STEERING
Section 12

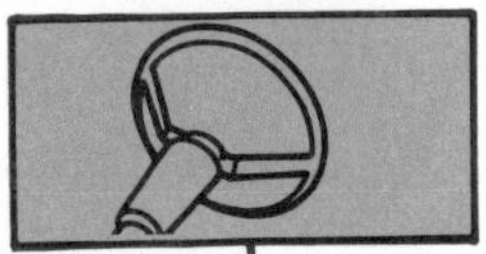

ACCESSORIES & EQUIPMENT
Section 5

SUSPENSION
Section 11

DRIVE AXLES
Section 8

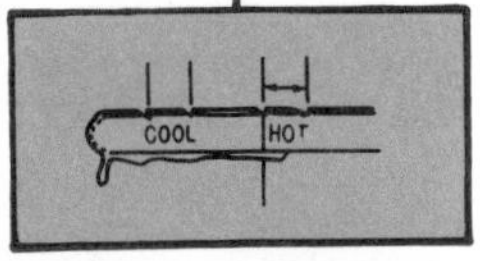

COOL
HOT

TRANSMISSION SERVICING
Section 13

SECTIONS 1 THROUGH 5
See Volume 1

ENGINES
Section 6

CLUTCHES
Section 7

DRIVE AXLES
Section 8

BRAKES
Section 9

WHEEL ALIGNMENT
Section 10

SUSPENSION
Section 11

STEERING
Section 12

TRANSMISSION SERVICING
Section 13

LATEST CHANGES & CORRECTIONS

GENERAL INDEX

PREFACE

This is the 1987 edition of Mitchell's Imported Cars, Light Trucks & Vans Tune-Up/Mechanical Service and Repair Manual.
This manual, like the many Mitchell publications which have preceded it, represents our commitment to professionalism in the automotive service market.

The automotive industry advances every year, and Mitchell pledges to advance and improve its products as we maintain the quality and usefulness of all our publications.

We cordially acknowledge the good will and mutual goals that exist in the automotive business, and it is in this spirit that we thank the automotive manufacturers, distributors, dealers and the entire automotive industry for their fine cooperation and assistance which have made this manual possible.

The Standard in Professional Estimating and Repair Information.

National Service Data

1987 IMPORTED CARS, LIGHT TRUCKS & VANS SERVICE & REPAIR

ENGINE
CHASSIS

VOLUME 2

Published By
MITCHELL INTERNATIONAL, INC.
P.O. BOX 26260
SAN DIEGO, CALIFORNIA 92126-0260

ISBN 0-8470-0064-8

Mitchell International, Inc.

ACKNOWLEDGEMENT

Mitchell International, Inc. thanks the domestic and import automobile and light truck manufacturers, distributors, and dealers for their generous cooperation and assistance which make this manual possible.

Published By

MITCHELL INTERNATIONAL, INC.
9889 Willow Creek Road
P.O. Box 26260
San Diego, California 92126-0260

For Subscription Information:
CALL TOLL FREE 800-854-7030. In California CALL TOLL FREE 800-421-0159.
Or WRITE: P.O. Box 26260, San Diego, CA 92126-0260

ISBN 0-8470-0064-8

Introduction

You now have the most complete and up-to-date Service and Repair Manual available to the professional mechanic. Our staff of experts has spent thousands of hours gathering and processing service and repair information from sources throughout the automotive industry. More than 800 separate articles, providing step-by-step Testing, Adjusting and Repair procedures for 1987 IMPORTED CARS LIGHT TRUCKS & VANS, are contained in this year's two-volume edition.

To use this manual in the most efficient and profitable way possible, please take the time to read the following instruction, "How To Find the Information". This will enable you to quickly locate the car model and the mechanical procedure you need, without wasting time thumbing through unnecessary pages.

HOW TO FIND THE INFORMATION

3 Quick Steps

(1) On the inside cover, you'll find the contents of this manual. Locate the section you want, and notice that it has a Black square next to it.

THUMB INDEX SPOT

ENGINES
Section 6

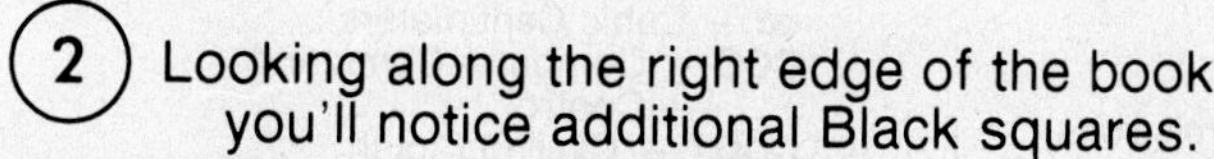

(2) Looking along the right edge of the book, you'll notice additional Black squares.

Match the Black square of the section listed on the cover with the Black square in line with it on the book's edge, then turn directly to that section.

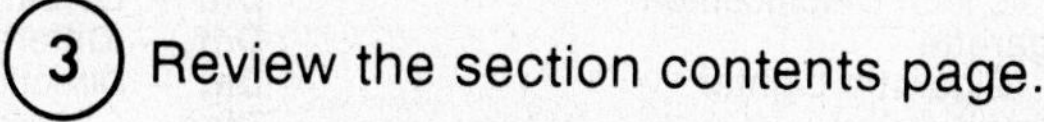

(3) Review the section contents page.

After locating the specific article and starting page needed, turn to the beginning of the article.

OR...

Determine, which volume you require...Volume I for Tune-Up and Electrical information, Volume II for Engine or Chassis information. Go directly to the expanded GENERAL INDEX located at the rear of that manual.
Go to the first page of the index and scan the contents page for what type of information you need. Using the alphabetical guide, as you would any type of reference index, locate what model you are working on and go to that page.

Mitchell's Abbreviations

ABBREVIATIONS MOST OFTEN USED

NOTE: **The following list of abbreviations, used most frequently in Mitchell's Service & Repair Manuals, is provided for your assistance. Although the majority of these abbreviations will be found in Mitchell's Wiring Diagrams, you may also find some of them used in articles dealing with Tune-Up, CEC, Emission, Fuel Systems, Electrical, Air Conditioning, Body Repair and other such subjects.**

CAUTION: **As some abbreviations may have more than one application, exercise caution that the definition provided here is logical for your vehicle's situation. For example, reason would help you determine whether "Alt." stands for Alternator, Altitude or for neither (an unlisted) definition.**

A

A – Amperes
AAC – Auxiliary Air Control
AAS – Auto Adjust Suspension
ABDC – After Bottom Dead Center
ABS – Anti-Lock Brake System
Abs. – Absolute
AC – Alternating Current
Ack. – Acknowledge
A/C – Air Conditioning
A/C Cltch. – A/C Clutch
Accel. – Accelerator
Accum. – Accumulator
Accy. – Accessory
A/Cl. – Air Cleaner
ACT – Air Charge Temperature
Actu. – Actuator
Actv. – Active
ACV – Air Control Valve
Adj. – Adjust or Adjustable
ADL – Automatic Door Lock
Adv. – Advance
AFC – Airflow Controlled
A.I.R. or **AIR** – Air Injection Reactor
AIR Sel. – AIR Selector
ALCL – Assembly Line Communication Link
ALDL – Assembly Line Data (Diagnostic) Link
Alm. – Alarm
Alt. – Alternator
Alt. or **Alti.** – High Altitude Emissions
Amb. – Ambient
AMC – American Motors Corporation
Amm. – Ammeter
Amp – Ampere
Amp. – Amplifier
Ant. – Antenna
Anti.-Dsl. – Anti-Diesel
Antic. – Anticipate
Assy. – Assembly (Wir. Diag. Only)
A/T – Automatic Transaxle or Transmission
ATDC – After Top Dead Center
ATC – Automatic Temperature Control
ATF – Automatic Transmission Fluid
Auto. – Automatic
Auto. Trans. – Automatic Transaxle or Transmission
Aux. – Auxiliary
Avg. – Average
AXOD – Automatic Overdrive Transaxle

B

Bap. Sens. – Barometric Absolute Pressure Sensor
Baro. – Barometric
Batt. – Battery
BBDC – Before Bottom Dead Center
Bbl. – Barrel
BCM – Body Control Module
Bk. – Back
Bk. Rest – Back Rest
Blst. – Ballast
Blwr. – Blower
Brkr. – Breaker
BTDC – Before Top Dead Center
Bulkhd. – Bulkhead
BTU – British Thermal Units
B/U or **B-U** – Back-Up
Buz. – Buzzer

C

C or **C°** – Celcius
C³I – Computer Controlled Coil Ignition
C4 – Computer Controlled Catalytic Converter
Calib. – Calibration
Calif. – California
Can. – Canada
Can. – Canister
Can. Prg. – Canister Purge
Canc. – Cancel
Cap. – Capacitor or Capacity
Carb. – Carburetor
CARB – California Air Resources Board
Cat. – Catalyst
CB – Circuit Breaker
CC – Cruise Control
cc – Cubic Centimeters
CCC – Computer Command Control
CCOT – Cycling Clutch Orifice Tube
CCP – Controlled Canister Purge
CCW – Counterclockwise
CEC – Computerized Emission Control
CEC – Computerized Engine Control
CFI – Central Fuel Injection
Chng. – Change
Chg. – Charge or Charging
Chk. – Check
Chk. Eng. – Check Engine
CI – Cubic Inches
CID – Cubic Inch Displacement
Cig. – Cigarette
Cig. Ltr. – Cigarette Lighter
Circ. – Circuit
Circ. Brkr. – Circuit Breaker
CIS – Continuous Injection System
CIS-E – CIS-Electronic
Ckt. – Circuit
CL – Closed Loop
CLCC – Closed Loop Carburetor Control
Clch. – Clutch
Clk. – Clock
Clmn. – Column
Clmt. – Climate
Clrnc. – Clearance
Clstr. – Cluster
CMH – Cold Mixture Heater
Cmpnstr. – Compensator
Cmptr. – Computer
Cncld. – Concealed
Cntr. – Central or Center
Cnvnc. – Convenience
CO – Carbon Monoxide
CO_2 – Carbon Dioxide
Co-Ax. – Co-Axial
Colng. – Cooling
Colnt. – Coolant
Comb. – Combination
Comp. – Compressor
Compens. – Compensation
Compt. – Compartment
Cond. – Condenser
Conn. – Connector or Connection
Cont. – Continued or Control
Conv. – Convertible or Converter
Convs. – Conversion
Count. – Counter
Crnr. – Corner
Crnrng. – Cornering
CRT – Cathode Ray Tube
CRTC – Cathode Ray Tube Controller
Ctrl. – Control
Ctrlld. – Controlled
Ctrllr. – Controller
CTS – Coolant Temperature Switch
Ctsy. – Courtesy
Cu. In. – Cubic Inches
CV – Constant Velocity
CW – Clockwise
Cyl. – Cylinder

D

"D" – Drive
DC – Direct Current
Damp. – Damper
Decel. – Deceleration
Def. – Defroster
Defog. – Defogger
Deg. – Degree
De-Ice. – De-Icer
Del. – Delay
Desig. – Designation
Detec. – Detector
Deton. – Detonation
Detrnt. – Deterrent
DFI – Digital Fuel Injection
Dft. – Defeat
Diff. – Differential
Dir. – Direction or Directional
Diag. – Diagnostic
Dig. – Digital
Dim. – Dimmer
Disp. – Display
Dist. – Distribution
Distr. – Distributor
Dlx. – Deluxe
Dly. – Delay
Dn. – Down
Dnshft. – Downshift
Dr. – Door
Drop. – Dropping
Drvr. – Driver
Dsl. – Diesel
Dstnc. – Distance

Mitchell's Abbreviations

ABBREVIATIONS MOST OFTEN USED (Cont.)

E

EAC - Electronic Air Control
EBCV - Electric Air Bleed Control Valve
ECA - Electronic Control Assembly
ECC - Electronic Chassis Control
ECC - Electronic Climate Control
ECC - Electronic Computer Control
ECCS - Electronic Concentrated Engine Control System
ECI - Electronically Controlled Injection
ECM - Electronic Control Module
Econ. - Economy
ECS - Emission Control System
ECS - Electronic Control Suspension
ECT - Electronic Control Transmission
ECT - Engine Coolant Temperature
ECU - Electronic Control Unit
EEC - Electronic Engine Control
EEC - Evaporative Emission Control
EFI - Electronic Fuel Injection
EFE - Early Fuel Evaporator
EGO - Exhaust Gas Oxygen
EGO Sens. Gnd. - EGO Sensor Ground
EGR - Exhaust Gas Recirculation
EGRC - EGR Control
EGRV - EGR Vent
EIS - Electronic Ignition System
ELC - Electronic Level (Load) Control
Elec. - Electric
Elect. - Electronic
Emis. or **Emiss.** - Emission
Eng. - Engine
EPA - Environmental Protection Agency
EPS - Electronic Power Steering
ESA - Electronic Spark Advance
ESC - Electronic Spark Control
EST - Electronic Spark Timing
Evap. - Evaporator or Evaporative
EVRV - Electronic Vacuum Regulator Valve
Ex. or **Exc.** - Except or Excluding
Exch. - Exchange
Exh. - Exhaust
Ext. - Exterior
Extd. - Extend

F

F or **F°** - Fahrenheit
F/B - Fuse Box or Block
F/B - Feedback
FBC - Feedback Carburetor
Fed. - Federal
FFOT - Ford Fixed Orifice Tube
FICD - Fast Idle Control Device
Flshr. - Flasher
Freq. - Frequency
Fnt. - Front
Fnt. WD - Front Wheel Drive
F/Rly. Pnl. - Fuse/Relay Panel
Frwd. - Forward
Ft. Lbs. or **ft. lbs.** - Foot Pounds
Func. - Function
Fus. - Fusible
Fus. Link - Fusible Link
4WD - Four-Wheel Drive
4WS - Four-Wheel Steering
FWD - Front Wheel Drive

G

g - Grams
Ga. - Gauge
Gal. or **Gals.** - gallons
Gen. - Generator
Gnd. - Ground
Gov. - Governor

H

Harn. - Harness
Haz. - Hazard
HC - Hydrocarbons
H/D - Heavy Duty
Headlt. - Headlight
HEI - High Energy Ignition
Hg - Mercury
Hgt. - Height
Hi. - High
Hi. Alt. - High Altitude
High Alt. - High Altitude
Hi-Spd. - High Speed
Hndl. - Handle
HO - High Ouput
HP - Horsepower
HP - High Performance
Hrn. - Horn
Hsg. - Housing
Htr. - Heater
HTR - Heavy Truck
Hyd. - Hydraulic
Hz - Hertz (Cycles Per Second)

I

IAC - Idle Air Control
IAS - Idle Air Stepper
IC - Integrated Circuit
I.D. - Inside Diameter
Ign. - Ignition
Ign. Gnd. - Ignition Ground
Ign. Mod. Sens. - Ignition Module Sensor
IIA - Integrated Ignition Assembly
ILC - Idle Load Control
Illum. - Illumination
In. - Inch or Inches
In. - Input
Incand. - Incandescent
INCH Lbs. - Inch Pounds
Ind. - Indicator
Infl. - Inflate
Info. - Information
In. Hg - Inches of Mercury
Inhib. - Inhibitor
Inj. - Injector or Injection
IN. Lbs. - Inch Pounds
Inp. - Input
Inst. - Instrument
Inst. Clstr. - Instrument Cluster
Int. - Interior
Interm. - Intermittent
Intgrtd. - Integrated
Intgrtn. - Integration
Intrpt. - Interrupt
Invrtr. - Inverter
ISC - Idle Speed Control
ISS - Idle Stop Solenoid

J

J/B - Junction Box
Jmpr. - Jumper
Junc. - Junction

K

KAPWR - Keep Alive Power
kg - Kilograms
kg/cm² - Kilograms Per Square Centimeter
k/ohms - 1000 ohms
Key. - Keyless

L

L - Liter
Lat. - Latched
Lbs. - Pounds
LCD - Liquid Crystal Display
L/D - Light Duty
LED - Light Emitting Diode
L. Fnt. - Left Front
LFT - Left
Lftgte. - Liftgate
LH - Left-hand
Lic. - License
Lk. - Lock
Lmtr. - Limiter
Lo. - Low
Lps. - Lamps
LR - Left Rear
Lt. - Light
Lt. Duty - Light Duty
Ltr. - Lighter
Ltr. - Limiter
Lug. - Luggage
Lvl. - Level
L4 - Straight 4-Cylinder
L6 - Straight 6-Cylinder

M

Ma - Milliamps
MAF - Mass Airflow
Mag. - Magnetic
Maint. - Maintenance
Man. - Manual
Man. - Manifold
Man. Trans. - Manual Transaxle or Transmission
Man. Stg. - Manual Steering
MAP - Manifold Absolute Pressure
MAT - Manifold Air Temperature
MCU - Microprocessor Control Unit
Mem. - Memory
Merc. - Mercury
Mesg. - Message
Mfd. - Microfarads
Mic. - Microphone
Mir. - Mirror
Mixt. - Mixture
mkg - Meter Kilogram
mm - Millimeters
Mod. - Module
Mon. - Monitor
MPC - Manifold Pressure Controlled
MPH - Miles Per Hour
MPI - Multi-Point Injection
Mtr. - Motor
M/T - Manual Transaxle or Transmission

N

"N" - Neutral Position
N.m - Newton Meter
NCA - No Color Available
Neut. - Neutral
No. or **#** - Number
Norm. - Normal
NOx - Oxides of Nitrogen

Mitchell's Abbreviations

ABBREVIATIONS MOST OFTEN USED (Cont.)

O

O – Oxygen
O_2 – Oxygen
OBC – On-Board Computer
OC – Oxidation Catalyst
OL – Open Loop
Oper. – Operated
Opt. – Options or Optional
O/D – Overdrive
Ozs. – Ounces

P

"P" – "PARK" Position
Pass. – Passenger
P/C – Printed Circuit
PCV – Positive Crankcase Ventilation
PFI – Port Fuel Injection
PGM-FI – Programmed Fuel Injection
PIP – Profile Ignition Pick-Up
Pkg. – Package
P/N – Park/Neutral
Pneu. – Pneumatic
Pnl. – Panel
Pos. – Positive
Postn. – Position
Pot. – Potentiometer
PPM – Parts Per Million
Pres. – Pressure
Prgmr. – Programmer
Pri. – Primary
PRNDL – Park, Reverse, Neutral, Drive, Low
PROM – Programmable Read Only Memory
Prtl. – Partial
P/S – Power Steering
psi – Pounds Per Square Inch
P/S Pres. Sw. – Power Steering Pressure Switch
PTO – Power Take Off
Pts. – Pints
Pwr. – Power

Q

Qts. – Quarts

R

R – Rear
Rad. – Radiator
R/B – Relay Box
Rcvr. – Receiver
Recirc. – Recirculator
Rdcr. – Reducer
Reduct. – Reduction
Ref. – Reference
Reg. – Regulator
Rel. – Release
Res. – Resistor
Resist. – Resistance
Retrac. – Retract or Retractor
Rev. – Revolution
Rheo. – Rheostat
Rly. – Relay
Rly. Up – Relay Up
RPM – Revolutions Per Minute
Rplnsg. – Replenishing
Rsm. – Resume
Rt. – Right
Rtd. – Retard
Rt. Fnt. – Right Front
RH or **RTH** – Right-hand
Rtrn. – Return
RWD – Rear Wheel Drive

S

Satlt. – Satellite
S/B – Seat Belt
SCC – Spark Control Computer
Sec. – Secondary
Sel. – Selector or Selection
Sen. or Sens. – Sensor
Send. – Sender
Sfty. – Safety
Shld. – Shield
Sig. – Signal
Sol. – Solenoid
Sole-Vac. – Solenoid Vacuum
Spd. – Speed
Speedo. – Speedometer
SPFI – Sequential Port Fuel Injection
SRS – Supplementary Restraint System
SSI – Solid State Ignition
St. – Start
Stab. – Stabilizer
Sta. Wag. – Station Wagon
Std. – Standard
Stop Lt. – Stop Light
Strkr. – Striker
Strtr. – Starter
Strng. – Steering
Supp. – Supply
Susp. – Suspension
Sw. – Switch
Swover. – Switchover
Sys. – System

T

TAB – Thermactor Air By-Pass
TAC – Thermostatic Air Cleaner
Tach. – Tachometer
TAD – Thermactor Air Diverter
Taillt. – Taillight
TBI – Throttle Body Injection
TCC – Torque Converter Clutch
TDC – Top Dead Center
Temp. – Temperature
Tens. – Tension
Tens. Rdcr. – Tension Reducer
Term. – Terminal
TFI – Thick Film Integrated
Therm. – Thermostat or Thermistor
Throt. – Throttle
TPS or **Th. Sens.** – Throttle Position Sensor
T-Q – Thermo-Quad
Trans. – Transaxle/Transmission
Transis. – Transistor
Trnsmtr. – Transmitter
Tripmdr. – Tripminder
Turbo – Turbocharger
T.V. – Throttle Valve
TVS – Thermal Vacuum Switch
TWC – Three Way Catalytic
Twilt. – Twilight
2WD – 2-Wheel Drive
Typ. – Typical

U

Unlat. – Unlatched

V

V – Volts
V6 – V6 Engine
V8 – V8 Engine
Vac. – Vacuum
Var. – Variable
VATS – Vehicle Anti-Theft System
VCC – Viscous Clutch Converter
Veh. – Vehicle
Vert. – Vertical
VIN – Vehicle Identification Number
Vlv. – Valve
Volt. – Voltage
V. Pwr. – Vehicle Power
VSS – Vehicle Speed Sensor

W

Warn. – Warning
Wshr. – Washer
W/B – Wheelbase
Wdo. – Window
Wip. – Wiper
W/Shield – Windshield
WOT – Wide Open Throttle
W/ – With
W/O – Without
W/W – Washer/Wiper

X

Xcvr. – Transceiver
Xmit – Transmit/Transmitter

SECTION 6

ENGINES

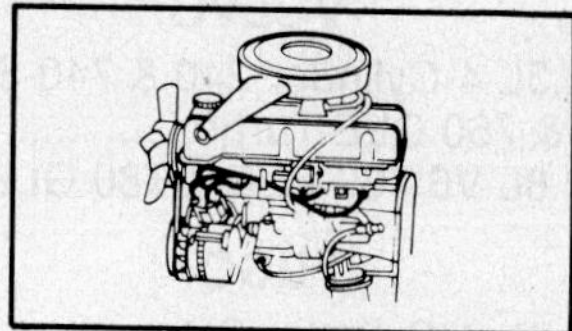

CONTENTS

1987 ENGINE IDENTIFICATION — **Page**
All Models 6-3

TROUBLE SHOOTING
Gasoline Engines 6-9
Diesel Engines 6-12
Engine Cooling 6-541

ENGINE OVERHAUL PROCEDURES
All Engines 6-14

ACURA
1.6L 4-Cylinder Integra 6-29
2.5L & 2.7L V6 Legend 6-39

ALFA ROMEO
2.5L V6 Milano 6-53

AUDI
1.8L 4-Cylinder 4000S 6-63
2.22L 5-Cylinder Coupe GT, 4000CS Quattro, 5000CS Quattro, 5000CS Turbo & 5000S 6-74
2.3L 5-Cylinder 5000S 6-74

BMW
2.5L & 2.7L 6-Cylinder 325, 325e, 325es, 325i, 325is & 528e 6-82
3.5L 6-Cylinder 535i, 635CSi & 735i 6-90

CHRYSLER MOTORS — **Page**
1.5L & 1.6L 4-Cylinder Colt 6-251
2.0L 4-Cylinder Colt Vista (2WD & 4WD) & Ram-50 6-261
2.6L 4-Cylinder Conquest, Ram-50 & Ram Raider 6-271

FORD MOTOR CO.
1.3L 4-Cylinder Festiva 6-98
1.6L 4-Cylinder Tracer 6-202
2.3L 4-Cylinder Merkur XR4Ti 6-106

GENERAL MOTORS
1.0L 3-Cylinder Chevrolet Sprint 6-115
1.5L 4-Cylinder Chevrolet Spectrum 6-125

HONDA
1.3L, 1.5L, 1.8L & 2.0L 4-Cylinder Accord, Civic & Prelude 6-133

HYUNDAI
1.5L 4-Cylinder Excel 6-251

ISUZU
1.5L 4-Cylinder I-Mark 6-125
1.9L, 2.0L & 2.3L 4-Cylinder Impulse, P'UP & Trooper II 6-154
2.2L 4-Cylinder Diesel P'UP & Trooper II 6-164

JAGUAR
4.2L 6-Cylinder XJ6 III 6-172
5.3L V12 XJS 6-181

MAZDA
1.3L Rotary RX7 6-189
1.6L 4-Cylinder 323 6-202
2.0L & 2.2L 4-Cylinder B2200 & 626 6-210
2.6L 4-Cylinder B2600 Truck 6-271

MERCEDES-BENZ
2.3L 4-Cylinder 190E 6-218
2.5L 5-Cylinder & 3.0L 6-Cylinder Turbo Diesel 190D, 300D, 300TD & 300SDL 6-227
2.6L & 3.0L 6-Cylinder 190E, 260E & 300E 6-235
4.2L & 5.6L V8 420SEL, 560SEC, 560SEL & 560SL 6-243

MITSUBISHI
1.5L & 1.6L 4-Cylinder Mirage & Precis 6-251
1.8L, 2.0L & 2.4L 4-Cylinder Cordia, Galant, Pickup, Tredia & Van/Wagon 6-261
2.6L 4-Cylinder Montero, Pickup & Starion 6-271

NISSAN
1.6L 4-Cylinder Pulsar NX & Sentra 6-279
1.6L 16-Valve 4-Cylinder Pulsar NX SE 6-290
2.0L 4-Cylinder Stanza & 200SX XE 6-298
2.4L 4-Cylinder Pathfinder & Pickup 6-306
3.0L V6 Maxima, Pathfinder, Pickup, 200SX & 300ZX 6-318

NOTE: **ALSO SEE GENERAL INDEX.**

CONTENTS (Cont.)

PEUGEOT Page

2.0L 4-Cylinder 505 Liberte 6-326
2.2L 4-Cylinder 505, 505 GL, 505 GLS, 505 S & 505 STI 6-333
2.8L V6 505 STI & 505 STX 6-339

PORSCHE

2.5L 4-Cylinder 924-S, 944, 944-S & 944 Turbo 6-350
3.2L & 3.3L 6-Cylinder 911 Carrera & 911 Turbo 6-365

SAAB

2.0L 4-Cylinder 900, 900S, 900 Turbo, 9000S & 9000 Turbo 6-384

STERLING

2.5L V6 825 6-39

SUBARU

1.2L 4-Cylinder Justy 6-391
1.6L & 1.8L 4-Cylinder Brat & Hatchback 6-401
1.8L OHC 4-Cylinder Coupe (3-Door), Sedan, Station Wagon & XT Coupe 6-409

SUZUKI

1.3L 4-Cylinder Samurai 6-418

TOYOTA

1.5L & 1.6L 8-Valve 4-Cylinder Corolla & Tercel Wagon 6-428

TOYOTA (Cont.) Page

1.5L 12-Valve 4-Cylinder Tercel (Except Wagon) 6-439
1.6L 16-Valve 4-Cylinder Corolla & MR2 6-450
2.0L 3S-FE & 3S-GE 4-Cylinder Camry & Celica 6-461
2.2L 4-Cylinder Van 6-474
2.4L 4-Cylinder Pickup & 4Runner 6-482
2.8L 6-Cylinder Cressida 6-490
3.0L Twin Camshaft 6-Cylinder Supra 6-499
4.2L 6-Cylinder Land Cruiser 6-510

VOLKSWAGEN

1.8L & 1.8L 16-Valve 4-Cylinder Cabriolet, Fox, Golf, GTI, Jetta, Jetta GLI & Scirocco 6-63
2.1L Opposed 4-Cylinder Vanagon & Vanagon Syncro 6-517
2.22L 5-Cylinder Quantum & Quantum Syncro 6-74

VOLVO

2.3L 4-Cylinder 240 & 740 Series & 760 GLE Turbo 6-526
2.8L V6 760 GLE & 780 GLE 6-339

YUGO

1.1L 4-Cylinder GV 6-533

ENGINE COOLING

General Cooling System Servicing 6-542
Engine Coolant Specifications 6-544
Heater Core Replacement 6-548

NOTE: ALSO SEE GENERAL INDEX.

1987 Engine Identification

ALL MODELS

ACURA

INTEGRA

Engine identification code is located on engine block directly above starter motor.

ENGINE CODE

Application	Code
1.6L	D16A1

LEGEND

Engine identification code is located on engine block behind timing belt upper cover below oil filler cap.

ENGINE CODE

Application	Code
Coupe 2.7L	C27A1
Sedan 2.5L	C25A1

ALFA ROMEO

GRADUATE, QUADRIFOGLIO & VELOCE

Engine identification code is located on left rear side of engine block on pad near bellhousing.

ENGINE CODE

Application	Code
2.0L	01544

MILANO

Engine identification code is located on rear side of engine block below left cylinder head surface.

ENGINE CODE

Application	Code
2.5L	019.13

AUDI

4000S

Engine identification code is located on machined pad at left side of engine block near ignition distributor.

ENGINE CODE

Application	Code
1.8L	MG

COUPE GT, 4000CS QUATTRO, 5000S, 5000CS QUATTRO & 5000CS TURBO

Engine identification code is located on machined pad just below cylinder head on left side of block.

ENGINE CODE

Application	Code
Coupe GT	
2.22L	KX
2.3L	NF
4000CS Quattro	
2.22L	JT
5000S	
2.22L	KZ
2.3L	NF
5000CS Turbo	
2.22L	MC
5000CS Quattro	
2.22L Turbo	MC

BMW

325 SERIES & 528e

Engine displacement and identification number are stamped on a pad on lower left side of engine block.

ENGINE CODE

Application	Code
325i & 325is	2.5L
All Others	2.7L

535i, 535is, 653CSi, L6, L7 & 735i

Engine displacement and identification number are stamped on top rear of engine block on bellhousing flange.

ENGINE CODE

Application	Code
535i, 535is, 653CSi L6, L7 & 735i	3.5L

CHRYSLER MOTORS & MITSUBISHI

The Vehicle Identification Number (VIN) is stamped on metal plate located near lower left corner of windshield. Engine can be identified by the 8th character of VIN number. Engine code numbers are stamped on top edge of front side of cylinder block.

ENGINE CODE

Application	Engine Model	Engine Vin Code
1.5L	G15B	K
1.6L Turbo	G32B	F
1.8L Turbo	G62B	G
2.0L	G63B	D
2.4L	G64B	L
2.6L		
Non-Turbo	G54B	E
Turbo	G54B	H
Turbo & Intercooler	G54B	N

1987 Engine Identification

ALL MODELS (Cont.)

FORD MOTOR CO.

FESTIVA

The Vehicle Identification Number (VIN) is stamped on metal plate attached to instrument panel located near lower left corner of windshield. Engine can be identified by the 8th character of VIN number.

ENGINE CODE

Application	Code
1.3L	K

MERKUR XR4Ti

The Vehicle Identification Number (VIN) is stamped on metal plate attached to instrument panel located near lower left corner of windshield. Engine can be identified by the 8th character of VIN number.

ENGINE CODE

Application	Code
2.3L Turbo	W

TRACER

The Vehicle Identification Number (VIN) is stamped on metal plate attached to instrument panel located near lower left corner of windshield. Engine can be identified by the 11th character of VIN number.

ENGINE CODE

Application	Code
1.6L	
Carbureted	7
EFI	5

GENERAL MOTORS

CHEVROLET SPECTRUM

The Vehicle Identification Number (VIN) is stamped on metal plate located near lower left corner of windshield. Engine can be identified by the 8th character of VIN number.

ENGINE CODE

Application	Code
1.5L	7
1.5L Turbo	9

CHEVROLET SPRINT

The Vehicle Identification Number (VIN) is stamped on metal plate located near lower left corner of windshield. Engine can be identified by the 8th character of VIN number.

ENGINE CODE

Application	Code
1.0L	5
1.0L Turbo	2

HONDA

ACCORD, CIVIC & PRELUDE

Engine serial number is located on right front corner of engine block just below cylinder head on Accord and Prelude models. Engine serial number is located under hood on the corner of left front fender on CRX, CRX HF, Hatchback, Sedan and Wagon models and on right front fender on CRX Si models. Engine serial number is also located on pad near starter motor. The first 5 characters of engine serial number is used for engine identification.

ENGINE CODE

Application	Code
1.3L	D13A2
1.5L	
Carbureted	D15A2
EFI	D15A3
1.8L	A18A1
2.0L	
Carbureted	A20A1
EFI	A20A3

HYUNDAI

EXCEL

The engine identification number is stamped on top edge of right front side of cylinder block.

ENGINE CODE

Application	Code
1.5L	J

ISUZU

I-MARK

The Vehicle Identification Number (VIN) is stamped on metal plate attached to instrument panel located near lower left corner of windshield. Engine can be identified by the 8th character of VIN number. Engine serial number is stamped on flange near transaxle mounting toward front of vehicle.

ENGINE CODE

Application	Code
1.5L	
Non-Turbo	7
Turbo	9

IMPULSE, P'UP & TROOPER II

The Vehicle Identification Number (VIN) is stamped on metal plate attached to instrument panel located near lower left corner of windshield. Engine can be identified by the 8th character of VIN number.

ALL MODELS (Cont.)

ENGINE CODE

Application	Code
Impulse	
1.9L	A
2.0L Turbo	F
P'UP	
1.9L	A
2.2L Diesel	S
2.3L	L
2.2 Turbo Diesel	U
Trooper II	
2.3L	L
2.2L Turbo Diesel	U

JAGUAR

XJ6 III

Engine serial number is stamped on top of cylinder block at rear of engine. Number is also stamped on Commission Plate located in engine compartment. No code number is used for engine identification.

XJS

Engine serial number is stamped on top rear of cylinder block, between cylinder heads. No code number is used for engine identification.

MAZDA

B2200 & B2600 PICKUP

Engine serial number and model code is located on cylinder block pad behind alternator mount on the B2600 or below distributor on the B2200 model.

ENGINE CODE

Application	Code
B2200 2.2L	F2
B2600 2.6L	G54B

RX7

Engine code is stamped on the left front of engine block in front of oil filler tube. The engine serial number is stamped on the pad located behind alternator.

ENGINE CODE

Application	Code
1.3L	
Non-Turbo	13B
Turbo	13B

323

Engine model and serial number are located on right rear of engine block.

ENGINE CODE

Application	Code
1.6L	B6

626

Engine model and serial numbers are located on front of engine block just below spark plug.

ENGINE CODE

Application	Code
2.0L	
Non-Turbo	FE
Turbo	FE

MERCEDES-BENZ

190D, 300D, 300TD & 300 SDL

Engine identification is stamped on tag located at left rear side of engine crankcase. First 6 characters are used for engine identification.

ENGINE CODE

Application	Code
190D 2.5L	
Diesel	602.911
Turbo Diesel	602.961
300D 3.0L	603.960
300TD 3.0L Turbo Diesel	603.960
300SDL 3.0L Turbo Diesel	603.961

190E

Engine identification is stamped on tag located at left rear side of engine crankcase. First 6 characters are used for engine identification.

ENGINE CODE

Application	Code
2.3L	102.985
2.6L	103.942

260E & 300E

The engine identification number is located on right side of engine crankcase in front of engine mount.

ENGINE CODE

Application	Code
260E 2.6L	103.940
300E 3.0L	103.983

420 & 560 SERIES

The engine identification number is located on left rear side of engine crankcase.

ENGINE CODE

Application	Code
420SEL 4.2L	116.965
560SEC & 560SEL 5.6L	117.968
560SL 5.6L	117.967

1987 Engine Identification

ALL MODELS (Cont.)

NISSAN

MAXIMA, 200SX SE & 300ZX

On Maxima and 300ZX and 200SX SE with 3.0L, engine serial number is located on top rear of cylinder block just below cam cover.

ENGINE CODE

Application	Code
Maxima 3.0L	VG30E
200SX SE 3.0L	VG30E
300ZX 3.0L	
Non-Turbo	VG30E
Turbo	VG30ET

PULSAR, SENTRA & 200SX XE

On Pulsar, Sentra, Stanza, and 200SX XE with 2.0L, engine serial number is located on rear corner of engine block just below exhaust manifold.

ENGINE CODE

Application	Code
Pulsar NX 1.6L	E16i
Pulsar NX SE 1.6L (16-Valve)	CA16DE
Sentra 1.6L	
Carbureted	E16s
Fuel Injection	E16i
Stanza & Stanza Wagon 2.0L	CA20E
200SX XE 2.0L	
Non-Turbo	CA20E
Turbo	CA18ET

PATHFINDER, PICKUP & VAN

On Pathfinder, Pickup and Van models with 2.4L, engine serial number is located in center of engine block on exhaust manifold side. On Pickup and Pathfinder models with 3.0L, engine serial number is located on pad behind right cylinder head.

ENGINE CODE

Application	Code
Pathfinder & Pickup	
2.4L	Z24i
3.0L	VG30i
Van 2.4L	Z24i

PEUGEOT

505 SERIES

Engine codes are stamped on tag riveted to engine block. On all models except the 2.8L, tag is located on left rear corner of engine block below starter motor. On the 2.8L, tag is located on left front of engine block in front of oil filter. First 3 characters are used for engine identification.

ENGINE CODE

Application	Code
2.0L	136
2.2L	851
2.2L Turbo	176
2.8L	154

PORSCHE

911 CARRERA & 911 TURBO

Engine identification number is stamped in machined pad on left of crankcase next to fan housing. First character indicates unit type, 2nd character indicates engine type and 3rd character indicates model year.

NOTE: **Porsche identification of engine type series is 930/25 for the 911 Carrera and 930/68 for the 911 Turbo.**

ENGINE CODE

Application	Code
911 Carrera 3.2L	64H
911 Turbo 3.3L	68H

924S, 944, 944S & 944 TURBO

Engine identification number is located on left side of engine crankcase next to clutch housing. First 2 characters of engine identification number indicate engine version and 3rd character indicates model year. Remaining characters are engine serial number used to indicate if A/T or M/T transmission is used.

ENGINE CODE

Application	Engine Type	Code
924S & 944 2.5L		
A/T	M44/08	43H 60001-90000
M/T	M44/07	43H 00001-60000
944S 2.5L		
M/T	M44/40	42H 00001-60000
944 Turbo 2.5L		
M/T	M44/51	45H 00001-10000

928S4

The engine identification number is stamped on the front reinforcing rib in the top half of the crankcase. First 2 characters of engine identification number indicate engine version and 3rd character indicates model year. Remaining characters are engine serial number.

ENGINE CODE

Application	Engine Type	Code
928S4 5.0L		
A/T	M82/42	81H 00001-01000
M/T	M82/41	81H 05001-10000

1987 Engine Identification

ALL MODELS (Cont.)

SAAB

900, 900S, 900 TURBO, 9000S & 9000 TURBO

Engine number is stamped on machined pad on lower left front of engine block on 900 series. On 9000 series, engine number is located on metal tag attached on front of engine block in the center.

ENGINE CODE

Application	Code
900 2.0L	
A/T	B2012I03AH
M/T	B2012I03MH
900S 2.0L	
A/T	B2022I13AH
M/T	B2022I13MH
900 Turbo 2.0L	
A/T	B2022L13AH
M/T	B2022L13MH
9000S 2.0L	....
9000 Turbo 2.0L	
A/T	B2023L13AH
M/T	B2023L13MH

STERLING

825

The Vehicle Identification Number (VIN) is stamped on firewall directly behind engine. Engine can be identified by the 8th character of VIN number. Engine number is stamped on cylinder block face of front bank below camshaft drive belt cover.

ENGINE CODE

Application	Code
2.5L	P

SUBARU

ALL MODELS

The Vehicle Identification Number (VIN) is stamped on metal plate located near lower left corner of windshield on Justy models and on firewall in center of engine compartment on all other models. Engine can be identified by the 6th character of VIN number. Engine serial number is stamped on rear of engine block on Justy models and on right side at front of crankcase on all other models.

ENGINE CODE

Application	Code
Brat 1.8L	
2WD	4
4WD	5
Coupe, Sedan & Wagon 1.8L	
2WD	4
4WD W/Air Suspension	7
4WD W/O Air Suspension	5

ENGINE CODE (Cont.)

Application	Code
Hatchback	
1.6L	2
1.8L	
2WD	4
4WD	5
Justy 1.2L	
2WD	7
4WD	8
XT Coupe 1.8L	
2WD	4
4WD	7

SUZUKI

SAMURAI

The Vehicle Identification Number (VIN) is stamped on left front door pillar. Engine can be identified by the 6th character of VIN number. Engine identification number is stamped on left rear of cylinder block.

ENGINE CODE

Application	Code
1.3L	5

TOYOTA

ALL MODELS

Engine identification number is stamped on rear of engine block directly below distributor on Camry and Celica. Engine identifiction number is stamped on right side of block on Supra, Cressida and Van models while number is stamped on left side on all others.

ENGINE CODE

Application	Code
Camry 2.0L	3S-FE
Celica 2.0L	3S-GE or 3S-FE
Corolla (FWD) 1.6L	4A-C
Corolla (RWD) 1.6L	4A-C
Corolla FX-16 1.6L	4A-GE
Corolla GT-S 1.6L	4A-GE
Cressida 2.8L	5M-GE
Land Cruiser 4.2L	2F
MR2 1.6L	4A-GE
Pickup 2.4L	
Carbureted	22R
EFI	22R-E
Turbo	22R-TE
4Runner 2.4L	
EFI	22R-E
Turbo	22R-TE
Supra 3.0L	
Non-Turbo	7M-GE
Turbo	7M-GTE
Tercel 1.5L	
Wagon	3A-C
Sedan	3E
Van 2.2L	4Y-E

1987 Engine Identification

ALL MODELS (Cont.)

VOLKSWAGEN

ALL MODELS

Engine identification number is stamped on left side of engine block below head on Fox models. On Vanagon and Vanagon Synchro number is stamped on block below crankcase breather hose. On Quantum and Quantum Synchro models number is stamped on left side of engine block. On all other models engine identification number is stamped on engine block near distributor.

ENGINE CODE

Application	Code
Cabriolet 1.8L	JH
Golf & Jetta 1.8L	GX
GTI & GLI 1.8L	PL
Quantum & Quantum Syncro 2.2L	KX
Scirocco 1.8L	PL
Vanagon & Vanagon Syncro 2.1L	MV
Fox 1.8L	UM

VOLVO

ALL MODELS

Engine identification number is located on label on timing belt cover and is stamped on left front corner of engine block on 2.3L and 2.3L Turbo. On the 2.8L, number is stamped on front center of engine block behind water pump on 740 and 760 series and on front of right bank for 780 series.

Vehicle identification number is located on center of right front fender on 240 series and above right headlight assembly on 740, 760 and 780 series. Engine can be identified by 6th and 7th characters of VIN number.

ENGINE CODE

Application	Engine Number	VIN Code
240DL & 240GL 2.3L		
A/T	1289093	88
M/T	1289092	88
740 GL & 740 GLE 2.3L		
A/T	1289075	88
M/T	1289074	88
740 & 760 GLE		
2.3L Turbo		
A/T	1289081	87
M/T	1289080	87
760 GLE 2.8L		
A/T	1289515	69
780 GLE 2.8L		
A/T	1289521	69

YUGO

GV

Engine identification code is located on metal tag located next to hood brace and stamped on right rear corner of engine block behind exhaust manifold.

ENGINE CODE

Application	Code
1.1L	128 A. 064

Engine Trouble Shooting

GASOLINE ENGINE TROUBLE SHOOTING

CONDITION	POSSIBLE CAUSE	CORRECTION
Engine Lopes At Idle	Intake manifold-to-head leaks	Replace manifold gasket, see ENGINES
	Blown head gasket	Replace head gasket, see ENGINES
	Worn timing gears, chain or sprocket	Replace gears, chain or sprocket
	Worn camshaft lobes	Replace camshaft, see ENGINES
	Overheated engine	Check cooling system, see COOLING
	Blocked crankcase vent valve	Remove restriction
	Leaking EGR valve	Repair leak and/or replace valve
	Faulty fuel pump	Replace fuel pump
Engine Has Low Power	Leaking fuel pump	Repair leak and/or replace fuel pump
	Excessive piston-to-bore clearance	Install larger pistons, see ENGINES
	Sticking valves or weak valve springs	Check valve train components, see ENGINES
	Incorrect valve timing	Reset valve timing, see ENGINES
	Worn camshaft lobes	Replace camshaft, see ENGINES
	Blown head gasket	Replace head gasket, see ENGINES
	Clutch slipping	Adjust pedal and/or replace components, see CLUTCHES
	Engine overheating	Check cooling system, see COOLING
	Auto. trans. pressure regulator valve faulty	Replace pressure regulator valve
	Auto. trans. fluid level too low	Add fluid as necessary, see TRANSMISSIONS
	Improper vacuum diverter valve operation	Replace vacuum diverter valve
	Vacuum leaks	Inspect vacuum system and repair as required
	Leaking piston rings	Replace piston rings, see ENGINES
Faulty High Speed Operation	Low fuel pump volume	Replace fuel pump
	Leaking valves or worn valve springs	Replace valves and/or springs, see ENGINES
	Incorrect valve timing	Reset valve timing, see ENGINES
	Intake manifold restricted	Remove restriction
	Worn distributor shaft	Replace distributor
Faulty Acceleration	Improper fuel pump stroke	Remove pump and reset pump stroke
	Incorrect ignition timing	Reset ignition timing
	Leaking valves	Replace valves, see ENGINES
	Worn fuel pump diaphragm or piston	Replace diaphragm or piston
Intake Backfire	Improper ignition timing	Reset ignition timing
	Faulty accelerator pump discharge	Replace accelerator pump
	Improper choke operation	Check choke and adjust as required
	Defective EGR valve	Replace EGR valve
	Fuel mixture too lean	Reset air/fuel mixture
	Choke valve initial clearance too large	Reset choke valve initial clearance
Exhaust Backfire	Vacuum leak	Inspect and repair vacuum system
	Faulty vacuum diverter valve	Replace vacuum diverter valve
	Faulty choke operation	Check choke and adjust as required
	Exhaust system leak	Repair exhaust system leak
Engine Detonation	Ignition timing too far advanced	Reset ignition timing
	Faulty ignition system	Check ignition system
	Spark plugs loose or faulty	Retighten or replace plugs
	Fuel delivery system clogged	Inspect lines, pump and filter for clog
	EGR valve inoperative	Replace EGR valve
	PCV system inoperative	Inspect and/or replace hoses or valve
	Vacuum leaks	Check vacuum system and repair leaks
	Excessive combustion chamber deposits	Remove built-up deposits
	Leaking, sticking or broken valves	Inspect and/or replace valves
External Oil Leakage	Fuel pump improperly seated or worn gasket	Remove pump, replace gasket and seat properly
	Valve cover gasket broken	Replace valve cover gasket
	Oil filter gasket broken	Replace oil filter and gasket
	Oil pan gasket broken or pan bent	Straighten pan and replace gasket
	Timing chain cover gasket broken	Replace timing chain cover gasket

Engine Trouble Shooting

GASOLINE ENGINE TROUBLE SHOOTING (Cont.)

CONDITION	POSSIBLE CAUSE	CORRECTION
External Oil Leakage (Cont.)	Rear main oil seal worn	Replace rear main oil seal
	Oil pan drain plug not seated properly	Remove and reinstall drain plug
	Camshaft bearing drain hole blocked	Remove restriction
	Oil pressure sending switch leaking	Remove and reinstall sending switch
Excessive Oil Consumption	Worn valve stems or guides	Replace stems or guides, see ENGINES
	Valve "O" ring seals damaged	Replace "O" ring seals, see ENGINES
	Plugged oil drain back holes	Remove restrictions
	Improper PCV valve operation	Replace PCV valve
	Engine oil level too high	Remove excess oil
	Engine oil too thin	Replace with thicker oil
	Valve stem oil deflectors damaged	Replace oil defelctors
	Incorrect piston rings	Replace piston rings, see ENGINES
	Piston ring gaps not staggered	Reinstall piston rings, see ENGINES
	Insufficient piston ring tension	Replace rings, see ENGINES
	Piston ring grooves or oil return slots clogged	Replace piston rings, see ENGINES
	Piston rings sticking in grooves	Replace piston rings, see ENGINES
	Piston ring grooves excessively worn	Replace piston and rings, see ENGINES
	Compression rings installed upside down	Replace compression rings correctly, see ENGINES
	Worn or scored cylinder walls	Rebore cylinders or replace block
	Mismatched oil ring expander and rail	Replace oil ring expander and rail, see ENGINES
	Intake gasket dowels too long	Replace intake gasket dowels
	Excessive main or connecting rod bearing clearance	Replace main or connecting rod bearings, see ENGINES
No Oil Pressure	Low oil level	Add oil to proper level
	Oil pressure sender or gauge broken	Replace sender or gauge
	Oil pump malfunction	Remove and overhaul oil pump, see ENGINES
	Oil pressure relief valve sticking	Remove and reinstall valve
	Oil pump passages blocked	Overhaul oil pump, see ENGINES
	Oil pickup screen or tube blocked	Remove restriction
	Loose oil inlet tube	Tighten oil inlet tube
	Loose camshaft bearings	Replace camshaft bearings, see ENGINES
	Internal leakage at oil passages	Replace block or cylinder head
Low Oil Pressure	Low engine oil level	Add oil to proper level
	Engine oil too thin	Remove and replace with thicker oil
	Excessive oil pump clearance	Reduce oil pump clearance, see ENGINES
	Oil pickup tube or screen blocked	Remove restrictions
	Oil pressure relief spring weak or stuck	Eliminate binding or replace spring
	Main, rod or cam bearing clearance excessive	Replace bearing to reduce clearance, see ENGINES
High Oil Pressure	Improper grade of oil	Replace with proper oil
	Oil pressure relief valve stuck closed	Eliminate binding
	Oil pressure sender or gauge faulty	Replace sender or gauge
Noisy Main Bearings	Inadequate oil supply	Check oil delivery to main bearings
	Excessive main bearing clearance	Replace main bearings, see ENGINES
	Excessive crankshaft end play	Replace crankshaft, see ENGINES
	Loose flywheel or torque converter	Tighten attaching bolts
	Loose or damaged vibration damper	Tighten or replace vibration damper
	Crankshaft journals out-of-round	Re-grind crankshaft journals
	Excessive belt tension	Loosen belt tension
Noisy Connecting Rods	Excessive bearing clearance or missing bearing	Replace bearing, see ENGINES
	Crankshaft rod journal out-of-round	Re-grind crankshaft journal
	Misaligned connecting rod or cap	Remove rod or cap and re-align
	Incorrectly tightened rod bolts	Remove and re-tighten rod bolts

GASOLINE ENGINE TROUBLE SHOOTING (Cont.)

CONDITION	POSSIBLE CAUSE	CORRECTION
Noisy Pistons and Rings	Excessive piston-to-bore clearance	Install larger pistons, see ENGINES
	Bore tapered or out-of-round	Rebore block
	Piston ring broken	Replace piston rings, see ENGINES
	Piston pin loose or seized	Replace piston pin, see ENGINES
	Connecting rods misaligned	Re-align connecting rods
	Ring side clearance too loose or tight	Replace with larger or smaller rings
	Carbon build-up on piston	Remove carbon
Noisy Valve Train	Worn or bent push rods	Replace push rods, see ENGINES
	Worn rocker arms or bridged pivots	Replace rocker arms or pivots, see ENGINES
	Dirt or chips in valve lifters	Remove lifters and remove dirt/chips
	Excessive valve lifter leak-down	Replace valve lifters, see ENGINES
	Valve lifter face worn	Replace valve lifters, see ENGINES
	Broken or cocked valve springs	Replace or reposition springs
	Too much valve stem-to-guide clearance	Replace valve guides, see ENGINES
	Valve bent	Replace valve, see ENGINES
	Loose rocker arms	Retighten rocker arms, see ENGINES
	Excessive valve seat run-out	Re-face valve seats, see ENGINES
	Missing valve lock	Install new valve lock
	Excessively worn camshaft lobes	Replace camshaft, see ENGINES
	Plugged valve lifter oil holes	Eliminate restriction or replace lifter
	Faulty valve lifter check ball	Replace lifter, see ENGINES
	Rocker arm nut installed upside down	Remove and reinstall correctly
	Valve lifter incorrect for engine	Remove and replace valve lifters
	Faulty push rod seat or lifter plunger	Replace plunger or push rod
Noisy Valves	Improper valve lash	Re-adjust valve lash, see ENGINES
	Worn or dirty valve lifters	Clean and/or replace lifters
	Worn valve guides	Replace valve guides, see ENGINES
	Excessive valve seat or face run-out	Re-face seats or valve face
	Worn camshaft lobes	Replace camshaft, see ENGINES
	Loose rocker arm studs	Re-tighten rocker arm studs, see ENGINES
	Bent push rods	Replace push rods, see ENGINES
	Broken valve springs	Replace valve springs, see ENGINES
Burned, Sticking or Broken Valves	Weak valve springs or warped valves	Replace valves and/or springs, see ENGINES
	Improper lifter clearance	Re-adjust clearance or replace lifters
	Worn guides or improper guide clearance	Replace valve guides, see ENGINES
	Out-of-round valve seats or improper seat width	Re-grind valve seats
	Gum deposits on valve stems, seats or guides	Remove deposits
	Improper spark timing	Re-adjust spark timing
Broken Pistons/Rings	Undersize pistons	Replace with larger pistons, see ENGINES
	Wrong piston rings	Replace with correct rings, see ENGINES
	Out-of-round cylinder bore	Re-bore cylinder bore
	Improper connecting rod alignment	Remove and re-align connecting rods
	Excessively worn ring grooves	Replace pistons, see ENGINES
	Improperly assembled piston pins	Re-assemble pin-to-piston, see ENGINES
	Insufficient ring gap clearance	Install new rings, see ENGINES
	Engine overheating	Check cooling system
	Incorrect ignition timing	Re-adjust ignition timing
Excessive Exhaust Noise	Leaks at manifold to head, or to pipe	Replace manifold or pipe gasket
	Exhaust manifold cracked or broken	Replace exhaust manifold, see ENGINES

Engine Trouble Shooting

DIESEL ENGINE TROUBLE SHOOTING

NOTE: **Diesel engine mechanical diagnosis is the same as gasoline engines for items such as noisy valves, bearings, pistons, etc. The following trouble shooting covers only items pertaining to diesel engines**

CONDITION	POSSIBLE CAUSE	CORRECTION
Engine Won't Crank	Bad battery connections or dead batteries	Check connections and/or replace batteries
	Bad starter connections or bad starter	Check connections and/or replace starter
Engine Cranks Slowly, Won't Start	Bad battery connections or dead batteries	Check connections and/or replace batteries
	Engine oil too heavy	Replace engine oil
Engine Cranks Normally, But Will Not Start	Glow plugs not functioning	Check glow plug system
	Glow plug control not functioning	Check glow plug controller
	Fuel not injected into cylinders	Check fuel injectors
	No fuel to injection pump	Check fuel delivery system
	Fuel filter blocked	Replace fuel filter
	Fuel tank filter blocked	Replace fuel tank filter
	Fuel pump not operating	Check pump operation and/or replace pump
	Fuel return system blocked	Inspect system and remove restriction
	No voltage to fuel solenoid	Check solenoid and connections
	Incorrect or contaminated fuel	Replace fuel
	Incorrect injection pump timing	Re-adjust pump timing
	Low compression	Check valves, pistons, rings, see ENGINES
	Injection pump malfunction	Inspect and/or replace injection pump
Engine Starts, Won't Idle	Incorrect slow idle adjustment	Reset idle adjustment
	Fast idle solenoid malfunctioning	Check solenoid and connections
	Fuel return system blocked	Check system and remove restrictions
	Glow plugs go off too soon	See glow plug diagnosis
	Injection pump timing incorrect	Reset pump timing
	No fuel to injection pump	Check fuel delivery system
	Incorrect or contaminated fuel	Replace fuel
	Low compression	Check valves, piston, rings, see ENGINES
	Injection pump malfunction	Replace injection pump
	Fuel solenoid closes in RUN position	Check solenoid and connections
Engine Starts/Idles Rough Without Smoke or Noise	Incorrect slow idle adjustment	Reset slow idle
	Injection line fuel leaks	Check lines and connections
	Fuel return system blocked	Check lines and connections
	Air in fuel system	Bleed air from system
	Incorrect or contaminated fuel	Replace fuel
	Injector nozzle malfunction	Test and/or replace nozzles
Engine Starts and Idles Rough Without Smoke or Noise, But Clears After Warm-Up	Injection pump timing incorrect	Reset pump timing
	Engine not fully broken in	Put more miles on engine
	Air in system	Bleed air from system
	Injector nozzle malfunction	Check nozzles
Engine Idles Correctly, Misfires Above Idle	Blocked fuel filter	Replace fuel filter
	Injection pump timing incorrect	Reset pump timing
	Incorrect or contaminated fuel	Replace fuel
Engine Won't Return to Idle	Fast idle adjustment incorrect	Reset fast idle
	Internal injection pump malfunction	Replace injection pump
	External linkage binding	Check linkage and remove binding
Fuel Leaks on Ground	Loose or broken fuel line	Check lines and connections
	Internal injection pump seal leak	Replace injection pump
Loss of Engine Power	Restricted air intake	Remove restriction
	EGR valve malfunction	Replace EGR valve
	Blocked or damaged exhaust system	Remove restriction and/or replace components
	Blocked fuel tank filter	Replace filter
	Restricted fuel filter	Remove restriction and/or replace filter

DIESEL ENGINE TROUBLE SHOOTING (Cont.)

CONDITION	POSSIBLE CAUSE	CORRECTION
Loss of Engine Power (Cont.)	Blocked vent in gas cap	Remove restriction and/or replace cap
	Tank-to-injection pump fuel supply blocked	Check fuel lines and connections
	Blocked fuel return system	Remove restriction
	Incorrect or contaminated fuel	Replace fuel
	Blocked injector nozzles	Remove nozzle and remove blockage, see FUEL
	Low compression	Check valves, rings, pistons, see ENGINES
Cylinder Knocking Noise	Injector nozzles sticking open	Test injectors and/or replace
	Very low nozzle opening pressure	Test injectors and/or replace
Loud Engine Noise With Black Smoke	Basic timing incorrect	Reset timing
	EGR valve malfunction	Replace EGR valve
	Internal injection pump malfunction	Replace injection pump
	Incorrect injector pump housing pressure	Check pressure and adjust
Engine Overheating	Cooling system leaks	Check cooling system and repair leaks
	Belt slipping or damaged	Check tension and/or replace belt
	Thermostat stuck closed	Remove and replace thermostat, see COOLING
	Head gasket leaking	Replace head gasket
Oil Light on at Idle	Low oil pump pressure	Check oil pump operation, see ENGINES
	Oil cooler or line restricted	Remove restriction and/or replace cooler
Engine Won't Shut Off	Injector pump fuel solenoid does not return fuel valve to OFF position	Remove and check solenoid and replace if needed
	VACUUM PUMP DIAGNOSIS	
Excessive Noise	Loose pump-to-drive assembly screws	Tighten screws
	Loose tube on pump assembly	Tighten tube
	Valves not functioning properly	Replace valves
Oil Leakage	Loose end plug	Tighten end plug
	Bad seal crimp	Remove and re-crimp seal

Engine Overhaul Procedures

ALL ENGINES

DESCRIPTION

Examples used in this article are general in nature and do not necessarily relate to a specific engine or system. Illustrations and procedures have been chosen to guide the mechanic through the engine overhaul process. Descriptions of cleaning, inspection, and assembly processes are included.

ENGINE IDENTIFICATION

Engine may be identified from Vehicle Identification Number (VIN) stamped on a metal tab. Metal tab may be located in different locations due to manfacturer. Engine identification number or serial number is located on cylinder block. Location varies with manufacturer.

INSPECTION PROCEDURES

Engine components must be inspected to meet manufacturer's specifications and tolerances during overhaul. Proper dimensions and tolerances must be met to obtain proper performance and maximum engine life.

The use of micrometers, depth guages and dial indicator is used for checking tolerances during engine overhaul. Magnaflux, magnaglo, dye-check, ultrasonic and x-ray inspection procedures are used for parts inspection.

MAGNETIC PARTICLE INSPECTION

Magnaflux & Magnaglo

Magnaflux is an inspection technique used to locate material flaws and stress cracks. Component is subjected to a strong magnetic field. Entire component or a localized area can be magnetized. Component is coated with either a wet or dry material that contains fine magnetic particles.

Cracks which are outlined by the particles cause an interruption of magnetic field. Dry powder method of magnaflux can be used in normal lighting and crack appears as a bright line.

Florescent liquid is used along with a Blacklight in the Magnaglo magnaflux system. Darkened room is required for this procedure. The crack will appear as a glowing line. Complete demagnetizing of component upon completion is required on both procedures. Magnetic particle inspection applies to ferrous materials only.

PENETRANT INSPECTION

Zyglo

The Zyglo process coats material with a fluorescent dye penetrant. Component is often warmed to expand cracks that will be penetrated by the dye. Using darkened room and Blacklight, component is inspected for cracks. Crack will glow brightly.

Developing solution is often used to enhance results. Parts made of any material, such as aluminum cylinder heads or plastics, may be tested using this process.

Dye Check

Penetrating dye is sprayed on the previously cleaned component. Dye is left on component for 5-45 minutes, depending upon material density. Component is then wiped clean and sprayed with a developing solution. Surface cracks will show up as a bright line.

ULTRASONIC INSPECTION

If an expensive part is suspected of internal cracking, Ultrasonic testing is used. Sound waves are used for component inspection.

X-RAY INSPECTION

This form of inspection is used on highly stressed components. X-ray inspection may be used to detect internal and external flaws in any material.

PRESSURE TESTING

Cylinder heads can be tested for cracks using a pressure tester. Pressure testing is performed by plugging all but one of the holes of cylinder head and injecting air or water into the open passage.

Leaks are indicated by the appearance of wet or damp areas when using water. When air is used, it is necessary to spray the head surface with a soap solution. Bubbles will indicate a leak. Cylinder head may also be submerged in water heated to specified temperature to check for cracks created during heat expansion.

CLEANING PROCEDURES

All components of an engine do not have the same cleaning requirements. Physical methods include bead blasting and manual removal. Chemical methods include solvent blast, solvent tank, hot tank, cold tank and steam cleaning of components.

BEAD BLASTING

Manual removal of deposits may be required prior to bead blasting, followed by some other cleaning method. Carbon, paint and rust may be removed using bead blasting method. Components must be free of oil and grease prior to bead blasting. Beads will stick to grease or oil soaked areas causing area not to be cleaned.

Use air pressure to remove all trapped residual beads from component after cleaning. After cleaning internal engine parts made of aluminum, wash thoroughly with hot soapy water. Component must be thoroughly cleaned as glass beads will enter engine oil resulting in bearing damage.

CHEMICAL CLEANING

Solvent tank is used for cleaning oily residue from components. Solvent blasting sprays solvent through a syphon gun using compressed air.

The hot tank, using heated caustic solvents, is used for cleaning ferrous materials only. DO NOT clean aluminum parts such as cylinder heads, bearings or other soft metals using the hot tank. After cleaning, flush parts with hot water.

A non-ferrous part will be ruined and caustic solution will be diluted if placed in the hot tank. Always use eye protection and gloves when using the hot tank.

Use of a cold tank is for cleaning of aluminum cylinder heads, carburetors and other soft metals. A less caustic and unheated solution is used. Parts may be left in the tank for several hours without damage. After cleaning, flush parts with hot water.

Steam cleaning, with boiling hot water sprayed at high pressure, is recommended as the final cleaning process when using either hot or cold tank cleaning.

ALL ENGINES (Cont.)

SHEET METAL PARTS

Examples of sheet metal parts are rocker covers, front and side covers, oil pan and bellhousing dust cover. Glass bead blasting or hot tank may be used for cleaning.

Ensure all mating surfaces are flat. Deformed surfaces should be straightened. Check all sheet metal parts for cracks and dents.

INTAKE & EXHAUST MANIFOLDS

Using solvent cleaning or bead blasting, clean manifolds for inspection. If intake manifold has an exhaust crossover, all carbon deposits must be removed. Inspect manifolds for cracks, burned or erroded areas, corrosion and damage to fasteners.

Exhaust heat and products of combustion, cause threads of fasteners to corrode. Replace studs and bolts as necessary. On "V" type intake manifolds, sheet metal oil shield must be removed for proper cleaning and inspection. Ensure all manifold parting surfaces are flat and free of burrs.

CYLINDER HEAD REPLACEMENT

REMOVAL

Remove intake and exhaust manifolds and valve cover. Cylinder head and camshaft carrier bolts (if equipped), should be removed only when engine is cold. On many aluminum cylinder heads, removal while hot will cause cylinder head warpage. Mark rocker arm or overhead cam components for location.

Remove rocker arm components or overhead cam components. Components must be installed in original location. Individual design rocker arms may utilize shafts, ball-type pedestal mounts or no rocker arms. For all design types, wire components together and identify according to corresponding valve. Remove cylinder head bolts. Note length and location. Some applications require cylinder head bolts be removed in proper sequence to prevent cylinder head damage. *See Fig. 1.* Remove cylinder head.

INSTALLATION

Ensure all surfaces and head bolts are clean. Check that head bolt holes of cylinder block are clean and dry to prevent block damage when bolts are tightened. Clean threads with tap to ensure accurate bolt torque.

Install head gasket on cylinder block. Some manufacturer's may recommend sealant be applied to head gasket prior to installation. Note that all holes are aligned. Some gasket applications may be marked so certain area faces upward. Install cylinder head using care not to damage head gasket. Ensure cylinder head is fully seated on cylinder block.

Some applications require head bolts be coated with sealant prior to installation. This is done if head bolts are exposed to water passages. Some applications require head bolts be coated with light coat of engine oil.

Install head bolts. Head bolts should be tightened in proper steps and sequence to specification. *See Fig. 1.* Install remaining components. Tighten all bolts to specification. Adjust valves if required. See VALVE ADJUSTMENT in this article.

NOTE: Some manufacturer's require that head bolts be retightened after specified amount of operation. This must be done to prevent head gasket failure.

Fig. 1: Typical Cylinder Head Tightening Sequence

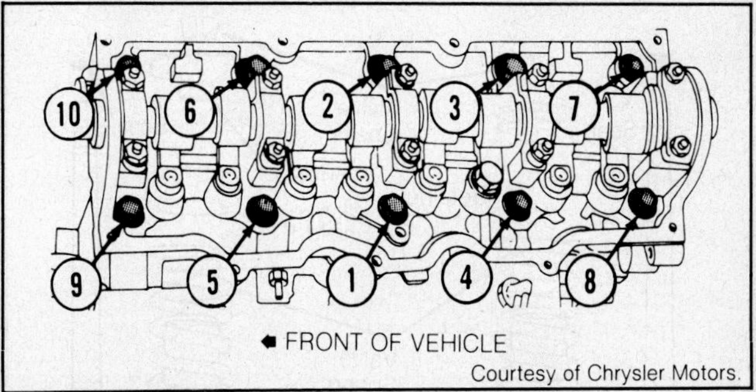

Reverse tightening sequence for removal.

VALVE ADJUSTMENT

Engine specifications will indicate valve train clearance and temperature at which adjustment is to be made on most models. In most cases, adjustment will be made with a cold engine. In some cases, both a cold and a hot clearance will be given for maintenance convenience.

On some models, adjustment is not required. Rocker arms are tightened to specification and valve lash is automatically set. On some models with push rod actuated valve train, adjustment is made at push rod end of rocker arm while other models do not require adjustment.

Clearance will be checked between tip of rocker arm and tip of valve stem in proper sequence using a feeler gauge. Adjustment is made by rotating adjusting screw until proper clearance is obtained. Lock nut is then tightened. Engine will be rotated to obtain all valve adjustments to manufacturer's specifications.

Some models require hydraulic lifter to be bled down and clearance measured. Different length push rods can be used to obtain proper clearance. Clearance will be checked between tip of rocker arm and tip of valve stem in proper sequence using a feeler gauge.

On overhead cam engines designed without rocker arms actuate valves directly on a cam follower. A hardened, removable disc is installed between the cam lobe and lifter. Clearance will be checked between cam heel and adjusting disc in proper sequence using a feeler gauge. Engine will be rotated to obtain all valve adjustments.

On overhead cam engines designed with rocker arms, adjustment is made at push rod end of rocker arm. Ensure that the valve to be adjusted is riding on the heel of the cam on all engines. Clearance will be checked between tip of rocker arm and tip of valve stem in proper sequence using a feeler gauge. Adjustment is made by rotating adjusting screw until proper clearance is obtained. Lock nut is then tightened. Engine will be rotated to obtain all valve adjustments to manufacturer's specifications.

Engine Overhaul Procedures

ALL ENGINES (Cont.)

CYLINDER HEAD OVERHAUL

DISASSEMBLY

Mark valves for location. Using valve spring compressor, compress valve springs. Remove valve locks. Carefully release spring compressor. Remove retainer or rotator, valve spring, spring seat and valve. *See Fig. 2.*

Fig. 2: Exploded View of Intake & Exhaust Valve Assemblies

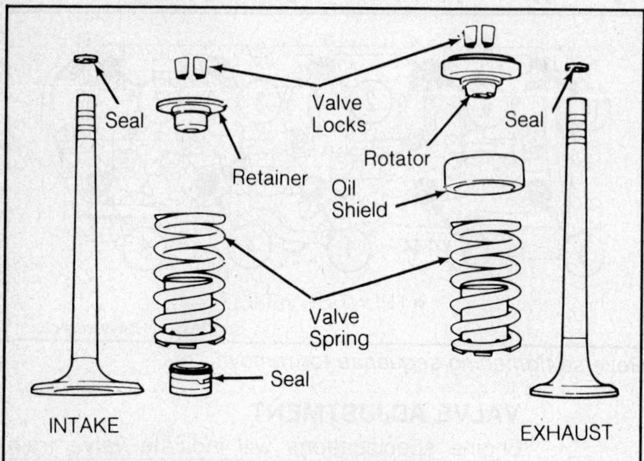

Courtesy of General Motors Corp.

CLEANING & INSPECTION

Clean cylinder head and valve components using approved cleaning methods. Inspect cylinder head for cracks, damage or warped gasket surface. Place straightedge across gasket surface. Determine clearance at center of straightedge. Measure across both diagonals, longitudinal centerline and across the head at several points. *See Fig. 3.*

On cast cylinder heads, if warpage exceeds .003" (.08 mm) in a 6" span, or .006" (.15 mm) over total length, cylinder head must be resurfaced. On most aluminum cylinder heads, if warpage exceeds .002" (.05 mm) in any area, cylinder head must be resurfaced. Warpage specification may vary with manufacturer.

Cylinder head thickness should be measured to determine amount of material which can be removed before replacement is required. Cylinder head thickness must not be thinner than manufacturer's specifications.

If cylinder head required resurfacing, it may not align properly with intake manifold. On "V" type engines, misalignment is corrected by machining intake manifold surface that contacts cylinder head. Cylinder head may be machined on surface that contacts intake manifold.

Using oil stone, remove burrs or scratches from all sealing surfaces.

VALVE SPRINGS

Inspect valve springs for corroded or pitted valve spring surfaces which may lead to breakage. Polished spring ends caused by a rotating spring, indicates that spring surge has occurred. Replace springs showing evidence of these conditions.

Inspect valve springs for squareness using a 90 degree straightedge. *See Fig. 4.* Replace valve spring if out-of-square exceeds manufacturer's specification.

Fig. 3: Checking Cylinder Head for Warpage

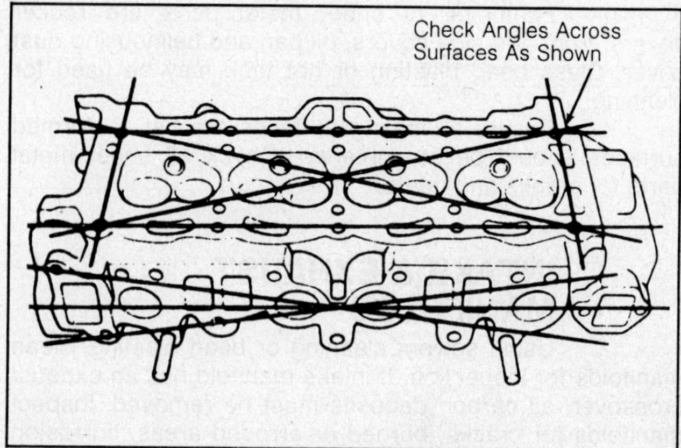

Courtesy of General Motors Corp.

Fig. 4: Checking Valve Spring Squareness

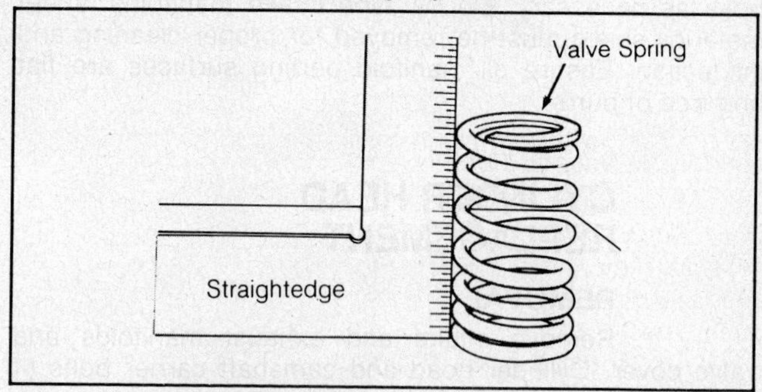

Courtesy of Ford Motor Co.

Using vernier caliper, measure free length of all valve springs. Replace springs if not within specification. Using valve spring tester, test valve spring pressure at installed and compressed heights. *See Fig. 5.*

Usually compressed height is installed height minus valve lift. Replace valve spring if not within specification. It is recommended to replace all valve springs when overhauling cylinder head.

Fig. 5: Checking Valve Spring Pressure

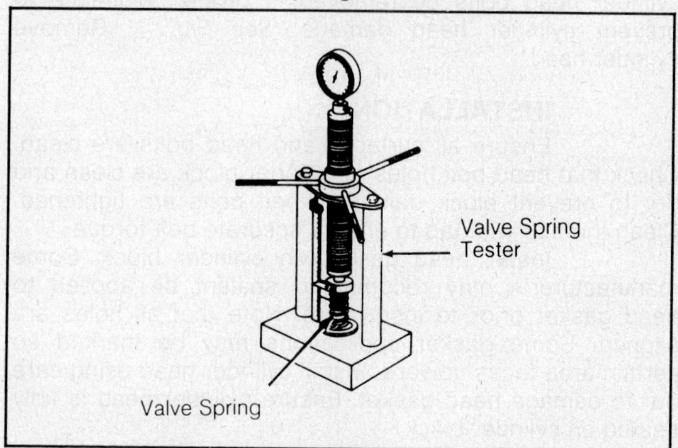

Courtesy of General Motors Corp.

VALVE GUIDE

Measuring Valve Guide Clearance

Check valve stem-to-guide clearance. Ensure valve stem diameter is within specifications. Install valve in valve guide. Install dial indicator assembly on cylinder

ALL ENGINES (Cont.)

head with tip resting against valve stem just above valve guide. See Fig. 6.

Fig. 6: Measuring Valve Stem-to-Guide Clearance

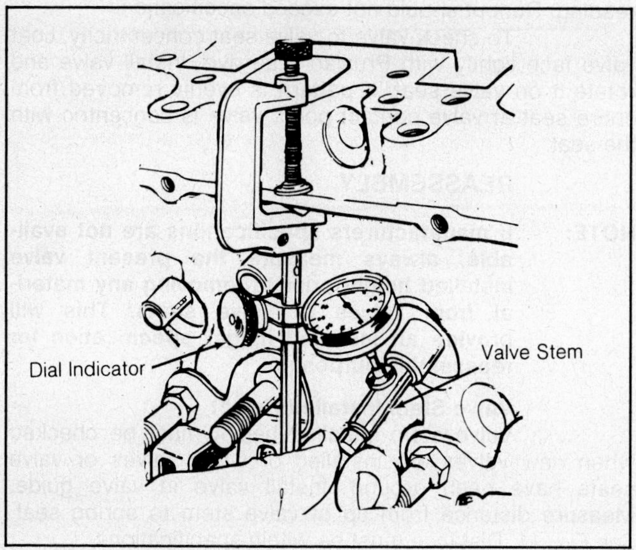

Courtesy of General Motors Corp.

Lower valve approximately 1/16" below valve seat. Push valve stem against valve guide as far as possible. Adjust dial indicator to zero. Push valve stem in opposite direction and note reading. Clearance must be within specification.

If valve guide clearance exceeds specification, valves with oversize stems may be used or valve guide must be replaced. On some applications, a false guide is installed, then reamed to proper specification. Valve guide reamer set is used to ream valve guide to obtain proper clearance for new valve.

Reaming Valve Guide

Select proper reamer for valve stem. Reamer must be of proper length to provide clean cut through entire length of valve guide. Install reamer in valve guide and rotate to cut valve guide. *See Fig. 7.*

Replacing Valve Guide

Replace valve guide if clearance exceeds specification. Valve guides are either pressed, hammered or shrunk in place, depending upon cylinder head design and type of metal used.

Remove valve guide from cylinder head by pressing or tapping out with a stepped drift. *See Fig. 8.* Once valve guide is installed, distance from cylinder head to top of valve guide must be checked. This distance must be within specification.

Aluminum heads are often heated before installing valve guide. Guide is sometimes chilled in dry ice before installation. Combination of a heated head and chilled guide insures a tight guide fit upon assembly. The new guide must be reamed to specification.

VALVES & VALVE SEATS

Valve Grinding

Valve stem O.D. should be measured in several area to indicate amount of wear. Replace valve if not within specification. Valve margin area should be measured to ensure that valve can be ground. *See Fig. 9.*

Fig. 7: Reaming Valve Guides

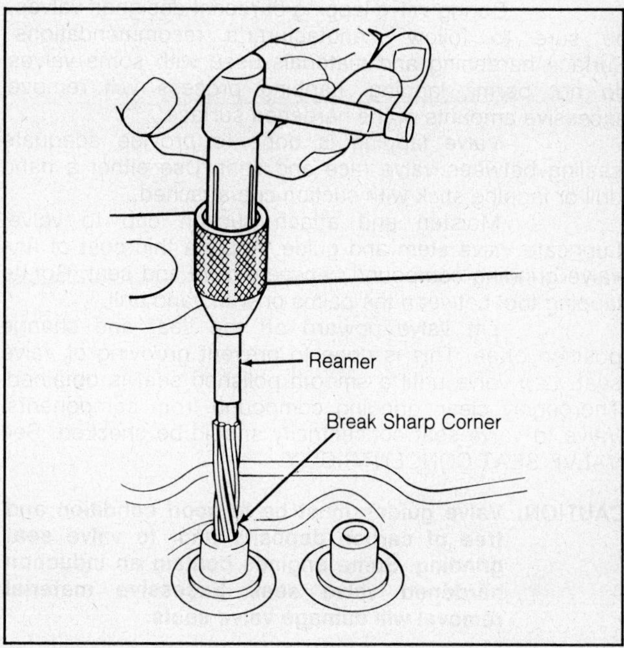

Courtesy of General Motors Corp.

Fig. 8: Typical Valve Guide Remover & Installer

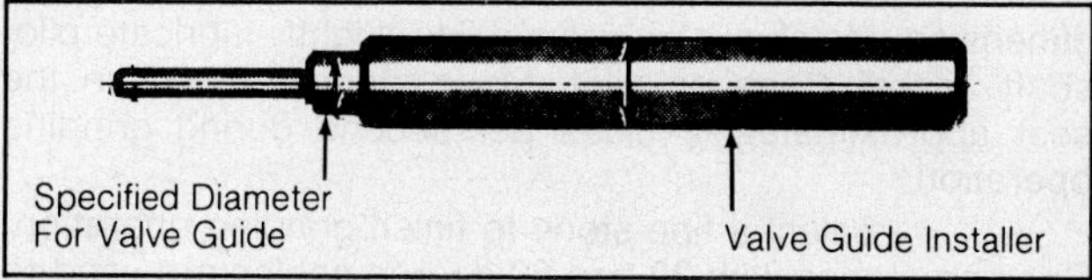

Courtesy of Chrysler Motors.

If valve margin is less than specification, this will burn the valves. Valve must be replaced. Due to minimum margin dimensions during manufacture, some new type valves cannot be reground.

Fig. 9: Measuring Valve Head Margin

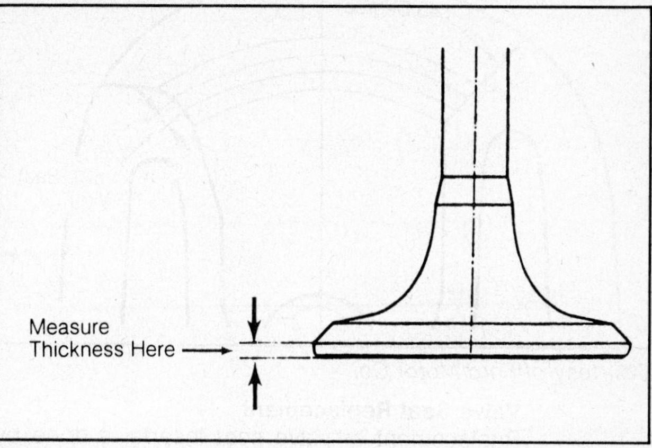

Courtesy of General Motors Corp.

Resurface valve on proper angle specification using valve grinding machine. Follow manufacturer's instructions for valve grinding machine. Specifications may indicate a different valve face angle than seat angle.

Measure valve margin after grinding. Replace valve if not within specification. Valve stem tip can be refinished using valve grinding machine.

Engine Overhaul Procedures

ALL ENGINES (Cont.)

Valve Lapping

During valve lapping of recent designed valves, be sure to follow manufacturer's recommendations. Surface hardening and materials used with some valves do not permit lapping. Lapping process will remove excessive amounts of the hardened surface.

Valve lapping is done to provide adequate sealing between valve face and seat. Use either a hand drill or lapping stick with suction cup attached.

Moisten and attach suction cup to valve. Lubricate valve stem and guide. Apply a thin coat of fine valve grinding compound between valve and seat. Rotate lapping tool between the palms or with hand drill.

Lift valve upward off the seat and change position often. This is done to prevent grooving of valve seat. Lap valve until a smooth polished seat is obtained. Thoroughly clean grinding compound from components. Valve to valve seat concentricity should be checked. See VALVE SEAT CONCENTRICITY.

CAUTION: **Valve guides must be in good condition and free of carbon deposits prior to valve seat grinding. Some engines contain an induction hardened valve seal. Excessive material removal will damage valve seats.**

Valve Seat Grinding

Select coarse stone of correct size and angle for seat to be ground. Ensure stone is true and has a smooth surface. Select correct size pilot for valve guide dimension. Install pilot in valve guide. Lightly lubricate pilot shaft. Install stone on pilot. Move stone off and on the seat approximately 2 times per second during grinding operation.

Select a fine stone to finish grinding operation. Grinding stones with 30 and 60 degree angles are used to center and narrow the valve seat as required. *See Fig. 10.*

Fig. 10: Adjusting Valve Seat Width

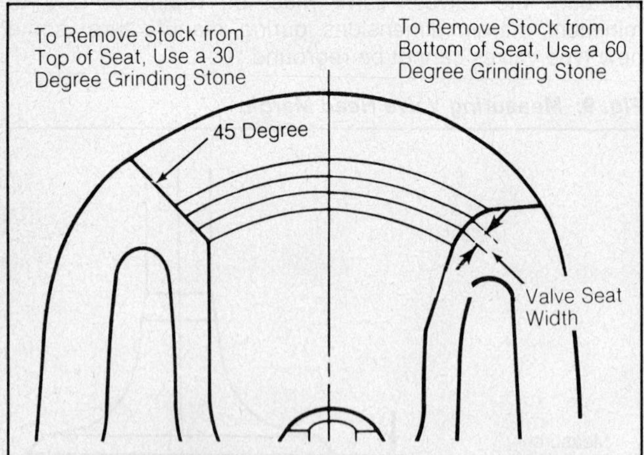

Courtesy of Ford Motor Co.

Valve Seat Replacement

Replacement of valve seat inserts is done by cutting out the old insert and machining an oversize insert bore. Replacement oversize insert is usually chilled and the cylinder head is sometimes warmed. Valve seat is pressed into the head. This operation demands specialized machine shop equipment.

Valve Seat Concentricity

Using dial gauge, install gauge pilot in valve guide. Position gauge arm on the valve seat. Adjust dial indicator to zero. Rotate arm 360 degrees and note reading. Runout should not exceed specification.

To check valve to valve seat concentricity, coat valve face lightly with Prusian Blue dye. Install valve and rotate it on valve seat. If pattern is evenly removed from entire seat at valve contact point, valve is concentric with the seat.

REASSEMBLY

NOTE: **If manufacturers specifications are not available, always measure the present valve installed height prior to removing any material from valves or valve seats. This will provide an installed height specification for reassembly purposes.**

Valve Stem Installed Height

Valve stem installed height must be checked when new valves are installed or when valves or valve seats have been ground. Install valve in valve guide. Measure distance from tip of valve stem to spring seat. *See Fig. 11.* Distance must be within specifications.

Fig. 11: Measuring Valve Stem Installed Height

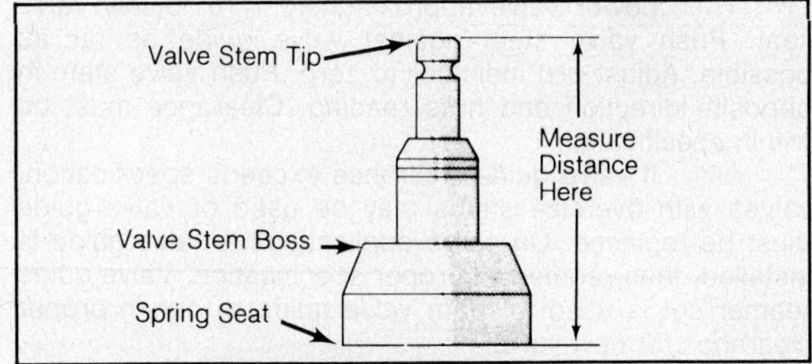

Courtesy of General Motors Corp.

VALVE STEM OIL SEALS

Valve stem oil seals must be installed on valve stem. *See Fig. 2.* Seals are needed due to pressure differential at the ends of valve guides. Atmospheric pressure above intake guide combined with manifold vacuum below guide causes oil to be drawn into the cylinder.

Exhaust guides also have pressure differential created by exhaust gas flowing past the guide, creating a low pressure area. This low pressure area draws oil into the exhaust system.

Replacement (On Vehicle)

Mark rocker arm or overhead cam components for location. Remove rocker arm components or overhead cam components. Components must be installed in original location. Remove spark plugs. Valve stem oil seals may be replaced by holding valves against seats using air pressure.

Air pressure must be installed in cylinder using an adapter for spark plug hole. An adapter can be constructed by welding air hose connection to spark plug body with porcelain removed.

Rotate engine until piston is at top of stroke. Install adapter in spark plug hole. Apply a minimum of 140 psi (9.8 kg/cm²) line pressure to adapter. Air pressure should hold valve closed. If air pressure does not hold

ALL ENGINES (Cont.)

valve closed, check for damaged or bent valve. Cylinder head must be removed for service.

Using valve spring compressor, compress valve springs. Remove valve locks. Carefully release spring compressor. Remove retainer or rotator and valve spring. Remove valve stem oil seal.

If oversized valves have been installed, oversized oil seals must be used. Coat valve stem with engine oil. Install protective sleeve over end of valve stem. Install new oil seal over valve stem and seat on valve guide. Remove protective sleeve. Install spring seat, valve spring and retainer or rotator. Compress spring and install valve locks. Remove spring comperssor. Ensure valve locks are fully seated.

Install rocker arms or overhead cam components. Tighten all bolts to specification. Adjust valves if required. Remove adpater and install spark plugs, valve cover and gasket.

VALVE SPRING INSTALLED HEIGHT

Valve spring installed height should be checked during reassembly. Measure height from lower edge of valve spring to the upper edge. DO NOT include valve spring seat or retainer. Distance must be within specifications. If valves and/or seats have been ground, an additional valve spring seat may be required to correct spring height. *See Fig. 12.*

Fig. 12: Measuring Valve Spring Installed Height

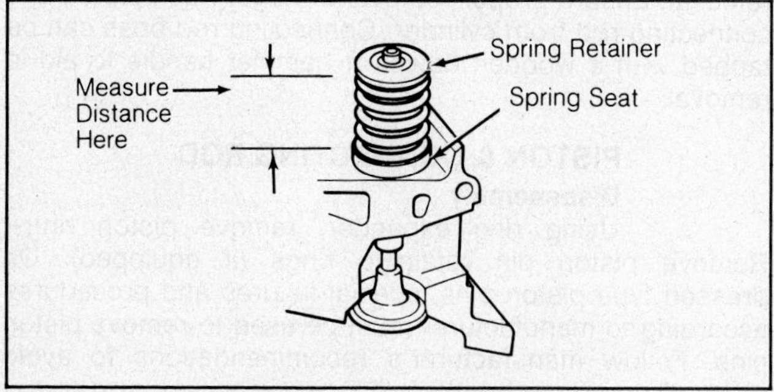

Courtesy of Ford Motor Co.

ROCKER ARMS & ASSEMBLIES

Rocker Studs

Rocker studs are either threaded or pressed in place. Threaded studs are removed by locking 2 nuts on the stud. Unscrew the stud by turning the jam nut. Coat new stud threads with Loctite and install. Tighten to specification.

Pressed in stud can be removed using a stud puller. Ream stud bore to proper specification and press in a new oversize stud. Pressed in studs are often replaced by cutting threads in the stud bore to accept a threaded stud.

Rocker Arms & Shafts

Mark rocker arms for location. Remove rocker arm retaining bolts. Remove rocker arms. Inspect rocker arms, shafts, bushings and pivot balls (if equipped) for excessive wear. Inspect rocker arms for wear in valve stem contact area. Measure rocker arm bushing I.D. Replace bushings if excessively worn.

The rocker arm valve stem contact point can be reground, using special fixture for valve grinding machine. Remove minimum amount of material as possible. Ensure all oil passages are clear. Install rocker arms in original locations. Ensure rocker arm is properly seated in push rod. Tighten bolts to specification. Adjust valves if required. See VALVE ADJUSTMENT in this article.

Push Rods

Remove rocker arms. Mark push rods for location. Remove push rods. Push rods can be steel or aluminum, solid or hollow. Hollow push rods must be internally cleaned to ensure oil passage to rocker arms is cleaned. Check push rods for damage, such as loose ends on steel tipped aluminum types.

Check push rod for straightness. Roll push rod on a flat surface. Using feeler gauge, check clearance at center. Replace push rod if bent. The push rod can also be supported at each end and rotated. A dial indicator is used to detect bends in the push rod.

Lubricate ends of push rod and install push rod in original location. Ensure push rod is properly seated in lifter. Install rocker arm. Tighten bolts to specification. Adjust valves if required. See VALVE ADJUSTMENT in this article.

LIFTERS

HYDRAULIC LIFTERS

Before replacing a hydraulic lifter for noisy operation, ensure noise is not caused by worn rocker arms or valve tips. Hydraulic lifter assemblies must be installed in original locations. Remove rocker arm assembly and push rod. Mark components for location. Some applications require intake manifold, or lifter cover removal. Remove lifter retainer plate (if used). To remove lifters, use a hydraulic lifter remover or magnet. Different type lifters are used. *See Fig. 13.*

On sticking lifters, disassemble and clean lifter. DO NOT mix lifter components or positions. Parts are select-fitted and are not interchangeable. Inspect all components for wear. Note amount of wear in lifter body-to-camshaft contact area. Surface must have smooth and convex contact face. If wear is apparent, carefully inspect cam lobe.

Inspect push rod contact area and lifter body for scoring or signs of wear. If body is scored, inspect lifter bore for damage and lack of lubrication. On roller type rollers, inspect roller for flaking, pitting, loss of needle bearings and roughness during rotation.

Measure lifter body O.D. in several areas. Measure lifter bore I.D. of cylinder block. Some models offer oversized lifters. Replace lifter if damaged.

If lifter check valve is not operating, obstructions may be preventing it from closing or valve spring may be broken. Clean or replace components as necessary.

Check plunger operation. Plunger should drop to bottom of the body by its own weight when assembled dry. If plunger is not free, soak lifter in solvent to dissolve deposits.

Lifter leak-down test can be performed on lifter. Lifter must be filled with special test oil. New lifters contain special test oil. Using lifter leak-down tester, perform leak-down test following manufacturer's instructions. If leak-down time is not within specifications, replace lifter assembly.

ALL ENGINES (Cont.)

Lifters should be soaked in clean engine oil several hours prior to installation. Coat lifter base, roller (if equipped) and lifter body with ample amount of molykote or camshaft lubricant. *See Fig. 13.* Install lifter in original location. Install remaining components. Valve lash adjustment is not required on most hydraulic lifters. Preload of hydraulic lifter is automatic. Some models may require adjustment.

Fig. 13: Typical Hydraulic Valve Lifter Assemblies

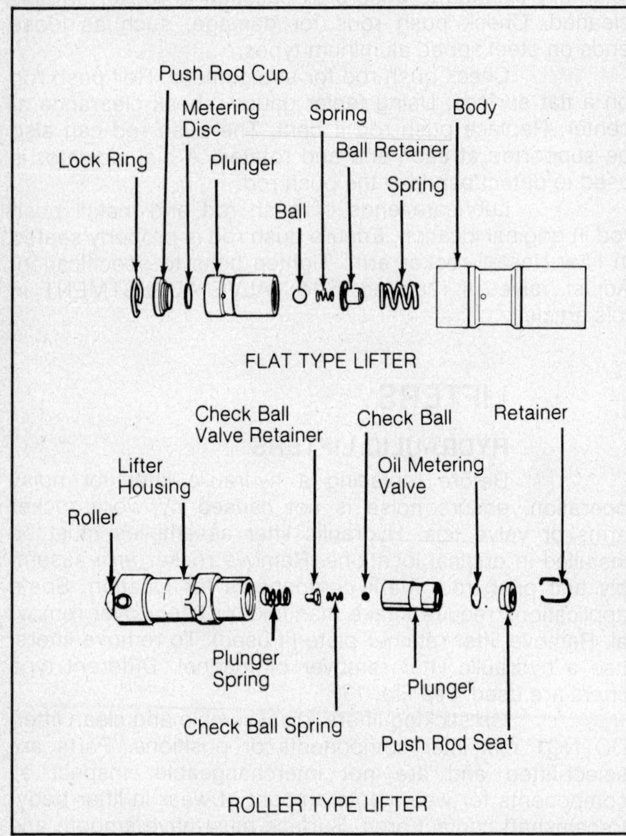

Courtesy of General Motors Corp.

Mechanical Lifters

Lifter assemblies must be installed in original locations. Remove rocker arm assembly and push rod. Mark components for location. Some applications require intake manifold, or lifter cover removal. Remove lifter retainer plate (if used). To remove lifters, use lifter remover or magnet.

Inspect push rod contact area and lifter body for scoring or signs of wear. If body is scored, inspect lifter bore for damage and lack of lubrication. Note amount of wear in lifter body-to-camshaft contact area. Surface must have smooth and convex contact face. If wear is apparent, carefully inspect cam lobe.

Coat lifter base, roller (if equipped) and lifter body with ample amount of molykote or camshaft lubricant. Install lifter in original location. Install remaining components. Tighten bolts to specification. Adjust valves. See VALVE ADJUSTMENT in this article.

PISTONS, CONNECTING RODS & BEARINGS

RIDGE REMOVING

Ridge in cylinder wall must be removed prior to piston removal. Failure to remove cylinder ridge prior to removing pistons will cause piston damage in piston ring locations.

With piston at bottom dead center, place rag in bore to trap metal chips. Install ridge reamer in cylinder bore. Adjust ridge reamer using manufacturer's instructions and remove ridge. DO NOT remove an excessive amount of material. Ensure ridge is completely removed.

PISTON & CONNECTING ROD REMOVAL

Note top of piston. Some pistons may contain a notch, arrow or be marked "FRONT". Piston must be installed in proper direction to prevent damage with valve operation.

Check that connecting rod and cap are numbered for cylinder location and which side of cylinder block the number faces. Proper cap and connecting rod must be installed together. Connecting rod cap must be installed on connecting rod in proper direction to ensure bearing lock procedure. Mark connecting rod and cap if necessary. Pistons must be installed in original location.

Remove cap retaining nuts or bolts. Remove bearing cap. Install stud protectors on connecting rod bolts. This protects cylinder walls from scoring during removal. Ensure proper removal of ridge. Push piston and connecting rod from cylinder. Connecting rod boss can be tapped with a wooden dowel or hammer handle to aid in removal.

PISTON & CONNECTING ROD

Disassembly

Using ring expander, remove piston rings. Remove piston pin retaining rings (if equipped). On pressed type piston pins, special fixtures and procedures according to manufacturer must be used to remove piston pins. Follow manufacturer's recommendations to avoid piston distortion or breakage.

Cleaning & Inspection

Remove all carbon and varnish from piston. Pistons and connecting rods may be cleaned in cold type chemical tank. Using ring groove cleaner, clean all deposits from ring grooves. Ensure all deposits are cleaned from ring grooves to prevent ring breakage or sticking. DO NOT attempt to clean pistons using wire brush.

Inspection

Inspect pistons for nicks, scoring, cracks or damage in ring areas. Connecting rod should be checked for cracks using Magnaflux procedure. Piston diameter must be measured in manufacture's specified area.

Using telescopic gauge and micrometer, measure piston pin bore of piston in 2 areas, 90 degrees apart. This is done to check diameter and out-of-round.

Install proper bearing cap on connecting rod. Ensure bearing cap is installed in proper location. Tighten bolts or nuts to specification. Using inside micrometer, measure inside diameter in 2 areas, 90 degrees apart.

ALL ENGINES (Cont.)

Connecting rod I.D. and out-of-round must be within specification. Measure piston pin bore I.D. and piston pin O.D. All components must be within specification. Subtract piston pin diameter from piston pin bore in piston and connecting rod to determine proper fit.

Connecting rod length must be measured from center of crankshaft journal inside diameter to center of piston pin bushing using proper caliper. Connecting rods must be the same length. Connecting rods should be checked on an alignment fixture for bent or twisted condition. Replace all components which are damaged or not within specification.

PISTON & CYLINDER FIT

Ensure cylinder is checked for taper, out-of-round and properly honed prior to checking piston and cylinder fit. See CYLINDER BLOCK in this article. Using dial bore gauge, measure cylinder bore. Measure piston at right angle to piston pin in center of piston skirt area. Subtract piston diameter from cylinder bore diameter. The difference is piston-to-cylinder clearance. Clearance must be within specification. Mark piston for proper cylinder location.

ASSEMBLING PISTON & CONNECTING ROD

Install proper fitted piston on connecting rod for proper cylinder. Ensure piston marking on top of piston (if equipped) is in correspondence with connecting rod and cap number. *See Fig. 14.*

Lubricate piston pin and install in connecting rod. Ensure piston pin retainers are fully seated (if equipped). On pressed type piston pins, follow manufacturer's recommended procedure to avoid distortion or breakage.

Fig. 14: Typical Piston Pin Installation

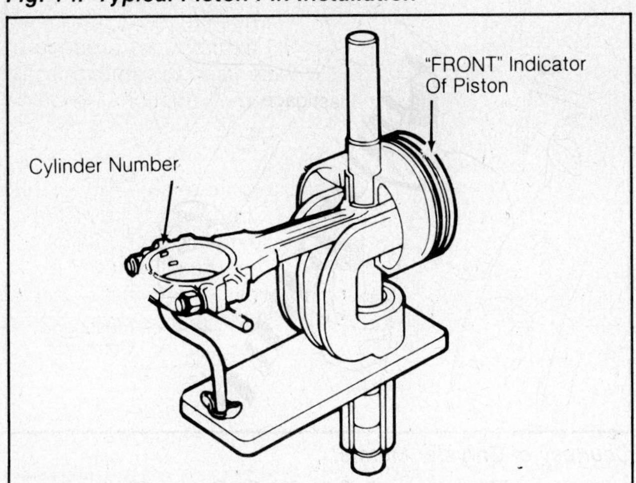

Courtesy of Ford Motor Co.

CHECKING PISTON RING CLEARANCES

Piston rings must be checked for side clearance and end gap. For checking end gap, install piston ring in cylinder which it is to be installed. Use an inverted piston and push ring to bottom of cylinder in smallest cylinder diameter.

Using feeler gauge, check ring end gap. *See Fig. 15.* Piston ring end gap must be within specification. Ring breakage will occur with insufficient ring end gap.

Some manufactures, insufficient ring end gap may be corrected by using a fine file while other manufactures recommend using another ring set. Mark rings for proper cylinder installation after checking end gap.

Fig. 15: Checking Piston Ring End Gap

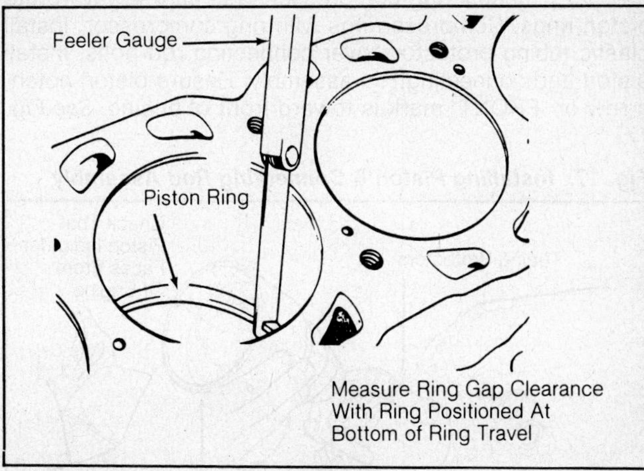

Courtesy of General Motors Corp.

For checking side clearance, install rings on piston. Using feeler gauge, measure clearance between piston ring and piston ring land. Check side clearance in several areas around piston. Side clearance must be within specification.

If side clearance is excessive, piston ring grooves can be machined to accept oversized piston rings (if available). Normal practice is to replace piston.

PISTON & CONNECTING ROD INSTALLATION

Cylinders must be honed prior to piston installation. See CYLINDER HONING under CYLINDER BLOCK in this article.

Fig. 16: Typical Piston Ring End Gap Positioning

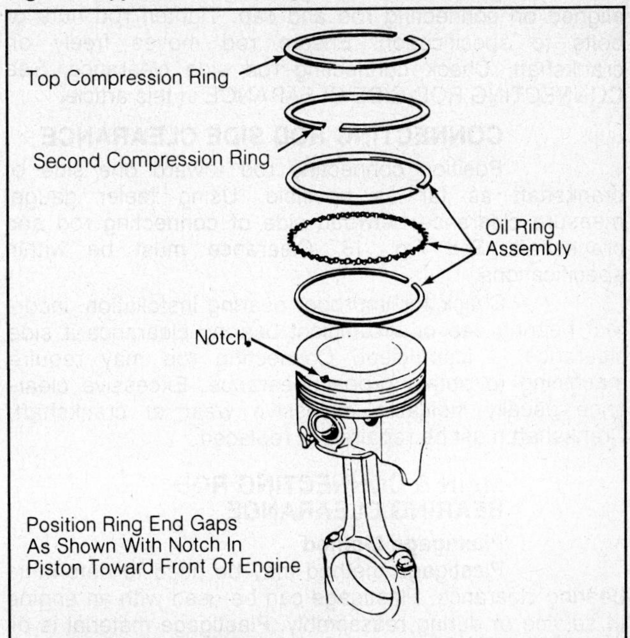

Courtesy of General Motors Corp.

ALL ENGINES (Cont.)

Install upper connecting rod bearings. Lubricate upper bearings with engine oil. Install lower bearings in rod caps. Ensure bearing tabs are properly seated. Position piston ring gaps according to manufacturer's recommendations. *See Fig. 16.* Lubricate pistons, rings and cylinder walls.

Install ring compressor. Use care not to rotate piston rings. Compress rings with ring compressor. Install plastic tubing protectors over connecting rod bolts. Install piston and connecting rod assembly. Ensure piston notch, arrow or "FRONT" mark is toward front of engine. *See Fig. 17.*

Fig. 17: Installing Piston & Connecting Rod Assembly

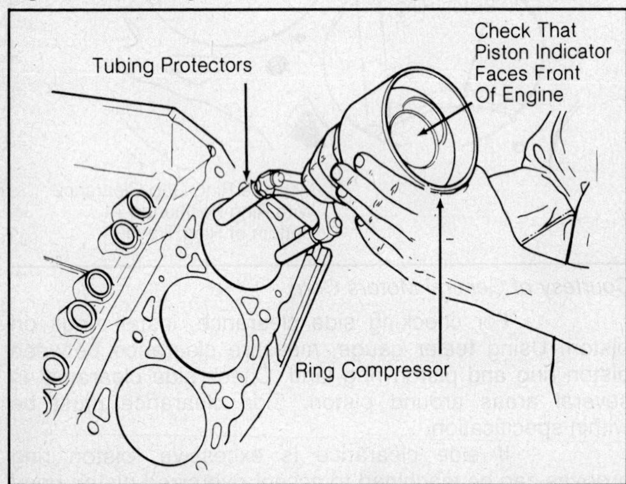

Courtesy of Ford Motor Co.

Carefully tap piston into cylinder until rod bearing is seated on crankshaft journal. Remove plastic protectors. Install rod cap and bearing. Lightly tighten connecting rod bolts. Repeat procedure for remaining cylinders. Check bearing clearance. See MAIN & CONNECTING ROD BEARING CLEARANCE in this article.

Once clearance is checked, lubricate journals and bearings. Install bearing caps. Ensure marks are aligned on connecting rod and cap. Tighten rod nuts or bolts to specification. Ensure rod moves freely on crankshaft. Check connecting rod side clearance. See CONNECTING ROD SIDE CLEARANCE in this article.

CONNECTING ROD SIDE CLEARANCE

Position connecting rod toward one side of crankshaft as far as possible. Using feeler gauge, measure clearance between side of connecting rod and crankshaft. *See Fig. 18.* Clearance must be within specifications.

Check for improper bearing installation, incorrect bearing cap or insufficient bearing clearance if side clearance is insufficient. Connecting rod may require machining to obtain proper clearance. Excessive clearance usually indicates excessive wear at crankshaft. Crankshaft must be repaired or replaced.

MAIN & CONNECTING ROD BEARING CLEARANCE

Plastigage Method

Plastigage method may be used to determine bearing clearance. Plastigage can be used with an engine in service or during reassembly. Plastigage material is oil soluble.

Fig. 18: Measuring Connecting Rod Side Clearance

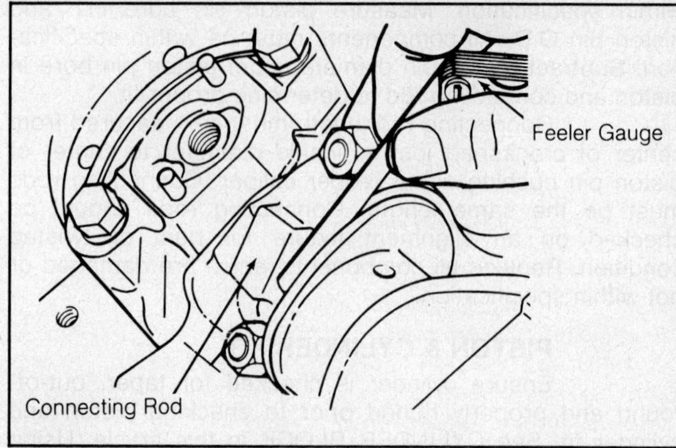

Courtesy of General Motors Corp.

Ensure journals and bearings are free of oil or solvent. Oil or solvent will dissolve material and false reading will be obtained. Install small piece of Plastigage along full length of bearing journal. Install bearing cap in original location. Tighten bolts to specification.

CAUTION: DO NOT rotate crankshaft while Plastigage is installed. Bearing clearance will not be obtained if crankshaft is rotated.

Remove bearing cap. Compare Plastigage width with scale on Plastigage container to determine bearing clearance. *See Fig. 19.* Rotate crankshaft 90 degrees. Repeat procedure. This is done to check journal eccentricity. This procedure can be used to check oil clearance on both connecting rod and main bearings.

Fig. 19: Measuring Bearing Clearance

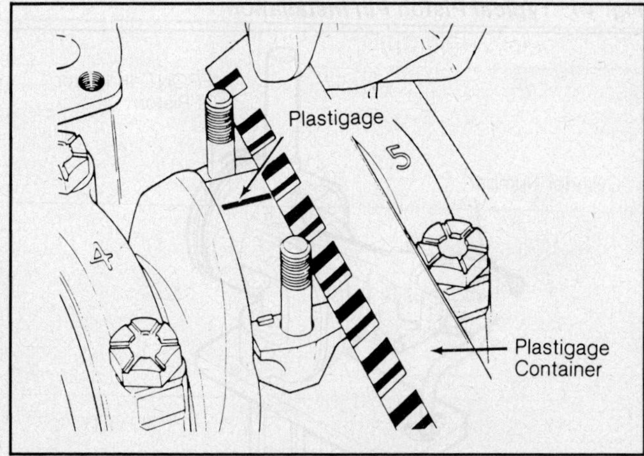

Courtesy of Chrysler Motors.

Micrometer & Telescopic Gauge Method

A micrometer is used to determine journal diameter, taper and out-of-round dimensions of the crankshaft. See INSPECTION under CRANKSHAFT & MAIN BEARINGS in this article.

With crankshaft removed, install bearings and caps in original location on cylinder block. Tighten bolts to specification. On connecting rods, install bearings and caps on connecting rods. Install proper connecting rod cap on corresponding rod. Ensure bearing cap is installed in original location. Tighten bolts to specification.

ALL ENGINES (Cont.)

Using a telescopic gauge and micrometer or inside micrometer, measure inside diameter of connecting rod and main bearings bores. Subtract each crankshaft journal diameter from the corresponding inside bore diameter. This is the bearing clearance.

CRANKSHAFT & MAIN BEARINGS

REMOVAL

Ensure all main bearing caps are marked for location on cylinder block. Some main bearing caps have an arrow stamped on it which must face front of engine. Remove main bearing cap bolts. Remove main bearing caps. Carefully remove crankshaft. Use care not to bind crankshaft in cylinder block during removal.

CLEANING & INSPECTION

Thoroughly clean crankshaft using solvent. Dry with compressed air. Ensure all oil passages are clear and free of sludge, rust, dirt, and metal chips.

Inspect crankshaft for scoring and nicks. Inspect crankshaft for cracks using Magnaflux procedure. Inspect rear seal area for grooving or damage. Inspect bolt hole threads for damage. If pilot bearing or bushing is used, check pilot bearing or bushing fit in crankshaft. Inspect crankshaft gear for damaged or cracked teeth. Replace gear if damaged. Check that oil passage plugs are tight (if equipped).

Using micrometer, measure all journals in 4 areas to determine journal taper, out-of-round and undersize. *See Fig. 20.* Some crankshafts can be reground to the next largest undersize, depending on the amount of wear or damage. Crankshafts with rolled fillet cannot be reground and must be replaced.

Fig. 20: Measuring Crankshaft Journals

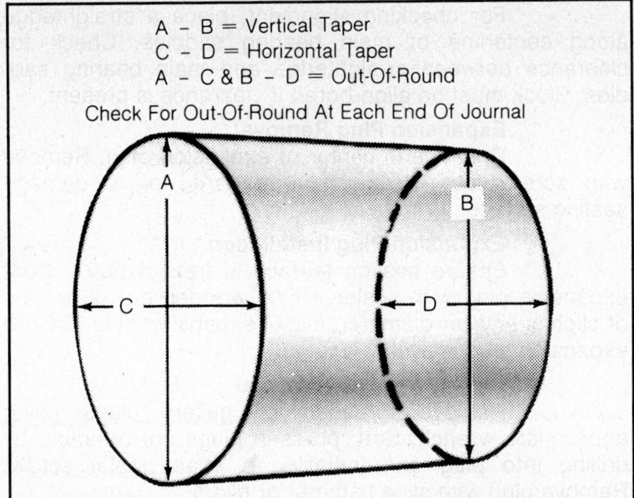

Courtesy of Ford Motor Co.

Crankshaft journal runout should be checked. Install crankshaft in "V" blocks or bench center. Position dial indicator with tip resting on the main bearing journal area. *See Fig. 21.* Rotate crankshaft and note reading. Journal runout must not exceed specification. Repeat procedure on all main bearing journals. Crankshaft must be repaired or replaced if runout exceeds specification.

Fig. 21: Measuring Crankshaft Main Bearing Journal Runout

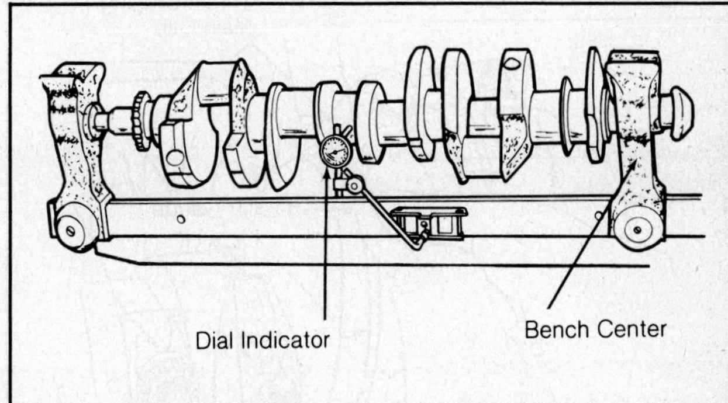

Courtesy of General Motors Corp.

INSTALLATION

Install upper main bearing in cylinder block. Ensure lock tab is properly located in cylinder block. Install bearings in main bearing caps. Ensure all oil passages are aligned. Install rear seal (if removed).

Ensure crankshaft journals are clean. Lubricate upper main bearings with clean engine oil. Carefully install crankshaft. Check each main bearing clearance using Plastigage Method. See MAIN & CONNECTING ROD BEARING CLEARANCE in this article.

Once clerance is checked, lubricate lower main bearing and journals. Install main bearing caps in original location. Install rear seal in rear main bearing cap (if removed). Some rear main bearing caps require sealant to be applied in corners to prevent oil leakage.

Install and tighten all bolts except thrust bearing cap to specification. Tighten thrust bearing cap bolts finger tight only. Thrust bearing must be aligned. On most applications, crankshaft must be moved rearward then forward. Procedure may vary with manufacturer. Thrust bearing cap is then tightened to specification. Ensure crankshaft rotates freely. Crankshaft end play should be checked. See CRANKSHAFT END PLAY in this article.

CRANKSHAFT END PLAY

Dial Indicator Method

Crankshaft end play can be checked using dial indicator. Mount dial indicator on rear of cylinder block. Position dial indicator tip against rear of crankshaft. Ensure tip is resting against flat surface.

Pry crankshaft rearward. Adjust dial indicator to zero. Pry crankshaft forward and note reading. Crankshaft end play must be within specification. If end play is not within specification, check for faulty thrust bearing installation or worn crankshaft. Some applications offer oversized thrust bearings.

Feeler Gauge Method

Crankshaft end play can be checked using feeler gauge. Pry crankshaft rearward. Pry crankshaft forward. Using feeler gauge, measure clearance between crankshaft and thrust bearing surface. *See Fig. 22.*

Crankshaft end play must be within specification. If end play is not within specification, check for faulty thrust bearing installation or worn crankshaft. Some applications offer oversized thrust bearings.

ALL ENGINES (Cont.)

Fig. 22: Checking Crankshaft End Play

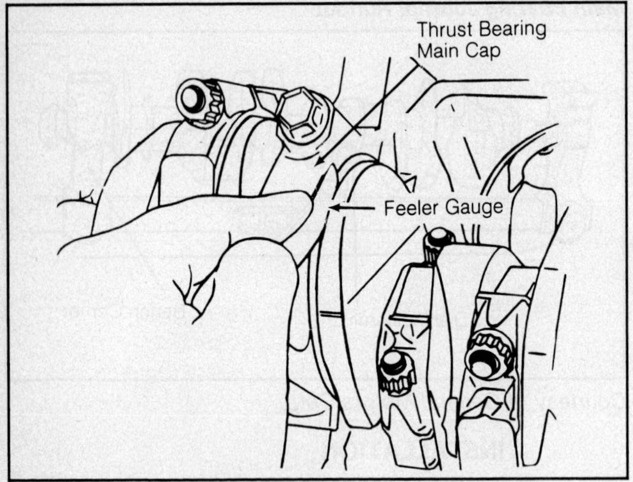

Courtesy of General Motors Corp.

CYLINDER BLOCK

Block Cleaning

Only cast cylinder blocks should be hot tank cleaned. Aluminum cylinder blocks should be cleaned using cold tank method. Cylinder block is cleaned in order to remove carbon deposits, gasket residue and water jacket scale. Remove oil galley plugs, freeze plugs and cam bearings prior to block cleaning.

Block Inspection

Visually inspect the block. Check suspected areas for cracks using the Dye Penetrant inspection method. Block may be checked for cracks using the magnaflux method.

Cracks are most commonly found at the bottom of cylinders, main bearing saddles, near expansion plugs, between cylinders and water jackets. Inspect lifter bores for damage. Inspect all head bolt holes for damaged threads. Threads should be cleaned using a thread chaser tap to ensure proper head bolt torque. Consult machine shop concerning possible welding and machining (if required).

Cylinder Bore Inspection

Inspect bore for scoring or roughness. Cylinder bore is dimensionally checked for out-of-round and taper using dial bore gauge. For determining out-of-round, measure cylinder parallel and perpendicular to the block centerline. Difference in the 2 readings is the bore out-of-round. Cylinder bore must be checked at top, middle and bottom of piston travel area.

Bore taper is obtained by measuring bore at the top and bottom. If wear has exceeded allowable limits, block must be honed or bored to next available oversize piston dimension.

Cylinder Honing

Cylinder must be properly honed to allow new piston rings to properly seat. Cross-hatching at correct angle and depth is critical to lubrication of cylinder walls and pistons.

A flexible drive hone and power drill are commonly used. Drive hone must be lubricated during operation. Mix equal parts of kerosene and SAE 20W engine oil for lubrication.

Apply lubrication to cylinder wall. Operate cylinder hone from top to bottom of cylinder using even strokes to produce 45 degree cross-hatch pattern on the cylinder wall. DO NOT allow cylinder hone to extend below cylinder during operation.

Recheck bore dimension after final honing. Wash cylinder wall with hot soapy water to remove abrasive particles. Blow dry with compressed air. Coat cleaned cylinder walls with lubricating oil.

Deck Warpage

Check deck for damage or warped gasket surface. Place a straightedge across gasket surface of the deck. Using feeler gauge, measure clearance at center of straightedge. Measure across width and length of cylinder block at several points.

If warpage exceeds specifications, deck must be resurfaced. If warpage exceeds manufacturer's maximum tolerance for material removal, replace block.

Deck Height

Distance from crankshaft centerline to block deck is called the deck height. Measure and record front and rear main journals of crankshaft. To compute this distance, install crankshaft and retain with center main bearing and cap only. Measure distance from crankshaft journal to block deck, parallel to cylinder centerline.

Add one half of main bearing journal diameter to distance from crankshaft journal to block deck. This dimension should be checked at front and rear of cylinder block. Both readings should be the same.

If difference exceeds specifications, cylinder block must be repaired or replaced. Deck height and warpage should be corrected at the same time.

Main Bearing Bore & Alignment

For checking main bearing bore, remove all bearings from cylinder block and main bearing caps. Install main bearing caps in original location. Tighten bolts to specification. Using inside micrometer, measure main bearing bore in 2 areas 90 degrees apart. Determine bore size and out-of-round. If diameter is not within specification, block must be align-bored.

For checking alignment, place a straightedge along centerline of main bearing saddles. Check for clearance between straightedge and main bearing saddles. Block must be align-bored if clearance is present.

Expansion Plug Removal

Drill hole in center of expansion plug. Remove with screwdriver or punch. Use care not to damage sealing surface.

Expansion Plug Installation

Ensure sealing surface is free of burrs. Coat expansion plug with sealer. Using wooden dowel or pipe of slightly smaller diameter, install expansion plug. Ensure expansion plug is evenly located.

Oil Gallery Plug Removal

Remove threaded oil gallery plugs using appropriate wrench. Soft, press-in plugs are removed by drilling into plug and installing a sheet metal screw. Remove plug with slide hammer or pliers.

Oil Gallery Plug Installation

Ensure threads or sealing surface is clean. Coat threaded oil gallery plugs with sealer and install. Replacement soft press-in plugs are driven in place with a hammer and drift.

ALL ENGINES (Cont.)

CAMSHAFT

CLEANING & INSPECTION

Clean camshaft with solvent. Ensure all oil passages are clear. Inspect cam lobes and bearing journals for pitting, flaking or scoring. Using micrometer, measure bearing journal O.D.

Support camshaft at each end with "V" blocks. Position dial indicator with tip resting on center bearing journal. Rotate camshaft and note reading. If reading exceeds specification, replace camshaft.

Check cam lobe lift by measuring base circle of camshaft using micrometer. Measure again at 90 degrees to tip of cam lobe. Cam lift can be determined by subtracting base circle diameter from tip of cam lobe measurement.

Different lift dimensions are given for intake and exhaust cam lobes. Reading must be within specifications. Replace camshaft if cam lobes or bearing journals are not within specifications.

Inspect camshaft gear for chipped, eroded or damaged teeth. Replace gear if damaged. On camshafts using thrust plate, measure distance between thrust plate and camshaft shoulder. Replace thrust plate if not within specification.

CAMSHAFT BEARINGS

Removal & Installation

Remove camshaft rear plug. Camshaft bearing remover is assembled with shoulder resting against bearing to be removed according to manufacturer's instructions. Tighten puller nut until bearing is removed. Remove remaining bearings, leaving front and rear bearings until last. These bearings act as a guide for camshaft bearing remover.

To install new bearings, puller is rearranged to pull bearings toward the center of block. Ensure all lubrication passages of bearing are aligned with cylinder block. Coat new camshaft rear plug with sealant. Install camshaft rear plug. Ensure plug is even in cylinder block.

CAMSHAFT INSTALLATION

Lubricate bearing surfaces and cam lobes with ample amount of Molykote or camshaft lubricant. Carefully install camshaft. Use care not to damage bearing journals during installation. Install thrust plate retaining bolts (if equipped). Tighten bolts to specification. On overhead camshafts, install bearing caps in original location. Tighten bolts to specification. Check end play.

CAMSHAFT END PLAY

Using dial indicator, check end play. Position dial indicator on front of engine block. Position indicator tip against camshaft. Push camshaft toward rear of engine and adjust indicator to zero.

Move camshaft forward and note reading. Camshaft end play must be within specification. End play may be adjusted by relocating gear, shimming thrust plate or replacing thrust plate according to manufacturer.

TIMING CHAINS & BELTS

TIMING CHAINS

Timing chains will stretch during operation. Limits are placed upon amount of stretch before replacement is required. Timing chain stretch will alter ignition timing and valve timing.

For checking timing chain stretch, rotate crankshaft to eliminate slack from one side of timing chain. Mark reference point on cylinder block. Rotate crankshaft in opposite direction to eliminate slack from remaining side of timing chain. Force other side of chain outward and measure distance between reference point and timing chain. *See Fig. 23.* Replace timing chain and gears if not within specification.

Fig. 23: Measuring Timing Chain Stretch

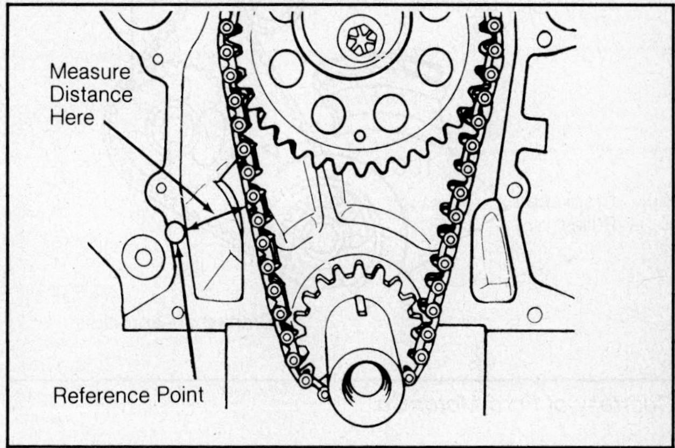

Courtesy of Ford Motor Co.

Timing chains must be installed so that timing marks on camshaft gear and crankshaft gear are aligned according to manufacturer. *See Fig. 24.*

Fig. 24: Typical Gear Timing Mark Alignment

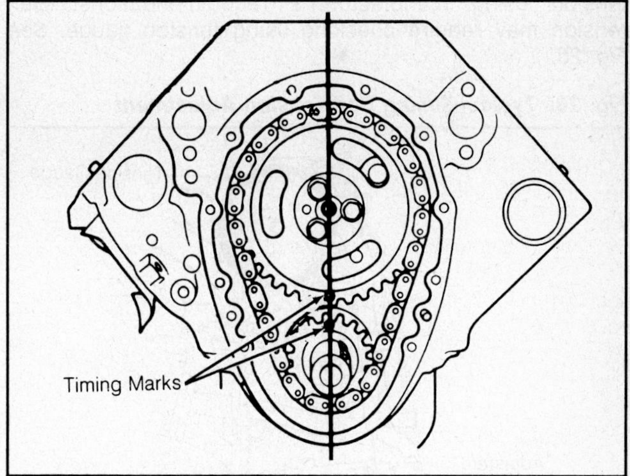

Courtesy of General Motors Corp.

TIMING BELTS

Cogged tooth belts are commonly used on overhead cam engines. Inspect belt teeth for rounded corners or cracking. Replace belt if cracked, damaged or missing teeth, or is oil soaked.

Used timing belt must be installed in original direction of rotation. Inspect all sprocket teeth for wear. Replace all worn sprockets. Sprockets are marked for timing purposes. Engine is positioned so that crankshaft sprocket mark will be upward. Camshaft sprocket is aligned with reference mark on cylinder head and timing belt is installed. *See Fig. 25.*

Engine Overhaul Procedures

ALL ENGINES (Cont.)

Fig. 25: Typical Camshaft Belt Sprocket Alignment

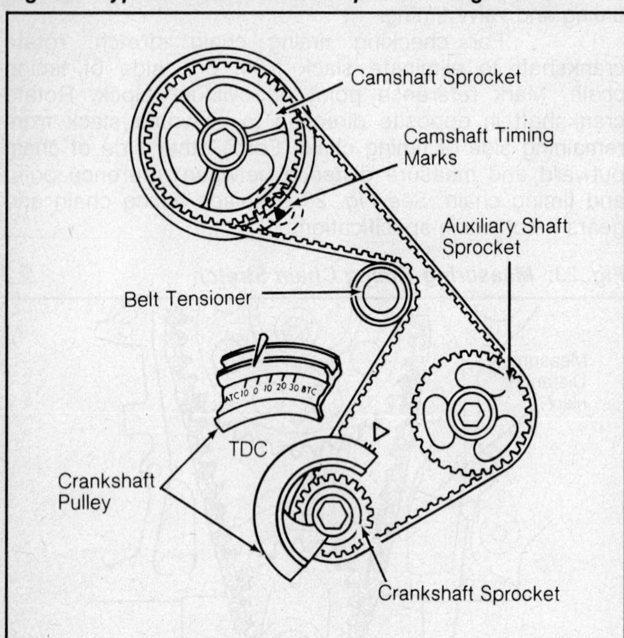

Courtesy of Ford Motor Co.

TENSION ADJUSTMENT

If guide rails are used with spring loaded tensioners, ensure at least half of original rail thickness remains. Spring loaded tensioner should be inspected for damage.

Ensure all timing marks are aligned. Adjust belt tension using manufacturer's recommendations. Belt tension may require checking using tension gauge. *See Fig. 26.*

Fig. 26: Typical Timing Belt Tension Adjustment

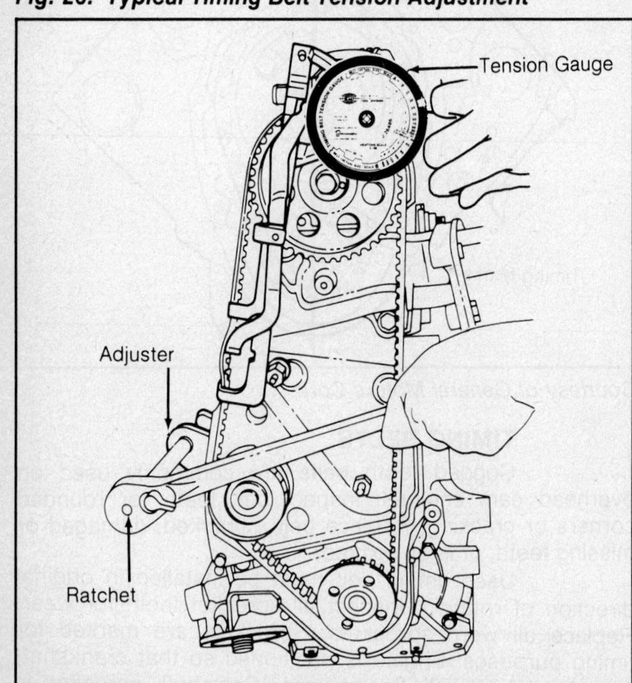

Courtesy of General Motors Corp.

TIMING GEARS

TIMING GEAR BACKLASH & RUNOUT

On engines where camshaft gear operates directly on crankshaft gear, gear backlash and runout must be checked. To check backlash, install dial indicator with tip resting on tooth of camshaft gear. Rotate camshaft gear as far as possible. Adjust indicator to zero. Rotate camshaft gear in opposite direction as far as possible and note reading.

To determine timing gear runout, mount dial indicator with tip resting on face edge of camshaft gear. Adjust indicator to zero. Rotate camshaft gear 360 degrees and note reading. If backlash or runout exceed specifications, replace camshaft and/or crankshaft gear.

REAR MAIN OIL SEAL INSTALLATION

One-Piece Type Seal

For one-piece type oil seal installation, coat block contact surface of seal with sealer if seal is not factory coated. Ensure seal surface is free of burrs. Lubricate seal lip with engine oil and press seal into place using proper oil seal installer. *See Fig. 27.*

Fig. 27: Installing Typical One-Piece Oil Seal

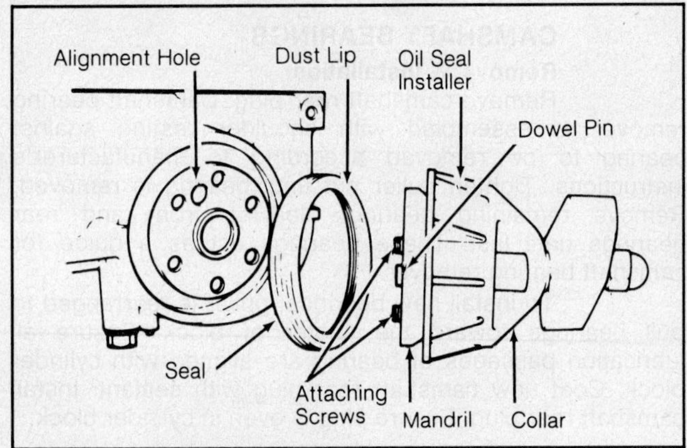

Courtesy of General Motors Corp.

Rope Type Seal

For rope type rear main oil seal installation, press seal lightly into seat area. Using seal installer, fully seat seal in bearing cap or cylinder block.

Trim seal ends even with block parting surface. Some applications require sealer to be applied on main bearing cap prior to installation. *See Fig. 28.*

Fig. 28: Typical Rope Seal Installation

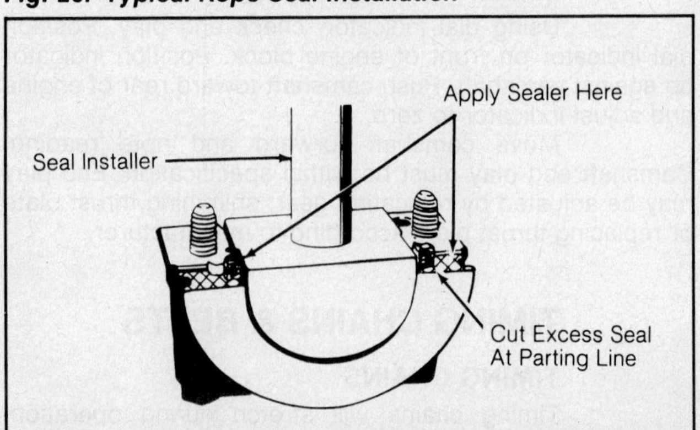

Courtesy of General Motors Corp.

ALL ENGINES (Cont.)

Split-Rubber Type Seal

Follow manufacturer's procedures when installing split-rubber type rear main oil seals. Installation procedures vary with engine type. See appropriate ENGINE article in this section. *See Fig. 29.*

Fig. 29: Typical Split-Rubber Seal Installation

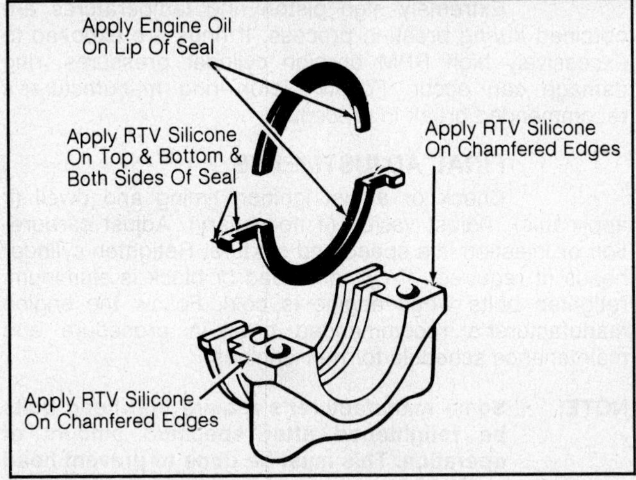

Courtesy of American Motors/Renault Corp.

OIL PUMP

ROTOR TYPE

Oil pump rotors must be marked for location prior to removal. *See Fig. 30.* Remove outer rotor and measure thickness and diameter. Measure inner rotor thickness. Inspect shaft for scoring or wear. Inspect rotors for pitting or damage. Inspect cover for grooving or wear. Replace components if not within specification or if damaged.

Measure outer rotor-to-body clearance. Replace pump assembly if clearance exceeds specification. Measure clearance between rotors. *See Fig. 31.* Replace shaft and both rotors if clearance exceeds specifications.

Install rotors in pump body. Position straightedge across pump body. Using feeler gauge, measure clearance between rotors and straightedge. Pump cover wear is measured using a straightedge and feeler gauge. Replace pump if clearance exceeds specification.

Fig. 30: Typical Rotor Type Oil Pump

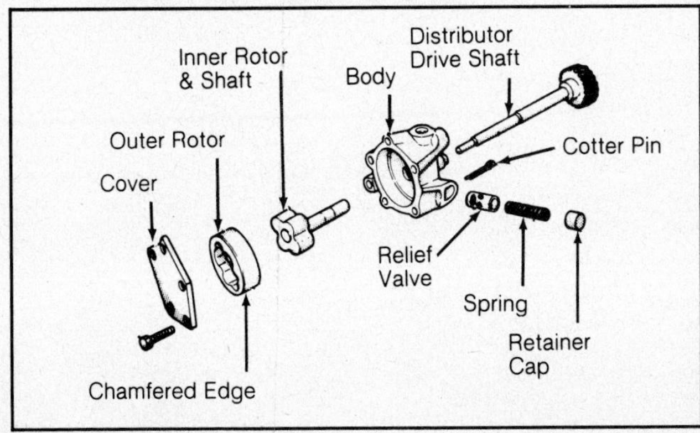

Courtesy of Chrysler Motors.

Fig. 31: Measuring Rotor Clearance

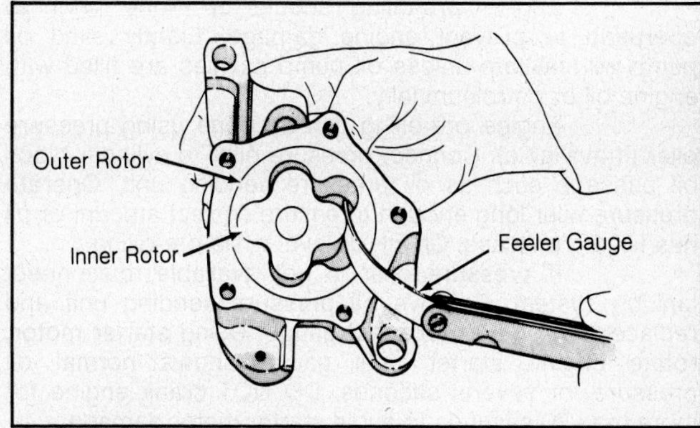

Courtesy of Chrysler Motors.

GEAR TYPE

Oil pump gears must be marked for location prior to removal. *See Fig. 32.* Remove gears from pump body. Inspect gears for pitting or damage. Inspect cover for grooving or wear.

Measure gear diameter and length. Measure gear housing cavity depth and diameter. *See Fig. 33.* Replace components if not within specification or are damaged.

Pump cover wear is measured using a straightedge and feeler gauge. Pump is to be replaced if warpage or wear exceeds specifications or mating surface of pump cover is scratched or grooved.

Fig. 32: Typical Gear Type Oil Pump

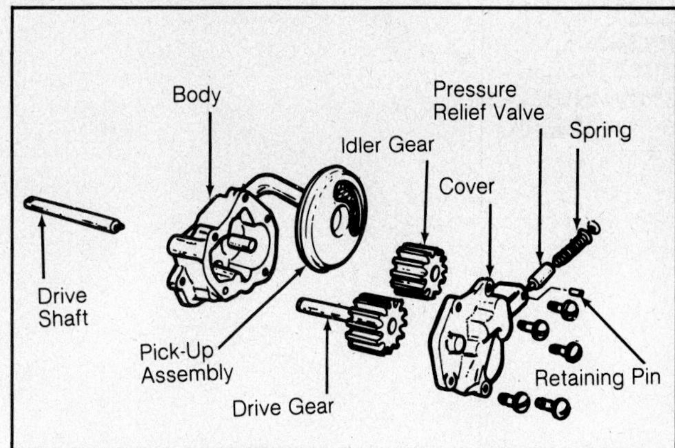

Courtesy of Chrysler Motors.

Fig. 33: Measuring Oil Pump Gear Cavity

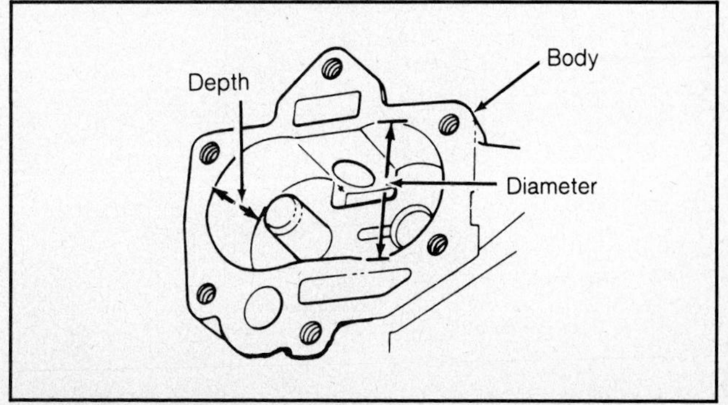

Courtesy of General Motors Corp.

ALL ENGINES (Cont.)

ENGINE PRE-OILING

Engine pre-oiling should be done prior to operation to prevent engine damage. Lightly oiled oil pump will cavitate unless oil pump cavities are filled with engine oil or petroleum jelly.

Engine pre-oiling can be done using pressure oiler (if available). Connect pressure oiler to cylinder block oil passage such as oil pressure sending unit. Operate pressure oiler long enough to ensure correct amount of oil has filled crankcase. Check oil level while pre-oiling.

If pressure oiler is not available, disconnect ignition system. Remove oil pressure sending unit and replace with oil pressure test gauge. Using starter motor, rotate engine starter until gauge shows normal oil pressure for several seconds. DO NOT crank engine for more than 30 seconds to avoid starter motor damage.

Ensure oil pressure has reached the most distant point from the oil pump. Reinstall oil pressure sending unit. Reconnect ignition system. Start engine and proceed to BREAK-IN PROCEDURE.

BREAK-IN PROCEDURE

Operate engine at low speed while checking for coolant, fuel and oil leaks. Stop engine. Recheck coolant and oil level. Adjust if necessary.

CAMSHAFT

Break-in procedure is required when new or reground camshaft has been installed. Operate and maintain engine speed between 1500-2500 RPM for approximately 30 minutes. Procedure may vary due to manufacturer's recommendations.

PISTON RINGS

Piston rings require a break-in procedure to ensure seating of rings to cylinder walls. Serious damage may occur to rings if correct procedures are not followed.

Extremely high piston ring temperatures are obtained during break-in process. If rings are exposed to excessively high RPM or high cylinder pressures, ring damage can occur. Follow piston ring manufacturer's recommended break-in procedure.

FINAL ADJUSTMENTS

Check or adjust ignition timing and dwell (if applicable). Adjust valves (if necessary). Adjust carburetion or injection idle speed and mixture. Retighten cylinder heads (if required). If cylinder head or block is aluminum, retighten bolts when engine is cold. Follow the engine manufacturer's recommended break-in procedure and maintenance schedule for new engines.

NOTE: **Some manufacturer's require that head bolts be retightened after specified amount of operation. This must be done to prevent head gasket failure.**

ENGINE TROUBLE SHOOTING

See ENGINE TROUBLE SHOOTING at beginning of ENGINE section.

1.6L 4-CYLINDER

Integra

NOTE: **For engine repair procedures not covered in this article, see ENGINE OVERHAUL PROCEDURES articles at beginning of this section.**

ENGINE CODING

ENGINE IDENTIFICATION

Engine identification code is located on engine block, above starter motor. Code is also stamped under hood, on corner of right front fender (directly behind headlight door).

ENGINE IDENTIFICATION CODE

Application	Code
1.6L	D16A1

ENGINE, MANIFOLDS & CYLINDER HEAD

ENGINE

Removal

1) Apply parking brake and block rear wheels. Disconnect battery cables and remove battery. Remove hood. Raise and support front of vehicle. Remove front wheels.

2) Remove engine splash shield. Drain engine oil, transaxle fluid, and coolant. Disconnect exhaust pipe. Disconnect air intake ducts.

3) On manual transaxle models, disconnect clutch cable. On automatic transaxle models, remove center console. Place shift lever in Reverse and remove adjuster pin. *See Fig. 1.*

Fig. 1: Automatic Transaxle Shift Linkage

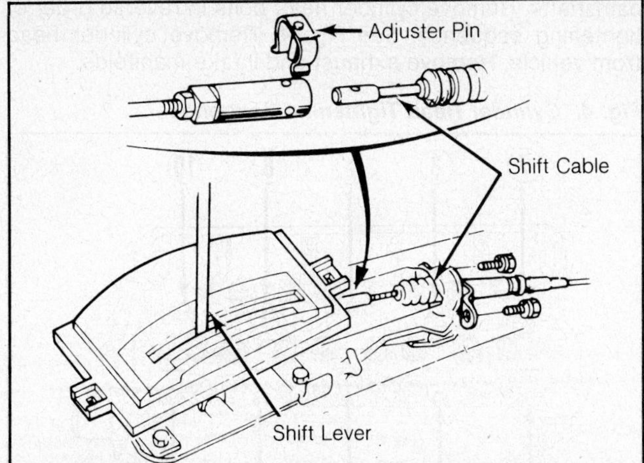

Courtesy of American Honda Motor Co., Inc.

4) On all models, disconnect transaxle ground cable. Place a shop towel on top of fuel filter and relieve fuel injection system pressure by slowly loosening fuel injection service bolt. *See Fig. 2.*

5) Remove battery tray. Disconnect wiring harness and connectors from right fender apron. Disconnect emission control box and remove from firewall. Disconnect ignition coil wiring and cruise control cable.

Fig. 2: Fuel Injection Service Bolt

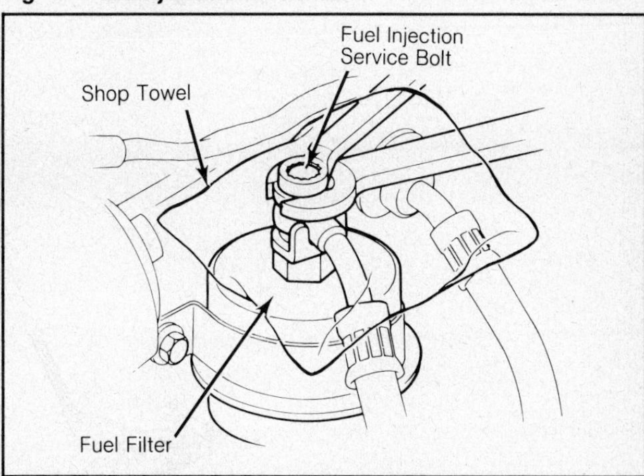

Courtesy of American Honda Motor Co., Inc.

6) Disconnect throttle cable and fuel return hose (near throttle cable). Disconnect power brake unit and cruise control servo vacuum hose. Remove vacuum canister. Disconnect ground strap (on valve cover) and wiring harness from left fender apron.

7) Remove power steering pump drive belt. Remove steering pump and set aside. DO NOT disconnect hoses. Disconnect radiator and heater hoses. On automatic transaxle models, disconnect transmission oil cooler hoses.

8) On all models, remove clip and disconnect speedometer cable from transaxle housing. DO NOT remove speedometer gear holder, or speedometer gear may fall into transaxle housing.

9) On A/C models, loosen A/C compressor idler pulley bolt and nut. Remove drive belt from A/C compressor. Remove A/C compressor and set aside. DO NOT disconnect refrigerant lines.

10) On all models, disconnect drive axles. Slide pin retainer and use a 5/16" pin punch to disconnect transaxle shift rod. Disconnect shift lever torque rod from rear of engine.

11) Disconnect alternator wire harness connectors. Remove belt tensioner bolt and remove drive belt from alternator. Remove alternator. Attach engine hoist to block and raise hoist to remove slack from chain. Remove rear engine/transaxle mount bracket.

12) Remove front engine/transaxle mount. Remove engine side mount bolt. Carefully lift engine and transaxle assembly about 6". Check for and remove any hoses, wires or other components which are still attached to both engine and chassis. Remove engine and transaxle from vehicle.

Installation

1) To install, reverse removal procedure. Tighten engine/transaxle mounts in specified sequence. *See Fig. 3.* Improper engine mount tightening will result in excessive engine vibration and premature engine mount wear.

2) When installing drive axles, use new spring clips. Insert drive axles until spring clips "click" into groove of differential side gear. Make sure all wires and hoses are connected properly. Check that all control cables are not bent or pinched, and are adjusted properly.

3) On manual transaxle models, adjust clutch pedal free play. Ensure transaxle shifts smoothly. On

Acura Engines

1.6L 4-CYLINDER (Cont.)

Fig. 3: Engine/Transaxle Mount Tightening Sequence

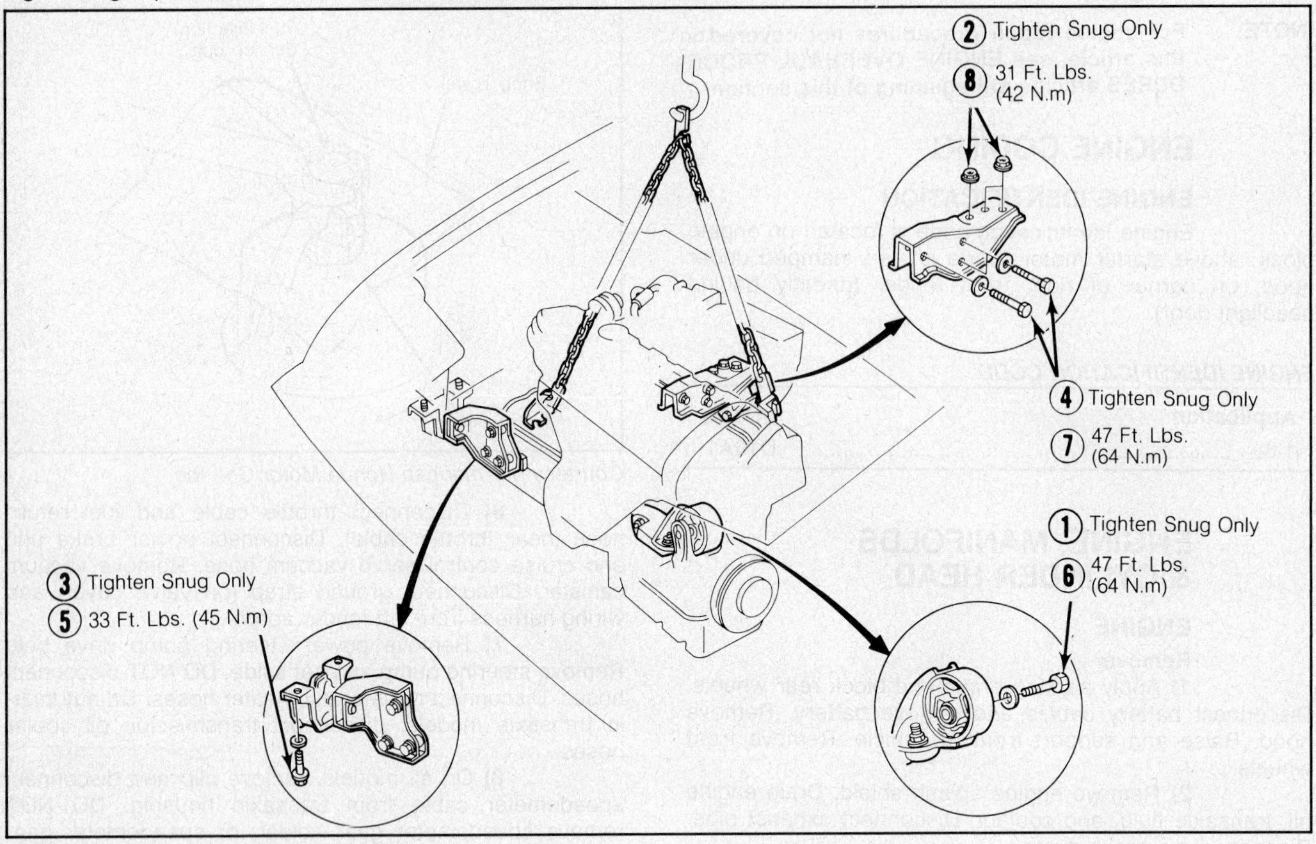

Courtesy of American Honda Motor Co., Inc.

automatic transaxle models, check that gear position agrees with shift indicator.

4) On all models, adjust tension of all drive belts. Restore all fluids to proper level. Open heater valve and loosen thermostat housing bleed bolt to bleed cooling system.

CYLINDER HEAD

Removal

1) Disconnect negative battery cable. Drain cooling system. Disconnect air intake ducts and remove air cleaner cover. Disconnect engine ground strap from top of engine valve cover.

2) Place a shop towel on top of fuel filter and relieve fuel injection system pressure by slowly loosening fuel injection service bolt. *See Fig. 2.* Disconnect throttle cable from throttle body.

3) Disconnect vacuum hose from power brake unit. Disconnect spark plug wires and remove distributor assembly. Disconnect fuel vapor canister hoses. Disconnect emission control box hoses from intake manifold.

4) On models with A/C, disconnect idle control solenoid hoses. On all models, disconnect cylinder head and intake manifold wiring harnesses. Disconnect electrical lead at oxygen sensor.

5) Disconnect radiator and heater hoses from cylinder head. Remove hose between thermostat housing and intake manifold. Disconnect exhaust pipe from exhaust manifold. Remove bolts attaching exhaust and intake manifolds and bracket.

6) Disconnect hose between intake manifold and breather chamber. Remove engine valve cover and timing belt upper cover. Turn crankshaft counterclockwise to bring piston in cylinder No. 1 to TDC of compression stroke.

7) Loosen timing belt tensioner adjustment bolt. Slip timing belt off camshaft pulleys. Remove camshafts. Remove cylinder head bolts in reverse order of tightening sequence. *See Fig. 4.* Remove cylinder head from vehicle. Remove exhaust and intake manifolds.

Fig. 4: Cylinder Head Tightening Sequence

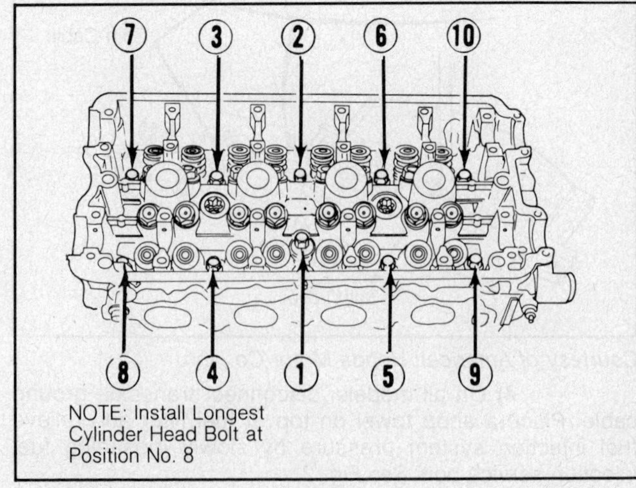

Courtesy of American Honda Motor Co., Inc.

1.6L 4-CYLINDER (Cont.)

Installation

1) Ensure all mating surfaces are clean. Check cylinder block surface for warpage. Engine block warpage must not exceed .004" (.10 mm).

2) Measure cylinder head for warpage. If warpage is less than .002" (.05 mm), install cylinder head. If warpage is between .002-.008" (.05-.20 mm), resurface cylinder head. Maximum resurface limit is .008" (.20 mm).

3) Make sure that cylinder head dowel pins, oil control jet, and "O" ring are installed in block. Install intake manifold on head and tighten nuts in a criss-cross pattern, beginning with inner nuts.

4) Ensure No. 1 piston is still on TDC. Install and tighten cylinder head bolts in 2 steps and in sequence. *See Fig. 4*. To complete installation, reverse removal procedure.

MANIFOLDS

Removal & Installation

Remove cylinder head with manifold(s) attached. Remove exhaust and/or intake manifold(s). To install manifolds, reverse removal procedure. Tighten intake manifold nuts in a crisscross pattern.

CAMSHAFT

TIMING BELT

Removal

1) Turn crankshaft counterclockwise to bring piston in cylinder No. 1 to TDC of its compression stroke. Remove all drive belts. Remove crankshaft pulley.

2) Remove engine valve cover and upper timing belt cover. Remove lower timing belt cover from engine block. Loosen timing belt tensioner to relieve tension on timing belt.

3) If timing belt is being reused, mark direction of belt rotation before removing. Slide belt off pulleys. Remove bolts, washers, camshaft pulleys, and Woodruff key (if necessary).

Installation

1) Ensure No. 1 piston is still on TDC. Install Woodruff keys, camshaft pulleys, washer, and retaining bolts (if removed). Position "UP" mark on pulleys at top. Align grooves on pulleys. *See Fig. 5*.

2) Install timing belt on pulleys. Use care not to excessively bend or twist belt. Make sure that arrow on used belt points in original direction of rotation.

3) Rotate crankshaft counterclockwise 3 teeth on camshaft pulleys to create tension on belt. Tighten tensioner adjustment bolt. Reverse removal procedure to complete installation.

CAMSHAFTS

Removal

Remove timing belt and camshaft pulleys. Remove distributor. Starting at ends and working toward middle, loosen camshaft journal cap bolts. Check camshaft end play and remove camshaft. Remove rocker arms (if necessary).

Inspection

1) Check camshaft lobes and bearing journals for excessive wear or damage. Place camshaft on "V" blocks and measure runout. Total runout must not exceed .002" (.06 mm).

Fig. 5: Camshaft Timing Marks

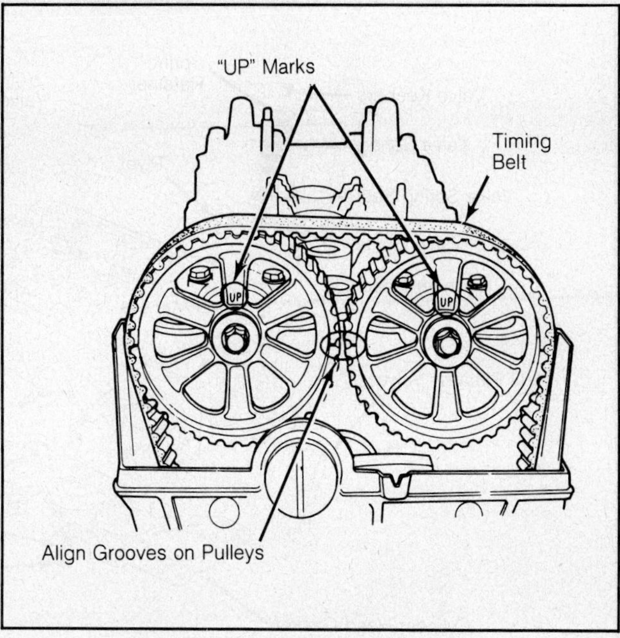

Courtesy of American Honda Motor Co., Inc.

2) Clean camshaft journals, camshaft journal caps, and cylinder head journal surfaces. Install camshaft on head and place a piece of Plastigage across each journal. Install camshaft journal caps and tighten bolts.

3) Remove camshaft journal caps and measure widest part of Plastigage on each journal. If camshaft oil clearance exceeds limit, replace camshaft. If camshaft has been replaced, replace cylinder head.

Installation

1) Oil camshaft journals and journal surfaces in caps and cylinder head. Install camshaft(s) with keyway pointing upward (No. 1 piston at TDC). Install camshaft journal bearing caps.

2) Starting with center caps and working outward, tighten camshaft journal bolts to 86 INCH lbs. (10 N.m). *See Fig. 6*. Turn each bolt 2 turns at a time to ensure rocker arms do not bind.

3) Using Camshaft Seal Driver (07947-SB00100), drive in camshaft seals. To complete installation of camshaft, reverse removal procedure. Adjust valve clearance. See VALVE CLEARANCE ADJUSTMENTS.

CAMSHAFT OIL SEALS

Removal & Installation

Remove timing belt and camshaft pulleys. See TIMING BELT. Pry out oil seals. Apply oil to camshafts and inner lip of oil seals. Install oil seals with spring side facing in. Using Camshaft Seal Driver (07947-SB00100), drive in camshaft seals. To complete installation of camshaft oil seals, reverse removal procedure.

CAMSHAFT END PLAY

Loosen rocker arm adjustment screws. Pry camshaft toward distributor side of engine. Attach dial indicator and zero it against pulley end of camshaft. Pry camshaft away from dial indicator and check end play. Desired end play is .002-.006" (.05-.15 mm). Maximum allowable end play is .020" (.50 mm). If end play exceeds limit, replace camshaft.

Acura Engines

1.6L 4-CYLINDER (Cont.)

Fig. 6: Exploded View of Cylinder Head, Camshaft & Rocker Arm Assemblies

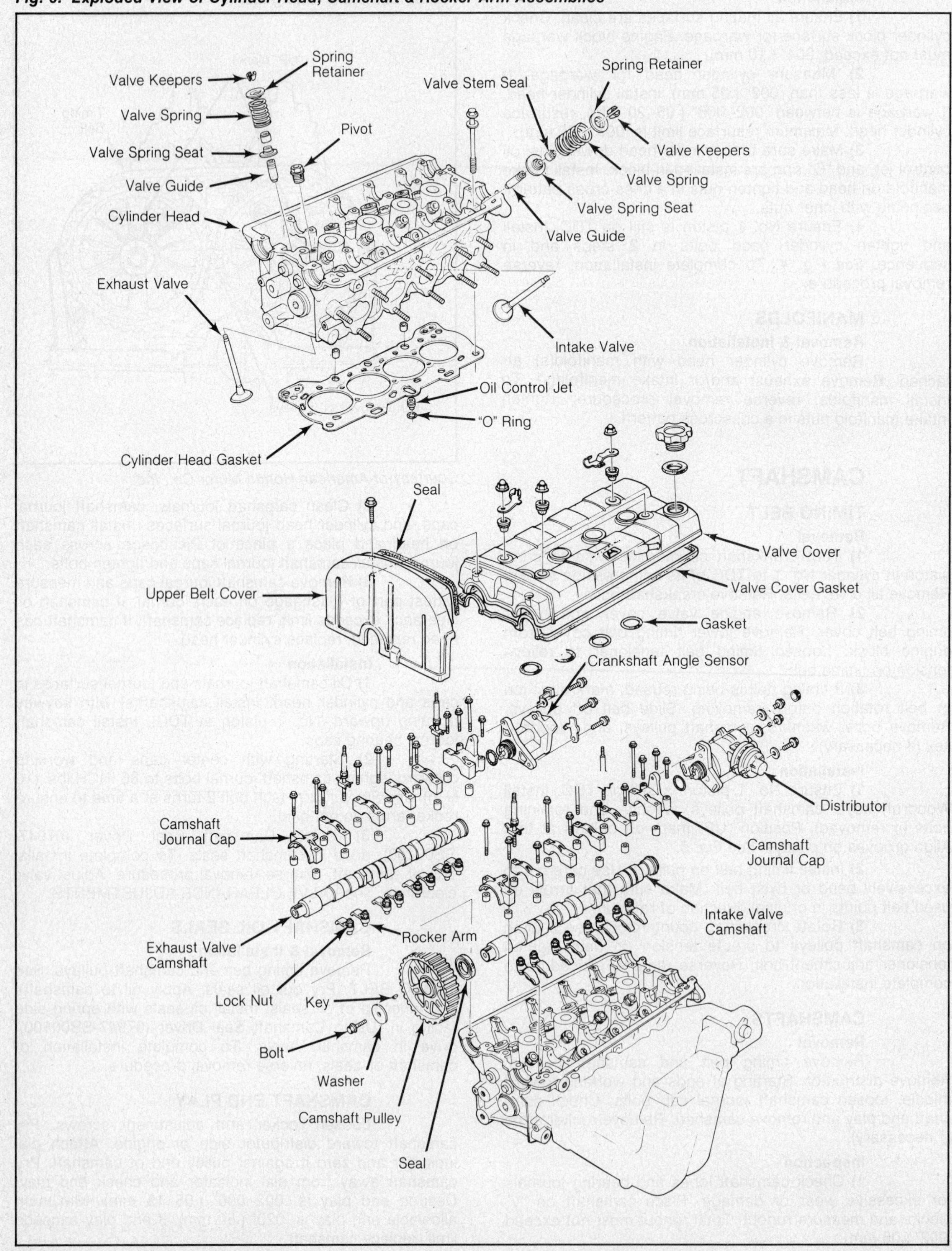

Courtesy of American Honda Motor Co., Inc.

1.6L 4-CYLINDER (Cont.)

VALVES

NOTE: **For engine repair procedures not covered in this article, see ENGINE OVERHAUL PROCEDURES articles at beginning of this section.**

VALVE ARRANGEMENT

Right Side - All Intake valves.
Left Side - All Exhaust valves.

VALVE GUIDE SERVICING

Inspection

Disassemble cylinder head. Measure valve stem diameters. Replace worn or damaged valves. Install valves in corresponding valve guides. Measure valve stem-to-valve guide clearance with a dial indicator placed on valve head.

Removal

1) Heat cylinder head to 300°F (150°C). Fabricate valve guide remover from an air-impact chisel. *See Fig. 7.* Using an air hammer and valve guide remover, force valve guide 5/64" toward combustion chamber.

Fig. 7: Valve Guide Remover Dimensions

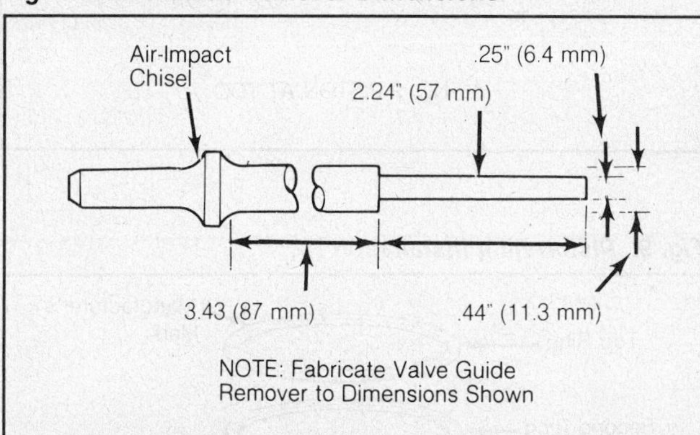

Courtesy of American Honda Motor Co., Inc.

2) Turn head over. Working from combustion chamber side of head, drive valve guide out toward camshaft side of head. If valve guide does not move, drill valve guide using a 5/16" drill bit, then try to drive it out once more.

Installation

1) Cool new valve guides in refrigerator for several hours. Remove new valve guides from refrigerator as needed. Slip a 15/64" steel washer and correct driver attachment over Valve Guide Driver (07942-6570100).

2) Install new valve guides from camshaft side of cylinder head. Drive each guide into heated head until attachment bottoms on head. It may be necessary to reheat cylinder head.

3) Intake valve guide installed height must be .79" (20 mm). Exhaust valve guide installed height must be .75" (19 mm). Using cutting oil, ream new valve guides by rotating Valve Guide Reamer (07984-6570100) clockwise the full length of valve guide bore.

VALVE STEM OIL SEALS

When installing valve stem oil seals, ensure that seals for intake valves have a White spring around neck of seal. Oil seals for exhaust valves have a Black spring around neck of seal.

VALVE SPRINGS

Removal

Remove cylinder head from engine. Using valve spring compressor, remove valve keepers, retainer, and springs. Keep parts in order for installation.

Inspection

Check valve springs for squareness. Out-of-square must not exceed .063" (1.6 mm). Measure free length of valve springs.

Installation

1) Check valve stem installed height before installing springs. If valve stem installed height exceeds limit, replace valve. If installed height is still incorrect, replace cylinder head.

2) Install springs with closely wound coils toward cylinder head or with painted part of spring on cylinder head. Install retainers and keepers. Tap end of each valve stem lightly with a plastic hammer. Measure valve spring installed height.

VALVE STEM INSTALLED HEIGHT

Application	In. (mm)
Exhaust	
New	1.770 (44.97)
Service Limit	1.802 (45.76)
Intake	
New	1.802 (45.76)
Service Limit	1.833 (46.57)

VALVE CLEARANCE ADJUSTMENTS

1) Adjust valves when engine temperature is 100°F (38°C) or less. Remove valve cover. Rotate crankshaft counterclockwise so No. 1 piston is on TDC of compression stroke.

2) Ensure "UP" marks on camshaft pulleys are up and grooves are aligned. *See Fig. 8.* Adjust valve clearance on No. 1 cylinder. Loosen lock nuts and turn adjustment screws until clearance is correct. Slide feeler gauge between camshaft lobe and rocker arm.

3) Rotate crankshaft 180 degress (camshaft pulleys turn 90 degrees) so No. 3 piston is on TDC of compression stroke. Ensure grooves on camshaft pulleys are up. *See Fig. 8.* Adjust valve clearance on No. 3 cylinder.

4) Rotate crankshaft 180 degrees so No. 4 piston is on TDC of compression stroke. Make sure grooves on camshaft pulleys align with cylinder head surface (180 degrees apart). *See Fig. 8.* Adjust valve clearance on No. 4 cylinder.

5) Rotate crankshaft 180 degrees so No. 2 piston is on TDC of compression stroke. Ensure grooves in camshaft pulleys are up. *See Fig. 8.* Adjust valve clearances on No. 2 cylinder.

VALVE CLEARANCE SPECIFICATIONS

Application	In. (mm)
Exhaust	.0059-.0075 (.15-.19)
Intake	.0051-.0067 (.13-.17)

1.6L 4-CYLINDER (Cont.)

Fig. 8: Position of Camshaft Pulleys for Valve Clearance Adjustment

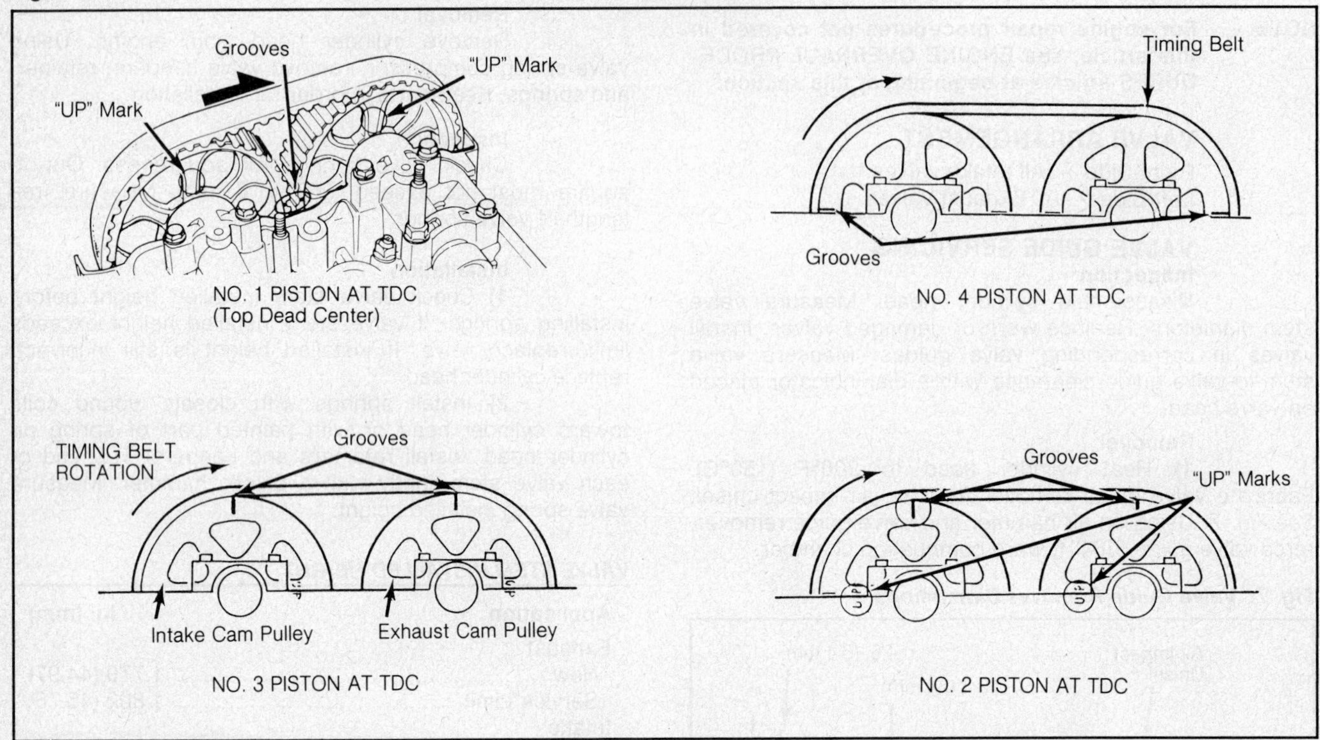

Courtesy of American Honda Motor Co., Inc.

PISTONS, PINS & RINGS

PISTON & ROD ASSEMBLY

Removal

1) Remove oil pan and cylinder head. Remove crankshaft oil seal cover, oil screen, and oil pump. Turn crankshaft so No. 2 and No. 3 crankpins are at the bottom.

2) Remove any ridge from top of cylinder bore. Mark connecting rod and cap for cylinder identification. Remove rod cap. Push piston and rod assembly out top of cylinder block. Install cap on rod from which removed.

Installation

1) Lubricate piston, rings, and cylinder bore with engine oil. Install piston rings and properly space ring end gaps on piston. *See Fig. 9*. Install piston and rod into cylinder bore.

2) Ensure arrow on piston faces timing belt side of engine and oil hole in connecting rod is positioned toward intake manifold. Install and tighten rod cap.

FITTING PISTONS

1) Measure cylinder bore out-of-round and taper. If either out-of-round or taper exceeds .002" (.05 mm), rebore cylinder for oversize pistons.

2) Measure piston-to-cylinder bore clearance. If clearance exceeds .003" (.07 mm), use micrometers to calculate difference between cylinder bore and piston diameter. If clearance exceeds limit, rebore cylinder and install oversize piston.

3) If cylinder bore is okay, hone cylinder to obtain a 60 degree cross-hatch pattern. After honing, wash cylinder bore with hot soap and water. Air dry cylinder bore and apply engine oil to prevent rusting.

Fig. 9: Piston Ring Installation

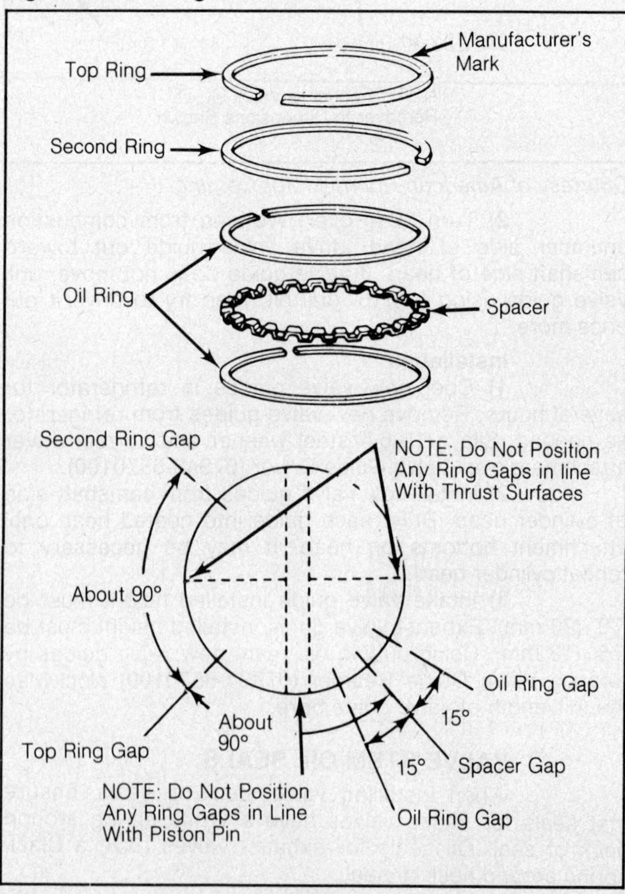

Courtesy of American Honda Motor Co., Inc.

PISTON DIAMETERS [1]

Application	In. (mm)
Standard (New) [2]	2.9520-2.9524 (74.98-74.99)
.25 O/S	2.9618-2.9622 (75.23-75.24)
.50 O/S	2.9716-2.9720 (75.48-75.49)

[1] - Measured at .63" (16 mm) from bottom of skirt.
[2] - Service limit is 2.9516" (74.97 mm).

CYLINDER BORE DIAMETERS [1]

Application	In. (mm)
Standard (New) [2]	2.9528-2.9535 (75.00-75.02)
.25 O/S	2.9612-2.9625 (75.215-75.248)
.50 O/S	2.9711-2.9724 (75.465-75.498)

[1] - Cylinder bore taper and out-of-round must not exceed .002" (.05 mm).
[2] - Service limit is 2.9555" (75.07 mm).

PISTON PIN REPLACEMENT

Removal

1) Install Piston Base Head (07973-SB00100) and Piston Pin Base Insert (07973-SB00400) into Base (07973-6570002). Turn handle on Piston Pin Driver (07973-PE00301) so piston driver length is 2.09" (53 mm).

2) Place piston on base and press out piston pin. When removing or installing piston pin, set piston in press with embossed side facing up. Be sure recessed part of piston aligns with lugs on base insert.

Inspection

1) Measure diameter of piston pin. Zero dial indicator to piston pin diameter. Insert gauge in piston boss to measure piston pin-to-piston clearance.

2) Piston pin-to-piston clearance must be .0004-.0009" (.010-.022 mm). If piston pin clearance is greater than .0009" (.022 mm), use an oversize piston pin and recheck clearance.

3) Check difference between piston pin diameter and connecting rod small end diameter. Piston pin-to-connecting rod interference must be .0006-.0016" (.014-.040 mm).

Installation

1) Ensure piston and connecting rod are positioned as shown. Turn handle on Piston Pin Driver (07973-PE00301) so piston driver length is 2.09" (53 mm).

2) Install Piston Pin Collar (07973-PE00200) in piston and connecting rod. Lightly oil new piston pin. Place piston on base and press in piston pin.

CRANKSHAFT & ROD BEARINGS

MAIN BEARINGS

1) Remove rear crankshaft oil seal cover, oil screen, and oil pump. Turn crankshaft so No. 2 and No. 3 crankpins are at the bottom. Remove connecting rod caps and bearings.

2) Ensure main bearing caps are marked for identification. Remove main bearing caps and bearing halves. Lift crankshaft out of block, being careful not to damage journals.

3) Check crankshaft for runout, out-of-round, and taper. If any measurement exceeds service limit, replace crankshaft.

4) Install crankshaft in block. Check oil clearance using Plastigage method. If engine is in vehicle, support counterweights and check only one bearing at a time. Tighten main bearing caps to 40 ft. lbs. (55 N.m).

5) If oil clearance is incorrect, remove crankshaft and upper bearing half. Install a new bearing (same color code) and recheck oil clearance. If oil clearance is still incorrect, try the next larger or smaller bearing and check oil clearance once more.

6) If proper oil clearance cannot be obtained by using larger or smaller bearings, replace crankshaft and repeat procedure.

Fig. 10: Crankshaft Main Journal & Bearing Identification Codes

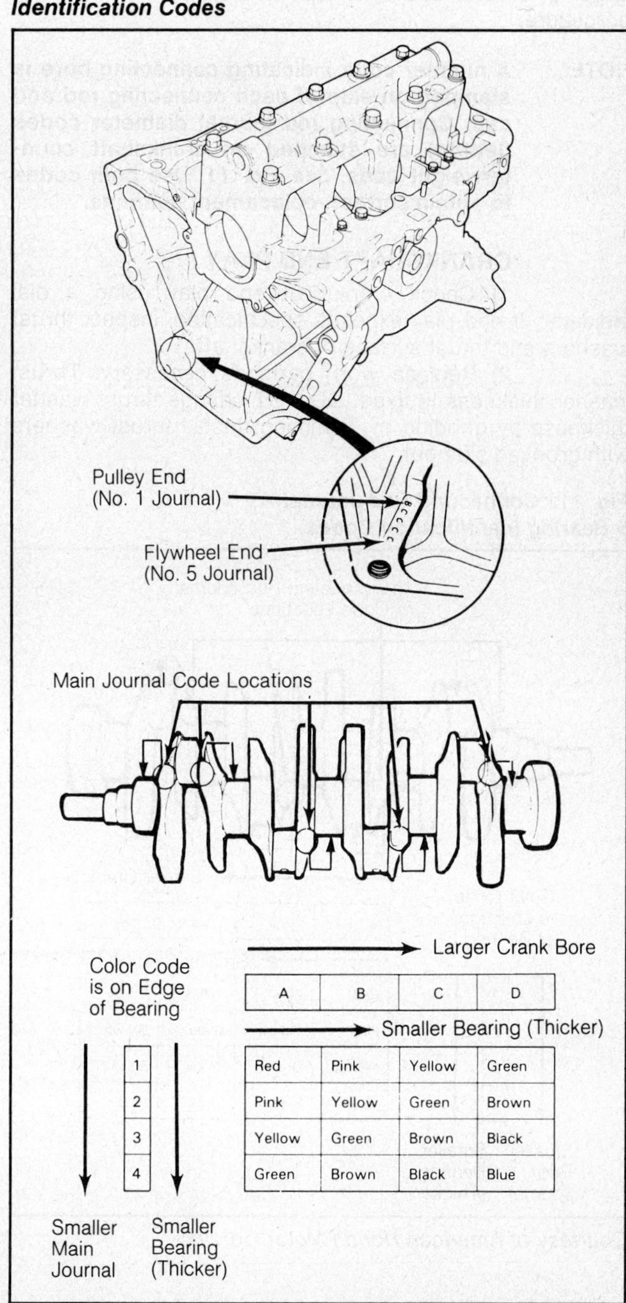

Courtesy of American Honda Motor Co., Inc.

Acura Engines

1.6L 4-CYLINDER (Cont.)

NOTE: A letter code indicating main journal bore diameters is stamped on cylinder block. See Fig. 10. Use these codes, along with crankshaft main journal diameter numbers, to obtain correct replacement bearings.

CONNECTING ROD BEARINGS

1) Check oil clearance using Plastigage method. Tighten bearing cap to 23 ft. lbs. (32 N.m).

2) If oil clearance is incorrect, remove connecting rod upper bearing half. Install a new bearing (same color code) and recheck oil clearance. DO NOT shim or file cap to adjust oil clearance.

3) If oil clearance is still incorrect, try the next larger or smaller bearing and check oil clearance once more. If proper oil clearance cannot be obtained by using larger or smaller bearings, replace crankshaft and repeat procedure.

NOTE: A number code indicating connecting bore is stamped on side of each connecting rod and cap. Connecting rod journal diameter codes (letters) are stamped on crankshaft counterweight pads. *See Fig. 11*. Use both codes to obtain correct replacement bearings.

CRANKSHAFT END PLAY

1) Check crankshaft end play using a dial indicator. If end play exceeds specification, inspect thrust washers and thrust surface of crankshaft.

2) Replace worn parts as necessary. Thrust washer thickness is fixed. DO NOT change thrust washer thickness by grinding or shimming. Install thrust washers with grooved side out.

Fig. 11: Connecting Rod Journal & Bearing Identification Codes

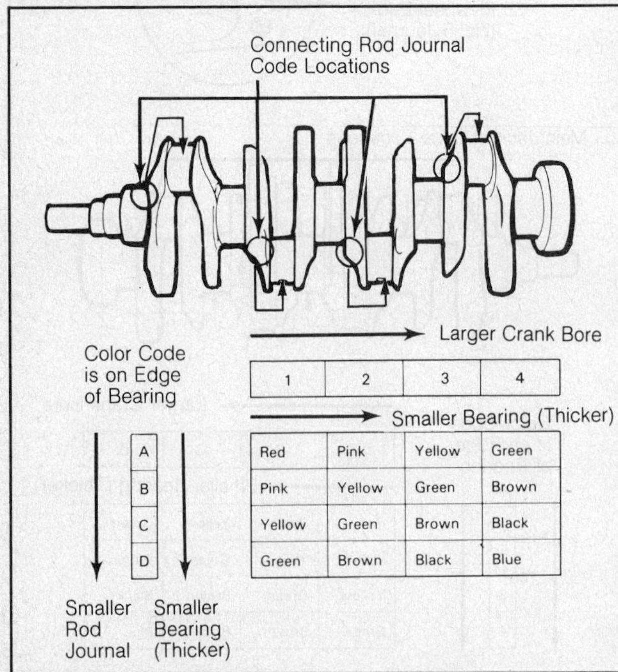

Courtesy of American Honda Motor Co., Inc.

FRONT & REAR CRANKSHAFT OIL SEALS

1) Remove rear crankshaft oil seal cover, oil screen, and oil pump. Remove rear seal from cover. Remove front seal from oil pump housing.

2) Use Oil Seal Driver (07947-6340000) to install front seal. Gently tap new oil seal into housing until it bottoms. Coat crankshaft and rear seal lip with engine oil. Use Driver (07749-0010000) with Driver Attachment (07948-SB00101) to install rear seal.

ENGINE OILING

ENGINE OILING SYSTEM

A rotor-type oil pump draws oil from oil pan and delivers it under pressure to main and connecting rod bearings. An oil hole in each connecting rod lubricates thrust side of piston and cylinder wall. An oil passage carries oil to camshaft and rocker arms. Oil spray lubricates valve stems.

CRANKCASE CAPACITY

Crankcase capacity is 3.2 qts. (3.0L) without oil filter replacement; 3.7 qts. (3.5L) when replacing oil filter. Capacity is 4.2 qts. (4.0L) after engine disassembly.

NORMAL OIL PRESSURE

Oil pressure at idle should be 21 psi (1.5 kg/cm²). Oil pressure at 3000 RPM should be 60-78 psi (4.2-5.5 kg/cm²).

OIL PUMP

Removal

Drain engine oil. Align "T" mark on crankshaft pulley with mark on cover. Remove valve cover and upper timing belt cover. Remove alternator belt, crankshaft pulley, and timing belt lower cover. Loosen belt tensioner and remove timing belt and driven pulley. Remove oil pan, oil screen, and oil pump assembly.

Disassembly

Remove 5 screws from pump housing, then separate housing and cover. Remove cotter pin, collar, spring, and relief valve.

Inspection

1) Check radial clearance between inner and outer rotor. Place a straightedge over pump housing and check axial clearance between outer pump rotor and pump housing.

OIL PUMP SPECIFICATIONS

Application	In. (mm)
Inner Rotor-to-Outer Rotor Radial Clearance	[1] .006 (.15)
Housing-to-Outer Rotor Axial Clearance	[2] .001-.003 (.03-.08)
Housing-to-Outer Rotor Radial Clearance	[1] .004-.007 (.10-.18)

[1] – Service limit is .008" (.20 mm).
[2] – Service limit is .006" (.15 mm).

1.6L 4-CYLINDER (Cont.)

2) Check radial clearance between pump housing and outer rotor. Inspect both rotors and pump housing for scoring or damage. Check that relief valve slides freely in bore. Replace parts as necessary.

Reassembly

Install relief valve assembly. Install front crankshaft oil seal in pump housing. See FRONT & REAR CRANKSHAFT OIL SEALS in this article. Install oil pump housing cover. Apply locking compound to pump housing screws. Make sure oil pump turns freely.

Installation

1) Install dowel pins and "O" ring in cylinder block. Clean oil pump mating surfaces. Apply Liquid Sealant (08740-99986) to cylinder block mating surface of oil pump.

2) Apply sealant to threads of inner bolt holes to prevent oil leaks. Install oil pump before sealant dries. Install oil screen and oil pump. Wait at least 30 minutes before filling crankcase with oil.

ENGINE COOLING

WATER PUMP

Removal

Remove timing belt. See TIMING BELT procedure in this article. Remove water pump and "O" ring seal.

Installation

1) To install water pump, reverse removal procedure. Loosen cooling system bleed bolt on thermostat housing. Fill radiator with coolant. When air bubbles no longer appear in coolant, close bleed bolt.

2) With radiator cap off, start engine. Allow engine to run until fan comes on at least twice. Add more coolant as necessary to bring level to bottom of filler neck. Install cap and check for leaks.

NOTE: **For further information on cooling systems, see ENGINE COOLING section.**

TIGHTENING SPECIFICATIONS

Application	Ft. Lbs. (N.m)
A/C Compressor/Bracket Bolts	33 (45)
Alternator Belt Adjustment Bolt	17 (23)
Alternator Mount Bolt	33 (45)
Battery Tray Bolts	17 (23)
Camshaft Pulley Bolt	27 (37)
Crankshaft Pulley Bolt	83 (112)
Connecting Rod Nuts	23 (31)
Cylinder Head Bolts	[1] 47 (64)
Engine Block-to-Side Engine Mount Bolts	29 (39)
Engine Block-to-Transaxle Housing Bolts	33 (45)
Exhaust Manifold	
Bolts	17 (23)
Nuts	26 (35)
Exhaust Pipe Flange Nuts	40 (54)
Flywheel Bolts	87 (118)
Intake Manifold Nuts	16 (22)
Intermediate Shaft Bolts	29 (39)
Main Bearing Cap Bolts	40 (54)
Oil Pump Screen Nuts	17 (23)
Power Steering Pump Bolts	35 (47)
Rocker Arm Lock Nuts	18 (24)
Rocker Arm Pivot Bolt	47 (64)
Timing Belt Adjustment Bolt	33 (45)
Torque Converter Drive Plate Bolts	54 (73)
Transaxle Mount-to-Transaxle Housing Bolts	33 (45)
	INCH Lbs. (N.m)
A/C Compressor Idler Pulley Bolt	86 (10)
Camshaft Journal Bolt	86 (10)
Crankshaft Seal Cover Bolts	108 (12)
Distributor Mount Bolts	86 (10)
Fuel Service Bolt	108 (12)
Oil Pan Bolts	108 (12)
Oil Pump Bolts	108 (12)
Shift Lever Torque Rod Bolt	86 (10)
Timing Belt Cover Bolts	86 (10)
Valve Cover Nuts	86 (10)

[1] – Tighten cylinder head in two steps. First tighten bolts to 22 ft. lbs. (30 N.m), and then tighten bolts to specification listed.

ENGINE SPECIFICATIONS

GENERAL SPECIFICATIONS

Year	DISPLACEMENT Cu. In.	DISPLACEMENT Liters	Fuel System	HP@RPM	Torque Ft. Lbs.@RPM	Compr. Ratio	BORE In.	BORE mm	STROKE In.	STROKE mm
1987	97	1.6L	Elect. Fuel Inj.	113@6250	99@5500	9.3:1	2.95	75	3.54	90

Acura Engines

1.6L 4-CYLINDER (Cont.)

ENGINE SPECIFICATIONS (Cont.)

VALVES

Engine Size & Valve	Head Diam. In. (mm)	Face Angle	Seat Angle	Seat Width In. (mm)	Stem Diameter In. (mm)	Stem Clearance In. (mm)	Valve Lift In. (mm)
1.6L							
Intake	1.177-1.185 (29.90-30.10)	45°	45°	[1] .049-.061 (1.25-1.55)	[2] .2591-.2594 (6.580-6.590)	[3] .0015-.0040 (.04-.10)	.....
Exhaust	1.059-1.067 (26.90-27.10)	45°	45°	[1] .049-.061 (1.25-1.55)	[4] .2579-.2583 (6.550-6.560)	[5] .004-.006 (.10-.15)	.....

1 – Seat width service limit .08" (2.0 mm).
2 – Intake valve stem diameter service limit .2591" (6.580 mm).
3 – Intake valve stem clearance service limit .006" (.15 mm).
4 – Exhaust valve stem diameter service limit .2579" (6.550 mm).
5 – Exhaust valve stem clearance service limit .008" (.20 mm).

CRANKSHAFT MAIN & CONNECTING ROD BEARINGS

Engine	MAIN BEARINGS				CONNECTING ROD BEARINGS		
	Journal Diam. In. (mm)	Clearance In. (mm)	Thrust Bearing	Crankshaft End Play In. (mm)	Journal Diam. In. (mm)	Clearance In. (mm)	Side Play In. (mm)
1.6L	2.1644-2.1654 (54.976-59.000)	[1] .0009-.0017 (.023-.043)	No. 4	[2] .004-.014 (.10-.36)	1.7707-1.7717 (44.976-45.000)	[3] .0008-.0015 (.020-.038)	[4] .006-.012 (.15-.30)

1 – Main bearing oil clearance service limit is .002" (.05 mm).
2 – Crankshaft end play service limit is .018" (.46 mm).
3 – Connecting rod oil clearance service limit is .002" (.05 mm).
4 – Connecting rod side play service limit is .016" (.40 mm).

PISTONS, PINS & RINGS

Engine	PISTONS	PINS		RINGS		
	Clearance In. (mm)	Piston Fit In. (mm)	Rod Fit In. (mm)	Ring No.	End Gap In. (mm)	Side Clearance In. (mm)
1.6L	[1] .0004-.0024 (.010-.060)	.0004-.0009 (.010-.023)	[2] .0006-.0016 (.015-0.040)	No. 1	[3] .006-.014 (.15-.36)	[4] .0012-.0024 (.030-.060)
				No. 2	[3] .006-.014 (.15-.36)	.0012-.0022 (.030-.055)
				Oil	[5] .008-.028 (.20-.71)	.....

1 – Piston-to-cylinder wall clearance service limit is .003" (.08 mm).
2 – Interference fit.
3 – Piston ring end gap service limit is .024" (.60 mm).
4 – Piston ring side clearance service limit is .005" (.13 mm).
5 – Oil control ring end gap service limit is .032" (.80 mm).

VALVE SPRINGS

Engine	Free Length In. (mm)	PRESSURE Lbs. @ In. (Kg @ mm)	
		Valve Closed	Valve Open
1.6L			
Intake	[1] 1.803 (45.80)	....	.....
Exhaust	[2] 1.854 (47.09)	....	....

1 – Intake valve spring free length service limit is 1.763" (44.80 mm).
2 – Exhaust valve spring free length service limit is 1.815" (46.10 mm).

CAMSHAFT

Engine	Journal Diam. In. (mm)	Clearance In. (mm)	Lobe Lift In. (mm)
1.6L	....	[1] .002-.004 (.05-.010)	....

1 – Camshaft oil clearance service limit is 0.006" (0.15 mm).

Acura & Sterling Engines

2.5L & 2.7L V6

Acura: Legend
Sterling: 825

NOTE: **For engine repair procedures not covered in this article, see ENGINE OVERHAUL PROCEDURES articles at beginning of this section.**

ENGINE CODING

ENGINE IDENTIFICATION

Engine identification code is located on engine block, behind timing belt upper cover (below oil filler cap).

ENGINE IDENTIFICATION CODES

Application	Code
2.5L	C25A1
2.7L	C27A1

ENGINE, MANIFOLDS & CYLINDER HEAD

ENGINE

Removal

1) Apply parking brake and block rear wheels. Disconnect battery cables and remove battery. Remove battery tray. Remove hood. Raise and support front of vehicle.

2) Remove front wheels. Remove engine splash shield. Drain engine oil, transaxle fluid, and coolant. Disconnect exhaust pipe. Remove air intake tube, air cleaner, and resonator tube as an assembly.

3) Disconnect oil pressure switch wire from oil filter case. Disconnect coolant hoses from engine oil cooler. Drain oil from oil filter case. Remove oil filter case from engine block.

4) Disconnect heater and radiator hoses. On automatic transaxle models, disconnect transmission oil cooler hoses from bottom of radiator. Disconnect wiring harness from right rear corner of engine compartment (next to power steering pump).

5) Disconnect wiring and hoses from power steering pump. Disconnect main fuse wiring from engine compartment relay box. Disconnect coil wire, primary lead, and condenser connector. Remove ground cables from cylinder head and transaxle.

Fig. 1: Fuel Injection Service Bolt

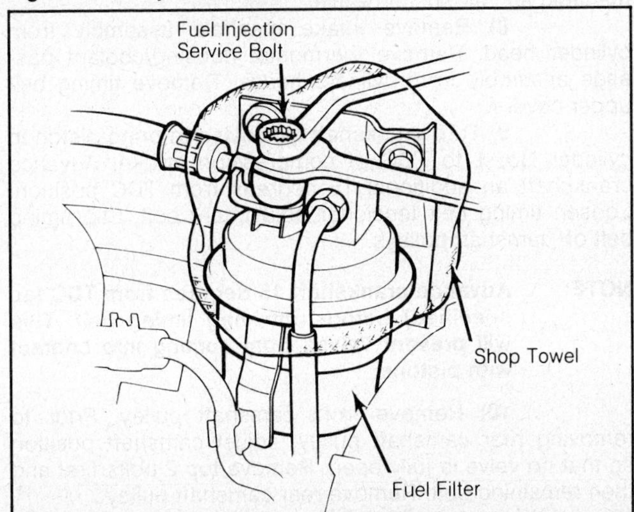

Courtesy of American Honda Motor Co., Inc.

6) Disconnect vacuum hose from cruise control actuator. Disconnect vacuum hose from power brake unit. Place a shop towel on top of fuel filter and relieve fuel injection system pressure by slowly loosening fuel injection service bolt. *See Fig. 1.*

7) Disconnect throttle cable from throttle body. Disconnect rubber tubes from emission control box (on firewall). Remove A/C compressor and set aside. DO NOT disconnect refrigerant lines.

8) On manual transaxle models, remove clutch cylinder. On automatic transaxle models, remove center console. Place shift lever in Reverse and remove adjuster pin. *See Fig. 2.* On all models, disconnect drive axles.

Fig. 2: Automatic Transaxle Shift Linkage

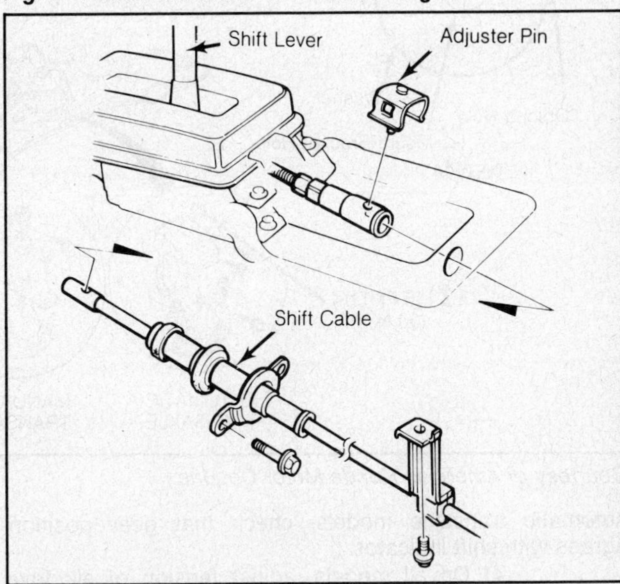

Courtesy of American Honda Motor Co., Inc.

9) Slide pin retainer and use an 5/16" pin punch to disconnect transaxle shift rod. Disconnect shift lever torque rod from rear of engine. Remove speed sensor (next to shift lever torque rod).

10) Attach engine hoist to block and raise hoist to remove slack from chain. Remove bolt from rear torque rod. Remove front/rear engine mount nuts. Remove bolts from side engine mount and pivot mount up and out of way.

11) Carefully lift engine and transaxle assembly about 6". Check for and remove any hoses, wires or other components which are still attached to both engine and chassis. Remove engine and transaxle from vehicle.

Installation

1) To install, reverse removal procedure. Tighten engine mounts in specified sequence. *See Fig. 3.* Improper engine mount tightening will result in excessive engine vibration and premature engine mount wear.

2) When installing drive axles, use new spring clips. Insert drive axles until spring clips "click" into groove of differential side gear. Make sure all wires and hoses are connected properly. Ensure control cables are not bent or pinched, and are adjusted properly.

3) On manual transaxle models, adjust clutch pedal free play. Make sure transaxle shifts smoothly. On

Acura & Sterling Engines

2.5L & 2.7L V6 (Cont.)

Fig. 3: Engine Mount Tightening Sequence

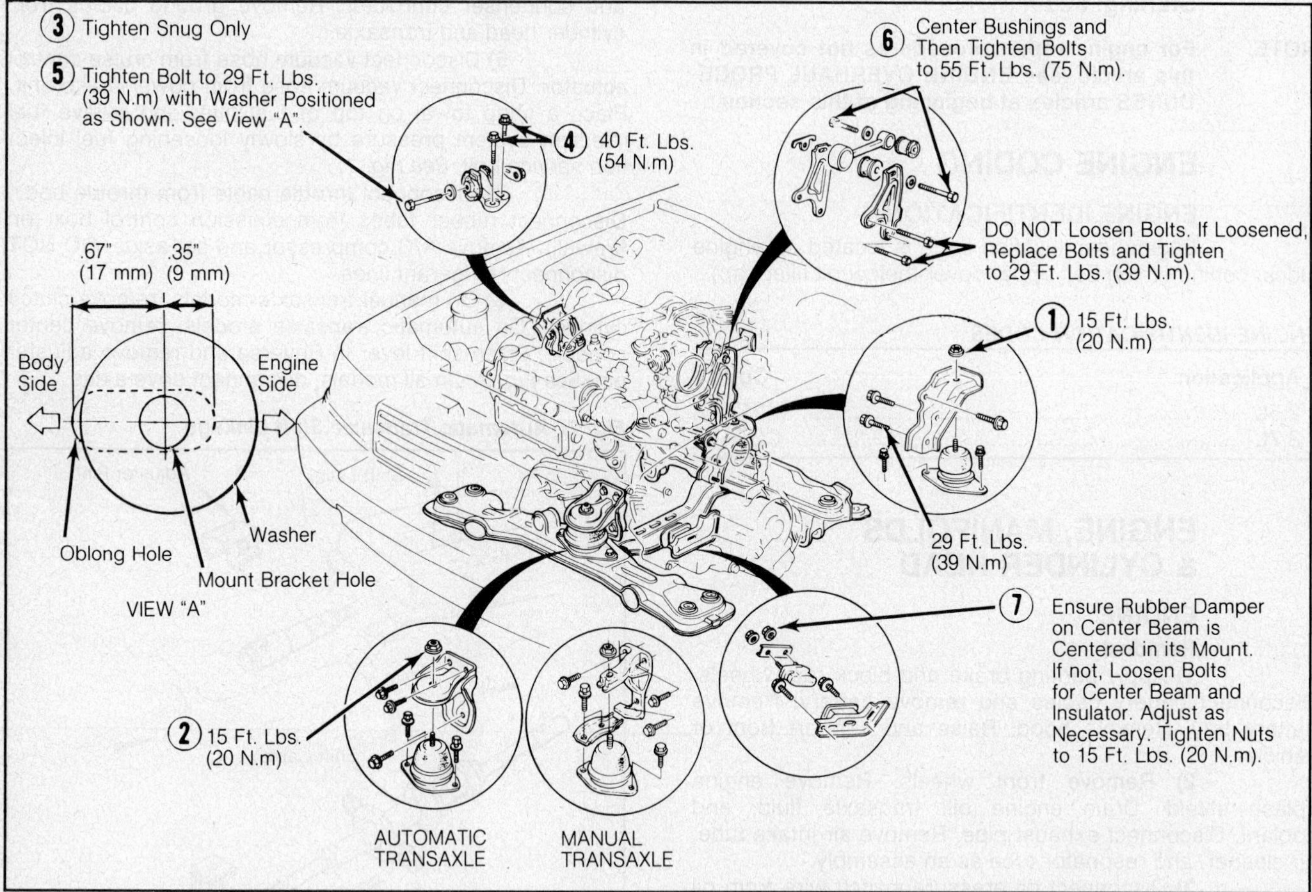

Courtesy of American Honda Motor Co., Inc.

automatic transaxle models, check that gear position agrees with shift indicator.

4) On all models, adjust tension of all drive belts. Restore all fluids to proper level. Open heater valve and loosen thermostat housing bleed bolt to bleed cooling system.

CYLINDER HEAD

Removal

1) Disconnect negative battery cable. Drain cooling system. Disconnect power brake unit vacuum hose. Disconnect engine ground strap from cylinder head and transaxle housing. Remove air cleaner cover.

2) Disconnect condenser, ignition coil wire, and ignition coil primary wiring. Place a shop towel on top of fuel filter and relieve fuel injection system pressure by slowly loosening fuel injection service bolt. *See Fig. 1*. Disconnect throttle cable from throttle body.

3) Disconnect fuel vapor canister vacuum hose (at throttle body). Disconnect engine harness from cylinder head and intake manifold. Disconnect oxygen sensor wire.

4) Disconnect radiator and heater hoses from cylinder head. Remove hose between thermostat housing and intake manifold. Disconnect exhaust pipe from exhaust manifold. Disconnect pipe and coolant by-pass outlet hose.

5) Disconnect spark plug wires and remove distributor assembly. Remove intake manifold, wire harness, and alternator pulley covers. Remove alternator and belt.

6) Remove power steering pump. On models with A/C, disconnect idle control solenoid hoses. Disconnect cruise control actuator (if equipped). On all models, disconnect exhuast pipe from manifolds. Remove air cleaner base mount bolts.

7) Disconnect hose between intake manifold and breather chamber. Remove air cleaner base. Remove EGR tube from cylinder head. Remove exhaust manifold cover nuts. Remove air suction tube nuts from exhaust manifold and air suction valve.

8) Remove intake manifold assembly from cylinder head. Remove thermostat housing/coolant passage assembly from cylinder heads. Remove timing belt upper covers.

9) Turn crankshaft clockwise to bring piston in cylinder No. 1 to TDC of compression stroke. Advance crankshaft an additional 15 degrees from TDC position. Loosen timing belt tensioner adjustment bolt. Slip timing belt off camshaft pulleys.

NOTE: Advance crankshaft 15 degrees from TDC (as specified) before removing timing belt. This will prevent valves from coming into contact with pistons.

10) Remove front camshaft pulley. Prior to removing rear camshaft pulley, adjust camshaft position so that no valve is fully open. Remove top 2 bolts first and then remaining bolt. Remove rear camshaft pulley.

2.5L & 2.7L V6 (Cont.)

Fig. 4: Exploded View of Intake Manifold Assemblies

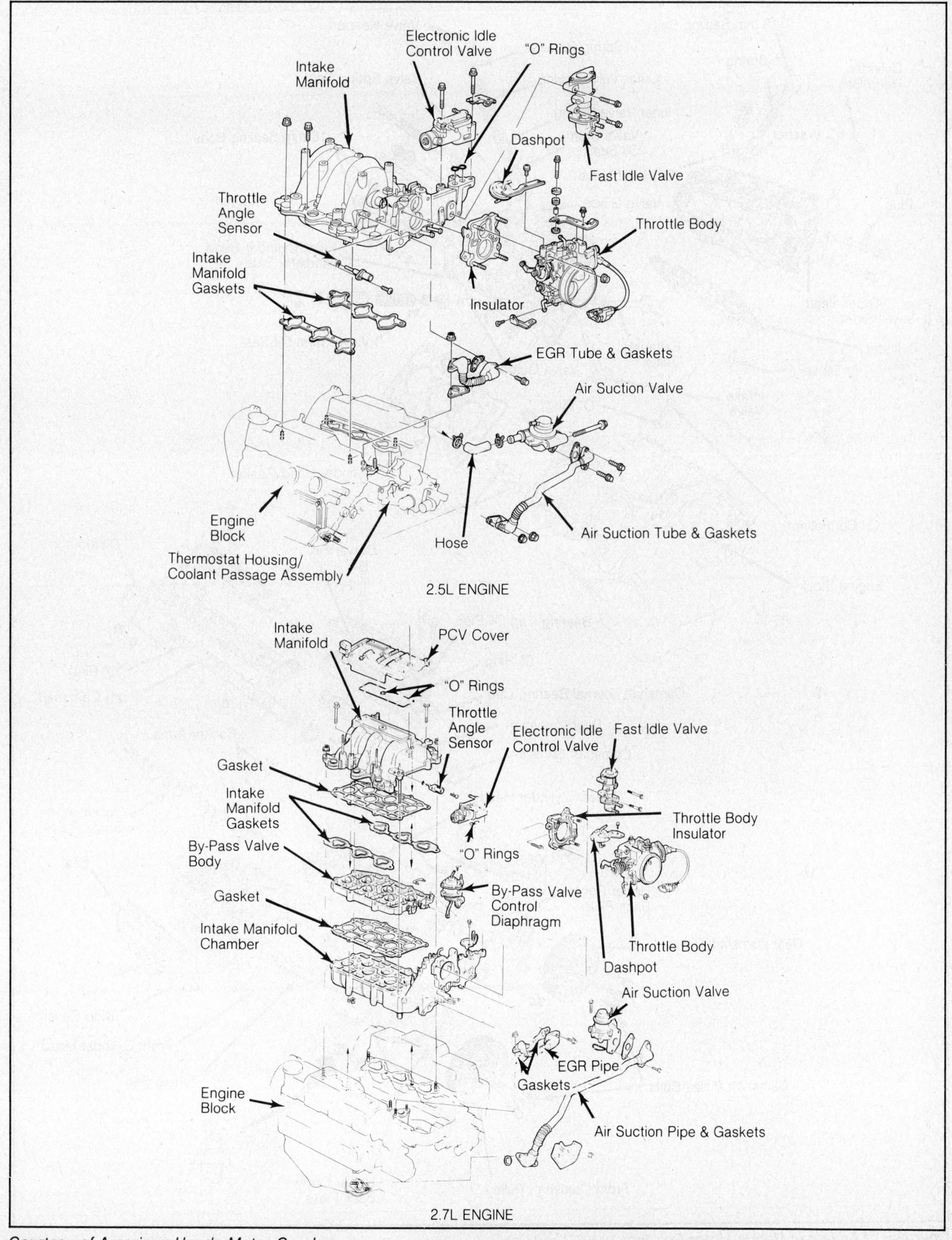

Courtesy of American Honda Motor Co., Inc.

2.5L & 2.7L V6 (Cont.)

Fig. 5: Exploded View of Cylinder Head Assembly

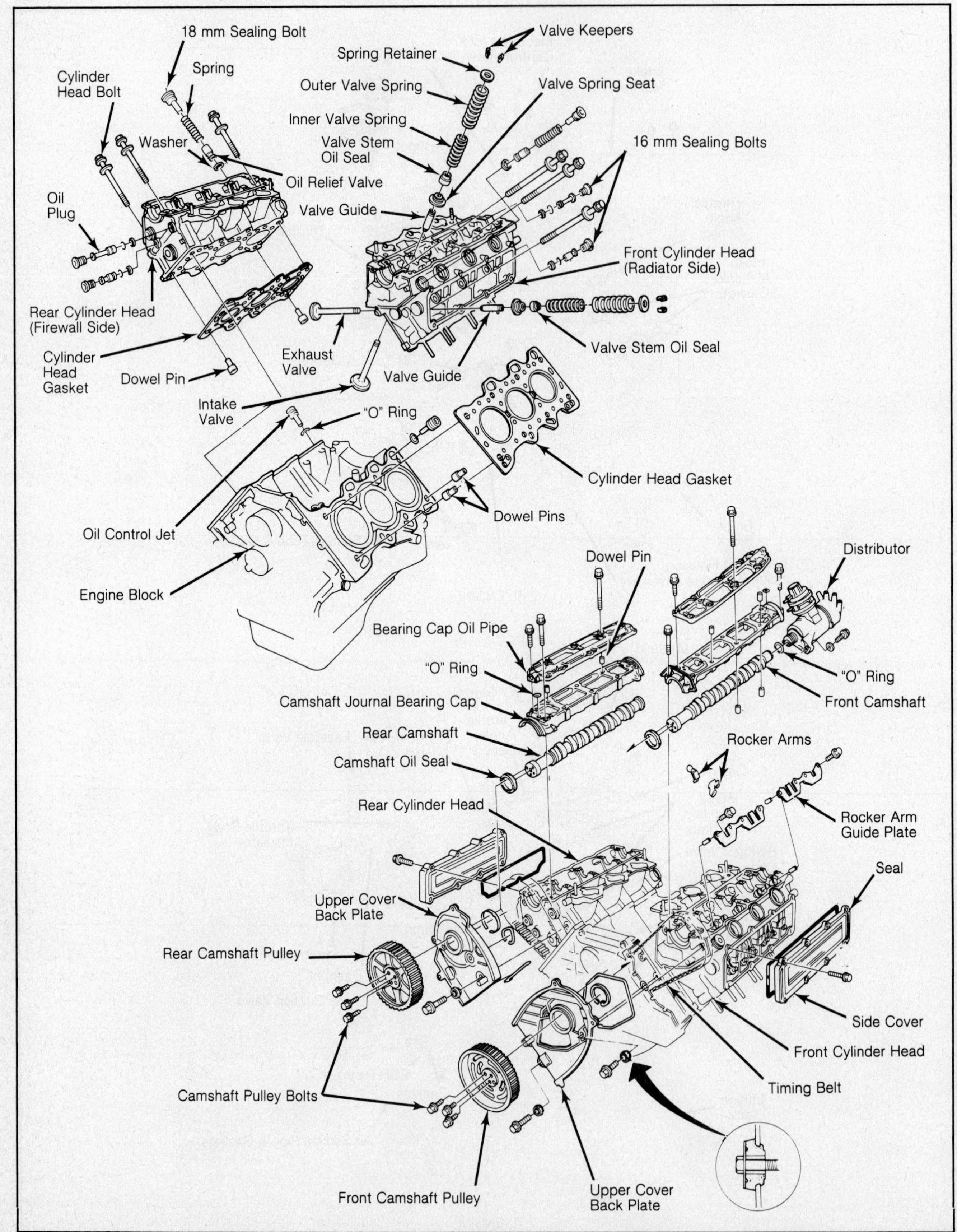

Courtesy of American Honda Motor Co., Inc.

2.5L & 2.7L V6 (Cont.)

11) Remove upper cover back plates. Remove valve covers. Remove cylinder head side covers. Remove bearing cap pipes and camshaft journal bearing caps. Remove camshafts.

12) Remove rocker arms and push rods. Mark parts for installation reference. Remove cylinder head bolts in reverse order of tightening sequence. *See Fig. 6.* Remove cylinder head from vehicle.

Fig. 6: Cylinder Head Tightening Sequence

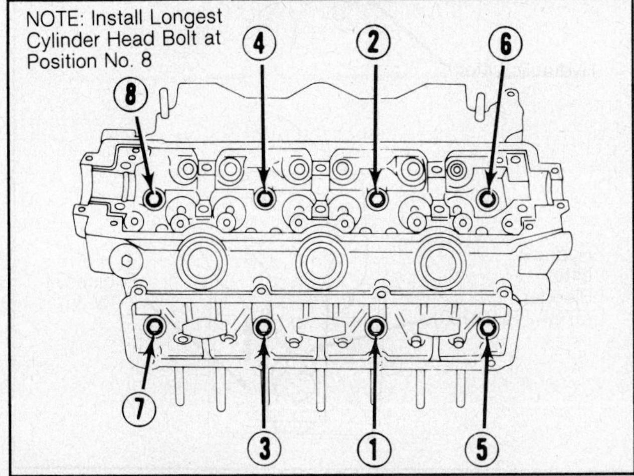

Courtesy of American Honda Motor Co., Inc.

Installation

1) Ensure all mating surfaces are clean. Check cylinder block surface for warpage. Engine block warpage must not exceed .004" (.10 mm).

2) Measure cylinder head warpage. If warpage is less than .002" (.05 mm), install cylinder head. If warpage is between .002-.008" (.05-.20 mm), resurface cylinder head. Maximum resurface limit is .008" (.20 mm).

3) Make sure cylinder head dowel pins, oil control jets, and "O" rings are installed in block. Install exhaust manifolds on heads and tighten nuts in a criss-cross pattern, beginning with inner nuts.

4) Ensure No. 1 piston is on TDC. Install and tighten cylinder head bolts in 2 steps and in sequence. *See Fig. 6.* To complete installation, reverse removal procedure.

NOTE: With cylinder heads completely reassembled, allow engine to sit for at least 5 minutes to allow hydraulic lifters to fill up with oil.

5) After 5 minutes, remove all spark plugs. Have an assistant crank engine, insert thumb over spark plug hole, and check for compression at each cylinder. Crank engine several times to ensure compression exists.

6) If any cylinder does not have compression, it may be necessary to disassemble cylinder head and check hydraulic lifters. If compression exists, install spark plugs and start engine.

MANIFOLDS

Removal & Installation

Intake and exhaust manifold removal procedure not available from manufacturer. Use illustration as a guide. *See Fig. 4.* To install, reverse removal procedure.

CAMSHAFTS

TIMING BELT

Removal

1) Turn crankshaft clockwise to bring piston in cylinder No. 1 to TDC of compression stroke. Remove pulley cover and harness cover from timing belt upper cover. Remove engine harness clamp (above side engine mount).

2) Support timing belt side of engine. Remove bolts from side engine mount and pivot mount up and out of way. Remove engine splash guard. Loosen A/C idle pulley adjustment bolt. Remove A/C belt and compressor. DO NOT disconnect refrigerant lines.

3) Remove alternator and power steering pump. DO NOT disconnect fluid lines. Remove timing belt covers. Remove crankshaft pulley. Remove timing belt lower covers.

4) Loosen timing belt tensioner to relieve tension on timing belt. If timing belt is being reused, mark direction of belt rotation before removing. Slide belt off pulleys.

Installation

1) Remove spark plugs. Turn crankshaft clockwise to bring piston in cylinder No. 1 to TDC of compression stroke. Advance crankshaft an additional 15 degrees from TDC position.

Fig. 7: Timing Belt Adjustment

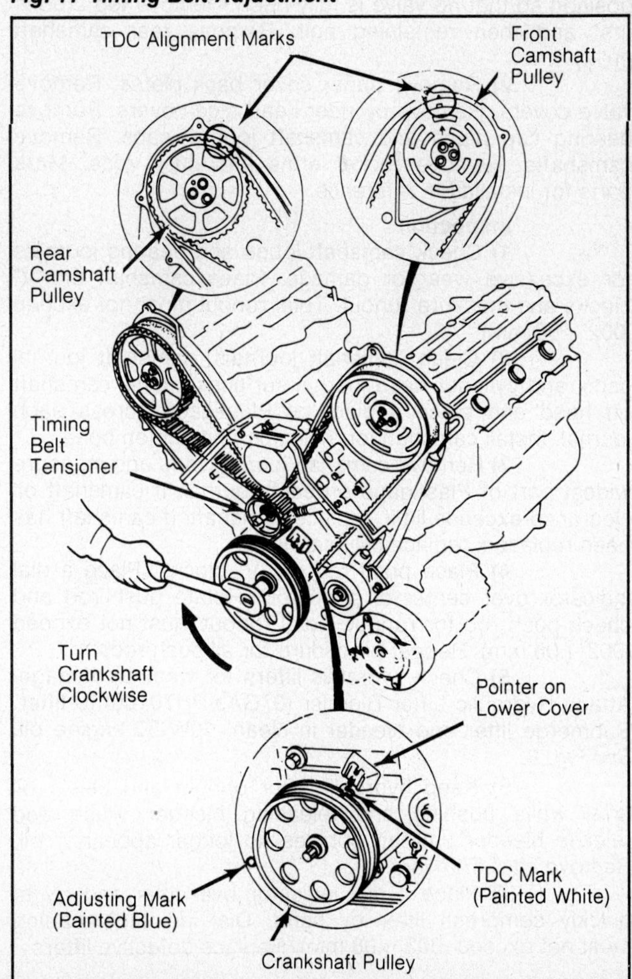

Courtesy of American Honda Motor Co., Inc.

2.5L & 2.7L V6 (Cont.)

2) Using holder, rotate front and rear camshaft pulleys to compression stroke (TDC position) of No. 1 cylinder. Return crankshaft pulley 15 degrees to TDC position. All components should now be at TDC position.

3) Push timing belt tensioner to full release position and snug adjuster bolt. Install timing belt over crankshaft pulley, front camshaft pulley, water pump pulley, tensioner, and then over rear camshaft pulley. *See Fig. 7*.

4) Rotate crankshaft clockwise 5-6 turns to seat timing belt in camshaft pulleys. Continue turning crankshaft clockwise to bring piston in cylinder No. 1 to TDC of compression stroke.

5) Rotate crankshaft 9 teeth on rear camshaft pulley. Blue mark on crankshaft pulley should match pointer on lower cover. Loosen timing belt tensioner bolt to create tension on timing belt. Tighten adjuster bolt. Reverse removal procedure to complete installation.

NOTE: **After timing belt installation, rotate engine clockwise several times to ensure that valves do not come in contact with pistons.**

CAMSHAFTS, ROCKER ARMS, HYDRAULIC LIFTERS & PUSH RODS

Removal

1) Remove timing belt. Remove front camshaft pulley. Before removing rear pulley, adjust camshaft position so that no valve is fully open. Remove top 2 bolts first and then remaining bolt. Remove rear camshaft pulley.

2) Remove upper cover back plates. Remove valve covers. Remove cylinder head side covers. Remove bearing cap pipes and camshaft journal caps. Remove camshafts. Remove rocker arms and push rods. Mark parts for installation reference.

Inspection

1) Check camshaft lobes and bearing journals for excessive wear or damage. Place camshaft on "V" blocks and measure runout. Total runout must not exceed .002" (.06 mm).

2) Clean camshaft journals, camshaft journal caps, and cylinder head journal surfaces. Install camshaft on head and place a piece of Plastigage across each journal. Install camshaft journal caps and tighten bolts.

3) Remove camshaft journal caps and measure widest part of Plastigage on each journal. If camshaft oil clearance exceeds limit, replace camshaft. If camshaft has been replaced, replace cylinder head.

4) Place push rod on "V" blocks. Place a dial indicator over center of push rod. Rotate push rod and check push rod for runout. Total runout must not exceed .002" (.06 mm). Repeat procedure for all push rods.

5) Check hydraulic lifters for wear or damage. Attach Hydraulic Lifter Bleeder (07GAJ-PH70100) to lifter. Submerge lifter and bleeder in clean, 10W-30 engine oil. *See Fig. 8*.

6) Keep hydraulic lifter upright and below oil level while pushing and releasing bleeder. Push and release bleeder until air bubbles no longer appear in oil. Remove lifter from jar.

7) Place a dial indicator over lifter and try to quickly compress lifter by hand. Dial indicator reading must not exceed .003" (.08 mm). Replace defective lifters.

Fig. 8: Checking Hydraulic Lifters

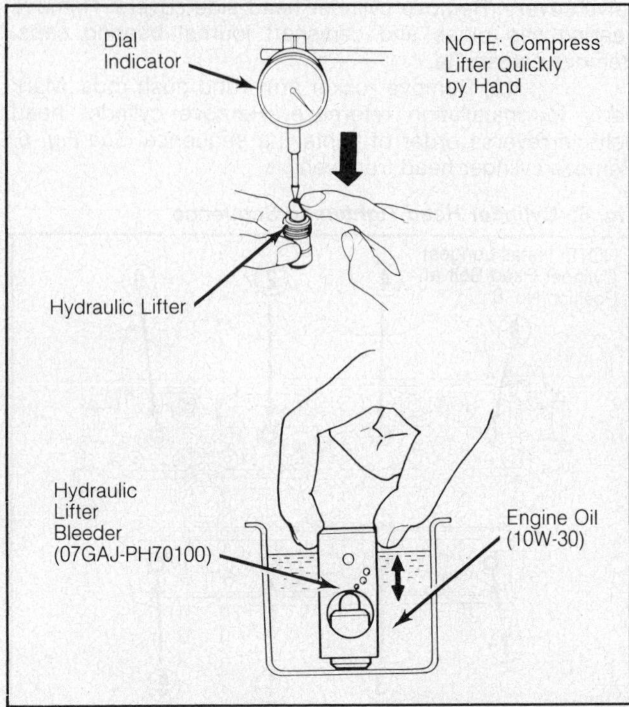

Courtesy of American Honda Motor Co., Inc.

Installation

1) Pour engine oil into cylinder head hydraulic lifter holes (up to level of oil passage). Install hydraulic lifters. DO NOT rotate lifters while inserting them.

2) Pour engine oil into 2 oil passage holes in cylinder head (next to camshaft journal surfaces). Loosen rocker arm adjustment screws and lock nuts. Install push rods and rocker arms in their original position.

3) Turn crankshaft clockwise to bring piston in cylinder No. 1 to TDC of compression stroke. Advance crankshaft an additional 15 degrees from TDC position.

NOTE: **Advance crankshaft 15 degrees from TDC as specified. This will prevent valves from coming into contact with pistons.**

4) Install rear camshaft on cylinder head. Adjust cam position so that no valve is fully open. Install front camshaft and oil seals. Apply sealant to camshaft oil seal mounting surfaces and on cylinder head contact surfaces.

5) Install and temporarily tighten camshaft journal bearing caps to 108 INCH lbs. (12 N.m). If engine is out of vehicle, use 35 mm Seal Driver (07746-0030400) to seat camshaft seals.

6) If engine is installed in vehicle, use a screwdriver and 35 mm Seal Driver (07746-0030400) to pry camshaft seals into place. Ensure camshaft oil seals contact bearing cap.

7) Starting with center caps and working outward, tighten camshaft journal bolts. *See Fig. 9*. Install timing belt upper cover plates. Install camshaft pulleys and timing belt. See TIMING BELT. Adjust valves. See VALVE/ROCKER ARM ADJUSTMENT.

NOTE: **With cylinder heads completely reassembled, allow engine to sit for at least 5 minutes to allow hydraulic lifters to fill up with oil.**

2.5L & 2.7L V6 (Cont.)

Fig. 9: Camshaft Journal Bearing Cap Tightening Sequence

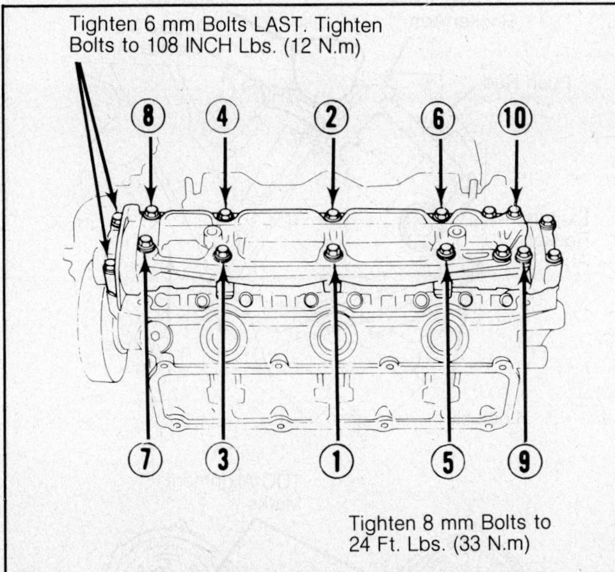

Courtesy of American Honda Motor Co., Inc.

8) After 5 minutes, remove all spark plugs. Have an assistant crank engine, place thumb over spark plug hole, and check for compression at each cylinder. Crank engine several times to ensure compression exists.

9) If any cylinder does not have compression, it may be necessary to disassemble cylinder head and check hydraulic lifters. If compression exists, install spark plugs and start engine.

CAMSHAFT OIL SEALS

Removal & Installation

1) Remove timing belt and camshaft pulleys. See TIMING BELT. Pry out oil seals. Apply oil to camshafts and inner lip of oil seals.

2) Use a screwdriver and 35 mm Seal Driver (07746-0030400) to pry camshaft seals into place. Ensure camshaft oil seals contact bearing cap. Reverse removal procedure to complete installation.

CAMSHAFT END PLAY

1) With rocker arms and push rods removed, install camshafts and camshaft journal bearing caps. Tighten bolts to specifications. *See Fig. 9*. Pry camshaft toward pulley side of engine.

2) Attach dial indicator and zero it against pulley end of camshaft. Pry camshaft away from dial indicator and check end play. Desired end play is .002-.006" (.05-.15 mm). Maximum allowable end play is .020" (.50 mm).

VALVES

VALVE ARRANGEMENT

Intake manifold side – All intake valves.
Exhaust manifold side – All exhaust valves.

VALVE GUIDES

Inspection

Disassemble cylinder head. Measure valve stem diameters. Replace worn or damaged valves. Install valves in corresponding valve guides. Measure valve stem-to-valve guide clearance with a dial indicator placed on valve head.

Removal

1) Heat cylinder head to 300°F (150°C). Fabricate valve guide remover from an air-impact chisel. *See Fig. 10*. Using an air hammer and valve guide remover, force valve guide 5/64" toward combustion chamber.

Fig. 10: Valve Guide Remover Dimensions

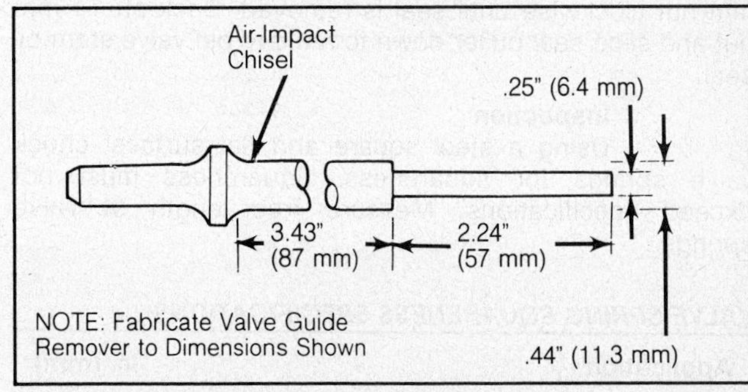

Courtesy of American Honda Motor Co., Inc.

2) Turn head over. Working from combustion chamber side of head, drive valve guide out toward camshaft side of head. If valve guide does not move, drill valve guide using a 5/16" drill bit. Guide should now come out.

Installation

1) Cool valve guides in refrigerator for several hours. Remove valve guides from refrigerator as needed. Slip a 15/64" steel washer and correct driver attachment over Valve Guide Driver (07942-6570100).

2) Install valve guides from camshaft side of cylinder head. Drive each guide into head until attachment bottoms on head. It may be necessary to reheat cylinder head.

3) Intake valve guide installed height must be .79" (20 mm). Exhaust valve guide installed height must be .83" (21 mm) Using cutting oil, ream new valve guides by rotating Valve Guide Reamer (07984-6570100) clockwise the full length of valve guide bore.

4) Remove reamer while continuing to turn reamer clockwise. After reaming valve guide, thoroughly clean valve guide. Check valve stem-to-valve guide clearance.

VALVE STEM OIL SEALS

When installing valve stem oil seals, check that seals for intake valves have a White spring around neck of seal. Oil seals for exhaust valves have a Black spring around neck of seal.

VALVE SPRINGS

Removal

1) If cylinder head is removed from engine, install a spring compressor over valves and compress springs. Remove valve keepers, retainer, and springs. Keep parts in order for installation.

2) If cylinder head is installed in vehicle, remove camshafts. Remove intake valve rocker arms, exhaust valve rocker arms, and push rods. Remove rocker shaft and exhaust valve rocker arms.

3) With piston of cylinder being worked on at TDC, insert a spark plug air fitting into spark plug hole.

2.5L & 2.7L V6 (Cont.)

Apply shop air to combustion chamber to keep valves closed. Compress valve springs.

4) If valve stem oil seal is being replaced, place Valve Stem Oil Seal Puller (07936-PH7000A) over valve. Turn 14 mm nut on puller counterclockwise until it reaches handle.

5) Let seal puller slide out of collar. Hold collar against nut and insert seal puller under valve step oil seal. Slide collar down over seal puller until it rests on valve spring seat.

6) Hold puller handle stationary and turn 14 mm nut clockwise until seal is removed. Back-off 14 mm nut and slide seal puller down to remove old valve stem oil seal.

Inspection

Using a steel square and flat surface, check valve springs for squareness. Squareness must not exceed specifications. Measure free length of valve springs.

VALVE SPRING SQUARENESS SPECIFICATIONS

Application	In. (mm)
Exhaust	
Inner Spring	.063 (1.60)
Outer Spring	.067 (1.70)
Intake	
2.5L	
Inner Spring	.066 (1.68)
Outer Spring	.076 (1.93)
2.7L	.076 (1.93)

Installation

1) Check valve stem installed height before installing springs. If valve stem installed height exceeds limit, replace valve. If installed height is still incorrect, replace cylinder head.

2) Install springs with closely wound coils toward cylinder head or with painted part of spring on cylinder head. Install retainers and keepers. Tap end of each valve stem lightly with a plastic hammer.

VALVE STEM INSTALLED HEIGHT

Application	In. (mm)
Exhaust	
New	1.870 (47.50)
Service Limit	1.900 (48.26)
Intake	
New	1.969 (50.00)
Service Limit	1.998 (50.75)

VALVE/ROCKER ARM ADJUSTMENT

1) Rotate crankshaft clockwise so No. 1 piston is on TDC of compression stroke. Marks on camshaft pulleys and TDC mark on crankshaft pulley should align. *See Fig. 7*.

2) Ensure exhaust valves on cylinders No. 1, No. 2, and No. 4 are closed. Turn adjustment screw on exhaust valve of cylinder No. 1. *See Fig. 11*. When screw contacts valve, turn adjustment screw an additional one and a half turns (1 1/2). Tighten lock nut.

Fig. 11: Valve/Rocker Arm Adjustment

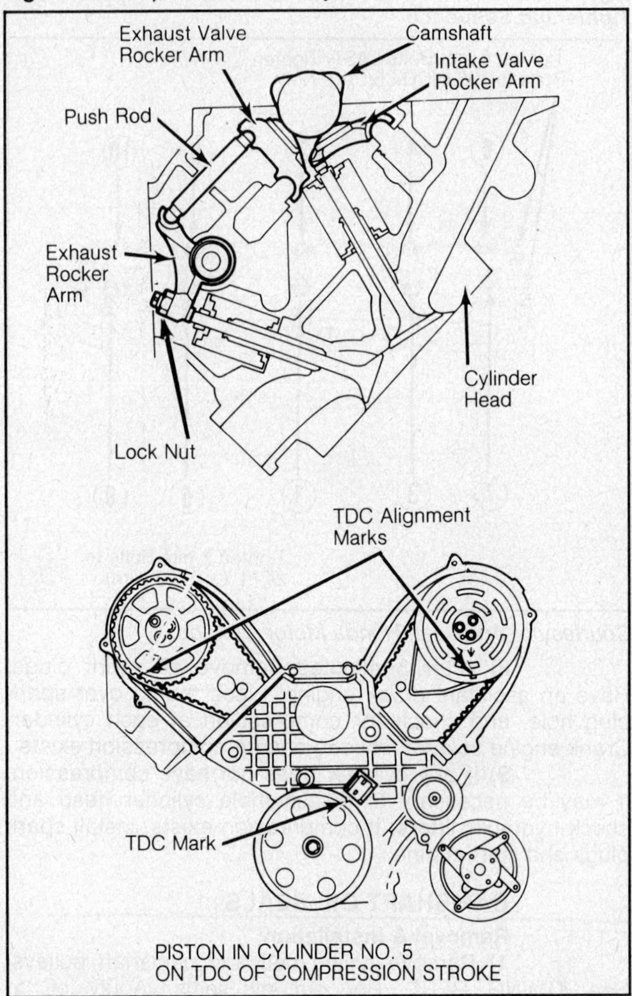

Courtesy of American Honda Motor Co., Inc.

3) Adjust exhaust valve screws on cylinders No. 2 and No. 4 using same procedure. Rotate crankshaft one turn clockwise so No. 5 piston is on TDC of compression stroke. *See Fig. 11*. Ensure exhaust valves on cylinders No. 3, No. 5, and No. 6 are closed.

4) Turn adjustment screw on exhaust valve of cylinder No. 3. When screw contacts valve, turn adjustment screw an additional one and a half turns (1 1/2). Tighten lock nut. Adjust exhaust valve screws on cylinders No. 5 and No. 6 using same procedure.

PISTONS, PINS & RINGS

PISTON & ROD ASSEMBLY

Removal

1) Remove oil pan and cylinder head. Remove rear crankshaft oil seal cover. Remove oil screen and crankcase baffle plate. Remove oil pipe and oil pump. Remove main bearing cap bridge.

2) Remove any ridge from top of cylinder bore. Mark connecting rod and cap for cylinder identification. Remove rod cap. Push piston and rod assembly out top of cylinder block. Install cap on rod from which removed.

2.5L & 2.7L V6 (Cont.)

Installation

1) Lubricate piston, rings, and cylinder bore with engine oil. Install piston rings and properly space ring end gaps on piston. *See Fig. 12*. Install piston and rod into cylinder bore.

Fig. 12: Piston Ring Installation

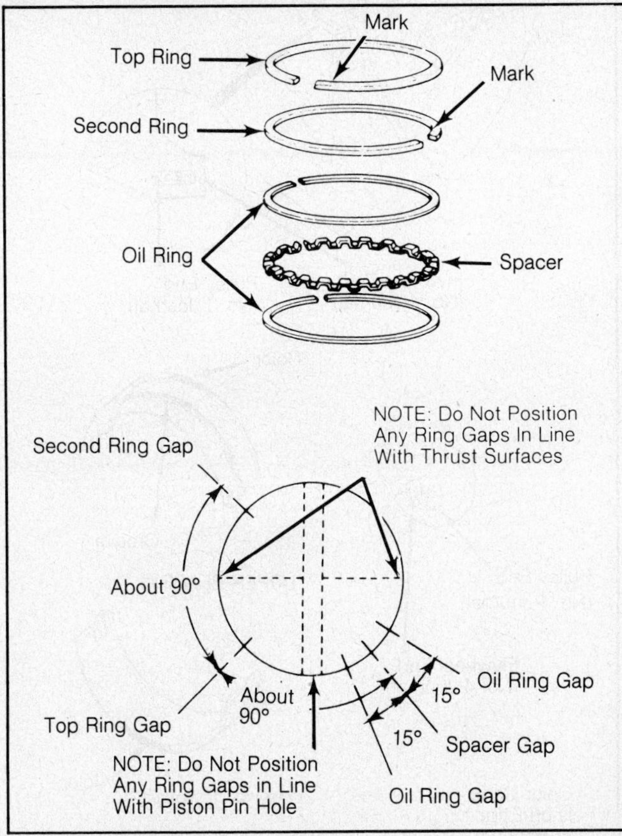

Courtesy of American Honda Motor Co., Inc.

2) Ensure that arrow on piston faces timing belt side of engine and that oil hole in connecting rod is positioned toward rear (firewall) side of engine. Install and tighten rod cap.

FITTING PISTONS

1) Measure cylinder bore at 3 places for out-of-round and taper. If either out-of-round or taper exceeds .002" (.05 mm), rebore cylinder for oversize pistons.

2) Insert piston in cylinder. Using a feeler gauge, determine piston-to-cylinder bore clearance. If clearance exceeds .003" (.07 mm), use micrometers to calculate difference between cylinder bore and piston diameter. If clearance exceeds limit, rebore cylinder and install oversize piston.

3) If cylinder bore is okay, hone cylinder to obtain a 60 degree cross-hatch pattern. After honing, thoroughly clean cylinder bore. Air dry cylinder bore and apply engine oil to prevent rusting.

CYLINDER BORE DIAMETERS [1]

Application	In. (mm)
2.5L	
Standard (New) [2]	3.3071-3.3079 (84.00-84.02)
.25 O/S	3.3169-3.3177 (84.25-84.27)
.50 O/S	3.3268-3.3276 (84.50-84.52)
2.7L	
Standard (New) [3]	3.4252-3.4259 (87.00-87.02)
.25 O/S	3.4350-3.4358 (87.25-87.27)
.50 O/S	3.4449-3.4457 (87.50-87.52)

[1] - Cylinder bore taper and out-of-round must not exceed .002" (.05 mm).
[2] - Service limit is 3.3098" (84.07 mm).
[3] - Service limit is 3.4279 (87.07 mm).

PISTON DIAMETERS [1]

Application	In. (mm)
2.5L	
Standard (New) [2]	
"A" Piston [3]	3.3065-3.3072 (83.986-84.004)
"B" Piston [4]	3.3061-3.3068 (83.976-83.994)
.25 O/S	3.3157-3.3167 (84.220-84.244)
.50 O/S	3.3256-3.3265 (84.470-84.494)
2.7L	
Standard (New) [2]	
"A" Piston [5]	3.4246-3.4253 (86.986-87.004)
"B" Piston [6]	3.3061-3.3068 (86.976-86.994)
.25 O/S	3.4337-3.4349 (87.216-87.247)
.50 O/S	3.4439-3.4446 (87.476-87.494)

[1] - Measured at .71" (18 mm) from bottom of skirt.
[2] - Piston identification letter is stamped on top of piston. Letters are also stamped on block as cylinder bore sizes.
[3] - Service limit is 3.3059" (83.970 mm).
[4] - Service limit is 3.3055" (83.960 mm).
[5] - Service limit is 3.4364" (86.970 mm).
[6] - Service limit is 3.4236" (86.960 mm).

FITTING RINGS

1) Use head of piston to push ring squarely into bore. Leave ring about 11/16" from bottom of bore. Using a feeler gauge, measure piston ring end gap. Compare measurement with specification.

2) Install rings onto piston. Note that 2nd compression ring inner edge is slightly chamfered. Using a feeler gauge, measure ring side clearance between ring and ring land. If ring lands are excessively worn, replace piston.

3) Properly space ring end gaps on piston. *See Fig. 12.* Make sure no end gaps are in line with piston pin or thrust face of piston. Install rings with manufacturer's mark facing up.

PISTON PIN REPLACEMENT

Removal

1) Install Piston Base Head (07GAF-PH60100) and Piston Pin Base Insert (07GAF-PH60300) into Base (07973-6570002). Turn handle on Piston Pin Driver (07973-PE00301) so driver length is 1.91" (48.5 mm).

2) Place piston on base and press out piston pin. When removing or installing piston pin, set piston in press with embossed side facing up. Be sure recessed part of piston aligns with lugs on base insert.

2.5L & 2.7L V6 (Cont.)

Inspection

1) Measure diameter of piston pin. Zero dial indicator to piston pin diameter. Insert gauge in piston boss to measure piston pin-to-piston clearance.

2) Piston pin-to-piston clearance must be .0005-.0009" (.013-.022 mm). If piston pin clearance is greater than .0009" (.022 mm), measure clearance once again using an oversize piston pin.

3) Check difference between piston pin diameter and connecting rod small end diameter. Piston pin-to-connecting rod interference fit must be .0005-.0013" (.013-.033 mm).

Installation

1) Ensure that piston and connecting rod are correctly positioned. Turn handle on Piston Pin Driver (07973-PE00301) so that piston driver length is 1.91" (48.5 mm).

2) Install Piston Pin Collar (07GAF-PH70100) in piston and connecting rod. Lightly oil new piston pin. Place piston on base and press in piston pin.

CRANKSHAFT & ROD BEARINGS

MAIN BEARINGS

1) Remove piston and connecting rod assemblies. See PISTON & ROD ASSEMBLY in this article. Ensure main bearing caps are marked for identification.

2) Remove main bearing cap bolts and bearing cap side bolts. Remove main bearing halves. Lift crankshaft out of block, being careful not to damage journals.

3) Check crankshaft for runout, out-of-round, and taper. If any measurement exceeds service limit, replace crankshaft.

4) Replace crankshaft in engine. Check main bearing oil clearance using Plastigage method. If engine is in vehicle, support counterweights and check only one bearing at a time.

5) Install bearing half, cap, and main bearing cap bridge. Tighten 9 mm main bearing cap bolts to 29 ft. lbs. (39 N.m). DO NOT rotate crankshaft. Tighten 11 mm main bearing cap bridge bolts to 50 ft. lbs. (68 N.m).

6) Install a new bearing (same color code) and recheck oil clearance. If oil clearance is still incorrect, try the next larger or smaller bearing and check oil clearance once more.

7) If proper oil clearance cannot be obtained by using larger or smaller bearings, replace crankshaft and repeat procedure.

NOTE: **A letter code or Roman numeral indicating main journal bore diameters is stamped on cylinder block. *See Fig. 13.* Use these codes, along with crankshaft main journal diameter numbers, to obtain correct replacement bearings.**

Fig. 13: Crankshaft Main Journal & Bearing Identification Codes

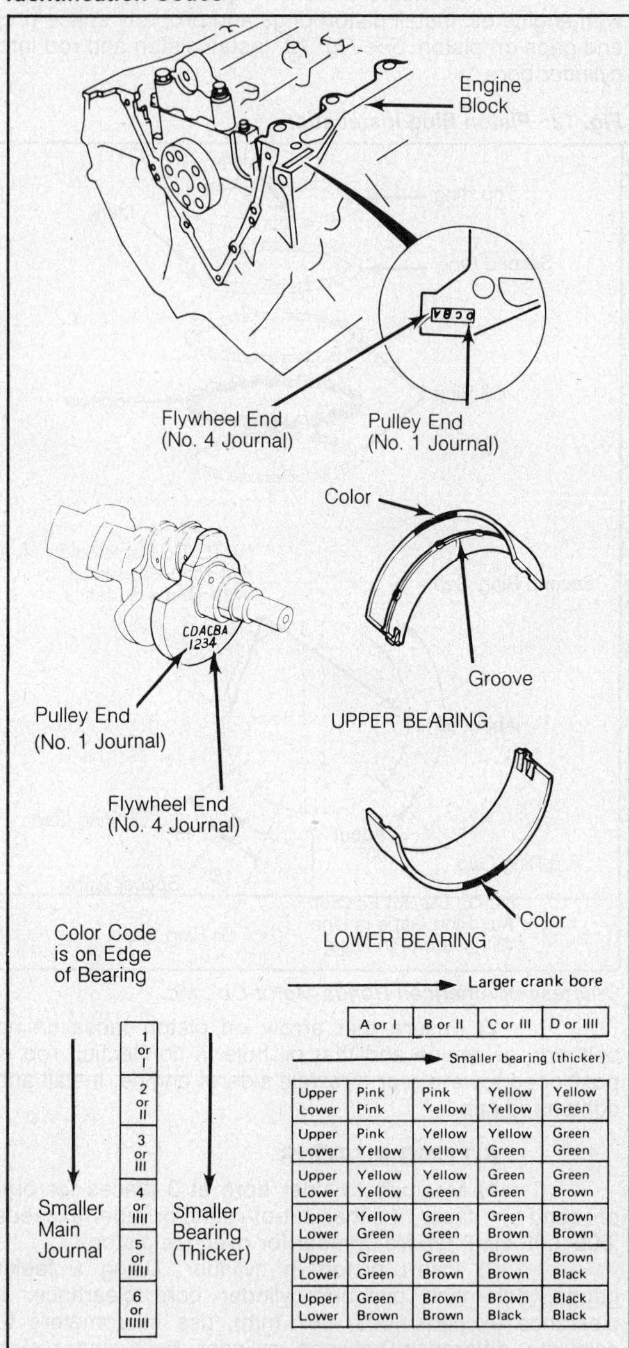

		A or I	B or II	C or III	D or IIII
1 or I	Upper Lower	Pink Pink	Pink Yellow	Yellow Yellow	Yellow Green
2 or II	Upper Lower	Pink Yellow	Yellow Yellow	Yellow Green	Green Green
3 or III	Upper Lower	Yellow Yellow	Yellow Green	Green Green	Green Brown
4 or IIII	Upper Lower	Yellow Green	Green Green	Green Brown	Brown Brown
5 or IIIII	Upper Lower	Green Green	Green Brown	Brown Brown	Brown Black
6 or IIIIII	Upper Lower	Green Brown	Brown Brown	Brown Black	Black Black

Courtesy of American Honda Motor Co., Inc.

CONNECTING ROD BEARINGS

1) Remove connecting rod caps and bearings. Clean connecting rod journal and bearing half with a clean shop towel. Check connecting rod bearing oil clearance using Plastigage method.

2) If oil clearance is incorrect, remove connecting rod upper bearing half. Install a new bearing (same color code) and recheck oil clearance. DO NOT shim or file cap to adjust oil clearance.

3) If oil clearance is still incorrect, try the next larger or smaller bearing and check oil clearance once

2.5L & 2.7L V6 (Cont.)

more. If proper oil clearance cannot be obtained by using larger or smaller bearings, replace crankshaft and repeat procedure.

NOTE: **A number code or Roman numeral indicating connecting bore is stamped on side of each connecting rod and cap. Connecting rod journal diameter codes (letters) are stamped on crankshaft counterweight pad. See *Fig. 14.* Use both these codes to obtain correct replacement bearings.**

Fig. 14: Connecting Rod Journal & Bearing Identification Codes

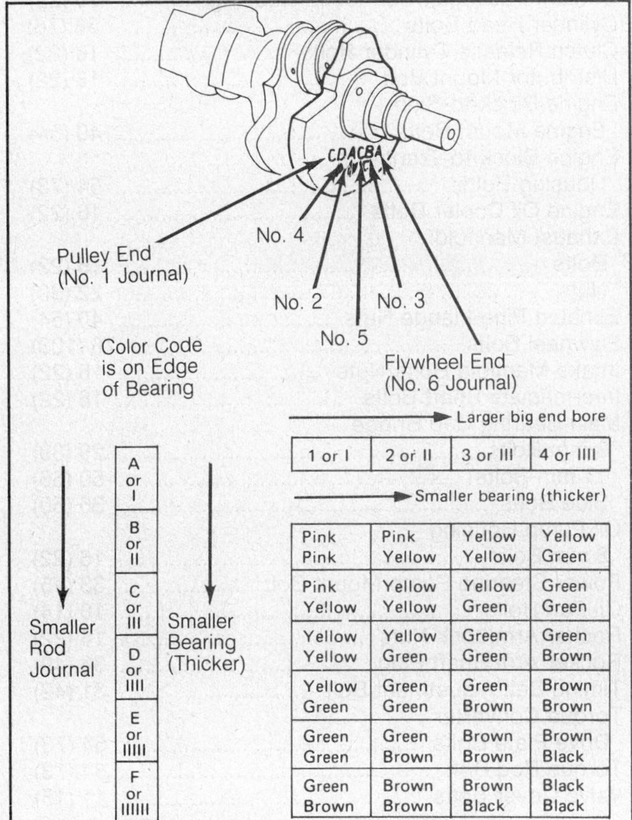

Courtesy of American Honda Motor Co., Inc.

CRANKSHAFT END PLAY

1) Check crankshaft end play with dial indicator. If end play exceeds specification, inspect thrust washers and thrust surface of crankshaft.

2) Replace worn parts as necessary. Thrust washer thickness is fixed. DO NOT change thrust washer thickness by grinding or shimming. Install thrust washers with grooved side out.

FRONT & REAR CRANKSHAFT OIL SEALS

1) Remove rear crankshaft oil seal cover. Remove oil screen and crankcase baffle plate. Remove oil pipe and oil pump. Remove front seal from oil pump housing.

2) Use Oil Seal Driver (07GAD-PH70200) to install front seal. Tap new oil seal into housing until it bottoms. Coat crankshaft and rear seal lip with engine oil. Use Driver (07749-0010000) with Driver Attachment (07948-SB00101) to install rear seal.

ENGINE OILING

ENGINE OILING SYSTEM

A rotor-type oil pump draws oil from oil pan and delivers it under pressure to main and connecting rod bearings. An oil hole in each connecting rod lubricates thrust side of piston and cylinder wall. An oil passage carries oil to camshaft and rocker arms. Oil spray lubricates valve stems.

CRANKCASE CAPACITY

Crankcase capacity is 4.2 qts. (4.0L) without oil filter replacement; 4.8 qts. (4.5L) when replacing oil filter. Capacity is 5.3 qts. (5.0L) after engine disassembly.

NORMAL OIL PRESSURE

Oil pressure at idle should be 20 psi (1.4 kg/cm²). Oil pressure at 3000 RPM should be 71-82 psi (5.0-5.8 kg/cm²).

OIL PUMP

Removal

1) Drain engine oil. Align "TDC" mark on crankshaft pulley with mark on cover. Remove upper timing belt cover. Remove alternator, power steering, and A/C compressor drive belts. Remove engine splash guard.

2) Remove crankshaft pulley and timing belt lower cover. Loosen belt tensioner. Remove timing belt and driven pulley. Remove oil filter assembly. Remove oil pan. Remove oil screen and crankcase baffle plate. Remove oil pipe and oil pump.

Disassembly

Remove 5 screws from pump housing. Separate housing and cover. Remove cotter pin, collar, spring, and relief valve. *See Fig. 15.*

Fig. 15: Oil Pump Assembly

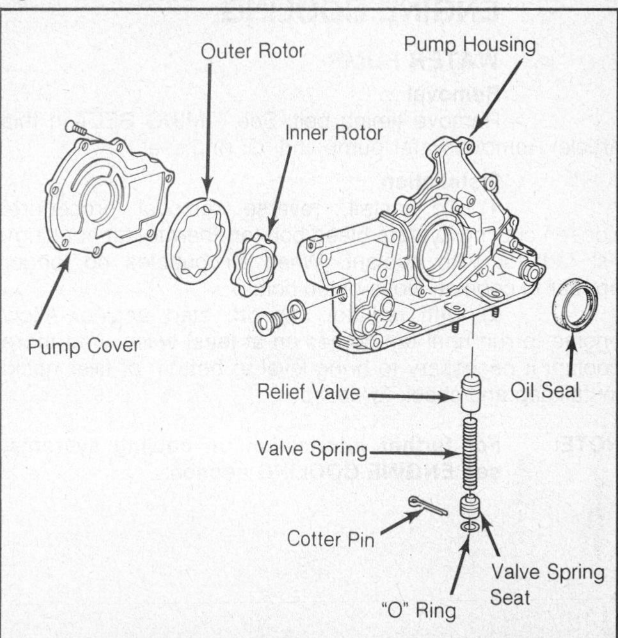

Courtesy of American Honda Motor Co., Inc.

2.5L & 2.7L V6 (Cont.)

Inspection

1) Check radial clearance between inner and outer rotor. Place a straightedge over pump housing, check axial clearance between outer pump rotor and pump housing.

2) Check radial clearance between pump housing and outer rotor. Inspect both rotors and pump housing for scoring or damage. Check that relief valve slides freely in bore. Replace parts as necessary.

OIL PUMP SPECIFICATIONS

Application	In. (mm)
Inner Rotor-to-Outer Rotor	
Radial Clearance	[1] .002-.007 (.05-.18)
Housing-to-Outer Rotor	
Axial Clearance	[2] .001-.003 (.03-.08)
Housing-to-Outer Rotor	
Radial Clearance	[3] .004-.007 (.10-.18)

[1] – Service limit is .008" (.20 mm).
[2] – Service limit is .005" (.13 mm).
[3] – Service limit is .008" (.20 mm).

Assembly

Install relief valve assembly. Install front crankshaft oil seal in pump housing. See FRONT & REAR CRANKSHAFT OIL SEALS in this article. Install oil pump housing cover, applying locking compound to pump housing screws. Make sure oil pump turns freely.

Installation

1) Install dowel pins and "O" ring in cylinder block. Clean oil pump mating surfaces. Apply Liquid Sealant (08740-99986) to cylinder block mating surface of oil pump.

2) Apply sealant to threads of inner bolt holes to prevent oil leaks. Install oil pump before sealant dries. Install oil screen and oil pump. Wait at least 30 minutes before filling crankcase with oil. Reverse removal procedure to complete installation.

ENGINE COOLING

WATER PUMP

Removal

Remove timing belt. See TIMING BELT in this article. Remove water pump and "O" ring seal.

Installation

1) To install, reverse removal procedure. Loosen cooling system bleed bolt (on thermostat housing). Fill radiator with coolant. When air bubbles no longer appear in coolant, close bleed bolt.

2) With radiator cap off, start engine. Allow engine to run until fan comes on at least twice. Add more coolant if necessary to bring level to bottom of filler neck. Install cap and check for leaks.

NOTE: **For further information on cooling systems, see ENGINE COOLING section.**

TIGHTENING SPECIFICATIONS

Application	Ft. Lbs. (N.m)
A/C Compressor Bolts	16 (22)
A/C Compressor Bracket Bolts	32 (43)
Alternator Bracket Bolt	
8 mm Bolts	16 (22)
10 mm Bolt	32 (43)
Alternator Mount Bolt	16 (22)
Camshaft Cap Bolts	
10 mm Bolt	24 (33)
Camshaft Pulley Bolts	23 (31)
Crankshaft Pulley Bolt	83 (112)
Connecting Rod Nuts	33 (45)
Coolant Passage/Thermostat Housing	16 (22)
Cylinder Head Bolts	[1] 56 (76)
Clutch Release Cylinder Bolts	16 (22)
Distributor Mount Bolt	16 (22)
Engine Block-to-Side	
Engine Mount Bolts	40 (54)
Engine Block-to-Transaxle	
Housing Bolts	54 (73)
Engine Oil Cooler Bolts	16 (22)
Exhaust Manifold	
Bolts	16 (22)
Nuts	22 (30)
Exhaust Pipe Flange Nuts	40 (54)
Flywheel Bolts	76 (103)
Intake Manifold Bolts/Nuts	16 (22)
Intermediate Shaft Bolts	16 (22)
Main Bearing Cap Bridge	
9 mm Bolts	29 (39)
11 mm Bolts	50 (68)
Side Bolts	36 (50)
Oil Pump Housing	
8 mm Bolts	16 (22)
Power Steering Pump Mount Bolt	33 (45)
Oil Pan Bolts	10 (14)
Rocker Arm Lock Nuts	16 (22)
Rocker Arm Shaft Plug	36 (49)
Timing Belt Adjustment Bolt	31 (42)
Torque Converter	
Drive Plate Bolts	54 (73)
Torque Rod Bolt	54 (73)
Valve Cover Bolts	11 (15)
	INCH Lbs. (N.m)
Camshaft Cap Bolts	
6 mm Bolts	108 (12)
Crankshaft Seal Cover Bolts	108 (12)
Cylinder Head Side Cover Bolts	108 (12)
Fuel Service Bolt	108 (12)
Oil Pump Housing	
6 mm Bolts	108 (12)
Oil Pump Screen Nuts	108 (12)
Timing Belt Cover Bolts	86 (10)

[1] – Tighten cylinder head in two steps. First tighten bolts to 29 ft. lbs. (39 N.m), and then tighten bolts to specification listed.

Acura & Sterling Engines

2.5L & 2.7L V6 (Cont.)

ENGINE SPECIFICATIONS

GENERAL SPECIFICATIONS

Year	DISPLACEMENT		Fuel System	HP@RPM	Torque Ft. Lbs.@RPM	Compr. Ratio	BORE		STROKE	
	Cu. In.	Liters					In.	mm	In.	mm
1987	153 163	2.5L 2.7L	Fuel Inj. Fuel Inj.	151@5800 161@5900	154@4500 162@4500	9.0:1 9.0:1	3.30 3.43	84 87	2.95 2.95	75 75

VALVES

Engine Size & Valve	Head Diam. In. (mm)	Face Angle	Seat Angle	Seat Width In. (mm)	Stem Diameter In. (mm)	Stem Clearance In. (mm)	Valve Lift In. (mm)
2.5L & 2.7L							
Intake	1.295-1.303 (32.89-33.10)	45°	45°	[1] .049-.061 (1.25-1.55)	[2] .2591-.2594 (6.580-6.590)	[3] .0015-.0040 (.04-.10)	.....
Exhaust	1.079-1.087 (27.40-27.60)	45°	45°	[1] .049-.061 (1.25-1.55)	[4] .2579-.2583 (6.550-6.560)	[5] .004-.006 (.10-.15)	.....

[1] – Seat width service limit .08" (2.0 mm).
[2] – Intake valve stem diameter service limit .258" (6.55 mm).
[3] – Intake valve stem clearance service limit .006" (.15 mm).
[4] – Exhaust valve stem diameter service limit .257" (6.53 mm).
[5] – Exhaust valve stem clearance service limit .009" (.23 mm).

CRANKSHAFT MAIN & CONNECTING ROD BEARINGS

Engine	MAIN BEARINGS				CONNECTING ROD BEARINGS		
	Journal Diam. In. (mm)	Clearance In. (mm)	Thrust Bearing	Crankshaft End Play In. (mm)	Journal Diam. In. (mm)	Clearance In. (mm)	Side Play In. (mm)
2.5L & 2.7L	2.5187-2.5197 (63.976-64.000)	[1] .0009-.0019 (.024-.048)	No. 3	[2] .004-.014 (.10-.36)	2.0463-2.0472 (51.976-52.000)	[3] .0010-.0020 (.025-.050)	[4] .006-.012 (.15-.30)

[1] – Main bearing oil clearance service limit is .002" (.05 mm).
[2] – Crankshaft end play service limit is .018" (.46 mm).
[3] – Connecting rod oil clearance service limit is .002" (.05 mm).
[4] – Connecting rod side play service limit is .016" (.40 mm).

PISTONS, PINS & RINGS

Engine	PISTONS	PINS		RINGS		
	Clearance In. (mm)	Piston Fit In. (mm)	Rod Fit In. (mm)	Ring No.	End Gap In. (mm)	Side Clearance In. (mm)
2.5L	[1] .0002-.0013 (.006-.034)	.0005-.0009 (.013-.023)	[2] .0005-.0013 (.013-0.032)	No. 1 & 2	[3] .008-.014 (.20-.35)	[4] .0008-.0018 (.020-.045)
				Oil	[6] .008-.028 (.20-.71)	.....
2.7L	[1] .0002-.0013 (.006-.034)	.0005-.0009 (.013-.023)	[2] .0005-.0013 (.013-.032)	No. 1	[3] .008-.014 (.20-.35)	[4] .0006-.0018 (.015-.045)
				No. 2	[5] .014-.019 (.35-.50)	[4] .0006-.0018 (.015-.045)
				Oil	[6] .008-.028 (.20-.70)	.....

[1] – Piston-to-cylinder wall clearance service limit is .003" (.08 mm).
[2] – Interference fit.
[3] – Piston ring end gap service limit is .024" (.60 mm).
[4] – Piston ring side clearance service limit is .005" (.13 mm).
[5] – Piston ring end gap service limit is .030" (.75 mm).
[6] – Oil control ring end gap service limit is .032" (.80 mm).

Acura & Sterling Engines

2.5L & 2.7L V6 (Cont.)

ENGINE SPECIFICATIONS (Cont.)

VALVE SPRINGS

Engine	Free Length In. (mm)	PRESSURE Lbs. @ In. (Kg @ mm) Valve Closed	Valve Open
2.5L			
Intake			
Inner	[1] 1.89 (48.0)	....	.....
Outer	2.16 (54.9)	....	.....
Exhaust			
Inner	[2] 1.79 (45.5)	....	.....
Outer	[3] 1.93 (49.0)	....	.....
2.7L			
Intake	[1] 2.12 (53.9)	....	.....
Exhaust			
Inner	[2] 1.77 (44.9)	....	....
Outer	[3] 1.95 (49.5)	....	....

[1] – Intake valve spring free length service limit is 2.05" (52.0 mm).
[2] – Inner exhaust valve spring free length service limit is 1.73" (43.9 mm).
[3] – Outer exhaust valve spring free length service limit is 1.91" (48.6 mm).

CAMSHAFT

Engine	Journal Diam. In. (mm)	Clearance In. (mm)	Lobe Lift In. (mm)
2.5L & 2.7L	.....	[1] .002-.006 (.05-.015)	.....

[1] – Camshaft oil clearance service limit is .02" (.5 mm).

Alfa Romeo Engines

2.5L V6

Milano

ENGINE CODING

ENGINE IDENTIFICATION

Engine identification code is located on left rear corner of engine block, near engine block/cylinder head mating surface.

ENGINE IDENTIFICATION CODE

Application	Code
2.5L	AR01911

ENGINE, MANIFOLDS & CYLINDER HEAD

NOTE: For engine repair procedures not covered in this article, see ENGINE OVERHAUL PROCEDURES article at beginning of this section.

ENGINE

Removal

1) Place vehicle over hoist. Open hood and remove battery. Disconnect engine compartment hood light wiring. Disconnect hose at windshield washer pump. Remove hood.

2) Disconnect power brake unit vacuum hose at air intake box one-way valve. *See Fig. 1*. Disconnect cable from airflow sensor and slide it out of bracket. Disconnect idle speed by-pass hose and fuel vapor recirculation hose from right side of air intake box.

3) Disconnect oil vapor breather hose from right valve cover. Disconnect fuel vapor recirculation hose from air intake duct. Disconnect hose from auxiliary air solenoid valve (below air intake duct). Remove air filter cover, airflow meter, and air intake duct as an assembly.

4) Remove air filter and air filter housing. Disconnect fuel line from back of intake manifold. Disconnect fuel line from fuel pressure regulator. Disconnect electrical wiring from thermostat housing. Release wiring harness bundle from brackets at thermostat housing and at timing belt covers.

5) Disconnect ground strap and remove intake air box guard (below air intake box). Disconnect wiring from fuel injectors, throttle position sensor, and cold start injector.

6) Disconnect wires from auxiliary air solenoid valve, oil pressure sending unit (on engine block), low oil pressure sending unit (on back of cylinder head). Disconnect starter, junction block wires, and oxygen sensor leads (on firewall, behind engine).

7) Disconnect junction block wires from left fender panel. Disconnect ignition cables from ignition coil and distributor. Disconnect A/C compressor clutch wiring and ground cable.

8) Disconnect wiring from cooling fan and cooling fan thermoswitch (on lower right side of radiator). Disconnect engine ground cable from power steering pump bracket. Disconnect throttle cable from throttle body and bracket. *See Fig. 1*.

9) Drain cooling system. Disconnect top radiator hose and heater return hose at radiator. Disconnect radiator breather hose. Disconnect heater hose at 3-way fitting (between engine and firewall). Remove radiator and cooling fan assembly.

10) Loosen A/C compressor belt idler pulley nut and remove drive belt. Remove nut (on A/C compressor) and bolts securing A/C compressor bracket to crankcase (under vehicle). Move A/C compressor to right and lock in this position (if necessary disconnect refrigerant lines).

11) Loosen bolts securing power steering pump to rear bracket. *See Fig. 1*. Loosen bolts securing front power steering pump bracket to left cylinder head. Remove power steering pump drive belt. Remove power steering pump bolts and set pump aside.

12) Place transmission in Neutral and raise vehicle on hoist. Drain engine oil. Remove bolt and clamp securing oxygen sensor wiring. Disconnect exhaust manifolds.

13) Remove nuts securing catalytic converter to exhaust manifolds. Loosen clamp and remove bolts securing catalytic converter to support. Detach rubber rings and remove catalytic converter and exhaust pipe center section.

14) Remove heat shield and crossmember. *See Fig. 1*. Remove gear selector bellows bolt and disconnect rod. Remove 4 bolts and move gear selector lever support out of way. Remove flywheel protection plate.

15) Rotate propeller shaft and alternately remove nuts and bolts connecting propeller shaft to flywheel and clutch fork. Remove bolts and detach rear engine mount from body.

16) Remove nuts and central propeller shaft support. Remove bolts and rear crossmember. Use Support (A.2.0075) and a post type lift to raise rear axle. Remove propeller shaft from clutch fork. Lower lift and remove propeller shaft.

17) Remove rear engine mount bracket. Install a lever on rear engine mount to direct engine during removal. Remove nuts from side engine mounts. Lower vehicle. Remove bolts from side engine mounts. Attach engine hoist to block and raise hoist to remove slack from chain.

18) Carefully lift engine about 6". Check for and remove any hoses, wiring or other components which are still attached to both engine and chassis. Remove engine from vehicle.

Installation

1) To install, reverse removal procedure. Install a lever on rear engine mount to direct engine during installation. Slowly lower engine and center over engine mounts. Install bolts on side engine mounts.

2) Raise vehicle on hoist. Install nuts on side engine mounts. Remove lever from rear engine mount. Restore all fluids to proper level and adjust drive belts.

INTAKE PLENUM & RUNNERS

Removal & Installation

Loosen clamps on rubber sleeves of intake plenum. Remove intake plenum, throttle body, and rubber sleeves. Remove bolts securing injectors to intake runners. Remove intake runners and gaskets. To install, reverse removal procedure.

CYLINDER HEAD

Removal

1) Remove external components and timing belt. Remove valve covers and gaskets. Remove spark

Alfa Romeo Engines

2.5L V6 (Cont.)

Fig. 1: Engine Removal Disconnect Points

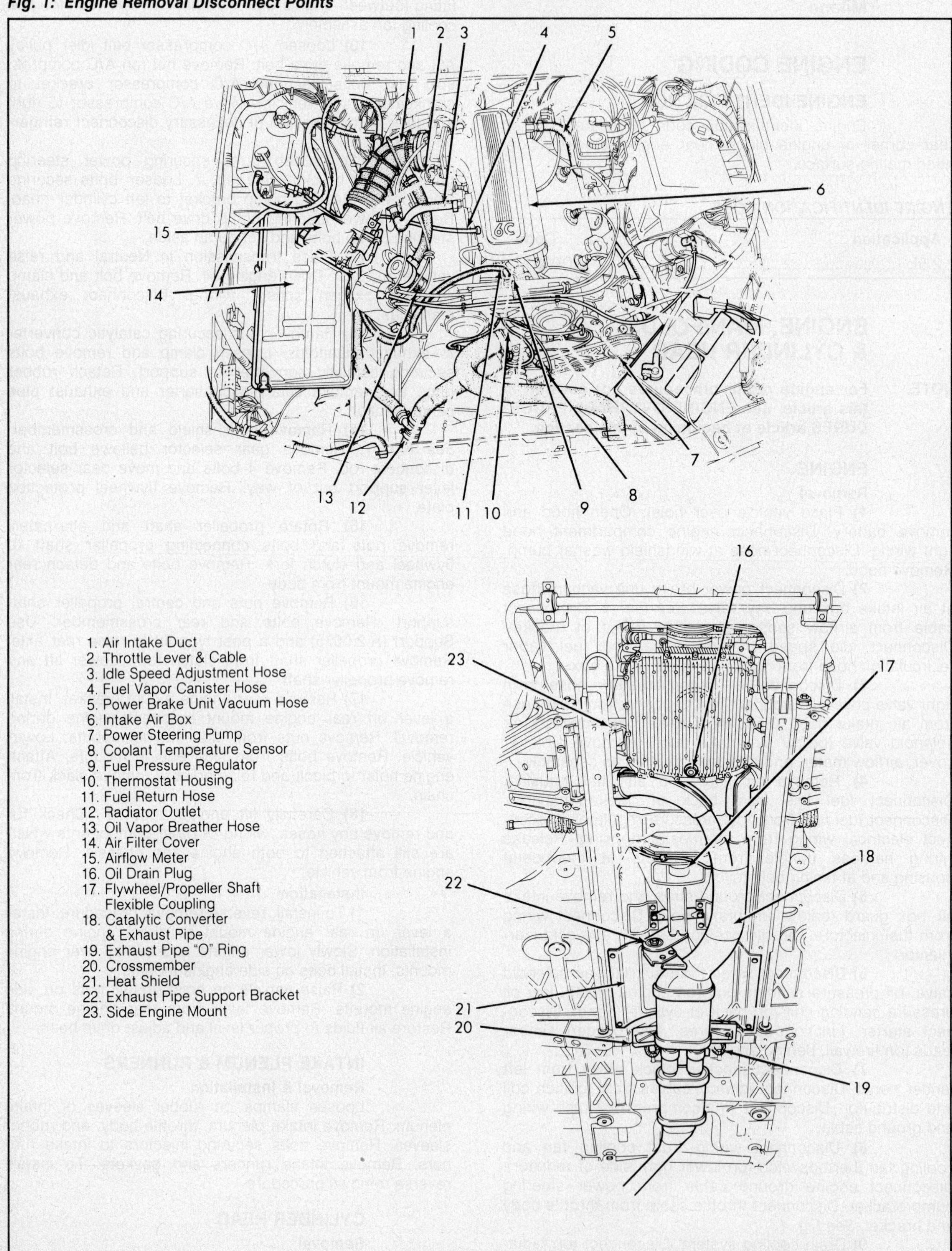

Courtesy of Alfa Romeo Auto S.p.A.

2.5L V6 (Cont.)

plug well gaskets. *See Fig. 4*. Using a magnetic retriever, remove oil pump/distributor drive gear from right cylinder head.

2) Remove cylinder head nuts. Remove cylinder head from engine, being careful not to damage engine block studs. Remove cylinder head gasket, cylinder liner rings, and oil passage "O" ring.

Installation

1) Make sure piston in cylinder No. 1 is at TDC of compression stroke. Piston is at TDC if "P" (TDC notch) on crankshaft pulley aligns with reference pin. *See Fig. 2*.

Fig. 2: Cylinder Head Tightening Sequence

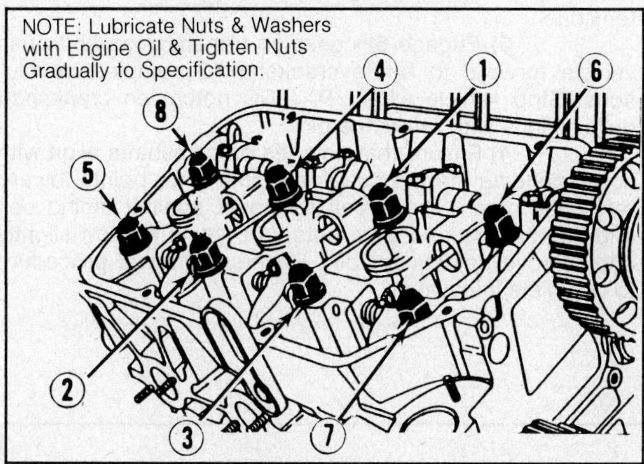
NOTE: Lubricate Nuts & Washers
with Engine Oil & Tighten Nuts
Gradually to Specification.
4
1
6
8
5
2
3
7

Courtesy of Alfa Romeo Auto S.p.A.

2) If installed, remove Cylinder Liner Holder (A.2.0117) and Washers (A.2.0362). Install cylinder liner rings, cylinder head gasket, and oil passage "O" ring.

3) Use Camshaft Holder (A.2.0361) to turn camshaft until notches on camshaft align with corresponding mark on caps. Install cylinder head on engine block. Lubricate engine studs, washers, and cylinder head nuts with clean engine oil.

4) Tighten cylinder head nuts in specified sequence. *See Fig. 2*. After 600 miles, loosen cylinder head nuts 1 turn. Lubricate washers and nuts with engine oil and retighten heads to 65 ft. lbs. (88 N.m).

CAMSHAFT

TIMING BELT COVERS

Removal

1) Disconnect negative battery cable. Unplug connector from airflow sensor and release cable from bracket. Disconnect hose from air intake duct and separate duct from throttle body.

2) Disconnect idle speed adjustment hose from air intake box. *See Fig. 1*. Disconnect air hose and wiring to auxiliary air solenoid valve. Remove auxiliary air solenoid valve from timing belt cover.

3) Disconnect distributor vacuum hose from throttle body. Disconnect oil vapor hose from timing belt cover. Disconnect fuel vapor canister hose from air intake box.

Fig. 3: Timing Belt Replacement

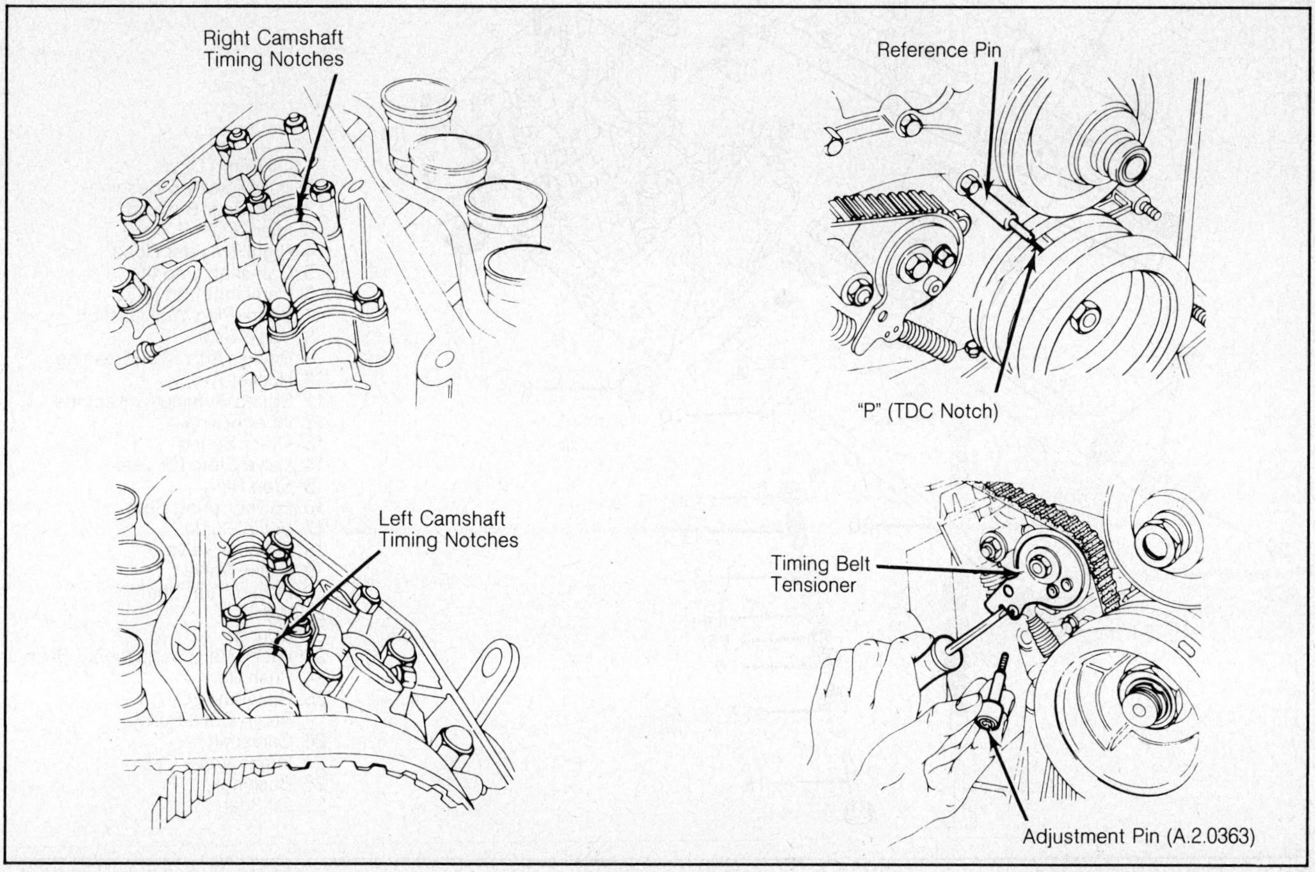

Right Camshaft Timing Notches

Reference Pin

"P" (TDC Notch)

Left Camshaft Timing Notches

Timing Belt Tensioner

Adjustment Pin (A.2.0363)

Courtesy of Alfa Romeo Auto S.p.A.

Alfa Romeo Engines

2.5L V6 (Cont.)

4) Disconnect pressure regulator hose. Remove air filter cover, air intake duct, and oil vapor separator. Remove air filter. Disconnect spark plug leads, coil lead, and remove distributor cap. Remove timing belt covers.

Installation

To install, reverse removal procedure.

TIMING BELT

Removal

1) Remove timing belt covers. See TIMING BELT COVERS. Remove drive belts. Disconnect coolant hoses and wiring from thermostat housing. Remove coolant temperature sending unit from thermostat housing. Clean spark plug seats and remove spark plugs.

2) Remove bolt, screws, and timing belt cover. Engage 5th gear on transmission and push vehicle forward until "P" (TDC notch) on crankshaft pulley aligns with reference pin. *See Fig. 3.*

3) Ensure that notches on camshafts align with corresponding mark on caps and that rotor points toward reference notch marked on distributor body. Make sure piston in cylinder No. 1 is at TDC of compression stroke (both valves closed).

4) Lift arm of timing belt tensioner and insert Adjustment Pin (A.2.0363) in block to keep tensioner arm up. Loosen nuts on tensioner arm, press tensioner downward to end of travel, and then tighten top nut. Remove timing belt from pulleys.

Installation

1) Check that engine is on TDC of compression stroke by installing TDC Adapter (C.6.0183) and dial indicator into spark plug seat of cylinder No. 1. Ensure that "P" (TDC notch) on crankshaft pulley aligns with reference pin and that notches on camshafts align with corresponding mark on caps.

2) Install timing belt over crankshaft pulley, left cylinder head, right cylinder head, distributor drive gear, and over belt tensioner pulleys. Loosen top nut on belt tensioner.

3) Engage 5th gear on transmission and push vehicle forward to rotate crankshaft 2 complete revolutions. Stop vehicle when "P" (TDC notch) on crankshaft pulley aligns with reference pin.

4) Ensure that notches on camshafts align with corresponding mark on caps and that rotor points toward reference notch. Press belt tensioner against timing belt and tighten tensioner arm nuts. Lift tensioner arm slightly and remove adjustment pin. Reverse removal procedure to complete installation.

Fig. 4: Exploded View of Cylinder Head Assembly

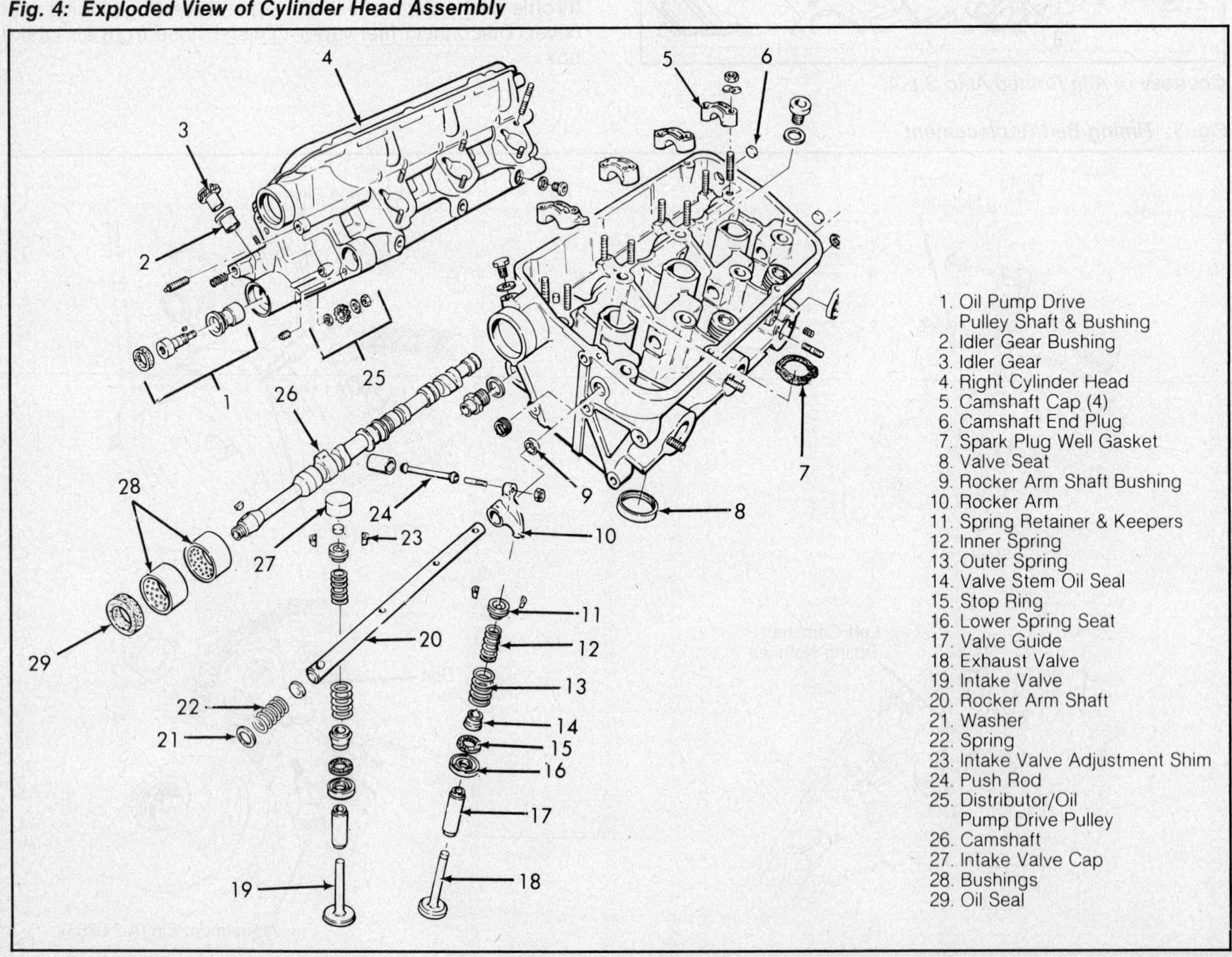

Courtesy of Alfa Romeo Auto S.p.A.

DISTRIBUTOR/OIL PUMP DRIVE PULLEY

Removal & Installation

Bend tab of nut securing drive gear. Use Camshaft Holder (A.2.0361) to hold drive pulley while removing nut from end of shaft. *See Fig. 4.* Remove nut and washer. Remove shaft, pulley, and spacer from cylinder head. Remove oil seal from cylinder head cavity. To install, reverse removal procedure.

CAMSHAFT

Removal

1) Use Camshaft Holder (A.2.0361) to prevent camshaft from rotating and remove nut on end of camshaft. Remove 3 bolts securing hub to end of camshaft.

2) Install Hub Puller (A.3.0521) on hub and turn puller center screw to withdraw hub from camshaft. Remove camshaft pulley and remove oil seal from cylinder head cavity.

3) Remove nuts and camshaft journal caps. Remove camshaft by raising rear part first and then sliding it out. *See Fig. 4.*

Installation

Lubricate camshaft journals with clean engine oil. Reverse removal procedure to complete installation.

ROCKER ARM ASSEMBLY

Removal

1) Remove tappets from cylinder head cavities and slide out push rods. Remove plug from rocker arm shaft support (on back of cylinder head). Insert a bolt into threaded shank of rocker arm shaft.

2) Gradually withdraw rocker arm shaft and catch washer, rocker arm, and spring one at a time. Remove intake valve tappet cups and corresponding adjustment shims one at a time. DO NOT mix cups and adjustment shims.

Installation

Lubricate rocker arm shaft journals and rocker arms with clean engine oil. Reverse removal procedure to complete installation.

VALVES

VALVE ARRANGEMENT

Intake Plenum Side – Intake valves.
Exhaust Manifold Side – Exhaust valves.

VALVES & VALVE SPRINGS

Removal

1) Insert Valve Support (A.2.0192) in spark plug well and lock it in place with Valve Support Nut (A.2.0359). Attach Loop (A.3.0522) to threaded shank of support nut. *See Fig. 5.*

2) Fit Yoke (A.3.0520) to Valve Spring Compressor Lever (A.3.0324). Hook lever onto loop and place yoke over valve spring. Compress valve springs and remove valve keepers. Remove spring retainer and springs.

3) Remove valve support assembly and valves. Using Valve Guide Seal Remover (A.3.0247), remove valve guide seals. Remove cap and spring seat. Remove valves, springs, and valve guide seals in remaining chambers, moving tool group each time.

Installation

To install, reverse removal procedure.

Fig. 5: Valve & Valve Spring Removal

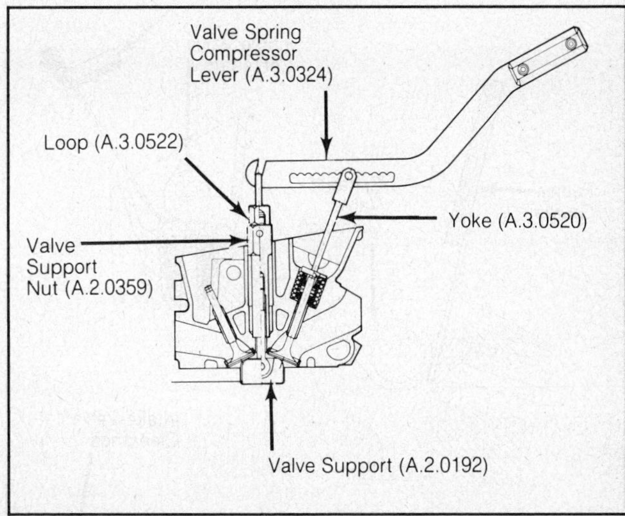

Courtesy of Alfa Romeo Auto S.p.A.

VALVE GUIDES

VALVE GUIDE SPECIFICATIONS

Application	In. (mm)
Valve Guide Clearance [1]	
Intake Valves	.0005-.0017 (.013-.043)
Exhaust Valves	.0016-.0031 (.040-.079)
Valve Guide-to-Cylinder Head	
Interference Fit	.0006-.0021 (.015-.053)
Valve Guide Installed Height	.402-.417 (10.20-10.60)

[1] – If a new valve guide is installed, use a .3543-.3549" (8.99-9.01 mm) reamer to ream inside diameter of valve guide. Check inside diameter after reaming and recheck valve guide clearance.

VALVE CLEARANCE ADJUSTMENT

1) Remove timing belt covers. See TIMING BELT COVERS. Remove oil from lubrication wells. Clean spark plug seats and remove spark plugs.

2) Use a feeler gauge to measure valve clearance between camshafts and valve tappet cups. *See Fig. 6.* Exhaust valve clearance should be .009-.010" (.23-25 mm). Intake valve clearance should be .019-.020" (.48-.50 mm).

3) If intake valve clearance is incorrect, note and record clearance on corresponding exhaust valve. Engage 5th gear on transmission and push vehicle forward until "P" (TDC notch) on crankshaft pulley aligns with reference pin. *See Fig. 3.*

4) Ensure that notches on camshafts align with corresponding mark on caps. Remove timing belt cover which protects timing belt. Use Camshaft Holder (A.2.0361) to hold camshaft while removing camshaft hub nut.

2.5L V6 (Cont.)

Fig. 6: Checking Valve Clearance Adjustment

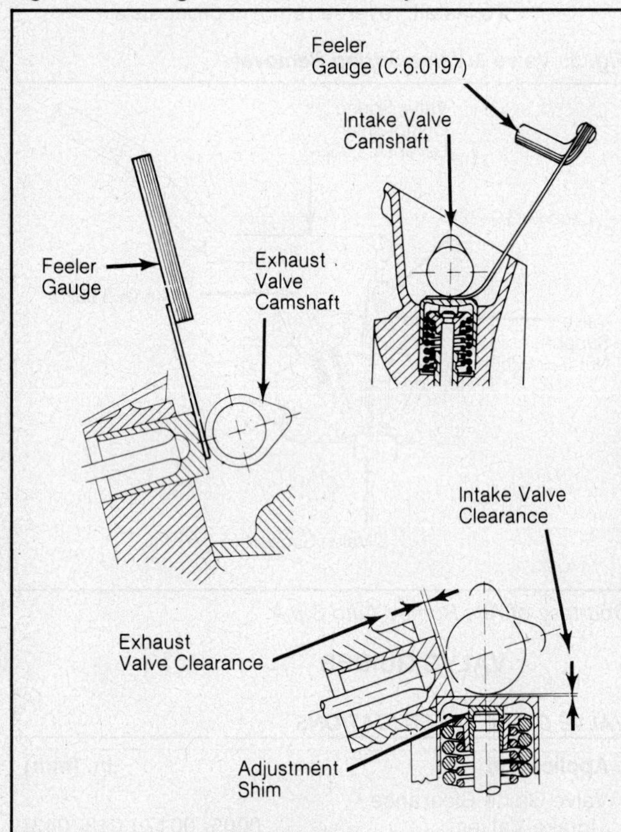

Courtesy of Alfa Romeo Auto S.p.A.

5) Remove 3 bolts securing hub to end of camshaft. Install Hub Puller (A.3.0521) on hub and turn puller center screw to withdraw hub from camshaft. Remove camshaft journal caps and camshaft.

6) Remove valve tappet cup(s) and adjustment shim(s). DO NOT mix cups and adjustment shims. Measure adjustment shim thickness (at center) and select a new adjustment shim that will restore valve clearance to specifications.

7) Lubricate and install selected adjustment shim(s) and cap(s). Install camshaft and camshaft journal caps. On right cylinder head, arrow on camshaft journal caps must face rear of engine. On left cylinder head, arrow on camshaft journal caps must face front of engine.

8) Rotate camshaft so that notches on camshafts align with corresponding mark on caps. Verify that "P" (TDC notch) on crankshaft pulley is still aligned with reference pin. *See Fig. 3.*

9) Using a new "O" ring, install camshaft hub. DO NOT tighten bolts at this time. Install and tighten camshaft hub nut. Tighten camshaft hub bolts. Check and adjust exhaust valve clearance (if necessary).

10) If exhaust valve clearance is incorrect, install Valve Adjuster (A.5.0220) over lock nut and loosen nut. Using adjuster, turn adjustment screw until valve clearance is correct.

11) Ensure camshafts are installed correctly by installing TDC Adapter (C.6.0183) and dial indicator into spark plug seat of cylinder No. 1. Engage 5th gear on transmission and push vehicle forward until piston in cylinder No. 1 is at TDC of compression stroke (as indicated by dial).

12) Ensure that "P" (TDC notch) on crankshaft pulley aligns with reference pin and that notches on camshafts align with corresponding mark on caps. *See Fig. 3.* Install timing belt covers.

CYLINDER BLOCK ASSEMBLY

CYLINDER LINERS

1) Measure cylinder liner at a point 13/32" below engine block surface and above 31/32" from bottom of liner. *See Fig. 7.* Cylinder liners are available in 3 grades and are identified by color. See CYLINDER LINER DIAMETER table for specifications.

2) Measure protrusion of cylinder liner beyond engine block surface. When measuring, install cylinder liner holder and tighten nuts to 10 ft. lbs. (13 N.m). Cylinder liner protrusion must be .0004-.0024" (.01-.06 mm). Cylinder liner out-of-round or taper must not exceed .0004" (.01 mm).

CYLINDER LINER DIAMETER

Application	In. (mm)
Grade "A" (Blue)	3.4640-3.4643 (87.985-87.994)
Grade "B" (Pink)	3.4644-3.4647 (87.995-88.004)
Grade "C" (Green)	3.4680-3.4651 (88.005-88.014)

Fig. 7: Cylinder Liner Measurements

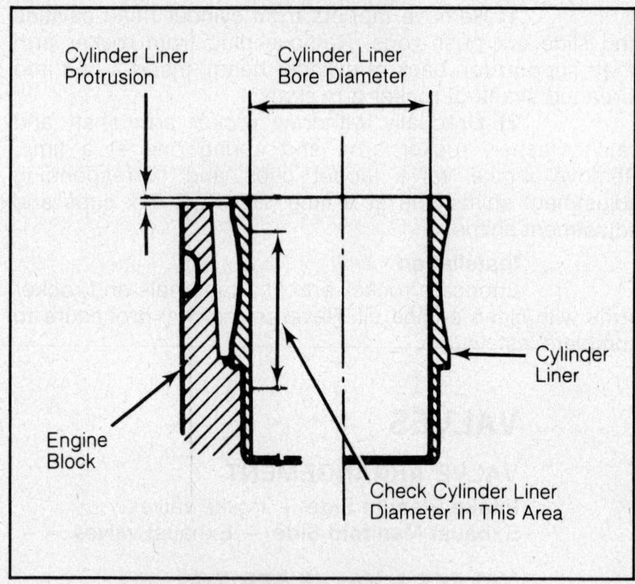

Courtesy of Alfa Romeo Auto S.p.A.

MAIN BEARING BORE

Crankcase main bearing bore diameter must be 2.5062-2.5069" (63.657-63.676 mm). Width of rear main bearing support shoulder should be 1.0413-1.0433" (26.45-26.50 mm).

PISTONS, PINS & RINGS

PISTON & ROD ASSEMBLY

Removal

1) Install Cylinder Liner Holders (A.2.0117) and Washers (A.2.0362) over engine block studs. Remove water pump bolts and alternator support bracket. Remove water pump and save gasket.

2) Install engine on engine stand and rotate engine so that oil pan is up. Remove oil pan and gasket. Using an Allen wrench, remove 3 bolts securing oil pump to block. Remove oil pump and save "O" ring.

3) Remove crankshaft pulley and front oil seal. See FRONT COVER/OIL SEAL in this article. Remove Flywheel Holder (A.2.0145) and rotate flywheel so that bolts retaining connecting rod cap are accessible.

4) Remove bolts, connecting rod cap, and lower bearing half. Rotate engine on stand until engine block is right side up. Remove cylinder liner holders and washer. Remove connecting rod, piston, and cylinder liners as an assembly. Remove "O" ring from bottom of cylinder liner.

Installation

1) Completely clean cylinder liners and install bottom "O" ring. Install cylinder liners in block, making sure thay are fully seated. Install cylinder liner holder, washers, and tighten nuts to 10 ft. lbs. (13 N.m).

2) Install dial indicators to Cylinder Liner Protrusion Gauge (C.6.0148). Place gauge assembly on a straightedge and zero dial indicators. *See Fig. 8*.

3) Place gauge assembly over cylinder block so that dial indicator stems rest on edge of cylinder liner. *See Fig. 8*. Cylinder liner protrusion must be .0004-.0024" (.01-.06 mm). Install piston/connecting rod assemblies by reversing removal procedure.

Fig. 8: Checking Cylinder Liner Protrusion

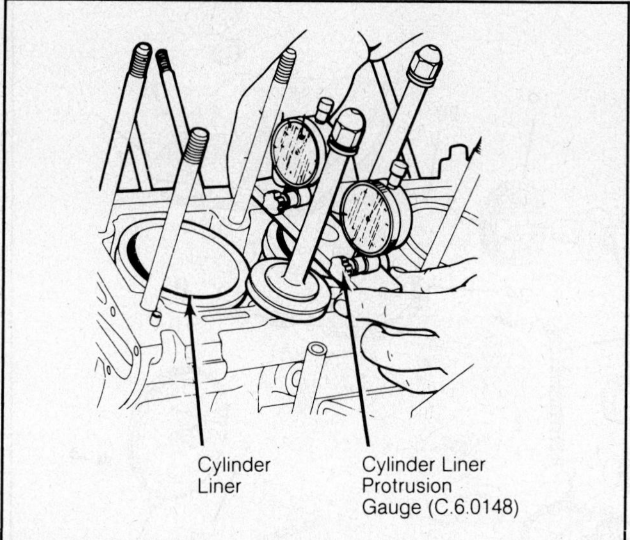

Courtesy of Alfa Romeo Auto S.p.A.

FITTING PISTONS

Measure piston diameter at .47" (12 mm) from bottom of skirt. Piston are available in 3 grades and are identified by color. See PISTON DIAMETER SPECIFICATIONS table.

PISTON DIAMETER SPECIFICATIONS

Application	In. (mm)
Grade "A" (Blue)	3.4620-3.4624 (87.935-87.945)
Grade "B" (Pink)	3.4624-3.4628 (87.945-87.955)
Grade "C" (Green)	3.4628-3.4632 (87.955-87.965)

PISTON PINS

1) Measure piston pin diameters. Standard piston pin diameter is .8659-.8660" (21.994-21.996 mm) for Black colored pins. Piston pin diameter is .8660-.8661" (21.996-22.000 mm) for White colored pins.

2) Measure piston pin bore diameter in piston. Standard piston pin bore diameter is .8663-.8664" (22.003-22.006 mm) for Black colored pins. Piston pin bore diameter is .8664-.8665" (22.006-22.009 mm) for White colored pins.

CRANKSHAFT & ROD BEARINGS

CRANKSHAFT MAIN BEARINGS

Removal

1) Remove front cover. Remove connecting rods and caps. Install Flywheel Holder (A.2.0145) on engine block to keep crankshaft from rotating. Remove flywheel bolts, flywheel holder, and flywheel.

2) Straighten lock tab from rear main bearing cap nuts. Remove lock nuts, nuts, and washers from main bearing caps. Remove main bearing caps and lower main bearing halves. Remove seals from sides of rear main bearing cap.

3) Remove rear main bearing oil seal from end of crankshaft. Remove thrust ring halves from rear main bearing flange. Remove crankshaft and upper main bearing halves.

Installation

To install crankshaft, reverse removal procedure. Check main bearing clearance using Plastigage. Ensure that grooves on thrust ring halves are facing crankshaft shoulder. With main bearing caps installed and tightened, measure crankshaft end play. Crankshaft end play must be .0032-.0104" (.080-.265 mm).

THRUST RING

Check thickness of thrust ring. Standard thrust ring thickness must be .0909-.0929" (2.310-2.360 mm).

FRONT COVER/OIL SEAL

Removal

1) Install Flywheel Holder (A.2.0145) on engine block to keep crankshaft from rotating. Straighten collar of crankshaft pulley nut. Remove crankshaft pulley nut, washer, and crankshaft pulley.

2) Remove crankshaft timing belt pulley and cupped washer. Remove bolt, washer, and plate securing hydraulic belt tensioner. Remove front cover bolts, cover, and gasket. Remove front oil seal from front cover.

Installation

1) Install front cover and hydraulic belt tensioner. Lubricate oil seal ring with engine oil and lip with Molykote grease. Using Seal Installer (A.3.0524), drive seal onto crankshaft.

2) Install flywheel holder to keep crankshaft from rotating. Install ring with crown of ring facing inward. Install crankshaft timing belt sprocket, crankshaft pulley, washer, and nut. Tighten nut and stake nut collar.

Alfa Romeo Engines

2.5L V6 (Cont.)

Fig. 9: Exploded View of Engine Block Assembly

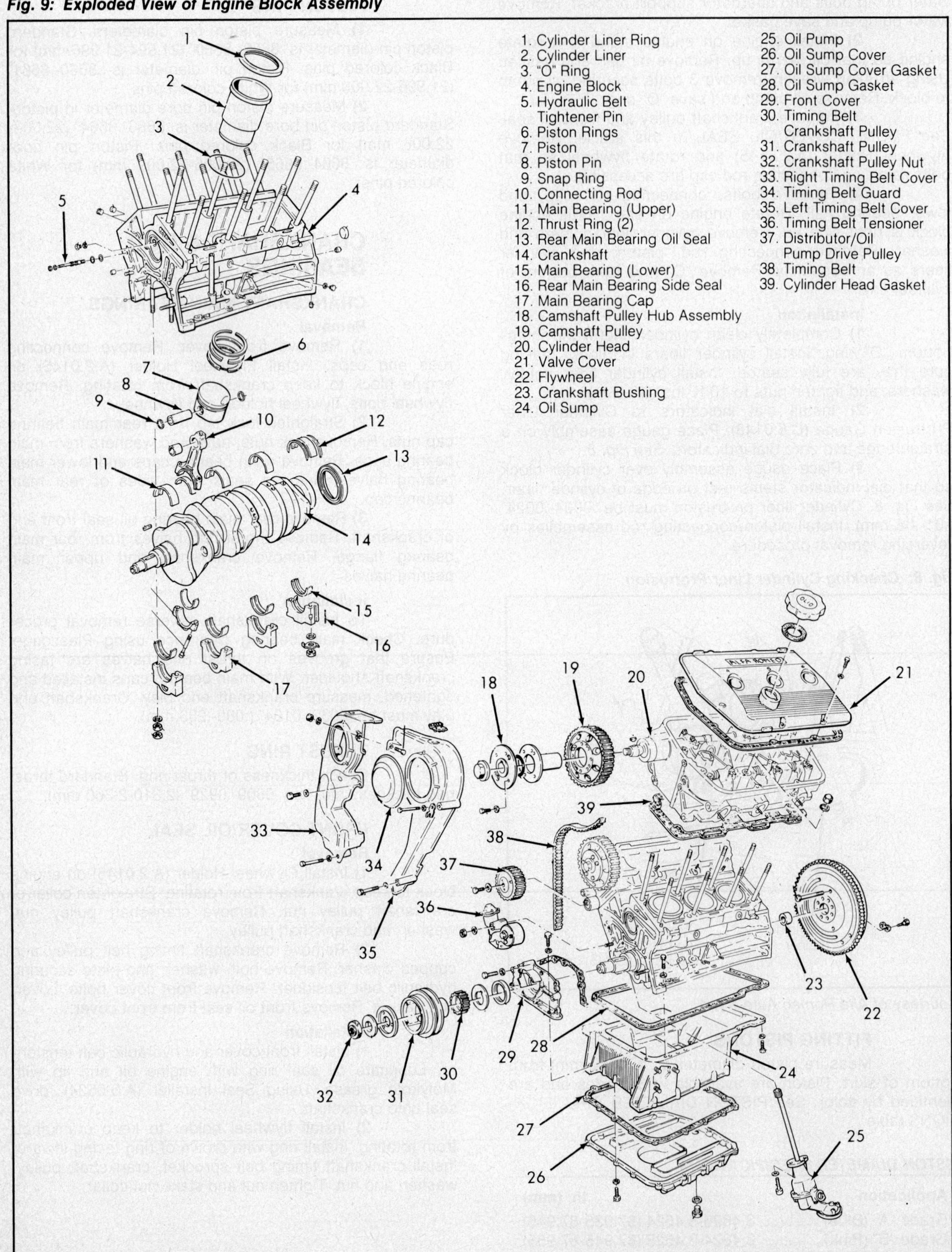

Courtesy of Alfa Romeo Auto S.p.A.

2.5L V6 (Cont.)

REAR MAIN BEARING OIL SEAL

Removal

Install Flywheel Holder (A.2.0145) on engine block to keep crankshaft from rotating. Remove flywheel bolts, flywheel holder, and flywheel. Remove rear main bearing cap and rear oil seal.

Installation

To install, reverse removal procedure. Drive seal onto crankshaft. Lubricate oil seal ring with engine oil and lip with Molykote grease. Using Seal Installer (A.3.0524), drive seal onto crankshaft.

ENGINE OILING

ENGINE OILING SYSTEM

Oil is drawn through oil pump screen and is delivered to oil filter. Oil is then forced to main bearings and connecting rod bearings. Rod bearings receive oil through oil passages drilled on crankshaft main bearing journals. A rotor-type pump is used.

CRANKCASE CAPACITY

Total oiling system capacity is 7.7 qts. (7.3L). Crankcase capacity after oil/filter change is 7.1 qts. (6.7L).

NORMAL OIL PRESSURE

Normal oil pressure at idle should be 7-21 psi (.5-1.5 kg/cm²). Oil pressure at 5500 RPM should be 57-85 psi (4-6 kg/cm²).

OIL PRESSURE RELIEF VALVE

Measure free length of oil pressure relief valve spring. Free length should be 1.941" (49.29 mm). Install pressure relief valve spring in spring tester and load reading with spring at 1.256" (31.90 mm). Spring load should be 38.2-39.6 lbs. (17-18 kg).

OIL PUMP

OIL PUMP SPECIFICATIONS

Application	In. (mm)
Driven Rotor Outside Diameter	1.933-1.935 (49.10-49.16)
Driven Rotor-to-Inner Rotor Clearance	.0016-.0114 (.040-.290)
Oil Pump Housing Inside Diameter	1.942-1.944 (49.33-49.38)
Rotor-to-Oil Pump Housing End Clearance	.0010-.0030 (.025-.075)

ENGINE COOLING

WATER PUMP

Removal

Remove timing belt and tensioner. See TIMING BELT. Use Wrench (A.2.0361) and remove bolt securing distributor drive pulley. Remove pulley. Disconnect hoses from thermostat housing. Remove bolts attaching water pump to engine block. Remove water pump and thermostat housing as an assembly.

Installation

To install, reverse removal procedure. Install drive belts and adjust tension. Restore all fluids to proper levels. Start engine and run it until it reaches normal operating temperature. Check for coolant leaks.

NOTE: For further information on cooling systems, see ENGINE COOLING section.

TIGHTENING SPECIFICATIONS

Application	Ft. Lbs. (N.m)
Belt Tensioner Pulley Bolt	15 (20)
Camshaft Journal Caps	[1] 12 (16)
Camshaft Hub Nut	85 (115)
Connecting Rod Cap Bolts	[1] 36 (49)
Crankshaft Pulley Nut	[1] 174 (235)
Cylinder Head Nuts	[2] 58 (78)
Flywheel Bolts	83 (112)
Intermediate Shaft Pulley Nut	62 (84)
Main Bearing Cap Nuts	[1] 58 (78)
Oil Pump Bolts	15 (20)
Propeller Shaft Coupling Bolts/Nuts	40 (55)
Propeller Shaft Central Crossmember Nuts	70 (95)
	INCH Lbs. (N.m)
Front Cover Bolts	72-82 (8-9)
Main Bearing Cap Lock Nuts	52-60 (6-7)
Valve Cover Bolts	82-96 (9-11)
Water Pump Bolts	72-82 (8-9)

[1] – With bolts/nuts lubricated.

[2] – With engine cold and washers, nuts, and stud threads lubricated. After 600 miles loosen nuts 1 turn and retighten nuts to 65 ft. lbs. (88 N.m) with washer and nuts surfaces lubricated.

ENGINE SPECIFICATIONS

GENERAL SPECIFICATIONS

Year	DISPLACEMENT		Fuel System	HP@RPM	Torque Ft. Lbs.@RPM	Compr. Ratio	BORE		STROKE	
	Cu. In.	Liters					In.	mm	In.	mm
1987	153	2.5	Fuel Inj.	157@5500	152@3200	9.0:1	3.46	80	2.69	68.3

Alfa Romeo Engines

2.5L V6 (Cont.)

ENGINE SPECIFICATIONS (Cont.)

VALVES

Engine Size & Valve	Head Diam. In. (mm)	Face Angle	Seat Angle	Seat Width In. (mm)	Stem Diameter In. (mm)	Stem Clearance In. (mm)	Valve Lift In. (mm)
2.5L							
Intake	1.608-1.614 (40.85-41.00)	45°	45°	.....	.3532-.3538 (8.972-8.987)	.0005-.0016 (.013-.040)	.....
Exhaust	1.433-1.441 (36.40-36.60)	45°	45°	.....	.3518-.3528 (8.935-8.960)	.0016-.0031 (.040-.080)	.....

CRANKSHAFT MAIN & CONNECTING ROD BEARINGS

Engine	MAIN BEARINGS				CONNECTING ROD BEARINGS		
	Journal Diam. In. (mm)	Clearance In. (mm)	Thrust Bearing	Crankshaft End Play In. (mm)	Journal Diam. In. (mm)	Clearance In. (mm)	Side Play In. (mm)
2.5L							
Red	2.3611-2.3615 (59.971-59.981)	.0002-.0019 (.005-.047)	No. 4	.0031-.0104 (.080-.265)	2.0468-2.0472 (51.990-52.000)	.0008-.0023 (.021-.060)	.008-.012 (.20-.30)
Blue	2.3607-2.3611 (59.961-59.971)	.0002-.0018 (.005-.045)	No. 4	.0031-.0104 (.080-.265)	2.0465-2.0468 (51.980-51.990)	.0009-.0024 (.023-.062)	.008-.012 (.20-.30)

PISTONS, PINS, RINGS

Engine	PISTONS	PINS		RINGS		
	Clearance In. (mm)	Piston Fit In. (mm)	Rod Fit In. (mm)	Ring No.	End Gap In. (mm)	Side Clearance In. (mm)
2.5L	.0016-.0023 (.040-.059)	.0002-.0005 (.004-.012)	[1]	No. 1 & 2	.012-.018 (.30-.45)	.0014-.0026 (.035-.067)
				Oil	.010-.016 (.25-.40)	.0010-.0022 (.025-.057)

[1] – Rod fit clearance is .0003-.0008" (.008-.021 mm) for Black colored pins, .0002-.0007" (.005-.018 mm) for White colored pins.

VALVE SPRINGS

Engine	Free Length In. (mm)	PRESSURE Lbs. @ In. (Kg @ mm)	
		Valve Closed	Valve Open
2.5L			
Inner	.....	29@1.20 (13@30.5)	50@.846 (23@21.5)
Outer	.....	55@1.28 (25@32.5)	106@.925 (48@23.5)

CAMSHAFT

Engine	Journal Diam. In. (mm)	Clearance In. (mm)	Lobe Lift In. (mm)
2.5L	1.0610-1.0618 (26.949-26.970)	.0012-.0033 (.030-.084)	.....

VALVE TIMING

Engine	INTAKE		EXHAUST	
	Open (BTDC)	Close (ABDC)	Open (BBDC)	Close (ATDC)
2.5L	36°50'	60°50'	59°55'	23°55'

1.8L & 1.8L 16-VALVE 4-CYLINDER

Audi: 4000S
Volkswagon: Cabriolet, Fox, Golf, GTI, Jetta, Jetta GLI, Scirocco

NOTE: **For engine repair procedures not covered in this article, see ENGINE OVERHAUL PROCEDURES article at beginning of this section.**

ENGINE CODING

ENGINE IDENTIFICATION

Stamped engine identification number is on machined pad at left side of engine block near ignition distributor. Letter prefix is engine identification code.

ENGINE IDENTIFICATION CODES

Application	Code
Audi	
4000S	MG
Volkswagen 8-Valve	
Cabriolet	JH
Fox	UM
Golf & Jetta	GX
Jetta GLI & GTI	RD
Scirocco	JH
All 16-Valve	PL

ENGINE, MANIFOLDS & CYLINDER HEAD

ENGINE

NOTE: **When removing longitudinally mounted engines, separate engine from transaxle before lifting it from engine compartment.**

Removal (Longitudinally Mounted)

1) Disconnect battery ground strap. Open radiator cap and set heater control to "WARM" position. Disconnect power steering pump from engine and place to side with hoses attached. Drain coolant. Leaving fuel lines connected, remove cold start valve, warm-up regulator, fuel injectors and airflow sensor assembly as necessary. Plug injector sockets and cap injectors. Secure all fuel components to right inner fender wall.

2) Disconnect wiring from radiator fan motor, thermo time switch and any components attached to engine. Remove radiator assembly with shroud and fan attached. Disconnect accelerator and clutch cables as necessary. Remove upper nut from left engine mount. Remove front engine mount. On models without A/C, proceed to step **4)**.

3) On models with A/C, remove A/C drive belt by loosening nuts on outer portion of crankshaft pulley. Remove 2 upper and 3 lower compressor mounting bracket bolts. Place compressor and bracket to side with hoses and wiring attached. Remove horn bracket, throttle valve housing, and auxiliary air regulator as necessary. Remove condenser and place to side with hoses attached.

4) Disconnect exhaust pipe at manifold. Remove starter motor. Remove all nuts from right engine mount. Remove bellhousing dust plate. On models with A/T, disconnect torque converter from drive plate by removing 3 bolts through starter opening. Hold transaxle up with Transaxle Support Assembly (3147 and 10-222A). Tighten hanger bar plate against transaxle with slight tension.

5) Attach lifting device to engine. Lift engine slowly until all engine mounts are clear. Remove right engine mount. Readjust hanger bar plate against transaxle. Remove remaining upper bolts holding engine to transaxle. Separate engine from transaxle. Lift engine, turning it so that body is cleared.

NOTE: **Lift engine carefully to avoid damage to transaxle mainshaft, clutch, and body. On models with automatic transaxle, secure torque converter to transaxle so that it cannot fall out.**

Installation

1) To install engine, reverse removal procedure. Use molybdenum disulfide grease on clutch release bearing and transaxle mainshaft. DO NOT lubricate release bearing guide sleeve. Place intermediate plate on locating dowels at rear of block, using grease to hold plate in place.

2) Carefully guide engine into vehicle and attach to transaxle, while keeping weight off engine mounts. Tighten lower bolts attaching engine to transaxle. Remove transaxle support bar and lower engine into position on mounts. Replace self-locking nuts on engine mounts. Install and tighten remaining bolts holding transaxle to engine.

3) Recharge A/C system. Final tightening of engine mounts and subframe bolts is done after engine is installed and running at idle speed. Adjust throttle and clutch cables. Adjust A/C belt tension with shims between pulley halves. Fill cooling system and ensure that radiator cooling fan cycles.

NOTE: **When removing transversely mounted engines, lift engine and transaxle from engine compartment as a unit. The intake manifold must be removed on 16-valve engines prior to engine removal.**

Removal (Transversely Mounted)

1) Remove battery from vehicle. Disconnect drive axles from transaxle flanges. Secure inner drive axle ends to body with wire. Remove springs holding together swivel joint of exhaust system. On models with power steering, remove pump and fluid reservoir with hoses attached. Secure pump and reservoir to crossmember with wire.

2) Remove radiator grille. On models with A/C, remove front trim panel and lower apron. Disconnect wiring at compressor and radiator fan shroud. Remove compressor and alternator drive belts. Disconnect condenser from crossmember and radiator, leaving hoses and ducting attached.

3) Disconnect vacuum hoses from idle boost valve. Remove air filter housing and airflow sensor assembly and place on radiator, leaving all fuel lines attached. Remove compressor from engine with hoses attached. Secure compressor and condenser out of way with wire.

NOTE: **When moving A/C parts that have hoses connected, use care to avoid kinking or flattening lines.**

4) Open coolant reservoir cap and drain coolant by removing coolant hoses. Disconnect wiring

1.8L & 1.8L 16-VALVE 4-CYLINDER (Cont.)

from radiator fan motor, thermo time switch, and headlights. Disconnect hood release cable from latch and apron. Remove radiator assembly with fan motor and shroud. Disconnect all wiring from electrical components that are attached to engine.

5) On vehicles with manual transaxle, disconnect wiring from transaxle mounted switches, upshift indicator vacuum switch and starter. Disconnect clutch and speedometer cables from transaxle. Plug speedometer cable opening. Disconnect gearshift rods from shifter bellcrank and remove bellcrank bracket.

6) On vehicles with automatic transaxles, disconnect battery cable from starter and CIS-E wiring harness. Disconnect accelerator and selector lever cables from levers and mounts with selector lever in "PARK".

7) On all models, disconnect accelerator cable at throttle valve linkage and mounting bracket. DO NOT disconnect throttle linkage. Remove cold start valve, warm-up valve and injectors from engine, leaving all fuel lines connected. Plug injector socket openings and cap injector tips. Disconnect all vacuum, vent, and preheat hoses.

8) Attach engine lifting device to 2 lifting eyes located at each end of cylinder head. Apply slight tension to lifting device with hoist. Remove rear engine mount. Disconnect transaxle mount. Remove through bolt from front mount. Lift engine/transaxle assembly slowly while turning unit slightly to clear front mount.

Installation

1) To install, reverse removal procedure. Make sure engine/transaxle assembly clears drive axles during lowering process. Connect rear engine mount, transaxle mount and front mount in sequence. ALL engine supports must be aligned with mount bushings before any mount bolts are tightened.

2) Connect and adjust accelerator cable, shift linkage, clutch linkage, and headlight alignment as necessary. Make sure all electrical components are connected correctly and wiring harnesses are properly routed. Check and adjust exhaust system alignment if necessary. Fill cooling system and make sure that cooling fan cycles properly.

CYLINDER HEAD & MANIFOLDS

Removal

1) Disconnect battery ground strap. Detach and remove air intake boot. If equipped, remove cold start valve, fuel injectors and control pressure regulator with lines connected. Plug injector seats and cap nozzles on fuel injectors and cold start valve.

2) Drain coolant from engine and disconnect any coolant hoses attached to cylinder head. Label and disconnect all vacuum, air and ventilation hoses attached to cylinder head and intake manifold.

3) Label and disconnect all electrical and ignition wiring attached to cylinder head and intake manifold. On 16-valve engine, remove upper half of intake manifold. *See Fig. 6.*

4) On all models, disconnect wire attached to oxygen sensor in exhaust manifold. Remove all drive belts. Remove alternator bracket from cylinder head. Remove upper timing belt cover. Remove camshaft cover.

5) Remove water pump pulley. Disconnect exhaust pipe from manifold. Disconnect throttle cable. If equipped, remove cruise control servo and linkage. Position No. 1 piston on TDC of compression stroke. Ensure that flywheel timing mark is on "0" (TDC).

6) Loosen timing belt tensioner. Remove timing belt from camshaft sprocket. Loosen head bolts in reverse order of tightening sequence. *See Fig. 1.* Remove cylinder head with manifold(s) attached.

CAUTION: If any head bolt(s) require replacement, new polygon head bolts must be replaced in COMPLETE sets only. Polygon head bolts do NOT require retorque subsequent to repairs.

Installation

1) Clean all gasket mating surfaces. Use straightedge to check cylinder head surface for warping. Cylinder head must be resurfaced if distortion exceeds .004" (.10 mm).

2) On 16-valve engine, minimum thickness of cylinder head after surfacing is 4.65" (118.1 mm). This dimension is measured from cylinder head gasket surface to machined surface of head where cylinder head bolt sits.

3) On all others, minimum thickness of cylinder head after surfacing is 5.22" (132.6 mm). This dimension is measured from cylinder head gasket surface to machined surface of head where camshaft cover gasket sits.

4) On all models, make sure cylinder head bolt holes in block are clean and dry. Place dry cylinder head gasket on cylinder block with word "OBEN" ("TOP") facing upward. Use no sealant on head gasket.

5) Install cylinder head with manifolds. Install head bolts Nos. 8 and 10 to align cylinder head. Install remaining head bolts. Polygon stretch head bolts must be sequentially tightened in 3 stages with engine cold. Tighten head bolts in proper sequence. *See Fig. 1.*

6) First tightening step is to 29 ft. lbs. (40 N.m). Second step is to 44 ft. lbs. (60 N.m). Third step is to turn bolts 180 degrees (1/2 turn) further in one continuous movement or in 2 separate 90 degree (1/4 turn) movements. Install remaining components in reverse order of removal. Ensure valve timing is correct. Install timing belt and adjust tension.

Fig. 1: Cylinder Head Bolt Tightening Sequence

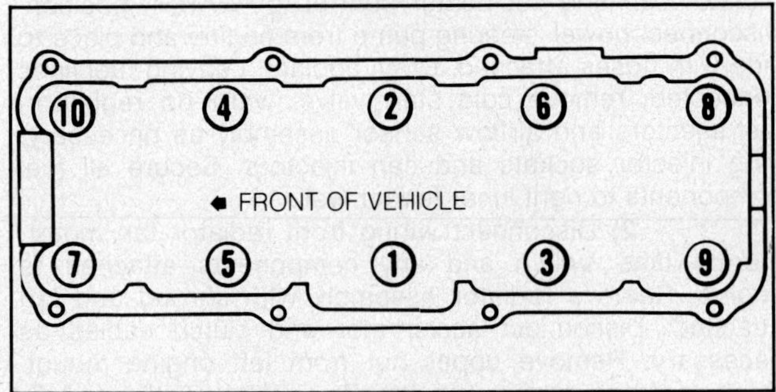

Courtesy of Volkswagen United States, Inc.

CAMSHAFT

TIMING BELT COVER

Removal & Installation

Outer cover consists of upper and lower parts. *See Fig. 2.* Inner (against block) timing belt cover is one piece. Remove all drive belts. Remove crankshaft and water pump pulleys. Remove outer covers. To install, reverse removal procedure.

1.8L & 1.8L 16-VALVE 4-CYLINDER (Cont.)

Fig. 2: 16-Valve Timing Belt Cover & Timing Belt Assembly

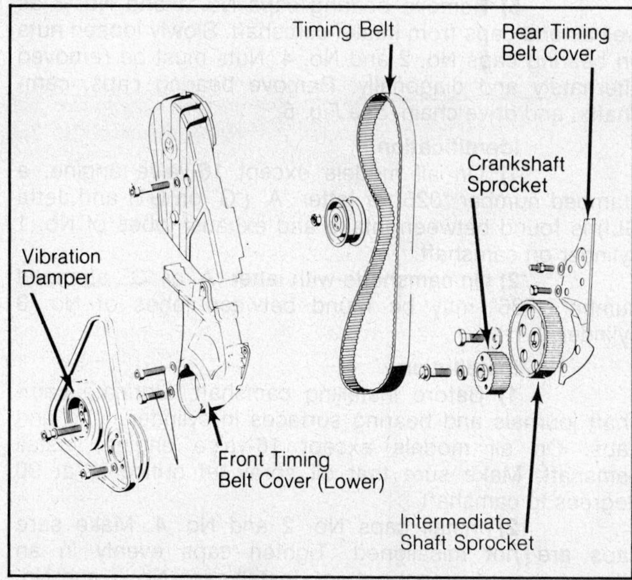

Courtesy of Volkswagen United States, Inc.

TIMING BELT

CAUTION: Never use camshaft sprocket attaching bolt to turn engine as timing belt could be stretched.

Removal

1) Remove all drive belts, crankshaft pulley, and vibration damper. Remove upper and lower timing belt outer covers. On 16-valve engine, remove upper half of intake manifold.

2) On all models, remove camshaft cover from cylinder head. Turn crankshaft to position No. 1 piston at TDC of compression stroke. Make sure distributor housing and flywheel timing marks are correctly aligned.

3) Loosen timing belt tensioner to relieve tension on timing belt. *See Fig. 2.* Slide timing belt off

Fig. 3: Aligning Intermediate Shaft & Crankshaft

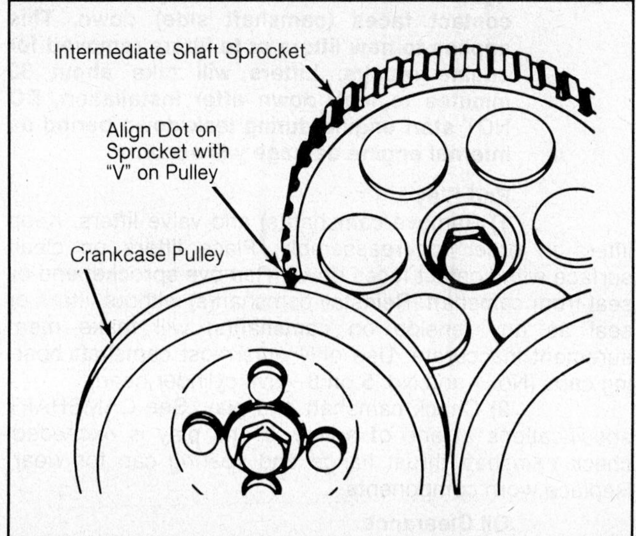

Courtesy of Volkswagen United States, Inc.

sprockets. Do not allow camshaft, crankshaft or intermediate sprockets to turn when removing timing belt.

Installation

1) Set crankshaft at point just before TDC compression for No. 1 cylinder. Place timing belt on crankshaft and intermediate shaft sprockets. Install crankshaft pulley and tighten all 4 bolts. Align mark on

Fig. 4: Setting Camshaft Timing Marks

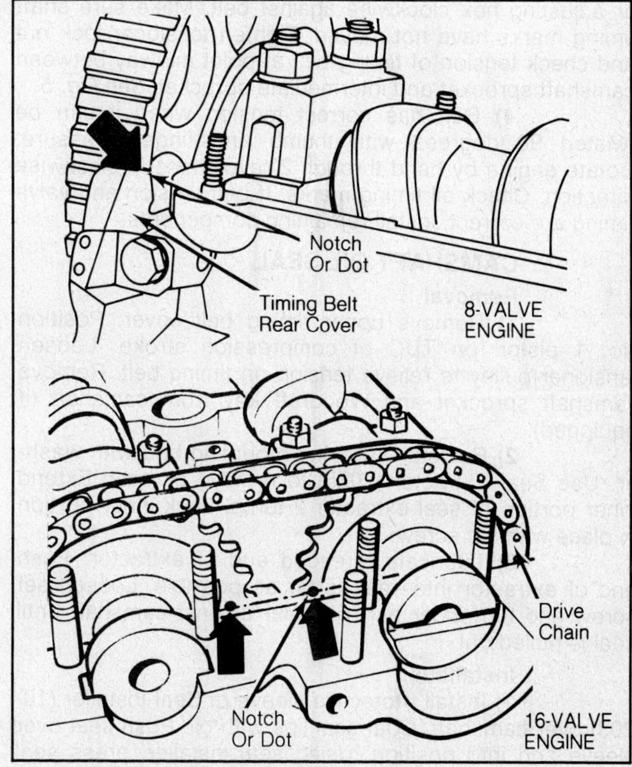

Courtesy of Volkswagen United States, Inc.

Fig. 5: Adjusting Timing Belt Tension

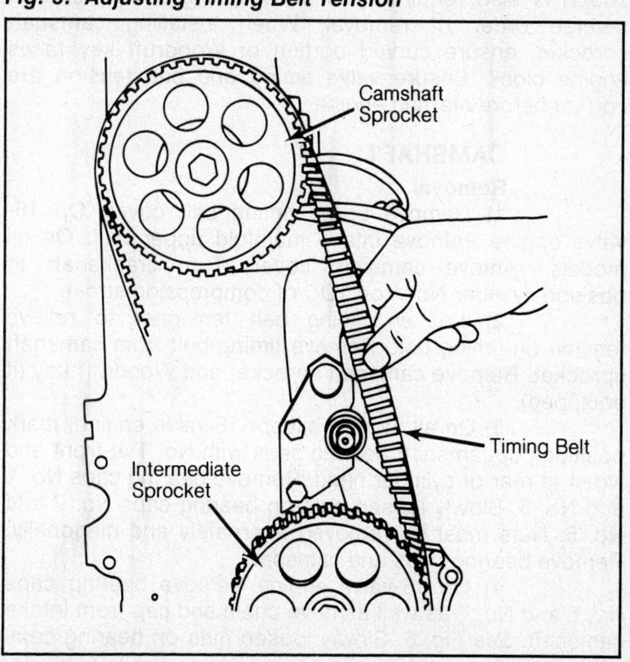

Courtesy of Volkswagen United States, Inc.

1.8L & 1.8L 16-VALVE 4-CYLINDER (Cont.)

crankshaft pulley with mark on intermediate shaft sprocket at TDC. *See Fig. 3.*

2) Position camshaft so mark on back of sprocket is in line with upper edge of timing belt rear cover. *See Fig. 4.* Both lobes for No. 1 cylinder should point upward at 45 degrees from camshaft follower so both valves are closed. Install timing belt on camshaft sprocket.

3) Adjust timing belt tension by turning tensioner adjusting hex clockwise against belt. Make sure shaft timing marks have not moved. Tighten tensioner lock nut and check tension of timing belt at point midway between camshaft sprocket and intermediate sprocket. *See Fig. 5.*

4) Belt has correct tension when it can be twisted 90 degrees with thumb and finger pressure. Rotate engine by hand through 2 revolutions in clockwise direction. Check all timing marks. If belt tension and valve timing are correct, install remaining components.

CAMSHAFT OIL SEAL

Removal

1) Remove upper timing belt cover. Position No. 1 piston on TDC of compression stroke. Loosen tensioner pulley to relieve tension on timing belt. Remove camshaft sprocket and Woodruff key from camshaft (if equipped).

2) Reinstall sprocket mounting bolt with washer. Use Seal Extractor (2085) to remove oil seal. Extend inner portion of seal extractor 2 turns. Lock inner portion in place with set screw.

3) Lubricate threaded end of extractor. Push end of extractor into seal as far as possible. Loosen set screw and turn inner part of puller against camshaft until seal is pulled out.

Installation

1) Install protective sleeve of Seal Installer (10-203) over camshaft. Coat seal lips with oil. Push seal over sleeve and into position. Using seal installer, press seal into bearing cap recess until flush.

2) On 16-valve engine, the use of Bolt (10-203/1) is also required. Install remaining components in reverse order of removal. When installing camshaft sprocket, ensure curved portion of Woodruff key faces engine block. Ensure valve timing and belt tension are correct before starting engine.

CAMSHAFT

Removal

1) Remove upper timing belt cover. On 16-valve engine, remove intake manifold upper half. On all models, remove camshaft cover. Turn crankshaft to position cylinder No. 1 on TDC of compression stroke.

2) Loosen timing belt tensioner to relieve tension on timing belt. Remove timing belt from camshaft sprocket. Remove camshaft sprocket and Woodruff key (if equipped).

3) On all models except 16-valve engine, mark positions of camshaft bearing caps with No. 1 at front and No. 4 at rear of cylinder head. Remove bearing caps No. 1 and No. 3. Slowly loosen nuts on bearing caps No. 2 and No. 5. Nuts must be removed alternately and diagonally. Remove bearing caps and camshaft.

4) On 16-valve engine, remove bearing caps No. 5 and No. 7 as well as drive chain end cap from intake camshaft. *See Fig. 6.* Slowly loosen nuts on bearing caps No. 6 and No. 8. Nuts must be removed alternately and diagonally.

5) Remove bearing caps No. 1 and No. 3 as well as end caps from intake camshaft. Slowly loosen nuts on bearing caps No. 2 and No. 4. Nuts must be removed alternately and diagonally. Remove bearing caps, camshafts, and drive chain. *See Fig. 6.*

Identification

1) On all models except 16-valve engine, a stamped number "026" or letter "A" ("G" on GTI and Jetta GLI) is found between intake and exhaust lobes of No. 1 cylinder on camshaft.

2) On camshafts with letter "A" or "G", stamped number "026" may be found between lobes of No. 3 cylinder.

Installation

1) Before installing camshaft, lubricate camshaft journals and bearing surfaces in cylinder head and caps. On all models except 16-valve engine, install camshaft. Make sure that oil spray jet orifice is at 90 degrees to camshaft.

2) Install caps No. 2 and No. 4. Make sure caps are not misaligned. Tighten caps evenly in an alternate and diagonal pattern. Install caps No. 1 and No. 3. Tighten all cap nuts evenly to 14 ft. lbs. (20 N.m).

3) On 16-valve engine, install camshafts and drive chain as an assembly. Ensure timing marks on camshaft are aligned. *See Fig. 4.* Tighten intake camshaft bearing caps No. 6 and No. 8 evenly in an alternate and diagonal pattern to 11 ft. lbs. (15 N.m).

4) Install remaining intake camshaft bearing caps and tighten to 11 ft. lbs. (15 N.m). Tighten exhaust camshaft bearing caps No. 2 and No. 4 evenly in an alternate and diagonal pattern to 11 ft. lbs. (15 N.m). Install remaining exhaust camshaft bearing caps and tighten to 11 ft. lbs. (15 N.m).

5) Install camshaft sprocket with Woodruff key facing engine block. Tighten camshaft sprocket bolt to 48 ft. lbs. (65 N.m). On all models, install remaining components in reverse order of removal. Make sure valve timing and belt tension are correct before starting engine.

CAMSHAFT INSPECTION

CAUTION: Hydraulic valve lifters are always stored with contact faces (camshaft side) down. This applies to new lifters or to lifters removed for engine repairs. Lifters will take about 30 minutes to leak down after installation. DO NOT start engine during leak-down period as internal engine damage will occur.

End Play

1) Remove camshaft(s) and valve lifters. Keep lifters in order for reassembly. Place lifters on clean surface with contact faces down. Remove sprocket and oil seal from camshaft. Reinstall camshaft(s) without lifters or seal as any tension on camshaft(s) will make measurement inaccurate. Use only outermost camshaft bearing caps (No. 1 and No. 5 on 8-valve cylinder head).

2) Check camshaft end play. See CAMSHAFT specifications at end of article. If end play is exceeded, check camshaft thrust flange and bearing cap for wear. Replace worn components.

Oil Clearance

1) Remove camshaft(s) and valve lifters. Keep lifters in order for reassembly. Place lifters on clean

1.8L & 1.8L 16-VALVE 4-CYLINDER (Cont.)

Fig. 6: Exploded View of 16-Valve Cylinder Head Assembly

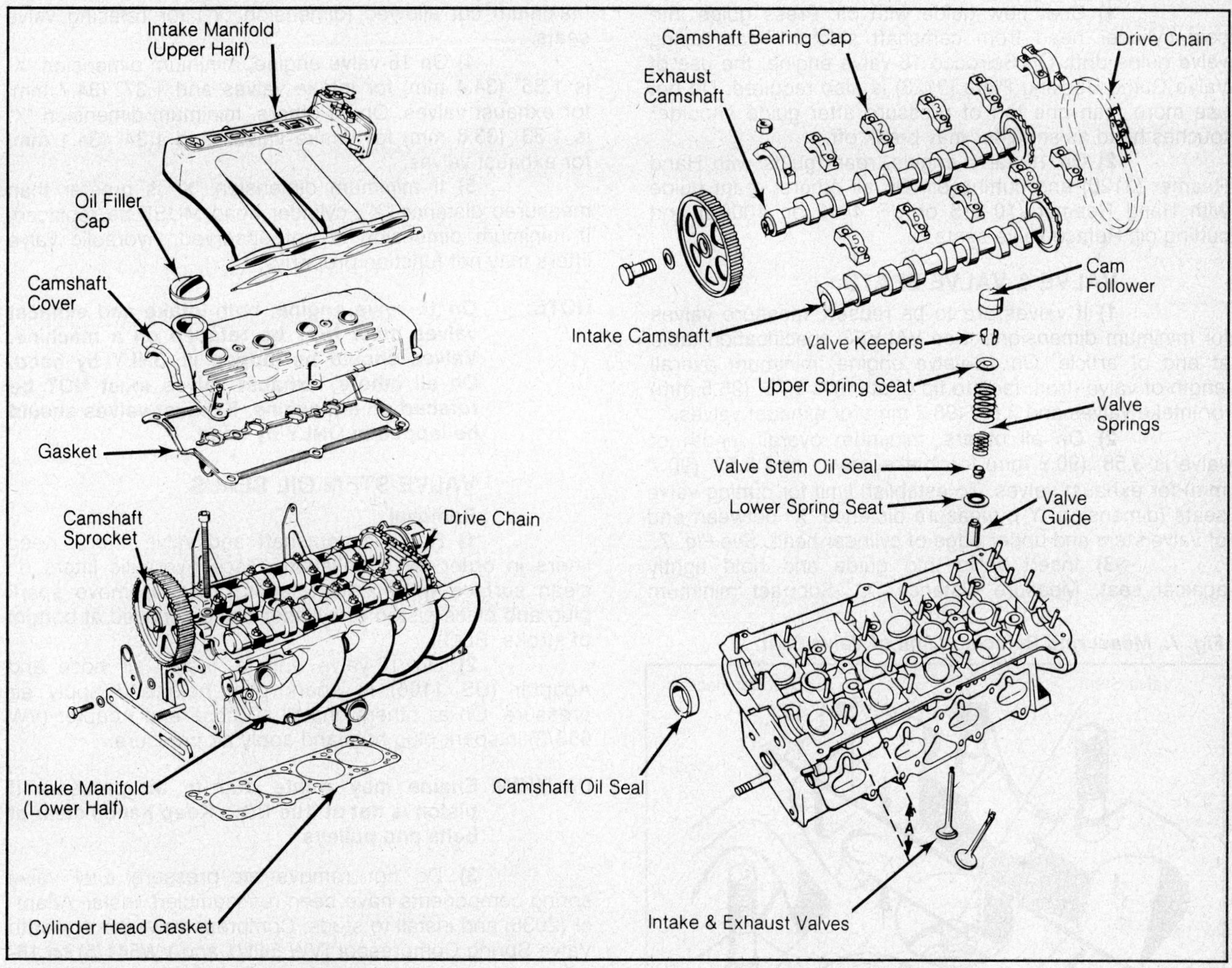

Courtesy of Volkswagen United States, Inc.

surface with contact faces down. Remove sprocket and oil seal from camshaft. Clean bearing caps, bearing seats, and camshaft journals.

2) Place camshaft(s) on cylinder head. Make sure that no lobes touch valves or valve spring retainers. Place Plastigage on camshaft journals parallel to length of camshaft. Install bearing caps in correct position and tighten cap nuts. DO NOT rotate camshaft with Plastigage installed.

3) Remove bearing caps and note oil clearance specification. See CAMSHAFT specifications at end of article. If limit is exceeded, repeat measurement with new camshaft installed. If limit is still exceeded with new camshaft in place, cylinder head must be replaced.

VALVES

VALVE ARRANGEMENT

Except 16 Valve

E-I-E-I-I-E-I-E (Front-to-rear).

16 Valve

Left Side - Intake Valves.

Right Side - Exhaust Valves.

VALVE GUIDES

Inspection

1) Make sure valve guides are clean and clear of debris. Attach dial indicator and Fixture (VW 387 or US 4420A) to mounting surface of cylinder head. Insert new valve into valve guide. Use correct valves in respective guides. End of valve stem must be flush with upper end of valve guide.

2) Tip of dial indicator must rest against side of valve head. Rock valve back and forth against tip of dial indicator. Maximum reading on dial indicator is .04" (1.0 mm) for intake valves and .05" (1.3 mm) for exhaust valves.

CAUTION: Replace valve guides in only those heads that have valve seats that can be resurfaced.

Removal

On 16-valve engine, use press, Valve Guide Drift (3121), and Support (30-23) to remove valve guides. On all others, use press and Valve Guide Drift (10-206) to remove valve guides. Press valve guides out of head from combustion chamber side.

Audi & Volkswagen Engines

1.8L & 1.8L 16-VALVE 4-CYLINDER (Cont.)

Installation

1) Coat new guide with oil. Press guide into cold cylinder head from camshaft side of head, using valve guide drift. On Scirocco 16-valve engine, the use of Valve Guide Backing Plate (3123) is also required. Do not use more than one ton of pressure after guide shoulder touches head as shoulder may break off.

2) On 16-valve engine, ream guide with Hand Reamer (3120) and cutting oil. On all others, ream guide with Hand Reamer (10-215 or US 4412 on 4000S) and cutting oil. Reface valve seats.

VALVE & VALVE SEATS

1) If valves are to be reused, measure valves for minimum dimensions. See VALVES specification table at end of article. On 16-valve engine, minimum overall length of valve (from face to tip of stem) is 3.76" (95.5 mm) for intake valves and 3.87" (98.2 mm) for exhaust valves.

2) On all others, minimum overall length of valve is 3.58" (90.9 mm) for intake valves and 3.57" (90.7 mm) for exhaust valves. To establish limit for cutting valve seats (dimension "Y"), measure distance "X" between end of valve stem and upper edge of cylinder head. *See Fig. 7.*

3) Insert valve into guide and hold tightly against seat. Measure distance "X". Subtract minimum dimension "X" from measured distance "X". Result is maximum cut allowed (dimension "Y") for refacing valve seats.

4) On 16-valve engine, minimum dimension "X" is 1.35" (34.4 mm) for intake valves and 1.37" (34.7 mm) for exhaust valves. On all others, minimum dimension "X" is 1.33" (33.8 mm) for intake valves and 1.34" (34.1 mm) for exhaust valves.

5) If minimum dimension "X" is greater than measured distance "X", cylinder head MUST be replaced. If minimum dimension is not observed, hydraulic valve lifters may not function properly.

NOTE: On 16-valve engine, both intake and exhaust valves must NOT be refaced on a machine. Valves should be lapped in ONLY by hand. On all others, exhaust valves must NOT be refaced on a machine. Exhaust valves should be lapped in ONLY by hand.

Fig. 7: Measuring Refacing Limit of Valve Seat

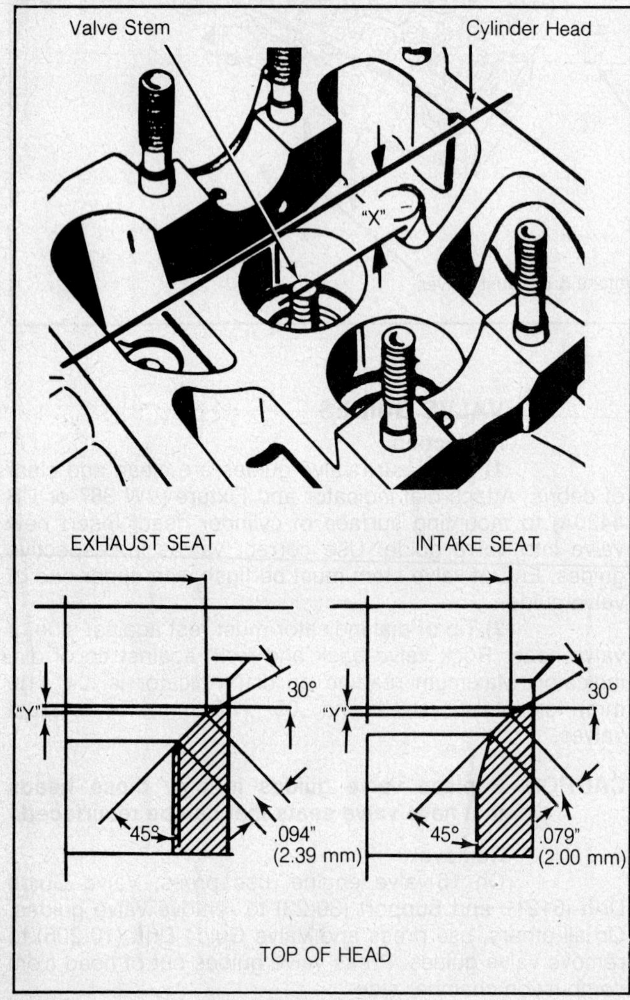

Courtesy of Volkswagen United States, Inc.

VALVE STEM OIL SEALS

Removal

1) Remove camshaft and valve lifters. Keep lifters in order for installation. Place hydraulic lifters on clean surface with contact faces down. Remove spark plug and place piston of cylinder being serviced at bottom of stroke (BDC).

2) On 16-valve engine, install air hose and Adapter (US 1106) in spark plug hole and apply air pressure. On all others, install air hose and Adapter (VW 653/3) in spark plug hole and apply air pressure.

CAUTION: Engine may rotate due to air pressure if piston is not at true BDC. Keep hands clear of belts and pulleys.

3) Do not remove air pressure until valve spring components have been reassembled. Install Adapter (2036) and install to studs. Compress valve springs with Valve Spring Compressor (VW 541/1 and VW541/5) on 16-valve engine.

4) Compress valve springs with Valve Spring Compressor (VW 541/1) on all others. Remove keepers, dual valve springs and both spring seats. Remove seal from valve stem.

Installation

Slide plastic protective sleeve onto valve stem. Lubricate new seal and push into place with Seal Installer (3129) on 16-valve engine. Use Seal Installer (10-204) on all other models. Install remaining components in reverse order of removal. Make sure valve timing is correct.

CAUTION: Hydraulic valve lifters are always stored with contact face down. This applies to new lifters or to lifters removed for engine repairs. Lifters will take about 30 minutes to leak down after installation. DO NOT start engine during leak-down period as internal engine damage will occur.

VALVE SPRINGS

Dual valve springs may be replaced with cylinder head installed on vehicle. To replace valve springs, use removal and installation procedure explained in VALVE STEM OIL SEALS. Both inner and outer valve springs must be replaced together if either is bad.

1.8L & 1.8L 16-VALVE 4-CYLINDER (Cont.)

HYDRAULIC VALVE LIFTERS

Inspection

1) Hydraulic valve lifters are not repairable or adjustable. Any worn, damaged or noisy lifter must be replaced as complete assembly. Some occasional valve/lifter noise is normal immediately after starting engine.

2) Run engine until radiator cooling fan has cycled at least once. Hold engine at steady 2500 RPM for 2 minutes. Allow engine speed to return to idle. If lifter is still noisy, go to next step.

3) On 16-valve engine, remove upper half of intake manifold. *See Fig. 6.* On all models, remove camshaft cover. Turn engine crankshaft until both camshaft lobes of cylinder to be checked point upward. Push down on lifter with wooden stick. If lifter can be compressed more than .004" (.10 mm), it must be replaced.

4) If hydraulic valve lifters are removed for engine repairs, keep them in correct order for installation. Store lifters on clean surface with contact surface facing down (upside down compared to installed position).

CAUTION: Hydraulic valve lifters are always stored with contact face down. This applies to new lifters or to lifters removed for engine repairs. Lifters will take about 30 minutes to leak down after installation. DO NOT start engine during leak-down period as internal engine damage will occur.

PISTONS, PINS & RINGS

OIL PAN

Removal

Drain engine oil. Attach lifting device or Support Bar (10-222) to engine. Raise engine slightly to support engine weight. If equipped, remove cover plate under engine. Remove both front bolts of subframe. Pull front end of subframe down to clear oil pan. Unbolt and remove oil pan.

Installation

Install oil pan with new gasket. DO NOT use any adhesive on gasket. Install oil pan bolts and tighten in diagonal pattern. Install subframe and cover plate (if equipped). Remove support bar from engine.

PISTON & ROD ASSEMBLY

Removal

Remove cylinder head, oil pan, and oil pump. Mark piston, rod and rod cap as to cylinder and position. Remove piston and rod assembly.

NOTE: All connecting rods must be in same weight class. Connecting rods of same weight class are only available in sets of 4.

Installation

1) Cover rod bolts with hose or tape to avoid damaging rod journals on crankshaft. Coat cylinder bore, piston and rings with engine oil. Ensure ring gaps are spaced 120 degrees apart and install ring compressor on piston.

2) Make sure that ring position does not change. Install piston and rod in correct bore, with arrow on piston head pointing toward front of engine. Forged casting marks on rod and cap must face toward intermediate shaft.

FITTING PISTONS

NOTE: Do not measure cylinder bore when block is on engine stand as block could be distorted. Resulting measurements would be inaccurate.

1)Measure cylinder out-of-round. Measure cylinder taper. If out-of-round or taper is excessive, block must be honed or bored to next oversize. Maximum deviation allowed from nominal dimensions, as shown in PISTON & CYLINDER DIMENSIONS table, is .003" (.08 mm).

2) Measure clearance between piston and cylinder wall. See PISTON, PINS, RINGS specifications at end of article. Install oversize pistons if wear limit is exceeded. Pistons have 4-digit number marked on face, which gives diameter in millimeters.

PISTON & CYLINDER DIMENSIONS

Size	Piston Diameter In. (mm)	Cylinder Bore In. (mm)
Standard	3.188 (80.98)	3.189 (81.01)
1st Over	3.198 (81.23)	3.199 (81.26)
2nd Over	3.208 (81.48)	3.209 (81.51)

FITTING RINGS

Measure ring end gap. Measure ring side clearance. See PISTONS, PINS, RINGS specifications at end of article. Install rings on piston with "TOP" mark facing upward. Recessed edge on outside of center ring must face piston pin (down). Ring end gaps should be spaced 120 degrees apart when piston is installed.

PISTON PIN REPLACEMENT

Removal

Remove circlip from pin bore groove. Use Piston Pin Drift (VW 222a or VW 207c) to remove and install piston pins. If pins are very tight, warm pistons to 140°F (60°C).

Installation

Assemble connecting rod to piston. Arrow on piston head and forged casting beads on connecting rod must face toward front of engine when assembly is installed. Use piston pin drift to install piston pin. Pin, piston and rod bushing should have interference fit. Install circlip into pin bore groove.

CRANKSHAFT & ROD BEARINGS

MAIN BEARINGS

1) Five main bearings are numbered front to rear. *See Fig. 8.* Measure bearing clearances. See CRANKSHAFT MAIN & CONNECTING ROD BEARINGS specifications at end of article. Replace parts as necessary.

2) When replacing bearings, install bearing halves with lubrication grooves into cylinder block. Plain bearing halves are installed in main bearing caps.

1.8L & 1.8L 16-VALVE 4-CYLINDER (Cont.)

CONNECTING ROD BEARINGS

Measure bearing clearances. Measure connecting rod side play. See CRANKSHAFT MAIN & CONNECTING ROD BEARINGS specifications at end of article. Replace parts as necessary. Install bearings and rod caps.

NOTE: Lubricate contact surface of rod nuts and tighten evenly to 22 ft. lbs. (30 N.m). Tighten both nuts an additional 90 degrees (1/4 turn).

CRANKSHAFT END PLAY

Use a feeler gauge to check crankshaft end play. Insert feeler gauge between No. 3 main bearing (thrust bearing) and crankshaft thrust face. Original thrust bearing uses plain shell with 4 separate washers while replacement thrust bearings have attached collar.

CRANKSHAFT REAR OIL SEAL

Removal

If engine is in vehicle, remove transaxle. Remove flywheel/flex plate, noting position of shim if used. Use Flywheel Lock (10-201) to hold flywheel/flex plate when loosening and tightening bolts. Carefully pry oil seal from seal flange.

Installation

1) Coat new seal lips with oil. Place Centering Sleeve (2003/2A) on crankshaft and start seal into place. Using Seal Installer (2003/1), press in seal until seated.

2) On models with flex plate, measure distance from back of block to face of flex plate (converter side) with intermediate plate removed. Distance must be 1.20-1.26" (30.5-32.1 mm), measured from lower left corner of block (high point). If distance is too small, install shim between end of crankshaft and flex plate.

3) Install intermediate plate, making sure it is located on dowel sleeves. Chamfered side of washer faces flex plate during installation. On all models, bolts with NO shoulder are tightened with locking compound to 55 ft. lbs. (75 N.m). Bolts with shoulder should be replaced with new bolts and tightened with locking compound to 74 ft. lbs. (100 N.m). Install remaining components.

CRANKSHAFT FRONT OIL SEAL

Removal

1) Remove all drive belts. Remove upper timing belt cover. Set No. 1 piston on TDC of compression stroke. Remove crankshaft pulley. Install Locking Retainer (3099) and loosen bolt that holds timing belt sprocket to crankshaft. Remove water pump pulley.

2) Remove lower timing belt cover. Loosen timing belt tensioner. Remove timing belt and drive sprocket. Install Allen head bolt from Seal Installer (3083) in end of crankshaft. Remove seal using Seal Extractor (2085) guided by bolt from installer.

Installation

1) Slide sleeve from Seal Installer (3083) onto crankshaft. Slide new seal over sleeve after dipping seal in fresh engine oil. Place thrust sleeve from installer over guide sleeve.

2) Press seal into place with thrust sleeve and Allen head bolt until seal is fully seated. Install crankshaft timing belt sprocket, making sure keyed lug on sprocket is fitted to machined groove in crankshaft. Use locking retainer to hold crankshaft.

3) Use oil to coat threads of bolt which secures timing belt sprocket to crankshaft. Install bolt and tighten to 148 ft. lbs. (200 N.m). Install remaining components. Make sure valve timing and timing belt tension are correct.

INTERMEDIATE SHAFT

END PLAY

Remove distributor prior to removing intermediate shaft. *See Fig. 8*. Measure intermediate shaft end play. Maximum end play is .010" (.25 mm). Replace parts as necessary.

OIL SEAL

If oil seal replacement is necessary, remove oil seal flange and press out seal. Lubricate new seal lips with oil. Install oil seal flange with oil return hole at bottom edge. Use Seal Installer (10-203) to press seal into place.

ENGINE OILING

ENGINE OILING SYSTEM

Oiling system is pressure feed system. A gear-type oil pump lifts oil from oil pan and pressure feeds it to crankshaft journals, camshaft bearings, and intermediate shaft. Other parts of system receive oil lubrication by drainage or splash method.

CRANKCASE CAPACITY TABLE

Model	With Filter Replacement	Without Filter Replacement
Cabriolet, Golf	3.7 Qts. 3.5 (L)	4.3 Qts. 4.1 (L)
Jetta, GLI, GTI	4.3 Qts. 4.1 (L)	4.7 Qts. 4.5 (L)
Fox	3.2 Qts. 3.0 (L)	3.8 Qts. 3.6 (L)
4000S	3.1 Qts. 2.9 (L)	3.7 Qts. 3.5 (L)

NORMAL OIL PRESSURE

Minimum oil pressure is 29 psi (2.0 kg/cm²) at 2000 RPM, with oil temperature of 176°F (80°C). Specification is for 20W/20 type engine oil.

OIL PUMP

Removal & Disassembly

Remove oil pan. Remove oil pump attaching bolts and lower pump away from engine. Remove pump pick-up bolts. Separate pick-up from pump body. Remove strainer cover from pick-up tube and clean strainer.

Inspection

1) With oil pump gears installed in pump housing, insert feeler gauge between drive gear and driven gear teeth (where teeth mesh). Measure pump gear backlash. Maximum backlash is .002-.008" (.05-.20 mm).

2) Place straightedge over pump housing. Insert feeler gauge between pump gears and straightedge. Maximum end play of gears is .006" (.15 mm).

Reassembly & Installation

Assemble pump in reverse order of disassembly. Prime oil pump prior to installing. Install pump in reverse order of removal procedures. Make sure engine has oil pressure after starting.

1.8L & 1.8L 16-VALVE 4-CYLINDER (Cont.)

Fig. 8: 16-Valve Engine Intermediate Shaft, Crankshaft & Main Bearing Asssembly

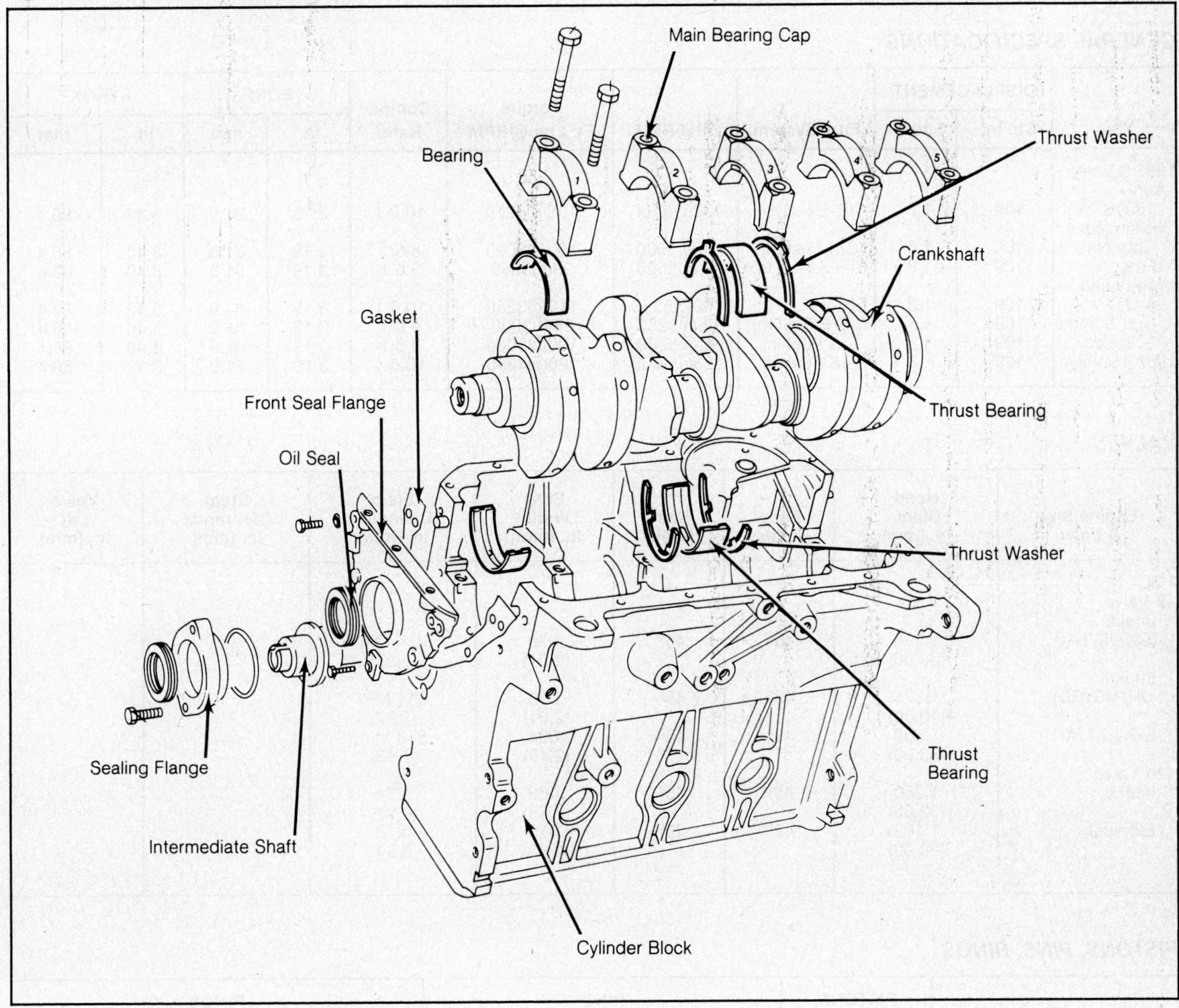

Courtesy of Volkswagen United States, Inc.

ENGINE COOLING

CAUTION: Coolant/water mixture should be used at all times. Only ethylene glycol based (phosphate-free) antifreeze may be used, as it protects aluminum/iron engines from corrosion.

WATER PUMP

Removal & Disassembly

1) Set heater control on dash to "WARM" position (partially opens heater control valve). Remove cap from expansion tank. Disconnect wiring and remove thermo-time switch from coolant flange on left side of head. Drain coolant. Remove alternator and drive belt.

2) Remove coolant hoses at pump housing. Remove water pump pulley. Remove bolts holding pump housing against engine block. Remove pump assembly. Unbolt and separate impeller portion from pump housing.

Reassembly & Installation

1) To reassemble, reverse disassembly procedure. Use new gasket between pump and housing. When installing pump assembly, use new "O" ring between pump housing and engine block. Open heater control valve fully. Add coolant to expansion tank until coolant comes out of thermo time switch opening on coolant flange.

2) Reinstall thermo time switch and connect wiring. Fill expansion tank 3/4" above full mark. Start and run engine until radiator cooling fans cycle on and off. Check coolant level. Fill expansion tank if necessary. Make sure coolant circulates (thermostat opens).

NOTE: For further information on cooling systems, see ENGINE COOLING section.

Audi & Volkswagen Engines

1.8L & 1.8L 16-VALVE 4-CYLINDER (Cont.)

ENGINE SPECIFICATIONS

GENERAL SPECIFICATIONS

	DISPLACEMENT						BORE		STROKE	
Year	Cu. In.	Liters	Fuel System	HP@RPM	Torque Ft. Lbs.@RPM	Compr. Ratio	In.	mm	In.	mm
1987 8-Valve										
Audi										
4000S	109	1.8	CIS-E Fuel Inj.	102@5500	105@3250	10.0:1	3.19	81.0	3.40	86.4
Volkswagen										
Cabriolet	109	1.8	CIS Fuel Inj.	90@5500	100@3000	8.5:1	3.19	81.0	3.40	86.4
Fox	109	1.8	CIS-E Fuel Inj.	81@5500	93@3250	9.0:1	3.19	81.0	3.40	86.4
Jetta GLI & GTI	109	1.8	CIS-E Fuel Inj.	102@5250	110@3250	10.0:1	3.19	81.0	3.40	86.4
Golf & Jetta	109	1.8	CIS-E Fuel Inj.	85@5250	96@3000	9.0:1	3.19	81.0	3.40	86.4
Scirocco	109	1.8	CIS Fuel Inj.	90@5500	100@3000	8.5:1	3.19	81.0	3.40	86.4
1987 16-Valve	109	1.8	CIS Fuel Inj.	123@5800	120@4250	10.0:1	3.19	81.0	3.40	86.4

VALVES

Engine Size & Valve	Head Diam. In. (mm)	Face Angle	Seat Angle	Seat Width In. (mm)	Stem Diameter In. (mm)	Stem Clearance In. (mm)	Valve Lift In. (mm)
1.8L							
8-Valve							
Intake (GX/JN/UM)	1.496 (38.00)	45°	45°	.079 (2.01)	.314 Min. (7.97)	.....	.....
Intake (JH/MG/RD)	1.575 (40.00)	45°	45°	.079 (2.01)	.314 Min. (7.97)	.....	.....
Exhaust (All)	1.300 (33.00)	45°	45°	.094 (2.40)	.313 Min. (7.95)	.....	.....
16-Valve							
Intake	1.260 (32.00)	45°	45°	.065 (1.65)	.274 (6.97)	.....	.....
Exhaust	1.102 (28.00)	45°	45°	.070 (1.80)	.273 (6.94)	.....	.....

PISTONS, PINS, RINGS

	PISTONS	PINS		RINGS		
Engine	Clearance In. (mm)	Piston Fit In. (mm)	Rod Fit In. (mm)	Ring No.	End Gap In. (mm)	Side Clearance In. (mm)
1.8L	.0011 [1] (.028)	[2]	Interference	All	.012-.018 [3] (.30-.46)	.0008-.0020 [4] (.020-.050)

[1] – Wear limit is .003" (.08 mm).

[2] – Light press fit at 140°F (60°C).

[3] – Wear limit is .04" (1.0 mm).

[4] – Wear limit is .006" (.15 mm).

1.8L & 1.8L 16-VALVE 4-CYLINDER (Cont.)

ENGINE SPECIFICATIONS (Cont.)

CRANKSHAFT MAIN & CONNECTING ROD BEARINGS

	MAIN BEARINGS				CONNECTING ROD BEARINGS		
Engine	Journal Diam. In. (mm)	Clearance In. (mm)	Thrust Bearing	Crankshaft End Play In. (mm)	Journal Diam. In. (mm)	Clearance In. (mm)	Side Play In. (mm)
1.8L							
Std. Size	2.124-2.125 [1] (53.96-53.98)	.001-.003 [2] (.03-.07)	No. 3	.003-.007 [3] (.07-.17)	1.880-1.881 [1] (47.76-47.78)	.0011-.0034 [4] (.028-.088)	.015 Max. (.38)
1st U/Size	2.114-2.115 (53.71-53.73)				1.871-1.872 (47.51-47.53)		
2nd U/Size	2.104-2.105 (53.46-53.48)				1.860-1.861 (47.26-47.28)		
3rd U/Size	2.095-2.096 (53.21-53.23)				1.851-1.852 (47.01-47.03)		

[1] – Out-of-round limit is .001" (.03 mm).
[2] – Wear limit is .007" (.17 mm).
[3] – Wear limit is .010" (.25 mm).
[4] – Wear limit is .005" (.12 mm).

CAMSHAFT

Engine	Journal Diam. In. (mm)	Clearance In. (mm)	Lobe Lift In. (mm)
1.8L [1]	1.34 (34.0)	.004 Max. (.10)	.....

[1] – Camshaft end play limit is .006" (.15mm).

TIGHTENING SPECIFICATIONS

Application	Ft. Lbs. (N.m)
Camshaft Bearing Cap Nuts	
8-Valve	14 (20)
16-Valve	11 (15)
Camshaft Sprocket Bolt	
8-Valve	58 (80)
16-Valve	48 (65)
Connecting Rod Cap Nut	[1] 22 (30)
Crankshaft Pulley Nut	14 (20)
Crankshaft Sprocket Bolt	148 (200)
CV Joint-to-Flange	33 (45)
Cylinder Head Bolt (Engine Cold)	
Step 1	29 (40)
Step 2	44 (60)
Step 3	[2]
Engine-to-Transaxle Bolts	
M10	33 (45)
M12	56 (75)

TIGHTENING SPECIFICATIONS (Cont.)

Application	Ft. Lbs. (N.m)
Engine/Transaxle-to-Body	
Longitudinally Mounted Unit	
Front Mount-to-Body	18 (25)
Side Mounts-to-Subframe	25 (35)
Transversely Mounted Unit	
Front Mount-to-Body Bolt	
Front	51 (70)
Rear	25 (35)
Front Mount-to-Trans. Bolt	33 (45)
Front Mount Through Bolt	36 (50)
Rear Mount-to-Bushing Bolt	18 (25)
Rear Mount-to-Engine Bolt	18 (25)
Rear Mount Through Bolt	58 (80)
Trans. Mount-to-Bushing Bolt	43 (60)
Trans. Mount Bushing-to-Body	18 (25)
Exhaust Pipe-to-Manifold Nut	25 (35)
Flywheel-to-Crankshaft Bolt [3]	
Without Shoulder	56 (75)
With Shoulder [4]	74 (100)
Intermediate Shaft Sprocket Bolt	
8-Valve	58 (80)
16-Valve	48 (65)
Main Bearing Cap Bolts	47 (65)
Manifold Fasteners	
8-Valve	18 (25)
16-Valve	15 (20)
Power Steering Pump-to-Bracket Nut	14 (20)
Timing Belt Tensioner Nut	33 (45)
Torque Converter-to-Drive Plate Bolt	
Longitudinally Mounted	14 (20)
Transversly Mounted	22 (30)

[1] – Turn nuts an additional 90 degrees (1/4 turn) after reaching specified torque.
[2] – Turn bolts 180 degrees (1/2 turn) further in one continous movement. Two separate 90 degree (1/4 turn) movements may also be used.
[3] – Use locking compound.
[4] – Always use new bolts.

2.22L & 2.3L 5-CYLINDER

Audi: Coupe GT, 4000CS Quattro, 5000CS Turbo, 5000CS Quattro, 5000S
Volkswagen: Quantum, Quantum Syncro

NOTE: **For engine repair procedures not covered in this article, see ENGINE OVERHAUL PROCEDURES article at beginning of this section.**

ENGINE CODING

ENGINE IDENTIFICATION

Engine number is stamped on machined pad just below cylinder head on left side of block. Letter prefix indicates engine type.

ENGINE IDENTIFICATION CODES

Application	Code
Audi	
Coupe GT (2.22L)	KX
4000CS Quattro (2.22L)	JT
5000S (2.22L)	KZ
5000CS Turbo, 5000CS Quattro (2.22L)	MC
All (2.3L)	NF
Volkswagen	
Quantum, Quantum Syncro (2.22L)	KX

ENGINE, MANIFOLDS & CYLINDER HEAD

ENGINE

Removal

1) Disconnect battery ground cable. Open heater control valve fully. Open cap on coolant expansion tank. Remove engine mounting bolt holding coolant pipe at bellhousing. Remove all coolant hoses. Remove ground strap from left engine mount. Remove upper radiator cover. Remove power steering pump with hoses attached. Tie pump aside.

2) Disconnect wiring from engine mounted components. Remove fuel injectors, cold start valve and control pressure regulator, leaving fuel lines attached. Plug injector sockets and cap injectors and cold start valve. Remove throttle rod. Remove front engine stop. On Coupe GT and 4000CS models with M/T, remove lower grille.

3) On Quantum (with A/T), Coupe GT and 4000CS (with M/T), belt pulley on crankshaft must be removed. Hold pulley in place with Locking Spanner (2084). Using Extension (2079), remove crankshaft bolt through grille opening. Remove 2 and loosen other 2 pulley bolts. Loosen pulley with light taps. Remove 2 remaining bolts and belt pulley, leaving drive sprocket in place on crankshaft.

4) Remove alternator adjusting and mounting bolts. Tie alternator aside with wires attached. Remove alternator bracket from engine block. Loosen clamps and remove air duct. Disconnect all vacuum hoses leading to engine. Disconnect fuel feed and return lines. Disconnect breather hose from valve cover. Remove air filter cover.

5) If equipped with automatic transmission, remove coolant hoses at ATF cooler. Remove coolant hose flange from engine block. Remove cover for right engine mount. Loosen left and right engine mounts at frame. Detach ground strap from mounting bracket.

6) Remove all but one bolt holding engine to transmission. If A/C equipped, remove compressor drive belt. Disconnect wire from compressor clutch. Remove compressor mount bolts from engine. Hang compressor aside with hoses connected. Disconnect starter wires. Remove both front subframe bolts. On 4000CS Quattro, remove subframe and press ball joint off strut.

7) On all models, disconnect exhaust pipe from manifold and exhaust pipe support at transmission. Remove starter. Working through starter mounting hole, remove 3 bolts holding torque converter to flex plate (if equipped). Remove lower bolts which hold engine to transmission. Detach shift rod (or clutch cable) from transmission. Attach Support Bar (VW 785/1) under transmission.

8) Ensure all wiring, hoses, lines, cables and linkages are disconnected from engine. Attach lifting device to engine and lift engine slightly. On 5000CS Turbo and 5000CS Quattro models, remove left engine mount. On all models, adjust support bar to contact transmission. Remove last bolt holding engine to transmission.

9) Separate engine from transmission. On Quantum models, lift engine without allowing it to turn. On 5000 models, lift engine while turning it right. On Coupe GT and 4000CS Quattro models, lift engine while turning it left. On models with A/T, secure torque converter in transmission.

Installation

1) Reverse removal procedure to install engine. On 4000 Quattro models tighten subframe bolts in following order: left rear, right rear, left front, right front. On all models, ensure starter wires will not touch engine block or exhaust system. When installing belt pulley on crankshaft, align dimple on pulley with nub on sprocket. Use Loctite 573 on both threads and contact surface of crankshaft bolt.

2) Adjust tension of power steering pump, alternator and A/C compressor belts. Refill cooling system. Adjust accelerator cable or throttle linkage rods. Tighten engine mounting bolts with engine running at idle speed. Ensure cooling fan cycles properly.

CYLINDER HEAD & MANIFOLDS

Removal

1) Disconnect battery ground strap. Drain cooling system. Disconnect coolant hoses from head. Disconnect all vacuum hoses from intake manifold. Disconnect all electrical and ignition wires at cylinder head and intake manifold.

2) Remove fuel injectors and cold start valve, leaving fuel lines attached. Cap injectors and cold start valve and plug injector sockets. Remove air duct from throttle housing. Remove throttle rods or cables from throttle valve housing.

3) Disconnect fuel supply and return lines at fuel distributor. Remove airflow sensor and fuel distributor. Disconnect exhaust pipe from manifold or turbocharger. Remove turbocharger unit (if equipped). Remove upper radiator cover. Remove drive belts.

4) Remove power steering pump and position aside with hoses connected. Remove camshaft cover and timing belt cover. *See Fig. 1.* Loosen water pump bolts to relieve tension on timing belt. Remove timing belt. Remove water pump to replace "O" ring.

NOTE: **Sealing "O" ring between water pump and cylinder block should be replaced whenever water pump bolts are loosened as leak may occur if old "O" ring is reused.**

2.22L & 2.3L 5-CYLINDER (Cont.)

Fig. 1: Timing Belt, Sprockets & Covers

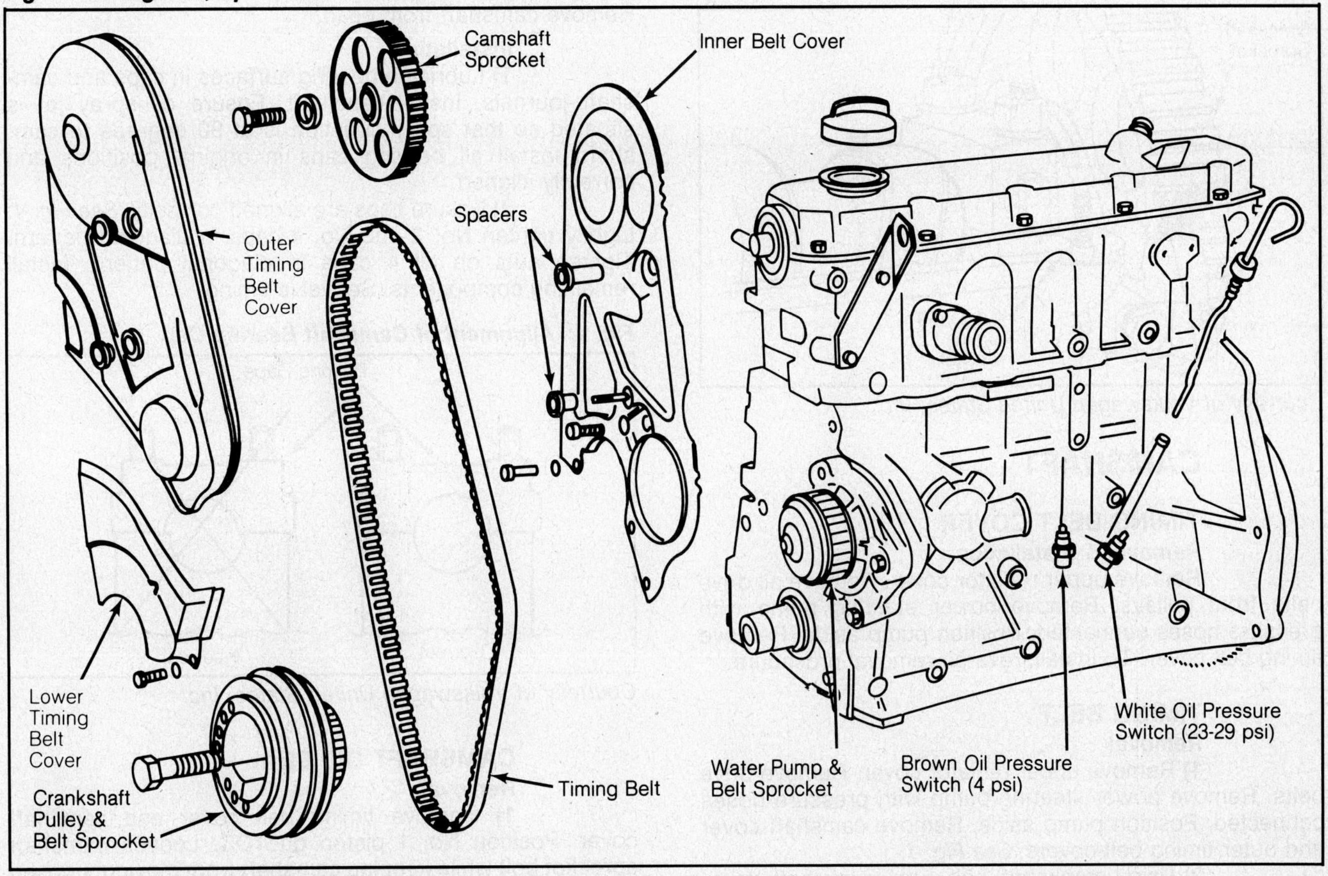

Courtesy of Volkswagen United States, Inc.

5) Loosen head bolts in reverse order of tightening sequence. *See Fig. 2.* Ensure all wiring, hoses and lines have been disconnected from cylinder head and intake manifold before lifting head from block. Remove cylinder head with intake manifold attached.

Fig. 2: Cylinder Head Tightening Sequence

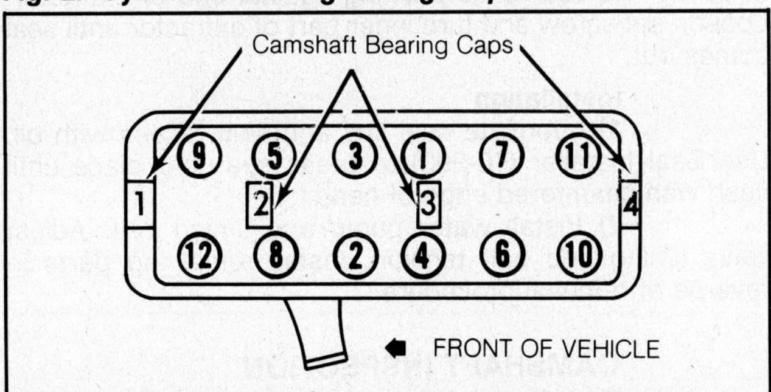

Courtesy of Volkswagen United States, Inc.

CAUTION: If head bolt(s) require replacement, install new polygon bolts in complete sets only. Polygon head bolts do not require retorque procedure at 1000 mile service following repair.

Installation

1) Check cylinder head for warping with straightedge. Maximum warp allowable is .004" (.10 mm). Minimum thickness of head after machining, measured from head gasket surface to camshaft cover gasket surface, is 5.226" (132.75 mm).

2) Install head gasket dry with part number facing upward. Use locating pins to hold gasket in place. Before installing cylinder head, turn crankshaft until all pistons are about equal distance from TDC to prevent any open valves from hitting pistons. Position head correctly and install bolts No. 9 and 11 to align head. Remove locating pins and install remaining bolts.

3) Tighten cylinder head bolts in 3 stages. *See Fig. 2.* First step of head bolt tightening procedure is to 29 ft. lbs. (40 N.m). Second step is to 43 ft. lbs. (60 N.m). Third step is an additional 180 degrees in one movement (two 90 degree movements are acceptable).

4) Set engine to TDC of compression stroke on No. 1 cylinder. Turn camshaft until timing mark on sprocket is aligned with upper edge of camshaft cover gasket (or rear timing belt cover). *See Fig. 3.* Install water pump with NEW sealing "O" ring, leaving bolts loose enough to move pump body.

5) Install timing belt. Turn water pump body counterclockwise to increase belt tension. Tension is correct when belt can be twisted 90 degrees using finger pressure at point midway between camshaft sprocket and water pump sprocket. Recheck valve timing. Complete installation in reverse order of removal.

Fig. 3: Aligning Camshaft Sprocket

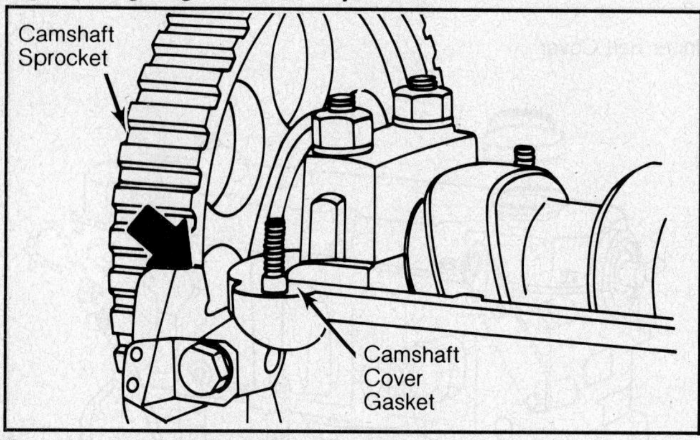

Courtesy of Volkswagen United States, Inc.

CAMSHAFT

TIMING BELT COVER

Removal & Installation

Remove upper radiator cover. Remove all drive belts from pulleys. Remove power steering pump with pressure hoses connected. Position pump aside. Remove timing belt cover. To install, reverse removal procedure.

TIMING BELT

Removal

1) Remove upper radiator cover. Remove drive belts. Remove power steering pump with pressure hoses connected. Position pump aside. Remove camshaft cover and outer timing belt covers. *See Fig. 1.*

2) Using crankshaft bolt, turn crankshaft clockwise to TDC of compression stroke on No. 1 cylinder. Align timing mark on back of camshaft sprocket with upper edge of gasket. *See Fig. 3.*

3) Loosen water pump adjusting bolts to relieve tension on timing belt. Remove timing belt. Remove water pump to check sealing "O" ring. Do not allow crankshaft or camshaft to move.

Installation & Valve Timing

1) Both camshaft lobes on No. 1 cylinder must point upward. Mark (notch or dot) on back of camshaft sprocket must be aligned with top of valve cover gasket or rear timing belt cover. Crankshaft must be at TDC for No. 1 cylinder. Flywheel TDC mark must be aligned with index point on transmission housing.

2) Install water pump with new sealing "O" ring. Install timing belt. Turn water pump body counterclockwise to increase belt tension. Tension is correct when belt can be twisted 90 degrees using finger pressure at point midway between camshaft sprocket and water pump sprocket. Recheck valve timing. Complete installation in reverse order of removal.

VALVE TIMING

See TIMING BELT INSTALLATION & VALVE TIMING.

CAMSHAFT

Removal

Remove timing belt. If necessary, mark camshaft bearing caps No. 1 to No. 4 (front to rear). Loosen nuts holding No. 2 and No. 4 caps in diagonal pattern. Remove No. 2 and No. 4 caps. Loosen nuts holding No. 1 and No. 3 caps in diagonal pattern. Remove No. 1 and No. 3 caps. Remove camshaft from head.

Installation

1) Lubricate bearing surfaces in caps and camshaft journals. Install camshaft. Ensure oil spray jet is situated so that spray direction is at 90 degrees to camshaft. Install all bearing caps in original positions and correctly aligned.

2) Ensure caps are aligned correctly. *See Fig. 4.* Lightly tighten No. 2 and No. 4 caps in diagonal pattern. Tighten nuts on all 4 caps in diagonal pattern. Install remaining components. Set valve timing.

Fig. 4: Alignment of Camshaft Bearing Cap

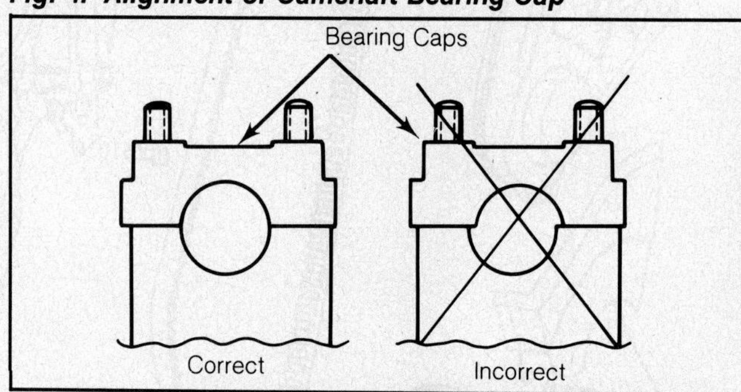

Courtesy of Volkswagen United States, Inc.

CAMSHAFT OIL SEAL

Removal

1) Remove timing belt cover and camshaft cover. Position No. 1 piston on TDC. Loosen camshaft sprocket bolt while keeping camshaft from moving. Loosen water pump adjusting bolts to relieve tension on timing belt.

2) Remove timing belt. Remove water pump to check sealing ring. Remove camshaft sprocket and Woodruff key. Install sprocket bolt 3 turns into end of camshaft and secure with lock nut. Use Seal Extractor (2085) to remove camshaft oil seal.

3) Back inner portion of extractor 3 or 4 turns out from outer portion. Lock inner part with set screw on outer part. Lubricate threaded head of seal extractor and thread it into seal while pushing against end of extractor. Loosen set screw and turn inner part of extractor until seal comes out.

Installation

1) Lubricate seal lips and seal recess with oil. Use Seal Installer (10-203) to press seal into place until flush with chamfered edge of head.

2) Install water pump and timing belt. Adjust valve timing and belt tension. Install remaining parts in reverse of removal procedure.

CAMSHAFT INSPECTION

End Play

Remove valve lifters. Check camshaft end play. If end play exceeds limit, check camshaft thrust flange and bearing cap for wear. Replace worn components.

CAUTION: Hydraulic valve lifters are always stored with contact face down. This applies to new lifters or to lifters removed for engine repairs. Lifters will take about 30 minutes to leak down after installation. DO NOT start engine during leak-down period as internal engine damage will occur.

2.22L & 2.3L 5-CYLINDER (Cont.)

Removal

1) Remove camshaft. Remove hydraulic lifters. Keep in order for reassembly. Remove spark plug of cylinder to be serviced. Turn crankshaft until piston is at BDC.

2) Install air hose and Adapter (VW 653/3) in spark plug hole and apply line pressure of at least 87 psi. Do not remove line pressure until valve spring components are reassembled.

CAUTION: **Be aware that engine can rotate due to air pressure if piston is not at true BDC. Keep hands clear of belts and pulleys.**

3) Use Spring Compressor (VW 541/1 or 2036). Compress valve spring and remove keepers, retainers and springs. Take out seals with Seal Remover Pliers (10-218).

Installation

Slide protective plastic sleeve onto valve stem. Lubricate new seal and push into place with Seal Installer (10-204). Install remaining components in reverse order of removal. Ensure valve timing is correct.

HYDRAULIC VALVE LIFTERS

NOTE: **Hydraulic valve lifters are not repairable or adjustable. Any worn, damaged or noisy lifter must be replaced as complete assembly. Some occasional valve/lifter noise is normal immediately after starting engine.**

Checking

1) Run engine until radiator cooling fan has cycled at least once. Hold engine at steady 2500 RPM for 2 minutes. Allow engine speed to return to idle. If lifter is still noisy, replace it.

2) Remove camshaft cover. Turn engine by crankshaft bolt until both camshaft lobes of cylinder to be checked point upward. Push down on lifters with wooden stick. If lifter compresses more than .004" (.10 mm), it must be replaced.

3) If hydraulic valve lifters are removed for engine repairs, keep them in correct order for reassembly. Store lifters on clean surface with contact surface facing down. This is upside down compared to installed position.

CAUTION: **Hydraulic valve lifters are always stored with contact face down. This applies to new lifters as well as to lifters removed for engine repairs. Lifters will take about 30 minutes to leak down after installation. DO NOT start engine during leak-down period as internal engine damage will occur.**

PISTONS, PINS & RINGS

OIL PAN

Removal

Remove 2 front bolts of subframe. Drain engine oil. Remove dipstick. Remove flywheel dust cover. Remove rear pan bolts. Remove remaining pan bolts and lower pan from engine.

Installation

Clean all gasket mating surfaces. Make sure flange of oil pan is not distorted. Install oil pan with new gasket. Tighten pan bolts in criss-cross pattern. Replace dipstick and flywheel dust cover. Tighten subframe bolts.

PISTON & ROD ASSEMBLY

Removal

1) Drain oil and coolant. Remove cylinder head and oil pan. Place piston to be removed at bottom of cylinder and cover with cloth to collect metal cuttings. Use ridge reamer to remove ridge or deposit from upper end of cylinder bore.

2) Before removing piston and rod from engine, mark rod and rod cap for cylinder identification. Remove rod cap and carefully push piston and rod out top of cylinder. Loosely install rod cap to rod for reassembly.

Piston Identification

Piston recess is measured from face of piston, to bottom of dish in top of piston. The compression height of these pistons, is measured from face of piston to top of wrist pin opening. See PISTON IDENTIFICATION table.

Installation

1) Coat cylinder bore, piston and rings with engine oil. Ensure ring end gaps are spaced 120 degrees apart. Install ring compressor on piston, making sure position of rings does not change.

2) Install piston and rod in original bore. Arrow on piston head faces toward front of engine. Forged marks (lumps) on rod and cap must also face toward front of engine. Make sure connecting rod bolts do not damage bearing journals on crankshaft.

PISTON IDENTIFICATION

Engine	Recess	Compression Height
MC	15 mm	30 mm
KX, JT	8.1 mm	22.2 mm
NF	4.4 mm	33.3 mm

FITTING RINGS

Measure piston ring end gap. Measure ring side clearance. Install compression rings on piston with "TOP" mark facing upward. Recessed edge on outside of center ring must face down toward piston pin. Oil scraper ring can be installed either way. Space ring end gaps 120 degrees apart.

PISTON PIN REPLACEMENT

Removal

Remove circlip from pin bore groove. Use Piston Pin Drift (VW 207C) to remove and install piston pin. If pin is too tight, warm pistons to about 140°F (60°C) and then install pin.

Installation

Assemble connecting rod to piston. Arrow on piston head and forged marks on connecting rod must face toward front of engine when assembly is installed. Use pin drift to install piston pin. Install circlip into pin bore groove.

CRANKSHAFT & ROD BEARINGS

MAIN BEARINGS

1) Main bearing caps are numbered one through 6 (front to rear). Never interchange bearing caps. Use Plastigage method for measuring bearing clearances. See CRANKSHAFT MAIN & CONNECTING ROD BEARINGS specifications at end of article.

2) When replacing bearings, install grooved bearing halves into cylinder block. Plain bearing halves are installed in main caps. Lubricate crankshaft journals and bearings prior to installation.

CONNECTING ROD BEARINGS

Use Plastigage method for measuring bearing clearances. Use feeler gauge to check connecting rod side clearance. See CRANKSHAFT MAIN & CONNECTING ROD BEARINGS specifications at end of article.

CRANKSHAFT END PLAY

Use feeler gauge to check crankshaft end play. Insert feeler gauge between No. 4 main bearing (thrust bearing) and crankshaft journal thrust face. See CRANKSHAFT MAIN & CONNECTING ROD BEARINGS specifications at end of article.

FRONT CRANKSHAFT OIL SEAL

Removal

1) Remove lower grille. Remove timing belt cover. Loosen water pump to remove timing belt. Remove water pump to replace sealing "O" ring. Use Crankshaft Lock (2084) to hold crankshaft.

2) Remove crankshaft damper/pulley bolt with Spanner (2079). Remove pulley with belt drive sprocket. Using Seal Remover (2086), carefully pry seal from oil pump housing.

Installation

1) Lightly coat new seal lip and outer edge with oil. Using Seal Installer (2080) and Guide Sleeve (2080A), press in seal until seated. Install crankshaft damper with timing belt. Install water pump with new sealing ring. Mount crankshaft lock on crankshaft pulley.

2) Use Loctite 573 on crankshaft damper bolt and install. Use spanner and torque wrench to tighten crankshaft pulley bolt. Torque specification only applies if torque wrench handle and spanner are in a straight line.

3) Remove tools and adjust timing belt tension. Make sure valve timing is correct. Install remaining parts in reverse order of disassembly.

REAR CRANKSHAFT OIL SEAL

Removal

Index mark flywheel/drive plate to crankshaft before removal. Remove flywheel/drive plate. Note position of any shims used. Using Seal Remover (2086), carefully pry oil seal from seal flange.

Installation

1) Coat lips of new seal with oil. Position seal in place and start by hand. Using Seal Installer (2003/1), press seal in until seated. There must be sufficient clearance between drive plate (A/T models) and back of engine block. Bolt torque converter tightly to crankshaft without shim.

2) Measure inside of drive plate from top edge of lip to face of plate where torque converter attaches. Measure from top edge of lip to engine block on both sides of block. Subtract inside measurement from outside measurement. If result is in range of .68-.74" (17.2-18.8 mm), no shim is required between drive plate and end of crankshaft. If result is smaller than range, shim is required.

3) Remove bolts and coat with locking compound. Install flywheel/flex plate with correct shim (if required) and tighten bolts. Note that notch on outer washer of flex plate faces toward torque converter on models with A/T. Replace shoulder bolts with new bolts. Install remaining components.

ENGINE OILING

ENGINE OILING SYSTEM

Slipper gear-type pump is used. Oil pump is mounted at front of engine and driven by crankshaft. *See Fig. 7.* Oil is lifted from pan by oil suction tube, which extends from oil pump. Oil is then fed to internal engine moving parts. Lubrication is either by pressure feed or drainage method.

Turbocharged engines use oil spray to aid in cooling piston crown and skirt. Oil is sprayed into underside of piston by nozzles which are installed at bottom of each cylinder. If oil nozzles are removed, coat retaining bolt threads with locking compound on installation.

CRANKCASE CAPACITY

On 5000 models, capacity is either 5.0 qts. (4.5L) with filter replacement or 4.5 qts. (4.0L) if filter is not replaced. On Coupe GT, Quantum and 4000CS Quattro models, capacity is either 3.7 qts. (3.5L) with filter replacement or 3.2 qts. (3.0L) if filter is not replaced.

NOTE: **Whenever turbocharger is replaced or rebuilt, engine oil and BOTH oil filters must be replaced.**

OIL PRESSURE

Oil pressure is 29 psi (2.0 kg/cm^2) at 2000 RPM. Measurement is to be made with fresh oil at temperature of 176°F (80°C).

OIL PRESSURE RELIEF VALVE

Oil pressure relief valve opens at 77-91 psi (5.3-6.3 kg/cm^2).

OIL PRESSURE WARNING SYSTEM

1) Dynamic oil pressure warning system is used on this motor. Control unit with buzzer is mounted on relay panel adapter. Dual oil pressure switches are on side of block. *See Fig. 1.*

2) Contacts of both switches are open with engine off. If oil pressure drops below 4.0 psi (.3 kg/cm^2) while engine is running, contacts of Brown oil pressure switch will open. Buzzer will sound and oil pressure symbol will appear on instrument panel.

3) If oil pressure drops below 23-29 psi (1.6-2.0 kg/cm^2) with engine running at 2500 RPM, contacts of White oil pressure switch will open. Buzzer will sound and oil pressure symbol will appear on instrument panel.

OIL PUMP

Removal & Disassembly

1) Remove all drive belts from crankshaft pulley. Remove power steering pump (with hoses connected) and position aside. Remove timing belt covers. Loosen crankshaft damper/pulley bolt.

2) Turn crankshaft to position No. 1 piston at TDC after compression stroke. Loosen water pump adjusting bolts. Turn water pump to relieve tension on timing belt.

3) Remove lower timing belt cover. Ensure crankshaft position has not changed. Remove damper-/pulley from crankshaft with drive sprocket attached. Remove dipstick.

4) Drain engine oil and remove oil pan. Remove oil suction tube from oil pump. Remove oil pump.

Oil Clearance

1) Remove camshaft and valve lifters. Keep lifters in order for reassembly. Place hydraulic lifters on clean surface with contact faces down. Remove sprocket and oil seal from camshaft. Clean bearing caps, bearing seats and camshaft journals.

2) Place camshaft on cylinder head. Ensure lobes do not touch valves or valve spring retainers. Place Plastigage on camshaft journals parallel to length of camshaft. Install bearing caps in correct position and tighten cap nuts. DO NOT rotate camshaft with Plastigage installed.

3) Remove bearing caps and read clearace. If wear limit is exceeded, repeat measurement with new camshaft installed. If wear limit is still exceeded with new camshaft, cylinder head must be replaced.

VALVES

VALVE ARRANGEMENT

E-I-E-I-I-E-I-E-I-E (Front-to-rear).

VALVE GUIDES

Inspection

1) Clean valve guides. Attach dial indicator and Adapter (VW 387) to mounting surface of cylinder head. Insert new valve into valve guide. End of valve stem must be flush with end of valve guide.

2) Rock valve head back and forth against tip of dial indicator to measure clearance between stem and guide. If reading exceeds limits, replace guides and/or valves. See VALVES specifications at end of article.

Removal

Use press and Valve Guide Drift (10-206) to remove and install guides. Press guides out from combustion chamber side of head.

Installation

Coat new guides with oil. Press guides into head from camshaft side. Press guides in as far as possible. Do not use more than one ton of pressure after guide shoulder is seated as guide shoulder may break. Ream guide by hand to proper size.

VALVES & SEATS

CAUTION: NEVER rework exhaust valves on machine. Lap exhaust valves by hand only.

1) If intake valves are to be refaced, they must exceed minimum standards. Measure intake valve stem diameter. Measure exhaust valve stem diameter. Measure overall length of valves. See VALVES specifications at end of article.

2) One of 2 limits for cutting valve seats (dimension "y") is determined by measured distance "X" between stem end of closed stem and upper face of cylinder head (where camshaft cover gasket rests). *See Fig. 5.* Insert valve into guide and hold tightly against seat.

3) Measure distance "X". Subtract minimum dimension "X" from measured distance "X". Result is maximum cut allowed (dimension "y") for refacing valve seats. Minimum dimension "X" is 1.33" (33.8 mm) for intake valves and 1.34" (34.1 mm) for exhaust valves.

NOTE: If minimum dimension "X" is greater than measured distance "X", cylinder head must be replaced. If minimum dimension is not observed, hydraulic valve lifters may not function properly.

Fig. 5: Measuring Refacing Limit Of Valve Seats

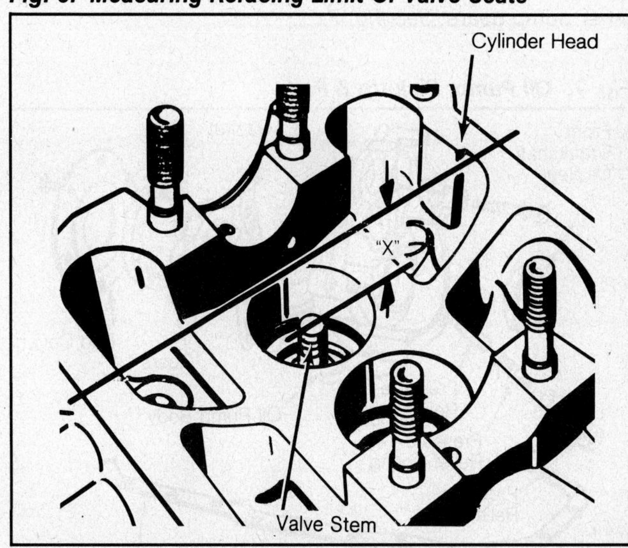

Courtesy of Volkswagen United States, Inc.

4) On all models, second limit for maximum amount of material that may be removed from seat is determined by distance "D" from lower face of cylinder head to edge of 45 degrees valve seat angle. *See Fig. 6.* Maximum distance "D" for intake seats is .36" (9.2 mm). On 4000CS Quattro models, maximum distance "D" for exhaust seats is .38" (9.6 mm) and .35" (9.0 mm) on all others.

5) Do not reface exhaust valves on machine. Lap exhaust valves only by hand. Be sure to remove all traces of grinding compound from valves and guides after valves have been lapped into seats.

VALVE STEM OIL SEALS

NOTE: Valve stem seals may be replaced with cylinder head installed on vehicle.

CAUTION: Hydraulic valve lifters are always stored with contact face down. This applies to new lifters or to lifters removed for engine repairs. Lifters will take about 30 minutes to leak down after installation. DO NOT start engine during leak-down period as internal engine damage will occur.

Fig. 6: Measuring Refacing Limits of Valve Seats

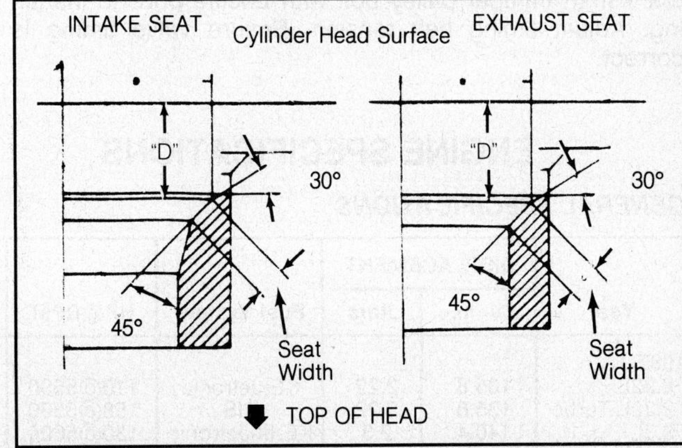

Courtesy of Volkswagen United States, Inc.

Audi & Volkswagen Engines

2.22L & 2.3L 5-CYLINDER (Cont.)

Remove end cover from pump housing. Lift out outer and inner pump gears. *See Fig. 7.*

Fig. 7: Oil Pump, Pick-Up & Pan

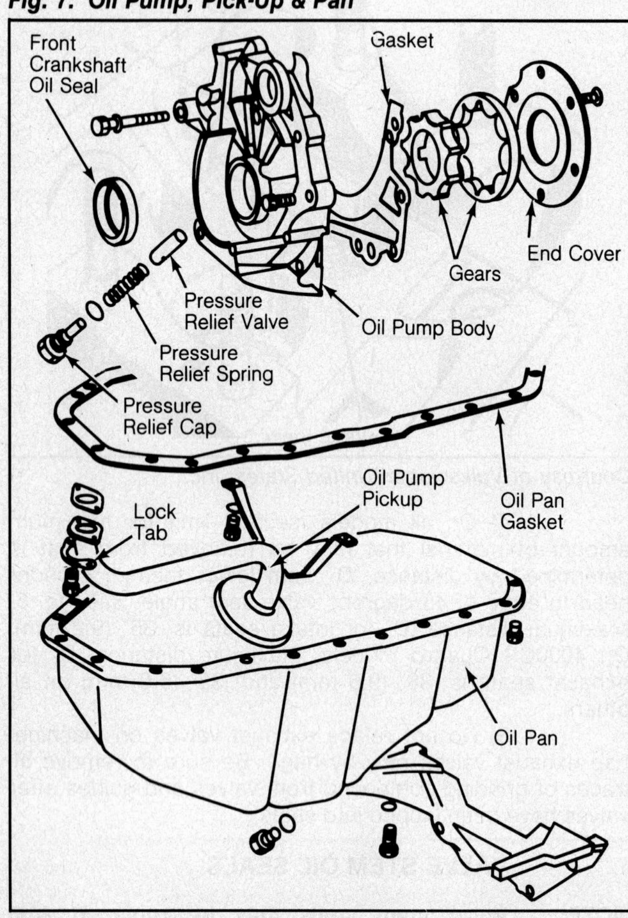

Courtesy of Volkswagen United States, Inc.

Inspection & Reassembly

Inspect end cover, housing and gears for wear or scoring. Replace end cover if scored. If pump gears require replacement, replace only in pairs. Install gears in pump housing with triangular mark facing end cover. Install end cover.

Installation

Prime oil pump prior to installing. Install oil pump in reverse of removal procedure. Coat threads of crankshaft damper/pulley bolt with Loctite prior to installing. Adjust timing belt tension. Ensure valve timing is correct.

ENGINE COOLING

WATER PUMP

Removal

1) Drain cooling system. Remove timing belt covers. Turn crankshaft to TDC for No. 1 cylinder. Align timing marks on flywheel and camshaft gear with reference marks.

2) Loosen water pump to relieve tension on timing belt. Remove timing belt. Do not allow crankshaft or camshaft to move. Remove water pump.

NOTE: If remanufactured water pump is being used, check "O" ring size. Some pumps are resurfaced and require a 5 mm "O" ring. These pumps will have numeral "5" stamped in mounting flange.

Installation

Install water pump in reverse of removal procedure, using new "O" ring. Ensure valve timing is correct prior to installing remaining components.

NOTE: For further information on cooling systems, see ENGINE COOLING section.

TIGHTENING SPECIFICATIONS

Application	Ft. Lbs. (N.m)
Camshaft Bearing Cap Nuts	14 (20)
Camshaft Sprocket Bolt	58 (80)
Connecting Rod Cap Nuts	37 (50)
Crankshaft Damper/Pulley Bolt [1]	[2] 258 (350)
Cylinder Head Bolts	
Step 1	29 (40)
Step 2	43 (60)
Step 3	Plus 180 Degree (1/2 Turn)
Exhaust Manifold-to-Head Nuts	18 (25)
Exhaust Manifold-to-Turbocharger Nuts	43 (60)
Exhaust Pipe-to-Turbocharger Nuts	22 (30)
Flywheel-to-Crankshaft Bolts [1]	
Without Shoulder	55 (75)
With Shoulder [3]	74 (100)
Intake Manifold Bolts	18 (25)
Main Bearing Cap Bolts	47 (65)
Oil Return Line	
Bracket-to-Turbocharger Nut	18 (25)
Torque Converter-to-Drive Plate Bolts	22 (30)

[1] – Use locking compound.
[2] – Applies only when using Spanner (2079) and torque wrench. Torque wrench must be in-line with spanner handle.
[3] – Always use new bolts.

ENGINE SPECIFICATIONS

GENERAL SPECIFICATIONS

Year	DISPLACEMENT		Fuel System	HP@RPM	Torque Ft. Lbs.@RPM	Compr. Ratio	BORE		STROKE	
	Cu. In.	Liters					In.	mm	In.	mm
1987										
2.22L	135.8	2.22	KE-Jetronic	110@5500	122@2500	8.5:1	3.19	81.0	3.40	86.4
2.22L Turbo	135.8	2.22	CIS	158@5500	166@2500	7.8:1	3.19	81.0	3.40	86.4
2.3L	140.4	2.3	KE-III-Jetronic	130@5600	140@4000	10:1	3.25	82.5	3.40	86.4

Audi & Volkswagen Engines

2.22L & 2.3L 5-CYLINDER (Cont.)

ENGINE SPECIFICATIONS (Cont.)

VALVES

Engine Size & Valve	Head Diam. In. (mm)	Face Angle	Seat Angle	Seat Width In. (mm)	Stem Diameter In. (mm)	Stem Clearance In. (mm)	Valve Lift In. (mm)
2.22L							
Intake [1]	1.496 (38.00)	45°	45° [3]	.079 [4] (2.00)	.314 (7.98)	.039 (1.0)	.....
Exhaust [2]	1.300 (33.00)	45°	45° [3]	.094 [5] (2.40)	.313 (7.95)	.051 (1.3)	
2.3L							
Intake	1.575 (39.87)	45°	45° [3]	.079 [6] (2.00)	.314 (7.98)	.039 (1.0)	.....
Exhaust [2]	1.300 (33.00)	45°	45° [3]	.094 [5] (2.40)	.313 (7.95)	.051 (1.3)	.....

[1] – Overall length is 3.58" (90.9 mm). [2] – Overall length is 3.57" (90.8 mm). [3] – Correction angle is 30 degrees.
[4] – Diameter limit is 1.47" (37.2 mm). [5] – Diameter limit is 1.28" (32.4 mm). [6] – Diameter limit is 1.55" (39.5 mm).

PISTONS, PINS & RINGS

Engine	PISTONS Clearance In. (mm)	PINS Piston Fit In. (mm)	PINS Rod Fit In. (mm)	RINGS Ring No.	RINGS End Gap In. (mm)	RINGS Side Clearance In. (mm)
2.22L, 2.3L	.001-.003 [1] (.03-.08)	[2]	Interference	All	.010-.020 [3] (.25-.50)	.0008-.003 [4] (.020-.08)

[1] – Wear limit is .003" (.08 mm). [2] – Push fit at 140°F (60°C). [3] – Wear limit is .04" (1.0 mm). [4] – Wear limit is .004" (.10 mm).

CRANKSHAFT MAIN & CONNECTING ROD BEARINGS

Engine	MAIN BEARINGS Journal Diam. In. (mm)	MAIN BEARINGS Clearance In. (mm)	MAIN BEARINGS Thrust Bearing	MAIN BEARINGS Crankshaft End Play In. (mm)	CONNECTING ROD BEARINGS Journal Diam. In. (mm)	CONNECTING ROD BEARINGS Clearance In. (mm)	CONNECTING ROD BEARINGS Side Play In. (mm)
2.22L, 2.3L							
Std. Size	2.2818-2.2826 [1] (57.958-57.978)	.0006-.003 [2] (.015-.08)	No. 4	.003-.007 [3] (.08-.18)	1.880-1.881 [1] (47.76-47.78)	.0006-.0024 [4] (.015-.062)	.016 Max. (.41)
1st U/Size	2.2720-2.2728 (57.708-57.728)				1.870-1.871 (47.51-47.53)		
2nd U/Size	2.2621-2.2629 (57.458-57.478)				1.860-1.861 (47.26-47.28)		
3rd U/Size	2.2523-2.2531 (57.208-57.228)				1.850-1.852 (47.01-47.03)		

[1] – Out-of-round limit is .001" (.03 mm). [3] – Wear limit is .010" (.25 mm). [2] – Wear limit is .006" (.16 mm). [4] – Wear limit is .005" (.13 mm).

CAMSHAFT

Engine	Journal Diam. In. (mm)	Clearance In. (mm)	Lobe Lift In. (mm)
2.22L, 2.3L [1]			
All	.....	.004 (.10) Max.	.....

[1] - Maximum end play is .001" (.03 mm).

BMW Engines

2.5L & 2.7L 6-CYLINDER

325, 325e, 325es, 325i, 325is, 528e

NOTE: **For engine repair procedures not covered in this article, see ENGINE OVERHAUL PROCEDURES article at beginning of this section.**

ENGINE CODING

ENGINE IDENTIFICATION

The engine displacement and identification numbers are stamped on a pad on the lower left side of engine block.

ENGINE IDENTIFICATION CODE

Model	Engine
325i & 325is	2.5L
325, 325e, 325es & 528e	2.7L

ENGINE, MANIFOLDS & CYLINDER HEAD

NOTE: **Vehicle transmission must be removed prior to engine removal.**

TRANSMISSION

Removal (Manual Transmission)

1) Remove exhaust system and support brackets from vehicle. Disconnect propeller shaft at rear of transmission. Remove heat shield from center support bearing.

2) Remove center support bearing bracket. Lower propeller shaft at center support bearing and pull propeller shaft from transmission.

3) Remove clutch slave cylinder, leaving hydraulic line connected. Remove speedometer cable and unplug back-up light switch.

4) Pull up boot from floor shift lever, remove circlip and pull shift lever up and out. Support transmission and remove crossmember. Remove transmission.

Removal (Automatic Transmission)

1) Disconnect exhaust system and remove support brackets. Disconnect accelerator cable from transmission and disconnect bracket. Drain transmission oil. Remove filler tube and plug opening.

2) Disconnect oil cooler lines from transmission. Label and disconnect all wiring attached to transmission. Remove cover plate. Mark installed positions of speed and reference mark sensors. Remove sensors.

3) Remove 4 bolts securing torque converter to drive plate. Disconnect shift rod from lever. Disconnect propeller shaft coupling at rear of transmission.

4) Remove heat shield and center support bearing bracket. Lower propeller shaft at center support bearing and pull propeller shaft from transmission. Support transmission.

5) Remove crossmember and lower transmission to rest on front axle carrier. Place transmission jack under transmission. Separate and remove transmission and torque converter from engine.

Installation

1) To install, reverse removal procedure. Before installing transmission, ensure torque converter is properly seated.

2) When installing propeller shaft, push center support bearing forward .08" (2.0 mm) to preload bracket and tighten nuts.

3) When installing sensors, note that Black plug of speed sensor faces ring gear. Gray ring of reference mark sensor faces flywheel. If plugs are reversed, engine will not start.

ENGINE

Removal

1) Remove hood and disconnect battery cables from battery. Remove transmission. Remove splash guard from under engine. Drain cooling system and remove radiator. Remove power steering pump (leaving hoses connected) and secure away from engine.

2) Remove A/C compressor (with hoses connected) and secure away from engine. Remove accelerator cable. If equipped, remove cruise control cable from engine.

3) Label and disconnect all electrical and ignition wiring that might interfere with engine removal. Ensure that wiring harness in glove box is disconnected and pull through hole in firewall.

4) Label and disconnect all coolant, ventilation, fuel and vacuum hoses (or lines) that might interfere with engine removal. Remove air cleaner with airflow sensor.

5) Remove nuts from engine mounts. Ensure no wiring, hoses or lines are attached to engine. Attach lifting chain and hoist to engine. Carefully lift engine from vehicle.

Installation

To install engine, reverse removal procedures. Ensure that all hoses, lines and electrical connections are restored to original position. Bleed cooling system.

CYLINDER HEAD

Removal

1) Disconnect battery ground cable. Drain cooling system. Remove splash guard from bottom of engine. Disconnect exhaust pipe from manifold.

2) Disconnect accelerator and cruise control cables from throttle valve housing. Remove cable to automatic transmission (if equipped). Disconnect attached hoses and electrical wiring. Remove air cleaner with airflow sensor.

3) Label and disconnect all coolant hoses attached to cylinder head. Label and disconnect all fuel ventilation and vacuum hoses from cylinder head and intake manifold.

4) Label and disconnect all electrical and ignition wiring that might interfere with cylinder head removal. If necessary, disconnect electrical plug in glove box and pull wiring through hole in firewall.

5) Remove valve cover. Remove upper engine timing belt cover and distributor cap.

6) Set No. 1 piston on TDC of compression stroke. Timing pointer and vibration damper mark should align. No. 6 cylinder valves should overlap.

7) Remove timing belt from camshaft sprocket. Remove cylinder head bolts in reverse of tightening sequence. Install locating pins in bolt holes to keep rocker arm shafts from turning. Remove cylinder head.

Inspection

Cylinder head may be machined if necessary. Minimum height from engine block mating surface to valve cover surface is 4.909" (124.70 mm). Use a .012" (.30 mm) thicker head gasket if cylinder head is machined.

Installation

1) Clean all gasket mating surfaces. Remove oil from threaded holes in cylinder block. Clean and lubricate bolt heads and threads. Using new head gasket, install cylinder head and bolts.

2) Tighten head bolts in sequence using 3 steps as outlined in TIGHTENING SPECIFICATIONS table. Bring engine to normal operating temperature. On third step, using Torque Wrench (11 2 110), retighten head bolts to torque angle of 20-30 degrees.

3) Install camshaft sprocket and timing chain (or timing belt). Ensure valve timing is correct. Install remaining components in reverse order of removal, using new gaskets where required. Adjust valves. Check ignition timing and adjust idle.

NOTE: **DO NOT retighten head after 600 miles.**

Fig. 1: Cylinder Head Tightening Sequence

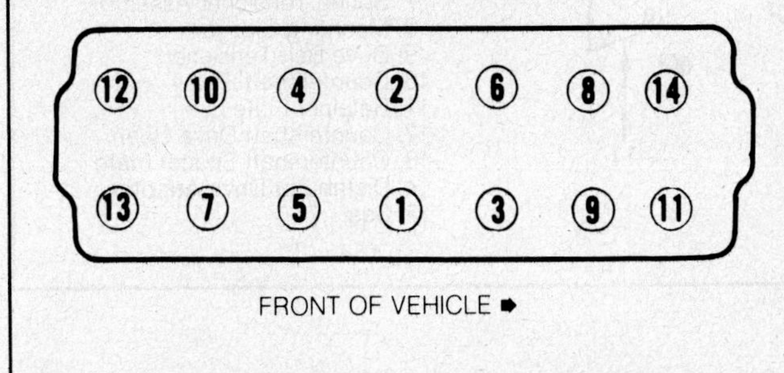

CAMSHAFT

CAUTION: **Inspect camshaft sprocket for stamped code. If code (w + p 2 86) is stamped on camshaft sprocket, sprocket MUST BE REPLACED. Failure to replace sprocket can result in breakage and severe engine damage at low mileage. Replace sprocket with new Camshaft Sprocket (11 31 1 284 273).**

Removal

1) Remove cylinder head. Mount Camshaft Removal Tools (11 1 060) and (00 1 490). Mount cylinder head on head stand. Remove oil feed line. Adjust valve clearance on all valves to specification.

2) Turn camshaft 15 degrees and mount Camshaft Removal Tool (11 1 106). Push intake rocker arms of cylinders No. 2 and 4 forward and align camshaft removal tool in such a manner that tabs rest on eccentrics of rocker arms. Remove thrust plate. Carefully pull out camshaft.

NOTE: **To avoid contact between valve heads, tighten nuts on exhaust side to stop and tighten intake side slightly. Check valve head clearance during procedure.**

Installation

1) Install camshaft in head and tighten thrust plate bolts to specifications. Camshaft must turn freely. Rotate camshaft until valves of No. 6 cylinder overlap.

2) If adapter was removed from front of camshaft, coat bolt threads with Loctite 270 before installation. Install oil pipe so oil bores will spray between rocker arms and cams of intake and exhaust valves.

3) Use new seals between oil pipe and rocker supports as well as under head of attaching bolts. Continue assembly in reverse order of removal.

Fig. 2: Rocker & Valve Assembly

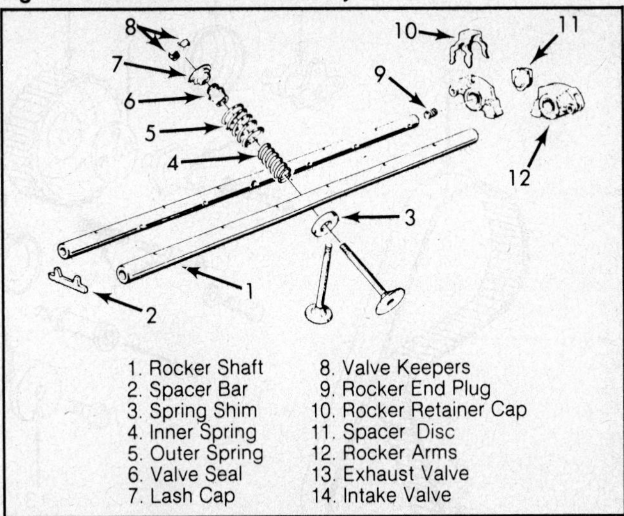

Courtesy of BMW of North America, Inc.

ROCKER ARM ASSEMBLY

Removal

1) Remove camshaft. Set up Camshaft Removal Tools (11 1 060) and (00 1 490) and attach to cylinder head using one head bolt. Remove sprocket retainer bolt and take off sprocket. Remove front and rear rocker arm plugs and guide plate. Remove rocker arm spring clamps.

2) To remove exhaust rocker arm, valves of No. 6 cylinder must overlap. Push in rocker arms of No. 1 cylinder and turn camshaft on adapter to intake side until all rocker arms are relaxed.

3) To remove intake rocker arm shafts, turn camshaft on adapter to exhaust side and move rocker arms until all rocker arms are relaxed. Pull out rocker arm shaft. Replace worn rocker arm shafts and rocker arms.

Installation

Install rocker arm shafts in reverse order of removal. Rocker arm shafts should be installed so that large oil bores face down toward valve guides. Ensure that small oil bores and grooves for guide plate, face in.

NOTE: **Be careful of springs popping out when removing rocker arm shafts.**

CAMSHAFT OIL SEAL

Removal

Place No. 1 cylinder on TDC of compression stroke. Align ignition timing and valve timing marks. Mark rotation direction and remove timing belt. Remove camshaft sprocket and thrust plate. Remove oil seal and round cord seal from thrust plate.

Installation

Lubricate oil seals with engine oil. Replace oil seal and round cord seal on thrust plate. Use Seal Aligner (11 2 212) when installing thrust plate. Install remaining components in reverse order of removal.

BMW Engines

2.5L & 2.7L 6-CYLINDER (Cont.)

Fig. 3: Camshaft Drive Assembly

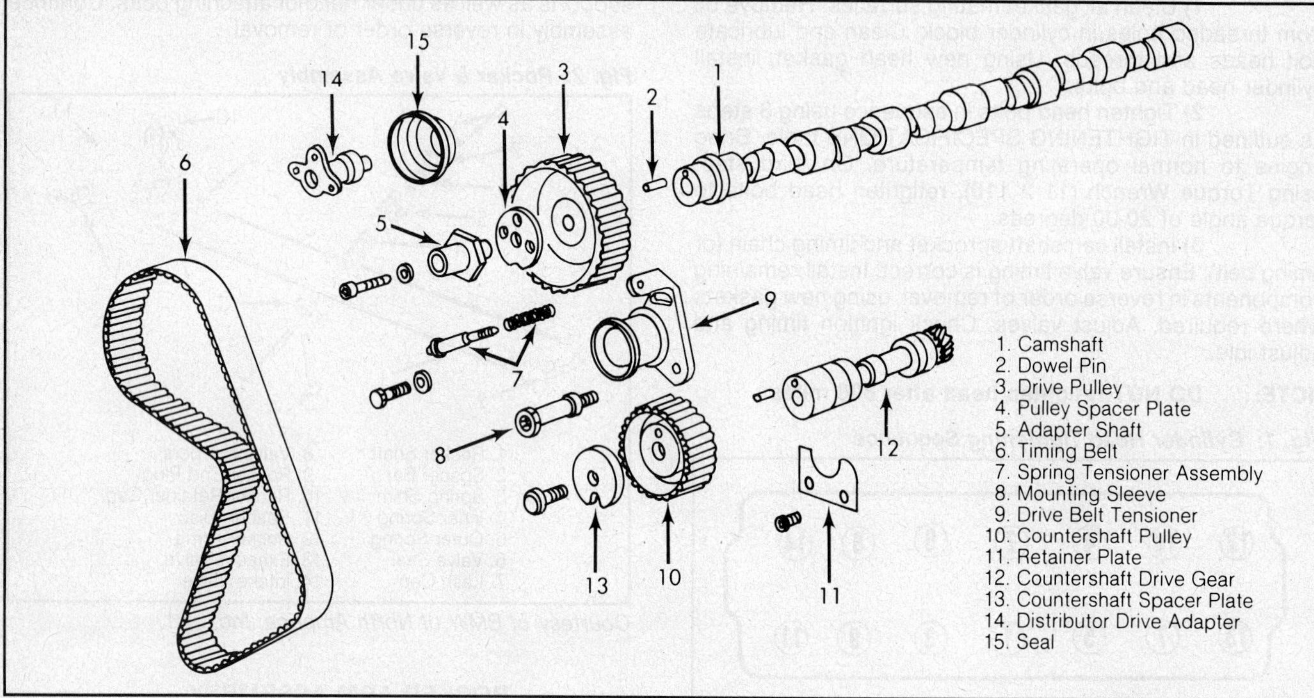

Courtesy of BMW of North America, Inc.

CAMSHAFT END PLAY

Insert feeler gauge between thrust plate and camshaft sprocket. Replace camshaft thrust plate if end thrust is excessive. Recheck end play.

TIMING BELT COVER

Removal

1) Remove all drive belts. Remove pulley and vibration damper. Hold crankshaft in place and remove center bolt from vibration damper hub.

2) Using a puller, remove vibration damper hub from crankshaft. Remove crankshaft sprocket from crankshaft using a puller. Hold intermediate shaft sprocket in place and remove attaching bolt, washer and sprocket.

3) Remove 3 oil pan-to-cover bolts. Loosen remaining oil pan bolts. Remove remaining attaching bolts and timing belt cover.

Installation

1) Clean gasket mating surfaces. Coat oil pan-to-cover gasket with gasket sealer. Install Centering Tool (11 2 211) on crankshaft and on intermediate shaft to align front cover.

2) Using new gasket, install and tighten timing belt cover. When installing crankshaft sprocket, lettering must face forward. Install remaining components in reverse order of removal procedure.

TIMING BELT COVER OIL SEALS

Removal & Installation

Remove timing belt cover. Remove crankshaft and intermediate shaft oil seals from cover. Using seal installer, install new seals until flush. Coat seal lips with oil prior to installing cover.

TIMING BELT & SPROCKET

Removal

1) Remove distributor cap and rotor. Remove cover surrounding distributor. Turn crankshaft to position No. 1 piston at TDC of compression stroke.

2) Ensure timing marks on vibration damper and pointer are aligned. Arrow on camshaft must be aligned with timing mark on cylinder head. *See Fig. 4.*

3) Remove timing belt cover. Loosen tensioner and position away from timing belt to relieve tension. Tighten tensioner adjusting bolt to keep tensioner in retracted position.

4) If installing same timing belt, mark rotation direction on timing belt before removing. Remove timing belt.

Installation

1) Ensure arrow on camshaft sprocket is still aligned with timing mark on cylinder head. Ensure timing mark on crankshaft sprocket is aligned with notch in cover (about one o'clock position). *See Fig. 4.*

2) Install timing belt on sprockets. Loosen tensioner adjusting bolt to allow tension on timing belt. Turn crankshaft in direction of normal rotation until timing belt tightens. Tighten tensioner bolts. Install remaining components in reverse order of removal.

VALVE TIMING

For valve timing procedure see TIMING BELT & SPROCKET.

TIMING BELT TENSIONER

Removal & Installation

Remove timing belt cover. Place piston of No. 1 cylinder on TDC of compression stroke. Remove timing belt tensioner. To install, reverse removal procedure. Check valve timing.

2.5L & 2.7L 6-CYLINDER (Cont.)

Fig. 4: Timing Sprockets Alignment

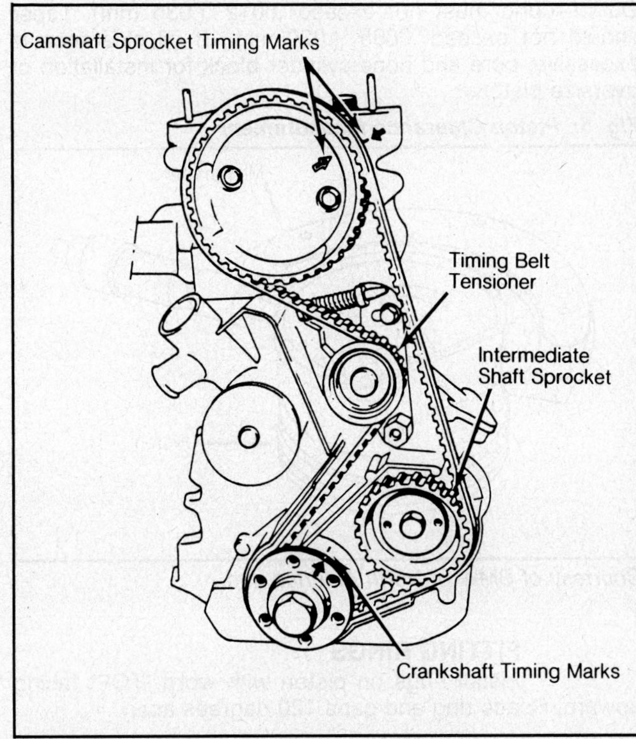

Mark rotation direction on timing belts that will be used.
Courtesy of BMW of North America, Inc.

INTERMEDIATE SHAFT

Removal & Installation

Remove timing belt cover. Remove guide plate and pull out intermediate shaft. To install, reverse removal procedure. Intermediate shaft bearings in engine block are not replaceable.

VALVES

VALVE ARRANGEMENT

Left Side - Intake valves.
Right Side - Exhaust valves.

VALVE ROCKER SERVICE

Removal

1) Remove cylinder head from engine. Remove camshaft sprocket. Adjust valve clearance of all valves to specification. Remove front and rear rubber plugs on either side of rocker shafts.

2) Remove thrust plate from rocker shaft (at front of head). Remove spring lips from rockers. Turn camshaft so that valves of No. 6 cylinder overlap.

3) Rotate camshaft 1/4 turn against normal direction of rotation while pushing rockers for cylinders No. 3 and 4 to rear of cylinder head. Push all remaining rockers to front of cylinder head.

4) When camshaft is clear of rockers, both rocker shafts can be removed. Mark all rocker arms, so that they may be installed in their original locations.

Inspection

Check rocker arms and shafts for excessive wear. Oil clearance should be .0006-.0020" (.016-.052 mm). Replace all worn parts.

Installation

Install rocker arm shaft assembly in reverse order of removal. Install rocker shafts with large oil holes facing downward. Ensure small oil holes and thrust plate grooves in rocker shafts face inward. Straight surface of retaining clips are installed in rocker shaft grooves.

VALVE GUIDES

1) If valve-to-guide clearance is excessive, drive out guide toward combustion chamber side of cylinder head. Check size of valve guide bore in cylinder head. Valve guide bore diameter should be the same as guide outside diameter.

2) Valve guides are available in 3 oversizes. Oversize diameters are 13.1, 13.2 and 13.3 mm. When installing valve guides, heat cylinder head to 122°F (50°C) and chill valve guide to -238°F (-150°C).

3) Drive guide into cylinder head from top. Stepped end of valve guide must face camshaft. Guide must protrude .551-.591" (14.0-15.0 mm) from top of cylinder head. Ream valve guide for correct oil clearance.

VALVE STEM OIL SEALS

Remove valve springs and pull off old seal. When replacing valve stem oil seals, use protective sleeve over valve stem to avoid damage to new seals. Lubricate seal with oil and install.

VALVE SEATS

1) When replacing valve seat, remove old seat by turning out with cutting tool.

2) When cutting bore for valve seat inserts, allow for shrink fit. Replacement (oversize) valve seats are available in .0078" (.200 mm) and .016" (.40 mm) outside diameters. See VALVE SEAT DIAMETER table. The valve seat insert shrink fit specification is .006" (.15 mm).

3) When installing new seat, heat cylinder head to about 122°F (50°C) and chill valve seat to about -238°F (-150°C). See VALVE SEAT DIAMETER table.

VALVE SPRINGS

NOTE: **Install springs with paint stripe (tight coil end) against cylinder head.**

Inspection

Check spring free length. Check spring pressure using valve spring tester. Replace defective springs with new springs of same color code.

VALVE CLEARANCE ADJUSTMENT

1) Adjust valves in firing order (1-5-3-6-2-4), with piston of cylinder being adjusted at TDC of compression stroke. Use a feeler gauge to measure clearance between rocker arm eccentric and tip of valve.

2) To adjust valve clearance, loosen nut on rocker arm and insert a rod in eccentric hole. Rotate eccentric until proper clearance is obtained and tighten lock nut.

VALVE SEAT DIAMETER

Application	Diameter In. (mm)
Intake	
Standard	1.659 (42.15)
.2 mm O.S.	1.667 (42.35)
.4 mm O.S.	1.675 (42.55)
Exhaust	
Standard	1.482 (37.65)
.2 mm O.S.	1.490 (37.85)
.4 mm O.S.	1.498 (38.05)

VALVE CLEARANCE ADJUSTMENT

Application	In. (mm)
Intake & Exhaust	
Cold	.010 (.25)
Hot	.012 (.30)

PISTONS, PINS & RINGS

OIL PAN

Removal

Remove splash guard. Disconnect electrical plug from side of block and remove flywheel cover. Remove oil pan bolts. Remove oil pump and oil pan.

Installation

Clean gasket mating surfaces and coat with gasket sealer. Using new gasket, install oil pump and pan in reverse order of removal. Install remaining components to complete installation.

PISTON & ROD ASSEMBLY

Removal

1) Remove engine. Remove cylinder head, oil pan and oil pump. If necessary, mark rod and cap for cylinder identification. Remove rod cap.

2) Remove ridge at top of cylinder bore. Push piston and rod assembly out of top of block. Install rod cap on same connecting rod.

3) If replacing pistons or rods, ensure they are in same weight class as existing piston or rods. Weight class is stamped on piston crown with "+" or "–".

Installation

1) Install rings on piston and space end gaps 120 degrees apart. Coat piston and cylinder walls with engine oil. Install ring compressor on piston.

2) Install piston and rod assembly with arrow on piston head toward front of engine. Install rod bearings. Using new rod bolts and nuts, install and tighten rod caps.

FITTING PISTONS

1) Arrow on piston heads indicate direction of installation. Weight class is indicated by a "+" or "–" sign. All pistons must be in same weight class. Maximum weight difference between pistons is .35 oz. (10 g).

2) Measure piston diameter 90 degrees to pin bore and at specified height from bottom of piston skirt. *See Fig. 5.* Piston crown is stamped with diameter and arrow of installation direction.

3) Measure cylinder at top, middle and bottom. Out-of-round must not exceed .0012" (.030 mm). Taper should not exceed .0008" (.020 mm). If oil clearance is excessive, bore and hone cylinder block for installation of oversize pistons.

Fig. 5: Piston Clearance Measurement

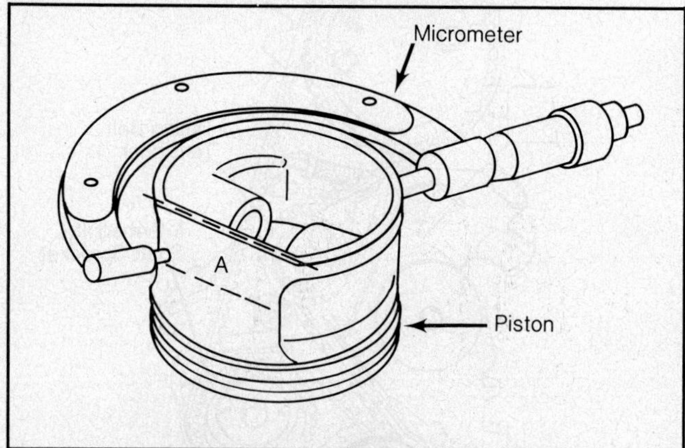

Courtesy of BMW of North America, Inc.

FITTING RINGS

Install rings on piston with word "TOP" facing upward. Space ring end gaps 120 degrees apart.

PISTON PIN REPLACEMENT

1) Remove circlip from pin bore groove. Push pin from piston and connecting rod. Piston pins and pistons must be replaced as matched set.

2) Replacement bushings may be used if pin is not worn. DO NOT machine connecting rods. Ream bushing so pin slides through under thumb pressure.

3) Assemble connecting rod to piston so rod bearing locating lugs will be on exhaust side of engine and arrow on piston head will face toward front of engine.

CRANKSHAFT & ROD BEARINGS

CRANKSHAFT MAIN BEARINGS

NOTE: Crankshafts are specially treated and can only be ground by the factory.

1) Use Plastigage method to measure main bearing clearances. Standard crankshafts are marked with Red or Blue dots on side of counterweights. Crankshaft is cast with "W" on center counterweight.

2) Factory ground crankshafts are identified by paint stripes marked on first counterweight. This indicates either first, second or third undersize. There are 2 undersizes available for 2.7L engine.

3) Factory ground crankshafts are supplied with bearings which are also color coded. If Red and Blue bearing shells are used in combination, ensure shells of same color are on same side of crankshaft. For example, all Red bearings should be in cylinder block and all Blue bearings should be in main bearing caps.

4) If 3 different color (Yellow, Green and White) bearings are used, match bearing shells to color codes on bearing journals and crankcase. If crankcase mark is missing, install both shells according to crankshaft color code.

2.5L & 2.7L 6-CYLINDER (Cont.)

CONNECTING ROD BEARINGS

Use Plastigage method to measure connecting rod bearing clearances. Measure clearances one at a time. Mark connecting rod and cap for cylinder identification before removing caps. Whenever rod bearing caps are removed, rod cap bolts and nuts should be replaced.

CRANKSHAFT END PLAY

Attach dial indicator to crankcase with indicator point contacting flywheel. Push flywheel forward and zero dial indicator. Pull flywheel rearward and record crankshaft end play. If end play is excessive, replace thrust bearing.

REAR MAIN BEARING OIL SEAL

Removal

1) Remove transmission and flywheel. Remove 2 rear oil pan bolts. Loosen remaining oil pan bolts. Carefully separate seal retainer from oil pan gasket.

2) Remove seal retainer from rear of crankcase. Remove oil seal from seal retainer.

Installation

1) Coat oil pan gasket at seal retainer contact surface with sealing compound. Install oil seal into retainer.

2) Install Aligning Tool (11 2 213) on crankshaft. Coat seal lips with oil and install retainer and seal. Install remaining components.

ENGINE OILING

CRANKCASE CAPACITY

Capacity is 4.2 qts. (4.0L) without filter replacement; 4.5 qts. (4.3L) with filter replacement.

NORMAL OIL PRESSURE

Oil pressure should be 7-14 psi (.5-1.0 bar) at idle. Maximum oil pressure at top RPM should be 72-87 psi (5.0-6.0 bar).

OIL PRESSURE RELIEF VALVE

The oil pressure relief valve opens at about 68-74 psi (4.8-5.2 bar).

ENGINE OILING SYSTEM

A gear type oil pump is used. Pump shaft is driven by distributor shaft. The pump is attached to bottom of crankcase. A safety valve in the oil pump prevents oil pressure from becoming excessive.

A pressure relief valve (screwed into crankcase) is connected directly into main oil galley. When oil pressure reaches predetermined maximum value, valve opens to allow oil to return to crankcase.

Oil pump pressure feeds oil through drilled passages within the block to lubricate all internal engine parts. Upper valve train components are lubricated by drainage method.

OIL PUMP

Removal

Remove oil pan. Remove 3 attaching bolts and remove oil pump.

Disassembly & Inspection

Remove cover to gain access to oil screen and gears. Remove snap ring, spring and oil pressure relief valve. Check all parts for excessive wear or scoring. Spring length must be 1.724-1.740" (43.8-44.2 mm).

Reassembly & Installation

Assemble oil pump in reverse order of disassembly. To install, reverse removal procedures. Ensure drive shaft engages with distributor shaft when installing.

OIL PUMP SPECIFICATIONS

Application	In. (mm)
Clearance Between Rotors	.005-.008 (.12-.20)
Clearance Over Rotors	.002-.004 (.04-.10)
Outer Rotor-to-Pump Body	.004-.006 (.10-.15)
Spring Free Length	2.677 (67.99)

ENGINE COOLING

WATER PUMP

Removal

1) Drain coolant. Remove distributor rotor and cap. Remove distributor cover. Remove fan and drive belt from pulley. Remove rubber guard and lift out cover from behind pulley.

2) Remove water pump pulley. Compress tensioner spring and pin near top of water pump and clamp in compressed position. Note installed position of pin to water pump. Remove coolant hoses from water pump. Remove water pump.

Installation

Using new gasket, install water pump. Adjust drive belt tension. Refill and bleed cooling system.

NOTE: For further information on cooling systems, see ENGINE COOLING.

TIGHTENING SPECIFICATIONS

Application	Ft. Lbs. (N.m)
Camshaft Sprocket	47-50 (65-70)
Camshaft Thrust Plate	100-106 (135-144)
Connecting Rod Caps	
Step 1	15 (20)
Step 2	[1]
Cylinder Head Bolts	
Step 1 [2]	29-33 (40-45)
Step 2 [3]	44-47 (60-65)
Step 3	[4]
Exhaust Manifold	16-18 (22-24)
Flywheel Bolts (Use Loctite)	71-81 (98-112)
Intake Manifold	22-24 (30-33)
Intermediate Shaft Sprocket	40-47 (55-64)
Main Bearing Caps	44-49 (60-67)
Oil Pump	15-17 (20-24)
Vibration Damper Hub	283-311 (390-430)

[1] – Using special (Angle-Calibrated) Torque Wrench (11 2 110), tighten bolts an additional 70 degrees.

[2] - Wait 15 minutes after following this step before continuing to next step.

[3] - Run engine at operating temperature for 25 minutes.

[4] – Using special (Angle-Calibrated) Torque Wrench (11 2 110), tighten bolts an additional 20-30 degrees.

BMW Engines

2.5L & 2.7L 6-CYLINDER (Cont.)

ENGINE SPECIFICATIONS

GENERAL SPECIFICATIONS

Year	DISPLACEMENT Cu. In.	DISPLACEMENT Liters	Fuel System	HP@RPM	Torque Ft. Lbs.@RPM	Compr. Ratio	BORE In.	BORE mm	STROKE In.	STROKE mm
1987										
325i & 325is	152	2.5	Fuel Inj.	168@5800	164@4300	8.8:1	3.31	84.0	2.96	75.0
325e & 528e	164	2.7	Fuel Inj.	121@4250	170@3250	9.0:1	3.31	84.0	3.19	81.0

VALVES

Engine Size & Valve	Head Diam. In. (mm)	Face Angle	Seat Angle	Seat Width In. (mm)	Stem Diameter In. (mm)	Stem Clearance In. (mm)	Valve Lift In. (mm)
2.5L [1]							
Intake	.....	45.5°	45°	.....	.275 (7.0)	.006 Max. (.15)	.....
Exhaust	1.417 (36.0)	45.5°	45°	.....	.275 (7.0)	.006 Max. (.15)	.....
2.7L [1]							
Intake	.....	45.5°	45°	.....	.275 (7.0)	.006 Max. (.15)	.....
Exhaust	1.339 (34.0)	45.5°	45°	.....	.275 (7.0)	.006 Max. (.15)	.....

[1] – Minimum valve head margin on intake valves is .051" (1.3 mm) and .079" (2.0 mm) on exhaust.

PISTONS, PINS & RINGS

Engine	PISTONS Clearance In. (mm)	PINS Piston Fit In. (mm)	PINS Rod Fit In. (mm)	RINGS Ring No.	RINGS End Gap In. (mm)	RINGS Side Clearance In. (mm)
2.5L & 2.7L	.0004-.0016 (.01-.04)	.....	Push Fit	No. 1	.012-.020 (.30-.50)	.0016-.0028 (.040-.072)
				No. 2	.012-.020 (.30-.50)	.0012-.0024 (.030-.062)
				Oil	.010-.020 (.25-.50)	.0008-.0017 (.020-.042)

CRANKSHAFT MAIN & CONNECTING ROD BEARINGS

Engine	MAIN BEARINGS Journal Diam. In. (mm)	MAIN BEARINGS Clearance In. (mm)	MAIN BEARINGS Thrust Bearing	MAIN BEARINGS Crankshaft End Play In. (mm)	CONNECTING ROD BEARINGS Journal Diam. In. (mm)	CONNECTING ROD BEARINGS Clearance In. (mm)	CONNECTING ROD BEARINGS Side Play In. (mm)
2.5L & 2.7L							
Red Code	2.3614-2.3618 (59.98-59.99)	.0012-.0028 (.030-.070)	No. 6	.0031-.0064 (.080-.163)	1.7707-1.7713 (44.975-44.991)	.0012-.0028 (.030-.070)	.....
Blue code	2.3611-2.3614 (59.97-59.98)						

BMW Engines

2.5L & 2.7L 6-CYLINDER (Cont.)

ENGINE SPECIFICATIONS (Cont.)

VALVE SPRINGS

Engine	Free Length In. (mm)	PRESSURE Lbs. @ In. (Kg @ mm)	
		Valve Closed	Valve Open
2.5L & 2.7L	[1]	[1]	[1]

[1] – Information not available from manufacturer.

CAMSHAFT

Engine	Journal Diam. In. (mm)	Clearance In. (mm)	Lobe Lift In. (mm)
2.5L & 2.7L [1 3]	[2]	[2]	[2]

[1] – Maximum axial clearance .008" (0.2 mm).
[2] – Information not available from manufacturer.
[3] - Radial play is .0006-0020" (.016-.052 mm).

BMW Engines

3.5L 6-CYLINDER

535i, 635CSi, 735i

NOTE: **For engine repair procedures not covered in this article, see ENGINE OVERHAUL PROCEDURES article at beginning of this section.**

ENGINE CODING

ENGINE IDENTIFICATION

On 535i, 635CSi and 735i models, displacement and identification numbers are on top rear of engine block on bellhousing flange.

ENGINE IDENTIFICATION CODE

Application	Code
535i, 635CSi & 735i	3.5L

CAUTION: **Before performing any work on vehicles equipped with Supplemental Restaint System (SRS), disconnect SRS control unit. Use EXTREME caution when testing or repairing any electrical equipment on or around steering column (air bag might deploy).**

ENGINE, MANIFOLDS & CYLINDER HEAD

NOTE: **Vehicle transmission must be removed prior to engine removal.**

MANUAL TRANSMISSION

Removal

1) Remove exhaust system and support brackets from vehicle. Disconnect propeller shaft at rear of transmission. Remove heat shield from center support bearing.

2) Remove center support bearing bracket. Lower propeller shaft at center support bearing and pull propeller shaft from transmission. Remove speed and reference mark sensors.

3) Remove clutch slave cylinder, leaving line connected. Remove speedometer cable and disconnect plug from back-up light switch.

4) Pull up boot from floor shift lever. Remove circlip and pull shift lever up and out. Support transmission and remove crossmember. Remove transmission.

Installation

1) To install, reverse removal procedure. When installing propeller shaft, use new lock nuts at rubber coupling. Only tighten nuts (never bolts) to avoid stress on coupling.

2) When installing propeller shaft, push center support bearing forward .08" (2.0 mm) to preload bracket and tighten nuts.

3) When installing speed and reference mark sensors, note that Black plug of speed sensor faces ring gear. Gray ring of reference mark sensor faces flywheel. If plugs are reversed, engine will not start.

AUTOMATIC TRANSMISSION

Removal

1) Disconnect exhaust system and remove support brackets. Disconnect bracket and accelerator cable from transmission. Drain transmission oil. Remove filler tube and plug opening.

2) Disconnect oil cooler lines from transmission. Label and disconnect all wiring attached to transmission. Remove cover plate from transmission. Mark installed positions of speed and reference mark sensors. Remove sensors.

3) Remove 4 bolts securing torque converter to drive plate. Disconnect shift rod from lever. Disconnect propeller shaft coupling at rear of transmission.

4) Remove heat shield and center support bearing bracket. Lower propeller shaft at center support bearing and pull propeller shaft from transmission. Support transmission.

5) Remove crossmember and lower transmission to rest on front axle carrier. Place transmission jack under transmission. Separate and remove transmission and torque converter from engine.

Installation

1) To install transmission and remaining components, reverse removal procedures. Before installing transmission, ensure torque converter is properly seated.

2) When installing propeller shaft, push center support bearing forward .08" (2.0 mm) to preload bracket. Tighten nuts.

3) When installing sensors, note that Black plug of speed sensor faces ring gear and Gray ring of reference mark sensor faces flywheel. If plugs are reversed, engine will not start.

ENGINE

Removal

1) Remove hood. Disconnect battery cables from battery. Remove transmission. Remove splash guard from under engine. Drain cooling system and remove radiator. Remove power steering pump (leaving hoses connected) and secure away from engine.

2) Remove A/C compressor with hoses connected (If equipped). Secure away from engine. Remove accelerator cable. Remove cruise control cable from engine (if equipped).

3) Label and disconnect all electrical and ignition wiring that might interfere with engine removal. Disconnect wiring harness in glove box and pull through hole in firewall.

4) Label and disconnect all coolant, ventilation, fuel and vacuum hoses (or lines). Remove air cleaner with airflow sensor.

5) Remove nuts from engine mounts. Ensure no wiring, hoses or lines are attached to engine. Attach lifting chain and hoist to engine. Carefully lift engine from vehicle.

Installation

To install engine, reverse removal procedures. Ensure that all hoses, lines and electrical connections are installed in original positions. Bleed cooling system.

CYLINDER HEAD

Removal

1) Disconnect battery ground cable. Drain cooling system. Remove splash guard from bottom of engine. Disconnect exhaust pipes from manifolds.

2) Disconnect accelerator and cruise control cables from throttle valve housing, including cable to automatic transmission (if equipped). Disconnect attached hoses and electrical wiring. Remove air cleaner with airflow sensor.

3.5L 6-CYLINDER (Cont.)

3) Label and disconnect all coolant hoses attached to cylinder head. Label and disconnect all fuel, ventilation and vacuum hoses (or lines) from cylinder head and intake manifold.

4) Label and disconnect all electrical and ignition wiring. If necessary, disconnect electrical plug in glove box, and pull wiring through hole in firewall.

5) Remove valve cover. Set No. 1 piston on TDC of compression stroke. Timing pointer and mark on vibration damper should align. Valves of No. 6 cylinder should overlap.

6) Remove timing chain tensioner plug, spring and piston. Remove camshaft sprocket. Remove cylinder head bolts in reverse of tightening sequence. Install locating pins in bolt holes to keep rocker arm shafts from turning. Remove cylinder head.

Inspection

Cylinder head may be machined if necessary. Minimum height is 5.063" (128.6 mm). Use a .012" (.30 mm) thicker head gasket if cylinder head is machined.

Installation

1) Clean all gasket mating surfaces. Remove oil from head bolt threaded holes in cylinder block. Clean and lubricate threads of head bolts. Using new head gasket, install cylinder head and bolts.

2) Tighten head bolts in 4 steps. See TIGHTENING SPECIFICATIONS chart in this article. *See Fig. 1.*

3) Using special Torque Wrench (11 2 110), retighten head bolts to specified torque angle. Never loosen bolts during tightening sequence; turn only in tightening direction.

NOTE: **DO NOT retorque head after 600 miles.**

Fig. 1: Cylinder Head Tightening Sequence

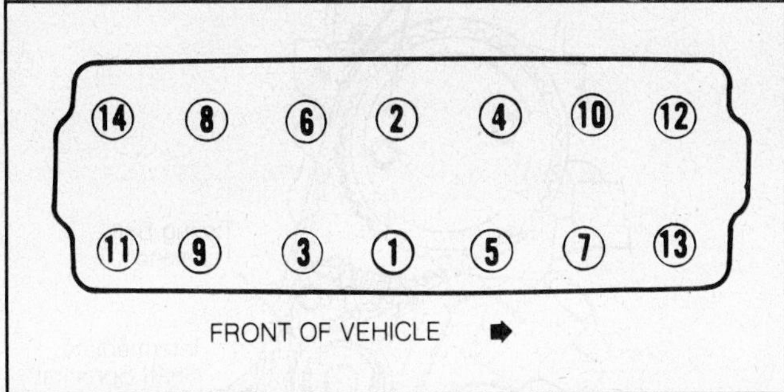

Use angle-calibrated torque wrench for final tightening (engine warm).

4) Install camshaft sprocket and timing chain (or timing belt). Ensure valve timing is correct. Install remaining components in reverse order of removal, using new gaskets where required. Adjust valves.

CAMSHAFT

Removal

1) Remove cylinder head. Mount Rocker Arm Compressor (11 1 060) on Cylinder Head Stand (00 1 490). Mount cylinder head on head fixture. Remove oil feed line. Adjust valve clearance of all valves to specification.

2) Turn camshaft 15 degrees and mount Cam Remover (11 1 061). Push intake rocker arms of cylinders No. 2 and No. 4 forward. Align special tool in such a manner that tabs rest on eccentrics of rocker arms. Remove thrust plate. Pull out camshaft.

NOTE: **To avoid contact between valve heads, tighten nuts on exhaust side to stop and then tighten intake side slightly. Check valve head clearance as procedure progresses.**

Installation

1) Install camshaft in head and tighten thrust plate bolts. Camshaft must turn easily. Turn camshaft to TDC position on camshaft flange (valves of No. 6 cylinder overlap). Remove compression tool. *See Fig. 2.*

2) If adapter was removed from front of camshaft, coat bolt threads with Loctite 270 before installation. Install oil pipe so oil bores will spray between rocker arms and cams of intake and exhaust valves.

3) Use new seals between oil pipe and rocker supports as well as under head of attaching bolts. Continue assembly in reverse order of removal.

Fig. 2: Camshaft Flange Position for Compression Tool Installation & Removal

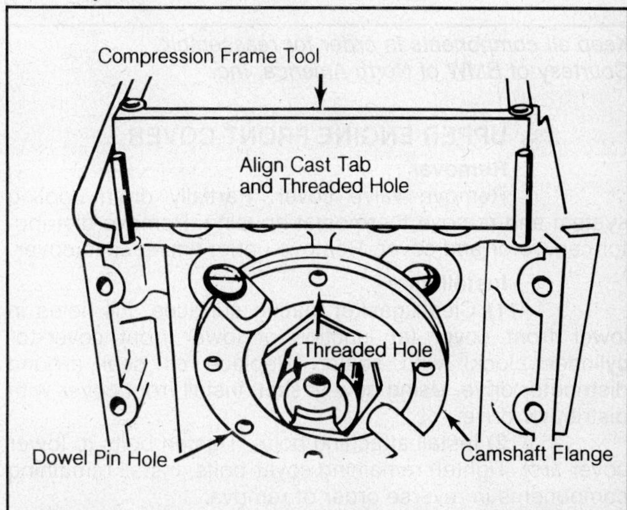

Position flange as shown when removing and installing camshaft sprocket. Courtesy of BMW of North America, Inc.

ROCKER ARM ASSEMBLY

Removal

1) Remove camshaft and remove end cover. Remove rocker arm shaft end plugs. If necessary, hold turning rocker arm shafts using dowel pin.

2) Push back rocker arms and thrust washers. Lift out retainer circlips and remove rocker arm shaft dowel pin. Screw Rocker Arm Shaft Remover (11 3 060) in rocker arm shaft. Drive out rocker arm shafts with an impact hammer.

NOTE: **Be careful of springs popping out when removing rocker arm shafts.**

Inspection

Check rocker arms and shaft for excessive wear. Oil clearance should be .0006-.0020" (.016-.052 mm). Replace all worn parts.

Installation

To install rocker arm shafts, reverse removal procedure. Align rocker arm shafts so that cylinder head bolts fit in openings. Insert rocker arm shaft retainer dowel pins.

3.5L 6-CYLINDER (Cont.)

Fig. 3: Rocker Arm Assembly

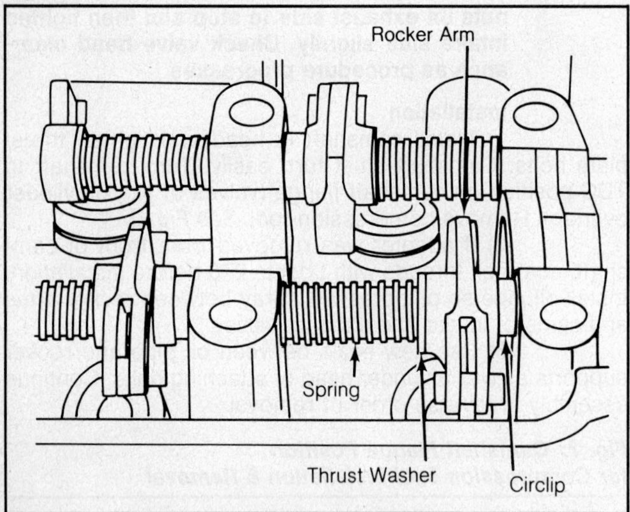

Keep all components in order for reassembly.
Courtesy of BMW of North America, Inc.

UPPER ENGINE FRONT COVER

Removal

Remove valve cover. Partially drain cooling system and remove thermostat housing. Remove distributor cap, rotor and cover. Remove upper timing case cover.

Installation

1) Clean gasket mating surfaces. Fill holes in lower front cover (at junction of lower front cover-to-cylinder block) with sealer. Replace oil seal around distributor drive. Using new gasket, install front cover with distributor drive.

2) Install attaching bolts. Tighten bolts to lower cover first. Tighten remaining cover bolts. Install remaining components in reverse order of removal.

LOWER ENGINE FRONT COVER

Removal

1) Remove upper engine front cover. Remove fan. Remove drive belts from crankshaft and fan pulleys. Hold crankshaft in place and remove vibration damper and hub. Remove chain tensioner piston.

2) Remove water pump pulley. Remove alternator and bracket. Remove and set aside power steering pump. Remove oil pan-to-front cover attaching bolts.

3) Loosen remaining oil pan bolts. Remove remaining cover attaching bolts. Carefully separate lower front cover from oil pan.

Installation

Clean gasket mating surfaces. Apply gasket sealer to oil pan gasket and to oil pan-to-cylinder block junction. Install lower engine front cover. Install remaining components in reverse order of installation. Adjust TDC position sensor after installing.

FRONT COVER OIL SEAL

Removal

Remove fan shroud and all drive belts. Remove nut on crankshaft. Remove vibration damper and hub. Pry out oil seal.

Installation

Pack lip of new oil seal with grease. Use Seal Installer (11 1 273) to press in seal. Install remaining components in reverse order of removal.

TIMING BELT & SPROCKET

Removal

1) Remove distributor cap and rotor. Remove cover surrounding distributor. Turn crankshaft to position No. 1 piston on TDC of compression stroke.

2) Ensure timing marks on vibration damper and pointer are aligned. Arrow on camshaft must be aligned with timing mark on cylinder head. *See Fig. 4*.

3) Remove timing belt cover. Loosen tensioner and position away from timing belt to relieve tension. Tighten tensioner adjusting bolt to keep tensioner in retracted position.

4) If installing same timing belt, mark normal direction of rotation on timing belt before removing. Remove timing belt.

Installation

1) Ensure arrow on camshaft sprocket is still aligned with timing mark on cylinder head. Ensure timing mark on crankshaft sprocket is aligned with notch in cover (approximately one o'clock position). *See Fig. 4*.

2) Install timing belt on sprockets. Loosen tensioner adjusting bolt to allow tension on timing belt. Turn crankshaft in direction of normal rotation until timing belt tightens. Tighten tensioner bolts. Install remaining components in reverse order of removal.

Fig. 4: Timing Sprockets Alignment

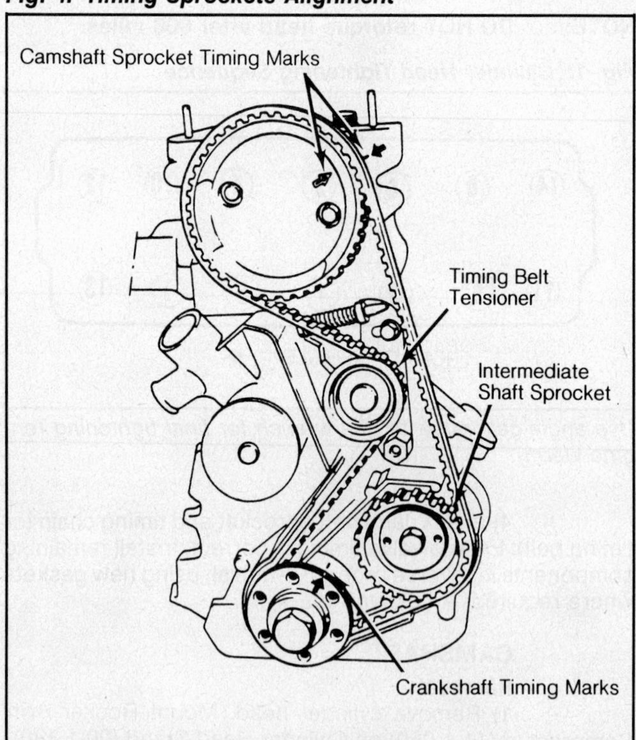

Mark rotation direction on timing belts that will be reused.
Courtesy of BMW of North America, Inc.

3.5L 6-CYLINDER (Cont.)

TIMING CHAIN & SPROCKETS

Removal

1) Remove upper and lower engine front cover. Rotate crankshaft until No. 1 cylinder is on TDC at end of compression stroke. Timing mark on front cover should align with notch in vibration damper.

2) Remove camshaft sprocket with timing chain attached. Remove chain from camshaft and crankshaft sprockets.

3) If crankshaft sprocket removal is necessary, remove oil pan. Remove oil pump sprocket and drive chain. Remove Woodruff key from crankshaft. Using a puller, remove crankshaft sprocket.

Installation

1) Install components in reverse order of removal. Oil pump drive chain has correct tension if chain gives under slight thumb pressure midway between sprockets. Adjusting shims are available for adjusting oil pump drive chain tension.

2) Ensure No. 1 piston is still on TDC of compression stroke. When installing timing chain and camshaft sprocket, ensure camshaft flange is correctly positioned. *See Fig. 4*.

VALVE TIMING

Use procedures outlined in TIMING CHAIN & SPROCKETS.

TIMING BELT TENSIONER

Removal & Installation

Remove timing belt cover. Place piston of No. 1 cylinder on TDC of compression stroke. Remove timing belt tensioner. To install, reverse removal procedures. Check valve timing.

TIMING CHAIN TENSIONER

CAUTION: Timing chain tensioner piston assembly is under high spring pressure. Use care when unscrewing tensioner plug.

Removal & Disassembly

Carefully remove tensioner plug. Remove spring and piston assembly. Remove piston, check ball and metering disc from piston sleeve. *See Fig. 5*. Clean all parts thoroughly and blow out with compressed air.

Fig. 5: Tensioner Components

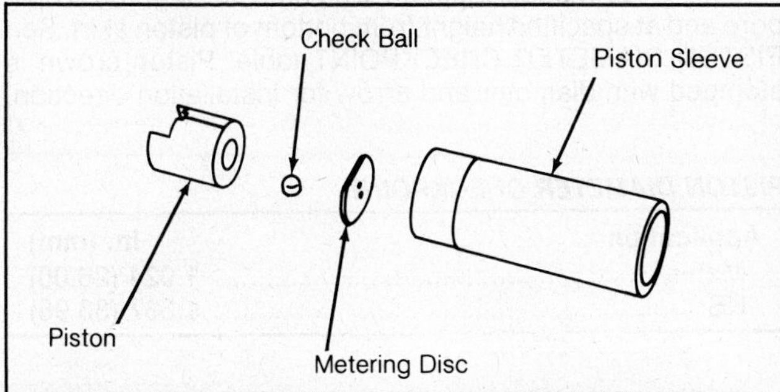

Piston assembly must be purged of air after installing.
Courtesy of BMW of North America, Inc.

Reassembly & Installation

1) Reassemble piston parts in reverse order of disassembly. Ensure metering disc does not block bleed slots in piston. Remove rocker cover.

2) Install piston assembly and spring in lower front cover. Tapered end of spring must face tensioner plug. Install plug and lightly tighten. Fill tensioner piston oil pocket (in lower front cover) with engine oil.

3) Piston must be purged of air. Using a screwdriver, move tensioning rail back and forth against piston until oil runs out around tensioner plug threads. Tighten tensioner plug. Install remaining components.

INTERMEDIATE SHAFT

Removal & Installation

Remove timing belt cover. Remove guide plate and pull out intermediate shaft. To install, reverse removal procedures. Bearings in engine block are not replaceable.

VALVES

VALVE ARRANGEMENT

Left Side - Intake valves.
Right Side - Exhaust valves.

Removal

1) Remove cylinder head from engine. Remove camshaft sprocket. Adjust valve clearance of all valves to specification. Remove front and rear rubber plugs on either side of rocker shafts.

2) Remove thrust plate from rocker shafts (at front of head). Remove spring clips from rockers. Turn camshaft so valves of cylinder No. 6 overlap.

3) Rotate camshaft 1/4 turn against normal direction of rotation, while simultaneously pushing rockers for cylinders No. 3 and No. 4 to rear. Push all remaining rockers toward front of cylinder head.

4) When camshaft is clear of rockers, both rocker shafts can be removed. Ensure that all rockers are in order for later installation.

Installation

Install rocker arm shaft assembly in reverse order of removal. Install rocker shafts with large oil holes facing downward. Ensure small oil holes and thrust plate grooves in rocker shafts face inward. Straight surface of retaining clips should be installed in rocker shaft grooves.

VALVE GUIDES

1) If valve-to-guide clearance is excessive, drive out guide toward combustion chamber side of head. Check size of valve guide bore in cylinder head. Valve guide bore diameter should be equal to guide outside diameter.

2) Valve guides are available in 3 oversizes. Oversize diameters are .555" (14.1 mm), .559" (14.2 mm) and .563" (14.3 mm). When installing guide, heat cylinder head to 122°F (50°C). Using Freon or Liquid Nitrogen, chill valve guide to about -238°F (-150°C).

3) Drive guide into cylinder head from top. Stepped end of valve guide must face camshaft installed guide. Guide height is .513" (13.5 mm). Ream valve guide for correct oil clearance.

3.5L 6-CYLINDER (Cont.)

VALVE STEM OIL SEALS

Remove valve springs and pull off old seal. When replacing valve stem oil seals, use protective sleeve over valve stem to avoid damage to new seals. Lubricate seal with oil and install.

VALVE SEATS

1) When replacing valve seat, remove old seat by turning out with cutting tool. When cutting bore for valve seat inserts, allow for shrink fit. Valve seat insert shrink fit specification is .006" (.15 mm).

2) When installing new seat, heat head to about 122°F (50°C). Using Freon or Liquid Nitrogen chill valve seat to about -238°F (-150°C). See VALVE SEAT DIAMETER table.

VALVE SEAT DIAMETER

Application	Diameter In. (mm)
Intake	
Standard	1.856 (47.15)
.2 mm O.S.	1.864 (47.35)
.4 mm O.S.	1.872 (47.55)
Exhaust	
Standard	1.581 (40.15)
.2 mm O.S.	1.589 (40.35)
.4 mm O.S.	1.596 (40.55)

VALVE SPRINGS

NOTE: Install springs with paint stripe (tight coil end) against head.

Inspection

Check spring free length. Check spring pressure in a valve spring tester. Replace defective springs with new springs of same color code.

NOTE: The intake valve spring with "S" mark, has an installed height of 1.457-1.535" (37-39 mm).

VALVE CLEARANCE ADJUSTMENT

1) Adjust valves in firing order (1-5-3-6-2-4), with piston of cylinder to be adjusted set at TDC of compression stroke. Use a feeler gauge to measure clearance between rocker arm eccentric and tip of valve.

2) To adjust valve clearance, loosen nut on rocker arm and insert a rod in eccentric hole. Rotate eccentric until proper clearance is obtained and tighten lock nut.

VALVE CLEARANCE ADJUSTMENT

Application	In. (mm)
Intake & Exhaust	
Cold	.012 (.30)
Hot	.014 (.35)

PISTONS, PINS & RINGS

OIL PAN

Removal

1) Drain engine oil and remove wire from oil level switch (if equipped). On 735i models, remove sway bar. On all models, remove power steering pump with hoses connected. Remove mounting bracket attached to oil pan and front cover.

2) Remove alternator and bracket. Remove transmission bellhousing cover. Remove engine mount bolts. Raise and support engine from above. Remove oil pan bolts.

3) Lower pan and move toward front of engine. Turn crankshaft until No. 5 and No. 6 connecting rod are above crankcase sealing surface. Remove oil pan.

Installation

Clean gasket mating surfaces and coat with gasket sealer. Using new gasket, install oil pan in reverse order of removal. Install remaining components to complete installation.

PISTON & ROD ASSEMBLY

Removal

1) Remove engine. Remove cylinder head, oil pan and oil pump. If necessary, mark rod and rod cap for cylinder identification. Remove rod cap.

2) Remove ridge at top of cylinder bore. Push piston and rod assembly out top of block. Install rod cap on connecting rod from which removed.

3) If replacing pistons or rods, ensure they are in same weight class as existing piston or rods. Weight class is stamped on piston crown with a "+" or "-".

Installation

1) Install rings on piston and space end gaps 120 degrees apart. Coat piston and cylinder walls with engine oil. Install ring compressor on piston.

2) Install piston and rod assembly with arrow on piston head toward front of engine. Install rod bearings. Using new rod bolts and nuts, install and tighten rod caps.

FITTING PISTONS

1) Arrow on piston heads indicate direction of installation. Weight class is indicated by a "+" or "-" sign. All pistons must be in same weight class. Maximum weight difference between pistons can be .35 oz. (10 grams).

2) Measure piston diameter 90 degrees to pin bore and at specified height from bottom of piston skirt. See PISTON DIAMETER CHECKPOINT table. Piston crown is stamped with diameter and arrow for installation direction.

PISTON DIAMETER CHECKPOINT

Application	In. (mm)
Mahle	1.024 (26.00)
KS	1.337 (33.95)

3) Measure cylinder at top, middle and bottom. Out-of-round and taper should not exceed .0004" (.010 mm). If oil clearance is excessive, bore and hone cylinder block for installation of oversize pistons.

3.5L 6-CYLINDER (Cont.)

Fig. 6: Piston Diameter Checkpoint

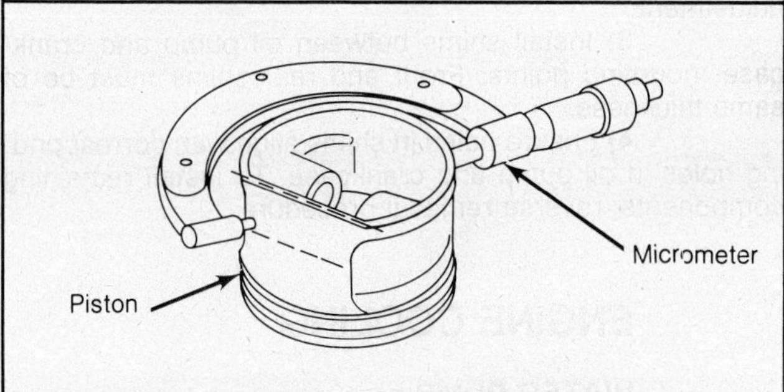

Courtesy of BMW of North America, Inc.

PISTON DIAMETER SPECIFICATIONS

Application	In. (mm)
Standard	3.5027 (88.97)
Special	3.5059 (89.05)
1st O.S.	3.5126 (89.22)
2nd O.S.	3.5224 (89.47)

FITTING RINGS

1) Place piston rings squarely into cylinder bore about 9/16" from bottom of bore. Use a feeler gauge to measure ring end gap.

2) With rings installed on piston, use a feeler gauge to measure ring side clearance. Take measurement around entire circumference of piston, between top of ring and ring land.

3) Install rings on piston with word "TOP" facing upward. Space ring end gaps 120 degrees apart.

PISTON PIN REPLACEMENT

1) Remove circlip from pin bore groove. Push pin from piston and connecting rod. Piston pins and pistons must be replaced as matched set.

2) All pistons and connecting rods must be in same weight class. DO NOT machine connecting rod.

3) Assemble connecting rod to piston with oil hole in rod's small end and arrow on piston head on same side. When installed, arrow on piston and rod's small end oil hole will face front of engine.

CRANKSHAFT & ROD BEARINGS

CRANKSHAFT MAIN BEARINGS

NOTE: **Crankshafts are specially treated and can only be ground by the factory.**

1) Use Plastigage to measure main bearing clearances. Standard crankshafts are marked with Red or Blue dots on side of counterweights. The crankshaft is cast with a "K" on center counterweight.

2) Factory ground crankshafts are identified by paint stripes marked on 1st counterweight. This indicates either 1st, 2nd or 3rd undersize (3 undersizes are available).

3) Factory ground crankshafts are supplied with bearings which are also color coded. If Red and Blue bearing shells are used in combination, ensure shells of same color are on same side of crankshaft. For example, all Red bearings in cylinder block and all Blue in main bearing caps.

4) If 3 different color (Yellow, Green and White) bearings are used, match bearing shells to color codes on bearing journals and crankcase. If crankcase mark is missing, install both shells according to crankshaft color code.

CONNECTING ROD BEARINGS

Use Plastigage to measure connecting rod bearing clearances. Measure clearances one at a time. Mark connecting rod and cap for cylinder identification before removing caps. Whenever rod bearing caps are removed, rod cap bolts and nuts should be replaced.

CRANKSHAFT END PLAY

Attach a dial indicator to crankcase with indicator point contacting flywheel. Push flywheel forward and zero dial indicator. Pull flywheel rearward and record crankshaft end play. If end thrust is excessive, replace thrust bearing.

REAR MAIN BEARING OIL SEAL

Removal

1) Remove transmission and flywheel. Remove 2 rear oil pan bolts. Loosen remaining oil pan bolts. Carefully separate seal retainer from oil pan gasket.

2) Remove seal retainer from rear of crankcase. Remove oil seal from seal retainer.

Installation

1) Coat oil pan gasket at seal retainer contact surface with sealing compound. Install oil seal into retainer.

2) Install Aligning Tool (11 2 213) on crankshaft. Coat seal lips with oil and install retainer and seal. Install remaining components.

ENGINE OILING

ENGINE OILING SYSTEM

A rotor-type oil pump is used. Pump is chain driven off of crankshaft sprocket. Pressure regulating valve is integral with oil pump.

Oil pump pressure feeds oil to full-flow oil filter. From oil filter, oil is circulated through drilled passages to all moving parts of the engine. Upper valve train components and timing chain are lubricated through drainage or splash method.

CRANKCASE CAPACITY

Capacity is 5.3 qts. (5.0L) without filter replacement, and 6.1 qts. (5.8L) with filter replacement.

NORMAL OIL PRESSURE

Oil pressure should be 7-28 psi (0.5-2.0 kg/cm²) at idle. Maximum oil pressure at peak RPM should be about 57-71 psi (4.0-5.0 kg/cm²).

OIL PRESSURE RELIEF VALVE

For all models, oil pressure relief valve opens at approximately 68-74 psi (4.8-5.2 kg/cm²).

BMW Engines

3.5L 6-CYLINDER (Cont.)

OIL PUMP

Removal

Remove oil pan. Remove oil pump drive sprocket and detach from chain. Remove oil pump.

Disassembly

1) Unscrew union and remove relief valve spring and plunger from pump body. Remove pick-up tube and cover from pump body. Clean all parts and dry with compressed air.

2) If inner rotor replacement is required, remove pump sprocket hub from rotor shaft using a puller. Install new rotor in pump body and press hub onto rotor shaft to a distance of 1.740-1.748" (44.20-44.40 mm) between hub and rotor faces.

Inspection

1) Using a feeler gauge, measure clearance between outer rotor and pump body. Measure clearance between inner and outer rotor.

2) Lay straightedge over pump body. Insert a feeler gauge between straightedge and rotors and measure clearance over rotors. Replace all worn parts.

3) Check free length of relief valve spring. If measurement is less than specified, replace spring.

OIL PUMP SPECIFICATIONS

Application	In. (mm)
Clearance Between Rotors	.005-.008 (.12-.20)
Clearance Over Rotors	.002-.004 (.04-.10)
Outer Rotor-to-Pump Body	.004-.006 (.10-.15)
Spring Free Length	2.677 (67.99)

Reassembly

Reassemble oil pump in reverse order of disassembly, using new parts where required.

Installation

1) Prime oil pump. To install, reverse removal procedure. Check oil pump drive chain tension.

2) Chain tension is correct if chain gives when slight thumb pressure is exerted midway between oil pump and crankshaft sprockets. Shims are available for tension adjustment.

3) Install shims between oil pump and crankcase mounting points. Front and rear shims must be of same thickness.

4) Ensure holes in shims align with corresponding holes in oil pump and crankcase. To install remaining components, reverse removal procedure.

ENGINE COOLING

WATER PUMP

Removal & Installation

Loosen drive belts. Remove fan, spacer and pulley from water pump. Remove lifting eye near top of water pump. Remove coolant hose from water pump and remove pump. Using new gasket, install water pump in reverse order of removal.

NOTE: For further information on cooling systems, see ENGINE COOLING.

TIGHTENING SPECIFICATIONS

Application	Ft. Lbs. (N.m)
Camshaft Thrust Plate	100-106 (135-144)
Connecting Rod Caps	38-41 (51-55)
Cylinder Head Bolts	
Step 1	42-45 (58-62)
Step 2	Wait 15 Minutes
Step 3	30-36 Degrees
Step 4 [1]	30-40 Degrees
Exhaust Manifold	16-18 (22-25)
Flywheel Bolts (Use Loctite)	75-83 (104-115)
Main Bearing Caps	42-45 (58-62)
Oil Pan Bolts	7-8 (9-11)
Timing Belt Cover Bolts	7-8 (9-11)
Vibration Damper Hub	311-325 (430-450)

[1] – Run engine at operating temperature for 25 minutes, and tighten to specified torque angle.

ENGINE SPECIFICATIONS

GENERAL SPECIFICATIONS

Year	DISPLACEMENT Cu. In.	DISPLACEMENT Liters	Fuel System	HP@RPM	Torque Ft. Lbs.@RPM	Compr. Ratio	BORE In.	BORE mm	STROKE In.	STROKE mm
1987 535i, 635CSi, & 735i	209	3.5	Fuel Inj.	182@5400	214@4000	8.0:1	3.62	92.0	3.38	86.0

VALVES

Engine Size & Valve	Head Diam. In. (mm)	Face Angle	Seat Angle	Seat Width In. (mm)	Stem Diameter In. (mm)	Stem Clearance In. (mm)	Valve Lift In. (mm)
3.5L [1]							
Intake	1.811 (46.0)	45.5°	45°	.039-.071 (1.0-1.8)	.....	.006 Max. (.15)	.....
Exhaust	1.496 (38.0)	45.5°	45°	.051-.083 (1.3-2.1)	.....	.006 Max. (.15)	.....

[1] – Minimum valve head margin on intake valves is .051" (1.3 mm) and .079" (2.0 mm) on exhaust.

BMW Engines

3.5L 6-CYLINDER (Cont.)

ENGINE SPECIFICATIONS (Cont.)

PISTONS, PINS & RINGS

	PISTONS	PINS		RINGS		
Engine	Clearance In. (mm)	Piston Fit In. (mm)	Rod Fit In. (mm)	Ring No.	End Gap In. (mm)	Side Clearance In. (mm)
3.5L	.0008-.002 (.02-.05)	.0002 Max. (.005)	Push Fit	No. 1	.012-.020 (.30-.50)	.0020-.0032 (.050-.082)
				No. 2	.008-.016 (.20-.40)	.0016-.0028 (.040-.072)
				Oil	.010-.020 (.25-.50)	.0008-.0020 (.020-.050)

CRANKSHAFT MAIN & CONNECTING ROD BEARINGS

	MAIN BEARINGS				CONNECTING ROD BEARINGS		
Engine	Journal Diam. In. (mm)	Clearance In. (mm)	Thrust Bearing	Crankshaft End Play In. (mm)	Journal Diam. In. (mm)	Clearance In. (mm)	Side Play In. (mm)
3.5L [1]							
Red Code	2.3614-2.3618 (59.98-59.99)	.0012-.0028 (.030-.070)	No. 4	.0033-.0069 (.085-.174)	1.8888-1.8894 (47.975-47.991)	.0012-.0028 (.030-.070)	.....
Blue Code	2.3611-2.3614 (59.97-59.98)						

[1] – On 3.5L engine, radial crankshaft bearing play is .0012-.0028" (.03-.07 mm).

VALVE SPRINGS

Engine	Free Length In. (mm)	PRESSURE Lbs. @ In. (Kg @ mm) Valve Closed	Valve Open
3.5L	6.122 (155.5)	[1]	[1]

[1] – Information on specifications not available from manufacturer.

CAMSHAFT

Engine	Journal Diam. In. (mm)	Clearance In. (mm)	Lobe Lift In. (mm)
3.5L[1]	[2]	[2]	[2]

[1] – End play clearance is .0012-.0071" (.03-.18 mm). Camshaft radial play is .0006-.0020" (.016-.050 mm).

[2] – Information on specifications not available from manufacturer.

Ford Motor Co. Engines

1.3L 4-CYLINDER

Festiva

NOTE: For engine repair procedures not covered in this article, see ENGINE OVERHAUL PROCEDURES article at beginning of this section.

ENGINE CODING

ENGINE IDENTIFICATION

Engine may be identified by Vehicle Identification Number (VIN), stamped on metal tab attached to instrument panel. Tab is close to windshield on driver's side and visible through windshield. This VIN contains a 20 character number. The 8th character identifies engine and 10th character establishes model year.

ENGINE IDENTIFICATION CODE

Engine	Code
1.3L	K

ENGINE, CYLINDER HEAD & MANIFOLDS

ENGINE

NOTE: When removing engine mounts, mark and note location and position to ensure proper installation.

Removal

1) Remove battery and battery tray. Index hood-to-hinge and remove hood. Drain coolant. Drain engine oil and transaxle fluid. Remove air cleaner assembly, oil dipstick, cooling fan and radiator assembly. Remove throttle cable and bracket from carburetor.

2) Disconnect speedometer cable at transaxle. Mark and disconnect fuel lines at fuel pump. Plug fuel lines to keep dirt out and avoid fuel leakage. Remove heater hoses. Remove brake booster vacuum hose. Mark and remove vacuum hoses at carburetor that connect to chassis.

3) Remove charcoal canister hoses connecting engine. Disconnect coil, distributor, fan temperature switch, temperature sending unit, starter, back-up light, neutral safety switch, alternator, carburetor, oxygen sensor and EGR position sensor wiring harness.

4) Remove alternator and brackets. Remove engine ground strap. Raise vehicle and remove catalytic converter. Disconnect A/C compressor without removing hoses and set aside. Disconnect lower control arms from knuckles. Separate halfshafts and install Differential Plugs (T87C-7025-C). See FWD AXLE SHAFTS & CV JOINTS article in this section.

5) Remove clutch control cable and shift control cable rod. Remove stabilizer bar from shift transaxle. Support engine assembly with hoist. Remove rear crossmember mount bolts at chassis. Remove front engine mount nut through hole in crossmember. Remove rear engine mount nuts at crossmember.

6) Remove crossmember. Lower vehicle and attach engine lifter hooks. Remove right engine mount bolt. Remove engine and transaxle assembly through bottom of vehicle.

Installation

1) Attach hoist to engine assembly and position in vehicle from the bottom. Support engine in chassis and install engine mount bolts through mounts. Raise vehicle and install front engine mount nut. Tighten nut to specifications.

2) Position crossmember onto mounts and chassis. Tighten rear nut. Install mount-to-crossmember nuts and tighten. Remove differential plugs and install halfshafts. To complete installation, reverse removal procedure. Tighten all bolts/nuts to specifications. Fill all fluid levels to proper level.

INTAKE MANIFOLD

NOTE: Fuel pump is attached to head and may be removed to access bolts.

Removal

Disconnect negative battery cable. Drain cooling system. Remove air cleaner. Disconnect throttle cable and bracket at carburetor. Mark and disconnect vacuum hoses, fuel hoses and wiring at carburetor. Remove intake manifold bolts. Remove intake manifold and gasket.

Installation

Clean all gasket mating surfaces. Ensure surface is free from burrs, scratches and cracks. Always replace gasket. Position gasket and manifold to cylinder head. Install bolts and tighten to specifications. To complete installation, reverse removal procedure.

EXHAUST MANIFOLD

Removal

1) Raise vehicle. Remove catalytic converter inlet pipe at exhaust manifold. Remove pulse air tube nuts at inlet pipe. Remove inlet pipe support bracket bolts. Lower vehicle and remove air cleaner assembly. Remove 4 exhaust manifold heat shroud bolts and remove shroud.

2) Disconnect oxygen sensor connector. Remove pulse air routing bracket bolt and bracket. Remove pulse air tube and gaskets. Remove exhaust manifold nuts and remove exhaust manifold. Remove gasket from inlet pipe and cylinder head.

Installation

Position new gasket on cylinder head and inlet pipe. Install exhaust manifold and nuts. Tighten nuts to specifications. To complete installation, reverse removal procedure. Tighten all bolts/nuts to specifications.

CYLINDER HEAD

Removal

1) Disconnect battery ground cable. Mark and disconnect fuel lines at fuel pump. Remove accessory belts, water pump pulley, crankshaft pulley, timing belt covers, timing belt tensioner, timing belt, valve cover, exhaust and intake manifold. Drain cooling system.

2) Mark and remove electrical connectors, vacuum hoses, spark plug wires from spark plugs and remove spark plugs. Remove fuel pump. Remove distributor cap. Disconnect vacuum hoses and ECM connector at distributor. Disconnect wiring from distributor-to-coil.

3) Index distributor-to-mount and remove hold-down bolt. Remove distributor assembly. Remove engine ground strap and front and rear engine lifting hooks. Remove upper radiator hose, by-pass hose and bracket.

1.3L 4-CYLINDER (Cont.)

4) Remove bolts retaining rocker arm shaft and remove rocker arm assemblies. Remove cylinder head bolts. Loosen head and remove head and gasket.

Inspection

1) Thoroughly clean and check gasket mating surface of cylinder head and block. Check cylinder for cracks, nicks, burrs or damage. Using a straightedge and feeler gauge, ensure cylinder head and block warpage does not exceed .006" (.15 mm), over entire gasket area.

2) If not within specifications, machine cylinder head and/or block gasket surface. Maximum machining allowed is .008" (.20 mm). If more machining is required, block and/or cylinder head must be replaced.

Installation

1) Before installation always perform inspection. Place new head gasket properly on block. Carefully place cylinder head in position on block. Install head bolts. Tighten bolts in sequence and in 2 steps. *See Fig. 1.*

2) To complete installation, reverse removal procedure. Tighten all bolts/nuts to specifications. Fill all fluid levels to proper level.

Fig. 1: Cylinder Head Bolt Installation

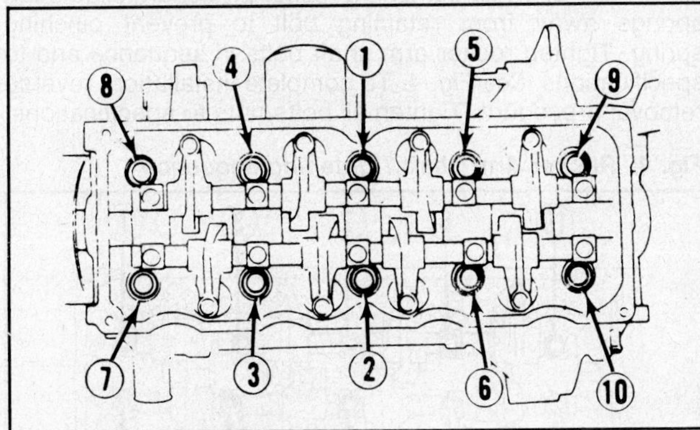

Courtesy of Ford Motor Co.

CAMSHAFT

TIMING BELT COVER

Removal & Installation

Remove accessory belts. Remove water pump pulley. Remove crankshaft damper. Remove 7 bolts retaining upper cover half and lower cover half to engine front. Remove both covers. To install, reverse removal procedure.

TIMING BELT

NOTE: Always rotate engine in direction of normal operation. Rotating crankshaft backwards can cause belt to jump timing.

Checking Timing

Remove upper timing belt cover. Set crankshaft to No. 1 cylinder, TDC. Crankshaft damper timing notch should be aligned with "TC" mark on lower timing belt cover. Check camshaft sprocket timing mark with notch on head. All timing marks should all be in alignment. *See Fig. 2.*

Fig. 2: Timing Mark Alignment

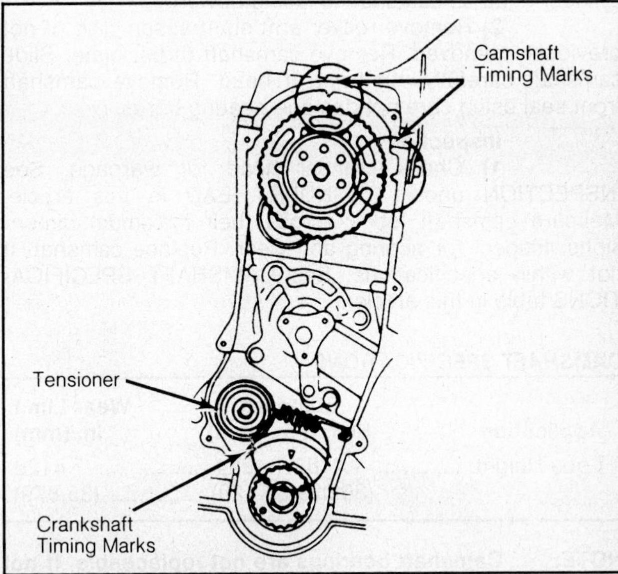

Courtesy of Ford Motor Co.

Timing Adjustment

1) If camshaft or crankshaft timing marks do not align, reset timing belt. Remove spark plugs. Rotate crankshaft and align timing mark on crankshaft sprocket with timing mark on oil pump housing. Number one cylinder must be on compression stroke, TDC. *See Fig. 2.*

2) Remove tensioner. Remove belt from camshaft sprocket. Rotate camshaft and align camshaft sprocket timing mark with timing mark on cylinder head. Ensure No. 1 cylinder valves are at TDC on compression stroke. Reinstall timing belt on camshaft sprocket and install tensioner. Recheck timing mark alignment.

Removal

Remove accessory belts, water pump pulley, crankshaft damper and upper and lower timing belt covers. Mark installed timing belt direction of rotation to ensure belt is installed in the same direction. Remove timing belt tensioner pulley bolt. Remove tensioner pulley, spring and spring cover. Remove timing belt.

Installation

1) Ensure timing belt and sprockets are clean and not worn or damaged. Align crankshaft and camshaft timing marks. See TIMING ADJUSTMENT in this article. Position belt on crankshaft sprocket. Ensure belt is installed as marked at removal.

2) Position belt on camshaft sprocket. Install timing belt tensioner spring, spring cover and pulley. Tighten tensioner pulley bolt to specifications. To complete installation, reverse removal procedure. Tighten all bolts/nuts to specifications.

FRONT COVER & OIL SEAL

Removal & Installation

Front cover is the housing for the oil pump. See OIL PUMP under ENGINE OILING in this article.

CAMSHAFT & BEARINGS

Removal

1) Remove fuel pump if not previously removed. Place cylinder head assembly on blocks or pins with gasket surface upward. With valves installed, clean

1.3L 4-CYLINDER (Cont.)

combustion chamber with wire brush and drill. Turn cylinder head so camshaft is facing upward.

2) Remove rocker arm shaft assemblies, if not previously removed. Remove camshaft thrust plate. Slide camshaft carefully out front of head. Remove camshaft front seal using care not damage bearing bores.

Inspection

1) Check cylinder head for warpage. See INSPECTION under CYLINDER HEAD in this article. Measure camshaft lobes across their maximum dimensions. Inspect for scoring and wear. Replace camshaft if not within specifications. See CAMSHAFT SPECIFICATIONS table in this article.

CAMSHAFT SPECIFICATIONS

Application	Standard Height In. (mm)	Wear Limit In. (mm)
Lobe Height	1.4185-1.4224 (36.029-36.129)	1.4126 (35.879)

NOTE: **Camshaft bearings are not replaceable. If not within specifications, replace cylinder head and/or camshaft.**

2) Measure camshaft bearing journals and cylinder head bores. *See Fig. 3.* Subtract camshaft bearing journal O.D. from cylinder head bore I.D. to obtain oil clearance. If clearance is not within specifications, replace head and/or camshaft. See CAMSHAFT JOURNAL & CLEARANCE SPECIFICATIONS table in this article.

Fig. 3: Measuring Camshaft

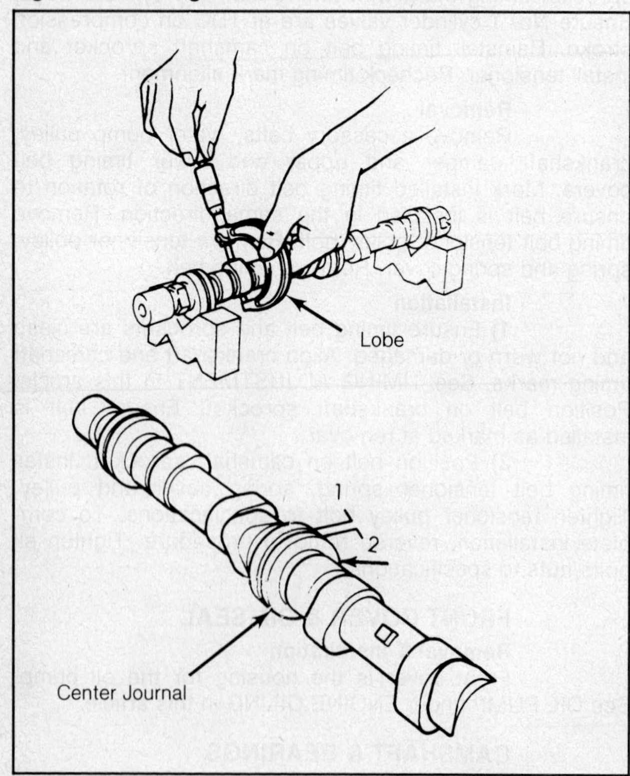

Courtesy of Ford Motor Co.

CAMSHAFT JOURNAL & CLEARANCE SPECIFICATIONS

Application	Standard In. (mm)
Front & Rear Journal [1]	1.7103-1.7112 (43.440-43.465)
Center Journal [1]	1.7079-1.7100 (43.410-43.435)
Front & Rear Bore Clearance [2]	.0014-.0033 (.035-.085)
Center Bore Clearance [2]	.0026-.0045 (.065-.115)

[1] – Out-of-round limit for all camshaft journals is .002" (.05 mm).
[2] – Service limit is .0059" (.15 mm).

Installation

1) Oil camshaft and carefully insert camshaft. Install thrust plate. Install camshaft front seal. Install rocker arm shaft assemblies to original location. Ensure oil holes in rocker arm shaft face downward.

2) While tightening rocker arm shaft, slide shaft springs away from retaining bolt to prevent pinching spring. Tighten rocker arm shaft bolts in sequence and to specifications. *See Fig. 4.* To complete installation, reverse removal procedure. Tighten all bolts/nuts to specifications.

Fig. 4: Rocker Arm Shaft Tightening Sequence

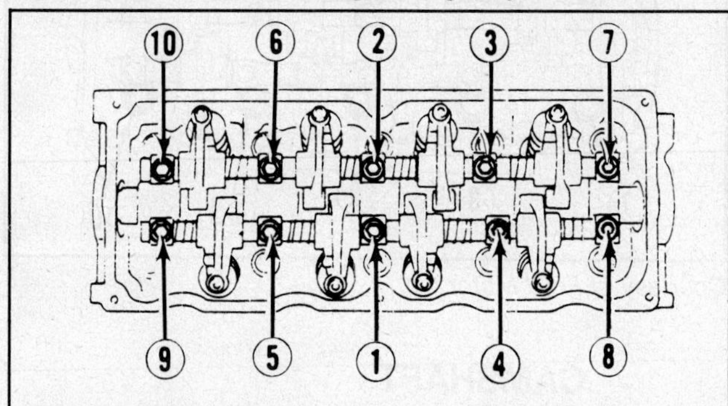

Courtesy of Ford Motor Co.

CAMSHAFT END PLAY

1) Measure camshaft end play with thrust plate in position. Install dial indicator to front of head, with pointer on camshaft center. Pry camshaft fully rear and zero dial indicator.

2) Pry camshaft fully forward and note dial indicator reading. Standard end play is .002-.007" (.05-.18 mm) with a limit of .008" (.20 mm). If end play exceeds specifications, replace thrust plate and recheck end play.

CAMSHAFT LOBE LIFT

Check lift of each lobe in order and note reading. Measure distance between major and minor diameters of each cam lobe. If readings from lobe to lobe vary, replace camshaft and all rocker arms.

VALVES

VALVE ARRANGEMENT

Right Side - Intake valves.
Left Side - Exhaust valves.

NOTE: **"Right" and "Left" refer to right and left side of engine, NOT vehicle.**

ROCKER ARM SHAFT ASSEMBLY

Removal & Installation

Remove valve cover. Keep components in order of removal to ensure reassembly to original position. Remove rocker arm shaft retaining bolts and remove rocker arm shaft assembly. To install, reverse removal procedure.

CAMSHAFT OIL SEAL

See REMOVAL under CAMSHAFT & BEARINGS in this article.

VALVE SEATS

NOTE: **Valve seat replacement information not available at this time. Replace guides, BEFORE grinding valve seats.**

VALVES & LIFTERS

Inspection

1) Lifter assemblies must be installed in original location as removed. Clean and inspect lifters for wear, cracks and leak-down rate. See LIFTER SPECIFICATIONS table in this article. Place lifter in leak-down tester and check for leak-down rate of .125" (3.17 mm) in 2-8 seconds with a 50 lb. load.

2) Inspect lifter-to-cam lobe contact area for wear and abnormalties. Check lifter-to-bore clearance. If not within specifications, replace necessary components.

LIFTER SPECIFICATIONS

Application	In. (mm)
Lifter Diameter	.8422-.8427 (21.39-21.40)
Lifter-to-Bore Clearance	[1] .0007-.0027 (.018-.069)

[1] – Service limit is .005" (.127 mm).

VALVE CLEARANCE ADJUSTMENTS

Adjustments

1) Warm engine to normal operating temperature. Remove valve cover. Place No. 1 cylinder at TDC on compression stroke. Check and adjust No. 1 and 2 intake and No. 1 and 3 exhaust valve clearance.

2) Using feeler gauge, measure distance between rocker arm and camshaft contact area. Rotate crankshaft one full turn so No. 4 cylinder is at TDC of compression stroke. Check and adjust remaining valves. See VALVE CLEARANCE SPECIFICATIONS table in this article.

VALVE CLEARANCE SPECIFICATIONS

Application	In. (mm)
Intake	.012 (.30 mm)
Exhaust	.012 (.30 mm)

VALVE GUIDES

Remove cylinder head, camshaft, and valves. Check valve stem-to-guide clearance. If clearance exceeds specifications, replace valve guides and/or valves. See ENGINE SPECIFICATIONS tables at end of this article.

VALVE SPRINGS

Inspection

Inspect valve springs for cracks or damage. Measure installed height. See VALVE SPRING HEIGHT table in this article. Measure free length and out-of-square. Maximum out-of-square is .059" (1.5 mm). See ENGINE SPECIFICATIONS tables at end of this article.

VALVE SPRING HEIGHT

Engine	Installed Height In. (mm)
1.3L	1.531-1.594 (38.89-40.49)

CYLINDER BLOCK ASSEMBLY

Inspection

1) Using staightedge and feeler gauge, ensure cylinder block cylinder head surface is flat within .006" (.15 mm) over entire surface. If not within specifications, cylinder block surface can be machined a maximum of .008" (.20 mm).

2) If more machining is required, replace cylinder block and or cylinder head. Check cylinder bore for wear, out-of-round, taper and piston fit. See CYLINDER BORE SPECIFICATIONS table. Oversize pistons are available in .010 and .020" (.25 and .50 mm).

CYLINDER BORE SPECIFICATIONS

Application	In. (mm)
Cylinder Diameter	
Standard	2.7953-2.7960 (71.000-71.019)
Limit	2.8020 (71.17)
Difference	.0007 (.019)
Piston-To-Bore	.0015-.0020 (.030-.052)
Limit	.006 (.15)

PISTONS, PINS & RINGS

OIL PAN

Removal

Disconnect battery ground cable. Raise vehicle and drain engine oil. Remove flywheel housing dust cover. Remove oil pan retaining bolts, nuts and stiffners. Rotate crankshaft while removing oil pan. Clean gasket mating surfaces thoroughly.

Installation

Ensure gasket surfaces are clean. Apply oil resistant sealer across the joint line of cylinder block and front and rear engine covers. *See Fig. 5.* To complete installation, reverse removal procedure.

1.3L 4-CYLINDER (Cont.)

Fig. 5: Oil Pan Sealing Points

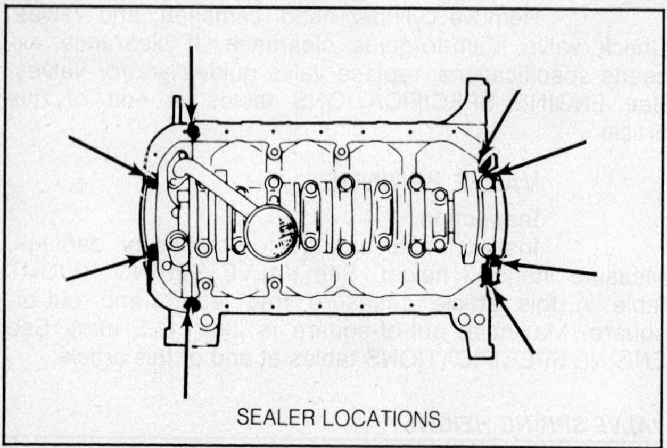

Courtesy of Ford Motor Co.

Fig. 6: Piston Ring Positioning

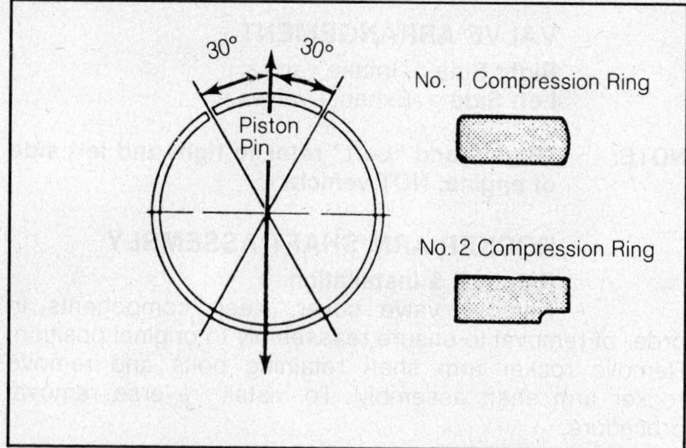

Courtesy of Ford Motor CO.

PISTON & ROD ASSEMBLY

Removal

Remove cylinder head assembly. Remove oil pan. Tap piston out top of cylinder block. Repeat procedure for remaining pistons. Keep in order to ensure installation to original position.

Installation

Position piston assembly in correct cylinder bore. Align piston mark "F", located at piston pin bore area, toward engine front. To complete installation, reverse removal procedure. Tighten all bolts/nuts to specifications.

FITTING PISTONS

1) With piston assembly removed, remove piston rings and clean piston. Measure piston outer diameter in thrust direction, below oil ring groove. Standard diameter is 2.793-2.794" (70.954-70.974 mm). Place piston in cylinder from which it was removed, upside down.

2) Using a feeler gauge, measure the clearance between piston and cylinder bore. If not within specifications, bore cylinder and replace piston as necessary. See CYLINDER BORE SPECIFICATIONS table in this article.

FITTING RINGS

Install rings on piston. Ensure marked side of rings are in proper position. Set ends of rings to proper position. *See Fig. 6.*

PISTON PIN REPLACEMENT

CAUTION: Ensure rod and piston are reassembled properly.

Removal

1) With piston removed and cleaned, mark piston-to-rod to ensure proper reassembly. Improper oiling and damage may occur if improperly installed. Using Piston Pin Remover/Installer Set (D81L-6135-A) and instructions, place piston and rod assembly in press.

2) Apply pressure and press piston pin from piston assembly. Keep all removed components together for reassembly. Remove piston and rod from press and inspect.

Inspection

Using a micrometer, measure outside diameter of piston pin in several areas. Measure inside diameter of piston pin. Measure inside diameter of piston pin bore and rod pin bore. Replace components as necessary. See PIN SPECIFICATIONS table in this article.

PIN SPECIFICATIONS

Application	In. (mm)
Pin O.D.	.7866 (19.980)
Pin I.D.	.524 (13.309)
Pin-to-Rod Clearance	.0-.00102 (.0-.26)
Pin-to-Piston Clearance	.0003-.0005 (.0076-.0127)

Reassembly

With rod, piston and pin within specifications, use piston pin set to reassemble. Ensure piston-to-rod is in proper position as marked at removal. Lubricate pin with engine oil prior to reassembly. With piston assembly reassembled, rod should fall by its own weight with piston held horizontally. Repeat procedure for remaining pistons.

CRANKSHAFT & ROD BEARINGS

CRANKSHAFT MAIN BEARINGS

NOTE: If replacing bearing inserts with engine in vehicle, keep at least 2 caps tight while servicing others.

Removal

1) Drain oil and remove oil pan. Check and ensure the main bearing caps are marked for location and position to engine front. Caps must be installed to original location and position.

2) Remove main bearing cap bolts. Remove caps and lower bearing inserts. Use bearing remover or fabricated cotter key to remove upper bearing insert. Rotate crankshaft in normal direction of operation only. Repeat procedure for remaining main bearings.

NOTE: If bearing clearance is to be measured with engine in vehicle, support crankshaft with piece of wood and jack, or a false reading may result.

1.3L 4-CYLINDER (Cont.)

Inspection

Check bearings for abnormal wear. Check crankshaft for grooves, scratches and pitting. Using Plastigage method, check clearance of main bearing-to-crankshaft. Always keep at least 2 bearings and caps tight during clearance check. See ENGINE SPECIFICATIONS tables at end of article.

Installation

Lubricate and install new bearings in cap and block. Match bearing tangs with the notch in cap and block. Position cap in its proper location and position. Install cap bolts and tighten to specifications. Repeat procedure for remaining main bearings.

CONNECTING ROD BEARINGS

Inspection

With piston removed, check rod bearing for abnormal wear. Check crankshaft journal. Check rod bearing-to-crankshaft clearance with Plastigage. Machine or replace as necessary. See ENGINE SPECIFICATIONS tables at end of this article.

THRUST BEARING ALIGNMENT

Inspection

Check crankshaft end play with dial indicator attached to front of crankshaft. Pry crankshaft fully rear and zero indicator. Pry crankshaft fully forward and note reading. If not within specifications, replace as necessary. See THRUST BEARING SPECIFICATIONS table in this article. See ENGINE SPECIFICATIONS tables at end of this article.

THRUST BEARING SPECIFICATIONS

Application	In. (mm)
Length	1.1990-1.2010 (30.4546-30.5054)
End Play Service Limit	.012 (.305)

REAR MAIN BEARING OIL SEAL

Removal

Remove transaxle. See appropriate REMOVAL article under TRANSMISSION SERVICING section. Remove flywheel or flexplate. Remove rear engine plate (if equipped). Remove rear main oil seal retainer and press rear main oil seal out.

Installation

Clean seal surface in retainer. Lubricate oil seal inside and outside. Install seal retainer on engine. Install seal in retainer with hollow side of seal facing engine. Using Rear Main Seal Installer (T87C-6701-A), install rear main oil seal. To complete installation, reverse removal procedure.

ENGINE OILING

ENGINE OILING SYSTEM

Oiling system is force-feed type, using a full-flow oil filter. Oil is retrieved from oil pan by oil pump pick-up tube and distributed to oil filter. Oil is filter and routed throughout the engine. *See Fig. 7.*

Fig. 7: Engine Oiling System

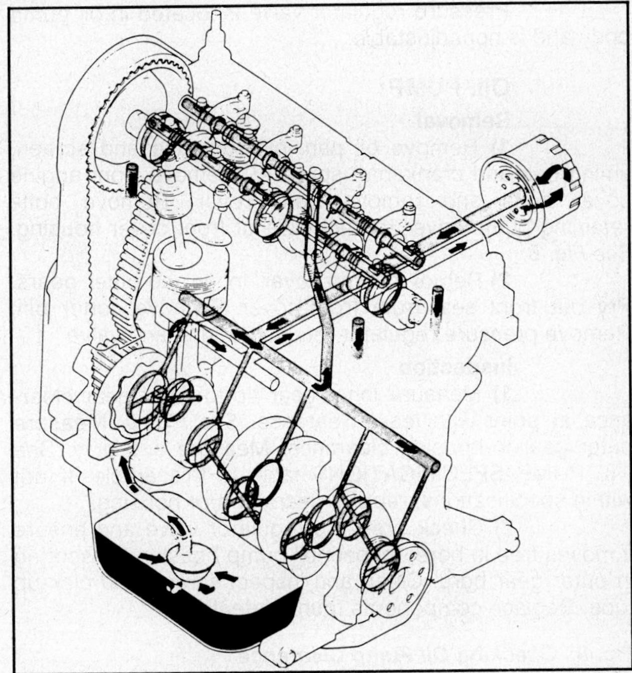

Courtesy of Ford Motor Co.

CRANKCASE CAPACITY

Crankcase capacity is 3.6 qts. (3.4L) without filter change and 3.9 qts. (3.7L) with filter change. Always check level with dipstick and never overfill.

NORMAL OIL PRESSURE (HOT)

Normal oil pressure is 40-60 psi (2.8-4.2 kg/cm²) at 2000 RPM.

Fig. 8: Exploded View of Oil Pump

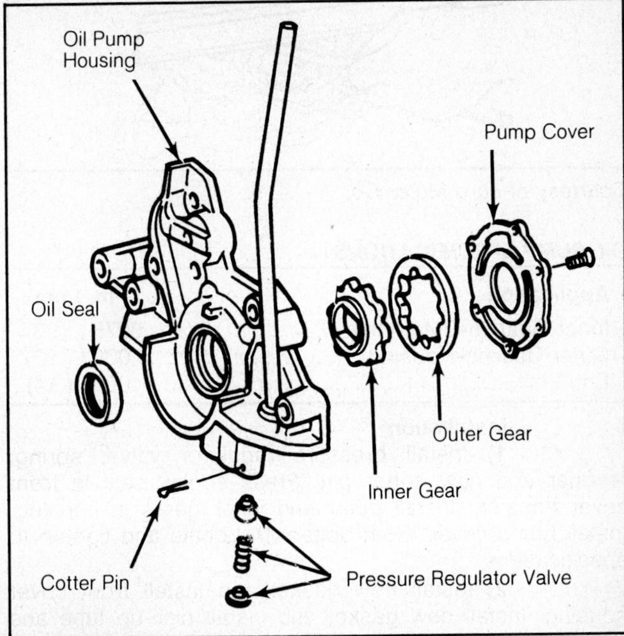

Courtesy of Ford Motor Co.

Ford Motor Co. Engines

1.3L 4-CYLINDER (Cont.)

PRESSURE REGULATOR VALVE

Pressure regulator valve is located in oil pump body and is nonadjustable.

OIL PUMP

Removal

1) Remove oil pan, pick-up tube and screen, timing belt and crankshaft sprocket. Remove front engine cover bolts and remove front cover. Remove bolts retaining pump cover to back side of front cover housing. *See Fig. 8.*

2) Remove pump cover, inner and outer gears. Pry out front seal from front cover. Remove cotter pin. Remove pressure regulator retainer, spring and valve.

Inspection

1) Measure inner gear tip-to-outer gear clearance at point with least clearance. *See Fig. 9.* Measure outer gear-to-housing clearance. Measure end play. See OIL PUMP SPECIFICATIONS table in this article. If not within specifications, replace gears and/or housing.

2) Check pressure regulator valve and ensure it moves free in bore. Inspect oil pump housing for scoring in outer gear bore. Clean and inspect screen and pick-up tube. Replace components found defective.

Fig. 9: Checking Oil Pump Clearance

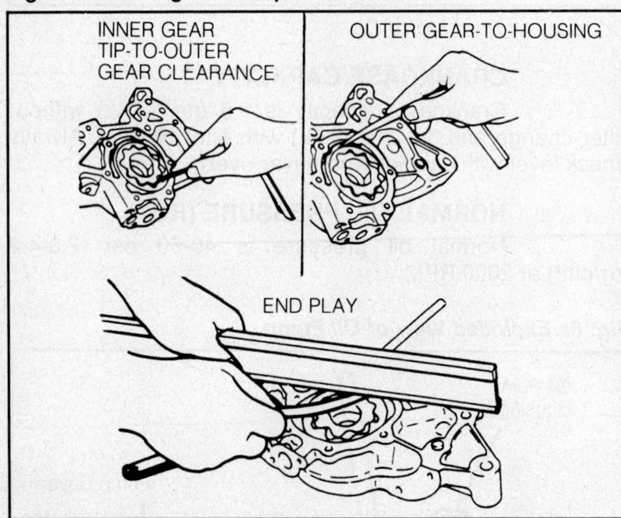

Courtesy of Ford Motor Co.

OIL PUMP SPECIFICATIONS

Application	In. (mm)
Inner Gear-to-Outer Gear	.0078 (.198)
Outer Gear-to-Housing	.0087 (.22)
End Play	.0055 (.14)

Installation

1) Install pressure regulator valve, spring, retainer and new cotter pin. Press a new seal in front cover housing. Install outer and inner gears in housing. Install pump cover. Coat bolts with Loctite and tighten to specifications.

2) Install new gasket and install front cover housing. Install new gasket and install pick-up tube and screen. Tighten all bolts/nuts to specifications. To complete installation, reverse removal procedure.

ENGINE COOLING

WATER PUMP

Removal & Installation

Remove timing belt. Loosen cap at coolant recovery tank and drain cooling system. Remove lower radiator hose and heater return hose from water pump. Remove water pump retaining bolts and remove water pump. Clean gasket surface and replace gasket. To install, reverse removal procedure.

NOTE: For more information, see ENGINE COOLING SYSTEMS article at the end of this section.

TIGHTENING SPECIFICATIONS

Application	Ft. Lbs. (N.m)
Timing Belt Tensioner	
Adjusting Bolt	14-19 (19-26)
Camshaft Sprocket Bolt	36-45 (49-61)
Connecting Rod Nut	
Step One	11-13 (15-18)
Step Two	22-25 (30-34)
Crankshaft Damper Bolt	80-94 (109-128)
Crankshaft Pulley Bolt	11-15 (15-20)
Crossmember-to-Body Bolt	27-46 (37-62)
Cylinder Head Bolt	
Step One	35-40 (48-54)
Step Two	56-60 (76-81)
Distributor Clamp Bolt	14-22 (19-30)
Exhaust Manifold-to-Cylinder Head	
Step One	5-7 (7-9)
Step Two	12-17 (16-23)
Flywheel Bolt	71-76 (96-103)
Front Cover Housing Bolt	14-19 (19-26)
Front Engine Mount Nut	27-46 (37-54)
Intake Manifold-to-Cylinder Head	14-19 (19-26)
Main Bearing Cap Bolt	
Step One	22-27 (30-37)
Step Two	40-43 (54-59)
Oil Pan Drain Plug	22-30 (30-41)
Pulse Air Tube Nut	23-34 (31-46)
Rear Engine Mount Nut	27-46 (37-62)
Rocker Arm Shaft Bolt	16-21 (22-29)
Side Engine Mount Bolt	27-46 (37-62)
Spark Plug	11-17 (15-23)
Thermostat Housing Bolt	14-22 (19-30)
Water Outlet Bolt	14-22 (19-30)
Water Pump-to-Block	14-19 (19-26)
Water Pump Pulley	36-45 (49-61)
	INCH Lbs. (N.m)
Camshaft Thrust Plate Bolt	69-108 (8-12)
Oil Pan Bolt	69-78 (8-9)
Oil Pressure Sender	108-156 (12-18)
Oil Pump Cover Bolt	90-130 (10-15)
Pickup Tube-to-Oil Pump Bolt	69-95 (8-11)
Rear Engine Plate Bolt	69-95 (8-11)
Temperature Sender	48-84 (5-10)
Timing Belt Cover Bolt	69-95 (8-11)
Valve Cover Bolt	44-79 (5-9)

Ford Motor Co. Engines

1.3L 4-CYLINDER (Cont.)

ENGINE SPECIFICATIONS

GENERAL SPECIFICATIONS

Year	DISPLACEMENT		Fuel System	HP@RPM	Torque Ft. Lbs.@RPM	Compr. Ratio	BORE		STROKE	
	Cu. In.	Liters					In.	mm	In.	mm
1987	80.8	1.3	2 Bbl.	58@5000	73@3500	9.7:1	2.78	71.0	3.29	83.60

VALVES

Engine Size & Valve	Head Diam. In. (mm)	Face Angle	Seat Angle	Seat Width In. (mm)	Stem Diameter In. (mm)	Stem Clearance In. (mm)	Valve Lift In. (mm)
Intake	....	45°	45°	.043-.067 (1.1-1.7)	.2744-.2750 (6.970-6.985)	.008 (.20)	.....
Exhaust	....	45°	45°	.043-.067 (1.1-1.7)	.2742-.2748 (6.965-6.980)	.008 (.20)	.....

PISTONS, PINS & RINGS

Engine	PISTONS	PINS		RINGS		
	Clearance In. (mm)	Piston Fit In. (mm)	Rod Fit In. (mm)	Ring No.	End Gap In. (mm)	Side Clearance In. (mm)
1.3L	.006 (.15)	.0003-.0005 (.008-.013)	.0-.0012 (.0-.26)	1 & 2	.006-.012 (.15-.31)	[1] .001-.003 (.0254-.0762)
				3	.008-.028 (.20-.71)	Snug Fit

[1] – Side clearance service limit is .006" (.15 mm).

CRANKSHAFT MAIN & CONNECTING ROD BEARINGS

Engine	MAIN BEARINGS				CONNECTING ROD BEARINGS		
	Journal Diam. In. (mm)	Clearance In. (mm)	Thrust Bearing	Crankshaft End Play In. (mm)	Journal Diam. In. (mm)	Clearance In. (mm)	Side Play In. (mm)
1.3L	1.9661-1.9668 (49.939-49.957)	[1] .0009-.0017 (.0229-.0432)	No. 3	[2] .003-.011 (.0762-.2794)	1.5724-1.5731 (39.939-39.957)	[1] .0009-.0017 (.0229-.0432)	.012 (.31)

[1] – Bearing clearance service limit is .0039" (.10 mm).
[2] – Crankshaft end play service limit is .012" (.31 mm).

VALVE SPRINGS

Engine	Free Length In. (mm)	PRESSURE Lbs. @ In. (Kg @ mm)	
		Valve Closed	Valve Open
1.3L	1.717 (43.61)	....	....

CAMSHAFT

Engine	Journal Diam. In. (mm)	Clearance In. (mm)	Lobe Lift In. (mm)
1.3L	[1] 1.7103-1.7112 (43.442-43.465) [3] 1.7091-1.7100 (43.411-43.434)	[2] .0014-.0033 (.036-.084) [4] .0026-.0045 (.0660-.1143)	....

[1] – For No. 1 and 3.
[2] – For front and rear.
[3] – For No. 2.
[4] – For center.

Ford Motor Co. Engines

2.3L 4-CYLINDER

Merkur XR4Ti

NOTE: **For engine repair procedures not covered in this article, see ENGINE OVERHAUL PROCEDURES article at beginning of this section.**

ENGINE CODING

ENGINE IDENTIFICATION

Engine may be identified by Vehicle Identification Number (VIN), stamped on metal tab attached to instrument panel. Tab is close to windshield on driver's side and visible from outside. VIN number is also stamped on Safety Certification Decal, mounted on the left front door lock panel. The VIN number contains 17 characters. The 8th character identifies engine.

ENGINE IDENTIFICATION CODE

Engine	Code
2.3L Turbo	W

ENGINE, CYLINDER HEAD & MANIFOLDS

ENGINE

Removal

1) Disconnect battery ground cable. Disconnect ground strap near right hood hinge. Mark hood-to-hinge location and remove hood. Depressurize EFI fuel system by connecting vacuum pump to fuel pressure regulator valve. Apply a minimum of 25 in. Hg for at least 3 minutes.

NOTE: **It is recommended to mark electrical connectors and vacuum hoses, to ensure correct reassembly.**

Fig. 1: Electrical Connectors & Locations

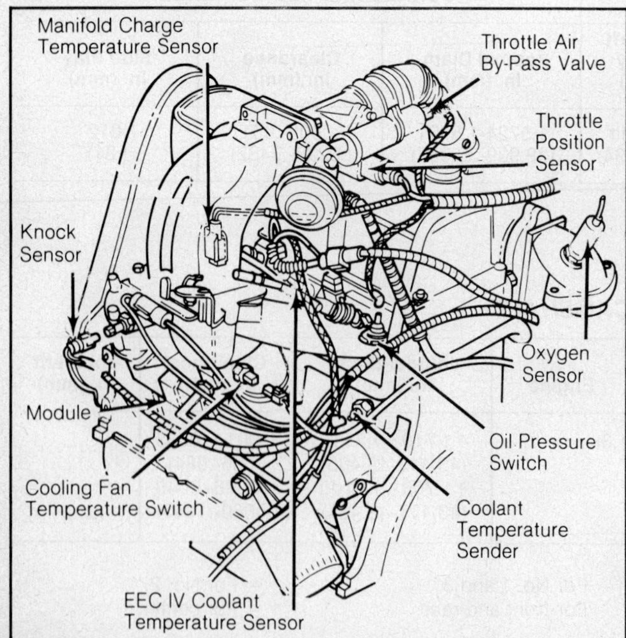

Courtesy of Ford Motor Co.

2) Remove cooling system expansion tank cap and drain radiator. Disconnect radiator upper hose at radiator. On manual transmission, also remove air vent hose at radiator. Remove radiator upper attaching bolts. Disconnect cooling fan wiring connector. Remove oil dipstick.

3) Remove vacuum hose from EGR valve. Disconnect fuel injection wiring harness connector. Remove remaining electrical connectors. *See Fig. 1.*

4) Using Quick Connect Remover/Replacer (T82L-9500-AH), disconnect fuel return line. Disconnect throttle cable and transmission kickdown cable (if equipped). Remove throttle cable bracket. Disconnect vacuum supply hose from vacuum tee, located by master cylinder.

5) Remove alternator from mounting bracket and secure out of way. Remove power steering pump and secure out of way. Remove turbocharger inlet tube. Disconnect Orange ground wire at turbocharger inlet elbow. Disconnect vacuum hose at tee located at turbocharger inlet elbow.

6) Remove A/C compressor from its mounting and secure out of way. On automatic transmission models, remove transmission dipstick tube attaching nut at turbocharger outlet flange. Disconnect coolant supply and return hoses at heater control valve.

7) Remove transmission cooler lines at radiator (if equipped). Raise vehicle. On manual transmission models, remove radiator refill tube, located at bottom of radiator.

8) Remove lower radiator hose. Remove radiator retaining bolts and remove radiator out bottom of vehicle. Remove chassis ground strap from A/C compressor bracket. Remove starter. Remove nuts attaching catalytic converter inlet pipe to turbocharger.

9) Remove inlet pipe-to-catalytic converter bolts. Remove support bracket bolt and remove inlet pipe. On manual transmission models, remove bolt retaining rear engine cover to flywheel housing.

10) Rotate crankshaft (clockwise only), and remove flexplate-to-torque converter bolts through starter housing. Remove nut retaining engine mount to crossmember. Remove bolts retaining transmission to engine. Upper bolts may be loose and left in transmission housing if removal is prevented.

11) If necessary to gain access to bolts, support transmission on jack and remove mount nuts securing transmission. Remove nuts securing drive shaft center bearing support. Lower transmission for bolt access. With bolts removed, reinstall transmission and drive shaft. Lower vehicle.

12) Attach engine hoist to engine at left front and right rear. Support transmission with a jack. Raise engine until engine mounts clear crossmember. Remove engine mount assemblies from engine. Pull engine away from transmission and remove engine.

Installation

To install, reverse removal procedure. Ensure torque converter is properly seated in transmission front pump. Torque converter should move free until bolted to flexplate. Tighten bolts/nuts to specifications. See TIGHTENING SPECIFICATONS table at end of article.

2.3L 4-CYLINDER (Cont.)

INTAKE MANIFOLD

Removal (Upper Intake)

1) Disconnect battery ground cable. Disconnect throttle cable from throttle linkage. On automatic transmission models, disconnect kickdown cable from throttle linkage. Remove throttle cable bracket assembly and set aside. Disconnect fuel pressure regulator vacuum hose at intake manifold.

2) Disconnect PCV hose at intake manifold. Disconnect vacuum tee suply hose at intake manifold. Loosen hose clamps and remove turbocharger outlet hose. Remove EGR bolts and remove EGR and gasket. Remove nut attaching pulse damper to bracket and remove pulse damper.

3) Remove engine oil dipstick. Remove dipstick tube attaching bolt at intake manifold. Remove 2 nuts retaining pulse damper bracket to intake manifold. Disconnect air by-pass valve and TPS connector.

4) Remove attaching bolts and nuts from throttle body and remove throttle body and gasket. Remove upper intake manifold attaching bolts and remove upper intake manifold and gasket.

Installation

Thoroughly clean all gasket mating surfaces and replace gaskets. To complete installation, reverse removal procedure. Tighten all bolts/nuts in proper sequence and to specifications. *See Fig. 2.* See TIGHTENING SPECIFICATIONS table at end of this article.

Fig. 2: Upper & Lower Intake Manifold Tightening Sequence

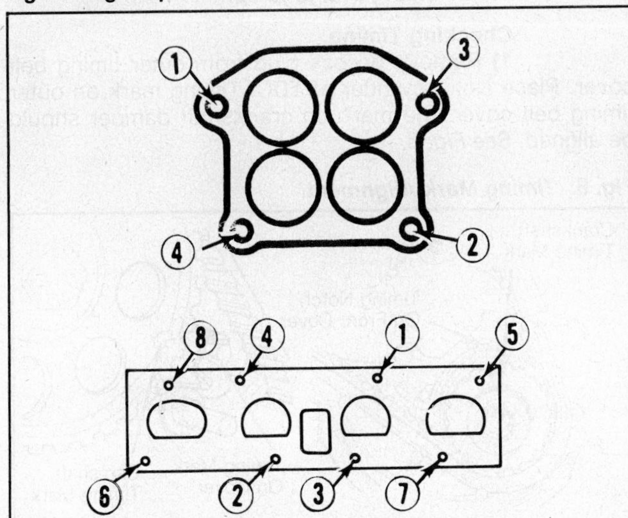

Courtesy of Ford Motor Co.

Removal (Lower Intake)

1) Disconnect battery ground cable and drain cooling system. Disconnect knock sensor, fan temperature sensor, EEC-IV coolant temperature sensor, fuel injection wiring harness and coolant temperature sender connectors. *See Fig. 1.*

2) Disconnect coolant by-pass line from lower intake manifold. Depressurize EFI fuel system by connecting vacuum pump to fuel pressure regulator valve. Apply a minimum of 25 in. Hg for at least 3 minutes. Remove vacuum pump.

3) Disconnect fuel supply line from fuel supply manifold. *See Fig. 3.* Using Quick Connect Remover/Replacer (T82L-9500-AH), disconnect fuel return line. Remove pulse damper and place aside. Remove upper intake manifold. See REMOVAL (UPPER INTAKE) in this article.

4) Remove 8 lower intake manifold bolts and remove lower manifold. Remove 2 bolts retaining each fuel injector and remove 4 fuel injectors. Remove fuel supply manifold assembly.

Fig. 3: Removal of Fuel Supply Line

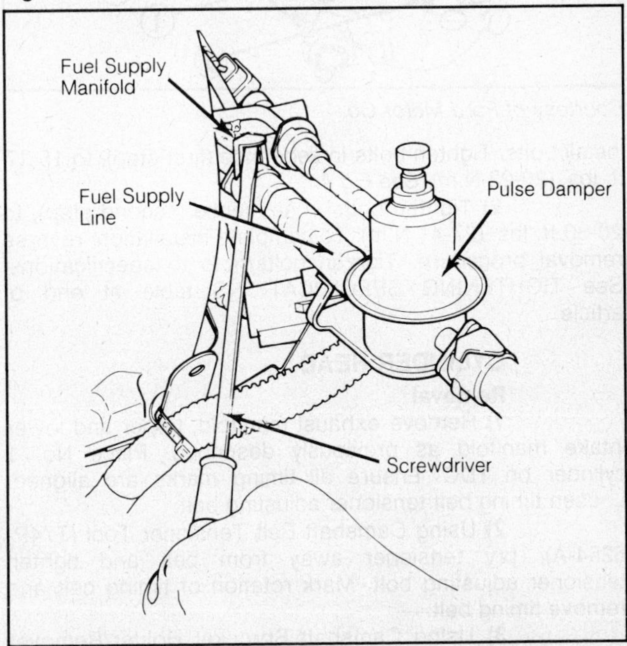

Courtesy of Ford Motor Co.

Installation

1) Thoroughly clean and check gasket mating surfaces and replace all gaskets. Surfaces must be flat and smooth. Position lower intake manifold and install 4 upper bolts finger tight. Install 4 lower bolts finger tight. Tighten bolts in sequence and to 12-15 ft. lbs. (16-20 N.m). *See Fig. 2.*

2) Reverse removal procedure to complete installation. Tighten all bolts/nuts to specifications. See TIGHTENING SPECIFICATIONS table at end of article.

EXHAUST MANIFOLD

Removal

1) Loosen cap on coolant expansion tank. Drain coolant from radiator. Remove return heater hose from water pump. Remove coolant pipe routing bracket at right front side of valve cover. Remove expansion tank hose at the coolant pipe. Disconnect turbocharger oil supply line at turbocharger.

2) Disconnect turbocharger coolant supply and return tube at turbocharger. Disconnect PCV tube at turbocharger air inlet adapter. Remove nuts retaining tubrocharger to exhaust manifold. Remove turbocharger support bracket and air tube.

3) Remove turbocharger assembly from exhaust manifold. Remove exhaust manifold bolts and remove exhaust manifold assembly.

Installation

1) Ensure mating surfaces are thoroughly cleaned and smooth. Place exhaust manifold to head and

Fig. 4: Exhaust Manifold Tightening Sequence

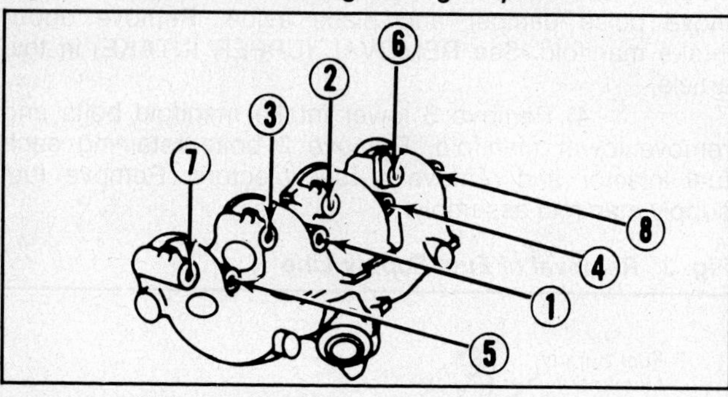

Courtesy of Ford Motor Co.

install bolts. Tighten bolts in sequence (first step), to 15-17 ft. lbs. (20-23 N.m). *See Fig 4.*

2) Tighten bolts in sequence (second step), to 20-30 ft. lbs. (27-41 N.m). To complete installation, reverse removal procedure. Tighten bolts/nuts to specifications. See TIGHTENING SPECIFICATIONS table at end of article.

CYLINDER HEAD

Removal

1) Remove exhaust manifold, upper and lower intake manifold as previously described. Place No. 1 cylinder on TDC. Ensure all timing marks are aligned. Loosen timing belt tensioner adjusting bolt.

2) Using Camshaft Belt Tensioner Tool (T74P-6254-A), pry tensioner away from belt and tighten tensioner adjusting bolt. Mark rotation of timing belt and remove timing belt.

3) Using Camshaft Sprocket Holder/Remover (T74P-6256-B), remove camshaft sprocket. Slide belt guide off camshaft. Loosen timing belt tensioner adjusting bolt. Remove spring bolt, spring stud and adjusting bolt. Remove belt tensioner.

4) Remove cylinder head bolts. Loosen cylinder head from gasket and block. Remove cylinder head assembly and gasket.

Inspection

1) Thoroughly clean and check mating surface of head and block. Check cylinder head for cracks, nicks, burrs or damage. Using a straightedge and feeler gauge, ensure cylinder head and block warpage does not exceed .003" (.762 mm) in any 6" (152 mm) span.

2) DO NOT machine surface of head or block more than .010" (.25 mm) from original surface. If cylinder head or block is out of specifications, head and/or block must be replaced.

Installation

1) Place new head gasket on block, with marked side ("Front-Up") in proper position. Carefully lower cylinder head assembly onto block. Ensure head fits over dowels in block.

2) Place new valve cover gasket on valve cover, with Contact Cement (D7AZ-19B508-A), and install at later time. Oil cylinder head bolts lightly and install in cylinder head. Tighten head bolt in sequence and 2 steps. *See Fig. 5.*

3) First step, tighten to 50-60 ft. lbs. (68-81 N.m) and second step, tighten to 80-90 ft. lbs. (108-122 N.m). To complete installation, reverse removal procedure. Tighten all bolts/nuts to specifications. See TIGHTENING SPECIFICATIONS table at end of article.

Fig. 5: Cylinder Head Tightening Sequence

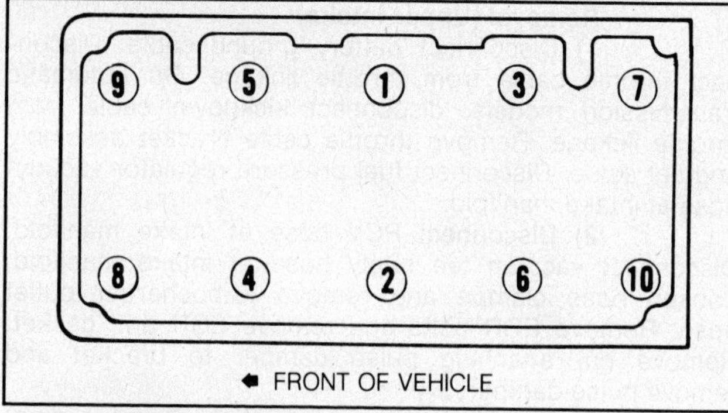

Courtesy of Ford Motor Co.

CAMSHAFT

TIMING BELT COVER

Removal & Installation

Remove A/C compressor belt and alternator belts. Remove timing belt cover retaining bolts and remove timing belt cover. For installation, reverse removal procedure.

TIMING BELT

NOTE: **Always turn engine clockwise. Due to tensioner arrangement, backward rotation may cause timing belt to jump.**

Checking Timing

1) Remove access plug from outer timing belt cover. Place No. 1 cylinder at TDC. Timing mark on outer timing belt cover and mark on crankshaft damper should be aligned. *See Fig. 6.*

Fig. 6: Timing Mark Alignment

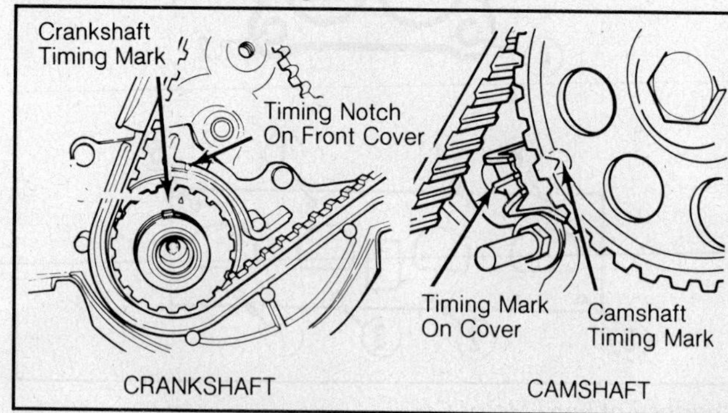

Courtesy of Ford Motor Co.

2) Look through access hole and check timing mark on camshaft sprocket with pointer on inner timing belt cover. *See Fig. 6.* Remove distributor cap and check rotor position. Rotor should be at No. 1 spark plug tower. If timing marks are not aligned, adjustment or component replacement is necessary.

Timing Adjustment

1) Camshaft and crankshaft sprockets contain timing marks which indicate TDC. Camshaft can be 180 degrees out and still have timing marks aligned. Ensure No. 1 cylinder valves are closed when camshaft timing mark is aligned with inner cover timing mark. *See Fig. 6.*

2.3L 4-CYLINDER (Cont.)

2) Crankshaft has 2 different timing marks to indicate TDC. A timing mark on crankshaft damper and outer timing belt cover is for setting engine timing. A timing mark on crankshaft sprocket and a notch on inner cover are used for timing belt installation.

3) Auxiliary sprocket drives the distributor assembly. With crankshaft and camshaft timing marks in alignment, distributor rotor must face No. 1 spark plug tower. Ensure camshaft is at No. 1 cylinder and valves are closed, not 180 degrees out.

Removal

1) Remove timing belt outer cover. Position No. 1 cylinder at TDC. Check location of camshaft and crankshaft sprocket timing marks. Check location of distributor rotor position. If all timing marks do not align, align camshaft sprocket mark with inner cover timing mark. Ensure camshaft is on No. 1 cylinder TDC.

2) Loosen belt tensioner adjustment bolt. Using Camshaft Belt Tensioner Tool (T74P-6254-A), release belt tensioner from belt and tighten adjusting bolt to hold tensioner.

3) Remove crankshaft damper pulley and belt guide. Remove timing belt and replace if necessary.

Installation

1) Position crankshaft sprocket, camshaft sprocket and distributor rotor in proper position. See TIMING ADJUSTMENT in this article. Place timing belt around crankshaft sprocket. Keeping belt on crankshaft sprocket, route belt around auxiliary sprocket.

2) Ensure rotor is at No. 1 spark plug tower. Route timing belt around camshaft sprocket and position belt at tensioner. Loosen tensioner adjusting bolt and allow tensioner to tighten belt.

3) Recheck all timing alignment marks and readjust if necessary. Ensure distributor rotor is at No. 1 spark plug tower. Reverse removal pocedure to complete installation. Set engine timing to specifications.

FRONT COVER & OIL SEAL

Removal & Installation

1) Remove timing belt. Using Crankshaft Sprocket Remover (T74P-6306-A), remove crankshaft sprocket. Using Front Cover Seal Remover (T74P-6700-B), remove front cover seal.

2) Remove front cover retaining bolts and oil pan-to-front cover bolts. Remove front cover and gasket. To install, reverse removal procedure.

CAMSHAFT & BEARINGS

Removal

1) With cylinder head removed, place head assembly on blocks or pins with camshaft facing up. Using Front Cover Seal Remover (T74P-6700-B), remove camshaft seal.

2) Using Valve Spring Compressor (T74P-6565-A), compress valve and spring assembly. Remove camshaft follower out and over lifter. Ensure all components are kept in order of removal for installation.

3) With camshaft followers removed, remove lock plate at rear of camshaft. Slide camshaft out front of cylinder head. Remove plug from rear of camshaft.

4) Using Camshaft Bearing Kit (T65L-6250-A), remove No. 3 and 4 bearing from rear of head. Remove No. 1 and 2 bearing from front of head. Clean and inspect camshaft bearing journals.

Inspection

Check cylinder head for warpage. See INSPECTION under CYLINDER HEAD in this article. Measure camshaft lobes across their maximum and minimum dimensions. The difference is lobe lift. Inspect for scoring and wear. Replace camshaft and followers if not within specifications. See CAMSHAFT SPECIFICATIONS table in this article.

CAMSHAFT SPECIFICATIONS

Application	Standard Lift In. (mm)	Wear Limit In. (mm)
Lobe Lift	.400 (10.2)	.005 (.127)

Installation

1) Oil camshaft bearing journal in cylinder head. Using Camshaft Bearing Kit (T65L-6250-A), install No. 2 and No. 3 bearing. Ensure oil holes are aligned and lube bearing before installing.

2) Install front bearing. Install No. 4 bearing with .001-.010" (.03-.25 mm), clearance from rear face of bearing bore and bearing. This will prevent interference with camshaft lock plate.

3) To complete installation, reverse removal procedure. Thoroughly lube bearings and camshaft before installing. Ensure camshaft plug at rear of camshaft is reinstalled. Tighten all bolts/nuts to specifications.

CAMSHAFT END THRUST

Using large screwdriver between camshaft sprocket and cylinder head, measure camshaft end thrust. Replace thrust plate at rear of cylinder head if end play is too great. Standard is .001-.007" (.025-.178 mm); service limit is .009" (.229 mm).

VALVES

VALVE ARRANGEMENT

E-I-E-I-E-I-E-I (Front-to-rear).

VALVE GUIDES

Remove cylinder head, camshaft and valves spring assemblies. Check valve stem-to-guide clearance. If clearance exceeds service limits, replace or recondition valve guide and or valves. See ENGINE SPECIFICATIONS tables at end of this article.

VALVE SPRINGS

Check installed height, out-of-square and free length of valve spring. If not within specification, install .030" (.76 mm) spacer between spring and pad or replace spring as necessary. See ENGINE SPECIFICATIONS tables at end of this article.

VALVE SPRING HEIGHT

Engine	Installed Height In. (mm)
2.3L	1.531-1.594 (38.89-40.49)

Ford Motor Co. Engines

2.3L 4-CYLINDER (Cont.)

HYDRAULIC LIFTERS

Inspection

1) Lifter assemblies must be installed in original locations. Clean and inspect lifters. Place lifter upright in Leak-Down Tester (6500-E) and check for leak-down rate of .125" (3.17 mm) in 2-8 seconds with a 50 lb. load.

2) Inspect lifter-to-cam lobe contact area for wear and abnormalties. Check lifter-to-bore clearance. If not within specifications, replace necessary components.

LIFTER SPECIFICATION

Application	In. (mm)
Lifter Bore	.8430-.8449 (21.41-21.46)
Lifter Diameter	.8422-.8427 (21.39-21.40)
Lifter-to-Bore Clearance	[1] .0007-.0027 (.018-.069)

[1] – Service limit is .005" (.127 mm).

CYLINDER BLOCK ASSEMBLY

CLEANING & INSPECTION

1) Check block-to-cylinder head surface for flatness. Maximum of .003" (.076 mm), per any 6" area is allowed. Block surface can be ground a maximum of .010" (.254 mm), from original.

2) Check cylinder bore for out-of-round and taper. Measure bore 1.0" (25.4 mm), below top of cylinder block and at point below piston ring travel area. Check piston fit in cylinder bore. If not within specifications, cylinder must be bored.

PISTONS, PINS & RINGS

OIL PAN

Removal

1) Disconnect battery negative cable and low oil level connector from dipstick (if equipped). Raise vehicle and drain oil. Remove starter. Mark steering column coupling-to-steering gear shaft. Remove steering column coupling pinch bolt.

2) Remove nut retaining engine mount to crossmember. Lower vehicle and attach Engine Support Bar (D79P-6000-B), to vehicle and engine. Raise engine as far as possible. Raise vehicle.

3) Remove bolts retaining steering gear to crossmember. Pull steering gear out and away from crossmember, disconnecting steering coupling from steering gear shaft. Use care not to damage gear hoses.

4) Place a jack under crossmember and remove bolts retaining crossmember and side rail. Lower jack and crossmember. Remove oil pan attaching bolts and remove oil pan.

Installation

1) Clean all gasket mating surfaces. Apply an even coat of adhesive on oil pan side of gaskets. Place gaskets on oil pan and allow to dry past wet stage. Apply sealer to seam at front engine cover-to-engine block. Install front saddle seal on front engine cover.

2) Install rear saddle seal on rear main bearing cap. Apply sealer to seam between engine block and rear main bearing cap. Apply sealer to corners of front and rear saddle seal. To complete installation, reverse removal procedure. Tighten bolt/nuts to specifications.

PISTON & ROD ASSEMBLY

Installation

1) Before installing, see CLEANING AND INSPECTION under CYLINDER BLOCK ASSEMBLY in this article. Note notch/arrow on piston top and ensure mark faces front of engine.

NOTE: Piston rings are marked and must be installed properly on pistons.

2) Install rings on pistons and properly space piston ring gaps. Place oil ring expander ends at piston front, 20 degrees either side of piston pin. Install oil ring segment gap at rear of piston, 80 degrees apart and not aligned with piston pin. Install compression rings 80 degrees apart and not aligned with piston pin.

3) Install rod nuts and evenly tighten to 25-30 ft. lbs. (34-41 N.m). Tighten rod nuts again to 30-36 ft. lbs. (41-49 N.m). Repeat procedure for remaining pistons. To complete installation, reverse removal procedure. Tighten all bolts/nuts to specifications.

PISTON RING GROOVE WIDTH

Application	In. (mm)
Compression Rings	.080-.081 (2.032-2.057)
Oil Ring	.188-.189 (4.775-4.801)

FITTING PISTONS

1) Inspect pistons for wear, cracks, ring groove wear or breakage and size. Check for glaze on thrust side of piston. This indicates a bent rod. Check cylinder block and bore. Check piston-to-cylinder bore clearance.

2) Measure diameter of cylinder bore at top, middle and bottom. Cylinder bore out-of-round should not be more than .0015" (.038 mm). Cylinder bore taper should not be more than .010" (.25 mm). Measure piston skirt diameter at piston pin center and 90 degrees to pin axis.

PISTON SIZE & CODE

Code	In. (mm)
Blue	3.7776-3.7782 (95.951-95.966)
Red	3.7764-3.7770 (95.921-95.936)
Oversize	3.7788-3.7794 (95.982-95.997)

FITTING PISTON PINS

NOTE: Removing/Installating Kit (D81L-6135-A), is required for piston pin removal and installation. Kit usage instructions are included with kit.

Disassembly

Mark piston-to-rod for reassembly to original position. Note rod oiling hole-to-notch/arrow on piston, to ensure proper position at reassembly. *See Fig. 7.* Using proper kit tooling, position assembly in press. Apply pressure and press piston pin out of piston assembly. Do not mix disassembled components.

2.3L 4-CYLINDER (Cont.)

Fig. 7: Piston & Rod Position

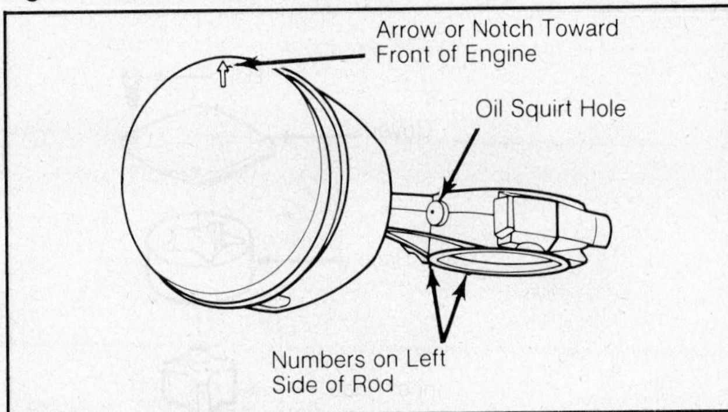

Courtesy of Ford Motor Co.

Inspection

Thoroughly check piston pin bore for cracks, wear and bore diameter. Measure piston pin diameter, length, piston-to-pin clearance and rod pin bore. If not within specifications, replace necessary components. Always check replaced components to ensure proper fitting.

PISTON PIN SPECIFICATIONS

Application	In. (mm)
Piston Pin Bore	.912-.913 (23.163-23.190)
Rod Pin Bore	.9096-.9102 (23.104-23.119)
Pin Diameter	.912-.914 (23.163-23.216)
Pin Length	3.01-3.04 (76.454-77.216)
Piston-to-Pin Clearance	.0003-.0005 (.0076-.0127)

Reassembly

1) Insert piston pin in piston pin bore. Measure and record amount that piston pin protudes evenly on each side of piston. Remove piston pin. Align rod and piston as marked and noted at disassembly. Position rod in piston.

2) Lubricate piston pin and insert pin into piston. Place piston, rod, pin and tooling in press. Check that piston is free on pin during reassembly. Press pin through piston until recorded amount from step **1)** is achieved. Ensure rod is centered in piston.

CRANKSHAFT & ROD BEARINGS

CRANKSHAFT MAIN BEARINGS

MAIN BEARING SPECIFICATIONS

Application	In. (mm)
Main Bearing Journal	
Out-of-Round	.0006 (.01524)
Taper	.0006 (.01524)
Main Bearing Standard	
Wall Thickness [1]	.0951-.0956 (2.41554-2.42824)

[1] – If bearings are .002" (.051 mm) undersize, add .001" (.0254 mm) to standard thickness.

THRUST BEARING

NOTE: Rear face of thrust bearing must be flush for final tightening of main bearing cap bolts.

Inspection

Check crankshaft end play with crankshaft bearing caps installed. Crankshaft end play is .004-.008" (.10-.20 mm). Maximum end play is .012" (.30 mm). Replace center main thrust bearing (upper and lower) if necessary.

REAR MAIN BEARING OIL SEAL

Removal

Remove transmission assembly. Remove flywheel or flexplate. Using a sharp awl, punch hole into seal metal surface between lip and block. Using a slide hammer, remove seal.

CAUTION: DO NOT damage crankshaft seal surfaces. Remove deposits with crocus cloth, but DO NOT polish seal surface. A polished surface can cause poor sealing or early seal wear.

Installation

Clean seal bore and crankshaft seal surface. Apply Oil (XO-10-40-QSP), to inner lip of seal and crankshaft sealing surface. Position seal on Seal Installer (T82L-6701-A), and install seal. Reverse removal to complete installation. Tighten nuts/bolts to specifications.

FRONT CRANKSHAFT OIL SEAL

Removal & Installation

Remove accessory belts and crankshaft damper. Remove timing belt cover and belt. Remove crankshaft timing belt sprocket and belt guide. Using Front Cover Seal Remover (T74P-6700-B), remove seal. Install seal with Front Seal Installer (T74P-6150-A). Reverse removal to complete installation.

AUXILIARY SHAFT & SEAL

Removal

Remove accessory belts, timing belt cover and timing belt. Using Cam Sprocket Holding/Removing Tool (T74P-6256-B), remove auxiliary sprocket. Using Front Cover Seal Remover (T74P-6700-B), remove seal. Remove auxiliary shaft cover, gasket and thrust plate. Carefully remove shaft.

Inspection

Inspect bearings and auxiliary shaft journals for damage or wear. Replace shaft and/or bearings as necessary. Auxiliary shaft bearing clearance is .0006-.0026" (.015-.066 mm). Auxiliary shaft end play is .001-.007" (.0254-.1778 mm). Use Slide Hammer (T59L-100-B) and Puller (T58L-101-A) to remove bearings from block.

Installation

Align bearing oil holes with holes in block. Using Bearing Driver (T57T-7003-A), install bearings. Coat shaft with engine oil and slide into cylinder block. Reverse removal procedure to complete installation. Tighten all nuts/bolts to specifications.

2.3L 4-CYLINDER (Cont.)

ENGINE OILING

ENGINE OILING SYSTEM

Oiling system is force-feed type, using a full-flow oil filter. Oil is retrieved from oil pan by oil pump pick-up tube and distributed to oil filter. Oil is filter and routed throughout the engine. *See Fig. 8.*

Fig. 8: Engine Oiling System

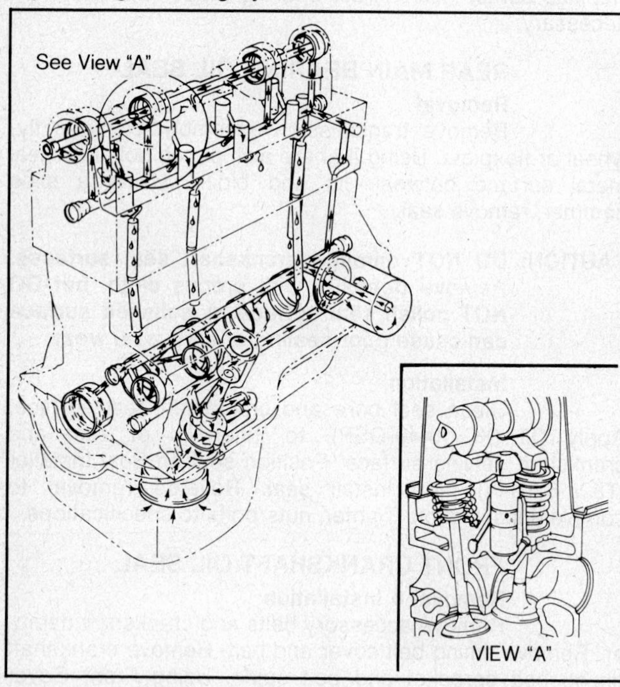

Courtesy of Ford Motor Co.

CRANKCASE CAPACITY

Crankcase capacity is 4.5 qts. (4.3L) without filter change and 5 qts. (4.7L) with filter change. Always check level with dipstick and never overfill.

NORMAL OIL PRESSURE (HOT)

Normal oil pressure is 40-60 psi (2.8-4.2 kg/cm²) at 2000 RPM.

PRESSURE REGULATOR VALVE

Pressure regulator valve is located in oil pump body and is nonadjustable.

OIL PUMP

Removal

Remove oil pan and gaskets. Remove pick-up tube mount bolt from No. 4 main bearing cap. Remove oil pump attaching screws and remove pump. Remove oil pump intermediate shaft.

Disassembly

Remove pick-up tube mounting bolts. Remove pick-up tube and gasket. Remove cover attaching bolts and remove cover. Remove inner rotor and outer race. Drill hole in relief valve retaining plug and pry out plug. Remove spring and valve. *See Fig. 9.*

Inspection

Wash components in solvent and blow dry. Check oil pump body for scoring in outer race bore. Minor scoring is normal, but if cover surface is worn, scored or

Fig. 9: Exploded View of Oil Pump Assembly

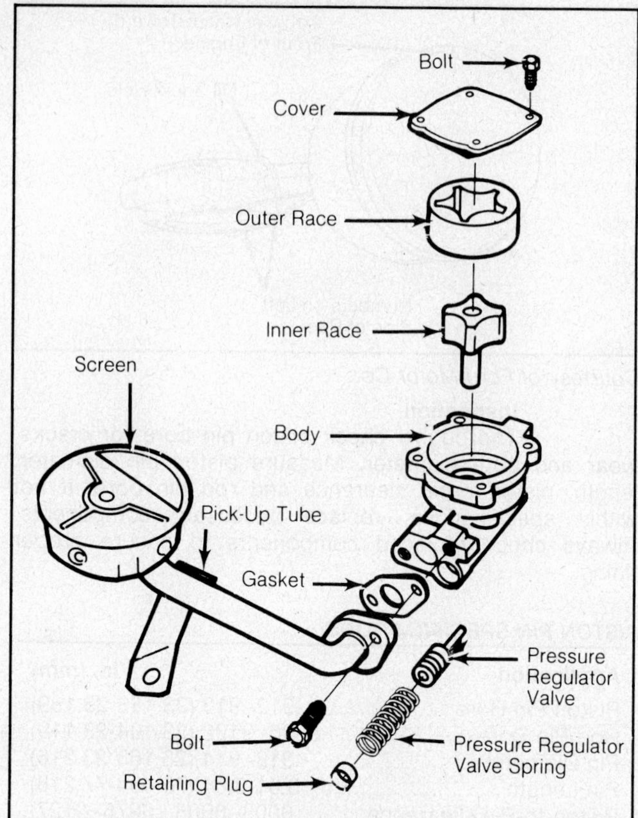

Courtesy of Ford Motor Co.

grooved, replace pump. Measure clearance of body-to-outer race with feeler gauge. Measure clearance at rotor tip-to-outer race. See OIL PUMP SPECIFICATIONS table in this article.

Reassembly

Oil all parts thoroughly. Install oil pump relief valve, spring and new plug. Tap plug in until it bottoms in its bore. Install outer race and inner rotor. Install oil pump cover and tighten bolts to specifications.

NOTE: Face identification mark (dimple) on outer race outward and on same side as mark on rotor. Rotor assembly and race are serviced as an assembly only.

Installation

To install, reverse removal procedure and use new pick-up tube gasket. Oil pump must be free to rotate after installation.

OIL PUMP SPECIFICATIONS

Application	Specification
Outer Race-to-Housing	.001-.013" (.02-.33 mm)
Relief Valve Spring	
Clearance	.0022" (.057 mm)
Tension	16.2 lbs. (6.5 kg)@1.20" (30.4 mm)
Relief Valve	
Bore Clearance	.0022" (.057 mm)
Rotor Tip	
End Clearance	.010" (.254 mm)
Rotor Assembly End Clearance	.004" (.10 mm)

Ford Motor Co. Engines

2.3L 4-CYLINDER (Cont.)

ENGINE COOLING

WATER PUMP

Removal

Drain cooling system and disconnect negative battery cable. Remove accessory belts, water pump pulley and timing belt cover. Loosen expansion tank cap. Disconnect radiator hose and heater hose from water pump. Remove water pump attaching bolts, water pump and gasket.

Installation

Clean all gasket surfaces. Reverse removal to complete installation. Fill, bleed and check system for leaks.

NOTE: For information, see ENGINE COOLING SYSTEMS article at the end of this section.

ENGINE SPECIFICATIONS

GENERAL SPECIFICATIONS

Year	DISPLACEMENT		Fuel System	HP@RPM	Torque Ft. Lbs.@RPM	Compr. Ratio	BORE		STROKE	
	Cu. In.	Liters					In.	mm	In.	mm
1987 2.3L Turbo	140	2.3	EFI	175@5000	200@3000	8.0:1	3.78	96.0	3.126	79.40

VALVES

Engine Size & Valve	Head Diam. In. (mm)	Face Angle	Seat Angle	Seat Width In. (mm)	Stem Diameter In. (mm)	Stem Clearance In. (mm)	Valve Lift In. (mm)
Intake	1.730-1.740 (43.94-44.20)	44°	45°	.060-.080 (1.52-2.03)	.3416-.3423 (8.67-8.69)	.0010-.0027 (.025-.068)	[1] .400 (10.16)
Exhaust	1.49-1.51 (37,8-38.3)	44°	45°	.070-.090 (1.78-2.29)	.3411-.3418 (8.66-8.68)	.0015-.0032 (.038-.081)	[1] .400 (10.16)

[1] – Intake and exhaust valve lift at zero lash is .390" (9.91 mm).

PISTONS, PINS & RINGS

Engine	PISTONS	PINS		RINGS		
	Clearance In. (mm)	Piston Fit In. (mm)	Rod Fit In. (mm)	Ring No.	End Gap In. (mm)	Side Clearance In. (mm)
2.3L	.0030-.0038 (.076-.097)	.0003-.0005 (.008-.013)	Press Fit	1 & 2	.010-.020 (.25-.51)	[1] .002-.004 (.05-.10)
				3	.015-.055 (.38-1.40)	Snug Fit

[1] – Side clearance service limit is .006" (.152 mm).

CRANKSHAFT MAIN & CONNECTING ROD BEARINGS

Engine	MAIN BEARINGS				CONNECTING ROD BEARINGS		
	Journal Diam. In. (mm)	Clearance In. (mm)	Thrust Bearing	Crankshaft End Play In. (mm)	Journal Diam. In. (mm)	Clearance In. (mm)	Side Play In. (mm)
2.3L	2.3982-2.3990 (60.914-60.935)	[1] .0008-.0015 (.020-.038)	No. 3	[2] .004-.008 (.10-.20)	2.0465-2.0472 (51.981-51.999)	[1] .0008-.0015 (.020-.038)	[3] .0035-.0105 (.089-.267)

[1] – Bearing clearance service limit is .0008-.0026" (.020-.066 mm).
[2] – Crankshaft end play service limit is .012" (.30 mm).
[3] – Connecting rod bearing side play service limit is .014" (.356 mm).

Ford Motor Co. Engines

2.3L 4-CYLINDER (Cont.)

ENGINE SPECIFICATIONS (Cont.)

VALVE SPRINGS

Engine	Free Length In. (mm)	PRESSURE Lbs. @ In. (Kg @ mm)	
		Valve Closed	Valve Open
2.3L	1.877 (47.68)	71-79@1.52 (32-36@38.6)	152-156@1.52 (69-71@28.4)

CAMSHAFT

Engine	Journal Diam. In. (mm)	Clearance In. (mm)	Lobe Lift In. (mm)
2.3L	1.7713-1.7720 (44.991-45.009)	.001-.003 (.03-.08)	.400 (10.16)

TIGHTENING SPECIFICATIONS

Application	Ft. Lbs. (N.m)
Auxiliary Shaft Sprocket Bolt	28-40 (38-54)
Belt Tensioner Adjustment Bolt	14-21 (19-29)
Belt Tensioner Pivot Bolt	28-40 (38-54)
Belt Tensioner Spring Stud	14-21 (19-29)
Camshaft Sprocket Bolt	50-71 (68-96)
Connecting Rod Nut	
Step 1	25-30 (34-41)
Step 2	30-36 (41-49)
Coupling Pinch Bolt	12-15 (16-20)
Crankshaft Damper Bolt	100-120 (136-163)
Crossmember-to-Side Rail Bolt	38-47 (56-64)
Cylinder Head Bolt	
Step 1	50-60 (68-81)
Step 2	80-90 (108-122)
EGR Bolt	14-21 (19-29)
Engine Mount Nut	50-70 (68-95)
Exhaust Manifold-to-Head Bolt	
Step 1	15-17 (20-23)
Step 2	20-30 (27-41)
Flywheel Bolt	54-64 (73-87)
Intake Manifold-to-Head Nut	14-21 (19-29)
Main Bearing Cap Bolt	
Step 1	50-60 (68-81)
Step 2	80-90 (108-122)
Oil Pump-to-Block Bolt	14-21 (19-29)
Oil Pump Pick-Up Tube-to-Pump Bolt	14-21 (19-29)
Steering Gear Bolt	[1] 10 (15)
Throttle Body-to-Upper Manifold Nut	12-15 (16-20)
Turbocharger-to-Manifold Nut	28-40 (38-54)
Upper-to-Lower Intake Manifold Bolt	15-22 (20-30)
	INCH Lbs. (N.m)
Air By-Pass Valve Bolt	6-8 (.7-.9)
Auxiliary Shaft Cover Bolt	72-108 (8-12)
Auxiliary Shaft Thrust Plate Bolt	72-108 (8-12)
Camshaft Thrust Plate Bolt	72-108 (8-12)
Cylinder Front Cover Bolt	72-108 (8-12)
Oil Pan Bolt	96 (11)
Oil Pump Cover Bolt	90-130 (10-15)
Valve Cover Bolt	60-96 (7-11)
TPS Bolt	14-16 (1.6-1.8)

[1] – Tighten an additional 90 degrees.

1.0L 3-CYLINDER

Chevrolet Sprint

NOTE: For engine repair procedures not covered in this article, see ENGINE OVERHAUL PROCEDURES article at beginning of this article.

ENGINE CODING

ENGINE IDENTIFICATION

Engine can be identified by the 8th character in the Vehicle Identification Number (VIN). VIN is stamped on a metal plate located on top of dash panel, on lower left corner of windshield.

ENGINE IDENTIFICATION CODE

Application	Code
1.0L 2-Bbl.	5
1.0L EFI Turbo	2

ENGINE, MANIFOLDS & CYLINDER HEAD

ENGINE

Removal

1) On models with EFI, depressurize fuel system by removing fuel tank cap to release fuel vapors. Start engine, disconnect fuel pump relay connector and wait until engine stops running.

NOTE: On EFI models, main relay and fuel pump relay are identical. Identify fuel pump relay by color of wires as follows: (Pink, Pink/White, White/Blue, White/Blue). *See Fig. 1.*

Fig. 1: Fuel Pump Wire Connector (EFI models)

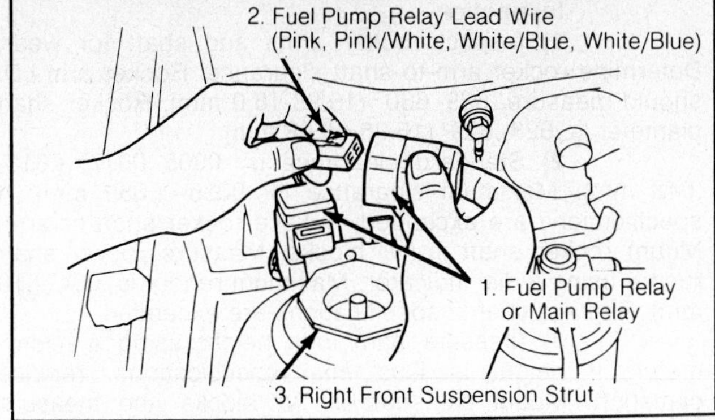

Courtesy of General Motors Corp.

2) On all models, disconnect battery cables. Remove battery, battery tray and hood. Remove air canister or intercooler on EFI Turbo models. Drain coolant and remove radiator hoses. Disconnect cooling fan wires.

3) Remove radiator and cooling fan as an assembly. Disconnect fuel lines and heater hoses. Identify, mark and remove vacuum lines and hoses at engine. Disconnect accelerator cable at carburetor or throttle body. Remove fresh air duct.

4) Disconnect speedometer and clutch cable with bracket at transaxle. Label and disconnect engine and transaxle wiring. Loosen A/C compressor adjusting bolt. Remove drive belt splash shield. Raise vehicle and disconnect exhaust pipe at manifold.

5) Loosen A/C compressor pivot bolt. Remove drive belt and A/C compressor mounting bracket. Disconnect gearshift control shaft and gearshift extension rod at transaxle. Drain transaxle and engine oil. Disconnect ball joints and drive axles.

6) On EFI Turbo models, remove radiator and front bumper from damper flange. Remove turbocharger covers and exhaust bolts. Remove upper and lower exhaust pipes together. Remove air inlet pipe, oil pipe from cylinder block and water hoses.

7) Remove engine torque rods and transaxle mount nut. Lower vehicle and remove engine side mount and mount nuts. Install chain hoist and remove engine and transaxle as an assembly.

Installation

Lower engine and transaxle into vehicle. Install rear mount nut. Raise vehicle and support engine. Remove front mount and bracket at frame. Align stud of motor mount with hole in engine bracket. Lower engine and install bolts into frame bracket. To complete installation, reverse removal procedure.

INTAKE MANIFOLD

Removal

1) Depressurize fuel system on EFI models. Disconnect negative battery cable. Drain coolant and disconnect coolant hoses at intake manifold.

2) On EFI models, remove surge tank together with throttle body.

3) Disconnect warm air, fresh air, secondary air and vacuum hoses. Disconnect EGR modulator. Remove air cleaner assembly or intercooler on EFI Turbo models.

4) On EFI models, disconnect fuel injector couplers and delivery pipes with injectors. On all models, disconnect throttle control cable and electrical leads. Remove emission control and fuel hoses. On models with carburetor, remove choke heater hoses.

5) Remove electrical leads and couplers at intake manifold. Remove emission control, coolant and brake booster hoses from intake manifold. Remove bolts and intake manifold from cylinder head.

Installation

1) Clean all mating surfaces. Using a new gasket, install intake manifold on cylinder head. Install wire harness clamps. Ensure that wires do not interfere with fuel pump. On models with carburetor, install 3-Way Solenoid Valve (TWSV) with terminals facing down and away from carburetor. Tighten manifold nuts and bolts to 14-20 ft. lbs. (18-27 N.m).

2) On EFI models, install fuel rails with injectors. If injectors were removed from delivery pipe, replace "O" ring with new one prior to installation.

3) Install vacuum lines and coolant hoses. Connect emission control hoses. Connect electrical leads for cooling fan, thermal switch, coolant temperature gauge switch and TWSV.

NOTE: On models equipped with carburetors, ensure that Blue harness connector is connected to Blue TWSV terminal and Black harness connector is connected to Black TWSV terminal.

4) Refill cooling system. Connect negative battery cable. Ensure throttle cable is properly adjusted.

1.0L 3-CYLINDER (Cont.)

EXHAUST MANIFOLD

Removal

1) Disconnect negative battery cable and raise vehicle. Remove turbocharger on EFI Turbo models. Remove exhaust pipe at manifold. Remove lower heat shield bolt. Disconnect secondary air pipe and remove A/C compressor drive belt (if equipped).

2) On Turbo models, disconnect turbocharger assembly, pipes and intercooler.

3) Lower vehicle. Remove A/C compressor lower adjusting brace (if equipped). Remove spark plug wires and O_2 sensor wire from sensor and block. Remove exhaust manifold hot air shroud and hoses at secondary air valve.

4) Remove secondary air valve and tubing. Remove exhaust manifold. Clean mating surfaces of manifold and cylinder head.

Installation

Install manifold using new gasket. Tighten manifold nuts and bolts to 14-20 ft. lbs. (18-27 N.m). To complete installation, reverse removal procedure.

CYLINDER HEAD

Removal

1) Disconnect negative battery cable and drain coolant. Remove air cleaner. On EFI Turbo models remove intercooler, pipes and hoses to airflow meter.

2) Remove rocker arm cover and distributor. Remove throttle control cable, emission control hoses, coolant hoses and electrical connectors to engine.

3) On EFI models, depressurize fuel system before removing fuel hoses. Remove brake booster vacuum hose. Remove crankshaft pulley, outer timing belt cover, timing belt and tensioner. Disconnect O_2 sensor lead. Remove exhaust pipe at manifold and secondary air valve.

4) Remove fuel pump and rocker shaft assemblies. Remove engine side mount at cylinder head. Loosen and remove cylinder head bolts. Remove cylinder head and manifolds as an assembly.

Inspection

1) Remove manifolds from cylinder head. Remove carbon from combustion chambers. Check cylinder head for cracks in valve ports, combustion chambers and head surface. Using a straightedge and feeler gauge, check head gasket mating surface for warpage. Maximum allowable warpage of cylinder head is .002" (.05 mm). If specifications are exceeded, correct surface or replace cylinder head.

2) Correct mating surface warpage with a surface plate and No. 400 sandpaper. Place sandpaper on surface plate and rub cylinder head surface against sandpaper to remove high spots. Should this method fail to correct warpage, replace cylinder head.

3) Measure flatness of intake and exhaust manifold mating surfaces. Maximum allowable warpage is .004" (.10 mm). If specifications are exceeded, correct surface or replace cylinder head.

Installation

1) Position cylinder head gasket with "TOP" mark facing up and toward crankshaft pulley side of cylinder block. Position cylinder head on gasket and tighten cylinder head bolts in sequence. *See Fig. 2.*

Fig. 2: Cylinder Head Tightening Sequence

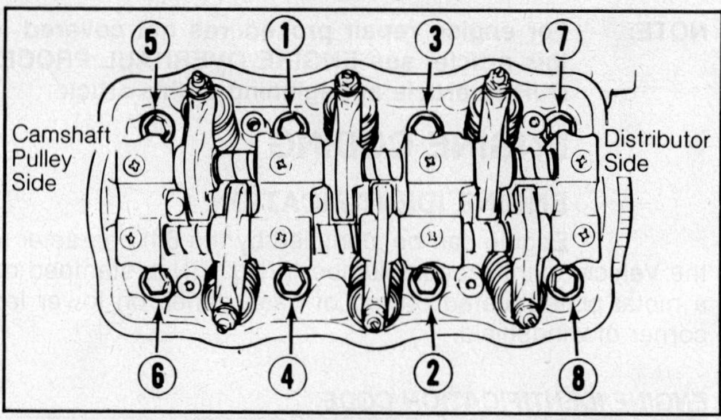

Courtesy of General Motors Corp.

2) Install camshaft and timing belt. See TIMING BELT in this article. To complete installation, reverse removal procedure. Adjust valve clearance and check all engine fluids. See VALVE CLEARANCE ADJUSTMENT in this article.

CAMSHAFT

CAMSHAFT

Removal

1) Disconnect negative battery cable. Remove rocker cover. Loosen valve adjuster lock nuts and back off adjusting screws. Remove rocker shaft mounting bolts and rocker shafts.

2) Remove distributor, fuel pump and fuel pump push rod. Remove crankshaft pulley, timing belt outer cover and timing belt. See TIMING BELT. Using Camshaft Lock Holder (J-34836) to hold camshaft pulley, loosen pulley bolt. Remove bolt, pulley and camshaft from cylinder head.

Inspection

1) Inspect rocker arms and shaft for wear. Determine rocker arm-to-shaft clearance. Rocker arm I.D. should measure .629-.630" (15.98-16.0 mm). Rocker shaft diameter is .628-.629" (15.95-15.98 mm).

2) Standard clearance is .0005-.0017" (.013-.043 mm). Maximum clearance is .0035" (.089 mm). If specifications are exceeded, replace rocker shaft or arm. Mount rocker shaft in "V" blocks. Measure rocker shaft runout using a dial indicator. Maximum runout is .004" (.10 mm). Replace shaft if specifications are exceeded.

3) Measure cam lobe height using a micrometer. If height is less than specifications, replace camshaft. Mount camshaft in "V" blocks and measure runout. Maximum runout is .0039" (.01 mm).

CAMSHAFT LOBE HEIGHT

Application	In. (mm)
Intake Lobe	[1] 1.501 (38.13)
Exhaust Lobe	[1] 1.501 (38.13)
Fuel Pump Drive Lobe	[2] 1.575 (40.00)

[1] – Wear limit is 1.497" (38.03 mm).
[2] – Wear limit is 1.559" (39.60 mm).

1.0L 3-CYLINDER (Cont.)

4) Inspect camshaft journals for wear and damage. Measure journal shaft diameter and journal bore diameter to determine journal clearance. *See Fig. 3.* Journal clearance should measure .002-.0036" (.05-.09 mm). If journal clearance exceeds .006" (.15 mm), replace camshaft and/or cylinder head.

Fig. 3: Camshaft Journal Identification

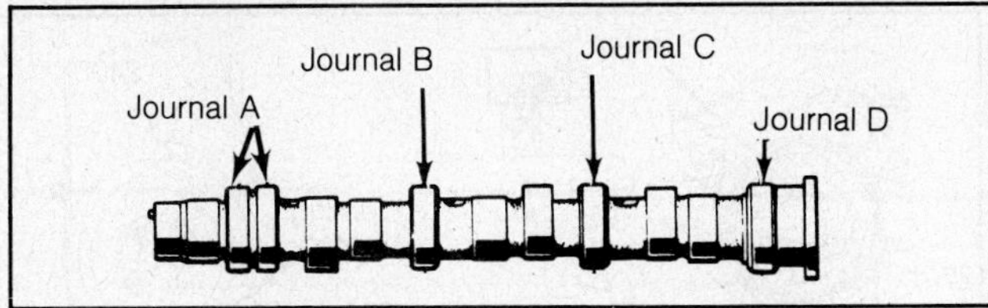

Courtesy of General Motors Corp.

Installation

1) Apply engine oil to camshaft lobes, journals and oil seal on cylinder head. Install camshaft. Install timing belt inner cover and camshaft sprocket. Align sprocket keyway and tighten bolt to 41-46 ft. lbs. (56-62 N.m).

2) Apply engine oil to fuel pump actuating rod. Install rod, gasket and fuel pump. Apply engine oil to rocker shaft and rocker arms.

NOTE: **Dimensions of intake and exhaust rocker shaft stepped ends differ. Intake rocker shaft stepped end O.D. is .55" (14.0 mm). Exhaust rocker shaft is .59" (15.0 mm). Shafts are NOT interchangeable.**

3) Position intake rocker arm shaft with its stepped end facing camshaft pulley side. Position exhaust rocker arm shaft with its stepped end facing the distributor side.

4) Arrange rocker arms and springs on top of valves. *See Fig. 4.* Install rocker arm shafts and tighten shaft support screws to 84-108 INCH lbs. (10-13 N.m). Install gasket, distributor case and distributor on cylinder head.

Fig. 4: Exploded View of Rocker Arm Assembly

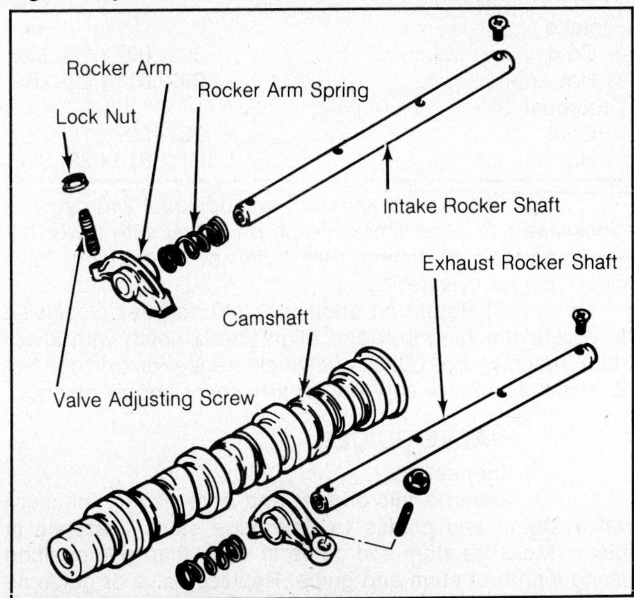

Courtesy of General Motors Corp.

5) Install belt tensioner, timing belt, outside cover, crankshaft sprocket and water pump pulley. Adjust valve clearance. Install rocker arm cover. Adjust ignition timing. To complete installation, reverse removal procedure.

TIMING BELT

Removal

1) Disconnect negative battery cable. Loosen water pump pulley bolts. Remove A/C compressor adjusting bolt (if equipped). Loosen alternator adjusting bolt and raise vehicle.

2) Remove drive belt splash shield and body plug in right fender. Remove alternator and A/C drive belt (if equipped). Remove crankshaft and water pump pulleys. Remove bolts from bottom of timing belt cover.

3) Lower vehicle and remove top timing belt cover. Remove rocker arm cover. Loosen rocker arm adjusting screws. Remove distributor cap. Loosen timing belt tensioner bolt and stud.

4) Slide belt tensioner upward to facilitate timing belt removal. Remove timing belt. Remove tensioner, tension plate and tensioner spring. Inspect timing belt for wear or cracks and replace if necessary.

Installation

1) Insert lug of tensioner plate into tensioner hole. Install tensioner, plate and spring. Hand tighten tensioner bolt and stud. Ensure proper plate movement. If no movement occurs between plate and tensioner, remove tensioner and plate and reinsert lug into tensioner hole.

2) Rotate camshaft sprocket clockwise and align timing mark on camshaft sprocket with "V" mark on timing belt cover. Rotate crankshaft and align punch mark on timing belt sprocket with arrow on oil pump.

Fig. 5: Aligning Timing Marks

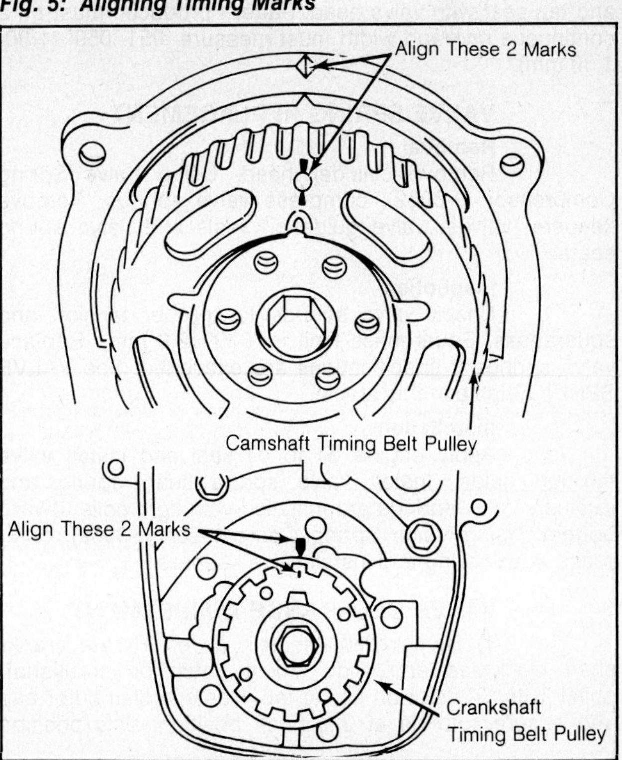

Courtesy of General Motors Corp.

1.0L 3-CYLINDER (Cont.)

3) With marks aligned, install timing belt onto sprockets so that drive side of belt is free of any slack with tensioner plate pushed up. To remove slack in timing belt, turn crankshaft one revolution clockwise after installing timing belt.

4) After removing slack, tighten tensioner stud nut. Tighten tensioner bolt to 17-21 ft. lbs. (23-28 N.m). Install timing belt outer cover. Align keyway on crankshaft sprocket and tighten 4 bolts to 84-108 INCH lbs. (10-13 N.m).

5) Install water pump pulley and drive belt. Adjust drive belt to proper tension. Adjust valve clearance. To complete installation, reverse removal procedure.

VALVES

VALVE ARRANGEMENT

Rear of vehicle – Intake valves.
Front of vehicle – Exhaust valves.

VALVES

1) Remove carbon from valves and inspect for wear, burn or distortion at face and stem. Replace as necessary. Measure thickness of margin on valve head. Intake and exhaust valve margin thickness should measure .039" (1.0 mm). Minimum margin thickness on intake valves is .024" (.60 mm) and .028" (.70 mm) on exhaust valves.

2) Inspect end face of each valve stem for wear. If necessary, grind end face of valve. If grinding removes .020" (.50 mm) or more, replace valve.

3) Inspect each valve for radial runout using a dial gauge and "V" block. Rotate valve slowly during inspection. Maximum radial runout is .003" (.08 mm).

4) Check contact pattern of each valve. Rotate and tap seat with valve head. Pattern produced must be a continuous ring and width must measure .051-.059" (1.30-1.50 mm).

VALVE SPRING REPLACEMENT

Removal

Remove cylinder head. Using Valve Spring Compressor (J-8062), compress valve springs. Remove keepers, valves, valve guide oil seals and valve spring seats.

Inspection

Check valve springs for proper tension and squareness. Squareness limit is .079" (2.0 mm). Replace valve springs if specifications are exceeded. See VALVE SPRINGS table in this article.

Installation

Apply engine oil to oil seal and install valve through guide. Install valve spring seat, spring and retainer. Valve springs are installed with tight coils toward bottom. Using Valve Spring Compressor (J-8062), compress valve spring and install valve keepers.

VALVE CLEARANCE ADJUSTMENT

1) Remove rocker arm cover. Rotate crankshaft clockwise and align timing notch on crankshaft pulley with "0" mark on timing tab. Remove distributor cap and ensure rotor is at 3 o'clock position. This position indicates engine is at compression stroke, TDC No. 1 cylinder.

2) Using a feeler gauge between rocker arm and valve stem, check intake and exhaust valve clearance on cylinder No. 1. After adjustment, tighten lock nut to 11-13 ft. lbs. (15-19 N.m).

Fig. 6: Correct Shaft Positions for Adjusting Valves

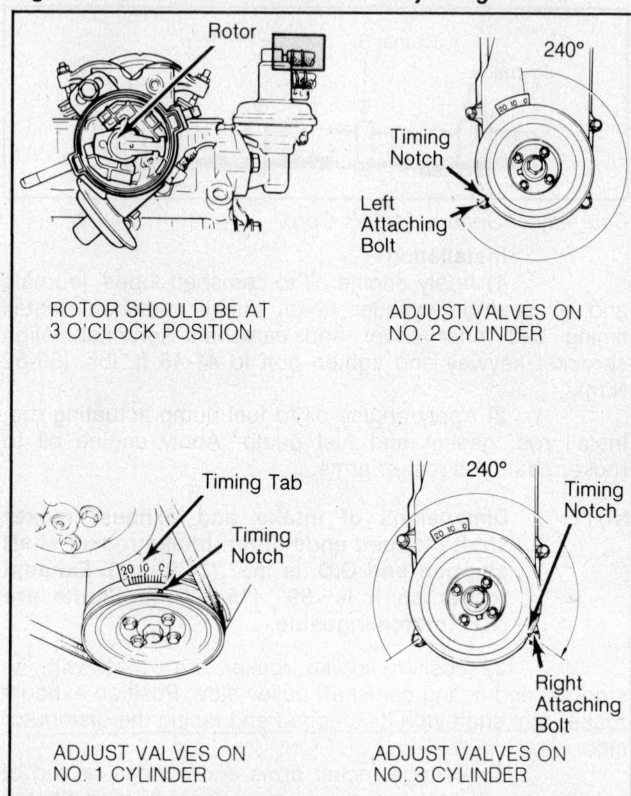

Courtesy of General Motors Corp.

VALVE LASH CLEARANCE

Application	In. (mm)
Intake	
Cold	.005-.007 (.13-.18)
Hot	.009-.011 (.23-.28)
Exhaust	
Cold	.007-.009 (.18-.23)
Hot	.011-.013 (.28-.32)

3) Rotate crankshaft an additional 240 degrees clockwise and align timing notch on pulley with lower left attaching bolt of timing belt outer cover. Check valve clearance for cylinder No. 3.

4) Rotate an additional 240 degrees clockwise from left attaching bolt and align timing notch with lower right attaching bolt. Check valve clearance for cylinder No. 2. Install distributor cap, rocker arm cover and air cleaner.

VALVE GUIDES

Inspection

Using a micrometer and bore gauge, measure valve stems and guides to determine stem clearance in guide. Measure stem and guide at more than one position along length of stem and guide. Replace valve or guide as necessary.

1.0L 3-CYLINDER (Cont.)

Removal

Remove valve springs, retainers, valves, valve guide oil seals and valve spring seats. Place disassembled parts in order, so they can be installed in their original positions. Using Valve Guide Remover/Installer (J-34833), drive valve guide out from combustion side to valve spring side.

Installation

1) Prior to valve guide installation, ream valve guide bore in cylinder head with Reamer (J-34832) or a .472" (12.0 mm) reamer. Reamer will remove burrs caused by valve guide removal. Ensure diameter of bore is within specifications.

2) Heat cylinder head to 176-212°F (80-100°C). Drive valve guide into guide bore using Valve Guide Remover/Installer (J-34834). Drive guide until installer contacts cylinder head. After installation, top of guide should measure .055" (14.0 mm) from surface of cylinder head.

3) Ream valve guide bore with Reamer (J-34831) or a .472" (7.0 mm) reamer. After reaming, clean bore. Install valve spring seat. Install new oil seal using Oil Seal Installer (J-34835). Ensure seal is properly seated, using only hand pressure. To complete installation, reverse removal procedure.

VALVE SEATS

1) Exhaust valve seats require the use of 3 cutters. To prepare the valve seat for final machining, 15 degree and 75 degree cutters are used. The third cutter or grinding wheel is used to produce the desired seat width at a 45 degree angle.

2) Intake valve seats use the same sequence as exhaust valve seats, except the second cut is at a 60 degree angle. Lap valves on seats in 2 steps. Use a coarse lapping compound, followed by lapping with a fine compound.

PISTONS, PINS & RINGS

PISTON & ROD ASSEMBLY

Removal

1) Drain engine oil. Remove cylinder head and oil pan from cylinder block. Remove oil pump strainer. Mark pistons, connecting rods and connecting rod caps for proper cylinder identification.

2) Remove rod caps and install a piece of hose over threads of rod bolts. Remove carbon ridge from top of cylinder. Push piston and connecting rod out through top of cylinder.

3) Remove rings from piston. Position arrow on piston head facing up. Using an arbor press and Piston Pin Remover/Installer (J-34838), press piston pin from connecting rod and piston.

Inspection

Inspect pistons for cracks, scoring and other damage. Replace pistons if damaged. With connecting rod installed, measure connecting rod side clearance. If side clearance exceeds specifications, replace connecting rod.

Installation

1) Apply engine oil to piston pin bores and connecting rod bushing. Position connecting rod with oil hole on left side of connecting rod. Using Piston Pin Remover/Installer (J-34838), position piston so arrow of piston faces up.

Fig. 7: Removing & Installing Piston Pin

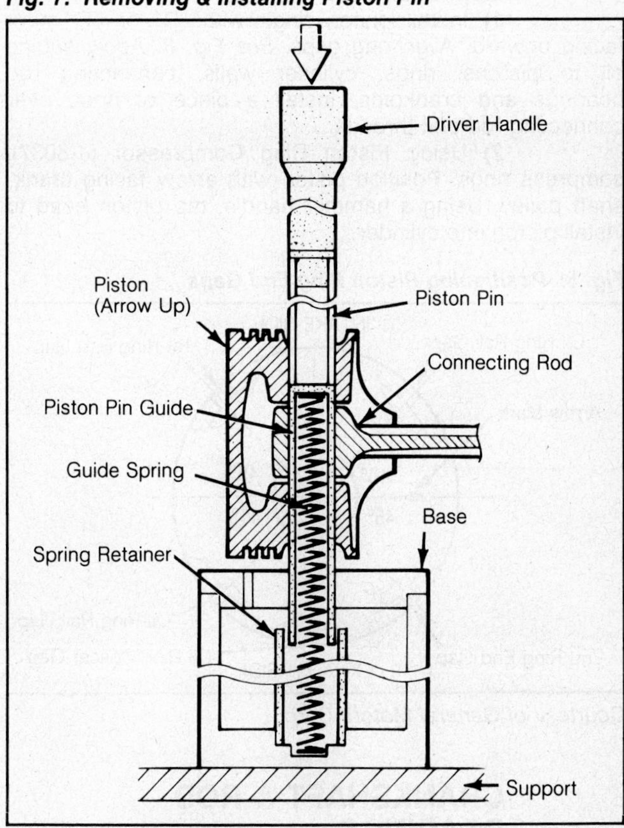

Courtesy of General Motors Corp.

2) Using an arbor press, insert piston pin until line marked on driver handle is flush with flat surface of piston.

FITTING PISTONS & RINGS

1) Check cylinder bores for scratches, roughness or ridges which indicate excessive wear. Using a cylinder bore gauge, measure cylinder bore in thrust and axial directions. Take measurements at 1.96" (50.0 mm) and again at 3.74" (95.0 mm) from top of cylinder bore.

2) There are 3 numbers stamped on top of cylinder block, toward crankshaft pulley side. They identify cylinder bore diameter. The left number identifies cylinder No. 1, the center number identifies cylinder No. 2 and the number to the right identifies cylinder No. 3.

3) Measure bore diameter, taper and out-of-round. If specifications are exceeded, rebore all cylinders to next oversize. Measure outer diameter of piston and determine piston-to-bore clearance. Measure piston .060" (15.0 mm) from bottom of piston skirt at a 90 degree angle to piston pin bore.

4) Piston-to-bore clearance should be .0008-.0015" (.02-.04 mm). Numbers stamped on piston heads identify piston outer diameter. Pistons are stamped with either a "1" or "2". When installing standard pistons, ensure that piston is matched with cylinder. Oversize pistons are available in .010" (.25 mm) and .020" (.50 mm).

5) Insert ring into top of cylinder bore and measure end gap using a feeler gauge. If end gap exceeds specifications, replace ring.

6) Clean pistons. Insert new ring in piston groove. Use a feeler gauge to determine side clearance. If side clearance exceeds specifications, replace ring.

1.0L 3-CYLINDER (Cont.)

Installation

1) Install piston rings with "R" or "T" mark facing upward. Align ring gaps. *See Fig. 8.* Apply engine oil to pistons, rings, cylinder walls, connecting rod bearings and crankpins. Install a piece of hose over connecting rod bolt threads.

2) Using Piston Ring Compressor (J-8037), compress rings. Position piston with arrow facing crankshaft pulley. Using a hammer handle, tap piston head to install piston into cylinder.

Fig. 8: Positioning Piston Ring End Gaps

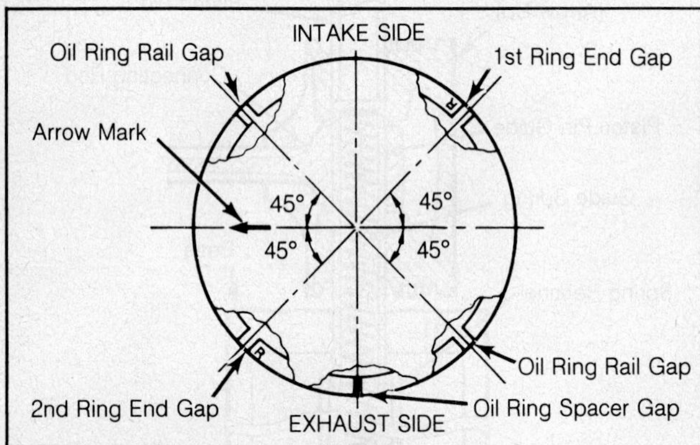

Courtesy of General Motors Corp.

CRANKSHAFT & ROD BEARINGS

FRONT OIL SEAL

Removal & Installation

1) Remove oil pump from block. Disassemble oil pump. Remove front oil pump seal. Install new seal on pump. Install 2 alignment pins and oil pump gasket on block. Position Oil Seal Guide (J-34853) onto crankshaft and lubricate outside of guide with oil.

2) Install oil pump assembly. Tighten mounting bolts to specifications. Check seal to ensure seal lip is not turned up. Remove guide. Trim gasket even with oil pump and oil pan mounting surface on block.

REAR MAIN OIL SEAL

Removal & Installation

Remove oil pan. Remove clutch, pressure plate and flywheel. Remove rear main seal housing. Remove seal from housing. Install new seal in housing. Install new gasket. Lubricate seal and install housing onto block. Trim gasket even with oil pan mounting surface on block.

CRANKSHAFT

Removal

1) With engine removed from vehicle, remove alternator belt, water pump pulley, crankshaft pulley, timing belt cover, timing belt and distributor cap. Loosen rocker arms. Remove crankshaft timing sprocket. Remove alternator adjusting bracket.

2) Remove oil pan, oil pump, clutch assembly and rear main seal housing. Remove oil pump pick-up screen. Mark connecting rods and remove rod caps. Remove main bearing caps and crankshaft from cylinder block.

Inspection

1) Inspect crankshaft for wear or damage. Measure crankshaft for out-of-round and taper with a micrometer. Out-of-round or taper must not exceed .0004" (.01 mm).

2) Mount crankshaft in "V" blocks and measure crankshaft runout using a dial indicator on No. 2 journal. If runout exceeds .0023" (.06 mm), replace crankshaft.

3) Position crankshaft in cylinder block with bearings and journal bearing caps installed. Using a dial indicator, measure crankshaft end play. Standard end play measurement is .004-.012" (.11-.31 mm). Maximum end play is .015" (.38 mm). If specifications are exceeded, replace thrust bearing.

4) Inspect main bearings for pitting, scratches, wear or damage. If any of these conditions are found, replace entire set of bearings. Check oil clearance of main bearings using Plastigage method.

Installation

1) Apply engine oil to all crankshaft journals and bearings. Install main bearing halves into cylinder block and main bearing caps. Install bearing caps with arrow pointing toward crankshaft pulley side.

2) Tighten bearing caps to specifications in 2 or 3 steps. Begin tightening sequence with No. 1 cylinder bearing cap (crankshaft pulley side). Tighten in numerical order (1, 2, 3, 4) toward rear bearing cap No. 4. After installation, ensure crankshaft turns freely by hand. See TIGHTENING SPECIFICATIONS table at the end of this article.

3) Apply oil to lip of rear main oil seal and install oil seal housing and gasket. Tighten housing bolts to 84-108 INCH lbs. (10-13 N.m). Cut edges of gasket so it is flush with cylinder block. To complete installation, reverse removal procedure. Check all engine fluids and adjust valve clearance.

MAIN BEARINGS

Standard Bearing

1) If bearings are damaged or exceed specifications, select a new standard bearing using the following procedure. Locate 4 numbers stamped on crankshaft counterweight of cylinder No. 1.

2) The first number (left) indicates journal diameter at No. 1 bearing cap. The second number indicates journal diameter at No. 2 bearing cap. The third number indicates journal diameter at No. 3 bearing cap. The fourth number indicates journal diameter at No. 4 bearing cap. *See Fig. 9.*

CRANKSHAFT JOURNAL DIAMETER [1]

Stamped Number	Journal Diameter In. (mm)
1	1.7714-1.7716 (44.994-45.000)
2	1.7712-1.7714 (44.988-44.994)
3	1.7710-1.7712 (44.982-44.988)

[1] – This table only applies to standard crankshafts.

1.0L 3-CYLINDER (Cont.)

Fig. 9: Location of Stamped Numbers on Counterweights

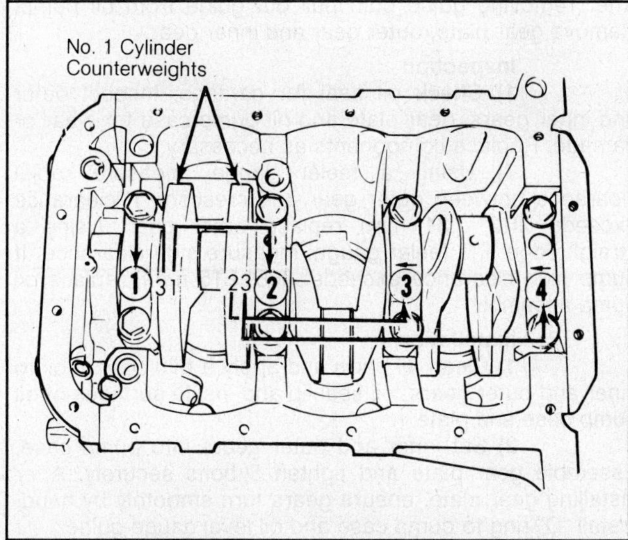

Courtesy of General Motors Corp.

3) Measure bearing cap bore diameter without bearing installed. There are 4 letters stamped on oil pan mating surface of cylinder block indicating cap bore diameter.

4) Reading from left-to-right, first letter applies to cap No. 1, second letter applies to No. 2 cap, third letter applies to No. 3 cap and fourth letter applies to No. 4 cap. See CRANKSHAFT BEARING JOURNAL BORE table.

CRANKSHAFT BEARING JOURNAL BORE

Letter [1]	Cap Diameter In. (mm)
A	1.9292-1.9294 (49.002-49.007)
B	1.9294-1.9296 (49.007-49.012)
C	1.9296-1.9298 (49.012-49.017)

[1] – Letters only indicate cap diameter. Diameter must be measured.

STANDARD BEARING SELECTION

Letter	1	2	3
A	Green	Black	No Paint
B	Black	No Paint	Yellow
C	No Paint	Yellow	Blue

NOTE: **There are 5 sizes of standard bearings. Paint marks are applied for identification purposes. Each color indicates thickness at center of bearing.**

5) From numbers stamped on crankshaft counterweights of cylinder No. 1 and letters stamped on oil pan mating surface, determine new standard size bearing to be installed on each journal.

6) Use Plastigage method to measure main bearing clearance. If clearance still exceeds specifications, use next size thicker bearing and remeasure. When replacing crankshaft or cylinder block for any reason, select new standard bearings by referring to numbers and letters.

Fig. 10: Location of Stamped Letters on Cylinder Block

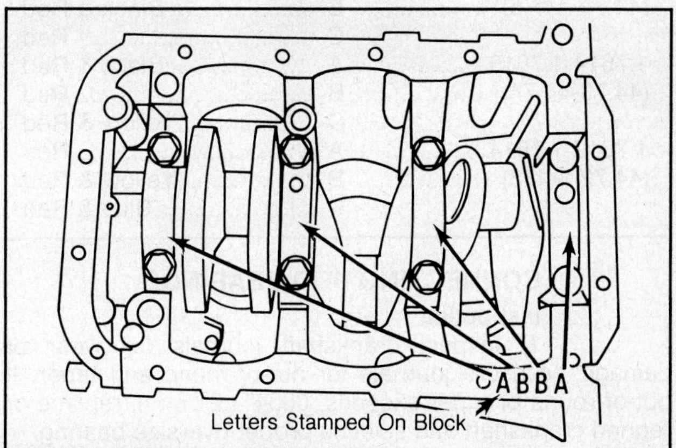

Courtesy of General Motors Corp.

MAIN BEARING IDENTIFICATION

Color Code	Bearing Thickness In. (mm)
Green	.0786-.0787 (1.996-2.000)
Black	.0787-.0788 (2.000-2.002)
No Paint	.0788-.0789 (2.002-2.004)
Yellow	.0789-.0790 (2.004-2.007)
Blue	.0790-.0791 (2.007-2.009)

Oversize Bearing

1) The following procedure is used to select an oversize bearing in the event that the crankshaft must be repaired or replaced. Regrind journal to finished diameter of 1.7612-1.7618" (44.734-44.75 mm).

2) Measure reground journal with a micrometer. From measurement obtained and letters stamped on oil pan mating surface, select new undersize bearing.

NOTE: **Oversize bearings are available in 5 sizes. Paint marks are applied for identification purposes. Each color indicates thickness at center of bearing.**

CRANKSHAFT JOURNAL OVERSIZE BEARINGS

Color Code	Bearing Thickness In. (mm)
Green & Red	.0835-.0836 (2.121-2.123)
Black & Red	.0836-.0837 (2.123-2.126)
Red Only	.0837-.0838 (2.126-2.129)
Yellow & Red	.0838-.0839 (2.129-2.131)
Blue & Red	.0839-.084 (2.131-2.134)

1.0L 3-CYLINDER (Cont.)

CRANKSHAFT JOURNAL OVERSIZE BEARING SELECTION

Journal Dia. In. (mm)	Block Letter	Bearing Color
1.7616-1.7618	A	Green & Red
(44.74-44.75)	B	Black & Red
	C	Red
1.7614-1.7616	A	Black & Red
(44.73-44.74)	B	Red
	C	Yellow & Red
1.7612-1.7614	A	Red
(44.72-44.73)	B	Yellow & Red
	C	Blue & Red

CONNECTING ROD BEARINGS

Inspection

1) Inspect crankshaft journals for wear or damage. Measure journals for out-of-round and taper. If out-of-round or taper exceeds .0004" (.01 mm), replace or regrind crankshaft and select a proper oversize bearing.

2) Inspect bearing shells for signs of pitting, burn or flaking and observe contact pattern. Bearings are available in standard and .010" (.25 mm) oversize.

Bearing Selection

1) Clean crankshaft journals and bearings to be installed. Using Plastigage method, check oil clearance. When installing rod caps, ensure that arrow on cap points to crankshaft pulley side.

2) Install connecting rod with bearing on crankshaft journal. Tighten bolts to specifications. Using a feeler gauge, measure side clearance. If specifications are exceeded, replace connecting rod.

ENGINE OILING

ENGINE OIL SYSTEM

A gear type pump assembly is mounted on front lower case and is driven directly by crankshaft. Oil under pressure from pump passes through oil filter. Flow is then diverted through 2 passages in cylinder block. One passage reaches crankshaft journal bearings and connecting rod journal bearings. The second passage directs oil under pressure to lubricate camshaft and valve train.

CRANKCASE CAPACITY

Crankcase capacity is 3.7 qts. (3.5L) including oil filter.

OIL PRESSURE

Oil pressure is 42.7-54.0 psi (3.0-4.2 kg/cm²) at 3000 RPM.

OIL PUMP

Removal

1) Disconnect negative battery cable. Remove timing belt. See TIMING BELT. Raise vehicle and drain oil. Remove flywheel dust cover. Disconnect exhaust pipe at manifold. Remove oil pan and strainer.

2) Remove crankshaft timing belt pulley. It may be necessary to lock flywheel to remove pulley bolt. Remove alternator and A/C compressor mounting brackets (if equipped). Remove alternator adjusting bolt and upper timing belt cover bolt. Remove oil pump bolts and oil pump.

Disassembly

Remove oil level gauge guide from oil pump. After removing guide bolt, pull out guide from oil pump. Remove gear plate, outer gear and inner gear.

Inspection

1) Check oil seal for damage. Inspect outer and inner gears, gear plate and oil pump case for wear or damage. Replace components as necessary.

2) Using a feeler gauge, measure radial clearance between outer gear and crescent. If clearance exceeds .012" (.31 mm) replace outer gear. Using a straightedge and feeler gauge, measure side clearance. If pump side clearance exceeds .006" (.15 mm), replace oil pump assembly.

Installation

1) Clean all parts and apply a thin coat of oil to inner and outer gears, oil seal lip and inside surfaces of oil pump case and plate.

2) Set inner and outer gears into pump case. Assemble gear plate and tighten 5 bolts securely. After installing gear plate, ensure gears turn smoothly by hand. Install "O" ring to pump case and oil level gauge guide.

3) Install 2 oil pump pins and oil pump gasket on cylinder block. Slide Oil Seal Guide (J-34853) on crankshaft. Apply oil to seal guide and install oil pump.

4) Install 7 oil pump bolts with 4 short bolts at top of oil pump and longer bolts on either side of cylinder block. Tighten bolts to 84-108 INCH lbs. (10-13 N.m). Ensure oil seal lip is not turned up and remove oil seal guide.

5) Trim edge of gasket that might bulge until it is smooth and flush with cylinder block. Install timing belt guide with curved side facing oil pump.

6) Install Woodruff key and crankshaft timing belt sprocket. Tighten sprocket bolt to 47-54 ft. lbs. (65-75 N.m). Install timing belt and tensioner. Adjust intake and exhaust valves. Connect negative battery cable. Check all engine fluids. Perform oil pressure check.

ENGINE COOLING

WATER PUMP

Removal

Disconnect negative battery cable and drain cooling system. Remove water pump belt, crankshaft sprocket, timing belt outer cover, timing belt and timing belt tensioner. Loosen water pump attaching bolts and remove water pump.

Installation

1) Install water pump to cylinder block. Install rubber seals between water pump and oil pump and between water pump and cylinder head. Install timing belt tensioner, timing belt and timing belt outer cover.

2) Install crankshaft pulley, water pump pulley and water pump drive belt. Adjust drive belt. Adjust valve clearance and install rocker arm cover and air cleaner. Fill cooling system and connect negative battery cable.

NOTE: **For further information on cooling systems, see COOLING SYSTEMS.**

General Motors

1.0L 3-CYLINDER (Cont.)

ENGINE SPECIFICATIONS

GENERAL SPECIFICATIONS

Year	DISPLACEMENT		Fuel System	HP@RPM	Torque Ft. Lbs.@RPM	Compr. Ratio	BORE		STROKE	
	Cu. In.	Liters					In.	mm	In.	mm
1987	61 61	1.0 1.0	2 Bbl. MFI Turbo	48@5100 70@5500	57@3200 79@3500	9.5 8.3	2.91 2.91	74 74	3.03 3.03	77 77

VALVES

Engine Size & Valve	Head Diam. In. (mm)	Face Angle	Seat Angle	Seat Width In. (mm)	Stem Diameter In. (mm)	Stem Clearance In. (mm)	Valve Lift In. (mm)
1.0L							
Intake	.....	45°	45°	.0512-.059 (1.3-1.5)	.2742-.2748 (6.965-6.98)	.0008-.0019 (.020-.050)	.....
Exhaust	.....	45°	45°	.0512-.059 (1.3-1.5)	.2737-.2742 (6.952-6.965)	.0014-.0025 (.035-.065)	.....

CRANKSHAFT MAIN & CONNECTING ROD BEARINGS

Engine	MAIN BEARINGS				CONNECTING ROD BEARINGS		
	Journal Diam. In. (mm)	Clearance In. (mm)	Thrust Bearing	Crankshaft End Play In. (mm)	Journal Diam. In. (mm)	Clearance In. (mm)	Side Play In. (mm)
1.0L	[1] 1.7714-1.7716 (44.994-45.00) [2] 1.7712-1.7714 (44.988-44.994) [3] 1.7710-1.7712 (44.982-44.988)	.0008-.0015 (.020-.040)	2	.0044-.0122 (.112-.310)	1.6529-1.6535 (41.98-42.00)	.0012-.0019 (.030-.050)	.0039-.0078 (.100-.198)

[1] – Specification given for journal marked No. 1.
[2] – Specification given for journal marked No. 2.
[3] – Specification given for journal marked No. 3.

PISTONS, PINS & RINGS

Engine	PISTONS	PINS		RINGS		
	Clearance In. (mm)	Piston Fit In. (mm)	Rod Fit In. (mm)	Ring No.	End Gap In. (mm)	Side Clearance In. (mm)
1.0L	.0008-.0015 (.020-.040)	Slip Fit	Press Fit	1	.0079-.0129 (.200-.330)	.0012-.0027 (.030-.060)
				2	.0079-.0137 (.200-.350)	.0079-.0023 (.200-.060)
				3	.0079-.0275 (.200-.700)	.....

1.0L 3-CYLINDER (Cont.)

ENGINE SPECIFICATIONS (Cont.)

CAMSHAFT

Engine	Journal Diam. In. (mm)	Clearance In. (mm)	Lobe Lift In. (mm)
1.0L	[1] 1.7372-1.7381 (44.125-44.15) [2] 1.7451-1.746 (44.325-44.35) [3] 1.753-1.7539 (44.525-44.55) [4] 1.7609-1.7618 (44.725-44.75)	.002-.0036 (.05-.091)	.....

[1] – Specification given for journal A.
[2] – Specification given for journal B.
[3] – Specification given for journal C.
[4] – Specification given for journal D.

VALVE SPRINGS

Engine	Free Length In. (mm)	PRESSURE Lbs. @ In. (Kg @ mm)	
		Valve Closed	Valve Open
1.0L	1.9409 (49.3)	54.7-64.3 @ 1.63 (24.8-29.2 @ 41.5)	.....

TIGHTENING SPECIFICATIONS

Application	Ft. Lbs. (N.m)
Camshaft Pulley Bolt	41-46 (56-62)
Connecting Rod Cap Bolts	24-26 (33-35)
Crankshaft Pulley Bolt	47-54 (65-75)
Crankshaft Main Bearing Cap Bolts	36-41 (49-56)
Cylinder Head Bolts	46-51 (62-69)
Exhaust Manifold Bolts	14-20 (19-27)
Exhaust Pipe Flange Nuts	30-43 (41-58)
Flywheel Mounting Bolts	41-47 (56-64)
Intake Manifold Bolts	14-20 (19-27)
Rocker Arm Lock Nut	11-13 (15-18)
Timing Belt Tensioner Lock Bolt	17-21 (23-28)
	INCH Lbs. (N.m)
Oil Pan Attaching Bolts	84-108 (10-13)
Oil Pump Housing Bolts	84-108 (10-13)
Rear Main Oil Seal Housing Bolts	84-108 (10-13)
Rocker Shaft Attaching Screws	84-108 (10-13)
Water Pump Attaching Bolts	84-108 (10-13)

1.5L & 1.5L TURBO 4-CYLINDER

Chevrolet: Spectrum
Isuzu: I-Mark

NOTE: **For engine repair procedures not covered in this article, see ENGINE OVERHAUL PROCEDURES article at beginning of this section.**

ENGINE CODING

ENGINE IDENTIFICATION

The Vehicle Identification Number (VIN) is stamped on a metal plate attached to the left top of dash panel. Engine can be identified by the 8th character in the VIN on all models. The 10th character identifies the model year. Engine serial number is also stamped on engine transaxle mounting flange under exhaust manifold.

ENGINE IDENTIFICATION CODE

Application	Code
1.5L 2-Bbl.	7
1.5L EFI Turbo	9

ENGINE, MANIFOLDS & CYLINDER HEAD

ENGINE

Removal

1) On EFI Turbo models, fuel system must be depressurized before disconnecting any fuel lines or injectors. To depressurize, loosen fuel filler cap to relieve pressure from fuel tank, disable fuel pump and run engine until it dies.

2) Disconnect negative battery cable. Remove hood from vehicle. Disconnect fuel lines. Remove air duct and air cleaner assembly. Disconnect power steering hoses. Discharge A/C system. Disconnect A/C hose assembly and plug openings.

3) Drain cooling system. Disconnect upper and lower radiator hoses. Remove heater hoses at engine. Remove transmission cooler lines on automatic transmission models. Label and disconnect vacuum hoses. Disconnect clutch, select and shift cables on manual transmission models.

4) Disconnect speedometer cable. Disconnect distributor high tension lead. Disconnect engine electrical harness connectors. Remove battery and battery tray. Remove ground lead from valve cover. Remove engine control cables.

5) Raise and support vehicle. Remove front wheels. Disconnect tie rod ends from steering knuckles using Remover (J-21687-02). Disconnect lower ball joints from lower control arm. Loosen, but DO NOT remove, upper strut-to-body attaching bolts.

6) Pry drive axle shafts from transaxle assembly. DO NOT damage oil seals when removing axle shafts. Disconnect front exhaust pipe from engine. Lower vehicle. Attach engine hoist to hangers on engine. Raise engine to remove weight from mounts.

7) Remove torque rod from body. Remove right side engine mounting rubber. Remove front engine mount through bolt and nut. Remove rear engine mount through bolt. Ensure all hoses and wiring are disconnected. Remove engine with transaxle assembly.

8) Remove engine mounts, torque rod and bracket from engine. Remove transaxle undercover. Remove main harness cable assembly. Separate transaxle from engine.

Installation

To install, reverse removal procedure. Adjust drive belts. Check all fluid levels

INTAKE MANIFOLD

NOTE: **Replace intake manifold if cylinder head mounting surface is warped more than .016" (.40 mm).**

Removal (EFI Turbo Engines)

1) Fuel system must be depressurized before disconnecting any fuel lines or hoses. Disconnect battery cables.

2) Disconnect engine wiring harness assembly, vacuum lines, hoses and throttle valve assembly from turbocharger.

3) Remove fuel injectors with pipe. Remove intake manifold. Check intake manifold for cracks or warpage.

Installation

To install, reverse removal procedure. Use new fuel injector "O" rings, intake manifold, and throttle body gaskets. Tighten mounting nuts and bolts to specifications.

Removal (Carburetor Engines)

1) Disconnect negative battery cable. Drain coolant. Remove alternator adjusting bolt. Disconnect all hoses to air cleaner assembly. Disconnect intake air temperature switch wiring connector. Remove air cleaner assembly. Label and disconnect vacuum hoses to carburetor.

2) Disconnect by-pass, heater and fuel hoses. Remove fuel vapor hose from charcoal canister. Disconnect electrical connectors to carburetor and EFE heater. Remove throttle cable. Remove carburetor mounting bolts. Remove carburetor and EFE heater.

3) Disconnect PCV, vacuum advance and EGR 3-way hose. Disconnect A/C wiring. Disconnect coolant temperature sending unit wire. Disconnect ground wires from intake manifold. Remove intake manifold mounting bolts. Remove intake manifold. Check intake manifold for cracks or warpage.

Installation

To install, reverse removal procedure. Tighten mounting nuts and bolts to specification. Use new intake manifold, carburetor base and EFE heater gaskets.

EXHAUST MANIFOLD

NOTE: **Replace exhaust manifold if cylinder head mounting surface is warped more than .016" (.40 mm).**

Removal (EFI Turbo Engines)

1) Disconnect negative battery cable. Remove upper, lower and manifold heat shields. Disconnect turbocharger pipe from throttle valve assembly and air cleaner.

2) Raise vehicle and disconnect exhaust pipe from exhaust manifold.

3) Remove turbocharger assembly from wastegate manifold. Remove exhaust manifold and check for cracks or warpage.

1.5L & 1.5L TURBO 4-CYLINDER (Cont.)

Installation

To install, reverse removal procedure. Use new exhaust manifold, wastegate manifold, turbocharger and flange gaskets. Tighten mounting nuts and bolts to specification.

Removal (Carburetor Engines)

1) Disconnect negative battery cable. Disconnect O_2 sensor wiring. Disconnect hot air cover and tubing and air injection pipe. Raise vehicle. Disconnect exhaust pipe from exhaust manifold.

2) Lower vehicle. Remove exhaust manifold mounting bolts and nuts. Check exhaust manifold for cracks or warpage.

Installation

To install, reverse removal procedure. Tighten mounting nuts and bolts to specification. Use new exhaust manifold and flange gaskets.

CYLINDER HEAD

Removal

1) Disconnect negative battery cable. Drain cooling system. Remove intake and exhaust manifolds, as indicated in this article. Disconnect spark plug wires at spark plugs.

2) Disconnect thermostat housing at cylinder head. Remove distributor from cylinder head. Disconnect all vacuum hoses to components on intake manifold and cylinder head. Disconnect fuel lines. Disconnect wire connectors. Disconnect throttle cable.

3) Disconnect power steering belt. Support engine. Remove right side motor mount and bracket at front cover. Disconnect A/C and alternator belts. Align timing marks.

4) Remove timing belt cover. Loosen timing belt tensioner pulley. Remove timing belt from camshaft timing pulley. Remove alternator bracket bolt at intake manifold. Remove power steering mounting and through bolts.

5) On carburetor models, disconnect heater hose to intake manifold and carburetor fuel line at fuel pump. Remove fuel pump. Remove rocker cover. Remove cylinder head bolts in proper sequence. *See Fig. 1.* Remove cylinder head.

Fig. 1: Cylinder Head Bolt Removal Sequence

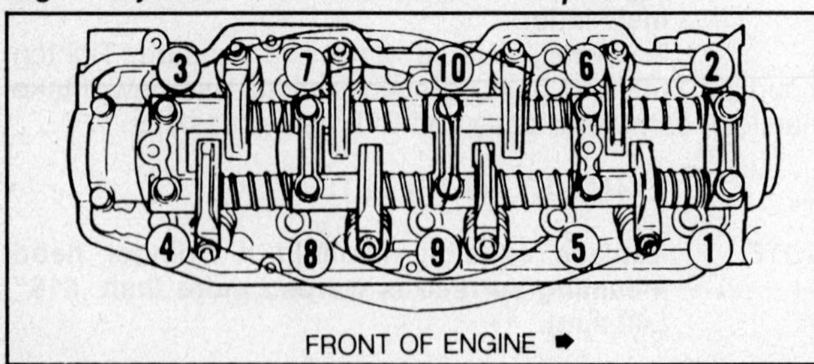

Courtesy of General Motors Corp.

Inspection

1) Remove gasket material from head. Remove carbon from combustion chambers and ports. Check head for cracks in water jackets, combustion chambers, and exhaust ports. Replace head if cracked.

2) Check head for warpage using a feeler gauge and straightedge. Check exhaust manifold, intake manifold and block mating surfaces. Repair or replace cylinder head as necessary. Maximum manifold surface warpage is .016" (.40 mm). Maximum head gasket surface warpage is .008" (.20 mm).

NOTE: DO NOT remove more than .016" (.40 mm) material when resurfacing cylinder head. Standard head thickness is 3.386" (86.00 mm).

Installation

Install new head gasket. Install cylinder head. Lubricate head bolts with engine oil. Tighten head bolts to specification. *See Fig. 2.* To complete installation, reverse removal procedure. Adjust valve clearance to specification.

Fig. 2: Cylinder Head Bolt Tightening Sequence

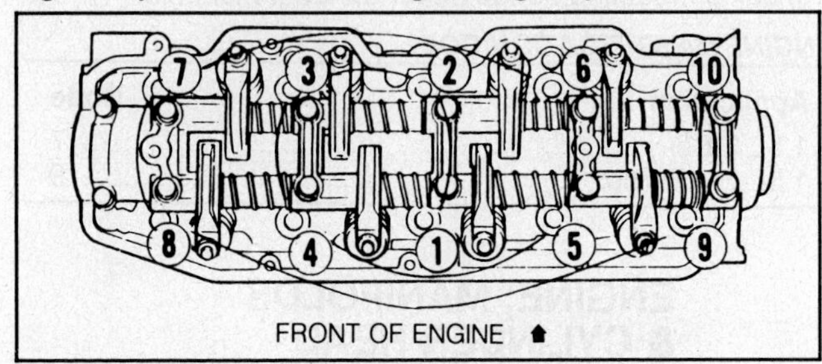

Courtesy of General Motors Corp.

CAMSHAFT

ROCKER SHAFT ASSEMBLY & CAMSHAFT

Removal

1) Disconnect negative battery cable. Align timing mark on crankshaft pulley so mark on crank pulley is aligned with zero degree mark on front cover. Remove rocker cover. Loosen camshaft pulley bolts. Ensure crankshaft and camshaft do not rotate.

2) Loosen timing belt tensioner and remove belt from camshaft pulley. Remove rocker shaft assemblies. *See Fig. 3.* Remove camshaft pulley. Remove distributor. Remove camshaft from cylinder head. Remove camshaft seal.

Fig. 3: Removing Rocker Shaft Assembly

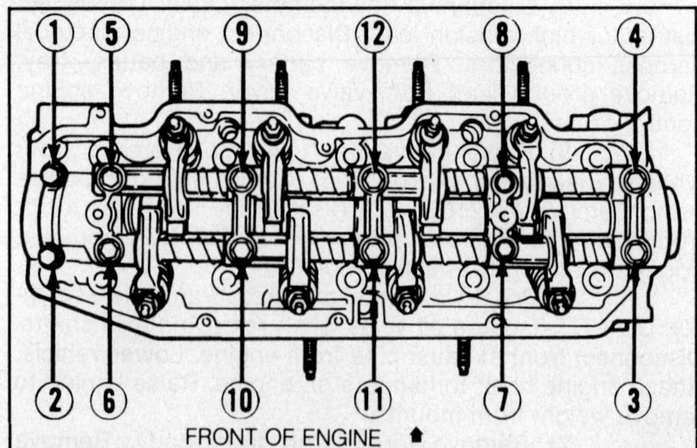

Courtesy of General Motors Corp.

Inspection

1) Measure camshaft lobe height and journal diameter. Replace camshaft if lobes are worn beyond 1.426" (36.22 mm) or if journals are worn beyond 1.0157"

1.5L & 1.5L TURBO 4-CYLINDER (Cont.)

(25.798 mm). Wear should be even across journals and lobes. Replace camshaft if worn unevenly. Place camshaft on "V" blocks. Measure camshaft runout with a dial indicator. Replace camshaft if runout is more than .004" (.10 mm).

2) Reinstall camshaft on cylinder head. Install camshaft bearing caps and tighten to specification. Measure camshaft journal oil clearance using Plastigage method. Replace cylinder head and/or camshaft if clearance is beyond specification.

3) Install dial indicator and measure camshaft end play. Replace cylinder head and/or camshaft if end play is more than .008" (.20 mm). Measure distributor drive slot. Drive slot width should be .196" (4.98 mm).

4) Check rocker shaft outer diameter. Minimum rocker shaft diameter is .624" (15.85 mm). Place rocker shaft on "V" blocks. Measure rocker shaft runout. Maximum runout is .016" (.40 mm).

5) Measure rocker arm inside diameter. Subtract rocker shaft diameter from rocker arm inside diameter to obtain rocker arm-to-rocker shaft oil clearance. Maximum oil clearance is .008" (.20 mm).

Installation

Lubricate and install camshaft with dowel pin in 12 o'clock position. *See Fig. 4*. Apply sealer to cylinder head mating surface of No. 1 and No. 5 rocker shaft mounting brackets. Lubricate and install new camshaft oil seal using Seal Installer (J-35268). To complete installation, reverse removal procedure. Adjust timing belt.

Fig. 4: Aligning Camshaft Sprocket Timing Marks

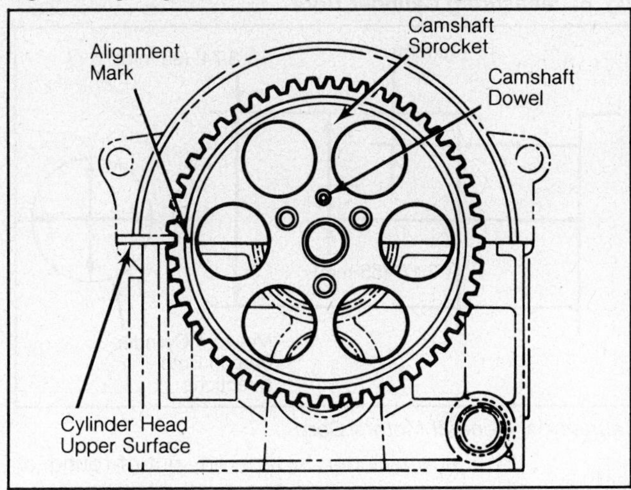

Courtesy of General Motors Corp.

TIMING BELT & SPROCKETS

Removal

1) Remove engine and mount on stand. Remove accessory drive belts. Remove engine mounting bracket from timing cover. Rotate crankshaft so No. 4 cylinder is at TDC on compression stroke. Align crankshaft pulley with zero degree mark on timing belt cover.

2) Remove starter and install Flywheel Holder (J-35271). Remove crankshaft bolt. Remove crankshaft boss and pulley. Remove timing belt cover. Ensure camshaft pulley mark is aligned with upper surface of head and dowel pin is at 12 o'clock position. Loosen belt tensioner attaching bolt.

3) Insert Allen wrench into pulley tensioner attaching bolt. Loosen timing belt tensioner by rotating pulley clockwise. Remove timing belt. Remove rocker cover. Remove crankshaft pulley. Loosen camshaft pulley attaching bolts. Remove camshaft pulley.

Inspection

Check timing belt for cracks and wear. Check for missing or damaged timing belt teeth. Check timing belt outer circumference for excessive hardness at 3-5 points around belt. Replace belt if worn, damaged, oil contaminated or excessively hard.

Installation

To install, reverse removal procedure. There must be no slack in the belt after it has been installed.

VALVES

VALVE ARRANGEMENT

Right Side - Exhaust valves.
Left Side - Intake valves.

NOTE: **"Right" and "Left" refer to right and left side of the engine NOT the vehicle.**

VALVE CLEARANCE ADJUSTMENT

1) Rotate crankshaft until No. 4 piston is at TDC on compression stroke. Align crankshaft pulley timing mark with zero degree mark on timing scale. Adjust intake valve in No. 3 and No. 4 cylinders. Adjust exhaust valve in No. 2 and No. 4 cylinders. See VALVE CLEARANCE ADJUSTMENT table.

2) Rotate crankshaft 360 degrees until No. 1 cylinder is at TDC on compression stroke. Adjust intake valve in No. 1 and No. 2 cylinders. Adjust exhaust valve in No. 1 and No. 3 cylinders. Reinstall rocker cover.

VALVE CLEARANCE ADJUSTMENT

Application	In. (mm)
Intake	.006 (.15)
Exhaust	.010 (.25)

VALVE STEM OIL SEALS

Removal

Remove rocker cover and rocker shafts. Remove spark plugs. Apply compressed air into cylinder to hold valve in place. Using Spring Compressor (J-26513-A), compress valve spring. Remove valve locks and retainer. Remove valve spring, seal and spring seat.

Installation

To install, reverse removal procedure. Lubricate and install new seal.

VALVES

Removal

Remove cylinder head from block. Compress valve spring using Valve Spring Compressor (J-8062). Remove valve locks and retainer. Remove valve spring, oil seal and spring seat. Remove valve from combustion chamber side of head.

Inspection

1) Measure valve face angle. If valve face angle is not 45 degrees, replace valve. Measure valve head margin. If valve head margin is less than .0315" (.800 mm), replace valve. Inspect valve stem tip for wear and damage. Replace if necessary.

1.5L & 1.5L TURBO 4-CYLINDER (Cont.)

2) Measure valve stem diameter. Intake valve stem diameter should be .274-.275" (6.959-6.985 mm). Exhaust valve stem diameter should be .2740-.2744" (6.959-6.969 mm). Replace valve and guide as a set.

Installation

To install, reverse removal procedure. Lubricate valve stem before installing.

VALVE SPRINGS

Check valve spring free height. Replace valve spring if free height is less than 1.85" (47 mm). Measure valve spring for out-of-square. Painted area of valve spring should be facing downward. Maximum out-of-square is .04" (1.0 mm). Measure valve spring preload at valve spring installed height. Valve spring preload should be 47.4 lbs. (21.5 kg) at 1.57" (39.9 mm).

VALVE GUIDE

Removal & Installation

1) Using Valve Guide Remover/Installer (J-35267), drive out valve guide toward combustion chamber side of head. Apply engine oil to outside of replacement valve guide.

2) Install valve guide using Valve Guide Remover/Installer (J-35267) from camshaft side of head. Drive in valve guide until valve guide protrudes .669" (17 mm) from top of cylinder head. *See Fig. 5.* Ream valve guide as necessary.

Fig. 5: Installing Valve Guide

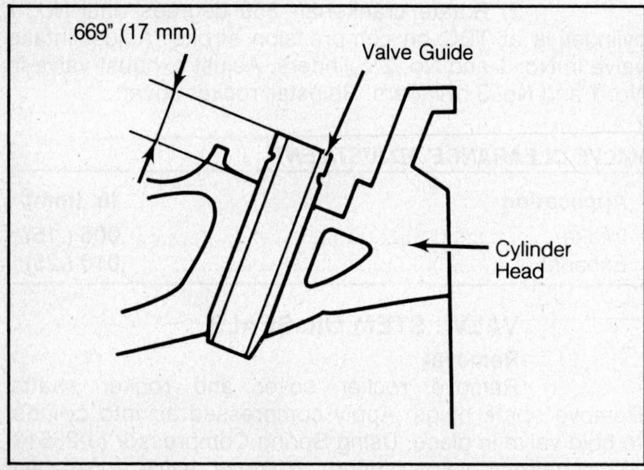

Courtesy of General Motors Corp.

VALVE SEATS

1) Check valve depression into cylinder head. Valve depression should be less than .0197" (.500 mm). Replace seat or cylinder head as necessary. Measure valve seat contact width. Regrind or replace seat if contact surface width is not within specification or contact surface is damaged or rough.

2) If reworking seat, check valve guide first. Arc weld rod to valve seat at several points. Allow rod to cool for a few minutes. This will cause valve seat to shrink. Remove valve seat from head. Clean seat area in cylinder head.

3) Heat cylinder head with steam. Cool valve seat insert with dry ice. Press valve seat into cylinder head. After installing seat, machine to specification. Lap seat and valve.

PISTONS, PINS & RINGS

PISTON & CONNECTING ROD ASSEMBLY

Removal

Remove cylinder head, oil pan and screen. Ensure connecting rods and rod caps are marked on big end for reassembly reference. Remove carbon ridge from cylinder bores. Remove connecting rod caps. Remove connecting rod and piston assembly through top of cylinder block.

Installation

1) To install, lubricate all internal surfaces with engine oil before installation. Ensure mark on piston head faces front of engine. Use ring compressor to compress rings, without changing ring gap position. Install piston and connecting rod assembly into cylinder block in original position.

2) Tap lightly on piston dome with wooden hammer handle while guiding connecting rod onto crankshaft. Install rod cap onto proper piston and connecting rod assembly. Tighten attaching bolts to specification. Install cylinder head and oil pan.

FITTING PISTONS

1) Check block for distortion, cracks, scratches or other abnormalities. Measure bores at top, center and bottom of piston ring travel for taper and out-of-round. *See Fig. 6.*

Fig. 6: Measuring Cylinder Bore

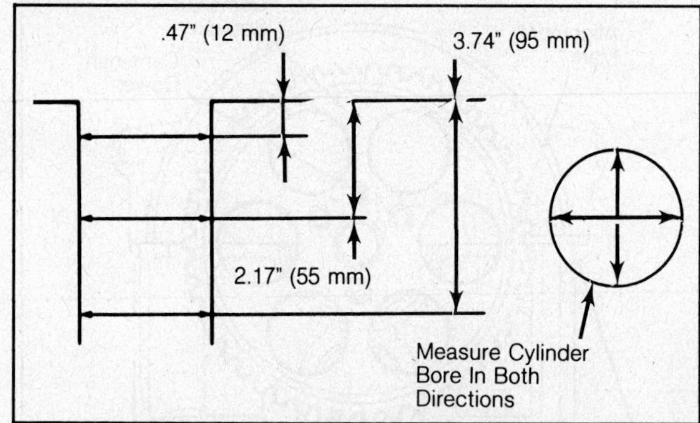

Courtesy of General Motors Corp.

2) If any cylinder is tapered, out-of-round or cylinder walls are badly scuffed or scored, block must be bored or honed and new oversized pistons and rings installed. See CYLINDER BORE SPECIFICATIONS table.

CYLINDER BORE SPECIFICATIONS

Piston Size	Cylinder Bore In. (mm)	Limit In. (mm)
Standard	3.0315-3.0330 (77.000-77.040)	3.0394 (77.200)
.50 Oversize	3.0512-3.0528 (77.500-77.540)	3.0590 (77.700)
1.0 Oversize	3.0709-3.0724 (78.000-78.040)	3.0724 (78.040)

3) Bore or hone all cylinders to same oversize. Do not bore only one cylinder. Bore or hone cylinders in sequence, skipping adjacent cylinders to prevent heat

1.5L & 1.5L TURBO 4-CYLINDER (Cont.)

distortion. Standard pistons are available in 4 sizes. See STANDARD PISTON APPLICATION table.

STANDARD PISTON APPLICATION

Size Mark	In. (mm)
A	3.0299-3.0303 (76.960-76.970)
B	3.0303-3.0307 (76.970-76.980)
C	3.0307-3.0310 (76.980-76.990)
D	3.0311-3.0314 (76.990-77.000)

NOTE: Replacement pistons are available in standard, .50 mm and 1.0 mm oversizes. Oversize pistons are stamped on crown to indicate oversize.

4) Measure outside diameter of piston by measuring at a point .079" (2.0 mm) from bottom of skirt below pin boss, and at 90 degrees to pin bore. Determine cylinder boring finish dimension.

PISTON PINS

1) Check piston pin outer diameter at 3 positions along length of pin. Measure pin 90 degrees to the first set of measurements. *See Fig. 7.* Standard piston pin outer diameter should be .7085-.7088" (17.996-18.005 mm). Minimum piston pin diameter is .7075" (17.970 mm).

Fig. 7: Measuring Piston Pin Diameter

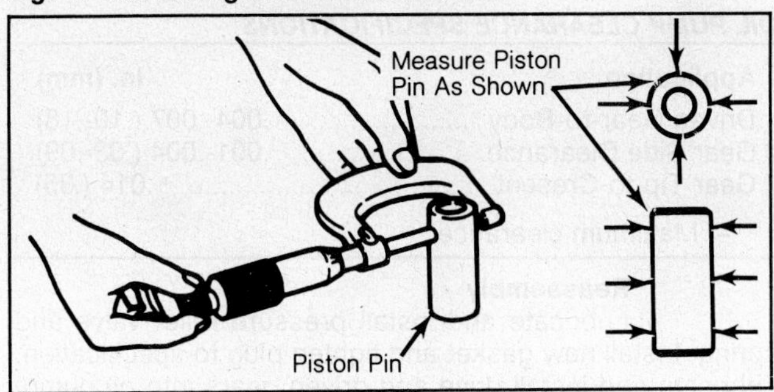

Courtesy of General Motors Corp.

2) Measure inside diameter of connecting rod small end. Piston pin-to-connecting rod clearance should be .000787-.001614" (.020-.041 mm). Measure piston pin-to-piston clearance. Piston pin-to-piston clearance should be .00024-.00043" (.006-.011 mm).

PISTON RINGS

1) Measure piston ring side and end clearance for all pistons and replace rings as necessary. When replacing ring in cylinder bore not needing reconditioning, check ring end gap at lower part of cylinder that is less worn.

2) Compression ring end gap should be .010-.014" (.25-.35 mm). Oil ring end gap should be .004-.024" (.10-.60 mm). Rings are available in standard, .50 mm oversize and 1.0 mm oversize.

3) Install oil ring first without using a ring expander. Spacer expander gap should be installed 90 degrees from side rail gaps. Rails should turn smoothly when installed. *See Fig. 8.*

Fig. 8: Positioning Piston Ring End Gaps

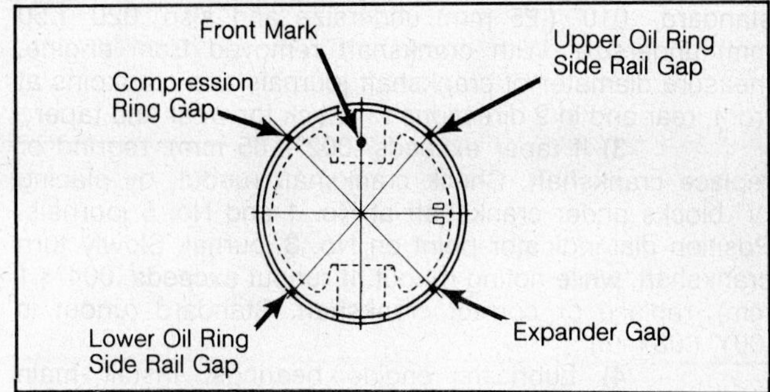

Courtesy of General Motors Corp.

CRANKSHAFT & ROD BEARINGS

CRANKSHAFT FRONT OIL SEAL

Removal & Installation

Remove oil pump from block. Pry seal from oil pump using a screwdriver. Be careful not to damage oil pump case when removing seal. Install new seal using Seal Installer (J-35269). Lubricate oil seal lip with engine oil. Install Seal Guide (J-35270) on crankshaft. Install oil pump assembly. To complete installation, reverse removal procedure.

CRANKSHAFT REAR OIL SEAL

Removal & Installation

Remove transaxle. Disconnect exhaust pipe bracket. Remove oil pan. Remove rear seal retainer. Remove crankshaft rear oil seal from retainer. Clean seal retainer. Install new oil seal. Apply sealer to seal retainer and lubricate oil seal lip. Install seal retainer to block. To complete installation, reverse removal procedure.

CRANKSHAFT MAIN BEARINGS

1) Remove main bearing caps. *See Fig. 9.* Check main bearing clearances using Plastigage method. If clearance is excessive, install new bearings. If clearance is still excessive, regrind crankshaft and install undersize bearings.

Fig. 9: Removing Main Bearing Cap Bolts

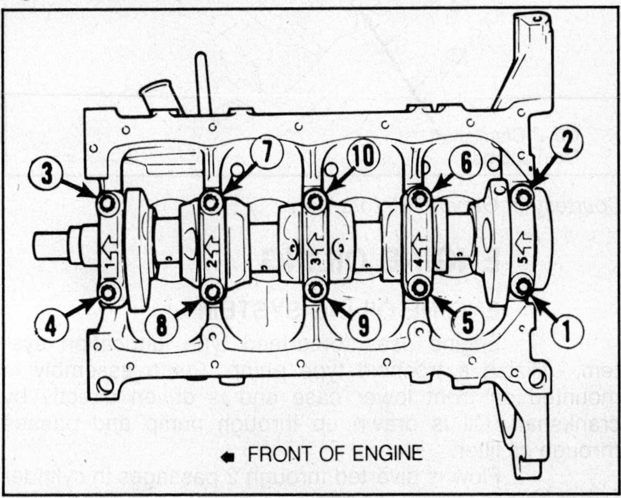

Courtesy of General Motors Corp.

1.5L & 1.5L TURBO 4-CYLINDER (Cont.)

2) Replacement bearings are available in standard, .010" (.25 mm) undersize and also .020" (.50 mm) undersize. With crankshaft removed from engine, measure diameter of crankshaft journals and crankpins at front, rear and in 2 directions to check for wear and taper.

3) If taper exceeds .002" (.05 mm), regrind or replace crankshaft. Check crankshaft runout, by placing "V" blocks under crankshaft at No. 1 and No. 5 journals. Position dial indicator point on No. 3 journal. Slowly turn crankshaft, while noting runout. If runout exceeds .004" (.1 mm), replace or correct crankshaft. Standard runout is .001" (.03 mm).

4) Lubricate engine bearings. Install main bearing caps in original position with arrow pointing toward front of engine. Lubricate main bearing cap bolts. Tighten main caps to specification in reverse order of removal. Ensure crankshaft turns freely.

CONNECTING ROD BEARINGS

Mark connecting rod and cap for cylinder identification and remove rod cap. Check bearing clearance using Plastigage method. If clearance is excessive, install new bearings. Replacement bearings are available in standard, .010" (.25 mm) undersize and also .020" (.50 mm) undersize.

THRUST BEARING

1) Install bearings in engine block. *See Fig. 10.* Position crankshaft in place. Install thrust bearing on both sides of No. 2 crankshaft journal.

2) Check crankshaft end clearance. If clearance is greater than .012" (.30 mm), replace thrust bearing.

Fig. 10: Installing Crankshaft Thrust Bearing

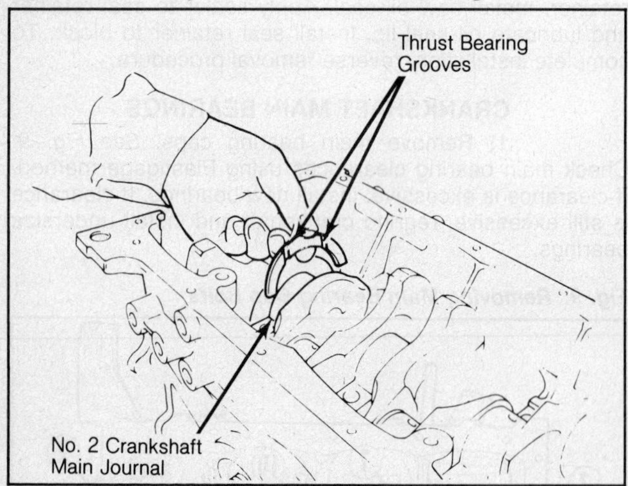

Courtesy of General Motors Corp.

ENGINE OILING

ENGINE OILING SYSTEM

Engine uses force-feed type lubrication system, utilizing a trochoid type pump. Pump assembly is mounted on front lower case and is driven directly by crankshaft. Oil is drawn up through pump and passes through oil filter.

Flow is diverted through 2 passages in cylinder block. One passage reaches crankshaft journal bearings and connecting rod journal bearings and the other flows up to cylinder head through No. 4 rocker shaft bracket to lubricate camshaft and valve train.

CRANKCASE CAPACITY

Crankcase capacity is 3.4 qts. (3.2L) with oil filter.

OIL PRESSURE

Oil pressure should be 57-85 psi (4-6 kg/cm²) at 3800 RPM.

OIL PUMP

Removal

Remove engine from vehicle. Drain engine oil. Remove alternator belt. Remove starter. Install Flywheel Holder (J-35271). Remove crankshaft pulley and boss. Remove timing belt cover and timing belt. Remove crankshaft timing belt pulley. Remove oil pan. Remove oil pump pick-up tube assembly. Remove oil pump assembly.

Disassembly

Remove gasket from block and oil pump. Remove pressure relief valve plug, gasket, spring and valve. Remove oil pump cover. Remove oil pump drive and driven gears.

Inspection

Check oil pump housing for cracks or damage. Ensure pressure relief valve slides freely. Check pressure relief valve spring for wear or damage. Check oil pump drive and driven gear for wear or damage. Check oil pump clearance. See OIL PUMP CLEARANCE SPECIFICATIONS table.

OIL PUMP CLEARANCE SPECIFICATIONS

Application	In. (mm)
Driven Gear-to-Body	.004-.007 (.10-.18)
Gear Side Clearance	.001-.004 (.03-.09)
Gear Tip-to-Cresent	[1] .014 (.35)

[1] – Maximum clearance.

Reassembly

Lubricate and install pressure relief valve and spring. Install new gasket and tighten plug to specification. Lubricate and install drive and driven gears into oil pump. Install oil pump cover. Tighten mounting bolts to specification. Ensure gears rotate smoothly.

Installation

Lubricate front oil seal. Install Seal Guide (J-35270) on crankshaft. Install oil pump assembly and tighten mounting bolts to specification. To complete installation, reverse removal procedure.

ENGINE COOLING

WATER PUMP

Removal & Installation

Drain cooling system. Remove power steering belt. Remove timing belt. See TIMING BELT & SPROCKETS in this article. Remove timing belt tensioner pulley and spring. Remove water pump mounting bolts. Remove water pump and gasket. To install, reverse removal procedure. Tighten mounting bolts to specification.

NOTE: **For further information on cooling systems, see ENGINE COOLING section.**

1.5L & 1.5L TURBO 4-CYLINDER (Cont.)

ENGINE SPECIFICATIONS

GENERAL SPECIFICATIONS

Year	DISPLACEMENT		Fuel System	HP@RPM	Torque Ft. Lbs.@RPM	Compr. Ratio	BORE		STROKE	
	Cu. In.	Liters					In.	mm	In.	mm
1987	90 90	1.5 1.5	2-Bbl. EFI	70 @ 5400 110@5400	87 @ 3400 120@3500	9.6:1 8.0:1	3.03 3.03	77 77	3.11 3.11	79 79

VALVES

Engine Size & Valve	Head Diam. In. (mm)	Face Angle	Seat Angle	Seat Width In. (mm)	Stem Diameter In. (mm)	Stem Clearance In. (mm)	Valve Lift In. (mm)
1.5L							
Intake	.....	45°	45°	.047-.063 (1.19-1.60)	.274-.275 (6.96-6.99)	.0009-.0022 (.023-.056)	.....
Exhaust	.....	45°	45°	.047-.063 (1.19-1.60)	.2740-.2744 (6.96-6.97)	.0012-.0025 (.030-.063)	.....

CRANKSHAFT MAIN & CONNECTING ROD BEARINGS

Engine	MAIN BEARINGS				CONNECTING ROD BEARINGS		
	Journal Diam. In. (mm)	Clearance In. (mm)	Thrust Bearing	Crankshaft End Play In. (mm)	Journal Diam. In. (mm)	Clearance In. (mm)	Side Play In. (mm)
1.5L	1.8865-1.8873 (47.917-47.937)	.0008-.0020 (.020-.051)	No. 2	.0024-.0095 (.061-.241)	1.5720-1.5726 (39.929-39.944)	.0010-.0023 (.025-.058)	.008-.014 (.20-.36)

PISTONS, PINS & RINGS

Engine	PISTONS	PINS		RINGS		
	Clearance In. (mm)	Piston Fit In. (mm)	Rod Fit In. (mm)	Ring No.	End Gap In. (mm)	Side Clearance In. (mm)
1.5L	.0012-.0020 (.030-.051)	.0002-.0004 (.006-.011)	Press Fit	No. 1	.010-.014 (.25-.36)	.0010-.0026 (.025-.066)
				Oil	.004-.024 (.10-.60)	.....

CAMSHAFT

Engine	Journal Diam. In. (mm)	Clearance In. (mm)	Lobe Lift In. (mm)
1.5L	1.021-1.022 (25.93-25.96)	.002-.004 (.05-.10)	[1]

[1] – Lobe height is 1.426" (36.22 mm).

VALVE SPRINGS

Engine	Free Length In. (mm)	PRESSURE Lbs. @ In. (Kg @ mm)	
		Valve Closed	Valve Open
1.5L	[1] 1.9095 (48.50)	47.4 @ 1.57 (21.5 @ 39.9)	.....

[1] – Maximum out-of-square is .04" (1.0 mm).

1.5L & 1.5L TURBO 4-CYLINDER (Cont.)

ENGINE SPECIFICATIONS (Cont.)

TIGHTENING SPECIFICATIONS

Application	Ft. Lbs. (N.m)
Connecting Rod Cap Bolts	25 (34)
Crankshaft Pulley Bolt	109 (148)
Cylinder Head Bolts	
Step 1	29 (39)
Step 2	58 (79)
Engine Mounting Bracket Bolt	17 (23)
Exhaust Manifold Bolts & Nuts	17 (23)
Exhaust Manifold Flange Bolts	42 (57)
Exhaust Pipe-to-Converter Bolts	20 (27)
Flywheel Bolts	[1] 22 (30)
Intake Manifold Bolts & Nuts	17 (23)
Main Bearing Cap Bolts	68 (92)
Oil Pump Cover Screws	27 (37)
Oil Pump Pick-Up Bolts	13 (18)
Oil Pump Pressure Relief Valve Plug	27 (37)
Rocker Shaft Bracket Bolts	16 (22)
Starter Bolts	37 (50)
Timing Belt Tensioner Bolt	37 (50)
Water Pump Bolts	17 (23)
	INCH Lbs. (N.m)
Camshaft Pulley Bolts	86 (10)
Oil Pan Mounting Bolts	86 (10)
Oil Pump Mounting Bolts	86 (10)
Rocker Cover Bolts	84 (9)

[1] – Then tighten bolts an additional 45 degrees.

Honda Engines

1.3L, 1.5L, 1.8L & 2.0L 4-CYLINDER

Accord, Civic, Prelude

NOTE: **For engine repair procedures not covered in this article, see ENGINE OVERHAUL PROCEDURES article at beginning of this section.**

ENGINE CODING

ENGINE IDENTIFICATION

Engine serial number is located on right front corner of engine block just below cylinder head on Accord and Prelude models. Engine serial number is located under hood on the corner of left front fender on CRX, CRX HF, Hatchback, Sedan and Wagon models and on right front fender on CRX Si models. Engine serial number is also located on pad near starter motor. The first 5 characters of engine serial number is used for engine identification.

ENGINE CODE

Application	Code
1.3L	D13A2
1.5L	
Carbureted	D15A2
EFI	D15A3
1.8L	A18A1
2.0L	
Carbureted	A20A1
EFI	A20A3

ENGINE, MANIFOLDS & CYLINDER HEAD

ENGINE

Removal (Accord & Prelude)

1) Apply parking brake and block rear wheels. Disconnect battery cables. Mark hood hinges in reference to location on hood. Remove hood.

2) Raise and support front of vehicle on safety stands. Drain engine oil, transaxle fluid, and coolant. Remove engine splash guard.

3) Remove air intake duct, air filter and air cleaner case. Disconnect wiring and vacuum hoses and remove air cleaner housing. Disconnect throttle cable from carburetor.

4) On fuel injected models, place shop towel on top of fuel filter and relieve fuel injection system pressure by slowly loosening service bolt. *See Fig. 1.* Disconnect fuel hoses from pressure regulator and fuel rail. Disconnect throttle cable from throttle body.

5) On all models, disconnect high tension coil wire and ignition primary wires from ignition coil. Disconnect electrical harness connectors near both shock towers and battery tray.

6) Disconnect ground cables near fuse block and from top of valve cover. Disconnect and mark vacuum hoses from left rear of engine compartment near brake booster.

7) Remove power steering hose clamp bolt from front of cylinder head near No. 4 spark plug. On carbureted engines, disconnect fuel hose at fuel filter. On all models, remove emission control box from right side of firewall. Allow box to hang next to engine.

8) Disconnect and mark vacuum hoses at fuel vapor canister. Disconnect vacuum hose from brake booster. On carbureted engines, remove air jet controller. Mark and remove vacuum hoses near brake booster.

Fig. 1: Accord Fuel Filter Service Bolt

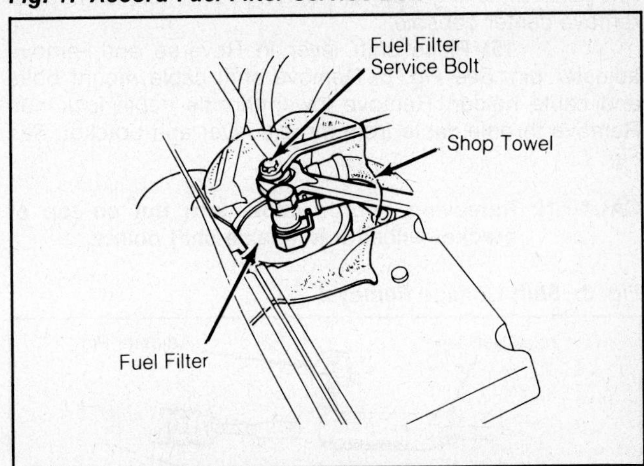

Courtesy of American Honda Motor Co., Inc.

9) On all models, disconnect radiator and heater hoses from engine. On models with cruise control, disconnect cruise control servo vacuum hoses and remove servo.

10) On manual transaxle models, loosen clutch cable adjustment nut and disconnect cable from release arm. Disconnect transaxle ground strap.

11) On automatic transaxle models, disconnect and plug transaxle cooler lines. On all models, remove speed sensor retaining bolt. Remove speed sensor. DO NOT disconnect hoses. *See Fig. 2.* Loosen power steering pump adjusting bolt. Remove drive belt. Remove power steering pump. DO NOT disconnect hoses.

Fig. 2: Speed Sensor Cable Removal

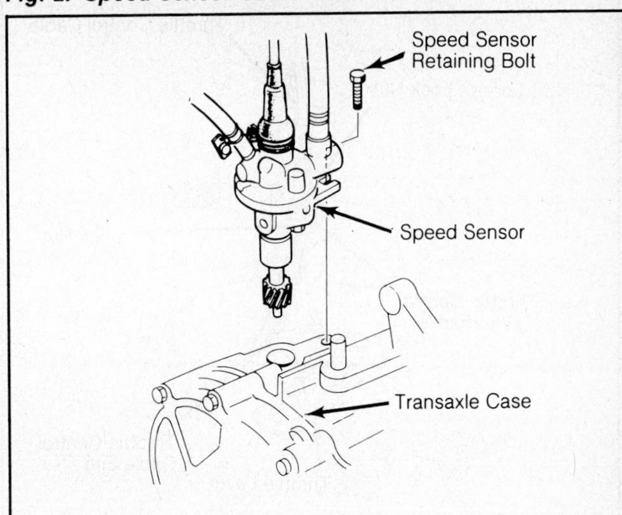

Courtesy of American Honda Motor Co., Inc.

12) On models with A/C, loosen A/C compressor belt adjustment bolt. Remove drive belt. Disconnect A/C compressor clutch lead. Remove A/C compressor mount bolts. Remove compressor and secure to bulkhead. DO NOT disconnect hoses.

13) On all models, disconnect and mark alternator wiring harness. Loosen adjusting bolt. Remove

1.3L, 1.5L, 1.8L & 2.0L 4-CYLINDER (Cont.)

drive belt and alternator. Remove center beam located underneath engine. Disconnect exhaust pipe from exhaust manifold.

14) On manual transaxle models, disconnect shift lever torque rod from clutch housing. Remove shift rod yoke attaching bolt. On automatic transaxle models, remove center console.

15) Place shift lever in Reverse and remove adjuster pin. *See Fig. 3.* Remove shift cable mount bolts and cable holder. Remove lower throttle cable lock nut. Remove throttle cable from throttle lever and bracket. *See Fig. 4.*

CAUTION: Removing throttle cable lock nut on top of bracket will alter transaxle shift points.

Fig. 3: Shift Linkage Removal

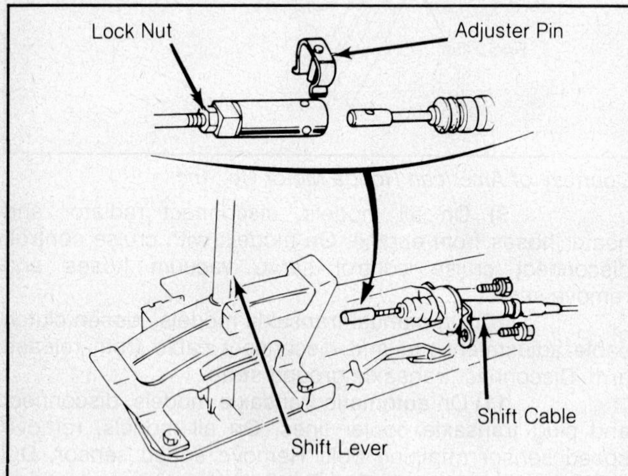

Courtesy of American Honda Motor Co., Inc.

Fig. 4: Throttle Control Cable Removal

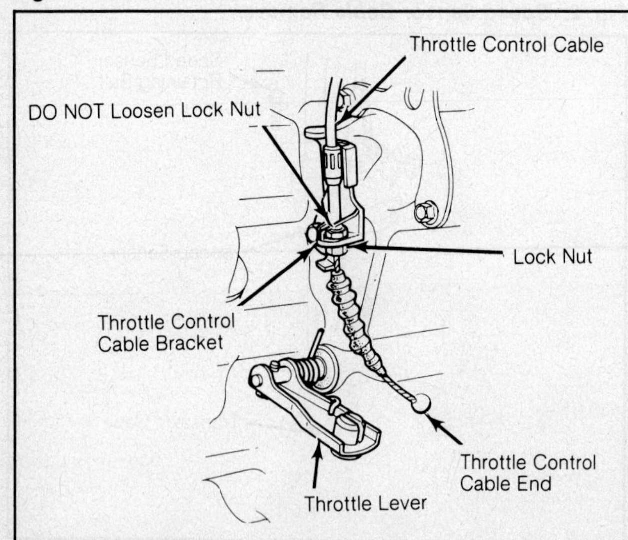

Courtesy of American Honda Motor Co., Inc.

16) On all models, remove drive axles. See FWD AXLE SHAFTS in DRIVE AXLES section. Attach chain to engine. Raise enough to tighten chain slack. Remove bolt from rear torque rod at engine. Loose remaining torque rod bolt. Move torque rod toward bulkhead.

17) Remove engine mount bolts located on front and rear and near timing belt cover. Ensure engine is free from all components. Remove engine and transaxle from vehicle. *See Fig. 6.*

Installation

1) Reverse removal procedure for installation. Tighten engine mounts to specification and in proper sequence. *See Fig. 6.* Improper engine mount tightening will result in excessive engine vibration and premature engine mount wear.

2) Use new spring clips when installing drive axles. Install drive axles until spring clip "clicks" in groove of differential side gear. Ensure all wires and hoses are connected properly. Ensure proper cable mounting.

3) On all models, adjust throttle cable tension. On manual transaxle models, adjust clutch pedal free play. Ensure transaxle shifts smoothly. On automatic transaxle models, ensure gear position agrees with shift indicator. Adjust tension of all drive belts. Restore all fluids to proper level. Open heater valve and loosen thermostat housing bleed bolt to bleed cooling system.

Removal (Civic)

1) Apply parking brake and block rear wheels. Disconnect battery cables. Remove battery and mount. Disconnect windshield washer fluid hose from hood. Mark hood hinges in reference to location on hood. Remove hood. Remove engine splash shield.

2) Remove wheelwell splash shields. Drain engine oil, transaxle fluid, and coolant. On carbureted models, disconnect air intake duct, hot air duct, and hoses to air cleaner housing.

3) Remove air cleaner cover and filter. Remove bolts and/or nuts securing air cleaner housing. Remove air cleaner housing. On fuel injected models, disconnect air intake duct.

4) Place shop towel on top of fuel filter and relieve fuel injection system pressure by slowly loosening service bolt approximately one turn. *See Fig. 5.*

5) Once fuel pressure is released, remove fuel line from fuel filter. Disconnect fuel return hose from pressure regulator. On all models, disconnect throttle cable and clutch cable (if equipped).

6) On all models, disconnect wiring harness at emission control box located in front of engine timing belt cover. Lift control box from bracket. Position control box next to engine.

Fig. 5: Civic Fuel Filter Service Bolt

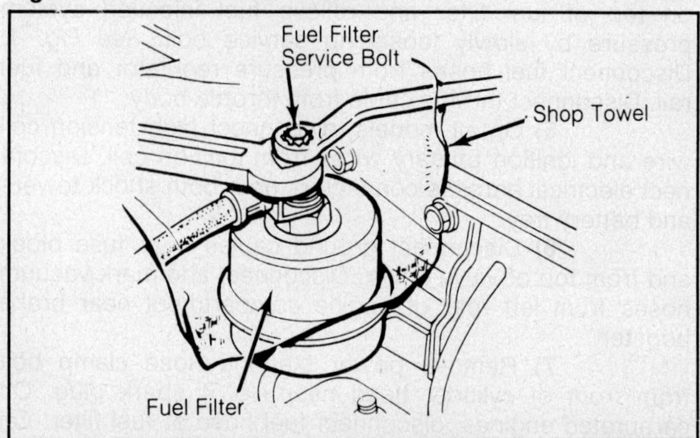

Courtesy of American Honda Motor Co., Inc.

1.3L, 1.5L, 1.8L & 2.0L 4-CYLINDER (Cont.)

Fig. 6: Accord & Prelude Engine Mount Location & Tightening Sequence

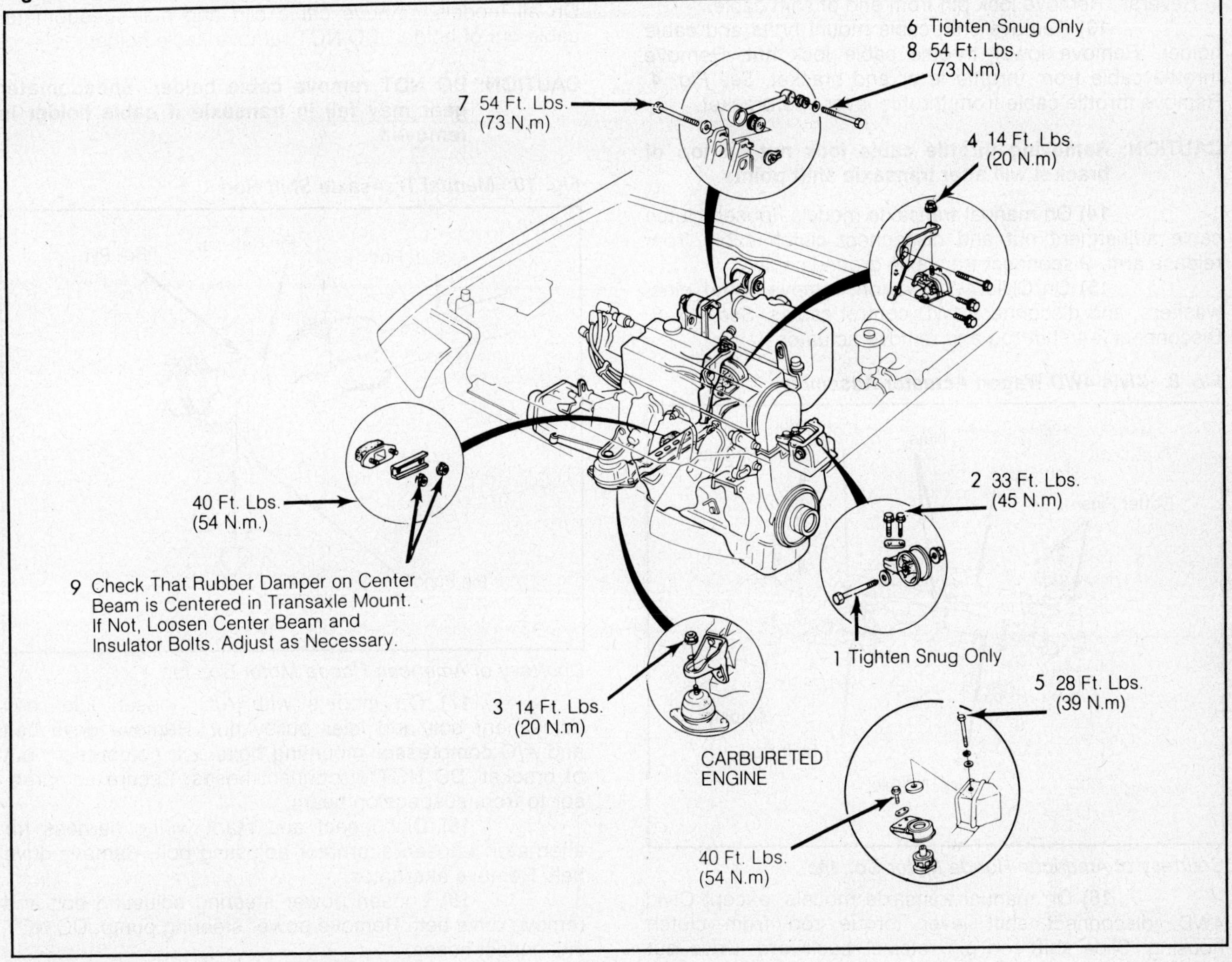

6 Tighten Snug Only
8 54 Ft. Lbs.
(73 N.m)
7 54 Ft. Lbs.
(73 N.m)
4 14 Ft. Lbs.
(20 N.m)
40 Ft. Lbs.
(54 N.m.)
9 Check That Rubber Damper on Center
Beam is Centered in Transaxle Mount.
If Not, Loosen Center Beam and
Insulator Bolts. Adjust as Necessary.
2 33 Ft. Lbs.
(45 N.m)
1 Tighten Snug Only
5 28 Ft. Lbs.
(39 N.m)
3 14 Ft. Lbs.
(20 N.m)
CARBURETED
ENGINE
40 Ft. Lbs.
(54 N.m)

Courtesy of American Honda Motor Co., Inc.

7) On carbureted models, disconnect high tension coil wire and ignition primary wires from ignition coil. On fuel injected models, disconnect high tension coil wire and ignition primary wires from distributor.

8) On all models, disconnect engine harness at right shock tower. Disconnect engine ground strap from engine valve cover. Disconnect brake booster vacuum hose. On models with A/C, remove idle air control solenoid located above and just right of brake booster.

9) On carbureted models, disconnect wiring harness at emission control box on right side of firewall. Lift control box and position next to engine. Disconnect purge control solenoid vacuum hose at fuel vapor canister.

10) On California and high altitude carbureted models, remove air jet controller from left shock tower. Remove emission control boxes from left front fender in front of engine timing belt cover.

11) On carbureted models, disconnect hoses at fuel pump. Remove fuel pump cover (if equipped) and fuel pump. *See Fig. 7.* On all models, mark hoses and distributor for location. Disconnect ignition and spark plug wires and vacuum hoses at distributor. Remove distributor.

Fig. 7: Civic Distributor Assembly

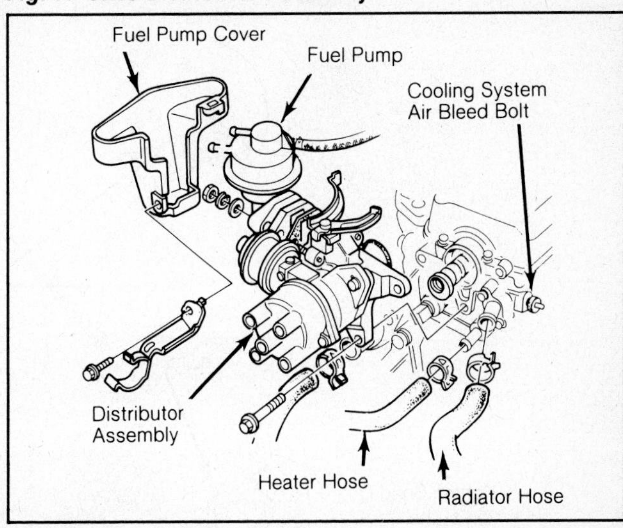

Fuel Pump Cover
Fuel Pump
Cooling System
Air Bleed Bolt
Distributor
Assembly
Heater Hose
Radiator Hose

Courtesy of American Honda Motor Co., Inc.

12) Disconnect radiator and heater hoses. On automatic transaxle models, disconnect and plug transaxle cooler lines. Remove center console. Place shift lever in Reverse. Remove lock pin from end of shift cable.

13) Remove shift cable mount bolts and cable holder. Remove lower throttle cable lock nut. Remove throttle cable from throttle lever and bracket. *See Fig. 4.* Remove throttle cable from throttle lever and bracket.

CAUTION: Removing throttle cable lock nut on top of bracket will alter transaxle shift points.

14) On manual transaxle models, loosen clutch cable adjustment nut and disconnect clutch cable from release arm. Disconnect transaxle ground cable.

15) On Civic 4WD wagon, remove cotter pins, washers, and disconnect 4WD control cables. *See Fig. 8.* Disconnect 2-4 shift rod and remove actuator.

Fig. 8: Civic 4WD Wagon Actuator Assembly

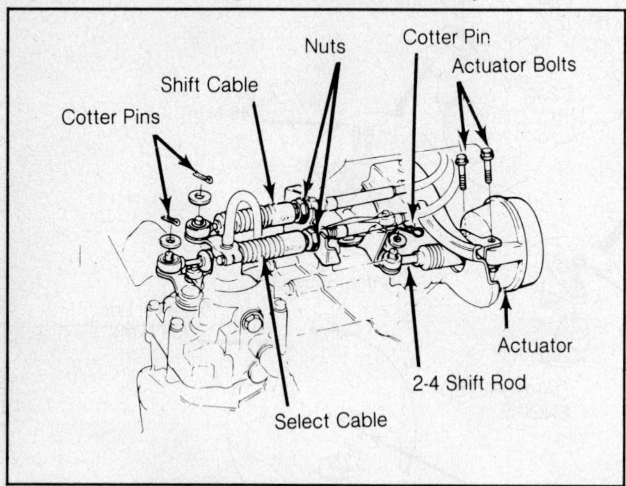

Courtesy of American Honda Motor Co., Inc.

16) On manual transaxle models, except Civic 4WD, disconnect shift lever torque rod from clutch housing. Slide shift rod pin retainer backward. Drive out roll pin with a punch, and disconnect shift rod. *See Fig. 10.* On all models, remove cable clip and pull speedometer cable out of holder. DO NOT remove cable holder.

CAUTION: DO NOT remove cable holder. Speedometer gear may fall in transaxle if cable holder is removed.

Fig. 10: Manual Transaxle Shift Rod

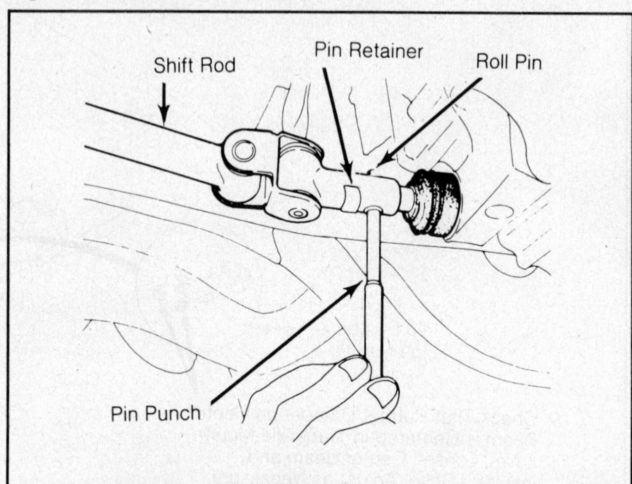

Courtesy of American Honda Motor Co., Inc.

17) On models with A/C, loosen idler belt adjustment bolt and idler pulley nut. Remove drive belt and A/C compressor mounting bolts. Lift compressor out of bracket. DO NOT disconnect hoses. Secure compressor to front suspension beam.

18) Disconnect and mark wiring harness for alternator. Loosen alternator adjusting bolt. Remove drive belt. Remove alternator.

19) Loosen power steering adjusting bolt and remove drive belt. Remove power steering pump. DO NOT disconnect hoses.

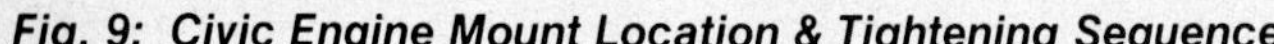

Fig. 9: Civic Engine Mount Location & Tightening Sequence

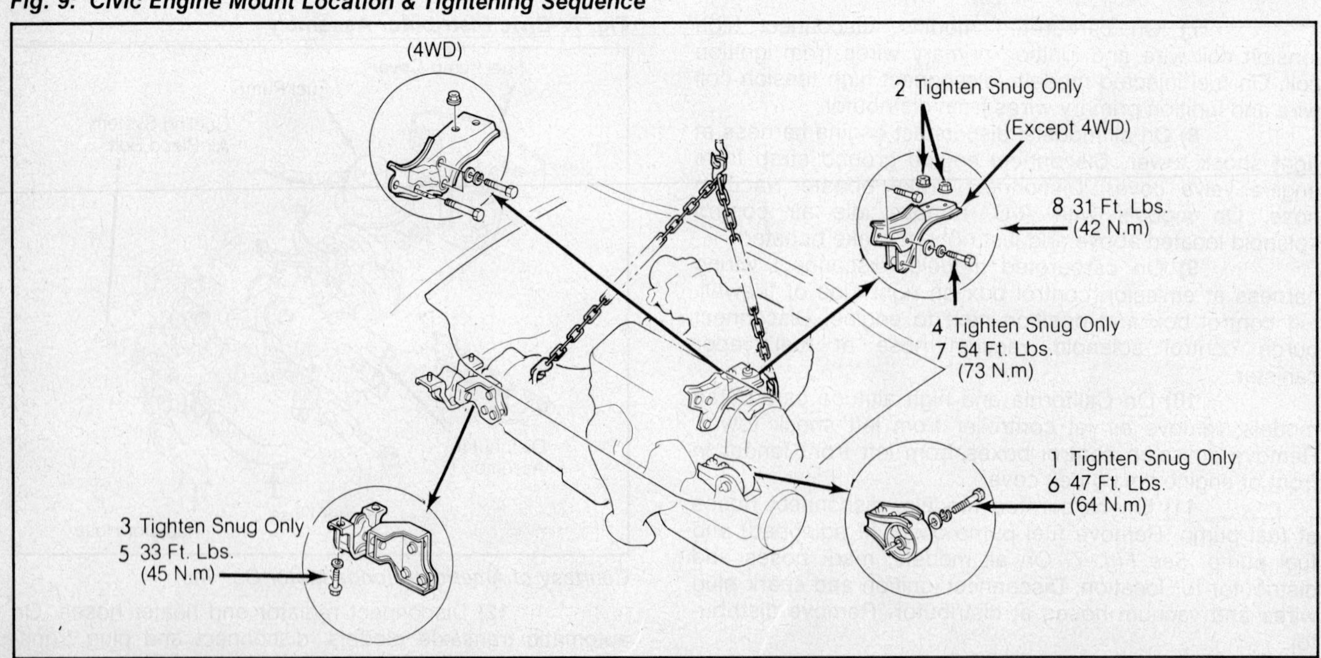

Courtesy of American Honda Motor Co., Inc.

20) On all models, raise and support front of vehicle. Remove drive axles. See FWD AXLE SHAFTS in DRIVE AXLES section. Disconnect propeller shaft from transaxle (4WD wagon only).

21) On all models, remove exhaust pipe from exhaust manifold. Attach chain to engine. Raise enough to remove chain slack. Remove rear transaxle mount bracket. Remove bolts from front and side mounts. *See Fig. 9.* Ensure engine is free from all components. Remove engine and transaxle from vehicle.

Installation

1) Reverse removal procedure for installation. Tighten engine mounts to specification and in proper sequence. *See Fig. 9.* Improper engine mount tightening will result in excessive engine vibration and premature engine mount wear.

2) Use new spring clips when installing drive axles. Install drive axles until spring clip "clicks" in groove of differential side gear. Ensure all wires and hoses are connected properly. Ensure proper cable mounting.

3) When installing speedometer cable, align tab on cable with slot of cable holder. Install clip with bent leg on grooved side. Pull lightly on cable to ensure cable is properly seated.

4) On all models, adjust throttle cable tension. On manual transaxle models, adjust clutch pedal free play. Ensure transaxle shifts smoothly. On automatic transaxle models, ensure gear position agrees with shift indicator. Adjust tension of all drive belts. Restore all fluids to proper level. Open heater valve and loosen thermostat housing bleed bolt to bleed cooling system.

CYLINDER HEAD

CAUTION: DO NOT remove cylinder head until coolant is below 100°F (38°C). Cylinder head damage may occur if removed above specified temperature.

Removal (Accord & Prelude)

1) Disconnect negative battery cable. Drain cooling system. Disconnect vacuum hose from brake booster. Remove ground cable from valve cover. Disconnect radio noise condenser, ignition coil wire and primary wire connector.

2) Disconnect electrical leads from distributor and remove vacuum hoses. Disconnect and mark emission control box vacuum hoses located on right side of bulkhead from intake manifold tubing.

3) On carbureted models, remove air cleaner cover and air filter. Mark hoses for location and remove hoses from air cleaner. Disconnect electrical leads from fuel cut-off solenoid, automatic choke and temperature gauge sending unit. Disconnect fuel lines and throttle cable from carburetor. Mark and remove hoses from air jet controller.

4) On fuel injected models, remove air intake duct. Remove air cleaner cover. Place shop towel on top of fuel filter and relieve fuel injection system pressure by slowly loosening service bolt. *See Fig. 1.* Disconnect fuel hoses from pressure regulator and fuel rail.

5) Disconnect throttle cable from throttle body. Disconnect fuel vapor canister hose from throttle body. Disconnect connectors for fuel injectors, TA sensor and ground terminal.

6) Disconnect electrical leads at throttle, crankshaft angle and oxygen sensors. Disconnect TW sensor, and EGR valve wiring. Remove wiring harness clamps.

7) On all models, disconnect radiator, heater and by-pass hoses from cylinder head. Remove hose between thermostat housing and intake manifold. Disconnect valve body connecting pipe to by-pass hose outlet.

8) Remove power steering pump. DO NOT disconnect hoses. Remove power steering pump bracket from cylinder head. On models with A/C, disconnect and mark vacuum hoses from idle control solenoid.

9) Remove the cruise control actuator (if equipped). On all models, raise and support front of vehicle. Remove engine splash shield. Remove exhaust pipe and bracket from exhaust manifold. Remove air cleaner base mount bolts. Disconnect intake manifold-to-breather chamber hose.

10) Remove valve cover and timing belt upper cover. Rotate engine crankshaft counterclockwise to bring No. 1 cylinder to TDC of compression stroke. Loosen timing belt tensioner adjustment bolt. Remove timing belt from camshaft sprocket.

11) Loosen cylinder head bolts in 1/3 turn increments, repeating sequence until all bolts are loose. Remove cylinder head bolts. Remove cylinder head. Ensure all brackets are disconnected from intake and exhaust manifolds. Remove exhaust and intake manifolds from cylinder head.

Inspection

1) Clean cylinder head and components using approved cleaning methods. Inspect cylinder head for cracks or damage. Check cylinder head warpage.

2) Cylinder head does not require resurfacing if warpage is less than minimum specification. Resurfacing is required if warpage exceeds minimum specification.

3) Measure cylinder head thickness. Cylinder head thickness must not be less than minimum specification after resurfacing. See CYLINDER HEAD SPECIFICATIONS table. Replace cylinder head if less than specification.

CYLINDER HEAD SPECIFICATIONS

Application	In. (mm)
All Models	
Thickness	
Maximum	3.54 (89.9)
Minimum	3.53 (89.7)
Warpage	.002 (.05)

Installation

1) Ensure mating surfaces are clean. Install intake and exhaust manifold using new gaskets. Tighten nuts in 3 steps to specification. Use a criss-cross pattern starting with inner nuts.

2) Ensure cylinder head dowel pins are installed in cylinder block. Install "O" ring seal on oil control jet and install in cylinder block. Ensure No. 1 piston is at TDC location. Position camshaft with camshaft gear grooves aligned with valve cover surface. *See Fig. 11.*

3) Install cylinder head. Coat cylinder head bolts with light coat of engine oil and install. Cylinder head bolts must be tightened in 2 steps, using proper sequence. *See Fig. 12.* Tighten to specification. See TIGHTENING SPECIFICATIONS table at end of article. Install and adjust timing belt. See TIMING BELT under CAMSHAFT in this article.

Honda Engines

1.3L, 1.5L, 1.8L & 2.0L 4-CYLINDER (Cont.)

4) To complete installation, reverse removal procedure. Tighten all bolts to specification. Adjust valves. See VALVE CLEARANCE ADJUSTMENT under VALVES in this article. Apply non-hardening sealant to rounded surfaces of front and rear camshaft caps before installing valve cover gasket.

Fig. 11: Accord & Prelude Camshaft Timing Marks

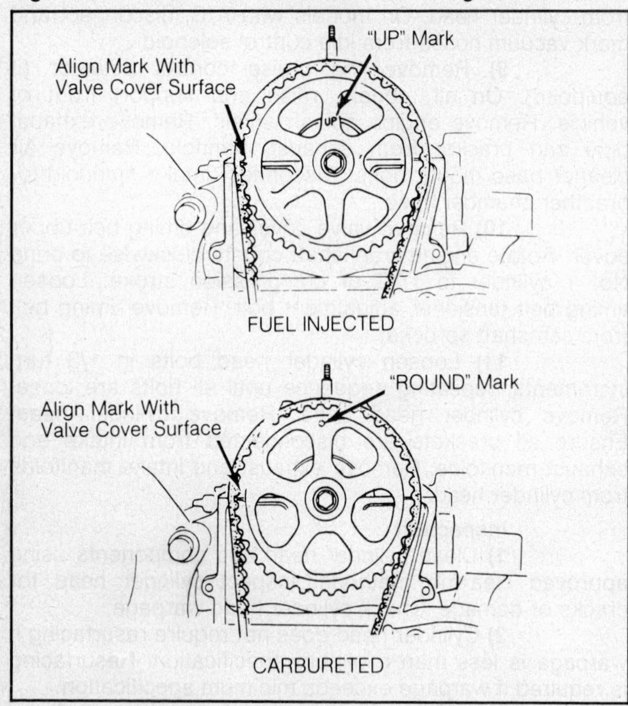

Courtesy of American Honda Motor Co., Inc.

Fig. 12: Cylinder Head Tightening Sequences

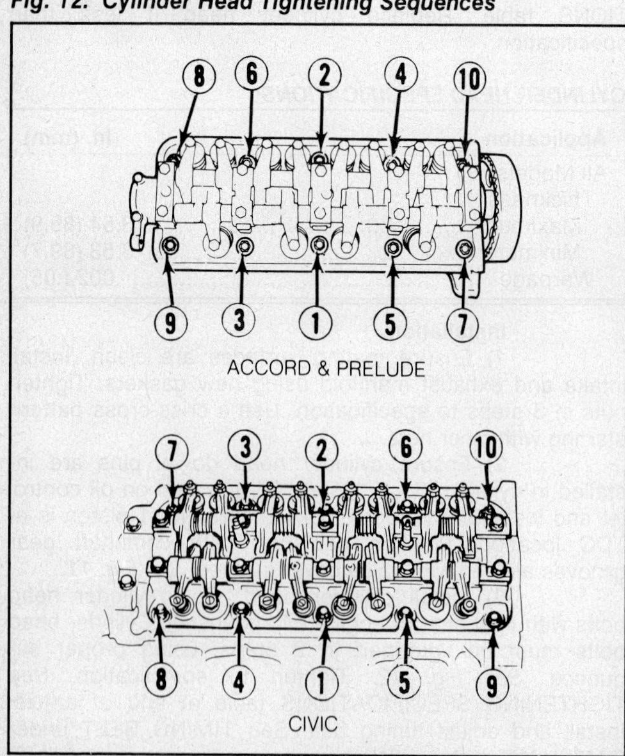

Courtesy of American Honda Motor Co., Inc.

Removal (Civic)

1) Disconnect negative battery cable. Drain cooling system. Disconnect air intake duct. Remove air cleaner cover. Disconnect brake booster vacuum hose at intake manifold. Remove ground cable from valve cover.

2) Disconnect electrical leads from fuel cut-off solenoid, choke, and thermosensor. On fuel injected models, place shop towel on top of fuel filter and relieve fuel injection system pressure by slowly loosening service bolt. *See Fig. 5.* Disconnect fuel return hose from pressure regulator and fuel filter hose.

3) Disconnect throttle cable at throttle body. Disconnect connectors for fuel injectors. Disconnect connectors for the TA, TW, throttle, crankshaft angle and oxygen sensors.

4) On carbureted models, disconnect throttle cable at carburetor, and air jet controller hoses (if equipped). On all models, mark and remove spark plug wires from spark plugs. Remove distributor.

5) Disconnect vacuum hoses at charcoal canister. Mark vacuum hoses from control box located on right of bulkhead. Remove vacuum hoses from tubing manifold.

6) On A/C equipped models, disconnect idle control solenoid hoses. On all models, disconnect radiator and heater hoses from cylinder head. Remove hose between thermostat housing and intake manifold.

7) Remove exhaust manifold and bracket retaining bolts. Remove exhaust manifold. Remove intake manifold and bracket retaining bolts. Disconnect hose from intake manifold and breather chamber.

8) Remove valve cover and upper timing belt cover. Rotate engine counterclockwise until No. 1 cylinder is at TDC of compression stroke. Timing mark on timing belt cover and crankshaft pulley should be aligned.

9) Remove timing belt from camshaft pulley. See TIMING BELT in this article. Loosen cylinder head bolts in 1/3 turn increments, repeating sequence until all bolts are loose. Ensure all brackets are disconnected from intake and exhaust manifolds. Remove cylinder head.

Inspection

See INSPECTION for ACCORD & PRELUDE in this article.

Installation

1) Ensure mating surfaces are clean. Install intake manifold using new gasket. Tighten nuts in 3 steps to specification. Use a criss-cross pattern starting with inner nuts.

2) Ensure cylinder head dowel pins are installed in cylinder block. Install "O" ring seal on oil control jet and install in cylinder block. Ensure No. 1 piston is at TDC location. Position camshaft gear with "UP" mark facing upward and grooves aligned with valve cover surface. *See Fig. 13.*

3) Install cylinder head. Cylinder head bolts must be tightened in 2 steps, using proper sequence. *See Fig. 12.* Tighten to specification. See TIGHTENING SPECIFICATIONS table at end of article.

4) Install exhaust manifold and bracket. Tighten bolts to specification. Install and adjust timing belt. To complete installation, reverse removal procedure. Tighten all bolts to specification. Adjust valves. See VALVE CLEARANCE ADJUSTMENT under VALVES in this article.

5) Install valve cover. Tighten bolts to specification. On specified models, valve cover bolts must be tightened in proper sequence. *See Fig. 14.*

1.3L, 1.5L, 1.8L & 2.0L 4-CYLINDER (Cont.)

Fig. 13: Civic Camshaft Timing Marks

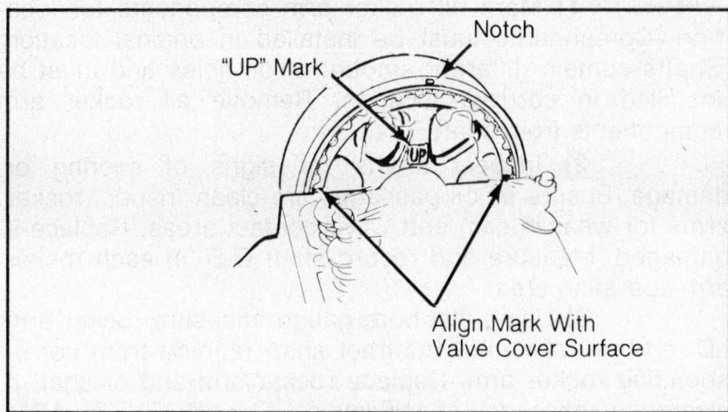

Courtesy of American Honda Motor Co., Inc.

Fig. 14: Civic 1.3L & CRX HF Valve Cover Tightening Sequence

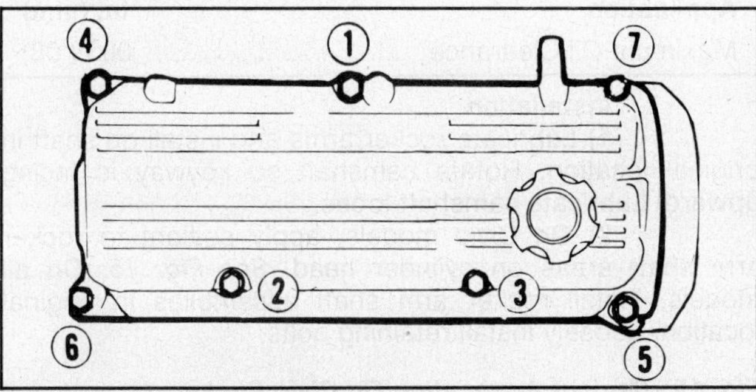

Courtesy of American Honda Motor Co., Inc.

MANIFOLDS

Removal

Disconnect exhaust pipe from exhaust manifold. Remove exhaust manifold and bracket retaining bolts. Remove exhaust manifold. For intake manifold, disconnect wiring and vacuum hoses from intake manifold. Remove intake manifold and bracket retaining bolts. Remove intake manifold and gasket.

Installation

Install intake and exhaust manifold using new gasket. Tighten nuts in 3 steps to specification. Use a criss-cross pattern starting with inner nuts.

CAMSHAFT

TIMING BELT

Removal

1) Rotate crankshaft counterclockwise to position No. 1 cylinder to TDC of compression stroke. Remove all drive belts. On Accord and Prelude models, remove water pump pulley.

2) On all models, remove engine valve cover and upper timing belt cover. Ensure camshaft timing marks are aligned with valve cover surface and "UP" or "ROUND" mark is upward. *See Figs. 11 and 13.*

3) Remove crankshaft pulley. Remove lower timing belt cover from engine block. Loosen timing belt tensioner to relieve timing belt tension.

4) If timing belt is being reused, mark direction of belt rotation before removing. Remove timing belt from camshaft and crankshaft gears. Remove camshaft gear (if necessary).

Inspection

Inspect timing belt for wear on rounded edges of drive teeth. Inspect belt for signs of oil contamination. Replace belt if damaged or contaminated. Inspect all drive gears for wear in drive belt area. Replace as necessary.

Installation

1) Ensure No. 1 piston is at TDC of compression stroke. Install camshaft gear, washer, and retaining bolt (if removed). Tighten retaining bolt to specification. Ensure camshaft timing marks are aligned with valve cover surface and "UP" or "ROUND" mark is upward. *See Figs. 11 and 13.*

2) Install timing belt. Use care not to excessively bend or twist belt. Ensure belt is installed in original direction of rotation. Belt tension must be adjusted.

CAUTION: Belt tension must be adjusted when engine temperature is cold.

3) Rotate crankshaft counterclockwise 3 teeth on camshaft pulley to create tension on belt. Tighten tensioner adjustment bolt to specification.

4) Install washer on crankshaft bolt with flat side toward the pulley. Tighten retaining bolt to specification. Reverse removal procedure to complete installation. Tighten all bolts to specification.

5) On specified Civic models, valve cover bolts must be tightened in proper sequence. *See Fig. 14.* On Accord and Prelude models, apply non-hardening sealant to rounded surfaces of front and rear camshaft caps before installing valve cover gasket.

CAMSHAFT

Removal

Remove timing belt and camshaft pulley. See TIMING BELT in this article. Remove distributor. Check camshaft end play prior to removing rocker arm assemblies. See CAMSHAFT END PLAY in this article. Remove rocker arm assemblies. See ROCKER ARM SHAFT ASSEMBLY under VALVES in this article. Remove camshaft and seal.

Inspection

1) Inspect camshaft lobes and journals for flaking, pitting or scoring. Measure camshaft lobe height. Replace if not within specification. See CAM LOBE HEIGHT SPECIFICATIONS table at end of article. Check camshaft runout. Runout must not exceed .002" (.06 mm).

2) Using Plastigage method, check camshaft clearance. Install camshaft on cylinder head. Install rocker arm shaft assembly. See ROCKER ARM SHAFT ASSEMBLY under VALVES in this article. Tighten bolts to specification.

3) Replace camshaft if clearance exceeds specification. See CAMSHAFT table at end of article. Cylinder head must be replaced if beyond specification and camshaft has been replaced.

Installation

1) Lubricate camshaft journals and journal surfaces in caps and cylinder head. Install camshaft with keyway pointing upward. Ensure No. 1 piston at TDC. Using Camshaft Seal Installer (07947-SB00100), install seal with spring side facing inward.

2) Install rocker arm shaft assembly. Install timing belt. Tighten all bolts to specification. Install new "O" ring on distributor. Install distributor. Reverse removal procedure to complete installation.

CAMSHAFT END PLAY

1) Camshaft end play should be checked prior to rocker arm removal. Loosen all valve adjusting screws. This is done to relieve pressure from camshaft. Using a screwdriver, pry camshaft toward distributor end of engine.

2) Install dial indicator on rear of cylinder head. Position dial indicator tip against distributor drive end. Adjust dial indicator to zero.

3) Pry camshaft away from dial indicator and note reading. If end play is not within specification, replace camshaft. See CAMSHAFT END PLAY SPECIFICATIONS table.

CAMSHAFT END PLAY SPECIFICATIONS

Application	In. (mm)
Desired End Play	.002-.006 (.05-.15)
Maximum End Play	.02 (.5)

CAMSHAFT OIL SEAL

Removal & Installation

1) Remove timing belt. See TIMING BELT in this article. Remove camshaft gear. Pry out oil seal. Apply oil to camshaft and inner lip of oil seal.

2) Install oil seal with spring side facing inward. Using Camshaft Seal Installer (07947-SB00100), install seal. Reverse removal procedure to complete installation. Tighten bolts to specification.

VALVES

VALVE ARRANGEMENT

NOTE: Valve arrangement listed is from timing belt side of head to distributor side of head. On Civic and CRX engines, letter "A" indicates auxiliary intake valve, letter "E" indicates exhaust valve.

Accord & Prelude
Firewall Side – Intake valves.
Exhaust Manifold Side – Exhaust valves.

Civic & CRX
Firewall Side – Intake valves.
Exhaust Manifold Side – A-E-E-A-A-E-E-A.

ROCKER ARM SHAFT ASSEMBLY

CAUTION: Rocker arms shaft assembly must be marked for location prior to removing cylinder head. Each shaft contains different oil passages and must be installed in correct location.

Removal

Remove valve cover. Starting at ends and working toward center, loosen rocker arm bolts 2 turns at a time using a criss-cross pattern. This procedure must be followed until bolts are loosened to prevent rocker arm shaft and valve damage. Remove rocker arm shaft assembly. Mark each rocker arm shaft assembly for location on cylinder head.

CAUTION: Rocker arms must be marked for location prior to removing from shaft. Each component must be installed in original location.

Cleaning & Inspection

1) Mark all rocker arm components for location. Components must be installed in original location. Shafts contain different amount of oil holes and must be installed in corrrect location. Remove all rocker arm components from shaft.

2) Inspect shafts for signs of scoring or damage. Ensure all oil passages are clear. Inspect rocker arms for wear in cam and valve contact areas. Replace if damaged. Measure and record shaft O.D. in each rocker arm operating area.

3) Using dial bore gauge, measure rocker arm I.D. and out-of-round. Subtract shaft reading from corresponding rocker arm. Replace rocker arm and or shaft if clearance exceeds specification. See ROCKER ARM SPECIFICATIONS table.

ROCKER ARM SPECIFICATIONS

Application	In. (mm)
Maximum Oil Clearance	.003 (.08)

Installation

1) Lubricate rocker arms and install on shaft in original location. Rotate camshaft so keyway is facing upward. Lubricate camshaft lobes.

2) On Civic models, apply sealant to rocker arm shaft areas on cylinder head. *See Fig. 15.* On all models, install rocker arm shaft assemblies in original location. Loosely install retaining bolts.

Fig. 15: Sealant Application On Civic Rocker Arm Shaft Assemblies

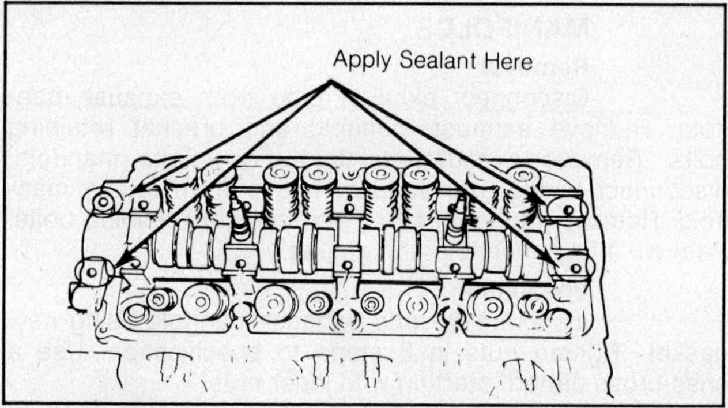

Courtesy of American Honda Motor Co., Inc.

3) Using Camshaft Seal Installer (07947-SB00100), install seal. Using proper sequence, tighten rocker arm shaft retaining bolts to specification in 2 turn increments. *See Fig. 16.* Ensure rocker arms do not bind on valves during tightening procedure.

4) Adjust valves. See VALVE CLEARANCE ADJUSTMENT in this article. On Accord and Prelude models, apply non-hardening sealant to rounded surfaces of front and rear camshaft caps before installing valve cover gasket.

5) On all models, install valve cover. Tighten bolts to specification. On specified Civic models, valve cover bolts must be tightened in proper sequence. *See Fig. 14.*

VALVE SERVICING

1) Mark valves for location. Disassemble cylinder head. Measure valve stem diameter. Replace

1.3L, 1.5L, 1.8L & 2.0L 4-CYLINDER (Cont.)

Fig. 16: Rocker Arm Tightening Sequences

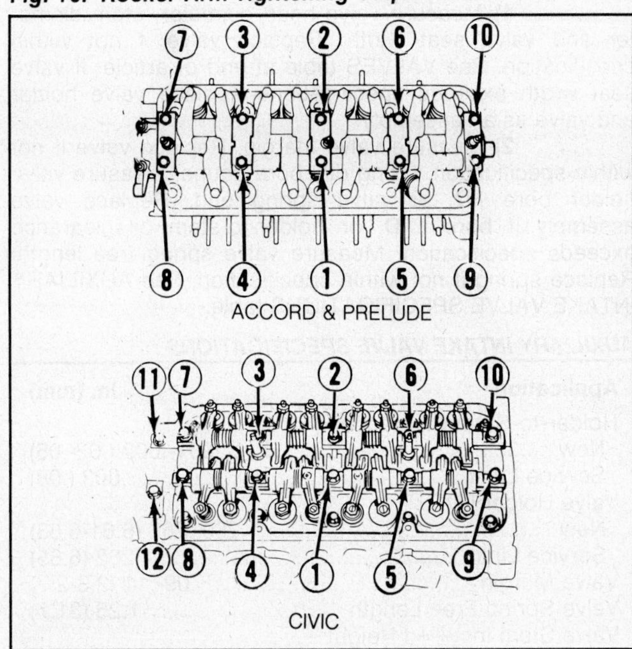

Courtesy of American Honda Motor Co., Inc.

valves not within specification. See VALVES table at end of article.

2) Measure valve margin. Replace valves if valve margin is not within specification. See VALVE MARGIN SPECIFICATIONS table. Remeasure valve margin after grinding valves.

VALVE MARGIN SPECIFICATIONS

Application	In. (mm)
Accord & Prelude	
Intake	
Standard	.053-.065 (1.35-1.65)
Service Limit	.045 (1.15)
Exhaust	
Standard	.065-.077 (1.65-1.95)
Service Limit	.057 (1.45)
Civic	
Intake	
Standard	.041-.053 (1.05-1.35)
Service Limit	.039 (.99)
Exhaust	
Standard	.065-.077 (1.65-1.95)
Service Limit	.057 (1.45)

VALVE GUIDE

Inspection

Disassemble cylinder head. Measure valve stem-to-guide clearance. Replace valves not within specification. See VALVES table at end of article. Valve guide I.D. can be measured using telescopic gauge. Replace guides not within specification. See VALVE GUIDE INSIDE DIAMETER table.

Removal

1) Heat cylinder head to 300°F (150°C). Using valve guide remover, drive valve guide from camshaft side

VALVE GUIDE INSIDE DIAMETER

Application	In. (mm)
Accord & Prelude	
Intake	[1] .260-.261 (6.60-6.63 mm)
Exhaust	[2] .276-.277 (7.01-7.03 mm)
Civic	
All Valves	[1] .260-.261 (6.60-6.63 mm)

[1] – Service limit is .262" (6.65 mm).
[2] – Service limit is .278" (7.06 mm).

to combustion side approximately .078" (1.98 mm). This is done to aid in valve guide removal.

2) Install valve guide remover in combustion chamber side of valve guide. Drive valve guide out toward camshaft side of head. If valve guide will not move, drill valve guide out using 5/16" drill bit. Repeat valve guide removal procedure.

NOTE: Valve guides should be chilled for at least one hour prior to installation.

Installation

1) Install new valve guides working from camshaft side of cylinder head. Cylinder head may need to be reheated during valve guide installation. Valve guide installed height must be checked.

2) Ensure valve guide is located at proper specified height. See VALVE GUIDE HEIGHT SPECIFICATIONS table. Ream new valve guides using valve guide reamer to obtain proper clearance.

VALVE GUIDE HEIGHT SPECIFICATIONS

Application	In. (mm)
Accord & Prelude	
All Guides	.61 (15.5)
Civic	
CRX	
Intake	.79 (20.0)
Exhaust	.75 (19.0)
All Others	
Intake	.69 (17.5)
Exhaust	.63 (16.0)

VALVE SEAT

Grind valve seats to proper seat angle. Check valve seat width after grinding. Valve seat width must be adjusted to specification. See VALVES table at end of article.

VALVE STEM OIL SEALS

When installing valve stem oil seals, ensure intake valve seals contain a White spring around neck of seal while exhaust valves contain a Black spring.

VALVE SPRINGS

Inspection

Measure free length of valve springs. Replace valve springs if not within specification. See VALVE SPRINGS table at end of article. Inspect valve springs for squareness. Replace valve if not within specification. See VALVE SPRING SQUARENESS SPECIFICATIONS table.

1.3L, 1.5L, 1.8L & 2.0L 4-CYLINDER (Cont.)

VALVE SPRING SQUARENESS SPECIFICATIONS

Application	In. (mm)
Accord & Prelude	.068 (1.72)
Civic	.069 (1.75)

Installation

1) Install valve in proper location. Measure valve stem installed height before installing springs. If valve stem installed height exceeds specification, replace valve. See VALVE STEM INSTALLED HEIGHT SPECIFICATIONS table.

2) If installed height still exceeds specification, valve seat is located too deep in cylinder head. Replace cylinder head. Install springs with closely wound coils or painted area toward cylinder head.

VALVE STEM INSTALLED HEIGHT SPECIFICATIONS

Application	In. (mm)
Accord & Prelude	
Intake	[1] 1.913 (48.59)
Exhaust	[2] 1.876 (47.66)
Civic	
Intake & Exhaust	[3] 1.896 (48.16)

[1] - Service limit is 1.943" (49.34 mm).
[2] - Service limit is 1.906" (48.41 mm).
[3] - Service limit is 1.927" (48.95 mm).

AUXILIARY INTAKE VALVES

Removal

1) Remove auxiliary valve holder nut using Auxiliary Chamber "T" Wrench (07907-6570001). Using Remover Handle (07936-3710100), Weight (07936-3710200), and Auxiliary Valve Remover (07741-0010100), remove valve holder assembly.

2) Compress spring and disassemble valve assembly. Mark valves and springs for location. Components must be installed in original location. Remove "O" ring from valve holder. *See Fig. 17.*

Fig. 17: Exploded View of Auxiliary Intake Valve

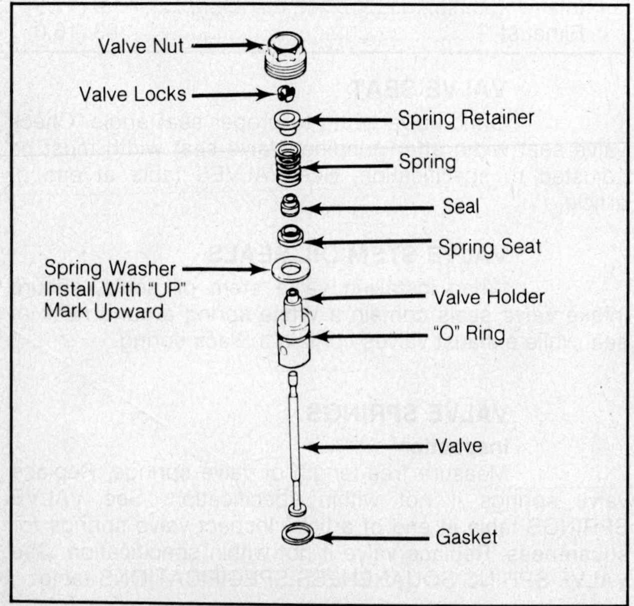

Courtesy of American Honda Motor Co., Inc.

Inspection

1) Measure valve head diameter, stem diameter and valve seat width. Replace valve if not within specification. See VALVES table at end of article. If valve seat width exceeds specifications, replace valve holder and valve as an assembly.

2) Measure valve margin. Replace valve if not within specification. Using dial bore gauge, measure valve holder bore I.D. at valve spring end. Replace valve assembly if bore I. D. or holder-to-stem oil clearance exceeds specification. Measure valve spring free length. Replace spring if not within specification. See AUXILIARY INTAKE VALVE SPECIFICATIONS table.

AUXILIARY INTAKE VALVE SPECIFICATIONS

Application	In. (mm)
Holder-to-Stem Clearance	
New	.001-.002 (.02-.05)
Service Limit	.003 (.08)
Valve Holder I.D.	
New	.260-.261 (6.61-6.63)
Service Limit	.262 (6.65)
Valve Margin	.09-.11 (2.3-2.7)
Valve Spring Free Length	1.25 (31.7)
Valve Stem Installed Height	
New	1.311 (33.29)
Service Limit	1.347 (34.21)

Installation

1) Install valve in valve holder. Measure valve stem installed height. Replace valve assemby if not within specification. See AUXILIARY INTAKE VALVE SPECIFICATIONS table.

2) Install valve in holder. Install spring washer with "UP" mark facing valve spring. Install spring seat, seal, spring and retainer. *See Fig. 17.* Compress spring and install valve keepers. Ensure valve keepers are fully seated.

3) Install new "O" ring and gasket on valve holder. Coat lock nut threads and "O" ring with molylube. Install valve assembly in cylinder head. Align dowel pin with cylinder head groove. Using "T" wrench, tighten holder nut to specification.

CAUTION: Valve clearance adjustment must be performed when cylinder head temperature is less than 100°F (38°C) or less.

VALVE CLEARANCE ADJUSTMENT

1) Remove valve cover. Rotate crankshaft counterclockwise until No. 1 piston is on TDC of compression stroke. The "ROUND" hole or "UP" mark on camshaft gear should be upward. *See Figs. 11 and 13.* Ensure grooves on camshaft gear are aligned with cylinder head surface.

2) Adjust valve clearances to specification on No. 1 cylinder. See VALVE CLEARANCE SPECIFICATIONS table. Rotate crankshaft 180 degrees (camshaft pulley turns 90 degrees). The "ROUND" hole or "UP" mark should not be visible. Adjust valve clearances on No. 3 cylinder.

3) Rotate crankshaft 180 degrees. Ensure both grooves on camshaft gear align with cylinder head surface. Adjust valve clearances on No. 4 cylinder. Rotate crankshaft 180 degrees.

4) Round hole or "UP" mark on camshaft gear should be visible. Adjust valve clearances on No. 2

1.3L, 1.5L, 1.8L & 2.0L 4-CYLINDER (Cont.)

cylinder. Ensure crankshaft pulley bolt did not loosen during valve adjustment. Tighten to specification if loosened.

5) On Accord and Prelude models, apply non-hardening sealant to rounded surfaces of front and rear camshaft caps before installing valve cover gasket. On all models, install valve cover. Tighten bolts to specification. On specified Civic models, valve cover bolts must be tightened in proper sequence. *See Fig. 14.*

VALVE CLEARANCE SPECIFICATIONS

Application	In. (mm)
Accord & Prelude	
Intake	.005-.007 (.12-.17)
Exhaust	.010-.012 (.25-.30)
Civic	
Intake & Auxiliary	.007-.009 (.17-.22)
Exhaust	.009-.011 (.22-.27)

CYLINDER BLOCK

CLEANING & INSPECTION

1) Inspect cylinder block for cracks, warpage, bore diameter, taper and out-of-round. Repair or replace block if not within specification.

2) Cylinder block on Accord and Prelude models are stamped with 4 letters either "A" or "B". *See Fig. 18.* Letters should be read from left to right for cylinder Nos. 1 through 4. Letters are used to indicate bore dimension. See ENGINE BLOCK SPECIFICATIONS table.

Fig. 18: Accord & Prelude Cylinder Block Letter Location

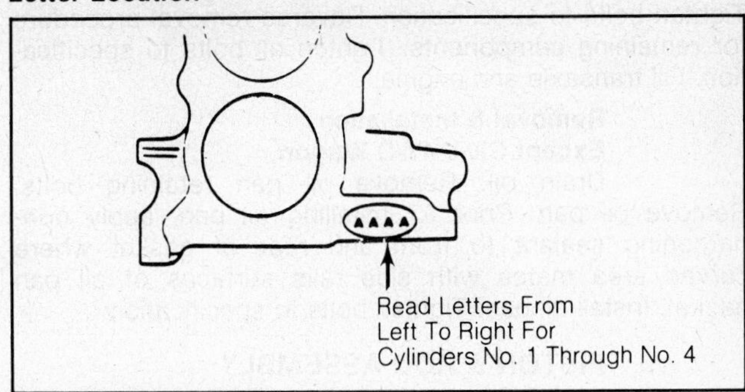

Courtesy of American Honda Motor Co., Inc.

ENGINE BLOCK SPECIFICATIONS

Application	In. (mm)
Cylinder Bore Diameter	
Accord	
"A" Standard	[1] 3.2562-3.2566 (82.707-82.717)
"B" Standard	[2] 3.2559-3.2563 (82.699-82.710)
.30 Oversize	3.2681-3.2685 (83.009-83.019)
Civic	
Standard	[5] 2.9134-2.9142 (74.000-74.020)
.25 Oversize	2.9218-2.9231 (74.213-74.246)
.50 O/S 1.3L Only	2.9317-2.9330 (74.465-74.498)
Cylinder Out-Of-Round	
All Models	.002 (.05)
Cylinder Taper	
All Models	.002 (.05)
Warpage	
All Models	.004 (.10)
Prelude	
Carbureted	
"A" Standard	[3] 3.1500-3.1504 (80.010-80.020)
"B" Standard	[4] 3.1496-3.1500 (79.999-80.010)
.25 Oversize	3.1594-3.1598 (80.248-80.258)
.50 Oversize	3.1693-3.1697 (80.500-80.510)
Fuel Injected	
"A" Standard	[1] 3.2562-3.2566 (82.707-82.717)
"B" Standard	[2] 3.2559-3.2562 (82.699-82.707)
.30 Oversize	3.2681-3.2685 (83.009-83.019)

[1] – Service limit is 3.2578" (82.748 mm).
[2] – Service limit is 3.2574" (82.737 mm).
[3] – Service limit is 3.1516" (80.050 mm).
[4] – Service limit is 3.1512" (80.040 mm).
[5] – Service limit is 2.917" (74.09 mm).

PISTONS, PINS & RINGS

OIL PAN

Removal Civic 4WD Wagon

1) Remove engine and transmission splash shield. Drain engine oil and transaxle fluid. Remove exhaust pipe. Disconnect propeller shaft from transaxle. Remove left cover from transfer case. *See Fig. 19.*

2) Remove shim, "O" ring, drive gear and drive gear thrust shim. Remove driven gear assembly, shim and "O" ring from transfer case. Remove transfer case from clutch housing. Remove clutch case cover. Remove oil pan retaining bolts. Remove oil pan.

Fig. 19: 4WD Wagon Transfer Case Assembly

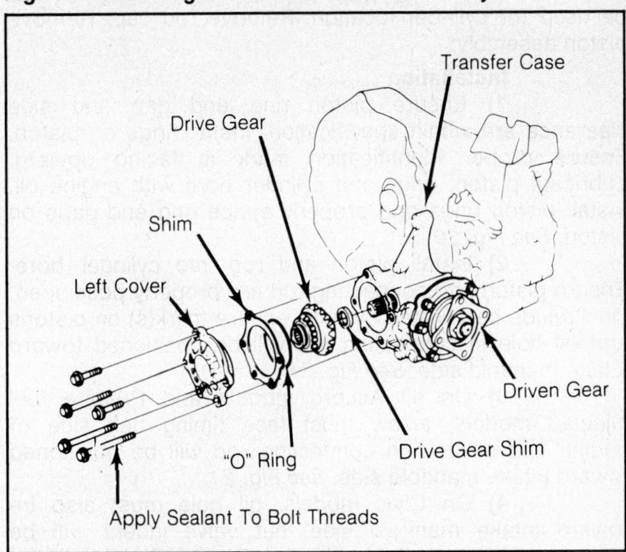

Courtesy of American Honda Motor Co., Inc.

Installation

1) Apply sealant to both sides of oil pan gasket at corners. Install oil pan. Tighten bolts to specification in a criss-cross pattern. Apply sealant on clutch housing-to-transfer case housing. Install transfer case on clutch housing.

2) Coat transfer case retaining bolts with sealant. Install and tighten to specification. Install new "O" ring on left cover. Lubricate drive gear with engine oil. Install shim, drive gear, shim and left cover. Coat retaining bolts with sealant. Install and tighten bolts to specification.

3) Install shim and driven gear assembly. Tighten bolts to specification. Reverse removal procedure for remaining components. Tighten all bolts to specification. Fill transaxle and engine.

Removal & Installation
Except Civic 4WD Wagon

Drain oil. Remove oil pan retaining bolts. Remove oil pan. Prior to installing oil pan, apply non-hardening sealant to front and rear of gasket where curved area mates with side rails surfaces of oil pan gasket. Install oil pan. Tighten bolts to specification.

PISTON & ROD ASSEMBLY

Removal

1) Remove cylinder head. See CYLINDER HEAD in this article. Remove oil pan. On Accord and Prelude models, remove oil screen and baffle plate. On all models, turn crankshaft so No. 2 and 3 crankpins are at bottom.

NOTE: On Civic models, rear crankshaft oil seal, oil pump and oil pump screen may require removal for main bearing cap removal. Main bearing cap assembly may require removal to gain access to connecting rod cap bolts. Ensure main bearing cap assembly is marked for location.

2) Ensure cylinder ridge is removed. Mark connecting rod and cap for cylinder identification. Connecting rod and cap are marked with number which is used for rod tolerance specification. This number is not to be used for cylinder location. Remove rod cap. Remove piston assembly.

Installation

1) Ensure piston ring end gap and side clearance are within specification. Install rings on piston. Ensure proper identification mark is facing upward. Lubricate piston, rings and cylinder bore with engine oil. Install piston rings and properly space ring end gaps on piston. *See Fig. 20.*

2) Install piston and rod into cylinder bore. Ensure piston and connecting rod are properly positioned. On Prelude carbureted models, square mark(s) on pistons and oil hole in connecting rod will be positioned toward intake manifold side. *See Fig. 21.*

3) On all Accord models and Prelude fuel injected models, arrow must face timing belt side of engine and oil hole in connecting rod will be positioned toward intake manifold side. *See Fig. 21.*

4) On Civic models, oil hole must also be toward intake manifold side, but valve indent will be toward exhaust manifold side. *See Fig. 21.* Check bearing clearance using Plastigage method. Tighten rod cap nuts to specification. See TIGHTENING SPECIFICATIONS table at end of article. Ensure rod moves freely on crankshaft. Check connecting rod side clearance.

FITTING PISTONS

Measure cylinder bore and piston skirt diameter. Piston skirt diameter should be measured at 90 degree angle to piston pin and at proper distance from bottom of piston skirt. Skirt measurement should be made at approximately .63" (16.0 mm) on Civic and .83" (21.0 mm) on Accord and Prelude models. Clearance between piston and cylinder bore must be within specification.

Fig. 20: Piston Ring End Gap Locations

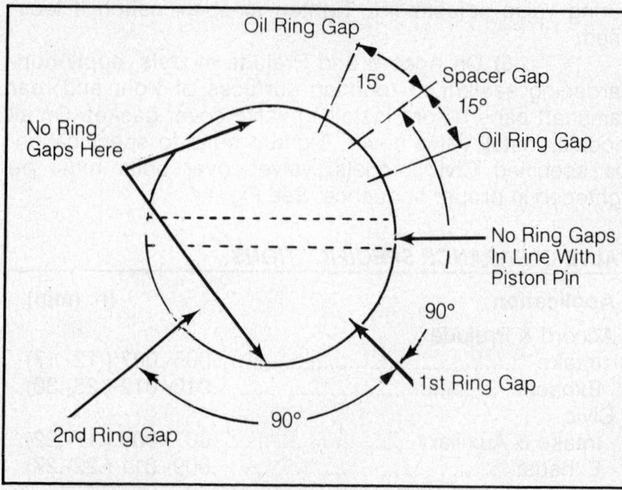

Courtesy of American Honda Motor Co., Inc.

Fig. 21: Piston-to-Connecting Rod Location

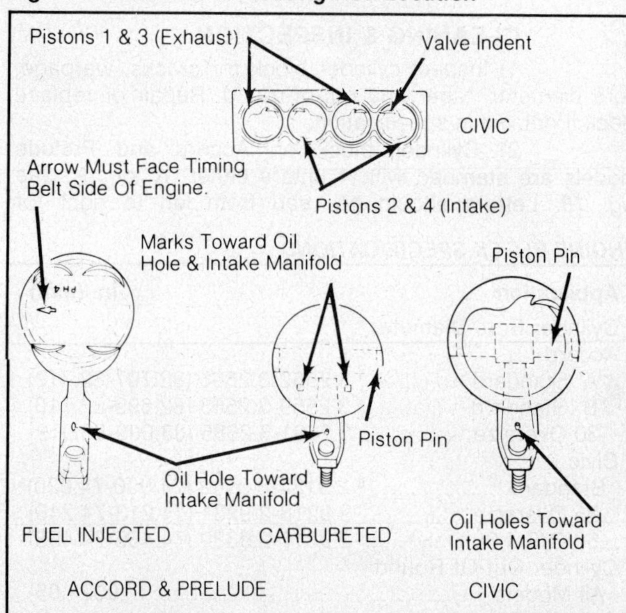

Courtesy of American Honda Motor Co., Inc.

PISTON PIN REPLACEMENT

Removal

1) On all models except Civic with HF engine, install Piston Base Head (07973-SB00100) and Piston Pin Base Insert (07973-PE00400) into Base (07973-6570002). Rotate handle on Piston Pin Driver (07973-PE00301) so driver end aligns with first groove (Civic) and second groove (Accord and Prelude) of driver body.

2) Install Pilot Collar (07973-SB00200) for Accord and Prelude or (07973-PE00200) for Civic models against piston pin. *See Fig. 22.*

3) Place piston on base with embossed mark facing upward. Embossed mark is located on piston just below oil control ring next to piston pin bore. Ensure piston recessed area aligns with lugs on pilot collar. Using hydraulic press, press pin from piston.

NOTE: **When removing or installing piston pin, place piston in press with embossed mark facing upward. Ensure piston recessed area aligns with lugs on pilot collar.**

Fig. 22: Typical Piston Pin Removal

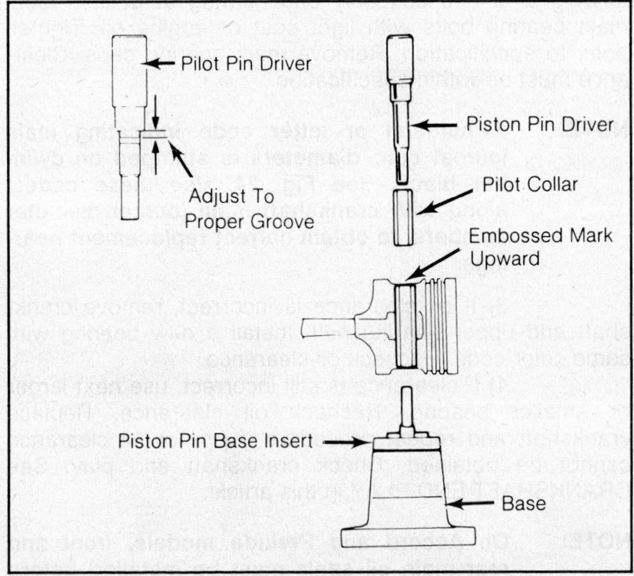

Courtesy of American Honda Motor Co., Inc.

4) On Civic models with HF engine, grind .04" (1.0 mm) from top of Piston Base Head (07973-6570101). *See Fig. 23.* Install Piston Base Head (07973-6570101) and Piston Pin Base Insert (07973-6570400) into Base (07973-6570002).

5) Adjust Piston Pin Driver (07973-65702001) length to 1.96" (49.8 mm). Place piston on base with embossed mark facing upward. Install Pilot Collar (07973-6340200).

6) Embossed mark is located on piston just below oil control ring next to piston pin bore. Ensure piston recessed area aligns with lugs on pilot collar. Using hydraulic press, press pin from piston.

Fig. 23: Piston Base Head Modification

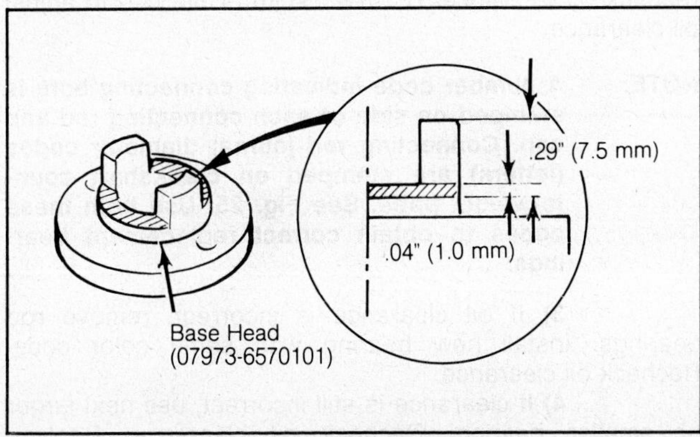

Courtesy of American Honda Motor Co., Inc.

Inspection

1) Inspect piston for cracks or damage in ring areas. Measure piston skirt diameter. Piston skirt diameter should be measured at 90 degree angle to piston pin and at proper distance from bottom of piston skirt. Skirt measurement should be made at approximately .63" (16.0 mm) on Civic and .83" (21.0 mm) on Accord and Prelude models.

2) Cylinder block on Accord and Prelude models are stamped with 4 letters either "A" or "B". *See Fig. 18.* Letters should be read from left to right for cylinder Nos. 1 through 4. Letters are used for indicating piston diameter. Replace piston if not within specification. See PISTON DIAMETER SPECIFICATIONS table.

PISTON DIAMETER SPECIFICATIONS

Application	In. (mm)
Accord [1]	
"A" Standard	[2] 3.2551-3.2555 (82.679-82.689)
"B" Standard	[3] 3.2547-3.2551 (82.669-82.679)
.30 Oversize	3.2669-3.2673 (82.979-82.989)
Prelude [1]	
Carbureted	
"A" Standard	[5] 3.1488-3.1492 (79.979-79.989)
"B" Standard	[6] 3.1484-3.1488 (79.969-79.979)
.25 Oversize	3.1583-3.1587 (80.220-80.230)
.50 Oversize	3.1681-3.1685 (80.469-80.479)
Fuel Injected	
"A" Standard	[2] 3.2551-3.2555 (82.679-82.689)
"B" Standard	[3] 3.2547-3.2551 (82.669-82.679)
.30 Oversize	3.2669-3.2673 (82.979-82.989)
Civic [4]	
Standard	[7] 2.9122-2.9130 (73.969-73.909)
Standard (HF Eng.)	[8] 2.9118-2.9123 (73.959-73.972)
.25 Oversize	2.9218-2.9231 (74.215-74.248)
.25 O/S (HF Eng.)	2.9216-2.9222 (74.208-74.223)
.50 O/S (1.3L Eng.)	2.9317-2.9330 (74.465-74.498)

[1] – Measured at .83" (21.0 mm) from bottom of skirt.
[2] – Service limit is 3.2547" (82.669 mm).
[3] – Service limit is 3.2543" (82.659 mm).
[4] – Measured at .63" (16.0 mm) from bottom of skirt.
[5] – Service limit is 3.1484" (79.969 mm).
[6] – Service limit is 3.1480" (79.959 mm).
[7] – Service limit is 2.912" (73.964 mm).
[8] – Service limit is 2.911" (73.939 mm).

3) Measure piston pin bore I.D. Clearance between piston and pin must be within specification. Measure clearance between connecting rod and piston pin. Clearance must be within specification. See PISTONS, PINS, RINGS table at end of article. Recheck clearance using an oversized pin.

PISTON PIN SPECIFICATIONS

Application	In. (mm)
Accord & Prelude	
Standard	.7872-.7874 (19.994-20.000)
Oversize	.7873-.7875 (19.997-20.003)
Civic	
HF Engine	
Standard	.6691-.6693 (16.994-17.000)
Oversize	.6692-.6694 (16.997-17.003)
All Others	
Standard	.7478-.7480 (18.994-19.000)
Oversize	.7479-.7481 (18.997-19.003)

4) Measure piston pin O.D. Replace piston pin if not within specification. See PISTON PIN SPECIFICATIONS table.

5) Measure connecting rod crankshaft journal I.D. with cap bolts tightened to specification. See CONNECTING ROD SPECIFICATIONS table.

CONNECTING ROD SPECIFICATIONS

Application	In. (mm)
Accord & Prelude	1.89 (48.0)
Civic	
HF Engine	1.65 (41.9)
All Others	1.77 (44.9)

CAUTION: Ensure piston is installed with reference point in accordance with oil hole in connecting rod.

Installation

1) Position piston on connecting rod. Ensure piston is installed in accordance with oil hole in connecting rod. *See Fig. 21.* Turn handle on piston pin driver so end of driver aligns with upper groove on driver for Accord and Prelude or lower groove for Civic models.

2) Install pilot collar in piston and connecting rod. Lightly oil piston pin. Place piston on base with embossed mark upward. Ensure piston recessed area aligns with lugs on pilot collar. Using hydraulic press, install pin in piston.

CRANKSHAFT & ROD BEARINGS

MAIN BEARINGS

Removal

1) On Accord and Prelude, remove oil screen and baffle plate (if equipped). On Civic, remove rear crankshaft oil seal cover, oil screen and oil pump. Ensure connecting rod and main bearing caps are marked for location. Rotate crankshaft so Nos. 2 and 3 crankpins are at bottom.

2) Remove connecting rod caps and bearings. Remove main bearing caps. Ensure all components are placed in correct order. Remove crankshaft. Remove main bearings from cylinder block. Mark bearings for location. Bearings must be installed in original location if reused.

Inspection

Inspect crankshaft for cracks, damaged keyway or threads. Measure journal diameters. Check crankshaft for runout, out-of-round, and taper. Replace crankshaft if not within specification. See CRANKSHAFT WEAR SPECIFICATIONS table.

CRANKSHAFT WEAR SPECIFICATIONS

Application	Standard In. (mm)	Service Limit In. (mm)
Out-of-Round	.0002 (.005)	.0004 (.010)
Runout		
Accord	.0009 (.024)	.0016 (.040)
Prelude		
Fuel Injected	.0009 (.024)	.0016 (.040)
Carbureted	.0012 (.030)	.0024 (.060)
Civic	.0012 (.030)	.002 (.06)
Taper	.0002 (.005)	.0004 (.010)

Installation

1) Install upper main bearings in cylinder block. Ensure oil hole is aligned. Lubricate bearings with engine oil. Install crankshaft in block. Install thrust washer with grooved side outward. Check main bearing clearance using Plastigage method.

2) If engine is in vehicle, support counterweights and check only one bearing at a time. Coat main bearing bolts with light coat of engine oil. Tighten bolts to specification. Remove main bearing caps. Clearance must be within specification.

NOTE: A numeral or letter code indicating main journal bore diameters is stamped on cylinder block. See Fig. 24. Use these codes, along with crankshaft main journal diameter numbers, to obtain correct replacement bearings.

3) If oil clearance is incorrect, remove crankshaft and upper bearing half. Install a new bearing with same color code. Recheck oil clearance.

4) If clearance is still incorrect, use next larger or smaller bearing. Recheck oil clearance. Replace crankshaft and repeat procedure if proper oil clearance cannot be obtained. Check crankshaft end play. See CRANKSHAFT END PLAY in this article.

NOTE: On Accord and Prelude models, front and rear main oil seals must be installed before main bearing cap is tightened to specification once oil clearance is correct. See FRONT & REAR MAIN BEARING OIL SEALS in this article.

5) Install connecting rod caps and bearings. Tighten to specification. Install remaining components. Tighten all bolts to specification.

CONNECTING ROD BEARINGS

1) Ensure bearing cap and connecting rod are marked for location. Remove connecting rod caps and bearings. Install bearings. Check bearing clearance using Plastigage method. Tighten nuts to specification.

2) Clearance must be within specification. Replace connecting rod bearing assembly if oil clearance is incorrect. Install a new bearing of same color code, and recheck oil clearance. DO NOT shim or file cap to adjust oil clearance.

NOTE: A number code indicating connecting bore is stamped on side of each connecting rod and cap. Connecting rod journal diameter codes (letters) are stamped on crankshaft counterweight pads. See Fig. 25. Use both these codes to obtain correct replacement bearings.

3) If oil clearance is incorrect, remove rod bearings. Install new bearing with same color code. Recheck oil clearance.

4) If clearance is still incorrect, use next larger or smaller bearing. Recheck oil clearance. Replace crankshaft and repeat procedure if proper oil clearance

1.3L, 1.5L, 1.8L & 2.0L 4-CYLINDER (Cont.)

Fig. 24: Crankshaft Main Journal & Bearing Identification Codes

Flywheel End (No. 5 Journal)
Pulley End (No. 1 Journal)
ACCORD & PRELUDE
Pulley End (No. 1 Journal)
Flywheel End (No. 5 Journal)
CIVIC
Main Journal Code Locations

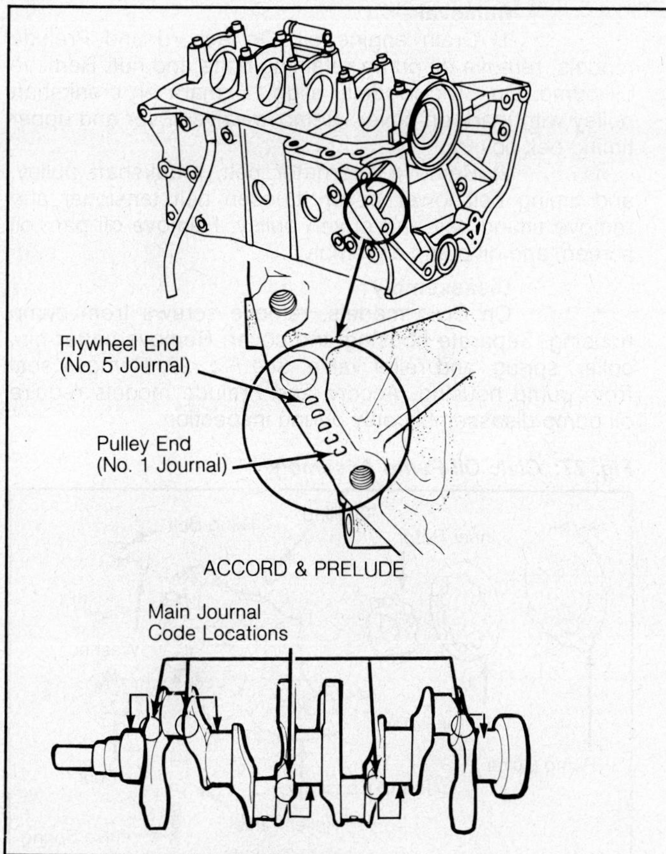

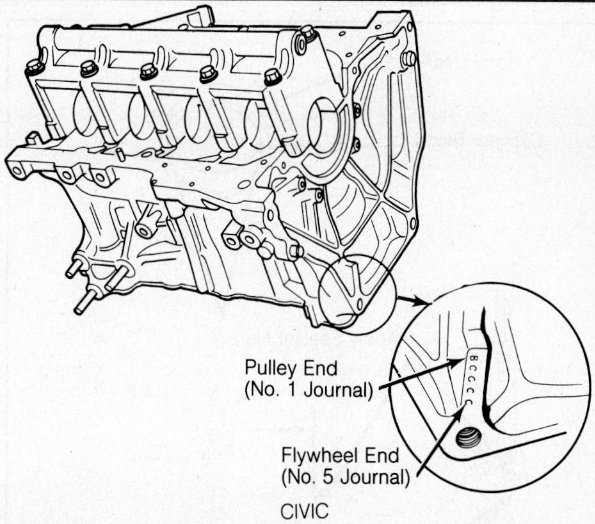

Color Code Is On The Edge Of Bearing → Larger Crank Bore; → Smaller Bearing (Thicker); ↓ Smaller Main Journal; ↓ Smaller Bearing (Thicker)

	I or A	II or B	III or C	IIII or D
1	Red	Pink	Yellow	Green
2	Pink	Yellow	Green	Brown
3	Yellow	Green	Brown	Black
4	Green	Brown	Black	Blue

Courtesy of American Honda Motor Co., Inc.

Fig. 25: Connecting Rod Journal & Bearing Identification Codes

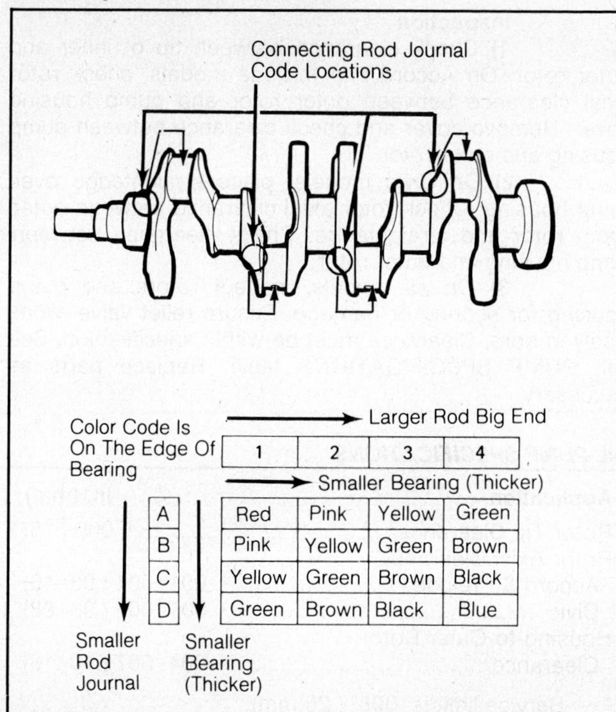

	1	2	3	4
A	Red	Pink	Yellow	Green
B	Pink	Yellow	Green	Brown
C	Yellow	Green	Brown	Black
D	Green	Brown	Black	Blue

Courtesy of American Honda Motor Co., Inc.

cannot be obtained. Check connecting rod side clearance after proper clearance is obtained.

CRANKSHAFT END PLAY

If not within specification, inspect thrust washers and thrust surface of crankshaft. Replace damaged components. Thrust washer thickness is fixed. DO NOT change thrust washer thickness by grinding or shimming. Install thrust washers with grooved side outward.

FRONT & REAR CRANKSHAFT OIL SEALS

Accord & Prelude

1) Install oil seals before tightening No. 1 and No. 5 main bearing caps. Ensure seal bore in cap is dry. Apply non-hardening sealant to inside of seal bore, and at cap-to-block parting line. *See Fig. 26.*

2) Coat crankshaft and seal lip with engine oil. Apply light coat of grease to sealing surfaces of both seals. Fill spring side seal with grease to retain spring during installation.

3) Use Oil Seal Driver (07947-SB00200) for front seal and Driver (07749-001000) with Driver Attachment (07948-SB00101) for rear seal. Install seal with part number facing outward.

4) Install seal until seal driver bottoms. Tighten main bearing caps to specification.

1.3L, 1.5L, 1.8L & 2.0L 4-CYLINDER (Cont.)

Fig. 26: Installing Accord & Prelude Main Bearing Oil Seal

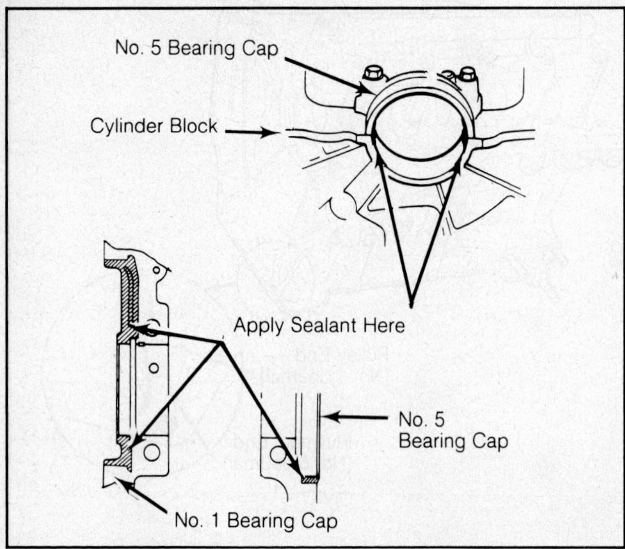

Courtesy of American Honda Motor Co., Inc.

Civic

1) Remove rear crankshaft oil seal cover from rear of cylinder block. Drive seal from oil seal cover. Remove seal from oil pump. It may be necessary to remove oil screen and oil pump. See OIL PUMP in this article.

2) Coat seal lips with engine oil. Using Oil Seal Driver (07947-6340000), install front seal. Install seal until it bottoms in housing. Coat crankshaft and rear seal lip with engine oil. Using Driver (07749-0010000) and Driver Attachment (07948-SB00101), install rear seal with part number facing outward.

3) Apply non-hardening sealant to oil seal cover sealing surface of cylinder block. Sealant bead must be centered on sealing surface. Coat oil seal cover retaining bolt threads with sealant.

4) Install oil seal cover. Use care not to damage seal during installation. Tighten bolts to specification.

ENGINE OILING

ENGINE OILING SYSTEM

Rotor-type oil pump provides oil pressure. Oil pressure is delivered to main and connecting rod bearings. Oil hole in connecting rod provides lubrication for thrust side of piston and cylinder wall. Pressure relief valve is located in oil filter base for Accord and Prelude models and in oil pump on Civic models.

CRANKCASE CAPACITY

Crankcase capacity for all engines is 3.2 qts. (3.0L) without oil filter replacement or 3.7 qts. (3.5L) with filter replacement.

NORMAL OIL PRESSURE

Minimum oil pressure at idle should be 14 psi (1.0 kg/cm²) for Accord and Prelude or 21 psi (1.5 kg/cm²) for Civic. Oil pressure at 3000 RPM for Accord and Prelude should be 54-65 psi (3.8-4.6 kg/cm²) or 48-60 psi (3.4-4.2 kg/cm²) for Civic.

OIL PUMP

Removal

1) Drain engine oil. On Accord and Prelude models, remove oil pump retaining bolts and nut. Remove oil pump. On Civic models, align "T" mark on crankshaft pulley with mark on cover. Remove valve cover and upper timing belt cover.

2) Remove alternator belt, crankshaft pulley, and timing belt lower cover. Loosen belt tensioner and remove timing belt and driven pulley. Remove oil pan, oil screen, and oil pump assembly.

Disassembly

On Civic models, remove screws from pump housing. Separate housing and cover. Remove cotter pin, collar, spring, and relief valve. *See Fig. 27.* Remove seal from pump housing. Accord and Prelude models require oil pump disassembly only during inspection.

Fig. 27: Civic Oil Pump Assembly

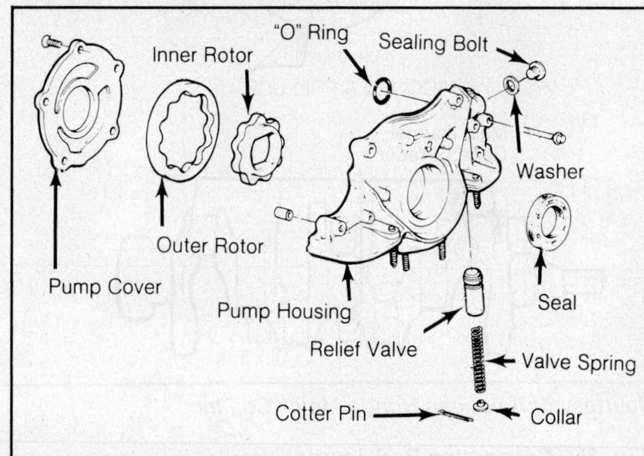

Courtesy of American Honda Motor Co., Inc.

Inspection

1) Check clearance between tip of inner and outer rotor. On Accord and Prelude models, check rotor axial clearance between outer rotor and pump housing cover. Remove cover and check clearance between pump housing and outer rotor.

2) On Civic models, place straightedge over pump housing. Check rotor axial clearance between outer pump rotor and straightedge. Check clearance between pump housing and outer rotor.

3) On all models, inspect rotors and pump housing for scoring or damage. Ensure relief valve slides freely in bore. Clearance must be within specification. See OIL PUMP SPECIFICATIONS table. Replace parts as necessary.

OIL PUMP SPECIFICATIONS

Application	In. (mm)
Rotor Tip Clearance	[1] .006 (.15)
Rotor Axial Clearance	
Accord & Prelude	[2] .001-.004 (.03-.10)
Civic	[2] .001-.003 (.03-.08)
Housing-to-Outer Rotor Clearance	[3] .004-.007 (.10-.18)

[1] – Service limit is .008" (.20 mm).
[2] – Service limit is .006" (.15 mm).
[3] – Service limit is .008" (.20 mm).

1.3L, 1.5L, 1.8L & 2.0L 4-CYLINDER (Cont.)

Reassembly

1) On Accord and Prelude models, install oil pump housing cover and "O" ring. Apply locking compound to pump housing retaining screws. Tighten to specification.

2) On Civic models, install relief valve assembly. Install front crankshaft oil seal in pump housing. See FRONT & REAR CRANKSHAFT OIL SEALS in this article. Install oil pump housing cover. Apply locking compound to pump housing screws. Tighten to specification. Ensure oil pump turns freely.

Installation

1) On Accord and Prelude models, apply sealant around "O" ring groove. Install new "O" ring. Install new gasket to pump housing. Install oil pump. Tighten bolts to specification. Ensure oil pump turns freely.

2) On Civic models, install dowel pins and "O" ring in cylinder block. Clean oil pump mating surfaces. Apply Liquid Sealant (08740-99986) to cylinder block mating surface of oil pump.

3) Apply sealant to threads of inner bolt holes. Install oil pump. Install oil screen. Tighten bolts to specification.

ENGINE COOLING

WATER PUMP

Removal

Drain radiator. On Accord and Prelude models, remove alternator drive belt and water pump pulley. On Civic models, remove timing belt. See TIMING BELT in this article. On all models, remove water pump retaining bolts. Remove water pump and "O" ring seal.

Installation

To install, reverse removal procedure using new "O" rings. Tighten bolts to specification. Loosen cooling system bleed bolt on thermostat housing. Fill radiator with coolant. Close bleed bolt when steady stream of coolant appears.

NOTE: **For further information on cooling systems, see ENGINE COOLING section.**

ENGINE SPECIFICATIONS

GENERAL SPECIFICATIONS

Year	DISPLACEMENT		Fuel System	HP@RPM	Torque Ft. Lbs.@RPM	Compr. Ratio	BORE		STROKE	
	Cu. In.	Liters					In.	mm	In.	mm
1987										
Accord										
DX & LX	119	2.0	2-Bbl.	98@5500	.....	9.1:1	3.25	82.7	3.58	91.0
Accord LXi	119	2.0	Fuel Inj.	110@5500	.....	8.8:1	3.25	82.7	3.58	91.0
Civic 1.3L	82	1.3	2-Bbl.	60@5500	.....	10.0:1	2.91	74.0	3.07	78.0
Civic 1.5L	91	1.5	2-Bbl.	76@6000	.....	9.2:1	2.91	74.0	3.41	86.5
Civic Si										
& CRX Si	91	1.5	Fuel Inj.	91@5500	.....	8.7:1	2.91	74.0	3.41	86.5
Civic (4WD)	91	1.5	2-Bbl.	74@6000	.....	9.2:1	2.91	74.0	3.41	86.5
CRX (HF)	91	1.5	2-Bbl.	58@4500	.....	9.6:1	2.91	74.0	3.41	86.5
Prelude DX	112	1.8	2 x 1-Bbl.	100@5500	.....	9.1:1	3.15	80.0	3.58	91.0
Prelude Si	119	2.0	Fuel Inj.	110@5500	.....	8.8:1	3.26	82.7	3.58	91.0

1.3L, 1.5L, 1.8L & 2.0L 4-CYLINDER (Cont.)

ENGINE SPECIFICATIONS (Cont.)

VALVES

Engine Size & Valve	Head Diam. In. (mm)	Face Angle	Seat Angle	Seat Width In. (mm)	Stem Diameter In. (mm)	Stem Clearance In. (mm)	Valve Lift In. (mm)
Accord & Prelude (1.8L & 2.0L)							
Intake	1.177-1.185 (29.89-30.09)	45°	45°	[1] .049-.061 (1.25-1.55)	[2] .2591-.2594 (6.581-6.588)	[3] .001-.002 (.03-.05)	.....
Exhaust	1.374-1.382 (34.89-35.10)	45°	45°	[1] .049-.061 (1.25-1.55)	[4] .2732-.2736 (6.939-6.949)	[5] .002-.004 (.05-.10)	.....
Civic (1.3L & CRX HF 1.5L)							
Intake	1.177-1.185 (29.89-30.09)	45°	45°	[1] .049-.061 (1.25-1.55)	[6] .2591-.2594 (6.581-6.588)	[3] .001-.002 (.03-.05)	.....
(1.5L) Intake	1.059-1.067 (26.90-27.10)	45°	45°	[1] .049-.061 (1.25-1.55)	[6] .2591-.2594 (6.581-6.588)	[3] .001-.002 (.03-.05)	.....
(1.3L & 1.5L)							
Exhaust Carbureted	1.138-1.146 (28.90-29.11)	45°	45°	[1] .049-.061 (1.25-1.55)	[7] .2579-.2583 (6.550-6.560)	[8] .002-.003 (.05-.08)	.....
Exhaust Fuel Injected	1.295-1.303 (32.89-33.09)	45°	45°	[1] .049-.061 (1.25-1.55)	[7] .2579-.2583 (6.550-6.560)	[8] .002-.003 (.05-.08)	.....
Auxiliary	.47-.48 (11.9-12.1)	45°	45°	[9] .014-.019 (.36-.48)	[7] .2587-.2593 (6.571-6.586)	[3] .001-.002 (.03-.05)	.....

1 – Service limit is .08" (2.0 mm).
2 – Service limit is .258" (6.55 mm).
3 – Service limit is .003" (.08 mm).
4 – Service limit is .272" (6.90 mm).
5 – Service limit is .005" (.12 mm).
6 – Service limit is .258" (6.55 mm).
7 – Service limit is .257" (6.53 mm).
8 – Service limit is .004" (.11 mm).
9 – Service limit is .040" (1.01 mm).

PISTONS, PINS & RINGS

Engine	PISTONS Clearance In. (mm)	PINS Piston Fit In. (mm)	PINS Rod Fit In. (mm)	RINGS Ring No.	RINGS End Gap In. (mm)	RINGS Side Clearance In. (mm)
Accord & Prelude 2.0L	[1] .0008-.0016 (.020-.040)	.0005-.0009 (.013-.023)	.0005-.0013 (.013-.033)	No. 1	[2] .008-.014 (.20-.36)	[3] .0012-.0024 (.030-.060)
				No. 2	[2] .012-.017 (.30-.43)	[3] .0012-.0024 (.030-.060)
				Oil	[4] .008-.035 (.20-.88)	.....
Civic 1.3L	[1] .0004-.0020 (.010-.050)	.0004-.0009 (.010-.023)	.0008-.0016 (.020-.040)	No. 1	[2] .006-.014 (.15-.36)	[3] .0012-.0024 (.030-.060)
				No. 2	[2] .006-.014 (.15-.36)	[3] .0012-.0022 (.030-.055)
				Oil	[5] .008-.024 (.20-.60)	.....
Civic 1.5L	[1] .0004-.0020 (.010-.050)	.0004-.0009 (.010-.023)	.0008-.0016 (.020-.040)	No. 1	[2] .006-.014 (.15-.36)	[3] .0012-.0024 (.030-.060)
				No. 2	[2] .006-.014 (.15-.36)	[3] .0012-.0022 (.030-.055)
				Oil	[5 6] .008-.024 (.20-.60)	.....
Prelude 1.8L	[1] .0008-.0016 (.020-.040)	.0005-.0009 (.013-.023)	.0005-.0013 (.013-.033)	No. 1	[2] .006-.010 (.15-.25)	[3] .0008-.0018 (.020-.045)
				No. 2	[2] .008-.014 (.20-.36)	[3] .0008-.0018 (.020-.045)
				Oil	[4] .008-.020 (.20-.50)	.....

1 – Service limit is .003" (.08 mm).
2 – Service limit is .02" (.6 mm).
3 – Service limit is .005" (.13 mm).
4 – Service limit is .04" (1.0 mm).
5 – Service limit is .03" (.7 mm).
6 – Measurement given is carbureted models. Fuel injected models is .012-.035" (.30-.88 mm) with service limit of .04" (1.0 mm).

1.3L, 1.5L, 1.8L & 2.0L 4-CYLINDER (Cont.)

ENGINE SPECIFICATIONS (Cont.)

CRANKSHAFT MAIN & CONNECTING ROD BEARINGS

Engine	MAIN BEARINGS				CONNECTING ROD BEARINGS		
	Journal Diam. In. (mm)	Clearance In. (mm)	Thrust Bearing	Crankshaft End Play In. (mm)	Journal Diam. In. (mm)	Clearance In. (mm)	Side Play In. (mm)
Accord & Prelude 2.0L	1.9673-1.9683 (49.970-49.994)	[1] [2] .0010-.0022 (.025-.056)	No. 4	[3] .004-.014 (.10-.36)	1.7707-1.7717 (44.976-45.001)	[2] .0008-.0015 (.020-.038)	[4] .006-.012 (.15-.30)
Civic 1.3L	1.7707-1.7717 (44.976-45.000)	[2] .0009-.0017 (.023-.043)	No. 4	[3] .004-.014 (.10-.36)	1.4951-1.4961 (37.976-38.000)	[2] .0008-.0015 (.020-.038)	[4] .006-.012 (.15-.30)
Civic 1.5L	1.9676-1.9685 (49.977-50.000)	[2] .0009-.0017 (.023-.043)	No. 4	[3] .004-.014 (.10-.36)	[5] 1.6526-1.6535 (41.976-42.000)	[2] .0008-.0015 (.020-.038)	[4] .006-.012 (.15-.30)
Prelude 1.8L	1.9673-1.9683 (49.970-49.994)	[2] .0010-.0022 (.025-.056)	No. 4	[3] .004-.014 (.10-.36)	1.7707-1.7717 (44.976-45.001)	[2] .0008-.0015 (.020-.038)	[4] .006-.012 (.15-.30)

[1] – Measurement given is for Nos. 1, 2, 4 & 5 main bearings. No. 3 main bearing clearance is .0013-.0024" (.033-.060 mm).
[2] – Service limit is .003" (.07 mm).
[3] – Service limit is .018" (.46 mm).
[4] – Service limit is .016" (.40 mm).
[5] – Clearance on 1.5L HF engine is 1.4951-1.4961" (37.976-38.000 mm).

CAMSHAFT

Engine	Journal Diam. In. (mm)	Clearance In. (mm)	Lobe Lift In. (mm)
Accord & Prelude			
No. 1, 3 & 5	.....	[1] .002-.004 (.05-.10)	
No. 2 & 4	.....	[2] .005-.007 (.13-.17)	.....
Civic	.....	[1] .002-.004 (.05-.10)	.....

[1] – Service limit is .006" (.15 mm).
[2] – Service limit is .009" (.23 mm).

Honda Engines

1.3L, 1.5L, 1.8L & 2.0L 4-CYLINDER (Cont.)

ENGINE SPECIFICATIONS (Cont.)

CAM LOBE HEIGHT SPECIFICATIONS

Model	Intake [1] In. (mm)	Exhaust In. (mm)	Aux. In. (mm)
Accord			
Carb.			
A/T	1.5174 (38.541)	1.5200 (38.607)	....
M/T	1.5148 (38.477)	1.5218 (38.653)	....
Fuel Inj.	1.5296 (38.853)	1.5274 (38.796)	....
	1.5198 (38.604)	....	....
Civic 1.3L	1.5645 (39.739)	1.5654 (38.762)	1.7447 (44.315)
Civic 1.5L			
Carb.			
A/T	1.5894 (40.370)	1.5902 (40.391)	1.7447 (44.315)
M/T	[2] 1.5894 (40.370)	[3] 1.5902 (40.391)	1.7447 (44.315)
Fuel Inj.			
A/T	1.6096 (40.884)	1.5902 (40.391)	1.7447 (44.315)
M/T	1.6089 (40.866)	1.5902 (40.391)	1.7447 (44.315)
Prelude			
Carb.			
A/T	1.522 (38.67)	1.513 (38.42)	....
	1.505 (38.22)	....	....
M/T	1.530 (38.86)	1.532 (38.92)	....
	1.512 (38.41)	....	....
Fuel Inj.	1.5296 (38.853)	1.5274 (38.796)	....
	1.5198 (38.604)	....	....

[1] – Some models contain 2 intake valves.
[2] – On HF engines, intake is 1.6151" (41.024 mm).
[3] – On HF engines, exhaust is 1.6165" (41.060 mm).

VALVE SPRINGS

Engine	Free Length In. (mm)	PRESSURE Lbs. @ In. (Kg @ mm) Valve Closed	Valve Open
Accord & Prelude			
Intake	1.94 (49.2)	.....	.....
Exhaust			
Inner	1.57 (39.8)	.....	.....
Outer	1.96 (49.8)	.....	.....
Civic 1.3L			
Intake & Exhaust	1.93 (49.1)	.....	.....
Auxiliary	1.25 (31.7)	.....	.....
Civic 1.5L Carbureted			
Intake & Exhaust	1.87 (47.6)	.....	.....
Auxiliary	1.25 (31.7)	.....	.....
Civic 1.5L Fuel Injected			
Intake & Exhaust			
Inner	1.73 (43.9)	.....	.....
Outer	1.86 (47.2)	.....	.....
Civic 1.5L HF			
Intake & Exhaust	1.69 (42.9)	.....	.....
Auxiliary	1.25 (31.7)	.....	.....

1.3L, 1.5L, 1.8L & 2.0L 4-CYLINDER (Cont.)

ENGINE SPECIFICATIONS (Cont.)

TIGHTENING SPECIFICATIONS (ACCORD & PRELUDE)

Application	Ft. Lbs. (N.m)
A/C Compressor Bracket Bolt	35 (47)
Air Suction Tube	51 (69)
Alternator Bracket Adjustment Bolt	18 (24)
Alternator Bracket Bolt	33 (45)
Camshaft Pulley Bolt	27 (37)
Center Beam Bolt	36 (49)
Connecting Rod Nut	23 (31)
Crankshaft Pulley Bolt	83 (112)
Cylinder Head Bolt	
Step 1	22 (30)
Step 2	49 (66)
EGR Tube	36 (49)
Engine Torque Rod Bolt	54 (73)
Exhaust Manifold Bolt	17 (23)
Exhaust Pipe Flange Nut	40 (54)
Exhaust Pipe-To-Tailpipe Bolt	16 (22)
Flywheel Bolt	76 (103)
Main Bearing Cap Bolt	49 (66)
Manifold Nut	
Exhaust	23 (31)
Intake	16 (22)
Power Steering Adjustment Nut	21 (28)
Power Steering Pump Bolt	33 (45)
Rocker Arm Support Bolt	
8 mm Bolt	16 (22)
Shift Rod Yoke Bolt	16 (22)
Thermostat Housing Nut	16 (22)
Timing Belt Adjuster Bolt	31 (42)
Torque Converter	
Drive Plate Bolt	54 (73)
Valve Adjustment Nut	14 (19)
	INCH Lbs. (N.m)
Distributor Mount Bolt	108 (12)
Fuel Filter Service Bolt	108 (12)
Oil Filter Base Bolt	108 (12)
Oil Pan Bolt	84 (9)
Oil Pan Nut	84 (9)
Oil Pump Bolt	120 (14)
Oil Pump Cover Screw	60 (7)
Oil Pump Screen Bolt	108 (12)
Oil Screen Bolt	108 (12)
Rocker Arm Support Bolt	
6 mm Bolt	108 (12)
Shift Cable Mount Bolt	108 (12)
Shift Lever Torque Rod Bolt	84 (9)
Timing Belt Cover Bolt	84 (9)
Valve Cover Nut	84 (9)
Water Pump Bolt	108 (12)

TIGHTENING SPECIFICATIONS (CIVIC)

Application	Ft. Lbs. (N.m)
A/C Compressor Bracket Bolt	33 (45)
Air Suction Pipe Bolt	18 (24)
Alternator Adjustment Bolt	17 (23)
Alternator Bracket Bolt	33 (45)
Auxiliary Valve Nut	58 (79)
Camshaft Pulley Bolt	27 (37)
Connecting Rod Nut	20 (27)
Crankshaft Pulley Bolt	83 (112)
Cylinder Head Bolt & Nut	
Step 1	22 (30)
Step 2	43 (58)
Distributor Assembly Mount Bolt	17 (23)
Exhaust Manifold Bracket Bolt	
Carbureted	17 (23)
Fuel Injected	33 (45)
Exhaust Pipe Flange Nut	25 (34)
Exhaust Pipe-To-Tailpipe Bolt	16 (22)
Flywheel Bolt	76 (103)
Fuel Pump Mount Nut	17 (23)
Main Bearing Cap Bolt	36 (49)
Manifold Bolt & Nut	
Exhaust	23 (31)
Intake	16 (22)
Oil Cooler Center Bolt	58 (79)
Oil Screen Nut	17 (23)
Propeller Shaft Bolt	24 (33)
Rocker Arm Support Bolt	16 (22)
Timing Belt Adjuster Bolt	35 (48)
Transfer Case Cover Bolt	33 (45)
Transfer Case Driven Gear Bolt	19 (26)
Torque Converter	
Drive Plate Bolt	54 (73)
Upper Intake Manifold Bolt	
8 mm Bolt	16 (22)
Valve Adjustment Nut	14 (19)
	INCH Lbs. (N.m)
Air Suction Pipe Nut	84 (9)
Crankshaft Rear Oil Seal	
Cover Bolt	108 (12)
Fuel Filter Service Bolt	108 (12)
Oil Pan Bolt	108 (12)
Oil Pan Nut	108 (12)
Oil Pump Bolt	108 (12)
Oil Pump Cover Screw	48 (5)
Oil Screen Bolt	108 (12)
Shift Lever Torque Rod	84 (9)
Thermostat Housing Bolt	108 (12)
Timing Belt Cover Bolt	84 (9)
Upper Intake Manifold Bolt	
6 mm Bolt	108 (12)
Valve Cover Bolt 1.3L	108 (12)
Valve Cover Nut	84 (9)
Water Pump Bolt	108 (12)

Isuzu Engines

1.9L, 2.0L TURBO & 2.3L 4-CYLINDER

Impulse, P'UP, Trooper II

NOTE: For I-Mark 1.5L engine see GENERAL MOTORS & ISUZU ENGINES, 1.5L & 1.5L TURBO 4-CYLINDER.

NOTE: For engine repair procedures not covered in this article, see ENGINE OVERHAUL PROCEDURES article at beginning of this section.

ENGINE CODING

ENGINE IDENTIFICATION

Engine may be identified by the eighth character of the Vehicle Identification Number (VIN). The VIN is stamped on a metal tab, located on top of instrument panel at lower left of windshield. Engine serial number is stamped on top right front corner of engine block on the 1.9L (G200Z) engines. The 2.0L Turbo (4ZC1) engine serial number is stamped on left rear corner of the engine block. The 2.3L (4ZD1) engine serial number is stamped on the top deck of the cylinder block in the center of the right side.

ENGINE IDENTIFICATION CODES

Application	Code
Impulse & P'UP (1.9L)	A
Impulse (2.0L Turbo)	F
P'UP & Trooper II (2.3L)	L

ENGINE, MANIFOLDS & CYLINDER HEAD

ENGINE

Removal & Installation (Impulse)

1) Disconnect battery cables. Remove hood strut. Scribe hinge positions on hood and remove hood. Remove lower engine cover. Drain crankcase oil and cooling system. Remove lower and upper radiator hoses. Disconnect transmission oil cooler line (if equipped).

2) Discharge A/C system. Disconnect receiver-drier line. Disconnect A/C compressor line at condenser. Remove A/C compressor and set aside. Remove air duct-to-cylinder head cover/turbocharger (if equipped). Remove throttle body/intercooler air duct hose (if equipped). Disconnect accelerator cable at throttle body. On turbo models, disconnect air duct-to-intercooler hose.

3) Depressurize fuel system. Disconnect injection pipe-to-pressure regulator hose and fuel hose from fuel injection line at rear of engine. Disconnect canister purge hoses from vacuum chamber and at 3-way connector. Disconnect vacuum switching valve hoses from vacuum chamber and at 3-way connector.

4) Disconnect wiring from inner fender panel to cylinder head. Remove coil high tension wire. On models with digital instrument panel, disconnect boost sensor wiring and vacuum hose.

5) Disconnect oil pressure sending unit, oil pressure switch and coolant temperature sensor wiring. Disconnect knock sensor and I-TEC wiring. Disconnect crankshaft position sensor wiring at distributor. Disconnect starter wiring and engine-to-rear crossmember ground cable.

6) Remove right engine mount nut. Remove air intake duct at front of engine. Remove radiator reservoir hose. Disconnect alternator and oxygen sensor wiring. Disconnect cruise control-to-vacuum chamber hose. Disconnect automatic transmission control wiring (if equipped).

7) Disconnect power brake unit vacuum hose from intake manifold. Disconnect heater hoses. Remove heat shield from left engine mount and remove mount bolt. Disconnect power steering lines. Remove propeller shaft. Disconnect speedometer cable. Disconnect shift lever from automatic transmission (if equipped).

8) Remove clutch slave cylinder from manual transmission (if equipped). Remove exhaust pipe bracket and catalytic converter. Disconnect exhaust pipe from exhaust manifold. Support engine and remove rear engine mount. Remove engine and transmission from vehicle. To install, reverse removal procedure.

Removal & Installation (P'UP & Trooper II)

1) Complete step number **1)** of Impulse engine removal procedure. Disconnect hoses and remove air filter assembly. Disconnect hot air supply hose. Disconnect alternator wiring. Remove exhaust pipe from manifold.

2) Release tension from clutch control cable. Disconnect O_2 sensor wiring (if equipped). Disconnect heater hoses. Disconnect supply hoses to air switching valves (if equipped).

NOTE: On 4x4 vehicles, separate engine and transmission before removing engine from vehicle. Remove engine/transmission as a unit on 2WD vehicles.

3) Disconnect fuel lines, hoses and ground cable from engine. Disconnect wiring and throttle cable. Disconnect transmission wiring. Remove engine mount bolts and reaction plate.

4) Disconnect A/C compressor hoses (if equipped). Remove radiator and cooling fan. Remove transmission shift lever assembly from inside cab. Disconnect parking brake cable and return spring.

5) Disconnect drive shaft at transmission. Remove clutch return spring and disconnect clutch cable. Remove exhaust pipe bracket from transmission. Disconnect speedometer cable.

6) Raise engine slightly and remove rear engine mounting bolts. Raise engine at front and remove from vehicle. Separate engine from transmission. To install, reverse removal procedures.

INTAKE MANIFOLD

Removal & Installation

Drain cooling system. Disconnect top radiator hose. Remove A/C compressor and bracket (if equipped). Disconnect EGR pipe from rear of intake manifold. Disconnect throttle cable, wiring, fuel and vacuum hoses. Remove intake manifold and throttle body/intercooler or carburetor as an assembly. To install, reverse removal procedure.

EXHAUST MANIFOLD

Removal & Installation

Disconnect EGR pipe. Remove heat shield. Disconnect exhaust pipe. Disconnect oxygen sensor wiring. On turbo models, disconnect oil supply, water supply and return lines at turbocharger. Separate turbocharger from exhaust manifold. Remove exhaust manifold. To install, reverse removal procedure.

CYLINDER HEAD

Removal (1.9L)

1) Remove valve cover, gasket and front plug. Remove camshaft sprocket bolt. Position timing chain and sprocket between guide and tensioner. Insert a screwdriver along right side of chain and depress tensioner lock lever rearward. Push in on tensioner adjustment shoe and lock tensioner in retracted position by releasing lever. *See Fig. 1.*

NOTE: **A timing chain is used on 1.9L engines. A timing belt is used on 2.0L Turbo & 2.3L engines.**

2) Start with outer nuts and work inward to loosen camshaft brackets. Remove camshaft brackets and nuts. Remove cylinder head-to-front cover bolts. Starting with outer bolts and working inward, loosen cylinder head bolts using Head Bolt Wrench (J-24239-01). Remove cylinder head and gasket.

Removal (2.0L & 2.3L)

1) Remove tension spring and loosen tensioner adjusting bolt. Move tension sprocket toward water pump. Remove timing belt, sprocket, tensioner and spring. Hold camshaft sprocket stationary and remove camshaft sprocket nut. Remove sprocket and guide plate.

2) Start with outer nuts and work inward to loosen camshaft brackets. Remove camshaft brackets and nuts. Remove cylinder head-to-front cover bolts. Starting with outer bolts and working inward, loosen cylinder head bolts using Head Bolt Wrench (J-24239-01). Remove cylinder head and gasket.

Installation (All Engines)

1) Clean gasket surfaces. Clean head bolts and threads in cylinder block. Install new head gasket with side marked "TOP" up. Apply a thin coat of engine oil to head bolt threads. Install cylinder head, but do not tighten bolts.

2) Apply a thin coat of oil to front cover bolts and install. Tighten cylinder head bolts and front cover bolts to specifications. Tighten cylinder head bolts in sequence. *See Fig. 2.* Reverse removal procedure to complete installation.

CAMSHAFT

ENGINE FRONT COVER

Removal (1.9L)

Remove cylinder head. Remove oil pan. Remove oil pump pick-up tube. Remove drive belts. Remove vibration damper assembly. Remove A/C compressor and mounting brackets (if equipped). Remove distributor.

Installation

1) Install front cover gasket. Position No. 1 piston at TDC of compression stroke. Turn punch mark on oil pump drive gear towards oil filter. Align center of dowel pin with mark on pump case. *See Fig. 3.*

2) Install front cover by engaging pinion gear with oil pump drive gear on crankshaft. Ensure that punch mark on oil pump drive gear is toward engine. Mark may be seen through clearance between front cover and block with oil pan removed.

Fig. 1: Locking Timing Chain Tensioner on 1.9L models

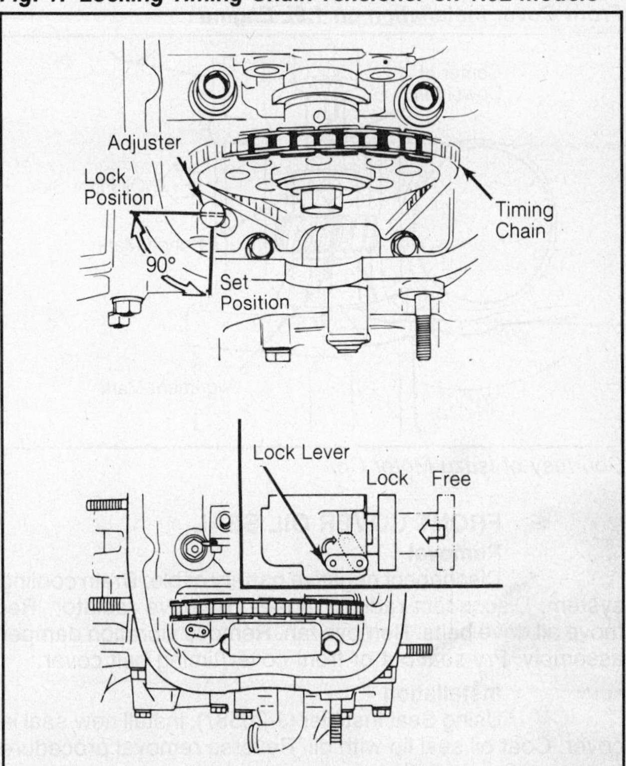

Courtesy of Isuzu Motor Co.

Fig. 2: Cylinder Head Tightening Sequence

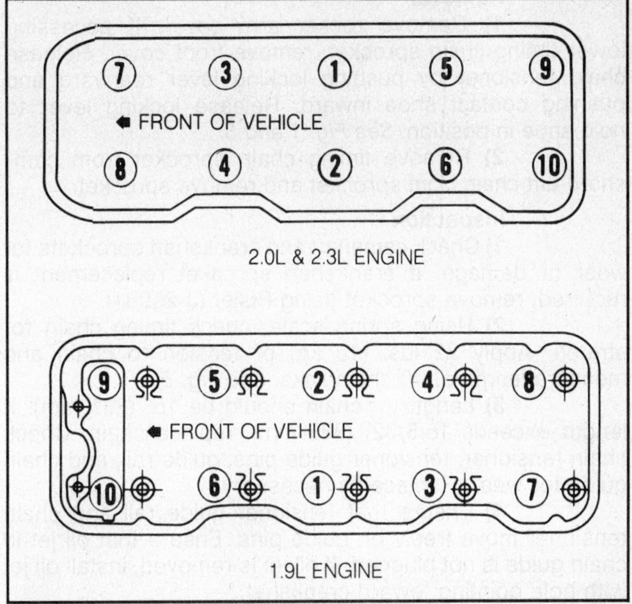

Courtesy of Isuzu Motor Co.

3) Ensure that slot at end of oil pump shaft (as viewed from top of front cover) is parallel with front face of cylinder block. Slot is offset towards the front, when No. 1 cylinder is at TDC of compression stroke. *See Fig. 12.* Reverse removal procedure to complete installation.

Isuzu Engines

1.9L, 2.0L TURBO & 2.3L 4-CYLINDER (Cont.)

Fig. 3: Aligning Oil Pump for Front Cover Installation on 1.9L Engine

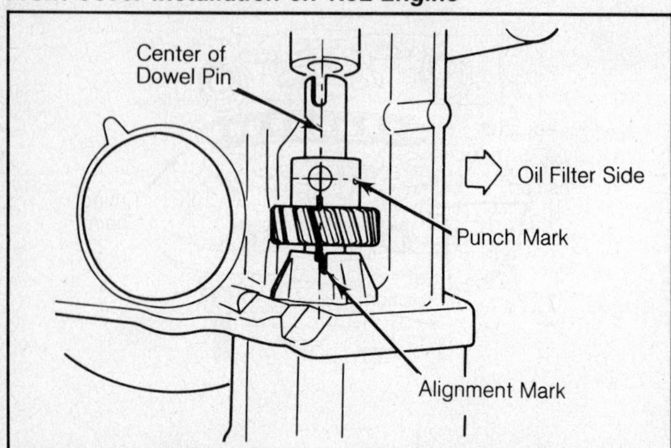

Courtesy of Isuzu Motor Co.

FRONT COVER OIL SEAL

Removal

Disconnect negative battery cable. Drain cooling system. Disconnect radiator hoses. Remove radiator. Remove all drive belts. Remove fan. Remove vibration damper assembly. Pry seal out of front cover/timing belt cover.

Installation

Using Seal Installer (J-26587), install new seal in cover. Coat oil seal lip with oil. Reverse removal procedure to complete installation.

TIMING CHAIN & SPROCKETS (1.9L)

Removal

1) Remove rocker arm cover. If accessing lower timing chain sprocket, remove front cover. Release chain tensioner by pushing locking lever rearward and pushing contact shoe inward. Release locking lever to hold shoe in position. *See Fig. 1 and 5.*

2) Remove timing chain sprocket from camshaft. Lift chain from sprocket and remove sprocket.

Inspection

1) Check camshaft and crankshaft sprockets for wear or damage. If crankshaft sprocket replacement is required, remove sprocket using Puller (J-25031).

2) Using spring scale, check timing chain for stretch. Apply 22 lbs. (10 kg) of tension to chain and measure length of 40 chain links. *See Fig. 5.*

3) Length of chain should be 15" (381 mm). If length exceeds 15 5/32" (385 mm), replace chain. Check chain tensioner, tensioner guide pins, guide rail, and chain guide for wear. Replace as necessary.

4) Ensure that tensioner guide rail and chain tensioner move freely on guide pins. Ensure that oil jet in chain guide is not plugged. If oil jet is removed, install oil jet with hole pointing toward crankshaft.

Installation

1) Install lower timing sprocket and pinion gear with grooved side toward front cover. Rotate crankshaft so that key groove faces upward (No. 1 piston on TDC).

2) Install timing chain by aligning marked chain link plate with mark on crankshaft sprocket. Ensure that side of chain with most links between marked link plates is on chain guide side (exhaust) of engine. *See Fig. 4.*

3) Install chain on camshaft sprocket. Ensure that marked plate aligns with triangular mark on sprocket. Install sprocket on camshaft. Ensure that marks on sprockets are still aligned with marked plates. Reverse removal procedure to complete installation.

Fig. 4: Aligning Timing Chain & Sprockets (1.9L)

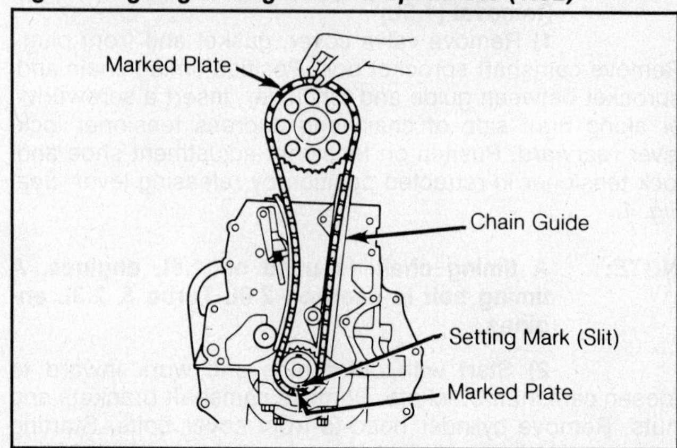

Courtesy of Isuzu Motor Co.

TIMING BELT & SPROCKETS (2.0L & 2.3L)

Removal

1) Position No. 1 cylinder on compression stroke. Align timing marks. Remove timing belt cover. Remove spring from tension pulley. Loosen adjusting bolt and move pulley toward water pump. Remove timing belt.

2) Remove tension pulley and spring. Remove crankshaft timing pulley and guide plate. Secure camshaft sprocket and remove camshaft sprocket nut.

CAUTION: DO NOT rotate camshaft or crankshaft with timing belt removed. Valve damage may occur.

3) Remove sprocket and guide plate. Repeat procedure for oil pump sprocket. Remove oil pump and water pump. Remove engine front cover.

Inspection

1) Timing belt must be handled carefully. Do not bend belt in an arc less than .79" (20 mm) in radius. Avoid twisting or kinking belt. Do not allow belt to become contaminated by water, oil, dirt or other contaminates.

2) Inspect belt for cracks or damage. Replace belt if necessary. Use a rubber hardness tester, and replace belt if any test shows over "90" durometers.

3) Measure outside diameter of crankshaft, camshaft, oil pump sprockets and tensioner. If specifications are exceeded, replace sprocket. See TIMING SPROCKET SPECIFICATIONS table.

4) Measure tension pulley spring length and force. If length exceeds 3.105" (78.87 mm) or force is less than 53-57 lbs. (24-26 kg), replace spring.

Installation

1) Install inner belt guard (if removed). Install oil pump sprocket. Install camshaft guide plate and camshaft sprocket. Hold sprocket and tighten mounting bolt.

2) Install crankshaft timing sprocket with keyway at 12 o'clock position. Install tensioner sprocket and spring. Push sprocket assembly toward water pump and temporarily tighten mounting bolt.

3) Rotate crankshaft until mark on timing sprocket aligns with mark on front crankshaft seal housing.

Fig. 5: Timing Chain & Tensioner Servicing (1.9L Engine)

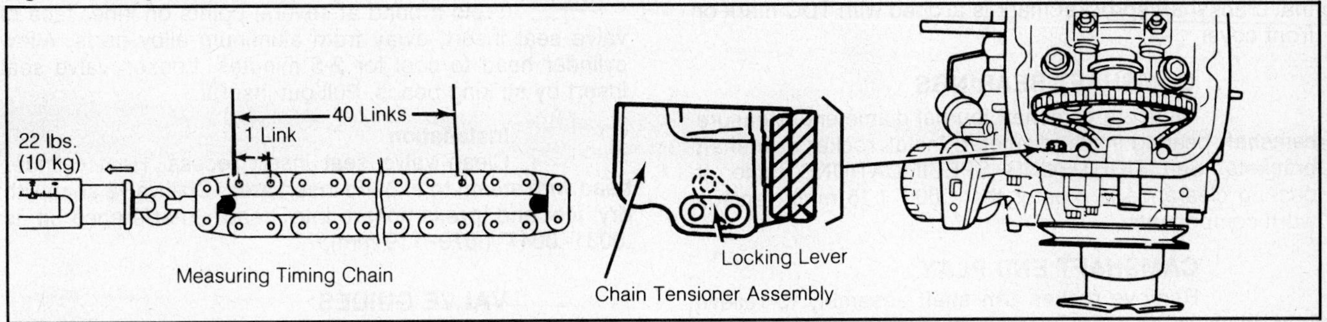

Courtesy of Isuzu Motor Co.

TIMING SPROCKET SPECIFICATIONS

Application	Standard In. (mm)	Limit In. (mm)
Camshaft	5.202 (132.03)	5.198 (131.93)
Crankshaft	2.574 (65.33)	2.570 (65.23)
Oil Pump	4.485 (113.84)	4.481 (113.74)
Tensioner	2.364 (60.00)	2.356 (59.80)

Rotate camshaft sprocket until timing mark aligns with mark on inner camshaft cover. Ensure No. 4 cylinder is at TDC on compression stroke. *See Fig. 6*.

4) Position timing belt over crankshaft sprocket, oil pump sprocket, camshaft sprocket and tensioner. Ensure that belt is positioned in sequence given and without slack between sprockets. Loosen tension sprocket adjusting bolt to allow spring tension to tighten belt. Tighten adjusting bolt temporarily.

5) Install crankshaft damper and rotate crankshaft 2 complete revolutions in opposite direction of engine rotation until marks on crankshaft timing pulley and front oil seal retainer are aligned. Loosen tensioner lock bolt, allowing tesioner spring to adjust tensioner. Tighten tensioner lock bolt.

6) Install timing belt cover. Install crankshaft damper assembly. To complete installation, reverse removal procedure. Install all drive belts.

CAMSHAFT

Removal

1) On 1.9L engine, remove valve cover. Rotate camshaft until No. 4 cylinder is on TDC of compression stroke. Remove distributor cap and mark rotor position on housing. Lock timing chain tensioner by depressing and turning slide pin 90 degrees clockwise. *See Fig. 1*.

2) Check chain for slack after locking tensioner. Remove camshaft sprocket with timing chain attached. DO NOT separate chain and sprocket.

3) On 2.0L and 2.3L models, remove valve cover. Rotate crankshaft until No. 4 piston is at TDC of compression stroke. Remove timing belt cover and timing belt. Remove camshaft timing belt sprocket and guide plate.

4) On all models, remove rocker arm shaft and bracket assembly. Remove camshaft.

Fig. 6: Aligning Timing Belt Sprockets (2.0L & 2.3L)

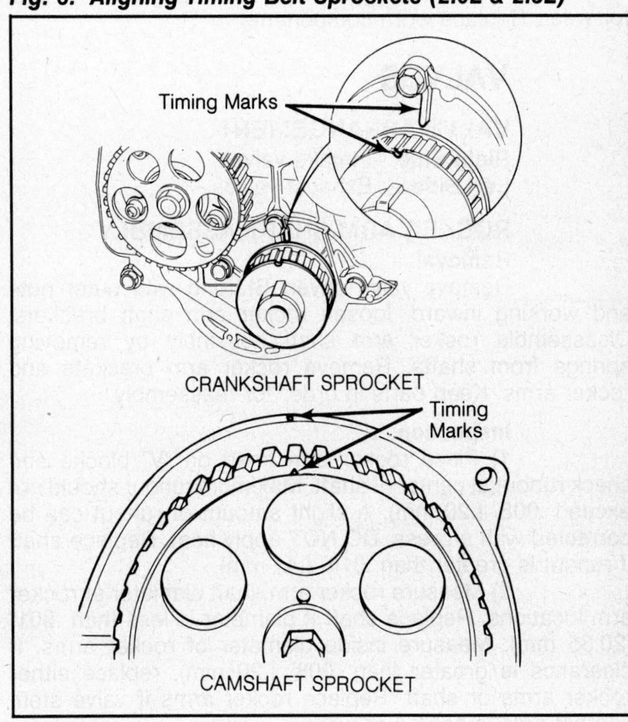

Courtesy of Isuzu Motor Co.

Inspection

1) Inspect camshaft lobes and journals for wear or damage. Measure height of camshaft lobes. Replace camshaft if measurement is less than 1.432" (36.37 mm).

2) Measure camshaft journals. If journal diameter is less than 1.331" (33.83 mm) or if difference between largest and smallest journal is more than .002" (.05 mm), replace camshaft.

3) Place camshaft on "V" blocks and check runout at center journal. If runout exceeds .004" (.10 mm), replace camshaft. A slight amount of runout can be corrected with a press. DO NOT apply heat.

Installation

1) Apply heavy coat of engine oil to camshaft journals and lobe surfaces. Install camshaft and rocker arm shaft brackets so that mark on camshaft thrust flange is aligned with mark on No. 1 rocker arm shaft bracket. Ensure that crankshaft sprocket mark is aligned with TDC mark on front cover.

2) Reverse removal procedure to complete installation. Ensure that rotor and mark on distributor housing are aligned when No. 4 cylinder is in firing position. Check that crankshaft sprocket mark is aligned with TDC mark on front cover.

CAMSHAFT BEARINGS

Measure camshaft journal diameters. Measure camshaft bearing inside diameter. Install rocker arm shaft brackets. See TIGHTENING SPECIFICATIONS table. If bearing clearance is greater than .006" (.15 mm), replace worn components.

CAMSHAFT END PLAY

Remove rocker arm shaft assembly to relieve load on camshaft. Install camshaft. Measure camshaft end play using a dial indicator. If end play exceeds .008" (.20 mm), check camshaft thrust flange or thrust groove in head for wear. Replace worn components.

VALVES

VALVE ARRANGEMENT

Right Side – Intake valves.
Left Side – Exhaust valves.

ROCKER ARM SHAFT ASSEMBLY

Removal

Remove valve cover. Starting with outer nuts and working inward, loosen rocker arm shaft brackets. Disassemble rocker arm shaft assembly by removing springs from shafts. Remove rocker arm brackets and rocker arms. Keep parts in order for reassembly.

Inspection

1) Place rocker arm shaft on "V" blocks and check runout at center of shaft. Maximum runout should not exceed .008" (.20 mm). A slight amount of runout can be corrected with a press. DO NOT apply heat. Replace shaft if runout is greater than .016" (.41 mm).

2) Measure rocker arm shaft diameter at rocker arm locations. Replace shaft if diameter is less than .801" (20.35 mm). Measure inside diameter of rocker arms. If clearance is greater than .008" (.20 mm), replace either rocker arms or shaft. Replace rocker arms if valve stem contact area is scored or worn.

Installation

1) Reassemble rocker arm shaft components in original positions. Cylinder number on upper face of brackets must point toward front of engine. Longer rocker shaft must be installed on exhaust side. Punch marks on rocker arm shafts must be positioned at front and point up.

2) Coat rocker arm shaft, rocker arms, and valve stems with engine oil. Install rocker arm shaft assembly on cylinder head. Align camshaft mark with mark on No. 1 rocker arm shaft bracket. On 2.0L and 2.3L engines, apply silicone gasket material to No. 1 rocker arm bracket mounting surface on cylinder head.

3) Starting with inner nuts and working outward, tighten brackets in steps. Adjust valve clearance and install valve cover.

VALVE SEATS

Inspection

With valves installed in cylinder head, check depth of valve head below cylinder head surface. If depth is more than .067" (1.70 mm), replace valve seat insert.

Removal

Weld a bead at several points on inner face of valve seat insert, away from aluminum alloy parts. Allow cylinder head to cool for 2-5 minutes. Loosen valve seat insert by striking beads. Pull out inserts.

Installation

Clean valve seat insert recess. Heat cylinder head with steam to expand insert area. Chill valve seat with dry ice and press insert into head. Interference fit is .0031-.0047" (.079-.119 mm).

VALVE GUIDES

Inspection

Measure valve guide and corresponding valve for wear. If stem-to-guide clearance is greater than .008" (.20 mm) on intake valves or .0097" (.246 mm) on exhaust valves, replace valve guides and valves as necessary.

Removal

Working from combustion chamber side of head, use Valve Guide Driver (J-26512-1) to drive guide out of head. Remove lower spring seat.

Installation

Lubricate outside of new guide with engine oil. Working from camshaft side of head, drive valve guide into position. Valve guide installed height should be .634-.642" (16.10-16.30 mm) above cylinder head surface.

VALVE SPRINGS

Removal & Installation

1) Remove rocker arm cover and shaft assembly. Use air pressure and remove springs as described in ENGINE OVERHAUL PROCEDURES article. Check valve springs. If spring is more than .0827" (2.100 mm) out-of-square, replace spring.

2) Lubricate valve stem and lower spring seat. Install lower spring seat. Slide new seal over valve stem and onto guide. Ensure that oil seal lip fits into groove in valve guide. To complete installation, reverse removal procedure.

VALVE CLEARANCE ADJUSTMENT

Ensure that rocker arm shaft brackets are tightened to specifications. Set No. 1 piston at TDC of compression stroke. Adjust clearance of No. 1 and No. 2 intake, and No. 1 and No. 3 exhaust valves. Turn crankshaft 360 degrees to place No. 4 piston on TDC of compression stroke. Adjust remaining valves.

VALVE CLEARANCE ADJUSTMENTS

Application	In. (mm)
Cold	
Intake	.006 (.15)
Exhaust	.010 (.25)
Hot	
Intake	.008 (.20)
Exhaust	.012 (.30)

Fig. 7: Sealer Application Points for Oil Pan Installation

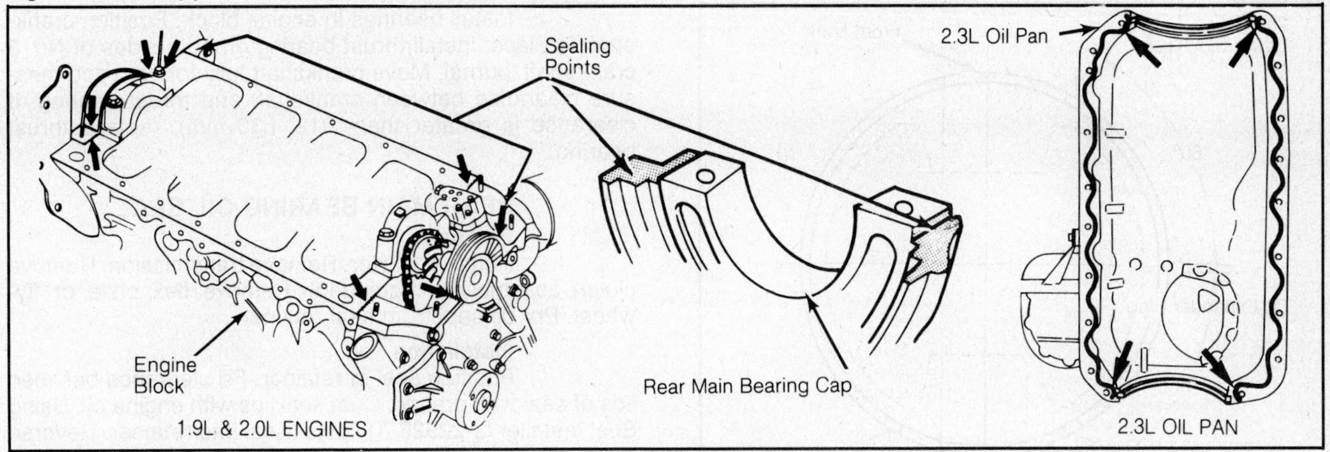

Courtesy of Isuzu Motor Co.

PISTONS, PINS & RINGS

OIL PAN

Removal & Installation

Remove engine from vehicle. Remove oil pan. When installing oil pan, apply a thin coat of non-hardening sealer to engine block. *See Fig. 7*. Ensure that contact area between main bearing cap and cylinder block are sealed. Reverse removal procedure to complete installation.

NOTE: The 2.3L oil pan uses a bead of silicone sealant between the block and oil pan. A gasket is used between the upper and lower pan sections. The 1.9L and 2.0L Turbo should always be reassembled using a gasket between the oil pan and cylinder block.

PISTON & ROD ASSEMBLY

Removal

1) Remove cylinder head and oil pan. Check connecting rods and caps for cylinder identification. Place rod and cap identification marks on starter side of engine. Remove carbon deposits or ridge from upper part of cylinder wall.

2) Remove connecting rod caps. Protect rod bolts to prevent rod journal damage. Push piston and connecting rod out top of engine block.

Installation

Lubricate bearings and piston rings with engine oil. On 1.9L models, install piston and rod assembly with mark on piston facing front of engine and cylinder identification number on connecting rod on starter side of engine.

On 2.0L and 2.3L engines, install piston and rod assembly with mark on piston and "ISUZU" on connecting rod facing forward.

FITTING PISTONS

Engine Block Inspection

1) Inspect engine block upper surface for distortion using a straightedge and feeler gauge. Distortion limit is .016" (.40 mm).

2) If distortion is more than .008" (.20 mm) but less than .016" (.41 mm), block may be resurfaced. Measure cylinder bore diameter.

3) Engine block must be rebored if measurement is more than .008" (.20 mm) over standard size. See CYLINDER BORE SIZES table. Variation between bore diameters after honing should be .0008" (.020 mm) or less.

CYLINDER BORE SIZES

Application	Standard Size In. (mm)
1.9L	3.433-3.434 (87.20-87.22)
2.0L	3.465-3.466 (88.00-88.04)
2.3L	3.516-3.517 (89.30-89.34)

FITTING RINGS

Position compression rings so that "N", "NPR", "T" or "TOP" mark is upward. Ensure rings turn freely in ring grooves. Piston ring size may be identified using mark on rings. *See Fig. 8*.

PISTON RING IDENTIFICATION

Application	Marking / Color Code
Standard	
1st Compression Ring	None
2nd Compression Ring	None
Oil Control Ring	Red
.5 mm Oversize	
1st Compression Ring	50
2nd Compression Ring	50
Oil Control Ring	Blue
1.0 mm Oversize	
1st Compression Ring	100
2nd Compression Ring	100
Oil Control Ring	Yellow

PISTON PIN REPLACEMENT

Removal

Use an arbor press and Piston Pin Remover (J-24086) to press piston pin out of piston and connecting rod assembly.

Isuzu Engines

1.9L, 2.0L TURBO & 2.3L 4-CYLINDER (Cont.)

Fig. 8: Piston Ring Gap Spacing

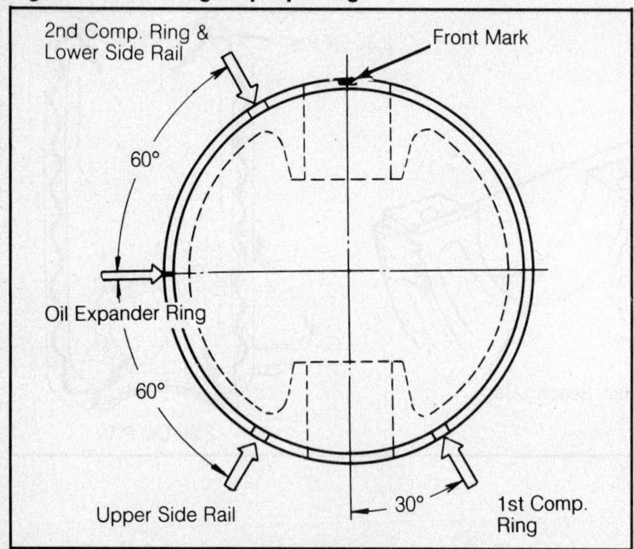

Lower side rail and second compression ring share same gap position on piston. Courtesy of Isuzu Motor Co.

Installation

Inspect oil jet on connecting rod for obstructions and clean as necessary. Assemble connecting rod with front mark on piston and "ISUZU" stamp on connecting rod on same side. Lightly oil pin bores in piston and rod. Press pin into piston and rod.

CRANKSHAFT & ROD BEARINGS

CRANKSHAFT MAIN BEARINGS

1) Use Plastigage method to check main bearing clearances. If clearances are exceeded, install undersize bearings. Replacement bearings are available in standard, .010" (.25 mm) undersize and .020" (.50 mm) undersize.

2) Remove crankshaft from engine. Measure crankshaft journals and crankpins to check for wear and taper. If taper exceeds .002" (.05 mm), replace or correct crankshaft.

3) Check crankshaft runout by placing "V" blocks under crankshaft at No. 1 and No. 5 journals. Position dial indicator point on No. 3 journal. Slowly turn crankshaft, while noting runout. If runout exceeds .004" (.10 mm), replace or correct crankshaft. Standard runout is .001" (.03 mm) or less.

4) Lubricate engine bearings. Install main bearing caps with arrow pointing toward front of engine. Tighten caps gradually and in sequence of caps No. 3, No. 4, No. 2, No. 5 and No. 1. Tighten caps to specification. Ensure that crankshaft turns freely.

CONNECTING ROD BEARINGS

Ensure connecting rod and cap are marked on starter side of engine for cylinder identification. Remove rod cap. Check bearing clearance using Plastigage. If clearance exceeds specifications, install new bearing. Replacement bearings are available in standard, .010" (.25 mm) undersize and .020" (.50 mm) undersize.

THRUST BEARING ALIGNMENT

Install bearings in engine block. Position crankshaft in place. Install thrust bearing on both sides of No. 3 crankshaft journal. Move crankshaft fully forward and measure clearance between crankshaft and thrust bearing. If clearance is greater than .012" (.30 mm), replace thrust bearing.

REAR MAIN BEARING OIL SEAL

Removal

Remove starter. Remove transmission. Remove clutch assembly (if equipped). Remove flex plate or flywheel. Pry oil seal from seal retainer.

Installation

Position seal in retainer. Fill clearance between lips of seal with grease. Coat seal lips with engine oil. Using Seal Installer (J-22928-A), install seal into retainer. Reverse removal procedure to complete installation.

ENGINE OILING

ENGINE OILING SYSTEM

A full-flow oil filter and trochoid-type oil pump are used. The oil pump delivers filtered oil to main oil gallery and crankshaft journals. Oil passages in crankshaft feed oil to connecting rod journals. Engine cylinder bore and piston pins are lubricated by oil spray from oil jet located on connecting rods.

An oil passage from No. 3 crankshaft journal delivers oil to cylinder head. Oil is fed to rocker arms by oil ports in rocker arm shaft assemblies. An oil well on top of cylinder head provides lubrication for camshaft. On 1.9L engines, the timing chain and sprockets are lubricated by oil spray from oil jet located on chain guide.

CRANKCASE CAPACITY

OIL REFILL QUANTITY

Application	Quarts (Liters)
1.9L	
With Filter	5.28 (5.0)
2.0L	
With Filter	3.8 (3.6)
Without Filter	3.4 (3.2)
2.3L	
With Filter	4.4 (4.2)
Without Filter	4.0 (3.8)
Overhaul	5.2 (4.9)

OIL PRESSURE

Oil pressure should be approximately 57 psi (4 kg/cm^2) at 1400 RPM (1.9L and 2.0L) or 3000 RPM (2.3L).

OIL PRESSURE RELIEF VALVE

Oil pressure relief valve opens at approximately 57-71 psi (4-5 kg/cm^2).

1.9L, 2.0L TURBO & 2.3L 4-CYLINDER (Cont.)

Fig. 9: Oil Pump Assembly (1.9L)

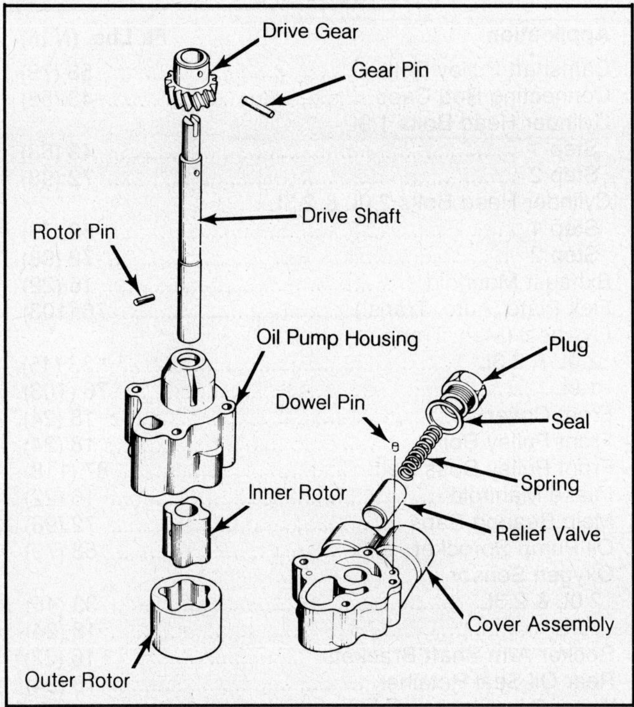

Courtesy of Isuzu Motor Co.

OIL PUMP

Removal

On 2.0L and 2.3L engines, remove front cover, timing belt and oil pump as outlined in TIMING BELT & SPROCKETS. On 1.9L models, remove valve cover and distributor. Remove oil pan. Remove oil pick-up tube from block, then remove tube from oil pump. Remove oil pump.

Inspection

Measure oil pump clearances. Replace oil pump if clearance exceeds specifications.

OIL PUMP SPECIFICATIONS [1]

Application	In. (mm)
Rotor Shaft Clearance	.0028-.0043 (.071-.109)
Rotor Tip Clearance	
All	.005-.006 (.13-.15)
Rotor-to-Pump Housing	
1.9L	.006-.008 (.16-.22)
2.0L & 2.3L	.009-.0014 (.24-.36)
Rotor-to-Pump Cover	
1.9L	.001-.004 (.03-.09)
2.0L & 2.3L	.002-.004 (.04-.09)

1 – Production/rebuild tolerances are given. Maximum allowable wear limits are +.002 (.05).

Installation

1) On 2.0L and 2.3L engines, follow installation procedures under TIMING BELT & SPROCKETS. On 1.9L engines, align mark on camshaft with mark on No. 1 rocker arm shaft bracket. Align notch on crankshaft pulley with "O" mark on front cover. When 2 sets of marks are aligned, No. 4 piston is at TDC of compression stroke.

Fig. 10: Oil Pump Assembly (2.0L & 2.3L)

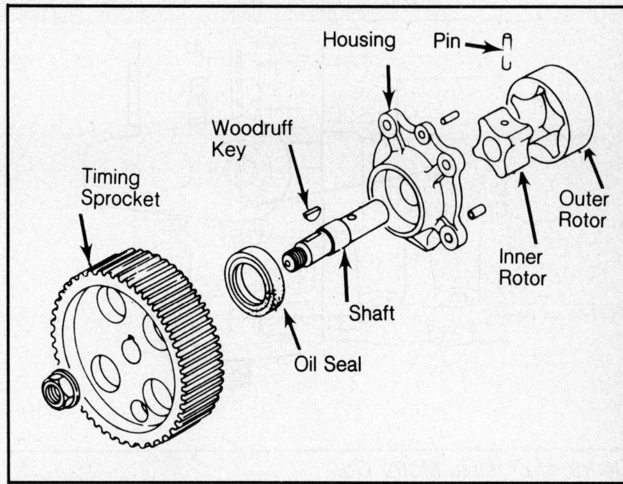

Courtesy of Isuzu Motor Co.

2) Ensure that marks on oil pump inner and outer rotors are aligned. Engage oil pump drive gear with pinion gear on crankshaft. Ensure that alignment mark is facing to the rear and approximately 20 degrees in a clockwise direction away from crankshaft. *See Fig. 11.*

3) Ensure that mark on drive gear is facing rear of engine with oil pump installed. Slot at end of drive shaft must be parallel with front face of cylinder block, and offset forward. *See Fig. 12.*

4) Install pump cover by fitting it to dowel pins, then install mounting bolts. Install relief valve assembly and oil pipe rubber hose. Reverse removal procedure to complete installation.

Fig. 11: Installing Oil Pump on 1.9L Models

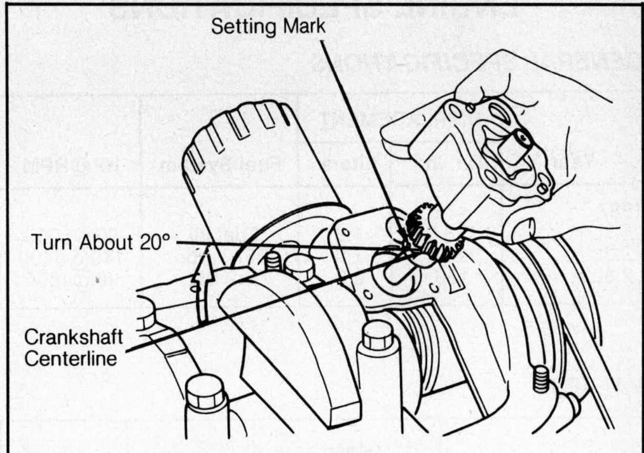

Courtesy of Isuzu Motor Co.

ENGINE COOLING

WATER PUMP

Removal

Disconnect negative battery cable. Remove lower cover and drain cooling system. Remove fan belts. Remove fan and fan pulley. Remove air pump drive pulley. Remove water pump.

Installation

To install, reverse removal procedure.

Isuzu Engines

1.9L, 2.0L TURBO & 2.3L 4-CYLINDER (Cont.)

Fig. 12: Checking Oil Pump Drive Shaft Alignment (1.9L)

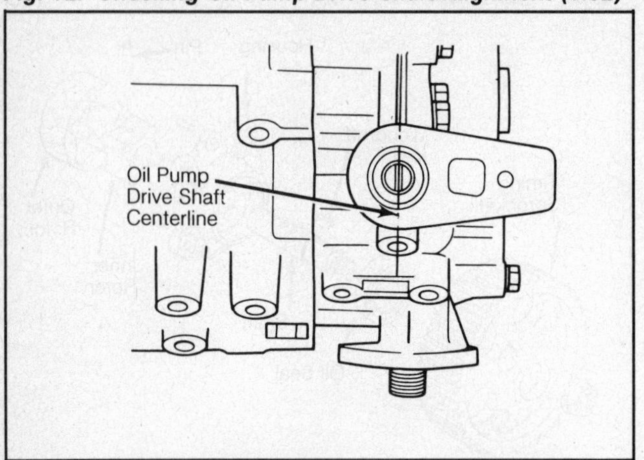

Courtesy of Isuzu Motor Co.

NOTE: For further information on cooling systems, see ENGINE COOLING section.

TIGHTENING SPECIFICATIONS

Application	Ft. Lbs. (N.m)
Camshaft Pulley Bolts	58 (79)
Connecting Rod Caps	43 (58)
Cylinder Head Bolts 1.9L	
Step 1	43 (58)
Step 2	72 (98)
Cylinder Head Bolts 2.0L & 2.3L	
Step 1	58 (79)
Step 2	72 (98)
Exhaust Manifold	16 (22)
Flex Plate (Auto. Trans.)	76 (103)
Flywheel (Man. Trans.)	
2.0L & 2.3L	[1] 33 (45)
1.9L	76 (103)
Front Cover	18 (24)
Front Pulley Bolts	18 (24)
Front Pulley Boss Bolt	87 (118)
Intake Manifold	16 (22)
Main Bearing Caps	72 (98)
Oil Pump Sprocket	58 (79)
Oxygen Sensor	
2.0L & 2.3L	33 (45)
1.9L	18 (24)
Rocker Arm Shaft Brackets	[2] 16 (22)
Rear Oil Seal Retainer	18 (24)
Water Pump	
2.0L & 2.3L	14 (19)
1.9L	18 (24)

[1] – With Loctite applied to first thread.

[2] – Tighten No. 9 and 10 bolts to 72 INCH lbs. (8 N.m) on 2.0L models.

ENGINE SPECIFICATIONS

GENERAL SPECIFICATIONS

Year	DISPLACEMENT		Fuel System	HP@RPM	Torque Ft. Lbs.@RPM	Compr. Ratio	BORE		STROKE	
	Cu. In.	Liters					In.	mm	In.	mm
1987										
1.9L	118.9	1.9	Fuel Inj.	90@5000	146@3000	9.2	3.43	87	3.29	82
2.0L	121.7	2.0	EFI Turbo	140@5400	166@3000	7.9	3.46	88	3.29	82
2.3L	138	2.3	1x2 Bbl.	96@4600	128@2200	8.3	3.52	89.3	3.54	90

VALVES

Engine Size & Valve	Head Diam. In. (mm)	Face Angle	Seat Angle	Seat Width In. (mm)	Stem Diameter In. (mm)	Stem Clearance In. (mm)	Valve Lift In. (mm)
1.9L							
Intake	1.67 (42.4)	45°	45°	.048-.063 (1.21-1.60)	.315 (8.00)	.0009-.0022 (.023-.056)	.....
Exhaust	1.34 (34.0)	45°	45°	.048-.063 (1.21-1.60)	.315 (8.00)	.0015-.0031 (.038-.079)	.....
2.0L & 2.3L							
Intake	1.67 (42.4)	45°	45°	.048-.063 (1.21-1.60)	.315 (8.00)	.0009-.0022 (.023-.056)	.....
Exhaust	1.42 (36.1)	45°	45°	.048-.063 (1.21-1.60)	.315 (8.00)	.0015-.0031 (.038-.079)	.....

Isuzu Engines

1.9L, 2.0L TURBO & 2.3L 4-CYLINDER (Cont.)

ENGINE SPECIFICATIONS (Cont.)

PISTONS, PINS & RINGS

Engine	PISTONS Clearance In. (mm)	PINS Piston Fit In. (mm)	PINS Rod Fit In. (mm)	RINGS Ring No.	RINGS End Gap In. (mm)	RINGS Side Clearance In. (mm)
1.9L	.0018-.0026 (.045-.065)	.0002-.0004 (.006-.011)	.0012-.0016 (.030-.041)	1 & 2	.014-.020 (.35-.50)	.0010-.0024 (.025-.060)
				Oil	.008-.035 (.20-.90)	.0008 min (.020)
2.0L & 2.3L	.0018-.0026 (.045-.065)	.0002-.0004 (.006-.011)	.00012-.0008 (.003-.020)	1	.012-.018 (.30-.46)	.0010-.0024 (.025-.060)
				2	.010-.016 (.25-.41)	.0008-.0022 (.020-.055)
				Oil	.008-.028 (.20-.71)	.0008 min. (.020)

CRANKSHAFT MAIN & CONNECTING ROD BEARINGS

Engine	MAIN BEARINGS Journal Diam. In. (mm)	MAIN BEARINGS Clearance In. (mm)	MAIN BEARINGS Thrust Bearing	MAIN BEARINGS Crankshaft End Play In. (mm)	CONNECTING ROD BEARINGS Journal Diam. In. (mm)	CONNECTING ROD BEARINGS Clearance In. (mm)	CONNECTING ROD BEARINGS Side Play In. (mm)
1.9L, 2.0L & 2.3L	2.2032-2.2038 (55.920-55.935)	.0008-.0025 (.021-.064)	No. 3	.002-.010 (.06-.25)	1.9276-1.9282 (48.925-48.940)	.0007-.0029 (.019-.075)	.008-.013 (.02-.33)

CAMSHAFT

Engine	Journal Diam. In. (mm)	Clearance In. (mm)	Lobe Lift In. (mm)
1.9L, 2.0L & 2.3L	1.339 (34.0)	.0030-.0043 (.065-.110)	1.451 (36.85)

VALVE SPRINGS

Engine	Free Length In. (mm)	PRESSURE Lbs. @ In. (Kg @ mm) Valve Closed	PRESSURE Lbs. @ In. (Kg @ mm) Valve Open
1.9L, 2.0L & 2.3L	1.8951 (48.1)	56 @ 1.61 (25.4 @ 41.0)	....

VALVE TIMING

Engine	INTAKE Open (BTDC)	INTAKE Close (ABDC)	EXHAUST Open (BBDC)	EXHAUST Close (ATDC)
1.9L, 2.0L & 2.3L	21°	65°	55°	20

Isuzu Engines

2.2L 4-CYLINDER DIESEL & TURBO DIESEL

P'UP, Trooper II

NOTE: **For engine repair procedures not covered in this article, see ENGINE OVERHAUL PROCEDURES articles at beginning of this section.**

ENGINE CODING

ENGINE IDENTIFICATION

Engine identification code is 8th character of the Vehicle Identification Number (VIN). The VIN is stamped on a metal tab, located on top of instrument panel near lower left of windshield. Engine serial number is stamped on a machined pad, located at front of engine block.

ENGINE IDENTIFICATION CODE

Engine	Code
2.2L Diesel	
Non-Turbo	U
Turbo	S

ENGINE, MANIFOLDS & CYLINDER HEAD

ENGINE

Removal (P'UP)

1) Remove hood. Disconnect battery cables and remove battery. Remove lower engine cover. Drain coolant, crankcase and transmission. Remove air cleaner assembly. Remove radiator hoses and drive belts.

2) Remove fan, fan shroud, radiator grille and radiator. Disconnect accelerator control cable. Disconnect A/C compressor control cable (if equipped). Disconnect fuel hoses from injection pump.

3) Disconnect transmission wiring. Disconnect vacuum hose at fast idle actuator and wiring at fuel cut solenoid. Disconnect sensing resistor, thermoswitch and A/C compressor switch wiring.

4) Disconnect heater hoses. Disconnect vacuum hoses from vacuum pump. Disconnect alternator wiring. Disconnect exhaust pipe from manifold and remove mounting bracket from engine backing plate. Disconnect wiring from starter.

5) On 2WD models, remove transmission gearshift lever. Disconnect speedometer and ground cables from transmission. Disconnect propeller shaft at differential and remove shaft.

6) Remove return spring and clutch cable from clutch release lever. Remove cable through stiffener bracket. Remove rear transmission mount bolts. Attach engine hoist. Raise engine and transmission. Remove rear crossmember.

7) Remove transmission rear extension mounting nuts. Remove engine mounting bolt and nuts. Ensure that engine and transmission are completely disconnected. Pull engine forward. Remove engine and transmission as an assembly.

8) On 4WD models, remove return spring from transfer gearshift lever. Remove transmission and transfer gearshift levers. Remove transmission gearshift lever quadrant. Remove starter.

9) Disconnect speedometer cable. Disconnect rear propeller shaft at differential. Disconnect driveshaft center bearing and remove propeller shafts. Disconnect clutch cable. Remove flywheel cover and transfer case. Remove rear transmission mounting bolts.

10) Support transmission. Remove rear crossmember. Support engine. Remove transmission-to-engine mounting bolts. Turn transmission 90 degrees clockwise and remove transmission. Ensure that engine is completely disconnected. Pull engine forward. Carefully remove engine.

Removal (Trooper II)

1) Disconnect battery ground cable. Remove engine hood. Remove battery assembly. Remove splash cover. Drain cooling system by opening drain plugs on radiator and on cylinder block. Disconnect air cleaner hose.

2) Disconnect upper water hose at engine side. Remove cooling fan and fan shroud. Disconnect lower water hose at engine side. Remove radiator grill. Remove radiator attaching bolts. Remove radiator.

3) Disconnect accelerator control cable from injection pump side. Disconnect air conditioning compressor control cable (if equipped). Disconnect fuel hoses from injection pump. Disconnect battery cable from body. Disconnect transmission wiring. Disconnect vacuum hose from fast idle actuator.

4) Disconnect fuel cut solenoid. Disconnect sensing resistor, thermoswitch, and A/C compressor switch connectors. Disconnect heater hoses. Disconnect vacuum hose at master-vac. Disconnect vacuum hose from vacuum pump. Disconnect alternator wiring at connector.

5) Disconnect exhaust pipe mounting bracket from engine backing plate. Disconnect starter motor wiring. Disconnect battery cable from starter motor. Slide transmission and transfer gearshift lever boot upwards. Remove gearshift lever attaching bolts. Remove return spring from transfer gear shift lever and remove levers.

6) Remove transmission. Remove engine mounting bolts and nuts. Install engine lift hangers on front and rear. Ensure that engine is slightly raised before removing engine mounting bolts and nuts. Ensure that all parts have been removed or disconnected from engine that are fastened to frame side. Move engine toward front of vehicle. When front part of engine is raised slightly above horizontal, remove engine.

Installation

Replace engine mounts showing signs of deterioration, separation or unusual wear. Reverse removal procedure to complete installation. On 4WD models, install transfer gearshift lever with transfer case in "2H" position. Check fluid levels. Adjust clutch.

MANIFOLDS

Removal

Remove air cleaner assembly. Disconnect exhaust pipe from exhaust manifold. Remove intake and exhaust manifolds. Remove manifold gasket.

Installation

Install intake/exhaust manifold gasket with mark turned up and pointing outward. Reverse removal procedure to complete installation.

CYLINDER HEAD

Removal

1) Remove lower engine cover. Drain cooling system. Remove intake and exhaust manifolds. Disconnect upper radiator hose from engine. Remove fan and fan shroud.

2.2L 4-CYLINDER DIESEL & TURBO DIESEL (Cont.)

2) Disconnect injection pipes. Remove nozzle holder nozzle holder assembly. Remove valve cover. Starting with outer bolts and working inward, loosen rocker arm shaft brackets.

Fig. 1: Cylinder Head Tightening Sequence

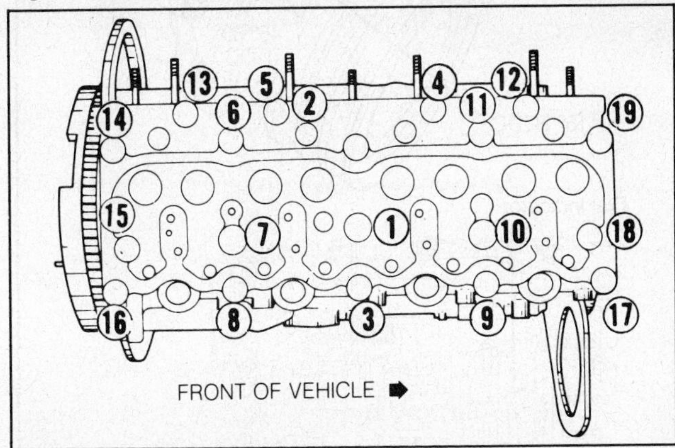

Courtesy of Isuzu Motor Co.

3) Remove rocker arm shaft assembly. Remove push rods. Remove joint bolt and disconnect leak-off pipe. Loosen head bolts in reverse order of tightening sequence. Remove cylinder head and gasket.

Installation

Install head gasket with "TOP" mark facing up. Install and tighten cylinder head. *See Fig. 1*. Install push rods and rocker arm shaft assembly. *See Fig. 2*. Reverse removal procedure to complete installation.

Fig. 2: Rocker Arm Shaft Assembly Tightening Sequence

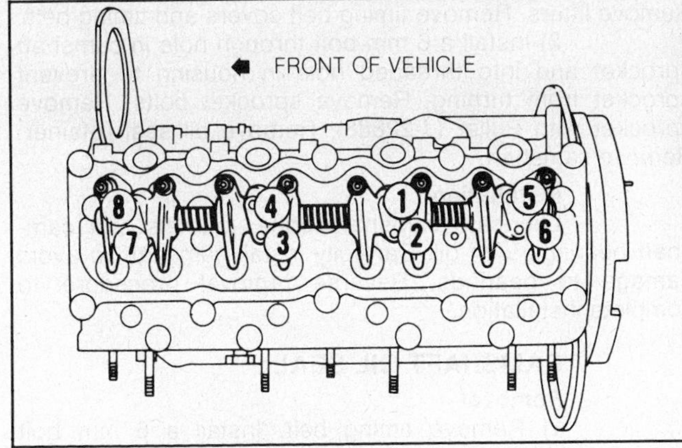

Courtesy of Isuzu Motor Co.

CAMSHAFT

TIMING BELT COVERS

Removal & Installation

Remove lower engine cover. Drain cooling system. Remove battery. Remove fan, fan shroud, top radiator hose and drive belts. Remove 4 crankshaft pulley bolts and crankshaft pulley. Remove timing belt covers. To install, reverse removal procedure.

TIMING BELT & VALVE TIMING

Removal

1) Remove timing belt covers. Position No. 1 cylinder at TDC of compression stroke. Ensure injection pump and camshaft sprocket timing marks are aligned. *See Fig. 3*.

2) Remove injection pump pulley flange bolts and remove flange. Remove tensioner spring without using excess force on spring. Remove tension pulley nut and tensioner assembly. Remove timing belt.

Fig. 3: Timing Belt Sprocket Alignment

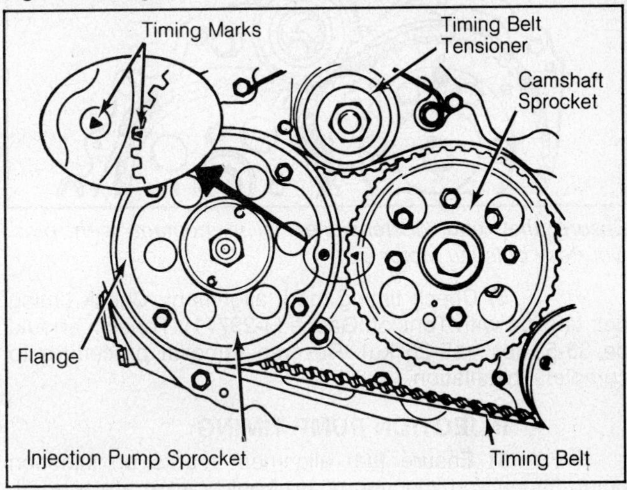

Courtesy of Isuzu Motor Co.

Installation

1) Ensure that timing marks on injection pump, camshaft sprockets, crankshaft pulley and timing pointer are aligned. *See Fig. 4*. Install timing belt over crankshaft sprocket, camshaft sprocket and injection pump sprocket.

Fig. 4: Timing Mark Alignment

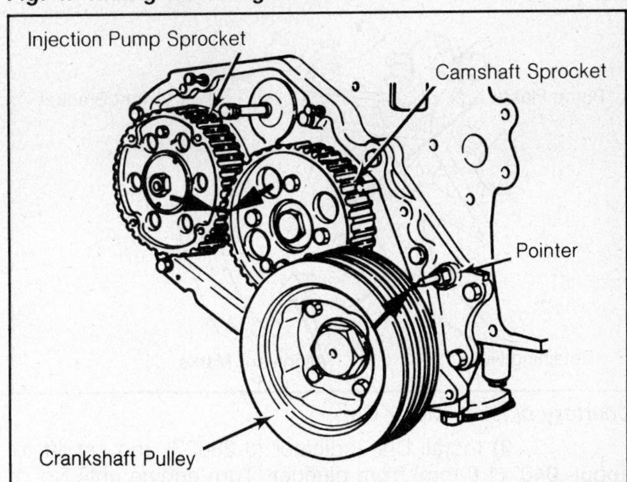

Heavy Black arrows show points of timing mark alignment. Courtesy of Isuzu Motor Co.

2) Install tensioner assembly so that end of tensioner is in contact with 2 pins on timing pulley housing. *See Fig. 5*. Hand tighten nut. Install tension spring. Tighten nut to 22-36 ft. lbs. (30-49 N.m).

3) Turn crankshaft 2 complete revolutions in normal direction of rotation, then turn crankshaft 90 degrees past TDC. Loosen tensioner nut completely and allow tensioner to take up slack. Tighten nut.

4) Install and tighten injection pump pulley flange. Ensure hole in flange lines up with triangular timing mark on pump sprocket. *See Fig. 3*. Turn crankshaft 2

more turns, bringing No. 1 cylinder to TDC on compression stroke.

Fig. 5: Timing Belt Tensioner Installation

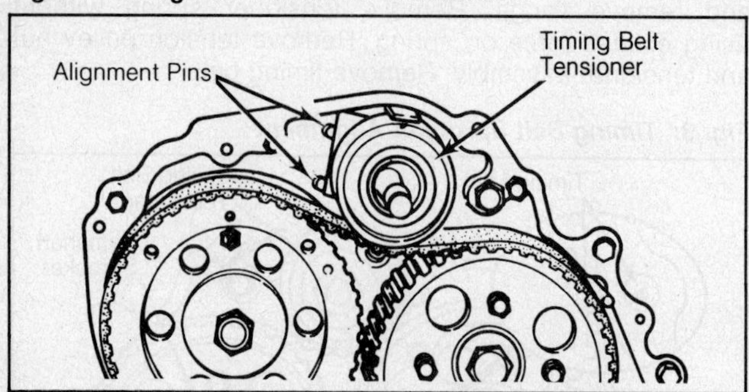

Ensure that end of tensioner is in contact with pins. Courtesy of Isuzu Motor Co.

5) Check timing mark alignment. Check timing belt tension with Tension Gauge (J-29771). Tension should be 33-55 lbs. (15-25 kg). Reverse removal procedure to complete installation.

INJECTION PUMP TIMING

1) Ensure that alignment marks on injection pump flange and injection pump front bracket are aligned. *See Fig. 6*. Place No. 1 cylinder at TDC of compression stroke.

2) With timing belt cover removed, ensure that timing belt is properly tensioned and that sprocket timing marks are aligned. Disconnect injection pipe from pump. Remove distributor head screw.

Fig. 6: Injection Pump Alignment Marks

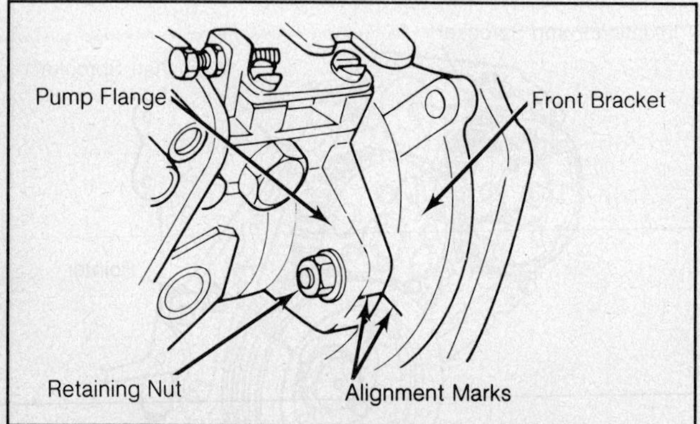

Courtesy of Isuzu Motor Co.

3) Install Dial Indicator (J-28827) and set lift to about .040" (1.0 mm) from plunger. Turn engine until No. 1 cylinder is 45-60 degrees BTDC. Calibrate dial indicator to zero. Turn crankshaft pulley slightly in both directions and check that gauge indication is stable.

4) Turn crankshaft in normal direction of rotation until 15 degrees BTDC mark on Federal non-turbo, 13 degrees BTDC mark on Calif. non-turbo, or 10 degrees mark on turbo models is aligned with timing pointer. Dial indicator should read .020" (0.5 mm).

5) If indicator reading is not correct, hold crankshaft in place and loosen nuts on injection pump flange. Move injection pump until correct reading is obtained. Tighten nuts and recheck reading.

Fig. 7: Injection Pump Timing Adjustment

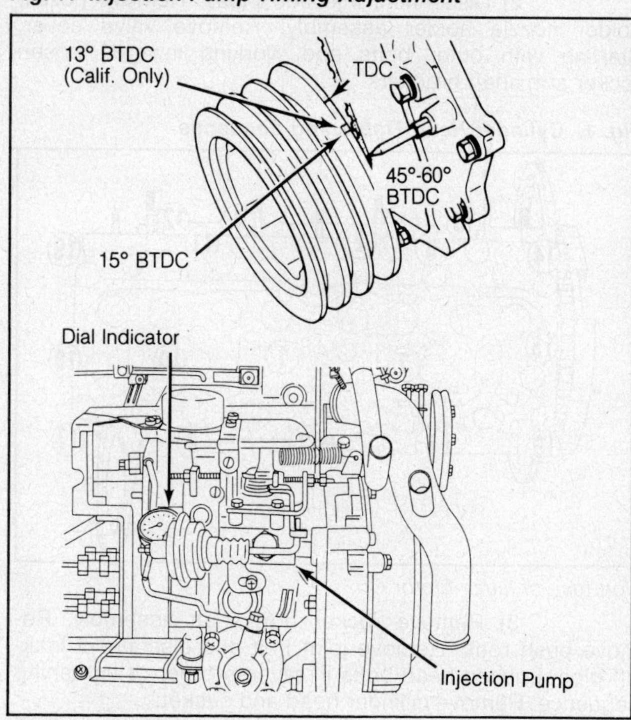

Courtesy of Isuzu Motor Co.

CAMSHAFT

Removal

1) Remove engine from vehicle. Remove valve cover, rocker arm shaft assembly and push rods. Remove lifter cover and rocker oil feed pipe from side of engine. Remove lifters. Remove timing belt covers and timing belt.

2) Install a 6 mm bolt through hole in camshaft sprocket and into threaded hole in housing to prevent sprocket from turning. Remove sprocket bolts. Remove sprocket with Puller (J-22888). Remove oil seal retainer. Remove camshaft.

Installation

Lubricate camshaft lobes, journals and camshaft bearings with oil. Carefully install camshaft to avoid damage to bearings. Reverse removal procedure to complete installation.

CAMSHAFT OIL SEAL

Removal

1) Remove timing belt. Install a 6 mm bolt through hole in camshaft sprocket and into threaded hole in housing to prevent sprocket from turning.

2) Remove sprocket bolts. Remove sprocket using Puller (J-22888). Remove oil seal retainer and oil seal.

Installation

Install oil seal into retainer until seated. Reverse removal procedure to complete installation.

CAMSHAFT BEARINGS

Removal & Installation

Remove and install bearings using Camshaft Bearing Remover and Installer (J-29764). Ensure that oil holes in bearings are aligned with those in engine block.

CAMSHAFT END PLAY

1) Remove timing belt covers. Attach a dial indicator to engine block with indicator point on camshaft sprocket center bolt. Push camshaft rearward and zero dial indicator.

2) Pry camshaft forward and note end play. Maximum allowable end play is .008" (.20 mm). If end play exceeds specification, camshaft oil pump drive gear or oil pump gear is worn and should be replaced.

VALVES

VALVE ARRANGEMENT

E-I-I-E-E-I-I-E (Front-to-rear).

ROCKER ARM SHAFT ASSEMBLY

Removal

Remove valve cover. Starting with outer bolts and working inward, loosen rocker arm shaft brackets. Remove rocker arm shaft assembly. If disassembly is necessary, remove end snap rings and keep parts in order.

Installation

To install, reverse removal procedure. Starting with outer bolts and working inward, tighten attaching bolts evenly. *See Fig. 2.*

VALVE GUIDE SERVICING

Inspection

Using dial indicator, check valve stem-to-guide clearance. Position dial indicator point about .400" (10 mm) above end of guide. Rock valve stem back and forth and measure movement. If movement exceeds .008" (.20 mm), replace valve guide and valve.

Removal

Working from combustion chamber side of cylinder head, drive out old guide with Driver (J-26512).

Installation

Coat outer surface of guide with engine oil. Working from top side of head, drive guide into head with Driver (J-26512). Guide should project from cylinder head .472" (12 mm). Always replace valve guide and valve as a set.

VALVE STEM OIL SEALS

Removal

Remove rocker arm shaft assembly. Position piston of cylinder to be serviced on TDC. Using Spring Compressor (J-29760), compress spring and remove valve locks. Release pressure and remove spring retainer and springs. Remove valve stem oil seal.

Installation

Apply engine oil to inner face of oil seal and valve stem. Install oil seal. Install inner and outer springs with Green side (closed-coil end) toward cylinder head. Reverse removal procedure to complete installation.

VALVE SEAT INSERTS

Inspection

With valves installed in cylinder head, check depth of valve head below cylinder head surface. If depth exceeds .080" (2.0 mm), replace valve seat insert.

Removal

Arc-weld a bead of metal around inner face of seat. Allow seat to cool a few minutes. Using screwdrivers, pry out valve seat.

Installation

Using arbor press, install new seat. Grind seat to correct width and angle. Lap valve and seat to complete installation.

VALVE SPRINGS

Removal & Installation

To remove and install valve springs, use procedure outlined in VALVE STEM OIL SEAL removal and installation.

Inspection

Measure spring for free length and spring tension with a valve spring tester. Using a flat surface and steel square, check valve springs for squareness. Take measurement between top of spring and square, while slowly rotating spring. Out-of-square must not exceed .040" (1.0 mm). Replace springs that fail tests.

HOT PLUGS (COMBUSTION CHAMBERS)

Inspection

Measure hot plug depth in cylinder head with straightedge and feeler gauge. If depth exceeds .0008" (.02 mm), hot plug must be replaced.

Removal

Using a 1/8 - 3/16" brass drift inserted through injection nozzle hole, drive out hot plug.

Installation

Install lock ball into groove of glow plug. Align lock ball with groove in cylinder head and drive plug in. Using bench press and a piece of metal over plug, press hot plug into position using 5-5.5 tons pressure. Grind plug flush with surface of cylinder head.

VALVE CLEARANCE ADJUSTMENT

Ensure rocker arm shaft brackets are properly tightened. Set No. 1 cylinder to TDC of compression stroke. Adjust clearance of No. 1 and No. 2 intake valves, and No. 1 and No. 3 exhaust valves. Turn crankshaft 1 full turn to place No. 4 cylinder to TDC of compression stroke. Adjust remaining valves.

VALVE CLEARANCE SPECIFICATIONS

Application	In. (mm)
All Valves (Cold)	.016 (.41)
All Valves (Hot)	.015 (.37)

PISTONS, PINS & RINGS

OIL PAN

Removal & Installation

Remove engine from vehicle. Remove oil pan bolts. Remove oil pan. To install, reverse removal procedure.

PISTON & ROD ASSEMBLY

Removal

1) Remove engine from vehicle. Remove cylinder head. Remove crankcase and oil pan as an

2.2L 4-CYLINDER DIESEL & TURBO DIESEL (Cont.)

assembly. Remove oil pipe sleeve nut from engine block. Remove attaching bolts. Remove oil pump with oil pipe attached.

2) Remove carbon deposits from upper edge of cylinder wall. Remove rod cap. Push piston/rod assembly out of cylinder block.

Installation

1) Lightly oil rings, piston and cylinder wall. Make sure ring gaps are properly spaced. *See Fig. 8.* Make sure bearing halves are properly seated in connecting rod and cap.

2) Install ring compressor and compress rings. Install piston in cylinder with mark toward front of engine. Install and tighten rod cap. Reverse removal procedure to complete installation.

Fig. 8: Piston Ring Gap Locations

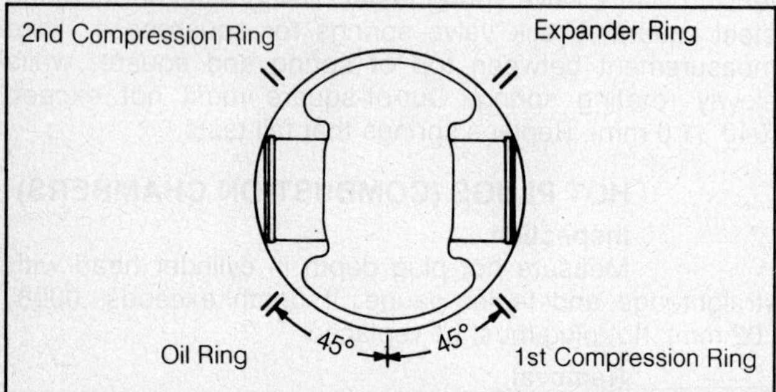

Courtesy of Isuzu Motor Co.

FITTING PISTONS

1) Measure cylinder bore diameter at 5/8" (16 mm) and 4 1/2" (114 mm) below engine block surface. Take measurements in-line with and at 90 degrees to crankshaft centerline. If reading is greater than 3.512" (89.2 mm), rebore cylinder.

2) Measure piston skirt diameter at 2 1/2" (63.5 mm) from top of piston and at right angle to piston pin. Subtract piston reading from cylinder diameter to determine piston-to-cylinder wall clearance. Clearance should be .0014-.0022" (.036-.056 mm).

PISTON DIAMETER SPECIFICATIONS

Application	In. (mm)
Standard	3.463-3.464 (87.96-87.99)
.5 mm Oversize	3.485-3.487 (88.46-88.49)
1 mm Oversize	3.502-3.506 (88.96-88.99)

FITTING RINGS

1) Position rings into cylinder bore at a point where bore diameter is smallest. Ring must be square in bore. Measure ring end gap with a feeler gauge.

2) Remove rings from bore and check ring side clearance. Ensure rings turn freely in ring grooves. When installing rings on pistons, ensure that gaps are properly positioned. *See Fig. 8.*

3) Install rings on piston as follows: Expander ring, oil ring, 2nd compression ring (grooved), then 1st compression ring. Install compression rings with "N" mark facing upward.

PISTON PIN REPLACEMENT

Removal

Place piston/rod assembly in soft-jawed vise. Remove snap rings from piston. Use a brass rod to drive out piston pin.

Inspection

1) Check connecting rod for distortion and parallelism. Correct or replace connecting rod if distortion exceeds .008" (.20 mm) or parallelism exceeds .006" (.15 mm) per 3.94" (100.0 mm) of length.

2) Measure inside diameter of connecting rod bushing and outside diameter of piston pin. If clearance is greater than .002" (.05 mm), replace piston pin or bushing. Check interference fit between piston pin and piston pin bore in piston.

3) Interference fit should be .0-.0002" (.004 mm). Measure piston pin outside diameter at several points around circumference. Pin diameter should be 1.062-1.063" (26.97-27.00 mm) for Non-Turbo engines and 1.140-1.141" (28.97-29.00 mm) for Turbo engines. If pin diameter is less than minimum specification, replace piston pin.

Bushing Replacement

Remove piston pin bushing using press and Piston Pin Remover/Installer (J-29765). Install bushing on connecting rod and ream to obtain .0003-.0008" (.008-.020 mm) standard clearance.

Installation

Heat piston to about 176°F (80°C). Assemble rod to piston so that front mark on piston and "ISUZU" mark on rod are on same side. Rod cap match marks will be on combustion chamber side of piston. *See Fig. 9.* Coat piston pin with oil and install. Install snap rings.

Fig. 9: Positioning Rod to Piston

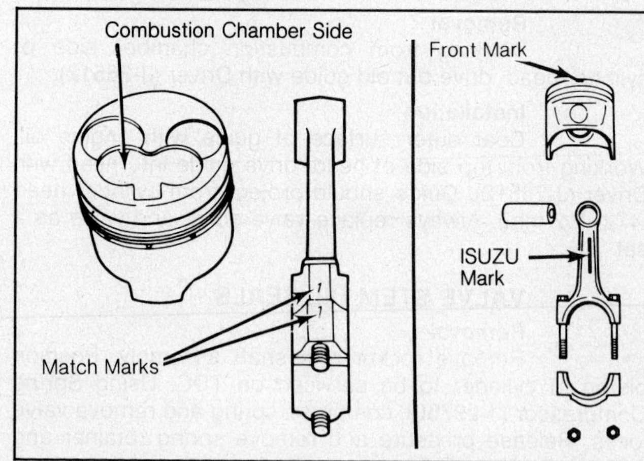

Courtesy of Isuzu Motor Co.

CRANKSHAFT & ROD BEARINGS

MAIN BEARINGS

1) Use Plastigage method to check main bearing clearances. If clearance is greater than .005" (.12 mm), replace crankshaft and/or bearings. Crankshaft journals and crankpins cannot be reground.

Isuzu Engines

2.2L 4-CYLINDER DIESEL & TURBO DIESEL (Cont.)

2) Remove crankshaft from engine. Measure crankshaft journals and crankpins to check for wear and taper. If crankshaft journal diameter is less than 2.358" (59.90 mm), replace crankshaft. If crankpin diameter is less than 2.083" (52.90 mm), replace crankshaft.

3) Check crankshaft runout. If runout exceeds .0024" (.061 mm), replace crankshaft. Standard runout is .001" (.03 mm) or less.

4) Lubricate main bearings. Install thrust bearing with grooved thrust face turned outward. Install arch gaskets on No. 1 and No. 5 bearing caps. Use silicone sealer to hold gasket in place. Gasket should not project more than .002" (.05 mm) from fitting face of cap. *See Fig. 10*.

5) Apply thin coat of silicone sealer to fitting face of No. 1 and No. 5 bearing caps. *See Fig. 10*. Install bearing caps. Ensure that No. 1 and No. 5 arch gasket protrusions fit properly.

6) Install bearing cap with "A" mark on rear face in No. 2 position. Tighten caps gradually and in sequence 3, 4, 2, 5 and 1. Ensure that crankshaft turns freely.

Fig. 10: Arch Gasket & Sealer Installation

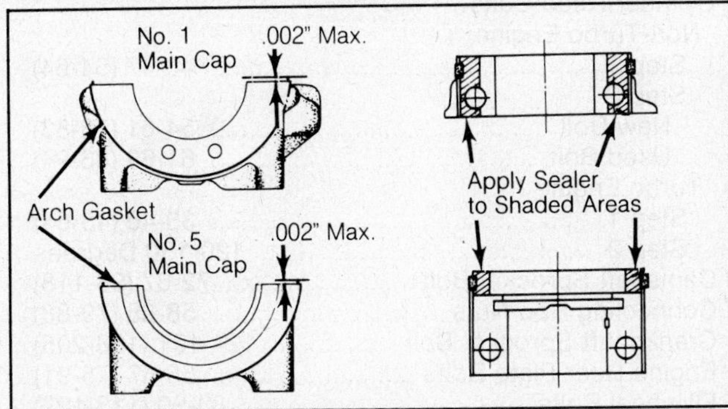

Install bearing caps before sealer sets up. Courtesy of Isuzu Motor Co.

CONNECTING ROD BEARINGS

Mark connecting rod and cap for cylinder identification. Remove rod cap. Check bearing clearance using Plastigage. If crankpin is not worn and clearance is excessive, install new bearings.

THRUST BEARING ALIGNMENT

Move crankshaft fully to one end. Using a feeler gauge, measure clearance between crankshaft and thrust bearing. If clearance is greater than .012" (.30 mm), replace thrust bearing.

REAR MAIN BEARING OIL SEAL

Removal

Remove engine from vehicle. Remove pressure plate, disc and flywheel. Remove rear oil seal.

Installation

Coat seal lip with engine oil. Using Seal Installer (J-22928), install new seal. Reverse removal procedure to complete installation.

CRANKSHAFT FRONT OIL SEAL

Removal

Remove camshaft oil seal retainer. Keep crankshaft from turning and remove crankshaft pulley bolt. Using Puller (J-29752), remove crankshaft sprocket. Remove front oil seal dust cover. Remove oil seal.

Installation

Coat seal lip with engine oil. Using Seal Installer (J-24250), install new oil seal. Install dust cover. Using Pulley Installer (J-26587), install crankshaft sprocket and pulley. Reverse removal procedure to complete installation.

ENGINE OILING

ENGINE OILING SYSTEM

A rotor-type oil pump is used in Non-Turbo 2WD models. A gear-type oil pump is used in Turbo and 4WD models. Oil drawn from crankcase passes through a strainer, then to oil pump.

Oil is delivered to full-flow oil filter, oil cooler and main oil gallery. By-pass valves are incorporated into oil filter and oil cooler.

Main oil gallery supplies oil to lubricate crankshaft and connecting rod bearings. Oil gallery feeds oil to vacuum pump, camshaft and turbocharger (if equipped). From camshaft, oil is routed to feed rocker arm shaft assembly and upper valve train components.

Oil is fed from oil gallery to oil jet pipe, which sprays oil from below pistons to lubricate cylinder walls and piston pins. Oil spray from oil jets aids in piston cooling.

CRANKCASE CAPACITY

Capacity on P'UP is 6.0 quarts (5.7L) with oil filter replacement; 5.6 quarts (5.3L) without filter replacement. Capacity on Trooper II is 6.4 quarts (6.0L) with filter and cooler.

NORMAL OIL PRESSURE

Normal oil pressure is 50 psi (3.5 kg/cm²).

OIL PUMP

Removal

Remove engine from vehicle. Remove crankcase and oil pan as an assembly. Remove oil pipe sleeve nut from engine block. Remove attaching bolts. Remove oil pump with oil pipe attached.

Inspection (Non-Turbo 2WD Models)

1) Disassemble oil pump and clean parts thoroughly. Inspect for signs of unusual wear or damage. With rotors installed in pump, place a straightedge over housing. Using a feeler gauge, measure clearance between rotors and straightedge.

2) If clearance is .006" (.15 mm), replace rotor set (pin, shaft, inner and outer rotors). Using a feeler gauge, measure clearance between inner and outer rotors. If clearance is greater than .0055" (.14 mm), replace rotor set.

3) Using a feeler gauge, measure clearance between outer rotor and pump housing. If clearance is greater than .011" (.27 mm), replace pump. Check clearance between rotor shaft and pump body. If clearance is greater than .008" (.20 mm), replace pump.

Inspection (Turbo & 4WD Models)

1) Disassemble oil pump and clean parts thoroughly. Inspect for signs of unusual wear or damage. Using a feeler gauge, check clearance between pump

2.2L 4-CYLINDER DIESEL & TURBO DIESEL (Cont.)

body inner wall and gear tips. If clearance is greater than .005-.0055" (.13-.14 mm), replace gear set (drive gear shaft and pin).

Fig. 11: Oil Pump Assemblies

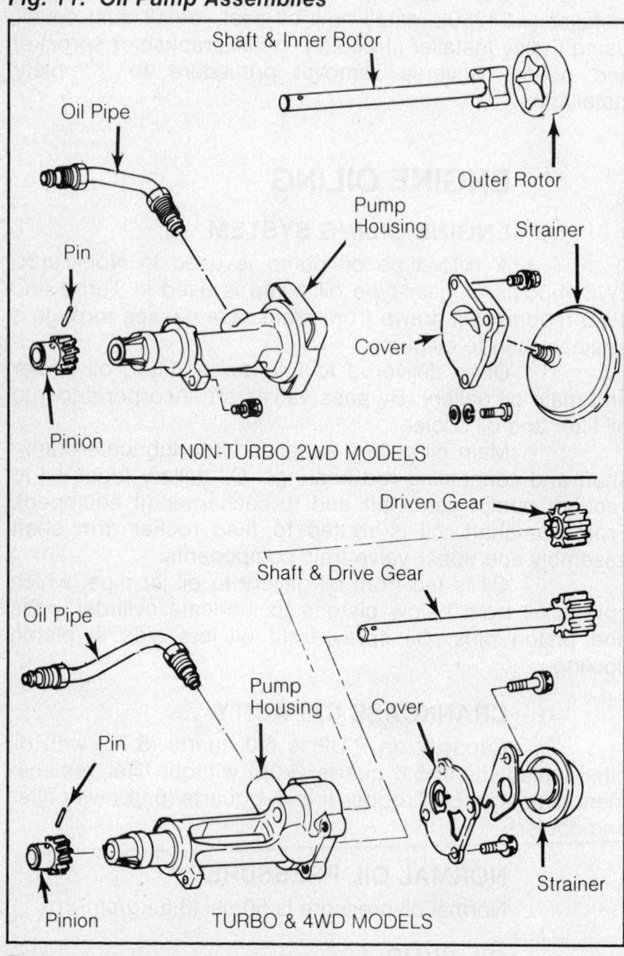

Thoroughly clean all parts prior to measuring clearances. Courtesy of Isuzu Motor Co.

2) With gears installed in pump, place a straightedge over pump housing. Using a feeler gauge, measure clearance between gears and straightedge. If clearance is greater than .0016-.0037" (.041-.094 mm), replace pump.

Installation

Assemble pump. Reverse removal procedure to complete installation.

ENGINE COOLING

WATER PUMP

Removal

Remove lower engine cover and drain cooling system. Remove battery, fan, fan shroud and upper radiator hose. Remove drive belts and fan pulley. Remove water pump retaining bolts and remove pump.

Installation

Install water pump using a new gasket. Reverse removal procedure to complete installation.

NOTE: For further information on cooling systems, see ENGINE COOLING section.

TIGHTENING SPECIFICATIONS

Application	Ft. Lbs. (N.m)
Cylinder Head Bolts	
Non-Turbo Engine	
Step 1	40-47 (54-64)
Step 2	
New Bolt	54-61 (73-83)
Used Bolt	61-69 (83-94)
Turbo Engine	
Step 1	33-40 (45-54)
Step 2	120-150 Degrees
Camshaft Sprocket Bolt	72-87 (98-118)
Connecting Rod Nuts	58-65 (79-88)
Crankshaft Sprocket Bolt	124-151 (168-205)
Engine Rear Plate Bolts	55-67 (75-91)
Flywheel Bolts	83-90 (113-122)
Main Bearing Cap Nuts	116-130 (157-176)
Manifolds Nuts (Intake & Exhaust)	10-17 (14-23)
Injection Pump Timing Pulley Bolt	42-52 (57-71)
Oil Jet Pipe Bolts	24-27 (33-37)
Oil Jets	22 (30)
Oil Cooler Bolts	54-61 (73-83)
Rocker Arm Shaft Bolts	10-17 (14-23)
Timing Belt Tensioner Bolts	79-94 (107-127)

ENGINE SPECIFICATIONS

GENERAL SPECIFICATIONS

Year	DISPLACEMENT		Fuel System	HP@RPM	Torque Ft. Lbs.@RPM	Compr. Ratio	BORE		STROKE	
	Cu. In.	Liters					In.	mm	In.	mm
1987										
Non-Turbo	136.6	2.2	Fuel Inj.	62@4300	96@2000	21:1	3.46	88	3.62	92
Turbo	136.6	2.2	Fuel Inj.	80@4000	125@2500	21.0:1	3.46	88	3.62	92

Isuzu Engines

2.2L 4-CYLINDER DIESEL & TURBO DIESEL (Cont.)

ENGINE SPECIFICATIONS (Cont.)

VALVES

Engine Size & Valve	Head Diam. In. (mm)	Face Angle	Seat Angle	Seat Width In. (mm)	Stem Diameter In. (mm)	Stem Clearance In. (mm)	Valve Lift In. (mm)
2.2L							
Intake	.....	45°	45°	.047-.059 (1.20-1.50)	.310-.315 (7.88-8.00)	.0015-.0027 (.039-.068)	.....
Exhaust	.....	45°	45°	.047-.059 (1.20-1.50)	.309-.315 (7.85-8.00)	.0025-.0037 (.064-.093)	.....

CRANKSHAFT MAIN & CONNECTING ROD BEARINGS

	MAIN BEARINGS				CONNECTING ROD BEARINGS		
Engine	Journal Diam. In. (mm)	Clearance In. (mm)	Thrust Bearing	Crankshaft End Play In. (mm)	Journal Diam. In. (mm)	Clearance In. (mm)	Side Play In. (mm)
2.2L	2.3591-2.3594 (59.921-59.929)	.0011-.0033 (.028-.085)	No. 3	.0012 Max. (.300)	2.0835-2.0839 (52.921-52.931)	.0016-.0047 (.040-.120)	.....

PISTONS, PINS & RINGS

	PISTONS	PINS		RINGS		
Engine	Clearance In. (mm)	Piston Fit In. (mm)	Rod Fit In. (mm)	Ring No.	End Gap In. (mm)	Side Clearance In. (mm)
2.2L						
Non-Turbo	.0014-.0022 (.036-.056)	.0002 [1] (.004)	.0003-.0008 (.008-.020)	No. 1	.008-.016 (.20-.41)	.002-.003 (.05-.07)
				No. 2	.008-.016 (.20-.41)	.001-.002 (.03-.06)
				Oil	.008-.016 (.20-.41)	.0008-.0021 (.020-.054)
Turbo	.0014-.0022 (.036-.056)	.0002 [1] (.004)	.0003-.0008 (.008-.020)	No. 1	.008-.016 (.20-.41)	.005-.006 (.05-.08)
				No. 2	.008-.016 (.20-.41)	.002-.003 (.05-.07)
				Oil	.008-.016 (.20-.41)	.0012-.0028 (.030-.070)

1 – Interference fit.

VALVE SPRINGS

Engine	Free Length In. (mm)	PRESSURE Lbs. @ In. (Kg @ mm) Valve Closed	Valve Open
2.2L			
Inner	1.89 (47.9)	12-14@1.46 [1] (5.5-6.3@37.0)	.....
Outer	1.86 (47.3)	43-49@1.54 [1] (19.7-22.2@39.0)	.....

1 – Compressed height as measured in spring tension tester.

CAMSHAFT

Engine	Journal Diam. In. (mm)	Clearance In. (mm)	Lobe Lift In. (mm)
2.2L	1.87-1.89 (47.6-48.0)	.0047 Max. (.012)	1.597 (40.57)

VALVE TIMING

	INTAKE		EXHAUST	
Engine	Open (BTDC)	Close (ABDC)	Open (BBDC)	Close (ATDC)
2.2L	16°	54°	56°	14

Jaguar Engines

4.2L 6-CYLINDER

XJ6 III

NOTE: **For engine repair procedures not covered in this article, see ENGINE OVERHAUL PROCEDURES articles at beginning of this section.**

ENGINE CODING

ENGINE IDENTIFICATION

Engine can be identified by the number stamped on top of cylinder block at rear of engine and on identification plate in engine compartment.

ENGINE, MANIFOLDS & CYLINDER HEAD

CAUTION: **The fuel injection system must be depressurized before disconnecting any fuel system component. Disconnect fuel pump relay and crank engine for a few seconds to depressurize system.**

NOTE: **Engine and transmission are removed as an assembly.**

ENGINE

Removal

1) Remove hood and disconnect battery. Drain engine oil and cooling system. Disconnect radiator hoses and remove radiator and fan shroud. Remove right wiring harness cover and disconnect headlights. Disconnect wiring and A/C hoses from diagonal fender support rods and remove rods.

2) Disconnect fuel lines and plug all openings. Disconnect wiring from A/C compressor. Remove drive belt and remove A/C compressor. Do not disconnect refrigerant hoses. Disconnect wiring from alternator.

3) Disconnect exhaust pipes from exhaust manifolds. Remove engine ground strap. Disconnect transmission oil cooler lines. Remove air cleaner. Disconnect airflow meter wiring. Remove airflow meter and bracket.

4) Remove power steering pump and place out of the way. Do not disconnect power steering hoses. Disconnect wiring, hoses, vacuum pipes and throttle cable from top of engine. Disconnect injector harness, ground lead and starter lead. Lift fresh air intake out of position and remove heater hose and water valve.

5) Install Engine Support (MS 53A). Raise front of vehicle and support with safety stands. Remove rear and intermediate exhaust heat shields. Remove plate between oil pan and transmission. Place floor jack under rear of engine and raise it slightly. Remove rear transmission mount attaching bolts and remove transmission mount.

6) Remove drive shaft companion flange bolts from rear of transmission. Disconnect selector lever cable and speedometer cable. Raise vehicle, remove safety stands and lower vehicle.

7) Attach engine sling to lifting eyes attached to cylinder head and support engine. Remove engine support.

8) Place floor jack, with a piece of wood, under transmission. Remove front engine mounts. Carefully raise the engine and move it forward to clear steering rack housing. Remove engine/transmission assembly.

Installation

Carefully lower engine/transmission assembly into vehicle. Ensure that engine clears steering rack housing. Reverse removal procedure to complete installation. Check all fluid levels.

INTAKE MANIFOLD

Removal

1) Depressurize fuel system. Remove air cleaner assembly. Remove airflow meter and disconnect hoses from throttle housing. Disconnect cable from airflow meter throttle switch. Remove throttle cable, kickdown cable and service interval counter cable, if used.

2) Remove breather and fuel tubes from fuel rail. Remove thermostat housing. Disconnect ignition coil harness and remove coil. Remove distributor cap and spark plug wires. Remove connectors from auxiliary air valve cold start injector, coolant temperature sensor and thermostatic switch.

NOTE: **When removing lower manifold nuts note position of all mounting clips for hoses and wiring.**

3) Remove fuel injection harness and disconnect fuel hoses from cold start injector regulator and fuel rail. Remove intake manifold attaching nuts. Remove intake manifold and gasket.

Installation

Install new intake manifold gasket on studs of cylinder head. Reverse removal procedure to complete installation.

EXHAUST MANIFOLDS

Removal

1) Remove hardware securing steering pinion heat shield. Remove hardware securing heat shield to exhaust manifold. Remove A/C compressor heat shield.

2) Disconnect oxygen sensor from exhaust pipes. Remove exhaust pipes from exhaust manifolds. Remove exhaust manifold from cylinder head. Note position of dipstick tube and dipstick standoffs.

Installation

To install, reverse removal procedure.

Fig. 1: Camshaft Timing

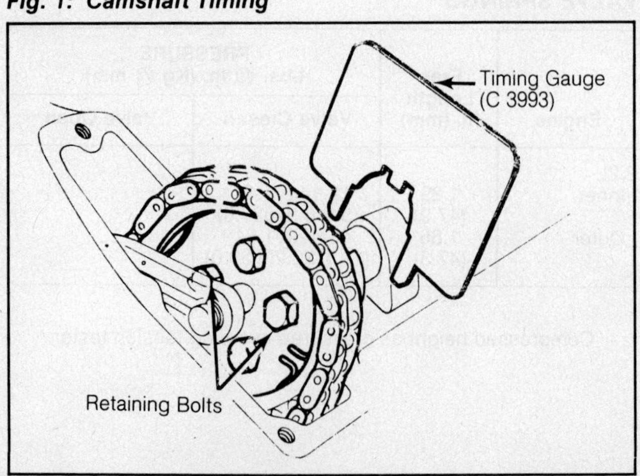

Courtesy of Jaguar Cars Inc.

Jaguar Engines

4.2L 6-CYLINDER (Cont.)

CYLINDER HEAD

Removal

1) Depressurize fuel injection system and drain cooling system. Disconnect wiring and A/C hoses from fender support rods and remove rods. Disconnect radiator hoses. Remove camshaft covers. Remove nuts attaching breather housing to front of cylinder head and remove breather.

CAUTION: The crankshaft must not be rotated while the camshaft sprockets are disconnected and cylinder head is still in place. When the cylinder head is removed, support cylinder head on wooden blocks placed at ends of cylinder head to prevent valve damage.

2) Remove bolt securing dipstick tube to manifold. Disconnect exhaust pipes from exhaust manifold. Disconnect fuel lines and plug all openings. Disconnect spark plug wires, temperature sensor lead and engine ground from manifold.

3) Remove air cleaner. Disconnect airflow meter hoses and remove airflow meter. Disconnect throttle and kickdown cables. Disconnect heater hoses and remove camshaft oil feed tubes by removing banjo bolts from back of cylinder head.

4) Raise front of vehicle and support with safety stands. Turn the crankshaft until the 2 camshaft timing notches are below the camshafts. Remove the 2 accessible bolts from each camshaft flange. Turn the crankshaft 1 complete revolution and loosen two remaining bolts.

5) Loosen lock nut on idler sprocket shaft. Slacken timing chain tension by pressing in on serrated adjuster pin and rotating Timing Chain Adjuster (JD 2B) in a clockwise direction. *See Fig. 2.* Remove remaining bolts.

NOTE: Do not remove wire snap rings from camshaft sprockets unless precision readjustment of cam timing using Timing Gauge (C3993) is necessary.

Fig. 2: Adjusting Upper Timing Chain

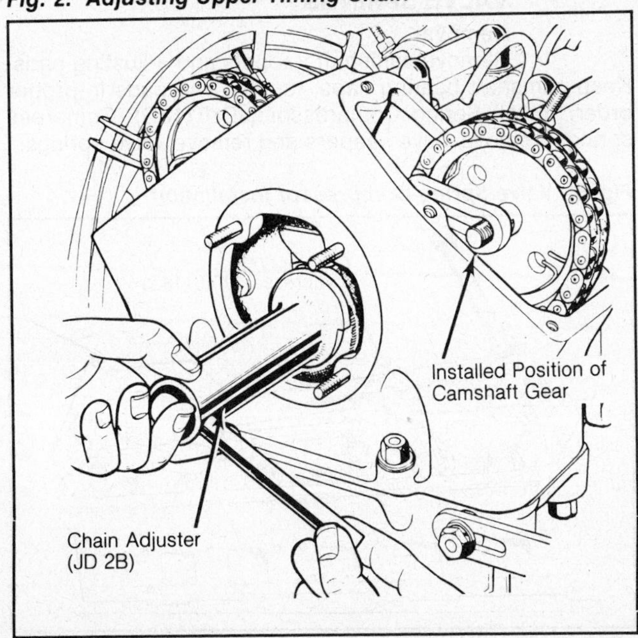

Courtesy of Jaguar Cars Inc.

6) Remove sprockets from camshaft and slide sprockets up the support brackets. Mark sprocket plates and camshafts for reassembly. Remove cylinder head domed nuts and 6 nuts securing front of cylinder head. Lower vehicle and remove cylinder head. Care must be taken when handling cylinder head to avoid bending valves.

Installation

1) Install new head gasket. Ensure "TOP" mark is upward. Rotate crankshaft until No. 6 (front) cylinder is at TDC, with distributor rotor pointing approximately forward in-line with engine. Align camshafts using Timing Gauge (C3993). *See Fig. 1.*

CAUTION: When camshafts are disconnected independent movement of individual camshaft may cause valve to valve contact and damage.

2) Lower cylinder head into position and install spark plug wire holders and lifting brackets. Install cylinder head domed nuts and 6 nuts securing front of cylinder head. Tighten nuts to specification in proper sequence. *See Fig. 3.*

Fig. 3: Jaguar XJ6 Cylinder Head Tightening Sequence

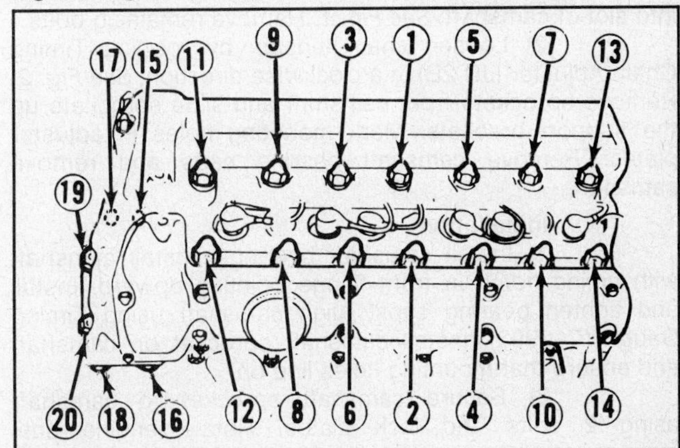

Courtesy of Jaguar Cars Inc.

3) Locate sprockets on camshaft flanges and ensure both holes in each flange are in alignment with mounting holes marked during removal. If necessary, remove snap ring and reposition adjuster plate. *See Fig. 4.*

Fig. 4: Exploded View of Camshaft Sprocket Assembly

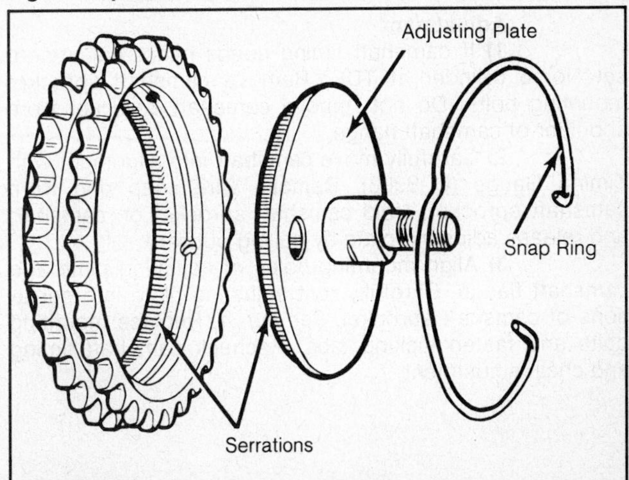

Courtesy of Jaguar Cars Inc.

Jaguar Engines

4.2L 6-CYLINDER (Cont.)

4) Secure adjuster plates to camshaft using 2 bolts and lock plates. Rotate engine until remaining holes are accessible. Install bolts and bend up lock plate tabs. Set timing chain tension by turning Timing Chain Adjuster (JD 2B) in a counterclockwise direction. DO NOT use excessive force to tighten chain. Tighten lock nut.

5) Ensure that No. 6 (front) cylinder is at TDC (with pointer opposite "0" on timing scale) and recheck position of camshafts using Timing Gauge (C 3993). Reverse removal procedure to complete installation. Check ignition timing and perform exhaust emission test.

CAMSHAFTS

CAUTION: The crankshaft must not be rotated while the camshaft sprockets are disconnected and cylinder head is still in place.

Removal

1) Remove camshaft covers. Remove nuts attaching breather housing to front of cylinder head and remove breather. Loosen lock nut on idler sprocket shaft. Remove the 2 accessible bolts from each camshaft flange. Rotate crankshaft until valve timing gauge can be fitted into slot of camshaft. *See Fig. 1*. Remove remaining bolts.

2) Loosen chain tension by rotating Timing Chain Adjuster (JD 2B) in a clockwise direction. *See Fig. 2*. Remove sprockets from camshaft and slide sprockets up the support brackets. Mark mounting holes in adjuster plates. Remove camshaft bearing caps and remove camshaft.

Installation

1) Install camshaft bearings. Install camshaft with timing notch in front flange pointing upward. Install and tighten bearing caps. Align camshaft using Timing Gauge (C 3993). Install camshaft sprocket on camshaft and ensure that mounting holes line up.

2) Secure camshaft sprocket to camshaft using 2 bolts and lock plates. Rotate engine until remaining holes are accessible. Install bolts and bend up lock plate tabs. Set timing chain tension by turning Timing Chain Adjuster (JD 2B) in a counterclockwise direction. Tighten lock nut.

3) Ensure that No. 6 (front) cylinder is at TDC (with pointer opposite "0" on timing scale) and recheck position of camshafts using Timing Gauge (C 3993). Reverse removal procedure to complete installation.

Adjustment

1) If camshaft timing needs minor adjustment set No. 6 cylinder at TDC. Remove camshaft sprocket mounting bolts. Do not remove camshaft sprocket from shoulder of camshaft flange.

2) Carefully move camshaft into alignment with Timing Gauge (C 3993). Remove wire snap ring from camshaft sprocket. Hold camshaft sprocket on camshaft and release adjusting plate by pulling outward.

3) Align mounting holes of adjusting plate and camshaft flange. Carefully refit adjusting plate into serrations of camshaft sprocket. *See Fig. 4*. Replace mounting bolts and fasten locking tabs. Recheck camshaft timing and chain adjustment.

VALVES

VALVE ARRANGEMENT

Right Side – Intake valves.
Left Side – Exhaust valves.

NOTE: When installing oversize replacement guides, check O.D. of guide to be used. If necessary, ream cylinder head bore to obtain proper interference fit.

VALVE GUIDES

Removal

Check valve stem clearance. Replace valve guide if stem clearance is more than .001-.004" (.03-.10 mm). Replace valve guides by heating head in boiling water for 30 minutes. Drive guides out of head from combustion chamber side.

Installation

Coat new guide with graphite grease and install snap ring. Reheat cylinder head and drive in new guides from top until snap ring is seated in groove.

REPLACEMENT VALVE GUIDES

Application	Size Mark	Dimension In. (mm)
Standard	No Mark	.501-.502 (12.73-12.75)
1st Oversize	1 Groove	.503-.504 (12.78-12.80)
2nd Oversize	2 Grooves	.506-.507 (12.85-12.88)
3rd Oversize	3 Grooves	.511-.512 (12.98-13.00)

NOTE: Support cylinder head on wooden blocks to prevent damaging valves.

VALVE SPRINGS

Removal

Remove camshaft, tappets and adjusting pads. Keep camshaft bearing caps, tappets and pads in proper order. Install Spring Compressor (JD 6118C). Compress springs, remove valve keepers and remove valve springs.

Fig. 5: Valve Spring Compressor Installation

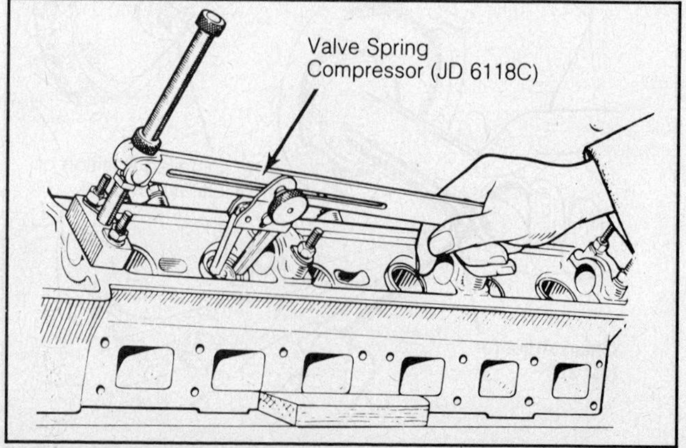

Courtesy of Jaguar Cars Inc.

Installation

Replace springs, if necessary. Reverse removal procedure to complete installation.

VALVE CLEARANCE ADJUSTMENT

CAUTION: If checking valve clearance with cylinder head removed, the camshafts must be fitted and checked one at a time. If one camshaft is rotated while the other is in position, interference between inlet and exhaust valves is likely to occur. Keep camshaft bearing shells, tappets and pads in proper order.

1) Remove camshaft covers. Rotate camshafts and record clearance between cam lobe and tappets. Remove camshaft, if adjustment is required. See CAMSHAFT removal in this article. Remove tappets and adjusting pads from valves that need adjustment.

Fig. 6: Valve Tappet & Guide Assembly

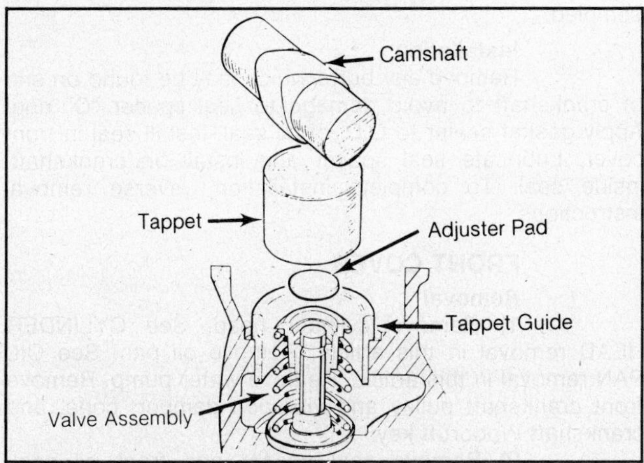

Courtesy of Jaguar Cars Inc.

2) Subtract specified valve clearance from actual (measured) valve clearance. Select a new adjusting pad that is equal to difference between the two readings. Adjusting pads are available in increments of .001" (.03 mm), from .085" (2.16 mm) to .110" (2.79 mm). Adjusting pads are marked with letters "A" to "Z" respectively.

3) Install correct adjusting pads and tappets. Reverse removal procedure to complete valve clearance adjustment.

VALVE CLEARANCE SPECIFICATIONS

Aplication	In. (mm)
All Valves	.012-.014 (.305-.356)

PISTONS, PINS & RINGS

PISTON & ROD ASSEMBLY

NOTE: Piston and connecting rod assemblies are numbered to their corresponding position in engine. No. 1 cylinder is at rear of engine. Front of engine is toward timing cover at front of vehicle.

Removal

Remove cylinder head and oil pan. See CYLINDER HEAD and OIL PAN REMOVAL in this article. Remove nuts from connecting rods and remove bearing caps. Push piston and rod assembly out of cylinder. Note numbers on connecting rods, they will normally face the exhaust side of engine when piston marking faces front.

Installation

Coat bearing shells and journals with oil. Compress piston rings and insert piston and rod assembly so that "FRONT" stamp on piston is toward front of engine. Tighten connecting rod nuts to 36-38 ft. lbs. (49-52 N.m). If new piston and rods are being installed they should be stamped with the number of the bore in which they are to be installed. Reverse removal procedure to complete installation.

PISTON RINGS

Check ring end gap and side clearance. Install oil control ring in bottom groove. Ensure that expander ends do not overlap. Install compression rings in top 2 grooves with "TOP" side up. The top compression ring is chrome-plated and cargraph coated, the Red coating must not be removed.

PISTON PINS

Remove snap rings and push piston pin out of piston. Piston pins and pistons are a matched set, do not mix. Piston pins are color coded. The O.D. of Red piston pins is .8751-.8752" (22.228-22.230 mm), the O.D. of Green piston pins is .8750-.8751" (22.225-22.228 mm). Install new snap rings.

FITTING PISTONS

1) Check piston-to-cylinder wall clearance to determine if proper clearance exists. Ensure that reboring does not exceed .020" (.51 mm), as oversize pistons are available in .020" (.51 mm) only.

2) If replacing pistons with standard sizes (no reboring), note the following list of piston grades and select replacement piston of same grade. Piston grade is stamped in piston crown and on top face of block adjacent to cylinder.

3) Grade "S" pistons are 3.6252-3.6262" (92.080-92.105 mm) in diameter across bottom of skirt and at right angles to piston pins. Honed diameter of bore must be .0007-.0013" (.018-.033 mm) greater than measured diameter of piston.

STANDARD PISTON GRADING

Stamp Mark	Cylinder Diameter In. (mm)
F	3.6250-3.6253 (92.075-92.083)
G	3.6254-3.6257 (92.085-92.093)
H	3.6258-3.6261 (92.095-92.103)

CYLINDER LINERS

1) Should reboring require more than .020" (.51 mm), new cylinder liners must be installed. Press out worn cylinder liners from below. Lightly coat block cylinder wall and outer top half of cylinder liner with a jointing compound.

2) Press in new liner until it is flush with top of block. Bore out and hone liner to correspond with grade

Jaguar Engines

4.2L 6-CYLINDER (Cont.)

of piston being installed. Following reboring, the plugs in the main oil gallery should be removed and cylinder block oil ways thoroughly cleaned. When dry, coat interior of crankcase with an oil and heat resistant paint.

CRANKSHAFT & ROD BEARINGS

MAIN & CONNECTING ROD BEARINGS

1) Remove connecting rod and main bearing caps, keeping parts in order for reassembly. Measure bearing clearances, using Plastigage. If wear or out-of-round exceeds .003" (.08 mm), grind crankshaft and install undersize bearings.

NOTE: Hardened crankshafts MUST NOT be reground. Hardened crankshafts have a Black surface finish. The hardened crankshaft Part No. is EAC-6719. They were installed in engines 8L168437 and later.

2) Undersize bearings are available in .010" and .020" (.25 mm and .51 mm) only. If grinding exceeds .020" (.51 mm), replace crankshaft. Install main and connecting rod caps and tighten to specified torque.

REAR MAIN BEARING OIL SEAL

NOTE: The following procedure must be performed before crankshaft is installed.

1) Apply a thin coat of gasket sealant to oil seal grooves 1 inch from parting face. Carefully tap new rear oil seal halves into position, then roll seal into retainer until ends do not protrude. Do not cut seal ends.

2) When both halves are properly in place, secure oil seal retainer with Allen head screws. Attach rear main bearing cap without bearings and torque to 72 ft. lbs. (98 N.m). Attach rear oil seal housing to cylinder block using 3 Allen head screws.

3) Apply a thin coat of graphite grease to inside surface of oil seal and insert Sizing Gauge (JD 17B). *See Fig. 7.* Press tool inward and turn until it is fully seated. Remove sizing gauge by pulling and twisting in opposite direction. Remove oil seal retainer and install crankshaft.

Fig. 7: Rear Oil Seal Installation

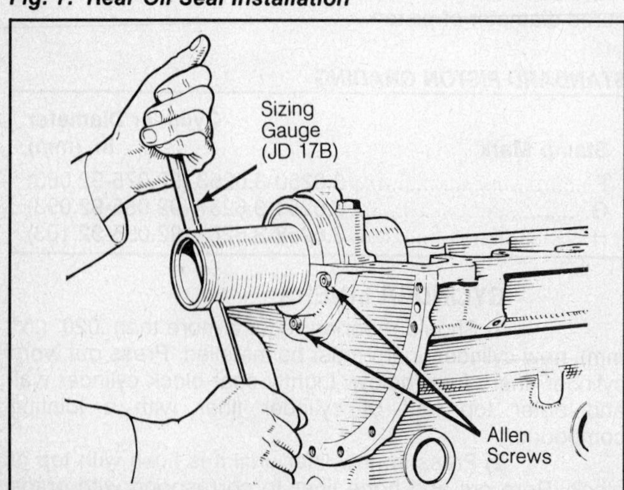

Courtesy of Jaguar Cars Inc.

THRUST BEARINGS

Thrust washers are used on center main bearing to adjust end play. If beyond specification, standard as well as .004" (.10 mm) oversize thrust washers are available. Install thrust washers with White metal side (grooved side) facing outward. Crankshaft end play is .004" (.10 mm).

FRONT CRANKSHAFT OIL SEAL & FRONT COVER

OIL SEAL

Removal

1) Remove oil pan. See OIL PAN removal in this article. Remove front crankshaft pulley and vibration damper, cone, and crankshaft Woodruff key.

2) Remove seal spacer and front oil seal. Always replace "O" ring inside seal spacer when disassembled.

Installation

Remove any burrs which may be found on end of crankshaft to avoid damage to seal spacer "O" ring. Apply gasket sealer to O.D. of oil seal. Install seal in front cover. Lubricate seal spacer and install on crankshaft, inside seal. To complete installation, reverse removal instructions.

FRONT COVER

Removal

1) Remove cylinder head. See CYLINDER HEAD removal in this article. Remove oil pan. See OIL PAN removal in this article. Remove water pump. Remove front crankshaft pulley and vibration damper, cone, and crankshaft Woodruff key.

2) Remove seal spacer and front oil seal. Always replace "O" ring inside seal spacer when disassembled. Remove idler pulley and and timing plate. Remove front cover.

Installation

Remove any burrs which may be found on end of crankshaft to avoid damage to seal spacer "O" ring. Apply gasket sealer to O.D. of oil seal. Install seal in front cover. Install new front cover gaskets on locating dowels in engine block. Install front cover. Lubricate seal spacer and install on crankshaft, inside seal. To complete installation, reverse removal instructions.

TIMING CHAINS

TIMING CHAIN REPLACEMENT

Removal

1) Remove cylinder head. See CYLINDER HEAD removal in this article. Remove water pump and oil pan. Remove vibration damper, cone and crankshaft Woodruff key. Remove timing gear cover, timing pointer, spacer, and front oil seal.

2) Remove oil slinger from crankshaft. Remove bottom timing chain tensioner and chain guide retaining screws. Remove conical filter behind tensioner. Loosen 4 cap screws securing top timing chain assembly. Do not remove cap screws at this point. *See Figs. 8 and 9.*

3) Remove crankshaft timing sprocket and chain assembly. Be sure to remove spacers, top timing

4.2L 6-CYLINDER (Cont.)

Fig. 8: Exploded View of Timing Gear & Chain Assembly

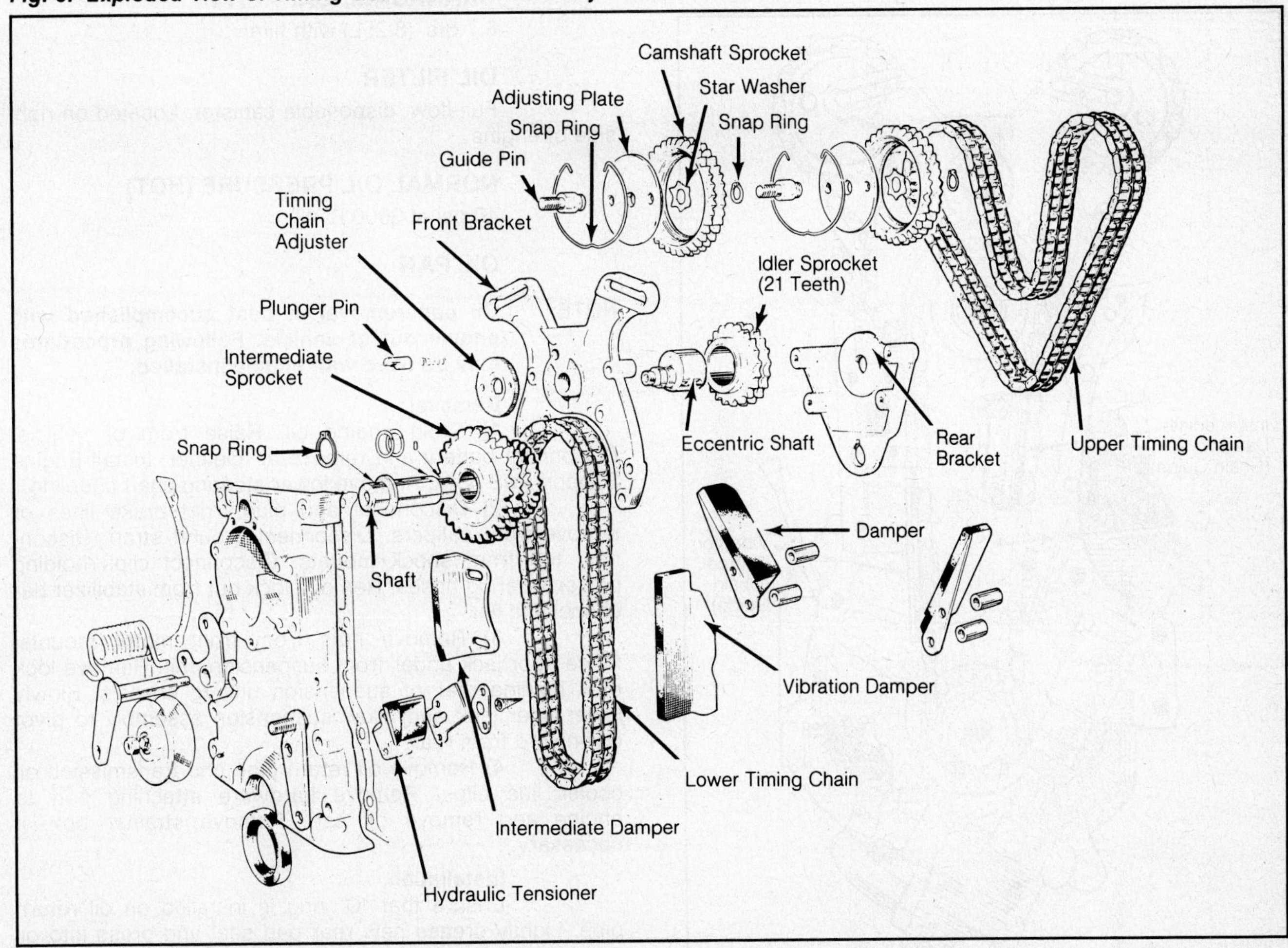

Courtesy of Jaguar Cars Inc.

chain dampers, and top timing chain retainer. Disengage camshaft sprockets from top chain. Remove nut and serrated washer from idler shaft. Remove serrated pin, plunger, and spring.

4) Remove nuts retaining front mounting bracket to rear mounting bracket. Remove timing chains from intermediate and idler sprockets. Remove idler shaft, idler sprocket, and bushing from rear mounting bracket. Remove snap ring and press intermediate shaft from rear mounting bracket. Note location of bushing and shim under intermediate sprocket.

Installation

1) Insert eccentric idler shaft in hole of front mounting bracket. Position spring and plunger in bracket and install serrated plate on shaft. Loosely secure plate using washer and nut.

2) Attach idler sprocket (21 teeth) to idler shaft. Install intermediate sprocket (large gear forward) on intermediate shaft. Install shim in rear mounting bracket. Install shaft assembly in rear mounting bracket, ensuring roll pin engages in slot. Install snap ring.

3) Install top timing chain (longer chain) on small intermediate sprocket, and lower timing chain on large sprocket. Loop top chain beneath idler sprocket and secure top mounting bracket to rear bracket.

4) Install 4 long cap screws and spring washers to front mounting bracket and attach dampers, chain support plate, and spacers to cap screws. Equalize loops of top timing chain and locate camshaft sprockets in loops. Rotate eccentric idler shaft to lift idler sprocket to its highest position between camshaft sprockets.

5) Ensure Woodruff key is installed in crankshaft. Install crankshaft sprocket, but do not fully seat at this time. Loop bottom timing chain beneath crankshaft sprocket, then tap sprocket until it is fully seated. Position and secure crankshaft sprocket assembly.

6) Install, but do not tighten, bottom timing chain guides. Insert conical filter into hole of cylinder block. Screw rubbing block into tensioner ratchet until .125" (3.2 mm) exists between rubbing block and body. Locate tensioner on shims as necessary to ensure rubbing block runs central on chain, and secure using 2 cap screws and lock plate.

7) Place slip gauge or spacer card supplied with new tensioner between rubbing block and body of tensioner to maintain a clearance of .125" (3.2 mm). Adjust intermediate damper to touch chain.

8) Tighten cap screws and bend up tabs of lock plate. Remove slip gauge and tap chain or rubbing block to release ratchet. Position oil slinger on crankshaft. Install timing cover, oil pan and cylinder head to complete installation.

Jaguar Engines

4.2L 6-CYLINDER (Cont.)

Fig. 9: Lower Timing Chain Assembly

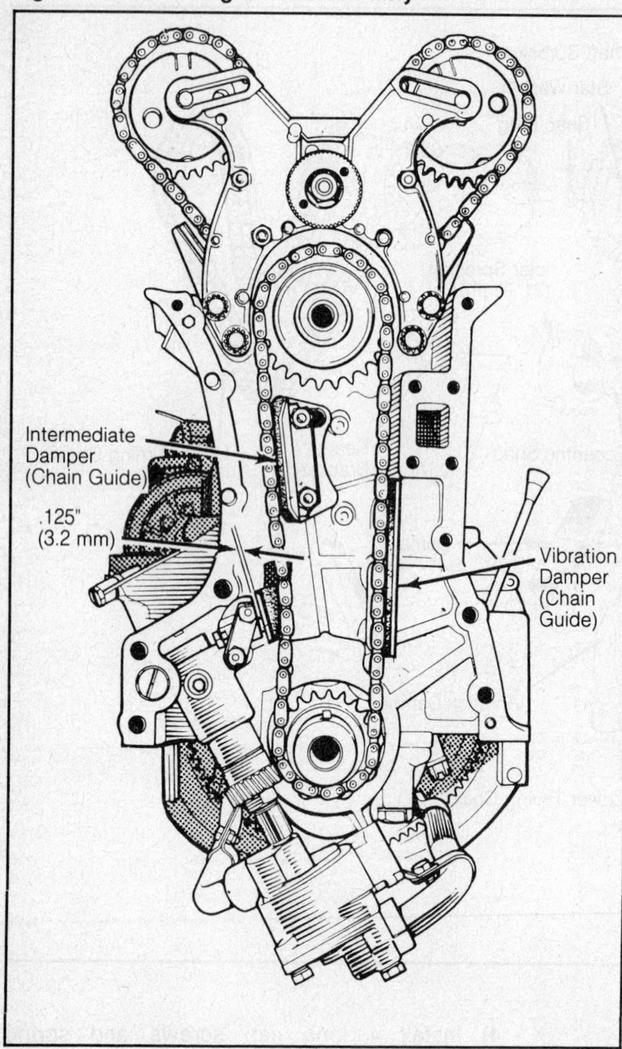

Courtesy of Jaguar Cars Inc.

Fig. 10: Oil Pump & Delivery Tubes

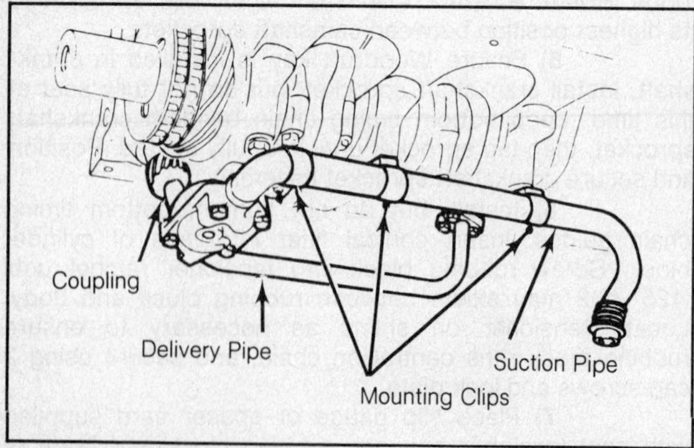

Courtesy of Jaguar Cars Inc.

ENGINE OILING SYSTEM

ENGINE OILING

Lubrication is provided by a gear-driven eccentric rotor-type pump.

CRANKCASE CAPACITY

8.7 qts. (8.25L) with filter.

OIL FILTER

Full-flow, disposable canister. Located on right side of engine.

NORMAL OIL PRESSURE (HOT)

40 psi at 3000 RPM.

OIL PAN

NOTE: **Oil pan removal is best accomplished with engine out of vehicle. Following procedures may be used with engine installed.**

Removal

1) Drain engine oil. Raise front of vehicle. Disconnect battery and remove air cleaner. Install Engine Support (MS 53A). Remove lower steering shaft coupling.

2) Disconnect and plug front brake lines or remove front calipers. Disconnect ground strap. Disconnect top front shock mounts. Disconnect clips holding power steering hoses. Remove lock nut from stabilizer bar connecting link.

3) Remove nuts from front motor mounts. Place floor jack under front suspension unit. Remove lock nuts holding rear of suspension unit to chassis. Slowly lower floor jack and allow suspension assembly to pivot downward from rear.

4) Remove oil return pipe and transmission oil cooler line clips. Remove hardware attaching pan to engine and remove oil pan. Remove strainer box, if necessary.

Installation

Ensure that "O" ring is installed on oil return pipe. Lightly grease new rear pan seal and press into oil pan groove. Do not trim ends. Install new oil pan gasket. Reverse removal procedure to complete installation.

OIL PUMP

Removal

Remove oil pan. Remove suction and delivery pipes. Remove bolts attaching oil pump to front main bearing cap. Remove pump and coupling sleeve at top of drive shaft. *See Fig. 11.*

Disassembly

1) Remove bolts and take off bottom cover. Remove inner and outer rotors. Inner rotor is pinned to drive shaft and cannot be disassembled.

2) Check clearances of inner and outer rotor lobes, outer rotor-to-body and rotor-to-cover plate. Place drive shaft in a soft-jawed vise and check that rotor is tight on pin.

Reassembly

Install outer rotor into pump body with chamfered end first. Reassemble oil pump in reverse order of disassembly.

Installation

Replace "O" rings on suction and delivery pipes. Ensure that suction pipe is on center line of engine and that connecting rods do not make contact when crankshaft is rotated. Install delivery pipe brackets on main bearing cap bolts. *See Fig. 10.* Reverse removal procedure to complete installation.

4.2L 6-CYLINDER (Cont.)

MAXIMUM OIL PUMP CLEARANCES

Application	In. (mm)
Inner-to-Outer Rotor	.006 (.15)
Outer Rotor-to-Body	.010 (.25)
Rotor-to-Cover (End Play)	.0025 (.064)

Fig. 11: Exploded View of Oil Pump

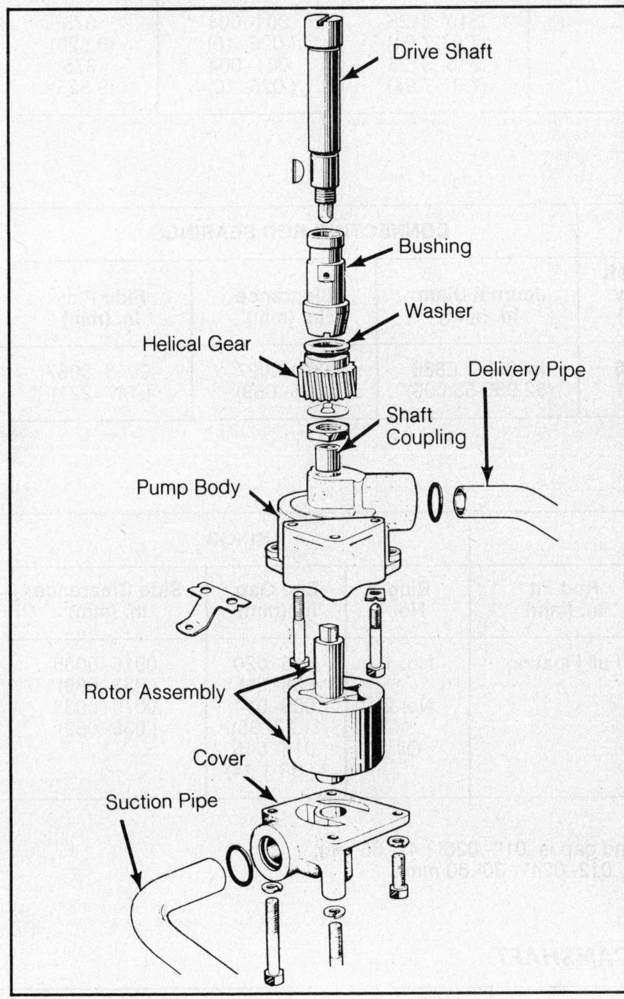

Courtesy of Jaguar Cars Inc.

ENGINE COOLING

WATER PUMP

Removal

1) Drain radiator. Remove radiator and fan shroud. Remove fan belts and fan hub assembly. Remove idler adjusting bolt. Remove hardware securing idler pulley to housing. Remove heater supply and manifold hoses from water pump.

2) Remove steering pump belt. Remove A/C compressor belt. Loosen steering pump bolts and remove adjusting bolt from special stud. Remove special stud. Remove cap screws securing thermostat housing. Remove housing and by-pass hose as an assembly.

3) Remove cap screws securing water pump and remove pump.

Installation

Tighten cap screws evenly to avoid distortion. Reverse removal procedure to complete installation.

NOTE: For information on cooling systems capacities and other cooling system components, see appropriate article in ENGINE COOLING SYSTEMS section.

TIGHTENING SPECIFICATIONS

Application	Ft. Lbs. (N.m)
Camshaft Connecting Rod Caps	36-38 (49-52)
Crankshaft Damper Bolt	125-150 (169-203)
Cylinder Head Nuts	50-52 (68-71)
Flywheel Bolts	64-67 (87-91)
Main Bearing Caps	69-72 (94-98)
Rear Transmission Mount	
5/16" Bolt	8-10 (11-14)
3/8" Bolt	27-32 (37-43)
Torque Converter Mounting	35 (47)
	In. Lbs. (N.m)
Cover (Domed Nuts)	84-96 (9-11)
Camshaft Bearing Caps	108 (12)

ENGINE SPECIFICATIONS

GENERAL SPECIFICATIONS

Year	DISPLACEMENT		Fuel System	HP@RPM	Torque Ft. Lbs.@RPM	Compr. Ratio	BORE		STROKE	
	Cu. In.	Liters					In.	mm	In.	mm
1987	258.4	4.2	Fuel Inj.	176 @ 4750	219 @ 2500	8.1:1	3.625	92.07	4.173	106

Jaguar Engines

4.2L 6-CYLINDER (Cont.)

ENGINE SPECIFICATIONS (Cont.)

VALVES

Engine Size & Valve	Head Diam. In. (mm)	Face Angle	Seat Angle	Seat Width In. (mm)	Stem Diameter In. (mm)	Stem Clearance In. (mm)	Valve Lift In. (mm)
4.2 L							
Intake	1.87-1.88 (47.50-47.75)	45°	44.5°	.....	.310-.3125 (7.87-7.94)	.001-.004 (.025-.10)	.375 (9.525)
Exhaust	1.620-1.630 (41.15-41.40)	45°	44.5°	.....	.310-.3125 (7.87-7.94)	.001-.004 (.025-.10)	.375 (9.525)

CRANKSHAFT MAIN & CONNECTING ROD BEARINGS

Engine	MAIN BEARINGS				CONNECTING ROD BEARINGS		
	Journal Diam. In. (mm)	Clearance In. (mm)	Thrust Bearing	Crankshaft End Play In. (mm)	Journal Diam. In. (mm)	Clearance In. (mm)	Side Play In. (mm)
4.2 L	2.7500-2.7505 (69.850-69.860)	.0008-.0025 (.020-.064)	Center	.004-.006 (.10-.15)	2.0860-2.0866 (52.980-53.000)	.001-.0027 (.025-.069)	.0058-.0087 (.147-.221)

PISTONS, PINS & RINGS

Engine	PISTONS	PINS		RINGS		
	Clearance In. (mm)	Piston Fit In. (mm)	Rod Fit In. (mm)	Ring No.	End Gap In. (mm)	Side Clearance In. (mm)
4.2 L	.0007-.0013 (.018-.033)	Full Floating	Full Floating	No. 1	.015-.020 (.38-.51)	.0015-.0035 (.038-.089)
				No. 2	.009-.014 [1] (.23-.35)	.0015-.0035 (.038-.089)
				Oil	.015-.045 [2] (.38-1.14)	[3]

[1] – Beginning with engine serial No. 8L103841, No. 2 compression ring end gap is .016-.026" (.41-.66 mm).
[2] – Beginning with engine serial No. 8L103841, oil control ring end gap is .012-.024" (.30-.60 mm).
[3] – Self-expanding.

VALVE SPRINGS

Engine	Free Length In. (mm)	PRESSURE Lbs. @ In. (Kg @ mm)	
		Valve Closed	Valve Open
4.2 L			
Inner	1.66-1.72 (42.0-43.7)	.....	.....
Outer	1.94-2.00 (49.3-50.8)	.....	.....

CAMSHAFT

Engine	Journal Diam. In. (mm)	Clearance In. (mm)	Lobe Lift In. (mm)
4.2 L	.9990-.9995 (25.375-25.387)	.0005-.002 (.013-.051)	.....

VALVE TIMING

Engine	INTAKE		EXHAUST	
	Open (BTDC)	Close (ABDC)	Open (BBDC)	Close (ATDC)
4.2 L	15°	57°	57°	15°

5.3L V12

XJS

NOTE: For engine repair procedures not covered in this article, see ENGINE OVERHAUL PROCEDURES articles at beginning of this section.

ENGINE CODING

ENGINE IDENTIFICATION

Engine number is stamped on cylinder block at rear of engine, between cylinder heads.

ENGINE, MANIFOLDS & CYLINDER HEADS

CAUTION: The fuel injection system must always be depressurized before disconnecting any fuel system component. Disconnect fuel pump relay and crank engine for a few seconds to depressurize system.

ENGINE

Removal

1) Remove hood and drain cooling system. Depressurize fuel and air conditioning systems. Disconnect battery. Remove right harness cover and disconnect headlights. Remove harness clips from right fender support rod and move harness out of the way.

NOTE: Engine and transmission are removed as an assembly.

2) Disconnect coil, pick-up module, ballast resistor and move harness out of the way. Remove receiver-drier clamps and relays from top rail. Remove the fan shroud attaching nuts. Disconnect the thermostatic switch harness and move out of the way. Remove right fender support rod.

3) Remove air cleaner assemblies. Remove the air anti-recirculation panel and fan attaching nuts. Remove lower radiator grille and grommets. Remove oil cooler to radiator attaching screws. Carefully position A/C condenser assembly out of the way.

4) Remove top radiator hose and disconnect remaining hoses from thermostat housings. Disconnect transmission cooler hoses from radiator and plug all openings. Disconnect expansion pipe and heater return hoses from radiator. Remove engine oil cooler and carefully move radiator forward.

5) Loosen fan belt and remove fan/clutch assembly. Disconnect bottom radiator hose and coolant level probe from radiator. Carefully remove radiator assembly. Remove left fender support rod.

6) Disconnect fuel hoses from fuel cooler and plug all openings. Disconnect the compressor to fuel cooler hose and plug all openings. Remove fuel cooler from left side air cleaner back plate.

7) Loosen power steering pump belt and remove pump. Position pump out of the way and remove pump bracket. Carefully disconnect A/C hoses from receiver-drier and condenser assembly. Plug all openings and remove condenser assembly.

8) Disconnect engine and alternator harness. Disconnect fuel feed hoses from engine and plug all openings. Disconnect vacuum hoses from brake vacuum reservoir. Disconnect brake servo hose and manifold one-way valve. Remove hose from firewall and move brake hose assembly out of the way.

9) Disconnect vacuum tubes from rear of right intake manifold. Remove bolt securing transmission dipstick tube and remove tube assembly. Disconnect starter solenoid from relay and starter feed wire from firewall connector.

10) Disconnect throttle switch, oil pressure switch, temperature sensor and ballast resistor. Disconnect cruise control harness, if used. Remove fresh air grille and remove hardware securing water valve to firewall. Disconnect hoses from water valve and remove valve.

11) Remove starter relay from firewall. Disconnent vacuum feed tube from manifold cross pipe. Disconnect kickdown switch wires and throttle cable from engine. Disconnect cruise control cable, if used. Install engine support (MS 53A) above rear engine lifting eyes and support engine.

12) Raise and support vehicle. Remove steering gear heat shields and disconnect exhaust pipes from exhaust manifolds. Place floor jack under rear transmission mount and raise it slightly. Remove mount attaching bolts and remove mount.

13) Remove intermediate and rear heat shields. Remove drive shaft attaching bolts and remove drive shaft. Disconnect speedometer cable. Lower engine slightly and disconnect shift cable. Disconnect ground strap and lower vehicle.

14) Place floor jack with a piece of wood under transmission and remove engine support. Attach engine sling and support engine, being careful not to damage thermostatic vacuum switch or tubes.

NOTE: Chains of engine hoist must be of sufficient length to ensure that distance between lifting eyes and hook of hoist is 34.5" from front eyes to hook and 41" from rear eyes to hook.

15) Remove nuts from front engine mounts. Loosen lower nuts on right engine mount. Carefully raise engine 2-3". Push engine off to one side until engine clears steering gear.

16) Rear of engine must be kept as high as possible to allow oil pan to clear steering rack housing. Continue to raise engine, being careful not to damage A/C expansion valve or evaporator unions. Remove engine/transmission assembly.

Installation

Ensure that engine mount fiber discs are installed. Carefully lower engine into position and tighten front engine mounts. Reverse removal procedure to complete installation. Check all fluid levels and charge A/C system.

INTAKE MANIFOLDS

Removal (Right Side)

1) Disconnect battery. Remove air cleaner and depressurize fuel system. Remove screws securing pipe to fuel injection overflow valve. Remove spacer from left valve. Disconnect manifold pressure hose from "T" and manifold.

2) Release clip securing fuel pipe to fuel rail and disconnect hose. Release throttle linkage from bellcrank. Disconnect vacuum hoses from throttle housing. Release clamp securing air pipe to rubber elbow and disconnect pipe.

Jaguar Engines

5.3L V12 (Cont.)

3) Remove plastic clips securing harness to fuel rail. Disconnect electrical connectors from fuel injectors and cold start injector. Disconnect ground strap from manifold ram tube. Disconnect brake vacuum hose from one-way valve. Disconnect transmission, diverter valve and heater vacuum hoses from rear of intake manifold.

4) Remove throttle return spring. Remove hardware securing intake manifold to cylinder head. Remove clamp securing air rail to check valve connecting hose. Remove air rail and discard "O" rings. Release clamp securing hose to fuel crossover pipe and disconnect hose at fuel rail.

5) Remove EGR valve from throttle housing. Remove spacers from line mounting clips on intake manifolds. Carefully remove intake manifold assembly. Plug inlet ports and transfer components to replacement intake manifold, if necessary.

Installation

Install new air rail sealing rings and gaskets. Reverse removal procedure to complete installation. Check throttle linkage adjustment. See article in FUEL SYSTEMS.

Removal (Left Side)

1) Disconnect battery. Remove air cleaner and depressurize fuel system. Remove fender support rod. Remove screws securing pipe to fuel injection overflow valve.

2) Release clamp securing pressure regulator return hose to fuel rail and disconnect hose. Disconnect manifold pressure hose from intake manifold. Disconnect vacuum hose from throttle housing and electrical connectors from kickdown switch. Release throttle linkage from bellcrank.

3) Remove electrical harness from fuel rail. Disconnect electrical connectors from fuel injectors and cold start injector. Disconnect brake vacuum hose from one-way valve. Remove throttle return spring. Release clamp securing idle air valve pipe to rubber elbow and disconnect pipe.

4) Remove hardware securing intake manifold to cylinder head. Remove screws securing air rail clips to manifold ram tubes. Remove clamp securing air rail to check valve connecting hose. Remove air rail and discard "O" rings.

5) Remove EGR valve from throttle housing. Remove intake manifold stud spacers. Carefully remove intake manifold assembly. Plug inlet ports and transfer components to replacement intake manifold, if necessary.

Installation

Install new air rail sealing rings. Reverse removal procedure to complete installation. Check throttle linkage adjustment.

EXHAUST MANIFOLDS

Removal

1) Disconnect battery. Raise front of car. Remove steering rack heat shields. Disconnect oxygen sensors from exhaust pipes. Remove bolts securing exhaust pipes to manifold. Separate exhaust pipes from manifolds and lower car.

2) Depressurize fuel system and remove intake manifold from side being serviced. See appropriate procedures in this article.

3) Remove self-tapping screws securing starter solenoid heat shield to main heat shield from right exhaust manifold. Remove set screws securing heat shield to exhaust manifolds. Remove nuts securing exhaust manifolds to cylinder heads and carefully remove exhaust manifolds.

Installation

To install, reverse removal procedure.

NOTE: **The following procedure may be used for removal of either cylinder head. The right side intake manifold and camshaft cover must always be removed to allow access to timing chain tensioner.**

CYLINDER HEAD

Removal

1) Disconnect battery and drain cooling system. Remove air filter, right intake manifold, and right camshaft cover, if either head is to be removed. Remove left intake manifold and camshaft cover only if left cylinder head is to be removed.

NOTE: **Align camshaft using Timing Gauge (C 3993) on cylinder head being removed. If both heads are to be removed, align right camshaft.**

2) Rotate crankshaft until timing notches in camshaft flanges are pointing down. Remove the two accessible camshaft sprocket mounting bolts (per camshaft) and lock tabs. Rotate crankshaft until Timing Gauge (C 3993) can be inserted in slot in camshaft front flange. *See Fig. 1*.

3) Remove rubber grommet from front of timing cover. Insert blade of Screwdriver (JD 42-2) through timing cover hole and release timing chain tensioner.

Fig. 1: Valve Timing Gauge in Position for Timing Chain Removal or Installation

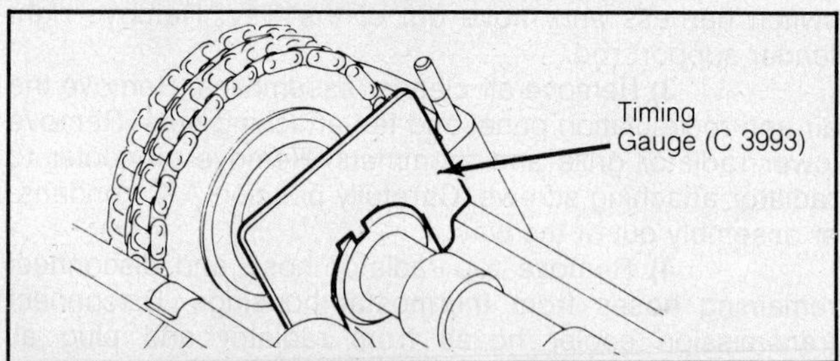

Courtesy of Jaguar Cars Inc.

4) Using Tensioner Retractor (JD 44), fully retract timing chain tensioner. Remove special tools, as soon as the locking catch engages on step. Disconnect remaining camshaft sprocket mounting bolts from camshaft and install Sprocket Retainers (JD 40). *See Figs. 2 and 5*.

5) Remove self-tapping screws securing starter solenoid heat shield from right cylinder head. Remove set screws securing heat shield to exhaust manifold. Remove nuts securing exhaust pipe to exhaust manifold. See EXHAUST MANIFOLDS in this article.

6) Remove camshaft oil feed banjo bolts at rear of cylinder heads. Remove A/C compressor. Remove nuts securing cylinder heads to timing cover. Remove cable clips from studs. Loosen cylinder head nuts, working from center of head outward. Remove cylinder heads and place on wooden blocks to prevent damaging valves. Discard old gaskets.

5.3L V12 (Cont.)

CAUTION: Do not rotate engine, unless Cylinder Liner Retainers (JD 41) have been attached to cylinder heads. If cylinder liners are allowed to move upward, the sealing area between the cylinder liner and block may become contaminated.

Fig. 2: Retracting Timing Chain Tensioner

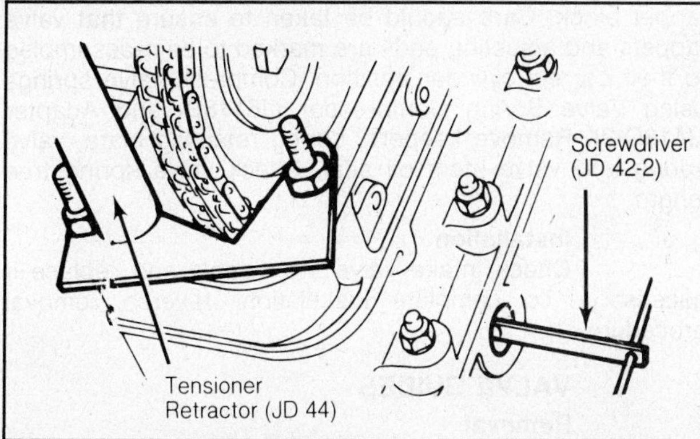

Courtesy of Jaguar Cars Inc.

Installation

1) Remove distributor cap. Attach a dial indicator to cylinder head stud. Rotate crankshaft to set No. 1 piston (right bank) to TDC of compression stroke. Check that the degree plate attached to the front of the oil pan is indicating 0 degrees on the crankshaft pulley. The distributor rotor will point at approximately 5 degrees from pick-up module.

2) Turn camshaft until Timing Gauge (C3993) can be inserted in slot in camshaft front flange. Remove cylinder liner retainer. Install cylinder head gasket with "TOP" side up. Install cylinder head and tighten retaining nuts to: 7/16" 49-52 ft. lbs. (66-71 N.m), 3/8" 27-28 ft. lbs. (36-38 N.m). *See Fig. 3.*

Fig. 3: Cylinder Head Tightening Sequence

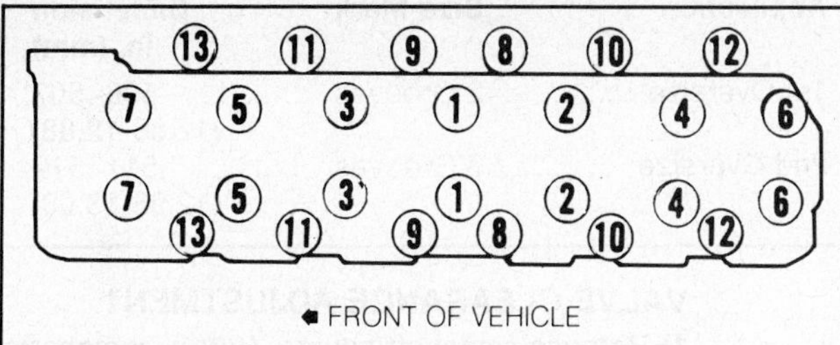

Courtesy of Jaguar Cars Inc.

3) Tighten cylinder head-to-timing cover nuts. Remove sprocket retainer and check alignment of sprocket holes. If camshaft and sprocket holes are not in alignment, remove snap ring which holds camshaft coupling to sprocket and disengage coupling from splines.

4) Rotate sprocket plate until retaining bolt holes are aligned. Bolt coupling to camshaft. Engage sprocket with coupling and install snap ring. Remove timing gauge. Repeat procedures for left cylinder head.

5) Rotate engine until remaining camshaft sprocket retaining bolts can be installed. Insert blade of Screwdriver (JD 42-2) through hole in timing cover and trip locking catch. Install rubber grommet. Reverse removal procedure to complete installation. Check all fluid levels and set ignition timing.

ENGINE FRONT COVER, OIL SEAL & TIMING CHAIN

FRONT COVER

Removal

1) With engine removed from chassis remove cylinder heads and oil pan. Remove oil pump adapter tubes and oil pump adapter. Remove alternator and power steering pump. Remove air injection (smog) pump and A/C compressor.

2) Remove water pump. Remove crankshaft damper bolt, damper and cone. Remove hardware securing alternator and smog pump brackets.

3) Remove bolts securing timing cover. Note length and relative position of bolts and dowel pins. Remove timing cover. Discard oil seal and gaskets.

Installation

To install, reverse removal procedure.

Fig. 4: Detail of Front Cover & Oil Seal

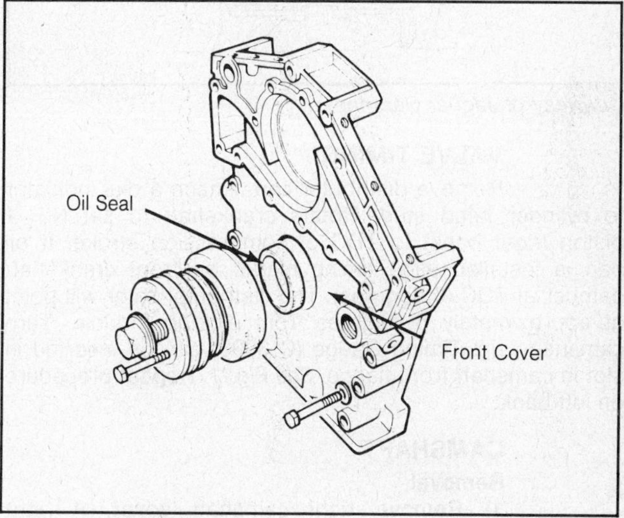

Courtesy of Jaguar Cars Inc.

OIL SEAL

Removal

1) Remove drive belts from crankshaft pulley. Remove fan and hub assembly. Remove outer nut, and pulley.

2) Remove crankshaft damper securing bolt. Remove crankshaft damper, mounting cone and Woodruff key. Pry out old oil seal and remove seal bushing.

Installation

Clean all parts and inspect seal contact areas for scratches or damage. Install new oil seal. Reverse removal procedures to complete installation.

TIMING CHAIN

Removal

Remove front cover as previously described. Install Intermediate Shaft Retainer (JD 39) on intermediate shaft (jackshaft). *See Fig. 5.* Disconnect timing chain from camshaft and jackshaft sprockets. Remove crankshaft sprocket and chain. To avoid disturbing position of distributor do not turn crankshaft with timing chain removed.

Installation

To install, reverse removal procedure.

Jaguar Engines

5.3L V12 (Cont.)

Fig. 5: Timing Chain Details

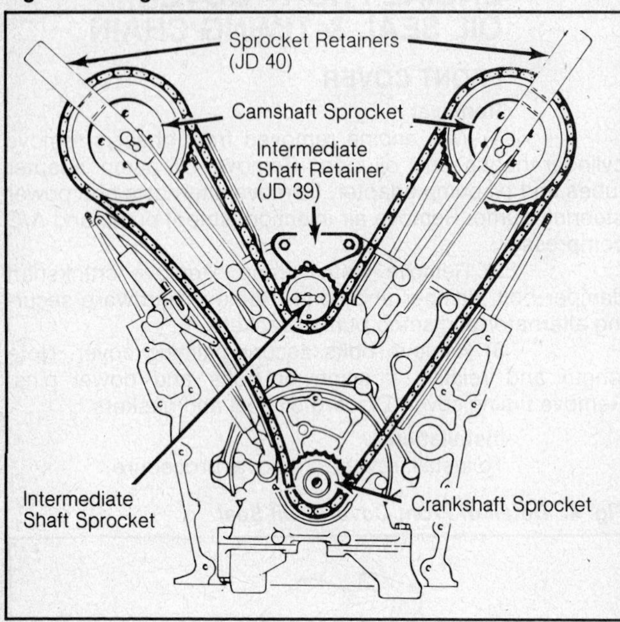

Courtesy of Jaguar Cars Inc.

VALVE TIMING

Remove distributor cap. Attach a dial indicator to cylinder head stud. Rotate crankshaft to set No. 1 piston (right bank) to TDC of compression stroke. If oil pan is installed align timing marks on front crankshaft damper at TDC (0 degrees). The distributor rotor will point at approximately 5 degrees from pick-up module. Turn camshaft until Timing Gauge (C 3993) can be inserted in slot in camshaft front flange. *See Fig. 1.* Repeat procedure on left bank.

CAMSHAFT

Removal

1) Remove right camshaft cover, if right camshaft is to be removed. Remove both camshaft covers, if left camshaft is to be removed. Remove rubber grommet from front of timing cover. Insert blade of Screwdriver (JD 42-2) through timing cover hole and release timing chain tensioner.

2) Using Tensioner Retractor (JD 44), fully retract timing chain tensioner. Remove special tools, as soon as the locking catch engages on step. Rotate crankshaft until timing notch in camshaft flanges face down. Remove 2 camshaft sprocket bolts. Rotate engine until Timing Gauge (C 3993) can be installed in slot in camshaft front flange.

3) Remove remaining sprocket retaining bolts. Attach Sprocket Retainers (JD 40) on sprocket pins. Sprocket retainers will hold sprockets in place on sprocket retaining struts. *See Fig. 5.* Do not rotate engine with camshaft disconnected. Loosen camshaft bearing cap nuts, starting with center cap and working outward. Remove bearing caps and camshaft out of tappet block.

Installation

To install, reverse removal procedure. Carefully recheck camshaft timing before final installation of camshaft covers.

VALVES

VALVE ARRANGMENT

E-I-E-I-E-I-I-E-I-E-I-E (Both sides, front-to-rear).

VALVE SPRINGS

Removal

Remove cylinder head, camshaft and valve tappet block. Care should be taken to ensure that valve tappets and adjusting pads are marked to be reassembled to their correct cylinder position. Compress valve springs using Valve Spring Compressor (J6118B) and Adapter (J118C-2). Remove keepers, spring retaining plate, valve spring and valve stem oil seal. Check valve spring free length.

Installation

Check intake valve stem seals and replace if necessary. To complete installation, reverse removal procedure.

VALVE GUIDES

Removal

Check valve guide-to-valve stem clearance. Replace valve guide if stem clearance is not within specification. Replace valve guides by heating head in boiling water for 30 minutes. Drive guides out of head from combustion chamber end.

Installation

Coat new guides with graphite grease and install snap ring. Reheat cylinder head and drive new guides from top until snap ring is seated in groove.

NOTE: When installing oversize replacement guides, check O.D. of guide to be used. If necessary, ream cylinder head bore to obtain proper interference fit.

REPLACEMENT VALVE GUIDES

Application	Size Mark	Dimension In. (mm)
1st Oversize	2 Grooves	.506-.507 (12.85-12.88)
2nd Oversize	3 Grooves	.511-.512 (12.98-13.00)

VALVE CLEARANCE ADJUSTMENT

1) Remove camshaft covers. Rotate camshafts and record clearance between cam lobe and tappets. Remove camshaft, if adjustment is required. See CAMSHAFT removal in this article. Remove tappets and adjusting pads from valves that need adjustment. Always return tappets to their original tappet bore.

2) Subtract specified valve clearance from actual (measured) valve clearance. Select a new adjusting pad that is equal to difference between the 2 readings. Adjusting pads are available in increments of .001" (0.03 mm), from .085" (2.16 mm) to .110" (2.79 mm). Adjusting pads are marked with letters "A" to "Z" respectively.

3) Install correct adjusting pads and tappets. Reverse removal procedure to complete valve clearance adjustment.

5.3L V12 (Cont.)

VALVE CLEARANCE SPECIFICATIONS

Application	In. (mm)
All Valves	.010-.012 (.25-.30)

VALVE TAPPET BLOCK

Removal

Remove camshaft, tappets, and adjusting pads. Remove Allen bolts attaching tappet block to cylinder head. Carefully tap block loose and remove it from the cam bearing studs.

Installation

Clean mating surfaces of cylinder head and tappet block. Inspect mating surfaces for scratches or damage. Apply gasket sealer to mating surfaces and refit tappet block. Tighten Allen bolts to specification.

PISTON, RINGS & PINS

OIL PAN

Removal

1) Drain engine oil. Disconnect battery and remove air cleaners. Raise front of vehicle. Install Engine Support (MS 53A). Remove lower steering shaft coupling.

2) Disconnect and plug front brake lines or remove front calipers. Disconnect ground strap. Disconnect top front shock mounts. Disconnect clips holding power steering hoses. Remove lock nut from stabilizer bar connecting link.

3) Remove nuts from front motor mounts. Place floor jack under front suspension unit. Remove lock nuts holding rear of suspension unit to chassis. Slowly lower floor jack and allow suspension assembly to pivot downward from rear.

4) Remove rear steel section of oil pan. This will allow access to interior main pan bolts. Remove cast aluminum main pan.

Installation

Replace "O" rings in oil cooler by-pass at front of pan. Install new gaskets. Install oil pan sections. Install transmission cooler line clips on pan bolts. Reverse removal instructions to complete installation procedure.

PISTON & ROD ASSEMBLY

Removal

Remove cylinder heads and oil pan. Install Cylinder Liner Retainers (JD 41) Remove oil pump adapters and oil pick-up and supply tubes. Rotate crankshaft until bearing cap to be removed is accessible. Remove nuts, bearing cap and bearing. Push piston and rod assembly out of cylinder.

Installation

Coat all parts with engine oil and make sure that piston ring gaps are evenly spaced around circumference of piston. Compress piston rings and insert piston and rod assembly so that "FRONT" stamp on top of piston faces front of engine. Reverse removal procedure to complete installation.

PISTON RINGS

Check ring end gap and side clearance. Install oil control ring in bottom groove. *See Fig. 6*. Ensure that expander ends do not overlap. Install compression rings in top two grooves with "TOP" side up. The top compression ring is chrome-plated and cargraph coated. DO NOT remove the Red coating.

Fig. 6: Exploded View of Piston Assembly

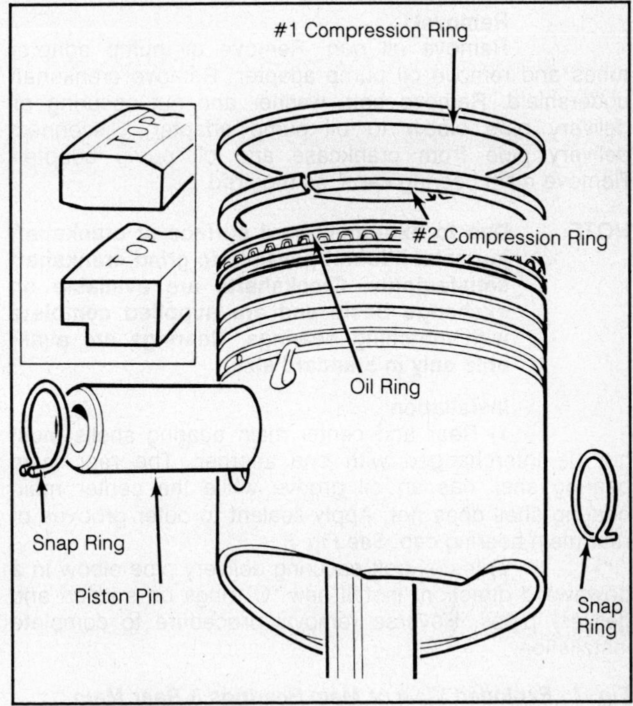

Courtesy of Jaguar Cars Inc.

PISTON PINS

Remove snap rings and push piston pin out of piston. Piston pins and pistons are a matched set, do not mix. The connecting rods must be installed so that "FRONT" stamp on piston faces front of engine. The chamfer on crankshaft end of connecting rod should face the crankpin radius.

FITTING PISTONS

Check piston-to-cylinder wall clearance to determine if proper clearance exists. If liner or piston is worn, replacement must be same grade as the one removed.

CYLINDER LINERS

NOTE: **If new liners are to be installed, they must be of same grade designation as old liners. Grade A-Red 3.543" (89.98 mm), or B-Green 3.544" (90.01 mm).**

Press out cylinder liners from below. Smear cylinder liners with Hylomar, or equivalent sealant prior to installation. Press cylinder liners into cylinder block. Care must be taken to ensure the block and cylinder liner mating surfaces are clean and free of dirt. Remove excessive sealant. Ensure liners are correctly seated and install Cylinder Liner Retainers (JD 41).

CRANKSHAFT & ROD BEARINGS

NOTE: **While it is possible to replace main bearing shells with engine in vehicle, this should only be done when it is certain that crankshaft is not damaged.**

Jaguar Engines

5.3L V12 (Cont.)

MAIN BEARINGS

Removal

Remove oil pan. Remove oil pump adapter tubes and remove oil pump adapter. Remove crankshaft undershield. Remove bolt, washer and nut securing oil delivery pipe elbow to oil pump adapter. Disconnect delivery pipe from crankcase and oil pump adapter. Remove main bearing caps, as required.

NOTE: **Due to extremely hard surface of crankshaft journals, it is not possible to grind crankshaft satisfactorily. Crankshafts are available on exchange basis and are supplied complete with matching bearings. Bearings are available only in standard size.**

Installation

1) Rear and center main bearing shells must not be interchanged with one another. The rear main bearing shell has an oil groove while the center main bearing shell does not. Apply sealant to outer grooves of rear main bearing cap. *See Fig. 8.*

2) Install bolt securing delivery pipe elbow in a downward direction. Install new "O" rings on suction and delivery pipes. Reverse removal procedure to complete installation.

Fig. 7: Exploded View of Main Bearings & Rear Main Oil Seal Assembly

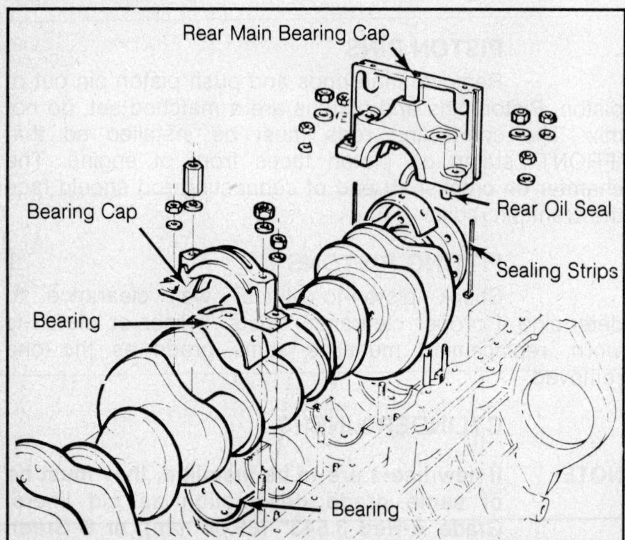

Courtesy of Jaguar Cars Inc.

REAR MAIN OIL SEAL REPLACEMENT

NOTE: **Rear oil seal replacement must be performed before installation of crankshaft.**

1) Apply sealant to outer grooves of rear main bearing cap. Apply one drop of Loctite to oil seal grooves. Install new oil seal halves in grooves of rear main bearing cap. Install main bearing cap on cylinder block and tighten.

2) Apply a small amount of graphite grease to oil seal. Insert Oil Seal Sizing Tool (JD 17B and JD 17B-1). Press tool inward and rotate until fully seated.

3) Remove rear main bearing cap. Coat oil seal with graphite grease. Position crankshaft in block. Apply Loctite 567 pipe sealant to bearing cap. *See Fig. 8.* Install main bearing cap and tighten to specifications.

Fig. 8: Sealing Rear Main Cap

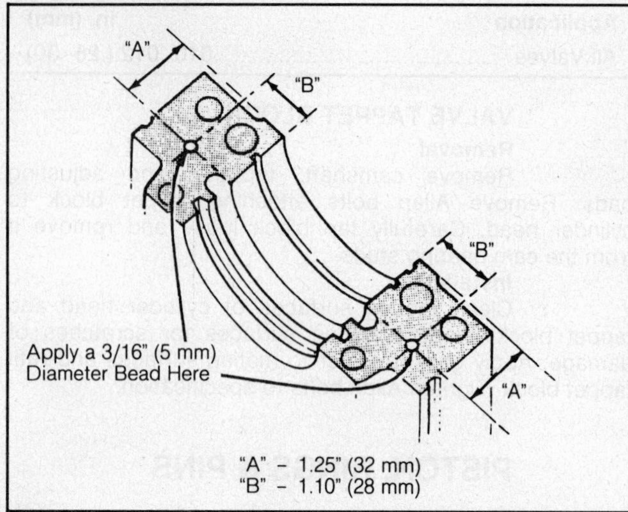

Courtesy of Jaguar Cars Inc.

THRUST BEARING ALIGNMENT

Measure crankshaft end play. Thrust bearing washers are used on center main bearing cap to adjust end play. Select thrust washers that bring end play within specification. Install thrust washers with grooved side facing outward.

ENGINE OILING

ENGINE OILING SYSTEM

Lubrication is provided by a gear-driven eccentric-type pump. Oil from pump goes through a full-flow oil filter to all moving engine components. Oil is then passed through an oil cooler and returned to oil pan.

CRANKCASE CAPACITY

11 qts. (10.2L) with filter.

OIL FILTER

Full-flow, disposable element.

NORMAL OIL PRESSURE

Information not available from manufacturer.

OIL PRESSURE REGULATOR VALVE

Nonadjustable. Located at oil filter assembly.

NOTE: **Oil pan removal is best accomplished with engine out of vehicle. Following procedures may be used with engine installed.**

OIL PUMP

Oil pump uses internal and external gears and crescent type cut-off. Drive gear is concentric around crankshaft nose. *See Fig. 9.*

Removal

Remove cylinder heads and oil pan. Remove timing cover and timing chain tensioner. Remove spacer from crankshaft. Remove timing chain and sprocket from crankshaft. Remove Woodruff key. Remove oil pump. Do not rotate crankshaft while oil pump is removed.

Jaguar Engines

5.3L V12 (Cont.)

Disassembly

1) Remove 8 bolts and lock washers and remove pump cover from gear housing. Mark drive and driven gear faces for reassembly reference. Remove both gears, and clean thoroughly.

2) Check condition of all gears. Remove burrs with fine file. Install driven gear and check radial clearance between gear and housing. Checks should not be taken at any of the 6 radial flats on the gear.

Fig. 9: Measuring Oil Pump Clearances

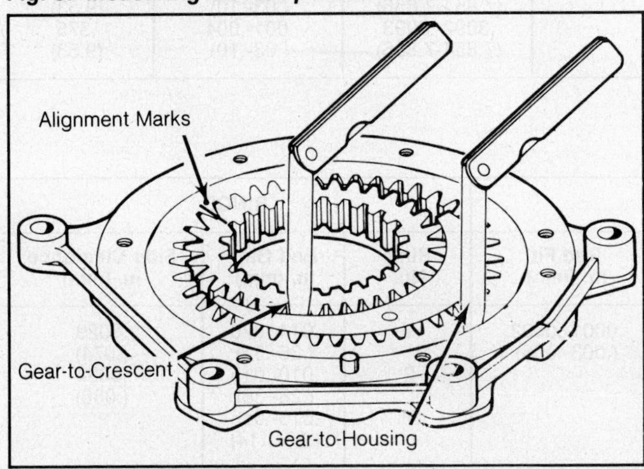

Courtesy of Jaguar Cars Inc.

3) Reinstall drive gear and check radial clearance between gear and crescent. Check gear end play by placing straightedge across joint face of housing and measure clearance between straightedge and gear. See MAXIMUM OIL PUMP CLEARANCE table.

Reassembly

Lubricate all gears with clean engine oil, check that surfaces are clean. Reverse disassembly procedure to complete assembly.

Installation

To install, reverse removal procedure.

MAXIMUM OIL PUMP CLEARANCE

Application	In. (mm)
Driven Gear-to-Housing	.005 (.13)
Drive Gear-to-Crescent	.006 (.15)
Gear End Play	.005 (.13)

ENGINE COOLING

WATER PUMP

Removal

1) Drain and remove radiator. Remove fan shroud and mounting bracket and move out of the way. Remove fan/clutch assembly. Remove fan belt. Remove idler pulley adjusting bolt. Remove hardware attaching idler pulley housing. Remove studs. Remove steering pump.

NOTE: **Exchange water pumps do not come with pulley. Pulley must be removed before sending in defective pump. Install pulley on pump before placing on engine. Aluminum idler pulleys have been replaced by stronger iron pulleys, (EAC 8097).**

2) Remove A/C compressor pump belt. Loosen steering pump pivot bolts enough to remove adjustment bolt from stud. Remove stud. Remove thermostatic switch housing and bottom hose assembly.

3) Loosen upper hose clamp on engine cross pipe. Remove set screws and washers attaching water pump. Pull pump out and downward to clear cross pipe hose.

Installation

To install, reverse removal procedure.

NOTE: **Improved material Thermostat Housing Gaskets are available, (EAC 7048) right side and (EAC 7047) left side.**

NOTE: **For further information on cooling systems, see ENGINE COOLING section.**

TIGHTENING SPECIFICATIONS

Application	Ft. Lbs. (N.m)
Crankshaft Main Bearing Nuts	
1/2"	59-62 (80-84)
3/8"	27-28 (36-38)
Connecting Rod Nuts	40-41 (54-56)
Crankshaft Pulley Bolts	125-150 (169-203)
Cylinder Head	
7/16" Nuts	49-52 (66-71)
3/8" Nuts	27-28 (36-38)
Flywheel-to-Crankshaft Bolts	63-66 (85-89)
	In. Lbs. (N.m)
Camshaft Cap Nuts	120 (14)
Thermostat Housing	96-108 (11-12)

ENGINE SPECIFICATIONS

GENERAL SPECIFICATIONS

Year	DISPLACEMENT		Fuel System	HP@RPM	Torque Ft. Lbs.@RPM	Compr. Ratio	BORE		STROKE	
	Cu. In.	Liters					In.	mm	In.	mm
1987	326	5.3	Fuel Inj.	262@5000	290@3000	12.5:1	3.543	90	2.756	70

5.3L V12 (Cont.)

ENGINE SPECIFICATIONS (Cont.)

VALVES

Engine Size & Valve	Head Diam. In. (mm)	Face Angle	Seat Angle	Seat Width In. (mm)	Stem Diameter In. (mm)	Stem Clearance In. (mm)	Valve Lift In. (mm)
5.3L							
Intake	1.620-1.630 (41.15-41.40)	45°	44.5°	.....	.3092-.3093 (7.854-7.856)	.001-.004 (.03-.10)	.375 (9.53)
Exhaust	1.355-1.365 (34.42-34.67)	45°	44.5°	.....	.3092-.3093 (7.854-7.856)	.001-.004 (.03-.10)	.375 (9.53)

PISTONS, PINS, RINGS

Engine	PISTONS Clearance In. (mm)	PINS Piston Fit In. (mm)	PINS Rod Fit In. (mm)	RINGS Ring No.	RINGS End Gap In. (mm)	RINGS Side Clearance In. (mm)
5.3L	.0012-.0017 (.030-.040)	Push Fit	.0001-.0002 (.003-.005)	1	.014-.020 (.36-.51)	.0029 (.074)
				2	.010-.015 (.25-.38)	.0034 (.086)
				Oil	.015-.045 (.38-1.14)	[1]

[1] – Oil ring is self expanding.

CRANKSHAFT MAIN & CONNECTING ROD BEARINGS

Engine	MAIN BEARINGS Journal Diam. In. (mm)	MAIN BEARINGS Clearance In. (mm)	MAIN BEARINGS Thrust Bearing	MAIN BEARINGS Crankshaft End Play In. (mm)	CONNECTING ROD BEARINGS Journal Diam. In. (mm)	CONNECTING ROD BEARINGS Clearance In. (mm)	CONNECTING ROD BEARINGS Side Play In. (mm)
5.3L	3.0007-3.0012 (76.218-76.230)	.0015-.0030 (.038-.076)	Center	.004-.006 (.10-.15)	2.2994-2.3000 (58.405-58.420)	.0015-.0034 (.038-.086)	.007-.013 (.18-.33)

VALVE SPRINGS

Engine	Free Length In. (mm)	PRESSURE Lbs. @ In. (Kg @ mm) Valve Closed	PRESSURE Lbs. @ In. (Kg @ mm) Valve Open
5.3L			
Inner	1.734 (44.04)	.....	.....
Outer	2.103 (53.42)	.....	.....

VALVE TIMING

Engine	INTAKE Open (BTDC)	INTAKE Close (ABDC)	EXHAUST Open (BBDC)	EXHAUST Close (ATDC)
5.3L	17°	59°	59°	17°

CAMSHAFT

Engine	Journal Diam. In. (mm)	Clearance In. (mm)	Lobe Lift In. (mm)
5.3L	1.0615-1.0620 (26.962-26.975)	.001-.003 (.03-.08)	.....

Mazda Engines

1.3L ROTARY

RX7

ENGINE CODING

ENGINE IDENTIFICATION

Engine identification number is stamped on front engine housing below alternator and behind distributor (crank angle sensor).

ENGINE IDENTIFICATION CODES

Application	Code
1.3L	RE 13B

ENGINE

REMOVAL & INSTALLATION

1) Remove hood and disconnect negative battery cable. Drain engine oil and coolant. Remove air intake pipe, relief silencer hose and air cleaner assembly. On turbocharged models, remove battery and battery tray. On all models, remove cooling fan, radiator hoses and heater return hose. Disconnect coolant level sensor and radiator switch at radiator.

2) Remove transmission fluid hoses (if equipped) from radiator. Remove radiator and cowling. On turbocharged models, remove intercooler. On all models, disconnect accelerator cable, cruise control cable and vacuum hose (non-turbo only). Remove brake vacuum hose and Bypass Air Control (BAC) air hose (non-turbo). Remove boost sensor vacuum hose.

3) On turbocharged models, remove split air pipe and disconnect oxygen sensor connector. Remove insulator covers. Remove front catalytic converter upper nut. On all models, disconnect engine harness connector.

4) Remove high tension leads from spark plugs. Disconnect distributor (crank angle sensor) connector and alternator connector. Disconnect oil pressure gauge connector and engine ground. Remove canister hose, fuel hoses and heater hose. Plug fuel hoses. Disconnect oil cooler pipe and bracket.

5) Disconnect automatic transmission oil pipe bracket (if equipped). Remove clutch release cylinder (if equipped). Remove power steering pump drive belt and pump. Remove A/C compressor drive belt and compressor. Remove pump and compressor with hoses still connected and wire out of the way.

6) Raise and support vehicle. Remove engine undercover. Remove exhaust pipe cover and catalytic converter insulator. Disconnect secondary air pipe and hose from catalytic converter. Disconnect exhaust pipe bracket. Disconnect exhaust pipe from exhaust manifold. Remove starter.

7) Remove bolts attaching engine to transmission. Support front of transmission with jack and remove left and right engine mount nuts. Attach sling to engine and take up slack. Slowly remove engine from vehicle. To install engine, reverse removal procedure. Return all fluids to specified levels.

8) To install engine, reverse removal procedure. Return all fluids to specified levels. Adjust drive belt tension. Check cooling fan-to-shroud clearance.

DISASSEMBLY

External Components

1) Remove A/C pump and P/S pump brackets. Remove left engine mount and spark plugs. Mount engine on engine stand. Remove dipstick, oil filler pipe and oil filter and body. Remove oil pressure gauge and distributor (crank angle sensor).

2) Remove air pump drive belt, air pump and bracket. Remove alternator drive belt and alternator. Remove clutch cover and clutch disc (if equipped) using Ring Gear Brake (49 F011 101).

3) Remove metering oil connecting rod. Remove throttle and dynamic chamber assembly and gasket from intake manifold. On turbocharged models, remove air control valve vacuum piping. Remove air control valve. On all models, remove exhaust manifold, insulator, insulator cover and gasket. Remove primary fuel injector and delivery pipe.

4) On turbocharged models, remove switching actuator. Remove water pipe from intake manifold. Remove turbocharger and insulator. Seal turbocharger to prevent dirt from entering. On all models, remove air hose assembly.

5) Remove exhaust manifold oil nozzle and metering oil tube. Remove intake manifold. Remove housing oil nozzle and metering oil tube. Remove metering oil pump. Remove eccentric shaft pulley assembly. Remove water pump. Remove engine harness and vacuum piping as an assembly. Remove EGR valve. Remove dynamic chamber bracket. Remove oil inlet pipe.

Internal Components

1) Remove right engine mount, oil pan bolts, oil pan and oil strainer. If equipped with M/T, attach Ring Gear Brake (49 F011 101) to flywheel. If equipped with A/T, attach Counterweight Stopper (49 1881 055) to counterweight. This will prevent eccentric shaft from turning.

2) Remove eccentric shaft lock bolt, washer and "O" ring. Remove eccentric shaft by-pass valve, spring and pulley boss.

3) Remove oil pressure control valve. Remove front cover, gasket and "O" ring. Remove distributor drive gear. Remove oil pump sprocket lock nut and lock washer. Remove oil pump drive sprocket, eccentric shaft sprocket and drive chain as an assembly. *See Fig. 1.*

Fig. 1: Removing Eccentric Shaft & Oil Pump Sprockets

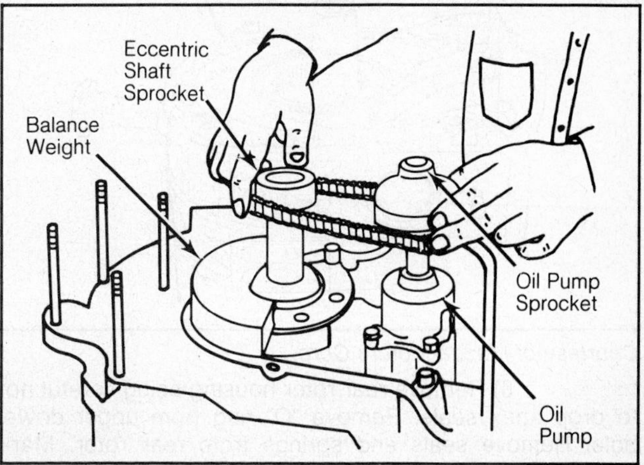

Courtesy of Mazda Motors Corp.

1.3L ROTARY (Cont.)

4) Remove baffle plate (turbo only). Remove oil pump. Remove key, balance weight, thrust washer, needle bearing and spacer from eccentric shaft. If equipped with M/T, remove flywheel nut. Remove flywheel using puller. Remove Woodruff key and ring gear brake.

5) If equipped with A/T, mark position of drive plate to retainer. Remove 6 bolts, retainer and drive plate. Remove flywheel nut. Remove counterweight using puller. Remove Woodruff key and counterweight stopper.

6) Remove rear housing bolts in sequence. *See Fig. 2*. Loosen in 2 or 3 steps. Lift rear housing off shaft. Remove any seals stuck to housing, and place them back in original positions. Remove sealing rubbers and oil seal from rear housing. Remove pressure regulator from rear housing.

Fig. 2: Loosening Rear Housing Bolts

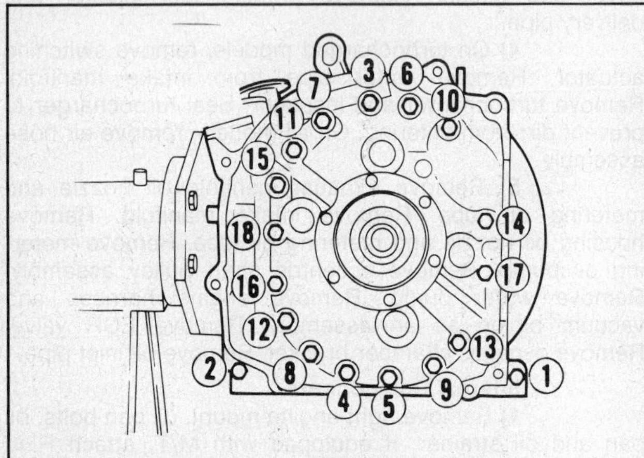

Courtesy of Mazda Motors Corp.

7) Remove apex seal side pieces from rear rotor. Mark for proper reassembly. Attach Dowel Puller (49 0813 215A), and pull tubular dowels off rear rotor housing. *See Fig. 3*.

Fig. 3: Extracting Tubular Dowels from Engine

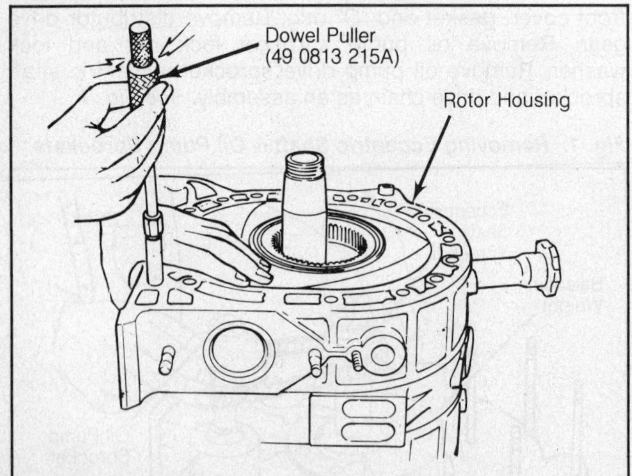

Courtesy of Mazda Motors Corp.

8) Remove rear rotor housing being careful not to drop apex seals. Remove "O" ring from upper dowel hole. Remove seals and springs from rear rotor. Mark seals and springs for proper reassembly. Remove rear rotor. Place on clean pad with internal gear side down. If seals stick on intermediate housing, place back in original position on rear rotor.

Fig. 4: Exploded View of Housing Assembly

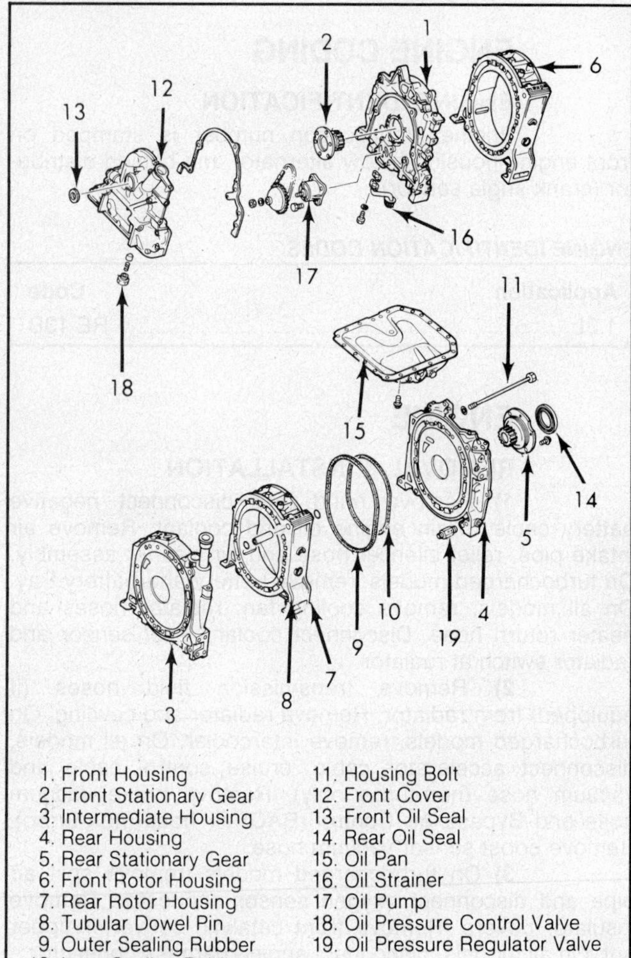

Courtesy of Mazda Motors Corp.

9) Remove all seals and springs from rear rotor. Mark seals, springs and rotor for proper reassembly. Remove tubular dowels from intermediate housing using dowel puller. Remove intermediate housing while turning and pushing eccentric shaft up. Do not remove eccentric shaft.

10) If seals stick to intermediate housing surface, place back in original position on front rotor. Remove sealing rubbers. Remove side pieces from front rotor and mark for reassembly. Remove front rotor housing being careful not to drop apex seals. Remove "O" ring from upper dowel hole.

11) Remove eccentric shaft. Remove front rotor. Place on clean pad with internal gear side down. Remove all seals and springs from front rotor. Mark seals, springs and rotor for proper reassembly.

12) Remove outer oil seal from each rotor. Remove inner oil seal. Remove oil seal springs. Remove "O" ring from oil seal.

INSPECTION & OVERHAUL

Front, Intermediate & Rear Housings

1) Clean housings using extra fine emery paper to remove carbon deposits from rotor running

1.3L ROTARY (Cont.)

Fig. 5: Exploded View of Rotors & Eccentric Shaft Assembly

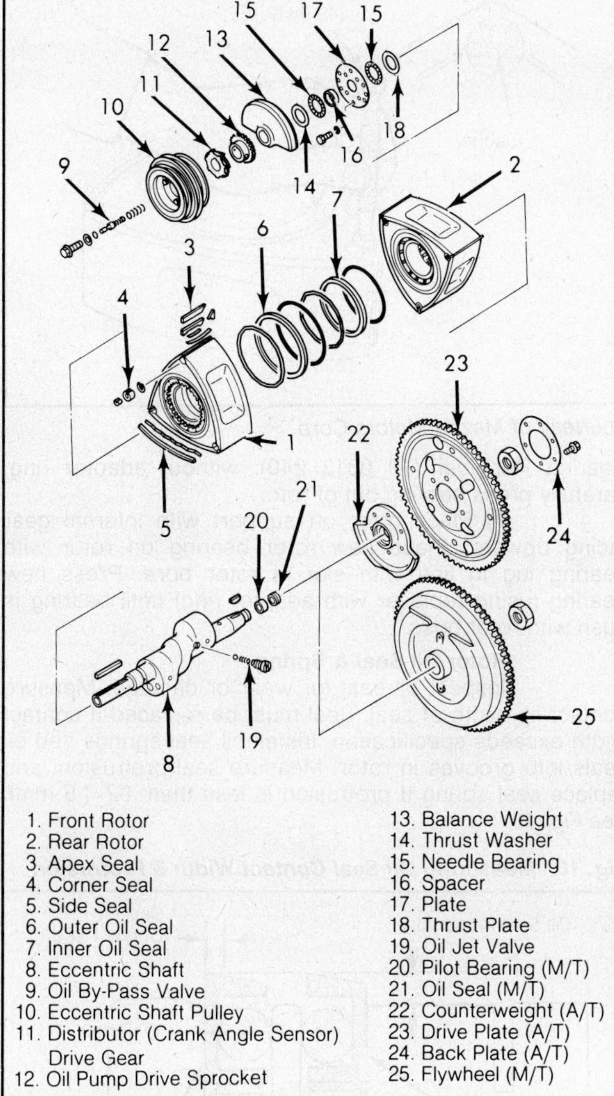

Courtesy of Mazda Motors Corp.

Fig. 6: Checking Housing Distortion with Straightedge

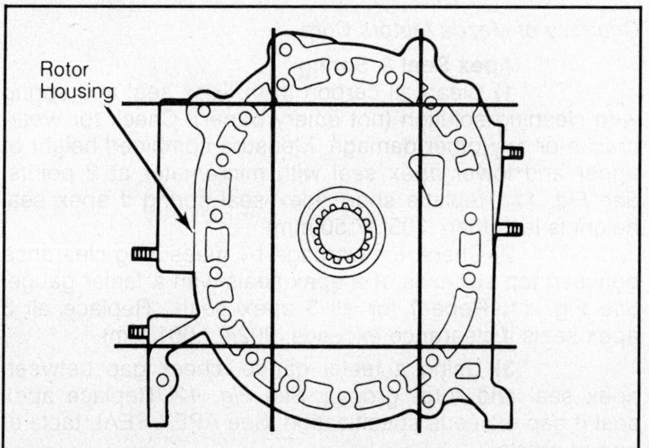

Courtesy of Mazda Motors Corp.

surface. Use a cloth or brush soaked in solvent or thinner to remove sealing agent.

2) Check front, intermediate, and rear housings for distortion. Place a straightedge across housing surface. *See Fig. 6.* Measure distortion by inserting feeler gauge between housing and straightedge. Replace housing if distortion exceeds specification.

3) Using a dial indicator and Gauge Body (49 0727 570), measure rotor sliding surface stepped wear pattern on all 3 housings. Check oil seal and side seal step wear by moving dial indicator from inside to outside of each seal tracking pattern. *See Fig. 7.*

OIL SEAL STEP WEAR

Location	Limit
Inside Side Seal	.0004" (.010 mm)
Outside Side Seal	.004" (.10 mm)
Oil Seal	.0008" (.020 mm)

Fig. 7: Checking Oil Seal & Side Seal Step Wear

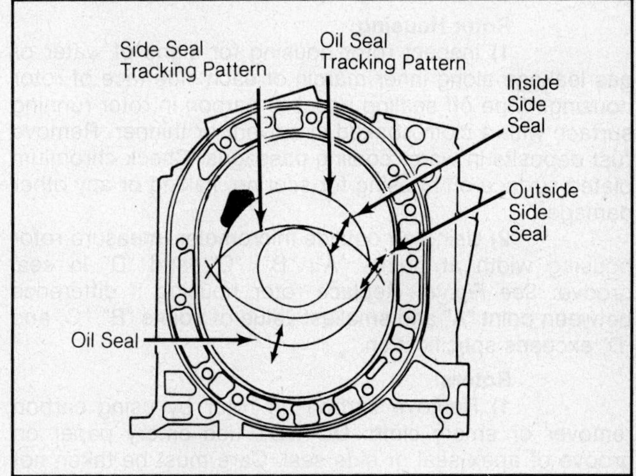

Courtesy of Mazda Motors Corp.

Stationary Gears & Main Bearing

1) Inspect front and rear stationary gears for cracked, scored, worn or chipped teeth. Replace stationary gear assembly if necessary. Measure inner diameter of main bearing and outer diameter of bearing journal on eccentric shaft. If clearance exceeds specification, replace bearing.

2) To replace main bearing, remove stationary gear assembly. To remove stationary gear assembly, remove plate, needle bearing and thrust plate from front stationary gear. Remove bolts from rear stationary gear. Using Main Bearing Replacer (49 0813 235), drive stationary gear out of housing.

3) Place rear stationary gear in press with flange side down. Using main bearing replacer, without adapter ring, press main bearing out of gear. Align lug on new bearing with slot on gear. Press new bearing into gear until adapter ring just contacts gear flange.

4) To install rear stationary gear, apply petroleum jelly to new "O" ring and install on gear. Apply sealant to gear flange. Install gear to housing so slot is aligned with dowel pin on housing. Install front gear with thrust plate, needle bearing and plate. Tighten bolts to specification.

Mazda Engines

1.3L ROTARY (Cont.)

Fig. 8: Checking Rotor Housing Width for Distortion

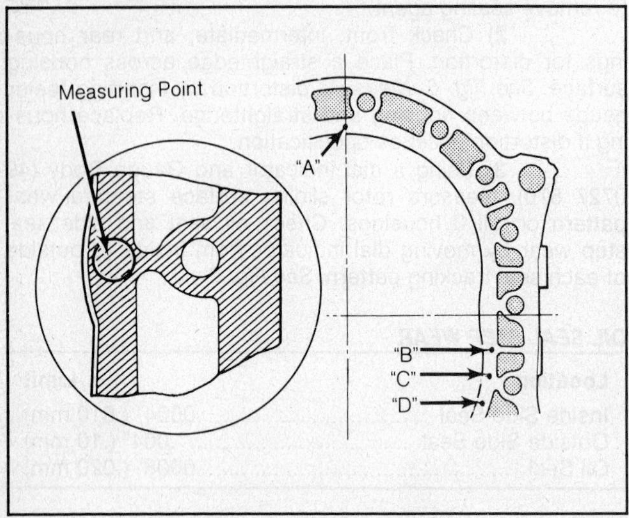

Courtesy of Mazda Motors Corp.

Rotor Housing

1) Inspect rotor housing for signs of water or gas leakage along inner margin of each side face of rotor housing. Wipe off sealing agent or carbon in rotor running surface with a cloth soaked in solvent or thinner. Remove rust deposits in water cooling passages. Check chromium plated surface on housing for scoring, flaking or any other damage.

2) Using an outside micrometer, measure rotor housing width at points "A", "B", "C", and "D" in seal groove. *See Fig. 8*. Replace rotor housing if difference between point "A" and smallest value of points "B", "C" and "D" exceeds specification.

Rotors

1) Remove carbon on rotor by using carbon remover or emery cloth. DO NOT use emery paper on groove of apex seal or side seal. Care must be taken not to damage soft material coating on side surfaces of rotor. Wash rotor in cleaning solvent and dry using compressed air.

2) Inspect rotor for wear or damage, and check internal gear for cracked, scored, worn or chipped teeth. Measure rotor width at 3 points on face of internal rotor gear. Compare maximum rotor width dimension with rotor housing width dimension "A" to determine clearance. *See Fig. 8*.

3) If clearance is greater than specification, replace rotor assembly. If clearance is less than specification, strike internal gear lightly with plastic hammer to reseat. Recheck clearance.

4) Check rotor corner seal bores for wear using Go-No-Go Gauge (49 0839 165). *See Fig. 9*. If neither end of gauge fits into rotor bores, use original corner seals. If "no-go" end of gauge does not fit into rotor bores, while "go" end does, replace corner seals. If both ends of gauge fit into bores, replace rotor.

5) Check rotor bearing for wear, flaking or scoring. Measure inner diameter of rotor bearing and outside diameter of rotor bearing journal on eccentric shaft. Replace rotor bearing if clearance exceeds specification.

6) To replace rotor bearing, place rotor on support with internal gear facing down. Using Rotor Bearing Replacer (49 0813 240), without adapter ring, carefully press bearing out of rotor.

Fig. 9: Checking Corner Seal Bore Wear

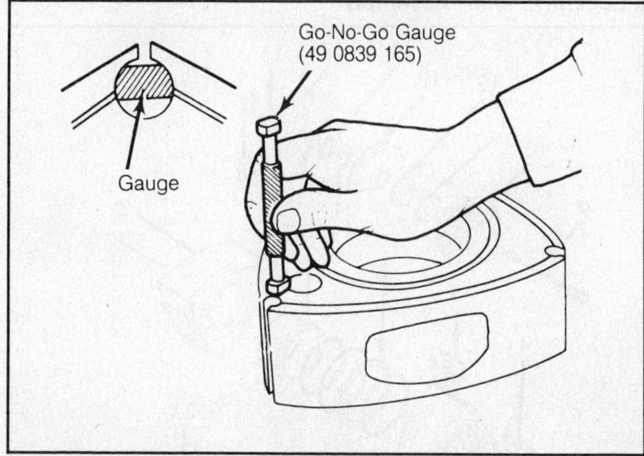

Courtesy of Mazda Motors Corp.

7) Place rotor on support with internal gear facing upward. Place new rotor bearing on rotor with bearing lug in line with slot in rotor bore. Press new bearing (using replacer with adapter ring) until bearing is flush with rotor boss.

Rotor Oil Seal & Spring

Inspect oil seal for wear or damage. Measure contact lip width of seal. Seal must be replaced if contact width exceeds specification. Install oil seal springs and oil seals into grooves in rotor. Measure seal protrusion, and replace seal spring if protrusion is less than .02" (.5 mm). *See Fig. 10*.

Fig. 10: Measuring Oil Seal Contact Width & Protrusion

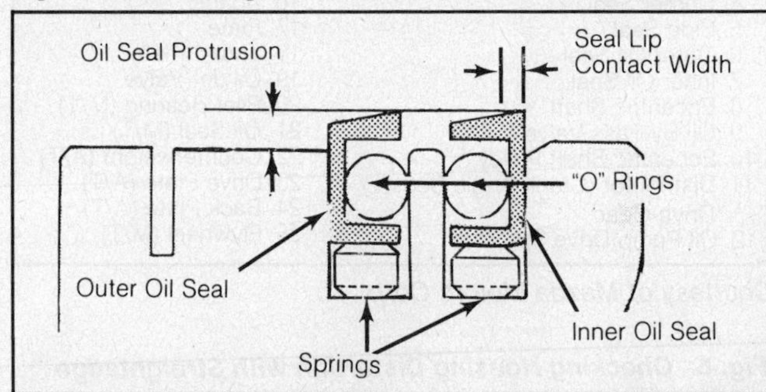

Courtesy of Mazda Motors Corp.

Apex Seal & Spring

1) Clean all carbon from apex seal and spring with cleaning solution (not emery paper). Check for wear, cracks or any other damage. Measure combined height of upper and lower apex seal with micrometer at 2 points. *See Fig. 11*. Replace short apex seal spring if apex seal height is less than .295" (7.50 mm).

2) Check for warpage by measuring clearance between top surfaces of 2 apex seals with a feeler gauge. *See Fig. 11*. Repeat for all 3 apex seals. Replace all 3 apex seals if clearance exceeds .0024" (.061 mm).

3) Using a feeler gauge, check gap between apex seal and rotor groove. *See Fig. 12*. Replace apex seal if gap exceeds specification. See APEX SEAL table at end of article.

1.3L ROTARY (Cont.)

Fig. 11: Checking Apex Seal Height & Warpage

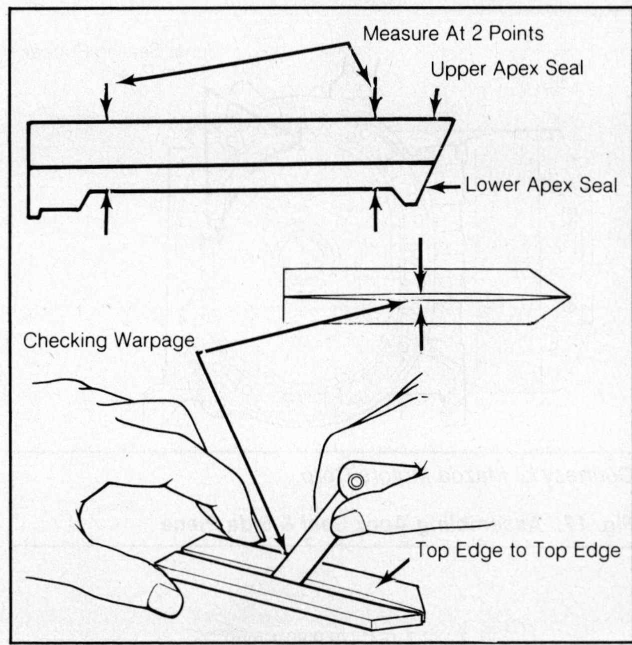

Courtesy of Mazda Motors Corp.

Fig. 12: Measuring Apex, Side & Corner Seal Clearance

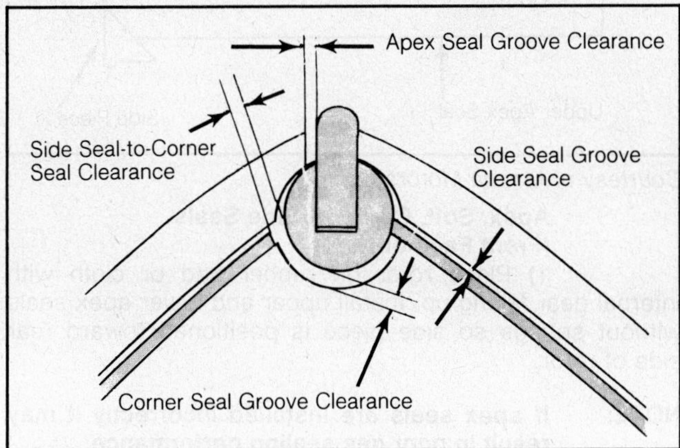

Courtesy of Mazda Motors Corp.

4) Check apex seal spring for wear and free height. *See Fig. 13*. Replace long spring if free height is less than .18" (4.6 mm). Replace short spring if free height is less than .12" (3.0 mm).

Fig. 13: Checking Apex Seal Spring Free Height

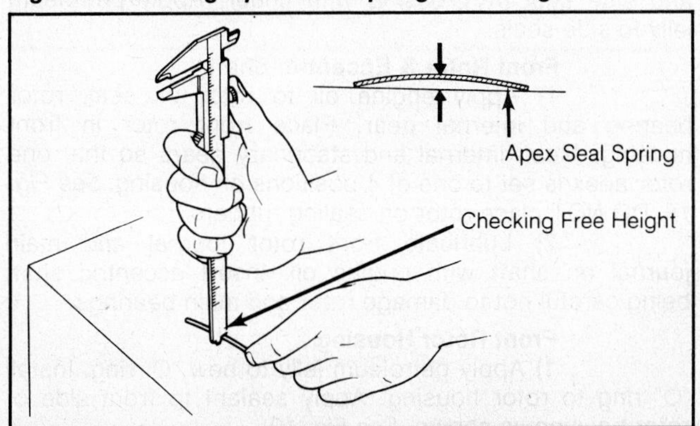

Courtesy of Mazda Motors Corp.

Side Seal & Spring

1) Clean all carbon from side seal and spring using a cleaning solution. Do not use emery paper. Inspect seal for wear or damage. With side seal and spring installed, press seal with finger and check that it moves freely in groove. Check that seal protrudes a minimum of .02" (.5 mm) above rotor face. If not, replace side seal or spring.

2) Check gap between side seal and groove with feeler gauge. *See Fig. 12*. Replace side seal if gap exceeds specification.

3) Install cylindrical corner seals in rotor and check gap between side seals and corner seals. *See Fig. 12*. Insert feeler gauge between end of side seal and round corner seal. Replace side seals if gap exceeds specification.

4) When replacing side seals, adjust gap between side seal and corner seal by filing one end of side seal. Use a fine-cut file and shape cut to match contour of corner seal. Adjust gap to .002-.006" (.05-.15 mm).

Corner Seal, Soft Seal & Spring

Clean carbon from corner seals and check for wear or damage. Install corner spring and seal in rotor groove. Check free movement of seal by pressing with finger. Check corner seal protrusion from rotor surface. Replace corner seals or springs if corner seals protrude less than .02" (.5 mm).

Eccentric Shaft

1) Thoroughly clean eccentric shaft in cleaning solution and blow out oil passages with compressed air. Inspect shaft for scratching or scoring of bearing journals and possible blocked oil passages.

2) Place eccentric shaft in 2 "V" blocks. Mount a dial indicator and check runout on slim end of shaft by rotating shaft slowly. Replace shaft if runout exceeds .0047" (.119 mm). Check oil jet for weak spring and stuck or damaged steel check ball.

Oil Pump Drive Chain & Sprockets

Check oil pump drive chain for broken links. Check oil pump sprockets for cracks, wear or damaged teeth. Replace parts as necessary.

Auxiliary Port Valves

Replace valves if damaged, cracked or abnormally worn.

REASSEMBLY

Rotor Inner & Outer Oil Seals

1) Place rotor on rubber pad or cloth. Install oil seal springs in their respective rotor grooves. Fit each spring edge in stopper hole. Oil seal springs have been painted in Cream or Blue color.

2) Cream-colored springs must be placed on front face of rotors. Blue springs go on rear face of rotors. When installed, painted side of spring must face oil seal (upward). *See Fig. 14*.

3) Install new oil seal without "O" ring in rotor groove. Check that oil seal moves smoothly in groove when pushed by hand. Be careful not to deform lip of oil seal.

4) Apply engine oil to new "O" ring and install in oil seal. Position inner oil seal in groove so that square edge of spring fits in notch of oil seal. Press inner oil seal into position by using a used oil seal. Lip of inner oil seal should be about .016" (.41 mm) below surface of rotor. *See Fig. 15*.

1.3L ROTARY (Cont.)

Fig. 14: Installing Oil Seal Spring on Rotor

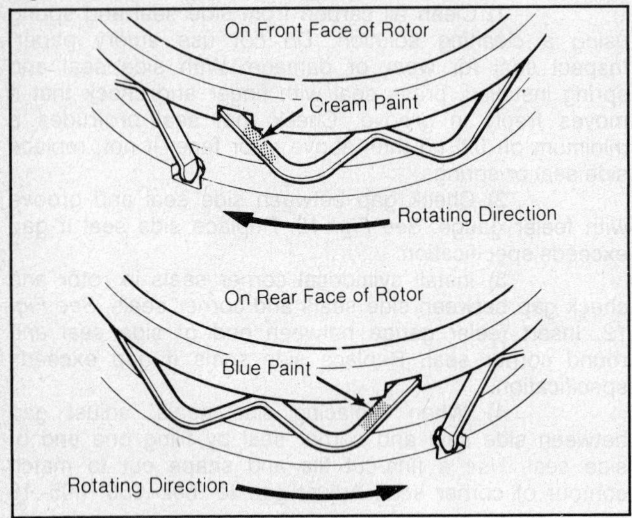

Courtesy of Mazda Motors Corp.

Fig. 15: Installing Inner Oil Seal on Rotor

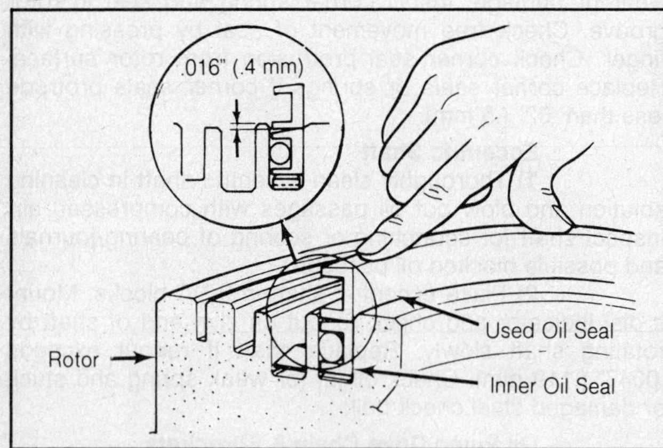

Courtesy of Mazda Motors Corp.

5) Install remaining oil seal springs and oil seals. Be careful not to deform lip of oil seal. Push each oil seal slowly by hand to confirm smooth movement.

Front Housing

1) Mount front housing to engine stand. Position thrust plate with chamfer facing toward front housing. Install needle bearing and plate and tighten bolts to specification.

2) Apply petroleum jelly to new outer and inner sealing rubbers. Install outer sealing rubber so White paint faces side wall in groove. Install inner sealing rubber so Blue paint faces outer wall in groove and seam is positioned properly. *See Fig. 16.*

3) After installation, check that sealing rubbers are not twisted. Apply engine oil to front housing contact surfaces, stationary gear and main bearing. DO NOT apply engine oil to sealing rubbers.

Apex Seal & Side Piece

Clean surfaces of apex seal and side piece with solvent where adhesive is to be applied. Assemble apex seal and side piece with Loctite 312 and Primer NF. Check length of assembled seal. *See Fig. 17.* Sliding and side surfaces should be flush. Cut away any extra adhesive.

Fig. 16: Positioning Inner Sealing Rubber on Housings

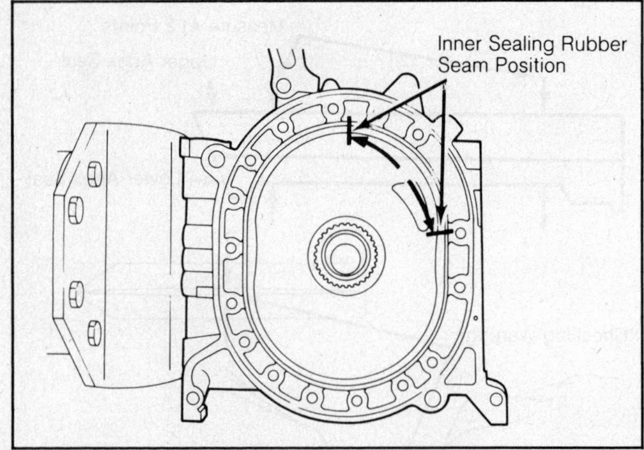

Courtesy of Mazda Motors Corp.

Fig. 17: Assembling Apex Seal & Side Piece

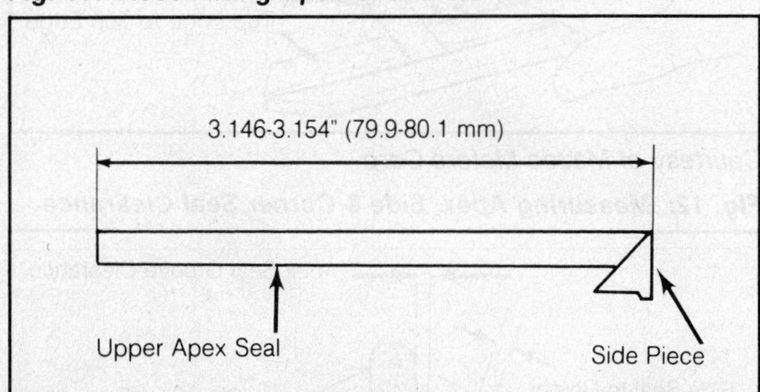

Courtesy of Mazda Motors Corp.

Apex, Soft, Corner & Side Seals (Front Face of Rotor)

1) Place rotor on rubber pad or cloth with internal gear facing up. Install upper and lower apex seals without springs so side piece is positioned toward rear side of rotor.

NOTE: **If apex seals are installed incorrectly it may result in poor gas sealing performance.**

2) Install soft seal into corner seal. Install corner seal springs and seals into bores. Chamfered surface should face bottom of groove. Install side seal springs and seals so painted surface faces bottom of groove.

3) Ensure smooth movement of each corner and side seal by pressing with finger. Apply petroleum jelly to side seals.

Front Rotor & Eccentric Shaft

1) Apply engine oil to rotor oil seal, rotor bearing and internal gear. Place front rotor in front housing. Mesh internal and stationary gears so that one rotor apex is set to one of 4 positions on housing. *See Fig. 18.* DO NOT place rotor on sealing rubbers.

2) Lubricate front rotor journal and main journal on shaft with engine oil. Insert eccentric shaft being careful not to damage rotor and main bearings.

Front Rotor Housing

1) Apply petroleum jelly to new "O" ring. Install "O" ring to rotor housing. Apply sealant to front side of rotor housing as shown. *See Fig. 19.*

1.3L ROTARY (Cont.)

Fig. 18: Positioning Rotor Apex for Reassembly

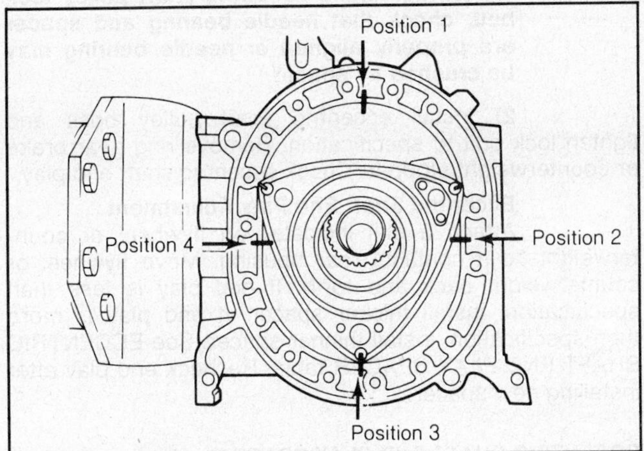

Courtesy of Mazda Motors Corp.

Fig. 19: Applying Sealant to Housing

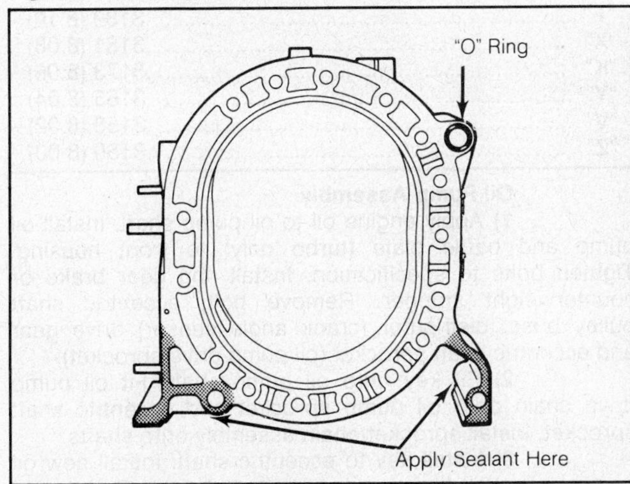

Courtesy of Mazda Motors Corp.

2) Apply engine oil to housing rotor running surface. Install front rotor housing on front housing. Apply engine oil to tubular dowels. Install dowels in front rotor housing holes and into front housing.

Apex Seal Springs & Soft, Corner & Side Seals (Rear Face of Rotor)

1) Install short apex seal springs. Insert long apex seal springs. Both ends of each spring should support back of apex seal. *See Fig. 20.*

2) Install soft seal into corner seal. Install corner seal springs and seals into bores. Chamfered surface should face bottom of groove.

3) Install side seal springs and seals so painted surface faces bottom of groove. Ensure smooth movement of each corner and side seal by pressing with finger.

Intermediate Housing

1) Apply petroleum jelly to new outer and inner sealing rubbers. Install outer sealing rubber so White paint faces side wall in groove. Install inner sealing rubber so Blue paint faces outer wall in groove and seam is positioned properly. *See Fig. 16.*

Fig. 20: Positioning Apex Seal Springs

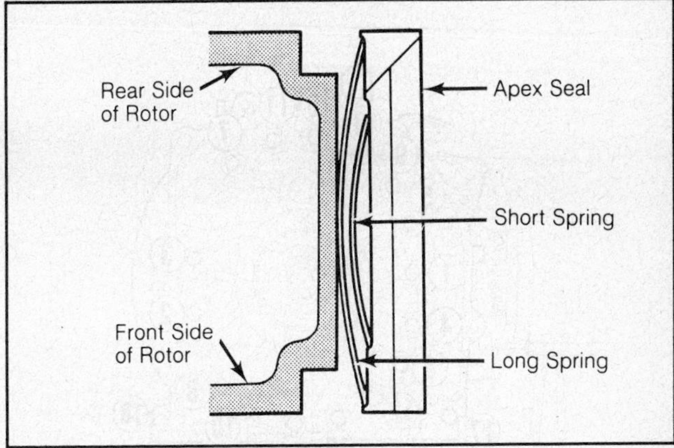

Courtesy of Mazda Motors Corp.

2) After installation, check that sealing rubbers are not twisted. Apply engine oil to housing contact surfaces. DO NOT apply engine oil to sealing rubbers.

3) Apply engine oil to rotor oil seal on rear side of front rotor. Apply petroleum jelly to new "O" ring. Install "O" ring to housing. Apply sealant to housing in area shown. *See Fig. 19.*

4) Turn eccentric shaft so rear rotor journal faces intake and exhaust side. Pull eccentric shaft out about 1.0" (25 mm). DO NOT pull shaft out more than 1.5" (38 mm). Carefully install intermediate housing over eccentric shaft and set on front rotor housing.

5) Install outer and inner sealing rubbers to rear side of intermediate housing using same method as in step **1)**. Apply engine oil to contact surfaces. DO NOT apply engine oil to sealing rubbers.

Rear Rotor, Rotor Seals & Rear Rotor Housing

Install rotor seals, rear rotor and rear rotor housing by following assembly procedure for front rotor seals, front rotor and front rotor housing.

Rear Housing

1) Apply engine oil to new rear oil seal and groove of rear stationary gear. Install oil seal into rear stationary gear. Install oil regulator valve and tighten to specification.

2) Apply petroleum jelly to new outer and inner sealing rubbers. Install outer sealing rubber so White paint faces side wall in groove. Install inner sealing rubber so Blue paint faces outer wall in groove and seam is positioned properly. *See Fig. 16.*

3) After installation, check that sealing rubbers are not twisted. Apply engine oil to housing contact surfaces, stationary gear and main bearing. DO NOT apply engine oil to sealing rubbers.

4) Apply engine oil to rotor oil seal on rear side of rear rotor. Apply petroleum jelly to new "O" ring. Install "O" ring to housing. Apply sealant to housing in area shown. *See Fig. 19.*

5) Install rear housing on rear rotor housing. Check that side pieces of front and rear apex seals are not wedged between rotor housing and side housing.

6) Apply engine oil to new seal washers and housing bolt threads. Install bolts and tighten gradually and in proper sequence. *See Fig. 21.* Turn eccentric shaft to make sure rotation is easy and smooth.

Mazda Engines

1.3L ROTARY (Cont.)

Fig. 21: Rear Housing Tightening Sequence

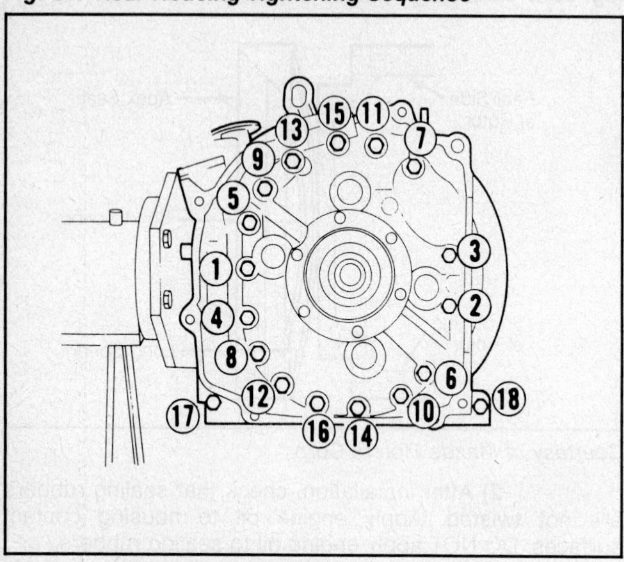

Courtesy of Mazda Motors Corp.

Flywheel (M/T)

Apply engine oil to oil seal in rear housing. Install Woodruff key and flywheel on eccentric shaft. Apply locking compound to eccentric shaft threads. Apply sealer to lock nut surface that contacts flywheel. Hold flywheel with Ring Gear Brake (49 F011 101), and tighten lock nut to specification.

Counterweight & Drive Plate (A/T)

1) Apply engine oil to oil seal in rear housing. Install Woodruff key on eccentric shaft. Align counterweight with key and install on eccentric shaft. Apply locking compound to eccentric shaft threads. Apply sealer to lock nut surface that contacts counterweight.

2) Hold counterweight with Stopper (49 1881 055), and tighten lock nut. Install drive plate on counterweight with hole in counterweight and drive plate aligned. *See Fig. 22.* Install back plate and tighten bolts to specification.

Fig. 22: Aligning Drive Plate & Counterweight Holes

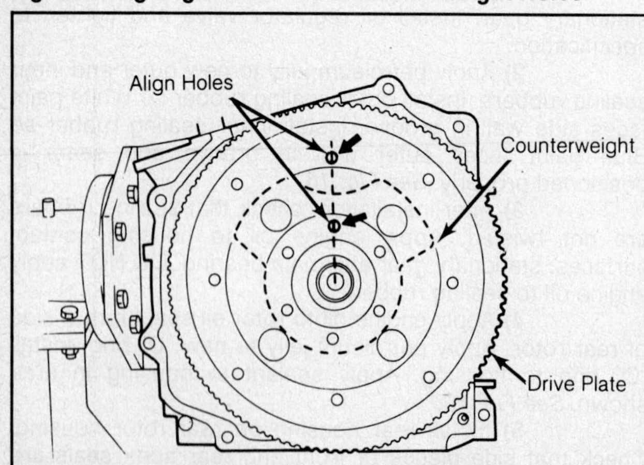

Courtesy of Mazda Motors Corp.

Balance Weight, Bearing & Spacer

1) Install the following parts to eccentric shaft: needle bearing, spacer, thrust washer, balance weight, oil pump drive sprocket and distributor (crank angle sensor) drive gear with chamfer towards housing.

NOTE: **Before tightening eccentric shaft pulley lock bolt, check that needle bearing and spacer are properly aligned or needle bearing may be crushed by spacer.**

2) Install eccentric shaft pulley boss and tighten lock bolt to specification. Remove ring gear brake or counterweight stopper. Check eccentric shaft end play.

Eccentric Shaft End Play Adjustment

Attach a dial indicator on flywheel or counterweight so it contacts rear housing. Move flywheel or counterweight back and forth. If end play is less than specification, install thicker spacer. If end play is more than specification, install thinner spacer. See ECCENTRIC SHAFT END PLAY SPACER table. Recheck end play after installing new spacer.

ECCENTRIC SHAFT END PLAY SPACER

I.D. Mark	Thickness In. (mm)
"S"	.3197 (8.12)
"T"	.3189 (8.10)
"X"	.3181 (8.08)
"K"	.3173 (8.06)
"Y"	.3165 (8.04)
"V"	.3158 (8.02)
"Z"	.3150 (8.00)

Oil Pump Assembly

1) Apply engine oil to oil pump shaft. Install oil pump and baffle plate (turbo only) to front housing. Tighten bolts to specification. Install ring gear brake or counterweight stopper. Remove bolt, eccentric shaft pulley boss, distributor (crank angle sensor) drive gear and eccentric shaft sprocket (oil pump drive sprocket).

2) Fit key onto oil pump shaft. Fit oil pump drive chain onto oil pump sprocket and eccentric shaft sprocket. Install sprocket/chain assembly onto shafts.

3) Install key to eccentric shaft. Install new oil pump sprocket lock washer and lock nut. Tighten to specification and bend lock washer tab. Install distributor (crank angle sensor) drive gear with chamfered surface facing housing.

Front Cover & Eccentric Shaft Pulley Boss

1) Apply engine oil to new front oil seal and groove of front cover. Install oil seal in front cover. Install oil pressure control valve in front cover and tighten to specification.

Fig. 23: Checking Pulley Boss Protrusion

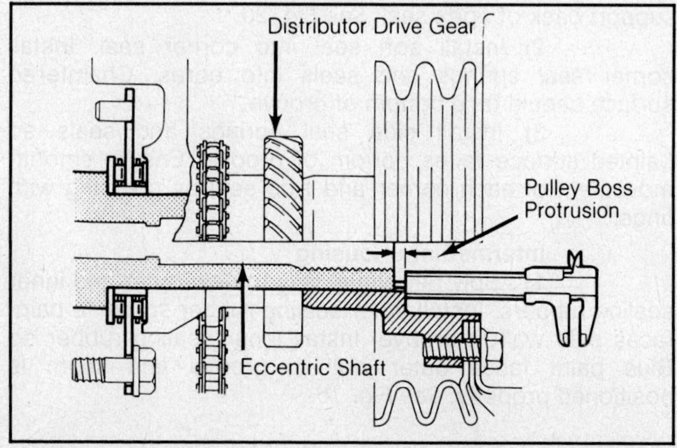

Courtesy of Mazda Motors Corp.

1.3L ROTARY (Cont.)

2) Install new "O" ring on front housing oil passage. Lubricate front cover oil seal lip and install front cover and new gasket on front housing. Tighten to specification. Install eccentric shaft pulley boss.

3) Install lock bolt and tighten by hand. Remove bolt and measure pulley boss protrusion. *See Fig. 23*. If boss protrudes more than .0961" (2.440 mm), needle bearing may be misaligned. Remove and reassemble so needle bearing is aligned correctly.

4) Install by-pass valve and spring into eccentric shaft. Apply engine oil to new "O" ring and install on lock bolt. Apply locking compound to lock bolt threads. Apply sealant to flange face of lock bolt. Install lock bolt with new washer. Tighten to specification.

Oil Strainer & Oil Pan

1) Install oil strainer and new gasket on front housing. Tighten to specification. Cut off excess gasket from front cover along oil pan mounting surface. Clean mating surfaces of housing and oil pan.

2) Apply a 1/4" bead of silicone sealer on mounting surface of oil pan (to inside of bolt holes). Install gasket on oil pan. Apply a similar bead of sealer to gasket. Install oil pan and right engine mount. Tighten bolts gradually to specification.

External Components

1) To complete reassembly, reverse removal procedures. Install water pump with new gasket. Ensure shims are used on studs where gasket does not mount. Install oil nozzles and connect metering oil tubes with new washers. Oil tube ends are colored for proper positioning. See OIL TUBE END COLORS table.

Fig. 24: Checking Metering Oil Connecting Rod Clearance

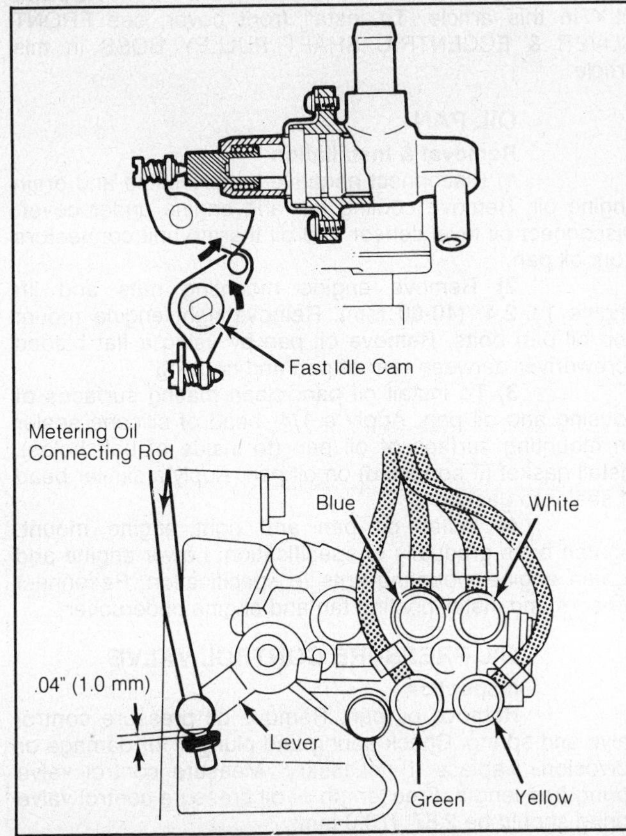

Courtesy of Mazda Motors Corp.

OIL TUBE END COLORS

Color	Position
White	Front Rotor Housing
Yellow	Rear Rotor Housing
Blue	Front Inlet Port
Green	Rear Inlet Port

2) Insert mixing plate into intermediate housing with White paint facing up. Install metering oil connecting rod to throttle body and lever of metering oil pump. Set fast idle cam. Check clearance. *See Fig. 24*. Adjust using shims if necessary. Connect oil tubes to metering oil pump. *See Fig. 24*.

3) Rotate eccentric shaft until Yellow mark (leading timing mark) aligns with indicator pin on front cover. Apply engine oil to new distributor (crank angle sensor) "O" ring and install. Apply engine oil to distributor (crank angle sensor) driven gear. Match mark on distributor (crank angle sensor) housing and driven gear and install in front housing.

4) On non-turbo engines, install new intake manifold gasket. Install auxiliary ports in side of engine housing so larger side of pin aligns with index mark on gasket. *See Fig. 25*.

Fig. 25: Installing Auxiliary Port Valves

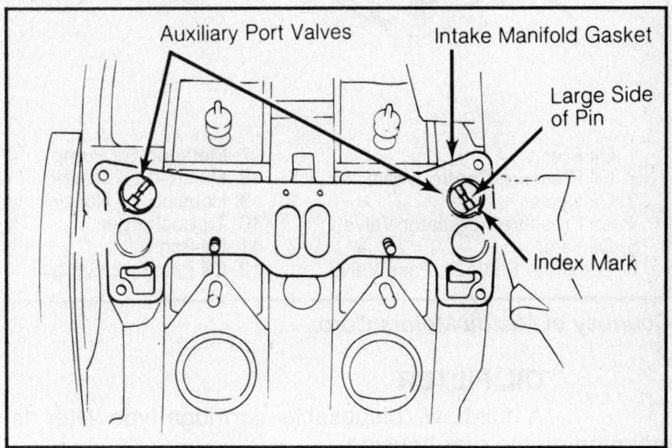

Courtesy of Mazda Motors Corp.

ENGINE OILING

ENGINE OILING SYSTEM

A two rotor oil pump produces pressure necessary for proper internal engine lubrication. Oil pump is mounted on front housing and is chain driven by eccentric shaft. Oil pressure is limited by a regulator valve and pressure control valve. Full-flow oil filter and oil cooler are used on engine.

The engine uses a metering oil pump to ensure proper rotor seal lubrication. The metering oil pump delivers oil to intake manifold and also to direct oil ports located in both rotor housings. Metering pump control lever is actuated by a rod connected to throttle lever. Oil pressure control valve is located in front cover and is designed to open at 156 psi (11 kg/cm²).

CRANKCASE CAPACITY

Crankcase capacity for 1.3L engine is 6.1 qts. (5.8L), including filter.

Mazda Engines

1.3L ROTARY (Cont.)

Fig. 26: Engine Oiling System

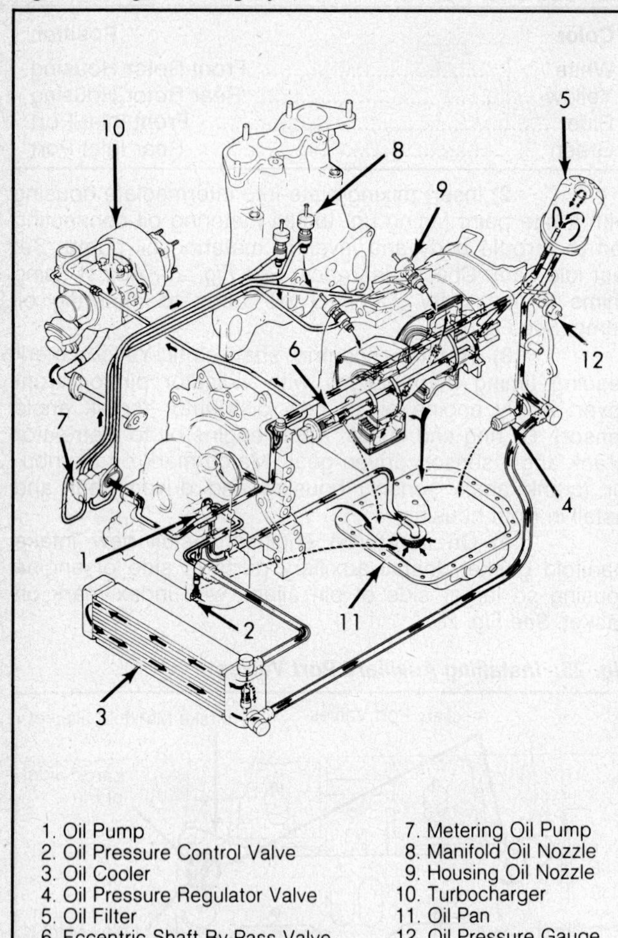

Courtesy of Mazda Motors Corp.

OIL FILTER

A full-flow, disposable cartridge-type filter is mounted on the rear housing.

NORMAL OIL PRESSURE

Normal oil pressure is 13-38 psi (.9-2.7 kg/cm²) at idle speed; 64-78 psi (4.5-5.5 kg/cm²) at 3000 RPM.

OIL PUMP

NOTE: **Oil pump is mounted on front engine housing. Front engine cover must be removed to remove oil pump. See INTERNAL COMPONENTS in DISASSEMBLY section at beginning of this article.**

Disassembly

Remove snap ring, rear outer and inner rotor, key, set screw and middle plate. Remove front outer and inner rotor, key and shaft. *See Fig. 27.*

Inspection

1) Insert a feeler gauge between lobes of both rotors and check clearance. Replace both rotors if clearance exceeds .006" (.15 mm). Check clearance between outer rotor and pump housing with a feeler gauge. If clearance exceeds .012" (.30 mm), replace rotor or oil pump housing.

Fig. 27: Exploded View of Oil Pump Assembly

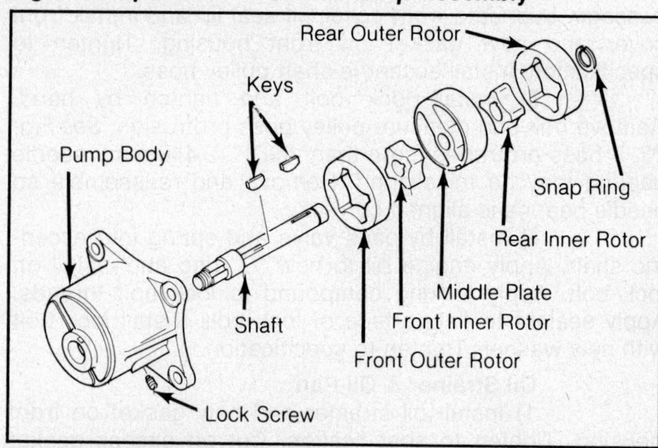

Courtesy of Mazda Motors Corp.

2) Place straightedge across pump body mounting surface, and check rotor end play with feeler gauge. Place straightedge across oil pump body mounting surface on front engine housing and check clearance. If clearance exceeds .006" (.15 mm), resurface or replace oil pump body.

Reassembly

1) To assemble oil pump, reverse disassembly procedure. Assembly marks on inner and outer rotors must be aligned and facing front engine housing. Apply Loctite to set screw and install in pump body.

2) Align set screw with recess portion of middle plate. Lightly peen area around set screw to keep it from coming off. Rotate shaft by hand and check for smooth rotation.

3) To install oil pump, see OIL PUMP ASSEMBLY in this article. To install front cover, see FRONT COVER & ECCENTRIC SHAFT PULLEY BOSS in this article.

OIL PAN

Removal & Installation

1) Disconnect negative battery cable and drain engine oil. Remove cooling fan and engine under cover. Disconnect oil level sensor and oil thermo unit connectors from oil pan.

2) Remove engine mounting nuts and lift engine 1.6-2.4" (40-60 mm). Remove right engine mount and oil pan bolts. Remove oil pan by using a flat bladed screwdriver between rear of pan and housing.

3) To install oil pan, clean mating surfaces of housing and oil pan. Apply a 1/4" bead of silicone sealer on mounting surface of oil pan (to inside of bolt holes). Install gasket (if equipped) on oil pan. Apply a similar bead of sealer to gasket.

4) Install oil pan and right engine mount. Tighten bolts gradually to specification. Lower engine and tighten engine mounting nuts to specification. Reconnect sensors and install cooling fan and engine undercover.

OIL PRESSURE CONTROL VALVE

Inspection

Remove oil pan. Remove oil pressure control valve and spring. Check spring and plunger for damage or corrosion. Replace if necessary. Measure control valve spring free length. Free length of oil pressure control valve spring should be 2.87" (73.0 mm).

1.3L ROTARY (Cont.)

METERING OIL PUMP

Adjustment & Inspection

1) Check metering pump clearance by setting fast idle cam against metering pump actuating lever. Check and adjust clearance of metering pump rod at pump lever. *See Fig. 24*. Clearance should not exceed .04" (1.0 mm). Ensure that lever contacts stop on metering pump.

2) Remove oil metering check valves from intake manifold and rotor housings. Test each check valve by blowing air into oil supply end. Air should pass through valve. Blow air into opposite end of valve. Air flow should be blocked.

OIL COOLER

Inspection

Check oil cooler for damage, cracks or leaks. Check oil cooler by-pass valve operation by draining engine oil and removing plug and by-pass valve from bottom of oil cooler. Submerge valve in container of engine oil heated to 149°F (65°C). Check that valve protrudes a minimum of .20" (5.0 mm).

ECCENTRIC SHAFT BY-PASS VALVE

Inspection

Remove cooling fan and drive belts. Remove eccentric shaft lock bolt, washer, "O" ring, by-pass valve and spring. Submerge valve in container of engine oil heated to 140°F (60°C). Check that valve protrudes a minimum of .24" (6.0 mm).

ENGINE COOLING

WATER PUMP

Removal & Installation

1) Disconnect negative battery cable. Turn eccentric shaft so top mark on pulley is aligned with indicator pin on front housing. Drain cooling system. Remove cooling fan and P/S and A/C drive belts (if equipped). Remove air pump, alternator and drive belts.

2) Remove eccentric shaft pulley. Remove upper and lower radiator hoses. Remove coolant reservoir and by-pass hoses. Disconnect water thermo sensor and water thermo switch (A/T only). Remove water pump.

3) To install water pump, reverse removal procedure. Install water pump with new gasket. Ensure shims are used on studs where gasket does not mount. Tighten to specification.

NOTE: **For more information, see ENGINE COOLING SYSTEMS article at the end of this section.**

TIGHTENING SPECIFICATIONS

Application	Ft. Lbs. (N.m)
A/C & P/S Bracket	
M10 Bolts	23-34 (32-46)
M12 Bolts	41-59 (55-80)
Air Pump Bracket Bolts	14-19 (19-25)
Air Pump Bolts	
Long	12-17 (16-23)
Short	17-22 (23-30)
Alternator Bolts	
Long	27-38 (37-52)
Short	14-19 (19-25)
Alternator Bracket Bolt	16-22 (22-30)
Back Plate-to-Drive Plate (A/T)	32-45 (44-61)
Clutch Cover Bolts	13-20 (18-26)
Counterweight Lock Nut (A/T)	289-362 (392-491)
Dynamic Chamber Bracket	14-19 (19-25)
Eccentric Shaft Pulley Bolt	80-98 (108-132)
EGR Valve	14-19 (19-25)
Engine Harness & Vacuum Piping	14-19 (19-25)
Exhaust Manifold Nuts	23-34 (32-46)
Flywheel Lock Nut (M/T)	289-362 (392-491)
Front Cover Bolts	12-17 (16-23)
Front Stationary Gear Plate Bolts	12-17 (16-23)
Fuel Delivery Pipe Assembly	14-19 (19-25)
Intake Manifold Bolts	14-19 (19-25)
Left Engine Mount	41-59 (55-80)
Oil Inlet Pipe Bolts (Turbo)	12-17 (16-23)
Oil Nozzles-to-Housing/Manifold	12-17 (16-23)
Oil Pump Sprocket Nut	23-34 (32-46)
Oil Pressure Control Valve Plug	29-36 (39-49)
Oil Pressure Gauge	8-12 (11-16)
Oil Regulator Valve	65-80 (88-108)
Rear Housing Bolts	23-29 (32-39)
Rear Stationary Gear Bolts	12-17 (16-23)
Right Engine Mount-to-Oil Pan	46-69 (63-93)
Spark Plugs	9-13 (13-18)
Throttle & Dynamic Chamber	14-19 (19-25)
Turbocharger Nuts	32-40 (44-54)
Turbocharger Water Pipe	18-26 (24-35)
Water Pump Nuts	13-20 (18-26)
	INCH Lbs. (N.m)
Distributor Bolt	69-95 (8-11)
Metering Oil Pump-to-Housing	69-95 (8-11)
Oil Pan Bolts	69-95 (8-11)
Oil Strainer Bolts	61-87 (7-10)
Oil Pump-to-Housing	61-87 (7-10)
Turbocharger Insulator Nuts	69-95 (8-11)

Mazda Engines

1.3L ROTARY (Cont.)

ENGINE SPECIFICATIONS

GENERAL SPECIFICATIONS

Year	Cu. In.	Liters	Fuel System	HP@RPM	Torque Ft. Lbs.@RPM	Compr. Ratio	ROTOR HOUSING WIDTH In.	ROTOR HOUSING WIDTH mm
1987	80.0	1.3	Fuel Injected	[1] 146@6500	[2] 138@3500	[3] 9.4:1	[4] 3.150	[4] 80.01

[1] – On turbocharged models, horsepower is 182@6500 RPM.
[2] – On turbocharged models, torque is 183 Ft. Lbs.@3500 RPM.
[3] – On turbocharged models, compression ratio is 8.5:1.
[4] – Maximum width shown. Minimum width is 3.1485" (79.972 mm).

ROTOR HOUSING, SIDE HOUSINGS & ROTOR

Engine	ROTOR HOUSING		FRONT, INTERMEDIATE & REAR HOUSING		ROTOR		
	Width In. (mm)	Distortion Limit In. (mm)	Width In. (mm)	Distortion Limit In. (mm)	Width In. (mm)	Housing-to-Rotor Clearance In. (mm)	Land Protrusion In. (mm)
1.3L							
Front	[1] 3.150 (80.01)	.0024 (.061)	1.575 (40)	.0016 (.041)	[2] 3.144 (79.85)	[3] .0047-.0083 (.119-.211)	.....
Center			1.969 (50)	.0016 (.041)			
Rear	[1] 3.150 (80.01)	.0024 (.061)	2.362 (60)	.0016 (.041)	3.144 (79.85)	[3] .0047-.0083 (.119-.211)	

[1] – Maximum width shown. Minimum width is 3.1485" (79.972 mm).
[2] – Maximum width shown. Minimum width is 3.142" (79.80 mm).
[3] – Limit is .004" (.10 mm).

APEX SEAL

Engine	Length In. (mm)	Seal Width In. (mm)	Height In. (mm)	SEAL-TO-HOUSING Clearance In. (mm)	SEAL-TO-HOUSING Wear Limit In. (mm)	SEAL-TO-ROTOR Groove Clearance In. (mm)	SEAL-TO-ROTOR Wear Limit In. (mm)
1.3L	[1] 3.154 (80.10)	[1] .0763 (1.939)	[3] .315 (8.00)	.....	.....	[4] .0020-.0040 (.051-.101)	.006 (.15)

[1] – Maximum length shown. Minimum length is 3.146" (79.90 mm).
[2] – Maximum width shown. Minimum width is .0752" (1.910 mm).
[3] – Maximum height shown. Minimum height is .256" (6.50 mm).
[4] – On turbocharged models, groove clearance is .0024-.0040" (.062-.101 mm).

SIDE SEAL

Engine	Thickness In. (mm)	Height In. (mm)	SEAL-TO-GROOVE Clearance In. (mm)	SEAL-TO-GROOVE Limit In. (mm)	SIDE SEAL-TO-CORNER SEAL Clearance In. (mm)	SIDE SEAL-TO-CORNER SEAL Limit In. (mm)
1.3L	.0260-.0270 (.661-.686)	.1122-.1240 (2.850-3.150)	.0011-.0031 (.028-.078)	.004 (.10)	.002-.006 (.05-.15)	.016 (.40)

Mazda Engines

1.3L ROTARY (Cont.)

ENGINE SPECIFICATIONS (Cont.)

ECCENTRIC SHAFT MAIN & ROTOR BEARINGS

Engine	MAIN BEARINGS			ROTOR BEARINGS	
	Journal Diameter In. (mm)	Clearance In. (mm)	Eccentric Shaft End Play In. (mm)	Journal Diameter In. (mm)	Clearance In. (mm)
[1] 1.3L	1.6918-1.6923 (42.970-42.985)	[2] .0016-.0031 (.041-.079)	[3] .0016-.0028 (.041-.071)	2.9122-2.9128 (73.970-73.985)	[2] .0016-.0031 (.041-.079)

[1] – Maximum eccentric shaft runout is .0047" (.119 mm).
[2] – Wear limit is .004" (.10 mm).
[3] – Wear limit is .0035" (.090 mm).

CORNER SEAL

Engine	Diameter In. (mm)	Height In. (mm)	SEAL-TO-GROOVE		SIDE SEAL-TO-CORNER SEAL	
			Clearance In. (mm)	Limit In. (mm)	Clearance In. (mm)	Limit In. (mm)
1.3L	.4327-.4336 (10.990-11.014)	.268-.276 (6.80-7.01)	.....	.....	.002-.006 (.05-.15)	.016 (.40)

OIL SEAL

Engine	Height In. (mm)	SEAL LIP CONTACT WIDTH	
		Standard In. (mm)	Limit In. (mm)
1.3L	[1] .228 (5.80)	Less than .02 Less than (.5)	.....

[1] – Maximum height shown. Minimum height is .220" (5.58 mm).

PORT TIMING

Engine	INTAKE		EXHAUST	
	Open (ATDC)	Close (ABDC)	Open (BBDC)	Close (ATDC)
1.3L	[1 3] 32°	[2 4] 40°	75°	48°

[1] – 32 degrees Primary & Secondary, and 45 degrees Auxiliary.
[2] – 40 degrees Primary, 30 degrees Secondary, and 80 degrees Auxiliary.
[3] – On turbocharged models, 32 degrees Primary & Secondary.
[4] – On turbocharged models, 50 degrees Primary & Secondary.

Mazda Engines

1.6L 4-CYLINDER

Ford Motor Co.: Tracer
Mazda: 323

NOTE: **For engine repair procedures not covered in this article, see ENGINE OVERHAUL PROCEDURES article at beginning of this section.**

ENGINE CODING

ENGINE IDENTIFICATION

Engine number is stamped on pad on upper right rear of engine deck.

ENGINE IDENTIFICATION CODE

Application	Code
1.6L	B6

ENGINE, MANIFOLDS & CYLINDER HEAD

ENGINE

Removal & Installation

1) Disconnect negative battery cable. Mark hinge location and remove hood. Drain engine oil, coolant and transaxle fluid. Remove battery and carrier. Remove air cleaner assembly and dipstick. Remove cooling fan and radiator assembly. Remove accelerator cable and cruise control cable (if equipped).

2) On EFI equipped engines, relieve fuel pressure before disconnecting any fuel hoses (run engine with fuel pump connector disconnected until engine stalls). Disconnect speedometer cable and fuel hoses. Disconnect heater hoses and brake vacuum hose. Disconnect 3-way solenoid valve hoses and canister hoses. Disconnect engine harness connectors and engine ground. Remove radiator hoses.

3) Disconnect secondary air pipe (if equipped) and exhaust pipe. Remove A/C compressor and P/S pump (if equipped) and wire out of way. Do not disconnect hoses. Remove drive shafts, shift control cable or rod and clutch cable (if equipped). Remove engine splash shield, inner fender panel and engine mounts. Remove engine and transaxle as an assembly. To install, reverse removal procedure. Check all fluid levels.

CYLINDER HEAD

Removal

1) Disconnect negative battery cable. Drain engine coolant. Remove air cleaner assembly and dipstick. Remove accelerator cable and cruise control cable (if equipped). On EFI equipped engines, relieve fuel pressure before disconnecting any fuel hoses (run engine with fuel pump connector disconnected until engine stalls).

2) Disconnect fuel hoses and remove fuel pump (carbureted models). Remove heater hoses, brake vacuum hose and canister hose. Disconnect engine harness connectors. Remove high tension leads, distributor and spark plugs. Remove secondary air pipe assembly from exhaust manifold (carbureted models). Remove front engine hanger and ground wire.

3) Remove upper radiator hose and coolant by-pass hose and bracket. Remove intake manifold assembly. Remove exhaust manifold insulator and exhaust manifold. Remove timing belt. See TIMING BELT in this article. Remove camshaft pulley and rear engine hanger. Remove rocker cover. Remove cylinder head bolts gradually and in sequence. *See Fig. 1.* Remove cylinder head.

Inspection

Check cylinder head for warpage. Check cylinder head thickness. See CYLINDER HEAD SPECIFICATIONS table.

CYLINDER HEAD SPECIFICATIONS

Application	In. (mm)
Maximum Warpage	.006 (.15)
Standard Thickness	4.228-4.236 (107.40-107.60)
Grinding Limit	.008 (.20)

Installation

Clean all gasket mating surfaces. Install new cylinder head gasket. Tighten cylinder head bolts in 2 steps and in sequence. *See Fig. 2.* Install camshaft pulley. Install timing belt. See TIMING BELT. To install remaining components, reverse removal procedure. Ensure distributor blade is aligned with small oil holes before installation.

Fig. 1: Cylinder Head Bolt Removal Sequence

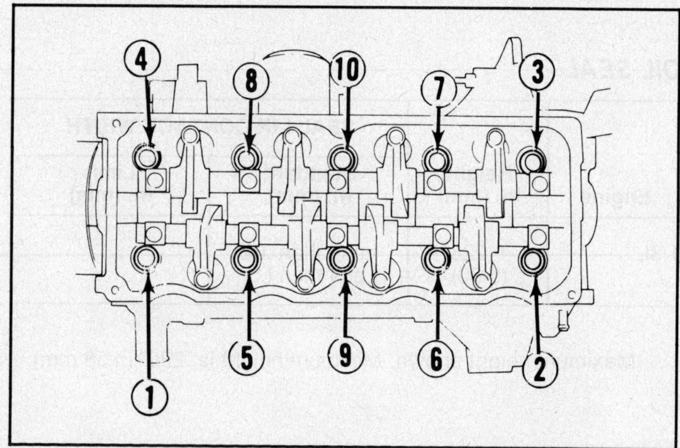

Courtesy of Mazda Motors Corp.

Fig. 2: Cylinder Head Bolt Tightening Sequence

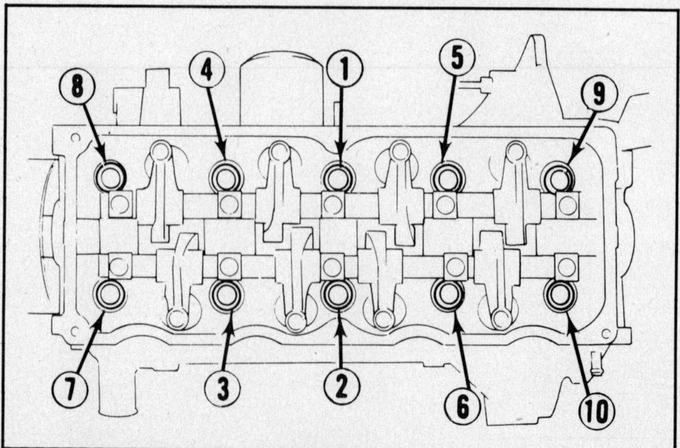

Courtesy of Mazda Motors Corp.

1.6L 4-CYLINDER (Cont.)

CAMSHAFT

TIMING BELT

Removal

1) Disconnect negative battery cable. Remove engine side cover, A/C and P/S drive belt (if equipped). Remove alternator belt and alternator. Remove water pump pulley, crankshaft pulley and baffle plate. Remove upper and lower timing belt cover.

2) Turn crankshaft to align matching mark of camshaft pulley with cylinder head and cylinder head cover timing mark. *See Fig. 3.* Mark timing belt direction of rotation for proper reassembly. Remove timing belt tensioner, spring and timing belt.

Inspection

Replace timing belt if any oil, grease or moisture is present. Inspect for damage, wear, peeling, cracking or hardening. Replace if necessary. Check belt tensioner for smoothness or abnormal noise. Inspect belt pulley and camshaft pulley teeth for wear or damage. DO NOT clean tensioner or pulleys with cleaning fluids. Wipe clean with soft rag.

NOTE: Never forceably twist, turn inside out, or bend timing belt. Belt MUST be replaced after 60,000 miles.

Fig. 3: Timing Belt Reference Marks

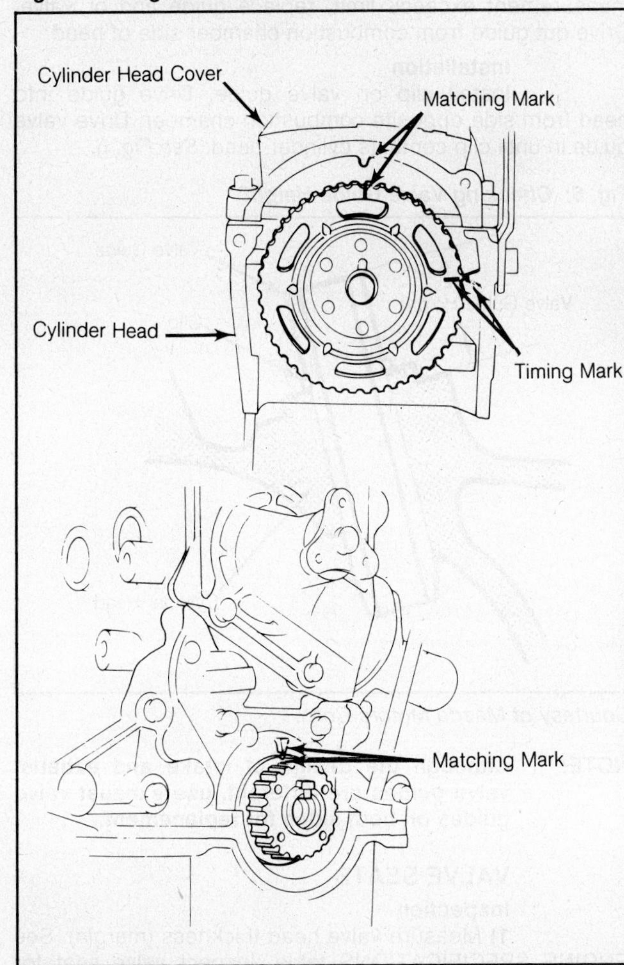

Courtesy of Mazda Motors Corp.

Installation

1) Ensure timing mark on crankshaft pulley is aligned with matching mark on oil pump. *See Fig. 3.* Also ensure matching mark on camshaft pulley is aligned with cylinder head mark.

2) Install tensioner and spring so spring is fully extended. Install belt and loosen the tensioner lock bolt. Turn crankshaft twice in direction of rotation and align matching marks. Ensure timing marks are correctly aligned. Tighten timing belt tensioner lock bolt.

3) Using hand pressure, measure deflection of timing belt between crankshaft pulley and camshaft pulley. Standard belt deflection should be .35-.51" (9.0-13.0 mm). *See Fig. 4.* If belt tension is not correct, repeat step **2)** or replace tensioner spring. To complete installation, reverse removal procedure.

Fig. 4: Timing Belt Deflection

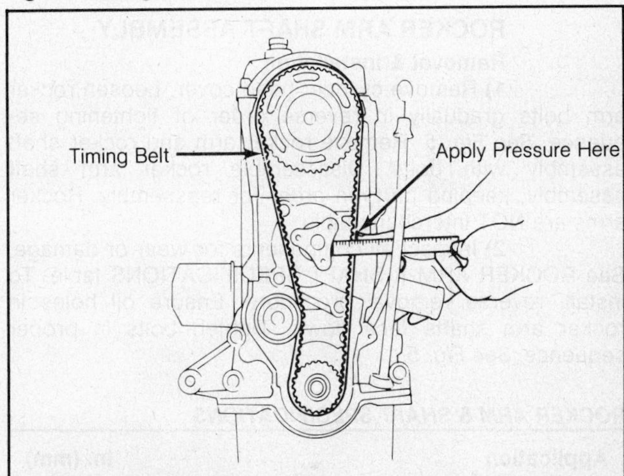

Courtesy of Mazda Motors Corp.

CAMSHAFT & FRONT OIL SEAL

Removal

Remove cylinder head. Remove rocker arm shaft assembly. See ROCKER ARM SHAFT ASSEMBLY. Remove camshaft front seal, thrust plate and camshaft.

Inspection

1) Inspect camshaft lobes for scoring or wear. Measure camshaft lobe height. Measure bearing journals. Measure front oil seal contact surface. Measure fuel pump cam lobe height. Check camshaft for bent condition (runout). Replace camshaft if not to specification.

CAMSHAFT SPECIFICATIONS [1]

Application	In. (mm)
End Play	.002-.007 (.05-.18)
Wear Limit	.008 (.20)
Front Oil Seal	
Contact Surface	1.1796-1.1811 (29.961-30.000)
Camshaft Runout	.0012 (.030)
Standard Lobe Height	
Intake & Exhaust	1.4378-1.4437 (36.519-36.669)
Wear Limit	1.4329 (36.394)
Standard Fuel Lobe Height	1.331-1.346 (33.80-34.19)
Wear Limit	1.323 (33.60)

[1] – For journal diameters and oil clearance specifications, see ENGINE SPECIFICATIONS tables at end of this article.

1.6L 4-CYLINDER (Cont.)

2) Measure camshaft end play with thrust plate installed. If end play exceeds limit, replace thrust plate or camshaft. Measure camshaft bearing-to-journal oil clearance. Replace camshaft or cylinder head if not to specification.

Installation

Apply engine oil to journals and bearings. Insert camshaft in position. Install thrust plate. Apply a thin coat of engine oil to camshaft oil seal and cylinder head. Tap camshaft oil seal into cylinder head. To complete installation, reverse removal procedure.

VALVES

VALVE ARRANGEMENT

Intake Manifold Side - Intake valves.
Exhaust Manifold Side - Exhaust valves.

ROCKER ARM SHAFT ASSEMBLY

Removal & Installation

1) Remove cylinder head cover. Loosen rocker arm bolts gradually in reverse order of tightening sequence. *See Fig. 5.* Remove rocker arm and rocker shaft assembly with bolts. Disassemble rocker arm shaft assembly, keeping parts in order for reassembly. Rocker arms are NOT interchangeable.

2) Inspect all components for wear or damage. See ROCKER ARM & SHAFT SPECIFICATIONS table. To install, reverse removal procedure. Ensure oil holes in rocker arm shafts face down. Tighten bolts in proper sequence. *See Fig. 5.*

ROCKER ARM & SHAFT SPECIFICATIONS

Application	In. (mm)
Rocker Arm Bore	.7087-.7097 (18.000-18.027)
Shaft Diameter	.7070-.7079 (17.959-17.980)
Rocker Arm-to-Shaft Clearance	
Standard	.0008-.0027 (.020-.068)
Maximum	.004 (.10)

Fig. 5: Rocker Arm Tightening Sequence

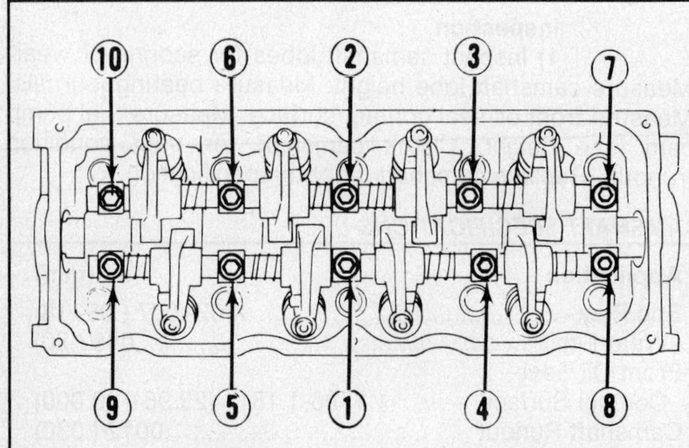

Courtesy of Mazda Motors Corp.

VALVE SPRINGS & SEALS

Removal

Compress valve springs with spring compressor. Remove keepers and spring seats. Remove springs and valve stem seals from cylinder head. It may be necessary to use a pair of pliers to remove seals.

Inspection

Inspect parts for cracks or damage. Check spring free length. See ENGINE SPECIFICATIONS table. Check valve springs for squareness. Spring out-of-square limit is .059" (1.5 mm). Replace valve springs if necessary.

Installation

Apply a coat of engine oil to inner surface of valve seal. Install valve seals. Install valve spring with narrow pitched end toward cylinder head. Install spring retainer and tap on end lightly to seat assembly.

VALVE GUIDES

Removal & Inspection

1) Remove cylinder head. Remove valve springs, valve stem seals and valves. Mark for proper reassembly. Measure valve guide bore and height. See VALVE GUIDE SPECIFICATIONS table.

VALVE GUIDE SPECIFICATIONS

Application	In. (mm)
Valve Guide Bore	
Intake & Exhaust	.2760-.2768 (7.010-7.030)
Installed Height	.520-.543 (13.20-13.79)

2) Measure valve stem diameter. See ENGINE SPECIFICATIONS table. Insert valve in corresponding guide and measure valve stem-to-valve guide clearance. If measurement exceeds limit, replace guide and or valve. Drive out guide from combustion chamber side of head.

Installation

Install clip on valve guide. Drive guide into head from side opposite combustion chamber. Drive valve guide in until clip contacts cylinder head. *See Fig. 6.*

Fig. 6: Checking Valve Guide Height

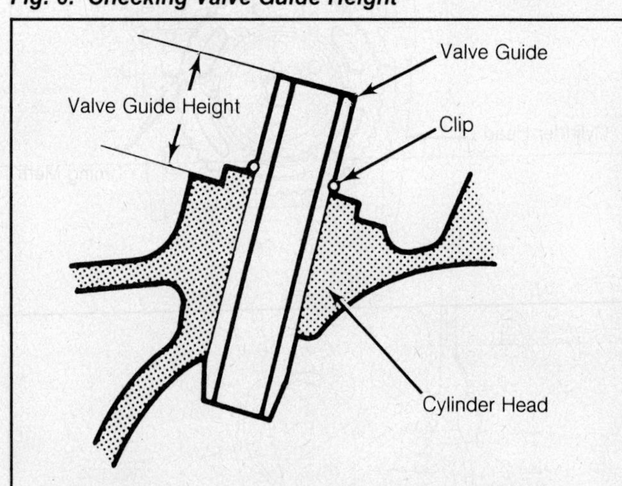

Courtesy of Mazda Motors Corp.

NOTE: **Although the design of intake and exhaust valve guides are different, use exhaust valve guides on both sides for replacement.**

VALVE SEATS

Inspection

1) Measure valve head thickness (margin). See ENGINE SPECIFICATIONS table. Inspect valve seat for damage. Measure seat angle and width. Grind valve seats if necessary. Use compound to seat valve and valve seat.

Mazda Engines

1.6L 4-CYLINDER (Cont.)

Check that contact surface is at center of valve face. Check valve stem installed height. Standard installed height is 1.535" (39.00 mm).

2) If height is 1.555-1.575" (39.50-40.00 mm), valve can be used as is. If height is 1.575-1.614" (40.00-41.00 mm), insert a shim into spring seat area so that height is 1.535" (39.00 mm). If height is more than 1.614" (41.00 mm), replace valve seat or cylinder head.

VALVE CLEARANCE ADJUSTMENTS

Set No. 1 cylinder at TDC of compression stroke. Adjust valve clearance for No. 1 intake and exhaust, No. 2 intake and No. 3 exhaust. Valve clearance for both intake and exhaust is .012" (.30 mm) with engine warm. Rotate crankshaft one revolution so No. 4 piston is at TDC of compression stroke. Adjust remaining valve clearances.

CYLINDER BLOCK ASSEMBLY

Inspection

Check cylinder block for leakage, cracks or scoring of cylinder walls. Check head gasket surface for warpage. Grind if necessary. Measure cylinder bore diameter. If wear exceeds limit, bore and hone cylinders for installation of oversize pistons.

CYLINDER BLOCK SPECIFICATIONS

Application	In. (mm)
Maximum Warpage	.006 (.15)
Grinding Limit	.008 (.20)
Bore Diameter	
Standard	3.0709-3.0717 (78.000-78.019)
Maximum	3.0776 (78.171)
Out-of-Round Limit	.0007 (.019)
Taper Limit	.0007 (.019)

PISTONS, PINS & RINGS

OIL PAN

Removal & Installation

1) Disconnect negative battery cable. Drain oil and remove engine splash shields. On 323 models, disconnect exhaust pipe.

2) On Tracer models, remove right front inner fender panel. Remove engine-to-flywheel housing support brackets. Remove flywheel housing inspection cover.

3) On all models, remove oil pan stiffeners, oil pan and gasket. Gasket is re-usable. To install, reverse removal procedure. Clean gasket mounting surfaces. Apply sealant across joint line of block and front and rear engine covers.

PISTON & ROD ASSEMBLY

Removal

Remove cylinder head, oil pan and oil strainer. Mark connecting rods and caps for reassembly reference. Remove ridge at top of cylinder with ridge reamer (if necessary). Remove rod caps. Push piston and rod assembly out top of cylinder. Be careful not to damage crankshaft journals or scratch cylinder walls. Remove piston from rod. See PISTON PIN REPLACEMENT.

Inspection

1) Check connecting rod for twisted or bent condition. Check connecting rod center-to-center length. Measure connecting rod small and large bores. See CONNECTING ROD SPECIFICATIONS table.

2) Inspect pistons for burns, scoring, cracking or scratches. Measure piston diameter 90 degrees to pin bore, .65" (16.5 mm) below lower ring groove. Standard piston diameter is 3.0691-3.0694" (77.954-77.964 mm). Use piston diameter and cylinder bore measurements to determine the piston-to-cylinder bore clearance.

NOTE: Oversize pistons and rings are available in .010" (.25 mm) and .020" (.50 mm) sizes.

CONNECTING ROD SPECIFICATIONS

Application	In. (mm)
Center-to-Center	5.230-5.234 (132.85-132.95)
Maximum Twist or Bend	.0016 (.040)
Small End Bore	.7854-.7859 (19.948-19.961)
Large End Bore	1.8898-1.8904 (48.000-48.016)
Big End Width	.8598-.8618 (21.838-21.890)

Installation

1) Install piston rings on piston. Space ring gaps properly. *See Fig. 7.* Ensure "R" is facing up on compression rings and oil rings turn smoothly after installing on piston. Lubricate piston rings, pistons and cylinder walls with engine oil.

Fig. 7: Piston Ring Gap Spacing

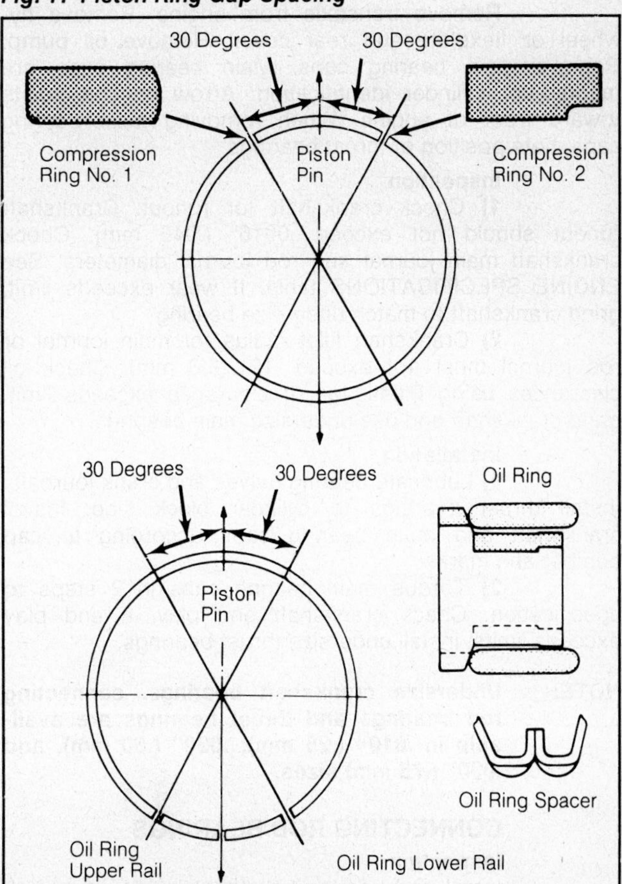

Courtesy of Mazda Motors Corp.

Mazda Engines

1.6L 4-CYLINDER (Cont.)

2) Install ring compressor onto piston without changing position of rings. Install piston and rod assembly. Ensure "F" mark on piston pin boss is facing front of engine. Install rod caps and tighten rod bolts in 2 steps to specification. Install oil strainer, oil pan and cylinder head.

PISTON PIN REPLACEMENT

Removal

Using a hydraulic press and proper piston pin removal and installation set, remove piston pin out of piston and rod. Mark pin, rod and piston for proper reassembly.

Inspection

Inspect piston bore, piston pin and connecting rod bore for excessive wear. Measure piston pin outer diameter. Outer diameter should be .7864-.7866" (19.974-19.980 mm).

Installation

Ensure connecting rod oil groove is opposite "F" mark on piston. Apply engine oil to piston pin and connecting rod bore. Press in piston pin. Required pressure should be 1100-3300 lbs. (500-1500 kg). After installation, ensure connecting rod falls from its own weight when piston is held horizontally.

CRANKSHAFT & ROD BEARINGS

MAIN BEARINGS

Removal

Remove transaxle from engine. Remove flywheel or flexplate and rear cover. Remove oil pump. Remove main bearing caps. Main bearing caps are marked for cylinder identification. Arrow on cap points toward front of engine. When removing main bearing caps, note position of thrust bearings.

Inspection

1) Check crankshaft for runout. Crankshaft runout should not exceed .0016" (.040 mm). Check crankshaft main journal and rod journal diameters. See ENGINE SPECIFICATIONS table. If wear exceeds limit, grind crankshaft to match undersize bearing.

2) Crankshaft fillet radius for main journal or rod journal must not exceed .12" (3.0 mm). Check oil clearances using Plastigage. If clearance exceeds limit, grind crankshaft and use undersize main bearings.

Installation

1) Lubricate bearing halves and crank journals. Install thrust bearings to cylinder block side. Install crankshaft and main bearing caps according to cap number and mark.

2) Torque main bearing caps in 2 steps to specification. Check crankshaft end play. If end play exceeds limits, install undersize thrust bearings.

NOTE: Undersize crankshaft bearings, connecting rod bearings and thrust bearings are available in .010" (.25 mm), .020" (.50 mm), and .030" (.75 mm) sizes.

CONNECTING ROD BEARINGS

Inspection

Install rod bearing halves into connecting rod. Install rod and piston assembly. Position Plastigage on crankpin. Place rod cap and bearing in position and tighten. Ensure mating marks on cap and rod are aligned. Remove cap and check oil clearance. If clearance exceeds limit, grind crankshaft and use undersize bearings. Check connecting rod side play before installing rod caps.

REAR MAIN BEARING OIL SEAL

Removal & Installation

With flywheel and oil pan removed, remove rear cover. Remove seal from cover. Lubricate cover, new seal and lips. Press oil seal into cover. Install rear cover with a new gasket. Tighten cover to specification. Cut away gasket that protrudes out from rear cover assembly.

ENGINE OILING

CRANKCASE CAPACITY

Crankcase capacity is 3.2 qts. (3.0L) without oil filter replacement; 3.6 qts. (3.4L) when replacing oil filter.

Fig. 8: Mazda 1.6L Engine Oiling System

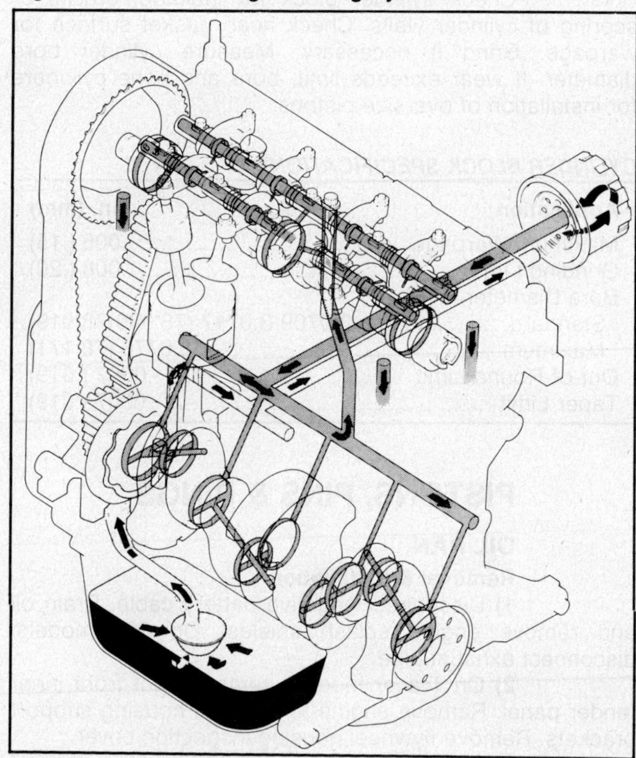

Courtesy of Mazda Motors Corp.

NORMAL OIL PRESSURE

Oil pressure should be 50-64 psi (3.5-4.5 kg/cm²) with engine warm and at 3000 RPM.

OIL PRESSURE RELIEF VALVE

Relief valve opening pressure is 14 psi (1.0 kg/cm²).

OIL PUMP

Removal & Disassembly

Remove lower timing cover, timing belt pulley and oil pan. Remove oil strainer and remove oil pump from engine block. Remove screws on oil pump cover with

1.6L 4-CYLINDER (Cont.)

impact driver. Remove pump cover, outer gear, inner gear and split pin. Remove plunger assembly and oil seal.

Inspection

1) Check for distortion or damage to pump body or cover. Check for weak or damaged plunger and plunger spring. Measure following clearances: inner gear tooth tip to outer gear and outer gear to pump body.

2) Using a straightedge positioned over pump body and above both gears, measure clearance between gear to straightedge. Replace gear assembly or oil pump body if clearances are not within limits.

OIL PUMP SPECIFICATIONS

Application	In. (mm)
Inner Gear Tooth Tip-to-Outer Gear	
Standard	.0008-.0063 (.020-.160)
Maximum	.0079 (.200)
Outer Gear-to-Pump Body	
Standard	.0035-.0071 (.090-.180)
Maximum	.0087 (.220)
Rotor-to-Cover	
Standard	.0012-.0043 (.030-.110)
Maximum	.0055 (.139)

Assembly & Installation

Apply engine oil to pump body and new oil seal. Press oil seal in flush with front of pump body. To complete assembly and install, reverse removal and disassembly procedure. Apply locking compound to pump cover screws.

ENGINE COOLING

WATER PUMP

Removal & Installation

Remove timing belt. Drain engine coolant. Disconnect water inlet pipe from water pump. Remove water pump. To install, reverse removal procedure.

NOTE: **For further information on cooling systems, see ENGINE COOLING section.**

TIGHTENING SPECIFICATIONS

Application	Ft. Lbs. (N.m)
Camshaft Pulley Nut	36-45 (49-61)
Connecting Rod Cap Nuts	
Step 1	25-30 (34-41)
Step 2	37-41 (50-56)
Crankshaft Pulley Bolt	10-13 (14-18)
Cylinder Head Bolts	
Step 1	35-40 (48-54)
Step 2	56-60 (76-81)
Distributor Bolt	14-22 (19-30)
Engine Hanger Bolts	
Front	27-38 (37-52)
Rear	14-19 (19-26)
Engine Mount Bolts	27-46 (37-62)
Exhaust Manifold Bolts	
Step 1	5-7 (7-9)
Step 2	12-17 (16-23)
Exhaust Pipe Bolts	23-34 (31-46)
Flywheel Bolts	71-76 (96-103)
Fuel Pump Bolts	17-22 (23-30)
Intake Manifold Bolts	14-19 (19-26)
Main Bearing Cap Bolts	
Step 1	22-27 (30-37)
Step 2	40-43 (54-59)
Oil Pan Drain Plug	22-30 (30-41)
Oil Pump Bolts	14-19 (19-26)
Spark Plug	11-17 (15-23)
Rocker Arm Bolts	16-21 (22-28)
Timing Belt Pulley Bolt	80-94 (108-128)
Timing Belt Tensioner Bolt	14-19 (19-26)
Water Pump Bolts	14-19 (19-26)
	INCH Lbs. (N.m)
Cylinder Head Cover Bolts	43-78 (5-9)
Oil Strainer Bolts	69-95 (8-11)
Oil Pan Bolts	69-95 (8-11)
Rear Cover Assembly Bolts	69-95 (8-11)
Timing Belt Cover Bolts	69-95 (8-11)

ENGINE SPECIFICATIONS

GENERAL SPECIFICATIONS

Year	DISPLACEMENT		Fuel System	HP@RPM	Torque Ft. Lbs.@RPM	Compr. Ratio	BORE		STROKE	
	Cu. In.	Liters					In.	mm	In.	mm
1987	97.4	1.6	EFI	82@5000	92@2500	9.3:1	3.07	78	3.29	83.6

Mazda Engines

1.6L 4-CYLINDER (Cont.)

ENGINE SPECIFICATIONS (Cont.)

VALVES

Engine Size & Valve	Head Diam. In. (mm)	Face Angle	Seat Angle	Seat Width In. (mm)	Stem Diameter In. (mm)	Stem Clearance In. (mm)	Valve Lift In. (mm)
1.6L							
Intake	[1] 1.492-1.500 (37.89-38.10)	45°	45°	[3] .0433-.0669 (1.099-1.699)	[4] .2744-.2750 (6.969-6.985)	[6] .0010-.0024 (.025-.060)	.....
Exhaust	[2] 1.256-1.264 (31.90-32.10)	45°	45°	[3] .0433-.0669 (1.099-1.699)	[5] .2742-.2748 (6.965-6.979)	[6] .0012-.0026 (.030-.065)	.....

[1] – Minimum intake valve head thickness (margin) is .04" (1.0 mm). On Ford Motor Co. Tracer models, margin is .02" (.5 mm).
[2] – Minimum exhaust valve head thickness (margin) is .05" (1.3 mm). On Ford Motor Co. Tracer models, margin is .04" (1.0 mm).
[3] – Maximum valve seat runout is .0016" (.040 mm).
[4] – Minimum diameter is .2724" (6.920 mm).
[5] – Minimum diameter is .2722" (6.915 mm).
[6] – Maximum valve stem-to-guide clearance is .008" (.20 mm).

CRANKSHAFT MAIN & CONNECTING ROD BEARINGS

Engine	MAIN BEARINGS Journal Diam. In. (mm)	MAIN BEARINGS Clearance In. (mm)	MAIN BEARINGS Thrust Bearing	MAIN BEARINGS Crankshaft End Play In. (mm)	CONNECTING ROD BEARINGS Journal Diam. In. (mm)	CONNECTING ROD BEARINGS Clearance In. (mm)	CONNECTING ROD BEARINGS Side Play In. (mm)
1.6L	[1] 1.9661-1.9668 (49.938-49.956)	[2] .0009-.0017 (.024-.042)	No. 4	[3] .0031-.0111 (.079-.282)	[1] 1.7693-1.7699 (44.940-44.956)	[2] .0011-.0027 (.028-.068)	[4] .0043-.0103 (.110-.262)

[1] – Maximum journal out-of-round is .002" (.05 mm). Grinding limit is .030" (.75 mm).
[2] – On Ford Motor Co. Tracer models, main bearing clearance is .0011-.0027" (.028-.068 mm) and connecting rod bearing clearance is .0009-.0017" (.024-.042 mm). On all models, wear limit is .004" (.10 mm).
[3] – Maximum end play is .012" (.30 mm).
[4] – Maximum side play is .012" (.30 mm).

PISTONS, PINS & RINGS

Engine	PISTONS Clearance In. (mm)	PINS Piston Fit In. (mm)	PINS Rod Fit In. (mm)	RINGS Ring No.	RINGS End Gap In. (mm)	RINGS Side Clearance In. (mm)
1.6L	[1] .0015-.0020 (.039-.052)	.00030-.00050 (.0076-.0127)	0-.00102 (0-.0259)	1	.006-.012 (.15-.30)	[1] .0012-.0026 (.030-.065)
				2	.006-.012 (.15-.30)	.0012-.0026 (.030-.065)
				Oil	[2] .008-.028 (.20-.70)	.....

[1] – Maximum clearance is .006" (.15 mm).
[2] – Wear limit is .04" (1.0 mm).

1.6L 4-CYLINDER (Cont.)

ENGINE SPECIFICATIONS (Cont.)

CAMSHAFT

Engine	Journal Diam. In. (mm)	Clearance In. (mm)	Lobe Lift In. (mm)
1.6L			
Front & Rear	[1] 1.7115-1.7125 (43.440-43.465)	[2] .0014-.0033 (.035-.085)	.....
Center	[1] 1.7104-1.7113 (43.410-43.435)	[2] .0026-.0045 (.065-.115)	.....

[1] – Maximum out-of-round is .002" (.05 mm).
[2] – Maximum oil clearance is .006" (.15 mm).

VALVE SPRINGS

Engine	Free Length In. (mm)	PRESSURE Lbs. @ In. (Kg @ mm) Valve Closed	Valve Open
1.6L	[1] 1.717 (43.61)	....	

[1] – Limit is 1.665" (42.29 mm).

VALVE TIMING

Engine	INTAKE Open (BTDC)	Close (ABDC)	EXHAUST Open (BBDC)	Close (ATDC)
1.6L	14°	52°	52°	14°

Mazda Engines

2.0L & 2.2L 4-CYLINDER

B2200, 626

NOTE: **For information on Mazda 2.6L 4-cylinder engine, see Chrysler Motors Imports 2.6L 4-cylinder engine article.**

ENGINE CODING

ENGINE IDENTIFICATION

Engines can be identified by the engine code number that is stamped on a pad behind the alternator and below No. 1 spark plug.

ENGINE IDENTIFICATION CODE

Application	Code
2.0L	FE
2.2L	F2

NOTE: **For engine repair procedures not covered in this article, see ENGINE OVERHAUL PROCEDURES article at beginning of this section.**

ENGINE, MANIFOLDS & CYLINDER HEAD

ENGINE

Removal (B2200)

1) Remove hood after marking hinge location. Drain engine oil and coolant. Disconnect negative battery cable. Remove air cleaner assembly and dipstick. Remove cooling fan and radiator shroud. Disconnect accelerator and cruise control cables. Disconnect fuel hoses from carburetor.

2) Disconnect power brake unit and heater hoses. Remove 3-way solenoid valves and vacuum sensor assembly. Remove duty solenoid valve assembly and vacuum switch. Disconnect vacuum hoses at vapor canister. Disconnect engine harness at alternator. Disconnect engine ground strap from rear of engine.

3) Remove radiator hoses and radiator. Remove secondary air pipe assembly. Disconnect exhaust pipe from manifold. Remove A/C compressor and power steering pump without disconnecting hoses (if equipped).

4) Remove starter motor. Remove gusset plates. Remove rear cover. Remove bolts attaching transmission to engine. Support transmission. Remove engine mount bolts. Attach engine sling. Remove engine from vehicle.

Removal (626 & 626 Turbo)

1) Remove hood after marking hinge location. Drain engine oil, transaxle fluid and coolant. Disconnect negative battery terminal. Remove air cleaner. Disconnect fuel supply hose and accelerator cable.

2) Disconnect speedometer cable, clutch release cylinder (M/T), or control cable (A/T). Remove engine ground wire and related wire connector. Disconnect vacuum hose from power brake unit. Remove 3-way valve vacuum switch and bracket. Disconnect heater hoses. Disconnect wiring to engine and transaxle.

3) Remove air vent hose and vacuum hoses. Remove electric fan and radiator. On A/C equipped models, remove subtank, alternator and A/C compressor. On all models, remove front wheels, splash shields, power steering pump and drive axles.

4) Disconnect shift linkage and shifter extension bar (M/T). Remove flexible joints, bolts and nuts. Remove torque stopper. Disconnect exhaust pipe from manifold. Remove engine and transaxle mounting nuts. Remove engine and transaxle as an assembly from vehicle.

Installation (All Models)

To install engine, reverse removal procedure. Check all fluid levels.

CYLINDER HEAD & MANIFOLDS

Removal (B2200)

1) Disconnect negative battery cable. Drain cooling system. Turn crankshaft to position No. 1 piston at TDC. Remove air cleaner assembly. Remove cooling fan and radiator shroud. Disconnect accelerator cable.

2) Disconnect fuel hoses from carburetor. Remove fuel pump (M/T). Disconnect power brake unit and heater hoses. Remove 3-way solenoid valves and vacuum sensor assembly.

3) Remove duty solenoid valve assembly. Disconnect vacuum hoses at vapor canister. Disconnect engine harness at alternator. Remove spark plug wires, spark plugs and distributor. Remove secondary air pipe assembly. Remove upper radiator hose and coolant bypass hose.

4) Remove intake manifold and carburetor as an assembly. Remove exhaust manifold heat shield and manifold. Remove upper timing belt cover. Remove timing belt. See TIMING BELT.

5) Disconnect engine ground strap and rear engine hanger. Remove valve cover and gasket. Remove cylinder head bolts gradually in reverse order of tightening sequence. *See Fig. 1.* Break cylinder head loose from engine block and remove head from vehicle.

Fig. 1: Cylinder Head Tightening Sequence

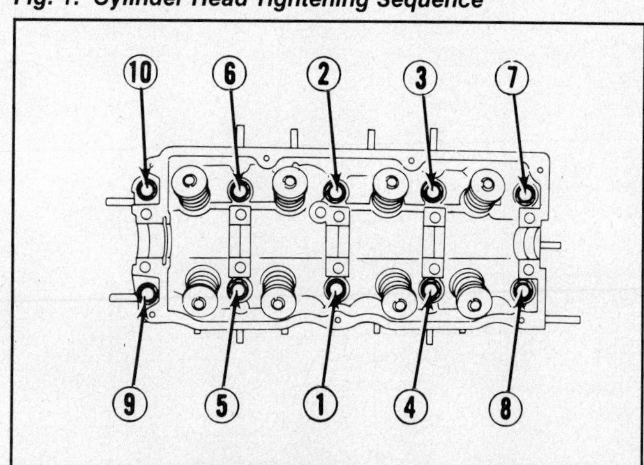

Courtesy of Mazda Motors Corp.

Removal (626 & 626 Turbo)

1) Disconnect negative battery cable. Drain cooling system. Turn crankshaft to position No. 1 piston at TDC. Disconnect accelerator cable and secondary air pipe. Remove distributor from rear housing. Remove rear housing.

2) Disconnect air hose and secondary air pipe assembly. Remove oil pipe, oil return hose and 3 turbocharger insulators (if equipped). Remove front catalytic converter-to-turbocharger bracket. Disconnect catalytic converter from exhaust manifold.

2.0L & 2.2L 4-CYLINDER (Cont.)

3) Remove turbocharger coolant hoses and EGR pipe. Remove exhaust manifold and turbocharger assembly (if equipped). Remove intake manifold and fuel injection assembly. Remove timing belt upper cover. Remove timing belt. See TIMING BELT.

4) Remove valve cover and gasket. Remove cylinder head bolts gradually in reverse order of tightening sequence. *See Fig. 1.* Break cylinder head loose from engine block and remove head from vehicle.

Inspection

Check cylinder head for warpage. Check cylinder head thickness. See CYLINDER HEAD SPECIFICATIONS table.

CYLINDER HEAD SPECIFICATIONS

Application	In. (mm)
Maximum Warpage	.006 (.15)
Standard Thickness	3.620-3.624 (91.95-92.05)
Grinding Limit	.008 (.20)

Installation (All Models)

To install, reverse removal procedure. Clean all gasket mating surfaces. Install new cylinder head gasket. Tighten head bolts gradually in sequence. *See Fig. 1.* Ensure new style surface treated plain washers are used on cylinder head bolts. Use new seal washers with valve cover bolts. Apply sealant to corners of cylinder head before installing valve cover.

CAMSHAFT

TIMING BELT

Removal

1) Disconnect negative battery cable. On B2200 models, drain cooling system. Remove cooling fan and shroud. Remove distributor from front housing. Remove cooling fan pulley and bracket. Remove secondary air pipe assembly.

2) On all models, remove alternator drive belt and A/C and P/S drive belts (if equipped). Remove crankshaft pulley and baffle plate. Remove timing belt covers. Align camshaft pulley with front housing timing mark. *See Fig. 2.* Mark an arrow on timing belt to indicate direction of travel. Remove tensioner lock bolt, tensioner and spring. Remove timing belt.

Inspection

Replace timing belt if any oil, grease or moisture is present. Inspect for damage, wear, peeling, cracking or hardening. Replace if necessary. Check belt tensioner for smoothness or abnormal noise. Inspect belt pulley and camshaft pulley teeth for wear or damage. DO NOT clean tensioner or pulleys with cleaning fluids. Wipe clean with soft rag.

NOTE: Never forceably twist, turn inside out, or bend timing belt. Belt MUST be replaced after 60,000 miles.

Installation

1) Align camshaft pulley with front housing timing mark. Align crankshaft pulley with pointer on oil pump body. *See Fig. 2.* Install tensioner, lock bolt and tensioner spring. Position timing belt tensioner to its limit of travel toward the intake manifold side and partially tighten lock bolt.

2) Install timing belt onto crankshaft pulley and then camshaft pulley. Install timing belt from tension side (right side, as viewed from engine front). If timing belt is being reused, ensure that arrow is pointing in direction of travel.

3) Loosen tensioner lock bolt to apply tension. To apply equal tension to each side of timing belt, turn crankshaft 2 revolutions in direction of travel. Tighten tensioner lock bolt. Check for proper alignment of timing marks.

4) On 2.0L engines, check for proper belt tension by measuring amount of deflection midway between crankshaft and camshaft pulleys when force of 22 lbs. (10 kg) is applied. *See Fig. 2.* Deflection should be .43-.51" (11-13 mm). If tension is incorrect, repeat step **3)**.

5) Reverse removal procedure to complete installation. On 2.2L engines, ensure distributor housing and drive gear marks are aligned. Turn crankshaft until No. 1 piston is at TDC. Install distributor into housing with marks facing straight up.

Fig. 2: Timing Belt Reference Marks & Deflection

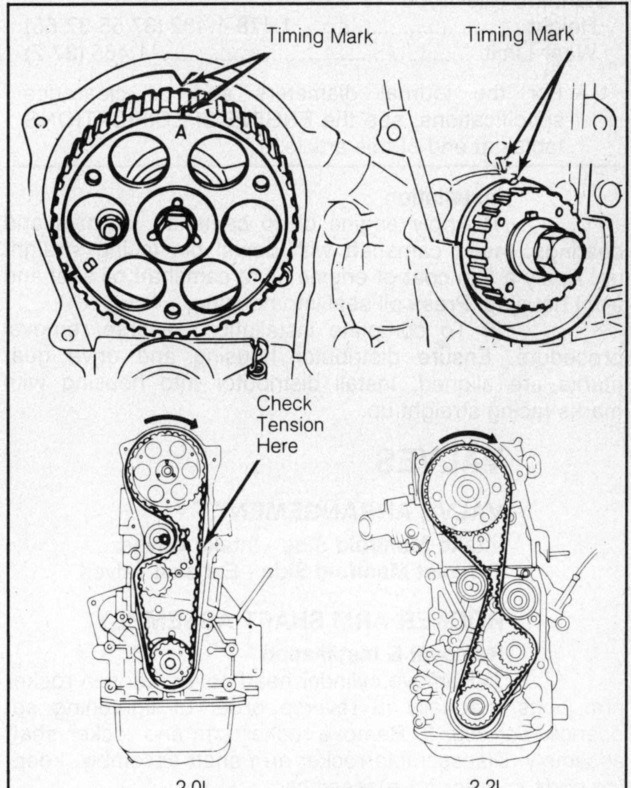

Courtesy of Mazda Motors Corp.

CAMSHAFT & FRONT OIL SEAL

Removal

Remove timing belt. Remove camshaft pulley. Remove front housing/oil seal assembly. On 2.2L engines with M/T, remove fuel pump. On 2.0L engines, remove distributor housing on rear of cylinder head. On all engines, remove rocker arm shaft assembly. See ROCKER ARM SHAFT ASSEMBLY. Remove camshaft. On 2.2L engines, remove rear seal cap.

Inspection

1) Inspect camshaft lobes for scoring or wear. Measure camshaft lobe height. Measure bearing journals.

Mazda Engines

2.0L & 2.2L 4-CYLINDER (Cont.)

Measure camshaft front oil seal contact surface. Measure fuel pump cam lobe height. Check camshaft for bent condition (runout). Replace camshaft if not to specification.

2) Measure camshaft end play. If end play exceeds limit, replace camshaft or cylinder head. Measure camshaft bearing-to-journal oil clearance. Replace cylinder head or camshaft caps if not to specification.

CAMSHAFT SPECIFICATIONS [1]

Application	In. (mm)
End Play	.003-.006 (.08-.16)
Wear Limit	.008 (.20)
Front Oil Seal	
Contact Surface	1.3370-1.3386 (33.961-34.000)
Camshaft Runout	.0012 (.030)
Standard Lobe Height	
2.0L	1.5021-1.5060 (38.152-38.252)
Wear Limit	1.4962 (38.002)
2.2L	1.4970-1.4990 (38.034-38.084)
Wear Limit	1.4910 (37.859)
Standard Fuel Lobe	
Height	1.478-1.482 (37.55-37.65)
Wear Limit	1.465 (37.2)

[1] - For the journal diameters and oil clearance specifications, see the ENGINE SPECIFICATIONS tables at end of this article.

Installation

1) Apply engine oil to camshaft journals and bearings. Insert camshaft with dowel pin facing straight up. Apply a thin coat of engine oil to camshaft oil seal and front housing. Press oil seal into housing.

2) To complete installation, reverse removal procedure. Ensure distributor housing and drive gear marks are aligned. Install distributor into housing with marks facing straight up.

VALVES

VALVE ARRANGEMENT

Intake Manifold Side - Intake valves.
Exhaust Manifold Side - Exhaust valves.

ROCKER ARM SHAFT ASSEMBLY

Removal & Installation

1) Remove cylinder head cover. Loosen rocker arm bolts gradually in reverse order of tightening sequence. *See Fig. 3.* Remove rocker arm and rocker shaft assembly. Disassemble rocker arm shaft assembly, keeping parts in order for reassembly.

2) Inspect all components for wear or damage. See ROCKER ARM & SHAFT SPECIFICATIONS table. To install, reverse removal procedure. Apply thin coat of sealant to each end of cylinder head. Ensure rocker shaft oil holes in center camshaft caps face each other. Tighten bolts in proper sequence. *See Fig. 3.*

ROCKER ARM & SHAFT SPECIFICATIONS

Application	In. (mm)
Rocker Arm Bore	.6300-.6310 (16.000-16.027)
Shaft Diameter	.6286-.6293 (15.966-15.984)
Rocker Arm-to-Shaft Clearance	
Standard	.0006-.0024 (.016-.061)
Maximum	.004 (.10)

Fig. 3: Rocker Arm Tightening Sequence

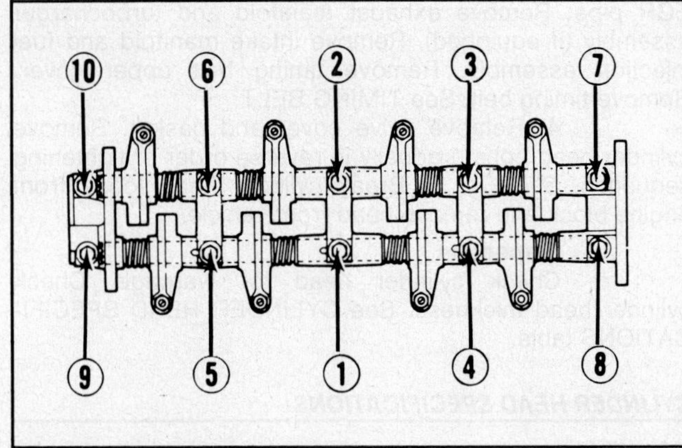

Courtesy of Mazda Motors Corp.

VALVE SPRINGS & SEALS

Removal

Remove cylinder head. Remove rocker arm assembly and camshaft. Compress valve springs with spring compressor. Remove keepers and spring seats. Remove springs and valve stem seals from cylinder head. It may be necessary to use a pair of pliers to remove seals.

Inspection

Inspect parts for cracks or damage. Check spring free length and out-of-square condition. Outer valve spring out-of-square must not exceed .07" (1.8 mm). Inner valve spring out-of-square must not exceed .06" (1.5 mm). Replace parts if necessary.

Installation

Apply a coat of engine oil to inner surface of valve seal. Install valve seals using Installer (49 G030 160). Outer valve spring is an unequal pitch type. Install spring so that end with closer pitch is on cylinder head side. Tap end of valve stem lightly with a plastic hammer after installing valve keepers.

VALVE GUIDES

Removal & Inspection

1) Remove valve springs, valve stem seals and valves. Mark for proper reassembly. Measure valve guide bore and height. *See Fig. 4.* See VALVE GUIDE SPECIFICATIONS table.

VALVE GUIDE SPECIFICATIONS

Application	In. (mm)
Valve Guide Bore	
Intake & Exhaust	.3177-.3185 (8.070-8.090)
Installed Height	.752-.772 (19.10-19.60)

2) Measure valve stem diameter. See ENGINE SPECIFICATIONS table. Insert valve in corresponding guide and measure valve stem-to-valve guide clearance. If measurement exceeds limit, replace guide and or valve. Drive out guide from combustion chamber side of head.

Installation

Install clip on valve guide. Drive guide into head from side opposite combustion chamber. Drive valve guide in until clip contacts cylinder head. *See Fig. 4.*

2.0L & 2.2L 4-CYLINDER (Cont.)

NOTE: Although the design of intake and exhaust valve guides are different, use exhaust valve guides on both sides for replacement.

Fig. 4: Checking Valve Guide Height

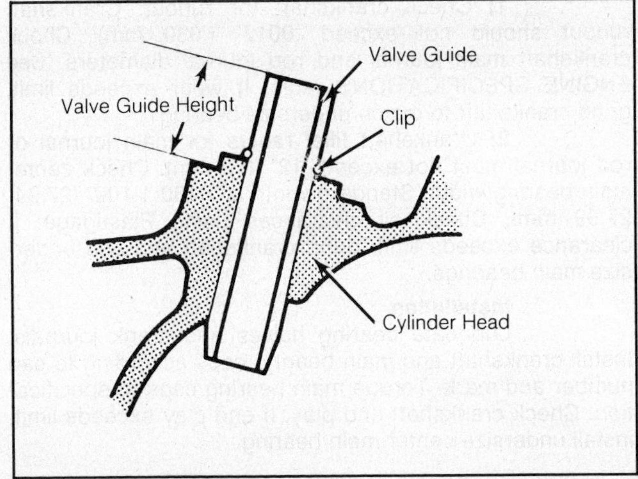

Courtesy of Mazda Motors Corp.

VALVE SEATS

Inspection

1) Measure valve head thickness (margin). See ENGINE SPECIFICATIONS table. Inspect valve seat for damage. Measure seat angle and width. Grind valve seats if necessary. Use compound to seat valve and valve seat. Check that contact surface is at center of valve face. Check valve stem installed height. Standard installed height is 1.831" (46.50 mm).

2) If height is 1.831-1.850" (46.50-47.00 mm), valve can be used as is. If height is 1.850-1.890" (47.00-48.00 mm), insert a shim into spring seat area so that height is 1.831" (46.50 mm). If height is more than 1.890" (48.00 mm), replace valve seat or cylinder head.

VALVE CLEARANCE ADJUSTMENT

2.0L Only

Warm engine to normal operating temperature. Bring No. 1 piston to TDC and adjust No. 3 and No. 4 intake valves and No. 2 and No. 4 exhaust valves. Turn crankshaft one revolution to bring No. 4 piston to TDC. Adjust clearance of remaining valves.

VALVE CLEARANCE SPECIFICATIONS (2.0L ONLY)

Application	In. (mm)
Intake	.012 (.30)
Exhaust	.012 (.30)

CYLINDER BLOCK ASSEMBLY

Inspection

Check cylinder block for leakage, cracks or scoring of cylinder walls. Check head gasket surface for warpage. Grind if necessary. Measure cylinder bore diameter. If wear exceeds limit, bore and hone cylinders for installation of oversize pistons.

CYLINDER BLOCK SPECIFICATIONS

Application	In. (mm)
Maximum Warpage	.006 (.15)
Grinding Limit	.008 (.20)
Bore Diameter	
Standard	3.3859-3.3866 (86.000-86.019)
Maximum	3.392 (86.17)
Out-of-Round Limit	.006 (.15)
Taper Limit	.0007 (.019)

PISTONS, RINGS & PINS

OIL PAN

Removal

1) Disconnect negative battery cable. Drain engine oil. On B2200 models, remove engine splash shield and engine crossmember. Disconnect steering linkage at idler control arm. Remove 2 gussets and flywheel inspection cover. Remove oil pan and baffle plate.

2) On 626 models, remove engine torque stopper and right front wheel assembly. Remove wheel-well splash shield and front exhaust pipe. Support engine and remove motor mount. Remove flywheel inspection cover. Remove oil pan.

Installation

To install, reverse removal procedure. On 626 models, apply sealant to oil pan and install. Do not apply sealant to both block and oil pan. On B2200 models, apply sealant to baffle plate and oil pan and install. Add oil, start engine and check for leaks.

PISTON & ROD ASSEMBLY

Removal

Remove cylinder head. Remove oil pan, baffle plate (2.2L only) and oil strainer. Mark connecting rods and caps for reassembly reference. Remove ridge at top of cylinder with ridge reamer (if necessary). Remove rod caps. Push piston and rod assembly out top of cylinder. Be careful not to damage crankshaft journals or scratch cylinder walls.

Inspection

Inspect pistons for burns, scoring, cracking or scratches. Measure piston diameter 90 degrees to pin bore, .71" (18.0 mm) below oil ring groove. Standard piston diameter is 3.3837-3.3845" (85.944-85.964 mm). Use piston diameter and cylinder bore measurements to determine the piston-to-cylinder bore clearance.

NOTE: Oversize pistons and rings are available in .010" (.25 mm) and .020" (.50 mm) sizes.

Installation

1) Install piston rings on piston. Space ring gaps properly. *See Fig. 5.* Ensure "R" is facing up on compression rings and oil rings turn smoothly after installing on piston. Lubricate piston rings, pistons and cylinder walls with engine oil.

2) Install ring compressor onto piston without changing position of rings. Install piston and rod assembly. Ensure "F" mark on piston pin boss is facing front of engine. Install rod caps and tighten rod bolts to specification. Install oil strainer, baffle plate (2.2L only) and oil pan. Install cylinder head.

2.0L & 2.2L 4-CYLINDER (Cont.)

Fig. 5: Piston Ring Gap Spacing

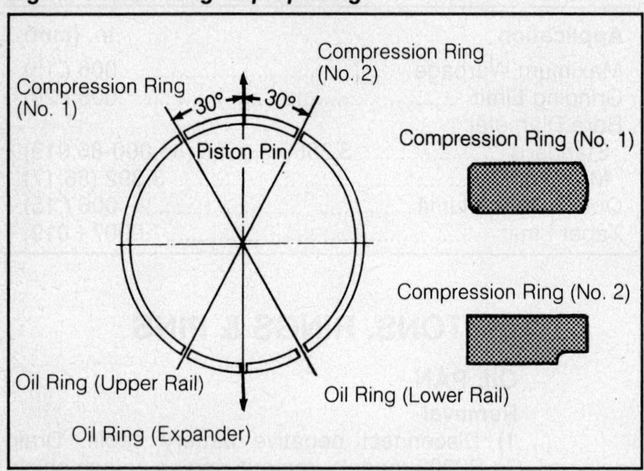

Courtesy of Mazda Motors Corp.

PISTON PIN REPLACEMENT

Removal

Using a hydraulic press and proper piston pin removal and installation set, remove piston pin out of piston and rod. Mark pin, rod and piston for proper reassembly.

Inspection

1) Check connecting rod for twisted or bent condition. Check connecting rod center-to-center length. Measure connecting rod small and large bores. See CONNECTING ROD SPECIFICATIONS table.

2) Inspect piston bore, piston pin and connecting rod bore for excessive wear. Measure piston pin outer diameter. Outer diameter should be .8651-.8654" (21.974-21.980 mm).

CONNECTING ROD SPECIFICATIONS

Application	In. (mm)
Center-to-Center	
2.0L	5.982-5.986 (151.95-152.05)
2.2L	6.238-6.242 (158.45-158.55)
Maximum Twist or Bend	
2.0L	.0016 (.040)
2.2L	.0024 (.060)
Small End Bore	.8640-.8646 (21.943-21.961)

Installation

Ensure connecting rod oil hole is opposite "F" mark on piston. Apply engine oil to piston pin and to connecting rod bore. Insert piston pin from piston side marked "F". Force required to install pin should be 1100-3300 lbs. (500-1500 kg). If force required is not within specifications, replace piston pin or connecting rod. After installation, ensure connecting rod falls from its own weight when piston is held horizontally.

CRANKSHAFT & ROD BEARINGS

MAIN BEARINGS

Removal

Remove transaxle from engine. Remove flywheel (M/T) or flexplate (A/T) and rear cover/oil seal assembly. Remove oil pump. Remove main bearing caps. Main bearing caps are marked for cylinder identification. Arrow on cap points toward front of engine. Note that cylinder block side of center main bearing is different than others.

Inspection

1) Check crankshaft for runout. Crankshaft runout should not exceed .0012" (.030 mm). Check crankshaft main journal and rod journal diameters. See ENGINE SPECIFICATIONS table. If wear exceeds limit, grind crankshaft to match undersize bearing.

2) Crankshaft fillet radius for main journal or rod journal must not exceed .12" (3.0 mm). Check center main bearing width. Standard width is 1.100-1.102" (27.94-27.99 mm). Check oil clearances using Plastigage. If clearance exceeds limit, grind crankshaft and use undersize main bearings.

Installation

Lubricate bearing halves and crank journals. Install crankshaft and main bearing caps according to cap number and mark. Torque main bearing caps to specification. Check crankshaft end play. If end play exceeds limit, install undersize center main bearing.

NOTE: Undersize crankshaft bearings, connecting rod bearings and center main bearing are available in .010" (.25 mm), .020" (.50 mm), and .030" (.75 mm) sizes.

CONNECTING ROD BEARINGS

Inspection

Install rod bearing halves into connecting rod. Install rod and piston assembly. Position Plastigage on crankpin. Place rod cap and bearing in position and tighten. Ensure mating marks on cap and rod are aligned. Remove cap and check oil clearance. If clearance exceeds limit, grind crankshaft and use undersize bearings. Check connecting rod side play before installing rod caps.

REAR MAIN BEARING OIL SEAL

Removal & Installation

Remove flywheel or flexplate. Remove oil pan. Remove rear cover. Remove seal from cover. Lubricate cover, new oil seal and seal lip. Press oil seal into cover. Install rear cover with new gasket. Tighten cover to specification. Cut away gasket that protrudes out from rear cover assembly. Install flywheel or flexplate using sealant on bolts.

ENGINE OILING

CRANKCASE CAPACITY

CRANKCASE CAPACITIES

Application	Qts. (L)
2.0L	
Oil Pan	3.8 (3.6)
Oil Filter	.32 (.3)
Total	4.5 (4.3)
2.2L	
Oil Pan	4.1 (3.9)
Oil Filter	.32 (.3)
Total	4.9 (4.6)

2.0L & 2.2L 4-CYLINDER (Cont.)

Fig. 6: 2.0L Engine Oiling System

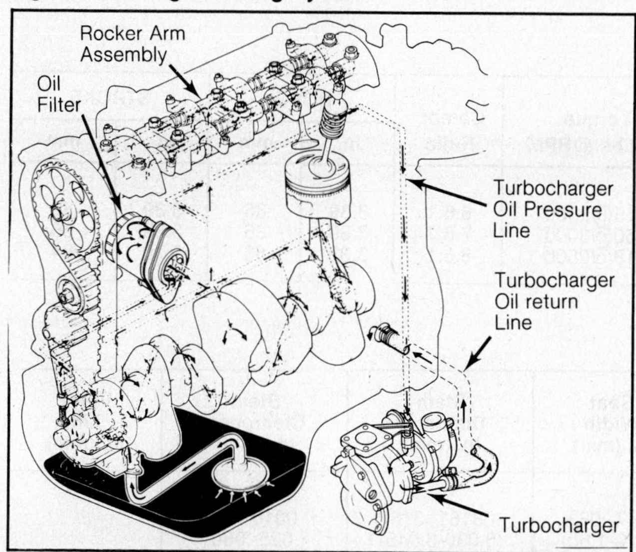

Turbo model shown. 2.2L engine is similiar. Courtesy of Mazda Motors Corp.

NORMAL OIL PRESSURE

Oil pressure should be 43-57 psi (3-4 kg/cm²) at 3000 RPM.

OIL PRESSURE RELIEF VALVE

Oil pressure relief valve opens at 11-17 psi (.8-1.2 kg/cm²).

OIL PUMP & OIL SEAL

Removal

Disconnect negative battery cable. Drain engine oil. Remove timing belt. See TIMING BELT. Remove crankshaft pulley bolt and pulley. Remove oil pan, oil strainer, baffle plate (2.2L only), engine bracket (2.0L only) and oil pump.

Disassembly

Use an impact driver to remove screws from pump cover. Remove cover from back of pump. Remove inner and outer pump gears. Remove snap ring and oil pressure control valve assembly. Remove oil seal from front of oil pump body.

Inspection

Check for distortion or damage to pump body or cover. Check for weak or damaged plunger and plunger spring. Using a straightedge positioned over pump body and above both gears, measure clearance between gear to straightedge (side clearance). Replace gear assembly or oil pump body if clearances are not within limits.

Reassembly

To reassemble, reverse disassembly procedure. On 2.0L engines, install outer gear with 2 punch marks facing oil pump body. On all engines, fill pump cavity with clean engine oil before installing cover. Apply Loctite to oil pump cover bolts and tighten.

Installation

To install, reverse removal procedure. Apply a thin coat of grease to "O" ring and install on pump. Apply engine oil to new oil seal and press in. Coat oil pump mating surfaces with sealant. Ensure that sealant does not enter oil passage.

OIL PUMP SPECIFICATIONS (2.0L)

Application	In. (mm)
Outer Gear Tooth Tip-to-Crescent	
Standard	.0078-.0126 (.200-.320)
Maximum	.0137 (.350)
Inner Gear Tooth Tip-to-Crescent	
Standard	.0105-.0150 (.267-.380)
Maximum	.016 (.40)
Outer Gear-to-Pump Body	
Standard	.0035-.0072 (.090-.184)
Maximum	.008 (.20)
Rotor-to-Cover Side Clearance	
Standard	.0012-.0025 (.030-.063)
Maximum	.004 (.10)

OIL PUMP SPECIFICATIONS (2.2L)

Application	In. (mm)
Inner Gear Tooth Tip-to-Outer Gear	
Standard	.0017-.0033 (.044-.084)
Maximum	.007 (.18)
Outer Gear-to-Pump Body	
Standard	.0035-.0069 (.090-.176)
Maximum	.008 (.20)
Rotor-to-Cover Side Clearance	
Standard	.0012-.0035 (.030-.090)
Maximum	.004 (.10)

ENGINE COOLING

WATER PUMP

Removal

1) Disconnect negative battery cable. Turn crankshaft so that No. 1 piston is at TDC. Drain coolant. On B2200 models, remove cooling fan, pulley and radiator shroud. On 626 models, remove wheelwell splash shield. On all models, remove alternator drive belt and timing belt upper cover.

2) On 626 models, remove crankshaft pulley. On all models, remove timing belt lower cover and tensioner. On B2200 models, remove timing belt idler. On all models, remove timing belt. See TIMING BELT. Remove water pump inlet pipe and gasket. Remove water pump, gasket (2.0L) or "O" ring (2.2L).

Installation

To install, reverse removal procedure. Apply a coating of petroleum jelly to water pump "O" ring. Always use new "O" ring. Apply petroleum jelly to inlet pipe "O" ring (if equipped). Fill cooling system.

NOTE: **For more information, see ENGINE COOLING SYSTEMS article at the end of this section.**

Mazda Engines

2.0L & 2.2L 4-CYLINDER (Cont.)

ENGINE SPECIFICATIONS

GENERAL SPECIFICATIONS

Year	DISPLACEMENT		Fuel System	HP@RPM	Torque Ft. Lbs.@RPM	Compr. Ratio	BORE		STROKE	
	Cu. In.	Liters					In.	mm	In.	mm
1987										
626	121.9	2.0L	L-Jetronic	93@5000	115@2500	8.6:1	3.39	86	3.39	86
626 Turbo	121.9	2.0L	L-Jetronic	120@5000	150@3000	7.8:1	3.39	86	3.39	86
B2200	134.2	2.2L	2-Bbl	85@4500	118@2500	8.6:1	3.39	86	3.70	94

VALVES

Engine Size & Valve	Head Diam. In. (mm)	Face Angle	Seat Angle	Seat Width In. (mm)	Stem Diameter In. (mm)	Stem Clearance In. (mm)	Valve Lift In. (mm)
2.0L & 2.2L							
Intake	[1] 1.732 (43.99)	45°	45°	.047-.063 (1.19-1.60)	[3] .3161-.3167 (8.030-8.045)	[4] .0010-.0024 (.025-.060)	.....
Exhaust	[2] 1.417 (35.99)	45°	45°	.047-.063 (1.19-1.60)	[5] .3159-.3165 (8.025-8.040)	[4][6] .0010-.0024 (.025-.060)	.....

[1] – Minimum intake valve head thickness (margin) is .02" (.5 mm).
[2] – Minimum exhaust valve head thickness (margin) is .04" (1.0 mm).
[3] – Minimum diameter is .3142" (7.980 mm).
[4] – Maximum valve stem-to-guide clearance is .008" (.20 mm).
[5] – Minimum diameter is .3140" (7.975 mm).
[6] – On 2.2L engine, stem clearance is .0012-.0026" (.030-.067 mm).

CRANKSHAFT MAIN & CONNECTING ROD BEARINGS

Engine	MAIN BEARINGS				CONNECTING ROD BEARINGS		
	Journal Diam. In. (mm)	Clearance In. (mm)	Thrust Bearing	Crankshaft End Play In. (mm)	Journal Diam. In. (mm)	Clearance In. (mm)	Side Play In. (mm)
2.0L & 2.2L	[1] 2.3598-2.3605 (59.937-59.955)	[2] .0012-.0019 (.031-.049)	No. 3	[3] .0031-.0071 (.079-.180)	[1] 2.0056-2.0061 (50.940-50.955)	[4] .0010-.0026 (.027-.067)	[5] .004-.010 (.10-.25)

[1] – Maximum journal out-of-round is .002" (.05 mm). Grinding limit is .030" (.75 mm).
[2] – Wear limit is .003" (.08 mm).
[3] – Maximum end play is .012" (.30 mm).
[4] – Wear limit is .004" (.10 mm).
[5] – Maximum side play is .012" (.30 mm).

PISTONS, PINS & RINGS

Engine	PISTONS	PINS		RINGS		
	Clearance In. (mm)	Piston Fit In. (mm)	Rod Fit In. (mm)	Ring No.	End Gap In. (mm)	Side Clearance In. (mm)
2.0L & 2.2L	[1] .0014-.0030 (.036-.075)	0-.0009 (0-.024)	Press	No. 1	.008-.014 (.20-.35)	[1] .0012-.0028 (.030-.070)
				No. 2	.006-.012 (.15-.30)	[1] .0012-.0028 (.030-.070)
				Oil	[2] .012-.035 (.30-.89)	.....

[1] – Maximum clearance is .006" (.15 mm).
[2] – Wear limit is .04" (1.0 mm).

Mazda Engines

2.0L & 2.2L 4-CYLINDER (Cont.)

ENGINE SPECIFICATIONS (Cont.)

VALVE SPRINGS

Engine	Free Length In. (mm)	PRESSURE Lbs. @ In. (Kg @ mm)	
		Valve Closed	Valve Open
2.0L & 2.2L			
Inner	[1] 1.73 (44.0)	.....	.....
Outer	[2] [3] 2.05 (52.0)	.....	.....

[1] – Limit is 1.68" (42.7 mm).
[2] – Limit is 2.00" (50.8 mm).
[3] – On 2.2L engine, limit is 1.98" (50.4 mm).

CAMSHAFT

Engine	Journal Diam. In. (mm)	Clearance In. (mm)	Lobe Lift In. (mm)
2.0L & 2.2L			
Front & Rear	[1] 1.2575-1.2584 (31.940-31.965)	[2] .0014-.0033 (.035-.085)	.....
Center	[1] 1.2563-1.2573 (31.910-31.935)	[2] .0026-.0045 (.066-.115)	.....

[1] – Maximum out-of-round is .002" (.05 mm).
[2] – Maximum oil clearance is .006" (.15 mm).

VALVE TIMING

Engine	INTAKE		EXHAUST	
	Open (BTDC)	Close (ABDC)	Open (BBDC)	Close (ATDC)
2.0L				
626	16°	54°	54°	16°
626 Turbo	16°	54°	54°	16°
2.2L	13°	57°	58°	12°

TIGHTENING SPECIFICATIONS

Application	Ft. Lbs. (N.m)
Camshaft Pulley Bolt	35-48 (47-65)
Connecting Rod Cap Nuts	
2.0L	37-41 (50-56)
2.2L	48-51 (65-69)
Coolant Inlet Pipe Bolts	14-19 (19-25)
Cylinder Head Bolts (Cold)	59-64 (80-87)
Drive Plate Bolts (A/T)	71-76 (96-103)
End Plate Bolts	
2.0L	14-22 (19-30)
2.2L	14-19 (19-25)
Engine Bracket Bolts (2.0L)	27-38 (37-52)
Engine Hanger Bolts	14-22 (19-30)
Engine Mount Bolts	27-46 (37-63)
Exhaust Manifold Nuts	16-21 (22-29)
Flywheel Bolts (M/T)	71-76 (96-103)
Front Housing Bolts	14-19 (19-25)
Fuel Pump Bolts	14-19 (19-25)
Intake Manifold Nuts	14-19 (19-25)
Main Bearing Cap Bolts	61-65 (82-88)
Oil Cooler Bolts (2.0L)	22-29 (30-39)
Oil Pump Bolts	
M8	14-19 (19-25)
M10	27-38 (37-52)
Rear Housing Bolts (2.0L)	14-19 (19-25)
Rocker Arm Shaft Bolts	13-20 (18-27)
Thermostat Cover Bolts	14-22 (19-30)
Timing Belt Crankshaft Pulley Bolt	
2.0L	116-123 (157-167)
2.2L	108-112 (146-152)
Timing Belt Idler (2.2L)	27-38 (37-52)
Timing Belt Tensioner Bolt	28-38 (38-52)
Torque Stopper Bolts (2.0L)	45-56 (61-76)
Water Pump Bolts	14-19 (19-25)
	INCH Lbs. (N.m)
Cooling Fan Bolts (2.2L)	35-43 (4-5)
Crankshaft Pulley Bolt	113-148 (13-17)
Oil Baffle Plate (2.2L)	69-104 (8-12)
Oil Strainer Bolts	69-104 (8-12)
Oil Pan Bolts	61-104 (7-12)
Rear Cover Bolts	69-104 (8-12)
Timing Belt Covers	61-87 (7-10)
Valve Cover	
2.0L	26-35 (3-4)
2.2L	35-42 (4-5)

Mercedes-Benz Engines

2.3L 4-CYLINDER

190E

NOTE: **For engine repair procedures not covered in this article, see ENGINE OVERHAUL PROCEDURES article at beginning of this section.**

ENGINE CODING

ENGINE IDENTIFICATION

The engine family designation is shown on the emission control information plate (attached to radiator crossmember). The 1st character identifies the model year ("H" for 1987) while the 4th and 5th characters identify the engine displacement.

ENGINE IDENTIFICATION CODE

Application & Engine Size	Engine [1] Designation	Engine Family (Engine Code)
190E 2.3L	102.985	HMB2.3V6FA11

[1] – The engine designation code must be used when ordering parts or when obtaining technical information. This number identifies specific engine.

CAUTION: **On models with Supplemental Restraint System (SRS), observe the following precautions: Before any repairs are performed, disconnect and shield battery ground. Disconnect 10-point SRS connector under passenger's foot rest. Use extreme caution when working around steering column. Models with SRS may be identified by a SRS light below tachometer.**

ENGINE, MANIFOLDS & CYLINDER HEAD

ENGINE

Removal

1) Place hood in vertical position by releasing levers on hood supports. Slowly push hood upward so detent lever engages at left hood support.

2) Disconnect positive side of battery. Remove rubber strip above firewall. Remove clips and pivot battery holder upward. Place battery positive cable over engine.

3) Drain engine coolant. Remove radiator and air filter. Discharge A/C system. Disconnect and plug hoses from pump to chassis. Drain oil from power steering pump and disconnect hoses.

4) Disconnect throttle linkage and coolant hoses. Disconnect all vacuum, oil, fuel, and electrical lines leading from engine. Remove TDC transmitter cable from test socket. Remove test socket from holder.

5) Unbolt engine shock absorber from frame. Remove engine stop bracket. Push holding strap for tachometer shaft out of link and disconnect ground cable.

6) Disconnect drive shaft from transmission. Loosen exhaust heat shield. Loosen center support bearing and slide shaft rearward. Remove exhaust pipe.

7) Remove tachometer drive support from transmission cover. On manual transmission models, disconnect hydraulic line to clutch slave cylinder. On automatic transmission models, disconnect shift linkage.

8) Attach chain hoist to lifting eyes of engine and take up slack. Remove rear engine support bracket and mount. Unbolt front engine mounts. Remove engine and transmission at an angle of 45 degrees.

Installation

1) To install, reverse removal procedure. Check engine mounts, engine shock absorber, coolant, oil and fuel hoses. On manual transmission models, inspect pilot bearing in rear of crankshaft.

2) Check position of right front engine mount shield. Adjust engine stop. Recharge A/C system. Check ignition timing and idle speed. Check engine for leaks.

CYLINDER HEAD

Removal

1) Place hood in vertical position. Drain cooling system and remove air cleaner assembly. Disconnect negative battery cable.

2) Remove coolant hose from thermostat housing. Disconnect all coolant, fuel, vacuum, and electric lines connected to cylinder head and intake manifold.

3) Disconnect throttle linkage by pushing plastic guide out of its seat in the slotted lever. Pull throttle cable through slot and set aside. Disconnect intake manifold support bracket.

4) Disconnect oil dipstick tube from exhaust manifold. Disconnect automatic transmission dipstick tube from rear of cylinder head. Remove brackets for A/C line at front of cylinder head. Loosen upper hose clamp of thermostat by-pass line.

5) Disconnect hydraulic lines and remove level control pressure pump from front of cylinder head (if equipped). Remove alternator belt and tensioner adjusting bolt.

NOTE: **On models with level control system, remove socket head cap screw from front of camshaft and remove drive coupling.**

6) Loosen alternator bracket mounting bolts on water pump. Pivot alternator bracket away from cylinder block to gain access to timing chain tensioner. Disconnect exhaust system at exhaust manifold. Remove valve cover and set No. 1 piston at TDC.

7) Carefully remove chain tensioner nut (spring tension). Remove sealing ring and tensioner spring. Mark camshaft timing gear-to-timing chain position. Remove camshaft sprocket. Remove chain guide locating pin from cylinder head. *See Fig. 2.*

8) Loosen and remove head bolts in reverse order of tightening sequence. Remove bolts (8 mm) at front inside portion of head. Attach hoist to lifting eyes on head, and remove cylinder head from engine.

9) Throughly clean all mating surfaces of head and cylinder block. Remove chain tensioner plunger from front timing cover.

Installation

1) To install, reverse removal procedure. Ensure that No. 1 piston is at TDC. Place head gasket in position. Ensure locating dowels are aligned. If cylinder head bolt length is greater than 4.80" (122 mm), replace head bolt.

2) Install and tighten head bolts. *See Fig. 1.* Use new seals and gaskets when installing components. Run engine until warm and check all fluid levels.

2.3L 4-CYLINDER (Cont.)

Fig. 1: Cylinder Head Tightening Sequence

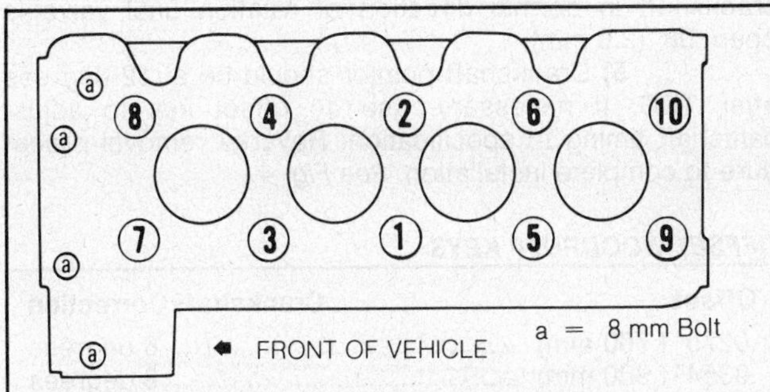

Courtesy of Mercedes-Benz of North America.

CAMSHAFT

TIMING CHAIN COVER

Removal

1) Drain engine oil and coolant. Disconnect negative battery cable. Remove air cleaner and radiator. Slacken and remove all drive belts. Remove valve cover and water pump.

2) Remove bolts for tensioning rod on A/C compressor. Remove A/C mounting bracket. Set engine to TDC for No. 1 piston. Remove vibration damper or hub for crankshaft drive belt.

3) Remove TDC transmitter and ignition distributor. Disconnect throttle linkage and pull throttle cable out through slot in slotted lever. Disconnect sway bar from frame.

4) Remove engine shock absorber and front engine stop. On vehicles with automatic transmission, remove transmission oil cooler lines from oil cooler and plug end of lines.

5) Remove engine ground strap. Disconnect exhaust system from exhaust manifold and swivel downward. Disconnect front and rear engine mounts. Remove oil pan and place on frame crossmember.

6) Attach hoisting chain to front lifting eye and lift engine upward. Remove oil pump suction pipe bracket. Remove 8 mm hex bolts from inside front of cylinder head.

7) Tap timing cover locating dowel pins toward rear and remove cover bolts. Carefully pull off timing cover in a slightly downward direction so that cylinder head gasket is not damaged. Remove seal ring from crankshaft if necessary.

Installation

1) Clean all mating surfaces. Replace seal on oil pump cover. Lightly glue gasket at several points. Trim gasket to fit front cover. Leave center portion of gasket for timing cover bolt.

2) Coat sealing surface of timing cover with a thin coat of gasket sealant. Carefully position timing cover. Turn inner gear of oil pump so that the 2 locating dowels are in alignment with those on drive sleeve.

3) Position locating dowel pins and install timing cover bolts. Install spacing ring. If timing cover sealing ring has been removed, install new sealing ring.

4) To complete installation, reverse removal procedure. Replace oil pan gasket. Check for proper adjustment of TDC transmitter. See TDC TRANSMITTER in this article. Check ignition timing.

TIMING CHAIN

Removal & Installation

1) A master link (split) timing chain is available for replacement without dismantling engine. Remove air cleaner, valve cover, and spark plugs. Use a chain link remover to remove master link from timing chain.

2) Remove old link and insert new master link with new chain attached. Turn crankshaft (by hand) slowly in direction of rotation while feeding new chain in and removing old chain. Ensure that chain does not slip on sprockets. Install master link from rear so retainer will be at front of engine.

NOTE: DO NOT rotate engine using camshaft sprocket bolt. DO NOT rotate engine in reverse direction. Prior to rotating crankshaft, switch ignition off and pull out plug for TDC transmitter of ignition distributor (Green cable) on switching unit.

3) Install connecting link clip with closed end facing direction of rotation. Rotate crankshaft through one complete revolution and check that camshaft timing mark is aligned. *See Fig. 3.* To complete installation, reverse removal procedure.

Fig. 2: Timing Chain Installation

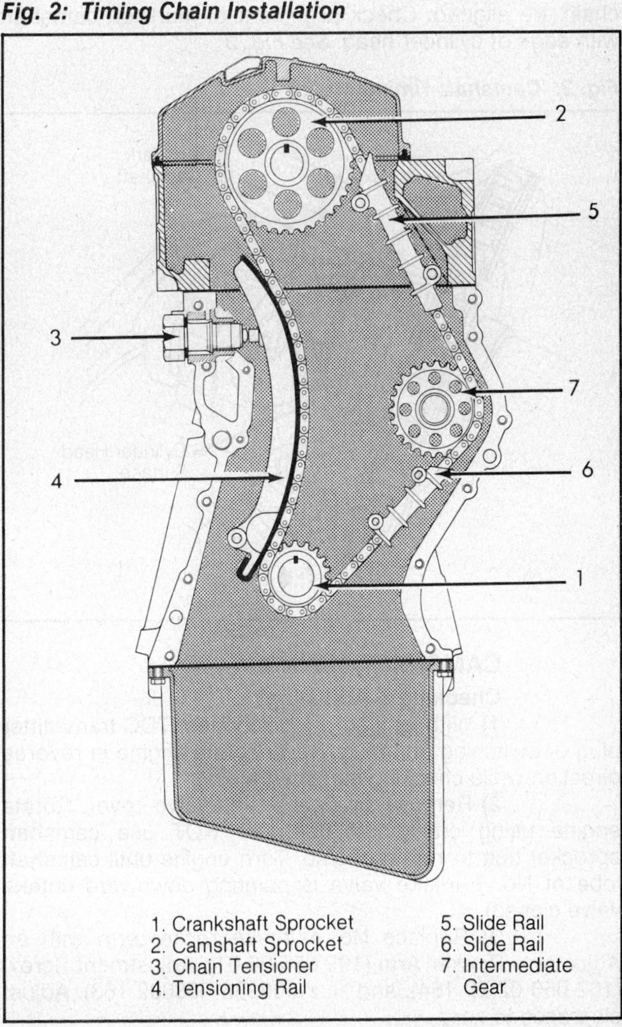

Courtesy of Mercedes-Benz of North America.

2.3L 4-CYLINDER (Cont.)

CAMSHAFTS

Removal

1) Remove air cleaner and valve cover. Set No. 1 piston at TDC. Mark on flange of camshaft must be in alignment with edge on cylinder head. *See Fig. 3.*

2) Mark camshaft sprocket and timing chain in relation to each other. Carefully remove chain tensioner nut (under spring tension), sealing ring and tensioner spring.

3) Remove camshaft bolt and sprocket. Remove rocker arm bearing caps. Remove and mark ball sockets from spring retainers. Remove camshaft. Remove Woodruff key and spacing ring from camshaft. Check lobes of camshaft for wear or scoring. Replace camshaft if necessary.

NOTE: **On models equipped with level control system the pressure pump is driven from front of camshaft. With pump removed, remove socket head cap screw from front of camshaft and remove drive coupling.**

Installation

To install, reverse removal procedure. Make sure ball sockets are installed in original positions. Ensure that identifying marks on camshaft sprocket and timing chain are aligned. Check alignment of mark on camshaft with edge of cylinder head. *See Fig. 3.*

Fig. 3: Camshaft Timing Marks

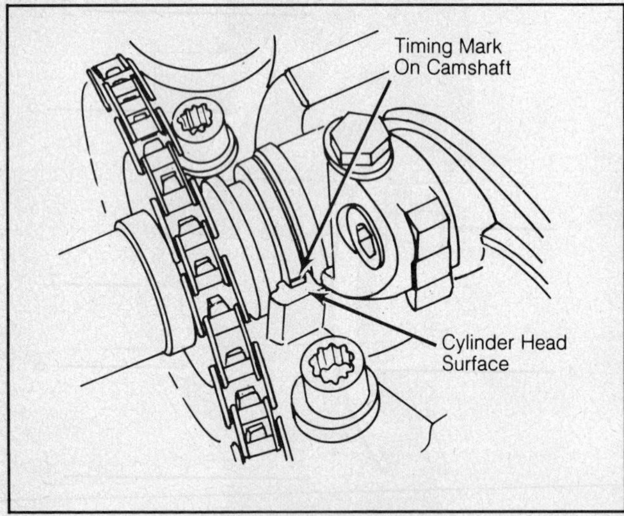

CAMSHAFT TIMING

Checking & Adjusting

1) With ignition off, disconnect TDC transmitter plug or switching unit plug. Never rotate engine in reverse direction while checking camshaft timing.

2) Remove air cleaner and valve cover. Rotate engine using crankshaft bolt. DO NOT use camshaft sprocket bolt to rotate engine. Turn engine until camshaft lobe of No. 1 intake valve is pointing downward (intake valve closed).

3) Replace No. 1 intake rocker arm with an Adjustable Rocker Arm (102 055 00 01), Adjustment Screw (102 050 02 20 164), and Nut (000936 008009 163). Adjust clearance to zero.

4) Install dial indicator with indicator stem resting vertically on valve spring retainer. Set indicator preload at .12" (3.0 mm) and zero dial indicator. Turn crankshaft in normal direction of rotation until valve is open .08" (2.0 mm).

5) Crankshaft pointer should be at 12 degrees after TDC. If necessary, use an offset key to adjust camshaft timing to specification. Reverse removal procedure to complete installation. *See Fig. 4.*

OFFSET WOODRUFF KEYS

Offset	Crankshaft Correction
.0275" (.700 mm)	6 degrees
.0354" (.900 mm)	8 degrees
.0433" (1.1 mm)	9 1/2 degrees
.0512" (1.3 mm)	11 1/2 degrees

Fig. 4: Offset Key Positioning

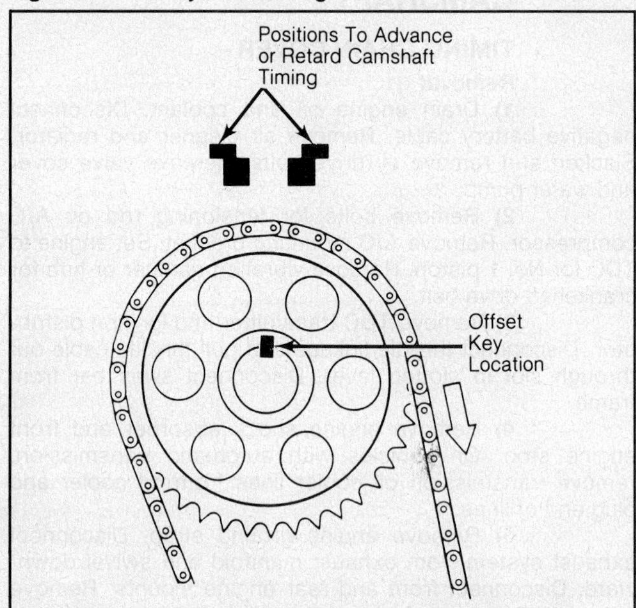

Courtesy of Mercedes-Benz of North America.

TDC TRANSMITTER

Positioning & Adjustment

1) Set engine to TDC of compression stroke for No. 1 piston. Remove valve cover and intake valve spring for No. 1 cylinder. Turn crankshaft from TDC approximately 10 degrees before TDC.

2) Position dial indicator on intake valve stem. Place dial indicator stem under a .079" (2 mm) preload to read piston position. Move crankshaft in normal drection of rotation until TDC position is located.

NOTE: **With cylinder head removed, position and zero a dial indicator directly over piston crown.**

3) With piston at TDC, zero dial indicator. Remove hex nut and TDC transmitter. Loosen dial indicator and place indicator stem under a .197" (5 mm) preload.

4) Rotate crankshaft backward from TDC until dial indicator reading is correct. See TDC TRANSMITTER SPECIFICATIONS table. In this position, piston travel at crankshaft is 20 degrees after TDC.

2.3L 4-CYLINDER (Cont.)

5) Place Locating Device (102 589 03 21 00) without handle into adjusting slide. Pin on vibration damper or crankshaft pulley should engage groove in locating device. If pin does not engage, loosen nut and correct position of adjusting slide.

6) With pin engaged, tighten nut and remove locating device. Insert TDC transmitter and tighten nut. Remove dial indicator and holder. Lubricate a new valve stem oil seal and install on intake valve stem. Install valve spring and check valve clearance.

TDC TRANSMITTER SPECIFICATIONS

Measurement Taken At	In. (mm)
Piston Crown	.12" (3.07)
Intake Valve	.106-.118 (2.70-3.00)

INTERMEDIATE GEAR SHAFT

Removal

1) Remove timing cover and chain tensioner. Mark timing chain-to-crankshaft sprocket position. Remove chain guides. Remove hex head mounting bolt through hole in intermediate gear face.

2) Remove locating plate from gear. Rotate crankshaft in opposite direction of rotation just enough to slacken timing chain on intermediate gear. Pull out intermediate gear shaft.

NOTE: **DO NOT rotate engine using camshaft sprocket bolt. Prior to rotating crankshaft, switch ignition off and pull out plug for TDC transmitter of ignition distributor (Green cable) on switching unit.**

Installation

To install, reverse removal procedure. Ensure that reference marks on crankshaft timing gear and chain align.

VALVES

VALVE ARRANGEMENT

Intake Manifold Side – Intake Valves
Exhaust Manifold Side – Exhaust Valves

ROCKER ARM ASSEMBLIES

Removal

Remove valve cover. With cam lobes pointing downward, remove cam bearing cap bolt at open end of rocker shaft bore. Install a bolt in the threaded end of the rocker shaft. Pull shaft from bearing cap. Remove rocker arm.

Installation

Lubricate camshaft lobe and rocker arm contact surfaces. Place rocker arm in position. Press down on valve end of rocker arm to collapse compensating valve. Install rocker shaft. Reverse removal procedure to complete installation.

Fig. 5: Sectional View of Valve Train Assembly

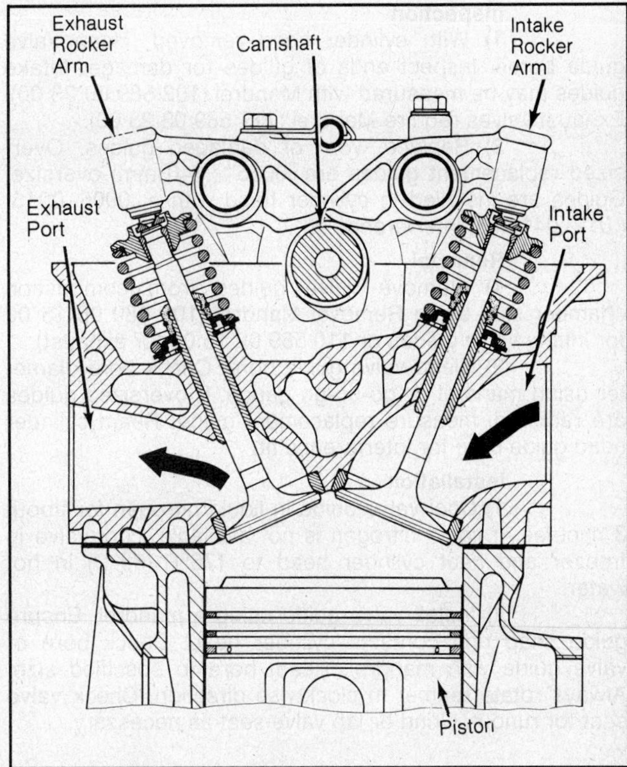

Courtesy of Mercedes-Benz of North America.

VALVE SPRINGS

Removal

1) Remove air cleaner, valve cover and spark plugs. Position crankshaft at TDC for cylinder being serviced. Remove oil pipe and rocker arm assembly.

2) Install Support Bracket (102 589 01 61 00) for spring compressor. Connect cylinder leak tester and pressurize cylinder. Attach Spring Compressor (102 589 00 61 00) to support bracket and position on valve spring retainer.

3) Compress valve spring and remove valve retainers. To avoid damage to valve, DO NOT remove valve spring without compressed air in cylinder. Remove valve spring retainer and valve spring.

4) Check valve spring and valve spring retainer. Check valve springs with a valve spring tester. Check spring force at specified length. If necessary, replace spring.

Installation

To install, reverse removal procedure. Ensure valve retainer is installed properly and numbers on camshaft bearing caps are aligned.

VALVE STEM OIL SEALS

Removal & Installation

1) Remove valve springs. Remove valve stem seals. DO NOT damage valve stem and valve guide. Remove any burrs from valve stem and guide.

2) Replace any damaged valve retainers or spring retainers. Lubricate valve stem seal and install. Install valve spring. To complete installation, reverse removal procedure.

Mercedes-Benz Engines

2.3L 4-CYLINDER (Cont.)

VALVE GUIDES

Inspection

1) With cylinder head removed, clean valve guide bores. Inspect ends of guides for damage. Intake guides may be measured with Mandrel (102 589 00 23 00). Exhaust valves require Mandrel (117 589 03 23 00).

2) Replace worn or damaged guides. Oversized replacement guides are .0055" (.140 mm) oversize. Guides are installed in cylinder head with a .0005-.0016" (.012-.041 mm) interference fit.

Removal

1) Remove valve guides from combustion chamber side using Removal Mandrel (102 589 06 15 00 for intake valve guides or 110 589 02 15 00 for exhaust).

2) Clean valve guide bore. Check bore diameter using mandrel or go-no-go gauge. If oversized guides are required, measure replacement guide. Ream cylinder head guide bore for interference fit.

Installation

1) Cool valve guide in liquid nitrogen for about 3 minutes. If liquid nitrogen is not available, cool valve in freezer and heat cylinder head to 176°F (80°C) in hot water.

2) Install valve guide using a mandrel. Ensure guide snap ring contacts cylinder head. Check bore of valve guide with mandrel. Ream bore to specified size. Always rotate reamer in clockwise direction. Check valve seat for runout. Grind or lap valve seat as necessary.

VALVE GUIDE SPECIFICATIONS

Application	O.D. In. (mm) [1]	I.D. In. (mm)
Intake	.5529-.5531 (14.044-14.051)	.3149-.3155" (8.000-8.015)
Exhaust	.5529-.5531 (14.044-14.051)	.3543-.3549 (9.000-9.015)

[1] – Oversize (Red) valve guide outside diameter is .5596-.5599" (14.214-14.222 mm). Cylinder head valve guide bore diameter should be .5524-.5526" (14.030-14.035 mm); .5590-.5592" (14.198-14.203 mm) for oversize valve guides.

VALVE CLEARANCE ADJUSTMENT

Engine is equipped with hydraulic valve lifters, valve clearance adjustment is not necessary.

VALVE SEATS

Removal & Installation

1) Remove valve seat inserts on a milling machine. Check valve guides and replace if necessary. Measure valve seat bore. A new valve seat ring with standard dimension can be used if bore meets specifications.

2) Pre-heat cylinder head in boiling water. Cool valve seat ring with liquid nitrogen. Install valve seat ring with a mandrel. Machine valve seat. *See Fig. 6.*

Fig. 6: Replacement Valve Seat Dimensions

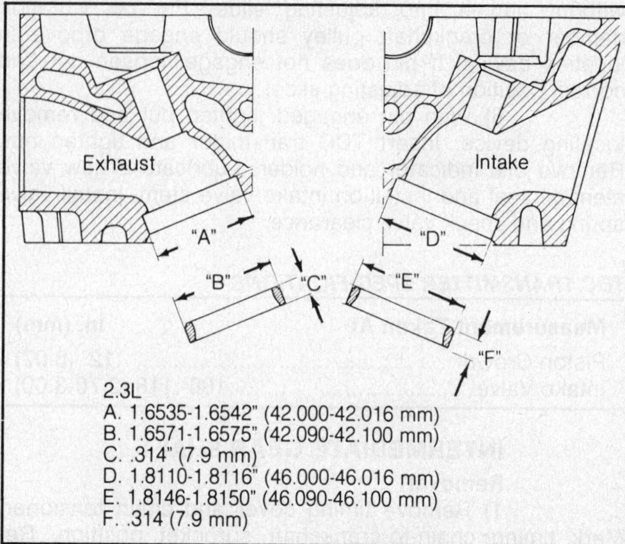

Courtesy of Mercedes-Benz of North America.

PISTONS, PINS & RINGS

PISTON & ROD ASSEMBLY

Removal

1) Remove engine from vehicle. Remove cylinder head, front timing cover, and oil pan. Remove connecting rod nuts and bearing caps. Check for any cylinder ridge lip and remove as necessary.

2) Push piston and rod assembly out top of cylinder. During removal, use care not to damage bearing surface. Remove piston pin snap ring and push out piston pin. Retain all components in proper order for reassembly.

Inspection

1) Check connecting rod for overheating discoloration and bearing damage. Check connecting rod bolts and replace if necessary.

2) Assemble connecting rod bearing cap and tighten connecting rod nuts. Measure connecting rod bearing bore. If bore diameter exceeds specifications by .0002" (.005 mm), replace connecting rods.

3) Check piston rings for land clearance and end gap. Ensure piston rings rotate freely. Using engine oil lubricate pistons. Pin fit into piston is a push fit.

NOTE: **When replacing connecting rods, ensure there is no difference in weight of connecting rods. Connecting rods are divided into 2 weight groups and are identified with one or 2 punch marks laterally on connecting rod.**

Installation

1) To install, reverse removal procedure. Lubricate piston pins and connecting rod bushings. Install pistons with diagonal splash bore in small end and arrow on top of piston pointing forward.

2) Push in piston pin manually. Insert piston pin snap ring into grooves. Lubricate cylinder bores, connecting rod bearing journals, connecting rod bearing shells and pistons.

3) Position ring gaps of piston rings uniformly along piston circumference. Fit ring compressor and install pistons with arrow pointing forward in cylinder bore. *See Fig. 7*. Install connecting rod bearing caps. Ensure reference marks are aligned.

2.3L 4-CYLINDER (Cont.)

PISTON & CYLINDER DIAMETERS

Piston Size & Group	Piston Diameter (mm)	Cylinder Diameter (mm)
Standard		
0	95.468-95.482	95.498-95.508
1	95.478-95.492	95.508-95.518
2	95.488-95.502	95.518-95.528
.5 mm Oversize		
0	95.968-95.982	95.998-96.008
1	95.978-95.992	96.008-96.018
2	95.988-96.002	96.018-96.028
1.0 mm Oversize		
0	96.468-96.482	96.498-96.508
1	96.478-96.492	96.508-96.518
2	96.488-96.502	96.518-96.528

Fig. 7: Top & Side View of Piston

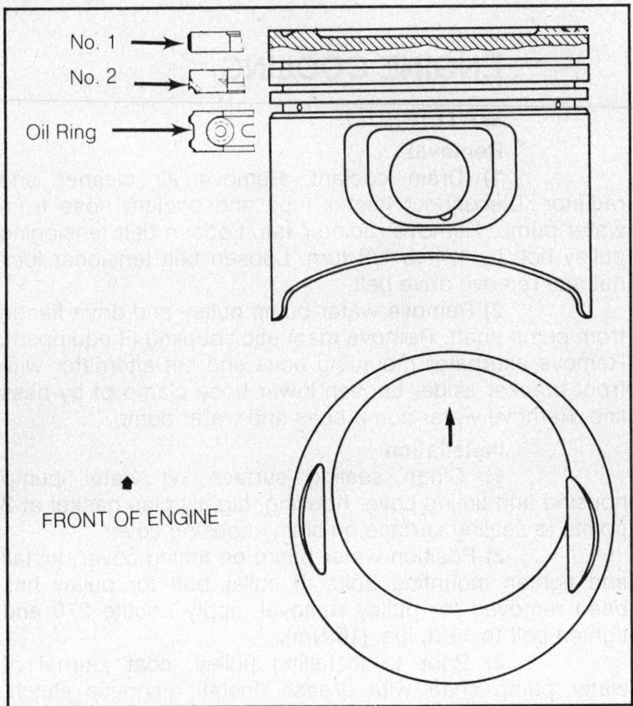

Courtesy of Mercedes-Benz of North America.

CRANKSHAFT & ROD BEARINGS

CRANKSHAFT MAIN BEARINGS

Inspection

1) Remove crankshaft from engine block. Clean crankshaft and inspect journals for cracks or damage. Cracked crankshafts must be replaced.

2) Damaged crankshafts may be reground. Journals must be hardened after grinding. *See Fig. 8.* Replace crankshaft if hardness test fails.

3) Install main caps. Lubricate main cap bolts and tighten to specification. Measure line bore. If line boring is necessary, DO NOT remove more than .008" (.02 mm) from main caps.

NOTE: The bearing cap register is offset .02" (.5 mm) from center. Bearing caps can only be installed in one direction.

Fig. 8: Crankshaft Hardening Specifications

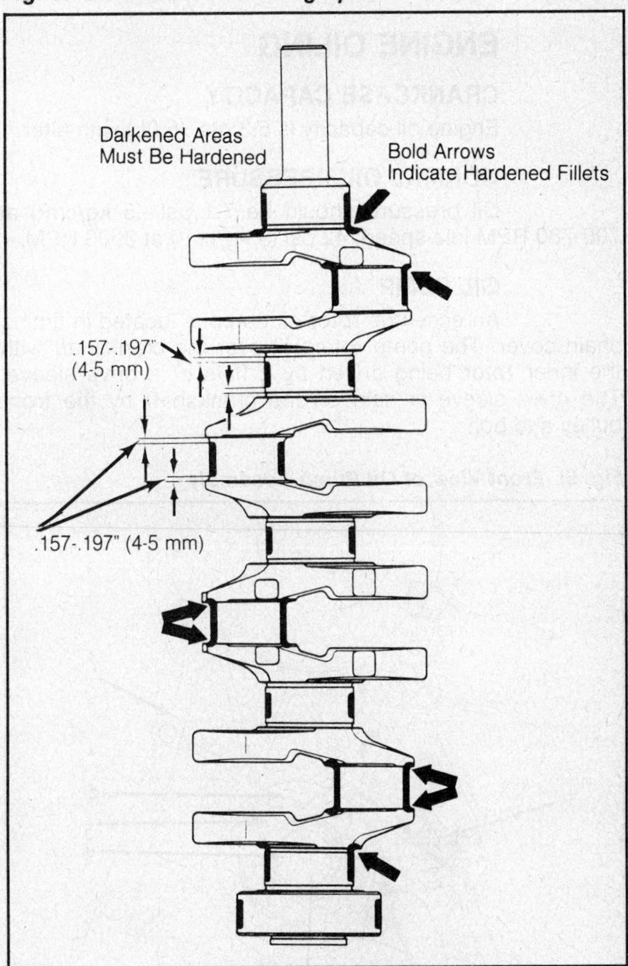

Courtesy of Mercedes-Benz of North America.

4) Install crankshaft bearings and tighten caps. Measure bearing diameter and record measurement. Measure crankshaft bearing journals and determine bearing clearance. Standard size bearings are color coded within the standard size tolerance range.

5) Standard size crankshaft bearing shells with Red identification markings are thicker than those with Yellow or Green markings. Bearings may be changed to obtain the correct clearance.

Installation

1) Lubricate bearing shells and crankshaft with engine oil and install crankshaft. Lubricate and install thrust washers and in registers in block and bearing cap.

2) Ensure that oil grooves in thrust washers face toward crankshaft webs. Install crankshaft bearing caps and tighten to specification. Measure crankshaft bearing end play. Rotate crankshaft manually and check for binding.

CONNECTING ROD BEARINGS

Inspection

Install bearing shells and tighten cap to 33 ft. lbs. (45 N.m). Measure connecting rod bearing diameter and record measurement. Measure corresponding connecting rod bearing journal and determine bearing clearance. If bearing clearance is incorrect, replace bearing shells. Connecting rod bearing shells without color coding are thicker than those with Blue markings.

ENGINE OILING

CRANKCASE CAPACITY

Engine oil capacity is 5.3 qts. (5.0L) with filter.

NORMAL OIL PRESSURE

Oil pressure should be 7.1 psi (.5 kg/cm²) at 700-780 RPM idle speed; 42 psi (3 kg/cm²) at 3000 RPM.

OIL PUMP

An eccentric rotor oil pump is located in timing chain cover. The pump rotors fit over the crankshaft with the inner rotor being driven by 2 flats of a drive sleeve. The drive sleeve is held on the crankshaft by the front pulley and bolt.

Fig. 9: Front View of Oil Pump Assembly

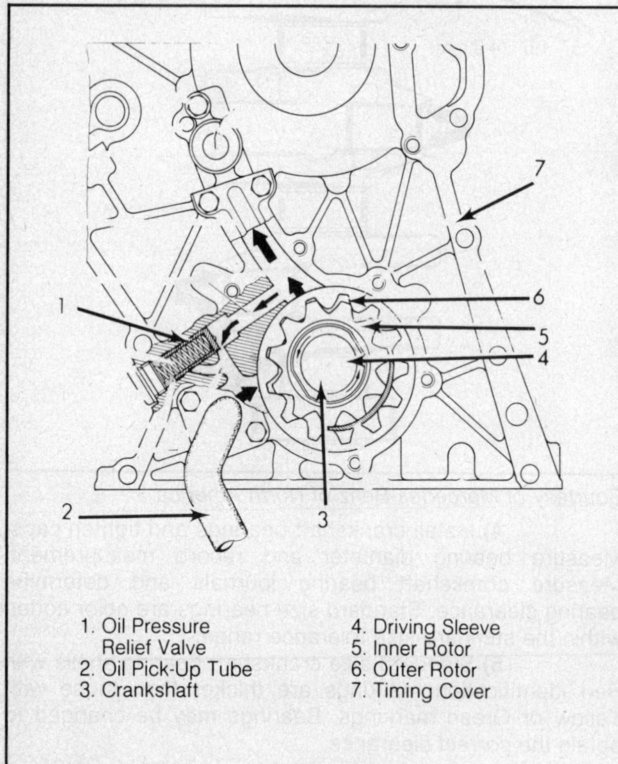

Courtesy of Mercedes-Benz of North America.

Removal

1) Remove timing chain cover. Remove oil suction pipe and oil strainer. Remove oil pump cover. Remove oil pump rotors from timing chain cover. Check driving sleeve for wear or damage.

2) If drive sleeve cannot be removed from crankshaft manually, remove with pump rotors. Clean and inspect rotors and case for damage. Rotor sets are available as replacement parts.

Installation

1) Lubricate oil pump rotors and install in timing cover. Replace seals and gaskets on suction pipe at pump housing.

2) Install oil pump housing on timing cover. Install suction pipe with oil strainer and with new gasket on oil pump cover. Ensure correct installation of gasket between flange of oil suction pipe and oil pump cover.

3) Check oil pump rotation for smoothness of operation. Install drive sleeve on crankshaft. Install timing housing cover. Run engine and check for leaks.

ENGINE COOLING

WATER PUMP

Removal

1) Drain coolant. Remove air cleaner and radiator. Disconnect heater tube and coolant hose from water pump. Remove radiator fan. Loosen belt tensioning pulley bolt by 1/4 to 1/2 turn. Loosen belt tensioner lock nut and remove drive belt.

2) Remove water pump pulley and drive flange from pump shaft. Remove magnetic coupling (if equipped). Remove alternator mounting bolts and set alternator with front bracket aside. Loosen lower hose clamp of by-pass line. Remove water pump bolts and water pump.

Installation

1) Clean sealing surface on water pump housing and timing cover housing. Lightly glue gasket at 2 points to sealing surface on timing housing cover.

2) Position water pump on timing cover. Install and tighten mounting bolts. If collar bolt for pulley has been removed for pulley removal, apply Loctite 270 and tighten bolt to 11 ft. lbs. (15 Nm).

3) Prior to installing pulley, coat journal of water pump shaft with grease. Install magnetic clutch. Install drive belt. DO NOT use lubricant to install belt.

4) Turn belt tensioner adjusting nut until indicator aligns with the 4th mark. Tighten tensioner bolt. To complete installation, reverse removal procedure.

NOTE: **For more information, see ENGINE COOLING SYSTEMS article at end of this section.**

ENGINE SPECIFICATIONS

GENERAL SPECIFICATIONS

Year	DISPLACEMENT		Fuel System	HP@RPM	Torque	Compr.	BORE		STROKE	
	Cu. In.	Liters			Ft. Lbs.@RPM	Ratio	In.	mm	In.	mm
1987 2.3L	140.3	2.3	Fuel Inj.	120@5000	136@3500	8.0:1	3.759	95.50	3.159	80.25

Mercedes-Benz Engines

2.3L 4-CYLINDER (Cont.)

ENGINE SPECIFICATIONS (Cont.)

VALVES

Engine Size & Valve	Head Diam. In. (mm)	Face Angle	Seat Angle	Seat Width In. (mm)	Stem Diameter In. (mm)	Stem Clearance In. (mm)	Valve Lift In. (mm)
2.3L							
Intake	1.807-1.815 (45.90-46.10)	45° +15'	45° +15'	.071-.098 (1.80-2.50)	.3131-.3138 (7.955-7.970)	.0012 (.030)	.....
Exhaust	1.531-1.539 (38.90-39.10)	45° +15'	45° +15'	.059-.098 (1.50-2.50)	.3519-.3527 (8.938-8.960)	.0012 (.030)	.....

PISTONS, PINS & RINGS

Engine	PISTONS	PINS		RINGS		
	Clearance In. (mm)	Piston Fit In. (mm)	Rod Fit In. (mm)	Ring No.	End Gap In. (mm)	Side Clearance In. (mm)
2.3L	.0006-.0016 (.016-.040)	[1] Push Fit	[2] Push Fit	No. 1	.012-.022 (.30-.55)	.0012-.0033 (.030-.085)
				No. 2	.012-.022 (.30-.55)	.0004-.0012 (.010-.030)
				Oil	.010-.020 (.25-.50)	.0004-.0018 (.010-.045)

[1] – Piston pin clearance in piston is .00008-.00047" (.0020-.0120 mm) when new.
[2] – Piston pin clearance in connecting rod bushing is .00027-.00071" (.0070-.0180 mm) when new.

CRANKSHAFT MAIN & CONNECTING ROD BEARINGS

Engine	MAIN BEARINGS				CONNECTING ROD BEARINGS		
	Journal Diam. In. (mm)	Clearance In. (mm)	Thrust Bearing	Crankshaft End Play In. (mm)	Journal Diam. In. (mm)	Clearance In. (mm)	Side Play In. (mm)
2.3L	2.281-2.282 (57.950-57.965)	.0010-.0018 (.025-.045)	Center	.002-.009 (.05-.23)	1.887-1.888 (47.955-47.965)	.0012-.0020 (.030-.050)	.004-.009 (.010-.23)

VALVE SPRINGS

Engine	Free Length In. (mm)	PRESSURE Lbs. @ In. (Kg @ mm)	
		Valve Closed	Valve Open
2.3L	1.93 (49.0)	.....	171-203 @ 1.20 (77-92 @ 30.5)

VALVE TIMING

Engine	INTAKE		EXHAUST	
	Open (BTDC)	Close (ABDC)	Open (BBDC)	Close (ATDC)
2.3L	[1]	11°	17.5°	12°

[1] – Intake valve opens 17 degrees after TDC.

CAMSHAFT

Engine	Journal Diam. In. (mm)	Clearance In. (mm)	Lobe Lift In. (mm)
2.3L	1.260 (32.000)	.0004-.002 (.010-.05)	.....

Mercedes-Benz Engines

2.3L 4-CYLINDER (Cont.)

ENGINE SPECIFICATIONS (Cont.)

TIGHTENING SPECIFICATIONS

Application	Ft. Lbs. (N.m)
Camshaft Bearing Caps	15 (21)
Camshaft Sprocket	59 (80)
Connecting Rod Bolts	
Step 1	30 (40)
Step 2	[1] Angle Tighten 90 Degrees
Crankshaft Damper Bolt	221 (300)
Cylinder Head Cover Nuts	11 (15)
Cylinder Head Bolts	
Step 1	52 (70)
Step 2	[1] Angle Tighten 90 Degrees
Step 3	[1] Angle Tighten 90 Degrees
8 mm Bolts (4)	19 (25)
Exhaust Manifold Bolts	15 (20)
Exhaust Pipe Nuts	22 (30)
Flywheel/Flexplate Bolts	
Step 1	26 (35)
Step 2	[1] Angle Tighten 90 Degrees
Front Engine Mount-to-Engine Carrier	30 (40)
Main Bearing Cap Bolts	66 (90)
Rear Engine Mount-to-Engine Carrier	15 (20)
Rear Engine Mount-to-Transmission Cover	52 (70)
Rocker Arm Bearing Bracket Bolts	15 (20)
Timing Chain Tensioner Plug	52 (70)
Timing Cover Bolts	17 (23)

[1] – DO NOT use torque wrench when angle tightening bolts.

Mercedes-Benz Engines

2.5L 5-CYLINDER & 3.0L 6-CYLINDER TURBO DIESEL

190D, 300D, 300TD, 300SDL

NOTE: **For engine repair procedures not covered in this article, see ENGINE OVERHAUL PROCEDURES article at beginning of this section.**

ENGINE CODING

ENGINE IDENTIFICATION

The engine family designation is shown on the emission control information plate (attached to radiator crossmember). The 1st character identifies the model year ("H" for 1987) while the 4th and 5th characters identify the engine displacement.

ENGINE IDENTIFICATION CODE

Application & Engine Size	Engine [1] Designation	Engine Family (Engine Code)
190D		
2.5L	602.911	HMB2.5D6JA14
2.5L Turbo	602.961	HMB2.5D9JF14
300D Turbo	603.960	HMB3.0D9KA18
300SDL Turbo	603.961	HMB3.0D9KA18
300TD Turbo	603.960	HMB3.0D9KA18

[1] – The engine designation code must be used when ordering parts or when obtaining technical information. This number identifies specific engine.

CAUTION: **On models with Supplemental Restraint System (SRS), observe the following precautions: Before any repairs are performed, disconnect and shield battery ground. Disconnect 10-point SRS connector under passenger's foot rest. Use extreme caution when working around steering column. Models with SRS may be identified by a SRS light below tachometer.**

ENGINE, MANIFOLDS & CYLINDER HEAD

ENGINE

Removal (190D)

1) Drain cooling system. Disconnect negative battery cable. Remove engine hood, radiator and fan shroud. Remove air filter with intake duct. Remove engine insulator cover from under vehicle.

2) Drain oil from power steering pump reservoir and disconnect hoses. Remove A/C compressor with hoses attached and set aside.

3) Remove throttle control linkage with shaft and set aside. Disconnect all coolant, vacuum, oil, fuel and electrical lines and hoses which lead to engine. Disconnect exhaust system at exhaust manifold.

4) Remove support for exhaust pipe at transmission. If equipped with level control, remove pump and set aside, leaving lines connected.

5) Remove engine mount bolts at chassis. Remove drive shaft shield and disconnect drive shaft at transmission. Disconnect engine shock absorbers at chassis. At transmission, disconnect shift lever and all electrical connections.

6) Remove transmission crossmember. Attach sling to lifting eyes and hoist engine/transmission assembly out at an angle of about 45 degrees. Separate engine/transmission assembly.

Installation

Lower engine/transmission assembly into position and reverse removal procedure to complete installation. Replenish engine fluid levels and check injection pump timing, if necessary.

Removal (300 SDL)

1) Open hood to vertical position. Drain cooling system. Disconnect negative battery cable. Remove air filter with intake duct.

2) Drain oil from power steering pump reservoir and disconnect hoses. Remove A/C compressor and set compressor aside. DO NOT disconnect refrigerant hoses.

3) Remove control linkage with shaft and set aside. Disconnect all coolant, vacuum, oil, fuel, and electrical lines which lead to engine. Loosen oil filter cover and raise slightly. Disconnect exhaust system at turbocharger.

4) Disconnect exhaust pipe at exhaust manifold. Remove lateral support from exhaust pipe at transmission. Remove level control pump and set aside, leaving lines connected.

5) Remove engine mount bolts at chassis. Remove drive shaft shield and disconnect drive shaft at transmission. Disconnect engine shock absorber at chassis. Disconnect shift lever and all electrical connections at transmission.

6) Remove transmission crossmember retaining bolts and remove crossmember. Attach sling to lifting eyes and hoist engine/transmission assembly out at an angle of about 45 degrees. Separate engine/transmission assembly.

Installation

To install engine, reverse removal procedure. Check engine mounts, engine shock absorbers, oil and fuel hoses and replace components as required. Check positioning of heat shields on engine mounts.

INTAKE & EXHAUST MANIFOLDS

Removal

Remove air cleaner assembly. Remove all vacuum lines and electrical connections that would interfere with manifold removal. Remove manifold retaining bolts and remove manifold.

Installation

Clean gasket mating surfaces. Install manifold, using new gasket. Reverse removal procedure to complete installation.

CYLINDER HEAD

Removal

NOTE: **Keep bolts in order during disassembly.**

1) Place hood in vertical position. Drain cooling system. Disconnect negative battery cable and coolant hoses attached to cylinder head. Remove air cleaner. If equipped with level control, remove pump and set aside, leaving lines connected.

2) If equipped with power steering, remove pump with bracket and fuel filter and set aside. Detach all remaining electrical connections, coolant, fuel and vacuum

2.5L 5-CYLINDER & 3.0L 6-CYLINDER TURBO DIESEL (Cont.)

lines from cylinder head and intake manifold. Remove bracket bolt for oil dipstick guide tube.

3) Disconnect exhaust pipe from exhaust manifold and at transmission support. Remove throttle control linkage and set aside. Remove injection lines, and cover all connections. Remove EGR pipe line between EGR valve and exhaust manifold.

4) Remove injection lines and intake manifold. Remove exhaust manifold support at manifold. Remove air intake pipe above valve cover. Remove valve cover. Loosen, but do not remove camshaft sprocket bolt. Rotate crankshaft by using socket tool on crankshaft pulley so that No. 1 cylinder is at TDC on compression stroke.

5) Mark camshaft sprocket and timing chain for reassembly. Remove camshaft and timing gear. Lower timing chain into chain box. Uniformly loosen all camshaft bearing caps. Remove timing chain guide rail from cylinder head. Remove camshaft sprocket.

6) Loosen and remove head bolts in reverse order of tightening sequence. *See Fig. 1.* Attach sling to lifting eyes on head and lift head from engine. Thoroughly clean all mating surfaces of head and cylinder block.

Installation

1) Ensure that No. 1 piston is at TDC. Place head gasket into position. Ensure locating dowels are in correct position. Install cylinder head on block. Install cylinder head bolts. Tighten cylinder head bolts using 4 step angle tightening method (final 2 steps require angle tightening).

2) To complete installation, reverse removal procedure. Adjust valve clearance. Use new seals and gaskets when installing all components. *See Fig. 1.*

CAMSHAFT

TIMING CHAIN

Removal

1) A split link timing chain is available for repairs without dismantling engine. Remove glow plugs and camshaft cover. Remove air cleaner adapter. Cover chain guard with cloth and grind open both pins of a link in the timing chain.

2) Remove old link and insert new split link with new chain attached. Turn crankshaft slowly in direction of rotation. Feed new chain in and old chain out. Ensure that chain does not slip on sprockets. Install master (split) link from rear so that retaining clip will be at front of engine.

Installation

1) Using Chain Press (000 589 57 43 00), place outer flange of connecting link into press. The outer flange is held magnetically. Place chain press on connecting link, and press flange on to stop. Force locking spring in opposite direction of engine rotation into grooves of chain pins.

2) Install chain tensioner. Rotate crankshaft and check adjusting mark in TDC position of engine

Fig. 2: Timing Chain & Related Components

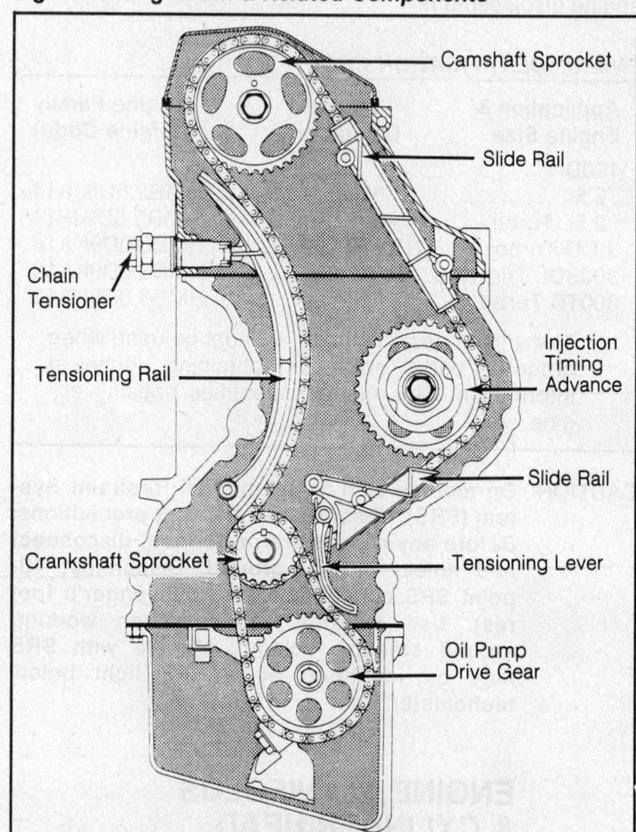

Courtesy of Mercedes-Benz of North America.

Fig. 1: Cylinder Head Tightening Sequence

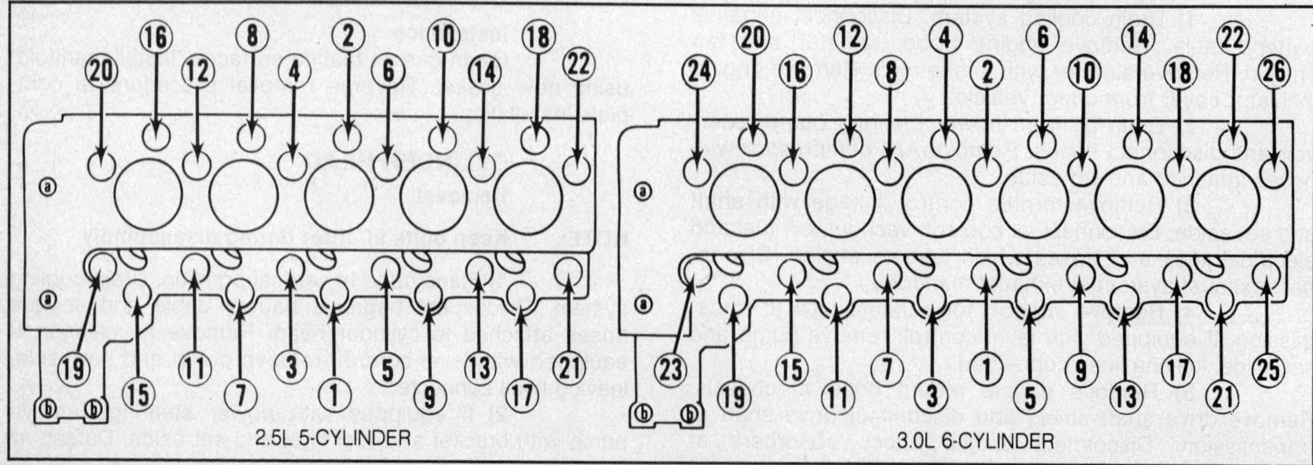

Courtesy of Mercedes-Benz of North America.

2.5L 5-CYLINDER & 3.0L 6-CYLINDER TURBO DIESEL (Cont.)

rotation. If adjusting mark is not as specified, check timing of crankshaft and timing of injection pump. To complete installation, reverse removal procedure.

VALVE TIMING

NOTE: **DO NOT use camshaft sprocket bolt to turn engine. DO NOT rotate engine in reverse direction while checking or setting valve timing.**

1) Remove valve cover and injection nozzles. Turn crankshaft until No. 1 intake cam lobe is pointing upward. Install Dial Indicator Holder (363 589 02 21 00) on cylinder head at No. 1 intake valve.

2) Position dial indicator on valve tappet with a preload of .12" (3.0 mm). Set indicator dial to zero.

3) Dial indicator shaft should be in a vertical position on valve tappet. Turn crankshaft in direction of rotation until intake valve opens .078" (2.00 mm).

4) Check camshaft timing marks. *See Fig. 3.* Crankshaft degree marks should indicate 11 degrees ATDC.

Fig. 3: Camshaft Timing Mark Locations

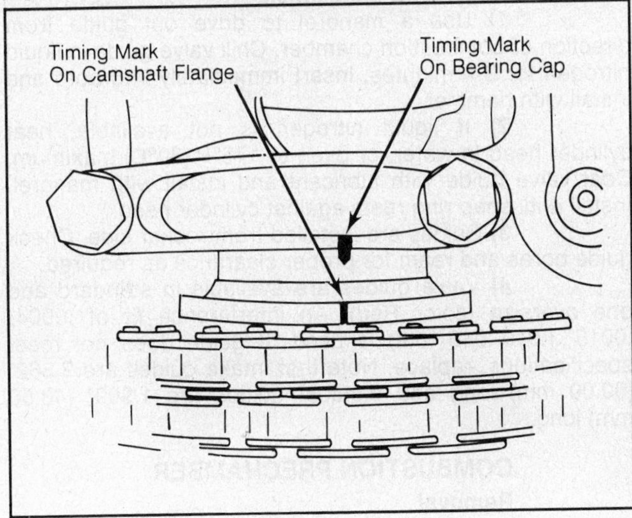

Courtesy of Mercedes-Benz of North America.

CAMSHAFT

NOTE: **DO NOT use camshaft sprocket bolt to rotate engine. DO NOT rotate engine in reverse direction while measuring valve timing.**

Removal

1) Remove valve cover. Set crankshaft to TDC of No. 1 cylinder. Remove chain tensioner. Mark camshaft sprocket/timing chain position. Remove camshaft sprocket.

2) On vehicles with level control, camshaft sprocket and drive sleeve are fastened with a hex head bolt. Remove oil pump, and set pump aside. Leave lines attached.

3) Evenly loosen all camshaft bearing bolts and remove camshaft bearing caps. Remove camshaft in upward direction. Remove and inspect camshaft locating snap ring. Release valve tappets with Vacuum Lifter (601 589 05 33 00).

Installation

1) Install camshaft locating snap ring in cylinder head. Lubricate camshaft and place into cylinder head (without tappets). Position camshaft bearing cap and tighten in sequence to 18 ft. lbs. (25 N.m). Ensure proper placement of bearing caps.

2) When checking camshaft rotation a 30 mm long socket head cap screw may be substituted for the original fastener. If camshaft is hard to turn, loosen bearing caps individually.

NOTE: **If a new camshaft is being installed or cylinder head has been machined, check camshaft for ease of rotation.**

3) Identify tight bearing. Measure camshaft journal and bearing. Polish or machine bearing clearance to .002-.003" (.05-.08 mm). Check camshaft runout.

4) Lubricate and install valve tappets. Install camshaft and bearing caps. Tighten bearing caps uniformly to specification. Install camshaft sprocket. Check valve timing. To complete installation, reverse removal procedure.

CAMSHAFT BEARINGS

1) Inspect camshaft bearings for wear. Replace as necessary. If camshaft journals are worn, grind, and fit undersize bearings.

2) Bearing on No. 1 journal controls camshaft end play. Place bearing on camshaft and install retaining ring.

3) Using a feeler gauge, measure clearance between camshaft flange and bearing. Lap bearing flange to adjust clearance.

VALVES

HYDRAULIC VALVE TAPPETS

NOTE: **Store valve tappets in upright position (open end up). The basic installation dimension of valve tappets cannot be adjusted.**

Removal

1) Run engine 5 minutes at 3000 RPM. Remove valve cover. Set camshaft lobe of respective valve tappet on base circle (camshaft lobe should point upward). Use mandrel to push against valve tappet, or try to move valve tappet manually.

2) If valve tappet has clearance, or compresses quickly, check specifications. Measure and record distance from cylinder head/camshaft cover mating surface to valve tappet. Place measuring bridge over valve tappet on cylinder head surface.

3) Remove camshaft. Re-measure cylinder head surface to tappet. The difference between these measurements is the basic installation dimension. Specifications for new engine is .0010-.063" (.025-1.600 mm). Used engine specification is .0010-.098" (.025-2.489 mm).

4) Remove valve tappet if it compresses quickly or if the basic dimension is not within specification. Measure dimension "L" on valve tappet and record. *See Fig. 4.* Measure dimension "L2" on valve tappet. Dimension "L1" (difference between "L" and "L2") should be .70-.74" (18-19 mm).

Mercedes-Benz Engines

2.5L 5-CYLINDER & 3.0L 6-CYLINDER TURBO DIESEL (Cont.)

5) If dimension "L1" exceeds specifications, remove guide sleeve. Remove sleeve with pliers using a rotary motion. Ensure guide sleeve is not damaged.

6) Remove thrust pin and compression spring from guide sleeve. *See Fig. 4*. Clean components with compressed air. Blow through valve tappet at oil feed bore. Remove snap ring from guide sleeve.

Fig. 4: Hydraulic Valve Tappet Assembly

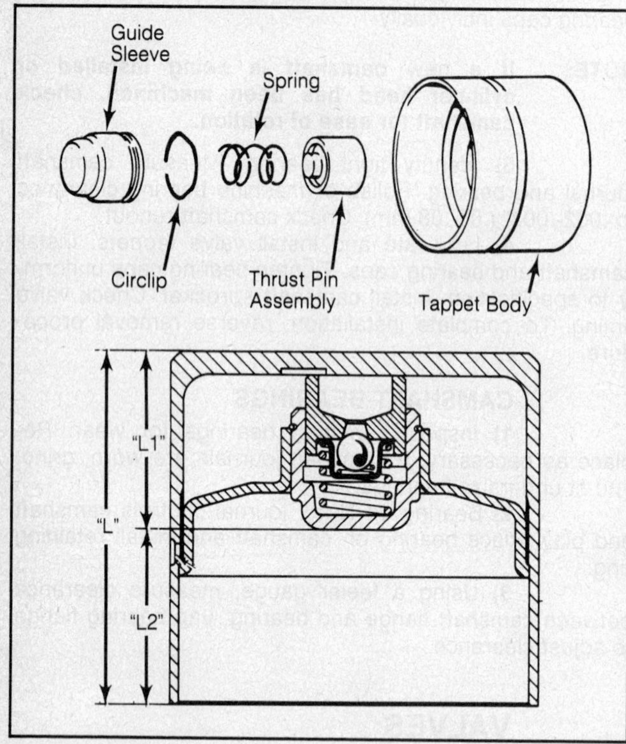

Courtesy of Mercedes-Benz of North America.

Installation

1) Install guide sleeve, compression spring, and thrust pin in valve tappet. Fill thrust pin with engine oil. Press on ball valve with a suitable pin, and purge chamber by pumping action.

2) Close ball valve and add oil, if required. Under light pressure, oil should not leak from ball valve. If oil flows out, replace complete valve tappet. *See Fig. 4*.

3) Fill valve tappet with engine oil and install vented thrust pin with guide. Push guide sleeve into valve tappet until snap ring engages. Check dimension "L1". *See Fig. 4*.

4) Check oil supply in cylinder head. For this purpose, remove plug from oil duct at rear of cylinder head. Blow compressed air into oil duct. Check outlet in tappet bore for oil flow. Lubricate and install valve tappets. To complete installation, reverse removal procedure.

VALVE SPRINGS

Removal

1) With cylinder head removed from cylinder block. Remove camshaft, chain tensioner, cooling fan and fan cover.

2) Remove valve tappets. Set engine at TDC for No. 1 cylinder. Install Supporting Bridge (601 589 02 59 00) on cylinder head, for valve spring compression.

CAUTION: When rotating engine, ensure timing chain is not pulled into timing cover.

3) Push valve spring retainer down with valve spring compressor. Remove valve retainers. Remove valve springs and valve spring retainers.

4) Check valve spring for proper height and tension (replace as necessary). Old valve seal may be pried off with screwdriver or pulled off with pliers.

Installation

Note that intake seals are color-coded Black and exhaust seals are Yellow. Position assembly sleeve over valve stem and press new seal onto guide with Installer (617 589 00 43 00). Install valve spring, collar, lock nut, and adjusting cap. To complete installation, reverse removal procedures.

VALVE GUIDES

Checking Valve Guides

After removal of valve spring and valve stem seal, valve guide wear can be determined by moving valve stem crosswise in relation to engine. Maximum allowed movement is .005" (.12 mm).

Removal & Installation

1) Use a mandrel to drive out guide from direction of combustion chamber. Chill valve guide in liquid nitrogen for 3-4 minutes. Insert immediately into bore and install with hammer.

2) If liquid nitrogen is not available, heat cylinder head in water, or oven to 176°F (80°C) maximum. Coat valve guide with lubricant and install with mandrel. Install until snap ring rests against cylinder head.

3) Guides are installed from rocker side. Check guide bores and ream for proper clearance as required.

4) Valve guides are available in standard and one oversize (color Red). An interference fit of .0004-.0015" (.010-.040 mm) is used. If guide does not meet specifications, replace. Note that intake guides are 2.362" (60.00 mm) long and exhaust guides are 1.909" (48.50 mm) long.

COMBUSTION PRECHAMBER

Removal

1) Remove injection lines from injectors. Loosen holders for injection lines, on intake manifold. Remove fuel return hoses from injection nozzles. Remove fuel pump regulator cable and lay aside. Remove nozzle holders and glow plugs.

2) Loosen threaded ring. Use an Impact Puller (601 589 06 33 00) and threaded mandrel to remove prechamber from cylinder head.

Inspection

1) Check and replace any damaged prechambers. Ball pin should not be burnt or covered with scale. If the burner tops show burn marks or cracks, remove intake manifold and check for traces of oil.

2) If oil moistened spots are found, check vacuum pump for damage or renew vacuum control unit on injection pump. Vacuum lines showing traces of oil will indicate which of the these parts has failed.

Installation

To install, reverse removal procedure. Position prechamber with lug pointing toward recess in cylinder head. Lubricate threaded ring and tighten to specification.

2.5L 5-CYLINDER & 3.0L 6-CYLINDER TURBO DIESEL (Cont.)

PISTON, PINS & RINGS

PISTON & ROD ASSEMBLY

Removal

Remove cylinder head and oil pan. Remove any ridge at top of cylinders. Remove connecting rod with piston. Remove piston pin snap ring and piston pin.

Installation

1) Place piston on connecting rod with arrow on piston crown facing forward. Number marks on rods face the left side of engine (intake manifold side). Coat piston pin with engine oil and press in by hand. Install piston pin snap rings.

2) Using motor oil, lubricate cylinder bores, rod bearing journals, rod bearing shells and pistons. Install rings. *See Fig. 5*. Arrange gaps of piston rings around piston circumference evenly.

3) Fit piston ring compressor and carefully install piston with arrow on crown facing forward. Place connecting rod bearing caps on connecting rods, with cap numbers aligned. Tighten rod cap nuts.

4) Measure piston above top of cylinder block with piston at TDC. Piston should project .020-.035" (.50-.90 mm) above block.

Fig. 5: 3.0L Piston Ring Installation

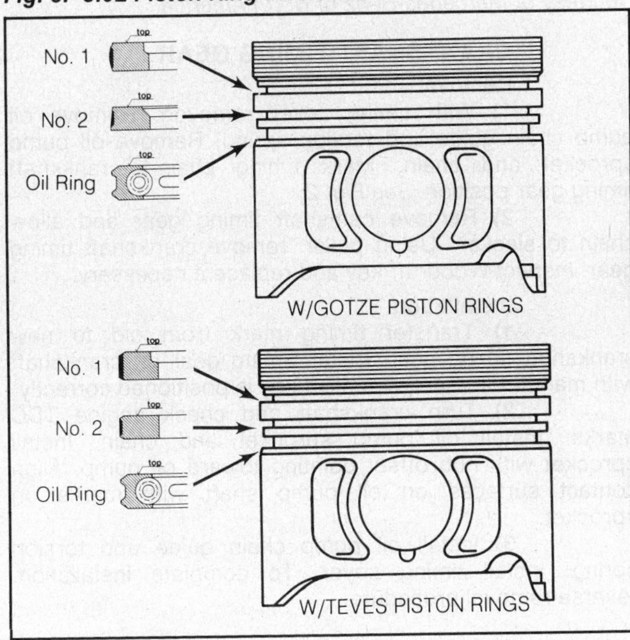

Courtesy of Mercedes-Benz of North America.

CYLINDER BLOCK ASSEMBLY

CYLINDER LINER

Removal & Installation

1) Using mandrel, press out cylinder liners. Clean and measure basic bore in cylinder block. If basic bore is beyond specification, replace engine block.

2) Press in new liners using a press and mandrel. Ensure liners seat in block.

3) Enlarge bore in 2 steps. Leave .0002" (.03 mm) in bores for honing purposes. Chamfer cylinder liners. *See Fig. 6*. Hone and measure cylinder bores and select matching pistons.

Fig. 6: Measuring Cylinder Bore Liner

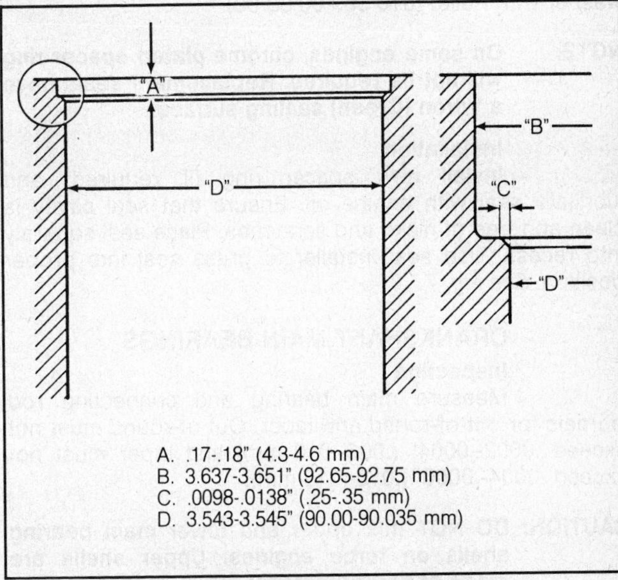

Courtesy of Mercedes-Benz of North America.

CRANKSHAFT & ROD BEARINGS

CRANKSHAFT FRONT OIL SEAL

Removal

Remove radiator and fan shroud. Remove front pulley and vibration damper. Pry old oil seal from

Fig. 7: Sectional View of Front Oil Seal

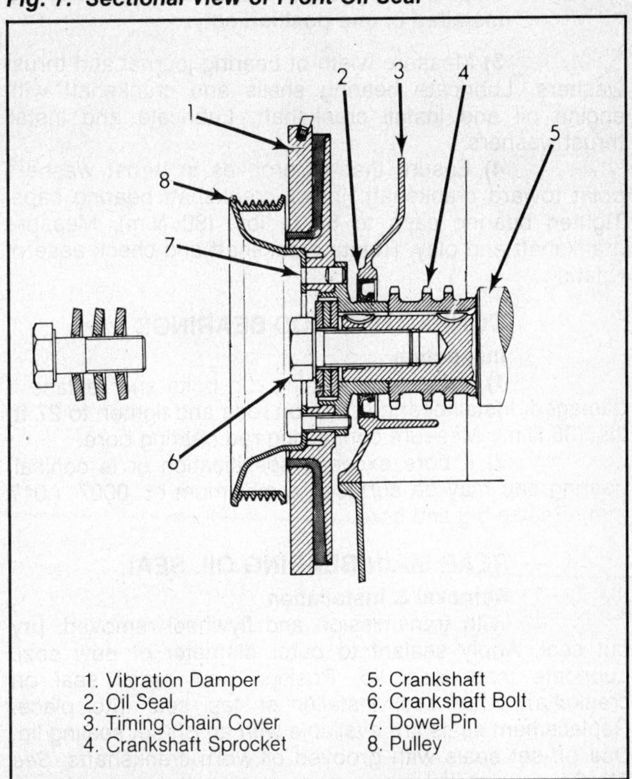

Courtesy of Mercedes-Benz of North America.

Mercedes-Benz Engines

2.5L 5-CYLINDER & 3.0L 6-CYLINDER TURBO DIESEL (Cont.)

front cover. If fitted with original seal, remove spacer washer with Puller (616 589 00 33 00).

NOTE: On some engines, chrome plated spacer ring will not be required. Replacement seals have a Vitron (Green) sealing surface.

Installation

Install new spacer ring (if required) and lubricate seal with engine oil. Ensure that seal cavity is clean and free of nicks and scratches. Place seal squarely into recess. Use seal installer to press seal into proper position. *See Fig. 7*.

CRANKSHAFT MAIN BEARINGS

Inspection

Measure main bearing and connecting rod journals for out-of-round and taper. Out-of-round must not exceed .0002-.0004" (.005-.010 mm) and taper must not exceed .0004-.0006" (.010-.015 mm).

CAUTION: DO NOT mix upper and lower main bearing shells on turbo engines. Upper shells are made of harder material.

Installation

1) Install main bearing and caps. Tighten to 65 ft. lbs. (85 N.m). Measure bearing bore and journal diameter.

2) Bearing clearance may be adjusted by bearing selection. Crankshaft bearing shells without a color code marking are thicker than those with a Blue color code.

NOTE: Main bearing caps are offset and may be installed in one position only.

3) Measure width of bearing journal and thrust washers. Lubricate bearing shells and crankshaft with engine oil and install crankshaft. Lubricate and install thrust washers.

4) Ensure that oil grooves in thrust washers point toward crankshaft. Install crankshaft bearing caps. Tighten bearing caps to 66 ft. lbs. (90 N.m). Measure crankshaft end play. Rotate crankshaft and check ease of rotation.

CONNECTING ROD BEARINGS

Inspection

1) Inspect connecting rod bolts and replace if damaged. Install bearing caps on rods and tighten to 27 ft. lbs. (36 N.m). Measure connecting rod bearing bore.

2) If bore exceeds specification or is conical, bearing cap may be surfaced a maximum of .0007" (.017 mm). Resize big end bore.

REAR MAIN BEARING OIL SEAL

Removal & Installation

With transmission and flywheel removed, pry out seal. Apply sealant to outer diameter of new seal. Lubricate inner seal lip. Position new radial seal on crankshaft. Use seal installer or tap seal into place. Replacement seals are available with an off-set sealing lip. Use off-set seals with grooved or worn crankshafts. *See Fig. 8*.

Fig. 8: Sectional View of Rear Crankshaft Oil Seal

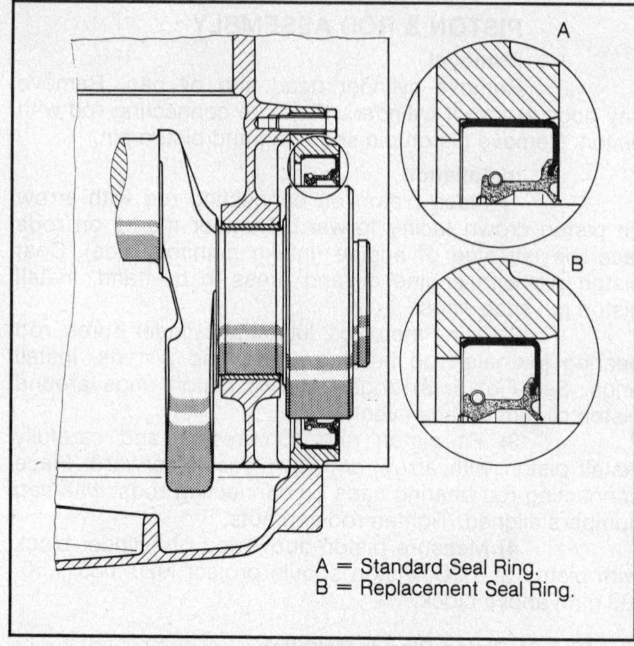

Courtesy of Mercedes-Benz of North America.

CRANKSHAFT TIMING GEAR

Removal

1) With timing cover removed. Remove oil pump chain guide and torsion spring. Remove oil pump sprocket and chain. Mark timing chain-to-crankshaft timing gear position. *See Fig. 2*.

2) Remove camshaft timing gear and allow chain to slacken. Using puller, remove crankshaft timing gear. Inspect Woodruff key and replace if necessary.

Installation

1) Transfer timing mark from old to new crankshaft timing gear. Install timing gear on crankshaft with mandrel. Ensure Woodruff key is positioned correctly.

2) Turn crankshaft and check engine TDC marks. Install oil pump sprocket and chain. Install sprocket with hub offset pointing toward oil pump. Align contact surfaces on oil pump shaft with marks on sprocket.

3) Install oil pump chain guide and torsion spring. Install timing cover. To complete installation, reverse removal procedure.

ENGINE OILING

ENGINE OILING SYSTEM

Engine lubrication is provided by a gear-type oil pump which supplies filtered oil to a main oil gallery. Oil is distributed from the main gallery to main and connecting rod bearings. Pistons, pins and pin bushings are splash lubricated.

A vertical oil passage from the main gallery supplies oil to intermediate sprocket shaft and bearings. Another oil passage supplies oil to oil pump drive shaft and helical gear.

A vertical passage supplies oil to front camshaft bearing. An external oil tube attached to the camshaft bearing lubricates other camshaft bearings and rocker arms.

2.5L 5-CYLINDER & 3.0L 6-CYLINDER TURBO DIESEL (Cont.)

Fig. 9: Engine Lubrication System

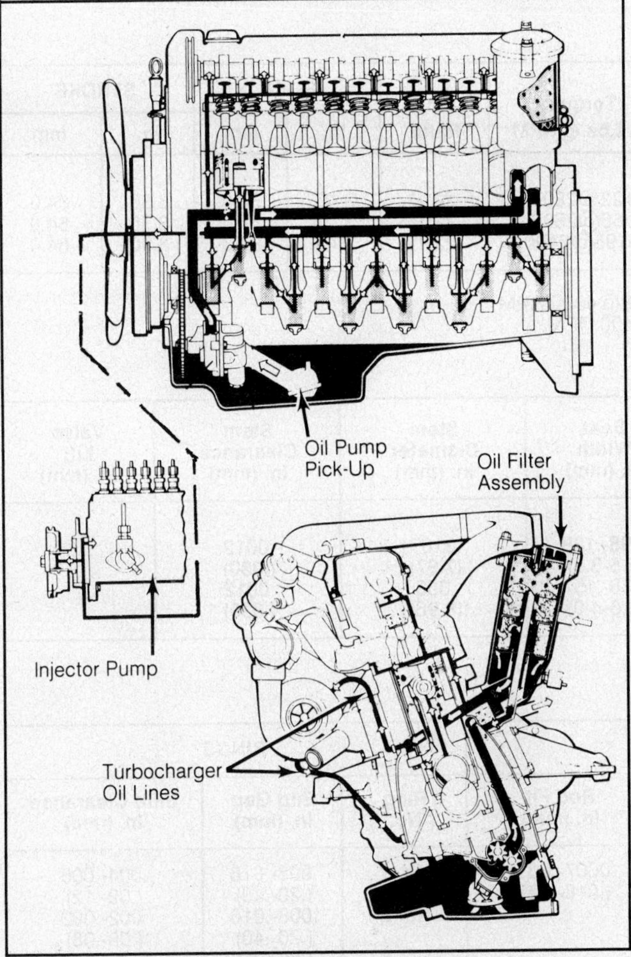

Courtesy of Mercedes-Benz of North America.

OIL PAN

Removal

1) Drain engine oil and raise engine hood to vertical position. Disconnect air cleaner duct and remove throttle control shaft. Disconnect battery. Drain coolant. Disconnect radiator hoses. Loosen fan shroud and place rearward over fan. Disconnect engine shock absorber.

2) Remove engine stop on oil pan. Disconnect drive shaft at transmission. Disconnect shift rods. Raise engine until oil pan can be removed. Disconnect turbo oil return line and RPM sensor (if equipped). Remove oil pan addition from right side of oil pan (3.0L only). Remove oil pan mounting bolts. Rotate crankshaft, if necessary, and remove pan.

Installation

1) Install new radial seal in groove at rear of pan. Ensure that mating surfaces are clean. Coat pan and gasket with sealing compound.

2) Place pan in position and insert dipstick guide tube (if removed). Install oil return line from turbocharger. To complete installation, reverse removal procedure.

OIL PUMP

Removal

Remove oil pan. Oil pump is chain driven and must have sprocket and chain removed prior to removal. Remove oil pump mounting bolts. Remove connecting pipe from engine block. Remove oil pump.

Installation

Use new "O" ring and insert connecting pipe. Ensure that sprocket and chain are properly mounted. Install oil pump. Mount sprocket on oil pump drive shaft and install tensioning rail and spring.

CRANKCASE CAPACITY

CRANKCASE CAPACITY SPECIFICATIONS

Application	Qts. (L)
Total Capacity	
2.5L	8.5 (8.0)
2.5L Turbo	8.7 (8.2)
3.0L	9.7 (9.2)
Oil Change & Filter	
2.5L	7.4 (7.0)
2.5L Turbo	7.4 (7.0)
3.0L	8.5 (8.0)

ENGINE COOLING

WATER PUMP

Removal

Drain cooling system and remove "V" belts. Remove overflow hose on fan shroud. Remove fan shroud and place over engine. Remove collar bolt for cooling fan and remove fan. Remove pulley from water pump. Remove water pump.

Installation

Coat new gasket with sealer, and mount pump on engine. Install fan and hub. Install and adjust belts. Fill radiator and expansion tank and run engine. After temperature reaches about 140°F (60°C), install radiator cap and check for leaks.

NOTE: For more information, see ENGINE COOLING SYSTEMS article at end of this section.

TIGHTENING SPECIFICATIONS

Application	Ft. Lbs. (N.m)
Camshaft Sprocket Bolt	58 (79)
Connecting Rod Caps Bolts	
Step 1	40 (55)
Step 2	Angle Tighten 90 Degrees
Crankshaft Front Hex Bolt	236 (320)
Cylinder Head Bolts (8 mm Bolts)	18 (25)
Cylinder Head Bolts (Hex Head) [1]	
Step 1	18 (25)
Step 2	[1] 30 (40)
Step 3	Angle Tighten 90 Degrees
Step 4	Angle Tighten 90 Degrees
Glow Plugs	36 (49)
Main Bearing Caps Bolts	66 (90)
Nozzle Holder in Prechamber	51-58 (69-79)
Prechamber Bolts	74-81 (100-110)

[1] - Setting time between steps No. 2 and 3 is 10 minutes.

2.5L 5-CYLINDER & 3.0L 6-CYLINDER TURBO DIESEL (Cont.)

ENGINE SPECIFICATIONS

GENERAL SPECIFICATIONS

Year	DISPLACEMENT		Fuel System	HP@RPM	Torque Ft. Lbs.@RPM	Compr. Ratio	BORE		STROKE	
	Cu. In.	Liters					In.	mm	In.	mm
1987										
2.5L	152.4	2.5	Diesel	93@4600	122@2800	22:1	3.43	87.0	3.30	84.0
2.5L Turbo	152.4	2.5	Diesel	123@4600	168@2800	22:1	3.43	87.0	3.30	84.0
3.0L Turbo	183.0	3.0	Diesel	[1] 143@4600	[2] 195@2400	22:1	3.43	87.0	3.30	84.0

[1] – Horsepower rating for the Federal 300SDL (603.961 engine) is 148@4600 RPM.
[2] – Torque rating for the Federal 300SDL (603.961 engine) is 201@2400 RPM.

VALVES

Engine Size & Valve	Head Diam. In. (mm)	Face Angle	Seat Angle	Seat Width In. (mm)	Stem Diameter In. (mm)	Stem Clearance In. (mm)	Valve Lift In. (mm)
2.5L & 3.0L							
Intake	1.520 (38.60)	45°	45°	.098-.138 (2.5-3.5)	.3137 (7.97)	.0012 (.030)	.....
Exhaust	1.377 (35.00)	45°	45°	.138-.157 (3.5-4.0)	.353 (8.96)	.0012 (.030)	.....

PISTONS, PINS & RINGS

Engine	PISTONS Clearance In. (mm)	PINS Piston Fit In. (mm)	PINS Rod Fit In. (mm)	RINGS Ring No.	RINGS End Gap In. (mm)	RINGS Side Clearance In. (mm)
2.5L & 3.0L	.0006-.0017 (.015-.043)	.0002-.0006 (.004-.015)	.0007-.0011 (.018-.029)	No. 1	.008-.016 (.20-.40)	.004-.005 (.09-.12)
				No. 2	.008-.016 (.20-.40)	.002-.003 (.05-.08)
				No. 3	.008-.016 (.20-.40)	.001-.0025 (.03-.065)

CRANKSHAFT MAIN & CONNECTING ROD BEARINGS

Engine	MAIN BEARINGS				CONNECTING ROD BEARINGS		
	Journal Diam. In. (mm)	Clearance In. (mm)	Thrust Bearing	Crankshaft End Play In. (mm)	Journal Diam. In. (mm)	Clearance In. (mm)	Side Play In. (mm)
2.5L & 3.0L	2.2815-2.2820 (57.95-57.96)	.0012-.0029 (.031-.073)	Center	.002-.009 (.05-.22)	1.8878-1.8883 (47.95-47.96)	.0012-.0029 (.031-.073)	.005-.010 (.12-.26)

VALVE SPRINGS

Engine	Free Length In. (mm)	PRESSURE Lbs. @ In. (Kg @ mm)	
		Valve Closed	Valve Open
2.5L & 3.0L	2.0 (50.8)	189.8@1.06 (850@27)	130.1@1.80 (648@28.5)

CAMSHAFT

Engine	Journal Diam. In. (mm)	Clearance In. (mm)	Lobe Lift In. (mm)
2.5L & 3.0L	1.218-1.2185 (30.94-30.95)	.002-.004 (.05-.10)	.....

Mercedes-Benz Engines

2.6L & 3.0L 6-CYLINDER

190E, 260E, 300E

NOTE: For engine repair procedures not covered in this article, see ENGINE OVERHAUL PROCEDURES article at beginning of this section.

ENGINE CODING

ENGINE IDENTIFICATION

The engine family designation is shown on the emission control information plate (attached to radiator crossmember). The 1st character identifies the model year ("H" for 1987) while the 4th and 5th characters identify the engine displacement. Engine code is also stamped on a machined pad just below second freeze plug.

ENGINE IDENTIFICATION CODE

Application & Engine Size	Engine [1] Designation	Engine Family (Engine Code)
190E 2.6L	103.942	HMB2.6V6FA18
260E 2.6L	103.940	HMB2.6V6FA18
300E 3.0L	103.983	HMB3.0V6FA12

[1] - The engine designation code must be used when ordering parts or when obtaining technical information. This number identifies specific engine.

CAUTION: On models with Supplemental Restraint System (SRS), observe the following precautions: Before any repairs are performed, disconnect and shield battery ground. Disconnect 10-point SRS connector under passenger's foot rest. Use extreme caution when working around steering column. Models with SRS may be identified by a SRS light below tachometer.

ENGINE, MANIFOLDS & CYLINDER HEAD

ENGINE

Removal (300E)

1) Raise hood to vertical position. Drain cooling system. Remove air cleaner. Disconnect negative battery cable.

2) On vehicles with level control, remove pressure pump with lines, and set aside. Remove A/C drier assembly and hose from compressor.

3) Disconnect all coolant, fuel, vacuum and electric lines at cylinder head and intake manifold. Disconnect throttle linkage. Pull throttle cable through slot bracket.

4) Remove valve cover with ignition cables and distributor cap. To remove distributor cap, use a "T" handle 5 mm hex wrench about 2 1/2" long. Remove distributor rotor.

NOTE: DO NOT rotate engine using camshaft sprocket bolt. DO NOT rotate engine in reverse direction. Prior to rotating crankshaft, switch off ignition and insert Safety Plug (102 589 02 21 21 00) into diagnosis socket.

5) Drain oil from power steering pump and disconnect hoses. Pull cable for TDC transmitter from test socket and remove test socket.

6) Disconnect engine shock absorber from frame side member. Remove engine stop bracket.

7) Disconnect drive shaft from transmission. Loosen slide piece as well as fastening bolts for drive shaft intermediate bearing. Push back propeller shaft as far as possible. Partially remove heat guide plate in vehicle floor.

8) Disconnect exhaust system at exhaust manifold. Disconnect speedometer at transmission cover. On manual transmission models, disconnect hydraulic line from clutch master cylinder. On automatic transmission models, remove lines to transmission oil cooler (plug ends of lines and fittings).

9) Attach hoist to lifting eyes on engine and take up slack. Remove rear engine support. From below, disconnect bolts on front engine mounts. Remove engine and transmission at a 45 degree angle.

Installation

1) To install, reverse removal procedure. Check engine mounts, engine shock absorber, coolant, oil and fuel hoses and replace if necessary. Before installing manual transmission, check pilot bearing on rear of crankshaft and release bearing, replace if necessary.

2) Check for proper installation of shielding on right front engine mount. Adjust engine stop. Recharge A/C system. Check ignition timing and idle speed adjustment.

CYLINDER HEAD

Removal (300E)

1) Remove lower splash panels. Drain coolant. Remove air filter assembly. Remove valve cover and ignition cables. Remove distributor cap and rotor.

2) Remove distributor drive plate and protective cover. Remove mounting bolts for distributor drive cover. Carefully tap off cover. Set crankshaft at TDC for No. 1 cylinder.

3) Remove chain tensioner plug and spring. Remove threaded ring and chain tensioner. Mark position of camshaft sprocket to camshaft. Apply paint dot adjacent to hole (in camshaft sprocket) with dowel pin.

4) Mark chain link and camshaft sprocket with paint dots. Remove 3 mounting bolts and pull off camshaft sprocket. Remove chain guide locating pin with impact puller.

5) Remove bracket for oil dipstick guide tube. Remove top bolt from intake manifold support bracket and

Fig. 1: Cylinder Head Tightening Sequence

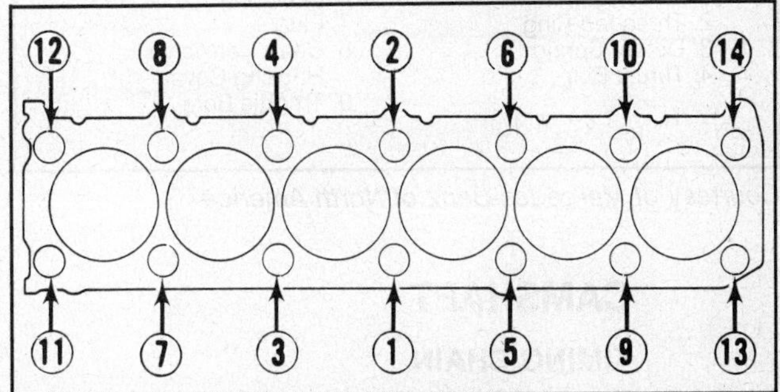

Courtesy of Mercedes-Benz of North America.

Mercedes-Benz Engines

2.6L & 3.0L 6-CYLINDER (Cont.)

loosen bottom bolt. Loosen hose clamp on coolant hose at water pump.

6) Disconnect exhaust system at exhaust manifold flanges. On automatic transmission equipped models, remove bracket for dipstick tube. Disconnect all electrical wiring.

7) Relieve pressure in fuel tank by opening and closing fuel tank cap. Disconnect fuel lines. Disconnect accelerator cable. Remove cylinder head bolts. Remove cylinder head with intake and exhaust manifolds attached.

Installation

1) Install new cylinder head gasket. Ensure head gasket is positioned on locating pins. With engine cold, tighten cylinder head bolts in proper sequence. *See Fig. 1.*

2) If camshaft was removed, set No. 1 piston at TDC. Lubricate camshaft and install with mark on camshaft flange aligned with mark on front camshaft bearing cap. *See Fig. 4.*

3) Clean sealing surfaces on cylinder head and top timing cover. Apply a small amount of sealer to groove, on left and right side of upper timing cover. Install contoured gasket in groove.

4) Install front cover using Guide Sleeve (103 589 00 14 00). Tighten 2 lower bolts first. Install cover, seal, and distributor driver. To complete installation, reverse removal procedure.

NOTE: Chain tensioner must be disassembled prior to installation. Pull thrust bolt toward right side of chain tensioner housing. See Fig. 2.

Fig. 2: Timing Chain Tensioner Assembly

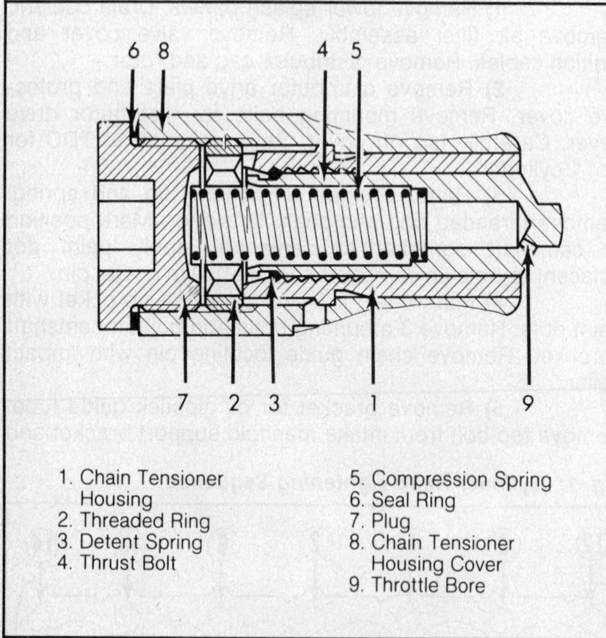

Courtesy of Mercedes-Benz of North America.

CAMSHAFT

TIMING CHAIN

Removal & Installation

1) A master link (split) timing chain is available for replacement without dismantling engine. Remove air cleaner, valve cover and spark plugs. Use a chain link remover to remove master link from timing chain.

2) Remove old link and insert new master link with new chain attached. Turn crankshaft (by hand) slowly in direction of rotation while feeding new chain in and removing old chain. Ensure that chain does not slip on sprockets. Install master link from rear so retainer will be at front of engine.

3) Install connecting link clip with closed end facing direction of rotation. Rotate crankshaft through one complete revolution and check that all timing marks are aligned. To complete installation, reverse removal procedure.

Fig. 3: Timing Chain & Sprockets

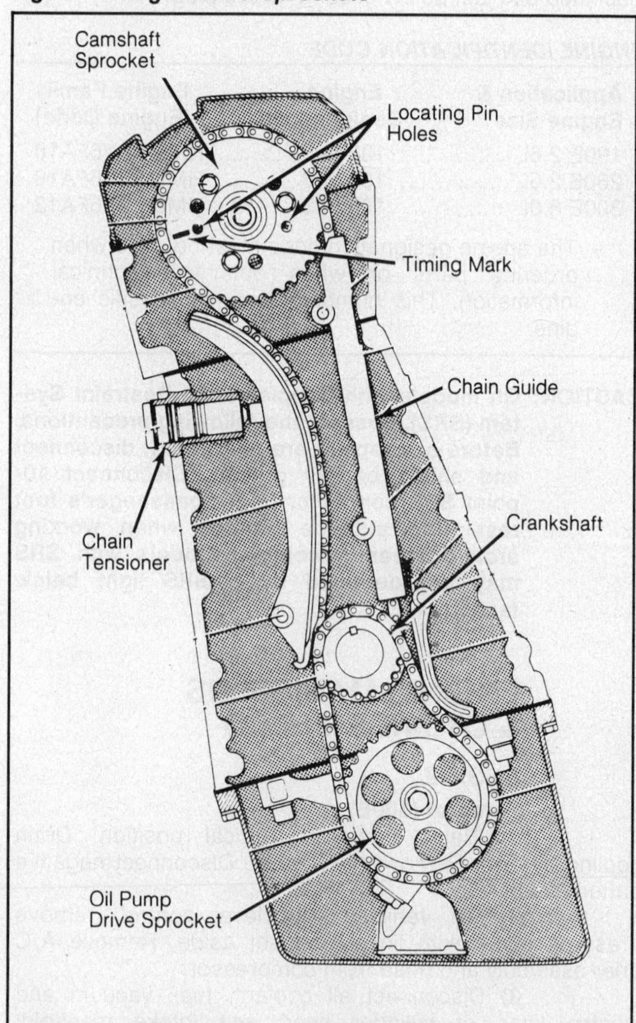

Courtesy of Mercedes-Benz of North America.

CAMSHAFT

Removal

1) Remove air cleaner and valve cover. Set No. 1 piston at TDC. Ensure that mark on flange of camshaft is aligned with mark on front camshaft bearing cap. *See Fig. 4.*

2) Mark camshaft sprocket and timing chain in relation to each other. Remove chain tensioner plug and spring. Remove threaded ring and chain tensioner.

3) Remove distributor cap and rotor. Remove distributor drive plate and protective cover. Remove

2.6L & 3.0L 6-CYLINDER (Cont.)

mounting bolts and distributor drive cover. Remove camshaft mounting bolts and sprocket.

4) Remove rocker arm bearing caps and camshaft. Check lobes of camshaft for wear or scoring. Replace camshaft if necessary. If camshaft bearing bores are damaged, a camshaft with oversized bearing journals is available as a replacement.

Fig. 4: Camshaft Timing Marks

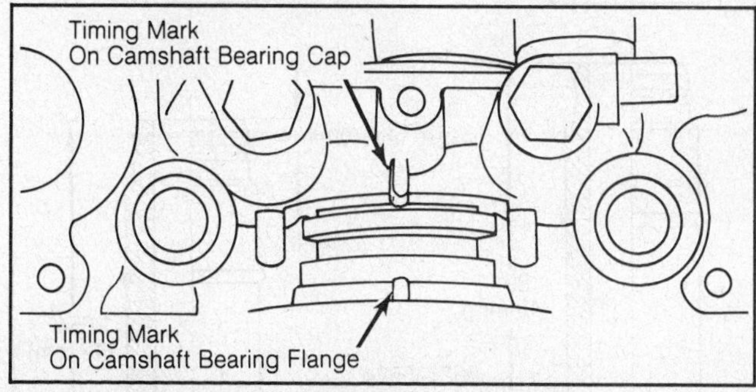

Courtesy of Mercedes-Benz of North America.

Installation

To install, reverse removal procedure. Ensure that identifying marks on camshaft sprocket and timing chain are aligned. Check alignment of mark on camshaft with mark on camshaft bearing cap. *See Fig. 4*.

CAMSHAFT TIMING

Checking

1) Using an adjustable rocker arm from another engine, fabricate a modified rocker arm to check camshaft timing. *See Fig. 5*. Remove valve cover and distributor guard.

2) Replace rocker arm with modified rocker arm, and set valve clearance to zero. Install dial indicator on cylinder head. Position indicator shaft parallel to valve stem for No. 1 intake valve and against valve spring retainer.

3) Position crankshaft to TDC for No. 1 cylinder. Ensure timing marks on camshaft and bearing cap are aligned. Preload indicator shaft .120" (3.0 mm) and zero dial indicator.

Fig. 5: Modified Rocker Arm For Checking Cam Timing

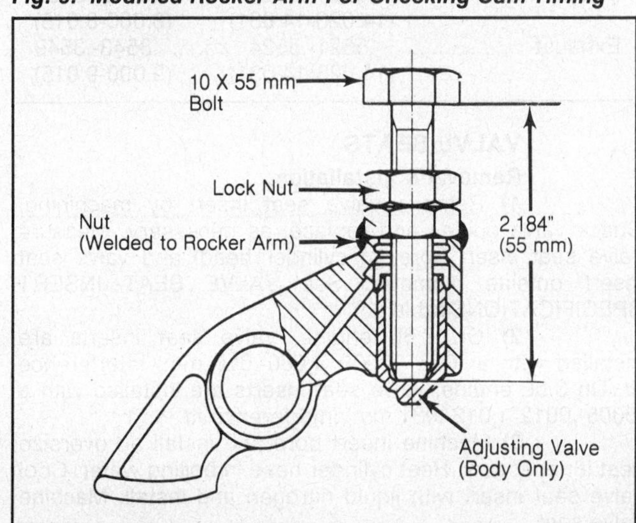

Courtesy of Mercedes-Benz of North America.

4) Turn crankshaft in direction of rotation until indicator reads .080" (2 mm). Read degrees on crankshaft. Intake valve should be open at 11.5 degrees after TDC. Exhaust valve should be open 18.6 degrees before BDC.

Adjustment

Adjust camshaft timing if not within 2 degrees of specification. Reverse the camshaft drive sprocket or select one of the alternate, alignment pin, holes to change timing 3 degrees. *See Fig. 3*.

VALVES

VALVE ARRANGEMENT

Intake Manifold Side – Intake Valves
Exhaust Manifold Side – Exhaust Valves

ROCKER ARM ASSEMBLIES

Removal

Remove valve cover. Position camshaft lobes of rocker arms to be removed downward. Remove camshaft bearing cap. Remove rocker pivot shaft. Shaft is threaded internally to aid removal. Use a bolt or slide hammer if shaft is tight.

Installation

1) Insert compensating valves. Ensure they are installed in their original rocker arm. Lubricate all bearing bores and shafts.

2) Before installing camshaft bearing cap, rotate crankshaft so that respective camshaft lobes are pointing downward. Install bearing cap No. 1 first and tighten to specification.

3) Install camshaft sprocket and other bearing brackets in sequence. To complete installation, reverse procedure. Check camshaft timing.

Fig. 6: Sectional View of Rocker Arm Assembly

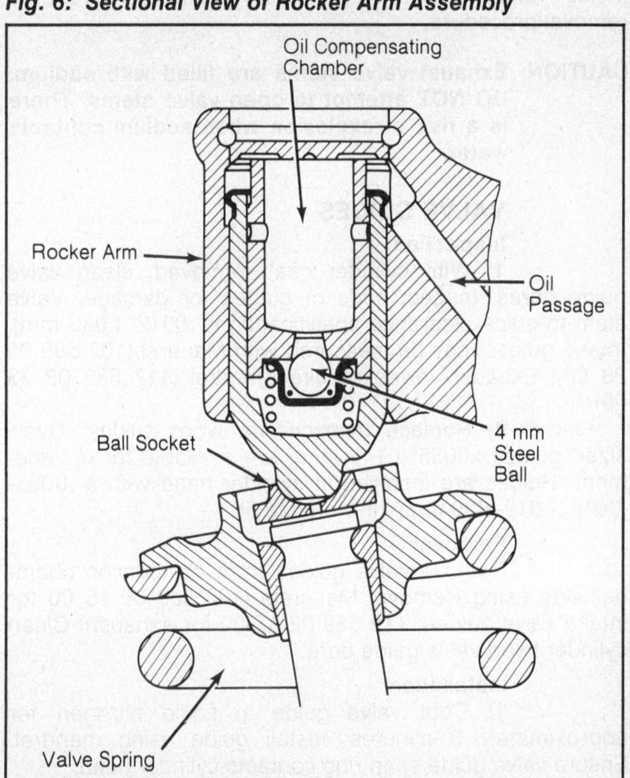

Courtesy of Mercedes-Benz of North America.

Mercedes-Benz Engines

2.6L & 3.0L 6-CYLINDER (Cont.)

VALVE SPRINGS

Removal (Off Vehicle)

1) Fasten cylinder head with 4 cylinder head bolts on Assembly Fixture (102 589 00 59 00). Remove camshaft and rocker arms.

2) Install Supporting Bridge (102 589 01 59 00) on cylinder head and remove valve springs with Valve Spring Compressor (102 589 00 61 00).

Removal (On Vehicle)

1) Remove air cleaner, valve cover, and spark plugs. Set engine to TDC for desired cylinder. Remove oil pipe and rocker arm assembly. Install Support Bracket (102 589 01 61 00) for spring compressor.

2) Connect cylinder leak tester and pressurize cylinder. Attach spring compressor to support bracket and position on valve spring retainer. Compress valve spring and remove valve retainer. DO NOT remove valve spring without compressed air in cylinder.

Inspection

Check valve springs with a valve spring tester or a valve spring scale. Check spring force at specified length. If not within specifications, replace spring.

Installation

To install, reverse removal procedure. Install camshaft bearing cap with oil pipe mounting lug facing rearward and numbers matched to cylinder head.

VALVE STEM OIL SEALS

Removal & Installation

1) Remove valve springs. Pry off valve seals. DO NOT damage valve stem or valve guide. Ensure valve seal are installed on the proper valve guide. *See Fig. 7*.

2) Deburr valve stem or groove. Replace dented valve cone halves, spring retainers, and pressure rings. Lubricate valve stem seal and push on manually. Install valve spring. To complete installation, reverse removal procedure.

CAUTION: Exhaust valve stems are filled with sodium. DO NOT attempt to open valve stems. There is a risk of explosion when sodium contacts water.

VALVE GUIDES

Inspection

1) With cylinder head removed, clean valve guide bores. Inspect ends of guides for damage. Valve stem-to-guide clearance specification is .0012" (.030 mm). Intake guides may be measured with Mandrel (102 589 00 23 00). Exhaust valves require Mandrel (117 589 03 23 00).

2) Replace damaged or worn guides. Oversized guides, .0055" (.140 mm), are available for replacement. Guides are installed in cylinder head with a .0005-.0012" (.012-.030 mm) interference fit.

Removal

Remove valve guides from combustion chamber side using Removal Mandrels (102 589 06 15 00 for intake valve guides; 110 589 02 15 00 for exhaust). Clean cylinder head valve guide bore.

Installation

1) Cool valve guide in liquid nitrogen for approximately 3 minutes. Install guide using mandrel. Ensure valve guide snap ring contacts cylinder head.

Fig. 7: Valve Seals & Guides

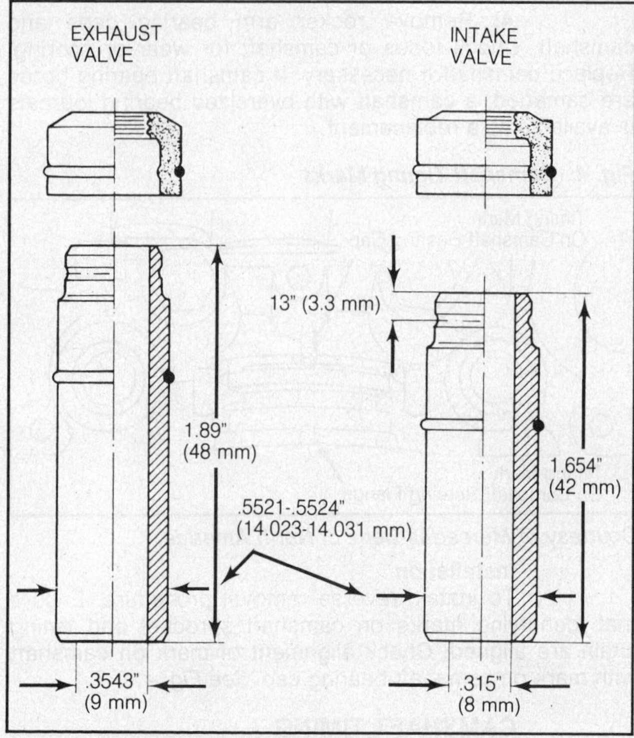

Courtesy of Mercedes-Benz of North America.

2) Ream valve guide I.D. to specified diameter. See VALVE GUIDE SPECIFICATIONS table. Always rotate reamer in clockwise direction. Check bore diameter using mandrel or go-no-go gauge.

3) If oversized guides are required, measure replacement guide. Ream cylinder head valve guide bore for interference fit. Check bore of valve guide with mandrel. Check valve seat for runout. Grind or lap valve seat as necessary.

VALVE GUIDE SPECIFICATIONS

Application	O.D. In. (mm)	I.D. In. (mm)
Intake	.5521-.5524 (14.023-14.031)	.3149-.3155 (8.000-8.015)
Exhaust	.5521-.5524 (14.023-14.031)	.3543-.3549 (9.000-9.015)

VALVE SEATS

Removal & Installation

1) Remove valve seat insert by machining. Check valve guides and replace, as necessary. Measure valve seat insert bore (in cylinder head) and valve seat insert outside diameter. See VALVE SEAT INSERT SPECIFICATIONS table.

2) On 2.6L engine, valve seat inserts are installed with a .0031-.0039" (.080-.010 mm) interference fit. On 3.0L engine, valve seat inserts are installed with a .0005-.0012" (.012-.031 mm) interference fit.

3) Machine insert bore and install an oversize seat if necessary. Heat cylinder head in boiling water. Cool valve seat insert with liquid nitrogen and install. Machine valve seat.

Mercedes-Benz Engines

2.6L & 3.0L 6-CYLINDER (Cont.)

VALVE SEAT INSERT SPECIFICATIONS

Application	Bore In. (mm)	O.D. In. (mm)
Exhaust Valve		
2.6L	1.476-1.477 (37.50-37.51)	1.479-1.480 (37.59-37.60)
3.0L	1.633-1.634 (41.50-41.51)	1.637-1.638 (41.59-41.60)
Intake Valve		
2.6L	1.673-1.674 (42.50-42.51)	1.677-1.678 (42.59-42.60)
3.0L	1.791-1.792 (45.50-45.51)	1.795-1.796 (45.59-45.60)

VALVE CLEARANCE ADJUSTMENT

Engine is equipped with hydraulic valve lifters, valve clearance adjustment is not necessary.

PISTONS, PINS & RINGS

PISTON & ROD ASSEMBLY

Removal

1) Remove engine from vehicle. Remove cylinder head, front timing cover, and oil pan. Remove connecting rod nuts and bearing caps. Check for any cylinder ridge lip and remove as necessary.

2) Push piston and rod assembly out top of cylinder. During removal, use care not to damage bearing surface. Remove piston pin snap ring and push out piston pin. Retain all components in proper order for reassembly.

Inspection

1) Check connecting rod for overheating discoloration and bearing damage. Check connecting rod bolts and replace if necessary.

Fig. 8: Top & Side View of Piston

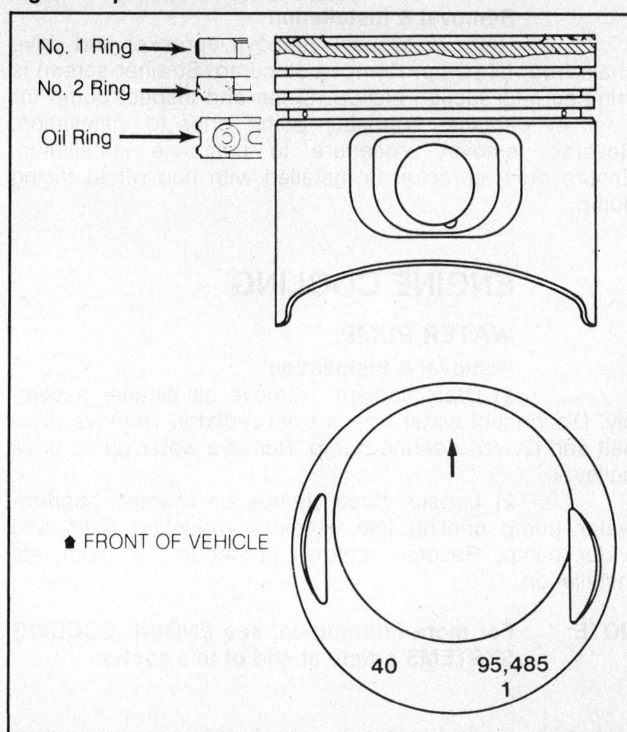

Courtesy of Mercedes-Benz of North America.

2) Assemble connecting rod bearing cap and tighten connecting rod nuts. Measure connecting rod bearing bore. If bore diameter exceeds specifications by .0002" (.005 mm), replace connecting rods.

3) Check piston rings for land clearance and end gap. Ensure piston rings rotate freely. Use engine oil to lubricate pistons. Pin fit into piston is a push fit.

Installation

1) To install, reverse removal procedure. Lubricate piston pins and connecting rod bushings. Position oil spray hole in connecting rod to point toward front of engine. Push piston pin in manually. Install piston pin snap rings.

2) Lubricate cylinder bores, connecting rod bearing journals, connecting rod bearing shells and pistons. Place ring compressor on pistons and push pistons into cylinder bores. Arrow on top of piston faces toward front of engine. *See Fig. 8.*

PISTON & CYLINDER DIAMETERS

Piston Size & Group	Piston Diameter (mm)	Cylinder Diameter (mm)
Standard		
0	95.468-95.482	95.498-95.508
1	95.478-95.492	95.508-95.518
2	95.488-95.502	95.518-95.528
.5 mm Oversize		
0	95.968-95.982	95.998-96.008
1	95.978-95.992	96.008-96.018
2	95.988-96.002	96.018-96.028
1.0 mm Oversize		
0	96.468-96.482	96.498-96.508
1	96.478-96.492	96.508-96.518
2	96.488-96.502	96.518-96.528

CRANKSHAFT & ROD BEARINGS

FRONT TIMING COVER

Removal

1) Drain engine coolant. Disconnect negative battery terminal. Remove air cleaner and radiator. Loosen pivot bolt 1/4 turn and turn adjusting nut to loosen drive belt. *See Fig. 9.*

2) Remove drive belt. Remove valve cover. Set engine to TDC of No. 1 cylinder. Remove cooling fan and belt tensioning assembly. Remove distributor cover.

3) Remove distributor, drive, and upper timing cover section. Remove crankshaft front pulley. Remove front pan bolts from timing cover.

4) Remove timing chain tensioner. *See Fig. 3.* Remove front cover bolts and pry cover forward, off locating dowels.

Installation

1) Clean all mating surfaces. Lightly glue front cover gasket in place at several points. Coat sealing surface of timing cover with sealing compound. Carefully install timing cover. Ensure oil pan gasket is not damaged.

2) If timing cover seal has been removed, install seal. Install upper timing cover with new gaskets.

Mercedes-Benz Engines

2.6L & 3.0L 6-CYLINDER (Cont.)

Install distributor drive and rotor. To complete installation, reverse removal procedure.

Fig. 9: Drive Belt Tensioning Assembly

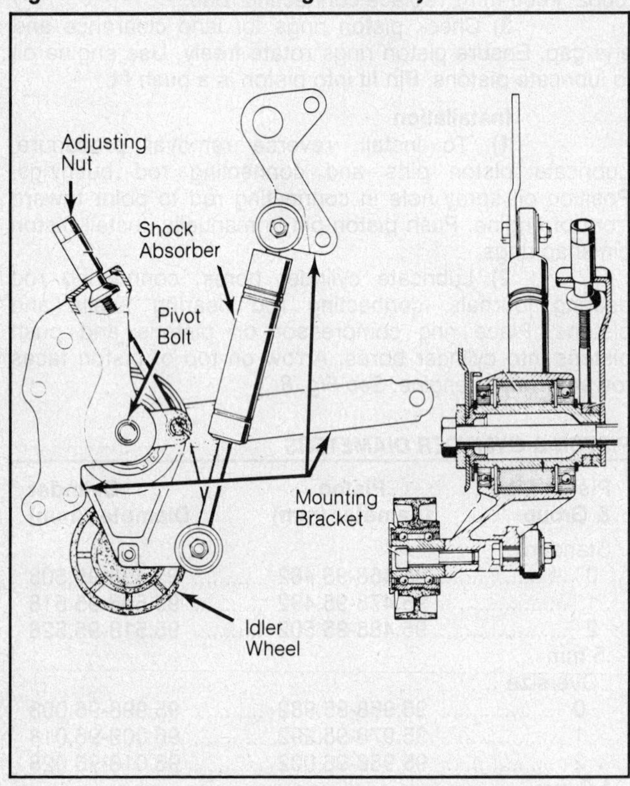

Courtesy of Mercedes-Benz of North America.

CRANKSHAFT MAIN BEARINGS

Inspection

1) Remove crankshaft from engine block. Clean crankshaft and inspect journals for cracks or damage. Cracked crankshafts must be replaced.

2) Damaged crankshafts may be reground. Journals must be hardened after grinding. Replace crankshaft if hardness test fails.

NOTE: **The register for the main bearing cap is offset .020" (.5 mm) from center. Bearing caps can only be installed in one direction.**

3) Install main caps. Lubricate main cap bolts and tighten to specification. Measure line bore. If line boring is necessary, DO NOT remove more than .008" (.02 mm) from main caps.

4) Install crankshaft bearings, and caps. Tighten to specification. Measure bearing diameter and record measurement. Measure crankshaft bearing journals and determine bearing clearance. Standard size bearings are color coded within the standard size tolerance range.

5) Standard size crankshaft bearing shells with Red identification markings are thicker than those with Yellow or Green markings. Bearings may be changed to obtain the correct clearance.

Installation

1) Lubricate bearing shells and crankshaft with engine oil and install crankshaft. Lubricate and install thrust washers and in registers in block and bearing cap.

2) Ensure that oil reliefs in thrust washers face toward crankshaft webs. Install crankshaft bearing caps and tighten to specification. Measure crankshaft bearing end play. Rotate crankshaft manually and check for binding.

CONNECTING ROD BEARINGS

Inspection

Axial movement of connecting rods is controlled by thrust surfaces in piston. Inspect thrust surfaces of small end bore. Small end bushing size is .8664-.8667" (22.007-22.013 mm). Big end bearing bore is 2.0315-2.0322" (51.600-51.619 mm). Install connecting rods on pistons with spray hole pointing towards front of engine.

NOTE: **When replacing connecting rods, ensure there is no difference in weight of connecting rods. Connecting rods are divided into 2 weight groups and are identified with one or 2 punch marks on bottom of connecting rod cap.**

ENGINE OILING

CRANKCASE CAPACITY

Total oil capacity is 6.9 qts. (6.5L). When changing the oil and filter 6.3 qts. (6.0L) of oil is required. An oil change only, requires 6 qts. (5.7L).

NORMAL OIL PRESSURE

Oil pressure should be 7.1 psi (.5 kg/cm²) at 700-780 RPM idle speed; 42 psi (3 kg/cm²) at 3000 RPM.

OIL PUMP

The oil pump is located in the oil pan and is chain driven from a sprocket at the front of the crankshaft. The oil pressure relief valve is in the oil pump and is set to open at 71 psi (5.0 kg/cm²).

Removal & Installation

Remove oil pan. Remove sprocket and drive chain from oil pump. Remove oil pump. Strainer screen is crimped into suction pickup. Clean and inspect pump for wear or damage. Lubricate pump prior to installation. Reverse removal procedure to complete installation. Ensure drive sprocket is installed with hub offset facing pump.

ENGINE COOLING

WATER PUMP

Removal & Installation

1) Drain coolant. Remove air cleaner assembly. Disconnect water hoses from radiator. Remove drive belt and power steering pump. Remove water pump drive pulley.

2) Loosen hose clamps on cylinder head-to-water pump cooling line. Remove mounting bolts and water pump. Reverse removal procedures to complete installation.

NOTE: **For more information, see ENGINE COOLING SYSTEMS article at end of this section.**

Mercedes-Benz Engines

2.6L & 3.0L 6-CYLINDER (Cont.)

ENGINE SPECIFICATIONS

NOTE: Complete specification information on 2.6L engine not available from manufacturer.

GENERAL SPECIFICATIONS

Year	DISPLACEMENT		Fuel System	HP@RPM	Torque Ft. Lbs.@RPM	Compr. Ratio	BORE		STROKE	
	Cu. In.	Liters					In.	mm	In.	mm
1987										
2.6L	158.6	2.6	Fuel Inj.	158@5800	162@4600	9.2:1	3.26	82.9	3.16	80.3
3.0L	180.8	3.0	Fuel Inj.	177@5700	188@4400	9.2:1	3.48	88.5	3.16	80.3

VALVES

Engine Size & Valve	Head Diam. In. (mm)	Face Angle	Seat Angle	Seat Width In. (mm)	Stem Diameter In. (mm)	Stem Clearance In. (mm)	Valve Lift In. (mm)
3.0L							
Intake	1.53 (43.0)	45°	45°	.071-.098 (1.8-2.5)	.3919-.3925 (9.955-9.970)	.0012-.0018 (.030-.045)	.....
Exhaust	1.53 (39.0)	45°	45°	.059-.098 (1.5-2.5)	.3518-.3527 (8.938-8.960)	.015-.0025 (.040-.062)	.....

PISTONS, PINS & RINGS

Engine	PISTONS	PINS		RINGS		
	Clearance In. (mm)	Piston Fit In. (mm)	Rod Fit In. (mm)	Ring No.	End Gap In. (mm)	Side Clearance In. (mm)
3.0L	.0007.-0015 (.017-.038)	.0005-.0007 (.013-.018)	.0003-.0007 (.008-.018)	No. 1	.012-.022 (.304-.558)	.002-.003 (.050-.076)
				No. 2	.012-.022 (.304-.558)	.0004-.0012 (.010-.016)
				Oil	.010-.016 (.254-.406)	.0004-.0018 (.010-.045)

CRANKSHAFT MAIN & CONNECTING ROD BEARINGS

Engine	MAIN BEARINGS				CONNECTING ROD BEARINGS		
	Journal Diam. In. (mm)	Clearance In. (mm)	Thrust Bearing	Crankshaft End Play In. (mm)	Journal Diam. In. (mm)	Clearance In. (mm)	Side Play In. (mm)
3.0L	2.2817-2.2819 (57.955-57.960)	.0010-.0018 (.025-.045)	No. 5	.002-.009 (.051-.228)	1.8880-1.8884 (47.955-47.965)	.0010-.0018 (.025-.045)	.004-.010 (.10-.25)

CAMSHAFT

Engine	Journal Diam. In. (mm)	Clearance In. (mm)	Lobe Lift In. (mm)
Standard	1.2178-1.2185 (30.934-30.950)	.0004-.002 (.010-.051)	.....
Oversize	1.2375-1.2380 (31.434-31.450)	.0004-.002 (.010-.051)	.....

VALVE SPRINGS

Engine	Free Length In. (mm)	PRESSURE Lbs. @ In. (Kg @ mm)	
		Valve Closed	Valve Open
3.0L In. & Ex.	1.93 (49.0)	.....	171-203@1.20" (77-92@30.5)

Mercedes-Benz Engines

2.6L & 3.0L 6-CYLINDER (Cont.)

ENGINE SPECIFICATIONS (Cont.)

VALVE TIMING

Engine	INTAKE		EXHAUST	
	Open (BTDC)	Close (ABDC)	Open (BBDC)	Close (ATDC)
2.6L	[1]	19.3	21.7	[2]
3.0L	[1]	17.2°	18.6°	[3]

[1] – Intake valve opens 11.5 degrees after TDC.
[2] – Exhaust valve closes 13.6 degrees before TDC.
[3] – Exhaust valve closes 13.7 degrees before TDC.

TIGHTENING SPECIFICATIONS

Application	Ft. Lbs. (N.m)
Camshaft Sprocket Bolts	15 (21)
Chain Tensioner Plug	37 (50)
Connecting Rod Bolts	
Step 1	22 (30)
Step 2	Angle Tighten 90 Degrees
Crankshaft Damper Bolt	221 (300)
Cylinder Head Bolts (Cold)	
Step 1	52 (70)
Step 2	Angle Tighten 90 Degrees
Step 3	Angle Tighten 90 Degrees
Drain Plug (Oil Pan)	18 (25)
Exhaust Manifold Bolts	22-24 (30-32)
Flywheel Bolts	
Step 1	22 (30)
Step 2	Angle Tighten 90 Degrees
Main Bearing Cap Bolts	
Step 1	40 (55)
Step 2	Angle Tighten 90 Degrees
Timing Cover Bolts	26 (35)

Mercedes-Benz Engines

4.2L & 5.6L V8

420SEL, 560SEC, 560SEL, 560SL

NOTE: **For engine repair procedures not covered in this article, see ENGINE OVERHAUL PROCEDURES article at beginning of this section.**

ENGINE CODING

ENGINE IDENTIFICATION

The engine family designation is shown on the emission control information plate (attached to radiator crossmember). The 1st character identifies the model year ("H" for 1987) while the 4th and 5th characters identify the engine displacement.

ENGINE IDENTIFICATION CODE

Application & Engine Size	Engine [1] Designation	Engine Family (Engine Code)
420SEL	116.965	HMB4.2V6FA10
560SEC	117.968	HMB5.6V6FA1X
560SEL	117.968	HMB5.6V6FA1X
560SL	117.967	HMB5.6V6FA20

[1] – The engine designation code but must be used when ordering parts or when obtaining technical information. This number identifies specific engine.

ENGINE, MANIFOLDS & CYLINDER HEADS

ENGINE

Removal

1) On 560SL remove engine hood. Remove complete exhaust system.

2) On other models, move engine hood to vertical position. Remove exhaust pipe at manifolds. Drain cooling system, using both left and right engine block drains. Disconnect and remove battery and bracket. Discharge air conditioning system and disconnect hose lines at compressor.

3) Disconnect coolant hoses. Remove radiator and engine cooling fan. Remove all vacuum, fuel and electrical lines leading to engine. Remove right drag link end from ball stud.

4) Drain power steering reservoir and disconnect hoses. Remove TDC test socket, and remove cable from TDC transmitter. Disconnect regulating shaft. Remove left and right engine shock absorbers.

5) Attach engine sling and hoist to engine and support engine. Remove engine mount bolts. Remove rear engine carrier with engine mount. Remove drive shaft.

6) Remove transmission linkage at transmission. Lift engine/transmission assembly to a 45 degree angle and carefully remove assembly from vehicle. Separate transmission from engine.

Installation

1) Ensure oil cooler and all hoses have been flushed and are free from contamination. Replace engine mounts and components as necessary.

2) Reverse removal procedure to complete installation. Recharge air conditioning system and check for leaks. Adjust engine idle speed as necessary.

INTAKE MANIFOLD

Removal & Installation

1) Disconnect negative battery cable. Partially drain coolant at cylinder block drain plug. Disconnect injection lines and fuel lines. Remove all vacuum hoses. Remove shift cable from automatic transmission.

2) Remove bearing bracket from throttle linkage and bearing bracket from throttle shaft. Disconnect cables and spark plug wiring. Disconnect vacuum lines from automatic transmission and power brake unit.

3) Remove cooling system hoses. Remove intake manifold. Clean intake manifold and check flange surfaces for warpage with straightedge. To install, reverse removal procedure.

EXHAUST MANIFOLD

Removal & Installation

Disconnect negative battery cable. Disconnect exhaust pipe from manifold and EGR line at 90 degree fitting. Remove exhaust manifold retaining bolts and remove exhaust manifold. To install, reverse removal procedure.

CYLINDER HEAD

NOTE: **Allow engine to cool before removing cylinder head. Several specially shaped Allen wrenches are required for cylinder head bolt removal and replacement.**

Removal

1) Remove left and right cylinder block drain plugs and drain cooling system. Remove air cleaner and battery. Remove fuel line and injectors. Disconnect fuel injection linkage.

2) Disconnect all fuel and electrical lines leading to intake manifold and remove intake manifold. Remove A/T fluid filler pipe from attachment to cylinder head. Remove alternator and mounting bracket. Remove distributor and power steering pump with mounting bracket.

3) On right cylinder head, disconnect power steering pump hoses and set aside. Remove ignition distributor. Remove slide rail after removing camshaft sprocket.

4) On left cylinder head, disconnect exhaust pipe from manifold and EGR line at 90 degree fitting. Remove chain tensioner and slide rails. Mark camshaft sprocket and timing chain position for reassembly reference. Remove sprocket from camshaft. Using specially shaped Allen wrenches, remove head bolts and lift off cylinder head.

Installation

1) Ensure all mating surfaces are clean. Install new cylinder head gaskets. Ensure mating surfaces are not damaged. Install cylinder head bolt in rear camshaft bearing bracket before installing head. Tighten cylinder head bolts. *See Fig. 1*.

2) To complete installation, reverse removal procedure. Run engine at normal operating temperature. Slightly loosen head bolts individually, and retighten to specification.

Mercedes-Benz Engines

4.2L & 5.6L V8 (Cont.)

Fig. 1: Cylinder Head Tightening Sequence

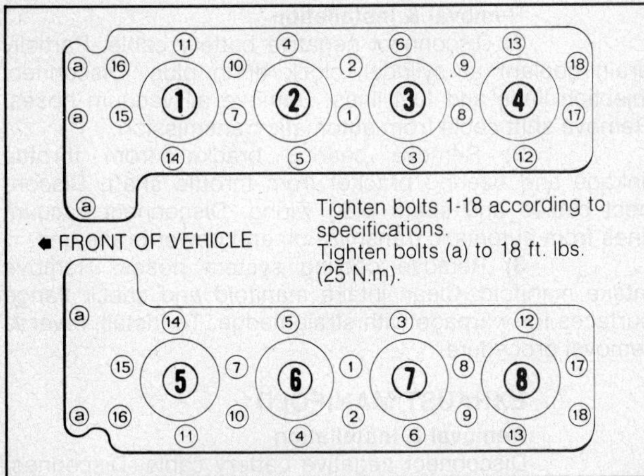

Courtesy of Mercedes-Benz of North America.

CAMSHAFTS

TIMING CHAIN

Removal & Installation

1) A split link timing chain is available for repairs without dismantling engine. Set No. 1 piston at TDC. DO NOT use camshaft sprocket bolts to rotate engine. Remove spark plugs and camshaft covers. Remove air cleaner adapter. Cover chain guard and grind open both pins of a link in the timing chain.

2) Remove old link and install new spit link with new chain attached. Turn crankshaft slowly in normal direction while feeding in new chain and removing old chain. Ensure that chain does not slip on sprockets. Install master link from rear of chain so retaining clip faces front of engine.

3) Install retaining clip with closed end facing direction of rotation. Rotate crankshaft one complete revolution and check for proper alignment of timing marks. To complete installation, reverse removal procedure. Check cam timing. Set distributor rotor alignment.

CHAIN TENSIONER

1) Remove air injector pipe and 3 bolts fastening chain tensioner. Remove chain tensioner. *See Fig. 2.*

2) To check tensioner, place vertically in container of oil with oil covering flange. Actuate plunger to fill tensioner with oil. After filling with oil and venting air, plunger should allow slow and even compression.

3) To install, reverse removal procedure. Use new gasket and tighten bolts evenly. Pressure pin of tensioner must press against lug of tensioning rail.

VALVE TIMING

Checking

1) Valve timing is measured at intake valves No. 1 and 6. Remove hydraulic valve lifters and replace with Adjustable Rocker Arms (116 050 11 20). Adjust to zero clearance against base circle of camshaft lobe.

2) Attach dial indicator with pointer resting vertically on valve spring retainer. Indicator must have .120" (3.00 mm) preload and dial should be set at "0".

3) Rotate engine in direction of normal rotation until pointer moves .080" (2.00 mm), leaving a preload of .040" (1.0 mm). Readings should be in accordance with valve timing chart. Repeat procedure for No. 6 intake valve.

Fig. 2: Timing Chain & Sprockets

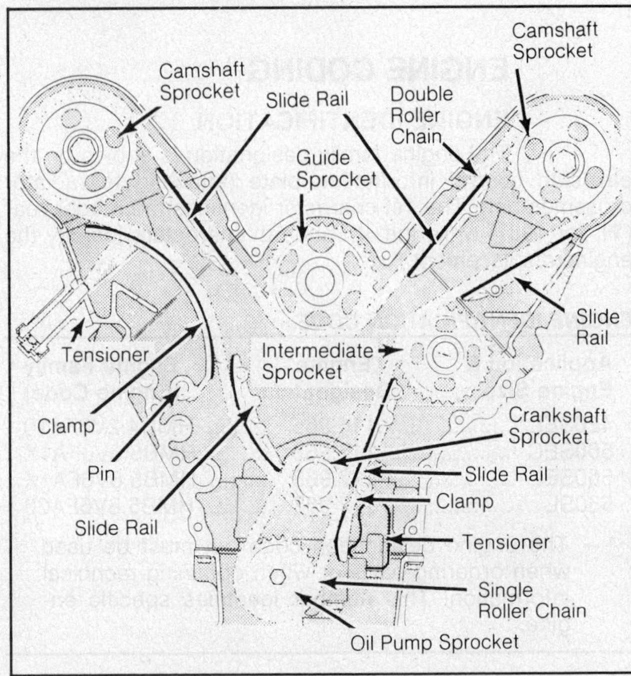

Courtesy of Mercedes-Benz of North America.

Adjusting

1) If timing requires correction, install an offset Woodruff key or new timing chain. *See Fig. 3.* An offset by one tooth on camshaft sprocket results in about 18 degrees at crankshaft.

2) An offset Woodruff key will advance or retard camshaft timing depending on the direction of installation. Mark camshaft sprockets and timing chain in relation to each other. Remove respective camshaft sprocket. Place rag under camshaft and remove Woodruff key.

3) Insert selected Woodruff key. Install camshaft sprocket and align with marks. Wide collar on camshaft sprocket should face camshaft. Do not tighten mounting bolt at this time. Mount opposite camshaft sprocket.

4) Tighten mounting bolt to 74 ft. lbs. (100 N.m). After checking and adjusting valve timing, reinstall hydraulic lifters and adjust for proper base setting.

Fig. 3: Offset Woodruff Key Location

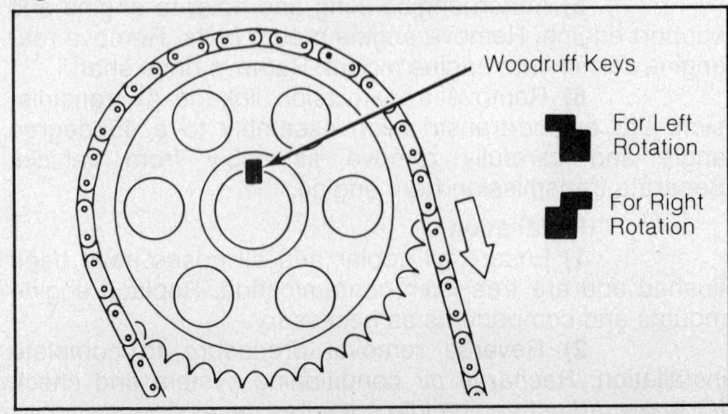

4.2L & 5.6L V8 (Cont.)

CAMSHAFT & BEARINGS

Removal

1) Remove valve covers. Remove fuel pump relay. Set No. 1 piston at TDC on compression stroke and remove rocker arms. DO NOT use camshaft sprocket bolt to rotate engine. Mark sprockets and timing chain for reassembly.

2) Remove camshaft sprockets. Remove camshaft bearings, oil tube and camshaft as an assembly.

NOTE: **Install rocker arms in original position. If rocker arms are intermixed or replaced, check basic position of hydraulic compensating elements. Adjust if necessary.**

Installation

1) Assemble camshaft bearings on camshaft. Camshafts with smooth bearing journals must be installed on grooved bearings. Camshafts with an oil groove in journal must be installed in ungrooved bearings.

2) Place camshaft and bearing assembly on head. Note that outer bolt of left rear camshaft bearing must be inserted in bearing prior to mounting due to interference with brake unit. Oil line connections on bearings must be replaced to ensure proper oil pressure.

3) Tighten camshaft bearing mounting bolts and check that camshaft rotates freely. Mount compensating washer so that both inner and outer notches align with Woodruff key in camshaft. Install sprockets on camshafts with White reference marks facing camshaft. Ensure timing marks are aligned.

4) Install rocker arms and check basic clearance of lifters. See ADJUSTING LIFTERS TO BASE SETTING in this article. To complete installation, reverse removal procedure.

NOTE: **Rocker arms and camshafts must be replaced as sets. DO NOT use a new camshaft with used rocker arms or new rocker arms with a used camshaft. Camshaft journals may be reground and undersize bearings installed.**

DISTRIBUTOR DRIVE GEAR

Removal

1) With front timing cover removed, disconnect slide rails and timing chain tensioners as needed.

2) Remove chain from intermediate sprocket and pull sprocket from engine. Use puller to extract bushing from crankshaft and cover.

Installation

1) Press new bushings in position with lubricating groove at bottom. Lubricate bushings, and install intermediate sprocket.

2) With engine at TDC for No. 1 piston, check that mark on sprocket aligns with mark on crankshaft. To complete installation, reverse removal procedure.

VALVES

VALVE ARRANGEMENT

Right Bank – E-I-E-I-E-I-I-E (Front-to-rear).
Left Bank – E-I-I-E-I-E-I-E (Front-to-rear).

ROCKER ARMS

Removal & Installation

1) Rotate engine until respective cam lobe points upward. On 560SL, remove 4-point cable connector at ignition and fuel pump electrical junction box.

2) Compress valve spring using Spring Compressor (123 589 03 61 00). Mark each arm for installation in original position.

3) Note that rocker arms have a chamfer behind ball socket (lifter end). This prevents rocker arm from striking retaining cap of lifters. DO NOT use replacement rocker arms without this chamfer.

4) If replacing camshaft and rocker arms, check base setting of hydraulic valve lifters using Test Gauge (100 589 04 23 00). If any corrections are necessary, thrust plates are available in steps of .0014" (.355). See ADJUSTING LIFTERS TO BASE SETTING in this article.

NOTE: **Rocker arms and camshafts must be replaced as sets. DO NOT use a new camshaft with used rocker arms or new rocker arms with a used camshaft. Camshaft journals may be reground and undersize bearings installed.**

VALVE SPRINGS

Removal

Remove cylinder head from vehicle. Use spring compressor and remove rocker arms. Lift out thrust plate using a magnet. Remove valve keepers, inner and outer valve springs, and valve stem oil seals. *See Fig. 4.*

Installation

Replacement valve stem seals and protective sleeves are supplied in valve grind gasket set. Place protective sleeve over stem, lubricate and install seal. Install remaining components in reverse order of removal.

Fig. 4: Removing Valve Keepers

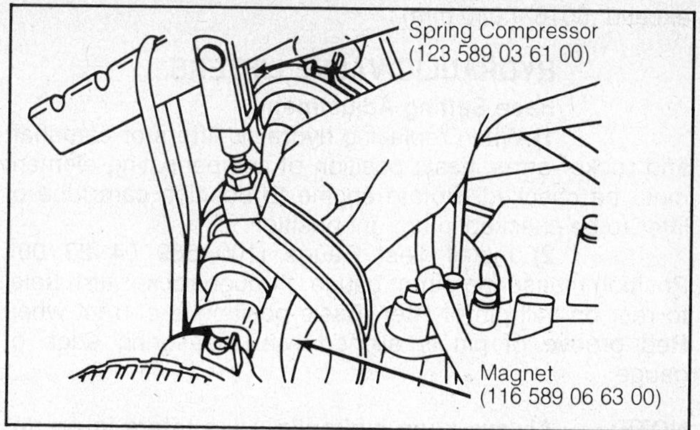

VALVE GUIDES

1) With cylinder head removed from vehicle, clean bores of valve guides. Carbon deposits may be removed with a valve guide hone.

2) Using a plug gauge, measure valve guides. If guide is beyond specification, replace guide.

3) Using a valve guide mandrel, remove guide from combustion chamber side of cylinder head. Inspect valve guide bore in cylinder head and ream to next oversize.

4.2L & 5.6L V8 (Cont.)

4) Heat cylinder head to approximately 194°F (90°C), or cool valve guide in liquid nitrogen. Coat guide bore with oil and install valve guide.

5) Ensure valve guide snap ring retainer is properly installed. Recheck valve guide clearance and that valve moves freely in guide.

Fig. 5: Installing Valve Stem Seals

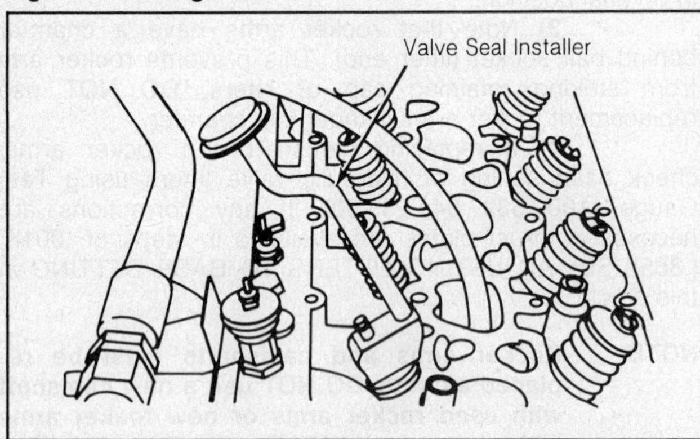

VALVE SEATS

1) Check valve guide prior to removing valve seat. See VALVE GUIDES in this article. If valve seat is worn, carefully remove it by machining with a valve seat remover.

2) Thoroughly clean receiving bore and check its diameter. If diameter is within specifications, install a new valve seat ring of the same size. If diameter is not within specifications, machine bore to next oversize.

3) Heat cylinder head in water to approximately 140°F (60°C). Place pre-cooled seat ring into bore. To position seat ring, lightly tap ring using mandrel and plastic or rubber hammer.

4) Machine valve seat to correct width. Check valve seat for runout. DO NOT machine rounded bead on lower part of valve seat. Valve seat runout should not exceed .0016" (.040 mm).

HYDRAULIC VALVE LIFTERS

Base Setting Adjustment

1) When replacing hydraulic lifters or camshaft and rocker arms, basic position of compensating element must be checked. Rotate engine to position cam lobe of lifter to be checked in upright position.

2) Install Test Gauge (100 589 04 23 00). Position measuring pin of gauge, through rocker arm hole, to rest on ball pin of lifter. Basic position is correct when Red groove of pin is aligned with measuring edge of gauge.

NOTE: **Always keep hydraulic valve lifters in an upright position. Rocker arms and valve lifters should always be reinstalled in original locations. When checking and adjusting lifter settings, crank engine (with ignition off) for 30 seconds with starter.**

3) If groove is below measuring edge, a plus deviation is indicated, requiring a thinner thrust plate. Entire groove showing above measuring edge indicates a minus deviation and requires a thicker thrust plate.

4) To correct setting, remove rocker arm and thrust plate. Install thinner or thicker thrust plate as required and reinstall rocker arm. Repeat measuring procedure. Position is correct when center of measuring groove aligns with edge of gauge.

CYLINDER BLOCK ASSEMBLY

The aluminum alloy cylinders are very sensitive to damage and scratches, as well as contamination. When honing, the cylinder bores must be sized to available pistons. The specified piston clearance must be observed.

In the event of excessive scoring or cylinder wear, the cylinders may be machine bored (if proper procedures are used). When boring or honing cylinders, ensure the "Sunnen Silcone-Lapping" procedure is used. This process exposes the silicone crystals, in the bores, for the pistons to contact.

NOTE: **DO NOT attempt replacement of pistons if facilities for the "Sunnen" procedure are not available. If the "Silicone-Lapping" procedure is not done, piston seizure will result.**

CYLINDERS

Inspection

1) The differences in markings on cylinder running surfaces are between "optical streaks" and "seizure streaks". Optical streaks are about 1/8" wide and are caused by ring gap.

2) If honing traces are still visible within the optical streaks, this condition is normal and the cylinder is still reusable if running surface is smooth, round and within tolerance.

3) For cylinders with "seizure streaks" however, the honing traces are no longer seen. Cylinders in this condition must be rebored. Piston assemblies of the proper weight and size must be installed. Seizure streaks are caused by piston skirt contact against cylinder wall.

4) Any streaks in the vertical direction in the area of wrist pin travel are considered optical streaks. These streaks are considered normal, since there is very little contact between piston body and cylinder wall.

NOTE: **When measuring cylinder bores, ensure the cylinder wall surface is not scratched.**

PISTONS, PINS & RINGS

PISTON & ROD ASSEMBLY

Removal

1) With cylinder head and oil pan removed, remove connecting rod nuts and bearing caps. Ensure bearing surface is not damaged during removal procedure.

2) Remove piston pin snap ring and push out piston pin. Retain all components in proper order for reassembly.

Inspection

1) Measure cylinder bores at top, bottom and center of bore in at least 2 directions. If measurement exceeds specification by .004" (.10 mm), cylinders must be bored and new pistons fitted.

2) Check rings for proper end gap and side clearance. Replace piston and/or rings if not within specifications.

4.2L & 5.6L V8 (Cont.)

Installation

1) Lubricate piston pins and connecting rod bushings. Push in piston pin (do not heat piston) and install circlips.

2) Stagger ring gaps on piston and fit ring compressor. Install piston and rod assembly with arrow on piston facing toward front of engine.

3) Install rod caps. Tighten rod cap nuts and check clearances. Ensure markings on rods and caps match.

PISTON PINS

Removal

Piston pins are retained with circlips in pistons. To remove pins, remove circlips and push pins out.

Installation

To install, reverse removal procedure. Ensure that arrow on piston crown faces front (timing chain end) and that bearing retaining notch in connecting rod faces toward outside of engine. Lubricate pin and push into piston and rod assembly by hand.

CRANKSHAFT & ROD BEARINGS

CRANKSHAFT MAIN BEARINGS

1) Install main bearing caps to cylinder block without bearings. Measure line bore. Offset bearing caps can be centered by lightly tapping them with a plastic hammer. *See Fig. 6*.

2) Measure main and connecting rod bearings at front and rear to check taper. If beyond .0006" (.015 mm), carefully remove excess material from one side of bearing cap using surface plate.

3) Install bearings and tighten bolts. Measure bearings or install crankshaft and check bearing clearance with Plastigage. Specified main bearing clearance is .0018-.0033" (.045-.084 mm).

Fig. 6: Measuring Main Bearing Bore Diameter

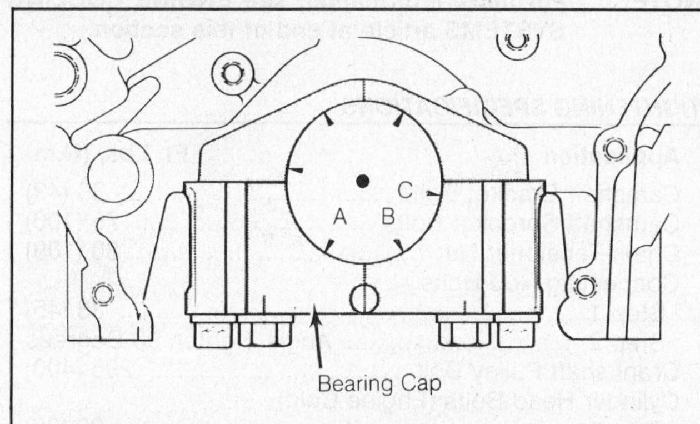

Courtesy of Mercedes-Benz of North America.

4) Oversized bearings are available to adjust bearing clearance. Ensure crankshaft turns freely when selected bearings are installed.

5) When proper clearance is obtained, clean and lubricate bearings and install crankshaft. Tighten main cap bolts in sequence to specification. *See Fig. 7*.

6) Use a feeler gauge to check crankshaft end play. Insert feeler gauge between number 3 main bearing (thrust bearing) and crankshaft thrust face. Crankshaft end play should be .004-.009" (.10-.23 mm).

Fig. 7: Crankshaft Main Bearing Tightening Sequence

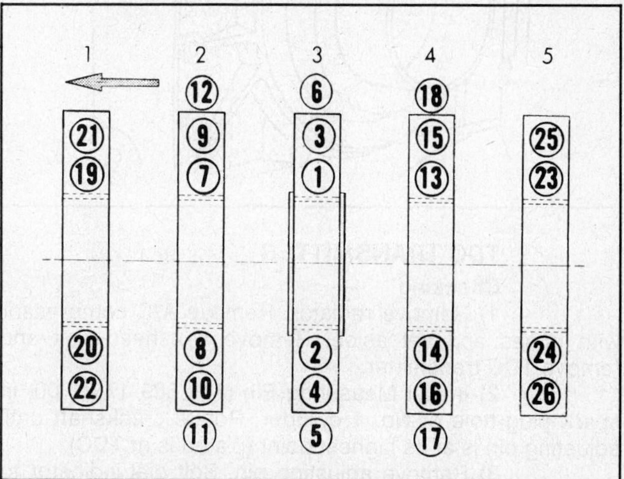

Courtesy of Mercedes-Benz of North America.

FRONT CRANKSHAFT OIL SEAL

Removal

With engine removed from vehicle, remove all "V" belts. Mark for installation alignment reference, and remove vibration damper, pulley and hub. Remove oil seal. Ensure crankshaft and housing bore are not damaged.

Installation

Lubricate housing bore and seal lip with oil. Install oil seal with Installer Sleeve (110 589 07 61 00). To complete installation, reverse removal procedure.

REAR MAIN BEARING OIL SEAL

Removal

1) Remove engine from vehicle. Remove flywheel assembly. Pry out old seal. Clean sealing surfaces.

2) Check crankshaft running surface for scoring. A special oil seal is available with a different sealing lip offset. Use this seal if crankshaft is scored.

Installation

1) Lubricate lip of seal, and place seal into position in rear engine cover. Place Conical Sleeve (116 589 03 43 00) over crankshaft and place cover in position. *See Fig. 8*.

2) Ensure pan gasket is not damaged. Install flywheel drive plate. Flywheel drive plate can only be mounted in one position due to offset of one mounting bolt.

Mercedes-Benz Engines

4.2L & 5.6L V8 (Cont.)

Fig. 8: Installing Rear Cover & Seal

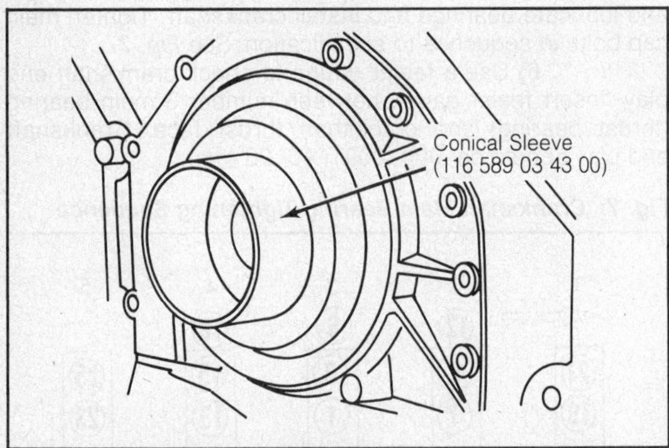

TDC TRANSMITTER

Checking

1) Remove radiator. Remove A/C compressor with hoses and set aside. Remove hex head bolt and remove TDC transmitter.

2) Install Measuring Pin (115 589 17 21 00) in spark plug hole of No. 1 cylinder. Rotate crankshaft until adjusting pin is at its highest point (piston is at TDC).

3) Remove adjusting pin. Bolt dial indicator to TDC adapter. Set a pre-load of .20" (5.0 mm) on indicator pointer. Rotate crankshaft and accurately find TDC using dial indicator. Adjust indicator dial to "0" at TDC.

4) Rotate crankshaft in direction of rotation until dial indicator reads .120" (2.99 mm) on 4.2L engine and .140" (3.58 mm) on 5.6L engine. Insert Locator (102 589 03 21 00) in adjusting slide. Pin of vibration damper should engage in groove of locator.

5) With right cylinder head removed from engine, place dial indicator vertically on No. 1 piston. Find TDC and set indicator dial to "0". Rotate crankshaft in direction of rotation until dial indicator reads .120" (2.99 mm) on 4.2L engine and .140" (3.58 mm) on 5.6L engine.

6) Loosen adjusting slide and move until pin engages in locator. Install adjusting slide and remove locator. Insert TDC transmitter into mount. Remove dial indicator. Rotate crankshaft in direction of rotation. Remove tester from spark plug hole.

ENGINE OILING

OIL PAN

Removal (560SL)

1) Remove radiator and fan shroud. Remove front axle assembly. Remove A/C compressor and mounting bracket.

2) Remove support bracket between pan and transmission. Remove oil pan bolts and lower oil pan along with dipstick guide tube from engine.

Installation

To install pan, reverse removal procedure. Apply grease to clean mating surfaces and install new gasket.

Removal (All Others)

1) Remove A/C compressor and mounting bracket from engine. Remove drive belt tensioning pulley. Unbolt and remove oil pan lower half. Remove oil pump drive sprocket and mounting bolts. Remove oil pump.

2) Remove oil pan upper half retaining bolts and remove upper pan. Remove engine mount bolts. Loosen both engine shock absorbers. Remove radiator fan shroud. Lift engine until oil pan can be removed.

Installation

To install oil pan, reverse removal procedure.

CRANKCASE CAPACITY

Oil capacity is 8.5 qts. (8.0L) when oil filter is replaced.

NORMAL OIL PRESSURE

Oil pressure is 7 psi (.5 kg/cm²) at idle and 43 psi (3.0 kg/cm²) at 3000 RPM.

OIL PUMP

Removal

Drain oil and remove pan. Oil pump is chain driven. Sprocket and chain must be removed prior to pump removal. Remove 4 oil pump mounting bolts. Slide pump off drive shaft.

Installation

Mount oil pump on sprocket. The clamping sleeve in sprocket should enter cut-out of drive shaft. Install oil pump. Lock tensioning spring of chain tensioner with a screwdriver, against rotation when tightening oil pump retaining bolts.

ENGINE COOLING

WATER PUMP

Removal

Disconnect necessary water hoses and components from water pump housing. Remove distributor and 8 water pump mounting bolts Remove pump from vehicle.

Installation

To install, reverse removal procedure.

NOTE: **For more information, see ENGINE COOLING SYSTEMS article at end of this section.**

TIGHTENING SPECIFICATIONS

Application	Ft. Lbs. (N.m)
Camshaft Bracket Bolts	36 (49)
Camshaft Sprocket Bolts	75 (100)
Chain Tensioner Nut	80 (109)
Connecting Rod Bolts	
Step 1	33 (45)
Step 2	Angle Tighten 90 Degrees
Crankshaft Pulley Bolt	295 (400)
Cylinder Head Bolts (Engine Cold)	
Step 1	22 (30)
Step 2	43 (58)
Step 3	Angle Tighten 90 Degrees
Flywheel (Drive Plate) Bolts	
Step 1	25 (35)
Step 2	Angle Tighten 90 Degrees
Hydraulic Valve Lifters	36 (49)
Main Bearing Caps	
Large Bolts	37 (50)
Small Bolts	22 (30)
Oil Pressure Relief Valve	29 (39)

Mercedes-Benz Engines

4.2L & 5.6L V8 (Cont.)

ENGINE SPECIFICATIONS

GENERAL SPECIFICATIONS

Year	DISPLACEMENT		Fuel System	HP@RPM	Torque Ft. Lbs.@RPM	Compr. Ratio	BORE		STROKE	
	Cu. In.	Liters					In.	mm	In.	mm
1987										
4.2L	256	4.2	Fuel Inj.	201@5200	228@3600	9.0:1	3.62	92	3.11	78.9
5.6L	338	5.6	Fuel Inj.	[1] 238@4800	[2] 287@3500	9.0:1	3.80	96.5	3.73	94.8

[1] – Horsepower rating for the 560SL (117.967 engine) is 227@4750 RPM.
[2] – Torque rating for the 560SL (117.967 engine) is 279@3250 RPM.

VALVES

Engine Size & Valve	Head Diam. In. (mm)	Face Angle	Seat Angle	Seat Width In. (mm)	Stem Diameter In. (mm)	Stem Clearance In. (mm)	Valve Lift In. (mm)
4.2L Intake	1.74 (44.2)	45°	45°	.051-.079 (1.3-2.0)	.3523-.3531 (8.95-8.97)	.003 (.076)	.....
5.6L Intake	1.82 (46.2)	45°	45°	.051-.079 (1.3-2.0)	.3523-.3531 (8.95-8.97)	.003 (.076)	.....
4.2L & 5.6L Exhaust	1.54 (39.0)	45°	45°	.059-.079 (1.5-2.0)	.3523-.3531 (8.95-8.97)	.003 (.076)	.....

PISTONS, PINS & RINGS

Engine	PISTONS	PINS		RINGS		
	Clearance In. (mm)	Piston Fit In. (mm)	Rod Fit In. (mm)	Ring No.	End Gap In. (mm)	Side Clearance In. (mm)
4.2L	.0005-.0015 (.013-.038)	.....	.0002-.0007 (.005-.018)	No. 1	.014-.022 (.35-.55)	.002-.0036 (.050-.092)
				No. 2	.014-.022 (.35-.55)	.0016-.0030 (.040-.076)
				Oil	.010-.016 (.25-.40)	.0012-.0030 (.030-.076)
5.6L	.0006-.0017 (.017-.043)	....	.0003-.0007 (.008-.018)	No. 1	.008-.016 (.20-.40)	.003-.005 (.090-.120)
				No. 2	.008-.016 (.20-.40)	.002-.003 (.20-.38)
				Oil	.008-.016 (.25-.40)	.001-.002 (.03-.06)

CRANKSHAFT MAIN & CONNECTING ROD BEARINGS

Engine	MAIN BEARINGS				CONNECTING ROD BEARINGS		
	Journal Diam. In. (mm)	Clearance In. (mm)	Thrust Bearing	Crankshaft End Play In. (mm)	Journal Diam. In. (mm)	Clearance In. (mm)	Side Play In. (mm)
4.2 & 5.6L	2.517-2.518 (63.93-63.96)	.0018-.0033 (.045-.084)	.....	.004-.009 (.10-.23)	2.031 (51.6)	.0008-.0027 (.020-.068)	.009-.015 (.23-.38)

Mercedes-Benz Engines

4.2L & 5.6L V8 (Cont.)

ENGINE SPECIFICATIONS (Cont.)

CAMSHAFT

Engine	Journal Diam. In. (mm)	Clearance In. (mm)	Lobe Lift In. (mm)
4.2 & 5.6L			
No. 1	1.376-1.377 (34.95-34.98)	.0004-.0023 (.010-.058)	.....
No. 2 & 3	1.935-1.936 (49.16-49.18)	.0011-.0027 (.03-.07)	.....
No. 4 & 5	1.943-1.944 (49.36-49.38)	.0011-.0027 (.03-.07)	.....

VALVE TIMING

Engine	INTAKE Open (BTDC)	INTAKE Close (ABDC)	EXHAUST Open (BBDC)	EXHAUST Close (ATDC)
4.2L	[1]	21°	10°	[3]
5.6L	[2]	34°	17°	[4]

[1] – Intake valve opens 22 degrees after TDC.
[2] – Intake valve opens 27 degrees after TDC.
[3] – Exhaust valve closes 15 degrees before TDC.
[4] – Exhaust valve closes 10 degrees before TDC.

VALVE SPRINGS

Engine	Free Length In. (mm)	PRESSURE Lbs. @ In. (Kg @ mm) Valve Closed	Valve Open
4.2 & 5.6L			
Inner	1.77 (45)	24.7@1.3 (11.2@33)	50.7@846 (23@21.5)
Outer	1.95 (49.5)	67.24@1.65 (30.5@42)	194@1.2 (88@30.5)

Mitsubishi Engines

1.5L & 1.6L TURBO 4-CYLINDER

Chrysler Motors: Colt
Hyundai: Excel
Mitsubishi: Mirage, Precis

NOTE: **For engine repair procedures not covered in this article, see ENGINE OVERHAUL PROCEDURES article at beginning on this article.**

ENGINE CODING

ENGINE IDENTIFICATION

Engine may be identified from the Vehicle Identification Number (VIN). The VIN is stamped in a metal tag attached to upper left corner of instrument panel near windshield. The eighth character of the VIN identifies the engine size and the tenth character identifies the model year. Engine model code and serial number are stamped on top edge of engine block just below No. 1 spark plug on right side of block.

ENGINE IDENTIFICATION CODES

Application	Engine Model	Engine VIN Code
1.5L	G15B	K
1.6L [1]	G32B	F

[1] – Turbocharged engine.

ENGINE, MANIFOLDS & CYLINDER HEAD

ENGINE

NOTE: **Remove engine and transaxle as an assembly. If equipped with fuel injection, bleed off pressure from fuel main pipes and hoses.**

Removal

1) Disconnect fuel hoses. Remove rear seat cushion and carpet. Start engine and disconnect fuel pump connector. Wait until engine stops. Turn ignition key to "OFF" position. Disconnect negative battery cable. Plug fuel hoses to prevent leakage.

2) Remove battery and battery tray. Disconnect air cleaner assembly. Disconnect back-up light, engine, starter motor and A/C harness connectors. On 5-speed manual transaxle models, disconnect select control valve connector. Disconnect alternator and oil pressure sending unit harness connectors. Drain engine oil and coolant.

3) On automatic transaxle models, label and disconnect transaxle oil cooler lines. Plug lines to prevent contamination. On all models, remove radiator hoses. Remove radiator and cooling fan assembly. Disconnect ignition coil harness and coil wire. Disconnect engine ground cable.

4) Disconnect brake booster vacuum hose. Remove fuel supply, return and vapor hoses from engine. Disconnect vacuum hoses. Disconnect throttle cable. On manual transaxle models, disconnect clutch cable from transaxle.

5) On automatic transaxle models, disconnect control cable from transaxle. Disconnect speedometer cable from transaxle. Discharge A/C and disconnect A/C hoses at compressor (if equipped). Plug openings in compressor and hoses to prevent contamination. Remove power steering pump from engine. Wire power steering pump aside.

6) From under vehicle, remove undercover and drain transaxle. Disconnect and suspend exhaust pipe. Remove shift control rod and extension rod from manual transaxle. Disconnect stabilizer bar from lower arms. Disconnect ball joint from knuckle. Disconnect tie rod from end of knuckle.

7) On turbocharged models, disconnect engine oil cooler hoses at engine. On all models, remove right and left drive axle shafts and center bearing (if equipped) from transaxle case. Suspend axle shafts and lower arms with string to prevent damaging joints. Cover holes in transaxle case to prevent contamination.

NOTE: **Drive axle shaft retainer rings should be replaced whenever drive axle shafts are removed from transaxle.**

8) Suspend engine with chains attached to hoisting brackets. Remove front roll stopper insulator bolt. Remove rear roll stopper insulator bolt. Remove attaching nut from left mount insulator, but DO NOT remove bolt. Raise engine slightly. Ensure all cables, hoses and electrical harnesses are disconnected from engine.

9) Remove cover from inside right inner fender panel. Remove transaxle mounting bracket bolts. Remove left insulator bolt. Remove engine/transaxle assembly from vehicle while pushing transaxle side downward during removal.

Installation

1) To install, reverse removal procedure. Tighten mounting bolts and nuts to specification with weight of engine on insulators. Note that front and rear center member insulators and collars are different.

2) Front insulator is round and has a .79" (20 mm) collar. Rear insulator is octagonal shaped and has a .87" (22 mm) collar. Ensure front roll stopper identification hole faces forward. Replace all fluids and adjust all cables and linkages.

CYLINDER HEAD & MANIFOLDS

Removal (1.5L)

1) Drain cooling system and disconnect upper radiator hose. Remove breather hose and air cleaner. Remove vacuum hose, fuel hose and coolant hose. Label and remove spark plug wires. Remove distributor and carburetor. Remove intake manifold.

Fig. 1: Cylinder Head Bolt Tightening Sequence

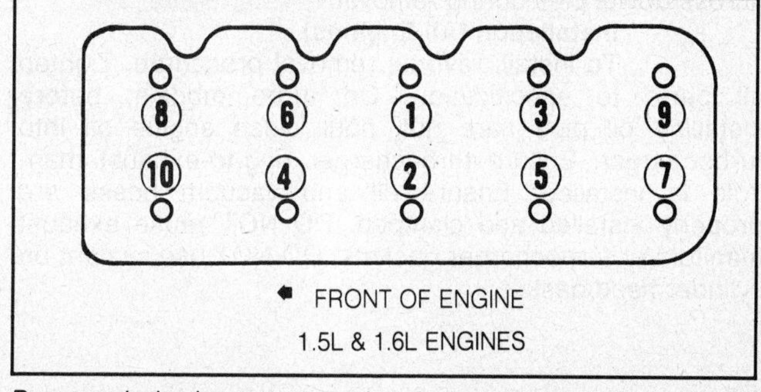

Remove bolts in reverse order during removal. Courtesy of Mitsubishi Motor Sales of America.

1.5L & 1.6L TURBO 4-CYLINDER (Cont.)

2) Remove heat shield and exhaust manifold assembly. Remove timing belt cover. Move timing belt tensioner toward water pump and secure. Remove timing belt from camshaft sprocket. Ensure belt stays on crankshaft sprocket. Remove rocker arm cover.

3) Loosen cylinder head bolts using Head Bolt Wrench (TW-10B), in reverse of tightening sequence. *See Fig. 1.* Loosen head bolts in 2 or 3 steps to prevent cylinder head warpage. Remove bolts and cylinder head.

CAUTION: Ensure exhaust system has cooled down before servicing.

Removal (1.6L)

1) Drain cooling system and remove upper radiator hose. Remove breather and purge hoses. Remove air cleaner assembly and fuel line. Remove vacuum hose at distributor and purge control valve. Label and disconnect spark plug wires. Remove distributor.

2) Disconnect heater hose at intake manifold. Disconnect water hose between cylinder head and injection mixer water case. Disconnect coolant temperature sending unit wire. Disconnect front exhaust pipe at exhaust manifold flange.

NOTE: It may be necessary to remove turbocharger from exhaust manifold before exhaust manifold can be removed.

3) Remove turbocharger heat protector. Remove oxygen sensor from catalytic converter. Remove converter-to-turbocharger nuts. Disconnect oil return hose from oil pan. Remove oil pipe from turbocharger and oil filter bracket. Remove air intake pipe connecting bolt. Disconnect water pipes from turbocharger. Remove turbocharger mounting nuts and remove turbocharger assembly from exhaust manifold.

4) Remove exhaust manifold. Remove intake manifold and injection mixer as an assembly. Remove timing belt upper front cover. Rotate crankshaft so that No. 1 piston is at TDC. Align camshaft sprocket timing marks. Mark timing belt with felt pen or chalk in alignment with timing mark on camshaft sprocket.

5) Remove camshaft sprocket bolt and camshaft sprocket with timing belt attached. DO NOT turn crankshaft. Ensure belt is prevented from disengaging from crankshaft or oil pump sprockets.

6) Remove 3 timing belt upper inner cover retaining bolts. Remove timing belt upper inner cover. Remove rocker cover. Loosen cylinder head bolts using Head Bolt Wrench (TW-10B), in reverse of tightening sequence. *See Fig. 1.* Loosen head bolts in 2 or 3 steps to prevent cylinder head warpage. Do not slide cylinder head across dowel pins during removal.

Installation (All Engines)

To install, reverse removal procedure. Tighten all parts to specification. On turbo models, before installing oil pipe flare nut, pour clean engine oil into turbocharger. Ensure turbocharger ring-to-exhaust manifold is installed. Ensure oil and vacuum hoses are properly installed and clamped. DO NOT reuse exhaust manifold or turbocharger gaskets. DO NOT use sealant on cylinder head gasket.

CAMSHAFT

ROCKER ARMS & SHAFTS

Removal (1.5L)

1) Remove breather hose and air cleaner. Remove timing belt cover. Remove rocker arm cover. Move timing belt tensioner toward water pump and secure. Remove timing belt from camshaft sprocket only. Remove camshaft sprocket.

2) Loosen rocker shaft mounting bolts and lift off rocker shaft, rocker arms and springs as an assembly. Remove bolts from shafts and slide off springs and rocker arms.

Installation

To install, reverse removal procedure. Ensure short springs for exhaust valves are used with right side rocker shaft assembly.

CAMSHAFT

Removal (1.5L)

Remove rocker arms and shafts. Remove cylinder head rear cover. Remove distributor, fuel pump and fuel pump push rod. Remove camshaft thrust case from rear of head and thrust case tightening bolt from top of head. Remove camshaft from rear of head.

Fig. 2: Installing Timing Belt on 1.5L Engine

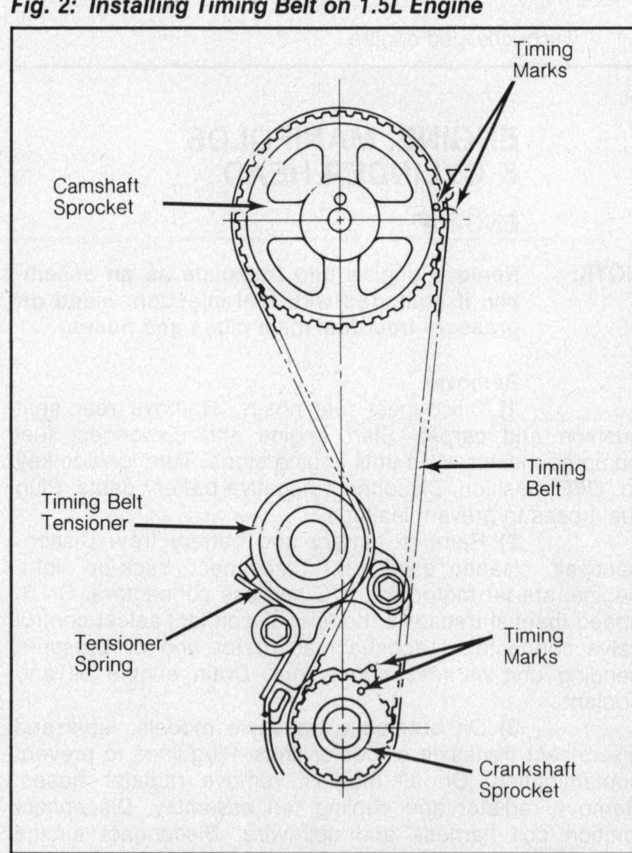

Courtesy of Mitsubishi Motor Sales of America.

Inspection

1) Check cam lobes for wear or damage. If exhaust cam lobe height is less than 1.480" (37.60 mm), replace camshaft. If intake cam lobe height is less than 1.484" (37.70 mm), replace camshaft.

1.5L & 1.6L TURBO 4-CYLINDER (Cont.)

2) Check camshaft bearing journals for damage, wear or seizure. Check camshaft bearing surface for damage, wear or seizure. Replace cylinder head if bearings are worn excessively. Check front oil seal lips for wear. Replace seal if worn.

Installation

1) To install, reverse removal procedure. Thoroughly lubricate camshaft and seal lips. Use Seal Installer (MD998306) to install camshaft oil seal. Ensure camshaft sprocket mark is aligned with timing mark on cylinder head. *See Fig. 2.*

2) Check camshaft end play. If excessive, replace thrust case and recheck. If end play is still excessive, check rear of camshaft journal for wear. If badly worn, replace camshaft.

3) Temporarily set valve clearance to cold engine settings. Readjust to hot engine settings when engine is at normal operating temperature.

Fig. 3: Rocker Arm Identification on 1.5L & 1.6L Engines

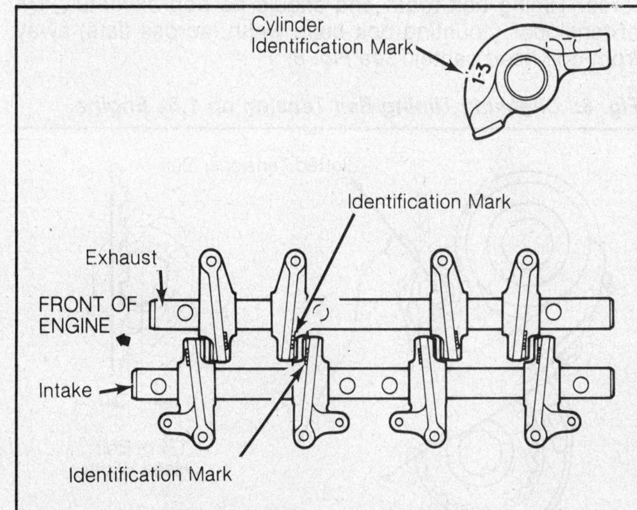

Numbers on rocker arms indicate cylinder application. Courtesy of Mitsubishi Motor Sales of America.

ROCKER ASSEMBLY & CAMSHAFT

Removal (1.6L)

1) Remove breather hoses and air cleaner. Disconnect spark plug wires and remove upper front timing belt cover. Turn crankshaft to TDC of compression stroke on No. 1 cylinder by aligning mark on upper inner cover with mark on camshaft sprocket. *See Fig. 4.*

2) Make reassembly mark with chalk or felt pen on timing belt in alignment with timing mark on camshaft sprocket. Slide camshaft sprocket (with belt attached) off camshaft. DO NOT turn crankshaft. Ensure belt is prevented from disengaging from crankshaft or oil pump sprockets.

3) Remove upper inner cover. Remove rocker cover. Remove camshaft bearing caps, rocker arms and rocker shafts as an assembly. Remove oil seal and distributor drive gear from camshaft. Remove camshaft.

Inspection

Check cam lobes for wear or damage. If cam lobe height is less than 1.4101" (35.817 mm), replace camshaft. Check camshaft bearing journals for damage, wear or seizure. Replace camshaft as necessary. Check camshaft bearing surface for damage, wear or seizure. Replace cylinder head if bearings are worn excessively.

Fig. 4: Aligning Camshaft Timing Marks on 1.6L Engine

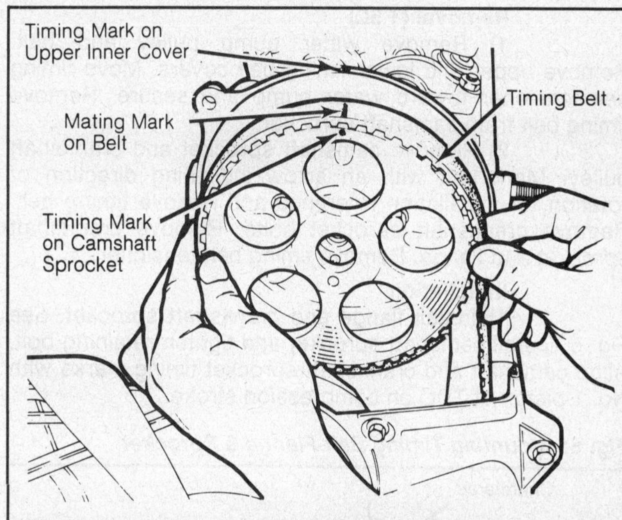

Courtesy of Mitsubishi Motor Sales of America.

Installation

1) Lubricate camshaft lobes and camshaft bearing journals and install camshaft into cylinder head. Check camshaft end play. Install rocker arm assembly to cylinder head. Insert camshaft bearing caps and tighten bolts.

2) Lubricate front O.D. of camshaft. Using Seal Installer (MD998364), install camshaft oil seal. Install upper inner cover and camshaft sprocket. If dowel pin hole on camshaft sprocket is not in alignment with dowel pin, lightly strike projections at No. 2 exhaust cam with a screwdriver to turn camshaft.

3) Reverse removal procedure to complete installation. Temporarily set valve clearance to cold engine settings. Readjust to hot engine settings when engine is at normal operating temperature. Apply sealer to cylinder head. *See Fig. 5.* Install rocker cover, air cleaner and breather hoses.

Fig. 5: Applying Sealer to Cylinder Head on 1.6L Engine

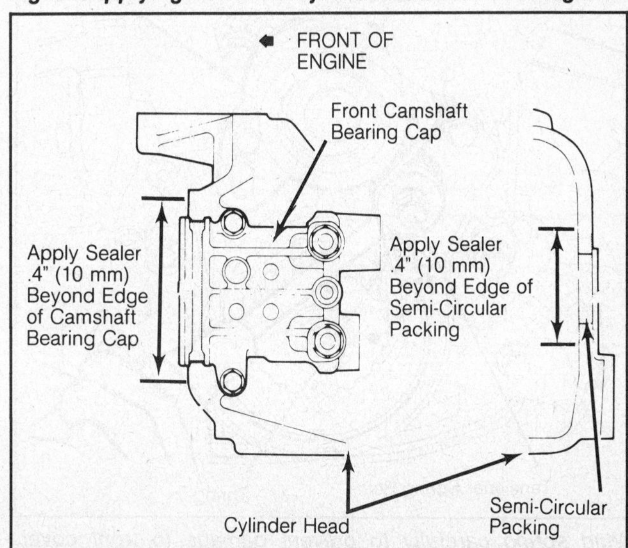

Courtesy of Mitsubishi Motor Sales of America.

1.5L & 1.6L TURBO 4-CYLINDER (Cont.)

TIMING BELT & SPROCKETS

Removal (1.5L)

1) Remove water pump pulley and belt. Remove upper and lower timing belt covers. Move timing belt tensioner toward water pump and secure. Remove timing belt from camshaft sprocket.

2) Remove camshaft sprocket and crankshaft pulley. Mark belt with an arrow indicating direction of rotation for installation reference and remove timing belt. Remove crankshaft sprocket bolts. Remove crankshaft sprocket and flange. Remove timing belt tensioner.

Installation

1) Install flange and crankshaft sprocket. *See Fig. 6*. Install camshaft sprocket and tighten retaining bolt. Align camshaft and crankshaft sprocket timing marks with No. 1 piston at TDC on compression stroke.

Fig. 6: Mounting Timing Belt Flange & Sprocket

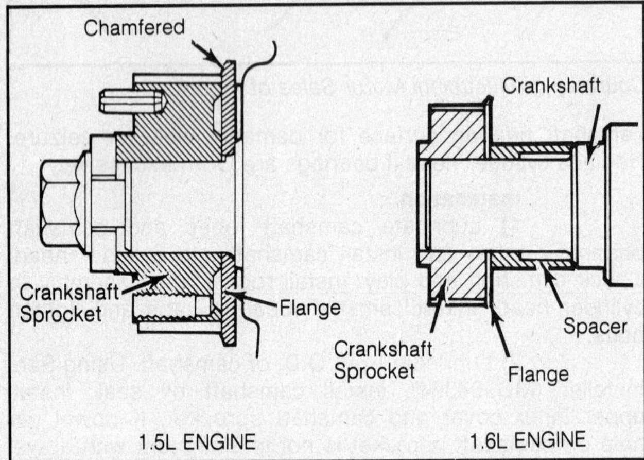

Installing flange incorrectly may damage belt. Courtesy of Mitsubishi Motor Sales of America.

2) Mount belt tensioner, spring and spacer. Temporarily tighten bolt. Position spring against tensioner first, then against case and tighten bolt. *See Fig. 7*. Position and secure tensioner toward water pump.

Fig. 7: Installing Timing Belt Tensioner on 1.5L Engine

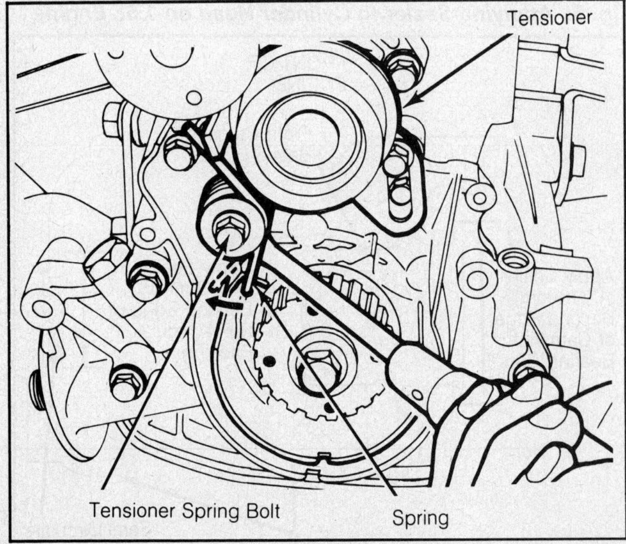

Wind spring carefully to prevent damage to front cover. Courtesy of Mitsubishi Motor Sales of America.

3) Install timing belt on crankshaft and camshaft sprockets. Ensure tension side is tight and timing marks are aligned when pressure is applied to turn camshaft in reverse direction.

4) Align dowel and install crankshaft pulley. Loosen tensioner spring bolt and then slotted tensioner bolt. This will give the timing belt only spring tension. Ensure tensioner and belt are properly positioned. With only spring tension applied to belt, tighten slotted tensioner bolt first and tensioner spring bolt last.

5) Slowly turn crankshaft one revolution clockwise and realign crankshaft sprocket timing mark at TDC. Do not push or shake belt while turning. Do not turn crankshaft in counterclockwise direction.

6) Loosen tensioner spring bolt first, then slotted tensioner bolt. Then tighten tensioner bolts by tightening slotted tensioner bolt first and tensioner spring bolt last.

7) Check belt tension by pushing tension side of timing belt in horizontally, using about 11 lbs. (5 kg) force. Timing belt tooth end should be approximately 1/4 of tensioner mounting bolt head width (across flats) away from bolt head center. *See Fig. 8*.

Fig. 8: Checking Timing Belt Tension on 1.5L Engine

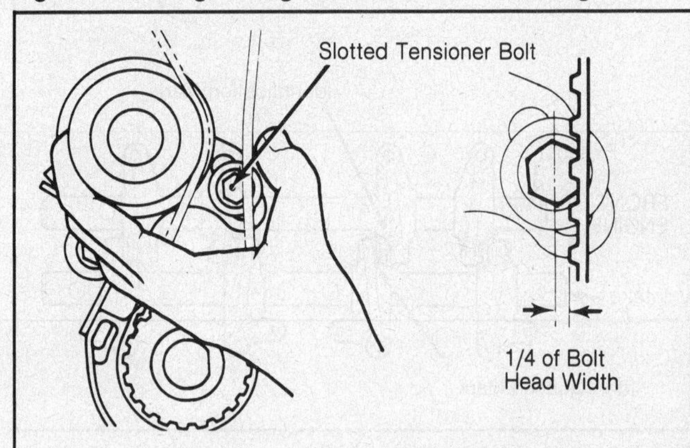

Courtesy of Mitsubishi Motor Sales of America.

Removal (1.6L)

1) Remove crankshaft pulley, upper and lower front timing belt covers and crankshaft sprocket bolt. Move tensioner to release belt tension and tighten nut to retain in this position.

2) Remove timing belt, camshaft sprocket, crankshaft sprocket and flange. Remove timing belt tensioner and upper and lower inner timing belt covers.

Installation

1) Install spacer, flange and crankshaft sprocket. *See Fig. 6*. Align crankshaft sprocket timing mark with front case timing mark. *See Fig. 9*. Lightly oil camshaft spacer and insert onto camshaft.

2) Install camshaft sprocket, tighten bolt to specification and align timing marks. Install tensioner spring and tensioner and temporarily tighten bolt. Rotate tensioner flange and install flange bolts.

3) Install tensioner spring with bent end at right angle on tensioner projection and straight end of spring on water pump body. *See Fig. 10*. Secure tensioner in position nearest water pump.

1.5L & 1.6L TURBO 4-CYLINDER (Cont.)

Fig. 9: Installing Timing Belt on 1.6L Engine

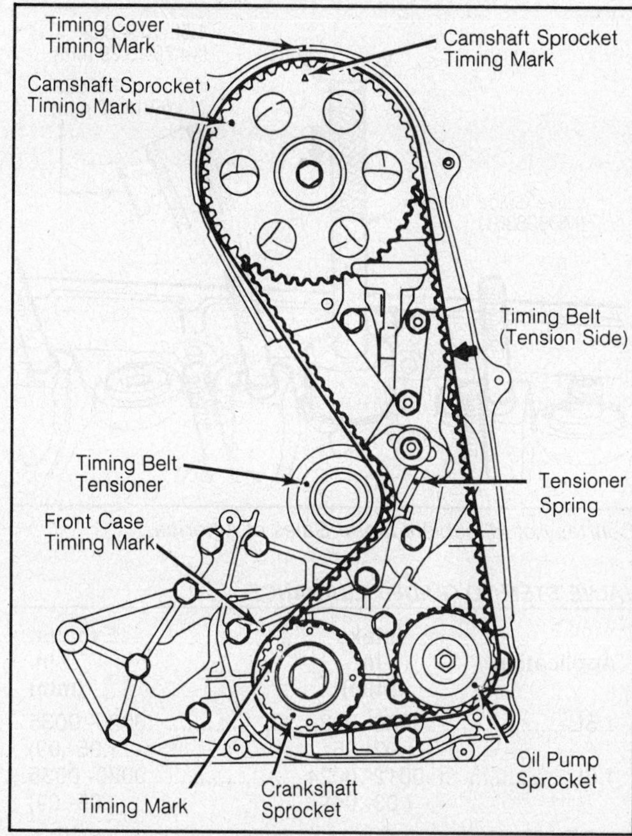

Courtesy of Mitsubishi Motor Sales of America.

Fig. 10: Installing Timing Belt Tensioner on 1.6L Engine

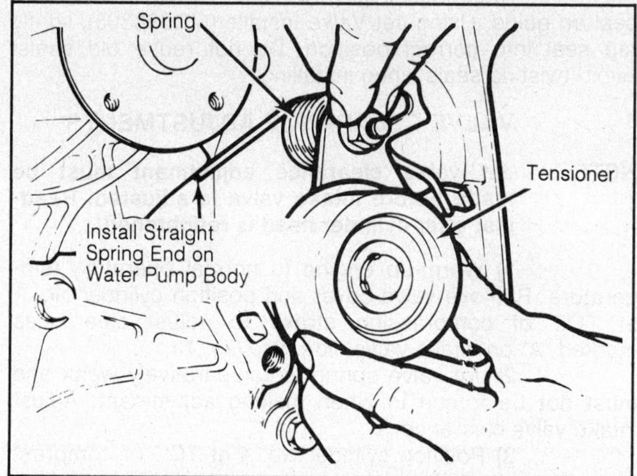

Courtesy of Mitsubishi Motor Sales of America.

4) Ensure all individual timing marks are aligned. Install timing belt on crankshaft sprocket, oil pump sprocket and camshaft sprocket.

5) Ensure tension side of belt is tight. Align dowel and temporarily install crankshaft pulley. Loosen tensioner bolt and nut so spring tension is applied to belt. Lightly push tensioner by hand to ensure belt and sprocket are in complete mesh.

6) Tighten tensioner nut, and then tighten bolt. Turn crankshaft smoothly one revolution clockwise, without pushing or jerking. DO NOT turn crankshaft counterclockwise. Loosen tensioner bolt and nut to allow spring pressure to tighten belt.

7) Retighten tensioner nut, then tighten bolt. Check tensioner adjustment by holding center of tension side of belt and seal line of inner cover between thumb and forefinger. *See Fig. 11.*

Fig. 11: Checking Timing Belt Tension on 1.6L Engine

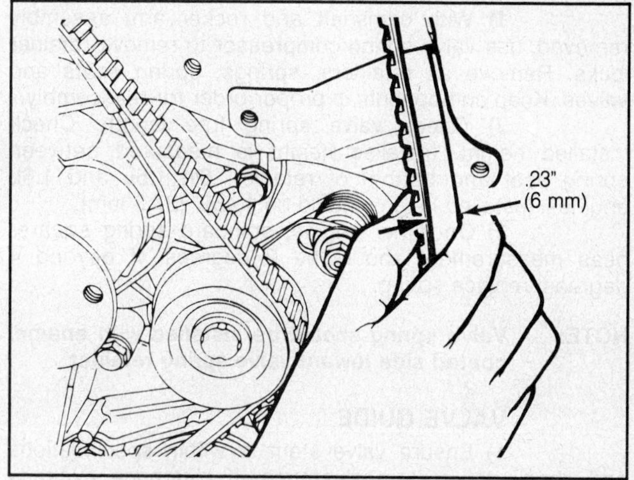

Courtesy of Mitsubishi Motor Sales of America.

8) Clearance should be .23" (6.0 mm). Readjust if necessary. Remove crankshaft pulley and install timing belt upper and lower front covers. Install crankshaft pulley and tighten.

VALVES

VALVE ARRANGEMENT

Left Side – Intake and jet valves.
Right Side – Exhaust valves.

NOTE: **"Right" and "Left" refer to right and left side of the engine NOT the vehicle.**

JET VALVES

Removal

1) Remove rocker arms and shafts. Using Jet Valve Socket (MD998310), remove jet valves. Disassemble valve using Spring Pliers (MD998309) to compress spring and remove retainer lock.

2) Ensure jet valve socket is not tilted with respect to center of valve when used. If socket is tilted, stem may be bent resulting in defective jet valve operation and a broken wrench.

3) Check valve head and seat for damage and ensure jet valve slides smoothly in body without play. Do not disturb jet valve and body combination. If defective, jet valve and body should be replaced as an assembly. Remove jet valve stem seals with pliers and discard.

Installation

1) Install new jet valve seal using Jet Valve Stem Seal Installer (MD998308). Apply oil to jet valve stem and install jet valve into body. Ensure jet valve stem slides smoothly in body.

2) Compress spring using spring pliers. Install spring, retainer and retainer lock. Do not damage valve

1.5L & 1.6L TURBO 4-CYLINDER (Cont.)

stem seal with bottom of retainer during installation. Install new "O" ring in jet valve body groove and lubricate with a light coat of oil.

3) Lubricate threaded portion and seating surface of jet valve assembly. Install jet valve assembly finger-tight. Tighten jet valve to specification using jet valve socket.

VALVE SPRINGS

1) With camshaft and rocker arm assembly removed, use valve spring compressor to remove retainer locks. Remove all retainers, springs, spring seats and valves. Keep components in proper order for reassembly.

2) Check valve spring free length. Check installed height. Installed height is measured between spring seat and bottom of retainer. On 1.5L and 1.6L engines, installed height should be 1.469" (37.3 mm).

3) On either engine, standard spring squareness measurement should be 2 degrees. If beyond 4 degrees, replace spring.

NOTE: Valve spring should be installed with enamel coated side toward valve spring retainer.

VALVE GUIDE

1) Ensure valve stem is within specifications and check valve stem clearance. If clearance exceeds service limits, replace valve guide with next oversize. See VALVE GUIDE OVERSIZES table.

VALVE GUIDE OVERSIZES

Size Mark	Guide Size (mm)	Cyl. Head Bore In. (mm)
1.5L		
5	.05	.4744-.4751 (12.050-12.068)
25	.25	.4823-.4830 (12.250-12.268)
50	.50	.4921-.4928 (12.500-12.518)
1.6L		
5	.05	.5138-.5145 (13.05-13.07)
25	.25	.5216-.5224 (13.25-13.27)
50	.50	.5315-.5323 (13.50-13.52)

2) Use a valve guide remover to drive out each guide toward bottom of cylinder head. Ream guide bore in cylinder head to specified size. See VALVE GUIDE OVERSIZES table.

3) Using Valve Guide Installer (MD998301), install new guides into head. *See Fig. 12.* Use of special tool makes it possible to install guide to predetermined height.

CAUTION: Do not use standard size valve guide for replacement. Be sure to install valve guide at room temperature.

4) Check guide clearance with new valve and ream as necessary.

Fig. 12: Installing Valve Guide

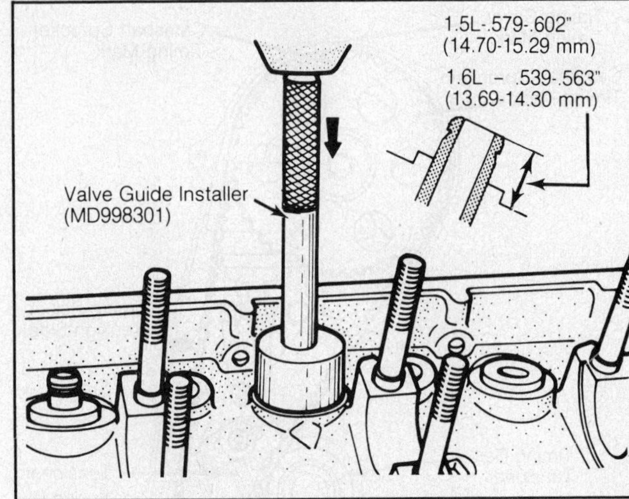

Courtesy of Mitsubishi Motor Sales of America.

VALVE STEM-TO-GUIDE CLEARANCE

Application	Intake In. (mm)	Exhaust In. (mm)
1.5L	.0080-.0020 (.02-.05)	.0020-.0035 (.05-.09)
1.6L	.0012-.0024 (.03-.06)	.0020-.0035 (.05-.09)

VALVE STEM OIL SEALS

After installing valve spring seat, place stem seal on guide. Using Jet Valve Installer(MD998308), lightly tap seal into correct position. Do not reuse old seals. Avoid twisting seals when installing.

VALVE CLEARANCE ADJUSTMENTS

NOTE: Jet valve clearance adjustment must be made before intake valve is adjusted. Readjust after cylinder head is retightened.

1) Warm-up engine to normal operating temperature. Remove valve cover and position cylinder No. 1 at TDC of compression stroke to adjust clearances marked "A" on intake valve side. *See Fig. 13.*

2) Jet valve spring is comparatively weak and must not be forced in when making adjustment. Adjust intake valve clearance.

3) Position cylinder No. 4 at TDC of compression stroke to adjust clearances marked "B" on intake valve side. Adjust by repeating steps **1)** and **2)**.

VALVE CLEARANCE SPECIFICATIONS

Application	Cold In. (mm)	Hot In. (mm)
Intake	.003 (.07)	.006 (.15)
Exhaust	.007 (.17)	.010 (.25)
Jet Valve	.007 (.17)	.010 (.25)

1.5L & 1.6L TURBO 4-CYLINDER (Cont.)

Fig. 13: Valve Clearance Adjusting Sequence

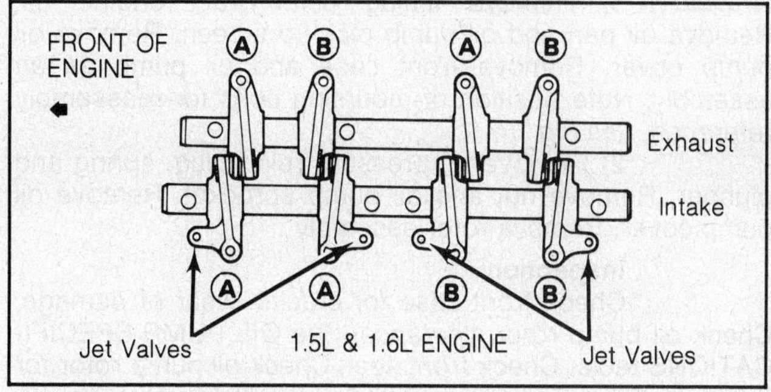

Courtesy of Mitsubishi Motor Sales of America.

PISTONS, PINS & RINGS

PISTON & CONNECTING ROD ASSEMBLY

Removal

Remove cylinder head, oil pan and screen. Ensure connecting rods and rod caps are marked for reassembly reference. Remove ridge from top of cylinder bores. Remove connecting rod caps. Remove connecting rod and piston assembly through top of cylinder block.

Installation

Lubricate all internal surfaces with engine oil before installation. Ensure front mark on piston head faces front of engine. Use ring compressor to compress rings, without changing their position. Install piston and connecting rod assembly into cylinder block in their original position.

PISTON PINS

Check piston bore fit. Pin should press in smoothly by hand at room temperature. When assembling, apply engine oil to outside of pin and to piston pin bore. Position rod to piston with identification mark upward. Align pin with installer, and press pin into piston and rod.

NOTE: Pin-to-rod fit at normal temperature requires 1,102-3,306 lbs. (500-1500 kg) to press pin through rod.

PISTON RINGS

1) Measure piston ring side and end clearance for all pistons. Replace rings as necessary. When replacing rings in cylinder bore not needing reconditioning, check ring end gap at lower part of cylinder that is less worn.

2) When replacing rings, be sure to use same size ring. Install rings on piston with end gaps staggered at 120 degree intervals. Ensure no ring gap is in line with thrust face of pin bore. Also ensure manufacturer's marks are facing upward when rings are installed.

CAUTION: Install oil ring first without using a ring expander. Spacer expander gap should be installed more than 45 degrees from side rail gaps. Rails should turn smoothly when installed.

Fig. 14: Positioning Piston Ring Gap

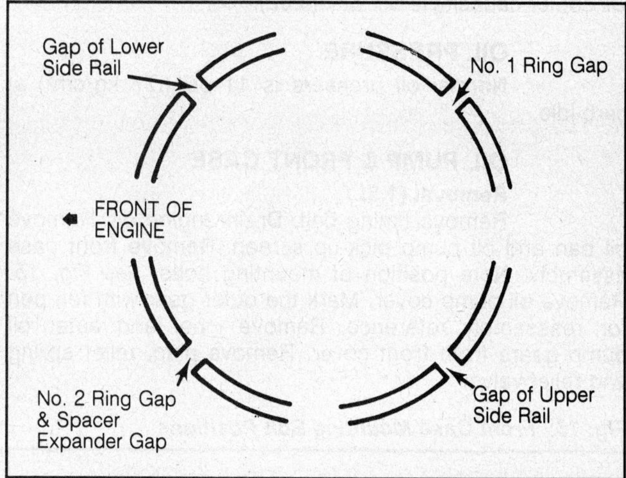

Courtesy of Mitsubishi Motor Sales of America.

CRANKSHAFT & ROD BEARINGS

MAIN & CONNECTING ROD BEARINGS

Removal & Installation

1) Remove timing belt train. Remove front case, flywheel, cylinder head assembly and oil pan. Remove rear plate and rear oil seal. Remove connecting rod caps. Remove main bearing caps and remove crankshaft.

2) Keep bearings in order for reassembly reference. Inspect each bearing for peeling, melting, seizure or improper contact. Replace defective bearings. Measure outside diameter of crankshaft and connecting rod journals to determine if out-of-round or tapered. Out-of-round or taper limits .0004" (.01 mm).

3) Use Plastigage method to measure bearing clearance. If clearance exceeds limits, bearing should be replaced or undersize bearing installed. Main and connecting rod bearings are available in .010" (.25 mm), .020" (.50 mm) and .030" (.75 mm) undersizes.

4) To install, reverse removal procedure. Lubricate bearings before installing. Tighten bolts to specification in 3 steps. Tighten main bearing caps in order of center, No. 2, No. 4, front and rear main caps.

THRUST BEARING

With crankshaft bearing caps installed, check thrust clearance (end play) by inserting feeler gauge between center main bearing and crankshaft thrust face. If clearance exceeds specified limits, replace center main bearing.

ENGINE OILING

ENGINE OILING SYSTEM

All engines use force-feed type lubrication system. The 1.5L engine uses a crescent-type pump and 1.6L engine uses a trochoid-type pump.

CRANKCASE CAPACITY

Crankcase capacity is 3.7 qts. (3.5L) for the 1.5L engine and 4.5 qts. (4.3L) for the 1.6L engine.

1.5L & 1.6L TURBO 4-CYLINDER (Cont.)

Capacity includes filter and cooler (if equipped on 1.6L). Oil cooler capacity is .21 qts. (.20L).

OIL PRESSURE

Normal oil pressure is 11 psi (.77 kg/cm²) at curb idle.

OIL PUMP & FRONT CASE

Removal (1.5L)

Remove timing belt. Drain engine oil. Remove oil pan and oil pump pick-up screen. Remove front case assembly. Note position of mounting bolts. *See Fig. 15.* Remove oil pump cover. Mark the outer gear with felt pen for reassembly reference. Remove inner and outer oil pump gears from front cover. Remove plug, relief spring and relief valve.

Fig. 15: Front Case Mounting Bolt Positions

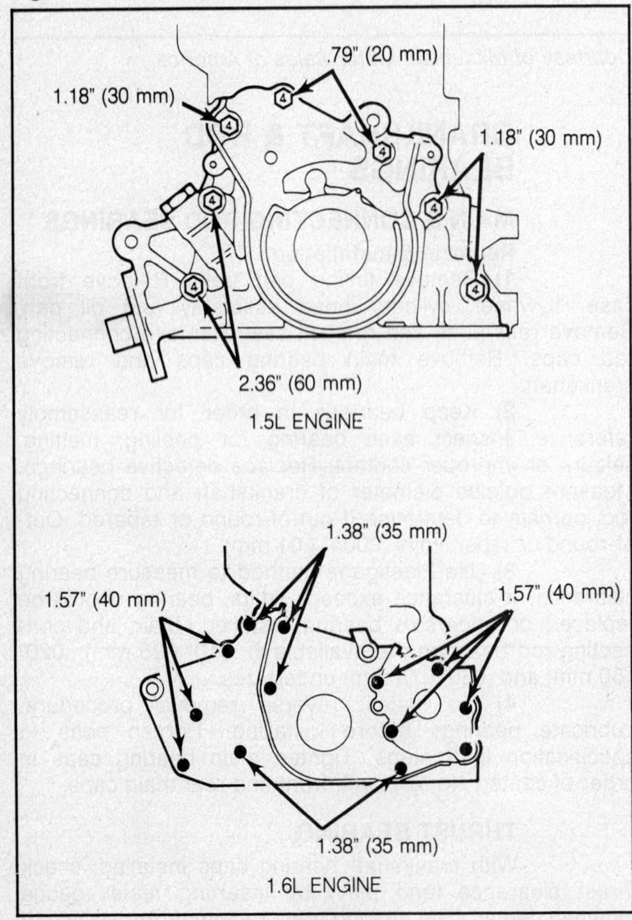

Ensure bolts are installed in original positions. Courtesy of Mitsubishi Motor Sales of America.

Inspection

1) Check front case for cracks or damage. Check front seal for worn or damaged lips. Check front case and oil pump cover for worn or damaged surfaces contacting gears. Check oil screen for clogging or damage. Check oil screen "O" ring.

2) Check oil pump gears for worn or damaged teeth. Check oil pump clearances. See OIL PUMP SPECIFICATIONS table. Ensure relief valve slides smoothly in bore. Check for a deformed or broken pressure relief spring.

Removal (1.6L)

1) Remove timing belt. Drain engine oil. Remove oil pan and oil pump pick-up screen. Remove oil pump cover. Remove front case and oil pump as an assembly. Note position of mounting bolts for reassembly reference. *See Fig. 15.*

2) Remove oil pressure relief plug, spring and plunger. Remove nut and oil pump sprocket. Remove oil pump cover. Remove rotor assembly.

Inspection

Check front case for cracks, wear or damage. Check oil pump rotor clearance. See OIL PUMP SPECIFICATIONS table. Check front seal. Check oil pump rotor for damage. Ensure pressure relief valve slides smoothly in bore. Check for a deformed or broken pressure relief spring. Replace damaged parts as necessary.

Installation (1.5L & 1.6L)

1) To install, reverse removal procedure. Ensure that gears are assembled in same direction as originally installed. Install new oil seal using a flat plate. Use new gasket and install front case assembly. Install front case mounting bolts in original positions. Install oil screen.

2) Apply a .16" (4.0 mm) bead of sealer into groove of oil pan flange. Tighten mounting bolts to specification.

CAUTION: Prior to installing oil pump, fill with sufficient amount of engine oil to prime pump.

OIL PUMP SPECIFICATIONS

Application	Clearance In. (mm)
1.5L Crescent-Type	
Inner Gear-to-Crescent	.0083-.0126 (.211-.320)
Gear End Play	.0016-.0039 (.041-.099)
Outer Gear-to-Case	.0039-.0079 (.10-.20)
Outer Gear-to-Crescent	.0087-.0173 (.22-.44)
1.6L Trochoid-Type	
Body Clearance	.0039-.0063 (.10-.16)
Drive Shaft-to-Cover Clear.	.0008-.0020 (.02-.05)
Side Clearance	.0024-.0047 (.06-.12)
Tip Clearance	.0016-.0047 (.04-.12)

ENGINE COOLING

WATER PUMP

Removal

1) Drain cooling system and disconnect battery. Remove drive belt, pulley and lower radiator hose to pump. Ensure that number 1 piston is at TDC of compression stroke.

2) Remove crankshaft pulley, timing belt covers, timing belt, camshaft sprocket, upper inner cover and timing belt tensioner. Remove pump mounting bolts noting length and position. Remove alternator brace. Remove pump from engine.

Installation

To install, use new gasket and reverse removal procedure. Ensure bolts are installed in their proper positions.

NOTE: For further information on cooling systems, see ENGINE COOLING section.

Mitsubishi Engines

1.5L & 1.6L TURBO 4-CYLINDER (Cont.)

TIGHTENING SPECIFICATIONS

Application	Ft. Lbs. (N.m)
Camshaft Bearing Cap Bolt	
1.6L	24-25 (33-35)
Camshaft Sprocket Bolt	
1.5L	47-54 (65-75)
1.6L	58-72 (79-98)
Center Member-to-Body Bolt	43-58 (80-100)
Connecting Rod Cap Bolt	24-25 (33-35)
Crankshaft Sprocket Bolt	
1.5L	51-72 (70-100)
1.6L	58-72 (80-100)
Cylinder Head Bolt	
Cold	51-54 (70-75)
Hot	58-61 (80-83)
Drive Plate-to-Crankshaft Bolt	94-101 (127-137)
Exhaust Manifold Nut	11-14 (15-19)
Exhaust Pipe-to-Manifold Bolt	11-18 (15-24)
Flywheel-to-Crankshaft Bolt	94-101 (127-137)
Front Case Bolt	
1.5L	9-10 (12-14)
1.6L	11-13 (15-17)
Front Roll Insulator Nut	33-43 (45-60)
Front Roll Stopper Bracket-to-Center Member Assembly Bolts	33-43 (45-60)
Intake Manifold Nut	11-14 (15-19)
Jet Valve	13-15 (18-20)
Left Motor Mount Insulator	
Large Nut	65-80 (90-110)
Small Nut	33-43 (45-60)

TIGHTENING SPECIFICATIONS (Cont.)

Application	Ft. Lbs. (N.m)
Left Motor Mount Bracket-to-Engine Bolts & Nuts	37-47 (50-65)
Lower Roll Insulator-to-Roll Damper Bracket Bolt	22-29 (30-39)
Main Bearing Cap Bolt	37-39 (50-53)
Oil Pump Sprocket Bolt (1.6L)	25-28 (34-39)
Rear Roll Insulator Nut	33-43 (45-60)
Rear Roll Stopper Bracket-to-Center Member Assembly Bolts	33-40 (45-54)
Rocker Arm Shaft Bolt (1.5L)	15-19 (20-26)
Timing Belt Tensioner Bolt or Nut	
1.5L	15-19 (20-26)
1.6L	16-22 (22-30)
Transaxle Bracket-to-Transaxle Bolts	
Automatic	65-80 (88-108)
Manual	40-43 (54-58)
Transaxle Insulator Bracket-to-Side Frame Bolts	22-29 (30-40)
Transaxle Mount Insulator Nut	66-80 (90-110)
	INCH Lbs. (N.m)
Crankshaft Pulley Bolt	
1.5L	108-120 (12-14)
1.6L	132-156 (15-18)
Oil Pan Bolt	54-66 (6-7)
Oil Pump Cover Bolt (1.6L)	72-84 (8-9)

ENGINE SPECIFICATIONS

GENERAL SPECIFICATIONS

Year	DISPLACEMENT		Fuel System	HP@RPM	Torque Ft. Lbs.@RPM	Compr. Ratio	BORE		STROKE	
	Cu. In.	Liters					In.	mm	In.	mm
1987	89.6 97.4	1.5 1.6	FBC ECI	68@5500 102@5500	82@3500 122@3200	9.4:1 7.6:1	2.97 3.03	75.5 76.9	3.23 3.39	82.0 86.0

VALVES

Engine Size & Valve	Head Diam. In. (mm)	Face Angle	Seat Angle	Seat Width In. (mm)	Stem Diameter In. (mm)	Stem Clearance In. (mm)	Valve Lift In. (mm)
1.5L & 1.6L							
Intake	[1] 1.34 (34)	45°	45°	.035-.051 (.9-1.3)	[3] .260 (6.6)	[4] .0008-.0020 (.02-.05)	[5] .346 (8.8)
Exhaust	[2] 1.18 (30)	45°	45°	.035-.051 (.9-1.3)	[3] .260 (6.6)	.0020-.0035 (.05-.09)	[5] .346 (8.8)

1 – On 1.6L engine 1.50" (38 mm).
2 – On 1.6L engine 1.22" (31 mm).
3 – On 1.6L engine .315" (8.0 mm).
4 – On 1.6L engine .0012-.0024" (.03-.06 mm).
5 – On 1.6L engine .362" (9.2 mm).

Mitsubishi Engines

1.5L & 1.6L TURBO 4-CYLINDER (Cont.)

ENGINE SPECIFICATIONS (Cont.)

PISTONS, PINS & RINGS

Engine	PISTONS	PINS		RINGS		
	Clearance In. (mm)	Piston Fit In. (mm)	Rod Fit In. (mm)	Ring No.	End Gap In. (mm)	Side Clearance In. (mm)
1.5L & 1.6L	.0008-.0016 (.02-.04)	[1]	[2] Press Fit	No. 1	[3] .008-.016 (.20-.40)	.0012-.0028 (.03-.07)
				No. 2	[4] .008-.016 (.20-.40)	.0008-.0024 (.02-.06)
				Oil	[5] .008-.020 (.20-.50)	.....

[1] – Thumb press fit without rod installed.
[2] – Press in at 1100-3300 lbs. at room temperature.
[3] – End Gap on 1.6L engine is .010-.016" (.25-.40 mm).
[4] – End Gap on 1.6L engine is .008-.014" (.20-.35 mm).
[5] – End gap on 1.6L engine is .008-.028" (.20-.71 mm).

CRANKSHAFT MAIN & CONNECTING ROD BEARINGS

Engine	MAIN BEARINGS				CONNECTING ROD BEARINGS		
	Journal Diam. In. (mm)	Clearance In. (mm)	Thrust Bearing	Crankshaft End Play In. (mm)	Journal Diam. In. (mm)	Clearance In. (mm)	Side Play In. (mm)
1.5L & 1.6L	[1] 1.890 (48)	.0008-.0028 (.02-.07)	No. 3	.002-.007 (.05-.18)	[2] 1.654 (42)	.0008-.0024 (.02-.06)	.004-.010 (.10-.25)

[1] – On 1.6L engine 2.244" (57 mm).
[2] – On 1.6L engine 1.772" (45 mm).

CAMSHAFT

Engine	Journal Diam. In. (mm)	Clearance In. (mm)	Lobe Lift In. (mm)
1.5L	1.80 (46)	[1] .0015-.0031 (.040-.080)	.....
1.6L	1.33 (34)	[2] .0020-.0035 (.051-.089)	.....

[1] – End play is .002-.008" (.05-.20 mm) on 1.5L engine.
[2] – End play is .002-.006" (.05-.15 mm) on 1.6L engine.

VALVE SPRINGS

Engine	Free Length In. (mm)	PRESSURE Lbs. @ In. (Kg @ mm)	
		Valve Closed	Valve Open
1.5L	1.756 (44.6)	53@1.469 (24@37.3)	.....
1.6L	1.800 (45.9)	62@1.469 (28.1@37.3)	.....

Mitsubishi Engines

1.8L TURBO, 2.0L & 2.4L 4-CYLINDER

Chrysler Motors: Colt Vista (2WD & 4WD), Ram-50
Mitsubishi: Cordia, Galant, Pickup, Tredia, Van/Wagon

NOTE: For engine repair procedures not covered in this article, see ENGINE OVERHAUL PROCEDURES article at beginning of this section.

ENGINE CODING

ENGINE IDENTIFICATION

Vehicle Identification Number (VIN) is stamped on a metal plate at upper left corner of instrument panel, near windshield. The eighth character identifies engine and tenth character identifies model year. Engine model code and serial number are stamped on top edge of right front side of cylinder block near alternator.

ENGINE IDENTIFICATION CODES

Application	Engine Model	Engine VIN Code
1.8L Turbo	G62B	G
2.0L	G63B	D
2.4L	G64B	L

ENGINE, MANIFOLDS & CYLINDER HEAD

ENGINE

Removal (Colt Vista)

NOTE: Remove engine and transaxle as an assembly.

1) Disconnect battery cables. Remove hood and air cleaner. Remove battery, battery tray and battery tray mounting bracket. Unplug oil pressure connectors to engine and power steering pump. Unplug harness connector for alternator. Disconnect high tension cable from ignition coil. Disconnect wiring to distributor. Disconnect engine ground from firewall.

2) Remove windshield washer tank. Disconnect vacuum hose from brake booster. Disconnect all other vacuum hoses. Drain coolant and remove reservoir tank. Disconnect upper and lower radiator hoses at engine and remove radiator. Disconnect heater hoses. Disconnect accelerator cable and speed control cable (if equipped) from carburetor. Disconnect speedometer cable.

3) Discharge A/C system. Disconnect hoses at compressor and plug openings to prevent contamination. Disconnect power steering hose at pump. Disconnect fuel return hose from carburetor. Disconnect main fuel hose from filter. Disconnect shift cables from transaxle case.

4) Raise vehicle and remove cover and lower plate. Drain transaxle and transfer case oil (if equipped). Disconnect exhaust pipe from manifold. On 4WD models, disconnect propeller shaft from transfer case.

5) Remove clutch release cylinder and disconnect hydraulic clutch piping. Disconnect driveshafts from transaxle case and cover holes in case to prevent contamination. Remove transfer case extension stopper bracket (if equipped).

NOTE: Remove 2 top bolts for transfer case extension stopper bracket (if equipped) from engine compartment.

6) Lower vehicle and remove nuts for bolt coupling the engine mounting bracket-to-body. DO NOT remove coupling bolt. Remove select control valves from transaxle insulator bracket. Remove nut for transaxle mounting insulator bolt. DO NOT remove coupling bolt. Remove front roll insulator installation nut. Remove rear insulator-to-engine coupling nut.

7) Remove radiator grille and bridge panel. Remove A/C condenser. Raise engine until weight is removed from mounts. Remove mounting bolts. Ensure all

Installation

NOTE: Replace drive axle shaft retainer ring each time drive axle shaft is removed.

To install, reverse removal procedure. Rear roll stopper insulator bolt should be installed after cross-member side has been mounted. Use care to align front engine mount locating holes without twisting insulator rubber. Tighten mounting bolts and nuts to specification with weight of engine on insulators. Replace all fluids, adjust all cables and linkages and check operation of gauges and meters.

Removal (Cordia, Galant & Tredia)

NOTE: Remove engine and transaxle as an assembly. On fuel injected models, fuel system must be depressurized before disconnecting fuel lines, prior to engine removal.

1) On fuel injected models, start engine and disconnect the electric fuel pump connector. Allow engine to run out of fuel. Turn ignition off. On all models, disconnect battery. Remove battery and battery tray. Drain engine and transaxle oil and radiator coolant. Remove hood and air cleaner assembly. Unplug inhibitor switch and pulse generator connector. Disconnect brake booster vacuum hose. Disconnect hose from canister and purge control valve.

2) Disconnect ground wire from right inner fender panel. Unplug front harness-to-engine harness connector. Discharge A/C system (if equipped). Drain power steering fluid. Remove electronic controlled suspension compressor and reserve tank assembly (if equipped). Disconnect transaxle control cable. Unplug alternator harness and oil pressure gauge connectors. Label and disconnect transaxle oil cooler hoses.

3) Unplug oxygen sensor connector. Disconnect ignition coil harnesses. Unplug engine harness-to-control harness. Disconnect coolant temperature switch. Disconnect throttle position sensor, idling control actuator and motor position sensor. Unplug injector connector from intake manifold. Remove harness protector bolt from surge tank.

4) Disconnect accelerator cable from actuator link. Disconnect fuel return hose and high pressure hose at manifold. Disconnect upper and lower radiator hoses. Disconnect heater hoses. Disconnect speedometer cable. Disconnect and plug A/C hoses at compressor. Disconnect power steering hoses at pump.

5) Raise and support vehicle. Disconnect exhaust pipe from the manifold. Support exhaust pipe with wire. On Galant models, remove knuckle from lower control arm ball joint using Remover (MB990778-01). Remove tie rod end from knuckle using Remover (MB990635-01). On all models, remove drive axles from transaxle case and cap holes in transaxle case to prevent contamination. Lower vehicle.

6) Connect engine hoist and remove slack from sling. Remove engine mount bracket-to-body nut. DO NOT remove bolt. Remove front roll stopper bracket upper nut. Remove rear roll stopper bracket upper nut. Remove cover from right inner fender panel. Remove transaxle mounting bracket bolts. Remove transaxle mounting insulator-to-bracket bolts. Remove transaxle mounting bracket.

7) Lift engine slightly and remove engine mounting bracket and roll stopper bolts. Ensure all hoses, cables and wiring are disconnected from the engine. Remove engine while tilting transaxle down.

Installation

NOTE: Replace drive axle shaft retainer ring each time drive axle shaft is removed.

1) To install, reverse removal procedure. Ensure arrow on mounting stopper of engine mount bracket faces center part of engine. Ensure front roll stopper bracket identification hole faces front of body.

2) On Galant models, check insulator clearance before engine weight is applied to front and rear roll stoppers. Temporarily tighten front roll stopper bracket. Center hole of insulator to lower edge of bracket should be 1.8-2.0" (46.7-52.7 mm). *See Fig. 1.* Temporarily tighten rear roll stopper bracket. Insulator clearance should be .23-.35" (6-9 mm). *See Fig. 2.*

Fig. 1: Checking Galant Front Roll Stopper Insulator

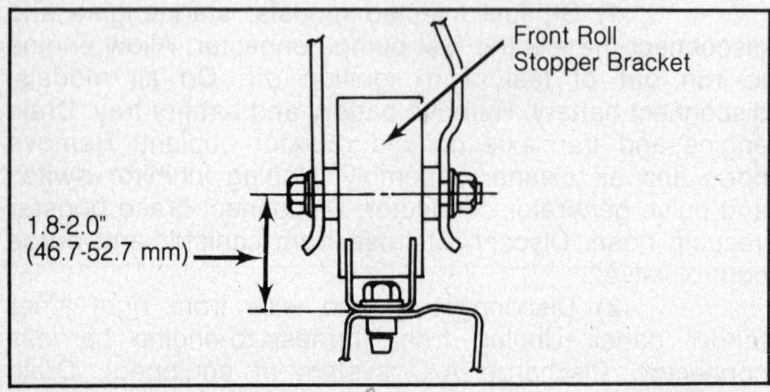

Ensure weight of engine is not on insulator. Courtesy of Mitsubishi Motor Sales of America.

Fig. 2: Checking Galant Rear Roll Stopper Insulator

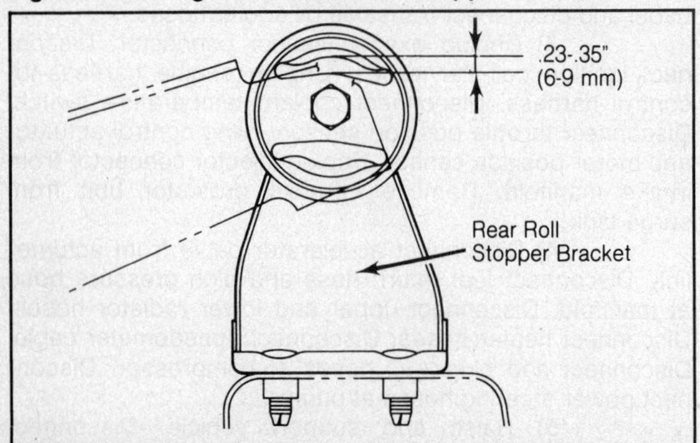

Ensure weight of engine is not on insulator. Courtesy of Mitsubishi Motor Sales of America.

3) On all models, tighten all mounting nuts and bolts to specification. Adjust transaxle control cable and throttle cable.

Removal (Pickup & Ram-50)

NOTE: Remove engine and transmission as an assembly.

1) Disconnect negative battery cable. Remove hood and air cleaner. Disconnect heater and brake booster vacuum hoses. Disconnect fuel hoses and accelerator cable. Disconnect engine ground cable.

2) Disconnect wiring from starter, alternator, coil and coolant temperature and oil pressure sending units. Remove radiator assembly. Disconnect clutch cable and remove front exhaust pipe.

3) Remove power steering pump (if equipped). Remove undercover and other protective transmission covers (if equipped). Disconnect speedometer cable, back-up light harness and 4WD indicator light switch (if equipped).

4) Mark for reference and remove propeller shafts. Remove gearshift lever assembly. Support transmission. Disconnect rear insulator from transmission and remove crossmember.

5) Support transfer case with a jack and remove transfer case mounting bracket and support insulator. Remove plate from side frame. Disconnect mounting bracket from transfer case. Remove front engine insulator mounting nuts. Attach lifting cables. With front of engine tilted upward, remove engine/transmission assembly diagonally from vehicle.

Installation

To install, reverse removal procedure. Use care to align front engine mount locating holes without twisting insulator rubber. Tighten mounting bolts and nuts to specification with weight of engine on insulators. Replace all fluids. Adjust all cables and linkages. Check operation of gauges and meters.

Removal (Van/Wagon)

NOTE: Engine and transmission is lowered under floor as an assembly.

1) Depressurize fuel system by starting engine with disabled fuel pump and wait until engine dies.

2) Engine compartment is under front seats. Remove front seats and engine compartment cover/lid. Cover behind driver's seat will also give access to battery.

3) Disconnect battery and all electrical connectors to engine and transmission, disconnect speedometer and throttle cables.

4) Remove radiator fan shroud, radiator upper and lower hoses, and heater hoses. Remove A/C compressor and all vacuum and fuel lines.

5) Remove strut bars and exhaust pipe connections. Remove transmission control cable connections and propeller shaft.

6) Firmly support oil pan with jack and wooden blocks. Remove engine support front insulator assemblies. Do not raise engine too much to avoid component damage.

7) Remove rear engine mounting bolt and engine mounting bolts and nuts to crossmember.

8) Ensure all hoses, cables and wirings are disconnected from engine. Slowly, lower engine down.

Mitsubishi Engines

1.8L TURBO, 2.0L & 2.4L 4-CYLINDER (Cont.)

Installation

1) To install, reverse removal procedure. Align hole to the positioning boss of engine support front insulator assemblies.

2) Run the shift control cables throught the insulator mounting bracket and attach crossmember to the body.

3) Tighten all mounting nuts and bolts to specification. Adjust control and throttle cables. Reconnect all hoses, cables and wiring connectors.

CYLINDER HEAD & MANIFOLDS

Removal

1) Drain cooling system. Remove breather hose and air cleaner. Disconnect necessary wiring. Remove vacuum and coolant hoses. Disconnect accelerator linkage and spark plug wires. Position cylinder No. 1 at TDC of compression stroke. Remove distributor, throttle body or carburetor, and intake manifold.

2) Remove exhaust manifold and gasket. On turbocharged models, remove heat shield and oxygen sensor. Remove turbocharger-to-catalytic converter nuts. Disconnect oil feed and return pipes. Remove air intake pipe connecting bolt and turbocharger mounting bolts. Remove turbocharger from exhaust manifold.

3) On all models, remove crankshaft and water pump pulleys. Remove timing belt front upper and lower covers. Mark timing belt, indicating direction of rotation, if belt is to be reused. Remove timing belt, camshaft sprocket and valve cover.

4) Remove camshaft bearing cap bolts. On 2.0L and 2.4L engines, install Auto-Lash Adjuster Holder (MD998443) on rocker arm to make sure adjusters do not fall out. Remove rocker shaft assembly and camshaft. Loosen cylinder head bolts, in reverse of tightening sequence, using Head Bolt Wrench (MD998051-01). *See Fig. 3.*

Inspection

Check cylinder head gasket surface for warpage by using straightedge and feeler gauge. If warpage exceeds .004" (.10 mm), lightly machine head surface or replace cylinder head. If machined, do not remove more than .008" (.20 mm) from head.

Installation

1) Install cylinder head gasket with gasket identification mark facing cylinder head. See CYLINDER HEAD GASKET IDENTIFICATION MARK table. DO NOT apply sealant to gasket or mating surfaces. Install cylinder head and head bolts.

CYLINDER HEAD GASKET IDENTIFICATION MARK

Application	Mark
1.8L	62
2.0L	63
2.4L	64

2) Tighten bolts in sequence to 1/2 of tightening specification, then tighten to final specification. *See Fig. 3.* Install camshaft sprocket and timing belt, ensuring timing mark alignment and belt tension are correct.

3) Reverse removal procedure to complete installation. Replace coolant. Adjust belts, valves and accelerator cable. With engine at operating temperature, adjust timing and idle speed.

Fig. 3: Cylinder Head Tightening Sequence

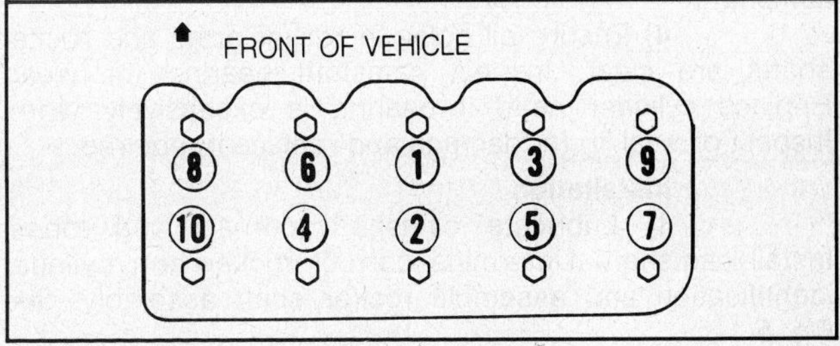

Reverse sequence when removing bolts. Courtesy of Mitsubishi Motor Sales of America.

CAMSHAFT

ROCKER SHAFT ASSEMBLY & CAMSHAFT

Removal

1) Remove upper timing belt and rocker shaft covers. Loosen camshaft sprocket bolt until it can be turned by hand. Rotate crankshaft until No. 1 cylinder is at TDC of compression stroke. Camshaft timing mark should be at pointer on cylinder head. *See Fig. 4.*

Fig. 4: Aligning Camshaft Timing Mark

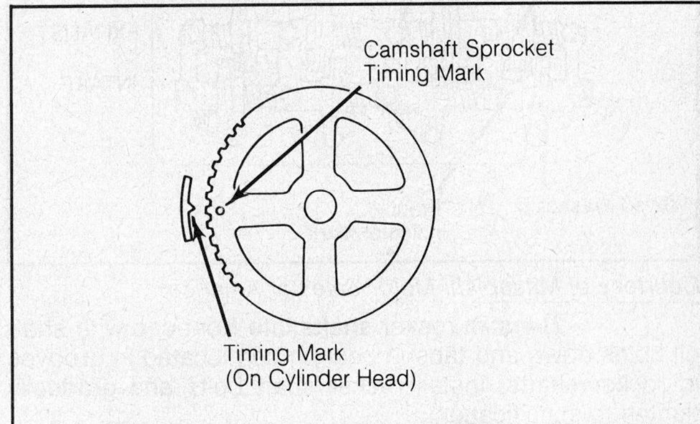

Courtesy of Mitsubishi Motor Sales of America.

2) Remove camshaft sprocket bolt. Remove camshaft sprocket and timing belt from camshaft. Place sprocket onto holder on lower timing belt cover. Remove camshaft bearing cap bolts.

3) On 2.0L and 2.4L engines, install Auto-Lash Adjuster Holder (MD998443) onto rocker arms to make sure adjusters do not fall out. Remove rocker arms, shafts and bearing caps as an assembly. Remove rocker arms, springs and caps from shafts. Keep rocker arms and adjusters in order for reassembly reference. Remove camshaft from cylinder head.

Inspection

1) Inspect rocker arm cam contact surface for pitting and wear. Check adjustment screw contact surface for wear and out-of-round. Inspect rocker shaft bore for loose fit on shaft.

2) Inspect rocker arm shaft for wear on rocker arm contact surfaces. Inspect camshaft for wear and damage on journals, lobes, fuel pump drive cam, distributor drive gear and oil seal contact surface.

3) On 1.8L turbo models, if camshaft lobe height is less than 1.641" (41.68 mm), replace camshaft. On 2.0L models, if camshaft lobe height is less than 1.637" (41.57 mm), replace camshaft. On 2.4L models, if cam-

1.8L TURBO, 2.0L & 2.4L 4-CYLINDER (Cont.)

shaft lobe height is less than 1.649" (41.88 mm), replace camshaft.

4) Ensure oil holes in rocker arms and rocker shafts are clear. Inspect camshaft bearing for wear. Replace cylinder head if bearing is excessively worn. Inspect oil seal lip for damage and replace if required.

Installation

1) Lubricate camshaft journals and lobes. Install camshaft. Determine correct rocker arm cylinder identification and assemble rocker shaft assembly. *See Fig. 5.*

NOTE: **Do not tilt auto-lash adjuster more than necessary to prevent oil in adjuster from spilling out. If oil leaks out, adjuster must be bled.**

Fig. 5: Assembling Rocker Shaft

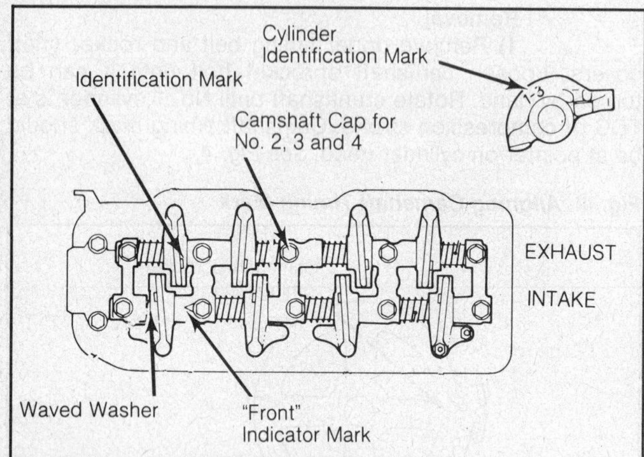

Courtesy of Mitsubishi Motor Sales of America.

2) Install rocker shafts into front cap with shaft oil holes down and tabs in bearing cap located in grooves in rocker shafts. Install rocker shaft bolts and gradually tighten to specification.

3) Turn camshaft until dowel pin is at 12 o'clock position. Install camshaft sprocket and timing belt. Ensure timing mark alignment and belt tension are correct. Reverse removal procedure to complete installation.

4) Adjust valves to specification. See VALVE CLEARANCE SPECIFICATIONS table. Apply sealant to top surface of cylinder block and above semi-circular packing at rear of head. Install valve cover.

TIMING BELTS & SPROCKETS

Camshaft Timing Belt Adjustment

1) Disconnect negative battery cable. Remove upper front timing belt cover or timing cover access cover (if equipped). Check timing belt for cracks or peeling. Turn crankshaft in clockwise direction only and position second tooth past timing mark on camshaft sprocket, in alignment with timing mark on cylinder head. *See Fig. 6.*

2) Using a screwdriver, pry out timing belt tensioner adjustment bolt and nut access covers, located in lower front timing belt cover, above and to the right of timing mark indicator.

3) Loosen belt tensioner nut and bolt 180-200 degrees. Do not loosen more than necessary, they might fall into lower cover. Insert screwdriver from top of timing cover. Slightly push tensioner toward belt, and then release.

Fig. 6: Adjusting Camshaft Timing Belt Without Removing Lower Cover or Replacing Belt

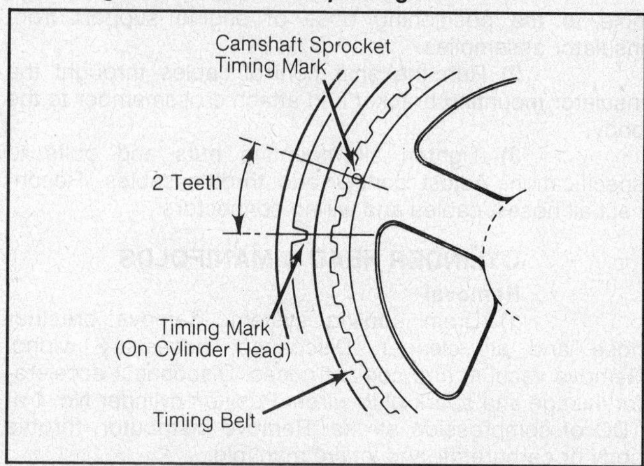

Courtesy of Mitsubishi Motor Sales of America.

4) This will allow spring to readjust, using only its own spring pressure. First tighten tensioner mounting bolt located in lower access hole, then tighten nut in upper hole.

5) Make certain bolt is tightened first. Tightening nut first will cause belt tension to be too tight. Install access covers and upper front timing cover. Reconnect battery.

Removal

1) Disconnect negative battery cable. Position No. 1 cylinder at TDC of compression stroke. Remove crankshaft and water pump pulleys. Remove upper and lower front timing belt covers.

2) Relieve camshaft timing belt tensioner pressure and secure tensioner toward water pump. If camshaft timing belt is to be reused, mark belt with an arrow indicating direction of rotation and remove belt.

3) Remove camshaft and crankshaft sprocket bolts. Remove camshaft sprocket, crankshaft sprocket and crankshaft flange. Remove plug on left side of cylinder block. Insert a screwdriver to keep left silent shaft in position. *See Fig. 13.*

4) Remove oil pump sprocket. Loosen right silent shaft sprocket mounting bolt until it can be turned by hand. Remove belt tensioner "B" and timing belt "B". Remove crankshaft sprocket "B" from crankshaft.

Inspection

1) Inspect back of belt for being hard, non-elastic and having a glossy surface. If no mark is produced when fingernail is forced into it, replace belt.

2) Check for rounded sides on belt. Sides of belt should be straight and clear-cut. Flaking, peeling, cracking and separating rubber from canvas also indicates belt warrants replacement. Cracks are most evident at base of tooth.

3) Abnormal wear most often occurs on load side of tooth. Fluffy canvas, unclear canvas texture, belt color changed to White from rubber missing, reduced tooth width or a missing tooth warrant belt replacement.

Installation

1) Install crankshaft sprocket "B", flange and crankshaft sprocket ensuring flange is installed correctly. *See Fig. 7.* Lightly oil right silent shaft spacer and insert spacer with chamfered end toward seal.

Mitsubishi Engines

1.8L TURBO, 2.0L & 2.4L 4-CYLINDER (Cont.)

Fig. 7: Installing Crankshaft Sprockets

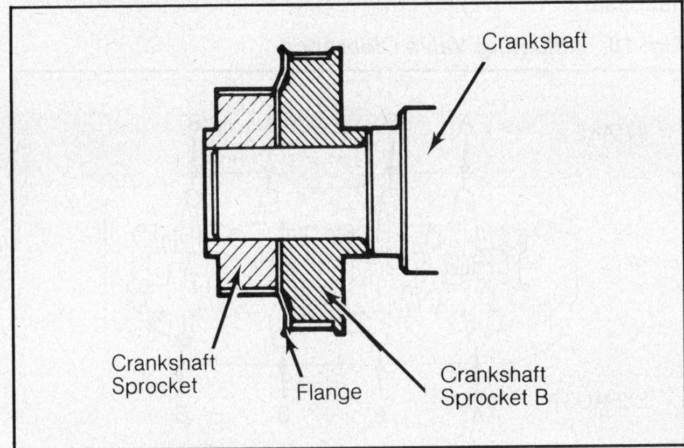

Courtesy of Mitsubishi Motor Sales of America.

2) Install right silent shaft sprocket (if removed) and finger-tighten bolt. Align crankshaft sprocket and silent shaft sprocket timing marks with corresponding marks on front case. *See Fig. 8.*

Fig. 8: Aligning Sprocket Timing Marks for Timing Belt "B"

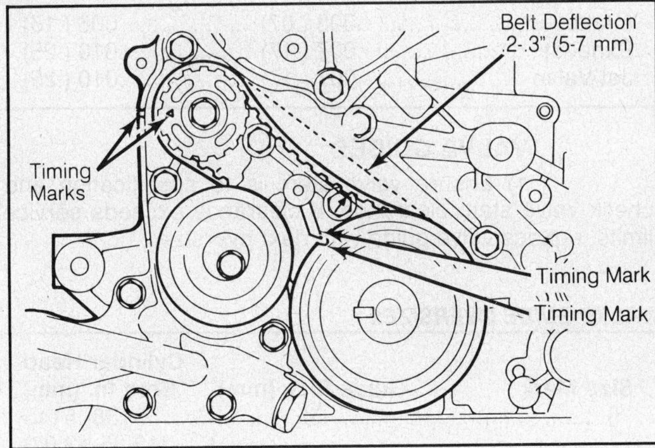

Courtesy of Mitsubishi Motor Sales of America.

3) Install timing belt "B", ensuring tension side has no slack. Install tensioner "B" so only light pressure is on belt. Ensure flange on tensioner is mounted away from engine and finger-tighten bolt.

4) Lift tensioner with finger tip until slack is removed from tension side of belt. Tighten tensioner bolt, being careful to prevent turning shaft. Ensure timing marks are in alignment. Tighten right silent shaft bolt.

5) Check belt tension by pressing center of tension side inward, using index finger and measuring belt deflection. Deflection should be .20-.30" (5.0-7.0 mm). Readjust if not within specification.

6) Align camshaft timing belt sprockets with corresponding timing marks. *See Fig. 9*. To ensure oil pump sprocket is in correct alignment, insert screwdriver shaft in hole on left side of block. *See Fig. 13*.

7) If screwdriver cannot be inserted at least 2.4" (60.0 mm), turn oil pump sprocket one revolution and realign marks. Insert screwdriver. Leave screwdriver inserted until timing belt installation is complete.

8) With tensioner secured fully toward water pump, install timing belt in order of crankshaft sprocket, oil pump sprocket and camshaft sprocket. Ensure tension side of belt has no slack.

Fig. 9: Aligning Timing Marks on Camshaft Timing Belt Sprockets

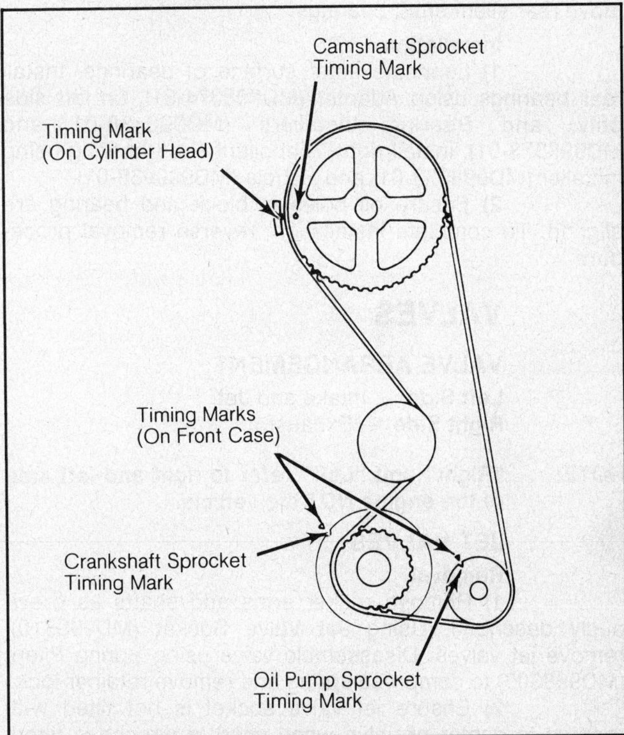

Courtesy of Mitsubishi Motor Sales of America.

9) Loosen tensioner mounting bolt and nut to allow only tensioner spring pressure to tighten belt. Check belt to ensure each tooth is in proper mesh with camshaft sprocket.

10) Tighten slot-side bolt before tightening nut. Otherwise, tension bracket will turn and belt will be overtensioned. Ensure all timing marks are in correct alignment. Remove screwdriver and install plug in block.

11) Turn crankshaft, clockwise only, one revolution. Loosen mounting nut and bolt to allow tensioner to readjust and tighten slot-side bolt, then tighten nut.

12) Hold belt and seal line of undercover, between thumb and forefinger, at center of tension side. Measure clearance between belt and seal line. Clearance should be .55" (14.0 mm). Reverse removal procedure to complete reassembly.

SILENT SHAFTS & BEARINGS

Removal

1) Remove timing belts and sprockets as previously described. Remove oil filter and oil pan. Remove oil pump pick-up screen and gasket. Remove oil pressure relief valve plunger plug and gasket. Remove oil pressure relief valve and spring from oil filter bracket.

2) Remove 4 bracket mounting bolts. Remove oil filter bracket and gasket. Remove plug from oil pump portion of front cover. Remove plug from left side of block and insert screwdriver at least 2.4" (60 mm). Remove oil pump driven gear and left silent shaft retaining bolt.

3) Remove front cover mounting bolts and front cover. Remove left and right silent shafts from block. Check silent shaft bearing journals for wear and seizure. Check silent shaft bearings.

4) Using Bearing Removers (MD998371-01 and MIT304204), remove right front silent shaft bearing.

1.8L TURBO, 2.0L & 2.4L 4-CYLINDER (Cont.)

Using Adapter (MD998374-01), on left side only, and Bearing Removers (MD998372-01 and MIT304204), remove rear silent shaft bearings.

Installation

1) Lubricate inner surface of bearings. Install rear bearings using Adapter (MD998374-01), on left side only, and Bearing Installers (MB990438-01 and MD998373-01). Install right front silent shaft bearing using Installer (MD998373-01) and Handle (MB990938-01).

2) Ensure oil holes in block and bearing are aligned. To complete installation, reverse removal procedure.

VALVES

VALVE ARRANGEMENT

Left Side - Intake and Jet.
Right Side - Exhaust.

NOTE: **"Right" and "Left" refer to right and left side of the engine NOT the vehicle.**

JET VALVES

Removal

1) Remove rocker arms and shafts as previously described. Using Jet Valve Socket (MD998310), remove jet valves. Disassemble valve using Spring Pliers (MD998309) to compress spring and remove retainer lock.

2) Ensure jet valve socket is not tilted with respect to center of valve when used. If wrench is tilted, stem may be bent, resulting in defective valve operation and a broken wrench.

Inspection

1) Check valve head and seat for damage. Ensure jet valve slides smoothly in body without play. Check jet valve face and jet body seat for seizure or damage. Check jet valve spring for deterioration, cracks or wear.

2) Do not disturb jet valve and body combination. If defective, jet valve and body should be replaced as an assembly. Spring can be replaced separately, if defective.

Installation

1) Install new jet valve oil seal using Installer (MD998308). Apply oil to jet valve stem and carefully insert jet valve into body. Ensure valve slides smoothly after installation.

2) Compress spring and install retainer lock, using care to prevent damaging valve stem. Install "O" ring on jet body. Lubricate "O" ring, jet body threads and seat surface.

3) Install jet valve assembly hand tight, then tighten to specification using socket. Use care to avoid tilting socket and damaging jet valve assembly.

VALVE CLEARANCE ADJUSTMENT

NOTE: **Jet valve clearance adjustment must be made before intake valve is adjusted and after cylinder head is retightened.**

1) Remove valve cover and position cylinder No. 1 at TDC of compression stroke. Adjust clearance on valves marked "A". *See Fig. 10.*

2) Position cylinder No. 4 at TDC of compression stroke. Adjust valves marked "B". *See Fig. 10.* After completing adjustment, check idle speed and readjust if necessary.

Fig. 10: Adjusting Valve Clearance

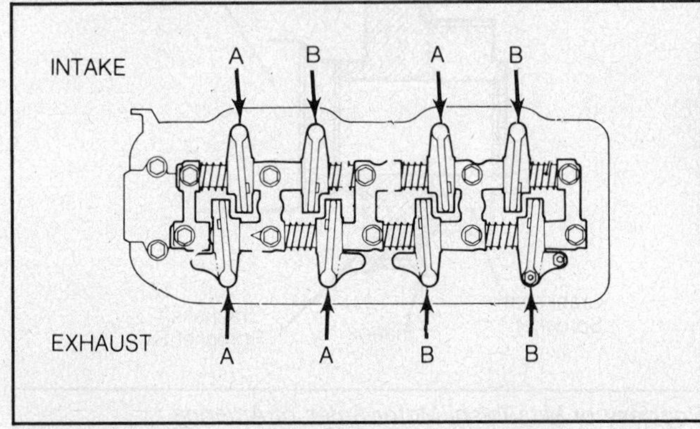

Ensure intake valve adjustment screw is fully loosened when adjusting jet valve. Courtesy of Mitsubishi Motor Sales of America.

VALVE CLEARANCE SPECIFICATIONS

Application	Cold In. (mm)	Hot In. (mm)
Intake	.003 (.07)	.006 (.15)
Exhaust	.007 (.17)	.010 (.25)
Jet Valve	.007 (.17)	.010 (.25)

VALVE GUIDES

1) Ensure valve stem is to specification and check valve stem clearance. If clearance exceeds service limits, replace valve guide with next oversize.

VALVE GUIDE OVERSIZES

Size Mark	Guide Size (mm)	Cylinder Head Bore In. (mm)
5	.05	.5138-.5145 (13.05-13.07)
25	.25	.5216-.5224 (13.25-13.27)
50	.50	.5315-.5322 (13.50-13.52)

Fig. 11: Removing & Installing Valve Guide

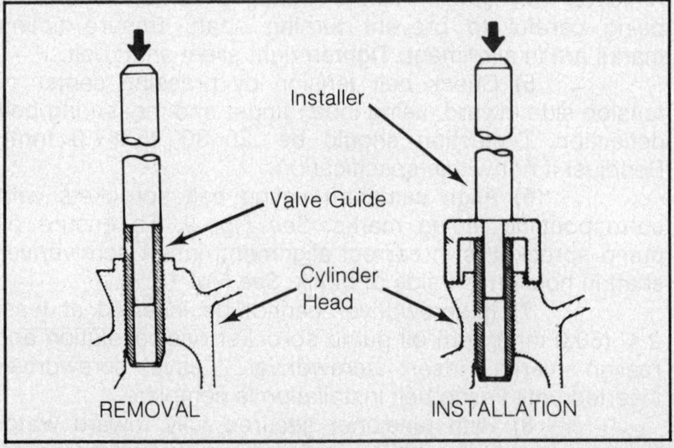

Install valve guide at room temperature. Courtesy of Mitsubishi Motor Sales of America.

1.8L TURBO, 2.0L & 2.4L 4-CYLINDER (Cont.)

2) Using a Valve Guide Remover/Installer (MD998115), drive out each guide toward combustion chamber. Machine guide bore in cylinder head to outside diameter of guide being installed. *See Fig. 11.*

3) To install, drive new guides in from top of head, using Remover/Installer (MD998115) with adapter, to ensure guide is installed to predetermined height. Guide should protrude .59" (15.0 mm) above head surface when properly installed. Check guide I.D. and ream as necessary.

VALVE SEATS

1) Check valve seat for evidence of overheating or improper contact with valve face. Replace or rework seat, as necessary. If reworking seat, check valve guide first. Replace guide as required. Recondition valve seat with grinder or cutter to specified contact width.

2) Remove valve seat ring by thinning down with a cutter, then machine seat bore to outside diameter and height of oversize valve seat ring. See VALVE SEAT OVERSIZES table for seat hole diameter.

NOTE: **Do not install valve seat ring at room temperature. This will damage seat hole and prevent seat from fitting tightly.**

3) Cool valve seat ring and press seat into cylinder head. After installing valve seat ring, machine to specification. After reworking seat, valve and valve seat should be lapped with compound.

VALVE SEAT OVERSIZES

Oversize (mm)	Seat Hole Diameter In. (mm)
Intake	
.30	1.744-1.745 (44.30-44.33)
.60	1.756-1.757 (44.60-44.63)
Exhaust	
.30	1.508-1.509 (38.30-38.33)
.60	1.520-1.521 (38.60-38.63)

VALVE STEM OIL SEALS

After installing valve spring seat, place new stem seal on guide. Using Seal Installer (MD998377), lightly tap seal into position until installer bottoms on spring seat.

VALVE SPRINGS

1) With camshaft and rocker arm assembly removed, use valve spring compressor to remove retainer locks. Remove all retainers, springs, spring seats and valves. Keep components in proper order for reassembly.

2) Check valve spring load, free length and spring squareness. Standard spring squareness should be 1.5 degrees or less. If beyond 2 degrees, replace spring. Install spring with identification color toward retainer.

PISTONS, PINS & RINGS

PISTON & CONNECTING ROD ASSEMBLY

Removal

Remove cylinder head, oil pan and screen. Ensure connecting rods and rod caps are marked on big end for reassembly reference. Remove carbon ridge from cylinder bores. Remove connecting rod caps. Remove connecting rod and piston assembly through top of cylinder block.

Installation

To install, lubricate all internal surfaces with engine oil before installation. Ensure "arrow" mark on piston head faces front of engine.

FITTING PISTONS

1) After checking block for distortion, cracks, scratches or other abnormalities, measure bores at top, center and bottom of No. 1 piston ring travel for taper and out-of-round.

2) If any cylinder has more than .0008" (.020 mm) taper or out-of-round, or if cylinder walls are badly scuffed or scored, block must be bored or honed and new oversized pistons and rings installed.

3) Bore or hone all cylinders to same oversize. Do not bore only one cylinder. Bore or hone cylinders in sequence, skipping adjacent cylinders to prevent heat distortion.

NOTE: **Replacement pistons are available in standard, .25 mm, .50 mm, .75 mm and 1.0 mm oversizes. Oversize pistons are stamped on crown to indicate oversize.**

4) Measure outside diameter of piston by measuring at a point .079" (2.00 mm) from bottom of skirt below pin boss, and at 90 degrees to pin bore. Determine cylinder boring finish dimension.

PISTON PINS

1) Check piston pin-to-bore fit. Pin should press in smoothly by hand at room temperature. When assembling, apply engine oil to outside of pin and piston pin bore.

2) Position rod in piston with arrow mark on piston and identification mark on connecting rod facing upward. Align pin with pin installer, and press pin into piston and rod.

NOTE: **Pin-to-rod fit at normal temperature requires 1653-3858 lbs. (750-1750 kg) to press pin through rod.**

PISTON RINGS

1) Measure piston ring side and end clearance for all pistons and replace rings as necessary. When replacing ring in cylinder bore not needing reconditioning, check ring end gap at lower part of cylinder that is less worn.

2) When replacing a ring, be sure to use same size ring. Compression rings differ in scraping edge design. From a cross sectional view, ring No. 1 has a barrel shaped scraping edge and ring No. 2 has a tapered edge.

3) Install rings on piston with end gaps staggered at 120 degrees intervals. Ensure no ring gap is in line with thrust face of pin bore. Also ensure manufacturer's marks are facing upward when rings are installed. *See Fig. 12.*

4) Install oil ring first without using a ring expander. Spacer expander gap should be installed more than 45 degrees from side rail gaps. Rails should turn smoothly when installed.

Mitsubishi Engines

1.8L TURBO, 2.0L & 2.4L 4-CYLINDER (Cont.)

Fig. 12: Positioning Piston Ring Gaps

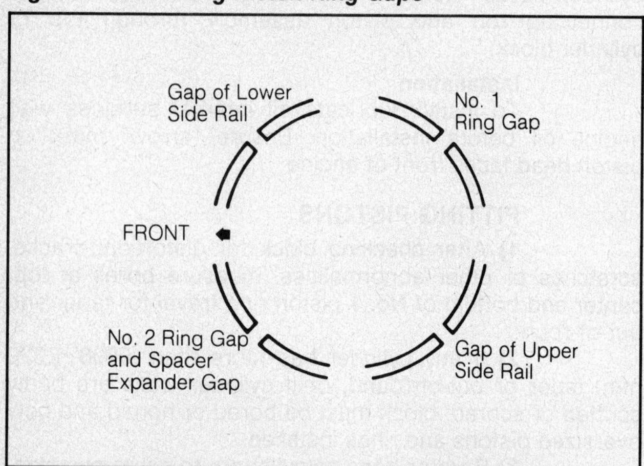

Stagger ring gaps to minimize compression loss. Courtesy of Mitsubishi Motor Sales of America.

CRANKSHAFT & ROD BEARINGS

MAIN & CONNECTING ROD BEARINGS

1) Inspect each bearing for peeling, melting, seizure or improper contact. Replace defective bearings. Measure outside diameter of crankshaft and connecting rod journals to determine if out-of-round or tapered.

2) Use Plastigage method to measure bearing clearance. If clearance exceeds limits, bearing should be replaced or undersize bearing installed. Undersize bearings are available in .25 mm, .50 mm and .75 mm undersizes.

3) Main bearing caps are installed with arrow directed toward front of engine and cap number in correct order. Gradually tighten cap bolts in 2 or 3 steps, before tightening to specification.

4) Connecting rod bearing caps are installed with bearing insert locking tabs, located on same side of rod. Ensure crankshaft turns freely and end play is within specification, after completing bearing installation.

THRUST BEARING ALIGNMENT

No. 3 main bearing is thrust bearing. With crankshaft bearing caps installed, check crankshaft end play by inserting feeler gauge between shoulder of center main bearing and crankshaft thrust face. If clearance exceeds specified limits, replace No. 3 main bearing.

ENGINE OILING

ENGINE OILING SYSTEM

Engine uses force-feed type lubrication system, utilizing a gear-type pump. Pump assembly is mounted on front of engine assembly. Oil pump driven gear is bolted to left silent shaft and is driven by camshaft timing belt.

CRANKCASE CAPACITY

Crankcase capacity is 4.2 quarts (4.0L) including filter on all models.

OIL PRESSURE

Oil pressure is 11.4 psi (.79 kg/cm²) or more at curb idle.

OIL PUMP & FRONT COVER

Removal

1) Remove timing belts as previously described. Remove oil filter and oil pan. Remove oil pump pick-up screen and gasket. Remove oil pressure relief valve plunger plug and gasket. Remove oil pressure relief valve and spring from oil filter bracket.

2) Remove 4 bracket mounting bolts. Remove oil filter bracket and gasket. Remove plug from oil pump portion of front cover. Remove plug from left side of block and insert screwdriver at least 2.4" (60.0 mm). Remove oil pump driven gear and left silent shaft retaining bolt.

3) Remove front cover mounting bolts and front cover. Keep mounting bolts in order for reassembly reference. Remove oil pump cover from the front cover. Mark gears for reassembly reference. Remove oil pump gears from front cover.

Fig. 13: Aligning Oil Pump Sprocket

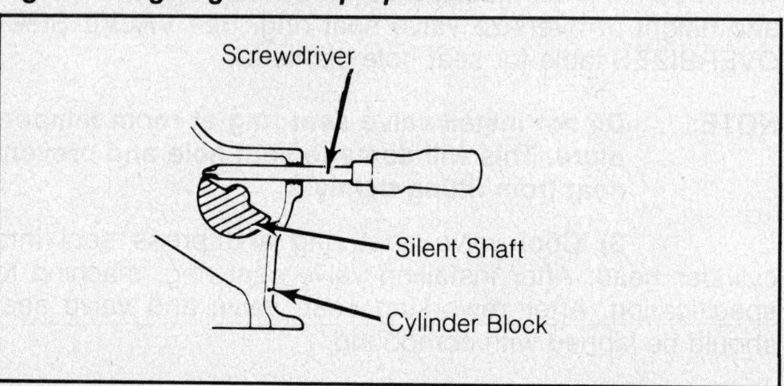

Silent shaft should be repositioned if screwdriver fails to insert 2.4" (60 mm). Courtesy of Mitsubishi Motor Sales of America.

Inspection

1) Inspect gears, front cover and seal for wear or damage. Reinstall gears as originally installed in front case and measure gear side clearance. Clearance should not exceed .005" (.13 mm).

2) Check gear contacting surfaces of front cover and oil pump cover for step wear. Replace front cover assembly if excessive clearance or step wear is evident.

Installation

1) Install oil pump gears in front case and align timing marks on gears with timing marks facing toward oil pump cover. *See Fig. 14*. Install pump cover and tighten bolts.

Fig. 14: Aligning Oil Pump Timing Marks

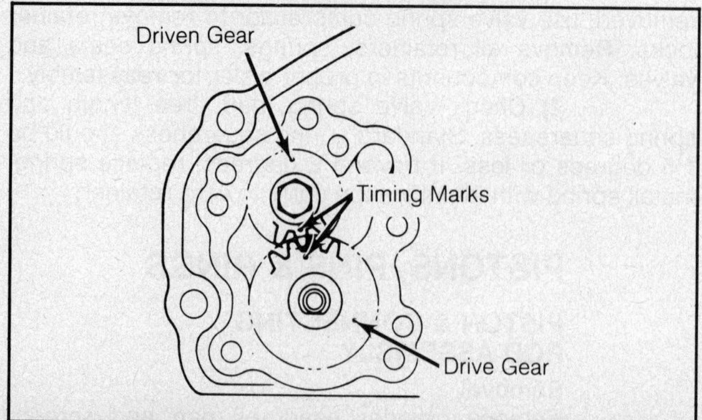

Timing marks face toward pump cover. Courtesy of Mitsubishi Motor Sales of America.

Mitsubishi Engines

1.8L TURBO, 2.0L & 2.4L 4-CYLINDER (Cont.)

2) Install Guide (MD998285-01) on end of crankshaft with smaller diameter toward front of engine. Lightly oil guide. Install new front cover gasket. Install front cover and lightly tighten 8 mounting bolts.

3) Insert screwdriver through plug hole in left side of block to keep left silent shaft in position. Tighten driven gear-to-silent shaft bolt. Install oil filter bracket and tighten front case bolts.

4) Apply sealant to 4 locations on cylinder block where oil seal case and front case join cylinder block. Install oil pan with new gasket. Reverse removal procedure to complete installation.

CAUTION: Prior to installing oil pump, fill with sufficient amount of engine oil to prime pump.

Fig. 15: Front Cover Bolt Locations

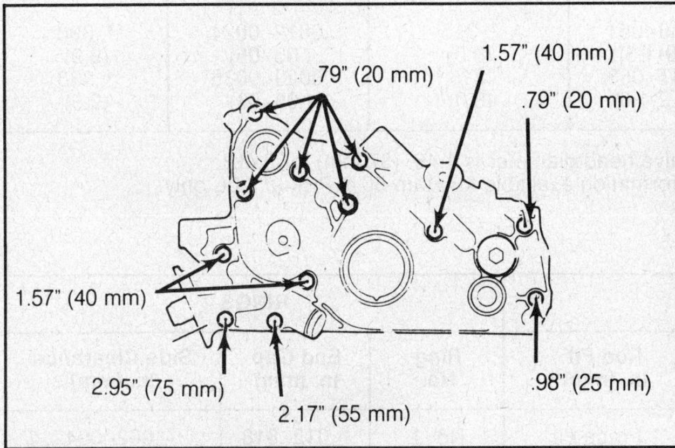

Courtesy of Mitsubishi Motor Sales of America.

CRANKSHAFT FRONT OIL SEAL

Removal & Installation

With front cover removed from block and disassembled, drive front seal from front cover. To install, tap new front seal into front cover. Install Crankshaft Front Oil Seal Guide (MD998285) to front of crankshaft. Lubricate guide with engine oil. Install front cover assembly on block. Tighten mounting bolts to specification.

CRANKSHAFT REAR OIL SEAL

With oil pan removed from block, remove rear main oil seal case. Drive old seal from case. Install new oil seal using Seal Installer (MD998376). Install oil separator into case with drain hole toward oil pan mounting surface. Install new case gasket and oil seal case to rear of block. Install oil pan.

ENGINE COOLING

WATER PUMP

Removal & Installation

Drain cooling system and disconnect battery. Remove drive belt and pulley. Remove mounting bolts and remove pump assembly from engine. To install, use new gasket and reverse removal procedure.

NOTE: For more information, see ENGINE COOLING SYSTEMS at the end of this section.

TIGHTENING SPECIFICATIONS

Application	Ft. Lbs. (N.m)
Camshaft Bearing Cap Bolts	14-15 (19-20)
Camshaft Sprocket Bolt	58-72 (78-98)
Coolant Temperature Sending Unit	22-28 (30-38)
Connecting Rod Cap Nuts	37-38 (49-51)
Crankshaft Pulley Bolt	15-21 (20-29)
Crankshaft Sprocket Bolt	80-94 (108-127)
Cylinder Head Bolts	
Cold	65-72 (89-98)
Hot	73-79 (99-107)
Drive Plate-to-Crankshaft Bolts	94-101 (127-137)
Engine Support Bracket Bolts	29-36 (39-49)
Exhaust Manifold Nuts & Bolts	11-14 (15-19)
Flywheel-to-Crankshaft Bolts	94-101 (127-137)
Front Cover Bolts	15-19 (20-26)
Front Roll Stopper Bracket-to-No. 1 Crossmember Nuts	29-36 (39-49)
Front Roll Stopper Insulator Nut	36-47 (49-65)
Heater Joint	15-28 (20-38)
Intake Manifold Bolts & Nuts	11-14 (15-19)
Jet Valve	13-15 (18-20)
Left Motor Mount Insulator	
Large Nut	43-58 (58-79)
Small Nut	22-29 (30-39)
Left Mounting Bracket-to-Engine Bolts & Nuts	36-47 (49-64)
Main Bearing Cap Bolts	37-39 (50-53)
Oil Pressure Relief Valve Plug	29-36 (39-49)
Oil Pump Cover Bolts	11-15 (15-20)
Oil Pump Sprocket Nut	
2.0L PU Only	36-48 (49-58)
All Other Models	25-28 (34-38)
Rear Roll Stopper Bracket-to-Rear Roll Stopper Stay Bolt	22-29 (30-39)
Rear Roll Stopper Insulator Nut	22-29 (30-39)
Rear Roll Stopper-to-No. 2 Crossmember Nuts	43-58 (58-78)
Silent Shaft Sprocket Bolt	25-28 (34-38)
Timing Belt Tensioner Nut	32-39 (42-53)
Transaxle Insulator Bracket-to-Fender Shield Bolts	29-36 (40-50)
Transaxle Mounting Bracket-to-	
Automatic	43-58 (58-78)
Manual	40-43 (54-58)
Transaxle Mount Insulator Nut	43-58 (58-79)
Water Pump Bolts	
M8 x 65	15-19 (20-26)
Others	9-11 (12-15)
	INCH Lbs. (N.m)
Heat Protector Bolt	60-84 (7-9)
Oil Pan Bolts	54-66 (6-7)
Oil Pressure Sending Unit	41-54 (4-6)
Rocker Arm Lock Nuts	108-156 (12-18)
Rocker Cover Bolts	48-60 (5-7)

Mitsubishi Engines

1.8L TURBO, 2.0L & 2.4L 4-CYLINDER (Cont.)

ENGINE SPECIFICATIONS

GENERAL SPECIFICATIONS

Year	DISPLACEMENT		Fuel System	HP@RPM	Torque Ft. Lbs.@RPM	Compr. Ratio	BORE		STROKE	
	Cu. In.	Liters					In.	mm	In.	mm
1987	109.5	1.8	TBI	116@5500	129@3000	7.5:1	3.17	(80.5)	3.46	(88)
	121.9	2.0	2-Bbl.	88@5500	108@3500	8.5:1	3.35	(85)	3.46	(88)
	143.4	2.4	TBI	110@4500	138@3500	8.5:1	3.41	(86.5)	3.94	(100)

VALVES

Engine Size & Valve	Head Diam. In. (mm)	Face Angle	Seat Angle	Seat Width In. (mm)	Stem Diameter In. (mm)	Stem Clearance In. (mm)	Valve Lift In. (mm)
1.8L, 2.0L & 2.4L							
Intake	[1] 1.693 (43)	45°	45°	.035-.051 (.9-1.3)	[2] .315 (8.0)	.0012-.0024 (.03-.06)	[4] .390 (9.9)
Exhaust	[3] 1.378 (35)	45°	45°	.047-.063 (1.2-1.6)	.315 (8.0)	.0020-.0035 (.05-.09)	[4] .390 (9.9)

[1] – Valve head diameter is 1.97" (50 mm) for 2.4L.
[2] – Valve stem diameter is .322" (8.2 mm) for 2.4L.
[3] – Valve head diameter is 1.46" (37 mm) for 2.4L.
[4] – Information available for Ram-50 & Pickup 2.0L only.

PISTONS, PINS & RINGS

Engine	PISTONS	PINS		RINGS		
	Clearance In. (mm)	Piston Fit In. (mm)	Rod Fit In. (mm)	Ring No.	End Gap In. (mm)	Side Clearance In. (mm)
1.8L, 2.0L & 2.4L	.0008-.0016 (.02-.04)	[1]	[2] Press Fit	No. 1	[3] .012-.018 (.30-.46)	.002-.004 (.05-.10)
				No. 2	[4] .008-.014 (.20-.35)	.001-.002 (.03-.05)
				Oil	.008-.028 (.20-.70)	.....

[1] – Thumb press fit without rod installed.
[2] – Press in at 1653-3858 lbs. at room temperature.
[3] – Ring end gap is .010-.016" (.25-.40 mm) on 2.0L and 2.4L.
[4] – Ring end gap is .008-.016" (.20-.40 mm) on 2.0L and 2.4L.

CRANKSHAFT MAIN & CONNECTING ROD BEARINGS

Engine	MAIN BEARINGS				CONNECTING ROD BEARINGS		
	Journal Diam. In. (mm)	Clearance In. (mm)	Thrust Bearing	Crankshaft End Play In. (mm)	Journal Diam. In. (mm)	Clearance In. (mm)	Side Play In. (mm)
1.8L, 2.0L & 2.4L	2.244 (57.00)	.0008-.0020 (.02-.05)	No. 3	.002-.007 (.05-.18)	1.772 (45.00)	.0008-.0020 (.02-.05)	.004-.010 (.10-.25)

CAMSHAFT

Engine	Journal Diam. In. (mm)	Clearance In. (mm)	Lobe Lift In. (mm)
1.8L, 2.0L & 2.4L	1.339 (34.00)	.002-.004 (.05-.10)	.....

VALVE SPRINGS

Engine	Free Length In. (mm)	PRESSURE Lbs. @ In. (Kg @ mm)	
		Valve Closed	Valve Open
1.8L	[1] 1.870 (47.5)	62@1.591 (28.1@40.4)	.....
2.0L & 2.4L	[2] 1.961 (49.8)	72@1.591 (32.7@40.4)	.....

[1] – Maximum out-of-square 1.5 degrees.
[2] – Maximum out-of-square 2.0 degrees.

Mitsubishi Engines

2.6L & 2.6L TURBO 4-CYLINDER

Chrysler Motors: Conquest, Ram-50, Ram Raider
Mazda: B2600 Truck
Mitsubishi: Montero, Pickup, Starion

NOTE: **For engine repair procedures not covered in this article, see ENGINE OVERHAUL PROCEDURES article at beginning of this section.**

ENGINE CODING

ENGINE IDENTIFICATION

Engine model code and serial number are stamped on right front side of engine block, just below No. 1 spark plug. The eighth character of Vehicle Identification Number (VIN), located on upper left side of instrument panel, can also be used to identify engine displacement.

ENGINE IDENTIFICATION

Application	Engine Model	Engine VIN Code
2-Bbl.	G54B	E
Turbo	G54B	H
Turbo [1]	G54B	N

[1] – With intercooler.

ENGINE, MANIFOLDS & CYLINDER HEAD

ENGINE

Removal (Conquest & Starion)

NOTE: **Remove engine and transmission as an assembly.**

1) Disconnect negative battery cable. Remove hood. Remove air cleaner and disconnect accelerator cable. Disconnect heater, fuel, boost sensor, and brake booster hoses. Drain radiator, transmission, and engine oil. Disconnect oil cooler lines. Unplug intake manifold ground cable connector.

2) Disconnect starter, alternator, fuel injection, ignition, and gauge wiring. Disconnect engine ground cable. Remove power steering pump and radiator assembly. Disconnect transmission oil cooler lines (if equipped). Remove rear catalytic converter. Disconnect speedometer cable and back-up light switch wiring.

3) Discharge A/C system. Remove propeller shaft, clutch release cylinder, engine mount bolts, and gearshift lever assembly. Support transmission. Remove insulator bolts and crossmember. Attach lifting cables and remove engine/transmission assembly.

NOTE: **Remove engine and transmission as an assembly.**

Removal (All Others)

1) Disconnect negative battery cable. Remove hood and air cleaner. Disconnect heater and brake booster vacuum hoses. Disconnect fuel hoses and accelerator cable. On Montero models, unplug carburetor wiring harness connectors.

2) Disconnect wiring from starter, alternator, coil, water temperature, and oil pressure sending units. Remove radiator assembly. On Montero models, remove clutch release cylinder from transmission. On all other models, disconnect clutch cable. On all models, remove front exhaust pipe. Disconnect engine ground cable.

3) Remove power steering pump (if equipped). Remove undercover and other protective transmission covers (if equipped). Disconnect speedometer cable, back-up light harness and 4WD indicator light switch (if equipped). On Montero models, disconnect vapor hose and purge hoses from purge control valve. Disconnect oxygen sensor.

4) On all models, mark propeller shafts for installation reference. Remove propeller shafts. Remove gearshift lever assembly. On automatic transmission models, remove oil cooler tubes and hoses. Support transmission. Disconnect rear insulator from transmission and remove crossmember.

5) Disconnect and remove transfer case mounting bracket. Support insulator from transfer case. Remove front engine insulator mounting nuts. Attach lifting cables. With front of engine tilted upward, remove engine/transmission assembly diagonally from engine compartment.

Installation (All Models)

To install, reverse removal procedure. Use care to align front engine mount locating holes without twisting insulator rubber. Using new tab lock washers, tighten mounting bolts and nuts to specifications with weight of engine on insulators. Replace all fluids. Adjust all cables and linkages. Check operation of gauges and meters.

CYLINDER HEAD & MANIFOLDS

Removal

1) Disconnect negative battery cable. Remove air cleaner assembly. Drain cooling system and disconnect hoses at cylinder head and intake manifold. Remove breather and purge hoses, vacuum hose at distributor, and purge control valve.

2) On fuel injected models, remove air intake hose from injector body. Disconnect electrical connectors at injectors, ISC servo, and throttle position sensor.

3) Disconnect accelerator cable, spark plug wires, and coolant temperature sending unit. Disconnect exhaust manifold from pipe. Remove distributor, fuel line, and fuel pump. Remove vacuum hoses. Remove exhaust manifold, intake manifold and carburetor (throttle body) assembly.

4) Remove rocker cover and gasket. Remove semi-circular seal. Rotate crankshaft until No. 1 piston is at TDC of compression stroke. Mark timing chain for reference, in-line with sprocket mark. Remove camshaft sprocket with timing chain and place on sprocket holder.

5) Install Auto-Lash Adjuster Holder (MD998443-01) on rocker arm to ensure adjuster does not fall out. Loosen camshaft bearing cap bolts. Leave bolts in end bearing caps so that rocker shaft can be removed as an assembly. Remove rocker arms and shafts as an assembly. Remove camshaft.

6) Loosen cylinder head bolts in reverse of tightening sequence. *See Fig. 1*. Remove bolts and lift off cylinder head. Use care not to slide head across alignment dowels.

2.6L & 2.6L TURBO 4-CYLINDER (Cont.)

Installation

1) Clean mating surfaces and use a new cylinder head gasket. Apply sealer to timing chain cover-to-block joint. DO NOT apply sealant to head gasket. Install gasket with identification mark toward cylinder head. Install cylinder head. To prevent damage to gasket, mating surfaces and alignment dowels, avoid sliding cylinder head.

2) Tighten cylinder head bolts to 1/2 of specification in sequence. *See Fig. 1*. Repeat procedure, tightening bolts to specification. DO NOT overtighten cylinder head-to-timing chain cover bolts. Reverse removal procedure to complete installation.

3) Temporarily set valve clearance to cold engine settings. Readjust to hot engine settings after engine is at normal operating temperature. Install rocker cover, air cleaner and breather hoses.

Fig. 1: Cylinder Head Bolt Tightening Sequence

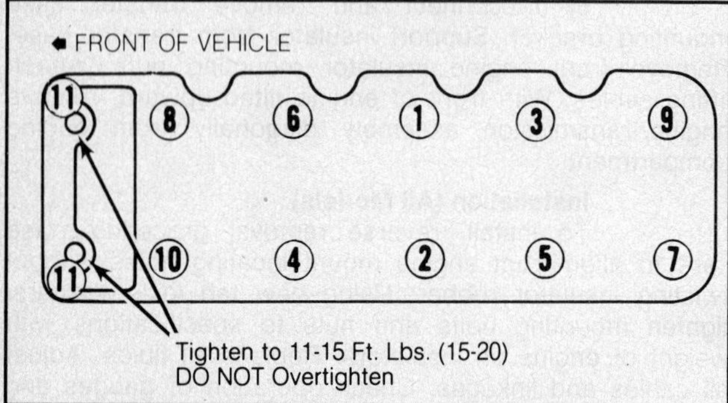

Reverse order when removing cylinder head. Courtesy of Mitsubishi Motor Sales of America.

CAMSHAFT

ROCKER ASSEMBLY & CAMSHAFT

Removal

1) Remove air cleaner, breather hoses, and purge line. Remove fuel pump and line. Disconnect spark plug wires and remove rocker cover. Remove breather and semi-circular seal. Slightly loosen camshaft sprocket bolt and turn crankshaft so No. 1 piston is at TDC of compression stroke. Mark timing chain and camshaft sprocket for installation reference.

2) Remove camshaft sprocket and hang sprocket on sprocket holder provided on timing chain lower front cover. Remove distributor drive gear, camshaft bearing caps, rocker arms, and rocker shafts as an assembly. Remove camshaft.

NOTE: **If front and rear bearing cap bolts are left inserted, rocker shafts can be removed as an assembly.**

Inspection

1) Check camshaft journals, fuel pump drive drive cam and distributor drive gear teeth for wear or damage. Replace if necessary.

2) Camshaft journal diameter should be 1.34" (34.0 mm), height of fuel pump cam drive 1.46" (37.0 mm), intake and exhaust cam height 1.67" (42.4 mm), and cam end play should be .004-.008" (.1-.2 mm).

Fig. 2: Rocker Shaft Alignment Marks

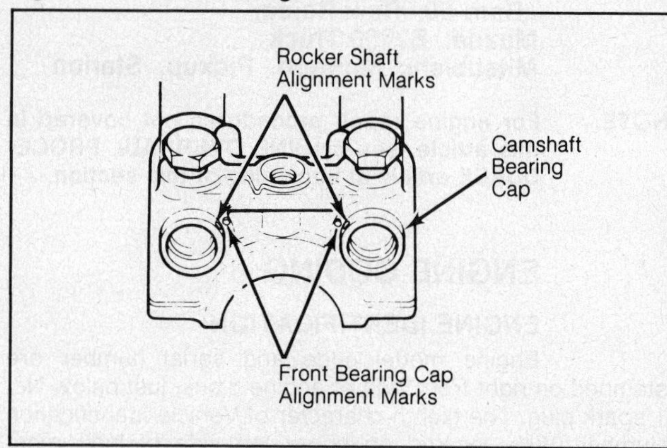

Courtesy of Mitsubishi Motor Sales of America.

Installation

1) Lubricate camshaft lobes and camshaft bearing journals. Install camshaft to cylinder head. Install rocker arm assembly to cylinder head. Insert camshaft bearing cap bolts and tighten to specification.

2) Install camshaft sprocket and distributor drive gear to camshaft. Tighten camshaft locking bolt. Install timing chain. Adjust valve clearance to specification. To complete installation, reverse removal procedure.

Fig. 3: Exploded View of Rocker Assembly

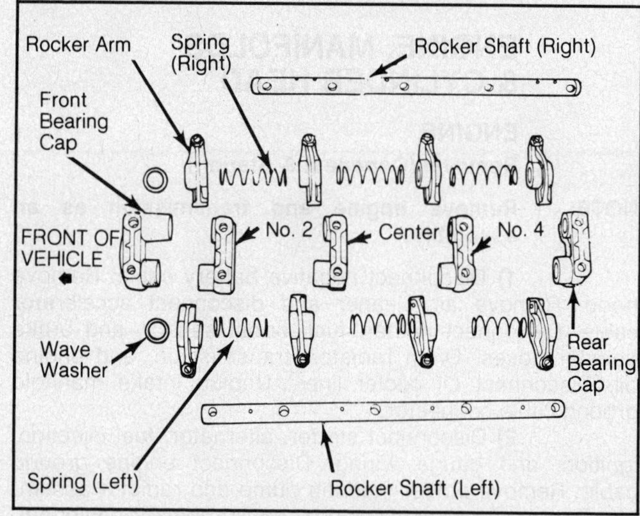

Courtesy of Mitsubishi Motor Sales of America.

COUNTERBALANCE DRIVE CHAIN

Removal

1) Drain coolant and engine oil. Disconnect negative battery cable. Remove rocker cover, breather, and semi-circular seal. Remove alternator, fan belt, fan, water pump pulley, and water pump. Remove distributor and oil pan.

2) Remove crankshaft pulley and timing chain case. Remove chain guides "A", "B", and "C", sprocket locking bolts, and crankshaft sprocket. Remove both counterbalance shaft sprockets and drive chain. *See Figs. 4 and 5.*

Installation

1) To install, reverse removal procedure. Ensure mating marks on sprockets align with plated links

2.6L & 2.6L TURBO 4-CYLINDER (Cont.)

on counterbalance chain. Adjust tension by installing guides "A" and "C".

2) Shake counterbalance shaft sprockets to take slack from chain. Adjust guide "B" so there will be .040-.140" (1.0-3.5 mm) clearance between guide and chain at point "P". Tighten guide mounting bolts and complete assembly.

Fig. 4: Exploded View of Counterbalance Shafts & Drive Chain

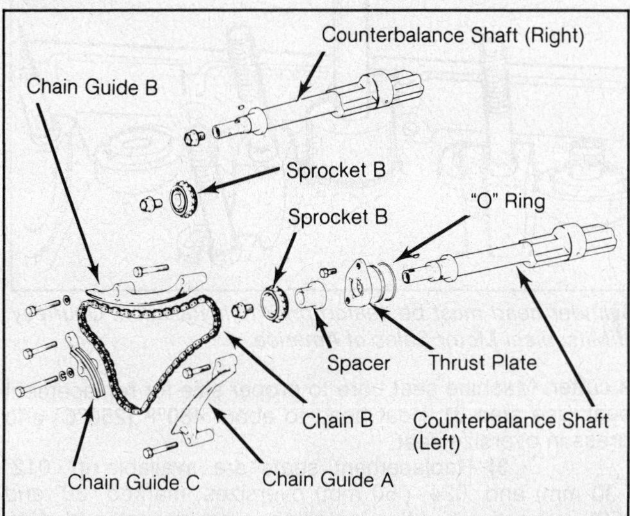

Right counterbalance shaft is driven by oil pump. Courtesy of Mitsubishi Motor Sales of America.

COUNTERBALANCE SHAFTS

Removal

1) With counterbalance drive chain removed, remove oil pump mounting bolts. Insert screwdriver through plug hole in left side of block to keep silent shaft from rotating.

2) Remove bolt holding oil pump driven gear and counterbalance shaft together. Remove oil pump mounting bolts and oil pump. Withdraw right counterbalance shaft.

Fig. 5: Counterbalance Drive Chain

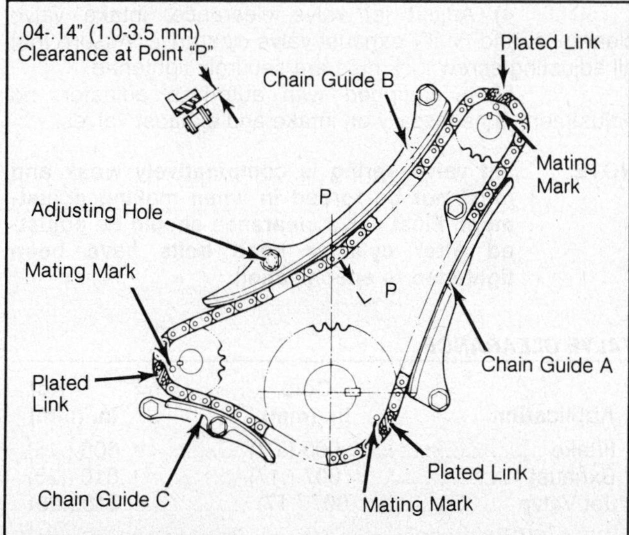

Align plated links with mating marks. Courtesy of Mitsubishi Motor Sales of America.

NOTE: If oil pump driven gear-to-counterbalance shaft locking bolt is hard to loosen, remove the oil pump and counterbalance shaft as an assembly.

3) Remove thrust plate, supporting front of left counterbalance shaft, by threading 8 mm diameter bolts into plate holes at same time. Withdraw left counterbalance shaft from cylinder block.

Installation

To install, reverse removal procedure.

COUNTERBALANCE SHAFT BEARINGS

Removal & Installation

1) Remove counterbalance shaft front bearings from block using Counterbalance Shaft Bearing Puller (MD998371-01). Remove rear bearing using Countershaft Bearing Pullers (MIT304204).

2) To install, lubricate outside of bearings. Install rear bearings using Counterbalance Shaft Bearing Installers (MD998373-01 and MD990938-01). Install front bearings using Counterbalance Shaft Bearing Installer (MD990938-01).

TIMING CHAIN

Removal & Installation

1) Remove counterbalance drive chain as previously described. Remove chain tensioner and right and left chain guides. Remove camshaft sprocket and timing chain.

2) To install, reverse removal procedure. Rotate crankshaft until No. 1 piston is at TDC of compression stroke. Align mating marks on sprockets and chain. *See Fig. 6.*

Fig. 6: Camshaft Sprocket Alignment & Installation

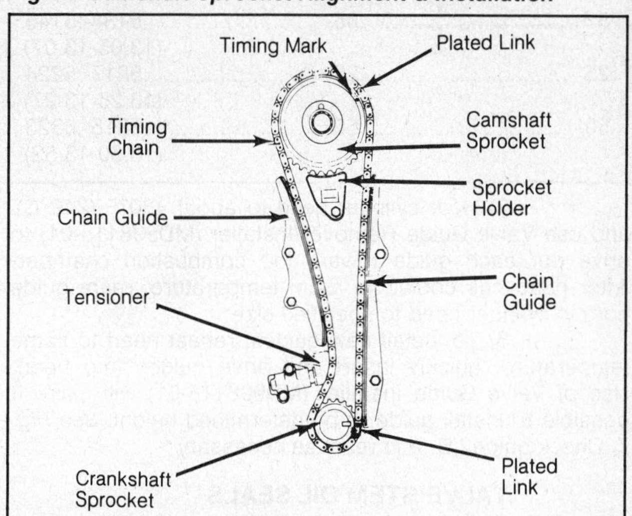

Align plated links with timing marks on sprockets. Courtesy of Mitsubishi Motor Sales of America.

VALVES

VALVE ARRANGEMENT

Left Side - Intake and jet valves.
Right Side - Exhaust valves.

NOTE: "Right" and "Left" refer to right and left side of the engine NOT the vehicle.

2.6L & 2.6L TURBO 4-CYLINDER (Cont.)

JET VALVES

Using Jet Valve Socket (MD998310), remove jet valves. Disassemble valve using Spring Pliers (MD998309) to compress spring and remove retainer lock. Check valve head and seat for damage and ensure jet valve slides smoothly in body without play.

CAUTION: Ensure jet valve socket is not tilted with respect to center of valve. If socket is tilted, stem may bend and result in improper valve operation. Do not attempt to repair jet valve assembly. If defective, replace jet valve as an assembly.

VALVE SPRINGS

1) With camshaft and rocker arm assembly removed, compress valve spring and remove retainer locks (keepers). Remove all retainers, springs, spring seats, and valves, keeping in proper order for reassembly.

2) Check valve spring free length and pressure. Standard spring squareness should be 1 1/2 degrees or less. Replace spring if beyond 2 degrees out of square.

VALVE GUIDE SERVICE

1) Check valve stem-to-guide clearance, and if clearance exceeds service limits as listed in table, replace valve guide with next oversize component. Guides are available in various oversizes. See VALVE GUIDE OVERSIZES table.

VALVE GUIDE OVERSIZES

Size Mark	Guide Oversize (mm)	Cyl. Head Bore In. (mm)
5	.05	.5138-.5145 (13.05-13.07)
25	.25	.5217-.5224 (13.25-13.27)
50	.50	.5315-.5323 (13.50-13.52)

2) Heat cylinder head to about 480°F (249°C), and use Valve Guide Remover/Installer (MD998115-01) to drive out each guide toward the combustion chamber. After head has cooled to room temperature, ream guide bore in cylinder head to specified size.

3) To install new guides, reheat head to same temperature, quickly insert and drive guides into head. Use of Valve Guide Installer (MD998115-01) will make it possible to install guide to predetermined height. *See Fig. 7.* Check guide I.D. and ream as necessary.

VALVE STEM OIL SEALS

After installing valve spring seat, place stem seal on guide. Use Valve Seal Installer (MD998377-01) and lightly tap seal into position. Do not reuse old seals or twist seals when installing.

VALVE SEAT

1) Check valve seats by measuring installed height of spring between the spring seat and retainer with all spring components installed.

2) Standard dimension is 1.590" (40.4 mm) with an additional wear limit of .039" (1.0 mm). Replace valve seat if beyond limit. To remove valve seat, thin down with

Fig. 7: Valve Guide Installation

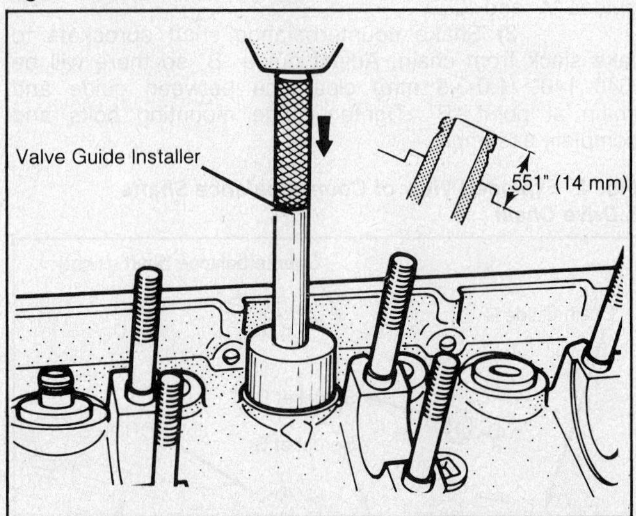

Cylinder head must be heated prior to installation. Courtesy of Mitsubishi Motor Sales of America.

a cutter. Machine seat bore to proper size for replacement seat, see step **3)**. Heat head to about 480°F (250°C) and press in oversize seat.

3) Replacement seats are available in .012" (.30 mm) and .024" (.60 mm) oversizes, marked "30" and "60" respectively. After installing, machine valve seat to specification.

VALVE CLEARANCE ADJUSTMENT

1) Ensure timing marks on camshaft sprocket and chain are aligned. With head assembly installed, adjust valves in 1-3-4-2 cylinder sequence, according to following procedure.

2) At TDC on compression stroke, for cylinder being adjusted, loosen rocker arm nuts. Turn adjusting screw to adjust valve clearance to specification.

3) Complete engine assembly and temporarily install rocker cover. Warm engine until coolant temperature is 170-180°F (77-82°C). With piston at TDC of compression stroke, back intake valve adjusting screw off 2 or more turns.

4) Adjust jet valve clearance, intake valve clearance, and finally exhaust valve clearance. Assure that all adjusting screw lock nuts are securely tightened.

5) If equipped with auto-lash adjuster, no adjustment is necessary on intake and exhaust valves.

NOTE: Jet valve spring is comparatively weak and must not be forced in when making adjustment. Final valve clearance should be adjusted after cylinder head bolts have been tightened to specification.

VALVE CLEARANCE

Application	Cold In. (mm)	Hot In. (mm)
Intake	[1] .003 (.07)	[1] .006 (.15)
Exhaust	[1] .007 (.17)	[1] .010 (.25)
Jet Valve	.007 (.17)	.010 (.25)

[1] – Valve clearance is zero when equipped with auto-lash adjuster.

2.6L & 2.6L TURBO 4-CYLINDER (Cont.)

PISTONS, PINS & RINGS

PISTON & CONNECTING ROD ASSEMBLY

Removal

Remove cylinder head and oil pan. Ensure connecting rods and rod caps are marked for reassembly reference. Remove rear main seal housing. Remove carbon ridge from cylinder bores. Remove connecting rod caps. Remove connecting rod and piston assembly through top of cylinder block.

Installation

To install, lubricate all internal surfaces with engine oil before installation. Ensure front mark on piston head faces front of engine.

FITTING PISTONS

1) After checking block for cracks, scratches or other abnormalities, measure bores at 3 levels to check distortion. If any distortion exceeds .001" (.02 mm) from standard bore size, block must be rebored and oversize pistons installed.

NOTE: **Pistons are available in standard, .010" (.25 mm), .020" (.50 mm), .030" (.75 mm) and .040" (1.0 mm) oversizes. Oversize pistons are stamped on crown to indicate oversize amount.**

2) Check outside diameter of piston by measuring at a point .079" (2.00 mm) from bottom of skirt and at 90 degrees to pin bore. Determine amount of cylinder reboring required to meet specified clearance.

PISTON PINS

NOTE: **Identification mark on connecting rod faces toward front of engine.**

Check pin fit in piston bore without rod. At room temperature, pin should press in smoothly by hand. When assembling, apply engine oil to outside of pin and to piston pin bore. Position rod and piston marks (indicating front) upward. Align pin with installer and press pin into piston and rod.

NOTE: **Pin-to-rod fit at normal temperature will require 1,653-3,858 lbs. (750-1,750 kg) to press piston through rod.**

PISTON RINGS

NOTE: **Compression rings differ in scraping edge design. From a cross sectional view, ring No. 1 has a barrel shaped scraping edge and ring No. 2 has a tapered edge.**

Install rings on piston with end gaps staggered at 120 degree intervals. *See Fig. 8.* Ensure no ring gap is in line with thrust face of pin bore. Also ensure manufacturer's marks are facing upward when rings are installed.

CAUTION: **Install oil ring first without using a ring expander. Expander gap should be installed more than 45 degrees from side rail gaps, and rails should turn smoothly when installed.**

Fig. 8: Piston Ring Gap Positions

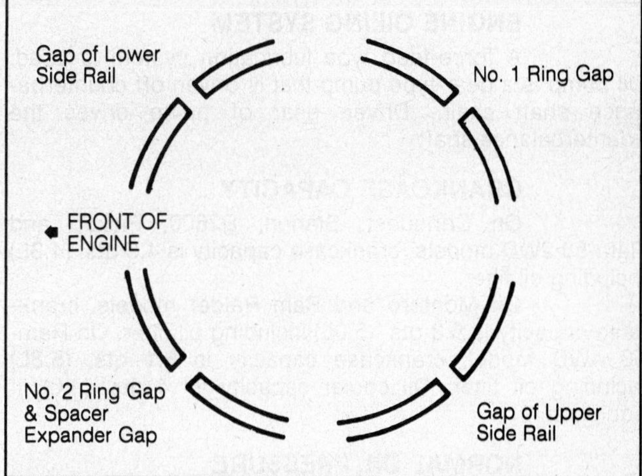

Stagger ring gaps to minimize compression loss. Courtesy of Mitsubishi Motor Sales of America.

PISTON RING SIZES

Ring Size	Size Mark
Standard	No Mark
.010" (.25 mm) Oversize	25
.020" (.50 mm) Oversize	50
.030" (.75 mm) Oversize	75
.040" (1.00 mm) Oversize	100

CRANKSHAFT & ROD BEARINGS

MAIN BEARINGS

1) With engine removed from vehicle, remove oil pan and cylinder head. Remove piston and rod assemblies as previously described. Remove crankshaft bearing caps.

2) Inspect each bearing for peeling, melting, seizure or improper contact. Replace defective bearings. Measure outside diameter of crankshaft, should be 2.36 inch (60 mm) and crank pin should be 2.09 inch (53 mm) to determine if out-of-round or taper. Service limit for both is .0004 inch (0.01 mm).

3) Use Plastigage method to check bearing clearance. If clearance exceeds limits, bearing should be replaced or undersize bearing installed. Undersize bearings are available in .010" (.25 mm), .020" (.50 mm), and .030" (.75 mm) undersizes.

NOTE: **Do not turn crankshaft with Plastigage installed.**

THRUST BEARING ALIGNMENT

Center main bearing is thrust bearing. With crankshaft bearing caps installed, check thrust bearing end play by inserting feeler gauge between center main bearing and crankshaft thrust face. If clearance exceeds specified limits, replace center main bearing.

2.6L & 2.6L TURBO 4-CYLINDER (Cont.)

ENGINE OILING

ENGINE OILING SYSTEM

A force-feed type lubrication system is used. Oil pump is a gear-type pump that is driven off counterbalance shaft chain. Driven gear of pump drives the counterbalance shaft.

CRANKCASE CAPACITY

On Conquest, Starion, B2600, Pickup and Ram-50 2WD models, crankcase capacity is 4.5 qts. (4.3L) including oil filter.

On Montero and Ram Raider models, crankcase capacity is 5.3 qts. (5.0L) including oil filter. On Ram-50 4WD model, crankcase capacity is 6.1 qts. (5.8L) including oil filter. Oil cooler capacity is .4 qts. (.4L), if equipped.

NORMAL OIL PRESSURE

Minimum oil pressure for all models is 11.4 psi (80 kg/cm²) at idle.

OIL PUMP

Removal

Oil pump is mounted at lower right side of engine block and driven by counterbalance shaft drive chain. For removal, see COUNTERBALANCE SHAFTS.

Installation

To install, reverse removal procedure. Ensure oil pump gear mating marks are aligned and Woodruff key on counterbalance shaft fits in keyway of driven gear. *See Fig. 9.*

CAUTION: Prior to installing oil pump, prime pump with .33 oz. (10 cc) of engine oil.

Fig. 9: Oil Pump Gear Mating Marks

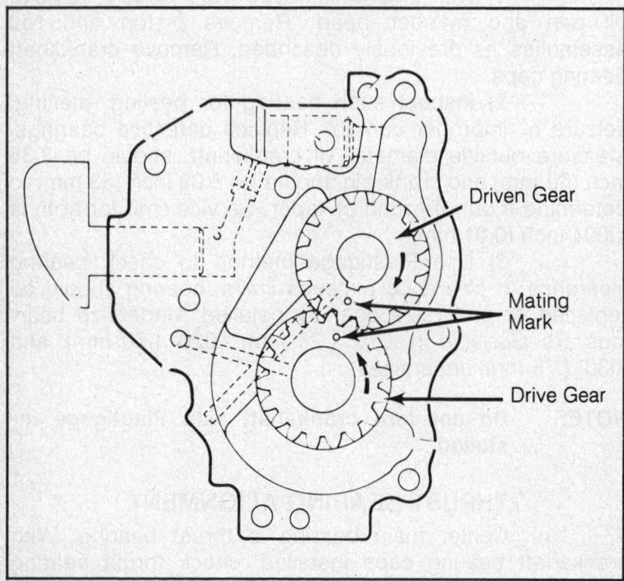

Align marks during assembly. Courtesy of Mitsubishi Motor Sales of America.

OIL PUMP SPECIFICATIONS

Application	Clearance In. (mm)
Drive Gear Side Clearance	.0032-.0055 (.08-.14)
Drive Gear-to-Bearing	.0008-.0020 (.02-.05)
Drive Gear-to-Rear Bearing	.0016-.0028 (.04-.07)
Driven Gear Side Clearance	.0024-.0047 (.06-.12)
Gear Tip-to-Body Clearance	.0043-.0059 (.11-.15)

ENGINE COOLING

WATER PUMP

Removal & Installation

Drain cooling system and disconnect battery. Remove fan shroud (if equipped) and lower radiator hose. Remove drive belt, cooling fan, fan clutch, and pulley. Remove water pump. To install, reverse removal procedure using new gasket.

NOTE: For further information on cooling systems, see ENGINE COOLING section.

TIGHTENING SPECIFICATIONS

Application	Ft. Lbs. (N.m)
Camshaft Bearing Cap Bolt	14-15 (19-20)
Camshaft Sprocket Bolt	37-43 (50-58)
Connecting Rod Cap Nut	33-34 (45-47)
Crankshaft Sprocket Bolt	80-94 (108-127)
Cylinder Head Bolt (Cold)	65-72 (89-98)
Cylinder Head Bolt (Hot)	72-79 (98-107)
Cylinder Head-to-Timing Cover Bolt	11-15 (15-20)
Engine Mount-to-Engine Bolt	10-14 (13-19)
Engine Mount-to-Crossmember Bolt	22-29 (30-39)
Exhaust Manifold Bolt Or Nut	11-14 (15-19)
Flywheel or Drive Plate-to-Crankshaft Bolt	94-101 (127-137)
Intake Manifold Bolt Or Nut	11-14 (15-19)
Jet Valve	13-15 (18-20)
Main Bearing Cap Bolt	55-61 (75-83)
Oil Pump Sprocket Bolt	22-28 (30-38)
Silent Shaft Sprocket Bolt	44-50 (59-68)
	INCH Lbs. (N.m)
Oil Pump Mounting Bolt	72-84 (8-10)
Rocker Arm Adjusting Nut	108-156 (12-18)

Mitsubishi Engines

2.6L & 2.6L TURBO 4-CYLINDER (Cont.)

ENGINE SPECIFICATIONS

GENERAL SPECIFICATIONS

Year	DISPLACEMENT		Fuel System	HP@RPM	Torque Ft. Lbs.@RPM	Compr. Ratio	BORE		STROKE	
	Cu. In.	Liters					In.	mm	In.	mm
1987 B2600	155.9	2.6	2-Bbl.	109@5000	142@3000	7.0:1	3.59	91.1	3.86	98.0
Conquest & Starion	155.9	2.6	EFI	145@5000	185@2500	7.0:1	3.59	91.1	3.86	98.0
Conquest TSi	155.9	2.6	EFI	176@5000	223@2500	7.0:1	3.59	91.1	3.86	98.0
Montero	155.9	2.6	2-Bbl	109@5000	142@3000	7.0:1	3.59	91.1	3.86	98.0
Pickup	155.9	2.6	2-Bbl.	109@5000	142@3000	8.2:1	3.59	91.1	3.86	98.0
Ram Raider	155.9	2.6	2-Bbl	106@5000	142@2500	8.7:1	3.59	91.1	3.86	98.0
Ram-50	155.9	2.6	2 Bbl	106@5000	142@2500	8.7:1	3.59	91.1	3.86	98.0
Starion ESI	155.9	2.6	EFI	176@5000	223@2500	7.0:1	3.59	91.1	3.86	98.0

VALVES

Engine Size & Valve	Head Diam. In. (mm)	Face Angle	Seat Angle	Seat Width In. (mm)	Stem Diameter In. (mm)	Stem Clearance In. (mm)	Valve Lift In. (mm)
2.6L							
Intake	1.81 (46)	45°	45°	.035-.051 (.9-1.3)	.315 (8.0)	.0012-.0024 (.03-.06)	.413 (10.5)
Exhaust [1]	1.50 (38)	45°	45°	.047-.063 (1.2-1.6)	.315 (8.0)	.0020-.0035 (.05-.09)	.413 (10.5)

[1] – Valve stem is chromium flash plated on intercooled models.

PISTONS, PINS & RINGS

Engine	PISTONS	PINS		RINGS		
	Clearance In. (mm)	Piston Fit In. (mm)	Rod Fit In. (mm)	Ring No.	End Gap In. (mm)	Side Clearance In. (mm)
2.6L	.0008-.0016 (.02-.04)	[1]	[2] Press Fit	No. 1	[3] .012-.020 (.30-.50)	.002-.004 (.05-.10)
				No. 2	.010-.016 (.25-.40)	.001-.002 (.02-.05)
				Oil	[4] .012-.031 (.30-.80)	.....

[1] – Thumb press fit without rod installed.
[2] – Press in at 1653-3858 (lbs.) at room temperature.
[3] – On Montero & Pickups, end gap is .012-.018" (.30-.45 mm).
[4] – On Montero & Pickups, end gap is .012-.024" (.30-.60 mm).

CRANKSHAFT MAIN & CONNECTING ROD BEARINGS

Engine	MAIN BEARINGS				CONNECTING ROD BEARINGS		
	Journal Diam. In. (mm)	Clearance In. (mm)	Thrust Bearing	Crankshaft End Play In. (mm)	Journal Diam. In. (mm)	Clearance In. (mm)	Side Play In. (mm)
2.6L	2.362 (60)	.0008-.0020 (.02-.05)	No. 3	.002-.007 (.05-.18)	2.087 (53)	.0008-.0024 (.02-.06)	.004-.010 (.10-.25)

Mitsubishi Engines

2.6L & 2.6L TURBO 4-CYLINDER (Cont.)

ENGINE SPECIFICATIONS (Cont.)

CAMSHAFT

Engine	Journal Diam. In. (mm)	Clearance In. (mm)	Lobe Lift In. (mm)
2.6L			
Int. & Exh.	1.339 (34)	.002-.004 (.05-.10)	.....

VALVE SPRINGS

Engine	Free Length In. (mm)	PRESSURE Lbs. @ In. (Kg @ mm)	
		Valve Closed	Valve Open
2.6L	[1] 1.961 (49.8)	72@1.591 (32.7@40.4)	.....

[1] – Not exceeding 2.0 degrees out of square.

Nissan Engines

1.6L 4-CYLINDER

Pulsar NX, Sentra

NOTE: For engine repair procedures not covered in this article, see ENGINE OVERHAUL PROCEDURES article at the beginning of this section.

ENGINE CODING

ENGINE IDENTIFICATION

Engine serial number is stamped on a machined pad, located beneath the exhaust manifold, at left rear side of the engine. The 2nd character of the VIN code represents engine model.

ENGINE IDENTIFICATION CODES

Application	Code
Pulsar NX & Sentra (1.6L Carb.)	E16S
Sentra (1.6L EFI)	E16i

ENGINE, MANIFOLDS & CYLINDER HEAD

ENGINE

NOTE: It is recommended that engine and transaxle be removed as a unit. If necessary, separate the engine from transaxle after removal.

Removal

1) Install fender cover and block wheels. Mark hood hinge positions. Remove hood. Remove battery and support bracket. Remove air cleaner and fresh air duct and place a clean shop towel over carburetor or throttle body inlet. Drain coolant. Remove radiator, shroud and cooling fan.

2) Remove power steering pump, bracket, A/C compressor and idler pulley (if equipped). Do not discharge systems. Secure components away from engine. Disconnect accelerator cable. Loosen 3 top bolts from struts.

3) Raise and support vehicle. Remove undercover. Disconnect front exhaust pipe from exhaust manifold. Disconnect all linkages, cables, vacuum hoses, and wiring from transaxle and label accordingly. Plug pinion gear hole once speedometer cable is removed.

4) Remove lower ball joints and discard mount nuts. Drain gear oil from transaxle. Remove both drive shafts from transaxle. Do not damage oil seals.

5) Label and disconnect all vacuum, fuel, air hoses and electrical wiring between engine and chassis. Attach lifting sling and engine hoist to engine. Disconnect engine and transaxle mounts. Lift engine and transaxle from vehicle.

Installation

Reverse removal procedure to install engine and transaxle. Use new nuts when installing ball joints. Ensure all hoses, cables, and wires are properly connected.

INTAKE MANIFOLD

Removal

1) Remove air cleaner and fresh air duct. Disconnect accelerator and choke cables. Disconnect fuel line at carburetor or throttle body opening, and plug openings. Remove intake manifold support bracket.

2) Remove all wiring, coolant and vacuum hoses interfering with intake manifold removal and label accordingly. Remove fuel pump and EGR valve assembly (if necessary). Remove intake manifold-to-cylinder head mount nuts. *See Fig. 1.* Remove carburetor from intake manifold assembly (if necessary).

Installation

Install intake manifold assembly using new gaskets. Ensure manifold and head mating surfaces are free of nicks, warpage or other damage. To complete installation, reverse removal procedure.

EXHAUST MANIFOLD

Removal

1) Remove exhaust air induction tube bracket and EGR tube at EGR valve side. If necessary, remove distributor and high tension cables. Remove exhaust manifold cover, EGR and exhaust air induction tubes.

2) Detach front exhaust pipe from manifold. When removing exhaust manifold mount bolts, note that center mount nut is of different diameter. Remove manifold.

Installation

Install exhaust manifold assembly using new gaskets. Ensure manifold and head mating surfaces are free of nicks, warpage or other damage. To complete installation, reverse removal procedure.

CYLINDER HEAD

Removal

1) Turn crankshaft until No. 1 piston is at TDC of compression stroke. Check timing marks to ensure correct timing setting. Remove alternator and bracket. Remove power steering pump and A/C compressor and bracket (if equipped). Do not discharge systems. Secure components away from engine.

2) Remove exhaust and intake manifolds. Remove rocker cover and gasket, water pump pulley and pump. Note bolt lengths and locations for reassembly reference.

3) If necessary, remove thermostat housing and distributor. Remove crankshaft pulley and damper. Remove upper and lower outer front dust cover mount bolts. Remove covers and gaskets.

4) Disconnect all hoses, cables, and wires interfering with cylinder head removal and label accordingly. Mark timing belt rotation direction. See TIMING BELT. Loosen timing belt tensioner and remove timing belt.

NOTE: There are 3 different lengths of cylinder head bolts. Note bolt length and location during removal for reassembly reference.

5) Remove camshaft sprocket and jackshaft pulley. Remove upper inner cover mount bolts and cover. Loosen head bolts gradually, in reverse order of tightening sequence. *See Fig. 2.* Remove cylinder head.

Inspection

1) Check cylinder head for cracks, flaws or damage. Replace as necessary. Inspect head and block mating surfaces for warpage. Warpage limit is .004" (.10 mm) or less.

2) If beyond limit, refinish surface. Maximum surface grinding limit of head and/or block is .008" (.20 mm). Replace head and/or block if machined or warped beyond service limit.

Nissan Engines

1.6L 4-CYLINDER (Cont.)

Fig. 1: Exploded View of Engine Components

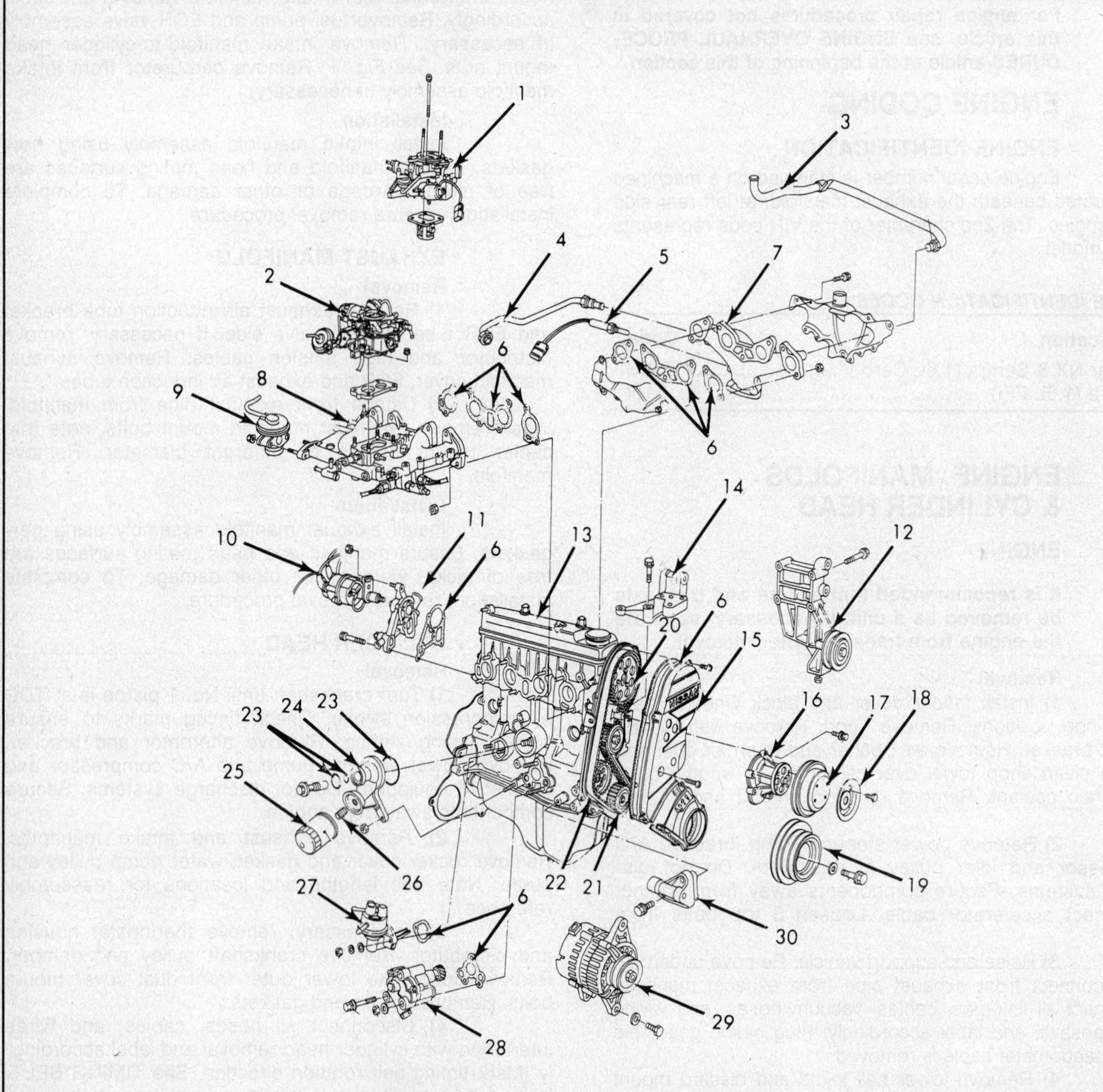

1. Throttle Body
2. Carburetor
3. Air Injection Pipe
4. EGR Tube
5. Oxygen Sensor
6. Gasket
7. Exhaust Manifold
8. Intake Manifold
9. EGR Valve
10. Distributor
11. Coolant Oulet Housing
12. Air Conditioner Bracket
13. Rocker Cover
14. Power Steering Oil Pump
15. Front Cover
16. Water Pump
17. Water Pump Pulley
18. Pulley Cover Plate
19. Crankshaft Pulley
20. Camshaft Timing Pulley
21. Camshaft Timing Pulley
22. Jackshaft Timing Pulley
23. "O" Ring
24. Oil Filter Adapter
25. Oil Filter
26. Oil Filter Stud
27. Fuel Pump
28. Oil Pump
29. Alternator
30. Engine Mounting Bracket

Courtesy of Nissan Motor Co., U.S.A.

1.6L 4-CYLINDER (Cont.)

Fig. 2: Cylinder Head Tightening Sequence

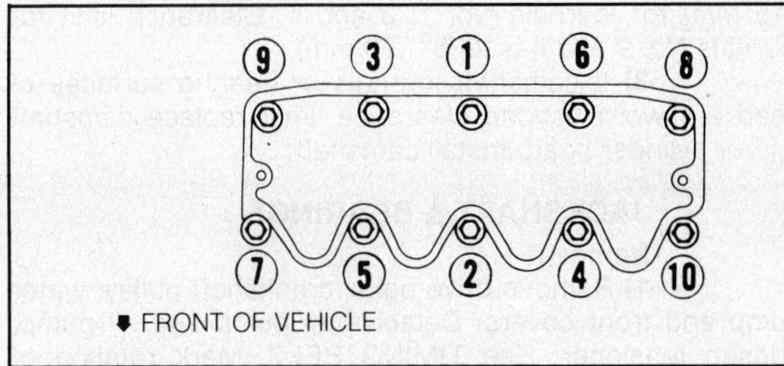

Courtesy of Nissan Motor Co., U.S.A.

NOTE: **Do not apply sealant to mating surfaces of cylinder head and block.**

Installation

1) Thoroughly clean mating surfaces of cylinder head and block. Ensure No. 1 piston is at TDC of compression stroke. Install new cylinder head gasket on dowel pins. Install cylinder head assembly.

2) Ensure camshaft sprocket mark aligns with cylinder head inner cover mark and crankshaft sprocket mark aligns with cylinder block inner cover mark. *See Fig. 3.*

3) Install cylinder head bolts in proper locations. Sequentially tighten bolts evenly, in 5 stages. Tighten cylinder head bolts to 22 ft. lbs. (29 N.m) and then to 51 ft. lbs. (69 N.m). Loosen all bolts completely. Retighten all head bolts in sequence to 22 ft. lbs. (29 N.m). Tighten all bolts to final torque of 54 ft. lbs. (74 N.m). *See Fig. 2.*

4) To complete installation, reverse removal procedure. When installing timing belt, ensure crankshaft and camshaft are in proper alignment and timing belt rotation is correct. See TIMING BELT. Adjust valve clearance. After engine has run for several minutes, allow it to cool down and recheck head bolt torque.

CAMSHAFT

TIMING BELT

NOTE: **After removing timing belt, do not rotate crankshaft or camshaft; piston-to-valve contact may result.**

Removal

1) Turn crankshaft until No. 1 piston is at TDC of compression stroke. Check timing marks to ensure correct timing. Remove accessory drive belts. Remove water pump plate, pulley, pump and gasket.

2) Remove crankshaft pulley and spacer. Remove outer, upper and lower front cover mount bolts and front dust covers. Remove timing belt tensioner, spring and timing belt.

Inspection

Check timing belt for cracks, wear, oil soaked or damaged belt grooves. Check tensioner for binding condition. Inspect tensioner surface and clean as necessary. Do not use oil or grease. Check for spring wear. Replace any component that is damaged or excessively worn.

Installation

1) Ensure No. 1 piston is at TDC on compression stroke. Camshaft dowel pin should be at 12 o'clock position. Check that camshaft sprocket mark aligns with inner cylinder head cover mark and crankshaft sprocket mark aligns with inner cylinder block cover mark. *See Fig. 3.*

Fig. 3: Timing Belt Alignment Procedure

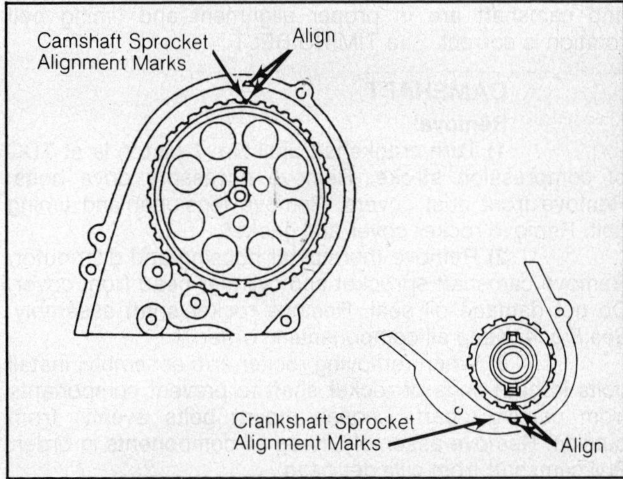

Courtesy of Nissan Motor Co., U.S.A.

NOTE: **When installing a used belt, mount belt in same direction as it was previously rotating and in conjuction with the engine rotating direction.**

2) Install tensioner and rotate clockwise about 70-80 degrees. Tighten lock nut. Place timing belt on sprockets. Ensure belt is not loose around jackshaft and camshaft sprockets.

3) Loosen tensioner lock nut so tensioner pushes on timing belt. Turn camshaft sprocket about 20 degrees (2 cogs) clockwise. Tighten nut while preventing tensioner from turning in "free" direction. To complete installation, reverse removal procedure.

ENGINE FRONT COVERS & OIL SEAL

Removal

1) Remove accessory drive belts. Remove water pump plate, pulley and pump. Remove crankshaft pulley and spacer. Remove upper and lower outer front cover mount bolts. Remove upper and lower outer front covers.

2) Remove timing belt tensioner and timing belt. See TIMING BELT. Remove jackshaft sprocket. Remove crankshaft sprocket and spacer. Remove cylinder block inner cover mount bolts, cover, gasket and oil seal collar. Mark direction of timing belt rotation at this time.

3) Remove jackshaft pulley. Using a seal driver/installer, drive out jackshaft and crankshaft oil seals from their covers.

NOTE: **Replace front cover seals whenever cylinder block cover is removed.**

Installation

1) Lubricate new oil seal lips with oil. Using seal driver/installer, drive seals into position. Thoroughly clean mating surfaces. Apply sealer to both sides of cylinder block gasket.

2) Install oil seal collar. Install cylinder block inner cover and tighten mount bolts. Do not damage oil seal lips during installation. Reverse removal procedure to complete installation.

3) Lubricate new oil seal lip with engine oil. Using seal driver/installer, drive seal into position. Align oil pump and crankshaft locating notches and install oil pump assembly.

4) To complete installation, reverse removal procedure. When installing timing belt, ensure crankshaft and camshaft are in proper alignment and timing belt rotation is correct. See TIMING BELT.

CAMSHAFT

Removal

1) Turn crankshaft until No. 1 piston is at TDC of compression stroke. Remove accessory drive belts. Remove front dust covers. Remove tensioner and timing belt. Remove rocker cover and gasket.

2) Remove thermostat housing and distributor. Remove camshaft sprocket and cylinder head front cover. Do not damage oil seal. Remove rocker shaft assembly. *See Fig. 4*. Keep all components in order.

3) When removing rocker arm assembly, install bolts in both ends of rocker shaft to prevent components from coming apart. Loosen mount bolts evenly, from outside. Remove assembly. Keep all components in order. Pull camshaft from cylinder head.

Inspection

1) Check camshaft, journals, and cam lobe surface for bend, wear or damage. Refer to CAMSHAFT SPECIFICATIONS chart. Check bend with camshaft in "V" blocks. If camshaft journal or cylinder head bearing surface is worn beyond maximum limit, replace camshaft and/or cylinder head.

2) With camshaft sprocket installed, check tooth surface for flaws or excessive wear. Install dial indicator with pointer mounted to flat surface of sprocket. Check for runout. Standard sprocket runout limit is .004" (.10 mm) or less. Replace sprocket if worn or beyond specification.

CAMSHAFT SPECIFICATIONS

Application	In. (mm)
Standard Lobe Height	
Intake	1.4128-1.4226" (35.884-36.134 mm)
Exhaust	1.4031-1.4130" (35.640-35.890 mm)
Camshaft End Play	.016 (.40)
Maximum Bend Limit	.004" (.10 mm)
Journal Inside Diameter	
Standard Clearance	
No. 1, 3 & 5	.0014-.0030" (.035-.076 mm)
No. 2 & 4	.0031-.0047" (.078-.119 mm)
Camshaft Bearing Inside Diameter	
Standard	1.1255-1.1260" (28.587-28.600)

Installation

1) Coat camshaft with engine oil and carefully install into engine. Do not damage camshaft bearing surfaces during installation. Install rocker arm assembly.

2) Install upper, inner dust cover (if equipped). Install camshaft sprocket, tensioner, timing belt, and related components. Install outer front covers. To complete installation, reverse removal procedure.

CAMSHAFT BEARINGS

Clearance Check

1) With camshaft removed, measure inside diameter of camshaft bearing surface of cylinder head with telescopic gauge. Measure outside diameter of camshaft journal with micrometer.

2) Camshaft bearing clearance limit is .006" (.15 mm) for journals No. 1, 3 and 5. Clearance limit for journals No. 2 and 4 is .008" (.20 mm).

3) If camshaft journals or bearing surfaces of head are worn beyond clearance limit, replace camshaft and/or cylinder head. Install camshaft.

JACKSHAFT & BEARINGS

Removal

1) Remove drive belts, crankshaft pulley, water pump and front covers. Detach fuel pump and oil pump. Loosen tensioner. See TIMING BELT. Mark rotation of and remove timing belt. Remove jackshaft sprocket.

2) Remove jackshaft locating plate mounting bolt and plate. Take out jackshaft. Do not damage bearing surfaces during removal.

Inspection

1) With jackshaft removed, measure inside diameter of jackshaft bushing surfaces in cylinder block with inside dial gauge. Measure outside diameter of jackshaft journals with micrometer. Refer to JACKSHAFT SPECIFICATIONS chart.

2) Replace jackshaft bearings in cylinder block if clearances are beyond limit. With jackshaft locating plate installed, tighten locating plate mount bolt and check for excessive end play. Refer to JACKSHAFT SPECIFICATIONS chart.

3) Mount dial gauge with pointer set on end of jackshaft. If end play is beyond specification, replace locating plate, jackshaft and/or inner bearings. Inspect jackshaft fuel pump cam lobe and oil pump drive gear for excessive wear or damage. If lobe or gear is excessively worn, replace jackshaft. Refer to JACKSHAFT SPECIFICATIONS chart.

JACKSHAFT SPECIFICATIONS

Application	In. (mm)
Bushing Inside Diameter	
Front Bushing	1.2606-1.2632" (32.020-32.085)
Rear Bushing	1.1268-1.1293" (28.620-28.685)
End Play	.0018-.0041" (.045-.105)
Fuel Pump Lobe Diameter	
Standard	1.094-1.098" (.27.80-27.90)
Journal Outside Diameter	
Front Standard	1.2593-1.2598" (31.987-32.000)
Rear Standard	1.1255-1.1260" (28.587-28.600)
Journal-to-Bushing Clearance	
Standard	.0008-.0039" (.020-.098)
Maximum	.006" (.15 mm)

Installation

1) Using bearing remover and proper adapters, remove jackshaft bearings. Pull front bearing out from front of block. Using long drift, push out rear expansion plug. Remove rear bearing from rear of engine.

2) Install front and rear jackshaft bearings using bearing installer tool. Ensure bearing oil holes are aligned with cylinder block oil holes. Coat with sealant and install rear jackshaft expansion plug.

3) Coat jackshaft with engine oil and install. Install locating plate and tighten mounting bolt. To complete installation, reverse removal procedure.

1.6L 4-CYLINDER (Cont.)

Fig. 4: Exploded View of Camshaft & Crankshaft Assemblies

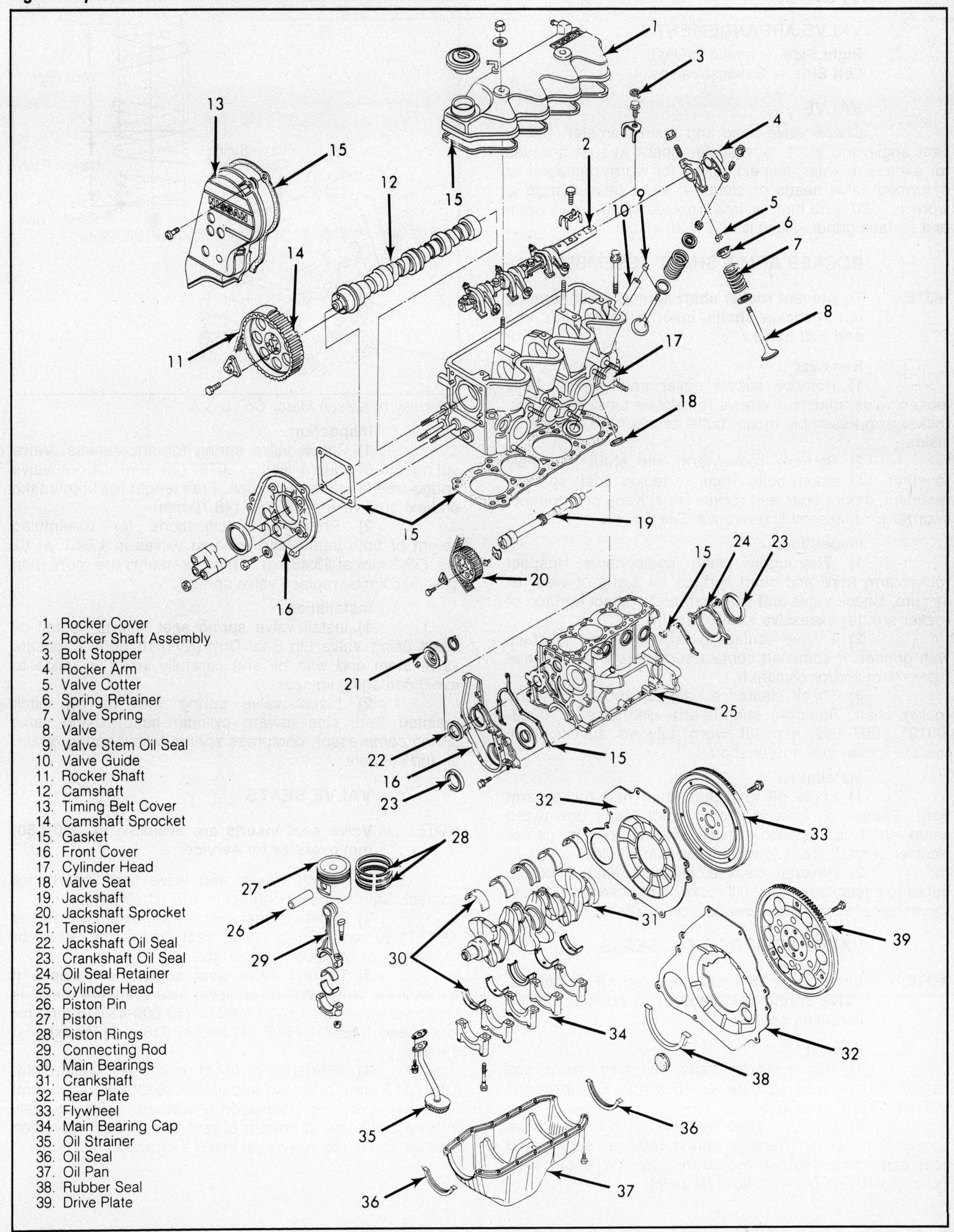

Courtesy of Nissan Motor Co., U.S.A.

Nissan Engines

1.6L 4-CYLINDER (Cont.)

VALVES

VALVE ARRANGEMENT

Right Side - Intake valves.
Left Side - Exhaust valves.

VALVE

Check valve head and stem diameter. Check seat angle and valve face angle. Check keeper grooves for excessive wear. Inspect valves for worn, damaged or deformed valve heads or stems. If valve head margin is worn to .020" (.50 mm) or less, replace valve. Valve stem end surface grinding limit is .008" (.20 mm).

ROCKER ARM & SHAFT ASSEMBLY

NOTE: **To prevent rocker shaft springs from slipping out of rocker shafts, insert bracket bolts into end bolt holes.**

Removal

1) Remove rocker cover and gasket. Fully loosen valve adjusting screws to remove tension. Loosen rocker arm assembly mount bolts evenly from outside to inside.

2) Remove rocker arm and shaft assembly together with mount bolts. Remove rocker shaft springs, retainers, mount bolts and rocker arms. Keep components in order for reassembly reference. *See Fig. 4*.

Inspection

1) Thoroughly clean components. Inspect rocker arm bore and shaft surface for signs of wear or seizure. Check valve and camshaft end contact surface of rocker arm for excessive wear or scuffing.

2) If valve contact surface is worn, resurface with grinder. If camshaft contact surface is worn, replace rocker arm and/or camshaft.

3) Check clearance between rocker arm and rocker shaft. Standard shaft-to-arm clearance is .0003-.0019" (.007-.049 mm). If worn beyond specification, replace rocker arm and/or shaft.

Installation

1) Apply oil to rocker shaft and rocker arm bore. Ensure oil hole in rocker shaft faces downward when shaft is installed. Check that cut-out in center retainer of shaft faces toward exhaust manifold.

2) Reverse disassembly and removal procedures to assemble and install rocker arm assembly. Adjust valves to cold clearance specification of .009" (.22 mm).

VALVE SPRINGS & OIL SEALS

NOTE: **Valve stem lip seals are used on all guides. Valve spring seat must be in position before installing seal.**

Removal

1) With cylinder head removed, compress valve spring using Valve Spring Compressor (KV101072S0). *See Fig. 5*.

2) Remove valve keepers. Carefully release spring compressor. Remove spring retainer, springs, oil seal and valve seat. If necessary, use Valve Lip Seal Puller (KV10107900) to remove oil seals.

Fig. 5: Valve Spring Removal & Replacement

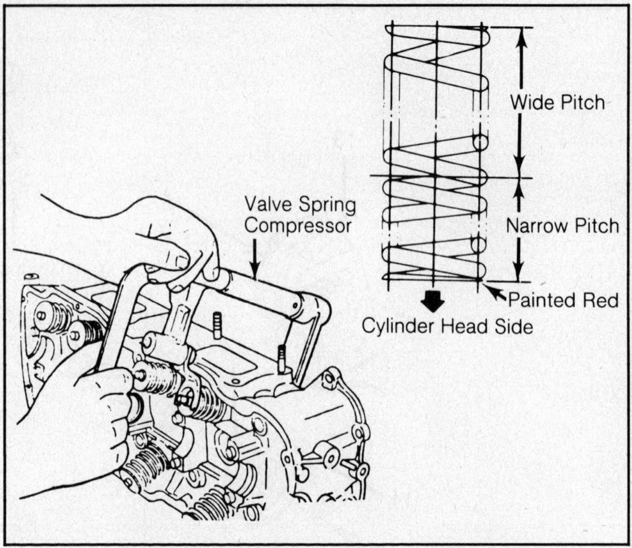

Courtesy of Nissan Motor Co., U.S.A.

Inspection

1) Check valve spring for squareness. Valve spring out-of-square limit is .079" (20 mm). Check valve spring free length and tension. Free length for both intake and exhaust valves is 1.838" (46.70 mm).

2) Pressure specifications for assembled height of both intake and exhaust valves is 1.543" at 52 lbs. (39.2 mm at 23.43 kg). If measurements are more than specified limits, replace valve spring.

Installation

1) Install valve spring seat inserts. Install oil seals using Valve Lip Seal Drift (KV10107500). Lubricate valve stem end with oil and carefully insert in guide to avoid damaging lip seal.

2) Install valve spring with narrow pitch (painted Red) side toward cylinder head. Using valve spring compressor, compress spring. Install spring retainer and keepers.

VALVE SEATS

NOTE: **Valve seat inserts are available in .020 (.50) mm oversize for service.**

1) Check valves and valve seat inserts for contact. Standard seat contact is .059" (1.50 mm).

2) Standard seat contact for exhaust insert is .071" (1.80 mm). Check valve seat inserts for pitting or looseness at valve contact surface.

3) Correct valve seat surface or replace if excessively worn. When replacing insert, ensure insert is recessed into head 1.6929-1.6935" (43.000-43.016 mm) for intake and 1.4567-1.4573" (37.000-37.016 mm) for exhaust insert.

4) Interference fit of insert is .0032-.0044" (.081-.113 mm) for intake and .0025-.0038" (.064-.096 mm) for exhaust. During installation ensure insert fits squarely in bore and seats at bottom of recess. Steel adhesive can also be applied to valve seat insert if desired.

1.6L 4-CYLINDER (Cont.)

VALVE CLEARANCE ADJUSTMENTS

NOTE: Valve clearance adjustment is made with engine warm but not running. For assembly purposes with engine cold, adjust valves to .009" (.22 mm).

1) Warm engine to normal operating temperature. Turn ignition switch to "OFF" position. Remove 2 air inlet tube bolts. Remove air inlet. Remove 2 air cleaner bracket bolts from rocker cover. Remove air cleaner.

2) Disconnect beather tube connecting air cleaner to rocker cover. Disconnect large tube to air pipe. Disconnect medium tube toward end of rocker cover. Remove flexible duct to exhaust manifold. Disconnect ignition wires from the spark plugs.

3) Remove 2 top rocker cover nuts. Remove rocker cover. Remove distributor cap. Turn steering wheel all the way to the right and remove hole plug from right front fender well.

4) Rotate crankshaft until No. 1 cylinder is at TDC on compression stroke. Ensure timing is correct by checking alignment of timing marks. Adjust valves No. 1, 2, 3 and 6. *See Fig. 6*. Loosen valve rocker adjusting screw lock nut and turn adjusting screw until specified clearance of .011" (.28 mm) is obtained.

5) Rotate crankshaft and bring No. 4 cylinder to TDC on compression stroke. Recheck timing marks to ensure correct timing. Adjust remaining valves No. 4, 5, 7 and 8. *See Fig. 6*. Loosen valve rocker adjusting screw lock nut and turn adjusting screw until specified clearance of .011" (.28 mm) is obtained.

6) After adjustment, hold adjusting screw and tighten rocker arm lock nut. Recheck clearances. To reassemble, replace rocker cover gasket and reverse disassemble procedure.

Fig. 6: Valve Clearance Adjustment Sequence

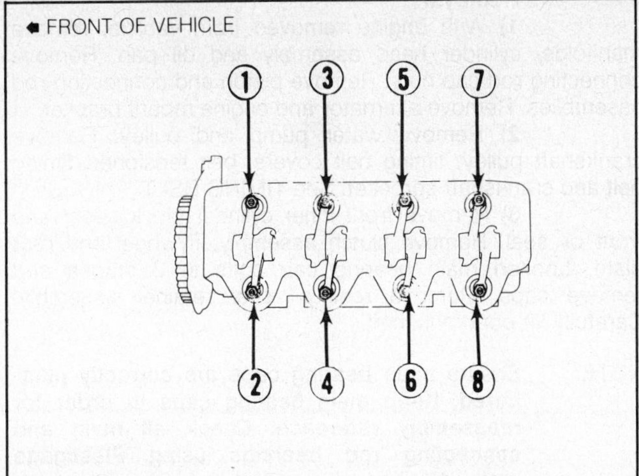

Courtesy of Nissan Motor Co., U.S.A.

VALVE GUIDES

Inspection

1) Measure clearance between valve stem and valve guide. Refer to VALVE GUIDE SPECIFICATIONS chart. Maximum guide-to-stem clearance is .004" (.10 mm) for all models. Insert valve into guide and move left and right, parallel with rocker arm. If tip moves .008" (.20 mm) or more, clearance is beyond maximum limit.

2) If clearance is beyond limits and valve stem is not worn, valve guide must be replaced. To replace guide, heat cylinder head to 300-320°F (150-160°C). Using long drift, drive old guide out from combustion chamber side.

3) With cylinder head at room temperature, ream cylinder head guide hole to fit new guide. Standard valve guide outside diameter is .4737-.4742" (12.033-12.044 mm). Interference fit of guide in cylinder head guide hole is .0018-.0029" (.045-.074 mm). Reheat cylinder head and install new guide.

4) Ensure guide projects above cylinder head surface .579-.602" (14.70-15.30 mm). Use reamer to finish guide bore to .2758-.2764" (7.005-7.020 mm). Check and reface valve seat surface as necessary.

VALVE GUIDE SPECIFICATIONS

Application	In. (mm)
Valve Guide-to-Stem Clearance	
Intake	.0008-.0020" (.020-.050 mm)
Exhaust	.0018-.0030" (.045-.075 mm)

PISTONS, PINS & RINGS

PISTON & ROD ASSEMBLY

Removal

1) With manifolds, cylinder head and oil pan removed, measure diameter of cylinder bore. Check for excessive wear, taper and out-of-round. If any of these measurements exceed maximum specifications provided in ENGINE SPECIFICATIONS chart, block will need to be bored.

2) If cylinder block measures okay, remove connecting rod nuts and ensure that connecting rods and caps are correctly numbered. Remove rod cap with bearing half. Check top of cylinder bore for ridge. If scraper will not remove carbon build-up, remove using ridge reamer.

Inspection

1) Carefully push piston and rod assembly out of block. Check connecting rod for bend or twist using rod aligner tool. Bend and twist limit is .002" (.05 mm) per 3.94" (100 mm) of length.

2) Install connecting rods with bearings onto crankshaft connecting rod journals. Measure rod side play clearance. Play at big end must be .0040-.0146" (.100-.370 mm). Replace rod or repair connecting rod if not within specifications.

NOTE: Applying a short piece of tubing to connecting rod cap studs will prevent damage to crankshaft during installation. If connecting rod is replaced, ensure weight difference between rods is no more than .25 oz. (7 g).

Installation

1) Ensure that "TOP" mark on compression rings is facing upward. Oil rings, piston and cylinder bore. Install piston and rod assembly. Ensure ring gaps are set 180 degrees apart. Do not set ring gaps on thrust side of piston or in line with piston pin. *See Fig. 7*. Ensure bearing halves are properly seated in rod and cap.

1.6L 4-CYLINDER (Cont.)

Fig. 7: Positioning Piston Ring End Gaps

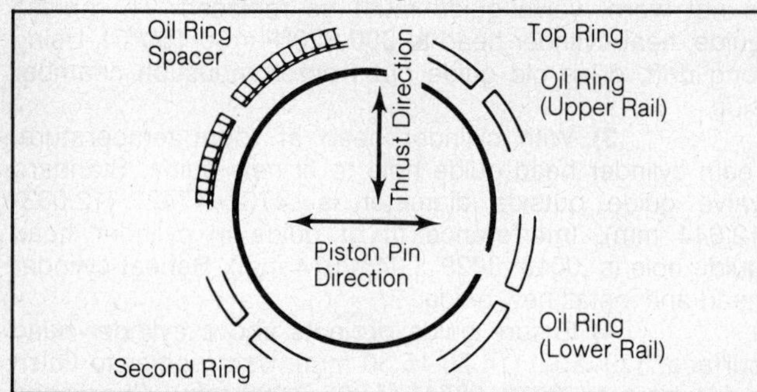

Courtesy of Nissan Motor Co., U.S.A.

2) Install piston in cylinder with notch mark on piston top toward front of engine. Oil jet of connecting rod should face right side of cylinder block. Install cylinder head and oil pan.

FITTING PISTONS & RINGS

1) Visually inspect cylinder block for cracks or flaws. Using bore gauge, measure cylinder bore for excessive wear, out-of-round and taper. If out-of-round exceeds .0006" (.015 mm) or taper exceeds .0008" (.020 mm), boring of cylinder block will be necessay. When one cylinder is bored, all cylinders must be bored.

NOTE: **Before machining block, main bearing caps must be installed and tightened to specifications. To prevent distortion due to excessive heat, bore cylinders in the following order No. 2-4-1-3.**

2) Determine piston oversize according to amount of wear in cylinder. See ENGINE SPECIFICATIONS chart. By measuring piston at thrust face and adding piston-to-cylinder clearance, finish hone of cylinder may be determined. Measure bore halfway down cylinder and 90 degrees to crankshaft center line.

PISTON DIAMETER SPECIFICATIONS

Application	In. (mm)
Standard	2.9908-2.9928 (75.967-76.017)
.0008" (.02 mm) O/S	2.9916-2.9936 (75.987-76.037)
.0197" (.50 mm) O/S	3.0105-3.0125 (76.467-76.517)

3) After honing cylinder to final fit, measure piston-to-cylinder clearance using pull scale and feeler gauge. Extracting force to pull scale should be 1.1-3.3 lbs. (0.5-1.5 kg) using .0016" (.040 mm) feeler gauge.

NOTE: **Pistons and rings are available in .0008" (.02 mm) and .0197" (.50 mm) oversize. Piston and cylinder must be at 68°F (20°C) when checking piston fit.**

4) If pistons are reused, de-carbon piston and ring grooves with scraper and piston groove cleaner tool. Clean oil slots in bottom land of oil ring groove. Check for scratches, wear or damage.

5) Measure piston ring end gap. End gap limit is .040" (1.0 mm). Replace rings if beyond limit. Measure side clearance of rings in grooves as each ring is installed. Side clearance limit is .008" (.20 mm). When installing rings, ensure stamped "TOP" mark on each ring faces up.

PISTON PIN REPLACEMENT

1) Piston pin is press fit into connecting rod and has sliding fit in piston. To remove, set piston and rod assembly with correct adapters into Hydraulic Press (KV10107400). Press pin out of rod.

2) Measure diameter of piston pin, piston pin hole and rod small end. Determine pin-to-piston and pin-to-rod clearance. Standard piston pin diameter is .7478-.7480" (18.995-19.000 mm). Standard piston pin hole inside diameter is .7481-.7485" (19.003-19.012 mm).

3) Check pin-to-piston clearance and pin-to-rod interference fit in specifications table. To assemble piston and rod, hold piston and rod in proper alignment and insert pin. *See Fig. 8*. Assemble with oil hole of rod big end toward right side of block.

Fig. 8: Removing & Installing Piston Pin

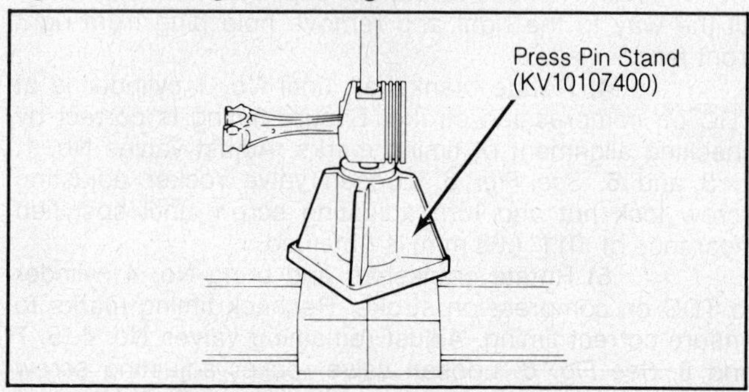

Courtesy of Nissan Motor Co., U.S.A.

CRANKSHAFT & ROD BEARINGS

CRANKSHAFT

Removal

1) With engine removed from vehicle, remove manifolds, cylinder head assembly and oil pan. Remove connecting rod cap nuts. Remove piston and connecting rod assemblies. Remove alternator and engine mount bracket.

2) Remove water pump and pulley. Remove crankshaft pulley, timing belt covers, belt tensioner, timing belt and crankshaft sprocket. See TIMING BELT.

3) Remove front inner cylinder block cover and front oil seal. Remove clutch assembly, flywheel and rear plate. Loosen main bearing cap bolts in 2 stages and remove caps. Remove rear oil seal retainer assembly. Carefully lift out crankshaft.

NOTE: **Ensure main bearing caps are correctly numbered. Keep main bearing caps in order for reassembly reference. Check all main and connecting rod bearings using Plastigage method.**

Inspection

1) Thoroughly clean and inspect crankshaft. Blow out oil passages with compressed air. Check crankshaft main journals and connecting rod journals for scoring, wear, cracks, taper and out-of-round. Standard taper and out-of-round limit is .0004" (.010 mm) or less. Maximum taper and out-of-round is .0012" (.030 mm).

2) Check crankshaft for bend by placing on "V" blocks. Use dial indicator at center journal of crankshaft.

1.6L 4-CYLINDER (Cont.)

Standard bend is .0016" (.05 mm) or less. If bend exceeds .0031" (.08 mm) replace crankshaft.

3) Check crankshaft pilot bushing for wear or damage. If necessary, pull bushing from crankshaft using Pilot Bushing Puller (ST16610001) or equivalent. Clean bushing hole. Insert bushing to .16" (4 mm). Do not damage bushing edge or insert.

4) Check flywheel friction surface for cracks, damage, hot spots or wear. Measure friction surface runout using a dial indicator. Runout limit is .006" (.15 mm). Resurface or replace flywheel if not within limits. Check tooth surfaces of ring gear for flaws or wear. Replace ring gear if necessary.

Installation

1) Install main bearing halves into engine block. Make sure that all bearings are on their correct journals. Journal No. 3 requires a thrust bearing. Upper and lower bearings are not interchangeable. Main bearing (block side) has an oil supply groove.

2) Apply oil to main bearing surface and install crankshaft. Install main bearing caps so number on bearing cap faces toward water pump.

3) Tighten main bearing caps in 2 or 3 stages, starting at center bearing and working outward. Crankshaft should rotate smoothly.

4) Check crankshaft end play. SEE THRUST BEARING ALIGNMENT. Install rear oil seal retainer. To complete installation, reverse removal procedure.

THRUST BEARING ALIGNMENT

Thrust bearing is installed on No. 3 main bearing journal. Check crankshaft end play by inserting a feeler gauge between flange of thrust bearing and crankshaft. Standard end play is .002-.007" (.05-.18 mm) and service limit is .012" (.30 mm). *See Fig. 9.*

Fig. 9: Checking Crankshaft End Play

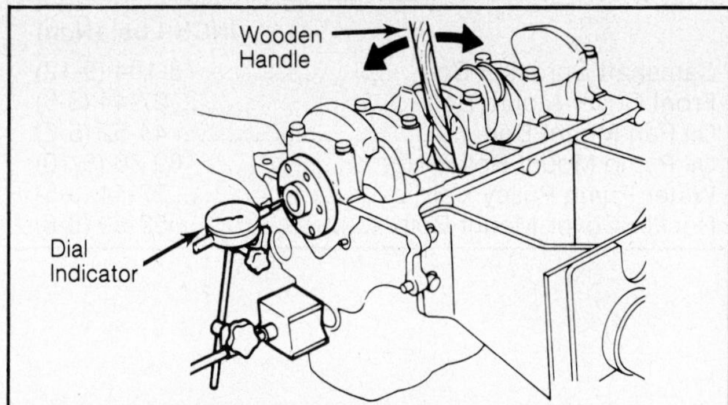

Courtesy of Nissan Motor Co., U.S.A.

REAR MAIN BEARING OIL SEAL

NOTE: When replacing front or rear oil seal, note seal mounting direction.

Removal

With engine removed from vehicle, remove clutch assembly. Remove flywheel and engine end plate. Remove oil pan and oil seal retainer assembly. Check oil seal mounting direction for reassembly reference. Drive out old seal from retainer, using a seal driver/installer.

Installation

Lubricate seal lips. Using seal driver/installer, drive seal into position. Install oil seal retainer. Reverse removal procedure to complete installation.

ENGINE OILING

ENGINE OILING SYSTEM

Pressure is provided to oiling system by a trochoid rotor type pump. Oil pump is mounted on side of crankcase and is driven by auxiliary shaft. Oil pump feeds oil from pan to full-flow oil filter.

Oil is then pumped into main oil gallery of crankcase where it is distributed to crankshaft journals and main bearing journals. From this point oil is fed to the camshaft journals and from center camshaft journal to rocker arm shaft to lubricate rocker arms and valves. Cylinder walls and piston pins are lubricated by oil squirt hole in connecting rod. *See Fig. 10.*

CRANKCASE CAPACITY

Oil capacity is 3.5 qts. (3.2L) with filter change.

OIL FILTER

Oiling system uses a full-flow, replaceable element.

NORMAL OIL PRESSURE

Oil pressure is 43 psi (3 kg/cm²) at 1700 RPM.

OIL PRESSURE RELIEF VALVE

Relief valve is nonadjustable and is located in the oil pump cover.

Fig. 10: Engine Oiling System

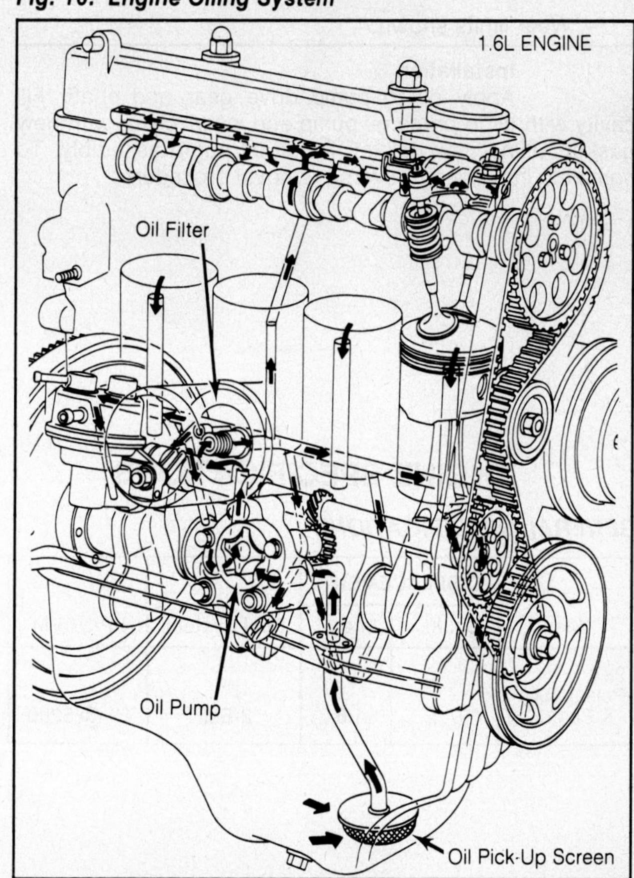

Courtesy of Nissan Motor Co., U.S.A.

Nissan Engines

1.6L 4-CYLINDER (Cont.)

OIL PUMP

Removal

1) Place drain pan under oil pump assembly. Loosen alternator lower bolts. Remove alternator belt and adjusting bracket bolt. Set alternator aside to gain working clearance.

2) Disconnect oil pressure gauge harness. Remove pump mount bolts and oil pump assembly. Remove pump cover bolts. Remove outer rotor. Remove regulator valve. Check all clearances using a feeler gauge. If beyond wear limit, replace entire pump assembly.

NOTE: **Inner rotor and drive gear cannot be disassembled. If placed in vise, do not distort pump body and cover.**

Inspection

Inspect pump body, cover and pump rotors for cracks and excessive wear. Check inner rotor shaft for looseness in pump body. Check oil pressure regulator valve sliding surface and valve spring. If damaged, replace valve seat.

OIL PUMP CLEARANCES

Application	[1] In. (mm)
Outer Rotor-to-Inner Rotor Tip Clearance	.0047 (.120)
Outer Rotor-to-Pump Body	.006-.008 (.15-.21)
Rotor-to-Straightedge	.0047 (.120)

[1] – Wear limits shown.

Installation

Apply oil to pump drive gear and shaft. Fill cavity with oil to prime oil pump and install cover with new gasket. Using new gasket, install oil pump assembly. To complete installation, reverse removal procedure.

ENGINE COOLING

WATER PUMP

NOTE: **The water pump cannot be disassembled. If defective, replace as a unit.**

Removal

Drain coolant. Remove power steering drive belt. Remove power steering pump (if equipped). Do not drain oil. Remove alternator drive belt and alternator. Remove A/C compressor drive belt (if equipped).

Inspection

Inspect water pump body and vane for rust and corrosion. Check pump bearing for excessive end play or rough operation. Replace water pump if any wear or damage is found.

Installation

To install, use new gasket and reverse removal procedure. Ensure gasket contact surfaces are clean.

NOTE: **For more information, see ENGINE COOLING SYSTEMS article at the end of this section.**

TIGHTENING SPECIFICATIONS

Application	Ft. Lbs. (N.m)
Cylinder Head Bolt	51-54 (69-74)
Connecting Rod Cap Nut	23-27 (31-37)
Crankshaft Pulley Bolt	80-94 (108-127)
Drive Plate Bolt	69-76 (93-103)
Flywheel Mount Bolt	58-65 (78-88)
Main Bearing Cap Bolt	36-43 (49-59)
Manifold Mount Nut	12-15 (16-21)
Rocker Arm Lock Nut	12-15 (16-21)
Rocker Arm Shaft Bolt	13-15 (18-21)
Timing Belt Tensioner Lock Nut	12-15 (16-21)
	INCH Lbs. (N.m)
Camshaft Sprocket Bolt	78-104 (9-12)
Front Cover Mount Bolt	27-44 (3-5)
Oil Pan Mount Bolt	44-52 (5-6)
Oil Pump Mount Bolt & Nut	69-86 (8-10)
Water Pump Pulley Bolt	27-44 (3-5)
Rocker Cover Mount Bolt	52-69 (6-8)

ENGINE SPECIFICATIONS

GENERAL SPECIFICATIONS

Year	DISPLACEMENT		Fuel System	HP@RPM	Torque Ft. Lbs.@RPM	Compr. Ratio	BORE		STROKE	
	Cu. In.	Liters					In.	mm	In.	mm
1987 Pulsar NX & Sentra	97.5	1.6	2-Bbl.	69 @ 5200	92 @ 3200	9.4:1	2.99	76.0	3.46	88.0

1.6L 4-CYLINDER (Cont.)

ENGINE SPECIFICATIONS (Cont.)

VALVES

Engine Size & Valve	Head Diam. In. (mm)	Face Angle	Seat Angle	Seat Width In. (mm)	Stem Diameter In. (mm)	Stem Clearance In. (mm)	Valve Lift In. (mm)
1.6L							
Intake	1.457 (37)	45°	45°	.059 (1.50)	.2744-.2750 (6.970-6.985)	.0008-.0020 (.020-.050)	.....
Exhaust	1.181 (30)	45°	45°	.071 (1.80)	.2734-.2740 (6.945-6.960)	.0018-.0030 (.045-.075)	.....

PISTONS, PINS & RINGS

Engine	PISTONS	PINS		RINGS		
	Clearance In. (mm)	Piston Fit In. (mm)	Rod Fit In. (mm)	Ring No.	End Gap In. (mm)	Side Clearance In. (mm)
1.6L	.0009-.0017 (.023-.043)	.0003-.0005 (.008-.012)	[1] .0007-.0015 (.017-.038)	1	.008-.014 (.20-.35)	.0016-.0029 (.040-.070)
				2	.006-.012 (.15-.30)	.0012-.0025 (.030-.063)
				Oil	.012-.035 (.30-.90)	.0020-.0057 (.050-.145)

[1] – Interference fit.

CRANKSHAFT MAIN & CONNECTING ROD BEARINGS

Engine	MAIN BEARINGS				CONNECTING ROD BEARINGS		
	Journal Diam. In. (mm)	Clearance In. (mm)	Thrust Bearing	Crankshaft End Play In. (mm)	Journal Diam. In. (mm)	Clearance In. (mm)	Side Play In. (mm)
1.6L	1.9663-1.9671 (49.943-49.964)	.0012-.0022 [1] (.031-.056)	No. 3	.0020-.0071 (.050-.180)	1.5730-1.5738 (39.954-39.974)	.0004-.0017 (.10-.044)	.020 (.50)

[1] – Main bearing clearance for No. 1, 3 and 5 shown, clearance for No. 2 and 4 is .0012-.0036" (.031-.092 mm).

CAMSHAFT

Engine	Journal Diam. In. (mm)	Clearance In. (mm)	Lobe Lift In. (mm)
1.6L			
No. 1, 3 & 5	1.6515-1.6522 (41.949-41.965)	.0014-.0030 (.035-.076)	[1]
No. 2 & 4	1.6498-1.6505 (41.906-41.922)	.0031-.0047 (.078-.119)	.....

[1] – Camshaft lobe height for 1.6L is 1.4128-1.4226" (35.884-36.134 mm) for intake and 1.4031-1.4130" (35.640-35.890 mm) for exhaust.

VALVE SPRINGS

Engine	Free Length In. (mm)	PRESSURE Lbs. @ In. (Kg @ mm)	
		Valve Closed	Valve Open
1.6L	1.839 (46.70)	52 @ 1.54 (23 @ 39.2)	.....

1.6L 16-VALVE 4-CYLINDER

Pulsar NX SE

NOTE: For engine repair procedures not covered in this article, see ENGINE OVERHAUL PROCEDURES articles at beginning of this section.

NOTE: "Left" and "Right" refer to front and rear side of the engine, NOT the vehicle.

ENGINE CODING

ENGINE IDENTIFICATION

Engine identification number is located on left side of the cylinder block at the No. 4 cylinder.

ENGINE IDENTIFICATION CODES

Application	Code
Pulsar NX SE Coupe	CA16DE

ENGINE, MANIFOLDS & CYLINDER HEAD

ENGINE

Removal

1) Drain radiator coolant. Remove belts from cooling fan, A/C compressor and steering pump. Raise front of vehicle on stands. Remove front wheels and undertrays.

2) Unbolt front brake calipers and move aside. Disconnect lower suspension and steering rod ball joints. Remove steering spindle-to-strut bolts. Disconnect drive shafts from differential housing.

NOTE: Engine and transaxle are removed as a single unit. Transaxle may be removed separately from beneath vehicle for independent service.

3) Remove transaxle support rod and front exhaust pipe section. Disconnect front and rear engine shock straps. Remove air filter and disconnect wiring, vacuum lines and water hoses.

4) Disconnect transaxle shift linkage and throttle control linkage. Lift engine slightly and remove or disengage all engine mounts. Lift engine out of chassis. Ensure brake lines and master cylinder are not damaged when removing engine.

Installation

Ensure insulators are positioned on engine mounts. Lower engine onto engine mounts. Reverse removal procedures to complete installation.

MANIFOLDS & CYLINDER HEAD

NOTE: Removal procedure is with engine removed from chassis.

Removal

1) Ensure No. 1 cylinder is at TDC. Remove timing belt. See TIMING BELT removal instructions in CAMSHAFT section of this article. Remove camshaft cover from cylinder head.

CAUTION: DO NOT rotate camshafts or crankshaft with timing belt removed or valve damage may occur.

2) Remove breather/oil separator from top of cylinder head. Loosen cylinder head bolts. Remove cylinder head.

Inspection & Disassembly

1) Check cylinder head for distortion and overall thickness. See CYLINDER HEAD MEASUREMENTS table. When surfacing cylinder head, remove camshaft pulleys and camshafts. *See Fig. 1 and 2.*

CYLINDER HEAD MEASUREMENTS

Application	In. (mm)
Distortion	Less than .004 (.10)
Height [1]	4.957-4.965 (125.9-126.1)
Machining Limit (Block + Head)	.008 (.20)

[1] – Measured from center of camshaft bore to mounting surface.

2) Hold camshafts with wrench when removing camshaft drive pulley bolts. Remove drive belt tensioner pulley and rear belt shield. Remove camshaft bearing caps gradually in 2 or 3 steps.

3) Remove front camshaft oil seals. Remove camshafts. Remove hydraulic valve lifters. Always set valve lifters with their flat contact face sitting up. DO NOT lay them on their side or with contact surface down. *See Fig. 7.*

Fig. 1: Measuring Cylinder Head

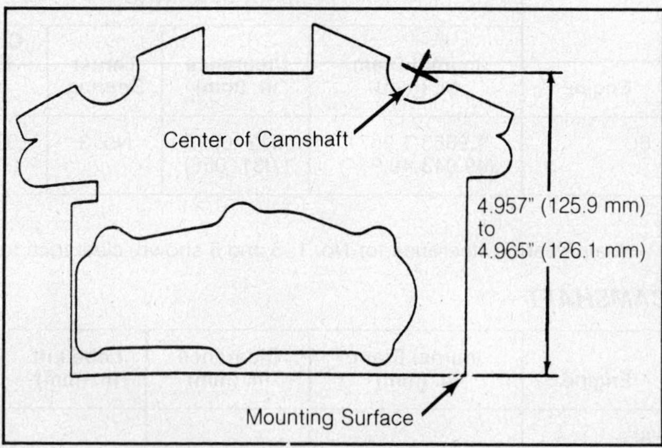

Courtesy of Nissan Motor Co., U.S.A.

Installation

1) Ensure No. 1 cylinder is at TDC and camshaft sprockets are aligned with marks on inner shroud. Install cylinder head on engine block. Install washers on head bolts with flat side of washers against cylinder head.

2) Lubricate bolt threads and contact surface. Tighten cylinder head to specification. *See Fig. 3.* Install timing belt and adjust tension. See TIMING BELT adjustment instructions in CAMSHAFT section of this article. Replace timing belt cover and remaining components to complete installation.

1.6L 16-VALVE 4-CYLINDER (Cont.)

Fig. 2: Removing Camshaft Drive Pulley

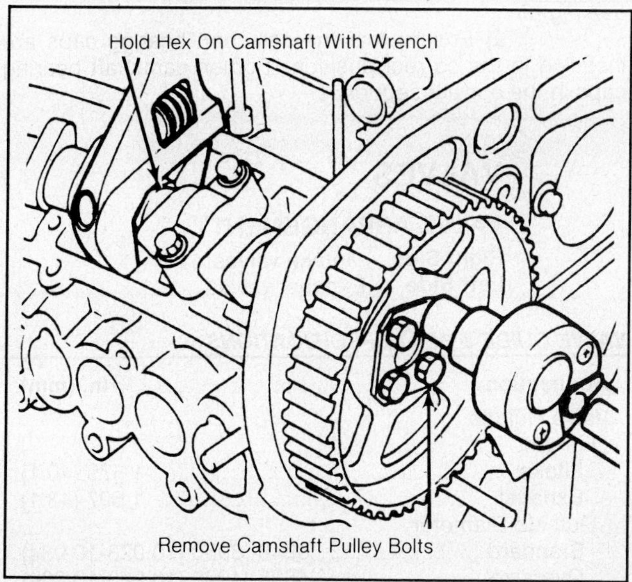

Courtesy of Nissan Motor Co., U.S.A.

CAMSHAFTS

TIMING BELT

Removal

1) Drain engine coolant and remove upper radiator hose. Remove undertray from right side. Remove drive belts from power steering pump and A/C compressor. Remove water pump pulley.

2) Remove crankshaft angle sensor. *See Fig. 4.* Mark sensor and timing belt cover for reassembly reference. Support engine with hoist or jack. Remove front engine mount support.

3) Remove upper timing belt cover. Align timing marks on camshaft belt pulleys and inner timing belt shroud. *See Fig. 5.* Remove right side inner fender panel to gain access to crankshaft. Remove pulley and timing belt.

Inspection

Visually check condition of timing belt. Replace belt if worn, broken or cracked. Check belt tensioning and idler pulleys. Ensure pulleys rotate smoothly. Check tensioner pulley return spring for distortion or corrosion.

Installation

1) Install crankshaft pulley and belt guide plates. Ensure No. 1 cylinder is at TDC on the compression stroke. Align camshaft sprockets with marks on inner shield. Install timing belt.

2) Align marks on timing belt and pulleys. *See Fig. 5.* Ensure there are 39 teeth between the marks on the camshaft pulleys and 48 teeth between the marks on the crankshaft pulley and exhaust cam pulley. *See Fig. 5.*

3) Loosen mounting nut on tensioner pulley. Install crankshaft bolt and a spacer and turn engine 2 revolutions. Tighten tensioner pulley nut. Install timing belt covers.

4) Install crankshaft pulley and washer. Install engine mount. Install crankshaft position sensor and water pump pulley. Ensure reference marks on crankshaft position sensor are aligned.

5) Install power steering and A/C drive belts. Install upper radiator hose and refill coolant.

Fig. 4: Removing Crank Angle Sensor

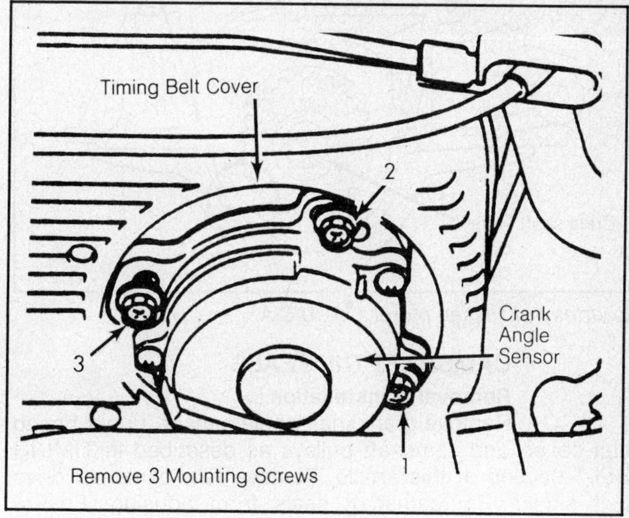

Courtesy of Nissan Motor Co., U.S.A.

Fig. 3: Cylinder Head & Camshaft Tightening Sequence

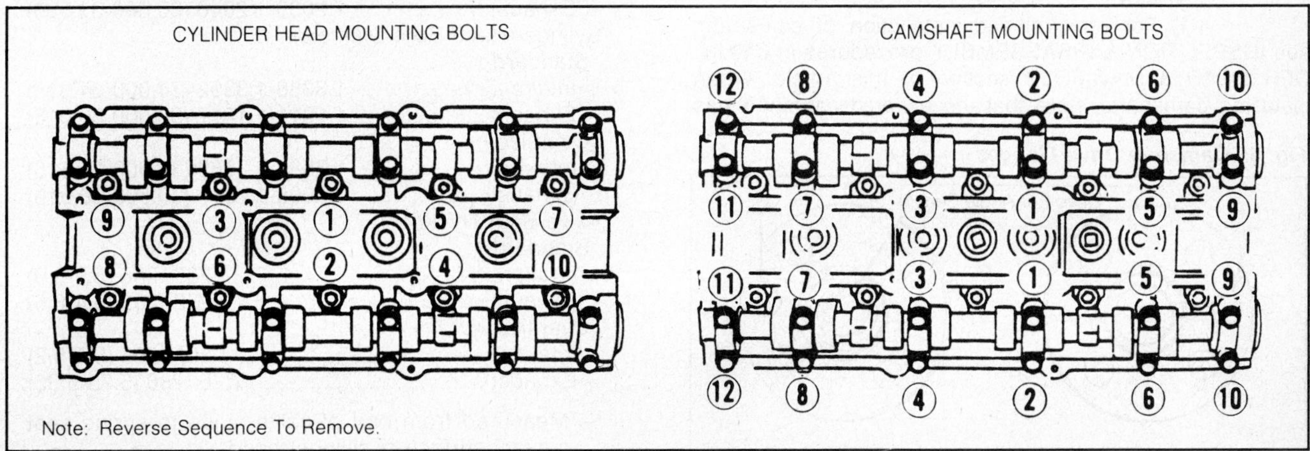

Courtesy of Nissan Motor Co., U.S.A.

1.6L 16-VALVE 4-CYLINDER (Cont.)

Fig. 5: Aligning Camshaft Timing Marks

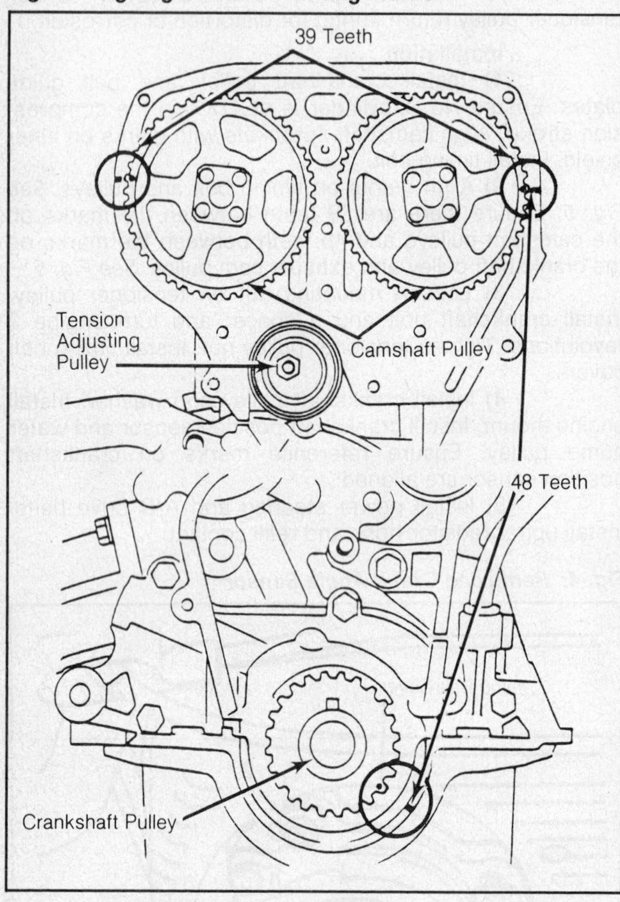

Courtesy of Nissan Motor Co., U.S.A.

CAMSHAFT OIL SEALS

Removal & Installation

Remove crankshaft angle sensor, upper timing belt cover, and camshaft pulleys as described in TIMING BELT section of this article. Remove rear camshaft drive belt shield. Pry camshaft seals from housing. Ensure camshaft seal surface is not damaged. Lubricate seal and drive into position. Reverse removal instructions to complete installation.

CAMSHAFTS & BEARINGS

1) For removal and installation of camshafts see INSPECTION & DISASSEMBLY procedures in CYLINDER HEAD & MANIFOLD section of this article. When installing camshafts, note that the exhaust camshaft has the internal splines to drive the crankshaft position sensor. *See Fig. 6.*

Fig. 6: Camshaft Drive Flanges

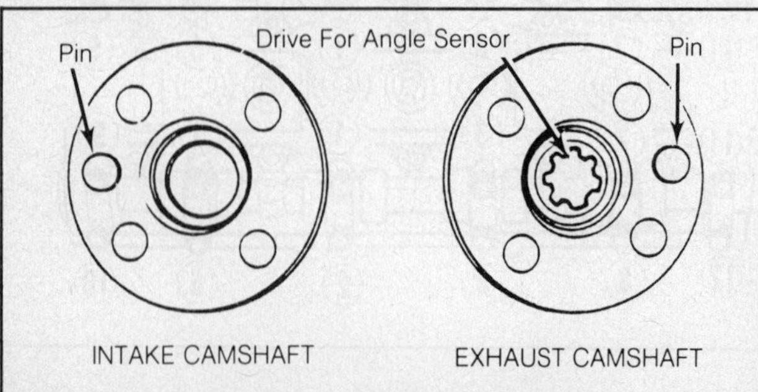

Courtesy of Nissan Motor Co., U.S.A.

2) Ensure that the camshaft bearing caps are installed in the correct position. Tighten camshaft bearing caps in the correct sequence.

VALVES

VALVE ARRANGEMENT

Right Side – Intake valves.
Left Side – Exhaust valves.

VALVE GUIDE & SEAT SPECIFICATIONS

Application	In. (mm)
Valve Guides	
Length	
Intake	1.579 (40.1)
Exhaust	1.697 (43.1)
Outside Diameter	
Standard	.3946-.3950 (10.023-10.034)
Oversize	.4025-.4029 (10.223-10.234)
Inside Diameter	
Intake & Exhaust	.2362-.2369 (6.000-6.018)
Guide Bore In Cylinder Head	
Standard	
Intake	.3921-.3928 (9.960-9.978)
Exhaust	.3927-.3935 (9.975-9.996)
Oversize	.4010-.4014 (10.185-10.196)
Interference Fit	
Standard	
Intake	.0018-.0029 (.045-.074)
Exhaust	.0011-.0023 (.027-.059)
Oversize	.0011-.0019 (.027-.049)
Stem to Guide Clearance	
Intake	.0008-.0021 (.020-.053)
Exhaust	.0016-.0029 (.040-.074)
Maximum Wear Limit	.004 (.10)
Installation Height [1]	.594-.602 (15.1-15.3)
Valve Seats	
Outside Diameter	
Standard	
Intake	1.3417-1.3424 (34.080-34.096)
Exhaust	1.1842-1.1849 (30.080-30.096)
Oversize	
Intake	1.3614-1.3620 (34.580-34.596)
Exhaust	1.2039-1.2046 (30.580-30.596)
Cylinder Head Bore Diameter	
Standard	
Intake	1.3386-1.3392 (34.000-34.016)
Exhaust	1.1811-1.1817 (30.000-30.016)
Oversize	
Intake	1.3583-1.3589 (34.500-34.516)
Exhaust	1.2008-1.2014 (30.500-30.516)
Valve Seat Thickness	
Standard	
Intake	.232-.236 (5.9-6.0)
Exhaust	.252-.256 (6.4-6.5)
Oversize	
Intake	.201-.205 (5.1-5.2)
Exhaust	.226-.230 (5.75-5.85)

[1] – Measured from end of valve guide to spring seat contact surface of cylinder head.

1.6L 16-VALVE 4-CYLINDER (Cont.)

VALVE SEATS

Removal & Installation

1) Bore out seat until it collapses and may be removed from cylinder head. Ensure machining does not contact cylinder head material during removal. Machine cylinder head to specifications for installation of replacement seat.

2) Heat cylinder head to 302-320°F (150-160°C). Press fit seat into cylinder head. Cut or grind seat to fit valve using 30, 45, and 60 degree cuts. Lap valve to seat.

VALVE GUIDES

Removal & Installation

1) Heat cylinder head to 302-320°F (150-160°C). Drive out guide using a press or a hammer and valve guide driver. When cylinder head is cold, ream guide bore in cylinder head to correct size. See VALVE GUIDE & SEAT SPECIFICATIONS table.

2) After machining, heat cylinder head to 302-320°F (150-160°C). Press replacement guide into cylinder head. Ream valve guide to finished dimension.

VALVE CLEARANCE ADJUSTMENTS

Valves are actuated by hydraulic cam followers. These followers are not adjustable. DO NOT disassemble cam followers. If valve lifter can be depressed more than .040" (1.00 mm) by finger pressure air may be present in follower. To bleed air run engine at 1,000 RPM for 10 minutes. If noise is still present, replace follower.

CAM FOLLOWER DIMENSIONS

Application	In. (mm)
Valve Lifter Diameter	1.2187-1.2191 (30.955-30.965)
Guide Bore Diameter	1.2205-1.2210 (31.000-31.013)

Fig. 7: Correct Position To Set Cam Followers

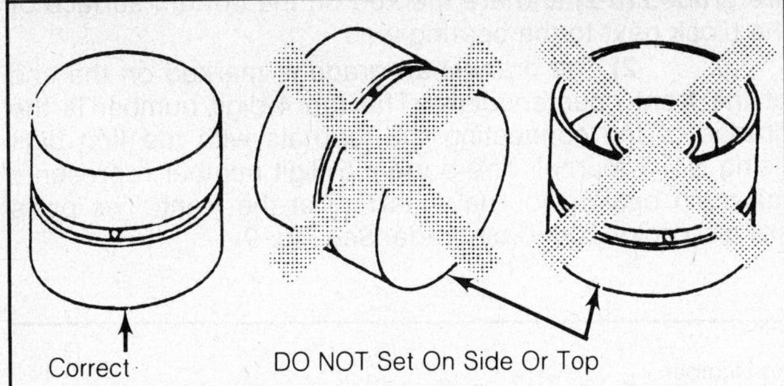

Courtesy of Nissan Motor Co., U.S.A.

VALVE SPRINGS

Removal & Installation
Cylinder Head Removed

Remove camshafts. Use Valve Spring Compressor (KV10111300) to remove valve springs. Remove valve stem seals using Slide Hammer Remover (KV10107901). Install valve springs with the narrow pitch or painted end towards the cylinder head.

Removal & Installation
Cylinder Head On Engine

1) Position piston at TDC of its compression stroke. Remove throttle body and camshaft cover. Remove timing belt and camshafts. Remove spark plug.

2) Install adapter in spark plug hole and apply air pressure (about 70 psi) to cylinder. Use spring compressor to remove valve springs. Use slide hammer to remove stem seals.

3) Always lubricate new stem seal prior to installation. Install new seal using Seal Driver (KV10107501). Reverse removal procedure to complete installation.

CYLINDER BLOCK ASSEMBLY

INSPECTION

Ensure cylinder block is within specifications. See CYLINDER BLOCK SPECIFICATIONS table. During boring procedures, allow cylinders to cool before measuring block. Factory engines are assembled with blocks and pistons graded for dimensional tolerance. Cylinder grade (1-5) is stamped on the top of the block on the right side. Pistons are stamped on the top near the front index mark (1-5). Always match grades of pistons and bores when replacing a piston in a bore that has not been rebored.

CYLINDER BLOCK SPECIFICATIONS

Application	In. (mm)
Deck Distortion Limits	.0039 (.100)
Cylinder Block Height	8.0610-8.0649 (204.75-204.85)
Maximum Machining Limit (Block + Head)	.008 (.20)
Cylinder Bores	
Standard Diameter	3.0689-3.0709 (77.95-78.00)
Wear Limit	.0079 (.20)
Out-of-Round Limit	.0006 (.015)
Taper Limit	.0004 (.010)
Rebore Sequence	Cyl. 2-4-1-3
Piston Clearance	.0006-.0014 (.015-.035)

PISTON, PINS & RINGS

OIL PAN

Removal

1) Drain engine oil. Remove splash shields and undertray. Remove center support brace and front exhaust pipe. Remove front engine shock strap.

2) Remove engine mount plates to allow access to oil pan. Remove pan bolts. If pan does not release easily, DO NOT use screwdrivers to pry pan from block as flange will deform.

3) Slide Seal Cutter (KV10111100) between pan and block by tapping into place with a hammer. Tap cutter along to break seal. Remove all traces of sealant from cylinder block and oil pan.

Installation

1) Apply a continous bead of liquid gasket seal to mating surface of oil pan. Sealant bead should be .138-.177" (3.5-4.5 mm) wide. Apply sealant in center of groove on grooved pans.

2) If mounting flange is flat apply sealant between mounting bolt holes and inner edge of pan. Install oil pan on cylinder block within 5 minutes of applying sealant. Allow sealant to set for a minimum of 30 minutes before refilling oil or starting engine.

1.6L 16-VALVE 4-CYLINDER (Cont.)

Fig. 8: Piston & Rod Installation References

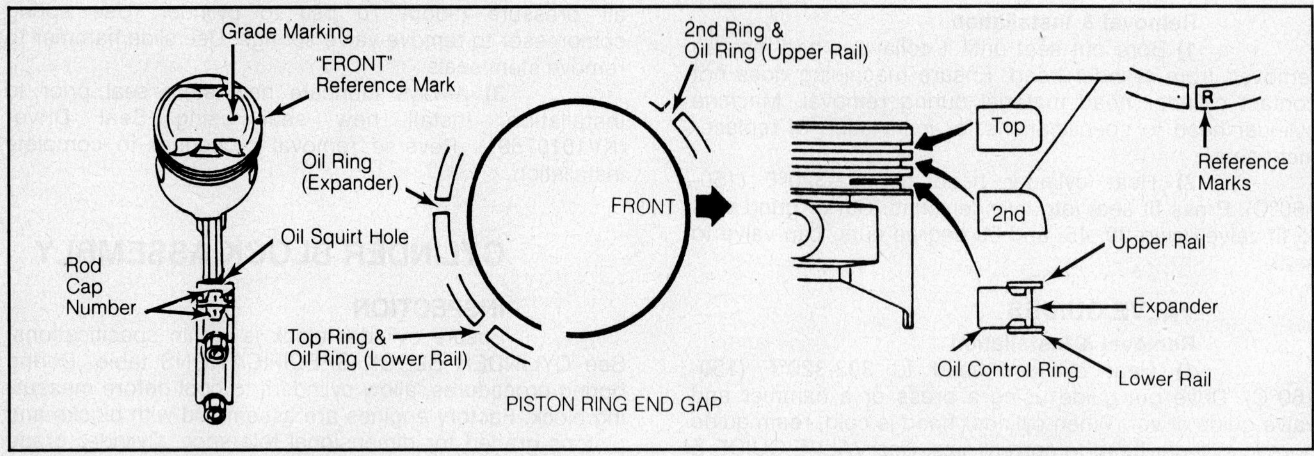

Courtesy of Nissan Motor Co., U.S.A.

PISTON & ROD ASSEMBLY

Removal

Remove cylinder head and oil pan. Remove piston an rod assemblies from engine. To disassemble piston and rod, heat piston to 140-158°F (60-70°C) and push out piston pin.

Inspection

Measure piston pin, small end bushing and piston. Ensure tolerances are within specification. Measure piston ring end gap and side clearance. Bend and torsion limit for connecting rods is .004" (.10 mm) per 3.94" (100 mm) of rod length.

Installation

1) Ensure piston is correctly positioned on connecting rod. *See Fig. 8.* Lubricate piston pin with oil and install with press. Piston should move smoothly after assembly.

2) Install rings on piston. Install rod bearings so that oil hole in bearing is aligned with hole in connecting rod.

3) Position rings on piston. *See Fig. 8.* Install piston in cylinders. Ensure mark on piston top faces front of engine. Install rod cap and tighten to specification.

4) Measure connecting rod side clearance. Side clearance should be .0079-.0138" (.20-.35 mm). Maximum wear limit is .016" (.4 mm).

CRANKSHAFT & ROD BEARINGS

CRANKSHAFT MAIN BEARINGS

Removal

1) Remove engine and place on work stand. Drain oil and coolant. Remove timing belt, water pump and cylinder head. Remove oil pan and oil pump. Remove pistons. Remove rear seal plate.

2) Remove oil pump pick-up tube. Remove rods and pistons. Loosen main bearing caps in sequence. *See Fig. 9.* Remove crankshaft and bearings.

Inspection

1) Measure main bearing clearance using a micrometer or Plastigage method. Main bearing assembly clearance is .0008-.0019" (.021-.048 mm). Maximum wear limit is .004" (.10 mm). Factory production line engines use grade markings to control tolerance. Main bearing bores are graded (0-2) and are marked on the bottom surface of the block next to the bearing web.

2) The crankshaft grade is marked on the end of the front counterweight. The top 4-digit number is the grades of the connecting rod journals with the first digit being No. 1 journal. The bottom 5-digit number represents the main bearing journals starting at the front. The parts are also color coded by grade. *See Fig. 9.*

Fig. 9: Main Bearing Tightening Sequence

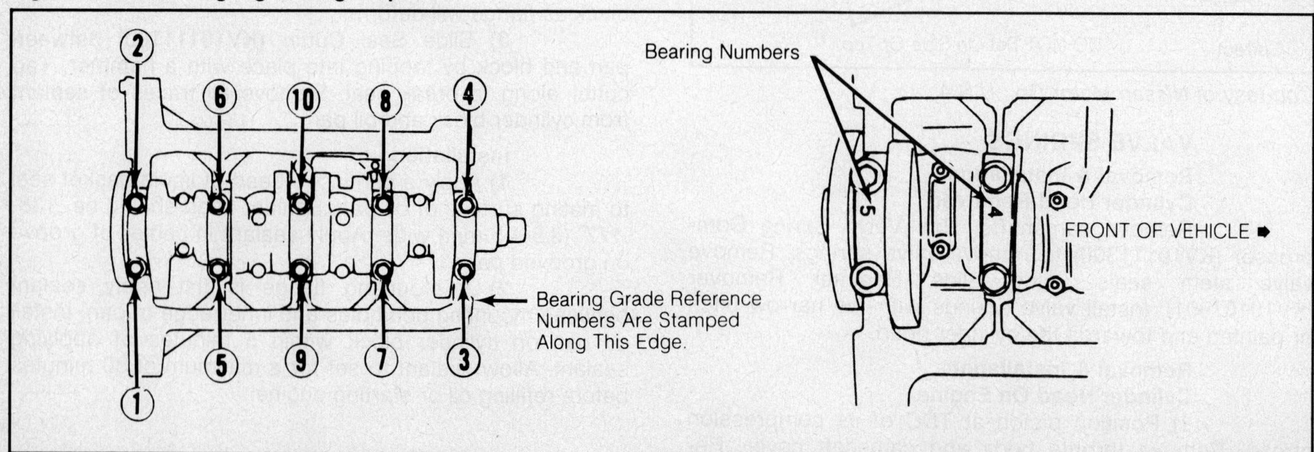

Courtesy of Nissan Motor Co., U.S.A.

1.6L 16-VALVE 4-CYLINDER (Cont.)

BEARING IDENTIFICATION COLOR CODES

Grade	Color
0	Black
1	Brown
2	Green
3	Yellow
4	Blue

MAIN BEARING GRADE SELECTION

Bearing Bore	Journal	Bearing Insert
0	0	0
0	1	1
0	2	2
1	0	1
1	1	2
1	2	3
2	0	2
2	1	3
2	2	4

Installation

1) Install main bearings in block. Ensure upper bearings which have oil grooves are positioned on cylinder block side. Lubricate bearing surfaces with engine oil. Install crankshaft.

2) Install bearing caps. Ensure numbers on caps are correctly positioned with the No. 1 cap being at the front of the engine. Move crankshaft forward and backwards to center thrust bearing.

3) Tighten to specification. Measure crankshaft end play at center main bearing.

CONNECTING ROD BEARINGS

Inspection & Identification

If crankshaft has been replaced, select correct grade bearing size from selection table. The 4-digit number on the front crankshaft web indicates the journal grade for each connecting rod journal (1-4).

ROD BEARING GRADE SELECTION

Journal Grade	Bearing Insert
0	0
1	1
2	2

Installation

Ensure that the connecting rod is installed in the correct direction on the piston. Align the rod cap markings with the markings on the rod. Install the bearings with the oil holes aligned. Lubricate threads of rod bolts and tighten to specification.

REAR MAIN BEARING OIL SEAL

Removal & Installation

Remove transaxle from vehicle. Remove fly-wheel. Pry oil seal from seal housing. Lubricate sealing lip of new seal and crankshaft flange. Tap new seal into housing using a mandrel.

ENGINE OILING

ENGINE OILING SYSTEM

A cresent-gear type pump is used to pressurize the oil system. A check valve (mounted in the block) is used to maintain pressure for the hydraulic valve lifters.

CRANKCASE CAPACITY

When changing oil and filter use 3.4 qts. (3.2L). An oil change only, requires 3.0 qts. (2.8L). Refill oil to "H" level on dipstick. Do not overfill. Tighten drain plug to 22-30 ft. lbs. (30-40 N.m).

TESTING OIL PRESSURE

Test figures for oil pressure testing are based on the use of SAE 10W-30 engine oil in good condition. Oil temperature should be 171-181°F (77 -83°C). Install a mechanical oil pressure guage in place of the oil pressure sender, below the oil filter. Check oil pressure in neutral. See OIL PRESSURE TESTING table.

OIL PRESSURE TESTING

RPM	psi (kg/cm²)
Idle	Minimum 11 (.8)
2000	67 (4.7)
6000	85 (6.0)

Fig. 10: Lubrication System Diagram

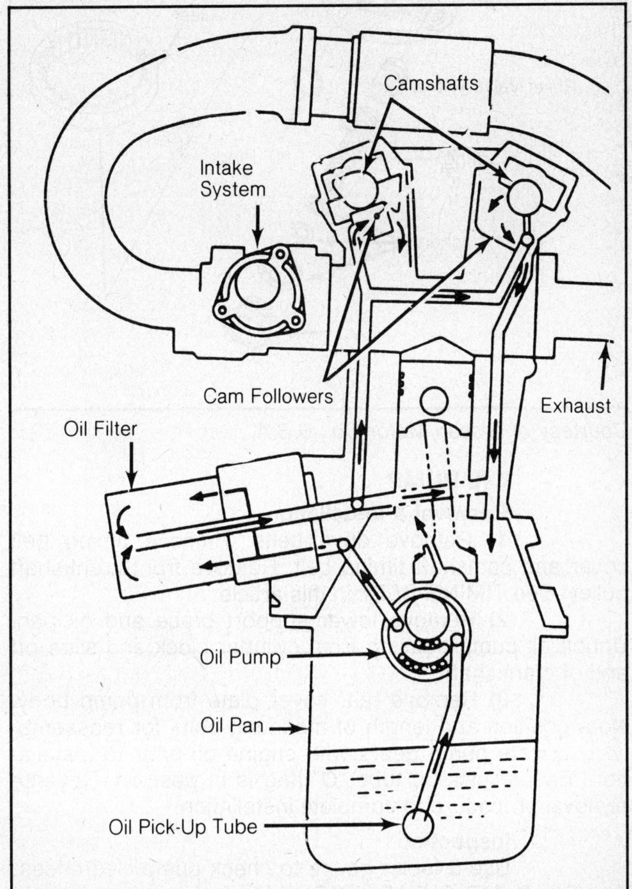

Courtesy of Nissan Motor Co., U.S.A.

1.6L 16-VALVE 4-CYLINDER (Cont.)

OIL PRESSURE RELIEF VALVE

Removal

With oil pan removed, oil pressure relief valve is servicable from bottom of oil pump. *See Fig. 11*. There is an oil filter by-pass valve located in the oil filter base. It is a spring loaded ball type valve.

Inspection & Testing

Visually inspect components for wear or damage. Lightly lubricate valve plunger with engine oil and ensure it will fall from the bore in the pump body under its own weight. Valve should open at 68-74 psi (4.8-5.2 kg/cm²). Oil filter by-pass valve can be tested by pushing ball off seat with a small drift. This valve will by-pass the oil filter should it become plugged.

Fig. 11: Oil Pump Assembly

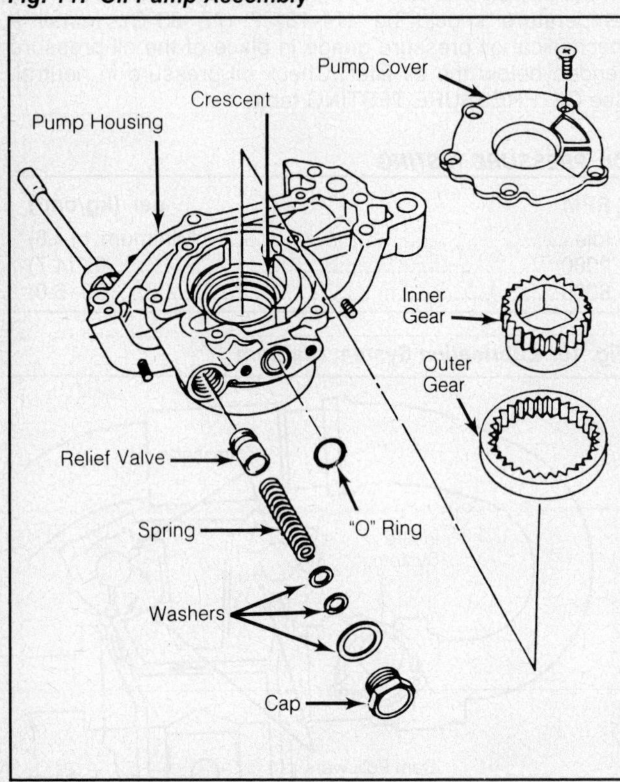

Courtesy of Nissan Motor Co., U.S.A.

OIL PUMP

Removal & Installation

1) Remove drive belts. Remove timing belt cover and camshaft timing belt. Remove front crankshaft pulley. See TIMING BELT in this article.

2) Remove lower support brace and oil pan. Unbolt oil pump housing from cylinder block and slide off end of crankshaft.

3) Remove rear cover plate from pump body. Note position and length of mounting bolts for reassembly. Lubricate pump gears with engine oil prior to installation. Ensure pick-up tube "O" ring is in position. Reverse removal procedure to complete installation.

Inspection

Use a feeler gauge to check pump clearances. See OIL PUMP CLEARANCE table. If clearances exceed specification replace both gears or entire pump.

OIL PUMP CLEARANCE

Application	In. (mm)
Pump Body-to-Outer Gear	.0043-.0079 (.11-.20)
Inner Gear-to-Crescent	.006-.010 (.15-.26)
Outer Gear-to-Crescent	.008-.012 (.21-.32)
Body-to-Inner Gearf	.002-.0035 (.05-.090)
Body-to-Outer Gear	.002-.004 (.05-.11)

ENGINE COOLING

WATER PUMP

Removal & Installation

Drain coolant from block and radiator. Block drain plug is located at left rear of cylinder block. Remove drive belt and pulley. Remove timing belt cover. Disconnect supply hose and unbolt water pump. Ensure coolant solution does not contact camshaft drive belt during work procedure. Replace water pump as a complete unit. Reverse removal procedure to complete installation.

NOTE: For more information, see ENGINE COOLING SYSTEMS article at the end of this section.

TIGHTENING SPECIFICATIONS

Applications	Ft. Lbs. (N.m)
Camshaft Pulley Bolts	10-14 (14-19)
Crankshaft Pulley Bolt	105-112 (142-152)
Cylinder Head Bolts	
Step 1	22 (29)
Step 2	76 (103)
Step 3	Loosen All Bolts
Step 4	22 (29)
Step 5	90 Degrees or 76 (103)
Connecting Rod Cap Bolts	
Step 1	10-12 (14-16)
Step 2	30-33 (41-44)
EGR Tube Nut	25-33 (34-44)
EGR Valve	13-17 (18-23)
Exhaust Manifold-to-Cyl. Head Nuts	27-35 (37-48)
Exhaust Manifold-to-Pipe Bolts	31-35 (42-48)
Flywheel-to-Crankshaft Bolts	61-69 (83-93)
Intake Manifold Nuts	14-19 (20-25)
Main Bearing Cap Bolts	33-40 (44-54)
Oxygen Sensor	13-17 (18-24)
Oil Pan Drain Plug	22-29 (29-39)
Oil Pressure Switch	7-12 (10-16)
Oil Pressure Relief Valve	29-51 (39-69)
Throttle Chamber	13-16 (18-22)
Timing Belt Idler	23-31 (31-42)
Timing Belt Tensioner	16-22 (22-29)
Water Drain Plug (Block)	40-54 (54-74)
	INCH Lbs. (N.m)
Air Regulator Valve	43-52 (5-6)
Camshaft Bearing Caps	84-108 (10-12)
Crank Angle Sensor	61-70 (7-8)
Oil Pump Mounting Bolts	96-120 (11-14)

1.6L 16-VALVE 4-CYLINDER (Cont.)

ENGINE SPECIFICATIONS

GENERAL SPECIFICATIONS

Year	DISPLACEMENT Cu. In.	DISPLACEMENT Liters	Fuel System	HP@RPM	Torque Ft. Lbs.@RPM	Compr. Ratio	BORE In.	BORE mm	STROKE In.	STROKE mm
1987 Pulsar NX SE	98	1.6	Fuel Inj.	113 @ 6400	99 @ 4800	10:1	3.07	78.0	3.29	83.6

VALVES

Engine Size & Valve	Head Diam. In. (mm)	Face Angle	Seat Angle	Seat Width In. (mm)	Stem Diameter In. (mm)	Stem Clearance In. (mm)	Valve Lift In. (mm)
1.6L							
Intake	1.225 (31.1)	45.5°	45°	.....	.2348-.2354 (5.965-5.980)	.0008-.0021 (.020-.053)	.335 (8.5)
Exhaust	1.10 (28.2)	45.5°	45°	.....	.2341-.2346 (5.945-5.960)	.0016-.0029 (.040-.073)	.335 (8.5)

PISTONS, PINS & RINGS

Engine	PISTONS Clearance In. (mm)	PINS Piston Fit In. (mm)	PINS Rod Fit In. (mm)	RINGS Ring No.	RINGS End Gap In. (mm)	RINGS Side Clearance In. (mm)
1.6L	.0010-.0018 (.025-.045)	-.0002-0 (-.004-0)	.0002-.0007 (.005-.017)	No. 1	.009-.015 (.22-.39)	.0016-.0029 (.040-.073)
				No. 2	.0075-.0177 (.19-.45)	.0012-.0025 (.030-.063)
				Oil	.008-.030 (.20-.76)	.0010-.0033 (.025-.085)

CRANKSHAFT MAIN & CONNECTING ROD BEARINGS

Engine	MAIN BEARINGS Journal Diam. In. (mm)	MAIN BEARINGS Clearance In. (mm)	MAIN BEARINGS Thrust Bearing	MAIN BEARINGS Crankshaft End Play In. (mm)	CONNECTING ROD BEARINGS Journal Diam. In. (mm)	CONNECTING ROD BEARINGS Clearance In. (mm)	CONNECTING ROD BEARINGS Side Play In. (mm)
1.6L	2.0847-2.0856 (52.951-52.975)	.0008-.0019 (.021-.048)	No. 3	.0020-.0071 (.05-.18)	1.7698-1.7706 (44.954-44.974)	.0007-.0018 (.018-.045)	.0079-.0138 (.20-.35)

VALVE SPRINGS

Engine	Free Length In. (mm)	PRESSURE Lbs. @ In. (Kg @ mm) Valve Closed	PRESSURE Lbs. @ In. (Kg @ mm) Valve Open
1.6L In. & Ex.	1.697 (43.1)	53 @ .31 (24 @ 8)	121 @ .650 (55 @ 16.5)

CAMSHAFT

Engine	Journal Diam. In. (mm)	Clearance In. (mm)	Lobe Lift In. (mm)
1.6L	1.0998-1.1006 (27.935-27.955)	.0018-.0035 (.045-.090)	.335 (8.5)

VALVE TIMING

Engine	INTAKE Open (BTDC)	INTAKE Close (ABDC)	EXHAUST Open (BBDC)	EXHAUST Close (ATDC)
1.6L	15°	53°	59°	9°

Nissan Engines

2.0L 4-CYLINDER

Stanza, 200SX XE

NOTE: **For engine repair procedures not covered in this article, see ENGINE OVERHAUL PROCEDURES article at beginning of this section.**

ENGINE CODING

ENGINE IDENTIFICATION

The engine serial number is located on left side of cylinder block, just below cylinder head mating surface.

ENGINE IDENTIFICATION CODES

Application	Code
Stanza & 200SX XE	CA20E

ENGINE, MANIFOLDS & CYLINDER HEAD

ENGINE

NOTE: **Remove the engine and transaxle as a single unit.**

Removal

1) Mark hood hinge positions. Remove hood. Remove battery and support bracket. Remove radiator reservoir tank. Remove air intake duct. Remove undertray. Drain coolant. Remove radiator and cooling fan.

2) Remove power steering pump, bracket, A/C compressor, and idler pulley (if equipped). Do not discharge systems. Secure components away from engine. Disconnect front exhaust pipe from exhaust manifold.

3) Disconnect accelerator cable. Disconnect linkage, cables, vacuum hoses, and wiring from transaxle. Remove speedometer cable and plug bore. Remove EGR vacuum control valve, with bracket, from body.

4) Remove lower ball joints and discard mounting nuts. Drain gear oil from transaxle. Loosen 3 top bolts from struts. Remove both drive shafts from transaxle. Ensure oil seals are not damaged.

5) Label and disconnect all vacuum, fuel, air hoses, and electrical wiring between engine and chassis. Attach lifting sling and engine hoist to engine. Disconnect engine and transaxle mounts. Lift engine and transaxle from vehicle.

Installation

1) Install engine mounting brackets and insulators on engine. Align notches in left side mount support and collar when installing support. There should be no clearance between mount support and vehicle body when installed.

2) When installing front mount support, position oblong hole in support so the insulator is in center of bracket. With mount supports installed, tighten buffer rod adjusting bolt to prevent rubber from deforming.

3) Reverse removal procedure to install engine and transaxle. Use new nuts when installing ball joints. Ensure all hoses, cables, and wires are properly attached.

INTAKE MANIFOLD

Removal

1) Remove air intake duct. Disconnect throttle body cable. Disconnect main fuel line and plug opening. Remove intake manifold support bracket.

2) Remove all wiring, coolant, and vacuum hoses interfering with intake manifold removal. Remove fuel pump and EGR valve assembly. Remove nuts attaching intake manifold to cylinder head. Remove intake manifold assembly.

Installation

Install intake manifold assembly using new gaskets. Manifold and head mating surfaces must be free of nicks or other damage. To complete installation, reverse removal procedure.

EXHAUST MANIFOLD

Removal

1) Remove exhaust air induction tube bracket and EGR tube at EGR valve. If necessary, remove distributor and high tension cable. Remove exhaust manifold cover.

2) Disconnect front exhaust pipe from manifold. When removing exhaust manifold mounting bolts, note center mount nut is a different diameter than the others. Remove manifold.

Installation

Install exhaust manifold assembly using new gaskets. Manifold and head mating surfaces must be free of nicks or other damage. To complete installation, reverse removal procedure.

CYLINDER HEAD

Removal

1) Turn crankshaft until No. 1 piston is at TDC on compression stroke. Remove alternator and bracket. Remove power steering pump and A/C compressor (if equipped). Do not discharge systems. Secure components away from engine.

2) Remove exhaust and intake manifolds as previously described. Remove valve cover and gasket. Remove oil and water pumps. Note bolt lengths and locations for reassembly reference.

3) Remove thermostat housing and distributor, if necessary. Remove crankshaft pulley and damper. Remove upper and lower outer front dust cover mount bolts. Remove covers and gaskets.

CAUTION: **After timing belt is removed, do not rotate crankshaft or camshaft.**

NOTE: **There are 3 different lengths of cylinder head bolts. Note locations during removal for reassembly reference.**

4) Disconnect all hoses, cables, and wires interfering with cylinder head removal. Remove fuel pump mounting bolts, spacer, and pump. Mark timing belt rotation direction. Loosen timing belt tensioner and remove timing belt.

5) Loosen head bolts, in reverse order of tightening sequence. Remove cylinder head. *See Fig. 1*.

Inspection

1) Check cylinder head for cracks, flaws, or damage. Inspect cylinder head and block mating surfaces for distortion. Distortion limit is .004" (.10 mm).

Nissan Engines

2.0L 4-CYLINDER (Cont.)

Fig. 1: Cylinder Head Tightening Sequence & Machining Limit

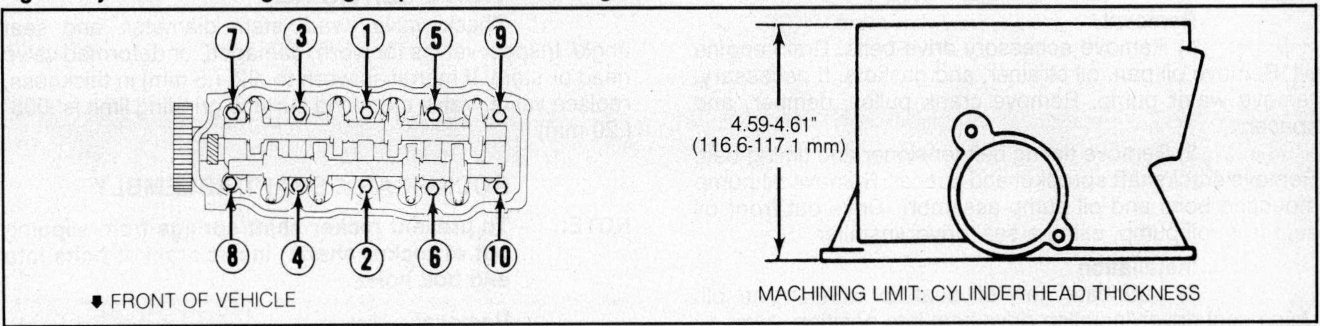

Courtesy of Nissan Motor Co., U.S.A.

2) If beyond limit, refinish surface. Maximum machining limit of cylinder head or block is .008" (.20 mm). Replace cylinder head and/or block if machined or warped beyond service limit. *See Fig. 1.*

NOTE: Do not apply sealant to mating surfaces of cylinder block and head.

Installation

1) Thoroughly clean cylinder head and block mating surfaces. Ensure No. 1 piston is at TDC on compression stroke. Install new cylinder head gasket on dowel pins. Install cylinder head.

2) Install cylinder head bolts. Temporarily tighten all cylinder head bolts in sequence to 22 ft. lbs. (29 N.m). *See Fig. 1*. Tighten all cylinder head bolts in sequence to 58 ft. lbs. (79 N.m). Loosen all cylinder head bolts completely. Tighten all cylinder head bolts in sequence to 54-61 ft. lbs. (74-83 N.m). Install timing belt and front cover.

3) To install distributor, align mark on distributor gear to mark on shaft. Turn rotor shaft counterclockwise, on distributor cap side, about 15 degrees and install.

4) After checking bolts for correct location, install water and oil pumps. Install drive belt tensioner. Do not tighten tensioner bolts to final specification before drive belt is installed.

5) Install timing belt plate and crankshaft sprocket with mating marks facing forward. See TIMING BELT in this article. *See Fig. 2.*

Fig. 2: Timing Belt Alignment Procedure

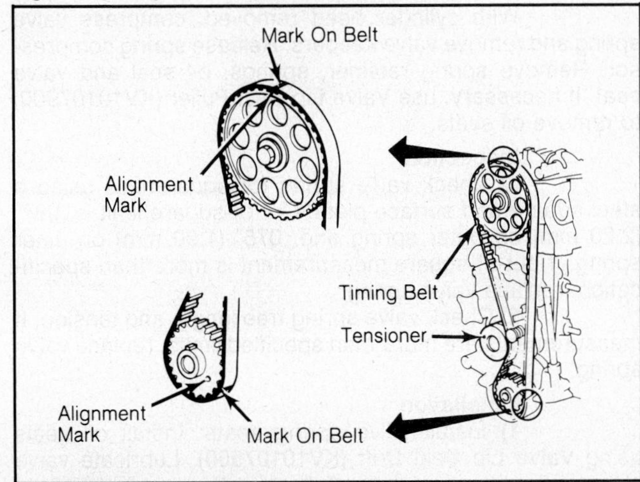

Courtesy of Nissan Motor Co., U.S.A.

Fig. 3: Adjusting Timing Belt Tension

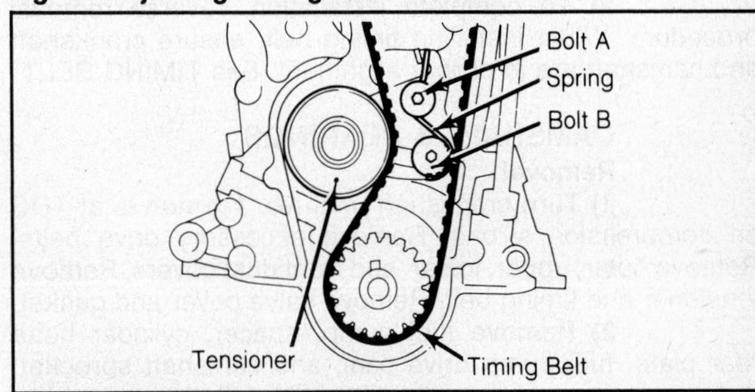

Courtesy of Nissan Motor Co., U.S.A.

6) Install new crankshaft front oil seal in oil pump. Install upper and lower front covers with new gaskets. Tighten mounting bolts. Install crankshaft plate, pulley damper, and pulley.

7) To complete installation, reverse removal procedure. After engine has run for several minutes, allow it to cool and retighten cylinder head bolts to specification.

CAMSHAFT

TIMING BELT

Removal

1) Turn crankshaft until No. 1 piston is at TDC on compression stroke. Remove cooling fan, radiator shroud and accessory drive belts.

NOTE: After timing belt is removed, do not rotate crankshaft or camshaft.

2) Remove upper and lower dust cover mount bolts. Remove upper and lower covers and gaskets. Remove timing belt tensioner, bracket, and timing belt.

Installation

1) Do not tighten tensioner bolts to final specification before drive belt is installed. Install timing belt. Align belt mark to camshaft and crankshaft sprocket marks. *See Fig. 2.*

2) Tighten belt tensioner and assemble spring. To set spring, hook one end on bolt "B" side. Hook the other end on tensioner bracket pawl. Tighten bolt "B" and then bolt "A". *See Fig. 3.*

3) Belt tension will automatically be at the specified value. Install lower front cover with gaskets and tighten mount bolts. Install plate and front pulley damper. Complete installation by reversing removal procedure.

FRONT COVER OIL SEAL

Removal

1) Remove accessory drive belts. Drain engine oil. Remove oil pan, oil strainer, and gaskets. If necessary, remove water pump. Remove crank pulley, damper, and spacer.

2) Remove timing belt tensioner and timing belt. Remove crankshaft sprocket and spacer. Remove oil pump mounting bolts and oil pump assembly. Drive out front oil seal from oil pump, using a seal driver/installer.

Installation

1) Lubricate new oil seal lip with engine oil. Using seal driver/installer, drive seal into position. Align oil pump and crankshaft locating notches and install oil pump assembly.

2) To complete installation, reverse removal procedure. When installing timing belt, ensure crankshaft and camshaft are in proper alignment. See TIMING BELT.

CAMSHAFT & BEARINGS

Removal

1) Turn crankshaft until No. 1 piston is at TDC on compression stroke. Remove accessory drive belts. Remove outer, upper, lower, and front dust covers. Remove tensioner and timing belt. Remove valve cover and gasket.

2) Remove fuel pump, spacer, cylinder head rear plate, fuel pump drive cam, and camshaft sprocket. Before rocker arm assembly removal, fully loosen rocker arm adjusting screws.

3) When removing rocker arm assembly, loosen mount bolts evenly, from the outside. Remove assembly. Keep all components in order. Pull camshaft from cylinder head.

Inspection

Check camshaft to ensure measurements are within specifications. See CAMSHAFT SPECIFICATIONS table.

CAMSHAFT SPECIFICATIONS

Application	In. (mm)
Runout Limit	.002 (.05)
Lobe Height	
Intake	1.5049-1.5081 (38.225-38.305)
Exhaust	1.5283-1.5315 (38.819-38.899)
Lobe Wear Limit	.008 (.20)
End Play	.008 (.20)
Bearing Clearance (Wear Limit)	.004 (.10)
Maximum Sprocket Runout	.004 (.10)

Installation

1) Coat camshaft with engine oil and carefully install into engine. Do not damage camshaft bearing surfaces during installation. Install rocker arm assembly.

2) Install upper, inner dust cover (if equipped), camshaft sprocket, tensioner, timing belt, and related components. Install outer front covers. To complete installation, reverse removal procedure.

VALVES

VALVE ARRANGEMENT

Right Side - Intake valves.
Left Side - Exhaust valves.

VALVE SERVICING

Check valve head, stem diameter, and seat angle. Inspect valves for worn, damaged, or deformed valve head or stem. If margin is worn to .02" (.5 mm) in thickness, replace valve. Valve stem end surface grinding limit is .008" (.20 mm).

ROCKER ARM SHAFT ASSEMBLY

NOTE: **To prevent rocker shaft springs from slipping out of rocker shafts, insert bracket bolts into end bolt holes.**

Removal

1) Remove valve cover and gasket. Fully loosen valve adjusting screws to remove tension. Loosen rocker arm assembly mount bolts evenly, from outside-to-inside.

2) Remove rocker arm and shaft assembly together with mount bolts. Remove rocker arm springs and shaft mount bolts. Slide rocker arms off rocker shafts. *See Fig. 4*. Keep components in order for reassembly reference.

Inspection

1) Thoroughly clean components. Inspect rocker arm bore and shaft surface for signs of wear or seizure. Check valve and camshaft end contact surface of rocker arm for excessive wear or scuffing.

2) If valve contact surface is worn, resurface with grinder. If camshaft contact surface is worn, replace rocker arm and camshaft.

3) Check clearance between rocker arm and rocker shaft. Standard shaft-to-arm clearance is .0003-.0019" (.007-.049 mm). If worn beyond specification, replace rocker arm or shaft.

Installation

1) Apply oil to rocker shaft and rocker arm bore. Intake rocker shaft has identification mark (slit on front surface) but exhaust shaft does not. Both rocker shafts must be assembled with punched marks on front surface facing 12 o'clock position to identify oil hole direction. *See Fig. 4*.

2) Reverse removal procedure to install rocker arm assembly. Adjust valve clearance.

VALVE SPRINGS

Removal

With cylinder head removed, compress valve spring and remove valve keepers. Release spring compressor. Remove spring retainer, springs, oil seal and valve seat. If necessary, use Valve Lip Seal Puller (KV10107900) to remove oil seals.

Inspection

1) Check valve spring for squareness using a steel square and surface plate. Out-of-square limit is .087" (2.20 mm) on outer spring and .075" (1.90 mm) on inner spring. If out-of-square measurement is more than specification, replace valve spring.

2) Check valve spring free length and tension. If measurements are more than specified limits, replace valve spring.

Installation

1) Install valve spring seats. Install oil seals using Valve Lip Seal Drift (KV10107500). Lubricate valve stem end with oil and carefully insert in guide to avoid damaging lip seal.

Fig. 4: Installing Rocker Arm & Rocker Shaft Assembly

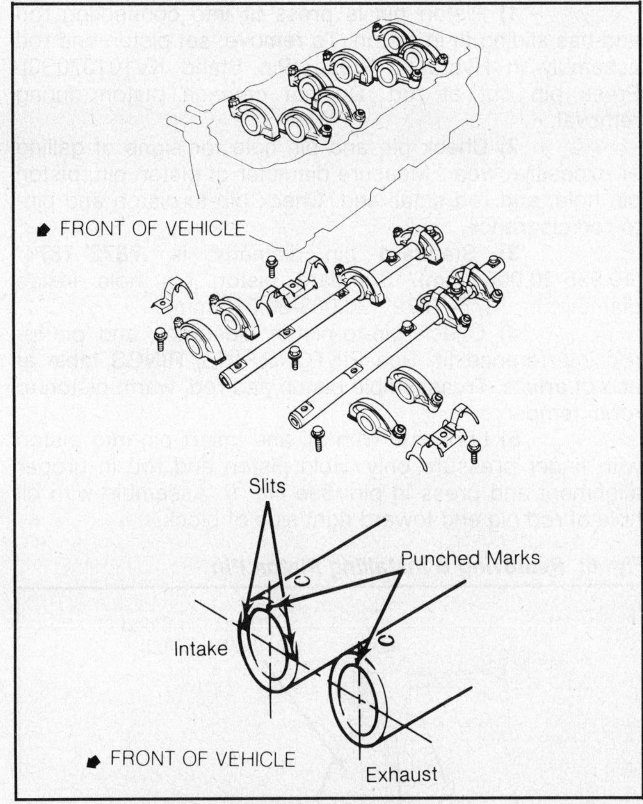

Courtesy of Nissan Motor Co., U.S.A.

2) Install valve spring (uneven pitch type) with narrow pitch side toward cylinder head. Using valve spring compressor, compress spring. Install retainer and keepers.

VALVE SPRING INSTALLED HEIGHT

Check valve spring by applying specified load and measuring spring height. If spring height or pressure do not meet specifications, replace spring. See VALVE SPRING specification table.

VALVE GUIDES

Inspection & Replacement

1) With valve in valve guide and off seat approximately 3/8", position dial indicator against edge of valve head. Move valve left and right, parallel with rocker arm. If valve moves more than .008" (.20 mm), clearance is beyond maximum limit.

2) If clearance is beyond limit and valve stem is not worn, the valve guide must be replaced. To replace guide, heat cylinder head to 302-320°F (150-160°C).

3) Using drift, drive old guide out from combustion chamber side. With head at room temperature, ream cylinder head guide hole to fit new guide. See VALVE GUIDE & SEAT SPECIFICATIONS table.

4) Reheat cylinder head and install new guide. Ensure guide projects above cylinder head surface. Ream guide. Check and reface valve seat surface as necessary.

VALVE GUIDE & SEAT SPECIFICATIONS

Application	In. (mm)
Valve Guides	
Guide-to-Stem Clearance	
Rebuild Specifications	
Intake	.0008-.0021 (.020-.053)
Exhaust	.0016-.0029 (.040-.053)
Maximum Wear Specification	
Intake & Exhaust	.004 (.10)
Valve Guide O.D.	.4340-.4344 (11.023-11.034)
Valve Guide I.D.	.2756-.2764 (7.000-7.020)
Interference Fit	.0011-.0023 (.027-.059)
Installation Height	
Guide End-to-Spring Seat	.402-.409 (10.20-10.40)
Valve Seats	
Seat Contact Width	
Intake	.071-.083 (1.80-2.10)
Exhaust	.055-.071 (1.40-1.80)
Interference Fit	
Intake	.0032-.0044 (.081-.113)
Exhaust	.0025-.0038 (.064-.096)

VALVE CLEARANCE ADJUSTMENTS

1) Adjust valves when motor is warm. With air cleaner and valve cover removed, rotate crankshaft until No. 1 cylinder is at TDC on compression stroke. Adjust valves as follows: No. 1 intake and exhaust, No. 2 intake and No. 3 exhaust. See VALVE CLEARANCE SPECIFICATIONS table.

2) Rotate crankshaft 360 degrees until No. 4 cylinder is at TDC on compression stroke. Adjust remaining valves, No. 2 exhaust, No. 3 intake and No. 4 intake and exhaust. After adjustment, hold adjusting screw and tighten rocker arm lock nut. Recheck clearances.

VALVE CLEARANCE SPECIFICATIONS [1]

Application	In. (mm)
Intake & Exhaust	.012 (.30)

[1] – For assembly purposes, with engine cold, adjust intake valves to .008" (.21 mm) and exhaust valves to .009" (.23 mm).

PISTONS, PINS & RINGS

PISTON & ROD ASSEMBLY

Removal

1) With cylinder head and oil pan removed, remove connecting rod nuts. Remove rod cap with bearing half. Check top of cylinder bore for ridge. If scraper will not remove carbon build-up, remove using ridge reamer.

2) Push piston and rod assembly, with bearing half, out through top of block. Rod caps must be kept with their respective piston and rod assembly and are not interchangeable.

Inspection

1) Check connecting rod for bend or twist. Bend and twist limit is .004" (.10 mm) or less in 3.94" (100 mm) of length.

2) Install rod and bearing on crankpin. Measure rod side clearance. Replace rod if not to specification.

NOTE: **If connecting rod is replaced, ensure weight difference between rods is no more than .25 oz. (7 g).**

Installation

1) Oil the rings, piston, and cylinder bore. Install piston and rod assembly. Ensure ring gaps are set 180 degrees apart. Do not set on thrust side of piston or in-line with piston pin. *See Fig. 5.*

Fig. 5: Positioning Piston Ring End Gaps

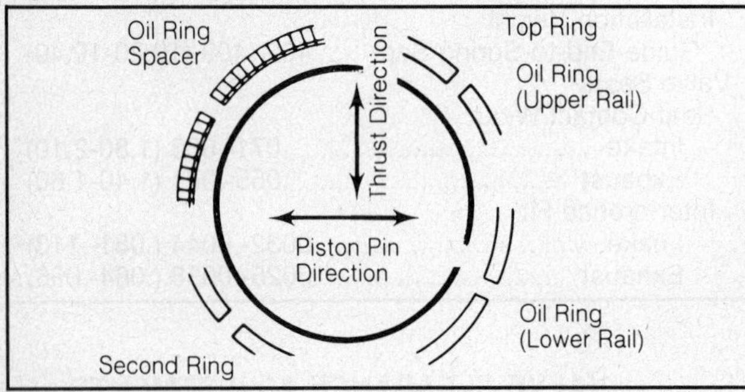

Courtesy of Nissan Motor Co., U.S.A.

2) Install ring compressor. Install piston in cylinder with notch mark on piston top toward front of engine.

3) Install rod caps. Oil jet of connecting rod should face right side of cylinder block. Install cylinder head and oil pan.

FITTING PISTONS & RINGS

1) Visually inspect cylinder block for cracks or flaws. Using bore gauge, measure cylinder bore for out-of-round or excessive taper. If out-of-round or taper exceeds .0008" (.020 mm), refinish bore. When one cylinder is bored, all must be bored.

NOTE: **Before block machining operations, ensure main bearing caps are installed and tightened to specification. To prevent block distortion, bore cylinders in sequence – No. 2-4-1-3.**

2) Determine piston oversize according to amount of wear in cylinder. See PISTON DIAMETER SPECIFICATION table. By measuring piston at thrust face and adding mean of piston-to-cylinder clearance, finish hone of cylinder may be determined. Measure bore halfway down cylinder and 90 degrees to crankshaft center line.

PISTON DIAMETER SPECIFICATIONS

Application	In. (mm)
Standard	3.3254-3.3274 (84.465-84.515)
.5 mm O/S	3.3451-3.3470 (84.965-85.015)
1 mm O/S	3.3648-3.3667 (85.465-85.515)

NOTE: **Pistons and rings are available in .5 mm and 1 mm oversize for service. Ensure piston and cylinder are at 68°F (20°C) when checking piston fit.**

PISTON PIN REPLACEMENT

1) Piston pin is press fit into connecting rod and has sliding fit in piston. To remove, set piston and rod assembly in Hydraulic Press (Pin Stand KV101070S0). Press pin out of rod. Do not damage piston during removal.

2) Check pin and pin hole for signs of galling or excessive wear. Measure diameter of piston pin, piston pin hole, and rod small end. Check pin-to-piston and pin-to-rod clearance.

3) Standard pin diameter is .7872-.7874" (19.995-20.000 mm). Standard piston pin hole inside diameter is .7875-.7879" (20.003-20.012 mm).

4) Check pin-to-piston clearance and pin-to-rod interference fit. See PISTONS,PINS, RINGS table at end of article. To assemble piston and rod, warm piston to room temperature.

5) Lubricate with oil and insert pin into piston with finger pressure only. Hold piston and rod in proper alignment and press in pin. *See Fig. 6.* Assemble with oil hole of rod big end toward right side of block.

Fig. 6: Removing & Installing Piston Pin

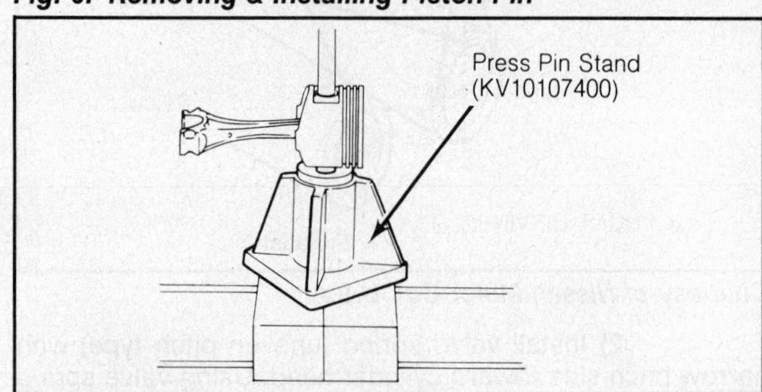

Courtesy of Nissan Motor Co., U.S.A.

CRANKSHAFT & ROD BEARINGS

CRANKSHAFT

Removal

1) With engine removed from vehicle, remove cylinder head assembly and oil pan. Remove connecting rod cap nuts. Remove piston and connecting rod assemblies. Remove alternator and engine mount bracket.

2) Remove crankshaft pulley, timing belt covers, belt tensioner, timing belt, and crankshaft sprocket. Remove oil pump and front oil seal.

3) Remove clutch assembly, flywheel, and rear plate. Loosen main bearing cap bolts, in 2 stages, and then remove caps. Remove rear oil seal retainer assembly. Carefully lift out crankshaft.

NOTE: **Keep main bearing caps in order for reassembly reference. Check all main and connecting rod bearings, using Plastigage method.**

Inspection

Clean and inspect crankshaft. Blow out oil passages with compressed air. Check crankshaft journals and crank pins for scoring, wear, cracks, taper, and out-of-round. Ensure crankshaft is within tolerances. See CRANKSHAFT SPECIFICATIONS table.

Installation

1) Install main bearing halves into engine block. Ensure that all bearings are on correct journal. Journal No. 3 requires a thrust bearing. Upper and lower bearings are not interchangeable.

2) Apply oil to main bearing surface and install crankshaft. Install main bearing caps so numbers on bearing caps are in a row, starting from front of engine. Tighten main bearing caps in 2 or 3 stages, starting at center bearing and working outward. Ensure crankshaft rotates smoothly.

CRANKSHAFT SPECIFICATIONS

Application	In. (mm)
Out-of-Round Limit	.0004 (.010)
Bend	.002 (.05)

3) Check crankshaft end play. See THRUST BEARING ALIGNMENT. Install rear oil seal retainer. Reverse removal procedure to complete installation.

THRUST BEARING ALIGNMENT

Thrust bearing is installed on No. 3 main bearing journal. Check crankshaft end play by inserting a feeler gauge between flange of thrust bearing and crankshaft.

REAR MAIN BEARING OIL SEAL

NOTE: When replacing front or rear oil seal, note installation direction.

Removal

With engine removed from vehicle, remove clutch assembly. Remove flywheel and engine end plate. Remove oil pan and oil seal retainer assembly. Check oil seal mounting direction for reassembly reference. Drive out old seal from retainer, using a seal driver/installer.

Fig. 7: Checking Crankshaft End Play

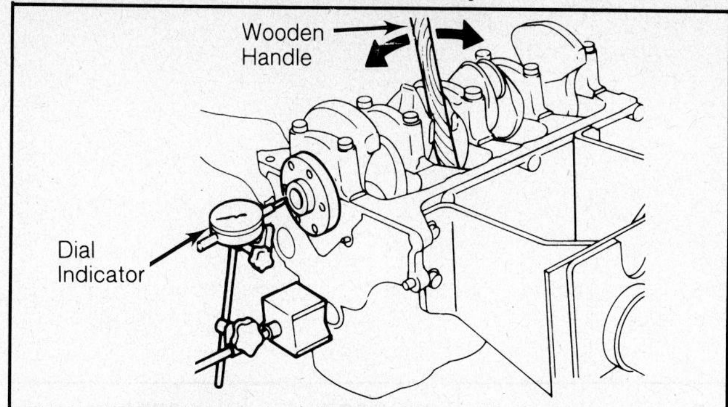

Courtesy of Nissan Motor Co., U.S.A.

Installation

Lubricate seal lips. Using seal driver/installer, drive seal into position. Install oil seal retainer. Reverse removal procedure to complete installation.

ENGINE OILING

ENGINE OILING SYSTEM

Pressure is provided to oiling system by an inner-gear type pump. Oil pump is mounted on front of crankshaft, and is driven by crankshaft. Oil pump feeds oil from pan to full-flow oil filter. Oil is then pumped into main oil gallery of crankcase where it is split into 2 circuits.

Oil is distributed to main bearings and to cylinder head oil gallery. From main bearings, oil is fed to connecting rods. Cylinder walls and piston pins are lubricated by oil squirt hole in connecting rod. From cylinder head, oil gallery oil is fed to No. 4 camshaft bracket, which feeds camshaft, rocker shaft, and rocker arm. *See Fig. 8.*

CRANKCASE CAPACITY

Oil capacity is 4.1 qts. (3.9L) with filter.

OIL PRESSURE

Oil pressure is 54-60 psi (3.8-4.2 kg/cm^2) at 2000 RPM.

PRESSURE RELIEF VALVE

Pressure relief valve is nonadjustable and is located in oil pump cover.

Fig. 8: Engine Oiling System

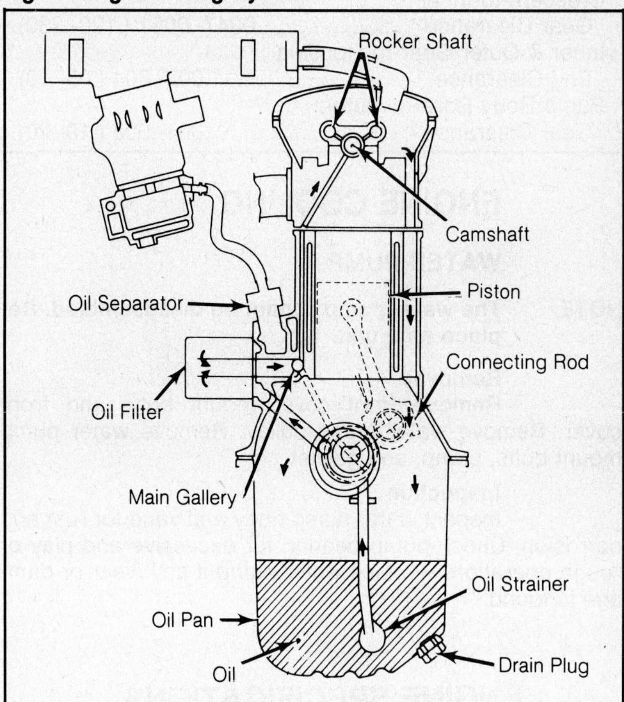

Courtesy of Nissan Motor Co., U.S.A.

OIL PUMP

Removal

1) Drain engine oil. Remove oil pan and oil strainer. Remove water pump belt, crankshaft pulley, and damper. Remove timing belt tensioner, timing belt, and crankshaft sprocket.

NOTE: After timing belt is removed, do not rotate crankshaft and camshaft.

2) Remove oil pump mount bolts and oil pump assembly. Check gear-to-cresent and gear-to-body clearance with a feeler gauge. Use a straightedge and feeler gauge to check end clearance of gears to housing and cover.

Nissan Engines

2.0L 4-CYLINDER (Cont.)

Inspection

Inspect pump body, cover, and inner and outer gears for cracks and excessive wear. If beyond wear limit, replace entire pump assembly. Check oil pressure regulator valve sliding surface and valve spring. If damaged, replace valve set.

Installation

1) When installing timing belt, ensure crankshaft and camshaft are in proper positions and locating marks on belt and sprockets align. Apply sealant to outside diameter of oil seal before installation.

2) After installing new oil seal, align locating notches of oil pump and crankshaft and install oil pump assembly. To complete installation, reverse removal procedure.

OIL PUMP SPECIFICATIONS

Application	In. (mm)
Crescent-to-Outer Gear Clearance	.0083-.0126 (.210-.320)
Crescent-to-Inner Gear Clearance	.0047-.0091 (.120-.230)
Inner & Outer Gear-to-Housing End Clearance	.002-.004 (.05-.10)
Pump Body Bore-to-Outer Gear Clearance	.004-.008 (.10-.20)

ENGINE COOLING

WATER PUMP

NOTE: **The water pump cannot be disassembled. Replace as a unit.**

Removal

Remove front cover mount bolts and front cover. Remove water pump pulley. Remove water pump mount bolts, pump, and gasket.

Inspection

Inspect water pump body and vane for rust and corrosion. Check pump bearing for excessive end play or rough operation. Replace water pump if any wear or damage is found.

Installation

To install, use new gasket and reverse removal procedure. Ensure gasket contact surfaces are clean.

NOTE: **For further information on cooling systems, see ENGINE COOLING section.**

TIGHTENING SPECIFICATIONS

Application	Ft. Lbs. (N.m)
Camshaft Lock Plate Bolt	58-65 (78-88)
Camshaft Sprocket Bolt	58-65 (78-88)
Connecting Rod Cap Nut	24-27 (32-36)
Crankshaft Pulley Bolt	9-10 (12-14)
Crankshaft Pulley Damper Bolt	90-98 (123-132)
Cylinder Head Bolt	54-61 (74-83)
Drive Plate Bolt	72-80 (98-108)
Exhaust Manifold Bolt	14-22 (20-29)
Exhaust Outlet-to-Turbocharger	16-22 (22-29)
Flywheel Mount Bolt	72-80 (98-108)
Fuel Pump Cam Bolt	58-65 (78-88)
Idler Bracket Bolt	36-43 (49-59)
Main Bearing Cap Bolt	33-40 (44-54)
Manifold Bolt & Nut	13-17 (18-24)
Oil Pump Bolt	9-12 (12-16)
Rocker Arm Lock Nut	13-16 (18-22)
Rocker Arm Shaft Bolt	13-16 (18-22)
Timing Belt Tensioner Bolt	13-16 (18-22)
	INCH Lbs. (N.m)
Cylinder Head Rear Cover Bolt	53-89 (6-10)
Front Cover Mount Bolt	27-44 (3-5)
Fuel Injector	27-35 (3-4)
Oil Pan Mount Bolt	44-62 (5-7)
Oil Pump Bolt	106-142 (12-16)
Rear Oil Seal Retainer Bolt	35-53 (4-6)
Valve Cover Mount Bolt	9-27 (1-3)

ENGINE SPECIFICATIONS

GENERAL SPECIFICATIONS

Year	DISPLACEMENT		Fuel System	HP@RPM	Torque Ft. Lbs.@RPM	Compr. Ratio	BORE		STROKE	
	Cu. In.	Liters					In.	mm	In.	mm
1987 Stanza & 200SX XE	120.4	2.0	EFI	102 @ 5200	116 @ 3200	8.5:1	3.33	84.5	3.46	88.0

Nissan Engines

2.0L 4-CYLINDER (Cont.)

ENGINE SPECIFICATIONS (Cont.)

VALVES

Engine Size & Valve	Head Diam. In. (mm)	Face Angle	Seat Angle	Seat Width In. (mm)	Stem Diameter In. (mm)	Stem Clearance In. (mm)	Valve Lift In. (mm)
2.0L							
Intake	1.614-1.622 (41)	45.5°	45°	.071-.083 (1.80-2.10)	.2742-.2748 (6.965-6.980)	.0008-.0021 (.020-.053)	.394 (10)
Exhaust	1.378-1.386 (35)	45.5°	45°	.055-.071 (1.40-1.80)	.2734-.2740 (6.945-6.960)	.0016-.0029 (.040-.073)	.394 (10)

PISTONS, PINS, RINGS

Engine	PISTONS	PINS		RINGS		
	Clearance In. (mm)	Piston Fit In. (mm)	Rod Fit In. (mm)	Ring No.	End Gap In. (mm)	Side Clearance In. (mm)
2.0L	.0010-.0018 (.025-.045)	.0003-.0005 (.008-.012)	[1] -.0007-.0015 (-.017-.038)	1	.010-.014 (.25-.35)	.0016-.0029 (.040-.073)
				2	.006-.010 (.15-.25)	.0012-.0025 (.030-.063)
				Oil	.008-.024 (.20-.60)	.....

[1] – Specification given is for an interference fit.

CRANKSHAFT MAIN & CONNECTING ROD BEARINGS

Engine	MAIN BEARINGS				CONNECTING ROD BEARINGS		
	Journal Diam. In. (mm)	Clearance In. (mm)	Thrust Bearing	Crankshaft End Play In. (mm)	Journal Diam. In. (mm)	Clearance In. (mm)	Side Play In. (mm)
2.0L [1]	2.0847-2.0852 (52.951-52.964)	.0016-.0024 (.040-.060)	No. 3	[2] .0020-.0071 (.050-.180)	1.7701-1.7706 (44.961-44.974)	.0008-.0024 (.020-.060)	.008-.012 (.20-.30)

[1] – Main nad rod journal out of round limit is .0012 (.030).
[2] – Maximum wear limit is .012 (.30).

CAMSHAFT

Engine	Journal Diam. In. (mm)	Clearance In. (mm)	Lobe Lift In. (mm)
2.0L	[1] 1.8085-1.8092 (45.935-45.955)	[2] .004 (.10)	[3] In. .335 (8.5) Ex. .374 (9.5)

[1] – No. 5 journal is 1.8077-1.8085" (45.915-45.935 mm).
[2] – Maximum clearance shown.
[3] – Camshaft lobe height is 1.5289-1.5309" (38.843-38.884 mm).

VALVE TIMING

Engine	INTAKE		EXHAUST	
	Open (BTDC)	Close (ABDC)	Open (BBDC)	Close (ATDC)
2.0L	12°	48°	54°	18°

VALVE SPRINGS

Engine	Free Length In. (mm)	PRESSURE Lbs. @ In. (Kg @ mm)	
		Valve Closed	Valve Open
2.0L			
Outer	1.959 (49.77)	47 @ 1.58 (21 @ 40.0)	.....
Inner	1.736 (44.10)	24 @ 1.38 (11 @ 35.0)	.....

Nissan Engines

2.4L 4-CYLINDER

Pathfinder, Pickup

NOTE: **For engine repair procedures not covered in this article, see ENGINE OVERHAUL PROCEDURES article at the beginning of this section.**

ENGINE CODING

ENGINE IDENTIFICATION

Engine identification number is stamped on left side of cylinder block between the exhaust manifold ports.

ENGINE IDENTIFICATION CODES

Application	Code
2.4L	Z24i

ENGINE, MANIFOLDS & CYLINDER HEAD

ENGINE

Removal

1) Disconnect negative battery cable. Drain oil and coolant. Remove radiator with shroud and cooling fan. Remove undercover. Remove A/C compressor and power steering pump (if equipped). Wire compressor and pump out of working area. Do not drain oil from power steering pump or discharge A/C system.

2) On 2WD models, disconnect harness from starter motor. On 4WD models, remove starter motor. On all models, disconnect exhaust manifold from exhaust front tube. Remove front exhaust tube.

3) On 2WD models, disconnect rear propeller shaft from transmission. Remove transmission-to-rear engine mounting bracket bolts. Remove transmission member. Remove front engine mounting bolts. Lift and remove engine.

4) On 4WD models, disconnect front propeller shaft from front differential carrier. Remove front drive shaft bolts. Remove front differential carrier fixing bolts and remove front differential carrier member.

5) On 4WD models, remove differential front mounting bolts. Remove transmission-to-rear engine mounting bracket nuts. Remove front engine mounting bolts. Lift up engine. Remove engine to transmission fixing bolts. Lift and remove engine.

Installation

Replace rubber engine mounts showing signs of deterioration or separation. Ensure proper placement of all electrical harnesses and/or vacuum lines. Reverse removal procedure to complete installation.

INTAKE & EXHAUST MANIFOLDS

Removal

1) Disconnect negative battery cable. Drain cooling system and crankcase. Remove air cleaner assembly and carburetor. Ensure to label all vacuum lines and electrical connections. Detach spark plug wires and cap from distributor.

2) Remove EGR tube crossing valve cover. Remove bolt holding coolant and fuel lines to head. Remove heater hoses. Disconnect fuel line, alternator wiring and all other related components.

3) Remove large vacuum hose from brake booster. Remove upper radiator hose from outlet. Mark position of distributor and remove it from front case assembly. If equipped with air conditioning or power steering, partial disassembly may be required for manifold removal.

4) Remove exhaust air induction tubes. Disconnect exhaust system from exhaust manifold. Remove exhaust manifold cover from manifold and hot air duct. Remove intake manifold assembly with EGR valve, PCV valve, water inlet and accelerator wire bracket attached. *See Fig. 1*.

Installation

When installing manifolds, use new gaskets. Ensure mating surfaces of cylinder head and manifolds are clean, flat and free of nicks or other damage. Set mount studs in cylinder head before installing intake manifold, to aid in alignment. To complete installation, reverse removal procedure.

CYLINDER HEAD

Removal

1) Disconnect negative battery cable. Drain cooling system. Remove power steering pump drive belt. Remove power steering pump, idler pulley and power steering brackets. *See Fig. 1*.

2) Disconnect front exhaust tube from exhaust manifold. *See Fig. 2*. Remove rocker cover. Set No. 1 cylinder at TDC of compression stroke.

3) Loosen camshaft sprocket bolt. Using Chain Stopper (KV101050800), support timing chain. *See Fig. 3*. Remove camshaft sprocket.

4) Remove cylinder head mounting bolts in reverse order of tightening sequence. *See Fig. 4*. Remove bolts securing cylinder head-to-front cover. Remove cylinder head with intake and exhaust manifold.

Disassembly

Remove intake manifold with injector body and exhaust manifold. Remove rocker shaft assembly together with securing bolts. Do not remove bolts at No. 1 and No. 5 brackets. Removal will cause rocker shaft bracket and rocker to spring out. Remove camshaft. Remove valves, valve springs and related parts using Valve Spring Compressor (ST12070000).

Inspection

1) Check cylinder head for cracks, flaws or damage. Repair or replace as necessary. Inspect head and block mating surfaces for warpage. Warpage limit is .004" (.10 mm) or less. If beyond limit, refinish surface.

2) Maximum surface grinding limit of "A" (head) plus "B" (block) is .008" (.20 mm). Replace head and/or block if machined or warped beyond specification.

3) Using calipers, measure cylinder head height. Cylinder head height should be 3.886-3.902" (98.7-99.1 mm). If cylinder head height is not within specifications, replace cylinder head.

4) After resurfacing cylinder head, check that camshaft rotates freely by hand. If resistance is felt, the cylinder head must be replaced.

Installation

1) Prior to installation, set No. 1 piston at TDC of compression stroke. Ensure mating surfaces of cylinder head and block are clean. Install cylinder head and new gasket.

2.4L 4-CYLINDER (Cont.)

Fig. 1: Exploded View of External Engine Components

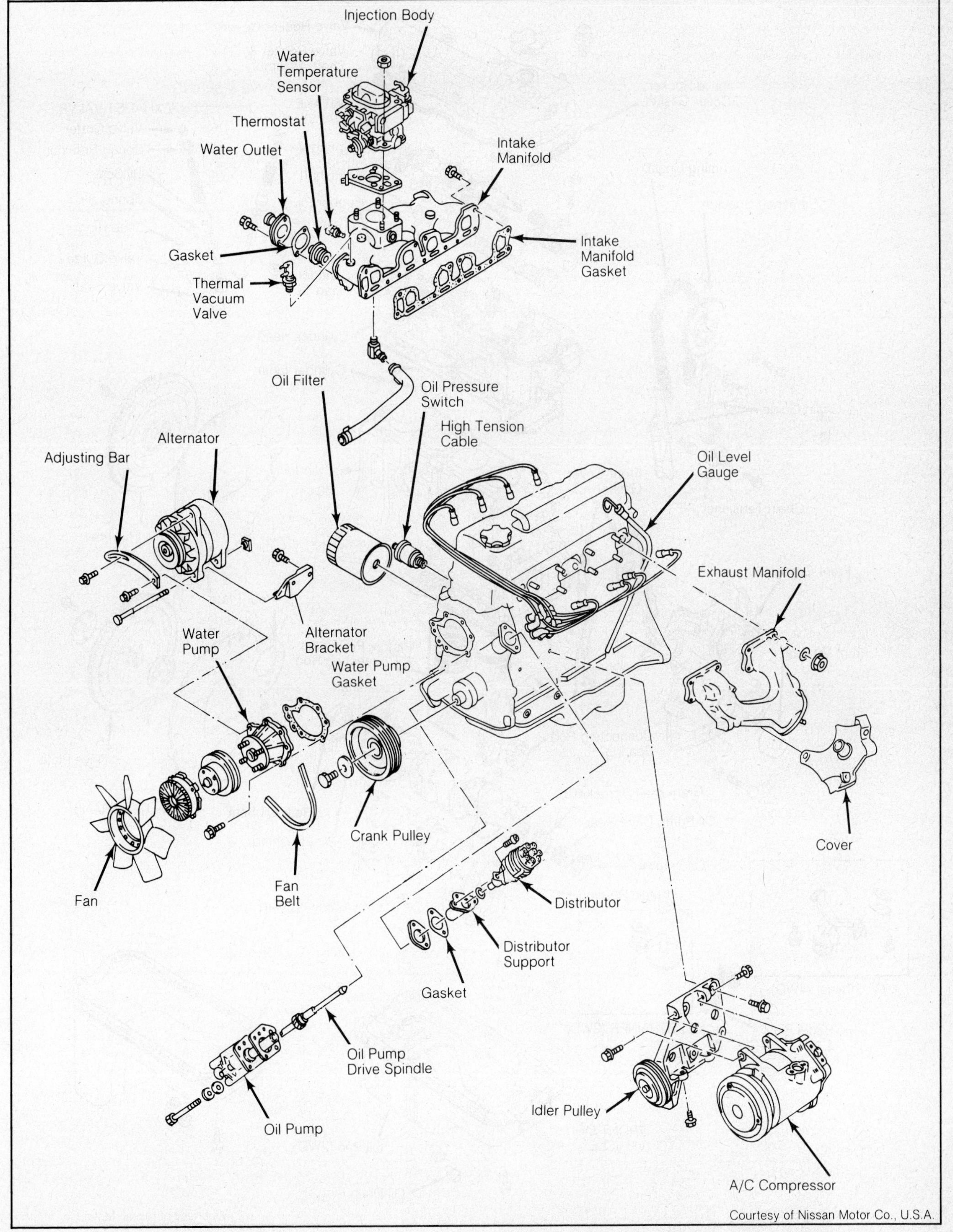

Courtesy of Nissan Motor Co., U.S.A.

Nissan Engines

2.4L 4-CYLINDER (Cont.)

Fig. 2: Exploded View of Z24i Engine

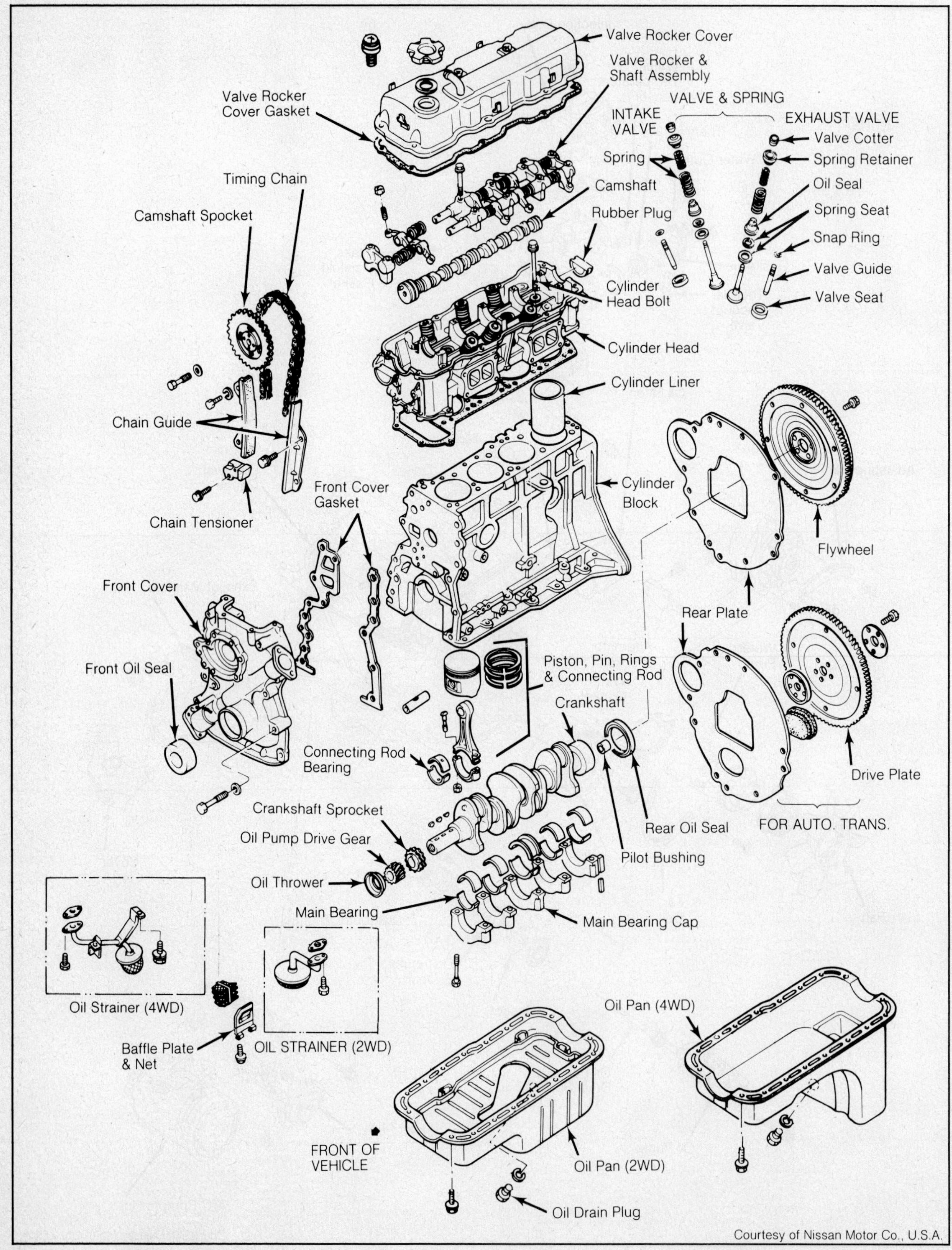

2.4L 4-CYLINDER (Cont.)

Fig. 3: Holding Timing Chain with Chain Stopper

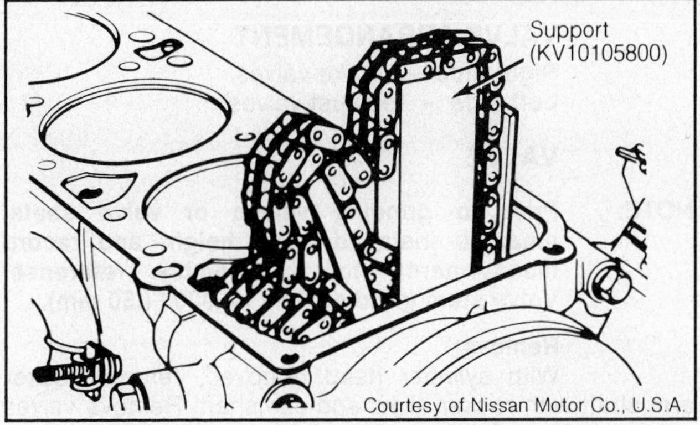

Courtesy of Nissan Motor Co., U.S.A.

2) Follow tightening sequence, and tighten head bolts to 22 ft. lbs (29 N.m). *See Fig. 4*. Tighten head bolts to 58 ft. lbs (78 N.m). Loosen all bolts completely. Tighten head bolts to 22 ft. lbs (29 N.m). Tighten head bolts to 54-61 ft. lbs (74-83 N.m).

3) Ensure that front pin is positioned at upper surface of camshaft. Set chain on camshaft by aligning each mating mark. Then install camshaft sprocket to camshaft. Apply sealant to sealant point of cylinder head and rubber plug. Install rubber plug.

4) See VALVE CLEARANCE ADJUSTMENTS and adjust valve clearance. Install rocker cover, power steering pump, idler pulley and brackets, power steering pump drive belt. Connect exhaust manifold and exhaust tube.

5) Install cylinder head and head bolts. Temporarily tighten No. 1 and No. 2 head bolts to 14 ft. lbs. (19 N.m). Install and align sprockets and timing chain. Install remaining components in reverse order of removal procedure, using new seals, gaskets and sealant where required.

6) Tighten head bolts in 3 steps, in sequence, to final specified torque. *See Fig. 4*. Run engine for several minutes, allow engine to cool down and recheck head bolt torque.

Fig. 4: Cylinder Head Tightening Sequence

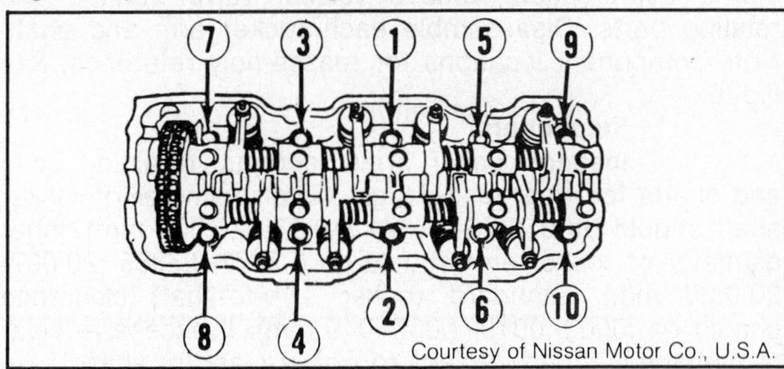

Courtesy of Nissan Motor Co., U.S.A.

CAMSHAFT

ENGINE FRONT COVER

Removal

1) Drain coolant and crankcase oil. Remove air cleaner. Remove intake and exhaust manifolds as previously described, label all wiring and vacuum lines for reassembly reference.

2) Remove distributor and wiring from front case assembly. Remove oil pan, oil strainer and oil pump drive spindle. Remove all related wiring from alternator, engine harness and other pertinent sub-systems and label accordingly.

3) Remove alternator and secure out of working area. Remove cylinder head as previously described. Remove radiator shroud and radiator. Remove fan, fan pulley and water pump. Remove crankshaft front pulley. Note position and remove front cover bolts for reassembly purposes. Remove front cover and gaskets.

Inspection

1) Check height difference between cylinder block upper face and front cover upper face. Difference must not exceed .006" (.15 mm). Correct as necessary.

2) Check oil seal surface of crankshaft for nicks or damage. Repair as necessary. Front cover mount bolts are of different lengths. Ensure bolts are in proper locations during installation.

Installation

1) Before installation, apply sealant at mating corners of oil pan gasket, cylinder head gasket and front cover gaskets. Press new oil seal in front cover with dust seal lip at outside.

2) Apply lithium grease to sealing lip of oil seal before cover is installed. Using new gaskets and sealant, install front cover and related components in reverse order of removal procedure.

TIMING CHAIN & SPROCKETS

Removal

1) Drain coolant and crankcase. Set No. 1 piston at TDC of compression stroke. Ensure timing marks are aligned and that rotor is pointing to No. 1 cylinder under distributor cap.

2) Remove air cleaner, alternator and wiring. Remove distributor and wires. Remove all wiring and hoses necessary for removal of manifolds and cylinder head and label.

3) Remove intake and exhaust manifolds. Remove valve cover and gasket. Remove camshaft sprocket and slowly lower timing chain down into front case. Remove cylinder head. Install Timing Chain Support (KV10105800). *See Fig. 3*.

4) Remove radiator shroud and radiator. Remove fan, fan pulley, water pump and front crankshaft pulley. Remove front case assembly. Remove timing chain tensioner and chain guide. Remove timing chain. Remove oil thrower, oil pump drive gear and crankshaft sprocket.

Inspection

1) Check camshaft sprocket tooth surface for flaws and wear. Replace if damaged. Install sprocket on camshaft and check for runout. Camshaft sprocket runout limit using total indicator reading is .004" (.10 mm).

2) Replace sprocket, if runout exceeds specification. Check timing chain for damage and excessive wear at roller links. Replace timing chain if faulty or stretched. Check chain tensioner and guide for excessive wear or defect. Replace as necessary.

Installation

1) Locate No. 2 hole of camshaft sprocket over camshaft dowel pin. Align timing chain mark with No. 2 mark on sprocket. Install timing chain onto crankshaft sprocket. Ensure to align marks on timing chain with marks on crankshaft sprocket.

2) Both sprocket timing marks will be towards right side of engine. *See Fig. 5*. Adjust chain guide tensioner to zero lash.

Nissan Engines

2.4L 4-CYLINDER (Cont.)

3) Install oil pump gear with large chamfered inner face towards rear. Set timing chain with mating marks aligned with crankshaft and camshaft sprockets. Complete installation in reverse order of removal procedure.

Fig. 5: Crankshaft & Camshaft Timing Chain Alignment

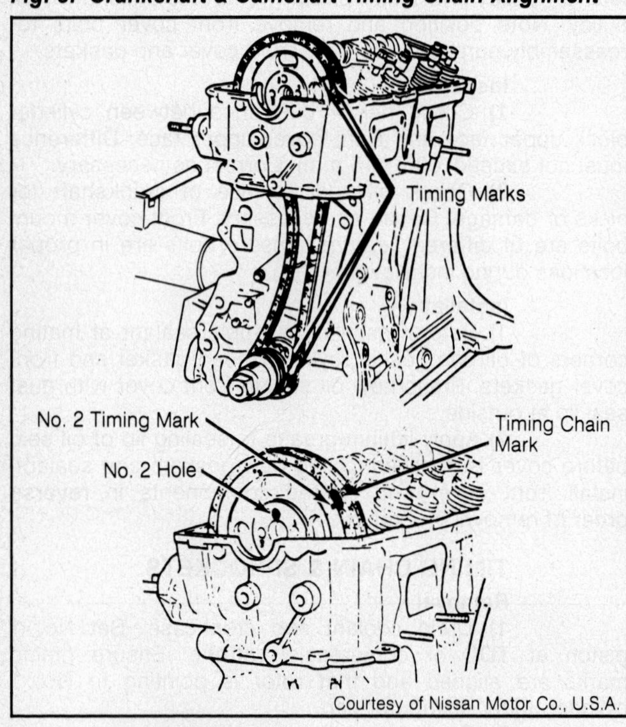

Courtesy of Nissan Motor Co., U.S.A.

CAMSHAFT

Removal

With cylinder head removed, loosen rocker arm bolts evenly, rotating from outside to inside in sequence. Do not remove bolts from each end bracket of rocker arm shaft assembly. Doing so, assembly will spring apart. Remove rocker arm assembly. Remove camshaft.

Inspection

Measure camshaft bearing journals. Measure cylinder head camshaft journal bearing inside diameter. Check CAMSHAFT SPECIFICATIONS. Place camshaft in "V" blocks and check camshaft runout. Check camshaft lobe height.

CAMSHAFT SPECIFICATIONS

Application	In. (mm)
Standard Lobe Heigth	1.515-1.517 (38.48-38.53)
Maximum Lobe Wear	.0098 (.25)
Camshaft End Play	.008 (.20)
Maximum Runout	..008 (.20)
Maximum Journal-to-Bushing Clearance	.004 (.10)

Installation

1) Install camshaft on cylinder head with front camshaft dowel pin at 12 o'clock position. Install rocker arm assembly by aligning rocker arm shaft on dowel pin of cylinder head.

2) Place cylinder head on wooden blocks to allow for valve space. Tighten rocker arm bolts evenly, in 2 or 3 steps, in an outward sequence from center bracket.

VALVES

VALVE ARRANGEMENT

Right Side – Intake valves.
Left Side – Exhaust valves.

VALVE

NOTE: **Prior to grinding valves or valve seats, measure installed valve height and record measurments for reassembly reference. Valve stem grinding limit is .020" (.50 mm).**

Removal

With cylinder head removed, remove rocker arm shaft with rocker arms and camshaft. Remove valves using Valve Spring Compressor (ST12070000 or KV101092S0). Keep disassembled parts in order.

Inspection

1) Inspect valve head diameter, stem diameter and seat angle. Inspect valves for worn, damaged or deformed valve head or stem. Inspect valve keeper grooves for excessive wear.

2) If valve head is worn to .020" (.50 mm) margin thickness, replace valve. Valve stem end surface grinding limit is .020" (.50 mm).

Installation

Install valve spring seat insert and oil seal over top of valve guide. Place springs in position with close-coiled (painted Red) end toward cylinder head. Use compressor to install valve spring, lubricated valve, valve retainers and keepers.

ROCKER ARM & SHAFT

Removal & Diassembly

1) Remove valve cover and gasket. Remove intake manifold with injection body and exhaust manifold. Loosen rocker arm mounting bolts. When loosening bolts, evenly loosen from outside in sequence. Do not remove bolts at No. 1 and No. 5 brackets since rocker shaft bracket and rocker will spring out.

2) Remove rocker shaft assembly together with securing bolts. Remove camshaft. *See Fig. 6*. Using spring compressor, remove valves, valve springs and relating parts. Disassemble each rocker arm and shaft. Note component locations for reassembly reference. *See Fig. 6*.

Inspection

Inspect rocker arms, springs, retaining bolts and shafts for wear or damage. Outer diameter of rocker shaft should be 0.7866-0.7874 (19.979-20.000 mm). Inner diameter of rocker arm should be 0.7877-0.7885 (20.007-20.0.28 mm). Standard rocker arm-to-shaft clearance should be .0003-.0019" (.007-.049 mm). If excessive wear or damage is found, replace rocker arm and/or shaft.

Reassembly & Installation

NOTE: **Discard old oil seal and install new one. Apply a coat of engine oil to sealing lips of oil seal and frictional surfaces of moving parts.**

1) With valves and camshaft assembled on cylinder head, assemble rocker shaft. *See Fig. 6*. Ensure camshaft dowel pin is at front side of cylinder head and positioned at 12 o'clock. Install rocker arm shaft brackets, rocker arms and springs on shaft. *See Fig. 6*.

2.4L 4-CYLINDER (Cont.)

NOTE: Rocker arm shaft brackets use alphabetical identification marks on each bracket and cylinder head location. *See Fig. 6.*

Fig. 6: Installing Rocker Arm & Shaft Assembly

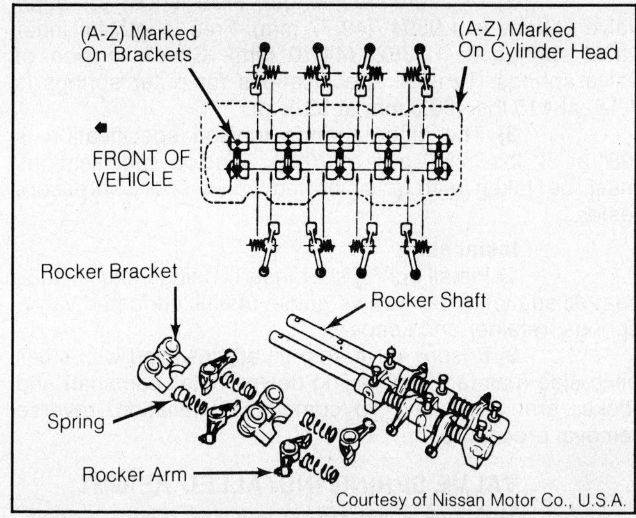

Courtesy of Nissan Motor Co., U.S.A.

2) Intake rocker shaft has an identification slit on front surface of rocker shaft. Exhaust rocker shaft has only a punch mark. Both shafts should be installed so that punch marks on front surface face up. Marks are used to identify oil hole direction and must be installed correctly for lubrication purposes. *See Fig. 7.*

Fig. 7: Assembling Rocker Arm Shafts Using Identification Marks

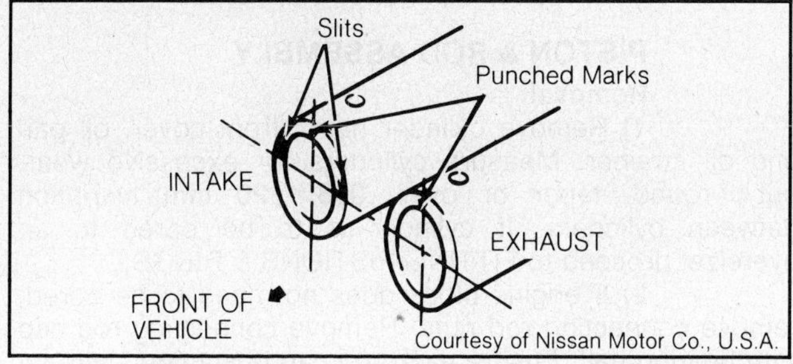

Courtesy of Nissan Motor Co., U.S.A.

3) Valve rocker arms are the same for intake and exhaust valve rocker arms for No. 1 and No. 3 cylinders are marked with "1". Rocker arms for No. 2 and No. 4 cylinders are marked with "2".

4) Do not mix rocker arms from original locations. Mount rocker shaft assembly onto alignment dowel pin in head. Tighten bolts gradually, in 2 or 3 steps from center outward.

5) Set cylinder head on blocks to allow space for valves to open during rocker shaft tightening process. After assembling cylinder head, turn camshaft until valves for No. 1 piston are at TDC of compression stroke (both valves closed).

VALVE SEATS

1) Check valves and valve seat inserts for pitting or excessive wear at valve face contact surface. Standard intake valve seat contact is .083" (2.1 mm). Exhaust valve seat contact width is .067" (1.7 mm). Correct valve seat surface or replace if excessively worn.

NOTE: Replacement valve seat inserts of .020" (.50 mm) oversize are available for service. Prior to replacing valve seat, the valve guide should be checked for wear. If replacment is necessary, valve guide replacement should always be done first.

2) To remove old inserts, set machine depth to prevent boring beyond bottom face of valve seat insert in cylinder head. Use a drilling guide (such as a mandrel in the valve guide) to cut old valve seat insert out of cylinder head. Ensure valve seat recess is centered on valve guide for correct seat replacement.

3) Heat cylinder head to 302-392°F (150-200°C). Apply Loctite to valve seat insert and install seat insert. Ensure that insert seats firmly against bottom face of recess. Cut valve seats to correct depth, face angle and seat width of valve being installed. Reface valve.

VALVE CLEARANCE ADJUSTMENTS

NOTE: Valves should be adjusted with engine at normal operating temperature, but not running. Cold specifications are provided for initial settings after assembly.

1) Remove air cleaner and cover carburetor with clean shop towel. Remove distributor high tension wire and valve cover.

2) Set No. 1 cylinder at TDC of compression stroke. Ensure timing is correct by noting the position of the timing marks. Ensure rotor is pointing to No. 1 cylinder when distributor cap is removed.

3) Using a feeler gauge, adjust clearances for valves 1, 2, 4 and 6. To adjust valve clearance, insert feeler gauge between valve stem end and rocker arm adjusting screw. *See Fig. 8.*

4) When correct measurement reading is obtained, there should be a slight drag on the feeler gauge while removing it. Set No. 4 cylinder at TDC of compression stroke and adjust valves No. 3, 5, 7 and 8.

5) Valve clearances for both intake and exhaust valves are .012" (.30 mm). Tighten rocker arm jam nuts to specification and recheck clearances.

Fig. 8: Valve Adjustment Sequence

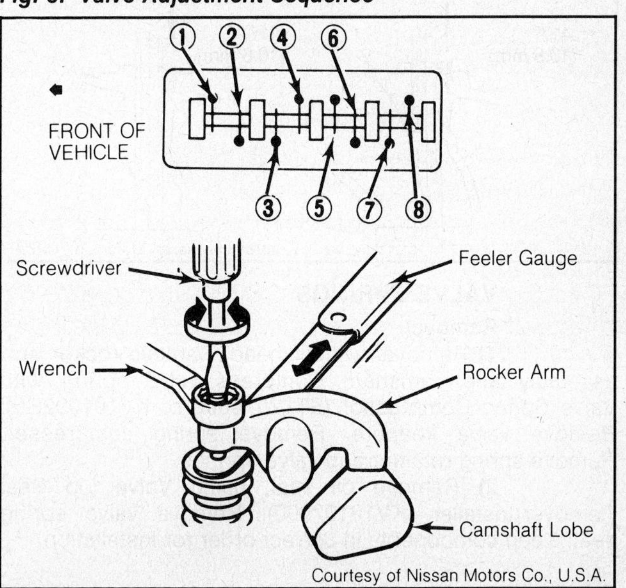

Courtesy of Nissan Motors Co., U.S.A.

2.4L 4-CYLINDER (Cont.)

VALVE GUIDES

Removal

Heat head to 302-392°F (150-200°C). Remove guide from combustion chamber side using Guide Remover (ST11320000). With head at room temperature, ream guide hole to specification. See VALVE GUIDE SPECIFICATION table.

Inspection

Measure clearance between valve stem and valve guide. See VALVE GUIDE SPECIFICATIONS table. If any part does not meet specifications, replace or repair. If clearance exceeds specification and valve stem is not worn, replace guide.

VALVE GUIDE SPECIFICATIONS

Application	In. (mm)
Standard Stem-to-Guide Clearance	
Intake Valve	.0008-.0021 (.020-.053)
Exhaust Valve	.0016-.0029 (.040-.073)
Maximum Stem-to-Guide Clearance	.004 (.10)
Standard Guide Hole Diameter	.4718-.4723 (11.985-11.996)
Standard Guide Outside Diameter	.4733-.4738 (12.023-12.034)
Interference Fit Valve Guide-to-Head	.0011-.0019 (.027-.049)
Ream Guide Hole	4797-.4802 (12.185-12.196)

NOTE: **Valve guides of .008" (.20 mm) oversize are available.**

Installation

1) To install guide, reheat head. Fit snap ring on new valve guide and lubricate outside diameter of replacement guide. Press new guide into head until snap ring contacts head surface. *See Fig. 9.*

2) Use Reamer (ST11032000) to finish guide bore to .3150-.3157" (8.000-8.018 mm). Reface valve seat surface, after valve guide repair or replacement is completed.

Fig. 9: Installing Intake & Exhaust Valve Guides

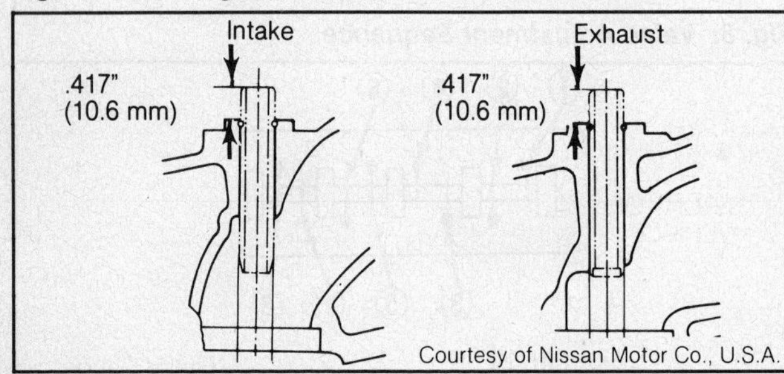

VALVE SPRINGS

Removal

1) Remove cylinder head. Remove rocker arm assembly and camshaft. Compress valve spring with Valve Spring Compressor (ST12070000 or KV101092S0). Remove valve keepers. Remove spring compresser. Remove spring retainer and valve springs.

2) Remove oil seal, using Valve Lip Seal Remover/Installer (KV10107900). Remove valve spring seat. Keep components in correct order for installation.

Inspection

1) Check valve springs for squareness using steel square and surface plate. Standard out of square limit is .087" (2.2 mm) for outer spring and .075" (1.9 mm) for inner spring.

2) Measure free length. Free length for outer valve springs is 1.9594" (49.77 mm). Free length for inner valve springs is 1.7362" (44.10 mm). Check tension of valve springs. Tension specifications for outer springs is 1.18" at 115 lbs. (30.0 mm at 52.3kg).

3) The inner springs tension specification is .98" at 57 lbs. (25.0 mm at 26kg). Tension specifications must be taken with a calibrated valve spring pressure tester.

Installation

1) Install spring seat insert. Using installer tool, seat oil seal onto each valve guide. Install lubricated valve, springs, retainer and keepers.

2) Ensure valve springs are installed with small pitch side (painted Red) facing down. Install camshaft and rocker arm assembly. To complete installation, reverse removal procedure.

VALVE SPRING INSTALLED HEIGHT

1) Check valve spring installed height. Specifications for outer valve spring installed heights are 1.57" (23.0 mm at 40kg) at 50.7 lbs. Specifications for inner springs are 1.38" (11.0 mm at 35kg) at 24.3 lbs.

2) Installed spring heights are tested with a calibrated spring tester. If any measurements are not within specifications, replace spring.

PISTON, PINS & RINGS

PISTON & ROD ASSEMBLY

Removal

1) Remove cylinder head, front cover, oil pan and oil strainer. Measure cylinders for excessive wear, out-of-round, taper or over .008" (.20 mm) variation between cylinders. If cylinder is to be bored to an oversize, proceed to FITTING PISTIONS & RINGS.

2) If engine block does not need to be bored, remove connecting rod nuts. Remove connecting rod cap with bearing half. Ensure each rod cap is stamped with an identification number which matches its mating connecting rod.

Inspection

1) Check connecting rods for bend or torsion using rod aligner. Standard bend and torsion limit is .0012" (.03 mm) and maximum limit is .002" (.05 mm), per 3.94" (100.0 mm) of length.

2) Install connecting rod with bearings, on crank journal and tighten to 33-40 ft. lbs. (45-54 N.m). Measure rod side thrust clearance. Standard clearance at connecting rod big end is .008-.012" (.20-.30 mm). Maximum limit is .024" (.60 mm). Replace or recondition rod if specifications are exceeded.

Installation

1) Apply oil to rings, piston and cylinder wall. Ensure ring gaps are approximately 180 degrees apart and not located on thrust side of piston or in line with piston pin.

2) Ensure grade mark stamped on top of piston is toward front of engine and oil hole on rod faces right side of block. *See Fig. 10.* Install cylinder head, front

2.4L 4-CYLINDER (Cont.)

cover and related components. Install oil pan with new gasket. Tighten bolts evenly, in a crossing pattern. Do not overtighten.

Fig. 10: Installing Piston & Rod Assembly

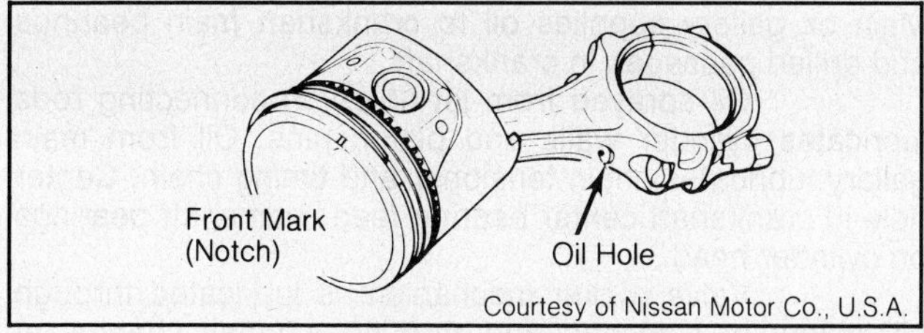

Courtesy of Nissan Motor Co., U.S.A.

FITTING PISTONS & RINGS

1) Inspect cylinder block for cracks or flaws. Using dial bore gauge, measure cylinder bore for out-of-round, taper or excessive wear. If bore out-of-round or taper exceeds .0006" (.015 mm), the cylinder will need to be bored. When any one cylinder is bored, all cylinders must be bored.

NOTE: **Before cylinder block machining operations, ensure main bearing caps are installed and tightened to specification. Bore cylinders in the order of No. 2-4-1-3 to prevent distortion.**

2) Determine piston oversize according to amount of wear in cylinder. Standard cylinder bore diameter is 3.5039-3.5093" (89.000-89.010 mm). Cylinder bore wear limit is .008" (.20 mm).

3) Measure piston diameter at thrust face. Standard piston diameter is 3.5026-3.5029" (88.965-88.975 mm). Add piston-to-cylinder clearance. Piston-to-cylinder clearance should be .0010-.0018 (.025-.045 mm). Finish hone of cylinder may then be determined.

4) After honing cylinder to final fit, measure piston-to-cylinder clearance using pull scale and feeler gauge. With piston and cylinder at room temperature (70°F (20°C), a force of .4-3.3 lbs. (.2-1.5 kg) should be obtained when extracting a .0016" (.04 mm) feeler gauge.

NOTE: **If only piston rings are replaced, measure gap at bottom of bore. Oversize pistons and rings are available in .02 mm, .50 mm and 1.0 mm.**

5) When installing piston rings, ensure stamped mark on ring faces up. Ensure that oil ring spacers are properly positioned and all oil rings are butted correctly to each other. *See Fig. 11.*

Fig. 11: Installation Order of Piston Rings

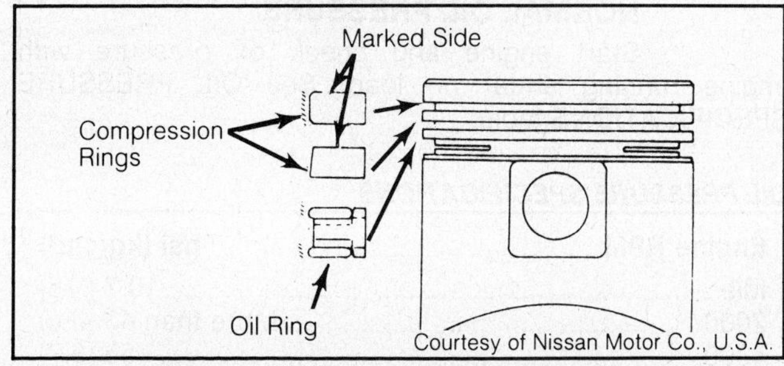

Courtesy of Nissan Motor Co., U.S.A.

PISTON PIN REPLACEMENT

1) Piston pin is press fit into connecting rod and has sliding fit in piston. To remove piston pin, set piston and rod assembly with correct adapters in Hydraulic Press (ST13030001) and press pin out of connecting rod. Do not damage piston during removal.

2) Check pin and pin hole for signs of galling or excessive wear. Using micrometer and telescopic hole gauge, measure diameter of piston pin, piston pin hole and rod small end. Determine pin-to-piston and pin-to-rod clearance.

3) Standard piston pin diameter is .8265-.8267" (20.993-20.998 mm). Standard piston pin hole inside diameter is .8268-.8271" (21.001-21.008 mm). Standard rod small end diameter is .8254-.8259" (20.956-20.978 mm).

4) Check pin-to-piston and pin-to-rod clearance. Refer to ENGINE SPECIFICATIONS chart for tolerances. To assemble piston and rod, warm piston to room temperature. Insert lubricated piston pin into piston with finger pressure only. Hold piston and rod in proper alignment, using proper adapters press in piston pin. Assemble with oil hole of rod big end toward right side of block.

CRANKSHAFT & ROD BEARINGS

CRANKSHAFT MAIN BEARINGS

Removal

1) With engine removed from vehicle, remove manifolds, cylinder head and oil pan. Remove flywheel and rear plate. Remove oil strainer, oil pump and drive spindle.

2) Remove front cover, chain tensioner, guide and timing chain. Remove oil slinger, oil pump drive gear and crankshaft sprocket. Remove piston and rod assemblies.

3) Ensure that main bearing caps are stamped to identify which number main web they are machined to fit. Remove main bearing caps, starting from outside and working towards center in sequence. Use Puller (KV101041SO) to remove center and rear main bearing caps. *See Fig. 12.*

NOTE: **Keep main bearing caps in order for reassembly reference.**

Fig. 12: Removing Center & Rear Main Bearing Caps

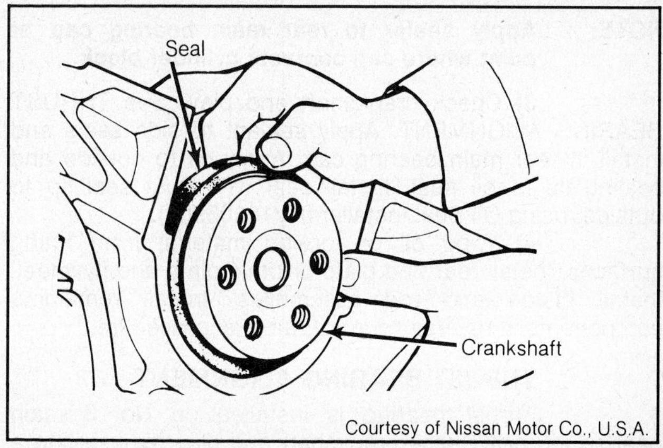

Courtesy of Nissan Motor Co., U.S.A.

4) Remove rear oil seal and crankshaft. Remove baffle plate and steel net from crankcase.

Inspection

1) Check crankshaft journals for scoring, wear, cracks, taper and out-of-round. See CRANKSHAFT SPECIFICATIONS table. Check crankshaft for runout by placing on "V" blocks. Check crankshaft pilot bushing for wear or damage.

2) If bushing is excessively worn, pull bushing from crankshaft using Pilot Bushing Puller (ST16610001). Clean bushing hole. Insert new bushing to .160" (4.0 mm). Do not damage bushing edge or insert bushing excessively.

3) Check flywheel friction surface for cracks, hot spots, damage or wear. Measure friction surface runout using a dial indicator. Runout limit is .006" (.15 mm). Resurface or replace flywheel if not within specifications. Check tooth surfaces of ring gear for flaws or wear. Replace ring gear if necessary.

CRANKSHAFT SPECIFICATIONS

Application	In. (mm)
Standard taper & Out-of-round limit	.0004 (.01) or Less
Maximum taper & Out-of-round	.0012 (.03)
Standard runout limit	.001 (.025)
Maximum runout	.002 (.05)

Installation

1) Install baffle plate and steel net into crankcase. Install upper main bearing halves into block. Ensure bearings are correctly mated to journal and positioned correctly. Journal No. 3 requires a thrust bearing. Bearings for No. 1 and No. 5. are the same. Bearings for No. 2 and No. 4 are the same.

NOTE: Upper and lower bearings are not interchangeable. Upper bearings have an oil groove and must be installed to the block portion. Ensure that all foreign material is clear from block main bearing oil feed holes.

2) Apply lubricant to upper main bearing surfaces. Install crankshaft. Install numbered main bearing caps with arrow pointing toward front. Shift crankshaft forward. Tighten main bearing caps, in 2 or 3 steps, starting at center bearing and working outward. Ensure crankshaft rotates smoothly.

NOTE: Apply sealer to rear main bearing cap at point where cap contacts cylinder block.

3) Check crankshaft end play. See THRUST BEARING ALIGNMENT. Apply sealant to side seals and install in rear main bearing cap. Apply oil to outside and sealing lip of oil seal. Install seal with dust seal lip to outside, using Oil Seal Installer (KV10105500).

4) Wipe oil or foreign material from fitting surfaces. Install rear end plate or drive plate and flywheel. Install piston and rod assemblies. Install remaining components in reverse order of removal procedure.

THRUST BEARING ALIGNMENT

Thrust bearing is installed on No. 3 main bearing journal. Check crankshaft end play by inserting a feeler gauge between flange of thrust bearing and crankshaft. Standard end play is .002-.007" (.05-.18 mm) and service limit is .012" (.30 mm).

ENGINE OILING

ENGINE OILING SYSTEM

Oil drawn from pan passes through screen to oil pump and is delivered to oil filter and main oil gallery. Main oil gallery supplies oil to crankshaft main bearings and drilled passages in crankshaft.

Oil sprayed from jet holes on connecting rods lubricates cylinder walls and piston pins. Oil from main gallery lubricates chain tensioner and timing chain. Center hole in crankshaft center bearing feeds camshaft bearings on cylinder head.

Valve rocker mechanism is lubricated through oil gallery in camshaft and through a small channel at base circle portion of each cam. Rocker arms and valves are lubricated through small holes in oil pipe and held in place by 4 bolts. Pump is driven by helical gear on crankshaft which also drives distributor shaft.

Fig. 13: Cutaway View of Engine Oiling System

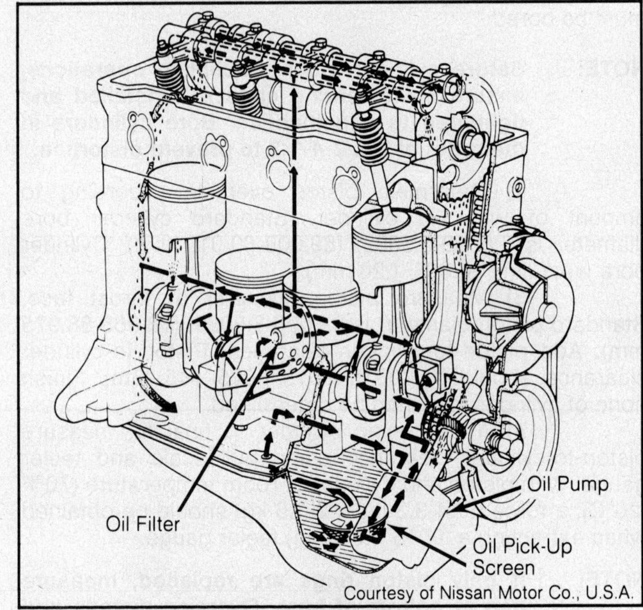

Courtesy of Nissan Motor Co., U.S.A.

CRANKCASE CAPACITY

For 2WD models, crankcase capacity is 4.0 qts. (3.8L) with oil filter. For 4WD models, crankcase capacity is 4.5 qts. (4.3L) with oil filter.

OIL FILTER

A full-flow, disposable cartridge filter is used.

NORMAL OIL PRESSURE

Start engine and check oil pressure with engine running under no load. See OIL PRESSURE SPECIFICATIONS table.

OIL PRESSURE SPECIFICATIONS

Engine RPM	[1] psi (kg/cm²)
Idle	10.7 (.75)
2000	More than 43 (3.0)
4000	53 (3.7)
6000	57 (4.0)

2.4L 4-CYLINDER (Cont.)

OIL PUMP

Removal

1) Pump assembly is installed at bottom right of front cover and held in place by 4 bolts. Pump is driven by helical gear on crankshaft and in turn drives distributor shaft.

2) Set No. 1 piston at TDC of compression stroke. Check distributor rotor position for reassembly reference. Remove mount bolts. Remove oil pump and drive spindle assembly.

Inspection

1) Remove cover and gasket from oil pump body. Remove gears. *See Fig. 13.* Wash parts with solvent. Inspect for wear or damage.

2) Using a feeler gauge, check clearances. See OIL PUMP SPECIFICATION table. With rotor in pump body and gasket installed, place straightedge over rotor. Check clearance between rotor and straightedge. Clearance should not exceed .0031" (.08 mm).

NOTE: Oil pump rotors and body are not serviced separately. If excessively worn or damaged, replace pump rotor set or complete pump assembly.

Installation

1) Install outer pump rotor with larger chamfered portion facing pump body side. Ensure distributor rotor is in same position as before removal. Fill pump housing with oil. Align punch mark on drive spindle with hole in pump. *See Fig. 14.*

2) Using new gasket, install oil pump and drive spindle assembly. Ensure drive spindle tip securely fits distributor fitting hole. Tighten all bolts to specification.

Fig. 14: Aligning Oil Pump Timing Marks

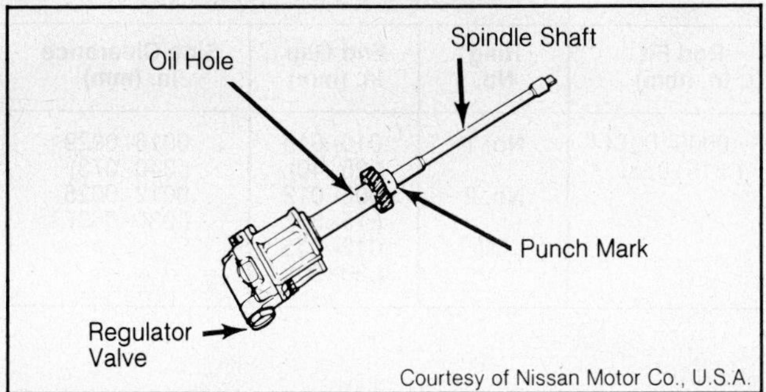

OIL PUMP SPECIFICATIONS

Application	[1] In. (mm)
Outer Rotor-to-Body Clearance	.0059-.0083 (.15-.21)
Rotor Side Clearance	
(Rotor to Bottom Cover) [2]	.0083 (.21)
Rotor Tip Clearance	.0047 (.12)

[1] – Wear limit specifications given.
[2] – Clearance is checked with gasket in place.

OIL PAN

Removal

1) Remove undercover. Drain engine oil. On 2WD models, remove front suspension crossmember. On 4WD models, remove front differential carrier member bolts. Remove front differential carrier fixing bolts and support differential carrier.

2) On 4WD models, remove transmission to rear engine mounting bracket nuts. Remove engine mounting bolts or nuts. Lift up engine. If necessary, disconnect exhaust tubes. On all models, remove oil pan.

Installation

Remove all traces of old gasket from mating surfaces. Apply a continuous bead of liquid gasket to mating surfaces. To complete installtion, reverse removal procedure.

ENGINE COOLING

WATER PUMP

Removal

To remove water pump, slowly open radiator cap to release system pressure. Drain coolant from drain plug on left rear of cylinder block. Remove upper radiator shroud. Loosen alternator bracket and remove fan belt. Remove power steering belt (if equipped). Remove fan. Remove pump mount bolts. Remove water pump with fan pulley, fan coupling and gasket.

Inspection

Inspect water pump body and vane for corrosion. Check pump bearing for excessive play or rough operation. Inspect fan coupling for oil leakage or bent bi-metal. Check thermostat for proper operation. Pressure leak test entire cooling system. Replace pump or components as necessary.

NOTE: Water pump and fan coupling cannot be disassembled. Replace as a unit.

Installation

Using new gasket, install water pump by reversing removal procedure. Adjust belt tension and fill cooling system. Check hoses for proper attachments and damage. After running engine for several minutes, check for leaks.

NOTE: For more information, see ENGINE COOLING SYSTEMS article at the end of this section.

Nissan Engines

2.4L 4-CYLINDER (Cont.)

ENGINE SPECIFICATIONS

GENERAL SPECIFICATIONS

Year	DISPLACEMENT		Fuel System	HP@RPM	Torque Ft. Lbs.@RPM	Compr. Ratio	BORE		STROKE	
	Cu. In.	Liters					In.	mm	In.	mm
1987										
Federal	119.1	2.0	2-Bbl.	95 @ 5200	112 @ 2800	9.4:1	3.35	85	3.39	86
50 State [1]	145.8	2.4	2-Bbl.	103 @ 4800	134 @ 2800	8.3:1	3.50	89	3.78	96

[1] – Only gasoline engine available in Calif. Pickups, and may also be used in some Federal Pickups.

VALVES

Engine Size & Valve	Head Diam. In. (mm)	Face Angle	Seat Angle	Seat Width In. (mm)	Stem Diameter In. (mm)	Stem Clearance In. (mm)	Valve Lift In. (mm)
2.4L							
Intake	1.654 (42)	45°	45.5°	.079 (2.00)	.3136-.3142 (7.965-7.980)	[1] .0008 [1] (.020)	.....
Exhaust	1.496 (38)	45°	45.5°	.067 (1.70)	.3128-.3134 (7.945-7.960)	[1] .009 [1] (.023)	.....

[1] – Specification given for cold measurement. Clearance for hot measurement is .012" (.30)

PISTONS, PINS & RINGS

Engine	PISTONS	PINS		RINGS		
	Clearance In. (mm)	Piston Fit In. (mm)	Rod Fit In. (mm)	Ring No.	End Gap In. (mm)	Side Clearance In. (mm)
2.4L	.0010-.0018 (.025-.045)	.0003-.0005 (.008-.012)	[1] .0006-.0014 (.015-.035)	No. 1	.010-.016 (.25-.40)	.0016-.0029 (.040-.073)
				No. 2	.006-.012 (.15-.30)	.0012-.0025 (.030-.063)
				Oil	.012-.035 (.30-.90)	.....

[1] – Interference fit.

CRANKSHAFT MAIN & CONNECTING ROD BEARINGS

Engine	MAIN BEARINGS				CONNECTING ROD BEARINGS		
	Journal Diam. In. (mm)	Clearance In. (mm)	Thrust Bearing	Crankshaft End Play In. (mm)	Journal Diam. In. (mm)	Clearance In. (mm)	Side Play In. (mm)
2.4L	2.1631-2.1636 (54.942-54.955)	.0008-.0024 (.020-.062)	No. 3	.002-.007 (.05-.18)	1.9670-1.9675 (49.961-49.974)	.0005-.0021 (.012-.054)	.008-.012 (.20-.30)

Nissan Engines

2.4L 4-CYLINDER (Cont.)

ENGINE SPECIFICATIONS (Cont.)

VALVE SPRINGS

Engine	Free Length In. (mm)	PRESSURE Lbs. @ In. (Kg @ mm)	
		Valve Closed	Valve Open
2.4L			
Inner	1.736 (44.10)	24.3@1.38 (11@35)	57@0.98 (26@25)
Outer	1.959 (49.77)	50.7@1.57 (23@40)	115.3@1.18 (52.3@30)

TIGHTENING SPECIFICATIONS

Application	Ft. Lbs. (N.m)
Alternator Bracket Bolt	29-43 (39-59)
Camshaft Sprocket Bolt	87-116 (118-157)
Clutch Cover Bolt	12-15 (16-21)
Connecting Rod Nut	33-40 (44-54)
Crankshaft Pulley	87-116 (118-157)
Cylinder Block Drain Plug	22-29 (29-39)
Cylinder Head Mount Bolt	54-61 (74-83)
Flywheel Mount Bolt	101-116 (137-157)
Main Bearing Cap Bolt	33-40 (44-54)
Manifold	
Exhaust Mount Bolt	12-15 (16-21)
Intake Mount Bolt	12-15 (16-21)
Oil Drain Plug	22-29 (29-39)
Oil Pump Mount Bolt	8-11 (11-15)
Rocker Shaft	
Bracket Bolt	11-18 (15-25)
Starter Motor Bolts	22-29 (29-39)
Transmission-to-Cylinder Mount Bolt	
Short Bolt	22-29 (29-39)
Long Bolt	29-36 (39-49)
Valve Clearance Adjusting Screw	
Lock Nut	12-16 (16-22)
	INCH Lbs. (N.m)
Cam Chain	
Guide Bolt	51-86 (6-10)
Tensioner Bolt	51-86 (6-10)
Cylinder Head-to-Front Cover Bolt	35-86 (4-10)
Front Cover Mount Bolt	
6 mm	35-86 (4-10)
8 mm	86-144 (10-16)
Oil Pan Mount Bolt	43.2-61.2 (5-7)
Oil Pump Mount Bolt	96-132 (11-15)
Valve Rocker Cover Bolt	8-26 (1-3)

CAMSHAFT

Engine	Journal Diam. In. (mm)	Clearance In. (mm)	Lobe Lift In. (mm)
2.4L	1.2967-1.2974 (32.935-32.955)	.0018-.0035 (.045-.090)	.218 (5.55)

Nissan Engines

3.0L & 3.0L TURBO V6

Maxima, Pathfinder, Pickup, 200SX, 300ZX

NOTE: **For engine repair procedures not covered in this article, see ENGINE OVERHAUL PROCEDURES article at beginning of this section.**

ENGINE CODING

ENGINE IDENTIFICATION

Engine type and serial numbers are stamped into a machined pad, located at the right rear of cylinder block, below rear cam cover.

ENGINE IDENTIFICATION CODES

Application	Code
Maxima, 200SX & 300ZX (3.0L)	VG30E
Pathfinder & Pickup (3.0L)	VG30i
300ZX Turbo (3.0L)	VG30ET

ENGINE, MANIFOLDS & CYLINDER HEAD

ENGINE

NOTE: **On engine removal for 300ZX models, support transmission prior to disconnecting engine from transmission. On Maxima models, disconnect drive axles. Remove engine and transaxle as a unit.**

Removal

1) Block wheels and mark hinge locations on hood for installation reference, and remove. In order to bleed off fuel pressure, start engine. Remove fuel pump fuse from fuse block with engine running. After engine stalls, crank engine 2 or 3 times. Turn ignition switch to "OFF" position. Install fuel pump fuse into fuse block.

2) Remove battery. Remove power steering pump and A/C compressor (if equipped) with hoses connected. Drain cooling system and engine crankcase. Remove radiator hoses and air cleaner. Disconnect fuel and canister hoses and label. Remove canister.

3) On automatic transmission/transaxle models, disconnect oil cooler lines. Remove radiator and shroud. Remove lower splash guard (if equipped). Disconnect accelerator linkage. Remove wiring to starter, alternator, oil pressure switch, neutral switch, back-up light switch, EGR solenoid valve, electronic fuel injection harness and connector. Label all wiring for installation.

4) Disconnect throttle valve switch, cold start valve, air regulator, vacuum cutting solenoid (manual transmission/transaxle models), auxiliary cooling fan (if equipped) and distributor. Label all electrical wiring and vacuum lines. On turbocharged models, remove vacuum control modulator and engine oil cooler hoses at oil filter bracket.

5) Disconnect ground cable to engine. Remove high tension coil wire. Disconnect wire for block terminal. Disconnect fuel return and fuel charge. Remove heater and vacuum hoses. Disconnect clutch linkage (if equipped). Disconnect exhaust pipe from exhaust manifold. Install engine hoist and raise engine slightly to remove pressure from motor mounts. Disconnect 4 motor mount retaining nuts and bolts. Remove engine.

Installation

To install, reverse removal procedure. Adjust accelerator control system. Refill fluids before starting engine. Adjust drive belt tension. Run engine for a brief period of time and check for fluid leaks.

INTAKE MANIFOLD

Removal

1) Bleed off fuel pressure. Disconnect battery and drain cooling system by removing drain cocks in cylinder block. Disconnect vacuum and coolant lines attached to intake manifold and label accordingly. Remove throttle body linkage. Remove collector cover and collector. *See Fig. 1.*

Fig. 1: Collector Removal Sequence

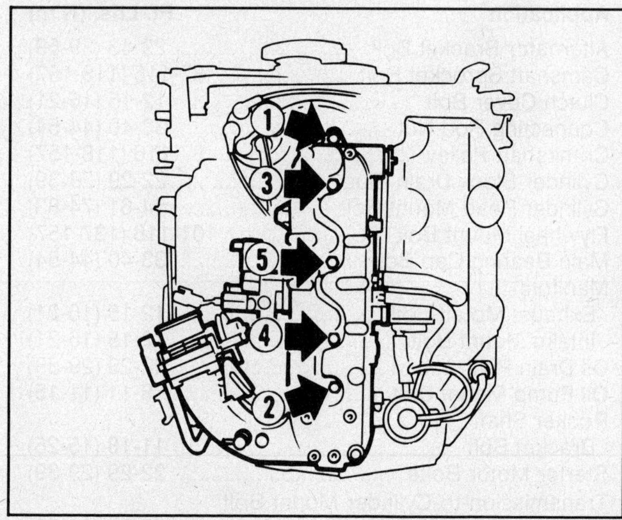

Courtesy of Nissan Motor Co., U.S.A.

2) Disconnect fuel line and components that interfere with removal. Remove intake manifold bolts using removal sequence. *See Fig. 2.* Remove intake manifold and fuel injector fuel lines as an assembly.

Fig. 2: Intake Manifold Removal Sequence

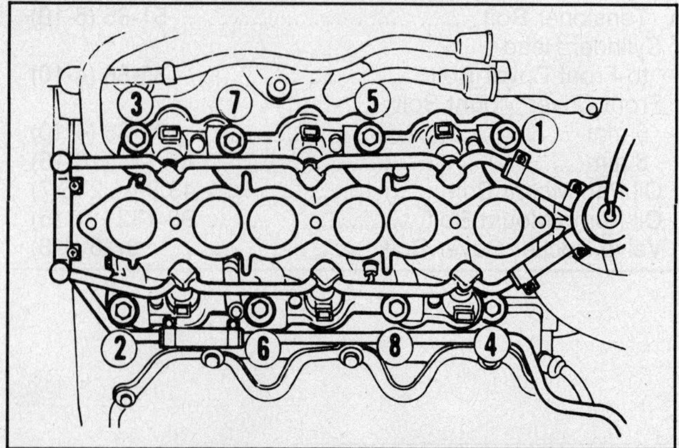

Courtesy of Nissan Motor Co., U.S.A.

Installation

Using new gaskets, install intake mainfold assembly. Tighten bolts in reverse order of removal sequence. *See Fig. 2.* Ensure that all electrical and

3.0L & 3.0L TURBO V6 (Cont.)

vacuum lines are properly connected. To complete installation, reverse removal procedure.

EXHAUST MANIFOLD

Removal

Remove exhaust manifold covers. Disconnect exhaust manifold connecting tube at rear of engine. Disconnect exhaust system from left exhaust manifold using reverse order of tightening sequence. *See Fig. 3*. On turbocharged models, disconnect oil passage tube and remove turbocharger.

Fig. 3: Exhaust Manifold Tightening Sequence

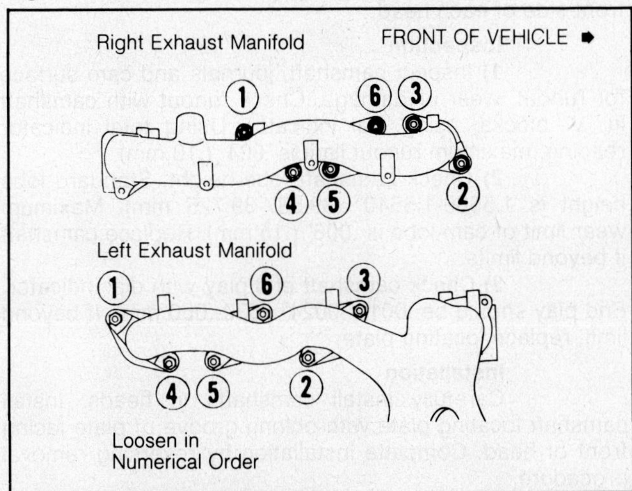

Courtesy of Nissan Motor Co., U.S.A.

Installation

To install, reverse removal procedure. Use new gaskets and follow exhaust manifold tightening sequence. *See Fig. 3*.

CYLINDER HEAD

Removal

1) Release pressure from fuel supply system. Set cylinder No. 1 to TDC of compression stroke. Ensure that timing marks are aligned. Disconnect negative battery cable. Drain cooling system by removing drain cocks in cylinder block.

2) Remove air cleaner. Disconnect upper radiator hose and heater hoses. Remove collector cover and collector. Disconnect vacuum lines and coolant hoses attached to intake manifold and label. Remove air regulator and all hoses as an assembly.

3) Remove spark plug wires at plug end. Remove EGR control valve, vacuum switching valve and hoses as an assembly. Remove fuel lines, vacuum hoses and canister purge hose pressure regulator and label. Remove thermostat housing and attached switches as an assembly.

4) Remove PCV valve hose and EGR tube. On turbocharged models, remove turbocharger. Remove intake manifold and fuel rail as an assembly. Remove drive belts. Remove exhaust manifold covers. Disconnect exhaust manifold connecting tube.

5) Mark timing belt and camshaft pulleys before removal. Remove cylinder head mounting bolts in reverse order of tightening sequence. *See Fig. 4*. Bolts should be loosened in 2 or 3 stages.

6) Remove camshaft pulleys and rear timing cover. Remove timing belt and valve covers. Remove cylinder head with exhaust manifold attached. If necessary, remove exhaust manifold from cylinder head. Remove exhaust manifold bolts in reverse order of tightening sequence. *See Fig. 3*.

Inspection

Check cylinder head for cracks, flaws or damage. Inspect cylinder head and block mating surfaces for warpage. Warpage limit is .004" (.10 mm). If beyond limit, resurface head. Maximum surface grinding limit of head and/or block is .008" (.20 mm). Replace head and/or block if machined or warped beyond service limit.

Installation

NOTE: Cylinder head bolts No. 4, 5, 12 and 13 are longer than other head bolts. See Fig. 4.

Installation

1) Set No. 1 piston at TDC of compression stroke. Crankshaft pulley timing mark should line up with mark on oil pump housing. Knock pin of camshaft should be in 12 o'clock position during installation of cylinder head. Ensure that mating surfaces of cylinder head and block are clean. Install cylinder head and gasket. DO NOT use sealer.

CAUTION: DO NOT rotate crankshaft and camshafts separately or valve-to-piston contact may take place.

2) Oil threads and install head bolts. Tighten head bolts in 5 stages as shown in CYLINDER HEAD

Fig. 4: Cylinder Head Bolt Tightening Sequence

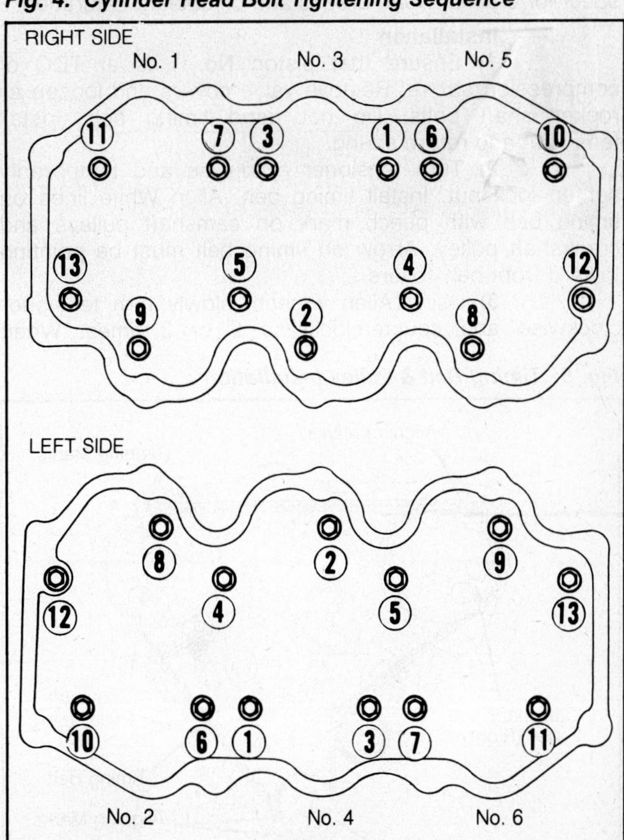

Loosen cylinder head bolts in reverse sequence. Courtesy of Nissan Motor Co., U.S.A.

Nissan Engines

3.0L & 3.0L TURBO V6 (Cont.)

BOLT TIGHTENING SEQUENCE chart. *See Fig. 4*. After assembly is completed, run engine for several minutes and allow to cool down. Recheck head bolt torque.

CYLINDER HEAD BOLT TIGHTENING SEQUENCE

Stages	Ft. Lbs. (N.m)
1st	22 (29)
2nd	43 (59)
3rd	Loosen All Bolts
4th	22 (29)
5th	40-47 (54-64)

CAMSHAFT

TIMING BELT

Removal

1) Release fuel pressure from system. Raise and support vehicle. Remove right wheel and engine side cover. Lower vehicle and drain cooling system. Remove cooling fan duct. Remove engine coolant reservoir. Remove actuator and remove radiator hoses. Do not allow coolant to contact drive belts.

2) Remove front upper and lower belt covers. Remove drive belts and set No. 1 cylinder at TDC of compression stroke. Remove idler bracket of compressor drive belt and crankshaft pulley. Remove timing belt by removing timing belt tensioner and return spring.

Inspection

Visually inspect condition of timing belt. Inspect for cracks, wear, breaks and oil/coolant saturation.

Installation

1) Ensure that piston No. 1 is at TDC of compression stroke. Remove valve covers and loosen all rocker shaft bolts. Do not bend timing belt. Install tensioner and return spring.

2) Turn tensioner clockwise and temporarily tighten lock nut. Install timing belt. Align White lines on timing belt with punch mark on camshaft pulleys and crankshaft pulley. Arrow on timing belt must be pointing toward front belt covers.

3) Using Allen wrench, slowly turn tensioner clockwise and counterclockwise 2 or 3 times. When camshafts and crankshaft marks are aligned, tighten tensioner lock nut. *See Fig. 5*. Ensure that camshaft lobes are correctly positioned. Tighten rocker shaft bolts in 2 stages. To complete installation, reverse removal procedures.

Fig. 5: Timing Belt & Pulley Installation

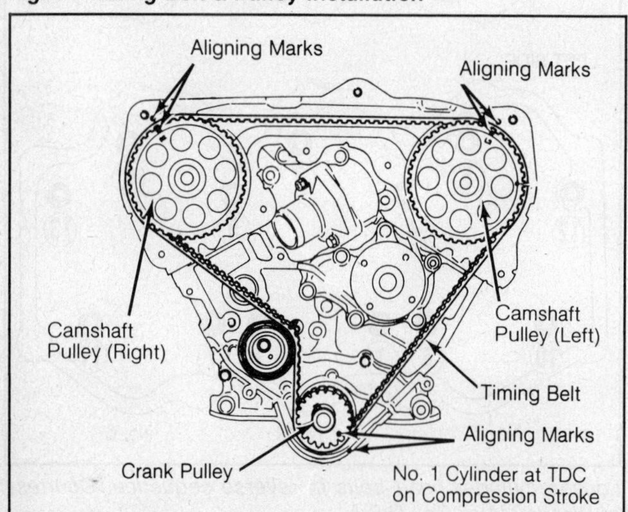

Courtesy of Nissan Motor Co., U.S.A.

CAMSHAFTS

Removal

Remove cylinder heads and remove rocker shafts with rocker arms. Secure hydraulic valve lifters with wire so they will not drop from lifter guide. If lifters are removed from lifter guide, ensure that they installed in original bore. Remove lifter guide. Remove camshaft from front side of each head.

Inspection

1) Inspect camshaft, journals and cam surface for runout, wear or damage. Check runout with camshaft in "V" blocks, using dial indicator. Using total indicator reading, maximum runout limit is .004" (.10 mm).

2) Check camshaft lobe height. Standard lobe height is 1.5566-1.5640" (39.537-39.725 mm). Maximum wear limit of cam lobe is .006" (.15 mm). Replace camshaft if beyond limits.

3) Check camshaft end play with dial indicator. End play should be .0012-.0024" (.030-.060 mm). If beyond limit, replace locating plate.

Installation

Carefully install camshafts in heads. Install camshaft locating plate with oblong groove of plate facing front of head. Complete installation by reversing removal procedure.

CAMSHAFT BEARINGS

Measure inner diameter of camshaft bearings and outer diameter of camshaft journals. Maximum bearing clearance is .006" (.15 mm). If worn or damaged, replace camshaft and/or cylinder head assembly.

VALVES

VALVE ARRANGEMENT

Right Bank – E-I-E-I-E-I (Front-to-rear).
Left Bank – I-E-I-E-I-E (Front-to-rear).

VALVES

Inspect valves for worn, damaged or deformed valve head or stem. If valve head margin is worn to .020" (.50 mm) or less, replace valve. Valve stem end surface grinding limit is .020" (.50 mm). Inspect valve stem keeper grooves for excessive wear. Replace valves as necessary.

VALVE GUIDES

1) Measure clearance between valve stem and guide. Insert valve in guide and move left or right. If tip moves .008" (.2 mm) or more, replace guide.

2) To ease removal, heat cylinder head to 300-320°F (150-160°C). Replace valve guide, using press and guide remover. Force guide from cylinder head from combustion chamber side. With head at room temperature, ream valve guide bore to .4400-.4408" (11.175-11.196 mm) for intake and .4793-4802" (12.175-12.196 mm) for exhaust.

3) Reheat head. Press service guide into cylinder head. Guide should extend from spring side of

3.0L & 3.0L TURBO V6 (Cont.)

cylinder head about .520-.528" (13.2-13.4 mm). Measurement is taken from outer valve spring seat surface of cylinder head. Ream valve guide to .2756-.2763" (7.000-7.018 mm) for intake and .3150-.3154" (8.000-8.011 mm) for exhaust. Regrind valve seat, to restore compatibility with new valve guide.

VALVE SEATS

Check valve seats for pitting at valve contact surface. Replace as necessary. To replace valve seat insert, heat cylinder head to 302-320°F (150-160°C). Remove old valve seat insert from recess in head. Apply metal adhesive to back of new insert and press fit into recess of cylinder head. Valve seat inserts of .020" (.050 mm) are available for service.

VALVE SPRING

Inspection

1) Check valve springs for squareness. Outer valve spring squareness must be less than .087" (2.20 mm) and inner spring must be less than .075" (1.90 mm).

2) Valve spring installed height pressure for inner springs is .984" at 57 lbs. (25 mm at 26 kg). Outer spring installed height pressure is 1.181" at 117 lbs. (30.0 mm at 53.4 kg). Replace spring if not to specification.

NOTE: **Outer valve spring has an uneven pitch design. Install spring with its narrow pitch side toward cylinder head.**

HYDRAULIC VALVE LIFTERS

NOTE: **Do not place hydraulic valve lifters in an upside down position or air will be allowed to enter lifter cavity. Do not disassemble lifters or lose their original installation position.**

Removal

Remove valve covers and remove rocker arms in correct sequence. Remove rocker guides. Wire lifters to lifter guide to prevent damage and loss of original location. Remove lifter guide with lifters and remove camshaft. Ensure that bearings and cam lobes are not.

Installation

To install valve lifters, reverse removal procedures.

PISTONS, PINS & RINGS

PISTON & ROD ASSEMBLY

Removal

1) With cylinder head and oil pan removed, use dial bore gauge to measure cylinder bore for excessive wear, taper and out-of-round. Refer to ENGINE SPECIFICATIONS chart for tolerances.

2) If cylinder bore measures okay, remove connecting rod nuts. Remove rod cap with bearing half. Check top of cylinder bore for ridge. If scraper will not remove carbon build-up, remove using ridge reamer.

3) Push piston and rod assembly out through top of block, ensuring not to damage reusable piston. Rod caps must be kept with their respective pistons. Connecting rod and piston assemblies are not interchangeable.

Inspection

Bend and torsion limit is .004" (.10 mm), per 3.94" (100 mm) of length. Install rod with bearings onto connecting rod journal. Measure rod side thrust clearance. Play at large end should be .0079-.0138" (.20-.35 mm). Replace rod if not to specification.

Installation

1) Wash cylinder walls with hot soapy water and dry with compressed air. Apply oil to rings, piston and cylinder bore. Ensure ring gaps are set 180 degrees apart. Do not set ring gap on thrust side of piston or in line with piston pin.

2) Install piston in cylinder with mark on piston top facing upward and oil supply hole of connecting rod toward right side of block. With piston installed, ensure rod and bearings are seated firmly against crankshaft journal.

FITTING PISTONS & RINGS

1) Visually inspect cylinder block for cracks or flaws. Using bore gauge, measure cylinder bore for excessive wear, out-of-round or taper. Wear limit is .0008" (.020 mm). Out-of-round and taper limit is .0006" (.150 mm). Check for scratches or seize marks. If seize marks are found, hone cylinder.

NOTE: **If either cylinder block or piston is replaced, select piston of same grade as the grade number stamped on cylinder block upper face.**

2) Measure piston-to-cylinder clearance using pull scale and feeler gauge. Extracting force of pull scale should be .4-3.3 lbs. (.2-1.5 kg) using a .0016" (.40 mm) feeler gauge. Measure rings for maximum end gap of .017" (.44 mm). Also measure for max. side clearance of .040" (.0016 mm). Replace pistons and rings if beyond limit.

PISTON PINS

1) Using press and adapters, remove pin from piston and rod. Check pin and bores for signs of sticking, excessive wear or damage. Measure pin bore diameter in piston and outside diameter of pin. Standard pin diameter is .8265-.8267" (20.993-20.998 mm).

2) Determine pin-to-piston clearance. Standard clearance is .0003-.0004" (.008-.010 mm). If wear exceeds specification, replace both piston and pin. Pin must fit into piston with light thumb pressure at room temperature.

3) Piston pin is press fitted in rod. Standard interference fit of piston pin-to-rod is .0009-.0016" (.022-.040 mm). If rod is replaced, ensure new rod is within .25 oz. (7 g) of defective rod.

CRANKSHAFT & ROD BEARINGS

CRANKSHAFT

Removal

1) Drain coolant and remove water pump. Drain oil and remove engine. Mount engine on engine stand. Remove timing belt covers and timing belt. Remove intake manifold. Remove cylinder heads.

2) Remove oil pan and oil pump. Remove flywheel or drive plate. Remove rear plate and cover. Remove pistons. Remove main bearing cap cradle-frame in sequence. *See Fig. 6.* Remove crankshaft.

Nissan Engines

3.0L & 3.0L TURBO V6 (Cont.)

Fig. 6: Main Bearing Cap Cradle-Frame Removal

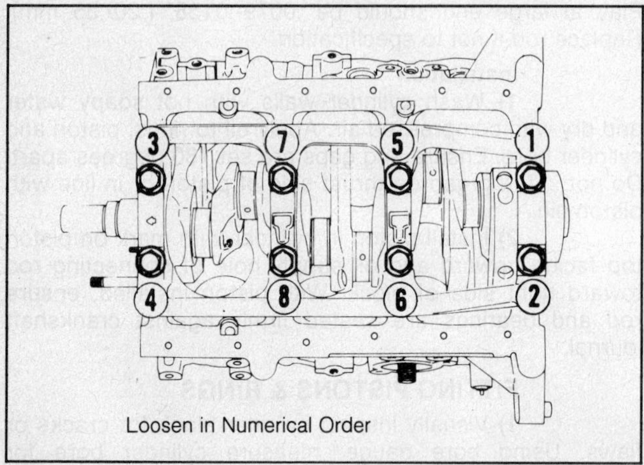

Courtesy of Nissan Motor Co., U.S.A.

Inspection

1) Check crankshaft main journals and connecting rod journals for scoring, wear or cracks. Taper and out-of-round of journals must not exceed .0002" (.006 mm). Check crankshaft for runout by placing on "V" blocks.

2) Set dial indicator pointer at center main journal of crankshaft. If runout exceeds .004" (.10 mm), replace crankshaft. Measure crankshaft journals to determine main bearing and rod bearing clearances.

3) Crankshaft (0 grade) main bearing journals should measure 2.4790-2.4793" (62.967-62.975 mm). Connecting rod journals should measure 1.9670-1.9675" (49.961-49.974 mm).

4) Standard main bearing clearance is .0011-.0022" (.028-.055 mm). Maximum main bearing clearance is .0035" (.090 mm). Standard connecting rod clearance is .0004-.0020" (.010-.052 mm). Connecting rod maximum clearance is .0035" (.090 mm).

Installation

1) Install main bearing halves into engine block. Ensure bearings are on correct journal and that all oil feed holes are clear. Journal No. 4 requires thrust bearing. Upper bearing halves have oil grooves and are not interchangeable with lower bearing halves. Apply oil to main bearing surface. Install crankshaft.

2) Tighten main bearing cap cradle-frame in 2 or 3 stages. Start at center bearing and work outward. *See Fig. 6*. Ensure crankshaft rotates smoothly. Check crankshaft end play. *See Fig. 7*. End play limit is .012" (.30 mm). If not within specification, replace No. 4 thrust bearing.

3) Install rear end plate and flywheel. Install piston and rod assemblies. Apply sealer to oil pan gasket. Install oil pan and remaining components in reverse order of removal procedure.

Fig. 7: Checking Crankshaft End Play

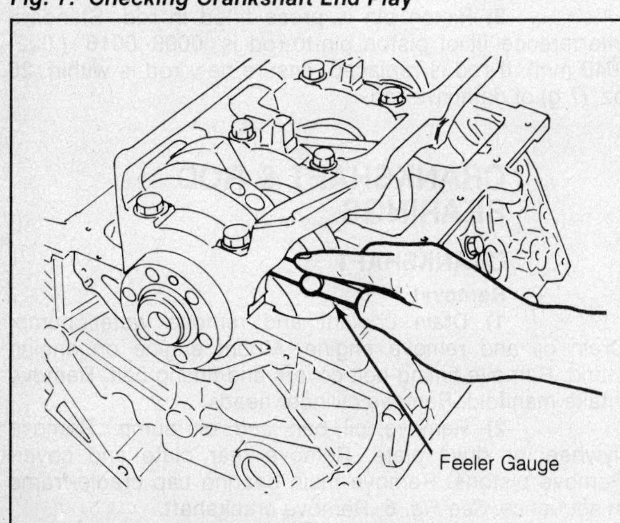

Courtesy of Nissan Motor Co., U.S.A.

CRANKSHAFT MAIN BEARINGS

1) Check bearings for scoring or wear. Replace if damaged. Clean oil from crankshaft. Check clearance using Plastigage method. Maximum main bearing clearance is .0035" (.090 mm). If not to specification, replace bearings.

2) If all crankshaft main bearings are replaced, it will be necessary to select bearing thickness. For example, if cylinder block main web grade number is one and crankshaft journal grade number is 2, main bearing grade number will be 3. *See Fig. 8* and CRANKSHAFT MAIN BEARING SPECIFICATIONS chart.

Fig. 8: Cylinder Block & Crankshaft Grade Numbers

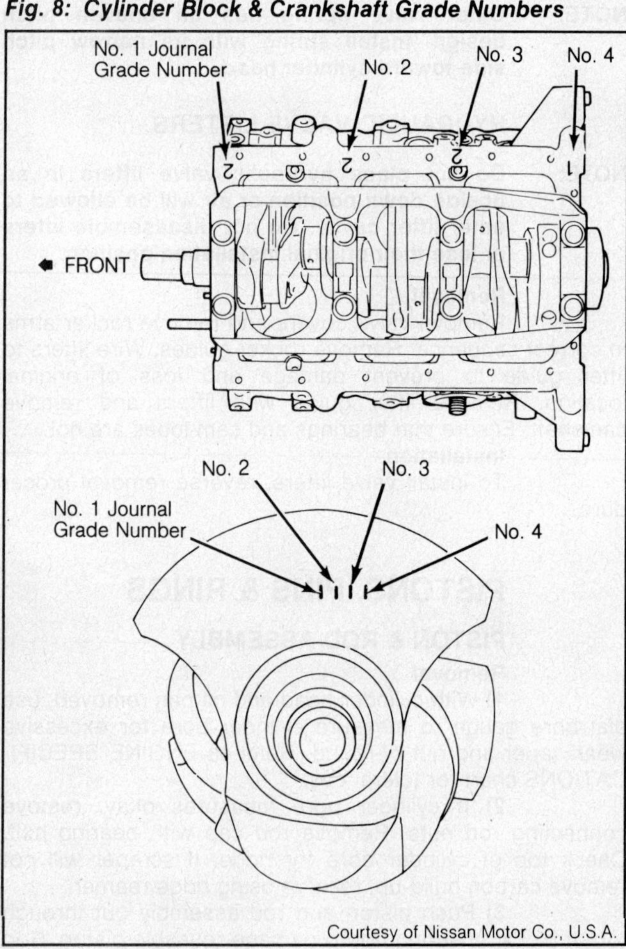

Nissan Engines

3.0L & 3.0L TURBO V6 (Cont.)

CRANKSHAFT MAIN BEARING SPECIFICATIONS

Grade No.	Thickness In. (mm)	ID Color
0	.0715-.0717 (1.817-1.821)	White
1	.0717-.0719 (1.821-1.825)	Brown
2	.0719-.0720 (1.825-1.829)	Green
3	.0720-.0722 (1.829-1.833)	Yellow
4	.0722-.0723 (1.833-1.837)	Blue

CONNECTING ROD BEARINGS

Check connecting rod bearing clearance using Plastigage method. Tighten connecting rod caps to 33-40 ft. lbs. (45-54 N.m). Maximum rod bearing clearance is .0035" (.090 mm). If not within specifications, replace bearings. Bearings are available in undersizes of .003" (.08 mm), .005" (.12 mm) and .010" (.25 mm).

ENGINE OILING

ENGINE OILING SYSTEM

Oil drawn from oil pan passes through a screen to oil pump. Oil is delivered to full-flow filter and main oil gallery. Main oil gallery supplies oil to crankshaft main bearings and drilled passages in crankshaft.

Passages from main gallery to lifter guides supply oil to camshaft, lifters and rocker arms. The turbocharger receives oil from main oil gallery.

CRANKCASE CAPACITY

Crankcase oil capacity is 4.25 qts. (4.0L) with filter change.

OIL FILTER

A full-flow oil filter with disposable cartridge is used.

OIL PRESSURE

Oil pressure should be 43 psi (3.0 kg/cm²) at 2000 RPM, depending upon engine condition and oil viscosity.

OIL PUMP

Removal & Installation

1) Drain engine oil. Remove oil pan and remove oil pump assembly. To disassemble pump, remove pump cover and gasket.

2) Remove pump gears from pump body. Remove regulator cap, valve and spring. Clean components with solvent. Inspect for wear or damage. Check OIL PUMP SPECIFICATIONS table and ensure clearances are to specification.

3) If not within specification, replace gear set or entire pump assembly. Replace gasket, "O" ring and seal. Assemble pump in reverse order of disassembly. Fill pump housing with oil before installing to front cover.

OIL PUMP SPECIFICATIONS

Application	Clearance In. (mm)
Body-to-Outer Gear	.0043-.0079 (.11-.20)
Inner Gear-to-Crescent	.0047-.0091 (.12-.23)
Outer Gear-to-Crescent	.0083-.0126 (.21-.32)
Housing-to-Inner Gear	.0020-.0035 (.05-.09)
Housing-to-Outer Gear	.0020-.0043 (.05-.11)

ENGINE COOLING

WATER PUMP

Removal & Installation

Drain cooling system and remove radiator shroud. Remove fan belts, fan and pulley. Remove mounting bolts and pump from front cover. To install, reverse removal procedure. Pressure check system for leaks after installation. Pressurization limit is 23 psi (1.6 kg/cm²).

NOTE: **For further information on cooling systems, see ENGINE COOLING section.**

TIGHTENING SPECIFICATIONS

Application	Ft. Lbs. (N.m)
Camshaft Pulley Bolt	58-65 (78-88)
Camshaft Locating Plate	58-65 (78-88)
Connecting Rod Nut	33-40 (44-54)
Crankshaft Pulley Bolt	90-98 (123-132)
Cylinder Head Bolt	40-47 (54-64)
Exhaust Connecting Tube	16-20 (22-27)
Exhaust Manifold Bolt	13-16 (18-22)
Flywheel Mount Bolt	72-80 (98-108)
Intake Manifold Bolt	12-14 (16-20)
Intake Manifold Nut	17-20 (24-27)
Main Bearing Cap Bolt	67-74 (90-100)
Oxygen Sensor (Non Turbo)	30-37 (40-50)
Oxygen Sensor (Turbo)	13-17 (18-24)
Timing Belt Tensioner Bolt	32-42 (43-58)
Turbocharger Bolt	33-40 (44-54)
Turbo Oil Feed Tube Bolt	11-14 (15-20)
Water Pump Bolt	12-15 (16-21)
	INCH Lbs. (N.m)
Oil Pan Bolt	43-61 (5-7)
Oil Pump Cover Bolt	35-44 (4-5)
Oil Pump-to-Front Cover Bolt	106-142 (12-16)
Rear Oil Seal Retainer Bolt	53 (6)
Timing Belt Cover	27-44 (3-5)
Turbo Oil Return Tube	89-106 (10-12)

Nissan Engines

3.0L & 3.0L TURBO V6 (Cont.)

ENGINE SPECIFICATIONS

GENERAL SPECIFICATIONS

Year	DISPLACEMENT Cu. In.	DISPLACEMENT Liters	Fuel System	HP@RPM	Torque Ft. Lbs.@RPM	Compr. Ratio	BORE In.	BORE mm	STROKE In.	STROKE mm
1987										
Pickup & Pathfinder										
VG30i	180.6	3.0	Fuel Inj.	140 @ 5200	157 @ 3600	9:1	3.43	87	3.27	83
Maxima										
VG30E	180.6	3.0	Fuel Inj.	152 @ 5200	167 @ 3600	9:1	3.43	87	3.27	83
200SX										
VG30E	180.6	3.0	Fuel Inj.	160 @ 5200	173 @ 4000	9:1	3.43	87	3.27	83
300ZX										
VG30E	180.6	3.0	Fuel Inj.	160 @ 5200	173 @ 4000	9:1	3.43	87	3.27	83
VG30ET	180.6	3.0	Fuel Inj.	200 @ 5200	227 @ 3600	7.8:1	3.43	87	3.27	83

VALVES

Engine Size & Valve	Head Diam. In. (mm)	Face Angle	Seat Angle	Seat Width In. (mm)	Stem Diameter In. (mm)	Stem Clearance In. (mm)	Valve Lift In. (mm)
3.0L							
Intake	1.65 (42.0)	45.5°	45°	[1] .070 (1.75)	.2742-.2748 (6.965-6.980)	.0008-.0021 (.020-.053)	.....
Exhaust	1.38 (35.0)	45.5°	45°	.067 (1.70)	.3136-.3138 (7.965-7.970)	[2] .0016-.0029 (.040-.073)	.....

[1] - Pathfinder and Pickup is .083" (2.10 mm).
[2] - Pathfinder and Pickup is .0012-.0018" (.030-.046 mm).

PISTONS, PINS & RINGS

Engine	PISTONS Clearance In. (mm)	PINS Piston Fit In. (mm)	PINS Rod Fit In. (mm)	RINGS Ring No.	RINGS End Gap In. (mm)	RINGS Side Clearance In. (mm)
3.0L	.0010-.0018 (.025-.046)	.0003-.0004 (.008-.010)	[1] .0009-.0016 (.022-.040)	No. 1	[2] .008-.017 (.20-.44)	.0016-.0029 (.040-.073)
				No. 2	.007-.017 (.18-.44)	.0012-.0025 (.030-.063)
				Oil	.008-.030 (.20-.76)	[3] .0006-.0075 (.015-.190)

[1] - Interference fit.
[2] - Pathfinder and Pickup is .008-.013" (.21-.34 mm).
[3] - Pathfinder and Pickup is .006-.0073" (.015-.185 mm).

CRANKSHAFT MAIN & CONNECTING ROD BEARINGS

Engine	MAIN BEARINGS Journal Diam. In. (mm)	MAIN BEARINGS Clearance In. (mm)	MAIN BEARINGS Thrust Bearing	MAIN BEARINGS Crankshaft End Play In. (mm)	CONNECTING ROD BEARINGS Journal Diam. In. (mm)	CONNECTING ROD BEARINGS Clearance In. (mm)	CONNECTING ROD BEARINGS Side Play In. (mm)
3.0L	2.4790-2.4793 [1] (62.967-62.975)	.0011-.0022 (.028-.055)	End No. 4	.002-.0067 (.05-.17)	1.9670-1.9675 (49.961-49.974)	.0004-.0020 (.010-.052)	.008-.014 (.20-.35)

[1] – Grade No. 0 is shown. Grade No. 1 is 2.4787-2.4790" (62.959-62.967 mm) and Grade No. 2 is 2.4784-2.4787" (62.951-62.959 mm).

Nissan Engines

3.0L & 3.0L TURBO V6 (Cont.)

ENGINE SPECIFICATIONS (Cont.)

VALVE SPRINGS

Engine	Free Length In. (mm)	PRESSURE Lbs. @ In. (Kg @ mm)	
		Valve Closed	Valve Open
3.0L			
Inner	1.736 (44.10)	57.3 @ .984 (26 @ 25.0)	.....
Outer	2.016 (51.20)	117.7 @ 1.181 (53. @ 30.0)	.....

VALVE TIMING

Engine	INTAKE		EXHAUST	
	Open (BTDC)	Close (ABDC)	Open (BBDC)	Close (ATDC)
3.0L	[1] 20°	[1] 52°	62°	10°

[1] - Pathfinder, Pickup and 200SX is 16° (BTDC) and 56° (ABDC).

CAMSHAFT

Engine	Journal Diam. In. (mm)	Clearance In. (mm)	Lobe Lift In. (mm)
3.0L	1.8472-1.8480 (46.920-46.940)	[1] .0024-.0041 (.060-.105)	.....

[1] - 200SX is .0018-.0035" (.045-.090 mm).

Peugeot Engines

2.0L 4-CYLINDER

ENGINE CODING

ENGINE IDENTIFICATION

Vehicle Identification Number (VIN) is attached to top of radiator support, above center of grille. The sixth character identifies the engine and the tenth character identifies model year. Engine Identification Number (EIN) is stamped on camshaft tunnel boss on left side of block, near starter.

ENGINE IDENTIFICATION CODES

Application	Engine Model	Engine VIN Code
2.0L	XN6	1

ENGINE, MANIFOLDS & CYLINDER HEAD

ENGINE

Removal

1) Remove hood, battery and fan shroud. Drain radiator. Remove upper and lower hoses. Remove electrical lead from cooling fan switch. Remove radiator. Remove rubber duct hose at throttle body.

2) Remove fuel supply return hoses and cold start injector hose. Remove PCV hose and electrical connectors from cold start injector and fuel distributor. Remove fuel hoses and electrical connector from control pressure regulator.

3) Remove fuel injectors, mixture regulator and air filter. Remove A/C compressor and A/C hose clamp near alternator (if equipped). Disconnect accelerator cable and electrical harness near brake master cylinder.

4) Remove diagnostic plug for TDC sensor, located near ignition coil. Remove high tension lead from coil. Remove vacuum hoses from charcoal canister.

5) Remove heater hose near power steering reservoir. Remove oxygen sensor (Lambda) wire near vacuum switches. Disconnect air injection hose to catalytic converter. Remove vacuum switches support and 3-wire electrical connector nearby. Install engine sling assembly.

Fig. 1: Positioning Support Plate for Torque Converter During Engine Removal

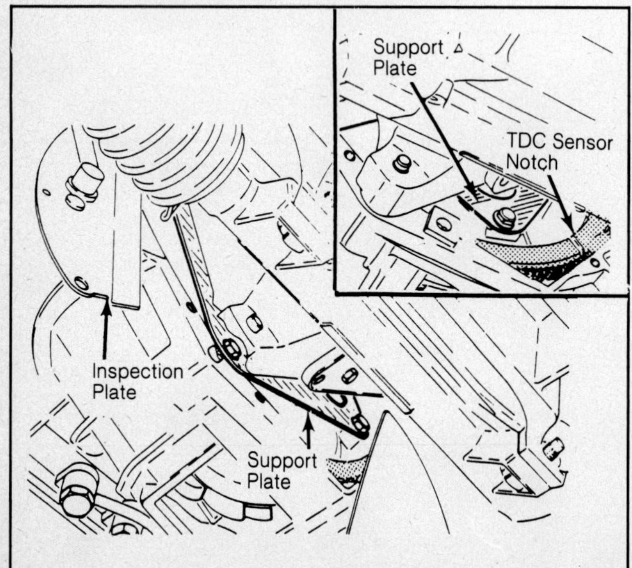

Courtesy of Peugeot Motor of America, Inc.

6) Remove starter and clutch housing bolts. Remove left and right engine mounts. Remove 3 power steering pump bolts and set pump aside. Remove exhaust header pipe.

7) Remove inspection plates from clutch housing. On vehicles with automatic transmission, remove inspection plate without altering TDC sensor adjustment as follows: Position torque converter support plate. *See Fig. 1.* Mark TDC sensor notch in reference to support plate. Support torque converter with Clamp (8.0315-A).

8) Remove A/C condenser and set aside. Leave hoses connected. Remove receiver-drier and set aside. Lift engine with engine sling assembly until top of bellhousing contacts lower firewall. *See Fig. 2.*

Fig. 2: Removing Engine from Vehicle

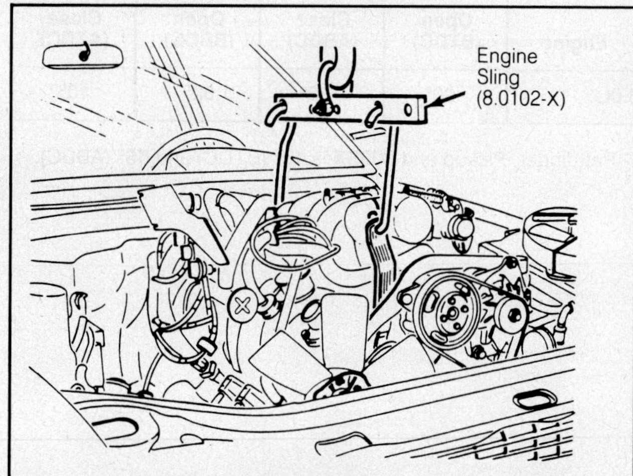

Courtesy of Peugeot Motor of America, Inc.

9) Install transmission support. Disengage engine from transmission and lift engine carefully out of engine compartment. Check for electrical leads, cables, hoses or pipes that have not been detached from engine.

Installation

1) To install engine, reverse removal procedure. On vehicles with automatic transmissions, lubricate torque converter centering nipple with Calysol Grease (F 3015).

2) Position TDC sensor notch and align reference marks made during removal. Coat 4 torque converter bolts with Loctite and tighten. Use ring gear Locking Pawl (8.0110-J) when tightening bolts.

3) On vehicles with manual transmissions, lightly lubricate splines, front and mainshaft pilot bushings with assembly lube. Place gearshift lever in gear. Tighten engine mount-to-crossmember bolts and engine-to-clutch housing bolts.

4) If TDC sensor is new, adjust by bringing 3 nipples in contact. If reusing TDC sensor, deburr 3 nipples so gap of .067" (1.7 mm) exists between sensor and ring gear.

5) Refill cooling system, engine crankcase and automatic transmission. Check power steering fluid.

6) To adjust accelerator cable, depress accelerator pedal against its stop, placing a .20" (5 mm) spacer between pedal and stop (full throttle position). Connect cable to throttle drum.

7) Rotate drum to full throttle position. Exert slight pull on cable housing stop to place control under slight load. Install clip to obtain minimum gap between clip and common manifold.

8) To adjust kickdown cable, place throttle plate in idle position. Extend cable to obtain a maximum play of .02" (.5 mm) between cable housing stop and cable travel limiter. Tighten cable on drum.

CYLINDER HEAD & MANIFOLDS

Removal

1) Drain cooling system including cylinder block. Disconnect battery. Remove exhaust header pipe and oxygen sensor. Remove mounting brackets for intake manifold plenum and runners.

2) Pull intake manifold plenum off runners. Remove distributor cap, injectors, and diagnostic plug bracket. Disconnect electrical connector near ignition coil and remove high tension lead from coil. Remove all clamps and wire ties from vicinity of ignition coil. Remove vacuum hoses from charcoal canister.

3) Remove air pump outlet hose at pump. Remove upper wire and lower connector from thermo-time switch. Remove sliding bolt from air pump-to-alternator bracket. Remove upper and lower radiator hoses. Remove heater hose and power steering reservoir.

4) Remove radiator, fan and fan shroud. Remove water pump belt from pulley. Remove thermostatic air slide valve bracket. Remove vacuum hoses, coolant hoses, and thermostatic wire from valve. Remove 2 large hoses from diverter valve. Remove bracket from valve. Remove air injection assembly.

5) Remove heater hose near dipstick and remove auxiliary air device. Remove remaining electrical connectors from switches or sensors mounted in cylinder head. Remove rocker arm oil feed pipe. Disconnect all vacuum hoses remaining on intake manifold side of engine.

6) Remove spark plug wire brackets and wires. Remove valve cover. Remove cooling fan brush holder. Remove sealing rings from spark plug tubes. Remove rocker arm assembly and push rods.

7) Use prying handles to break cylinder head loose. Install Cylinder Liner Retainers (8.0132) to prevent liners from moving.

Inspection

1) Plug passages in cylinder block for valve lifters and oil return. Clean and scrape cylinder block gasket surface. Run a tap in cylinder block bolt holes.

2) Check liner protrusion above block. Liner protrusion should be .0028-.0055" (.070-.140 mm) at engine centerline. No liner should protrude more than .0015" (.040 mm) above adjacent liner.

3) Clean cylinder head gasket surface and cylinder head bolts. Check for cylinder head warpage. Maximum allowable warpage is .004" (.10 mm).

4) Check cylinder head thickness. Original thickness is 3.636-3.648" (92.35-92.65 mm), with minimum permissable thickness being 3.616" (91.85 mm). If cylinder head must be surfaced, check thickness before and after surfacing to be sure thickness is within tolerances.

5) Clean and check valve lifters, using caution not to mix them. DO NOT scrape carbon off piston tops, as liner damage could result.

Installation

1) Using 2 Locating Guides (8.-115-BZ), install cylinder head. Install new head gasket with "DESSUS", "ALTO" or "TOP" facing up (toward cylinder head).

2) Install cylinder head and rocker arm assembly. Lightly tighten cylinder head bolts (with flat washers), using assembly lube on threads. Lightly tighten rocker shaft nuts. Remove 2 head guides. Install last 2 head bolts.

NOTE: Do not get oil in cylinder head bolt holes, as this could cause hydraulic blockage and prevent proper tightening.

3) Tighten head bolts to 36 ft. lbs. (49 N.m) and rocker shaft nuts to 11 ft. lbs. (15 N.m). *See Fig. 3.* Place Angular Head Torque Wrench (8.0129) on 2 center bolts (No. 1 and 2). Completely loosen No. 1 bolt and retighten to 14 ft. lbs. (20 N.m). Keep wrench in place and maintain tension on torque wrench.

Fig. 3: Cylinder Head Bolt Tightening Sequence

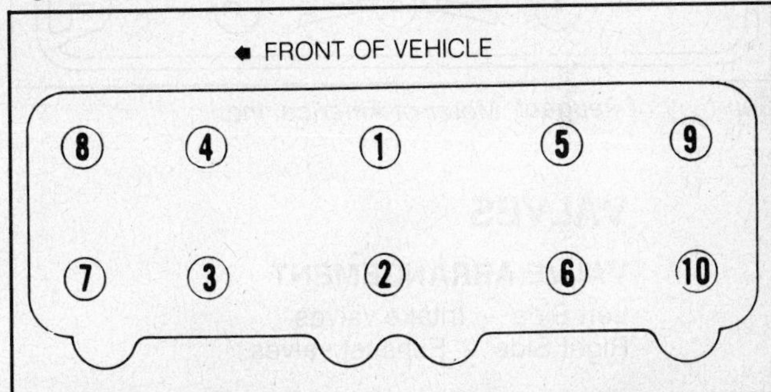

Head bolts must be retorqued after 1000-1500 miles. Courtesy of Peugeot Motor of America, Inc.

4) Position pointer on wrench at "0" notch by moving spring loop. Continue tightening until pointer lines up with "90" notch. Repeat entire procedure with No. 2 bolt. Then move wrench and complete tightening procedure in proper sequence.

5) If there is doubt concerning torque of any one bolt, loosen it completely and repeat all tightening procedures for that one head bolt. To install remaining components, reverse removal procedure. Refill cooling system and adjust valves.

6) Adjust intake valve clearance to .004" (.10 mm) and exhaust valves to .010" (.25 mm). After 1000-1500 miles, retorque cylinder head bolts (after engine has cooled for 6 hours), and adjust valve clearances to specification. See VALVE CLEARANCE ADJUSTMENT.

7) Adjust air pump and alternator belt tension at idler pulley. Loosen both idler pulley mounting bolts. Tighten nut directly above idler pulley to 36 ft. lbs. (49 N.m).

8) Tighten mounting bolts. Turn crankshaft one full turn to align belt on idler pulley. Loosen mounting bolts. Tighten idler pulley nut to 58 ft. lbs. (79 N.m). Retighten mounting bolts.

SPARK PLUG TUBE REPLACEMENT

Removal

With cylinder head supported, screw in spark plugs to prevent dirt from falling into cylinder. Remove tubes using mallet or extractor.

Peugeot Engines

2.0L 4-CYLINDER (Cont.)

NOTE: If spark plug tubes are removed, new tubes MUST be installed.

Installation

To install tubes, coat with sealing compound and insert so plug caps are facing correct position. *See Fig. 4*. When tube is fully seated, it will protrude 2.835" (72 mm) upward from cylinder head.

Fig. 4: Position of Spark Plug Tubes for Installation

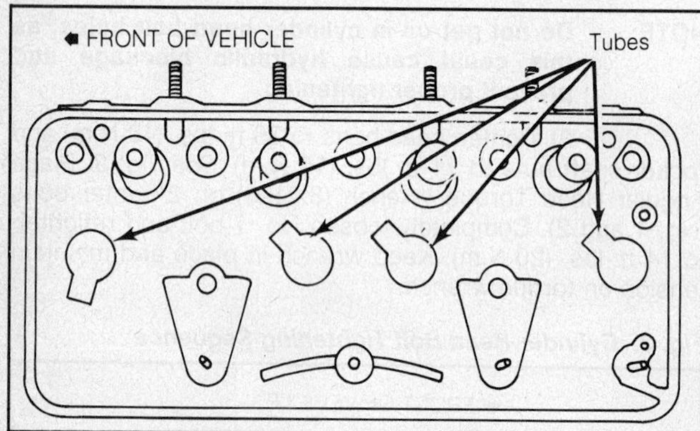

Courtesy of Peugeot Motor of America, Inc.

VALVES

VALVE ARRANGEMENT

Left Side – Intake valves.
Right Side – Exhaust valves.

NOTE: Cylinders and valves are numbered with No. 1 cylinder at flywheel end of engine.

VALVE SPRING REPLACEMENT

Intake Valve

1) Turn crankshaft in direction of engine rotation and position where exhaust valve just begins to open. Slide rocker arm off intake valve, then bring piston to TDC on compression stroke.

2) Using valve spring compressor, compress spring and remove keepers, spring retainer and spring.

Fig. 5: Removing Valve Spring with Valve Held in Place

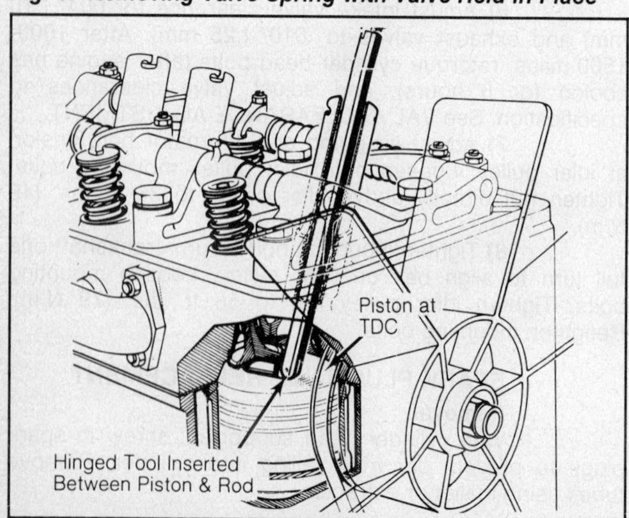

Courtesy of Peugeot Motor of America, Inc.

Exhaust Valve

1) Remove spark plug from cylinder. Rotate crankshaft in direction of engine rotation and bring intake valve to fully closed position. Slide rocker arm off exhaust valve.

2) Insert Hinge (0-0136) into spark plug hole and bring piston to TDC without forcing as tool is between piston and valve. Using spring compressor, compress spring and remove keepers, spring retainer and spring.

VALVE CLEARANCE ADJUSTMENT

NOTE: Engine must be allowed to cool at least 6 hours before adjusting valves. Adjust valves in firing order sequence (1-3-4-2). No. 1 cylinder is on flywheel end of engine.

1) Rotate engine until No. 1 exhaust valve is fully opened, then adjust No. 3 intake valve and No. 4 exhaust valve.

2) Rotate crankshaft 1/2 turn (180 degrees) until No. 3 exhaust valve is fully opened and adjust corresponding valves. See VALVE ADJUSTMENT SEQUENCE table. Continue procedure until all valves have been adjusted.

VALVE ADJUSTMENT SEQUENCE

Valve Open	Adjust Valves
E 1	I 3 & E 4
E 3	I 4 & E 2
E 4	I 2 & E 1
E 2	I 1 & E 3

VALVE CLEARANCE SPECIFICATIONS

Application	Intake In. (mm)	Exhaust In. (mm)
All Models	.004 (.10)	.010 (.25)

CAMSHAFT

ENGINE FRONT COVER & OIL SEAL

Removal

1) Drain engine oil and remove oil sump pan (if necessary). Remove radiator and fan belt. Remove crankshaft pulley retaining bolt and pulley. Remove idler pulley assembly.

2) Unscrew front cover retaining bolts. Remove cover. Using a seal driver, drive out old seal from front cover.

Installation

Using a seal driver, drive new oil seal into front cover. Install new gasket on front cover. Install front cover. To complete installation, reverse removal procedure.

TIMING CHAIN

Removal

1) Remove radiator, fan belt and spark plugs. Remove crankshaft pulley and timing chain cover. Disengage chain tensioner by removing plug and turning Allen bolt .118" (3.0 mm) clockwise.

2) Position camshaft to avoid any possible contact of valves and pistons when rotating crankshaft

2.0L 4-CYLINDER (Cont.)

with timing chain removed. *See Fig. 6*. Remove camshaft sprocket, timing chain, crankshaft sprocket, and Woodruff key.

Fig. 6: Proper Alignment of Camshaft & Crankshaft for Removing Timing Chain

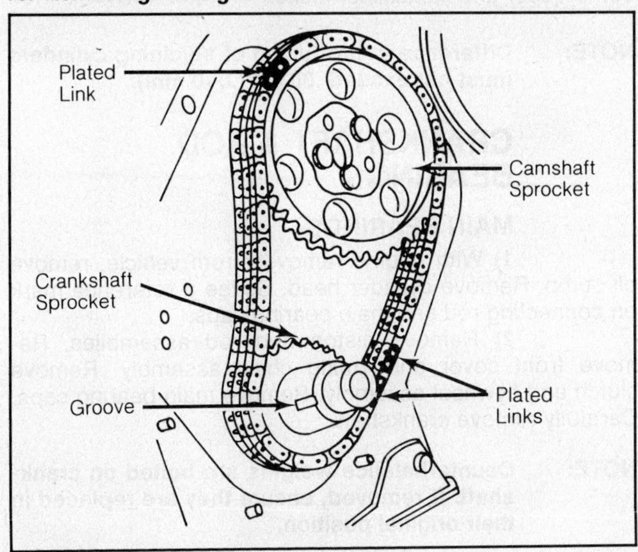

Courtesy of Peugeot Motor of America, Inc.

Installation

1) Hold crankshaft in original position and install Woodruff key and sprocket. Position camshaft and crankshaft. *See Fig. 7*.

2) Install timing chain first on camshaft sprocket, then on crankshaft sprocket. Ensure timing marks are in correct alignment. Fit camshaft with a new washer and tighten bolts. Bend up tabs.

Fig. 7: Proper Alignment of Camshaft & Crankshaft

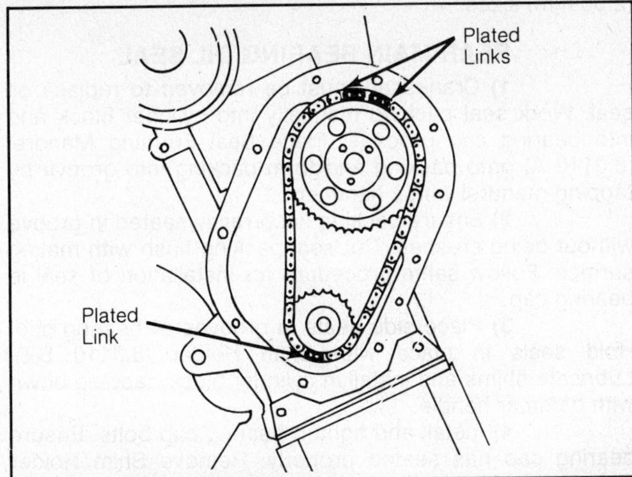

Courtesy of Peugeot Motor of America, Inc.

3) Engage chain tensioner (Renold) by adjusting Allen wrench clockwise. Install a new tab washer on plug and bend tab. On Sedis-style tensioner, turn pawl to the right.

NOTE: **Renold and Sedis chain tensioners are interchangeable as complete units only.**

4) Install thrust washers (if required) and timing chain cover. Install timing chain cover on 2 centering pins, being careful to protect seal. Install crankshaft pulley after cover bolts are tightened.

PISTONS, PINS & RINGS

PISTON & ROD ASSEMBLY

Removal

1) With engine removed and mounted on engine stand, remove intake and exhaust manifolds. Remove all auxiliary equipment, including alternator, air pump, and fuel pump. *See Fig. 8*.

2) Remove cylinder head as previously described. Remove oil pan and oil pump. Remove bearing caps, keeping them in original order. Remove pistons and connecting rods. Attach connecting rods to matching cap and mark rod assemblies 1-4.

Fig. 8: Cylinder Block & Cylinder Head Assembly

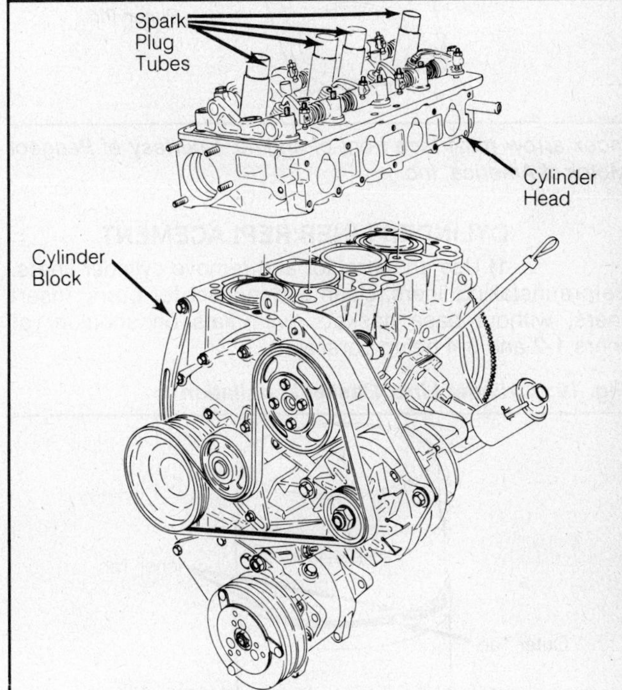

Courtesy of Peugeot Motor of America, Inc.

Installation

1) Install piston ring compressor on piston. Insert piston and rod assembly. Index arrow must face front of engine.

2) Push piston down cylinder and guide connecting rod with bearing over crankshaft journal. Install bearing cap and tighten.

NOTE: **Marks on rods and caps must be on same side.**

PISTON PIN REPLACEMENT

Remove snap rings and piston pin. Fit piston to rod with index mark "AV" at right angle to oil thrower hole so it will face front of engine. If necessary, heat piston in boiling water to insert pin. Install snap rings.

NOTE: **The "AV" mark on piston top must face front of engine. Pistons and liners must be matched by letter code. Number on top of**

Peugeot Engines

2.0L 4-CYLINDER (Cont.)

piston refers to piston pin code (1 - Blue, 2 - White, and 3 - Red).

Fig. 9: Piston & Rod Assembly with Index Marks & Codes

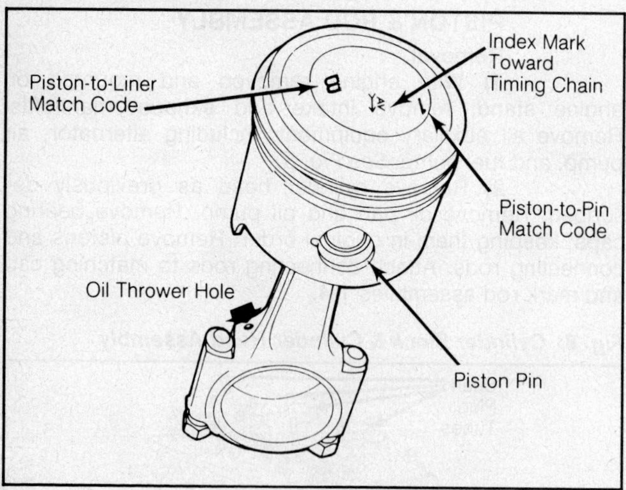

Index arrow must face front of engine. Courtesy of Peugeot Motor of America, Inc.

CYLINDER LINER REPLACEMENT

1) Use an extractor and remove cylinder liners. Before installing liners, clean and inspect for burrs. Insert liners, without base gaskets, with flats on shoulder of liners 1-2 and 3-4 being parallel.

Fig. 10: Cylinder Liner Gasket Installation

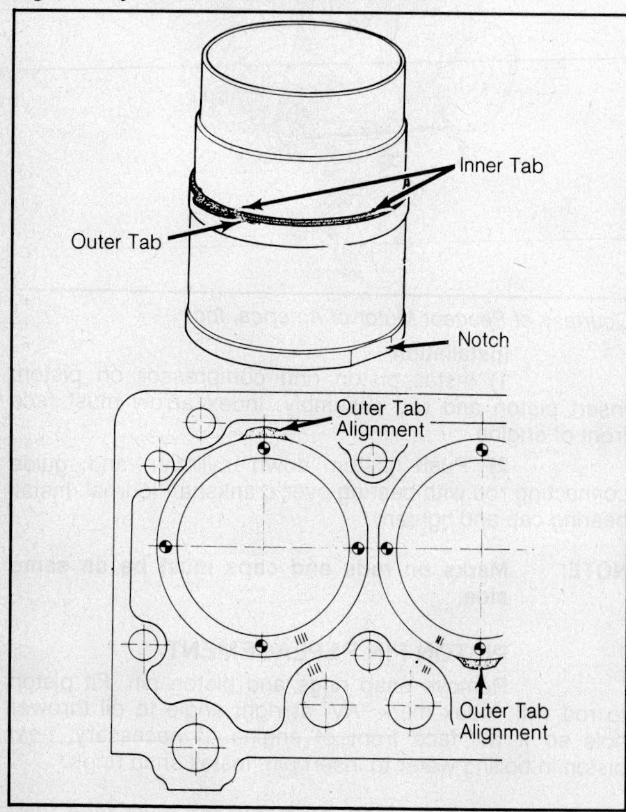

Gaskets are available in 4 different sizes. Courtesy of Peugeot Motor of America, Inc.

4) Fit gasket on liner. Engage gasket inner tabs in liner grooves. *See Fig. 10*. Position tab with reference mark at right angles to flat. Position liners with outer tabs in position. Install liner compressor to block. Seat liners and ensure protrusion is correct. Remove compressor and install liner locks.

NOTE: **Difference in protrusion of adjoining cylinders must not exceed .0015" (.040 mm).**

CRANKSHAFT & ROD BEARINGS

MAIN BEARINGS

1) With engine removed from vehicle, remove oil sump. Remove cylinder head. Scribe a reference mark on connecting rod and main bearing caps.

2) Remove piston and rod assemblies. Remove front cover and timing chain assembly. Remove clutch and flywheel assembly. Remove main bearing caps. Carefully remove crankshaft.

NOTE: **Counterbalance weights are bolted on crankshaft. If removed, ensure they are replaced in their original position.**

3) Use Plastigage method to measure main bearing clearances. Measure main bearing clearances one at a time.

THRUST BEARING WASHERS

Crankshaft thrust bearing washers are located at rear main bearing. Install crankshaft with original thickness thrust bearing washers and without rear main seal. Check end play. End play must not exceed .008" (.20 mm). If specification is exceeded, oversize thrust washers are available in .094" (2.40 mm), .096" (2.45 mm), and .098" (2.50 mm) sizes.

REAR MAIN BEARING OIL SEAL

1) Crankshaft must be removed to replace oil seal. Work seal packing manually into cylinder block and into bearing cap grooves. Place Seal Forming Mandrel (8.0110 A) onto packing and form packing into groove by tapping mandrel with a hammer.

2) Ensure packing is correctly seated in groove without being crushed. Cut seal packing flush with mating surface. Follow same procedure for installation of seal in bearing cap.

3) Place side seals in grooves of bearing cap. Hold seals in place with Shim Holder (8.0110 BZ). Lubricate shims and install in cylinder block, tapping down with hammer handle.

4) Install and tighten bearing cap bolts. Ensure bearing cap has seated properly. Remove Shim Holder (8.0110 BZ). Trim side seals with knife so they protrude .020" (.50 mm) above lower crankcase mating surface. Use Gauge (8.0110 D) for measurement.

ENGINE OILING

ENGINE OILING SYSTEM

A high output, gear-type oil pump is mounted to engine block lower surface and is operated by camshaft.

Peugeot Engines

2.0L 4-CYLINDER (Cont.)

NOTE: Do not alter piston/liner pairings.

2) Place a dial gauge and support on block face. Synchronize dial at "0" and "5". Check each liner at 4 different points, noting the highest reading. Maximum allowable difference between 2 opposite points must be less than .003" (.07 mm). If specification is exceeded, it may be necessary to change position of liners.

3) Select a base gasket for each liner which will give a protrusion of about .005" (.12 mm). Gaskets are available in 4 different sizes. Use only one gasket on each liner.

CRANKCASE CAPACITY

Crankcase capacity is 4.2 qts. (3.9L).

OIL FILTER

Oil filter is a full-flow cartridge type.

NORMAL OIL PRESSURE

Normal oil pressure is 28-51 psi (2-3.6 kg/cm²) at idle; 44-67 psi (3-4.7 kg/cm²) at 4000 RPM.

OIL PUMP

Removal & Installation

Remove oil pan. Turn engine to TDC on No. 1 cylinder. Remove oil pump. To install, reverse removal procedure. Check ignition timing.

NOTE: For further information on cooling systems, see ENGINE COOLING section.

ENGINE COOLING

WATER PUMP

Removal & Installation

Remove radiator and fan belt. Disconnect heater hose from pump and self-engaging fan brush holder. Remove water pump. To install, reverse removal procedure. Ensure contact surfaces are clean before installing new gasket.

TIGHTENING SPECIFICATIONS

Application	Ft. Lbs. (N.m)
Belt Tension Nut	[1] 58 (79)
Camshaft Retaining Plate Bolts	12 (16)
Camshaft Sprocket Bolts	16 (22)
Connecting Rod Nuts	29 (39)
Crankshaft Main Bearing Bolts	54 (73)
Crankshaft Pulley Bolts	123 (167)
Cylinder Head Bolts	[2]
Engine-to-Clutch Housing Bolts	40 (54)
Engine-to-Converter Housing Bolts	22 (30)
Engine Mounts-to-Crossmember Bolts	25 (34)
Flywheel-to-Crankshaft Bolts	49 (67)
Rocker Arm Support Nut	11 (15)
	INCH Lbs.
Oil Pump Mounting Bolts	84 (10)

[1] – First step, tighten to 36 ft. lbs. (49 N.m), turn engine one full turn, and retighten to 58 ft. lbs. (79 N.m).

[2] – See text for tightening procedure.

ENGINE SPECIFICATIONS

GENERAL SPECIFICATIONS

Year	DISPLACEMENT		Fuel System	HP@RPM	Torque Ft. Lbs.@RPM	Compr. Ratio	BORE		STROKE	
	Cu. In.	Liters					In.	mm	In.	mm
1987	120.3	2.0	CIS Lambda	97 @ 5000	116 @ 3500	8.35:1	3.465	88	3.189	81

VALVES

Engine Size & Valve	Head Diam. In. (mm)	Face Angle	Seat Angle	Seat Width In. (mm)	Stem Diameter In. (mm)	Stem Clearance In. (mm)	Valve Lift In. (mm)
2.0L							
Intake	1.67 (42.5)	30°	30°	.....	.315 (8.00)	.0008-.0015 (.02-.04)	.....
Exhaust	1.40 (35.5)	45°	45°	.....	.316 (8.02)	.....	.....

PISTONS, PINS, RINGS

Engine	PISTONS	PINS		RINGS		
	Clearance In. (mm)	Piston Fit In. (mm)	Rod Fit In. (mm)	Ring No.	End Gap In. (mm)	Side Clearance In. (mm)
2.0L	.002-.003 (.06-.08)	0-.0003 (0-.008)	Full Floating	No. 1	.008-.020 (.20-.50)	.....
				No. 2	.016-.022 (.40-.55)	.....
				Oil	.010-.016 (.25-.40)	.....

Peugeot Engines

2.0L 4-CYLINDER (Cont.)

ENGINE SPECIFICATIONS (Cont.)

CRANKSHAFT MAIN & CONNECTING ROD BEARINGS

Engine	MAIN BEARINGS				CONNECTING ROD BEARINGS		
	Journal Diam. In. (mm)	Clearance In. (mm)	Thrust Bearing	Crankshaft End Play In. (mm)	Journal Diam. In. (mm)	Clearance In. (mm)	Side Play In. (mm)
2.0L							
No. 1 (Rear)	2.1616-2.1646 (54.905-54.980)	.....	Rear	.003-.008 (.08-.20)	2.1123-2.1131 (53.652-53.673)	.0006-.003 (.016-.08)	.....
No. 2	2.2102-2.2112 (56.140-56.165)						
No. 3	2.2509-2.2515 (57.174-57.189)						
No. 4	2.3050-2.3060 (58.548-58.573)						
No. 5	2.3386-2.3392 (59.401-59.416)						

VALVE SPRINGS

Engine	Free Length In. (mm)	PRESSURE Lbs. @ In. (Kg @ mm)	
		Valve Closed	Valve Open
2.0L	[1] 1.57 (44)	.....	.....

[1] – Inner spring free length is 1.56" (39.6 mm).

2.2L 4-CYLINDER

Peugeot: 505

NOTE: **For engine repair procedures not covered in this article, see ENGINE OVERHAUL PROCEDURES article at beginning of this section.**

ENGINE CODING

ENGINE IDENTIFICATION

Vehicle Identification Number (VIN) is attached to top of radiator support, above center of grille. The sixth character identifies the engine and the tenth character identifies model year. Engine Identification Number (EIN) is stamped on lower left side of block, near the starter.

ENGINE IDENTIFICATION CODE

Application	Engine Model	Engine EIN Code
Non-Turbo 2.2L	ZDJL	851
Turbo 2.2L	N9T	A05

ENGINE, MANIFOLDS & CYLINDER HEAD

ENGINE

Removal

1) Remove hood, battery and fan shroud. Drain radiator and remove upper and lower hoses. Remove electrical lead from cooling fan switch, and remove radiator lower mounting bolts. Remove radiator. Remove rubber duct hose at throttle body.

2) Remove power steering pump without opening hydraulic circuit. After removal of power steering pump, reinstall bolts with their spacers to avoid oil leaks. Disconnect air conditioning compressor from engine. Do not discharge system.

3) Disconnect all wires between engine and body. Use care when removing injector harness as there is an 8-pin connector located behind relay support bracket.

4) Remove cruise control servo motor. Remove auxiliary air device connector. Install engine sling assembly. Disconnect turbocharger-to-front header pipe clamp (if equipped).

5) Remove inspection plates from clutch housing. Remove TDC sensor diagnostic plug located on reinforcement bracket.

6) Remove 5 upper clutch housing bolts. Do not remove 2 lower bolts at this time. Reinforcement bracket will be removed later.

7) Remove right mounting bolts at engine crossmember. Remove left engine mount bolts. Lift engine with engine sling assembly until top of clutch housing contacts lower firewall.

8) Install transmission support. Remove 2 remaining clutch housing bolts and reinforcement bracket. Disengage engine from transmission and lift engine from engine compartment.

Installation

1) To install engine, reverse removal procedure. Lightly lubricate splines, front and mainshaft pilot bushings with Molykote 321. Place gearshift lever in gear. Tighten engine mount-to-crossmember bolts and engine-to-clutch housing bolts.

2) If TDC sensor is new, adjust by bringing 3 nipples in contact with flywheel. If reusing TDC sensor, deburr 3 nipples and push TDC sensor against flywheel. Pull sensor back out .040" (1.0 mm) and tighten bolt.

3) Refill cooling system and crankcase. Check power steering fluid reservoir level.

4) Adjust accelerator cable. Place accelerator pedal at rest. Throttle flap should be against stop. Set retaining clip to obtain minimum play between clip and washer.

5) Check full throttle position. Depress accelerator pedal fully and ensure lever is against throttle flap. Compensating spring should be slightly compressed.

CYLINDER HEAD & MANIFOLDS

Removal (Non-Turbo Engine)

1) Disconnect battery. Drain cooling system including cylinder block. Remove radiator and fan shroud. Remove exhaust header pipe and oxygen sensor.

2) Disconnect A/C compressor. Do not discharge system. Remove A/C compressor mount. Remove alternator. Remove air cleaner with airflow sensor and air duct.

3) Remove intake manifold. Remove thermostat housing and auxiliary air device. Remove distributor cap and ignition wires. Remove upper radiator hose.

4) Align timing marks for crankshaft, camshaft and intermediate shaft. *See Fig. 1.* Remove crankshaft pulley bolt. Ensure that crankshaft does not rotate. Remove timing belt cover. Loosen timing belt tensioner bolts. Remove camshaft pulley and timing belt.

Fig. 1: Location of 2.2L Non-Turbo Engine Timing Marks

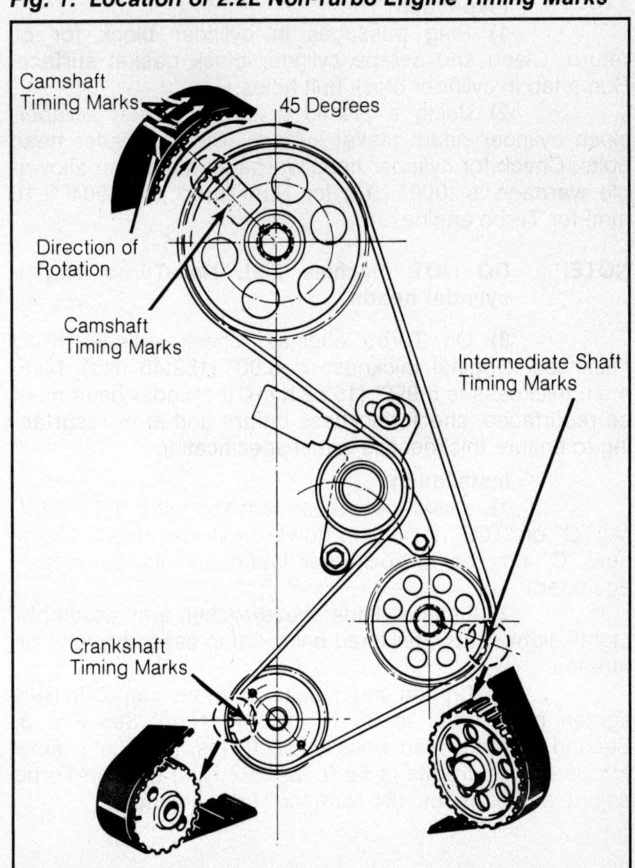

Courtesy of Peugeot Motor of America, Inc.

2.2L 4-CYLINDER (Cont.)

5) Remove valve cover. Remove cylinder head bolts and rocker arms. Using Handles (.0149), separate cylinder head from cylinder block. Install Cylinder Liner Retainers (.0132A1Z) to prevent liners from moving.

Removal (Turbo Engine)

1) Disconnect battery. Drain cooling system including cylinder block. Remove exhaust header pipe and oxygen sensor. Remove turbocharger lower mounting screws.

2) Disconnect A/C compressor. Do not discharge system. Remove A/C compressor mount. Remove access plug to hydraulic chain tensioner adjustment. Disconnect turbocharger lubrication feed pipe.

3) Insert screwdriver in tensioner plug hole. Push tensioner shaft in against its stop. Rotate shaft right about 1/3 turn. Remove distributor cap and ignition wires. Remove upper radiator hose. Remove turbocharger intake manifold tube.

4) Disconnect distributor wiring. Remove hoses from thermostat housing. Remove mounting clamps from intake manifold. Clear hose from studs. Move intake manifold to one side. Remove valve cover.

5) Position engine at TDC. The TDC notch on crankshaft pulley should be lined up with "0" notch on timing chain housing. No. 4 cylinder should be in firing position. *See Fig. 2.* Camshaft gear reference should be aligned with casting boss on cylinder head.

6) Remove distributor. Remove upper timing chain housing. Remove camshaft gear mounting bolts. Remove camshaft gear. Install timing chain Retaining Stirrups (.0934 R). Using Handles, (.0149), separate cylinder head from cylinder block.

Inspection

1) Plug passages in cylinder block for oil return. Clean and scrape cylinder block gasket surface. Run a tap in cylinder block bolt holes.

2) Using a plastic or wood gasket scraper, clean cylinder head gasket surface. Clean cylinder head bolts. Check for cylinder head warpage. Maximum allowable warpage is .005" (.13) for Non-Turbo and .004" (.10 mm) for Turbo engines.

NOTE: DO NOT machine 2.2L Non-Turbo engine cylinder heads.

3) On Turbo engines, check cylinder head thickness. Original thickness is 6.00" (152.40 mm). Minimum thickness is 5.992" (152.2 mm). If cylinder head must be resurfaced, check thickness before and after resurfacing to ensure thickness is within specification.

Installation

1) Install new head gasket with "DESSUS", "ALTO" or "TOP" facing up (toward cylinder head). Install new "O" ring on turbocharger lubricating flange inlet (if equipped).

2) Install cylinder head/rocker arm assembly. Lightly tighten cylinder head bolts, using assembly lube on threads.

3) Tighten head bolts in three steps. Initially tighten head bolts to 36 ft. lbs. (49 N.m). *See Fig. 3.* Second, tighten head bolts to 58 ft. lbs. (59 N.m.). Final torque on head bolts is 68 ft. lbs. (92 N.m) on Non-Turbo engine and 62 ft. lbs. (84 N.m) for Turbo engine.

Fig. 2: Location of 2.2L Turbo Engine Timing Marks

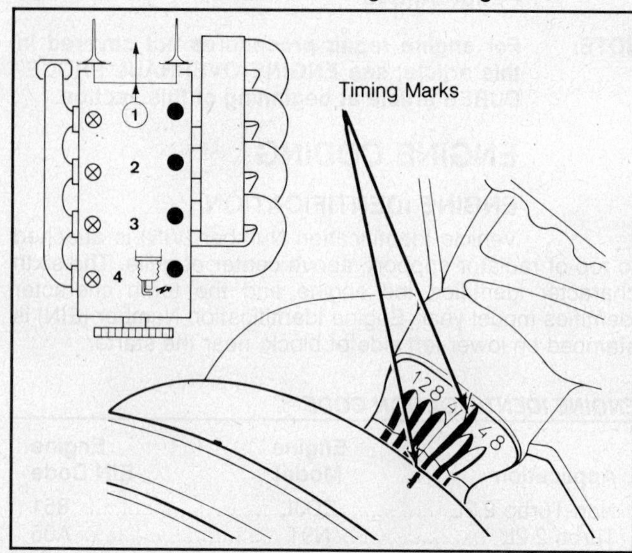

Courtesy of Peugeot Motor of America, Inc.

Fig. 3: Cylinder Head Bolt Tightening Sequence

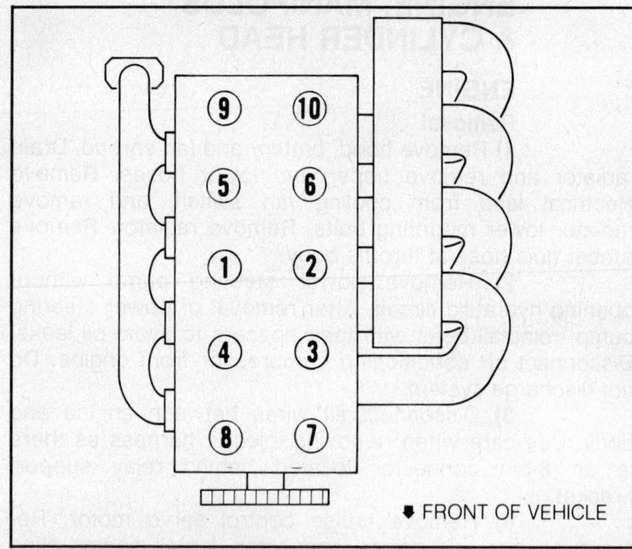

Courtesy of Peugeot Motor of America, Inc.

4) To install remaining components, reverse removal procedure. Refill cooling system, adjust valves and install distributor (Turbo engine).

5) To install distributor drive on Turbo engines, set engine at TDC with No. 4 cylinder in firing position. Install distributor drive with small side toward cylinder head. *See Fig. 4.*

6) To adjust static distributor timing, bring No. 1 cylinder to firing position. Align TDC notch on crankshaft pulley with "0" notch on timing chain housing.

7) Install distributor. Position distributor body reference in line with distributor rotor. Lock distributor in this position.

2.2L 4-CYLINDER (Cont.)

Fig. 4: 2.2L Turbo Distributor Drive Alignment

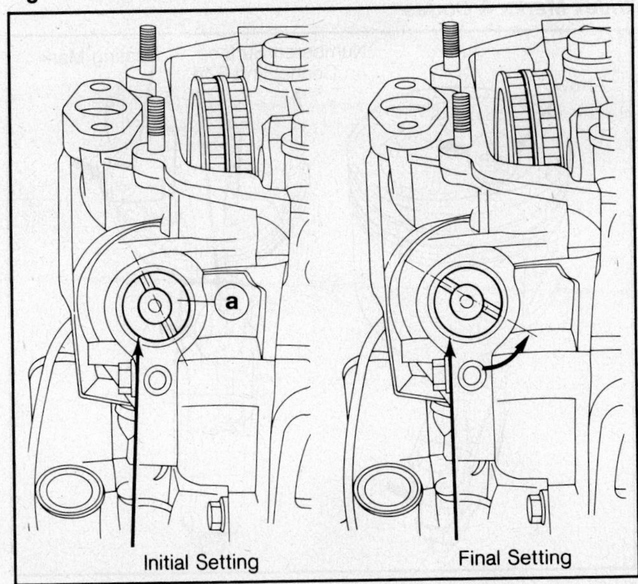

Courtesy of Peugeot Motor of America, Inc.

VALVES

VALVE ARRANGEMENT

Left side - Intake valves.
Right side - Exhaust valves.

VALVE CLEARANCE ADJUSTMENT

NOTE: **Engine must be allowed to cool at least 6 hours before adjusting valves. Adjust valves in firing order sequence (1-3-4-2). No. 1 cylinder is on flywheel end of engine.**

1) Rotate engine until No. 1 exhaust valve is fully opened, then adjust No. 3 intake valve and No. 4 exhaust valve.

2) Rotate crankshaft 1/2 turn (180 degrees) until No. 3 exhaust valve is fully opened and adjust corresponding valves. See VALVE ADJUSTMENT SEQUENCE table. Continue this procedure until all valves have been adjusted.

VALVE ADJUSTMENT SEQUENCE

Valve Open	Adjust Valves
E 1	I 3 & E 4
E 3	I 4 & E 2
E 4	I 2 & E 1
E 2	I 1 & E 3

VALVE CLEARANCE SPECIFICATIONS

Application	Intake In. (mm)	Exhaust In. (mm)
Non-Turbo	.004 (.10)	.010 (.25)
Turbo	.008 (.20)	.012 (.30)

CAMSHAFT

ENGINE FRONT COVER & OIL SEAL

Removal (Turbo Engine)

1) Drain coolant and engine oil. Remove radiator, fan and fan belt. Remove upper timing chain cover. Remove crankshaft pulley retaining bolt, and pulley.

2) Remove water pump. Unscrew front cover retaining bolts and remove cover. Use a seal driver to drive out old seal from front cover.

Installation

Using a seal driver, drive new seal into front cover. Install new gasket on front cover. Install front cover. To complete installation, reverse removal procedure.

TIMING BELT

Removal (Non-Turbo Engine)

1) Disconnect battery. Drain cooling system including cylinder block. Remove radiator and fan shroud. Remove thermostat housing and auxiliary air device.

2) Align timing marks for crankshaft, camshaft and intermediate shaft. *See Fig. 1.* Remove crankshaft pulley bolt and pulley. Ensure that crankshaft does not rotate. Remove timing belt cover. Loosen timing belt tensioner bolts and position tensioner out of way. Remove camshaft pulley and timing belt.

Installation

1) Ensure timing marks remain in alignment. *See Fig. 1.* Remove distributor cap and check rotor position. Distributor rotor must be at a 90 degree angle to the crankshaft. If not, turn intermediate shaft once or twice.

2) Install timing belt, centered on pulleys and tensioner. Loosen belt tensioner mounting bolts and allow spring to adjust timing belt. Tighten belt tensioner bolts.

3) To complete installation, reverse removal procedures. Crankshaft pulley bolt must be reinstalled using Loctite.

TIMING CHAIN

Removal (Turbo Engine)

1) Insert screwdriver in tensioner plug hole. Push tensioner shaft in against its stop. Rotate shaft right about 1/3 turn. Remove distributor cap and ignition wires. Remove upper radiator hose.

2) Disconnect distributor wiring. Remove hoses from thermostat housing. Remove turbocharger air intake tube. Remove valve cover.

3) Position engine at TDC. The TDC notch on crankshaft pulley should be lined up with "0" notch on timing chain housing. The No. 4 cylinder should be in firing position. *See Fig. 2.* Camshaft gear reference should be aligned with casting boss on cylinder head.

4) Remove distributor. Remove upper timing chain housing. Remove front cover. Remove oil pan. Remove oil pump gear, chain and pump assembly. Remove the camshaft gear mounting bolts. Remove camshaft gear. Remove timing chain.

2.2L 4-CYLINDER (Cont.)

Fig. 5: 2.2L Non-Turbo Camshaft & Crankshaft Alignment

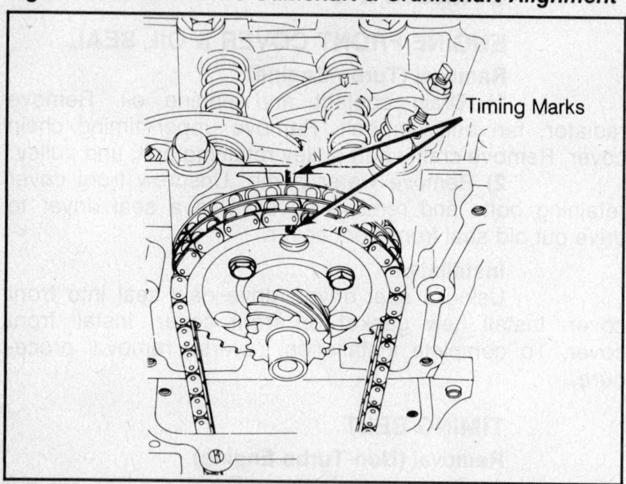

Courtesy of Peugeot Motor of America, Inc.

Installation

1) Set engine at TDC with No. 4 cylinder in firing position. Install distributor drive with small side toward cylinder head. *See Fig. 4*.

2) Adjust static distributor timing. Bring No. 1 cylinder to firing position. Align TDC notch on crankshaft pulley with "0" notch on timing chain housing.

3) Install distributor. Position distributor body reference in line with distributor rotor. Lock distributor in this position.

CAMSHAFT

Removal

1) Remove front grille assembly. Remove radiator hoses and radiator. Remove turbocharger tube. Remove spark plugs. Set engine to TDC on No. 4 cylinder firing position. Remove ignition wires and distributor.

2) Remove valve cover and upper front cover. Remove camshaft gear. Install timing chain Retaining Stirrups (.0934 R). Remove cylinder head rear inspection plate. Remove camshaft retaining plate. Loosen all rocker arm adjusting screws.

3) Remove rocker arm shafts, rocker arms, shaft spring and spacers. Set parts aside in proper order with respective rocker arm shaft. Remove camshaft.

Installation

To install, reverse removal procedure. See VALVE CLEARANCE ADJUSTMENTS.

PISTONS, PINS & RINGS

PISTON & ROD ASSEMBLY

Removal

1) With engine removed and mounted on engine stand, remove intake and exhaust manifolds. Remove all auxiliary equipment.

2) Remove cylinder head as previously described. Remove oil pan and oil pump. Remove bearing caps, keeping them in original order. Remove pistons and connecting rods. Attach connecting rods to matching cap and mark rod assemblies.

Installation

1) Install piston ring compressor on piston. Insert piston and rod assembly. Index arrow must face front of engine. *See Fig. 6.*

Fig. 6: Piston & Rod Assembly with Index Marks & Codes

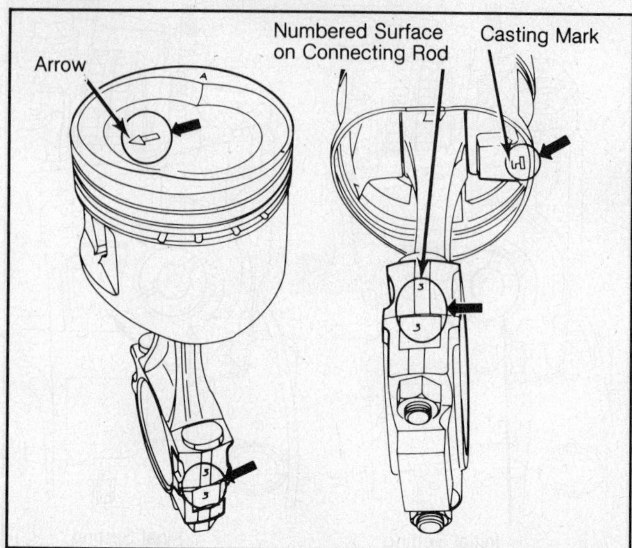

Index arrow must face front of engine. Courtesy of Peugeot Motor of America, Inc.

2) Push piston into cylinder. Guide connecting rod with bearing over crankshaft journal. Install bearing cap and tighten.

NOTE: **Marks on rods and caps must be on same side.**

PISTON PIN REPLACEMENT

Remove snap rings and piston pin. Fit piston to rod so arrow on top of piston will point toward front of engine and numbered surface of rod and cap will be on oil filter side of engine. If necessary, heat piston in boiling water to insert pin. Install snap rings. *See Fig. 6.*

CRANKSHAFT & ROD BEARINGS

MAIN BEARINGS

1) With engine removed from vehicle, remove oil sump. Remove cylinder head as previously described. Scribe a reference mark on connecting rod caps and main bearing caps.

2) Remove piston/rod assemblies. Remove front cover and timing chain assembly. Remove clutch/flywheel assembly. Remove main bearing caps and carefully remove crankshaft.

3) Fit main bearing half shells into cylinder block and main bearing caps. Lubricate main bearings and carefully place crankshaft in position.

4) Install main bearing caps and bolts. Tighten main bearing cap bolts in 2 or 3 steps, starting at center bearing and working outward. Ensure crankshaft rotates smoothly.

5) Measure main bearing clearances using Plastigage method.

THRUST BEARING WASHERS

Crankshaft thrust bearing washers are located at center main bearing. Install crankshaft with original thickness thrust bearing washers and with rear main seal.

Peugeot Engines

2.2L 4-CYLINDER (Cont.)

Check end play. End play must not exceed .010" (.25 mm). Oversize thrust washers are available in .0958" (2.433 mm), .0978" (2.484 mm), and .0998" (2.535 mm) sizes.

REAR MAIN BEARING OIL SEAL

Remove crankshaft and old rear oil seal. Place a drop of non-hardening cement in rear main seal carrier and cylinder block grooves. Install rope seals using Installer (-0134U) and Handle (-0110A3). Do not alter or modify length or shape of rope seals. *See Fig. 7.*

Fig. 7: Rear Main Seal Installation

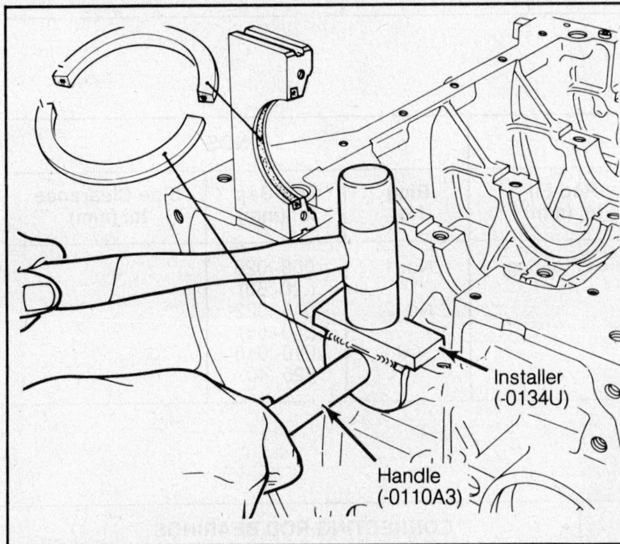

Courtesy of Peugeot Motor of America, Inc.

ENGINE OILING

ENGINE OILING SYSTEM

A high output, gear-type oil pump is mounted to engine block front lower surface and is operated by crankshaft chain.

CRANKCASE CAPACITY

Crankcase capacity is 5.3 qts. (5.0L).

OIL FILTER

The oil filter is a full-flow cartridge type.

NORMAL OIL PRESSURE

Normal oil pressure is 22 psi (1.5 kg/cm²) at 900 RPM and 51 psi (3.5 kg/cm²) at 2000 RPM. Maximum oil pressure is 81 psi (5.5 kg/cm²).

OIL PUMP

Removal & Installation

Remove oil pan. Turn engine to TDC on No. 4 cylinder. Remove oil pump. To install, reverse removal procedure. Check ignition timing.

ENGINE COOLING

WATER PUMP

Removal & Installation

Remove radiator and fan belt. Disconnect heater hose from pump and self-engaging fan brush holder. Remove water pump. To install, reverse removal procedure. Ensure contact surfaces are clean before installing new gasket.

NOTE: **For further information on cooling systems, see ENGINE COOLING section.**

TIGHTENING SPECIFICATIONS

Application	Ft. Lbs. (N.m)
Camshaft Sprocket Bolts	11 (15)
Connecting Rod Nuts	47 (64)
Crankshaft Main Bearing Bolts	80 (108)
Crankshaft Pulley Bolts	98 (133)
Cylinder Head Bolts	[1]
Engine-to-Clutch Housing Bolts	25 (34)
Engine Mount-to-Block Bolts	14 (20)
Engine Mount-to-Crossmember Bolts	25 (34)
Exhaust Manifold Bolts	14 (20)
Flywheel-to-Crankshaft Bolts	58 (79)
Intake Manifold Bolts	11 (15)
Oil Pump Mounting Bolts	14 (20)

[1] – See text for tightening procedure.

ENGINE SPECIFICATIONS

GENERAL SPECIFICATIONS

Year	DISPLACEMENT		Fuel System	HP@RPM	Torque Ft. Lbs.@RPM	Compr. Ratio	BORE		STROKE	
	Cu. In.	Liters					In.	mm	In.	mm
1987										
Non-Turbo	131.5	2.2	L-Jetronic EFI	120 @ 5000	131 @ 3500	8.8:1	3.46	88	3.50	89
Turbo	131.5	2.2	L-Jetronic EFI	150 @ 5000	180 @ 2750	7.5:1	3.61	91.7	3.21	81.6

Peugeot Engines

2.2L 4-CYLINDER (Cont.)

ENGINE SPECIFICATIONS (Cont.)

VALVES

Engine Size & Valve	Head Diam. In. (mm)	Face Angle	Seat Angle	Seat Width In. (mm)	Stem Diameter In. (mm)	Stem Clearance In. (mm)	Valve Lift In. (mm)
2.2L Turbo [1]							
Intake	1.67 (42.5)	30°	30°	.....	.315 (8.00)	.0008-.0015 (.02-.04)	.....
Exhaust	1.40 (35.5)	45°	45°	.....	.316 (8.02)	.....	.....

[1] – Information for 2.2L Non-turbo engine not available.

PISTONS, PINS & RINGS

Engine	PISTONS	PINS		RINGS		
	Clearance In. (mm)	Piston Fit In. (mm)	Rod Fit In. (mm)	Ring No.	End Gap In. (mm)	Side Clearance In. (mm)
2.2L Turbo [1]	.002-.003 (.06-.08)	0-.0003 (0-.008)	Full Floating	No. 1	.008-.020 (.20-.50)	.....
				No. 2	.016-.022 (.40-.55)	.....
				Oil	.010-.016 (.25-.40)	.....

[1] – Information for 2.2L Non-turbo engine not available.

CRANKSHAFT MAIN & CONNECTING ROD BEARINGS

Engine	MAIN BEARINGS				CONNECTING ROD BEARINGS		
	Journal Diam. In. (mm)	Clearance In. (mm)	Thrust Bearing	Crankshaft End Play In. (mm)	Journal Diam. In. (mm)	Clearance In. (mm)	Side Play In. (mm)
2.2L Turbo [1]							
No. 1 (Rear)	2.1616-2.1646 (54.905-54.980)	.....	Rear	.003-.008 (.08-.20)	2.1123-2.1131 (53.652-53.673)	.0006-.003 (.016-.08)	.....
No. 2	2.2102-2.2112 (56.140-56.165)						
No. 3	2.2509-2.2515 (57.174-57.189)						
No. 4	2.3050-2.3060 (58.548-58.573)						
No. 5	2.3386-2.3392 (59.401-59.416)						

[1] – Information for 2.2L Non-turbo engine not available.

VALVE SPRINGS

Engine	Free Length In. (mm)	PRESSURE Lbs. @ In. (Kg @ mm)	
		Valve Closed	Valve Open
2.2L Turbo [1]	[2] 1.57 (44)	.....	.....

[1] – Information for 2.2L Non-turbo engine not available.
[2] – Inner spring free length is 1.56" (39.6 mm).

Peugeot & Volvo Engines

2.8L V6

Peugeot: 505 STI, STX;
Volvo: 760 GLE, 780 GLE

ENGINE CODING

ENGINE IDENTIFICATION

Engine identification number is located on plate on front left side of engine block, in front of oil filter. Vehicle Identification Number (VIN) is located on top of instrument panel at lower left of windshield.

ENGINE IDENTIFICATION CODES

Application	Code
Peugeot	ZN3J
Volvo	B280F

ENGINE, MANIFOLDS & CYLINDER HEADS

ENGINE

Removal (Peugeot)

1) Remove hood, air filter, airflow sensor and intake preheater assembly. Remove fan, fan shroud and transmission cooler lines at radiator. Remove idle electronic regulation electrovalve located on right valve cover. Disconnect A/C compressor, power steering pump and reservoir from brackets and lay aside.

2) Drain cooling system. Remove battery and radiator overflow tank. Disconnect 2 ground cables from cylinder head. Disconnect 3 connectors from power supply cables. Remove accelerator and kickdown linkage. Do not disconnect cruise control cable.

3) Disconnect fuel feed, injector pump return and cruise control vacuum hoses. Disconnect steering column at coupling. Lower front crossmember about 1.9" (50 mm) using Bolts (1511C).

4) Remove 2 right header pipe nuts, 2 starter bolts, left header pipes and 2 bellhousing inspection plates. From rear of left cylinder head remove ignition sensor connector. Lock flywheel using Pawl (0134Q). Remove 4 torque converter bolts using Socket (KM-J36301). Remove flywheel locking pawl. Install a support under the transmission.

5) Hold torque converter in place with Clamp (0318), using care not to distort flywheel. Remove remaining torque converter bolts. Clear engine from compartment and rest it on Cradle (0134 A).

6) Remove 2 upper engine/transmission assembly bolts. Remove transmission dipstick tube bolt from cylinder head. Remove engine mount-to-crossmember nuts. Ensure torque converter is held in place with Clamp (0318). Using Hoist, (0135ZZ) remove engine until transmission contacts floorpan.

Installation

To install, reverse removal procedure.

Removal (Volvo)

1) Remove air cleaner, grille, grille crossmember, fan shroud and engine splash guard. Drain engine and transmission oil. Drain cooling system (each side of block) and disconnect all coolant hoses. Disconnect A/C compressor and move aside. DO NOT disconnect A/C hoses.

2) Remove radiator. Disconnect throttle cable, speedometer and battery ground cable. Disconnect and mark all electrical connections, hoses, and tubing that will interfere with engine removal.

3) Move gear selector to "P" and disconnect kickdown cable at throttle pulley. Drain transmission oil by disconnecting oil filler tube at oil pan.

4) Disconnect automatic transmission oil cooler pipes at radiator. Disconnect control rods at transmission. Disconnect solenoid wiring plug below shifter.

5) Attach a Crossmember Lifting Cradle (2810) and 2 Lifting Cradle Slings (5100) to engine. Support lifting cradle on engine hoist. Disconnect propeller shaft at transmission.

6) Disconnect exhaust pipe at joint in front of catalytic converter and remove exhaust pipe from exhaust pipe bracket. Remove rear engine mount and crossmember assembly. Remove nuts from front engine mounts and lift engine/transmission assembly from vehicle.

Installation

To install, reverse removal procedure.

CYLINDER HEADS & MANIFOLDS

Removal

1) The engine is equipped with camshaft driven counterweights at each end of the right bank cylinder head. The counterweights are timed in relation to the camshaft. The counterweights are installed in the front of the cylinder head, inside a support, and in the rear of the cylinder head.

2) If one or more cylinder heads are to be removed, the timing chain and sprocket assembly must be kept under tension. This procedure will avoid the removal of the timing chain cover. On the right cylinder head, keep the front counterweight drive pinion from turning. Move the countershaft support from its centering dowels seated in the head. Do not separate pinions from each other.

3) If both cylinder heads are to be removed, always remove the right cylinder head first. If one cylinder head is to be removed, follow the removal steps for that cylinder head only. Ensure cooling system is drained. Disconnect electrical and mechanical connections as necessary between intake manifold accessories and engine. Remove intake manifold. If removing right cylinder head, go to next step. If removing left cylinder head, go to step **8)**.

4) To remove right cylinder head, remove air filter, airflow sensor and junction hose assembly. Remove front grille, air intake preheat system, upper radiator hose and left header pipe at catalytic converter. Remove right header pipe. Remove fan, shroud and coolant hose.

5) Remove valve cover, plugs and bolts from end of head. *See Fig. 1.* Loosen camshaft pinion bolt. Turn crankshaft clockwise until No. 6 cylinder valves are in rocking position. Turn engine until end of rocker arm shaft is visible through left cut-out in camshaft sprocket.

6) Install camshaft Pinion Support (0134 W) on timing chain housing. Place tab of plate into pinion teeth. Hand tighten and lock bolts. *See Fig. 2.* Install bolt into counterweight support but do not tighten. Remove counterweight support bolts through access holes. Insert 2 screwdrivers into slots "A" and "B" and carefully pry support out of centering dowels. *See Fig. 3.*

7) Install Support (0134 X) on rear of head with pin "C" between 2 gear teeth. Tighten 2 bolts. *See Fig. 4.* Remove head bolts and rocker arm assembly. Loosen camshaft retainer bolts. Remove camshaft retainer from camshaft groove. Remove retainer bolt to clear camshaft from timing chain sprocket. Using 2 screwdrivers, move

2.8L V6 (Cont.)

camshaft until it contacts support. Using Levers (91.41), tilt and remove heads. To continue removal procedure for right cylinder head, go to step **11**).

Fig. 1: Removing Bolts & Plugs From Head

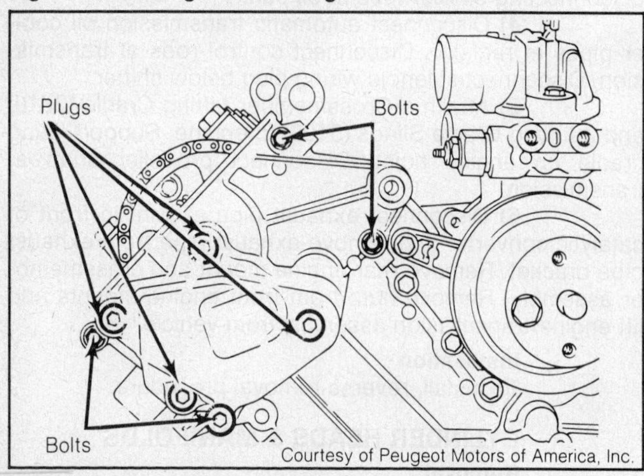

Fig. 2: Installing Camshaft Pinion Support (0134 W)

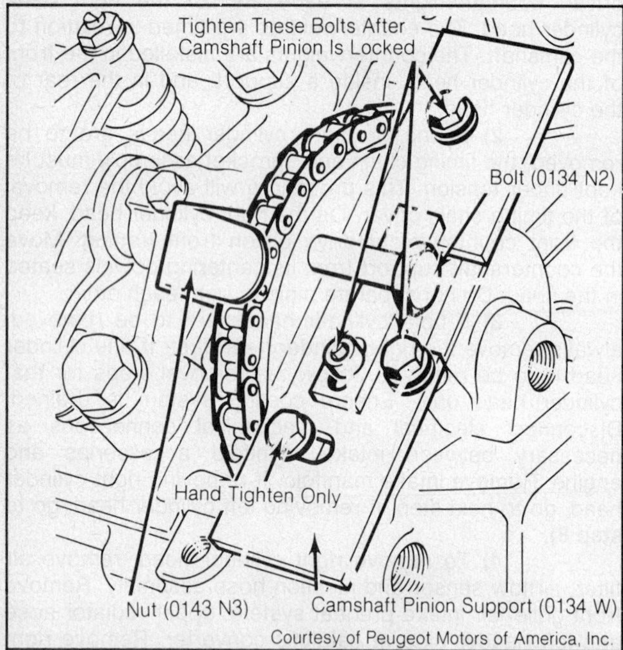

Fig. 3: Removing Counterweight Support

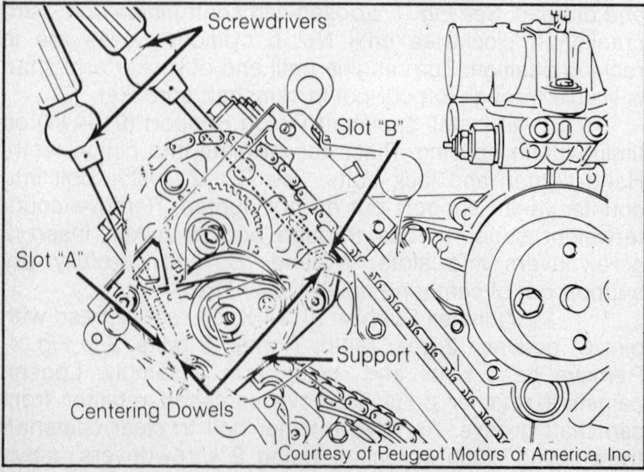

Fig. 4: Aligning Pin "C" Between Gear Teeth

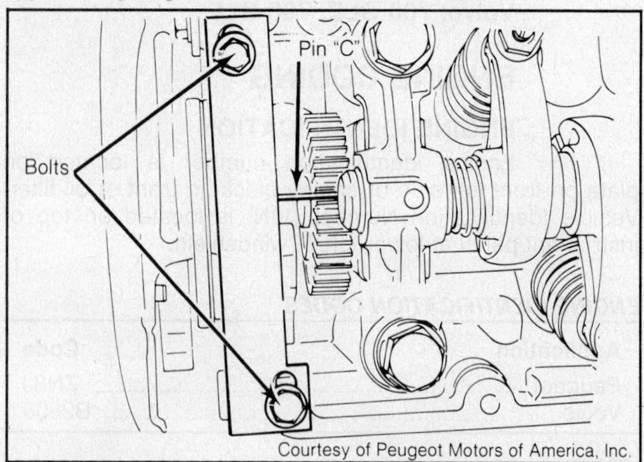

8) To remove left cylinder head, remove battery, overflow tank and bracket, and left exhaust manifold. Loosen power steering fluid reservoir and set aside. Remove valve cover. Turn crankshaft clockwise until No. 2 cylinder valves are in rocking positon. Rotate crankshaft an additional turn until camshaft pinion is positioned. *See Fig. 5.*

9) Remove distributor cap, rotor, distributor mounting bolts and camshaft sprocket mounting bolt. Remove coolant hose and fitting. *See Fig. 6.* Install Support (0134 N) on timing chain housing. Install bolts finger tight. Lock camshaft and tighten support bolts. *See Fig. 7.*

10) Remove or pull head bolts out as far as possible. Loosen camshaft retainer clamp bolts and pull clamp away from camshaft groove. Using a screwdriver, pry camshaft away from sprocket. Using Levers (91.41), tilt and remove heads.

Fig. 5: Positioning Camshaft Pinion

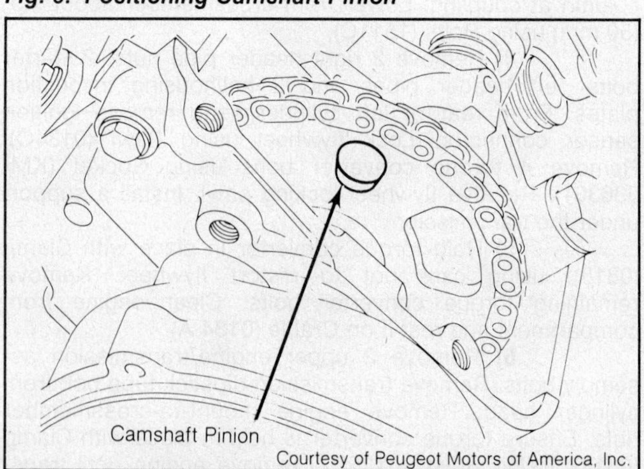

CAUTION: **When removing cylinder heads, Ensure cylinder liners DO NOT separate from seals at lower seat. If this happens, coolant can flow into crankcase.**

11) After removal, place cylinder head on wooden blocks to protect it from damage. Remove gasket and install Cylinder Liner Holders (5093). Use needle nose pliers to remove guide sleeves. When cleaning, remove cylinder holders one at a time.

2.8L V6 (Cont.)

Fig. 6: Removing Distributor Mounting Bolts

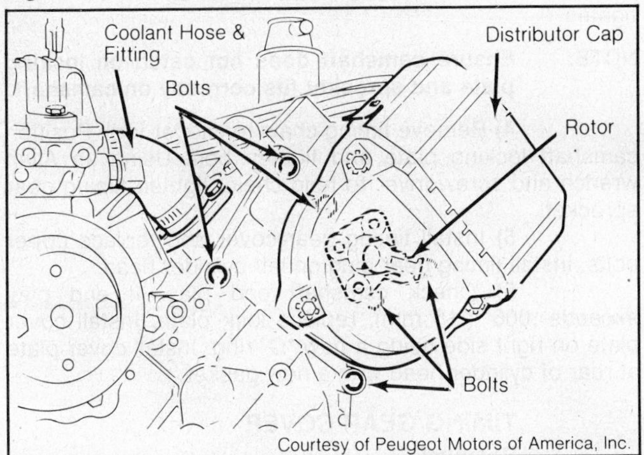

Fig. 7: Locking Camshaft & Tightening Support Bolts

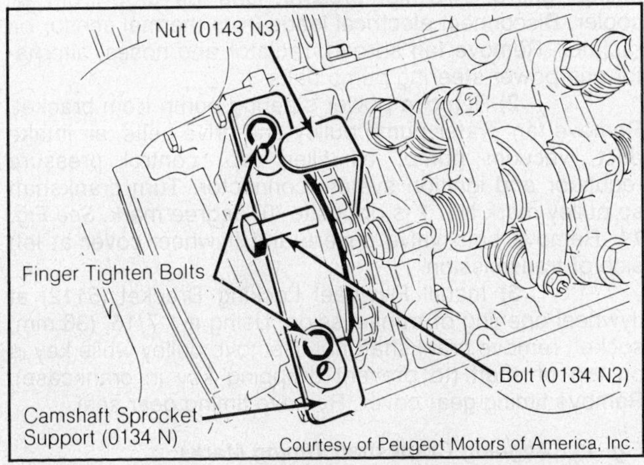

CAUTION: When cleaning, use plastic scraper to prevent scratching. Use compressed air to clean cylinder head bolt holes.

12) When replacing cylinder head gasket only, clean gasket surfaces and check for warpage. Clean valve cover. Use a steel rule and feeler gauge to check warpage. Maximum warpage is .002" (.05 mm) over 4" (100 mm) of length. If warpage exceeds measurement, replace cylinder head.

Installation

1) Ensure drive lugs of camshaft pinions are positioned as illustrated. *See Fig. 8.* Using same bolt as was used during removal, lock camshaft pinion. Reinstall locking Plate (0134 W). Insert a 3 mm pin in each dowel pin hole. Install centering dowels butted against pins. Use care not to drive dowels in too far.

2) Install new head gasket. Install camshaft retainer plate without locking bolt. Install head on engine block. Using an Allen wrench, tighten camshaft sprocket bolt. Coat camshaft retainer bolt with loctite and tighten to 114 INCH lbs. (12 N.m).

3) Clean all grease from rocker arm pads. Spray a light coat of Molykote on rocker arm pads. Install rocker arm assembly. Lubricate head bolts with engine oil and install. Tighten bolts, in order, to 44 ft. lbs. (60 N.m). Loosen all bolts, in order, and retighten to 15 ft. lbs. (20 N.m). Angle tighten all bolts, in order, an additional 105 degrees. *See Fig. 9.*

Fig. 8: Positioning Camshaft Pinion Drive Lug

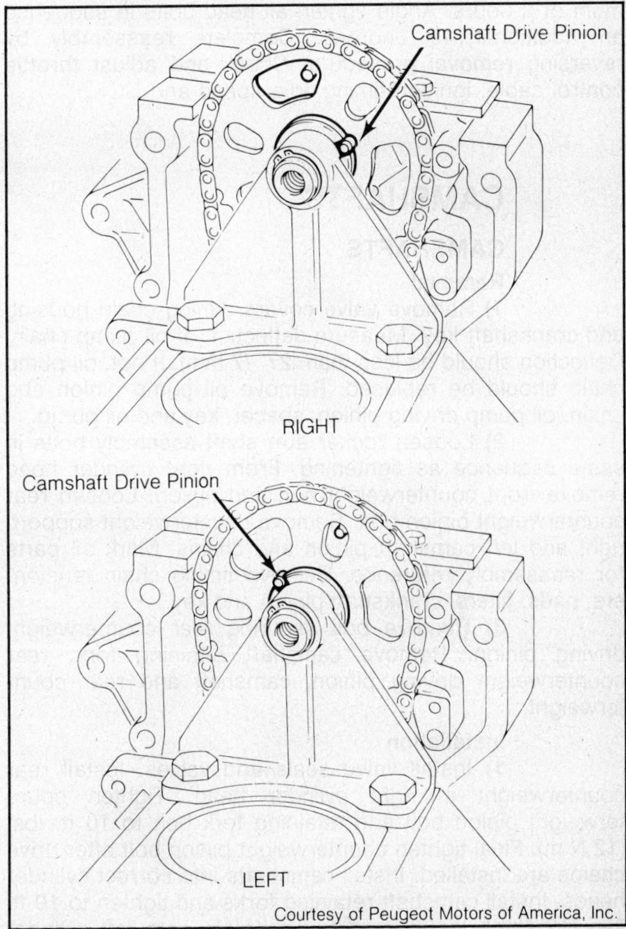

Fig. 9: Cylinder Head Tightening Sequence

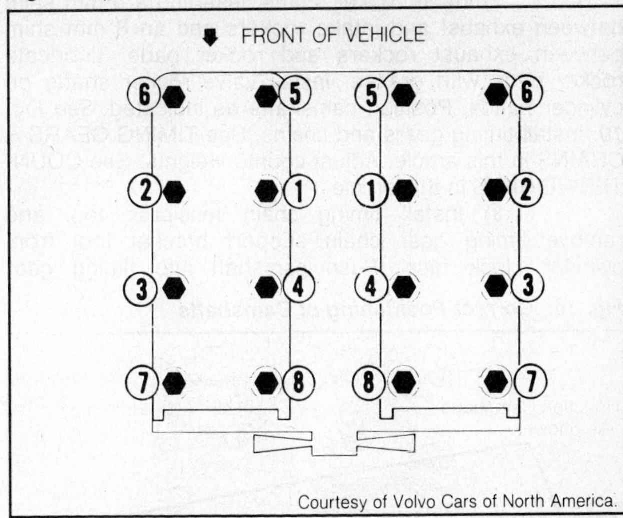

4) On right cylinder head install counterweight support and tighten bolt to 108 ft. lbs. (12 N.m). Tighten camshaft pinion bolt to 59 ft. lbs. (80 N.m). Coat Allen head plugs with Loctite and install. On left cylinder head tighten camshaft pinion bolt to 59 ft. lbs. (80 N.m). Install distributor cap and rotor.

5) Adjust valve clearance with engine cold. See VALVE CLEARANCE ADJUSTMENT in this article. Install valve covers and gaskets. Warm-up engine to normal

2.8L V6 (Cont.)

operating temperature. Allow engine to cool for a minimum of 2 hours. Angle tighten all head bolts in sequence an additional 45 degrees. Complete reassembly by reversing removal procedure. Check and adjust throttle control cable, ignition timing, idle speed and CO.

CAMSHAFTS

CAMSHAFTS

Removal

1) Remove valve covers, timing chain housing and crankshaft key. Measure deflection of oil pump chain. Deflection should be less than .27" (7 mm). If not, oil pump chain should be replaced. Remove oil pump pinion and chain, oil pump driving pinion, spacer, key and oil pump.

2) Loosen rocker arm shaft assembly bolts in same sequence as tightening. From right cylinder head remove front counterweight bolt and pinion. Loosen rear counterweight pinion bolt. Remove counterweight support, right and left camshaft pinion and chains. Mark all parts for reassembly reference. Remove timing chain tensioners, pads, filters, crankshaft pinion and key.

3) Remove bolt securing rear counterweight driving pinion. Remove camshaft retaining fork, rear counterweight driving pinion, camshaft and rear counterweight.

Installation

1) Install valve seals and valves. Install rear counterweight in right cylinder head. Tighten counterweight pinion bolt and retaining fork bolt to 10 ft. lbs. (12 N.m). Final tighten counterweight pinion bolt after drive chains are installed. Install camshafts into correct cylinder heads. Install camshaft retaining forks and tighten to 10 ft. lbs. (12 N.m). Install rear sealing plate onto left cylinder head.

2) Install rocker shafts, inserting a 5 mm shim between exhaust and intake rockers and an 8 mm shim between exhaust rockers and rocker pads. Lubricate rocker pads with grease. Install valve rocker shafts on cylinder heads. Position camshafts as indicated. *See Fig. 10.* Install timing gears and chains. See TIMING GEARS & CHAINS in this article. Adjust counterweights. See COUNTERWEIGHTS in this article.

3) Install timing chain tensioner tool and remove timing gear chain support bracket tool from cylinder block face. Push camshaft into timing gear sprocket. Install timing gear sprocket bolt but do not tighten.

NOTE: **Ensure camshaft does not catch on locking plate and sprocket fits correctly on camshaft.**

4) Remove timing chain tensioner tool. Position camshaft locking plate and tighten bolt. Using an Allen wrench and screwdriver to hold chain, tighten timing gear sprocket.

5) Install timing gear cover and replace upper bolts. Install timing gear plug on left cylinder head.

6) Check camshaft end play. If end play exceeds .006" (.15 mm), replace lock plate. Install cover plate on right side using a new "O" ring. Install cover plate at rear of cylinder head with a new gasket.

Fig. 10: Correct Positioning of Camshafts

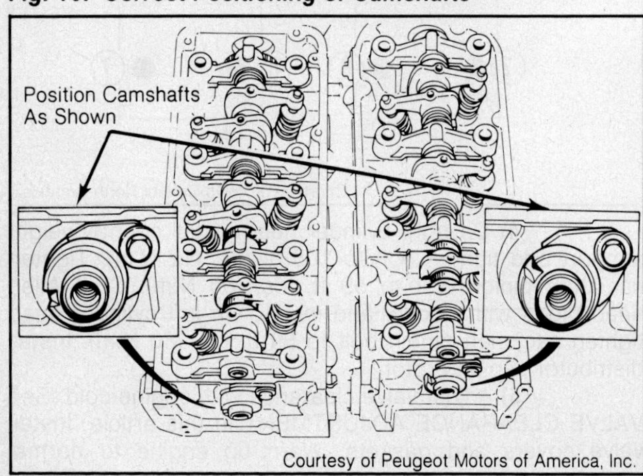

TIMING GEAR COVER

Removal

1) Disconnect battery ground cable. Remove splash guard, A/C compressor, and oil tube from oil cooler. Disconnect electrical leads from thermal sensor on radiator. Remove fan shroud, radiator and hoses, alternator and power steering pump belts.

2) Remove power steering pump from bracket. Remove fan, water pump pulley and drive belts, air intake duct, vacuum pump, oil filler cap, control pressure regulator and ignition system connector. Turn crankshaft so pulley mark No. 1 is opposite "0" degree mark. *See Fig. 11.* Remove both valve covers and flywheel cover at left side of transmission.

3) Install Flywheel Locking Bracket (5112) at flywheel opening of transmission. Using a 1 7/16" (36 mm) socket, remove crankshaft nut. Remove pulley while key is on top of shaft (to prevent dropping key in crankcase). Remove timing gear cover. Remove timing gear seal.

Fig. 11: Aligning Crankshaft Timing Marks

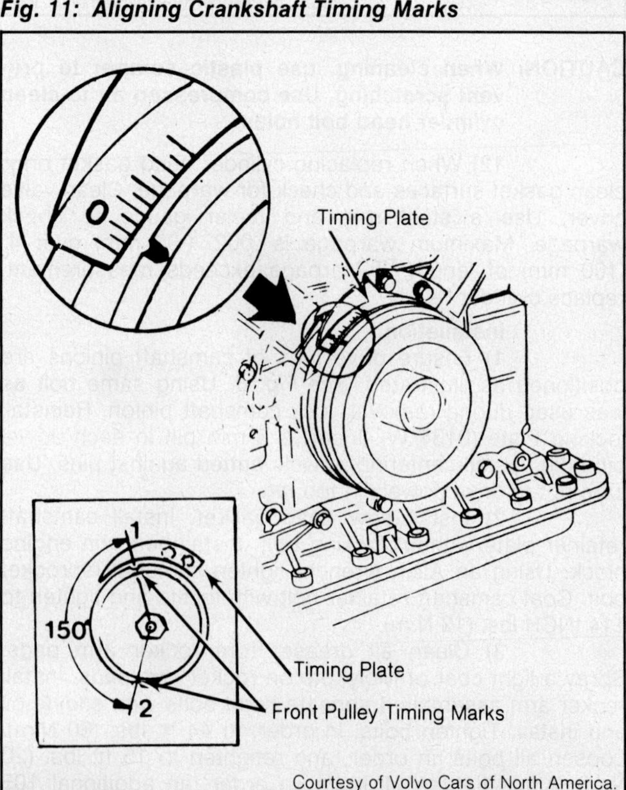

2.8L V6 (Cont.)

Installation

1) Clean surfaces and place gaskets on block and timing gear cover. Install cover and tighten bolts to 7-11 ft. lbs. (10-15 N.m). Using Crankshaft Oil Seal Driver (5103), install crankshaft oil seal.

2) Using flywheel locking bracket and a 1 7/16" (36 mm) socket, install crankshaft pulley and tighten crankshaft nut. Complete installation by reversing removal procedure.

CHAINS & SPROCKETS

Inspection

To perform a visual inspection of timing chain wear, remove left camshaft cover. Check position of chain tensioner rubbing block. *See Fig. 12.* Chain tensioner rubbing block should not protrude more than .315" (8 mm). Replace chains if beyond specification.

Fig. 12: Inspecting Timing Chain Tensioner

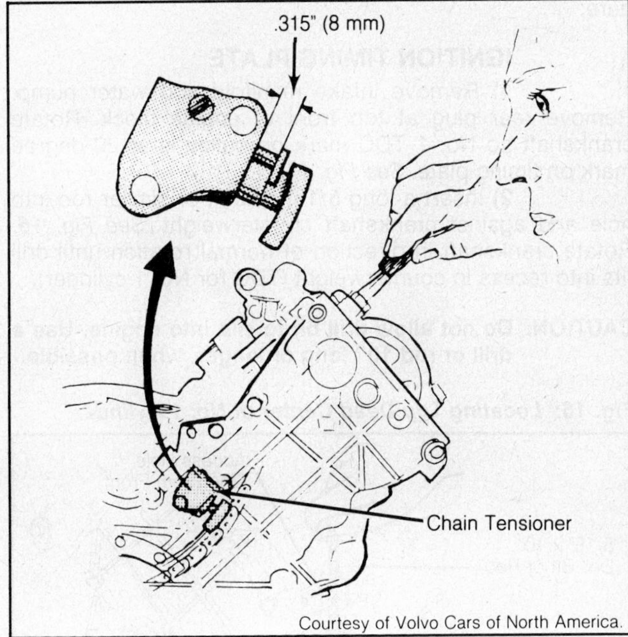

Courtesy of Volvo Cars of North America.

Removal

1) Remove timing gear cover. Use a 10 mm Allen wrench and screwdriver to remove camshaft bolts. Turn each timing gear chain tensioner lock 1/4 turn counterclockwise and push in piston to slacken camshaft chains.

2) Remove oil pump sprocket and chain, both tensioners, oil strainers, and all dampers. Remove camshaft sprockets and chains. Cover holes into crankcase to prevent items from falling in crankcase. From crankshaft, remove outer sprocket, inner double sprocket, and key. *See Fig. 13.*

Installation

1) Place inner key on crankshaft. Install inner double sprocket (line on sprocket should face outward). Install outer key and sprocket, new strainers, chain tensioners, and curved and straight dampers. Apply locking fluid to bolts.

2) Rotate crankshaft so key aligns with camshaft in left bank (No. 1 cylinder at TDC). Position camshaft with key pointing upward (rocker arms for No. 1 cylinder should have no clearance). *See Fig. 14.*

Fig. 13: Camshaft & Oil Pump Chain Drives

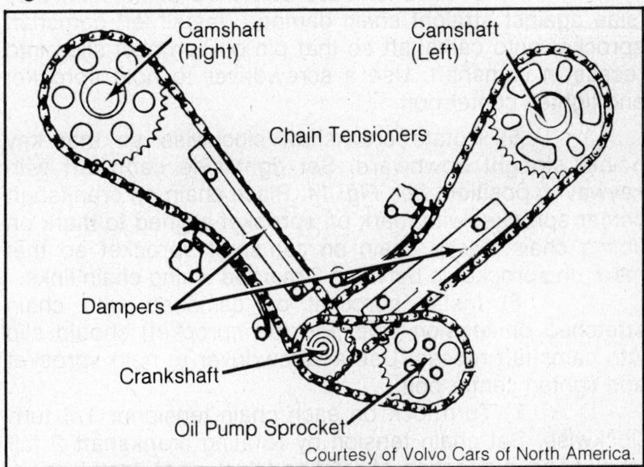

Courtesy of Volvo Cars of North America.

3) Place chain on camshaft sprocket with mark on sprocket between 2 marks on timing chain. *See Fig. 14.* Place chain on inner crankshaft sprocket so timing mark on sprocket is facing mark on crankshaft sprocket.

Fig. 14: Aligning Camshaft Sprocket Timing Marks

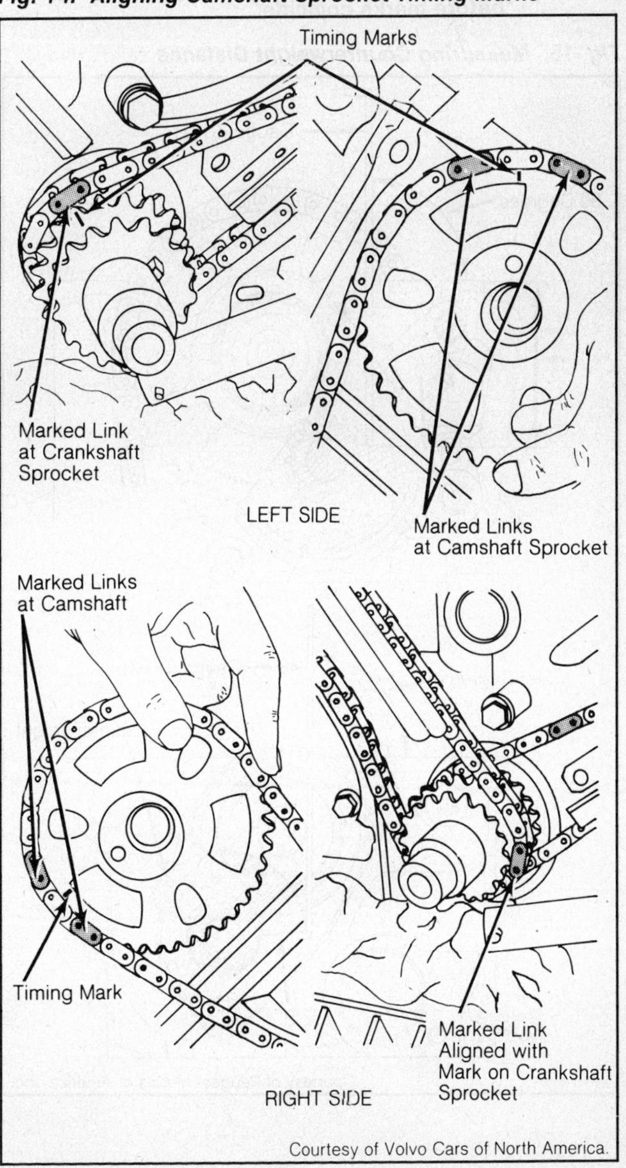

Courtesy of Volvo Cars of North America.

2.8L V6 (Cont.)

4) Chain should be stretched on tension side (side against straight chain damper). Install left camshaft sprocket onto camshaft so that pin on sprocket slips into recess in camshaft. Use a screwdriver to hold sprocket and tighten center bolt.

5) Rotate crankshaft clockwise so that key points straight downward. Set right side camshaft with keyway in position. *See Fig. 14.* Place chain on crankshaft center sprocket with mark on sprocket aligned to mark on timing chain. Place chain on camshaft sprocket so that mark on sprocket is between 2 marked timing chain links.

6) Install sprocket on camshaft with chain stretched on tension side. Pin (on sprocket) should slip into camshaft recess. Use a screwdriver to hold sprocket and tighten center bolt.

7) Turn lock on each chain tensioner 1/4 turn clockwise. Set chain tension by rotating crankshaft 2 full revolutions in direction of rotation (clockwise). Install chain and chain sprocket for oil pump.

NOTE: After initial rotation of crankshaft, marks on chains and sprockets will not coincide. It is necessary to rotate crankshaft several times before marks coincide.

Fig. 15: Measuring Counterweight Distance

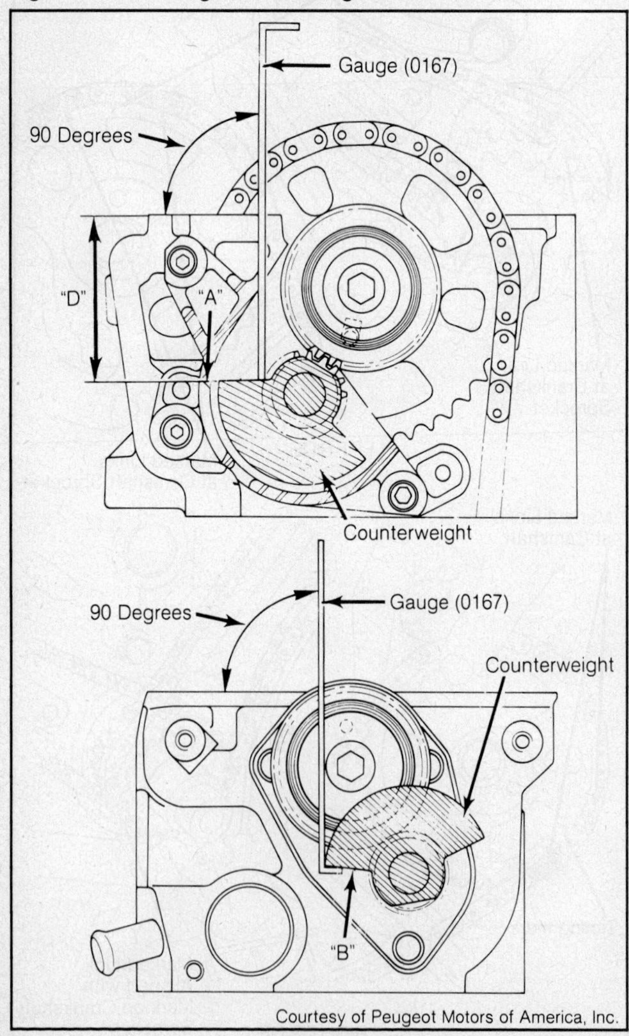

Courtesy of Peugeot Motors of America, Inc.

8) Place non-aligned end of Gauge (0.0167) on face "A" of front counterweight. Place angeled end of gauge under face "B" of rear counterweight. Check distance "D" between counterweight faces "A", "B" and valve cover gasket plane of cylinder head. Ensure distance lies within gauge marks. Incorrect counterweight setting by one tooth will cause a .20-.40" (5-10 mm) variation of distance "D". If variation is excessive, counterweights must be repositioned. *See Fig. 15.*

9) Install new gasket with timing gear cover. Apply locking compound to bolts and tighten to 11 ft. lbs. (15 N.m). Attach wiring harness to timing gear cover.

10) Install idler roller to timing gear cover. Using oil seal driver, install oil seal in timing cover. Install flywheel locking bracket at flywheel cover plate opening. Install pulley on crankshaft.

11) Tighten crankshaft nut. Remove flywheel locking bracket and install flywheel cover plate at transmission. Complete installation by reversing removal procedure.

IGNITION TIMING PLATE

1) Remove intake manifold and water pump. Remove rear plug at top front of engine block. Rotate crankshaft so No. 1 TDC mark on pulley is at 20 degree mark on timing plate. *See Fig. 11.*

2) Insert a long 5/16" drill bit or similar rod into hole and against crankshaft counterweight. *See Fig. 16.* Rotate crankshaft in direction of normal rotation until drill fits into recess in counterweight (TDC for No. 1 cylinder).

CAUTION: Do not allow drill bit to slip into engine. Use a drill or rod 10" long or longer, when possible.

Fig. 16: Locating Top Dead Center of No. 1 Cylinder

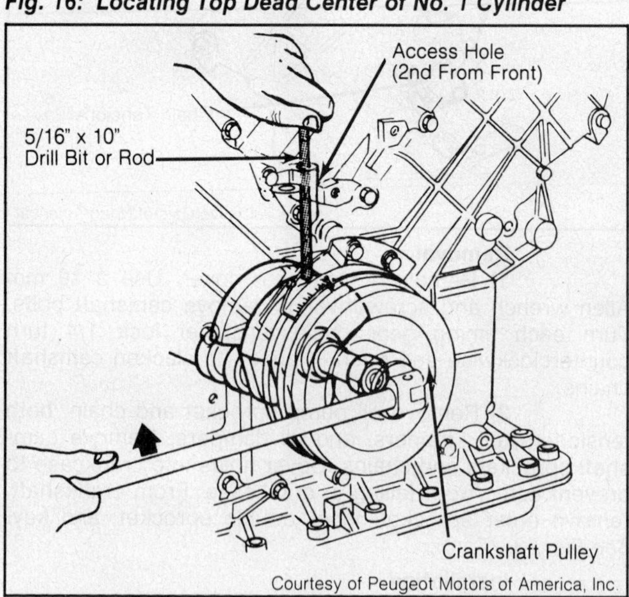

Courtesy of Peugeot Motors of America, Inc.

3) Loosen 2 bolts and adjust timing plate so that "0" degree mark is aligned with pulley mark. Tighten 2 bolts and remove drill bit or rod. Install plug with new seal and tighten to 26-30 ft. lbs. (35-40 N.m). Install water pump and intake manifold.

ROCKER ARM ASSEMBLY

Removal

1) Remove valve cover from cylinder head. Loosen rocker arm shaft bolts in sequence and remove

2.8L V6 (Cont.)

rocker arm shaft assembly. Remove lock ring from end of shaft. Remove rocker arms, shaft supports, spacer sleeves and springs.

2) Keep all parts in order for correct assembly. Remove lock bolt and rocker shaft support from rocker shaft. Check shaft-to-arm clearance. Clearance when new is .0005-.002" (.012-.054 mm). Replace worn parts as necessary.

Installation

1) Install rocker shaft support on rocker shaft with lubricating holes pointing downward. Flat top surface should face toward lock ring groove in other end of shaft. Tighten lock bolt.

2) Install thick spacer, exhaust rocker arm, thin spacer, intake rocker arm, spring and rocker shaft support, in order. Install lock ring in rocker shaft groove. *See Fig. 17.*

Fig. 17: Exploded View of Rocker Shaft Assembly

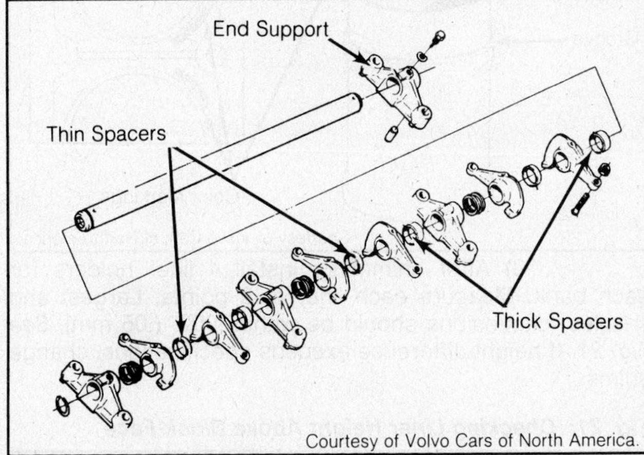

Courtesy of Volvo Cars of North America.

VALVES

VALVE ARRANGEMENT

Right Bank - E-I-E-I-E-I (Front-to-rear).
Left Bank - I-E-I-E-I-E (Front-to-rear).

VALVE SPRINGS & OIL SEALS

With cylinder head removed from engine, remove spark plugs, rear cover plate, lock plate and camshaft. Using a valve spring compressor, remove valve keepers, spring retainer, spring, lower spring seat and valve. Remove valve guide seal from guide. Mark valves for installation reference.

VALVE GUIDES

1) Check valve guides for wear. If replacement is necessary, press out guide using Removal Drift (5218). Ream hole in cylinder head to first or second oversize.

2) Heat cylinder head to 300°F (150°C) and cool valve guides to -95°F (-70°C). Press valve guides into cylinder head within 3-4 seconds. Use Installing Drift (5108) for intake or (5109) for exhaust, to press in new guides.

3) Using Reamer (5224), ream guides to .3150-.3158" (8.00-8.02 mm). Check for burrs and ensure valves move freely in guides. Install valve guide seals.

VALVE CLEARANCE ADJUSTMENT

1) Rotate crankshaft to bring No. 1 piston to TDC. *See Fig. 16.* In this position, both rocker arms for No. 1 cylinder should have clearance.

2) Check and adjust following cylinders for clearance: intake valves on cylinders 1, 2, and 4; exhaust valves on cylinders 1, 3, and 6. *See Fig. 18.*

Fig. 18: Valve Clearance Adjustment Sequence

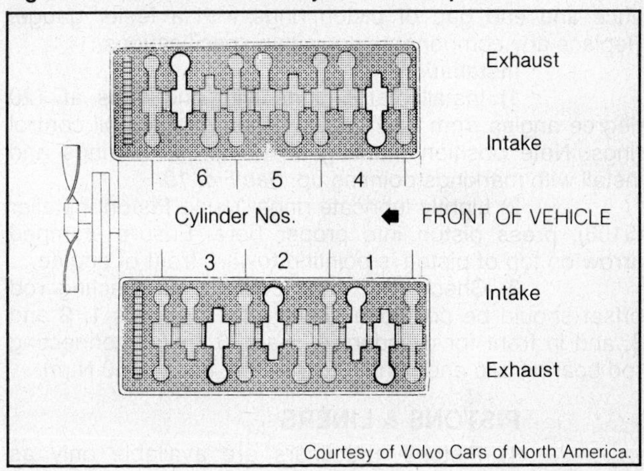

Courtesy of Volvo Cars of North America.

VALVE CLEARANCE SPECIFICATIONS

Valve	In. (mm)
Intake [1]	.004-.006" (.10-.15 mm)
Exhaust [1]	.010-.012" (.25-.30 mm)

[1] - Cold engine.

3) Rotate crankshaft one full turn, with mark again opposite "0" degree mark. Rocker arms for No. 1 cylinder will not have clearance. Check and adjust following cylinders for clearance: intake valves on cylinders 3, 5, and 6; exhaust valves on cylinders 2, 4, and 5. *See Fig. 18.*

PISTONS, PINS & RINGS

PISTON & ROD ASSEMBLIES

Removal

1) Remove lower crankcase and cylinder heads. Install cylinder liner holders to keep liners from

Fig. 19: Piston Ring Installation

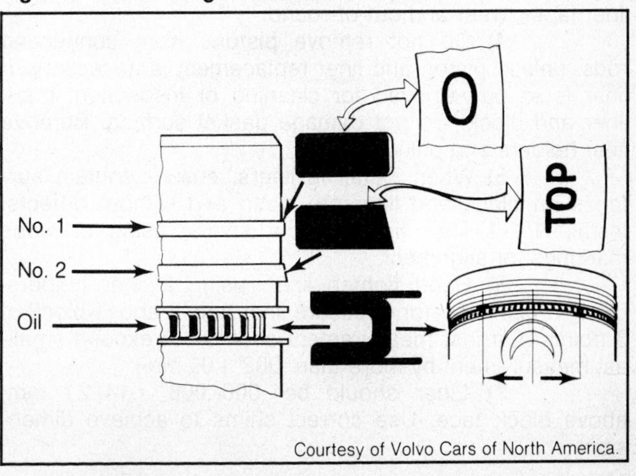

Courtesy of Volvo Cars of North America.

being pushed out with piston. Check connecting rod and crankshaft markings so piston assemblies can be installed in their original positions.

2) Connecting rods are marked "A" through "F" from rear of engine to front. Remove bearing cap nuts, bearing caps and push piston assembly out through top of bore. Remove big end bearing.

3) Remove piston rings. Clean ring grooves and piston of any carbon deposits. Measure side clearance and end gap of piston rings with a feeler gauge. Replace any components not within specifications.

Installation

1) Install piston rings with end gaps at 120 degree angles from each other. Offset gaps on oil control rings. Note position marking on compression rings and install with markings pointing up. *See Fig. 19.*

2) Lightly lubricate rings. Using Piston Installer (5106), press piston into proper bore. Ensure stamped arrow on top of piston is pointing toward front of engine.

3) Check rod offset position. Connecting rod offset should be positioned behind for cylinders 1, 2 and 3, and in front for cylinders 4, 5 and 6. Install connecting rod bearing cap and tighten to 33-37 ft. lbs. (45-50 N.m).

PISTONS & LINERS

1) Pistons and liners are available only as matched sets. Pistons are classified by diameter in 3 categories. Marking on piston top is either "A", "B" or "C", and corresponds to liners marked "1", "2" or "3" respectively.

2) Liners are marked in recesses at top of liner. Pistons and piston pins are also classified by diameters, with Blue, Red and White markings being used instead of numbers for proper matching.

PISTON & LINER DIAMETERS

Piston Designation	Diameter In. (mm)
"A" (for liner "1")	3.5815-3.5819 (90.97-90.98)
"B" (for liner "2")	3.5819-3.5823 (90.98-90.99)
"C" (for liner "3")	3.5823-3.5827 (90.99-91.00)
Liner Designation	**Diameter In. (mm)**
"1" (for piston "A")	3.5827-3.5831 (91.00-91.01)
"2" (for piston "B")	3.5831-3.5835 (91.01-91.02)
"3" (for piston "C")	3.5835-3.5839 (91.02-91.03)

3) Measure piston diameter at right angles to pin bore. Take measurements .32" (8.0 mm) above lower edge. With an bore gauge dial indicator, check cylinder liner taper, wear and out-of-round.

4) Do not remove pistons from connecting rods, unless piston and liner replacement is necessary. If liner is to be removed for cleaning or inspection, mark liner and block. Do not damage gasket surface. Remove liner holders and pull up liners.

5) When installing liners, ensure contact surfaces on block and liner are clean and without defects. Install No. 1 liner first (without shims) using previous markings for alignment.

6) Hand tighten liner, using 2 liner holders. Using a dial indicator, measure liner height above block at 3 points. Largest measurement should not exceed smallest measurement by more than .002" (.05 mm).

7) Liner should be .006-.008" (.14-.21 mm) above block face. Use correct shims to achieve dimension.

LINER SHIM THICKNESSES

Color	Thickness - In. (mm)
Blue	.0028-.0041 (.070-.105)
White	.0033-.0047 (.085-.120)
Red	.0041-.0055 (.105-.140)
Yellow	.0051-.0065 (.130-.165)

8) Install shims with color marking up. *See Fig. 20.* Inner tabs on shims should be in liner groove.

Fig. 20: Positioning Shims on Liners

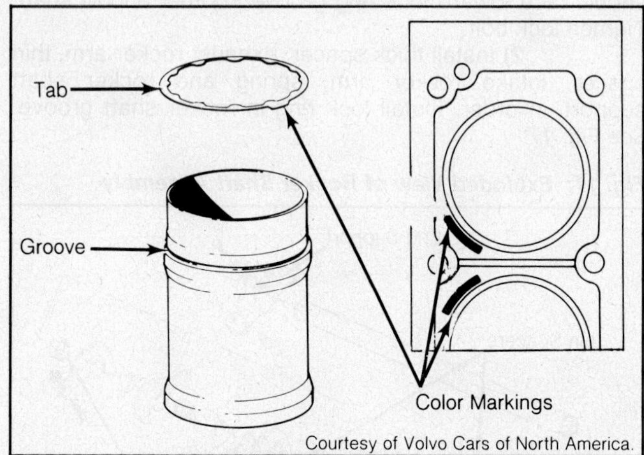

9) After shimming, install 4 liner holders for each bank. Measure each liner at 3 points. Largest and smallest dimensions should be within .002" (.05 mm). *See Fig. 21.* If height difference exceeds specifications, change shims.

Fig. 21: Checking Liner Height Above Block Face

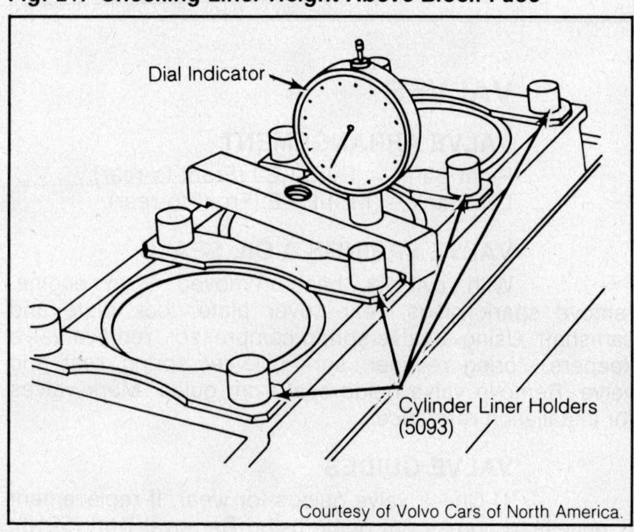

CRANKSHAFT & ROD BEARINGS

LOWER CRANKCASE

Removal

Remove oil pan, gasket, oil strainer and baffle plate. Remove crankcase bolts and main bearing nuts. Remove lower crankcase. Install main Bearing Cap Retainers (5096) on 2 outer bearings.

2.8L V6 (Cont.)

Installation

1) Install rubber "O" ring and sleeve for oil gallery. Clean and apply sealing compound to crankcase, and block surfaces. Remove main bearing cap retainers and install lower crankcase.

Fig. 22: Main Bearing Cap Tightening Sequence

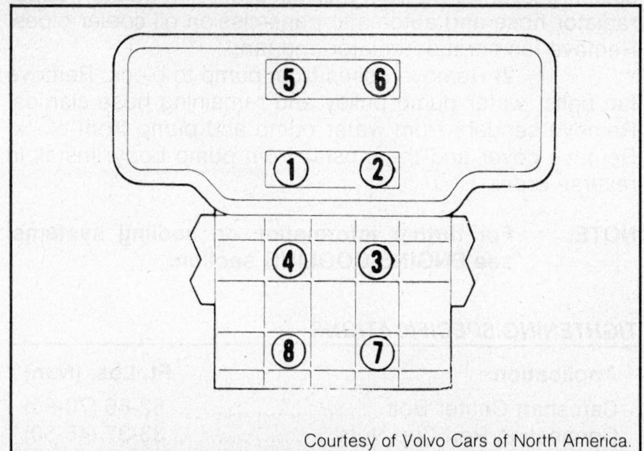

Courtesy of Volvo Cars of North America.

2) Ensure crankcase and block are flush at rear. Tighten bellhousing-to-crankcase bolts to 48 INCH lbs. (5 N.m). Tighten oiled crankcase bearing bolts to 22 ft. lbs. (30 N.m), then tighten an additional 75 degrees. Tighten crankcase pan-to-block bolts to 13 ft. lbs. (18 N.m). *See Fig. 22.* Install baffle plate, oil strainer, gasket and oil pan.

MAIN BEARINGS

Removal

1) Remove engine from chassis. See ENGINE REMOVAL section in this article. Remove oil pan, lower crankcase, and drive plate and spacer for automatic transmission. Remove rear crankshaft seal holder and pry out oil seal. Press in new seal, flush with seal holder.

2) Remove front pulley and timing chain cover. Remove timing chains and oil pump drive chain. Note location of markings on connecting rods. Remove connecting rod caps.

3) Check main bearing cap markings (marked 1 through 4, from rear-to-front). Remove main bearing retainers and caps. Remove upper and lower thrust bearings and lift out crankshaft. Remove main bearing inserts from block and caps.

NOTE: Thrust bearing is located on flywheel end of crankshaft.

Installation

1) Inspect crankshaft and measure journals for wear. Position oiled main bearings with oil holes to engine block. Carefully set crankshaft into place. Oil and install thrust bearings with notched ends in engine block groove.

2) Oil and install unnotched thrust bearings on crankshaft. Lubricate bearing shell and position in bearing cap. Install bearing cap and bearing retainers. Note that cap identification number faces front of engine.

3) Using a dial indicator, measure crankshaft end play and install thrust washers to adjust end play to .003-.011" (.07-.27 mm). Oil remaining bearing shells, place in caps and install. Ensure bearing cap numbers reference toward front of engine.

4) Install main bearing retainer on rear main cap and 1 nut on each remaining bearing cap to keep them in place until installation of lower crankcase. Install timing chains and tensioners.

5) Install connecting rod caps and tighten to specification. Check and adjust camshaft timing and install front chain cover. Install lower crankcase and tighten main caps. To complete installation reverse removal procedures.

CONNECTING ROD BEARINGS

Removal

Remove engine from chassis. See ENGINE REMOVAL section in this article. Remove lower oil pan and crankcase. Install main bearing retainers to hold crankshaft in place. Note location of identifying marks on connecting rods and caps. Remove caps and bearings.

Inspection & Service

Side clearance between connecting rod and crankshaft journal is .008-.015" (.20-.38 mm). If side clearance exceeds specification rod must be replaced. Connecting rod bolts are pressed in. Piston and rod assembly must be removed to replace bolts. Bearing clearance is .0011-.0031 (.030-.080 mm), check with Plastigage.

Installation

Lubricate and install bearing inserts. Tighten connecting rod nuts. Remove main bearing cap retainers. Install sleeve and "O" ring for oil gallery. Apply sealant and install lower crankcase. Tighten main bearing cap nuts to specification. Install lower oil pan.

ENGINE OILING

ENGINE OILING SYSTEM

Engine utilizes a force-feed lubrication system. Oil moves from oil pan through strainer to oil pump and full-flow oil filter mounted outside of engine block assembly. Oil is pressure fed from filter to drilled galleries in block.

Lubricant moves under pressure to main bearings, which are drilled to pass oil on to connecting rod and camshaft bearings, upward in block to rocker arm shafts.

Excess or run-off oil drains back down into oil pan through drain holes in cylinder head. Cylinder walls and piston rings are lubricated by splash from connecting rods.

CRANKCASE CAPACITY

Crankcase capacity is 6.9 quarts (6.5L) with oil filter change, and 6.3 quarts (6.0L) without filter change.

OIL PRESSURE

With engine warm and a new filter installed, minimum pressure should be 14.2 psi (1.0 kg/cm²) @ 900 RPM, and 57 psi (4 kg/cm²) @ 3000 RPM.

2.8L V6 (Cont.)

OIL PUMP SPECIFICATIONS

Application	In. (mm)
Backlash	[1] .007-.011 (.17-.27)
Bearing Clearance	
Driving Shaft	.0006-.0021 (.015-.053)
Bearing Clearance	
Idler Shaft	.0006-.0020 (.015-.051)
Clearance	
Tooth-to-Housing	[1] .0043-.0072 (.110-.185)
End Play	.0009-.0033 (.025-.084)
Relief Valve Spring Length	
No Load	3.52 (89.5)

[1] – Excluding bearing clearance.

OIL PUMP

Oil pump is serviced as a complete unit (housing cover with impeller and relief valve). Inspect housing, cover and gears for damage or wear. Replace if necessary.

Removal

Remove drive belts, crankshaft pulley and timing gear cover. Remove oil pump drive sprocket and chain. Remove 4 retaining bolts and lift out oil pump with gears.

Installation

Place gears on shaft and lubricate pump housing, gears and shaft. Install pump assembly, ensuring pump gears and shafts are centered in housing before tightening bolts. Install pump drive sprocket and chain. Install remaining components in reverse of removal order.

ENGINE COOLING

WATER PUMP

Removal & Installation

1) Disconnect negative battery cable. Drain coolant from both sides of block. Remove intake manifold, splash guard, wiring from thermal switch in radiator, upper radiator hose and automatic transmission oil cooler pipes. Remove fan shroud, radiator and fan.

2) Remove hoses from pump to block. Remove fan belts, water pump pulley and remaining hose clamps. Remove senders from water pump and pump from block. Remove cover and thermostat from pump body. Install in reverse order.

NOTE: For further information on cooling systems, see ENGINE COOLING section.

TIGHTENING SPECIFICATIONS

Application	Ft. Lbs. (N.m)
Camshaft Center Bolt	52-66 (70-90)
Connecting Rod Cap Nuts	33-37 (45-50)
Crankshaft Pulley Nut	177-206 (240-280)
Cylinder Head Bolts	[1]
Exhaust Manifold Bolts	11 (15)
Flywheel Bolts	33-37 (45-50)
Intake Manifold Bolts	11 (15)
Main Bearing Nuts	
Step 1	22 (30)
Step 2	[2]
Lower Crankcase Bolts	13 (18)
Transmission-to-Engine	30-36 (41-49)

[1] – See CYLINDER HEAD INSTALLATION section in this article.

[2] – Angle tighten an additional 75 degrees.

ENGINE SPECIFICATIONS

GENERAL SPECIFICATIONS

Year	DISPLACEMENT Cu. In.	DISPLACEMENT Liters	Fuel System	HP@RPM	Torque Ft. Lbs.@RPM	Compr. Ratio	BORE In.	BORE mm	STROKE In.	STROKE mm
1987	174	2.8	Fuel Inj.	136@5500	159@2700	8.8:1	3.58	91.0	2.87	73.0

VALVES

Engine Size & Valve	Head Diam. In. (mm)	Face Angle	Seat Angle	Seat Width In. (mm)	Stem Diameter In. (mm)	Stem Clearance In. (mm)	Valve Lift In. (mm)
2.8L							
Intake	1.73 (44)	29.5°	30°	.051-.067 (1.3-1.7)	.3135-.3145 (7.97-7.99)	.002 (.058)	....
Exhaust	1.46 (37)	44.5°	45°	.079-.094 (2.0-2.4)	.3127-.3141 (7.95-7.98)	.002 (.058)	....

2.8L V6 (Cont.)

ENGINE SPECIFICATIONS (Cont.)

PISTONS, PINS & RINGS

Engine	PISTONS Clearance In. (mm)	PINS Piston Fit In. (mm)	PINS Rod Fit In. (mm)	RINGS Ring No.	RINGS End Gap In. (mm)	RINGS Side Clearance In. (mm)
2.8L	.0007-.0015 (.020-.040)	.0006-.0008 (.010-.016)	-.0007--.0016 (-.020--.041) Press Fit	Comp. 1	.016-.024 (.40-.60)	.0018-.0029 (.045-.074)
				Comp. 2	.016-.024 (.40-.60)	.0010-.0021 (.025-.054)
				Oil	.016-.057 (.40-1.45)	.0004-.0092 (.009-.233)

CRANKSHAFT MAIN & CONNECTING ROD BEARINGS

Engine	MAIN BEARINGS Journal Diam. In. (mm)	MAIN BEARINGS Clearance In. (mm)	MAIN BEARINGS Thrust Bearing	MAIN BEARINGS Crankshaft End Play In. (mm)	CONNECTING ROD BEARINGS Journal Diam. In. (mm)	CONNECTING ROD BEARINGS Clearance In. (mm)	CONNECTING ROD BEARINGS Side Play In. (mm)
2.8L	2.7575-2.7583 (70.043-70.062)	.0014-.0034 (.038-.088)	.....	.0027-.0106 (.070-.270)	2.0577-2.0585 (52.267-52.286)	.0011-.0031 (.030-.080)	.008-.015 (.20-.38)

VALVE SPRINGS

Engine	Free Length In. (mm)	PRESSURE Lbs. @ In. (Kg @ mm) Valve Closed	PRESSURE Lbs. @ In. (Kg @ mm) Valve Open
2.8L	1.85 (47.1)	52-60@1.57 (23-27@40)	137-154@1.18 (61-69@30)

CAMSHAFT

Engine	Journal Diam. In. (mm)	Clearance In. (mm)	Lobe Lift In. (mm)
2.8L			
Front	1.5921-1.5931 (40.440-40.465)	.0013-.0033 (.035-.085)	.....
2nd	1.6157-1.6167 (41.040-41.065)		
3rd	1.6393-1.6403 (41.640-41.665)		
4th	1.6629-1.6639 (42.240-42.265)		

Porsche Engines

2.5L 4-CYLINDER

924-S, 944, 944-S, 944 Turbo

NOTE: For engine repair procedures not covered in this article, see ENGINE OVERHAUL PROCEDURES article at beginning of this section.

ENGINE CODING

ENGINE IDENTIFICATION

Engine identification code/serial number is stamped on left flange of engine block, near clutch housing. The identification code consists of the first 3 characters.

The first character denotes number of cylinders (4 = 4-cylinder engine). The second character is engine type (2 = 16 Valve DOHC, 3 = non-turbo, 5 = turbo). The third character is model year (H = 1987). The remaining characters are the engine serial number.

ENGINE IDENTIFICATION CODES

Application	Code
924S & 944 A/T	[1] 43 H
924S & 944 M/T	[2] 43 H
944S M/T	42 H
944 Turbo M/T	45 H

[1] – Engine serial numbers 60001-90000.
[2] – Engine serial numbers 00001-60000.

ENGINE, MANIFOLDS & CYLINDER HEAD

ENGINE

Removal
(924-S, 944 & 944-S)

1) Engine is removed from underneath vehicle. On manual transaxle vehicles, clutch bellhousing is removed with engine. Check hydraulic engine mounts for wear or damage before removal. See HYDRAULIC ENGINE MOUNTS in this article.

2) Raise and support vehicle. Disconnect negative battery cable. Remove front wheels. Disconnect battery positive cable and push through splash wall (with rubber grommet). Disconnect cruise control actuating cable, wiring and vacuum lines.

3) Disconnect 2 plugs for engine wiring harness. Unplug control unit harness connector (in passenger compartment, near steering column). Push control unit plug and wiring through firewall. Remove bracket (with sensor wire) on intake pipe.

4) Disconnect throttle cable and brake booster vacuum hose. Detach oxygen sensor plug and wire in metal lug on firewall. Remove air cleaner (with airflow sensor). Detach distributor cap, rotor and dust cap. Disconnect engine ground strap.

5) Disconnect and plug fuel lines. Attach Engine Support (VW 10-222A) to engine lifting bracket at front of engine. Hold engine in the installed position. Open heater valve. Remove cap on coolant expansion tank.

6) Remove splash shield. Drain cooling system. Disconnect exhaust system from engine. Remove starter. On manual transaxle, remove clutch slave cylinder with hydraulic line but do not disconnect line. Remove stabilizer bar from front suspension. Remove shield for right engine mount (on front crossmember).

NOTE: If control arm mounting bolts are disconnected, front end alignment must be checked.

7) Detach hydraulic engine mount from front crossmember. On vehicles equipped with power steering, disconnect (and plug) hydraulic lines. Mark universal joint position on steering gear. Remove joint from gear. Detach tie rod ends from steering arms.

8) Remove hydraulic engine mount from engine bracket (turn 180 degrees if necessary and remove from front). Pull down front crossmember enough to remove engine mount and universal joint. Disconnect left and right control arms from front crossmember. Remove front crossmember (with steering) from underneath.

9) On vehicles with air conditioning, loosen belt tensioner and remove A/C belt. Remove A/C compressor and mount. Suspend compressor from spring strut with wire. Do not disconnect refrigerant lines.

10) Detach coolant hoses from radiator, expansion tank and heater. Disconnect any remaining wiring and vacuum hoses. Remove radiator and cooling fans fron beneath vehicle.

11) Attach Engine Lifting Bracket (VW 3033) with short end toward rear of engine. Lift engine slightly and remove engine support. Remove lower bolts from central tube. Lower engine, pull forward and remove from underneath.

Removal (944 Turbo)

1) Remove upper section of air filter. Remove air induction tubes from rubber hose connections. Remove distributor cover, oil filter and power steering reservoir. Disconnect throttle cable and oxygen sensor plug.

2) Remove front lower trim panel and splash guard. Drain coolant and remove alternator vent duct. Remove radiator hoses and disconnect wires to cooling fan motors. Remove fans from below.

3) Remove radiator vent hoses and disconnect temperature switch. Remove coolant hoses from radiator expansion tank and turbo unit. Remove radiator from above.

4) Support engine with Engine Support (10-222A). Loosen drive belt tensioner on A/C compressor and remove belt. Remove A/C compressor and hang to side (leave hoses connected).

5) Remove front sway bar and brackets. Disconnect both side tie rods. Disconnect power steering hoses between steering pump and cooler. Remove power steering pump.

6) Remove lower control arm front pivot bolts and rear mounts. Remove universal joint from steering rod. Unbolt upper hydraulic engine mounts from engine support. Remove front crossmember and steering pump from below.

7) Unbolt deflection plate from starter and clutch housing and move rearward. Disconnect and remove starter. Disconnect slave cylinder from clutch housing, leaving lines connnected.

8) Remove exhaust system and catalytic converter at flanges on turbo and wastegate valve. Remove wastegate assembly and move bracket on bottom of transaxle rearward. *See Fig. 1.*

9) Remove upper transaxle mounting bolts. Disconnect heater hoses above exhaust manifold on cylinder head. Remove wiring harness and plugs. Discon-

2.5L 4-CYLINDER (Cont.)

Fig. 1: Turbo Exhaust System

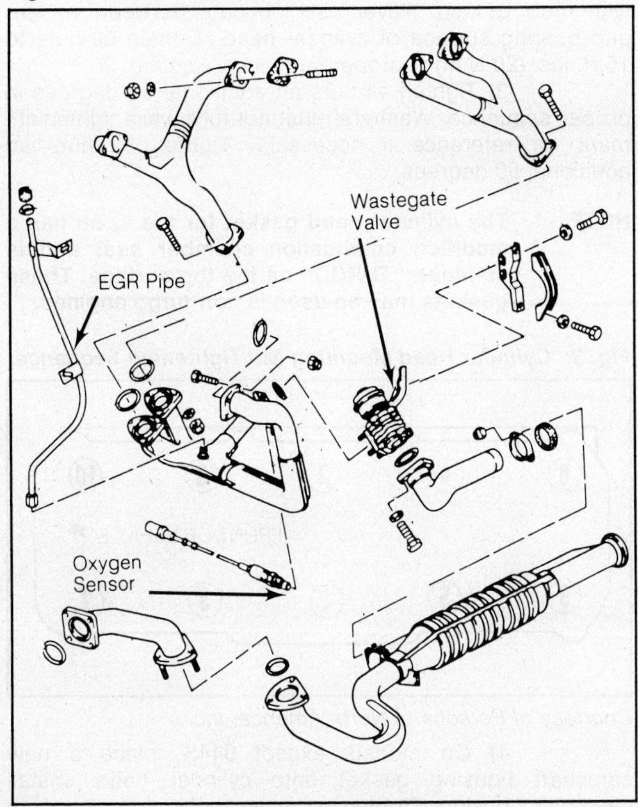

Courtesy of Porsche of North America, Inc.

nect vacuum hoses to brake booster. Disconnect diagnostic plug.

10) Attach engine sling and hoist assembly and support engine. Remove lower clutch housing bolts. Pull engine forward and disconnect ground cable from clutch housing. Remove wiring harness from firewall grommet. Unbolt drive shaft tube, and lower engine.

Installation

1) To install, reverse removal procedure. Check hydraulic engine mounts for wear or damage before installation. See HYDRAULIC ENGINE MOUNTS in this article. On manual transaxle models, insert clutch housing mounting bolts finger tight. Tighten housing bolts after hydraulic engine mount and front crossmember have been installed.

2) To install hydraulic engine mount, insert mount with twist lock positioned on stop (at right side rear), press top of mount into crossmember.

3) Tighten self-locking hydraulic engine mount-to-front crossmember nut. Next tighten hydraulic engine mount-to-engine bracket nuts. Tighten universal joint-to-steering gear nut.

4) After radiator installation, check for correct fit in rubber mounts. Secure coolant hose (between radiator and expansion tank) with 2 straps. Fill and bleed cooling system.

HYDRAULIC ENGINE MOUNTS

NOTE: **Right mount is subject to higher thermal temperatures and is more likely to fail or be damaged.**

Inspection

1) With engine in vehicle and mounts attached, check for knocking or vibration when engine is started. Check for engine vibration or rattle at idle.

2) Check for insufficient spring travel when pulling down on engine. Standard spring travel is .08-.12" (2-3 mm). Check mounts independently. Exhaust system may be used to apply leverage.

3) With mounts removed from vehicle, visually check for leaking fluid (alcohol/water), rubber peeling off, cracks or notches. Check mount height (as measured between weight bearing surfaces). Standard mount height is 2.72-2.80" (69.0-71.0 mm). Minimum compressed height is 2.56" (65.0 mm).

4) If hydraulic engine mount has failed, install new type (Gray) mount. Ensure each hydraulic engine mount has two 4 mm washers (steel or plastic) on new longer mounting bolts, between engine support bracket-to-mount mating surface. This allows flow-through ventilation of mount.

MANIFOLDS & CYLINDER HEAD

Removal

1) Disconnect battery ground cable. Remove coolant expansion tank cap. Remove splash guard. Drain coolant. Loosen tension rod mounting bolts, and tension rod lock nuts. Turn rod to loosen poly-rib belt. Remove belt.

2) Detach mounting bolts and remove camshaft drive belt outer cover (lower). Rotate crankshaft to set No. 1 cylinder to TDC of compression stroke. Remove distributor cap. Remove distributor rotor mounting screw. Remove rotor, dust cap and gasket.

3) Remove upper camshaft sprocket cover/distributor cap mount. Relax belt tension, and pull camshaft belt off camshaft sprocket. Remove 2 mounting bolts holding rear drive belt cover (camshaft bearing cap) to cylinder head. Disconnect fuel lines.

4) Remove plastic cover on fuel collection tube. Pull off wire plugs on fuel injectors and lay wiring harness aside. Remove aluminum plugs, coolant line and bolts. Remove camshaft cover mounting bolts. Detach housing from cylinder head.

NOTE: **Ensure hydraulic valve lifters do not fall out when housing is removed. DO NOT interchange lifters.**

5) Remove air cleaner assembly. Remove bolt from brace on air inlet manifold. Remove air inlet manifold by removing holder on oil dipstick tube. Remove hoses from brake booster and air inlet manifold. Remove retaining clamp on accelerator cable and inlet manifold/cylinder head mounting bolts.

6) Remove exhaust manifold/catalytic converter flange mounting bolts and detach exhaust system. Detach exhaust manifold-to-cylinder head nuts and remove exhaust manifolds.

7) Remove engine splash guard. Remove engine coolant and alternator vent tube. Unbolt exhaust pipe flange at turbo and remove turbo flange mounting bolt from cylinder block.

8) Disconnect coolant and oil pressure lines from turbo and remove turbo from exhaust manifold.

9) On 944 Turbo, remove hose from heater regulating valve and 2 screws on neck for coolant circuit.

2.5L 4-CYLINDER (Cont.)

Remove cylinder head mounting nuts in sequence. *See Fig. 3*. Remove cylinder head and discard gasket.

Inspection (924-S & 944)

1) Check cylinder head for distortion. Maximum warpage is .001" (.03 mm).

2) A maximum of .008" (.20 mm) may be removed from cylinder head surface. To determine if cylinder head has already been machined, measure distance "A". *See Fig. 2*.

3) The 8-valve cylinder head sealing surface (distance "A") is .941-.949" (23.90-24.10 mm). The minimum wear limit of distance "A" is .937" (23.80 mm).

Fig. 2: Cylinder Head Sealing Surface Distance

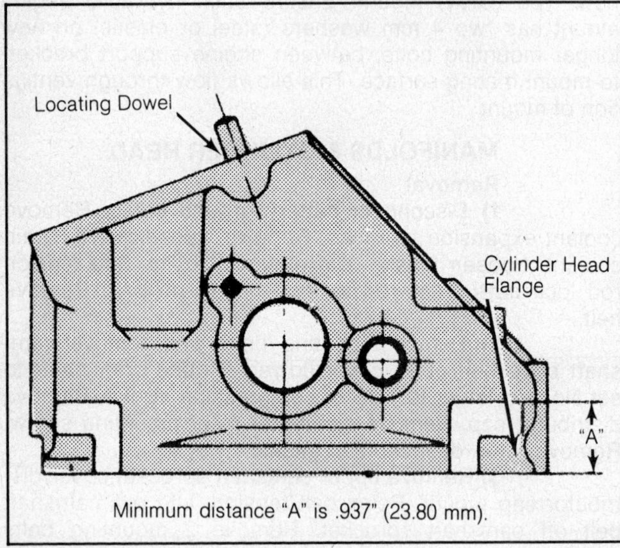

Courtesy of Porsche of North America, Inc.

4) When machining combustion chamber side sealing surface, always check camshaft housing side sealing surface for straightness. Before machining, plug oil bore of check valve and remove dowel pins.

Inspection (944 Turbo)

Check that ceramic lining in exhaust ports is not cracked, loose or damaged. Exhaust valve seat width is .098" (2.5 mm).

NOTE: **Although parts of the non-turbo and turbo cylinder heads appear identical, the cylinder head for the turbocharged engine differs from the non-turbo version in the following areas. The exhaust valve guides are longer and of different material. The check valve in the cylinder head oil pressure line has a smaller orifice, which allows more oil to be diverted to the crankshaft and turbo unit during initial starting. Turbo cylinder heads may be identified by a "T" stamped next to the cast part number.**

Installation (924-S, 944 & 944 Turbo)

1) Use 3 step "Angle Tightening Method" for all cylinder heads in conjunction with new cylinder head Nuts (999 076 028 02) and Washers (944 104 229 00). These nuts must be replaced at each repair as they are not reuseable.

2) Coat threads and contact surface of nuts with moly grease. Never use lubricant between washer and bearing surface of cylinder head. Tighten all nuts to 15 ft. lbs. (20 N.m) in proper sequence. *See Fig. 3.*

3) Tighten all nuts an additional 90 degrees in proper sequence. Washers must not turn while tightening, mark for reference if necessary. Tighten all nuts an additional 90 degrees.

NOTE: **The cylinder head gasket for the turbo has a modified combustion chamber seal and is stamped "TURBO" on the top surface. These gaskets may be used in non-turbo engines.**

Fig. 3: Cylinder Head Mounting Nut Tightening Sequence

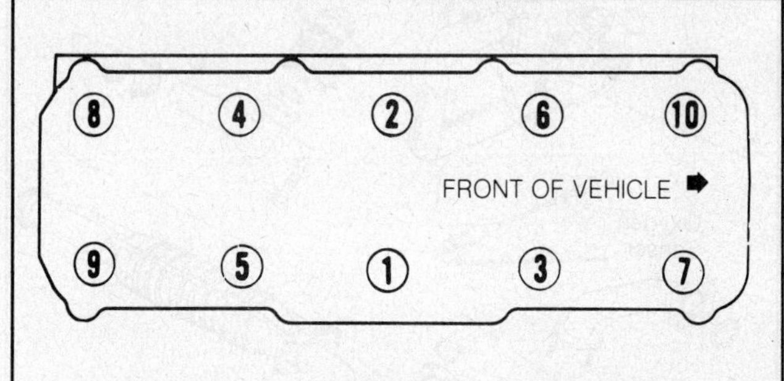

Courtesy of Porsche of North America, Inc.

4) On models except 944S, place a new camshaft housing gasket onto cylinder head. Install camshaft housing. Tighten mounting bolts and aluminum plugs.

5) Install drive belt. See CAMSHAFT DRIVE BELT in this article. Install exhaust manifold and tighten mounting nuts to 15-16 ft. lbs. (20-22 N.m). Check tightness of all remaining exhaust system mounting nuts.

6) When installing distributor cap, ensure locking boss on cap faces up. Align clamping hooks in cap so they are positioned horizontally and face left (as seen from front).

7) Place cap in position. Push in and turn hooks counterclockwise. Ensure clamping hooks are firmly engaged and cap fits tight. To complete installation, reverse removal procedure. Adjust poly-rib belt.

CAMSHAFT

CAUTION: **DO NOT rotate crankshaft with camshaft drive belt off or loose. Damage to internal components may result.**

CAMSHAFT & CAMSHAFT HOUSING

Removal (924-S, 944 & 944 Turbo)

Remove camshaft drive belt from drive gear. See DRIVE BELTS section of this article. Remove plugs (with seals) concealing top row of mounting bolts. Remove all housing mounting bolts. Disassemble camshaft housing components.

Removal (944-S)

1) Remove exhaust camshaft drive belt from drive gear. See DRIVE BELTS section of this article. Remove spark plug wiring from spark plugs. Remove camshaft cover from cylinder head.

2.5L 4-CYLINDER (Cont.)

2) Hold both camshafts in bearings with Camshaft Holder (9226). Remove all other bearing caps. Carefully release camshaft holder and remove both camshafts with chain and tensioner.

3) Camshafts on 944S are mounted directly in the cylinder head and there is no separate camshaft housing. After removing camshafts secure intake camshaft drive chain tensioner with wire.

Inspection
(924-S, 944 & 944 Turbo)

1) Inspect camshaft journals and journal bores in housing for wear and damage. Standard camshaft journal O.D. is 2.380-2.384" (60.46-60.56 mm). Standard camshaft housing bearing journal bore is 2.382-2.383" (60.50-60.53 mm). Replace components as necessary.

2) Check camshaft for excessive runout by placing camshaft in "V" blocks. Assemble dial indicator with pointer resting on camshaft journal. Maximum runout limit is .0008" (.020 mm). Replace camshaft if beyond limit.

3) With camshaft assembled in housing, install a dial indicator and check camshaft for end play. Standard end play is .004-.007" (.10-.18 mm). Replace bearing bracket if end play is beyond specification.

4) Camshaft lobe height for the exhaust lobes of the turbo motor camshaft is .433" (11 mm). All other camshaft lobes are .472" (12 mm). Camshafts may be identified by the last 2 digits of the numbers stamped on camshaft. The final digits of the turbo camshaft are 5R, the non-turbo 9R.

Inspection (944-S)

Inspection procedures for 944S cylinder head are not available from manufacturer.

Installation
(924-S, 944 & 944 Turbo)

1) Position gasket on cylinder head with oil supply bore for camshaft clear and in proper position. Housing is located on head with 2 dowel pins and mounted with Allen head bolts.

2) Install camshaft housing. Lightly lubricate plugs and seals with oil. Tighten housing to 29 ft. lbs. (40 N.m). If camshaft oil seal needs replacement, remove sprocket mounting bolt and washer. Remove drive belt sprocket.

3) Lubricate sealing lip of oil seal. Using Seal Driver (9202), install seal (with spacer) by driving in to its stop. Ensure arrow on outside of seal indicates direction of rotation.

Installation (944-S)

1) Place both camshafts in timing chain with cast bosses aligned with light colored chain links. Lubricate bearing surfaces with oil and place camshaft in bearings. *See Fig. 4.*

2) Mount camshafts on cylinder head with Camshaft Holder (9226). Install bearings and bearing caps on camshafts. Bearing caps are machined together with cylinder head and must always be installed in correct position.

3) Coat sealing surfaces of front and rear bearing caps with Loctite 574 before installation. Recheck camshaft position with gauge from Camshaft Holder (9226).

4) Use seal installer to drive seal on to drive end of camshaft. Lubricate camshaft and drive in seal.

Camshaft Chain Tensioner (944-S)

1) Remove camshaft cover and camshaft drive belt from exhaust camshaft drive pulley. Hold both camshafts in bearings with Camshaft Holder (9226). Remove all other bearing caps. Carefully release camshaft holder and remove both camshafts with chain.

NOTE: **Chain tensioner piston is under spring tension. Compress piston for removal and hold together with wire after removing.**

2) To install camshafts in cylinder head, align camshaft drive chain. Reverse removal procedure to complete installation.

DRIVE BELTS

NOTE: **When using drive belt tension gauge, always zero telltale gauge needle after lock pin is engaged (turned counterclockwise). Adjust drive belt tension only on a cold engine. Ensure gauge does not turn on belt and that slides remain flat on belt surface.**

Fig. 4: Camshaft Drive Chain Installation & Chain Tensioner

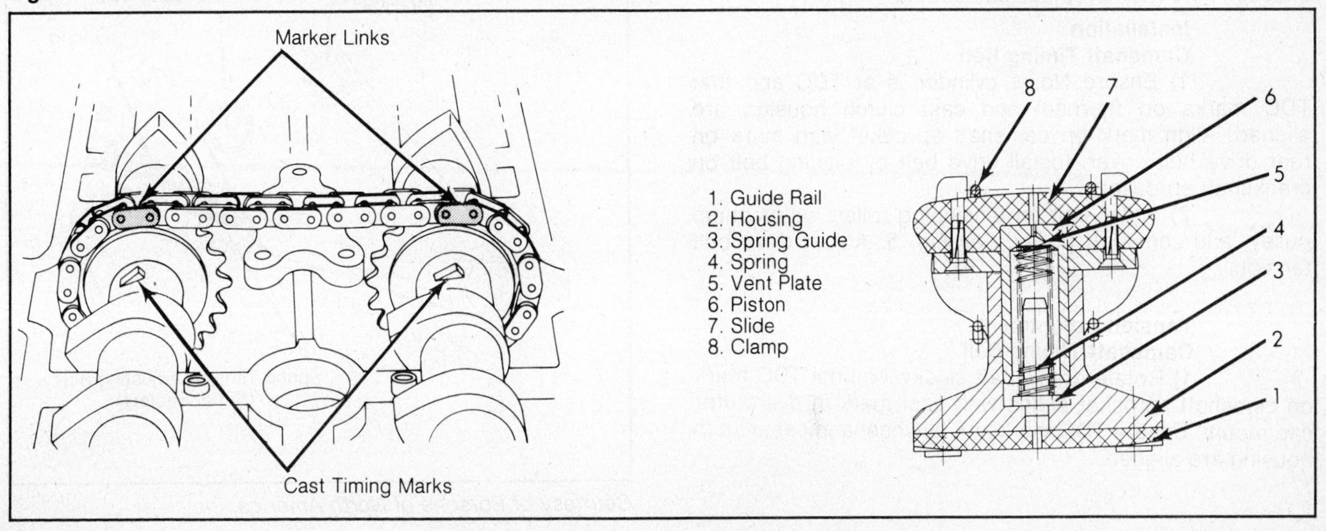

Porsche Engines

2.5L 4-CYLINDER (Cont.)

Fig. 5: Drive Belt Positioning

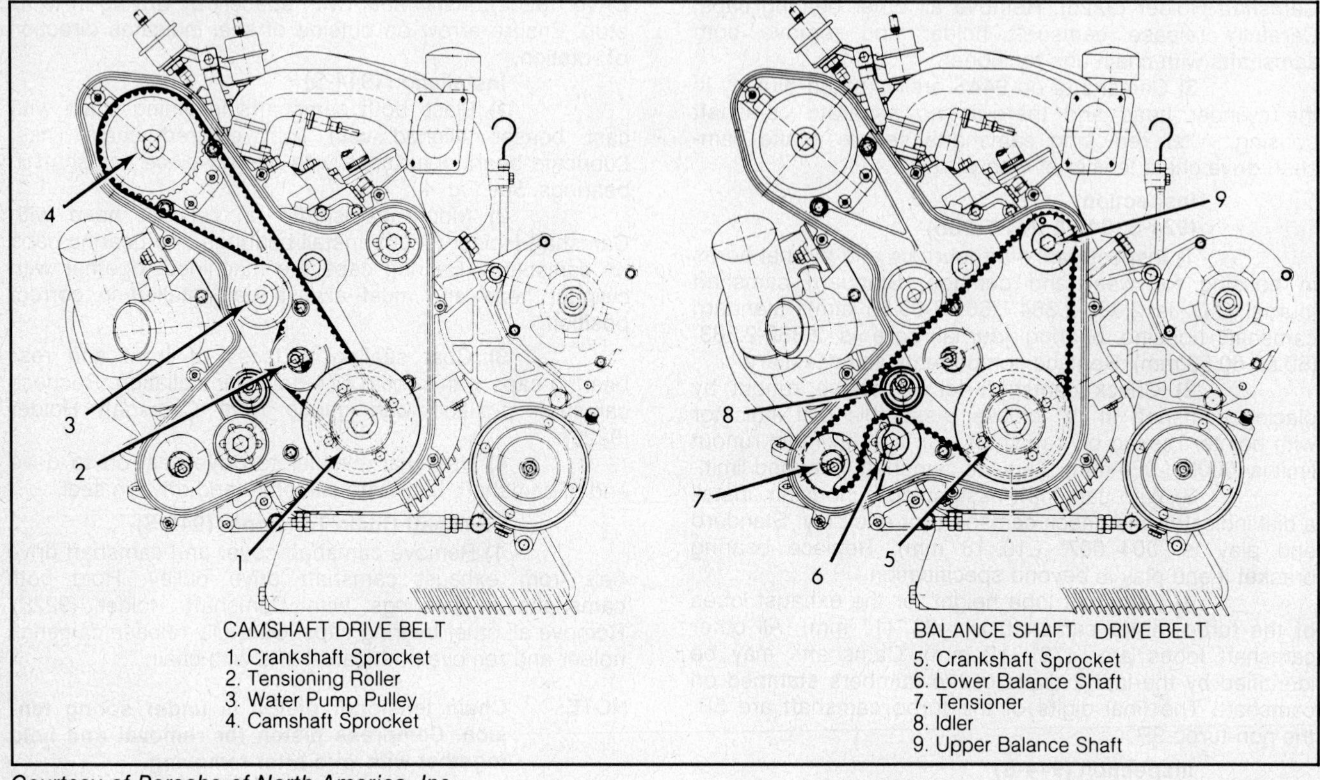

Courtesy of Porsche of North America, Inc.

CAMSHAFT DRIVE BELT

Removal

1) Check toothed belt alignment with upper belt cover removed and engine running. Mark belt travel direction before removal.

2) Disconnect battery ground cable. Remove alternator/compressor drive belt (poly-rib). Remove camshaft drive belt cover. Rotate crankshaft to set No. 1 cylinder to TDC of compression stroke.

3) Remove distributor cap. Remove distributor rotor and protective cap. Remove mount for distributor cap. Relax belt tension and remove camshaft drive belt from camshaft sprocket. Check drive belt for oil, dirt or excessive wear and replace as needed.

Installation

Camshaft Timing Belt

1) Ensure No. 1 cylinder is at TDC and that TDC marks on flywheel and cast clutch housing are aligned. Align mark on camshaft sprocket with mark on rear drive belt cover. Install drive belt by placing belt on crankshaft sprocket.

2) Install belt on tensioning roller, water pump pulley, and camshaft pulley. *See Fig. 5.* Adjust drive belt tension.

Tension Adjustment

Camshaft Timing Belt

1) Rotate crankshaft clockwise until TDC mark on camshaft sprocket aligns with cast mark in distributor cap mount. Ensure TDC marks on flywheel and cast clutch housing are aligned.

NOTE: **The 944-S intake camshaft is driven by a chain from the center of the exhaust camshaft. For information on camshaft alignment, see 944-S CAMSHAFT INSTALLATION procedure in this article.**

2) Loosen tensioner adjustment bolts. *See Fig. 6.* Spring will force tension idler against belt. Tighten adjustment bolts to 15 ft. lbs. (20 N.m).

Fig. 6: Mechanical Belt Tensioner

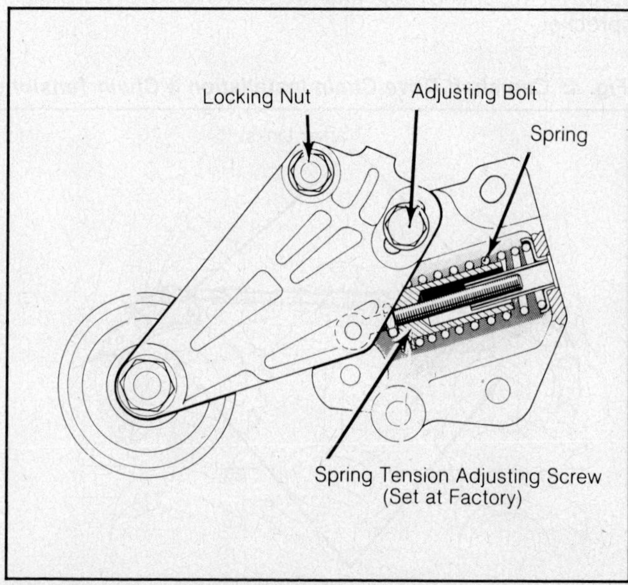

Courtesy of Porsche of North America, Inc.

Porsche Engines

2.5L 4-CYLINDER (Cont.)

Fig. 7: Belt Tension Gauge

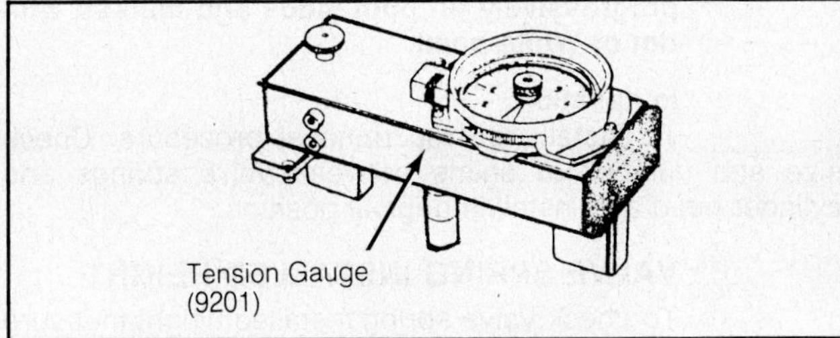

Courtesy of Porsche of North America, Inc.

CAUTION: DO NOT remove balance shaft sprocket mounting bolts to replace drive belt. Handle metal insert drive belts carefully.

NOTE: Mark belts if reused to ensure original direction of travel is maintained. DO NOT interchange belts.

BALANCE SHAFT DRIVE BELT

Removal

1) Remove splash guard. Loosen bolts of pressure adjusting rod (for alternator/compressor drive belt) slightly before loosening lock nuts. Loosen adjusting rod tension. Remove alternator belt.

2) Remove vent hose. Remove drive belt cover. Turn crankshaft (clockwise only) until TDC mark on camshaft sprocket is aligned with cast mark on distributor cap mount.

NOTE: TDC marks on flywheel and cast clutch housing must also be aligned.

3) Ensure marks on upper and lower balance shaft sprockets align with marks on rear drive belt cover. *See Fig. 8*. Loosen idler pulley so pulley does not touch drive belt. Mark belt travel direction. Remove belt.

Installation

1) Ensure crankshaft, camshaft and balance shaft sprockets are aligned. *See Fig. 8*.

2) Install drive belt. Ensure side of belt with color coded tooth faces out. Adjust drive belt tension. Complete installation by reversing removal procedure.

Adjustment

1) With splash shield and poly-rib belt removed, remove vent hose and drive belt cover. Loosen idler pulley so pulley does not touch drive belt. Turn crankshaft clockwise until TDC mark on camshaft sprocket is aligned with cast mark in distributor cap mount.

2) Ensure TDC marks on flywheel and clutch housing align. Check position of balance shaft sprockets. Marks on sprockets should be aligned with marks on rear drive belt cover.

3) For upper shaft, align groove "O" with Woodruff key. For lower shaft, align unmarked groove with Woodruff key. *See Fig. 8*. Prepare drive belt tension gauge for testing. Pull out lock pin on tension gauge and push out gauge pin opposite lock pin. Zero telltale needle.

4) Slide tension gauge onto belt. Push in gauge needle until lock pin is heard to engage. Read value from dial gauge. On engine with slotted guide roller, tension should be 2.4-3.0 dial value for both new and used belts.

Fig. 8: Balance Shaft Drive Belt Positioning

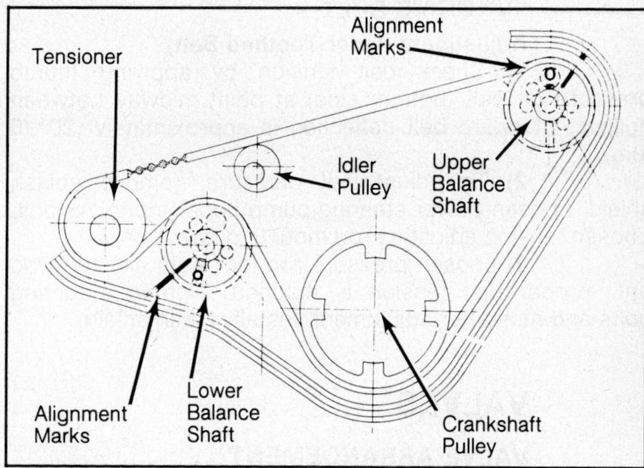

Courtesy of Porsche of North America, Inc.

5) If adjustment is necessary, turn tensioner clockwise to tighten and counterclockwise to loosen. Tighten tensioner nut. After adjusting drive belt tension, adjust idler pulley position.

6) Use Adjusting Gauge (9207) or a .020" (.50 mm) feeler gauge to ensure .020" (.50 mm) clearance between drive belt (at lower balance shaft sprocket) and idler pulley is maintained when upper portion of drive belt is preloaded .04-.08" (1.0-2.0 mm).

7) Tighten idler pulley. *See Fig. 8*. If correct gap cannot be reached, turn idler pulley 180 degrees and repeat adjustment. Tighten mounting nut. Install and adjust poly-rib belt.

DRIVE BELT TENSION GAUGE TABLE

Drive Belt Application	Tension (Gauge Dial Value)
Balance Shaft	
New or Used	2.4-3.0
Alternator/Compressor "Poly-Rib" Type	
New or Used	9.0-10.0

ALTERNATOR/COMPRESSOR POLY RIB DRIVE BELT

Adjustment

1) Prepare drive belt tension gauge for testing. Pull out lock pin on tension gauge and push out gauge pin opposite lock pin. Zero telltale needle.

2) Slide gauge carefully onto belt. Push in gauge measuring needle until lock pin is heard to engage. Read value from dial gauge and correct belt tension as needed.

3) The belt should have a tension of 9.0-10.0 dial value for both new and used belts. Pull out lock pin and remove gauge.

CAUTION: On drive belts with 6 ribs, adjust tension to specification and turn adjusting rod 2 complete turns for additional tension.

4) To adjust belt tension, loosen bolts at end of pressure adjusting rod. Loosen adjusting rod lock nuts and turn rod to obtain correct belt tension.

Porsche Engines

2.5L 4-CYLINDER (Cont.)

POWER STEERING PUMP "V" DRIVE BELT

Adjustment (Inner-Toothed Belt)

1) Check belt tension by applying thumb pressure on belt (bottom side) at point midway between pulleys. Standard belt deflection is approximately .20" (5 mm).

2) To adjust belt pressure, remove splash shield. Loosen power steering pump upper mounting bolt. Loosen tension adjusting rod mounting bolts.

3) Loosen pressure rod lock nuts and turn rod until proper belt tension is reached. Tighten mounting bolts and nuts after adjustment. Install splash shield.

VALVES

VALVE ARRANGEMENT

924-S, 944 & 944 Turbo

I-E-I-E-I-E-I-E (Front-to-rear).

944-S

Right Side – Exhaust valves.

Left Side – Intake valves.

HYDRAULIC VALVE LIFTERS

NOTE: **Use care to ensure lifters are always installed in original positions. DO NOT interchange lifter order. Store lifters so that oil bores face up.**

Inspection

(Except 944-S)

Check hydraulic lifters and bores in housing for excessive wear. Standard lifter O.D. is 1.4954-1.4959" (37.982-37.996 mm). Standard lifter bore is 1.4963-1.4971" (38.007-38.027 mm). Replace lifters and/or camshaft housing if worn beyond specification.

VALVE SERVICING

Inspection

(Except 944-S)

1) Standard clearance is .003" (.08 mm) for intake and exhaust valves. Replace valve and/or guide as needed. If valve is to be reused and stem tip shows signs of wear, ensure overall length is still at standard specification.

2) Standard overall valve length is 4.39" (111.5 mm) for intake valves and 4.41" (111.9 mm) for exhaust valves. If not to specification, replace valves.

CAUTION: **The exhaust valves for the turbo engine have a hollow stem which is partially filled with sodium. These valves must be disposed of properly and no attempt must be made to open the valve stem.**

VALVE SPRINGS

Removal

With cylinder head removed from engine, remove valve springs using Overhead Valve Spring Compressor (US 1020). Remove keepers and lift off retainer, inner and outer springs and shims. Ensure valve springs are to specification.

NOTE: **Inner and outer valve springs are wound progressively on both sides and marked with dot of White paint.**

Installation

To install, reverse removal procedure. Check size and number of shims between valve springs and cylinder head and install in original position.

VALVE SPRING INSTALLED HEIGHT

To check valve spring installed height measure distance between shim or valve spring seat and top of valve stem. *See Fig. 9.* Install Valve Spring Height Gauge (9138/1) on valve with spring retainer, keepers and shim(s). Read measurement on gauge and correct installed height, if required, by adding or removing shims.

Fig. 9: Installed Valve Spring Height Measurement

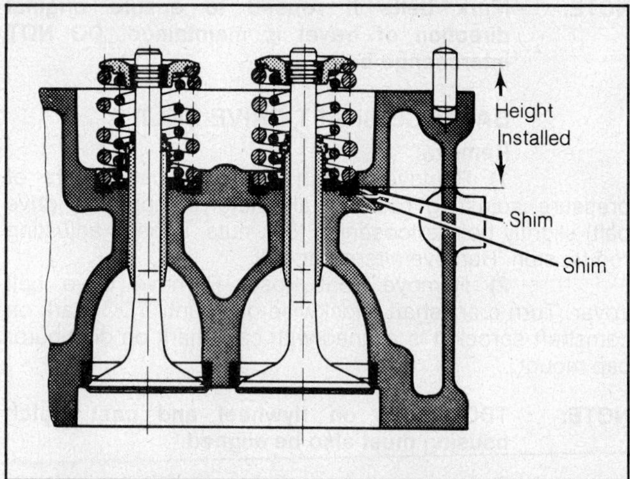

Courtesy of Porsche of North America, Inc.

NOTE: **Valve spring shims are available in .020" (.50 mm) and .040" (1.00 mm) thicknesses for spring height adjustment.**

VALVE SPRINGS

Engine	Free Length In. (mm)	Installed Height
924-S & 944		
Inner	1.73 (44.0)	.....
Outer	2.03 (51.5)	.....
944-S		
Inner	1.484	.....
Outer		
Intake	1.780 (45.2)	1.42 +.020 (36.0 +.5)
Exhaust	1.780 (45.2)	1.38 +.020 (35.0 +.5)
944 Turbo		
Inner	1.73 (44.0)	.....
Outer	2.28 (58.0)	.....

VALVE STEM OIL SEALS

With cylinder head and valve springs removed, use Seal Remover (3047 or 10-218), to remove valve seal. Use caution to prevent marring guide. Place plastic sleeve

2.5L 4-CYLINDER (Cont.)

(from Porsche 924 valve stem seal kit) on valve stem. Lubricate seal with oil and push into place using Pressure Pad (9202).

VALVE GUIDES

Inspection

1) Place new valve in guide with valve stem end flush with mating surface of cylinder head and camshaft housing. Mount dial indicator, in Holder (VW 387), on cylinder head with pointer shaft at 90 degrees to valve stem and pointer positioned on valve head.

2) Rock valve back and forth in guide and note indicator reading. Measurement must not exceed .032" (.80 mm) for both intake and exhaust valves. When replacing valve guides see VALVE GUIDE SPECIFICATIONS table for size information.

VALVE GUIDE SPECIFICATIONS

Application	924, 944, 944 Turbo	944S
Intake I.D.	.3543-.3549 (9.000-9.015)	.....
Intake O.D.	.522 (13.27)	.....
Guide Bore/Head	.512 (13.01)	.....
Press Fit/Head	.0024-.0031 (.060-.080)	.....

Installation

1) Cool valve guide with dry ice and coat with talcum powder. Heat cylinder head to 374°F (190°C). Using Valve Guide Installer (9221), press guide into cylinder head. Press in from camshaft side until guide reaches stop.

NOTE: DO NOT keep cylinder head heated at 374°F (190°C) for more than 90 minutes.

2) Using Valve Guide Reamer (3015), ream valve guides for proper valve stem clearance. After guide replacement, valve seat inserts must also be machined.

VALVE SEATS

1) With head removed and components disassembled, inspect valve seat inserts for proper seat width, depth, excessive wear and/or damage. Standard seat width is .059-.075" (1.50-1.90 mm) for exhaust seats and .071-.087" (1.80-2.20 mm) for intake seats. Exhaust valve seats for turbocharged engines should be .098" (2.5 mm) wide. Recut or replace seat insert as necessary.

CAUTION: When cutting valve seats, ensure only minimum amount of metal is removed to prevent premature wear of valves and seats.

2) After valve seat inspection and/or repair, check insert seat depth by installing respective valve and spring assembly. Measure distance from valve stem tip-to-camshaft housing mount surface. Standard distance is .52-.55" (13.2-14.1 mm). Maximum distance is .57" (14.5 mm).

NOTE: The maximum valve seat depth wear limit must not be exceeded or improper hydraulic lifter function will result.

PISTON, PINS & RINGS

FITTING PISTONS

1) To check pistons for excessive wear, measure diameter approximately 2.4" (61 mm) down from top of piston crown, at 90 degree offset from piston pin bore. Piston repair sizes are standard, first oversize and second oversize, with 3 tolerance groups for each size.

2) Standard tolerance group mark stamped on piston crown is either "0", "1" or "2". Tolerance group stampings indicate if piston is standard, .0004" (.010 mm) or .0008" (.020 mm) oversize of its particular repair size. See PISTON OVERSIZE & TOLERANCE GROUP CODE table.

NOTE: Tolerance group marks are stamped on cylinder block head gasket surface, in-line with each bore center line. Piston tolerance group mark is stamped on piston crown. Pistons and cylinders must match. Different tolerance groups may be used in one engine.

PISTON OVERSIZE & TOLERANCE GROUP CODE

Piston Repair Size	Piston Diameter In. (mm)	Cylinder Bore Diameter In. (mm)
KS Standard	3.9359-3.9365 (93.973-93.987)	[1] 3.9368-3.9372 (99.995-100.005)
	3.9363-3.9369 (99.983-99.997)	[2] 3.9372-3.9376 (100.005-100.015)
	3.9367-3.9373 (99.993-100.007)	[3] 3.9376-3.9380 (100.015-100.025)
1st Oversize	3.9556-3.9562 (100.473-100.487)	[4] 3.9565-3.9569 (100.495-100.505)
	3.9560-3.9566 (100.483-100.497)	[5] 3.9569-3.9573 (100.505-100.515)
	3.9564-3.9570 (100.493-100.507)	[6] 3.9573-3.9577 (100.515-100.525)
2nd Oversize	3.9753-3.9759 (100.973-100.987)	[7] 3.9762-3.9766 (100.995-100.005)
	3.9757-3.9763 (100.983-100.997)	[8] 3.9766-3.9770 (101.005-101.015)
	3.9761-3.9767 (100.993.-101.007)	[9] 3.9770-3.9774 (101.015-101.025)

[1] – Piston tolerance group code is "0".
[2] – Piston tolerance group code is "1".
[3] – Piston tolerance group code is "2".
[4] – Piston tolerance group code is "I0".
[5] – Piston tolerance group code is "I1".
[6] – Piston tolerance group code is "I2".
[7] – Piston tolerance group code is "II0".
[8] – Piston tolerance group code is "II1".
[9] – Piston tolerance group code is "II2".

3) When measuring cylinder bore and out-of-round tolerances, ensure crankcase lower section is installed and tightened to specification. Using a bore gauge, measure bore approximately 2.4" (61 mm) from upper edge of cylinder block, 90 degrees offset from piston pin bore.

Porsche Engines

2.5L 4-CYLINDER (Cont.)

4) Standard out-of-round tolerance is .0004" (.010 mm) and maximum tolerance is .0008" (.020 mm). Standard piston-to-cylinder bore clearance is .0003-.0013" (.008-.032 mm) and maximum clearance is .0032" (.080 mm).

5) If piston-to-cylinder clearance or out-of-round tolerance is beyond specification, cylinder bores may be machined for next oversize piston. If necessary, cylinder bores may be machined separately since oversize piston is the same weight as standard piston.

NOTE: **Due to cylinder block composition (aluminum alloy) and bore finish (silicone), vehicle manufacturer recommends using only Sunnen brand Automatic Cylinder Honing Machine (CK-10) with Honing Head (CK-3000), special Honing Stone Set (EHU-123, C30-J84 or JHU-820 and C30-Co3-81) and Silicone Paste (AN-30).**

CAUTION: **Before honing procedure, ensure upper and lower cylinder block sections are bolted together. Tighten to specification or cylinder bore distortion may result.**

6) When honing cylinders to size, ensure initial honing procedure brings cylinder bore size to within .004" (.10 mm) of finished size. Second (final) honing procedure should bring cylinder to within .0008" (.020 mm).

7) After final honing procedure, polish bore to final size and treat with Sunnen silicone mixture according to manufacturer's instructions. After honing and polishing procedures are complete, cut upper cylinder edge to a 30 degree chamfer .02" (.5 mm) wide.

8) Before assembly, thoroughly clean upper and lower block assemblies of emery particles and silicone paste. Ensure pistons are installed with rounded edges of valve pockets facing right side (forward direction) and arrows on piston crowns facing pulley.

PISTON PIN

1) Remove circlips and piston pins from pistons. Mark piston and pin for each cylinder. Inspect piston(s) for excessive wear. See FITTING PISTONS and FITTING RINGS.

NOTE: **Piston pin bore is offset by .058" (1.50 mm) on 924S and 944 engine, and .039" (1.00 mm) on 944S and 944 Turbo engine. Arrow on piston crown faces front pulley. Piston pin diameter is .9447-.9448" (23.996-24.000 mm).**

2) Check piston pin-to-connecting rod bushing clearance. See CRANKSHAFT & CONNECTING RODS. If clearance is beyond .0013" (.032 mm), replace piston/pin assembly or install new rod bushing as necessary.

3) When installing pin into piston, heat piston to 140°F (60°C). Slide pin into piston in a single motion. If installation is tight, lubricate pin bore lightly. Install pin circlips with end gap at top or bottom.

FITTING RINGS

1) Position each piston ring approximately 2/3 down into cylinder bore. Measure ring end gap. Check side clearance of rings in piston ring grooves.

2) Install rings on piston with "TOP" (or lettering) facing upward. Adjust end gap spacing so each scraper ring end gap is offset 45 degrees from expander ring ends and side rail gaps offset 90 degrees from each other.

3) Install compression rings so gaps are offset 120 degrees. Ensure no ring gap is in-line with thrust face of pin bore.

4) Install Ring Compressor (US 1008 A) on piston/rings assembly. With end gaps properly positioned, tighten compressor. Lubricate cylinder bore and piston assembly lightly with oil.

5) Position piston/compressor assembly over cylinder bore and lightly tap piston assembly down into bore. Ensure rounded edges of valve cut-outs face right side.

CYLINDER BLOCK ASSEMBLY

CYLINDER BLOCK

CAUTION: **DO NOT attempt piston replacement if facilities for Sunnen honing procedure are not available. If "silcone-lapping" step is omitted, piston seizure may result.**

NOTE: **The crankcase upper and lower sections, as well as balance shaft bearing caps, are machined together and cannot be replaced separately.**

CRANKCASE LOWER SECTION

Crankcase Sealing

1) It is not necessary to remove old sealant for repairs. New sealant will dissolve the old. Remove any grease from surface so that after cleaning solution has dried, new sealant can be applied.

NOTE: **If old sealant must be removed, use a fine steel brush. Do not damage sealing surfaces during cleaning.**

2) Using a short-pile velour roller, apply a very thin coat of anaerobic sealant (Loctite 574, Orange) to lower crankcase section in areas of oil intake and sealing surface around flywheel.

3) After applying sealant, install lower crankcase section to cylinder block within 10 minutes. Install mounting nuts and washers so that rounded side of washers and lettered side of nuts face up.

4) When tightening lower crankcase section to cylinder block, ensure 10 mm nuts are tightened in 2 steps and 12 mm nuts are tightened in 3 steps, in proper sequence. *See Fig. 10*.

CRANKCASE MAIN BEARING BORE MEASUREMENTS

NOTE: **Main bearing bores should be measured and resized (if necessary) whenever upper cylinder block and lower crankcase section are disassembled for repair.**

1) Attach upper cylinder block to holding fixture. Assemble lower crankcase section without crankshaft assembly or bearing inserts. Lightly tighten all lower crankcase section mounting nuts by hand.

2) Align both upper and lower crankcase sections. Tighten lower crankcase mounting bolts to proper torque, in sequence. *See Fig. 10*. Using an inside micrometer, cross-check main bearing bores and realign as needed.

3) Measure crankcase main bearing bores. Standard I.D. for all main bearing bores is 2.9528-2.9535" (75.000-75.019 mm). If bores are too tight, ream to standard size. If bores are too large, ream (in 2 steps) to bearing oversize of 2.9626-2.9633" (75.250-75.269 mm).

Fig. 10: Crankcase Lower Section Tightening Sequence

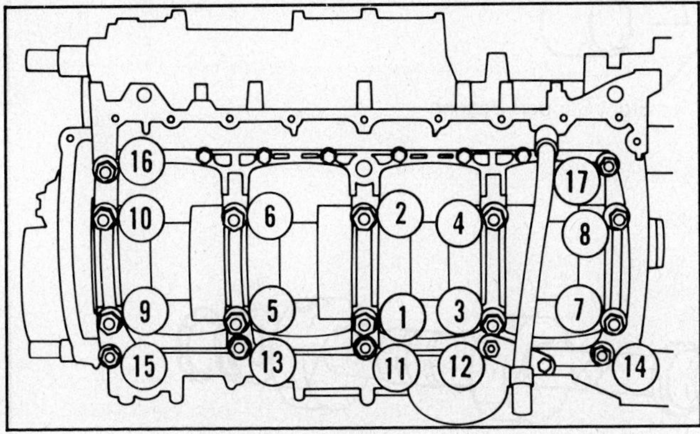

CRANKSHAFT & ROD BEARINGS

NOTE: **Replacement crankshaft main and rod bearings are available in standard and .010" (.25 mm), .020" (.50 mm) and .030" (.75 mm) oversize and undersize.**

MAIN BEARINGS

1) When inspecting crankshaft, check main bearing insert bores in cylinder block/lower crankcase section for straightness and size. See CRANKCASE MAIN BEARING BORE MEASUREMENTS in this article. Assemble lower crankcase section to cylinder block with main bearing inserts installed.

2) Using bore gauge and micrometer (or Plastigage method), measure all main bearing inserts I.D. and crank journals O.D. to check insert-to-journal clearances. Maximum clearance is no more than .006" (.16 mm). Grind crankshaft and replace bearing inserts as necessary.

NOTE: **A new main bearing design was put into production during the 1985 model year. When replacing main bearings always use late type bearings. The new bearings have a .394" (10 mm) oil feed slot instead of the older .275" (7 mm) slot. The new bearings also have additional oil slots at the bearing split lines.**

CONNECTING ROD BEARINGS

1) Using Plastigage and/or micrometer and bore gauge, check connecting rods and crankshaft for proper bearing-to-journal clearance. Maximum clearance is .004" (.10 mm).

2) Regrind crankshaft and replace rod bearing inserts if clearance is greater than specification. When replacing rod bearing inserts on crankshaft, inspect connecting rod bearing insert bore for excessive wear or damage. Replace rod as necessary.

NOTE: **Connecting rod stretch bolts should never be reused. Replace rod bolts whenever connecting rods are disassembled.**

CAUTION: **New connecting rod nuts are available with ribbed, nut-to-rod cap, contact surface. Use these nuts whenever rods are reassembled. Do not use old type (smooth) rod nuts or engine damage may result.**

3) With new inserts installed and rods assembled in their proper positions, check rod side clearance. If side clearance is more than .004-.016" (.10-.40 mm), replace rod(s).

THRUST BEARING END PLAY

1) Check crankshaft thrust bearing size and end play. Number 3 main bearing is the thrust bearing. Standard thrust bearing width is 1.184" (30.08 mm).

2) With crankshaft and inserts installed and cylinder block/lower crankcase section assembled, mount dial indicator using Indicator Adapter (VW 387). Position pointer on crankshaft end. Measure end play and change thrust bearing if not within specification.

CRANKSHAFT OIL SEAL

1) Install Crankshaft Oil Seal Guide (9203) onto end of crankshaft. Lubricate new oil seal sealing lip with oil. Slide seal over guide.

2) Remove seal guide. Using Oil Seal Installer (9126), ensure seal is still aligned with bore and tap into position. Crankshaft oil seal (flywheel end) can be installed with crankcases assembled.

BALANCE SHAFTS

BALANCE SHAFTS & BEARINGS

NOTE: **Both balance shafts are identical and rotate at twice crankshaft speed. Front balance shaft bearings, which guide shafts axially, are pressed into upper and lower front bearing housings. Rear bearings are integral with the cylinder block and housing/cover. Each shaft is sealed with an oil seal and 2 "O" rings. Balance shaft covers are machined and matched to cylinder block. Coding numbers stamped on covers and block must match.**

1) Balance shaft journal diameter is 1.2195-1.2201" (30.975-30.991 mm). Front bearing flange cap bushing bore is 1.3386-1.3393" (34.000-34.019 mm).

2) Replace balance shafts, if not to specification. If sleeve in upper bearing housing flange cap must be replaced, remove and replace with Sleeve Remover/Installer (9210). On final assembly, thoroughly clean balance shaft cover.

NOTE: **If necessary, heat cover with hot air blower to melt old sealant and/or use Loctite Adhesive Remover (60646).**

2.5L 4-CYLINDER (Cont.)

Fig. 11: Disassembled View of Balance Shafts

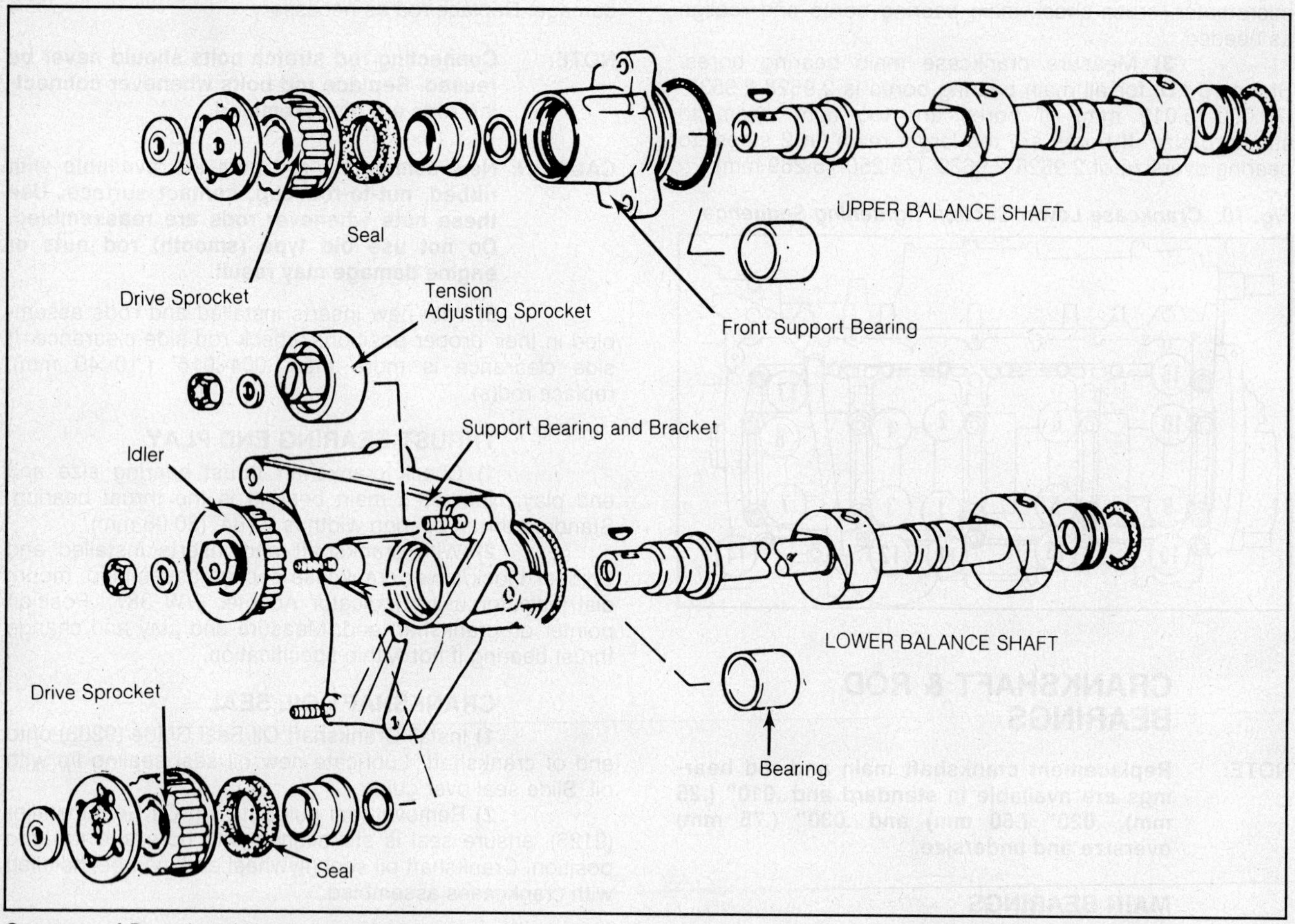

Seal
Drive Sprocket
Tension Adjusting Sprocket
UPPER BALANCE SHAFT
Front Support Bearing
Support Bearing and Bracket
Idler
LOWER BALANCE SHAFT
Drive Sprocket
Bearing
Seal

Courtesy of Porsche of North America, Inc.

3) Apply thin coat of sealant (Loctite 638) to sealing surfaces. Install cover on engine and tighten all nuts and bolts finger tight. Mount upper bearing housing with a lightly oiled "O" ring but do not tighten mounting bolts at this time.

4) Tighten cover bolts to specification in sequence and in 2 steps. *See Fig. 12.* Check movement of balance shaft between each tightening step. Tighten front bearing housing bolts.

Fig. 12: Balance Shaft Cover Tightening Sequence

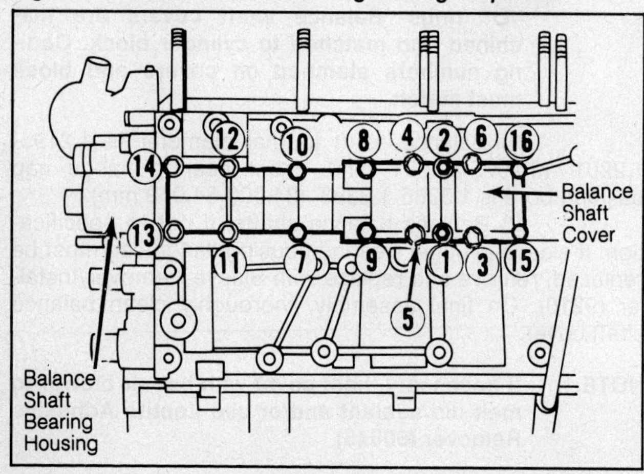

Courtesy of Porsche of North America, Inc.

BALANCE SHAFT OIL SEALS & DRIVE SPROCKETS

Removal

With alternator/compressor drive belt, front belt cover and balance shaft drive belt removed, loosen balance shaft sprocket mounting bolt. Remove bolt, washer and sprocket for each balance shaft. Note position of each sprocket on balance shaft for installation reference. Remove oil seals as necessary and discard.

NOTE: Balance shaft oil seals have different diameters and sealing lips. Arrow stamped on front of each seal must point in rotating direction of related balance shaft.

Installation

1) Lubricate new oil seal sealing lip with oil and install with spacer. Using Oil Seal Driver (9202) and hammer, install upper and lower balance shaft oil seals. Position both balance shaft Woodruff key grooves facing up.

2) Install upper and lower balance shaft sprockets over Woodruff keys and onto shafts. Ensure upper sprocket collar plate notch aligns with notch in rear belt cover notch (1 o'clock position) and lower sprocket collar plate notch aligns with rear cover lower rib (8 o'clock position).

NOTE: Only upper Woodruff key groove is marked with an "O" on balance shaft sprockets.

2.5L 4-CYLINDER (Cont.)

3) On both sprockets, coat mounting bolt with Loctite 574. Install mounting bolts, washers and collar plates. Ensure upper sprocket collar is mounted so that "O" mark can be seen in large, round opening in collar and locating tab engages in unmarked sprocket groove.

4) Ensure lower sprocket collar is mounted so that "O" mark is visible in square opening of collar plate and locating tab protrudes into "O" marked sprocket groove. Using Sprocket Holder (9200), tighten mounting bolts to specification.

ENGINE OILING

ENGINE OILING SYSTEM

Engine utilizes a wet sump oil system. An oil cooler is located in a housing on engine and uses coolant as a heat exchanger. Cooler housing is also used as an oil filter and oil pressure sending unit mount. The oil pump is a crescent gear type pump located in a separate housing that is bolted to front of crankcase.

An oil pressure relief valve is located inside the oil pump housing. A splined drive sleeve drives oil pump by way of an axial connection with the inner gear. Oil pump draws in oil from oil pan through oil filter screen. *See Fig. 13.* Filter screen tube is mounted on crankcase lower section and is sealed with an "O" ring. Oil continues to oil pump through a bore in crankcase upper and lower sections.

Sealing surfaces around suction bore are coated with sealant (Loctite 574). Oil delivered by pump enters a short bore in crankcase upper section. From there, oil reaches pressure relief valve and oil cooler. After being cooled, oil passes through oil filter and pressure sending unit and enters main bore. Main bearings are supplied by main oil bore. Connecting rod bearings receive oil from crankshaft.

Oil for left balance shaft rear bearing comes from crankshaft thrust bearing (No. 3). Right balance shaft is supplied by a separate bore off of main bore. An oil bore in each balance shaft supplies oil to front flange bearings.

A gallery passes through crankcase to cylinder head and camshaft housing. Camshaft housing has branching bore to supply oil to camshaft and lifters. A check valve is installed to prevent oil from flowing down cam supply bore when engine is not operating.

CRANKCASE CAPACITY

Crankcase oil capacity is 6.87 qts. (6.5L) with filter change.

OIL FILTER & OIL COOLER

The oil filter housing is mounted on the left side of the engine block and the cooler is internally mounted and cooled by engine coolant.

NORMAL OIL PRESSURE

Oil pressure at normal operating temperature and 5000 RPM should be 58 psi (4.08 kg/cm²).

OIL PUMP

Removal

Remove drive belts and related components noting locations for reassembly reference. Drain oil. Loosen oil pan mounting bolts and lower pan approximately .39" (10 mm), to allow gasket to separate from pump. Do not damage pan gasket during pump removal. Detach oil pump mounting bolts. Remove oil pump.

Fig. 13: Oil Flow Circuit Diagram

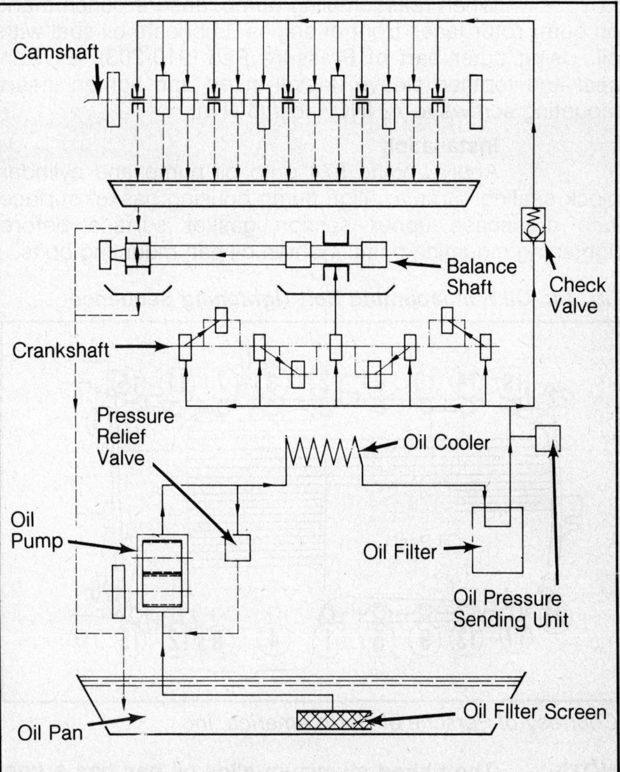

Courtesy of Porsche of North America, Inc.

Disassembly

Remove splined sleeve. Remove 2 mounting screws from inside housing. Using Pressure Pad (10-203), drive out insert through rear of housing. Remove inner and outer rotors. Pry out oil seal and discard. Inspect pump components for excessive wear or damage.

Inspection

1) Check splined sleeve for worn teeth and looseness on shaft. Inspect inner and outer rotors for nicks, scoring or chipped rotor teeth. Check outer rotor-to-pump housing for excessive looseness. Replace oil pump assembly as necessary.

2) If low or no oil pressure is observed when cold starting (after vehicle has been sitting or parked overnight), it is possible air is being drawn into lubrication system between suction and pressure sections of pump.

3) To correct pressure problem, disassemble and thoroughly clean pump and dry with compressed air. Coat outer diameter of rear housing insert, over entire width, with Loctite (574). Replace oil seal and "O" ring.

4) Remove pressure relief valve. Clean relief valve bore and valve. Ensure valve moves freely in bore and seats properly in block. If preceeding procedures correct low pressure problem, remove oil pan and related components to allow lower crankcase section to be removed.

5) Remove lower crankcase section and clean sealing surfaces. Apply Loctite (574) to sealing surfaces. Reinstall lower crankcase section and oil pan.

Porsche Engines

2.5L 4-CYLINDER (Cont.)

Reassembly

When reassembling pump, ensure punch mark on outer rotor faces front of engine. Lubricate oil seal with oil. Using outer part of Pressure Pad (910-203), drive in seal and toothed sleeve. Install insert and tighten insert mounting screws to 72 INCH lbs. (8 N.m).

Installation

Apply Loctite 574 onto oil pump and cylinder block sealing surface. Align pump housing gasket surface with crankcase upper section gasket surface before tightening mounting bolts. Tighten oil pan mounting bolts.

Fig. 14: Oil Pan Mounting Bolt Tightening Sequence

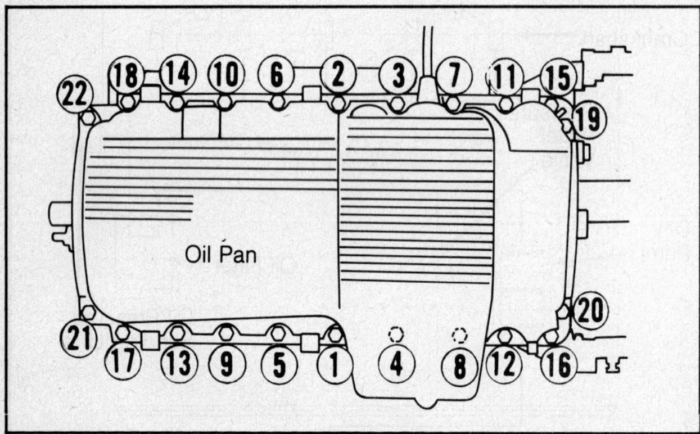

Courtesy of Porsche of North America, Inc.

NOTE: **The ribbed aluminum alloy oil pan has a one-piece rubber gasket that requires a 2-step tightening sequence to ensure proper sealing. See Fig.14. Oil pan is equipped with an oil pan insert (splash guard) to keep oil drag on crankshaft to a minimum.**

OIL PAN

Removal & Installation

When removing oil pan, ensure oil intake pipe is not damaged. Ensure oil pan insert is cleaned (by opening tabs) whenever oil pan is removed and mounting bolt is coated with Loctite (270). If dipstick guide tube is removed or loose, reseal with Loctite (638). If oil intake pipe is removed, replace seal.

OIL PRESSURE RELIEF VALVE

Valve & Bushing Replacement

Remove relief valve bushing by unscrewing with pliers and discard. Do not damage crankcase during bushing removal. Coat new bushing (at lower scored surface) with Loctite (648 or 638). Drive bushing into position using Bushing Driver (9215) which will also center oil cooler housing.

NOTE: **Replacement oil pressure relief valve (944 107 035 11) should be installed during any service related to oil pressure or oil cooler problems.**

ENGINE COOLING

WATER PUMP

Water pump is mounted on front of cylinder block and is driven by the backside of the camshaft toothed drive belt. The water pump drive pulley serves as an idler for the drive belt.

The water pump on the turbo engine has an additional thermostat mounted inside the hose outlet fitting on front of pump.

Removal

1) Remove radiator and intake hoses to access front of engine. Remove drive belts for alternator and steering pump. Remove "V" belt pulley from front of crankshaft.

2) Remove timing belt outer shield. Remove distributor cap and base drive plate. Remove balancer shaft drive belt and idler pulleys.

CAUTION: **DO NOT rotate crankshaft with cam drive belt disconnected or valve damage may occur.**

3) Turn crankshaft to TDC and check alignment of camshaft drive belt pulley. Remove camshaft drive belt and idlers. Remove rear belt guard plate. Remove heater hose from water pump. Remove water pump.

Installation

1) Replace all "O" rings and seals. Coat pump drive shaft sealing ring lightly with oil. Coat pump housing seals with Loctite 638. Install water pump and hoses.

2) Install rear belt guard plate. Install camshaft drive belt. See DRIVE BELT section of this article. Carefully check alignment of camshaft and balance shaft drive belts and pulleys. Reverse removal procedures to complete installation.

TURBOCHARGER COOLING

Water is drawn from the engine block by the water pump and circulated to the body of the turbocharger housing. A thermostat located in the hose fitting of the water pump controls water flow. The thermostat opens at a temperature of 180°F (82°C). If the temperature in the cooling line of the turbocharger, of a non-running motor, reaches 239°F (115°C), an electric water pump is switched on. This pump circulates water from the expansion tank, thru the turbocharger and back to the expansion tank via a check valve.

NOTE: **For additional information on cooling systems see ENGINE COOLING section.**

Porsche Engines

2.5L 4-CYLINDER (Cont.)

ENGINE SPECIFICATIONS

GENERAL SPECIFICATIONS

Year	DISPLACEMENT		Fuel System	HP@RPM	Torque Ft. Lbs.@RPM	Compr. Ratio	BORE		STROKE	
	Cu. In.	Liters					In.	mm	In.	mm
1987										
924-S	151	2.5	Fuel Inj.	147 @ 6000	190 @ 3000	9.7:1	3.94	100.0	3.11	78.9
944	151	2.5	Fuel Inj.	147 @ 6000	190 @ 3000	9.7:1	3.94	100.0	3.11	78.9
944-S	151	2.5	Fuel Inj.	190 @ 6000	230 @ 4300	10.9:1	3.94	100.0	3.11	78.9
944 Turbo	151	2.5	Turbo/Fuel Inj.	217 @ 5800	330 @ 3500	8.0:1	3.94	100.0	3.11	78.9

VALVES

Engine Size & Valve	Head Diam. In. (mm)	Face Angle	Seat Angle	Seat Width In. (mm)	Stem Diameter In. (mm)	Stem Clearance In. (mm)	Valve Lift In. (mm)
924-S & 944							
Intake	1.77 (45.0)	45°	[1] 45°	.067 (1.70)	.353 (8.97)	.031 (.80)	.472 (12.00)
Exhaust	1.57 (40.0)	45°	[1] 45°	.079 (2.00)	.352 (8.95)	.031 (.80)	.472 (12.00)
944-S							
Intake	1.457 (37.00)	45°	45°	.059-.075 (1.50-1.90)	.2744 (6.969)	.001-.002 (.03-.05)	.433 (11.00)
Exhaust	1.339 (34.00)	45°	45°	.071-.086 (1.80-2.20)	.2732 (6.940)	.002-.003 (.05-.07)	.393 (10.00)
944 Turbo [2]							
Intake	1.77 (45.0)	45°	[1] 45°	.067 (1.70)	.353 (8.97)	.031 (.80)	.472 (12.00)
Exhaust	1.57 (40.0)	45°	[1] 45°	.098 (2.50)	.352 (8.95)	.031 (.80)	.433 (11.00)

[1] – Valve seat throat angle (valve guide side) is 60°; Valve seat top angle (combustion chamber side) is 30°.
[2] – Valve dimensions same as non-turbo. Material differs for both intake and exhaust.

PISTONS, PINS & RINGS

Engine	PISTONS Clearance In. (mm)	PINS Piston Fit In. (mm)	PINS Rod Fit In. (mm)	RINGS Ring No.	RINGS End Gap In. (mm)	RINGS Side Clearance In. (mm)
924-S, 944, 944-S 944 Turbo	[1] .0003-.0013 (.008-.032)	Interference	.0007-.0013 (.018-.032)	1	.0079-.0177 (.200-.450)	.0019-.0032 (.050-.082)
				2	.0079-.0177 (.200-.450)	.0016-.0028 [2] (.040-.072)
				Oil	.0149-.0557 (.380-1.400)	.0009-.0054 (.023-.137)

[1] – Wear limit is .0031" (.080 mm).
[2] – "Mahle" ring side clearance shown. "KS" manufactured ring side clearance is .0019-.0032" (.050-.082 mm).

CRANKSHAFT MAIN & CONNECTING ROD BEARINGS

Engine	MAIN BEARINGS Journal Diam. In. (mm)	MAIN BEARINGS Clearance In. (mm)	MAIN BEARINGS Thrust Bearing	MAIN BEARINGS Crankshaft End Play In. (mm)	CONNECTING ROD BEARINGS Journal Diam. In. (mm)	CONNECTING ROD BEARINGS Clearance In. (mm)	CONNECTING ROD BEARINGS Side Play In. (mm)
924-S, 944 944-S 944 Turbo	[1] 2.755-2.756 (69.971-69.990)	.0008-.0038 (.020-.098)	No. 3	.0043-.0122 (.110-.312)	2.0461-2.0468 (51.971-51.990)	.0008-.0028 (.020-.070)	.0039-.0157 (.100-.400)

[1] – Standard crankcase main bearing bore diameter is 2.9528-2.9535" (75.000-75.019 mm). Oversize bore diameter is 2.9626-2.9633" (75.250-75.269 mm).

Porsche Engines

2.5L 4-CYLINDER (Cont.)

ENGINE SPECIFICATIONS (Cont.)

VALVE TIMING

Engine	INTAKE		EXHAUST	
	Open (BTDC)	Close (ABDC)	Open (BBDC)	Close (ATDC)
924-S & 944	1°(ATDC)	49°	47°	1°
944-S	4°(ATDC)	40°	36°	4°(BTDC)
944 Turbo	1°(ATDC)	49°	43°	3°(BTDC)

TIGHTENING SPECIFICATIONS

Application	Ft. Lbs. (N.m)
Balance Shaft Bearing Cover [1]	
Step 1: 2 Bolts @ Bearing (8 mm)	11 (15)
Step 2	
6 mm	7 (10)
8 mm	15 (20)
Step 3: 2 Bolts @ Bearing (8 mm)	24 (33)
Balance Shaft Sprocket Mounting Bolt	33 (45)
Belt Tensioner Mounting Bolts	33 (45)
Camshaft Housing Mounting Bolts	15 (20)
Camshaft Plugs (Aluminum)	30 (40)
Camshaft Sprocket	
Hex Mounting Bolt	33 (45)
Polygon Mounting Bolt	47-51 (65-70)
Connecting Rod Nut [2]	54 (75)
Coolant Pipe Adapter	15 (20)
Crankcase Lower Section Mounting Nuts	
6 mm	6 (8)
8 mm	15 (20)
10 mm	
Step 1	15 (20)
Step 2	37 (50)

TIGHTENING SPECIFICATIONS (Cont.)

Application	INCH Lbs. (N.m)
12 mm	
Step 1	15 (20)
Step 2	37 (50)
Step 3	66 (90)
Crankshaft-to-Sprocket Mounting Bolt	155 (210)
Crossmember (Front) Mounting Bolt	63 (85)
Cylinder Head Mounting Nut	
Step 1	15 (20)
Step 2	90 Degrees
Step 3	90 Degrees
Exhaust Flanges (Turbo)	
8 mm	15-18 (20-25)
12 mm	30-33 (40-45)
Flywheel-to-Crankshaft Mounting Bolt	66 (90)
Guide Roller-to-Water Pump Housing	33 (45)
Oil Cooler Housing Drain Plug	25 (35)
Oil Pan Drain Plug	37 (50)
Oil Pressure Switch	25 (35)
Oil Pressure Relief Valve	33 (45)
Transaxle-to-Clutch Housing Mounting Bolt	31 (42)
Universal Joint-to-Steering Gear Nut	22 (30)
Water Drain Plug (Cylinder Block)	15 (20)
	INCH Lbs. (N.m)
Camshaft Bearing Cap Bolts	96 (8)
Oil Pan Mounting Bolts	
Step 1	36 (4)
Step 2	96 (8)
Transport Clamp-to-Camshaft Housing	96 (8)

[1] – Check movement of balance shaft between each tightening step.

[2] – Use only new nuts, lubricated lightly with oil.

Porsche Engines

3.2L & 3.3L 6-CYLINDER

911 Carrera, 911 Turbo

NOTE: For engine repair procedures not covered in this article, see ENGINE OVERHAUL PROCEDURES article at beginning of this section.

ENGINE CODING

ENGINE IDENTIFICATION

An 8 character engine identification number is die-stamped on cooling air blower fan support near oil temperature sensor. The first character indicates engine type (6 = 6 cylinder), second character of number identifies vehicle type, and third character indicates model year (H = 1987), and last 5 characters indicate engine serial number.

NOTE: Porsche identification of engine type series is 930/25 for the 911 Carrera (USA) and 930/68 for the 911 Turbo (USA).

ENGINE IDENTIFICATION CODES

Application	Code
911 Carrera	64H
911 Turbo	68H

ENGINE, MANIFOLDS & CYLINDER HEADS

ENGINE

NOTE: The engine/transaxle assembly is removed as a unit. Manufacturer recommends that all self-locking nuts, lock washers, cotter pins and circlips be replaced whenever removed.

Removal

1) Place vehicle on jack stands at lift points. Disconnect battery ground cable. Detach A/C compressor from mounting brackets (if equipped). Leave compressor in vehicle with hoses connected.

CAUTION: If A/C compressor hoses are to be disconnected, air conditioner system must be discharged before hose removal and recharged after installation.

2) Remove air cleaner cover with air filter cartridge. Disconnect bottom hose for crankcase breather. Detach top hose on oil tank from intake hose/throttle housing. Detach hoses on air valve. Plug hoses.

3) Disconnect hose from active carbon canister on air cleaner. Remove hose between fan and heat exchangers. Remove cover from central electrical board. Pull off multiple pin plug on control board and high voltage lead on ignition coil.

4) Disconnect central engine ground on No. 1 cylinder intake pipe. Press in clamp and pull upper plug off connector board (wire to temperature sensor, cylinder No. 3). Pull center plug (wire to speed sensor) and lower plug (wire to reference mark sensor) off connector board.

5) Disconnect oxygen sensor plug and oxygen sensor heating plug. Remove fuel lines at filter, and at return line. Disconnect brake booster hose. Remove rear tunnel cover from passenger compartment.

6) Pull rubber boot (in tunnel) forward, over selector rod. Loosen shift rod coupling set screw (Allen head). Pull coupling off transaxle shift rod. Disconnect electronic speedometer sensor wires (in tunnel). Remove rubber sleeve with wire plug.

7) Drain crankcase. Disconnect and plug oil line and hose on engine and oil tank. Ensure oil line fitting is held securely when loosening to prevent damage. Remove heater hoses at heat exchangers. Remove rear stabilizer bar.

8) Disconnect ground strap at body and battery wires at starter. Disconnect accelerator linkage from pedal. Remove clutch cable retainer. Disconnect clutch cable from release lever after loosening cable at holder. Detach spring that positions lever on transmission, and push lever forward.

CAUTION: The spring will expand after passing a pressure point so release lever will snap forward.

9) Remove clutch release lever from release lever shaft. Loosen drive shaft flange (Allen head) mounting bolts from transaxle assembly. Remove rear cowl panel screws. Detach cowl panel with seal. Place jack under engine/transaxle assembly. Apply upward pressure to relieve tension on motor mounts.

10) Remove engine/transaxle carrier mounting bolts. Lower engine/transaxle assembly slightly. Pull off multiple pin plug (on shock absorber crossmember) and airflow sensor plug. Lower jack and roll engine/transaxle assembly out toward rear of vehicle.

11) Detach wires at starter and back-up light switch. Remove circlip on top of accelerator linkage, and disconnect linkage. If necessary, disconnect clutch cable and release lever circlip. Remove lever and rubber ring. Remove transaxle from engine.

Fig. 1: Turbo Exhaust System

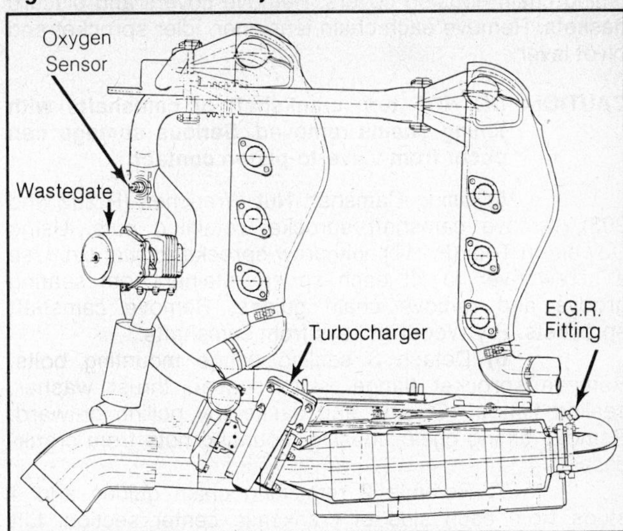

Courtesy of Porsche of North America, Inc.

CAUTION: Ensure secondary air injection pipes are not damaged during engine removal. See Fig. 2.

Porsche Engines

3.2L & 3.3L 6-CYLINDER (Cont.)

Installation

1) Before attaching engine to transaxle check input shaft for runout. Check clutch release bearing for wear and replace if necessary.

2) Lubricate release bearing guide tube, input shaft splines, starter shaft pilot bushing, and flywheel nut.

3) DO NOT clamp heater hoses. Slide heater hoses onto heat exchangers just before engine/transmission assembly is in final installation position.

4) To complete installation, reverse removal procedure. After engine/transmission assembly is installed, adjust clutch free play as needed.

CYLINDER HEADS & MANIFOLDS

Removal (Non-Turbo)

1) Detach fuel injection system/intake manifold pipes (with plastic insulators and aluminum gaskets). Remove distributor cap and spark plug wires. Remove all cooling air ducts and cover shrouds.

NOTE: Each cylinder has a separate head. If camshaft housing is removed, any single head may be removed. If camshaft housing is left attached to cylinder heads, cylinder heads and camshaft housing may be removed as an assembly.

2) Detach air ducts connecting cooling air blower outlets and heat exchanger inlets (with cover shrouds). Remove muffler at connecting flanges.

3) Remove engine mounting bracket, cooling fan pulley and "V" belt. Loosen band strap attaching alternator/blower housing. Pull housing rearward. Disconnect alternator cables. Remove blower housing with alternator.

4) Using Exhaust Manifold Wrenches (P 205 and P 217), remove heat exchangers. Disconnect timing chain tensioner oil supply lines between crankcase and timing chain housing covers. Remove covers and discard gaskets. Remove each chain tensioner, idler sprocket and pivot lever.

CAUTION: DO NOT turn crankshaft or camshafts with timing chains removed. Serious damage can occur from valve-to-piston contact.

5) Using Camshaft Nut Wrenches (P 202 and 203), remove camshaft sprocket retaining nuts. Using Dowel Pin Tool (P 212), withdraw sprocket dowel pin. Use a screwdriver to lift each spring retainer from seating groove and remove chain guides. Remove camshaft sprockets. Pry Woodruff keys from camshafts.

6) Detach 3 sealing flange mounting bolts. Remove sprocket flange, shim spacer, thrust washer, sealing flange, "O" ring and gasket by pulling outward. Remove timing chain housing mounting nuts from crankcase.

7) Remove 2 remaining chain guides and 4 studs from each side of crankcase center section. Lift spring retainer from seating groove in each stud, and remove studs. Remove chain guides. Remove oil cooler from engine (if equipped).

8) To remove all 3 cylinder heads and camshaft housing as an assembly, remove rocker arm cover and gasket. Loosen cylinder head nuts in sequence. Remove 3 cylinder heads and camshaft housing assembly off cylinder studs.

NOTE: To remove a single head, remove rocker arm covers and gaskets. Using an 5 mm Allen wrench, loosen and remove rocker arm shafts. Rocker arm must be off camshaft lobe to remove shaft. Remove rocker arms. Remove camshaft and camshaft carrier. Remove cylinder head.

NOTE: Mark rocker arm shafts in relation to rocker arms and rocker arms in relation to camshaft housing for reassembly reference.

9) Remove rocker arms. Detach 3 upper camshaft housing Allen head mounting bolts. Note locations for reassembly reference. Remove remaining camshaft housing mounting nuts and spring washers. Remove camshaft housing.

10) Using Temperature Sensor Remover (9222), remove temperature sensor from rear of No. 3 cylinder head. Using Cylinder Head Nut Remover (P 119), remove cylinder head nuts and lift off each cylinder head. Mark cylinder heads and cylinders for reassembly in original positions.

NOTE: A head gasket is not used. Cylinder head seats directly onto cylinder sealing surface.

Removal (Turbo)

1) Follow non-turbo engine removal procedure. In addition, perform the following procedures. Disconnect pressure hose between turbo outlet and duct. Disconnect the oil pressure lines from turbo unit. Drain oil from oil trap and remove. Remove rear sheet metal and rubber seal. Remove muffler.

2) Disconnect air injection pipe from catalytic converter. Disconnect air inlet line from turbo. Disconnect turbo from exhaust inlet pipe and remove turbo and

Fig. 2: Air Injection System

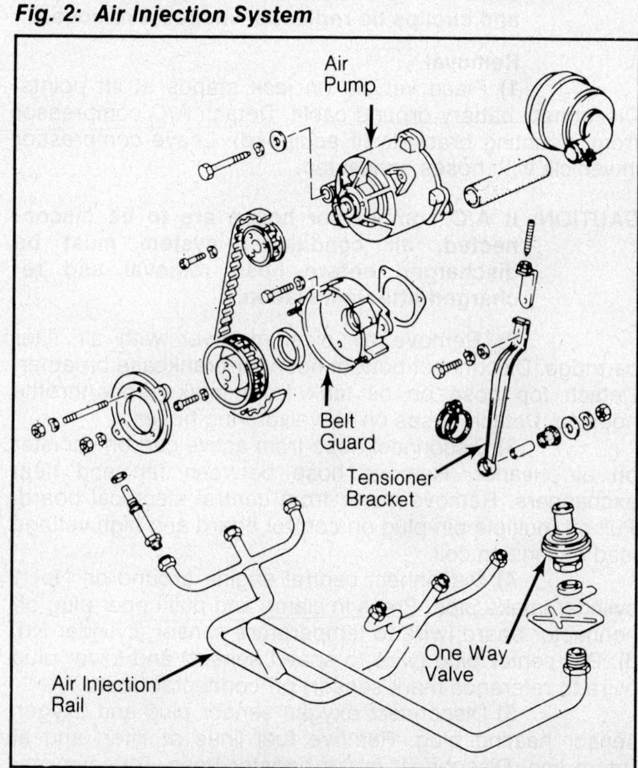

Courtesy of Porsche of North America, Inc.

3.2L & 3.3L 6-CYLINDER (Cont.)

converter. Disconnect oxygen sensor and wastegate control lines.

3) Disconnect exhaust line couplings and remove wastegate, by-pass muffler and exhaust lines. Disconnect air injection system hoses at diverter valve and check valve. Remove supply tubes from air injection nozzles in cylinder heads. *See Fig. 2.*

Fig. 3: Turbo System

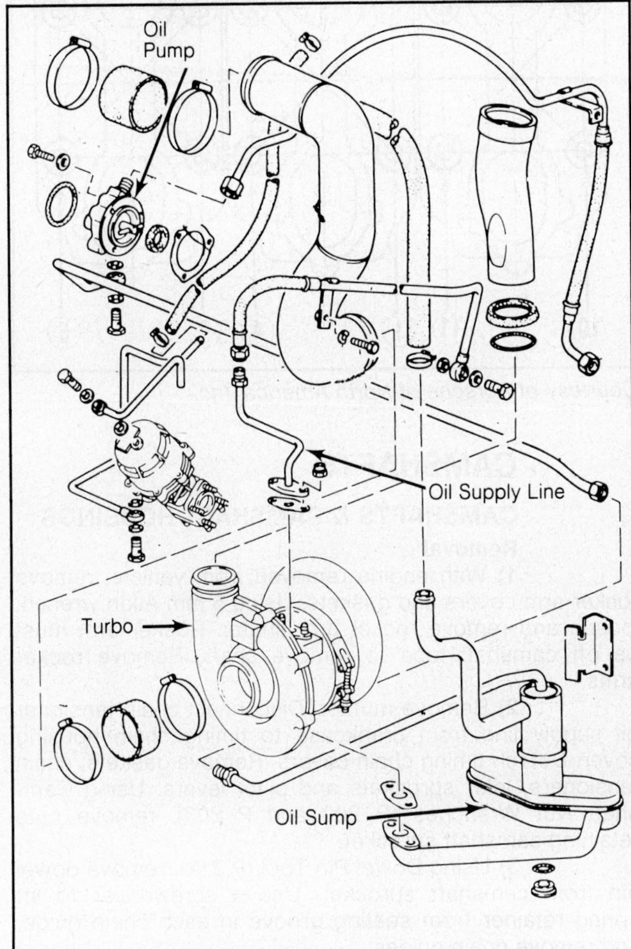

Courtesy of Porsche of North America, Inc.

4) Remove inner cooling ducting, mounting bolts, and inner cooler. Remove turbo oil pump from drive on end of camshaft or remove oil lines and drive belt from air injection pump. *See Fig. 3.*

Inspection

1) Check cylinder head and camshaft housing mating surfaces for cleanliness, wear, and damage. Repair or replace as necessary. Check cylinder head distortion (flatness) with feeler gauge and straightedge.

2) Standard cylinder head distortion limit (at cylinder seating area) is .006" (.15 mm) maximum. DO NOT machine cylinder head surface. If beyond specification, replace head.

3) Inspect camshaft housing for camshaft bearing bore surface wear or damage. See CAMSHAFTS & CAMSHAFT HOUSINGS in this article. Check rocker arm shaft bores for excessive wear, nicks or other damage. See ROCKER ARMS in this article. Replace camshaft housing as necessary.

Installation

1) If cylinder heads and camshaft housing were removed individually, install cylinder heads and oil return tubes on cylinders at the same time. Coat ends of oil return tubes and "O" rings with oil for easier installation. Install cylinder head nuts finger tight at this time.

2) Install cool air shrouds in their proper positions and attach clamps. Apply light coat of Loctite 573 sealing compound (Green) between camshaft housing and cylinder head sealing surfaces. Assemble camshaft housing onto mounting studs.

3) Install new camshaft housing mounting nuts with spring washers. Lightly tighten nuts while sealer is still soft to ensure a good seal. Install 3 Allen bolts in their proper locations. Tighten all camshaft housing retainers progressively, in a crisscross pattern.

NOTE: **Camshaft housings are interchangeable, but camshafts are not. If camshaft housing is relocated to opposite side, apply sealant and install appropriate housing end cover.**

4) Tighten cylinder head nuts while checking that camshaft does not bind in housing. See CYLINDER HEAD TIGHTENING PROCEDURE in this article. Tighten nuts in proper sequence. *See Fig. 5.* With cylinder head nuts tightened to specification, camshaft must rotate freely.

5) If cylinder heads and camshaft housing were removed as an assembly, install cooling air shrouds and fasten with spring clips. Place new "O" rings on both ends of oil return tubes and coat with engine oil.

6) Place cylinder heads/camshaft housing assembly onto cylinder studs. At the same time, insert both oil return tubes in their seats in crankcase and camshaft housing. Ensure tubes are properly seated.

CAUTION: To ensure camshaft housing is not warped in the process of tightening cylinder head nuts, remove all rocker arms and shafts before tightening.

7) Install new spring washers and retaining nuts onto cylinder head studs. Tighten cylinder head nuts. See step **4)** of this procedure. When tightening nuts to specification, turn camshaft to check for possible binding.

Fig. 4: Exploded View of Camshaft Sprocket Flange & Sealing Components

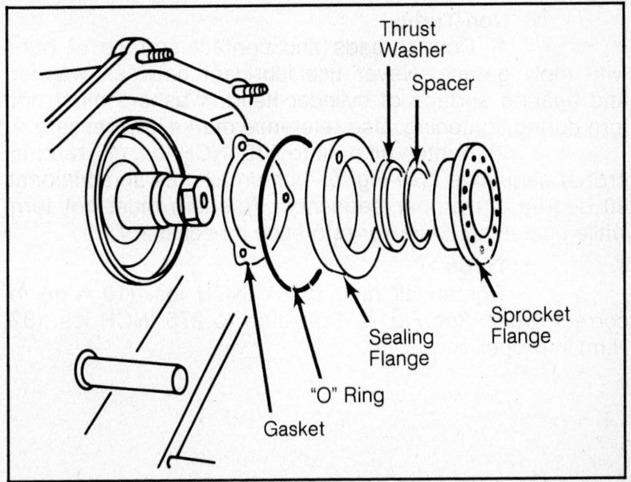

3.2L & 3.3L 6-CYLINDER (Cont.)

8) Install rocker arms and shafts with shafts positioned so that machined grooves in shaft are centered properly in bores of camshaft housing. *See Fig. 15.* Ensure grooves are positioned approximately .060" (1.52 mm) into bores. See ROCKER ARMS in this article.

9) Using Torque Wrench (P 210) and Allen Drive Adapter (P 211), tighten rocker arm shaft mounting bolts. Install new timing chain housing gaskets on crankcases. Install timing chain housing. Install new camshaft sealing flange gasket and "O" ring, sealing flange, thrust washer, shim spacer, camshaft sprocket, and Woodruff key. *See Fig. 4.*

NOTE: If crankcase was disassembled check intermediate shaft end play at this time. Set spacers and gaskets aside for final timing chain and cover reassembly.

10) Install timing chain guides and camshaft sprockets. Check timing chain alignment. See TIMING CHAIN & TENSIONERS in this article. Slide chain guides on mounting studs. Lift retaining spring with screwdriver and slide chain guide into place. Install chain tension pivot lever and idler sprocket. Ensure that oil holes in pivot stud face upward.

NOTE: When installing turbo, lubricate by placing 2-4 cc's of engine oil in oil pipe fitting. When installing new turbo, lubricate by cranking starter motor for 30 seconds with manifold pressure limiting switch disconnected.

11) Install timing chain and chain tensioners. Remove tensioner piston holders. Left tensioner may be positioned in only far enough to let camshaft nut be installed after valve timing. See VALVE TIMING in this article. Install timing chain housing covers, new gaskets and camshaft oil lines. Install heat exchangers. To complete installation, reverse removal procedure.

NOTE: Use "Angle Tightening Method" for all Porsche engines except 911 Turbo. Use new Yellow cylinder head Nuts (901 104 382 02). These nuts must be replaced at each repair as they are not reuseable.

CYLINDER HEAD TIGHTENING PROCEDURE

Non-Turbo

1) Coat threads and contact surface of nuts with moly grease. Never use lubricant between washer and bearing surface of cylinder head. Washers must not turn during tightening. Use reference marks if necessary.

2) Tighten all nuts to 132 INCH lbs. (15 N.m) in proper sequence. *See Fig. 5.* Tighten all nuts an additional 90 degrees in proper sequence. Washers must not turn while tightening. Mark for reference if necessary.

Turbo

Tighten all nuts to 84 INCH lbs. (10 N.m) in correct order. *See Fig. 5.* Retighten to 276 INCH lbs. (32 N.m) in proper sequence.

Fig. 5: Cylinder Head Tightening Sequence

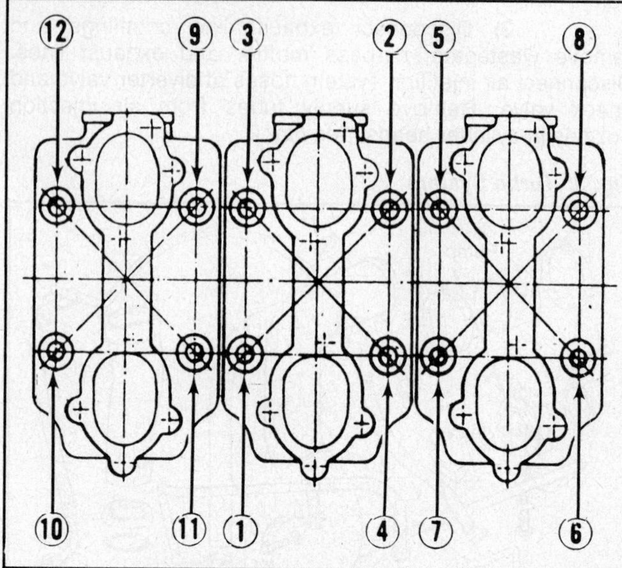

Courtesy of Porsche of North America, Inc.

CAMSHAFTS

CAMSHAFTS & CAMSHAFT HOUSINGS

Removal

1) With engine removed from vehicle, remove rocker arm covers and gaskets. Using 5 mm Allen wrench, loosen and remove rocker arm shafts. Rocker arm must be off camshaft lobe to remove shaft. Remove rocker arms.

2) Remove muffler. Disconnect chain tensioner oil supply line from crankcase to timing chain housing cover. Detach timing chain covers. Remove gaskets, chain tensioners, idler sprockets and pivot levers. Using Camshaft Nut Wrenches (P 202 and P 203), remove nuts retaining camshaft sprocket.

3) Using Dowel Pin Tool (P 212), remove dowel pin from camshaft sprocket. Use a screwdriver to lift spring retainer from seating groove in each chain guide, and remove chain guides.

4) Pull sprockets, sprocket flanges, shim spacers, and thrust washers from camshafts. Pry Woodruff keys from camshafts. Detach 3 mounting screws and remove each sealing flange with "O" ring and gasket. Withdraw each camshaft from its housing by pulling it rearward.

5) Check oil injection tubes in camshaft housing for damage. If replacement is needed, drill a 3/8" deep hole in end plug using a 1/2" drill bit. Cut 6 mm threads with bottoming tap and pull out end plug with 6 mm screw and spacer. DO NOT damage sealing surface during plug removal.

6) Before removing injection tube, note oil hole locations in tube for installation reference. Separate oil hole bores must face upward (toward valve covers). Double bores face cam bearing surface. Loosen centering screws and slide out injection tube.

Inspection

1) Inspect lobe working surfaces of both camshafts. Replace camshaft if excessively worn or

3.2L & 3.3L 6-CYLINDER (Cont.)

damaged. Check oil passages for blockage. Blow passages clear with compressed air or fill with oil and check for proper flow.

2) Inspect camshaft housing bearing journal bores for excessive wear or damage. Standard bore diameter is 1.8490-1.8500" (46.965-46.992 mm). Check O.D. of camshaft bearing journals. Standard journal diameter is 1.8474-1.8481" (46.924-46.942 mm).

3) With camshaft installed in housing, check for free rotation. If camshaft rotates freely, check clearance between camshaft and housing bearing surfaces. Standard clearance is .0009-.0025" (.025-.066 mm). Maximum clearance is .0039" (.102 mm). If beyond specification, replace camshaft and/or housing.

4) Check camshaft for proper end play. See CAMSHAFT END PLAY in this article. Check for runout, measuring at center bearing surface. Maximum runout is .0008" (.020 mm). Replace camshaft if beyond specifications.

Installation

1) Lubricate oil injection tube bore. Slide in new tube. Apply sealant to new end plug. Install plug about .012" (.30 mm) deeper than sealing surface. Expand plug before installation if it does not fit tightly in bore.

2) Install camshafts in housings. *See Fig. 6.* Install sealing flange with new gasket and "O" ring and tighten mounting bolts. Install thrust washer, shim spacer and Woodruff key. Install camshaft sprocket flange (sprocket flanges are interchangeable).

Fig. 6: Positioning Camshafts In Camshaft Housings

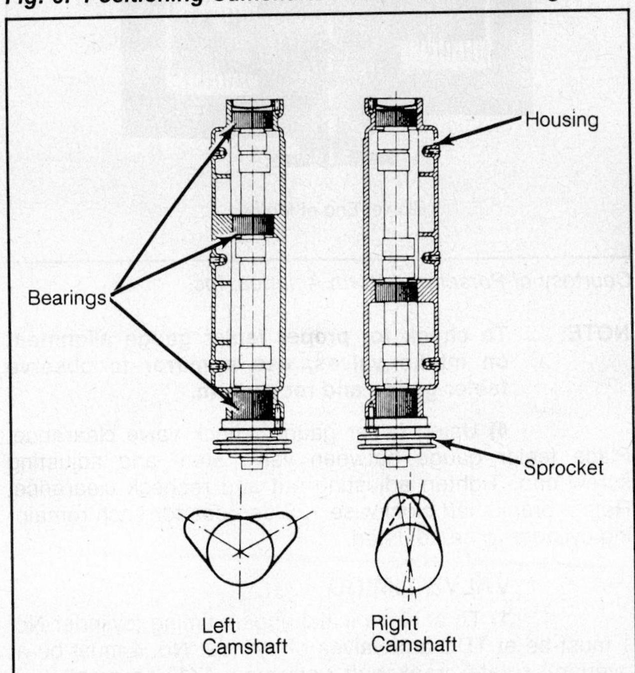

Courtesy of Porsche of North America, Inc.

3) Install timing chain and camshaft sprockets with sprockets in their proper locations. *See Fig. 7.* Check timing chain alignment. See TIMING CHAIN & TENSIONERS in this article. Install chain guides, sprocket dowels and sprocket mounting nuts. Install chain tensioners, pivot levers and idler sprockets.

Fig. 7: Left & Right Camshaft Sprocket Positions

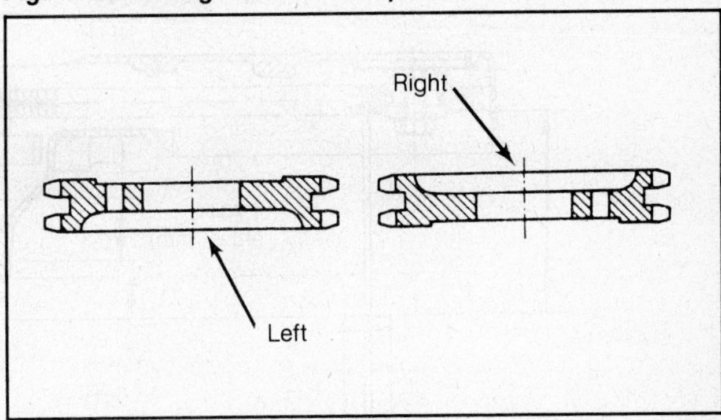

Courtesy of Porsche of North America, Inc.

4) Install rocker arm shaft assemblies and rocker arms. To complete installation, reverse removal procedure. Check and adjust valve timing as necessary. Install timing chain housing and rocker arm covers with new gaskets.

CAMSHAFT END PLAY

1) With camshaft and sprocket assembly installed in housing, attach a dial indicator with probe positioned on end of camshaft. Carefully move camshaft back and forth and measure axial end play.

2) Standard end play is .006-.008" (.15-.20 mm). Maximum end play is .016" (.40 mm). If play is excessive, replace aluminum sealing flange (and thrust washer if necessary) located behind camshaft sprocket flange.

TIMING CHAIN & TENSIONERS

Removal

1) With engine in vehicle, gain working clearance by removing muffler and rear cooling shroud. Remove chain tensioner oil supply lines from crankcase to timing chain tensioner fittings.

NOTE: **Timing chain tensioner has a fitting that protrudes through timing chain cover for oil supply line mounting bolt. Ensure "O" ring on fitting shank that seals chain cover is replaced whenever cover is removed.**

2) If equipped, remove ground strap from left side. Remove timing chain housing covers and gaskets. Turn crankshaft to bring No. 1 piston to TDC ("Z1" mark).

3) Remove chain tensioners, pivot lever and idler sprocket. Using Camshaft Nut Wrenches (P 202 and P 203), remove timing chain sprocket mounting nuts. Using Dowel Pin Tool (P 212), withdraw aligning dowel pins. *See Fig. 12.*

4) Lift spring retainers from their seating grooves and remove outer chain guides. Inspect chain guides and replace if worn or damaged. Remove sprockets.

5) Remove master link type timing chain by detaching master link clip and separating chain. Remove endless type timing chain by grinding 2 rivet ends from any one link. Remove link and chain.

NOTE: **Factory installed timing chain is an endless type. A master link type chain is available for replacement. If endless type chain is desired for replacement, crankcases must be split.**

Porsche Engines

3.2L & 3.3L 6-CYLINDER (Cont.)

Fig. 8: Timing Chains & Sprockets Alignment (Top View)

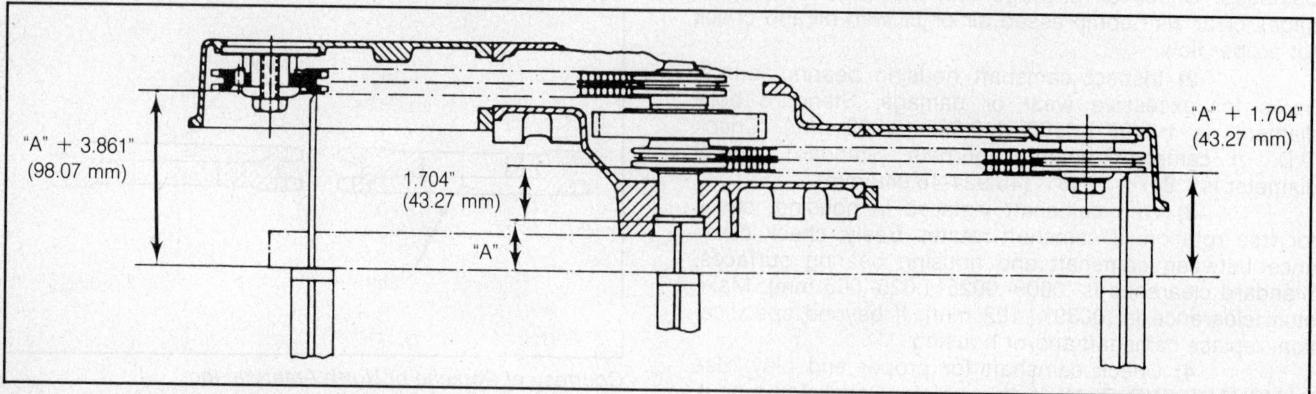

Courtesy of Porsche of North America, Inc.

CAUTION: When installing master link type chain, ensure master link clip is fully installed in pin grooves and closed end of clip faces direction of travel.

Installation

1) When installing chain tensioners, it is not necessary to fill or bleed tensioner. After timing chain and related components are installed, ensure that timing chain sprockets are parallel and aligned. *See Fig. 8*. Parallel misalignment of sprockets must not exceed .010" (.25 mm).

2) Seat intermediate shaft and camshafts against thrust collars (push towards flywheel) prior to measuring alignment.

3) Chain alignment may be adjusted with .02" (.5 mm) shim spacers between sprocket flange and sealing flange (if necessary). Normally, there are 3 shims under left camshaft sprocket (1-3 cylinders) and no shims under right camshaft sprocket. Ensure valve timing is correct. *See Fig. 10*. To complete installation, reverse removal procedure.

VALVES

VALVE CLEARANCE ADJUSTMENT

NOTE: **Valve clearance is to be adjusted ONLY with engine cold.**

1) Standard clearance is .004" (.10 mm). If valves or seats have been reground, set clearances to .006" (.15 mm) and run engine for 1/2 hour. Reset valves to .004" (.10 mm) after engine cools.

NOTE: **Adjust valves in firing order sequence: 1-6-2-4-3-5. As viewed from cooling air blower end of engine, the cylinders are numbered 1, 2, and 3 on driver's side of vehicle and 4, 5, and 6 on passenger's side. See Fig. 9.**

2) Remove cooling ducts between fan and heat exchangers. Remove timing chain cover. Check tightness of rocker arm shafts. If necessary, tighten rocker arm shafts to 156 in. lbs. (18 N.m).

3) Starting with No. 1 cylinder, turn pulley on crankshaft until both valves are closed (valves of No. 4 cylinder at overlap) and TDC mark ("Z1") on pulley aligned with crankcase joint or stripe on fan housing.

Fig. 9: Cylinder Numbering

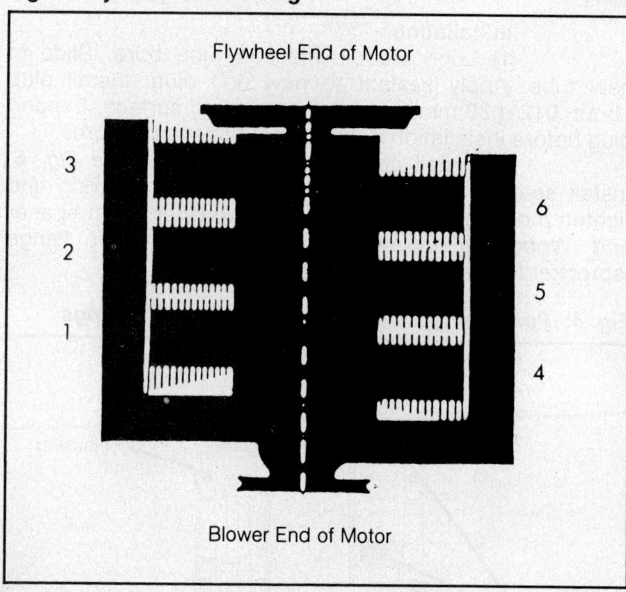

Courtesy of Porsche of North America, Inc.

NOTE: **To check for proper feeler gauge alignment on intake valves, use a mirror to observe feeler gauge and rocker arm.**

4) Using feeler gauge, check valve clearance. Place feeler gauge between valve stem and adjusting screw cap. Tighten adjusting nut and recheck clearance. Rotate crankshaft clockwise 120 degrees for each remaining cylinder to be adjusted.

VALVE TIMING

1) To achieve initial engine timing (cylinder No. 1 must be at TDC and valves of cylinder No. 4 must be at overlap), rotate crankshaft until mark "Z1" on crankshaft pulley aligns with crankcase vertical center joint (or stripe on fan housing).

CAUTION: Use extreme care when turning crankshaft or camshafts to avoid valve-to-piston contact. DO NOT turn crankshaft or camshafts if even the slightest resistance is felt or severe component damage could result.

3.2L & 3.3L 6-CYLINDER (Cont.)

Fig. 10: View of Engine from Blower End (Rear of Vehicle) Showing Valve Timing Marks

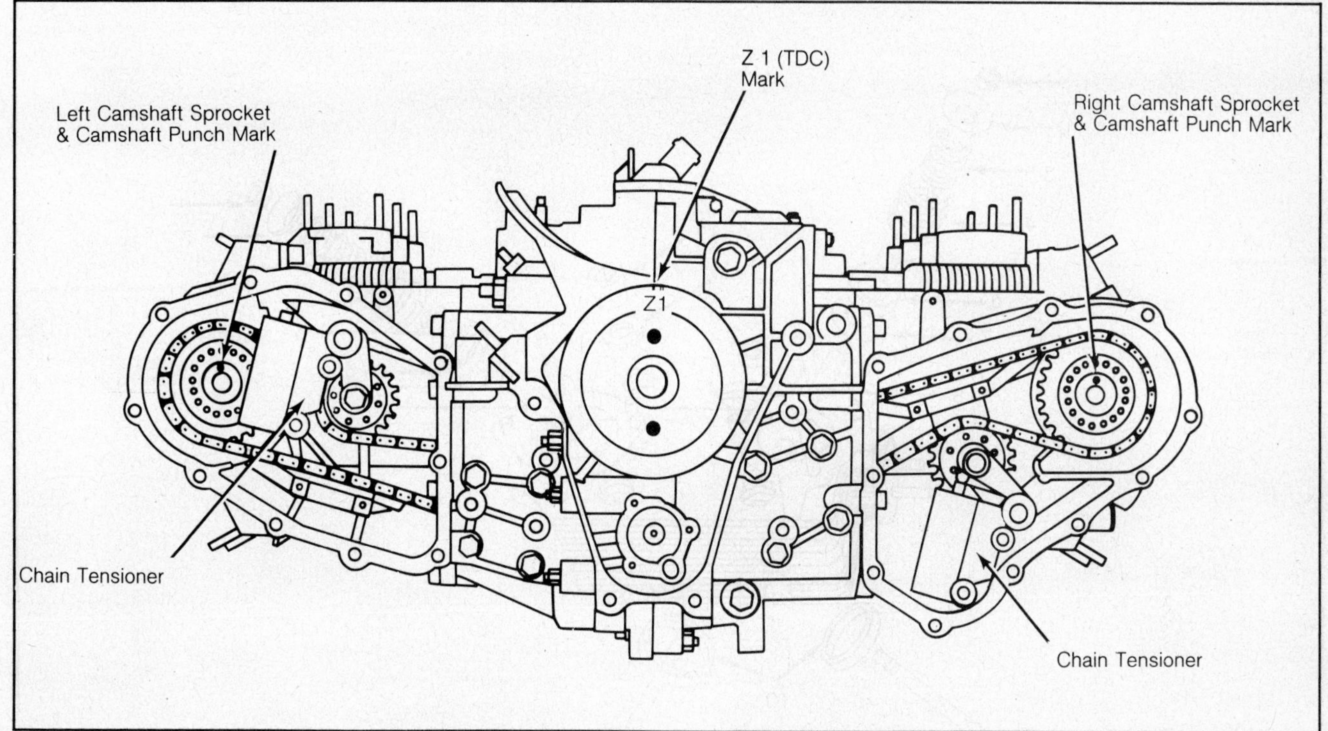

2) Using Camshaft Wrench (P 202), position both camshafts so punch marks point up (12 o'clock position). *See Fig. 10*. In this position, one sprocket bore will be aligned with one sprocket flange bore. Insert locating pin in aligned bores of both sprockets and flanges. *See Fig. 13.*

3) Using Wrench (P 9191), tighten sprocket mounting bolts finger tight while holding sprockets. Turn crankshaft 360 degrees and check timing marks. If one camshaft is out of time remove sprocket bolt and locating pin for that camshaft. Use Dowel Pin Tool (P 212).

4) Carefully turn misaligned camshaft to basic position (punch mark up) with camshaft wrench. Reinstall locating pin in the aligned bores and retighten sprocket mounting bolt. Turn crankshaft 2 complete turns to "Z1" mark and ensure all timing marks align.

5) Using feeler gauge, adjust valve clearance to .004" (.10 mm) on No. 1 and 4 cylinders. See VALVE CLEARANCE ADJUSTMENT in this article. Mount dial indicator on camshaft housing stud using Dial Gauge Holder (P 207). Position dial indicator probe exactly on edge of No. 1 intake valve spring retaining collar. Valve must be closed.

6) Adjust dial indicator to preload of .4" (10 mm) to provide for probe travel when cam lobe depresses valve. Zero dial indicator. While watching dial indicator, turn crankshaft approximately 360 degrees (clockwise) from "Z1" mark (TDC) until adjusting tolerance range is reached. See INTAKE VALVE LIFT table.

7) Detach sprocket mounting bolt and locating pin on left camshaft. Turn crankshaft until "Z1" mark on pulley aligns with crankcase joint. Install dowel pin in aligned bores of sprocket and sprocket flange. Use Dowel Pin Tool (P 212). *See Fig. 12.* Hold sprocket and tighten mounting bolt finger tight.

INTAKE VALVE LIFT @ TDC

Application	In. (mm)
911 Carrera [1]	.043-.055 (1.10-1.40)
911 Turbo [1]	.025-.031 (.65-.80)

[1] – Intake valve at overlap (TDC) with .004" (.10 mm) valve clearance.

8) Turn crankshaft 2 complete turns and recheck setting. The indicated value should be within tolerance. Tighten left camshaft mounting bolt to final specification. Transfer dial indicator to right housing. Ensure valve is closed. Set No. 4 cylinder at TDC (No. 1 cylinder at overlap). Repeat steps **6)** through **8)**.

VALVE GUIDES

1) Valve guides are pressed into heads. In order to avoid cylinder head damage from spreading valve guide end during removal, mill guide down to head surface on camshaft side. *See Fig. 11.*

2) If mill is not available, use a .433" (11 mm) drill bit to drill out guide. Using a drift, drive valve guide out into combustion chamber. Using a valve guide bore gauge, measure guide bore in cylinder head. Machine outside diameter of replacement guide to specification. See VALVE GUIDE SPECIFICATION TABLE.

3) Use lubricant when pressing in valve guides. After installation, machine valve guide I.D. using broach or fine boring mill. If necessary, valve guides can be finished with a reamer.

NOTE: **Removal of old valve guides will increase bore diameter in head. Replacement guides must be oversized and machined to match enlarged bore. Replacement valve guides are available in first and second oversizes.**

Porsche Engines

3.2L & 3.3L 6-CYLINDER (Cont.)

Fig. 11: Exploded View of 911 Carrera Cylinder Head

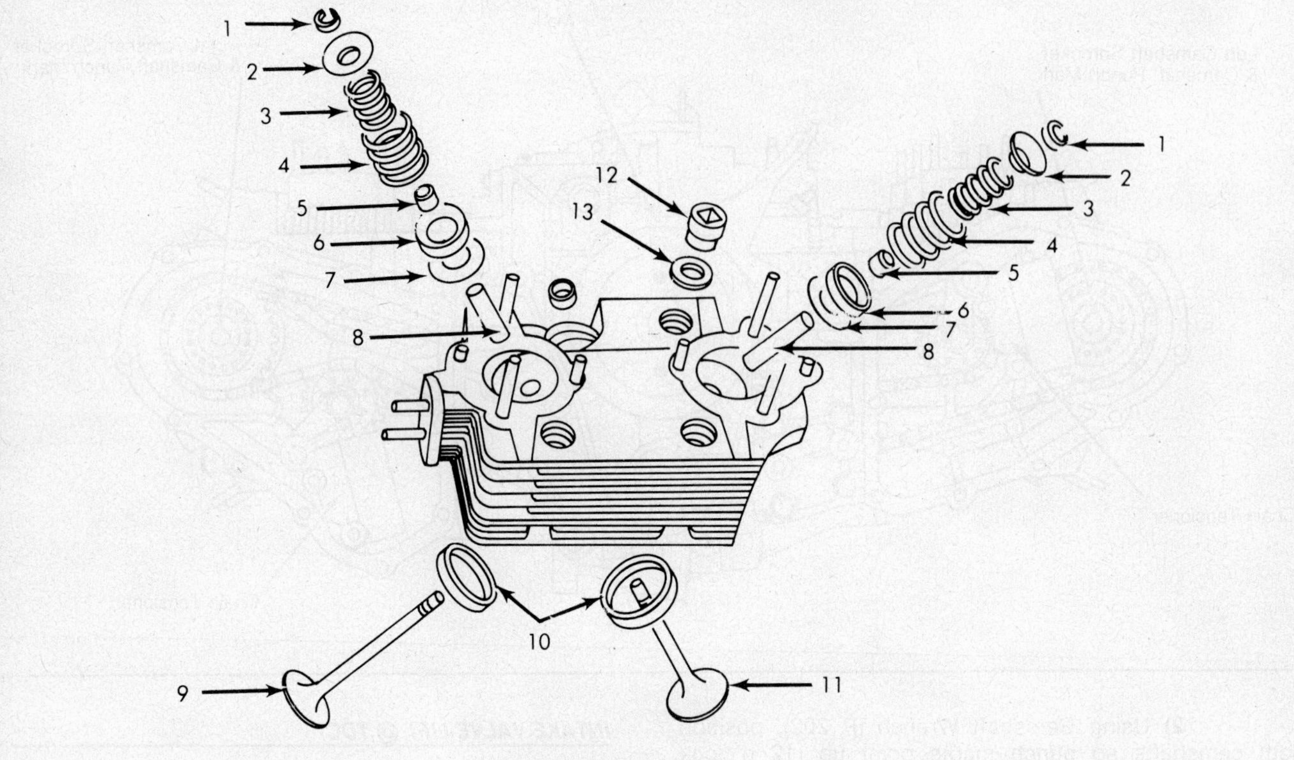

1
2
3
4
5
6
7
8
12
13
10
9
11
1. Valve Spring Keepers
2. Valve Spring Retainer Cap
3. Inner Valve Spring
4. Outer Valve Spring
5. Valve Seals
6. Valve Spring Seats
7. Valve Spring Spacer
8. Valve Guide
9. Exhaust Guide
10. Valve Seat
11. Intake Valve
12. Head Nut
13. Washer

VALVE GUIDE SPECIFICATION TABLE

Application	In. (mm)
Valve Guides	
OutsideDiameter	.5137-.5141 (13.049-13.060)
Inside Diameter	.3543-3549 (9.000-9.015)
Guide Bore In Cylinder Head	
Standard	.5118-.5125 (13.000-13.018)
Press Fit	
Production	.0012-.0023 (.031-.060)
Replacement	.0024-.0035 (.060-.090)
Installed Height [1]	.50-.52 (12.9-13.2)

[1] – See Fig. 13.

VALVE SEATS

1) To remove a valve seat, use a grinder. Machine away seat material until loose in cylinder head. Drive seat out. Measure I.D. of valve seat bore. If necessary, machine oversize valve seat to specified size for cylinder head bore. See VALVE SEAT SPECIFICATION TABLE.

Fig. 12: Installing Cam Sprocket Dowel Pin

Dowel Pin Tool (P 212)

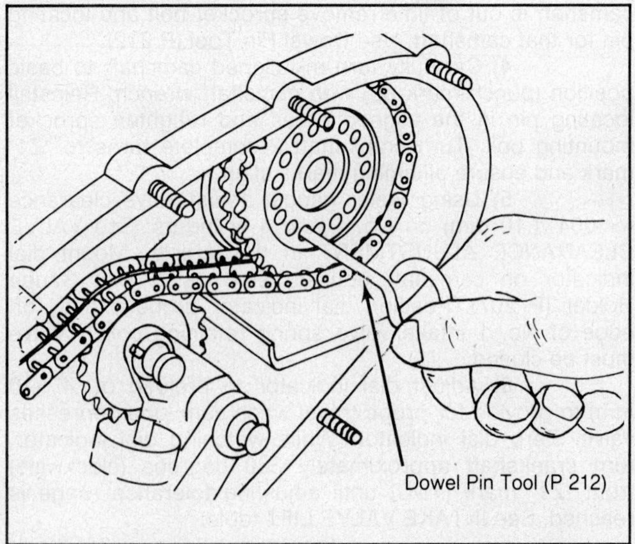

3.2L & 3.3L 6-CYLINDER (Cont.)

VALVE SEAT SPECIFICATION TABLE

Application	In. (mm)
Intake Seat	
Outside Diameter	
Standard	2.0339-2.0346 (51.661-51.680)
Oversize	2.0465-2.0472 (51.181-52.000)
Cylinder Head Bore	
Standard	2.0276-2.0287 (51.500-51.530)
Oversize	2.0402-2.0413 (51.820-51.850)
Exhaust Seat	
Outside Diameter	
Standard	1.7395-1.7402 (44.184-44.200)
Oversize	1.7616-1.7622 (44.744-44.760)
Cylinder Head Bore	
Standard	1.7323-1.7333 (44.000-44.025)
Oversize	1.7543-1.7553 (44.560-44.588)
Interference Fit	.0055-.0071 (.140-.180)

2) Heat cylinder head to about 392°F (200°C). Install new valve seat(s) using a drift of the proper size.

3) After valve seat installation, check insert depth by installing respective valve in guide and measuring distance from tip of valve stem to bottom of shim cavity (without shims). *See Fig. 13.* Standard valve tip-to-bottom of shim cavity distance is 1.799-1.823" (45.70-46.30 mm).

4) Allow cylinder head to cool slowly to room temperature. Reheat head to 392°F (200°C) and maintain this temperature for 2 hours. Again allow cylinder head to cool slowly to room temperature.

Fig. 13: Checking Valve Seat Insert Installed Depth

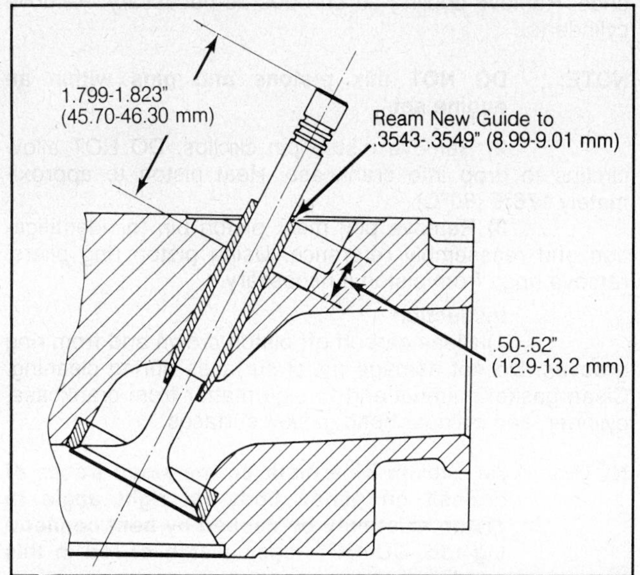

Courtesy of Porsche of North America, Inc.

5) If dimension is greater than specified, measure with new valve. If dimension is still beyond specification, valve seat insert has been cut too deep. Replace insert or cylinder head.

6) If valve seat must be recut, ensure original 3-angle valve seat is restored. Valve seat face angle is 45 degrees, top angle (combustion chamber side) is 30 degrees and throat angle (valve guide side) is 75 degrees.

7) After valve seat insert installation and 3-angle valve seat machining operation is performed, check valve seat insert runout using a dial indicator. If insert runout is more than .002" (.05 mm) recut valve face(s) or replace insert.

VALVES

1) Remove carbon from valve head. Using wire brush or wheel, clean valve thoroughly. Inspect valve for damaged head, scored or bent stem, and excessively worn or scored valve stem tip.

2) Check valve face and insert seat for burned or damaged areas. Grind or replace valve(s) and/or inserts as needed. Ensure valve stem-to-valve guide clearance is not beyond specification.

3) Standard clearance is .004" (.10 mm) for both intake and exhaust valves. Maximum clearance limit is .006" (.15 mm) for intake valves and .008" (.20 mm) for exhaust valves. Replace valve and/or guide as needed.

4) If valve is to be reused and has been ground, ensure overall length is still within specification. Standard overall valve length is 4.325-4.345" (109.85-110.35 mm) for intake valves and 4.258-4.278" (108.15-108.65 mm) for exhaust valves. If not within limits, replace valve(s).

VALVE STEM OIL SEALS

Removal

1) With rocker arm cover and spark plug(s) removed, position piston of cylinder concerned at BDC. Install adapter in spark plug hole, attach air line and apply air pressure.

2) Using a spring compressor, compress spring, detach valve keepers and remove valve springs with retainer. Pry valve stem oil seal from end of valve guide.

Installation

1) Lubricate end of valve guide with oil. Install new seal over stem, using caution to avoid damage to seal as it passes over keeper grooves.

2) Press seal over end of valve guide evenly. Install remaining components in reverse order of removal.

VALVE SPRINGS

1) With rocker arm cover and spark plug(s) removed, position piston of cylinder concerned at BDC. Install adapter in spark plug hole, attach air line and apply air pressure.

2) Using a spring compressor, compress spring, detach valve keepers and remove valve springs with retainer. Check springs for wear or fatigue and replace as necessary. Install springs with closely wound coils next to cylinder head.

3) Check installed height with Valve Spring Height Gauge (P 10C). *See Fig. 14.* Ensure height gauge fits spring retainer properly. If necessary, machine height gauge to fit.

4) Add or remove shim spacers under valve spring to attain specified installed height. Installed height for intake and exhaust valve springs is 1.346-1.358" (34.20-34.50 mm) for 911 Carrera and 1.307-1.331" (33.20-33.80 mm) for 911 Turbo, with valve closed.

CAUTION: The maximum valve spring installed height specification must not be exceeded. The minimum specification is prefered.

Porsche Engines

3.2L & 3.3L 6-CYLINDER (Cont.)

Fig. 14: Measurement of Valve Spring Installed Height

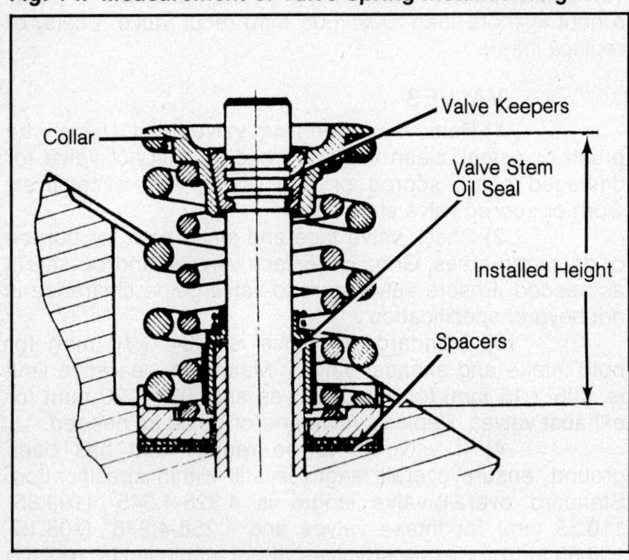

Courtesy of Porsche of North America, Inc.

ROCKER ARMS

1) With rocker arm covers and gaskets removed, rotate crankshaft and camshafts to relieve cam lobe pressure on rocker arm being worked on. If necessary, loosen nut on valve adjusting screw and back off adjusting screw.

NOTE: **Rocker arm and shaft assembly cannot be removed unless cam lobe pressure is relieved.**

2) Using a 6 mm Allen wrench, loosen rocker arm shaft bolt. Remove Allen head bolt, conical bushing, and conical nut. Slide rocker shaft out of cylinder head and remove rocker arm.

3) Check rocker arm, shaft bore and shaft for wear, replace as required. Install rocker arm shaft with Allen head bolt facing either No. 2 or No. 5 cylinder. Center shaft properly in housing and tighten Allen head bolt. *See Fig. 15.*

Fig. 15: Cross Section of Rocker Arm & Shaft Assembly

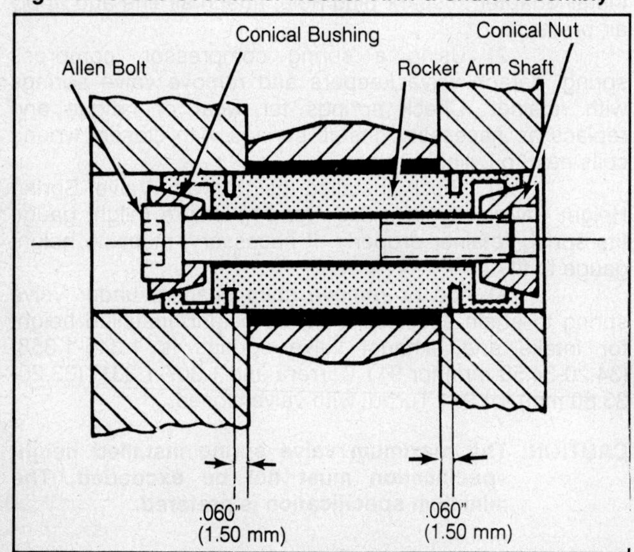

Courtesy of Porsche of North America, Inc.

ROCKER ARM SPECIFICATIONS

Application	Diameter In. (mm)	Limits In. (mm)
Rocker Arm Shaft Bore	.7086-.7093 (18.000-18.018)	[1]
Rocker Arm Shaft	.7083-.7086 (17.992-18.000)	[2] .0031 (.080)
Rocker Arm Bore	.7092-.7096 (18.016-18.027)	[2] .0031 (.080)
Rocker Arm Width	1.0157-1.0196 (25.800-25.900)	[3] .02 (.5)
Housing Width	1.0236-1.0241 (26.000-26.150)	[3] .02 (.5)

[1] – Rocker arm shaft is held firmly by wedge action.

[2] – Maximum wear limit for rocker arm-to-rocker shaft shown. Standard clearance is .0006-.0013" (.016-.035 mm).

[3] – Maximum wear limit for rocker arm-to-camshaft housing shown. The standard side clearance is .004-.014" (.10-.35 mm).

PISTON & CYLINDER ASSEMBLY

PISTONS, PINS, RINGS & CYLINDERS

Removal

1) With camshaft housing and cylinder head(s) removed, mark piston and cylinder for reassembly reference. Remove cooling air shrouds as necessary. Remove cylinder(s).

NOTE: **DO NOT mix pistons and pins within an engine set.**

2) Remove piston pin circlips. DO NOT allow circlips to drop into crankcase. Heat piston to approximately 176°F (80°C).

3) Remove pin, mark piston pin for identification and reassembly reference. Using piston ring pliers, remove rings from piston if necessary.

Inspection

1) Clean carbon off piston crown and from ring grooves. Do not damage metal surfaces during cleaning. Clean gasket material and foreign matter from crankcase, cylinder, and cylinder head gasket surfaces.

NOTE: **An uneven Blue mark or one-sided traces of deposit on piston body (at right angle to piston axis) may be caused by bent connecting rod. DO NOT reuse piston or rod in this condition.**

2) Inspect piston, rings and pin for each cylinder. Check piston pin fit. Check piston pin-to-connecting rod clearance. If clearance is beyond .002" (.05 mm), replace piston pin or install new rod bushing as necessary.

3.2L & 3.3L 6-CYLINDER (Cont.)

4) Inspect piston(s) for excessive wear. Piston diameter can be determined from size group marking stamped on piston crown. See PISTON & CYLINDER SIZES table.

PISTON & CYLINDER SIZES

Cylinder Size Marking	Bore Diameter [1] In. (mm)	Piston Diameter [1] In. (mm)
911 Carrera Mahle [2]		
0	3.7402-3.7404 (95.000-95.007)	3.7388-3.7392 (94.965-94.975)
1	3.7404-3.7407 (95.007-95.014)	3.7391-3.7394 (94.972-94.982)
2	3.7407-3.7409 (95.014-95.021)	3.7393-3.7397 (94.979-94.989)
3	3.7409-3.7413 (95.021-95.028)	3.7396-3.7399 (95.984-95.998)
911 Carrera KS [3]		
0	3.7402-3.7404 (95.000-95.007)	3.7358-3.7392 (94.963-94.977)
1	3.7404-3.7407 (95.007-95.014)	3.7398-3.7395 (94.970-94.984)
2	3.7407-3.7409 (95.014-95.021)	3.7392-3.7397 (94.977-94.991)
3	3.7409-3.7413 (95.021-95.028)	3.7395-3.7340 (95.984-95.998)
911 Turbo [4]		
0	3.8189-3.8192 (97.000-97.007)-	3.8130-3.8134 (96.850-96.860)
1	3.8192-3.8194 (97.007-97.014)	3.8133-3.8137 (96.857-96.867)
2	3.8194-3.8197 (97.014-97.021)	3.8133-3.8139 (96.864-96.874)
3	3.8197-3.8200 (97.021-97.028)	3.8138-3.8142 (96.871-96.881)

[1] - Replace piston(s) and cylinder(s) if clearance exceeds .006" (.15 mm).
[2] - Standard "Mahle" piston-to-cylinder clearance is .0010-.0017" (.025-.042 mm).
[3] - Standard "KS" piston-to-cylinder clearance is .0009-.0020" (.023-.052 mm).
[4] - Standard piston-to-cylinder clearance is .0010-.0020" (.025-.052 mm).

Installation

1) Lubricate piston and ring assemblies with oil. Ensure rings are correctly positioned on pistons (top mark up) with end gaps staggered. Install piston circlip with opening facing up or down.

2) Insert piston pin. See PISTON PIN in this article. Heat piston to about 176°F (80°C). Lubricate pin, and insert into piston until it contacts circlip.

3) Install remaining circlip. Ensure ring end gaps are staggered with oil scraper ring end gap at top. Using Piston Ring Compressor (P 8), compress rings. Care must be used to avoid ring damage.

4) Lightly oil cylinder bore. Install new base gasket and cylinder. Remove ring compressor.

CAUTION: Ensure that when cylinder is installed over studs, studs do not come in contact with cylinder fins. Broken fins reduce cooling and possible engine damage may result from overheating.

5) Check stud position by rotating cylinder back and forth while in installed position. If binding is found, check and straighten or replace studs as necessary. To complete installation, reverse removal procedure.

PISTON PIN

Piston pin is a press fit into piston. If piston pin can be inserted into piston while cold, a pin of larger diameter is necessary. Correct pin size is determined from color code (Black or White) marked on inside of piston pin boss. See PISTON PIN IDENTIFICATION table.

PISTON PIN IDENTIFICATION

Color	Piston Pin Bore Diameter	Piston Pin Diameter
White	.8660-.8661 (21.997-22.000)	.8661-.8662 (22.000-22.003)
Black	.8659-.8660 (21.994-21.997)	.8659-.8660 (21.994-21.997)

FITTING PISTONS

Piston pin bore is offset in piston. Piston installed direction is determined by marking stamped on piston dome (mark faces toward clutch) or by positioning flat spot on domed surface of piston facing intake valve. Only pistons from same manufacturer and of same weight class (with cylinders of same size) may be used in order to prevent engine imbalance. Maximum weight difference between one piston set (6) is .21 oz. (6 g).

1) Inspect "Nikasil" cylinder coating condition before performing tolerance and roundness measurements. See CYLINDER INSPECTION in this article. Measure pistons and cylinders for wear and out-of-round.

2) To check wear, measure piston diameter at 90 degrees to piston pin (at lower edge of pin bore). Piston is excessively worn if diameter (at measurement point) is .002" (.05 mm) below size when fitted. See PISTON & CYLINDER SIZES table in this article.

3) Using cylinder bore gauge, measure cylinder I.D. approximately 1.2" (30 mm) below top edge of bore. Cylinder wear limit (at point of measurement) is .003" (.08 mm).

4) To check cylinder out-of-round, measure cylinder diameter 1.2" (30 mm) below top edge of cylinder. Take one measurement in line with thrust face and another at 90 degrees to this measurement. If difference between the 2 measurements is more than .0016" (.040 mm), cylinder has exceeded out-of-round limit.

NOTE: Cylinder installed height is divided into 2 parts. Only cylinders of the same height reference mark (No. 5 or 6 within triangle stamped on lower flange) should be installed on the same bank.

5) Check cylinders for proper height. Cylinders marked with No. 5 (in triangle) are 3.236-3.237" (82.200-82.225 mm) and those marked with No. 6 are 3.237-3.238" (82.225-82.250 mm).

Porsche Engines

3.2L & 3.3L 6-CYLINDER (Cont.)

6) Cylinder-to-cylinder head sealing is metal-to-metal and there is no longer a sealing groove machined in cylinder head surface. Maximum runout of the cylinder sealing surface is .0015-.0032" (.040-.080 mm). Replace cylinder if worn or warped beyond specifications.

CYLINDER INSPECTION

1) When evaluating scored or streaky "Nikasil" coated cylinder running surfaces, it is often hard for the workshop to decide whether damage is already significant and requires repair of engine, or whether marks are insignificant. Use the following guidelines to determine cylinder wear.

2) Differences in markings on cylinder running surfaces are between "optical streaks" and "seizure streaks". Optical streaks are about 3 mm wide and are caused by ring end gap.

3) If honing traces are still visible within the optical streaks, this condition is normal and the cylinder is still reusable if running surface is smooth, round and within tolerance.

4) For cylinders with "seizure streaks", however, the honing traces are no longer seen. Cylinders in this condition must be replaced along with pistons of the proper weight and size. Seizure streaks are caused by piston skirt contacting cylinder walls, broken rings and/or lack of oil.

5) Any streaks in the vertical direction of wrist pin travel are considered optical streaks and are also a normal condition since there is very little contact between piston body (at the wrist pin area) and cylinder wall. These streaks are caused by oil breakdown and are primarily stains.

FITTING PISTON RINGS

1) Position piston rings in cylinder to height of cylinder base gasket. Measure ring gap. See PISTONS, PINS, RINGS in specifications section of this article.

2) Check side clearance of rings in piston ring grooves. Replace each piston's ring set if rings are beyond specification. Install rings on piston with "TOP" facing upward.

CRANKCASE ASSEMBLY

CRANKCASE HOUSING

Disassembly

1) With camshaft housings, cylinder heads, cylinders, timing chain covers, tensioners and sprockets removed, detach chain guides. Remove crankcase breather cover, oil pressure sensor, thermostat, and flywheel.

2) Dismantle and remove "V" belt pulley assembly. Detach and remove intermediate shaft axial adjustment cover. Detach breather outlet nozzle. Remove thermostat and oil pressure gauge.

3) Remove all 8 mm nuts connecting crankcase halves. Remove 2 cap nuts (under oil cooler flange) from No. 1 main bearing studs. Remove all through bolts. Loosen No. 7 main bearing stud nut (through left timing chain housing opening).

4) Lift left crankcase half from right crankcase half. Lift out crankshaft. Unfasten lock tabs on oil pump mounting nuts. Remove nuts and oil pump together with connecting shaft, intermediate shaft, and timing chains.

Inspection

1) Examine crankcase halves for cracks or damage. Inspect sealing surfaces for flatness and cleanliness. Repair or replace crankcase and related components as necessary.

2) Clean off gasket material with solvent and/or sharp-edged scraper. Clean out oilways with round wire brush, and flush out entire system of oil passages with solvent and compressed air. Ensure air emerges from all oil outlets.

NOTE: **Check that annular pressure relief groove cut around No. 7 main bearing through bolt (on left crankcase half sealing surface) is free of dirt or sealing compound at all times.**

3) Measure main bearing bores when crankcase is disassembled for repair. See CRANKCASE MAIN BEARING BORE MEASUREMENTS in this article. This procedure applies to engines of all model years. Inspect crankshaft and repair or replace as necessary. See CRANKSHAFT & CONNECTING RODS in this article.

4) If cylinder head stud has been broken above threads in crankcase, remove by first grinding broken stud flat. Center punch stud. Using a .250" (6.35 mm) carbide tip drill bit (in a drill press), drill approximately 5/8" into stud.

5) Drive screw extractor (No. 3 Snap-On) about 7/16" into bore. Heat crankcase housing in oven or with torch to about 392°F (200°C) to loosen grip of Loctite.

6) Turn out broken stud. Retap threads in crankcase and apply Loctite 270 and install a new "Dilivar" cylinder head stud.

NOTE: **The crankcase identifying mark ("0" or "1") for crankshaft and intermediate shaft center-to-center matching is stamped into left crankcase half, below alternator mount.**

Installation

1) Attach right crankcase half to work stand. Fit crankcase with matching crankshaft and intermediate shaft gears for proper center-to-center and backlash measurements before crankcase reassembly. See INTERMEDIATE SHAFT in this article.

2) After gear matching procedure, place intermediate shaft together with connecting shaft and oil pump (without timing chains) into crankcase. Turn shaft by hand and check that intermediate shaft, connecting shaft and oil pump run true (no visible runout) and without binding.

3) If runout is noted, correction may be possible by resetting each shaft's splines in relation to each other. Remove intermediate shaft, connecting shaft and oil pump from crankcase without disassembling.

4) If removed, install oil screens (at connecting webs below bearing supports) and fasten by bending sheet metal tabs over. Determine proper main bearing insert sizes. See CRANKSHAFT & CONNECTING RODS in this article.

5) Install No. 2-7 main bearing inserts into both crankcase halves. Ensure grooves machined in bearing supports of crankcase halves and bearing insert guide tabs align and oil passages in inserts and crankcase coincide.

6) Place No. 1 (blower end) main (thrust) bearing inserts in position in both crankcase halves. Place

3.2L & 3.3L 6-CYLINDER (Cont.)

new oil seal ring into groove of oil pump suction passages, in right crankcase half. Ensure seal ring is properly seated.

7) Install assembled oil pump, connecting shaft and intermediate shaft (with timing chains) in crankcase half. Install oil pump mounting nuts with new sheet metal lock tabs and bend tabs over lock nuts after tightening.

8) Install new "O" ring and oil seal in No. 8 bearing insert. Mark position of centering hole on insert flank and slide insert onto crankshaft journal. Using Connecting Rod Props (P 221), stand up cylinder No. 1 and 2 connecting rods.

9) Apply oil and molybdenum disulphide grease to all bearing journals. Install crankshaft assembly in right crankcase half with No. 8 bearing insert centering bore aligned with dowel pin in crankcase.

CAUTION: DO NOT allow dowel pin to fit into oil passage provided in bearing insert or oil will not reach bearing and severe engine damage will result.

10) Coat main bearing oil seal O.D. with sealant and ensure seal fits flush with outer crankcase exterior. Install Timing Chain Props (P 222) and remaining connecting rod props. Ensure new seal rings are installed in oil passage connecting left and right crankcases and between oil pump and left crankcase half.

11) Apply thin coat of sealant to both crankcase mating surfaces. Ensure no sealant reaches bearing insert seats or surfaces. Make a careful final inspection of component locations. Attach left crankcase half to right crankcase half.

12) Preassemble all through bolts by first placing double chamfer washer onto bolt (smooth side toward crankcase). Push on new "O" ring. Push through bolts into place from right crankcase half. Place another new "O" ring and double chamfer washer onto bolt. Hand tighten cap nuts at this time .

13) Install new "O" rings, double chamfer washers and cap nuts onto No. 1 main bearing studs (within oil cooler flange). Install a standard washer and nut onto No. 7 main bearing stud (within timing chain housing of left crankcase half).

14) Progressively tighten all main bearings through bolt cap nuts and stud nuts to 25 ft. lbs. (35 N.m). Start in center of cases and work outward in a clockwise, spiral pattern. Place new 8 mm spring washers onto all crankcase retaining studs and tighten nuts to 192-216 INCH. lbs. (22-24 N.m).

15) Ensure flywheel mating surfaces are free of grease and foreign matter. Install flywheel. Check to ensure crankshaft turns freely in crankshaft housing, ensuring timing chains remain clear. Complete remaining engine assembly as needed.

CRANKCASE MAIN BEARING BORE MEASUREMENTS

NOTE: Main bearing bores in crankcase must be measured and resized (if necessary) whenever crankcase halves are disassembled for repair.

1) Attach left crankcase half to mount fixture. Assemble both crankcase halves without intermediate shaft. Lightly tighten all crankcase main bearing studs and two 8 mm nuts at main bearing No. 1.

2) Align both crankcase halves using a plastic mallet. Ensure main bearing No. 8 is not offset in relation to each half. Using an inside micrometer, cross-check No. 8 main bearing bore and realign bore as needed.

3) Tighten all crankcase studs and both 8 mm nuts to proper torque. Measure all main bearing bores with an inside micrometer. Standard I.D. for all crankcase main bearing bores is 2.5591-2.5598" (65.000-65.019 mm).

4) If bores are too tight, ream bores to standard size. If bores are too large, ream light alloy crankcase bores (in 2 steps) to "B" bearing (oversize) of 2.5689-2.5696" (65.250-65.269 mm).

5) When reaming, use cutting oil on reamer and make initial cut to 2.4468" (62.150 mm). When reaming pressure-cast crankcases, cut in one pass, without oil. Ream to oversize specification of 2.5689" (65.250 mm).

INTERMEDIATE SHAFT

Center-to-Center Distance Check

1) Check identifying mark ("0" or "1") stamped into left crankcase half, below alternator mount and on crankshaft gear and intermediate shaft gear. Gears and crankcase may be paired together only as indicated.

2) If crankcase is stamped with a "0", the distance between shaft centers is 4.0935-4.0941" (103.975-103.990 mm). Install crankshaft gear with "0" and intermediate shaft gear with "0". Using dial indicator mounted to crankcase, ensure gear backlash is within .0011-.0019" (.029-.049 mm).

NOTE: Do not mix gears with different stamped number unless gear backlash falls within specification.

3) If crankshaft gear is stamped with "1" and intermediate shaft gear is stamped "0", gear backlash must be .0006-.0016" (.016-.042 mm). If crankshaft gear is stamped "0" and intermediate shaft gear is stamped "1", gear backlash must be .0007-.0017" (.017-.043 mm).

4) If crankcase is stamped with a "1", the distance between shaft centers is 4.0941-4.0945" (103.990-104.000 mm). Install crankshaft gear with "1" and intermediate shaft gear with "1". Ensure gear backlash is within .0050-.0016" (.012-.041 mm).

5) If crankshaft gear is stamped with "0" and intermediate shaft gear is stamped "1", gear backlash must be .0010-.0019" (.025-.049 mm). If crankshaft gear is stamped "1" and intermediate shaft gear is stamped "0", gear backlash must be .0010-.0018" (.025-.048 mm).

CAUTION: The bolt-on intermediate shaft gear is machined in position on the shaft to avoid improper gear meshing or out-of-roundness. DO NOT replace just the gear if worn. Replace both shaft and gear assembly.

Gear Inspection

1) With gear removed from intermediate shaft, place two .18" (4.5 mm) diameter steel rollers into gear teeth, 180 degrees apart from each other. Measure total O.D. distance of rollers and gear.

2) If measuring standard gear, the distance must be no less than 5.374" (136.50 mm). If gear is stamped with "1", the distance must be no less than 5.376" (136.55 mm). Replace crankshaft drive gear and intermediate shaft gear if not within specification.

3) In the case where engine has been run for a considerable time or during overhaul, the aluminum plugs on shaft end face must be removed and oil passages cleaned to remove residue. See PLUG REPLACEMENT in this article.

Oil Passage Plug Replacement

1) To remove pressed-in plugs, first drill out center of each plug with a .252" (6.40 mm) diameter drill. Thread plug with an 8 mm tap. Install a 8 x 65 mm bolt and carefully turn out plug.

2) Thoroughly clean intermediate shaft oil passages. Press in new plug while ensuring no damage is done to bearing oil passages in plug.

Bearing Service

With crankcase halves separated, lift out intermediate shaft and bearing inserts. Inspect bearing inserts and shaft journals for excessive wear or damage. See BEARING INSERT SPECIFICATIONS table in this article.

NOTE: Undersize intermediate shaft bearing inserts are NOT available.

BEARING INSERT SPECIFICATIONS [1]

Application	Inches (mm)
Front Blower Inserts	
Standard Journal (O.D.)	.9835-.9843" (24.980-25.000 mm)
Crankcase (I.D.)	1.0827-1.0835" (27.500-27.521 mm)
Rear Flywheel End	
Standard Journal (O.D.)	.9436-.9441" (23.967-23.980 mm)
Crankcase (I.D.)	1.0433-1.0441" (26.500-26.521 mm)
Standard Clearane	.0012-.0033" (.030-.084 mm)

[1] – Replace inserts and/or intermediate shaft as needed.

End Play Adjustment

A flanged bearing insert is used in crankcase to support rear journal of intermediate shaft. When installing insert, ensure alignment tab is seated in corresponding notch in insert cradle. If new inserts are installed, end play adjustment is normally not needed.

1) If crankcases are disassembled for resealing only, end play should be checked and adjusted with crankcases reassembled but before timing chain housings are installed.

2) Thrust end of intermediate shaft is designed to protrude beyond crankshaft housing. Spacers for adjusting end play are available in various thicknesses.

3) Using a depth gauge, check and record shaft overhang beyond crankcase housing. Use this specification during timing chain alignment. Place a new "O" ring in groove on intermediate shaft cover and install in crankshaft housing.

4) Install Dial Indicator Fixture (P 220) with probe positioned on face of intermediate shaft. Measure end play by moving shaft back and forth. Note end play.

5) Allowable shaft end play is .0016-.006" (.040-.16 mm). Replace intermediate shaft bearing inserts if beyond specification.

6) If necessary, adjust clearance by inserting proper size shim spacers (available in various thicknesses). After end play check, set shaft cover and spacers aside for final assembly.

CRANKSHAFT & CONNECTING RODS

1) Separate crankcase halves. Lift out crankshaft and connecting rods. Place crankshaft on stand and remove connecting rods. Inspect connecting rods for wear, damage and alignment. Check rod bearing inserts for excessive wear or damage and replace as necessary. See CONNECTING ROD BEARINGS.

2) Inspect connecting rod small end bushing for excessive wear or damage. Standard rod bushing I.D. is .8669-.8671" (22.020-22.033 mm). Standard piston pin O.D. is .8657-.8661" (21.994-22.000 mm). If piston pin-to-bushing clearance is more than .0022" (.055 mm) replace bushing.

3) New rod bushing O.D. is .9856-.9864" (25.035-25.055 mm). Connecting rod small end I.D. is .9842-.9850" (25.000-25.021 mm). Bushing is pressed into rod with interference fit of .0006-.0022" (.014-.055 mm). Check connecting rods for proper widths and center-to-center distance.

4) Standard small end rod/bushing width is 1.0228-1.0236" (25.980-26.000 mm). Standard large end rod width is .933-937" (23.70-23.80 mm). Ensure rod side clearance is within .008-.014" (.20-.35 mm). Rod center-to-center length is 5.032" (127.80 mm). Repair or replace connecting rod if not within specifications.

NOTE: Replacement connecting rods (without inserts) must have a weight difference of no more than .11 oz. (3 g).

5) Check main bearing inserts for excessive wear or damage and replace as necessary. See MAIN BEARINGS in this article. Inspect crankshaft main and rod bearing journals and oil seal surfaces for nicks, scratches and excessive wear or damage.

6) Replace crankshaft or regrind bearing journals as necessary. If oil seal surfaces are deeply scored, grind seal surfaces to 1.16" (29.5 mm) for cooling fan end and 3.52" (89.5 mm) for flywheel end.

7) After grinding, chamfer oil holes to a .02" (.5 mm) radius. Polish oil seal journals to 2-5 microns. Crankshaft main and rod bearing journals may be reground 4 times.

NOTE: Crankshaft bearing undersize color codes are: Blue paint dot for first undersize, Green dot for second undersize, Yellow dot for third undersize and White dot for fourth undersize.

8) If crankshaft is reground, plugs must be removed from oil passages. Thoroughly clean out passages and install and secure new plugs. Ensure all oilways are properly radiused and sharp edges chamfered.

CAUTION: If bearing journals are reground, crankshaft must have a surface hardness treatment done to restore journals to proper hardness.

9) After regrind, crankshaft must have a "Tenifer" treatment for 2 hours at 1060°F (570°C). After crankshaft heat treatment, polish all bearing journals. Magniflux complete crankshaft to check for cracks. If crankshaft is rebalanced after regrinding, ensure balance is within 10 cmg.

3.2L & 3.3L 6-CYLINDER (Cont.)

10) Check crankshaft runout. Maximum runout is .0016" (.040 mm) as measured on bearing journals No. 4 and 8 with journals No. 1 and 7 on "V" blocks. After "Tenifer" treatment, DO NOT attempt to straighten No. 3 and 5 bearing journals. All other main bearing journals may be straightened by applying pressure to the bearing journal webs.

11) Check distributor drive gear for wear or damage. If drive gear must be replaced, remove circlip and install gear puller with puller arms on timing gear. Pull timing gear, spacer and distributor drive gear off end of crankshaft as an assembly.

12) Remove spring washer. When installing new drive gear, note that 2 drive gears are available. Ensure gear marked with "P" faces the "V" belt drive pulley.

NOTE: **Incorrect installation of distributor drive gear will cause initial ignition timing to be off by approximately 13 degrees.**

13) For a gear marked with "P" and an additional "X" (scribed with an electric engraver), the "X" should face the "V" belt drive pulley. The location of the "P" mark on this gear does not matter.

NOTE: **Circlips are available in 4 thicknesses to take up axial end play between distributor and drive gear. Circlip with code mark "O" stamped on surface is 2.4 mm thick. Code "1" is 2.3 mm, code "2" is 2.2 mm and code "3" is 2.1 mm.**

14) Heat timing gear to approximately 302°F (150°C) in oil bath or on hot plate. Push gear onto crankshaft end. Timing gear shoulder should face flywheel. Heat drive gear to 212°F (100°C) and press on.

15) With spring washer, timing gear, spacer and drive gear installed on crankshaft, select proper circlip by first installing to check thickness. Install proper thickness circlip to take up axial play.

NOTE: **With proper distributor drive gear in place, the distributor rotor will turn clockwise.**

MAIN BEARINGS

1) Main bearing No. 8 is a special bearing with an external "O" ring and an internal oil seal. A steel dowel, pressed into crankcase, is used to locate No. 8 bearing and prevents it from turning. Crankshaft journals 1-7 are the same size.

2) When inspecting crankshaft, check main bearing insert bores in crankcase for size and straightness. See CRANKCASE MAIN BEARING BORE MEASUREMENTS in this article. Using a bore gauge and micrometer (or Plastigage method), assemble crankcases with inserts installed.

3) Measure all main bearing inserts I.D. and crank journals O.D. to check insert-to-journal clearances. Maximum clearance is no more than .0033" (.083 mm). Grind crankshaft and replace bearing inserts as necessary.

Fig. 16: Exploded View of Crankshaft Assembly

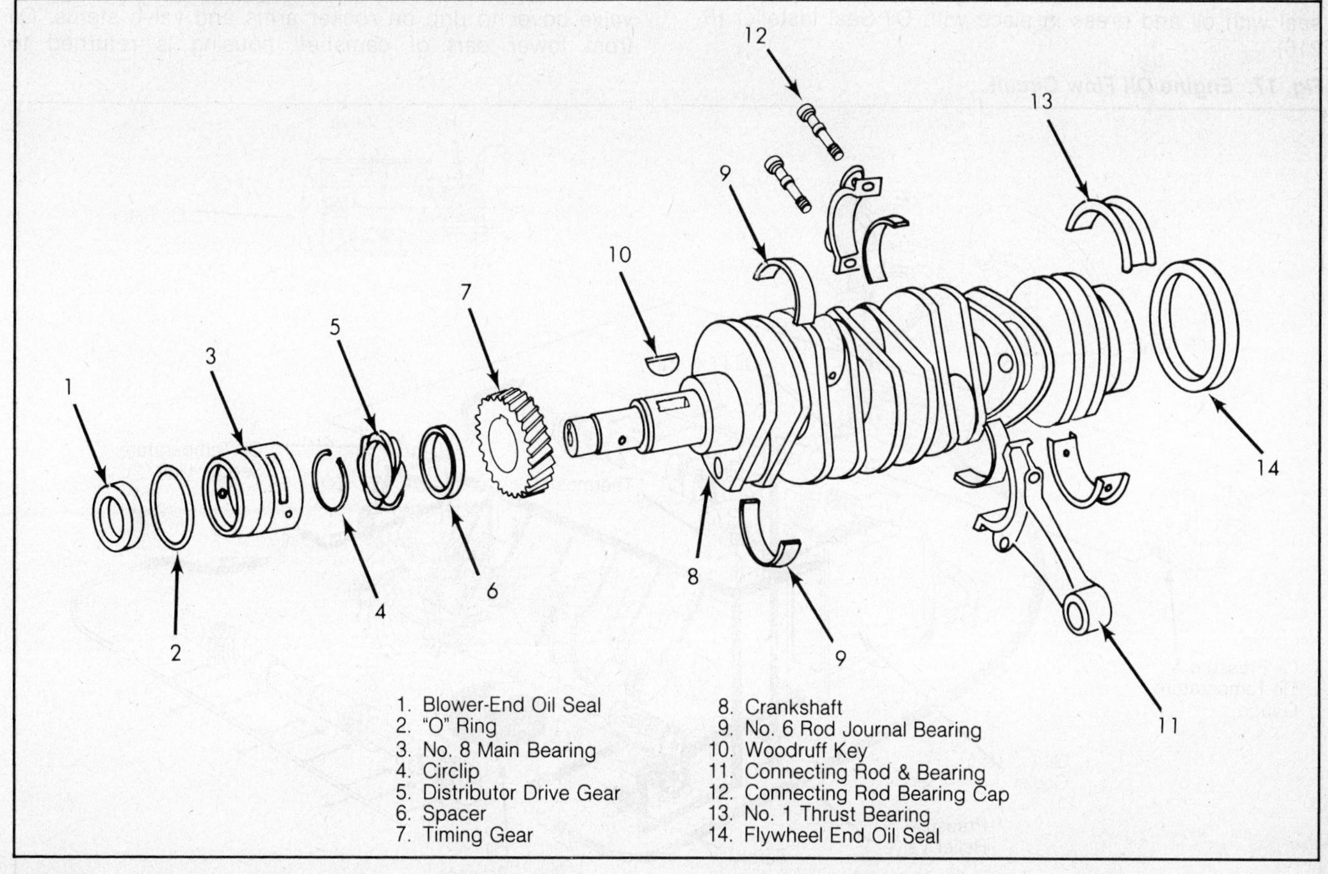

Porsche Engines

3.2L & 3.3L 6-CYLINDER (Cont.)

NOTE: **Connecting rod stretch bolts should never be reused. Replace rod bolts whenever connecting rods are disassembled.**

CONNECTING ROD BEARINGS

1) Using Plastigage or micrometer and hole gauge, check connecting rods and crankshaft for proper bearing-to-journal clearance. Maximum clearance .0039" (.099 mm).

2) Regrind crankshaft and replace rod bearing inserts if clearance is more than specification. When replacing rod bearing inserts on crankshaft, inspect connecting rod bearing insert bore.

3) To check, assemble rod and end cap using old rod bolts. Using bore gauge, measure rod big end I.D. Without insert, standard I.D. is 2.2047-2.2055" (56.000-56.019 mm). Replace connecting rod if beyond limits.

THRUST BEARING END PLAY

1) Check size and end play at No. 1 main (thrust) bearing. Standard thrust bearing width is 1.1024-1.1047" (28.000-28.060 mm). With crankshaft and inserts installed and crankcases temporarily assembled, mount dial indicator with pointer positioned on crankshaft end.

2) Carefully move crankshaft back and forth and record end play. Standard end play clearance is .0043-.0076" (.110-.195 mm). Maximum end play is .012" (.30 mm). Replace No. 1 main bearing inserts and/or crankshaft if excessive wear is present.

CRANKCASE OIL SEALS

Main Bearing (Blower End)

Remove belt pulley. Pry out old seal. Coat new seal with oil and press in place with Oil Seal Installer (P 216).

Main Bearing (Flywheel End)

Remove flywheel. Remove oil seal by prying out. Coat new seal outer edges with sealing compound. Press seal into crankcase with Oil Seal Driver (P 9126) until seal is flush with face of crankcase.

OIL CAPACITY

Standard oil capacity is 10.6 qts. (10L) when changing oil. Total engine capacity (with oil cooler) is 13.7 qts. (13L). Always check oil level with engine at idle speed and normal operating temperature. Difference between maximum and minimum marks on dipstick is approximately 1.9 qts. (1.8L).

OIL FILTER

Oil filter is a disposable, spin-on type.

NORMAL OIL PRESSURE

Oil pressure should be 60 psi (4.2 kg/cm²) at 5000 RPM with an oil temperature of 194°F (90°C).

ENGINE OILING

ENGINE OILING SYSTEM

Lubrication is dry sump type. Two independent oil pumps (built into one pump body) provide pressure and suction in system. The pressure pump draws oil from externally mounted oil tank and forces it through an oil cooler and to main, connecting rod, and intermediate shaft bearings. The suction pump removes oil from sump (through strainer) and forces it through oil filter to oil tank.

Camshaft bearings are oiled by external oil lines leading to camshaft housing. Oil splashes against valve cover to drip on rocker arms and valve stems. Oil from lower part of camshaft housing is returned to

Fig. 17: Engine Oil Flow Circuit

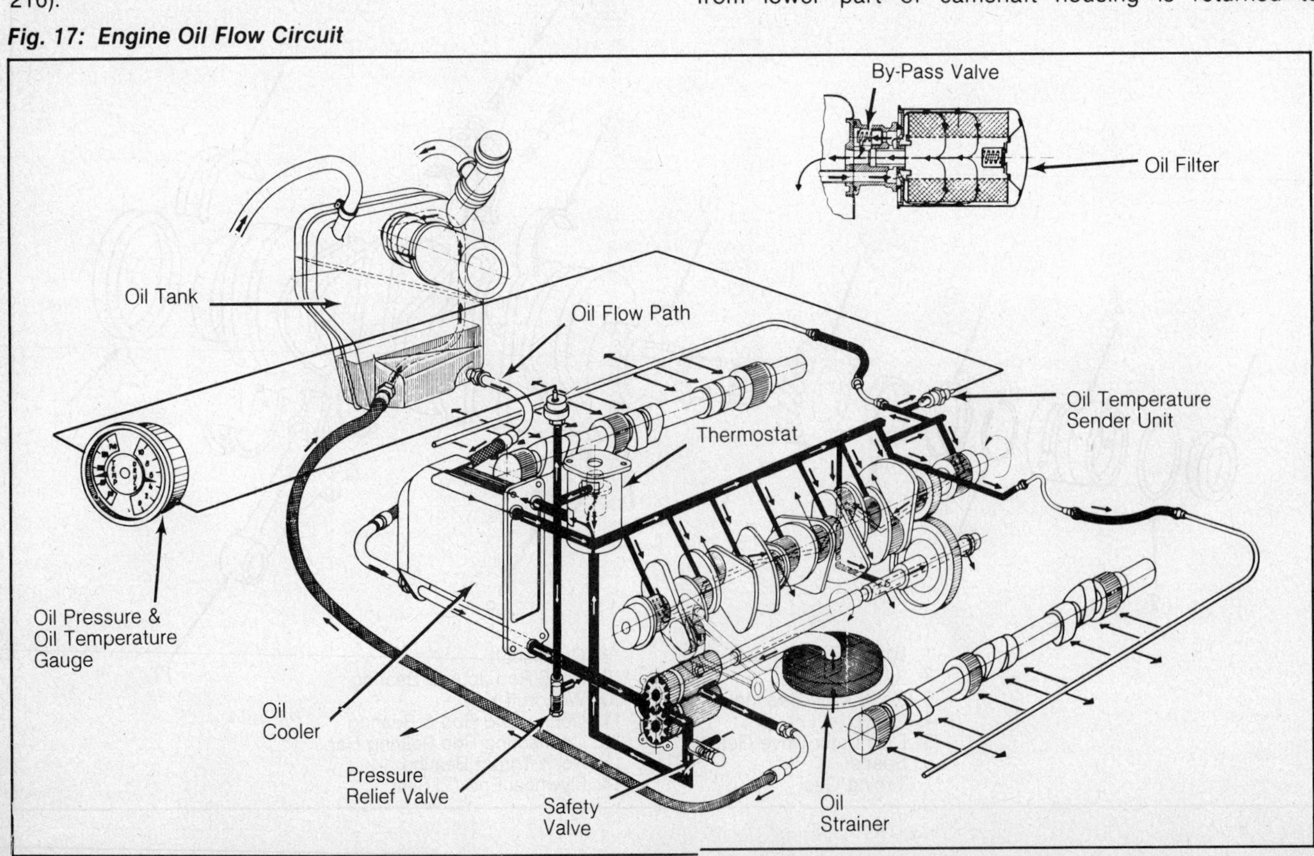

Courtesy of Porsche of North America, Inc.

3.2L & 3.3L 6-CYLINDER (Cont.)

crankcase by oil return pipes. Pressure is controlled by 4 separate valves. At low temperatures, below 176°F (80°C), a thermostatically controlled valve directs oil to engine. At higher temperatures, oil first flows through cooler and then to bearings.

A pressure relief valve directs oil into crankcase if pressure rises to 76.9-99.6 psi (5.4-7.0 kg/cm²). Additional safety and by-pass valves are built into the system to prevent damage from excessive pressure.

PRESSURE RELIEF & SAFETY VALVES

1) Identically constructed coil springs are used in pressure release and safety valves. The safety valve is set to operate at a higher pressure than the relief valve by greater compression of coil spring in its fitted position.

2) The spring for pressure release and safety valves is 2.75" (70 mm) long (in free length) with an O.D. of .48" (12.2 mm) and wire diameter of .055" (1.4 mm).

3) Fully compressed length is 1.31" (33.3 mm). Pressure exerted at length of 2.04" (52 mm) is 77 lbs. (342 N); at length of 1.81" (46 mm), pressure is 102 lbs. (454 N).

4) The pressure relief valve (in right crankcase half, across from thermostat) uses an aluminum washer and the safety valve (located in horizontal position in left crankcase half) uses a copper washer.

OIL PUMP

NOTE: **Engine oil pump may be removed only when crankcase halves are separated. See CRANKCASE HOUSING in this article. DO NOT attempt to repair a defective oil pump assembly. Replace unit as an assembly.**

Inspection

1) With oil pump removed from crankcases and shafts separated, drain remaining oil from pump, clean unit in solvent and dry with compressed air.

2) Check pump operation by rotating drive shaft at a steady speed. Examine sealing surfaces at oil inlet and outlet passages. If surfaces are damaged, drive shaft rotation is not smooth or pump pressure is inadaquate, replace oil pump assembly.

NOTE: **When installing engine oil pump (with connecting shaft and intermediate shaft attached), new sealing ring must be installed in grooves in right crankcase half main oil passage. Ensure ring is not trapped between crankcase inlet passage and centering groove on oil pump.**

ENGINE COOLING

A fan type cooling system is used in the 911 Carrera and 911 Turbo engine. Cooling is accomplished by means of an axial-type fan mounted on the alternator shaft. Fan system consists of an impeller, belt pulley, and blower housing. Impeller and belt pulley are attached to alternator shaft.

Fan delivers air for cooling engine, oil cooler, and alternator. Cooling air flows through upper molded plastic air ducts to cylinders and heads.

Baffle plates mounted to cylinders provide uniform distribution of air. A duct incorporated into upper air guide leads air flow directly to oil cooler. Ducting for air delivery to heat exchangers is on both sides of blower housing.

CAUTION: **It is essential that when air ducts and baffle plates are reinstalled, no openings or gaps exist, or cooling effectiveness will be seriously reduced with resultant major engine damage.**

COOLING AIR BLOWER

Blower may be removed (complete or with alternator only) with engine either in or out of vehicle. The air deflector plates between cylinders can only be detached with engine out of vehicle and camshaft housing(s) removed.

CAUTION: **DO NOT attempt to remove "V" belt by prying belt over pulley or severe belt damage may occur.**

Removal

1) Detach screws holding upper air channel. Using "V" Belt Pulley Holder (P 208), hold alternator pulley, loosen pulley mounting nut and remove belt. Remove nuts from blower housing mount strap and loosen strap.

2) Remove blower housing and alternator off locating peg and toward rear. Mark wiring connectors on alternator for reassembly reference. Detach wiring from alternator. Remove blower housing with alternator assembly.

Installation

1) Position blower housing and alternator on crankcase locating peg. Reconnect alternator wiring.

2) Check "V" belt condition and replace if signs of excessive wear (frayed edges and/or cracks in belt face) are present. Adjust "V" belt tension at this time.

CAUTION: **DO NOT allow oil or grease to contact "V" belt. DO NOT overtighten belt or bearing damage and belt breakage will result. DO NOT adjust belt with too low tension or excessive slippage may develop between belt and pulley, reducing air supply and causing engine overheating with resultant engine damage.**

Adjustment

1) Adjust blower drive belt by adding or removing spacer washers between impeller housing and pulley half. This will cause belt to ride higher or lower on pulley, thereby loosening or tightening drive belt.

2) Adjust initial "V" belt tension so belt can be pressed in about .394-.591" (10-15 mm) by hand pressure at mid point between pulleys. Remove one spacer washer from between pulley half and housing and install it in front of pulley section. Check for final belt deflection of .2" (5 mm).

NOTE: **If "V" belt is stretched to the point that only one spacer washer remains between pulley half and impeller housing, replace belt. Belt must not contact bottom of "V" in pulley.**

3) Install outer belt pulley half. Insert spacer washers not used for adjustment between outer pulley half and clamping cap so total number of washers (6) on shaft remains unaltered.

Porsche Engines

3.2L & 3.3L 6-CYLINDER (Cont.)

4) Tighten pulley mounting nut to 32-65 ft. lbs. (45-90 N.m). Check that pulley halves run true. If not, belt wear may be greatly increased. Maximum radial pulley runout is .006" (.15 mm) and maximum lateral runout is .008" (.20 mm). Run vehicle 30-60 miles. Check and readjust belt as necessary.

TIGHTENING SPECIFICATIONS

Application	Ft. Lbs. (N.m)
Alternator Pulley Nut	32-65 (45-90)
Camshaft (Hex Head) Bolt	87 (120)
Camshaft Sprocket Mounting Nut	103 (140)
Connecting Rod Cap Nut	
Step 1	14 (20)
Step 2	Angle Tighten 90 Degrees
Crankcase	
Pressure Relief Valve Plug	43 (60)
Safety Valve Plug	43 (60)
Through Bolt (9 mm)	[1] 25 (35)
Crankshaft Pulley Nut	[2] 58 (80)
Cylinder Head Mounting Nut	[4]
Engine Carrier Mounting Bolt	29 (40)
Flywheel Mounting Bolt	65 (90)
Main Bearing Caps	25 (35)
Oil Drain Plug	51 (70)
Oil Pressure Return Line Adapter	87 (120)
Oil Pressure Transmitter Adapter	25 (35)
Oil Pressure Transmitter-to-Adapter	25 (35)
Oxygen Sensor-to-Catalytic Converter	36-43 (50-60)
Spark Plug	18-22 (25-30)

TIGHTENING SPECIFICATIONS (Cont.)

Application	INCH Lbs. (N.m)
Camshaft Housing Cover Bolt	72 (8)
Camshaft Housing Mounting Nut (8 mm)	216 (25)
Crankcase Through Bolt (8 mm)	216 (25)
Crankshaft Sleeve W/Needle Bearing	84 (10)
Fan Housing Strap Bolt	108 (12)
Fuel Distribution Line Cap Nut	108 (12)
Intake Manifold	216 (25)
Oil Pressure Control Switch	[3] 168 (20)
Reactor to Cyl. Head (Turbo)	168-204 (14-17)
Rocker Arm Shaft Nut	156 (18)

[1] – Tighten through bolts and stud nuts progressively, starting at center main bearings and working clockwise outward, in a spiral pattern.

[2] – Pulley without air conditioner shown. Pulley with air conditioner mounting nut torque is 123 ft. lbs. (170 N.m).

[3] – Maximum torque shown.

[4] – See CYLINDER HEAD TIGHTENING PROCEDURE section of this article.

ENGINE SPECIFICATIONS

GENERAL SPECIFICATIONS

Year	DISPLACEMENT Cu. In.	Liters	Fuel System	HP@RPM	Torque Ft. Lbs.@RPM	Compr. Ratio	BORE In.	mm	STROKE In.	mm
1987										
911 Carrera	193.2	3.2	Fuel Inj.	200 @ 5900	185 @ 4800	9.5:1	3.74	95.0	2.93	74.4
911 Turbo	201.3	3.3	Turbo/Fuel Inj.	282 @ 5500	288 @ 4000	7.0:1	3.82	97	2.93	74.4

VALVES

Engine Size & Valve	Head Diam. In. (mm)	Face Angle	Seat Angle	Seat Width In. (mm)	Stem Diameter In. (mm)	Stem Clearance In. (mm)	Valve Lift In. (mm)
3.2L & 3.3L							
Intake	1.925-1.933 (48.90-49.10)	45°	45°	.055-.063 (1.40-1.60)	.3526-.3532 (8.958-8.970)	.004 (.10)	.043-.055 [1] (1.10-1.40)
Exhaust	1.629-1.638 (41.40-41.60)	45°	45°	.055-.063 (1.40-1.60)	.3518-.3523 (8.938-8.950)	.004 (.10)	.....

[1] – Intake valve lift is measured at TDC overlap with .004" (.10 mm) valve clearance. Valve lift for 911 Turbo is .025-.031" (.65-.80 mm), other valve specifications are same as 911 Carrera.

Porsche Engines

3.2L & 3.3L 6-CYLINDER (Cont.)

ENGINE SPECIFICATIONS (Cont.)

CRANKSHAFT MAIN & CONNECTING ROD BEARINGS

Engine	MAIN BEARINGS				CONNECTING ROD BEARINGS		
	Journal Diam. In. (mm)	Clearance In. (mm)	Thrust Bearing	Crankshaft End Play In. (mm)	Journal Diam. In. (mm)	Clearance In. (mm)	Side Play In. (mm)
3.2L & 3.3L							
Journals 1-7	2.3611-2.3618 (59.971-59.990)	.0003-.0028 (.010-.072)	No. 1	.008-.014 (.20-.35)	2.0855-2.0862 (52.971-52.990)	.0010-.0034 (.030-.088)	.008-.014 (.20-.35)
Journal 8	1.2197-1.2202 (30.980-30.993)	.0018-.0041 (.048-.104)					

PISTONS, PINS & RINGS

Engine	PISTONS	PINS		RINGS		
	Clearance In. (mm)	Piston Fit In. (mm)	Rod Fit In. (mm)	Ring No.	End Gap In. (mm)	Side Clearance In. (mm)
3.2L Carrera	.0009-.0020 [1] (.023-.044)	Press Fit [2]	.0007-.0015 (.020-.039)	No. 1	.004-.008 (.10-.20)	.003-.004 (.07-.10)
				No. 2	.004-.008 (.10-.20)	.001-.003 (.04-.07)
				Oil	.006-.012 [3] (.15-.30)	.0008-.0020 [3] (.02-.05)
3.3L Turbo	.0010-.0020 (.025-.052)	Press Fit [2]	.0007-.0015 (.020-.039)	No.1	.006-.012 (.15-.30)	.003-.004 (.040-.072)
				No. 2	.006-.012 (.15-.30)	.001-.003 (.040-.072)
				Oil	.006-.012 (.15-.30)	.0008-.0020 (.020-.052)

[1] – The clearance shown is for "KS" pistons. "Mahle" piston-to-cylinder clearance is .0010-.0017" (.025-.042 mm).
[2] – If piston pin can be inserted into piston while cold, a pin of larger diameter is necessary. See PISTON PIN in this article.
[3] – Clearance shown is for 1-piece oil ring.

VALVE TIMING

Engine	INTAKE		EXHAUST	
	Open (BTDC)	Close (ABDC)	Open (BBDC)	Close (ATDC)
3.2L Carrera	4°	50°	46°	0°
3.3L Turbo	3°(ATDC)	37°	27°	5°(BTDC)

VALVE SPRINGS

Engine	Free Length In. (mm)	PRESSURE Lbs. @ In. (Kg @ mm)	
		Valve Closed	Valve Open
3.2L Carrera			
Intake	[1]	44 @ 1.65-1.67 (20 @ 41.9-42.4)	171 @ 1.20-1.22 (80 @ 30.5-30.9)
Exhaust	[1]	44 @ 1.65-1.67 (20 @ 41.9-42.4)	160 @ 1.24-1.26 (75 @ 31.5-32.0)
3.3L Turbo	[2]		

[1] – When installing valve springs, use installed height of 1.347-1.358" (34.20-34.50 mm). Add or remove shims to correct height to lower limit if possible.
[2] – Installed height for 911 Turbo valve springs is 1.319" +/- .012" (33.5 +/- 0.3 mm).

Saab Engines

2.0L 4-CYLINDER

900, 900S, 900 Turbo, 9000S & 9000 Turbo

NOTE: **For engine repair procedures not covered in this article, see ENGINE OVERHAUL PROCEDURES article at beginning of this section.**

ENGINE CODING

ENGINE IDENTIFICATION

Engine number is stamped on a machined pad on engine block below CIS throttle housing.

ENGINE IDENTIFICATION CODES

Application	Code
900	
Man. Trans.	B2012I03MH
Auto. Trans.	B2012I03AH
900S & 9000S	
Man. Trans.	B2022D03MH
Auto. Trans.	B2022D03AH
900 & 9000 Turbo	
Man. Trans.	B2022L13MH
Auto. Trans.	B2022L13AH

ENGINE, MANIFOLDS & CYLINDER HEAD

ENGINE

NOTE: **Remove engine and transaxle as a unit. On 900 models, transaxle housing forms engine lower crankcase pan.**

Removal

1) Disconnect and remove battery. Disconnect windshield washer hose. Remove hood on 900 models. Drain cooling system. Disconnect ground strap between engine and chassis. Disconnect positive cable from starter motor. Disconnect servo vacuum hose at manifold. Remove bellows between airflow sensor and intake manifold.

2) Clean area around fuel distributor lines and detach lines at connectors. Cover fuel distributor line openings and plug fuel line ends. Remove air cleaner assembly. Remove mixture control unit. Disconnect EGR system (if equipped). Disconnect all coolant hoses.

3) On Turbo models, remove ignition coil. Disconnect turbocharger pressure line at turbocharger. Remove intercooler/throttle body unit. Remove airflow sensor with inlet pipe to turbocharger.

4) Disconnect ignition wiring connectors. Disconnect sensors, emission control and electrical power connections between chassis and engine/transaxle. Disconnect heating system and vacuum hoses.

5) Disconnect throttle control wire. Disconnect hydraulic lines at power steering pump (if equipped).

6) On manual transmission models, disconnect clutch line from slave cylinder and cap hose and slave cylinder opening. On 900 models, place gear lever in Neutral position. Drive front taper pin from shift rod joint. Separate joint from gearshift rod. On 9000 models, select 4th gear and separate rubber shift linkage joint.

7) On automatic transmission models, place gear selector in Park position. To remove selector cable retaining screw, push back spring loaded sleeve on shift rod and disconnect cable.

8) Remove protective cover from exhaust manifold. On all models, disconnect exhaust pipe at manifold. Disconnect speedometer cable at transmission. Remove inner universal joint clamps and bellows. On 900 models, place Spacer (83 93 209) between upper control arm and body to ensure that front suspension will be unloaded when car is raised.

9) Raise and support vehicle. Remove lower end piece from right side control arm. Remove rear transaxle mounting bolts and loosen front mounting nut so that mount can be lifted from bracket. Attach lifting hoist and raise engine/transaxle slightly.

10) Move engine/transaxle to right and remove left universal joint. Move engine/transaxle to left and remove right universal joint. Ensure all cables and lines are free of engine/transaxle. Remove engine/transaxle from vehicle.

Installation

1) Ensure universal joints are packed with grease. Position new gaskets on exhaust pipe flanges. Suspend and position engine/transaxle so front mount will locate in its bracket before rear mount.

2) Lower engine/transaxle assembly while guiding front mount into its bracket. Continue to lower assembly until rear of engine/transaxle is about 2" above mountings.

3) Move engine/transaxle to right and guide in left universal joint. Lower engine/transaxle into mountings while aligning right universal joint. Ensure exhaust pipe flanges line up.

4) Attach right end piece to control arm. Tighten universal joints. Install rear mounting bolts. Tighten all engine/transaxle mountings. To complete installation, reverse removal procedure.

CYLINDER HEAD & MANIFOLDS

Removal (Single Camshaft Engine)

1) Remove battery leads. Drain cooling system. Remove upper radiator hose. Remove PCV hose from valve cover. Remove wiring from distributor and temperature sending unit. Remove warm-up regulator and auxiliary air valve from cylinder head.

2) Raise front of vehicle until wheels are off ground. Remove distributor cap. Rotate engine until rotor tip aligns with TDC mark on distributor housing and timing mark aligns with "0". Lower vehicle.

3) Remove valve cover. Place a jack under transaxle case. Detach stay between right engine/transaxle mount and cylinder head and rotate it to one side. Jack up engine slightly. Support engine with a piece of wood between crossmember and transmission case.

4) Detach and support intake and exhaust manifolds. Detach sprocket from camshaft but secure chain to sprocket. Place sprocket between chain guide and tensioner.

5) Remove 2 timing cover-to-cylinder head bolts. Remove cylinder head bolts in reverse of order of tightening sequence. *See Fig. 1*. Remove cylinder head.

Installation

1) Position No. 1 piston at TDC position. Install cylinder head, using a new gasket. Install camshaft sprocket and chain. Position chain on sprocket. Ensure that chain is placed between chain guide and tensioner. Ensure camshaft timing marks are aligned. Refer to TIMING CHAIN ASSEMBLY section of this article.

2.0L 4-CYLINDER (Cont.)

2) Tighten cylinder head bolts in sequence to an initial setting of 44 ft. lbs. (60 N.m). Tighten bolts to a second setting of 66 ft. lbs. (90 N.m). After cylinder head assembly, run engine to normal temperature and then allow to cool for 30 minutes. Loosen and then retighten each bolt to 66 ft. lbs. (90 N.m). Finally, tighten each bolt an additional 90 degrees. *See Fig. 1.*

Fig. 1: Cylinder Head Tightening Sequence

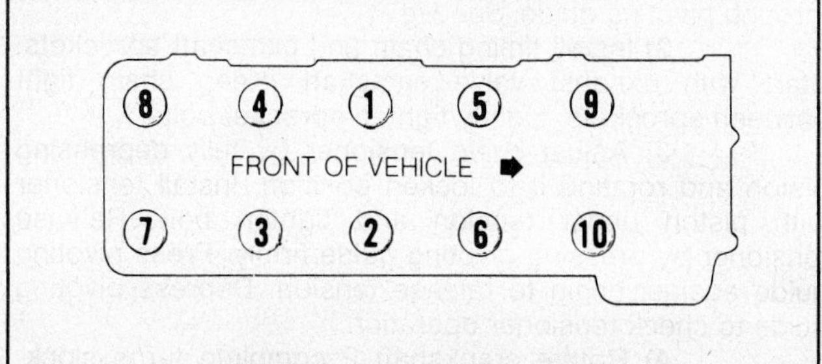

Courtesy of Saab-Scania of America, Inc.

3) Install cylinder head-to-timing cover bolts. Release timing chain tension by inserting Tension Release Bar (83 93 357) into tensioner catch and pulling upward. *See Fig. 2.*

Fig. 2: Chain Tensioner & Tension Release Bar

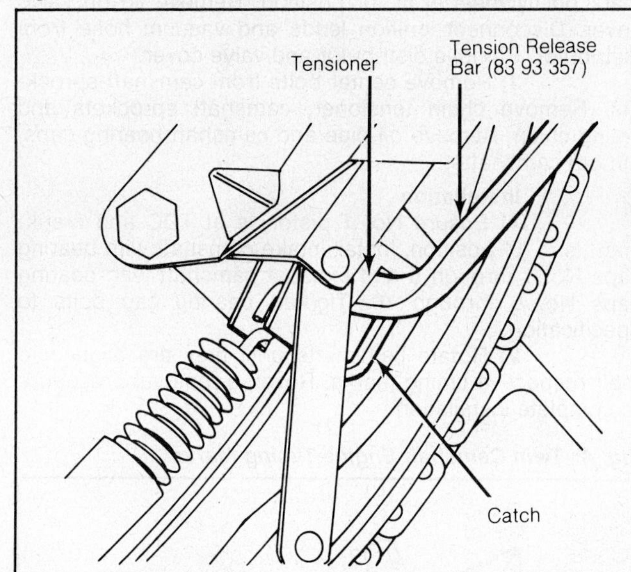

Courtesy of Saab-Scania of America, Inc.

4) Ensure sprocket is positioned on camshaft with marks on bearing cap, sprocket and screw holes aligned. If necessary, alter position of chain. Install camshaft sprocket retaining bolts using flat washers.

5) Using tension release bar, push tensioner catch down to apply tension on chain. To complete installation, reverse removal procedure.

Removal (Twin Camshaft Engine)

1) On 900 models, disconnect windshield washer hoses and remove hood. On all models, disconnect and remove battery. Drain cooling system and remove upper hose. Remove spark plug wires and distributor cap. Remove wiring from temperature sender and fuel injection system.

2) Remove distributor and distributor heat shield. Disconnect turbocharger inlet, outlet, and oil feed pipes (if equipped). Remove wastegate actuator from turbocharger. Detach turbocharger-to-transaxle bracket. Remove oil dipstick tube. Disconnect exhaust pipe. Remove exhaust manifold and turbocharger as a unit.

3) Remove air conditioning and power steering drive belts (if equipped). Remove air conditioning compressor and bracket. Remove intake manifold assembly. Remove 2 timing cover-to-cylinder head bolts. Remove right side engine mounting bolts.

4) Remove valve cover. Align timing mark on flywheel to "0" mark. Remove camshaft chain tensioner and sprockets. Support engine to a position allowing removal of cylinder head. Remove cylinder head bolts in reverse of tightening sequence. Fit a guide pin to one bolt hole. Remove cylinder head. Ensure timing chain pivoting guide is not damaged.

Installation

1) Place new gasket on cylinder block. Rotate crankshaft to TDC position of No. 1 piston. Align camshafts to their respective timing marks. Position timing chain in pivoting guide.

2) Tighten cylinder head bolts in sequence to an initial setting of 44 ft. lbs. (60 N.m). Tighten bolts to a second setting of 66 ft. lbs. (90 N.m). After cylinder head assembly, run engine to normal temperature and then allow to cool for 30 minutes. Loosen and then retighten each bolt to 66 ft. lbs. (90 N.m). Finally, tighten each bolt an additional 90 degrees. *See Fig. 1.*

3) Install 2 timing cover-to-cylinder head bolts. Install timing chain and camshaft sprockets, starting with exhaust valve camshaft. Keep chain tight between sprockets. Lightly tighten sprocket bolts.

4) Adjust chain tensioner by fully depressing piston and rotating tensioner into locked position. Install tensioner with piston under tension and tighten bolt. Release tensioner by pressing pivoting guide firmly. Press pivoting guide against chain to release tension. Depress pivoting guide to check tensioner operation.

5) Rotate crankshaft 2 complete turns clockwise. Check timing marks on crankshaft and camshafts. Tighten camshaft sprocket bolts to specification. Reverse removal procedure to complete installation.

CAMSHAFT – SINGLE CAMSHAFT ENGINE

TIMING CHAIN ASSEMBLY

Removal

1) Remove engine/transaxle from vehicle. Remove distributor cap. Rotate engine until rotor tip aligns with TDC mark on distributor housing. Remove valve cover.

2) Remove sprocket from camshaft and hang sprocket between tensioner and chain guide. Remove crankshaft pulley and oil pump. Remove water pump. Remove cylinder head-to-timing cover bolts.

3) Remove timing cover bolts and cover. Remove timing chain, camshaft sprocket, tensioner and chain guide.

Installation

1) Ensure crankshaft and camshaft timing marks are aligned. Install chain tensioner and chain guide.

Temporarily install camshaft sprocket. Position chain on camshaft and crankshaft sprockets. Ensure that chain is between tensioner and guide.

2) Install timing cover, oil pump and water pump. Release timing chain tension by inserting tension release bar into tensioner and pulling up. Place chain on camshaft sprocket. Ensure marks on camshaft bearing cap, sprocket and screw holes are aligned. Install camshaft sprocket using flat washers.

3) To tighten chain, insert tension release bar into tensioner catch and push down to turn catch over latch arm. *See Fig. 2*. To complete installation, reverse removal procedure.

CAMSHAFT

Removal

1) Remove distributor cap. Rotate engine until rotor tip aligns with TDC mark on distributor housing.

2) Remove valve cover and camshaft sprocket. Hang sprocket and chain between tensioner and chain guide. Remove camshaft bearing caps. Lift out camshaft.

Fig. 3: Single Camshaft Engine Timing Marks

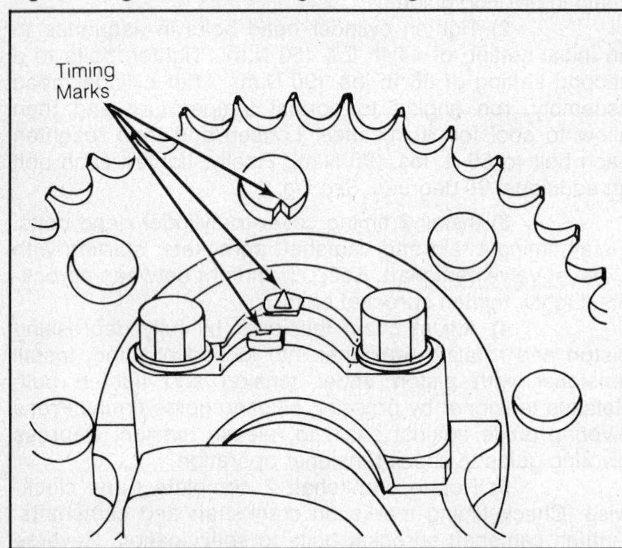

Courtesy of Saab-Scania of America, Inc.

Installation

Install camshaft bearing assembly so access ports are toward intake manifold. Ensure crankshaft is still at TDC position for No. 1 cylinder. To complete installation, reverse removal procedure.

CAMSHAFT – TWIN CAMSHAFT ENGINE

TIMING CHAIN ASSEMBLY

Removal

1) Remove engine/transaxle from vehicle. Position No. 1 piston at TDC and timing mark on flywheel in "0" position. Remove lid on valve cover. Disconnect ignition leads and vacuum hose from distributor. Remove distributor cap and valve cover.

2) Remove center bolts from camshaft sprockets. Ensure that camshafts remain at correct timing settings. Remove chain tensioner and camshaft sprockets. Remove crankshaft pulley and oil pump. Remove water pump pulley and water pump. Remove cylinder head-to-timing cover bolts.

3) Remove timing cover bolts and cover. Remove timing chain and crankshaft sprocket.

Installation

1) Ensure No. 1 piston is in TDC position and camshafts are aligned to their respective timing marks. Position timing chain around crankshaft sprocket and through pivoting guide. *See Fig. 4*.

2) Install timing chain and camshaft sprockets. Start with exhaust valve camshaft. Keep chain tight between sprockets. Lightly tighten sprocket bolts.

3) Adjust chain tensioner by fully depressing piston and rotating it to locked position. Install tensioner with piston under tension and tighten bolt. Release tensioner by pressing pivoting guide firmly. Press pivoting guide against chain to release tension. Depress pivoting guide to check tensioner operation.

4) Rotate crankshaft 2 complete turns clockwise and check timing marks on crankshaft and camshafts. Tighten camshaft sprocket bolts to specification. Reverse removal procedure to complete installation.

CAMSHAFT

Removal

1) With No. 1 piston at TDC, ensure timing mark on flywheel is at "0" position. Remove lid on valve cover. Disconnect ignition leads and vacuum hose from distributor. Remove distributor and valve cover.

2) Remove center bolts from camshaft sprockets. Remove chain tensioner, camshaft sprockets and timing chain. Remove oil pipe and camshaft bearing caps. Lift out camshafts.

Installation

1) Ensure No. 1 piston is at TDC and crankshaft is in "0" position. Install intake camshaft with bearing caps No. 1 through 5 and exhaust camshaft with bearing caps No. 6 through 10. Tighten bearing cap bolts to specification.

2) Rotate camshafts until they are aligned to their respective timing marks. Reverse removal procedure to complete installation.

Fig. 4: Twin Camshaft Engine Timing Marks

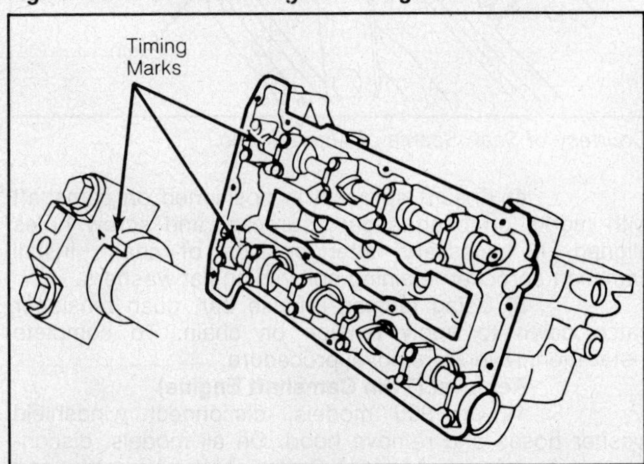

Courtesy of Saab-Scania of America, Inc.

2.0L 4-CYLINDER (Cont.)

VALVES – SINGLE CAMSHAFT ENGINE

VALVE ARRANGEMENT

E-I-I-E-E-I-I-E (Front-to-rear).

VALVE SPRINGS

NOTE: **Valve spring replacement is possible without removing cylinder head from engine.**

Removal

1) Remove camshaft. Replace spark plug with an air hose connector. Apply air pressure to cylinder. Remove valve depressors and adjusting pallets with a magnet.

2) Remove camshaft bearing support assembly. Compress valves and remove retainers (keepers) with a magnet.

Installation

To install, reverse removal procedure.

VALVE GUIDES

1) To inspect valve guides for wear, pull valve approximately .120" (3.0 mm) from its seat and check side play with a dial indicator. If play exceeds .020" (.50 mm), replace valve and/or valve guide.

2) To replace guide, flush hot water through head and pull valve guide from head using Guide Puller (83 92 631). To install, flush hot water through head and press in new valve guide from top.

VALVE CLEARANCE ADJUSTMENT

1) Remove valve cover. Rotate crankshaft so that cam lobe of valve to be measured is 180 degrees from valve. Insert feeler gauge through side access port. Measure clearance between heel of cam and valve depressor. *See Fig. 5.*

2) Clearance must be between .006-.012" (.15-.30 mm) for intake valves and .014-.020" (.35-.50 mm) for exhaust valves. If measured clearance of any valve exceeds specification, direct measuring of valves is required.

3) Install Valve Clearance Measuring Assembly (83 91 450) around cam lobe and on valve depressor. Insert dial indicator into clearance measuring assembly. Set dial indicator gauge to zero.

Fig. 5: Measuring Valve Clearance

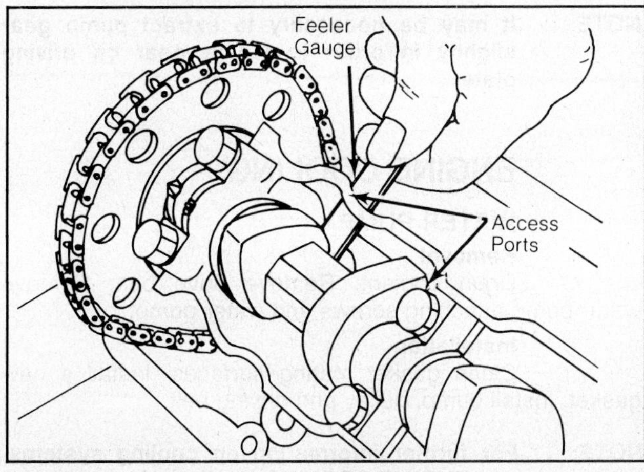

Courtesy of Saab-Scania of America, Inc.

4) Pull upward on measuring tool and valve depressor to obtain clearance readings for each valve. Valve clearances are determined by thickness of "pallets" (pads) that are under each valve depressor.

5) Intake valve pallets of increased thickness must be installed if direct measurements are not within .006-.012" (.15-.30 mm) of clearances in step **2)**.

6) Exhaust valve pallets of increased thickness must be installed if direct measurements are not within .016-.018" (.40-.45 mm) of clearances in step **2)**.

7) Add direct clearance and pallet thickness, to obtain correct new pallet thickness. Install new pallets. Install valve depressors and camshaft. Recheck valve clearance. Install valve cover.

VALVES – TWIN CAMSHAFT ENGINE

VALVE ARRANGEMENT

Left Side – Intake Valves.
Right Side – Exhaust Valves.

VALVE SPRINGS

NOTE: **Valve spring replacement is possible without removing cylinder head from engine.**

Removal

1) Remove camshafts. Use a magnet to remove lifters. Install Lifter Bore Sleeves (83 93 746) to protect lifter bores. Replace spark plug with air hose connector. Apply air pressure to cylinder.

2) Position Valve Retainer Remover (83 94 181) squarely on valve head and tap firmly with hammer. Remove retainers (keepers) with a magnet. Lift out spring and cap.

Installation

Replace spring and cap over valve stem. Position retainers (keepers) into groove in spring cap. Using Valve Retainer Remover (83 94 181) and Valve Retainer Installer Sleeve (83 94 207), carefully tap retainers into groove of valve stem. Reverse removal procedure to complete installation.

VALVE GUIDES

1) To check for valve guide wear, pull valve approximately .120" (3.0 mm) from its seat and check side play with a dial indicator. If play exceeds .020" (.50 mm), replace valve and/or valve guide.

2) To replace guide, flush hot water through head and pull valve guide from top of head using Guide Puller (83 93 811), Spacer (83 93 829) and Nut (83 93 845). To install, flush hot water through head and press in new valve guide from bottom.

VALVE CLEARANCE ADJUSTMENT

Valve clearance is automatically adjusted by use of hydraulic valve lifters.

PISTONS, PINS & RINGS

PISTON & ROD ASSEMBLY

Removal

Remove engine/transaxle assembly. Separate engine from transaxle. Mount engine on stand. Remove cylinder head. Ensure rods and rod caps are numbered. Push piston/rod assembly out of cylinder.

Installation

Ensure ring gaps are staggered before installing ring compressor. Compression ring gaps must be equally spaced from each other. Notch on piston top must face timing cover. Connecting rod numbers face exhaust side.

PISTON PIN REPLACEMENT

Piston pins are retained by circlips. Remove circlips and press out piston pins. Check pins and bearings for wear or damage and replace as required.

FITTING PISTONS

1) To fit pistons to cylinder bores, use a feeler gauge .500" (12.7 mm) wide and .0005-.0016" (.014-.040 mm) thick. Oil cylinder lightly and insert piston without rings.

2) Attach feeler gauge to a spring scale. Insert feeler gauge between piston and cylinder wall at right angles to piston pin. When feeler gauge can be pulled out of cylinder with a force of 1.8-2.6 lbs. (.82-1.20 kg), piston clearance is correct.

3) Repeat test at various bore depths. Graded standard and non-graded oversize pistons are available.

PISTON DIAMETER SPECIFICATIONS

Application	In. (mm)
Except Turbo	
Standard (AB)	3.5428-3.5431 (89.988-89.996)
Standard (C)	3.5435-3.5441 (90.004-90.020)
1st O/S	3.5623-3.5629 (90.482-90.497)
2nd O/S	3.5820-3.5826 (90.892-90.997)
Turbo	
Standard (AB)	3.5421-3.5424 (89.970-89.978)
Standard (C)	3.5427-3.5434 (89.986-90.002)
1st O/S	3.5614-3.5620 (90.460-90.475)
2nd O/S	3.5811-3.5817 (90.960-90.975)

4) Check piston rings for end gap and side clearance. Use an inverted piston to push ring down into bore. On worn bores, measure at lower end of bore.

5) Install rings on pistons. Stagger ring gaps. Compression ring gaps must be located 180 degrees from each other. Oil ring gaps must be equally spaced from each other.

CRANKSHAFT & ROD BEARINGS

MAIN & CONNECTING ROD BEARINGS

1) Remove connecting rod and main bearing caps. Measure journals with a micrometer. If out-of-round exceeds .002" (.051 mm), journals must be ground.

2) Use "V" blocks and a dial indicator to check crankshaft for bend. If bend exceeds .002" (.051 mm), crankshaft must be replaced or repaired.

3) Using Plastigage, check main bearing and connecting rod bearing journals. Use undersize bearings to obtain correct clearance.

THRUST BEARING ALIGNMENT

Center main bearing is thrust bearing. If end play exceeds specifications, install new thrust washer. Thrust washer oil grooves face toward crankshaft.

ENGINE OILING

ENGINE OILING SYSTEM

Oil pressure is generated by a gear-type oil pump with one gear wheel and an eccentric ring gear. Oil pump is mounted on timing cover and is driven by a driving plate mounted on crankshaft. Oil is circulated through a full flow filter, to oil channels which feed main bearings, rod bearings and valve train.

CRANKCASE CAPACITY

Oil capacity is 4.0 qts. (3.8L) with filter for engines without turbo. Turbocharged engine oil capacity is 4.75 qts. (4.5L).

OIL FILTER

Oil filter is a disposable, full-flow type.

NORMAL OIL PRESSURE

Oil pressure is 43 psi (3.0 kg/cm²) at 2000 RPM.

PRESSURE REGULATOR VALVE (PRV)

The nonadjustable PRV opens at 52-75 psi (3.6-5.2 kg/cm²).

OIL PUMP

Removal

Clean area around pump. Attach Locking Device (83 92 987) to flywheel ring gear. Remove crankshaft pulley retaining bolt and remove pulley from crankshaft. Remove oil pump retaining bolts and pump.

Inspection

Use a straightedge and feeler gauge to check end clearance between pump body and gear wheel.

Installation

Coat gear wheels with oil. Ensure ring gear is installed with mark on face visible. Position a new sealing ring into groove in pump body. Prime pump with oil and install on engine. Remove oil filter adapter casting and fill passage with oil. Reinstall casting.

NOTE: **It may be necessary to extract pump gear slightly in order to locate gear on driving plate.**

ENGINE COOLING

WATER PUMP

Removal

Drain coolant. Remove drive belt. Remove water pump attaching screws and water pump.

Installation

Clean gasket mating surfaces. Install a new gasket. Install pump, pulley and driving belt.

NOTE: **For further information on cooling systems, see ENGINE COOLING section.**

Saab Engines

2.0L 4-CYLINDER (Cont.)

ENGINE SPECIFICATIONS

GENERAL SPECIFICATIONS

Year	DISPLACEMENT		Fuel System	HP@RPM	Torque Ft. Lbs.@RPM	Compr. Ratio	BORE		STROKE	
	Cu. In.	Liters					In.	mm	In.	mm
1987										
900	121	2.0	CIS Lambda	110@5250	119@3500	9.25:1	3.54	90	3.07	78
900S & & 9000S	121	2.0	LH Jetronic	125@5500	123@3000	10.0:1	3.54	90	3.07	78
900 & 9000 Turbo	121	2.0	LH Jetronic	165@5500	195@3000	9.0:1	3.54	90	3.07	78

VALVES

Engine Size & Valve	Head Diam. In. (mm)	Face Angle	Seat Angle	Seat Width In. (mm)	Stem Diameter In. (mm)	Stem Clearance In. (mm)	Valve Lift In. (mm)
2.0L							
Single Cam							
Intake	1.654 (42.0)	44.5°	45°	.004-.008 (.10-.20)	.313-.314 (7.960-7.975)	.002 (.50)	.....
Exhaust	1.398 (35.5)	44.5°	45°	.004-.008 (.10-.20)	.313-.314 (7.960-7.975)	.002 (.50)	.....
Twin Cam							
Intake	1.25 (32)	44.5°	45°	.006 (.15)	.264-.274 (6.960-6.975)	.002 (.05)	.....
Exhaust	1.14 (29)	44.5°	45°	.006 (.15)	.274-.275 (6.975-6.980)	.002 (.05)	.....

PISTONS, PINS, RINGS

Engine	PISTONS	PINS		RINGS		
	Clearance In. (mm)	Piston Fit In. (mm)	Rod Fit In. (mm)	Ring No.	End Gap In. (mm)	Side Clearance In. (mm)
2.0L	.0008-.0020 (.020-.050)	.0002-.0006 (.005-.014)	.0002-.014 (.05-.35)	No. 1	.014-.021 (.35-.55)	.002-.003 (.050-.082)
				No. 2	.012-.018 (.30-.45)	.0016-.003 (.040-.082)
				Oil	.015-.055 (.38-1.40)	.....

CRANKSHAFT MAIN & CONNECTING ROD BEARINGS

Engine	MAIN BEARINGS				CONNECTING ROD BEARINGS		
	Journal Diam. In. (mm)	Clearance In. (mm)	Thrust Bearing	Crankshaft End Play In. (mm)	Journal Diam. In. (mm)	Clearance In. (mm)	Side Play In. (mm)
2.0L	2.283-2.284 (57.981-58.000)	.001-.002 (.020-.050)	Center	.003-.011 (.08-.28)	2.046-2.047 (51.981-52.000)	.001-.002 (.002-.050)	.....

Saab Engines

2.0L 4-CYLINDER (Cont.)

ENGINE SPECIFICATIONS (Cont.)

VALVE TIMING

Engine	INTAKE Open (BTDC)	INTAKE Close (ABDC)	EXHAUST Open (BBDC)	EXHAUST Close (ATDC)
2.0L				
900	10°	54°	46°	18°
900S & 9000S	16°	44°	61°	13°
Turbo	16°	56°	61°	13°

VALVE SPRINGS

Engine	Free Length In. (mm)	PRESSURE Lbs. @ In. (Kg @ mm) Valve Closed	PRESSURE Lbs. @ In. (Kg @ mm) Valve Open
2.0L			
Single Cam	1.700 (43.1)	.....	170-183@1.161 (77-83@29.5)
Twin Cam	1.770 (45)	.....	134-145@1.118 (61-66@28.4)

CAMSHAFT

Engine	Journal Diam. In. (mm)	Clearance In. (mm)	Lobe Lift In. (mm)
2.0L [1]			
Single Cam	1.139 (28.94)	.....	Int. .425 (10.8) Exh. .433 (11.0)
Twin Cam	1.1387-1.1392 (28.922- 28.935)	.....	Int. .340 (8.65) Exh. .340 (8.65)

[1] – End play is .003-.010" (.08-.25 mm) on single cam engines and .003-.014" (.08-.35 mm) on twin cam engines.

TIGHTENING SPECIFICATIONS

Application	Ft. Lbs. (N.m)
Camshaft Bearing Cap Bolts	
Single Camshaft Engine	13 (18)
Twin Camshaft Engine	11 (15)
Camshaft Sprocket Bolts	
Single Camshaft Engine	15 (20)
Twin Camshaft Engine	47 (64)
Crankshaft Pulley Bolts	141 (191)
Cylinder Head Bolts	
Step 1	44 (60)
Step 2	66 (90)
Step 3	66 (90)
Step 4	[1]
Exhaust Manifold Bolts	
Single Camshaft Engine	15 (20)
Twin Camshaft Engine	19 (26)
Flywheel Bolts	44 (60)
Intake Manifold Bolts	13 (18)
Main Bearing Bolts	81 (110)
Rod Bearing Bolts	41 (56)

[1] – Refer to text for tightening procedure.

Subaru Engines

1.2L 4-CYLINDER

Justy

NOTE: **For engine repair procedures not covered in this article, see ENGINE OVERHAUL PROCEDURES article at beginning of this section.**

ENGINE CODING

ENGINE IDENTIFICATION

The Vehicle Identification Number (VIN) is stamped on metal plate located near lower left corner of windshield. Engine can be identified by the 6th character in the VIN. Engine serial number is stamped on cylinder block machined pad located below distributor end of cylinder head.

ENGINE CODE

Application	Code
1.2L	
2WD	7
4WD	8

ENGINE, MANIFOLDS & CYLINDER HEAD

ENGINE

Removal

1) Position hood in widest position. Disconnect negative battery cable and cooling fan connections. Drain cooling system and remove radiator. Remove front bumper and grille.

2) Disconnect hood release cable. Remove radiator support member. Remove air cleaner and air intake duct. Disconnect and mark hoses to carburetor. Remove hose from brake booster.

3) Remove heater hoses. Disconnect clutch and accelerator cable. Disconnect speedometer cable from transmission. Remove support arm from engine to firewall. Disconnect and mark wiring at alternator, distributor and starter.

4) Raise and support vehicle. Remove lower engine covers. Disconnect exhaust pipes. Disconnect gearshift rod at transmission. Disconnect gearshift support rod at cylinder block.

5) Remove transverse link. *See Fig. 1.* Remove spring pin. Separate front axle shaft. *See Fig. 2.*

6) Remove engine and transmission mounting brackets. Install chain and raise engine slightly. Remove lower front engine mount bolts. Remove crossmember. Ensure all components are disconnected. Remove engine and transaxle.

Installation

Reverse removal procedures. Adjust clutch cable. Adjust fluid levels. Tighten bolts to specification.

CAUTION: **Transverse link-to-crossmember bolt must be tightened to specification with vehicle setting in proper operating height with no additional load.**

Fig. 1: Removing Transverse Link

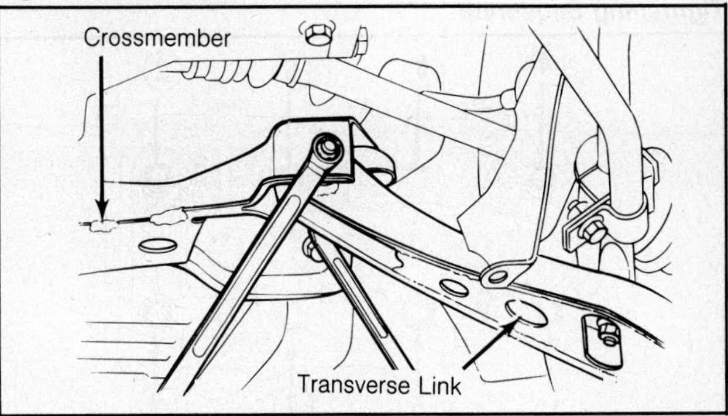

Courtesy of Subaru of America, Inc.

Fig. 2: Removing Spring Pin

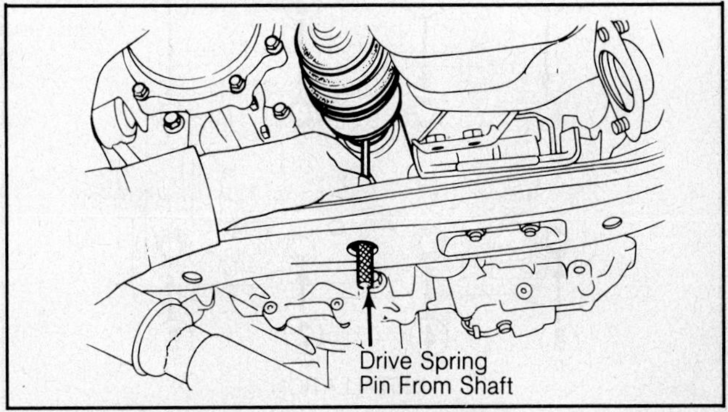

Courtesy of Subaru of America, Inc.

CYLINDER HEAD

Removal

1) Remove front bumper and grille. Drain cooling system. Remove air duct. Remove exhaust manifold. Remove accelerator cable.

2) Disconnect radiator and heater hoses. Disconnect and mark air cleaner and carburetor hoses. Disconnect wiring from distributor. Remove alternator drive belt. Remove air suction pipe from crankcase and intake manifold.

3) Using Pulley Holder (499205500), remove crankshaft pulley bolts. Remove crankshaft pulley. Remove timing belt. See TIMING BELT under CAMSHAFT in this article. Remove camshaft sprocket retaining bolts. Remove camshaft sprocket. Remove timing belt tensioner. Remove inner timing belt cover.

4) Remove PCV hose from valve cover. Remove valve cover. Remove cylinder head bolts in proper sequence. *See Fig. 3.* Remove cylinder head.

CAUTION: **Cylinder head bolts must be removed in proper sequence to prevent cylinder head damage.**

Inspection

1) Inspect cylinder head for cracks or damage. Check cylinder head warpage.

2) Cylinder head does not require resurfacing if warpage is less than minimum specification. Resurfacing is required if warpage exceeds minimum specification.

3) Measure cylinder head thickness. Cylinder head thickness must not be less than minimum specification after resurfacing. See CYLINDER HEAD SPECIFICATIONS table. Replace cylinder head if less than specification.

Subaru Engines

1.2L 4-CYLINDER (Cont.)

Fig. 3: Cylinder Head Bolt Removal & Tightening Sequence

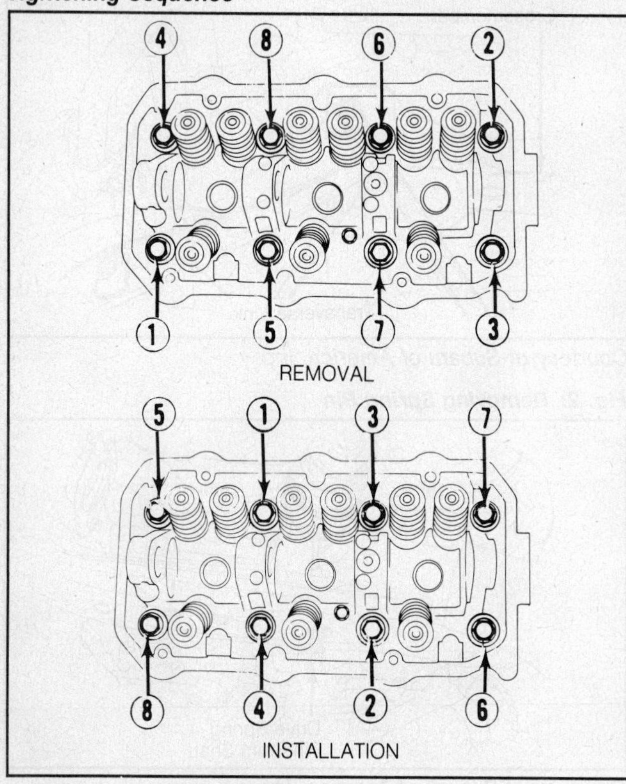

Courtesy of Subaru of America, Inc.

CYLINDER HEAD SPECIFICATIONS

Application	In. (mm)
All Models	
Thickness	
Maximum	4.39 (111.5)
Minimum	4.382 (111.30)
Warpage	
Minimum	.002 (.05)
Maximum	.008 (.20)

CAUTION: Cylinder head bolt tightness should be checked again after operating engine for short period and engine has obtained proper operating temperature. Ensure engine is cold prior to checking head bolts.

Installation

1) Ensure mating surfaces are clean. Install head gasket. Install cylinder head. Install head bolts and washers. Head bolts must be tightened in proper sequence. *See Fig. 3.* Tighten head bolts in 3 steps to specification. See TIGHTENING SPECIFICATIONS table at end of article.

2) Install and adjust timing belt. Reverse removal procedure for remaining components. Tighten all bolts to specification. Fill cooling system.

INTAKE MANIFOLD

Removal & Installation

1) Drain cooling system. Remove air cleaner. Remove heater and radiator hoses. Disconnect electrical connectors. Remove accelerator cable. Disconnect and mark vacuum hoses.

2) Remove air suction pipe. Remove intake manifold retaining bolts and nuts. Remove intake manifold and carburetor. For installation, reverse removal procedure using new gasket. Tighten all bolts to specification. Fill cooling system.

EXHAUST MANIFOLD

Removal & Installation

Remove exhaust manifold-to-flange bolts. Remove exhaust manifold retaining nuts. Remove exhaust manifold. Reverse removal procedure using new gasket for installation. Tighten all bolts to specification.

NOTE: Exhaust manifold retaining nuts are stainless steel. DO NOT use any other type of nut.

CAMSHAFT

TIMING BELT

Removal

1) Remove alternator drive belt. Using PULLEY HOLDER (499205500), loosen crankshaft pulley bolts. Rotate engine until No. 3 piston is at TDC. Remove crankshaft pulley retaining bolts using access hole in fenderwall housing.

2) Remove outer timing belt cover. Loosen tensioner retaining bolts. Move tensioner toward outside of engine. Tighten bolts to hold tensioner.

3) Mark timing belt for direction of rotation. Belt must be installed in original direction of rotation. Remove crankshaft belt drive sprocket plate and timing belt.

Inspection

Inspect timing belt for wear on rounded edges of drive teeth. Inspect belt for signs of oil contamination. Replace belt if damaged or contaminated. Inspect all drive sprockets for wear in drive belt area. Inspect tensioner for noise or grease leakage. Replace as necessary.

Installation

1) Using Pulley Holder (499205500), rotate camshaft to align camshaft sprocket mark with alignment mark on timing belt cover. *See Fig. 4.* Install crankshaft belt drive sprocket with flanged side facing inward (if removed). Rotate crankshaft so crankshaft belt drive sprocket aligns with crankcase alignment mark. *See Fig. 4.*

2) Remove valve cover (if not previously removed). Loosen valve adjusting screws to gain rocker arm free play. Install timing belt. Ensure timing belt is installed in original direction of rotation.

3) Loosen tensioner retaining bolts. Apply tension to timing belt. Tighten inner then outer tensioner retaining bolt. Ensure all timing marks are aligned.

4) Install crankshaft belt drive sprocket plate. Reverse removal procedure for remaining components. Tighten all bolts to specification. Adjust valve clearance. See VALVE CLEARANCE ADJUSTMENT under VALVES in this article.

Subaru Engines

1.2L 4-CYLINDER (Cont.)

Fig. 4: Aligning Timing Marks

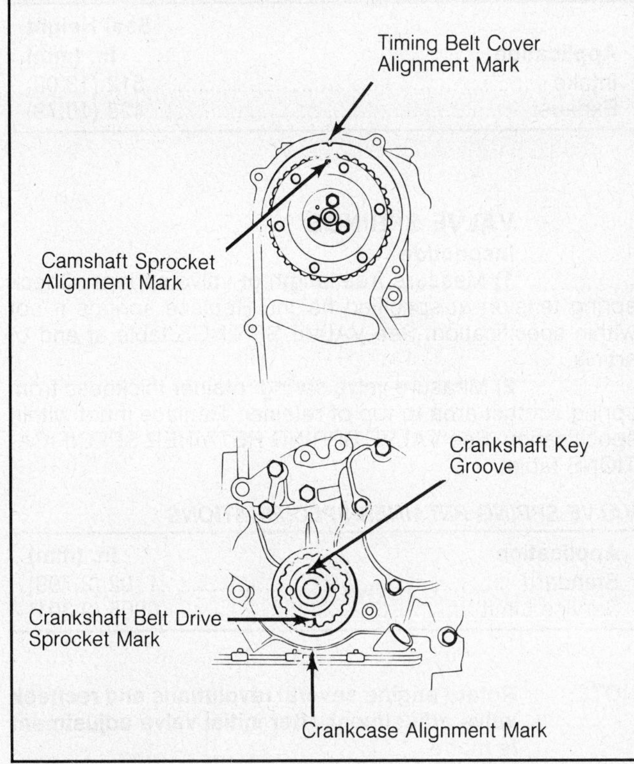

Courtesy of Subaru of America, Inc.

CAMSHAFT

Removal

1) Remove valve cover. Remove rocker arm assembly. See ROCKER ARM SHAFT ASSEMBLY in this article. Remove timing belt. See TIMING BELT in this article. Using Pulley Holder (499205500), remove camshaft drive pulley.

2) Mark distributor wires. Remove distributor. Remove camshaft retaining breaker case. Remove camshaft using care not to damage lobes and journals.

Inspection

1) Measure camshaft lobe height. Replace if not within specification. See CAM LOBE HEIGHT SPECIFICATIONS table.

2) Clean camshaft journals and cylinder head journal surfaces. Inspect journal areas for wear. Replace camshaft and or cylinder head if excessively worn.

CAM LOBE HEIGHT SPECIFICATIONS

Application	In. (mm)
Lobe Height	
Standard	1.4520-1.4528 (36.880-36.901)
Service Limit	.012 (.30)

Installation

1) Coat camshaft with ample amount of camshaft lubricant. Install camshaft in cylinder head. Install camshaft retainer breaker case. Check camshaft end play. See CAMSHAFT END PLAY in this article. Reverse removal procedure for remaining components. Tighten bolts to specification.

2) Adjust valve clearance. See VALVE CLEARANCE ADJUSTMENT under VALVES in this article. Install valve cover and new gasket. Tighten bolts to specification.

3) Install distributor. Distributor and camshaft contain an off-set coupling. Ensure coupling offset of camshaft and distributor are on the same side. Tighten retaining bolt.

CAMSHAFT END PLAY

Using dial indicator, check camshaft end play. End play must be within specification. See CAMSHAFT END PLAY SPECIFICATIONS table. If not within specification, grind retainer breaker case surface of cylinder head until end play is within specification.

CAMSHAFT END PLAY SPECIFICATIONS

Application	In. (mm)
End Play	
Standard	.0012-.0150 (.030-.383)
Service Limit	.020 (.50)

VALVES

VALVE ARRANGEMENT

Firewall Side - Intake valves.
Exhaust Manifold Side - Exhaust valves.

ROCKER ARM SHAFT ASSEMBLY

CAUTION: Rocker arm shaft assembly components must be marked for location prior to removal. Components must be installed in original location.

Removal

1) Remove valve cover. Position No. 1 piston on TDC. Loosen rocker arm adjusting screw lock nuts. Loosen adjusting screw until measurement from bottom of rocker arm to bottom of adjusting screw is .04" (1.0 mm).

2) Repeat procedure on remaining cylinders and rocker arms. Remove rocker arm shaft retaining bolt. Note location of all components. Carefully remove rocker arm shaft. DO NOT allow components to fall.

3) Remove rocker arms and spring washers. Mark components for location. Rocker Arm Shaft Guide (498005400) can be used in assisting in shaft removal if shaft is snug fit.

Inspection

Measure and record shaft O.D. in each rocker arm operating area. Using dial bore gauge, measure rocker arm I.D. and out-of-round. Subtract shaft reading from corresponding rocker arm. Replace rocker arm and or shaft if clearance exceeds specification. See ROCKER ARM SPECIFICATIONS table.

ROCKER ARM SPECIFICATIONS

Application	In. (mm)
Oil Clearance	.0006-.0022 (.015-.050)

Reassembly

1) Reverse removal procedure. Ensure components are installed in original location. Ensure rocker arm shaft is aligned with retaining bolt. Tighten rocker arm shaft retaining bolt.

2) Adjust valve clearance. See VALVE CLEARANCE ADJUSTMENT under VALVES in this article. Install valve cover and new gasket. Tighten bolts to specification.

VALVES

1) Disassemble cylinder head. Measure valve stem diameter. Replace valves not within specification. See VALVES table at end of article.

2) Measure valve margin. Replace valves if valve margin is not within specification. See VALVE MARGIN SPECIFICATIONS table. Remeasure valve margin after grinding valves.

VALVE MARGIN SPECIFICATIONS

Application	In. (mm)
Standard	.039 (.99)
Wear Limit	.020 (.50)

VALVE GUIDE

Inspection

Measure valve stem-to-guide clearance. Replace valves and valve guides not within specification. See VALVES table at end of article. Valve guide I.D. can be measured using telescopic gauge. Replace guides not within specification. See VALVE GUIDE SPECIFICATIONS table.

VALVE GUIDE SPECIFICATIONS

Application	In. (mm)
Guide I.D.	.2756-.2762 (7.000-7.015)
Installed Height	.807 (20.49)

Removal & Installation

1) Using Valve Guide Remover (399762103), drive valve guide from cylinder head. Use oversize valve guide when replacing valve guide.

2) Using Valve Guide Reamer (399762104), ream cylinder head for oversize valve guide. Using Valve Guide Installer (499765400), install valve guide. Valve guide installed height must be checked. Ensure valve guide is located at specified height. See VALVE GUIDE SPECIFICATIONS table.

VALVE SEAT

Grind valve seats to proper seat angle. Check valve seat width after grinding. Adjust seat width to specification. See VALVES table at end of article.

VALVE STEM OIL SEALS

When installing valve stem oil seals, ensure valve seals are proper height for valve application. See VALVE STEM OIL SEAL APPLICATION table. Use Valve Stem Installer (398852100) for seal installation.

VALVE STEM OIL SEAL APPLICATION

Application	Seal Height In. (mm)
Intake	.512 (13.00)
Exhaust	.425 (10.79)

VALVE SPRINGS

Inspection

1) Measure free length of valve springs. Check spring tension at specified height. Replace springs if not within specification. See VALVE SPRINGS table at end of article.

2) Measure valve spring retainer thickness from spring contact area to top of retainer. Replace if not within specification. See VALVE SPRING RETAINER SPECIFICATIONS table.

VALVE SPRING RETAINER SPECIFICATIONS

Application	In. (mm)
Standard	.1102 (2.799)
Service Limit	.0906 (2.301)

NOTE: **Rotate engine several revolutions and recheck valve adjustment after initial valve adjustment is made.**

VALVE CLEARANCE ADJUSTMENT

1) Position cylinder to be adjusted on TDC of compression stroke. Ensure piston is at TDC and valves are closed. Using Valve Adjuster (498767000), adjust valve clearance to specification. See VALVE CLEARANCE SPECIFICATIONS table. Tighten lock nut to specification.

2) Repeat procedure on remaining cylinders. Rotate engine several revolutions after completing valve adjustment. Recheck valve clearance.

VALVE CLEARANCE SPECIFICATIONS

Application	In. (mm)
Intake	.0051-.0067 (.129-.170)
Exhaust	.0091-.0106 (.231-.269)

CYLINDER BLOCK

CLEANING & INSPECTION

Inspect cylinder block for cracks, warpage, bore diameter, taper, out-of-round and deck height. Replace or repair cylinder block if not within specification. See CYLINDER BLOCK SPECIFICATIONS table.

CRANKCASE COVER

Removal

1) Disconnect negative battery cable. Drain engine oil and cooling system. Remove oil dipstick and guide. Disconnect and mark alternator wiring. Remove alternator drive belt and alternator.

2) Using Pulley Holder (499205500), remove crankshaft pulley. Remove outer timing belt cover. Remove

1.2L 4-CYLINDER (Cont.)

CYLINDER BLOCK SPECIFICATIONS

Application	In. (mm)
Bore Diameter	3.0709-3.0718 (78.000-78.023)
Bore Out-Of-Round	.002 (.05)
Bore Taper	.002 (.05)
Deck Height	7.87 (199.8)
Maximum Boring Limit	.039 (.99)
Warpage	.002 (.05)
Warpage Grind Limit	.008 (.20)

timing belt. See TIMING BELT in this article. Remove belt tensioner and camshaft sprocket.

3) Remove inner timing belt cover. Remove flywheel cover, oil pan and gasket. Remove air suction tube bracket. Remove water pump cover and water pump impeller. See WATER PUMP in this article. Remove crankcase cover retaining bolts. Remove crankcase cover.

Installation

Reverse removal procedure. Replace all gaskets and "O" rings. Tighten bolts to specification. Fill crankcase and cooling system.

PISTONS, PINS & RINGS

OIL PAN

Removal

1) Raise and support vehicle. Drain engine oil. Remove exhaust manifold cover. Remove lower engine covers. Disconnect header pipe from tailpipe.

2) Disconnect tailpipe hanger from engine mount. Install chain and slightly raise engine. DO NOT raise excessively. Engine must be supported for crossmember removal.

3) Remove support arm from engine to firewall. Remove crossmember from body and transaxle. Remove stabilizer bar from body. Remove transmission center mount. Remove flywheel cover. Disconnect air suction pipe. Remove oil pan and gasket.

Installation

Reverse removal procedure using new gasket. Tighten all bolts to specification. Fill with engine oil.

PISTON & ROD ASSEMBLY

Removal

1) Remove cylinder head. See CYLINDER HEAD in this article. Remove oil pan. Ensure cylinder ridge is removed. Mark connecting rod and cap for cylinder identification.

2) Note direction of recess areas in piston. Remove rod cap. Remove piston assembly.

Installation

1) Ensure piston ring end gap and side clearance are within specification. Install rings on piston. Ensure "R1" or "R2" mark for top and second ring is toward top of piston. Lubricate piston, rings and cylinder bore with engine oil.

2) Properly space ring end gaps on piston. *See Fig. 5.* Install piston and rod into cylinder bore. Ensure piston and connecting rod are properly positioned. Recess areas on piston must face intake manifold side. *See Fig. 6.*

Fig. 5: Piston Ring End Gap Locations

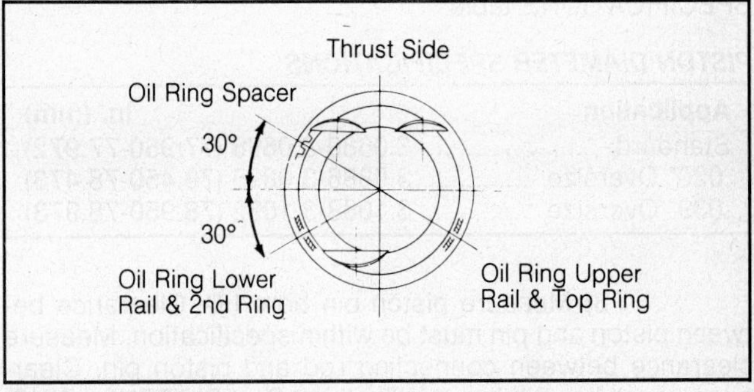

Courtesy of Subaru of America, Inc.

Fig. 6: Piston-to-Connecting Rod Location

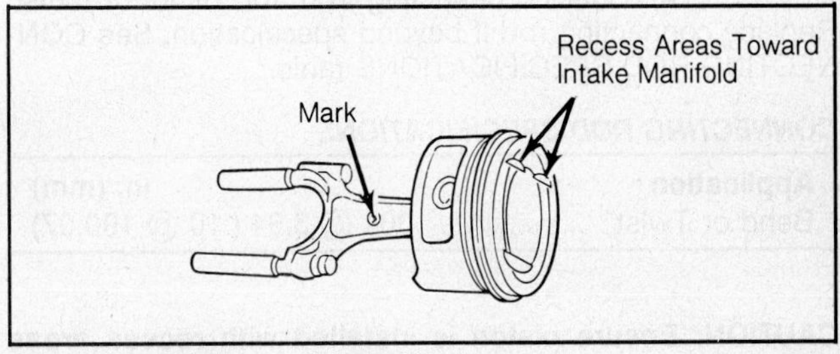

Courtesy of Subaru of America, Inc.

3) Check bearing clearance using Plastigage method. Tighten rod cap nuts to specification. See TIGHTENING SPECIFICATIONS table at end of article. Ensure rod moves freely on crankshaft. Check connecting rod side play. Replace connecting rod if not within specification.

FITTING PISTONS

Measure cylinder bore and piston skirt diameter. Piston skirt diameter should be measured at 90 degree angle to piston pin. Measure at approximately 1.673" (42.49 mm) from top of piston with normal temperature of 68°F (20°C). Clearance between piston and cylinder bore must be within specification. See PISTONS, PINS, RINGS table at end of article.

PISTON PIN REPLACEMENT

Removal

1) Note piston location in reference to mark on connecting rod. *See Fig. 6.* Use Piston Pin Press (499015400) for pin removal. Install spring and attachment in base. *See Fig. 7.*

2) Lubricate attachment guide hole, piston pin remover and piston pin installer with engine oil. Position piston pin installer in guide hole of attachment.

3) Position piston on attachment. Alignment mark on attachment must align with piston head direction. Install piston pin remover on piston pin. Using hydraulic press, remove piston pin.

Inspection

1) Inspect piston for cracks or damage in ring areas. Check ring side clearance. Replace piston if not within specification. See PISTONS, PINS, RINGS table at end of article.

2) Measure piston skirt diameter. Piston skirt diameter should be measured at 90 degree angle to piston pin. Measure at approximately 1.673" (42.49 mm) from top of piston with normal temperature of 68°F (20°C). Replace piston if not within specification. See PISTON DIAMETER SPECIFICATIONS table.

PISTON DIAMETER SPECIFICATIONS

Application	In. (mm)
Standard	3.0689-3.0698 (77.950-77.972)
.020" Oversize	3.0886-3.0895 (78.450-78.473)
.039" Oversize	3.1083-3.1092 (78.950-78.973)

3) Measure piston pin bore I.D. Clearance between piston and pin must be within specification. Measure clearance between connecting rod and piston pin. Clearance must be within specification. See PISTONS, PINS, RINGS table at end of article.

4) Check connecting rod for bend or twist. Replace connecting rod if beyond specification. See CONNECTING ROD SPECIFICATIONS table.

CONNECTING ROD SPECIFICATIONS

Application	In. (mm)
Bend or Twist	.004 @ 3.94 (.10 @ 100.07)

CAUTION: Ensure piston is installed with recess areas aligned with connecting rod mark.

Installation

1) Position piston on connecting rod. Ensure piston recess areas are installed in accordance with connecting rod mark. *See Fig. 6.* Lubricate attachment guide hole, piston pin remover, piston pin and piston pin bores of piston and connecting rod with engine oil.

2) Install piston pin installer on piston pin. Place assembly on base. *See Fig. 7.* Using press, install piston pin until piston pin remover bottoms in base.

Fig. 7: Installing Piston Pin

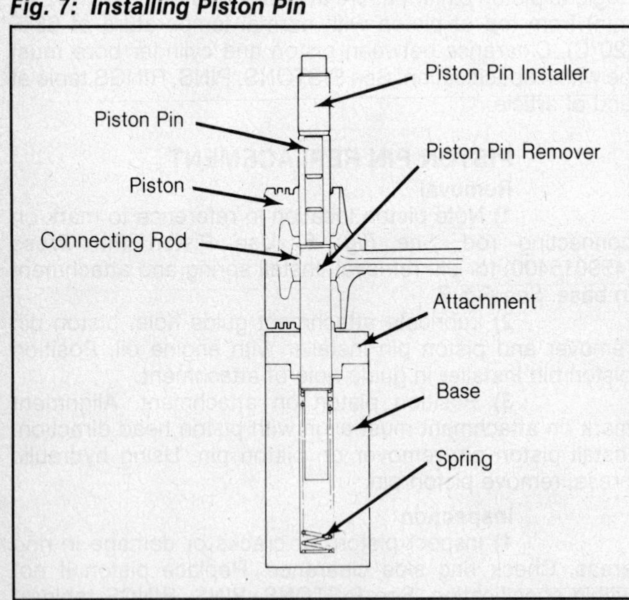

Courtesy of Subaru of America, Inc.

CRANKSHAFT & ROD BEARINGS

MAIN BEARINGS

Removal

1) Ensure connecting rod and main bearing caps are marked for location. Remove connecting rod caps and bearings. Remove main bearing caps.

2) Ensure all components are placed in correct order. Note alignment marks for balance shaft chain prior to removing crankshaft. *See Fig. 8.* Remove crankshaft. Remove main bearings from cylinder block. Mark bearings for location.

Inspection

Inspect crankshaft for cracks, damaged sprocket or threads. Measure journal diameters. Check crankshaft for runout, out-of-round, and taper. Replace or repair crankshaft if not within specification. See CRANKSHAFT WEAR SPECIFICATIONS table. Replace sprocket if damaged.

CRANKSHAFT WEAR SPECIFICATIONS

Application	In. (mm)
Grinding Limit	.0098 (.248)
Out-of-Round	.0012 (.030)
Runout	.0012 (.030)
Taper	.0008 (.020)

Installation

1) On crankshafts with main journal diameter of 1.6525-1.6529" (41.974-41.985 mm), note letter code stamped on oil pan mating surface of cylinder block. Select proper replacement bearing using letter code. See MAIN BEARING SELECTION table.

MAIN BEARING SELECTION

Letter Code	Bearing Color Code
A or B	Black
C or D	Green

2) Install upper main bearings in cylinder block. Ensure oil hole is aligned and bearing is properly seated. Lubricate bearings with engine oil. Install crankshaft in block.

3) Ensure crankshaft sprocket is properly aligned with Gold link of balancer shaft chain. Check all alignment marks and Gold links for proper alignment. *See Fig. 8.*

CAUTION: Main bearing caps must be installed in original location with arrow facing front of engine.

4) Install bearings in main bearing caps. Check oil clearance using Plastigage method. Main bearing caps must be installed in original location with arrow pointing toward front of engine.

5) Tighten bolts to specification. Remove main bearing caps. Clearance must be within specification. If oil clearance exceeds specification, replace bearing with new or undersized bearing.

6) Recheck oil clearance. Ensure crankshaft rotates freely with all main bearing caps installed. Check

Subaru Engines

1.2L 4-CYLINDER (Cont.)

Fig. 8: Aligning Balancer Shaft Chain

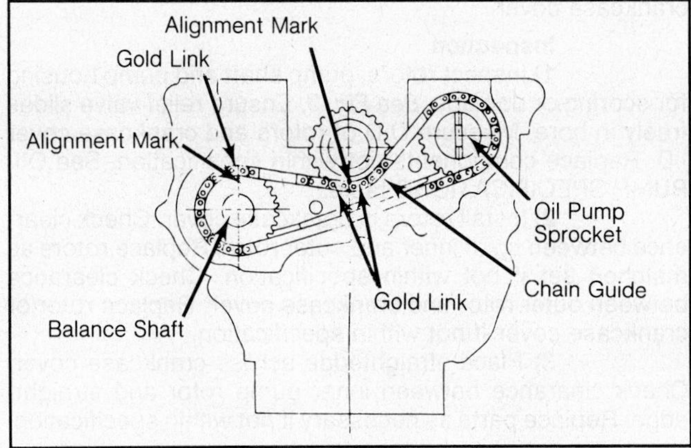

Courtesy of Subaru of America, Inc.

crankshaft end play. See CRANKSHAFT END PLAY in this article.

7) Tighten chain guide retaining bolts to specification (if loosened). Install connecting rod caps and bearings. Tighten to specification. Ensure connecting rods move freely on crankshaft. Install remaining components. Tighten bolts to specification.

CONNECTING ROD BEARINGS

1) Ensure bearing cap and connecting rod are marked for location. Remove connecting rod caps and bearings. Install replacement bearings. Check bearing clearance using Plastigage method. Tighten nuts to specification.

2) Clearance must be within specification. Replace connecting rod bearing assembly if oil clearance is incorrect. Recheck oil clearance. Ensure connecting rod will move freely after cap is tightened to specification. Check connecting rod side clearance after proper clearance is obtained.

CRANKSHAFT END PLAY

If not within specification, inspect thrust bearing or crankshaft for damage. Replace damaged components.

REAR CRANKSHAFT OIL SEAL

Removal & Installation

1) Remove flywheel. Pry seal from cylinder block. Note direction of seal lips. Ensure seal surfaces are free of burrs. Lubricate seal lips with engine oil.

2) Install Crank Seal Guide (498725500) on rear of crankshaft. Using Seal Press (498725600), install seal. Install flywheel. Tighten bolts to specification.

BALANCE SHAFT, CHAIN & OIL PUMP SPROCKET

Removal

1) Remove crankcase cover. See CRANKCASE COVER in this article. Remove crankshaft. Using dial indicator, measure thrust clearance of balance shaft. Chain guide must be replaced if clearance exceeds specification. See THRUST CLEARANCE SPECIFICATIONS table.

2) Remove chain and guide. *See Fig. 8.* Remove balance shaft. Use care not to damage bearing journals.

3) Inspect balance shaft bearings for scoring or wear. If front bearing requires removal, use Front Balance Press (498835901) and hydraulic press. Press front bearing from cylinder block.

4) Remove plug from rear of cylinder block. Using Rear Balance Press (498835801) and hydraulic press, remove bearing from block.

Inspection

1) Inspect balance shaft for scoring or wear in bearing journals. Inspect all sprockets for damage in chain drive area. Inspect chain and guide for damage and wear.

2) Place dial indicator on cylinder block with tip resting against oil pump sprocket. Check thrust clearance of oil pump sprocket. Replace oil pump sprocket if thrust clearance exceeds specification. See THRUST CLEARANCE SPECIFICATIONS table.

3) Inspect oil pump sprocket shaft for scoring or wear. Remove shaft from cylinder block if damaged.

THRUST CLEARANCE SPECIFICATIONS

Application	In. (mm)
Balance Shaft	.020 (.50)
Oil Pump Sprocket	.016 (.40)

Installation

1) If balance shaft sprocket requires replacement, remove and install sprocket using Pinion Bearing Replacer (498517000) and Crankshaft Sprocket Installer (499585400). Ensure sprocket is installed with alignment mark facing front of balance shaft.

2) Install oil pump sprocket shaft in cylinder block (if removed). Ensure oil holes are aligned with cylinder block. Install balance shaft bearings. Use Front Balance Press (498835901) for front bearing and Rear Balance Press (498835801) and Spacer (498835803) for rear bearing. Ensure oil holes are aligned with cylinder block.

3) Using rear balance press, install rear plug in cylinder block. Lubricate balance shaft with engine oil. Install balance shaft in cylinder block. Proper chain must be installed when different components are replaced. Determine proper components to be used when installing chain and guide. See CHAIN & GUIDE APPLICATION table.

CHAIN & GUIDE APPLICATION

Guide Used Color Code	Use Chain Part. No.	Use Chain Color Code
Chain Replacement Only		
White	12430KA060	Green
Blue	12430KA060	Green
Guide Replacement Only		
White	12441KA000	White
Blue	12441KA010	Blue
Green	12441KA000	White
Green	12441KA010	Blue
Chain & Guide Replacement		
White	12430KA060	Green
Blue	12430KA060	Green

4) Install guide and oil pump sprocket. DO NOT tighten guide bolts at this time. Rotate balance shaft and oil pump sprocket so Gold chain links can be installed in proper location. *See Fig. 8.*

Subaru Engines

1.2L 4-CYLINDER (Cont.)

5) Install chain. Install crankshaft. Once crankshaft is installed, tighten guide retaining bolts to specification. Ensure all alignment marks are aligned with Gold links. Reverse removal procedure for remaining components. Tighten bolts to specification.

ENGINE OILING

ENGINE OILING SYSTEM

Rotor-type oil pump provides oil pressure. Oil pump is driven by the crankshaft through drive sprocket and chain. Oil pressure is delivered to main and connecting rod bearings. Pressure relief valve is located in crankcase cover.

CRANKCASE CAPACITY

Crankcase capacity is 3.0 qts. (2.8L) with filter replacement.

NORMAL OIL PRESSURE

Minimum oil pressure at 1500 RPM should be 30 psi (2.1 kg/cm^2) and 47 psi (3.3 kg/cm^2) at 3000 RPM with oil temperature at 172-180°F (78-82°C).

Fig. 9: Exploded View of Crankcase Cover & Oil Pump

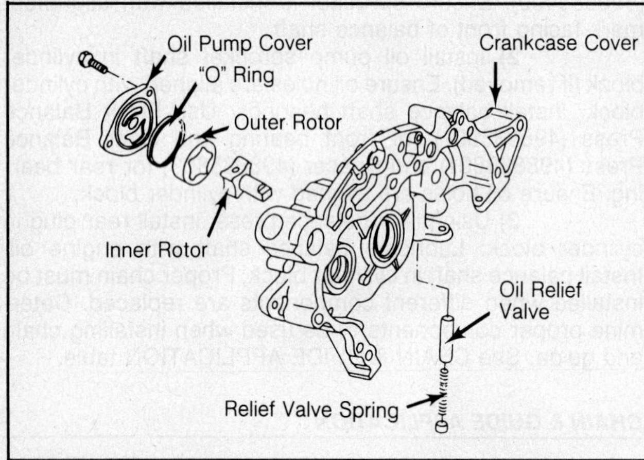

Courtesy of Subaru of America, Inc.

OIL PUMP

NOTE: **Oil pump clearances can be checked without removing oil pump. Remove oil pump cover and perform clearance inspection. See INSPECTION under OIL PUMP in this article.**

Removal

1) Drain engine oil and coolant. Remove dipstick and guide. Disconnect negative battery cable. Mark and remove wiring from alternator. Remove alternator drive belt and alternator.

2) Remove crankshaft pulley and outer timing belt cover. Remove timing belt. See TIMING BELT in this article. Remove camshaft drive sprocket. Remove inner timing belt cover.

3) Remove flywheel cover. Remove oil pan. See OIL PAN in this article. Remove crankcase cover. See CRANKCASE COVER in this article. Remove oil pump cover and "O" ring. Remove inner and outer rotor from crankcase cover.

Inspection

1) Inspect rotors, pump shaft and pump housing for scoring or damage. *See Fig. 9.* Ensure relief valve slides freely in bore. Measure O.D of rotors and crankcase cover I.D. Replace components not within specification. See OIL PUMP SPECIFICATIONS table.

2) Install rotors in crankcase cover. Check clearance between tip of inner and outer rotor. Replace rotors as matched set if not within specification. Check clearance between outer rotor and crankcase cover. Replace rotor or crankcase cover if not within specification.

3) Place straightedge across crankcase cover. Check clearance between inner pump rotor and straightedge. Replace parts as necessary if not within specification.

OIL PUMP SPECIFICATIONS

Application	In. (mm)
Case Cover I.D.	1.6028-1.6039 (40.711-40.739)
Case-To-Rotor	[1] .0059-.0083 (.149-.210)
Inner Rotor O.D.	1.693-1.1709 (29.700-29.740)
Outer Rotor O.D.	1.5957-1.5968 (40.530-40.558)
Rotor-To-Cover	[2] .0020-.0063 (.050-.160)
Rotor Tip Clearance	[3] .0008-.0059 (.020-.149)

[1] – Service limit is .0098" (.248 mm).
[2] – Service limit is .0071" (.180 mm).
[3] – Service limit is .0079" (.200 mm).

Installation

Reverse removal procedure. Use new gaskets and "O" rings. Tighten bolts to specification. Fill cooling system and engine oil.

ENGINE COOLING

WATER PUMP

Removal

1) Drain engine oil and coolant. Remove dipstick and guide. Disconnect negative battery cable. Remove connector from alternator. Remove alternator drive belt and alternator.

2) Remove crankshaft pulley and outer timing belt cover. Remove timing belt. See TIMING BELT in this article. Remove camshaft drive sprocket. Remove inner timing belt cover.

3) Remove flywheel cover. Remove oil pan. See OIL PAN in this article. Remove water pump cover. Install screwdriver against balance shaft to hold balance shaft from turning.

4) Remove impeller retaining bolt and impeller. *See Fig. 10.* Remove crankcase cover retaining bolts. Remove crankcase cover.

Disassembly

Position crankcase cover in hydraulic press. Using Mechanical Seal Remover (499715400) and Plate (499685510), press mechanical seal from crankcase cover.

Inspection

Inspect ceramic seal for cracks. Inspect mechanical seal and ceramic seal contact areas for wear or damage. Inspect impeller for corrosion or damage. Inspect oil seal for damage.

Subaru Engines

1.2L 4-CYLINDER (Cont.)

NOTE: When replacing impeller, mechanical seal must also be replaced.

Reassembly

Coat mechanical seal-to-cover surface with Three Bond (No. 1303). Using Mechanical Seal Installer (499795400) and hydraulic press, install mechanical seal.

CAUTION: Coat impeller with coolant prior to installation.

Fig. 10: Exploded View of Water Pump

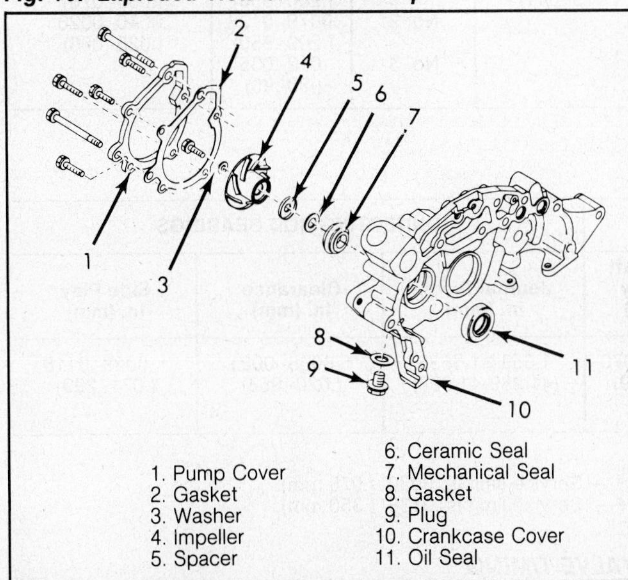

Courtesy of Subaru of America, Inc.

Installation

1) Install crankcase cover on cylinder block. Coat impeller with coolant and install. When installing new impeller, add one or 2 spacers and measure tip clearance.

2) Manually press impeller against balance shaft and measure tip clearance. Tip clearance must be within specificaton. See WATER PUMP TIP CLEARANCE table.

3) Install impeller retaining bolt. Tighten to specification. Install new gasket and pump cover. Tighten retaining bolts. Reverse removal procedure for remaining components. Use new gaskets and tighten all bolts to specification. Fill cooling system and engine oil.

NOTE: For further information on cooling systems, see ENGINE COOLING section.

WATER PUMP TIP CLEARANCE

Application	In. (mm)
Standard	.012-.035 (.30-.88)
Service Limit	.043 (1.09)

TIGHTENING SPECIFICATIONS

Application	Ft. Lbs. (N.m)
Connecting Rod Nut	29-33 (39-45)
Crankshaft Pulley Bolt	47-54 (64-73)
Cylinder Head Bolt	
Step 1	29 (39)
Step 2	43 (58)
Step 3	51 (69)
Engine Mount-To-Body Bolt	27-49 (37-66)
Exhaust Flange-To-Pipe Nut	34-64 (46-87)
Exhaust Manifold Nut	14-22 (19-30)
Exhaust Manifold-To-Flange Bolt	17-31 (23-42)
Flywheel Bolt	65-71 (88-96)
Intake Manifold Bolt	14-22 (19-30)
Main Bearing Cap Bolt	30-35 (41-47)
Support Arm-To-Engine Bolt	27-49 (37-66)
Transmission Mount-To-Body Bolt	27-49 (37-66)
Transverse Link-To-Crossmember Bolt	58 (79)
Valve Adjusting Screw Nut	12-17 (16-23)
	INCH Lbs. (N.m)
Camshaft Sprocket Bolt	100-108 (11-12)
Chain Guide Bolt	51-61 (5.7-6)
Oil Pan Bolt	40-48 (4-5)
Shift Rod-To-Transmission Bolt	84-132 (9-15)
Valve Cover Bolt	61-70 (6-8)
Water Pump Impeller Bolt	84-91 (9-10)

ENGINE SPECIFICATIONS

GENERAL SPECIFICATIONS

Year	DISPLACEMENT		Fuel System	HP@RPM	Torque Ft. Lbs.@RPM	Compr. Ratio	BORE		STROKE	
	Cu. In.	Liters					In.	mm	In.	mm
1987	72	1.2	2-Bbl.	66 @ 5200	70 @ 3600	9.0:1	3.07	77.9	3.27	83.0

VALVES

Engine Size & Valve	Head Diam. In. (mm)	Face Angle	Seat Angle	Seat Width In. (mm)	Stem Diameter In. (mm)	Stem Clearance In. (mm)	Valve Lift In. (mm)
1.2L							
Intake	....	45°	45°	.057 (1.44)	.2742-.2748 (6.964-6.979)	.0008-.0020 (.020-.050)	....
Exhaust	....	45°	45°	.08 (2.0)	.2734-.2740 (6.944-6.959)	.0016-.0028 (.040-.071)	....

Subaru Engines

1.2L 4-CYLINDER (Cont.)

ENGINE SPECIFICATIONS (Cont.)

PISTONS, PINS, RINGS

Engine	PISTONS Clearance In. (mm)	PINS Piston Fit In. (mm)	PINS Rod Fit In. (mm)	RINGS Ring No.	RINGS End Gap In. (mm)	RINGS Side Clearance In. (mm)
1.2L	.0015-.0024 (.038-.062)	.0005-.0007 (.012-.018)	.0007-.0016 (.018-.041)	No. 1	.0079-.0138 (.200-.350)	.0014-.0030 (.035-.076)
				No. 2	.0079-.0138 (.200-.350)	.0010-.0026 (.025-.066)
				No. 3	.012-.035 (.30-.90)	....

CRANKSHAFT MAIN & CONNECTING ROD BEARINGS

Engine	MAIN BEARINGS Journal Diam. In. (mm)	MAIN BEARINGS Clearance In. (mm)	MAIN BEARINGS Thrust Bearing	MAIN BEARINGS Crankshaft End Play In. (mm)	CONNECTING ROD BEARINGS Journal Diam. In. (mm)	CONNECTING ROD BEARINGS Clearance In. (mm)	CONNECTING ROD BEARINGS Side Play In. (mm)
1.2L	1.6525-1.6529 (41.974-41.985)	[1] .0006-.0018 (.015-.045)	No. 4	[2] .0031-.0070 (.078-.179)	1.6531-1.6535 (41.989-41.998)	[3] .0008-.0021 (.020-.053)	[4] .0028-.0118 (.071-.299)

[1] – Service limit is .0024" (.060 mm).
[2] – Service limit is .012" (.30 mm).
[3] – Service limit is .0030" (.075 mm).
[4] – Service limit is .0138" (.350 mm).

VALVE SPRINGS

Engine	Free Length In. (mm)	PRESSURE Lbs. @ In. (Kg @ mm) Valve Closed	PRESSURE Lbs. @ In. (Kg @ mm) Valve Open
1.2L	1.79-1.83 (46.50)	....	112.7-129.7@1.2 (51-58@31)

VALVE TIMING

Engine	INTAKE Open (BTDC)	INTAKE Close (ABDC)	EXHAUST Open (BBDC)	EXHAUST Close (ATDC)
1.2L	19°	57°	64°	24°

Subaru Engines

1.6L & 1.8L 4-CYLINDER

Brat & Hatchback

NOTE: **For engine repair procedures not covered in this article, see ENGINE OVERHAUL PROCEDURES article at beginning of this section.**

ENGINE CODING

ENGINE IDENTIFICATION

The engine can be identified by 6th character in the VIN. The VIN is stamped on a metal plate located on firewall in center of engine compartment. Engine identification number is stamped on a machined pad on right front side of engine crankcase.

ENGINE IDENTIFICATION CODES

Application	Code
1.6L 2WD	2
1.8L 2WD	4
1.8L 4WD	5

ENGINE, MANIFOLDS & CYLINDER HEAD

ENGINE

NOTE: **It is possible to remove engine with transaxle connected. Removal procedure given is with transaxle remaining in vehicle.**

Removal

1) Disconnect negative battery cable at battery and engine. Remove spare tire and support from engine compartment. Remove fuel canister and evaporation hoses. Pull up windshield washer reservoir and set behind strut.

2) Remove air cleaner. Remove all vacuum lines and label. Disconnect all electrical wiring and label. Disconnect accelerator and clutch cables. Remove power steering pump (if equipped). Remove oil pump and bracket assembly. Remove alternator and belt. Disconnect O_2 sensor.

3) Remove bolts retaining transaxle-to-engine. Do not remove starter. Drain coolant. Disconnect upper and lower radiator hoses. Remove ground wire. Remove radiator. Disconnect heater hoses. Disconnect exhaust pipe from exhaust manifold.

4) Remove front engine mount. Secure lifting chain or cable to engine hangers. Raise engine slowly, while raising transaxle with a floor jack. Move engine horizontally away from transaxle and separate. Remove engine.

Installation

To install, reverse removal procedure. Ensure correct adjustments are made to accelerator, pitching stopper (engine mount) and clutch cables. Always use new gaskets.

INTAKE MANIFOLD

Removal

1) Disconnect negative battery cable. Remove air cleaner assembly. Drain coolant and disconnect all hoses from manifold.

2) Disconnect throttle cable, vacuum lines, fuel lines and electrical connections to manifold and label. Remove distributor and wires. Remove alternator and air cleaner bracket.

3) Loosen both ends of EGR pipe and remove from rear of manifold. Remove manifold-to-cylinder head bolts, and remove manifold.

Installation

After cleaning mating surfaces and installing new gaskets, reverse removal procedure. Tighten all bolts to specification.

EXHAUST MANIFOLD

Removal

1) Remove air cleaner. Remove necessary hoses and lines. Remove hot air preheat tube from exhaust pipe. Disconnect O_2 sensor harness. Remove nuts which secure front exhaust manifold to exhaust port of engine.

2) Remove bolts connecting front exhaust pipe to rear exhaust pipe. Remove bolt connecting front exhaust pipe to support bracket at transaxle. Remove exhaust manifold.

Installation

1) When installing exhaust manifold, always use new gaskets and lock nuts. The manifold-to-engine gasket is installed with FLAT side toward engine.

2) To install, reverse removal procedure and tighten bolts to specification.

CYLINDER HEAD

Removal

1) Remove intake and exhaust manifolds. Remove valve covers, rocker arm shafts and push rods. *See Fig. 4.*

NOTE: **Keep push rods in correct order.**

2) Loosen cylinder head bolts in reverse of tightening sequence shown. *See Fig. 1.* Remove cylinder heads.

Fig. 1: Cylinder Head Tightening Sequence

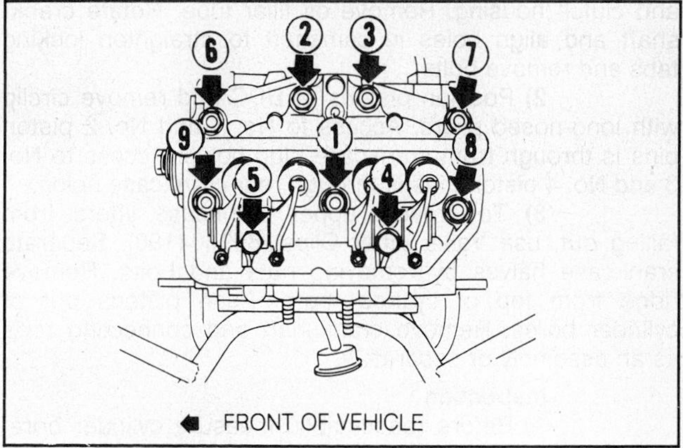

Courtesy of Subaru of America, Inc.

Inspection

1) Check cylinder head mating surface for warpage. Resurface if necessary. See CYLINDER HEAD SPECIFICATION table. Inspect intake and exhaust valve seats for corrrect surface contact and surface width. See VALVE specifications at end of article. If valve surface contact width is not within specifications, a replacement valve seat insert will be required.

Subaru Engines

1.6L & 1.8L 4-CYLINDER (Cont.)

CYLINDER HEAD SPECIFICATION

Application	In. (mm)
Warpage Limit	.002 (.05)
Grinding Limit	.02 (.50)
Standard Height	
1.6L	3.53 (89.6)
1.8L	3.57 (90.6)

2) Inspect intake and exhaust valve seats for correct surface contact and surface width. See VALVES specifications at end of article. If valve seat contact width is not within specifications, a replacement valve seat insert will be required.

Installation

1) Clean mating surfaces of cylinder head and crankcase so that they are free of oil, grease and dirt. Tighten rocker arm shaft in a progressive sequence, from center to outside.

NOTE: Apply head gasket sealant Three Bond 1201 or Dow Corning 92-024 to both sides of new cylinder head gasket. Install gasket quickly after applying sealant.

2) Before installing cylinder heads, coat all nut and bolt threads with oil. Tighten in sequence, in 3 successive steps. See TIGHTENING SPECIFICATIONS chart at end of article.

3) After tightening all cylinder head nuts and bolts, retighten center nut (No. 1) to ensure it is correctly torqued. Once engine is installed in vehicle, start engine and run for 10 minutes. Recheck cylinder head bolt torque.

CRANKCASE

Disassembly

1) Remove intake and exhaust manifolds. Remove cylinder heads. Remove transaxle. Remove water pump, oil pump and oil pan. Remove crankcase 14 mm Allen head plugs. Remove pressure plate, clutch, flywheel and clutch housing. Remove oil filler tube. Rotate crankshaft and align holes in camshaft to straighten locking tabs and remove bolts.

2) Position pistons at BDC and remove circlip with long-nosed pliers. Access to No. 1 and No. 2 piston pins is through front crankcase plug holes. Access to No. 3 and No. 4 piston pins is through rear crankcase holes.

3) To prevent upper crankcase lifters from falling out, use Valve Lifter Clips (899804100). Separate crankcase halves by removing nuts and bolts. Remove ridge from top of cylinder bore. Push pistons out of cylinder bores. Remove crankshaft and connecting rods as an assembly or separately.

Inspection

1) Before reassembly, measure cylinder bore. Refer to ENGINE SPECIFICATIONS chart for tolerances. Check for loose or bent stud bolts. Use Stud Bolt Wrench (898878600) when replacing stud bolts. Coat threads with a torque-holding sealant (Loctite 270) and tighten to 25-33 ft. lbs. (24-44 N.m).

2) Check stud bolt length. On 1.6L engines, length should measure 3.56-3.64" (90.5-92.5 mm), and on 1.8L engines it should measure 3.60-3.68" (91.5-93.5 mm). Check crankcase-to-cylinder head mating surface for warpage, and correct by grinding if necessary. Warping limit is .002" (.05 mm).

Reassembly

1) Lubricate all friction surfaces with engine oil prior to reassembly. Install lifters and use Lifter Clips (899804100) to hold lifters in place. Install bearings in crankcase half having No. 2 and No. 4 cylinders. Install crankshaft and camshaft so punch mark on camshaft gear is visible through chamfered hole in crankshaft gear. *See Fig. 3.*

2) Clean mating surfaces of crankcase and apply liquid gasket. Install water jacket "O" ring and back-up ring into crankcase half having No. 2 and No. 4 cylinders.

3) To complete reassembly, reverse disassembly procedure. Tighten crankcase halves and cylinder heads in sequence. *See Figs. 1 and 2*. Measure crankshaft end play and camshaft back lash.

Fig. 2: Crankcase Tightening Sequence

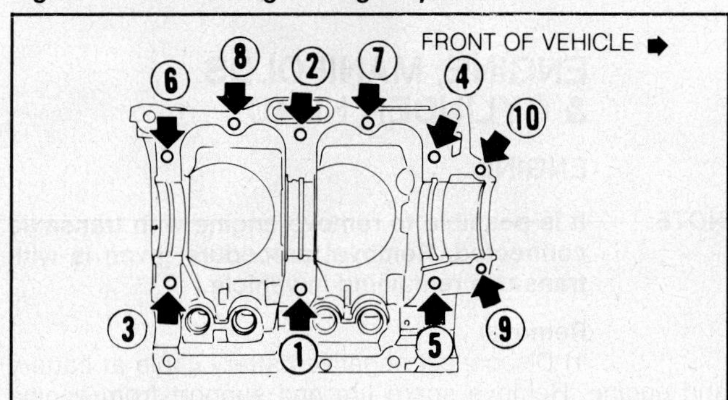

Courtesy of Subaru of America, Inc.

Fig. 3: Aligning Camshaft with Crankshaft

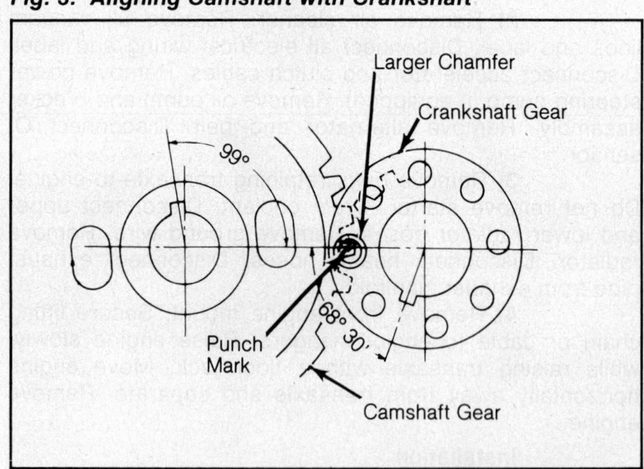

Camshaft gear mark should be visible through crankshaft gear chamfered hole. Courtesy of Subaru of America, Inc.

FRONT CRANKSHAFT OIL SEAL

1) Remove front pulley bolt and tap pulley lightly to disengage. Carefully pry old seal from crankcase. Install new seal using Installer (499067000).

2) Install crankshaft pulley. Apply oil to pulley bolt threads and liquid gasket (Three Bond 1215) on the flange seat. Prevent flywheel or flex plate from rotating and tighten to specification.

1.6L & 1.8L 4-CYLINDER (Cont.)

Fig. 4: Exploded View of Valve Train Assembly

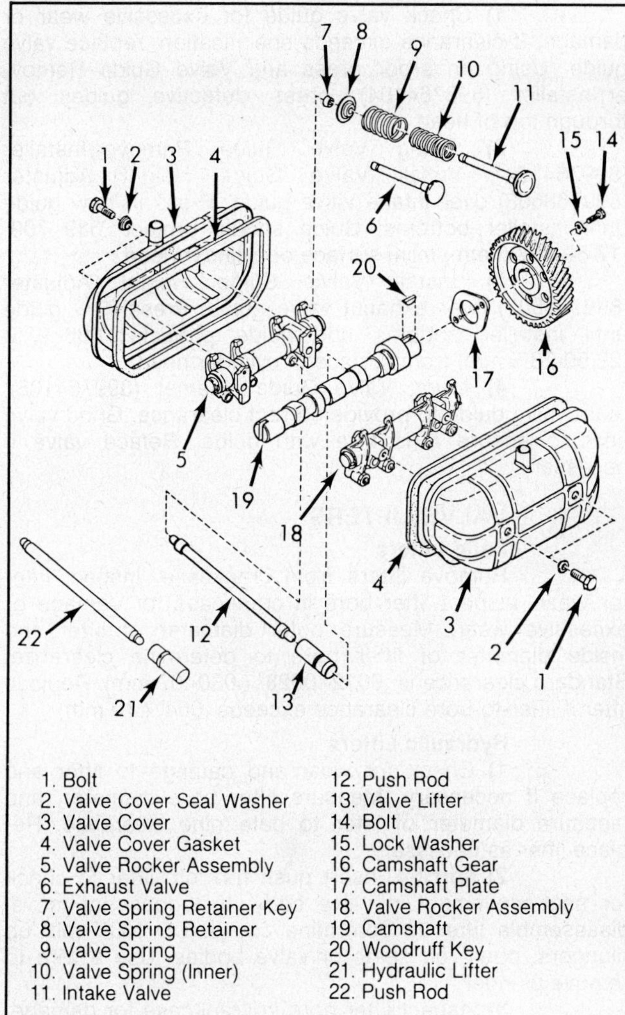

Courtesy of Subaru of America, Inc.

REAR MAIN BEARING OIL SEAL

1) Remove engine from vehicle. Remove transaxle from engine. Remove flywheel or torque converter flex plate to gain access to rear seal.

2) Pry oil seal from clutch housing and coat new seal with oil before installation. To install new oil seal, feed lip around crankshaft and push seal in by hand. Install flush with surface of clutch housing.

CAMSHAFT

Camshaft may be removed after crankcase has been separated. Visually inspect camshaft for cracks, excessive wear or damage. Replace camshaft as necessary. Inspect camshaft keyway groove. If defective, repair camshaft or replace key. Using a dial indicator, ensure runout does not exceed .002" (.05 mm).

NOTE: If camshaft is replaced, all valve lifters should also be replaced. Check identification marks. The 1.6L engine uses camshaft marked "51", while 1.8L engine with solid lifters uses camshaft marked "72". The 1.8L engine with hydraulic lifters uses camshaft marked "76".

CAMSHAFT END THRUST

Measure thrust clearance between camshaft and camshaft plate. Standard clearance is .0008-.0035" (.02-.09 mm). If clearance exceeds limit of .008" (.20 mm), replace camshaft plate.

CAM LOBE LIFT

Measure camshaft lobe height. Standard lobe height is 1.269-1.273" (32.24-32.34 mm) for camshafts used with solid lifters. Standard lobe height is 1.413-1.417" (35.90-36.00 mm) for camshafts used with hydraulic lifters. Wear limit specification is .006" (.15 mm). If camshaft wear exceeds specification, camshaft replacement is necessary.

TIMING GEAR

Measure camshaft gear runout with dial indicator. Replace camshaft if runout exceeds .010" (.25 mm). Measure backlash between camshaft gear and crankshaft gear. If backlash exceeds .004" (.10 mm), replace camshaft gear. Standard value of backlash is .0004-.0020" (.010-.050 mm).

CAMSHAFT BEARINGS

Bearings are not used for camshaft. Crankcase is machined to specifications. Oil clearance between camshaft and bore should be within specification. See CAMSHAFT specifications at end of article.

ROCKER ARM SHAFT ASSEMBLY

1) Check rocker arm shaft, rocker arm and bushing for wear or damage. Replace any worn parts. Pay special attention to position and number of all spring washers. *See Fig. 5.*

2) Measure outside diameter of rocker shaft and inner diameter of rocker arm to determine oil clearance. See ROCKER ASSEMBLY SPECIFICATIONS table.

3) If rocker arm surface is noticeably worn, replace rocker arm. If worn slightly in a stepped shape, use a valve refacer to correct. Replace rocker shaft spring washers if worn excessively. *See Fig. 5.*

ROCKER ASSEMBLY SPECIFICATIONS

Application	In. (mm)
Diameter	
Outside Rocker Shaft	.7080-.7088 (17.982-18.003)
Inside Rocker Arm	.7093-.7100 (18.016-18.034)
Oil Clearance	.0005-.0020 (.013-.52)

PUSH RODS

Check for damage and runout. Runout limit is .016" (.4 mm). Replace as necessary. Check oil hole for clogging and wear. Measure overall length of push rods. See PUSH ROD LENGTH table.

PUSH ROD LENGTH

Application	In. (mm)
1.6L	8.62-8.64 (219.0-219.4)
1.8L	
Solid Lifters	9.08-9.10 (230.7-231.1)
Hydraulic Lifters	9.12-9.14 (231.7-232.2)

Subaru Engines

1.6L & 1.8L 4-CYLINDER (Cont.)

Fig. 5: Exploded View of Rocker Arm Shaft Assembly

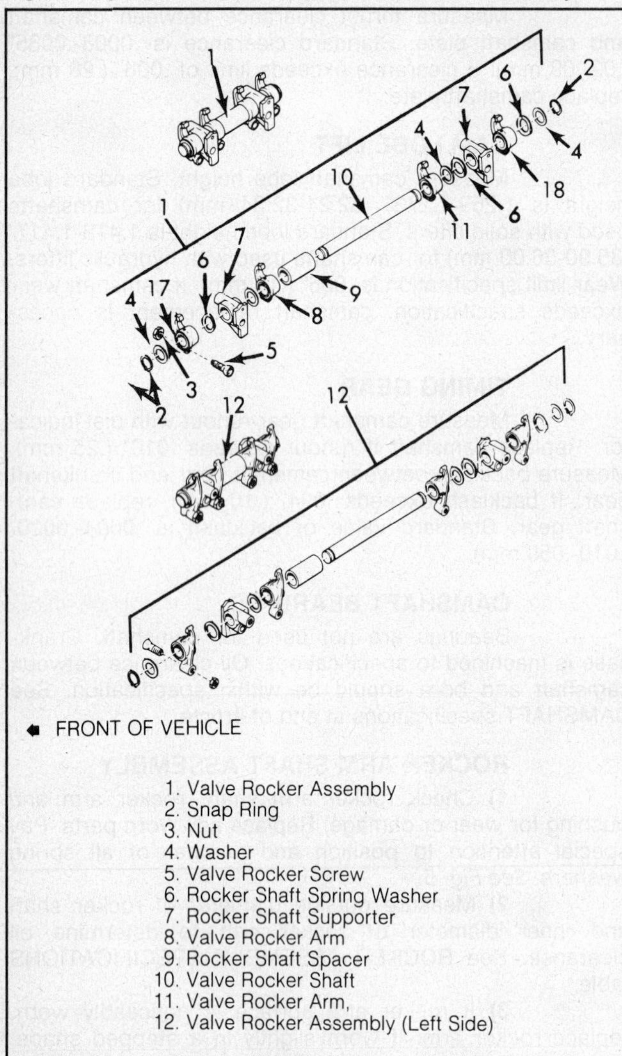

Courtesy of Subaru of America, Inc.

VALVES

VALVE ARRANGEMENT

I-E-E-I (Both banks, front-to-rear).

VALVE SPRINGS

Using Spring Compressor (899724100), remove valve keepers and spring retainer. Check springs under pressure and at free length. Replace if necessary. See VALVE SPRINGS in ENGINE SPECIFICATIONS chart at the end of this article. Install spring with wide spaced coil (paint marks) facing valve spring retainer.

VALVE STEM OIL SEALS

Valve stem oil seals are used only on intake valve guides. Remove old seal from intake valve guide. Using Oil Seal Installer (898858600), replace with a new seal. When fully installed, oil seal will measure .913" (23.2 mm) from cylinder head surface to top of oil seal. When inserting valve stem, lubricate and use care not to damage seal.

VALVE GUIDES

1) Check valve guide for excessive wear or damage. If clearance exceeds specification, replace valve guide. Using an arbor press and Valve Guide Remover/Installer (899764104), press defective guides out through top of head.

2) Using Valve Guide Remover/Installer (899764104), install Valve Guide Height Adjuster (899768603) over intake valve guide. Press in new guide until installer bottoms. Guide should project .689-.709" (17.50-18.00 mm) from surface of cylinder head.

3) Install Valve Guide Height Adjuster (899768602) over exhaust valve guide. Press new guide until installer bottoms and guide projects .886-.925" (22.50-23.5 mm) from surface of cylinder head.

4) Using Valve Guide Reamer (899764105), ream valve guide to provide correct clearance. Grind valve seat to ensure it is true with guide. Reface valve if necessary.

VALVE LIFTERS

Solid Lifters

Remove lifters from crankcase. Inspect lifter for wear. Inspect lifter bore in crankcase for damage or excessive wear. Measure outer diameter of lifter and inside diameter of lifter bore to determine clearance. Standard clearance is .0012-.0028" (.030-.07 mm). Replace lifter if lifter-to-bore clearance exceeds .004" (.10 mm).

Hydraulic Lifters

1) Check for wear and damage to lifter and replace if necessary. Measure lifter bore diameter, and measure diameter of lifter to determine clearance. Replace lifter as necessary.

2) Forcibly insert push rod into lifter to check for seat movement in valve body. If it does not move, disassemble lifter to determine cause. DO NOT mix up plungers, push rod seats or valve bodies. Use a wire to remove plunger.

3) Inspect lifter bore in crankcase for damage. Measure outer diameter of lifter and bore diameter to determine clearance. Standard clearance is .0008-.0035" (.020-.090 mm). Replace lifter if lifter-to-bore clearance exceeds .004" (.10 mm).

VALVE CLEARANCE ADJUSTMENT

With engine at ambient air temperature, rotate engine to TDC of compression stroke. Insert feeler gauge between rocker arm and valve stem. Firing order is 1-3-2-4. Cylinder identification numbers are stamped on engine case.

VALVE CLEARANCE SPECIFICATIONS

Application	In. (mm)
Intake	.010 (.25)
Exhaust	.014 (.35)

PISTONS, PINS & RINGS

PISTON & ROD ASSEMBLY

Removal

With engine removed from vehicle, remove manifolds. Remove cylinder heads, oil pump and oil pan. Remove clutch assembly, flywheel and clutch housing.

1.6L & 1.8L 4-CYLINDER (Cont.)

Remove pistons from bores and split crankcase. Remove connecting rods and crankshaft. See CRANKCASE in this article.

Inspection

1) Replace connecting rod if large or small end thrust surface is damaged. Using a connecting rod aligner, check for bend or twist. Limit of bend or twist per 3.94" (100 mm) is .004" (.10 mm).

2) Install connecting rod with bearing onto crankshaft. Tighten rod nuts to specification and measure side clearance. See CRANKSHAFT MAIN & CONNECTING ROD BEARINGS specifications at end of article.

3) Inspect small end bushing of connecting rod for excessive wear or foreign material saturation. Ensure cylinder wall oiling holes are clear from obstruction.

Installation

To install connecting rods and pistons, reverse removal procedures. See CRANKCASE in this article.

NOTE: **Each connecting rod has a mating cap. Ensure they are assembled correctly by checking their matching number. Position each connecting rod with marked side (logo) facing forward.**

FITTING PISTONS & RINGS

1) Measure cylinder bore .028" (.70 mm) from top of cylinder in-line with crankshaft and again 90 degrees from center line of crankshaft. Also measure down bore at 1.18" (30.0 mm) on 1.6L engines and 1.32" (33.5 mm) on 1.8L engines.

2) Measure piston 1.04" (26.3 mm) from bottom of skirt and 90 degrees from piston pin hole. Determine cylinder-to-piston clearance. See PISTON, PINS, RINGS specifications at end of article. If clearance is incorrect, replace pistons or bore all cylinders to fit oversize pistons.

3) If cylinder bore diameter exceeds 3.641-3.642" (92.48-92.51 mm), replace crankcase.

NOTE: **Measurement of both pistons and cylinder bores should be performed at 68°F (20°C). All cylinders must be bored to same size and use same size pistons.**

4) Check ring end gap and piston ring groove clearance. See PISTON, PINS, RINGS specifications at end of article. Check end gap at bottom of cylinder bore. Position pistons with oil rail stopper pin to center of case.

5) Install piston pin circlip, with dog ear facing out, on stopper pin side of piston. Fit piston rings with "R" or "N" marking facing up. When installing piston rings, ensure that ring end gaps are staggered around piston ring and not in-line with piston pin hole. *See Fig. 6.*

PISTON PINS

1) Check piston pins for damage, cracks, wear or distortion. Measure connecting rod bushing-to-piston pin clearance. Standard outer diameter of piston pin is .8265-.8268" (20.992-21.000 mm).

2) Check piston pin-to-connecting rod bushing bore clearance. See PISTON, PIN, RINGS specifications at end of article.

3) To remove bushing from connecting rod, use Bushing Remover/Replacer (499037000) and an arbor press. Ream bushing to fit standard pin.

Fig. 6: Piston Ring Gap Position

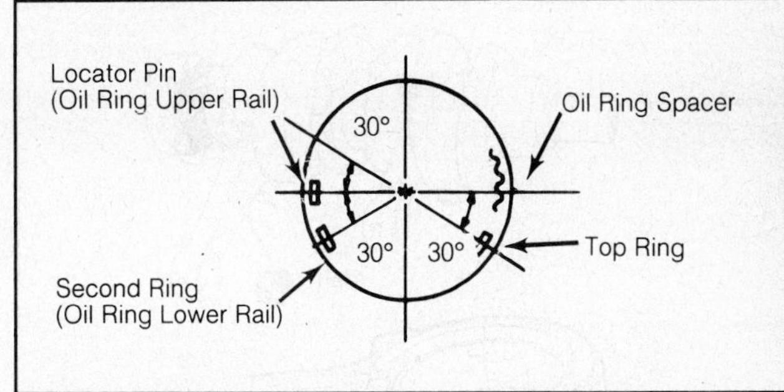

Courtesy of Subaru of America, Inc.

4) To replace bushing, coat with oil and press bushing into position. Drill two .12" (3.0 mm) oiling holes in bushing and ream bushing bore. Standard bushing bore measurement is .8268-.8274" (21.00-21.016 mm). After installation, ream and clean bushing to remove chips.

5) Check piston bore-to-piston pin clearance. See PISTON, PIN, RINGS specifications at end of article. Piston pin is a thumb push fit at 68°F (20°C).

CRANKSHAFT & ROD BEARINGS

CRANKSHAFT

1) Crankshaft can be removed after crankcase has been separated. Remove pistons. Remove connecting rods. Remove crankshaft. Clean crankshaft and using dye penetrant, inspect for cracks.

2) Measure crankshaft runout. Correct or replace crankshaft if runout exceeds specification. Measure for journal wear. See CRANKSHAFT & JOURNAL WEAR table.

CRANKSHAFT & JOURNAL WEAR

Application	In. (mm)
Grinding Limit	.0098 (.250)
Out-of-Round [1]	.0012 (.030)
Runout Limit	.0014 (.035)
Taper Limit	.0028 (.070)

[1] – Specification given is maximum allowance.

MAIN & CONNECTING ROD BEARINGS

1) Set crankshaft into crankcase. Measure thrust clearance at center bearing. See CRANKSHAFT MAIN & CONNECTING ROD BEARINGS specifications at end of article. If specification is exceeded, replace center main bearing.

2) Tighten main case bolts to specifications and measure oil clearance of crankshaft bearings. Measure oil clearance of connecting rod bearings. See CRANKSHAFT MAIN & CONNECTING ROD BEARINGS specifications at end of article.

NOTE: **Position each connecting rod with the marked side (logo) facing forward. Make sure connecting rods are assembled correctly by checking their matching number. See Fig. 7.**

Subaru Engines

1.6L & 1.8L 4-CYLINDER (Cont.)

Fig. 7: Connecting Rod Alignment Marks

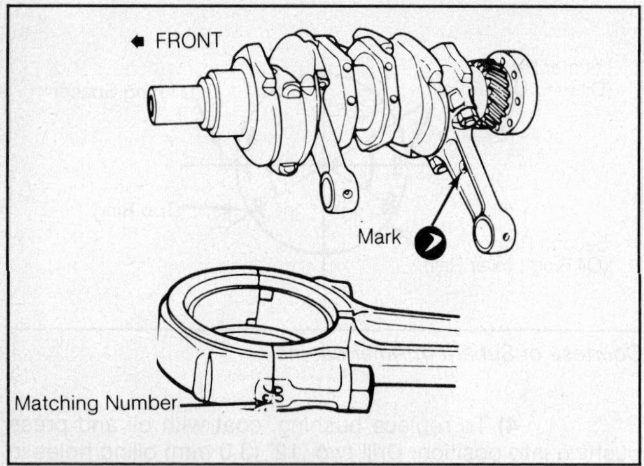

Courtesy of Subaru of America, Inc.

ENGINE OILING

ENGINE OILING SYSTEM

Oil is pressure-fed by a camshaft-driven trochoid type oil pump. Pump incorporates an oil relief and by-pass valve in its body. Oil pump is located externally on engine.

Oil from pump passes through oil filter to main oil gallery. To journals of camshaft and crankshaft. From there, oil goes to main bearings, piston pin bushings and cylinder walls. Oil then passes through valve lifters and push rods to oil rocker arms.

CRANKCASE CAPACITY

Crankcase capacity (including filter) is 3.7 qts. (3.5L) at the upper level mark, and 2.6 qts. (3.5L) at the lower level mark for 1.6L engine. For 1.8L engine, oil capacity is 4.2 qts. (4.0L) at the upper level mark, and 3.2 qts. (3.0L) at the lower level mark.

OIL FILTER

The oil filter is a full-flow disposable type.

NORMAL OIL PRESSURE

Oil pressure for 1.6L engine is 36 psi (2.5 kg/cm²) at 500 RPM, and 57 psi (4.0 kg/cm²) at 2500 RPM. For the 1.8L engine, oil pressure should be 50 psi (3.5 kg/cm²) at 500 RPM, and 57 psi (4.0 kg/cm²) at 2500 RPM.

PRESSURE REGULATOR VALVE

Valve is nonadjustable. It opens at 57-64 psi (4.0-4.5 kg/cm²).

OIL PUMP

Removal

Disconnect oil pressure sending unit lead (if necessary). Remove oil filter from pump. Remove 4 attaching bolts and pull pump forward.

Disassembly

Remove screws and lift cover and rotor from pump body. Remove "O" ring. Remove by-pass spring and ball. Unscrew plug and remove washers, spring and pressure relief valve.

Inspection

1) Measure rotor-to-drive gear and rotor-to-body clearance. Measure rotor side clearance and measure diameters of rotor and drive gear. Replace any component that exceed specifications.

2) Inspect relief valve spring, valve and pump body for wear or damage. Measure free length of relief spring. See OIL PUMP SPECIFICATIONS chart.

NOTE: **Make sure oil pump shaft is aligned with slot in camshaft when reassembling.**

Reassembly

Reassemble in reverse order, using all new gaskets and "O" rings.

Installation

Install oil filter on pump. Reverse removal procedure to complete installation.

OIL PUMP SPECIFICATONS

Application	In. (mm)
Drive Gear O.D.	1.169-1.171 (29.70-29.74)
Outer Rotor-to-Body Clearance	.001-.005 (.03-.13)
Relief Valve Spring Free Length	
1.6L	1.602 (40.7)
1.8L	1.461 (37.1)
Rotor O.D.	1.596-1.597 (40.53-40.56)
Rotor Side Clearance	.006-.008 (.15-.21)
Rotor-to-Drive Gear Clearance	.001-.005 (.03-.13)

ENGINE COOLING

WATER PUMP

Removal

Drain coolant. Disconnect lower radiator hose and by-pass hose. Loosen water pump pulley nuts to hand tight. Loosen alternator mounting bolts and remove drive belt. Remove timing belt front cover. Remove water pump mounting bolts and water pump.

Installation

Install water pump with new gasket and sealant. Install drive belt and hoses. Gradually tighten bolts alternately and evenly in several steps to prevent leakage. The clamps for the lower radiator hose should be positioned properly to prevent interference with drive belts. Pressure test cooling system at 23 psi (1.6kg/cm²) and check for leaks.

NOTE: **For further information on cooling systems, see ENGINE COOLING section.**

BRAT & HATCHBACK 1.6L & 1.8L 4-CYLINDER (Cont.)

ENGINE SPECIFICATIONS

GENERAL SPECIFICATIONS

Year	DISPLACEMENT		Fuel System	HP@RPM	Torque Ft. Lbs.@RPM	Compr. Ratio	BORE		STROKE	
	Cu. In.	Liters					In.	mm	In.	mm
1987										
1.6L	97	1.6	2-Bbl.	69@4800	86@2800	9.0:1	3.62	92	2.36	60
1.8L	109	1.8	2-Bbl.	73@4400	94@2400	[1] 8.7:1	3.62	92	2.64	67

[1] – On 4WD models, compression ratio is 7.7:1.

VALVES

Engine Size & Valve	Head Diam. In. (mm)	Face Angle	Seat Angle	Seat Width In. (mm)	Stem Diameter In. (mm)	Stem Clearance In. (mm)	Valve Lift In. (mm)
1.6L & 1.8L							
Intake	.....	45°	45°	.028-.051 (.7-1.3)	.3130-.3136 (7.950-7.965)	.0014-.0026 (.035-.065)	.....
Exhaust	.....	45°	45°	.039-.071 (1.0-1.8)	.3128-.3134 (7.945-7.960)	.0016-.0028 (.040-.070)	.....

PISTONS, PINS & RINGS

Engine	PISTONS	PINS		RINGS		
	Clearance In. (mm)	Piston Fit In. (mm)	Rod Fit In. (mm)	Ring No.	End Gap In. (mm)	Side Clearance In. (mm)
1.6L & 1.8L	.0004-.0016 (.010-.040)	.0002-.0004 (.004-.010)	0-.0009 (0-.022)	No.1	[1] .0079-.0138 (.20-.35)	[3] .0016-.0031 (.04-.08)
				No. 2	[1] .0079-.0138 (.20-.35)	[3] .0012-.0028 (.03-.07)
				No. 3	[2] .0079-.0354 (.20-.90)	.....

[1] – Limit .039" (1.0 mm). [2] – Limit .059" (1.5 mm). [3] – Limit .0059" (.15 mm).

CRANKSHAFT MAIN & CONNECTING ROD BEARINGS

Engine	MAIN BEARINGS				CONNECTING ROD BEARINGS		
	Journal Diam. In. (mm)	Clearance In. (mm)	Thrust Bearing	Crankshaft End Play In. (mm)	Journal Diam. In. (mm)	Clearance In. (mm)	Side Play In. (mm)
1.6L							
Front & Rear	1.9668-1.9673 (49.957-49.970)	[1] .0004-.0014 (.010-.035)	Center	[2] .0004-.0037 (.010-.095)	1.7715-1.7720 (44.995-45.010)	[3] .0008-.0028 (.020-.070)	[4] .0028-.013 (.07-.33)
Center	1.9673-1.9678 (49.970-49.982)	.0004-.0012 (.010-.030)					
1.8L							
Front & Rear	2.1636-2.1642 (54.995-54.970)	[1] .0004-.0012 (.010-.030)	Center	[2] .0004-.0037 (.010-.095)	1.7715-1.7720 (44.995-45.010)	[3] .0008-.0028 (.020-.070)	[4] .0028-.013 (.07-.33)
Center	2.1636-2.1642 (54.995-54.970)	.0004-.0010 (.010-.025)					

[1] – Limit front and rear, .0022" (.55 mm); limit center, .0018" (.045 mm). [2] – Limit .0118" (.30 mm). [3] – Limit .0039" (.100 mm).
[4] – Limit .016" (0.4 mm).

Subaru Engines

1.6L & 1.8L 4-CYLINDER (Cont.)

ENGINE SPECIFICATIONS (Cont.)

CAMSHAFT

Engine	Journal Diam. In. (mm)	Clearance In. (mm)	Lobe Lift In. (mm)
1.6L Front & Center	1.022-1.0226 (25.959-25.975)	[1] .0010-.0023 (.025-.059)	.....
1.8L Front & Center	1.2582-1.2589 (31.959-31.975)	[1] .0010-.0023 (.025-.059)	.....
1.6L & 1.8L Rear	1.4157-1.4163 (35.959-35.975)	[1] .0010-.0023 (.025-.059)	.....

[1] – Limit .0039" (.100 mm).

VALVE TIMING

Engine	INTAKE Open (BTDC)	INTAKE Close (ABDC)	EXHAUST Open (BBDC)	EXHAUST Close (ATDC)
1.6L	20°	60°	60°	20°
1.8L				
Manual	20°	60°	60°	20°
Automatic	20°	64°	64°	20°

TIGHTENING SPECIFICATIONS

Application	Ft. Lbs. (N.m)
Cylinder Head Nuts	
Step 1	22 (30)
Step 2	43 (58)
Step 3	47 (64)
Connecting Rod Nuts	29-31 (39-42)
Crankshaft Pulley Bolt	47-54 (64-73)
Crankcase Plug	46-56 (62-76)
Crankcase Halves	
6 mm Bolts	3-4 (4-5)
8 mm Bolts	17-20 (23-27)
10 mm Bolts	29-35 (39-48)
Intake Manifold Bolts	13-16 (18-22)
Flywheel Bolts	30-33 (41-45)
Rocker Arm Bolts	47 (64)

Subaru Engines

1.8L OHC 4-CYLINDER

Coupe (3-Door), Sedan, Station Wagon & XT Coupe

NOTE: **For engine repair procedures not covered in this article, see ENGINE OVERHAUL PROCEDURES article at beginning of this section.**

ENGINE CODING

ENGINE IDENTIFICATION

On all models, engine can be identified by 6th character of Vehicle Identification Number (VIN). The VIN is stamped on a metal plate located on front right side of engine compartment. Identification number of engine is stamped on a machined pad on right front of engine cylinder block.

ENGINE IDENTIFICATION CODES

Application	Code
1.8L 2WD	4
1.8L 4WD	5
1.8L 4WD	7

ENGINE, MANIFOLDS & CYLINDER HEADS

ENGINE

NOTE: **It is possible to remove engine with transaxle remaining in vehicle. Removal procedure given is with transaxle remaining in vehicle.**

Removal (Non-Turbocharged Engines)

1) Disconnect negative battery cable at battery and engine. Remove spare tire and spare tire support from engine compartment. Remove hoses, duct and boot from air cleaner. Remove air cleaner.

2) Disconnect fuel line from carbon canister. Disconnect carburetor inlet. Allow fuel to drain into a suitable container. Remove brake booster and heater control vacuum hoses from intake manifold. On automatic transaxle models, remove diaphragm vacuum hoses and transaxle cooler lines.

3) On all models, disconnect wiring harness connectors at engine, distributor, alternator, radiator, starter and accessories and label. Remove retaining clips. Disconnect accelerator cable from carburetor. On manual transaxle models, remove release lever spring. On hill-holder models, disconnect hill-holder cable.

4) On all models, remove exhaust pipe from exhaust manifold. Remove engine stabilizer bar. Remove accelerator cable. Remove and label evaporative control and vacuum hoses from engine. Remove timing hole plug. Remove 4 mounting bolts which retain engine to transaxle. Ensure that bolts do not fall into housing. Drain coolant. Disconnect radiator and reservoir hoses.

5) Remove upper radiator bolts and lift out radiator. Remove heater hoses from engine side. Remove starter motor. Remove power steering pump assembly and wire out of working area (if equipped). Remove A/C compressor and wire components out of working area (if equipped).

6) Disconnect O_2 sensor lead. Remove nuts securing engine mounts to crossmember. Lower vehicle and support transaxle with a floor jack. Ensure all components are disconnected and clear from engine. Lift engine with chain hoist attached to front and rear hangers, and separate engine from transaxle.

7) When separating engine from transaxle, ensure that torque converter remains with transaxle (automatic transaxle only). Remove engine completely and place on engine stand.

Removal (Turbocharged Engines)

1) Remove spare tire and support. Relieve fuel system pressure. Raise vehicle and disconnect fuel pump. Lower vehicle and crank engine about 5 seconds to relieve fuel pressure. Turn ignition switch to the "OFF" position. Remove battery ground cable at battery and engine.

2) Remove fuel and evaporative control hoses. Remove vacuum hoses and disconnect necessary wiring from engine, radiator, accessories and label. Remove air duct and airflow meter boot. Cover openings to keep out dirt and dust. Remove upper cover.

3) Remove accelerator cable. Remove center exhaust pipe and heat shield cover from transaxle. On XT models, remove entire cover assembly. Remove cooling fan and power steering pump assembly (if equipped). Wire pump out of working area.

4) On automatic transaxle models, remove timing hole plug. Remove 4 bolts connecting torque converter to flex plate. Use care that bolts do not fall into housing.

5) On manual transaxle models, remove clutch return spring and hill-holder cable. Remove engine stabilizer. Remove upper bolts attaching engine to transaxle. Drain coolant and remove radiator assembly. On automatic transaxle models, disconnect oil cooler lines.

6) Disconnect heater hoses at engine. Remove engine mounting nuts. Remove lower nuts connecting engine to transaxle. Connect sling to power steering bracket and engine stabilizer bracket. Support transaxle with a floor jack. Raise engine, remove from vehicle and place on engine stand.

Installation

To install, reverse removal procedures.

INTAKE MANIFOLD

Removal (Non-Turbocharged Engines)

1) Disconnect negative battery cable. Remove air cleaner assembly. Remove distributor and spark plug wires. Drain coolant and disconnect all hoses from manifold. Disconnect throttle cable, vacuum lines, fuel lines and electrical connections to manifold and label. *See Fig. 1*.

2) Before slackening alternator belt, loosen water pump pulley mounting nuts until finger tight. Remove alternator (except A/C models). Remove silencers and silencer hoses. Remove air suction valve and pipe together with brackets.

3) Loosen both ends of EGR pipe and remove from rear of manifold. Remove PCV hose and blow-by hose. Remove air bleed hose from thermostat case. Disconnect each harness. Remove 6 manifold-to-cylinder head bolts and remove manifold. *See Fig. 1*.

1.8L OHC 4-CYLINDER (Cont.)

Fig. 1: View of Carbureted Intake Manifold

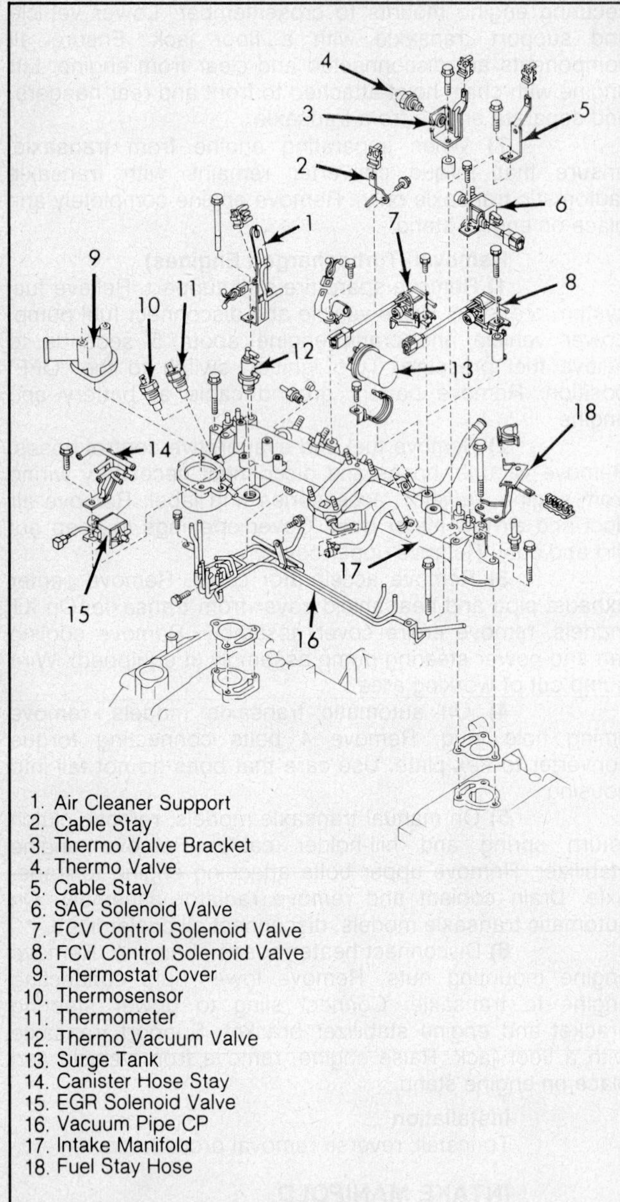

Courtesy of Subaru of America, Inc.

Removal (Turbocharged Engines)

1) Disconnect negative battery cable. Remove air duct to turbocharger. Remove air intake duct. Drain coolant and remove upper radiator hose. Remove turbocharger cooling hose and turbocharger. Remove front exhaust pipe from cylinder head. Remove distributor and spark plug wires. *See Fig. 2.*

2) Loosen water pump pulley mounting bolts until finger tight. Remove alternator (except A/C models). Remove PCV hose. Remove clips, ground terminal and knock sensor terminal. Remove wiring harness. Disconnect oil pressure switch. Disconnect remaining electrical wiring and vacuum lines as necessary. Label all wiring and vacuum lines.

3) Disconnect air bleed hose from intake manifold. Remove EGR pipe clamps. Remove EGR pipe cover and pipe. Remove bolts securing intake manifold-to-engine and remove intake manifold. *See Fig. 2.*

Fig. 2: Exploded View of Intake Manifold for Fuel Injected Engines

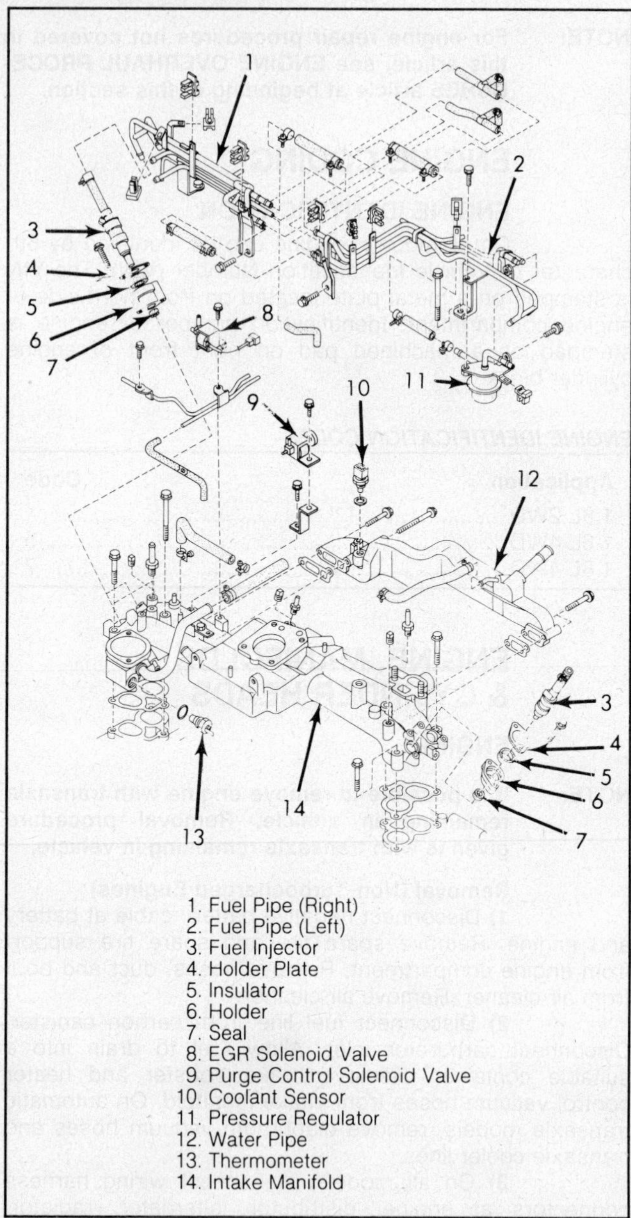

Courtesy of Subaru of America, Inc.

Installation

After cleaning mating surfaces and inspecting manifold, install new gaskets and reverse removal procedure.

EXHAUST MANIFOLD

Removal (Non-Turbocharged Engines)

Disconnect O_2 sensor harness. Remove air duct from upper shell cover. Loosen, but do not remove nuts which hold front exhaust pipe to manifold. Disconnect front and rear exhaust pipes. Disconnect front exhaust pipe and bracket.

Removal (Turbocharged Engines)

1) Remove turbocharger heat shields. Remove turbocharger. Remove nuts which hold turbo bracket to front exhaust pipe. Remove underguard and right undercover.

Subaru Engines

1.8L OHC 4-CYLINDER (Cont.)

2) Loosen engine mount bracket and engine stabilizer bar. Slightly raise engine until mount bolts protrude beyond surface of crossmember. Remove nuts which secure front exhaust manifold to exhaust port of engine. Remove exhaust manifold through clearance between crossmember and cylinder head.

Installation

When installing exhaust manifold, always use new gaskets and lock nuts. The gasket between manifold and engine is installed with the FLAT side toward engine. To install, reverse removal procedure and tighten bolts to specification.

CYLINDER HEAD

NOTE: Procedure given is with engine removed from vehicle.

Removal

1) Remove power steering pump and bracket (if equipped). Remove alternator, brackets and stabilizer bar (except A/C models). Remove knock sensor and fuel injectors (turbo models). Remove air bleed hose. Remove oil filler tube. Remove water pipe.

2) Remove crankshaft pulley by locking crankshaft with Flywheel Stopper (498277000) for manual transaxle models, or Drive Plate Stopper (498497000) for automatic transaxle models. Remove water pump pulley and pulley cover. Remove dipstick and tube. Remove belt cover plate (turbo models). Remove timing belt covers.

3) Loosen timing belt tensioner mounting bolts on No. 1 cylinder a half turn. Cover end of tensioner wrench clamping tips to avoid damage to crankshaft. Turn tensioner with Tensioner Wrench (499007000) to slacken belt and tighten mounting bolts. Mark direction of timing belt and remove.

4) Remove crankshaft sprocket. Remove crankshaft sprocket No. 2. Remove both tensioners together with tensioner spring. Remove belt idler. Remove camshaft sprockets by using Camshaft Sprocket Wrench (499207000). Remove timing belt covers. Remove water pump together with hose and pipe.

5) Remove oil pump by aligning notch in oil pump pulley with bolt position. Remove pump outer rotor from cylinder block. Remove clutch cover and clutch disc (except A/T models). Remove flywheel or flex plate. Remove spark plugs. Remove valve rocker covers.

6) Remove camshaft cases, camshaft support and camshafts as units. Remove rocker arms and valve lash adjusters, keeping adjusters upright and in correct order. On turbocharged models, remove turbocharger cooling pipe. Remove cylinder heads.

Disassembly & Inspection

1) Measure valve stem installed height. If measurement is not within specification, replace valve seat and or valve. Remove valve and valve guide seal.

2) Inspect cylinder head for damage. When disassembling cylinder head, ensure all parts are arranged in their relative order for reassembly purposes. Measure cylinder head mating surface for warpage. Warpage limit is .002" (.05 mm).

3) Inspect intake and exhaust seats for correct contact width. If contact surface widths are not within specification, regrind valve seats. Check clearance between valve stem and valve guide. See VALVES specifications at end of this article. If clearance is excessive replacement of valve guide is necessary. Refer to VALVE GUIDE in this article.

Reassembly & Installation

1) Install oil seals to valve guides using Oil Seal Installer (398852100). Coat stem of valve with engine oil and carefully insert through oil seal into valve guide. Install valve spring with closed coil end side facing downward towards cylinder head.

2) Install spring retainer. Install valve spring compressor and compress valve spring. Install valve keepers and slowly remove valve spring compressor. Before installing cylinder heads, coat bolt threads with oil. Install cylinder head gaskets and cylinder heads. Tighten cylinder head bolts in 3 successive steps. *See Fig. 3*. See TIGHTENING SPECIFICATIONS table.

3) After tightening all the cylinder head bolts, reverse removal procedures to complete installation. Tighten timing and drive belts.

Fig. 3: Cylinder Head Tightening Sequence

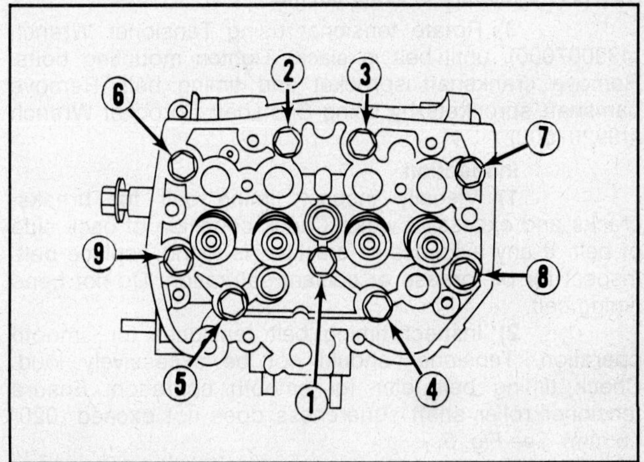

Courtesy of Subaru of America, Inc.

CAMSHAFTS

Removal

With engine removed from vehicle, remove camshaft cases, camshaft support and camshaft.

Inspection

Inspect camshaft. Measure camshaft lobe height. Measure camshaft runout. See CAMSHAFT specifications at end of article.

Installation

To install, reverse removal procedures.

TIMING BELTS & SPROCKETS

Removal

1) With engine removed from vehicle, remove crankshaft pulley. Lock crankshaft by using Flywheel Stopper (498277000) for manual transaxle models. For automatic transaxle models, use Drive Plate Stopper (498497000). Remove water pump pulley and pulley cover.

2) Remove dipstick and dipstick tube. Remove timing belt covers. Mark rotating direction of timing belts. Loosen timing belt tensioner mounting bolts on No. 1 cylinder. Turn tensioner to slacken belt and tighten mounting bolts. Remove timing belt. Loosen timing belt tensioner bolts on No. 2 cylinder. *See Fig. 4*.

1.8L OHC 4-CYLINDER (Cont.)

Fig. 4: Timing Belts & Engine Components

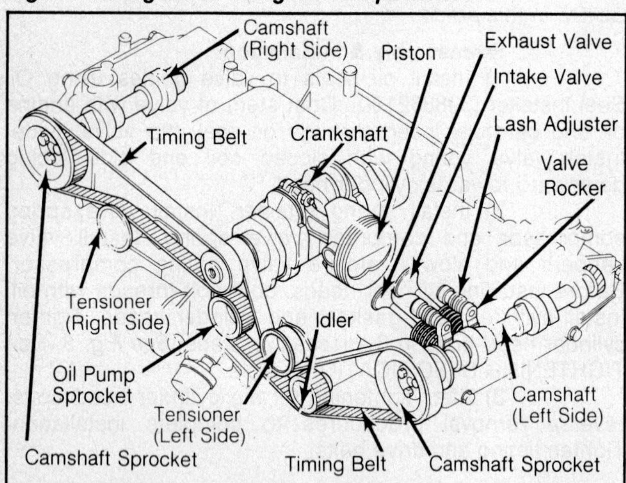

Courtesy of Subaru of America, Inc.

3) Rotate tensioner using Tensioner Wrench (499007000), until belt is slack. Tighten mounting bolts. Remove crankshaft sprocket and timing belt. Remove camshaft sprockets by using Camshaft Sprocket Wrench (499207000).

Inspection

1) Visually inspect timing belt for breaks, cracks and excessive wear. Check condition of back side of belt. If any evidence of cracking is found, replace belt. Inspect for oil, grease or coolant saturation. Do not bend timing belt.

2) Inspect timing belt tensioner for smooth operation. Tensioner should not be excessively loud. Check timing belt idler for smooth operation. Ensure tensioner roller shaft squareness does not exceed .020" (.5 mm). *See Fig. 5.*

Fig. 5: Tensioner Squareness Measuring Point

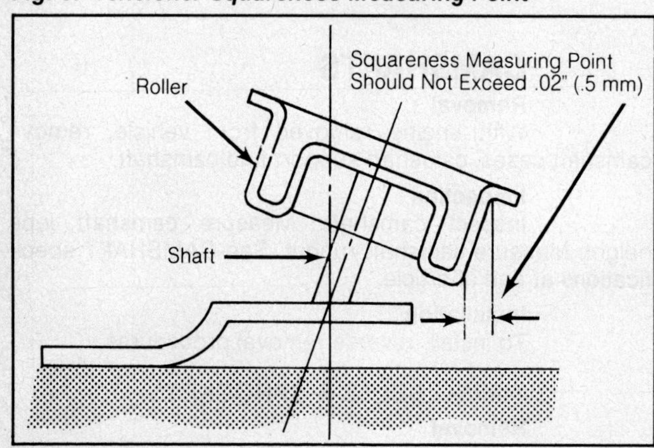

Courtesy of Subaru of America, Inc.

Installation

1) Install camshaft sprockets, using Camshaft Sprocket Wrench (499207000) to hold sprockets. Tighten bolts in 2 or 3 steps to specified torque. Install No. 1 and No. 2 belt tensioners. Install belt idler to cylinder block and tighten. Install No. 2 crankshaft sprocket (sprocket without dowel pin) to crankshaft. Install crankshaft pulley and tighten temporarily.

2) Align center mark on flywheel with mark on flywheel housing. Align mark on camshaft left sprocket with notch in belt cover. *See Fig. 7*. Attach timing belt No. 2 to crankshaft sprocket No. 2. Then install belt around oil pump sprocket, belt idler and camshaft sprocket in that order. Loosen tensioner No. 2 retaining bolt to allow tension upon the timing belt.

3) Push timing belt by hand to ensure smooth operation and movement of tensioner. Apply specified torque to camshaft sprocket in a counterclockwise direction using Belt Tensioner Wrench (499437000). While applying torque, tighten tensioner bolts. Ensure that flywheel timing marks are aligned.

4) Ensure that left side camshaft sprocket marks are in their correct positions. Ensure that all timing marks are aligned. *See Fig. 6 and 7*. Turn crankshaft one turn clockwise from position where the first timing belt (No. 2) was installed.

Fig. 6: Flywheel Timing Alignment Marks

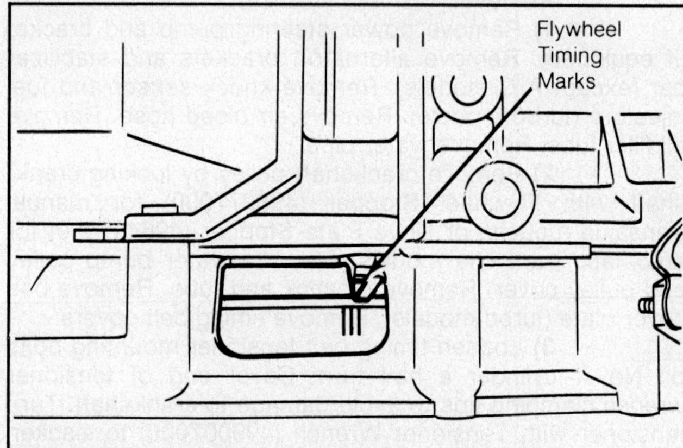

Courtesy of Subaru of America, Inc.

Fig. 7: Camshaft Timing Alignment Marks

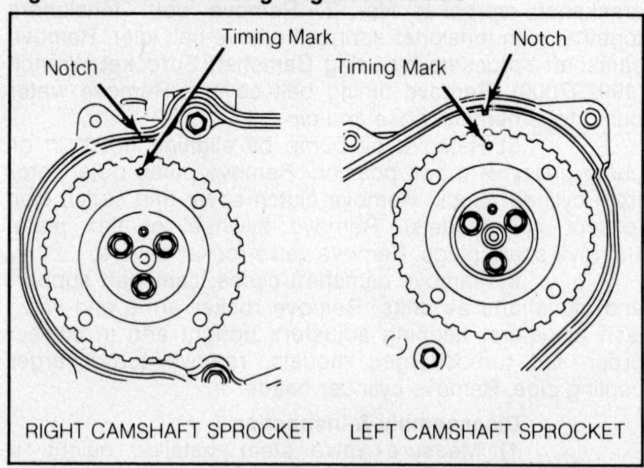

Courtesy of Subaru of America, Inc.

5) Align the center line of 3 lines marked on the flywheel with timing mark on flywheel housing. Install sprocket to crankshaft. Align timing mark on right side camshaft sprocket with notch in belt cover. *See Fig. 7*.

6) Install timing belt over sprockets, keeping slack out of side opposite tensioner. Loosen tensioner retaining bolts to apply tension to belt. Using Belt Tension Wrench (499437000), apply specified torque, while turning camshaft sprocket in counterclockwise direction. See TIMING BELT TENSION SPECIFICATIONS chart.

Subaru Engines

1.8L OHC 4-CYLINDER (Cont.)

7) While applying torque, tighten adjusting bolt first, then pivot bolt. Ensure that flywheel timing marks and camshaft right side timing marks are still in alignment. Reverse removal procedures to complete installation.

TIMING BELT TENSION SPECIFICATIONS

Application	Belt Tension	Torque
New Belt	33-55 lbs.	17-19 ft. lbs.
	(15-25 kg)	(24-25 N.m)
Used Belt	24-46 lbs.	10-12 ft. lbs.
	(11-21 kg)	(14-16 N.m)

VALVES

VALVE ARRANGEMENT

E-I-I-E (Both banks, front-to-rear).

VALVE SPRINGS

Removal

With cylinder heads removed, use Spring Compressor (899724100) to compress valve springs. Remove valve keepers and retainers. Remove and check springs under pressure. Check free length of springs. Replace if necessary. See VALVE SPRINGS in ENGINE SPECIFICATIONS chart at end of this article.

Installation

Install springs with closed coil end against cylinder head spring seat.

VALVE

With valves removed from cylinder head, inspect stem, head and keeper grooves for excessive wear or deformation. Check valve contact width and pattern for correct fit.

VALVE GUIDE

1) Check valve guide for wear or damage. If excessive wear is found, replace valve guide. Using an arbor press and Valve Guide Remover/Installer (399762103), press worn guides out through top of head.

2) Using same valve guide remover/installer, install Valve Guide Height Adjuster (899768603) over valve guide and press in new guide until installer bottoms and guide projects .689-.728" (17.50-18.50 mm) from surface of cylinder head.

3) Using Valve Guide Reamer (399762104), ream valve guide to provide correct clearance. Reface valve seat to new valve guide. Inspect valve seat to ensure it is true with guide.

VALVE LASH ADJUSTERS

With adjuster set in an upright position, push adjuster pivot piston down hard and quickly by hand. If pivot piston can be depressed more than .020" (.50 mm), put adjuster in a container of light oil and move pivot piston up and down until adjuster is within specification. If adjuster is still not within specification, replace adjuster.

VALVE CLEARANCE ADJUSTMENT

The valve clearance is automatically adjusted by use of hydraulic valve lash adjusters.

PISTONS, PINS & RINGS

PISTON & ROD ASSEMBLY

Removal

With engine removed from vehicle, remove cylinder heads, oil pump and oil pan. Remove clutch assembly, flywheel and clutch housing. Remove piston pins from connecting rods and split cylinder block. Remove connecting rods from crankshaft. See CYLINDER BLOCK in this article.

Inspection

1) Replace connecting rod if large or small end thrust surface is damaged. Using a connecting rod aligner, check for bend or twist. Limit of bend or twist per 3.94" (100 mm) is .0039" (.10 mm).

2) Install connecting rod with bearing onto crankshaft. Tighten rod nuts to specification and measure side clearance. See CRANKSHAFT MAIN & CONNECTING ROD BEARINGS in ENGINE SPECIFICATIONS chart at end of this article. Replace connecting rod if side clearance exceeds specified limits.

Installation

To install connecting rods and pistons, reverse removal procedures. See CYLINDER BLOCK in this article.

NOTE: **Each connecting rod has a mating connecting rod cap. Ensure they are assembled correctly by checking their matching number. Position each connecting rod with marked side (stamped) facing forward.**

FITTING PISTONS & RINGS

1) Measure cylinder bore .028" (.71 mm) from top of cylinder in line with crankshaft and again 90 degrees from centerline of crankshaft. Also measure bore at 2 intervals of 1.319" (33.5 mm) from top of cylinder.

2) Measure piston 1.059" (26.9 mm) from bottom of skirt and 90 degrees from piston pin hole. Determine clearance between cylinder and piston clearance. Clearance should be .0004-.0016" (.010-.040 mm). Maximum clearance is .0024" (.060 mm). If clearance is incorrect, replace pistons or bore all cylinders to fit oversize pistons.

3) If cylinder bore diameter exceeds .0118" (.30 mm) more than standard bore of 3.6214-3.6261" (91.983-92.105 mm) after boring and honing, replace cylinder block. Maximum allowable variation between cylinder bores is .002" (.050 mm).

NOTE: **Measurement of both pistons and cylinder bores should be performed at 68°F (20°C). All cylinders must be bored to same size and use same diameter oversize pistons.**

4) Check ring end gap and piston groove clearance. See ENGINE SPECIFICATIONS chart for tolerances. Check end gap at bottom of cylinder bore. Position pistons with oil rail stopper pin to center of case. Install piston pin circlip, with dog ear facing out, on stopper pin side of piston. Fit piston rings with "R" or "N" mark facing up.

PISTON PINS

1) Check piston pins for damage, cracks, wear or distortion. Check clearance between connecting rod

1.8L OHC 4-CYLINDER (Cont.)

piston pin. Standard outer diameter of piston pin is .8265-.8268" (20.993-21.001 mm).

2) Standard piston pin-to-connecting rod bushing bore press fit is 0-.0009" (0-.022 mm). If pin or bushing are worn beyond specification, replace bushing in connecting rod.

3) To remove bushing from connecting rod, use Bushing Remover/Replacer (499037000) and an arbor press. Ream bushing to fit standard pin.

4) To replace bushing, coat with oil and press bushing into position. Drill two .12" (3 mm) oiling holes in bushing and hone bushing bore. Bushing bore measurement is .8268-.8274" (21.000-21.016 mm). After installation, ream and clean bushing to remove chips.

5) Check piston bore-to-piston pin clearance. Standard clearance between piston pin and piston bore is .00004-.00059" (.0010-.0150 mm). Piston pin is a thumb push fit at 68°F (20°C).

CYLINDER BLOCK

DISASSEMBLY

1) Remove intake and exhaust manifolds. Remove cylinder heads. Remove water pump, oil pump and oil pan. Remove oil separator cover. Remove 14 mm Allen head plugs from crankcase. Position pistons No. 1 and 2 at BBDC and remove circlip with long-nosed pliers from piston pin bore.

2) Access to piston pins No. 1 and 2 is through front crankcase service holes. Remove piston pins using Piston Pin Remover (399094310). Access to No. 3 and No. 4 piston pins is through rear crankcase holes. Remove piston pins using piston pin remover.

NOTE: When separating cylinder block, do not allow connecting rods to fall and cause damage. Be sure to keep combinations of pistons, connecting rods and cylinders matched.

3) Remove all crankcase connecting bolts and separate cylinder block halves. Remove crankshaft and connecting rods. With dial bore gauge, measure cylinder bores for taper, out-of-round and excessive wear. See engine CYLINDER BLOCK SPECIFICATIONS chart for tolerances.

4) If cylinder bore is within specification, check top of cylinder for a ridge. If necessary, remove ridge using a ridge reamer. Remove pistons from cylinder bores.

Inspection

Measure cylinder bores. Inspect cylinder block for damage. Measure cylinder block mating surface for warpage. See CYLINDER BLOCK SPECIFICATIONS chart.

REASSEMBLY

1) Install crankshaft bearings to cylinder block halves. Install crankshaft into the left side of cylinder block half having No. 2 and No. 4 cylinders. Clean mating surfaces of cylinder block and apply liquid gasket. Install water jacket "O" ring. Back ring up into the cylinder block half possessing No. 2 and No. 4 cylinders.

2) Tighten cylinder block halves and cylinder heads in sequence to specified torque. To complete reassembly, reverse disassembly procedure. Make sure to check crankshaft thrust clearance.

CYLINDER BLOCK SPECIFICATIONS

Application	In. (mm)
Standard	
Cylinder Bore	3.6214-3.6226 (91.985-92.015)
Taper	
Standard	.0006 (.015)
Maximum	.002 (.050)
Out-Of-Round	
Standard	.0004 (.010)
Maximum	.002 (.050)
Warpage	
Maximum	.002 (.05)
Grinding Limit	.016 (0.40)

FRONT CRANKSHAFT OIL SEAL

Removal

Remove timing belts. Remove crankshaft sprocket. Carefully pry old seal from cylinder block.

Installation

Install new seal using Seal Installer (499567000). Reverse removal procedure to complete installation.

REAR MAIN BEARING OIL SEAL

Removal

Remove engine from vehicle. Remove flywheel or torque converter flex plate to gain access to rear oil seal. Carefully pry old seal from cylinder block.

Installation

Install new seal using Seal Installer (499587000). Reverse removal procedure to complete installation.

CRANKSHAFT & ROD BEARINGS

CRANKSHAFT

Removal & Inspection

1) Crankshaft can be removed after cylinder block has been separated. Remove connecting rods. Clean crankshaft and use dye penetrant to inspect for cracks.

2) Place crankshaft with front and rear journal resting in "V" blocks. Using a dial indicator on center journal, measure crankshaft runout. Correct or replace crankshaft if it exceeds specification. Using a micrometer, inspect crankshaft for excessive journal wear.

CRANKSHAFT & JOURNAL WEAR LIMITS

Application	In. (mm)
Out-of-Round	.0012 (.03)
Taper Limit	.0028 (.07)
Grinding Limit	.0098 (.25)
Runout Limit	.0014 (.035)

MAIN & CONNECTING ROD BEARINGS

1) With main bearings in block, set crankshaft into engine block. Using a feeler gauge, measure crankshaft thrust clearance (end play) at center bearing. If limit is exceeded, replace center main bearing (thrust bearing).

2) Wipe off oil and dust on surfaces to be measured. Install bearings in cylinder block and set

1.8L OHC 4-CYLINDER (Cont.)

crankshaft into cylinder block. Tighten crankcase bolts to specification and measure oil clearance of crankshaft bearings using Plastigage method.

3) Wipe off oil and dust on surfaces to be measured. Install bearings on connecting rod and cap. Tighten rod nuts to specification. Measure oil clearance of connecting rod bearings using Plastigage method.

4) Main bearings are available in standard, .001" (.03 mm), .002" (.05 mm) and .010" (.25 mm) undersize. Connecting rod bearings are available in standard, .0012" (.03 mm), .002" (.05 mm) and .0098" (.25 mm) undersize.

NOTE: Position each connecting rod with the marked side (stamped) facing forward. Make sure connecting rods are assembled correctly by checking their matching number. See Fig. 8.

Fig. 8: Connecting Rod Alignment Marks

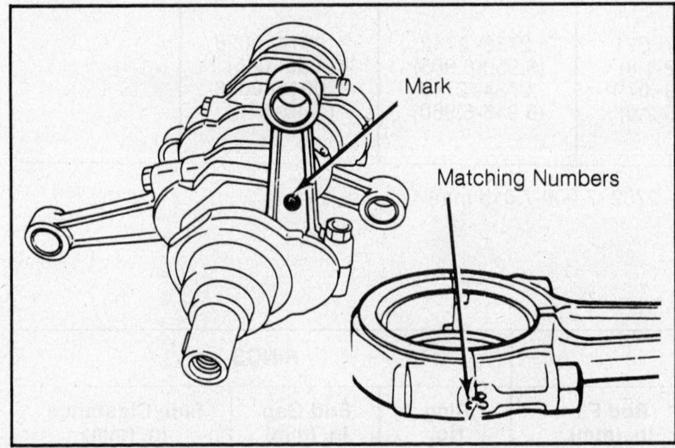

Courtesy of Subaru of America, Inc.

ENGINE OILING

ENGINE OILING SYSTEM

Oil is pressure fed by a timing belt driven trochoid type oil pump. Pump incorporates an oil relief and by-pass valve in its body. Oil pump is located externally on engine.

Oil from pump passes from main oil gallery to journals of crankshaft and camshafts. From there, oil goes to main bearings, piston pin bushings and cylinder walls. Oil passes through oil relief pipes to oil the rocker arms.

CRANKCASE CAPACITY

Crankcase capacity (including filter) is 4.2 qts. (4.0L) at the upper level mark, and 3.2 qts. (3.0L) at the lower level mark.

OIL FILTER

The oil filter is a disposable, full-flow paper cartridge type.

NORMAL OIL PRESSURE

The oil pressure should be 14 psi (1.5 kg/cm²) at 550 RPM, and 43 psi (3.0 kg/cm²) at 5000 RPM.

PRESSURE REGULATOR VALVE

Valve is nonadjustable. It opens at 57-64 psi (4.0-4.5 kg/cm²).

OIL PUMP

Removal

Remove timing belts as previously described. Align notches in oil pump pulley with oil pump mounting bolts, and remove bolts. Remove oil pump with oil filter, including outer rotor.

Disassembly

Remove oil filter from oil pump. Remove "O" ring. Remove oil pressure sending units. Remove oil pump pulley and pull out inner rotor. Unscrew plugs and remove by-pass spring and ball. Remove pressure relief spring and valve.

Inspection

Measure rotor-to-drive gear and rotor-to-body clearance. Measure rotor side clearance and measure diameters of rotor and drive gear. Replace any component that exceeds wear specification limits. Inspect relief valve spring, valve and pump body for wear or damage.

Reassembly

Using new "O" ring, reassemble in reverse order.

Installation

Install oil filter on pump. Reverse removal procedure to complete installation.

OIL PUMP SPECIFICATONS

Application	In. (mm)
Inner Rotor-to-Body Clearance	.002-.0063 (.05-.160)
Outer Rotor-to-Body Clearance	.004-.007 (.10-.18)
Inner Rotor O.D.	1.4035-1.4055 (35.650-35.700)
Outer Rotor O.D.	1.9665-1.9685 (49.950-50.000)
Relief Valve Spring Free Length	1.855 (47.10)

ENGINE COOLING

WATER PUMP

Removal

Drain coolant. Disconnect lower radiator hose and by-pass hose. Loosen water pump pulley nuts to hand tight. Loosen alternator mounting bolts and remove drive belt. Remove timing belt front cover. Remove water pump mounting bolts and water pump.

Installation

Install water pump, new gasket, drive belt and hoses. Gradually tighten bolts alternately and evenly in several steps to prevent leakage. The clamps for the lower radiator hose should be positioned properly to prevent interference with drive belts.

NOTE: For further information on cooling systems, see ENGINE COOLING section.

Subaru Engines

1.8L OHC 4-CYLINDER (Cont.)

ENGINE SPECIFICATIONS

GENERAL SPECIFICATIONS

Year	DISPLACEMENT		Fuel System	HP@RPM	Torque Ft. Lbs.@RPM	Compr. Ratio	BORE		STROKE	
	Cu. In.	Liters					In.	mm	In.	mm
1987										
1.8L	109	1.8	2-Bbl.	82@4800	101@2800	9.0:1	3.62	92	2.64	67
1.8L	109	1.8	Fuel Inj.	94@5200	101@2800	9.5:1	3.62	92	2.64	67
1.8L Turbo	109	1.8	Fuel Inj.	111@4800	134@2800	7.7:1	3.62	92	2.64	67

VALVES

Engine Size & Valve	Head Diam. In. (mm)	Face Angle	Seat Angle	Seat Width In. (mm)	Stem Diameter In. (mm)	Stem Clearance In. (mm)	Valve Lift In. (mm)
1.8L [1]							
Intake	.....	45°	45°	.047-.071 (1.2-1.8)	.2736-.2742 (6.950-6.965)	[2] .0014-.0026 (.035-.065)	
Exhaust	.....	45°	45°	.059-.079 (1.5-2.0)	.2734-.2740 (6.945-6.960)	[2] .0016-.0028 (.040-.070)	

[1] – Standard inside diameter of intake and exhaust valve guides are .2756-.2762 (7.000-7.015 mm)
[2] – Maximum clearance is .0059" (.149 mm)

PISTONS, PINS & RINGS

Engine	PISTONS	PINS		RINGS		
	Clearance In. (mm)	Piston Fit In. (mm)	Rod Fit In. (mm)	Ring No.	End Gap In. (mm)	Side Clearance In. (mm)
1.8L	[1] .0004-.0016 (.010-.040)	.00004-.00059 (.001-.015)	0-.0009 (0-.022)	No.1	[2] .0079-.0138 (.20-.35)	[2] .0016-.0031 (.04-.08)
				No. 2	[2] .0079-.0138 (.20-.35)	[2] .0012-.0028 (.03-.07)
				No. Oil	.012-.05 (.30-.9)	.....

[1] – Maximum clearance is .0024" (.060 mm).
[2] – Limit .059" (1.5mm).

CRANKSHAFT MAIN & CONNECTING ROD BEARINGS

Engine	MAIN BEARINGS				CONNECTING ROD BEARINGS		
	Journal Diam. In. (mm)	Clearance In. (mm)	Thrust Bearing	Crankshaft End Play In. (mm)	Journal Diam. In. (mm)	Clearance In. (mm)	Side Play In. (mm)
1.8L							
Front	2.1636-2.1642 (54.995-54.970)	[1] .0012-.0014 (.003-.036)	Center	[2] .0004-.0037 (.010-.095)	1.7715-1.7720 (44.995-45.010)	[3] .0008-.0028 (.020-.070)	[4] .0028-.013 (.07-.33)
Center	2.1636-2.1642 (54.995-54.970)	.0004-.0010 (.010-.025)					
Rear	2.1636-2.1642 (54.995-54.970)	.0012-.0014 (.003-.036)					

[1] – Limit front and rear, .0022" (.55mm); limit center, .0018" (.045 mm). [2] – Limit .0118" (.30 mm). [3] – Limit .004" (.10 mm).
[4] – Limit .016" (0.4 mm).

Subaru Engines

1.8L OHC 4-CYLINDER (Cont.)

ENGINE SPECIFICATIONS (Cont.)

CAMSHAFT

Engine	Journal Diam. In. (mm)	Clearance In. (mm)	Lobe Lift In. (mm)
1.8L [1] [2] [3]			
Front & Rear	1.4946-1.4953 (37.964-37.980)	[4] .0008-.0021 (.020-.054)	
Center	1.9080-1.9087 (48.464-48.480)	[4] .0008-.0021 (.020-.054)	

[1] – Maximum runout is .001" (.25 mm)
[2] – Lobe height is 1.571-1.575" (39.91-40.01 mm) for XT Non-Turbo and 1.565-1.569 (39.75-39.85 mm) for all others.
[3] – End play is .0012-.012" (.03-.26 mm).
[4] – Limit .0028" (.070 mm).

VALVE TIMING

Engine	INTAKE Open (BTDC)	INTAKE Close (ABDC)	EXHAUST Open (BBDC)	EXHAUST Close (ATDC)
1.8L				
Carbureted	3°	51°	47°	7°
Fuel Inj.				
Non-Turbo	12°	58°	58°	12°
Turbo	3°	51°	47°	7°

VALVE SPRINGS

Engine	Free Length In. (mm)	PRESSURE Lbs. @ In. (Kg @ mm) Valve Closed	PRESSURE Lbs. @ In. (Kg @ mm) Valve Open
1.8L [1]			
Outer Spring	1.996 (50.6)	49@1.63 (22@41.4)	.....
Inner Spring	1.980 50.29	21@1.516 (10@.059)	.....

[1] – Spring squareness is 0.087" (2.21).

TIGHTENING SPECIFICATIONS

Application	Ft. Lbs. (N.m)
Cylinder Head Nuts	
Step 1	22 (30)
Step 2	43 (58)
Step 3	47 (64)
Camshaft Case Bolts	13-15 (18-20)
Connecting Rod Nuts	29-31 (39-42)
Crankshaft Pulley Bolt	66-79 (89-107)
Crankcase Plug	46-56 (62-76)
Crankcase Halves	
8 mm Bolts	17-20 (23-27)
10 mm Bolts	29-35 (39-47)
Intake Manifold Bolts	13-16 (18-22)
Flywheel Bolts	51-55 (69-75)

Suzuki Engines

1.3L 4-CYLINDER

Samurai

NOTE: For engine repair procedures not covered in this article, see ENGINE OVERHAUL PROCEDURES article at the beginning of this section.

ENGINE CODING

ENGINE IDENTIFICATION

The Vehicle Identification Number (VIN) is stamped on a metal tag attached to left front pillar near the windshield. The sixth character of the VIN identifies engine size and the tenth character identifies model year. Engine model code and serial number are stamped on rear portion of left skirt of cylinder block.

ENGINE IDENTIFICATION CODE

Application	VIN
1.3L (Sixth Character)	5
1987 (Tenth Character)	H

ENGINE, MANIFOLDS & CYLINDER HEAD

ENGINE

NOTE: Remove engine and transmission as an assembly.

Removal

1) Disconnect battery cables. Disconnect positive battery cable and Black/Yellow lead wire from starter motor terminals. Disconnect White lead wire and coupler from alternator terminals. Disconnect lead wires from coolant temperature gauge and thermal switch. Gauge and switch are located on intake manifold. Disconnect ground wire from intake manifold.

2) Disconnect couplers from carburetor fuel cut-off solenoid, vent solenoid and mixture control soleniod. Disconnect couplers from the 3-way solenoid valve and vacuum switching valve. Remove warm air hose. Disconnect breather hose from air cleaner case. Remove air intake case from carburetor body and air inlet hose.

3) Disconnect accelerator cable from carburetor. Disconnect vacuum hoses of thermostatic controlled air cleaner. Disconnect canister from intake manifold. Remove fuel tank filler cap to release fuel vapor pressure in fuel tank. Reinstall fuel filler cap. Disconnect fuel supply line and return hoses from fuel pump.

4) Disconnect lead wire from oil pressure unit terminal and oxygen sensor lead wire at coupler. Disconnect lead wires of back-up light switch and 5th gear switch. Disconnect distributor lead wire at distributor coupler. Remove high tension wire from ignition coil. Drain radiator.

5) Disconnect hoses from thermostat cap and inlet pipe. Remove cooling fan and clutch. Remove fan shroud and radiator. Disconnect brake booster vacuum hose. Disconnect Black lead wire from distributor gear case at coupler. Remove 4 bolts fastening gear shift lever boot No. 2 and move boot upward. Move gear shift No. 1 to upper side of shift lever. Loosen 3 bolts on gear shift lever case and remove shift lever from lever case.

6) Raise vehicle. Disconnect muffler from exhaust manifold. Disconnect clutch cable from engine mounting bracket and clutch release lever. Drain transmission oil. Remove propeller shaft connecting transmission case to transfer case. Support engine with chain hoist.

NOTE: Install chain hoist on 2 hooks provided. One hook is mounted on intake manifold side and another on exhaust manifold side of engine.

7) Remove exhaust center pipe mounting bracket and 4 transmission mounting bolts. Remove pipe connected to chassis under transmission. Lower vehicle. Remove 4 bolts securing right and left engine mounting brackets. Ensure that all hoses, electrical wires and cables are disconnected. Remove engine. Remove clutch lower plate. Separate engine from transmission.

Installation

To install, reverse removal procedure. Tighten mounting bolts and nuts to specifications with weight of engine on insulators. Replace all fluids. Adjust all cables and linkages.

CYLINDER HEAD & MANIFOLDS

Removal

1) Drain cooling system. Disconnect upper radiator hose. Remove breather hose and air cleaner. Remove vacuum hose, fuel hose and coolant hose. Label and remove spark plug wires. Remove distributor and carburetor. Remove intake manifold.

2) Remove heat shield and exhaust manifold assembly. Remove timing belt cover. Loosen timing belt tensioner and secure. Remove timing belt from camshaft sprocket. Ensure that belt stays on crankshaft sprocket. Remove rocker arm cover.

3) Loosen cylinder head bolts in reverse order of tightening sequence. *See Fig. 1*. Loosen head bolts in 2 or 3 steps to prevent cylinder head warpage. Remove bolts and cylinder head.

Fig. 1: Cylinder Head Bolt Tightening Sequence

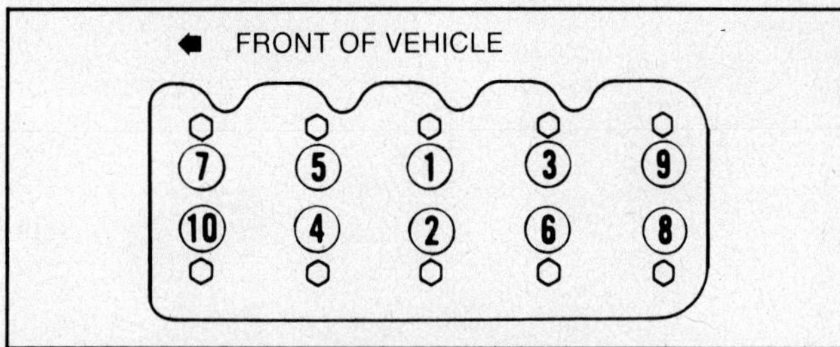

Courtesy of Suzuki of America Corp.

Inspection

1) Check cylinder head for evidence of water leakage or damage. Check cylinder head for cracks in intake and exhaust ports, combustion chambers and head surface. Check surface of head at 6 locations. *See Fig. 2*. Warpage limit of cylinder head is .002" (.05 mm).

2) If warpage exceeds specification, correct surface warpage by lapping head on a surface plate using No. 400 Waterproof Silicone Carbide abrasive paper. If lapping process is ineffective, replace cylinder head.

3) Check intake and exhaust manifold seating faces on cylinder head for warpage. Warpage limit for manifold seating faces is .004" (.10 mm). If warpage exceeds specification, correct warpage or replace cylinder head.

Installation

To install cylinder head, reverse removal process. Use new head and manifold gaskets. Tighten cylinder head and manifolds to specifications.

1.3L 4-CYLINDER (Cont.)

Fig. 2: Checking Cylinder Head Warpage

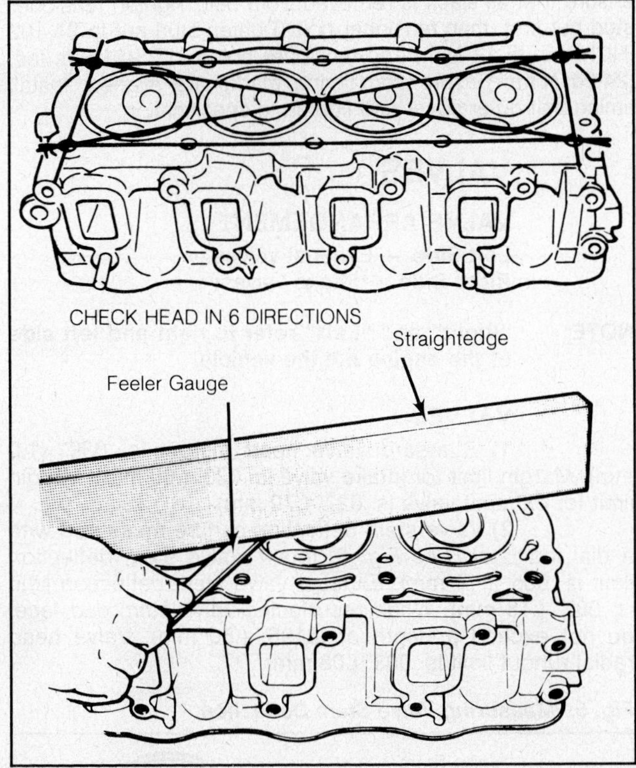

Courtesy of Suzuki of America Corp.

CAMSHAFT

ROCKER ARMS & SHAFTS

Removal

1) Remove breather hose and air cleaner. Remove alternator. Remove crankshaft pulley. Remove timing belt cover. Remove rocker arm cover. Loosen timing belt tensioner and secure. Remove timing belt from camshaft sprocket only. Remove camshaft sprocket. *See Fig. 3.*

2) Loosen 8 valve adjusting screws fully. Leave screws in place. Loosen rocker shaft securing screws. Remove rocker shaft, rocker arms and springs.

Installation

To install, reverse removal procedure. Rocker arm-to-shaft clearance limit is .0035" (.09 mm). Rocker arm shaft runout limit is .004" (.12 mm). If specifications are exceeded, replace shaft or rocker arms. If tip of rocker arm adjusting screw is worn, replace screw. If cam riding face of rocker arm is badly worn, replace rocker arm.

CAMSHAFT

Removal

Remove camshaft sprocket. *See Fig. 3.* Remove distributor and distributor case. Remove fuel pump and fuel pump push rod. Remove rocker cover, rocker arms and shafts. Remove camshaft from rear of head.

Inspection

1) Check cam lobes for wear or damage. If exhaust camshaft lobe height is less than 1.4724" (37.40 mm), replace camshaft. If intake camshaft lobe height is less than 1.4724" (37.40 mm), replace camshaft.

2) Camshaft journal dimension at sprocket end is 1.7687-1.7697" (44.925-44.950 mm). Remaining 4 journals are progressively stepped down in increments of .0079" (.20 mm). Check camshaft bearing journals and bearing surfaces for damage, wear or seizure.

3) Standard bearing clearance is .002-.0036" (.05-.091 mm). Bearing clearance limit is .0059" (.15 mm). If bearing wear exceeds specifications, replace cylinder head. Using dial indicator and "V" blocks, measure camshaft runout at center of shaft. If camshaft runout exceeds specifications, replace camshaft. Camshaft runout limit is .0039" (.10 mm).

Fig. 3: Installing Camshaft Sprocket

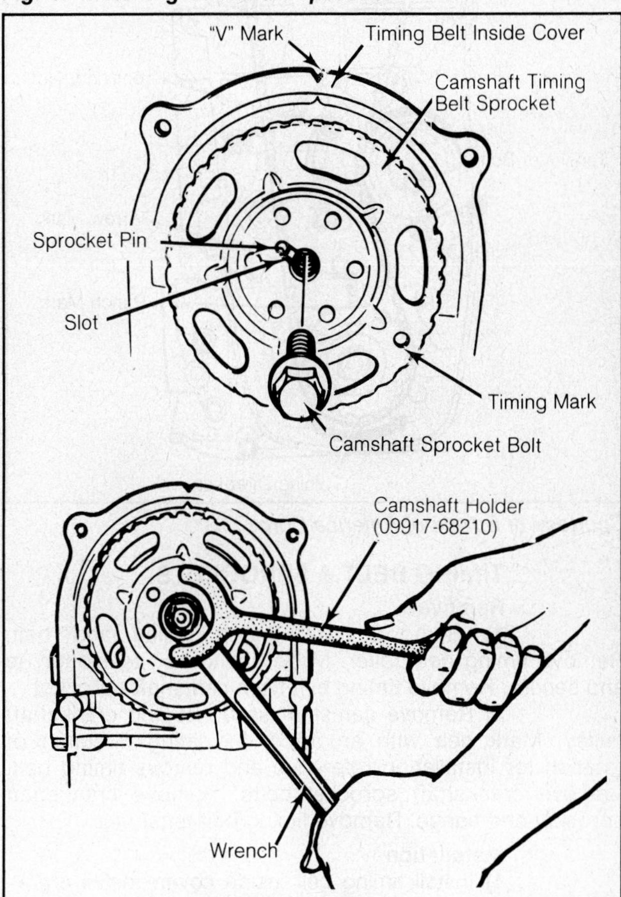

Courtesy of Suzuki of America Corp.

Installation

1) Lubricate camshaft lobes and camshaft bearing journals. Install camshaft in cylinder head. Install camshaft sprocket. Check camshaft end play. Install rocker arm assembly. Ensure that camshaft sprocket mark is aligned with timing mark on cylinder head. *See Fig. 4.*

2) Reverse removal procedure to complete installation. Temporarily set valve clearance to cold engine settings. Readjust to hot engine settings when engine is at normal operating temperature. Install rocker cover, air cleaner and breather hoses.

Suzuki Engines

1.3L 4-CYLINDER (Cont.)

Fig. 4: Timing Belt & Tensioner

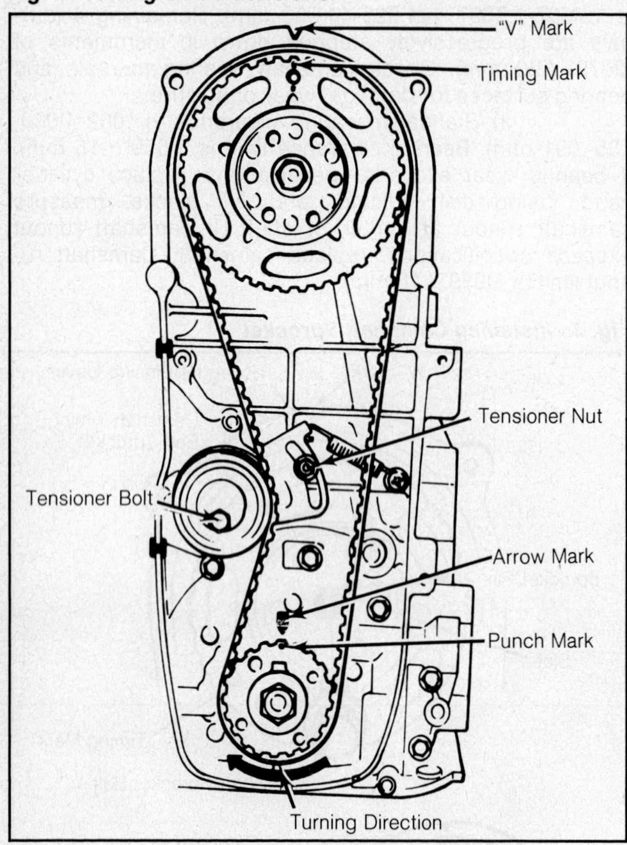

Courtesy of Suzuki of America Corp.

TIMING BELT & SPROCKETS

Removal

1) Remove water pump pulley and belt. Remove timing belt cover. Move timing belt tensioner up and secure. Remove timing belt from camshaft sprocket.

2) Remove camshaft sprocket and crankshaft pulley. Mark belt with an arrow indicating direction of rotation for installation reference and remove timing belt. Remove crankshaft sprocket bolts. Remove crankshaft sprocket and flange. Remove timing belt tensioner.

Installation

1) Install timing belt inside cover. Install crankshaft timing belt guide, key and sprocket. Concave side of timing belt guide faces oil pump. Tighten crankshaft timing belt sprocket bolt to specification. Install camshaft timing belt sprocket. Fit sprocket pin on camshaft into slot in camshaft sprocket. Tighten camshaft sprocket retaining bolt using Camshaft Holder (09917-68210). *See Fig. 3.*

2) Install timing belt tensioner plate on tensioner. Insert lug of tensioner plate in hole of tensioner. Install timing belt tensioner, tensioner plate and spring on cylinder block. Tighten tensioner bolts finger tight to allow movement during belt tension adjustment.

3) Loosen all valve adjusting screws fully before installing timing belt. Camshaft must be permitted to rotate freely during belt tension adjustment. Align timing mark on camshaft sprocket with "V" mark on timing belt inside cover.

4) Turn crankshaft clockwise until punch mark on crankshaft sprocket is aligned with arrow mark on oil pump. With timing marks aligned, install timing belt. Ensure that drive side of belt is free of slack. Move tensioner plate up with finger pressure and loosely secure tensioner bolt.

5) Turn crankshaft 2 revolutions clockwise to ensure that all slack is removed from belt. Tighten tensioner stud nut first, then tensioner bolt. Tighten stud nut to 84-102 INCH lbs. (9-12 N.m) and tensioner bolt to 17.5-21.5 ft. lbs. (24-30 N.m). Ensure that timing marks are aligned. Install timing belt outer cover and tighten to specification.

VALVES

VALVE ARRANGEMENT

Left Side - Exhaust valves.
Right Side - Intake valves.

NOTE: **"Right" and "Left" refer to right and left side of the engine not the vehicle.**

VALVES

1) Standard valve head margin is .039" (1.0 mm). Margin limit for intake valve is .023" (.60 mm). Margin limit for exhaust valve is .027" (.70 mm).

2) Valve stem deflection can be measured with a dial indicator. *See Fig. 5.* Intake valve stem deflection limit is .005" (.14 mm). Exhaust valve stem deflection limit is .007" (.18 mm). When resurfacing valve stem end face, do not exceed a depth of .0196" (.50 mm). Valve head radial runout limit is .003" (.08 mm).

Fig. 5: Measuring Valve Stem Deflection

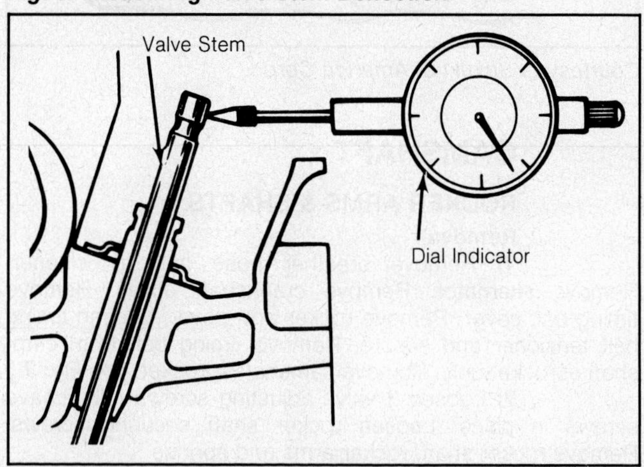

Courtesy of Suzuki of America Corp.

VALVE SEATS

Inspect valve seats for damage or wear. Replace or rework seat as necessary. Replace valve seat if specifications are exceeded. Remove valve seat by thinning down with a cutter. After thinning operation is completed, machine seat bore to proper size for replacement seat. Heat head to 480°F (249°C) and press in oversize seat. Install valve seat and machine to specifications.

VALVE STEM OIL SEALS

Install valve spring seat. Place lubricated stem seal on guide. Use Valve Stem Seal Installer (09917-98210) to press seal on guide with hand pressure only. When installer bottoms on head, seal is positioned properly. Do not reuse old seals. Avoid twisting seals when installing.

VALVE CLEARANCE ADJUSTMENT

1) Cylinder No. 1 is located at front of engine. Remove ignition timing inspection rubber plug from clutch

1.3L 4-CYLINDER (Cont.)

housing of transmission case. Turn crankshaft clockwise until line on flywheel with "T" mark above it lines up with match mark on transmission case. This will place No. 1 piston at TDC position.

2) Remove distributor cap. Ensure that rotor is pointing toward No. 1 distributor terminal. If rotor is not correctly positioned, rotate crankshaft clockwise 360 degrees until No. 1 piston is at TDC of compression stroke.

3) Ensure that engine has reached normal operating temperature. Remove valve cover. Loosen adjustment screw lock nuts. Adjust intake and exhaust valves of No. 1 cylinder, intake valve of No. 2 cylinder and exhaust valve of No. 3 cylinder.

4) Rotate crankshaft 360 degrees clockwise. Adjust intake valves of cylinder No. 3 and cylinder No. 4. Adjust exhaust valves of cylinder No. 2 and cylinder No. 4. Tighten adjusting screw lock nuts to specification. Install valve cover. Tighten cover bolts to specification.

Fig. 6: Valve Clearance Adjustment

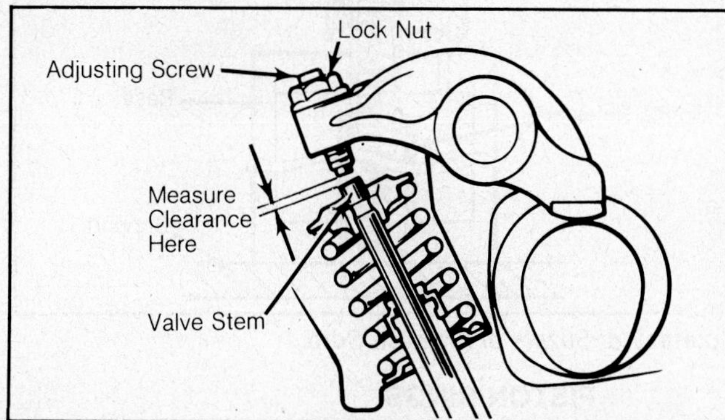

Courtesy of Suzuki of America Corp.

VALVE CLEARANCE SPECIFICATIONS

Valve	Hot	[1] Cold
Intake	.010" (.25 mm)	.006" (.15 mm)
Exhaust	.011" (.28 mm)	.007" (.18 mm)

[1] – Use for initial settings only.

VALVE GUIDES

1) Check valve stem clearance. If clearance exceeds specifications, replace with oversize valve guide. Oversize valve guide diameter is .0012" (.03 mm) larger than standard guide. Intake and exhaust guides are identical.

2) Use a valve guide remover to drive out guides toward combustion chamber. Ream guide bore in cylinder head with 12 mm Reamer (09916-37310). Heat cylinder head to 176-212°F (80-100°C).

3) Install new oversize guides in head. Valve guide protrusion for intake and exhaust guides is .550" (14.0 mm). Using Valve Guide Installer Attachment (09917-88210) and Valve Guide Installer Handle (09916-57321), drive in new valve guide until valve guide installer contacts cylinder head. Ream valve guide with 7 mm Reamer (09916-34520). Clean valve guide bore after reaming.

VALVE SPRINGS

1) Remove camshaft and rocker arms. Use Valve Spring Compressor (09916-14510) and Valve Lifter Attachment (09916-48210) to remove retainer locks. Remove retainers, springs, spring seats and valves. Keep components in proper order for reassembly.

2) Standard valve spring free length is 1.941" (49.30 mm). Replace spring if free length is 1.894" (48.10 mm) or less.

3) Use a valve spring tester to test spring pressure under load. Standard valve spring pressure is 54.7-64.3 lbs. (24.8-29.2 kg) at a compressed height of 1.63" (41.4 mm). Replace spring if pressure is less than 50.2 lbs. (22.8 kg) at a compressed height of 1.63" (41.5 mm).

4) Valve spring squareness should be .079" (2.0 mm) or less. If squareness exceeds specification, replace valve spring. Install valve springs with fine pitch end toward valve spring retainer.

PISTONS, PINS & RINGS

PISTON & ROD ASSEMBLY

Removal

1) Remove cylinder head. Remove oil level gauge guide, oil pan and screen. Remove flywheel using Flywheel Holder (09924-17810). Ensure that connecting rods and rod caps are marked for reassembly reference. Remove ridge from top of cylinder bores. Remove connecting rod caps.

2) Install protective hose over connecting rod bolts. Remove connecting rod and piston assembly through top of cylinder block. Scribe cylinder number on piston crown. Remove piston rings.

Installation

1) Mount connecting rod on aligner and inspect for bend and twist. Bend limit is .002" (.05 mm). Twist limit is .0039" (.10 mm). If necessary, replace connecting rod.

2) Lubricate all internal surfaces with engine oil before installation. Ensure that arrow on piston head faces front of engine. Ensure that lubrication jet in connecting rod faces intake side of engine.

3) Position piston ring gaps. *See Fig. 7.* Connecting rod side clearance limit is .0137" (.35 mm). Install cylinder head, oil pick-up screen and oil pan. Reverse removal procedure.

Fig. 7: Positioning Piston Ring Gaps

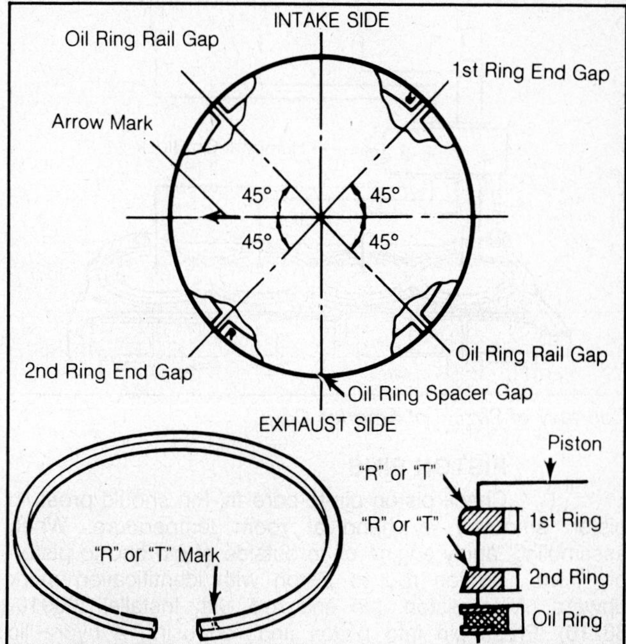

Courtesy of Suzuki of America Corp.

1.3L 4-CYLINDER (Cont.)

FITTING PISTONS

1) Inspect block for distortion of deck surface. Warpage limit is .0024" (.06 mm). Inspect block for cracks, scratches or other defects. Measure bores at 3 levels for taper, out-of-round and wear.

2) If bore wear exceeds .0015" (.04 mm), or taper and out-of-round exceed .0039" (.10 mm) from standard bore size, block must be rebored and oversize pistons installed. Pistons are available in .010" (.25 mm) and .020" (.50 mm) oversizes.

3) Check outside diameter of piston by measuring at a point .590" (15.0 mm) from bottom of skirt and at 90 degrees to pin bore. Standard pistons are available in 2 sizes in order to ensure correct piston-to-cylinder clearance. Each standard piston has a number "1" or number "2" stamped on piston crown.

4) The cylinder block is stamped with 4 numbers, either number "1" or number "2". The first number stamped on cylinder block indicates bore size of No. 1 cylinder. Second number indicates bore size of No. 2 cylinder. Third number indicates bore size of No. 3 cylinder. Fourth number indicates bore size of No. 4 cylinder.

5) Install piston stamped number "1" into cylinder stamped number "1". Use a piston stamped number "2" in a cylinder stamped number "2". *See Fig. 8.*

Fig. 8: Matching Pistons to Cylinders

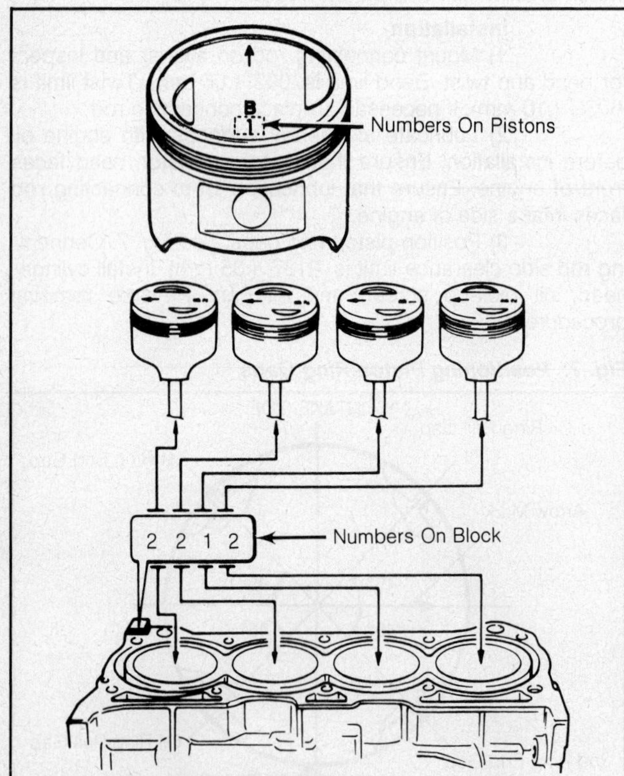

Courtesy of Suzuki of America Corp.

PISTON PINS

Check piston pin-to-bore fit. Pin should press in piston smoothly by hand at room temperature. When assembling, apply engine oil to outside of pin and to piston pin bore. Position rod to piston with identification mark upward. Align piston, pin and rod with Installer (09910-38210). Press pin into piston and rod using a hydraulic press. *See Fig. 9.*

Fig. 9: Installing Piston Pin

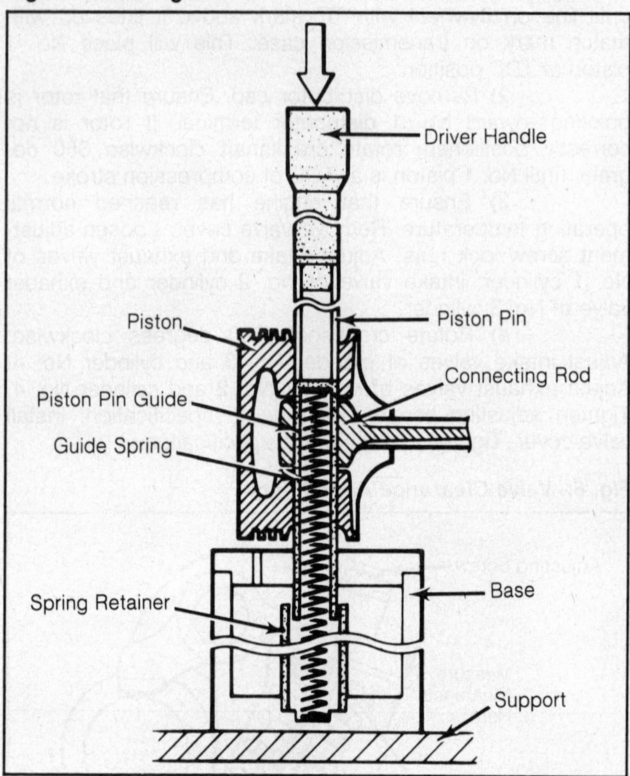

Courtesy of Suzuki of America Corp.

PISTON RINGS

1) Measure piston ring side and end clearance for all pistons. Replace rings as necessary. When replacing rings in cylinder bore not needing reconditioning, check ring end gap at lower part of cylinder that is less worn.

2) When replacing rings, ensure that same size ring is installed. Install rings on piston with end gaps staggered at 120 degree intervals. Ensure that ring gap is not in line with thrust face of pin bore. Manufacturer's marks face upward when rings are installed. *See Fig. 7.*

NOTE: **Install oil ring first without using a ring expander. Spacer gap should be installed not less than 45 degrees from rail gap. Rails should turn smoothly when installed.**

CRANKSHAFT & ROD BEARINGS

CRANKSHAFT MAIN BEARINGS

Removal & Installation

1) Remove front case. Remove timing belt, sprockets, pulley and tensioner. Remove flywheel, water pump, cylinder head assembly and oil pan. Remove rear main oil seal housing. Remove connecting rod caps. Remove main bearing caps. Remove crankshaft.

2) Keep bearings in order for reassembly reference. Inspect each bearing for peeling, melting, seizure or improper contact. Replace defective bearings. Measure outside diameter of crankshaft and connecting rod journals to determine out-of-round, taper and runout.

3) Use Plastigage method to measure bearing clearance. Main and connecting rod bearing out-of-round

1.3L 4-CYLINDER (Cont.)

and taper limit is .0004" (.010 mm). If clearance exceeds specifications, bearings should be replaced or undersize bearings installed. Undersize bearings are available in .010" (.25 mm).

4) To install, reverse removal procedure. Lubricate bearings before installing. Tighten bolts to specification in 3 steps. Tighten main bearing caps in order of center, No. 2, No. 4, front and rear main caps.

MAIN BEARING SELECTION

Standard Bearings

1) Standard main bearings are coded with a color patch and are available in 5 thickness variations. Upper half of bearing has an oil groove. Upper bearing half is installed in cylinder block. An arrow mark and number are embossed on each main bearing cap. *See Fig. 10*.

2) Ensure that arrow mark on main bearing cap faces toward crankshaft pulley. Bearing No. 1 is at crankshaft pulley end of engine. Remaining main bearings are numbered in ascending order.

Fig. 10: Stamped Numbers on Crank Webs of No. 2 & No. 3 Cylinders

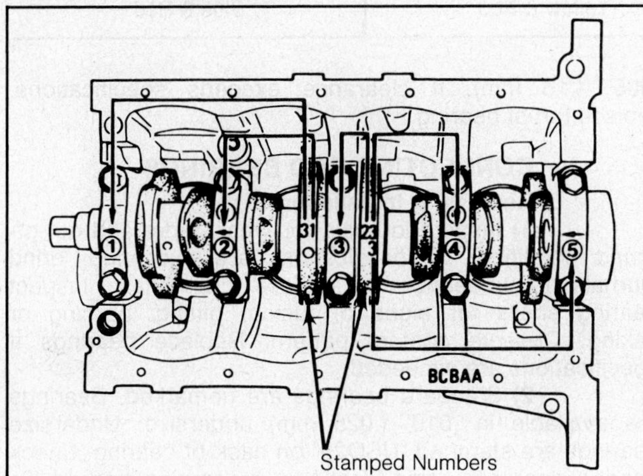

Courtesy of Suzuki of America Corp.

3) Crank webs of No. 2 and No. 3 cylinders have 5 stamped numbers. Journal diameter is represented by 3 numbers, "1", "2" and "3". *See Fig. 10*. The first, second, third, fourth and fifth stamped numbers on web indicate journal diameter of bearings "1", "2", "3", "4" and "5" respectively. Read stamped numbers from left to right.

4) Determine bearing cap bore diameter without bearing in place. Five letters are stamped on mating surface of cylinder block. *See Fig. 11*.

5) Cap bore diameter is represented by 3 letters, "A", "B" and "C". The first, second, third, fourth and fifth stamped letters indicate the cap bore diameter of bearing caps "1", "2", "3", "4" and "5" respectively. Five thickness variations of standard main bearings are available. Each color indicates thickness at center of bearing. *See Fig. 12*.

6) From number stamped on crankshaft webs of No. 2 and No. 3 cylinders and letters stamped on mating surface of cylinder block, refer to STANDARD BEARING CHART and determine new standard bearing to be installed on journal.

JOURNAL DIAMETERS

Stamped Numbers On Webs	Diameter In. (mm)
1	1.7714-1.7716 (44.994-45.000)
2	1.7712-1.7714 (44.988-44.994)
3	1.7710-1.7712 (44.982-44.988)

Fig. 11: Stamped Letters on Cylinder Block

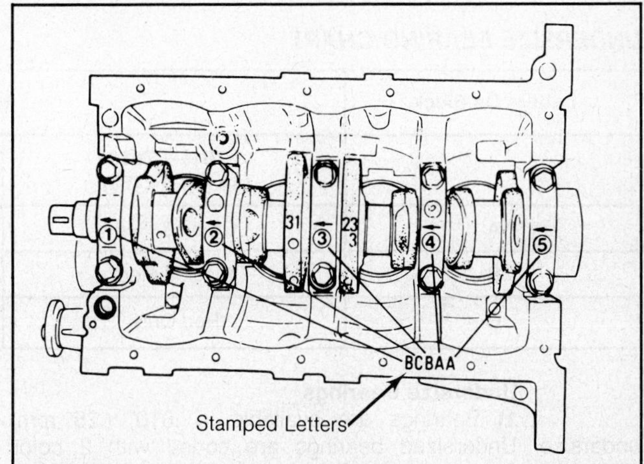

Courtesy of Suzuki of America Corp.

BEARING CAP BORE DIAMETERS

Stamped Letters On Block	Diameter In. (mm)
A	1.9292-1.9294 (49.000-49.006)
B	1.9294-1.9296 (49.006-49.012)
C	1.9296-1.9298 (49.012-49.018)

Fig. 12: Standard Main Bearing Color Mark

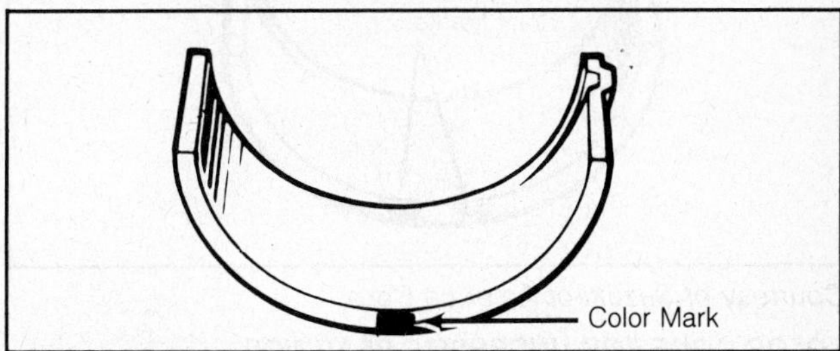

Courtesy of Suzuki of America Corp.

COLOR CODE FOR STANDARD BEARINGS

Color Painted	Bearing Thickness In. (mm)
Green	.0786-.0787 (1.996-1.999)
Black	.0787-.0788 (1.999-2.001)
No Paint	.0788-.0789 (2.001-2.004)
Yellow	.0789-.0790 (2.004-2.006)
Blue	.0790-.0791 (2.006-2.009)

Suzuki Engines

1.3L 4-CYLINDER (Cont.)

STANDARD BEARING CHART

Letters On Block	Numbers Stamped On Crankshaft Webs		
	1	2	3
A	Green	Black	No Color
B	Black	No Color	Yellow
C	No Color	Yellow	Blue

UNDERSIZE BEARING CHART

Letters On Block	Measured Journal Diameter In. (mm)		
	1.7616-1.7618 (44.744-44.750)	1.7614-1.7616 (44.738-44.744)	1.7612-1.7614 (44.732-44.738)
A	Green & Red	Black & Red	Red Only
B	Black & Red	Red Only	Yellow & Red
C	Red Only	Yellow & Red	Blue & Red

Undersize Bearings

1) Bearings are available in .010" (.25 mm) undersize. Undersized bearings are coded with 2 color patches and are available in 5 thickness variations. *See Fig. 13.*

2) Regrind journals .010" (.25 mm) undersize, to a finished diameter between 1.7612-1.7618" (44.732-44.750 mm). Using the finished diameter of the journal and letters stamped on mating surface of cylinder block, refer to UNDERSIZE BEARING CHART and select the undersized bearing to be installed. Use Plastigage measuring method to insure correct clearance of installed undersize bearing.

Fig. 13: Undersize Main Bearing Color Marks

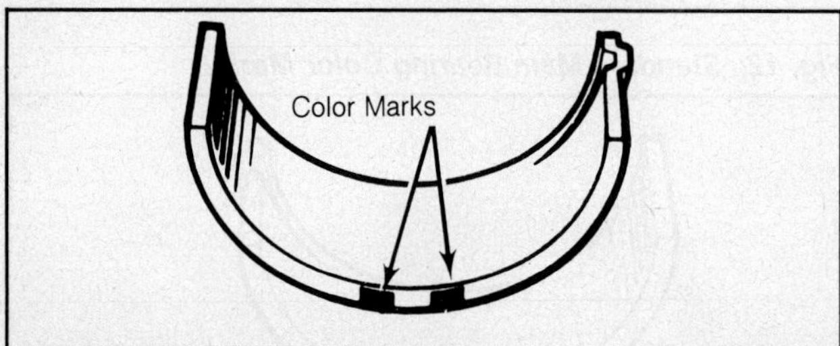

Courtesy of Suzuki of America Corp.

COLOR CODE FOR UNDERSIZE BEARINGS

Color Painted	Bearing Thickness In. (mm)
Green & Red	.0835-.0836 (2.121-2.123)
Black & Red	.0836-.0837 (2.123-2.126)
Red Only	.0837-.0838 (2.126-2.129)
Yellow & Red	.0838-.0839 (2.129-2.131)
Blue & Red	.0839-.0840 (2.131-2.134)

THRUST BEARING

With crankshaft bearing caps installed, check thrust clearance (end play) by inserting feeler gauge between center main bearing and crankshaft thrust face. Standard thickness of thrust bearing is .0984" (2.50 mm). Oversize thrust bearings are available in increments of .005" (.13 mm). If clearance exceeds specifications, replace thrust bearing.

CONNECTING ROD BEARINGS

Removal & Installation

1) Inspect journals for wear, taper and out-of-round condition. If specifications are exceeded, grind journals to undersize or replace crankshaft. Inspect bearing shells for signs of fusion, pitting, burning or flaking. Observe contact pattern. Replace bearings if specifications are exceeded.

2) Standard bearings are unmarked. Bearings are available in .010" (.025 mm) undersize. Undersize bearings are stamped "USO25" on back of bearing. Check bearing clearance using Plastigage measuring method. To install, reverse removal procedure. Tighten connecting rod nuts to specification.

REAR MAIN BEARING OIL SEAL

Removal

Remove flywheel. Remove oil seal housing. If oil seal is to be replaced, remove seal.

Inspection

Inspect oil seal housing for wear or damage. If seal lip is worn or damaged, replace seal. *See Fig. 14.*

Fig. 14: Rear Main Oil Seal & Housing

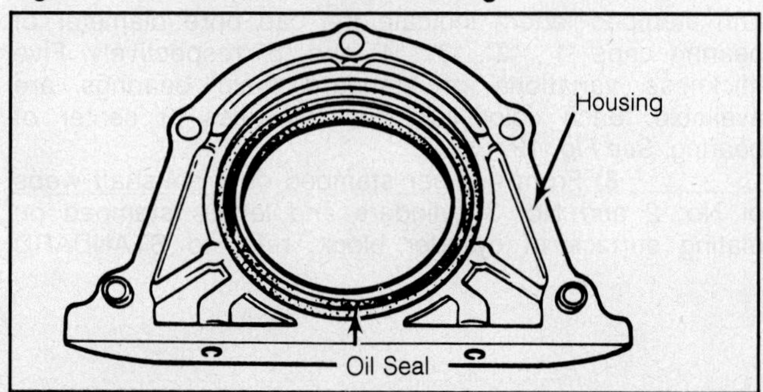

Courtesy of Suzuki of America Corp.

Suzuki Engines

1.3L 4-CYLINDER (Cont.)

Installation

Install oil seal in housing. Apply oil to seal lip. Install oil seal housing and new gasket. Tighten housing bolts to specification. Oil seal housing gasket will bulge after mounting bolts have been tightened. Trim excess gasket material flush with cylinder block and seal housing.

ENGINE OILING

ENGINE OILING SYSTEM

A force-feed type lubrication system is used. The oil pump is a trochoid-type pump mounted on the forward portion of the crankshaft.

CRANKCASE CAPACITY

Crankcase capacity is 3.9 qts. (3.7L). Capacity includes filter.

NORMAL OIL PRESSURE

Normal oil pressure is 42.7-59.7 psi (3.0-4.2 kg/cm²) at 3000 RPM.

OIL PUMP

Removal

1) Position No. 1 piston at TDC of compression stroke. Remove water pump, crankshaft pulley and alternator. Remove timing belt cover and timing belt. Drain engine oil. Remove oil dipstick and oil pan. Remove oil pump pick-up screen.

2) Remove oil pump assembly. Remove oil pump rotor plate. Mark outer gear with felt pen for reassembly reference. Remove inner and outer oil pump gears. Remove plug, relief spring and relief valve.

Inspection

1) Inspect oil pump housing for cracks or damage. Inspect oil screen for clogging or damage. Inspect oil screen "O" ring. Inspect oil pump gears for worn or damaged teeth. Ensure that relief valve slides smoothly in bore. Inspect pressure relief spring for damaged coils.

2) Using a feeler gauge, measure radial clearance between outer rotor and case. Radial clearance limit is .0122" (.31 mm). If clearance exceeds specification, replace outer rotor or case. *See Fig. 15.*

Fig. 15: Checking Oil Pump Radial Clearance

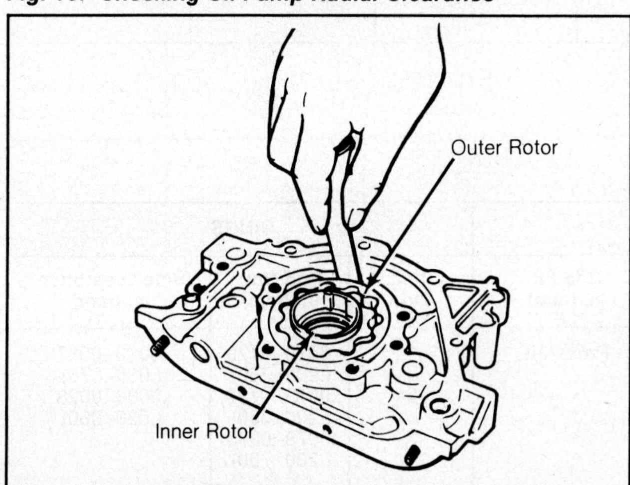

Courtesy of Suzuki of America Corp.

3) Using a feeler gauge and straightedge, measure side clearance. Side clearance limit is .0059" (.15 mm). If clearance exceeds specification, replace outer rotor or case. *See Fig. 16.*

Fig. 16: Checking Oil Pump Side Clearance

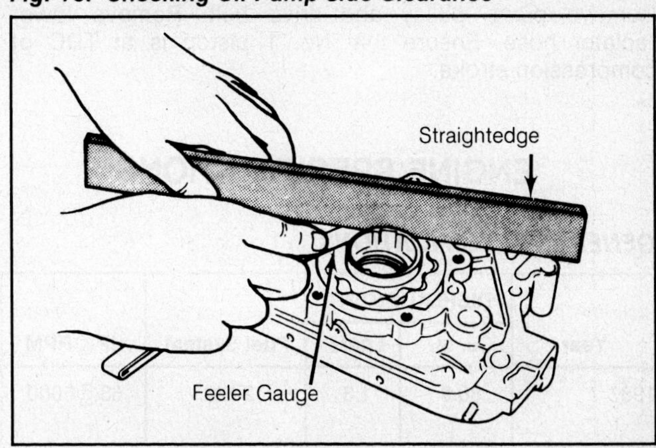

Courtesy of Suzuki of America Corp.

Installation

1) To install, reverse removal procedure. Ensure that gears are assembled in same direction as originally installed. Apply thin coat of engine oil to inner and outer rotors, lip portion of oil seal and inside surfaces of oil pump case and plate. Install inner and outer rotors.

2) Install gear plate. Tighten 5 screws to specification. Ensure that gears turn freely by hand after gear plate is installed. Install 2 oil pump pins, new dip stick "O" ring, new seal for oil pick-up tube and new oil pump gasket. Use Oil Seal Guide (09926-18210) to prevent damage to oil seal during installation of oil pump. *See Fig. 17.*

3) Apply engine oil to guide and install pump. Install dipstick guide with new seal. Tighten bolts to specification. Install oil pan using silicone type sealant. Tighten bolts to specification.

Fig. 17: Oil Seal Guide Installation

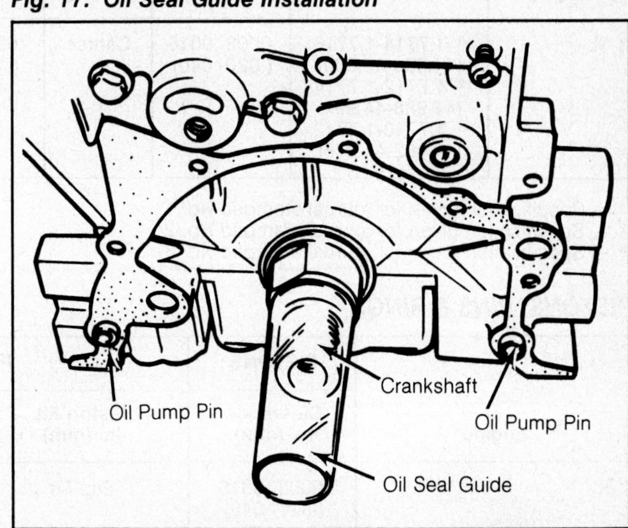

Courtesy of Suzuki of America Corp.

Suzuki Engines

1.3L 4-CYLINDER (Cont.)

ENGINE COOLING

WATER PUMP

Removal

1) Drain cooling system. Disconnect battery. Remove pump pulley and drive belt. Remove lower radiator hose. Ensure that No. 1 piston is at TDC of compression stroke.

2) Remove crankshaft pulley and timing belt cover. Loosen timing belt tensioner bolt and stud nut. Remove timing belt, camshaft sprocket and timing belt tensioner. Remove pump.

Installation

To install, use new gasket and reverse removal procedure.

NOTE: **For more information, see ENGINE COOLING SYSTEMS articles at the end of this section.**

ENGINE SPECIFICATIONS

GENERAL SPECIFICATIONS

Year	DISPLACEMENT		Fuel System	HP@RPM	Torque Ft. Lbs.@RPM	Compr. Ratio	BORE		STROKE	
	Cu. In.	Liters					In.	mm	In.	mm
1987	80.8	1.3	2-Bbl.	63@6000	74@3500	8.9:1	2.91	74.0	3.03	77.0

VALVES

Engine Size & Valve	Head Diam. In. (mm)	Face Angle	Seat Angle	Seat Width In. (mm)	Stem Diameter In. (mm)	Stem Clearance In. (mm)	Valve Lift In. (mm)
1.3L							
Intake	.....	45°	45°	.0512-.0590 (1.300-1.500)	.2742-.2748 (6.965-6.980)	.0008-.0019 (.020-.050)	.....
Exhaust	.....	45°	45°	.0512-.0590 (1.300-1.500)	.2737-.2742 (6.950-6.965)	.0014-.0025 (.035-.065)	.....

CRANKSHAFT MAIN & CONNECTING ROD BEARINGS

Engine	MAIN BEARINGS				CONNECTING ROD BEARINGS		
	Journal Diam. In. (mm)	Clearance In. (mm)	Thrust Bearing	Crankshaft End Play In. (mm)	Journal Diam. In. (mm)	Clearance In. (mm)	Side Play In. (mm)
1.3L	[1] 1.7714-1.7716 (44.994-45.000) [2] 1.7712-1.7714 (44.988-44.994) [3] 1.7710-1.7712 (44.982-44.988)	.0008-.0016 (.020-.040)	Center	.0044-.0122 (.112-.310)	1.6529-1.6535 (41.982-42.000)	.0012-.0019 (.030-.050)	.0039-.0078 (.100-.200)

[1] – Specification given for journal stamped No. 1.
[2] – Specification given for journal stamped No. 2.
[3] – Specification given for journal stamped No. 3.

PISTONS, PINS & RINGS

Engine	PISTONS	PINS		RINGS		
	Clearance In. (mm)	Piston Fit In. (mm)	Rod Fit In. (mm)	Ring No.	End Gap In. (mm)	Side Clearance In. (mm)
1.3L	.0008-.0016 (.020-.040)	Slip Fit	Press Fit	1	.0079-.0129 (.200-.330)	.0012-.0027 (.030-.070)
				2	.0079-.0137 (.200-.350)	.0008-.0023 (.020-.060)
				3	.0079-.0275 (.200-.700)	.....

Suzuki Engines

1.3L 4-CYLINDER (Cont.)

ENGINE SPECIFICATIONS (Cont.)

CAMSHAFT

Engine	Journal Diam. In. (mm)	Clearance In. (mm)	Lobe Lift In. (mm)
1.3L	[1] 1.7372-1.7381 (44.125-44.150) [2] 1.7451-1.7460 (44.325-44.350) [3] 1.7530-1.7539 (44.525-44.550) [4] 1.7609-1.7618 (44.725-44.750) [5] 1.7687-1.7697 (44.925-44.950)	.002-.0036 (.05-.091)	.....

[1] – Specification given for journal No. 1.
[2] – Specification given for journal No. 2.
[3] – Specification given for journal No. 3.
[4] – Specification given for journal No. 4.
[5] – Specification given for journal No. 5.

VALVE SPRINGS

Engine	Free Length In. (mm)	PRESSURE Lbs. @ In. (Kg @ mm)	
		Valve Closed	Valve Open
1.3L	1.9409 (49.300)	54.7-64.3 @ 1.63 (24.8-29.2 @ 41.5)	.....

TIGHTENING SPECIFICATIONS

Application	Ft. Lbs. (N.m)
Camshaft Sprocket Bolt	41-46 (56-62)
Connecting Rod Cap Nuts	24-27 (33-36)
Crankshaft Sprocket Bolt	48-54 (65-75)
Cylinder Head Bolts	46-52 (62-70)
Exhaust Manifold Bolts	13-20 (18-28)
Flywheel Bolts	42-47 (57-65)
Intake Manifold Bolts	13-20 (18-28)
Main Bearing Cap Bolts	37-41 (50-56)
Oil Pan Drain Plug	22-29 (30-40)
Rocker Arm Adjustment Lock Nuts	11-14 (15-19)
Transmission Case Bolts	16-25 (22-35)
	INCH Lbs. (N.m)
Alternator Pulley Bolts	90-108 (10-13)
Crankshaft Pulley Bolts	90-108 (10-13)
Distributor Case Bolts	72-102 (8-12)
Oil Pan Bolts	84-102 (9-12)
Oil Pressure Switch	102-126 (12-15)
Oil Pump Mounting Bolts	84-102 (9-12)
Oil Pump Strainer Bolts	84-102 (9-12)
Rear Main Seal Bolts	90-108 (10-13)
Rocker Arm Shaft Screws	84-102 (9-12)
Rocker Cover Bolts	36-42 (4-5)
Timing Belt Outer Cover Bolts	84-102 (9-12)
Water Pump Mounting Bolts	84-102 (9-12)
Water Pump Pulley Bolts	90-108 (10-13)

Toyota Engines

1.5L & 1.6L 8-VALVE 4-CYLINDER

Corolla, Tercel Wagon

NOTE: **For engine repair procedures not covered in this article, see ENGINE OVERHAUL PROCEDURES article at the beginning of this section.**

ENGINE CODING

ENGINE IDENTIFICATION

The serial number and code are stamped on left rear of engine block.

ENGINE IDENTIFICATION CODES

Application	Code
Corolla (1.6L)	4A-C
Tercel Wagon (1.5L)	3A-C

ENGINE, MANIFOLDS & CYLINDER HEAD

ENGINE

NOTE: **On Tercel Wagon models, separate engine from transaxle before removal. On Corolla models, remove engine and transmission or transaxle as a unit.**

Removal (Corolla RWD & Tercel Wagon)

1) Mark hinge locations and remove hood. Remove battery and carrier. Remove air cleaner assembly. Drain coolant. On 3A-C, wrap drive shaft boots with shop towels. On A/C equipped models, remove fan shroud. On all models, remove radiator, alternator, brackets, drive belts, fan, water pump (3A-C only) and hoses as necessary.

2) Detach A/C belt, compressor, condenser, power steering belt and pump with bracket (if equipped). Set assemblies aside. Do not discharge systems. Remove engine sub-wiring harness and set aside. On 3A-C, remove 4 upper transaxle-to-engine mount bolts. On automatic transmission equipped models, disconnect throttle linkage and oil cooler lines.

3) On 4A-C engines, remove emission control valve set. Disconnect oxygen sensor and air hose from air suction reed valve. From inside of vehicle, remove console box and disconnect shift lever. On all models, raise and support vehicle. Drain engine oil. On 3A-C, remove front exhaust pipe and bracket, differential plate bolts and oil cooler pipe (if equipped).

4) On 4A-C engines, remove front exhaust pipe and brackets from catalytic converter. Scribe alignment marks on differential and drive shaft flanges. Remove drive shaft assembly. Insert Transmission Shaft Plug (09325-12010) to prevent oil leakage.

5) On all models, disconnect engine-to-chassis electrical connections at engine. Disconnect carburetor linkage, fuel lines and heater hoses. On 3A-C manual transaxle, remove starter cable and windshield washer tank. Disconnect clutch pedal tension spring and release cable. On automatic transaxle equipped models, remove starter and torque converter cover.

6) On 4A-C engines, disconnect fuel line at fuel pump and front exhaust pipe at manifold flange. Disconnect speedometer cable and back-up light switch. Remove clutch slave cylinder. On automatic transmission equipped models, disconnect oil cooler lines and remove power steering gear housing. Place jack under transmission.

7) Remove engine rear mount and ground cable. Remove engine mount bolts from both side mounts. Attach hoist chain to engine and take up slack. Lift engine/transmission assembly from vehicle. Use caution to avoid damage to clutch and brake fluid reservoirs. Disconnect transmission and starter from engine after removal.

8) On 3A-C, support transaxle with floor jack. Remove engine mounts. Attach hoist to engine hangers. With hoist supporting engine, remove remaining lower transaxle mount bolts. Ensure all wiring and hoses are detached from engine before removal.

9) On manual transaxle equipped models, carefully lift and remove engine. On automatic transaxle equipped models, remove 4 torque converter mount bolts. Pull engine about 2" forward, disconnect torque converter and remove engine. Suspend clutch or converter housing.

Installation

1) With 4A-C engine connected to transmission, install starter. Carefully lower engine into position. Replace engine mount bolts and nuts. On manual transmission equipped models, install clutch slave cylinder and bleed hydraulic system as necessary. On 3A-C, install engine and connect to transaxle.

2) On all models, install all wiring, heater and vacuum hoses. Adjust drive belts. Add proper amount of engine and transmission oil and coolant. To complete installation, reverse removal procedure. Start engine and check for leaks.

Removal (Corolla FWD)

1) Remove battery and hood. Drain coolant from radiator and engine. Drain engine oil and transaxle fluid. Remove air cleaner hose and air cleaner. Remove coolant reservoir tank.

2) Disconnect fan motor wire. Disconnect radiator upper side hose from engine block. Disconnect radiator lower side hose from thermostat housing. Remove radiator with shroud.

3) Disconnect actuator cable, accelerator cable, and transaxle throttle cable from carburetor. Disconnect the Vacuum Control Valve (VCV), the oxygen sensor, back-up/neutral start switch, and coolant temperature switch.

4) Disconnect distributor lead, starter wire, electrical wires from engine, transaxle, oil pressure switch and A/C compressor.

5) Disconnect alternator wire, coolant temperature sender gauge, Electrical Air Bleed Control Valve (EBCV), Cold Mixer Heater (CMH), and fuel-cut solenoid. Disconnect vacuum hoses. Disconnect fuel hoses from fuel pump. Disconnect heater hoses from water inlet housing and cylinder head rear plate.

6) Disconnect power steering pump and A/C compressor without discharging and set aside. Disconnect speedometer cable from transaxle. On manual transaxle equipped models, remove clutch release cylinder without disconnecting pipe and hose.

7) Remove control cable clip and washers. Disconnect control cable from shift outer lever and select outer lever. Raise and support vehicle. Disconnect exhaust pipe from exhaust manifold. Disconnect front and rear mounting from crossmember.

1.5L & 1.6L 8-VALVE 4-CYLINDER (Cont.)

Fig. 1: Exploded View of Engine Cylinder Head & Block

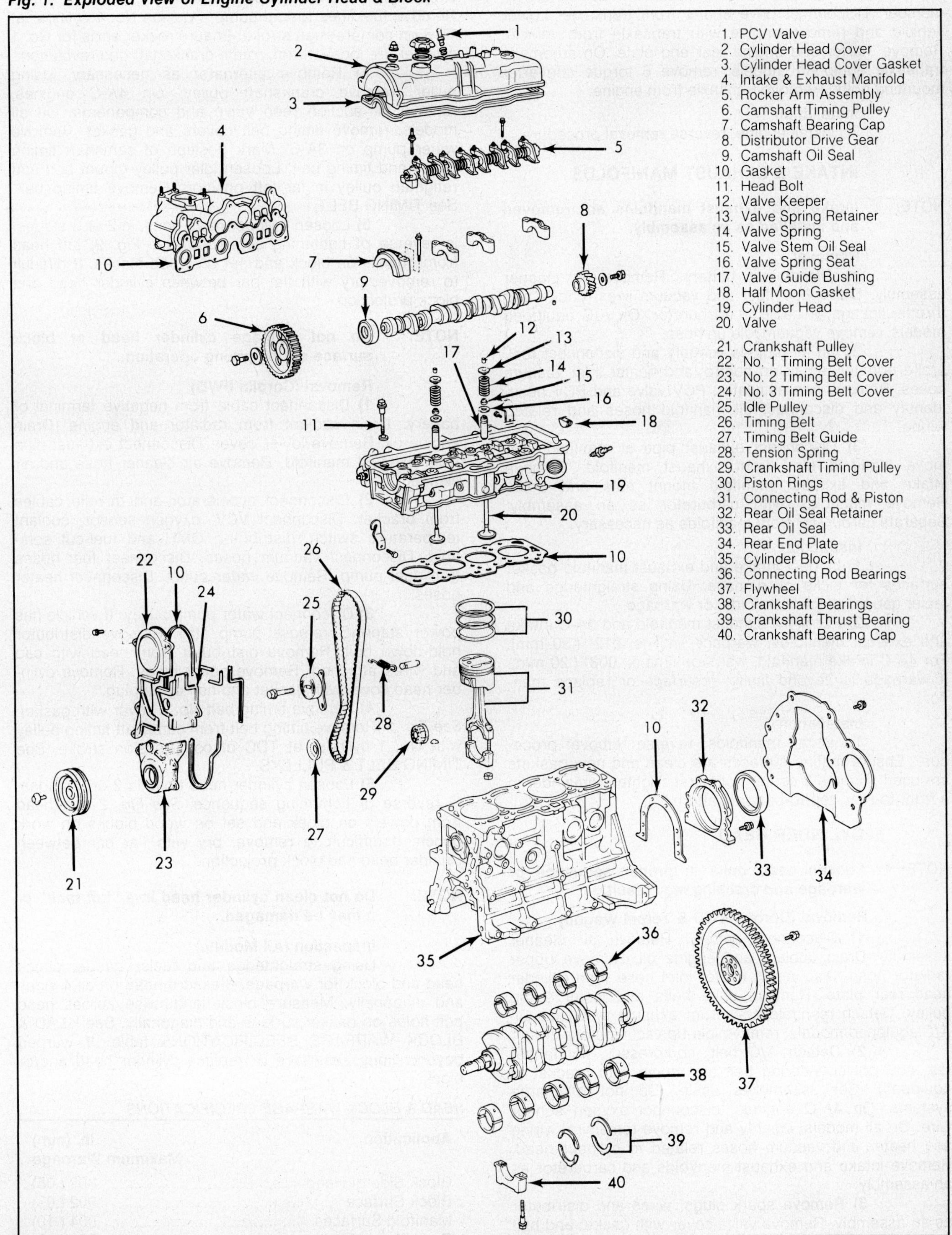

Courtesy of Toyota Motor Sales, U.S.A., Inc.

Toyota Engines

1.5L & 1.6L 8-VALVE 4-CYLINDER (Cont.)

8) Remove engine mounting center crossmember. Disconnect drive shafts from transaxle. Lower vehicle and remove engine with transaxle from vehicle. Remove starter and engine rear end plate. On automatic transaxle equipped models, remove 6 torque converter mounting bolts. Remove transaxle from engine.

Installation

To install engine, reverse removal procedure.

INTAKE & EXHAUST MANIFOLDS

NOTE: **Intake and exhaust manifolds are removed and installed as an assembly.**

Removal

1) Disconnect battery. Remove air cleaner assembly. Disconnect fuel and vacuum lines, choke and throttle linkage or cable at carburetor. On A/C equipped models, remove vacuum idle up hose.

2) On all models, identify and disconnect fuel, brake booster, emission control and heater inlet vacuum hoses. Remove heat insulator, PCV valve and PCV hose. Identify and disconnect all manifold hoses and related wiring.

3) Disconnect exhaust pipe at manifold. Remove manifold stay from exhaust manifold. Remove intake and exhaust manifold mount nuts and bolts. Remove manifolds with carburetor as an assembly. Separate carburetor from manifolds as necessary.

Inspection

1) Inspect intake and exhaust manifold gasket surfaces for nicks or damage. Using straightedge and feeler gauge, check manifolds for warpage.

2) For 4A-C exhaust manifold and 3A-C intake and exhaust manifolds, warpage limit is .012" (.30 mm). For 4A-C intake manifold, warpage limit is .008" (.20 mm). If warpage is beyond limits, resurface or replace manifolds.

Installation

To install manifolds, reverse removal procedure. Ensure mating surfaces are clean and new gaskets are used. Tighten 2 center bolts first. Tighten remainder in a front-to-rear, top-to-bottom pattern.

CYLINDER HEAD

NOTE: **Loosen head bolts in proper sequence or warpage and cracking may result.**

Removal (Corolla RWD & Tercel Wagon)

1) Disconnect battery. Remove air cleaner assembly. Drain coolant and engine oil. Remove upper radiator hose. Disconnect heater inlet hose from cylinder head rear plate. Remove drive belts and water pump pulley. Detach manifold stay from exhaust manifold. On A/C equipped models, remove idle-up vacuum hose.

2) Detach A/C belt, compressor, condenser fan, and power steering belt and pump with bracket (if equipped). Set assemblies aside. Do not discharge systems. On 4A-C engines, disconnect oxygen sensor wire. On all models, identify and remove remaining wiring and heater and vacuum hoses related to cylinder head. Remove intake and exhaust manifolds and carburetor as an assembly.

3) Remove spark plugs, wires and distributor as an assembly. Remove valve cover with gasket and half circle plug, alternator upper bracket and water outlet. Remove fuel lines to fuel pump. Position No. 1 cylinder at TDC on compression stroke. Ensure rocker arms for No. 1 cylinder are loose. If not, rotate crankshaft one revolution.

4) Remove alternator as necessary. Using puller, remove crankshaft pulley. On 4A-C engines, remove air suction reed valve and components. On all models, remove timing belt covers and gasket. Remove water pump on 3A-C. Mark position of camshaft timing pulley and timing belt. Loosen idler pulley mount bolt and retighten pulley in far left position. Remove timing belt. See TIMING BELT.

5) Loosen cylinder head bolts, in 2 or 3 stages, in reverse of tightening sequence. *See Fig. 2.* Lift head from dowels on block and set on wood blocks. If difficult to remove, pry with flat bar between cylinder head and block projection.

NOTE: **Do not damage cylinder head or block surface during prying operation.**

Removal (Corolla FWD)

1) Disconnect cable from negative terminal of battery. Drain coolant from radiator and engine. Drain engine oil. Remove lower cover. Disconnect exhaust pipe from exhaust manifold. Remove air cleaner hose and air cleaner.

2) Disconnect accelerator and throttle cables from bracket. Disconnect VCV, oxygen sensor, coolant temperature switch, distributor, CMH and fuel-cut solenoid. Disconnect vacuum hoses. Disconnect fuel hoses from fuel pump. Remove water outlet. Disconnect heater hoses.

3) Disconnect water pump pulley. If vehicle has power steering, remove pump stay. Remove distributor hold-down bolt. Remove distributor from head with cap and wires attached. Remove spark plugs. Remove cylinder head cover with gasket and half circle plug.

4) Remove timing belt No. 1 cover with gasket. *See Fig. 1.* Remove timing belt from camshaft timing pulley with No. 1 cylinder at TDC of compression stroke. See TIMING BELT & PULLEYS.

5) Loosen cylinder head bolts in 2 or 3 stages, in reverse of tightening sequence. *See Fig. 2.* Lift head from dowels on block and set on wood blocks on work bench. If difficult to remove, pry with flat bar between cylinder head and block projection.

NOTE: **Do not clean cylinder head in a "hot tank" or it may be damaged.**

Inspection (All Models)

Using straightedge and feeler gauge, check head and block for warpage. Measure head on all 4 sides and diagonally. Measure block lengthwise across head bolt holes on gasket surface and diagonally. See HEAD & BLOCK WARPAGE SPECIFICATIONS table. If warped beyond limits, resurface or replace cylinder head and/or block.

HEAD & BLOCK WARPAGE SPECIFICATIONS

Application	In. (mm) Maximum Warpage
Block Side of Head	.002 (.05)
Block Surface	.002 (.05)
Manifold Surfaces	.004 (.10)
Resurfacing Limit	.004 (.10)

1.5L & 1.6L 8-VALVE 4-CYLINDER (Cont.)

Installation

1) Ensure mating surfaces are clean and camshaft caps and rocker arm assembly are tightened properly. Apply oil to all sliding and rotating surfaces.

2) Install new head gasket and cylinder head. Tighten head bolts gradually, in 3 stages. *See Fig. 2.* Install timing belt and check valve timing and timing belt tension. To complete installation, reverse removal procedure.

3) Set valve clearance. Fill cooling system. Refill engine with oil. Check and set ignition timing and idle speed. Start engine and check for leaks. Run engine for several minutes, let cool and recheck cylinder head bolt torque.

Fig. 2: Cylinder Head Bolt Tightening Sequence

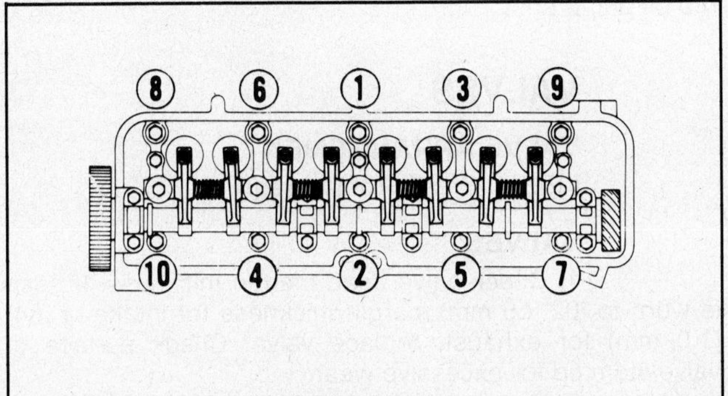

Courtesy of Toyota Motor Sales, U.S.A., Inc.

CAMSHAFT

TIMING BELT & PULLEYS

NOTE: **Do not bend or twist timing belt. Keep belt free of oil, water or dust.**

Removal

1) On Corolla models, remove right wheel and under cover. Drain cooling system if necessary. Disconnect radiator inlet hose and loosen water pump pully bolts. Remove alternator drive belt and alternator. Remove A/C compressor drive belt, A/C compressor and bracket (if equipped). Remove vane drive belt.

2) On Tercel Wagon models, remove radiator and air cleaner assembly. Remove drive belts. On all models, remove water pump pulley. *See Fig. 1.* On Tercel Wagon models, remove idler pulley bracket together with pulley (if equipped). Remove cylinder head cover. On Corolla models, remove timing belt covers and gaskets.

NOTE: **If reusing old timing belt, draw directional arrow on belt in direction of engine revolution. Place match marks on crankshaft and camshaft sprockets and belt.**

3) On all models, set No. 1 cylinder at TDC on compression stroke. Ensure No. 1 rocker arms are loose. Remove crankshaft pulley. Remove remaining timing belt cover and gasket. Remove timing belt guide.

4) Loosen idler pulley mount bolt, position pulley at far left and retighten mount bolt. Remove timing belt, idler pulley, and tension spring. Remove crankshaft timing sprocket. On Corolla models, remove cylinder head cover and gasket. On all models, remove camshaft timing sprocket.

5) On Corolla models, place jack under engine. Remove 2 under covers and 4 mounting bolts. Remove engine mounting bolt. Raise up engine and pull out timing belt.

Inspection

1) Check belt teeth for cracks or damage. If tooth damage is found, ensure camshaft, water pump or oil pump is not locked. If wear or cracks on flat belt face are found, check for nicks on one side of idler pulley lock.

2) If wear or damage to only one side of belt is found, check belt guide and alignment of each pulley and sprocket. If noticeable wear is found on belt teeth, check timing cover gasket for damage and proper installation.

3) Ensure there is no foreign material on sprocket teeth. Check timing belt idler pulley for smooth rotation. Replace if roughness or noise is found. Ensure that free length of tension spring is 1.705" (43.31 mm).

Installation

1) Install camshaft sprocket. On Corolla models, install cylinder head. On all models, install crankshaft sprockets. Loosen timing belt idler pulley mount bolt and install tension spring. Move pulley as far left as possible and retighten bolt. Install timing belt.

2) If reusing old belt, align marks made during removal. Install belt with arrow pointing in direction of revolution. Release idler pulley and place tension on belt.

3) If installing new belt, align crankshaft timing pulley and TDC mark on oil pump cover. Align front cam bearing cap mark and center of small hole on camshaft timing sprocket. *See Fig. 3.*

4) Slowly turn crankshaft 2 revolutions clockwise. Recheck timing marks. Measure belt tension on side opposite idler pulley while pushing belt toward pulley.

5) Deflection should be .24-.28" (6.0-7.0 mm), at tension of 4.4 lbs. (2 kg). *See Fig. 3.* If tension is incorrect, readjust with idler pulley. To complete installation, reverse removal procedure. *See Fig. 1.*

Fig. 3: Aligning Valve Timing Marks

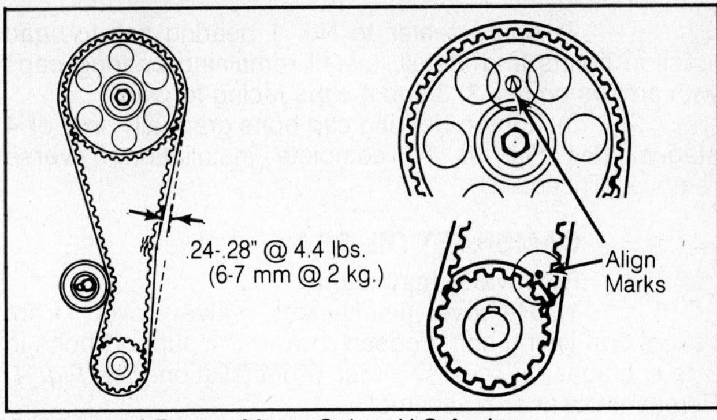

Courtesy of Toyota Motor Sales, U.S.A., Inc.

CAMSHAFT

Removal

1) Remove air cleaner assembly. Identify and remove all wiring and hoses interfering with valve cover removal. Remove valve cover and gasket. Remove engine front covers, gasket and timing belt. Loosen rocker arm support bolts in 3 to 4 stages, in reverse order of tightening sequence. *See Fig. 4.*

2) Remove rocker arm assembly. Secure camshaft. Remove camshaft timing sprocket. Before camshaft removal, measure end play. Remove camshaft bearing caps in the following sequence: front, rear, front center and rear center.

3) Keep bearing caps in order for reassembly reference. Remove camshaft and oil seal. Detach distributor drive gear mount bolt from camshaft and remove drive gear.

Inspection

1) Check end play. Check camshaft runout by placing camshaft in "V" blocks. Using micrometer, check camshaft lobe heights for excessive wear. See CAMSHAFT SPECIFICATIONS. If clearance is beyond limit, replace camshaft and/or cylinder head assembly.

2) Using micrometer, measure camshaft bearing journals. Inspect cam bearing caps for flaking or scoring. If caps are damaged or excessively worn, replace head and camshaft.

3) Check camshaft oil clearance, with camshaft and bearing caps tightened in place, using Plastigage method. Do not turn camshaft during measurement. Maximum clearance is .004" (.10 mm). If clearance is beyond limit, replace camshaft and cylinder head.

CAMSHAFT SPECIFICATIONS

Application	In. (mm)
End Play	
Standard	.003-.007 (.08-.18)
Maximum	.0098 (.25)
Maximum Runout	.0024 (.060)
Lobe Height	
Standard	
3A-C	1.5528-1.5531 (39.440-39.450)
4A-C	1.5508-1.5547 (39.390-39.490)
Minimum	1.5409 (39.140)

Installation

1) Coat camshaft and bearing caps with oil. Install camshaft. Apply grease to new oil seal lip and sealant on outside edge of seal. Install oil seal flush with cylinder head.

2) Apply sealer to No. 1 bearing cap-to-head junction points and install. Install remaining bearing caps with arrows on No. 2, 3 and 4 caps facing forward.

3) Tighten bearing cap bolts gradually, in 3 or 4 stages. *See Fig. 4.* To complete installation, reverse removal procedure.

CAMSHAFT OIL SEAL

Removal & Installation

1) Remove air cleaner, valve cover, front covers and timing belt. Loosen rocker arm support bolts in 3 to 4 stages, in reverse order of installation. *See Fig. 4.* Remove rocker arm assembly.

2) Secure camshaft and remove camshaft timing sprocket. Remove camshaft bearing caps in following sequence: front, rear, front center and rear center.

3) Keep caps in order for reassembly reference. Remove camshaft and oil seal. Inspect seal contact surface of camshaft for cracks or damage. Replace as necessary. Apply grease to lip of new oil seal and sealant to outside of seal.

4) Install oil seal. Install No. 1 bearing cap with sealant applied at cap-to-head junction points. Tighten bearing caps in 3 to 4 stages, in sequence. *See Fig. 4.*

CRANKSHAFT FRONT OIL SEAL

Removal & Installation

1) With oil pump removed from block, tap oil seal out using hammer and drift. Do not damage seal contact surface of pump. Apply grease to new oil seal. Replace using Seal Installer (09517-30011) for 3A-C or (09517-30010) for 4A-C.

NOTE: During installation, ensure oil seal is flush with oil pump body outer surface.

2) With pump installed, use knife to cut off lip of seal. Pry out seal. Inspect seal lip contact surface of crankshaft for cracks or damage and replace as necessary. Apply grease to new seal lip. Using seal installer, replace oil seal. Do not set seal more than .04" (1.0 mm) into oil pump body.

VALVES

VALVE ARRANGEMENT

I-E-E-I-I-E-E-I (Front-to-rear).

VALVES

1) Check valve head margin thickness. If head is worn to .02" (.5 mm) margin thickness for intake or .04" (1.0 mm) for exhaust, replace valve. Check surface of valve stem tip for excessive wear.

2) Standard valve length is 4.208" (106.88 mm) for intake and 4.204" (106.78 mm) for exhaust. Valve stem end surface grinding limit is .02" (.5 mm). If valve stem tip is worn, resurface with grinder or replace valve.

VALVE SPRINGS

Removal

1) With cylinder head, rocker arms and shaft assembly removed, remove cam bearing caps, seal and camshaft. Keep components in order for reassembly reference.

2) Press valve spring down with Spring Compressor (09202-43013). Remove valve keepers. Remove spring compressor. Remove spring retainer, spring, valve, oil seal and valve spring seat.

NOTE: Keep all valve train and camshaft components in order for reassembly reference.

Inspection

1) Valve springs must be .08" (2.0 mm) or less out-of-square. Check free length of springs. Replace any not within specification.

2) Using spring tester, check tension of each spring at specified installed height. Valve spring installed height is 1.52" (38.6 mm). Minimum installed tension is 46.3 lbs. (21 kg). Replace spring if not to specification.

Installation

Clean parts and lubricate with oil. To install, reverse removal procedure.

ROCKER ARMS & SHAFT ASSEMBLY

Removal

1) Remove air cleaner and valve cover. Loosen valve adjuster lock nuts. Back off adjuster screws. Loosen rocker arm support bolts in 3 to 4 stages, in reverse of tightening sequence. *See Fig. 4.* Remove rocker arm assembly.

1.5L & 1.6L 8-VALVE 4-CYLINDER (Cont.)

2) Check arm-to-shaft clearance by twisting rocker arm on shaft. Little or no movement should be felt. If movement is felt, disassemble rocker arm assembly and measure oil clearance. Mark parts for reassembly reference.

Inspection

1) Using dial indicator, measure inside diameter of rocker arm. Using micrometer, measure outside diameter of rocker shaft. Subtract rocker diameter from shaft diameter.

2) Determine clearance. Standard rocker arm-to-shaft clearance is .0004-.0019" (.010-.048 mm). If clearance exceeds .0024" (.060 mm), replace rocker arm and/or shaft.

3) Check cam end contact surface of rocker arm and valve contact surface of rocker arm adjusting screw. If worn excessively, grind or replace rocker arm and/or adjusting screw as necessary.

Installation

1) To install rocker arms, reverse removal procedure. Tighten rocker arm support bolts gradually, in 3 to 4 stages, in proper sequence. *See Fig. 4.*

Fig. 4: Rocker Arm Assembly & Bearing Cap Mount Bolt Tightening Sequence

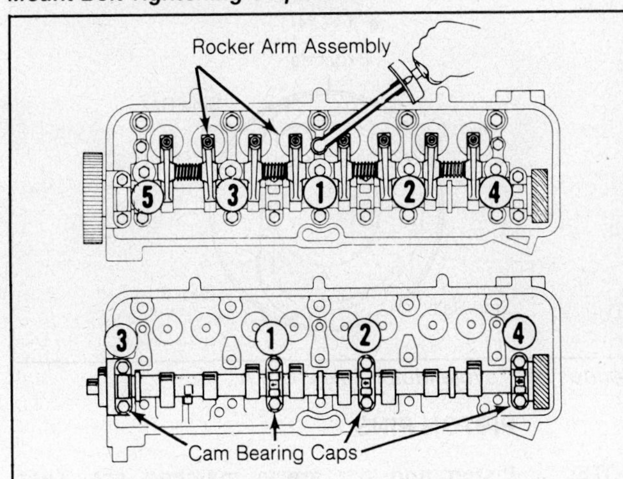

Courtesy of Toyota Motor Sales, U.S.A., Inc.

2) If necessary, loosen adjusting screws and nuts prior to installation of assembly. When assembling rocker shaft, shaft oil holes must face right, left and bottom. *See Fig. 5.*

Fig. 5: Assembling Rocker Arms & Shaft Assembly

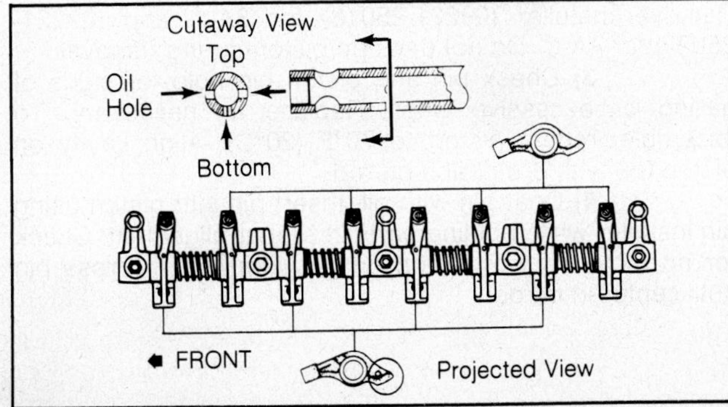

Courtesy of Toyota Motor Sales, U.S.A., Inc.

VALVE GUIDES

Clearance Check

Check valve guide clearance. Refer to VALVE GUIDE DIAMETER SPPECIFICATIONS. If clearance is beyond specification and stem is not worn, replace guide.

VALVE GUIDE DIAMETER SPECIFICATIONS

Application	In. (mm)
Inside Guide Diameter	.2760-.2768 (7.010-7.030)
Maximum Stem-to-Guide Clearance	
Intake	.0031 (.080)
Exhaust	.004 (.10)

NOTE: Replacement valve guides are available in .05 mm oversize.

Replacement

1) Using hammer and drift, tap guide firmly enough to break guide off flush with cylinder head surface. Remove snap ring. Gradually heat head to 194°F (90°C). Using Valve Guide Remover (09201-60011), drive guide out from camshaft side.

2) Measure cylinder head valve guide hole. Standard guide outside diameter is .4543-.4548" (11.540-11.551 mm). If hole-to-guide clearance is excessive, machine hole for oversized guide.

3) With head at room temperature, ream guide hole to fit new guide. Oversize guide outside diameter is .4563-.4567" (11.590-11.601 mm). To install valve guide, reheat cylinder head.

4) Using Valve Guide Installer (09201-60011), drive in new guide until snap ring contacts head. Using 7 mm reamer, finish guide bore to specified clearance. Reface valve seat surface, as needed, after valve or guide repair or replacement.

VALVE CLEARANCE ADJUSTMENT

NOTE: Valves should be adjusted with engine at normal operating temperature but not running. Cold specification is provided for initial settings after assembly.

1) With engine at normal operating temperature, stop engine and remove valve cover. Bring No. 1 piston to TDC of compression stroke. Ensure rockers on No. 1 are loose and No. 4 are tight.

2) Realign cut-out on damper pulley with zero degree timing mark on timing belt cover. Adjust Nos. 1 and 2 intake valves and Nos. 1 and 3 exhaust valves.

3) Rotate crankshaft one full turn (360 degrees) clockwise to realign timing mark on damper pulley with zero ("0") mark on timing cover. Adjust Nos. 3 and 4 intake valves and Nos. 2 and 4 exhaust valves. See VALVE CLEARANCE SPECIFICATIONS table.

VALVE CLEARANCE SPECIFICATIONS

Valve	Hot In. (mm)	Cold In. (mm)
Intake	.008 (.20)	.007 (.18)
Exhaust	.012 (.30)	.011 (.28)

1.5L & 1.6L 8-VALVE 4-CYLINDER (Cont.)

PISTONS, PINS & RINGS

PISTON & ROD ASSEMBLY

Removal

1) With cylinder head and oil pan removed, remove connecting rod nuts. Remove rod cap with bearing half. Remove any ridge before pushing piston out.

2) Cover rod bolts with short pieces of rubber hose to protect crankshaft journals from damage. Push piston/rod assembly, with bearing half, out through top of block.

Inspection

1) Using rod aligner, check connecting rod for bend or torsion. Bend and torsion limit is .002" (.05 mm), in 3.94" (100 mm) of length.

2) Install rod and bearings on crankpin. Measure side thrust clearance. Maximum play at big end is .012" (.30 mm). Replace rod if not to specification.

Installation

1) Install rings with code marks up. Ensure ring gaps are set 180 degrees apart and are not on thrust side of piston or in line with pin. *See Fig. 6*. Apply oil to rings, piston and bore. Install piston and rod assembly. Ensure bearing inserts are properly seated.

2) Install ring compressor. Install piston/rod assembly with cavity on piston top aligned with protrusion of rod and facing toward front of engine. *See Fig. 6*.

3) Ensure rod and cap marks align. Tighten caps to specification. Install cylinder head. Install new gasket and oil pan. Tighten pan bolts evenly, in a criss-cross pattern. Do not overtighten. Complete installation by reversing removal procedure.

FITTING PISTONS & RINGS

NOTE: **Pistons and rings are available in .50 mm, .75 mm and 1 mm oversize for 3A-C and .50 mm oversize for 4A-C engines.**

1) Inspect cylinder block for cracks or flaws. Using bore gauge, measure for out-of-round or excessive taper. If measurement exceeds .0008" (.020 mm), refinish bore. If one cylinder is bored, all must be bored. Check head gasket surface for warpage. Maximum limit is .002" (.05 mm).

NOTE: **Before cylinder block machining operations, ensure main bearing caps are installed and tightened to specification. Bore cylinders in order of No. 2-4-1-3 to prevent distortion.**

2) Determine piston oversize according to cylinder wear. Standard bore diameter is 3.0602" (77.73 mm) for 3A-C and 3.1890-3.1902" (81.000-81.030 mm) for 4A-C. Bore wear limit is .008" (.20 mm). Measure piston diameter at right angle to pin and .20" (5.0 mm) below oil ring groove. See PISTON DIAMETER SPECIFICATIONS table.

PISTON DIAMETER SPECIFICATIONS

Application	In. (mm)
Standard	
3A-C	3.0468-3.0480 (77.390-77.420)
4A-C	3.1850-3.1864 (80.90-80.93)

3) After honing cylinder to final fit, measure piston-to-cylinder clearance with parts at 70°F (20°C). Ensure difference of bore limit between cylinders is .002" (.05 mm) or less. If beyond limit, cylinders must be bored.

4) Measure side clearance of rings in grooves as each is installed. Check ring end gap. Install ring squarely in cylinder, using piston. If beyond limits, replace piston and/or rings. When installing rings, ensure code mark faces up. *See Fig. 6*.

Fig. 6: Positioning Piston Ring Gaps

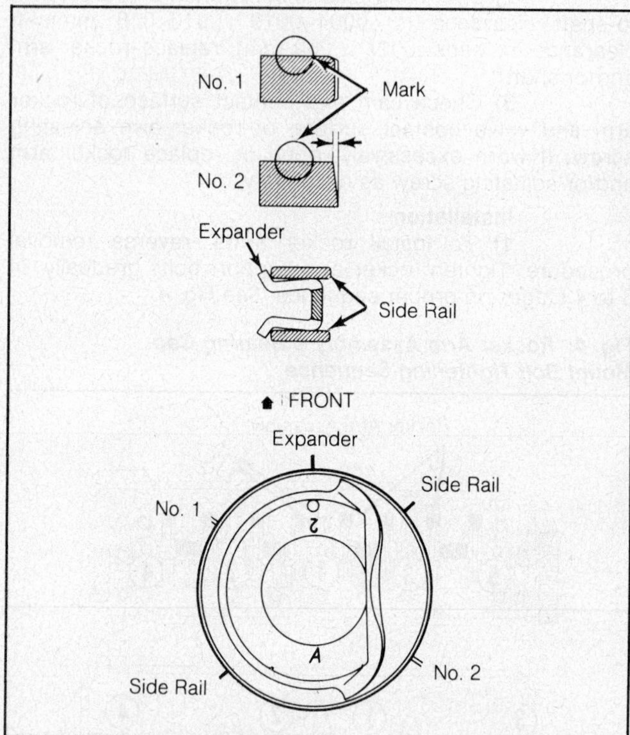

Courtesy of Toyota Motor Sales, U.S.A., Inc.

PISTON PINS

NOTE: **Piston and pin are a matched set. Keep piston, pin, rings and rod together for each cylinder.**

1) Check fit between piston and pin by moving piston back and forth on piston pin. If any movement is felt, replace piston and pin.

2) To remove piston pin, warm piston and rod assembly to about 70°F (20°C). Press out pin using Pin Remover/Installer (09221-25018) for 3A-C and (09221-25022) for 4A-C. Do not damage piston during removal.

3) Check pin and piston pin hole for signs of galling or excessive wear. Replace as necessary. To assemble, reheat piston to 70°F (20°C). Align cavity on piston top with protrusion on rod.

4) Coat pin with oil. Insert pin into piston using pin installer while holding parts in proper alignment. Check for no movement of piston on pin. *See Fig. 7*. Press pin until centered in rod.

Fig. 7: Assembling Piston & Connecting Rod

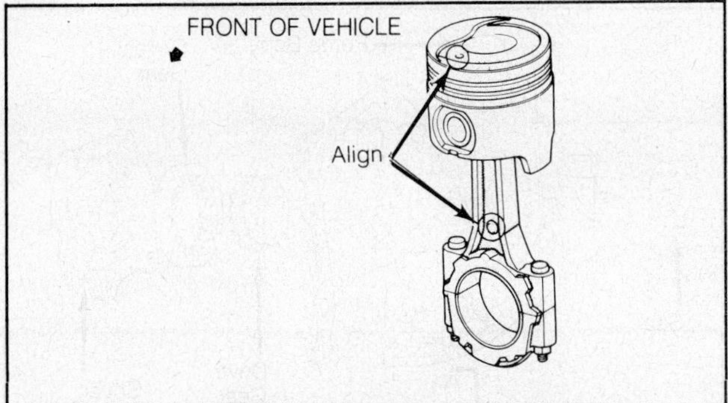

Courtesy of Toyota Motor Sales, U.S.A., Inc.

CRANKSHAFT & ROD BEARINGS

CRANKSHAFT

NOTE: **Cylinder block bearing marks are near No. 5 main bearing cap. The number stamped closest to flywheel edge of block corresponds to No. 5 main bearing.**

Removal

1) Remove engine from vehicle. Remove drive belts and front covers. Remove valve timing belt. Secure crankshaft and remove flywheel or drive plate, oil pan, oil pump and cylinder head. Remove piston and rod assemblies. Using punch, mark rods and caps for reassembly reference.

2) Remove main bearing caps and arrange caps, inserts and thrust washers in order. Remove rear oil seal retainer. Do not damage crankshaft sealing surface. Remove crankshaft. Remove upper main bearing halves.

NOTE: **If replacing main bearing, replace with one having the same number as marked on cylinder block. There are 3 sizes of standard bearings, marked 1, 2 or 3 accordingly.**

Inspection

1) Check crankshaft journals and crankpins for scoring, wear, cracks, taper and out-of-round. Maximum taper and out-of-round limit is .0008" (.020 mm). If beyond specification, replace crankshaft.

2) Check crankshaft runout by placing on "V" blocks. Use dial indicator at center journal. Maximum runout is .0024" (.060 mm). If beyond specification, replace crankshaft.

NOTE: **Pilot bearing in crankshaft rear opening is permanently lubricated and requires no additional cleaning or lubrication.**

3) Inspect crankshaft rear end pilot bearing. If damaged or excessively worn, replace pilot bearing using Bearing Remover (09303-35011) and Bearing Installer (09304-30012).

4) Check flywheel friction surface for cracks, damage or wear. Measure runout using dial indicator. Runout limit is .008" (.02 mm). Resurface or replace if beyond limits. Check tooth surfaces of ring gear for flaws or wear. Replace as necessary.

NOTE: **Main bearing caps are numbered and must be installed with arrows facing forward.**

Installation

1) Install main bearing inserts in block. Ensure insert oil holes are in proper alignment with block and bearing cap oil holes.

2) Apply oil to main bearing surfaces. Install upper thrust washers on center bearing and lower thrust washers on No. 3 main bearing cap with oil grooves facing out. Install crankshaft. Install bearing caps with arrows facing front of engine.

3) Shift crankshaft toward front of engine. Tighten bearing caps in 2 or 3 stages, starting at center bearing and working outward. Ensure crankshaft rotates smoothly. *See Fig. 8.*

4) Check end play using dial indicator with pointer set on crankshaft sprocket mount. Standard thrust washer thickness is .0961-.0980" (2.440-2.490 mm). Maximum end play is .012" (.30 mm) or less. If beyond specification, replace thrust washers.

5) Install rear oil seal retainer. Install flywheel or drive plate. Install piston and rod assemblies. To install remaining components, reverse removal procedure.

Fig. 8: Main Bearing Cap Tightening Sequence

Courtesy of Toyota Motor Sales, U.S.A., Inc.

CRANKSHAFT REAR OIL SEAL

Removal & Installation

1) Remove and separate engine/transaxle assembly. Remove flywheel or drive plate. With seal retainer removed from block, tap oil seal out using hammer and drift. Apply grease to new oil seal lip. Install using Seal Installer (09218-56010) for 3A-C and (09223-41020) for 4A-C.

2) With retainer installed, use knife to cut off lip of seal. Pry out seal. Inspect seal lip contact surface of crankshaft for cracks or damage. Replace as necessary. Apply grease to new oil seal lip. Using seal installer, replace oil seal.

ENGINE OILING

ENGINE OILING SYSTEM

Oil is circulated through the engine by pressure provided by a gear-type oil pump. Oil is drawn from the oil pan and circulated to a full-flow oil filter. From the filter, oil is directed to crankshaft main bearings that feed connecting rod bearings. The oil passage above No. 1 main bearing feeds camshaft and rocker arm shaft through No. 1 rocker support. Oil is then returned to pan. *See Fig. 9.*

Toyota Engines

1.5L & 1.6L 8-VALVE 4-CYLINDER (Cont.)

Fig. 9: Typical Engine Oiling System

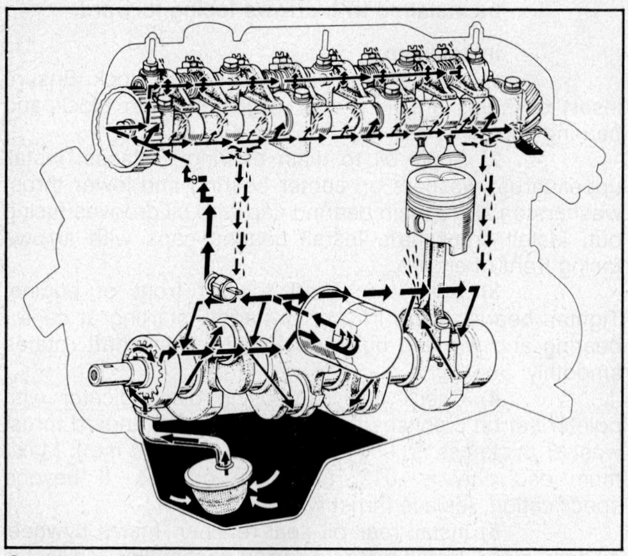

Courtesy of Toyota Motor Sales, U.S.A., Inc.

CRANKCASE CAPACITY

The crankcase capacity is 3.5 qts. (3.3L) with filter. Refill without filter is 3.2 qts. (3.0L).

NORMAL OIL PRESSURE

The normal oil pressure is 4.3 psi (.3 kg/cm²) at idle. At 3000 RPM the oil pressure should be 35.6-71.1 psi (2.5-5.0 kg/cm²).

OIL PRESSURE REGULATOR VALVE

The oil pressure regulator valve is located in the oil pump cover. It is a nonadjustable type valve.

OIL PUMP

Removal

1) Raise and support vehicle. Drain engine oil. Remove timing covers and timing belt. Using Oil Pan Sealant Cutter (09032-00100), remove oil pan. Do not use sealant cutter on pump side. Do not damage pan flange.

2) Remove oil strainer mount bolts and strainer. Remove dipstick and tube. Remove oil pump by tapping pump body with plastic hammer. Disassemble pump cover, drive gear, driven gear, oil seal and relief valve. *See Fig. 10.*

Inspection

1) Check gears for wear or damage. Install new oil seal using Seal Installer (09517-30011) for 3A-C and (09517-30010) for 4A-C. Do not install seal slantwise.

2) Measure drive gear-to-driven gear, side clearance, and gear-to-body clearances. If beyond specification, replace parts. Check relief valve for wear or damage. See OIL PUMP SPECIFICATIONS table. *See Fig. 10.*

Installation

1) Ensure mating surfaces are clean. Ensure pump drive gear spline teeth engage with large teeth of crankshaft.

2) Using new Seal Packing (102) pan gasket or silicone base sealant, install oil pan. Complete installation by reversing removal procedure.

Fig. 10: Exploded View of Oil Pump Assembly

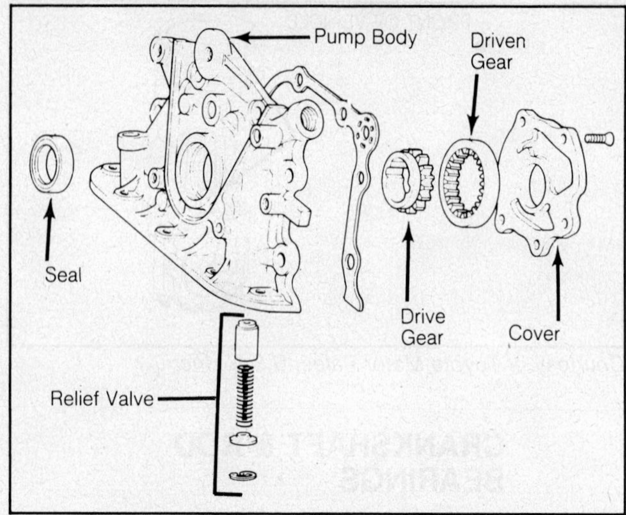

Courtesy of Toyota Motor Sales, U.S.A., Inc.

OIL PUMP SPECIFICATIONS

Application	In. (mm)
Drive Gear	
Tip-to-Cresent Clearance	.004-.010 (.10-.25)
	Limit .014 (.35)
Driven Gear	
Tip-to-Cresent Clearance	.002-.012 (.06-.31)
	Limit .014 (.35)
Gear Side Clearance	.001-.003 (.03-.08)
	Limit .004 (.10)
Driven Gear-to-Body Clearance	.004-.008 (.10-.19)
	Limit .008 (.20)

ENGINE COOLING

WATER PUMP

NOTE: Do not allow coolant onto timing belt during replacement or repair.

Removal

1) Drain cooling system. Loosen alternator pivot bolt, swing unit toward engine and remove drive belt. On A/C equipped models, remove fan shroud. Remove fluid coupling with fan, water pump pulley and drive belt.

2) Remove water outlet housing, by-pass pipe, water inlet housing, thermostat, timing belt upper cover and oil dipstick tube. Disconnect heater outlet hose from pipe and remove heater outlet pipe mounting bolt. Remove water pump.

Disassembly

1) Remove water pump suction cover mount bolts and pry off cover. Remove 4 stud bolts from pulley seat. Using hydraulic press and Pump Holder (09236-00100), press pulley seat off pump bearing shaft.

2) Heat pump body to about 185°F (85°C). Press out bearing, with impeller, from pump body. Press impeller off pump shaft/bearing assembly. Remove seal set from bearing assembly.

1.5L & 1.6L 8-VALVE 4-CYLINDER (Cont.)

Reassembly

1) Heat pump body to 185°F (85°C). Press bearing/shaft assembly into body until bearing race is flush with body top surface. Apply sealant to new seal set and press onto bearing assembly.

2) Press pulley seat onto pump bearing shaft. Distance between face of pulley seat and rear of pump body should be 3.0" (76 mm) for 3A-C and 3.34-3.40" (84.8-86.2 mm) for 4A-C.

3) Install new packing and seat into impeller. Apply oil to seal lip and rotor contact surfaces. Press impeller onto shaft to depth of .236" (6.0 mm). Install 4 stud bolts to pulley seat. After assembly, ensure impeller turns smoothly. *See Fig. 11.*

Fig. 11: Installing Impeller to Specified Depth

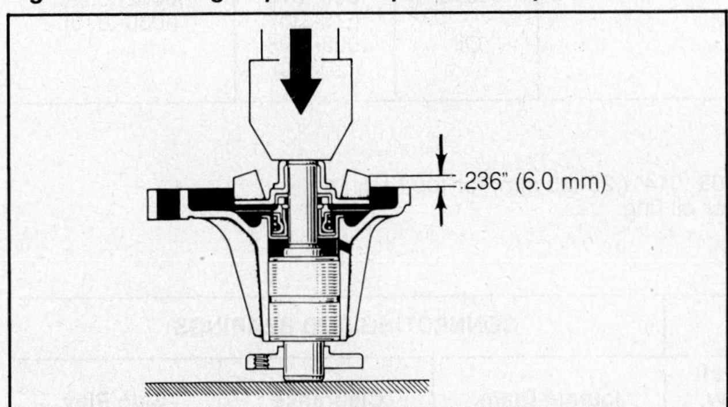

Courtesy of Toyota Motor Sales, U.S.A., Inc.

Installation

1) To install water pump, mount heater outlet pipe, with new gasket, to pump. Place new "O" ring gasket on clean block surface and mount pump. Install new "O" ring onto dipstick tube and mount to block.

2) To complete installation, reverse removal procedure. Adjust tension of drive belts, fill coolant system, start engine and check for leaks.

TIGHTENING SPECIFICATIONS

Application	Ft. Lbs. (N.m)
Camshaft Sprocket Bolt	29-39 (39-53)
Connecting Rod Cap Nut	26-32 (35-43)
Crankshaft Pulley Bolt	80-94 (109-128)
Cylinder Head Bolt	40-47 (54-64)
Distributor Drive Gear Mount Bolt	20-23 (27-31)
Exhaust Pipe-to-Manifold Mount Bolt	26-32 (36-44)
Flywheel Bolt	55-61 (75-83)
Main Bearing Cap Bolt	40-47 (54-64)
Manifold Nut	15-21 (20-29)
Oil Pump Mount Bolt	13-18 (18-24)
Rocker Shaft Support Bolt	17-19 (23-26)
Timing Belt Idler Mount Bolt	
3A-C	22-32 (30-43)
4A-C	26-36 (36-49)
	INCH Lbs.
Camshaft Bearing Cap Bolt	96-120 (11-14)

ENGINE SPECIFICATIONS

GENERAL SPECIFICATIONS

Year	DISPLACEMENT		Fuel System	HP@RPM	Torque Ft. Lbs.@RPM	Compr. Ratio	BORE		STROKE	
	Cu. In.	Liters					In.	mm	In.	mm
1987										
Corolla	96.8	1.6	2-Bbl.	70 @ 4800	85 @ 2800	9.0:1	3.19	81.0	3.03	77.0
Tercel	88.6	1.5	2-Bbl.	62 @ 4800	76 @ 2800	9.0:1	3.05	77.5	3.03	77.0

VALVES

Engine Size & Valve	Head Diam. In. (mm)	Face Angle	Seat Angle	Seat Width In. (mm)	Stem Diameter In. (mm)	Stem Clearance In. (mm)	Valve Lift In. (mm)
1.5L & 1.6L							
Intake	.....	44.5°	45°	.047-.063 (1.20-1.60)	.2744-.2750 (6.970-6.985)	.0010-.0024 (.025-.060)	.....
Exhaust	.....	44.5°	45°	.047-.063 (1.20-1.60)	.2742-.2748 (6.965-6.980)	.0012-.0026 (.030-.065)	.....

Toyota Engines

1.5L & 1.6L 8-VALVE 4-CYLINDER (Cont.)

ENGINE SPECIFICATIONS (Cont.)

PISTONS, PINS & RINGS

Engine	PISTONS Clearance In. (mm)	PINS Piston Fit In. (mm)	PINS Rod Fit In. (mm)	RINGS Ring No.	RINGS End Gap In. (mm)	RINGS Side Clearance In. (mm)
1.5L	.004-.005 (.10-.12)	[1] Press Fit	[1] Press Fit	No. 1	[2] .008-.016 (.20-.40)	.0016-.0031 (.04-.08)
				No. 2	.006-.014 (.15-.35)	.0012-.0028 (.03-.07)
				Oil	.004-.024 (.10-.60)	.....
1.6L	.004-.005 (.10-.12)	[1] Press Fit	[1] Press Fit	No. 1	[2] .010-.014 (.25-.35)	.0016-.0031 (.040-.080)
				No. 2	.006-.012 (.15-.30)	.0012-.0028 (.030-.070)
				Oil	.008-.028 (.20-.70)	.....

[1] – Piston and pin are available only as a set.
[2] – End gap for "TP" brand rings shown; for "Riken" brand, end gap is .008-.014" (.20-.35 mm) for top ring, .006-.012" (.15-.30 mm) for second ring and .012-.035" (.30-.90 mm) for oil ring.

CRANKSHAFT MAIN & CONNECTING ROD BEARINGS

Engine	MAIN BEARINGS Journal Diam. In. (mm)	MAIN BEARINGS Clearance In. (mm)	MAIN BEARINGS Thrust Bearing	MAIN BEARINGS Crankshaft End Play In. (mm)	CONNECTING ROD BEARINGS Journal Diam. In. (mm)	CONNECTING ROD BEARINGS Clearance In. (mm)	CONNECTING ROD BEARINGS Side Play In. (mm)
1.5L & 1.6L	1.8891-1.8898 (47.982-48.000)	.0005-.0019 (.012-.049)	Center	.0008-.0073 (.020-.185)	1.5742-1.5748 (39.985-40.000)	.0008-.0020 (.020-.051)	.006-.010 (.15-.25)

CAMSHAFT

Engine	Journal Diam. In. (mm)	Clearance In. (mm)	Lobe Lift In. (mm)
1.5L & 1.6L	1.1015-1.1022 (27.979-27.995)	.0015-.0029 (.037-.073)	.....

VALVE SPRINGS

Engine	Free Length In. (mm)	PRESSURE Lbs. @ In. (Kg @ mm) Valve Closed	PRESSURE Lbs. @ In. (Kg @ mm) Valve Open
1.5L & 1.6L	1.756 (44.60)	52@1.52 (23.6@38.6)	.....

1.5L 12-VALVE 4-CYLINDER

Tercel (Except Wagon)

ENGINE CODING

ENGINE IDENTIFICATION

Engine serial number is stamped on left rear side of block.

ENGINE IDENTIFICATION CODES

Application	Code
1.5L	3E

ENGINE, MANIFOLDS & CYLINDER HEAD

ENGINE

Removal

1) Remove battery and radiator reserve tank. Mark engine hood for installation reference and remove engine hood. Remove covers under engine. Drain coolant from radiator and engine. Radiator drain plug is on lower right corner of radiator. Engine drain plug is located by oil filter.

2) Disconnect cooling fan electrical connectors. Remove upper and lower radiator hose. Remove radiator mounting brackets and remove radiator assembly. Disconnect and remove windshield washer reservoir. On cruise control equipped models, disconnect control cable and connector. Remove 3 actuator mounting bolts and remove actuator.

3) Disconnect accelerator cable. On automatic transaxle models, disconnect throttle cable. On all models, disconnect and plug fuel hoses at fuel pump. Disconnect and remove charcoal canister. Disconnect vacuum hose from brake booster.

4) Disconnect heater inlet hose from water outlet housing. Disconnect heater outlet hose from heater water valve. Disconnect speedometer cable from transaxle. Disconnect control cables from transaxle. On manual transaxle models, remove clutch release cylinder and selecting bell crank from transaxle.

5) Remove front tire and wheel assemblies. Drain transaxle fluid. Apply brakes and remove dust cap, cotter pin, lock nut and wheel bearing nut. Remove and suspend brake caliper. Remove disc brake rotor. Separate tie rod from steering knuckle.

6) Remove bolts and nuts retaining strut assembly to steering knuckle. Wrap shop rags around inner and outer axle shaft boots to prevent damage. Using a soft hammer, tap axle shaft out of steering knuckle and hub assembly. Using Axle Shaft Puller (SST 09520-10021), pull axle shaft from transaxle. Repeat procedure for opposite side.

7) Mark and disconnect necessary electrical connectors. Disconnect wire harness from intake manifold. Remove bolt, nut, ground strap and intake manifold stay. Remove Vacuum Switching Valve (VSV). Remove power steering pump without disconnecting hoses and suspend out of way.

8) Remove air compressor (if equipped) without disconnecting hoses and suspend out of way. Disconnect and separate inlet pipe from exhaust manifold. Mark driveshaft and mounting flange for installation reference. Remove driveshaft assembly.

9) Attach engine lifting chain to engine lifting brackets. Remove rear engine mount through bolt. Remove 4 bolts and the rear mounting insulator. Remove front engine mount through bolt. Remove 3 bolts and mounting bracket from cylinder block. Remove upper right engine mounting insulator through bolt, 2 nuts and bolts. Remove mounting insulator.

10) Remove 5 bolts from left engine mounting bracket and remove bracket. Lift engine with transaxle out of vehicle. Use care to clear battery tray. Place engine and transaxle in a stand. Remove starter. Separate transaxle from engine. Remove clutch and pressure plate (if equipped). Remove flywheel or flexplate.

Installation

Install transaxle and components on engine. To install engine and transaxle assembly, reverse removal procedure. Tighten all bolts and nuts to specifications. Fill all fluid levels to proper level.

INTAKE MANIFOLD

Removal & Installation

No on vehicle removal and installation procedure available from manufacturer. Intake manifold removal and installation does not include cylinder head removal.

Inspection

Check mounting surface for warpage. Maximum allowed warpage is .0079" (.201 mm). Check for cracks and rough gasket mating surfaces. Replace as necessary.

EXHAUST MANIFOLD

Removal & Installation

No on vehicle removal and installation procedure available from manufacturer. Exhaust manifold removal and installation does not include cylinder head removal.

Inspection

Check mounting surface for warpage. Maximum allowed warpage is .0118" (.300 mm). Check for cracks and rough gasket mating surfaces. Replace as necessary.

CYLINDER HEAD

NOTE: **To prevent warping or cracking, allow engine to cool before removing components and follow the cylinder head bolt removal procedure given.**

Removal

1) Disconnect negative battery cable. Remove right cover under engine. Drain cooling system. See ENGINE under ENGINE, MANIFOLDS & CYLINDER HEAD in this article. Remove power steering pump and bracket without disconnecting hoses (if equiped). Suspend power steering pump out of way.

2) Remove air conditioning idler pulley (if equipped). Remove raditator hoses. Disconnect throttle cable from bracket. Disconnect automatic transaxle throttle cable (if equipped).

3) Remove timing belt. See TIMING BELT & SPROCKETS under CAMSHAFT in this article. Hold camshaft and remove bolt retaining camshaft sprocket. Remove camshaft sprocket.

1.5L 12-VALVE 4-CYLINDER (Cont.)

4) Disconnect heater inlet hose. Disconnect and plug fuel lines at fuel pump. Remove air suction hose and valve (if equipped). Disconnect brake booster vacuum hose from intake manifold. Disconnect coolant inlet hose. Disconnect coolant hose from intake manifold.

5) Mark and disconnect necessary electrical connectors and hoses. Remove evaporative emission control, VSV and No. 2 cold enrichment breaker VSV. Disconnect coolant by-pass hose from carburetor. Separate inlet pipe from exhaust manifold. Remove intake manifold stay and ground strap. Remove clamp bolt retaining wire harness to intake manifold.

6) Attach a dial indicator to cylinder head, with pointer on front of camshaft. Measure camshaft thrust clearance. See INSPECTION under CAMSHAFT in this article.

CAUTION: Cylinder head bolts MUST be removed in the sequence given.

7) Loosen and remove cylinder head bolts in 3 steps and in sequence. *See Fig. 1.* Mark and note head bolts for installation or replacement reference. Remove cylinder head assembly. If necessary, pry with bar between cylinder head and cylinder block protrusion by water pump.

Fig. 1: Cylinder Head Bolt Removal Sequence

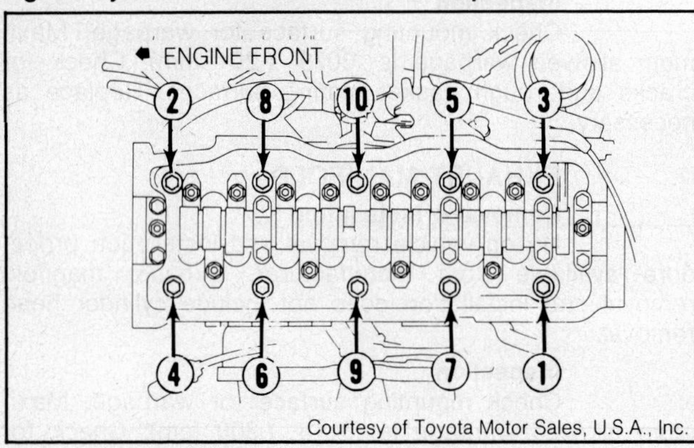

Courtesy of Toyota Motor Sales, U.S.A., Inc.

Inspection

1) Clean all gasket material from top of block. Clean cylinder head bolt holes in cylinder block and tap threads. Thoroughly clean carbon and gasket material from combustion chambers head and manifold surfaces. DO NOT scratch or damage gasket contact surfaces.

2) Using straightedge and feeler gauge, check cylinder head and block for warpage. Maximum warpage on all surfaces are .002" (.05 mm). If warpage exceeds specifications, replace cylinder head.

3) Using a dye penetrant, check combustion chamber intake and exhaust ports for cracks. Check cylinder head surface for cracks. Replace cylinder head if cracks are present.

Installation

1) Install a new cylinder head gasket over dowels on cylinder block. Ensure head gasket is installed properly. *See Fig. 2.* Place camshaft knock pin at 12 o'clock position and ensure crankshaft is at TDC. Position cylinder head assembly on installed head gasket.

CAUTION: Camshaft knock pin must be at 12 o'clock position and crankshaft must be at TDC. Valves may contact pistion if not as specified.

2) Lightly coat cylinder head bolt threads and under the bolt head with engine oil. Install cylinder head bolts to original position as marked at removal. Replace any head bolts which are deformed or stretched.

3) Using several passes in sequence, tighten cylinder head bolts evenly to 22 ft. lbs. (29 N.m). *See Fig. 3.* Retighten bolts 90 degrees in sequence, with torque wrench set at 36 ft. lbs. (49 N.m). If any bolt(s) at this time do not meet 36 ft. lbs (49 N.m) at 90 degrees, replace the bolt(s).

4) Final tightening of cylinder head bolts is an additional 90 degrees and in the proper sequence. To complete installation, reverse removal procedure. Tighten all bolts and nuts to specifications. Fill all fluid levels to proper level.

Fig. 2: Cylinder Head Gasket Installation

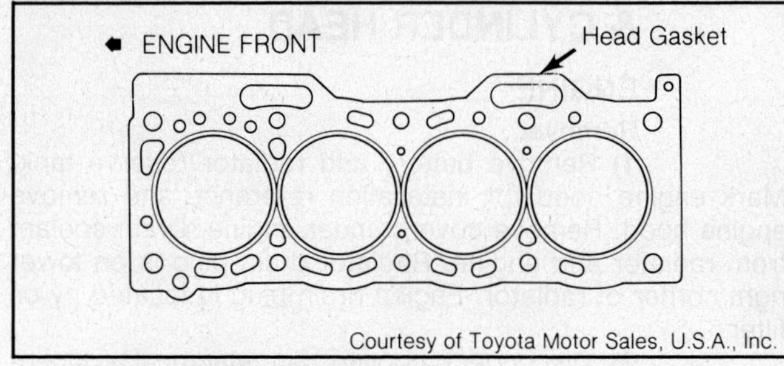

Courtesy of Toyota Motor Sales, U.S.A., Inc.

Fig. 3: Cylinder Head Bolt Installation

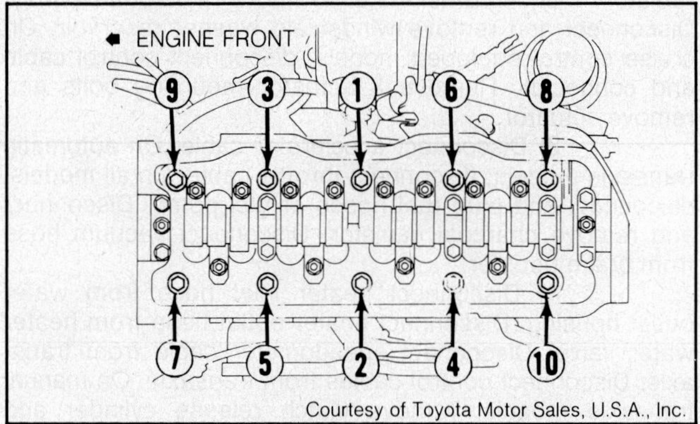

Courtesy of Toyota Motor Sales, U.S.A., Inc.

CAMSHAFT

TIMING BELT & SPROCKETS

Removal

1) Remove right tire and wheel assembly. Remove cover under engine. Remove accessory drive belts. Remove mounting bolt for VSV and remove air cleaner assembly. Remove spark plugs. Using a jack, slightly raise engine to relieve tension on upper right engine mount. Remove upper right mount through bolt, 2 nuts and bolts. Remove upper right mount assembly.

2) Disconnect PCV hose from PCV valve. Remove valve cover. Rotate crankshaft until crankshaft pulley is on TDC of compression stroke. Remove crankshaft drive belt pulley (if equipped). Remove crankshaft pulley with Pulley Remover (SST 09213-31021). Remove 8 bolts retaining upper and lower timing belt covers. *See Fig. 4.* Remove timing belt covers.

1.5L 12-VALVE 4-CYLINDER (Cont.)

Fig. 4: Exploded View of Timing Belt

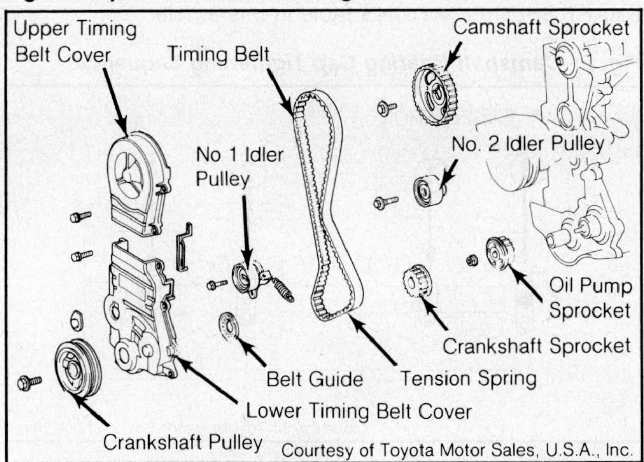

Courtesy of Toyota Motor Sales, U.S.A., Inc.

NOTE: **If reusing timing belt, mark rotation direction on belt to ensure installation to original position. Place match marks on timing belt, crankshaft, camshaft and oil pump sprockets.**

3) Remove timing belt guide from crankshaft. Remove No. 1 idler pulley tension spring. Loosen No. 1 idler pulley bolt and push pulley fully left. Tighten bolt to hold position. Remove timing belt. Remove No. 1 idler pulley and No. 2 idler pulley.

4) Pry crankshaft sprocket off crankshaft. Hold camshaft and remove camshaft sprocket. Using Pulley Holder (SST 09616-12011), remove oil pump sprocket.

Inspection

1) Check timing belt for contamination, wear or cracks. Replace as necessary. Check rotation of camshaft to ensure it does not bind. Check all sprockets for damage. Ensure idler pulleys rotate free and smooth.

2) Check tension spring free length. Check installed tension and length. Free length is 1.528" (38.8 mm). Installed tension should be 183 lbs. (8.3 kg) at a length of 2.157" (54.8 mm).

Fig. 5: Installing Camshaft Sprocket

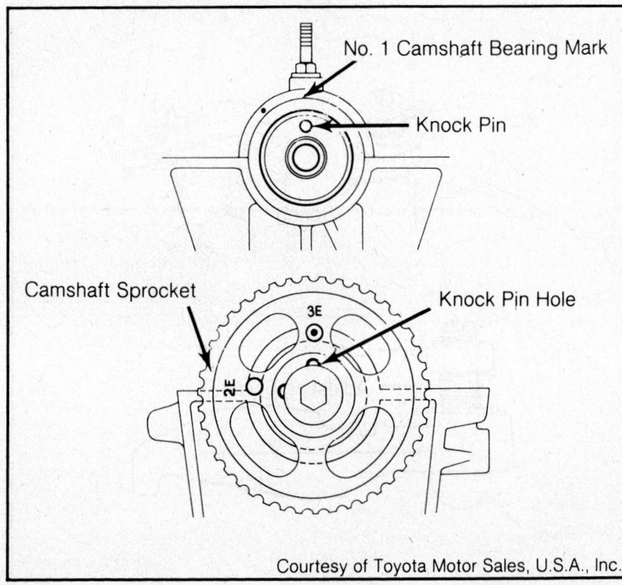

Courtesy of Toyota Motor Sales, U.S.A., Inc.

Installation

1) Align oil pump sprocket with oil pump shaft and install sprocket. Using pulley holder, install oil pump sprocket bolt and tighten to specifications. Align camshaft knock pin with mark on No. 1 camshaft bearing cap. *See Fig. 5.* Align camshaft sprocket knock pin hole,located below "3E" mark on sprocket. Install camshaft sprocket. *See Fig. 5.*

2) Hold camshaft and tighten camshaft sprocket bolt to specifications. Slide crankshaft sprocket on crankshaft. Align TDC mark on oil pump body and crankshaft sprocket. *See Fig. 6.* Install No. 1 idler pulley and position fully left. Install and tighten bolt.

Fig. 6: Aligning Crankshaft Sprocket With TDC Mark

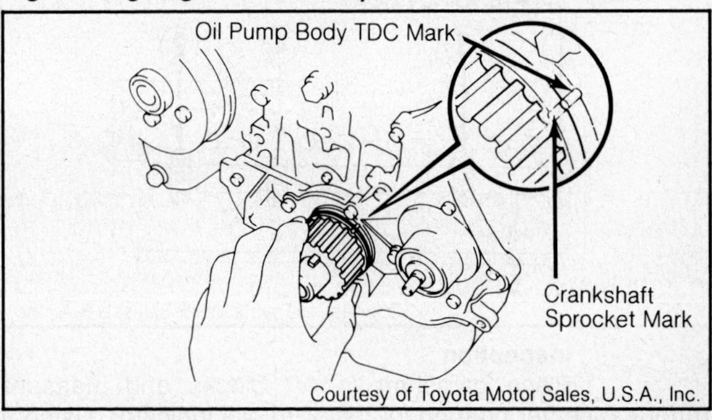

Courtesy of Toyota Motor Sales, U.S.A., Inc.

3) Install No. 2 idler pulley and tighten to specifications. Clean all sprockets and idler pulleys thoroughly. Align timing belt marks and direction (if reusing), made at removal. Install timing belt on crankshaft sprocket. Work around oil pump sprocket side to camshaft sprocket.

4) Loosen No. 1 idler pulley bolt and install tension spring. Temporarily install crankshaft pulley bolt. Turn crankshaft clockwise 2 revolutions (from TDC to TDC). Check all sprocket aligning marks and ensure marks are properly aligned. *See Fig. 7.*

Fig. 7: Timing Belt Installed Alignment

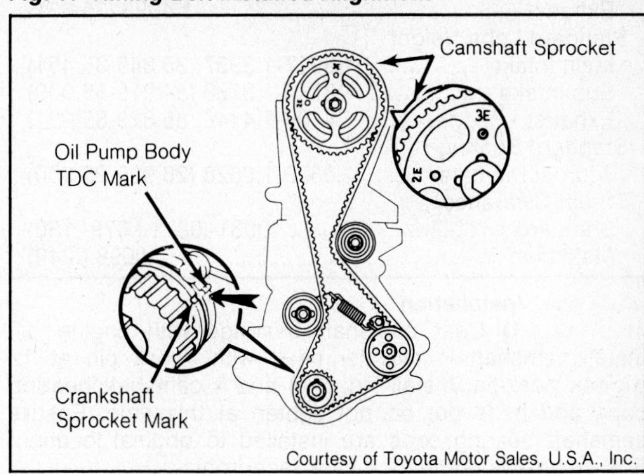

Courtesy of Toyota Motor Sales, U.S.A., Inc.

5) With sprockets properly aligned, tighten No. 1 idler pulley to specifications. Check and ensure there is belt tension between oil pump sprocket and No. 2 idler pulley. To complete installation reverse removal procedure. Tighten all bolts and nuts to specifications.

Toyota Engines

1.5L 12-VALVE 4-CYLINDER (Cont.)

CAMSHAFT

NOTE: On vehicle removal and installation procedure unavailable from manufacturer. Procedure given is with cylinder head removed.

Removal

Remove fuel pump from cylinder head. Number the camshaft bearing caps. Loosen each camshaft bearing cap bolt in several passes and in sequence. *See Fig. 8.* Remove camshaft bearing caps and keep in order. Remove camshaft and seal.

Fig. 8: Removing Camshaft Bearing Caps

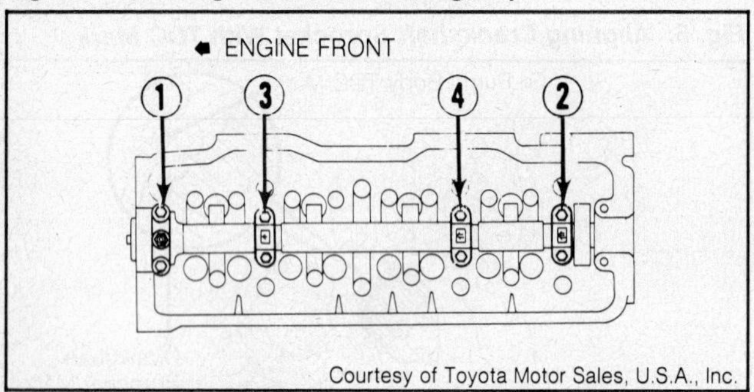

Inspection

Place camshaft in "V" blocks and measure runout at center bearing journal with dial indicator. Using a micrometer, measure each camshaft lobe height. Using a micrometer, measure each camshaft bearing journal. If camshaft is not within specifications, replace camshaft. See CAMSHAFT SPECIFICATIONS table in this article.

CAMSHAFT SPECIFICATIONS

Application	In. (mm)
Center Journal Runout	.0016 (.040)
Minimum Lobe Height	
Main Intake	1.3839 (35.151)
Sub Intake	1.3665 (34.709)
Exhaust	1.4028 (35.631)
Standard Lobe Height	
Main Intake	1.3917-1.3957 (35.349-35.451)
Sub Intake	1.3744-1.3783 (34.910-35.009)
Exhaust	1.4106-1.4146 (35.829-35.931)
Standard Bearing Journal Diameter	1.0622-1.0628 (26.980-25.560)
Thrust Clearance	
Standard	.0031-.0071 (.079-.180)
Maximum	.0098 (.249)

Installation

1) Coat camshaft bearings with engine oil. Install camshaft in cylinder head with knock pin at 12 o'clock position. Install No. 2, 3 and 4 camshaft bearing caps and bolts but do not tighten at this time. Ensure camshaft bearing caps are installed to original location. Ensure arrows on bearing caps face front.

2) Apply engine oil to new camshaft seal lip and install seal. Apply seal packing to No. 1 camshaft bearing cap and immediately install No. 1 bearing cap. Do not tighten to specifications at this time.

3) Tighten each camshaft bearing cap a little at a time and in sequence to specifications. *See Fig. 9.* Check camshaft thrust clearance. If not within specifications, replace cylinder head and/or camshaft. See CAMSHAFT SPECIFICATIONS table in this article.

Fig. 9: Camshaft Bearing Cap Tightening Sequence

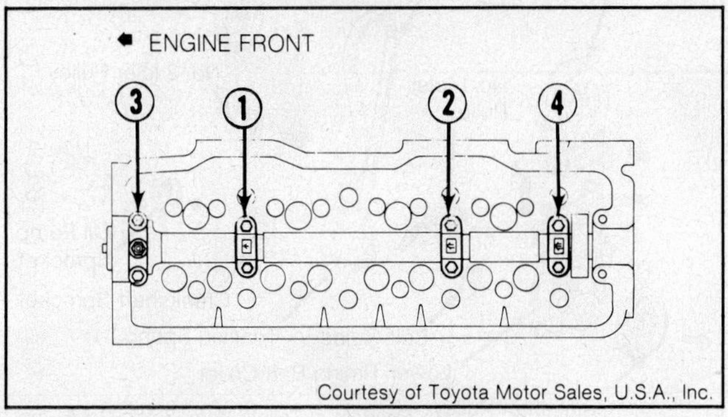

CAMSHAFT OIL SEAL

Removal & Installation

On-vehicle procedure unavailable from manufacturer. For out of vehicle procedure, see REMOVAL under CAMSHAFT in this article.

VALVES

VALVE ARRANGEMENT

Right Side – Intake valves.

Left Side – Exhaust valves.

NOTE: "Right" and "Left" refer to right and left side of the engine NOT the vehicle.

ROCKER ARMS

Removal

Remove camshaft. See REMOVAL under CAMSHAFT in this article. Loosen valve adjusting screw lock nut. Lift up on rocker arm spring and pry spring off

Fig. 10: Rocker Arm Adjusting Screw Position

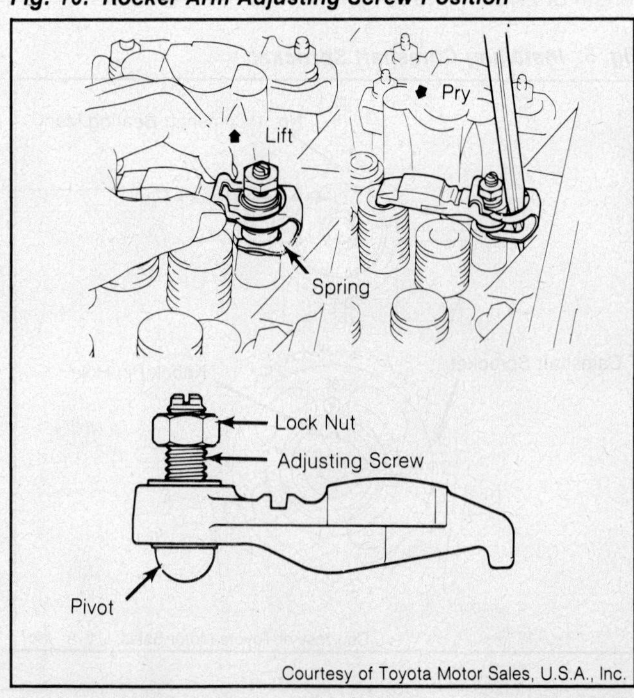

1.5L 12-VALVE 4-CYLINDER (Cont.)

with a screwdriver. *See Fig. 10.* Remove rocker arms and keep in order for installation to original location.

Installation

1) Properly position valve adjusting screw. *See Fig. 10.* Position a new rocker arm spring on rocker arm. Using a screwdriver, press the bottom lip of rocker arm spring until it fits into groove on rocker arm pivot.

2) Place valve adjusting screw in rocker arm pivot. Using a screwdriver, pry rocker arm spring onto rocker arm pivot. Pulling rocker arm up and down, ensure spring tension is on rocker arm and rocker arm does not rattle. To complete installation, reverse removal procedure.

CAMSHAFT BEARINGS

Removal & Installation

Check bearing clearance with Plastigage method. If clearance is greater than specifications, replace cylinder head. See ENGINE SPECIFICATIONS tables at end of this article.

VALVE GUIDE SERVICING

NOTE: Keep valves in order to ensure accurate measurement with matching valve guide.

Inspection

With cylinder head disassembled, measure inside diameter of valve guide. Measure outside diameter of matching valve stem. Subtract valve stem diameter from valve guide diameter. If clearance is greater than specifications, replace valve guide. See MAXIMUM VALVE CLEARANCE table in this article. See REPLACEMENT under VALVE GUIDE SERVICING in this article.

MAXIMUM VALVE CLEARANCE

Application	In. (mm)
Intake	.0031 (.079)
Exhaust	.0039 (.099)

Replacement

1) Using Valve Guide Replacer (SST 09201-70010), drive valve guide out through combustion side of cylinder head. Measure valve guide bore diameter of cylinder head.

2) Select the proper replacement valve guide to fit valve guide bore. See VALVE GUIDE BORE-TO-VALVE GUIDE table in this article. Using valve guide replacer, drive new valve guide into cylinder head from rocker arm side.

3) Installed valve guide must protrude from cylinder .5236-.5551" (13.299-14.100 mm). *See Fig. 11.* Using a 6 mm reamer, ream installed valve guide to obtain standard valve-to-valve guide clearance. See ENGINE SPECIFICAITONS tables at end of this article.

VALVE GUIDE BORE-TO-VALVE GUIDE

Guide Bore In. (mm)	Guide Size
.4331-.4341 (11.001-11.026)	Standard
.4342-.4360 (11.029-11.074) [1]	O/S 0.05

[1] – If guide bore exceeds .4341" (11.026 mm), machine guide bore to .4350-.4361" (11.049-11.077 mm) and use O/S guide.

Fig. 11: Installed Valve Guide

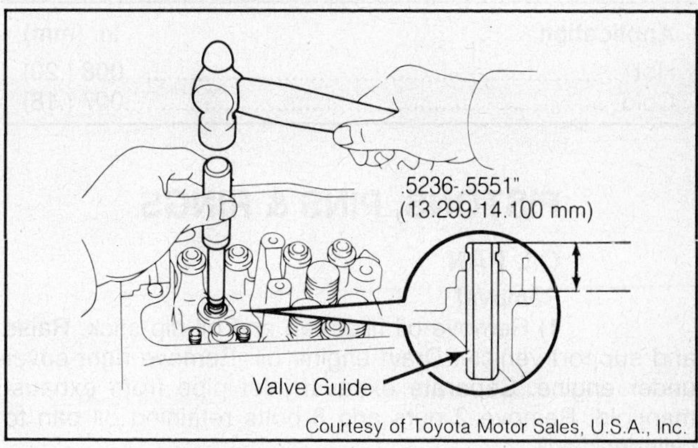

Courtesy of Toyota Motor Sales, U.S.A., Inc.

VALVE SEAT INSERTS

NOTE: Valve seat insert replacement procedure unavailable from manufacturer.

Inspection & Grinding

1) Check valve face-to-valve seat contact surface. Contact surface must be in middle of valve face. Contact surface must have a width of .047-.063" (1.194-1.60 mm). If contact surface is too high on valve face, use a 30 degree and 45 degree cutter on all valve seats.

2) If contact surface is too low on valve face, use a 75 degree and 45 degree cutter on intake valve seat and a 60 degree and 45 degree cutter on exhaust valve seat. With proper contact surface achieved, hand-lap valve and valve seat thoroughly.

VALVE SPRINGS

Inspection

With valve springs removed, check valve spring squareness and free length. Using a spring tester, measure valve spring tension at specified length. If valve spring(s) is not within specifications, replace valve spring(s). See VALVE SPRING SPECIFICATIONS table in this article.

VALVE SPRING SPECIFICATIONS

Application	Specifications
Free Length	1.6346" (41.52 mm)
Installed Tension	35.1 Lb. @ 1.3842" (15.91 kg @ 35.16 mm)
Maximum Out Of Square	.079" (2.01 mm)

VALVE CLEARANCE ADJUSTMENT

1) Align groove on crankshaft pulley with "O" mark on timing belt cover. Ensure rocker arms on No. 1 cylinder are loose and rocker arms on No. 4 cylinder are tight. If rocker arms are not correct, rotate crankshaft one complete revolution and recheck.

2) Measure clearance on No. 1 cylinder intake and exhaust, No. 2 cylinder intake and No. 3 cylinder exhaust. Rotate crankshaft one complete revolution. Measure clearance on No. 2 cylinder exhaust, No. 3 cylinder intake and No. 4 cylinder intake and exhaust.

3) Adjust clearance if not within specifications. See VALVE CLEARANCE ADJUSTMENT table in this article. Recheck valve clearance after adjustment.

1.5L 12-VALVE 4-CYLINDER (Cont.)

VALVE CLEARANCE ADJUSTMENT

Application	In. (mm)
Hot	.008 (.20)
Cold	.007 (.18)

PISTONS, PINS & RINGS

OIL PAN

Removal

1) Remove oil filler cap and oil dip stick. Raise and support vehicle. Drain engine oil. Remove right cover under engine. Separate exhaust inlet pipe from exhaust manifold. Remove 2 nuts and 8 bolts retaining oil pan to cylinder block.

2) Insert Seal Cutter (SST 09032-00100) between cylinder block and oil pan. Cut off applied sealer but DO NOT cut along oil pump body side. Remove oil pan. Remove oil strainer with "O" ring. Remove pressure regulator valve assembly.

CAUTION: DO NOT use solvent to clean gasket from mating surfaces.

Installation

1) Install presssure regulator valve and tighten to specifications. Apply engine oil to new "O" ring and install "O" ring on oil strainer. Install and tighten oil strainer.

2) Ensure gasket mating surfaces are clean and dry. Apply seal packing to oil pan surface. *See Fig. 12.* Install oil pan within 15 minutes. To complete installation, reverse removal procedure.

Fig. 12: Applying Seal Packing On Oil Pan

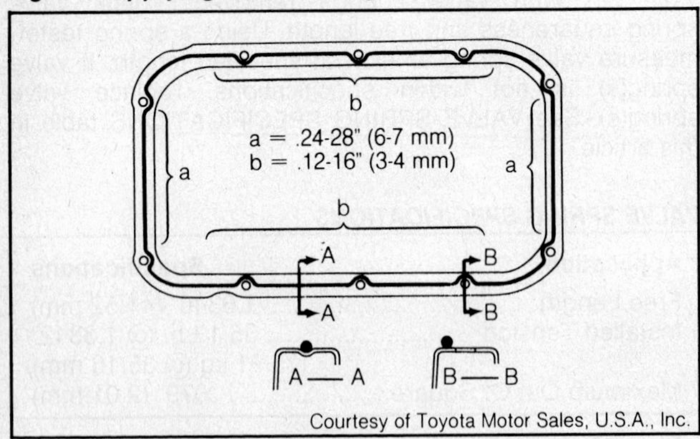

PISTON & ROD ASSEMBLY

Removal

1) With cylinder head and oil pan removed, remove ridge from top of each cylinder wall. Match mark rods and rod caps with installed cylinder number. Place an engine front mark on rod and/or piston if not marked from factory.

2) Using a dial indicator, measure connecting rod thrust clearance by moving rod back and forth. If clearance is greater than maximum specifications, replace connecting rod and/or crankshaft. See CONNECTING ROD THRUST CLEARANCE table in this article. Remove connecting rod cap nuts.

3) Lightly tap rod cap bolts with plastic hammer. Remove rod cap and lower bearing insert. Cover rod bolts to prevent damage. Push connecting rod and piston assembly out top of cylinder block.

CONNECTING ROD THRUST CLEARANCE

Application	In. (mm)
Standard Clearance	.0059-.0138 (.150-.351)
Maximum Clearance	.0177 (.450)

Installation

1) Apply new engine oil to cylinder bore, piston, crankshaft rod journal and rod bearing inserts. Cover rod bolts to prevent damage. Ensure piston ring gaps are positioned properly. *See Fig. 13.* Install a piston ring compressor.

2) Position engine front mark and push piston and upper bearing insert, into cylinder from which it was removed. Install matching connecting rod cap and lower bearing insert. Ensure rod cap engine front is positioned properly.

3) Apply a light coat of engine oil to rod bolt threads and under head of nut. Alternately tighten nuts to specifications in several steps. Rotate crankshaft and ensure it turns smoothly. Check rod thrust clearance.

Fig. 13: Installed Piston Rings

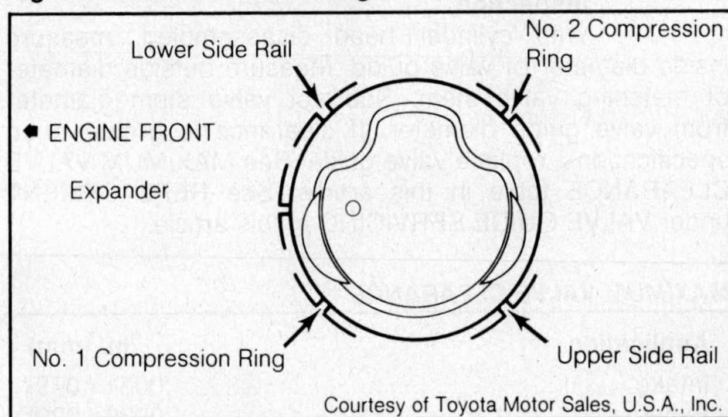

FITTING PISTON

1) Thoroughly clean piston and cylinder bore. DO NOT use wire brush. Measure out side diameter of piston at right anlges to piston pin center line and .87" (22.1 mm) from piston top.

2) Measure cylinder bore diameter in thrust direction. Take measurement .39" (9.9 mm) from top and bottom of cylinder bore. Take another measurement at middle of cylinder bore.

3) Subtract piston outside diameter from cylinder bore inside diameter. If clearance is greater than maximum specifications of .0079" (.201 mm), replace all 4 pistons and/or rebore all cylinders. See AVAILABLE PISTON SIZE table in this article.

AVAILABLE PISTON SIZE

Piston	In. (mm)
Standard	2.8709-2.8720 (72.921-72.949)
O/S 0.50	2.8905-2.8917 (73.419-73.449)

PISTON PIN REPLACEMENT

Removal & Installation

Piston pin is press fit. No cooling or heating for removal is required. Place match marks on components to ensure installation to original piston and connecting rod.

1.5L 12-VALVE 4-CYLINDER (Cont.)

Coat piston pin and pin bore with engine. Specified installing temperature is 68°F (20°C). To install, reverse removal procedure. Ensure engine front marks are properly positioned. *See Fig. 14.*

Fig. 14: Aligning Engine Front Marks

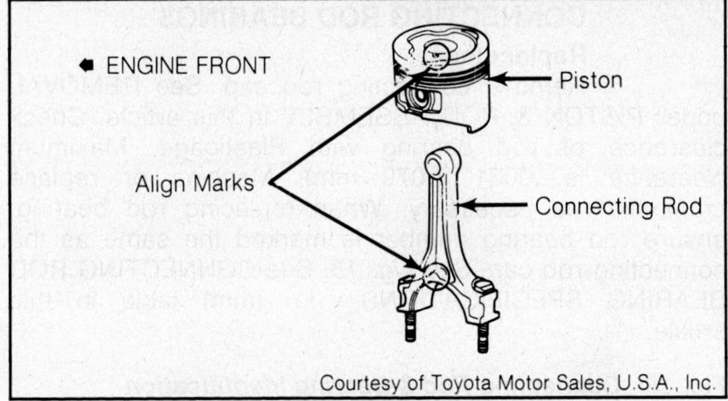

Courtesy of Toyota Motor Sales, U.S.A., Inc.

CRANKSHAFT & ROD BEARINGS

NOTE: Following procedures are with engine removed from vehicle.

CRANKSHAFT & MAIN BEARINGS

Removal

1) Remove cylinder head, oil pan, oil screen, pressure regulator, front crankshaft cover and rear oil seal retainer. Using dial indicator, measure crankshaft thrust clearance. If clearance is greater than maximum specifications, replace thrust washers as a set. See THRUST CLEARANCE SPECIFICATIONS table in this article.

THRUST CLEARANCE SPECIFICATIONS

Application	In. (mm)
Standard Clearance	.0008-.0087 (.020-.022.1)
Maximum Clearance	.012 (.31)
Thrust Washer Thickness	
Standard	.0957-.0976 (2.431-2.479)
O/S .125	.0981-.1001 (2.492-2.543)

2) Mark main bearing cap with engine front and order number for installation reference. Gradually loosen crankshaft main bearing bolts in several steps and in sequence. *See Fig. 15.* Remove main bearing cap with bearing inserts and thrust washers.

3) Place Plastigage on each main bearing journal. Install main bearing caps and inserts. Ensure main bearing cap front is located properly. Tighten main bearing bolts in 3 steps to specifications and in sequence. *See Fig. 16.* Remove main bearing bolts as in step **2)**.

4) Measure widest point on Plastigage. If clearance is greater than maximum, replace bearings and grind or replace crankshaft as necessary. See CRANKSHAFT PLASTIGAGE SPECIFICATIONS table in this article. With Plastigage specifications achieved, remove crankshaft from cylinder block.

CRANKSHAFT PLASTIGAGE SPECIFICATIONS

Application	In. (mm)
Standard Clearance	.0006-.0014 (.015-.036)
Maximum Clearance	.0031 (.079)
Replacement Cylinder Block	
Standard Clearance	.0007-.0018 (.018-.046)

Fig. 15: Main Bearing Cap Bolt Removing Sequence

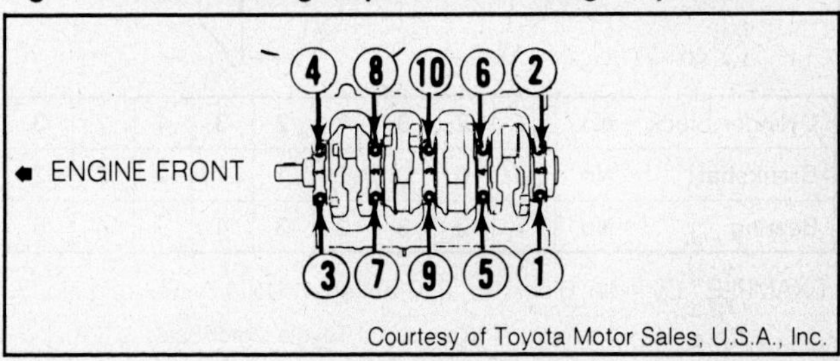

Courtesy of Toyota Motor Sales, U.S.A., Inc.

Fig. 16: Main Bearing Cap Bolt Tightening Sequence

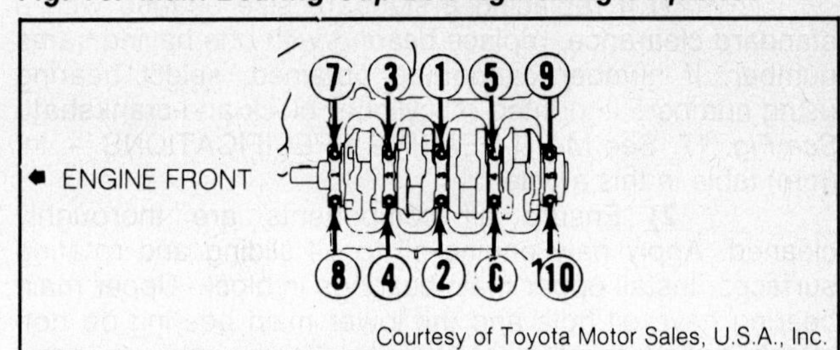

Courtesy of Toyota Motor Sales, U.S.A., Inc.

MAIN BEARING SPECIFICATIONS – In. (mm)

Bearing Size No.	Cylinder Block Main Journal Bore	Main Journal Diameter	Bearing Center Wall Thickness
0	....	1.9683-1.9685 (49.995-50.000)	....
1	2.1267-2.1269 (54.018-54.024)	1.9681-1.9683 (49.991-49.995)	0.786-0.0787 (1.997-2.000)
2	2.1270-2.1272 (54.025-54.031)	1.9679-1.9681 (49.985-49.990)	0.0788-0.0789 (2.001-2.004)
3	2.1272-2.1274 (54.031-54.036)	....	0.0789-0.0790 (2.004-2.007)
4	....	....	0.0790-0.0791 (2.007-2.010)
5	....	....	0.0791-0.0792 (2.010-2.012)
U/S 0.25	2.1267-2.1274 (54.018-54.036)	1.9585-1.9589 (49.745-49.755)	0.0834-0.0836 (2.118-2.124)

Toyota Engines

1.5L 12-VALVE 4-CYLINDER (Cont.)

Fig. 17: Selecting Main Bearing

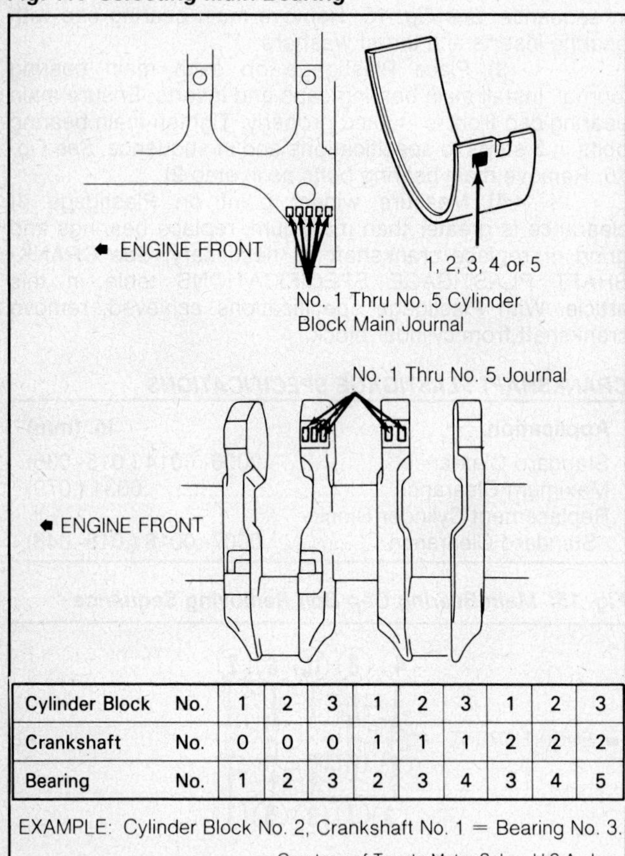

Cylinder Block	No.	1	2	3	1	2	3	1	2	3
Crankshaft	No.	0	0	0	1	1	1	2	2	2
Bearing	No.	1	2	3	2	3	4	3	4	5

EXAMPLE: Cylinder Block No. 2, Crankshaft No. 1 = Bearing No. 3.

Courtesy of Toyota Motor Sales, U.S.A., Inc.

Installation

1) If replacing a standard size bearing with a standard clearance, replace bearing with one having same number. If number cannot be obtained, select bearing using numbers imprinted on cylinder block and crankshaft. *See Fig. 17.* See MAIN BEARING SPECIFICATIONS - In. (mm) table in this article.

2) Ensure all components are thoroughly cleaned. Apply new engine oil to all sliding and rotating surfaces. Install upper main bearings in block. Upper main bearing have oil hole and the lower main bearing do not. Install upper thrust washers on center main bearing journal, with oil grooves facing outward.

3) Coat installed main bearings with new engine oil and install crankshaft. Install lower main bearings in main bearing caps. Install lower thrust washers on No. 3 main bearing cap with oil grooves facing outward. Install proper numbered main bearing cap. Ensure engine front mark faces proper direction.

4) Apply a light coat of new engine oil on main bearing cap bolt threads and under the heads of cap bolts. Tighten cap bolts to specification in 3 steps and in sequence. *See Fig. 16.* To complete installation, reverse removal procedure.

CONNECTING ROD BEARINGS

Replacement

Remove connecting rod cap. See REMOVAL under PISTON & ROD ASSEMBLY in this article. Check clearance of rod bearing with Plastigage. Maximum clearance is .0031" (.079 mm). Machine or replace crankshaft as necessary. When replacing rod bearing, ensure rod bearing number is marked the same as the connecting rod cap. *See Fig. 18.* See CONNECTING ROD BEARING SPECIFICATIONS - In. (mm) table in this article.

Fig. 18: Connecting Rod & Bearing Identification

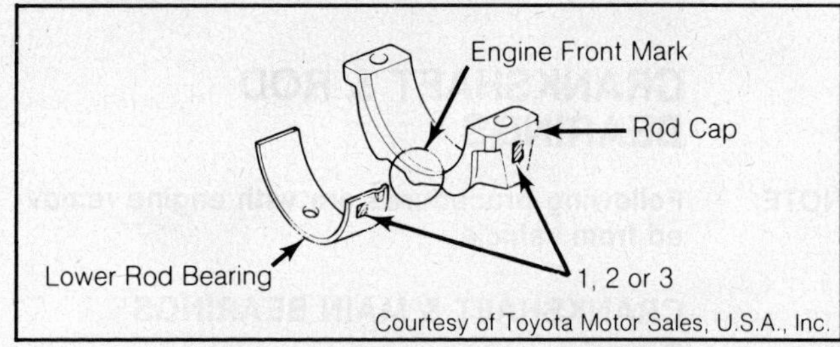

Courtesy of Toyota Motor Sales, U.S.A., Inc.

REAR MAIN BEARING OIL SEAL

Removal

Remove transaxle without removing engine. Remove clutch disc and pressure plate (if equipped). Remove flywheel or flexplate. Using a knife, cut off lip of oil seal. Tape end of flat screwdriver and pry out oil seal. Use care not to damage sealing surface.

Installation

Ensure sealing surface of crankshaft is not damaged. Apply multipurpose grease to new seal. Using Oil Seal Installer (SST 09223-41020), install oil seal squarely in oil seal retainer.

ENGINE OILING

CRANKCASE CAPACITY

Crankcase dry fill capacity is 3.6 qts. (3.4L). Drain and fill capacity without filter is 3.1 qts. (2.9L) and with filter is 3.4 qts. (3.2L).

CONNECTING ROD BEARING SPECIFICATIONS - In. (mm)

Bearing Size No.	Connecting Rod Inner Diameter	Crankshaft Rod Journal Diameter	Bearing Center Wall Thickness
1	1.8110-1.8113 (45.999-46.007)	1.6923-1.6929 (42.984-43.000)	0.0585-0.0587 (1.486-1.491)
2	1.8113-1.8116 (46.007-46.014)	1.6923-1.6929 (42.984-43.000)	0.0587-0.0589 (1.491-1.495)
3	1.8116-1.8118 (46.014-46.021)	1.6923-1.6929 (42.984-43.000)	0.0589-0.0590 (1.495-1.499)
U/S 0.251	1.8110-1.8118 (45.999-46.021)	1.6829-1.6833 (42.746-42.756)	0.0633-0.0636 (1.608-1.615)

1.5L 12-VALVE 4-CYLINDER (Cont.)

NORMAL OIL PRESSURE

Normal oil pressure is greater than 4.3 psi (.3 kg/cm²) at idle. At 3,000 RPM oil pressure should be 36-71 psi (2.5-5.0 kg/cm²).

OIL PRESSURE REGULATOR VALVE

Oil pressure regulator valve is located on lower cylinder block, under oil pan and on left side. It is a nonadjustable type valve.

CRANKSHAFT FRONT OIL SEAL

Removal & Installation

Remove timing belt and crankshaft sprocket. See REMOVAL under TIMING BELT & SPROCKETS in this article. Cut off lip of seal. Tape end of flat screwdriver and pry out seal. Apply multipurpose grease to new seal. Install seal with Front Seal Installer (SST 09214-60010). To complete installation, reverse removal procedure.

OIL PUMP & OIL SEAL

NOTE: Front cover is the housing for oil pump.

Removal

1) Remove timing belt. See REMOVAL under TIMING BELT & SPROCKETS in this article. Remove oil pan and oil strainer. See REMOVAL under OIL PAN in this article. Remove 9 bolts retaining front cover. Remove tension spring bracket.

2) Lightly tap front cover at the oil pan mating surface, with plastic hammer and remove front cover assembly. Remove "O" ring. Remove drive and driven gear. Pry out oil seal flat screwdriver.

Inspection

Check gears, cover and body for wear and damage. Measure clearance between driven gear and body. Measure clearance between both gear tips. Measure side clearance. If beyond specifications, replace necessary parts.

OIL PUMP SPECIFICATIONS

Application	In. (mm)
Driven Gear-to-Body Clearance	
Standard	.0039-.0063 (.100-.160)
Maximum	.0079 (.200)
Gear Side Clearance	
Standard	.0012-.0035 (.031-.089)
Maximum	.0039 (.099)
Gear Tip-to-Gear Tip Clearance	
Standard	.0024-.0059 (.061-.150)
Maximum	.0079 (.200)

Installation

Apply multipurpose grease to new oil seal. Using Pump Seal Installer (SST 09307-12010), install oil seal to a depth of .04" (1.0 mm) below pump body edge. Apply seal packing to front cover. *See Fig. 19.* To complete installation, reverse removal procedure.

Fig. 19: Applying Seal Packing To Front Cover

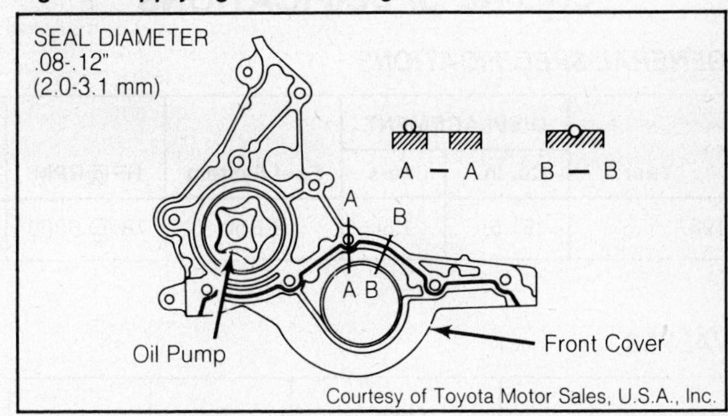

ENGINE COOLING

WATER PUMP

Removal

1) Remove right cover under engine. Drain coolant from radiator and engine. See step **1)** in REMOVAL under ENGINE in this article. Remove oil dipstick. Remove accessory drive belt. Remove intake manifold stay and ground strap. Disconnect coolant hose from carburetor.

2) Remove dipstick tube mounting bolt and pull out dipstick tube. Remove coolant hose from intake manifold. Remove water pump pulley. Remove bolt retaining coolant hose to side of cylinder block. Remove bolt, nuts and water pump assembly.

Installation

Apply seal packing to water pump. *See Fig. 20.* Install new "O" ring to inlet pipe. Apply a water and soap solution to "O" ring. Insert inlet pipe in water pump. Install water pump and tighten to specifications. To complete installation, reverse removal procedure.

Fig. 20: Applying Seal Packing To Water Pump

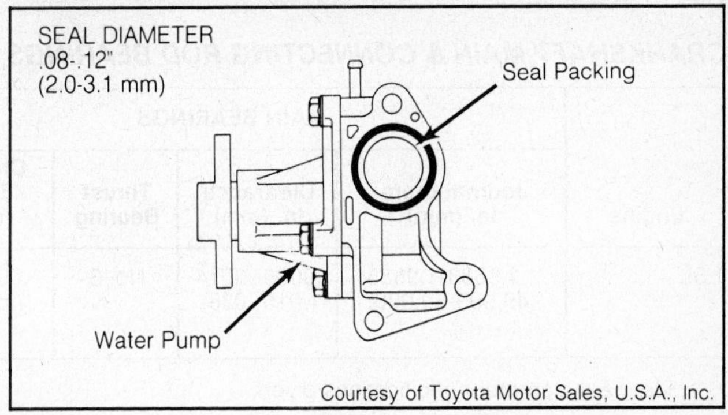

NOTE: For more information, see ENGINE COOLING SYSTEMS article at the end of this section.

1.5L 12-VALVE 4-CYLINDER (Cont.)

ENGINE SPECIFICATIONS

GENERAL SPECIFICATIONS

Year	DISPLACEMENT		Fuel System	HP@RPM	Torque Ft. Lbs.@RPM	Compr. Ratio	BORE		STROKE	
	Cu. In.	Liters					In.	mm	In.	mm
1987	91.5	1.5	2-Bbl.	78 @ 6000	87 @ 4000	9.3:1	2.88	73.2	3.43	87.1

VALVES

Engine Size & Valve	Head Diam. In. (mm)	Face Angle	Seat Angle	Seat Width In. (mm)	Stem Diameter In. (mm)	Stem Clearance In. (mm)	Valve Lift In. (mm)
1.5L							
Intake	.....	44.5°	45°	.047-.063 (1.20-1.60)	.2350-.2356 (5.970-5.985)	.0010-.0024 (.025-.061)	.....
Exhaust	.....	44.5°	45°	.047-.063 (1.20-1.60)	.2348-.2354 (5.965-5.980)	.0012-.0026 (.031-.066)	.....

PISTONS, PINS & RINGS

Engine	PISTONS	PINS		RINGS		
	Clearance In. (mm)	Piston Fit In. (mm)	Rod Fit In. (mm)	Ring No.	End Gap In. (mm)	Side Clearance In. (mm)
1.5L	.0028-.0035 (.071-.089)	.....	[1] Press Fit	No. 1	.0102-.0142 (.259-.361)	.0016-.0031 (.041-.079)
				No. 2	.0118-.0177 (.300-.450)	.0012-.0028 (.031-.071)
				Oil	.0059-.0157 (.150-.399)	.....

[1] – Piston and pin are available only as a set.

CRANKSHAFT MAIN & CONNECTING ROD BEARINGS

Engine	MAIN BEARINGS				CONNECTING ROD BEARINGS		
	Journal Diam. In. (mm)	Clearance In. (mm)	Thrust Bearing	Crankshaft End Play In. (mm)	Journal Diam. In. (mm)	Clearance In. (mm)	Side Play In. (mm)
1.5L	[1] 1.9683-1.9685 (49.995-50.000)	.0006-.0014 (.015-.036)	No. 3	.0008-.0087 (.020-.221)	1.6923-1.6929 (42.984-43.000)	.0006-.0019 (.015-.048)	.0059-.0138 (.150-.351)

[1] – Standard diameter specifications given.

CAMSHAFT

Engine	Journal Diam. In. (mm)	Clearance In. (mm)	Lobe Lift In. (mm)
1.5L	1.0622-1.0628 (26.980-26.995)	.0015-.0029 (.035-.072)	[1] 1.392-1.396 (35.35-35.45)

[1] – Main intake specifications given. Sub intake is 1.3744-1.3783" (34.910-35.009 mm). Exhaust is 1.4106-1.4116" (35.829-35.855 mm).

VALVE SPRINGS

Engine	Free Length In. (mm)	PRESSURE Lbs. @ In. (Kg @ mm)	
		Valve Closed	Valve Open
1.5L	1.6346 (41.519)	35.1 @ 1.3842 (15.9 @ 35.159)	.....

1.5L 12-VALVE 4-CYLINDER (Cont.)

ENGINE SPECIFICATIONS (Cont.)

TIGHTENING SPECIFICATIONS

Application	Ft. Lbs. (N.m)
Camshaft Bearing Cap Bolt	10 (14)
Camshaft Sprocket Bolt	37 (50)
Connecting Rod Cap Nut	[1] 29 (39)
Crankshaft Pulley Bolt	112 (152)
Cylinder Head Bolt	[2]
Engine-to-Automatic Transaxle	
10 mm Bolt	25 (34)
12 mm Bolt	47 (64)
Engine-to-Manual Transaxle	
10 mm Bolt	34 (46)
12 mm Bolt	47 (64)
Engine Lift Hook	
Front	15 (20)
Rear	43 (58)
Exhaust Manifold Nut	38 (52)
Exhaust Pipe-to-Exhaust Manifold	46 (62)
Flywheel Bolt	[3] 65 (88)
Flexplate	61 (83)
Front Engine Mount Through Bolt	58 (79)
Intake Manifold Bolts/Nuts	14 (19)
Left Engine Mount Bracket-to-	
Transaxle Bolt	35 (48)
Insulator Bolt	54 (73)
Main Bearing Cap Bolt	[1] 42 (57)
Oil Pump Sprocket Nut	20 (27)
Pressure Plate-to-Flywheel Bolt	14 (19)
Pressure Regulator Valve	22 (29)
Rear Engine Mount Bracket-to-	
Transaxle Bolt	43 (58)
M/T Insulator Bolt	47 (64)
A/T Insulator Bolt	35 (48)

TIGHTENING SPECIFICATIONS (Cont.)

Application	Ft. Lbs. (N.m)
Rear Engine Mount Insulator-to-	
Body (M/T) Bolt	47 (64)
Body (A/T) Bolt	35 (48)
Right Engine Mount Bracket-to-	
Cylinder Block	32 (43)
Insulator Bolt	47 (64)
Right Engine Mount Insulator-to-Right Member Bolt	35 (48)
Spark Plug	13 (18)
Timing Belt Idler Pulley	
No. 1 Bolt	13 (18)
No. 2 Bolt	20 (27)
Torque Converter Bolt	13 (18)
Water Pump Bolt/Nut	13 (18)
	INCH Lbs. (N.m)
Fuel Pump Nut	108 (12)
Oil Pan Bolts/Nuts	74 (8)
Oil Pump-to-Block	65 (7)
Oil Strainer-to-Block	65 (7)
Rocker Arm Adjusting Lock Nut	108 (12)

[1] – Tighten in several steps.
[2] – In sequence, tighten first to 22 ft. lbs. (30 N.m). Tighten second to 36 ft. lbs. (49 N.m). Final tighten is an additional 90 degrees.
[3] – Tighten in 2 or 3 steps in a cross pattern.

1.6L 16-VALVE 4-CYLINDER

Corolla, MR2

NOTE: **For engine repair procedures not covered in this article, see ENGINE OVERHAUL PROCEDURES article at beginning of this section.**

ENGINE CODING

ENGINE IDENTIFICATION

Engine serial number is stamped on left rear side of block.

ENGINE IDENTIFICATION CODES

Application	Code
1.6L	4A-GE

ENGINE, MANIFOLDS & CYLINDER HEAD

ENGINE

Removal (Corolla)

1) Mark hinge-to-hood. Remove hood and battery. Remove under engine covers. Drain coolant, engine oil and automatic transaxle fluid. Mark and remove vacuum hoses and electrical connectors. Remove air cleaner assembly.

2) Remove coolant reservoir tank and radiator, with cooling fan. Disconnect heater hoses at inlet housing, fuel inlet hose at fuel filter and hoses at air valve. Disconnect fuel return hose at pressure regulator.

3) On manual transaxle models, remove clutch slave assembly and disconnect charcoal canister vacuum hose. Mark and remove shift control cables. On automatic transaxle models, disconnect control cable at shift lever.

4) Disconnect speedometer and cruise control cables. Disconnect throttle linkage. Remove cruise control actuator (if equipped). Disconnect and remove ignition coil.

5) Remove right side kick panel and disconnect 4 connectors at junction block. Disconnect ECU connectors. Pull out engine main wire-to-engine compartment. Mark and disconnect junction block connectors, starter cable, ground strap terminals, washer change valve and cruise control connectors.

6) Disconnect vacuum hose at brake booster. Loosen power steering pulley nut. Loosen pulley to gain access to bolts behind pulley. Loosen idler pulley set nut and turn adjusting bolt. Remove belt. *See Fig. 1.*

Fig. 1: Idler Pulley Removal

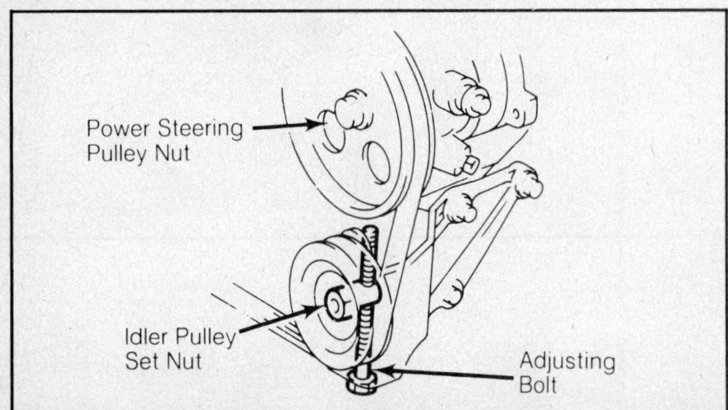

Courtesy of Toyota Motor Sales, U.S.A., Inc.

7) Remove A/C compressor belt. Remove 4 mounting bolts and move compressor aside. Loosen compressor bracket bolts and disconnect oil pressure connector. Loosen bolts behind power steering pump pulley. Remove pump bracket-to-engine bolts and remove as an assembly.

8) Disconnect and remove oxygen sensor. Disconnect oil cooler hoses. Raise vehicle. Remove catalytic converter hanger bolts. Remove exhaust hanger at engine. Disconnect exhaust pipe from manifold.

9) Remove 2 hole covers from crossmember and remove bolts from holes. Remove front engine mount through bolt and engine retaining bolts. Remove mount assembly. Remove 4 outer crossmember bolts and remove crossmember.

10) Remove both drive shafts. See FWD AXLE SHAFTS & CV JOINTS under DRIVE AXLES section. Lower vehicle. Attach hoist to engine lifting hooks. Disconnect right-hand engine mount assembly. Remove left-hand transaxle mount assembly.

11) Lift engine and transaxle out top of vehicle using care to clear wiring, hoses, cables, steering gear housing and throttle position sensor. Place assembly on stand and remove starter. On automatic transaxle models, remove 6 torque converter bolts.

12) Remove bolts retaining transaxle and remove transaxle. On manual transaxle, remove clutch and flywheel assembly. Remove rear engine plate. Remove A/C bracket and alternator assembly.

Installation

Install transaxle, starter, alternator and A/C bracket on engine. Attach engine hoist and lower engine into position. To complete installation, reverse removal procedure. Check all oil and coolant levels. Install hood, start engine and check for leaks.

Removal (MR2)

1) Disconnect battery. Remove fuel tank protector and under engine cover. Drain engine oil and coolant. Remove throttle cable, cruise control (if equipped), automatic transaxle throttle cable (if equipped) and speedometer cable.

2) Remove battery. Remove airflow meter assembly with air hose. Disconnect heater hoses from cylinder head rear cover and coolant inlet housing. Disconnect radiator hose, air bleeder hose and ground strap from coolant inlet housing.

3) Disconnect fuel line from filter. Disconnect return fuel line. Disconnect charcoal canister vacuum hose. Mark and disconnect engine wiring connectors, main wire connector and back-up light switch connector (manual transaxle).

4) Remove manual transaxle protector. Remove coolant reservoir tank. Remove A/C compressor belt. Remove alternator assembly. Disconnect radiator hose from coolant outlet housing. Disconnect vacuum hose from brake booster. Disconnect ignition coil wire.

5) Remove rear luggage compartment trim and disconnect circuit opening relay, ECU connectors and cooling fan computer connector. *See Fig. 2.* Loosen A/C compressor and remove belt. Remove compressor assembly and move compressor aside.

6) Disconnect manual transaxle control cables from shift outer lever and select lever. Remove clutch slave cylinder and bracket assembly from manual transaxle. Disconnect automatic transaxle control cable and oil cooler hoses. Disconnect engine oil cooler hoses. Raise vehicle.

1.6L 16-VALVE 4-CYLINDER (Cont.)

Fig. 2: Rear Luggage Compartment Connectors

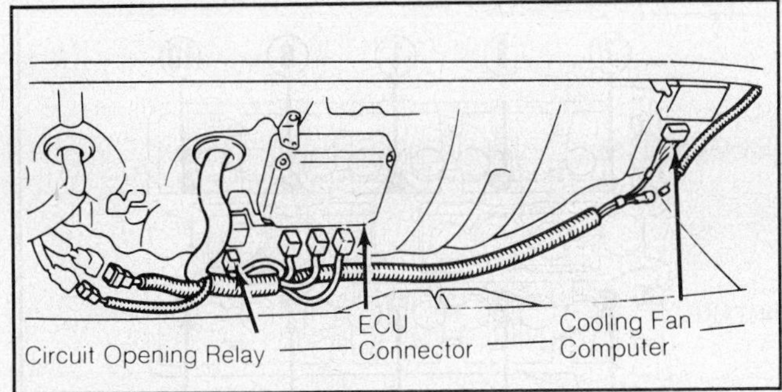

Courtesy of Toyota Motor Sales, U.S.A., Inc.

7) Disconnect exhaust pipe from exhaust manifold. Disconnect and remove oxygen sensor. Remove flywheel housing stiffener plate and inspection cover. Remove right-hand drive shaft and disconnect left-hand drive shaft from side gear shaft. See FWD AXLE SHAFTS & CV JOINTS under DRIVE AXLES section.

8) Remove front engine mount through bolt and engine retaining bolts. Remove front engine mount assembly. Repeat procedure and remove rear engine mount. Place a saddle type engine stand under vehicle. Lower vehicle until engine sets on stand.

9) Remove right-hand engine mount nuts, bolt and through bolt. Remove engine mount. Remove left-hand engine mount through bolt. Raise vehicle, using care not to damage throttle position sensor, wiring, hoses and cables. Remove engine and transaxle assembly.

10) Remove starter and transaxle from engine. On manual transaxle models, remove clutch assembly and flywheel. Mount engine on stand.

Installation

Install transaxle and starter to engine. Position engine assembly under vehicle and lower into position. Install engine mount bolts and nuts. To complete installation, reverse removal procedure. Check oil and coolant level. Start engine and check for leaks.

INTAKE MANIFOLD

Removal

1) Disconnect battery. Remove air cleaner assembly, throttle cable and speedometer cable clamp. Mark and disconnect vacuum hoses. Remove EGR valve with piping. Remove cold start injector pipe. Remove pulsation damper and disconnect fuel pipe from intake manifold and cylinder head rear cover.

2) Remove vacuum hose from pressure regulator. Remove fuel hose from connecting fuel pipe. Remove fuel pipe from cylinder head rear cover. Remove vacuum pipe and cylinder head rear cover. Remove delivery pipe with injectors.

3) Remove intake manifold bracket. Disconnect vacuum hose from intake air control valve. Remove vacuum switching valve with vacuum tank. Remove 2 nuts and 7 bolts retaining intake manifold to head. Remove intake manifold, air control valve and gaskets.

Inspection

Clean and check all gasket mating surfaces. Maximum warpage for intake manifold and air control valve surface is .002" (.05 mm). Replace manifold or air control valve if not within specifications.

Installation

Using new gaskets, assemble air control valve on intake manifold. Position manifold assembly to head and install bolts and nuts. Evenly tighten bolts starting from center and working outward. To complete installation, reverse removal procedure.

EXHAUST MANIFOLD

Removal & Installation

Disconnect exhaust pipe from exhaust manifold. Remove exhaust manifold heat insulator. Disconnect and remove oxygen sensor. Remove manifold bracket. Remove exhaust manifold retaining bolts and nuts. Remove manifold and gasket. Using new gaskets, reverse removal procedure for installation.

Inspection

Clean and check all gasket mating surfaces. Maximum warpage is .0118" (.30 mm). Replace manifold if not within specifications.

CYLINDER HEAD

NOTE: **To prevent warping or cracking, allow engine to cool before removing components.**

Removal

1) Remove under engine cover and drain coolant. Remove intake and exhaust manifolds. Disconnect brake booster vacuum hose. Remove heater hose from cylinder head rear cover. Remove radiator hose from coolant outlet housing.

2) Disconnect ignition coil and coolant by-pass hoses at auxiliary air valve. Remove vacuum pipe assembly from rear of cylinder head. Disconnect engine compartment wire connector from engine compartment main wire. Mark and disconnect cylinder head electrical components.

3) Mark and remove spark plug wires from spark plugs. Remove distributor cap. Set No. 1 cylinder at TDC, compression stroke. See TIMING BELT REMOVAL under CAMSHAFT in this article. Note position of distributor rotor and remove distributor. Remove accessory drive belts. Remove center valve cover and gasket. Remove both valve covers and gaskets. Check valve clearance. valve clearance.

4) Remove coolant outlet with by-pass pipe. Remove spark plugs. Slightly raise engine assembly and remove right-hand engine mount. Remove water pump pulley. Remove A/C idler pulley. Remove upper and center timing belt covers. Ensure all timing marks are in proper alignment and remove timing belt from camshaft sprockets.

5) Do not allow timing belt to shift on crankshaft sprocket. Hold camshaft secure and remove camshaft sprocket. Repeat procedure for other camshaft sprocket. Remove upper inner timing belt cover, located behind camshaft sprockets. Remove right-hand engine mount bracket. Check camshaft thrust clearance.

6) Loosen camshaft bearing cap bolts in 3 even steps and in sequence. *See Fig. 3.* Mark position of engine front, cap number and camshaft side on caps, if not already marked. Remove bearing caps, oil seals and camshafts. Remove cylinder head bolts in 3 even steps and in sequence. *See Fig. 4.*

CAUTION: **Failure to properly remove bolts may result in head warpage or cracking.**

1.6L 16-VALVE 4-CYLINDER (Cont.)

Fig. 3: Camshaft Bearing Cap Bolt Removal

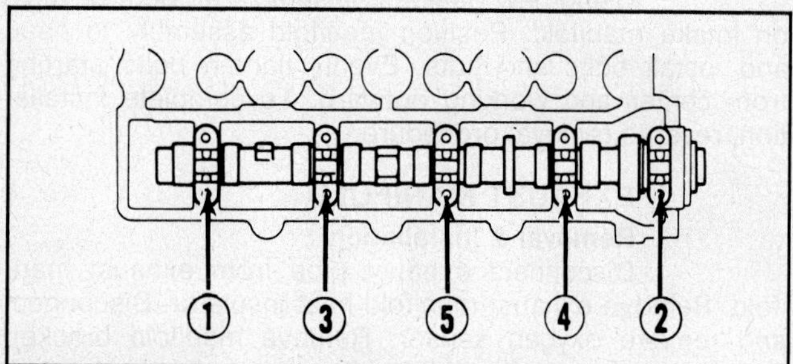

Courtesy of Toyota Motor Sales, U.S.A., Inc.

Fig. 4: Cylinder Head Bolt Removal

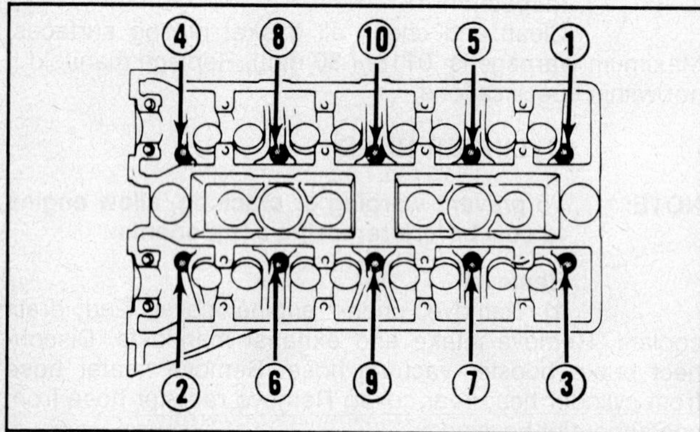

Courtesy of Toyota Motor Sales, U.S.A., Inc.

NOTE: Do not damage cylinder head or block surface during prying operation.

7) Lift cylinder head from dowels on cylinder block. If cylinder head is difficult to remove, pry with screwdriver between cylinder head and projection of cylinder block. Use care not to damage surface.

Inspection

Using feeler gauge and straightedge, check cylinder head for warpage. Maximum warpage for cylinder head and intake manifold surfaces is .002" (.051 mm). Maximum warpage for exhaust manifold surface is .0039" (.099 mm). Check head for cracks with dye penetrant. Replace as necessary. Tap cylinder block head bolt threads and blow clean with compressed air.

Installation

1) Thoroughly clean all gasket mating surfaces and carbon areas. Properly install new head gasket over dowels on block. Place cylinder head on block. Install short head bolts on intake side and long bolts on exhaust side. Lightly coat head bolt threads and under bolt head before installing. Tighten cylinder head bolts in 3 even steps and sequence. *See Fig. 5.*

2) Place camshafts in cylinder head and apply Seal Packing (08826-00080), to head. *See Fig. 6.* Ensure exhaust camshaft, with distributor drive gear, is on proper side of cylinder head. Install camshaft bearing caps to location as marked at removal. Ensure exhaust and intake sides are on proper camshaft sides.

3) Install camshaft bearing cap bolts. Tighten in 3 even steps and in sequence. *See Fig. 7.* Check camshaft thrust clearance. Apply grease to new camshaft oil seal lip and install oil seal. Ensure oil seals are installed squarely.

Fig. 5: Cylinder Head Tightening Sequence

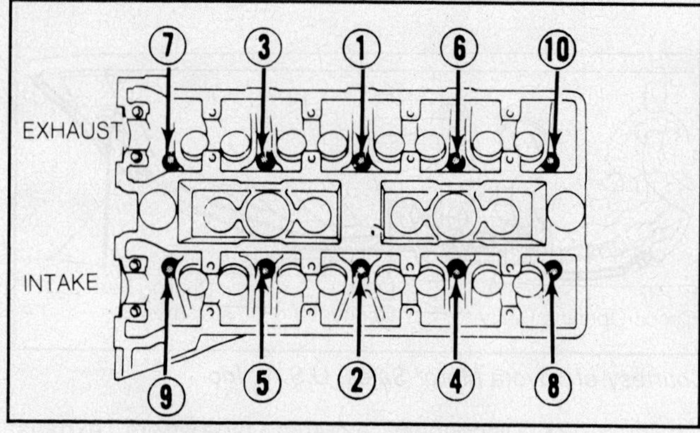

Courtesy of Toyota Motor Sales, U.S.A., Inc.

4) To complete installation, reverse removal procedure. Ensure all timing marks are in proper alignment before installing timing belt. Tighten all bolts/nuts to specifications.

Fig. 6: Camshaft & Seal Packing Installation

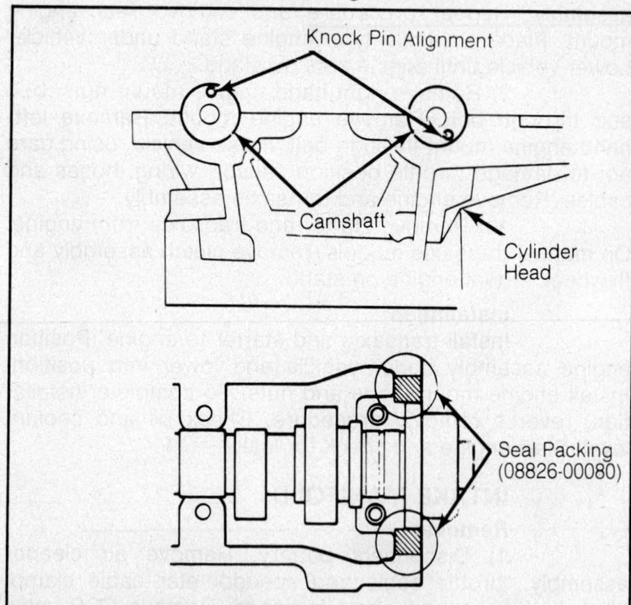

Courtesy of Toyota Motor Sales, U.S.A., Inc.

Fig. 7: Camshaft Bearing Cap Tightening Sequence

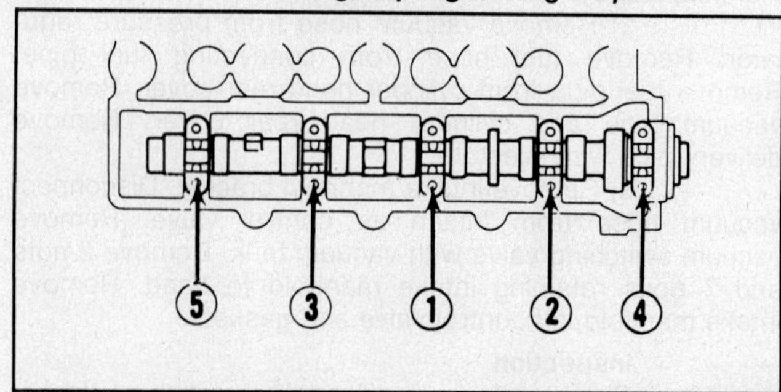

Courtesy of Toyota Motor Sales, U.S.A., Inc.

1.6L 16-VALVE 4-CYLINDER (Cont.)

CAMSHAFT

TIMING BELT

Removal

1) Remove right-hand wheel assembly, under engine cover and A/C belt (if equipped). Loosen water pump pulley bolts and remove accessory belts. Remove spark plugs and oil filler cap. Rotate crankshaft (clockwise only), and align timing mark on crankshaft damper with pointer on cover.

2) Look through oil filler hole and ensure cavity in camshaft is visible. *See Fig. 8.* This ensures No. 1 cylinder is at TDC on compression stroke. If cavity is not visible, rotate crankshaft one complete revolution and recheck cavity location.

Fig. 8: Camshaft Cavity Position

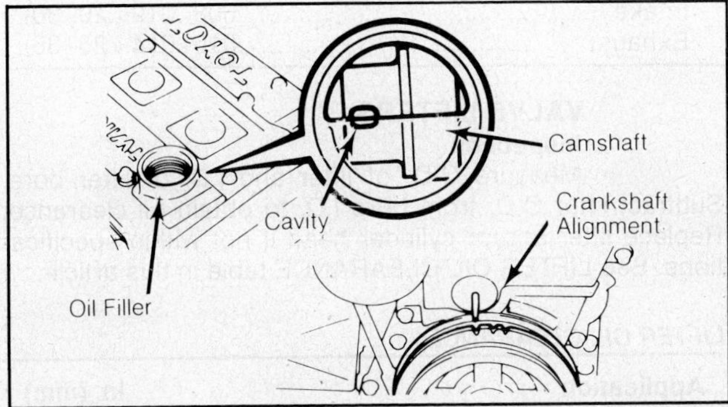

Courtesy of Toyota Motor Sales, U.S.A., Inc.

3) Disconnect ignition coil wiring, brake booster vacuum hose and cruise control vacuum hoses at intake manifold. Slightly raise engine with a jack. Remove right-hand engine mount assembly. Remove water pump pulley.

Fig. 9: Exploded View of Timing Belt & Components

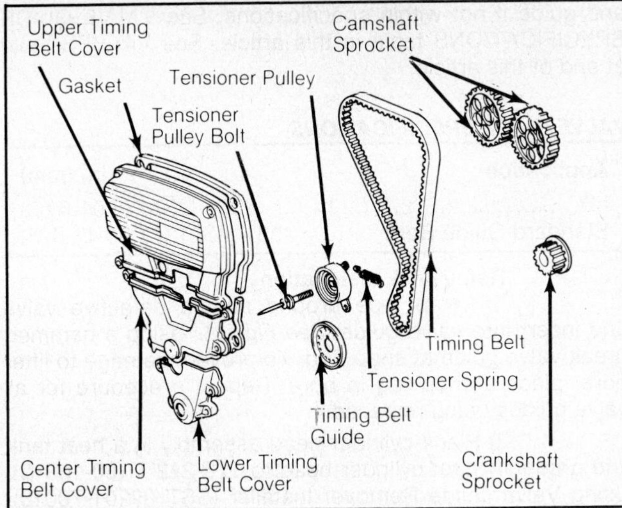

Courtesy of Toyota Motor Sales, U.S.A., Inc.

NOTE: **Timing cover bolts are of different lengths and must be installed to original location. Mark bolts at removal.**

4) Using Crankshaft Pulley Bolt Remover/Installer (SST 09213-70010 and 09330-00021), remove crankshaft pulley bolt. Using Pulley Remover (SST 09213-31021), remove crankshaft pulley. Remove 10 bolts retaining upper, center and lower timing belt covers and remove covers. *See Fig. 9.*

5) Remove timing belt guide. Mark installed direction of timing belt and belt tooth-to-sprocket tooth, if not replacing timing belt. Loosen belt tensioner bolt and move tensioner away from belt. Tighten tensioner bolt to hold tensioner away from belt and remove timing belt.

Inspection

Do not bend, twist or turn belt inside out or allow belt to contact any type of liquid. Check all sprockets for teeth wear or damage. Check belt teeth for wear, cracks, nicks or damage. Check tensioner spring. Free length is 1.713" (43.5 mm). Replace all components found to be defective.

Fig. 10: Aligning Timing Marks

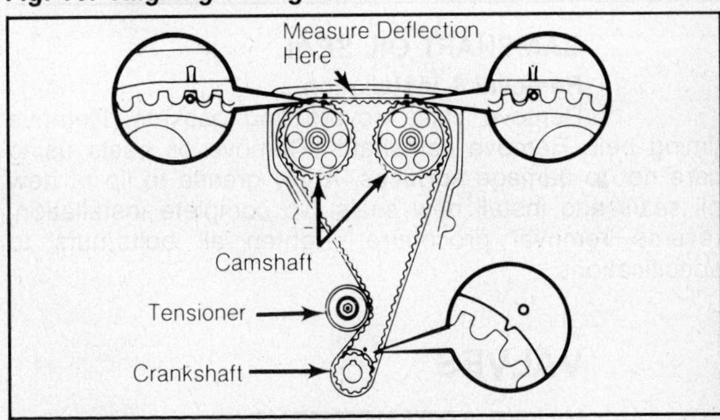

Courtesy of Toyota Motor Sales, U.S.A., Inc.

Installation

1) Ensure camshaft sprockets and crankshaft sprocket are clean and dry. Ensure all timing marks are in alignment. *See Fig. 10.* Place timing belt tensioner far left and tighten bolt.

2) Install timing belt. If reusing belt, ensure belt is installed to position marked at removal. Release tensioner and tighten bolt. Turn crankshaft 2 revolutions (clockwise only). Recheck timing marks and camshaft cavity location.

3) Measure belt deflection between both camshaft sprockets. Deflection should be 4.4 lbs. at .16" (2.0 kg at 4.0 mm). *See Fig. 10.* If deflection is incorrect, readjust with tensioner. To complete installation, reverse removal procedure.

FRONT COVER & OIL SEAL

Removal & Installation

Front cover is the body for the oil pump. See CRANKSHAFT FRONT OIL SEAL under ENGINE OILING in this article.

CAMSHAFTS & BEARINGS

NOTE: **Check end play before removing camshafts.**

Removal & Installation

The camshaft rides directly on cylinder head bearing surfaces and caps. Camshaft bearings are not replaceable. See step **3)-6)** under CYLINDER HEAD REMOVAL in this article.

Inspection

1) Measure camshaft runout and lobe height. Measure camshaft bearing journals. If not within specifications, replace camshaft and/or cylinder head assembly.

1.6L 16-VALVE 4-CYLINDER (Cont.)

2) Inspect camshaft bearing caps. Use Plastigage method to determine camshaft bearing clearance. If not within specifications, replace camshaft and/or cylinder head. See CAMSHAFT SPECIFICATIONS table in this article. See ENGINE SPECIFICATIONS table at end of this article.

CAMSHAFT SPECIFICATIONS

Application	In. (mm)
End Play	
Standard	.003-.008 (.08-.19)
Maximum	.010 (.25)
Maximum Runout	.002 (.04)
Lobe Height	
Standard	1.3998-1.4002 (35.555-35.565)
Minimum	1.3841 (35.155)

CAMSHAFT OIL SEAL

Removal & Installation

Remove valve covers and gaskets. Remove timing belt. Remove camshafts. Remove oil seals using care not to damage surfaces. Apply grease to lip of new oil seals and install new seals. To complete installation, reverse removal procedure. Tighten all bolts/nuts to specifications.

VALVES

VALVE ARRANGEMENT

Right Side – Intake valves.
Left Side – Exhaust valves.

NOTE: **"Right" and "Left" refer to right and left side of the engine NOT the vehicle.**

VALVE SEATS

NOTE: **Valve seat replacement information not available at this time. Replace valve guides BEFORE grinding valve seats.**

VALVE CLEARANCE ADJUSTMENTS

NOTE: **Mark valves, lifters and shims. They must be installed in original location as removed.**

1) With camshafts installed, place No. 1 cylinder on TDC, compression stroke. See TIMING BELT REMOVAL under CAMSHAFT in this article. Ensure timing marks are in alignment and No. 1 cylinder lifters are loose while No. 4 cylinder lifters are tight. If not, rotate crankshaft until this is achieved.

2) Measure clearance of cylinder No. 1 and 3 on exhaust side and cylinder No. 1 and 2 on intake side. Record measurements for determining replacements shims. Rotate crankshaft one complete revolution and measure remaining valves. Record these measurements. See VALVE CLEARANCE table in this article.

3) If not within specifications, rotate crankshaft until camshaft lobe is at lowest point of lifter to be adjusted. Rotate notch in lifter toward spark plug. Using Lifter Compressor (SST 09248-70012), compress lifter and remove shim with small screwdriver.

4) Using micrometer, measure thickness of removed shim. Add removed shim thickness to recorded clearance in step **2)**. Subtract .008" (.20 mm) for intake side and .010" (.25 mm) for exhaust side. Select shim with thickness as close as possible to obtain clearance specifications.

5) Shims are available in 17 sizes, in increments of .002" (.050 mm) starting with .0984" (2.5 mm). Recheck clearance after adjustments are made.

VALVE CLEARANCE

Application	In. (mm)
Cold	
Intake	.006-.010 (.15-.25)
Exhaust	.008-.012 (.20-.30)
Hot	
Intake	.008-.012 (.20-.30)
Exhaust	.010-.014 (.25-.36)

VALVE LIFTERS

Inspection

Measure O.D. of lifter and I.D. of lifter bore. Subtract lifter O.D. from bore I.D. to obtain oil clearance. Replace lifter and/or cylinder head if not within specifications. See LIFTER OIL CLEARANCE table in this article.

LIFTER OIL CLEARANCE

Application	In. (mm)
Standard	.0006-.0018 (.015-.046)
Maximum	.0039 (.10)

VALVE GUIDE SERVICING

Inspection

With valves removed, measure I.D. of valve guide and O.D. of valve stem. Subtract valve stem O.D. from valve guide I.D. to obtain clearance. Replace valve and guide if not within specifications. See VALVE GUIDE SPECIFICATIONS table in this article. See VALVES table at end of this article.

VALVE GUIDE SPECIFICATIONS

Application	In. (mm)
I.D.	.2366-.2374 (6.01-6.03)
Standard Guide Bore	.4331-.4341 (11.00-11.027)

Removal & Installation

1) Wrap tape around an old defective valve and insert into valve guide. *See Fig. 11.* Using a hammer, break valve guide at snap ring. To prevent damage to lifter bore, place a shop rag in bore. Repeat procedure for all valve guides being replaced.

2) Place cylinder head assembly in a heat tank and gradually heat cylinder head to 176-212°F (80-100°C). Using Valve Guide Remover/Installer (SST 09201-70010), remove valve guide(s). Reverse removal procedure to install guide. Drive guide in until snap ring on guide contacts cylinder head.

1.6L 16-VALVE 4-CYLINDER (Cont.)

Fig. 11: Removing Valve Guide

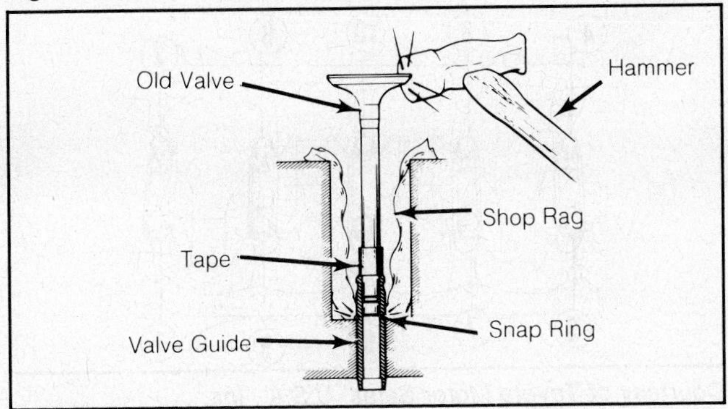

Courtesy of Toyota Motor Sales U.S.A., Inc.

VALVE SPRINGS

Inspection

Check squareness of valve springs. See VALVE SPRING SPECIFICATIONS table in this article. Check spring free length, installed tension and height. See ENGINE SPECIFICATIONS table at end of article. If not within specifications, replace springs.

VALVE SPRING SPECIFICATIONS

Application	In. (mm)
Maximum Squareness	.071 (1.8)
Installed Height	1.366 (34.7)

Installation

Install valves in location from which they were removed. Install new oil seals. Install spring seat, spring and spring retainer. Valve springs must be installed with the wide coils of spring upward and narrow coils downward. Tighten all bolts/nuts to specifications.

PISTONS, PINS & RINGS

OIL PAN

Removal

1) Raise vehicle and drain engine oil. Remove exhaust pipe from exhaust manifold. Remove 19 bolts and 2 nuts retaining oil pan. Insert Blade (SST 09032-00100) between oil pan and baffle plate and cut off sealer. Remove oil pan.

2) Remove pick-up tube and screen. Insert blade between baffle plate and cylinder block. Cut off sealer and remove baffle plate. Use care not to damage baffle plate flange.

Installation

1) Remove all gasket/sealer from surfaces. Do not use solvents and do not allow oil on surfaces. Apply Seal Packing (08826-00080) to oil pan surface and baffle plate surface. *See Fig. 12.* Do not allow seal packing near oil passages.

2) Install baffle plate-to-cylinder block within 5 minutes of seal packing application. Install new gasket on pick-up tube and install pick-up tube and screen. To complete installation, reverse removal procedure. Tighten all bolts/nuts to specifications.

Fig. 12: Seal Packing Application

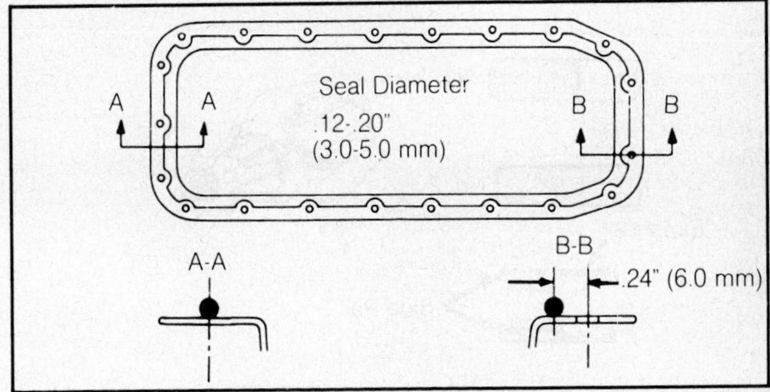

Courtesy of Toyota Motor Sales U.S.A., Inc.

PISTON & ROD ASSEMBLY

Removal

Remove cylinder head assembly. Remove oil pan. Tap piston out top of cylinder block. Repeat procedure for remaining pistons. Keep in order to ensure installation to original position.

Installation

Position piston assembly in correct cylinder bore. Align stamped cavity on top of piston with front of engine. Protrusion on connection rod must also align with cavity on top of piston. *See Fig. 13.* To complete installation, reverse removal procedure. Tighten all bolts/nuts to specifications.

Fig. 13: Piston & Connecting Rod Alignment

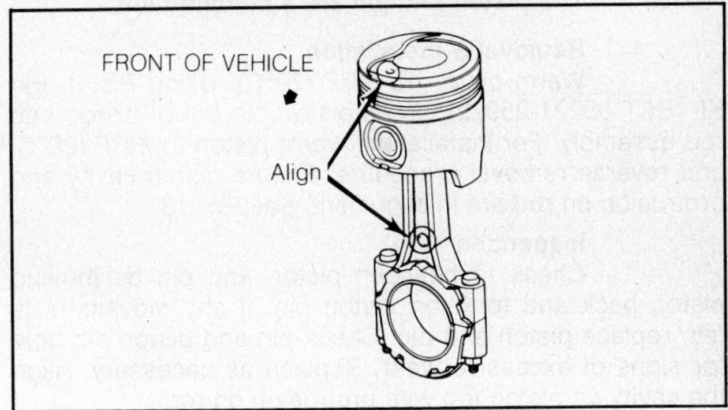

Courtesy of Toyota Motor Sales, U.S.A., Inc.

FITTING PISTONS

1) With piston assemblies removed, remove piston rings and clean piston. Measure piston outer diameter in thrust direction, at right angles to piston pin center line and 1.65" (42.0 mm) from piston skirt. Standard piston diameter is 3.1846-3.1858" (80.89-80.92 mm).

2) Measure cylinder bore in thrust direction, and subtract piston diameter measurement from cylinder bore measurement. Piston clearance must be .0039-.0047" (.10-.12 mm). Standard bore diameter is 3.1890-3.1902" (81.00-81.03 mm). If not within specifications, replace piston and/or cylinder block.

FITTING RINGS

Install rings on piston. Ensure marked side of rings are in proper position. Set ends of rings to proper position. *See Fig. 14.*

1.6L 16-VALVE 4-CYLINDER (Cont.)

Fig. 14: Positioning Piston Ring Gaps

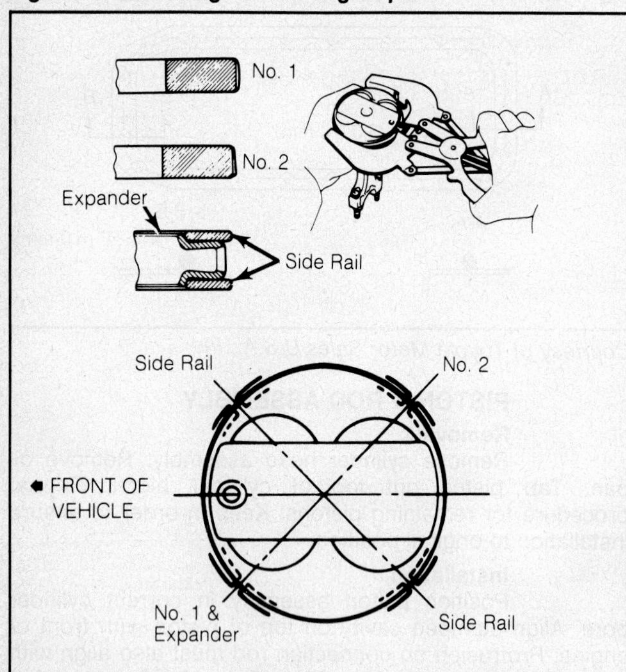

Courtesy of Toyota Motor Sales, U.S.A., Inc.

PISTON PINS REPLACEMENT

NOTE: The piston and pin are a matched set.

Removal & Installation

Warm piston to 68°F (20°C). Using Piston Pin Kit (SST 09221-25022), press piston pin out of piston and rod assembly. For installation, warm piston to 68°F (20°C) and reverse removal procedure. Ensure piston cavity and protrusion on rod are in alignment. *See Fig. 13.*

Inspection

Check fit between piston and pin by moving piston back and forth on piston pin. If any movement is felt, replace piston and pin. Check pin and piston pin hole for signs of excessive wear. Replace as necessary. Align the cavity on piston top with protrusion on rod.

CRANKSHAFT & ROD BEARINGS

CRANKSHAFT MAIN BEARINGS

NOTE: Ensure all rod and main bearing caps are marked with cylinder No. and engine front direction. Mark them if necessary.

Removal

1) With engine removed, remove oil pan, flywheel, rear engine plate and rear oil seal retainer. Remove piston and rod assemblies. Remove main bearing cap bolts in 3 even steps and in sequence. *See Fig. 15.*

2) Remove caps and lower bearing inserts. Keep all removed components together. Remove crankshaft. Remove upper main bearing inserts and upper thrust bearings (No. 3 journal).

Fig. 15: Main Bearing Cap Removal

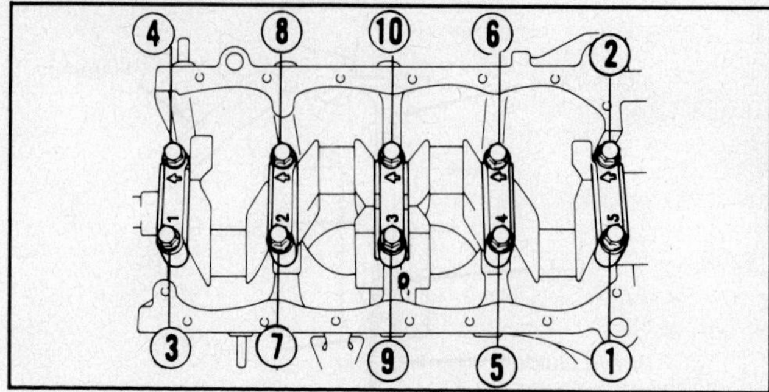

Courtesy of Toyota Motor Sales, U.S.A., Inc.

Inspection

1) Check main bearings and crankshaft for scoring or wear. Check bearing clearance using Plastigage method. Maximum main bearing clearance is .0039" (.10 mm). If not within specifications, replace main bearing inserts. Machine or replace crankshaft if necessary. See CRANKSHAFT SPECIFICATIONS table in this article.

Fig. 16: Main Bearing Insert Identification

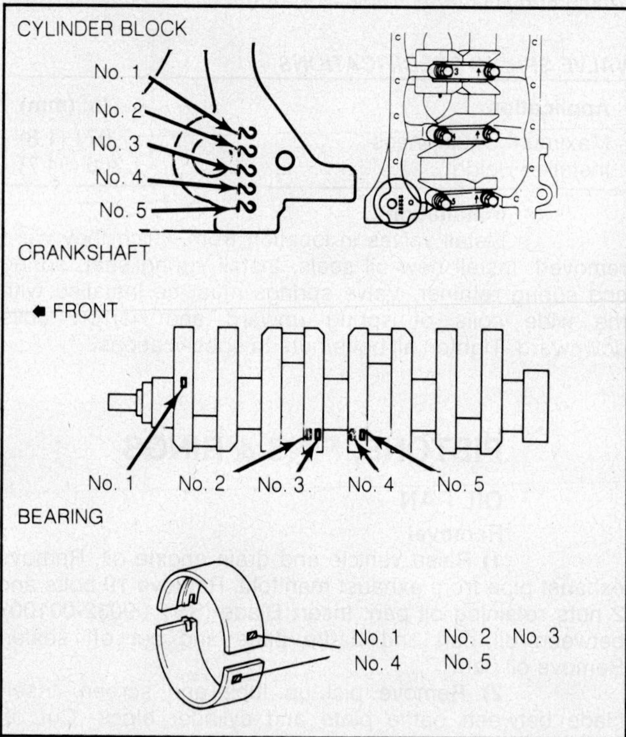

Courtesy of Toyota Motor Sales, U.S.A., Inc.

CRANKSHAFT SPECIFICATIONS

Application	In. (mm)
Crankshaft Runout [1]	.0024 (.06)
Journal Taper	
Maximum	.0008 (.02)
Out-of-Round	
Maximum	.0008 (.02)

[1] – Measured at center journal, with crankshaft in "V" blocks.

1.6L 16-VALVE 4-CYLINDER (Cont.)

2) If replacing bearing inserts, replace with one having same number as one which was removed. The cylinder block, crankshaft and bearing inserts are marked and must be used to determine the correct replacement bearing insert. *See Fig. 16.*

Installation

1) Ensure proper bearing inserts are being installed to proper journal. Place upper bearing inserts in block. Install No. 3 thrust bearings with oil grooves facing outward. Place matched bearing inserts in main bearing caps. Install No. 3 thrust bearings on cap with oil grooves facing outward.

2) Lubricate bearing insert surfaces with engine oil. Place crankshaft in block. Install main bearing caps. Lightly coat threads and under head of cap bolts with engine oil. Tighten main bearing cap bolts in 3 even steps and in sequence. *See Fig. 17.*

Fig. 17: Main Bearing Cap Tightening Sequence

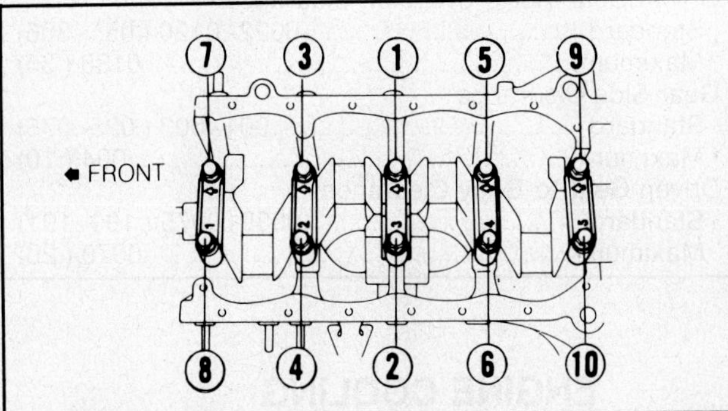

Courtesy of Toyota Motor Sales, U.S.A., Inc.

3) Ensure crankshaft rotates smoothly after completing installation. Check crankshaft end play and adjust as necessary. To complete installation, reverse removal. Tighten all bolts/nuts to specifications.

CONNECTING ROD BEARINGS

Inspection

With pistons removed, check rod bearings for abnormal wear. Check crankshaft journal and machine or replace as necessary. Check rod bearing-to-crankshaft clearance with Plastigage. See ENGINE SPECIFICATIONS table at end of this article.

THRUST BEARING ALIGNMENT

Inspection

Using dial indicator, measure thrust clearance while prying back and forth with screwdriver. If clearance exceeds specifications, replace thrust bearings as a set. See THRUST BEARING CLEARANCE SPECIFICATIONS table in this article.

THRUST BEARING CLEARANCE SPECIFICATIONS

Application	In. (mm)
Standard Clearance	.0008-.0087 (.02-.22)
Maximum Clearance	.0118 (.30)

REAR MAIN BEARING OIL SEAL

Removal & Installation

1) Remove transaxle. See appropriate REMOVAL article under TRANSMISSION SERVICING section. Remove flywheel or flexplate. Remove rear engine plate. Remove oil seal retainer and drive seal out.

2) Using Seal Installer (SST 09223-41929), install new oil seal. Lightly coat seal lip with grease. Replace oil seal retainer gasket and install retainer. Tighten bolts/nuts to specifications. To complete installation, reverse removal procedure.

CRANKSHAFT FRONT OIL SEAL

Removal & Installation

Remove oil pump. Remove oil seal from pump. Do not damage seal contact surface of pump. Apply grease to new oil seal. Replace using Seal Installer (09517-30010). Ensure oil seal is flush with oil pump body outer surface.

ENGINE OILING

ENGINE OILING SYSTEM

Oil is circulated through the engine by pressure provided by a gear-type oil pump. *See Fig. 18.* Oil is drawn from the oil pan and circulated to a full-flow oil filter. Oil from the filter is directed to crankshaft main bearings that feed connecting rod bearings. The oil passage above No. 1 main bearing, feeds camshafts and valve train.

Fig. 18: Typical Engine Oiling System

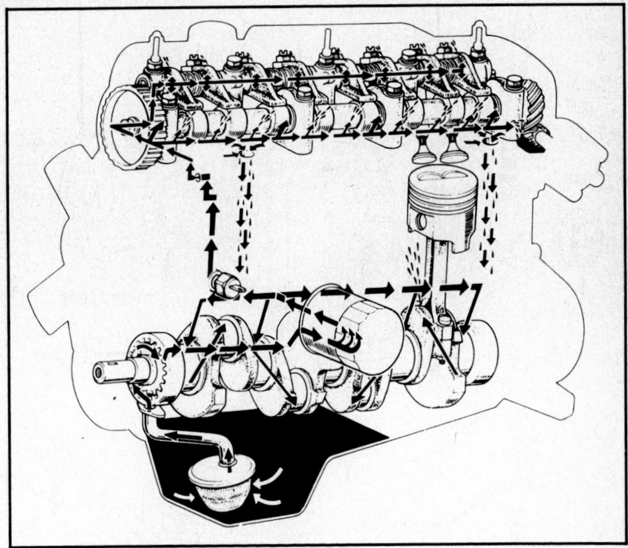

Courtesy of Toyota Motor Sales, U.S.A., Inc.

CRANKCASE CAPACITY

The crankcase capacity is 3.9 qts. (3.7L) with filter, 3.6 qts. (3.4L) without filter and 4.3 qts. (4.1L) for dry fill.

NORMAL OIL PRESSURE

Normal oil pressure at idle is greater than 4.3 psi (.3 kg/cm²) and at 3000 RPM oil pressure should be 36-71 psi (2.5-5.0 kg/cm²).

OIL PRESSURE REGULATOR VALVE

Oil pressure regulator valve is located in the oil pump cover. It is a nonadjustable type valve.

1.6L 16-VALVE 4-CYLINDER (Cont.)

OIL PUMP

Removal & Installation (Corolla)

1) Mark hinge-to-hood and remove hood. Drain engine oil and remove under engine cover. Remove 4 bolts retaining crossmember and remove crossmember. Remove oil pan. Remove pick-up tube and screen assembly.

2) Remove timing belt and crankshaft sprocket. Remove oil pan baffle plate. Remove oil dipstick tube. Remove 7 bolts retaining oil pump and remove remove oil pump. To loosen, tap oil pump from the inside with plastic hammer. *See Fig. 19.* Reverse removal procedure for installation. Ensure spline teeth of drive gear engages large teeth of crankshaft.

Removal & Installation (MR2)

1) Raise vehicle and drain engine oil. Remove exhaust pipe from exhaust manifold. Remove timing belt and crankshaft sprocket. Install right-hand engine mount. Remove oil pan, oil pump pick-up tube and screen.

2) Remove oil pan baffle plate. Remove dipstick tube. Remove 7 bolts retaining oil pump and remove oil pump. To loosen, tap oil pump from the inside with plastic hammer. *See Fig. 19.* Reverse removal procedure for installation. Ensure spline teeth of drive gear engages large teeth of crankshaft.

Fig. 19: Exploded View of Oil Pump Assembly

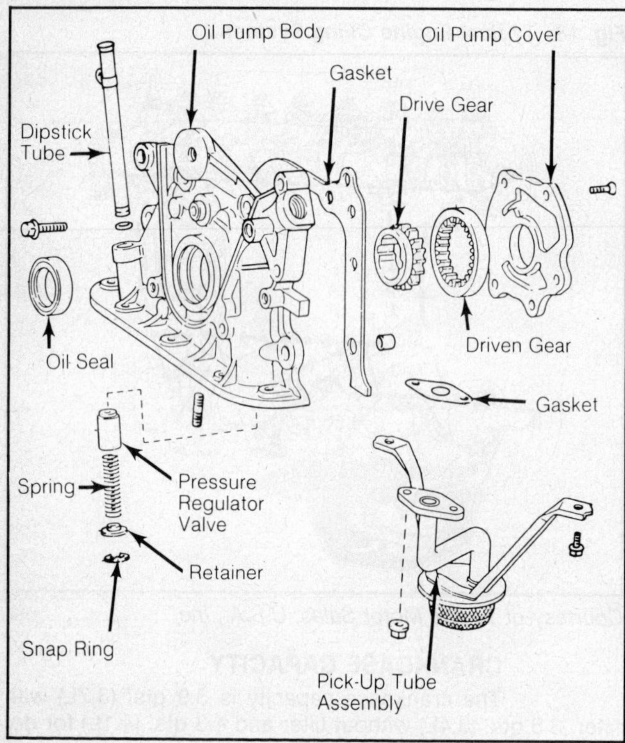

Courtesy of Toyota Motor Sales, U.S.A., Inc.

Disassembly

Remove 5 oil pump cover bolts and remove cover. Remove drive and driven gears. Remove snap ring, retainer, spring and pressure regulator valve.

Inspection

Check gears, cover and body for wear and damage. Measure clearance between driven gear and body. Measure clearance between both gear tips and crescent. Measure side clearance. If beyond specifications, replace necessary parts. Check relief valve for wear or damage.

OIL PUMP SPECIFICATIONS

Application	In. (mm)
Drive Gear Tip-to-Crescent Clearance	
Standard	.0042-.0098 (.107-.248)
Maximum	.0138 (.35)
Driven Gear Tip-to-Crescent Clearance	
Standard	.0022-.0120 (.055-.306)
Maximum	.0138 (.35)
Gear Side Clearance	
Standard	.001-.003 (.025-.075)
Maximum	.004 (.10)
Driven Gear-to-Body Clearance	
Standard	.0039-.0075 (.100-.191)
Maximum	.0079 (.20)

ENGINE COOLING

WATER PUMP

NOTE: **Do not allow coolant to contact timing belt.**

Removal

1) Drain cooling system. Remove A/C compressor drive belt and idler pulley (if equipped). Loosen water pump pulley bolts and remove alternator drive belt. Remove water pump pulley. Disconnect water inlet and water by-pass hoses from inlet pipe.

2) Remove water inlet pipe and "O" ring from rear of water pump. Remove oil dipstick tube and plug hole in oil pump body. Remove upper and center timing belt cover. Remove water pump retaining bolts and remove water pump.

Installation

Install new "O" ring on clean block surface and mount pump. Tighten bolts to specifications. Install dipstick tube with new "O" ring in place. To complete installation, reverse removal procedure. Adjust drive belt tension, fill coolant system and check for leaks.

NOTE: **For more information, see ENGINE COOLING SYSTEMS article at the end of this section.**

ENGINE SPECIFICATIONS

GENERAL SPECIFICATIONS

Year	DISPLACEMENT Cu. In.	DISPLACEMENT Liters	Fuel System	HP@RPM	Torque Ft. Lbs.@RPM	Compr. Ratio	BORE In.	BORE mm	STROKE In.	STROKE mm
1987	96.8	1.6	Fuel Inj.	112 @ 6600	97 @ 4800	9.0:1	3.19	81.0	3.03	77.0

1.6L 16-VALVE 4-CYLINDER (Cont.)

ENGINE SPECIFICATIONS (Cont.)

VALVES

Engine Size & Valve	Head Diam. In. (mm)	Face Angle	Seat Angle	Seat Width In. (mm)	Stem Diameter In. (mm)	Stem Clearance In. (mm)	Valve Lift In. (mm)
1.6L							
Intake	.....	44.5°	45°	.039-.055 (1.00-1.40)	.2350-.2356 (5.970-5.985)	.001-.0024 (.025-.06)	.....
Exhaust	.....	44.5°	45°	.039-.055 (1.00-1.40)	.2348-.2354 (5.965-5.980)	.0012-.0026 (.03-.07)	.....

PISTONS, PINS & RINGS

Engine	PISTONS	PINS		RINGS		
	Clearance In. (mm)	Piston Fit In. (mm)	Rod Fit In. (mm)	Ring No.	End Gap In. (mm)	Side Clearance In. (mm)
1.6L	.0039-.0047 (.099-.119)	.....	Press Fit [1]	No. 1	.0098-.0185 (.25-.47)	.0016-.0031 (.04-.08)
				No. 2	.0078-.0165 (.20-.42)	.0012-.0028 (.03-.07)
				Oil	.0118-.0402 (.30-1.02)	.....

[1] – Piston and pin are available only as a set.

CRANKSHAFT MAIN & CONNECTING ROD BEARINGS

Engine	MAIN BEARINGS				CONNECTING ROD BEARINGS		
	Journal Diam. In. (mm)	Clearance In. (mm)	Thrust Bearing	Crankshaft End Play In. (mm)	Journal Diam. In. (mm)	Clearance In. (mm)	Side Play In. (mm)
1.6L	1.889-1.890 (47.99-48.00)	.0006-.0013 (.015-.033)	No. 3	.0008-.0087 (.02-.22)	1.574-1.575 (39.99-40.00)	.0008-.0020 (.02-.05)	.006-.010 (.15-.25)

CAMSHAFT

Engine	Journal Diam. In. (mm)	Clearance In. (mm)	Lobe Lift In. (mm)
1.6L	1.0610-1.0616 (26.95-26.97)	.004 (.102)	1.400 (35.56)

VALVE SPRINGS

Engine	Free Length In. (mm)	PRESSURE Lbs. @ In. (Kg @ mm)	
		Valve Closed	Valve Open
1.6L	1.6177 (41.09)	34.8 @ 1.366 (15.8 @ 34.7)	.....

Toyota Engines

1.6L 16-VALVE 4-CYLINDER (Cont.)

ENGINE SPECIFICATIONS (Cont.)

TIGHTENING SPECIFICATIONS

Application	Ft. Lbs. (N.m)
Camshaft Sprocket Bolt	34 (46)
Connecting Rod Cap Nut	36 (49)
Crankshaft Damper Bolt	87 (118)
Cylinder Head Bolt	43 (58)
Engine-to-Transaxle	
10 mm Bolts	34 (46)
12 mm Bolts	47 (64)
Exhaust Manifold Bolts/Nuts	18 (24)
Exhaust Pipe-to-Exhaust Manifold	46 (62)
Flywheel Bolt	58 (79)
Flex Plate	47 (64)
Front Engine Mount Through Bolt	58 (79)
Intake Manifold Bolts/Nuts	20 (27)
Main Bearing Cap Bolt	43 (58)
Oil Pump Body Mount Bolt	13-18 (18-24)
Rear Engine Mount	
10 mm Bolt Head	38 (52)
12 mm Bolt Head	58 (79)
Right-Hand Engine Mount Bolt	58 (79)
Spark Plug	13 (18)
Timing Belt Idler Bolt	27 (37)
Torque Converter Bolt	20 (27)
	INCH Lbs. (N.m)
Camshaft Bearing Cap Bolt	108 (12)
Oil Pan Bolts/Nuts	43 (5)
Oil Pump Cover Bolt	72-108 (8-12)
Oil Pump Pick-Up Tube	82 (9)

2.0L 3S-FE & 3S-GE 4-CYLINDER

Camry, Celica

NOTE: For engine repair procedures not covered in this article, see ENGINE OVERHAUL PROCEDURES article at beginning of this section.

ENGINE CODING

ENGINE IDENTIFICATION

Engine serial number is stamped onto a machined pad, located on the right side of the engine block.

ENGINE IDENTIFICATION CODE

Application	Code
Camry & Celica	3S-FE
Celica	3S-GE

ENGINE, MANIFOLDS & CYLINDER HEAD

ENGINE

NOTE: Remove engine and transaxle as a unit.

Removal

1) Drain coolant. Remove hood and battery. Disconnect accelerator cable from throttle body. On automatic transaxle models, disconnect throttle cable with bracket from throttle body. On all models, disconnect and remove radiator.

2) Remove air cleaner assembly with airflow meter. Disconnect wiring from alternator, distributor, and coolant temperature sending unit. On automatic transaxle equipped models, disconnect coolant temperature switch. Mark components for installation reference. Disconnect power brake booster vacuum hose.

3) Label and disconnect vacuum hoses attaching A/C unit and cruise control to distribution block (if equipped). Label and disconnect EFI wiring. Pull EFI wiring out through right fender panel. Disconnect heater hoses.

4) Disconnect fuel hoses. Disconnect speedometer cable from transaxle. On manual transaxle models, remove clutch release cylinder without disconnecting tubing. Disconnect shifter linkage. On automatic transaxle models, disconnect transaxle control cable.

5) Remove A/C compressor and power steering pump and lay aside (if equipped). Raise and support vehicle. Disconnect both front drive shafts. Remove exhaust pipe.

6) Attach engine hoist to lift brackets on engine. Remove engine and transaxle mounts from brackets. Remove left transaxle mount bracket. Lift engine/transaxle assembly out of vehicle.

Installation

1) Using an engine hoist, slowly lower engine/transaxle assembly into engine compartment. Tilt transaxle down while lowering to clear neutral start switch, engine mount brackets and power steering gear housing.

2) Install engine mounts, brackets and crossmember. To complete installation, reverse removal procedure. Reconnect all wiring, fuel and vacuum hoses. Adjust drive belts. Fill radiator with coolant and engine/transaxle with oil.

INTAKE & EXHAUST MANIFOLDS

Removal

Remove intake manifold mounting bolts and intake manifold. Remove exhaust manifold mounting bolts, heat insulator and exhaust manifold.

Inspection

1) Inspect air intake chamber. Check intake and exhaust manifold gasket surfaces for nicks, warpage or damage. Intake and exhaust manifold warpage limit is .012" (.30 mm).

2) Air intake chamber warpage limit is .012" (.30 mm). If warpage is beyond specification, resurface or replace.

Fig. 1: Exploded View of 3S-FE Cylinder Head Components

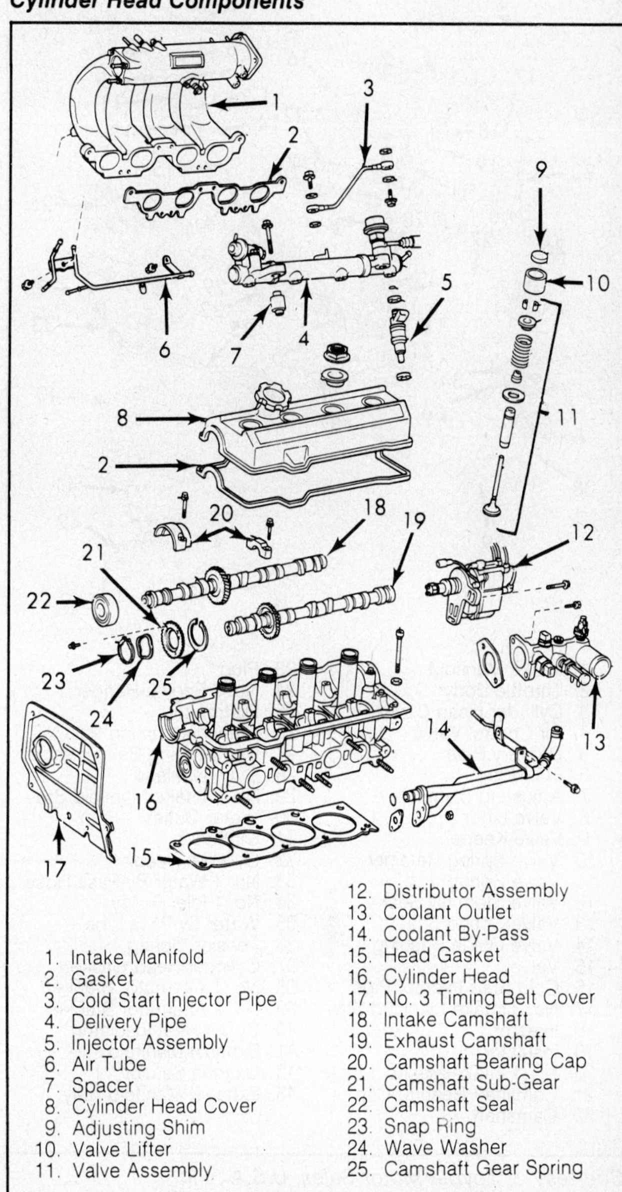

Courtesy of Toyota Motor Sales, U.S.A., Inc.

Toyota Engines

2.0L 3S-FE & 3S-GE 4-CYLINDER (Cont.)

Installation

Use new gaskets when installing intake and exhaust manifolds. To install, reverse removal procedure.

CYLINDER HEAD

Removal

1) Remove negative battery cable. Drain coolant. Remove ignition coil connector and high tension wire. Remove upper brace from front suspension. On automatic transaxle vehicles, disconnect throttle cable and bracket from throttle body. Remove accelerator cable and bracket from throttle body and air intake chamber.

Fig. 2: Exploded View of 3S-GE Cylinder Head Components

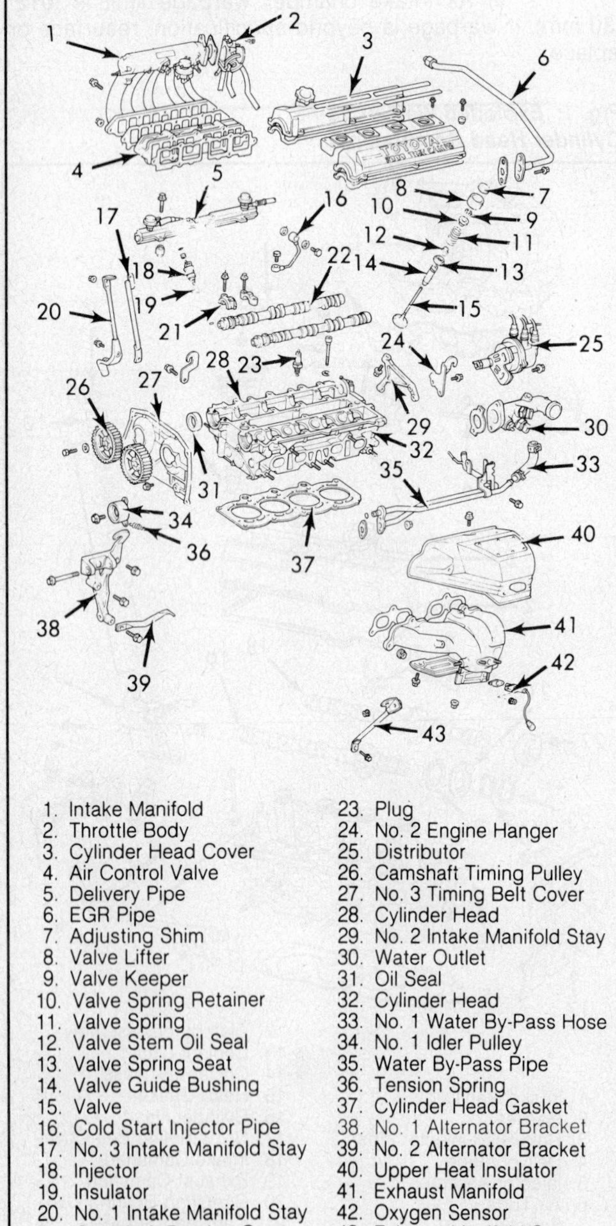

1. Intake Manifold
2. Throttle Body
3. Cylinder Head Cover
4. Air Control Valve
5. Delivery Pipe
6. EGR Pipe
7. Adjusting Shim
8. Valve Lifter
9. Valve Keeper
10. Valve Spring Retainer
11. Valve Spring
12. Valve Stem Oil Seal
13. Valve Spring Seat
14. Valve Guide Bushing
15. Valve
16. Cold Start Injector Pipe
17. No. 3 Intake Manifold Stay
18. Injector
19. Insulator
20. No. 1 Intake Manifold Stay
21. Camshaft Bearing Cap
22. Camshaft
23. Plug
24. No. 2 Engine Hanger
25. Distributor
26. Camshaft Timing Pulley
27. No. 3 Timing Belt Cover
28. Cylinder Head
29. No. 2 Intake Manifold Stay
30. Water Outlet
31. Oil Seal
32. Cylinder Head
33. No. 1 Water By-Pass Hose
34. No. 1 Idler Pulley
35. Water By-Pass Pipe
36. Tension Spring
37. Cylinder Head Gasket
38. No. 1 Alternator Bracket
39. No. 2 Alternator Bracket
40. Upper Heat Insulator
41. Exhaust Manifold
42. Oxygen Sensor
43. Exhaust Manifold Stay

Courtesy of Toyota Motor Sales, U.S.A., Inc.

2) Remove radiator reservoir tank. Remove cruise control actuator and bracket (if equipped). Remove air cleaner assembly, airflow meter and air cleaner hose. Remove alternator.

3) Remove oil pressure gauge, engine hangers and alternator upper bracket. Raise and support vehicle. Remove right-front wheel and cover from under right side of engine. Remove suspension lower crossmember.

4) Disconnect exhaust pipe from catalytic converter, remove oxygen sensor connector. Remove 6 bolts and manifold upper heat insulator. Remove 2 bolts and catalytic converter stay. Remove exhaust manifold and catalytic converter assembly. Disconnect oil, coolant and cold start injector switches.

5) Separate exhaust manifold from catalytic converter. Remove distributor. Remove coolant temperature sender connector, cold start injector time switch connector, radiator upper hose, coolant hoses, emission control vacuum hoses and coolant outlet and gasket. Remove coolant by-pass pipe.

6) Remove EGR valve and modulator. Remove throttle body and cold start injector tube. Remove air intake chamber air hose, throttle body air hose, power steering pump air hoses and air tube. Remove 2 bolts and intake manifold stay. Remove vacuum sensing hose. Remove intake manifold and gasket. On 3S-GE engines, remove No. 1 and 3 intake manifold stays. Remove ground strap, 2 VSV connectors, and power steering hoses.

7) Remove delivery pipe and injectors, spark plugs and camshaft timing pulley. Remove No. 1 idler pulley and tension spring.

8) On 3S-FE engines, remove 4 timing belt cover bolts. Support belt so meshing of crankshaft timing pulley and timing belt does not shift. Use care not to drop anything inside timing belt cover. Do not allow oil, coolant or dust to come in contact with timing belt.

Fig. 3: Cylinder Head Bolt Removal Sequence

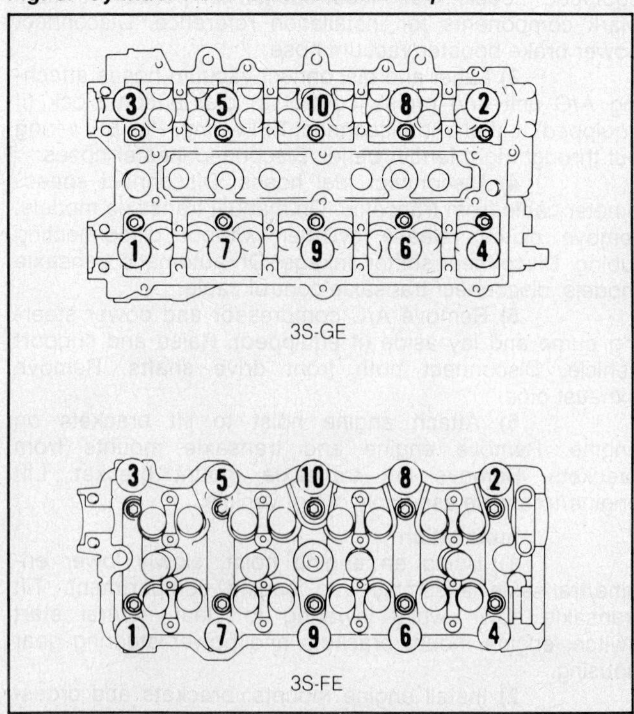

Courtesy of Toyota Motor Sales, U.S.A., Inc.

2.0L 3S-FE & 3S-GE 4-CYLINDER (Cont.)

9) Remove cylinder head cover nuts, grommets (if equipped), cover and gasket. Ensure grommets are arranged in correct order for reassembly reference. Remove camshafts as outlined under CAMSHAFT & TIMING BELT in this article.

10) Loosen and remove cylinder head bolts gradually, in 3 stages. *See Fig. 3.* Failure to remove cylinder head bolts in proper order can cause severe head damage. Lift cylinder head from dowels on cylinder block and place on wooden work stand.

Inspection

On 3S-FE cylinder head, maximum warpage on block side of head is .002" (.05 mm). On exhaust manifold side of head, maximum warpage is .0031" (.08 mm). On 3S-GE cylinder head, maximum warpage on intake manifold side of head is .008" (.20 mm). On exhaust manifold side of head, maximum warpage is .012" (.30 mm). If warpage is greater than specification, cylinder head must be replaced.

Installation

Position new cylinder head gasket on cylinder block. Install cylinder head on gasket. Put a light coat of oil on threads and under heads of cylinder head bolts. Install and tighten cylinder head bolts in reverse order of removal sequence. *See Fig. 3.* To install remaining components, reverse removal procedure. To install camshafts, see CAMSHAFT & TIMING BELT section.

CAMSHAFT & TIMING BELT

ENGINE FRONT COVERS

Removal & Installation (3S-FE)

Remove negative battery cable. Remove right front wheel. Remove lower right engine cover. Remove cruise control actuator and bracket. Remove drive belts, alternator and bracket. Raise engine enough to remove weight from right engine mount. Remove right engine mount bolt and insulaltor. Remove spark plugs. Remove No. 2 timing belt cover.

Removal & Installation (3S-GE)

Remove negative battery cable. Remove right front wheel. Remove right engine under cover. Remove spark plugs. Remove No. 2 timing belt cover with gasket. To install cover, reverse removal procedure.

TIMING BELT

Removal (3S-FE)

1) Remove negative battery cable. Remove right front wheel. Remove lower right engine cover. Remove cruise control actuator and bracket. Remove drive belts, alternator and bracket. Raise engine enough to remove weight from right engine mount. Remove right engine mount bolt and insulaltor. Remove spark plugs. Remove No. 2 timing belt cover.

2) Turn crankshaft pulley and align its groove with timing mark "0" on No. 1 timing belt cover. Ensure hole of camshaft timing pulley is aligned with alignment mark of bearing cap.

3) Remove timing belt from camshaft timing pulley. If timing belt is to be reused, place reference marks on belt and pulley. Loosen No. 1 idler pulley mount bolt and pull pulley as far left as possible and tighten pulley. Remove timing belt from camshaft timing pulley.

4) Using a Drive Shaft Holder (09278-54012) to hold camshaft pulley, remove bolt, plate washer and pulley from camshaft. Using a Crankshaft Pulley Holder (09213-54014) to hold crankshaft pulley, remove pulley mount bolt from crankshaft. Remove pulley.

5) Remove 4 bolts, No. 1 timing belt cover and gasket. Remove timing belt and belt guide. If timing belt is to be reused, place reference marks on belt and pulley. Remove No. 1 idler pulley and tension spring. Remove No. 2 idler pulley, crankshaft timing pulley and oil pump pulley.

Removal (3S-GE)

1) Remove negative battery cable. Remove right front wheel, lower engine cover, and radiator reservoir tank. Remove cruise control actuator with bracket. Position power steering fluid reservoir tank out of way. Remove alternator drive belt, alternator and bracket. *See Fig. 4.*

Fig. 4: Exploded View of 3S-GE Timing Belt Components

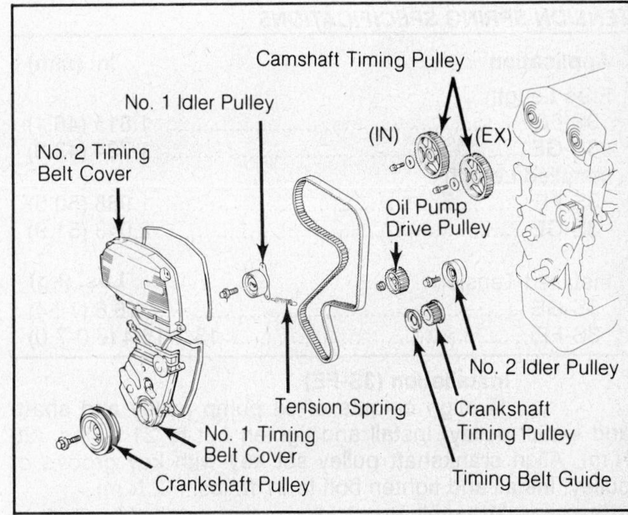

Courtesy of Toyota Motor Sales, U.S.A., Inc.

2) Remove power steering pump drive belt. Raise engine slightly. Remove right engine mounting insulator and bracket. Remove cylinder head covers with gaskets. Remove spark plugs. Remove No. 2 timing belt cover with gasket.

3) Turn crankshaft pulley and align groove with "0" mark on No. 1 timing belt cover. Ensure marks on camshaft timing pulleys and No. 3 timing belt are aligned. If marks are not aligned, turn crankshaft pulley one complete revolution.

4) Remove timing belt from camshaft timing pulleys. If old belt is to be reused, place reference marks for installation reference. Loosen No. 1 idler pulley bolt and move left as far as possible. Temporarily tighten set bolt and then relieve timing belt tension. Remove belt from camshaft timing pulley.

5) Support belt so meshing of crankshaft timing pulley and timing belt will not shift. Hold camshaft with wrench and remove pulley set bolts. Remove camshaft pulleys and pins. Using Crankshaft Pulley Holder (SST 09213-14010) to hold crankshaft pulley, remove pulley bolt. Using Puller (SST 09213-31021), remove crankshaft pulley.

6) Remove 6 bolts, No. 1 timing belt cover and gasket. Remove timing belt guide and timing belt. If reusing old belt, mark location and rotation for reinstallation reference. Remove No. 1 idler pulley and tension

2.0L 3S-FE & 3S-GE 4-CYLINDER (Cont.)

spring. Remove No. 2 idler pulley, crankshaft timing pulley and oil pump pulley.

Inspection

1) Check timing belt teeth for cracks or damage. If tooth damage is found, ensure camshaft, coolant pump or oil pump are not locked. If wear or cracks on flat belt face are found, check for nicks on one side of idler pulley lock.

2) If wear or damage to only one side of belt is found, check belt guide and alignment of each pulley and sprocket. If noticeable wear is found on belt teeth, check timing cover gasket for damage and proper installation. Ensure there is no foreign material on sprocket teeth.

3) Check idler pulleys for smooth rotation. Replace if roughness or noise is found. Inspect tension spring free length, installed tension and length. See TENSION SPRING SPECIFICATIONS table.

TENSION SPRING SPECIFICATIONS

Application	In. (mm)
Free Length	
3S-FE	1.815 (46.1)
3S-GE	1.724 (43.8)
Installed Length	
3S-FE	1.988 (50.5)
3S-GE	2.043 (51.9)
Installed Tension	**Lbs. (kg)**
3S-GE	16.6 (7.54)
3S-FE	13.2-15.4 (6.0-7.0)

Installation (3S-FE)

1) Align cutouts of oil pump pulley and shaft, and install pulley. Install and tighten nut to 21 ft. lbs. (28 N.m). Align crankshaft pulley set key with key groove of pulley. Install and tighten bolt to 31 ft. lbs. (42 N.m).

2) Install No. 2 idler pulley and tighten bolt to 31 ft. lbs. (42 N.m). Ensure pulley is clean and rotates smoothly. Temporarily install No. 1 idler pulley and tension spring. Pry pulley left as far as possible. Temporarily install timing belt. Ensure marks made at disassembly are aligned.

CAUTION: Timing belt should not be installed on a warm engine.

3) Install timing belt guide, ensuring cup side faces outward. Install No. 1 timing belt cover. Align crankshaft pulley set key with key groove of pulley and install. Tighten bolt to 80 ft. lbs. (108 N.m). Align camshaft knock pin with pulley knock pin groove and install. Install plate washer and tighten bolt to 40 ft. lbs. (54 N.m).

4) Turn crankshaft pulley and align its groove with "0" timing mark on No. 1 timing belt cover. Turn camshaft and align hole of camshaft timing pulley with alignment mark on bearing cap. Ensure marks made at disassembly are aligned and install timing belt.

5) Turn crankshaft pulley clockwise 2 turns from TDC to TDC. Tighten No. 1 idler pulley mount bolt to 31 ft. lbs. (42 N.m). Ensure belt tension is present as indicated. *See Fig. 5.* To complete installation, reverse removal procedure.

Installation (3S-GE)

1) Using Wrench (SST 09616-30011), hold oil pump pulley and tighten nut. Install timing pulley over crankshaft key. Install and tighten No. 2 idler pulley. Install timing belt idler pulley and tension spring. Pry timing belt idler pulley left as far as possible and temporarily tighten.

CAUTION: Ensure no oil or coolant is present on idler pulley.

2) Temporarily install timing belt. Engine must not be warm. If old timing belt was reused, align reference marks made during removal. Install timing belt on crankshaft, oil pump, water pump, and No. 2 idler pulley. Install timing belt guide with cup side facing outward.

3) Install No. 1 timing belt cover gasket and belt cover. Use Crankshaft Pulley Holder (SST 09213-14010), to hold crankshaft pulley. Install and tighten pulley bolt. Ensure crankshaft pulley groove aligns with "0" mark on No. 1 timing cover. If "0" mark is not aligned, turn crankshaft pulley and align its groove with "0" mark on No. 1 timing belt cover.

NOTE: Two types of camshafts are available: one with 2 holes on timing pulley contact surface and one with 5 holes on timing pulley contact surface. All replacement camshafts have 5 holes.

4) To align 2-hole type camshafts, use a wrench and turn camshafts so camshaft knock pin aligns with mark on No. 3 timing belt cover. *See Fig. 6.* On 5-hole type camshafts, use a wrench and align camshaft knock pin and No. 1 bearing cap mark. *See Fig. 7.*

NOTE: Two types of camshaft timing pulleys are available: one with 5 holes on the camshaft contact surface and one with one hole on the camshaft surface. All replacement pulleys have 5 holes.

Fig. 5: Checking Timing Belt Tension

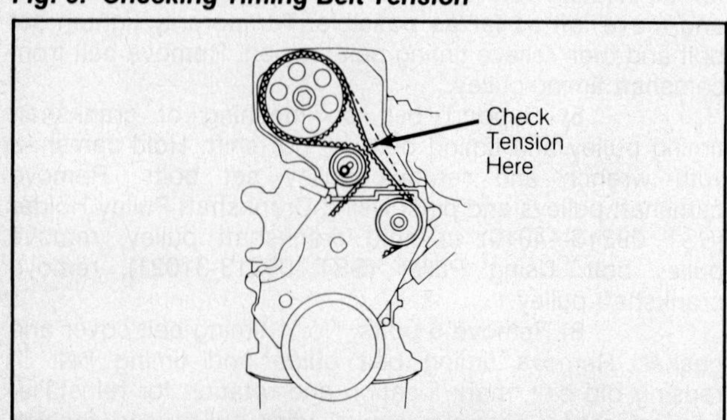

Courtesy of Toyota Motor Sales, U.S.A., Inc.

Fig. 6: Two-Hole Type Camshaft Alignment Marks

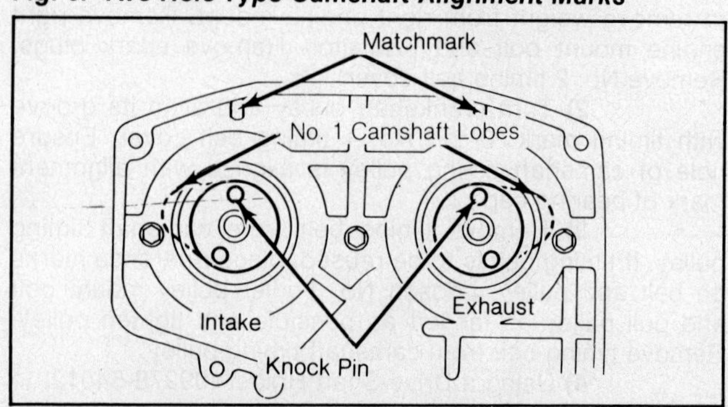

Courtesy of Toyota Motor Sales, U.S.A., Inc.

2.0L 3S-FE & 3S-GE 4-CYLINDER (Cont.)

Fig. 7: Five-Hole Type Camshaft Alignment Marks

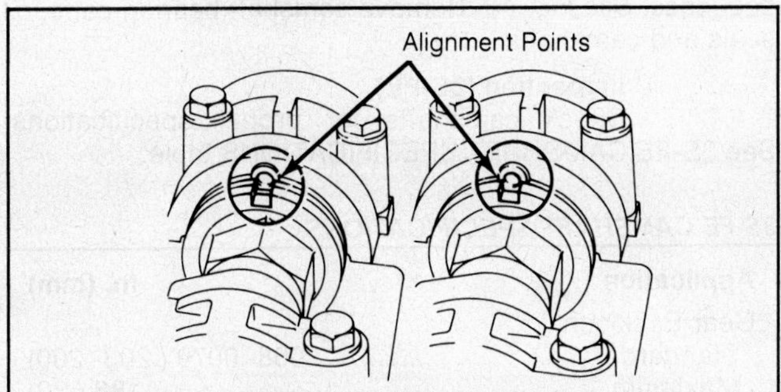

Courtesy of Toyota Motor Sales, U.S.A., Inc.

5) Install timing belt on pulleys. If reusing old belt, align marks made during removal. Be sure "S" mark on timing pulley faces outward. Align timing pulley mark with No. 3 timing belt cover mark. Install timing pulleys with belt. On one-hole type camshafts, match camshaft knock pin with camshaft timing pulley hole. *See Fig. 8.*

Fig. 8: One-Hole Type Camshaft Timing Pulley Alignment Marks

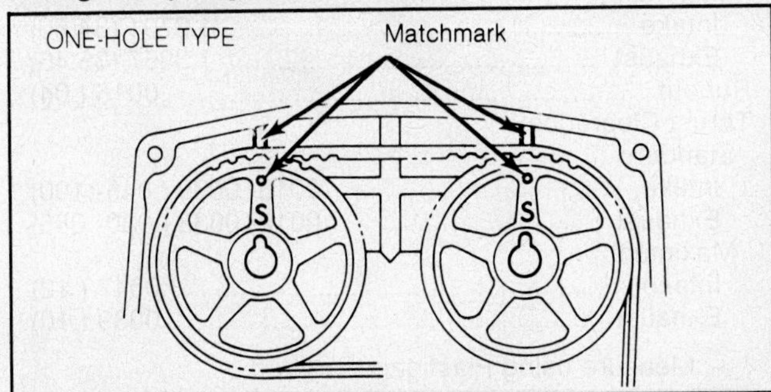

Courtesy of Toyota Motor Sales, U.S.A., Inc.

6) On 5-hole type camshafts, install knock pin into whichever camshaft timing pulley and camshaft holes are aligned. *See Fig. 9.* If holes are not aligned, turn camshaft. Hold camshaft with wrench and tighten pulley bolts to specification. Loosen No. 1 idler pulley set bolt and stretch timing belt. Use care not to loosen set bolt further than point where idler returns.

Fig. 9: Five-Hole Type Camshaft Timing Pulley Alignment Marks

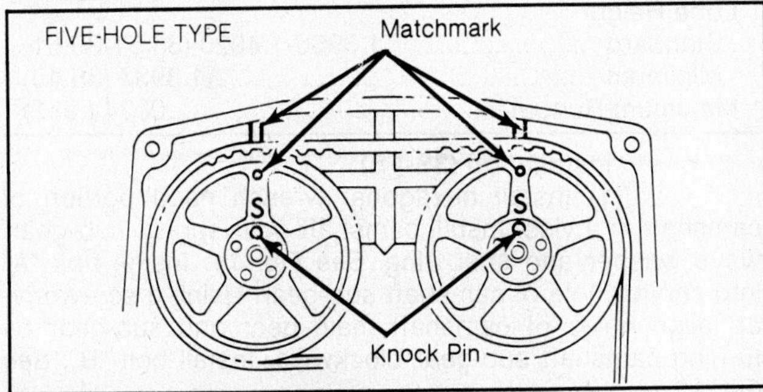

Courtesy of Toyota Motor Sales, U.S.A., Inc.

7) Turn crankshaft pulley clockwise 2 revolutions from TDC to TDC. Tighten No. 1 idler pulley set bolt to 31 ft. lbs. (43 N.m). Ensure belt has tension between crankshaft timing pulley and camshaft timing pulley on intake side. Check valve timing.

8) Install No. 2 timing belt cover, spark plugs, and cylinder head covers. Install right engine mounting insulator and bracket. Tighten bolts to specification. Lower engine and install power steering pump drive belt, alternator bracket, alternator and drive belt. Adjust drive belt tension. To complete installation, reverse removal procedure.

CAMSHAFT & CAMSHAFT HOUSING

Removal (3S-FE)

1) Remove cylinder head cover and timing belts. Because camshaft thrust clearance is very small, camshafts must be absolutely level when removed.

2) Set knock pin of intake camshaft at 10-45 degrees BTDC of camshaft angle. *See Fig. 10.* This position will allow the camshaft to be lifted evenly by the valve lifters pushing the No. 2 and No. 4 cylinder cam lobes.

3) Secure exhaust camshaft sub-gear to main gear with a 6 X 1.0 X 18 mm service bolt. *See Fig. 11.* When removing camshaft, ensure torsional spring force of sub-gear has been eliminated by installation of service bolt.

Fig. 10: Setting Camshaft Knock Pin

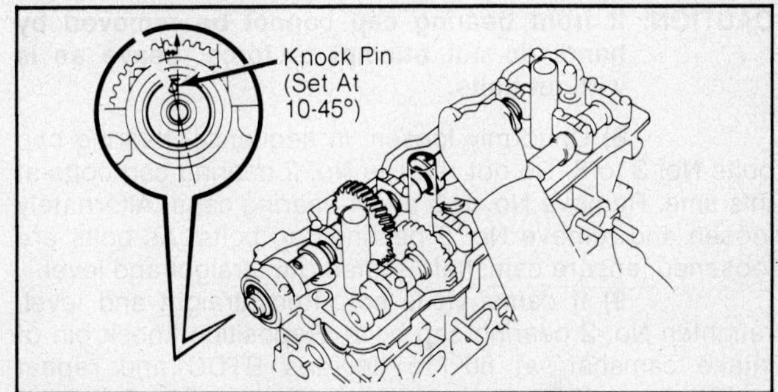

Courtesy of Toyota Motor Sales, U.S.A., Inc.

Fig. 11: Securing Exhaust Camshaft Sub-Gear

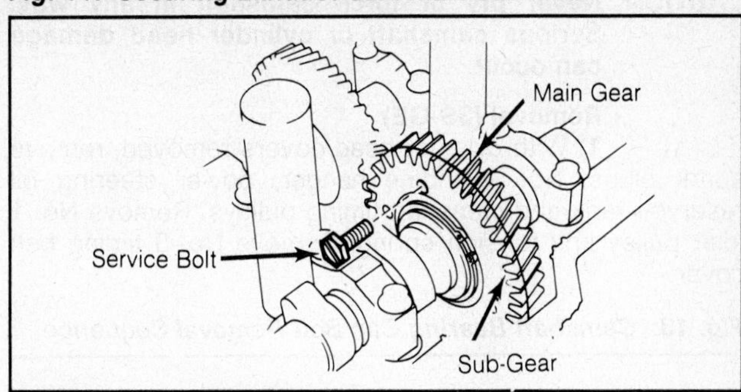

Courtesy of Toyota Motor Sales, U.S.A., Inc.

4) Remove camshaft rear bearing cap. Loosen and remove, in sequence, bearing cap bolts No. 3 to 8. *See Fig. 12.* Do not remove No. 3 bearing cap bolts at this time.

5) Remove No. 1, 2 and 4 bearing cap. Alternately loosen and remove No. 3 bearing cap bolts. As these bolts are loosened, ensure camshaft is lifted out straight and level.

6) If camshaft is not being lifted out straight and level, tighten bearing cap bolts No. 9 and 10, and reverse entire camshaft removal procedure. Reset knock pin of intake camshaft at 10-45 degrees BTDC. Remove No. 3 bearing cap and exhaust camshaft.

Toyota Engines

2.0L 3S-FE & 3S-GE 4-CYLINDER (Cont.)

Fig. 12: Bearing Cap Bolt Numbers

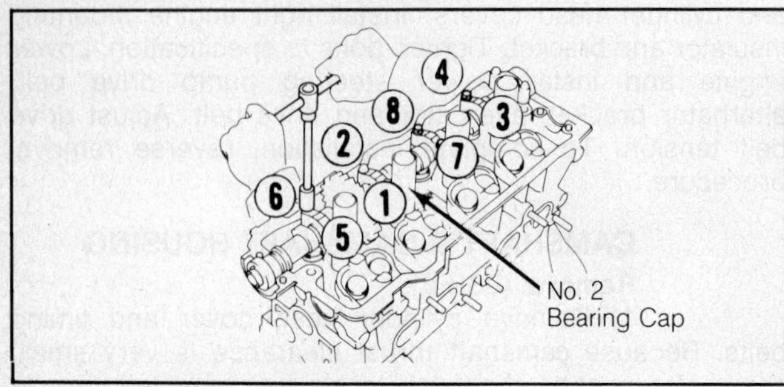

Courtesy of Toyota Motor Sales, U.S.A., Inc.

CAUTION: Never pry or force camshaft in any way. Serious damage to camshaft or cylinder head could occur.

7) To remove intake camshaft, set knock pin at 80-115 degrees BTDC of camshaft angle. This angle will allow No. 1 and 3 cylinder cam lobes of intake camshaft to be evenly pushed up by their valve lifters. Remove front bearing cap bolts No. 1 and 2. Remove front bearing cap and oil seal.

CAUTION: If front bearing cap cannot be removed by hand, do not attempt to force. Leave as is without bolts.

8) Uniformly loosen, in sequence, bearing cap bolts No. 3 to 8. Do not remove No. 2 bearing cap bolts at this time. Remove No. 1, 3 and 4 bearing caps. Alternately loosen and remove No. 2 bearing cap bolts. As bolts are loosened, ensure camshaft is lifted out straight and level.

9) If camshaft is not lifted straight and level, retighten No. 2 bearing cap bolts. Reposition knock pin of intake camshaft at 80-115 degrees BTDC and repeat entire camshaft removal procedure. Remove No. 2 bearing cap and camshaft.

CAUTION: Never pry or force camshaft in any way. Serious camshaft or cylinder head damage can occur.

Removal (3S-GE)

1) With cylinder head covers removed, remove spark plugs, No. 1 engine hanger, power steering oil reservoir tank and camshaft timing pulleys. Remove No. 1 idler pulley and tension spring. Remove No. 3 timing belt cover.

Fig. 13: Camshaft Bearing Cap Bolt Removal Sequence

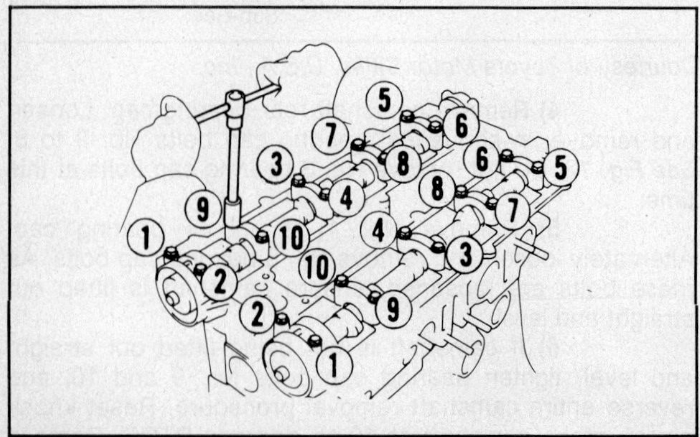

Courtesy of Toyota Motor Sales, U.S.A., Inc.

2) Loosen camshaft bearing cap bolts in sequence. *See Fig. 13.* Remove camshaft bearing caps, oil seals and camshafts.

Inspection (3S-FE)

Check camshafts for proper specifications. See 3S-FE CAMSHAFT SPECIFICATIONS table.

3S-FE CAMSHAFT SPECIFICATIONS

Application	In. (mm)
Gear Backlash	
Standard	.008-.0079 (.203-.200)
Maximum	.188 (.30)
Gear Spring End	
Free Distance	.886-.902 (22.5-22.9)
Journal Diameter	1.0614-1.0620 (26.959-26.975)
Journal Oil Clearance [1]	
Standard	.025-.062 (.0010-.0024)
Maximum	.0039 (.10)
Lobe Height	
Standard	
Intake	1.3744-1.3783 (34.910-35.010)
Exhaust	1.4000-1.4039 (35.560-35.660)
Maximum	
Intake	1.3701 (34.80)
Exhaust	1.3957 (35.45)
Runout	.0016 (.04)
Thrust Clearance	
Standard	
Intake	.0018-.0039 (.045-.100)
Exhaust	.0012-.0033 (.030-.085)
Maximum	
Intake	.0047 (.12)
Exhaust	.0039 (.10)

[1] – Measure using Plastigage method.

Inspection (3S-GE)

Check camshafts for proper specifications. See 3S-GE CAMSHAFT SPECIFICATIONS table.

3S-GE CAMSHAFT SPECIFICATIONS

Application	In. (mm)
Bearing-to-Journal Clearance	
Standard	.0010-.0024 (.025-.062)
Maximum	.003 (.08)
Journal Diameter	1.0614-1.0620 (26.959-26.975)
Lobe Height	
Standard	1.3980-1.4020 (35.51-35.61)
Minimum	1.3937 (35.40)
Maximum Runout	.0024 (.062)

Installation (3S-FE)

1) Install hexagonal wrench head portion of camshaft in a vise. Install camshaft gear spring, sub-gear, wave washer and snap ring. *See Fig. 14.* Install bolt "A" into service hole of camshaft sub-gear. Using a screwdriver, align holes of camshaft main gear and sub-gear by turning camshaft sub-gear clockwise. Install bolt "B". *See Fig. 15.*

NOTE: Ensure camshaft is level during installation.

2) Apply multi-purpose grease to thrust portion of camshaft. Install intake camshaft at 80 degrees BTDC of camshaft angle on cylinder head. Apply Seal Packing (08826-00080) to No. 1 bearing cap. *See Fig. 16.*

2.0L 3S-FE & 3S-GE 4-CYLINDER (Cont.)

3) Install bearing caps. Apply a light coat of engine oil on threads and under heads of bearing cap bolts. Install and tighten, in sequence, bearing cap bolts in 3 steps. *See Fig. 17.* Apply multi-purpose grease to new oil seal lip. Install oil seal.

Fig. 14: Installing Camshaft Components

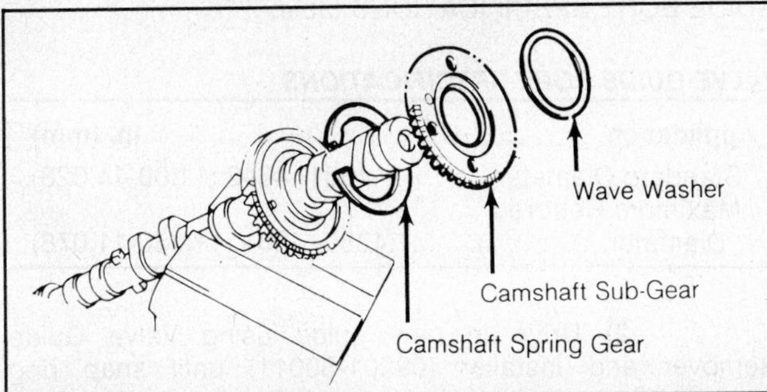

Courtesy of Toyota Motor Sales, U.S.A., Inc.

Fig. 15: Location of Bolts "A" & "B"

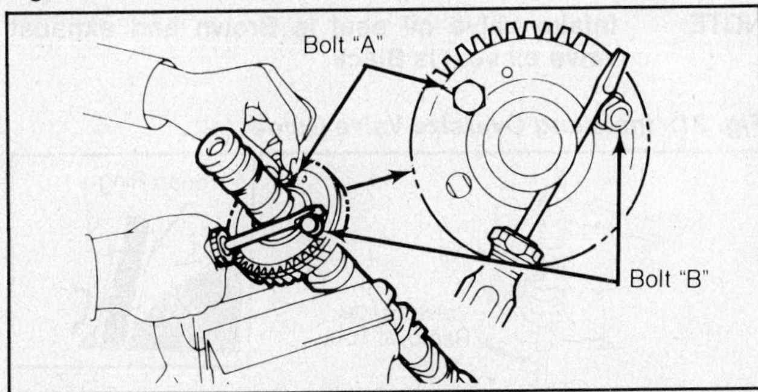

Courtesy of Toyota Motor Sales, U.S.A., Inc.

Fig. 16: Seal Packing Installation Location

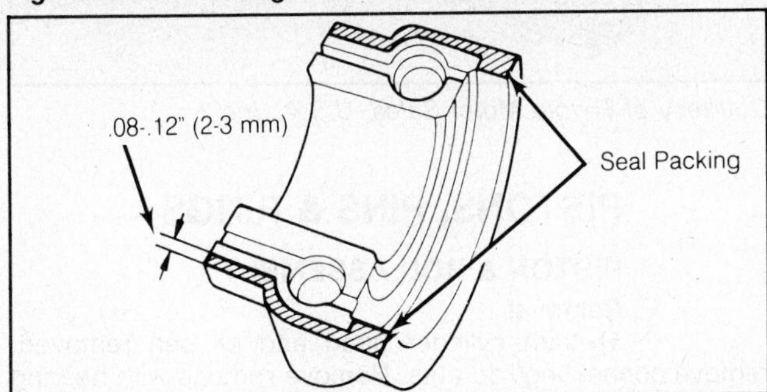

Courtesy of Toyota Motor Sales, U.S.A., Inc.

Fig. 17: Bearing Cap Bolt Tightening Sequence

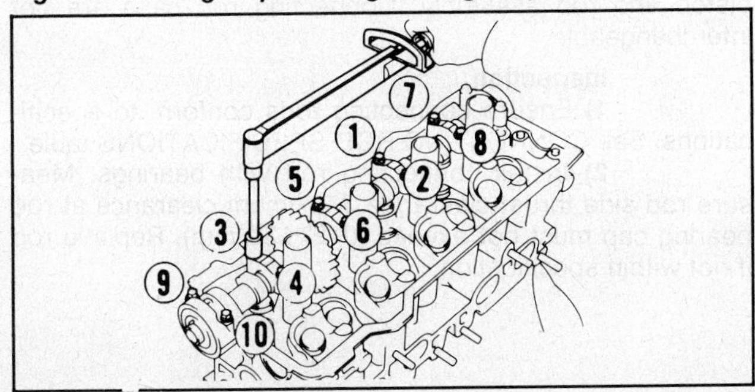

Courtesy of Toyota Motor Sales, U.S.A., Inc.

4) Set knock pin of intake camshaft at 10 degrees BTDC of camshaft angle. Apply multi-purpose grease to thrust portion of camshaft. Engage exhaust camshaft gear to intake camshaft gear by matching timing marks on each gear. Roll down exhaust camshaft onto bearing journals while engaging gears with each other.

NOTE: In addition to timing marks, assembly reference marks are present on each gear. Disregard these marks. See Fig. 18.

5) Turn intake camshaft in either direction, a little at at time, until exhaust camshaft sits in bearing journals evenly without rocking camshaft on bearing journals. Install bearing caps in proper locaton.

CAUTION: Camshaft must be evenly placed in bearing journals while tightening bearing caps.

Fig. 18: Timing Reference Marks

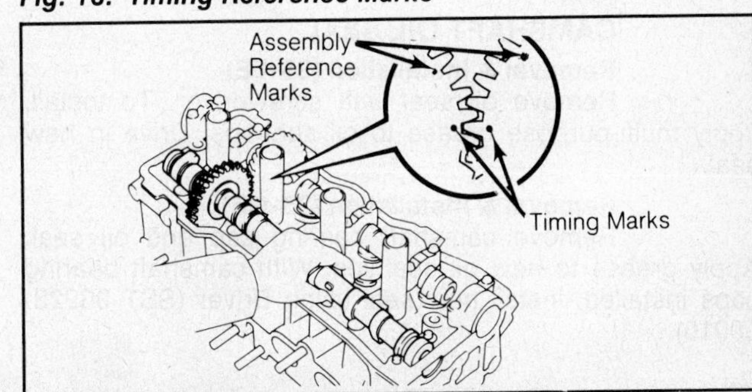

Courtesy of Toyota Motor Sales, U.S.A., Inc.

6) Apply a light coat of engine oil on threads and under heads of bearing cap bolts. Install and tighten, in sequence, bearing cap bolts in reverse order of

Fig. 19: Cylinder Head Seal Packing Installation

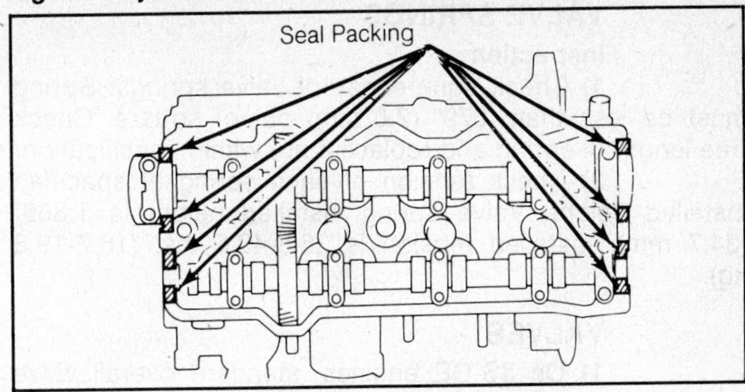

Courtesy of Toyota Motor Sales, U.S.A., Inc.

Fig. 20: Head Cover Grommet Installation

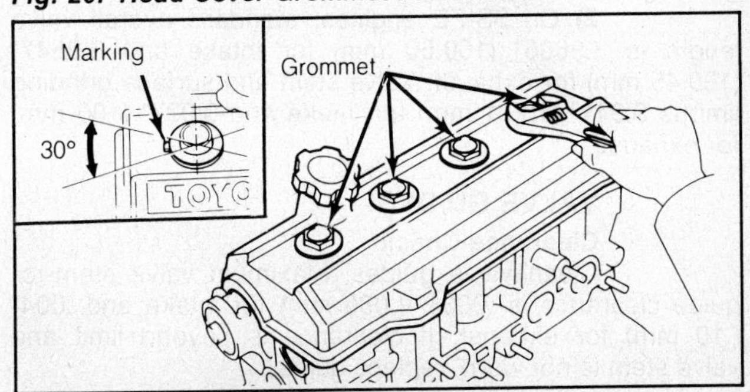

Courtesy of Toyota Motor Sales, U.S.A., Inc.

2.0L 3S-FE & 3S-GE 4-CYLINDER (Cont.)

removal. Remove service bolt. Install seal packing to cylinder head. *See Fig. 19.* Install gasket to head cover.

7) Install and tighten head cover with 4 grommets and nuts. Ensure grommets are installed so markings are properly positioned. *See Fig. 20.*

8) Install No. 3 timing belt cover. Install No. 1 idler pulley and tension spring, camshaft timing pulley, spark plugs and injector and delivery pipe. Install intake manifold. To complete installation, reverse removal procedure.

Installation (3S-GE)

Install bearing caps in numerical order from front. Ensure bearing cap arrows point toward front of engine. Install Seal Packing (08826-00080) to No. 1 bearing cap. Apply light coat of engine oil on threads and under heads of bearing cap bolts. Tighten bearing cap bolts in sequence to 14 ft. lbs. (19 N.m). To install remaining components, reverse removal procedure.

CAMSHAFT OIL SEAL

Removal & Installation (3S-FE)

Remove oil seal with screwdriver. To install, apply multi-purpose grease to oil seal lips. Drive in new seal.

Removal & Installation (3S-GE)

Remove camshaft bearing cap and oil seal. Apply grease to new oil seal lips. With camshaft bearing caps installed, install new seal using Driver (SST 09223-50010).

VALVES

VALVE ARRANGEMENT

Rear - Intake Valves
Front - Exhaust Valves

VALVE SPRINGS

Inspection

1) Check squareness of valve springs. Spring must be less than .079" (2.0 mm) out of square. Check free length of spring and replace if not within specification.

2) Check tension of each spring at specified installed height. Valve spring installed height is 1.366" (34.7 mm). Installed tension is 36.8-42.5 lbs. (16.7-19.3 kg).

VALVES

1) On 3S-GE engines, standard overall valve length is 4.0492" (102.850 mm) for intake and 4.0118" (101.900 mm) for exhaust. Valve stem end surface grinding limit is .028" (.70 mm).

2) On 3S-FE engines, standard overall valve length is 3.9606" (100.60 mm) for intake and 3.9547" (100.45 mm) for exhaust. Valve stem end surface grinding limit is 3.941" (100.1 mm) for intake and 3.937" (100 mm) for exhaust.

VALVE GUIDES

Clearance Check

Clean valve guides. Maximum valve stem-to-guide clearance is .0031" (.080 mm) for intake and .004" (.10 mm) for exhaust. If clearance is beyond limit and valve stem is not worn, replace guide.

Replacement

1) Using hammer and drift, tap valve guide firmly enough to break guide off flush with cylinder head surface. Remove snap ring. Gradually heat head to 230-266°F (110-130°C) in an oil bath. Using Valve Guide Driver (09201-60011), drive guide out toward block side. Measure cylinder head hole for valve guide. See VALVE GUIDE BORE SPECIFICATIONS table.

VALVE GUIDE BORE SPECIFICATIONS

Application	In. (mm)
Standard Diameter	.4331-.4342 (11.00-11.028)
Maximum Rebored Diameter	.4350-.4361 (11.050-11.078)

2) Drive in new guide using Valve Guide Remover and Installer (09201-60011) until snap ring comes in contact with cylinder head. *See Fig. 21.* Using an appropriate reamer, finish guide bore to specified clearance. Reface valve seat surface as necessary.

NOTE: **Intake valve oil seal is Brown and exhaust valve oil seal is Black.**

Fig. 21: Installing Oversize Valve Guide

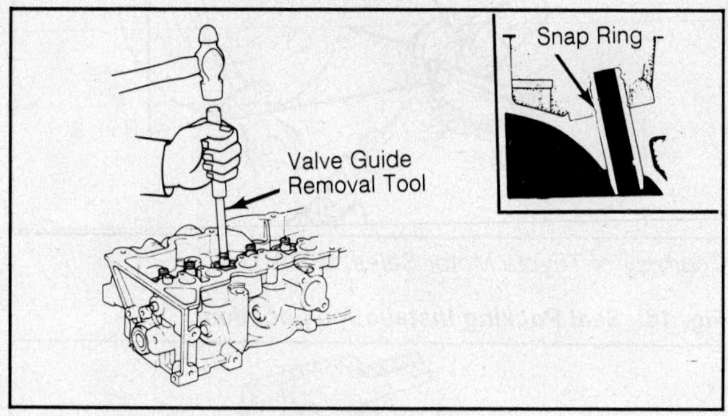

Courtesy of Toyota Motor Sales, U.S.A., Inc.

PISTONS, PINS & RINGS

PISTON & ROD ASSEMBLY

Removal

1) With cylinder head and oil pan removed, remove connecting rod nuts. Remove rod cap with bearing half. Remove cylinder bore ridge (if present).

2) Remove piston and rod assembly through top of block. Rod caps must be kept with their respective piston and rod assembly. Connecting rod caps are not interchangeable.

Inspection

1) Ensure connecting rods conform to specifications. See CONNECTING ROD SPECIFICATIONS table.

2) Install connecting rod with bearings. Measure rod side thrust clearance. Maximum clearance at rod bearing cap must not exceed .012" (.30 mm). Replace rod if not within specification.

2.0L 3S-FE & 3S-GE 4-CYLINDER (Cont.)

CONNECTING ROD SPECIFICATIONS

Application	In. (mm)
Thrust Clearance	.012 (.30)
Torsion Twist In 3.94" (100 mm) Length	
Minimum	.002 (.05)
Maximum	.006 (.15)

Installation

1) Oil rings, piston and cylinder bore. Install piston and rod assembly. Ensure ring gaps are set 180 degrees apart and code marks face up. Do not set on thrust side of piston or in line with piston pin. Ensure bearing halves are properly seated in rod and cap.

2) Install ring compressor. Install piston in cylinder with cavity on piston top aligned with straight edge of rod and facing front of engine. With piston installed, ensure rod and bearings are seated against crankshaft journal.

3) Install rod caps to their respective piston and rod assembly. Tighten connecting rod cap bolts to specification. Install cylinder head. Install new gasket and oil pan. Tighten pan bolts to specification. Complete installation by reversing removal procedure.

FITTING PISTONS & RINGS

1) Inspect cylinder block for cracks or flaws. If cylinder bore out-of-round or taper exceeds .0008" (.020 mm), refinish cylinder bore. When any one cylinder is bored, all cylinders must be bored. Maximum head contact surface warpage limit is .002" (.05 mm).

2) Determine piston oversize according to amount of wear in cylinder. Measure piston diameter at thrust face. Add piston-to-cylinder clearance. Finish hone of cylinder may then be determined. See PISTON & BORE SPECIFICATIONS table.

NOTE: Pistons and rings are available in .020" (.50 mm), .030" (.75 mm) and .040" (1.0 mm) oversize for service.

PISTON & BORE SPECIFICATIONS

Application	Diameter In. (mm)
Piston Size	
Standard	3.3061-3.3073 (83.975-84.005)
Bore Size	
Standard	3.3071-3.3073 (83.975-84.005)
Wear Limit	3.3181 (84.280)
Overbore Limit	3.3480 (85.040)

3) After honing cylinder to final fit, measure piston-to-cylinder clearance with piston and cylinder at room temperature of 70°F (20°C). Maximum clearance is .002" (.05 mm). Ensure bore difference between cylinders is .002" (.05 mm) or less. If more than specification, cylinders must be bored.

PISTON PINS

NOTE: Piston and pin are a matched set. Keep piston, pin, rings and rod together for each cylinder.

1) Check fit between piston and pin by trying to move piston back and forth on piston pin. If movement is felt, replace piston and pin.

2) To remove pin, warm piston and rod assembly to about 70°F (20°C). Press out pin using Piston Pin Installer/Remover (09221-25017).

3) Check pin and piston pin hole for signs of gouging or excessive wear. To assemble piston and rod, reheat piston to 70°F (20°C). Align cavity on piston with straightedge on connecting rod.

4) Hold piston and rod in proper alignment. Coat pin with oil and insert into the piston using a piston pin installer/remover. Ensure there is no movement of piston on pin.

CRANKSHAFT & ROD BEARINGS

CRANKSHAFT

Removal

1) Remove engine from vehicle. Remove drive belts and front covers. Remove valve timing belt. Secure crankshaft and remove flywheel or drive plate. Remove oil pan, oil pump and cylinder head. Remove piston and rod assemblies. Using punch, mark rods and caps for installation reference.

2) Remove main bearing caps and arrange caps, inserts and thrust washers in order for installation reference. Remove rear oil seal retainer. Do not damage crankshaft sealing surface. Remove crankshaft. Remove upper main bearing halves. Do not machine crankshaft.

NOTE: If replacing main bearings, replace with ones having the same number as marked on cylinder block. There are 5 sizes of bearings, marked "1", "2", "3", "4" or "5". See Fig. 22.

Fig. 22: Checking Standard Main Bearing Sizes

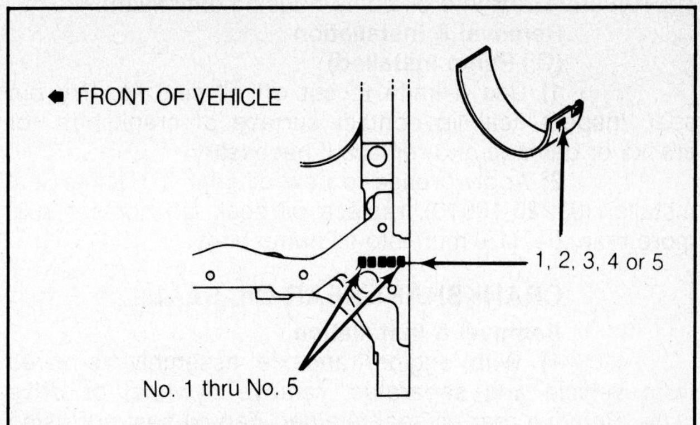

Courtesy of Toyota Motor Sales, U.S.A., Inc.

Inspection

1) Maximum taper and out-of-round is .0008" (.020 mm). Maximum allowable runout is .0024" (.060 mm). Maximum main bearing clearance is .003" (.08 mm).

2) If clearance is not to specification, main bearing inserts must be replaced with those having same number as marked on cylinder block. There are 3 sizes of standard main bearings, marked "1", "2" and "3".

3) Check bearing clearance using Plastigage method. Tighten rod caps to 36 ft. lbs. (49 N.m) on 3S-FE engines and 47 ft. lbs. (64 N.m) on 3S-GE engines. Maximum connecting rod bearing clearance is .0031" (.080 mm).

4) If not to specification, replace rod bearing inserts with ones having the same number as marked on bearing cap. Three sizes of standard rod bearing are available, marked "1", "2" and "3".

5) Check flywheel surface for cracks, damage or wear. Measure friction surface runout using a dial indicator. Runout limit is .004" (.10 mm).

Installation

1) Install main bearing halves in engine block. Ensure upper bearing halves have an oil hole and oil groove. Do not interchange inserts as crankshaft journal damage will result. Main bearing caps are numbered and must be installed with arrows facing front of engine.

2) Apply oil to main bearing surfaces. Install upper thrust washers on center bearing and lower thrust washers on No. 3 main bearing cap with oil grooves facing outward. Install crankshaft. Install main bearing caps with arrows facing front of engine.

3) Shift crankshaft toward front of engine. Tighten main bearing caps in 2 or 3 steps, starting at center bearing and working outward. Ensure crankshaft rotates smoothly. Check crankshaft end play. Maximum end play is .012" (.30 mm). Standard thrust washer thickness is .096-.098" (2.44-2.49 mm). If not within specification, replace No. 3 center main bearing thrust washers.

4) Install rear oil seal retainer. Install flywheel or drive plate. Install piston and rod assemblies. To install remaining components, reverse removal procedure.

CRANKSHAFT FRONT OIL SEAL

Removal & Installation
(Oil Pump Removed)

Remove oil seal using hammer and drift. Do not damage oil seal contact surface of oil pump. Apply grease to new oil seal lip. Using Seal Installer (09226-10010), drive seal into oil pump housing until flush.

Removal & Installation
(Oil Pump Installed)

1) Use a knife to cut off oil seal lip. Pry out seal. Inspect seal lip contact surface of crankshaft for cracks or damage and replace if necessary.

2) Apply grease to new oil seal lip. Using Seal Installer (09226-10010), replace oil seal. Do not set seal more than .04" (1.0 mm) into oil pump body.

CRANKSHAFT REAR OIL SEAL

Removal & Installation

1) With engine/transaxle assembly removed from vehicle and separated, remove flywheel or drive plate. Remove rear oil seal retainer. Tap oil seal out using hammer and drift. Apply grease to new oil seal lip. Using Seal Installer (09223-63010), install new seal.

2) If rear oil seal retainer is left installed, use a knife to cut off lip of oil seal. Pry out seal.

3) Inspect seal lip contact surface of crankshaft for damage and replace as necessary. Apply grease to new oil seal lip. Using Seal Installer (09223-63010), install new oil seal.

ENGINE OILING

ENGINE OILING SYSTEM

Oil is circulated through engine by a timing belt-driven oil pump. Oil is drawn from oil pan, circulated through a full-flow filter, then directed to crankshaft bearings and connecting rod bearings. Oil then passes through a galley that feeds camshaft bearings and rocker arms.

CRANKCASE CAPACITY

Crankcase capacity is 4.2 qts. (4.0L) with filter.

OIL FILTER

Oil filter is a full-flow, disposable type.

OIL PRESSURE

Normal oil pressure is 36-71 psi (2.5-5.0 kg/cm²) at 3000 RPM.

OIL PUMP

Removal

1) Raise and support vehicle. Drain engine oil. Remove lower right engine cover and oil dipstick. Remove oil pan without damaging flange.

2) Remove oil strainer mount bolts, strainer and "O" ring. Remove timing belt. Remove oil pump housing mount bolts. Carefully tap housing with plastic hammer to dislodge.

Disassembly

Remove oil pump body mount bolts, pump body, driven rotor and "O" ring. Hold sprocket in padded vise. Remove nut, sprocket, drive rotor and pump body. Remove snap ring, retainer, spring and relief valve piston. *See Fig. 23.*

Inspection

1) Measure clearance between driven rotor and pump body. Standard clearance is .004-.007" (.10-.17 mm). Maximum clearance is .008" (.20 mm). *See Fig. 24.*

2) Measure clearance between both rotor tips. Standard clearance is .0016-.0063" (.040-.160 mm). Maximum clearance is .008" (.20 mm). *See Fig. 24.*

3) Check relief valve components for wear or damage. Ensure relief valve operating pressure is within specification. Standard pressure is 51-63 psi (3.6-4.4 kg/cm²).

Fig. 23: Exploded View of Oil Pump

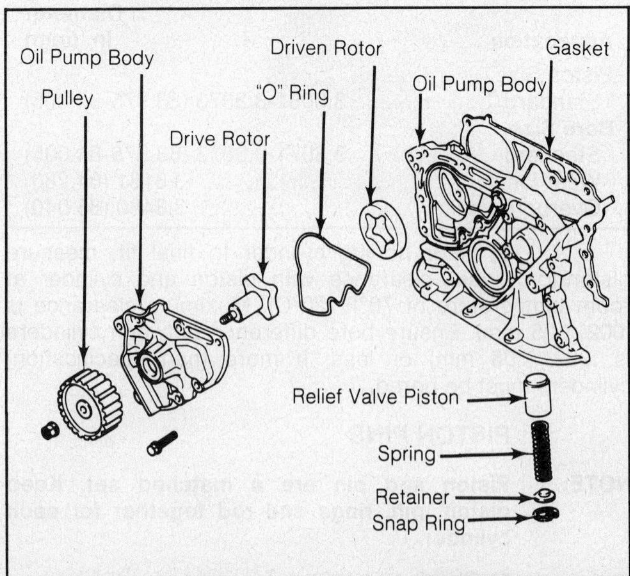

Courtesy of Toyota Motor Sales, U.S.A., Inc.

2.0L 3S-FE & 3S-GE 4-CYLINDER (Cont.)

Fig. 24: Checking Oil Pump Clearances

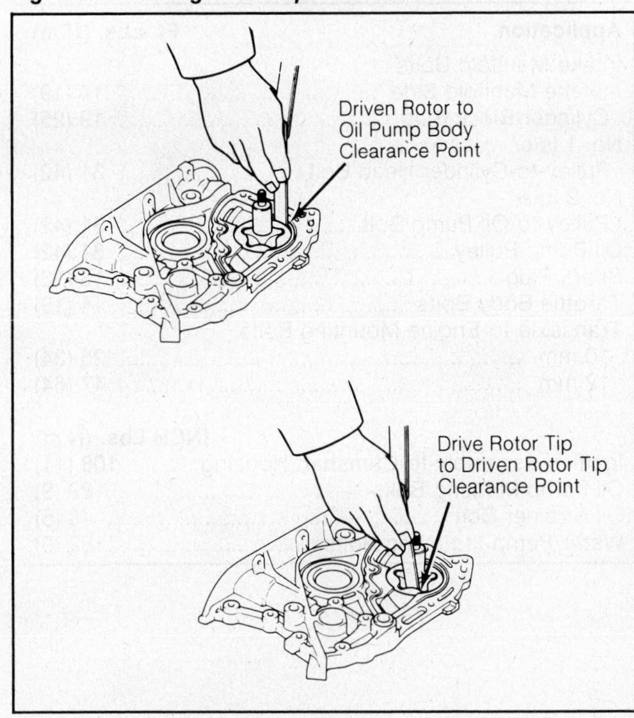

Courtesy of Toyota Motor Sales, U.S.A., Inc.

Reassembly

1) Install relief valve piston, spring, and retainer into pump body and secure with snap ring. Insert sprocket in drive rotor and install nut loosely. Hold sprocket in padded jaw vise and tighten nut to 16-23 ft. lbs. (22-31 N.m).

Fig. 25: Installing Oil Pan Gasket

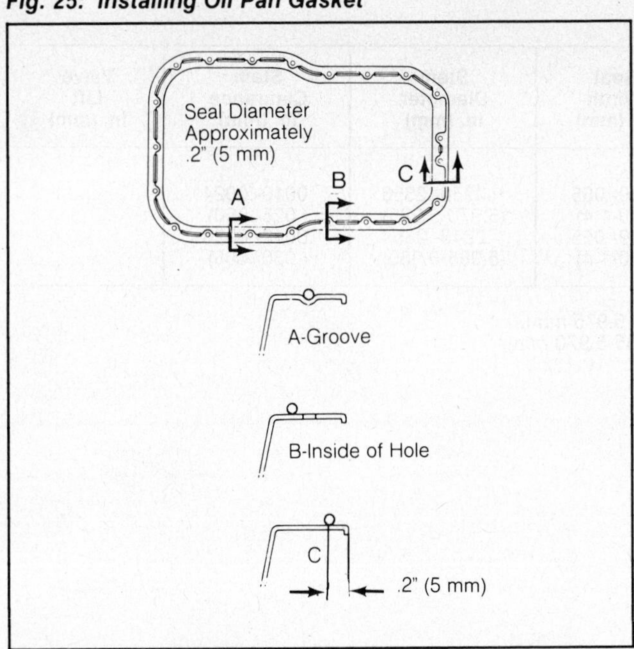

Courtesy of Toyota Motor Sales, U.S.A., Inc.

2) Place driven rotor into pump body with mark facing up. Install new "O" ring in body groove. Install pump body on pump housing.

Installation

1) Using new gasket, install pump housing onto cylinder block. Install timing belt. Install oil strainer with new "O" ring.

2) Clean old packing material from oil pan and apply new seal packing to oil pan. *See Fig. 25*. Install oil pan as soon as seal packing is applied.

3) To install remaining components, reverse removal procedure. Fill crankcase with oil, start engine and check for leaks.

ENGINE COOLING

WATER PUMP

Removal

1) Drain coolant. Remove drive and timing belts. Remove alternator adjusting bar. Disconnect radiator inlet hose. Disconnect coolant temperature switch connector from coolant inlet housing.

2) Disconnect coolant by-pass hose from water pump. Remove heater pipe mount bolts, heater pipe, and gasket. Remove 3 water pump assembly mounting bolts in sequence shown. *See Fig. 26*.

Fig. 26: Removing Water Pump Assembly Mount Bolts

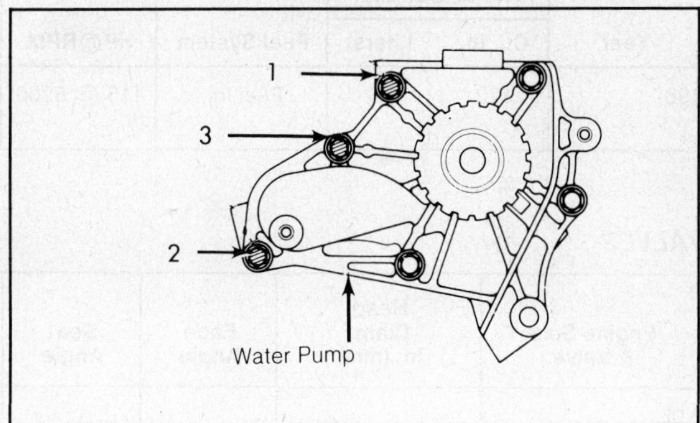

Courtesy of Toyota Motor Sales, U.S.A., Inc.

3) Remove remaining mounting bolts and tap water pump housing with plastic hammer to dislodge. Remove pump, "O" ring, and gasket.

Inspection

Check water pump impeller and pump body for cracks and damage of contact surfaces. Check pump bearing for roughness or noise. Ensure there is no sign of coolant leakage from drain hole. Check thermostat and radiator to ensure proper cooling system function.

Installation

To install, reverse removal procedure.

NOTE: **For further information on cooling systems, see ENGINE COOLING section.**

Toyota Engines

2.0L 3S-FE & 3S-GE 4-CYLINDER (Cont.)

TIGHTENING SPECIFICATIONS

Application	Ft. Lbs. (N.m)
Air Control Valve	14 (19)
Camshaft Housing Mounting Bolts	14 (19)
Camshaft Sprocket Mount Bolt	40 (54)
Connecting Rod Cap Bolts	
3S-GE	47 (64)
3S-FE	36 (49)
Crankshaft Main Bearing Cap Bolts	43 (59)
Crankshaft Sprocket Mount Bolt	80 (108)
Cylinder Head Mounting Bolts	
3S-FE	47 (64)
3S-GE	40 (54)
Engine Hanger No. 2 & Intake Manifold Stay No. 2 (3S-GE)	
12 mm Bolt	14 (19)
14 mm Bolt	29 (39)
Exhaust Manifold Bolts	
3S-GE	32 (43)
3S-FE	29 (39)
Flywheel Mounting Bolts	72 (98)

TIGHTENING SPECIFICATIONS (Cont.)

Application	Ft. Lbs. (N.m)
Intake Manifold Bolts	
Intake Manifold Side	14 (19)
Cylinder Block Side	19 (25)
No. 1 Idler	
Pulley-to-Cylinder Head Bolt	31 (42)
No. 2 Idler	
Pulley-to-Oil Pump Bolt	31 (42)
Oil Pump Pulley	31 (42)
Spark Plug	13 (18)
Throttle Body Bolts	14 (19)
Transaxle-to-Engine Mounting Bolts	
10 mm	25 (34)
12 mm	47 (64)
	INCH Lbs. (N.m)
Ignition Assembly-to-Camshaft Housing	108 (11)
Oil Pump Mouting Bolts	82 (9)
Oil Strainer Bolt	48 (5)
Water Pump Mounting Bolts	82 (9)

ENGINE SPECIFICATIONS

GENERAL SPECIFICATIONS

Year	DISPLACEMENT		Fuel System	HP@RPM	Torque Ft. Lbs.@RPM	Compr. Ratio	BORE		STROKE	
	Cu. In.	Liters					In.	mm	In.	mm
1987	122	2.0	Fuel Inj.	115 @ 5200	125 @ 4400	9.2:1	3.38	86	3.38	86

VALVES

Engine Size & Valve	Head Diam. In. (mm)	Face Angle	Seat Angle	Seat Width In. (mm)	Stem Diameter In. (mm)	Stem Clearance In. (mm)	Valve Lift In. (mm)
2.0L							
Intake	.....	44.5°	45°	.039-.055 (1.0-1.4)	[1] .2350-.2356 (5.970-5.985)	.0010-.0024 (.025-.060)	.....
Exhaust	.....	44.5°	45°	.039-.055 (1.0-1.4)	[2] .2348-.2354 (5.965-5.980)	.0012-.0026 (.030-.065)	.....

[1] – On 3S-GE engines, intake valve stem diameter is .2346-.2352" (5.960-5.975 mm).
[2] – On 3S-GE engines, exhaust valve stem diameter is .2344-.2350" (5.955-5.970 mm).

Toyota Engines

2.0L 3S-FE & 3S-GE 4-CYLINDER (Cont.)

ENGINE SPECIFICATIONS (Cont.)

PISTONS, PINS & RINGS

Engine	PISTONS	PINS		RINGS		
	Clearance In. (mm)	Piston Fit In. (mm)	Rod Fit In. (mm)	Ring No.	End Gap In. (mm)	Side Clearance In. (mm)
2.0L						
3S-FE	.0018-.0026 (.045-.065)	.....	Press Fit [1]	No. 1	.0106-.0193 (.270-.490)	.0012-.0028 (.030-.070)
				No. 2	.0106-.0197 (.270-.500)	.0012-.0028 (.030-.070)
				Oil	.0079-.0311 (.200-.790)	.0012-.0028 (.030-.070)
3S-GE	.0012-.0020 (.030-.050)	.....	Press Fit [1]	No. 1	.0130-.0213 (.330-.540)	.0012-.0028 (.030-.070)
				No. 2	.0079-.0173 (.200-.440)	.0008-.0024 (.020-.060)
				Oil	.0079-.0350 (.200-.790)	.....

[1] – The piston and pin are available only as a matched set.

CRANKSHAFT MAIN & CONNECTING ROD BEARINGS

Engine	MAIN BEARINGS				CONNECTING ROD BEARINGS		
	Journal Diam. In. (mm)	Clearance In. (mm)	Thrust Bearing	Crankshaft End Play In. (mm)	Journal Diam. In. (mm)	Clearance In. (mm)	Side Play In. (mm)
2.0L	2.1648-2.1654 (54.985-55.000)	.0007-.0015 [1] (.018-.037)	No. 3	.0008-.0087 (.020-.220)	1.8892-1.8898 (47.985-48.000)	.0009-.0022 (.023-.055)	.0063-.0123 (.160-.312)

[1] – The main bearing clearance for journal No. 3 is .0011-.0019" (.028-.047 mm).

CAMSHAFT

Engine	Journal Diam. In. (mm)	Clearance In. (mm)	Lobe Lift In. (mm)
2.0L			
3S-FE			
Intake	1.0614-1.0620 (26.959-26.975)	.0010-.0024 (.025-.062)	1.374-1.378 (34.91-35.01)
Exhaust	1.0614-1.0620 (26.959-26.975)	.0010-.0024 (.025-.062)	1.400-1.404 (34.56-35.66)
3S-GE	1.0614-1.0620 (26.959-26.975)	.0010-.0024 (.025-.062)	1.398-1.402 (35.51-35.61)

VALVE SPRINGS

Engine	Free Length In. (mm)	PRESSURE Lbs. @ In. (Kg @ mm)	
		Valve Closed	Valve Open
2.0L			
3S-FE	1.772 (45.0)	38.6 @ 1.366 (17.5 @ 34.7)	.....
3S-GE	1.6779 (42.62)	38.6 @ 1.366 (17.5 @ 34.7)	.....

Toyota Engines

2.2L 4-CYLINDER

Van

NOTE: **For engine repair procedures not covered in this article, see ENGINE OVERHAUL PROCEDURES article at beginning of this section.**

ENGINE CODING

ENGINE IDENTIFICATION

The engine serial number is stamped on right side of engine block below cylinder head. Vehicle Identification Number (VIN) is displayed in 3 locations on the vehicle. These locations are plate under front passenger seat carpet, on top left side of dash, and certification plate on left door post.

ENGINE IDENTIFICATION CODES

Application	Code
2.2L	4Y-E

ENGINE, MANIFOLDS & CYLINDER HEAD

ENGINE

Removal & Installation

1) Disconnect negative battery cable. Remove right seat. Remove engine service cover. Drain coolant. Disconnect hoses from radiator, heater outlet, brake booster, fuel inlet and outlet, and charcoal canister.

2) Remove hose from air cleaner. Remove power steering pump (if equipped). Disconnect accelerator cable and bracket from throttle body.

3) Disconnect wire connectors from coolant temperature sending unit, oil pressure switch, Integrated Ignition Assembly (IIA), A/C compressor, idle-up solenoid, and Vacuum Switching Valve (VSV).

4) If equipped with automatic transmission, disconnect 3 connectors at transmission. Disconnect coolant temperature switch, alternator, airflow meter, and solenoid resistor connectors.

5) Remove fan shroud. Remove fan clutch with fan and pulley. Remove driver's door pillar cover. Remove driver's seat belt retractor and cover. Disconnect Electronic Control Unit (ECU) connectors. Remove 4 air conditioning compressor mounting bolts. Remove compressor and secure out of way.

6) Raise and support vehicle about 40" off floor. Drain crankcase. Remove drive shaft. Remove exhaust pipe. Remove transmission control selector, shift cable(s), and clutch release cylinder.

7) Remove starter wiring. Remove starter. Disconnect speedometer cable. Disconnect back-up light connector. Disconnect transfer case indicator light (if equipped). Disconnect rear heater mode select and air mix cable at damper (if equipped). Disconnect rear heater hose connections.

8) Disconnect heater outlet hose. Disconnect cable from engine mounts. Remove lower engine cover. On automatic transmission equipped models, disconnect oil cooler lines.

9) Remove stabilizer bar. Remove stabilizer bar bracket from lower control arm. Scribe alignment marks on strut bar-to-strut bar rear nut. Remove strut bar from lower control arm. Support front and rear of engine. *See Fig. 1.*

10) Remove engine mounts from body. *See Fig. 2.* Lower engine and transmission. Remove engine mounting member from engine. Remove transmission from engine. To install engine, reverse removal procedure.

Fig. 1: Supporting Engine for Removal & Installation

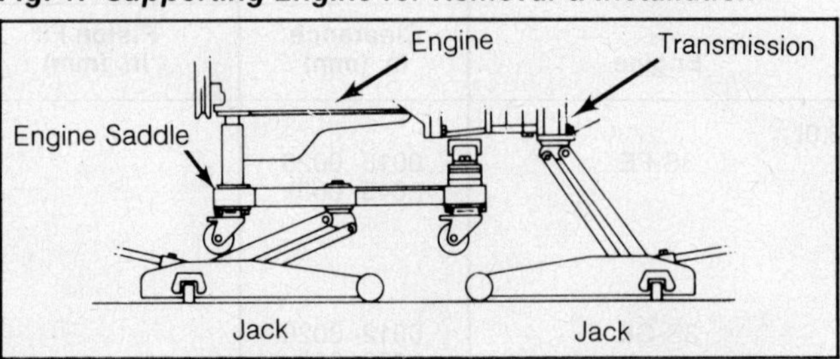

Courtesy of Toyota Motor Sales, U.S.A., Inc.

Fig. 2: View of Engine Mounting

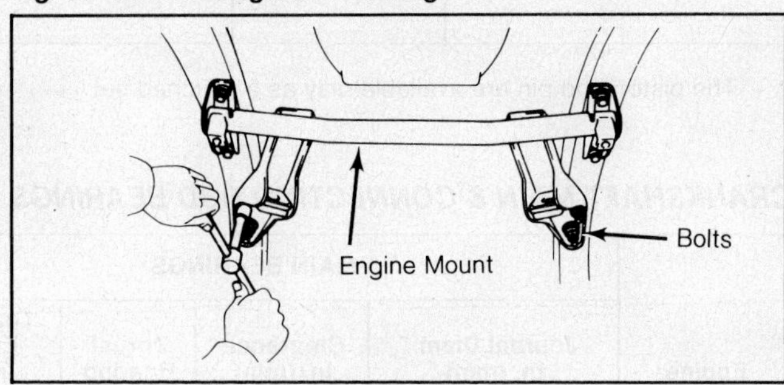

Courtesy of Toyota Motor Sales, U.S.A., Inc.

CYLINDER HEAD

Removal

1) Disconnect negative battery cable. Remove right seat. Remove engine service cover. Drain coolant and disconnect all coolant hoses. Drain oil pan. Remove power steering pump (if equipped).

2) Remove exhaust pipe and bracket. Disconnect accelerator cable with bracket from throttle body. Remove air cleaner and hoses.

3) Disconnect electrical connectors from coolant temperature sensor, start injector time switch, cold start injector, air valve, throttle position sensor, and oxygen sensor. Remove A/C coolant temperature switch (if equipped). *See Fig. 3.*

Fig. 3: Engine Electrical Connections

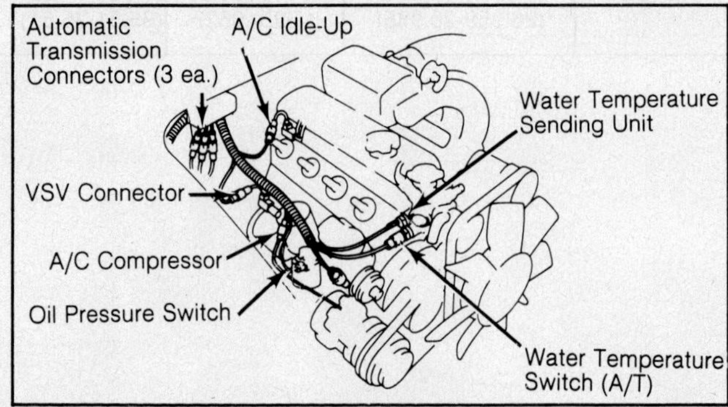

Courtesy of Toyota Motor Sales, U.S.A., Inc.

4) Disconnect hoses from radiator inlet, radiator breather, coolant reserve tank, heater outlet, PCV valve, and coolant by-pass. *See Fig. 4.*

2.2L 4-CYLINDER (Cont.)

Fig. 4: Engine Hose Connections

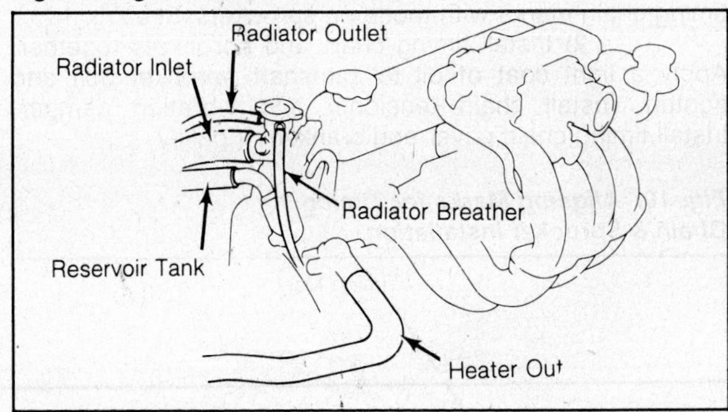

Courtesy of Toyota Motor Sales, U.S.A., Inc.

5) Label and disconnect emission control hoses and vacuum lines from brake booster and charcoal canister. Remove fuel injection throttle body. Remove 2 nuts attaching air intake chamber to EGR valve. Remove union nut attaching EGR valve to exhaust manifold. Remove EGR valve.

6) Disconnect start injector pipe and pressure regulator hose. Remove air intake chamber brackets. Remove air intake chamber with air valve. Remove wire clamp bolt at injector tube. Remove injector wire connections.

7) Remove exhaust manifold bracket. Remove heater pipe bracket. Remove fuel inlet union bolt from fuel filter. Remove fuel outlet hose. Remove intake and exhaust manifold.

8) Remove spark plugs and spark plug tubes. Remove valve cover. Remove rocker arm assembly. Remove push rods. Loosen head bolts in sequence, in 3 stages. *See Fig. 5.*

Fig. 5: Cylinder Head Bolt Removal Order

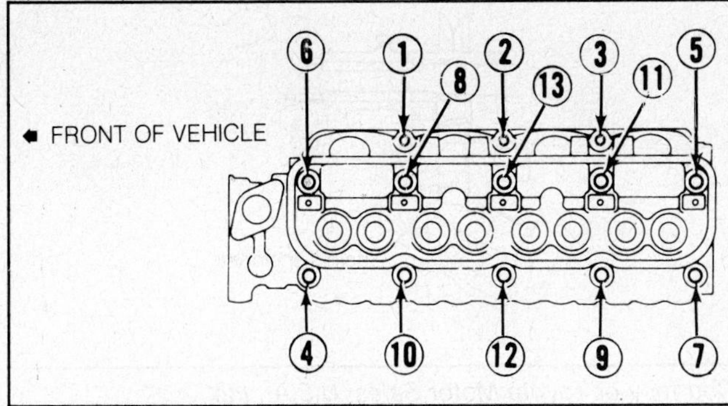

Courtesy of Toyota Motor Sales, U.S.A., Inc.

9) Remove cylinder head. Remove lifters from engine block. Keep lifters in correct order for reassembly reference.

Installation

To install cylinder head, reverse removal procedure. Tighten bolts to specification in proper sequence. *See Fig. 6.*

Fig. 6: Cylinder Head Bolt Tightening Sequence

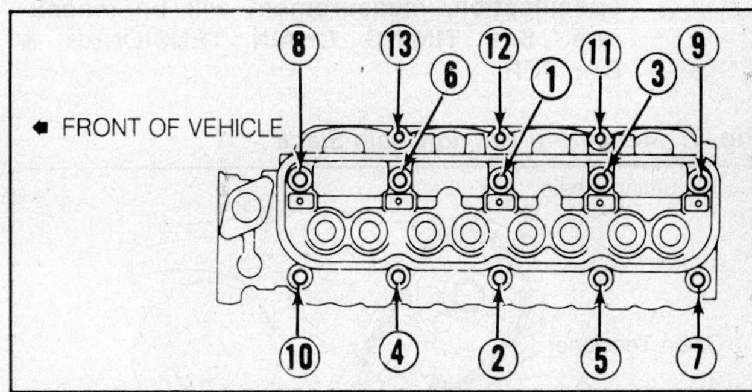

Courtesy of Toyota Motor Sales, U.S.A., Inc.

INTAKE & EXHAUST MANIFOLDS

Removal

1) Disconnect negative battery cable. Remove right seat. Remove engine service cover. Drain coolant and disconnect all coolant hoses. Drain oil pan. Remove power steering pump (if equipped).

2) Remove exhaust pipe and bracket. Disconnect accelerator cable with bracket from throttle body. Remove air cleaner and hoses.

3) Remove electrical connectors from coolant temperature sensor, start injector time switch, cold start injector, air valve, throttle position sensor, and oxygen sensor. Disconnect A/C coolant temperature switch (if equipped). *See Fig. 3.*

4) Disconnect hoses from radiator inlet, radiator breather, reserve tank, heater outlet, PCV valve, and coolant by-pass. *See Fig. 4.* Remove brake booster vacuum hose and charcoal canister hose.

5) Label and disconnect all emission control hoses. Remove throttle body. Remove 2 nuts attaching air intake chamber to EGR valve. Remove union nut attaching exhaust manifold to EGR valve and remove EGR valve.

6) Disconnect start injector pipe and pressure regulator hose. Remove air intake chamber brackets. Remove air intake chamber with air valve. Remove wire clamp bolt at injector tube.

7) Disconnect injector wire connections from injectors. Remove exhaust manifold bracket. Remove heater pipe bracket. Remove fuel inlet union bolt from fuel filter. Remove fuel outlet hose. Remove intake and exhaust manifolds.

Installation

To install manifolds, reverse removal procedure. Ensure mating surfaces are clean and new gaskets are used. Tighten 2 center bolts first, then top front, bottom rear, bottom front, and top rear bolts in order.

CAMSHAFT

TIMING CHAIN & GEAR

Checking for Stretch

1) Remove timing chain cover. With timing chain installed on engine, attach a spring scale to timing chain on tensioner side. Pull on chain with tension of 22 lbs. (10 kg). If distance between chain tensioner plunger and tensioner body exceeds .531" (13.5 mm), chain and sprockets must be removed and checked. *See Fig. 7.*

NOTE: **When checking distance between tensioner plunger and body, note thickness of tension-**

Toyota Engines

2.2L 4-CYLINDER (Cont.)

er head. If tensioner head is worn beyond specification, measurement will be inaccurate. See TIMING CHAIN TENSIONER & DAMPER.

Fig. 7: Measuring Timing Chain Slack

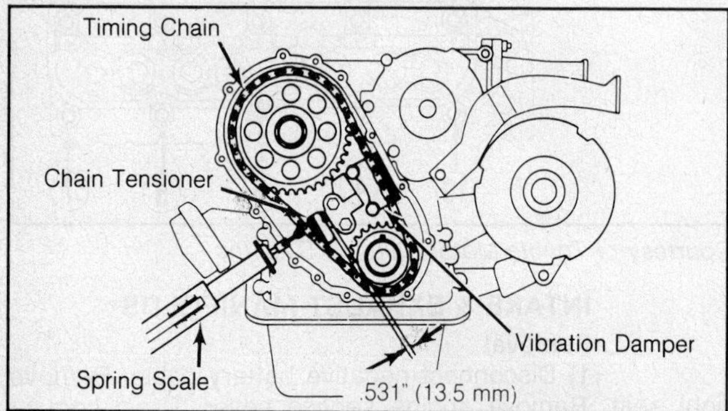

Courtesy of Toyota Motor Sales, U.S.A., Inc.

2) Timing chain may be inspected when removed from engine. Secure one link of timing chain and attach spring tension gauge to opposite end. *See Fig. 8.*

Fig. 8: Checking Timing Chain Elongation

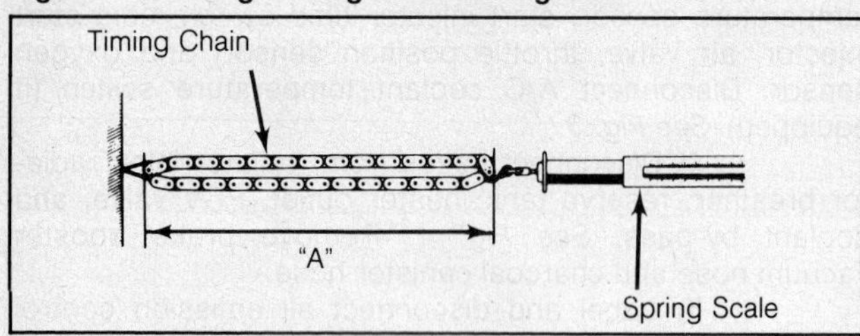

Courtesy of Toyota Motor Sales, U.S.A., Inc.

3) With 11 lbs. (5 kg) tension applied to chain, distance "A" should be no more than 11.47" (291 mm). If distance exceeds specification, replace chain.

Removal

1) Remove camshaft sprocket bolt and remove sprocket and chain. Pull crankshaft sprocket from crankshaft. Check sprockets for wear.

2) Wrap chain completely around crankshaft sprocket. Measure outside diameter of rollers with a Vernier caliper. If less than 2.34" (59 mm), replace sprocket. Measure camshaft sprocket in same manner. If less than 4.49" (114 mm), replace sprocket. *See Fig. 9.*

Installation

1) To correctly install sprockets and timing chain, set No. 1 piston to TDC of compression stroke.

Fig. 9: Measuring Chain & Sprocket for Wear

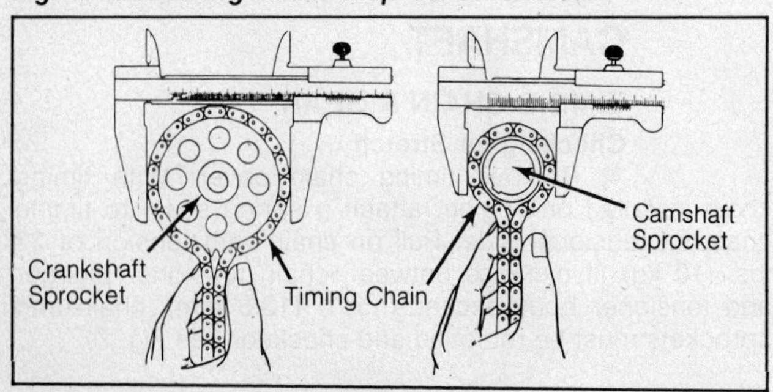

Courtesy of Toyota Motor Sales, U.S.A., Inc.

Align camshaft dowel pin with mark on thrust plate. Align timing chain marks with those on sprockets. *See Fig. 10.*

2) Install timing chain and sprockets together. Apply a light coat of oil to camshaft sprocket bolt and tighten. Install chain tensioner and vibration damper. Install timing chain cover and crankshaft pulley.

Fig. 10: Aligning Marks for Timing Chain & Sprocket Installation

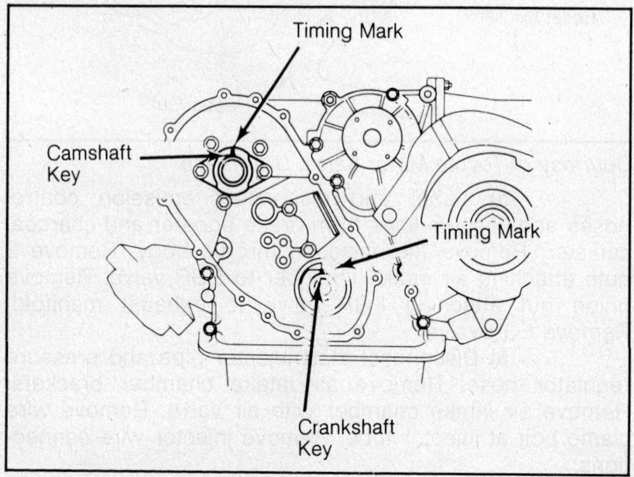

Courtesy of Toyota Motor Sales, U.S.A., Inc.

TIMING CHAIN TENSIONER & DAMPER

1) Inspect surfaces of tensioner plunger and bore of tensioner body. To test clearance, lubricate plunger and insert into plunger body. Cover oil passages with fingers and pull plunger out about halfway. Vacuum strong enough to return plunger should be felt.

Fig. 11: Measuring Chain Tensioner

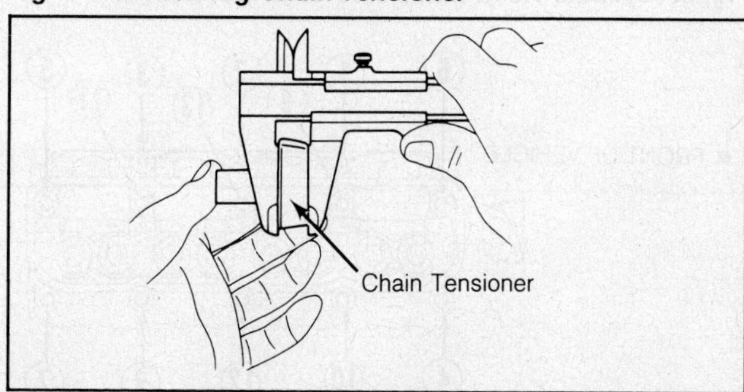

Courtesy of Toyota Motor Sales, U.S.A., Inc.

Fig. 12: Measuring Chain Damper

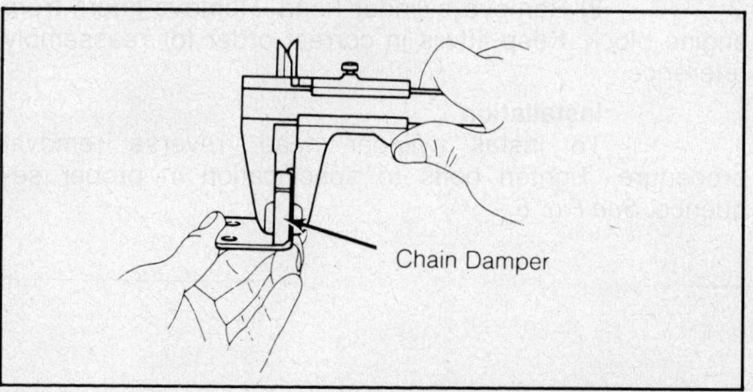

Courtesy of Toyota Motor Sales, U.S.A., Inc.

2) Measure thickness of tensioner head and chain damper. Tensioner head should be a minimum of .49" (12.5 mm) thick. Chain damper should be a minimum of .20" (5.0 mm) thick. *See Figs. 11 and 12.*

CAMSHAFT

Removal

1) Remove timing chain and sprockets. See TIMING CHAIN & GEAR in this article. Take off camshaft thrust plate. Remove front end plate from engine block.

2) Remove cylinder head, valve lifters, and distributor. Pull camshaft straight out, using care not to damage bearings or journals.

3) Check camshaft runout at number 2 journal by using a dial indicator. Maximum service runout limit is .0024" (.060 mm), and maximum journal out-of-round or taper is .0008" (.020 mm).

Installation

After installing camshaft, install timing gears and chain. See TIMING CHAIN & GEAR in this article. Install cylinder head with new gasket. See CYLINDER HEAD in this article. To install camshaft, reverse removal procedure.

CAMSHAFT END THRUST

With sprocket installed, check clearance between thrust plate and first bearing journal. If clearance exceeds .012" (.3 mm), replace thrust plate. If clearance is still excessive after replacing thrust plate, it will be necessary to replace camshaft.

CAM LOBE HEIGHT

Measure height of camshaft lobes, if less than specifications replace camshaft. See CAM LOBE HEIGHT TABLE.

CAM LOBE HEIGHT TABLE

Lobe	In. (mm)
Standard	
Intake	1.5205-1.5244 (38.621-38.720)
Exhaust	1.5208-1.5248 (38.628-38.730)
Minimum	
Intake	1.5063 (38.26)
Exhaust	1.5067 (38.27)

CAMSHAFT BEARINGS

Removal & Installation

1) Measure camshaft journal diameter and subtract from measured diameter of bearing bore to determine clearance. Bearings should be replaced if clearance exceeds limit. See CAMSHAFT specifications at end of article.

2) To replace bearings, remove camshaft expansion plug from rear of engine. Use Bearing Puller/Installer (09215-00100) to remove old bearings. To install bearings, use Bearing Puller/Installer (09215-00100) to draw bearings into cylinder block. Be sure oil holes in bearings are aligned with oil holes in cylinder block. Coat expansion plug with sealer and install.

VALVES

VALVE ARRANGEMENT

E-I-I-E-E-I-I-E (Front-to-rear).

ROCKER ARM ASSEMBLY

1) Remove air intake chamber and valve cover. Remove rocker arm assembly retaining bolts in 3 or 4 steps. Loosen in sequence of front, rear, front center, and rear center bolts. Remove rocker arm assembly.

2) Remove retaining clips from both ends of rocker arm shaft. Remove conical spring, rocker arms, springs, and support stands. Keep parts in order for reassembly reference.

3) Thoroughly clean and inspect all components. Check rocker arm-to-shaft clearance. If clearance exceeds .003" (.08 mm), replace rocker arms or shafts as necessary. Reface valve end of rocker arm if worn. Lubricate all components before assembly.

VALVE SPRINGS

Removal

With cylinder head removed, use Compressor (09202-43013) to compress valve springs and retainers. Remove valve spring retainer locks (keepers). Remove retainer, spring, seal and washer. Remove valves and components. Mark parts for reassembly reference.

Inspection

1) With valve spring removed, check length under specified load in a spring tester. Check free length. If not within specifications, replace valve spring.

2) Check valve spring squareness with a steel square. Replace spring if out-of-square more than specified limit. See VALVE SPRINGS specifications at end of article.

Installation

To install valve springs, reverse removal procedure and use new seals on valve stems. Compress springs and install keepers.

VALVE STEM LENGTH

Valve stem tips may be resurfaced on a valve grinder. Do not grind more than .020" (.5 mm) from valve stem tips. Standard intake valve length is 4.260" (108.2 mm). Exhaust valve length is 4.272" (108.5 mm).

VALVE MARGIN

Check valve head margin thickness, if less than specification replace valve. See MARGIN THICKNESS table.

MARGIN THICKNESS

Valve	In. (mm)
Standard	
Intake	.039-.055 (.99-1.39)
Exhaust	.051-.067 (1.29-1.70)
Minimum	
Intake	.020 (.50)
Exhaust	.031 (.80)

VALVE GUIDES

1) Measure valve guide inner diameter and valve stem outer diameter. If clearance exceeds specified

2.2L 4-CYLINDER (Cont.)

limit, replace valves and/or guides. See VALVES specifications at end of article.

NOTE: Cylinder head should be heated to about 212°F (100°C) before removal or replacement of valve guide.

2) To replace valve guide, break off upper portion of guide at snap ring. Drive remaining portion of guide out of head through combustion chamber with Driver (09201-60011).

3) Install snap ring on guide and install from top with driver. Drive in until snap ring contacts head. Guide projects .07" (1.8 mm) when properly installed. Ream guide for proper stem clearance.

NOTE: Oversize guides .002" (.05 mm) larger than original guides are available to obtain proper fit between guide and head.

HYDRAULIC VALVE LIFTERS

1) Using a leak-down tester, apply 44 lbs. (20 kg) of pressure to plunger. Measure leak-down time. Leak-down time should be 7-50 seconds for .04" (1 mm), after sliding down about .08" (2 mm), at a temperature of 68°F (20°C).

2) Check clearance between valve lifter and bore in crankcase. If clearance exceeds .004" (.1 mm), replace lifter.

VALVE CLEARANCE ADJUSTMENT

The valve clearance is automatically adjusted by use of hydraulic valve lifters and is not adjustable.

PISTONS, RINGS & PINS

PISTON & ROD ASSEMBLY

Removal

With engine removed from vehicle, remove cylinder head and oil pan. Remove ridge from top of cylinder bore before removing pistons. Mark each connecting rod and mating cap for reassembly. Remove piston and connecting rod assembly. Mark piston to ensure it is installed in same cylinder.

Installation

1) Ensure ring gaps are in correct position. *See Fig. 13.* Coat piston and rings with oil. To install piston and rod assembly, compress piston rings with a ring compressor. Install piston and rod assembly in crankcase with notch in piston facing front of engine.

2) Apply oil to crankshaft journals. Install connecting rod cap. Tighten connecting rod nuts to specification. Install cylinder head, oil pan, and engine as previously described.

FITTING PISTONS

1) Check cylinder head mating surface of engine block with a straightedge and feeler gauge. Replace block if warpage is more than .002" (.05 mm).

2) Measure cylinder bores in 3 places at 90 degrees to and parallel with crankshaft. If cylinder bores measure more than .008" (.2 mm) over standard, cylinders must be rebored.

3) When reboring, finish to final dimension by honing the last .0008" (.02 mm). Pistons and rings are available in .020" (.50 mm) oversize.

4) Measure diameter of piston .94" (24.0 mm) from top of piston at 90 degrees to piston pin. Standard piston diameter is 3.5797-3.5809" (90.924-90.954 mm). Standard between piston and cylinder wall is .0026-.0033" (.065-.085 mm).

5) If clearance exceeds specification, bore cylinder block to next oversize. Replace piston with next oversize piston. Check piston ring side clearance in piston. See FITTING RINGS in this article.

FITTING RINGS

1) Measure ring end gap at lowest part of piston travel about 4.33" (110 mm) from top surface of block. Clean piston ring grooves and measure ring side clearance. If clearance exceeds limit, replace ring and/or piston. See ENGINE SPECIFICATIONS in this article.

2) When installing rings, size and manufacturer marks must face upward. Position ring gaps as shown. *See Fig. 13.*

Fig. 13: Arranging Piston Ring Gaps

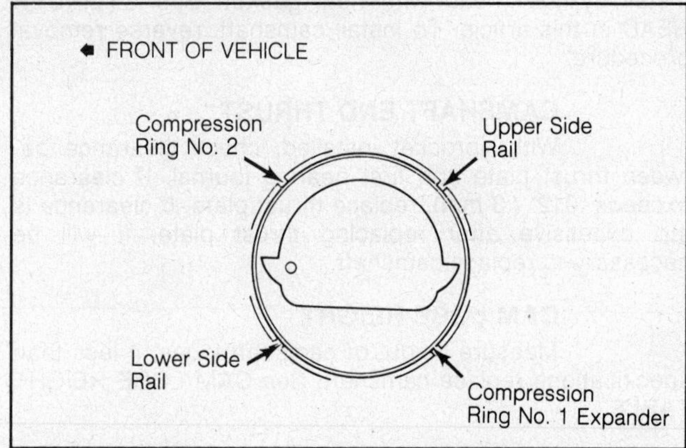

Courtesy of Toyota Motor Sales, U.S.A., Inc.

PISTON PIN REPLACEMENT

1) Check pin fit by rocking piston at right angle to pin. If any movement is felt, replace piston and pin.

2) Using Piston Pin Remover/Replacer (09221-25022), press pin from piston. Ensure pins, pistons, and connecting rods are marked for reassembly.

3) Thoroughly clean and inspect all components. Coat pin with engine oil. Using Piston Pin Remover/Replacer (09221-25022), press pin into piston. Piston and pin should be at 68°F (20°C) during pin removal and installation procedure. Ensure piston and connecting rod are in proper position before installing pin. *See Fig. 14.* If fit is loose, replace piston and pin.

Fig. 14: Assembling Piston & Rod

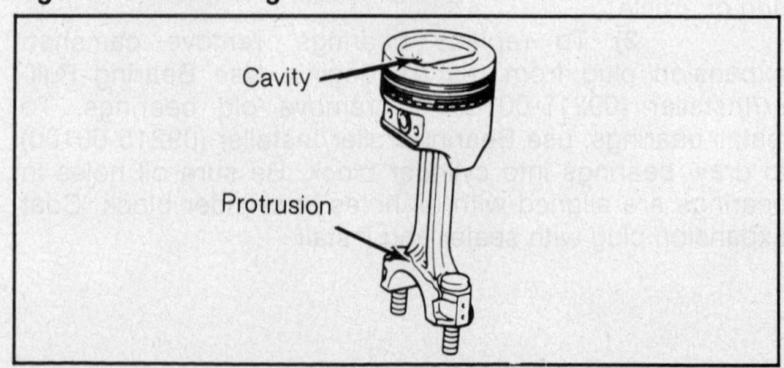

Courtesy of Toyota Motor Sales, U.S.A., Inc.

2.2L 4-CYLINDER (Cont.)

CRANKSHAFT & ROD BEARINGS

FRONT COVER OIL SEAL

Removal

1) Remove fan shroud, radiator, fan belts, and water pump pulley. Remove distributor and cold start injector. Remove crankshaft pulley center bolt.

2) Use Puller (09213-31021) to remove crankshaft pulley, being careful not to damage crankshaft. Remove 11 bolts retaining timing cover. Using screwdriver, pry timing cover off. Drive out old seal.

Installation

Using Seal Driver (09223-22010), install new oil seal. Coat lip of new seal with multipurpose grease. To complete installation, reverse removal procedure.

REAR MAIN BEARING OIL SEAL

Removal & Installation

1) Oil seal may be replaced with engine in vehicle and crankshaft installed. With transmission removed, remove 7 bolts on rear oil seal retainer. Drive old seal out of retainer.

2) Drive new seal into position using Seal Driver (09223-63010). Coat seal lip with multipurpose grease and install seal assembly. Install flywheel or flexplate and tighten to specification. To install rear main bearing oil seal, reverse removal procedure.

CRANKSHAFT MAIN BEARINGS

1) Thoroughly clean and inspect crankshaft. Blow out all oil passages with compressed air. Check crankshaft for runout at center main bearing journal with a dial indicator. Replace crankshaft if runout exceeds .0024" (.060 mm).

2) Measure main journals. If .0008" (.020 mm) out-of-round or taper is exceeded, crankshaft must be reground or replaced. Main bearings are available in .010" (.25 mm) undersize.

3) Main bearing clearance is checked by the Plastigage method. If clearance is greater than .004" (.10 mm), crankshaft must be ground to next undersize.

4) Install bearing halves in crankcase and main bearing caps. Lubricate bearings and install crankshaft. Install main bearing caps with arrows toward front. See THRUST BEARING CLEARANCE in this article.

5) Tighten cap bolts in 2 or 3 steps in following order: bearing caps No. 3, 4, 2, 5 and 1. Install remaining components in reverse order of removal. Note proper alignment of timing marks. See TIMING CHAIN & GEAR in this article.

CONNECTING ROD BEARINGS

1) Measure connecting rod journals. If taper or out-of-round exceeds .0008" (.020 mm), crankshaft must be reground or replaced. Connecting rod bearings are available in .010" (.25 mm) undersize.

2) Make sure bearing halves and crankshaft journals are thoroughly clean. Check oil clearance by Plastigage method. The limit of bearing clearance on connecting rod bearings is .004" (.10 mm). Install connecting rod cap and tighten nuts to specification.

THRUST BEARING CLEARANCE

Check thrust washer clearance at No. 3 main bearing with feeler gauge. If specification of .018" (.30 mm) is exceeded, install oversize thrust washer. Thrust washers are available in .0049" (.125 mm) and .010" (.25 mm) oversize. If clearance is excessive after installation of oversize thrust washers, replace crankshaft.

ENGINE OILING

ENGINE OILING SYSTEM

Oil is circulated through the engine by pressure provided by a rotor-type oil pump. Pump is mounted on bottom of crankcase and is driven by camshaft through distributor drive. Oil is drawn from oil pan and is circulated through a full-flow oil filter into main oil galley. Oil is then distributed to main and connecting rod bearing journals and camshaft bearing journals.

Cylinders and piston pins are lubricated by oil spraying from a hole in connecting rod. Oil is supplied to timing chain by oil from timing chain tensioner. Oil flows from No. 2 cam bearing journal to rocker arm shaft to lubricate rocker arms. Excess oil from rocker arm shaft lubricates valves and valve stems.

CRANKCASE CAPACITY

The crankcase capacity is 3.7 qts. (3.5L) with filter and 3.2 qts. (3L) without filter.

OIL FILTER

The oil filter is a disposable, full-flow type.

NORMAL OIL PRESSURE

With engine at normal operating temperature, normal oil pressure is 4.3 psi (.03 kg/cm²) at idle, 36-71 psi (2.5-5.0 kg/cm²) at 3000 RPM.

OIL PRESSURE REGULATOR VALVE

The pressure regulator valve is a nonadjustable type, mounted in oil pump. Regulator operating pressure is 51-63 psi (3.6-4.4 kg/cm²) at engine operating temperature.

OIL PUMP

Removal

Raise and support vehicle. Drain engine oil. Disconnect oil level sensor connector. Remove right and left stiffener plates. Remove 18 oil pan bolts and oil pan. Remove bolt from oil pump and pull out pump.

Inspection

1) Check rotor tip clearance. If tip clearance is beyond limit, replace rotors. Check clearance between drive rotors and cover using a straightedge and feeler gauge. If clearance exceeds specification, replace cover, pump body, or rotors.

2) Check clearance between outer rotor and pump body with feeler gauge. If clearance exceeds specification, replace pump body or rotors. Check pressure regulator spring and piston for wear or damage. Replace as necessary.

Toyota Engines

2.2L 4-CYLINDER (Cont.)

OIL PUMP SPECIFICATIONS

Application	In. (mm)
Standard	
Rotor Tip Clearance	.003-.005 (.07-.12)
Rotor-to-Cover Clearance	.001-.003 (.03-.07)
Rotor-to-Body Clearance	.004-.006 (.10-.15)
Maximum	
Rotor Tip Clearance	.008 (.20)
Rotor-to-Cover Clearance	.006 (.15)
Rotor-to-Body Clearance	.008 (.20)

Installation

To install oil pump, reverse removal procedure.

Fig. 15: Exploded View of Oil Pump

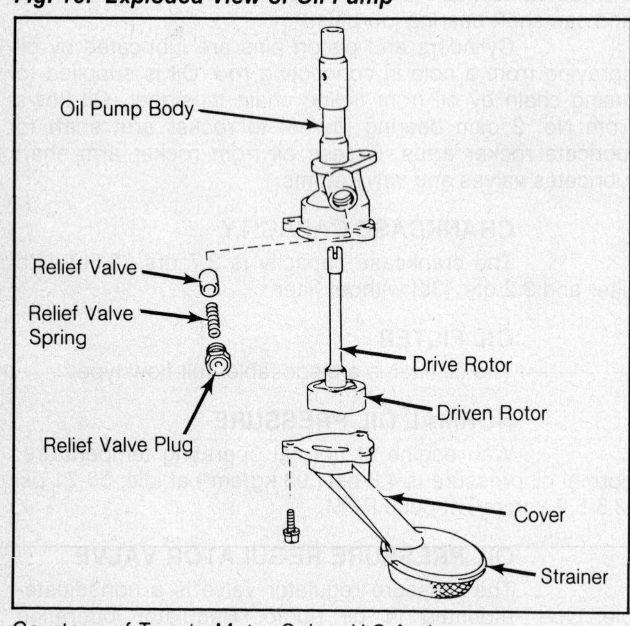

Courtesy of Toyota Motor Sales, U.S.A., Inc.

ENGINE COOLING

WATER PUMP

Removal & Installation

Drain cooling system and loosen drive belt. Disconnect radiator and heater hoses at pump. Loosen and remove fan belt. Remove mounting nuts attaching fan clutch to fan and pulley to pump. Remove drive belt adjusting bar. Remove water pump. To install water pump, reverse removal procedure.

NOTE: For further information on cooling systems, see ENGINE COOLING section.

TIGHTENING SPECIFICATIONS

Application	Ft. Lbs. (N.m)
Camshaft Sprocket Bolt	67 (90)
Camshaft Thrust Plate	13 (18)
Connecting Rod Cap Nuts	36 (49)
Crankshaft Pulley Bolt	116 (157)
Cylinder Head	
12 mm Bolts	14 (19)
14 mm Bolts	65 (88)
Drive Plate Bolts	54 (74)
Flywheel Bolts	61 (83)
Manifold-to-Cylinder Head Bolts	36 (49)
Main Bearing Cap Bolts	58 (78)
Rocker Arm Shaft Bolts	17 (24)
	INCH Lbs. (N.m)
Air Chamber-to-Throttle Body Bolts	108 (12)
Manifold-to-Air Chamber Bolts	108 (12)

ENGINE SPECIFICATIONS

GENERAL SPECIFICATIONS

Year	DISPLACEMENT Cu. In.	DISPLACEMENT Liters	Fuel System	HP@RPM	Torque Ft. Lbs.@RPM	Compr. Ratio	BORE In.	BORE mm	STROKE In.	STROKE mm
1987	137.0	2.2	Fuel Inj.	101@4400	133@3000	8.8:1	3.58	91	3.40	86

VALVES

Engine Size & Valve	Head Diam. In. (mm)	Face Angle	Seat Angle	Seat Width In. (mm)	Stem Diameter In. (mm)	Stem Clearance In. (mm)	Valve Lift In. (mm)
2.2L							
Intake	.....	44.5°	45° [1]	.047-.063 (1.20-1.60)	.3138-.3144 (7.970-7.985)	.004 (.10)	.....
Exhaust	.....	44.5°	45° [1]	.047-.063 (1.20-1.60)	.3136-.3142 (7.965-7.980)	.005 (.12)	.....

[1] – Correction angles are 30° and 60°.

Toyota Engines

2.2L 4-CYLINDER (Cont.)

ENGINE SPECIFICATIONS (Cont.)

PISTONS, PINS & RINGS

Engine	PISTONS Clearance In. (mm)	PINS Piston Fit In. (mm)	PINS Rod Fit In. (mm)	RINGS Ring No.	RINGS End Gap In. (mm)	RINGS Side Clearance In. (mm)
2.2	.0026-.0033 (.065-.085)	Press Fit	.0002-.0003 (.004-.008)	No. 1	.009-.019 (.22-.47)	.0012-.0028 (.03-.07)
				No. 2	.006-.017 (.15-.42)	.0012-.0028 (.03-.07)
				Oil	.008-.032 (.20-.82)	.....

CRANKSHAFT MAIN & CONNECTING ROD BEARINGS

Engine	MAIN BEARINGS Journal Diam. In. (mm)	MAIN BEARINGS Clearance In. (mm)	MAIN BEARINGS Thrust Bearing	MAIN BEARINGS Crankshaft End Play In. (mm)	CONNECTING ROD BEARINGS Journal Diam. In. (mm)	CONNECTING ROD BEARINGS Clearance In. (mm)	CONNECTING ROD BEARINGS Side Play In. (mm)
2.2L	2.2829-2.2835 (57.985-58.000)	.0008-.0020 (.020-.051)	No. 3	.0008-.009 (.020-.22)	1.8892-1.8898 (47.985-48.000)	.0008-.0020 (.020-.051)	.006-.010 (.16-.31)

VALVE SPRINGS

Engine	Free Length In. (mm)	PRESSURE Lbs. @ In. (Kg @ mm) Valve Closed	PRESSURE Lbs. @ In. (Kg @ mm) Valve Open
2.2L	1.85 [1] (47)	70.6@1.598 (32.0@40.6)	....

[1] – Squareness limit is .079" (2.01 mm)

CAMSHAFT

Engine	Journal Diam. In. (mm)	Clearance In. (mm)	Lobe Lift In. (mm)
2.2L [1]			
No. 1	1.8291-1.8297 (46.459-46.475)	.001-.003 [2] (.025-.081)	.....
No. 2	1.8192-1.8199 (46.209-46.225)	.001-.003 [2] (.025-.081)	.....
No. 3	1.8094-1.8100 (45.959-45.975)	.001-.003 [2] (.025-.081)	.....
No. 4	1.7996-1.8002 (45.709-45.725)	.001-.003 [2] (.025-.081)	.....
No. 5	1.7897-1.7904 (45.459-45.475)	.001-.003 [2] (.025-.081)	.....

[1] – Maximum camshaft runout measured at center journal is .0024" (.06 mm).

[2] – Clearance limit is .0039" (.10 mm)

Toyota Engines

2.4L 4-CYLINDER

Pickup, 4Runner

NOTE: For engine repair procedures not covered in this article, see ENGINE OVERHAUL PROCEDURES article at the beginning of this section.

ENGINE CODING

ENGINE IDENTIFICATION

Engine serial number is stamped on left side of cylinder block, behind the alternator. The last group of characters designates engine type.

ENGINE IDENTIFICATION CODES

Application	Code
Carburetor	22R
Fuel Injection	22R-E
Turbocharger	22R-TE

ENGINE, MANIFOLDS & CYLINDER HEAD

ENGINE

Removal

1) Disconnect the negative battery cable. Drain the cooling system. Disconnect the upper radiator hose from engine. On models with turbocharger, remove turbocharger assembly. On fuel injected engines, remove the air cleaner hose.

2) On all models, remove air cleaner. Disconnect exhaust pipe from exhaust manifold. Remove fan, radiator, shroud, hoses and upper bracket. Remove and support air conditioning compressor without discharging system (if equipped).

3) Disconnect heater hoses, fuel lines and brake booster hose from intake manifold. Disconnect and label all electrical wiring and emission control hoses for reassembly reference. Remove alternator and distributor.

4) On fuel injected engines, remove EGR modulator and air intake chamber with throttle body. Disconnect actuator, accelerator and throttle cables. Disconnect and label all fuel injection wiring and vacuum hoses. On carbureted engines, disconnect accelerator linkage.

5) On automatic transmission equipped models, disconnect transmission throttle cable and drain fluid. On power steering equipped models, remove pump from engine. Do not disconnect hoses. On manual transmission equipped models, remove shift lever and slave cylinder.

6) Raise and support vehicle. Disconnect front exhaust pipe. Remove engine undercover. Disconnect transmission shift linkage. On automatic transmission equipped models, disconnect cooler lines.

7) Remove drive shaft. Remove motor mount bolts (above crossmember). Attach engine hoist to engine. Place jack under transmission. Place wood block between firewall and cylinder head to prevent damage to heater hose. Remove rear transmission mounting bracket. Lift engine and transmission from vehicle.

Installation

To install engine, reverse removal procedure. Be sure to check all fluid levels and linkage adjustments prior to starting engine.

MANIFOLDS

Removal

Remove heater inlet pipe-to-cylinder head bolt. Remove No. 1 air pipe. Remove intake manifold with delivery pipe, injection nozzles and heater water inlet pipe as an assembly. Remove exhaust manifold bolts and exhaust manifold.

Installation

To install intake and exhaust manifolds, use new gaskets and reverse removal procedure.

CYLINDER HEAD

Removal

1) Disconnect negative battery cable. Drain engine oil and cooling system. Disconnect front exhaust pipe. On turbocharged models, remove turbocharger assembly. Remove air cleaner. Remove and label all hoses and linkages to intake manifold, carburetor (or air intake chamber on fuel injection) and cylinder head.

2) Disconnect upper radiator and heater hoses from cylinder head. Remove water by-pass tube bolts. Disconnect and label all electrical wiring, fuel lines, and vacuum hoses from cylinder head. On carbureted models, remove fuel pump from cylinder head. Remove distributor with cap and wires.

3) Remove power steering pump and set aside (if equipped). On fuel injected vehicles, remove EGR modulator with bracket and air intake chamber with throttle body. *See Fig. 1*. Disconnect and label all fuel injection wiring and linkages for reassembly reference.

4) Remove valve cover. Set No. 1 piston to TDC on compression stroke. Paint mating marks on camshaft sprocket and timing chain. Remove rubber half circle seal and cam sprocket retaining bolt.

5) Pull distributor drive gear and cam thrust plate off sprocket. Remove sprocket from camshaft. Allow sprocket and chain to rest in cylinder head. Remove chain cover bolt in front of camshaft sprocket.

6) Loosen cylinder head bolts, in 3 steps, in reverse order of tightening sequence. *See Fig. 2*. Remove rocker arm assembly. If necessary, pry equally at front and rear of rocker arm assembly to remove.

7) Lift head from dowels on block and set on wood blocks on work bench. If difficult to remove, pry with flat bar between cylinder head and block projection. Remove EGR valve, intake and exhaust manifolds.

Installation

1) Apply liquid sealer at 2 front corners of engine block and position head gasket over locating dowels. Place head in position and turn camshaft so dowel is at top.

2) Install rocker arm assembly over locating dowels and tighten head bolts in 3 steps. *See Fig. 2.* Continue installation in reverse of removal sequence. Ensure valve and ignition timing is properly set. Adjust valves.

CAMSHAFT

FRONT COVER OIL SEAL

Removal & Installation

1) Seal press fits into oil pump body at front of crankshaft. Remove crankshaft pulley bolt. Using gear puller, remove crankshaft pulley. Pry out seal.

Toyota Engines

2.4L 4-CYLINDER (Cont.)

Fig. 1: Exploded View of Cylinder Head & Cylinder Block Components

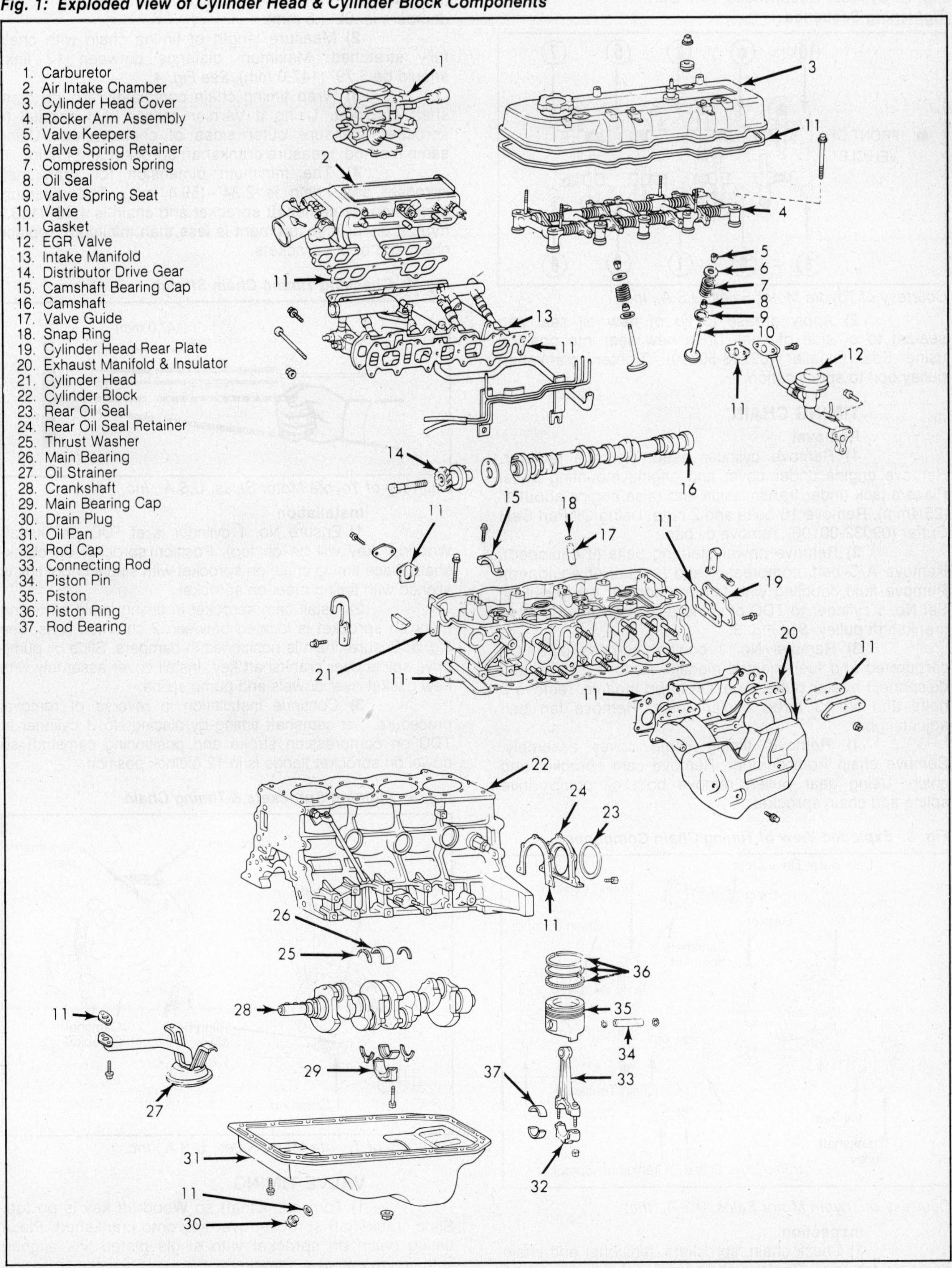

Courtesy of Toyota Motor Sales, U.S.A., Inc.

2.4L 4-CYLINDER (Cont.)

Fig. 2: Cylinder Head/Rocker Arm Bolt Tightening Sequence

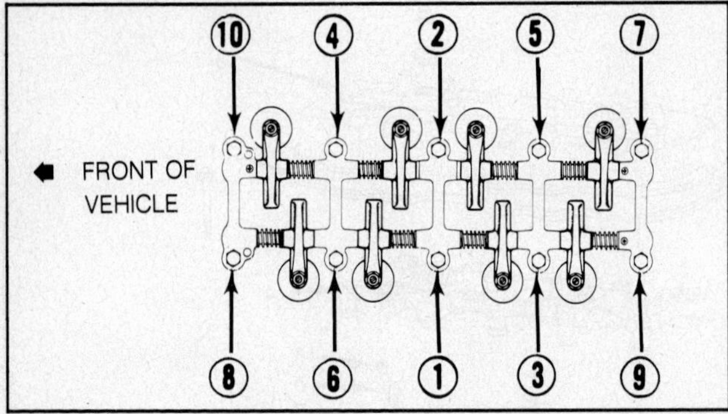

Courtesy of Toyota Motor Sales, U.S.A., Inc.

2) Apply grease to lip of new oil seal and sealant to outside of seal. Drive new seal into position using Seal Installer (09223-50010). Tighten crankshaft pulley bolt to specification.

TIMING CHAIN

Removal

1) Remove cylinder head. Remove radiator. Remove engine under cover and engine mounting bolts. Place a jack under transmission and raise engine about 1" (25.4mm). Remove 16 bolts and 2 nuts. Using Oil Pan Seal Cutter (09032-00100), remove oil pan.

2) Remove power steering belts (if equipped). Remove A/C belt, compressor and bracket (if equipped). Remove fluid coupling with fan and coolant pump pulley. Set No. 1 cylinder to TDC of compression stroke. Remove crankshaft pulley. *See Fig. 3.*

3) Remove No. 1 coolant by-pass pipe. On carbureted and fuel injected models, remove 2 bolts and disconnect heater outlet pipe. On turbo models, remove 2 bolts and No. 3 turbo coolant pipe. Remove fan belt adjusting bar.

4) Remove timing chain cover assembly. Remove chain from damper. Remove cam sprocket and chain. Using gear puller, remove both oil pump drive spline and chain sprocket.

Fig. 3: Exploded View of Timing Chain Components

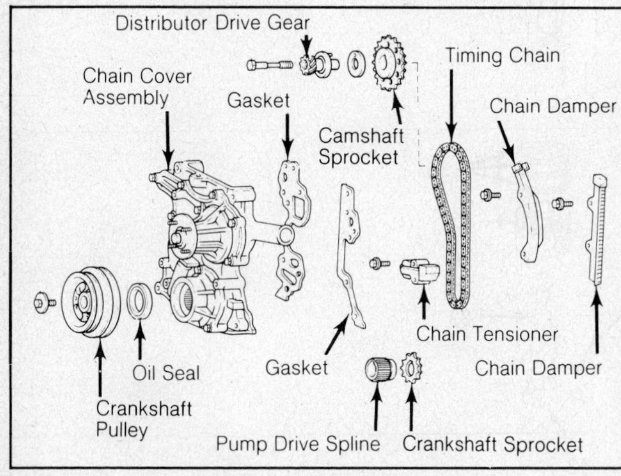

Courtesy of Toyota Motor Sales, U.S.A., Inc.

Inspection

1) Check chain, sprockets, tensioner and chain dampers for wear. Replace chain tensioner if width is less than .43" (11 mm). Minimum size for left and right chain dampers is .02" (.5 mm).

2) Measure length of timing chain with chain fully stretched. Maximum distance between 17 links should be 5.79" (147.0 mm). *See Fig. 4.*

3) Wrap timing chain completely around camshaft sprocket. Using a Vernier caliper held parallel to sprocket, measure outer sides of chain rollers. Using same method, measure crankshaft sprocket and chain.

4) The minimum dimension for crankshaft sprocket and chain is 2.34" (59.4 mm). The minimum dimension for camshaft sprocket and chain is 4.48" (113.8 mm). If either measurement is less than minimum, replace chain and both sprockets.

Fig. 4: Checking Timing Chain Stretch

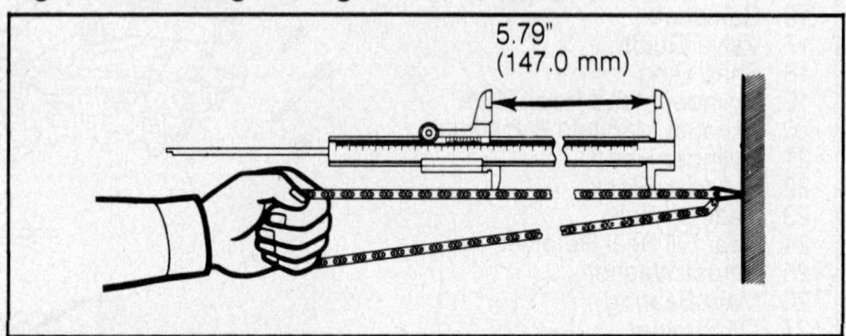

Courtesy of Toyota Motor Sales, U.S.A., Inc.

Installation

1) Ensure No. 1 cylinder is at TDC (crankshaft Woodruff key will be on top). Position sprocket on crankshaft. Place timing chain on sprocket with single bright link is aligned with timing mark on sprocket.

2) Install cam sprocket in timing chain so timing mark on sprocket is located between 2 chromed links. *See Fig. 5.* Ensure chain is positioned in dampers. Slide oil pump drive spline over crankshaft key. Install cover assembly with new gasket over dowels and pump spline.

3) Continue installation in reverse of removal procedure. Set camshaft timing by placing No. 1 cylinder at TDC on compression stroke and positioning camshaft so dowel on sprocket flange is in 12 o'clock position.

Fig. 5: Aligning Sprockets & Timing Chain

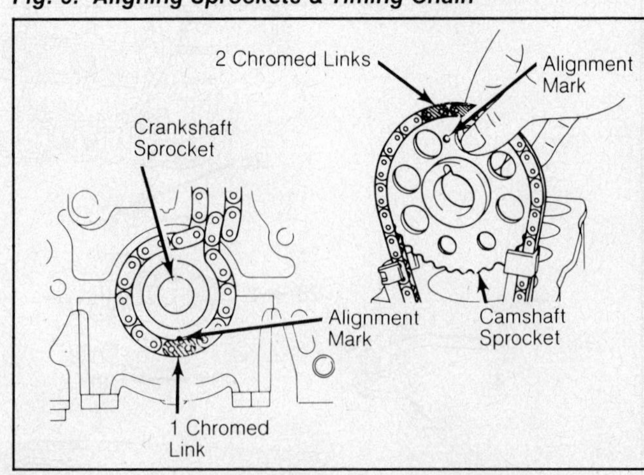

Courtesy of Toyota Motor Sales, U.S.A., Inc.

VALVE TIMING

1) Turn crankshaft so Woodruff key is on top. Slide crankshaft sprocket over key onto crankshaft. Place timing chain on sprocket with single plated link aligned with timing mark on sprocket.

2.4L 4-CYLINDER (Cont.)

2) Turn camshaft to locate dowel pin and stamped mark on camshaft at 12 o'clock position. Timing mark on camshaft sprocket must be between 2 plated links on timing chain. Single plated link on timing chain must be aligned with crankshaft sprocket timing mark.

CAMSHAFT

Removal

Remove cylinder head and rocker arm assembly. Remove camshaft bearing caps and lift out camshaft.

Inspection

1) Camshaft journal oil clearance may be checked using Plastigage method. If clearance exceeds specification, replace cylinder head and/or camshaft. Maximum clearance is .004" (.10 mm).

2) Maximum camshaft runout at center journal is .008" (.20 mm). Replace camshaft if runout is beyond limit. Replace camshaft if intake lobe height is less than 1.678-1.689" (42.62-42.90 mm), or exhaust lobe height is less than 1.681-1.684" (42.70-42.77 mm).

Installation

To install camshaft, reverse removal procedure. Install bearing caps in numbered order with arrows pointing toward front. Adjust valves.

VALVES

VALVE ARRANGEMENT

Right Side – Intake valves.
Left Side – Exhaust valves.

ROCKER ARM ASSEMBLY

1) If rocker arms appear loose, disassemble rocker arm assembly and measure rocker arm-to-shaft clearance. Clearance should be .0004-.0020" (.010-.050 mm), with a maximum limit of .0031" (.08 mm).

2) If clearance exceeds maximum limit, replace rocker arms and/or shafts. Reassemble in reverse of disassembly. Note that rocker arms are identical. *See Fig. 6.*

Fig. 6: Disassembled View of Rocker Arm Assembly

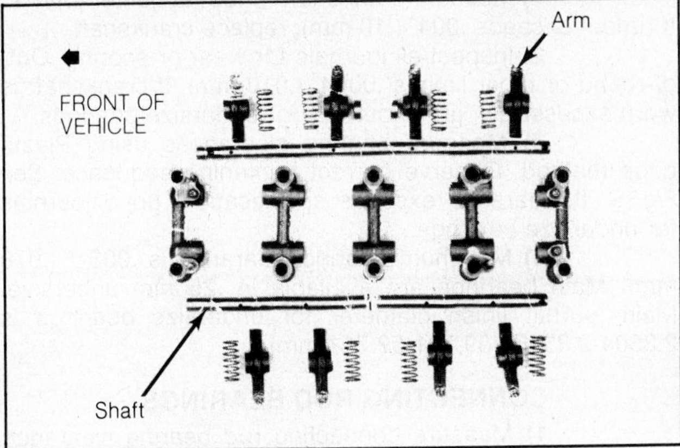

Courtesy of Toyota Motor Sales, U.S.A., Inc.

VALVE STEM OIL SEALS

Removal & Installation

1) Using a spring compressor, remove valve keepers. Remove spring retainer and springs. Remove valve stem oil seal from end of valve guide.

2) Slide a new oil seal over valve stem, using care not to damage seal as it passes over keeper grooves. Force seal over end of valve guide. To complete installation, reverse removal procedure.

VALVE CLEARANCE ADJUSTMENTS

1) Engine must be at normal operating temperature. Remove valve cover and rotate crankshaft until No. 1 piston is TDC on compression stroke. Measure clearance between rocker arm and valve stem.

2) Adjust No. 1 and No. 2 intake valves and No. 1 and No. 3 exhaust valves. Rotate crankshaft one complete revolution (360 degrees) and align timing mark at TDC. Adjust remaining valves.

VALVE CLEARANCE ADJUSTMENTS

Valve	In. (mm)
Intake	.008 (.20)
Exhaust	.012 (.30)

VALVE GUIDES

Removal & Installation

1) Measure diameter of valve guide and valve stem. Maximum clearance for exhaust valves is .0039" (.10 mm). Maximum clearance for intake valves is .0031" (.08 mm). If valve stem oil clearance exceeds specification, valve guides and valves must be replaced. Break off end of guide using punch and hammer. Heat cylinder head to about 194°F (90°C).

2) Using Valve Guide Remover (09201-60011) and hammer, drive old guide out through combustion chamber. Install new valve guide from top of head until snap ring contacts cylinder head. Ream valve guide with a .31" (8 mm) reamer for proper stem clearance.

VALVE SPRINGS

Check valve spring free length and squareness. If free length is less than 1.91" (48.5 mm) or out-of-square more than .063" (1.6 mm), replace spring. Use a spring tester and measure tension at installed height. Replace spring if less than specified.

PISTONS, PINS & RINGS

OIL PAN

Removal

Drain engine oil. Remove engine undercover. Detach steering idler arm bracket. Remove pitman arm and front crossmember. Remove oil pan.

Installation

Place gasket on pan and apply sealer to 4 corners where front cover and rear seal retainer join cylinder block. Install pan. To complete installation, reverse removal procedure.

PISTON & ROD ASSEMBLY

Removal

Remove cylinder head and oil pan. Remove ring ridge from top of cylinder. Mark rods and caps for correct assembly. Remove rod caps. Cover rod bolts with short length of hose to prevent crankshaft damage. Push piston/rod assembly out of block.

Installation

Lubricate piston, cylinder and journal with clean engine oil. Position rings, and install ring compressor. *See Fig. 7.* Stamped mark on ring must face upward. Install piston/rod assembly in proper position with notch on piston top facing forward.

FITTING PISTONS

1) Measure cylinder bore at top, bottom and center of piston travel. Measure in line with and at 90 degrees to crankshaft. Standard bore is 3.6220-3.6232" (91.998-92.029 mm) with a wear limit of .0008" (.020 mm). Maximum out-of-round is .0008" (.020 mm). Maximum taper is .0004" (.010 mm).

2) Measure piston at right angle to pin and just below oil ring groove. If not within specification, rebore cylinder and/or replace pistons. On 22R and 22R-E engines, pistons are available in .50 mm and 1.00 mm oversize diameters.

PISTON SIZE CHART

Application	In. (mm)
22R & 22R-E	
Standard	3.6209-3.6220 (91.970-92.000)
.5 mm O/S	3.6405-3.6417 (92.470-92.500)
1.0 mm O/S	3.6602-3.6614 (92.970-93.000)
22R-TE	3.6195-3.6207 (91.935-91.965)

FITTING RINGS

1) Measure compression ring end gap at bottom of ring travel. If not within specification, replace ring. Do not file ring end. Check clearance of ring in land groove. If side clearance is greater than maximum, replace piston.

2) Position rings on piston with code marks facing up. Position ring end gaps correctly. *See Fig. 7.*

Fig. 7: Correct Piston Ring Gap Arrangement

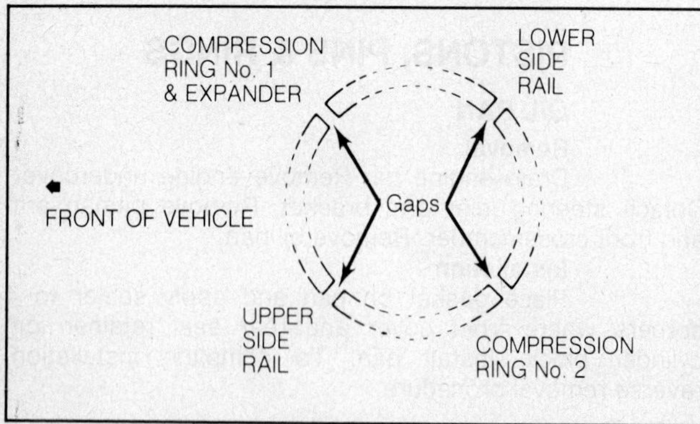

Courtesy of Toyota Motor Sales, U.S.A., Inc.

PISTON PIN REPLACEMENT

Removal

Heat piston to 176°F (80°C). Using hammer and driver, push piston pin out of piston and connecting rod.

Inspection

1) Measure clearance between rod bushing and piston pin. Replace rod bushing if clearance is greater than .0006" (.015 mm).

2) At 176°F (80°C), pin should push into piston with thumb pressure. If pin can be installed at lower temperature, replace pin and piston. The maximum rod bend limit is .002" (.05 mm) per 3.94" (100 mm). The maximum rod twist limit is .0059" (.15 mm) per 3.94" (100 mm). If rod is bent or twisted, replace rod.

NOTE: Piston and pin are a matched set. Use new snap rings for reassembly.

Installation

Heat piston to 176°F (80°C) and position piston and connecting rod so manufacturer's mark on rod and indent on piston crown face same direction. Push pin into piston and rod assembly. Install snap rings. *See Fig. 8.*

Fig. 8: Correct Alignment of Piston & Rod Assembly

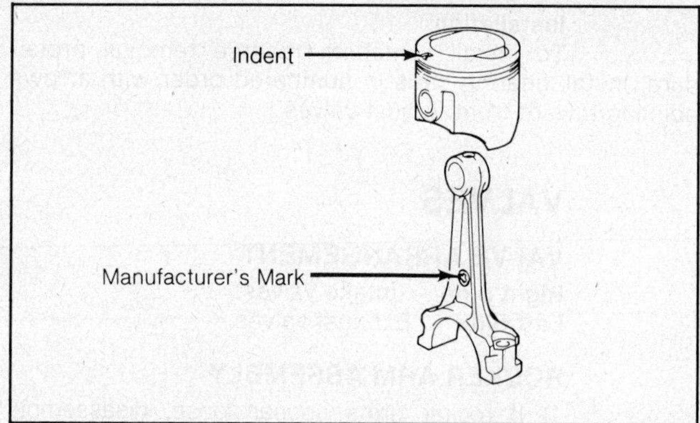

Courtesy of Toyota Motor Sales, U.S.A., Inc.

CRANKSHAFT & ROD BEARINGS

CRANKSHAFT MAIN BEARINGS

1) Measure crankshaft runout at center journal. If runout exceeds .004" (.10 mm), replace crankshaft.

2) Inspect all journals for wear or scoring. Out-of-round or taper limit is .0004" (.010 mm). If crankshaft is worn excessively, grind journals for undersize bearings.

3) Measure bearing clearances using Plastigage method. Observe correct tightening sequence. *See Fig. 9.* If clearance exceeds specification, grind journals for undersize bearings.

4) Maximum bearing clearance is .0031" (.078 mm). Main bearings are available in .25 mm undersize. Main journal finish diameter for undersize bearings is 2.3504-2.3508" (59.701-59.711 mm).

CONNECTING ROD BEARINGS

1) Measure connecting rod bearing clearance using Plastigage method. Replace bearings or grind crankshaft if clearance is greater than .0031" (.078 mm).

2) Regrind crankshaft to .010" (.25 mm) undersize if taper or out-of-round is greater than .0004" (.010 mm). Connecting rod journal diameter for undersize is 2.0748-2.0752" (52.699-52.710 mm).

2.4L 4-CYLINDER (Cont.)

Fig. 9: Main Bearing Tightening Sequence

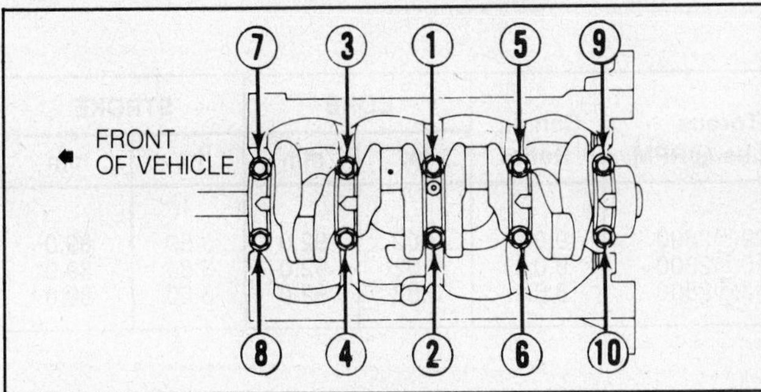

Courtesy of Toyota Motor Sales, U.S.A., Inc.

THRUST BEARING ALIGNMENT

Check crankshaft end play at thrust bearing with a feeler gauge. If end play exceeds limit of .012" (.30 mm), replace thrust washers. Oil grooves must be facing out.

THRUST WASHER SPECIFICATIONS

Size	Thickness In. (mm)
Standard	.1059-.1079 (2.690-2.740)
.125 O/S	.1084-.1104 (2.753-2.803)
.250 O/S	.1108-.1128 (2.815-2.865)

REAR MAIN BEARING OIL SEAL

Rear main bearing oil seal may be replaced with engine in vehicle. Remove transmission. Pry out old seal from retainer. Apply grease to lip of new oil seal. Using Seal Driver (09223-41010), drive oil seal in place.

ENGINE OILING

ENGINE OILING SYSTEM

Oiling system is force fed, utilizing a gear-type oil pump, driven from front of crankshaft. Oil from oil pan is pumped through a full-flow oil filter and then to oil galleys in cylinder block. Oil is fed to crankshaft bearings, timing chain assembly, camshaft and rocker arm assembly. *See Fig. 10.*

CRANKCASE CAPACITY

Engine oil capacity is 4.5 qts. (4.3L) including oil filter.

OIL FILTER

Oil filter is a full-flow, disposable type. Filter is located at right side of engine.

NORMAL OIL PRESSURE

Oil pressure at idle speed is 4.3 psi (.3 kg/cm²) and 36-71 psi (2.5-5.0 kg/cm²) at 3000 RPM.

OIL PRESSURE RELIEF VALVE

Relief valve is nonadjustable, with a 64 psi (4.5 kg/cm²) operating pressure.

OIL PUMP

Removal

Remove oil pan and strainer. Remove drive belts and crankshaft pulley. Remove 5 bolts and oil pump assembly. Remove oil pump drive spline from crankshaft

Fig. 10: Engine Oiling System

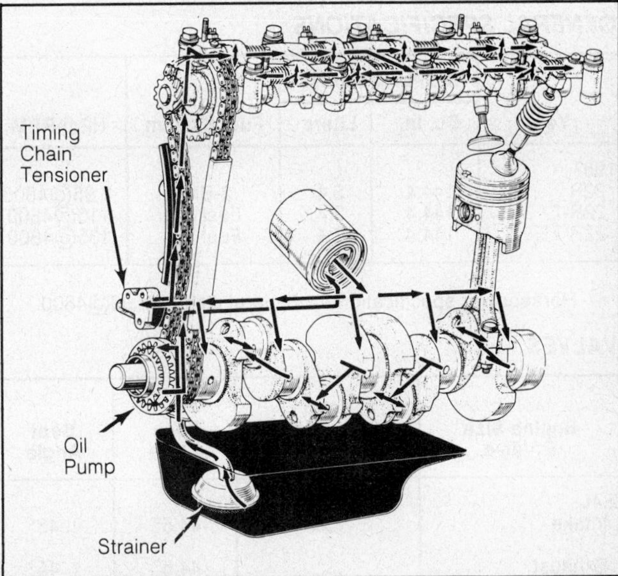

Courtesy of Toyota Motor Sales, U.S.A., Inc.

and "O" ring from engine block. Remove relief valve plug, spring and piston from pump body. Remove driven and drive gear from pump body.

Installation

Reassemble pump and lubricate seal lip. Install new "O" ring in block and apply sealer to upper bolt. Install and tighten pump. To complete installation, reverse removal procedure.

OIL PUMP SPECIFICATIONS

Application	Clearance In. (mm)
Drive Gear-to-Crescent	
Standard	.0087-.0098 (.221-.249)
Wear Limit	.012 (.30)
Driven Gear-to-Crescent	
Standard	.0059-.0083 (.149-.211)
Wear Limit	.012 (.30)
Driven Gear-to-Body	
Standard	.0035-.0059 (.088-.149)
Wear Limit	.008 (.20)
Gear Faces-to-Body	
Standard	.0012-.0035 (.030-.088)
Wear Limit	.0059 (.149)

ENGINE COOLING

WATER PUMP

Removal

Drain cooling system and loosen alternator pivot adjusting bolts. Pivot alternator toward engine to loosen drive belt. Remove fan clutch, pulley and fan belt. Remove 6 bolts and 3 nuts. Remove pump from engine.

Installation

To install water pump, use new gasket on clean mating surfaces and reverse removal procedure.

NOTE: For more information, see ENGINE COOLING SYSTEMS article at the end of this section.

Toyota Engines

2.4L 4-CYLINDER (Cont.)

ENGINE SPECIFICATIONS

GENERAL SPECIFICATIONS

Year	DISPLACEMENT		Fuel System	HP@RPM	Torque Ft. Lbs.@RPM	Compr. Ratio	BORE		STROKE	
	Cu. In.	Liters					In.	mm	In.	mm
1987										
22R	144.4	2.4	2-Bbl.	[1] 95@4800	129@2800	9.0:1	3.62	92.0	3.50	89.0
22R-E	144.4	2.4	Fuel Inj.	116@4800	140@2800	9.0:1	3.62	92.0	3.50	89.0
22R-TE	144.4	2.4	Fuel Inj.	135@4800	173@2800	8.0:1	3.62	92.0	3.50	89.0

[1] – Horsepower specification for Federal pickup is 99@4800.

VALVES

Engine Size & Valve	Head Diam. In. (mm)	Face Angle	Seat Angle	Seat Width In. (mm)	Stem Diameter In. (mm)	Stem Clearance In. (mm)	Valve Lift In. (mm)
2.4L							
Intake	.....	44.5°	[1] 45°	.047-.063 (1.19-1.60)	.3138-.3144 (7.970-7.985)	.0010-.0024 (.025-.061)	.....
Exhaust	.....	44.5°	[2] 45°	.047-.063 (1.19-1.60)	.3136-.3142 (7.965-7.980)	.0012-.0026 (.030-.065)	.....

[1] – Intake correction angles are 30 and 60 degrees.
[2] – Exhaust correction angles are 30 and 65 degrees.

PISTONS, PINS & RINGS

Engine	PISTONS	PINS		RINGS		
	Clearance In. (mm)	Piston Fit In. (mm)	Rod Fit In. (mm)	Ring No.	End Gap In. (mm)	Side Clearance In. (mm)
2.4L	[1] .0008-.0016 (.020-.040)	.....	.0002-.0004 (.005-.011)	No. 1	.0098-.0185 (.25-.47)	.008 (.20)
				No. 2	.0236-.0323 (.60-.82)	.008 (.20)
				Oil	.0079-.0224 (.20-.57)	.....

[1] – Specification is for 22R and 22R-E models. Specification for 22R-TE models is .0022-.0030" (.055-.075)

CRANKSHAFT MAIN & CONNECTING ROD BEARINGS

Engine	MAIN BEARINGS				CONNECTING ROD BEARINGS		
	Journal Diam. In. (mm)	Clearance In. (mm)	Thrust Bearing	Crankshaft End Play In. (mm)	Journal Diam. In. (mm)	Clearance In. (mm)	Side Play In. (mm)
2.4L	2.3616-2.3622 (59.984-60.000)	.0010-.0022 (.025-.055)	Center	.0008-.0087 (.020-.220)	2.0861-2.0866 (52.998-53.000)	.0010-.0022 (.025-.055)	.0063-.0102 (.160-.259)

CAMSHAFT

Engine	Journal Diam. In. (mm)	Clearance In. (mm)	Lobe Lift In. (mm)
2.4L [1]	1.2984-1.2992 (32.98-33.00)	.0004-.0020 (.010-.050)	.....

[1] – End play is .0031-.0071" (.08-.18 mm). Maximum is .0098" (.25 mm).

VALVE SPRINGS

Engine	Free Length In. (mm)	PRESSURE Lbs. @ In. (Kg @ mm)	
		Valve Closed	Valve Open
2.4L	1.909 (48.50)	66.1@1.59 (30@40.5)	.....

2.4L 4-CYLINDER (Cont.)

ENGINE SPECIFICATIONS (Cont.)

TIGHTENING SPECIFICATIONS

Application	Ft. Lbs. (N.m)
Camshaft Bearing Bolts	14 (20)
Camshaft Sprocket Bolt	58 (78)
Connecting Rod Cap Bolts	51 (69)
Crankshaft Pulley Bolt	116 (157)
Cylinder Head Bolts	58 (78)
Exhaust Manifold	33 (44)
Flywheel Bolts	80 (108)
Intake Manifold-to-Cylinder Head	14 (19)
Main Bearing Cap Bolts	76 (103)
Oil Cooler (22R-TE)	33 (44)
Timing Cover Bolts	
8 mm	9 (12)
10 mm	29 (39)
	INCH Lbs.
Oil Pan	108 (13)
Rear Oil Seal Retainer	108 (13)

Toyota Engines

2.8L 6-CYLINDER

Cressida

ENGINE CODING

ENGINE IDENTIFICATION

Engine code is stamped on a machined pad on right front of engine block. It is also printed on a sticker attached to cylinder head cover.

ENGINE IDENTIFICATION CODE

Application	Code
2.8L	5M-GE

ENGINE, MANIFOLDS & CYLINDER HEAD

ENGINE

Removal

1) Drain cooling system. Remove hood, battery and windshield washer tank. Remove air filter case, airflow meter and air intake connector. Remove throttle cable and bracket from camshaft cover.

2) Disconnect engine ground cable. Disconnect connectors from oxygen sensor, oil pressure sending switch, alternator and distributor wiring. Remove coolant temperature sending unit, starter and Electronic Controlled Transmission (ECT) connectors.

3) Label and disconnect all fuel lines, vacuum hoses and wiring attached to engine. Disconnect heater hoses. Remove glove box and computer. Disconnect 3 computer connectors. Remove Electronic Fuel Injection (EFI) wiring.

4) Remove upper radiator hose, fan shroud and fan clutch. Remove engine splash shield from under vehicle. Remove radiator and coolant recovery tank. Remove A/C compressor (if equipped). Do not discharge A/C system. Remove power steering pump without draining system and secure out of way. Remove engine mounting bolts.

5) On manual transmission models, remove shift lever from inside vehicle. On automatic transmission models, disconnect shift linkage at transmission. Raise and support vehicle. Disconnect exhaust pipe from exhaust manifold. Disconnect fuel line. On manual transmission models, remove clutch release cylinder.

6) On all models, remove propeller shaft and plug rear of transmission to prevent oil leakage. Support transmission with jack. Remove rear engine mount and crossmember.

7) Place wood block between firewall and cylinder head to prevent damage to heater hose. Lower jack supporting transmission and remove stands. Using an engine hoist, remove engine and transmission assembly from vehicle.

Installation

To install engine, reverse removal procedure. Check all fluid levels and linkage adjustments prior to starting engine.

INTAKE MANIFOLD

Removal

1) Disconnect battery and drain coolant. Remove air intake connector. Remove throttle cable from valve cover. Remove air valve hoses from air intake chamber. Disconnect No. 1 coolant by-pass hose from Idle Speed Control (ISC) valve body. Remove No. 2 coolant by-pass hose from throttle body.

2) Disconnect PCV hose from valve cover. Disconnect power brake booster hose from air intake chamber. Disconnect fuel hose from hose support. Label and disconnect all wiring from air intake chamber and intake manifold. To allow removal of vacuum pipe subassembly, label and disconnect emission control hoses from throttle body and air intake chamber.

3) Remove air intake chamber bracket, EGR cooler and vacuum pipe. Disconnect cold start fuel hose. Remove cold start injector. Remove No. 1 fuel pipe and coolant outlet housing. Remove air intake chamber. Remove distributor. Remove delivery pipe with injectors. Remove intake manifold.

Inspection

Check air intake chamber and intake manifold for surface warpage. Maximum warpage is .004" (.10 mm) for both. Replace if not to specification.

Installation

Clean all gasket surfaces and install new gasket. Install manifold assembly. Gradually tighten bolts working from center outward. Reverse removal procedure to complete installation.

EXHAUST MANIFOLD

Removal & Inspection

Remove the 2 heat insulators. Disconnect oxygen sensor and exhaust pipe. Remove exhaust manifold and gasket. Maximum exhaust manifold warpage is .030" (.75 mm). Replace if not to specification.

Installation

Clean manifold and cylinder head mating surfaces. Install exhaust manifold and new gasket. Tighten nuts to specification.

CYLINDER HEAD

Removal

1) Remove intake and exhaust manifolds. Remove distributor and spark plug wires from cylinder head. Without draining system, remove power steering pump and bracket. Secure pump out of way.

2) Disconnect and label all electrical wiring connected to engine. Remove timing belt and camshaft timing pulleys. Remove inner timing belt cover.

3) To prevent head warpage or cracking, cylinder head bolts must be removed in correct sequence. Loosen cylinder head bolts in 3 stages in reverse of tightening sequence. *See Fig. 1.*

Fig. 1: Cylinder Head Tightening Sequence

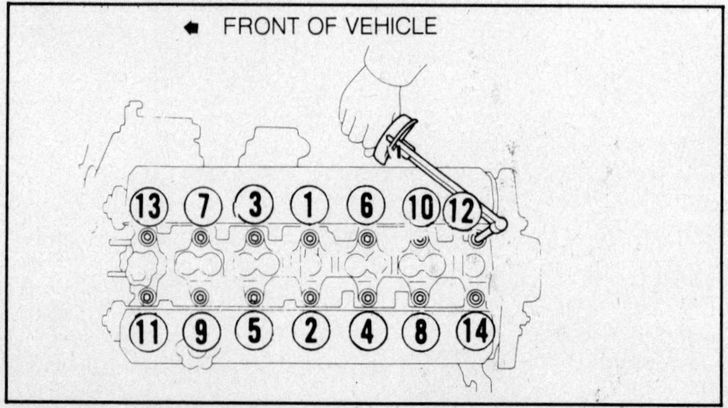

Courtesy of Toyota Motor Sales, U.S.A., Inc.

2.8L 6-CYLINDER (Cont.)

Inspection

Using a feeler gauge and precision straightedge, check cylinder head for warpage. Warpage limit for intake and exhaust manifold, cylinder head, and camshaft housing surfaces is .004" (.10 mm).

Installation

1) Clean all surfaces and apply sealer to both top front corners of block. Install new head gasket over dowels on block. Place cylinder head on block. Tighten cylinder head bolts in sequence, in 3 stages. *See Fig. 1*.

2) Install timing belt and camshaft timing pulleys. See TIMING BELT. To complete installation, reverse removal procedure.

CAMSHAFT

TIMING BELT COVERS

Removal

1) Engine front cover consists of 2 sections. Remove 4 bolts from top section and lift from block.

2) Remove crankshaft pulley bolt. Remove crankshaft pulley. Remove lower timing belt cover section. Loosen and remove all drive belts. *See Fig. 2*.

Fig. 2: Exploded View of Timing Belt & Components

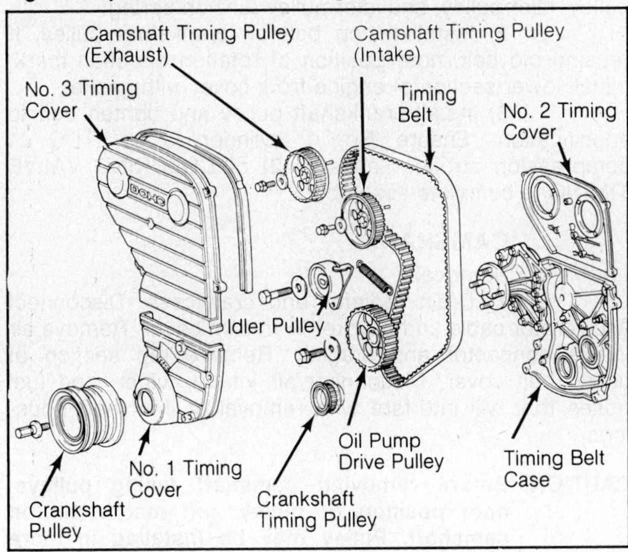

Courtesy of Toyota Motor Sales, U.S.A., Inc.

Installation

Thoroughly clean front covers and block mating surfaces. Use liquid sealer on front cover gaskets when assembling. Install crankshaft pulley and tighten to specification.

ENGINE FRONT COVER OIL SEAL

Removal

Remove upper and lower timing belt covers and timing belt. Remove crankshaft timing pulley with gear puller. Remove oil pump drive shaft pulley. Pry old seals out without damaging cover or retainer.

Installation

Apply engine oil to seal lip. Install oil seals using seal driver. Install pulleys. Tighten oil pump pulley bolt to specification. Install timing belt, covers and drive belts.

TIMING BELT & GEAR

Inspection

Inspect drive belt for wear, cracks or damage to teeth. Check pulleys for wear or damage. If defective, service or repair as necessary. Check idler pulley bearing for smooth operation. Idler pulley tension spring free length must be 2.72" (69.0 mm) or less. Replace spring if not to specification.

Checking Timing Belt Tension

1) Remove upper fan shroud. Remove air intake connector. Remove top section of timing belt cover. Remove oil filler cap and exhaust side cam cover. Rotate cam pulleys inward with 14 ft. lbs. (19 N.m) of torque. All timing belt slack should be at the top between pulleys. Check for tension with engine cold.

2) Press down on belt between pulleys with 4.4-6.6 lbs. (2-3 kg) of pressure. Belt deflection should be .16-.24" (4-6 mm) for a cold engine. Hot engine deflection should be .08-.16" (2-4 mm).

3) If tension is not within specification, rotate engine in direction of rotation to move belt slack to idler pulley side of engine.

4) Loosen idler pulley lock bolt and allow spring to take up belt slack. Tighten bolt to 36 ft. lbs. (49 N.m). Check tension and adjust if necessary.

Checking Valve Timing

1) Remove upper fan shroud, air intake connector, camshaft covers and No. 3 timing belt cover. Ensure No. 1 cylinder is on TDC of compression stroke. Ensure holes align with No. 2 timing belt cover and timing belt pulleys. *See Fig. 3*. If more than one tooth is misaligned between match marks, go to step **2)**. If less than one tooth is misaligned between match marks, go to step **4)**.

Fig. 3: Camshaft Pulley Match Marks

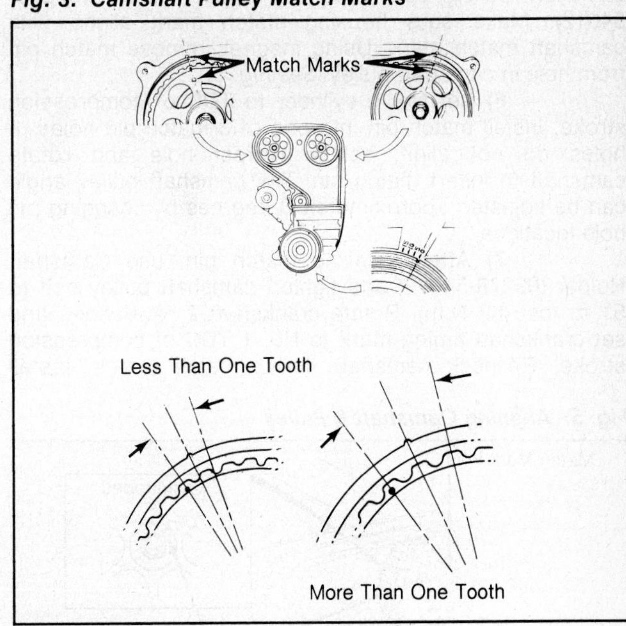

Courtesy of Toyota Motor Sales, U.S.A., Inc.

2) Loosen idler pulley set bolt. Position idler pulley to alternator side of engine. Install idler pulley set bolt finger tight. Remove timing belt. Using Pulley Holder (09278-54012), rotate camshaft to align match marks. Install timing belt. Loosen idler pulley set bolt and take up slack in belt.

Toyota Engines

2.8L 6-CYLINDER (Cont.)

3) Tighten idler pulley set bolt to 36 ft. lbs. (49 N.m). Ensure tension is equal between exhaust cam pulley-to-idler pulley and between intake cam pulley-to-oil pump drive pulley. Rotate engine 2 revolutions in direction of rotation and set No. 1 cylinder to TDC of compression stroke. Recheck camshaft pulley alignment marks. If there is less than one tooth misaligned, go to step **4)**. If there is more than one tooth misaligned, repeat step **2)**.

4) Clean camshaft match holes. Rotate camshaft pulley to align match hole in camshaft with hole in camshaft housing. *See Fig. 4.* Check timing position mark on crankshaft pulley. If timing marks are within 5 degrees of specification, no further adjustment is needed. Repeat procedure for both intake and exhaust. If timing marks are not within 5 degrees go to step **5)**.

Fig. 4: Aligning Camshaft Match Marks

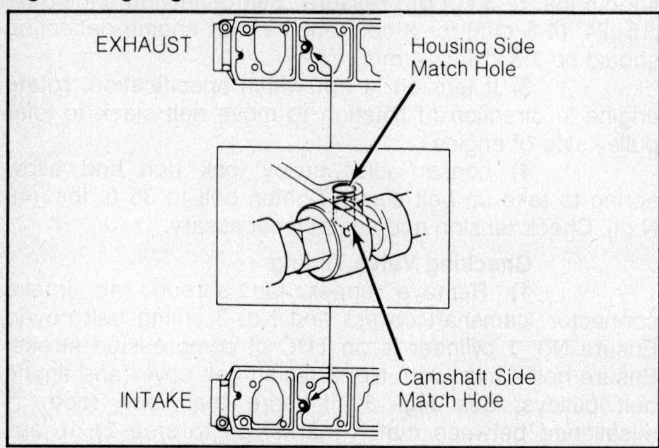

Courtesy of Toyota Motor Sales, U.S.A., Inc.

5) To realign camshaft and pulley, remove camshaft pulley bolt using Camshaft Holder (09278-54012). Make sure housing match mark aligns with camshaft match mark. Using magnet, remove match pin from hole in camshaft pulley. *See Fig. 5.*

6) Set No. 1 cylinder to TDC of compression stroke. Install match pin into one of 3 match pin holes. If holes do not align, select nearest hole and rotate camshaft to insert match pin. The camshaft pulley angle can be adjusted approximately 3 degrees by changing pin hole locations.

7) After installing match pin, use Camshaft Holder (09278-54012) and tighten camshaft pulley bolt to 51 ft. lbs. (69 N.m). Rotate crankshaft 2 revolutions and set crankshaft timing mark to No. 1 TDC of compression stroke. Recheck camshaft timing match marks. Install camshaft covers, timing belt cover, air intake connector and fan shroud.

Fig. 5: Aligning Camshaft & Pulley

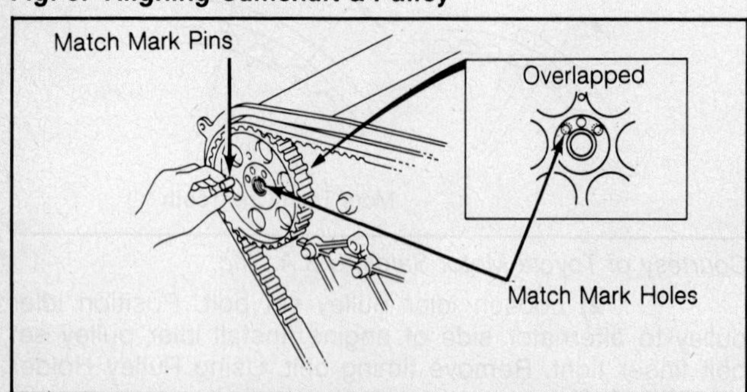

Courtesy of Toyota Motor Sales, U.S.A., Inc.

Removal

1) Disconnect negative battery cable. Remove all drive belts. Set No. 1 cylinder to TDC of compression stroke. Remove upper fan shroud, air intake connector and camshaft covers. Remove No. 3 timing belt cover.

2) To relieve timing belt tension, loosen idler pulley set bolt. Using gear puller, remove crankshaft pulley. Remove lower section of engine front cover.

3) If timing belt is to be reused, place a rotation direction mark on belt. Remove timing belt.

CAUTION: Before removing camshaft timing pulleys, note position of pulley and match pin on camshaft. Pulley may be installed in more than one position.

4) To remove camshaft timing pulley or oil pump drive pulley hold pulley with Camshaft Holder (09278-54011) and loosen set bolt. Remove exhaust valve cover and oil filler cap. Use a gear puller to remove crankshaft timing pulley.

Installation

1) Install oil pump drive pulley (if removed). Tighten bolt to specification. Install crankshaft timing pulley, idler pulley, and idler pulley tension spring.

2) Install timing belt on crankshaft pulley. If reusing old belt, note position of rotation direction mark. Install lower section of engine front cover with gasket.

3) Install crankshaft pulley and tighten bolt to specification. Ensure No. 1 cylinder is on TDC of compression stroke. See step **2)** of CHECKING VALVE TIMING to complete assembly.

CAMSHAFT

Removal

1) Drain radiator and crankcase. Disconnect accelerator cable and bracket from cam cover. Remove air intake connector and bracket. Remove top section of timing belt cover. Disconnect air intake, water, and fuel hoses that will interfere with removal of camshaft housings.

CAUTION: Before removing camshaft timing pulleys, note position of pulley and match pin on camshaft. Pulley may be installed in more than one position.

Fig. 6: Camshaft Housing Tightening Sequence

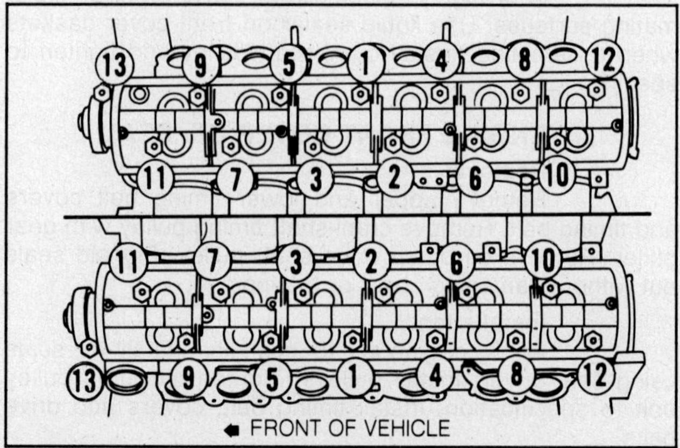

Courtesy of Toyota Motor Sales, U.S.A., Inc.

2.8L 6-CYLINDER (Cont.)

2) Relieve tension on timing belt. Using a spanner wrench, remove camshaft timing pulley set bolts. Noting position for reassembly, remove timing pulleys and match pins.

3) Remove valve covers. Loosen camshaft housings in reverse of tightening sequence. *See Fig. 6*. Lift off camshaft housings. Remove housing rear covers and pull out camshaft.

Inspection

Check camshaft runout at center journal. Maximum allowable runout is .002" (.04 mm). Check journal diameter. Check for scoring or excessive wear. Minimum cam lobe height on intake and exhaust lobe is 1.40" (35.5 mm).

Installation

Lubricate camshaft and housing journals. Place camshaft in position. Install housings on cylinder head. Tighten to specification in 3 stages. To complete assembly, reverse removal procedure.

CAMSHAFT END THRUST

Attach dial indicator and check end thrust at flange end. Maximum thrust is .012" (.30 mm). Specified standard thrust is .002-.010" (.05-.25 mm). If clearance is beyond specification, replace camshaft and/or housing.

CAMSHAFT BEARINGS

There are no camshaft bearings in camshaft housings. If clearance is beyond specification, replace housing.

VALVES

VALVE ARRANGEMENT

Left Side - Intake valves.
Right Side - Exhaust valves.

VALVE SPRINGS

Removal

1) Remove air cleaner assembly and valve cover. Remove camshaft housings. Keep parts in order for reassembly reference. Remove rocker arms and hydraulic lifters.

2) Springs may be removed with cylinder head on or off vehicle. Using valve spring compressor, remove valve retainer locks, retainers, springs, spring seat and oil seal.

Inspection

Check valve springs for free length, installed tension, installed height and squareness. If spring is out of square more than .079" (2 mm), it must be replaced.

Installation

To install valve springs and camshaft housing, reverse removal procedure. See TIMING BELT for information on timing camshafts and adjusting belt tension.

VALVE SPRING INSTALLED HEIGHT

Measure valve spring free length with Vernier caliper. Using a spring tester, check load when spring is compressed to its normal installed height. See VALVE SPRING INSTALLED HEIGHT table.

VALVE SPRING INSTALLED HEIGHT

Application	In. (mm)
Exhaust	1.69 (43.0)
Intake	1.57 (40.0)

VALVE STEM LENGTH & DIAMETER

If valve stem tip is worn, resurface with a valve grinder. Do not grind more than .020" (.5 mm). Minimum intake valve length is 4.232" (107.49 mm). Minimum exhaust valve length is 4.319" (109.71 mm). Intake valve stem diameter is .3138-.3144" (7.970-7.985 mm). Exhaust valve stem diameter is .3136-.3142" (7.965-7.980 mm).

VALVE GUIDE SERVICE

1) Break off valve guide bushing at snap ring and remove snap ring. Heat cylinder head to approximately 194°F (90°C) and drive out bushing toward combustion chamber. Use Guide Driver (09201-60011), to remove valve guides.

2) Replacement guides are available in standard and .05 mm oversize. Standard outer diameter is .512-.513" (13.00-13.03 mm). Oversize valve guide outer diameter is .514-.515" (13.05-13.08 mm).

3) With cylinder head at approximately 194°F (90°C), drive in new guide with Guide Driver (09201-60011) until snap ring makes contact with cylinder head. Use 8 mm hand reamer to provide specified stem clearance.

HYDRAULIC VALVE LASH ADJUSTERS

1) Lash adjusters should be checked for plunger stroke and leak-down. Tool must be made to depress check ball for plunger stroke check. *See Fig. 7*.

Fig. 7: Checking Plunger Stroke

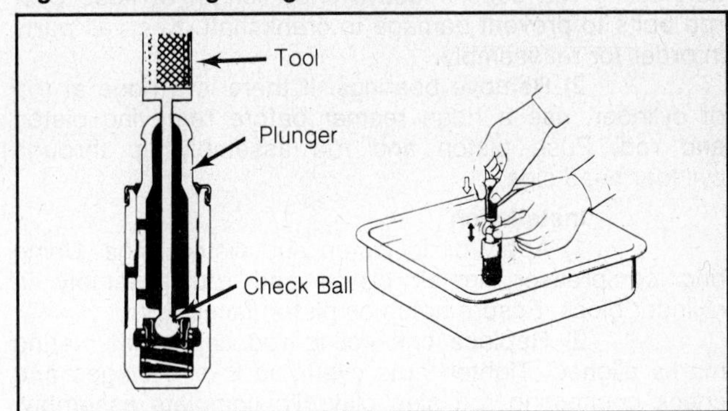

Courtesy of Toyota Motor Sales, U.S.A., Inc.

2) Immerse lash adjuster in light oil and depress check ball. Slide plunger up and down several times. Replace lifter if stroke exceeds .020" (.50 mm).

CAUTION: Do not disassemble hydraulic lash adjuster.

3) Using a leak-down tester, measure leak-down speed after plunger has been depressed about .08" (2 mm). Apply a pressure of 44.1 lbs. (20 kg.). Leak-down time is 2-7 seconds for a distance of .04" (1 mm).

VALVE CLEARANCE ADJUSTMENT

Valve clearance is automatically adjusted by use of hydraulic valve lash adjusters and is not adjustable.

Toyota Engines

2.8L 6-CYLINDER (Cont.)

OIL PRESSURE REGULATOR FOR LASH ADJUSTERS

Removal & Installation

Remove No. 3 timing cover. Remove timing belt tensioner. Remove oil pressure regulator and gasket from top of cylinder head. Unscrew relief valve and remove spring and relief valve. Inspect relief valve for scoring or wear. If damaged, replace valve assembly. To install oil pressure regulator, reverse removal procedure.

PISTONS, RINGS & PINS

OIL PAN

Removal

1) Raise and support vehicle. Drain engine oil and coolant. Disconnect air connector pipe from air cleaner. Remove oil level gauge. Disconnect upper radiator hose and loosen fan belts. Remove clutch fan and shroud.

2) Remove engine and flywheel housing undercovers. Remove exhaust pipe clamp and stiffener plates. Remove motor mount bolts on both sides of engine. Place a jack under transmission and raise engine about 2". Remove oil pan.

Installation

Clean oil pan and block thoroughly. Apply sealer to corners of new oil pan gasket. Install oil pan and gasket. Install remaining parts in reverse of removal sequence.

PISTON & ROD ASSEMBLY

Removal

1) Remove cylinder head and oil pan. Remove connecting rod caps. Place a short length of hose over rod bolts to prevent damage to crankshaft. Keep all parts in order for reassembly.

2) Remove bearings. If there is a ridge at top of cylinder, use a ridge reamer before removing piston and rod. Push piston and rod assembly up through cylinder head side.

Installation

1) Apply oil to piston and piston rings. Using ring compressor, install piston and rod assembly in cylinder block. Ensure notch on piston faces front.

2) Replace connecting rod caps with mating marks aligned. Tighten nuts evenly in 2 or 3 stages and check connecting rod side play. To complete assembly, reverse removal procedure.

FITTING PISTONS

1) Measure at top, center, and bottom of cylinder bore. Measure at 90 degrees and parallel to crankshaft center. If measurements are not within specification, rebore cylinder. See BORE DIAMETER SPECIFICATIONS table.

BORE DIAMETER SPECIFICATIONS

Application	Maximum Diameter In. (mm)
Standard	3.277 (83.25)
Oversize	
.50 mm	3.297 (83.75)
.75 mm	3.307 (84.00)
1.00 mm	3.316 (84.25)

2) Cylinder block surface warp limit is .002" (.05 mm). If taper or out-of-round exceeds .0008" (.020 mm), cylinders must be rebored. Cylinders must be bored to achieve piston clearance of .002-.003" (.05-.07 mm).

3) Measure piston diameter at right angles to piston pin centerline, .98" (25 mm) from piston head. See PISTON DIAMETER SPECIFICATIONS table.

PISTON DIAMETER SPECIFICATIONS

Application	Diameter In. (mm)
Standard	3.265-3.267 (82.93-82.98)
Oversize	
.50 mm	3.285-3.286 (83.43-83.48)
.75 mm	3.294-3.296 (83.68-83.73)
1.00 mm	3.304-3.306 (83.93-83.98)

4) Finish bore to final dimension by honing the last .0008" (.020 mm). Allow bore to cool after boring and honing to avoid erroneous readings while measuring.

FITTING RINGS

Check piston ring end gap at least worn part of cylinder. Measure ring side clearance in piston. Replace pistons and/or rings if not within specification. Install rings with mark on side of ring facing upward. Position piston ring gaps. *See Fig. 8.*

Fig. 8: Positioning Ring Gaps

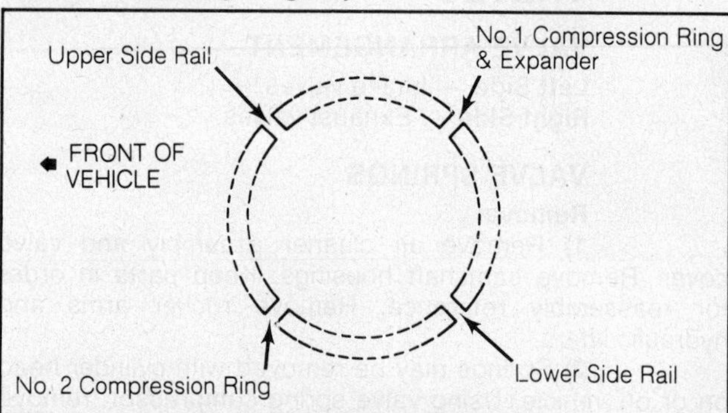

Courtesy of Toyota Motor Sales, U.S.A., Inc.

PISTON PIN REPLACEMENT

Removal

1) Try to move piston back and forth on piston pin. If any movement is felt, replace piston and pin. To disassemble piston and rod, remove circlips in piston pin hole with needle-nose pliers.

2) Heat piston to about 140°F (60°C). Remove pin by tapping lightly with plastic hammer. Keep piston, pin and rod together as a set.

Inspection

1) Check pistons and pins for wear or scoring. Inspect rod for bend or twist. The rod bend limit is .002" (.05 mm) per 3.94" (100 mm). The rod twist limit is .006" (.15 mm) per 3.94" (100 mm).

2) The oil clearance between piston pin and rod bushing must not exceed .0006" (.015 mm). If clearance is greater than specification, replace rod

2.8L 6-CYLINDER (Cont.)

bushing. Hone new rod bushing so oil clearance is .0002-.0004" (.005-.010 mm).

Fig. 9: Assembling Piston & Rod

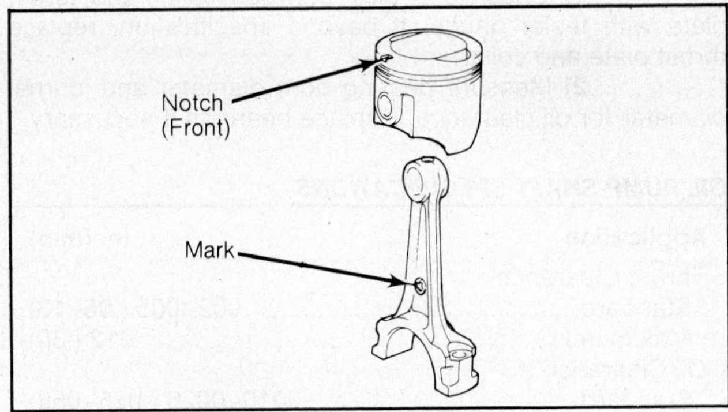

Courtesy of Toyota Motor Sales, U.S.A., Inc.

Installation

Install one circlip in piston and heat to about 140°F (60°C). Align piston notch with rod mark. Coat piston pin with engine oil and push pin in with thumb. Install remaining circlip.

CRANKSHAFT & ROD BEARINGS

MAIN BEARINGS

1) Check crankshaft runout with dial indicator. If runout exceeds .0024" (.060 mm), replace crankshaft. The taper and out-of-round limit for main and rod journals is .0008" (.020 mm).

2) Check main bearing clearance using Plastigage. Crankshaft may be reground for undersize bearings. Bearings are available in standard, .002" (.05 mm), .010" (.25 mm) and .020" (.50 mm) undersize. Tighten main bearing caps in sequence in 2 or 3 stages. *See Fig. 10.*

Fig. 10: Tightening Main Bearing Caps

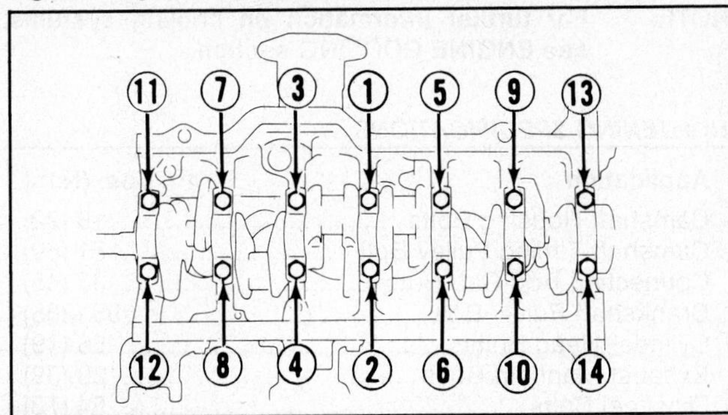

Courtesy of Toyota Motor Sales, U.S.A., Inc.

CONNECTING ROD BEARINGS

1) Measure connecting rod side play with dial indicator. If greater than .012" (.30 mm), rod must be replaced. Wipe off bearing journal, then check clearance with Plastigage.

2) If clearance exceeds .003" (.08 mm) and cannot be corrected with .002" (.05 mm) undersize bearings, or if taper or out-of-round exceeds .0008" (.020 mm), grind crankshaft to next undersize.

3) Connecting rod bearings are available in .002" (.05 mm), .010" (.25 mm), and .020" (.50 mm) undersize.

THRUST BEARING ALIGNMENT

1) Measure crankshaft end play with center (No. 4) main bearing and cap installed. If clearance exceeds .012" (.30 mm), replace thrust washers. Standard clearance is .002-.010" (.05-.25 mm).

2) Standard thrust washer thickness is .115" (2.92 mm) with .005" (.13 mm) and .010" (.25 mm) oversize available.

NOTE: **Install thrust washers with oil grooves facing outward.**

REAR MAIN OIL SEAL

1) Rear main oil seal may be replaced without removing oil pan. Remove transmission and flywheel for access to seal.

2) Inspect oil seal lip and replace if worn or damaged. Pry old seal out without damaging cover or retainer. Install seal using Seal Driver (09223-41010). Apply multipurpose lubricant to seal lip.

ENGINE OILING

ENGINE OILING SYSTEM

System is force-feed type, with a full-flow filtering unit. Pressure is delivered by a gear-driven oil pump. Oil travels from filter through cylinder block passages to lubricate internal components.

CRANKCASE CAPACITY

The crankcase capacity is 5.4 qts. (5.1L) with filter, 4.9 qts. (4.6L) without filter.

OIL FILTER

The oil filter is a full-flow, disposable type.

NORMAL OIL PRESSURE

Oil pressure at idle should be more than 3.6 psi (.25 kg/cm²). At 3000 RPM oil pressure is 36-71 psi (2.5-5.0 kg/cm²).

OIL PRESSURE RELIEF VALVE

The oil pressure relief valve is a nonadjustable type located in the oil pump. The oil pressure relief valve operating pressure is 63-71 psi (4.4-5.0 kg/cm²). There is also an oil pressure regulator valve for the hydraulic lifters. It is located in front of No. 1 spark plug on top of cylinder head.

OIL PUMP

Removal

Raise and support vehicle. Remove oil pan. See OIL PAN. Remove oil pump.

Disassembly

Remove snap ring, spacer, drive shaft gear and Woodruff key. Remove pump cover, pump shaft subassembly, driven gear, relief valve plug, gasket, spring and relief valve.

2.8L 6-CYLINDER (Cont.)

Inspection

Check oil pump for signs of wear or scoring. Measure body and side clearance. Measure gear backlash.

Fig. 11: Exploded View of Oil Pump

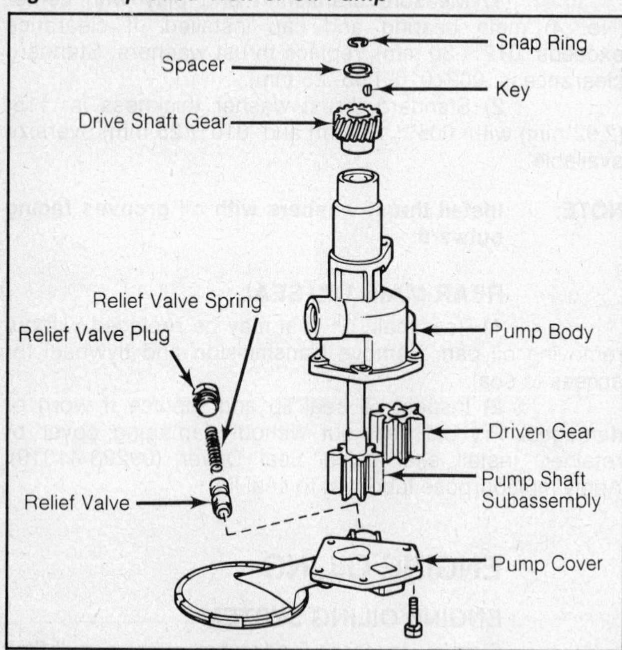

Courtesy of Toyota Motor Sales, U.S.A., Inc.

Reassembly

To reassemble pump, reverse disassembly procedure. Check pump operation by immersing inlet tube in engine oil. Turn pump shaft counterclockwise and check for oil discharge.

Installation

To install oil pump, reverse removal procedure.

OIL PUMP SPECIFICATIONS

Application	Wear Limit In. (mm)
Body Clearance	.008 (.20)
Gear Backlash	.035 (.90)
Side Clearance	.006 (.15)

OIL PUMP SHAFT

Removal

1) Oil pump shaft can be removed with engine in vehicle. Set No. 1 cylinder to TDC of compression stroke. Drain cooling system. Remove radiator and fan. Remove all drive belts.

2) Remove engine timing belt. Use a gear puller to remove crankshaft timing gear. Remove oil pump drive shaft pulley.

3) Remove bolts along right half of water pump. Remove timing belt case with water pump. Remove thrust plate bolt. Carefully pull oil pump shaft from engine block.

Inspection

1) Check end play between collar and thrust plate with feeler gauge. If beyond specification, replace thrust plate and collar.

2) Measure bearing bore diameter and journal diameter for oil clearance. Replace bearings if necessary.

OIL PUMP SHAFT SPECIFICATIONS

Application	In. (mm)
Thrust Clearance	
Standard	.002-.005 (.06-.13)
Maximum	.012 (.30)
Oil Clearance	
Standard	.0010-.0026 (.025-.066)
Maximum	.003 (.08)
Standard Journal Diameter	
Front	1.612-1.613 (40.95-40.97)
Rear	1.297-1.298 (32.95-32.97)

OIL PUMP GUIDE BUSHING

Oil pump drive bushing may be pressed out of cylinder block if worn. Install bushing with oil hole facing crankshaft and front mark facing front of cylinder block.

ENGINE COOLING

WATER PUMP

Removal

Drain cooling system. Loosen and remove drive belts and fan shroud. Remove 8 pump bolts and take off pump assembly.

Installation

Install water pump with water drain hole positioned down. To install water pump, use new gasket and reverse removal procedure.

NOTE: **For further information on cooling systems, see ENGINE COOLING section.**

TIGHTENING SPECIFICATIONS

Application	Ft. Lbs. (N.m)
Camshaft Housing Bolts	16 (22)
Camshaft Timing Pulley Bolt	51 (69)
Connecting Rod Cap Nuts	33 (45)
Crankshaft Pulley Bolt	195 (265)
Cylinder Head Bolts	58 (79)
Exhaust Manifold Bolts	29 (39)
Flywheel Bolts	54 (73)
Intake Manifold Bolts	13 (18)
Main Bearing Caps Bolts	75 (102)
Oil Pump-to-Engine Block Bolts	16 (22)
Rear Timing Cover Bolts	36 (49)

Toyota Engines

2.8L 6-CYLINDER (Cont.)

ENGINE SPECIFICATIONS

GENERAL SPECIFICATIONS

Year	DISPLACEMENT		Fuel System	HP@RPM	Torque Ft. Lbs.@RPM	Compr. Ratio	BORE		STROKE	
	Cu. In.	Liters					In.	mm	In.	mm
1987	170.8	2.8	Fuel Inj.	156@5200	165@4500	9.2:1	3.27	83	3.35	85

VALVES

Engine Size & Valve	Head Diam. In. (mm)	Face Angle	Seat Angle	Seat Width In. (mm)	Stem Diameter In. (mm)	Stem Clearance In. (mm)	Valve Lift In. (mm)
2.8L							
Intake	.....	44.5°	[1] 45°	.047-.063 (1.2-1.6)	.3138-.3144 (7.970-7.985)	.0010-.0024 (.025-.060)	.....
Exhaust	.....	44.5°	[1] 45°	.047-.063 (1.2-1.6)	.3136-.3142 (7.965-7.980)	.0012-.0026 (.030-.065)	

[1] - Correction angles for valve seats are 30° and 60°.

PISTONS, PINS & RINGS

Engine	PISTONS	PINS		RINGS		
	Clearance In. (mm)	Piston Fit In. (mm)	Rod Fit In. (mm)	Ring No.	End Gap In. (mm)	Side Clearance In. (mm)
2.8L	.0024-.0031 (.06-.08)	[1]	[2] .0002-.0004 (.005-.011)	No. 1	.009-.016 (.23-.41)	.0012-.0028 (.03-.07)
				No. 2	.0098-.0209 (.25-.53)	.0008-.0024 (.02-.06)
				Oil	.0040-.0201 (.10-.51)	

[1] - Piston pin standard diameter is .866-.867" (21.997-22.009 mm).
[2] - Limit is .0006" (.015 mm).

CRANKSHAFT MAIN & CONNECTING ROD BEARINGS

Engine	MAIN BEARINGS				CONNECTING ROD BEARINGS		
	Journal Diam. In. (mm)	Clearance In. (mm)	Thrust Bearing	Crankshaft End Play In. (mm)	Journal Diam. In. (mm)	Clearance In. (mm)	Side Play In. (mm)
2.8L	2.3625-2.3627 (60.007-60.012)	[1] .0012-.0048 (.030-.048)	[2] No. 4	.002-.010 (.05-.25)	2.1659-2.1663 (55.085-55.025)	[1] .0008-.0021 (.021-.053)	.006-.012 (.16-.30)

[1] - Maximum oil clearance for main and connecting rod bearings is .003" (.08 mm).
[2] - Standard thrust washer thickness is .1152-1171" (2.925-2.975 mm).

Toyota Engines

2.8L 6-CYLINDER (Cont.)

ENGINE SPECIFICATIONS (Cont.)

VALVE SPRINGS

Engine	Free Length In. (mm)	PRESSURE Lbs. @ In. (Kg @ mm)	
		Valve Closed	Valve Open
2.8L			
Intake	1.93 (49.1)	76.5-84.4@1.58 (34.7-38.3@40.0)	.....
Exhaust	2.07 (52.5)	73.4-80.9@1.69 (33.3-36.7@43.0	.....

CAMSHAFT

Engine	Journal Diam. In. (mm)	Clearance In. (mm)	Lobe Lift In. (mm)
2.8L			
No. 1	1.4944-1.4951 (37.959-37.975)	.0010-.0026 (.025-.066)	1.39-1.40 (35.47-35.67)
No. 2	1.6913-1.6919 (42.959-42.975)		
No. 3	1.7110-1.7116 (43.459-43.475)		
No. 4	1.7307-1.7313 (43.959-43.975)		
No. 5	1.7504-1.7510 (44.459-44.475)		
No. 6	1.7700-1.7707 (44.959-44.975)		
No. 7	1.7897-1.7904 (45.459-45.475)		

3.0L TWIN CAMSHAFT 6-CYLINDER

Supra

ENGINE CODING

ENGINE IDENTIFICATION

Engine serial number is stamped on a machined pad on right front of engine block. Engine code is printed on a sticker attached to front of valve cover.

ENGINE IDENTIFICATION CODE

Application	Code
3.0L	7M-GE

ENGINE, MANIFOLDS & CYLINDER HEAD

ENGINE

Removal

1) Remove hood. Disconnect negative battery cable. Remove lower engine cover. Drain coolant from engine block and radiator. Drain engine oil. Disconnect air hoses from airflow meter and power steering unit. Remove 3 attaching bolts from air cleaner case. Remove air cleaner with hoses attached.

2) Disconnect condenser fan motor connector. Disconnect radiator and coolant reservoir hoses. On automatic transmission models, disconnect and plug transmission cooler lines. On all models, remove radiator supports and radiator. Remove condenser fan motor connector.

3) Remove A/C, power steering and alternator drive belts. Remove water pump pulley and fluid coupling. Disconnect brake booster, heater valve, cruise control and charcoal canister hoses. Disconnect engine ground straps (one on left front fender apron and one at rear of engine). Label and disconnect electrical connections between engine and chassis.

4) Disconnect cruise control and accelerator cables. On automatic transmission models, disconnect throttle cable. On all models, disconnect heater hoses. Disconnect hoses from A/C compressor and power steering pump. Remove A/C compressor and power steering pump.

5) On manual transmission models, remove shift lever from inside vehicle. On all models, disconnect ground strap from fuel hose clamp. Disconnect fuel lines. Remove exhaust pipe. Remove propeller shaft and insert Transmission Oil Plug (09325-40010 for auto. trans. or 09325-20010 for man. trans.) to prevent oil leakage.

6) Disconnect speedometer cable. Remove manual shift linkage (auto. trans.). Remove No. 1 front crossmember. Remove clutch release cylinder (man. trans.). Using a jack, support transmission with wooden block between jack and transmission oil pan. Place wooden block between rear of cylinder head and firewall.

7) Remove rear engine support member from body with ground strap attached. Attach lifting chain to engine hangers. Remove engine mounting nuts and washers. Carefully lift engine/transmission assembly from engine compartment, ensuring all electrical wiring and hoses are disconnected.

8) Mount engine on engine stand. Remove oil cooler lines (auto. trans.). Separate transmission from engine. Remove clutch cover and clutch disc (man. trans.).

Installation

1) With engine connected to transmission, carefully lower engine/transmission assembly into engine compartment. Install clutch release cylinder. Bleed hydraulic system if necessary (man. trans.).

2) Install all wiring, heater and vacuum hoses. Adjust drive belts. Check engine oil, transmission oil and coolant levels. To complete installation, reverse removal procedure. Recheck ignition timing. Reinstall hood, start engine and check for leaks.

INTAKE MANIFOLD

NOTE: **Intake manifold is removed after removing cylinder head from engine. See CYLINDER HEAD removal procedure in this article.**

Removal

1) With cylinder head resting on wooden blocks, remove No. 2 timing belt cover. Remove alternator bracket, heater inlet hose and heater union.

2) Remove 3 fuel supply rail retaining bolts. Remove fuel supply rail with injectors attached. Do not

Fig. 1: Exploded View of Cylinder Head, Intake Manifold & Exhaust Manifold Assemblies

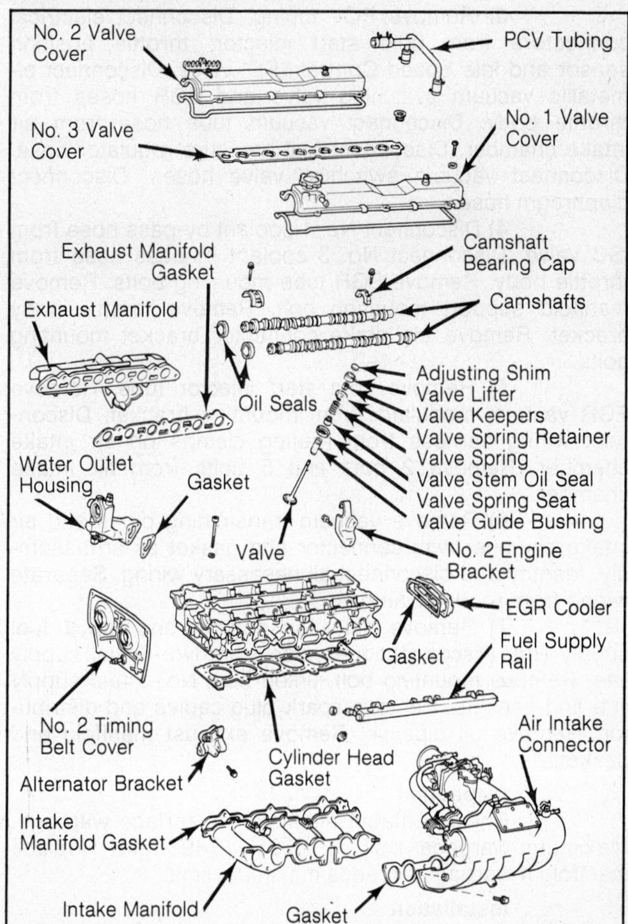

Courtesy of Toyota Motor Sales, U.S.A., Inc.

drop injectors. Remove 6 insulators and 3 collars from cylinder head. Remove EGR valve, vacuum switching valve, intake manifold and gasket.

Inspection

Check intake manifold and intake chamber for surface warpage. Maximum warpage limit is .004" (.10 mm). Replace manifold if warpage exceeds maximum limit.

Installation

Thoroughly clean all gasket surfaces and install new gasket. Install intake manifold. Install EGR valve. Install vacuum switching valve. Gradually tighten bolts, working from center outward. To complete installation, reverse removal procedure.

EXHAUST MANIFOLD

Removal

1) Disconnect negative battery cable. Drain coolant from engine block and radiator. Disconnect exhaust pipe from exhaust manifold. Disconnect cruise control cable, accelerator cable and throttle cable (auto. trans.). Disconnect ground strap at rear of engine.

2) Remove air cleaner hose with intake air connector tube (nearest fender panel). Disconnect cruise control vacuum hose and charcoal canister hose. Remove heater and radiator inlet hoses. Disconnect No. 3 PCV hose. Remove drive belt. Remove alternator and adjusting bracket.

3) Remove PCV tubing. Disconnect electrical connectors from cold start injector, throttle position sensor and Idle Speed Control (ISC) valve. Disconnect bi-metallic vacuum switching valve and EGR hoses from throttle body. Disconnect vacuum tube hose from air intake chamber. Disconnect fuel pressure regulator hose. Disconnect vacuum switching valve hoses. Disconnect diaphragm hose.

4) Disconnect No. 1 coolant by-pass hose from ISC valve. Disconnect No. 3 coolant by-pass hose from throttle body. Remove EGR tube mounting bolts. Remove manifold support mounting bolt. Remove throttle body bracket. Remove air intake connector bracket mounting bolts.

5) Remove cold start injector tube. Remove EGR vacuum modulator from mounting bracket. Disconnect wiring harness from routing clamps on air intake chamber. Remove 2 nuts and 5 bolts from air intake chamber.

6) Remove vacuum transmitting pipes and air intake chamber with connector and gasket as an assembly. Identify and disconnect all necessary wiring. Separate wiring from routing clamps.

7) Remove pulsation damper and No. 1 fuel supply line. Disconnect fuel hose from No. 3 fuel supply line. Remove mounting bolt, union bolt, No. 3 fuel supply line and gaskets. Remove spark plug cables and distributor. Remove oil dipstick. Remove exhaust manifold and gasket.

Inspection

Check exhaust manifold for surface warpage. Maximum warpage limit is .0295" (.749 mm). Replace manifold if warpage exceeds maximum limit.

Installation

Thoroughly clean all gasket surfaces and install new gasket. Install exhaust manifold and tighten nuts. To complete installation, reverse removal procedure.

CYLINDER HEAD

Removal

1) Remove timing belt. See TIMING BELT & SPROCKETS removal procedure in this article. Remove exhaust manifold as previously outlined. Remove union bolts and No. 4 coolant by-pass hose with gaskets at coolant outlet housing. Disconnect No. 6 coolant by-pass hose from coolant by-pass tube. Remove bolt, nuts, coolant outlet housing and gasket.

2) Remove accelerator link. Remove No. 1 and No. 2 valve covers. Using Clamp Adapter (09923-00010), remove heater hose clamp and No. 3 valve cover (cover between camshafts). Remove spark plugs.

3) Using 10 mm Hex Adapter (09043-38100), loosen cylinder head bolts in 3 stages in reverse order of tightening sequence. *See Fig. 2*. Cylinder head bolts must be removed in correct order to prevent warpage or cracking. Lift cylinder head off dowels on engine block. While lifting head, separate No. 5 coolant by-pass hose from union. Place head on wooden blocks on work bench.

NOTE: Cylinder head can be pried from engine block with screwdriver inserted between head and block projections only. Do not damage head or block surfaces during prying operation.

Fig. 2: Cylinder Head Tightening Sequence

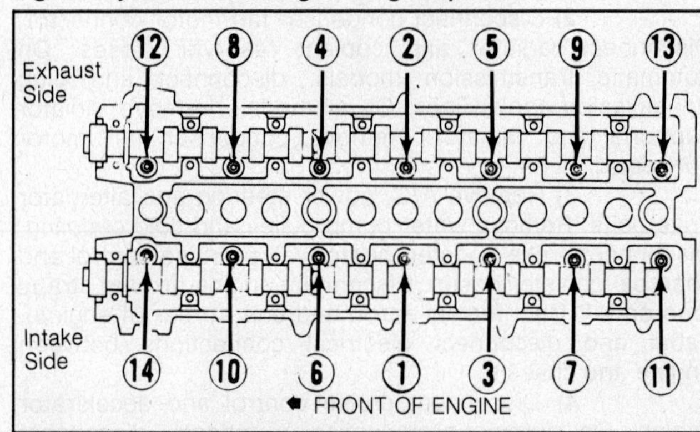

Tighten in sequence in 3 stages. Reverse tightening sequence to remove bolts in 3 stages. Courtesy of Toyota Motor Sales, U.S.A., Inc.

Installation

1) Clean all surfaces. Install oil seals at front of cylinder block. Install new head gasket. Ensure gasket is properly installed. *See Fig. 3*. Carefully lower cylinder head into position over dowels. Connect No. 5 coolant by-pass hose to the union.

2) Apply light coat of oil to threads and underside of cylinder head bolts. Using 10 mm Hex Adapter (09043-38100), tighten cylinder head bolts in 3 stages in tightening sequence. *See Fig. 2*. Install timing belt. See TIMING BELT & SPROCKETS installation procedure in this article. Install spark plugs.

3) Using Clamp Adapter (09923-00010), install heater hose clamp and No. 3 valve cover (cover between camshafts). Install seals on cylinder heads. *See Fig. 4*. Install No. 1 and No. 2 valve covers. Install accelerator link.

4) Install new coolant outlet housing gasket. Install coolant outlet housing with bolt and 2 nuts. Connect No. 6 coolant by-pass hose. Install new gaskets, union

3.0L TWIN CAMSHAFT 6-CYLINDER (Cont.)

and union bolt to coolant outlet housing. To complete installation, reverse removal procedure.

Fig. 3: Positioning of Seals & Gaskets For Cylinder Head Installation

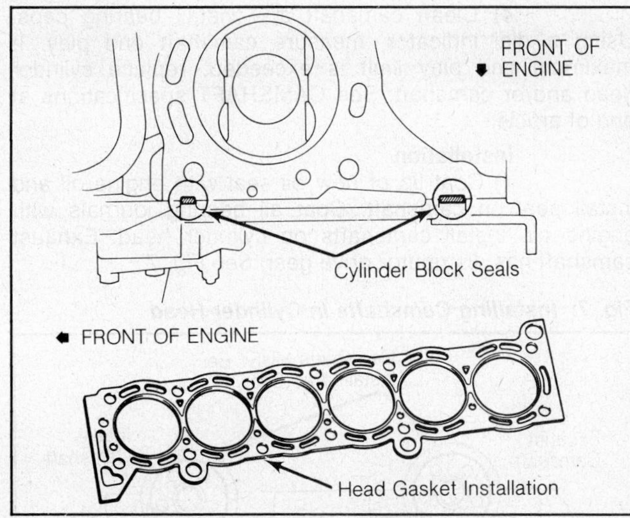

Courtesy of Toyota Motor Sales, U.S.A., Inc.

Fig. 4: Installing Cylinder Head Seals

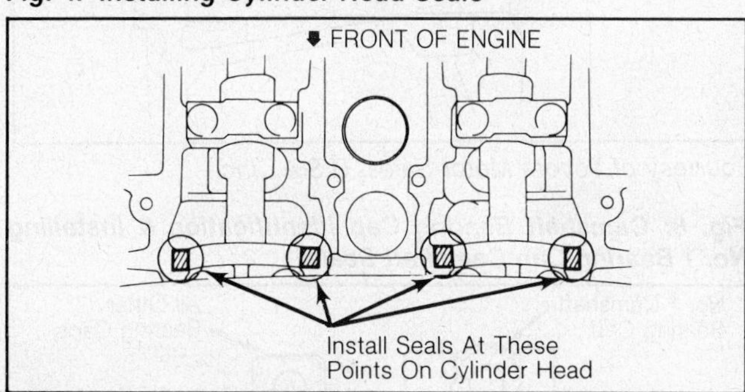

Courtesy of Toyota Motor Sales, U.S.A., Inc.

CAMSHAFTS

TIMING BELT & SPROCKETS

NOTE: **Timing belt should be replaced at 60,000 mile intervals.**

Removal

1) Remove radiator as previously outlined under ENGINE removal. Remove spark plugs. Remove thermostat housing, thermostat and gasket. Remove A/C belt. Remove fan. Remove power steering and alternator drive belts. Remove 5 bolts and one nut from No. 3 timing belt cover. Remove No. 3 timing belt cover and gasket. *See Fig. 5*.

2) Position No. 1 cylinder at TDC on compression stroke. Ensure "0" on No. 1 timing belt cover timing mark plate is aligned with pulley groove. Alignment marks on camshaft pulleys must be aligned with marks on No. 2 timing belt cover (cover behind pulleys). *See Fig. 6*. If timing belt is to be reused, place arrow on belt in direction of rotation.

3) Loosen idler pulley bolt. Pry the idler pulley as far left as it will go and tighten pulley bolt. Relieve timing belt tension and remove belt from camshaft and idler pulleys. Support belt in such a way that alignment marks on camshaft pulleys and crankshaft pulley are not disturbed.

Fig. 5: Exploded View of Timing Belt & Sprockets

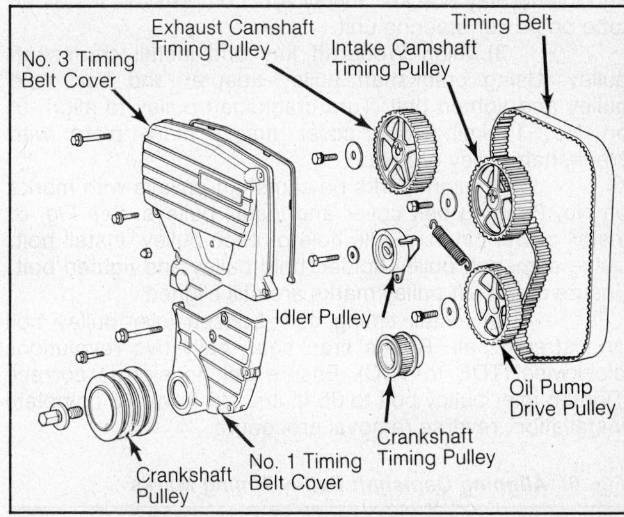

Courtesy of Toyota Motor Sales, U.S.A., Inc.

4) Using Camshaft Pulley Holder (09278-54012), hold pulley and remove bolt. Remove camshaft pulleys and dowel pins (center pin only on each pulley). Using Crankshaft Pulley Adapter and Bar (09213-70010 and 09330-00021), hold pulley and remove bolt. Using Crankshaft Pulley Puller (09213-31021), remove crankshaft pulley.

NOTE: **DO NOT use belt tension to hold pulleys while removing bolt.**

5) Remove air tube from power steering unit. Remove A/C compressor without disconnecting hoses. Remove A/C idler pulley bracket, A/C compressor bracket and No. 1 timing belt cover. Remove timing belt. Remove idler pulley and spring.

6) Using Crankshaft Timing Pulley Puller (09213-60017) and socket, remove crankshaft timing pulley. Using Oil Pump Drive Pulley Holder (09278-54012), remove oil pump drive pulley.

Inspection

1) Check belt teeth for cracks or damage. If tooth damage is found, ensure camshafts are not locked. If wear or cracks on flat belt race are found, check for nicks on one side of idler pulley lock.

2) If wear or damage to only one side of belt is found, check belt guide and alignment of each pulley and sprocket. If noticeable wear is found on belt teeth, check timing cover gasket for damage and proper installation.

3) Ensure there is no foreign material on sprocket teeth. Check timing belt idler pulley for smooth rotation. Replace if roughness or noise is found. Check free length of idler pulley tension spring. If free length is not 2.72" (69 mm), replace spring.

Installation

1) Install oil pump drive pulley. Using oil pump drive pulley holder, install and tighten pulley belt. Using Crankshaft Timing Pulley Installer (09214-60010), drive pulley onto crankshaft. Install idler pulley and spring. Pry the idler pulley as far left as it will go and tighten pulley bolt. Keep idler pulley clean.

3.0L TWIN CAMSHAFT 6-CYLINDER (Cont.)

2) With engine cold, install timing belt on crankshaft, oil pump drive and idler pulleys. If reusing old belt, install belt with arrow pointing in direction of rotation. Install No. 1 timing belt cover, A/C compressor bracket and idler pulley bracket. Install A/C compressor. Install air tube on power steering unit.

3) Align Woodruff key and install crankshaft pulley. Using crankshaft pulley adapter and bar, hold pulley and tighten bolt. Turn crankshaft pulley to align "0" on No. 1 timing belt cover timing mark plate with crankshaft pulley groove.

4) Align marks on camshaft pulleys with marks on No. 2 timing belt cover and install pulleys. *See Fig. 6*. Install dowel pin in middle hole of each pulley. Install bolt. Using camshaft pulley holder, hold pulley and tighten bolt. Ensure camshaft pulley marks are still aligned.

5) Install timing belt. Loosen idler pulley bolt and stretch belt. Rotate crankshaft pully two revolutions clockwise (TDC to TDC). Ensure belt tension is correct. Tighten idler pulley bolt to 36 ft. lbs. (49 N.m). To complete installation, reverse removal procedure.

Fig. 6: Aligning Camshaft Pulley Timing Marks

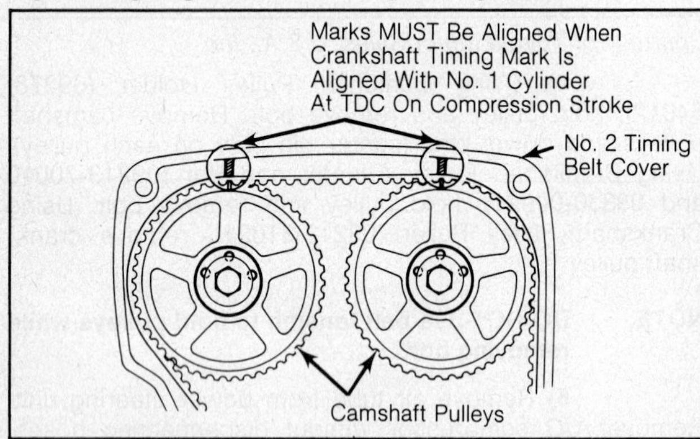

Courtesy of Toyota Motor Sales, U.S.A., Inc.

CAMSHAFTS

Removal

1) Remove cylinder head and intake manifold as previously outlined. See ENGINE, MANIFOLDS & CYLINDER HEAD in this article. Remove No. 2 engine bracket. Remove heater pipe union, gaskets and pipe. Remove EGR cooler.

2) Loosen bearing cap bolts in 3 stages in reverse order of tightening sequence. *See Fig. 9*. Remove bearing caps, oil seal and camshaft. Keep bearing caps in order for reassembly reference.

NOTE: Camshaft rides directly on cylinder head bearing surfaces and caps. There are no replaceable camshaft bearings in head.

Inspection

1) Clean camshaft. Measure runout. Mount dial indicator so tip is touching center journal. If runout exceeds limit, replace camshaft. Measure camshaft lobe height. If lobe height is less than minimum limit, replace camshaft.

2) Using a micrometer, measure camshaft journal diameter. If journal diameter is less than specified, replace camshaft. Clean camshaft bearing caps. Using Plastigage method, mount camshaft in cylinder head to measure camshaft oil clearance.

3) Install bearing caps with top of number (stamped in cap) facing front of head in numerical sequence. Tighten bearing cap bolts in 3 stages in tightening sequence. *See Fig. 9*. If maximum oil clearance is exceeded, replace cylinder head and/or camshaft.

4) Clean camshaft and install bearing caps. Using a dial indicator, measure camshaft end play. If maximum end play limit is exceeded, replace cylinder head and/or camshaft. See CAMSHAFT specifications at end of article.

Installation

1) Coat lip of new oil seal with engine oil and install seal on camshaft. Coat all bearing journals with engine oil. Install camshafts on cylinder head. Exhaust camshaft has distributor drive gear. *See Fig. 7*.

Fig. 7: Installing Camshafts In Cylinder Head

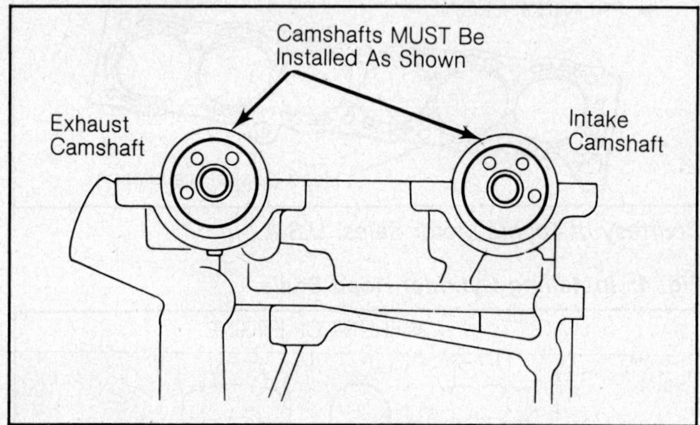

Courtesy of Toyota Motor Sales, U.S.A., Inc.

Fig. 8: Camshaft Bearing Cap Identification & Installing No. 1 Bearing Cap Camshaft Seals

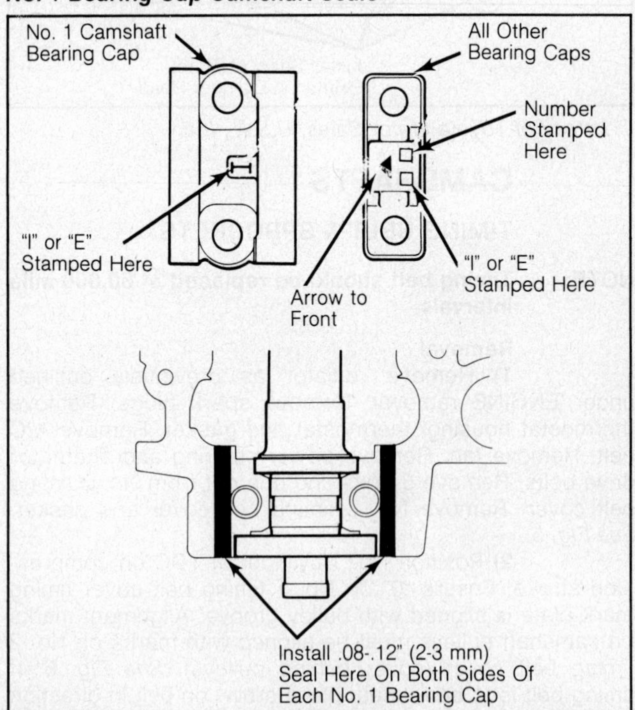

Courtesy of Toyota Motor Sales, U.S.A., Inc.

2) Install .08-.12" (2.0-3.0 mm) seal on each side of camshafts at No. 1 bearing cap locations. After

3.0L TWIN CAMSHAFT 6-CYLINDER (Cont.)

installing seals, install No. 1 bearing caps. No. 1 bearing caps are identified by "I" for intake side and "E" for exhaust side. *See Fig. 8*.

Fig. 9: Camshaft Bearing Cap Tightening Sequence

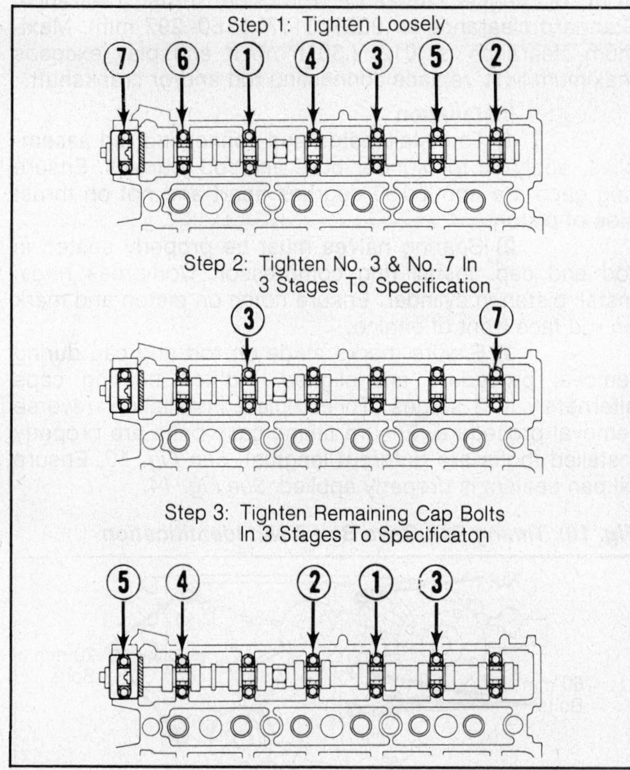

Courtesy of Toyota Motor Sales, U.S.A., Inc.

3) Install remaining bearing caps in correct order with arrows pointing toward front of cylinder head. Loosely tighten all bearing caps in tightening sequence. *See Step 1 in Fig. 9*. Using Camshaft Oil Seal Installer (09223-50010), drive in new camshaft oil seals.

4) Tighten No. 3 and No. 7 bearing caps to specification in 3 stages in sequence. *See Step 2 in Fig. 9*. Tighten all remaining bearing caps to specification in 3 stages in sequence. *See Step 3 in Fig. 9*. Recheck camshaft end play.

5) Install EGR cooler. Install heater pipe union, gaskets and pipe. Install No. 2 engine bracket. To complete installation, reverse removal procedure.

CAMSHAFT OIL SEALS

Removal & Installation

Camshafts must be removed to replace camshaft oil seals. See CAMSHAFTS in this article for removal and installation of oil seals.

VALVES

VALVE ARRANGEMENT

Right Side – Exhaust valves.
Left Side – Intake valves.

VALVE SPRINGS

Removal

1) Remove camshafts as previously outlined. Remove valve lifters and shims. Keep lifters and shims in order for reassembly reference. Using Valve Spring Compressor and Adapter (09202-43013-01 and 09202-00010-01), compress spring and remove 2 valve keepers.

2) Remove compressor and adapter. Remove spring retainer, spring, valve seat and valve. Arrange all components in order for reassembly reference. Pry out valve oil seals.

Inspection

1) Using steel square, measure squareness of valve springs. Replace spring if squareness limit is exceeded. Measure free length of valve springs. If free length is not within specification replace valve spring.

2) Using spring tester, check tension of each valve spring at specified installed height. If valve spring tension is not within specification replace spring. See VALVE SPRINGS specifications at end of article.

Installation

1) Clean all parts to be assembled. Apply oil to all sliding and rotating surfaces. Replace all gaskets and seals. Insert valves into cylinder head valve guide bushings, in correct sequence. Using Valve Stem Oil Seal Installer (09201-41020), install new oil seals on valve guide bushings.

2) Install spring seats, springs and spring retainers. Using spring compressor and adapter, compress spring and install 2 keepers around valve stem. Remove compressor and adapter. Lightly tap valve stem to ensure proper fit.

VALVE GUIDES

Clearance Check

Measure valve-to-guide clearance. See VALVES specifications at end of article. If clearance is greater than maximum limit, replace valve and/or guide.

NOTE: Replacement valve guides are available in .05 mm oversize.

Replacement

1) Insert an old valve wrapped with tape into valve guide. Tap valve with hammer firmly enough to break guide off flush with cylinder head surface. Do not damage lifter hole. Remove snap ring.

2) Using water or oil bath, gradually heat cylinder head to about 194°F (90°C). Using Valve Guide Remover/Installer (09201-70010), drive guide out from camshaft side. Using telescopic hole gauge, measure inside diameter of valve guide bore.

3) If valve guide bore is .4331-.4341" (11.001-11.026 mm), install standard valve guide. If valve guide bore is greater than .4341" (11.026 mm), rebore guide bushing bore to .4350-.4361" (11.049-11.077 mm).

4) To install valve guide, reheat cylinder head as explained in step **2)**. Using valve guide remover/installer, drive in new valve guide from camshaft side until snap ring contacts cylinder head. Using a sharp .24" (6.1 mm) reamer, ream valve guide until standard valve stem-to-guide clearance is obtained.

VALVE CLEARANCE ADJUSTMENT

Measuring Valve Clearance

1) With engine cold, remove valve covers. Place No. 1 cylinder on TDC of compression stroke. Ensure lifters on No. 1 cylinder are loose and lifters on No. 6 cylinder are tight. If not, turn crankshaft one complete revolution.

2) Using feeler gauge, measure and record clearance of intake valves on No. 1 and No. 4 cylinders and exhaust valves on No. 1 and No. 5 cylinders. Rotate crankshaft 2/3 turn (240 degrees). Measure and record clearance of intake valves on No. 3 and No. 5 cylinders and exhaust valves on No. 3 and No. 6 cylinders.

3) Rotate crankshaft another 2/3 turn (240 degrees). Measure and record clearance of intake valves on No. 2 and No. 6 cylinders and exhaust valves on No. 2 and No. 4 cylinders. If clearance is not within specification, change adjusting shim to adjust valve clearance. See VALVE CLEARANCE SPECIFICATIONS table.

VALVE CLEARANCE SPECIFICATIONS

Valve	In. (mm)
Intake	.0059-.0098 (.150-.249)
Exhaust	.0079-.0118 (.201-.300)

Adjusting Valve Clearance

1) To remove adjusting shim, depress valve lifter with Lifter Depressor (09248-70011). Before depressing lifter, position notch on depressor toward spark plug. Use small screwdriver to remove shim from top of lifter.

2) Measure thickness of shim removed with a micrometer. If valve clearance is greater than specified, use thicker shim. If valve clearance is less than specified, use thinner shim. Adjusting shims are available in .002" (.05 mm) increments ranging from .0984" (2.500 mm) to .1299" (3.299 mm). Install new shims using lifter depressor.

PISTONS, PINS & RINGS

PISTON & ROD ASSEMBLY

Removal

1) Remove engine as previously outlined and mount on engine stand. Remove timing belt and cylinder head as previously outlined. Remove 2 nuts attaching coolant by-pass housing to timing belt case. Remove 3 bolts attaching coolant by-pass pipe and hose to cylinder block. Remove housing, pipe and hose from block.

2) Remove ground strap from block. Remove vacuum control valve assembly with hoses attached. Remove 2 nuts attaching fuel return line and support to block. Remove return line, support and insulator. Remove engine mounting brackets. Remove oil filter and oil hole cover plate. Remove power steering pump bracket.

3) Remove oil pan. Remove timing belt case with water pump and gaskets. Remove bolt securing oil pump drive shaft in position. While turning oil pump drive shaft, slowly pull shaft out of block. Remove 5 bolts from rear crankshaft oil seal retainer. Remove retainer and seal assembly. Remove oil pump pick-up, tubes and oil pump.

4) Before removing bearing caps, mark caps and rods with punch for reassembly reference. Measure and record connecting rod thrust clearance with dial indicator. Using Plastigage method, measure and record bearing clearances.

5) Check top of cylinder bore for carbon ridge. If ridge is present, remove using ridge reamer. Cover rod bolts with short pieces of rubber hose. Push piston and rod assembly, with bearing half, out through top of block. Rod caps and bearings must be kept with respective piston and rod assembly. Rod caps are not interchangeable.

Inspection

1) Using a connecting rod aligner, check rod for bends or twists. Maximum bend limit is .002" (.05 mm) in 3.94" (100 mm) length, or less. Maximum twist limit is .0059" (.15 mm) in 3.94" (100 mm) length, or less.

2) Install connecting rod, with bearings, on crankpin with notch on piston and mark on rod facing front of engine. Measure rod side thrust clearance. Standard clearance is .0063-.0117" (.160-.297 mm). Maximum clearance is .012" (.30 mm). If end play exceeds maximum limit, replace connecting rod and/or crankshaft.

Installation

1) To install piston and connecting rod assemblies, apply oil to cylinder bore and rod journals. Ensure ring gaps are about 180 degrees apart and not on thrust side of piston.

2) Bearing halves must be properly seated in rod and cap. Install ring compressor. Compress rings. Install piston in cylinder. Ensure notch on piston and mark on rod face front of engine.

3) Ensure marks made on rod and cap during removal procedure are aligned. Tighten bearing caps alternately in 3 stages. To complete installation, reverse removal procedure. Ensure timing case bolts are properly installed (bolts are different lengths). *See Fig. 10.* Ensure oil pan sealant is properly applied. *See Fig. 14.*

Fig. 10: Timing Belt Case Bolt & Nut Identification

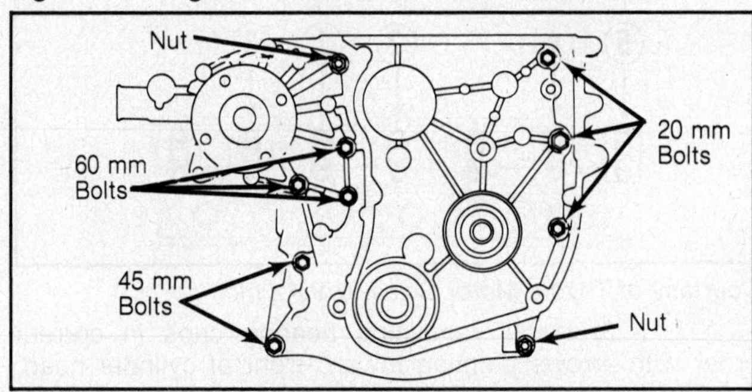

Courtesy of Toyota Motor Sales, U.S.A., Inc.

FITTING PISTONS & RINGS

NOTE: Pistons are available only in .50 mm oversize.

1) Remove all gasket material from cylinder block. Clean cylinder block with solvent and soft brush. Inspect cylinder block for scratches and rebore cylinder if necessary. Inspect cylinder block deck for warpage. If warpage exceeds limit of .002" (.05 mm), replace block.

2) Using bore gauge, measure cylinder bore for out-of-round and excessive taper. Record readings in axial and thrust directions of bore. Record readings at .39" (10 mm) from top of cylinder bore, at center of bore and at .39" (10 mm) from bottom of bore.

3) If maximum out-of-round limit and maximum taper limit of .0008" (.02 mm) are exceeded, rebore cylinder. When one cylinder is rebored, all cylinders must be rebored.

4) Determine piston oversize according to cylinder wear. Standard bore diameter is 3.2673-3.2693" (82.989-83.040 mm). Standard piston diameter is 3.2646-3.2665" (82.920-82.969 mm).

5) Using a micrometer, measure piston diameter at right angles to piston pin center line, .87" (22.1 mm) from top of piston head. To determine amount of cylinder rebore, add piston clearance of .0024-.0031" (.061-.079 mm) to measured piston diameter. From this figure, subtract maximum honing amount of .0008" (.020 mm).

3.0L TWIN CAMSHAFT 6-CYLINDER (Cont.)

6) After honing cylinder to final fit, measure piston-to-cylinder clearance with piston and cylinder at 70°F (21°C). Clearance should be .0024-.0031" (.061-.079 mm). Ensure that difference of bore limit between cylinders is less than .0008" (.020 mm).

7) If reusing pistons, decarbon ring grooves with groove cleaner or broken ring. Using solvent and soft brush (not wire brush), thoroughly clean piston. Check for scratches, wear or damage.

8) Measure side clearance of rings in grooves as each is installed. Check ring end gap. Install ring squarely in cylinder, using piston. If beyond limits, replace piston and/or rings. Install rings with code marks facing up.

PISTON PINS

NOTE: Piston and pin are a matched set. Keep piston, pin, rings and connecting rod together for each cylinder.

1) Check fit between piston and pin by moving piston back and forth on piston pin. If any movement is felt, replace piston and pin.

2) To separate piston from connecting rod, remove snap rings from piston with needle-nose pliers. Heat piston and rod assembly to 140°F (60°C). Drive pin out of piston with plastic-faced hammer and driver.

3) Measure clearance between connecting rod bushing and piston pin. Standard clearance is .0002-.0004" (.005-.010 mm). If maximum clearance of .0008" (.020 mm) is exceeded, replace connecting rod bushing. To replace bushing, use press and Connecting Rod Bushing Remover/Installer (09222-30010) to press out bushing.

4) Use press and bushing remover/installer to install bushing. Ensure oil holes in bushing and connecting rod are aligned. Hone new bushing to ensure standard clearance between piston pin and bushing.

5) Coat pin with oil. Install new snap ring on one side of piston. Install pin into piston and rod. See PISTONS, PINS & RINGS specifications at end of article. Ensure notch on piston and mark on connecting rod are aligned. *See Fig. 11*. Install other new snap ring.

Fig. 11: Assembling Piston & Connecting Rod

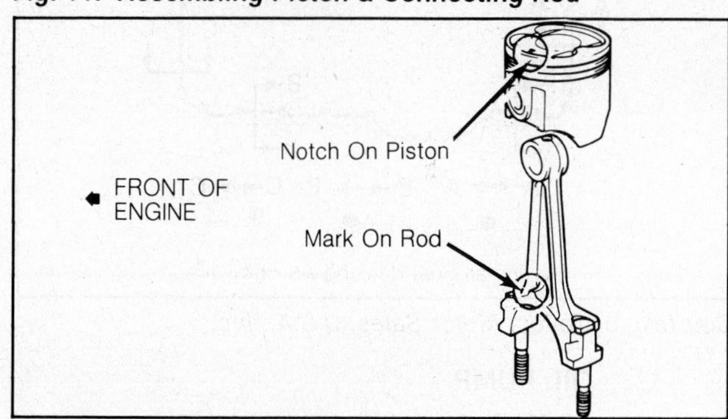

Courtesy of Toyota Motor Sales, U.S.A., Inc.

CRANKSHAFT & ROD BEARINGS

CRANKSHAFT

Removal

1) With engine removed and mounted on engine stand, remove piston assemblies as previously outlined. See PISTON & ROD ASSEMBLY in this article. Before removing crankshaft, measure and record crankshaft end play with dial indicator. See THRUST BEARING ALIGNMENT.

2) Loosen main bearing caps in 3 stages in reverse order of tightening sequence. *See Fig. 13*. Remove main bearing caps and arrange caps, inserts and thrust washers (No. 4 main bearing) in order. Remove crankshaft. Leave upper bearing halves and thrust washers for No. 4 main bearing inserted in block. Remove remaining upper bearing halves.

Inspection

1) Check crankshaft journals and crankpins for scoring, wear, cracks, taper and out-of-round. Maximum taper and out-of-round limit is .0008" (.020 mm). If maximum limits are exceeded, regrind or replace crankshaft.

2) Check crankshaft for bend by placing on "V" blocks. Use dial indicator at center journal. Replace crankshaft if maximum limit of .0024" (.061 mm) is exceeded.

Installation

1) Install upper main bearing halves in engine block. Ensure bearing halves are properly installed with oil holes aligned. *See Fig. 12*. Install upper thrust washers on center main bearing (No. 4) with oil grooves facing outward. Lubricate bearing faces with engine oil.

Fig. 12: Identification of Crankshaft Main Bearings

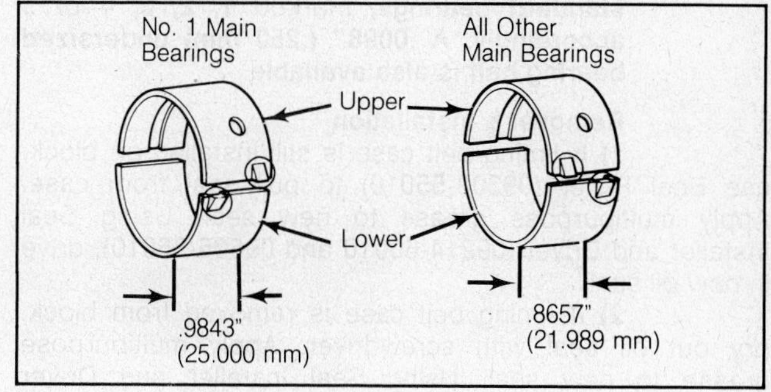

Courtesy of Toyota Motor Sales, U.S.A., Inc.

2) Install crankshaft. Install main bearing caps, with bearing halves installed, on corresponding journal with arrow facing front of engine block. Install thrust washers on No. 4 main bearing with oil grooves facing outward.

3) Tighten main bearing cap bolts in 3 stages in tightening sequence. *See Fig. 13*. Ensure crankshaft

Fig. 13: Crankshaft Main Bearing Cap Tightening Sequence

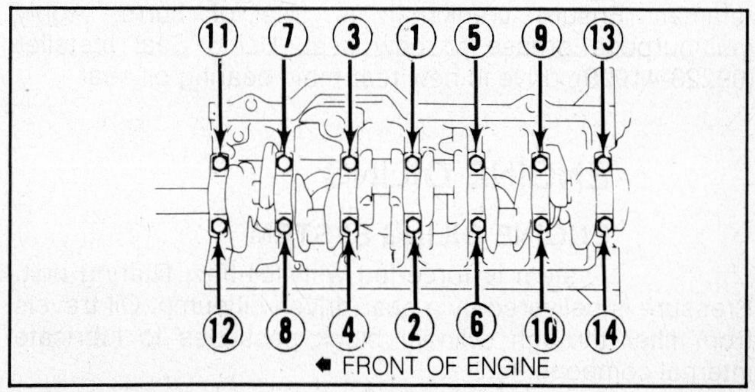

Courtesy of Toyota Motor Sales, U.S.A., Inc.

turns. Check crankshaft end play. See THRUST BEARING ALIGNMENT. Complete installation by reversing removal procedure.

THRUST BEARING ALIGNMENT

1) Thrust washers are installed on No. 4 main bearing journal. Check crankshaft end play.

2) See CRANKSHAFT MAIN & CONNECTING ROD BEARINGS specifications at end of article. If end play exceeds maximum limit, replace thrust washers as a set and/or replace crankshaft.

NOTE: **Thrust washers are available in standard thickness of .1152-.1171" (2.926-2.974 mm) and oversize of .1176-.1196" (2.988-3.038 mm).**

MAIN & CONNECTING ROD BEARING CLEARANCES

Check clearance using Plastigage method. If clearance exceeds maximum limit, replace bearings and/or grind crankshaft journals. See CRANKSHAFT MAIN & CONNECTING ROD BEARINGS specifications at end of article.

NOTE: **If replacing standard connecting rod or main bearing, replace with one having same number as marked on cylinder block oil pan mounting surface. There are 5 sizes of standard bearings, marked 1, 2, 3, 4 or 5 accordingly. A .0098" (.250 mm) undersized bearing half is also available.**

Removal & Installation

1) If timing belt case is still installed on block, use Seal Puller (09308-55010) to pull seal from case. Apply multipurpose grease to new seal. Using Seal Installer and Driver (09214-60010 and 09506-35010), drive in new oil seal.

2) If timing belt case is removed from block, pry out oil seal with screwdriver. Apply multipurpose grease to new seal. Using Seal Installer and Driver (09214-60010 and 09506-35010), drive in new oil seal.

REAR MAIN BEARING OIL SEAL

Removal & Installation

1) If rear oil seal retainer is removed from block, use screwdriver to remove seal. Apply multipurpose grease to new seal. Using Seal Installer (09223-41020), drive in new rear main bearing oil seal.

2) If rear oil seal retainer is still installed on block, cut off lip of oil seal with knife at 8 o'clock position. Cover crankshaft with shop towel and pry seal out of retainer. Ensure crankshaft is free of burrs. Apply multipurpose grease to new seal. Using Seal Installer (09223-41020), drive in new rear main bearing oil seal.

ENGINE OILING

ENGINE OILING SYSTEM

System is force-fed with full-flow filtering unit. Pressure is delivered by a gear-driven oil pump. Oil travels from filter through cylinder block passages to lubricate internal components.

CRANKCASE CAPACITY

Total oil capacity (dry) is 5.4 qts. (5.1L). Drain and refill capacity is 3.9 qts. (3.7L) without filter, and 4.7 qts. (4.4L) with filter.

NORMAL OIL PRESSURE

Normal oil pressure at idle should be more than 4.3 psi (.3 kg/cm²). At 3000 RPM, oil pressure should be 36-71 psi (2.5-5.0 kg/cm²).

OIL PRESSURE RELIEF VALVE

The oil pressure relief valve is a nonadjustable type located in the oil pump.

OIL PAN

Removal

1) Remove hood and lower engine cover. Drain engine oil. On models with automatic transmission, disconnect transmission oil cooler lines. On all models, remove No. 1 front crossmember. Remove front exhaust pipe bracket and stiffener plates.

2) Remove front wheel and tire assemblies. Remove brake hose brackets and clips. Loosen intermediate steering shaft pinch bolt. Disconnect intermediate steering shaft. Disconnect stabilizer bar links from lower control arms.

3) Attach engine lifting chain to engine hangers. Support engine and remove engine mounting nuts and washers. Remove electronic suspension actuators from strut assemblies. Remove top strut mounting bolts. Support front suspension member with floor jack. Remove 2 bolts and 4 nuts securing assembly to body. Lower suspension member and support on jack stands. Remove oil pan.

Installation

To install oil pan, reverse removal procedure. Ensure oil pan gasket sealant is properly applied. *See Fig. 14.* Fill engine with oil. Start engine and check for leaks. Check front wheel alignment.

Fig. 14: Sealing Oil Pan

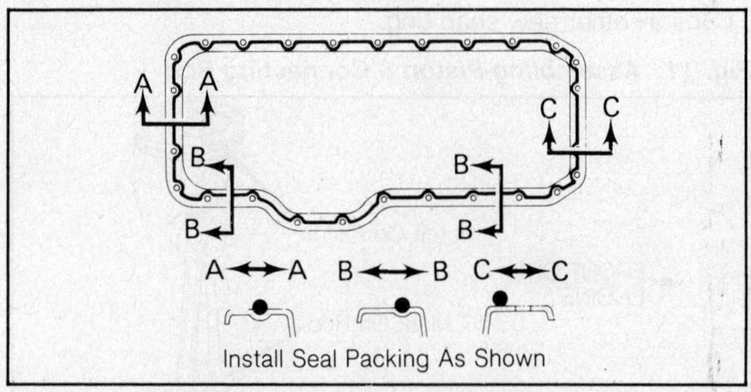

Courtesy of Toyota Motor Sales, U.S.A., Inc.

OIL PUMP

Removal

Remove oil pan as previously outlined. Unbolt and remove oil pump assembly.

Disassembly

Remove oil pick-up and discharge tubes. Unscrew relief valve plug. Carefully remove plug, spring and relief valve. Remove 5 bolts from pump cover. Remove cover and driven gear. Remove snap ring, shaft gear, Woodruff key and drive shaft. *See Fig. 15.*

3.0L TWIN CAMSHAFT 6-CYLINDER (Cont.)

Fig. 15: Exploded View of Oil Pump Assembly

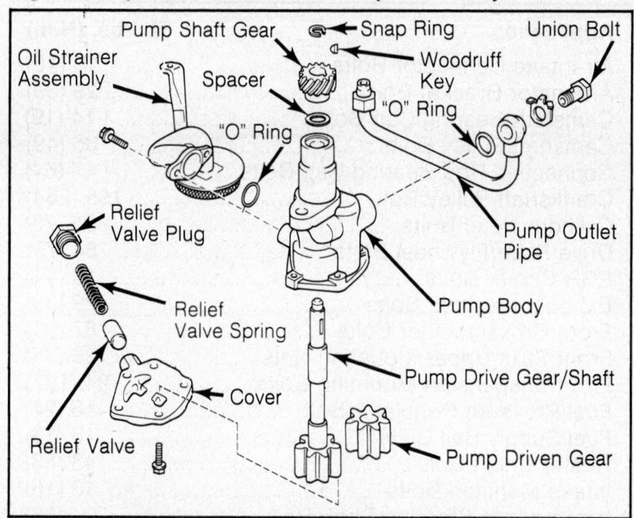

Courtesy of Toyota Motor Sales, U.S.A., Inc.

Inspection

Check relief valve for scoring or wear. If damaged, replace valve or pump assembly. Measure clearances between driven gear and pump body, drive gear and driven gear and check gear-to-body clearance.

Reassembly

Reassemble pump in reverse order of disassembly. Replace all "O" rings with new ones. After reassembly, check pump operation. Immerse inlet tube in clean engine oil and turn drive shaft counterclockwise. Oil should flow from discharge hole. Cover hole with thumb and turn drive shaft counterclockwise. Shaft should be difficult to turn.

Installation

Install oil pump. Clean gasket material from oil pan and block. Install oil pan with new gasket.

OIL PUMP SPECIFICATIONS

Application	In. (mm)
Driven Gear-to-Body	
Standard Clearance	.0041-.0069 (.104-.175)
Maximum Clearance	.008 (.20)
Drive Gear-to-Driven Gear	
Standard Backlash	.020-.024 (.51-.61)
Maximum Backlash	.035 (.89)
Gear-to-Body	
Standard Clearance	.0012-.0035 (.030-.089)
Maximum Clearance	.0059 (.150)

OIL PUMP DRIVE SHAFT, BEARINGS & BUSHINGS

Removal

Remove oil pump drive pulley. See TIMING BELT & SPROCKETS removal procedure. Remove oil pump drive shaft. See PISTON & ROD ASSEMBLY.

Inspection

1) Using a micrometer, measure and record oil pump drive shaft journal diameter. Standard journal diameter is 1.6126-1.6132" (40.960-40.975 mm) for front journal and 1.2976-1.2982" (32.959-32.974 mm) for rear journal.

2) Using a telescopic bore gauge, measure and record front and rear drive shaft bearing bore diameters. To obtain clearance, subtract journal diameter readings from bore diameter readings.

3) Standard clearance is .0010-.0026" (.025-.066 mm). If maximum clearance of .0031" (.078 mm) is exceeded, replace bearings and/or drive shaft.

4) Using Bearing Remover/Replacer Set (09215-00100), replace bearings. Replace No. 1 bearing using No. 2 bearing as a guide. Replace No. 2 bearing using No. 1 bearing as a guide.

NOTE: **Ensure bearing oil holes are aligned during replacement.**

5) Using a feeler gauge, measure drive shaft thrust clearance between thrust plate and collar. Standard thrust clearance is .0024-.0051" (.061-.130 mm). If maximum thrust clearance of .0118" (.30 mm) is exceeded, replace thrust plate and/or collar.

6) Mount Thrust Plate Puller (09950-20017) in vise. Install drive shaft in puller. Pull off thrust plate and collar. To replace thrust plate and collar, assemble on drive shaft and press into position. *See Fig. 16.*

7) To replace oil pump guide bushing, drive bushing out from outer side of engine block. To install bushing, drive bushing in from inner side of block. Ensure oil hole is aligned toward crankshaft side of engine block. Mark on bushing should face front of engine block. *See Fig. 17.*

Fig. 16: Assembling Thrust Plate & Collar on Oil Pump Drive Shaft

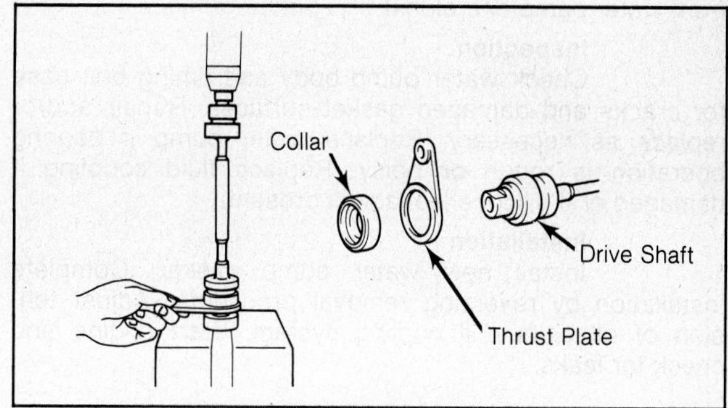

Courtesy of Toyota Motor Sales, U.S.A., Inc.

Fig. 17: Installing Oil Pump Guide Bushing

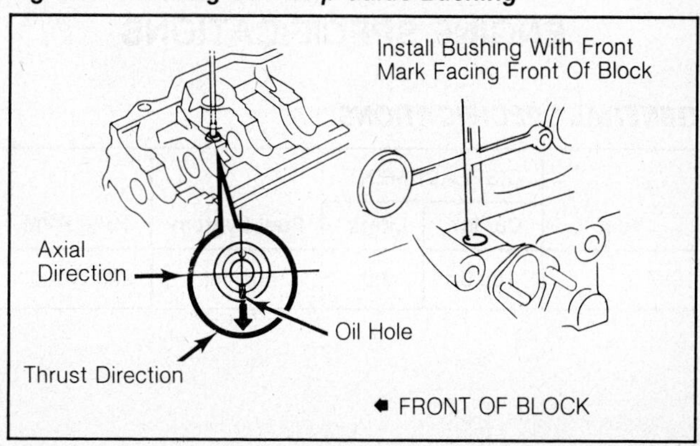

Courtesy of Toyota Motor Sales, U.S.A., Inc.

3.0L TWIN CAMSHAFT 6-CYLINDER (Cont.)

Installation

To install oil pump drive shaft, rotate drive shaft and slowly insert into cavity to avoid damaging bearing. To complete installation, reverse removal procedure.

OIL PUMP DRIVE SHAFT OIL SEAL

Removal & Installation

1) If timing belt case is removed from block, use screwdriver to remove seal. Apply multipurpose grease to new seal. Using Seal Installer and Driver (09214-60010 and 09506-35010), drive in new oil seal.

2) If timing belt case is still installed on block, cut off lip of oil seal with knife at 8 o'clock position. Tape screwdriver tip and carefully pry seal out. Check oil seal lip contact surface for cracks or damage. Apply multipurpose grease to new seal. Using Seal Installer (09214-41010), drive in new oil seal.

ENGINE COOLING

WATER PUMP

Removal

1) Drain coolant from block and radiator. Remove A/C belt. Loosen water pump pulley nuts. Remove alternator drive belt. Remove 4 nuts, fluid coupling and water pump pulley. Separate fan from fluid coupling.

2) Remove air tube from power steering pump. Remove 8 bolts and 2 nuts mounting water pump to block. Remove water pump and gasket. Clean all gasket material from water pump and block.

Inspection

Check water pump body and timing belt case for cracks and damaged gasket surfaces. Repair and/or replace as necessary. Replace water pump if bearing operation is rough or noisy. Replace fluid coupling if damaged or if silicone leakage is present.

Installation

Install new water pump gasket. Complete installation by reversing removal procedure. Adjust tension of all belts. Fill cooling system. Start engine and check for leaks.

NOTE: **For further information on cooling systems, see ENGINE COOLING section.**

ENGINE SPECIFICATIONS

GENERAL SPECIFICATIONS

Year	DISPLACEMENT Cu. In.	DISPLACEMENT Liters	Fuel System	HP@RPM	Torque Ft. Lbs.@RPM	Compr. Ratio	BORE In.	BORE mm	STROKE In.	STROKE mm
1987	180.3	3.0	Fuel Inj.	200@6000	185@4800	9.2:1	3.27	83	3.58	91

TIGHTENING SPECIFICATIONS

Application	Ft. Lbs. (N.m)
Air Intake Connector Bolts	13 (18)
Alternator Bracket Bolt	29 (39)
Camshaft Bearing Cap Bolts	[1] 14 (19)
Camshaft Pulley Bolts	36 (49)
Connecting Rod Bearing Cap Bolts	[1] 47 (64)
Crankshaft Pulley Bolt	195 (264)
Cylinder Head Bolts	[1] 58 (79)
Drive Plate/Flywheel Bolts	54 (73)
EGR Cooler Bolts	10 (14)
Exhaust Manifold Bolts	29 (39)
Front Crossmember Bolts	67 (91)
Front Strut Upper Mounting Nuts	26 (35)
Front Suspension Mounting Bolts	94 (127)
Fuel Pressure Regulator Bolt	18 (24)
Fuel Supply Rail Bolts	13 (18)
Heater Union Bolt	43 (58)
Intake Manifold Bolts	13 (18)
Intermediate Steering Shaft Bolt	24 (33)
Main Bearing Cap Bolts	[1] 75 (102)
No. 2 Engine Bracket	29 (39)
Oil Pump Drive Pulley Bolt	16 (22)
Oil Pump Mounting Bolts	16 (22)
Oil Pump Outlet Tube Union	25 (34)
Oil Pump Relief Valve Plug	27 (37)
Oil Pump Union Nut	25 (34)
Stabilizer Bar-to-Lower Arm	47 (64)
Timing Belt Idler Pulley Bolt	36 (49)
	INCH Lbs. (N.m)
Alternator Belt Adjusting Bolt	108 (12)
Cooling Fan Bolts	48 (5.4)
Fuel Return Line Support Bolt	108 (12)
Oil Pan Bolts & Nuts	108 (12)
Oil Pump Cover Bolts	65 (7)
Oil Pump Drive Shaft Retaining Nut	108 (12)
Oil Pump Strainer Bolts	108 (12)
Rear Main Oil Seal Retainer Bolts	108 (12)
Valve Cover Bolts	22 (2.5)
Coolant By-Pass-to-	
Timing Belt Case Nuts	120 (14)
Cylinder Block Bolts	108 (12)

[1] – Tighten bolts in 3 stages.

3.0L TWIN CAMSHAFT 6-CYLINDER (Cont.)

ENGINE SPECIFICATIONS (Cont.)

VALVES

Engine Size & Valve	Head Diam. In. (mm)	Face Angle	Seat Angle	Seat Width In. (mm)	Stem Diameter In. (mm)	Stem Clearance In. (mm)	Valve Lift In. (mm)
3.0L [1]							
Intake	.....	44.5°	[2] 45°	.039-.055 (1.00-1.40)	.2350-.2356 (5.969-5.984)	.0010-.0024 (.025-.061)	.....
Exhaust	.....	44.5°	[2] 45°	.039-.055 (1.00-1.40)	.2348-.2354 (5.964-5.979)	.0012-.0026 (.030-.066)	.....

[1] – Standard valve guide inside diameter is .2366-.2374" (6.010-6.030 mm).
[2] – Correction angles for valve seats are 30 degrees and 60 degrees.

PISTONS, PINS & RINGS

Engine	PISTONS	PINS		RINGS		
	Clearance In. (mm)	Piston Fit In. (mm)	Rod Fit In. (mm)	Ring No.	End Gap In. (mm)	Side Clearance In. (mm)
3.0L	.0024-.0031 (.061-.079)	[1] Interference Fit	.0002-.0004 (.005-.010)	No. 1	.0091-.0150 (.231-.381)	.0012-.0028 (.030-.071)
				No. 2	.0098-.0209 (.249-.531)	.0008-.0024 (.020-.061)
				Oil	.0039-.0201 (.099-.511)	.....

[1] – Piston pin is installed using thumb pressure with piston and rod assembly at 140°F (60°C). If pin can be installed at a lower temperature, replace piston assembly.

CRANKSHAFT MAIN & CONNECTING ROD BEARINGS

Engine	MAIN BEARINGS				CONNECTING ROD BEARINGS		
	Journal Diam. In. (mm)	Clearance In. (mm)	Thrust Bearing	Crankshaft End Play In. (mm)	Journal Diam. In. (mm)	Clearance In. (mm)	Side Play In. (mm)
3.0L	2.3620-2.3627 (59.995-60.013)	.0012-.0022 (.030-.056)	No. 4	.0020-.0098 (.051-.249)	2.0463-2.0472 (51.976-51.999)	.0012-.0019 (.030-.048)	.0063-.0117 (.160-.297)

VALVE SPRINGS

Engine	Free Length In. (mm)	PRESSURE Lbs. @ In. (Kg @ mm)	
		Valve Closed	Valve Open
3.0L [1]	1.6394 (41.641)	35@1.378 (16@35.00)	.....

[1] Spring squarness limit is .059" (1.50 mm)

CAMSHAFT

Engine	Journal Diam. In. (mm)	Clearance In. (mm)	Lobe Lift In. (mm)
3.0L [1] [2]			
No. 1	1.0610-1.0616 (26.949-26.965)	.0014-.0028 (.036-.071)	[3]
No. 2-No. 7	1.0586-1.0620 (26.888-26.975)	.0010-.0037 (.025-.094)	[3]

[1] – Runout limit is .0012" (.030 mm).
[2] – Standard end play is .0031-.0075" (.079-.191 mm).
[3] – Standard cam lobe height for intake and exhaust is 1.5102" (38.359 mm).

Toyota Engines

4.2L 6-CYLINDER

Land Cruiser

NOTE: For engine repair procedures not covered in this article, see ENGINE OVERHAUL PROCEDURES article at the beginning of this section.

ENGINE CODING

ENGINE IDENTIFICATION

Engine code is stamped on right side of cylinder block above starter motor.

ENGINE IDENTIFICATION CODES

Application	Code
4.2L	3F

ENGINE, MANIFOLDS & CYLINDER HEAD

ENGINE

Removal

1) Drain crankcase and cooling system. Remove battery. Remove hood and tip grille forward. Disconnect hoses and remove radiator. Remove air cleaner assembly and cover carburetor.

2) Disconnect throttle and choke controls to carburetor. Remove A/C compressor and condenser, if equipped. Disconnect alternator and ignition wiring between engine and chassis. Label and disconnect all vacuum and emission control hoses. Remove power steering pump and reservoir.

3) Remove engine, transmission undercovers, front propeller shaft and winch drive shaft. Place supporting device under transmission and transfer case. Remove bolts attaching transmission to bell housing. Disconnect exhaust pipe from manifold and fuel line at pump.

4) Attach hoist and sling to engine. Remove engine mount bolts and nuts. Move engine forward and upward to remove.

Installation

Use guide dowels in transmission bolt holes and lower into position. Use care when aligning clutch assembly over transmission pilot shaft. Continue installation in reverse sequence of removal.

INTAKE & EXHAUST MANIFOLDS

Removal

1) Disconnect battery and remove air cleaner. Disconnect throttle rod, choke rod, accelerator cable, vacuum line, and fuel line from carburetor.

2) Disconnect solenoid wire from ignition coil terminal. Remove carburetor assembly. Disconnect exhaust pipe from exhaust manifold. Remove manifold nuts, manifolds and gaskets.

Installation

1) Thoroughly clean all gasket surfaces and install new gaskets. Replace intake or exhaust manifold if warpage exceeds .079" (2.0 mm).

2) Install manifold assembly. Gradually tighten bolts to specification. *See Fig. 1.* Install remaining components in reverse of removal procedure.

Fig. 1: Intake & Exhaust Manifold Tightening Sequence

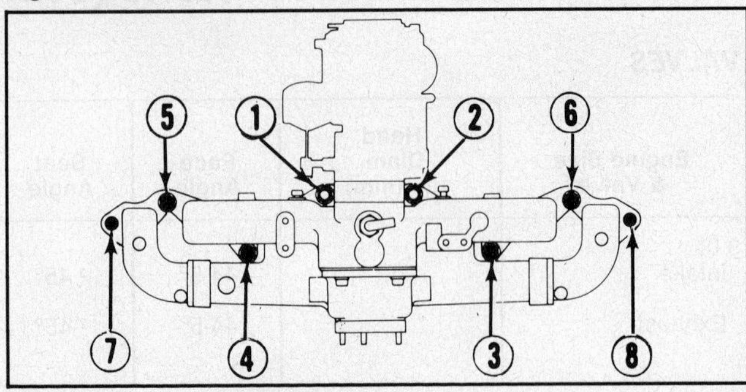

Courtesy of Toyota Motor Sales, U.S.A., Inc.

CYLINDER HEAD

Removal

1) Drain cooling system and remove air cleaner assembly. After marking for identification, disconnect spark plug wires, electrical connectors and vacuum hoses from head. Remove intake and exhaust manifold.

2) Remove valve cover and rocker arm assembly. Take out push rods, keeping them in order for installation. Loosen head bolts in 2 or 3 stages in reverse of tightening sequence. *See Fig. 2.* Remove cylinder head.

Inspection

1) Head surface warpage limit is .0059" (.15 mm). Manifold mounting surface warpage limit is .0039" (.10 mm).

2) If warpage exceeds specification, correct by machining or replacement. Maximum reface limit for both surfaces is .0079" (.20 mm).

Installation

1) Ensure all mating surfaces are clean. Place new head gasket on cylinder block. Ensure mating oil hole on push rod side is between No. 4 and 5 cylinder.

2) Install cylinder head and tighten bolts in 2 or 3 stages. *See Fig. 2.* To complete installation, reverse removal procedure.

Fig. 2: Cylinder Head Tightening Sequence

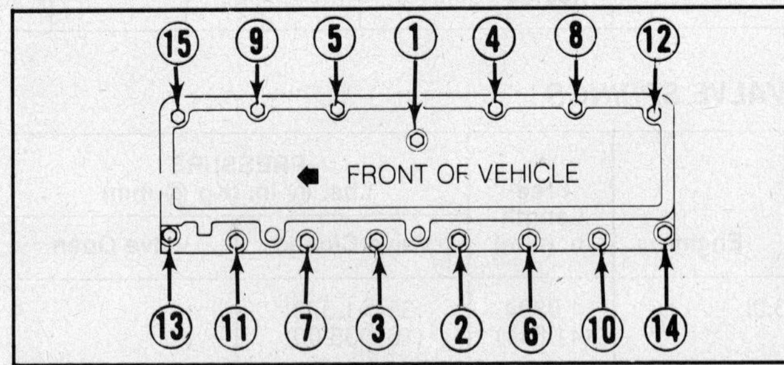

Courtesy of Toyota Motor Sales, U.S.A., Inc.

CAMSHAFT

TIMING GEAR

NOTE: Camshaft must be removed from engine for gear replacement. Due to model variations, engine may have to be removed from vehicle.

4.2L 6-CYLINDER (Cont.)

Inspection

Set engine to TDC of No. 1 cylinder. Drain cooling system and remove radiator. Remove engine front cover. Replace camshaft and crankshaft timing gears if gear backlash exceeds .008" (.20 mm).

Removal

1) Align timing marks. Remove camshaft thrust plate aligning bolts. *See Fig. 3.* Remove valve cover and engine side cover. Remove rocker arm shaft. Remove push rods and valve lifters. Note location for reinstallation reference. Remove camshaft.

Fig. 3: Aligning Timing Marks on Gears

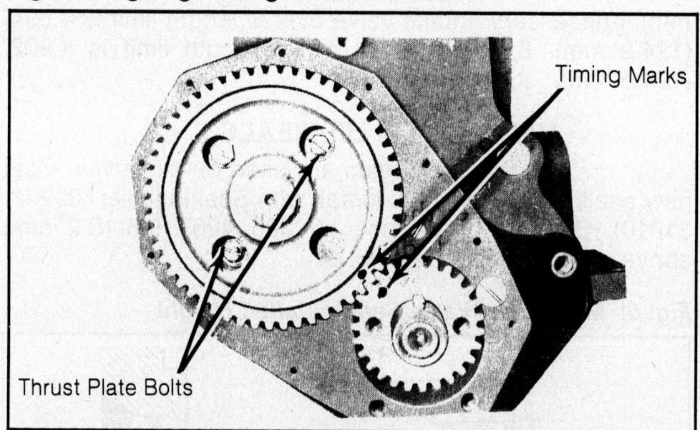

Courtesy of Toyota Motor Sales, U.S.A., Inc.

2) Remove snap ring and press timing gear off camshaft. Pry pulley key from crankshaft. Using gear puller, pull timing gear off crankshaft.

Installation

1) Install crankshaft timing gear and pulley key. Press new timing gear on camshaft. Oil camshaft journals and bearings and install camshaft.

2) Align timing marks on camshaft and crankshaft timing gears. *See Fig. 3.* If oil nozzle was removed, reinstall and stake in 2 places. Oil hole must face gears. *See Fig. 4.* To install remaining components, reverse removal procedure.

Fig. 4: Adjusting Oil Nozzle

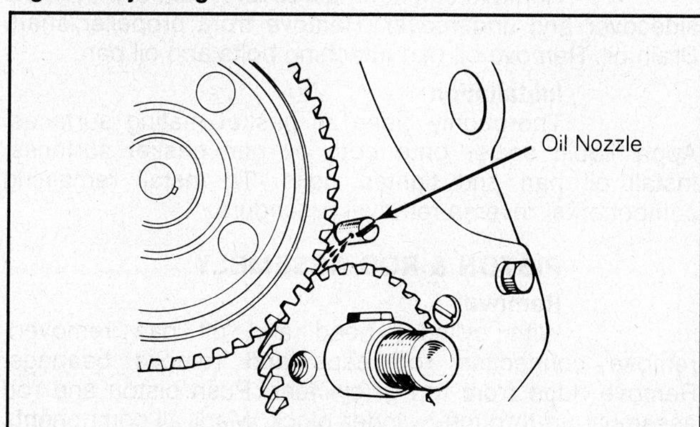

Courtesy of Toyota Motor Sales, U.S.A., Inc.

ENGINE FRONT COVER

Removal

Drain cooling system and remove radiator. Remove fan belts. Using a gear puller, remove crankshaft pulley. Remove timing gear cover bolts and cover.

Installation

1) Install cover and gasket. Apply liquid sealer on threads of lower 2 bolts. Use proper length bolts.

2) To locate cover properly, drive pulley into position with Pulley Installer (09214-60010). Tighten cover bolts. To complete installation, reverse removal procedure.

FRONT COVER OIL SEAL

Removal & Installation

Pry out old seal. Install new oil seal so open end of seal is toward inside of timing gear cover. Drive seal in place with Seal Installer (09515-35010).

CAMSHAFT

Removal & Installation

See TIMING GEAR in this article.

Inspection

1) Check camshaft for runout at center journal. If runout exceeds .0059" (.150 mm), replace camshaft. Measure end play between thrust plate and first camshaft journal with feeler gauge. Standard end play is .0079-.0103" (.200-.261 mm). If end play exceeds .012" (.30 mm), replace camshaft thrust plate.

2) Camshaft intake lobe limit is 1.496" (38.0 mm). Exhaust lobe limit is 1.492" (37.9 mm). If wear exceeds specification, replace camshaft.

CAMSHAFT BEARING

Removal

Drive out camshaft rear expansion plug from cylinder block. Remove bearings using Camshaft Bearing Remover/Installer (09215-00010).

Inspection

Inspect camshaft journals and bearings for wear or damage. If clearance exceeds specification, replace camshaft bearings and/or camshaft. Bearings are available in standard .010" and .020" (.25 and .50 mm) oversize.

Installation

Ensure oil holes of bearing align with oil holes in cylinder block. Coat rear expansion plug with sealer and reinstall plug in block.

VALVES

VALVE ARRANGEMENT

E-I-I-E-E-I-I-E-E-I-I-E (Front-to-rear).

ROCKER ARM SHAFT ASSEMBLY

Disassembly & Inspection

1) Note position of rocker arms and supports before disassembly. Check rocker arms and shaft for damage or wear. Measure oil clearance between rocker arms and shaft. Clearance should be .0007-.0017" (.018-.043 mm).

2) Check contact surface of rocker arm. If only lightly scored, reface with an oil stone. If badly scored, replace rocker arm.

Reassembly

Assemble rocker arms, springs and rocker shaft supports onto rocker arm shaft. Oil hole of shaft must be aligned with oil hole of No. 4 support. Install valve rocker shaft lock springs.

Toyota Engines

4.2L 6-CYLINDER (Cont.)

VALVE CLEARANCE ADJUSTMENTS

1) Valves are adjusted at normal operating temperature. Set No. 1 piston at TDC of compression stroke and align timing mark with pointer.

2) Adjust valves No. 1, 2, 3, 5, 7, and 9 (as numbered from front). Rotate crankshaft one complete turn and again align timing mark with pointer. Adjust remaining valves No. 4, 6, 8, 10, 11, and 12.

VALVE CLEARANCE SPECIFICATIONS

Valve	In. (mm)
Intake	.008 (.20)
Exhaust	.014 (.35)

VALVE GUIDES

1) Check clearance between valve stems and valve guides. If clearance exceeds .004" (.10 mm) for intake or .005" (.12 mm) for exhaust, replace valve and/or valve guide. To replace valve guide, drive toward combustion chamber with Remover/Installer (09201-60011).

2) Measure valve guide bore in cylinder. If guide bore is more than .5519" (14.018 mm), machine the bore to .5531-.5539" (14.050-14.068 mm).

3) Install .002" (.05 mm) oversize valve guide from top of cylinder head. Guide should extend .689" (17.5 mm) from top of cylinder head. *See Fig. 5.*

4) Intake valve guide length is 2.13" (54 mm). Exhaust valve guide length is 2.32" (59 mm). After installation, ream guide for proper clearance.

Fig. 5: Installing Valve Guides

Courtesy of Toyota Motor Sales, U.S.A., Inc.

VALVE LIFTERS

Check lifters and bores for wear or damage. Valve lifter standard diameter is .9902" (25.15 mm). Standard oil clearance is .0007-.003" (.019-.075 mm). If clearance exceeds specification, replace lifter with oversize lifter.

VALVE SPRINGS

Removal & Inspection

1) With cylinder head removed, use spring compressor to compress valve spring and remove retainer keepers. Remove spring retainer, spring, valve stem oil seal and spring seat.

2) Remove valves and keep in order. Check spring squareness, free height and tension at installed height. Spring should be square within .072" (1.8 mm).

Installation

1) Insert valve into valve stem guide. Install valve spring seat, valve spring, valve stem oil seal and valve spring retainer onto valve stem.

2) Use valve spring compressor to compress spring. Install valve spring retainer keepers. Ensure retainer keepers seat properly in valve stem groove.

VALVE STEM LENGTH

Valve stem tips may be resurfaced .02" (.50 mm) if necessary. Intake valve overall length limit is 4.894" (124.3 mm). Exhaust valve overall length limit is 4.902" (124.5 mm).

VALVE STEM OIL SEALS

Cup-type oil seals are used on all valves. Coat new seals with engine oil. Install with Seal Installer (09201-31010). Drive in a distance of .386-.406" (9.8-10.2 mm) above cylinder head. *See Fig. 6.*

Fig. 6: Measuring Valve Seal Installed Height

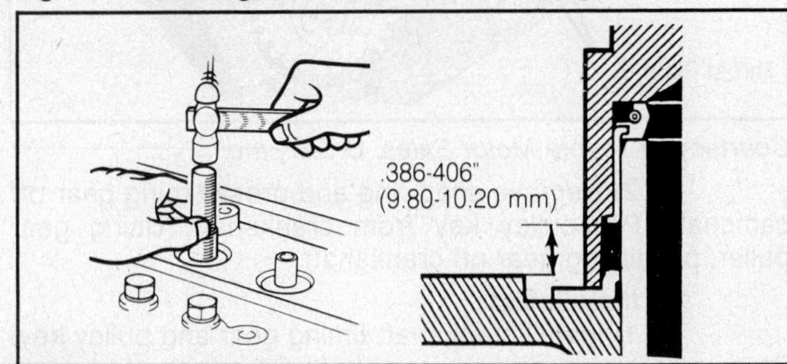

Courtesy of Toyota Motor Sales, U.S.A., Inc.

PISTONS, PINS & RINGS

OIL PAN

Removal

Remove engine undercovers. Remove flywheel sidecover and undercover. Remove front propeller shaft. Drain oil. Remove oil pan attaching bolts and oil pan.

Installation

Thoroughly clean all gasket mating surfaces. Apply liquid sealer onto both oil pan gasket surfaces. Install oil pan and tighten bolts. To install remaining components, reverse removal procedure.

PISTON & ROD ASSEMBLY

Removal

With cylinder head and oil pan removed, remove connecting rod caps and remove bearings. Remove ridge from top of cylinder. Push piston and rod assembly up through cylinder block. Mark all components for correct reassembly.

NOTE: **Cover rod bolts with a short piece of hose during removal and installation to prevent damage to crankshaft.**

Toyota Engines

4.2L 6-CYLINDER (Cont.)

Installation

1) Lubricate piston and rings. Position ring gaps. *See Fig. 7.* Use a ring compressor and install piston/rod assembly in proper position. Notch on piston must face FRONT and Toyota trademark on rod should face REAR.

2) Oil hole in rod faces right (camshaft) side. Install bearings and caps. Check for smooth rotation of crankshaft after tightening each bearing cap.

FITTING PISTONS

1) Measure cylinder bores at 90 degrees and parallel to crankshaft centerline. Also measure bores at top, center and bottom of piston travel.

2) If cylinder bore is worn beyond specification, cylinder must be bored and oversize pistons installed. Oversize pistons are available in .020", .040" and .060" (.50, 1.00 and 1.50 mm) sizes.

3) Measure piston with micrometer at bottom of skirt at right angles to piston pin. Standard piston diameter is 3.6992-3.7012" (93.96-94.01 mm). If worn beyond specification, replace piston.

CYLINDER BORE SPECIFICATIONS

Application	Wear Limits In. (mm)
Standard Bore	3.701-3.703 (94.00-94.05)
Bore Wear Limit	.008 (.20)
Taper	.0008 (.020)
Difference Between Cylinders	.002 (.05)

FITTING RINGS

1) Measure ring gaps in cylinder. If cylinder has not been bored, check gap with ring in lowest part of cylinder.

NOTE: Two types of rings are used: NP and Riken. Check PISTONS, PINS & RINGS table at end of article for ring gap specification.

2) Check clearance of piston ring in ring groove. If groove is worn beyond limit, replace piston. Install rings with marks facing upward.

PISTON PIN REPLACEMENT

Removal

Remove piston pin bolt and push piston pin from piston and connecting rod. Mark all parts for correct reassembly.

Inspection

1) Coat piston pin with engine oil. The piston pin should push into piston hole with thumb pressure.

2) Oil clearance limit between piston and piston pin is .0028" (.07 mm). If clearance is exceeded, replace piston and piston pin as a set .

3) Check connecting rod for bending or twisting. Bend limit per 3.94" (100 mm) is .002" (.05 mm). Twist limit per 3.94" (100 mm) is .006" (.15 mm).

Installation

1) Position piston and connecting rod so notch on top of piston faces forward and oil hole in connecting rod faces camshaft.

2) Push pin into assembly, and center pin in piston. Center connecting rod between piston pin bosses and tighten piston pin bolt.

Fig. 7: Spacing Piston Ring Gaps

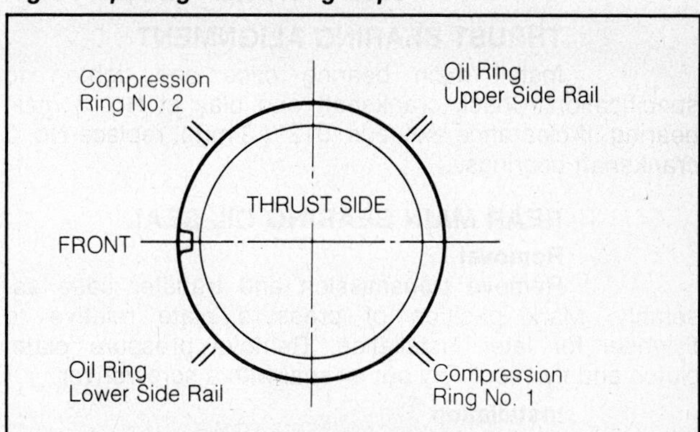

Courtesy of Toyota Motor Sales, U.S.A., Inc.

Fig. 8: Piston & Rod Assembly

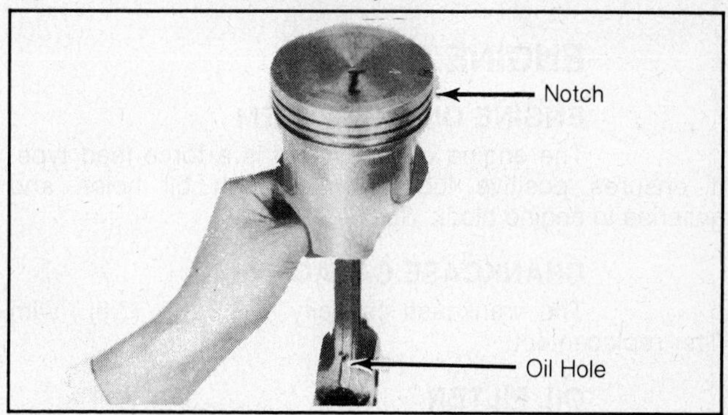

Courtesy of Toyota Motor Sales, U.S.A., Inc.

CRANKSHAFT & ROD BEARINGS

CRANKSHAFT MAIN BEARINGS

1) Check crankshaft for runout with a dial indicator on second or third main bearing journal. If runout exceeds .004" (.10 mm), replace crankshaft. If main bearing journal taper or out-of-round exceeds .0004" (.01 mm), grind crankshaft to next undersize.

2) Check main bearing oil clearance with Plastigage method. If clearance cannot be brought to specification by use of new standard size bearings, grind crankshaft to next undersize. Crankshaft bearings are available in .002", .010", and .020" (.05, .25, and .50 mm) undersizes.

NOTE: All main bearings are different. No. 1 (front) and No. 4 (rear) have oil holes and must be installed on block side. Arrow on connecting rod cap must face front.

CONNECTING ROD BEARINGS

1) Check connecting rod journals for wear, taper or out-of-round. The taper and out-of-round limit is .0004" (.01 mm). Grind crankshaft if worn beyond limit.

Toyota Engines

4.2L 6-CYLINDER (Cont.)

2) Check connecting rod oil clearance by Plastigage method. Grind crankshaft if new standard size bearings will not restore proper clearance. Undersize bearings are available in .002", .010", and .020" (.05, .25 and .50 mm).

THRUST BEARING ALIGNMENT

Install main bearing caps and tighten to specification. Check crankshaft end play at No. 3 main bearing. If clearance exceeds .012" (.3 mm), replace No. 3 crankshaft bearings.

REAR MAIN BEARING OIL SEAL

Removal

Remove transmission and transfer case assembly. Mark position of pressure plate relative to flywheel for later installation. Remove pressure plate, clutch and flywheel. Pry out oil seal with a screwdriver.

Installation

Use Seal Installer (09223-60010) to drive new seal into place. To complete installation, reverse removal procedure.

ENGINE OILING

ENGINE OILING SYSTEM

The engine oiling system is a force-feed type. It ensures positive lubrication through oil holes and galleries in engine block. *See Fig. 9.*

CRANKCASE CAPACITY

The crankcase capacity is 8.2 qts. (7.8L) with filter replacement.

OIL FILTER

The oil filter is a full-flow, cartridge-type with integral relief valve.

NORMAL OIL PRESSURE

The oil pressure is maintained at 50-64 psi (3.5-4.5 kg/cm²) by a safety valve in oil pressure regulator.

OIL PRESSURE REGULATOR VALVE

The oil pressure regulator valve is located in the oil pump and is nonadjustable.

OIL PUMP

Removal

With oil pan removed, remove bolts attaching oil strainer to crankcase. Remove oil pump mounting bolt and oil pump line. Remove pump from engine.

Disassembly

Remove oil pump cover, regulator valve plug and disassemble pump.

Inspection

Inspect all parts for wear or damage. Check regulator valve in valve bore for smooth operation. Install gears in housing and check for proper clearance.

Reassembly

1) To reassemble oil pump, reverse disassembly procedure. Ensure pump cover discharge hole faces toward pump body bolt hole.

Fig. 9: Engine Oiling System

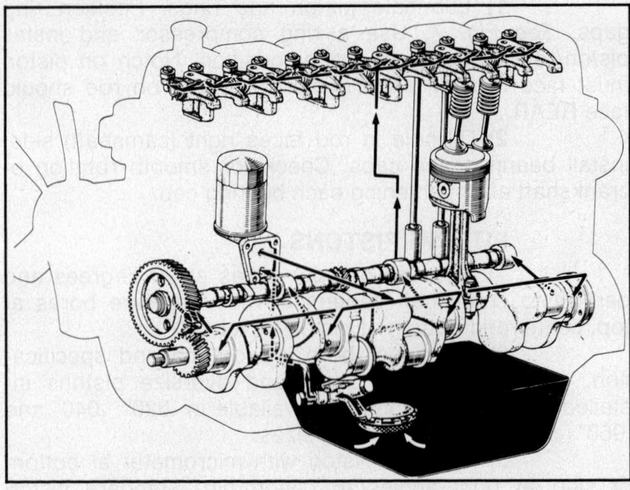

Courtesy of Toyota Motor Sales, U.S.A., Inc.

Fig. 10: Exploded View of Oil Pump Assembly

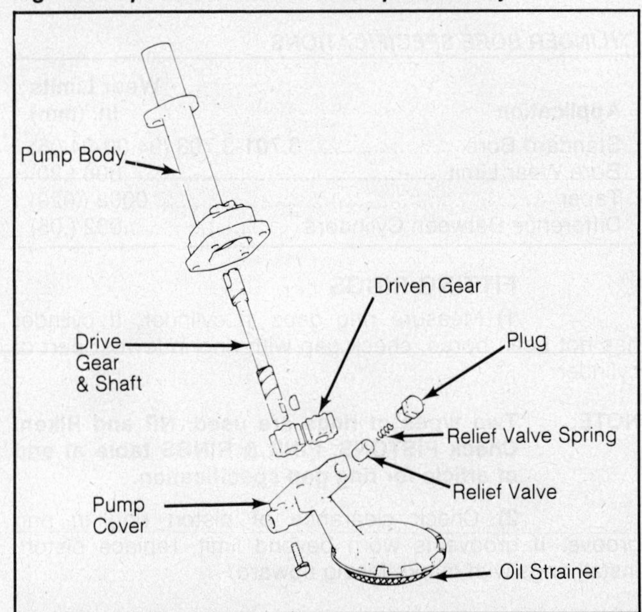

Courtesy of Toyota Motor Sales, U.S.A., Inc.

2) Check pump operation by submerging inlet line in fresh engine oil. Turn shaft clockwise with a screwdriver and check for oil flow from discharge hole. Cover discharge hole with thumb and turn shaft. Turning resistance should be felt.

OIL PUMP SPECIFICATIONS

Application	In. (mm)
Gear-to-Housing Clearance	
Standard	.0043-.0071 (.109-.180)
Wear Limit	.008 (.20)
Gear Backlash	
Standard	.020-.024 (.50-.60)
Wear Limit	.0375 (.952)
Gear Side Clearance	
Standard	.0012-.0035 (.030-.090)
Wear Limit	.0059 (.15)
Cover Wear	
Wear Limit	.0059 (.15)

Toyota Engines

4.2L 6-CYLINDER (Cont.)

Installation

Install pump on engine. Note lower end of distributor drive shaft aligns with oil pump shaft. To complete installation, reverse removal procedure.

ENGINE COOLING

WATER PUMP

Removal

Drain cooling system. Loosen alternator adjusting bar. Remove fan, fan pulley and fan belt. Remove lower radiator hose and heater hose from pump. Remove water pump retaining bolts, pump and gasket.

Disassembly

Remove rear plate and gasket. Press pulley seat off pump shaft. Heat pump housing to approximately 176°F (80°C). Press shaft and bearing assembly out through rear of housing. Press impeller off pump shaft and remove seal set. Inspect all parts for wear, cracks or damage.

Reassembly

1) Press bearing and shaft into pump housing. Apply liquid sealer to outside edge of seal set and press into pump housing.

2) Install packing and seal into impeller. Press impeller onto pump shaft. Impeller-to-housing clearance should be .03" (.75 mm).

3) Press pulley seat onto pump shaft to specified depth. Measure from front face of pulley seat to rear face of pump housing.

PULLEY SEAT INSTALLATION DEPTH

Type	Depth
Direct Drive	6.0" (152.3 mm)
Fan Clutch	4.6" (117.3 mm)

Installation

Ensure mating surface is clean and free from pitting or damage. Install pump with new gasket and tighten mounting bolts. To complete installation, reverse removal procedure. Adjust belt tension.

NOTE: **For more information, see ENGINE COOLING SYSTEMS article at the end of this section.**

TIGHTENING SPECIFICATIONS

Application	Ft. Lbs. (N.m)
Connecting Rod Bearing Caps	35-54 (48-73)
Crankshaft Main Bearing Caps	
No. 1 - No. 3	91-108 (124-147)
No. 4	76-94 (103-128)
Crankshaft Pulley Bolts	116-144 (158-196)
Cylinder Head Bolts	84-97 (114-132)
Flywheel Bolts	58-79 (79-107)
Manifold Nuts	29-36 (39-49)
Piston Pin Bolt	40-50 (54-68)
Rocker Arm-to-Cyl. Head	
8 mm Bolt	15-21 (20-29)
10 mm Bolt	22-32 (30-44)
	INCH Lbs.
Camshaft Thrust Plate Bolts	96-132 (11-15)

ENGINE SPECIFICATIONS

GENERAL SPECIFICATIONS

Year	DISPLACEMENT		Fuel System	HP@RPM	Torque Ft. Lbs.@RPM	Compr. Ratio	BORE		STROKE	
	Cu. In.	Liters					In.	mm	In.	mm
1987	257.9	4.2	2-Bbl.	125@3600	271@1800	8.3:1	3.70	94	4.00	101.6

VALVES

Engine Size & Valve	Head Diam. In. (mm)	Face Angle	Seat Angle	Seat Width In. (mm)	Stem Diameter In. (mm)	Stem Clearance In. (mm)	Valve Lift In. (mm)
4.2L [1]							
Intake	1.81 (46.0)	45.5°	45°	.055 (1.40)	.3138-.3144 (7.970-7.985)	.0012-.0024 (.030-.060)	.....
Exhaust	1.48 (37.5)	45.5°	45°	.067 (1.70)	.3134-.3140 (7.960-7.975)	.0016-.0028 (.040-.071)	.....

[1] - Maximum clearance for intake guides is .004" (.10 mm) and .005" (.12 mm) for exhaust.

Toyota Engines

4.2L 6-CYLINDER (Cont.)

ENGINE SPECIFICATIONS (Cont.)

PISTONS, PINS, RINGS

Engine	PISTONS Clearance In. (mm)	PINS Piston Fit In. (mm)	PINS Rod Fit In. (mm)	RINGS Ring No.	RINGS End Gap In. (mm)	RINGS Side Clearance In. (mm)
4.2L	.0012-.0020 (.030-.050)	.0003-.0005 (.008-.012)	Locked in Rod	No. 1	.0079-.0157 (.200-.400)	.0012-.0028 (.030-.071)
				No.2	.0079-.0157 (.200-.400)	.0008-.0024 (.020-.060)
				Oil (NP)	.0079-.0197 (.200-.500)	.0016-.0075 (.040-.190)
				Oil (Riken)	.0118-.0354 (.300-.900)	.0016-.0075 (.040-.190)

CRANKSHAFT MAIN & CONNECTING ROD BEARINGS

Engine	MAIN BEARINGS Journal Diam. In. (mm)	MAIN BEARINGS Clearance In. (mm)	MAIN BEARINGS Thrust Bearing	MAIN BEARINGS Crankshaft End Play In. (mm)	CONNECTING ROD BEARINGS Journal Diam. In. (mm)	CONNECTING ROD BEARINGS Clearance In. (mm)	CONNECTING ROD BEARINGS Side Play In. (mm)
4.2L							
No. 1	2.6367-2.6376 (66.972-66.996)	.0008-.0017 (.020-.044)	No. 3	.002-.006 (.06-.15)	2.1252-2.1260 (53.98-54.00)	.0008-.0024 (.020-.060)	.003-.009 (.08-.23)
No. 2	2.6957-2.6967 (68.472-68.496)						
No. 3	2.7548-2.7557 (69.972-69.996)						
No. 4	2.8139-2.8148 (71.472-71.496)						

VALVE SPRINGS

Engine	Free Length In. (mm)	PRESSURE Lbs. @ In. (Kg @ mm) Valve Closed	PRESSURE Lbs. @ In. (Kg @ mm) Valve Open
4.2L	2.028 (51.5)	71@1.693 (32.5@43.0)	.....

CAMSHAFT

Engine	Journal Diam. In. (mm)	Clearance In. (mm)	Lobe Lift In. (mm)
4.2L			
No. 1	1.8810-1.8888 (47.777-47.975)	.001-.003 (.025-.075)	.....
No. 2	1.8289-1.8297 (46.455-46.475)		
No. 3	1.7699-1.7707 (44.955-44.975)		
No. 4	1.7108-1.7116 (43.455-43.475)		

Volkswagen Engines

2.1L OPPOSED 4-CYLINDER

Vanagon, Vanagon Syncro

ENGINE CODING

ENGINE IDENTIFICATION

Engine number is stamped on right crankcase below breather. This horizontally-opposed 4-cylinder engine is water-cooled.

ENGINE IDENTIFICATION CODE

Application	Code
2.1L	MV

ENGINE, MANIFOLDS & CYLINDER HEAD

ENGINE

Removal

1) Disconnect negative battery cable. Remove air cleaner with airflow sensor and air intake duct. Disconnect wires from alternator. Disconnect wiring from fuel injectors, throttle valve switch and auxiliary air regulator.

2) Disconnect 2 vacuum hoses from charcoal filter valve. Disconnect and plug fuel return line at pressure regulator and fuel line from fuel pump at "T" fitting. Remove throttle cable from throttle valve lever. On automatic transaxle models, remove snap ring and spring from throttle rod.

3) On all models, mark and disconnect coil lead and wiring plug at distributor, wiring at oxygen sensor, oil pressure switch, temperature sensor and temperature sender. Disconnect wiring to coolant level warning switch, located in expansion tank. Mark and disconnect ground leads on top left side of crankcase.

4) Clamp off both radiator hoses at thermostat housing. Clamp off both heater hoses at right rear side of engine compartment. Open expansion tank cap. Remove drain plugs at bottom of cylinder heads and drain coolant. Disconnect coolant hoses from expansion tank at engine end. Remove expansion tank.

5) Disconnect brake booster vacuum line at check valve. Remove 2 upper bolts and nuts that hold engine to transaxle. On models with automatic transaxle, remove 3 bolts that attach torque converter to drive plate. These bolts are reached through hole on top of transaxle housing.

6) On automatic transaxle models, remove rod from kickdown lever. On all models, disconnect wiring at starter. On models with power steering, remove power steering pump with hoses attached. Secure pump in engine compartment. On models with A/C, remove compressor with hoses attached. Secure compressor in engine compartment.

7) Remove plates from left and right side of engine. Remove bolts from rear cover plate located at muffler and leave plate in place. On Vanagon Syncro, remove skid plate under engine and transaxle. On all models, loosen transaxle mount bolts for front bracket 3 turns. Loosen lower transaxle mount bolt.

8) Attach Support Bar (VW 785/1B) so support pad is about 4.75" (120.0 mm) below transaxle housing. Support engine with Jack Adapter (US 612/5) and transmission jack. Remove 4 bolts retaining engine carrier at frame. While lowering, adjust angle of engine and keep wiring out of way of oil filler tube.

9) Lower engine/transaxle assembly until transaxle rests on support bar. Remove 2 lower nuts that hold engine to transaxle. Separate engine from transaxle. Remove engine from vehicle. On automatic transaxle models, secure torque converter in transaxle.

Installation

1) On Vanagon Syncro, clean mating surface of engine and transaxle. Lightly coat surfaces with Silicone Adhesive Seal (AMV 176 005 05). Lubricate clutch release bearing and main shaft splines with Grease (MoS_2). DO NOT lubricate release bearing guide sleeve.

2) On all models, check release bearing and replace if necessary. Replace all self-locking nuts. Replace coolant drain plug gaskets. To install, reverse removal procedure. Check and adjust throttle cables and linkage. Fill and bleed cooling system. See WATER PUMP under ENGINE COOLING in this article.

Fig. 1: Exploded View of Engine Components

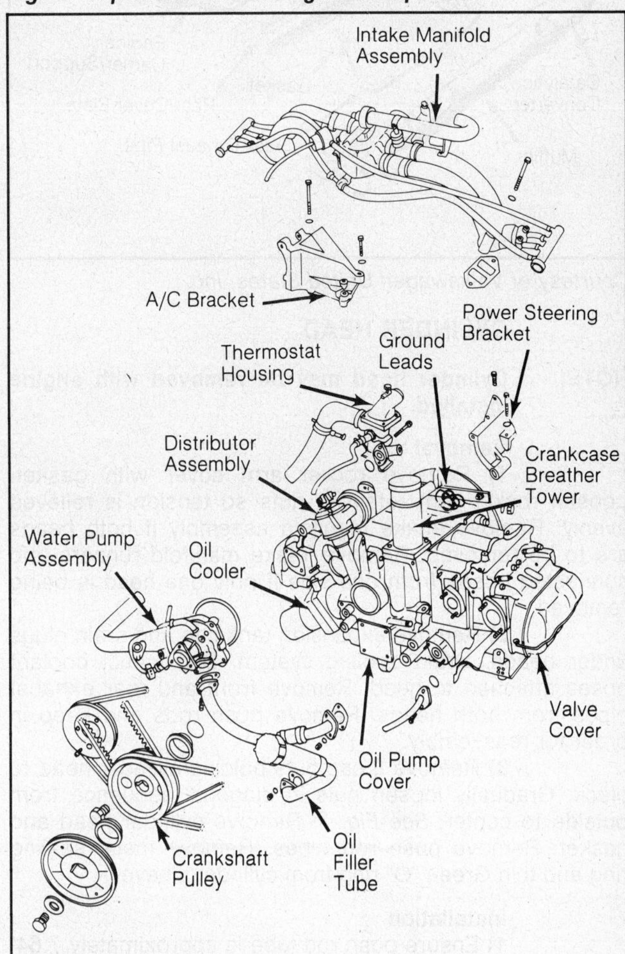

Courtesy of Volkswagen United States, Inc.

INTAKE MANIFOLD

Removal & Installation

Procedures for removal and installation are not available. Remove intake manifold and throttle valve as an assembly. *See Fig. 1.* Replace all gaskets at installation. See WATER PUMP under ENGINE COOLING in this article.

Volkswagen Engines

2.1L OPPOSED 4-CYLINDER (Cont.)

EXHAUST MANIFOLDS

Removal & Installation

Procedures for removal and installation were not available. *See Fig. 2.* Replace all gaskets at installation. Ensure metal surface of gaskets face cylinder head. Ensure all gasket mating surfaces are clean and smooth. Bleed cooling system.

Fig. 2: Exploded View of Exhaust Components

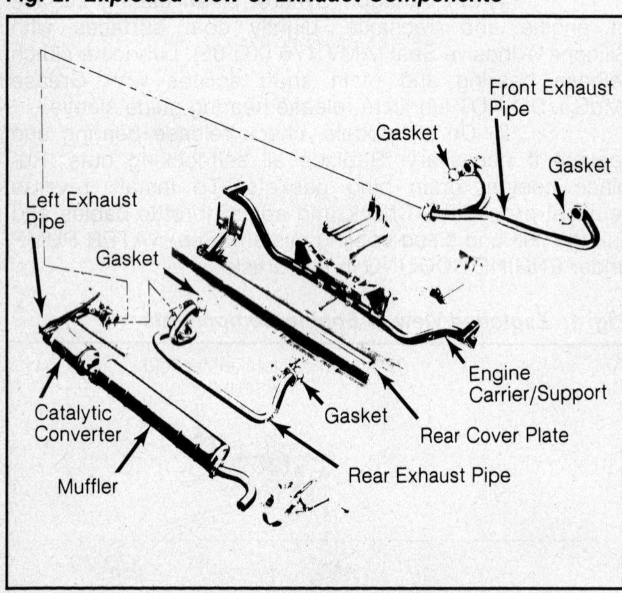

Courtesy of Volkswagen United States, Inc.

CYLINDER HEAD

NOTE: Cylinder head may be removed with engine installed.

Removal

1) Remove rocker arm cover with gasket. Loosen rocker arm retaining nuts so tension is relieved evenly. Remove intake manifold assembly if both heads are to be removed. Remove intake manifold runners and connected hoses from one side if only one head is being removed.

2) Remove expansion tank cap and drain plugs under heads. Drain cooling system. Disconnect coolant hoses attached to head. Remove front and rear exhaust pipes from both heads. Remove push rods and keep in order for reassembly.

3) Remove 8 cap nuts holding cylinder head to block. Gradually loosen nuts in diagonal sequence from outside to center. *See Fig. 3.* Remove cylinder head and gasket. Remove push rod tubes. Remove metal sealing ring and thin Green "O" ring from cylinder sleeve.

Installation

1) Ensure push rod tube is approximately 7.64" (194.0 mm), between inside edges of tube sealing "O" rings. *See Fig. 4.* Seam of tube faces upward and small end of tube is toward cylinder head. Always use new sealing rings and thoroughly clean mating surfaces.

2) Clean cylinder head sealing surface with solvent. Install new thin Green "O" ring and metal gasket on cylinder sleeves. Apply Sealing Compound (VW No. D 000 400) to center of new water jacket gasket. DO NOT use excessive sealant as cylinder head cooling passages may become plugged.

Fig. 3: Cylinder Head Nut Tightening Sequence

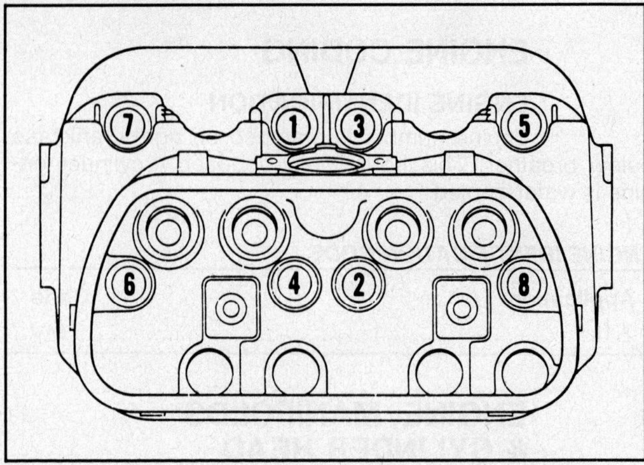

Courtesy of Volkswagen United States, Inc.

3) Coat sealing face of cap nuts with waterproof compound. Install and snug cap nut at No. 1 stud enough to install remaining cap nuts. Tighten cap nuts to first stage of 84 INCH lbs. (10 N.m) in sequence shown. *See Fig. 3.* Make sure push rod tubes are correctly seated.

4) Tighten cap nuts to final setting of 33 ft. lbs. (45 N.m). Install push rods, making sure that push rods fit into cups of lifters. Install rocker assembly with slots facing upward on shaft supports. Adjust hydraulic lifters after nuts attaching rocker assembly to head are tight. Install rocker cover with new gasket.

5) Install remaining parts in reverse order of removal. Use new exhaust flange gaskets with metal surface toward head. Always use new locking nuts. Use new gaskets on drain plugs. Fill and bleed cooling system. See WATER PUMP under ENGINE COOLING in this article.

Fig. 4: Push Rod Tube Length

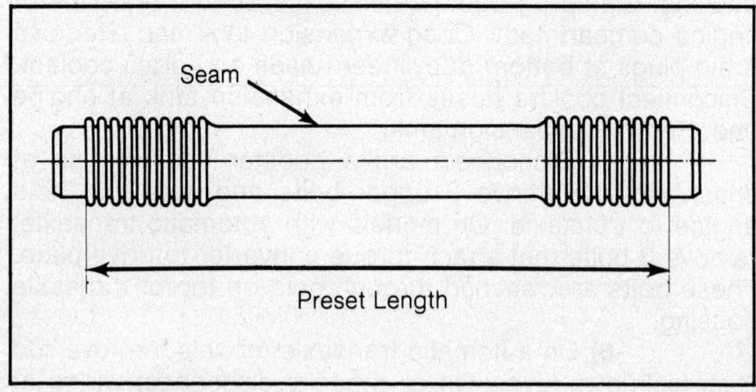

Courtesy of Volkswagen United States, Inc.

VALVES

VALVE ARRANGEMENT

E-I-I-E (Both heads).

VALVE SEATS

NOTE: DO NOT machine exhaust valves. They MUST be lapped into seats by hand.

2.1L OPPOSED 4-CYLINDER (Cont.)

If valves are to be reused, dimensions must be checked. Minimum length from stem tip to face is 4.823" (122.50 mm). Valve margin must not be less than .02" (.5 mm). See ENGINE SPECIFICATIONS tables at end of this article. Leak test all valves with solvent after reassembled in head.

VALVE LIFTERS

NOTE: **Intermittent lifter noise is considered normal after starting, during sudden acceleration, at high temperatures or at high engine speed.**

Removal

Remove rocker arm covers. Remove rocker arm shaft assembly. Remove push rods. Remove lower cover plate. Remove push rod tube with pliers or screwdriver. Remove lifters with magnet or lifter extractor. Keep lifters in order of removal to ensure reassembly to original location.

Inspection

1) If metal particles are found in engine oil, remove, disassemble and clean lifters. If damaged or worn, lifter MUST be replaced. Check camshaft lobes through lifter bore. Ensure lifter moves freely in bore.

2) Check and bleed lifters before installing. Apply firm thumb pressure to push rod socket. Push rod socket should NOT move. If socket moves, remove lock ring. Remove push rod socket, plunger, check ball, spring, check valve retainer and plunger spring.

3) Fill valve body bore with oil up to bleed hole. Insert plunger spring, check valve retainer, check valve spring, ball and plunger. Push downward on plunger and at the same time open ball check valve with scribe.

4) Place push rod socket into position. Use a valve guide to help compress lifter and place assembly horizontally in vise, bleeder hole facing up. Slowly tighten vise and compress lifter. Install lock ring. Recheck lifter.

CAUTION: **Failure to install lifters in same location will cause premature camshaft failure.**

Installation & Adjustment

1) Lightly oil lifter body and slide into lifter bore. Replace push rod tube sealing rings at each end. Compress push rod tube and position in cylinder block with seam facing upward. Small end of tube must be toward cylinder head.

2) Release push rod tube and allow it to expand into position. Ensure tube seats properly. Install push rods and ensure push rods are seated in lifter, not on lifter edge.

3) Install rocker arm shaft assembly. Tighten nuts evenly. Hydraulic valve lifters must be adjusted whenever rocker arm shafts have been removed and installed. Loosen lock nut. Back out adjusting screw until ball shaped end is flush with rocker arm surface.

4) Place No. 1 cylinder at TDC on compression stroke. Distributor rotor will align with mark on distributor housing. Adjust No. 1 cylinder by turning adjusting screws until contact with valve stem. Turn adjusting screw clockwise 2 turns and tighten lock nuts.

5) Rotate crankshaft 180 degrees. Use firing order and repeat procedure. Repeat until all have been adjusted. Install rocker arm cover with new gasket. Start engine and let idle until no lifter or valve noise is heard. Idle should be smooth and engine should have oil pressure.

VALVE GUIDES

NOTE: **Minor cracks between valve seats or between seat and spark plug thread are acceptable. Cracks may not exceed .019" (.50 mm) in width. Cracks may not extend beyond first coil of plug thread.**

1) Clean carbon from seats and port areas around guides. Measure clearance of valve stem-to-guide with dial indicator pointer on head of valve. Rock valve back and forth and note reading. Maximum clearance is .047" (1.20 mm). If guides are to be replaced, mount head securely with combustion chambers down.

2) Use step drill to remove shoulder of valve guide. Be careful to avoid cutting head or valve guide boss. Remove remaining guide with drift from top side, toward combustion chamber side. Coat new guide with oil and install with drift, from side opposite combustion chamber. Using cutting oil, ream guides to fit valves.

Removal

1) Valve springs may be removed with head installed or removed. If head is installed, apply air pressure to cylinder through spark plug hole to hold valves closed.

2) Compress spring retainer and springs. Remove keepers and release compressor. Remove retainer and both inner and outer springs. Make sure springs are not cracking and are of equal length.

Installation

Install inner and outer springs over valve stem. Install compressor and retainer. Compress retainer and springs. Install keepers, making sure that keepers fit properly in grooves of valve stem. Release compressor and remove air pressure if used.

ROCKER ARM ASSEMBLY

NOTE: **Hydraulic valve lifters must be adjusted whenever rocker shafts have been removed and installed.**

Removal & Installation

Remove rocker arm cover and gasket. Gradually remove 2 nuts holding rocker arm shaft assembly on head. Check adjusting screw surfaces for wear or damage. Make sure threads of adjusting screws and lock nuts move freely. To install, reverse removal procedure. Adjust lifters. See VALVE LIFTERS under VALVES in this article.

PISTONS, PINS & RINGS

PISTON & CYLINDER SLEEVE

Removal

1) With cylinder heads removed, mark pistons and cylinder sleeves with matching numbers. Note cylinder sleeve position for installation reference. Mark piston in relation to flywheel direction. Place piston at TDC.

2) Using slide hammer and Clamping Puller (3092), pull out sleeve until piston pin circlip is visible through hole in housing. Remove piston pin circlip. *See Fig. 5.*

3) Using Piston Pin Puller/Installer (3091), remove piston pin. If piston pin cannot be pulled out, use Reamer (3159) and remove burr in piston pin bore. Remove piston and cylinder sleeve.

Volkswagen Engines

2.1L OPPOSED 4-CYLINDER (Cont.)

4) Piston and sleeve at pulley end of crankshaft must be removed before removing piston and sleeve at flywheel end. Remove rubber sealing rings from cylinder sleeve. Clean all scale deposits and sealing compound from cylinder head and crankcase surfaces.

Fig. 5: Exploded View of Cylinder/Piston Assembly

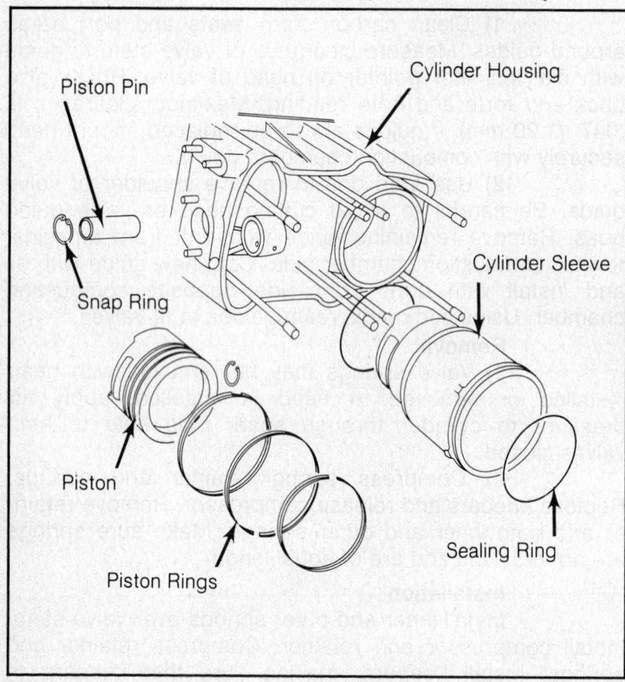

Installation

1) Install new sealing rings on sleeve. Thick Black ring is inner and thin Green ring is outer. Piston and sleeve assemblies at flywheel end of crankshaft must be installed first. Align all marks made and noted at removal.

2) Install piston in cylinder sleeve. Install piston pin circlip on flywheel side of piston. Place installing piston cylinder on TDC. Center connecting rod with Support (3090) and hold support position with rubber band.

3) Align connecting rod and piston. Install piston pin through access hole in housing with puller/installer. Install piston pin circlip. Make sure piston and rod move freely on pin. Push cylinder sleeve in until it bottoms out. To complete installation, reverse removal procedure.

FITTING PISTONS

1) Measure piston diameter at bottom of skirt, approximately .563" (15.10 mm) from edge and 90 degrees from pin bore. Measure inside diameter of cylinder sleeve .375-.625" (9.53-15.88 mm) from top of sleeve. Subtract cylinder sleeve reading from piston reading. See ENGINE SPECIFICATIONS tables at end of article.

2) Measure piston recess depth from top edge of crown to bottom of recess in crown. On Vanagon Syncro, measurement should be .610" (15.50 mm) and .458" (11.65 mm) on all other models. Replace piston and/or cylinder sleeve as necessary. Arrow on piston top faces flywheel end.

3) Size, weight and installation direction are marked on crown of piston. Weight group is indicated by "+" or "-" mark. Pistons marked "+", weigh 16.12-16.37 ozs. (457-464 g). Pistons marked "-", weigh 15.80-16.08 ozs. (448-456 g).

Fig. 6: Installing Piston Rings

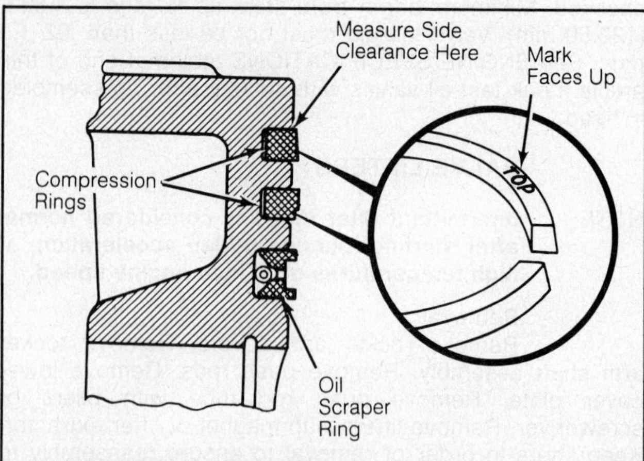

Courtesy of Volkswagen United States, Inc.

FITTING RINGS

1) Insert piston ring squarely into cylinder sleeve approximately .188" (4.76 mm) from bottom end. Use a feeler gauge and measure end clearance. See ENGINE SPECIFICATIONS tables at end of this article. If not within specifications, replace as necessary.

2) Install rings on piston with "TOP" mark facing piston crown. *See Fig. 6.* Use feeler gauge and measure side clearance between ring and piston. If not within specifications, replace rings and/or pistons. See ENGINE SPECIFICATIONS tables at end of this article.

CRANKCASE, CRANKSHAFT & CAMSHAFT

CRANKCASE

Disassembly

1) Remove engine from vehicle and place on engine stand. Remove manifolds, cylinder heads, pistons and cylinder sleeves. Note directional arrows on carrier and remove engine carrier assembly.

2) Mark pressure plate position for installation reference and remove pressure plate and clutch disc. Remove flywheel or flex plate. Remove crankcase breather tower. Remove distributor assembly. Index distributor drive shaft gear, to ensure installation to exact position.

3) Using Shaft Remover/Installer (VW 228b), pull drive shaft gear from cylinder block. Remove 2 shims located at bottom end of shaft gear and retain for installation. Remove water pump assembly. Remove thermostat housing. Remove oil filter and cooler. Pry out front and rear crankshaft seals.

4) Remove oil filler tube. Remove oil pump cover and gears. Using Puller (VW 201), remove oil pump housing and gasket. Remove lifters if not previously removed. Keep lifters in a marked order for installation. Remove nuts retaining case halves together.

5) Separate case halves. Use a rubber mallet if necessary. DO NOT use pry bars or levers between case halves. Oil leaks will occur even if no other damage is done. Lift camshaft from case. Remove crankshaft and connecting rods as an assembly. *See Fig. 7.*

6) If bearings are to be reused, mark them and remove from crankcase halves. Remove main bearing locating dowels. Remove metal camshaft plug.

2.1L OPPOSED 4-CYLINDER (Cont.)

Inspection

NOTE: Use only Sealant (AMV 188 000 02) on crankcase half mating surfaces.

Thoroughly clean all sealing compound from bolts, nuts and washers. If a Brownish color sealant is noticed on crankcase half mating surfaces thoroughly clean surfaces. If previously sealed with Sealant (AMV 188 000 02), clean only excess. Blow out all oil galleys with compressed air. Ensure studs are tight.

Reassembly

1) Ensure bearing locating dowels fit snug in case. Install main bearing and camshaft bearings in crankcases. Lubricate bearings with engine oil. Lay crankshaft and connecting rods into left case half. Properly align main bearings and locating dowels.

2) Install camshaft with "O" mark between marks on crankshaft gear. Check backlash of timing gears. Rotate crankshaft backward. If camshaft lifts out of bearing, install a smaller camshaft gear. Size of camshaft gear is marked on inner side of gear. Various sizes are available to acquire proper backlash. Coat edge of camshaft plug with sealant and install.

3) Install rear thrust washer with projection on thrust washer toward main bearing and separating line of crankcase. Projection on main bearing will fit in notches in crankcase. Oil holes must be in left half of crankcase. *See Fig. 8.*

4) Apply a thin layer of Sealant (AMV 188 000 02) to mating surfaces of both crankcase halves. Place right half of case over through studs and compress case halves together. Coat both sides of washers and face of cap nuts with Sealant (D3).

5) Tighten 8 mm nut above and behind No. 1 exhaust lifter bore first. Tighten all 10 mm nuts and then tighten all remaining 8 mm nuts. Place No. 1 cylinder on TDC. Install distributor drive gear with Shaft Remover/Installer (VW 228b). Ensure drive gear is in exact position as marked at removal.

6) Install remaining components in reverse procedure. Tighten all bolts/nuts to specifications. Fill fluid levels. Bleed cooling system. See WATER PUMP under ENGINE COOLING in this article.

CRANKSHAFT & ROD BEARINGS

Disassembly

1) Remove crankshaft and rods as assembly. Mark rod and rod caps with matching cylinder number. Note position of rod to ensure installation to original position. Remove rod cap nuts and discard nuts. Remove rod and cap.

2) Note position of rod bearing and remove bearing. Keep rod bearing with rod from which it was removed. Repeat procedure for remaining rods to be removed. If replacing rods, they must be replaced as a complete set of 4.

Fig. 7: Exploded View of Crankcase Assembly

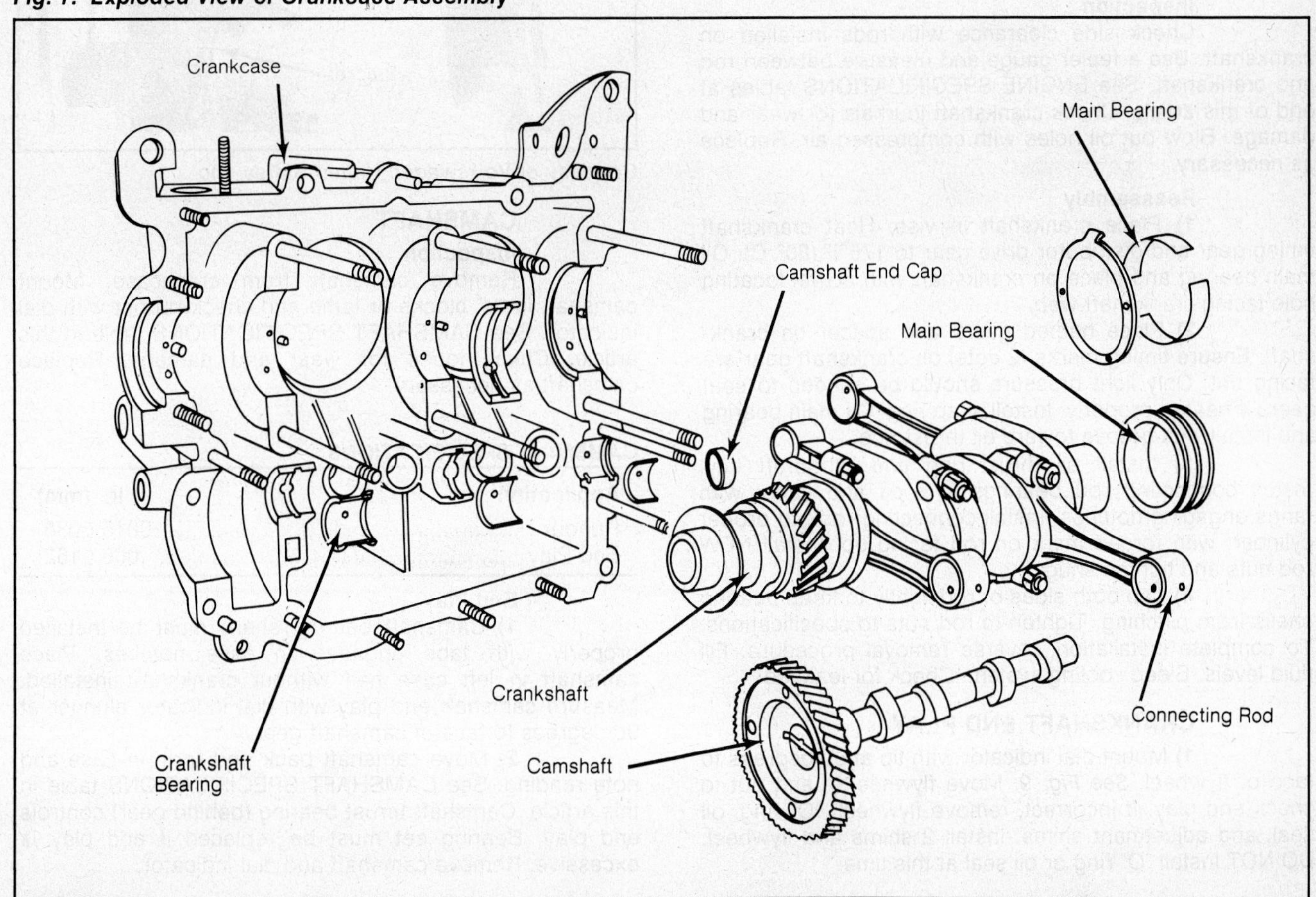

Courtesy of Volkswagen United States, Inc.

Volkswagen Engines

2.1L OPPOSED 4-CYLINDER (Cont.)

Fig. 8: Thrust Washer & Main Bearing Installation

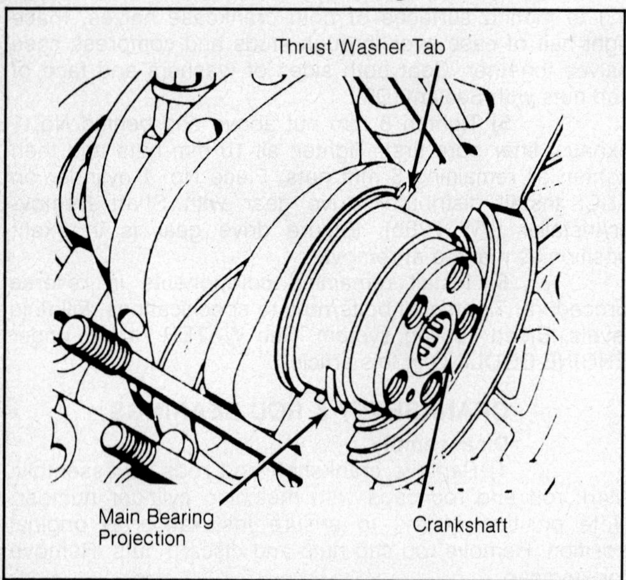

Courtesy of Volkswagen United States, Inc.

3) Note color mark(s) on crankshaft. Main bearings must be color coded the same. Remove Woodruff key and snap ring from crankshaft. Place assembly in press. Using Plate (VW 402), press off crankshaft timing gear and distributor drive gear.

Inspection

Check side clearance with rods installed on crankshaft. Use a feeler gauge and measure between rod and crankshaft. See ENGINE SPECIFICATIONS tables at end of this article. Check crankshaft journals for wear and damage. Blow out oil holes with compressed air. Replace as necessary.

Reassembly

1) Place crankshaft in vise. Heat crankshaft timing gear and distributor drive gear to 175°F (80° C). Oil main bearing and place on crankshaft with dowel locating hole facing crankshaft web.

2) Place heated gears and spacer on crankshaft. Ensure timing marks (2 dots) on crankshaft gear are facing out. Only light pressure should be needed to seat gears if heated properly. Install snap ring. Oil main bearing and install with groove toward oil thrust ring.

3) Install oil thrust ring and Woodruff key. Install connecting rod bearings in rods and caps, with tangs engaging notches. Install connecting rods to proper cylinder, with forged mark on rod facing up. Install NEW rod nuts and tighten snug.

4) Tap both sides of rod lightly to keep bearing shells from pinching. Tighten to rod nuts to specifications. To complete installation, reverse removal procedure. Fill fluid levels. Bleed cooling system. Check for leakage.

CRANKSHAFT END PLAY

1) Mount dial indicator with tip at 90 degrees to face of flywheel. *See Fig. 9.* Move flywheel in and out to check end play. If incorrect, remove flywheel, "O" ring, oil seal, and adjustment shims. Install 2 shims and flywheel. DO NOT install "O" ring or oil seal at this time.

NOTE: **Always use 3 shims to set or correct crankshaft end play.**

2) Repeat step **1)**. To determine thickness of third shim, take dial indicator reading and subtract desired end play. Value obtained is thickness of third shim. See EXAMPLE below. Install adjustment shims, "O" ring, seal, and flywheel. Tighten flywheel bolts and recheck crankshaft end play.

EXAMPLE:

Dial Indicator Reading	*.017" (.44 mm)*
Minus (Desired End Play)	*.004" (.10 mm)*
Thickness of Third Shim	*.013" (.34 mm)*

Fig. 9: Measuring & Adjusting Crankshaft End Play

Courtesy of Volkswagen United States, Inc.

CAMSHAFT

Inspection

Remove camshaft from crankcase. Mount camshaft in "V" blocks or lathe and check runout with dial indicator. See CAMSHAFT SPECIFICATIONS table in this article. Check lobes for wear and damage. Replace camshaft as necessary.

CAMSHAFT SPECIFICATIONS

Application	In. (mm)
Runout	.0015 (.038)
End Play	.006 (.162)

End Play

1) Camshaft bearing shells must be installed properly with tabs engaged in case notches. Place camshaft in left case half without crankshaft installed. Measure camshaft end play with dial indicator plunger at 90 degrees to face of camshaft gear.

2) Move camshaft back and forth in case and note reading. See CAMSHAFT SPECIFICATIONS table in this article. Camshaft thrust bearing (behind gear) controls end play. Bearing set must be replaced if end play is excessive. Remove camshaft and dial indicator.

Volkswagen Engines

2.1L OPPOSED 4-CYLINDER (Cont.)

REAR MAIN BEARING OIL SEAL

Removal & Installation

1) Remove flywheel or flex plate and pry out seal. Take care not to damage engine crankcase while prying out seal. Clean seating area for seal. Remove "O" ring from inside lip of flywheel. Check pilot bearing felt ring for damage.

2) Lightly oil lips of new flywheel seal and install on Seal Installer Guide (VW 191A). Attach Seal Installer Base (VW 191B) to crankshaft. Press seal and guide in until seal seats. Install lightly lubed new "O" ring into flywheel. Install flywheel.

FRONT CRANKSHAFT OIL SEAL

Removal

1) If single "V" belt type pulley is used, remove drive belt. Hold flywheel/drive plate through hole in crankcase while loosening or tightening pulley bolt. Pry out seal being careful not to damage crankcase.

2) If triple "V" belt type pulley is used, loosen A/C compressor or power steering pump (if equipped). Remove drive belts from crankshaft pulley. Loosen alternator and remove drive belt.

3) Remove coolant expansion tank and set aside. Remove screws and bolts from exhaust heat shield. Move heat shield down and away from installed position. Rotate pulley until alignment holes are horizontal.

4) Insert Alignment Plate (3149) into pulley. *See Fig. 10.* Place Pad (3149) across engine mounts with tabs pointing upward. Remove crankshaft pulley bolt and pulley. Pry out seal being careful not to damage crankcase.

Fig. 10: Removing Triple "V" Belt Type Pulley

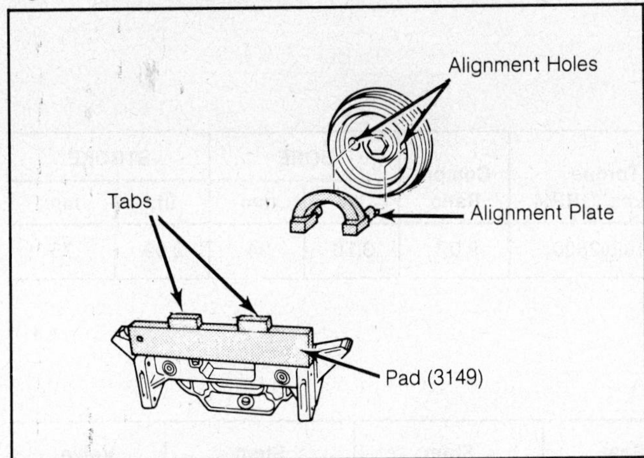

Courtesy of Volkswagen United States, Inc.

Installation

1) To install new seal on single pulley engine, coat seal lips with oil. Use Seal Installer (3088) and pulley bolt without washer to start seal into case. When seal is started, remove bolt and put washer on bolt. Tighten bolt with washer until stop is reached.

NOTE: On Vanagon Syncro, Seal Installer (3162) must be used.

2) On engine with triple pulley, coat seal lips with oil. Install with Seal Installer (3088) and bolt without washer. Tighten bolt until stop is reached. Reverse removal procedure to install pulley.

ENGINE OILING

ENGINE OILING SYSTEM

Gear-type oil pump at front of engine is driven by camshaft. Oil flows under full pressure from pump to filter to main bearing journals through oil galleys in crankcase casting. Crankshaft is cross-drilled to provide oil to connecting rod journals. Oil filter is connected to an oil cooler.

Oil galleys bring full pressure to camshaft journals and hydraulic valve lifters. Oil flows through hollow push rods to lubricate rocker arm assembly. Splash oil lubricates valve stems. Excess oil returns to crankcase through push rod tubes. Cylinder walls and piston pins are splash lubricated.

OIL CAPACITY

Oil capacity without filter is 4.2 qts. (4.0L). Oil capacity with filter is 4.7 qts. (4.5L).

OIL PRESSURE

Minimum oil pressure should be 29 psi (2 kg/cm²) at 2000 RPM with oil temperature of 176°F (80°C). Oil pressure warning light should go out at pressure of 2-6.5 psi (.15-.45 kg/cm²). Spring-loaded pressure relief valve opens when oil pressure becomes excessive.

OIL PUMP

Removal

Remove engine. Remove exhaust and engine carrier. Remove oil pump cover with 4 sealing nuts. Remove gears from pump housing. Install Puller (VW 201) and remove pump housing.

Inspection

1) Check pump housing for scoring. Ensure post for driven gear is tight in pump housing. Check lug of drive gear for excessive wear. Ensure machine surface of pump cover is smooth and flat.

2) Place gears in pump housing. Place straightedge across pump body and face of gears. Measure end play of gears to straightedge with feeler gauge. Maximum end play is .004" (.10 mm).

Installation

1) Lightly coat THICK oil pump housing gasket with sealer. Place over studs against crankcase. Carefully tap pump housing into crankcase with soft mallet. Ensure to align studs and pump housing. Avoid tearing gasket edge.

2) Place drive gear in pump housing and rotate until lug fits into groove on face of camshaft. Install driven gear, rotating crankshaft slightly to align gear teeth. Install dry THIN oil pump cover gasket over studs.

3) Place pump cover plate on studs. Tighten new sealing nuts in diagonal pattern. Sealing ring of nut faces oil pump cover. To complete installation, reverse removal procedure. Ensure proper oil pressure is present, after starting.

Volkswagen Engines

2.1L OPPOSED 4-CYLINDER (Cont.)

ENGINE COOLING

WATER PUMP

Removal

Remove expansion tank cap. Drain coolant at drain plugs on bottom of cylinder heads. Remove drive belt(s). Disconnect all hoses to water pump and thermostat housings. Remove water pump and thermostat housing as an assembly.

Installation

1) Clean all sealing surfaces and replace gaskets. Install water pump and thermostat housing assembly. Tighten bolts and nuts. Attach hoses and tighten clamps. Install drive belt and adjust so belt deflects .375-.563" (9.53-14.29 mm) with thumb pressure.

2) Fill and bleed cooling system. Set heater control valve to maximum heat. Open control valve for auxiliary heater under rear seat (if equipped). Remove radiator grille and raise front of vehicle about 16". Open bleeder screw on upper right corner of radiator.

3) Open bleeder valve in engine compartment (turn counterclockwise). Start filling expansion tank until full. Start and run engine at 2000 RPM. Keep topping tank until coolant flows from bleeder screw on radiator without any air bubbles. Add coolant until tank is full and install cap on tank.

4) Turn engine off and restart after 20 seconds. Open expansion tank cap with engine running at 2000 RPM. Close bleeder screw on radiator when coolant is flowing out. Add coolant to expansion tank until full and close tank tightly.

5) Close bleeder valve in engine compartment. Switch engine off. Top off refill tank to maximum mark. Attach pressure tester to expansion tank and run engine until cooling fan has cycled. After checking for leaks, remove tester. Tighten cap on expansion tank.

NOTE: **For further information on cooling systems, see ENGINE COOLING section.**

TIGHTENING SPECIFICATIONS

Application	Ft. Lbs. (N.m)
Connecting Rod Nuts	33 (45)
Coolant Pipe-to-Cylinder Head Nuts	15 (20)
Crankcase Half Nuts	
8 mm	15 (20)
10 mm	22 (30)
Cylinder Head Nuts	33 (45)
Drain Plug-to-Crankcase	19 (25)
Drive Plate-to-Crankshaft Bolts	66 (90)
Engine-to-Transaxle Nuts	22 (30)
Exhaust Flange-to-Cylinder Head Nuts	15 (20)
Flywheel-to-Crankshaft Bolts	81 (110)
Oil Pump-to-Crankcase Nuts	19 (25)
Pressure Plate-to-Flywheel Bolts	15 (20)
Pulley-to-Crankshaft Bolt	
Single "V" Pulley	44 (60)
Triple "V" Pulley	258 (350)
Rocker Shaft-to-Cylinder Head Nuts	19 (25)
Torque Converter-to-Drive Plate Bolts	15 (20)
Water Pump-to-Crankcase Bolts	15 (20)

ENGINE SPECIFICATIONS

GENERAL SPECIFICATIONS

Year	DISPLACEMENT		Fuel System	HP@RPM	Torque Ft. Lbs.@RPM	Compr. Ratio	BORE		STROKE	
	Cu. In.	Liters					In.	mm	In.	mm
1987	128	2.1	Digifant	90@4800	118@2800	9.0:1	3.70	94	2.99	76

VALVES

Engine Size & Valve	Head Diam. In. (mm)	Face Angle	Seat Angle	Seat Width In. (mm)	Stem Diameter In. (mm)	Stem Clearance In. (mm)	Valve Lift In. (mm)
2.1L							
Intake	1.575 (40.0)	45°	45°	.055-.098 (1.4-2.5)	.313-.314 (7.96-7.97)	[1] .0457 (1.19)	.....
Exhaust	1.34 (34.0)	45°	45°	.055-.098 (1.4-2.5)	.3508-.3512 (8.91-8.92)	[1] .047 (1.19)	.....

[1] – Measured with dial indicator pointer on head of valve and rocking valve back and forth.

Volkswagen Engines

2.1L OPPOSED 4-CYLINDER (Cont.)

ENGINE SPECIFICATIONS (Cont.)

PISTONS, PINS & RINGS

Engine	PISTONS	PINS		RINGS		
	Clearance In. (mm)	Piston Fit In. (mm)	Rod Fit In. (mm)	Ring No.	End Gap In. (mm)	Side Clearance In. (mm)
2.1L	[1] .001-.002 (.03-.06)	Full Floating	Full Floating	1	[2] .012-.018 (.30-.45)	[3] .0020-.0031 (.05-.08)
				2	[2] .012-.020 (.30-.50)	[4] .0016-.0028 (.04-.07)
				3	[5] .010-.016 (.25-.40)	[4] .001-.002 (.02-.05)

[1] – Wear limit .008" (.20 mm).
[2] – Wear limit .035" (.90 mm).
[3] – Wear limit .005" (.13 mm).
[4] – Wear limit .004" (.10 mm).
[5] – Wear limit .037" (.95 mm).

CRANKSHAFT MAIN & CONNECTING ROD BEARINGS

Engine	MAIN BEARINGS				CONNECTING ROD BEARINGS		
	Journal Diam. In. (mm)	Clearance In. (mm)	Thrust Bearing	Crankshaft End Play In. (mm)	Journal Diam. In. (mm)	Clearance In. (mm)	Side Play In. (mm)
2.1L							
No. 1	[1] 2.3614-2.3618 (59.980-59.990)	.....	No. 1	[2] .003-.005 (.07-.13)	2.1647-2.1652 (54.983-54.996)	.....	.028" (.70 mm)
No. 2 & 3	[3] 2.3614-2.3618 (59.980-59.990)						
No. 4	1.5742-1.5748 (39.984-40.000)						

[1] – Standard size with Blue dot. Standard size with Red dot is 2.3611-2.3614" (59.971-59.979 mm).
[2] – Wear limit .006" (.15 mm).
[3] – Standard size with Blue dot. Standard size with Red dot is 2.1642-2.1645" (54.971-54.979 mm).

Volvo Engines

2.3L 4-CYLINDER

240 Series
740 Series
760 GLE Turbo

NOTE: **For engine repair procedures not covered in this article, see ENGINE OVERHAUL PROCEDURES article at beginning of this section.**

ENGINE CODING

ENGINE IDENTIFICATION

Engine identification number is located on lower left corner of label on the camshaft timing belt cover and is stamped on the block behind the distributor. The Vehicle Identification Number (VIN) carries an engine code as its 7th and 8th characters.

ENGINE IDENTIFICATION CODES

Application	Code
B230F	88
B230FT (Turbo)	87

ENGINE, MANIFOLDS & CYLINDER HEAD

ENGINE

Removal

1) Remove battery. Disconnect windshield washer hose and engine compartment lamp. Remove hood. Remove rubber boot and snap ring at base of gearshift lever (manual transmission only).

2) Remove cap from expansion tank. Open radiator and engine drain cocks and drain coolant. Disconnect lower radiator hose at radiator, crankcase ventilation hose at cylinder head, and upper radiator hose at engine. Detach expansion tank hoses from radiator.

3) Disconnect oil cooler lines for automatic transmission at radiator. On Turbo, disconnect oil cooler lines and exhaust pipe from turbocharger. On all models, remove fan shroud screws, disconnect radiator, and lift radiator and fan shroud from vehicle.

4) Remove air cleaner and hose assembly. Remove vacuum hose to brake booster. Remove adjusting bar, drive belt and power steering pump.

5) Remove A/C crankshaft pulley and A/C drive belt (if equipped). Reinstall pulley loosely. Disconnect and remove compressor and bracket.

6) Mark and disconnect 4 vacuum hoses at engine and 2 carbon filter hoses. Remove wire or connector from distributor and high tension lead from coil. Remove starter motor cables and clutch cable clamp (if equipped) from starter.

7) Detach wiring harness from voltage regulator. Disconnect throttle cable at pulley. Disconnect A/C wire at solenoid, on intake manifold.

8) Remove fuel cap to relieve pressure, and remove fuel hoses from filter and return pipe. Remove guard plate for ballast resistor. Disconnect 2 connectors from intake manifold microswitch, wiring harness, and ballast resistor.

9) Disconnect heater hoses at firewall and drain oil from engine. Remove exhaust pipe flange nuts and gasket.

10) Remove front engine mounting bolts and front exhaust pipe mounting bracket. Disconnect gearshift control rod (automatic transmission) or clutch cable (manual transmission).

11) Disconnect speedometer cable, propeller shaft universal joint, and gearshift selector from control rod. If manual transmission has overdrive, disconnect wire to gearshift selector. Using a wooden block, place jack under transmission. Remove transmission support member.

12) Attach Lifting Sling (5035) to engine lifting eyes, and adjust Lifting Yoke (2810), so that engine weight is at its rearmost position.

13) Hoist slightly to release front engine mount dowels. Check for wires or hoses, and disconnect as necessary. Raise engine gradually till proper clearance is met, then readjust lifting yoke to forward position and lift engine from vehicle.

Installation

To install, reverse removal procedure. Check for proper installation of all lines, hoses and electrical leads.

INTAKE & EXHAUST MANIFOLDS

Removal

1) Disconnect battery ground cable. Drain coolant level to below intake manifold. Remove air bellows from injection unit to intake manifold. Disconnect PCV hoses at intake manifold and flame arrester.

2) Disconnect vacuum pump hose at intake manifold. Disconnect diverter valve hoses. Disconnect air pump with tensioner and position to one side.

3) Disconnect fuel lines from control pressure regulator, cold start injector, distributor pipe to engine, front fuel filter to engine, and injector lines.

4) Disconnect wiring at control pressure regulator, cold start injector, and auxiliary air valve.

5) On turbo models remove air delivery and intake hoses. Disconnect exhaust manifold at turbo. Disconnect turbo oil and cooling lines.

6) Disconnect throttle cable from intake manifold. Disconnect charcoal canister hoses and EGR valve hose from intake manifold. Remove intake manifold brace, attaching nuts, and intake manifold.

7) Disconnect transmission fill pipe from flywheel housing (automatic transmissions only). Remove attaching nuts and exhaust manifold.

Installation

To install, reverse removal procedure and install new manifold gaskets. Tighten nuts and bolts to specifications.

CYLINDER HEAD

CAUTION: **Do not rotate crankshaft or camshaft when drive belt has been removed. Pistons may strike valves.**

Removal

1) Drain cooling system at radiator and cylinder block. Disconnect battery ground cable. Remove fan, preheater hose (below fan shroud) and fan shroud. Loosen adjustments and remove all drive belts and water pump pulley.

2) Using center bolt on crankshaft, rotate crankshaft so that mark on camshaft pulley aligns

2.3L 4-CYLINDER (Cont.)

opposite marking on inner timing gear cover, and that crankshaft marking is opposite zero TDC on timing cover.

3) Remove tensioner nut and washer. Pull on timing gear belt to depress tensioner spring. Use a 3 mm drill bit to lock tensioner spring in place. Remove belt.

4) Remove camshaft sprocket and spacer washer. Remove stud bolt for timing belt tensioner.

5) Remove intake and exhaust manifolds. See INTAKE & EXHAUST MANIFOLDS section of this article.

6) Remove spark plug cables at spark plugs. Remove distributor cap from distributor and disconnect upper water hose at firewall.

7) Remove cylinder head bolts. Lift cylinder head from engine.

Installation

1) Install new head gasket with "TOP" mark upward. Be sure all contact surfaces are clean. Ensure that "O" ring for water pump sits correctly in groove. Position cylinder head over gasket.

2) Dip head bolts and washers in engine oil before installation. Install and tighten bolts in 3 stages in sequence. *See Fig. 1*. First tighten bolts to 15 ft. lbs. (20 N.m). Tighten next to 44 ft. lbs. (60 N.m). Angle tighten an additional 90 degrees.

3) Check valve adjustment. See VALVE CLEARANCE ADJUSTMENT section in this article. Reverse remainder of removal procedure to complete assembly.

Fig. 1: Cylinder Head Tightening Sequence

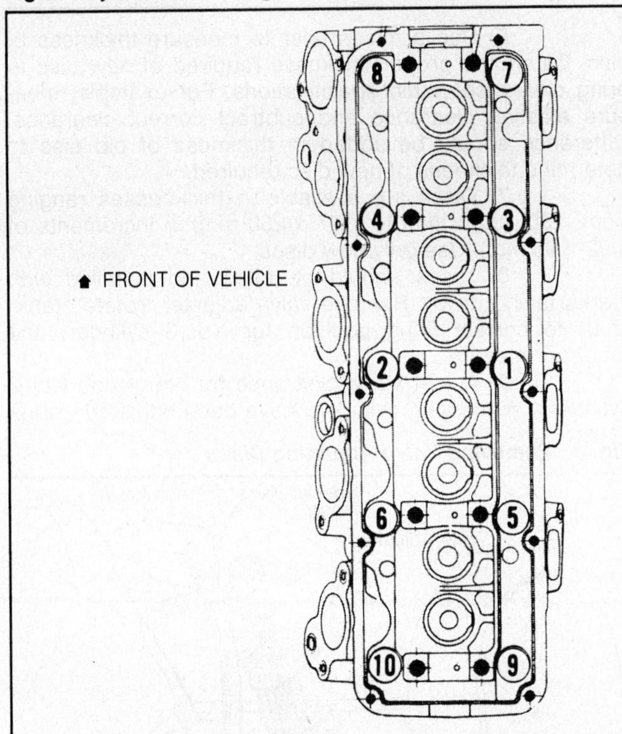

Courtesy of Volvo Cars of North America.

CAMSHAFT

NOTE: **Rear end of camshafts for B230FT engine are stamped with the letter "T". Camshafts for B230F are stamped with letter "M".**

Removal

1) Using center bolt on crankshaft, rotate crankshaft so that marking on camshaft pulley aligns opposite marking on timing gear cover. Ensure that crankshaft pulley mark aligns opposite zero degrees TDC on cover.

2) Remove timing belt cover. Remove belt tensioner nut and washer. Pull on belt to depress tensioner spring. Use a 3 mm drill bit to lock tensioner pulley in place. Remove belt, camshaft gear and spacer washer.

3) Remove valve cover and gasket. Check and note markings on camshaft bearing caps. Remove center bearing cap and install Holder (5021) to hold camshaft in place while removing remaining bearing caps.

4) Remove remaining bearing caps and take out front camshaft oil seal. Release screw on holder and lift out camshaft.

Inspection

Inspect bearing surfaces for damage. Camshaft bearings should have an inner diameter of 1.1811-1.1819" (30.00-30.02 mm).

Installation

Ensure that dowel for sprocket is UP (12 o'clock position) and lubricate all bearing and friction surfaces. To complete installation, reverse removal procedure.

TIMING BELT INSTALLATION

1) Install belt tensioner if previously removed. Align notch in crankshaft belt guide with timing mark on front cover.

2) Rotate intermediate shaft to align timing mark on sprocket with mark on belt guard. Align marks on camshaft belt pulley with timing mark on valve cover. *See Fig. 2*.

3) New drive belts have two lines on outer side of belt. Two lines should fit toward crankshaft marks.

4) Place belt over crankshaft sprocket first, then over intermediate shaft. Stretch belt on tension side and fit over camshaft sprocket. Slide back of belt inside tension roller.

5) Loosen nut on belt tensioner to permit spring tension to act against drive belt. Recheck timing marks for proper location and tighten tensioner nut. Attach pulley to front hub on crankshaft.

VALVES

NOTE: **Exhaust valves are stellite-coated and must not be machined. They may be lapped into valve seat. Use extreme care when disposing of damaged or worn sodium-filled exhaust valves. If the sodium contained in the valve comes into contact with water, a violent reaction will occur.**

VALVE ARRANGEMENT

E-I-E-I-E-I-E-I (Front-to-rear).

VALVE GUIDES

Removal & Installation

1) Heat cylinder head to 212°F (44°C) and press old guides out with Drift (5218), pressing toward

Volvo Engines

2.3L 4-CYLINDER (Cont.)

Fig. 2: Timing Marks for Crankshaft, Intermediate Shaft & Camshaft

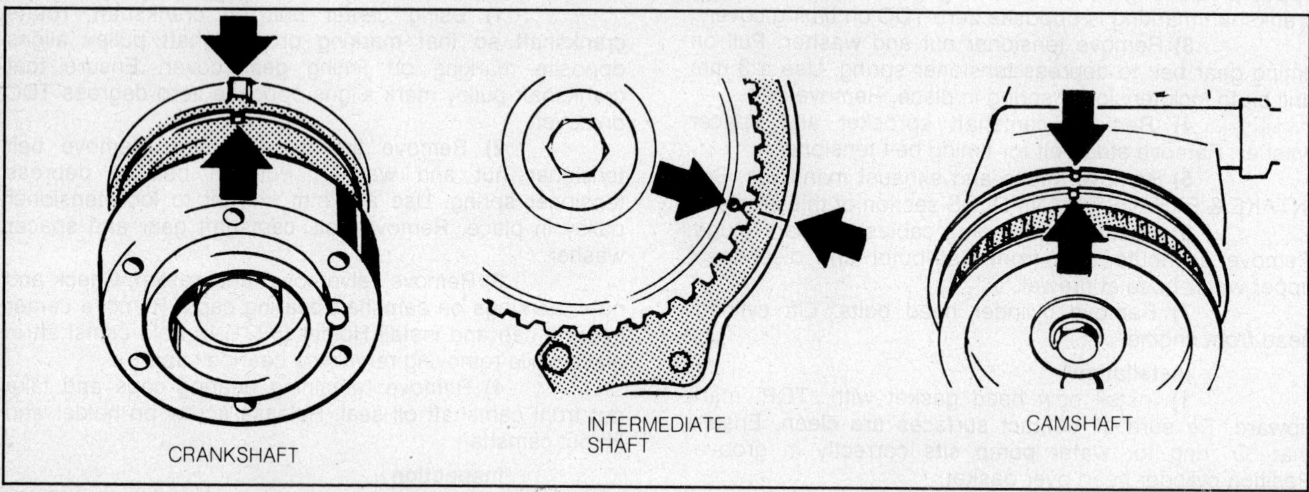

Courtesy of Volvo Cars of North America.

combustion chamber. Ensure that guide has not seized during removal. If so, valve guide bore must be reamed to oversize. With cylinder head at room temperature, use Intake Guide Drift (5027) and Exhaust Guide Drift (5028) to press in new guides.

2) Valve guides are available in standard size (no grooves) and 3 oversizes (1, 2 or 3 grooves). Ream oversize guides with proper Reamer (5161, 5162, or 5163 respectively).

3) Press in until drift contacts cylinder head to give proper height above cylinder head.

NOTE: Ensure that replacement guide is same size as old guide. At least 1980 lbs. (9000 N) force should be required to press in new guide. If not, head must be fitted with oversize guide.

VALVE SPRINGS

Removal

With cylinder head removed, compress valve springs using valve spring compressor tool, and remove valve retainers. Disassemble valve spring components and place valves in order in valve rack.

Installation

To install, place valves in position, fit valve guide seal, valve spring, valve collar and retainers.

VALVE CLEARANCE ADJUSTMENT

1) Valve clearance is adjusted with engine off. Engine may be either warm or cold. Remove valve cover.

2) Turn crankshaft center bolt until camshaft is in position for firing No. 1 cylinder. Both cam lobes should point up at equally large angles. Pulley timing mark should be zero degrees TDC.

3) Using feeler gauge, check valve clearance of No. 1 cylinder, measuring between camshaft lobe and discs. Intake and exhaust valves have same adjustment clearances.

4) If clearance is incorrect, line up notches in valve depressors at right angles to engine center line.

5) Install Press Tool (5022) to depress tappet. Remove adjusting disc with Special Pliers (5026). *See Fig. 3.*

VALVE CLEARANCE SPECIFICATIONS

When Checking	In. (mm)
Cold Engine	.012-.016 (.30-.41)
Hot Engine	.014-.018 (.36-.46)
When Adjusting	
Cold Engine	.014-.016 (.36-.41)
Hot Engine	.016-.018 (.41-.46)

6) Use a micrometer to measure thickness of disc. Determine proper thickness required of new disc to bring clearance within specifications. For example; measure existing clearance and subtract correct clearance. Difference should be added to thickness of old disc to determine thickness of new disc required.

7) Discs are available in thicknesses ranging from .130" (3.30 mm) to .177" (4.50 mm) in increments of .002" (.05 mm). Use only new discs.

8) Discs should be oiled and installed with marks facing down. Remove valve adjuster, rotate crankshaft to correct firing position for No. 3 cylinder, and repeat procedure.

9) Adjust valve clearance for No. 4 and No. 2 cylinders. When all 4 cylinders have been adjusted, rotate

Fig. 3: Removing Valve Adjusting Discs

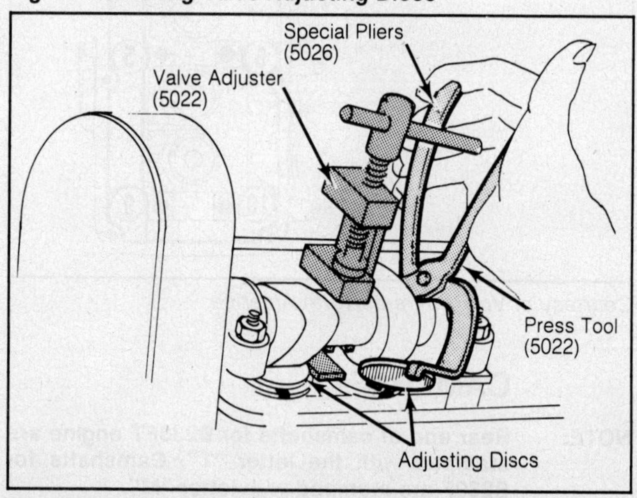

Courtesy of Volvo Cars of North America.

2.3L 4-CYLINDER (Cont.)

camshaft a few revolutions and recheck valve clearance for all cylinders. Position gasket on cylinder head and install valve cover.

CRANKSHAFT & ROD BEARINGS

MAIN & CONNECTING ROD BEARINGS

Removal

1) Remove oil pan. See OIL PAN REMOVAL section of this article. Identify and mark connecting rod caps and main bearing caps for installation reference.

2) Remove connecting rod caps and push pistons toward top of cylinders. Remove main bearing caps (one at a time) and thoroughly clean all bearing surfaces.

Installation

1) Measure all journals, using a micrometer. Out-of-roundness on main bearing journals should not exceed .00016" (.004 mm), and on connecting rod journals it should not exceed .00016" (.004 mm).

2) Reinstall main bearing caps, refit connecting rods to crankshaft and tighten all nuts and bolts to specifications. Reassemble engine in reverse order of removal.

REAR MAIN BEARING OIL SEAL

NOTE: **Note whether seal is flush with seal flange, or .12" (3.0 mm) from flange so that seal position is known when reinstalling.**

Removal

Remove transmission, clutch, and flywheel from engine. Pry seal out using a screwdriver.

Installation

1) Assemble Handle (1801) and Drift (5276) with all spacers. Apply oil to seal contact face and oil seal lips. Install seal on drift. If crankshaft shows signs of wear, seal should be pressed into housing further than before.

2) Remove one spacer from drift if old seal was flush with housing.

3) Remove two spacers from drift if old oil seal was .12" (3.0 mm) in deeper from housing face.

4) Leave both spacers in drift if crankshaft shows no signs of wear.

ENGINE FRONT COVER OIL SEALS

NOTE: **Excessive crankcase pressure due to a blocked flame guard, will cause oil seals to leak. Clean flame guard and recheck seals for leakage.**

Removal

1) Disconnect battery. Remove fan shroud, fan belt, and fan pulley. Loosen adjustments and remove A/C compressor and belts. Remove water pump pulley and upper timing belt cover.

2) Using center bolt on crankshaft, rotate crankshaft to position intermediate shaft, crankshaft and camshaft opposite their proper timing marks.

3) Remove crankshaft vibration damper/pulley, use Holding Fixture (5284). Remove timing belt cover.

4) Remove belt tensioner nut and washer. Pull on belt to depress tensioner spring. Use 3 mm drill bit to lock tensioner pulley in place. Remove timing belt.

5) Remove drive belt pulley from intermediate shaft. Remove timing belt tensioner and inner timing belt cover. Remove seal to be replaced.

NOTE: **Front cover removal is not necessary if only seals are being replaced.**

Installation

1) Clean and inspect all surfaces. Grease intermediate shaft seal and press into place using Sleeve (5025). Grease crankshaft seal and press into place using Sleeve (5283).

2) Install crankshaft vibration damper/pulley and intermediate drive belt pulley. To complete installation, refer to TIMING BELT INSTALLATION in this article.

ENGINE OILING

ENGINE OILING SYSTEM

Engine utilizes a force-feed type lubricating system. Oil circulates through oil pump to oil filter on outside of engine block assembly. Turbo models use an engine oil cooler.

From filter, oil is forced to drilled gallery in center of block, where it moves under pressure to main bearings. Main bearings are drilled to permit lubricant to pass on to connecting rod and camshaft bearings.

Oil from camshaft bearings is used to lubricate discs, valves, and cylinder head assembly. Cylinder walls and rings are lubricated by the splash from connecting rods. Excess oil returns to sump through drain holes in block assembly and through the drain hose connected to oil trap in upper block and secured to oil pump.

CRANKCASE CAPACITY

Oil capacity when oil filter is changed is 4.0 quarts (3.8L). Without a filter change capacity is 3.5 quarts (3.3L).

ENGINE OIL COOLER

An engine oil cooler is used on Turbo models. It is air cooled and is located at the side of the radiator. An engine oil thermostat, located at the oil cooler fitting, controls oil temperature.

NORMAL OIL PRESSURE

Oil pressure is 35-85 psi (2.5-6.0 kg/cm²) at 2000 RPM with engine at normal operating temperature.

OIL PAN

Removal

1) Raise and support front of vehicle. Drain engine oil. Remove splash guard. Remove engine mount nuts from underside of crossmember.

2) Release main steering shaft steering gear. Remove steering "U" joint lower bolt, loosen upper bolt and slide "U" joint up on shaft.

3) Install lifting bar and raise engine slightly. Remove front axle crossmember bolts. Pull down on crossmember.

4) Remove left engine mount. Remove support bracket (located between rear of oil pan and clutch housing). Remove oil pan bolts. Turn, and lower oil pan to remove.

Volvo Engines

2.3L 4-CYLINDER (Cont.)

Installation

To install oil pan, reverse removal procedure.

OIL PUMP

Removal

Remove oil pan and related parts. Remove oil pump. Disassemble and clean all parts thoroughly. Check all parts for excessive wear or signs of fatigue.

Inspection

1) Measure backlash clearance between pump gears. Clearance limits are .006-.014" (.15-.35 mm). Lay straightedge across pump body, above gears. Measure clearance between gear and straightedge. Clearance should be .0008-.0048" (.02-.12 mm).

2) Relief valve spring free length should be 1.543" (39.2 mm). When loaded to 10-12 lbs. (4.5-5.4 kg), spring length should be 1.033" (26.3 mm). When loaded to 13.6-17.2 lbs. (6.2-7.8 kg), spring length should be .827" (21.0 mm).

3) Pump drive shaft and gear are a matched set and must be replaced as an assembly. *See Fig. 4*.

Fig 4: Cutaway View of Oil Pump

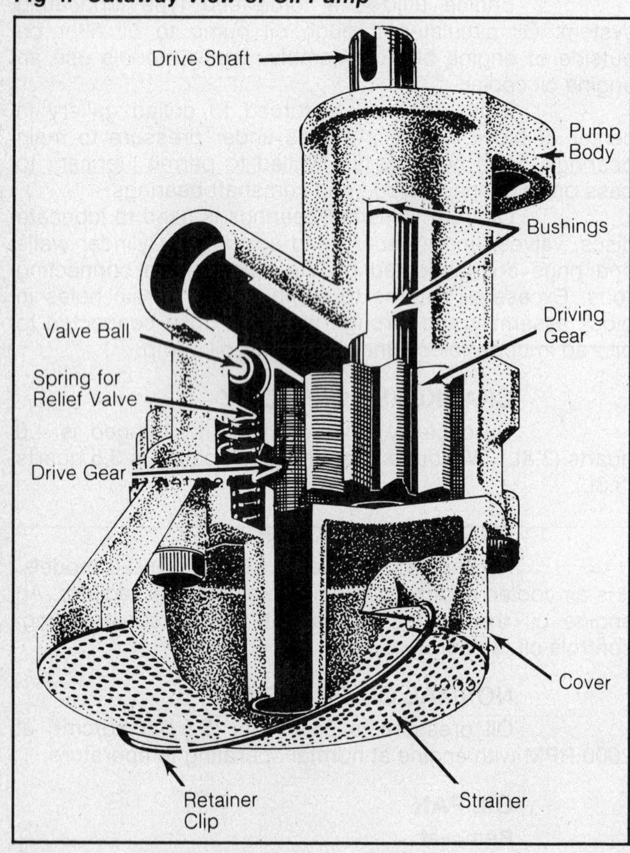

Courtesy of Volvo Cars of North America.

Installation

Install oil pump. Use new seals when attaching oil delivery pipe. Ensure oil pump properly engages pump drive shaft. Replace oil pan and related components.

ENGINE COOLING

WATER PUMP

Removal

1) Disconnect vacuum hose from water valve (On vehicles equipped with A/C). Turn heater control switch to "WARM". Remove expansion tank cap. Open drain cock on right side of cylinder block. Drain coolant.

2) Remove fan shroud, fan and preheating hose clamp (beneath fan shroud).

3) Loosen adjusters and remove belts and water pump pulley. Remove upper timing belt cover.

4) Remove nut and bolt retaining return pipe at water pump. Remove remaining nuts and bolts to remove water pump.

Installation

1) Clean all gasket and "O" ring surfaces. Ensure that contact area on head is not corroded. Install new gasket and "O" ring on water pump.

2) Install nuts and bolts so that pump does not slip, but can be moved upwards. Pry water pump upwards against cylinder head, while tightening nuts and bolts. Install return pipe.

3) Install components previously removed. Tighten drain cock and fill with coolant. Run engine and check for leaks.

NOTE: **For further information on cooling systems, see ENGINE COOLING section.**

TIGHTENING SPECIFICATIONS

Application	Ft. Lbs. (N.m)
Cylinder Camshaft Bearing Caps	15 (20)
Connecting Rod Caps [1]	
Step 1	15 (20)
Step 2	[2]
Cylinder Head Bolts	
Step 1	15 (20)
Step 2	44 (60)
Step 3	[2]
Drive Belt Tensioner Nut	37 (50)
Engine Mount Bolts	15 (20)
Exhaust Pipe-to-Turbo Nuts	18 (24)
Exhaust & Intake Manifold Bolts	15 (20)
Fan Bolts	33 (45)
Flywheel Bolts	50 (70)
Main Bearing Caps	80 (110)
Sprockets	
Camshaft	37 (50)
Intermediate Shaft	37 (50)
Crankshaft	
Step 1	44 (60)
Step 2	[2]

[1] – If bolts are reused length must not exceed 2.185" (55.5 mm).

[2] – Tighten an additional 90 degrees.

Volvo Engines

2.3L 4-CYLINDER (Cont.)

ENGINE SPECIFICATIONS

GENERAL SPECIFICATIONS

Year	DISPLACEMENT		Fuel System	HP@RPM	Torque Ft. Lbs.@RPM	Compr. Ratio	BORE		STROKE	
	Cu. In.	Liters					In.	mm	In.	mm
1987										
B230FT	141.0	2.3	Turbo/Fuel Inj.	160@5300	187@2900	8.7:1	3.780	96	3.150	80
B230F	141.0	2.3	Fuel Inj.	114@5400	136@2750	9.8:1	3.780	96	3.150	80

VALVES

Engine Size & Valve	Head Diam. In. (mm)	Face Angle	Seat Angle	Seat Width In. (mm)	Stem Diameter In. (mm)	Stem Clearance In. (mm)	Valve Lift In. (mm)
B230FT & B230F							
Intake	1.732 (44)	44.5°	45°	.051-.075 (1.30-1.91)	.3132-.3138 (7.955-7.970)	.0012-.0024 (.030-.060)	.374 [1] (9.5)
Exhaust	1.380 (35)	44.5°	45°	.066-.091 (1.70-2.31)	.3128-.3134 [2] (7.945-7.960)	.0024-.0035 (.060-.090)	.413 [1] (10.5)

1 – Except B230FT: Intake and exhaust lift for Turbo is .391" (9.9 mm)
2 – Except B230FT: Exhaust stem diameter for Turbo is .3136-.3142" (7.965-7.980 mm), measured .63" (16 mm) from top of stem.

PISTONS, PINS & RINGS

Engine	PISTONS	PINS		RINGS		
	Clearance In. (mm)	Piston Fit In. (mm)	Rod Fit In. (mm)	Ring No.	End Gap In. (mm)	Side Clearance In. (mm)
B230FT & B230F	.0004-.0012 (.010-.030)	Push Fit [1]	Push Fit [1]	1 Comp.	.012-.022 (.30-.55)	.0024-.0036 (.060-.092)
				2 Comp.	.012-.022 (.30-.55)	.0015-.0028 (.040-.072)
				Oil	.012-.024 (.30-.60)	.0012-.0025 (.030-.065)

1 – Push fit in piston; light thumb pressure (close running fit) in rod.

CRANKSHAFT MAIN & CONNECTING ROD BEARINGS

Engine	MAIN BEARINGS				CONNECTING ROD BEARINGS		
	Journal Diam. In. (mm)	Clearance In. (mm)	Thrust Bearing	Crankshaft End Play In. (mm)	Journal Diam. In. (mm)	Clearance In. (mm)	Side Play In. (mm)
B230FT & B230F [1]	2.1648-2.1653 [2] (54.986-55.000)	.0009-.0028 (.024-.072)	.....	.0032-.0106 (.080-.270)	1.9285-1.9293 [2] (48.984-49.005)	.0009-.0026 (.023-.067)	.006-.014 (.15-.35)

1 – Diameter of intermediate shaft front journal should be 1.8494-1.8504" (46.974-47.000 mm); middle journal, 1.6939-1.6949" (43.025-43.050 mm), and rear journal, 1.6900-1.6909" (42.926-42.948 mm). Intermediate shaft bearing clearances should be .0008-.0030" (.020-.075 mm). End play should be .008-.018" (.20-.46 mm).
2 – Maximum out-of-round is .0016" (.004 mm); taper limit is .0016" (.004 mm).

Volvo Engines

2.3L 4-CYLINDER (Cont.)

ENGINE SPECIFICATIONS (Cont.)

CAMSHAFT

Engine	Journal Diam. In. (mm)	Clearance In. (mm)	Lobe Lift In. (mm)
B230FT & B230F [1]	1.1791-1.1799 (29.950-29.970)	.0012-.0028 [2] (.030-.071)	.374 [3] (9.9) [3]

[1] – Rear of B230FT camshaft is stamped with letter "T"; B230F is stamped with letter "M".

[2] – End play is .004-.016" (.10-.40 mm).

[3] – B230FT only. Specifications for B230F: Intake lift .374" (9.5 mm), Exhaust lift .413" (10.5 mm).

VALVE SPRINGS

Engine	Free Length In. (mm)	PRESSURE Lbs. @ In. (Kg @ mm)	
		Valve Closed	Valve Open
B230FT & B230F	1.79 (45.5)	62-70@1.50 (28-32@38)	154-162@1.08 (70-78@27.5)

Yugo Engines

1.1L 4-CYLINDER

GV

NOTE: For engine repair procedures not covered in this article, see ENGINE OVERHAUL PROCEDURES article at beginning of this section.

ENGINE CODING

ENGINE IDENTIFICATION

Engine may be identified by the eighth character of the Vehicle Identification Number (VIN). The VIN is stamped on a metal tab, located on top of instrument panel at lower left of windshield. Engine serial number is stamped on engine block and on a metal tag next to hood brace.

ENGINE IDENTIFICATION CODE

Application	Code
1.1L	VX

ENGINE, MANIFOLDS & CYLINDER HEAD

ENGINE

NOTE: Engine and transaxle are removed as a unit by lowering assembly through the bottom of engine compartment.

Removal

1) Open hood and remove spare tire. Drain coolant. Disconnect battery cables. Remove air cleaner. Disconnect fuel supply and return hoses from carburetor. Disconnect distributor wires. Disconnect wires from alternator, starter, oil pressure sending unit, coolant temperature sending unit and back-up light switch.

2) Disconnect vacuum and fuel lines from carburetor. Disconnect accelerator cable from carburetor. Disconnect wires from carburetor choke and shut-off solenoid. Disconnect exhaust pipe from exhaust manifold. Disconnect heater hoses from engine. Disconnect radiator hoses. Remove clutch cable from clutch release lever.

3) Disconnect speedometer cable from transaxle. Install Lifting Sling (A. 60592) on engine. Using a hoist, place lifting sling under light tension. Remove front wheels. Disconnect tie rods using Remover (A. 47035). Remove sway bar, brackets and bushings. Note location and number of shims for reassembly purposes. Disconnect strut from knuckle.

4) Remove CV joint nuts from front wheels. Remove CV joints from knuckles. Secure axle shafts with wire to retain them in their differential seats. Remove exhaust pipe support bracket from transaxle housing. Disconnect ground strap from transaxle housing. Disconnect shift linkage. Remove crossmember. Remove engine mount bolts. Remove engine/transaxle by lowering assembly from bottom of vehicle.

Installation

To install engine, reverse removal procedure. Check all fluid levels.

MANIFOLDS & CYLINDER HEAD

Removal

1) Disconnect positive battery cable. Remove spare tire from engine compartment. Drain cooling system. Remove air cleaner. Disconnect fuel supply and return hoses from carburetor. Disconnect accelerator cable. Disconnect wires from distributor. Disconnect all hoses from carburetor and intake manifold.

2) Disconnect wires from carburetor choke and shut-off solenoid. Disconnect exhaust pipe from exhaust manifold. Disconnect heater hoses from engine. Remove upper radiator hose. Remove thermostat housing. Disconnect EGR line at valve and manifold. Remove timing belt cover. Remove air pump and support. Remove alternator without disconnecting wires.

3) Move alternator to one side. Loosen timing belt tensioner. Remove timing belt and camshaft sprocket. See TIMING BELT. Remove valve cover and gasket. Remove cylinder head bolts in reverse order of tightening sequence. *See Fig. 1.* Remove cylinder head, exhaust manifold and intake manifold with carburetor as an assembly.

Fig. 1: Cylinder Head Tightening Sequence

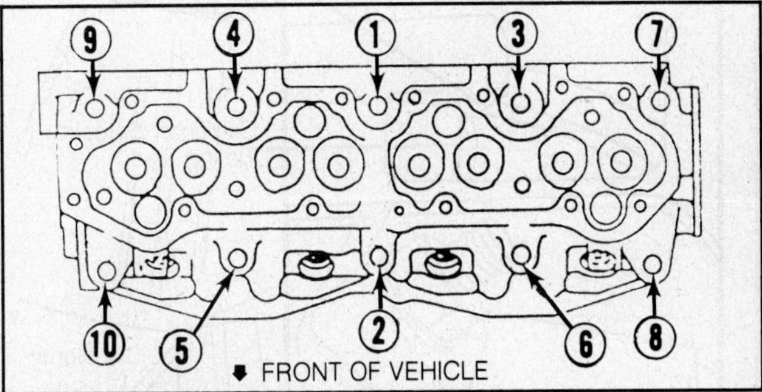

Courtesy of Yugo America, Inc.

NOTE: 1987 engines has 10 mm head bolts (17 mm hex). Lubricate all bolts and washers with engine oil before installation.

Installation

1) To install, reverse removal procedure. Tighten head bolts in two stages. Apply paint mark to one corner of each head bolt and a corresponding mark on the cylinder head. Tighten all bolts 90° (1st. step). Tighten all bolts to a second 90° (2nd. step).

2) Retighten head bolts after 1000 miles. *See Fig. 1.* Ensure that head gasket is aligned with block-to-head lubrication passage. Refill cooling system. Change oil and filter. Adjust valves, ignition timing and idle speed.

CAMSHAFT

TIMING BELT

Removal

Disconnect positive battery cable. Remove cooling fan and shroud. Remove crankshaft pulley. Remove timing belt covers. Align camshaft sprocket with timing mark. *See Fig. 2.* Loosen tensioner lock nut and move tensioner pulley toward engine mount. Tighten nut to secure tensioner in slack position. Remove and discard timing belt.

CAUTION: Timing belts cannot be reused. DO NOT readjust belt tension following initial installation of a new belt.

1.1L 4-CYLINDER (Cont.)

Installation

1) Align camshaft sprocket with timing mark. Align crankshaft sprocket with reference index. *See Fig. 2.* Position timing belt tensioner to its limit of travel toward engine mount and partially tighten lock nut. Install a new timing belt with slack on tensioner side. Loosen tensioner lock nut to apply tension. Tighten tensioner lock nut to 33 ft. lbs. (45 N.m).

2) To apply equal tension to each side of timing belt, turn crankshaft 2 revolutions in direction of travel. Tighten tensioner lock bolt. Check for proper alignment of timing marks. Reverse removal procedure to complete installation.

Fig. 2: Camshaft & Crankshaft Sprocket Alignment

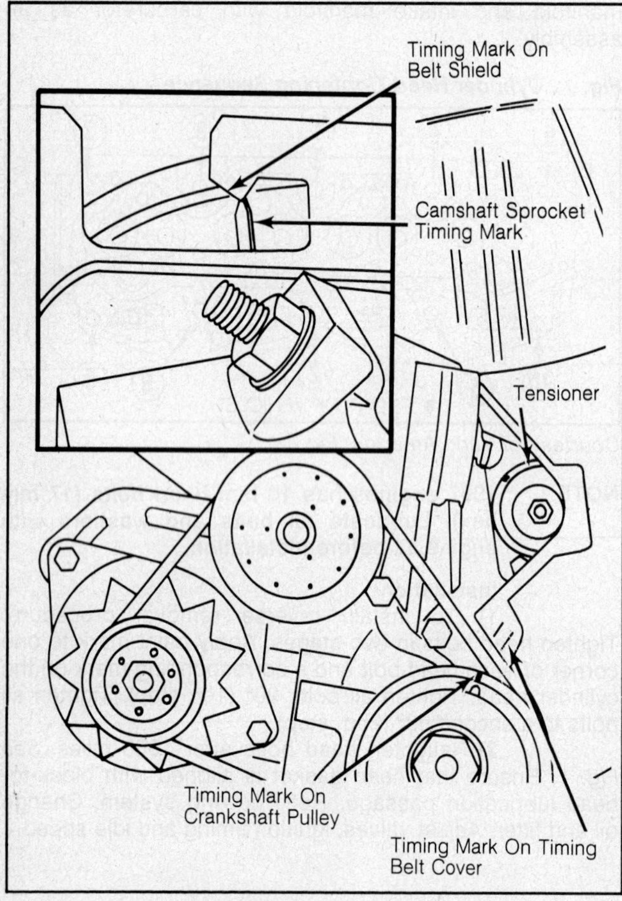

VALVES

VALVE ARRANGEMENT

E-I-I-E-E-I-I-E (Front-to-rear).

VALVES

Remove carbon from valves and inspect for wear, burn or distortion at face and stem. Intake and exhaust valve margin thickness should measure .020" (.50 mm). Inspect end face of each valve stem for wear. Do not grind more than .020" (.50 mm). Check contact pattern of each valve. Width must measure .080" (2.0 mm).

VALVE GUIDES

Inspection

Using a micrometer and bore gauge, measure valve stems and guides. Measure at more than one position along length of stem and guide.

Removal

Using Driver (A. 60395), drive valve guide out from combustion side to valve spring side of cylinder. *See Fig. 3.*

Fig. 3: Removing Valve Guides

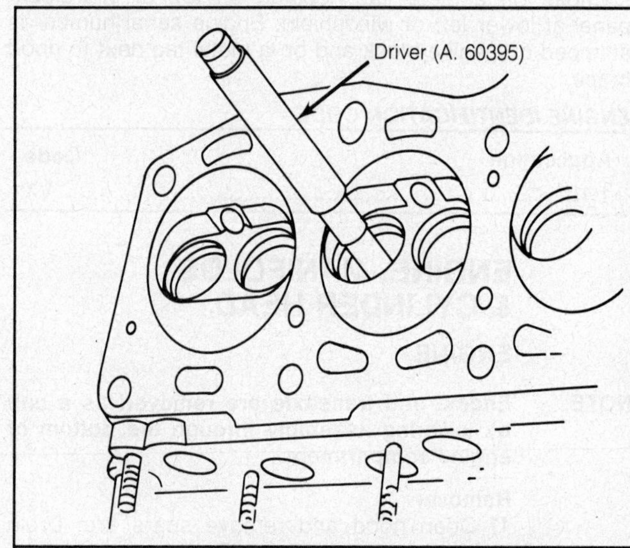

Installation

1) Valve guides are available with an outer diameter .008" (.20 mm) oversize. Drive valve guide into guide bore using Driver (A. 60462). Drive guide until driver contacts cylinder head. *See Fig. 4.*

2) Ream valve guide bore with Reamer (A. 90310). After reaming, clean bore. Install valve spring seat. Install new oil seal. Ensure seal is properly seated, using only hand pressure. Ensure diameter of bore is within specifications.

Fig. 4: Installing Valve Guides

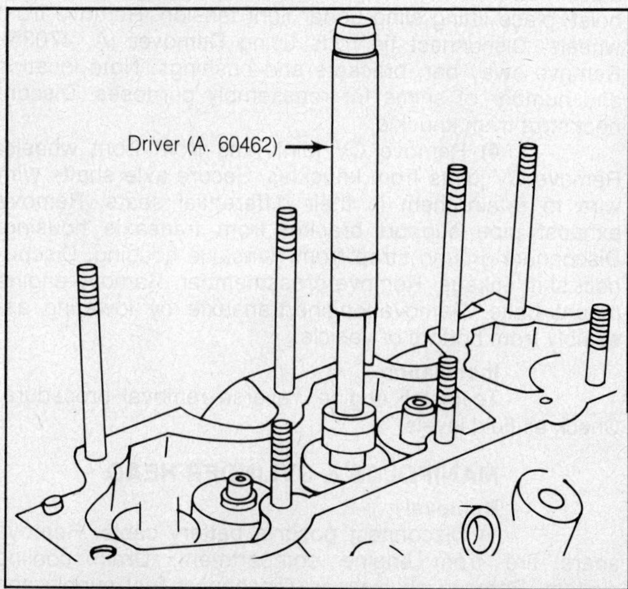

Fig. 5: Exploded View of Camshaft & Valve Components

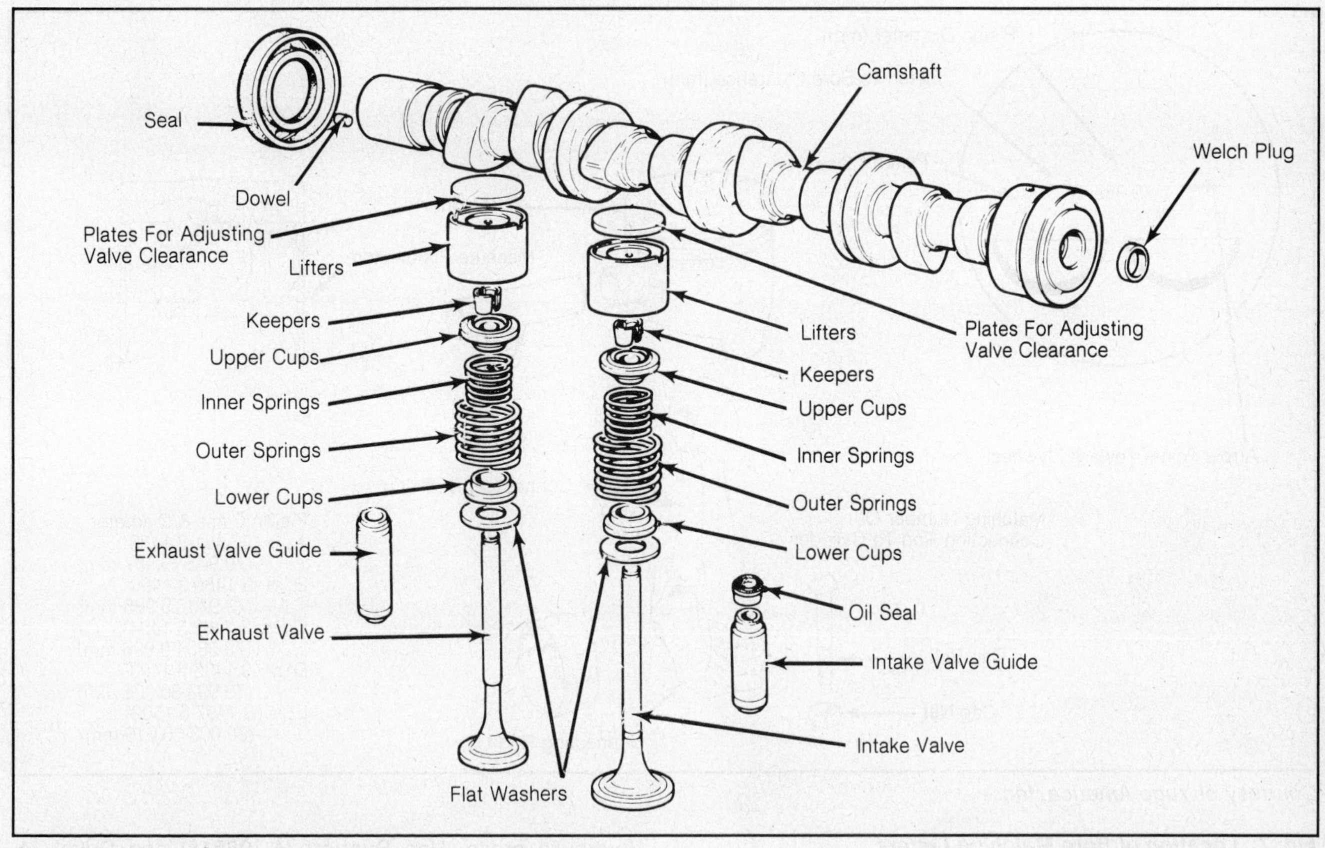

Courtesy of Yugo America, Inc.

VALVE CLEARANCE ADJUSTMENT

1) Adjust valve clearance with engine cold. Remove camshaft cover. Turn crankshaft until camshaft lobe is pointed up on valve to be checked. Measure clearance between shim and camshaft lobe. If clearance exceeds specifications, insert Lifter (A. 60421) to depress valve. Use Pliers (A. 87001) to remove plate from its seat.

2) After determining needed thickness, install new shim. Lifter clearance shims are available in a thickness range from .128-.185" (3.25-4.70 mm). Shim thickness is marked on one side of shim. Install marked side toward lifter.

VALVE CLEARANCE SPECIFICATIONS

Application	In. (mm)
Intake	.016 (.40)
Exhaust	.019 (.50)

PISTONS, RINGS & PINS

PISTON & ROD ASSEMBLY

Removal

Drain engine oil and coolant. Remove cylinder head. Remove oil pan. Remove oil pump and strainer. Remove carbon or ridge at top of cylinder. Place protective hoses over connecting rod bolts. Remove cap and bearing. Remove piston and rod assembly.

Installation

1) Apply a coat of oil to cylinder wall and rod bearing halves. Ensure that piston ring gaps are spaced 120 degrees apart. Place piston ring compressor over piston and tighten to compress rings. If more than one piston was removed, ensure that each piston is installed in original cylinder.

2) Install rings on pistons. Install third scraper ring first. Arrow stamped on top of piston must point to flywheel. Bore matching number, stamped on side of connecting rod, must be on opposite side of cylinder bore from auxiliary shaft. Ensure that piston class mark on piston top matches bore class mark stamped on cylinder block. *See Figs. 6 and 7*.

3) Position piston in cylinder bore with ring compressor resting on cylinder block surface. Ensure marks on connecting rod and connecting rod cap are in alignment. To complete installation, reverse removal procedure.

FITTING PISTONS

1) Measure cylinder bore for out-of-round and taper. Standard cylinder bore is 3.1496-3.1516" (80.00-80.05 mm). Cylinder bore maximum wear limit is .006" (.15 mm). If readings exceed specifications. Rebore cylinder to next oversize.

1.1L 4-CYLINDER (Cont.)

Fig. 6: Identification Marks on Pistons & Connecting Rods

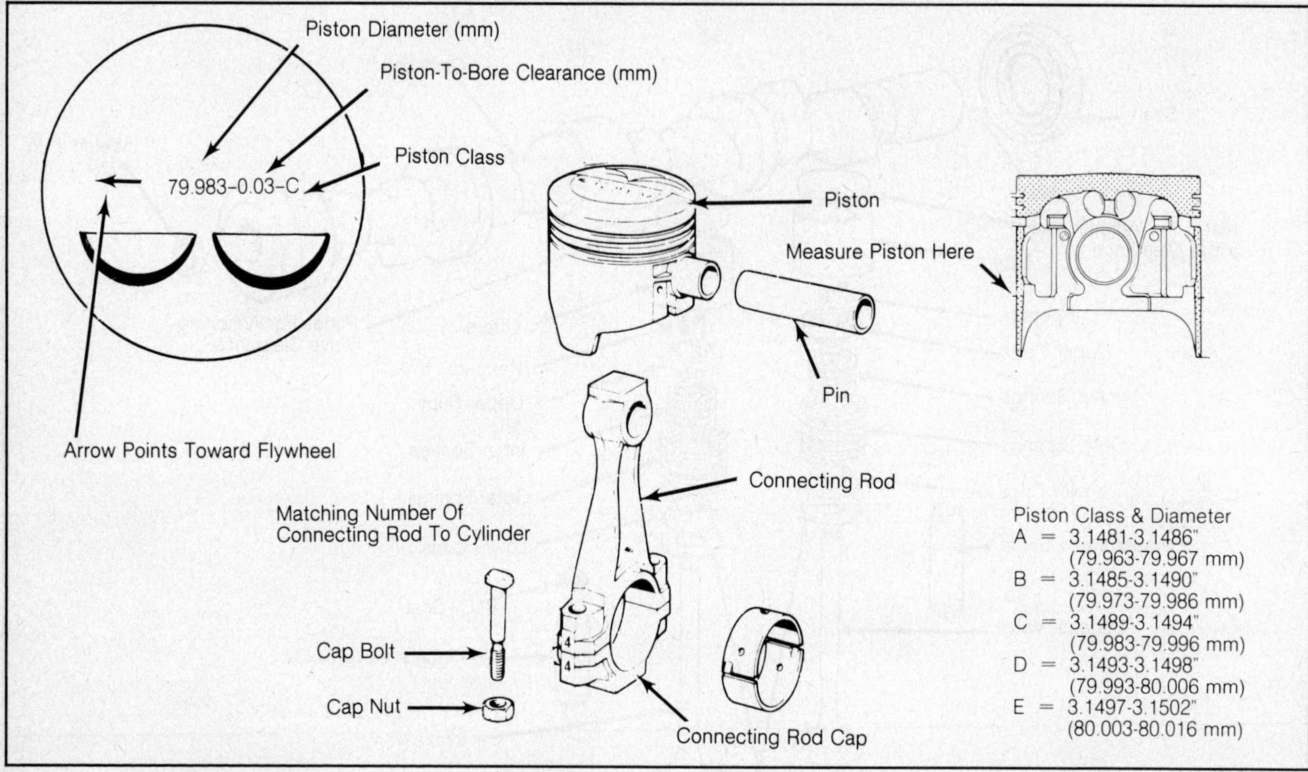

Courtesy of Yugo America, Inc.

Fig. 7: Location of Bore Matching Letters

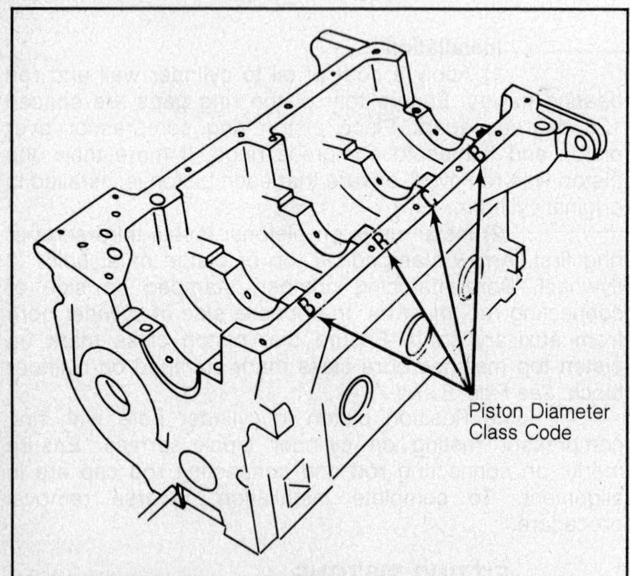

2) Piston diameter is stamped on top of piston. Ensure that piston class code matches bore class code stamped on cylinder block. *See Figs. 6 and 7*. Pistons are available in five oversizes, .004" (.10 mm), .008" (.20 mm), .016" (.40 mm), .024" (.60 mm) and .031" (.80 mm).

PISTON PIN REPLACEMENT

Removal

Piston pin floats in piston and is press fitted in connecting rod. Place piston and rod assembly in a hydraulic press. Use Support (A. 95615) and Driver (A. 60397) to press piston pin out of piston. *See Fig. 9*.

Installation

1) Heat connecting rod to a temperature of 464°F (240°C). Slide the selected piston pin over shaft of Driver (A. 60325). Install pilot on shaft end and lock pilot in

Fig. 8: Piston Pin Offset

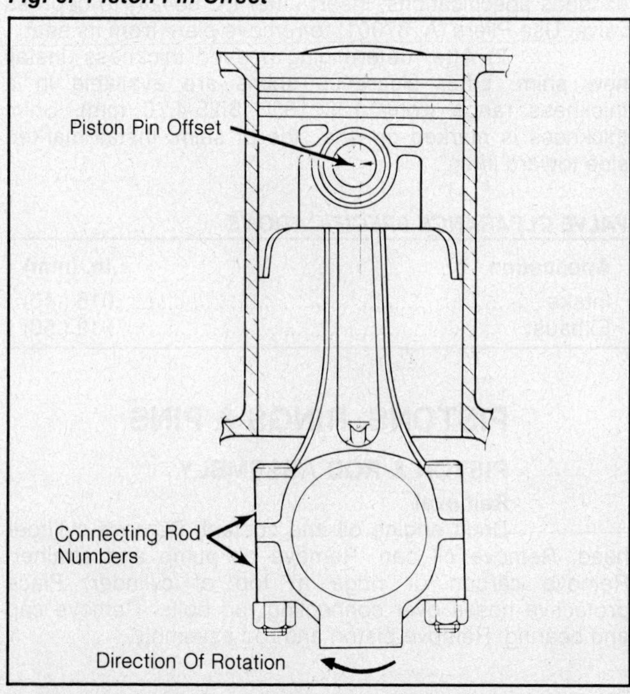

Courtesy of Yugo America, Inc.

1.1L 4-CYLINDER (Cont.)

place with screw finger tight. Remove rod from oven and clamp rod in a soft jawed vise. Place piston over small end of rod, positioned so that the number stamped on rod faces the piston pin offset side. *See Fig. 8.*

2) Line up pin bore with small end of connecting rod. Insert driver and piston pin until shoulder of driver bottoms against piston boss. Ensure connecting rod moves freely after assembly. *See Fig. 10.*

Fig. 9: Pressing Pin Out of Piston

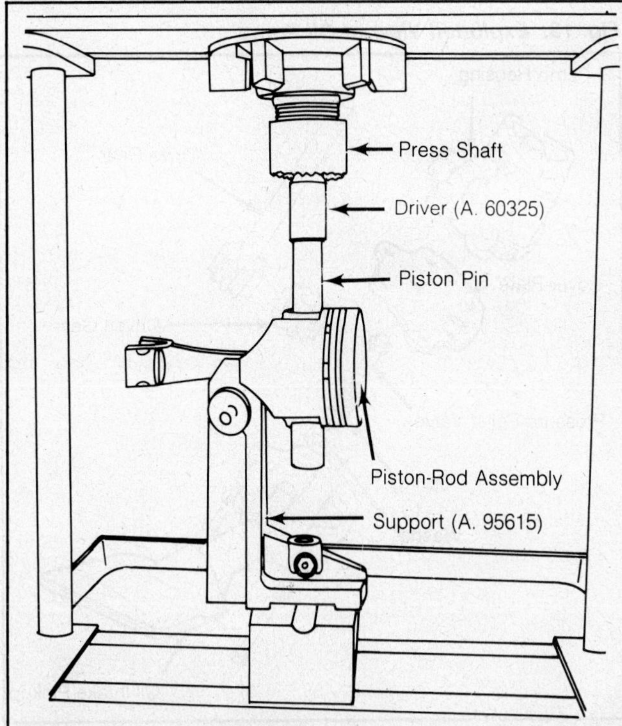

Courtesy of Yugo of America, Inc.

Fig. 10: Installing Piston Pin

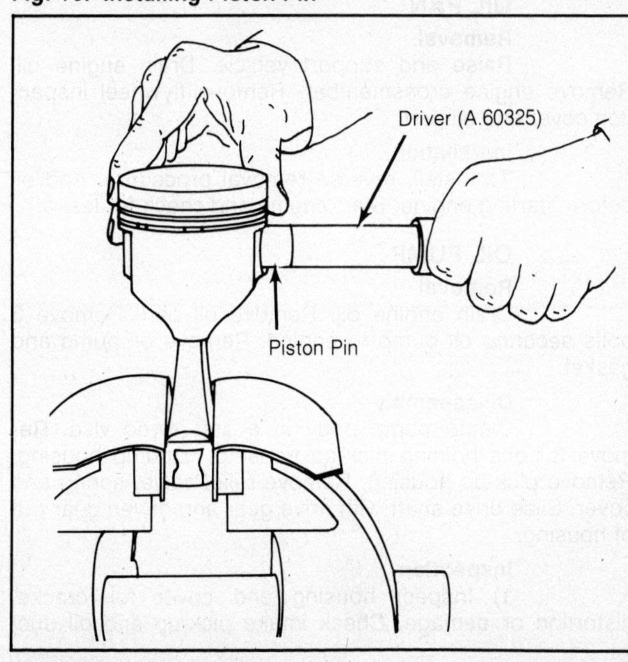

Courtesy of Yugo Of America, Inc.

3) Check fit of piston pin in rod using a torque wrench and Fixture (A. 95615). *See Fig. 12.* Install assembled piston, pin and rod in fixture. Using a torque wrench, ensure piston pin will not rotate when a force of 113 INCH lbs. (12.74 N.m) is applied.

4) Check alignment of piston and connecting rod assembly using a rod aligning fixture. Maximum allowable misalignment of rod axis is .004" (.10 mm), measured at the piston top. *See Fig. 11.*

Fig. 11: Checking Alignment of Piston & Rod Assembly

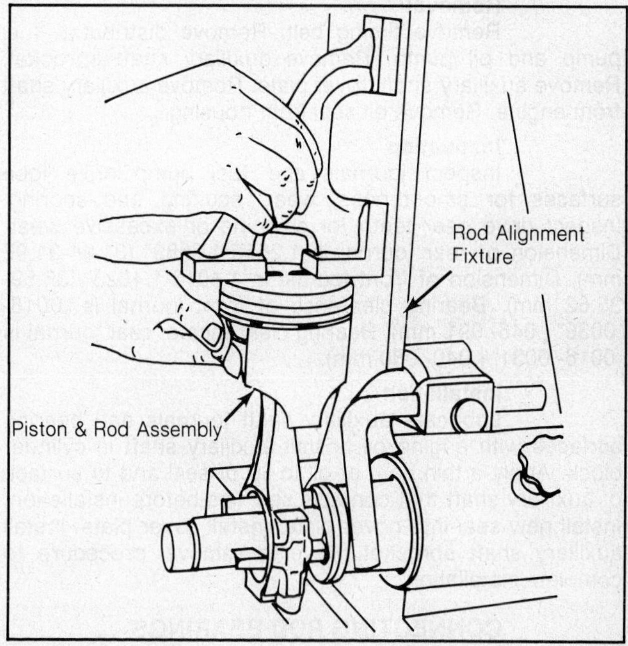

Courtesy of Yugo of America, Inc.

Fig. 12: Checking Fit of Pin in Connecting Rod

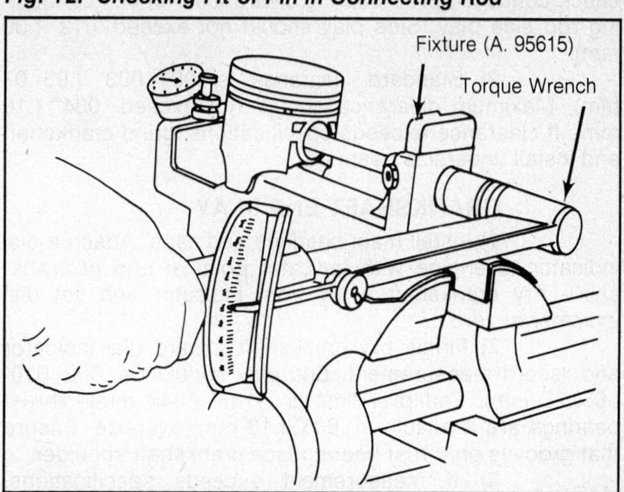

Courtesy of Yugo of America, Inc.

CRANKSHAFT & ROD BEARINGS

MAIN BEARINGS

Using Plastigage, check main bearing clearance. Standard clearance is .0014-.0033" (.040-.085 mm). Maximum clearance should not exceed .0033" (.085 mm).

If clearance exceeds specifications, grind crankshaft and install undersize bearings.

NOTE: Undersize crankshaft and connecting rod bearings are available in .010" (.25 mm), .020" (.50 mm) and .030" (.75 mm).

AUXILIARY SHAFT & OIL SEAL

Auxiliary shaft is driven by the timing belt and drives the ignition distributor, fuel pump and oil pump.

Removal

Remove timing belt. Remove distributor, fuel pump and oil pump. Remove auxiliary shaft sprocket. Remove auxiliary shaft cover plate. Remove auxiliary shaft from engine. Remove oil seal from housing.

Inspection

Inspect journals and fuel pump drive lobe surfaces for smoothness, wear, scuffing and scoring. Inspect drive gear teeth for chipping or excessive wear. Dimension of rear journal is 1.2575-1.2583" (31.94-31.96 mm). Dimension of front journal is 1.4013-1.4023" (35.59-35.62 mm). Bearing clearance of front journal is .0018-.0036" (.046-.091 mm). Bearing clearance of rear journal is .0016-.0031" (.040-.080 mm).

Installation

Lubricate auxiliary shaft journals and bearing surfaces with engine oil. Install auxiliary shaft in cylinder block. Apply a thin coat of oil to lip of seal and to surface of auxiliary shaft that contacts seal lips before installation. Install new seal into cover plate. Install cover plate. Install auxiliary shaft sprocket. Reverse removal procedure to complete installation.

CONNECTING ROD BEARINGS

1) Install rod bearing halves into connecting rod. Install rod and piston assembly. Using Plastigage, check connecting rod bearing clearances. Check connecting rod side play. Side play should not exceed .012" (.30 mm).

2) Standard clearance is .001-.003" (.03-.07 mm). Maximum clearance should not exceed .004" (.10 mm). If clearance exceeds specifications, grind crankshaft and install undersize bearings.

CRANKSHAFT END PLAY

1) Install main bearings and caps. Attach a dial indicator to engine with indicator point at end of crankshaft. Pry crankshaft away from indicator and set dial indicator at zero.

2) Firmly pry crankshaft toward dial indicator and record measurement. End play should be .002-.010" (.05-.25 mm). End play limit is .0137" (.348 mm). Thrust bearings are available in .005" (.13 mm) oversize. Ensure that grooves on thrust bearing face crankshaft shoulder.

3) If measurement exceeds specifications, inspect thrust bearing and thrust surface of crankshaft. Replace thrust bearing or grind crankshaft as necessary.

REAR MAIN BEARING OIL SEAL

Removal

Remove flywheel. Remove cover plate. Remove oil seal from cover plate.

Installation

Apply a thin coat of oil to lip of seal and to surface of crankshaft that contacts seal lips before installation. Install new seal into cover plate. Reverse removal procedure to complete installation.

ENGINE OILING

CRANKCASE CAPACITY

Crankcase capacity is 4.5 quarts (4.3L) including oil filter.

Fig. 13: Exploded View of Oil Pump

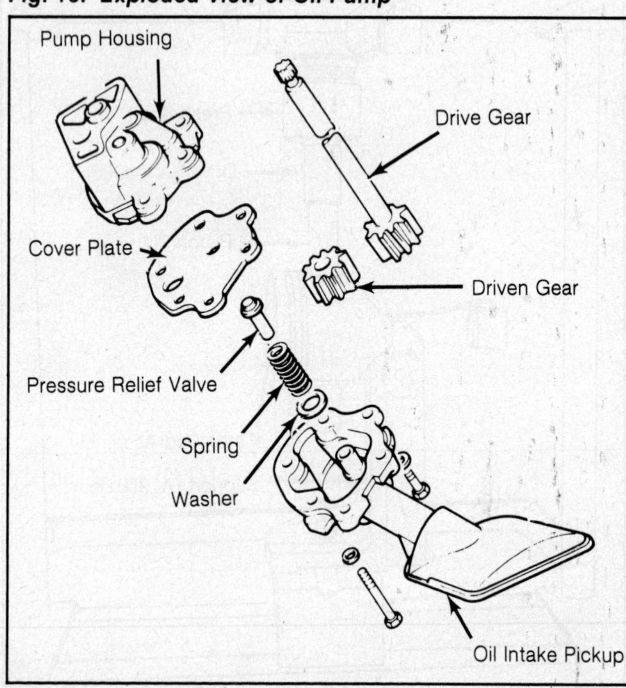

Courtesy of Yugo America, Inc.

OIL PAN

Removal

Raise and support vehicle. Drain engine oil. Remove engine crossmember. Remove flywheel inspection cover and oil pan.

Installation

To install, reverse removal procedure. Add oil before starting engine. Start engine and check for leaks.

OIL PUMP

Removal

Drain engine oil. Remove oil pan. Remove 3 bolts securing oil pump to engine. Remove oil pump and gasket.

Disassembly

Clamp pump body in a soft-jawed vise. Remove 3 bolts holding pick-up housing to pump housing. Remove pick-up housing. Remove relief valve, spring and cover. Slide drive shaft with drive gear and driven gear out of housing.

Inspection

1) Inspect housing and cover for cracks, distortion or damage. Check intake pick-up and oil duct

1.1L 4-CYLINDER (Cont.)

for clogging. Check plunger for wear. Check for weak or broken plunger spring. Measure oil pump clearances.

2) Backlash between gears is .006" (.15 mm) on a new pump. Replace housing and gears if backlash exceeds .010" (.25 mm).

3) Measure side clearance. Maximum side clearance is .006" (.15 mm). Replace worn or damaged parts. Measure gear length. Length should be 1.101-1.102" (27.967-28.00 mm).

4) Drive gear is mounted on shaft with an interference fit. Inspect for signs of drive gear play. Clearance between driven gear and its shaft is .0006-.002" (.017-.057 mm). Replace gear and shaft if clearance exceeds .004" (.10 mm).

5) Check clearance between pump drive shaft and housing. Clearance range is .0006-.0020" (.017-.057 mm). Replace drive shaft and housing if clearance exceeds .004" (.10 mm).

Reassembly

To reassemble, reverse disassembly procedure. Fill pump cavity with clean engine oil before installing cover. Apply Loctite to oil pump cover bolts.

Installation

To install, reverse removal procedure. Apply a thin coat of grease to "O" ring and install on pump. Coat oil pump mating surfaces with sealant. Ensure that sealant does not enter oil passage. Add engine oil.

ENGINE COOLING

WATER PUMP

Removal

Remove timing belt cover. Remove air pump and drive belt. Loosen alternator and remove drive belt. Drain cooling system until fluid level is below water pump. Remove 2 bolts holding intake pipe to water pump and remove pipe. Remove 4 pump mounting bolts. Remove water pump and gasket.

Installation

To install, reverse removal procedure. Use a new gasket. Fill cooling system.

THERMOSTAT

Removal

Drain cooling system until fluid level is below thermostat housing. Remove spare tire. Disconnect hoses from thermostat housing outlets. Remove 3 housing mounting bolts. Remove housing and gasket.

Installation

To install, reverse removal procedure. Use a new gasket. Fill cooling system.

NOTE: **For further information on cooling systems, see ENGINE COOLING section.**

TIGHTENING SPECIFICATIONS

Application	Ft. Lbs. (N.m)
Alternator Nuts	36 (49)
Breather Pipe-To-Crankcase Bolt	19 (25)
Camshaft Housing Bolts	14 (19)
Camshaft Sprocket Bolt	61 (83)
Crankshaft Pulley Nut	101 (137)
Connecting Rod Cap Nuts	38 (51)
Cylinder Head Bolts (90° Turn/Stage)	
First Stage	35 (47)
Second Stage	70 (95)
Exhaust Manifold Nuts	20 (27)
Flywheel Bolts	61 (83)
Intake Manifold Nuts	20 (27)
Main Bearing Cap Bolts	59 (80)
Spark Plugs	27 (37)
Tensioner Pulley Support Nut	33 (44)
	INCH Lbs. (N.m)
Air Pump Pulley Bolts	7.5 (10)

ENGINE SPECIFICATIONS

GENERAL SPECIFICATIONS

Year	DISPLACEMENT		Fuel System	HP@RPM	Torque Ft. Lbs.@RPM	Compr. Ratio	BORE		STROKE	
	Cu. In.	Liters					In.	mm	In.	mm
1987	68.12	1.1	2 Bbl.	55 @ 6000	52 @ 4600	9.2	3.150	80	2.185	55.5

VALVES

Engine Size & Valve	Head Diam. In. (mm)	Face Angle	Seat Angle	Seat Width In. (mm)	Stem Diameter In. (mm)	Stem Clearance In. (mm)	Valve Lift In. (mm)
1.1L							
Intake	1.053 (26.75)	45°	45°	.080	.3139-.3146 (7.97-7.99)	.0012-.0026 (.030-.066)	.362 (9.20)
Exhaust	1.053 (26.75)	45°	45°	.080	.3139-3146 (7.97-7.99)	.0012-.0026 (.030-.066)	.362 (9.20)

Yugo Engines

1.1L 4-CYLINDER (Cont.)

ENGINE SPECIFICATIONS (Cont.)

CRANKSHAFT MAIN & CONNECTING ROD BEARINGS

Engine	MAIN BEARINGS				CONNECTING ROD BEARINGS		
	Journal Diam. In. (mm)	Clearance In. (mm)	Thrust Bearing	Crankshaft End Play In. (mm)	Journal Diam. In. (mm)	Clearance In. (mm)	Side Play In. (mm)
1.1L	1.9994-2.0002 (50.785-50.805)	.0016-.0033 (.040-.085)	No. 5	.0021-.0104 (.055-.265)	1.7913-1.7920 (44.498-45.518)	.0014-.0034 (.036-.086)	.004-.010 (.10-.25)

PISTONS, PINS & RINGS

Engine	PISTONS	PINS		RINGS		
	Clearance In. (mm)	Piston Fit In. (mm)	Rod Fit In. (mm)	Ring No.	End Gap In. (mm)	Side Clearance In. (mm)
1.1L	.001-.002 (.024-.047)	.0003-.0007 (.008-.018)	Press Fit	No. 1	.0118-.0177 (.30-.45)	.0018-.0030 (.045-.077)
				No. 2	.0079-.0140 (.20-.35)	.0001-.0022 (.0025-.0558)
				Oil	.0079-.0140 (.20-.35)	.0008-.0019 (.02-.04)

CAMSHAFT

Engine	Journal Diam. In. (mm)	Clearance In. (mm)	Lobe Lift In. (mm)
1.1L			
No. 1	1.1787-1.1795 (29.939-29.959)	.0012-.0028 (.03-.07)	In. .362 (9.2)
No. 2	1.8872-1.8878 (47.935-47.950)		Ex. .364 (9.25)
No. 3	1.8951-1.8957 (48.135-48.150)		
No. 4	1.9030-1.9035 (48.335-48.350)		
No. 5	1.9108-1.9114 (48.535-48.550)		

VALVE TIMING

Engine	INTAKE		EXHAUST	
	Open (BTDC)	Close (ABDC)	Open (BBDC)	Close (ATDC)
1.1L	12°	52°	52°	12°

VALVE SPRINGS

Engine	Free Length In. (mm)	PRESSURE Lbs. @ In. (Kg @ mm)	
		Valve Closed	Valve Open
1.1L			
Inner	1.646 (41.8)	33 @ 1.220 (14.9 @ 31.0)	64 @ .846 (28.1 @ 21.5)
Outer	2.122 (53.9)	85 @ 1.417 (38.9 @ 36)	141 @ 1.043 (59.5 @ 26.5)

Engine Cooling

COOLING SYSTEM TROUBLE SHOOTING

CONDITION	POSSIBLE CAUSE	CORRECTION
Engine Overheats With or Without Coolant Loss	Low coolant level	Add coolant, see ENGINE COOLING
	Thermostat stuck closed	Replace thermostat, see ENGINE COOLING
	Faulty fan clutch	Replace fan clutch, see ENGINE COOLING
	Faulty electric fan motor	Replace motor
	Faulty thermal relay switches	Check switches and connections
	Water distribution tube clogged	Flush system, see ENGINE COOLING
	Radiator air flow passages blocked	Clean or replace radiator
	Incorrect coolant concentration	Refill with proper amount of coolant
	Incorrect ignition timing	Reset ignition timing
	Faulty ignition advance	Check and/or replace
	Exhaust system restricted	Correct restriction
	Broken or slipping fan belt	Replace fan belt
	Water pump shaft broken	Replace water pump, see ENGINES
	Leaking freeze plug(s)	Replace freeze plug(s)
	Faulty radiator pressure cap	Replace pressure cap, see ENGINE COOLING
Engine Overheats With Internal Coolant Leakage	Warped or cracked intake manifold	Replace intake manifold, see ENGINES
	Blown cylinder head gasket	Replace head gasket, see ENGINES
	Warped/cracked cylinder head/block	Resurface or replace head or block
Engine Fails to Reach Normal Temperature	Thermostat stuck in open position	Replace thermostat, see ENGINE COOLING
	Temperature gauge or light defective	Inspect gauge, light or sending unit
	Faulty temperature sending unit	Replace sending unit
	Faulty thermal relay switches	Replace switches
	Incorrect thermostat	Replace thermostat, see ENGINE COOLING
	Improper coolant level	Add coolant to proper level
Poor Coolant Flow	Plugged or restricted radiator	Flush or replace radiator
	Restricted cylinder head or block	Flush entire cooling system
	Collapsed lower radiator hose	Replace lower hose
	Faulty water pump	Replace water pump, see ENGINES
Radiator Foaming	Incorrect coolant concentration	Flush system, add proper amount of coolant
Coolant Loss	Radiator, reservoir or heater core leaks	Repair radiator, reservoir or heater
	Water pump seal or gasket leaking	Replace seal or gasket, see ENGINES
	Cylinder head gasket leaking	Replace head gasket, see ENGINES
	Incorrect cylinder head bolt torque	Retighten bolts, see ENGINES
	Air in system	Bleed cooling system, see ENGINE COOLING
	Faulty water control valve	Replace control valve
Recovery System Inoperative	Low coolant level	Add coolant as required
	Leak in system	Inspect system, see ENGINE COOLING
	Radiator cap loose or defective	Inspect and/or replace as required
	Overflow tube clogged or leaking	Remove tube restriction
	Recovery bottle vent restricted	Remove vent restriction
No Coolant Flow Through Heater Core	Plugged return pipe in water pump	Inspect or replace water pump, see ENGINES
	Heater hose collapsed or plugged	Remove restriction and/or replace hose
	Plugged heater core and/or thermostat	Remove blockage in core or housing
	Plugged cylinder head heater flow hole	Flush system, see ENGINE COOLING
	Faulty water valve	Replace water valve
Cooling System Noise	Fan contacting shroud	Reposition fan and/or shroud
	Loose water pump impeller	Replace water pump, see ENGINES
	Dry fan belt	Replace fan belt
	Rough surface on drive pulley	Smooth surface or replace pulley
	Water pump bearing worn	Replace water pump, see ENGINES
	Improper alignment of fan belts	Reposition and/or replace belts

Engine Cooling

GENERAL COOLING SYSTEM SERVICING

DESCRIPTION

The basic liquid cooling system consists of a radiator, water pump, thermostat, electric or belt-driven cooling fan, pressure cap, heater, and various connecting hoses and cooling passages in the block and cylinder head.

MAINTENANCE

DRAINING

Remove radiator cap and open heater control valve to maximum heat position. Open drain cocks or remove plugs in bottom of radiator and engine block. In-line engines usually have one plug or drain cock, while "V" type engines will have 2, one in each bank of cylinders.

CLEANING

A good cleaning compound removes most rust and scale. Follow manufacturer's instructions in the use of cleaner. If considerable rust and scale has to be removed, cooling system should be flushed. Clean radiator air passages with compressed air.

FLUSHING

CAUTION: Some manufacturer's use an aluminum and plastic radiator (identified by a note below the filler neck). Material used for cleaning and flushing must be compatible with aluminum.

1) Back flushing is an effective means of removing cooling system rust and scale. The radiator, engine and heater core should be flushed separately.

2) To flush radiator, connect flushing gun to water outlet of radiator and disconnect water inlet hose. To prevent flooding engine, use a hose connected to radiator inlet. Use air in short bursts to prevent damage to radiator. Continue flushing until water runs clear.

3) To flush engine, remove thermostat and replace housing. Connect flushing gun to water outlet of engine. Disconnect heater hoses from engine. Flush using short air bursts until water runs clean. Flush heater core as described for radiator. Ensure heater valve is set to maximum heat position before flushing heater.

REFILLING

To prevent air from being trapped in engine block, engine should be running when refilling cooling system. After system is full, continue running engine until thermostat is open, then recheck fill level. Do not overfill system.

THERMOSTAT

1) Visually inspect thermostat for corrosion and proper sealing of valve and seat. If satisfactory, suspend thermostat and a thermometer in a container with a 50/50 mixture of coolant and water. *See Fig. 1.*

2) Do not allow thermostat or thermometer to touch bottom of container. Heat water until thermostat just begins to open.

3) Read temperature on thermometer. This is the initial opening temperature and should be within specification. Continue heating water until thermostat is fully open and note temperature. This is the fully opened temperature. If either reading is not to specification, replace thermostat.

Fig. 1: Testing Thermostat in Anti-Freeze/Water Solution

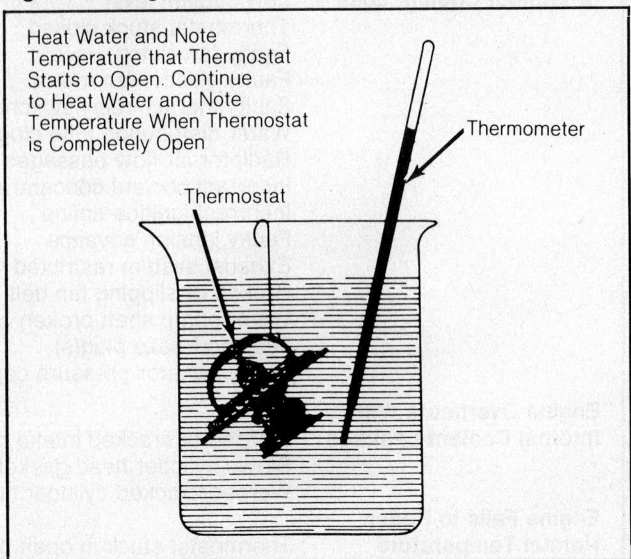

Support thermometer so it does not touch bottom of container.

PRESSURE TESTING

A pressure tester is used to check both radiator cap and complete cooling system. Test components as follows, following tool manufacturer's instructions.

Radiator Cap

Visually inspect radiator cap, then dip cap in water and connect to tester. Pump tester to bring pressure to upper limit of cap specification. If cap fails to hold pressure within specification, replace cap.

Cooling System

1) With engine off, wipe radiator filler neck seat clean. Fill radiator to correct level. Attach tester to radiator and pump until pressure is at upper limit of radiator rating.

2) If pressure drops, inspect for external leaks. If no leaks are apparent, detach tester and run engine until normal operating temperature is reached. Reattach tester and observe. If pressure builds up immediately, a possible leak exists from a faulty head gasket or crack in head or block.

Fig. 2: Testing Radiator Pressure Cap

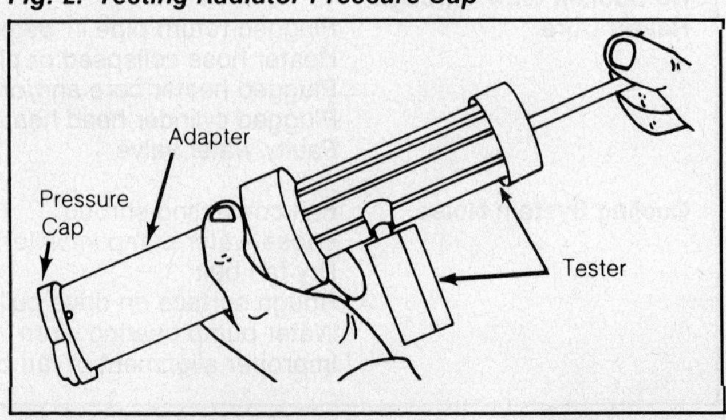

Wet cap gasket before testing.

GENERAL COOLING SYSTEM SERVICING (Cont.)

CAUTION: Pressure may build up quickly. Release any excess pressure or cooling system damage may result.

3) If there is no immediate pressure build up, pump tester to within system pressure range (on radiator cap). Vibration of gauge pointer indicates compression or combustion leak into cooling system. Isolate leak by shorting each spark plug wire to cylinder block. Gauge pointer should stop or decrease vibration when leaking cylinder(s) is shorted.

Fig. 3: Pressure Testing Cooling System

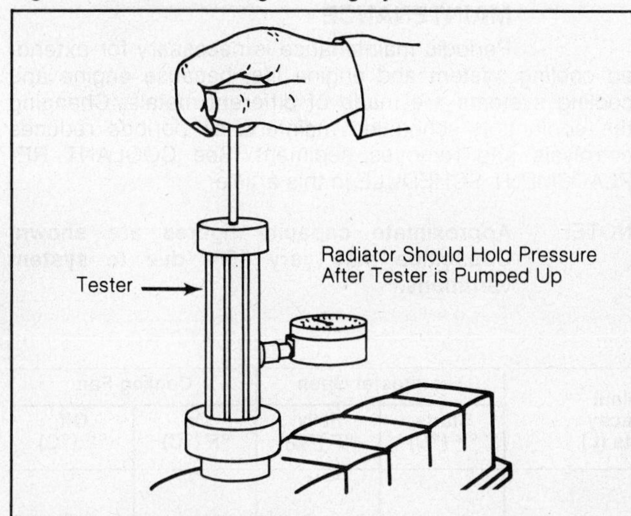

CAUTION: Do not disconnect spark plug wires while engine is operating, or operate engine with spark plug shorted for more than one minute, as catalytic converter may be damaged.

4) Check engine oil and automatic transmission fluid for signs of coolant. If so, an internal leak is indicated. If checks are negative and system holds pressure for 2 minutes, there are no serious leaks.

ANTI-FREEZE CONCENTRATION

NOTE: On models using aluminum engines or cooling system components, refer to Owners Manual for coolant requirements and recommendations. Aluminum components require a different formulation of coolant.

Test coolant concentration using coolant tester. Tester should have a temperature-compensating feature, as failure to take temperature into consideration could cause an error as large as 30°F (16°C). Follow tester manufacturer's instructions.

ELECTRIC COOLING FANS

DESCRIPTION

Electrically-driven fans are actuated by thermal relay switches. Thermal switches turn fan motor(s) on when necessary and shut fan motor(s) off when not needed. Some air conditioned vehicles are equipped with over-ride switches. These switches turn fan motor on whenever air conditioning system is operating. When system is turned off, fan motor control is returned to thermal relay.

TESTING

Disconnect fan motor wire connector and connect it with 14 gauge wire to a 12-volt battery. If fan runs, motor is okay. This indicates car battery, thermal switch, radiator fan switch, coolant relay, timer relay, coolant temperature switch, A/C relay or other component may be defective. If fan motor does not run when connected directly to a good battery, replace fan motor. See WIRING DIAGRAMS section.

Fig. 1: Typical Electric Cooling Fan

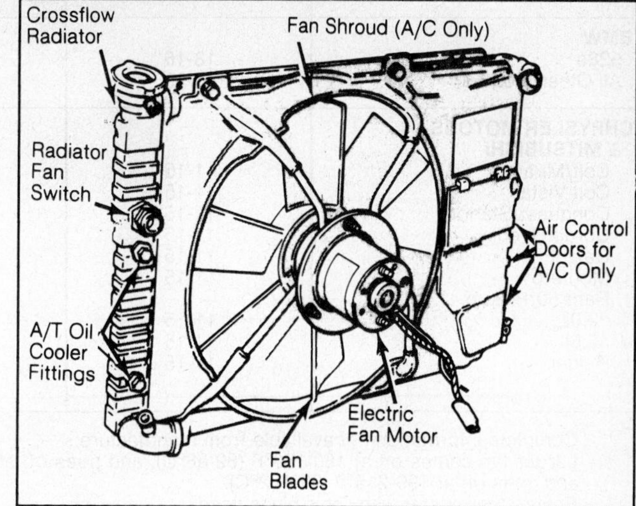

Engine Cooling

ENGINE COOLANT SPECIFICATIONS

DESCRIPTION

THERMOSTAT

Most thermostats are thermal wax pellet type. As coolant temperature rise the wax begins to expand. This expansion overcomes spring tension allowing the thermostat to open. Some thermostats also incorporate an additional bleed hole to allow a small amount of circulation and help eliminate air locks.

PRESSURE CAP

Modern cooling systems use a closed system type cap. This system allows for coolant to expand and build pressure, some coolant is permitted to bleed past the cap into the overflow tank. When the engine cools and coolant contracts, the cap allows the coolant in the overflow tank to siphon back into the system.

The pressure cap also increases pressure in the cooling system. The increased pressure raises the boiling point, one pound of pressure raises the boiling point approximately 3°F (16°C).

COOLANT MIXTURE ·

Engine coolant must be mixed with water to a specific percent. A 100% coolant mixture could cause system overheating or premature system failure. Coolants are designed to function best when mixed with water. The precentage of coolant to water can vary depending on climate condition, but a 50/50 mixture is a standard percentage.

Engine coolant should also include an aluminum protection additive. This will help protect against metal deterioration.

MAINTENANCE

Periodic maintenance is necessary for extended cooling system and engine life, because engine and cooling systems are made of different metals. Changing the coolant at scheduled maintenance periods reduces ectrolysis and removes sediment. See COOLANT REPLACEMENT SCHEDULE in this article.

NOTE: Approximate capacity figures are shown. Capacities may vary 15% due to system variations.

COOLING SYSTEM APPLICATION CHART

Application	Pressure Cap PSI	Coolant Capacity Quarts (L)	Thermostat Open		Cooling Fan	
			Starts °F (°C)	Fully °F (°C)	On °F (°C)	Off °F (°C)
ACURA						
Integra	11-15	6 (5.6)	172 (78)	196 (91)	194 (90)	187 (86)
Legend	14-17	9 (8.8)	172 (78)	196 (91)	194 (90)	187 (86)
ALFA ROMEO [1]						
Milano	10	12.7 (12.0)	182 (83)	203 (95)	187 (86)	.....
AUDI						
4-Cyl.	17-19	7.5 (7.0)	194 (90)	216 (102)	203 (96)	195 (91)
5-Cyl.	17-19	8.6 (8.1)	194 (90)	216 (102)	199 (93)	189 (88)
BMW						
528e	13-16	11.6 (11.0)	176 (81)	203 (95)	.....	.....
All Other Models	13-16	12.7 (12.0)	176 (81)	203 (95)	.....	.....
CHRYSLER MOTORS & MITSUBISHI						
Colt/Mirage	11-15	5.3 (5.0)	190 (88)	212 (100)	185 (85)	178 (81)
Colt Vista	11-15	7.4 (7.0)	190 (88)	212 (100)	185 (85)	178 (81)
Conquest/Starion	11-15	9.7 (9.2)	190 (88)	212 (100)	[2]	[2]
Cordia/Tredia	11-15	8.0 (7.7)	190 (88)	212 (100)	185 (85)	178 (81)
Galant	11-15	8.0 (7.5)	190 (88)	212 (100)	185 (85)	178 (81)
Montero	11-15	9.2 (8.7)	190 (88)	212 (100)	185 (85)	178 (81)
Ram-50/Pickup						
2.0L	11-15	7.4 (7.0)	190 (88)	212 (100)	185 (85)	178 (81)
2.6L	11-15	8.3 (7.9)	190 (88)	212 (100)	185 (85)	178 (81)
Raider	11-15	8.5 (8.0)	190 (88)	212 (100)	.....	.....

[1] - Complete information not available from manufacture.

[2] - Larger fan comes on at 180-190°F (82-88°C), and goes off at 172 -183°F (78-84°C). Smaller fan comes on at 207-217°F (97-103°C), and goes off at 199-216°F (93-102°C).

[3] - Ensure thermostat with jiggle pin is used.

[4] - Specification is given for large fan, small fan (upper temp. switch) comes on at 212°F (100°C)

[5] - Stage 1 is given, stage 2 engages at 198°F (92°C), and disengages at 187°F (87°C).

[6] - On turbo models, standard thermostats begin opening at 176-183°F (80-90°C).

[7] - It is also possible to have a thermostat that begins to open at 203°F (95°C), and is fully open at 212°F (100°C).

[8] - Engine compartment temperature switch comes on at 176°F (80°C), and goes off at 147°F (64°C).

[9] - Two pole switch specifications are given. Three pole switch first stage comes on at 198-208°F (92-98°C), and turns off at 183-196°F (84-91°C). Second stage will come on at 210-221°F (99-105°C), and goes off at 196-219°F (91-104°C).

[10] - First stage is given. Second stage comes on at 203-212°F (94-99°C), and goes off at 188°F (87°C).

[11] - Optional temperature switch comes on at 189°F (87°C).

ENGINE COOLANT SPECIFICATIONS (Cont.)

COOLING SYSTEM APPLICATION CHART (Cont.)

Application	Pressure Cap PSI	Coolant Capacity Quarts (L)	Thermostat Open Starts °F (°C)	Thermostat Open Fully °F (°C)	Cooling Fan On °F (°C)	Cooling Fan Off °F (°C)
FORD MOTOR CO. [1]						
Festiva	12-14	5.3 (5.0)	185 (85)	.....	194 (90)	.....
Merkur XR4Ti	14-18	9.0 (8.5)	192 (89)	212 (100)	210 (98)	.....
Tracer						
Auto. Trans.	11-15	6.3 (6.0)	185 (85)	212 (100)	207 (97)	194 (90)
Man. Trans.	11-15	5.3 (5.0)	185 (85)	212 (100)	207 (97)	194 (90)
GENERAL MOTORS						
Spectrum	13-17	6.8 (6.4)	179 (82)	203 (95)	205 (96)	197 (91)
Sprint	13	4.5 (4.3)	190 (88)	212 (100)	205 (96)	197 (91)
HONDA						
Accord & Prelude	11-15	7.9 (7.5)	180 (82)	203 (95)	193 (90)	183 (84)
Civic (All)						
1.3L	11-15	4.6 (4.4)	173 (78)	196 (91)	194 (89)	187 (86)
1.5L	11-15	5.8 (5.5)	173 (78)	196 (91)	194 (89)	187 (86)
HYUNDAI						
Excel	11-15	5.3 (5.0)	190 (88)	212 (100)	.....	.....
ISUZU						
I-Mark	13-17	6.8 (6.4)	180 (83)	203 (95)	.....	.....
Impulse	13-17	9.5 (9.0)	180 (82)	203 (95)	.....	.....
P'UP						
Diesel	13-17	9.5 (9.0)	180 (82)	203 (95)	.....	.....
Gas	13-17	8.5 (8.0)	180 (82)	203 (95)	.....	.....
Turbo Diesel	13-17	11.2 (10.6)	180 (82)	203 (95)	.....	.....
Trooper II	13-17	8.5 (8.0)	180 (82)	203 (95)	.....	.....
JAGUAR						
XJ6 III	15	19.2 (18.2)	190 (87)	203 (94)	205 (96)	167 (75)
XJS	15	22.4 (21.2)	[3] 178 (81)	203 (94)	205 (96)	167 (75)
MAZDA						
Pickup (All)	11-15	7.9 (7.5)	190 (87)	212 (100)	.....	.....
RX7						
Non-Turbo	11-15	7.7 (7.3)	180 (81)	203 (95)	207 (97)	194 (90)
Turbo	11-15	9.2 (8.7)	180 (81)	203 (95)	207 (97)	194 (90)
323						
Auto. Trans.	11-15	6.3 (6.0)	185 (85)	212 (100)	207 (97)	194 (90)
Man. Trans.	11-15	5.3 (5.0)	185 (85)	212 (100)	207 (97)	194 (90)
626	11-15	7.4 (7.0)	191 (87)	212 (100)	207 (97)	194 (90)
MERCEDES-BENZ [1]						
190D, 190E (2.3L)	.....	8.5 (8.0)	.....	.....	.....	.....
190E (2.6L), 300D, 300E, 260E	.....	9.5 (9.0)	.....	.....	.....	.....
300SDL, 300D, 300TD	.....	10.6 (10.1)	.....	.....	.....	.....
420SEL	.....	13.7 (13.0)	.....	.....	.....	.....
560SEC, 560SEL, 560SL	.....	13.7 (13.0)	.....	.....	.....	.....

1 - Complete information not available from manufacture.
2 - Larger fan comes on at 180-190°F (82-88°C), and goes off at 172 -183°F (78-84°C). Smaller fan comes on at 207-217°F (97-103°C), and goes off at 199-216°F (93-102°C).
3 - Ensure thermostat with jiggle pin is used.
4 - Specification is given for large fan, small fan (upper temp. switch) comes on at 212°F (100°C)
5 - Stage 1 is given, stage 2 engages at 198°F (92°C), and disengages at 187°F (87°C).
6 - On turbo models, standard thermostats begin opening at 176-183°F (80-90°C).
7 - It is also possible to have a thermostat that begins to open at 203°F (95°C), and is fully open at 212°F (100°C).
8 - Engine compartment temperature switch comes on at 176°F (80°C), and goes off at 147°F (64°C).
9 - Two pole switch specifications are given. Three pole switch first stage comes on at 198-208°F (92-98°C), and turns off at 183-196°F (84-91°C). Second stage will come on at 210-221°F (99-105°C), and goes off at 196-219°F (91-104°C).
10 - First stage is given. Second stage comes on at 203-212°F (94-99°C), and goes off at 188°F (87°C).
11 - Optional temperature switch comes on at 189°F (87°C).

Engine Cooling

ENGINE COOLANT SPECIFICATIONS (Cont.)

COOLING SYSTEM APPLICATION CHART (Cont.)

Application	Pressure Cap PSI	Coolant Capacity Quarts (L)	Thermostat Open		Cooling Fan	
			Starts °F (°C)	Fully °F (°C)	On °F (°C)	Off °F (°C)
NISSAN [1]						
Maxima	11-14	9.7 (9.2)	170 (77)	194 (90)	[4]	[4]
Pathfinder & Pickup						
2.4L	13	8.7 (8.2)	180 (82)	203 (95)	.....	.....
3.0L	13	10.5 (10.0)	180 (82)	203 (95)	.....	.....
Pulsar NX						
OHV	13	3.0 (2.8)	180 (82)	203 (95)	194 (90)	.....
DOHC	13	3.6 (3.4)	180 (82)	203 (95)	194 (90)	.....
Sentra	13	5.6 (5.3)	180 (82)	203 (95)	194 (90)	.....
Stanza						
Coupe	13	8.0 (7.6)	180 (82)	203 (95)	185 (85)	.....
Wagon	13	7.1 (6.7)	180 (82)	203 (95)	185 (85)	.....
Van						
Single Heater	13	9.2 (8.7)	180 (82)	203 (95)	.....	.....
Front & Rear Heater	13	9.6 (9.1)	180 (82)	203 (95)	.....	.....
200SX	13	9.1 (8.6)	180 (82)	203 (95)	.....	.....
300ZX						
Non-Turbo	11-14	11.1 (10.5)	170 (77)	194 (90)	.....	.....
Turbo	11-14	11.6 (11.0)	170 (77)	194 (90)	212 (100)	.....
PEUGEOT						
2.0L	14.3	7.9 (7.5)	179 (81)	205 (96)	[5] 190 (88)	[5] 181 (83)
2.2L Non-Turbo	14.3	7.9 (7.5)	179 (81)	205 (96)	[5] 190 (88)	[5] 181 (83)
2.2L Turbo	14.3	10.0 (9.5)	179 (81)	205 (96)	[5] 190 (88)	[5] 181 (83)
2.8L (V6)	14.3	10.0 (9.5)	179 (81)	205 (96)	[5] 190 (88)	[5] 181 (83)
PORSCHE						
944	22	8.5 (8.0)	182 (83)	194 (90)	.....	.....
SAAB						
900	13-18	10.5 (10.0)	[6] 191 (88)	.....	199 (93)	190 (88)
9000	13-18	9.5 (9.0)	[6] 191 (88)	.....	199 (93)	190 (88)
STERLING						
825	15	9.8 (9.2)	172 (78)	196 (91)	205 (96)	198 (92)
SUBARU						
All Models						
Except Justy	11	5.8 (5.5)	191 (88)	212 (98)	203 (94)	.....
Justy	11	4.5 (4.3)	185 (84)	208 (98)	198 (92)	.....
SUZUKI						
Samurai	12.8	5.3 (5.0)	[7] 179 (82)	[7] 203 (95)	.....	.....

[1] - Complete information not available from manufacture.
[2] - Larger fan comes on at 180-190°F (82-88°C), and goes off at 172 -183°F (78-84°C). Smaller fan comes on at 207-217°F (97-103°C), and goes off at 199-216°F (93-102°C).
[3] - Ensure thermostat with jiggle pin is used.
[4] - Specification is given for large fan, small fan (upper temp. switch) comes on at 212°F (100°C)
[5] - Stage 1 is given, stage 2 engages at 198°F (92°C), and disengages at 187°F (87°C).
[6] - On turbo models, standard thermostats begin opening at 176-183°F (80-90°C).
[7] - It is also possible to have a thermostat that begins to open at 203°F (95°C), and is fully open at 212°F (100°C).
[8] - Engine compartment temperature switch comes on at 176°F (80°C), and goes off at 147°F (64°C).
[9] - Two pole switch specifications are given. Three pole switch first stage comes on at 198-208°F (92-98°C), and turns off at 183-196°F (84-91°C). Second stage will come on at 210-221°F (99-105°C), and goes off at 196-219°F (91-104°C).
[10] - First stage is given. Second stage comes on at 203-212°F (94-99°C), and goes off at 188°F (87°C).
[11] - Optional temperature switch comes on at 189°F (87°C).

ENGINE COOLANT SPECIFICATIONS (Cont.)

COOLING SYSTEM APPLICATION CHART (Cont.)

Application	Pressure Cap PSI	Coolant Capacity Quarts (L)	Thermostat Open		Cooling Fan	
			Starts °F (°C)	Fully °F (°C)	On °F (°C)	Off °F (°C)
TOYOTA						
Camry						
W/Heater or A/C	11-15	7.4 (7.0)	180 (82)	203 (95)	194 (90)	181 (83)
W/O Heater or A/C	11-15	6.9 (6.5)	180 (82)	203 (95)	194 (90)	181 (83)
Celica	11-15	7.2 (6.8)	180 (82)	203 (95)	194 (90)	181 (83)
Corolla						
FWD	11-15	6.3 (6.0)	180 (82)	203 (95)	194 (90)	181 (83)
RWD	11-15	5.9 (5.6)	180 (82)	203 (95)	.....	.....
FX-16	11-15	6.3 (6.0)	180 (82)	203 (95)	199 (93)	181 (83)
Cressida	11-15	8.7 (8.2)	191 (88)	212 (100)	194 (90)	181 (83)
Land Cruiser	11-15	17.4 (16.5)	191 (88)	212 (100)	.....	.....
MR2	11-15	13.5 (12.8)	180 (82)	203 (95)	[8] 199 (93)	[8] 181 (83)
Pickup, 4Runner	11-15	8.9 (8.4)	191 (88)	212 (100)	.....	.....
Supra	11-15	8.6 (8.1)	191 (88)	212 (100)	.....	.....
Tercel	11-15	4.9 (4.6)	180 (82)	203 (95)	194 (90)	181 (83)
Van						
2WD	11-15	8.9 (8.4)	180 (82)	203 (95)	.....	.....
4WD	11-15	7.8 (7.4)	180 (82)	203 (95)	.....	.....
VOLKSWAGEN						
Cabriolet	17-21	5.1 (4.8)	185 (85)	221 (105)	[9] 203 (94)	[9] 189 (86)
Golf, GTI & Fox	17-21	7.3 (6.9)	185 (85)	221 (105)	[9] 203 (94)	[9] 189 (86)
Jetta (All)	17-21	7.3 (6.9)	185 (85)	221 (105)	[9] 203 (94)	[9] 189 (86)
Scirocco	17-21	5.1 (4.8)	185 (85)	221 (105)	[9] 203 (94)	[9] 189 (86)
Quantum (All)						
4-Cyl	17-19	6.3 (6.0)	185 (85)	221 (105)	203 (94)	195 (86)
5-Cyl	17-19	8.6 (8.1)	189 (87)	216 (102)	[9] 202 (94)	[9] 190 (87)
Vanagon	17-21	18.5 (17.5)	185 (85)	221 (105)	[10] 197 (91)	[10] 98 (18)
VOLVO						
240 Models						
Auto. Trans.	[11] 9.4-12.3	10.4 (9.8)	198 (92)	215 (102)	212 (100)	203 (95)
Man. Trans.	[11] 9.4-12.3	10.6 (10.0)	198 (92)	215 (102)	212 (100)	203 (95)
740 Models	[11] 9.4-12.3	10.0 (9.5)	198 (92)	215 (102)	212 (100)	203 (95)
760 Models						
GLE	9.4-12.3	10.6 (10.0)	198 (92)	215 (102)	[11] 212 (100)	203 (95)
Turbo	9.4-12.3	10.0 (9.5)	198 (92)	215 (102)	[11] 212 (100)	203 (95)
YUGO [1]						
GV	14.2	6.9 (6.5)	180 (85)	.....	198 (92)	188 (87)

1 - Complete information not available from manufacture.
2 - Larger fan comes on at 180-190°F (82-88°C), and goes off at 172 -183°F (78-84°C). Smaller fan comes on at 207-217°F (97-103°C), and goes off at 199-216°F (93-102°C).
3 - Ensure thermostat with jiggle pin is used.
4 - Specification is given for large fan, small fan (upper temp. switch) comes on at 212°F (100°C)
5 - Stage 1 is given, stage 2 engages at 198°F (92°C), and disengages at 187°F (87°C).
6 - On turbo models, standard thermostats begin opening at 176-183°F (80-90°C).
7 - It is also possible to have a thermostat that begins to open at 203°F (95°C), and is fully open at 212°F (100°C).
8 - Engine compartment temperature switch comes on at 176°F (80°C), and goes off at 147°F (64°C).
9 - Two pole switch specifications are given. Three pole switch first stage comes on at 198-208°F (92-98°C), and turns off at 183-196°F (84-91°C). Second stage will come on at 210-221°F (99-105°C), and goes off at 196-219°F (91-104°C).
10 - First stage is given. Second stage comes on at 203-212°F (94-99°C), and goes off at 188°F (87°C).
11 - Optional temperature switch comes on at 189°F (87°C).

Heater Core Replacement

ACURA

HEATER SYSTEMS ONLY

HEATER CORE ASSEMBLY

Removal (Integra)

Disconnect negative battery cable. Drain radiator coolant. Place drip pan under heater hoses and disconnect heater hoses at firewall. Disconnect heater valve cable from heater valve. Remove heater lower mounting nut. Remove console. Disconnect air mix cable from heater. Remove dashboard. Disconnect wire harness. Remove 2 heater mounting bolts. Pull heater away from body.

Installation

Install in reverse order of removal. Apply sealant to grommets. Do not interchange inlet and outlet hoses. Secure hose clamps. Loosen radiator bleed bolt. Refill radiator and reservoir tank with coolant. Tighten bleed bolt after trapped air has escaped. Connect cables and ensure proper adjustment.

MANUAL A/C-HEATER SYSTEMS

EVAPORATOR

Removal (Integra)

1) Disconnect battery negative terminal. Discharge the refrigerant. Disconnect receiver-drier line and suction hose from evaporator.

NOTE: **Cap the open fittings immediately to keep moisture and dirt out of the system.**

2) Remove screws, bolt and glove box frame. Remove the headlight retractor control unit with the bracket. Remove the console box and bracket. Unbolt dashboard lower bracket, and pry to ease evaporator removal.

Installation

Reverse removal procedure to install.

Removal (Legend)

1) Disconnect battery negative terminal. Discharge refrigerant. Disconnect receiver-drier line and suction hose from evaporator.

NOTE: **Cap the open fittings immediately to keep moisture out of the system.**

2) Remove glove box lower cover and glove box. Remove glove box frame and side duct. Disconnect wire harness from evaporator sensor connector. Remove tapping screws and mounting bolts. Pull evaporator away from the body.

Installation

Reverse removal procedure to install.

AUTOMATIC A/C-HEATER SYSTEMS

HEATER ASSEMBLY

Removal (Legend Coupe)

Removal

1) Drain radiator coolant. Place drain pan under heater hoses (as coolant will damage painted surfaces). Loosen clamp and disconnect heater hoses at heater.

Fig. 1: Integra & Legend Evaporator Assemblies

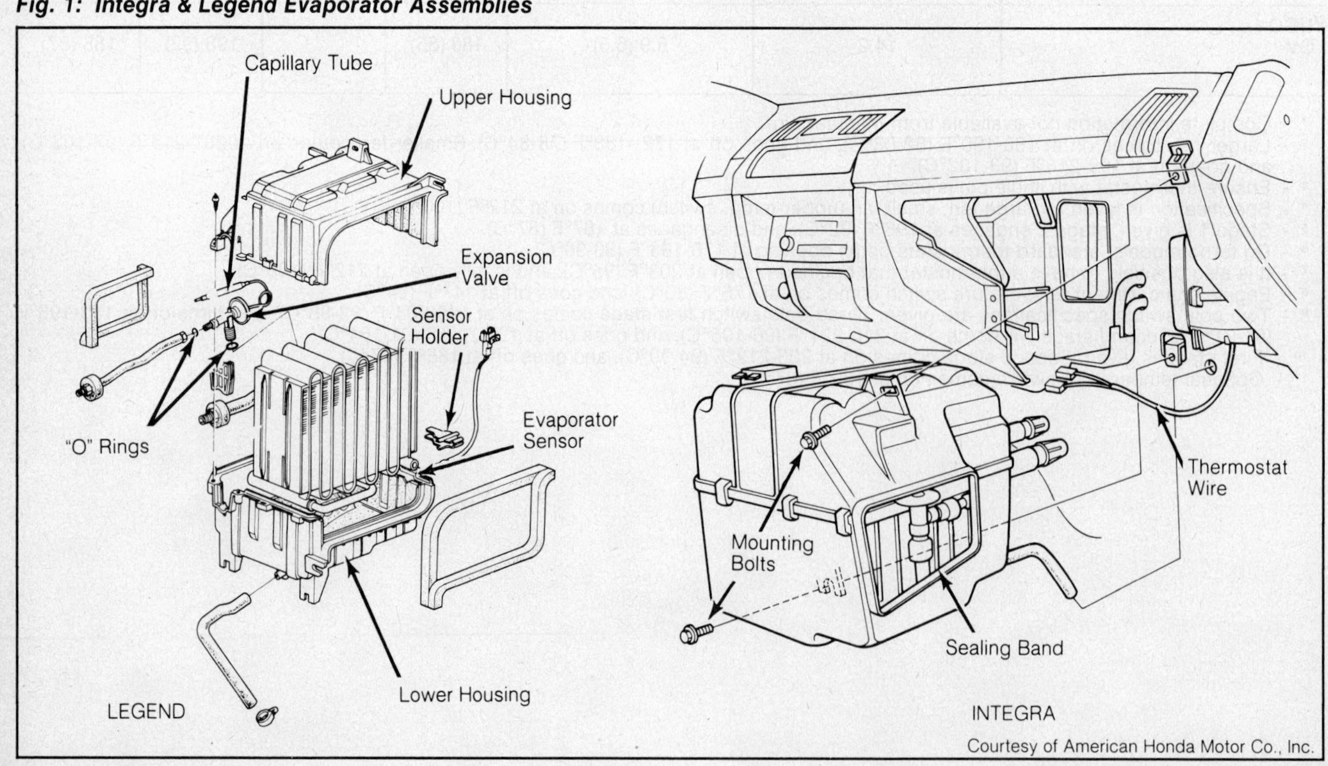

Courtesy of American Honda Motor Co., Inc.

Heater Core Replacement

ACURA (Cont.)

Fig. 2: Dashboard & Center Console Removal

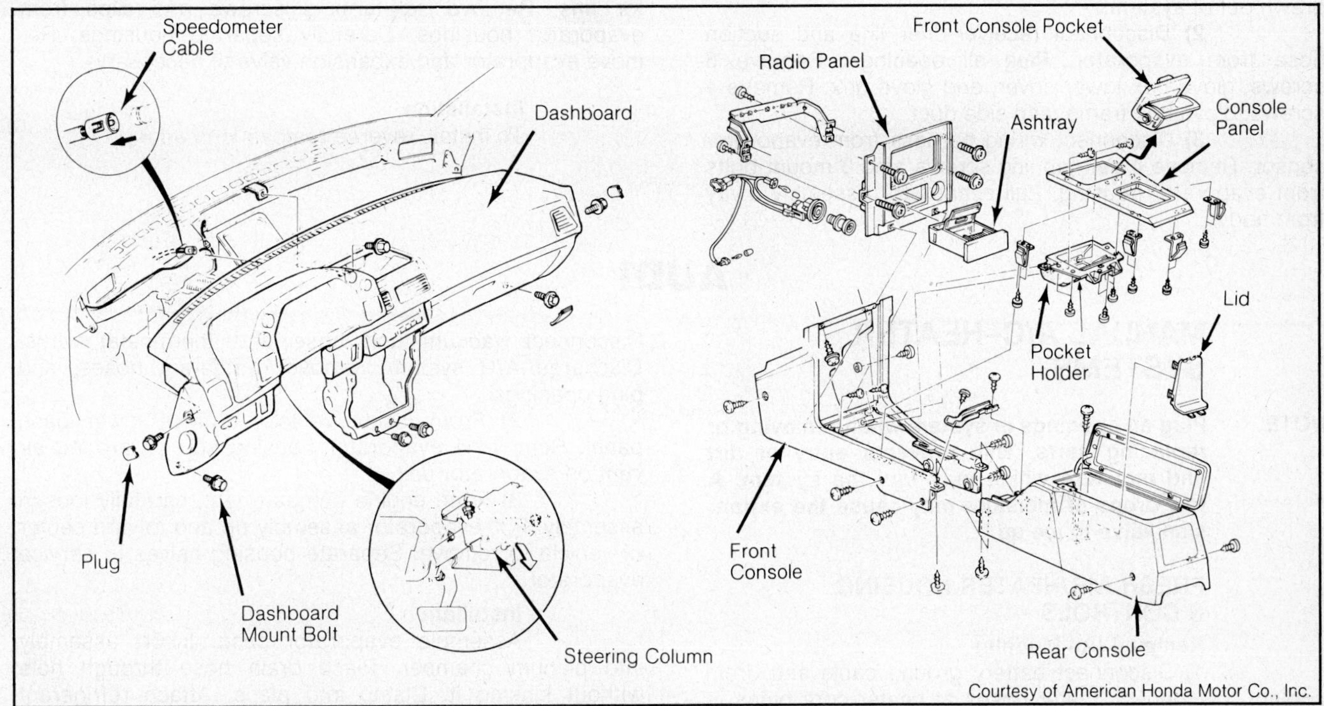

2) Remove dashboard. See DASHBOARD in this article. Remove side ducts. Disconnect wiring harness and vacuum hoses. Remove 2 heater mounting bolts, 2 nuts, and heater assembly from body.

Installation

To install, reverse removal procedure. Apply sealant to grommets. DO NOT interchange inlet/outlet hoses and make sure hose clamps are secure. Recharge A/C system and test system performance.

DASHBOARD

Removal (Legend Coupe)

1) Remove steering wheel, dashboard lower panel, and left air duct. Remove bolts, hood release, and disconnect hood release cable. Grasp parking brake lever and set parking brakes. Remove front center console pocket.

2) Remove 2 screws, console panel, an pocket holder. Remove 14 screws and front console. Unplug wire harness from connector holder and remove dashboard ground strap (above left air duct opening).

3) Remove radio panel (4 screws). Unplug wiring harness connectors, antenna cables, and wire tie. Remove radio assembly. Disconnect heater control cable(s). Remove center dashboard pocket (above clock).

4) Lower steering column. Remove 6 dashboard mount bolts (one in glove box opening, one in pocket opening, 2 on dashboard ends, and 2 on center console area). Pull dashboard toward rear of vehicle and disconnect speedometer cable.

Installation

To install, reverse removal procedure. Make sure dashboard fits correctly onto body. Before tightening dashboard mount bolts, ensure wiring harnesses are not pinched and that dashboard is not interfering with heater control cable(s).

EVAPORATOR

Removal

1) Disconnect negative battery terminal. Slowly discharge refrigerant from A/C system. DO NOT allow

Fig. 3: Evaporator Housing Assembly

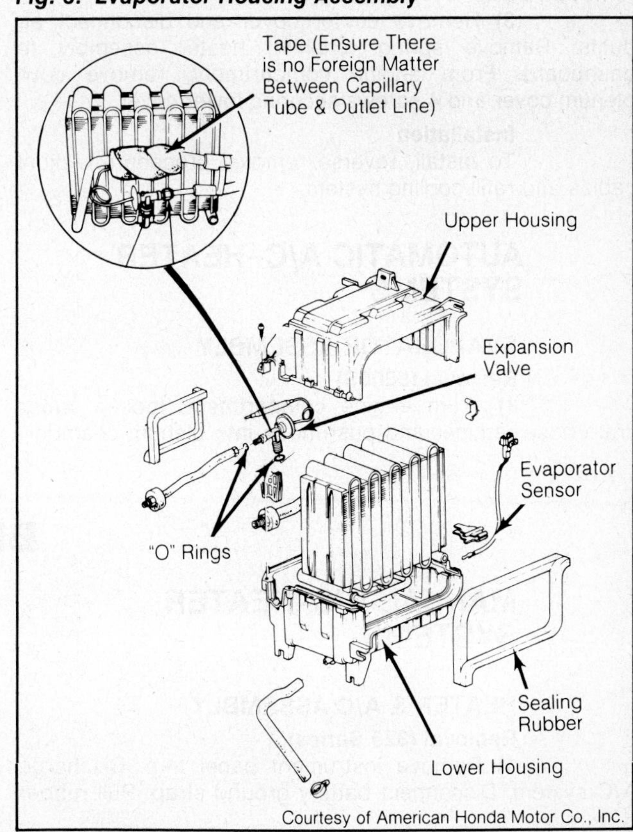

Heater Core Replacement

ACURA (Cont.)

refrigerant to escape too fast, as refrigerant oil will be drawn out of system.

2) Disconnect receiver-drier line and suction hose from evaporator. Plug all openings. Remove 5 screws, glove box lower cover, and glove box. Remove 4 screws, glove box frame, and side duct.

3) Disconnect wiring harness from evaporator sensor. Remove 4 self-tapping screws amd 3 mount bolts from evaporator housing. Pull evaporator assembly away from body.

4) Pull evaporator sensor away from evaporator fins. Remove self-tapping screws and clips from evaporator housings. Carefully separate housings. Remove evaporator and expansion valve (if necessary).

Installation

To install, reverse removal procedure.

AUDI

MANUAL A/C-HEATER SYSTEMS

NOTE: **Plug all openings in system when removing or replacing parts. This prevents entry of dirt and moisture which may foul the system. A few drops of moisture may cause the expansion valve to ice up.**

FRESH AIR/HEATER HOUSING & CONTROLS

Removal (All Models)

1) Disconnect battery ground cable and drain coolant. Disconnect heater hoses at heater core pipes in engine compartment. Disconnect temperature cable at water valve.

2) Remove console (if equipped). Remove left and right covers below dashboard. Pull out heater control knobs. Remove heater selector trim plate. Loosen screws for heater controls. Loosen screws for control panel and remove 4 center cover screws.

3) Remove center cover and disconnect air ducts. Remove spring retaining heater assembly to dashboard. From engine compartment, remove cowl plenum cover and 4 screws securing lower cover.

Installation

To install, reverse removal procedure. Adjust cables and refill cooling system.

AUTOMATIC A/C-HEATER SYSTEMS

EVAPORATOR ASSEMBLY

Removal (5000S)

1) From engine compartment, loosen water drain hose retainer and push hose into plenum chamber. Disconnect vacuum unit hose and thermostat wires. Discharge A/C system, remove refrigerant hoses, and plug openings.

2) From inside vehicle, remove lower dash panel. Remove 4 evaporator housing screws around air vent on evaporator unit.

3) From engine compartment, carefully loosen assembly. Pull evaporator assembly up and toward center of vehicle to remove. Separate housing halves to service evaporator.

Installation

Assemble evaporator case. Insert assembly into plenum chamber. Place drain hose through hole without kinking it. Clamp into place. Attach refrigerant lines loosely, and cement gasket into place around opening. Install screws, tighten hoses, and recharge system.

HEATER ASSEMBLY

Removal (5000S)

1) From engine compartment, disconnect battery cable, thermostat wiring, evaporator-heater duct clamp, temperature control cable and vacuum hose.

2) Remove electrical wiring, loosen restraining strap and remove coolant reservoir cap. Clamp heater hoses closed near heater core. Disconnect hoses from core. Upper hose goes to water pump, lower to cylinder head.

3) From inside vehicle, disconnect vacuum lines. Disconnect air ducts and electrical wiring. Remove 4 screws around evaporator housing opening. Lift heater assembly up into engine compartment. Remove grommet and control cable. Loosen clips and wiring harness.

Installation

To install, reverse removal procedure. Seal all air duct connections carefully to prevent air leaks.

BMW

MANUAL A/C-HEATER SYSTEMS

HEATER & A/C ASSEMBLY

Removal (325 Series)

1) Remove instrument panel trim. Discharge A/C system. Disconnect battery ground strap. Pull rubber sealing strip from firewall. Cut wire straps attaching wiring harness to heater cover and pull wiring out of way.

2) Remove cover attaching bolts and cover. Drain cooling system and disconnect heater hoses. Disconnect heater system wiring harness connector. Unscrew nut and bolt and remove heater mounting bracket. Disconnect and plug refrigerant lines.

3) Remove connector between heater and rear area heater duct on right and left sides. Unscrew mounting nuts and remove heater assembly with by-pass flaps closed.

Installation

To install, reverse removal procedure, making sure that all seals are installed correctly. Check oil level. Check system for proper operation.

EVAPORATOR ASSEMBLY

Removal (325 Series)

1) Disconnect battery ground cable. Remove package tray. Remove left side instrument panel trim. Discharge A/C system. Open glove box. Unscrew bolt and remove glove box trim.

2) Disconnect pins of retaining straps. Loosen nuts and remove glove box. Disconnect refrigerant lines from evaporator and plug. Remove attaching bolts and cover of blower motor.

3) Pull off electrical connecting plugs. Unscrew attaching bolts. Remove temperature switch and sensor from evaporator housing at the same time. Pull evaporator out of housing.

Installation

To install, reverse removal procedure, using new line coupling seals. Wrap line with refrigerant line insulating tape after installation.

HEATER ASSEMBLY

Removal (528e, 535i & 535is)

1) Disconnect battery ground. Pull up rubber strip and remove bolts and nuts from upper heater wall. *See Fig. 4.* Detach both heater hoses. Following procedures for removal of control panel, remove center console, leaving control panel and radio in vehicle.

2) Unscrew bolts from heater cover and remove cover. Remove insulating compound and disconnect pipe connections. Disconnect plug from multiple connector. Pull off plug from temperature sensor.

3) Unscrew bolts from blower support bracket and evaporator housing. Remove left and right fasteners from evaporator housing and remove housing. Pull off plugs, lift out air guides and remove heater.

Fig. 4: Disconnecting Upper Heater Wall

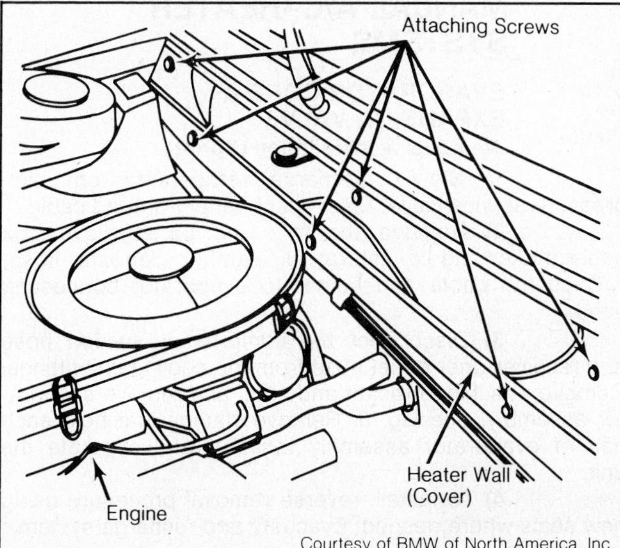

Installation

To install heater assembly, reverse removal procedures and note the following: replace all gaskets. Make sure heater ducts are attached properly. Add engine coolant and check heater operation.

HEATER CORE

Removal (528e, 535i & 535is)

Remove heater assembly from vehicle as outlined. Pull off air ducts. Lift housing sections out of holders. Lift out all clamps on heater. Take heater housing sections apart. Remove heater core.

EVAPORATOR HOUSING ASSEMBLY

Removal & Installation (528e, 535i & 535is)

1) Disconnect battery ground lead. Remove instrument panel at bottom left. Remove tray. Discharge refrigerant from system.

2) Unscrew bolts and take off trim panel. Remove insulation and disconnect lines. Insert plugs in open ends of lines immediately. Disconnect electrical plug.

3) Pull off plug on temperature sensor. Unscrew bolts and remove brackets. Unscrew bolts on left and right sides. Open left and right fasteners to remove evaporator housing. To install, reverse removal procedure.

HEATER & HEATER CORE

Removal (635CSi & L6)

1) Remove evaporator assembly. Remove right and left side mounting bolt. Disconnect and remove coolant hoses from heater core. Unscrew bolts and take off cover. Unscrew nuts on both sides of blower motor and remove heater assembly.

2) To remove heater core, remove 4 air guides. Push back retaining bar and remove blower shells. Lift off 13 retaining clips on heater housing. Take housing sections apart. Remove heater core.

Installation

To install, reverse removal procedure, making sure bearings of distributor flaps are located in their bores. Glue new foam rubber frame on heater core.

EVAPORATOR ASSEMBLY

Removal (635CSi & L6)

1) Remove evaporator housing. Lift off 7 clamps. Remove bolt from between 2 blower wheels. Cut out plastic rivet. Remove upper housing section with blower. Pull evaporator and expansion valve out of housing.

2) Unscrew connections from refrigerant lines and plugs. Remove sealing compound and disconnect clamp from evaporator. Remove evaporator.

Installation

1) To install evaporator and expansion valve, reverse removal procedure. Secure coil on pipe with clamp and protect against ambient temperature with insulating compound.

2) When reconnecting wires, refer to wiring diagram for wire colors and location. When attaching refrigeration lines to evaporator, use new seals and coat threads with refrigerant oil. Recharge A/C system. Check oil level and system operation.

Heater Core Replacement

BMW (Cont.)

REAR A/C UNIT

Removal (635CSi & L6)

Remove cooling box trim on left and right sides. Remove 4 retaining screws. Remove upper section trim panel. Disconnnect electrical plug. Remove rear seats. Remove 4 retaining screws from each side. Remove side trim panels. Remove air duct retaining screws and remove air duct. Remove electrical plug and remove transistor.

Installation

To install, reverse removal procedure.

AUTOMATIC A/C-HEATER SYSTEMS

HEATER ASSEMBLY

Removal & Installation (735i)

1) Drain coolant and discharge A/C system. Remove instrument panel. Pull off rubber trim. Remove wiring and drain hose from expansion tank. Remove expansion tank and set aside. DO NOT bend coolant hose.

2) Cut 5 wiring straps (on firewall). Remove screws and pull up cover. Disconnect heater hoses. Remove 5 bolts and nut from heater assembly (engine compartment side).

3) Remove 3 bolts from heater assembly, lift out ventilator ducts, and remove heater assembly. To install, reverse removal procedure.

HEATER CORE

Removal & Installation (735i)

1) Drain coolant. Remove center console. Remove 3 bolts from heater assembly. Remove 2 bolts and lift out right holder (next to accelerator pedal). Remove front ventilator drive motor. Disconnect in-car temperature sensor.

2) Remove 3 screws, loose wire straps, clips, and take off cover. Remove 8 bolts and heater pipes. Remove heater core from right side. To install, reverse removal procedure.

EVAPORATOR

Removal & Installation (735i)

1) Discharge A/C system. Remove instrument panel. Pull off rubber trim. Reove wiring and and drain hose from expansion tank. Remove expansion tank and set aside. DO NOT bend coolant hose. Cut 5 wiring straps (on firewall).

2) Remove screws and pull up cover. Remove nut, 2 screws, and bolt. Remove wiring, cut wire straps, and set aside. Disconnect wiring and gas cylinder rod from left side of glove box. Pull off trim, detach clips, and remove glove box.

3) Detach clips and lift out holder. Remove 3 screws and evaporator cover. Remove screw and lift out pipe. Remove expansion valve and evaporator. To install, reverse removal procedure.

CHEVROLET

NOTE: **For information covering Chevrolet Spectrum HEATER CORE REMOVAL & INSTALLATION, refer to the ISUZU HEATER SYSTEM article in this manual.**

HEATER BLOWER RESISTOR

Removal & Installation

Disconnect battery gound cable. Disconnect resistor electrical connector. Remove attaching screws and resistor. See TESTING in this article. To install, reverse removal procedure.

HEATER SYSTEMS ONLY

HEATER CORE

Removal & Installation (Sprint)

1) Drain radiator and disconnect both heater hoses from heater core. Remove glove box. Remove defroster hoses from heater case. Disconnect wiring connectors from blower motor and resistor.

2) Disconnect 3 control cables from heater case side levers. Remove center register, ashtray upper plate, and instrument panel stay.

3) On all models, remove heater assembly attaching nuts, and remove assembly. Remove retaining clips and separate housing halves. Remove heater core. To install, reverse removal procedure.

BLOWER MOTOR

Removal & Installation (Sprint)

Disconnect left defroster hose at blower motor case. Disconnect blower motor lead wire. Remove 3 attaching screws and blower motor. To install, reverse removal procedure.

MANUAL A/C-HEATER SYSTEMS

EVAPORATOR CORE & EXPANSION VALVE

Removal & Installation (Sprint)

1) Slowly discharge refrigerant from high pressure service valve. Disconnect battery ground cable.

2) Remove the following parts: glove box upper striker and lid, ashtray, air damper, defroster hose, A/C control cable and heater to evaporator connecting band.

3) Disconnect the compressor suction hose and receiver-drier outlet hose from the cooling unit fittings. Remove attaching bracket and nuts, and remove evaporator assembly. *See Fig. 5.* Remove clamps that hold each half of evaporator assembly together and separate the unit.

4) To install, reverse removal procedure using new seals where needed. Evacuate and recharge system.

CHEVROLET (Cont.)

Fig. 5: Sprint Evaporator Housing

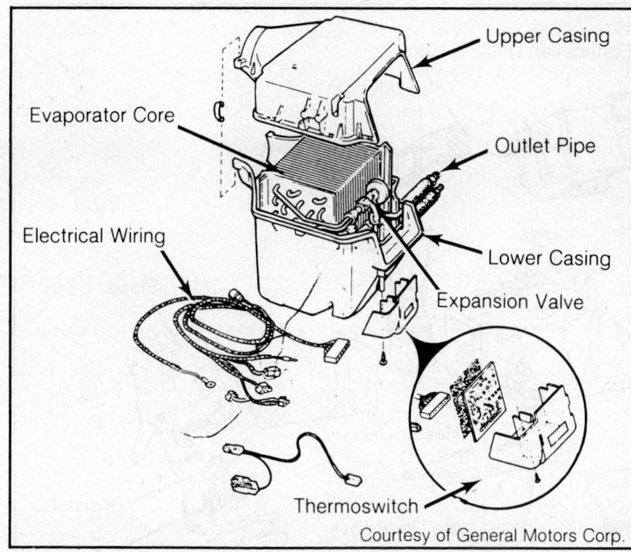

Spectrum is similar.

Removal & Installation (Spectrum)

1) Remove the insulator at outlet of evaporator and blower joint. Remove the thermo switch from the upper case. Remove the clips retaining the upper and lower halves of the evaporator case, remove the upper half of housing.

2) Carefully pull the thermoswitch capillary tube from the evaporator core. Remove the thermoswitch. Remove the evaporator core with the expansion valve, inlet and outlet lines attached.

3) Peel the insulation tape from the sensor expansion valve and the equalizer line connection. Disconnect the expansion valve intake pipe connection, the equalizer line and the evaporator outlet line and remove the core.

4) Cap or plug all open connections immediately. To install, reverse removal procedure, using new seals where needed. Evacuate and recharge system.

CHRYSLER MOTORS & MITSUBISHI

NOTE: **For information on Mitsubishi Precis heater, refer to HYUNDAI EXCEL & MITSUBISHI PRECIS Heater Systems article.**

NOTE: **For the purposes of this article, "Pickups" will refer to both Chrysler Motors Ram-50 and Mitsubishi Pickups.**

HEATER SYSTEMS

Chrysler Motors: Colt, Colt Vista, Raider, Ram-50
Mitsubishi: Cordia, Mirage, Montero, Pickup, Tredia, Van/Wagon

HEATER ASSEMBLY

Removal (Colt, Colt Vista & Mirage)

Disconnect battery ground cable. Move lever to "WARM" position. Drain engine coolant. Remove instrument panel. Remove the duct between the heater unit and blower assembly. Disconnect the heater hose at heater assembly. Remove heater assembly.

Installation

To install, reverse removal procedure. Make sure that hoses are clamped tightly and heater control valve is open while cooling system is refilled.

Removal (Conquest & Starion)

1) Remove steering wheel and column switch from steering shaft. Remove instrument cluster assembly. Remove front and rear console box assembly. Remove cover under instrument panel and glove box.

2) Insert tip of removal tool (MB990784) into space between instrument panel side cover and instrument panel side pad. Twist tool to remove left and right instrument panel side covers. Remove hood lock release handle and fuse block.

3) Insert a screwdriver from door glass side, and twist and pry side defroster grille forward to pull it out. Remove heater control knob. Remove screws, bolts and speed nuts from instrument panel.

4) Remove ash tray and light connector. Remove side defroster duct at instrument panel side. Remove main wiring harness connector for glove box, rear defogger, cigar lighter, rear wiper and rheostat.

5) Remove clock and pull instrument panel outward. Remove center reinforcement bolts. Loosen clamp for main harness. Remove panel.

6) Remove center ventilator duct, defroster duct, and lap heater duct. Remove center reinforcement bracket. Remove heater unit.

Installation (Conquest & Starion)

1) To install, reverse removal procedure. Install heater hoses and tighten clamps. The hose with painted mark should be connected to engine side.

2) Hook instrument panel on guide pin on dash board. Check to be sure that ventilator duct and wiring harness are correctly installed.

3) When glove box is being installed, first temporarily tighten each screw. After checking left and right clearances between glove box lid and instrument pad while lid is locked, tighten screws completely.

4) Place air outlet changeover lever at closed position. With heater side air outlet changeover damper lever in position, connect inner cable to lever and secure cable casing with clips.

5) Place heater control lever at the off position. Connect inner cable to lever and secure cable with clips.

6) Place inside/outside air changeover lever at fresh air position. With heater side inside/outside air changeover damper lever in position, connect inner cable

Heater Core Replacement

CHRYSLER & MITSUBISHI (Cont.)

Fig. 6: Exploded View of Cordia & Tredia Heater System

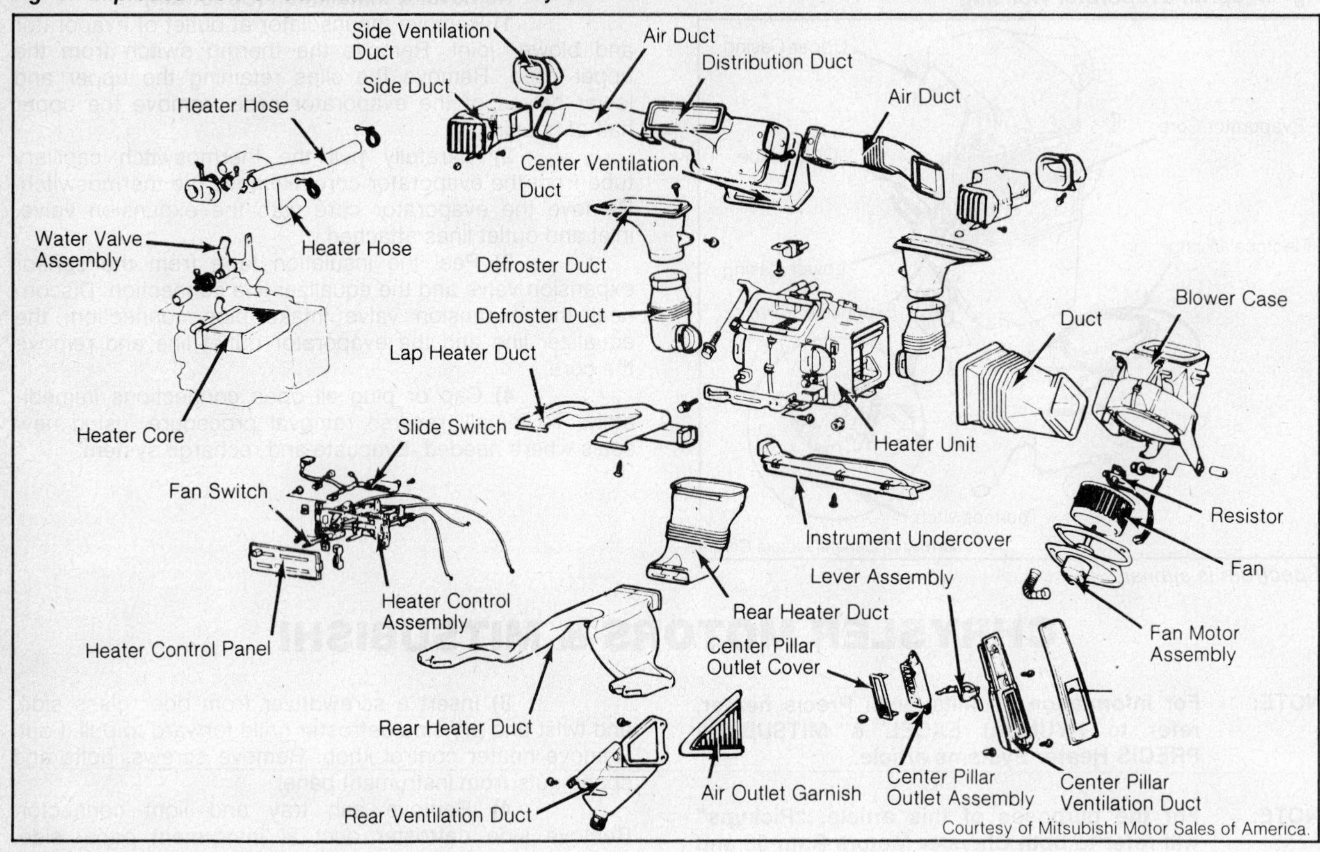

Cordia is shown, Tredia is similar.

to lever and secure cable with clips. Check all control cable adjustments and replenish coolant level.

Removal (Cordia & Tredia)

1) Disconnect negative cable from battery. Move heater control lever to the "WARM" position and drain coolant.

2) Remove steering wheel, glove box and cover under instrument panel. Remove heater duct, defroster ducts and 3 heater control wires.

3) Remove fuse block from instrument panel. Disconnect connectors for instrument panel. Remove heater control panel. Remove attaching screws of trim panel and remove trim panel by prying tabs of instrument case.

4) Disconnect speedometer cable from back of instrument case. Remove instrument cluster mounting screws, and pull instrument cluster out slightly. Disconnect all electrical connections and remove instrument cluster from instrument panel.

5) Remove left and right instrument panel covers, defroster garnish, floor console mount screws and instrument panel mounting screws and nuts.

6) Disconnect center ventilator duct and rear heater duct. Disconnect heater hose at heater unit. Remove heater unit.

7) Remove cover from heater box unit. Disconnect links for heater control valve and heater control flaps. Remove heater pipe clamps and remove heater core from heater unit.

Installation

1) To install, reverse removal procedure. Set air mixing damper at cold airflow position, and install the rod with the heater control valve fully closed.

2) Place air outlet changeover damper lever on heater unit at "VENT" postion. Confirm and make adjustment of each link to direct dampers.

3) Check for coolant leakage and for normal air flow after each control wire has been installed. Check for proper operation of heater control system.

Removal (Montero & Raider – Front)

1) Move temperature control lever to "WARM" position. Drain coolant from vehicle. Disconnect heater hoses from heater unit.

2) Remove steering wheel, center console, instrument cluster, lap heater ducts and release cable bracket. Remove fuse block, front speaker harness, right and left demister grilles.

3) Remove glove box and disconnect heater relay from front of wiring harness. Remove instrument panel mounting screws and remove instrument panel.

4) Remove center ventilator duct and defroster duct. Remove heater unit.

Removal (Montero & Raider – Rear)

Drain cooolant. Disconnect rear heater electrical connectors. Disconnect heater hoses at rear heater. Remove grommet upward. Remove cover mounting bolts. Remove cover. Remove rear heater assembly upward. Remove heater hose attaching clamps. Remove heater hoses attaching clips. Remove heater hose assembly.

Heater Core Replacement

CHRYSLER & MITSUBISHI (Cont.)

Fig. 7: Exploded View of Montero & Raider Front Heater System

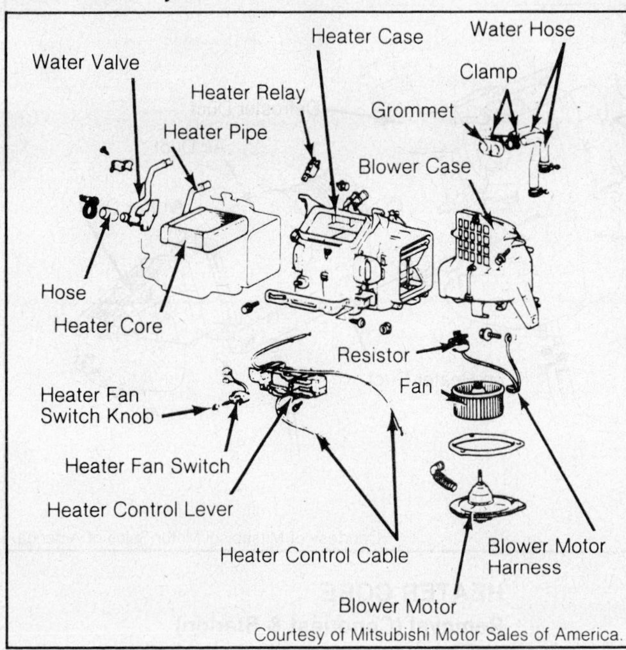

Courtesy of Mitsubishi Motor Sales of America.

Fig. 8: Exploded View of Montero & Raider Rear Heater System

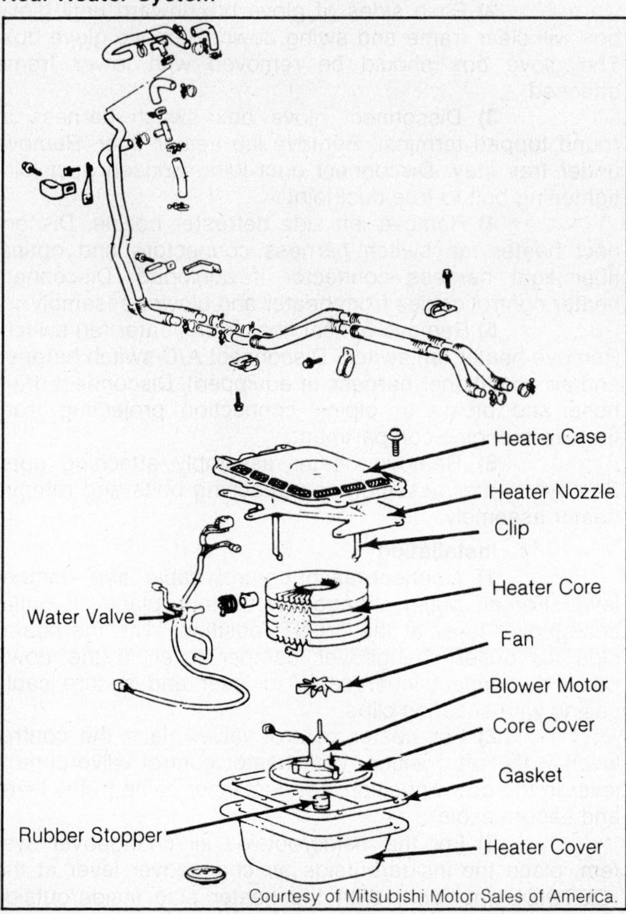

Courtesy of Mitsubishi Motor Sales of America.

Removal (Pickups)

1) Disconnect battery ground. Place heater control lever in "OFF" position. Drain coolant. Remove parcel tray, center ventilator grille and duct, and defroster duct.

2) Disconnect all control cables at heater side. Disconnect heater hose and harness from heater fan motor. Remove top mounting bolts and center mounting nuts and remove heater assembly.

Installation (Montero, Pickups & Raider)

1) Reverse removal procedure to install. Insert heater hoses fully into pipes and clamp them securely so they will not leak. When filling radiator with coolant, first open heater control valve fully and run engine to circulate coolant and discharge air from inside the heater and engine cooling system. Then stop engine and add coolant.

2) Adjust all control cables. When installing heater hose grommets, apply drying sealer. After installing heater control assembly, make sure each lever operates smoothly.

Removal & Installation (Van/Wagon–Front)

1) Move temperature control lever to "WARM" position. Drain coolant from vehicle. Disconnect heater hoses from heater unit.

2) Remove lap heater duct and defroster ducts. Remove steering wheel and column cover. Remove inspection cover from left, upper side of instrument panel.

3) Remove switch panel from instrument hood. Remove instrument hood. Disconnect instrument connectors and speedometer cable. Remove instrument cluster.

4) Remove brake fluid reservoir mounting bracket bolt. Remove dash center panel. Remove heater control panel. Disconnect all electrical connectors. Remove instrument panel mounting screws and remove instrument panel. Remove heater unit. Reverse procedure for installation.

Fig. 9: Exploded View of Pickup Heater System

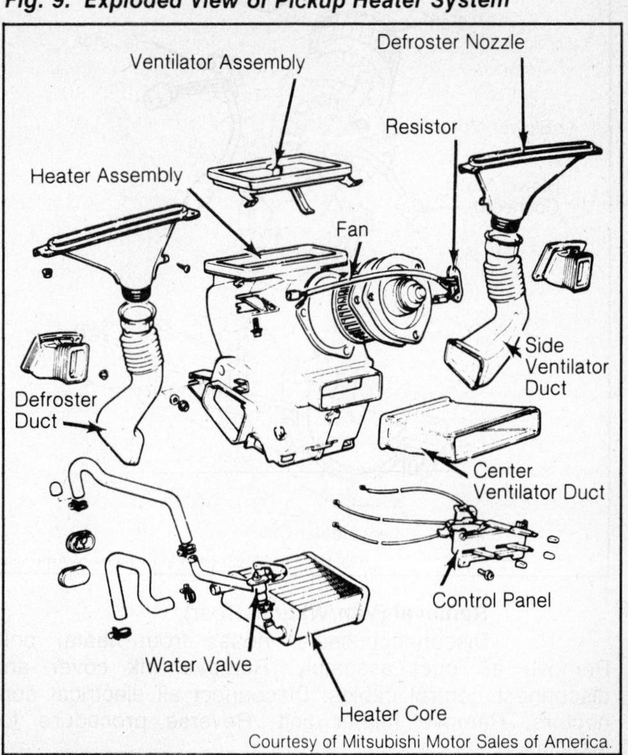

Courtesy of Mitsubishi Motor Sales of America.

Heater Core Replacement

CHRYSLER & MITSUBISHI (Cont.)

Fig. 10: Exploded View of Van/Wagon Front Heater System

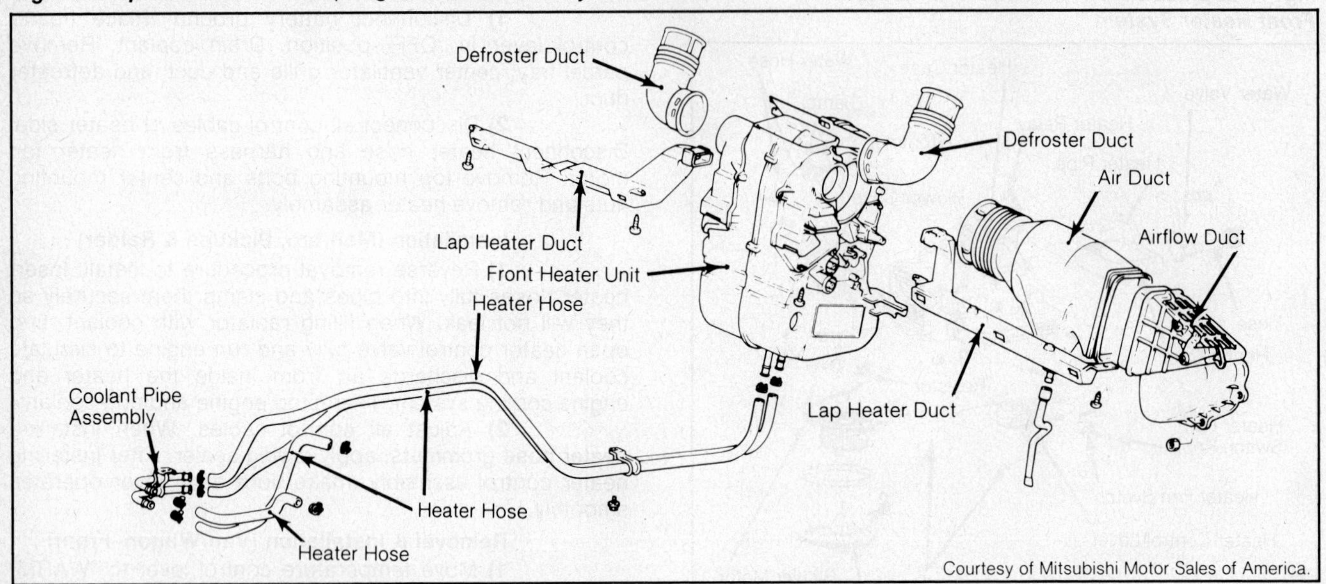

Fig. 11: Exploded View of Van/Wagon Rear Heater System

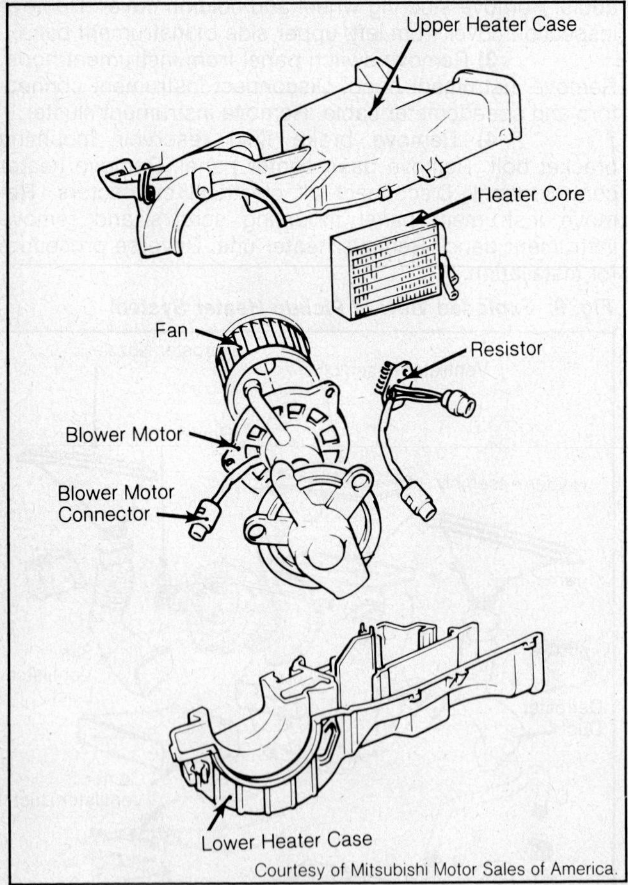

Removal (Van/Wagon-Rear)

Disconnect heater hoses from heater unit. Remove air duct assembly. Remove link cover and disconnect control cables. Disconnect all electrical connectors. Remove heater unit. Reverse procedure for installation.

HEATER CORE

Removal (Conquest & Starion)

1) Remove screws attaching right side console cover and remove side cover. Remove screw from lap heater duct. Disconnect duct and remove it.

2) Push sides of glove box inward until glove box will clear frame and swing down. Remove glove box. The glove box should be removed with lower frame attached.

3) Disconnect glove box switch harness at round topped terminal. Remove lap heater duct. Remove under tray stay. Disconnect duct joint. Loosen duct joint tightening bolt to free duct joint.

4) Remove left side defroster nozzle. Disconnect heater fan switch harness connectors and optical fiber light harness connector if equipped. Disconnect heater control cables from heater and blower assembly.

5) Remove optical fiber from heater fan switch. Remove heater fan switch. Disconnect A/C switch harness and air conditioner harness (if equipped). Disconnect drain hose and piping at piping connection projecting from firewall in engine compartment.

6) Remove heater assembly attaching nuts. Remove heater assembly top attaching bolts and remove heater assembly.

Installation

1) Connect each control cable and damper lever. For air outlet changeover system, place air outlet changeover lever at the "VENT" position. With the heater side air outlet changeover damper lever in the down position, connect inner cable to lever and secure cable casing with securing clips.

2) For heater control valve, place the control lever at the off position. With heater control valve control lever in the down position, connect inner cable to the lever and secure cable.

3) For the inside/outside air changeover system, place the inside/outside air changeover lever at the "OUTSIDE" position. With the heater side inside/outside air changeover damper lever in the down position, connect inner cable to the lever and secure cable casing.

CHRYSLER & MITSUBISHI (Cont.)

4) Check to make sure that each control lever moves smoothly. If there is any noise or stiff movement, apply multi-purpose grease to all moving parts.

Removal (Colt Vista, Cordia & Tredia)

Remove the cover. Disconnect links. Remove pipe clamps. Remove heater core from heater unit.

Installation

To install, reverse removal procedure. Confirm and make adjustment of each cable as necessary. Heater hoses should be inserted with a 1-1.2" (25-30 mm) overlap on outlet.

Removal & Installation (Colt & Mirage)

Remove heater hose. Remove pipe clamps. Remove water valve. Remove heater core from heater unit. Reverse procedure for installation.

Removal (Montero & Raider)

Remove the heater control lever arm. Remove the heater control valve cover. Remove the heater pipe and heater control valve. Disconnect the control arm linkage. Remove the control arm. Remove the heater core by moving it sideways.

Installation

To install, reverse removal procedure. Connect heater hoses with 1-1.2" (25-30 mm) overlap on outlet.

Removal (Van/Wagon–Front)

Remove the cover. Remove pipe clamps. Remove heater core from heater unit.

Installation

To install, reverse removal procedure. Confirm and make adjustment of each cable as necessary. Connect heater hoses with 1-1.2" (25-30 mm) overlap on outlet.

Removal (Van/Wagon–Rear)

Remove heater assembly as outlined previously. Separate upper and lower heater case and remove heater core.

Installation

To install, reverse removal procedure. Confirm and make adjustment of each cable as necessary. Connect heater hoses with 1-1.2" (25-30 mm) overlap on outlet.

MANUAL A/C–HEATER SYSTEMS

NOTE: **For removal and installation procedures for other system components, see HEATER SYSTEMS ONLY in this section.**

EVAPORATOR ASSEMBLY

Removal & Installation (Colt, Cordia, Mirage & Tredia)

Remove glove box. Remove liquid pipe connections and "O" rings from evaporator. Disconnect suction hose connection. Remove dash insert and lap heater duct. Remove defroster duct. Remove heater and blower duct joints. Disconnect A/C switch harness. Disconnect main harness connector. Remove evaporator unit mounting nuts and remove evaporator unit. Reverse procedure for installation.

Removal & Installation (Colt Vista)

Remove upper and lower glove compartments. Remove defrost duct. Disconnect harness connectors. Remove temperature control panel and cover. Remove temperature control unit. Remove A/C switch. Slowly disconnect high and low pressure lines from engine compartment. Remove drain tube from inside engine compartment. Remove evaporator unit mounting nuts. Remove evaporator unit. Reverse procedure for installation.

Removal & Installation (Montero & Ram-Raider)

Remove the glove box. Glove box should be removed with lower frame attached. Loosen the duct joint bolt to free the duct joint. Disconnect the A/C switch harness and A/C harness. Disconnect the drain hose.

Disconnect the piping at the piping connection projecting from the firewall in the engine compartment. Remove the evaporator unit top attaching bolts in the passenger compartment. Remove the cooling unit. Reverse procedure for installation.

Removal & Installation (Pickup Models)

Disconnect liquid pipe and suction hose connections. Remove glove box assembly. Remove air and defroster duct. Remove drain hose and clamp. Disconnect wiring connectors. Remove nut from firewall evaporator assembly mounting bracket. Reverse procedure for installation.

Removal & Installation (Van/Wagon Front)

Remove glove box and foot protector. Remove air selection control wire and clamp. Remove washer tank. Disconnect suction hose and liquid line connection. Disconnect engine compartment connector. Remove drain hose. Remove airflow box. Remove ducts. Disconnect main harness connector and A/C switch harness. Remove evaporator mounting bolts and evaporator. To install, apply compressor oil to liquid connection lines. Readjust air selection door. Reverse removal procedure to install.

Removal & Installation (Van/Wagon Rear)

Remove harness connector. Disconnect suction hose connection. Disconnect liquid line connection. Remove mounting bolts. Remove evaporator.

AUTOMATIC A/C–HEATER SYSTEMS

HEATER ASSEMBLY

Removal & Installation (Conquest, Starion)

1) Warm engine to normal operating temperature. Set temperature controls to warmest position. Turn engine off. Drain engine coolant and disconnect heater hoses. Remove front console and instrument panel.

2) Remove center and lap heater ducts. *See Fig. 12*. Remove center reinforcement and heater assembly. Remove servo motor by uncopling blend air damper and servo motor rod. Remove servo motor. To install, reverse removal procedure.

Heater Core Replacement

CHRYSLER & MITSUBISHI (Cont.)

Fig. 12: Exploded View of Heater Assembly

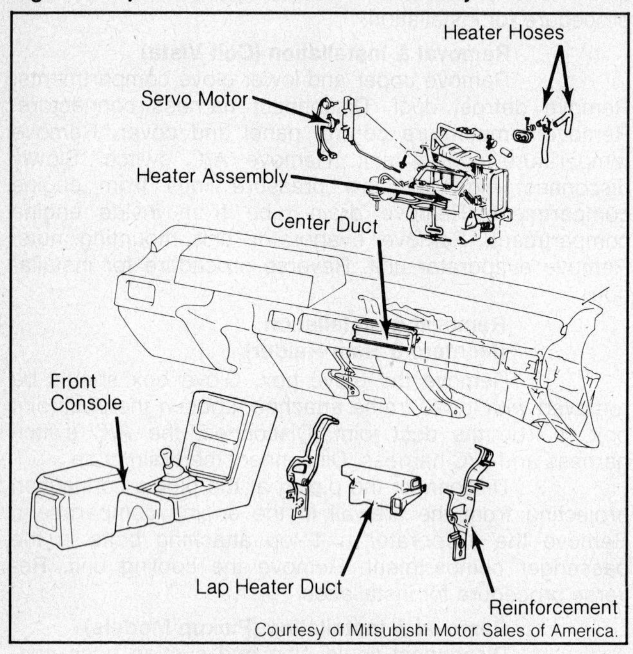

Courtesy of Mitsubishi Motor Sales of America.

HEATER CORE & WATER VALVE

Removal (Conquest & Starion)

Unlock water valve lever clip and disconnect link for blend air damper from water valve lever. Remove water valve clamp, hose clamp, hose and screw. Remove plate and heater core. If removal is difficult, remove damper lever first.

Installation

Install heater cover and water valve. Push water valve inward so that it rests in the closed position. Pull blend-air damper lever downward so that blend-air damper is completely closed.

EVAPORATOR ASSEMBLY & EXPANSION VALVE

Removal (Conquest & Starion)

1) Discharge A/C system. Remove liquid line, suction hose, nut, and grommet. *See Fig. 13.* Press inward on both sides and pull glove box rearward. Remove screws and glove box.

2) Remove instrument panel under cover, lap heater duct, side console duct, and frame. Remove defroster duct, duct joint, and drain hose. Disconnect wiring harness and vacuum hose. Remove bolt and evaporator assembly.

3) Remove harness, vacuum hose, and evaporator housing clips. Remove upper case, airflow sensor, and lower case. Remove evaporator, insulation, clip, and expansion valve.

Installation

To install, reverse removal procedure. Apply refrigerant oil to expansion valve and tubing "O" rings.

Fig. 13: Exploded View of Evaporator Assembly

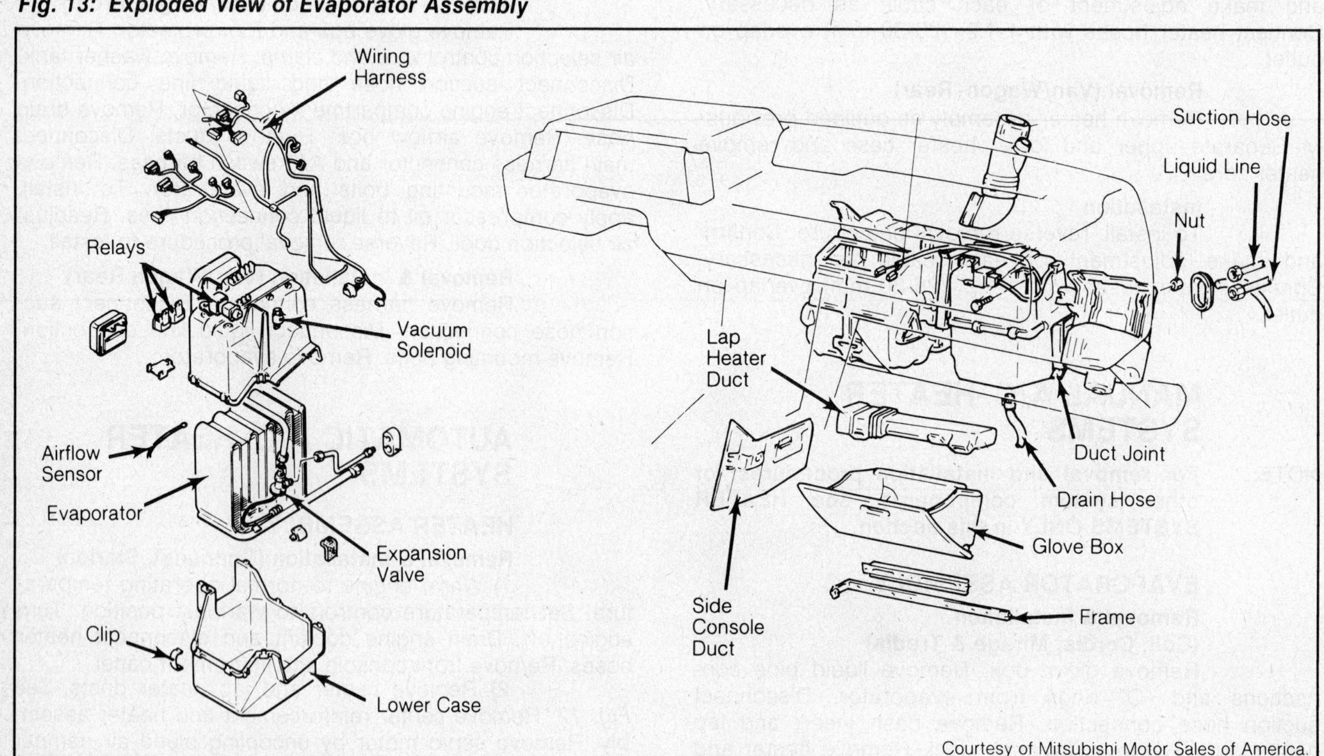

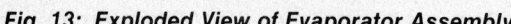

Courtesy of Mitsubishi Motor Sales of America.

Heater Core Replacement

FORD MOTOR CO.

ALL SYSTEMS

EVAPORATOR HOUSING

Removal & Installation (Festiva)

1) Disconnect negative battery cable. Discharge refrigerant. Disconnect evaporator refrigerant lines and plug. Remove glove box. Disconnect 2 electrical connectors from thermostat.

2) Disconnect cable from thermostat. remove wiring harness clamps from housing. Loosen clamp screws securing connector duct to evaporator housing. Remove drain hose. Remove air inlet duct.

3) Remove mounting bolts attaching evaporator housing to dash panel. Remove evaporator housing. To install, reverse removal procedure. Use new "O"-rings. Evacuate, charge and test system for proper operation.

EVAPORATOR

Removal & Installation (Festiva)

1) Remove evaporator housing. Remove clips securing upper and lower evaporator case halves. Remove upper housing. Remove thermostat, pull sensing tube from evaporator core fins as thermostat is removed. Remove evaporator from lower housing. Remove standoff insert from between inlet and outlet tubes.

2) Remove insulator from around capillary tube and expansion valve. Remove clamp securing capillary tube to suction tube. Disconnect evaporator tube fitting and expansion valve. To install, reverse removal procedures. Use new "O"-rings on all refrigerant line connections. Evacuate, charge and test system for proper operation.

HEATER CORE

Removal & Installation (Festiva)

1) Remove the air distribution plenum. Disconnect linkage connecting defroster doors. Remove attaching screw located near blower resistor. Turn housing around and remove attaching screw located near the blower motor opening.

2) Remove clips retaining blower housing halves. Separate blower housing halves. Remove heater core. Remove tube insert from heater core. To install, reverse removal procedures. Test system for proper operation.

EVAPORATOR ASSEMBLY

Removal & Installation (Merkur XR4Ti)

1) Disconnect both battery cables. Discharge refrigerant from A/C system using a manifold gauge set. Remove engine valve cover. Remove cowl insulator cover. Remove water valve retaining clip.

2) Remove battery shield. Disconnect EGR valve vacuum line and remove EGR valve. Remove 2 nut retaining A/C hose plate and seal to partition. Disconnect wiring harness from partition. Remove A/C lines to expansion valve Torx bolt.

3) Disconnect lines from expansion valve. Remove upper weather seal from partition. Remove 7 partition retaining screws. Remove drain valves. Pull partition up and remove. Disconnect de-icer wire connector.

4) Disconnect ground wire on evaporator. Remove evaporator mounting bolts. Remove cowl grille panel. Disconnect windshield wiper and arm assembly. Slide evaporator assembly upward and remove from vehicle. Reverse procedure for installation. Recharge and test A/C system.

EVAPORATOR VACUUM MOTOR

Removal & Installation (Merkur XR4Ti)

Remove evaporator assembly. See REMOVAL & INSTALLATION–EVAPORATOR ASSEMBLY in this article. Disconnect connecting arm from vacuum motor. Disconnect electrical connector. Remove evaporator vacuum motor mounting screws. Remove evaporator vacuum motor. Reverse procedure for installation. Recharge system.

EVAPORATOR CORE & BLOWER MOTOR

Removal & Installation (Merkur XR4Ti)

1) Remove evaporator assembly. See REMOVAL & INSTALLATION-EVAPORATOR ASSEMBLY in this article. Remove 3 access cover retaining screws. Pry cover upward. Remove 2 blower fan and deicing thermostat mounting screws.

2) Remove evaporator case retaining clips. Separate evaporator case. Remove blower motor retaining screw. Reverse procedure for installation, being careful to correctly align thermostat sensor. Recharge system.

HEATER ASSEMBLY

Removal & Installation (Merkur XR4Ti)

1) Disconnect negative battery cable. Drain coolant system. Disconnect heater hoses from heater core. Blow compressed air into upper core outlet to remove excess coolant. Disconnect cover plate and gasket from firewall. Remove center console.

2) Remove right side footwell trim panel. Detach heater cover lever. Disconnect glove box, combination switch and cigar lighter electrical connectors. Remove lower right dash panel.

3) Disconnect all duct hoses from heater assembly. Disconnect control cables from heater assembly. Remove heater assembly mounting bolts. Remove heater assembly. Reverse procedure for installation.

EVAPORATOR HOUSING

Removal & Installation (Tracer)

1) Disconnect negative battery cable. Discharge refrigerant. Disconnect evaporator refrigerant lines and plug. Remove evaporator tube grommets from bulkhead. Remove glove box. Disconnect 2 electrical connectors.

2) Remove air duct bands. Remove drain hose. Remove mounting bolts and nuts. Carefully remove evaporator. To install, reverse removal procedure. Use new "O" rings. Evacuate, charge and test system for proper operation.

EVAPORATOR

Removal & Installation (Tracer)

1) Remove evaporator housing. Remove clips securing upper and lower evaporator halves. Remove upper housing. Remove de-ice thermostat, pull sensing tube from evaporator core fins as thermostat is removed. Disconnect liquid line from inlet fitting of expansion valve.

2) Remove insulator from around capillary tube and expansion valve and remove. Remove evaporator tube fitting and expansion valve. To install, reverse

Heater Core Replacement

FORD MOTOR CO. (Cont.)

removal procedures. If installing a new evaporator, add .84-1.0 oz. of refrigerant oil. Use new "O" rings on all refrigerant line connections. Evacuate, charge and test system for proper operation.

HEATER CASE

Removal & Installation (Tracer)

1) Remove instrument panel assembly. Drain cooling system. Disconnect heater hoses from heater core extentsion tubes and plug tubes. Remove push pins securing defroster ducts to heater case.

2) Remove defroster ducts. Remove push pins retaining main air duct from heater case. Remove 2 push pins and one screw retaining lower carpet panel under heater case. Disconnect all wiring harness braces and remove. Remove 4 heater case upper and lower mounting bolts.

3) Remove mounting nut on passengers side. Remove 2 push pins attaching lower duct to heater case. Remove heater case by pulling it straight back, be careful not to damage extension tubes. To install, reverse removal procedures. Fill cooling system with coolant. Check for proper operation of heating system.

HEATER CORE

Removal & Installation (Tracer)

1) Remove heater case. Remove 3 screws attaching heater core cover to heater case and remove case. Remove tube braces. Remove heater case by pulling it straight back, be careful not to damage extension tubes. Remove outlet extension tube.

2) Looosen inlet extension tube hose clamp and remove extension tube. To install, reverse removal procedures. Fill cooling system with coolant. Check for proper operation of heating system.

HONDA

HEATER SYSTEMS ONLY

HEATER CORE

Removal (Accord)

1) Drain coolant from radiator. Place a pan underneath heater hoses to catch coolant when disconnecting heater hoses from firewall. Note which hose is inlet and which is outlet. Disconnect heater valve cable from heater valve. Remove lower heater mounting bolt.

2) Remove left side instrument panel and fuse block cover. Lower steering column. Disconnect all electrical connectors from rear of instrument panel. Mark for reassembly reference.

3) Remove heater control panel and bracket. Remove instrument panel center access panel, ashtray and 9 instrument panel mounting bolts. Remove heater assembly-to-firewall mounting bolts. Remove instrument panel.

4) Disconnect all cables, wires and vacuum hoses from heater assembly. Remove heater assembly-to-firewall mounting bolts. Remove heater assembly from vehicle.

Removal (Civic)

1) Drain coolant from radiator. Remove lower instrument panel. Disconnect heater hoses at firewall. Note which hose is inlet and which is outlet for reassembly reference. Catch coolant spillage in a pan.

2) Remove heater-to-firewall nut from inside engine compartment. Remove clip and cable at coolant valve. Disconnect heater ducts and control cables from heater assembly. Remove heater assembly upper bolts and remove assembly from vehicle.

Removal (Prelude)

NOTE: The heater core on Prelude can be removed without removing the heater assembly.

Drain coolant from radiator. Remove heater pipe cover and clamp. Remove heater core retaining plate. Pull out cotter pins from joint hose clamps and separate heater pipes. Catch coolant spillage in a pan. Remove heater core from heater housing.

Installation (All Models)

To install heater assembly, reverse removal procedures and note following: Make sure all electrical connectors are connected correctly. Make sure all control cables are connected and all doors operate properly. On Prelude, install new joint hose clamps and cotter pins. Make sure heater hoses are connected properly. Refill radiator and make sure heater system operaters properly.

MANUAL A/C-HEATER SYSTEMS

EVAPORATOR

Removal (Accord & Prelude)

1) Disconnect battery ground cable and discharge system. Disconnect suction hose and liquid line from evaporator. Cap open fittings immediately to keep moisture and dirt from entering system.

2) On Prelude, remove grommets from inlet and outlet fittings of evaporator. Remove both lower instrument panel covers. Disconnect the vacuum line and wiring harness from blower assembly.

3) Disconnect sealing band connecting blower motor assembly to evaporator case. *See Fig. 14.* Remove bolts attaching blower motor to firewall. Remove blower motor assembly.

4) Carefully disconnect wiring harness from thermostat. Remove evaporator assembly attaching bolts and remove evaporator from vehicle.

5) On Accord, remove self-tapping screws and glove box lower cover. Remove retaining screws and glove box. Remove drain hose from evaporator lower housing.

6) Loosen sealing band and slide it toward blower. Disconnect thermostat wire and remove from clamp at top of evaporator. Remove 3 retaining bolts and 2 self-tapping screws to remove evaporator. *See Fig. 14.*

HONDA (Cont.)

Fig. 14: Accord Evaporator & Blower Assembly

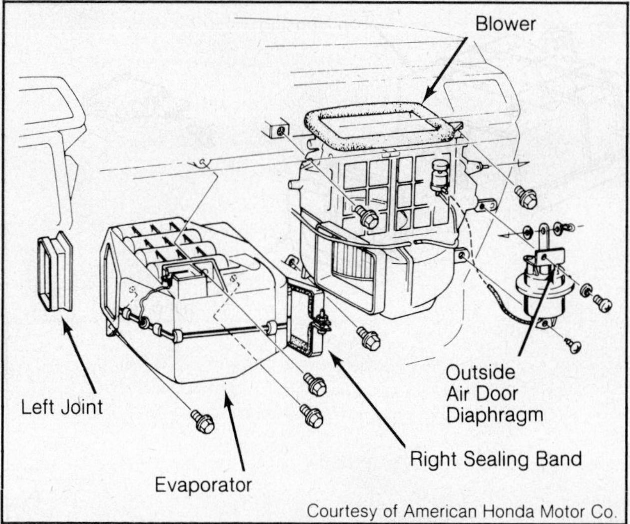

Fig. 15: Exploded View of Evaporator Assembly

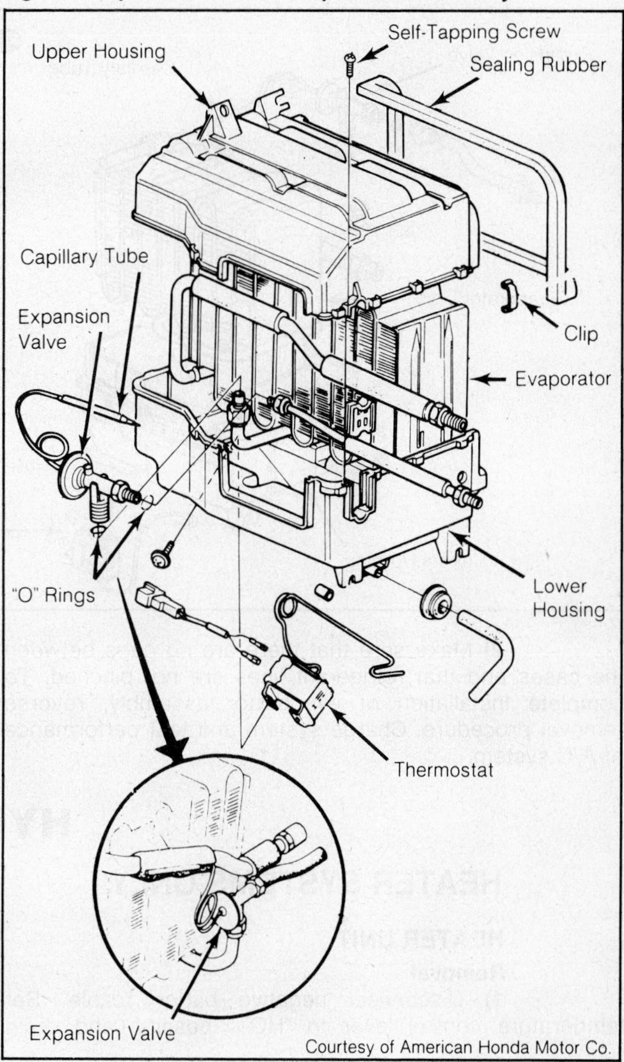

Installation (Accord & Prelude)

Reverse removal procedure and note the following; Install capillary tube in its original position. Make sure there are no gaps between evaporator case and that evaporator and blower sealing bands are secured tightly so no air will leak. If a new evaporator is installed, add one ounce of refrigerant oil before charging system.

EVAPORATOR

Removal (Civic & Civic CRX)

1) Disconnect battery negative terminal and discharge A/C system. Disconnect receiver-drier and suction hoses from evaporator core. *See Fig. 16.* Cap open fittings immediately to prevent moisture and dirt from entering A/C system.

2) On Hatchback and CRX models, remove glove box and frame. On Wagon models, remove passenger's tray. On all models, disconnect wire harness from thermostat.

3) Loosen sealing band screw and slide air duct off. Disconnect electrical wiring harness. Remove blower mounting bolts and remove blower and evaporator.

Disassembly (Civic & Civic CRX)

1) Remove self-tapping screws and clips from housing. Remove capillary tube of thermostat from evaporator fins.

2) Separate housings and remove evaporator covers. Remove expansion valve, if necessary. If replacing expansion valve, use new "O" rings. Remove all dirt from evaporator with compressed air. *See Fig. 16.*

Evaporator Reassembly (Civic & Civic CRX)

1) To reassemble, reverse disassembly procedures. Install expansion valve capillary tube against suction and wrap with tape. When reassembling evaporator housing, make sure there are no air gaps between the upper and lower housing.

2) If a new evaporator is installed, add one ounce. of refrigerant oil to evaporator before charging. Make sure routing of drain tube is correct.

Installation

1) Install thermostat and make sure capillary tube is installed in original position (in evaporator fins). Install evaporator to lower case (if required). Install upper case to lower case and install clamps and screws.

Fig. 16: Removal of Evaporator Assembly

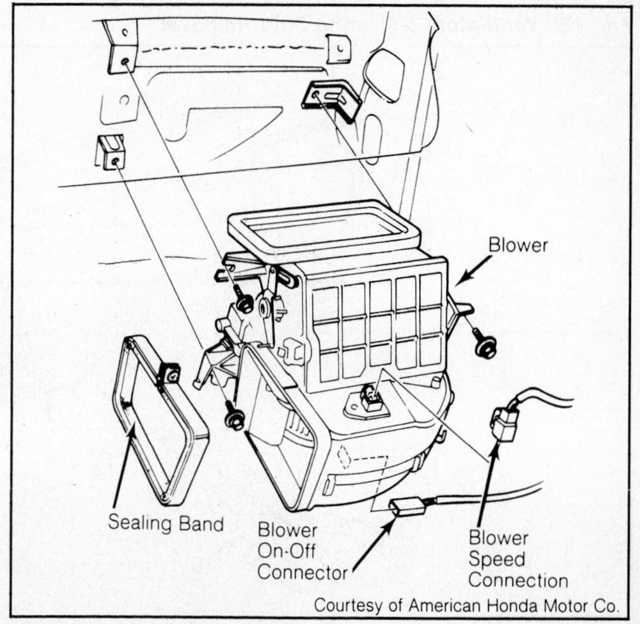

Heater Core Replacement

HONDA (Cont.)

Fig. 17: Removal of Evaporator Core & Expansion Valve from Evaporator Case

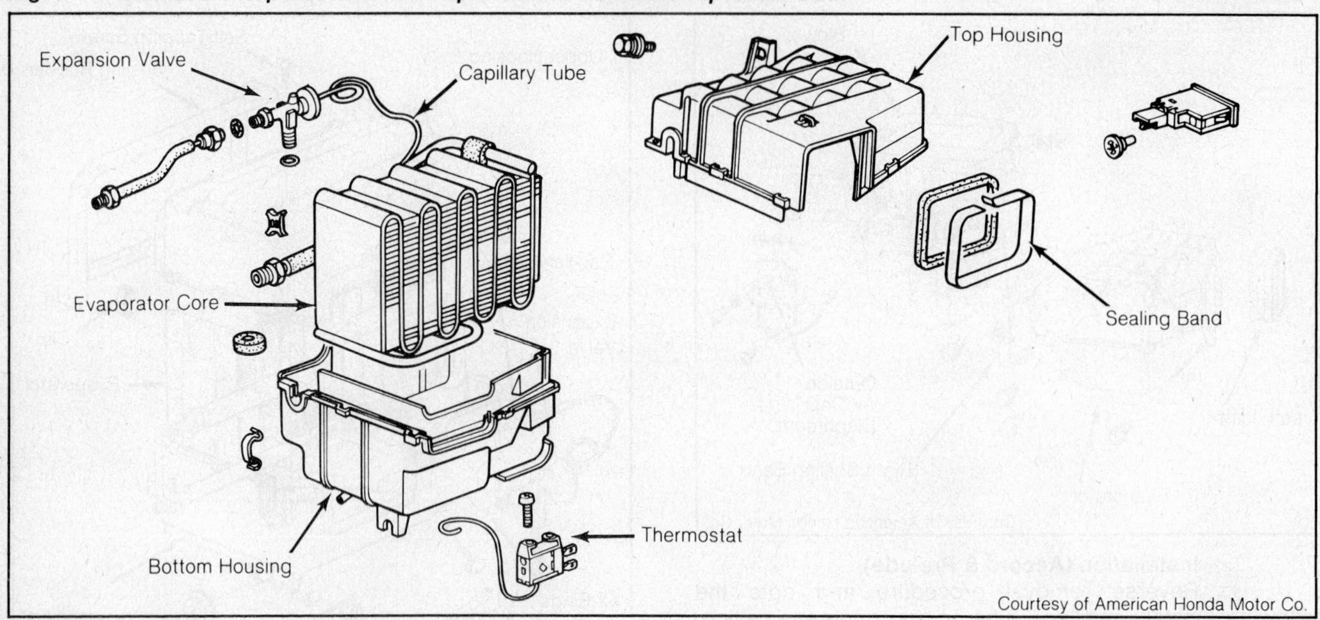

2) Make sure that there are no gaps between the cases and that refrigerant lines are not pinched. To complete installation of evaporator assembly, reverse removal procedure. Charge system and test performance of A/C system.

HYUNDAI

HEATER SYSTEMS ONLY

HEATER UNIT

Removal

1) Disconnect negative battery cable. Set temperature control lever to "HOT" position and drain

2) Remove lower dash pad. Remove supplement console and computer (if equipped). Loosen rear heating duct mounting screw. Push rear heating joint duct and pull at heating duct. *See Fig. 18.*

3) Disconnect heater control cable. Remove A/C unit (if equipped) or blower-to-heater duct. Loosen heater mounting bolts and remove heater unit.

Fig. 18: Ventilators & Heating Duct Removal

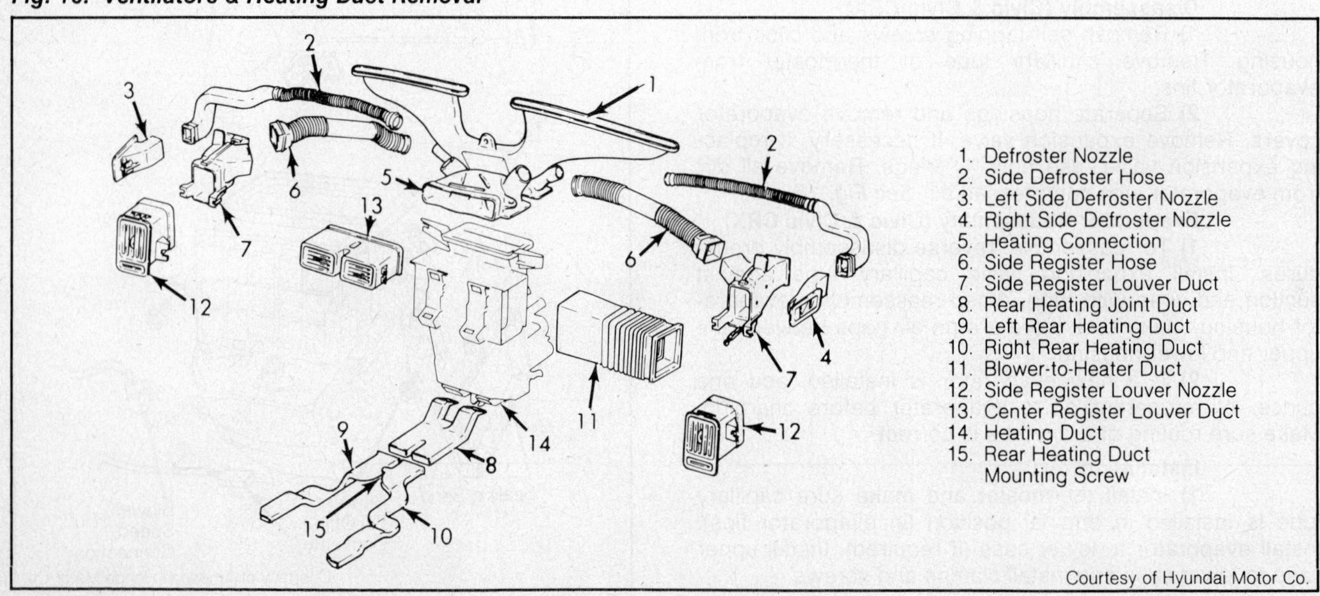

HYUNDAI (Cont.)

MANUAL A/C-HEATER SYSTEMS

EVAPORATOR & EXPANSION VALVE

Removal & Installation (Excel)

1) Remove negative battery cable. Discharge refrigerant from system. Disconnect liquid line and suction hose from evaporator and plug. Remove grommets from inlet and outlet tubes. Remove lower cover and glove box in that order .

2) Disconnect A/C electrical connector. Remove drain hose. Remove mounting bolts and nuts. Carefully lift out assembly. To disassemble the evaporator unit. Remove the clip, fixing the inlet and outler pipes. Remove the eight clamps, holding the upper case to the lower case.

3) Remove the cover from the lower case. Remove the thermostat. Remove the evaporator from the lower case. Disconnect the inlet pipe. Remove the insulator tape from the outler pipe, the clip, fixing the sensing bulb of the expansion valve, and remove the expansion valve. To install, reverse removal procedure.

Fig. 19: Exploded View of Evaporator Core Assembly

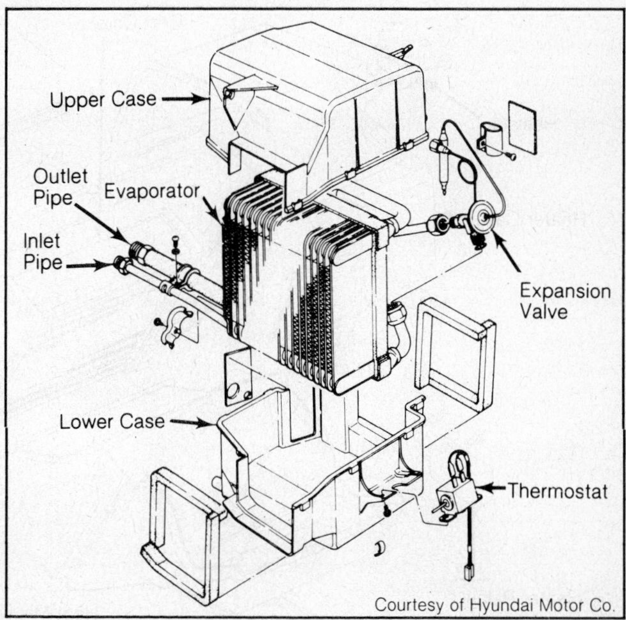

Courtesy of Hyundai Motor Co.

ISUZU

HEATER SYSTEMS ONLY

HEATER ASSEMBLY & CORE

Removal (All Models)

1) Disconnect battery ground cable and drain radiator. Disconnect heater hoses at core and plug core tubes. Remove instrument panel. See INSTRUMENT PANEL in this section. Disconnect blower motor duct. Disconnect wire harness. Remove attaching nuts and washers. Disconnect temperature cable at heater valve.

2) Remove heater assembly. Remove lower retaining clip from heater case and pry open lower part of heater assembly case. Remove heater core.

Installation

To install, reverse removal procedure. Adjust heater control cables.

INSTRUMENT PANEL

Removal (All Models)

1) Remove glove box hinge pins and slide out glove box. Remove steering wheel. Unscrew meter hood screws and meter assembly screws. Remove meter hood and meter assembly. Disconnect cable from speedometer boss. Remove side trim.

2) Remove fuse box fixing screws. Remove right and left air defroster ducts. Remove steering column fixing bolts. Lift instrument panel fixing screw covers. Unscrew 10 instrument panel fixing screws and remove instrument panel.

Installation

To install, reverse removal procedure.

REAR HEATER UNIT

NOTE: **The rear heater unit is under rear seat.**

Removal (Trooper II)

Remove rear seat. Remove hose clamps fastening heater hoses to rear heater unit. Remove bolts fastening rear heater unit to body. Disconnect wiring harness at connectors. Remove rear heater assembly from vehicle. To expose heater core and blower motor, remove cover fastening screws and remove cover.

Installation

To install, reverse removal procedure.

MANUAL A/C-HEATER SYSTEMS

NOTE: **For heater components removal and installation procedures, refer to HEATER SYSTEMS in this section.**

EVAPORATOR & EXPANSION VALVE

Removal & Installation (I-Mark)

1) Remove insulator. Remove thermo-switch. Disconnect retaining clips. Remove evaporator upper housing. Carefully pull out thermo-switch capillary tube from evaporator core. Remove evaporator lower housing.

2) Remove expansion valve intake pipe. Remove insulating tape from sensing bulb of the expansion valve and remove. Remove evaporator core. To install, reverse removal procedures.

3) If new core is to be installed, add 1.7 oz. of refrigerant oil to new core. Replace insulating tape around sensing bulb. Evacuate, recharge and test for proper operation.

A/C-HEATER ASSEMBLY

Removal & Installation (P'UP & Trooper II)

1) Disconnect refrigerent line flare nuts at evaporator core. Disconnect vacuum hose. Disconnect

Heater Core Replacement

ISUZU (Cont.)

Fig. 20: Exploded View of I-Mark & Spectrum Heater Unit

Courtesy of Isuzu Motor Co.

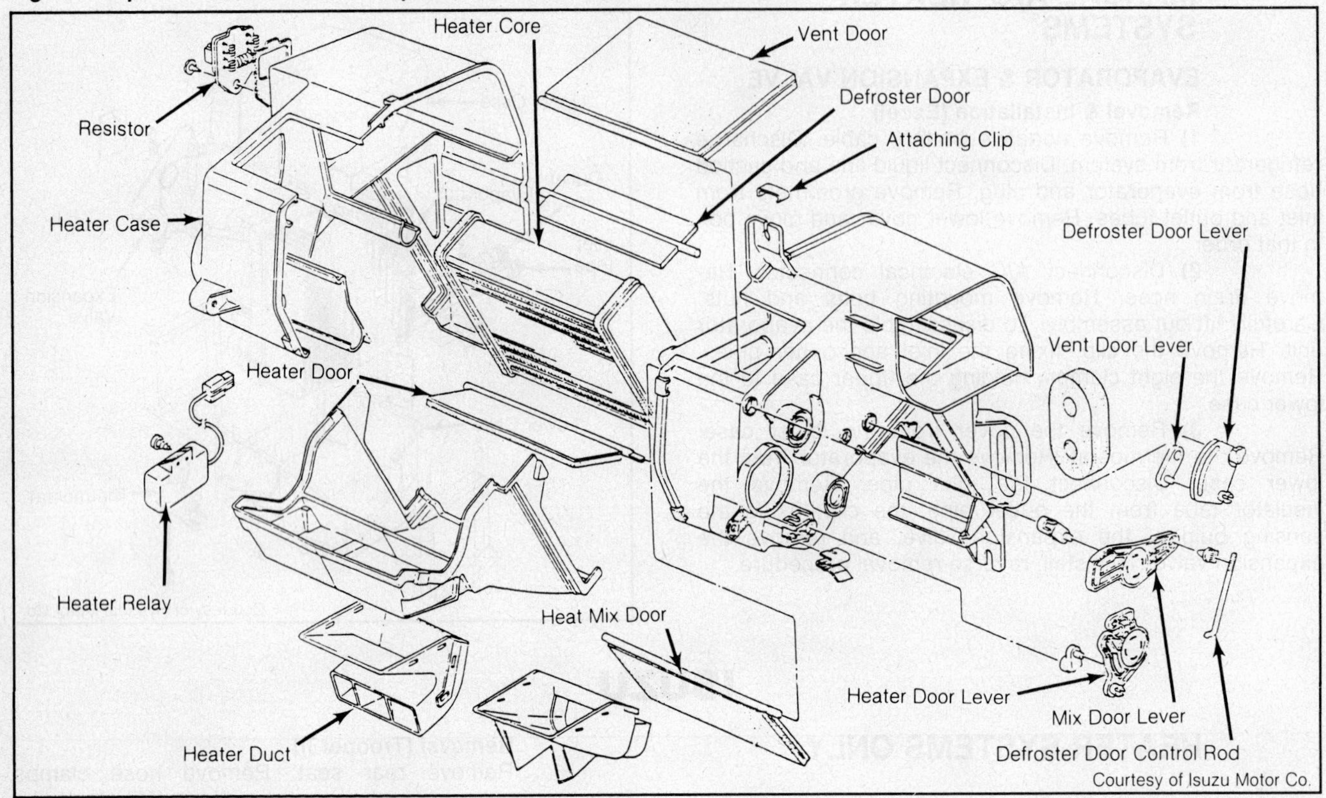

Fig. 21: Exploded View of P'UP and Trooper II Heater Unit

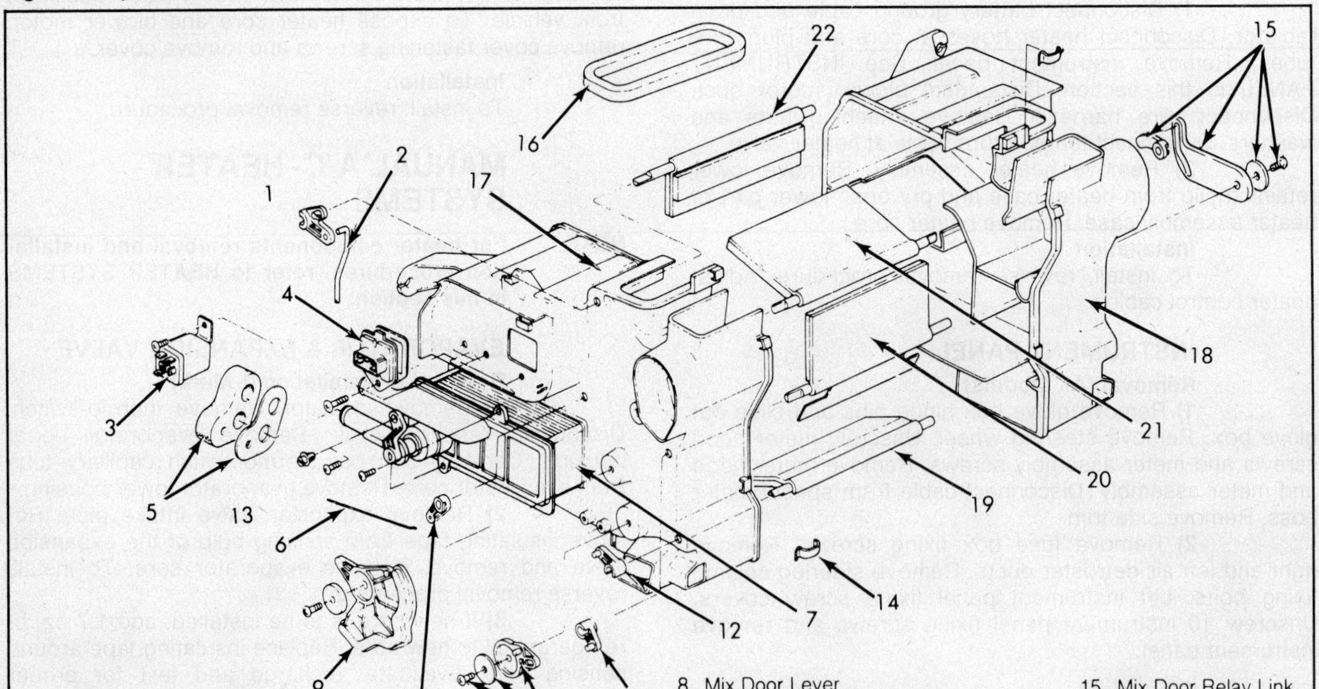

1. Defroster Door Lever
2. Defroster Door Control Rod
3. Relay
4. Resistor
5. Plate & Seal
6. Heater Valve Rod
7. Heater Core Assembly
8. Mix Door Lever
9. Main Mode Control Cam
10. Relay Link
11. Vent Door Lever
12. Heater Door Lever
13. Heater Valve
14. Attaching Clip
15. Mix Door Relay Link
16. Seal
17. Heater Case
18. Heater Door
19. Vent Door
20. Heat Mix Door
21. Defroster Door

Courtesy of Isuzu Motor Co.

Heater Core Replacement

ISUZU (Cont.)

Fig 22: Exploded View of Trooper II Rear Heater Unit

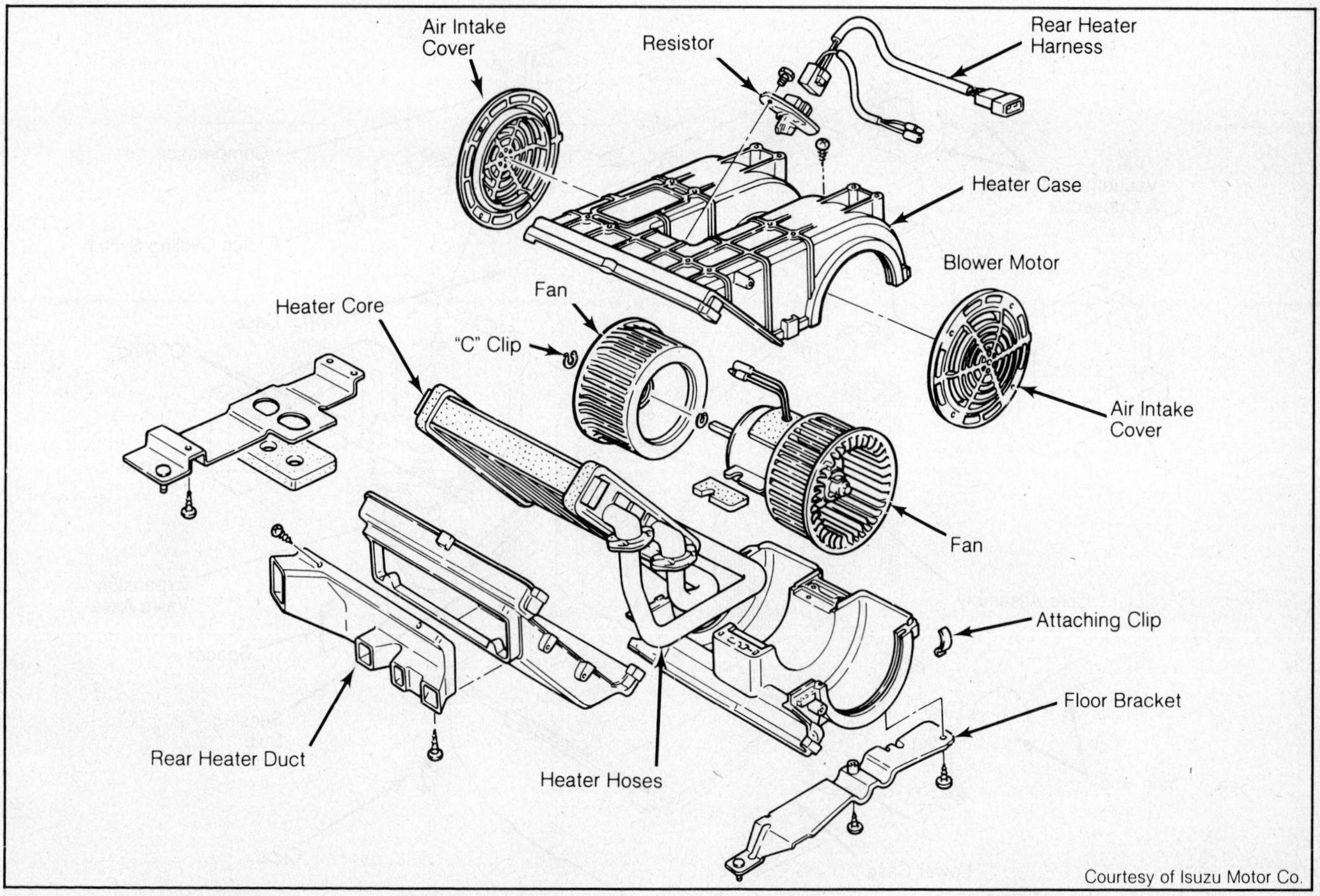

Fig. 23: Exploded View of Isuzu Manual A/C-Heater System Assembly

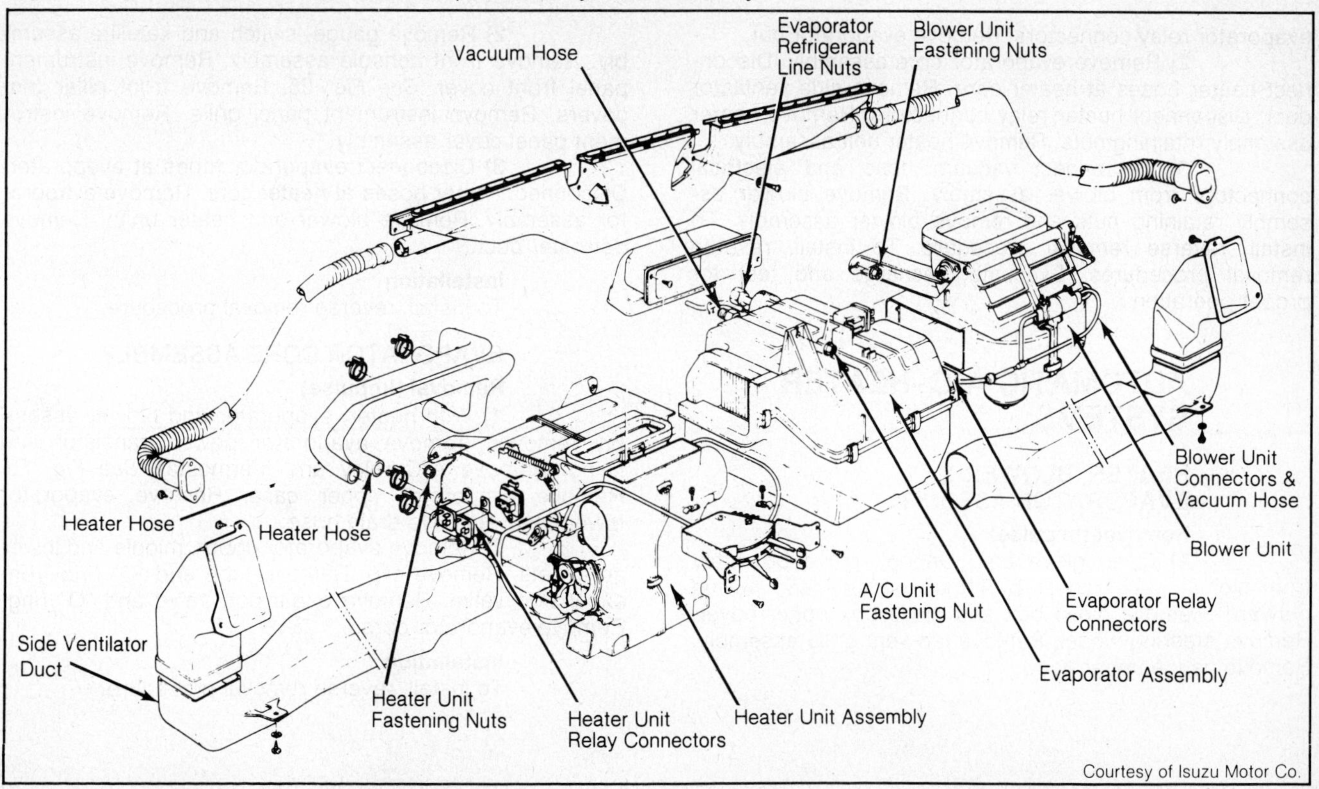

P'UP shown. I-Mark and Trooper II are similar.

Heater Core Replacement

ISUZU (Cont.)

Fig. 24: Exploded View Evaporator Core Assembly

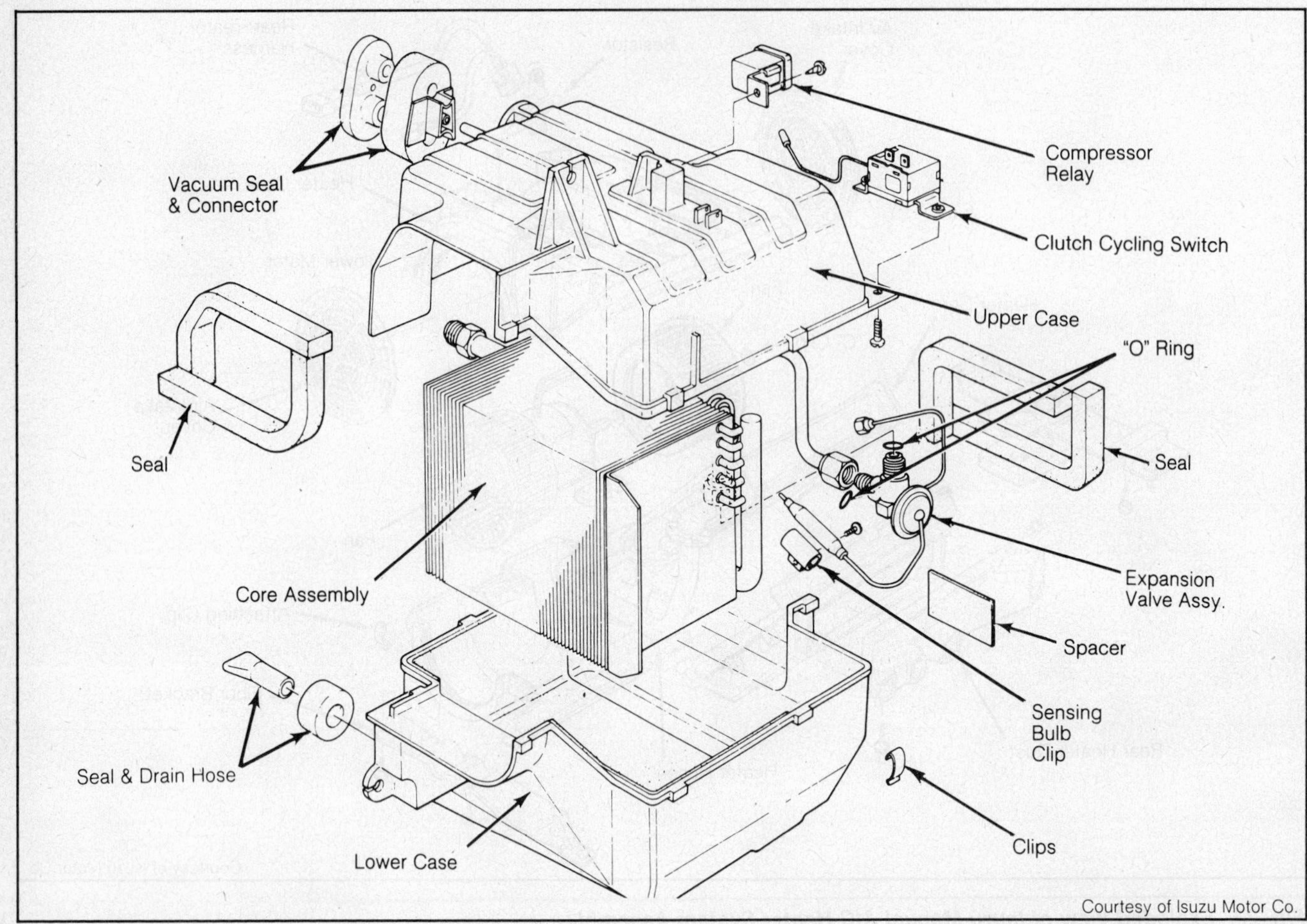

evaporator relay connectors. Remove evaporator nut.

2) Remove evaporator core assembly. Disconnect heater hoses at heater core. Remove side ventilator duct. Disconnect heater relay connectors. Remove heater assembly retaining nuts. Remove heater unit assembly.

3) Disconnect vacuum hose and electrical connectors from blower assembly. Remove blower assembly retaining nuts and remove blower assembly. To install, reverse removal procedure. To install, reverse removal procedures. Evacuate, recharge and test for proper operation.

AUTOMATIC A/C-HEATER SYSTEMS

HEATER, BLOWER & EVAPORATOR ASSEMBLY

Removal (Impulse)

1) Open glove box. Unhook glove box stay from slot in upper cover by lift up on stay and pulling outward. Remove glove box and glove box upper cover. Remove steering wheel. Remove lap vent grille assembly. Remove gauge upper hood.

2) Remove gauge, switch and satellite assembly. Remove front console assembly. Remove instrument panel front cover. *See Fig. 25*. Remove front pillar trim covers. Remove instrument panel grille. Remove instrument panel cover assembly.

3) Disconnect evaporator tubes at evaporator. Disconnect heater hoses at heater core. Remove evaporator assembly. Remove blower and heater units. Remove defroster duct.

Installation

To install, reverse removal procedure.

EVAPORATOR CORE ASSEMBLY

Removal (Impulse)

1) With heater, evaporator and blower assembly removed, remove evaporator power transistor and lining. Remove A/C relay and thermostat. *See Fig. 26*. Remove evaporator upper case. Remove evaporator lower case. Remove drain hose.

2) Remove evaporator upper, middle and lower grommets. Remove clip. Remove tube and "O" ring from expansion valve. Remove expansion valve and "O" ring. Remove evaporator core.

Installation

To install, reverse removal procedure.

Heater Core Replacement

ISUZU (Cont.)

Fig. 25: Instrument Panel Assembly

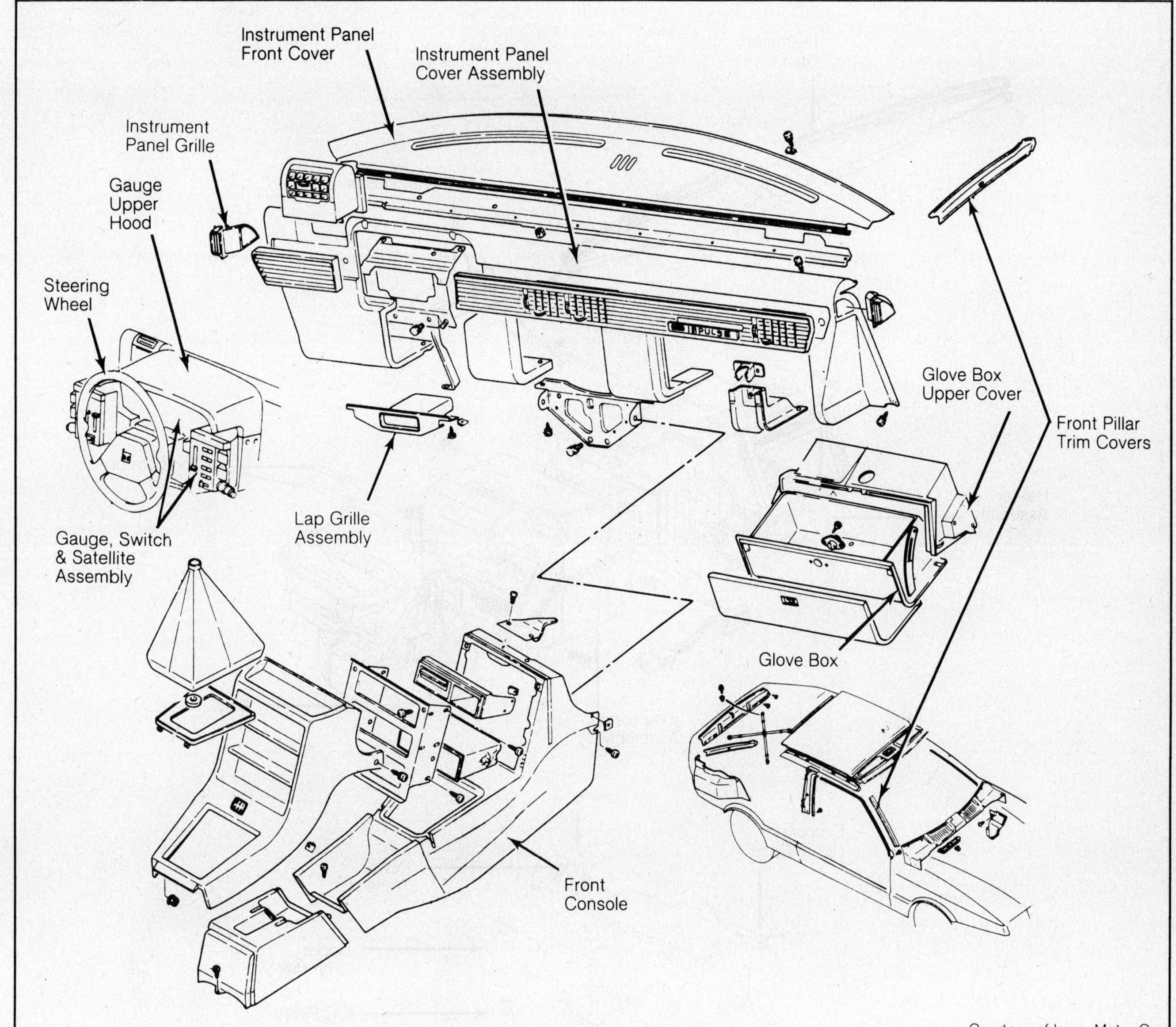

Courtesy of Isuzu Motor Co.

Heater Core Replacement

ISUZU (Cont.)

Fig. 26: Isuzu Heater, Blower & Evaporator Assembly

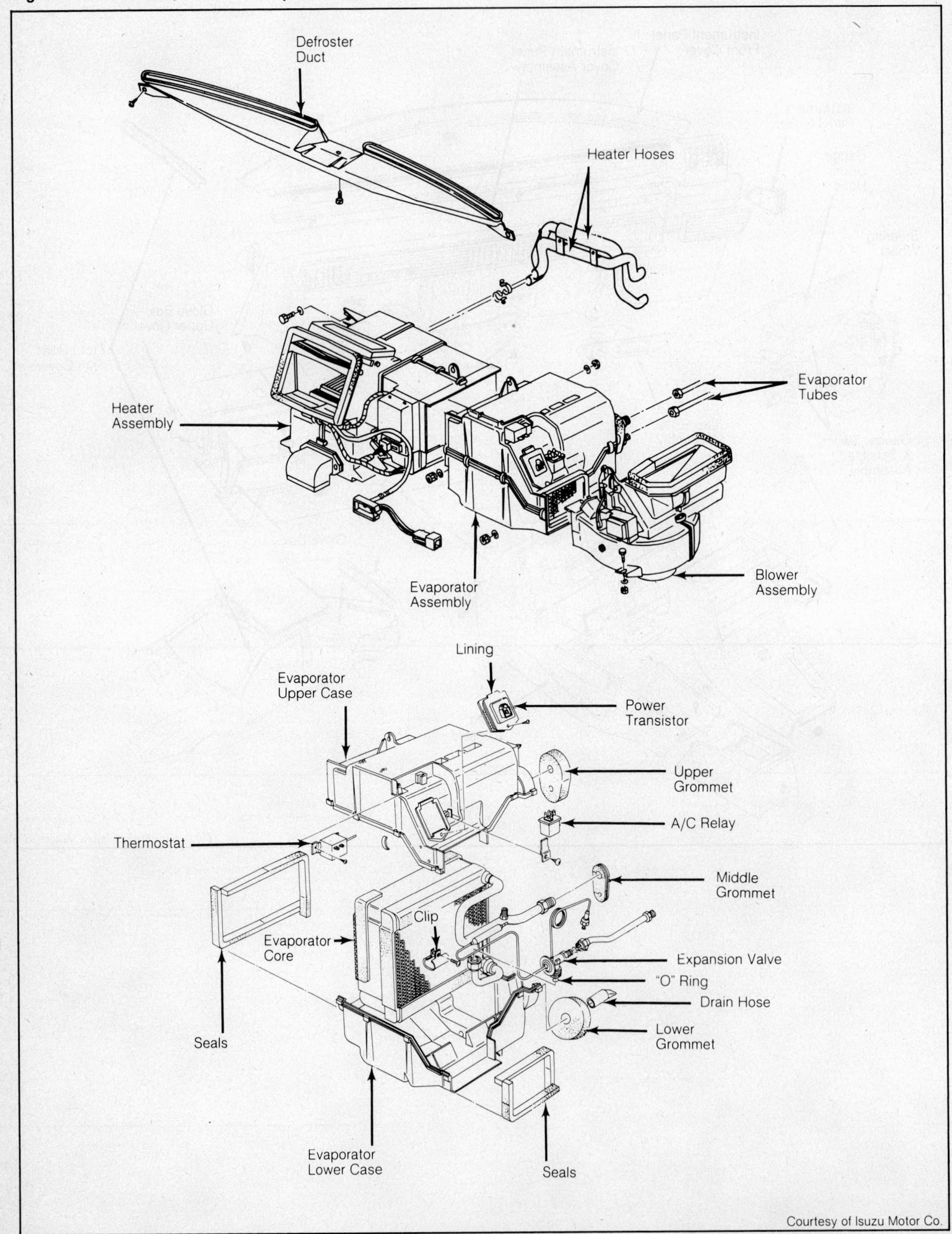

Heater Core Replacement

ISUZU (Cont.)

HEATER CORE ASSEMBLY

Removal (Impulse)

1) With heater, evaporator and blower assembly removed, disconnect wire harness. Remove heater control unit. Remove heater unit actuator and 2 shutter levers. Remove resistor assembly. Remove control unit and wire harness. Remove actuator, actuator-to-lever rod, and lever. *See Fig. 27.*

2) Disconnect cable from lever and remove lever. Remove heater unit thermostat. Remove lever rod. Remove actuator. Remove actuator lever rod and shutter lever. Remove heater core plate and lining. Remove duct.

3) Remove side rear and side front case assemblies. Remove lining. Remove left and right case assembly. Remove center upper, center, and center lower shutter assemblies. Remove heater core assembly.

Installation

To install, reverse removal procedure.

Fig. 27: Exploded View of Heater Assembly

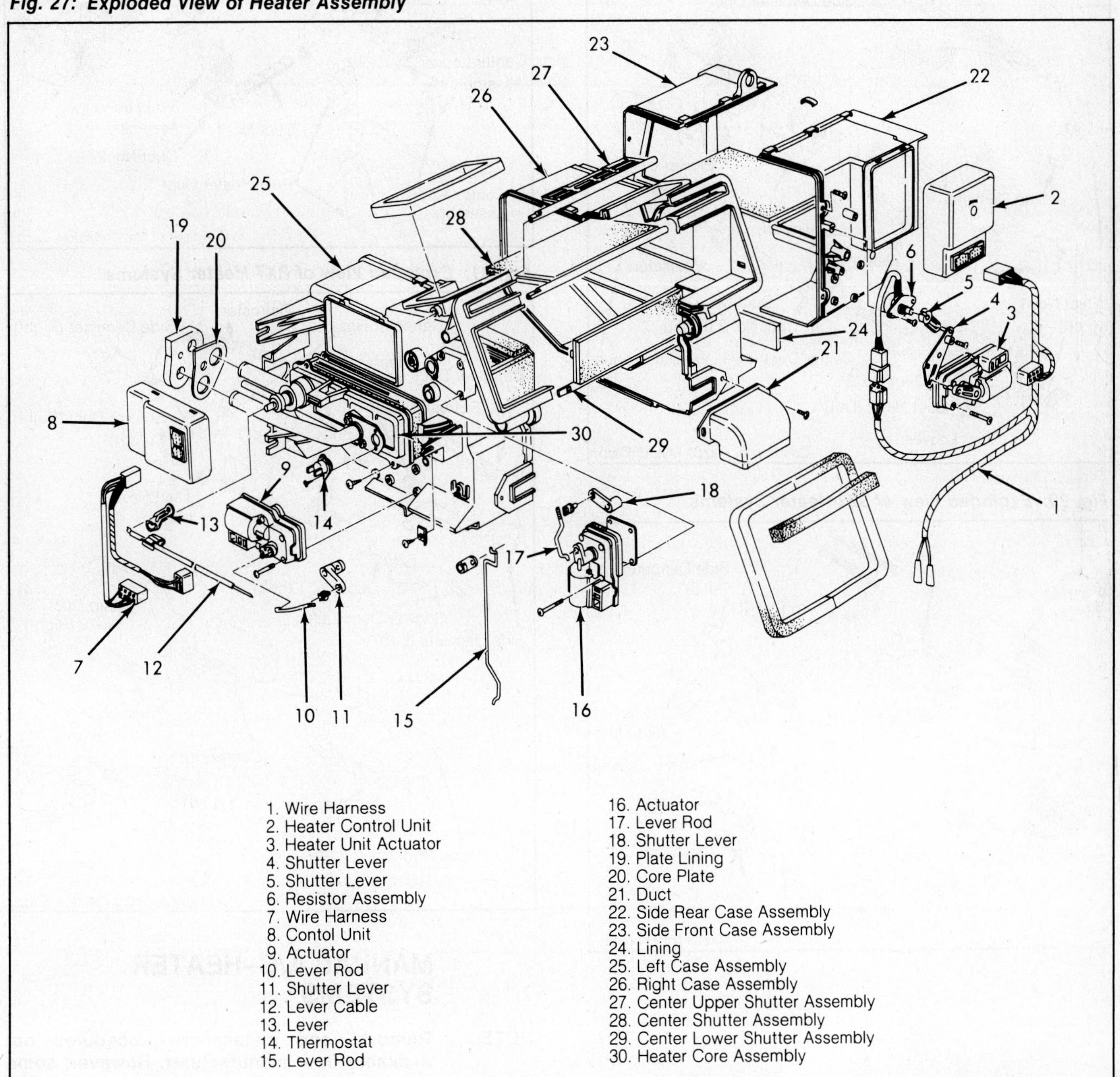

Heater Core Replacement

MAZDA

HEATER SYSTEMS ONLY

NOTE: Removal and installation procedures are not unavailable from manufacturer. However, exploded views of the systems have been provided.

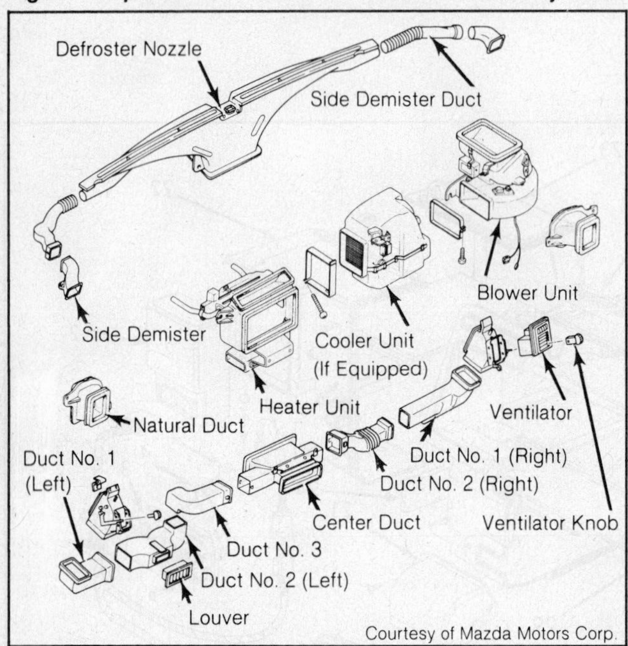

Fig. 28: Exploded View of B2200 & B2600 Heater Systems

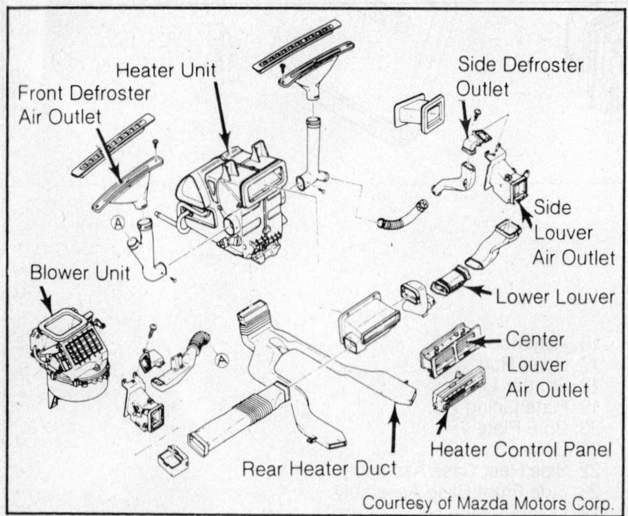

Fig. 29: Exploded View of 323 Heater Systems

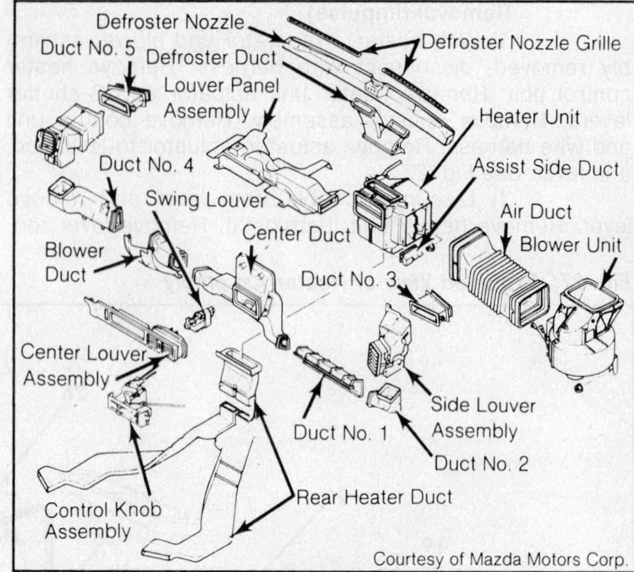

Fig. 30: Exploded View of 626 Heater Systems

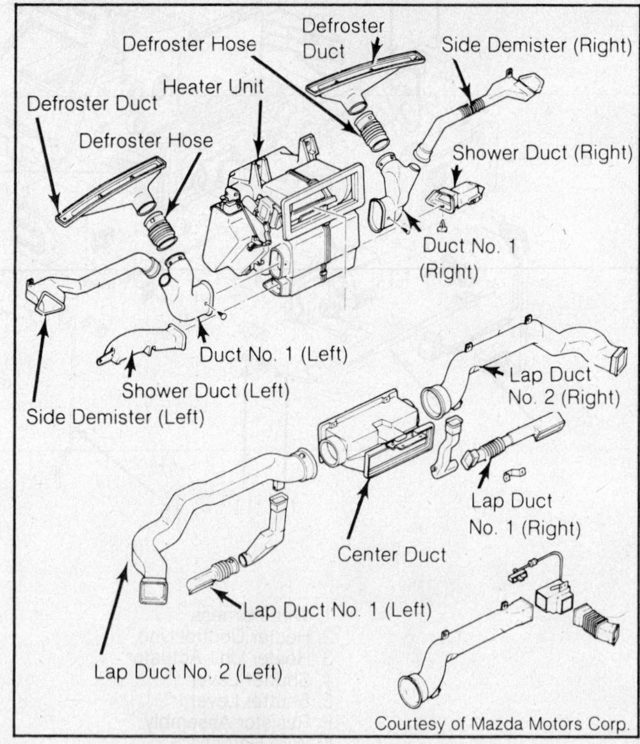

Fig. 31: Exploded View of RX7 Heater Systems

MANUAL A/C-HEATER SYSTEMS

NOTE: Removal and installation procedures not available from manufacturer. However, some component illustrations have been provided. See Figs. 32-37.

Heater Core Replacement

MAZDA (Cont.)

Fig. 32: B2200 & 2600 A/C System Components

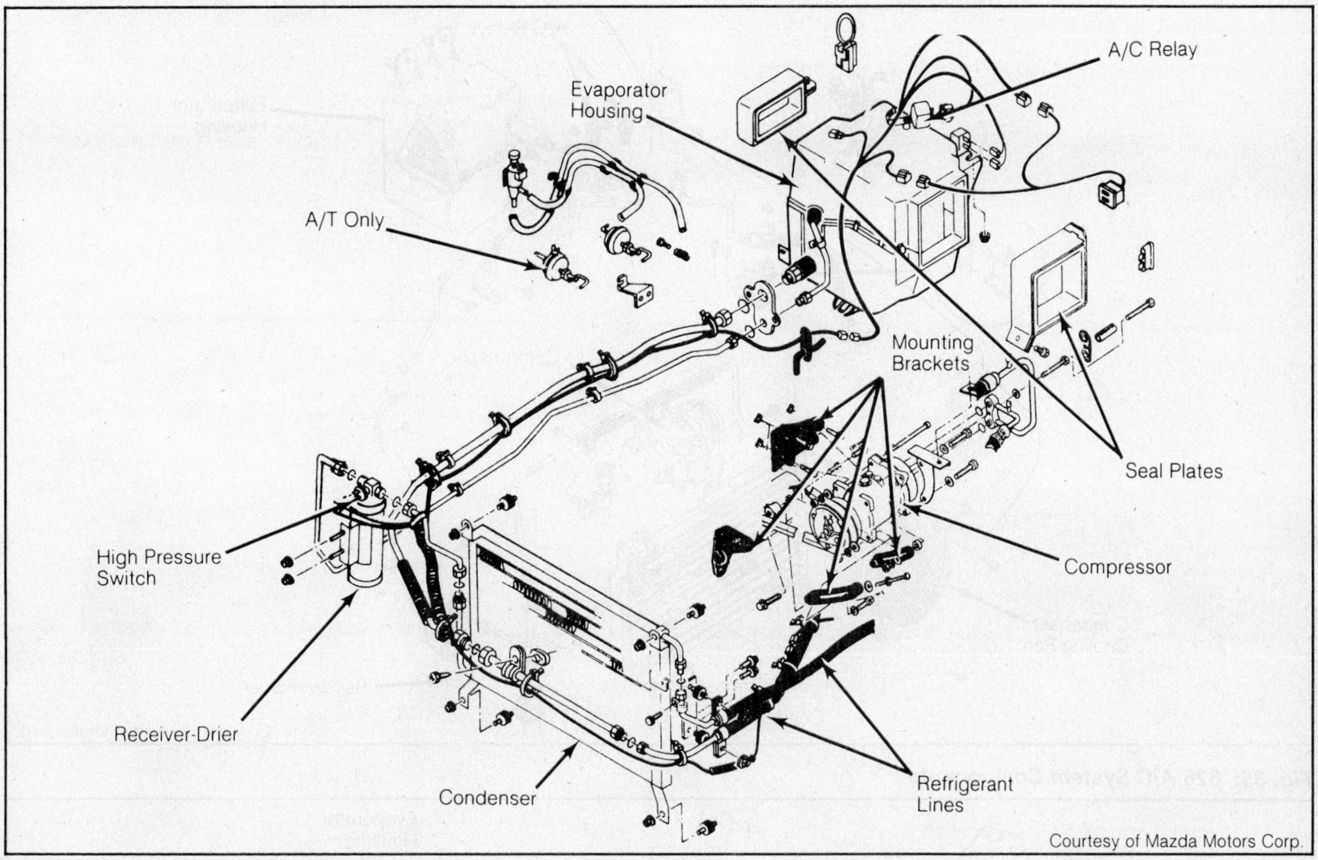

Fig. 33: RX7 A/C System Components

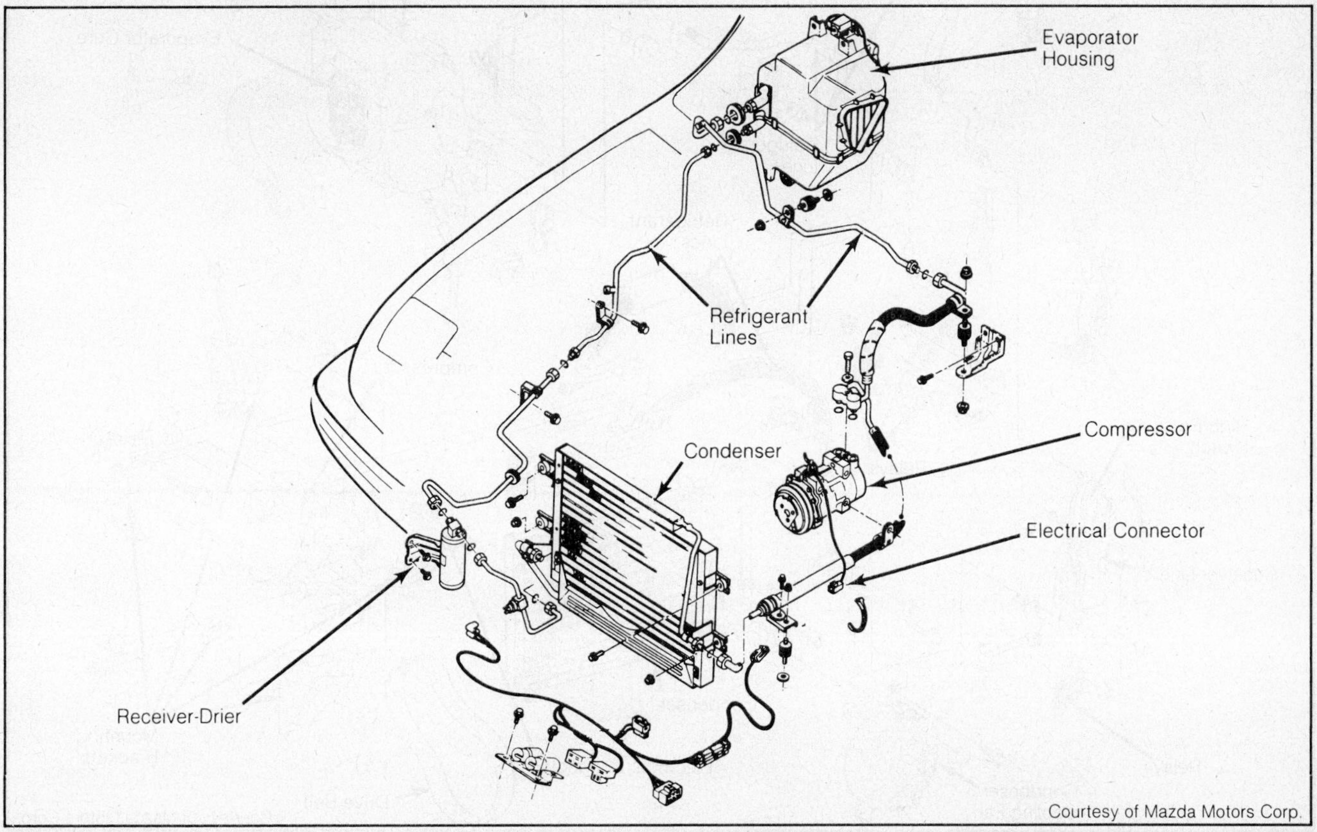

Heater Core Replacement

MAZDA (Cont.)

Fig. 34: 323 A/C System Components

A/C Relays
Evaporator Housing
Compressor
Condenser Cooling Fan
Receiver-Drier
Condenser
Courtesy of Mazda Motors Corp.

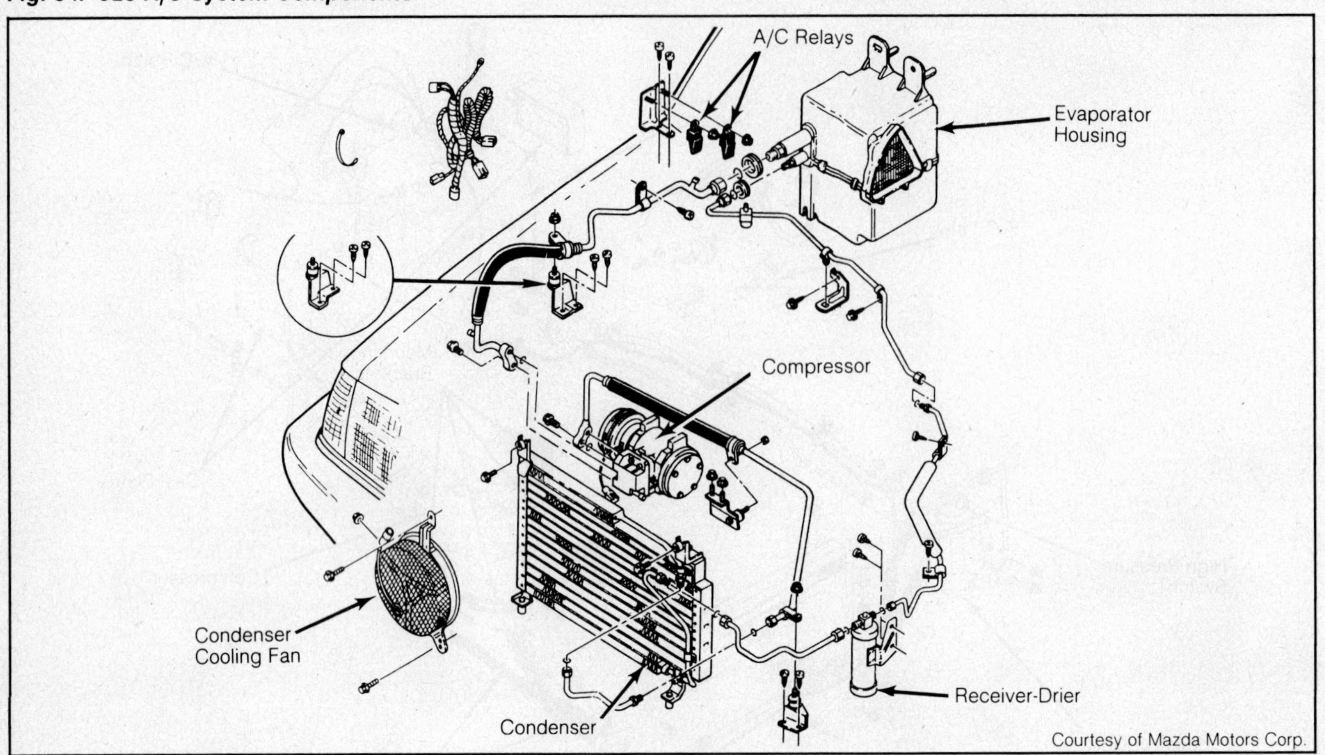

Fig. 35: 626 A/C System Components

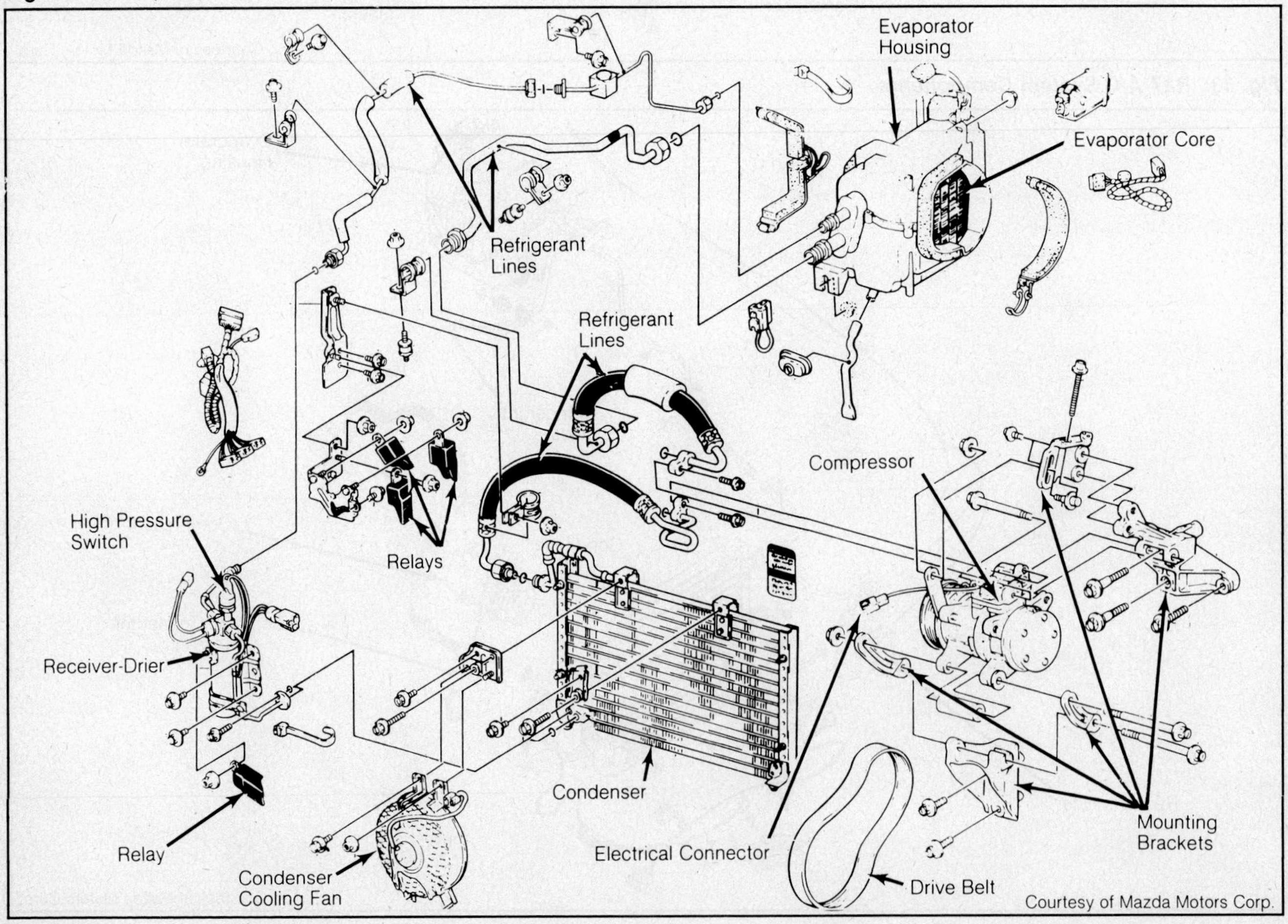

Evaporator Housing
Evaporator Core
Refrigerant Lines
Refrigerant Lines
Compressor
High Pressure Switch
Relays
Receiver-Drier
Condenser
Relay
Condenser Cooling Fan
Electrical Connector
Drive Belt
Mounting Brackets
Courtesy of Mazda Motors Corp.

MAZDA (Cont.)

Fig. 36: B2200 Evaporator Housing

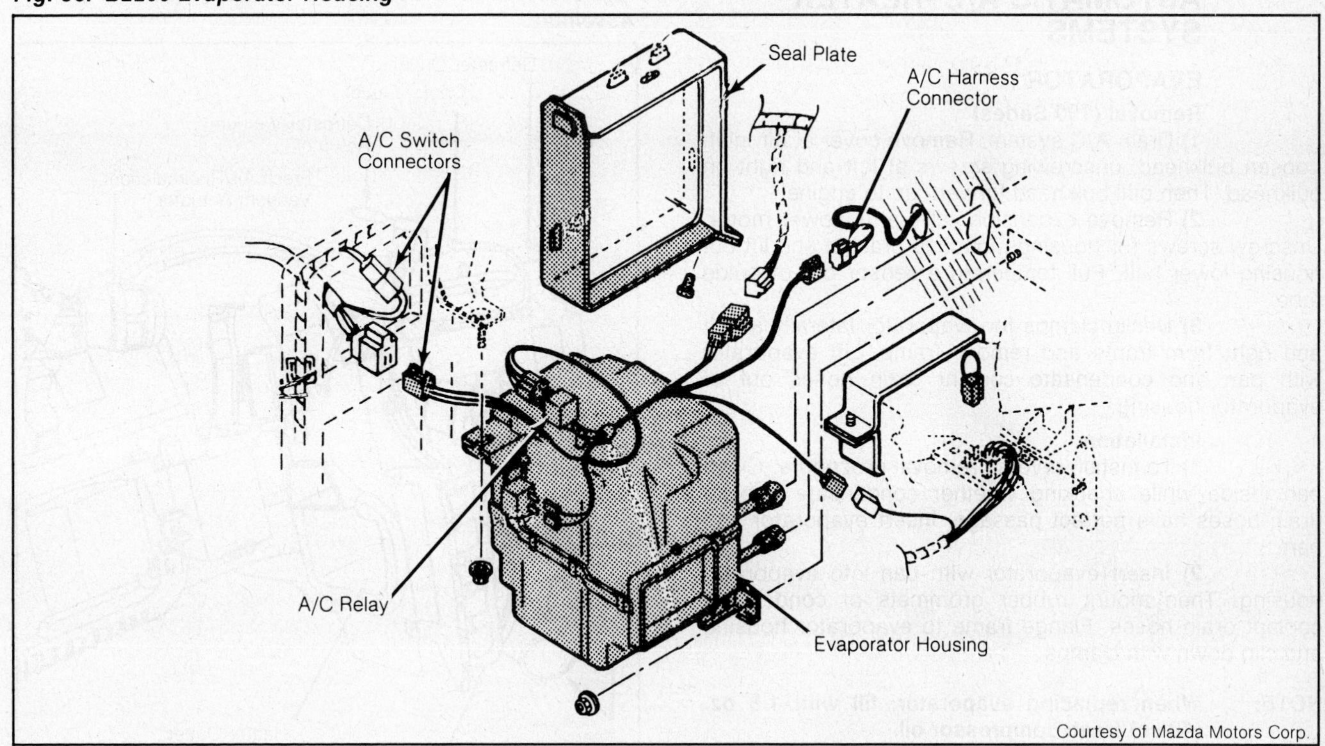

Fig. 37: RX7 Evaporator Housing

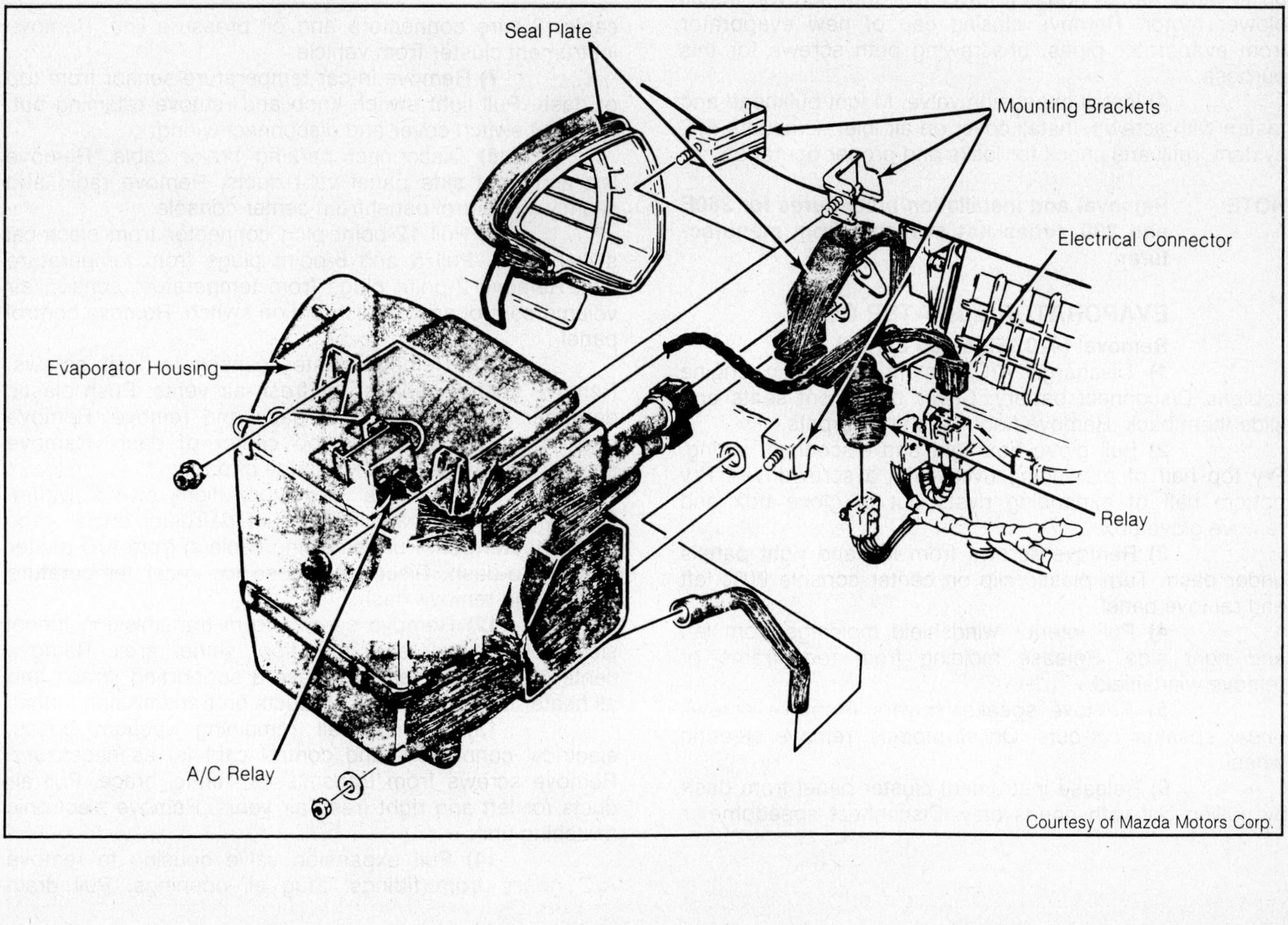

MERCEDES BENZ

AUTOMATIC A/C–HEATER SYSTEMS

EVAPORATOR

Removal (190 Series)

1) Drain A/C system. Remove cover at air inlet. Loosen bulkhead, unscrewing screws at left and right on bulkhead. Then pull bulkhead forward up to engine.

2) Remove expansion valve and blower motor. Unscrew screws for housing mounting bracket and lift out housing lower half. Pull temperature sensor out of guide tube.

3) Unclip clamps for evaporator laterally at left and right from frame and remove frame. Lift evaporator with pan and condensate coolant drain hoses out of evaporator housing.

Installation

1) To install, reverse removal procedure. Clean pan inside while checking whether condensate coolant drain hoses have perfect passage. Insert evaporator into pan.

2) Insert evaporator with pan into evaporator housing. Then mount rubber grommets of condensate coolant drain hoses. Flange frame to evaporator housing and clip down with clamps.

NOTE: **When replacing evaporator, fill with 1.3 oz. (40 cc) fresh compressor oil.**

3) Insert temperature sensor into guide tube up to stop. Mount housing lower half with screws. Install blower motor. Remove closing cap of new evaporator from evaporator pipes, unscrewing both screws for this purpose.

4) Install expansion valve. Mount bulkhead and fasten with screws. Install cover on air inlet. Evacuate A/C system, refill and check for leaks and proper operation.

NOTE: **Removal and installation procedures for 260E and 300 series not available from manufacturer.**

EVAPORATOR & HEATER CORE

Removal (420SEL & 560 Series)

1) Discharge A/C system and drain engine coolant. Disconnect battery. Cover both front seats and slide them back. Remove floor mats and carpets.

2) Pull glove box light and disconnect wiring. Pry top half of expanding rivets with a screwdriver. Pry bottom half of expanding rivets out of glove box and remove glove box.

3) Remove screws from left and right panels under dash. Turn plastic clip on center console 90% left and remove panel.

4) Pull interior windshield moldings from left and right side. Release molding from roof frame or remove windshield.

5) Remove speaker covers. Remove screws under speaker cut-outs. On all models, remove steering wheel.

6) Release instrument cluster panel from dash by pulling out with hands only. Disconnect speedometer cable, 2 wire connectors and oil pressure line. Remove instrument cluster from vehicle.

Fig. 38: 420SEL & 560 Series Heater-Evaporator Assembly

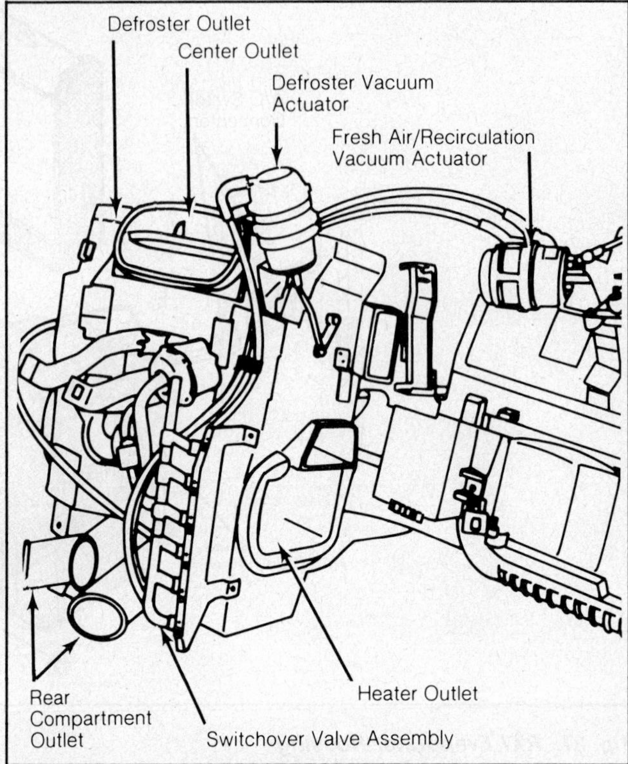

7) Remove in-car temperature sensor from top of dash. Pull light switch knob and remove retaining nut. Pull light switch cover and disconnect wiring.

8) Disconnect parking brake cable. Remove left and right side panel vent ducts. Remove radio and slightly lift control panel from center console.

9) Pull 12-point plug connector from electrical switch gear. Pull 5 and 6-point plugs from temperature dial. Remove 2-point plugs from temperature sensor, air volume control and air distribution switch. Remove control panel.

10) Remove center console-to-dash screws. Remove control cable(s) for fresh air vents. Push plastic defroster nozzle on top of dash and remove. Remove dash mounting screw at top center of dash. Remove screws beneath left and right side of dash.

11) Remove glove box light switch wiring. Slightly raise dash and make sure defroster ducts come out of heater box. Pull remaining cable(s) from A/C-heater housing-to-dash. Disconnect hose for in-car temperature sensor and remove dash.

12) Remove screws from transmission tunnel sides, center tray and near floor shifter area. Remove center console to rear. Remove 3 supporting straps and all heater hoses. Remove air ducts on transmission tunnel.

13) Remove all remaining vacuum hoses, electrical connectors and control cable(s) as necessary. Remove screws from transmission tunnel brace. Pull air ducts for left and right fresh air vents. Remove electronic switching unit.

14) Pull expansion valve housing to remove A/C hoses from fittings. Plug all openings. Pull drain

MERCEDES BENZ (Cont.)

hoses from both sides of A/C-heater housing. Pull electrical plug from switchover valve.

15) Remove remaining screws and nuts from support brackets. Pull A/C-heater unit housing complete with heater hoses from vehicle. Hold heater hoses up so coolant will not spill.

16) Remove clips from top of A/C-heater case. Remove heater core case and core unit. Pry 2 clamps from lateral member. Pull vacuum line to vacuum control motor. Disconnect actuator control rod and vacuum motor mounting screw.

17) Remove lateral member. Pull plastic shaft and shaft bearing rod out of A/C-heater housing. Pull temperature sensor from A/C-heater housing near expansion valve. Disconnect vacuum controls on main air flap.

18) Pry clips holding main flap housing and remove. Pry remaining clips around A/C-heater (evaporator-to-heater core) housing. Remove screws holding vacuum switchover valve to case. Remove left side panel.

19) Remove main air flap shaft. Separate A/C-heater housing and remove evaporator.

Installation

To install, reverse removal procedure. Make sure evaporator housing joining surfaces are well sealed during reassembly.

NISSAN

HEATER SYSTEMS ONLY

HEATER CORE & ASSEMBLY

NOTE: **Some heater core REMOVAL & INSTALLATION procedures are not available from manufacturer. However, exploded views of the systems have been provided.**

Removal (Pulsar NX & Sentra)

Set temperature lever to "HOT" position and drain engine coolant. Disconnect heater hoses at engine compartment. Remove cluster lid, glove box, heater control panel and trim pieces. Remove heater unit assembly.

Installation

To install, reverse removal procedure. Adjust cables and check system operation.

Fig. 39: Exploded View of Van Heater Assembly

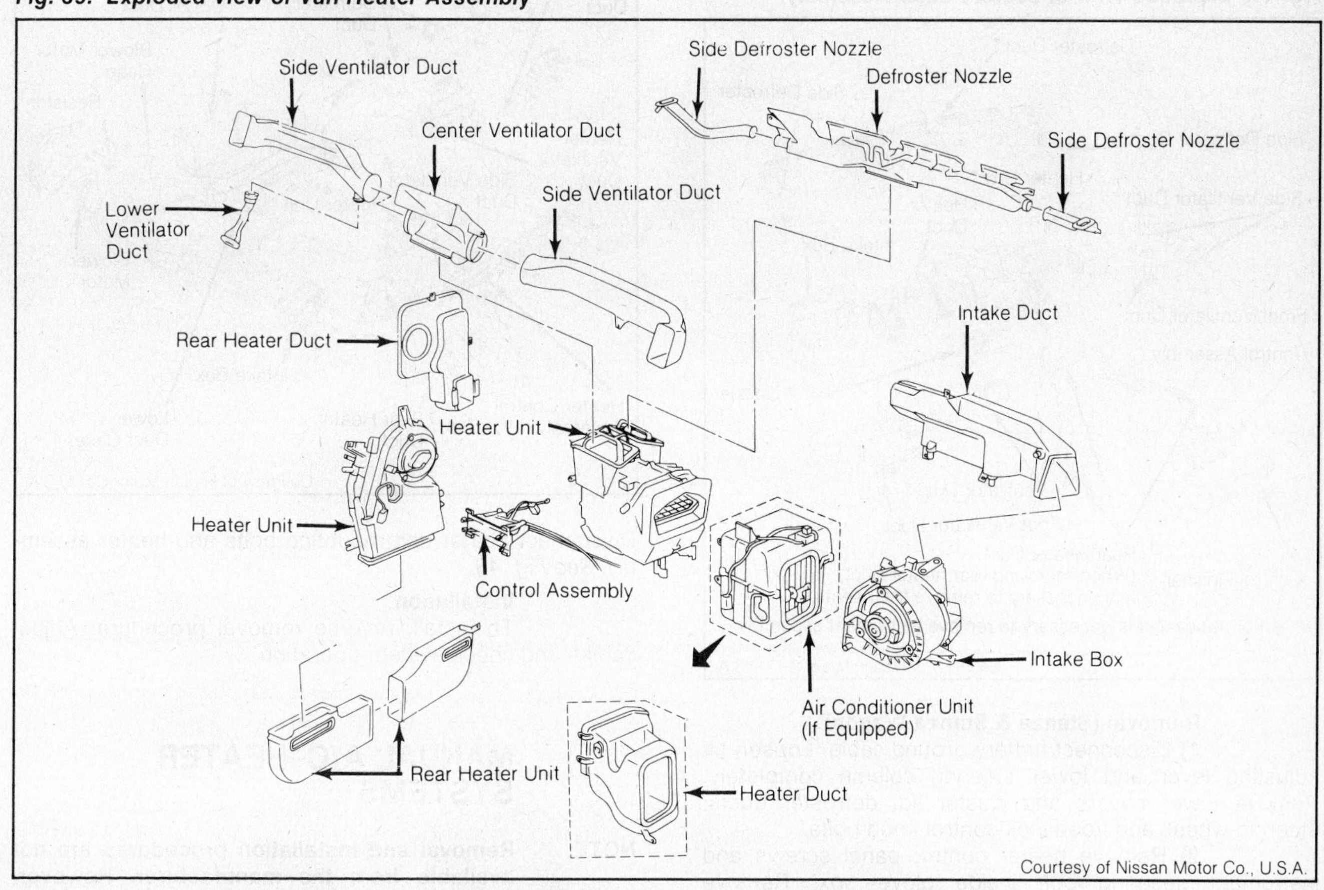

MERCEDES BENZ (Cont.)

Fig. 40: Exploded View of Pathfinder & Pickup Heater Assembly

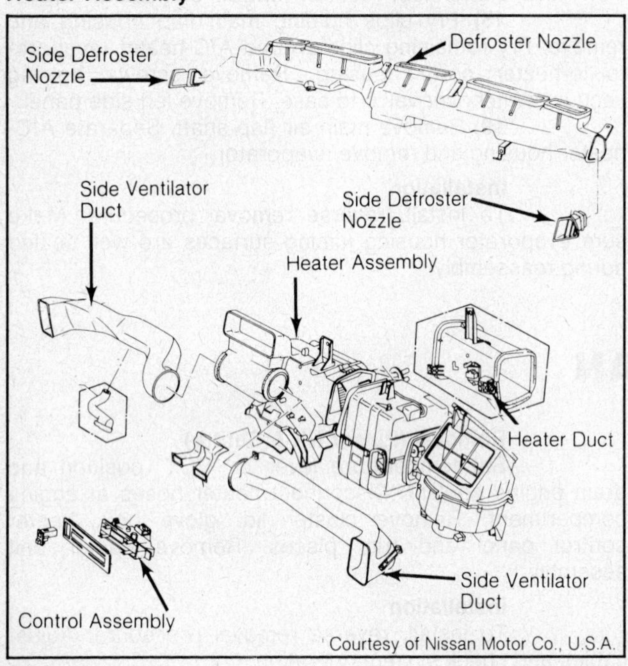

Fig. 41: Exploded View of 200SX Heater Assembly

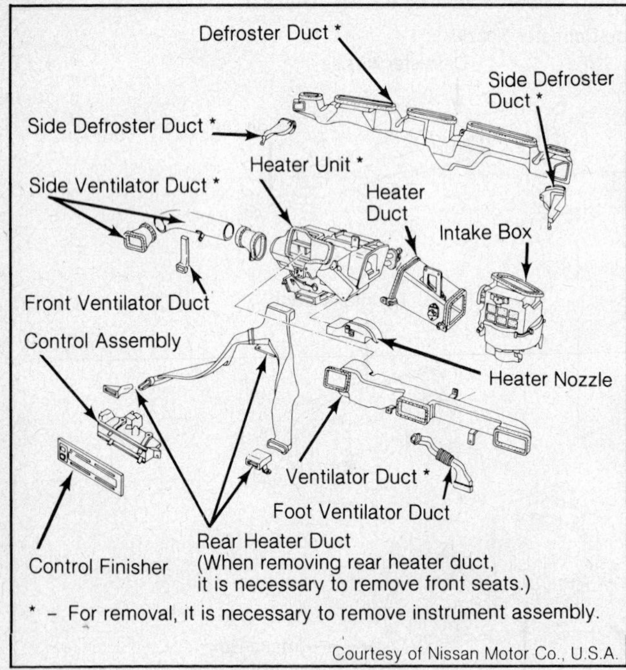

Removal (Stanza & Stanza Wagon)

1) Disconnect battery ground cable. Loosen tilt adjusting lever and lower steering column completely. Remove lower covers and cluster lid, defroster ducts, steering wheel, and hood lock control knob bolts.

2) Remove heater control panel screws and instrument securing bolt inside glove box. Remove instrument securing bolts, speedometer cable and harness connectors. Remove instrument panel.

3) Disconnect heater hoses and vacuum tubes at engine compartment. Remove heater control assembly.

Fig. 42: Exploded View of Pulsar NX & Sentra Heater Assembly

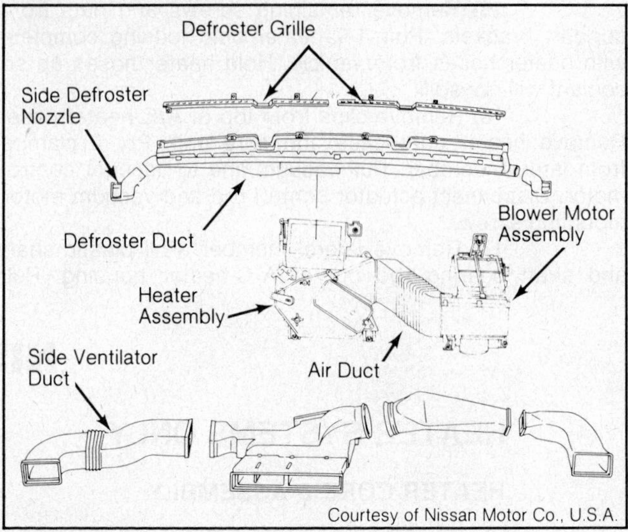

Fig. 43: Exploded View of Stanza & Stanza Wagon Heater Assembly

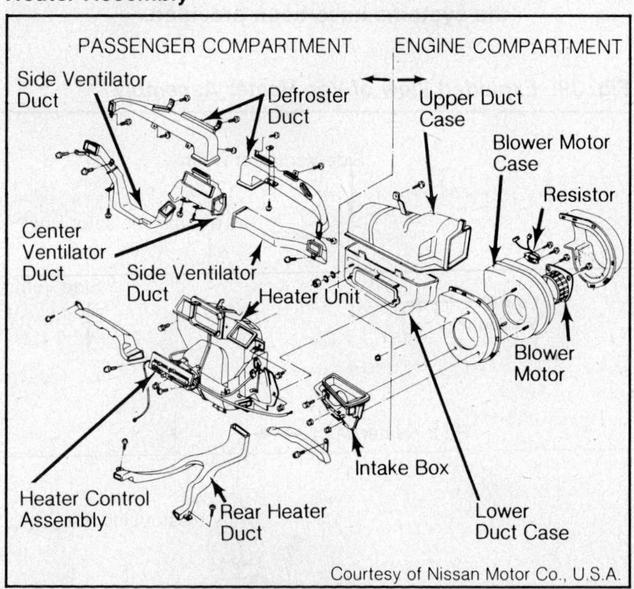

Disconnect heater unit mounting bolts and heater assembly. *See Fig. 43.*

Installation

To install, reverse removal procedure. Adjust cables and check system operation.

MANUAL A/C-HEATER SYSTEMS

NOTE: **Removal and installation procedures are not available from the manufacturer. However, component layout exploded views, as well as general removal and installation procedures are included as an outline for Removal and Installation operations. *See Figs. 44 thru 52.***

Heater Core Replacement

NISSAN (Cont.)

EVAPORATOR ASSEMBLY

NOTE: Evaporator core Removal and Installation procedures for 200SX and 300ZX are not available from manufacturer.

Removal (Maxima)

Remove instrument lower cover and cluster lid. Disconnect refrigerant lines and harness from cooling unit. Remove cooling unit with drain tube. Remove clips fixing upper case to lower case. Withdraw evaporator assembly.

Installation

To install, reverse removal procedure.

Removal (Pickup)

1) Disconnect battery. Discharge A/C system. Disconnect inlet and outlet hoses from evaporator and remove tube mounting bolt. Plug all openings. Remove steering column cover, package tray, and speedometer cable from speedometer.

2) Remove wiring for center illuminator, cigar lighter, rear defogger switch, clock, turn signal switch and other wiring (mark for re-installation).

3) Remove 11 panel retaining bolts (3 beneath windshield, 1 at bracket near steering column, 1 inside glove box, 2 at each end of panel and 2 above cluster cover). Remove blower motor assembly as described in this article.

4) Remove 3 evaporator assembly screws and take out evaporator assembly. Remove retaining clips, take off upper half of case and withdraw evaporator core.

Installation

To install, reverse removal procedure. If installing new evaporator core, add 2.4 oz. of compressor oil to new core before installation. Evacuate, recharge and leak test system.

Removal (Pulsar NX)

1) Disconnect battery ground cable. Discharge A/C system. Disconnect refrigerant lines from evaporator and plug lines and fittings. Remove piping grommet and cover. Remove passenger's side instrument lower cover and glove box. Remove attachment plate from instrument panel.

Fig. 45: Cutting Pulsar NX Instrument Panel for Evaporator Removal

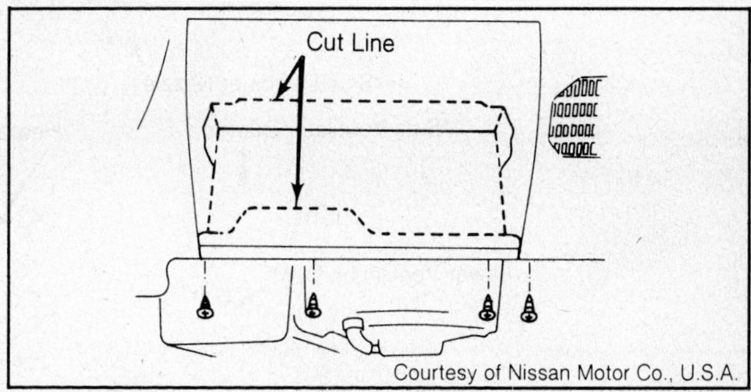

2) Cut instrument panel with hacksaw blade on cut lines. Before cutting, cover blower motor vent holes with tape. After cutting, brush shavings away from area around blower motor and remove tape. Remove blower motor unit. Remove evaporator assembly. *See Fig. 45.*

Installation

To install, reverse removal procedure. If installing new evaporator core, add compressor oil to new core before installation. Evacuate, recharge and leak test system.

Removal (Sentra)

Disconnect battery ground cable. Discharge system. Disconnect refrigerant lines from evaporator. Remove piping grommet and cover. Remove instrument panel by removing cluster lid, glove box, heater control panel and trim pieces. Remove evaporator assembly mounting bolts and remove assembly.

Fig. 44: Maxima Manual A/C-Heater Systems Component Layout

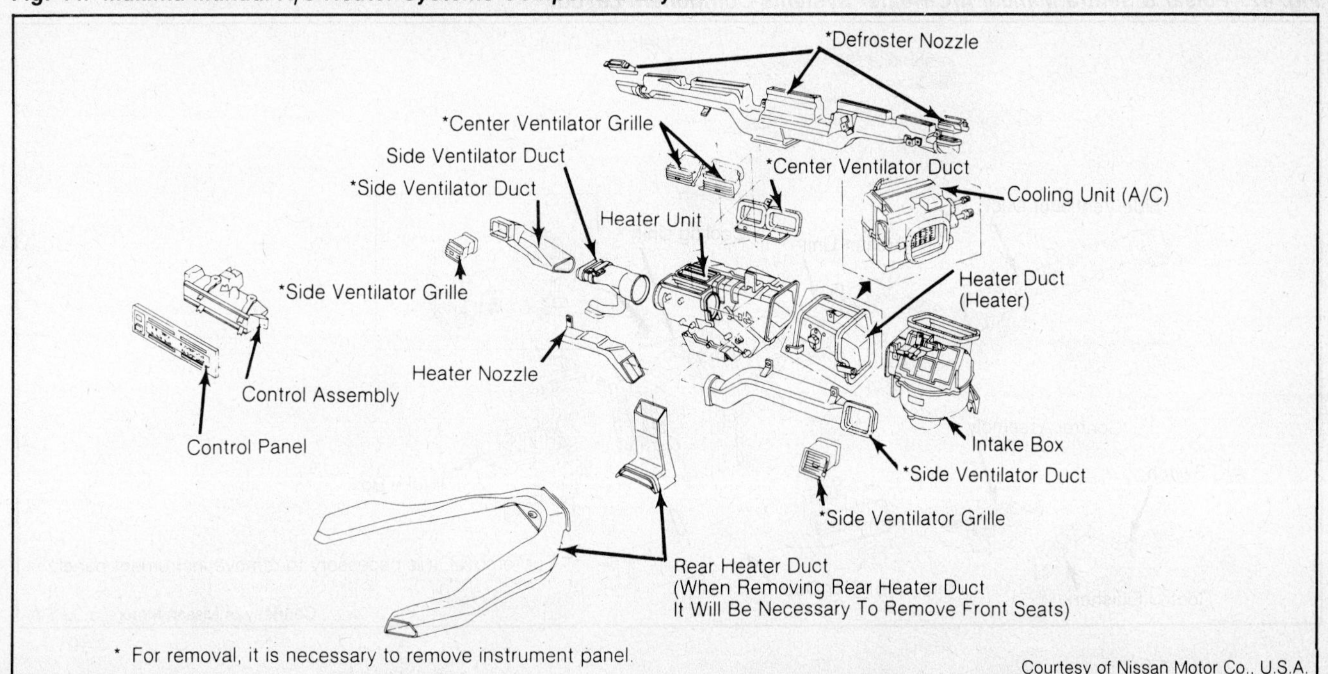

Heater Core Replacement

NISSAN (Cont.)

Fig. 46: Pathfinder/Pickup Manual A/C-Heater Systems Component Layout

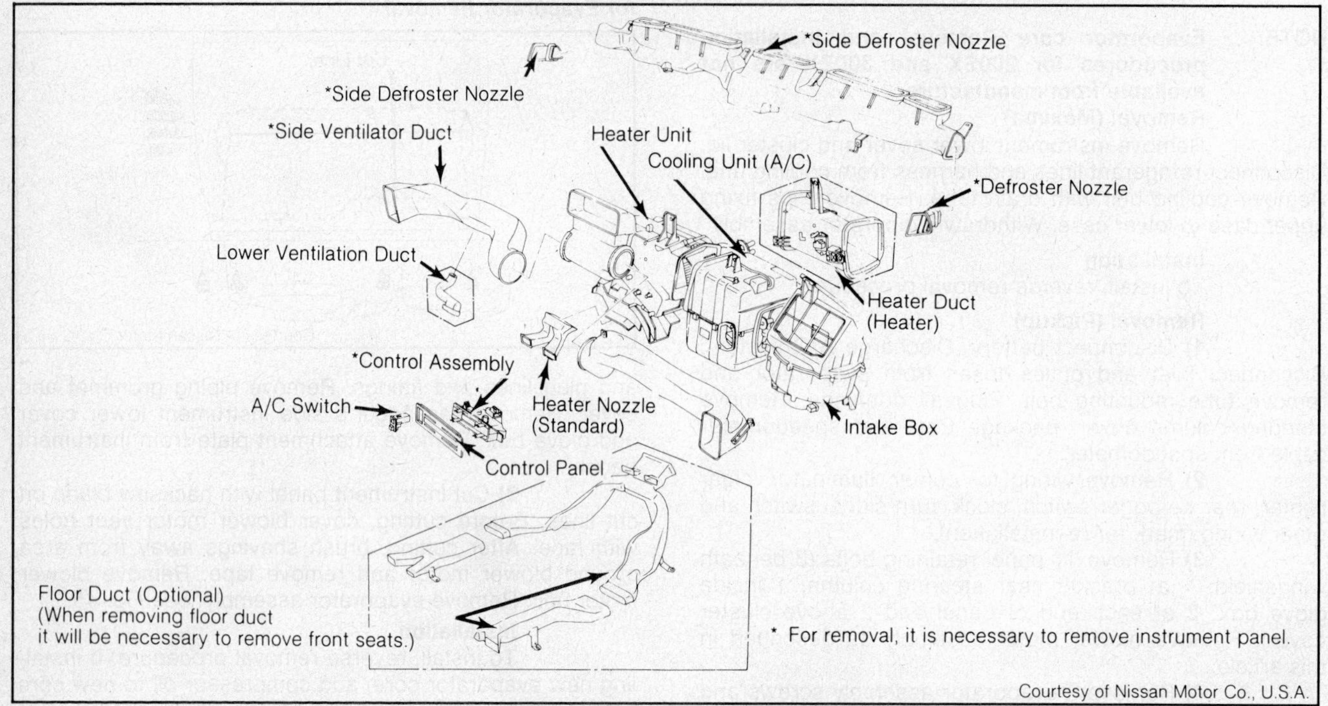

Installation

To install, reverse removal procedure. If installing new evaporator core, add compressor oil to new core before installation. Evacuate, recharge and leak test system.

Removal (Stanza)

1) Disconnect battery ground cable. Discharge refrigerant from system. Remove air cleaner. Disconnect vacuum check valve fixing bolt. Disconnect evaporator upper case fixing bolts.

2) Remove evaporator upper case while scraping off sealer. Disconnect inlet and outlet lines at evaporator and plug openings. Remove evaporator from evaporator lower case.

Installation

To install, reverse removal procedure. Use sealer to take up clearance between upper and lower cases.

Fig. 47: Pulsar & Sentra Manual A/C-Heater Systems Component Layout

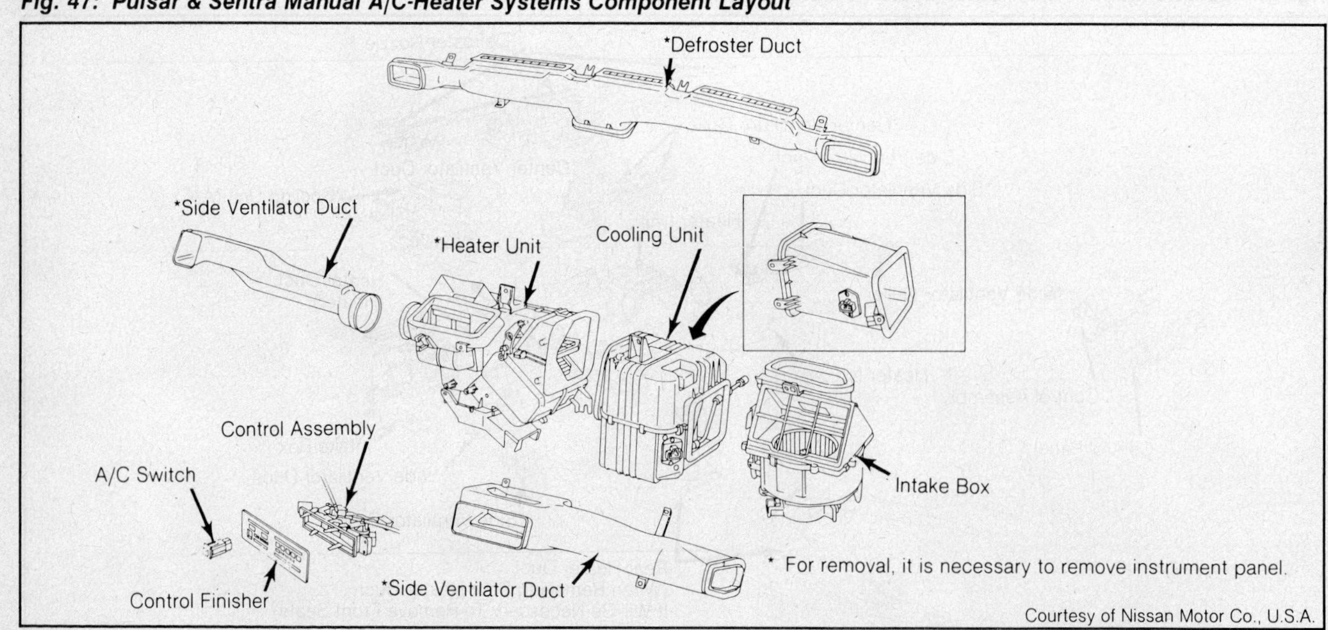

Heater Core Replacement

NISSAN (Cont.)

Fig. 48: Stanza Manual A/C-Heater Systems Component Layout

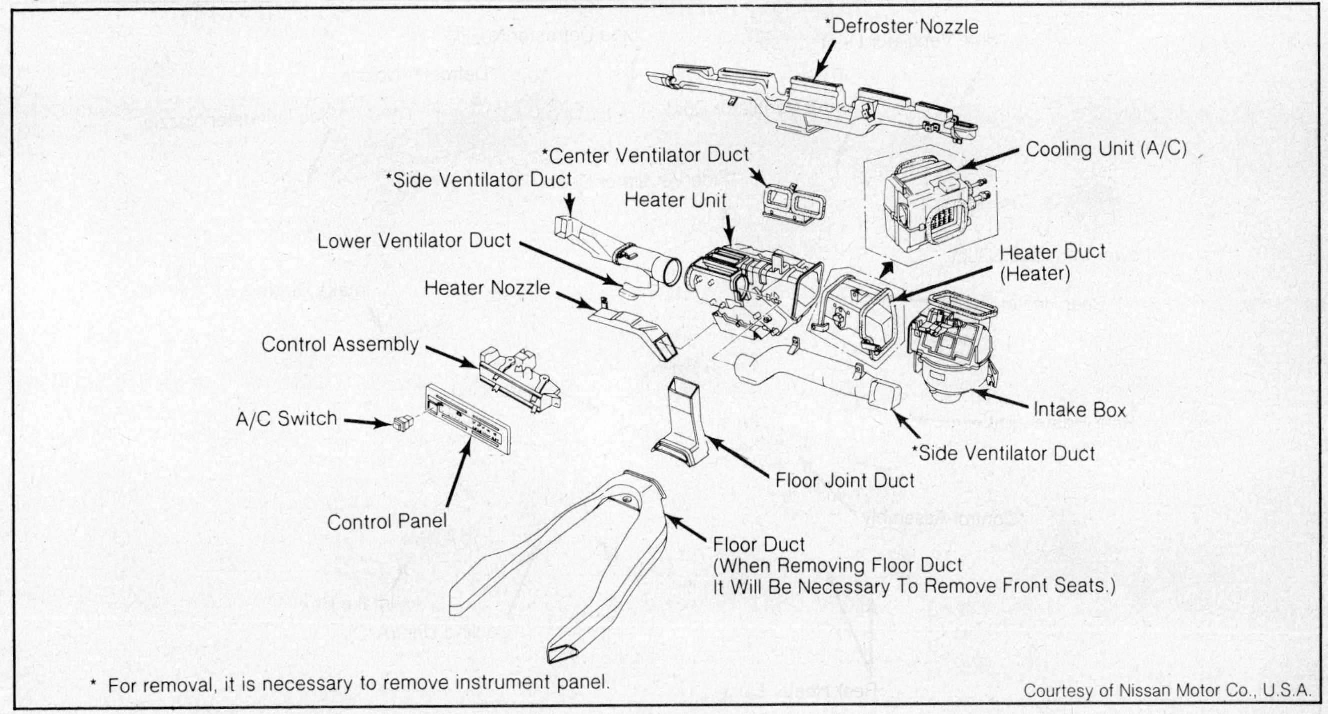

Fig. 49: Stanza Wagon Manual A/C-Heater Systems Component Layout

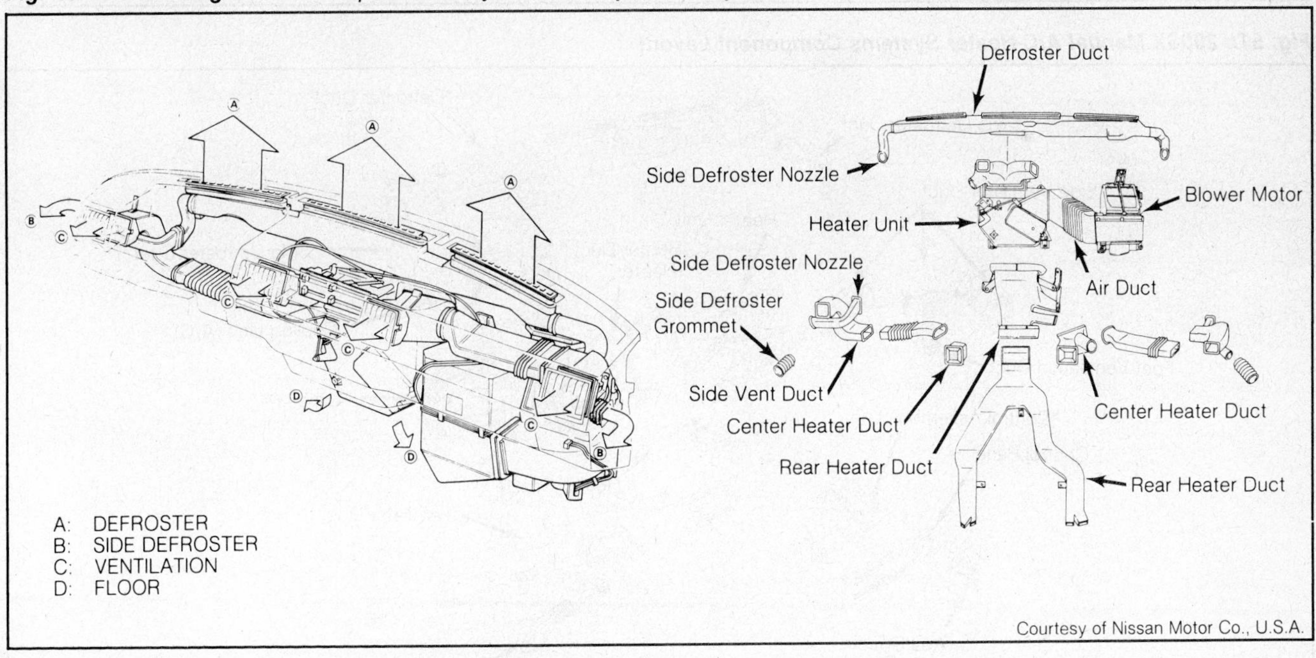

Heater Core Replacement

NISSAN (Cont.)

Fig. 50: Van Manual A/C-Heater Systems Component Layout

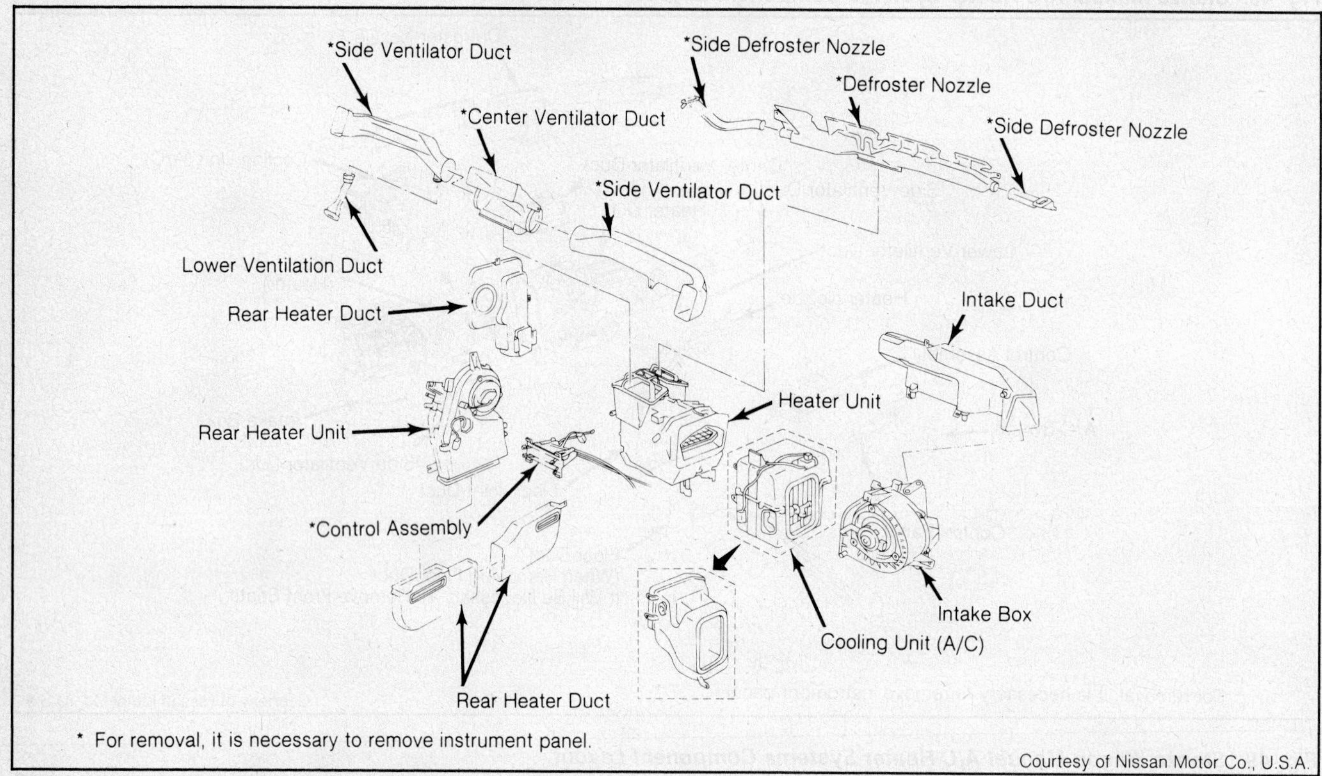

Fig. 51: 200SX Manual A/C-Heater Systems Component Layout

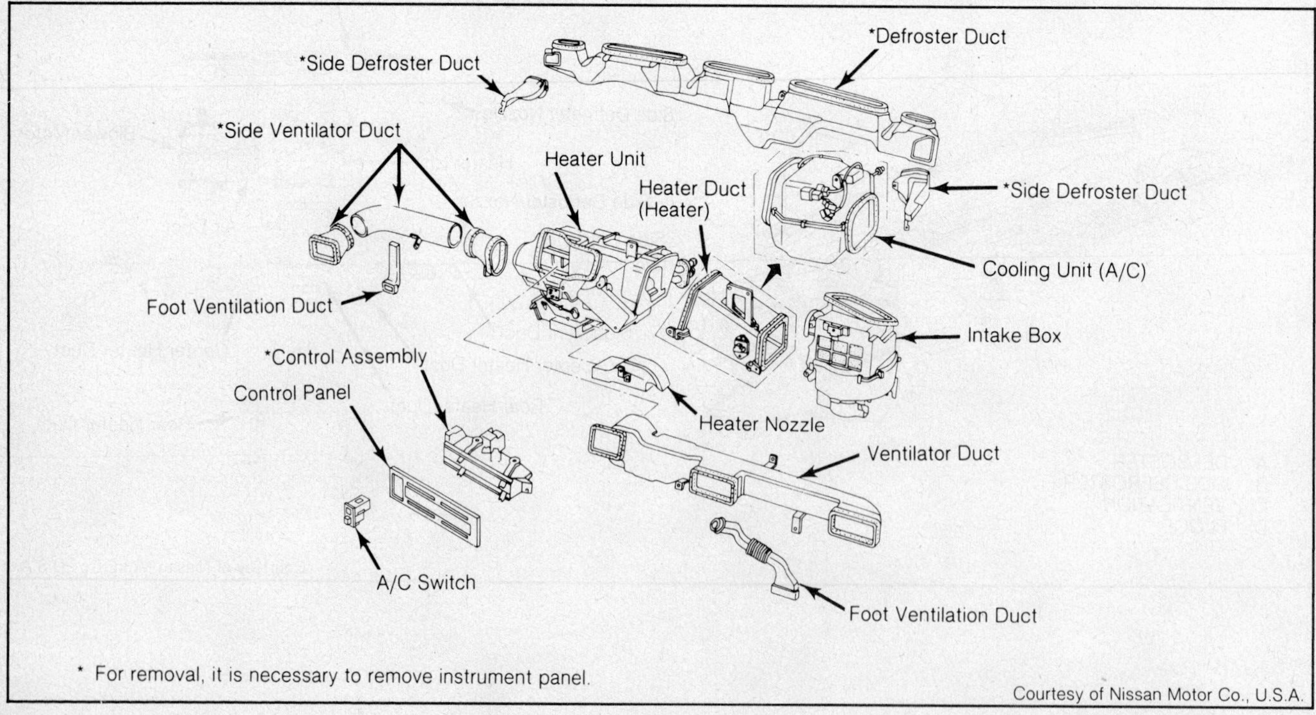

Heater Core Replacement

NISSAN (Cont.)

Fig. 52: 300ZX Manual A/C-Heater Systems Component Layout

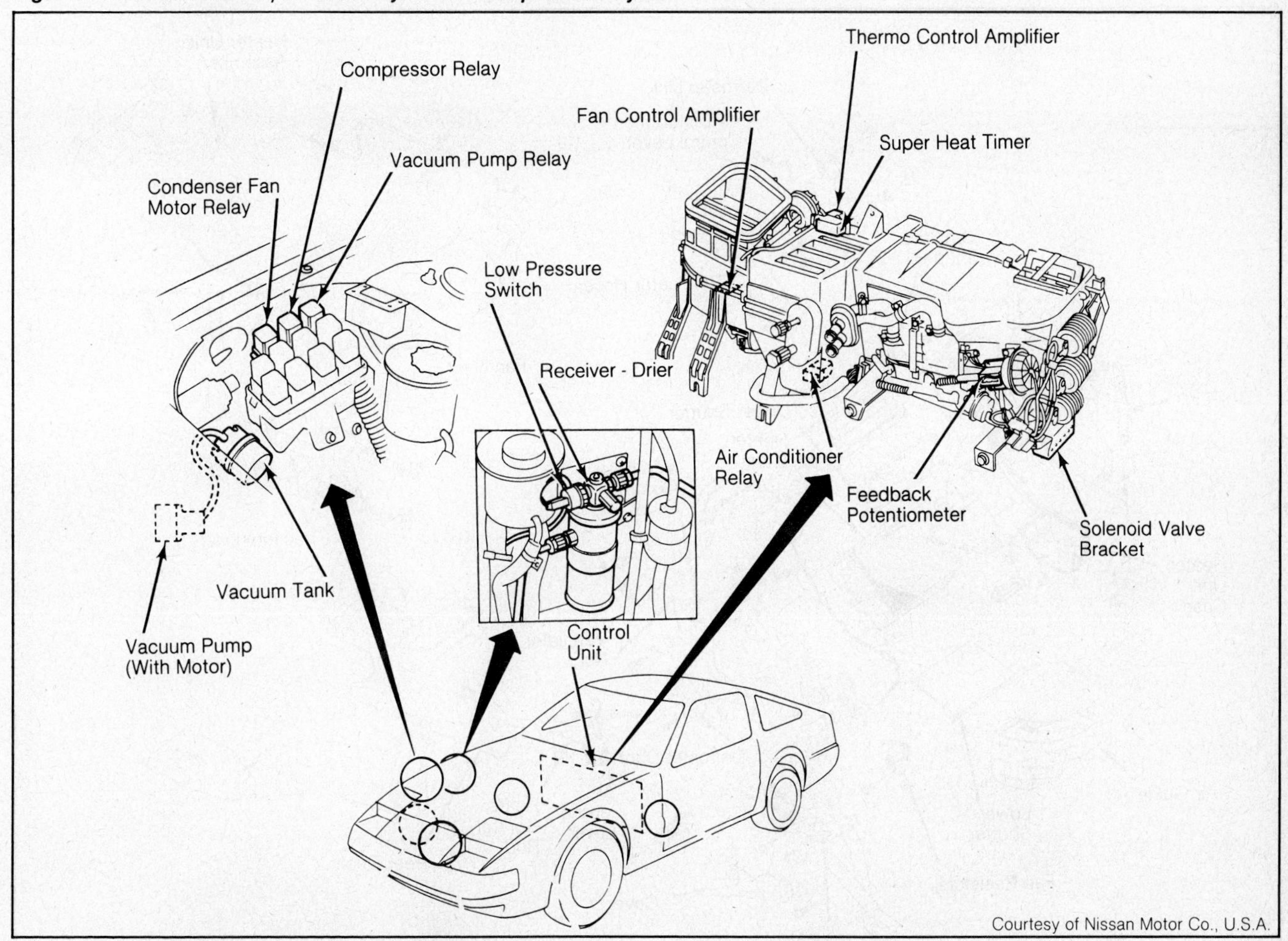

Courtesy of Nissan Motor Co., U.S.A.

AUTOMATIC A/C–HEATER SYSTEMS

NOTE: **For removal of basic A/C system components, see MANUAL A/C-HEATER SYSTEMS in MANUAL A/C-HEATER in this section.**

SUBARU

HEATER SYSTEMS ONLY

HEATER CORE UNIT

Removal (All Models)

1) Disconnect negative battery cable. Drain coolant. Disconnect both heater hoses. Remove heater hose grommet from firewall.

2) Remove radio, package tray and dash. Detach fan duct between fan motor assembly and heater unit. Remove defroster nozzles. Remove 2 bolts at upper part of heater unit. Lift heater unit 3/8" and remove from vehicle.

3) Remove heater control valve. Disconnect rod between left and right defroster shutters from plastic clamp. Pry clips off to separate heater unit and remove heater core or shutters as necessty.

Installation

To install, reverse removal procedure. Adjust control cables.

HEATER UNIT

Removal & Installation (Justy)

1) Disconnect battery ground cable. Drain coolant from radiator by removing drain plug. Remove outlet and inlet heater hoses by loosening hose clamp screws. Pull off right and left defroster ducts from defroster nozzles.

Heater Core Replacement

SUBARU (Cont.)

Fig. 53: Exploded View of 1600 & 1800 OHV Heater Assembly

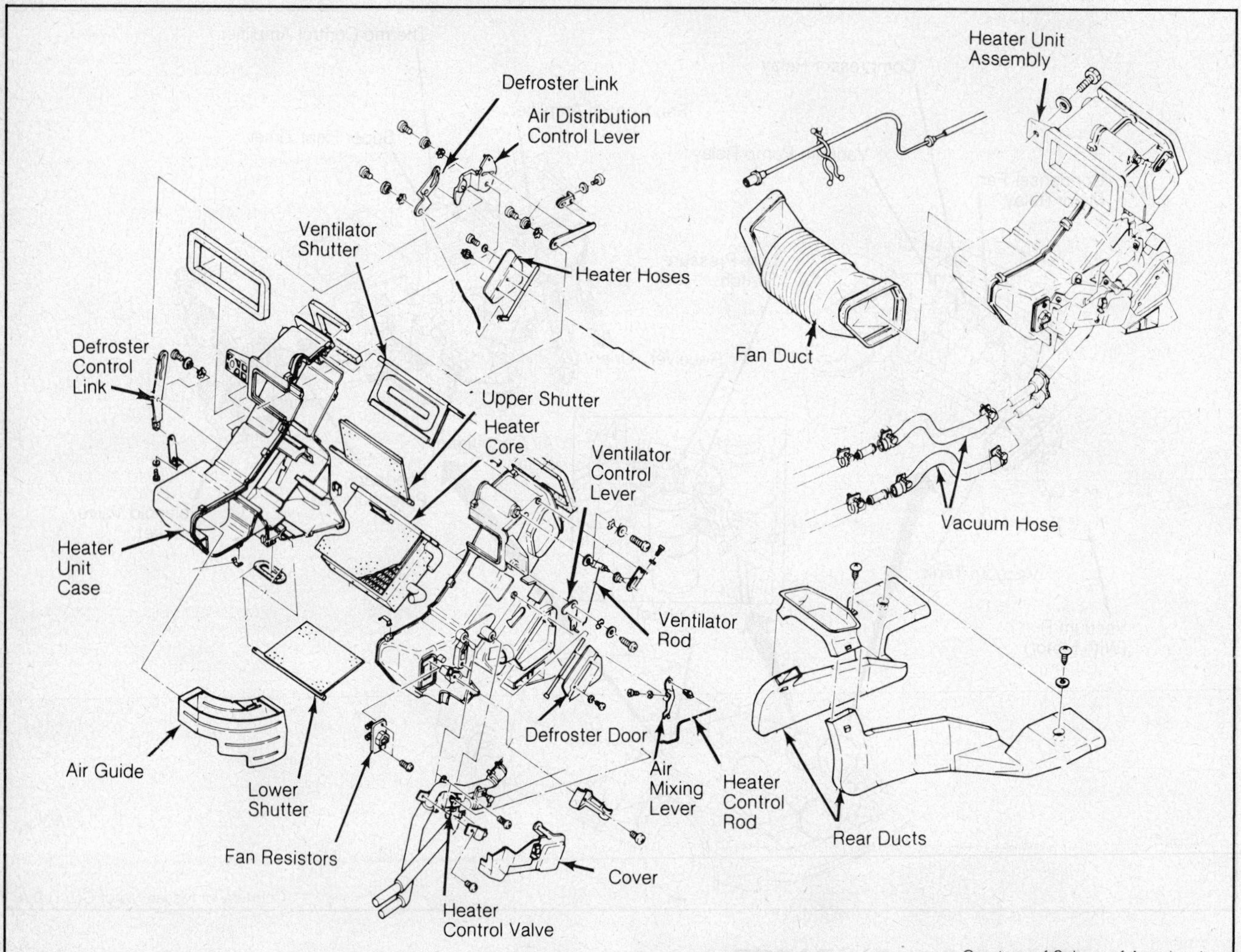

Courtesy of Subaru of America, Inc.

2) Pull ducts from heater unit. Disconnect wires between fan switch and blower motor. Disconnect air mix cable from heater unit. Disconnect mode cable from heater unit. Remove heater unit to instrument panel attaching bolt.

3) Open pocket, and pull pocket stopper clip toward inside. Turn pocket fully downward. Disconnect inside-outside air control cable from blower assembly. Remove instrument panel assembly. Remove heater unit attaching bolts and blower assembly attaching bolts.

4) Remove heater unit assembly with care not to spill residual coolant in heater core over passenger compartment floor. When removing heater unit assembly through body hole, use care to prevent damage to heater pipe. To install, reverse removal procedure.

Removal & Installation (XT Coupe)

Remove both heater hoses in engine compartment. Drain as much coolant from heater unit as possible, and plug heater pipes with cloth. Remove instrument panel. *See Fig. 55.* Unplug connector of harness coming from motor and temperature cable. Remove heater unit. To install, reverse removal procedure.

Removal & Installation (1.8L OHC)

Remove both heater hoses in engine compartment. Drain as much coolant from heater unit as possible,

Fig. 54: Exploded View of Justy Heater Unit

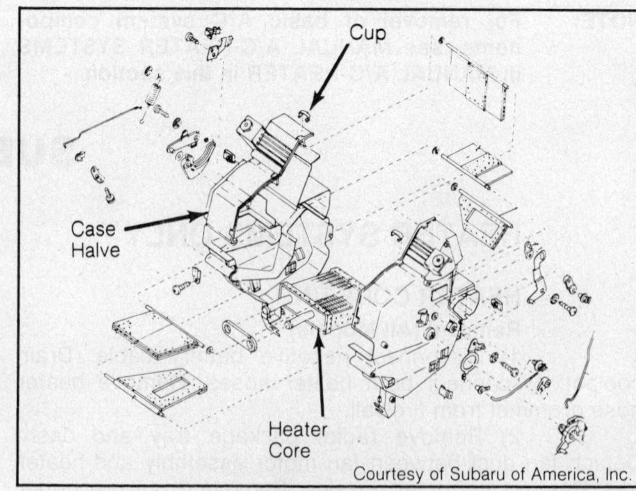

Courtesy of Subaru of America, Inc.

and plug disconnected hose with cloth. Disconnect temperature control cable and vacuum hose from heater unit joint. Remove console box. Remove instrument panel. *See Fig. 56.* Remove heater unit. To install, reverse removal procedure.

Heater Core Replacement

SUBARU (Cont.)

Fig. 55: Exploded View of XT Instrument Panel

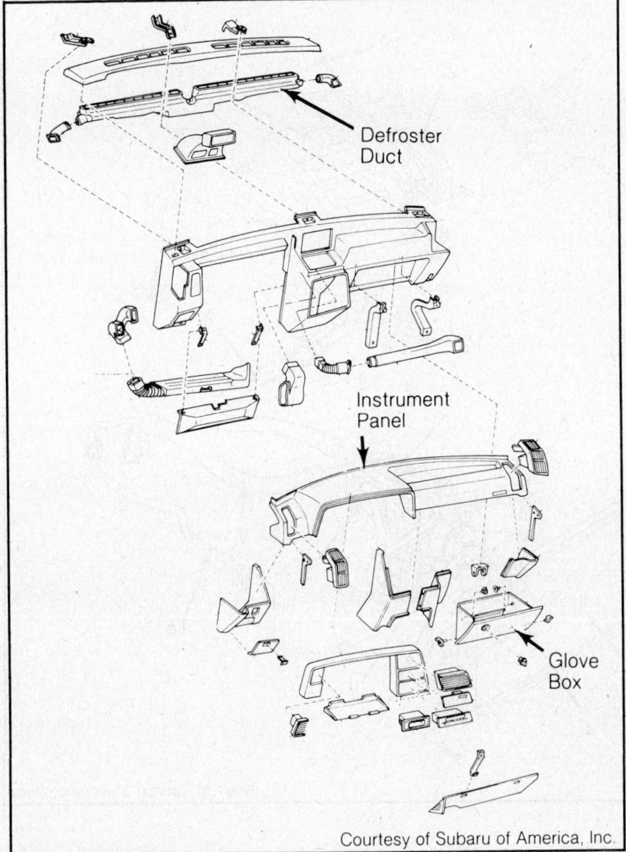

Fig. 56: Exploded View of 1800 OHC Instrument Panel

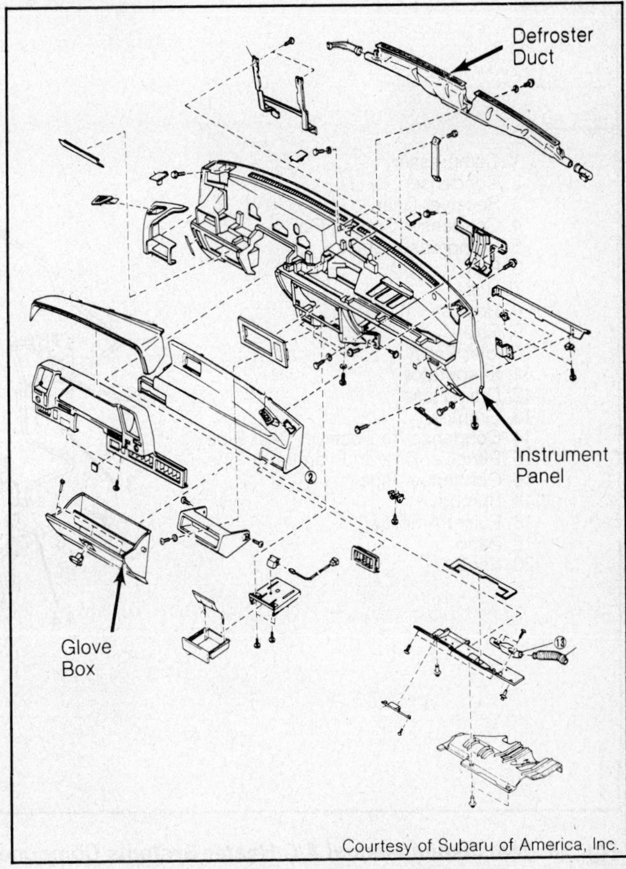

MANUAL A/C-HEATER SYSTEMS

EVAPORATOR

Removal & Installation (All Except XT Coupe)

1) Remove spare tire. Disconnect negative battery cable. Discharge refrigerant from system. Slowly disconnect lines from evaporator. Remove grommets for all hoses. Remove instrument panel lid and pocket.

2) Remove front shelf. Disconnect evaporator electrical connector. Remove 2 bands and loosen evaporator mounting bolts. Remove evaporator. Reverse procedure for installation.

Removal & Installation (XT Coupe)

1) Disconnect negative battery cable. Discharge refrigerant from system. Slowly disconnect A/C lines at evaporator to release remaining refrigerant.

2) Remove undercover. Remove pocket assembly. Disconnect electrical connectors from evaporator assembly. Remove 2 retaining bands & mounting bolts. Remove evaporator.

Installation

To install, reverse removal procedure. Use new "O" rings on pipe fittings. Make sure the wiring harness does not get caught between evaporator and vehicle when installing the evaporator. Evacuate and recharge A/C system. Test system for proper operation.

Heater Core Replacement

SUBARU (Cont.)

Fig. 57: Hitachi Manual A/C-Heater Systems Components

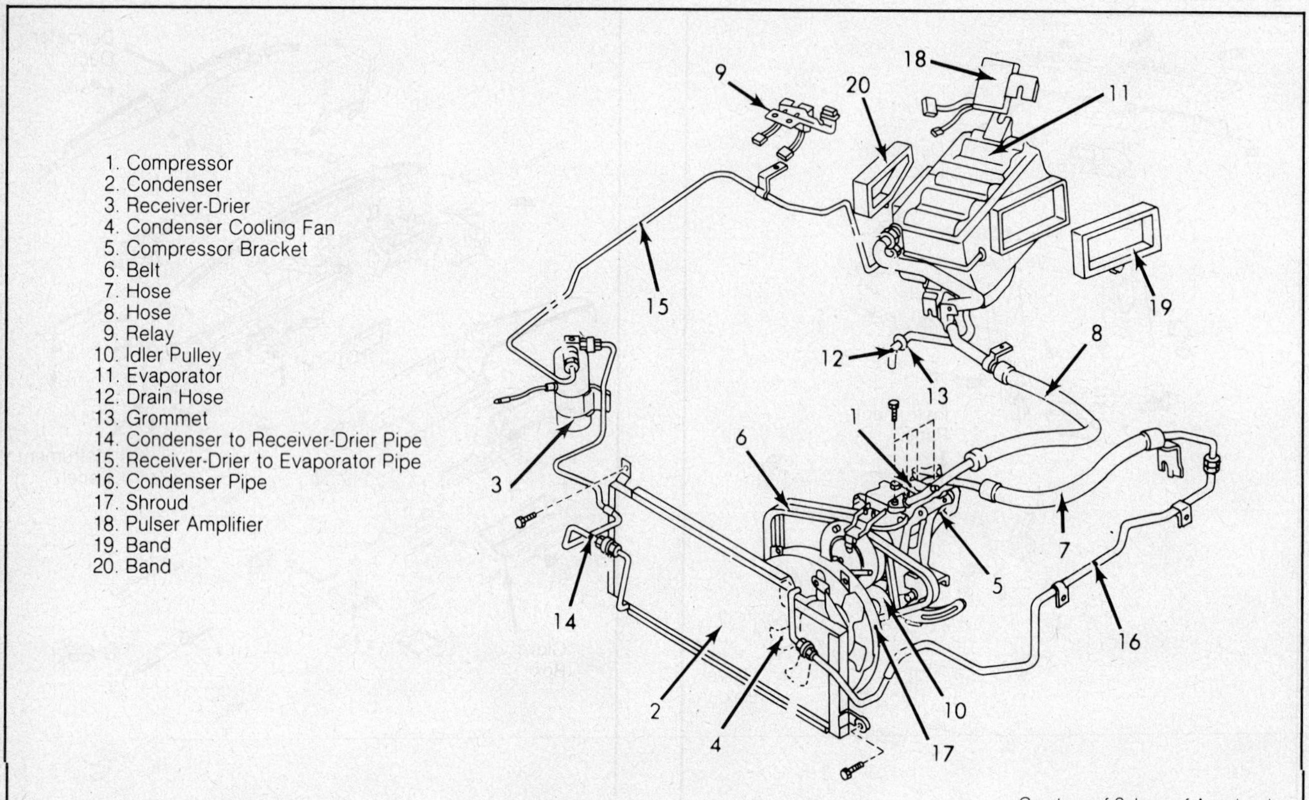

1. Compressor
2. Condenser
3. Receiver-Drier
4. Condenser Cooling Fan
5. Compressor Bracket
6. Belt
7. Hose
8. Hose
9. Relay
10. Idler Pulley
11. Evaporator
12. Drain Hose
13. Grommet
14. Condenser to Receiver-Drier Pipe
15. Receiver-Drier to Evaporator Pipe
16. Condenser Pipe
17. Shroud
18. Pulser Amplifier
19. Band
20. Band

Courtesy of Subaru of America, Inc.

Fig. 58: Matsushita Manual A/C-Heater Systems Components

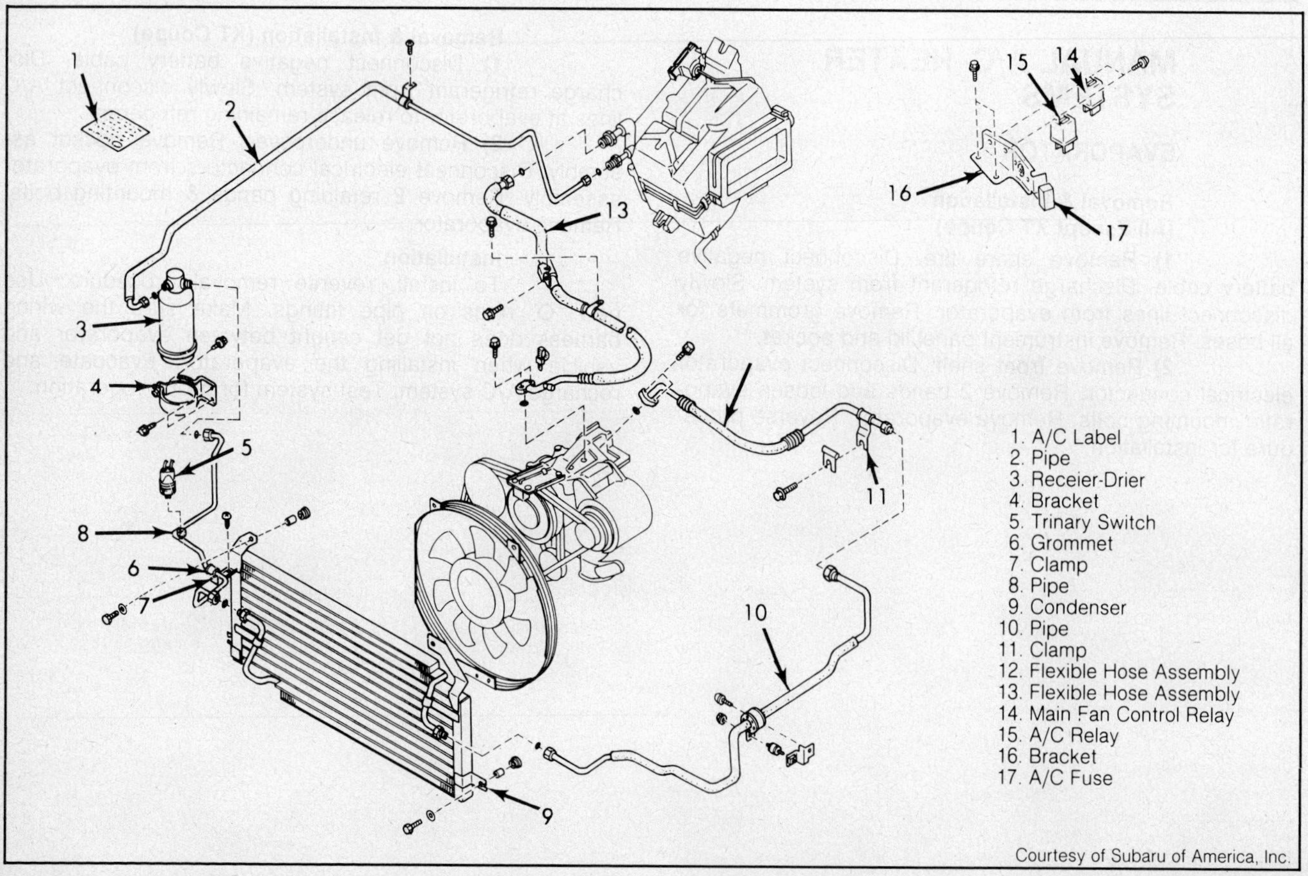

1. A/C Label
2. Pipe
3. Receier-Drier
4. Bracket
5. Trinary Switch
6. Grommet
7. Clamp
8. Pipe
9. Condenser
10. Pipe
11. Clamp
12. Flexible Hose Assembly
13. Flexible Hose Assembly
14. Main Fan Control Relay
15. A/C Relay
16. Bracket
17. A/C Fuse

Courtesy of Subaru of America, Inc.

Heater Core Replacement

SUZUKI

HEATER SYSTEMS ONLY

Removal (Samurai)

HEATER & BLOWER MOTOR

Removal

1) Disconnect battery negative cable. Drain cooling system. Disconnect heater inlet and outlet hoses at heater pipes. Remove instrument panel and speedometer assembly. See INSTRUMENT PANEL in this section.

Fig. 59: Exploded View of Samurai Heating System

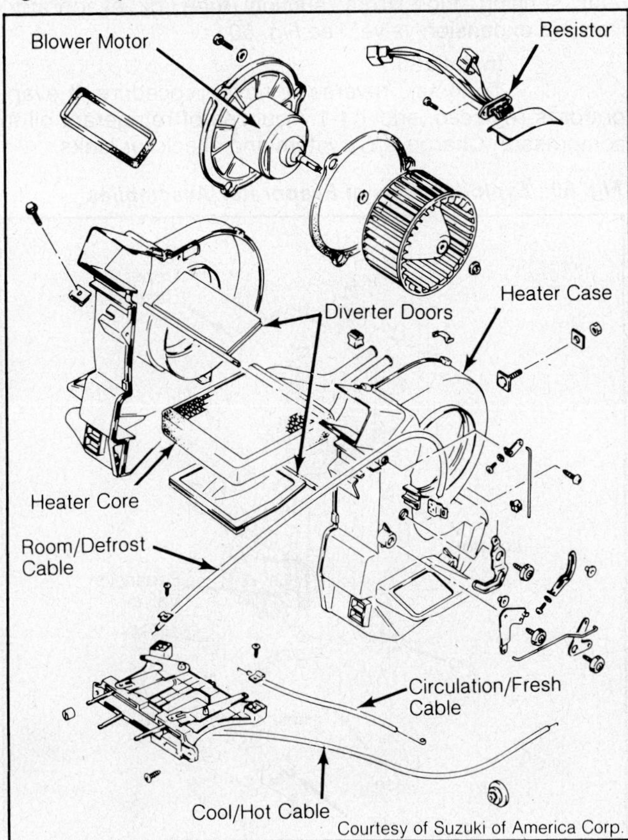

Courtesy of Suzuki of America Corp.

2) Loosen front door stopper screws. Remove steering column holder. Disconnect heater blower motor and resistor connectors. Loosen heater case securing nut on engine side. Remove heater assembly. Remove heater blower motor.

Installation

To install, reverse removal procedures. Ensure that heater and ventilator control cables are correctly routed. *See Fig. 59.* Refill radiator and reconnect negative battery cable.

INSTRUMENT PANEL

Removal (Samurai)

1) Take off horn pad and remove steering wheel using Steering Wheel Remover (09944-38210). Disconnect radio and remove (if equipped). Disconnect cigar lighter and remove (if equipped). Pull out ashtray and loosen ashtray plate screws.

2) Disconnect front hood opening cable from lock assembly. Loosen glove box stay screw and hood opening cable lock nut on back side of glove box. Disconnect cables from control lever. Pull out lever knobs and plate. Loosen lever case screws.

NOTE: **Ensure all hoses, wire harnesses, cables and screws are disconnected from instrument panel before removal.**

3) Remove defroster and side ventilator hoses. Disconnect instrument panel electrical connectors at speedometer and switches. Disconnect speedometer cable. Loosen clamps and release wiring harness from instrument panel. Unscrew instrument panel and remove.

Installation

To install, reverse removal procedures

TOYOTA

HEATER SYSTEMS ONLY

NOTE: **Removal & Installation procedures are not available from the manufacturer**

MANUAL A/C-HEATER SYSTEMS

EVAPORATOR ASSEMBLY

Removal (All Models)

1) Disconnect battery. Discharge A/C system. Detach inlet and outlet lines and grommets from evaporator. Plug openings.

2) Disconnect electrical leads from evaporator. Remove glove box and lower trim panel. Remove side air duct. Remove nuts and bolts and remove evaporator assembly.

Disassembly

1) Remove thermistor. Release spring clips holding covers together. Remove any screws at case joints. Separate upper and lower cases from evaporator core. Remove idle stablizing amplifier from lower case.

2) Remove heat insulator from outlet tube. Remove high side (inlet) line from expansion valve and remove expansion valve. Remove pressure switch.

Reassembly & Installation

Reverse disassembly and removal procedure. If installing new evaporator core, add 1.4-1.7 oz. of refrigerant oil to core prior to installation. Evacuate, recharge and leak test system.

Heater Core Replacement

TOYOTA (Cont.)

REAR EVAPORATOR

Removal & Installation (Van)

Discharge A/C system. Disconnect rear evaporator electrical connectors. Remove magnetic valve. Disconnect A/C lines from rear evaporator. Remove rear evaporator mounting bolts. Remove rear evaporator. Reverse procedure for installation. Evacuate and recharge A/C system.

AUTOMATIC A/C-HEATER SYSTEMS

THERMISTOR, EXPANSION VALVE & EVAPORATOR

Removal (Cressida)

1) Disconnect negative battery cable. Discharge A/C system. Disconnect equalizer tube from evaporator pressure regulator. Disconnect suction tube from outlet fitting. Disconnect liquid tube from inlet fitting. Cap all openings.

2) Remove grommets from inlet and outlet fittings. Remove glove box and under cover. Unplug connector and remove evaporator housing. Remove connectors from lower evaporator case. Remove 4 clips, 4 screws, upper case and lower evaporator case. Remove evaporator.

3) Disconnect liquid tube from inlet fitting of expansion valve. Remove packing and heat sensing tube from suction tube of evaporator. Remove expansion valve. *See Fig. 60*.

Installation

To install, reverse removal procedure. If evaporator is replaced, add 1.4-1.7 ounces of refrigerant oil to compressor. Charge A/C system and check for leaks.

Removal (Supra)

1) Disconnect negative battery cable. Discharge A/C system. Remove charcoal canister with bracket. Disconnect suction tube from outlet fitting. Disconnect liquid tube from inlet fitting. Cap all openings.

2) Remove grommets from inlet and outlet fittings. Remove glove box and under cover. Remove glove box cover and reinforcement. Remove electronic fuel injection and and anti-lock brake system computers. Unplug connector and remove evaporator housing.

3) Remove thermistor connector from upper evaporator case. Remove 3 clips, 4 screws, and upper case. Remove thermistor with thermistor holder. Remove lower evaporator case.

4) Remove evaporator. Disconnect liquid tube from inlet fitting of expansion valve. Remove packing and heat sensing tube from suction tube of evaporator. Remove expansion valve. *See Fig. 60*.

Installation

To install, reverse removal procedure. If evaporator is replaced, add 1.4-1.7 ounces of refrigerant oil to compressor. Charge A/C system and check for leaks.

Fig. 60: Exploded View of Evaporator Assemblies

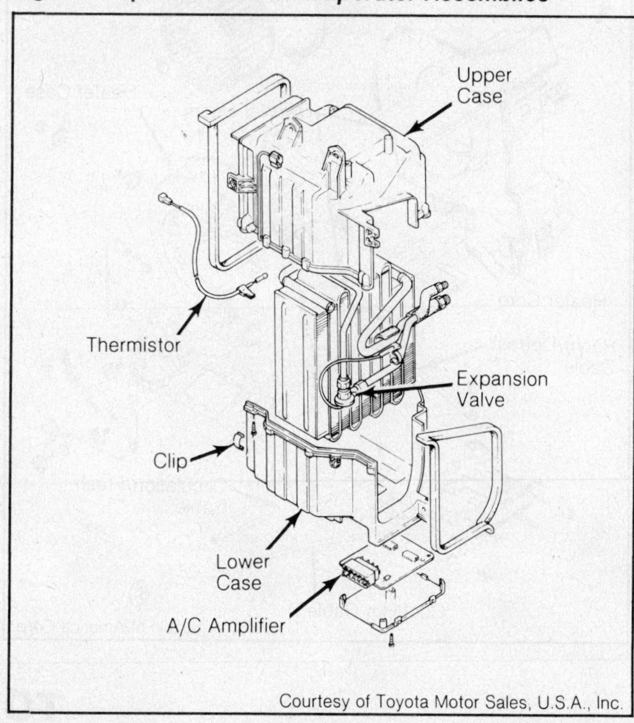

VOLKSWAGEN

HEATER SYSTEMS ONLY

NOTE: **Vanagon and Vanagon Syncro Removal & Installation for heater system information is not available from manufacturer.**

HEATER ASSEMBLY

Removal (Cabriolet, Fox & Scirocco)

1) Drain coolant from radiator. Loosen clamps and remove heater core hoses. Disconnect battery ground cable. Pull heater control knobs off. Remove trim plate and underdash access panels.

2) Disconnect wiring from blower motor and remove cable from temperature control lever. Pry spring clamp off with screwdriver and separate heater assembly halves. Remove heater core and blower motor.

Installation

To install, insert blower motor and heater core into right half of housing. Position left half and install spring clips. To complete installation, reverse removal procedure.

Removal (Golf, GTI, Jetta & Jetta GLI)

1) Disconnect negative battery cable. Drain coolant from radiator. Remove steering wheel. Remove lower left instrument panel retaining screws. Remove lower left instrument panel. Remove lower right instrument panel tray retaining screws.

2) Remove lower right instrument panel. Remove gearshift lever knob. Remove gearshift lever boot. Remove center console retaining screws. Slide center console rearward. Disconnect electrical connectors attached to center console. Remove center console.

3) Remove temperature control knobs. Remove trim plate. Remove radio. Remove switches from

VOLKSWAGEN (Cont.)

Fig. 61: Cabriolet, Fox & Scirocco Heater System Components

Courtesy of Volkswagen United States, Inc.

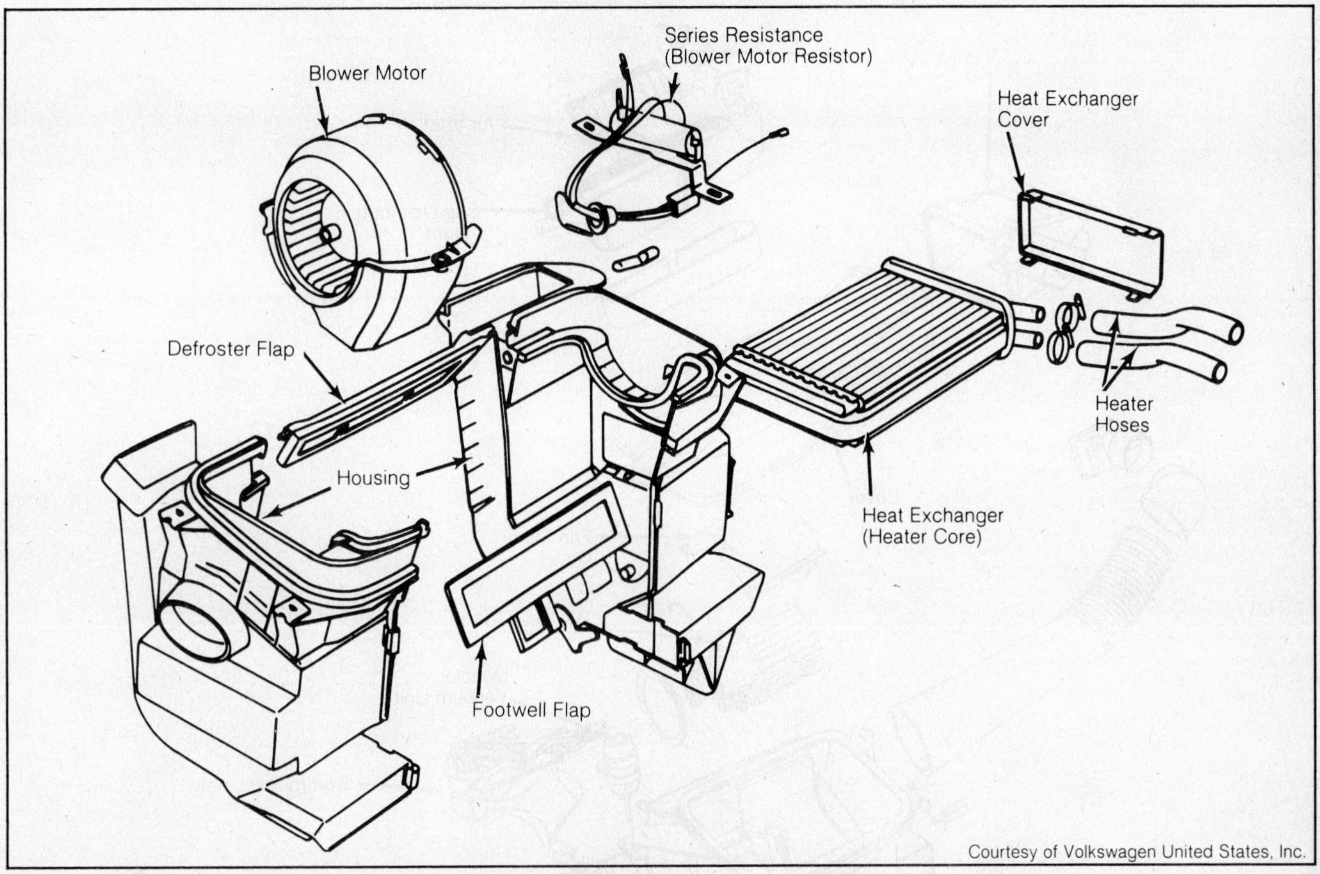

Fig. 62: Golf, GTI, Jetta & Jetta GLI Heater System Components

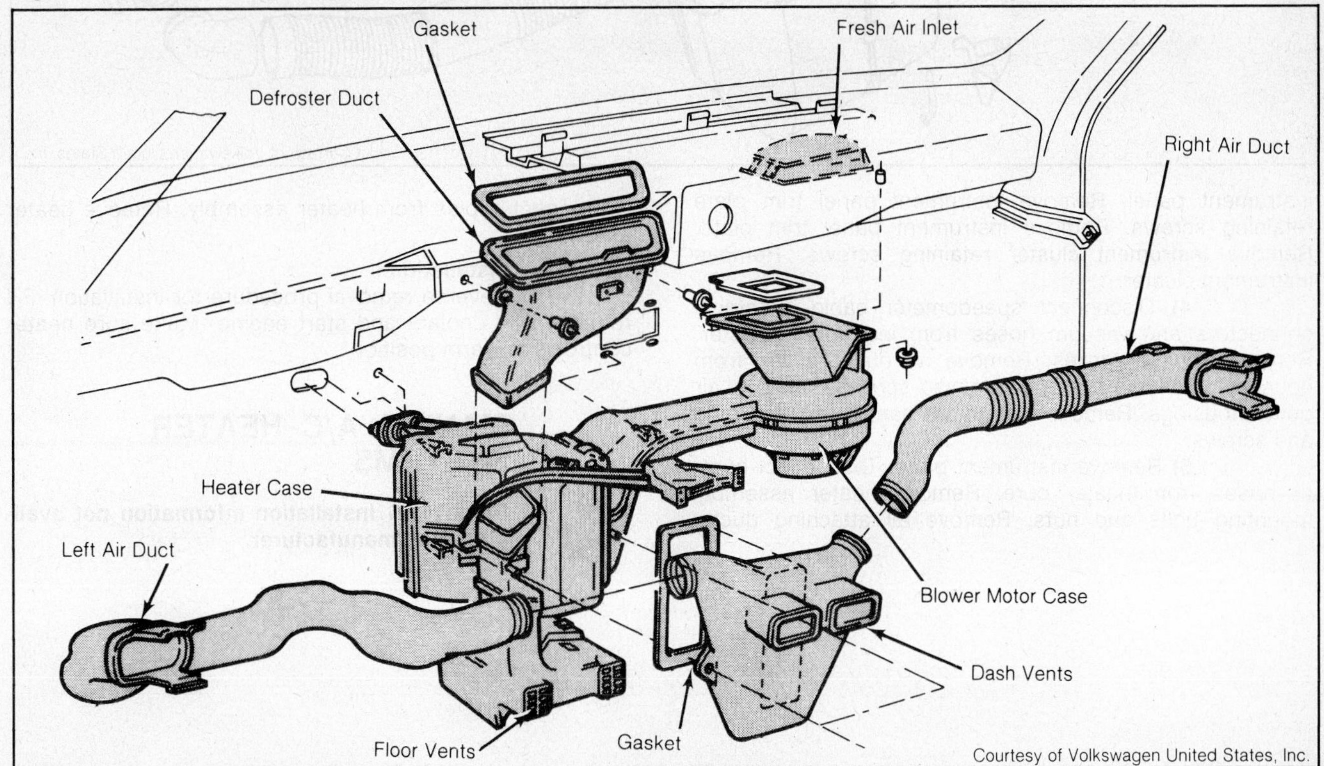

Courtesy of Volkswagen United States, Inc.

Heater Core Replacement

VOLKSWAGEN (Cont.)

Fig. 63: Exploded View of Volkswagen Cabriolet & Scirocco Manual A/C-Heater Systems Components

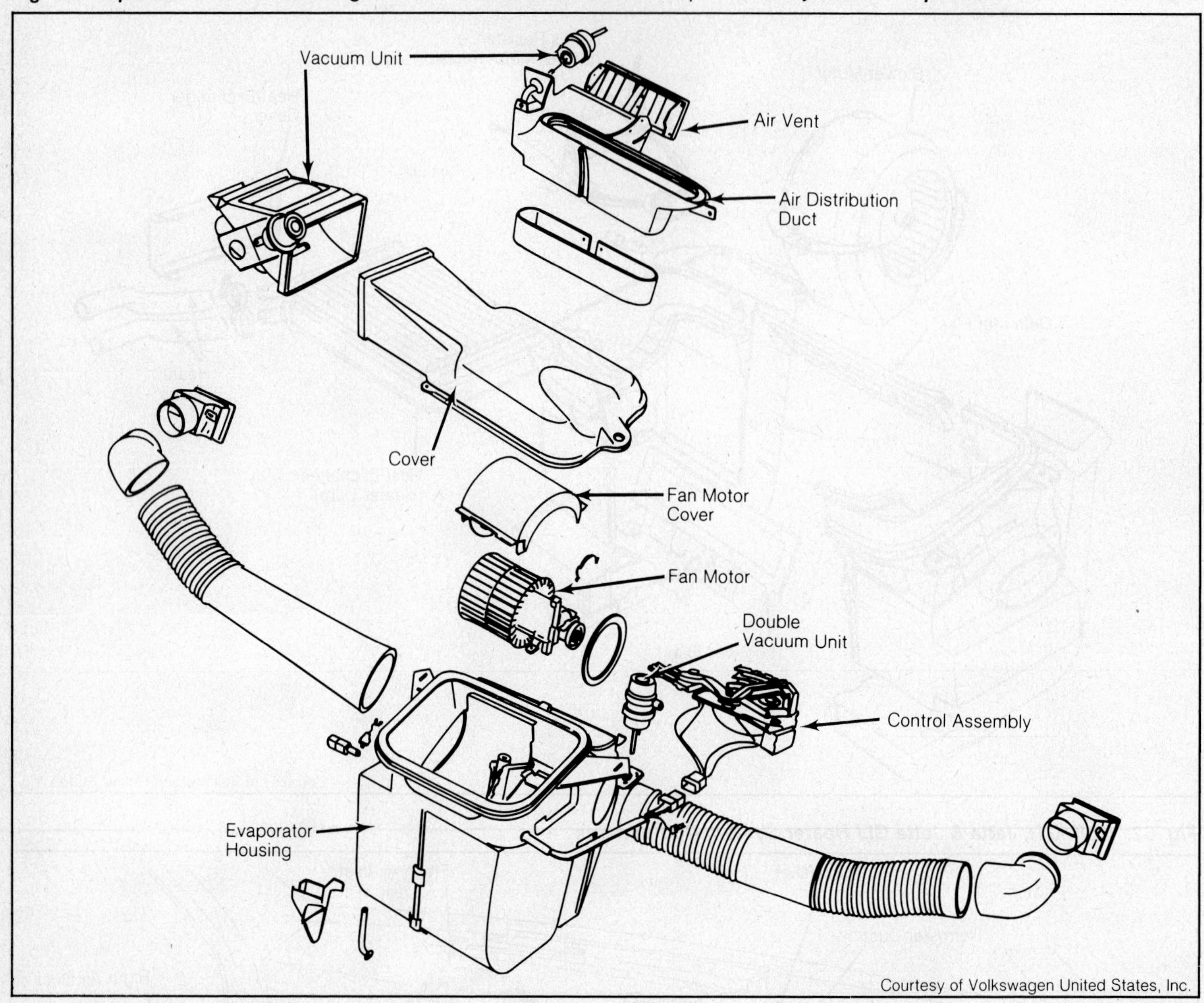

instrument panel. Remove instrument panel trim plate retaining screws. Remove instrument panel trim plate. Remove instrument cluster retaining screws. Remove instrument cluster.

4) Disconnect speedometer cable, electrical connectors and vacuum hoses from instrument cluster. Remove speaker grilles. Remove air outlet grilles from housings. Remove housing retaining screws. Remove air outlet housings. Remove instrument panel mounting nuts and screws.

5) Remove instrument panel. Disconnect heater hoses from heater core. Remove heater assembly mounting bolts and nuts. Remove all attaching ducts. Disconnect cables from heater assembly. Remove heater assembly.

Installation

Reverse removal procedure for installation. Fill radiator with coolant and start engine. Make sure heater control is in warm position.

MANUAL A/C-HEATER SYSTEMS

NOTE: **Removal & Installation information not available from manufacturer.**

Heater Core Replacement

VOLVO

MANUAL A/C-HEATER SYSTEMS

EVAPORATOR

Removal (All Models)

1) Disconnect battery terminals. Discharge A/C system. Remove right side panel from housing assembly. Remove A/C housing assembly insulation panel and glove box.

2) Disconnect defroster outlet and air channel and push to one side. Disconnect thermostat from cover and remove the putty from evaporator pipes. Disconnect attached hoses and pull out evaporator assembly.

Installation

To install, reverse removal procedure. Apply sealing putty or insulating tape to evaporator outlet around hoses and connections. Evacuate, recharge and leak test system.

HEATER CORE

Removal (All Models)

1) Drain engine coolant and disconnect battery negative cable. Remove heater hoses from heater core and plug pipes.

2) Remove clamps from hoses on evaporator and remove firewall door without loosening hoses to evaporator.

NOTE: **Be careful when moving A/C components as system is still under pressure.**

3) Remove central combined instrument panel, air hoses between housing assembly and left inner air vent, and vacuum hoses from vacuum motors for left defroster nozzle and left air outlet.

4) Remove left side panel from housing assembly. Fold floor mat out of way and disconnect rear floor duct from housing assembly. Disconnect pipe joints for heater system water hoses from firewall.

5) Loosen the upper screws 2 or 3 turns. Remove the lower screws from left support leg and upper and lower brackets from firewall.

6) Remove heater assembly right side panel, right side insulation panel, and glove box. Remove right side defroster jet and hose from housing assembly to right center jet. Fold carpet out of way and disconnect rear floor air duct.

7) Remove screws retaining right support leg and control panel. Disconnect ground wires from control plate and contact unit from blower motor switch. Disconnect thick Yellow wire from contact.

8) Separate vacuum hose connector and disconnect vacuum tank hose from connector. Move connector plate as far back on transmission tunnel as wires will permit. Remove previously loosened screws from firewall.

9) Disconnect thermostat attachment bellows from housing assembly and both clamps securing cover to

Fig. 64: Exploded View A/C-Heater Assembly

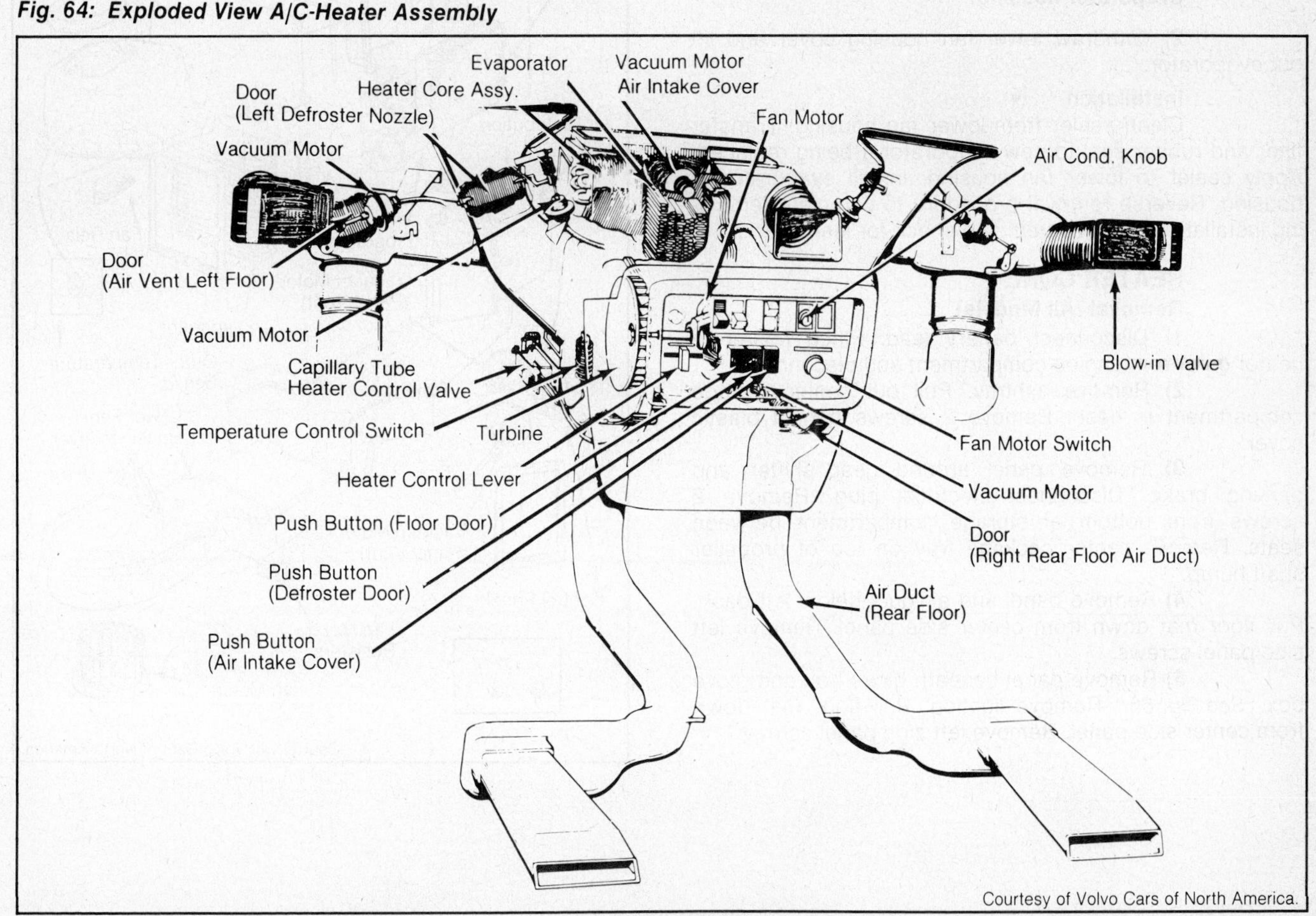

Heater Core Replacement

VOLVO (Cont.)

evaporator. Remove evaporator from housing assembly without disconnecting refrigerant hoses.

10) Place evaporator to right side of cowl. Remove housing assembly right outer end, turbine wheel, and inner end. Carefully remove heater assembly.

11) Remove left outer turbine wheel lock from end of shaft and remove turbine wheel. Use 2 screwdrivers to remove lock from end of shaft.

12) Remove screws retaining tunnel bracket and inner end. Lift off inner end and remove the air intake left door shaft lock. Remove screws retaining blower motor.

13) Disconnect heater hoses from housing assembly. Remove clamps for heater unit middle joint, lift off left half, and remove core assembly.

Installation

To install, reverse removal procedure.

AUTOMATIC A/C-HEATER SYSTEMS

EVAPORATOR

Removal (All Models)

1) Discharge refrigerant from system (plug open hoses). Disconnect evaporator connectors in engine compartment. Remove panel beneath glove box and glove box. *See Fig. 65.* Disconnect all electrical wires. Remove screws from lower fan housing.

NOTE: Two screws are hidden behind fan and evaporator housing.

2) Withdraw lower fan housing cover and lift out evaporator.

Installation

Clean sealer from lower fan housing. Transfer filter and rubber seal to new evaporator if being replaced. Apply sealer to lower fan housing. Install evaporator in housing. Reverse removal procedure to complete remaining installation. Refill system and check for leaks.

HEATER CORE

Removal (All Models)

1) Disconnect battery lead. Pinch hoses to heater core from engine compartment and disconnect.

2) Remove ashtray. Pull out center storage compartment in dash. Remove 2 screws behind plastic cover.

3) Remove panel around gear shifter and parking brake. Disconnect electrical plug. Remove 2 screws from bottom of storage compartment between seats. Remove center package tray on top of propeller shaft hump.

4) Remove panel and air duct below left dash. Pull floor mat down from center side panel. Remove left side panel screws.

5) Remove panel beneath glove box and glove box. *See Fig. 65.* Remove lighting. Pull floor mat down from center side panel. Remove left side panel screws.

6) Remove radio and radio compartment. Remove screws holding side panels to center dash brackets. Remove side panels.

7) Remove panel around control panel. Remove radio compartment console. Loosen screws holding control panel. Disconnect vacuum hoses and electrical plug to control panel and remove control panel.

8) Remove all vent ducts attached to distribution unit and center panel vent. Remove vacuum hoses to vacuum motors and aspirator. Remove distribution unit from vehicle.

9) Remove straps holding heater core to housing. Lift heater core from vehicle.

10) Remove panel from distribution unit. Replace vacuum motors as required.

Installation

To install, reverse removal procedure. Reconnect vacuum motor hoses as follows: Red to upper shutter for panel vents, Blue to defroster vents and Light Brown to lower shutter for panel vents.

Fig. 65: Exploded View of Automatic A/C-Heater Assembly

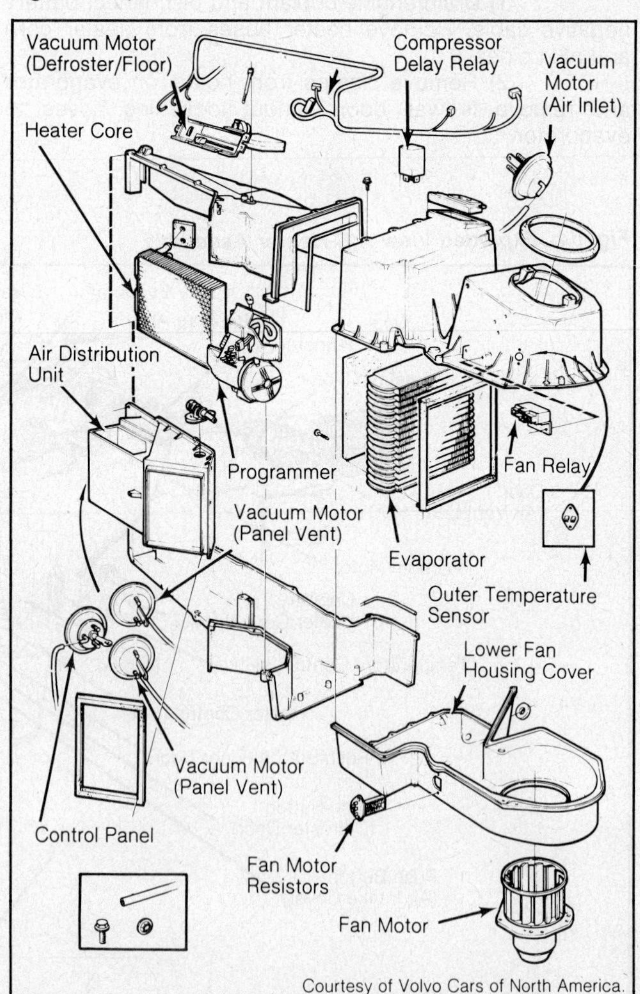

Heater Core Replacement

YUGO

HEATER SYSTEMS ONLY

HEATER ASSEMBLY

Removal (All Models)

1) To remove heater assembly, it will first be necessary to drain coolant both from engine radiator and heater core. To drain the heater core, move lever controlling the water valve, all the way to the right.

2) Loosen clips retaining hoses for heater water inflow and return. Remove attaching screw and nut from air admission shutter actuating rod. Remove air conveyor, after screw and plain washer have been taken out from inside.

3) Slide out heater core housing spring clips. Withdraw outside air admission shutter actuating rod. Remove heater valve control cable. Remove heater core. Back out fan housing attaching nuts from body. Disconnect Yellow and Blue/Black wires, feeding fan motor at fan switch.

NOTE: **Fan ground cable is located on left side of heater core and is released by unscrewing one of the nuts attaching fan assembly to the body.**

Installation

Fig. 66: Exploded View of Heater Assembly

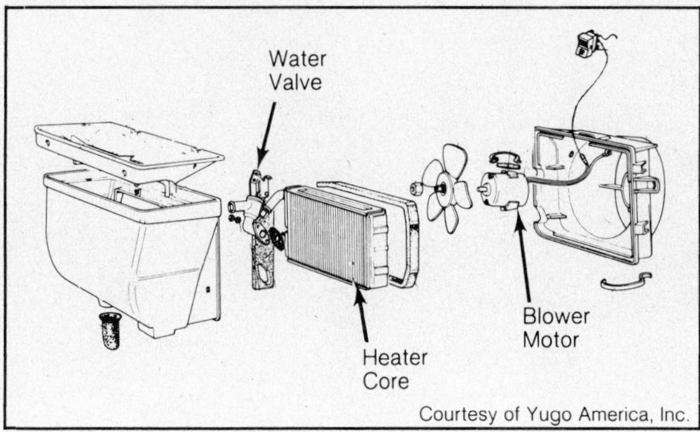

4) To install, reverse removal procedure, but take care to insert gasket between fan housing and body correctly, and to reconnect water hoses to engine, so these connections are water tight. Do not forget to reconnect the fan ground lead.

5) After refitting heater to vehicle, engine and heater radiators must be refilled with coolant. To ensure that heater core is properly filled, the engine should be run for a few minutes with lever all the way right, and the engine radiator topped off again.

MANUAL A/C-HEATER SYSTEMS

NOTE: **Removal & Installation information not available from manufacturer.**

Fig. 67: Exploded View of Underhood A/C Components

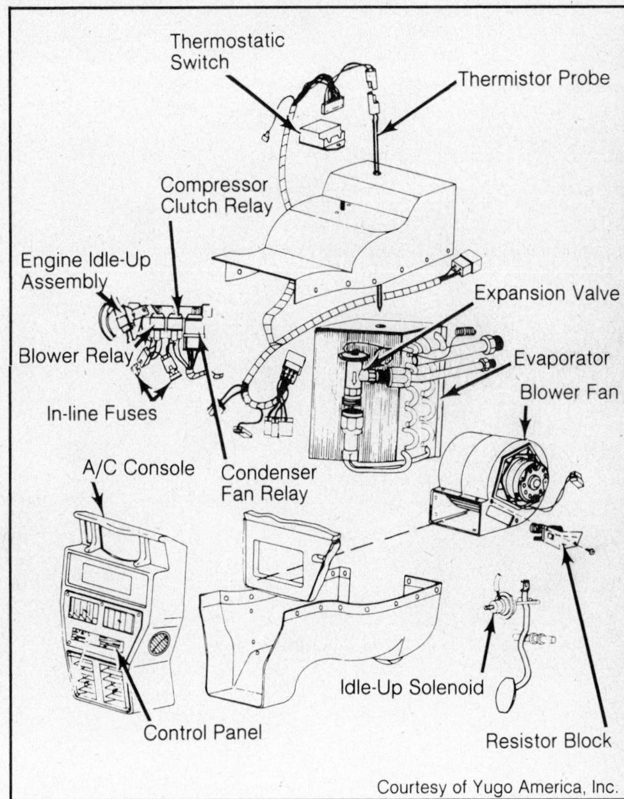

SECTION 7

CLUTCHES

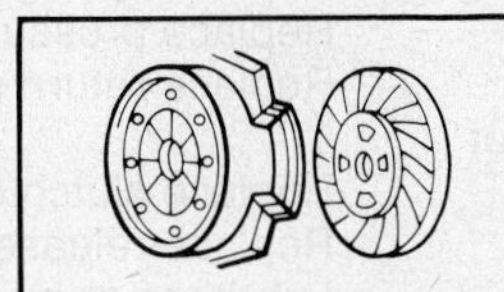

CONTENTS

TROUBLE SHOOTING Page

All Models 7-2

CLUTCHES

Acura 7-4
Alfa Romeo
Milano 7-7
Audi
Coupe GT & 4000S 7-8
4000CS Quattro & 5000 Series 7-10
BMW 7-12
Chrysler Motors
FWD 7-14
RWD 7-16
Ford Motor Co.
Festiva & Merkur XR4Ti 7-20
Tracer 7-33

CLUTCHES (Cont.) Page

General Motors 7-24
Honda 7-4
Hyundai 7-26
Isuzu
I-Mark 7-27
Impulse 7-28
P'UP & Trooper II 7-30
Mazda
FWD 7-33
RWD 7-37
Mercedes-Benz 190 Series 7-39
Mitsubishi
FWD 7-14
RWD 7-16
Nissan
All Except Pulsar NX, Sentra & Stanza 7-41
Pulsar NX, Sentra & Stanza 7-44
Peugeot 7-46
Porsche
911 Carrera & Turbo 7-47
Saab
900 7-48
9000 7-50
Sterling 825 7-52
Subaru 7-53
Suzuki Samurai 7-55
Toyota
All Except Tercel 7-56
Tercel 7-58
Volkswagen
Cabriolet, Golf, GTI
Jetta & Scirocco 7-60
Fox & Quantum 7-62
Vanagon 7-63
Volvo 7-64
Yugo 7-66

NOTE: **ALSO SEE GENERAL INDEX.**

CLUTCH TROUBLE SHOOTING

CONDITION	POSSIBLE CAUSE	CORRECTION
Chattering or Grabbing	Incorrect clutch adjustment	Adjust clutch
	Oil, grease or glaze on facings	Disassemble and clean or replace
	Loose "U" joint flange	See DRIVE AXLES
	Worn input shaft spline	Replace input shaft
	Binding pressure plate	Replace pressure plate
	Binding release lever	See CLUTCHES
	Binding clutch disc hub	Replace clutch disc
	Unequal pressure plate contact	Replace worn/misaligned components
	Loose/bent clutch disc	Replace clutch disc
	Incorrect transmission alignment	Realign transmission
	Worn pressure plate, disc or flywheel	Replace damaged components
	Broken or weak pressure springs	Replace pressure plate
	Sticking clutch pedal	Lubricate clutch pedal & linkage
	Incorrect clutch disc facing	Replace clutch disc
	Engine loose in chassis	Tighten all mounting bolts
Failure To Release	Oil or grease on clutch facings	Clean or replace clutch disc
	Incorrect release lever or pedal adjustment	See CLUTCHES
	Dust or dirt on clutch disc	Clean or replace
	Worn or broken clutch facings	Replace clutch disc
	Bent clutch disc or pressure plate	Replace damaged components
	Clutch disc hub binding on input shaft	Clean or replace clutch disc and/or input shaft
	Binding pilot bearing	Replace pilot bearing
	Sticking release bearing sleeve	Replace release bearing and/or sleeve
	Binding clutch cable	See CLUTCHES
	Defective clutch master cylinder	Replace master cylinder
	Defective clutch slave cylinder	Replace slave cylinder
	Air in hydraulic system	Bleed hydraulic system
Rattling	Weak or broken release lever spring	Replace spring and check alignment
	Damaged pressure plate	Replace pressure plate
	Broken clutch return spring	Replace return spring
	Worn splines on clutch disc or input shaft	Replace clutch disc and/or input shaft
	Worn clutch release bearing	Replace release bearing
	Dry or worn pilot bearing	Lubricate or replace pilot bearing
	Unequal release lever contact	Align or replace release lever
	Incorrect pedal free play	Adjust free play
	Warped or damaged clutch disc	Replace damaged components
Slipping	Pressure springs worn or broken	Replace pressure plate
	Oily, greasy or worn clutch facings,	Clean or replace clutch disc
	Incorrect clutch alignment	Realign clutch assembly
	Warped clutch disc or pressure plate	Replace damaged components
	Binding release levers or clutch pedal	Lubricate and/or replace release components
Squeaking	Worn or damaged release bearing	Replace release bearing
	Dry or worn pilot or release bearing	Lubricate or replace bearing assembly
	Pilot bearing turning in crankshaft	Replace pilot bearing and/or crankshaft
	Worn input shaft bearing	Replace bearing and seal
	Incorrect transmission alignment	Realign transmission
	Dry release fork between pivot	Lubricate release fork and pivot
Heavy and/or Stiff Pedal	Sticking release bearing sleeve	Replace release bearing and/or sleeve
	Dry or binding clutch pedal hub	Lubricate and align components
	Floor mat interference with pedal	Lay mat flat in proper area
	Dry or binding ball/fork pivots	Lubricate and align components
	Faulty clutch cable	Replace clutch cable
Noisy clutch pedal	Faulty interlock switch	Replace interlock switch
	Self-adjuster ratchet noise	Lubricate or replace self-adjuster
	Speed control interlock switch	Lubricate or replace interlock switch

CLUTCH TROUBLE SHOOTING (Cont.)

CONDITION	POSSIBLE CAUSE	CORRECTION
Clutch pedal sticks down	Binding clutch cable	See CLUTCHES
	Springs weak in pressure plate	Replace pressure plate
	Binding in clutch linkage	Lubricate and free linkage
Noisy	Dry release bearing	Lubricate or replace release bearing
	Dry or worn pilot bearing	Lubricate or replace bearing
	Worn input shaft bearing	Replace bearing
Transmission click	Weak springs in pressure plate	Replace pressure plate
	Release fork loose on ball stud	Replace release fork and/or ball stud
	Oil on clutch disc damper	Replace clutch disc
	Broken spring in slave cylinder	Replace slave cylinder

Clutches

ACURA & HONDA

Acura: Integra, Legend
Honda: Accord, Civic, CRX, Prelude

DESCRIPTION

Clutch is disc type, using a diaphragm spring to engage pressure plate. Clutch has a mechanical release system consisting of clutch pedal, cable, release lever and release bearing.

REMOVAL & INSTALLATION

CLUTCH ASSEMBLY

Removal (Accord & Prelude)

1) Place shift lever in Neutral. Disconnect the battery ground cable at battery and transaxle. Disconnect starter wiring. Disconnect backup light switch. Release engine subwiring harness from clamp at clutch housing.

2) Disconnect clutch cable at release arm. Remove 2 upper transaxle mount bolts. Raise and support vehicle. Drain transaxle oil. Remove front wheels.

3) Remove bolt securing speedometer drive holder and pull assembly out of transaxle. Disconnect shift lever torque rod from clutch housing. Remove bolt from shift rod clevis.

4) Disconnect tie rod ball joints. Remove lower arm ball joint bolt from right side lower control arm. Using a puller, disconnect ball joint from knuckle. Remove damper fork bolt.

5) Turn each steering knuckle to its most outboard position. With screwdriver, pry right side CV joint out approximately 1/2". Pull sub axle out of transaxle housing. Repeat on opposite side. Remove right side radius rod.

6) Remove torque arm bracket bolts from clutch housing. Remove damper bracket from transaxle. Remove clutch housing bolts from the front transaxle mount.

7) Remove clutch housing bolts from rear transaxle mounting bracket. Remove clutch cover. Remove starter motor and lower through chassis.

8) Remove front transaxle mounting bolt. Pull transaxle away from engine block to clear 2 locating pins. Lower transaxle using transaxle jack. If reusing clutch, mark pressure plate and flywheel.

Removal (Civic 2WD & Integra)

1) Disconnect ground cable at battery and transaxle. Release steering lock and put gear shift lever in Neutral. Disconnect wiring from starter. Disconnect back-up light switch and small ground cable.

2) Remove cable clip and pull speedometer cable out of holder. Do not remove speedometer housing. Disconnect clutch cable at release arm. On Civic, remove transaxle side starter mounting bolts and top transaxle bolts.

3) On all models, loosen front wheel lug nuts. Apply parking brake and block rear wheels. Raise front end on jack stands and remove front wheels. Support lower control arm with floor jack and remove ball joint cotter pin and nut.

CAUTION: Torsion bar tension on lower control arm will cause arm to jump when ball joint puller is being used. Position floor jack securely under lower control arm ball joint.

4) On all models, separate ball joint from front hub with ball joint remover. Slowly lower floor jack to release lower control arm. On Integra, remove front wheel spindle nut and pull front hub off driveshaft. Repeat procedure for other side.

5) On all models, secure a hoist chain to bolt on head and raise engine slightly to take weight off mounts. Drain transaxle and remove splash shields covering engine and right side wheel well.

6) Separate inlet pipe from exhaust manifold. On Civic, turn right steering knuckle outward as far as possible. On all models, pry right drive axle out of transaxle, approximately 1/2" with a screwdriver. Pull drive axle straight out completely. Repeat procedure for opposite side.

7) Disconnect shift lever torque rod from clutch housing. Slide pin retainer back, drive out spring pin using a pin punch, then disconnect shift rod. *See Fig. 1.*

Fig. 1: View of Shift Lever Torque Rod & Shift Rod

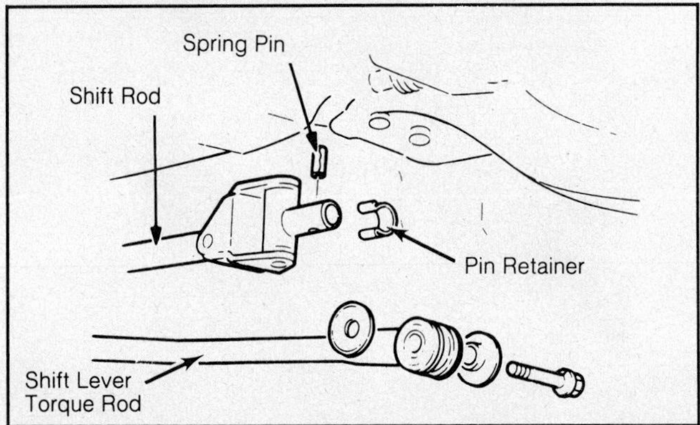

Courtesy of American Honda Motor Co., Inc.

8) Place a jack under transaxle and raise just enough to take weight off mounts. Remove bolts from front transaxle mount. Remove transaxle housing bolts from engine torque bracket.

9) Remove remaining transaxle bolts. Pull transaxle away from engine until mainshaft clears clutch pressure plate.

NOTE: On Civic 4WD, engine and transaxle must be removed as an assembly.

Removal (Civic 4WD)

1) Disconnect battery cables and remove battery. Disconnect windshield washer fluid hose from hood. Mark hood hinges for reference and remove hood. Remove engine splash shield.

2) Drain engine oil, transaxle fluid, and coolant. Remove air intake duct and air cleaner cover. Remove battery mount. Disconnect throttle cable, coil wire and ignition primary leads. Remove secondary ground cable and clutch cable.

3) On fuel injected models, place shop towel on top of fuel filter and relieve fuel injection system pressure by slowly loosening service bolt approximately one turn. Once fuel pressure is released, remove fuel line from fuel filter. Disconnect fuel return hose.

4) Disconnect wiring harness cable, sub harness connectors, and fuse holder connector located next to shock tower. Disconnect ignition wires at spark plugs and remove distributor. Disconnect No. 1 control box connector. Lift control box off its bracket and let it hang next to engine.

5) On carbureted models, disconnect ignition wires at spark plugs and remove distributor. On California and high altitude carbureted models, remove air jet controller from left shock tower. Remove No. 2 control box from left front fender in front of engine timing belt cover. Remove fuel pump cover and hoses. Remove fuel pump.

6) On models with A/C, loosen belt adjusting bolt and idler pulley nut. Remove compressor mounting bolts. Lift compressor out of bracket with hoses attached, and wire it up to front beam. Remove idle air control solenoid located above and just to the right of brake booster. Remove transaxle ground cable.

7) On models with power steering, remove power steering pump mounting bolts and drive belt. Pull pump away from its bracket without disconnecting hoses.

8) Slide retainer clip out of the way of roll pin on shift rod. Drive pin out and disconnect shift rod from transaxle. Remove cotter pins and disconnect 4WD shift control, and selector shift control cables from levers. Disconnect propeller shaft at transaxle yoke.

9) Disconnect radiator hoses and heater hoses. Remove speedometer cable clip and pull speedometer cable out of holder.

CAUTION: DO NOT remove cable holder. Speedometer gear may fall in transaxle if cable holder is removed.

10) Disconnect alternator wiring and remove alternator. Attach chain hoist to engine block hoist brackets and raise just enough to remove slack from chain.

11) Remove rear transaxle mount bracket. Remove bolt from front transaxle mount. Remove bolt from engine side mount.

12) Check that engine and transaxle assembly are completely free of any hoses or electrical wires. Carefully raise assembly out from vehicle.

13) Remove starter motor and 3 engine mount bolts. Remove intermediate shaft (if equipped). Separate transaxle from engine. Remove pressure plate and clutch disc. Remove flywheel. *See Fig. 2.*

Removal (Legend)

1) Disconnect battery positive and negative cables from battery. Remove starter and ground cables from transaxle. Disconnect all external electrical connectors from transaxle.

2) Loosen bolt attaching harness bracket at side of transaxle hanger, and release harness from transaxle. Loosen bolts at side of battery base and remove intake hose band. Remove air cleaner assembly with intake hose.

3) Remove clutch slave cylinder and clutch damper assembly from transaxle. Remove power steering speed sensor assembly with sensor hose in tact. Drain transaxle oil and remove right and left side drive axle shafts. Remove intermediate shaft assembly.

4) Remove shift rod and shift extension. Remove 2 bolts attaching torque rod bracket to upper part of clutch housing. Secure a transaxle jack under transaxle and remove sub frame center beam. Attach chain hoist evenly to both banks of engine and raise slightly until chain is tight.

5) Remove center stopper bracket from transaxle and remove clutch cover. Remove engine mounting bolts on front and on rear of transaxle. Remove starter mounting bolts and remove starter.

6) Remove remaining transaxle-to-engine bolts and carefully pull transaxle away from engine and slowly lower transaxle.

Inspection

1) Check pressure plate diaphragm spring fingers for wear or uneveness on release bearing contact points. Check spring finger height using Clutch Disc Aligner (07974-6890101) and feeler gauge. *See Fig. 3.*

2) Check that clearance between tool flange and fingers is no more than .04" (1.0 mm). Unevenness service limit of spring fingers is .04" (1.0 mm). Inspect pressure plate surface for wear, cracks, burning or warpage. Maximum face warpage is .006" (.15 mm). Measure with straight edge and feeler gauge at several points.

3) Check clutch disc lining for excessive wear, burned or oil soaked condition. Check clutch disc for loose rubber torsion dampers. Measure disc thickness,

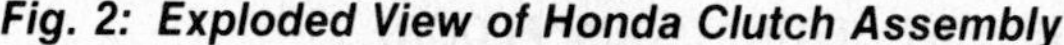
Fig. 2: Exploded View of Honda Clutch Assembly

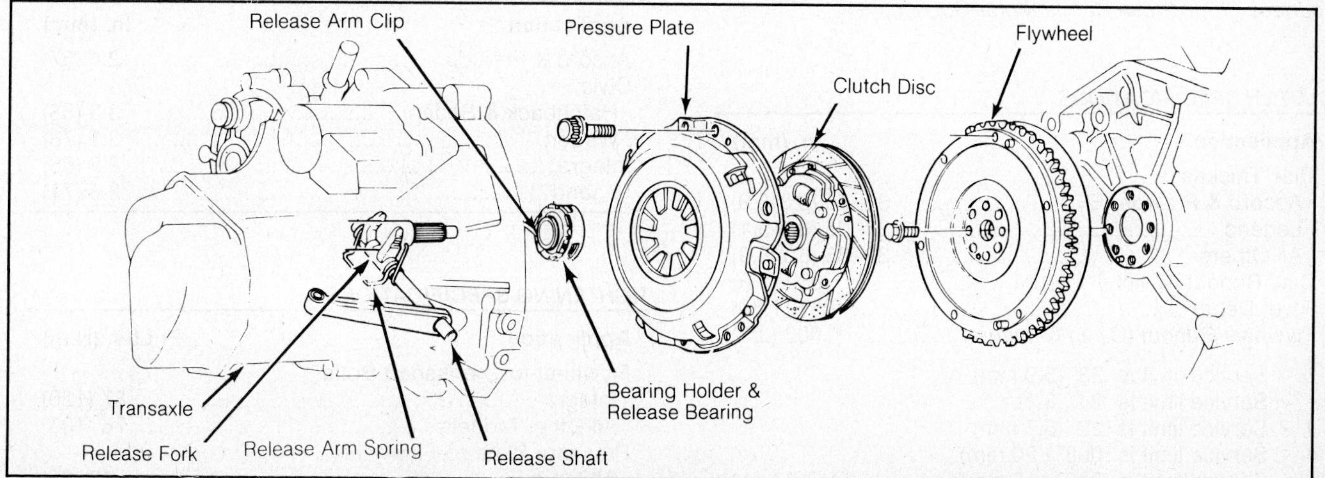

Courtesy of American Honda Motor Co.,Inc.

ACURA & HONDA (Cont.)

rivet depth. Check disc runout and flywheel runout. See CLUTCH SPECIFICATIONS chart.

Fig. 3: Checking Height on Diaphragm Springs With Aligner (07974-6890101) & Feeler Gauge.

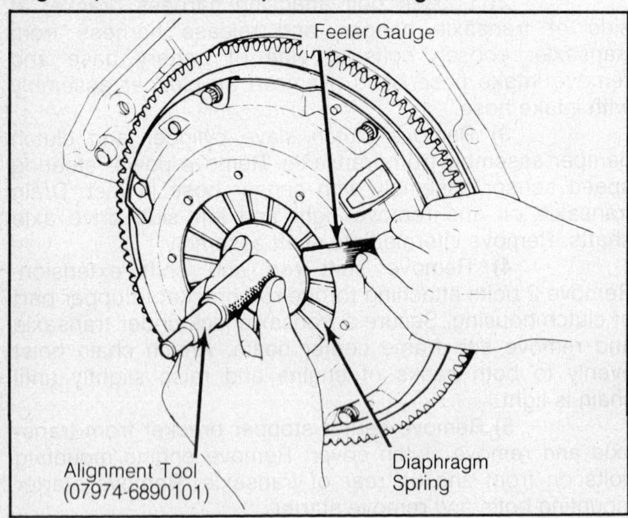

Courtesy of American Honda Motor Co., Inc.

Fig. 4: Clutch Adjustment Nut Location

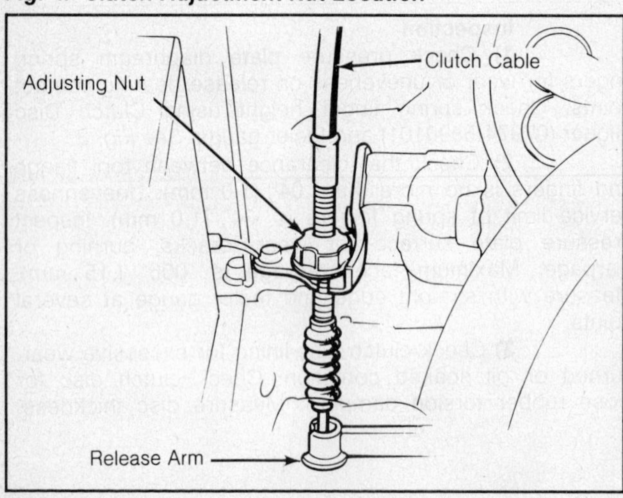

Courtesy of American Honda Motor Co., Inc.

CLUTCH SPECIFICATIONS

Application	In. (mm)
Disc Thickness	
Accord & Prelude (EFI)	[1] .33-.35 (8.3-8.9)
Legend	[2] .33-.36 (8.4-9.1)
All Others	[3] .32-.35 (8.1-8.9)
Disc Runout (Civic) & Integra	.039 (1.0)
Rivet Depth	[4] .051 (1.30)
Flywheel Runout (Civic) & Integra	[5] .002 (.05)

[1] – Service limit is .23" (5.9 mm).
[2] – Service limit is .24" (6.1).
[3] – Service limit is .22" (5.7 mm).
[4] – Service limit is .008" (.20 mm).
[5] – Service limit is .006" (.15 mm).

Installation

1) Align flywheel dowels with dowel holes in clutch cover. Using clutch alignment tool and ring gear holder, install disc and pressure plate. Tighten bolts evenly, in a criss-cross pattern, to final torque. Ensure that 2 dowel pins are installed in clutch housing.

2) Clean release bearing sliding surface. Apply molybdenum grease to release bearing sliding surface. Apply a light amount of grease to input shaft splines. DO NOT allow grease or dirt on clutch disc or pressure plate surfaces. To complete installation, reverse removal procedure. Refill all fluid to proper level. Adjust clutch pedal height, travel and freeplay.

CAUTION: New spring clips must be used on both axle shafts. Slide axles in until spring clips engage differential.

ADJUSTMENTS

CLUTCH PEDAL

Ensure that pedal return spring holds clutch pedal against stop pad. Turn adjusting nut clockwise to decrease cable adjustment and counterclockwise to increase cable adjustment. *See Fig. 4.*

CLUTCH PEDAL FREE PLAY

Application	In. (mm)
Accord & Prelude	5/8-1 (15.8-25.4)
Civic & Integra	7/16-1 1/8 (11.1-27.1)
Civic 4WD	5/8-7/8 (15.8-22.2)
Legend	11/32-19/32 (8.7-15.0)

RELEASE ARM FREE PLAY

Application	In. (mm)
Accord & Prelude	13/64-1/4 (5.3-6.4)
Legend	[1]
All Others	5/32-13/64 (4.0-5.0)

[1] – Adjust clutch pedal free play only.

DISENGAGEMENT HEIGHT (FROM FLOOR)

Application	In. (mm)
Accord & Prelude	2.4 (57)
Civic	
Hatchback & Sedan	3.3 (83)
Wagon	3.1 (78)
Integra	2.2 (56)
Legend	2.8 (71)

TIGHTENING SPECIFICATIONS

Application	Ft Lbs. (N.m)
Flywheel-to-Crankshaft Bolts	
Integra	87 (120)
All Other Models	76 (105)
Pressure Plate-to-Flywheel	
All Models	19 (26)

Clutches

ALFA ROMEO MILANO

DESCRIPTION

The clutch assembly is a dry disc type. The pressure plate is a diaphragm spring type. A prelubricated release bearing is operated by clutch master cylinder and slave cylinder.

REMOVAL & INSTALLATION

Removal and installation procedures for clutch-gearbox-differential assembly were not available from manufacturer.

OVERHAUL

CLUTCH UNIT

Disassembly

1) Remove clutch-gearbox-differential assembly. Mount and support assembly on work bench. Remove slave cylinder and release bearing fork. Remove rear shift lever from clutch assembly. Remove clutch cover-to-gearbox housing bolts.

2) Separate clutch cover and gearbox. *See Fig. 1.* Match mark drive shaft yoke and flywheel shaft end for reassembly. Remove yoke lock nut. Using a puller, remove yoke. Remove dust cover and clutch cover.

3) Match mark flywheel-to-pressure plate for reassembly reference. Remove pressure plate mount bolts. Remove release bearing, pressure plate and clutch disc as an assembly.

4) Place pressure plate on work table with friction surface up. Apply pressure to spring. Remove retaining ring holding release bearing to pressure plate. Separate bearing from pressure plate. Discard Belleville washer.

5) Using a puller, remove flywheel shaft bearing. Remove flywheel shaft-to-flywheel mounting bolts. Separate flywheel shaft from flywheel.

6) To dismantle clutch cover, remove 2 lock nuts retaining rear bearing. Remove front ball bearing. Discard "O" ring. Remove rear bearing using Puller (A.3.0401). Replace Belleville washer and "O" ring upon installation.

NOTE: **If pressure plate is excessively worn or damaged, manufacturer recommends entire clutch assembly be replaced with new or rebuilt unit.**

Inspection

1) Check clutch disc for wear, damage, burnt or oil saturated linings. Check release bearing. Inspect input shaft needle bearing for seizing marks or excessive wear. Replace components as necessary. Inspect flywheel shaft.

2) Replace if working sufaces are worn. Check flywheel shaft bearings. Replace of seized or excessiely worn. Inspect flywheel for wear, cracks, grooves or burnt friction surface.

3) Friction surface must be parallel to flywheel shaft mount surface within .0024" (.060 mm). Standard thickness, from friction surface-to-flywheel shaft side surface, is .43" (11.0 mm). If flywheel is resurfaced, ensure radius is remachined at outer edge of friction suface. If flywheel was reground or wear is more than .008" (.20

Fig. 1: Exploded View of Clutch Assembly

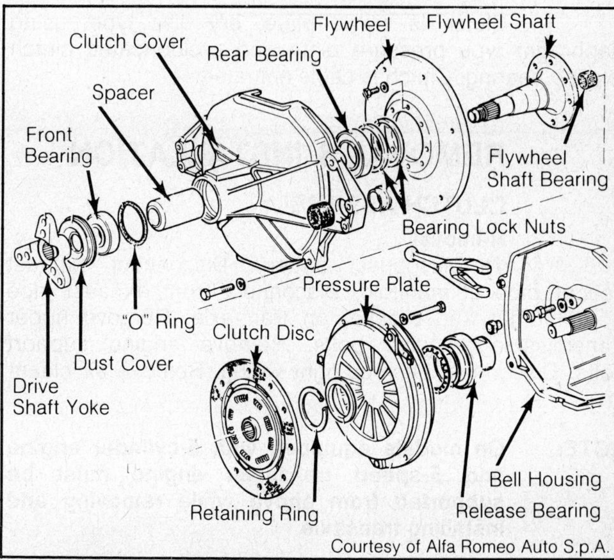

mm), replace entire clutch assembly with new or rebuilt unit.

Reassembly

1) To assemble clutch cover, drive rear bearing in using Bearing Installer (A.3.0282). Lock in place using lock nuts. Install spacer with beveled side toward front cover. Install new "O" ring in seat. Install front bearing.

2) Refit shift lever dust boot. Install release bearing. Apply Loctite to flywheel shaft mount bolts. Install flywheel on shaft. If needle bearing was removed, install using Bearing Installer (A.3.0405). Match index marks. Install flywheel and clutch disc.

3) Line up slots of clutch disc with Clutch Aligning Bar (A.4.0205). Install pressure plate with release bearing. Install pressure plate mount bolts onto flywheel. Check that pressure plate and clutch disc are tight and true to flywheel. Ensure clutch has initial idle travel. Remove alignment tool. Install clutch cover and dust cover.

4) Apply Loctite to clutch shaft and tighten yoke lock nut. Support pressure plate and tap on yoke to ensure yoke is fully seated. Lubricate release bearing guide sleeve, ball spindle and contact surface of release lever with grease. Install shift lever and tighten. To complete installation, reverse removal procedure. When installing release lever, ensure it is properly located on ball seat and release bearing seat.

ADJUSTMENTS

The clutch wear, pedal stroke and free play are automatically adjusted by operation of hydraulic system. No periodic adjustment is required.

TIGHTENING SPECIFICATIONS

Application	Ft. Lbs. (N.m)
Clutch Cover-to-Gearbox Bolt	21-23 (29-32)
Flywheel Shaft-to-Yoke Lock Nut	69-76 (93-103)
Flywheel Shaft-to-Flywheel Bolt	20-22 (28-31)
Pressure Plate-to-Flywheel Bolt [1]	13-16 (18-22)
Shift Lever Lock Nut	20-23 (28-32)

[1] - Tighten mount bolts evenly, in a diagonal pattern.

AUDI COUPE GT & 4000S

DESCRIPTION

Clutch is single plate, dry disc type, using diaphragm type pressure plate and prelubricated clutch release bearing. Clutch is cable actuated.

REMOVAL & INSTALLATION

CLUTCH ASSEMBLY

Removal

1) Disconnect battery. Disconnect exhaust header pipe at manifold. Disconnect front exhaust pipe from muffler and bracket on transaxle. Remove upper transmission-to-engine bolts. Remove engine support bolts. Disconnect back-up light wiring. Remove air cleaner.

NOTE: On models equipped with 5-cylinder engine and 5-speed transaxle, engine must be supported from above while removing and installing transaxle.

2) Remove bolt attaching shift rod coupling to rear of transaxle shifting shaft. Separate assemblies. Disconnect clutch cable at release lever. Disconnect speedometer cable.

3) Disconnect axle drive shafts at inner drive flanges. Remove starter. Remove front clutch housing cover plate. Remove remaining transaxle-to-engine bolts. Remove steering brackets (if necessary).

4) Support transaxle with jack and lift slightly. Remove transaxle rear mounts and brackets. Remove front support bolts. Pry transaxle away from engine and slide it out of vehicle.

NOTE: Ensure that axle shafts, drive shaft, tie rods and shift linkage do not interfere with transaxle removal.

Fig. 1: Exploded View of Clutch Assembly

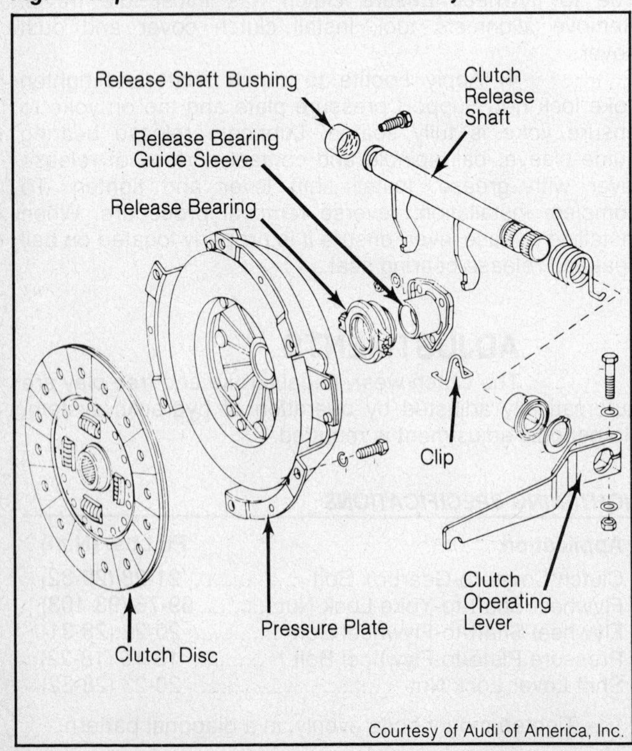

Courtesy of Audi of America, Inc.

5) Install Holder (10-201) on flywheel. Index mark pressure plate and flywheel for reinstallation in original position. Loosen pressure plate bolts 1/4 turn at a time in diagonal pattern. Slide pressure plate off flywheel dowels. Separate clutch disc. *See Fig. 1.*

Inspection

1) Clean and inspect pressure plate surface for cracks, burns and wear. Maximum pressure plate surface inward taper is .08" (.2 mm). Check diaphragm spring ends for wear or scores. Pressure plate may be used with scratches or scores to a maximum depth of .012" (.30 mm). If specifications are exceeded, replace pressure plate.

2) Inspect straps between pressure plate and cover for cracks. Ensure that rivets are secure and tight. Inspect clutch disc lining and splines for wear. Maximum clutch disc runout is .016" (.40 mm). If runout exceeds specifications, replace clutch disc.

Installation

To install, reverse removal procedure. Lubricate clutch disc splines lightly with molybdenum disulfide grease before assembly. Use clutch aligner to fit pressure plate and disc. Ensure flywheel and pressure plate index marks are aligned.

CLUTCH RELEASE BEARING

Removal & Installation

1) With transaxle separated from engine, remove retaining springs and clips securing release bearing to clutch fork. Bearing is prelubricated. DO NOT clean bearing in solvent. Rotate bearing and check for roughness or noise. If bearing is rough or noisy, replace release bearing.

2) Apply molybdenum disulfide grease to bearing contact points on clutch fork. Install retaining springs in retaining clips before sliding clips on release shaft. To install clutch components, reverse removal procedure.

CLUTCH PEDAL BUSHING

Removal & Installation

1) Check clutch release shaft and pedal bushings for free movement. If shaft is loose or binds, check and replace clutch pedal bushings. Remove retainer clip, pedal pivot pin and pedal assembly. Drive out old bushings using Bushing Removers (VW 401, VW 408a and VW 434).

NOTE: Ensure that new self-locking nuts and retainer clips are used during assembly. Lubricate bolts lightly with molybdenum disulfide grease.

2) Press in rubber bushing first. Lightly coat plastic bushing and install using Bushing Installers (VW 401, VW 411, VW 416b and VW 436a). Lubricate shaft and bushings. DO NOT grease guide sleeve. Install pedal assembly.

CLUTCH RELEASE SHAFT BUSHING

Removal & Installation

1) With transaxle out of vehicle and clutch components removed, install Bushing Removers (VW 771/15 and VW 771).

2) Using slide hammer, remove bushing from housing. Install new bushing with Bearing Installers (VW 295), (VW 439) or (VW 431).

AUDI COUPE GT & 4000S (Cont.)

3) Lubricate bushing and shaft with molybdenum disulfide grease and install bushing. Do not grease guide sleeve. To complete installation, reverse removal procedure.

PILOT BEARING

Removal & Installation

1) Lock flywheel in place, using Flywheel Holder (10-201). Install Pilot Bearing Remover (10-202). Remove bearing. Install pilot bearing with letters on bearing face out. Use Pilot Bearing Installer (VW 207c) on 4-cylinder models. Use Pilot Bearing installer (2026) on 5-cylinder models.

2) Seat bearing until distance from flywheel recess to bushing edge is .063" (1.6 mm) on 4-cylinder models. Seat bearing on 5-cylinder models to .219" (5.6 mm). Lubricate bearing and complete clutch and/or transaxle repair.

ADJUSTMENT

CLUTCH PEDAL FREE PLAY

1) Adjust clutch pedal free play by loosening and adjusting both lock nuts at clutch cable. Pedal free play is .590" (15.0 mm), measured at clutch pedal. Lock nuts have been replaced by spring clips on some models.

2) Clutch operating lever distance, from outside edge of clutch cable mount bracket (near oil filter) to flat upper edge of lever, is 6.656" (169.0 mm) for 5-speed, 4-cylinder models. Measurement is 7.594" (193 mm) for 5-speed, 5-cylinder models. Tip of lever (at cable attaching point) should be at same height as bottom of horizontal boss on lower left front of transaxle case.

TIGHTENING SPECIFICATIONS

Application	Ft. Lbs. (N.m)
Clutch Assembly-to-Flywheel Bolts	18 (25)
Clutch Release Shaft Retaining Bolt	11 (15)
Clutch Operating Lever Retaining Bolt	18 (25)
Guide Sleeve Mount Bolt	
4-Speed	7 (10)
5-Speed	11 (15)
Transaxle-to-Engine Bolts	40 (55)
Flywheel-to-Crankshaft Bolts	45 (61)

AUDI 4000CS QUATTRO & 5000 SERIES

DESCRIPTION

Clutch is single plate, dry disc type. Pressure plate is diaphragm spring type. Release bearing is pre-lubricated. Bearing is operated by slave cylinder push rod and release lever.

Slave cylinder is mounted on clutch housing and extends inside housing. Clutch pedal is connected to clutch master cylinder push rod fork using a clevis pin. Master cylinder is secured to clutch and brake pedal mounting brace.

REMOVAL & INSTALLATION

CLUTCH ASSEMBLY

Removal

1) Disconnect battery. Remove windshield washer bottle. Remove upper engine-to-transaxle bolts. Disconnect speedometer cable. Remove slave cylinder tensioning clip. Drive out slave cylinder lock pin. Remove cylinder with fluid line connected.

2) Support weight of engine. Remove exhaust pipe heat shield. Disconnect exhaust pipe at manifold. Disconnect axle drive shafts at transaxle and support with wire. Disconnect back-up light wire. Remove both shifting and adjusting rods.

3) Remove lower engine-to-transaxle mounting bolts. Remove starter and subframe cover shield. Slightly raise transaxle. Remove transaxle support bolts and bushings from both sides of subframe. Loosen both rear subframe mounting bolts. Remove right side transaxle bracket.

4) Slide transaxle off dowels and remove from vehicle. Index mark position of pressure plate on flywheel. Insert Flywheel Retainer (10-201). Loosen pressure plate mounting bolts evenly in diagonal pattern. Remove pressure plate and clutch disc.

Inspection

1) Check surface of clutch diaphragm spring fingers that contact release bearing for scores or wear. Pressure plate may be used if scores do not exceed .012" (.30 mm) in depth.

2) Check pressure plate for cracks, burn marks and scoring. Replace pressure plate if inward taper of disc contact face exceeds .012" (.30 mm) or if rivets are damaged or loose.

3) The maximum runout of clutch disc face is .020" (.50 mm). Measure runout at outer edge. Check disc splines for wear and rivets for tightness.

Installation

Clutch disc spring cage must face pressure plate. Clutch disc must slide freely with no radial play on input shaft. Lubricate input shaft splines with molybdenum grease. Align pressure plate index marks. Use Clutch Disc Aligner (10-213) to center disc. To install, reverse removal procedure.

CLUTCH RELEASE BEARING

Removal

1) Remove transaxle. Remove cap bolt and 2 retainer pieces at lower edge of release lever. Slide release lever and bearing out of bell housing.

2) Disengage circlip and retainer clips securing release bearing to lever. Separate bearing from lever. Remove guide sleeve (if necessary).

Inspection

Inspect clutch release bearing for wear or unusual noise. Do not wash bearing in solvent. If bearing is excessively rough or noisy, replace bearing. Inspect release lever and guide sleeve for excessive wear. Replace as necessary.

Installation

Lubricate ball cap located in clutch housing with grease. Do not grease plastic guide sleeve. Ensure clutch release lever locates directly to slave cylinder push rod tip. Push rod tip should be lubricated. To install, reverse removal procedure.

Fig. 1: Clutch Release Bearing with Related Components

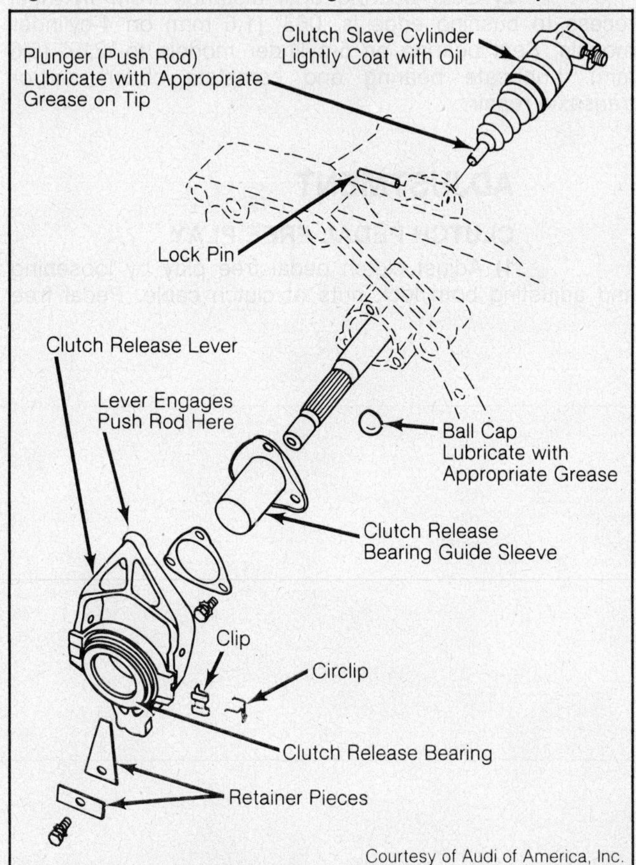

CLUTCH PEDAL BUSHING

Removal & Installation

1) Inspect clutch pedal bushings for free movement. Inspect for loose or binding shaft. Replace clutch pedal bushings if excessive wear is found. Detach slave cylinder clip at clevis and remove from pedal assembly. Remove retainer clip, pedal pivot pin and pedal assembly.

2) Remove old bushings. Press in new bushings. Ream new bushings to size. Install clutch pedal assembly. Replace all circlips and self-locking nuts. Bleed and adjust system.

NOTE: **Do not add DOT 5 silicone type brake fluid to system or severe component corrosion may result. Replace all internal components when repairing master or slave cylinder. Coat cups and piston with brake fluid paste before**

AUDI 4000CS QUATTRO & 5000 SERIES (Cont.)

installing. Replace all circlips and self-locking nuts.

CLUTCH MASTER CYLINDER

Removal

Disconnect and plug fluid lines. Separate cylinder from clutch pedal by removing circlip and clevis pin. Note circlip location for proper reassembly. Remove 2 bolts mounting master cylinder to pedal bracket. Remove master cylinder.

Fig. 2: Exploded View of Master Cylinder

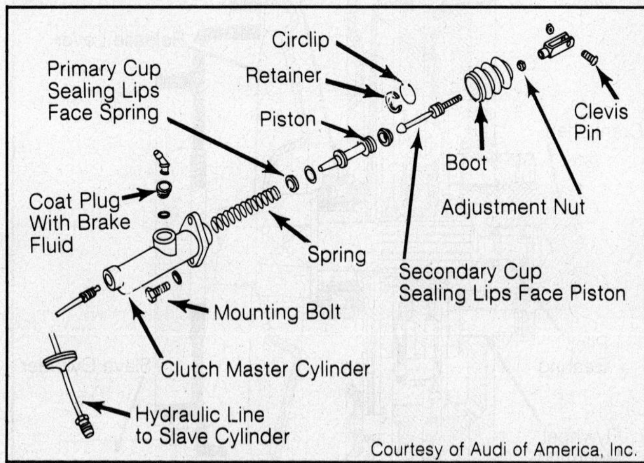

Inspection

1) Remove rubber boot, clevis and push rod. Remove snap ring. Remove snap ring spacer, piston, cups and spring. Check piston and cylinder bore for wear, nicks and corrosion.

2) If light honing does not clean up master cylinder bore, replace clutch master cylinder. Replace rubber parts during overhaul. Ensure secondary cup sealing lips face piston and primary cup sealing lips face spring.

Installation

To install master cylinder, reverse removal procedure. Bleed air from master cylinder fluid line. Do not use more than 35 psi (2.4 kg/cm²) in pressure bleeder when bleeding system. Check for proper clutch operation.

SLAVE CYLINDER

Removal

Working from under vehicle, remove tensioning clamp. Drive out slave cylinder lock pin located on top of transaxle. Slide cylinder back until push rod clears. Disconnect and plug fluid line.

Inspection

1) Remove slave cylinder push rod, rubber boot and retaining ring. Note ring location for proper installation. Remove piston, cup and spring. Check cylinder bore and piston for wear, nicks and corrosion.

2) Replace all internal components during slave cylinder overhaul. If corrosion in cylinder cannot be removed with light honing, replace slave cylinder assembly. Coat all internal rubber parts with brake fluid paste before installation.

Fig. 3: Exploded View of Slave Cylinder

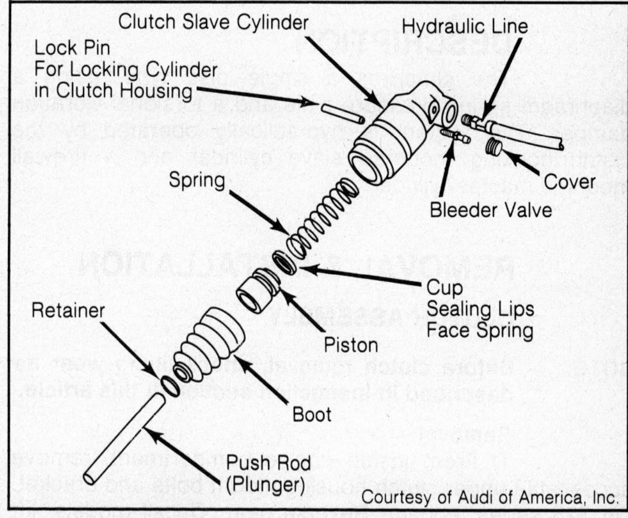

Installation

To install, reverse removal procedure. Coat outer housing machined surface of slave cylinder with light oil before installation. Bleed air from fluid line. Check for proper clutch operation and pedal height.

ADJUSTMENTS

CLUTCH PEDAL

Adjust master cylinder push rod. In rest position clutch pedal should stand 3/8" (10.0 mm) above brake pedal. Ensure return spring moves clutch pedal to end position after releasing. Excessive clutch plate wear will occur if pedal is allowed to rest on pedal mounting.

NOTE: **If clutch pedal is correctly adjusted but fails to return properly, inspect hydraulic system for airtight pedal bushing or jammed return spring.**

HYDRAULIC SYSTEM BLEEDING

Use pressure bleeding equipment to bleed system. Follow manufacturer's instructions. Do not use more than 35 psi (2.4 kg/cm²) in pressure bleeder when bleeding system.

TIGHTENING SPECIFICATIONS

Application	Ft. Lbs. (N.m)
Drive Shaft-to-Transmission Bolt	32 (43)
Engine-to-Transmission Bolt	
Upper Bolt	40 (54)
Lower Bolt	
Inner Bolt	33 (45)
Outer Bolt	14 (20)
Guide Sleeve Mount Bolt	11 (15)
Master Cylinder Mount Nut	14 (20)
Pedal Mount Assembly Bolt	18 (25)
Pressure Plate Bolt	18 (25)
Release Lever Retainer Bolt	11 (15)
Slave Cylinder Mount Bolt	14 (20)
Starter Bolt	40 (54)

Clutches

BMW

**BMW: 325 Series, 528 Series,
535 Series, 635CSi, 736i**

DESCRIPTION

The clutch is a single disc type, using a diaphragm spring pressure plate and a torsional vibration damper. The system is hydraulically operated by the clutch housing mounted slave cylinder and a firewall mounted master cylinder.

REMOVAL & INSTALLATION

CLUTCH ASSEMBLY

NOTE: **Before clutch removal, check lining wear as described in Inspection section in this article.**

Removal

1) From inside engine compartment, remove accessable upper clutch housing mount bolts and bracket. On 325 series, engage Reverse gear. On all models, lift shift lever dust boot and remove circlip holding lever. Remove selector rod from gearshift lever.

2) After noting component locations, remove shift lever. Raise and support vehicle. Remove front exhaust system components. Fit Clamp (26 1 011) to drive shaft flange. Remove bolts and discard lock nuts holding drive shaft flange to transmission shaft flange. Remove heat shield.

3) On 735i models, remove web under drive shaft tunnel. On all models, disconnect center support bearing and bracket. Remove drive shaft from front flange and position out of way. Support transmission with jack. Remove rear transmission mount and crossmember from body.

4) Remove clutch slave cylinder from clutch housing and set aside, leaving hydraulic line attached. Remove TDC sensors from bellhousing. Unplug electrical connectors from transmission. Remove transmission mount bolts. Pull transmission straight back and lower from vehicle.

NOTE: **On vehicles with speed and reference mark sensors, check component locations for proper reassembly reference. Black plug goes to starter ring gear and Gray plug goes to flywheel. Check and replace "O" rings as necessary. If sensors are reversed, engine WILL NOT start.**

5) Remove flywheel cover, clutch housing mount bolts and housing. Install Clutch Aligner (21 2 100) and Flywheel Holder (11 2 160). Loosen pressure plate bolts in diagonal pattern. Remove clutch assembly.

Inspection

1) Check clutch lining wear before removing transmission. Insert Liner Check Tool (21 2 060) into slave cylinder opening up to stop on tool grip. Replace disc if gap is more than .197" (5.0 mm). Minimum lining thickness is .295" (7.50 mm).

2) After removal, check lining for cracks, heat hardening or oil contamination. Mount disc on input shaft. Ensure linings are parallel within .006" (.15 mm). Mount dial indicator to transmission. Check disc hub runout.

3) Maximum runout should be less than .20" (5.08 mm) or .12" (3.0 mm) from disc outer edge. Check that hub slides smoothly on input shaft splines. Check end surface of diaphragm spring fingers for wear. Spring finger height should be less than .024" (.60 mm).

Fig. 1: Typical BMW Clutch Assembly

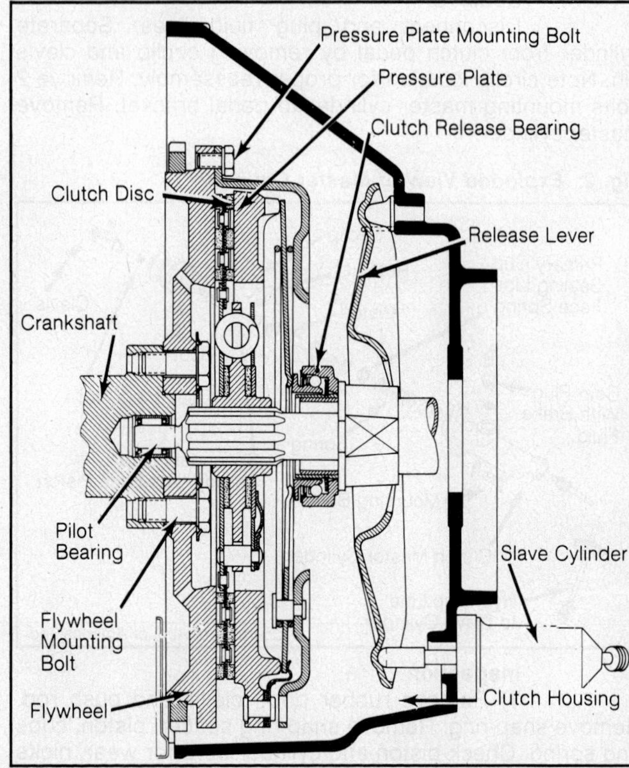

DO NOT allow oil, grease or dirt to contaminate clutch component friction surfaces. Courtesy of BMW of North America, Inc.

4) Check diaphragm springs for heat distortion, loose rivets, wear or damage. Inspect pressure plate and flywheel friction surfaces for cracks, distortion and proper thickness. Minimum flywheel thickness is .988" (25.10 mm) for 325e and 528e models. On 535i, 635CSi and 735i models minimum flywheel thickness should be 1.047" (26.60 mm).

5) Resurface or replace flywheel if runout is more than .004" (.10 mm). Pressure plate friction surface must be level. Light roughness may be dressed with fine emery cloth. If surfaces are deeply scored, resurface or replace defective parts.

Installation

1) Using alignment tool, install clutch disc and pressure plate. Install flywheel holding tool. Tighten pressure plate mount bolts evenly, in diagonal pattern. Install clutch housing.

2) Lightly apply molybdenum grease on contact surfaces of release bearing, disc hub splines, pressure plate and release lever. Install slave cylinder with bleeder screw at bottom.

3) Install drive shaft. To preload center bearing, move bracket .078" (2.0 mm) forward in slots. Install and tighten NEW drive shaft flange lock nuts. To complete installation, reverse removal procedure.

BMW (Cont.)

RELEASE BEARING & LEVER

Removal

With transmission and clutch housing removed from engine, remove spring from pivot end of release arm. Slide off arm and bearing assembly. Separate release bearing and measure for overall length of 1.93-1.97" (49.1-49.9 mm).

Installation

Coat contact points and pack lubricating groove of release bearing with molybdenum grease. To complete installation, reverse removal procedure.

CLUTCH MASTER CYLINDER

Removal

1) Remove trim under left side of instrument panel. On 325 series, remove accelerator cable. Remove bolt attaching master cylinder push rod to clutch pedal. Siphon brake fluid from reservoir.

2) Disconnect reservoir and hydraulic lines from clutch master cylinder. On 735i models only, remove windshield washer tank. Remove master cylinder mount bolts at firewall. Remove master cylinder from vehicle.

Installation

To install, reverse removal procedure. Bleed hydraulic system. On 635CSi and 735i models, ensure pedal over-center spring is engaged in pedal guide before attaching push rod.

CLUTCH SLAVE CYLINDER

Removal & Installation

Siphon fluid from reservoir. Remove slave cylinder from clutch housing. Disconnect hydraulic line and remove cylinder. To install, reverse removal procedure. Ensure cylinder is mounted with bleeder screw at bottom. Fill reservoir and bleed system.

OVERHAUL

CLUTCH MASTER CYLINDER

Disassembly & Reassembly

Remove master cylinder. Slide off dust boot and remove circlip holding push rod. Remove piston assembly. Clean components with denatured alcohol. Inspect cylinder bore for corrosion or scoring. Replace all rubber parts. Lubricate internal parts with brake fluid and reassemble. Adjust push rod length to approximately 5.5" (140 mm). *See Fig. 2.*

NOTE: Ensure that all pivot points on clutch pedal assembly are coated with Molykote 2 (or equivalent) prior to assembly.

CLUTCH SLAVE CYLINDER

Disassembly & Reassembly

Remove retaining ring. Remove push rod, boot and piston assembly. Clean internal parts with denatured alcohol. Inspect bore for scoring and corrosion. Replace all rubber parts. Ensure that all internal parts are lubricated with brake fluid and reassemble.

ADJUSTMENT

NOTE: The clutch pedal stroke and free play are automatically adjusted.

Fig. 2: Sectional View of Clutch Master Cylinder

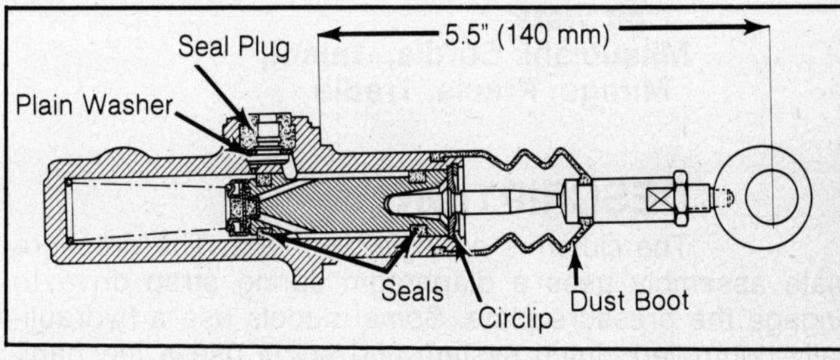

Courtesy of BMW of North America, Inc.

Fig. 3: Sectional View of Clutch Slave Cylinder

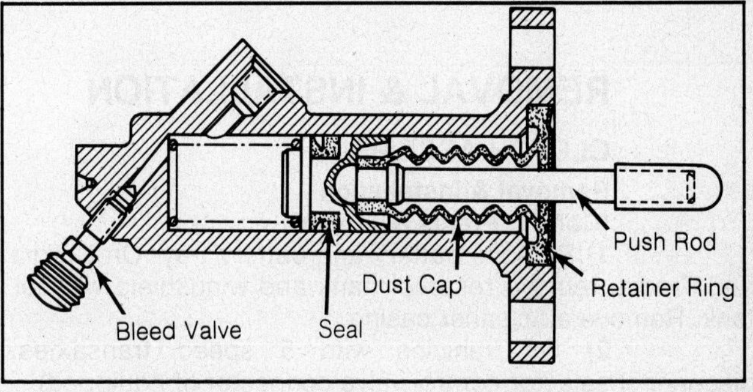

Replace all rubber components during overhaul.
Courtesy of BMW of North America, Inc.

HYDRAULIC SYSTEM BLEEDING

Ensure fluid reservoir is full. Attach bleeder hose to bleed screw on slave cylinder. Submerge end of hose in partially filled container of brake fluid. Slowly pump clutch pedal several times.

Hold pedal down on last stroke. Loosen bleeder screw to allow air to escape. Close bleeder screw and repeat until air is bled from system. Ensure fluid reservoir does not run dry during bleeding operation or complete hydraulic system must be rebled.

TIGHTENING SPECIFICATIONS

Application	Ft. Lbs. (N.m)
Clutch Housing-to-Engine Bolt	
8 mm Bolt	15-20 (21-27)
10 mm Bolt	29-36 (40-50)
12 mm Bolt	56-62 (78-86)
Cover-to-Clutch Housing Bolt	
8 mm Bolt	18-20 (24-27)
Clutch-to-Flywheel Bolt	16-17 (22-23)
Drive Shaft Flange Bolt	72 (98)
Master Cylinder Mount Bolt	16-17 (22-23)
Slave Cylinder-to-Housing Mount Bolt	17 (23)

CHRYSLER MOTORS & MITSUBISHI FWD

Chrysler Motors: Colt, Colt Vista
Mitsubishi: Cordia, Galant, Mirage, Precis, Tredia

DESCRIPTION

The clutch is a single disc type. The pressure plate assembly uses a diaphragm spring strap drive to engage the pressure plate. Some models use a hydraulically controlled clutch system and some use a mechanically-operated clutch release cable. The clutch pedal and a permanently lubricated release bearing complete the clutch system.

REMOVAL & INSTALLATION

CLUTCH ASSEMBLY

Removal & Installation (Cordia, Precis & Tredia)

1) Remove battery and battery tray. On Cordia and Tredia, remove reservoir tank and windshield washer tank. Remove air cleaner casing.

2) On vehicles with 5 speed transaxles, disconnect selector control valve connector (if equipped).

3) On all models, disconnect speedometer cable and clutch cable. Remove clutch release cylinder (where applicable). Disconnect back-up lamp harness and starter motor wiring. Remove starter motor and all upper transaxle-to-engine bolts.

3) Raise and support vehicle. Remove front wheels and engine under cover. Drain transaxle oil. Disconnect extension rod and shift control rod at transaxle.

4) Remove stabilizer bar and strut bar from right side lower control arm. Remove right and left side drive axle shafts and support out of the way. See FWD AXLE SHAFTS & CV JOINTS in DRIVE AXLE section.

5) Remove bellhousing cover. Support lower part of transaxle using a transaxle jack and remove remaining transaxle-to-engine bolts. Remove transaxle mount insulator bolt.

6) On Precis, remove blind cover from inside the right fender shield and remove transaxle bracket assembly.

7) Ensure that all cables, linkage and wires have been disconnected, and that transaxle will clear both drive axles. Slide transaxle assembly to the right and lower unit from vehicle.

8) Insert a clutch disc guide through clutch disc to prevent it from dropping. Diagonally loosen bolts in succession to avoid bending pressure plate flange during removal. Reverse removal procedures to install clutch assembly and transaxle. *See Fig. 1.*

Removal & Installation (All Others)

1) Remove battery and battery tray. Remove air cleaner casing assembly. Disconnect clutch cable at transaxle and remove from bracket. If clutch system is hydraulic, remove clutch release cylinder. Disconnect speedometer cable.

2) Disconnect both shifter and selector cables from linkage and remove from bracket. Disconnect back-up light harness and wiring for starter motor. Remove starter.

Fig 1: Exploded View of FWD Clutch Assembly

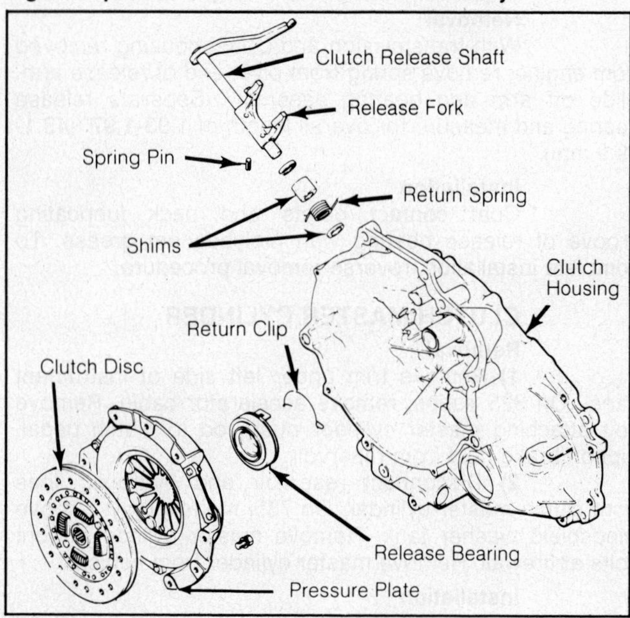

Courtesy of Chrysler Motors.

3) Raise and support vehicle. Remove front wheels and engine under cover (if equipped). Drain transaxle oil.

4) Remove bellhousing cover. Disconnect stabilizer bar, tie rod ends and lower control arm ball joint (if necessary).

5) Remove drive axle shafts and support out of the way. Do not damage axle boots. See FWD AXLE SHAFTS & CV JOINTS in DRIVE AXLE section.

6) Remove bolts attaching transaxle mount bracket to frame. Remove bracket attached to transaxle. On Colt and Mirage models, remove lower torque support rod.

7) Ensure that all cables, linkage, mounts and wires have been disconnected, and that transaxle clears both drive axles when removing. Insert a clutch disc aligning guide through clutch disc to prevent it from dropping.

8) Diagonally loosen pressure plate-to-flywheel bolts in succession to complete removal. Reverse removal procedures to install clutch assembly and transaxle. Check and adjust clutch pedal free play.

Inspection

1) Check release bearing for damage or abnormal noise. Replace bearing if contact surface area of release fork shows signs of wear. Replace release fork if worn. Do not clean bearing assembly in solvent.

2) Inspect outer casing of clutch cable for damage and cable for signs of fraying. Check cable for rough movement. Replace if necessary. Inspect hydraulic system components for fluid leakage and cylinder dust boot for cracks or deterioration.

3) Inspect pressure plate surface for wear, cracks, and/or discoloration. Check strap plate rivets for looseness and replace assembly if loose. Measure diaphragm spring ends for wear and uneven height. Replace assembly if difference between fingers exceed specifications. See SPRING FINGER HEIGHT table in this article.

CHRYSLER MOTORS & MITSUBISHI FWD (Cont.)

SPRING FINGER HEIGHT

Application	In. (mm)
Maximum Difference	.02 (.5)

4) Check clutch disc facing for loose rivets, uneven contact, deterioration, seizure and adhesion of grease or oil. Measure disc thickness or rivet sink limit (if necessary). Replace disc if not within specifications. See CLUTCH DISC THICKNESS SPECIFICATIONS table.

CLUTCH DISC THICKNESS SPECIFICATIONS

Application	In. (mm)
Disc Thickness	
Colt & Mirage	[1] .30-.32 (7.6-8.1)
Colt Vista	[2] .30-.32 (7.6-8.1)
Cordia, Galant & Tredia	.33-.35 (8.4-8.9)
Precis	[3]

[1] - On 1.6L engine thickness is .31-.34" (7.9-8.6 mm).
[2] - On 4WD thickness is .31-.34" (7.9-8.6 mm).
[3] - Rivet sink limit is .012" (0.3 mm)

CLUTCH MASTER CYLINDER

Removal & Installation

1) Drain hydraulic system at clutch release cylinder bleeder screw. Remove cotter pin, washer and clevis pin and disconnect push rod from clutch pedal.

2) Disconnect hydraulic line fitting at clutch master cylinder. Remove nuts retaining clutch master cylinder to firewall and remove master cylinder assembly. To install, reverse removal procedure.

CLUTCH RELEASE CYLINDER

Removal & Installation

1) Drain hydraulic system at clutch release cylinder bleeder screw. Disconnect hydraulic line fitting at release cylinder.

2) Remove "E" clip and clevis pin attaching push rod to clutch release arm. Disconnect hydraulic line at release cylinder. Remove bolts attaching cylinder to transaxle. Remove clutch release cylinder. To install, reverse removal procedure.

OVERHAUL

CLUTCH MASTER CYLINDER

Disassembly & Reassembly

1) Remove piston stop ring and remove damper and push rod assembly. Pull piston assembly out. Note position of resevoir band for reassembly and remove resevoir.

2) Apply DOT 3 brake fluid to components during reassembly. To complete Reassembly, reverse disassembly procedure. Ensure pistons move freely in their bores. Fill hydraulic system and bleed. Check for leaks and adjust clutch pedal free play.

CLUTCH RELEASE CYLINDER

Disassembly & Reassembly

1) Remove valve plate and spring on opposite end of bleeder plug. Remove push rod and boot. Cover piston assembly opening with a rag. Slowly apply compressed air to hydraulic line opening to force piston assembly out.

2) Apply DOT 3 brake fluid to components during reassembly. To complete Reassembly, reverse disassembly procedure. Ensure pistons move freely in their bores. Fill hydraulic system and bleed. Check for leaks and adjust clutch pedal free play.

Inspection

Clutch Master Cylinder & Clutch Release Cylinder

1) Check master cylinder and clutch release cylinder for leaks. Check hoses and lines for leaks, cracks or clogging. Clean cylinders and internal components in solvent and blow dry with compressed air.

2) Inspect all cylinder bores and piston assemblies for signs of rust or scoring. Check piston cups for wear or deformation. Inspect boots for deterioration.

3) Measure inside bore diameter of master cylinder and clutch release cylinder using a cylinder gauge. Measure bore diameter at 3 locations (bottom, middle and top) in 2 perpendicular directions.

4) Measure outside diameter of pistons for master cylinder and release cylinder with a micrometer. If master cylinder-to-piston clearance exceeds limit, replace master cylinder assembly. If release cylinder-to-piston clearance exceeds limit, replace release cylinder assembly. See CYLINDER CLEARANCE SPECIFICATIONS .

CYLINDER CLEARANCE SPECIFICATIONS

Application	In. (mm)
All Cylinder-to-Piston Clearance	.006 (.15)

ADJUSTMENT

CLUTCH PEDAL FREE PLAY

Application	In. (mm)
Colt & Mirage	[1] 0.8-1.2 (20.3-30.5)
Colt Vista & Galant	[2] .24-.51 (6.1-13.0)
Cordia & Tredia	0.6-0.8 (15.2-20.3)
Precis	0.8-1.2 (20.3-30.5)

[1] - On 1.6L engine free play is .24-.55" (6.1-14.0 mm).
[2] - On 4WD free play is .24-.51" (6.1-13.0 mm).

TIGHTENING SPECIFICATIONS

Application	Ft. Lbs. (N.m)
Pressure Plate-to-Flywheel Bolts	11-15 (15-20)
Transaxle-to-Engine	
8 mm Bolts	22-25 (30-34)
10 mm Bolts	32-40 (43-54)
Starter Mounting Bolts	16-25 (22-34)

CHRYSLER MOTORS & MITSUBISHI RWD

Chrysler Motors: Conquest, Raider, Ram-50
Mitsubishi: Montero, Pickup, Starion

DESCRIPTION

The clutch is a single disc type. The clutch cover assembly uses a diaphragm spring strap drive to engage the pressure plate. Some models use a hydraulically controlled clutch release system and some use a cable controlled clutch release system. The clutch pedal and a permanently lubricated release bearing complete the clutch release system.

REMOVAL & INSTALLATION

CLUTCH ASSEMBLY

Removal (2WD)

1) Disconnect negative ground cable from battery. Drain transmission fluid. Remove bolts from top of shift tower and remove shift lever assembly away from transmission. Disconnect backup light switch connector and speedometer cable. On Conquest and Starion, remove engine under cover and clutch release cylinder.

2) Remove exhaust pipe mounting bracket from exhaust and clutch housing (if equipped). Disconnect wiring from starter and remove starter motor. Support transmission with a jack and relieve weight of transmission from crossmember.

3) Remove rear engine mount from transmission and crossmember. Remove crossmember. Remove transmission-to-engine mounting bolts and draw transmission rearward until input shaft clears clutch assembly. Lower transmission from vehicle.

4) Index mark clutch cover and flywheel for reassembly. Using a crisscross pattern, alternately and evenly loosen clutch cover bolts in several steps. Remove clutch cover and clutch disc assembly.

Inspection

1) Check for excessive wear, warpage or damage to clutch disc. Measure rivet depth on clutch disc. *See Fig. 2.* Replace disc if rivet depth is not within specifications given.

Fig. 2: Measuring Rivet Depth With Gauge

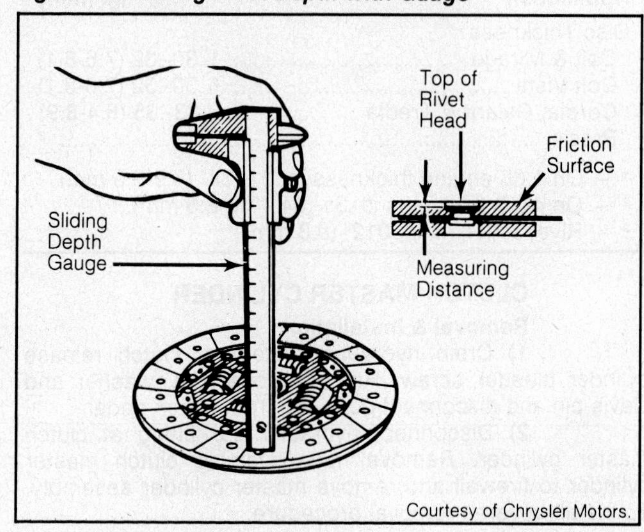

Fig. 1: Hydraulic Type Release Assembly

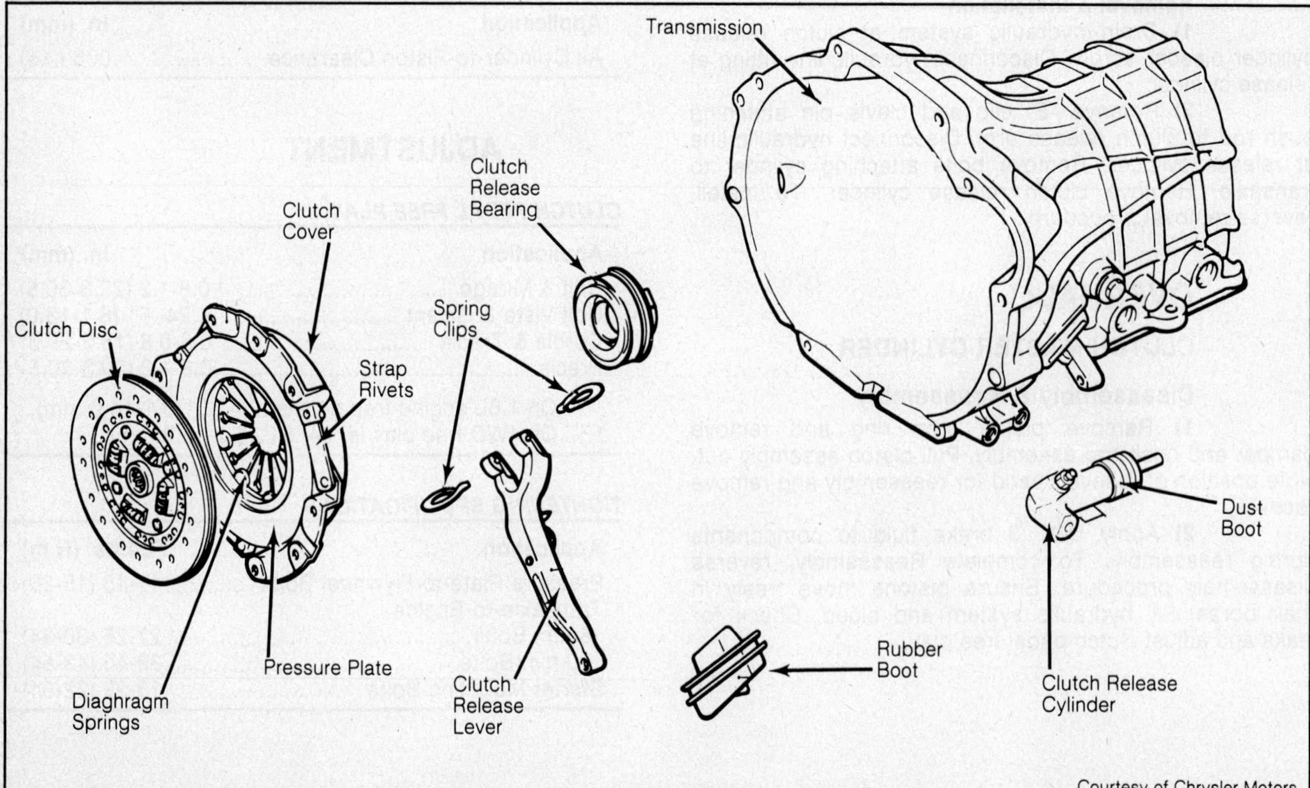

CHRYSLER MOTORS & MITSUBISHI RWD (Cont.)

Fig. 3: Cable Controlled Release Arm Assembly

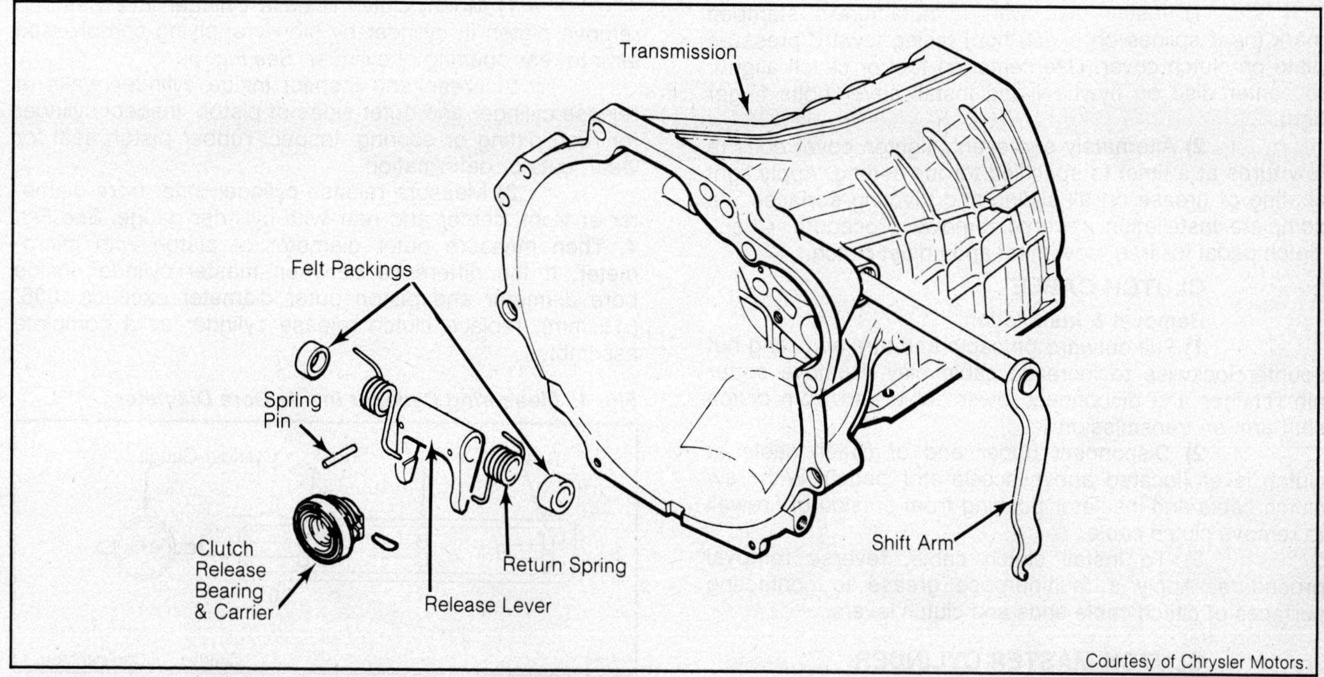

2) Inspect diaphragm spring of clutch cover for excessive wear of fingers and looseness of strap rivets. Check pressure plate for scoring or warpage. Using dial indicator, ensure that flywheel runout does not exceed specification given. Inspect flywheel for cracks, scoring or discoloration. Resurface or replace flywheel if necessary.

3) Check release bearing for rough rotation and/or excessive noise. Check diaphragm spring contact surface for abnormal wear. Inspect bearing and fulcrum contact points of release lever for abnormal wear. Check clutch cable (if equipped) for free movement and replace if necessary.

Installation

1) Install disc with manufacturers stamped mark (near splines on clutch hub) facing toward pressure plate on clutch cover. Use centering tool or clutch aligner to center disc on flywheel and install cover bolts finger tight.

2) Alternately and evenly tighten cover bolts (a few turns at a time) to specified torque setting. Apply light coating of grease on all sliding and pivoting surfaces. To complete installation, reverse removal procedure. Check clutch pedal for free movement and adjust clutch.

Removal (4WD)

1) Disconnect negative battery cable. Remove transmission/transfer case protector shield (if equipped). Drain transmission and transfer case fluids. Index mark and remove both front and rear propeller shafts.

2) On Montero and Ram Raider, remove both transmission and transfer case shift knobs and floor console. All models, disconnect backup light switch harness connector and speedometer cable. Disconnect exhaust pipe mounting bracket from exhaust pipe and remove bracket from front of clutch housing.

3) On cable controlled transmissions, pull down on clutch cable and turn adjusting nut counterclockwise to increase clutch cable free play. Disconnect clutch cable end from clutch release lever. On hydraulically controlled systems, remove clutch release cylinder bolts and remove cylinder.

4) On all models, disconnect 4WD indicator light switch harness. Support transmission/transfer case assembly with a suitable jack. Disconnect rear engine mount from transmission assembly and remove crossmember. Remove transfer case mount (if equipped) and mounting bracket. Disconnect wiring for starter and remove starter motor.

5) Remove transmission-to-engine mounting bolts and carefully draw transmission/transfer case assembly rearward until transmission input shaft clears clutch assembly. On vehicles with rear crossmember, tilt front of transmission/transfer case down to clear crossmember. Carefully lower assembly from vehicle.

6) Index mark clutch cover and flywheel for reassembly. Using a crisscross pattern, alternately and evenly loosen clutch cover bolts in several steps. Remove clutch cover and clutch disc assembly.

Inspection

1) Check for excessive wear, warpage or damage to clutch disc. Measure rivet depth on clutch disc. *See Fig. 2.* Replace disc if rivet depth is not within specifications given. Inspect diaphragm springs on clutch cover for excessive wear of fingers or looseness of strap rivets.

2) Check pressure plate on clutch cover and flywheel for scoring, heat cracks, warpage or discoloration. Using a dial indicator, measure flywheel runout. Resurface or replace flywheel if runout is greater then .005" (.13 mm).

3) Check release bearing for rough rotation and/or excessive noises. Replace if needed. Check diaphragm spring contact surface of clutch cover for abnormal wear. Inspect bearing and fulcrum contact points of release lever for abnormal wear. Replace if necessary.

CHRYSLER MOTORS & MITSUBISHI RWD (Cont.)

Installation

1) Install disc with manufacturers stamped mark (near splines on clutch hub) facing toward pressure plate on clutch cover. Use centering tool or clutch aligner to center disc on flywheel and install cover bolts finger tight.

2) Alternately and evenly tighten cover bolts (a few turns at a time) to specified torque setting. Apply light coating of grease on all sliding and pivoting surfaces. To complete installation, reverse removal procedure. Check clutch pedal for free movement and adjust clutch.

CLUTCH CABLE

Removal & Installation

1) Pull outward on cable and turn adjusting nut counterclockwise to increase cable play. Remove cotter pin retainer and disconnect lower cable end from clutch shift arm on transmission.

2) Disconnect upper end of clutch cable at clutch lever (located above accelerator pedal). Withdraw clutch cable and insulator bushing from outside of firewall to remove clutch cable.

3) To install clutch cable, reverse removal procedure. Apply a multipurpose grease to contacting surfaces of clutch cable ends and clutch levers.

CLUTCH MASTER CYLINDER

NOTE: **On some models, it may be necessary to remove the clutch fluid reservoir before removing clutch master cylinder.**

Removal & Installation

1) Drain hydraulic system at clutch release cylinder bleeder screw. Remove split pin, washer and clevis pin attaching push rod of master cylinder to clutch pedal. Disconnect push rod from clutch pedal.

2) Disconnect hydraulic line fitting at master cylinder. Remove 2 nuts retaining master cylinder to firewall and remove master cylinder assembly. Reverse removal procedure to install master cylinder.

Inspection

1) Remove piston stop ring from rear of master cylinder. Pull piston assembly outward and remove. Clean all components and inspect inside cylinder walls of master cylinder and outer piston for rust, pitting or scoring. Inspect piston cup for wear, cuts or deformation.

2) Measure master cylinder inside bore diameter in front, center and rear with cylinder gauge. *See Fig. 4*. Measure piston outer diameter with micrometer. If the difference between master cylinder inside diameter and piston outer diameter exceeds .006" (.15 mm), replace clutch master cylinder as a complete assembly.

CLUTCH RELEASE CYLINDER

Removal & Installation

1) Drain clutch hydraulic system at release cylinder bleeder screw. Remove eye bolt, hose and both sealing gaskets from cylinder. Remove release cylinder bolts and remove cylinder.

2) To install clutch release cylinder, reverse removal procedure. Add hydraulic fluid, bleed and adjust system.

Disassembly & Inspection

1) Mount clutch release cylinder in a vise and remove piston in cylinder by slowly applying compressed air into rear opening of cylinder. *See Fig. 5*.

2) Clean and inspect inside cylinder walls of release cylinder and outer sides of piston. Inspect cylinder for rust, pitting or scoring. Inspect rubber piston seal for wear, cuts or deformation.

3) Measure release cylinder inner bore diameter at front, center and rear with cylinder gauge. *See Fig. 4*. Then measure outer diameter of piston with micrometer. If the difference between master cylinder inside bore diameter and piston outer diameter exceeds .006" (.15 mm), replace clutch release cylinder as a complete assembly.

Fig. 4: Measuring Cylinder Inside Bore Diameter

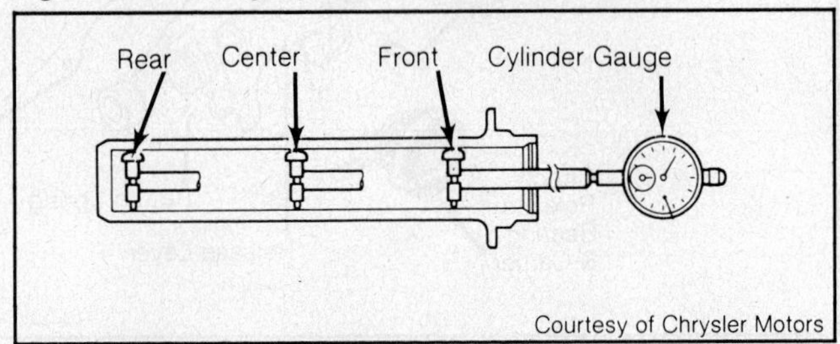

Fig. 5: Removing Release Cylinder Piston

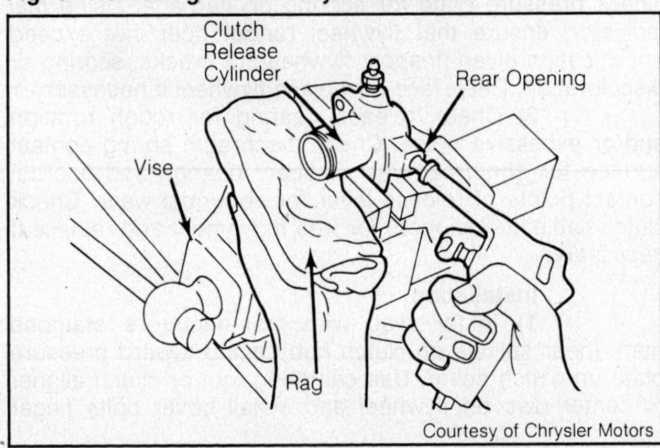

CLUTCH RELEASE SHIFT ARM

Removal & Installation

1) Remove return clips. Slide off release bearing carrier with bearing. Use a pin punch to remove shift arm spring pins and release lever assembly. *See Fig. 6*.

2) Slide shift arm outward to remove shift arm, release lever, 2 felt packings and 2 return springs. To install clutch release shift arm, reverse removal procedure and lubricate all contact surfaces.

Inspection

Inspect all pivoting areas, bearing and cable contact surfaces for abnormal wear. Check shift arm and lever for bends or cracks. Replace if necessary. Always lubricate shaft at pivot points and replace spring pins with new pins. *See Fig. 7*.

CHRYSLER MOTORS & MITSUBISHI RWD (Cont.)

ADJUSTMENTS

CLUTCH PEDAL FREE PLAY

Hydraulic

To adjust clutch pedal free play, hold master cylinder push rod (connected to clutch pedal) and loosen lock nut with wrench. Rotate push rod to lengthen (decrease) or shorten (increase) clutch pedal free play. Ensure that free play is within specifications given. Tighten lock nut.

Cable

To adjust clutch cable, lightly pull down on cable and turn adjusting nut until adjusting nut-to-insulator clearance measures .12-.16" (3-4 mm). *See Fig. 8.* After making adjustment, depress clutch pedal several times and recheck adjustment. Clutch cable adjustment should correspond with free play specification.

Fig. 6: Removing Shift Arm Spring Pins

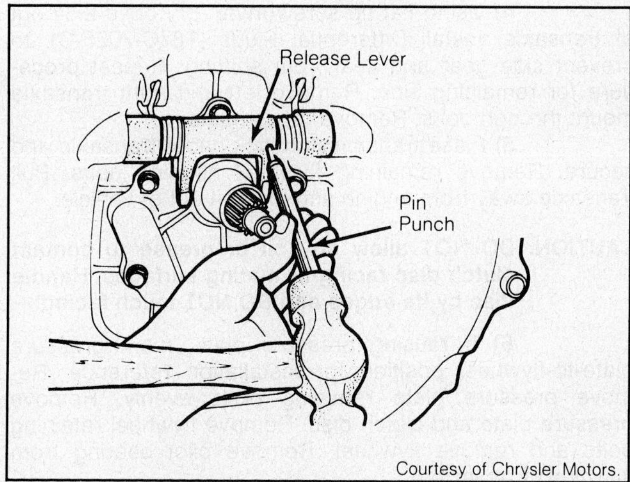

Courtesy of Chrysler Motors.

Fig. 7: Lubrication Points On Shift Arm

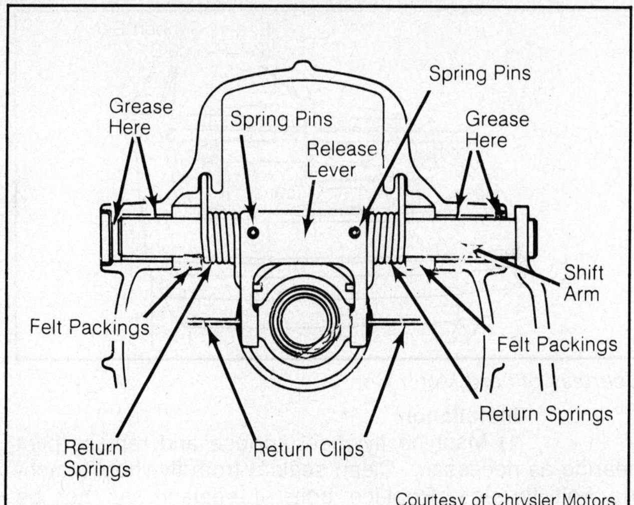

Courtesy of Chrysler Motors.

Fig. 8: Clutch Cable Measuring Distance

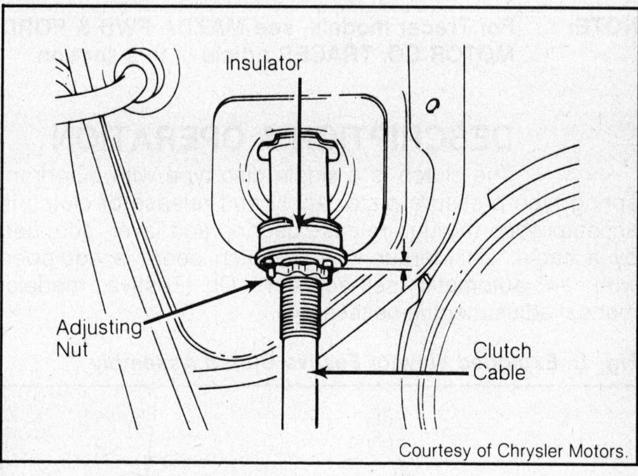

Courtesy of Chrysler Motors.

Fig. 9: Free Play Measuring Distance

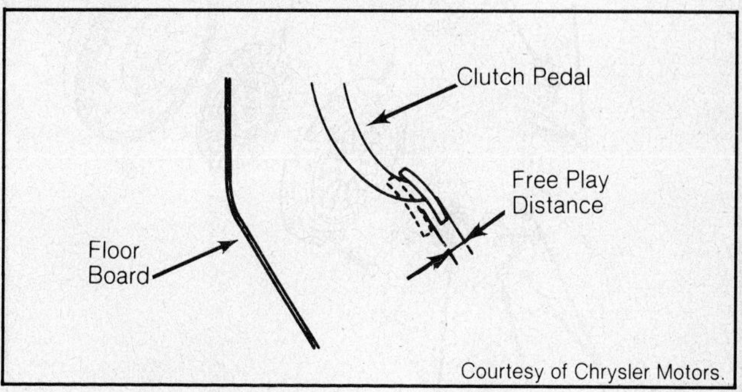

Courtesy of Chrysler Motors.

CLUTCH PEDAL FREE PLAY

Application	In. (mm)
Conquest & Starion	.2-.5 (6-13)
Montero & Ram Raider	.31-.63 (8-16)
Pickup & Ram-50	.8-1.4 (20-35)

CLUTCH RIVET DEPTH

Application	In. (mm)
All Models	
Minimum Depth	.012 (.3)

TIGHTENING SPECIFICATIONS

Application	Ft. Lbs. (N.m)
Clutch Cover bolt	1-16 (15-22)
Crossmember Bolt	
Conquest & Starion	7 (10)
All Others	41-54 (55-75)
Drain Plug	
Transmission	43 (60)
Transfer Case	22-25 (30-35)
Flywheel-to-Crankshaft Bolt	94-101 (130-140)
Propeller Shaft Bolt	36-43 (50-60)
Rear Engine MountBolt	
Conquest & Starion	14-17 (20-24)
All Others	13-18 (18-25)
Release Cylinder Bolt	22-30 (30-41)
Starter Motor Bolt	
Raider & Ram-50	20-25 (27-34)
All Others	16-23 (22-31)

Clutches

FORD MOTOR CO.

Festiva, Merkur XR4Ti

NOTE: **For Tracer models, see MAZDA FWD & FORD MOTOR CO. TRACER article in this section.**

DESCRIPTION & OPERATION

The clutch is a single disc type with diaphram spring type pressure plate. Apply and release of clutch is accomplished through release bearing and lever, actuated by a cable. On Merkur XR4Ti, clutch pedal is equipped with an automatic self-adjuster. On Festiva models, manual adjustment is necessary.

Fig. 1: Exploded View of Festiva Clutch Assembly

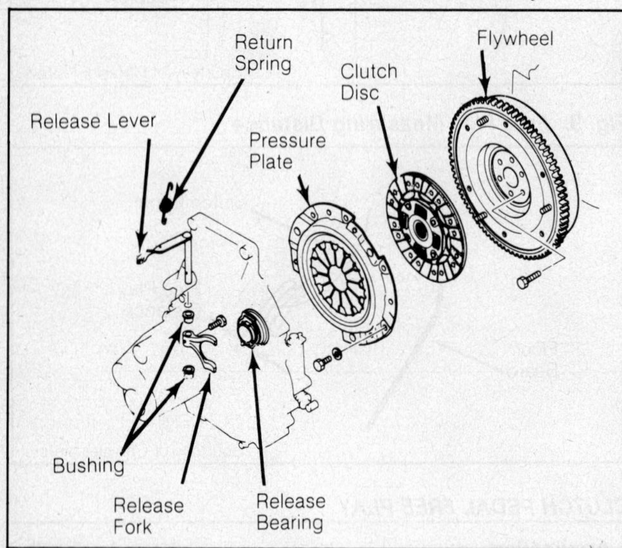

Courtesy of Ford Motor Co.

Fig. 2: Exploded View of Merkur XR4Ti Clutch Assembly

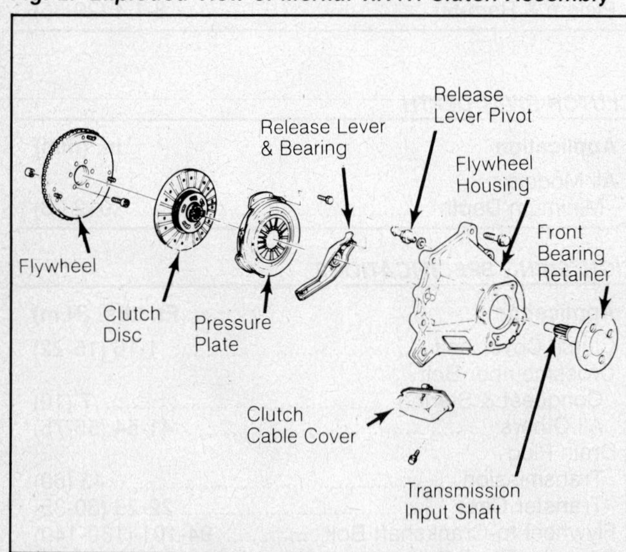

Courtesy of Ford Motor Co.

REMOVAL & INSTALLATION

CLUTCH ASSEMBLY

Removal (Festiva)

1) Disconnect battery negative cable. Disconnect backup light switch and neutral switch. Loosen clutch cable adjuster nut and disengage cable from release lever. Remove starter. Disconnect speedometer cable from transaxle.

2) Remove 2 top transaxle-to-engine bolts. Install Engine Support Bar (D79P-6000-B), to retain engine during transaxle removal. *See Fig. 3.* Raise vehicle. Remove bolt and nut retaining shift rod to input shift rail. Drain transaxle fluid. Remove front wheels.

3) Remove under engine covers. Apply brakes and loosen drive axle lock nut at hub. Remove stabilizer bar from lower control arm and body. Remove clamp bolt attaching steering knuckle to lower control arm ball joint. Pry ball joint out of steering knuckle.

4) Using flat tip screwdriver, pry drive axle out of transaxle. Install Differential Plugs (T87C-7025-C), to prevent side gear and seal from shifting. Repeat procedure for remaining side. Remove left and right transaxle mount through bolts. Remove crossmember.

5) Place transmission jack under transaxle and secure. Remove remaining flywheel housing bolts. Pull transaxle away from engine and lower it out of vehicle.

CAUTION: **DO NOT allow any oil or grease to contact clutch disc facing or mating surfaces. Handle disc by its edges and DO NOT touch facing.**

6) If reusing pressure plate, mark pressure plate-to-flywheel position for installation reference. Remove pressure plate retaining bolts evenly. Remove pressure plate and clutch disc. Remove flywheel retaining bolts and remove flywheel. Remove pilot bearing from flywheel (if replacing).

Fig. 3: Engine Support Bar Installed

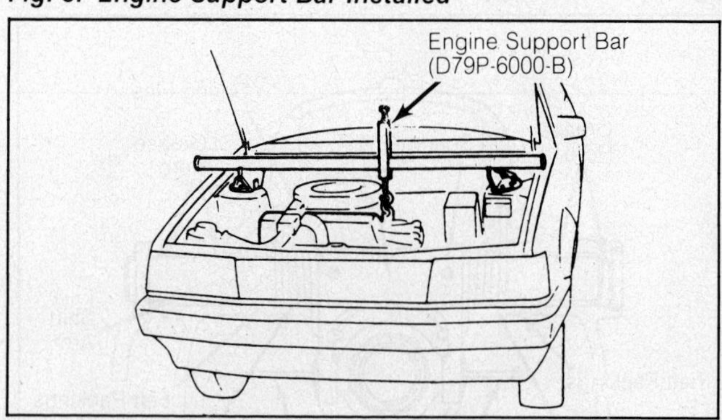

Courtesy of Ford Motor Co.

Installation

1) Machine flywheel surface and replace pilot bearing as necessary. Clean sealant from flywheel attaching bolt threads. Replace bolts if sealant can not be removed. Coat bolt threads with Stud and Bearing Mount Sealer (EOAZ-19554-B), and install flywheel. Tighten bolts to specifications.

2) Position clutch disc on flywheel with damper springs facing away from flywheel. Hold in place with Clutch Aligner (T77F-7137-A). Position pressure plate over clutch disc. Align marks, if reusing pressure plate.

FORD MOTOR CO. (Cont.)

3) Install pressure plate retaining bolts. Alternately tighten bolts to specifications. Remove clutch aligner. Place transaxle on transmission jack. Lightly coat input shaft splines with Clutch Grease (C1AZ-19590-B).

4) Install transaxle and remove transmission jack. Install crossmember and transaxle mount bolts. Remove differential plugs. Install new circlips on drive axles and install drive axles.

5) To complete installation, reverse removal procedure. Tighten all bolts/nuts to specifications. Adjust clutch pedal free play. Fill transaxle with Dexron II fluid.

Removal (Merkur XR4Ti)

1) Wedge a 7" block of wood under clutch pedal to disengage clutch cable self-adjuster. Place transmission in Neutral. Disconnect battery negative cable. Raise vehicle. Remove catalytic converter inlet pipe at turbocharger. Remove catalytic converter and inlet pipe as assembly.

2) Mark drive shaft-to-pinion flange. Remove drive shaft bolts at pinion flange. Remove center support bearing bracket bolts. Note and retain spacers. They MUST be installed to original location and position.

3) Separate drive shaft at pinion flange. Support center bearing and pull drive shaft out of transmission. Install a plug in extension housing seal to prevent fluid leakage.

4) Disconnect the wiring from starter. Remove starter attaching bolts, heat shield rear support bracket and transmission brace. Remove starter motor. Remove front stabilizer bar-to-body brackets and body stiffener rod. Place wooden block between stabilizer bar and body side rail.

5) Install transmission jack. Remove rear mount from transmission. Remove bolts attaching rear mount to body and remove rear mount. Loosen engine mount attaching nuts, leaving 2 or 3 threads protruding from nuts. Place block of wood against engine oil pan. Raise front of engine and lower transmission jack, until engine mount nuts contact crossmember.

6) Disconnect back-up light switch and neutral safety switch. Remove shift lever attaching bolts and raise shift lever out extension housing. Remove the snap ring and pull speedometer cable out of extension housing. Remove clutch release lever cover. Disengage clutch cable from release lever.

7) Remove speedometer cable routing clips bolts and position cable on left side of vehicle. Remove flywheel housing rear cover plate bolts. Remove top flywheel housing attaching bolts. Remove remaining flywheel housing attaching bolts.

8) Pull transmission rearward until flywheel housing contacts the vehicle body. Raise rear of transmission and pull rearward until clear of vehicle body. Lower rear of transmission and remove transmission.

CAUTION: DO NOT allow any oil or grease to contact clutch disc facing or mating surfaces. Handle disc by its edges and DO NOT touch facings.

9) Mark pressure plate-to-flywheel for installation reference. Install Clutch Aligner (T71P-7137-H), to hold assembly in position during removal. Loosen pressure plate bolts alternately. Remove pressure plate and clutch disc. *See Fig. 2.*

10) Remove flywheel bolts and remove flywheel. Use care not to drop flywheel during removal of last bolt. Using slide hammer and Pilot Bearing Puller (T58L-101-A), remove pilot bearing (if replacing).

Installation

1) Lightly coat pilot bearing bore with Clutch Grease (C1AZ-19590-B). Using clutch aligner and Pilot Bearing Replacer (T71P-7137-C), install pilot bearing with sealed surface facing outward (if removed).

2) DO NOT reuse pilot bearing, if removed for any reason. Lightly coat input shaft on transmission with Clutch Grease (C1AZ-19590-B). Install transmission by reversing removal procedure.

NOTE: Transmission fluid is a semi-synthetic oil. When adding or replacing, use ONLY E5RY-19C-547A (Ford specification ESD-M-2C175A).

3) To complete installation, reverse removal procedure. Tighten all bolts/nuts to specifications. Align all marks made at removal. Ensure drive shaft center bearing spacers are installed to original location and position as noted at removal. Check and fill transmission to proper level.

CLUTCH RELEASE LEVER & BEARING

NOTE: The clutch release bearing is prelubricated and permanently sealed. Never wash or soak bearing in cleaning solvent.

Removal & Installation

1) Remove transmission or transaxle. On Festiva models, remove release lever bolt and slide release bearing off. Remove release lever shaft and remove release lever. Lightly lube bearing I.D. and release lever contact surface with clutch grease. To complete installation, reverse removal. Align bolt hole in release lever and shaft. Apply Stud and Bearing Sealant (E0AZ-19554-B), to release lever bolt.

2) On Merkur XR4Ti models, pop release lever off pivot stud and slide lever and bearing off input shaft. Apply light film of clutch grease to transmission front bearing retainer, lever-to-bearing surfaces and bearing I.D. surface. Fill grease groove in release bearing hub and remove any excess grease. To complete installation, reverse removal.

Inspection

Check bearing rotation operation for roughness, sticking and noise. Check release lever and transmission/transaxle front bearing retainer for wear or damage. Check release lever shaft for bent, worn or damage. Check all mating surfaces for wear or damage. Replace components found to be defective.

PILOT BEARING

NOTE: DO NOT reuse pilot bearing if removed. Seal side of pilot bearing faces outward.

Removal & Installation

1) On Festiva models, remove transaxle, pressure plate, clutch disc and flywheel. Drive pilot bearing out of flywheel. Reverse procedure for installation.

2) On Merkur XR4Ti models, remove transmission, pressure plate and clutch disc. Using slide hammer and Pilot Bearing Puller (T58L-101-A), remove pilot bearing. Lightly coat pilot bearing bore with clutch grease.

Clutches

FORD MOTOR CO. (Cont.)

Using Clutch Aligner (T71P-7137-H) and Pilot Bearing Replacer (T71P-7137-C), install pilot bearing.

PEDAL SELF-ADJUSTER & CABLE

Removal (Merkur XR4Ti)

1) Disconnect negative battery cable. Remove sound-deadening panel, located under instrument panel. Remove left cowl trim panel attaching screws and pull left cowl trim panel away from body. Disconnect courtesy light wiring and remove panel.

2) Remove steering column lower shroud and left lower instrument panel attaching screws. Lower instrument panel, disconnect radio speaker wires and remove panel. Wedge a block of wood approximately 7" long under clutch pedal to disengage clutch cable self-adjuster.

3) Raise vehicle. Remove clutch release lever cover. Pull rearward on clutch release cable and disengage from release lever. Lower vehicle. Unhook clutch release cable from self-adjuster cam.

4) Using a hook, remove clutch pedal retaining clip. Remove clutch pedal and washer from shaft. Remove pedal bushings, adjuster sector and sector spring. Remove retaining clip from adjuster pawl shaft. Remove adjuster pawl, spring, and shaft. *See Fig. 4.*

Fig. 4: Merkur XR4Ti Self-Adjuster Components

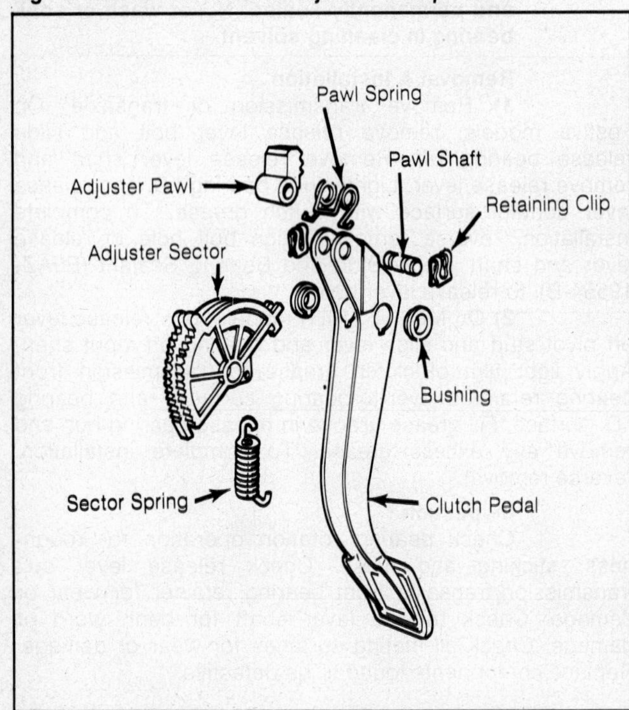

Courtesy of Ford Motor Co.

Installation

1) Install adjuster pawl, shaft, spring and retaining clip. Connect sector spring to clutch pedal and sector. Pull sector into position against spring tension and secure in position with pedal bushings. Lift pawl and rotate sector into position.

2) Lubricate bushings and pedal shaft with graphite-type grease and install pedal. Install pedal washer and retaining clip. Install cable, if previously removed. Position clutch release cable in adjuster sector. Position block of wood under clutch pedal. Raise vehicle. Connect clutch release cable to release lever and install cover.

3) Lower vehicle and remove block of wood. Position left lower instrument panel, connect radio speaker wires, and install attaching screw. Install steering column lower shroud. Position cowl trim panel, connect courtesy light wires, and install attaching screws. Install sound-deadening panel. Connect negative battery cable.

ADJUSTMENTS

CLUTCH PEDAL HEIGHT

Festiva

1) Disconnect clutch cable from release lever at transaxle. Move carpet and insulation out of way. Measure distance from upper center of pedal to dash panel. *See Fig. 5.* If not within specifications, ensure pedal mounting is not defective. See CLUTCH PEDAL HEIGHT table in this article.

2) Remove instrument panel bracket and air duct, located under steering column. Adjust stopper bolt until correct pedal height is achieved. Install clutch cable at transaxle. Check and adjust pedal freeplay. See CLUTCH PEDAL FREEPLAY under ADJUSTMENTS in this article.

3) Recheck pedal height. If connecting clutch cable changes pedal height, check cable for improper routing or binding. Reverse procedures to complete adjustment.

CLUTCH PEDAL HEIGHT

Application	In. (mm)
Festiva	8.209-8.304 (208.51-210.92)

Fig. 5: Measuring Pedal On Festiva

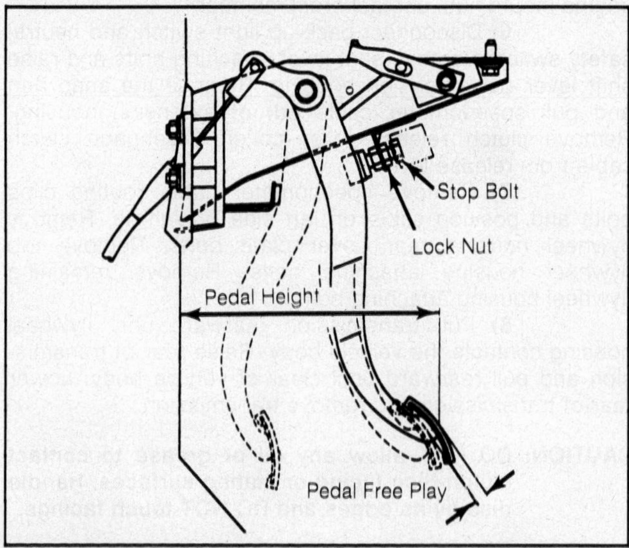

Courtesy of Ford Motor Co.

Clutches

FORD MOTOR CO. (Cont.)

CLUTCH PEDAL FREE PLAY

Festiva

1) Measure distance clutch pedal moves, from parked position to first indication of clutch application. Freeplay must be .35-.59" (8.89-14.99 mm). *See Fig. 5.*

2) If not within specifications, adjust clutch cable at transaxle until a clearance of .06-.10" (1.5-2.5 mm) is between release lever and cable adjusting pin. Recheck pedal freeplay. If not within specifications, check and repair release components. *See Fig. 6.*

Fig 6: Release Lever Clearance

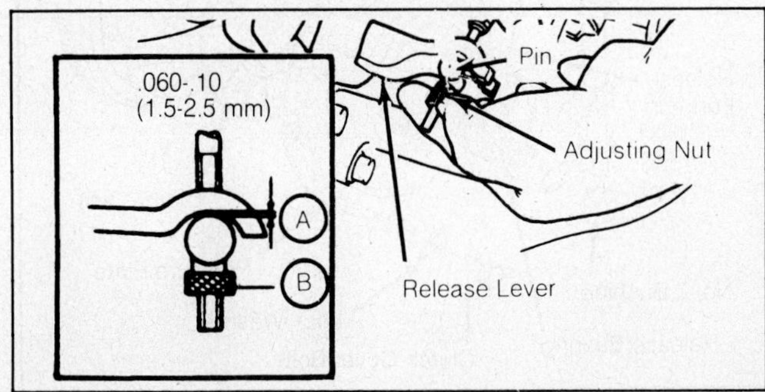

Courtesy of Ford Motor Co.

TIGHTENING SPECIFICATIONS

Application	Ft. Lbs. (N.m)
Engine Mount Stud Nut	50-70 (68-95)
Exhaust Pipe-to-Turbocharger Bolt	25-35 (34-48)
Flywheel-to-Crankshaft Bolt	
Festiva	71-76 (96-104)
Merkur XR4Ti	56-64 (73-87)
Flywheel Housing-to-Engine Bolts	
Festiva	47-66 (63-89)
Merkur XR4Ti	28-38 (38-51)
Front Wheel Lug Nuts	65-87 (88-118)
Lower Ball Joint Pinch Bolt	
Festiva	32-40 (43-54)
Pressure Plate-to-Flywheel Bolts	
Festiva	13-20 (18-27)
Merkur XR4Ti	15-19 (20-26)
Rear Engine Cover-to-Housing Bolt	
Merkur XR4Ti	28-38 (38-51)
Rear Mount-to-Transmission Bolt	50-70 (68-95)
Rear Transmission Mount-to-Body Bolt	25-35 (34-48)
Stabilizer Bracket-to-Body Bolt	
Festiva	23-34 (31-46)
Merkur XR4Ti	33-41 (45-56)
Starter Motor-to-Mount Bolt	
Merkur XR4Ti	15-20 (20-27)
	INCH Lbs. (N.m)
Release Lever Bolt	72-96 (8-11)

GENERAL MOTORS

Spectrum, Sprint

DESCRIPTION

The clutch is a single disc type, using a diaphragm spring to engage the pressure plate. The clutch is mechanically operated. If the clutch pedal is not depressed all the way or is released, the clutch start switch remains off. Starter motor will not run, even if the ignition key is in the "START" position.

REMOVAL & INSTALLATION

CLUTCH ASSEMBLY

Removal

1) Disconnect negative battery cable. Disconnect negative cable at transaxle. Disconnect speedometer cable and wire connectors from transaxle. Remove clutch cable from release lever. Drain transaxle oil.

2) On Spectrum, disconnect shift cables from transaxle. Remove air cleaner heat tube. Remove upper bolts attaching transaxle to engine.

3) On Sprint, remove air cleaner and heat pipe. Remove starter motor. Remove front and rear torque rod bolts at transaxle.

4) On all models, loosen lug nuts on front left wheel. Raise vehicle and remove left front wheel. On Spectrum, remove splash shield. Disconnect left tie rod at steering knuckle. Remove left tension rod.

5) On Sprint, remove exhaust pipe at exhaust manifold and at first exhaust hanger. Remove clutch housing lower plate. Remove gear shift control shaft and extension rod at transaxle.

6) On Spectrum, disconnect drive axles from transaxle. Remove shafts from transaxle case by pulling straight out. To prevent damage to oil seals, use care when removing drive axles from transaxle. Remove dust cover at clutch housing.

7) On Sprint, detach snap rings on right and left drive axles. Pry inboard joint out of differential side gear. Remove stabilizer bar mount bolts and ball stud bolt on the left side. Push down on stabilizer bar and detach the ball stud from the steering knuckle. Pull inboard joint, of left drive axle, out of transaxle. Remove front torque rod.

8) On all models, support transaxle with a jack. On sprint, remove mounting bolts from body and transaxle.

9) On all models, remove remaining bolts and nuts attaching transaxle to engine. Slide transaxle toward left side and lower transaxle from vehicle. Install clutch centering tool to support clutch assembly.

10) Look for "X" mark or White painted letter on clutch cover and "X" mark stamped on flywheel. If there are no markings, match mark flywheel and pressure plate for installation reference.

11) Loosen bolts attaching pressure plate to flywheel one turn at a time, until spring pressure is released. Remove bolts. Remove pressure plate and clutch disc.

Inspection

1) Clean flywheel friction surface of all oil, grease and metal deposits. Inspect flywheel for cracks, heat checking or other defects. Replace or machine as required.

2) Check wear on facings of clutch disc by measuring depth of each rivet head depression. On

Fig. 1: Exploded View of Sprint Clutch Assembly

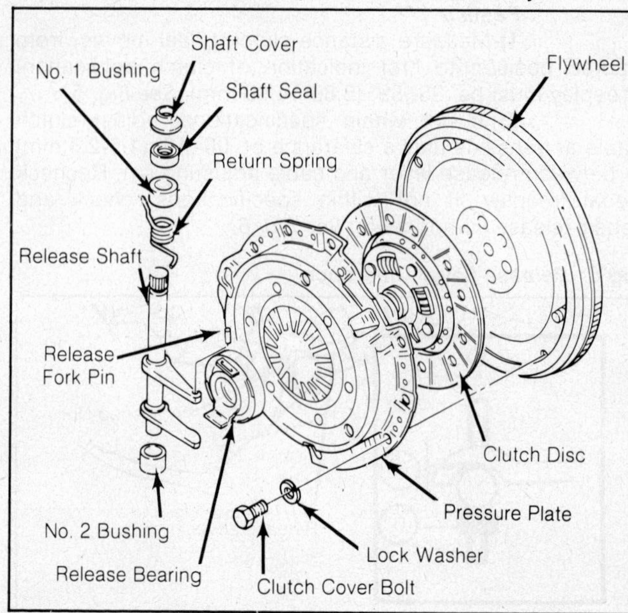

Courtesy of General Motors Corp.

Spectrum, sevice limit is .008" (.20 mm). On Sprint, service limit is .02" (.5 mm). If depth is found to have reached service limit at any of rivet head, replace clutch disc assembly.

3) Check diaphragm spring and pressure plate for wear or damage. If the spring or plate is excessively worn, or damaged, replace pressure plate assembly. Do not disassemble pressure plate.

Installation

1) Position clutch disc and pressure plate and support. Clutch disc is installed with damper springs toward transaxle. Install pressure plate bolts. Tighten bolts evenly and gradually until tight, to avoid possible clutch distortion.

2) See TIGHTENING SPECIFICATIONS at end of this article. Lightly lubricate release bearing sliding surfaces and input shaft with grease. Install transaxle and adjust clutch cable.

RELEASE BEARING

NOTE: **Damage to seals may result if bearings are placed in degreaser.**

Removal & Installation

1) Remove transaxle. Disconnect return spring from shaft fork. Remove clutch release bearing from transaxle. Inspect release bearing for rough rotation, wear or damage. If necessary, replace bearing.

2) Lightly lubricate release bearing with grease. Install clutch release bearing on transaxle retainer. Make sure bearing pads are located on fork ends (pads must be indexed) and both spring ends are in fork holes with spring completely seated in bearing groove. Install transaxle.

PILOT BEARING

Removal & Installation (Sprint)

Remove transaxle. Remove clutch cover and clutch disc. Remove pilot bearing. Inspect pilot bearing for rough rotation, wear or damage. If any of the above conditions are found, replace bearing. Install clutch disc and pressure plate. Install transaxle.

GENERAL MOTORS (Cont.)

CLUTCH START SWITCH

Removal & Installation

Disconnect negative battery cable. Disconnect wire at switch. Remove switch mounting screw at clutch pedal stop bracket. Disconnect switch from clutch pedal. To install, reverse removal procedure.

CLUTCH CABLE

Removal (Spectrum)

Disconnect negative battery cable. Loosen clutch cable adjusting nuts. Disconnect cable from release arm and cable bracket. Remove cable retaining bolt at clutch pedal. Disconnect cable from front of dash. Remove the clutch cable from vehicle.

Inspection

Inspect clutch cable and replace it if any of the following conditions are found: frayed, kinked, worn, excessive friction, or broken boots.

Installation

Apply grease to clutch cable pin before installing. Route cable through front of dash. Connect cable to the clutch pedal. Route clutch cable through bracket at transaxle. Connect clutch cable to release lever. Adjust clutch cable. Connect negative battery cable.

Removal (Sprint)

Disconnect negative battery cable. Remove clutch cable joint nut. Disconnect cable from release arm. Remove clutch cable bracket retaining bolts and remove bracket from cable. Remove cable retaining bolts at clutch pedal. Remove clutch cable from vehicle.

Inspection

Inspect clutch cable and replace it if any of the following conditions are found: frayed, kinked, worn, excessive friction, or broken boots.

Installation

Apply grease to hook and pin of clutch cable before installing. Connect cable to clutch pedal and install retaining bolts. Install clutch cable bracket on cable. Position bracket to transaxle and install retaining bolts. Connect clutch cable to release lever and install joint nut on cable. Adjust clutch cable. Connect negative battery cable.

ADJUSTMENTS

CLUTCH CABLE

Spectrum

Disconnect battery cables. Loosen adjusting nut. Pull cable to rear until it turns freely. Turn adjusting nut either clockwise or counterclockwise to adjust cable length. When pedal free play reaches .39-.79" (10-20 mm), release cable. Tighten lock nut securely. *See Fig. 2.*

CLUTCH PEDAL HEIGHT

Sprint

Adjust height of clutch pedal with clutch pedal stop bolt, so pedal is level with brake pedal. Tighten lock nut after adjusting.

Fig. 2: Spectrum Pedal Free Play

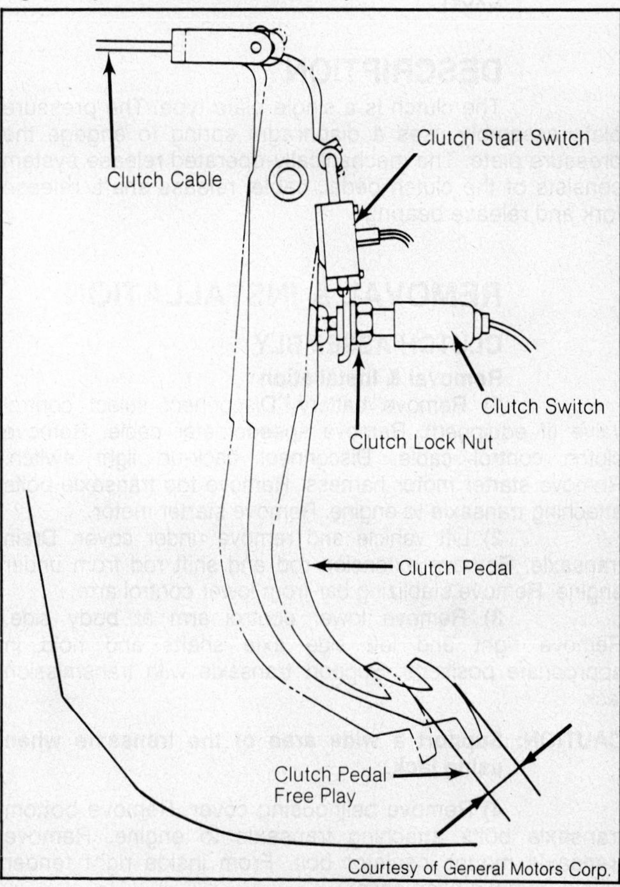

RELEASE ARM PLAY

Sprint

Check clutch release arm play by moving arm by hand. Arm play should be within .08-.16" (2-4 mm). If arm play is out of specification, loosen or tighten clutch cable joint nut as necessary.

CLUTCH START SWITCH

Apply parking brake firmly. Place gear shift lever in Neutral. Disconnect wire at switch. Loosen lock nut and screw switch out. Depress clutch pedal all the way to floor, and then return it back .4-1.1" (10-30 mm) along its travel from floor. Connect ohmmeter to switch. Slowly screw switch in until it is on. Hold switch at this position, and tighten lock nut. Connect wire.

TIGHTENING SPECIFICATIONS

Application	Ft. Lbs. (N.m)
Pressure Plate to-Flywheel Bolts	
Spectrum	14 (18)
Sprint	14-20 (18-28)
Start Switch Lock Nut	8-11 (10-15)

HYUNDAI

Excel

DESCRIPTION

The clutch is a single plate type. The pressure plate assembly uses a diaphragm spring to engage the pressure plate. The mechanically-operated release system consists of the clutch pedal, cable, release shaft, release fork and release bearing.

REMOVAL & INSTALLATION

CLUTCH ASSEMBLY

Removal & Installation

1) Remove battery. Disconnect select control valve (if equipped). Remove speedometer cable. Remove clutch control cable. Disconnect back-up light switch. Remove starter motor harness. Remove top transaxle bolts attaching transaxle to engine. Remove starter motor.

2) Lift vehicle and remove under cover. Drain transaxle. Remove extension rod and shift rod from under engine. Remove stablizing bar from lower control arm.

3) Remove lower control arm at body side. Remove right and left side axle shafts and hold in appropriate positions. Support transaxle with transmission jack.

CAUTION: Support a wide area of the transaxle when using jack.

4) Remove bellhousing cover. Remove bottom transaxle bolts attaching transaxle to engine. Remove transaxle mount insulator bolt. From inside right fender shield, remove blind cover.

5) Remove transaxle bracket assembly. Remove transaxle mount bracket. Slide transaxle assembly toward right and lower out of vehicle. Install clutch centering tool. Diagonally loosen bolts attaching pressure plate to flywheel, 2 turns at a time. *See Fig. 1.*

6) To install, reverse removal procedure.

Fig. 1: Exploded View of Hyundai Clutch Assembly

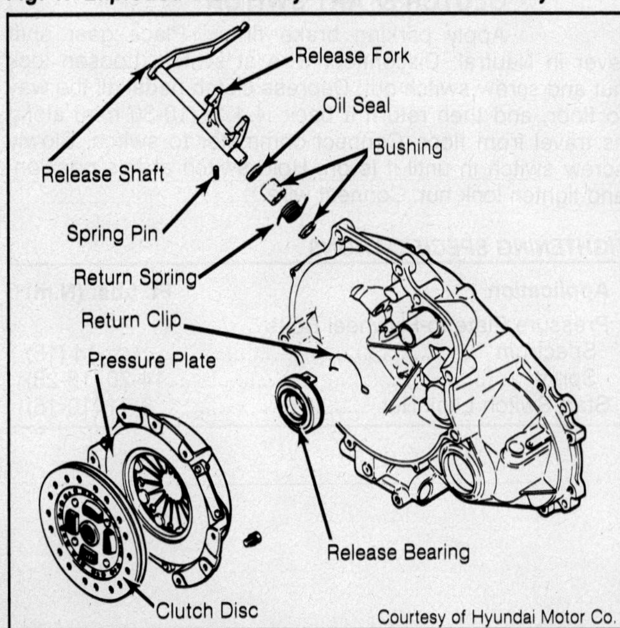

CLUTCH RELEASE BEARING

CAUTION: Release bearing is packed with grease. Do not use solvent. Clean with compressed air only.

Removal & Installation

1) Remove transaxle. Remove return clip. Remove release bearing. Remove spring pins from clutch release fork and shaft with a 3/16" pin punch. Remove clutch release shaft. Remove release fork, packings and return spring.

NOTE: Do not reuse spring pins.

2) Apply multipurpose grease to contact surfaces of release fork, shaft and bearing. Install release shaft. Install packings, return spring and release fork. Align lock pin holes of release fork and release shaft. Install 2 new spring pins. Ensure spring pin slot direction is at right angles to center line of control shaft.

3) Apply grease into groove of release bearing and install release bearing on front bearing retainer of transaxle. Install return clip to release bearing and fork.

ADJUSTMENTS

CLUTCH PEDAL

Turn adjusting bolt so distance from floor to clutch pedal is 7.3-7.5" (182-187 mm). Lightly pull clutch outer cable and turn adjusting nut until clearance between adjusting nut and holder is .20-.25" (5-6 mm). Check to ensure pedal free play is .8-1.2" (20-30 mm). Clutch disengagement stroke is 5.7" (145 mm). *See Fig. 2.*

Fig. 2: Measuring Pedal Height & Free Play

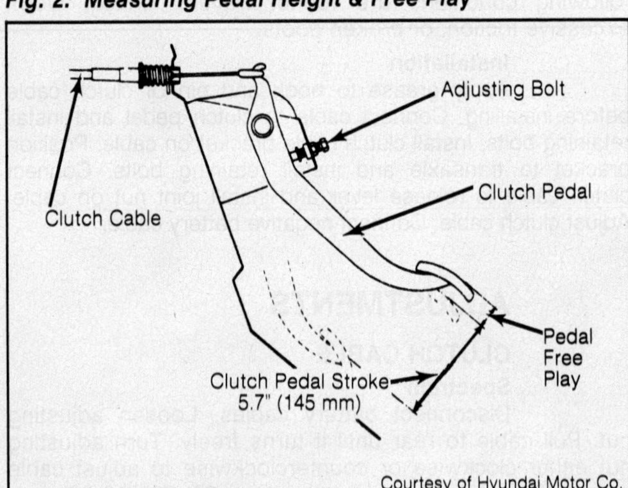

TIGHTENING SPECIFICATIONS

Application	Ft. Lbs. (N.m)
Back-Up Light Switch	22 (30)
Clutch Pedal Mounting Nut	12-17 (16-24)
Pressure Plate-to-Flywheel Bolts	11-15 (15-21)
Starter Motor Mounting Bolts	22-25 (30-34)
Transaxle Drain Plug	22-25 (30-34)
Transaxle-to-Engine Bolts	32-39 (43-53)

ISUZU I-MARK

DESCRIPTION

The disc clutch assembly uses a diaphragm spring to engage the pressure plate. The clutch has a mechanically-operated release system consisting of clutch pedal, clutch cable, release fork and release bearing.

REMOVAL & INSTALLATION

CLUTCH ASSEMBLY

Removal

1) Disconnect negative battery cable. Drain transaxle oil. Remove hood. Disconnect negative cable from transaxle. Remove air duct. Disconnect wiring connectors from transaxle. Disconnect speedometer cable from transaxle.

2) Disconnect clutch and shift cables from transaxle. Raise and support front end of vehicle. Disconnect right control arm end at knuckle. Remove left tension rod with bracket. Disconnect both rod ends at knuckle.

3) Being careful not to damage transaxle oil seals, use a screwdriver to pry out axle shafts. Raise engine and support transaxle with transmission jack. Remove bolts from center beam.

4) Lower and slant engine from engine support fixture. Remove bolts attaching clutch housing to engine. Remove transaxle assembly. Remove clutch cover and disc. *See Fig. 1.*

Fig. 1: Exploded View of I-Mark Clutch Assembly

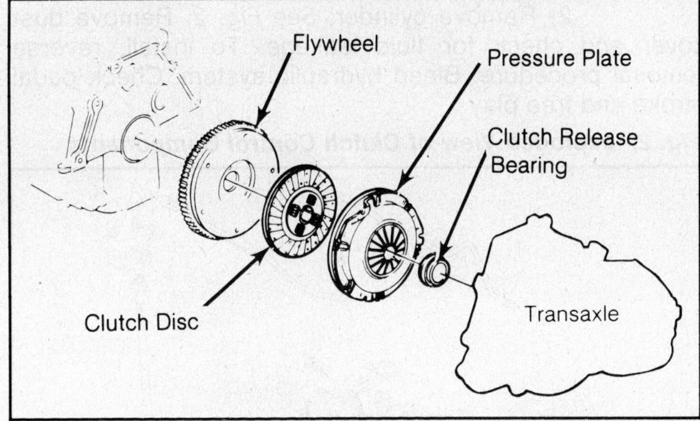

Courtesy of Isuzu Motor Co.

Inspection

1) Clean flywheel, pressure plate and clutch disc mating surfaces of all oil, grease, and metal deposits. Inspect for cracks, heat checking, warpage and other defects. Slight surface scoring can be removed with sandpaper. Replace or repair as required.

2) Check wear on facings of clutch disc by measuring depth of each rivet head depression. Minimum depth at any rivet is .007" (.20 mm). Replace clutch disc assembly if not within specification. Insure runout of clutch disc facing does not exceed .039" (1.0 mm).

3) Check diaphragm spring and pressure plate for wear or damage. If the spring or plate is excessively worn, or damaged, replace clutch cover assembly. Do not disassemble clutch cover assembly. If defective, replace assembly.

Installation

To install, reverse removal procedure. Adjust clutch cable and check transaxle oil level.

CLUTCH START SWITCH

Removal & Installation

Disconnect negative battery cable. Disconnect wire at switch. Remove switch mounting screw at clutch pedal stop bracket. Disconnect switch from clutch pedal. To install, reverse removal procedure.

CLUTCH CABLE

Removal

Disconnect negative battery cable. Loosen clutch cable adjusting nuts. Disconnect cable from release arm and cable bracket. Remove cable retaining bolt at clutch pedal. Disconnect cable from front of dash. Remove the clutch cable from vehicle.

Installation

Apply grease to clutch cable pin before installing. Route cable through front of dash. Connect cable to the clutch pedal. Route clutch cable through bracket at transaxle. Connect clutch cable to release lever. Adjust clutch cable. Connect negative battery cable.

ADJUSTMENTS

CLUTCH CABLE & PEDAL ADJUSTMENTS

1) Loosen cable adjusting nut from cable-to-transmission mounting bracket. Pull cable to rear until it turns freely. Turn adjusting nut either clockwise or counterclockwise to adjust cable length.

2) Release cable pedal free play should be .39-.79" (10-20 mm). Replace cable when minimum pedal free play cannot be obtained. Tighten lock nut securely.

PEDAL FREE PLAY & HEIGHT ADJUSTMENT

Application	In. (mm)
Free Play	.39-.79 (10-20)
Height	6.07 (154)

TIGHTENING SPECIFICATIONS

Application	Ft. Lbs. (N.m)
Center Beam Bolt	51 (69)
Clutch Housing-to-Engine Bolt	56 (76)
Drive Shaft	42 (57)
Pressure Plate Bolt	14 (18)
Tension Rod Frame Mount Bolt	48 (65)
Tension Rod-to-Control Arm	80 (108)

Clutches

ISUZU IMPULSE

DESCRIPTION

The clutch assembly is a single disc type, using a diaphragm spring to engage the pressure plate with a prelubricated release bearing. The clutch is operated by a firewall mounted master cylinder and clutch housing mounted slave cylinder.

REMOVAL & INSTALLATION

CLUTCH ASSEMBLY

Removal

1) Disconnect negative battery cable. From inside of vehicle, remove gear shift knob. Remove boot cover assembly from shift lever. Remove console assembly. Raise and support vehicle. Drain transmission oil. Remove front exhaust pipe assembly.

2) Remove 4 front drive shaft flange mount bolts. Remove front drive shaft. Remove speedometer cable assembly. Remove slave cylinder, and wire to vehicle frame.

3) Remove cover under transmission case. Position jack under transmission. Lower transmission slightly. Remove bolts retaining shifter quadrant cover to transmission case. Disconnect wiring from transmission.

4) Remove transmission mount bolts. Lower transmission from vehicle. Ensure starter is moved forward to prevent it from falling when mount bolts are removed. Index mark clutch assembly to flywheel for reassembly reference. Remove clutch assembly. *See Fig. 1.*

Fig. 1: Exploded View of Impulse Clutch Assembly

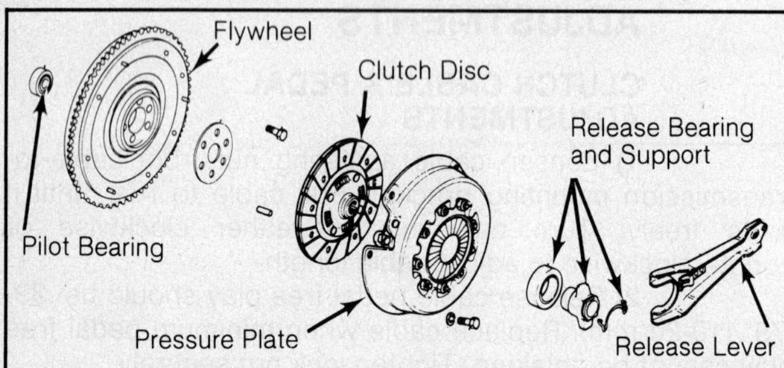

Courtesy of Isuzu Motor Co.

Inspection

1) Check clutch disc friction surfaces for cracks, heat hardening or contamination by dirt, oil or grease. Inspect damper springs. Replace disc if excessive play is found. Check rivet head depth.

2) Check disc lining thickness. Install disc on transmission input shaft. Mount dial gauge 90 degrees to lining surface and measure disc face runout. Check disc hub spline wear (play). Measure wear at outside diameter of disc. See CLUTCH DISC SPECIFICATIONS table.

3) Inspect pressure plate friction surfaces for cracks, distortion and proper thickness. Standard thickness is .51" (13 mm). Check diaphragm springs for heat distortion, loosened rivets, wear or damage.

4) Inspect flywheel friction surface. Resurface or replace if heavy wear marks or damage is evident. Standard surface depth is 1.26" (32 mm). Service limit is 1.22" (31 mm). Replace ring gear if teeth are worn or damaged.

NOTE: **Wash all clutch components except disc and release bearing in solvent. Blow dry with compressed air.**

CLUTCH DISC SPECIFICATIONS

Application	In. (mm)
Rivet Head Depth [1]	
G200Z Engine	.047 (1.20)
4ZC1-T Engine	.315 (8.00)
Free Thickness	
G200Z	.343 (8.70)
4ZC1-T	.331 (8.4)
Runout Limit	.04 (1.0)
Spline Wear Limit	.04 (1.0)

[1] – Standard head depth is given. Minimum head depth is .008" (.20 mm).

Installation

1) Lightly lubricate clutch release lever assembly, disc hub and top gear shaft splines and release bearing contact surfaces with molybdenum grease. Install release lever, spring and bearing assembly. Mount alignment tool. Install clutch assembly.

2) Tighten mount bolts evenly, in a diagonal pattern. With transmission mounted, clean and install magnetic drain plug and fill transmission. To complete installation, reverse removal procedure.

CLUTCH MASTER CYLINDER

Removal & Installation

1) Remove the hydraulic line from reservoir to master cylinder and plug opening. Disconnect hydraulic line from master cylinder to slave cylinder. From inside of vehicle, disconnect master cylinder push rod at clevis. Remove master cylinder mount bolts.

2) Remove cylinder. *See Fig. 2.* Remove dust cover and check for fluid leakage. To install, reverse removal procedure. Bleed hydraulic system. Check pedal stroke and free play.

Fig. 2: Exploded View of Clutch Control Components

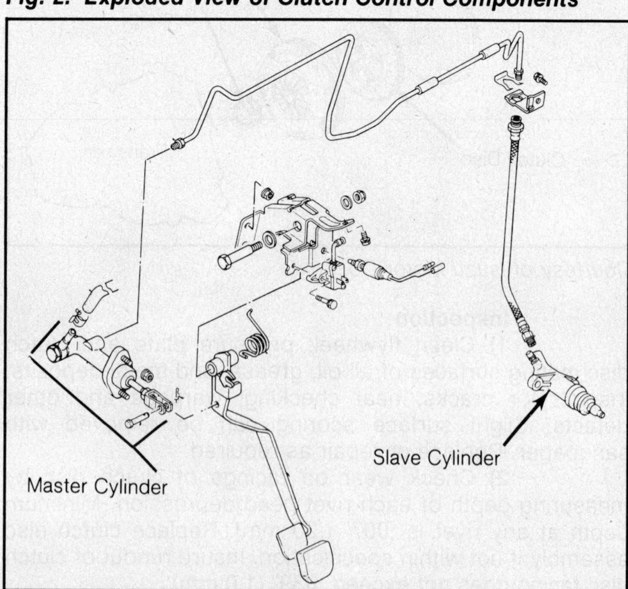

Courtesy of Isuzu Motor Co.

CLUTCH SLAVE CYLINDER

Removal & Installation

Disconnect hydraulic line from slave cylinder to master cylinder and plug opening. Remove bolts attaching

ISUZU IMPULSE (Cont.)

slave cylinder to clutch housing. Remove cylinder. To install, reverse removal procedure. Bleed hydraulic system. Check pedal stroke and free play.

PILOT BEARING

NOTE: The pilot bearing is permanently lubricated. Do not wash in solvent. Clean only with compressed air.

Removal

With clutch assembly removed, check pilot bearing for seizing, sticking, abnormal noise or wear by turning in thrust direction. Remove pilot bearing from crankshaft (if necessary).

Installation

Install pilot bearing in crankshaft bore. Bearing must be fitted against bottom face of bearing bore. To complete installation, reverse removal procedure.

OVERHAUL

CLUTCH MASTER & SLAVE CYLINDERS

Disassembly

1) Remove cylinder from vehicle, take out push rod and dust cover. On master cylinder, remove snap ring and piston stopper. Remove piston, spring seat and return spring.

2) On slave cylinder, remove piston, piston cup and piston spring as an assembly. Remove bleeder screw. *See Fig. 3 and Fig. 4*. Wash all parts in clean brake fluid and blow dry with compressed air.

Fig. 3: Exploded View of Clutch Master Cylinder

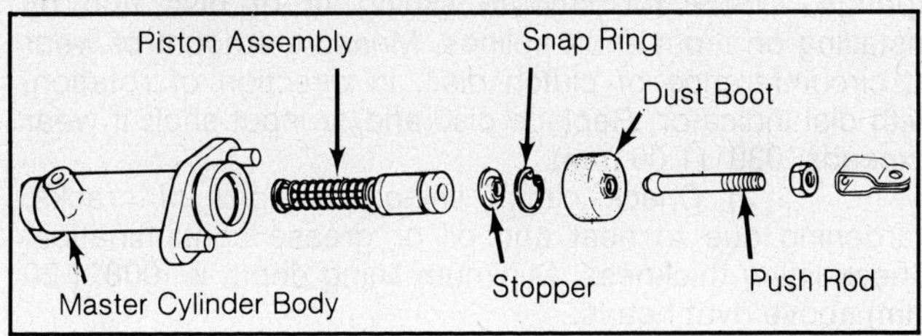

Courtesy of Isuzu Motor Co.

Inspection

Inspect all components for excessive wear or damage. Standard clearance between cylinder bore and piston is .0028" (.070 mm). If clearance between cylinder and piston exceeds .0059" (.150 mm), replace defective part. Replace rubber piston cup and dust cover during overhaul.

Reassembly

Ensure all recesses, openings and internal passages are clear of foreign matter. To assemble, coat parts with brake fluid. Reverse disassembly procedure. Bleed hydraulic system. Check pedal height and free play.

Fig. 4: Clutch Slave Cylinder Assembly

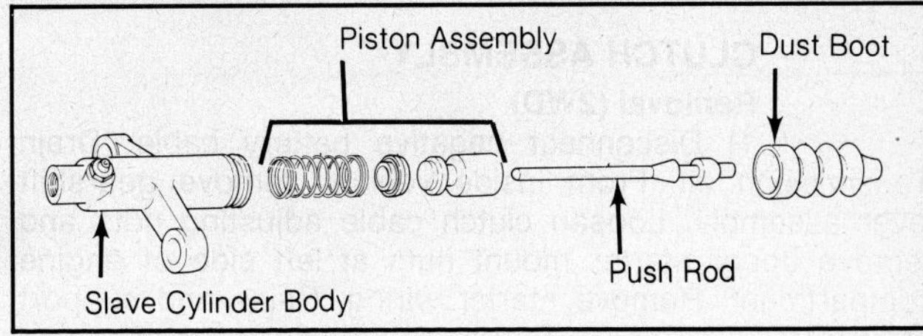

Courtesy of Isuzu Motor Co.

ADJUSTMENTS

CLUTCH PEDAL STROKE & FREE PLAY

The clutch pedal stroke and free play are automatically adjusted by operation of hydraulic system.

CLUTCH PEDAL HEIGHT

Adjust clutch pedal height by turning master cylinder push rod after lock nut has been loosened. Adjust clearance between clutch switch and pedal to .020-.059" (.50-1.50 mm). After adjustment, check that push rod is in contact with master cylinder piston.

TIGHTENING SPECIFICATIONS

Application	Ft. Lbs. (N.m)
Flywheel-to-Crankshaft Bolt	
G200Z Engine	76 (103)
4ZC1-T Engine	40 (54)
Pressure Plate-to-Flywheel Bolt	13 (18)
Propeller Shaft	
G200Z Engine	20 (27)
4ZC1-T Engine	23 (31)

ISUZU P'UP & TROOPER II

DESCRIPTION

The clutch assembly is a single disc type with a diaphragm spring to engage pressure plate. The clutch is mechanically operated release system consisting of clutch pedal, clutch cable, return spring, release fork and prelubricated release bearing.

REMOVAL & INSTALLATION

CLUTCH ASSEMBLY

Removal (2WD)

1) Disconnect negative battery cable. Drain transmission oil. From inside vehicle, remove gearshift lever assembly. Loosen clutch cable adjusting nuts and remove upper starter mount nuts at left side of engine compartment. Remove starter wiring. Raise and support vehicle.

2) Remove drive shaft. Remove speedometer and clutch cable. Remove starter lower bolt and starter. Disconnect exhaust pipe from manifold. Remove exhaust pipe bracket. Remove flywheel inspection cover and rear transmission support mount bolt. Support transmission. Remove rear transmission support from frame.

3) On 2WD P'UP, remove 2 lower flywheel cover mount bolts. Remove 2 bolts mounting frame bracket to rear mount. Using a jack, slightly raise transmission. Remove 4 bolts connecting crossmember to frame. Remove 2 bolts mounting transmission extension housing.

4) Lower engine and transmission assembly. Support rear of engine. Disconnect electrical leads at transmission. Remove bolts connecting transmission to engine. Remove transmission.

5) Index mark pressure plate to flywheel for reassembly reference. Install clutch assembly aligning tool. Remove retaining bolts evenly in a crisscross pattern.

Removal (4WD)

1) Disconnect negative battery cable. Drain transmission. Slide transmission and transfer case shift lever boots upward on levers. Remove gearshift lever mount bolts. Remove spring from transfer case shift lever and both levers. Remove starter mount bolts and starter.

2) Raise and support vehicle. Disconnect exhaust pipe from manifold. Remove exhaust hanger from transmission. Disconnect speedometer and ground cable at transmission. Disconnect rear drive shaft at differential. Remove 2 center bearing mount bolts.

3) Remove first and second rear drive shafts together. Disconnect front drive shaft at both ends. Remove return spring at clutch fork. Disconnect clutch cable from clutch fork. Pull clutch cable forward through stiffener bracket. Remove 2 lower flywheel guard mount bolts.

4) Remove 2 frame bracket-to-transmission rear mounting bolts and nuts. Raise engine and transmission assembly slightly. Remove 4 bolts connecting crossmember to frame bracket. Remove 2 rear mount bolts from transfer case. Support rear of engine.

5) Remove side case mount bolts and nuts. Use care not to lose shift rod detent spring and detent ball during side case removal. Remove side case. Disconnect electrical connectors from transmission. Remove shift cover and gasket from top of transfer case. Remove bolts attaching transmission to engine.

NOTE: **When removing 4WD transmission, swing transmission case 90 degrees clockwise for easier removal.**

6) Pull transmission straight back to clear clutch assembly. Tilt front of transmission down and remove. Index mark pressure plate and flywheel for reassembly reference. Loosen pressure plate attaching bolts evenly until pressure is relieved. Support clutch assembly with clutch aligning tool. Remove clutch assembly. *See Fig. 1*.

Fig. 1: Exploded View of Clutch Assembly

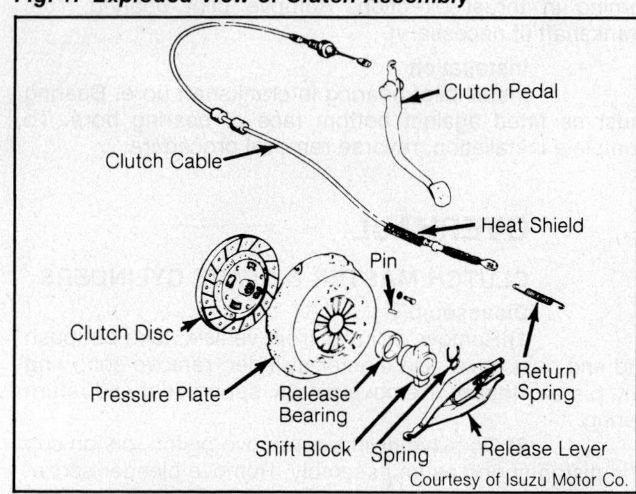

Courtesy of Isuzu Motor Co.

Inspection

1) Check clutch disc for burned, worn or damaged lining, loose rivets or very loose torsional springs. Check for smooth sliding fit of disc hub by installing on input shaft splines. Measure amount of wear at circumference of clutch disc, in direction of rotation, with dial indicator. Replace disc and/or input shaft if wear exceeds .039" (1.00 mm).

2) Check clutch lining for signs of cracks, hardening due to heat and oil or grease contamination. Check lining thickness. Minimum lining depth is .008" (.20 mm) above rivet heads.

3) Measure clutch disc runout, at outer edge, with dial indicator. Maximum runout is .039" (1.00 mm). Check friction surfaces of flywheel and pressure plate for scoring or roughness. Smooth slight roughness with fine emery cloth. Standard pressure plate thickness is .51" (13.0 mm). If surface is deeply scored, resurface or replace component.

4) Inspect pressure plate for cracks and distortion. Inspect diaphragm spring for heat distortion and loosened rivets. Check wire ring for wear.

5) Inspect release lever ball socket, release bearing contact face and ball retaining spring for damage. Spring must hold release lever tightly to ball stud.

Installation (2WD & 4WD)

1) Using aligning tool, install clutch assembly in original position. Tighten bolts evenly, in crisscross pattern. Lightly lubricate input shaft splines, clutch hub and release bearing contact surfaces with molybdenum grease.

2) To complete installation, reverse removal procedure. Readjust clutch pedal height and free play. Refill transmission.

ISUZU P'UP & TROOPER II (Cont.)

RELEASE BEARING

Removal

Remove clutch assembly. Remove release fork cover from transmission case. Remove release bearing-to-fork retaining spring. Remove release bearing with shift collar. Remove release fork from transmission ball stud.

NOTE: The release bearing is permanently lubricated. Do not wash in solvent. Clean only with compressed air and shop towel.

Inspection

Check contact areas of release bearing and release fork for excessive wear. Check release bearing and shift collar for noise or roughness by rotating by hand in thrust direction. Remove release bearing (if necessary). Inspect return spring and release bearing spring for wear.

Installation

Lubricate ball stud and install release fork. Lubricate shift collar and install release bearing and shift collar to release fork with retaining springs. Install clutch assembly.

PILOT BEARING

NOTE: Do not remove pilot bearing unless absolutely necessary. Release bearing is permanently lubricated. Do not wash in solvent. Clean only with compressed air and shop towel.

Removal

Remove clutch assembly. Check pilot bearing for seizing, sticking, abnormal noise or wear. Remove pilot bearing from crankshaft.

Installation

Install pilot bearing in crankshaft bore. Bearing must be fitted against bottom face of bearing fitting hole. Install clutch assembly by reversing removal procedure.

CLUTCH CABLE

Removal

1) Loosen clutch cable lock and adjusting nuts. Remove cable clip in engine compartment. Raise vehicle. Remove return spring from release lever. Remove clutch cable from release lever and slide it through retaining bracket. Disconnect cable from clutch pedal and remove.

2) Disconnect cable from hooked portion of clutch pedal and pull out toward engine compartment together with damper rubber. Use care not to damage rubber damper during removal. On all models, check cable assembly and/or damper rubber for fatigue or damage. Replace as necessary.

Installation

Slide cable through firewall and install clutch pedal. Install cable in original position through retaining bracket to release lever. Install clutch return spring. Adjust clutch cable and tighten lock nut.

CLUTCH MASTER CYLINDER

Removal & Installation

1) Remove hydraulic line from reservoir to master cylinder and plug opening. Disconnect hydraulic line from master cylinder to slave cylinder. From inside of vehicle, disconnect master cylinder push rod at clevis. Remove master cylinder mount bolts.

2) Remove cylinder. Remove dust cover and check for fluid leakage. To install, reverse removal procedure. Bleed hydraulic system. Check pedal stroke and free play.

CLUTCH SLAVE CYLINDER

Removal & Installation

Disconnect hydraulic line from slave cylinder to master cylinder and plug opening. Remove bolts attaching slave cylinder to clutch housing. Remove cylinder. To install, reverse removal procedure. Bleed hydraulic system. Check pedal stroke and free play.

OVERHAUL

CLUTCH MASTER & SLAVE CYLINDERS

Disassembly

1) Remove cylinder from vehicle, take out push rod and dust cover. On master cylinder, remove snap ring and piston stopper. Remove piston, spring seat and return spring.

2) On slave cylinder, remove piston, piston cup and piston spring as an assembly. Remove bleeder screw. *See Figs. 2 and 3*. Wash all parts in clean brake fluid and blow dry with compressed air.

Fig. 2: Exploded View of Clutch Master Cylinder

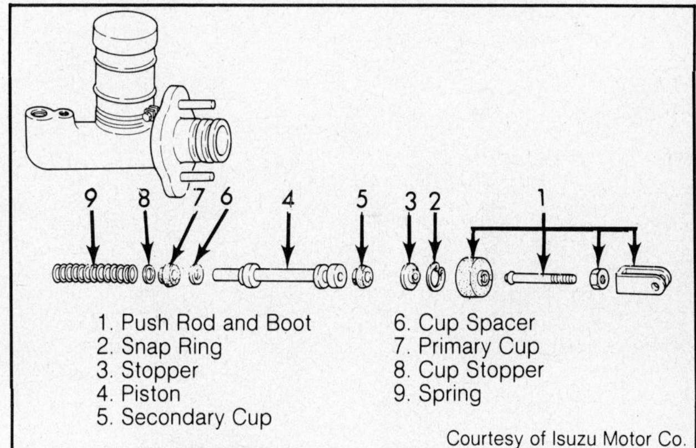

Courtesy of Isuzu Motor Co.

Inspection

Inspect all components for excessive wear or damage. Standard clearance between cylinder bore and piston is .0028" (.070 mm). If clearance between cylinder and piston exceeds .0059" (.150 mm), replace defective part. Replace rubber piston cup and dust cover during overhaul.

Reassembly

Ensure all recesses, openings and internal passages are clear of foreign matter. To assemble, coat parts with brake fluid. Reverse disassembly procedure. Bleed hydraulic system. Check pedal height and free play.

Fig. 3: Clutch Slave Cylinder Assembly

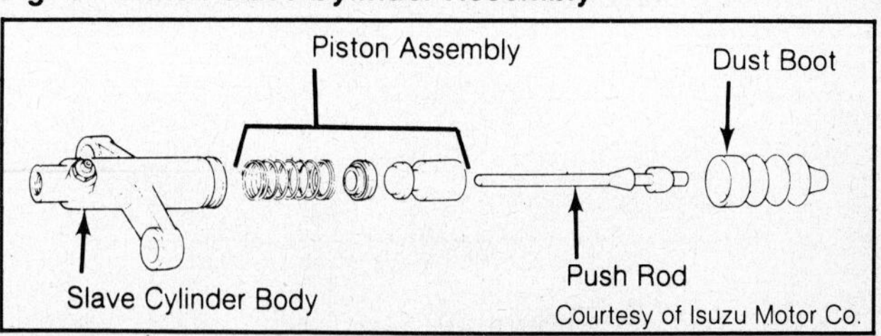

Courtesy of Isuzu Motor Co.

ISUZU P'UP & TROOPER II (Cont.)

ADJUSTMENTS

CLUTCH CABLE FREE PLAY

Pull outer cable into engine compartment. Rotate adjuster nut until washer damper rubber is brought into contact with firewall. Work pedal several times. Pull outer cable out again. Fully tighten adjusting nut. Back adjusting nut off until there is .2" (5 mm) between adjusting nut and washer damper rubber. Release outer cable. Tighten lock nut. *See Fig. 4*.

Fig. 4: Adjusting Clutch Cable Free Play

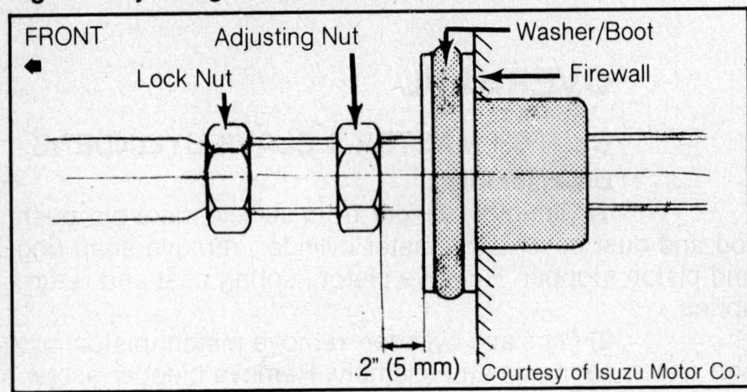

Courtesy of Isuzu Motor Co.

CLUTCH PEDAL HEIGHT & FREE PLAY

Adjust clutch switch setting so pedal height, from floor, is 6.9-7.2" (174-184 mm) for P'UP. For Trooper II, when adjusting clutch, pedal height should be 9.1-9.5" (231-241 mm). Insure clutch pedal free play is .8" (20 mm).

TIGHTENING SPECIFICATIONS

Application	Ft. Lbs. (N.m)
Flywheel-to-Crankshaft Bolts	40-70 (54-64)
Pressure Plate-to-Flywheel Bolts	12-14 (16-19)
Release Lever Ball Stud	29 (39)

MAZDA FWD & FORD MOTOR CO. TRACER

Ford Motor Co.: Tracer
Mazda: 323, 626

DESCRIPTION

The clutch is a single disc, diaphragm spring type. On 323 and 626 EFI models, clutch release mechanism is cable actuated. On 626 turbo, clutch release mechanism is hydraulically actuated. On Tracer models, carbureted engines use bevelled spring pressure plate and EFI engines use flat spring pressure plate. A prelubricated release bearing is used and is located in transaxle housing.

REMOVAL & INSTALLATION

CLUTCH ASSEMBLY

Removal

1) Disconnet negative battery cable. Remove air cleaner. Loosen front wheel nuts. Disconnect speedometer cable from transaxle. Remove clutch cable adjusting nut and pin at release lever. Remove clutch cable from release lever and remove clutch cable bracket from transaxle. Remove ground wire from transaxle.

2) Remove coolant pipe bracket. Remove secondary air pipe and EGR pipe bracket. Remove wire harness retaining clip. On 626 models, remove starter. Disconnect coupler for neutral switch and back-up light switch. Disconnect body ground connector. Remove 2 top transaxle-to-engine bolts.

3) Install an engine support bar to retain engine during transaxle removal. *See Fig. 1.* On 626 models, remove top 4 transaxle-to-engine bolts. Raise vehicle and drain transaxle fluid. Remove front wheels. Remove under engine cover and side covers.

Fig. 1: Typical Engine Support Bar

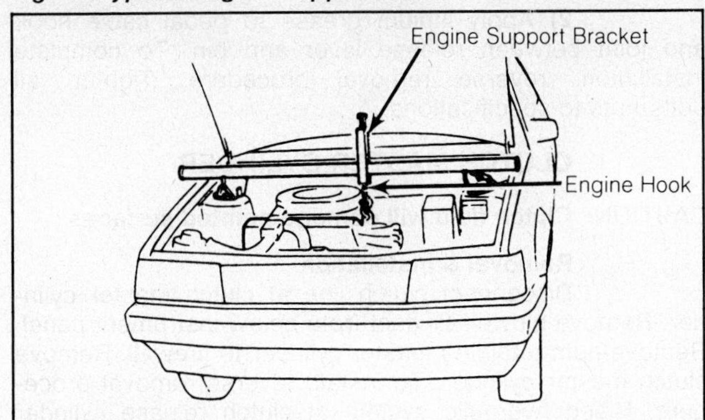

Courtesy of Ford Motor CO.

4) Remove front stabilizer bar. Remove pinch bolt retaining lower ball joint in spindle. Pry down lower control arm and separate lower ball joint from spindle.

5) On 323 and Tracer models, pull hub outward to remove drive axle from transaxle. To prevent boot and/or CV joint damage, keep drive shaft horizontal and do not allow CV joint to angle in excess of 20 degrees. Suspend drive axle to vehicle with wire. Repeat procedure for remaining side.

6) On 626 models, remove left drive axle by inserting pry bar between axle and transaxle case. DO NOT insert pry bar to deeply. Separate axle from side gear by tapping end of pry bar. Hold inner joint assembly and pull front hub assembly outward and remove axle from transaxle.

7) On 626 models, the right drive axle is attached to an inner shaft, which is splined into transaxle. Separate right drive axle from inner shaft with pry bar inserted between drive axle and inner shaft. Pull outward on hub and remove drive axle from inner shaft. Remove inner shaft mounting bracket bolts. Remove inner shaft and bracket assembly from transaxle.

8) Remove transaxle mount-to-crossmember bolts. Remove crossmember-to-vehicle bolts and remove crossmember. Remove bolt and nut retaining shift control rod to transaxle and slide control rod aside.

9) Remove bolt from shift extension bar mounting bracket and slide extension bar off bracket. Disconnect electrical wires at starter. Remove starter. Remove bolts retaining engine rear cover to clutch housing. Lower transaxle assembly with engine support bar.

10) Place transmission jack under transaxle. Disconnect engine mount from clutch housing, located by exhaust pipe. Remove remaining clutch housing-to-engine bolts and pull transaxle away from engine.

CAUTION: DO NOT allow any oil or grease to contact clutch disc facing or mating surfaces. Handle disc by its edges and DO NOT touch facing.

11) Install Clutch Aligner (T87C-7137-A), to hold assembly during removal. If reusing pressure plate, mark pressure plate-to-flywheel position for installation reference. Remove pressure plate retaining bolts evenly and one turn at a time.

12) Remove pressure plate and clutch disc. Remove flywheel retaining bolts and remove flywheel. Remove pilot bearing from flywheel, if replacing. *See Fig. 2.*

Fig. 2: Exploded View of Clutch Assembly

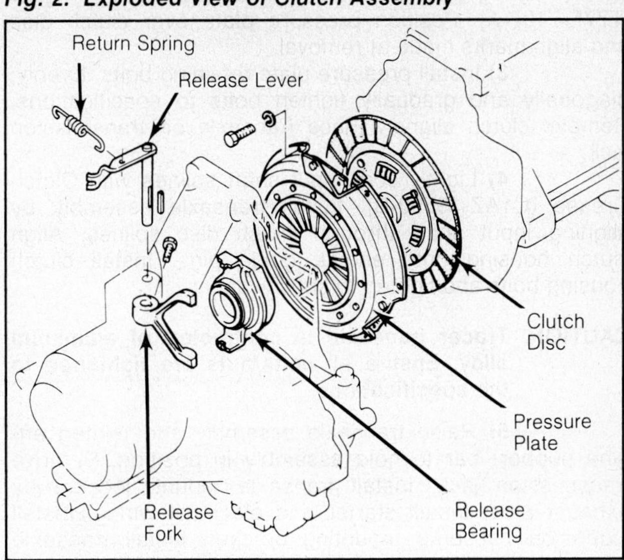

Courtesy of Mazda Motors Corp.

Inspection

1) Check disc for loose rivets, worn springs or oil contamination. Minimum lining height above rivet heads is .012" (.30 mm). Inspect flywheel and pressure plate for burns, scoring or grooves.

MAZDA FWD & FORD MOTOR CO. TRACER (Cont.)

2) Flywheel and pressure plate runout/warpage limit is .008" (.20 mm). Machine flywheel surface as necessary. Flywheel grinding limit is .020" (.51 mm). If flywheel ring gear is replaced, ensure chamfer on teeth face engine.

3) Mount clutch disc on input shaft. Check runout using dial indicator. Maximum runout is .04" (1.0 mm). Check disc hub and input shaft splines for excessive wear. Hub must slide smoothly on input shaft splines.

4) Check pilot bearing for excessive wear. Remove pilot bearing if replacing. On 626 models, install pilot bearing so that it is recessed .087-.110" (2.18-2.79 mm) below shoulder of crankshaft. Pack bearing with lithium based grease.

Installation

1) Machine flywheel surface and replace pilot bearing as necessary. Clean sealant from flywheel attaching bolt threads. Replace bolts if sealant can not be removed. Coat bolt threads with Stud and Bearing Mount Sealer (EOAZ-19554-B), and install flywheel. Tighten bolts in sequence and to specifications. *See Fig. 3.*

Fig. 3: Flywheel Tightening Sequence

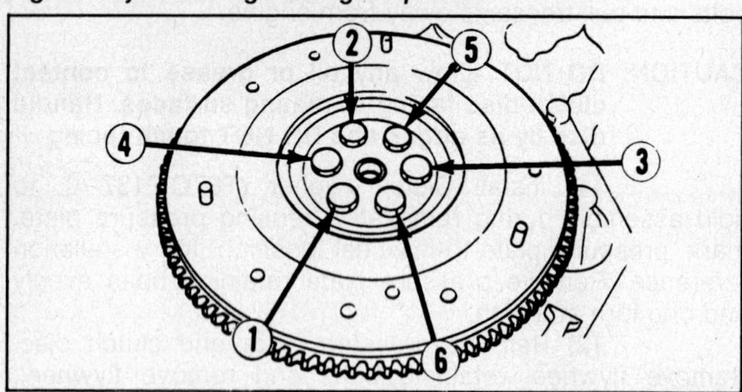

Courtesy of Ford Motor Co.

2) Position clutch disc on flywheel with damper springs facing outward. Hold in place with Clutch Aligner (T77F-7137-A). Position pressure plate over clutch disc and align marks made at removal.

3) Install pressure plate retaining bolts. Evenly, diagonally and gradually tighten bolts to specifications. Remove clutch aligner. Place transaxle on transmission jack.

4) Lightly coat input shaft splines with Clutch Grease (C1AZ-19590-B). Install transaxle assembly by aligning input shaft through clutch disc splines. Align clutch housing onto engine guide pins. Install clutch housing bolts and tighten to specifications.

CAUTION: Tracer transaxle is contructed of aluminum alloy. Ensure all bolts/nuts are tightened to the specifications.

5) Raise transaxle assembly and tighten engine support bar to hold assembly in position. Remove transmission jack. Install transaxle mount, located by exhaust pipe. Install starter and electrical wiring. Install extension bar onto mounting bracket. Install transaxle control rod.

6) Install crossmember and transaxle mount bolts. Install new circlips on drive axles and install drive axles. Ensure circlips are seated completely in transaxle. To complete installation, reverse removal procedure. Tighten all bolts/nuts to specifications.

CLUTCH RELEASE BEARING & FORK

NOTE: Release bearing is prelubricated, do not wash in solvent.

Removal & Installation

1) Disconnect return spring from release bearing. Remove bolt retaining release fork and lever together. Slide release bearing off input shaft and out of release fork. Pull release lever and shaft out top of flywheel housing and remove fork.

2) To install, reverse removal procedure. Align release lever shaft hole and fork bolt hole. Apply Stud and Bearing Mount Sealer (EOAZ-19554-B) to bolt and install. Tighten all bolt/nuts to specifications.

CLUTCH CABLE

Removal & Installation

1) Remove blower air duct from below instrument panel. Disconnect clutch cable from release lever. *See Fig. 4.* Remove nuts retaining clutch cable at firewall. Unhook clutch cable at clutch pedal. Pull clutch cable out from engine compartment side.

Fig. 4: Clutch Release Lever & Cable Adjustment

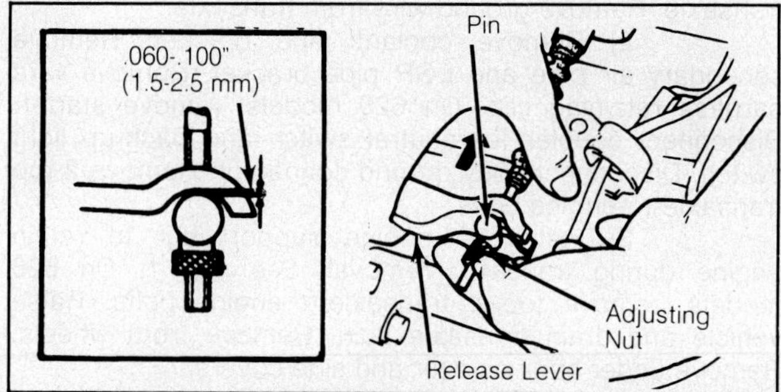

Courtesy of Mazda Motors Corp.

2) Apply lithium grease to pedal cable hook and joint between release lever and pin. To complete installation, reverse removal procedure. Tighten all bolts/nuts to specifications.

CLUTCH MASTER CYLINDER

CAUTION: Clutch fluid will damage painted surfaces.

Removal & Installation

Disconnect clutch line at clutch master cylinder. Remove blower air duct from below instrument panel. Remove nuts retaining master cylinder to firewall. Remove clutch master cylinder. To install, reverse removal procedure. Bleed hydraulic system at clutch release cylinder and check for leakage.

CLUTCH RELEASE CYLINDER

Removal & Installation

Remove air cleaner assembly. Remove tubing from flexible hose. Plug tubing and hose to prevent brake fluid from escaping. Remove mounting bolts and release cylinder from clutch housing. To install, reverse removal procedure. Bleed system at release cylinder and check for leakage.

MAZDA FWD & FORD MOTOR CO. TRACER (Cont.)

OVERHAUL

CLUTCH MASTER CYLINDER

Disassembly

1) Remove clutch master cylinder. Depress piston with a screwdriver and remove snap ring. Remove piston assembly by placing shop rag over piston bore and lightly applying compressed air to clutch line bore.

2) Remove primary cup and return spring. Remove reservoir cap and baffle. Drain fluid from reservoir. Work reservoir back and forth, while pulling upward and remove reservoir. Remove bushing (if necessary). *See Fig. 5.*

Fig. 5: Exploded View of Clutch Master Cylinder

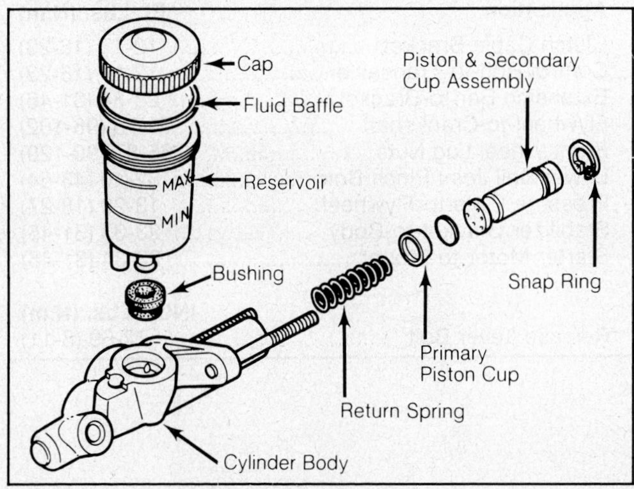

Courtesy of Mazda Motors Corp.

Inspection

Wash parts with clean clutch fluid. Check for wear, cracks or damage. Check piston bore and piston for wear or damage. Replace components as necessary.

Reassembly

Apply clean clutch fluid to cups and cylinder bore. Install new reservoir bushing (if removed). To complete reassembly, reverse removal. Bench bleed clutch master cylinder. Install clutch master cylinder. Bleed system at clutch release cylinder and check for leakage.

CLUTCH RELEASE CYLINDER

Disassembly

Remove clutch release cylinder. Remove flexible hose. Pull out push rod and boot. Remove piston and piston cup by placing shop rag over bore and lightly applying compressed air at flexible hose bore. Remove return spring, bleeder screw and steel ball. *See Fig. 6.*

Inspection

Wash parts in clean clutch fluid. Check for wear or damage to cylinder bore and piston. Replace components as necessary.

Reassembly

Install steel ball and bleeder screw. Install return spring with small diameter end facing outward. Install a new piston and cup assembly. Install push rod, boot, and flexible hose. Install clutch release cylinder and bleed system.

Fig. 6: Exploded View of Clutch Release Cylinder

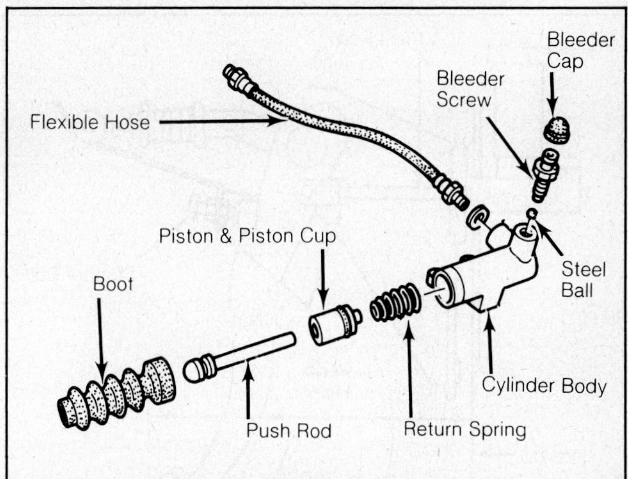

Courtesy of Mazda Motors Corp.

ADJUSTMENTS

CLUTCH PEDAL HEIGHT

Check clutch pedal height from upper center clutch pad-to-firewall. *See Figs. 7 and 8.* See CLUTCH PEDAL SPECIFICATIONS table in this article. If not within specifications, adjust by loosening lock nut and turning stopper or clutch switch.

Fig. 7: EFI Clutch Pedal Adjustment

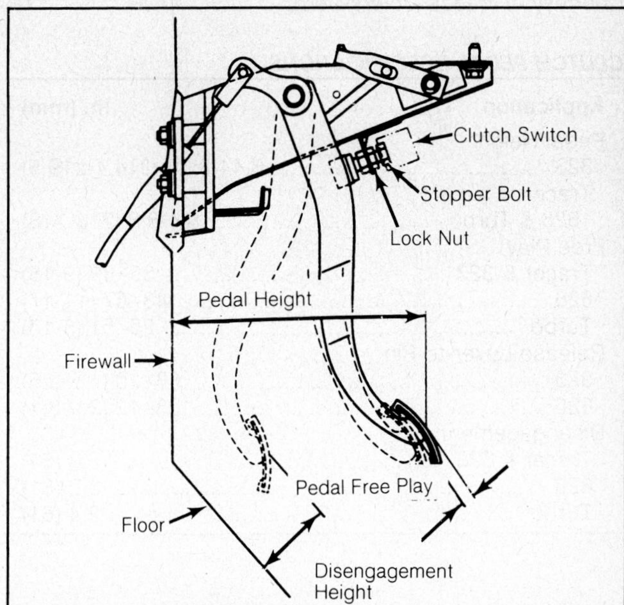

Courtesy of Mazda Motors Corp.

MAZDA FWD & FORD MOTOR CO. TRACER (Cont.)

Fig. 8: Turbo Clutch Pedal Adjustment

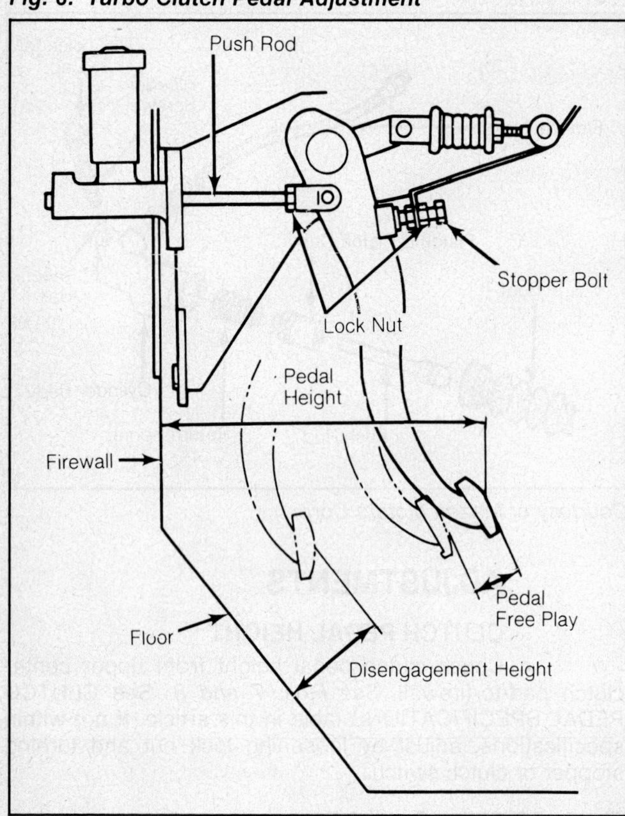

Courtesy of Mazda Motors Corp.

CLUTCH PEDAL SPECIFICATIONS

Application	In. (mm)
Pedal Height	
323	8.44-8.64 (214.4-219.5)
Tracer, 626 & Turbo	8.4-8.6 (213-218)
Free Play	
Tracer & 323	.35-.59 (9-15)
626	.43-.67 (11-17)
Turbo	.20-.51 (5-13)
Release Lever-to-Pin	
323	.06-.10 (1.5-2.5)
626	.08-.12 (2.0-3.1)
Disengagement	
Tracer & 323	3.3 (84)
626	3.2 (81)
Turbo	2.4 (61)

CLUTCH PEDAL FREE PLAY

1) Check clutch pedal free play by pushing lightly on clutch pedal until all free play is removed. *See Figs. 7 and 8.* See CLUTCH PEDAL SPECIFICATIONS table in this article. If not within specifications, adjust clearance at release lever. *See Fig. 4.* Check disengagement distance and readjust free play if necessary.

2) On turbo models, adjust free play by loosening lock nut on clutch master cylinder and turning push rod. *See Fig. 8.* Check disengagement distance and readjust free play if necessary.

TIGHTENING SPECIFICATIONS

Application	Ft. Lbs. (N.m)
Clutch Cable Bracket	12-17 (16-23)
Control Rod-to-Transaxle	12-17 (16-23)
Extension Bar-to-Bracket	23-34 (31-46)
Flywheel-to-Crankshaft	71-75 (96-102)
Front Wheel Lug Nuts	65-87 (90-120)
Lower Ball Joint Pinch Bolt	32-40 (43-54)
Pressure Plate-to-Flywheel	13-20 (18-27)
Stabilizer Bracket-to-Body	23-33 (31-45)
Starter Motor-to-Mount	23-34 (31-46)
	INCH Lbs. (N.m)
Release Lever Bolt	72-69 (8-11)

Clutches

MAZDA RWD

B2200, B2600, RX7

DESCRIPTION

The clutch assembly is a disc, diaphragm spring type. The hydraulically-operated clutch release system uses a firewall-mounted master cylinder and a release cylinder attached to the bellhousing.

REMOVAL & INSTALLATION

CLUTCH ASSEMBLY

Removal (RX7)

1) Disconnect negative battery cable. Place shift lever in Neutral. Remove shift knob. Remove console box (if equipped). Remove shift lever dust boot, lever and related components. Remove air cleaner.

2) Raise and support vehicle. Remove drive shaft. Remove under covers. Remove any interfering exhaust components. Remove clutch release cylinder without discharging system.

3) Remove starter, speedometer cable and related electrical connections. Place support under rear of engine. Remove bolts attaching transmission to engine. Remove crossmember.

4) Slide transmission back until input shaft is clear of bellhousing. Remove transmission from vehicle. Install flywheel holder. Index mark position of clutch cover to flywheel.

5) Remove clutch cover and disc. Before removing flywheel, check flywheel runout. Remove clutch release bearing and fork. *See Fig. 1*.

Fig. 1: Exploded View of RWD Clutch Assembly

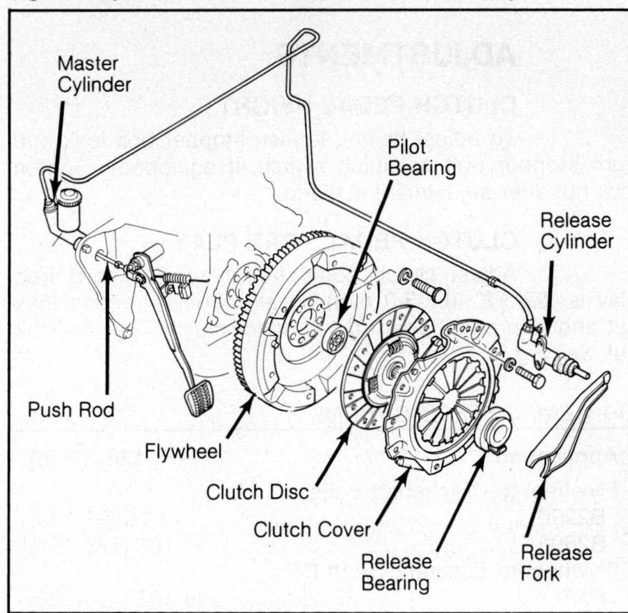

Courtesy of Mazda Motors Corp.

Removal (B2200, B2600)

1) Disconnect negative battery cable. Raise and support vehicle. Drain transmission oil. Remove console and gear shift lever. Remove drive shaft(s) and disconnect speedometer cable from transmission.

2) Disconnect wiring harness. Remove return spring. Disconnect parking brake cables. Remove release cylinder and gusset plate. Disconnect and move exhaust pipe out of way. Remove crossmember.

3) Remove bolts attaching transmission to engine. Pull transmission from vehicle. Remove clutch cover mounting bolts. Remove clutch cover and disc.

Inspection

1) Check disc for loose rivets, worn springs or oil contamination. Minimum lining height above rivet heads is .012" (.30 mm). Inspect flywheel and pressure plate for burns, scoring or grooves.

2) Check runout for flywheel and pressure plate. Resurface or replace flywheel and/or pressure plate if out of specification. See CLUTCH RUNOUT table. If flywheel ring gear is replaced, ensure chamfer on flywheel teeth faces engine.

3) Mount clutch disc on input shaft. Check runout using dial indicator, replace if out of specification. See CLUTCH RUNOUT table. Check disc hub and input shaft splines for excessive wear. Hub must slide smoothly on input shaft splines.

CLUTCH RUNOUT

Application	In. (mm)
Flywheel, Pressure Plate	.008 (.20)
Disc	
B2200, B2600	.03 (.7)
RX7	.04 (1.0)

Installation

1) Lightly coat input shaft splines, release bearing and fork contact areas with molybdenum disulphide grease. Center clutch assembly. Clutch cover and flywheel "O" alignment marks must be aligned.

2) Tighten clutch cover bolts evenly, in diagonal pattern. To complete installation, reverse removal procedure.

RELEASE BEARING & FORK

Removal & Installation

1) Remove clutch assembly. Remove release bearing and fork. Turn release bearing by hand in both direction. Replace if bearing is rough or noisy.

2) Inspect release fork for damage. Replace if necessary. Lightly apply molybdenum disulphide grease to clutch component contact areas and sliding surfaces. To complete installation, reverse removal procedure.

CLUTCH MASTER CYLINDER

Removal & Installation

Disconnect hydraulic line and master cylinder mounting nuts. Unhook clutch pedal from push rod. Remove master cylinder. To install, reverse removal procedure and bleed hydraulic system.

Clutches

MAZDA RWD (Cont.)

CLUTCH RELEASE CYLINDER

Removal & Installation

Raise and support vehicle. Disconnect and plug fluid hose. Remove nuts attaching release cylinder to clutch housing. Remove release cylinder. To install, reverse removal procedure and bleed hydraulic system.

OVERHAUL

CLUTCH MASTER CYLINDER

Disassembly (RX7)

1) Drain brake fluid. Remove reservoir connector bolt and reservoir. Remove piston stop ring, washer and piston assembly. Separate piston, cups and return spring. Wash parts in clean brake fluid. *See Fig. 2.*

2) Check all parts for wear, damage or deformation. Standard piston-to-cylinder bore clearance is .001-.004" (.032-.102 mm). If clearance exceeds .006" (.15 mm), replace master cylinder. Coat all components with clean brake fluid before assembly.

Fig. 2: Exploded View of Clutch Master Cylinder

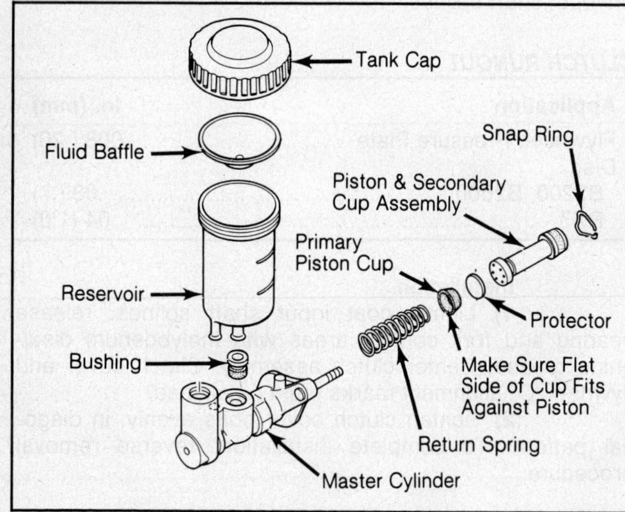

Courtesy of Mazda Motors Corp.

Reassembly

1) Install primary cup with flat side against piston. Ensure compensating port is open. To complete assembly, reverse disassembly procedure. After assembly, fill reservoir with clean brake fluid.

2) Bench bleed master cylinder. Install master cylinder and bleed hydraulic system.

Disassembly (B2200, 2600)

1) Remove clutch master cylinder from vehicle. While pressing down on piston with a screwdriver, remove snap ring. Remove piston and secondary cup assembly. Remove by blowing compressed air through clutch line. Use a rag to prevent parts from flying out.

2) Remove primary cup and return spring. Remove tank cap and baffle. Remove reservoir tank and bushing (if necessary).

Reassembly

Install new bushing. Install reservoir tank, baffle and tank cap. Install new return spring, primary cup, and piston and secondary cup assembly. While pushing down on piston, install snap ring. Bench bleed master cylinder. Install master cylinder and bleed hydraulic system.

CLUTCH RELEASE CYLINDER

Disassembly (RX7)

Remove release cylinder. Detach dust boot and release rod. Remove piston and cup assembly from cylinder. Use compressed air if required. Remove return spring, bleeder screw and valve.

Reassembly

1) Wash parts in clean brake fluid. Check all parts for wear or damage. Replace parts as needed.

2) Before assembly, coat pistons and cups with clean hydraulic fluid. To complete reassembly, reverse disassembly procedure.

Disassembly (B2200, 2600)

Remove unit from vehicle. Disconnect flexible hose. Pull out push rod and boot. Remove piston and piston cup by blowing compressed air through oil passage. Use a rag to prevent piston and cup assembly from flying out. Remove return spring, bleeder cap, screw and steel ball.

Reassembly

Install steel ball, bleeder screw, bleeder cap, return spring, and piston and cup assembly. Make sure that direction of return spring and piston cup assembly are correct. Narrow end of spring goes toward piston. Install release rod, boot, and flexible hose. Reinstall clutch release cylinder and bleed hydraulic system.

ADJUSTMENTS

CLUTCH PEDAL HEIGHT

To adjust height, loosen stopper bolt lock nut. Turn stopper bolt or clutch switch (if equipped). Tighten lock nut after adjustment is made.

CLUTCH PEDAL FREE PLAY

Adjust clutch pedal free play. Standard free play is .02-.12" (0.6-3.0 mm) on all models. Loosen lock nut and turn pedal push rod to specification. Tighten lock nut. *See Fig. 3.*

TIGHTENING SPECIFICATIONS

Application	Ft. Lbs. (N.m)
Flywheel-to-Crankshaft Bolts	
B2200	71-76 (96-103)
B2600	94-101 (128-137)
Flywheel-to-Eccentric Shaft Bolt	
RX7	289-362 (400-500)
Clutch Cover-to-Flywheel Bolts	20 (26)

MERCEDES-BENZ 190 SERIES

DESCRIPTION

Clutch housing and transmission are integral. Clutch is a single disc with diaphragm spring type pressure plate. Clutch actuation is hydraulic. A clutch pedal mounted master cylinder applies hydraulic pressure to a clutch housing mounted slave cylinder. Clutch free play is adjusted automatically. Clutch release bearing is sealed and prelubricated.

REMOVAL & INSTALLATION

Removal

1) Disconnect battery ground cable. Ensure insulating mat is covered for protection when lowering transmission. Support transmission with vehicle jack or pit lift.

2) Remove rear engine mount. Remove engine carrier on frame floor. Remove exhaust holder on transmission. Remove shielding above propeller shaft center bearing. Loosen but DO NOT remove clamping nut of propeller shaft.

3) Loosen bolts for propeller shaft center bearing. Remove propeller shaft on transmission. Ensure companion plate remains on propeller shaft. Loosen fitted sleeves on universal flange. Push companion plate away from universal flange.

4) In order to lower transmission to required height, disconnect exhaust unit on rear suspension. Lower transmission carefully and suspend with wire. Remove tachometer drive cable from rear of transmission. Remove holder for line on clutch housing.

5) Remove clutch slave cylinder from housing. Move cylinder with hydraulic line to rear until push rod is free of clutch housing. Remove clip locks and shift rods from intermediate shift levers on shift bracket.

6) Remove starter motor. Remove bellhousing bolts (remove upper 2 bolts last). Rotate transmission 45 degrees left and pull transmission out of pilot bearing. Lower rear of transmission. Remove transmission. Remove clutch pressure plate and disc.

NOTE: **Tilt transmission to rear only after pulling input shaft well out of clutch plate. Damage to clutch disc will occur if shaft is not clear.**

Inspection

1) Measure wear of clutch driven plate at slave cylinder using Check Gauge (115 589 07 23 00). Automatic adjusting (free play) clutch actuation will not indicate wear of clutch actuating system.

2) Slip Check Gauge (115 589 07 23 00) into groove of plastic shim on clutch slave cylinder. If notch marks disappear in flange, clutch disc is fully operational. If notch marks of check gauge inserted to stop remain visible, wear limit of clutch disc has been attained. Replace clutch disc if specifications are exceeded.

3) Inspect clutch pressure plate for heat cracks and score marks. Inspect diaphragm spring for fractures. Inspect diaphragm spring tongues for wear and uniform hardness. Align diaphragm spring tongues (if required). Maximum wear of spring tongues is .120" (.30 mm).

4) Inspect flywheel for burns, cracks and score marks. Touch up clutch pressure plate and flywheel with coarse emery cloth. Inspect clutch disc for oil saturation, mechanical damage, lining cracks and lining thickness. Inspect stop bolts, spring windows, torsion springs and hub for wear and score marks. Replace components as necessary.

Installation

1) Place slave cylinder and hydralic line above transmission. Using an aligning tool, center clutch disc on flywheel. Install pressure plate. Tighten bolts 1 to 1 1/2 turns at a time until tight.

NOTE: **When installing propeller shaft to transmission, raise engine and transmission with jack. Tighten propeller shaft center bearing clamp nut to 22-29 ft. lbs. (30-39 N.m).**

2) During installation, ensure clutch is fully seated in flywheel recess. To complete installation, reverse removal procedure. Bleed hydraulic system. Check clutch pedal and shift linkage adjustment.

RELEASE BEARING & LEVER

Removal

Remove release bearing from bearing tube on front transmission cover. Move release lever down and left. Pull release lever from ball pin on clutch housing.

Installation

To install, reverse removal procedure. Apply light coat of lubricant to all bearing and lever contact surfaces.

CLUTCH MASTER CYLINDER

Removal

1) Remove floor mats and lining from driver's compartment. Remove cover under instrument panel. Siphon fluid from reservoir to below minimum mark. Loosen input line of reservoir by pulling elbow out of rubber clamping ring on master cylinder.

2) Disconnect pressure line from master cylinder. Unscrew master cylinder from pedal assembly. Remove master cylinder and connecting hose. Push rod should remain on clutch pedal.

Installation

To install, reverse removal procedure. Refill fluid level in reservoir. Bleed hydraulic system. Adjust master cylinder push rod clearance. See ADJUSTMENTS in this article.

CLUTCH SLAVE CYLINDER

Removal

Disconnect hydraulic line from slave cylinder. Plug hydraulic line with rubber cap to prevent loss of fluid. Remove bolts attaching cylinder to clutch housing. Remove slave cylinder and push rod from housing as an assembly.

CAUTION: **Ensure plastic shim is installed between cylinder and housing. Shim is recessed to accommodate inspection gauge.**

Installation

1) To install, place shim with grooved end against clutch housing and hold in position. Notches in shim must face outward.

2) Insert slave cylinder with push rod into clutch housing. Install and tighten mounting bolts. Connect hydraulic line to cylinder. Bleed hydraulic system.

MERCEDES-BENZ 190 SERIES (Cont.)

Fig. 1: Mercedes-Benz 190 Series Clutch Assembly

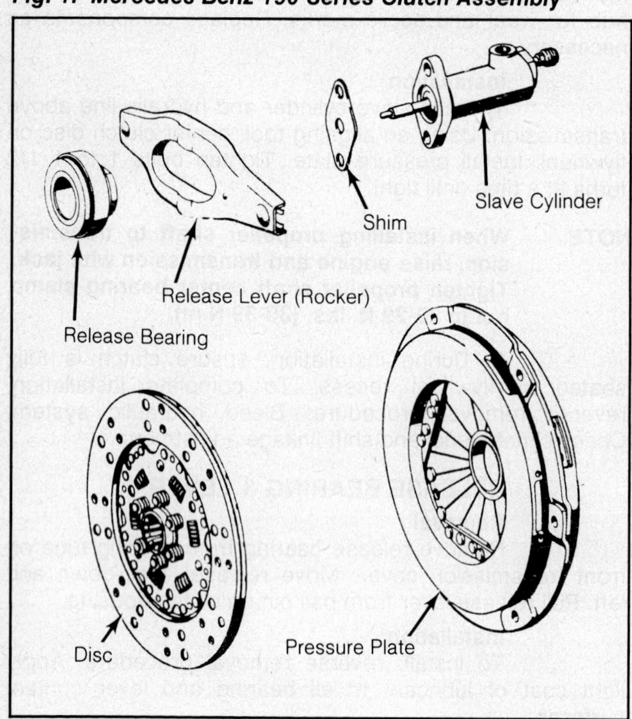

Courtesy of Mercedes-Benz of North America.

Fig. 2: Checking for Clutch Disc Wear

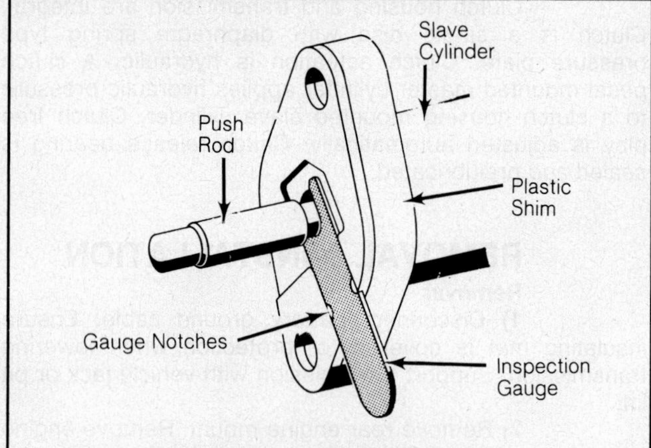

Courtesy of Mercedes-Benz of North America.

Fig. 3: Exploded View of Clutch Pedal Assembly

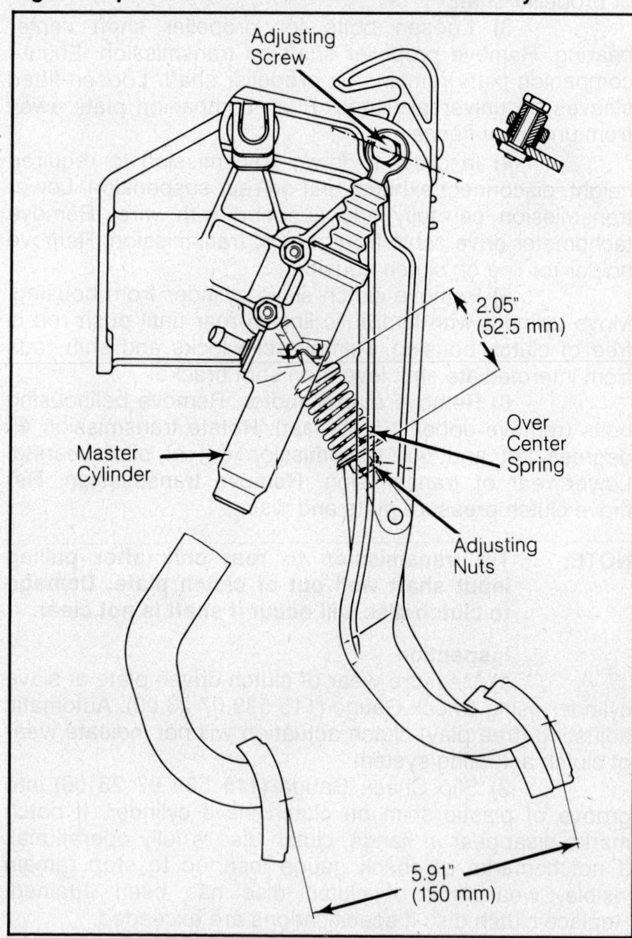

Courtesy of Mercedes-Benz of North America.

ADJUSTMENTS

OVER-CENTER SPRING

Adjust nuts at bottom of over-center spring. Spring length measured across retainers is 2.050" (52.5 mm). Improper adjustment will result in failure of pedal to return when released or excessive pressure required to depress pedal.

MASTER CYLINDER PUSH ROD CLEARANCE

Adjust master cylinder push rod length to a clearance of .008" (.20 mm) between push rod and piston. To adjust, loosen hex nut of eccentric adjusting screw and turn screw. Tighten hex nut after adjustment.

CHECKING CLUTCH DISC WEAR

Wear on clutch disc is checked using special inspection gauge. With slave cylinder installed on clutch housing, insert inspection gauge in groove of plastic shim. Disc is serviceable if notches on gauge disappear in flange. If notches remain visible, wear limit has been exceeded. Replace disc. *See Fig. 2.*

TIGHTENING SPECIFICATIONS

Application	Ft. Lbs. (N.m)
Center Bearing Clamp Nut	22-29 (30-39)

Clutches

NISSAN – EXC. PULSAR NX, SENTRA & STANZA

DESCRIPTION

Clutch is dry, single disc type. All models use diaphragm spring type pressure plate and prelubricated clutch release bearing. Clutch operates by firewall mounted master cylinder and clutch housing mounted slave cylinder. All models use nonadjustable slave cylinder assembly.

Fig. 1: Typical Nissan Hydraulic Clutch System

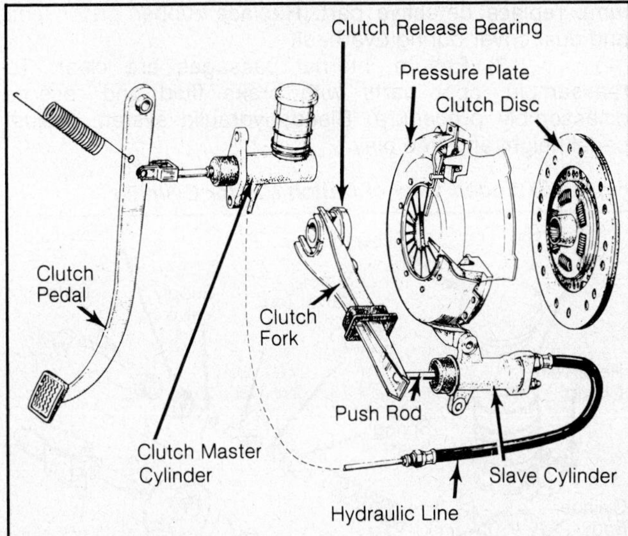

Courtesy of Nissan Motor Co., U.S.A.

REMOVAL & INSTALLATION

CLUTCH ASSEMBLY

Removal (Except Maxima & Van)

1) Disconnect battery and accelerator linkage. Remove console box. Place shift lever in Neutral. Remove shift lever boot, snap ring or nut, shift lever pin and shift lever. Raise and support vehicle. Disconnect exhaust pipe from manifold. If required, remove bolts mounting exhaust pipe bracket-to-extension housing or rear engine crossmember. Remove exhaust pipe insulator.

2) Disconnect back-up light, neutral, overdrive and transmission controlled spark connectors (if equipped). Disconnect speedometer cable on all except 4WD models. Index mark drive shafts and companion flanges prior to removal. On 4WD models, remove primary and front drive shafts. Remove front differential carrier crossmember.

3) Remove slave cylinder. On all except 4WD, separate center support bearing from crossmember. Remove drive shaft. On all models, plug rear of transmission to prevent fluid loss. Support engine and transmission with jacks. Loosen rear engine mount attaching bolt.

4) Remove rear engine mount bracket. Remove starter and engine-to-transmission bolts. Slide transmission rearward and remove. Loosen pressure plate bolts, using a crisscross pattern, until spring pressure is relieved. Remove pressure plate and clutch disc.

Removal (Maxima)

1) Disconnect speedometer cable. Remove clutch slave cylinder heat shield and slave cylinder. Remove both drive shafts using the following procedure. Remove brake caliper assembly without disconnecting brake hose. Do not twist brake hose. Support caliper by a piece of wire.

2) Remove wheel bearing lock nut. Lightly tap on drive shaft to separate drive shaft from steering knuckle. Separate tie rod from steering knuckle. Remove lower ball joint securing nuts. Remove drive shaft from transaxle.

3) Support engine and remove transmission mounting bolts. Remove transmission. Loosen pressure plate bolts, using a criss-cross pattern, until spring pressure is relieved. Remove pressure plate and clutch disc.

Removal (Van)

Remove drive shaft. Remove shift linkage. Carefully support engine and remove transmission. Remove pressure plate and clutch disc.

Inspection

1) Slide clutch disc on input shaft of transmission. Using a dial indicator mounted to transmission, check runout at specified radius from centerline of hub. See CLUTCH DISC RUNOUT SPECIFICATIONS table. Inspect friction surface of disc for wear, grease or oil. On all models, minimum distance from rivet head-to-disc surface is .012" (.3 mm). Replace parts as necessary.

CLUTCH DISC RUNOUT SPECIFICATIONS

Application	Radius In. (mm)	Runout In. (mm)
Pickup & Pathfinder		
V-6	4.72 (120)	.040 (1.0)
4-Cylinder	4.53 (115)	.040 (1.0)
Diesel	4.23 (108)	.040 (1.0)
Maxima	4.53 (115)	.040 (1.0)
Van	4.23 (107)	.040 (1.0)
200SX		
4-Cylinder	4.23 (107)	.040 (1.0)
V-6	4.53 (115)	.040 (1.0)
300ZX		
Non-turbo	4.53 (115)	.040 (1.0)
Turbo	4.72 (120)	.040 (1.0)

2) Check disc spline backlash at outer diameter of disc. Maximum backlash is .039" (.99 mm). Inspect flywheel for damage. Replace or resurface flywheel as necessary. Inspect clutch cover thrust rings for wear or damage by shaking cover assembly and listen for chattering noise. Lightly tap on rivets and listening for crackling noise. Either noise indicates worn thrust rings and complete assembly must be replaced.

Installation (All Models)

1) Lightly lubricate clutch disc splines with molybdenum grease. Slide onto mainshaft splines several times. Remove disc and wipe off excess grease. Slip clutch assembly over guide dowels. Use clutch aligning tool to center disc and pressure plate.

2) Tighten bolts evenly, one turn at a time, in a crisscross pattern. To complete installation, reverse removal procedure. Adjust linkage and pedal. Check and refill transmission lubricant. Bleed clutch hydraulic system.

CLUTCH MASTER CYLINDER

Removal & Installation

1) Disconnect clutch master cylinder push rod at clevis by removing snap ring. Disconnect hydraulic line from clutch master cylinder-to-slave cylinder. On 300ZX models only, remove windshield washer tank and electronic fuel injection resistor.

2) On all models, remove clutch master cylinder mount bolts and remove cylinder. Remove master cylinder dust cover (if equipped). To install, reverse removal procedure. Bleed hydraulic system. Adjust pedal height and free play.

CLUTCH DAMPER

Removal & Installation

Remove hydraulic lines from clutch damper. Remove clutch damper from bracket. To install, reverse removal procedure. Bleed hydraulic system and adjust pedal height and free play.

CLUTCH SLAVE CYLINDER

Removal & Installation

Remove clutch fork return spring (if equipped). Disconnect hydraulic line from slave cylinder. Remove bolts attaching cylinder to clutch housing and remove slave cylinder. To install, reverse removal procedure. Bleed hydraulic system and adjust pedal height and free play.

CLUTCH RELEASE BEARING & LEVER

Removal

With transmission removed from vehicle, remove dust boot from clutch housing. Disconnect release lever return spring and retaining clips holding release bearing to lever. Remove bearing and lever as an assembly through front of clutch housing. Remove bearing from collar using puller.

Installation

Assemble bearing onto inner sleeve using a press. Do not press on outer race. Apply molybdenum grease to inside surface of bearing collar, release bearing contact points, release bearing, ball pin in clutch housing and ball contact points on release lever. To complete installation, reverse removal procedure.

PILOT BEARING

Removal

With transmission, clutch assembly and release bearing components removed, pull pilot bearing from crankshaft with Bearing Puller (ST16610001). Do not lubricate bearing or wash in solvent. Clean only with compressed air.

Installation

Before installing new bearing, clean crankshaft bearing hole and check for nicks or damage. Insert bearing into crankshaft until distance between flange end and bearing is .16" (4.1 mm) for all models. Do not damage edge of pilot bearing or insert too deep into crankshaft bore.

OVERHAUL

NOTE: **More than one manufacturer supplies master and slave cylinders. Do not interchange parts. Ensure overhaul kit matches cylinder. Do not use mineral oil to clean components or rubber parts will be destroyed.**

CLUTCH MASTER CYLINDER

Disassembly & Reassembly

1) Remove cylinder and filler cap. Drain fluid. Remove dust cover and stopper ring. Remove push rod and stopper. Remove supply valve stopper, piston, spring seat and return spring. *See Fig. 2*.

2) Wash parts in clean brake fluid. Blow dry with compressed air. Inspect for excessive wear or damage. If cylinder-to-piston clearance exceeds .006" (.15 mm), replace defective part. Replace rubber piston cup and dust cover during overhaul.

3) Ensure internal passages are clear. To reassemble, coat parts with brake fluid and reverse disassembly procedure. Bleed hydraulic system. Adjust pedal height and free play.

Fig. 2: Exploded View of Clutch Master Cylinder

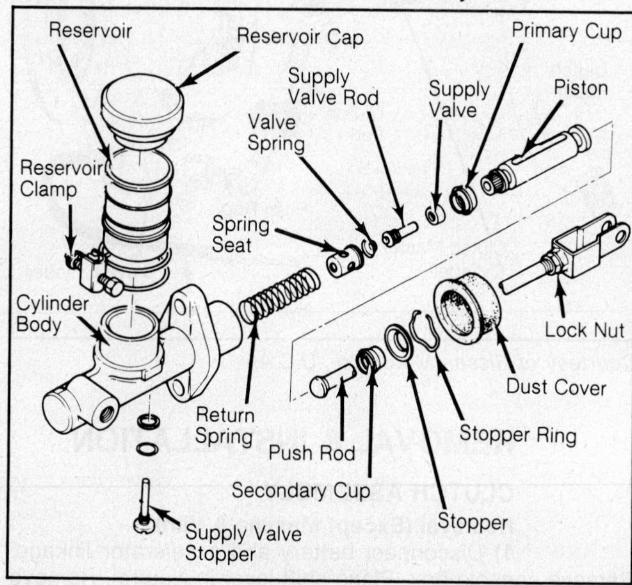

Courtesy of Nissan Motor Co., U.S.A.

CLUTCH SLAVE CYLINDER

Disassembly & Reassembly

1) Remove cylinder. Remove push rod and dust cover. Remove piston, cup and spring as an assembly. Remove bleeder screw. *See Fig. 3*. Wash parts in clean brake fluid. Inspect for wear or damage.

Fig. 3: Clutch Slave Cylinder Assembly

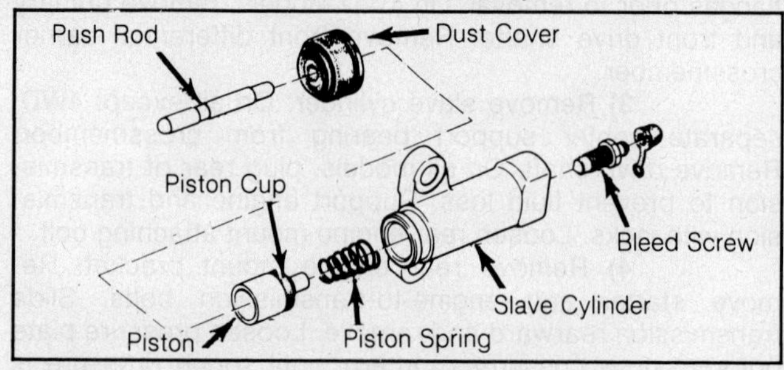

Courtesy of Nissan Motor Co., U.S.A.

2) If cylinder-to-piston clearance exceeds .006" (.15 mm), replace defective part. Always replace piston cup and dust cover. To reassemble, coat parts with brake fluid and reverse disassembly procedure. Ensure piston cup is installed properly. Bleed hydraulic system.

NISSAN – EXC. PULSAR NX, SENTRA & STANZA (Cont.)

CLUTCH DAMPER

Disassembly & Reassembly

1) Remove 4 cover mount screws. Do not let oil touch damper rubber. Remove damper rubber, piston and cup. Clean parts in brake fluid. Check cylinder bore and piston for wear or damage. If cylinder-to-piston clearance exceeds .006" (.15 mm), replace defective parts. Replace piston cup during overhaul.

2) Check damper rubber for cracks, deformation and elasticity. Replace as necessary. To reassemble, reverse disassembly procedure. Lubricate parts in brake fluid. Bleed hydraulic system. Adjust pedal height and free play.

ADJUSTMENTS

PEDAL HEIGHT & FREE PLAY

On all models, adjust pedal height by turning pedal stopper adjusting nut or clutch switch. *See Fig. 4.* On all models, free play is adjusted to .04-.20" (1-5 mm) by turning clutch master cylinder push rod in or out.

Fig. 4: Clutch Pedal Height & Free Play Adjustment

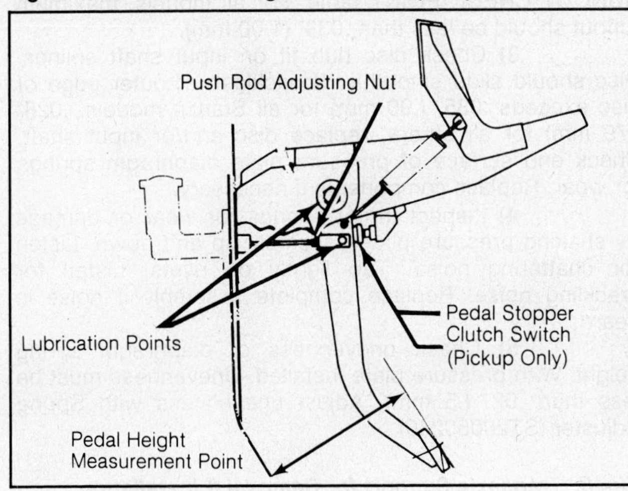

Courtesy of Nissan Motor Co., U.S.A.

HYDRAULIC SYSTEM BLEEDING

NOTE: **On models with clutch damper, bleed hydraulic system in sequence of slave cylinder, clutch damper and clutch master cylinder.**

1) Fill reservoir with brake fluid. Fit hose to bleeder screw. Place opposite end of hose into container partially filled with brake fluid. Slowly pump clutch pedal 2 or 3 times. Hold to floor.

2) Break bleeder screw loose. Allow air to vent. Close bleeder screw. Allow pedal to return. Repeat until no air bubbles are present in discharged fluid. Do not let fluid reservoir run dry during bleeding operation or complete hydraulic system must be rebled.

TIGHTENING SPECIFICATIONS

Application	Ft. Lbs. (N.m)
Clutch Cover-to-Flywheel Bolts [1]	
Turbo	25-33 (33-45)
Non-Turbo	16-22 (22-30)
Crossmember-to-Body Bolts	23-31 (31-42)
Engine-to-Transmission Bolt	
Maxima	29-40 (39-54)
All Others	29-36 (39-49)
Flex Hose-to-Slave Cylinder Nut	12-15 (17-21)
Flywheel	
Van, Pickup, Pathfinder	101-116 (137-157)
All Others	72-80 (98-108)
Slave Cylinder Mount Bolt	22-30 (30-40)
Starter Motor-to-Housing Bolts	29-39 (39-53)

[1] – Tighten bolts evenly, in a diagonal pattern.

Clutches

NISSAN PULSAR NX, SENTRA & STANZA

DESCRIPTION

The clutch assembly is a single, dry disc type with a diaphragm spring pressure plate. Clutch actuation is mechanical, using an adjustable cable connected to the pedal and release fork. Pilot and release bearings are prelubricated and sealed.

Fig. 1: Exploded View of Clutch Assembly

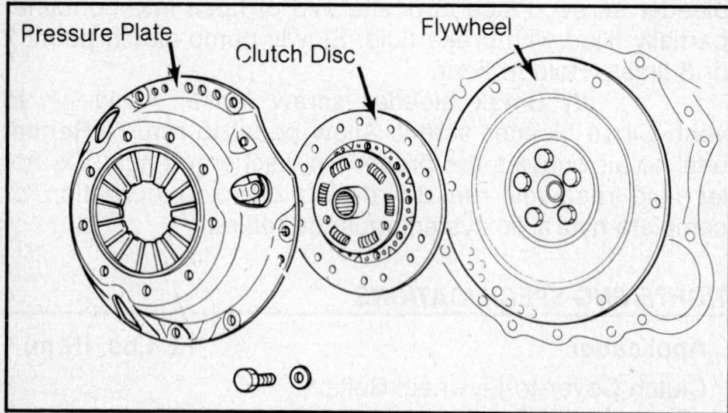

Courtesy of Nissan Motor Co., U.S.A.

REMOVAL & INSTALLATION

CLUTCH ASSEMBLY

Removal

1) Remove battery and battery holding plate. Remove air cleaner and airflow meter. Remove front wheels and drain transaxle gear oil. Remove bolts attaching steering knuckle to strut assembly. Pull drive shaft ends out of transaxle and install support bar to prevent disruption or rotation of gears.

CAUTION: During drive shaft removal, use care to avoid damaging lip of oil seal.

2) Remove wheel house protector or undercover. Separate control rod and support rod from transaxle. *See Fig. 2.* On Stanza models, disconnect exhaust pipe from engine manifold and frame bracket.

3) On all models, remove engine gusset mount bolts and transmission protector or engine mount. On Sentra and Pulsar NX, disconnect clutch cable. On Stanza models, remove clutch slave cylinder and support out of work area.

Fig. 2: Control Rod & Support Rod Location

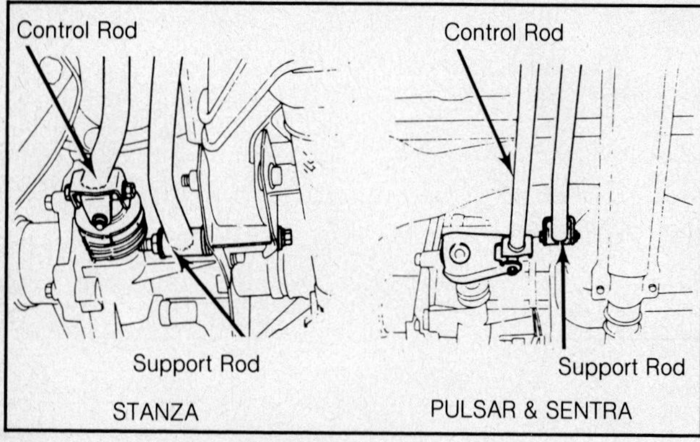

Courtesy of Nissan Motor Co., U.S.A.

4) Disconnect speedometer cable, back-up and neutral switch wires. Support rear of engine with jack. Remove transfer case (if equipped). Remove starter. Support transaxle with jack. *See Fig. 3.*

5) Remove engine mount bolts. Remove bolts mounting engine to transaxle. Slide transaxle away from engine. Loosen pressure plate bolts evenly in crisscross pattern. Remove disc and pressure plate. *See Fig. 1.*

NOTE: Bearings are prelubricated and must not be cleaned with solvents. Wash all other clutch components, except disc, in solvent.

Inspection

1) Light roughness on pressure plate and flywheel may be dressed with fine emery cloth. If surfaces are deeply scored, replace defective parts. Check clutch disc for wear. Standard clutch lining thickness is .138" (3.5 mm). Minimum height of lining above rivet heads is .012" (.3 mm).

2) Check disc runout by mounting disc onto input shaft. Mount dial indicator to transmission case with indicator plunger against face of disc. Runout must be measured at correct distance from hub center. See RUNOUT CHECK POINT table. For all models, maximum runout should be less than .039" (1.00 mm).

3) Check disc hub fit on input shaft splines. Disc should slide smoothly. If backlash at outer edge of disc exceeds .035" (.90 mm) for all Stanza models, .028" (.70 mm) for all others, replace disc and/or input shaft. Check end surface of pressure plate diaphragm springs for wear. Replace components if necessary.

4) Inspect thrust springs for wear or damage by shaking pressure plate assembly up and down. Listen for chattering noise. Tap lightly on rivets. Listen for crackling noise. Replace complete assembly if noise is heard.

5) Check unevenness of diaphragm spring height. With pressure plate installed. Unevenness must be less than .02" (.5 mm). Adjust unevenness with Spring Adjuster (ST20050240).

Fig. 3: Transaxle Support for Removal & Installation

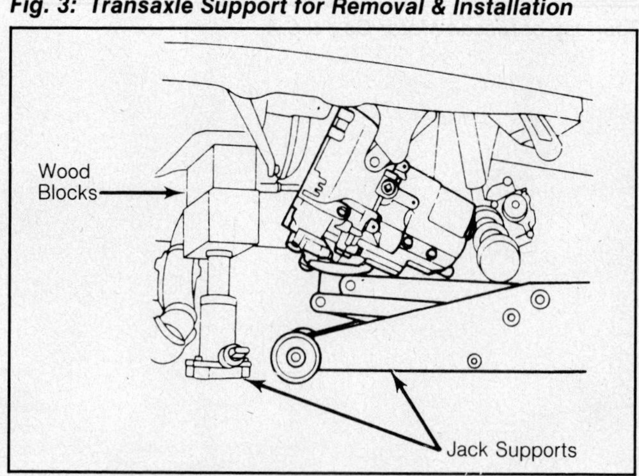

Courtesy of Nissan Motor Co., U.S.A.

NISSAN PULSAR NX, SENTRA & STANZA (Cont.)

RUNOUT CHECK POINT (Measured From Hub Center)

Application	In. (mm)
Pulsar NX	
16-Valve	3.74 (95.0)
8-Valve	3.54 (90.0)
Sentra	3.54 (90.0)
Stanza Models	4.23 (108.0)

Installation

1) Apply grease to input shaft splines and contact surfaces of release fork and bearing. Slide disc onto spline shaft several times. Remove and wipe excess grease from components. Install clutch assembly and align with clutch aligning tool.

NOTE: Do not allow grease or oil to contaminate clutch facing or other friction surfaces.

2) Tighten bolts evenly in a diagonal pattern. Remove clutch assembly centering tool. Reinstall transaxle in reverse order of removal procedure. Refill transaxle with oil. Adjust pedal height and free play. *See Fig 4.*

CLUTCH CABLE

Removal (Pulsar NX & Sentra)

Remove instrument lower cover. Disengage lock nut on release lever and disconnect clutch cable. Disconnect cable from clutch pedal. Remove clutch cable.

Installation

To install cable, reverse order of removal. Apply grease to both ends of cable and return spring.

CLUTCH RELEASE FORK & BEARING

Removal

Remove transaxle from engine. Disconnect spring from release bearing and note location for proper installation. Remove bearing. Align release fork retaining pins with cavity in clutch housing. Using a pin punch, drive out retaining pins. Pull out clutch control shaft. Release lever and spring can now be removed.

Inspection

Check contact areas of release bearing and fork for excessive wear. Check release bearing for noise or roughness by hand rotating in thrust direction. Inspect return spring and release bearing spring for wear. Replace components as necessary.

Installation

1) Using a lithium based grease, lubricate inner groove of release bearing. Lubricate contact surfaces of release fork, bearing and contact surfaces of control shaft and housing. Do not use excessive lubricant on clutch sliding components.

2) Install release fork, return spring and control shaft. Align holes in control shaft and release fork. Drive in retaining pins. Install release bearing spring on bearing. When installing release bearing, verify bearing spring is secured on fork.

ADJUSTMENTS

PEDAL HEIGHT

The clutch pedal height is adjusted by means of an adjustable pedal stopper located just below pedal hinge. Loosen lock nut and adjust stopper for correct pedal height.

PEDAL FREE PLAY

Pulsar NX & Sentra

Free play is adjusted at release lever end of clutch cable. Loosen lock nut and adjust cable until free play is .10-.14" (2.5-3.5 mm). *See Fig. 4.*

Fig. 4: Adjusting Clutch Pedal Free Play

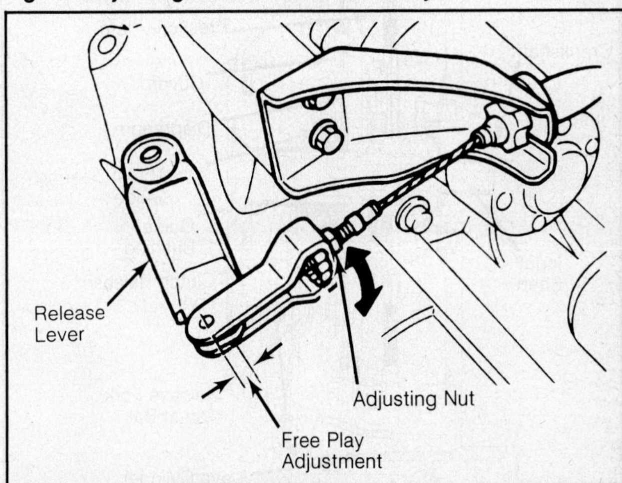

Applicable to Pulsar NX and Sentra models. Courtesy of Nissan Motor Co., U.S.A.

Stanza

The free play is adjusted at clutch master cylinder push rod. Adjust rod until free travel between push rod and master cylinder is .04-.12" (1.0-3.0 mm).

TIGHTENING SPECIFICATIONS

Application	Ft. Lbs. (N.m)
Engine-to-Transaxle Bolts	41-43 (56-58)
Flywheel-to-Crankshaft Bolts	
Pulsar NX & Sentra	58-65 (78-88)
Stanza	72-80 (98-108)
Pedal Stopper Bolt Lock Nut	
Pulsar NX & Sentra	9-11 (12-15)
Stanza	12-19 (16-25)
Pressure Plate-to-Flywheel Bolts [1]	
Pulsar NX	16-22 (22-29)
Sentra & Stanza	12-15 (16-21)

[1] – Tighten mount bolts evenly, in a diagonal pattern, to final torque.

PEUGEOT

DESCRIPTION

The clutch is a single disc, diaphragm spring type. The hydraulic actuated clutch, uses a firewall mounted master cylinder and a bellhousing mounted slave cylinder.

A prelubricated clutch release bearing is also used. No adjustments, with the exception of bleeding the hydraulic system, are necessary.

Fig. 1: Sectional View of Clutch Assembly

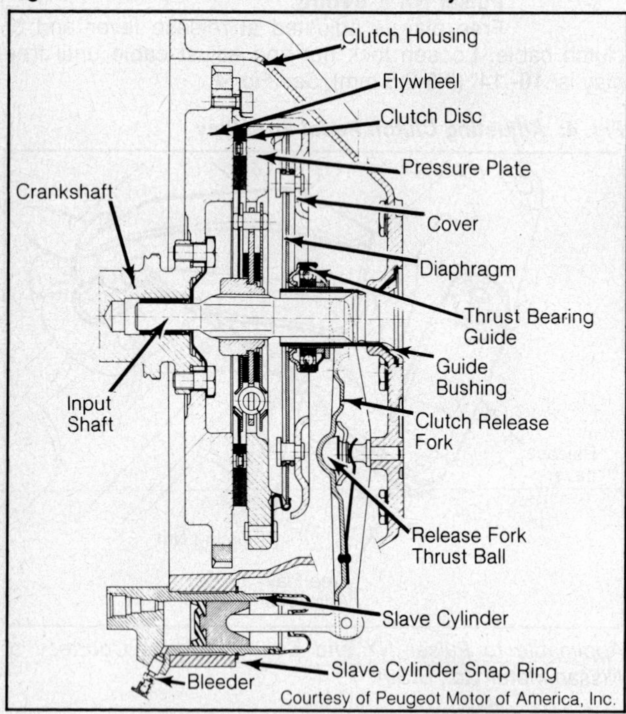

Courtesy of Peugeot Motor of America, Inc.

REMOVAL & INSTALLATION

CLUTCH ASSEMBLY

Removal

1) Raise hood. Disconnect negative battery cable. Remove fan shroud, noting that lower mount is snapped in place. Disconnect front header pipe and wire on Lambda sensor. Remove heat shield. Disconnect air injection hose. Remove front seat track floor brace. Disconnect rear tail pipe brackets.

2) Disconnect rear axle mounts. Mark position of steering column at steering box and disconnect column from box. On each side of crossmember, install one bolt in place of original bolt and thread completely. Remove 2 remaining bolts on crossmember.

3) Lower crossmember. Back off torque tube. Using an M 10 x 150 bolt, mount Insert Plate (8.0403 SZ). Clear transmission shaft. Remove inspection plates on bellhousing. Place jack under transmission and remove torque tube bolts. Disconnect front mount for gear selector rod.

4) Disconnect shifting link rod, selector link rod, back-up light switch wire, and speedometer cable. Remove slave cylinder circlip and disconnect flexible hose bracket. Remove bolts mounting transmission to engine. Remove starter bolts.

5) Lower transmission jack and twist transmission on its axis, while pulling it toward rear of vehicle.

6) Remove transmission from vehicle. Mark pressure plate cover in relation with flywheel. Diagonally unscrew 6 bolts using a 6 mm Allen wrench. Remove clutch pressure plate and disc. Clean, check and replace worn parts.

Installation

To install clutch, reverse removal procedure.

CLUTCH RELEASE BEARING & FORK

Removal

Remove slave cylinder from clutch housing. Remove release bearing from fork by turning it counterclockwise. Remove clutch fork by pulling it outward until backing spring is disengaged from ball stud.

NOTE: **Bearing is self-lubricated. DO NOT wash in any cleaning solution. Lubricate with motor oil when installing.**

Installation

Smear guide sleeve with Molycote. Position retaining jaw with long flange toward starter housing, then engage release bearing with clutch fork by rotating bearing clockwise. Pack rubber cup on ball stud with grease. To complete installation, reverse removal procedure.

PILOT BUSHING

Removal & Installation

Bushing is press fit in rear of crankshaft. Bushing must be replaced if excessive clearance with transmission input shaft is evident. Remove and install bushing using puller and driver.

CLUTCH MASTER CYLINDER

Removal & Installation

Disconnect and plug master cylinder hydraulic lines from fluid reservoir and slave cylinder. Remove bolts securing master cylinder to pedal assembly and remove master cylinder. To install, reverse removal procedure and bleed hydraulic system.

CLUTCH SLAVE CYLINDER

Removal & Installation

Disconnect hydraulic line at slave cylinder. Remove snap ring securing cylinder in clutch housing. Slide slave cylinder from clutch housing mounting. To install, reverse removal procedure. Bleed hydraulic system.

NOTE: **Overhaul procedures for clutch slave cylinder and master cylinder are not provided by manufacturer.**

TIGHTENING SPECIFICATIONS

Application	Ft. Lbs. (N.m)
Bellhousing Bolts	40 (54)
Clutch Cover	11 (15)
Drain Plug	20 (27)
Front Crossmember Bolts	31 (42)
Front Seat Track Reinforcement Bolts	13 (18)
Header Pipe Bolts	25 (34)
Rear Differential Mount Bolts	27 (37)
Starter Bolts	15 (20)
Steering Coupling Bolts	13 (18)
Torque Tube Bolts	40 (54)

PORSCHE 911 CARRERA & 911 TURBO

DESCRIPTION

The clutch assembly on the 911 Carrera is hydraulically operated, and is a rubber damped, single plate, clutch. The 911 Turbo clutch assembly is mechanically operated, and uses an adjustable cable. The clutch is a single disc with a diaphragm spring pressure plate.

REMOVAL & INSTALLATION

CLUTCH ASSEMBLY

Removal

1) Raise and support vehicle. Disconnect negative battery cable and remove air cleaner. Remove engine block vent hose. Plug vent cover hole (If equipped). Remove A/C compressor and set aside. Do not remove hoses.

2) Remove relay plate cover. Disconnect engine wires at relay plate, adapter plug, relay plate socket and ignition control unit. Remove fuel hoses at filter and return line. Disconnect accelerator linkage.

3) Remove rear center tunnel cover in passenger compartment. Slide boot forward over shift selector rod. Disconnect coupling from inner shift rod. Disconnect speedometer sensor wires in tunnel. Drain engine oil. Plug hoses on engine and oil tank.

4) Remove heater hoses at exchangers and remove rear stabilizer. Disconnect ground strap at body and battery wires at starter. Disconnect accelerator linkage from pedal and clutch cable at transaxle. Remove axle shafts from flanges at transaxle.

5) Place jack under engine/transaxle assembly and lift slightly. Do not damage secondary air injection pipes. Loosen transaxle and engine mount bolts. Lower assembly from vehicle.

6) Remove circlip from clutch release lever shaft. Remove lever and rubber ring. Remove transaxle mount bolts and pull transaxle from engine. Mark pressure plate and flywheel for reassembly. Insert clutch alignment tool. Loosen bolts evenly, in diagonal pattern. Separate clutch assembly from engine.

Installation

1) Ensure marks on flywheel and clutch are aligned. Tighten pressure plate bolts evenly, in a diagonal pattern. Use clutch alignment tool to center disc. When installing new clutch, balancing marks on clutch and flywheel should be offset 180 degrees.

2) With transaxle installed, pull release lever away from engine. Ensure that there is at least .78" (19.8 mm) clearance between release lever and transaxle housing. To complete installation, reverse removal procedure.

CLUTCH RELEASE BEARING

Removal

Bearing is removed with pressure plate. Remove by laying pressure plate on bearing and removing snap ring on flywheel side of clutch fingers. Remove bearing along with washers.

Installation

Apply thin coat of lubricant to guide tube and friction surfaces. Reverse removal procedure, to complete installation.

ADJUSTMENT

NOTE: **On 911 Carrera clutch operating mechanism is hydraulically actuated. No free play or pedal adjustment is necessary.**

CLUTCH ADJUSTMENT

1) Clutch free play is checked at transaxle adjusting lever (due to auxiliary clutch spring). With cable snug, adjust play at lever to .04" (1.0 mm).

2) Clutch pedal travel may be adjusted at stop on floor plate. Release travel should be .965-1.004" (24.5-25.5 mm) when measured at cable end.

NOTE: **If rubber sleeve over clutch cable is not installed completely to clutch release lever, clutch cable may bind.**

Fig. 1: Clutch Adjusting Mechanism

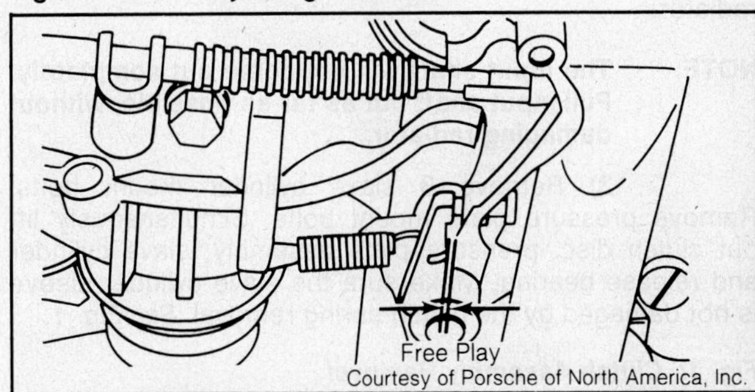

Courtesy of Porsche of North America, Inc.

PEDAL ADJUSTMENT

1) With engine running at operating temperature, reverse gear should engage silently when pedal is fully depressed. Release lever should move .6" (15 mm) to completely release clutch.

2) If cable housing rests on bottom of guide clamp when pedal is fully depressed, inner cable must be adjusted at yoke end. Measure from threaded cable end of yoke to outer edge of lock nut.

3) Adjust if not within .7-.9" (17-22 mm). If arc of cable is too large and allows cable slip out of guide clamp when pedal is released, shorten inner cable at yoke end.

TIGHTENING SPECIFICATIONS

Application	Ft. Lbs. (N.m)
Clutch Cover Bolt	18 (25)
Engine-to-Transaxle Nut	32 (45)
Flywheel Mount Bolt	66 (90)
Starter Mount Nut	34 (47)

Clutches

SAAB 900

DESCRIPTION

The clutch is a single dry plate, diaphragm spring type. The clutch operation is hydraulically activated by a clutch master cylinder which applies pressure to the transaxle-mounted slave cylinder.

REMOVAL & INSTALLATION

CLUTCH ASSEMBLY

Removal

1) Disconnect preheater hose. Remove clutch cover housing. Depress clutch pedal and install Spacer Ring (83 90 023) between diaphragm spring fingers and pressure plate cover. Spacer ring must be used to keep clutch disengaged while removing components.

NOTE: If clutch cannot be disengaged normally, compress diaphragm spring with Compressor (83 93 175) to install spacer ring.

2) Unhook shaft cover spring clip. Remove input shaft cover and unscrew plastic propeller. Install 8 mm bolt in end of input shaft. Using Shaft Remover Fork (83 93 175) and a hammer, pop input shaft out toward radiator.

NOTE: The input shaft will not come out completely. Pull input shaft out as far as possible, without damaging radiator.

3) Remove 3 slave cylinder mount bolts. Remove pressure plate mount bolts. Simultaneously lift out clutch disc, pressure plate assembly, slave cylinder and release bearing. Make sure the slave cylinder sleeve is not damaged by the clutch during removal. *See Fig. 1.*

Fig. 1: Clutch Assembly Removal

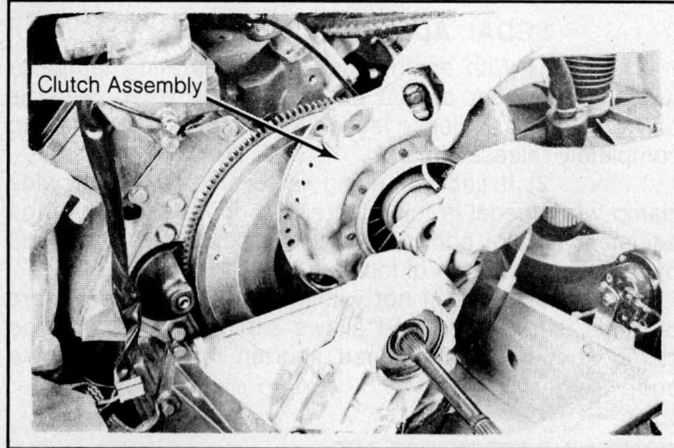

Courtesy of Saab-Scania of America, Inc.

CLUTCH MEASUREMENT TABLE

Application	In. (mm)
Disc Compressed Thickness	
Non-Turbo	.28-.30 (7.1-7.6)
Turbo	.27-.29 (6.9-7.4)
Disc-to-Pressure Plate Clearance	
Unloaded	.05 (1.27)

On-Vehicle Inspection

1) With clutch assembly installed, remove inspection plate on top of clutch cover and look through inspection hole. Measure distance between plastic sleeve front edge and front edge of machined surface on slave cylinder housing.

2) Replace worn clutch disc if distance is less than .08" (2.0 mm). Distance for a new clutch disc is .35" (9.0 mm).

3) Ensure that loaded, compressed thickness of disc is within specification. Ensure unloaded disc-to-pressure plate clearance is within specification. See CLUTCH MEASUREMENT TABLE.

Off-Vehicle Inspection

1) Check flywheel and pressure plate friction surfaces for burns, cracks or scoring. Measure surface warpage. At pressure plate inner edge, maximum taper is .0012" (.030 mm). Resurface pressure plate if necessary.

2) Ensure clutch release bearing turns freely. If bearing is noisy, rough or dry, it must be replaced. DO NOT clean bearing with solvent, use only compressed air.

Installation

1) Before installing clutch, check input shaft seal condition. If necessary, replace seal. Reassemble clutch assembly. Install components simultaneously. Loosely install pressure plate mounting bolts.

2) Hardened side of release bearing must face clutch assembly. Lightly coat input shaft splines with molybdenum grease. Tap shaft into position. Ensure splined shaft engages with splines of both the disc and flywheel bearing. Apply Loctite to slave cylinder bolts. Install slave cylinder.

NOTE: When removing spacer, do not depress clutch pedal further than necessary. Seal lip may be pressed too far, causing hydraulic leak and seal damage.

3) Tighten pressure plate bolts evenly. Ensure plastic sleeve with circlip is installed with slave cylinder. Depress clutch pedal and remove spacer. To complete installation, reverse removal procedure.

CLUTCH MASTER CYLINDER

Removal

1) Remove lower instrument panel. Panel attaching bolts are located behind the ashtray and on each side of the engine compartment. One of the side bolts is located near the fuse panel, the other is near the plastic bottle inside the right fenderwell.

2) Remove push rod pin at clutch pedal. Remove master cylinder mount nuts from firewall. From inside engine compartment, remove fluid flex hose from reservoir-to-cylinder and plug opening. Remove hydraulic line at rear of cylinder. Remove master cylinder.

Installation

To install, reverse removal procedure and bleed system.

CLUTCH SLAVE CYLINDER

Slave cylinder removal is accomplished during clutch assembly removal. See CLUTCH ASSEMBLY.

SAAB 900 (Cont.)

OVERHAUL

NOTE: Wash cylinder components with clean brake fluid. Do not use any form of mineral oil for cleaning cylinder components.

CLUTCH MASTER CYLINDER

Disassembly

1) Pull back rubber cover. Remove circlip, push rod and stop washer. Remove piston assembly, convex washer, rear piston seal and return spring. Inspect cylinder bore and piston assembly. *See Fig. 2.*

2) Replace complete master cylinder if bore or piston assembly shows signs of excessive wear or damage.

Fig. 2: Exploded View of Clutch Master Cylinder

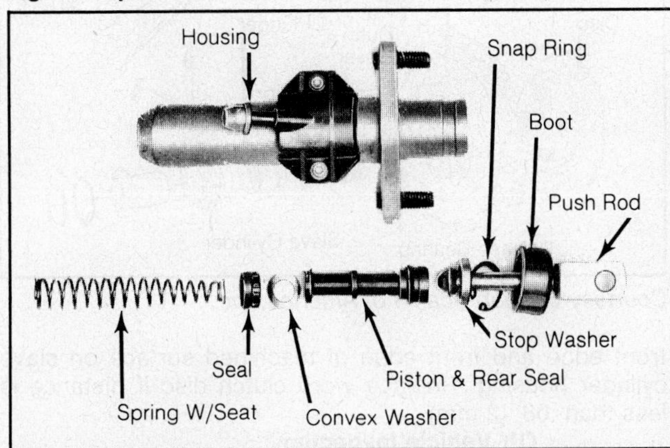

Courtesy of Saab-Scania of America, Inc.

Reassembly

1) Install return spring and retainer. Lubricate piston and seals with clean brake fluid. Install seals, convex washer and piston. Convex side of washer must face master cylinder piston. *See Fig. 3.*

Fig. 3: Master Cylinder Convex Washer Installation

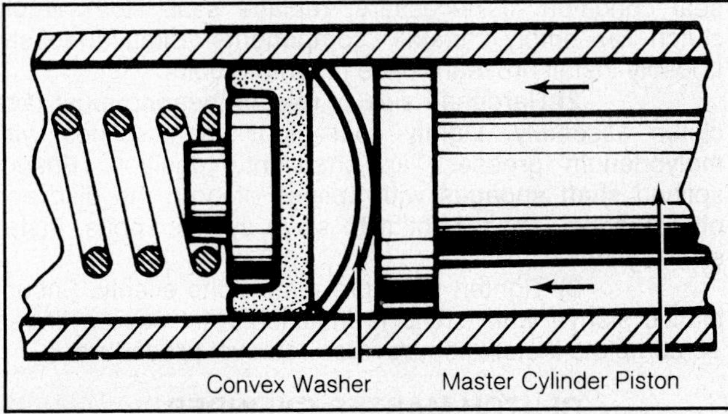

Courtesy of Saab-Scania of America, Inc.

2) Install push rod, washer and retaining ring. Install rubber cover. Install cylinder and bleed system.

CLUTCH SLAVE CYLINDER

NOTE: Sleeve rides on machined surface of cylinder body and doubles as dust cover.

Disassembly

1) Remove clutch release bearing from slave cylinder. Set slave cylinder with release bearing end facing up. Press cylinder sleeve out. Remove "O" ring from sleeve flange. Remove piston, lip seal and related components.

2) Clean and inspect slave cylinder housing-to-sleeve bore, sleeve inside bore and outside surface, piston assembly and all rubber components. Replace slave cylinder assembly if cylinder bore, sleeve or piston assembly are excessively worn or damaged. *See Fig. 4.*

Fig. 4: Clutch Slave Cylinder

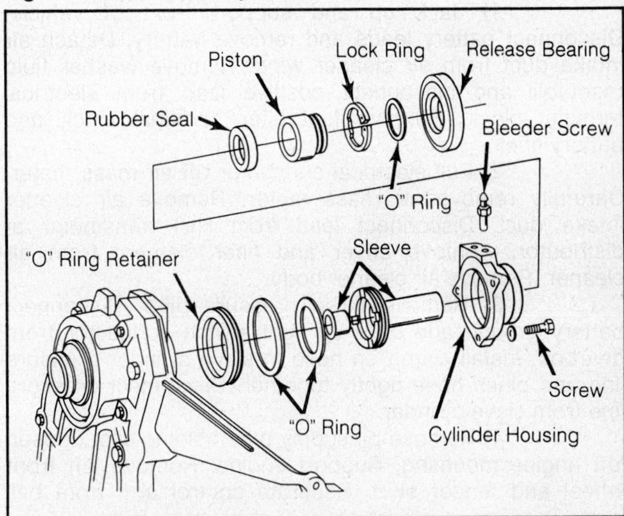

Courtesy of Saab-Scania of America, Inc.

Reassembly

1) Before beginning reassembly, lightly coat lip seal and piston with rubber grease. DO NOT coat "O" ring. Fit "O" ring to sleeve flange. Slide seal lip on sleeve. Coat sleeve flange with brake fluid. Insert sleeve into cylinder. Push seal lip part way into cylinder.

2) Guide sleeve and cylinder together by pushing on piston until lock rings and "O" ring are in position. Place slave cylinder on support and seat sleeve into cylinder. Fit release bearing to piston. Install cylinder. Bleed system.

ADJUSTMENTS

PEDAL STROKE & FREE PLAY

The clutch pedal stroke and free play are automatically adjusted by operation of hydraulic system.

TIGHTENING SPECIFICATIONS

Applications	Ft. Lbs. (N.m)
Flywheel-to-Crankshaft Bolt	43 (59)
Slave Cylinder Retaining Nut	10 (14)
Mount Bolt (8 mm)	17 (21)
Transaxle Drain Plug	33 (49)

Clutches

SAAB 9000

DESCRIPTION

The clutch is a single dry plate diaphragm spring type. The hydraulically-operated clutch is activated by a master cylinder which applies pressure to the slave cylinder within the gearbox. The clutch is completely self-adjusting.

REMOVAL & INSTALLATION

CLUTCH ASSEMBLY

Removal

1) Jack up and support front of vehicle. Disconnect battery leads and remove battery. Detach air intake duct from air cleaner wing. Remove washer fluid reservoir and disconnect positive lead from electrical terminal block. Remove fuel filter, terminal block and battery shelf.

2) Pull electrical connector off air mass meter. Carefully remove air mass meter. Remove air cleaner intake duct. Disconnect lead from Hall transmitter at distributor. Remove cover and filter element from air cleaner. Remove air cleaner body.

3) Remove turbo pressure pipe. Disconnect battery ground and back-up light switch connector from gearbox. Install clamp on hose in slave cylinder pressure line and pinch hose tightly together. Disconnect pressure line from slave cylinder.

4) Remove oil supply pipe holding clip. Loosen left engine mounting. Support engine. Remove left front wheel and fender skirt. Seperate control arm from ball joint.

5) Disconnect speedometer cable and remove carefully so pinion does not fall down into gearbox. Separate 2 halves of selector-rod joint and remove clip from dust cover on intermediate drive shaft.

6) Unbolt steady bar from inlet manifold. Unbolt starter motor from gearbox and push steady bar out of way. Let starter motor hang from electrical leads.

7) Leave one bolt in position in top flange between engine and gearbox. Remove other bolts and install Locating Dowels (8392128).

8) Loosen 2 subframe pivot mountings and remove 4 securing bolts. Unbolt front and rear mounting bracket. Remove 4 securing bolts at back of subframe.

9) Remove bolts securing lower attachment point for wheel-arch bracket and let subframe hang from anti-roll bar. Loosen top nut for anti-roll bar. Unbolt anti-roll bar link from suspension arm and remove supension arm.

10) Loosen clip securing rubber gaiter on inboard universal joint. Withdraw drive shaft and install protective covers to open ends of gaiter and driver cup.

11) Attach lifting sling to gearbox and remove remaining bolt. Withdraw gearbox past locating dowels and lower to ground. Install flywheel locking tool to top locating dowel. Lift off clutch assembly and remove clutch assembly. *See Fig. 1*.

On-Vehicle Inspection

With clutch assembly installed, remove inspection plate on top of clutch cover and look through inspection hole. Measure distance between plastic sleeve front edge and front edge of machined surface on slave cylinder housing. Replace worn clutch disc if distance is less than .08" (2 mm).

Fig. 1: Exploded View of Clutch Assembly

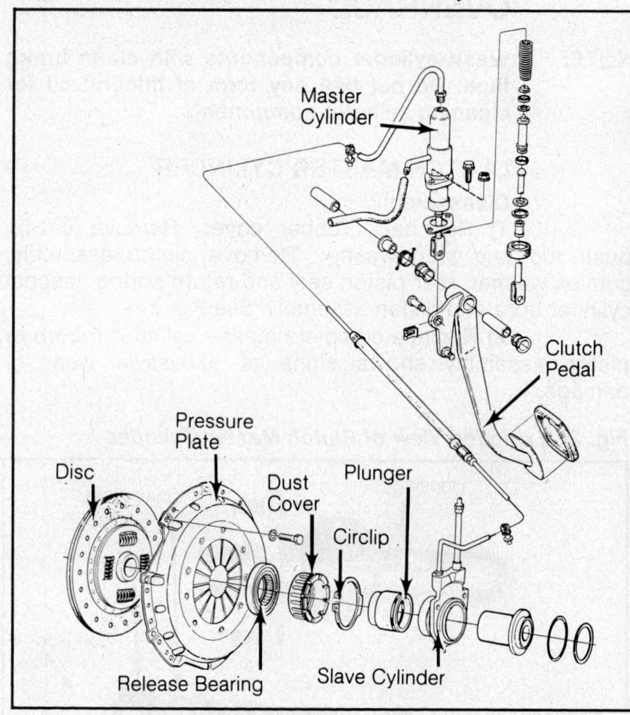

Courtesy of Saab-Scania of America, Inc.

Off-Vehicle Inspection

1) Check flywheel and pressure plate friction surfaces for signs of scoring or distortion. If deeply scored or excessively worn, resurface pressure plate.

2) Ensure clutch release bearing turns freely. If bearing is noisy, rough or dry, it must be replaced. DO NOT clean bearing with solvent. Use only compressed air.

Installation

1) Before installing clutch, check input shaft seal condition. If necessary, replace seal. Reassemble clutch assembly. Install components simultaneously. Loosely install pressure plate mounting bolts.

2) Hardened side of release bearing must face clutch assembly. Lightly coat input shaft splines with molybdenum grease. Tap shaft into position. Ensure splined shaft engages with splines of both the disc and pilot bearing. Apply Loctite to slave cylinder bolts. Install slave cylinder.

3) Tighten pressure plate bolts evenly. Ensure plastic sleeve with circlip is installed with slave cylinder. To complete installation, reverse removal procedure.

CLUTCH MASTER CYLINDER

Removal

1) From inside vehicle, remove trim panel above brake pedal. Remove clip and withdraw clevis pin from master cylinder pushrod. Place a sheet of cardboard under clutch pedal to protect carpet against drops of clutch fluid.

Clutches

SAAB 9000 (Cont.)

2) Detach supply hose from cylinder and plug end of hose. Detach pressure line from master cylinder. Remove mounting bolts and lift out cylinder.

Installation

Position master cylinder and install mounting bolts. Check gasket between cylinder body and car body for damage. Connect pressure line to master cylinder and install supply hose. Tighten mounting bolts and pressure line. To complete installation, reverse removal procedure.

CLUTCH SLAVE CYLINDER

Removal

Remove gearbox. Remove release bearing. Disconnect pressure line and bleed nipple. Loosen 3 mounting screws and remove slave cylinder.

Installation

Install slave cylinder into the clutch housing and tighten screws evenly in sequence to 72-89 INCH lbs. (8-10 N.m). Install release bearing. Replace bleed nipple and connect pressure pipe.

CLUTCH PEDAL

Removal

Remove trim panel above brake pedal. Remove clip and withdraw clevis pin securing master cylinder pushrod to pedal. Remove lock nut, unhook spring and remove pedal and spring.

Installation

Attach spring onto pedal bracket and pedal. Install a new lock nut and thighten lock nut to 31.3 ft. lbs. (42 N.m). Insure that all spring coils are on plastic sleeve. Install clevis pin and replace trim panel.

OVERHAUL

CLUTCH MASTER CYLINDER

Disassembly

1) Pull back dust cover, remove circlip and remove the pushrod. Withdraw plunger assembly complete with spring. Remove spring, seal retainer, recuperating seal and washer. Carefully remove plunger seal. *See Fig. 2*.

Fig. 2: Exploded View of Clutch Master Cylinder

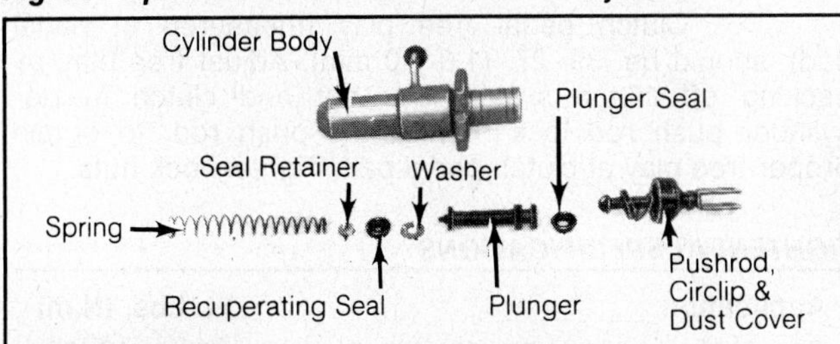

Courtesy of Saab-Scania of America, Inc.

2) If plunger seals are loose, drain and replace contaminated fluid. If cylinder has a smooth surface free of scoring, replace seals only. Otherwise, install a new master cylinder.

Reassembly

Wash master cylinder in clean brake fluid before reassembly. Lubricate plunger and seals with rubber grease. Install return spring and seal retainer. Install washer and plunger complete with seals. Install pushrod, circlip and dust cover. Replace dust cover if damaged.

CLUTCH SLAVE CYLINDER

Disassembly

Remove release bearing sleeve and tap out stuffing box. Push plunger out of bore and carefully remove 2 seals from plunger. Replace slave cylinder assembly if cylinder bore, sleeve or piston assembly are excessively worn or damaged. *See Fig. 3*.

Fig. 3: Clutch Slave Cylinder

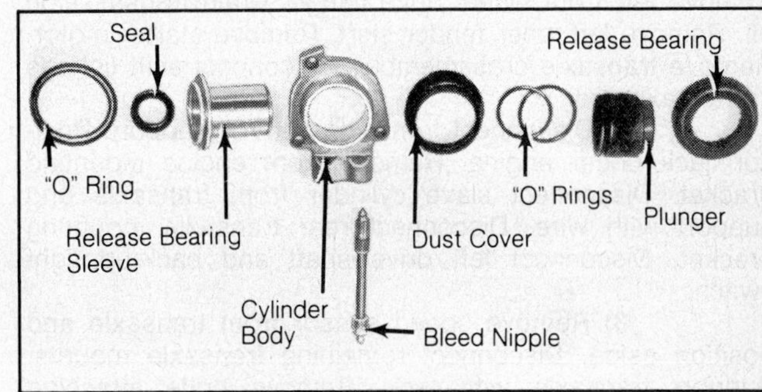

Courtesy of Saab-Scania of America, Inc.

Reassembly

Insure that slave cylinder is perfectly clean. Clean with brake fluid. Install dust cover retainer .43" (11 mm) from the machined edge of cylinder body. Install new "O" rings on plunger and lubricate with brake fluid. Install plunger in bore so flange for release bearing is slightly foward of dust cover.

ADJUSTMENTS

PEDAL STROKE & FREE PLAY

The clutch pedal stroke and free play are automatically adjusted by operation of the hydraulic system.

TIGHTENING SPECIFICATIONS

Applications	Ft. Lbs. (N.m)
Anti-Roll Bar Clamp Bolt	30-40 (40-54)
Anti-Roll Bar End Nut	30-40 (40-54)
Back-Up Light Switch	15-18 (20-24)
Engine-to-Gearbox Bolts	40-74 (54-100)
Engine Mounting Bolts	36-67 (49-91)
Flywheel-to-Crankshaft Bolts	43 (59)
Master Cylinder Mounting Bolts	16 (22)
Pressure Plate Bolts	11-20 (14-27)
Starter Motor	28-35 (38-47)
Subframe Mounting Bolts	32-42 (44-57)
Suspension Arm-to-Ball Joint	15-20 (20-27)
Transaxle Drain Plug	29-37 (39-50)

Clutches

STERLING 825

DESCRIPTION

The clutch is a single dry disc type, using a diaphragm spring type pressure plate and a clutch release bearing mounted inside the transmission. The clutch is operated by the use of a firewall mounted master cylinder and a transaxle mounted slave cylinder.

REMOVAL & INSTALLATION

CLUTCH ASSEMBLY

Removal

1) Remove air cleaner. Raise front of vehicle. Remove left front wheel drive flange. Drain transmission oil. Remove left inner fender skirt. Remove starter motor. Remove transaxle crossmember. Disconnect shift linkage at transaxle.

2) Disconnect transaxle anti-roll support. Position jack under engine. Remove front engine mounting bracket. Disconnect slave cylinder from transaxle and support with wire. Disconnect rear transaxle mounting bracket. Disconnect left drive shaft and back-up light switch.

3) Remove speed sensor from transaxle and position aside. Disconnect remaining transaxle mounts. Support transaxle with jack. Remove bolts attaching transaxle to engine. Disconnect right drive shaft. Remove transaxle. Remove pressure plate bolts in a crisscross pattern. Remove pressure plate and clutch disc.

Installation

Apply light amount of grease to release bearing sliding surfaces and input shaft. To complete installation, reverse removal procedure.

CLUTCH RELEASE BEARING

Removal

With transaxle removed, pull release fork away from transaxle and slide bearing off transaxle input shaft.

Installation

To install, coat pivoting points between bearing and operating shaft with multipurpose grease. Slide bearing onto input shaft. Position release fork to pivot ball and bearing.

NOTE: **Bearing is prelubricated. DO NOT wash in solvent.**

CLUTCH MASTER CYLINDER & DAMPER

Removal

Disconnect and plug fluid lines. Separate cylinder from clutch pedal by removing clevis pin. Remove nuts in passenger compartment mounting master cylinder to firewall. Remove nuts in engine compartment mounting damper to firewall. Remove master cylinder and damper.

Inspection

1) Disassemble master cylinder. *See Fig. 1.* Check piston and cylinder bore for wear, nicks and corrosion. Replace parts if necessary.

2) Replace rubber parts during overhaul. Ensure secondary cup sealing lips face piston and primary cup sealing lips face spring.

Fig. 1: Exploded View of Master Cylinder

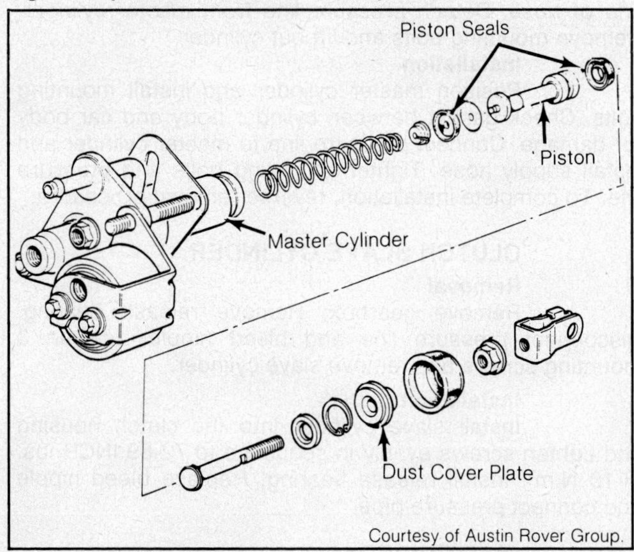

Installation

To install master cylinder, reverse removal procedure. Bleed air from master cylinder fluid line. Check for proper clutch operation.

CLUTCH SLAVE CYLINDER

Removal

Working from under vehicle, remove cylinder mounting bolts. Disconnect and plug fluid line.

Inspection

Remove slave cylinder push rod rubber boot. Remove piston, cup and spring. Do not attempt to remove plastic filter from base of cylinder. Check cylinder bore and piston for wear, nicks and corrosion. Replace parts as necessary.

Installation

To install, reverse removal procedure. Bleed air from fluid line. Check for proper clutch operation.

ADJUSTMENT

CLUTCH PEDAL FREE PLAY

Clutch pedal free play (measured at pedal pad), should be .39-.27" (1.0-7.0 mm). Adjust free play by backing off clutch switch lock nut and clutch master cylinder push rod lock nut. Rotate push rod, to obtain proper free play at clutch pedal pad. Tighten lock nuts.

TIGHTENING SPECIFICATIONS

Application	Ft. Lbs. (N.m)
Clutch Assembly-to-Flywheel Bolts	19 (26)
Drive Shaft-to-Transmission Nuts	53 (72)
Transaxle Mount(s) Bolts	30-33 (40-45)
Transmission-to-Engine Bolts	55 (75)

SUBARU

DESCRIPTION

The clutch is single, dry disc type using a diaphragm spring pressure plate. System is controlled by a cable running from pedal assembly to clutch release lever. The release bearing is a self-aligning design.

Fig. 1: Exploded View of Clutch Assembly

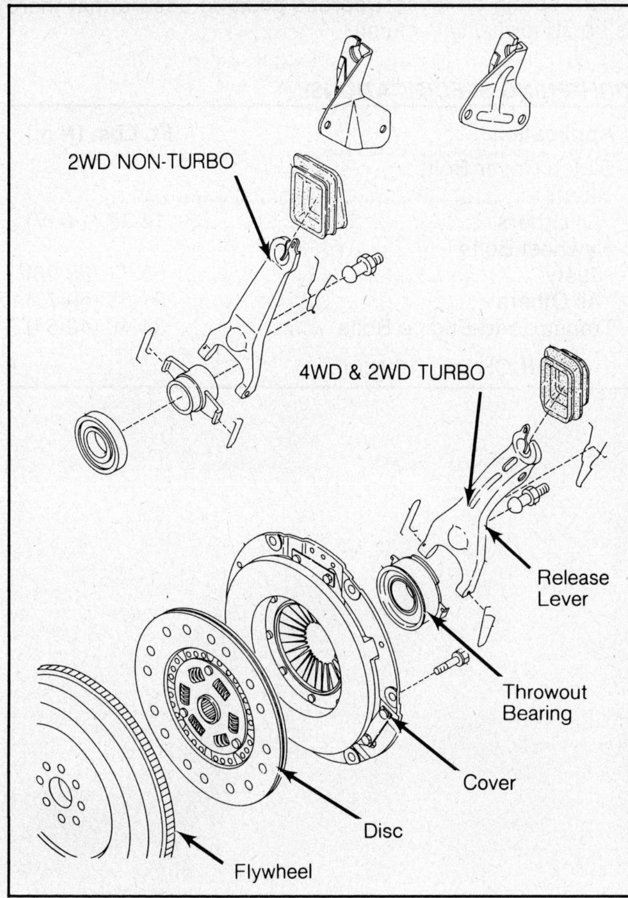

Courtesy of Subaru of America, Inc.

REMOVAL & INSTALLATION

CLUTCH

Removal (All Except Justy)

1) Prop open hood. Remove spare tire. Disconnect ground cable from engine. Remove spare tire support. Remove hill-holder cable, lock nut and clips. Remove clutch cable with return spring, lock nut, adjusting nut and clips. Remove air cleaner and air duct. Remove speedometer cable and clip.

2) Label and disconnect wiring and hoses connected between engine and vehicle body. Remove starter, radiator and cooling fan assembly. Remove power steering pump, air conditioning compressor and place to side of work area (if equipped). Raise vehicle. Remove center exhaust pipe. Move rear exhaust pipe away from work area.

3) Remove propeller shaft (4WD). Plug opening at rear of extension housing. Remove shift linkage from selector lever. Remove stabilizer bar from transverse link. Remove hand brake cable bracket from transverse link. Remove transverse link. Using a punch, drive out each axle shaft spring pin. Separate side axle shafts from drive shafts.

4) Disconnect engine and transaxle mounts. Remove interfering crossmember(s). Remove engine with transaxle from vehicle. Remove mounting nuts and bolts attaching engine to transaxle. Remove engine. Remove pressure plate and clutch disc. Remove release bearing, bearing holder and clutch release lever.

Inspection

1) Light roughness on pressure plate and flywheel may be dressed with fine emery cloth. If surfaces are deeply scored, replace defective parts. Check clutch disc for wear. Minimum height of lining above rivet heads is .012" (.3 mm).

2) Check disc runout by mounting disc onto Clutch Disc Guide (499747000 for Non-Turbo engines and 499747100 for all others). Mount dial indicator with indicator plunger against face of disc. Face runout must be measured from disc hub center at a distance of 3.7" (95 mm) for Non-Turbo engines, and 4.2" (107 mm) for all others. Maximum runout should be less than .03" (.7 mm).

3) Check clutch release bearing for seizure, damage and rough rotation. Replace if defective.

Installation

1) Install clutch release lever and release bearing holder. Before assembly, lubricate following points with a light coat of molybdenum disulphide grease: inner groove of release bearing holder, contact surface of lever and pivot, contact surface of lever and holder, and transaxle mainshaft spline.

2) Install retainer spring into lever. While pushing lever onto pivot, fit retainer spring onto pivot. Install release lever sealing diaphragm. Using clutch alignment tool, position clutch disc against flywheel. Note front and rear of clutch disc.

3) Position pressure plate so it is off-set 120 degrees or more between "0" mark on flywheel "0" mark on pressure plate. Tighten clutch cover installing bolts gradually. Each bolt should be tightened in a criss-cross fashion to 11-13 ft. lbs. (15-18 N.m).

4) Remount engine and transaxle on body. To complete installation, reverse removal procedure. Ensure new spring pins are installed in axle shafts.

Removal (Justy)

1) Open and support engine hood. Disconnect battery negative terminal. Disconnect hoses and cables from air cleaner. Remove air cleaner. Disconnect wiring from starter. Remove starter. Disconnect speedometer cable and back-up light switch. Remove transaxle ground strap.

2) Attach lifting device to transaxle lifting bracket. Remove mount assembly attaching transaxle to vehicle body. Mount Engine Supporter (921540000), between radiator body mount and engine. Mount another supporter, between engine and removed transaxle mount (On vehicle body).

3) Lift up transaxle slightly. Remove undercovers. Disconnect rear exhaust pipe from front exhaust pipe and vehicle body. Remove center crossmember. Remove transverse link. Remove each axle spring pin and separate each axle shaft.

Clutches

SUBARU (Cont.)

4) Remove transaxle mounting bracket. Disconnect gearshift rod and brace from transaxle. Remove bolts mounting transaxle to engine and separate. Lift transaxle up and out of vehicle. Remove release bearing, release bearing fork and seal from transaxle. Remove pressure plate and clutch disc from flywheel.

Inspection

1) Light roughness on pressure plate and flywheel may be dressed with fine emery cloth. If surfaces are deeply scored, replace defective parts. Check clutch disc for wear. Minimum height of lining above rivet heads is .012" (.3 mm).

2) Check disc runout by mounting disc onto Clutch Disc Guide (499745500). Mount dial indicator with indicator plunger against face of disc. Runout must be measured at 6.7" (170 mm) from hub center. Maximum runout should be less than .02" (.5 mm).

3) Check clutch release bearing for seizure, damage and rough rotation. Replace if defective.

Installation

Before installation, lightly grease release bearing-to-release bearing fork contact area, release bearing fork pivot and transaxle input shaft. Using clutch alignment tool, position clutch disc against flywheel. Position clutch cover against disc. Tighten cover bolts in a criss-cross manner. To complete installation, reverse removal procedure. Ensure new spring pins are installed in axle shafts.

ADJUSTMENTS

CLUTCH PLAY

Remove release lever return spring from lever. Adjust nut so play is .12" (3.0) at lever end. Be sure not to twist cable during adjustment. Upon completion of adjustment, securely lock adjusting nut with lock nut. Install return spring on lever. Depress pedal to assure that there is no abnormality in clutch.

TIGHTENING SPECIFICATIONS

Application	Ft. Lbs. (N.m)
Clutch Cover Bolts	
Justy	[1]
All Others	14-17 (14-17)
Flywheel Bolts	
Justy	65-71 (88-96)
All Others	51-55 (69-75)
Transaxle-to-Engine Bolts	34-40 (46-54)

[1] – 90 INCH lbs. (10 N.m).

SUZUKI SAMURAI

DESCRIPTION

Clutch is a single disc using a diaghragm spring type pressure plate. The clutch operation is mechanically operated by a clutch cable.

REMOVAL & INSTALLATION

CLUTCH ASSEMBLY

Removal

1) Remove shift lever boot. Remove shift lever case cover bolts and remove shift lever. Disconnect negative battery cable. Disconnect back-up light and 5th gear switch. Disconnect starter motor wiring and remove stater. Remove clamps attaching fuel hoses to transmission case. Drain transmission oil.

2) Disconnect clutch cable from clutch release lever. Remove both propeller shafts. Remove clutch inspection plate. Remove bolts and nuts fastening engine-to-transmission. Remove crossmember and center exhaust pipe. Remove transmission rear mounting bracket. Lower transmission from vehicle.

3) Install flywheel holder. Match mark pressure plate-to-flywheel. Remove 6 bolts securing pressure plate to flywheel. Remove pressure plate and clutch disc. Remove clutch release bearing. *See Fig. 1.*

Fig. 1: Exploded View of Clutch Assembly

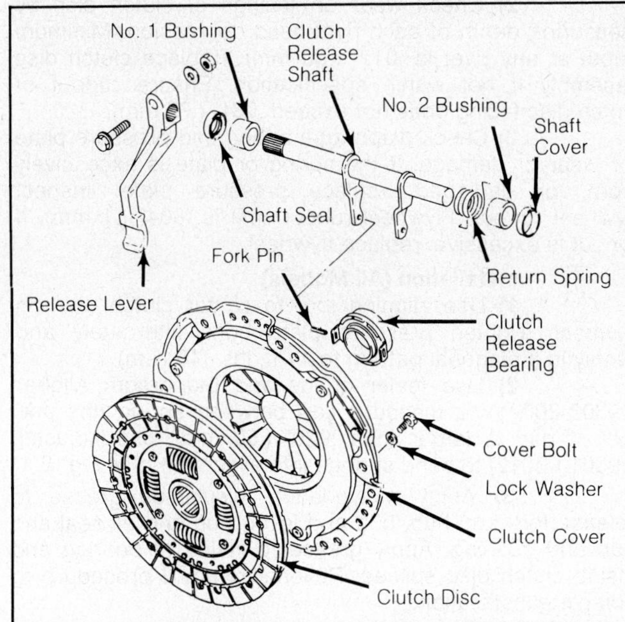

Courtesy of Suzuki of America Corp.

Inspection

1) Check flywheel and pressure plate contact surface for damage. Replace clutch disc if rivet head depression is found to have reached .02" (.5 mm) or less. Standard depression is .05" (1.2 mm). Mount clutch disc on transmission input shaft. Turn disc back and forth to check backlash.

2) Replace disc assembly if backlash exceeds .03" (.8 mm). Inspect pressure plate assembly for loose diaphragm spring rivets. Check diaphragm fingers for wear. Replace parts as necessary.

Installation

Install clutch alignment tool. Position clutch disc to pressure plate and align index marks. Tighten pressure plate-to-flywheel bolts in a diagonal pattern. Complete installation by reversing removal procedure.

CLUTCH RELEASE BEARING

Removal

Remove clutch assembly. Remove clutch release fork pin and remove bearing from transmission input shaft bearing retainer.

NOTE: **Replace release bearing if it sticks, rattles or makes abnormal noise when spun or turned.**

Installation

Before installing release bearing, apply grease to its inner surface. Reverse removal procedures to complete installation.

CLUTCH RELEASE SHAFT

Removal

1) Remove clutch release bearing. Remove release lever. Check for cracks and binding of shaft. Remove return spring from clutch release shaft.

2) Position Clutch Release Bushing Remover (09925-48210) against bushing No. 2 and lightly tap out bushing and cap. Repeat procedure and remove bushing No. 1 with seal. *See Fig. 1.*

Installation

Install release shaft, apply grease to release fork contact surfaces. Apply grease to both ends of clutch cable. To complete installation, reverse removal procedures. Clutch release arm bolt and nut should be tightened to 90-138 INCH lbs. (10-16 N.m).

PILOT BEARING

Removal

Remove clutch assembly. Remove pilot bearing by using Bearing Remover (09917-58010).

Inspection

Replace pilot bearing if it sticks, rattles or makes abnormal noise when spun or turned by hand.

Installation

Apply grease to pilot bearing. Install pilot bearing to flywheel.

ADJUSTMENTS

PEDAL HEIGHT

Loosen stop bolt lock nut. Turn stop bolt so that clutch pedal is level with brake pedal. Tighten lock nut after adjusting.

CLUTCH PEDAL FREE PLAY

If clutch pedal free play is not between .8-1.1" (20-30 mm), adjust it with clutch cable end nuts on transmission..

TIGHTENING SPECIFICATIONS

Application	Ft. Lbs. (N.m)
Flywheel Mounting Bolts	41.5-47.0 (57-65)
Pressure Plate-to-Flywheel Bolts	13.5-20.0 (18-28)
Transmission-to-Engine Bolts	32-39 (43-53)
Starter Mount Bolt	16-23 (22-31)

Clutches

TOYOTA – EXCEPT TERCEL

DESCRIPTION

Clutch is a single disc, hydraulically operated by a firewall mounted master cylinder and clutch housing mounted slave cylinder. Slave cylinder is nonadjustable. Clearance is automatically compensated by internal design of cylinder.

Fig. 1: Exploded View of Typical Clutch Arrangement

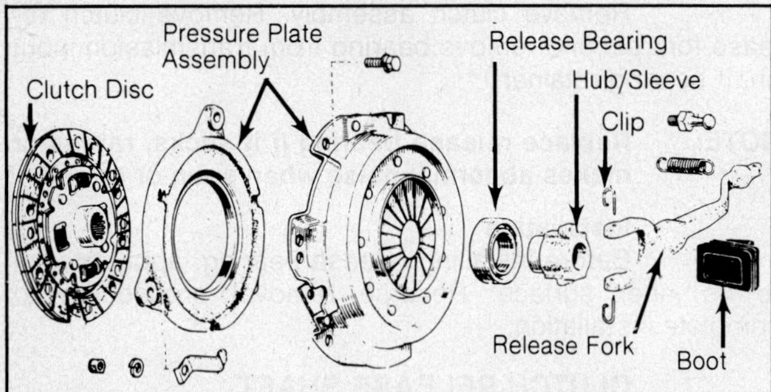

Courtesy of Toyota Motor Sales, U.S.A., Inc.

REMOVAL & INSTALLATION

CLUTCH ASSEMBLY

Removal (RWD Exc. MR2)

1) Disconnect battery cable. Remove air cleaner. Drain cooling system. Remove upper radiator hose. On Land Cruiser, remove cowl side trim, heater duct on transmission hump and front carpet or mat. On all models, remove shift lever boot, shifter assembly and starter. On Land Cruiser, remove transfer case levers.

2) On all models, raise and support vehicle. Remove protective cover from under engine (if equipped). Remove clutch slave cylinder with hydraulic line connected. Disconnect front exhaust pipe from manifold and converter. Remove exhaust pipe from vehicle.

3) Disconnect speedometer cable and electrical leads from transmission. Remove drive shaft(s). Insert plug into extension housing to prevent oil spillage.

4) Support engine. Support transmission with transmission jack. Remove rear support crossmember. Remove transmission-to-engine bolts. Pull transmission (including transfer case on Land Cruiser) to rear. Lower and remove transmission from vehicle.

5) Mark pressure plate and flywheel for reassembly reference. Loosen pressure plate attaching bolts alternately and evenly until pressure plate is released. Remove clutch disc and pressure plate.

Removal (FWD)

1) Remove negative battery cable. Remove air cleaner. Disconnect back-up light switch connector. Remove speedometer cable. Disconnect control cable. Remove water inlet. Remove clutch slave cylinder. Remove engine undercover.

2) Remove exhaust pipe assembly. Disconnect front and rear engine/transaxle mount. Remove engine/transaxle crossmember. Disconnect drive shafts from transaxle. Disconnect left steering knuckle from lower control arm. Remove left drive shaft.

3) Remove starter. Disconnect ground strap. Remove engine rear plate. Raise engine and transaxle slightly. Remove left engine mount. Remove bolts attaching engine to transaxle. Lower engine left side and remove transaxle.

4) Mark pressure plate and flywheel for reassembly reference. Loosen pressure plate attaching bolts alternately and evenly until pressure plate is released. Remove clutch disc and pressure plate.

Removal (MR2)

1) Remove negative battery cable. Drain gear oil. Disconnect back-up light switch connector. Remove speedometer cable. Remove water inlet. Remove engine undercover. Remove fuel tank protector. Disconnect control cable.

2) Remove control cable bracket and clutch release cylinder. Remove exhaust pipe assembly. Disconnect drive shaft from side gear shaft. Remove starter. Remove engine rear plate. Remove front engine mount. Remove rear engine mount. Remove left engine mount. Disconnect transaxle bolts from engine. Lower engine left side and remove transaxle. Remove side gear shaft from transaxle.

3) Mark pressure plate and flywheel for reassembly reference. Loosen pressure plate attaching bolts alternately and evenly until pressure plate is released. Remove clutch disc and pressure plate.

Inspection (All Models)

1) Clean flywheel, pressure plate and clutch disc mating surfaces of all oil, grease, and metal deposits. Inspect for cracks, heat checking, warpage and other defects. Slight surface scoring can be removed with sandpaper. Replace or repair as required.

2) Check wear on facings of clutch disc by measuring depth of each rivet head depression. Minimum depth at any rivet is .012" (.30 mm). Replace clutch disc assembly if not within specification. Ensure runout of clutch disc facing does not exceed .031" (.79 mm).

3) Check diaphragm spring and pressure plate for wear or damage. If the spring or plate is excessively worn, or damaged, replace pressure plate. Inspect flywheel runout. Flywheel runout limit is .004" (.1 mm). If runout is excessive, replace flywheel.

Installation (All Models)

1) Use aligning tool to center clutch disc on flywheel. Tighten pressure plate bolts alternately and evenly in a diagonal pattern to 14 ft. lbs. (18 N.m).

2) Use feeler gauge and Diaphragm Aligner (09302-20021) to measure gap between spring tips and tool. If gap is larger than .020" (.50 mm), use Adjuster (09301-00012) to bend springs into alignment. *See Fig. 2.*

3) Apply molybdenum disulphide grease to release fork and hub, hub and lever, hub and oil seal and hub and bushing. Apply grease to inside of bearing and inside clutch disc splines. Reverse removal procedure to complete installation.

CLUTCH MASTER CYLINDER

Removal & Installation

1) On Van models, disconnect negative battery cable. Remove the 5 instrument cluster finish panel retaining screws and remove panel. Remove the 4 combination meter retaining screws.

2) Disconnect speedometer cable and wiring connectors. Remove combination meter. Remove air duct. On all models, disconnect master cylinder push rod at clutch pedal. Disconnect hydraulic line at cylinder. Remove cylinder from firewall.

TOYOTA – EXCEPT TERCEL (Cont.)

Fig. 2: Diaphragm Spring Tip Alignment Check

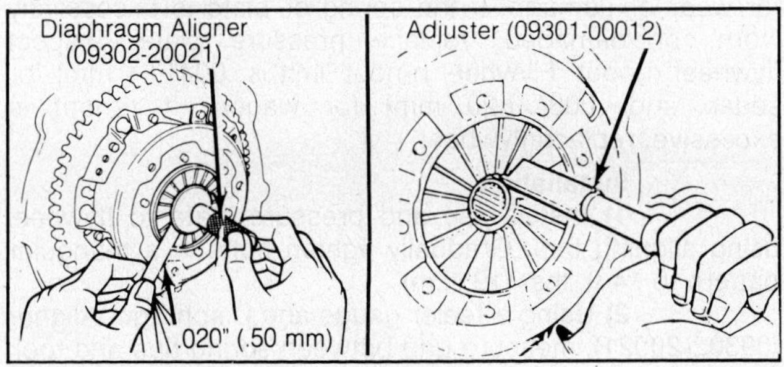

Courtesy of Toyota Motor Sales, U.S.A., Inc.

3) To install, reverse removal procedure. Adjust pedal height and free play. See ADJUSTMENTS in this article. Bleed hydraulic system.

CLUTCH RELEASE BEARING

Removal & Installation

1) Remove transmission. Check release bearing for freedom of rotation. To remove bearing, disconnect retaining clips from bearing collar and remove.

2) Replace bearing if necessary. Press new bearing on sleeve. Lightly grease all contact surfaces. To install, reverse removal procedure.

PILOT BEARING

Removal & Installation

Remove pilot bearing from crankshaft with puller. Coat new bearing with multipurpose grease and drive into crankshaft.

Fig. 3: Exploded View of Typical Clutch Master Cylinder

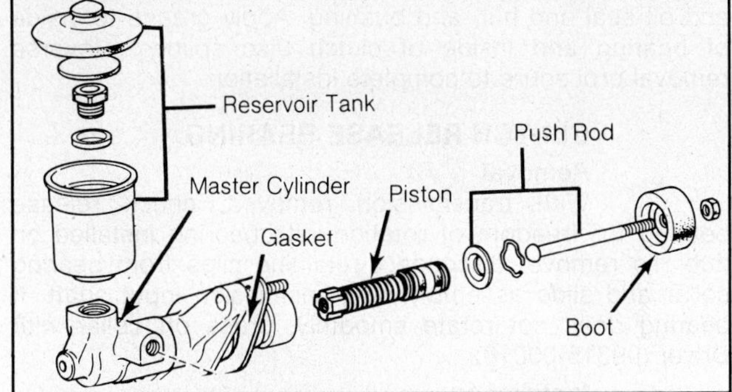

Courtesy of Toyota Motor Sales, U.S.A., Inc.

OVERHAUL

CLUTCH MASTER CYLINDER

Disassembly

Clamp master cylinder in a soft-jawed vise. Remove hold-down bolt and reservoir. Pull back boot and remove snap ring on push rod. Remove piston, push rod, cup and remaining internal components.

Reassembly

Wash all parts in clean brake fluid. Inspect for wear or damage. Dip cylinder cups in clean brake fluid. Reassemble components in reverse order of disassembly.

CLUTCH SLAVE CYLINDER

Disassembly & Reassembly

Remove rubber boot and push rod. Remove piston assembly and spring. Remove bleeder screw. Wash all parts in clean brake fluid. Inspect for wear or damage. Dip piston in clean brake fluid. Reassemble components in reverse order of disassembly.

Fig. 4: Exploded View of Slave Cylinder

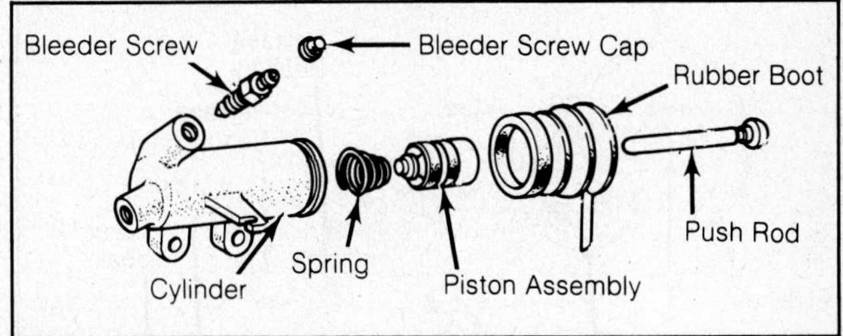

Courtesy of Toyota Motor Sales, U.S.A., Inc.

ADJUSTMENTS

PEDAL HEIGHT & FREE PLAY

Adjust pedal stop bolt at top of pedal assembly to adjust pedal height. To adjust free play, loosen lock nut on master cylinder push rod and turn push rod in or out to specified free play. Tighten lock nut.

PEDAL FREE PLAY

Application	In. (mm)
Corolla RWD	
4A-C Engine	.2-.6 (5-15)
4A-GE Engine	.5-.9 (13-23)
Land Cruiser	1.2-2.0 (30-50)
All Others	.2-.6 (5-15)

CLUTCH FORK FREE PLAY

Land Cruiser

Clutch fork free play is distance slave cylinder push rod moves before moving clutch fork. To adjust free play, loosen lock nut at slave cylinder. Turn push rod tip while holding push rod nut with wrench. Free play should be .16-.20" (4.0-5.0 mm). Tighten lock nut and recheck.

TIGHTENING SPECIFICATIONS

Application	Ft. Lbs. (N.m)
Clutch Cover Bolts	14 (19)
Transmission-to-Engine Bolts	
Corolla RWD	
Upper 2 Bolts	53 (72)
All Other Bolts	27 (37)
Land Cruiser	
17 mm Bolts	53 (72)
14 mm Bolts	47 (64)
Truck, Van & 4-Runner	53 (72)
All Other Models	
12 mm Bolt	47 (64)
10 mm Bolt	34 (46)

TOYOTA TERCEL

DESCRIPTION

Clutch is single disc using diaphragm spring type pressure plate. Actuation is mechanical, using an adjustable cable connected to clutch pedal and release fork. A permanently lubricated release bearing is used.

Fig. 1: Exploded View of Clutch Components

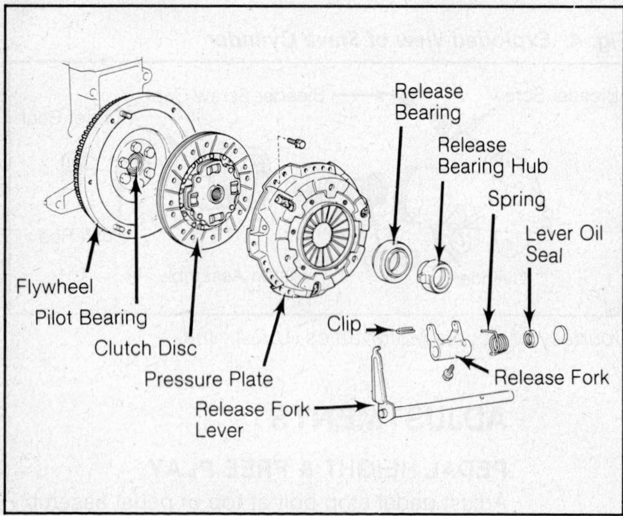

Courtesy of Toyota Motor Sales, U.S.A., Inc.

REMOVAL & INSTALLATION

CLUTCH ASSEMBLY

Removal

1) Disconnect battery negative cable. Remove air cleaner inlet duct. Disconnect clutch cable. Drain cooling system and disconnect upper hose from engine. Remove upper transaxle set bolt. Remove both drive shafts. Remove starter.

2) On 4WD models, remove console box. Remove snap ring and remove shift lever from inside vehicle. Raise and support vehicle. Remove drive shaft and insert plug into extension housing. Disconnect 4WD link and 4WD switch wiring.

3) Remove front exhaust pipe and exhaust clamp on side of transaxle. Remove stiffener plate. Disconnect back-up light switch wire and speedometer cable. On 2WD models, remove No. 1 gear shift rod and lever housing rod.

4) Remove rear support member. Place a wooden block between engine and dash panel. Remove 4 transaxle bolts. Disconnect rear bond cable. Remove transaxle.

5) Loosen pressure plate bolts gradually until spring pressure is released. Remove pressure plate and disc.

Inspection

1) Clean flywheel, pressure plate and clutch disc mating surfaces of all oil, grease, and metal deposits. Inspect for cracks, heat checking, warpage and other defects. Slight surface scoring can be removed with sandpaper. Replace or repair as required.

2) Check wear on facings of clutch disc by measuring depth of each rivet head depression. Minimum depth at any rivet is .012" (.30 mm). Ensure runout of clutch disc facing does not exceed .031" (.79 mm). Replace clutch disc assembly if not within specifications.

3) Check diaphragm spring and pressure plate for wear or damage. If the spring or plate is excessively worn, or damaged, replace pressure plate. Inspect flywheel runout. Flywheel runout limit is .004" (.1 mm) for sedan and .008" (.20 mm) for wagon. If runout is excessive, replace flywheel.

Installation

1) Install disc and pressure plate to flywheel using aligning tool. Gradually tighten bolts in a triangular pattern to 14 ft. lbs. (19 N.m).

2) Using a feeler gauge and Diaphragm Aligner (09302-20021), measure gap between spring tips and tool. If gap is larger than .020" (.50 mm), use Adjuster (09301-00012) to bend springs until alignment is correct. *See Fig. 2.*

Fig. 2: Diaphragm Spring Tip Alignment Check

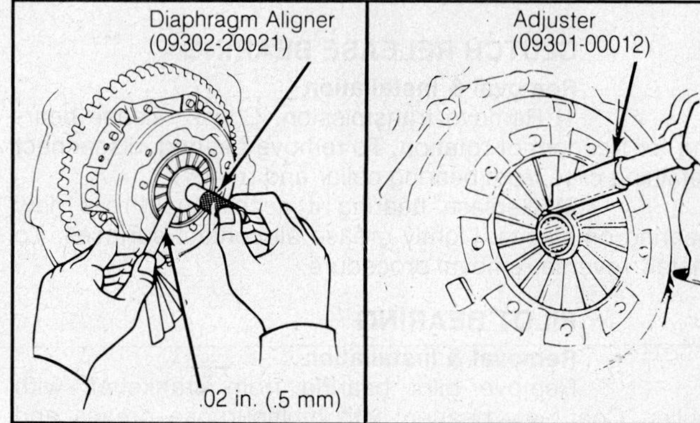

Courtesy of Toyota Motor Sales, U.S.A., Inc.

3) Apply multipurpose grease to the following contact points: release fork and hub, hub and lever, hub and oil seal and hub and bushing. Apply grease to inside of bearing and inside of clutch disc splines. Reverse removal procedure to complete installation.

CLUTCH RELEASE BEARING

Removal

With transmission removed, check release bearing for freedom of rotation with bearing installed on hub. To remove, disconnect retaining clips from bearing collar and slide assembly off transmission input shaft. If bearing does not rotate smoothly, press off collar with Driver (09315-00010).

Installation

Use press and driver to install new bearing on sleeve. Lightly grease inner groove of bearing collar and all contact surfaces. To complete installation, reverse removal procedure.

PILOT BEARING

Removal & Installation

If pilot bearing is worn or damaged, remove from crankshaft with puller. Coat new bearing with multipurpose grease and install in crankshaft with appropriate driver.

ADJUSTMENTS

PEDAL HEIGHT

Measure distance from floor panel to upper surface of clutch pedal. Adjust pedal stopper bolt if not

TOYOTA TERCEL (Cont.)

within specifications. See PEDAL HEIGHT SPECIFICATIONS table in this article. *See Fig. 3.*

PEDAL HEIGHT SPECIFICATIONS

Application	In. (mm)
Tercel	7.130-7.440 (181.10-188.98)

Fig. 3: Pedal Height & Free Play Measurement Points

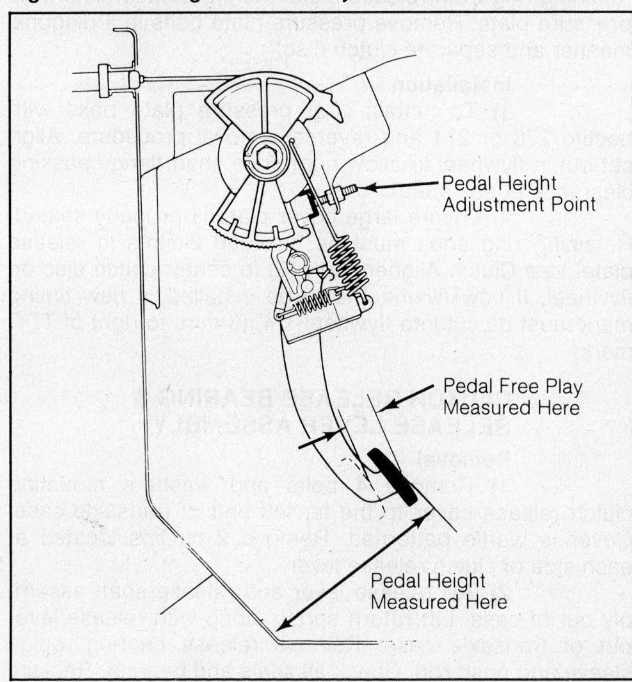

Courtesy of Toyota Motor Sales, U.S.A., Inc.

CLUTCH PEDAL FREE PLAY

Sedan

Check and adjust pedal free play as necessary. *See Fig 3.* See PEDAL FREE PLAY table in this article. Adjust pedal free play at clutch master cylinder push rod.

Wagon

Check and adjust pedal free play as necessary. *See Fig 3.* See PEDAL FREE PLAY table in this article. To adjust, pull slightly on release cable and position pedal selector pawl to give free play. Depress pedal several times and recheck pedal play.

PEDAL FREE PLAY

Application	In. (mm)
Tercel	
Sedan	.04-.19 (1.0-5.0)
Wagon	.08-1.10 (2.0-28.0)

TIGHTENING SPECIFICATIONS

Application	Ft. Lbs. (N.m)
Pressure Plate	14 (19)
Transaxle-to-Engine	
14mm Bolt	29 (39)
17mm Bolt	43 (58)

VOLKSWAGEN CABRIOLET, GOLF, GTI, JETTA & SCIROCCO

DESCRIPTION

The clutch is a single dry disc type, using a diaphragm spring type pressure plate and a clutch release bearing mounted inside the transaxle. The clutch is cable operated.

REMOVAL & INSTALLATION

CLUTCH ASSEMBLY

NOTE: **Transaxle is lowered out of vehicle. Engine remains installed.**

Removal

1) Disconnect battery ground. Attach an engine support assembly. Remove left transaxle mount bolts and mount. Disconnect back-up light wires, speedometer drive cable (plug hole) and clutch cable. *See Fig. 1.*

Fig. 1: Clutch Cable Routing & Adjusting Location

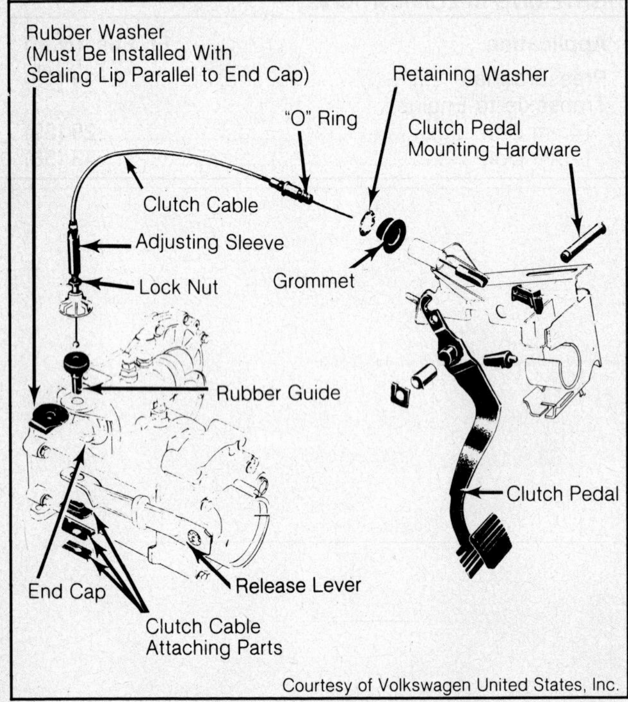

Courtesy of Volkswagen United States, Inc.

2) Remove upper clutch housing-to-transaxle bolts. Remove starter. On models equipped with a flywheel which has cut-outs, align flywheel lug with boss on bellhousing. On all models, disconnect shift linkage at rod lever and relay lever. Remove front selector rod.

NOTE: **Vehicles with cut-outs in flywheel can be identified by a stud/nut at right engine-to-transaxle mounting position. Flywheel on this type vehicle MUST be aligned before separating engine/transaxle.**

3) Remove exhaust pipe bracket. Remove transaxle rear mount and support transaxle on jack. Disconnect left and right drive shafts at transaxle and wire out of way. Remove large plate cover bolts (plate remains on engine). Remove small cover bolts and cover.

4) Remove the right engine-to-transaxle bolt (stud/nut). On vehicles with cut-outs in flywheel, pull transaxle away from engine to clear dowels. Lower and remove transaxle. On all other vehicles, pull transaxle away from engine, while cocking engine so right drive flange clears flywheel. Lower and remove transaxle.

5) With transaxle removed from engine, install Holder (VW558) to ring gear or pressure plate. Pry retaining ring from release plate and lift release plate from pressure plate. Remove pressure plate bolts in a diagonal manner and separate clutch disc.

Installation

1) To install, coat pressure plate bolts with Loctite 270 or 271 and reverse removal procedure. Align cut-out in flywheel to allow right drive shaft flange passing clearance (if equipped).

2) Ensure large cover plate is properly seated. Retaining ring ends must be between 2 slots in release plate. Use Clutch Aligner (VW547) to center clutch disc on flywheel. If new flywheel is to be installed, a new timing mark must be cut into flywheel 1/4" (6 mm) to right of TDC mark.

CLUTCH RELEASE BEARING & RELEASE LEVER ASSEMBLY

Removal

1) Remove 4 bolts and washers mounting clutch release cover to the far left end of transaxle case. Cover is waffle patterned. Remove 2 circlips located at each side of clutch release lever.

2) Pull release lever and release shaft assembly out of case. Lift return spring along with release lever out of transaxle case. Remove release bearing, guide sleeve and push rod. Check all seals and bearing. Replace defective parts.

Installation

1) Coat ends of push rod with multipurpose grease and insert back into position. Grease sliding surface of bearing and guide sleeve.

2) Position return spring and release lever inside transaxle case. Return spring center hook should fit on top of release lever lug. Spring end hooks must point down to hold release lever away from release bearing.

3) Lightly coat release shaft with multipurpose grease. Fit shaft. Work release lever until splines on release shaft mesh with those in release lever.

4) Install circlips. Make sure when release lever is in normal position that return spring has tension. Fit gasket and cover.

ADJUSTMENT

PEDAL TRAVEL

1) Hook a tape measure over top of clutch pedal pad. Tape hook to pad to hold it in place. Pull tape through steering wheel and record measurement at centerline of wheel rim.

2) Press clutch pedal to floor with foot, using normal force for a shift while vehicle is stationary. Record measurement at centerline of wheel rim. If difference between 2 measurements is 4.6" (117 mm) or more, no further adjustments are necessary.

VOLKSWAGEN CABRIOLET, GOLF, GTI, JETTA & SCIROCCO (Cont.)

3) If difference is less than 4.6" (117 mm), adjustments to floor covering will be necessary. Remove push nut from stud behind pedal bracket. Remove left scuff plate from driver's door.

4) Separate carpet from floor on driver's side wheelwell. Lay carpet back into position and measure to see if required amount of travel has been obtained. If so, finish by tucking carpet under hinge pillar and scuff plate.

5) If clutch pedal travel is still short of 4.6" (117 mm), pull back carpet again and cut away portion of floor insulation that is between floorpan and area where pedal bottoms out. Reinstall carpet.

CLUTCH PEDAL FREE PLAY

1) Fully depress clutch pedal 5 times. Loosen lock nut "A". Insert Adjusting Gauge (US 5043). Raise clutch release lever at transaxle until resistance is felt.

2) Turn adjusting sleeve "B" until zero free play is obtained at adjusting gauge. Tighten cable lock nut "A" to 36-48 INCH lbs. (4-6 N.m). Remove adjusting tool. Check clutch free play at clutch release lever. It should be .224-.248" (5.70-6.30 mm). *See Fig. 2.*

TIGHTENING SPECIFICATIONS

Application	Ft. Lbs. (N.m)
Cover Plate Bolt	11 (15)
Drive Shaft-to-Transaxle Bolt	32 (44)
Flywheel Bolts	14 (19)
Pressure Plate Bolts	54 (73)
Transaxle-to-Engine Bolts	55 (75)

Fig. 2: Adjusting Clutch Cable

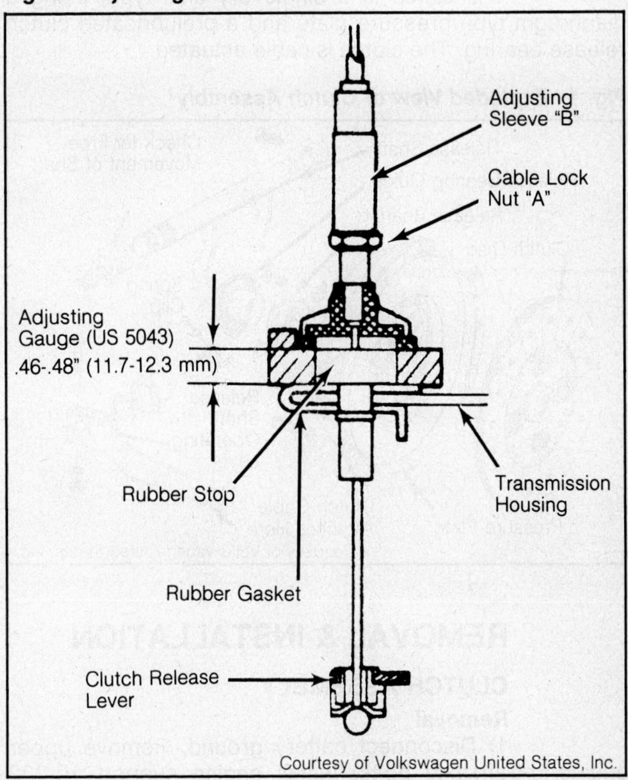

VOLKSWAGEN FOX & QUANTUM

DESCRIPTION

The clutch is a single dry disc type, using a diaphragm type pressure plate and a prelubricated clutch release bearing. The clutch is cable actuated.

Fig. 1: Exploded View of Clutch Assembly

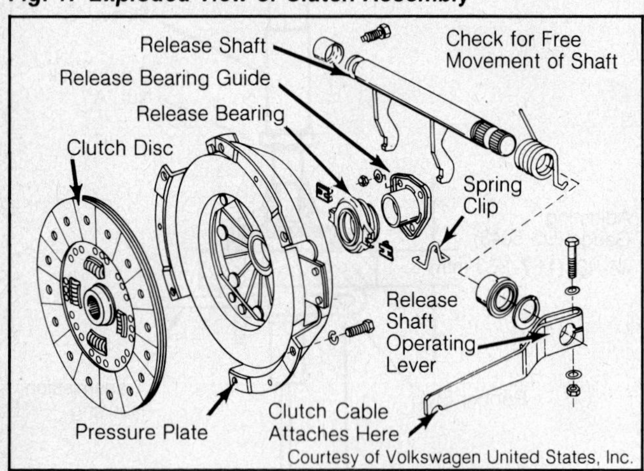

REMOVAL & INSTALLATION

CLUTCH ASSEMBLY

Removal

1) Disconnect battery ground. Remove upper engine-to-transaxle bolts. Install engine support 10-222 and hold engine in place. Remove air cleaner. Detach speedometer cable. Unhook clutch cable. Disconnect exhaust pipe at manifold. Remove transaxle-to-steering rack bracket bolts. Remove engine support bolts. Remove front muffler and exhaust pipe.

2) Remove drive shafts at transaxle. Disconnect back-up light wiring. Remove cover plate bolts. Remove starter. Remove shift rod couping bolt. Pry off shift rod couping ball. Pull off shift rod coupling from shift rod.

3) Position transaxle lift under transaxle and lift up slightly. Loosen bolt "A" and remove bolt "B" from rear transaxle mount. Remove rubber mount. *See Fig. 2.* Remove 3 front transaxle support bolts. Remove lower engine-to-transaxle bolts.

4) Pry transaxle away from engine. Remove transaxle by lowering transaxle lift. Lock flywheel to prevent rotation and index mark pressure plate and flywheel for reassembly referance. Loosen pressure plate bolts 1/4 turn at a time, working in a diagonal pattern. Slide pressure plate off flywheel dowels.

Installation

1) Using a clutch alignment tool, fit pressure plate with clutch. Make sure index marks are observed. Loosely attach clutch assembly.

2) Tighten pressure plate bolts in a crisscross pattern about 2 turns at a time. Position transaxle to engine. Make sure mainshaft splines are clean and lubricated lightly with molybdenum disulphide grease.

3) Reverse removal procedure to install remaining components. Make sure all engine-to-transaxle mounts are aligned and free of tension before tightening bolts and nuts.

Fig. 2: Transaxle Support Assembly

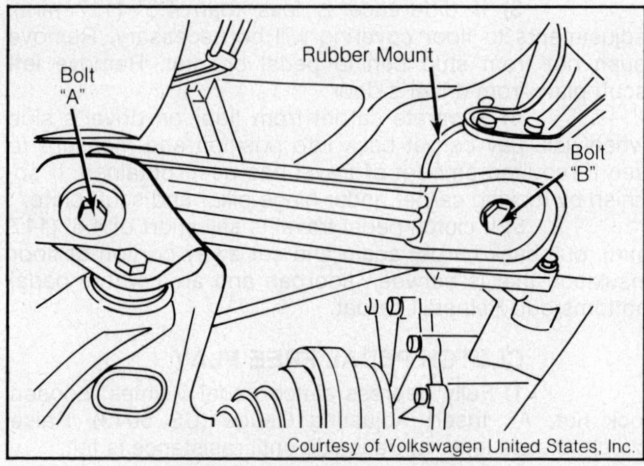

CLUTCH RELEASE BEARING

Removal

With transaxle removed, remove retaining clips and springs from release bearing. Slide bearing off bearing guide.

Installation

To install, lubricate metal guide sleeve with molybdenum disulphide paste. Coat pivoting points between bearing and operating shaft with multipurpose grease. Position bearing to shaft and install retaining clips and springs.

NOTE: Release bearing is prelubricated. DO NOT wash in solvent.

CLUTCH CABLE

Removal

Loosen cable adjusting nuts and free clutch cable housing from support bracket. Separate cable from clutch operating lever (mounted on side of clutch housing). Disconnect cable at pedal and force cable and housing into passenger compartment and remove.

Installation

To install new cable, reverse removal procedure and adjust pedal free play.

NOTE: If new clutch cable has been installed, recheck clutch pedal free play after 300 miles.

ADJUSTMENT

CLUTCH PEDAL FREE PLAY

Clutch pedal free play (measured at pedal pad) should be 9/16" (14 mm). Adjust free play at support bracket on transaxle case by adjusting cable housing length with lock nuts on cable housing.

TIGHTENING SPECIFICATIONS

Application	Ft. Lbs. (N.m)
Pressure Plate-to-Flywheel Bolts	18 (24)
Drive Shaft-to-Transaxle Bolts	
8 mm Bolts	33 (45)
10 mm Bolts	59 (80)
Transaxle-to-Engine Bolts	40 (54)

VOLKSWAGEN VANAGON

DESCRIPTION

The clutch is a single disc, diaphragm spring type. The clutch is hydraulically operated by a firewall mounted master cylinder and a slave cylinder mounted on clutch housing. The slave cylinder is nonadjustable. The clearance is automatically compensated for by internal design of slave cylinder.

REMOVAL & INSTALLATION

CLUTCH ASSEMBLY

Removal

1) Disconnect negative battery cable. Remove bolts attaching top of engine to transaxle. Remove bracket for accelerator cable. Remove left drive shaft from transaxle and support with a wire.

2) Remove clutch cable bracket from transaxle. Remove clutch slave cylinder from mounting bracket and hang on a wire (DO NOT disconnect hydraulic line).

3) Disconnect back-up light wires. Disconnect starter wires and remove starter. Remove right drive shaft from transaxle and support with a wire. Support engine using VW Engine Support (VW 785/1B).

4) Remove shift rod support and shift linkage from transaxle. Support transaxle using transmission jack. Disconnect ground strap from body. Remove front transaxle mount from body.

5) Lower front part of transaxle by loosening spindle of Engine Support (VW 785/1B) until there is enough room to remove transaxle. Remove remaining bolts attaching engine to transaxle. Pull transaxle off of engine guide studs and remove from vehicle.

6) Lock flywheel with flywheel retainer tool. Mark position of pressure plate on flywheel for reassembly reference. Loosen pressure plate-to-flywheel bolts evenly in a diagonal fashion and remove clutch assembly.

Installation

1) Apply molybdenum disulfide grease to release bearing. Clean splines of transaxle input shaft and lubricate lightly with molybdenum disulfide powder. Position clutch disc against flywheel and center using clutch alignment tool.

2) Install pressure plate and tighten bolts evenly in a diagonal fashion. Install transaxle by reversing removal procedure. Tighten front transaxle mounts. Insert rear bolt for slave cylinder before installing. Position air deflector plates correctly.

CLUTCH RELEASE BEARING

Removal

Remove transaxle. Pry off clip retainers from bearing and disengage spring clips. Remove release bearing by sliding off guide tube.

NOTE: **Do not wash bearing in solvent or cleaning solution. Wipe with dry cloth to clean.**

Installation

Lubricate release shaft and release bearing pivot points with molybdenum disulfide grease. Position bearing on shaft and install spring clips and retainers. Make sure clips are correctly positioned. *See Fig. 1*.

Fig. 1: Clutch Release Bearing Assembly

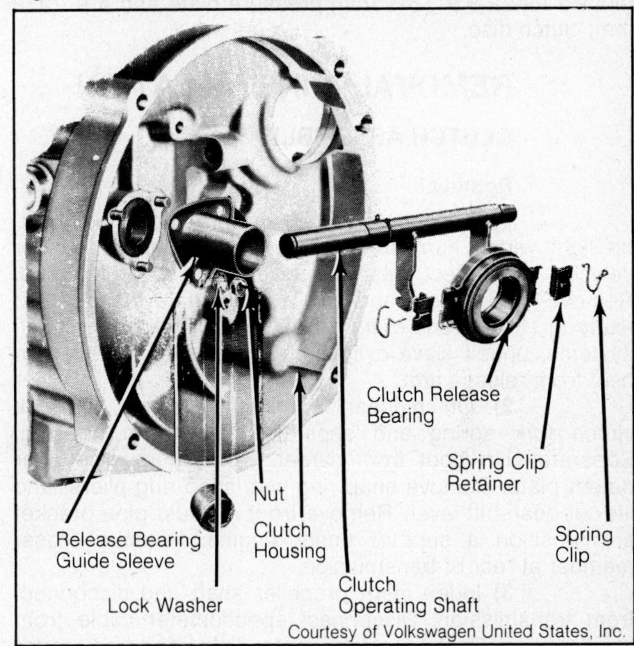

CLUTCH MASTER CYLINDER

Removal

Disconnect master cylinder push rod at clutch pedal by removing cotter pin and clevis. Disconnect hydraulic line at cylinder. Remove cylinder attaching bolts and remove cylinder from firewall.

Installation

To install, reverse removal procedure and bleed system.

CLUTCH SLAVE CYLINDER

Removal

Disconnect hydraulic line from slave cylinder. To disconnect slave cylinder, push rod from clutch lever ball. Remove mounting bolts and remove cylinder.

Installation

Grease clutch lever ball lightly. Insert rear bolt to slave cylinder and install on vehicle. Install front bolt. Attach hydraulic line and clutch lever. Bleed system.

TIGHTENING SPECIFICATIONS

Application	Ft. Lbs. (N.m)
Axle Shaft-to-Transaxle Bolts	33 (45)
Drain Plug	14 (20)
Engine-to-Transaxle Nuts & Bolts	22 (30)
Flywheel-to-Crankshaft Bolts	80 (110)
Pressure Plate-to-Flywheel Bolts	18 (25)

Clutches

VOLVO

DL, GL, Turbo, 760 GLE

DESCRIPTION

Clutch is single dry disc type, using a diaphragm spring type pressure plate. All DL, GL and Turbo models use a 8.5" (216 mm) clutch disc. The 760 GLE models use a 9.5" (241 mm) pressure plate and a 9" (229 mm) clutch disc.

REMOVAL & INSTALLATION

CLUTCH ASSEMBLY

Removal

1) Disconnect battery ground cable and back-up light wiring harness connector. Working from under vehicle, disconnect gearshift lever from gearshift rod. Remove lock screw and pin, and hold lever to avoid exerting force on transmission. On hydraulic clutch systems, unbolt slave cylinder from housing and disconnect from release arm.

2) On mechanical clutch systems, unhook clutch fork spring and separate cable from housing. Separate shift boot from carpet. Remove reverse gear detent plate. Remove snap ring with snap ring pliers, and lift out gearshift lever. Remove front exhaust pipe bracket and position a support under engine. Remove cross-member at rear of transmission.

3) Index mark propeller shaft and disconnect from transmission. Disconnect speedometer cable from transmission. Remove starter motor bolts, and free starter from clutch housing. Remove clutch housing cover plates and all bolts except 2 at bottom. Install transmission jack and remove last 2 clutch housing bolts.

4) Pull transmission to rear, and turn to clear propeller shaft tunnel. Lower transmission from vehicle. Loosen pressure plate bolts gradually in a diagonal pattern and remove clutch assembly. Check pilot bearing and flywheel surface for any cracks or excess wear.

Installation

Reverse removal procedure, making sure that flywheel and pressure plate are free from grease. Using alignment tool, install clutch disc with long side of hub facing back. Install pressure plate, and tighten bolts gradually in a diagonal pattern. Adjust clutch fork free travel.

NOTE: Since differences in pressure plates and bearings exist between models, components must never be interchanged.

CLUTCH CABLE

Removal & Installation

1) Raise vehicle, disconnect return spring and loosen cable. Disconnect cable from fork, bellhousing and clamp at fuel filter.

NOTE: There is no return spring on Turbo models.

2) Remove underdash panel. Remove locking pin and rubber bushing. Pull cable out of firewall. To install, reverse removal procedure. Adjust clutch fork free play to specification.

Fig. 1: Volvo Mechanical Linkage Clutch System

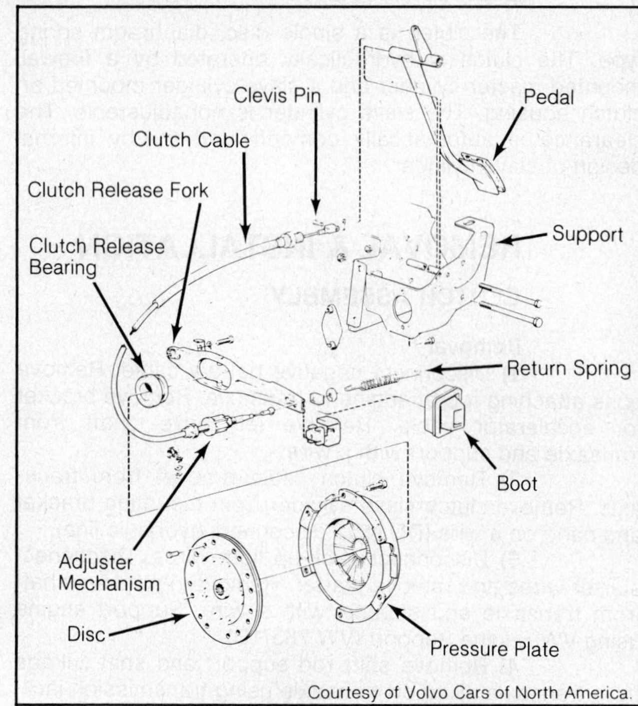

Courtesy of Volvo Cars of North America.

CLUTCH MASTER CYLINDER

Removal

1) Remove panel under instrument panel. Remove pin and locking spring from clutch pedal. Disconnect hose from clutch fluid reservoir.

Fig. 2: Volvo Hydraulic Clutch System

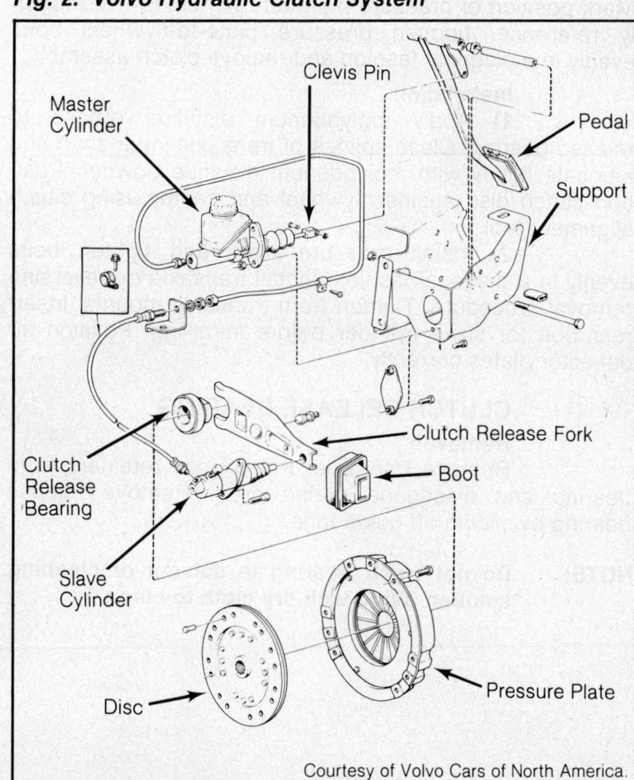

Courtesy of Volvo Cars of North America.

VOLVO (Cont.)

NOTE: **Hydraulic brake fluid may damage vehicle paint.**

2) Screw out nipple from cylinder housing, and place container under it to collect fluid. Remove bolts holding cylinder and remove cylinder.

Installation

To install, secure cylinder. Connect nipple and hose from fluid reservoir. Install pin and locking spring making sure there is .04" (1.0 mm) clearance between push rod and piston. Adjust if necessary. Install panel under instrument panel. Fill reservoir with fluid and bleed system.

CLUTCH SLAVE CYLINDER

Removal & Installation

Disconnect hose from slave cylinder. Remove slave cylinder mounting bolts and remove cylinder. To install reverse removal procedure and bleed hydraulic system.

OVERHAUL

MASTER CYLINDER

Disassembly

Remove dust shield and push rod. Remove snap ring and washer. Pull out piston and remove spring. Remove seals from piston and thoroughly clean and inspect.

Reassembly

To assemble, soak new piston seals in brake fluid and install on piston. Install spring and piston in cylinder. Install washer and snap ring. Install dust shield and push rod.

SLAVE CYLINDER

Disassembly

Remove dust shield and push rod. Remove snap ring and pull out piston and spring. Remove piston seal.

Reassembly

To assemble, immerse new seals in brake fluid and install on piston. Install spring and piston in cylinder. Install snap ring, dust shield and push rod.

HYDRAULIC CLUTCH BLEEDING

1) Fill brake fluid reservoir. Connect bleeder wrench to bleeder screw on slave cylinder and submerge end of hose in a jar containing brake fluid.

2) Have an assistant depress clutch pedal and bleed system until air bubbles are no longer present. Tighten bleeder screw and refill reservoir to proper level.

PILOT BEARING

Removal & Installation

Remove bearing using Puller (4090). Pack bearing with heat-resistant grease and install into crankshaft using proper size driver.

ADJUSTMENT

CLUTCH FREE PLAY

Using adjustment mechanism attached to clutch housing, set free play. Adjustment is correct when approximately .04-.12" (1.0-3.0 mm) clutch fork free play is obtained.

Fig. 3: Adjusting Clutch Free Play

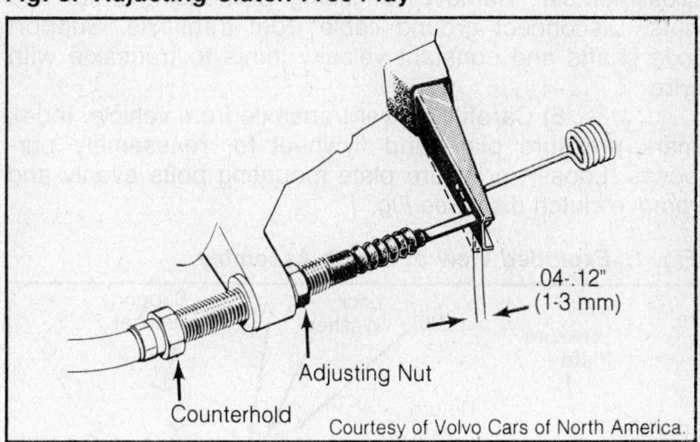

Courtesy of Volvo Cars of North America.

TIGHTENING SPECIFICATIONS

Application	Ft. Lbs. (N.m)
Engine-to-Transmission Bolt	25-35 (35-50)

Clutches

YUGO

DESCRIPTION

The clutch is a dry, single plate, diaphragm spring type. The clutch control mechanism is mechanically operated and consists of the clutch pedal, clutch cable, release lever and release bearing.

REMOVAL & INSTALLATION

CLUTCH ASSEMBLY

Removal

1) Disconnect negative battery cable. Remove spare tire. Raise and support front end of vehicle. Drain transaxle oil. Unscrew ring nut from transaxle housing. Remove speedometer cable. Disconnect clutch cable from release lever and unhook return spring. Support engine and unscrew bellhousing top bolts.

2) Remove front wheel hub cap. Unscrew constant velocity joint hub nuts. Remove left front wheel. Disconnect left tie rod from steering arm. Remove sway bar by unscrewing nuts on control arms and bolts on body brackets.

3) Remove bolt holding control arm to body. Disconnect back-up light switch wires. Disconnect exhaust pipe bracket and gearshift linkage. Remove starter motor.

4) Remove flywheel cover. Remove lower crossmember. Remove remaining bellhousing bolts and nuts. Disconnect ground cable from transaxle. Support axle shafts and constant velocity joints to transaxle with wire.

5) Carefully lower transaxle from vehicle. Index mark pressure plate and flywheel for reassembly purposes. Loosen pressure plate mounting bolts evenly and remove clutch disc. *See Fig. 1.*

Fig. 1: Exploded View of Clutch Assembly

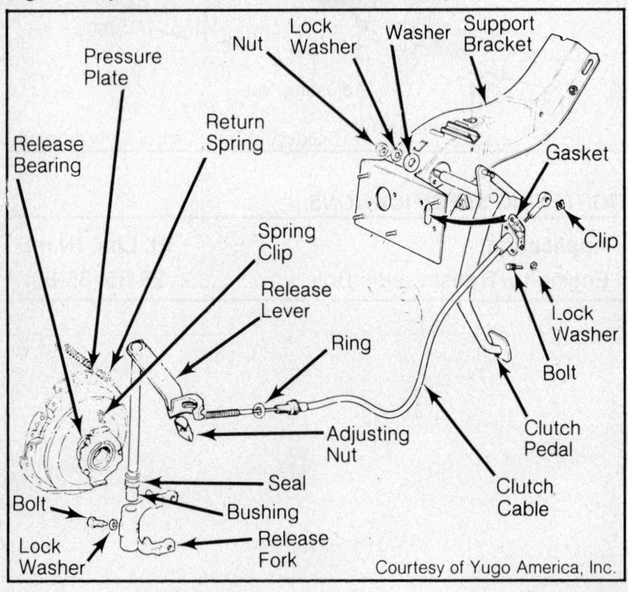

Inspection

1) Check flywheel and pressure plate friction surfaces for signs of cracks, scoring or burns. Minor imperfections can be removed from pressure plate with medium grit emery cloth. If deeply scored or excessively worn, replace pressure plate.

2) Ensure clutch disc is not warped. Check that surface of friction material is not less than .059" (1.50 mm) from rivet heads. Check that fingers of diaphragm spring are not broken, cracked or misaligned. Check that springs, plate or splines are not damaged. Replace disc if damaged. Check mounting hardware for damage and replace (if necessary).

Installation

1) If flywheel was removed, replace and tighten mounting bolts to specification. Make sure clutch and flywheel surfaces are clean. Position clutch disc and pressure plate, align index marks and loosely attach pressure plate to flywheel.

2) Install clutch alignment tool and gradually tighten mounting bolts to specification. Remove alignment tool, lightly coat transaxle input shaft with molybdenum grease and install transaxle. To complete installation, reverse removal procedure.

RELEASE BEARING

Removal

1) Remove clutch assembly. Disconnect spring clip and remove release bearing. Ensure clutch release bearing turns freely. If bearing is noisy, rough or dry, it must be replaced.

2) Check that lever moves freely and does not bind. If binding, disassemble by removing holding bolt and lock washer. Check bearing surfaces and shaft bushing for wear. Replace bushing if worn.

NOTE: **DO NOT clean release bearing with solvent. Use only compressed air.**

Installation

Coat contact surface with molybdenum grease. To complete installation, reverse removal procedure.

CLUTCH CABLE & PEDAL

Removal

1) To remove cable, disconnect clip from pin on clutch pedal. Remove cable eyelet from pin. In engine compartment, remove spare tire. Remove nuts holding cable in lever. Remove threaded end of cable from lever and remove ring. Remove 2 bolts and remove cable.

2) To remove pedal, remove clutch pedal mounting nut and washers. Slide pedal shaft out of bracket.

Installation

Lightly coat contact surface between release lever and cable nut with molybdenum grease. To install clutch cable, reverse removal procedure.

ADJUSTMENTS

PEDAL FREE PLAY

Adjust clutch pedal free play to 1" (25 mm).

TIGHTENING SPECIFICATIONS

Applications	Ft. Lbs. (N.m)
Clutch & Brake Pedal Bracket Nut	11 (15)
Clutch Pedal Pivot Shaft Nut	11 (15)
Flywheel Bolts	61 (83)
Pressure Plate Bolts	12 (16)
Release Fork Bolt	19 (26)

SECTION 8

DRIVE AXLES

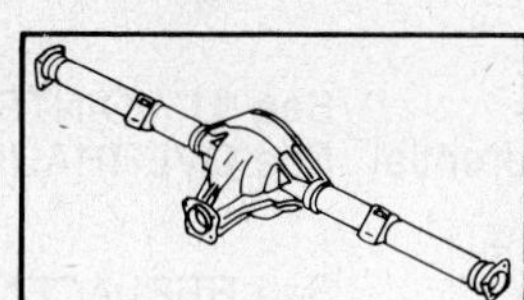

CONTENTS

TROUBLE SHOOTING Page

All Models 8-2

GEAR TOOTH PATTERNS

All Models 8-4

FWD AXLE SHAFTS

All Models 8-5

DRIVE AXLES

Audi 4000CS Quattro & 5000CS Quattro 8-29
BMW Integral Carrier 8-33
Chrysler Motors
- Front Axle - 4WD (Raider, Ram-50) 8-46
- Integral (Colt Vista 4WD & Conquest) 8-37
- Rear Axle (Raider & Ram-50) 8-51

Ford Motor Co. (Merkur XR4Ti) 8-57
Honda Rear Axle (Civic Wagon 4WD) 8-62
Isuzu
- Front Axle - 4WD (P'UP & Trooper II) 8-66
- Integral (Impulse Non-Turbo) 8-71
- Rear Axle (Impulse Turbo, P'UP & Trooper II) 8-76

Jaguar 8-82
Mazda
- (RX7, B2200 & B2600) 8-88

Mercedes-Benz 8-94
Mitsubishi
- Front Axle - 4WD (Montero & Pickup) 8-46
- Integral (Starion) 8-37
- Rear Axle (Montero, Pickup & Van/Wagon) 8-51

Nissan
- Front Axle - 4WD (Pathfinder & Pickup) 8-102
- Integral Housing (200SX, 300ZX & Stanza Wagon 4WD) 8-109
- Separate Carrier (4WD Pathfinder & Pickup) 8-115
- Model C200 Rear Axle (4WD Pathfinder, Pickup 4WD & Van) 8-119

Peugeot Split Housing - I.R.S. 8-124
Porsche Drive Axles 8-132
Subaru 4WD Rear 8-135
Suzuki 8-139
Toyota
- Integral Housing - Except Van 8-143
- Integral Housing - Van (4WD Front) 8-152
- Separate Carrier 8-154

Volvo 8-164
Volkswagen Quantum Syncro 8-29

LOCKING HUBS

All Manufacturers 8-169

NOTE: ALSO SEE GENERAL INDEX.

Drive Axles

TROUBLE SHOOTING RWD VEHICLES

CONDITION	POSSIBLE CAUSE	CORRECTION
General Knocking or Clunking	Excessive differential side gear clearance	See OVERHAUL in DRIVE AXLES
	Worn rear axle pinion shaft	See OVERHAUL in DRIVE AXLES
	Worn case or differential cross shaft in case	See OVERHAUL in DRIVE AXLES
	Excessive end play of axle shafts-to-differential cross shaft	See OVERHAUL in DRIVE AXLES
	Gear teeth mutilated	See OVERHAUL in DRIVE AXLES
	Improper axle shaft spline fit	See OVERHAUL in DRIVE AXLES
	Total axle backlash too great	See OVERHAUL in DRIVE AXLES
	Incorrect driveline angle	See ADJUSTMENT in PROPELLER SHAFTS ALIGNMENT
Clunking During Initial Engagement	Excessive differential side gear clearance	See OVERHAUL in DRIVE AXLES
	Excessive ring and pinion backlash	See OVERHAUL in DRIVE AXLES
	Worn or loose pinion shaft	See OVERHAUL in DRIVE AXLES
Gear Howl or Whine	Improper pinion depth	See OVERHAUL in DRIVE AXLES
	Improper ring gear backlash adjustment	See OVERHAUL in DRIVE AXLES
	Improper ring gear runout	See OVERHAUL in DRIVE AXLES
	Improper bearing preload	See OVERHAUL in DRIVE AXLES
	Excessive pinion bearing wear	See OVERHAUL in DRIVE AXLES
Clicking or Chatter on Turns	Wrong lubricant in differential	Drain and refill differential
	Clutch plates worn	See LUBRICATION in POSITIVE TRACTION DIFFERENTIALS
	Differential side gears or pinion worn	See OVERHAUL in DRIVE AXLES
Knock or Click Approximately Every Second Revolution	Flat spot on rear wheel bearing	See OVERHAUL in DRIVE AXLES
Grunt Noise on Stops	Lack of lubricant in propeller shaft slip yoke	See "U" JOINTS in PROPELLER SHAFTS
Groan in Forward or Reverse	Wrong lubricant in differential	Change to proper lubricant
Knock in Drive Line in High Gear at 10 MPH	Worn or damaged universal joints	See "U" JOINTS
	Side gear hub counterbore in differential worn oversize	See OVERHAUL in DRIVE AXLES
Ping, Snap or Click in Drive Line	Loose upper or lower control arm bushing bolts	See REPLACEMENT in REAR SUSPENSION
	Loose companion flange	See OVERHAUL in DRIVE AXLES
Scraping Noise	Slinger, companion flange or end yoke rubbing on rear axle carrier	See OVERHAUL in DRIVE AXLES
Car Will Not Move	Broken axle shaft	See OVERHAUL in DRIVE AXLES
	Broken pinion stem	See OVERHAUL in DRIVE AXLES
	Axle lock-up	See OVERHAUL in DRIVE AXLES
	Broken gear teeth	See OVERHAUL in DRIVE AXLES
	Broken wheel bearing	See OVERHAUL in DRIVE AXLES
Axle Backlash	Excessive ring and pinion clearance	See OVERHAUL in DRIVE AXLES
	Loose fitting differential pinion shaft	See OVERHAUL in DRIVE AXLES
	Excessive side gear-to-case clearance	See OVERHAUL in DRIVE AXLES
Leakage at Differential or Driveshaft	Rough outside surface on splined yoke	See OVERHAUL in DRIVE AXLES
	Drive pinion seal or nut	See OVERHAUL in DRIVE AXLES
	Axle cover gasket, or axle shaft seal	See OVERHAUL in DRIVE AXLES

TROUBLE SHOOTING RWD VEHICLES (Cont.)

CONDITION	POSSIBLE CAUSE	CORRECTION
Roughness, Shudder or Vibration Upon Heavy Acceleration	Double cardan joint ball seats worn, and ball set spring may be broken	See "U" JOINTS in PROPELLER SHAFTS
	Excessive joint angle	See PROPELLER SHAFTS
	Sticking inboard joint assembly	See "U" JOINTS in PROPELLER SHAFTS
	Worn or damaged inboard or outboard joints	See "U" JOINTS in PROPELLER SHAFTS
Roughness, Vibration or Body Boom Experienced at Any Speed	Rough rear wheel bearings	See OVERHAUL in DRIVE AXLES
	Unbalanced or damaged propeller shaft	Check and/or balance propeller shaft
	Unbalanced or damaged tires	Check and/or balance tires
	Worn or damaged "U" joints	See "U" JOINTS in PROPELLER SHAFTS
	Bent or damaged drive shaft, or undercoating on drive shaft	Check drive shaft balance
	Tight "U" joints	Lubricate or replace as necessary
	Burrs or gouges on companion flange	Resurface or replace flange
	Drive shaft or companion shaft runout too great	Repair or replace as necessary
	Excessive looseness at slip yoke spline	See OVERHAUL in DRIVE AXLES

TROUBLE SHOOTING FWD VEHICLES

CONDITION	POSSIBLE CAUSE	CORRECTION
Grease Leaks	Joint boot torn, split or cracked	See DISASSEMBLY in FWD AXLES SHAFTS
Clicking Noise on Cornering	Damaged or worn outboard joint	See DISASSEMBLY in FWD AXLES SHAFTS
Clunk Noise on Acceleration	Damaged or worn inboard joints Transaxle gears or bearings	See DISASSEMBLY in FWD AXLES SHAFTS
Vibration or Shudder on Acceleration	Sticking, damaged or worn joints Excessive alignment or spring height	See DISASSEMBLY in FWD AXLES SHAFTS
Squealing or Humming	Insufficient or Improper Joint Lubrication	See DISASSEMBLY in FWD AXLES SHAFTS
	Wheel Bearing Problem	See HUB & BEARING ASSEMBLY in FWD AXLES SHAFTS

GEAR TOOTH PATTERNS

INSPECTION

Clean lubricant from internal parts, then rotate gears and inspect for wear or damage. Mount a dial indicator to housing and check backlash at several points around ring gear. Backlash must be within specifications at all points. If no defects are found, check gear tooth contact pattern.

GEAR TOOTH CONTACT PATTERN

NOTE: **Drive pattern should be well centered on ring gear teeth. Coast pattern should be centered but may be slightly toward toe of ring gear teeth.**

1) Paint ring gear teeth with a marking compound. Apply some form of load to differential case to resist rotation. Rotate pinion gear until ring gear has made one full revolution .

2) Rotate pinion gear in opposite direction to complete one full revolution of ring gear. Examine ring gear teeth for contact pattern. Correct as necessary by moving appropriate shims. Backlash between drive gear and pinion must be maintained within specified limits until correct tooth pattern is obtained.

ADJUSTMENTS

GEAR BACKLASH & PINION SHIM CHANGES

NOTE: **Change in tooth pattern is directly related to change in shim and/or backlash adjustment.**

1) With no change in backlash, moving pinion further from ring gear moves drive pattern toward heel and top of tooth, and moves coast pattern toward toe and top of tooth.

2) With no change in backlash, moving pinion closer to ring gear moves drive pattern toward toe and bottom of tooth, and moves coast pattern toward heel and bottom of tooth.

3) With no change in pinion shim thickness, an increase in backlash moves ring gear further from pinion. Drive pattern moves toward heel and top of tooth, and coast pattern moves toward heel and top of tooth.

4) With no change in pinion shim thickness, a decrease in backlash moves ring gear closer to pinion gear. Drive pattern moves toward toe and bottom of tooth, and coast pattern moves toward toe and bottom of tooth.

Fig. 1: Gear Tooth Contact Pattern

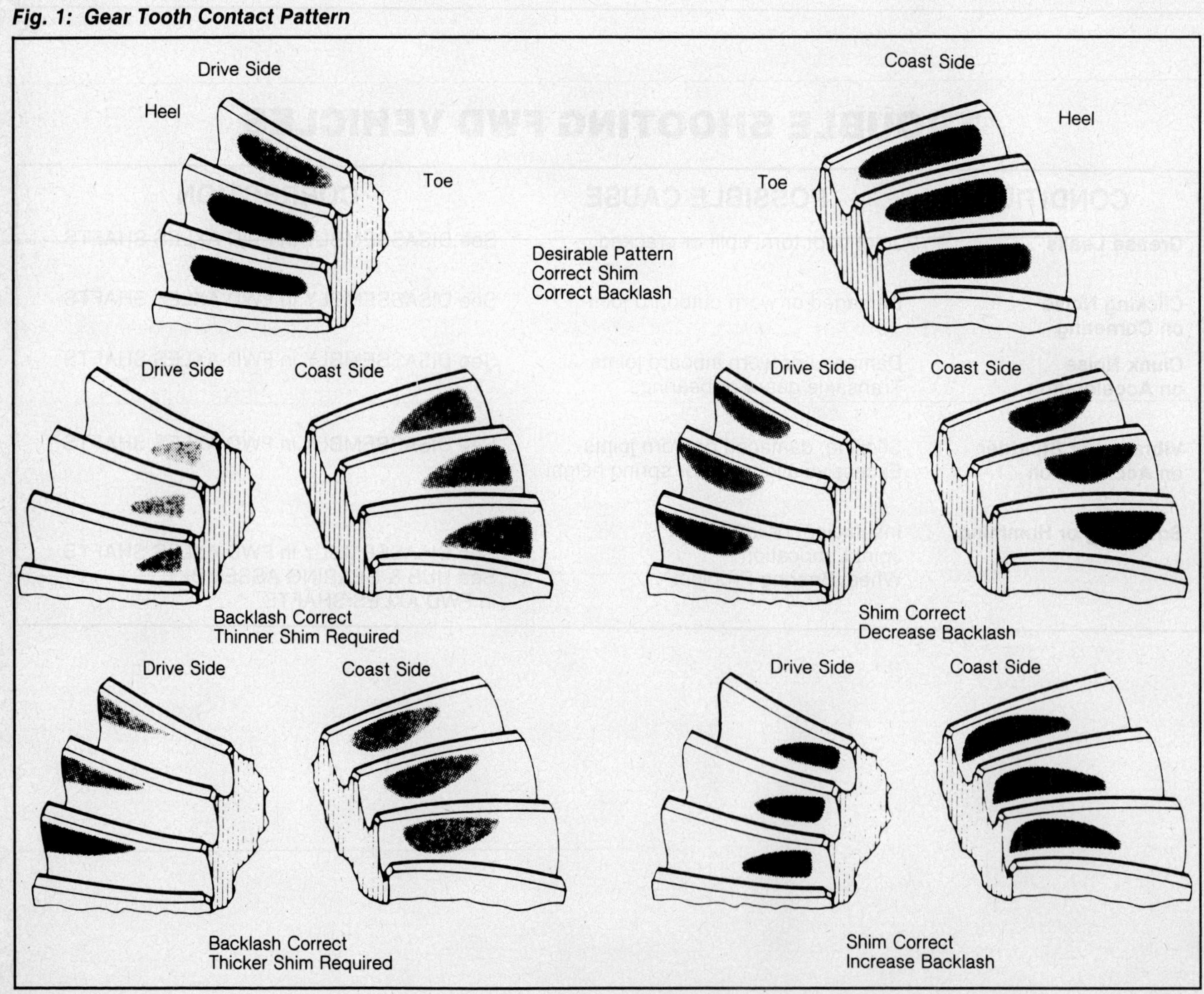

FWD Axle Shafts

ALL MODELS

Acura, Audi, Chrysler Motors, Ford Motor Co., General Motors, Honda, Hyundai, Isuzu, Mazda, Mitsubishi, Nissan, Saab, Sterling, Subaru, Suzuki, Toyota, Volkswagen, Yugo

DESCRIPTION

Axle shafts transfer power from transaxle to driving wheels. All axle shafts consist of a shaft and flexible Constant Velocity (CV) joint at each end. Inner CV joint is splined or bolted to transaxle. Outer CV joint is splined to hub assembly and secured by axle shaft nut.

The inner and outer CV joints are enclosed by a CV joint boot. The boot maintains lubrication in the joint and prevents contamination from entering the joint. Boots must be replaced when signs of leakage or cracks are present. The inner CV joint can be repaired without replacing assembly. The outer CV joint must be replaced as an assembly.

There are 3 different types of axle shaft CV joints. The Double Offset Joint (DOJ). The Birfield Joint (BJ) and the Tripod Joint (TJ) (sometimes referred to as tripot).

On Audi, Toyota Camry and Corolla, and Volkswagen models, the inner CV joint is bolted to differential case drive flanges. On Subaru models, inner CV joint is splined onto differential output shafts and secured with a pin. On Saab models, inner CV joint housing is pressed into differential side gear and secured with a snap ring. On all other models, inner CV joint is splined into differential side gear and held with a retaining ring.

TROUBLE SHOOTING

TROUBLE SHOOTING CHART

Condition	Possible Cause
Grease Leaks	CV boot torn or cracked
Clicking Noise on Cornering	Damaged outer CV
Clunk Noise on Acceleration	Damaged inner CV
Vibration or Shudder on Acceleration	Sticking, damaged or worn CV Misalignment or spring height

REMOVAL, DISASSEMBLY, REASSEMBLY & INSTALLATION

AXLE SHAFTS

CAUTION: **Vehicle weight must not be allowed to rest on wheel bearings and hub WITHOUT axle shaft installed and axle shaft nut tightened to specification.**

Removal (Acura & Sterling)

1) Remove wheel/tire assembly and drain transaxle fluid. Remove axle shaft lock tab from nut and loosen nut by applying brakes. On Legend models, remove damper pinch bolt and damper fork bolt. Remove damper fork. *See Fig. 1.*

Fig. 1: Damper Fork & Pinch Bolt Location

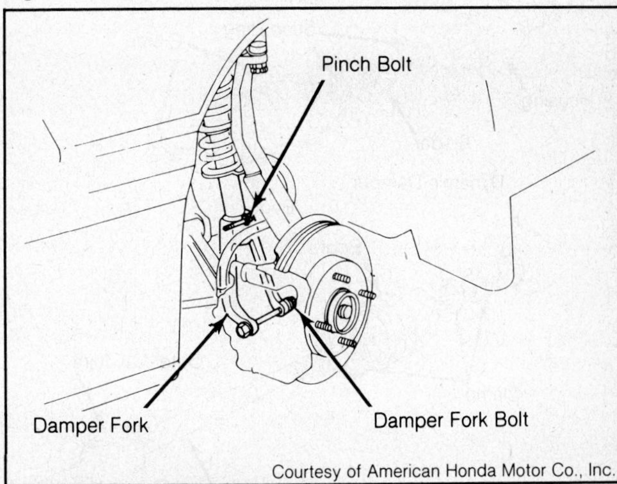

Acura shown, Sterling is similar.

2) On Integra models, raise lower control arm with a floor jack. On all models, remove lower ball joint cotter pin and nut. Using a bearing puller, separate the lower control arm and steering knuckle. Pull steering knuckle outward and remove axle shaft from hub assembly. Use a plastic hammer to drive axle out if necessary.

CAUTION: **Do not pull on inboard CV joint or disassembly may occur. Be careful not to damage seals.**

3) Using a screwdriver, carefully pry the inner CV joint and shaft assembly approximately .5" (12 mm). This will dislodge the retaining ring from transaxle or intermediate shaft. Grip both sides of the inner CV joint and remove the axle shaft from vehicle.

CAUTION: **Do not disassemble the outer CV joint. This must be replaced as an assembly.**

Disassembly (Acura & Sterling)

NOTE: **Mark roller to roller groove alignment to ensure proper reassembly.**

1) Remove axle shaft from vehicle and place on work bench. Remove inner CV joint boot clamps and discard. Slide boot toward the outer CV joint to access inner CV joint. *See Fig. 2.*

2) Index axle shaft, inner CV joint housing and spider roller to ensure reassembly to original location and position. Remove housing from spider assembly. Index rollers and spider to ensure reassembly to original location. Remove rollers from spider.

3) Remove snap ring securing spider to axle shaft and remove spider. Remove stopper ring and slide boot off axle shaft. Remove outer CV joint boot clamps. Slide boot off axle shaft inner CV joint end. Do not disassemble outer CV joint. Replace as an assembly only.

Reassembly (Acura & Sterling)

1) Thoroughly clean and inspect axle shaft. Replace all defective parts. Place outer CV joint boot into position but do not install clamps. Assemble inner CV joint.

FWD Axle Shafts

ALL MODELS (Cont.)

Fig. 2: Exploded View of Acura Axle Shaft

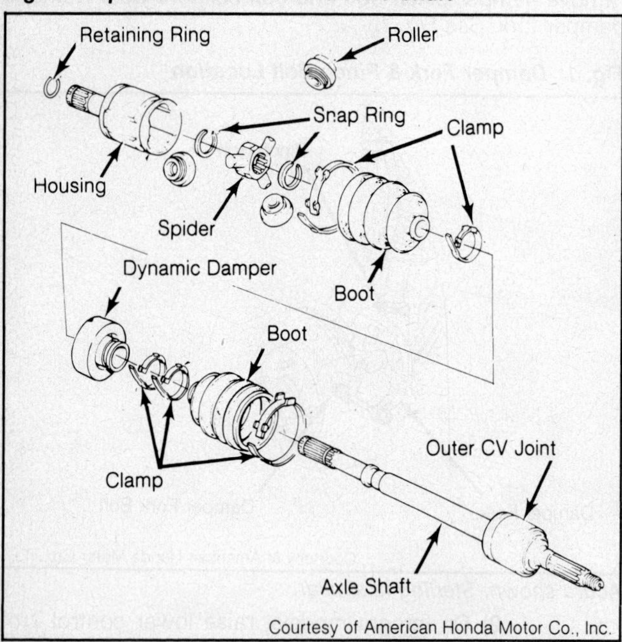

Legend model is shown, Sterling is similar.

2) Install stopper ring in groove on axle shaft. Install spider and snap ring. Lube spider and inside bore of rollers and install rollers. Ensure rollers are aligned with marks made at disassembly and high side of rollers are facing upward.

NOTE: Sterling gives no specifications for axle shaft lengths.

3) Pack inner CV joint housing with grease. Align housing marks made at disassembly and install housing on spider assembly. Adjust the standard length of axle shaft. *See Figs. 3, 4 and 5.* Position boots halfway between full compression and full extension and install new boot clamps.

4) Lightly tap doubled-over portion of boot clamp to reduce their height. Install a new retaining ring on end of inner CV joint and install axle shaft.

Installation (Acura & Sterling)

1) Measure the assembled axle shaft and ensure length is within specifications. *See Fig. 3 or 5.* Install damper to specified position. *See Fig. 4.* Install a new retaining ring in groove at end of axle shaft. Install new bands on boots.

Fig. 3: Assembled Acura Integra Axle Shaft Length

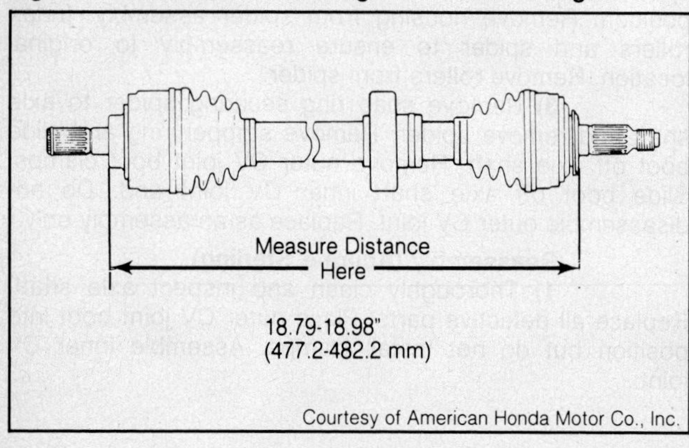

Fig. 4: Installation of Assembled Acura Integra Damper

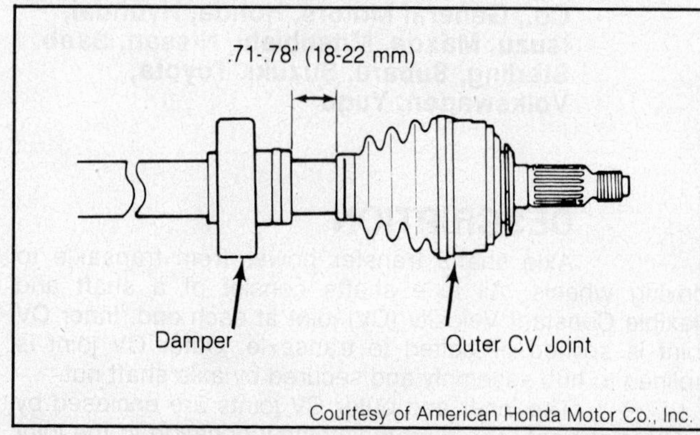

2) Slide axle into transaxle or intermediate shaft. Ensure retaining ring seats fully in groove. Check by attempting to pull axle out of installed position.

3) Pull hub assembly away from axle shaft and slide axle into hub assembly. Install axle shaft nut and lightly tighten. Position ball joint in hub. Raise lower control arm with floor jack and install ball joint nut. Tighten nut to specification.

4) Install cotter pin and secure. Remove floor jack. Tighten axle shaft nut to specification.

Fig. 5: Legend Axle Shaft Length

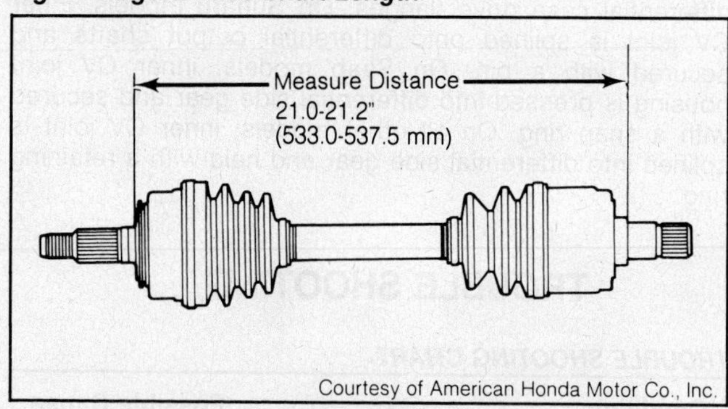

Removal (Audi & Volkswagen)

1) Remove hub cap. Loosen axle shaft nut. Raise and support vehicle. Remove axle nut and wheel. Remove Allen bolts connecting inner CV joint to transmission case flange. *See Fig. 6.*

2) On 5000S models with automatic transaxle, remove sway bar brackets. On all other models, mark position of both ball joint flanges on control arms. Remove ball joint from control arm and pull pivot mounting outward while removing axle shaft. Press axle shaft out of hub with puller and guide past transaxle.

NOTE: Axle shafts should be disassembled ONLY to replace defective rubber boots. If boots are replaced, check all components for wear or damage and replace assembly if necessary.

Disassembly (Audi & Volkswagen)

1) On inner CV joint, remove circlip from axle shaft and drive protective cap from CV joint. Place axle shaft in Holder (VW402) and press CV joint from shaft with Adapter (VW408a), supporting hub to prevent damage.

2) Pivot hub and cage assembly out of inner joint. Push out and remove balls. Align ball hub grooves with cage and remove hub. *See Fig. 7.*

ALL MODELS (Cont.)

Fig. 6: Exploded View of Typical Audi & Volkswagen Axle Shaft Assembly

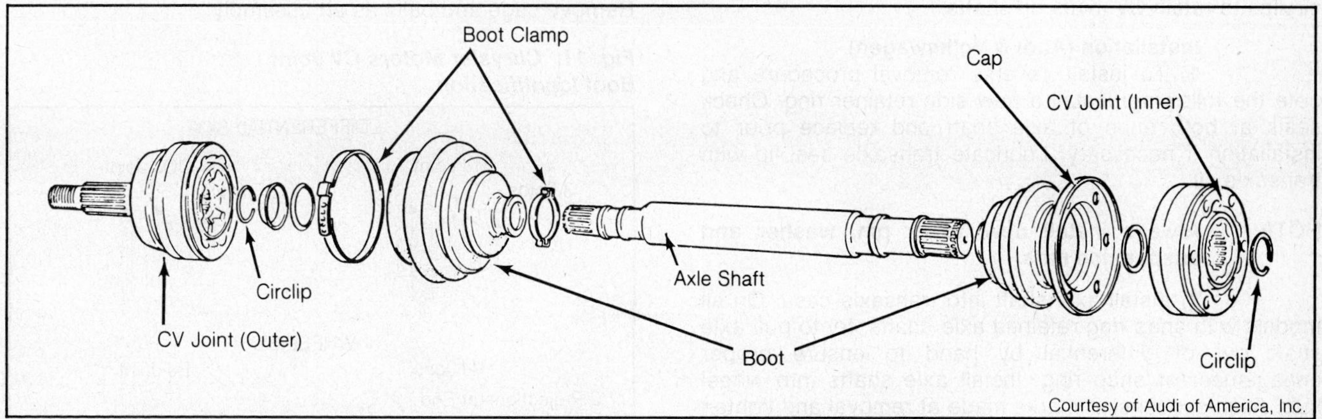

NOTE: Inner CV joint and ball hub are matched sets. DO NOT interchange with outer joint. CV joint balls cannot be interchanged between CV joints.

Fig. 7: Removing Audi & Volkswagen Inner CV Joint Ball Hub

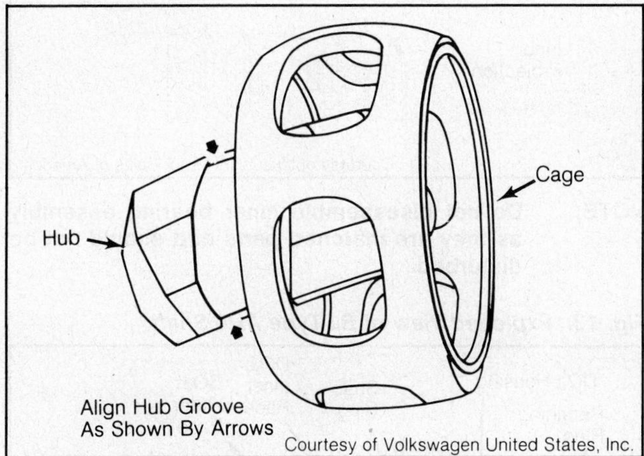

3) Remove and discard inner boot clamp and boot. On outer CV joint, spread circlip inside ball hub and drive CV joint off axle shaft with brass drift by tapping on hub. Mark position of ball hub and outer joint. Tilt cage and remove each ball.

4) Align cage perpendicular to joint. Align 2 large openings of cage with raised portions of joint and remove cage and hub. Position one retainer of hub in large opening and remove hub by tilting outward. Remove and discard outer boot and clamp.

Reassembly (Audi & Volkswagen)

1) To reassemble CV joints, reverse disassembly procedure and note the following: lubricate joints with 3 ozs. of molybdenum disulphide grease. After inserting balls into inner CV joint hub and cage, insert hub and cage into joint in a perpendicular position.

2) Chamfer of ball hub splines must face larger diameter of joint. Rotate ball and cage into position and ensure CV joint wide ball groove and narrow hub groove are on same side of joint. *See Fig. 8.* Joint is correctly assembled if hub can move over shaft splines by hand.

3) Outer CV joint alignment marks must match after reassembly. Replace dust boots and clamps. Install

Fig. 8: Installing Audi & Volkswagen Ball Hub & Cage

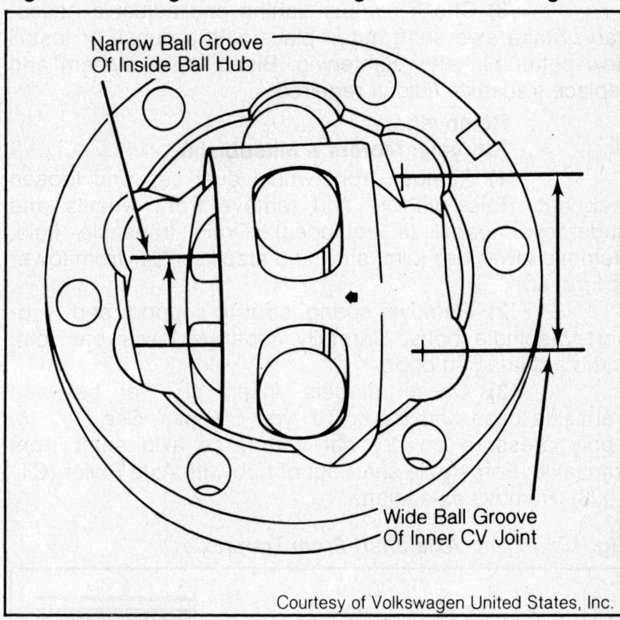

CV joints onto axle shaft with inside ball hub chamfer facing shaft.

4) Outer CV joint must be assembled with dished washer concave side facing thrust washer and convex side of thrust washer facing CV joint. *See Fig. 9.*

Fig. 9: Installation of Audi & Volkswagen Dished & Thrust Washers

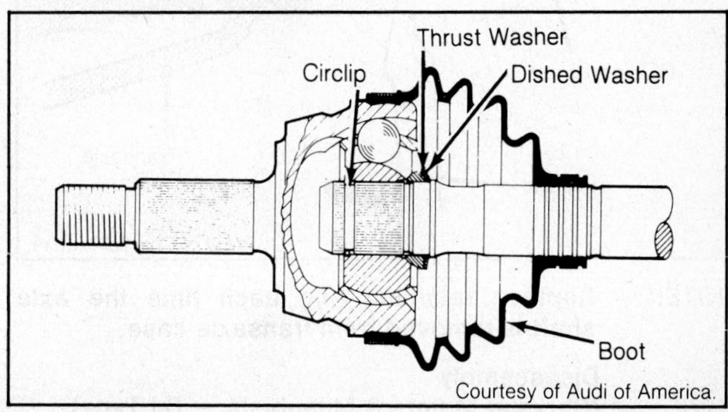

5) Inner CV joint must be assembled with dished washer concave side facing CV joint when installed on shaft. Install boot clamps with open end facing

FWD Axle Shafts

ALL MODELS (Cont.)

opposite direction of normal rotation. Always use new circlips to retain CV joints on shafts.

Installation (Audi & Volkswagen)

1) To install, reverse removal procedure and note the following: install a new side retainer ring. Check seals at both ends of axle shaft and replace prior to installation if necessary. Lubricate transaxle seal lip with transaxle oil.

NOTE: Always install new cotter pin, washer and suspension nuts.

2) Install axle shaft into transaxle case. On all models with snap ring retained axle shafts, try to pull axle shaft out of differential by hand to ensure proper engagement of snap ring. Install axle shafts into wheel hub. Align suspension marks made at removal and tighten nuts. On Audi Coupe models, apply (D6) locking compound to splines.

3) Check camber setting and adjust if necessary. Stake axle shaft nut in place with a punch or install new cotter pin after tightening. Bleed brake system and replace transaxle fluid, if required.

Removal
(Chrysler Motors & Mitsubishi)

1) Remove front wheel dust cap and loosen lock nut. Raise vehicle and remove front wheels and undercover panel (if equipped). Drain transaxle fluid. Remove lower ball joint, strut and stabilizer bar from lower control arm.

2) Remove spring strut-to-support and support-to-spindle bolts. Carefully separate lower ball joint without damaging boot.

3) On all models, insert pry bar between transaxle case and BJ or TJ type CV joint. *See Fig. 10.* Apply pressure on pry bar and force axle shaft from transaxle. Force axle shaft out of hub with Axle Puller (CT-1003). Remove axle shaft.

Fig. 10: Prying Axle Shaft From Transaxle

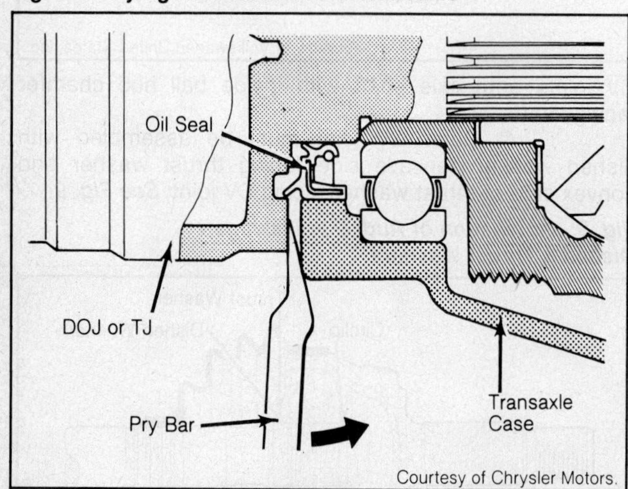

Courtesy of Chrysler Motors.

NOTE: Replace retaining ring each time the axle shaft is removed from transaxle case.

Disassembly
(Chrysler Motors & Mitsubishi – BJ Type)

Identify CV joint boot application. *See Figs. 11 and 12.* Remove inner joint boot. Remove circlip from joint and remove outer race. Remove snap ring and inner race. Remove cage and balls as an assembly.

Fig. 11: Chrysler Motors CV Joint Boot Identification

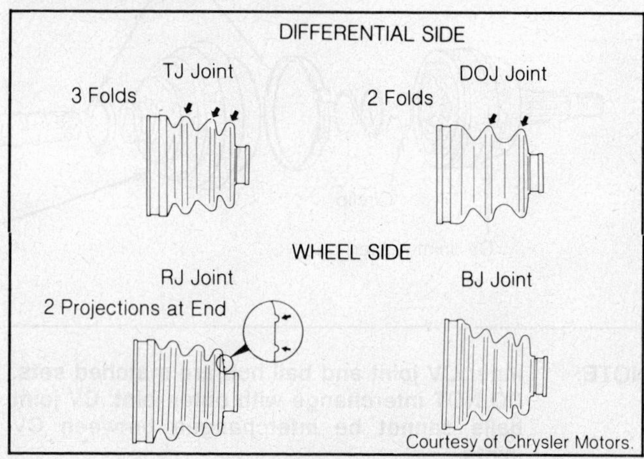

Courtesy of Chrysler Motors.

Fig. 12: Mitsubishi CV Joint Boot Identification

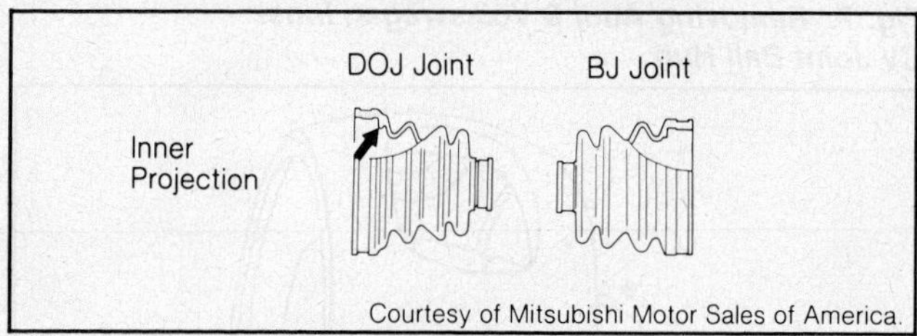

Courtesy of Mitsubishi Motor Sales of America.

NOTE: Do not disassemble inner bearing assembly as they are matched parts and should not be disturbed.

Fig. 13: Exploded View of BJ Type Axle Shaft

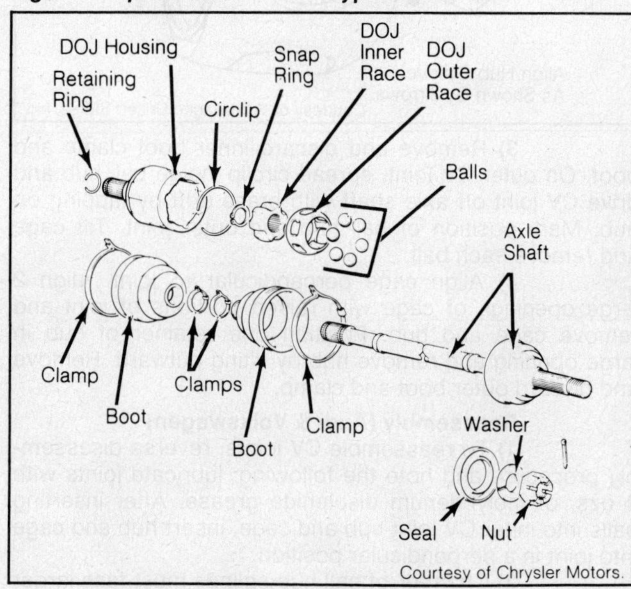

Courtesy of Chrysler Motors.

Reassembly
(Chrysler Motors & Mitsubishi - BJ Type)

To assemble, reverse disassembly procedure and note the following: apply grease to inner and outer races. Install CV joint assembly on shaft with chamfered edge of inner race facing outer edge of shaft. Install new boots and place boot clamps 3.5" (90 mm) apart.

ALL MODELS (Cont.)

Disassembly
(Chrysler Motors & Mitsubishi - TJ Type)

Remove inner joint boots. Pull axle shaft out from inner case. Remove snap ring and take out spider assembly. Clean, but do not disassemble, spider assembly. Remove outer boots.

Fig. 14: Exploded View of TJ Type Axle Shaft

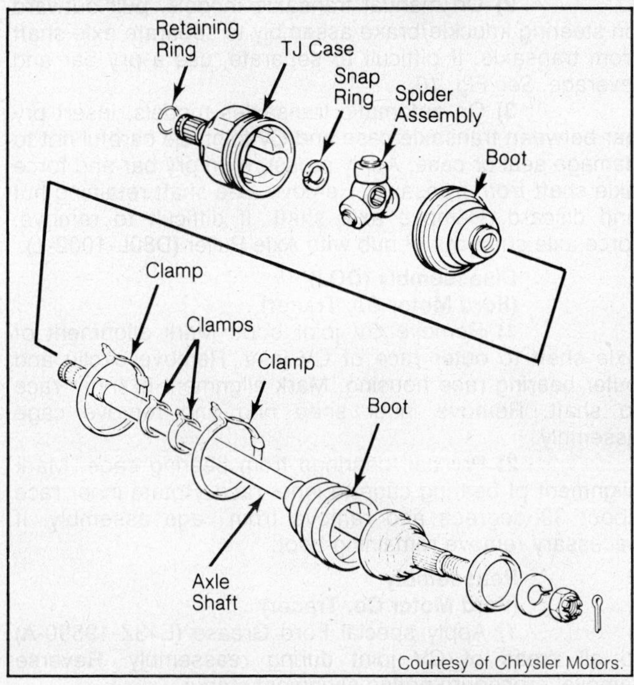

Reassembly
(Chrysler Motors & Mitsubishi - TJ Type)

To assemble, reverse disassembly procedure. Apply grease to the inner and outer races. Install new boots and place boot clamps 3.0" (75 mm) apart.

CAUTION: Outer CV joint on all models cannot be serviced. If joint is found to be worn or damaged, complete axle shaft assembly must be replaced. Always replace inboard housing spring clip when axle shafts are removed.

Installation
(Chrysler Motors & Mitsubishi)

1) To install, reverse removal procedure and note the following: install a new side retainer ring. Check seals at both ends of axle shaft and replace prior to installation if necessary. Lubricate transaxle seal lip with transaxle oil.

NOTE: Always install new cotter pin, washer and suspension nuts.

2) Install axle shaft into transaxle case. On all models with snap ring retained axle shafts, try to pull axle shaft out of differential by hand to ensure proper engagement of snap ring. Install axle shafts into wheel hub. Align suspension marks made at removal and tighten nuts.

3) Check camber setting and adjust if necessary. Stake axle shaft nut in place with a punch or install new cotter pin after tightening. Bleed brake system and replace transaxle fluid, if required.

Removal (Ford Motor Co. Festiva)

1) Raise and support vehicle. Remove lower underbody splash shields. Drain transaxle fluid. Remove front wheels and loosen axle shaft lock nut. Remove stabilizer bar from control arm. Remove joint clamp bolt from lower control arm. Pry downward and separate steering knuckle from ball joint.

2) Pry axle shaft from transaxle using a flat tip screwdriver or pry bar. Remove axle shaft from hub. If difficult to remove, use axle puller. Remove axle shaft from transaxle. Plug openings with Plugs (T87C-7025-C).

Disassembly (DOJ)
(Ford Motor Co. Festiva)

1) Label and remove CV joint boot. Mark alignment of axle shaft to outer race of CV joint. Remove circlip and outer bearing race housing. Mark alignment of inner race to shaft. Remove inner snap ring and remove cage assembly.

2) Pry ball bearings from bearing cage. Mark alignment of bearing cage to inner race. Rotate inner race about 30 degrees and remove from cage assembly. If necessary, remove remaining boot.

Fig. 15: Exploded View of Festiva Axle Shafts

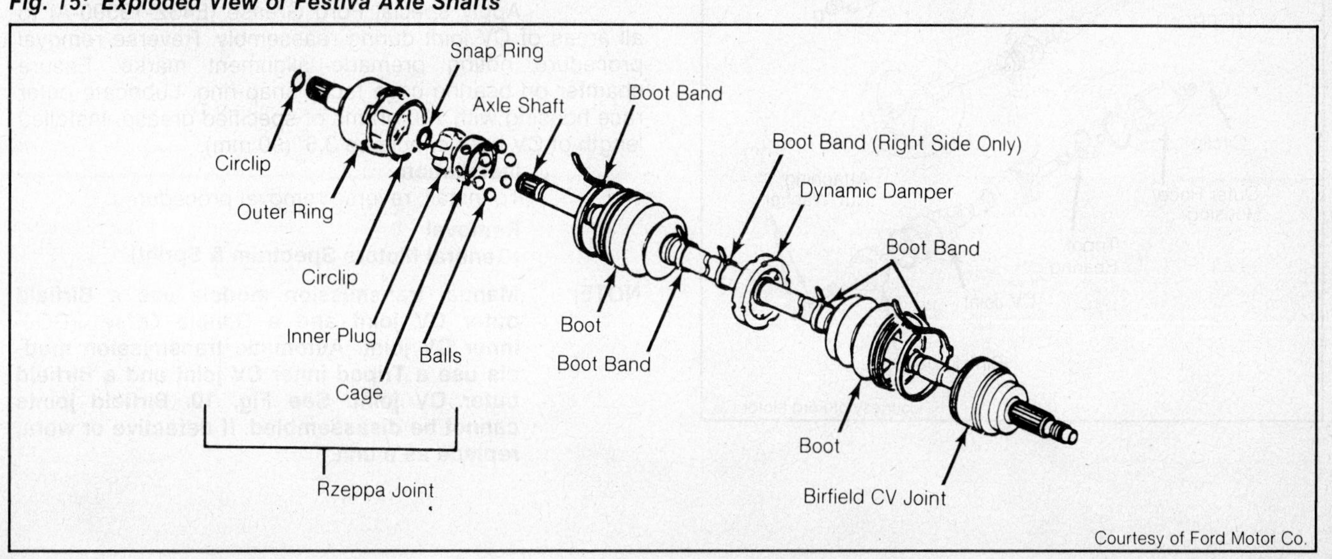

FWD Axle Shafts

ALL MODELS (Cont.)

Reassembly (Ford Motor Co. Festiva)

1) Apply Special Ford Grease (E43Z-19590-A) to all areas of CV joint during reassembly. Reverse removal procedure noting premade alignment marks. Ensure chamfer on bearing cage faces snap ring. Lubricate outer race housing with 40-60 grams of specified grease.

2) Install right side dynamic damper at a distance of 19.99-19.27" (482.5-489.5 mm) from outboard end of axle shaft. Installed length of CV boot should be 3.5" (90 mm).

Installation (Ford Motor Co. Festiva)

1) To install, reverse removal procedure and note the following: install a new side retainer ring. Check seals at both ends of axle shaft and replace prior to installation if necessary. Lubricate transaxle seal lip with transaxle oil.

NOTE: **Always install new cotter pin, washer and suspension nuts.**

2) Install axle shaft into transaxle case. On all models with snap ring retained axle shafts, try to pull axle shaft out of differential by hand to ensure proper engagement of snap ring. Install axle shafts into wheel hub. Align suspension marks made at removal and tighten nuts.

Removal (Ford Motor Co. Tracer)

NOTE: **Manual transmission models use a Birfield outer CV joint and a Double Offset (DOJ) inner CV joint. Automatic transmission models use a Tripot inner CV joint and a Birfield outer CV joint. Birfield joints cannot be disassembled. If defective or worn, replace as a unit.**

Fig. 16: Exploded View of Tracer Axle Shafts

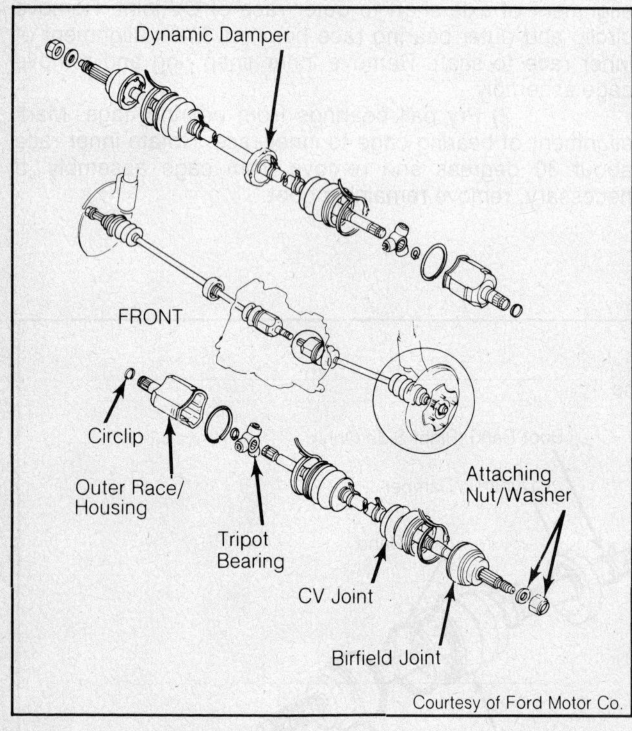

Courtesy of Ford Motor Co.

1) Raise and support vehicle. Remove lower underbody splash shields. Drain transaxle fluid. Remove front wheels and loosen axle shaft lock nut. Remove lower control arm ball joint clamp bolt. Separate steering knuckle from ball joint.

2) On manual transaxle models, pull outward on steering knuckle/brake assembly to separate axle shaft from transaxle. If difficult to separate, use a pry bar and leverage. *See Fig. 10*.

3) On automatic transaxles models, insert pry bar between transaxle case and CV joint. Be careful not to damage seal or case. Apply pressure on pry bar and force axle shaft from transaxle. Remove axle shaft retaining nut and discard. Remove axle shaft. If difficult to remove, force axle shaft out of hub with Axle Puller (D80L-1002-L).

Disassembly (DOJ)
(Ford Motor Co. Tracer)

1) Remove CV joint boot. Mark alignment of axle shaft to outer race of CV joint. Remove circlip and outer bearing race housing. Mark alignment of inner race to shaft. Remove inner snap ring and remove cage assembly.

2) Pry ball bearings from bearing cage. Mark alignment of bearing cage to inner race. Rotate inner race about 30 degrees and remove from cage assembly. If necessary remove remaining boot.

Reassembly
(Ford Motor Co. Tracer)

1) Apply special Ford Grease (E43Z-19590-A) to all areas of CV joint during reassembly. Reverse removal procedure noting alignment marks.

2) Ensure chamfer on bearing cage faces snap ring. Lubricate outer race housing with 40-60 grams of specified grease. Installed length of CV boot should be 3.5" (90 mm).

Disassembly (Tripot)
(Ford Motor Co. Tracer)

Remove boot clamp and boot. Paint an alignment mark of axle shaft to outer race of CV joint. Remove circlip and outer bearing race housing. Mark alignment of inner race to shaft. Remove snap ring and remove tripot assembly using a soft brass drift and hammer.

Reassembly (Ford Motor Co. Tracer)

Apply special Ford Grease (E43Z-19590-A) to all areas of CV joint during reassembly. Reverse removal procedure noting premade alignment marks. Ensure chamfer on bearing cage faces snap ring. Lubricate outer race housing with 100 grams of specified grease. Installed length of CV boot should be 3.5" (90 mm).

Installation

To install, reverse removal procedures.

Removal
(General Motors Spectrum & Sprint)

NOTE: **Manual transmission models use a Birfield outer CV joint and a Double Offset (DOJ) inner CV joint. Automatic transmission models use a Tripod inner CV joint and a Birfield outer CV joint. See Fig. 10. Birfield joints cannot be disassembled. If defective or worn, replace as a unit.**

ALL MODELS (Cont.)

1) Raise and support vehicle. Remove tire and wheel. Remove cotter pin and drive axle nut. Drain transaxle fluid. Remove stabilizer (if equipped). Pry inner CV joint from transaxle using a large screwdriver to detach snap ring.

2) Remove brake hose retaining clip at strut. Disconnect flex hose from caliper. Remove and support caliper aside. Remove rotor and splash shield. Disconnect tie rod end.

Fig. 17: General Motors Spectrum & Sprint FWD Axleshafts

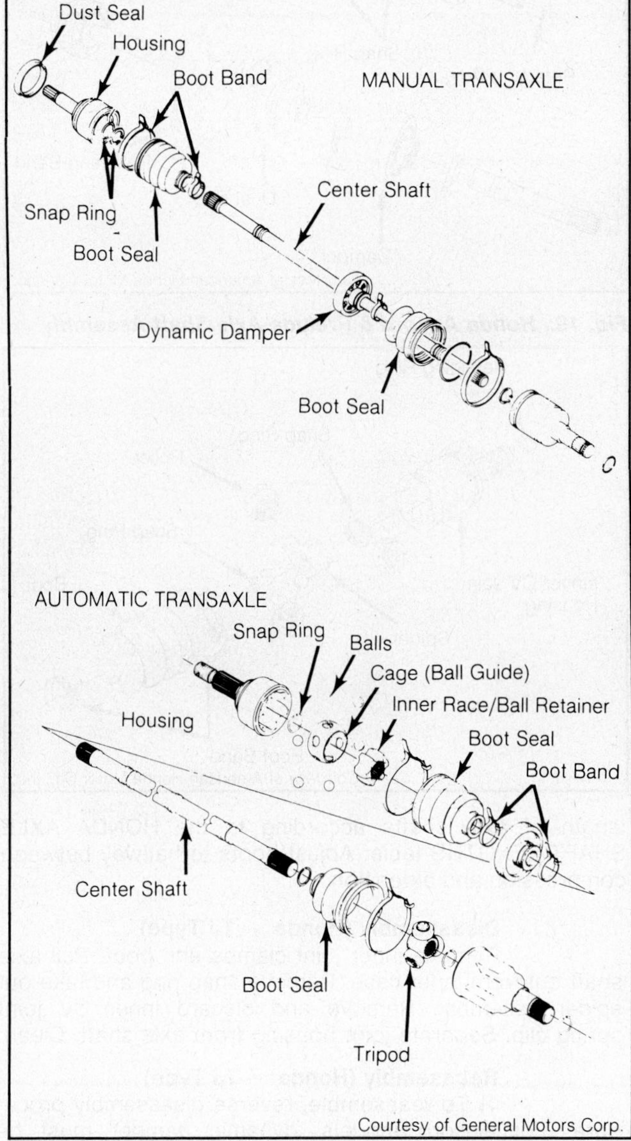

Courtesy of General Motors Corp.

3) Remove 2 ball joint-to-control arm and strut rod mounting nuts and bolts. Remove 2 strut-to-steering knuckle attaching nuts and bolts. Remove hub and knuckle assembly. Support drive axle. Remove shaft from transaxle. Remove axle shaft from vehicle. Be careful not to damage dust boots.

Disassembly
(General Motors Spectrum & Sprint)

1) Remove boot retaining bands from inner CV joint. Pry out circlip with screwdriver. Slide bellows inward on shaft. Pry out 6 balls from CV joint. Rotate ball guide to align with projected portion of ball retainer.

2) Slide ball guide toward bellows. Remove snap ring from shaft. Inspect bellows for cracks and damage. Replace as necessary.

Reassembly
(General Motors Spectrum & Sprint)

1) Reverse disassembly procedure and note the following: apply a light coat of grease to axle shaft before installing bellows. Fill bellows 1/2 full with grease. Ensure ball retainer is installed with smaller diameter toward the inside.

2) Install circlip so that end gap is positioned away from ball groove. Ensure bellows is not collapsed after installation.

Disassembly Tripod Joint
(General Motors Spectrum & Sprint)

Remove boot retaining bands from inner CV joint. Mark alignment of of housing to shaft. Slide back housing from joint. Remove snap ring from axle shaft. Mark alignment of tripod to shaft and remove with brass drift and hammer. Remove boot from shaft. Remove dynamic damper, if necessary.

Reassembly
(General Motors Spectrum & Sprint)

Reverse disassembly procedure and note the following: insert tripod on shaft with shorter spline poistioned outward. Ensure all alignment marks are aligned. Fill tripod housing with 140-150 grams of grease.

Installation
(General Motors Spectrum & Sprint)

1) To install, reverse removal procedure and note the following: install a new side retainer ring. Check seals at both ends of axle shaft and replace prior to installation if necessary. Lubricate transaxle seal lip with transaxle oil.

NOTE: Always install new cotter pin, washer and suspension nuts.

2) Install axle shaft into transaxle case. On all models with snap ring retained axle shafts, try to pull axle shaft out of differential by hand to ensure proper engagement of snap ring. Install axle shafts into wheel hub. Align suspension marks made at removal and tighten nuts.

3) Check camber setting and adjust if necessary. Stake axle shaft nut in place with a punch or install new cotter pin after tightening. Bleed brake system and replace transaxle fluid, if required.

FWD Axle Shafts

ALL MODELS (Cont.)

Removal (Honda DOJ & TJ Type)

1) Raise and support vehicle. Remove front wheels and tires. Drain transaxle oil. Spread locking tab on spindle nut. Remove nut using 32 mm socket. Support lower control arm with a floor jack.

2) On Prelude and Accord models, remove damper fork-to-strut and damper fork-to-lower control arm attaching bolts. On all models, remove ball joint bolt. Separate ball joint from knuckle.

3) If equipped, remove stabilizer bar bolts. Slowly lower floor jack to allow lower control arm to lower. Use a plastic hammer to tap lower control arm free from knuckle.

4) Pull front hub outward, clear of drive axle. Pry inboard CV joint out approximately .5" (12 mm) to force spring clip past groove in differential side gear splines. Remove drive axle from transaxle.

NOTE: **DO NOT pull on inner CV joint. CV joint may come apart.**

Disassembly (Honda - DOJ Type)

1) Mark roller-to-roller groove alignment prior to disassembly. Remove boot clamps from CV joints. Slide inner boot up drive axle to access inner CV joint. Wipe grease from joint. Remove large retaining ring and separate shaft with ball bearing from housing. Remove and discard spring clip. *See Fig. 18.*

2) Remove dust cover from axle shaft. Remove snap ring and ball bearing assembly from shaft. Remove outer dust boot from shaft. Pry balls from cage using a screwdriver. Remove race from cage. Clean and inspect all components.

HONDA AXLE SHAFT LENGTHS

Model	Inches (mm)
Accord	
Right	19.9-20.1" (506.0-510.5)
Left	
M/T	31.7-31.9" (805-809.5)
A/T	32.0-32.1" (812-816.5)
Civic	
Left	30.354-30.551" (771.0-776.0)
Right	18.5430-18.740" (471.0-476.0)
Prelude	
Left	
Fuel Injected	
M/T	31.7-31.9" (805-809.5)
A/T	32.0-32.1" (812-816.5)
Carburetted	
M/T	31.5-31.7" (800-804.5)
A/T	31.8-32.0" (809-813.5)
Right	
Fuel Injected	9.9-20.1" (506-510.5)
Carburetted	20.2-20.4" (514-518.5)

NOTE: **Outer CV joint on all models cannot be serviced. If joint is found to be defective, replace complete assembly.**

Reassembly (Honda - DOJ Type)

To reassemble, reverse disassembly procedure. Thoroughly pack high quality molybdenum disulfide grease into the inboard joint and both boots. On Civic models, install dynamic damper into orginal position (if removed). Install new boots and boot clamps. Adjust but do not disassembly spider assembly. Remove outer joint clamps and boot. *See Fig. 19.*

Fig. 18: Exploded View of Honda Civic Axle Shaft

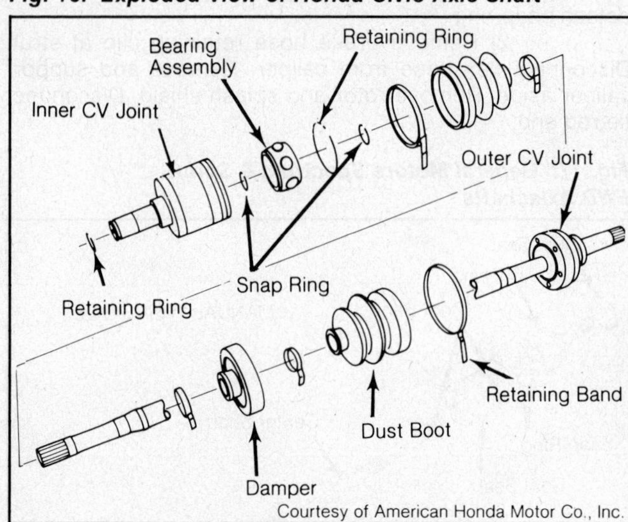

Fig. 19: Honda Accord & Prelude Axle Shaft Assembly

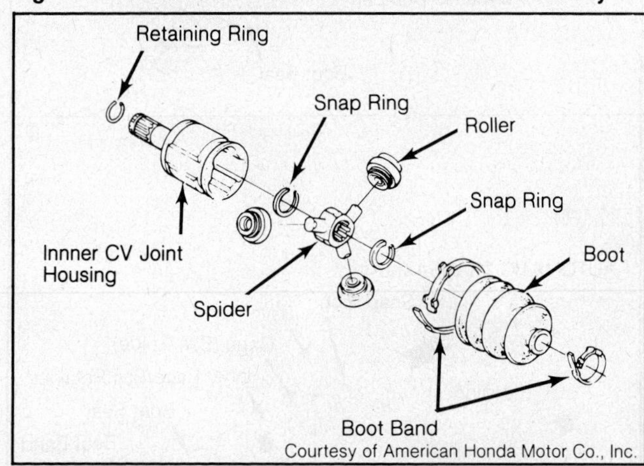

length of axle shafts according to the HONDA AXLE SHAFT LENGTHS table. Adjust boots to halfway between compression and extension.

Disassembly (Honda - TJ Type)

Remove inner joint clamps and boot. Pull axle shaft out from inner case. Remove snap ring and take out spider assembly. Remove and discard inner CV joint spring clip. Separate joint housing from axle shaft. Clean,

Reassembly (Honda - TJ Type)

1) To reassemble, reverse disassembly procedure. For Accord models, dynamic damper must be installed 0.2-0.28" (3-7 mm) from end of boot on outer axle shaft end. *See Fig. 20.* Press ball bearings into race until firmly seated.

2) Install ball bearing race with chamfered end toward small end of bearing cage. Thoroughly pack both inner and outer CV joints with grease supplied with kit.

3) Adjust length of axle shaft by adjusting boot position. *See Fig. 21.* Also see HONDA AXLE SHAFT LENGTHS table.

ALL MODELS (Cont.)

Fig. 20: Adjusting Damper Position on Honda Accord Axle Shaft

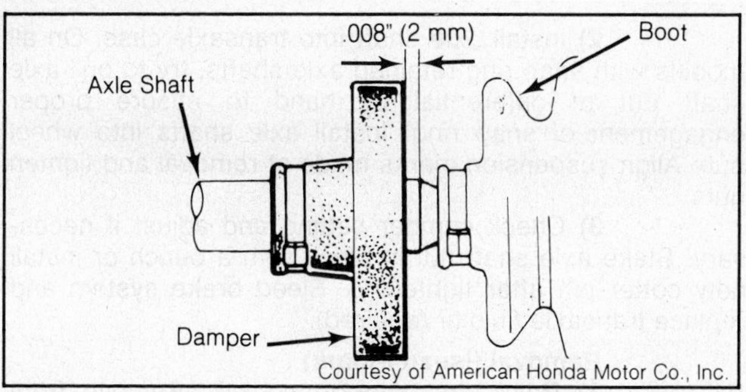

Fig. 21: Measuring Honda CV Joint Assembled Length

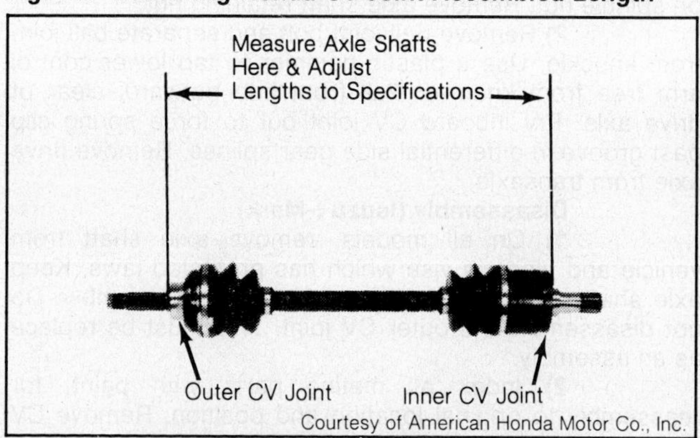

Installation (Honda DOJ & TJ Types)

1) To install, reverse removal procedure and note the following: install a new side retainer ring. Check seals at both ends of axle shaft and replace prior to installation if necessary. Lubricate transaxle seal lip with transaxle oil.

NOTE: Always install new cotter pin, washer and suspension nuts.

2) Install axle shaft into transaxle case. On all models with snap ring retained axle shafts, try to pull axle shaft out of differential by hand to ensure proper engagement of snap ring. Install axle shafts into wheel hub. Align suspension marks made at removal and tighten nuts.

3) Check camber setting and adjust if necessary. Stake axle shaft nut in place with a punch or install new cotter pin after tightening. Bleed brake system and replace transaxle fluid (if required).

Removal (Hyundai)

1) Apply the brakes and loosen axle shaft nut. Remove the under cover protector. Remove lower ball joint and strut bar from the lower control arm. Use caution not to damage ball joint boot. Replace if necessary.

2) Drain fluid from transaxle. Using a pry bar between transaxle case and CV joint case, pry axle shaft from transaxle. *See Fig. 22.* Use caution not to damage oil seal or transaxle case. Place a clean shop cloth in transaxle hole to prevent foreign material from entering.

3) Using Axle Shaft Puller (09526-11001), force drive shaft out of hub assembly. Note position of spacer and retain for reassembly to original position and location. Remove axle shaft from vehicle.

Fig. 22: Exploded View of Hyundai Axle Shaft

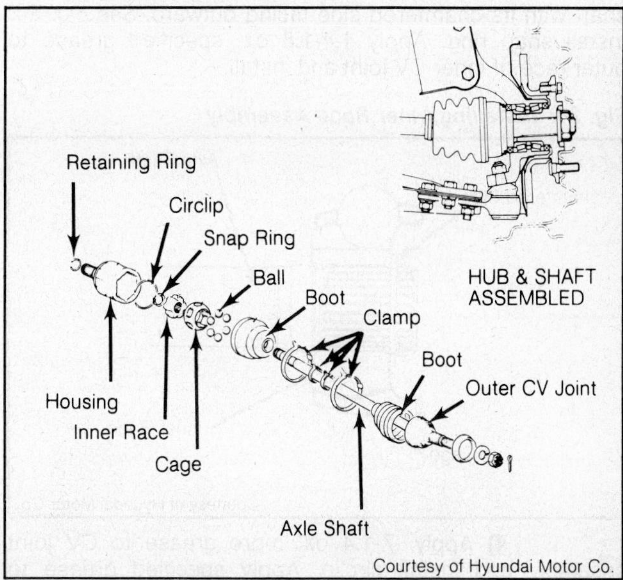

Disassembly (Hyundai)

1) Remove axle shaft from vehicle and place on work bench. Remove the inner CV joint boot clamp. Slide the boot away from the outer housing. Using a small screwdriver, remove the circlip retaining housing to the inner CV joint assembly.

2) Remove drive shaft from the inner CV joint outer race. Remove snap ring retaining inner race, cage and balls and remove assembly from axle shaft. Tape axle shaft splines to prevent damaging boot and remove inner CV joint boot. Remove outer CV joint boot clamps and remove the boot.

CAUTION: Use only BD-K2 grease. Do not mix grease.

Reassembly (Hyundai)

1) Thoroughly inspect inner and outer CV joint and boot. Replace defective components. Wrap tape around drive shaft splines to prevent damage to boot during installation. Install dynamic damper 15.0" (383.5 mm) from center of CV joint. *See Fig. 25.*

2) Apply a light film of grease to axle shaft and install both boots. Ensure correct boot is installed on proper CV joint. *See Fig. 23.* Apply specified grease to inner race and cage of inner CV joint.

Fig. 23: Inner & Outer CV Joint Boot Identification

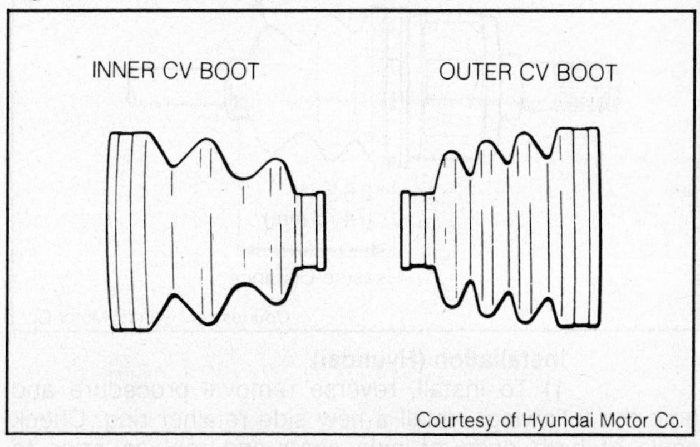

FWD Axle Shafts

ALL MODELS (Cont.)

3) Install inner race and cage assembly on axle shaft with its chamfered side facing outward. *See Fig. 24.* Install snap ring. Apply 1.4-1.8 oz. specified grease to outer race of inner CV joint and install.

Fig. 24: Installing Inner Race Assembly

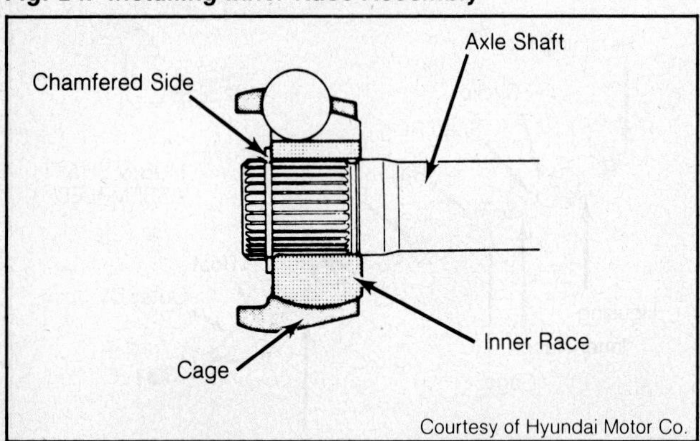

4) Apply .7-1.4 oz. more grease to CV joint assembly and install circlip. Apply specified grease to outer CV joint assembly without overfilling. Slide boots over CV joints. Install boot clamps on the outer CV joint.

Fig. 25: Dynamic Damper Installation Position

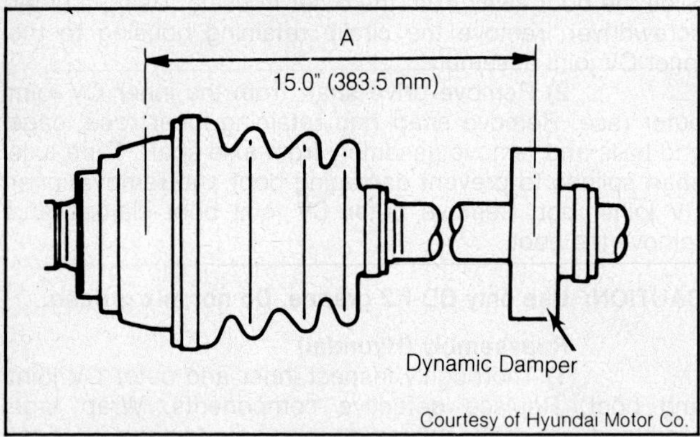

5) Place inner CV joint boot clamps in position. Measure the distance from clamp to clamp. The distance must be 2.6-3.4" (74-76 mm). *See Fig. 26.* Install axle shaft.

Fig. 26: Installation of Inner CV Joint Boot Clamps

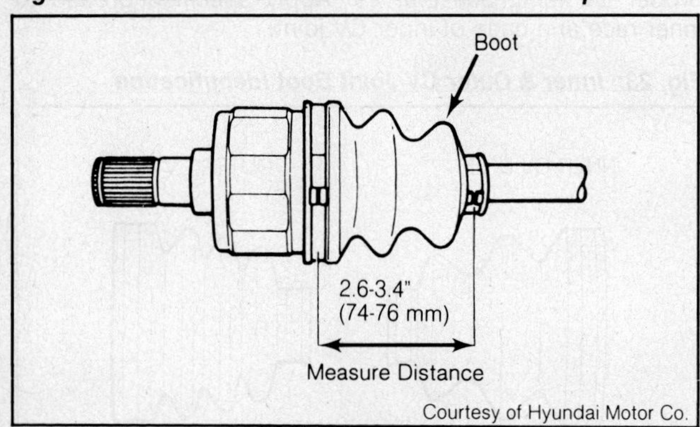

Installation (Hyundai)

1) To install, reverse removal procedure and note the following: install a new side retainer ring. Check seals at both ends of axle shaft and replace prior to installation if necessary. Lubricate transaxle seal lip with transaxle oil.

NOTE: Always install new cotter pin, washer and suspension nuts.

2) Install axle shaft into transaxle case. On all models with snap ring retained axle shafts, try to pull axle shaft out of differential by hand to ensure proper engagement of snap ring. Install axle shafts into wheel hub. Align suspension marks made at removal and tighten nuts.

3) Check camber setting and adjust if necessary. Stake axle shaft nut in place with a punch or install new cotter pin after tightening. Bleed brake system and replace transaxle fluid (if required).

Removal (Isuzu I-Mark)

1) Raise and support vehicle. Remove front wheels and tires. Drain transaxle oil. Spread locking tab on spindle nut. Remove axle shaft retaining nut.

2) Remove ball joint bolt and separate ball joint from knuckle. Use a plastic hammer to tap lower control arm free from knuckle. Pull front hub outward, clear of drive axle. Pry inboard CV joint out to force spring clip past groove in differential side gear splines. Remove drive axle from transaxle.

Disassembly (Isuzu I-Mark)

1) On all models, remove axle shaft from vehicle and place in vise which has protected jaws. Keep axle shaft clean during disassembly and reassembly. Do not disassemble the outer CV joint. This must be replace as an assembly.

2) Index all mating parts with paint, for reassembly to original location and position. Remove CV joint boot clamps and slide boot away from inner CV joint.

3) On manual transaxle vehicles, remove clip ring retaining inner CV joint to the housing with a flat tip screwdriver. Index shaft end and mating inner CV joint assembly to ensure reassembly to original position.

4) Remove snap ring retaining inner CV joint to shaft. Remove inner CV joint from axle shaft. Insert a small flat tip screwdriver between inner ring and cage and remove the balls. Index inner ring and cage.

5) Turn cage 30 degrees and pull it away from inner ring. Wrap end of shaft with tape to prevent damage to boot during removal. Slide boot off axle shaft. Remove dynamic damper only if replacing. Remove outer CV joint boot clamps and remove boot. Do not disassemble outer joint.

6) On automatic transaxle vehicles, index housing, tripod and axle shaft for reassembly to original position. Using needle nose pliers, remove clip ring from inner CV joint and housing. Remove housing from CV joint.

7) Remove snap ring retaining tripod to axle shaft. Using a hammer and drift, drive tripod off axle shaft. Wrap axle shaft end with tape. Remove inner CV joint boot. Remove dynamic damper if necessary. Remove outer CV joint boot clamps and remove boot.

Reassembly (Isuzu I-Mark)

1) On all models, pack outer CV joint with grease, provided with service kit. Install dynamic damper if removed. Wrap tape around axle shaft end and slide outer boot into position. Slide inner CV joint boot on axle shaft far enough to reassemble CV joint.

2) On models with automatic transaxles align marks on tripod and axle shaft. Install tripod on axle shaft using a hammer and drift. Install snap ring. Apply lithium grease to tripod assembly. Align marks on tripod, axle shaft and housing. Position housing and install clip ring.

ALL MODELS (Cont.)

3) On models with manual transaxles, fill outer CV joint with grease. Slide boot into position over outer CV joint. Align index marks on inner ring and cage. Reassemble cage over inner race and install the balls. Align index marks on inner CV joint assembly and axle shaft. Install assembly on shaft and install snap ring.

4) On all models, position boot over CV joint and install clip ring. Carefully position boot in grooves on axle shaft and housing. Using new boot clamps, position clamps so the folded portion is opposite the forward revolving direction of axle shaft.

Installation (Isuzu I-Mark)

To install, reverse removal procedures.

Removal (Mazda 323)

1) Raise vehicle and support with stands. Drain transaxle fluid. Remove wheel/tire assembly. Remove side covers. Raise lock tab on axle shaft nut. Apply brakes and loosen axle shaft nut but do not remove nut.

2) On manual transaxles, remove stabilizer bushings assembly from lower control arm.

3) On all models, remove lower ball joint clamp bolt and nut. Pry down the lower control arm and disconnect ball joint from steering knuckle. Insert a pry bar between inner CV joint and transaxle bearing housing. Use caution not to insert pry bar to far and cause damage to seal.

Fig. 27: Removing Mazda Axle Shaft With Manual Transaxle

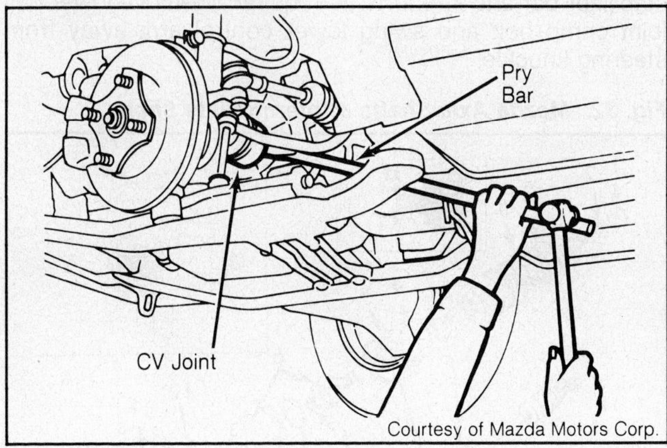

Fig. 28: Removing Mazda Axle Shaft With Automatic Transaxle

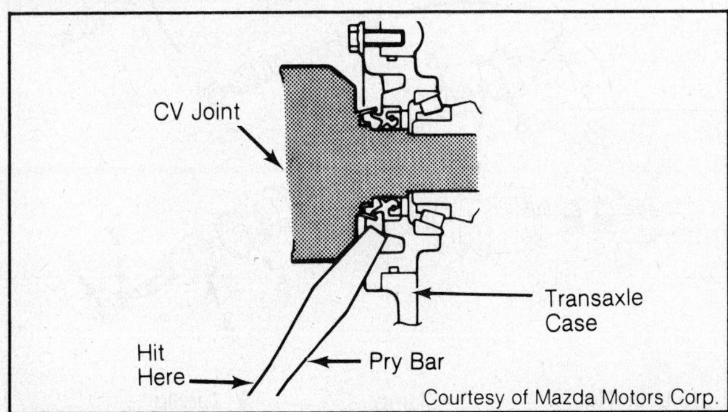

4) Carefully tap end of pry bar lightly to unseat inner CV joint assembly at transaxle. *See Figs. 27 and 28.* Do not remove at this time. On manual transaxle, it may not be necessary to pry inner CV joint. Grip hub assembly and carefully pull outward.

5) Remove axle shaft nut. Pull out on hub assembly and remove axle shaft from hub. A bearing puller may be used to push axle shaft from hub. Remove axle shaft from transaxle and install Differential Side Gear Holder (49G 030 455) to prevent contamination.

Disassembly (Mazda 323 Auto. Trans.)

1) Place in vise which has protected jaws. Keep axle shaft clean during disassembly and reassembly. DO NOT disassemble the outer CV joint. This must be replaced as an assembly.

2) Index all mating parts with paint, for reassembly to original location and position. Remove CV joint boot clamps and slide boot away from inner CV joint.

3) Index housing, tripod and axle shaft for reassembly to original position. Using needle nose pliers, remove clip ring from inner CV joint and housing. *See Fig. 29.* Remove housing from CV joint.

Fig. 29: Exploded View of 323 Auto. Trans. Axle Shaft

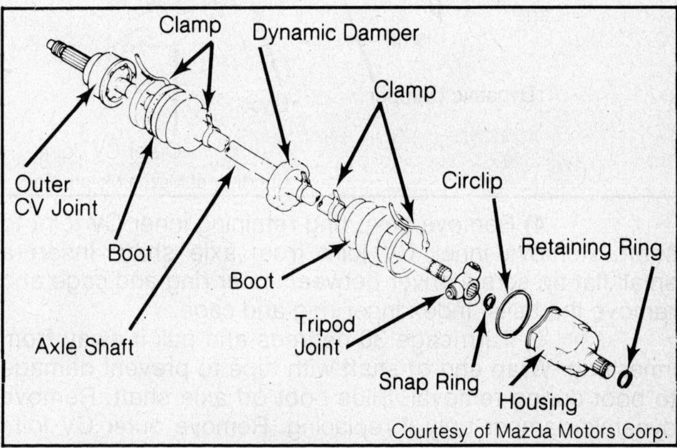

4) Remove snap ring retaining tripod to axle shaft. Using a hammer and drift, drive tripod off axle shaft. Wrap axle shaft end with tape. Remove inner CV joint boot. Remove dynamic damper if necessary. Remove outer CV joint boot clamps and remove boot.

Reassembly (Mazda 323 Auto. Trans.)

1) Pack outer CV joint with grease (lithium), provided with service kit. Install dynamic damper if removed. Wrap tape around axle shaft end and slide outer boot into position. Slide inner CV joint boot on axle shaft far enough to reassemble CV joint.

2) Align marks on tripod and axle shaft. Install tripod on axle shaft using a hammer and drift. Install snap ring. Apply lithium grease to tripod assembly. Align marks on tripod, axle shaft and housing. Position housing and install clip ring.

3) Using new boot clamps, position clamps so the folded portion is opposite of the forward revolving direction of axle shaft. Fold boot clamp back by pulling on end of clamp with pliers. Lock end of clamp by bending locking clip.

Disassembly (Mazda 323 Man. Trans.)

1) Place in vise which has protected jaws. Keep axle shaft clean during disassembly and reassembly. Do not disassemble the outer CV joint. This must be replaced as an assembly.

2) Index all mating parts with paint, prior to disassembly for reassembly to original location and position. Remove CV joint boot clamps and slide boot away from inner CV joint.

3) Remove clip ring retaining inner CV joint to the housing with a flat tip screwdriver. *See Fig. 30.* Index

ALL MODELS (Cont.)

shaft end and mating inner CV joint assembly to ensure reassembly to original position.

Fig. 30: Exploded View of 323 Man. Trans. Axle Shaft

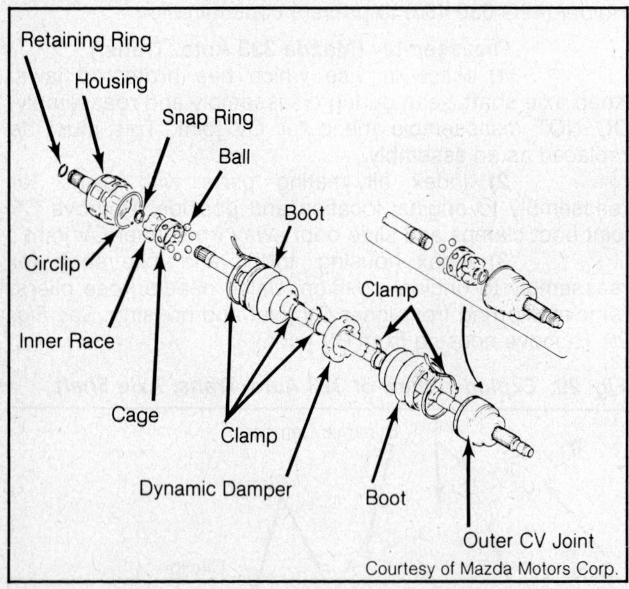

Courtesy of Mazda Motors Corp.

4) Remove snap ring retaining inner CV joint to shaft. Remove inner CV joint from axle shaft. Insert a small flat tip screw driver between inner ring and cage and remove the balls. Index inner ring and cage.

5) Turn cage 30 degrees and pull it away from inner ring. Wrap end of shaft with tape to prevent damage to boot during removal. Slide boot off axle shaft. Remove dynamic damper only if replacing. Remove outer CV joint boot clamps and remove boot. Do not disassemble outer joint.

Reassembly (Mazda 323 Man. Trans.)

1) Replace all defective parts. Pack CV joint during reassembly with grease (molybdenum disulfide), provided with service kit. Install dynamic damper, if removed. Lightly grease axle shaft. Wrap axle shaft end to prevent damage to boot during reassembly.

NOTE: Inner and outer CV joint boots are different. Ensure proper boot is being installed.

2) Fill outer CV joint with grease. Slide boot into position over outer CV joint. Align index marks on inner ring and cage. Reassemble cage over inner race and install the balls. Align index marks on inner CV joint assembly and axle shaft. Install assembly on shaft and install snap ring.

3) Position boot over CV joint and install clip ring. Carefully position boot in grooves on axle shaft and housing. Using new boot clamps, position clamps so the folded portion is opposite of the forward revolving direction of axle shaft.

4) Fold the clamp back by pulling on the end with pliers. Lock the end of the band by bending locking clip. Repeat procedure for opposite boot. Install axle shaft in vehicle.

Installation (Mazda 323)

1) Measure assembled axle shaft to ensure dynamic damper position is within specifications. *See Fig. 31.* Replace retaining ring on transaxle end of axle shaft. Check all seals and sealing surfaces to ensure proper seating. Replace as necessary.

Fig. 31: Measuring Mazda 323 Dynamic Damper

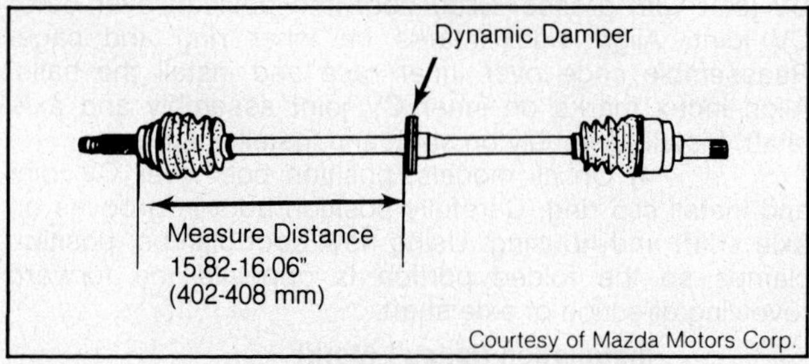

Courtesy of Mazda Motors Corp.

2) Remove differential side gear holder and insert axle shaft. Pull and push axle shaft to ensure retaining ring is fully seated. Pull outward on hub assembly and insert axle shaft in hub. Install a new axle shaft nut, but do not tighten at this time.

3) Install lower ball joint in steering knuckle and install clamp bolt. Tighten clamp bolt to specifications. Install stabilizer bar and tighten to specifications. Apply the brake and tighten axle shaft nut to specifications.

NOTE: Do not damage rubber boots of axle shaft. Always carry and store shaft in level position.

Removal (Mazda 626)

1) Raise and support vehicle. Drain transaxle fluid. Remove wheel/tire assembly and axle hub cap. Apply brakes. Loosen axle shaft lock nut. Remove stabilizer bar and supports as required. Remove lower ball joint crimp bolt and swing lower control arm away from steering knuckle.

Fig. 32: Mazda Axle Shafts & Intermediate Shaft

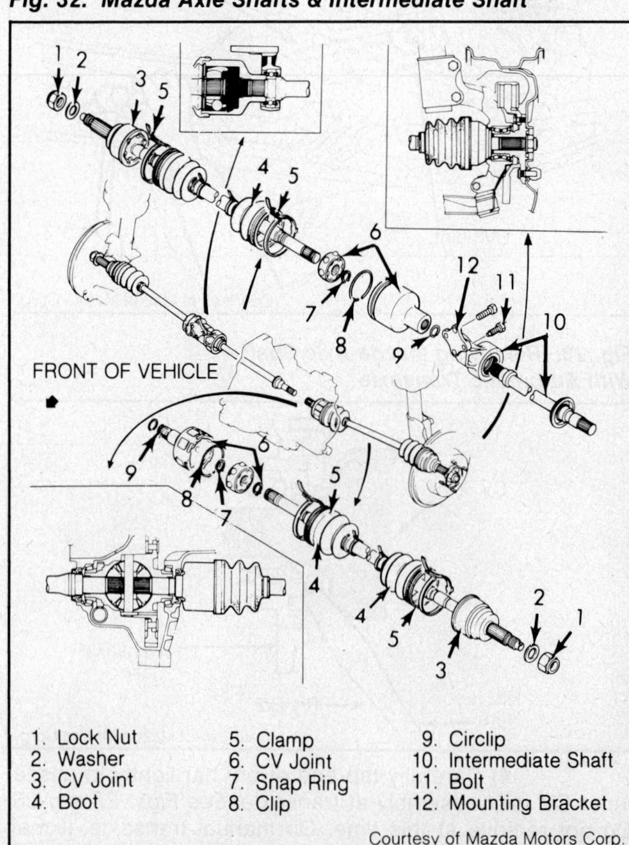

Courtesy of Mazda Motors Corp.

2) On manual transaxle models, insert pry bar between left inner CV joint and transaxle. Hit pry bar to

ALL MODELS (Cont.)

remove shaft. *See Fig. 10.* On automatic transaxle models, insert pry bar between left inner CV joint and transaxle. Tap end of pry bar lightly to remove axle shaft.

3) Use pry bar on right inner CV joint to uncouple axle shaft from intermediate shaft. Pull axle shaft out of wheel hub. If required, unbolt intermediate shaft mounting bracket and remove from vehicle.

Disassembly (Mazda 626 Man. Trans.)

1) Remove axle shaft from vehicle and place in vise which has protected jaws. Keep axle shaft clean during disassembly and reassembly. Do not disassemble the outer CV joint. This must be replace as an assembly.

2) Index all mating parts with paint, for reassembly to original location and position. Remove CV joint boot clamps and slide boot away from inner CV joint.

3) Remove clip ring retaining inner CV joint to the housing with a flat tip screwdriver. *See Fig. 32.* Index shaft end and mating inner CV joint assembly to ensure reassembly to original position.

Fig. 33: Exploded View of 626 Auto. Trans. Axle Shaft

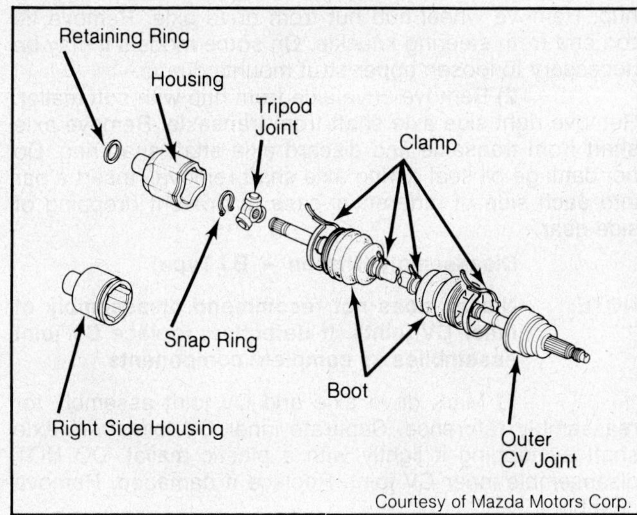

4) Remove snap ring retaining inner CV joint to shaft. Remove inner CV joint from axle shaft. Insert a small flat tip screw driver between inner ring and cage and remove the balls. Index inner ring and cage.

5) Turn cage 30 degrees and pull it away from inner ring. Wrap end of shaft with tape to prevent damage to boot during removal. Slide boot off axle shaft. Remove dynamic damper only if replacing. Remove outer CV joint boot clamps and remove boot. Do not disassemble outer joint.

Reassembly (Mazda 626 Man. Trans.)

1) Replace all defective parts. Pack CV joint during reassembly with grease (molybdenum disulfide), provided with service kit. Install dynamic damper, if removed. Lightly grease axle shaft. Wrap axle shaft end to prevent damage to boot during reassembly.

NOTE: **Inner and outer CV joint boots are different. Ensure proper boot is being installed. The outer CV joint boot has less ribs.**

2) Fill outer CV joint with grease. Slide boot into position over outer CV joint. Align index marks on inner ring and cage. Reassemble cage over inner race and install the balls. Align index marks on inner CV joint assembly and axle shaft. Install assembly on shaft and install snap ring.

3) Position housing over CV joint and install clip ring. Carefully position boot in grooves on axle shaft and housing. Using new boot clamps, position clamps so the folded portion is opposite of the forward revolving direction of axle shaft.

4) Fold the clamp back by pulling on the end with pliers. Lock the end of the band by bending locking clip. Repeat procedure for opposite boot. Install axle shaft in vehicle.

MAZDA 626 AXLE SHAFT LENGTH

Application	Length In. (mm)
Right Side	
Automatic	13.79 (350)
Manual	13.98 (355)
Left Side	
Automatic	13.79 (350)
Manual	13.98 (355)
Shaft Capacity	.94 (24)

Disassembly (Mazda 626 Auto. Trans.)

1) Remove axle shaft from vehicle and place in vise which has protected jaws. Keep axle shaft clean during disassembly and reassembly. DO NOT disassemble the outer CV joint. This must be replace as an assembly.

Fig. 34: Measuring Axle Shaft Length

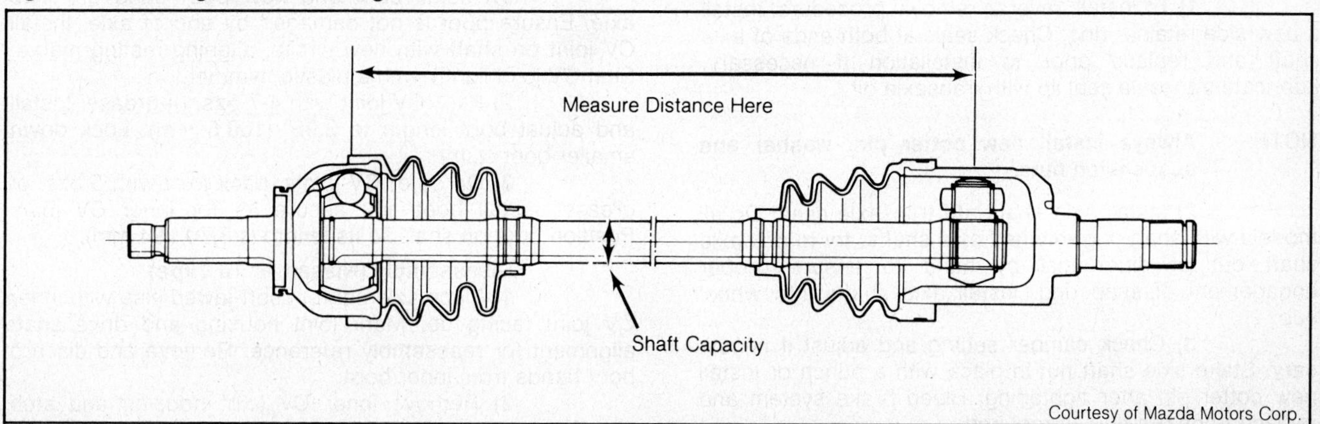

FWD Axle Shafts

ALL MODELS (Cont.)

Fig. 35: Exploded View of Man. Trans. Axle Shaft

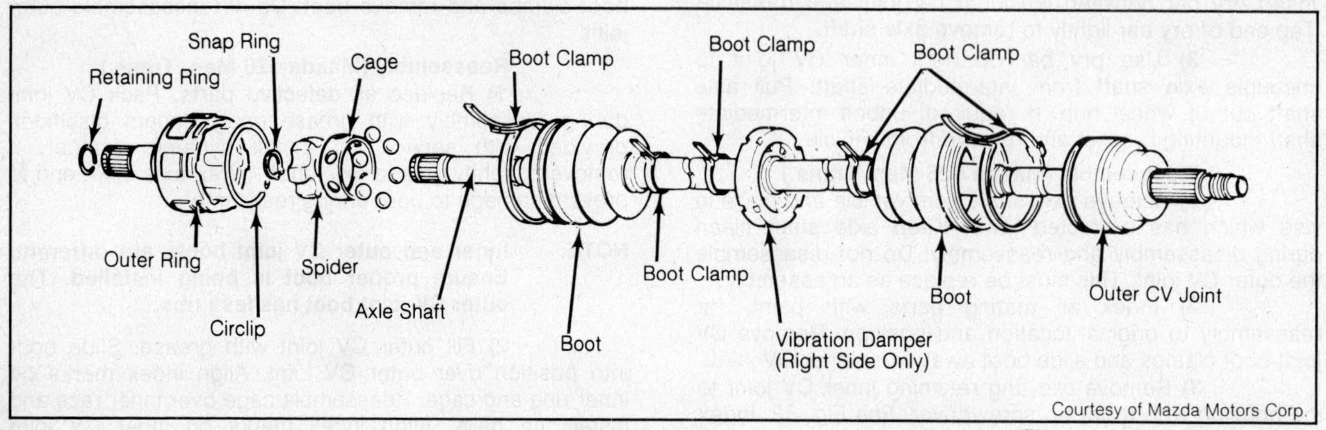

2) Index all mating parts with paint, prior to disassembly for reassembly to original location and position. Remove CV joint boot clamps and slide boot away from inner CV joint.

3) Index housing, tripod and axle shaft for reassembly to original position. Using a needle nose plier, remove clip ring from inner CV joint and housing. *See Fig. 35.* Remove housing from CV joint.

4) Remove snap ring retaining tripod to axle shaft. Using a hammer and drift, drive tripod off axle shaft. Wrap axle shaft end with tape. Remove inner CV joint boot. Remove dynamic damper if necessary. Remove outer CV joint boot clamps and remove boot.

Reassembly (Mazda 626 Auto. Trans.)

1) Pack outer CV joint with grease (lithium), provided with service kit. Install dynamic damper if removed. Wrap tape around axle shaft end and slide outer boot into position. Slide inner CV joint boot on axle shaft far enough to reassemble CV joint.

2) Align marks on tripod and axle shaft. Install tripod on axle shaft using a hammer and drift. Install snap ring. Apply lithium grease to tripod assembly. Align marks on tripod, axle shaft and housing. Position housing and install clip ring.

3) Using new boot clamps, position clamps so the folded portion is opposite of the forward revolving direction of axle shaft. Fold boot clamp back by pulling on end of clamp with pliers. Lock end of clamp by bending locking clip. Repeat procedure for opposite boot. Install axle shaft in vehicle.

Installation (Mazda 626)

1) To install, reverse removal procedure. Install a new side retainer ring. Check seals at both ends of axle shaft and replace prior to installation if necessary. Lubricate transaxle seal lip with transaxle oil.

NOTE: Always install new cotter pin, washer and suspension nuts.

2) Install axle shaft into transaxle case. On all models with snap ring retained axle shafts, try to pull axle shaft out of differential by hand to ensure proper engagement of snap ring. Install axle shafts into wheel hub.

3) Check camber setting and adjust if necessary. Stake axle shaft nut in place with a punch or install new cotter pin after tightening. Bleed brake system and replace transaxle fluid (if required).

Removal (Nissan)

1) Raise and support vehicle. Remove wheel and tire. Remove brake caliper and pry cotter pin out of hub. Remove wheel hub nut from drive axle. Remove tie rod end from steering knuckle. On some models it may be necessary to loosen upper strut mounting nuts.

2) Remove drive axle from hub with soft mallet. Remove right side axle shaft from transaxle. Remove axle shaft from transaxle and discard axle shaft snap ring. Do not damage oil seal during axle shaft removal. Insert a bar into each side of differential case to prevent dropping of side gear.

Disassembly (Nissan – BJ Type)

NOTE: Nissan does not recommend disassembly of inner CV joints. If defective, replace CV joint assemblies as complete components.

1) Mark drive axle and CV joint assembly for reassembly reference. Separate inner CV joint from axle shaft by tapping it lightly with a plastic mallet. DO NOT disassemble inner CV joint. Replace if damaged. Remove dust boot.

2) On outer CV joint, remove and discard boot bands. Mark outer CV joint-to-shaft position for reassembly reference. Remove and discard snap ring. Remove slide joint housing. Remove snap ring.

3) Remove ball cage, inner race and balls as a unit. Remove snap ring and dust boot. Inspect parts for wear or damage. Replace if damaged or defective.

Reassembly (Nissan – BJ Type)

1) Install boot and new boot band on drive axle. Ensure boot is not damaged by end of axle. Install CV joint on shaft with new circlip, aligning mating marks. Seat CV joint lightly with a plastic hammer.

2) Pack CV joint with 4-7 ozs. of grease. Install and adjust boot length to 3.96" (100.5 mm). Lock down smaller boot clamp.

3) On outer CV joints, pack joint with 5 ozs. of grease. Install boot and secure as for inner CV joint. Position boot on shaft so its length is 3.70" (94 mm).

Disassembly (Nissan – TJ Type)

1) Place axle shaft in soft-jawed vise with inner CV joint facing up. Mark joint housing and drive shaft alignment for reassembly reference. Remove and discard boot bands from inner boot.

2) Remove inner CV joint housing and stub axle from axle shaft. Remove snap ring and mark spider

ALL MODELS (Cont.)

Fig. 36: Exploded View of Nissan Axle Shaft Assemblies

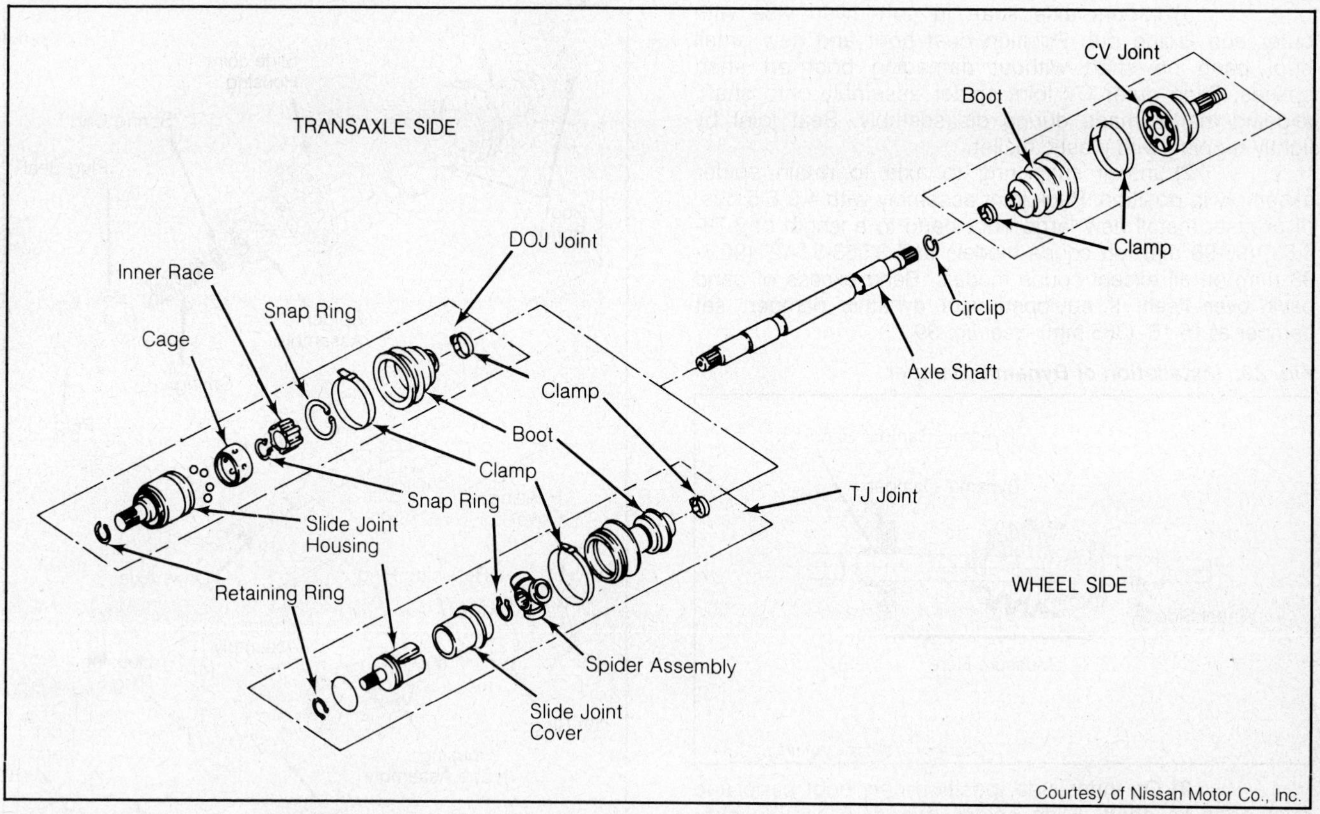

Courtesy of Nissan Motor Co., Inc.

Pulsar NX models are shown, other models are similar.

Fig. 37: Exploded View of Nissan Drive Axle (DOJ Type)

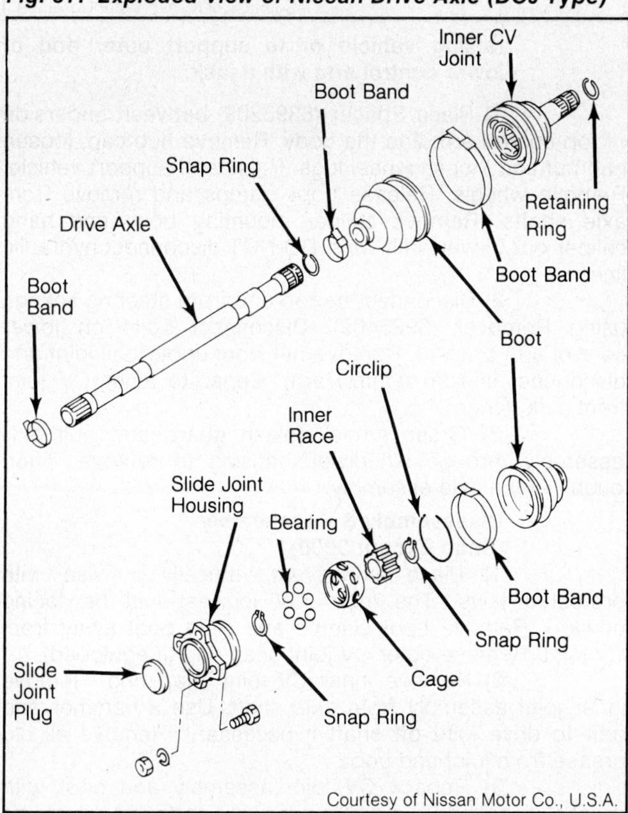

Courtesy of Nissan Motor Co., U.S.A.

assembly-to-shaft position for reassembly reference. *See Fig. 38.*

3) Discard snap ring and press off spider assembly without dropping axle shaft. CV joint on wheel side cannot be disassembled, if damage or wear are evident, change joint as a unit. If wheel side boot is damaged, mark joint to shaft alignment and remove retaining snap ring. Remove tripod joint, boot and boot bands. Inspect drive axles and CV joints for wear and damage. Replace as necessary.

Fig. 38: Removing Nissan Inner CV Joint (TJ Type)

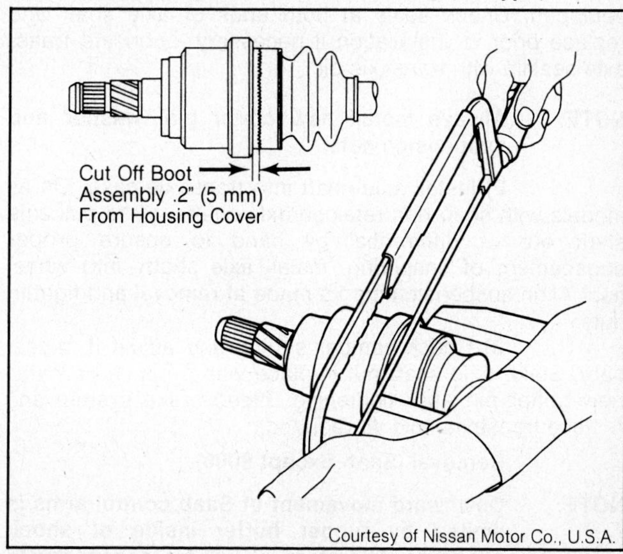

Courtesy of Nissan Motor Co., U.S.A.

ALL MODELS (Cont.)

Reassembly (Nissan - TJ Type)

1) Mount axle shaft in soft-jawed vise with outer end facing out. Position dust boot and new small boot band on shaft without damaging boot on shaft splines. Slide outer CV joint spider assembly onto shaft, aligning marks made during disassembly. Seat joint by lightly tapping with plastic mallet.

2) Install snap ring to axle to retain spider assembly in position. Pack joint assembly with 4.0-6.5 ozs. of grease. Install new large boot band to a length of 3.78-3.86" (96-98 mm) on coupe models and 3.563-3.642" (90.5-98 mm) on all except coupe models. Bend excess of band back over itself. If equipped with dynamic damper, set damper at 15.16" (385 mm). *See Fig. 39.*

Fig. 39: Installation of Dynamic Damper

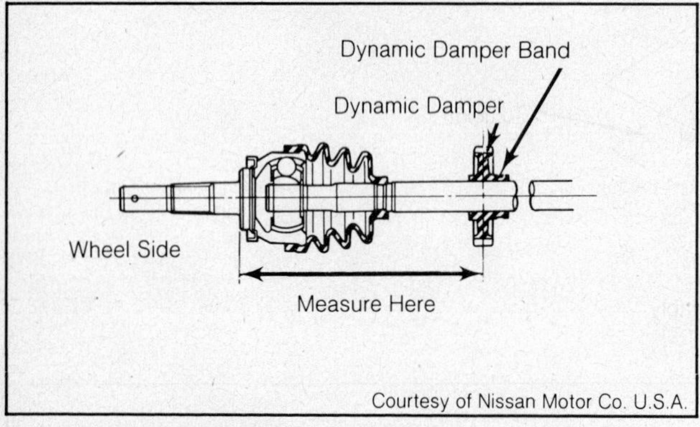

Courtesy of Nissan Motor Co. U.S.A.

3) On inner side, position new boot band and dust boot on shaft. Slide spider (tripod) assembly onto shaft, aligning marks made during disassembly. Press spider assembly into position. Retain in position with new snap ring (round surface facing spider assembly).

4) Pack CV joint assembly with 6.0-8.0 ozs. of grease. Install spider joint housing. Position dust boot on shaft so its length is 4.00-4.07" (101.5-103.5 mm) on coupe models and 3.76-3.83" (95.5-97.5 mm) on all models except the coupe. Secure small band in position without deforming or buckling dust boot.

Installation (Nissan)

1) To install, reverse removal procedure and note the following: install a axle shaft retainer ring, if equipped. Check seals at both ends of axle shaft and replace prior to installation if necessary. Lubricate transaxle seal lip with transaxle oil.

NOTE: Always install new cotter pin, washer and suspension nuts.

2) Install axle shaft into transaxle case. On all models with snap ring retained axle shafts, try to pull axle shaft out of differential by hand to ensure proper engagement of snap ring. Install axle shafts into wheel hub. Align suspension marks made at removal and tighten nuts.

3) Check camber setting and adjust if necessary. Stake axle shaft nut in place with a punch or install new cotter pin after tightening. Bleed brake system and replace transaxle fluid (if required).

Removal (Saab Except 9000)

NOTE: Downward movement of Saab control arms is limited by rubber buffer inside of shock absorber. Therefore, it will be necessary to install a special Spacer (8393209) before raising vehicle or to support outer end of lower control arm with a jack.

Fig. 40: Exploded View of Nissan Drive Axle (TJ Type)

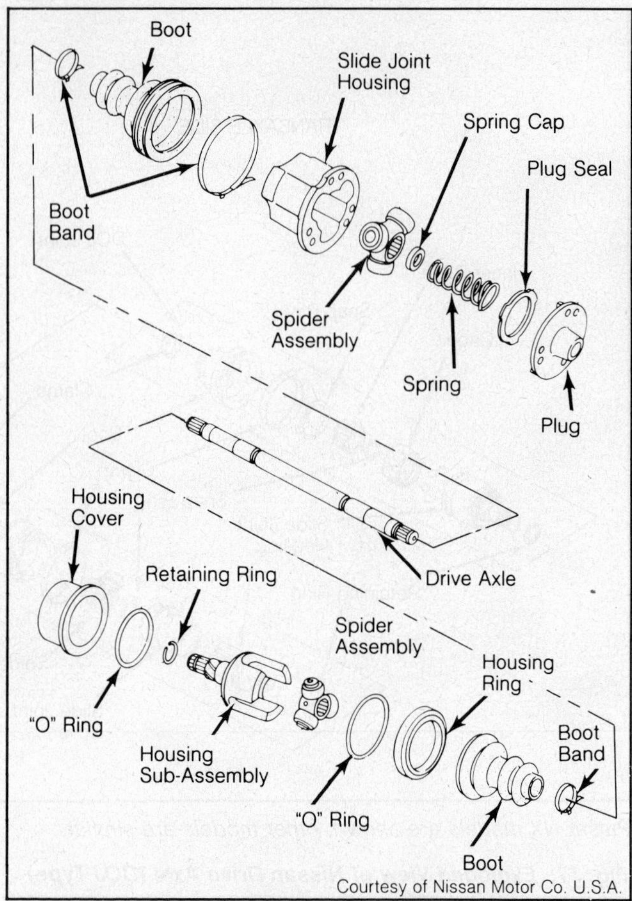

Courtesy of Nissan Motor Co. U.S.A.

1) Place Spacer (8393209) between underside of top control arm and the body. Remove hub cap, loosen hub nut and loosen wheel lugs. Raise and support vehicle. Remove wheels. Release boot clamps and remove from axle shafts. Remove caliper mounting bolts and hang caliper out of way with wire. DO NOT disconnect hydraulic line.

2) Disconnect tie rod end from steering linkage using Remover (8995409). Disconnect bolts on lower control arm bracket. Remove nut from upper ball joint and disconnect it from control arm. Separate inner CV joint from axle flange.

3) Grasp wheel splash guard and pull axle assembly through wheelwell housing to remove. Thoroughly clean axle assembly.

Disassembly & Reassembly (Saab Except 9000)

1) Place axle shaft vertically in vise with protected jaws. The inner CV joint should be facing upward. Remove boot clamps and slide boot away from CV joint. Remove outer CV joint snap ring (if equipped).

2) Remove inner CV joint snap ring. Remove inner joint assembly from axle shaft. Use a hammer and drift to drive joint off shaft if necessary. Remove all old grease from joint and boot.

3) Repack CV joint assembly and boot with grease supplied in kit. Replace all parts found to be defective. Replace boots if cracked or leaking. Always use new boot clamps. Reverse procedure for reassembly.

FWD Axle Shafts

ALL MODELS (Cont.)

Fig. 41: Sectional View of Saab Steering Knuckle

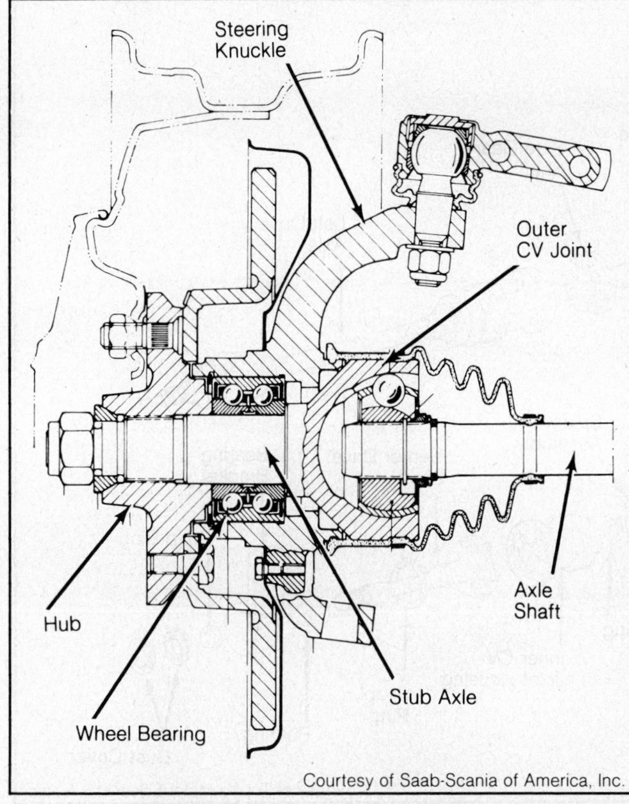

Courtesy of Saab-Scania of America, Inc.

Installation (Saab Except 9000)

1) Install axle shaft through wheelwell housing. Mount any needle bearings which may have fallen out of inner CV joint on ends of "T" piece. Attach inner CV joint to axle flange. Install upper ball joint into steering knuckle. Mount tie rod end to steering arm. Mount brake caliper.

2) Reinstall front wheel and lower vehicle. Tighten hub lock nut. Secure in place by peening into locking groove. Pump brake pedal several times to seat brake pads.

Removal (Saab 9000)

1) Raise vehicle and support with stands. Apply the brakes and loosen axle shaft nut. Remove wheel/tire assembly. Remove inner wheelwell insert. Loosen inner CV joint boot clamp. Remove flexible brake hose mounted to shock absorber.

2) Remove bolts securing shock absorber to steering knuckle. Pull outward on the upper hub assembly and remove inner CV joint from transaxle. Cover the CV joint boots to prevent damage. Cover the holes to prevent contamination from entering transaxle.

3) Remove axle shaft nut. Remove axle shaft from hub assembly. If necessary, tap axle shaft end with soft hammer to remove.

NOTE: **Axle shafts cannot be disassembled. If damaged or defective, replace as complete assembly.**

Installation (Saab 9000)

1) Check boots for cracks and leakage. Replace as necessary. Insert axle shaft into hub and install axle nut. Do not tighten axle shaft nut at this time. Remove hole covers. Push upward on hub assembly and insert inner CV joint into transaxle.

2) Position steering knuckle and shock absorber. Install mounting bolts and tighten. Attach flexible brake hose to shock absorber. Tighten inner CV joint boot clamp. Ensure inner CV joint and boot is positioned properly.

3) Apply brake and tighten axle shaft nut. Install inner wheelwell insert. Install wheel/tire assembly. Check camber setting and adjust if necessary. Stake axle shaft nut in place with a punch or install new cotter pin after tightening. Bleed brake system and replace transaxle fluid, if required.

Removal (Subaru)

1) Apply parking brake. Remove front wheel cap and cotter pin. Loosen castle nut and wheel nuts. Raise and support vehicle. Remove front tires and wheels. Remove brake caliper assembly from brake disc. Remove disc brake cover. Remove disc brake assembly. Drive out spring connecting axle shaft to differential and discard.

2) Disconnect tie rod end from linkage using a puller. Remove bolt retaining housing to strut. Remove ball joint of transverse link from housing. Remove housing and axle shaft assembly as a unit. Remove housing from axle shaft by using Puller (922493000) and Adapter (921122000).

Disassembly (Subaru)

1) Straighten bent claw of larger end of boot on DOJ side. Loosen band by means of screwdriver or pliers, taking care not to damage boot. Remove boot band from small end of DOJ boot in same manner.

2) Remove larger end of boot on DOJ side. Pry and remove round circlip located at neck of outer race on DOJ side with a screwdriver. Remove outer race on DOJ side from shaft assembly.

3) Wipe off grease and remove balls. Move cage to boot side. Remove snap ring with snap ring pliers. Remove inner race of DOJ. Remove cage of DOJ from shaft and remove boot from DOJ. Pull out boot on CV joint side.

Reassembly (Subaru)

To reassemble, reverse disassembly procedure. Grease CV joint and DOJ with Molylex No. 2 grease.

NOTE: **DO NOT disassemble the outer CV joint. Replace the CV joint and axle shaft as an assembly.**

Installation (Subaru)

1) To install, reverse removal procedure and note the following: install a new side retainer ring (if equipped). Check seals at both ends of axle shaft and replace prior to installation if necessary. Lubricate transaxle seal lip with transaxle oil.

NOTE: **Always install new cotter pin, washer and suspension nuts.**

2) Install axle shaft into transaxle case. On all models with snap ring retained axle shafts, try to pull axle shaft out of differential by hand to ensure proper engagement of snap ring. Install axle shafts into wheel hub. Align suspension marks if made at removal and tighten nuts.

3) Check camber setting and adjust if necessary. Stake axle shaft nut in place with a punch or install new cotter pin after tightening. Bleed brake system and replace transaxle fluid (if required).

FWD Axle Shafts

ALL MODELS (Cont.)

Fig. 42: Exploded View of Camry Axle Shaft

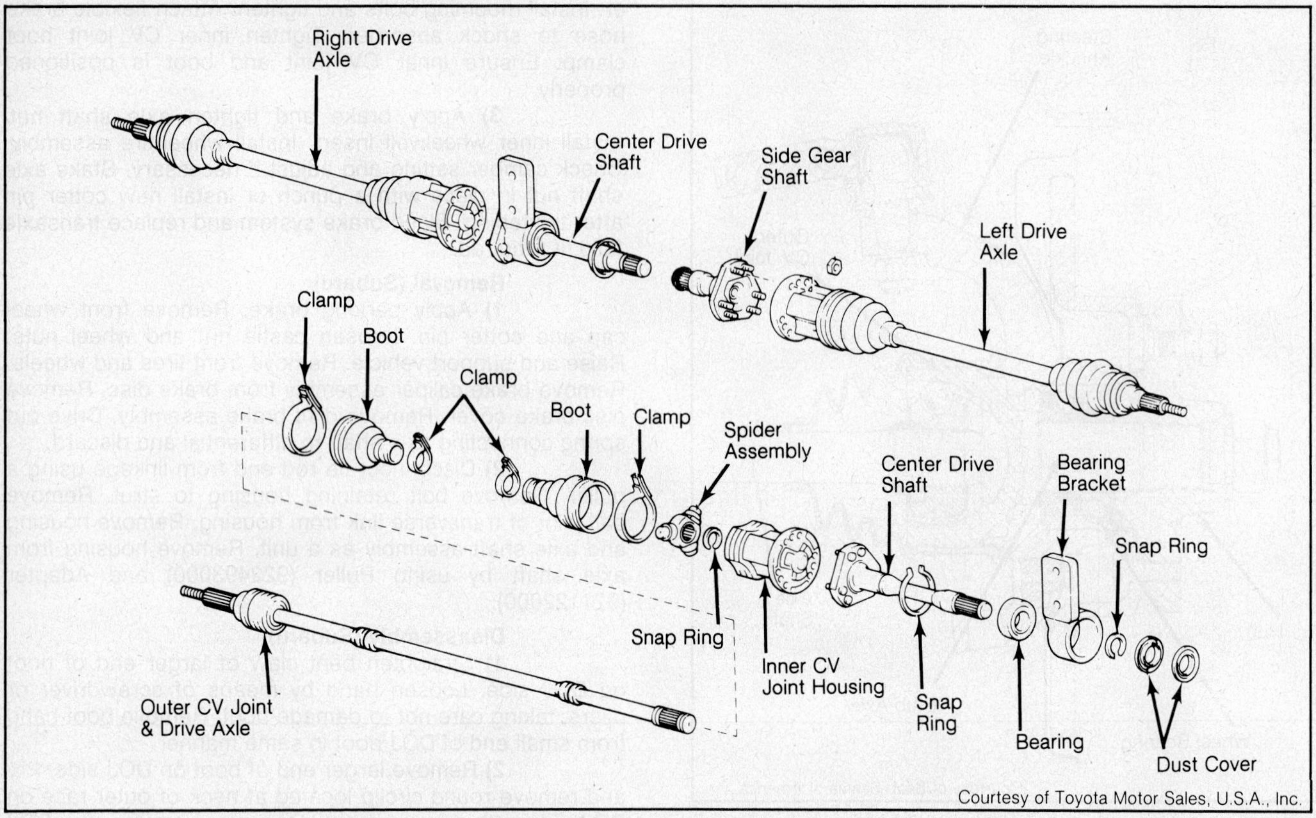

Courtesy of Toyota Motor Sales, U.S.A., Inc.

Removal (Toyota Camry)

1) Remove hub cap, cotter pin and locknut. Loosen and remove locknut from wheel bearing. Remove engine undercover. Remove front fender apron seal. Apply the brakes and remove 6 retaining bolts and nuts on each axle shaft flange. Disconnect steering knuckle from lower ball joints. Drain transaxle fluid. Remove axle shafts from transaxle. Loosen center drive shaft locknut.

2) Remove snap ring from bearing bracket and pull out center drive shaft. Push side gear shaft into differential. Measure distance and note distance between transaxle case and side gear shaft. Pull the center drive shaft out of transaxle. Inspect side gear and side gear shaft seal for damage, replace if neccessary.

Removal (Toyota Celica)

1) The Celica has 2 different types of front axle shafts: the ST161 and the ST162. The ST161 series is retained to the transaxle by 6 bolts and nuts. The right axle axle is bolted to a center drive shaft. The ST162 series is retained by a snap ring with the center drive shaft part of the CV joint. *See Fig. 43.*

2) Remove hub cap, cotter pin and lock nut. Apply the brakes and remove adjusting nut. Remove cover located under engine (if equipped).

3) On ST162 series, drain transaxle fluid and remove the protector cover located on the left side of transaxle. On the ST161 series, loosen 6 nuts (each axle), retaining axle shaft to center drive shaft or side gear shaft.

4) On both series, remove tie rod from the steering knuckle. Disconnect steering knuckle from the lower control arm. Cover CV joint boot with a shop cloth to protect from damage during removal.

5) On ST161 series, use Puller (SST09950-20017) and separate the axle shaft from steering knuckle.

Fig. 43: Exploded View of Celica Axle Shaft

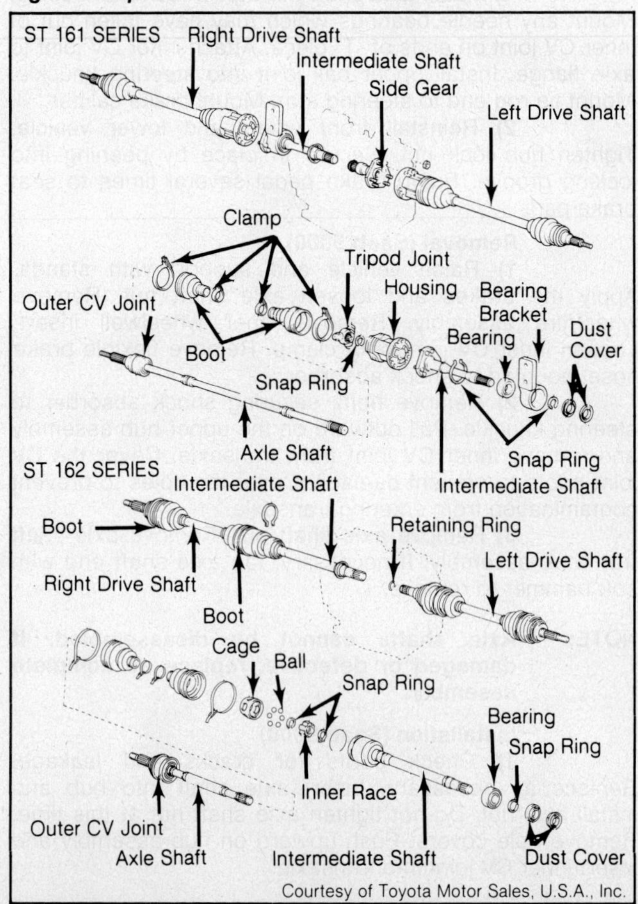

Courtesy of Toyota Motor Sales, U.S.A., Inc.

FWD Axle Shafts

ALL MODELS (Cont.)

Remove the 6 retaining nuts at transaxle and remove the axle.

6) On the ST162 series, left axle shaft, index the shaft and measure the distance from the transaxle case and index mark. Note distance for reassembly. Using Puller (SST09520-32060), remove the axle shaft from transaxle. Using Puller (SST09950-20016), remove the axle shaft from steering knuckle.

7) On ST162 series, right axle shaft, remove shaft from steering knuckle with Puller (SST09950-20016). Remove snap ring from center drive shaft and remove the center drive shaft and axle shaft as an assembly.

8) On ST161 series, drain the transaxle fluid. Using pliers, remove the snap ring from the center drive shaft and remove the center drive shaft. Always discard snap ring and replace with new one.

Removal (Toyota Corolla)

1) Remove hub cap, cotter pin and lock nut. Apply brakes and remove adjusting nut. Apply brakes and loosen the nuts retaining axle shaft to transaxle. Remove engine undercover. Loosen 6 nuts retaining front drive shaft to differential side gear shaft. Remove brake caliper and rotor. Do not remove brake line or support caliper by the brake line. *See Fig. 44.*

Fig. 44: Exploded View of Toyota Corolla Axle Shaft

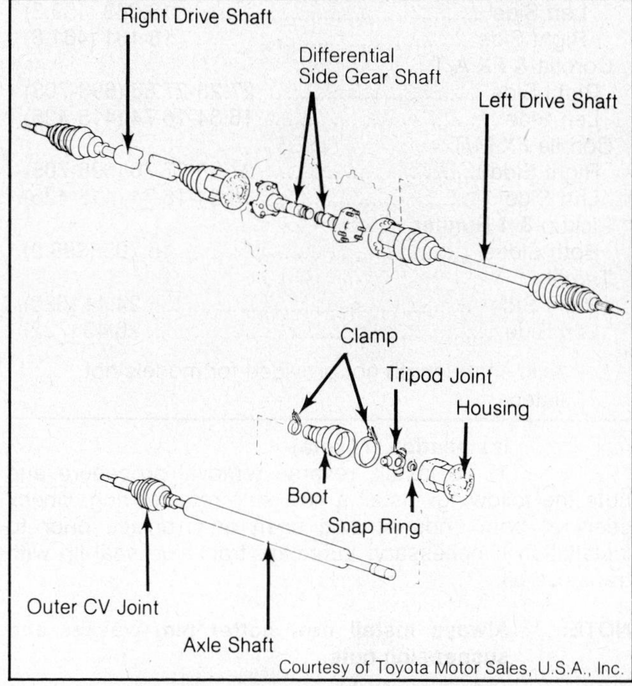

2) Disconnect steering knuckle from lower control arm. Using Puller (SST09950-2017), remove axle shaft from steering knuckle. Cover CV joint boot with shop cloth to prevent damage. Remove retaining nuts and remove axle shaft.

Removal (Toyota Pickup & 4Runner)

1) Place free wheeling hub cover in the "FREE" position. On all models, remove the hub cover. Remove the spindle bolt and washer. Remove the hub body mounting nuts and washers. Remove cone washers by tapping on bolt heads with brass drift and hammer. Remove hub body.

2) On automatic locking hubs, use a screwdriver and remove snap ring. Remove the brake subassembly. Using a torx socket, remove screws and remove the brake drum. Remove adjusting nut if necessary.

Fig. 45: Exploded View of 4Runner Axle Shaft

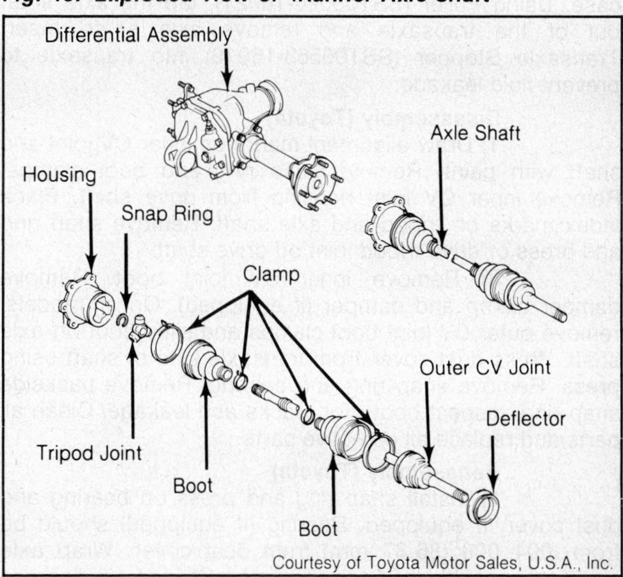

3) Loosen retaining nuts attaching axle shaft to front differential. Remove snap ring from axle shaft. Remove retaining nuts and slide axle shaft toward steering knuckle until free from differential. Pull axle shaft down and away out of steering knuckle.

Removal (Toyota Tercel)

1) Remove engine undercover and drain gear oil. Remove hub cap, cotter pin and lock nut. Apply brakes and remove adjusting nut. Remove brake caliper. Do not remove brake line or support caliper by brake line. Remove brake rotor.

Fig. 46: Exploded View of Tercel Axle Shaft

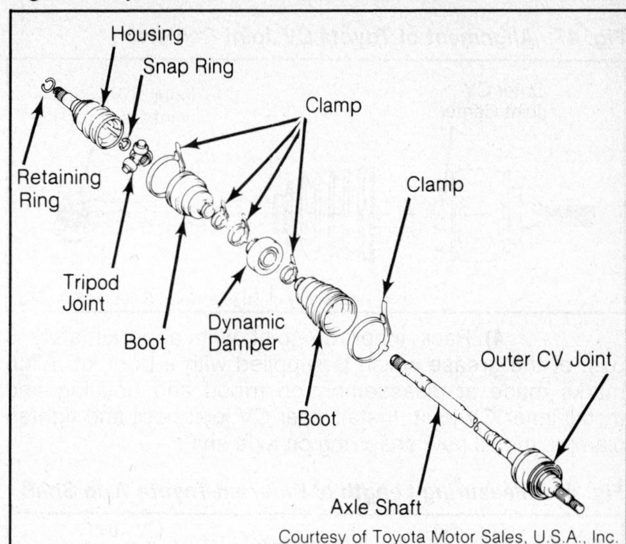

2) Disconnect tie rod from steering knuckle. Index shock absorber lower bracket and the camber adjusting cam to ensure reassembly to original position. Remove the shock absorber mounting bolts and disconnect from steering knuckle. Remove axle shaft from steering knuckle.

FWD Axle Shafts

ALL MODELS (Cont.)

3) Place shop cloth on CV joint boot to prevent damage during removal. Push axle shaft all the way into transaxle and measure distance of axle shaft to transaxle case. Using Puller (SST09520-10021), tap the axle shaft out of the transaxle and remove axle shaft. Insert Transaxle Stopper (SST09563-16010) into transaxle to prevent fluid leakage.

Disassembly (Toyota)

1) Draw alignment marks on inner CV joint and shaft with paint. Remove snap ring and boot clamps. Remove inner CV joint housing from drive shaft. Place index marks on tripod and axle shaft. Remove snap ring and press or drive tripod joint off drive shaft.

2) Remove inner CV joint boot. Remove damper clamp and damper (if equipped). On all models, remove outer CV joint boot clamps and slide boot off axle shaft. Press dust cover from transaxle side of shaft using press. Remove snap ring and bearing. Remove backside snap ring. Inspect boots for cracks and leakage. Clean all parts and replace all defective parts.

Reassembly (Toyota)

1) Install snap ring and press on bearing and dust cover, if equipped. Bearing (if equipped) should be from .004-.008 (86-87 mm) from dust cover. Wrap axle shaft splines with vinyl tape to protect boot from damage during reassembly. Slide new boots onto axle shaft. Place boot clamp rings loosely over boots with open end of clamp away from direction of rotation.

2) Do not tighten clamps at this time. Place beveled side of tripod onto shaft with beveled splines facing outer joint and align reference marks made at disassembly. Before tapping tripod into final position, align centers of inner and outer CV joints. *See Fig. 47.*

3) Using a brass drift and hammer, tap tripod into position and install new snap ring. Pack outer CV joint and boot with approximately 5 ozs. of the grease which is supplied with a boot kit. Install outer boot and tighten clamps.

Fig. 47: Alignment of Toyota CV Joint Centers

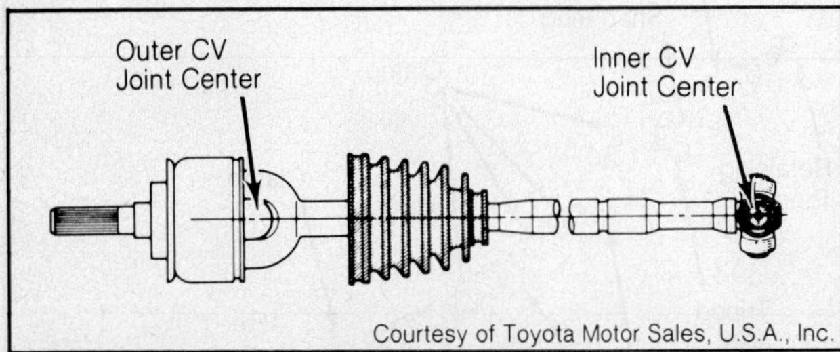

4) Pack inner CV joint with approximately 8 ozs. of the grease which is supplied with a boot kit. Align marks made at disassembly on tripod and housing and install inner CV joint. Install inner CV joint boot and tighten clamps. Install new snap ring on axle shaft.

Fig. 48: Measuring Length of Different Toyota Axle Shaft

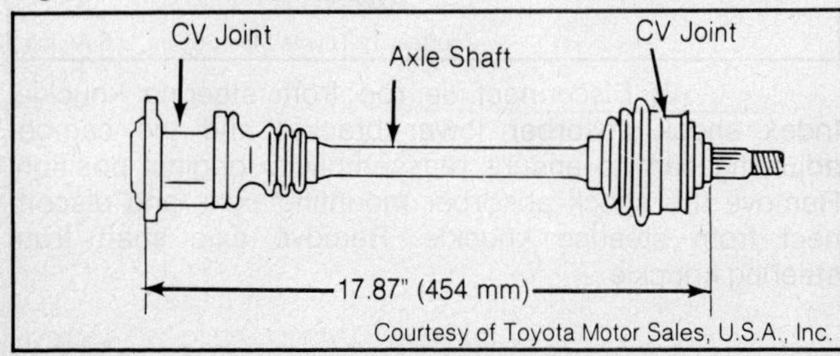

5) On Camry models, standard axle shaft length is 17.744" (455 mm) for all axles except right side on diesel models. See TOYOTA AXLE SHAFT LENGTH table in this article. Ensure boots are not deformed when axle shaft is at standard length. *See Fig. 48.*

6) On Tercel models, install damper to left axle shaft. Position balancer 15.98" (406 mm) from end of outer CV joint. Tighten clamps. *See Fig. 49.*

Fig. 49: Locating Toyota Damper on Axle Shaft

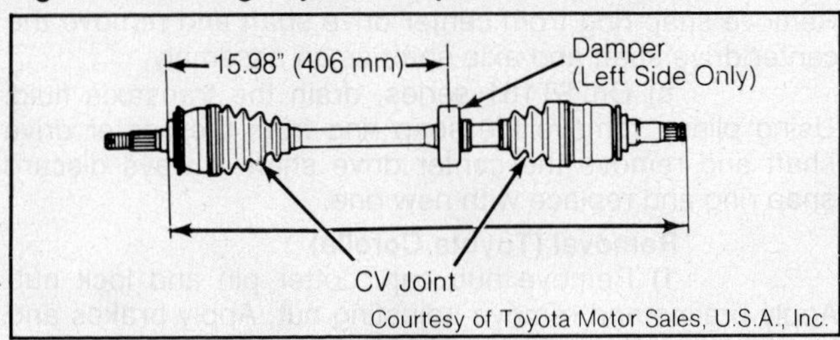

TOYOTA AXLE SHAFT LENGTH

Application	[1] Length In. (mm)
Celica	
3S-GE	
Left Side	18.083 (459.3)
Right Side	18.181 (461.8)
Corolla & FX A/T	
Right Side	27.28-27.68 (693-703)
Left Side	16.34-16.74 (415-425)
Corolla FX M/T	
Right Side	27.36-27.76 (695-705)
Left Side	16.34-16.74 (415-425)
Pickup & 4 Runner	
Both Sides	15.705 (398.9)
Tercel	
Right Side	24.41 (620)
Left Side	28.43 (722)

[1] – Axle shaft length not provided for models not listed.

Installation (Toyota)

1) To install, reverse removal procedure and note the following: install a new side retainer ring. Check seals at both ends of axle shaft and replace prior to installation if necessary. Lubricate transaxle seal lip with transaxle oil.

NOTE: **Always install new cotter pin, washer and suspension nuts.**

2) Install axle shaft into transaxle case. On all models with snap ring retained axle shafts, try to pull axle shaft out of differential by hand to ensure proper engagement of snap ring. Install axle shafts into wheel hub. Align suspension marks made at removal and tighten nuts.

3) Check camber setting and adjust if necessary. Stake axle shaft nut in place with a punch or install new cotter pin after tightening. Bleed brake system and replace transaxle fluid (if required).

Removal (Yugo)

1) Drain oil from transaxle. Unscrew axle boot flange nuts and screws. Remove outer clamps on CV joint boots and pull boots back along axle shaft. Ensure CV joints are completely uncovered. *See Fig. 50.*

ALL MODELS (Cont.)

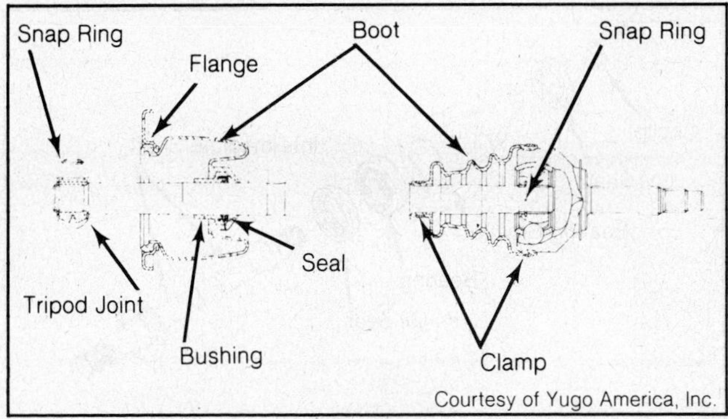

Fig. 50: Sectional View of Yugo Axle Shaft

Courtesy of Yugo America, Inc.

2) Clean grease off CV joints. Remove snap ring located inside the outer CV joint assembly. Remove shaft end from its seat in the joint. Turn wheel to enable shafts to be fully removed from their seats in the transaxle. Remove axle shaft from vehicle.

Disassembly & Reassembly (Yugo)

1) Remove axle shaft from vehicle. Remove snap ring from inner CV joint end of axle shaft and remove tripod from axle shaft. Remove boot, bushing and seal as an assembly. Clean polished sealing surface with either emery cloth or solvent. Replace all sealing components when removed.

2) Use Spreader (A.70375) and spread boot. Remove bushing and install new bushing. Install Adapter (A.70375 J) over end of axle shaft and slide boot assembly on shaft. Install tripod and snap ring. Install axle shaft in vehicle.

Installation (Yugo)

1) To install, reverse removal procedure and note the following: install a new side retainer ring. Check seals at both ends of axle shaft and replace prior to installation if necessary. Lubricate transaxle seal lip with transaxle oil.

NOTE: **Always install new cotter pin, washer and suspension nuts.**

2) Install axle shaft into transaxle case. On all models with snap ring retained axle shafts, try to pull axle shaft out of differential by hand to ensure proper engagement of snap ring. Install axle shafts into wheel hub. Align suspension marks made at removal and tighten nuts.

3) Check camber setting and adjust if necessary. Stake axle shaft nut in place with a punch or install new cotter pin after tightening. Bleed brake system and replace transaxle fluid (if required).

REMOVAL & INSTALLATION

INTERMEDIATE AXLE SHAFTS

Removal & Installation (Acura)

1) Drain fluid from transaxle. Remove axle shaft from intermediate shaft. See AXLE SHAFTS under REMOVAL & INSTALLATION in this article. Remove mounting bolts securing intermediate shaft. Integra uses 3, 10 mm bolts and the Legend uses 3, 8 mm bolts and one 10 mm bolt.

Fig. 51: Legend Intermediate Shaft Assembly

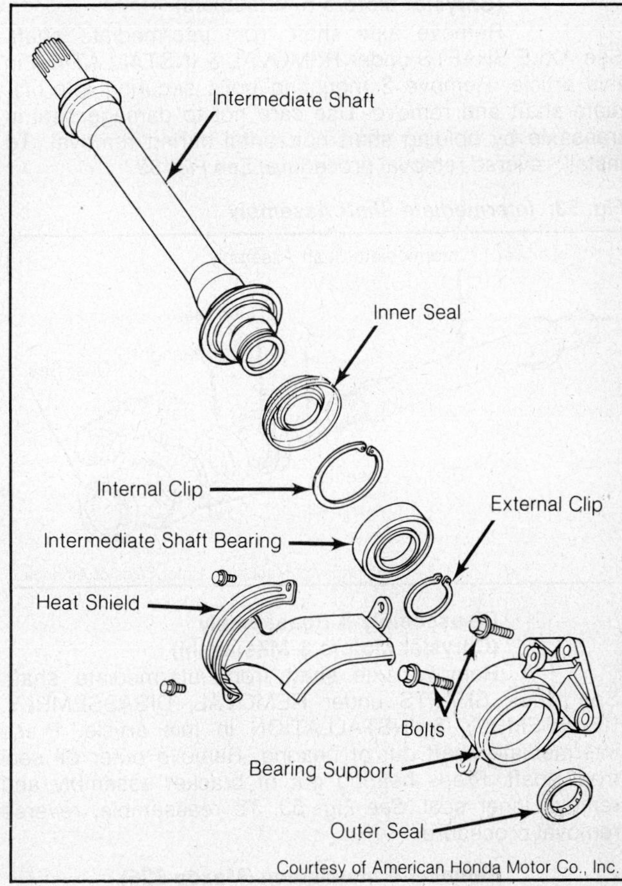

Courtesy of American Honda Motor Co., Inc.

2) Lower the bearing support close to steering gearbox and remove intermediate shaft from differential. Use care not to damage seal in transaxle by holding shaft horizontal during removal. To install, reverse removal procedure.

Disassembly & Reassembly (Acura)

Remove heat shield from bearing support (if equipped). Remove intermediate shaft outer seal. Remove one 40 mm external circlip. Press intermediate shaft out of bearing. Remove intermediate shaft inner seal. Remove 68 mm internal circlip. Press intermediate shaft bearing out of bearing support. *See Fig. 52.*

Fig. 52: Exploded View of Integra Intermediate Shaft

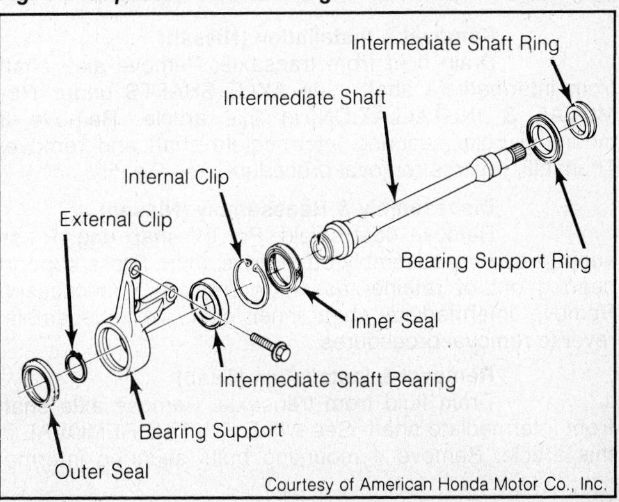

Courtesy of American Honda Motor Co., Inc.

FWD Axle Shafts

ALL MODELS (Cont.)

Removal & Installation (Chrysler Motors & Mitsubishi)

Remove axle shaft from intermediate shaft. See AXLE SHAFTS under REMOVAL & INSTALLATION in this article. Remove 2 mounting bolts securing intermediate shaft and remove. Use care not to damage seal in transaxle by holding shaft horizontal during removal. To install, reverse removal procedure. *See Fig. 53.*

Fig. 53: Intermediate Shaft Assembly

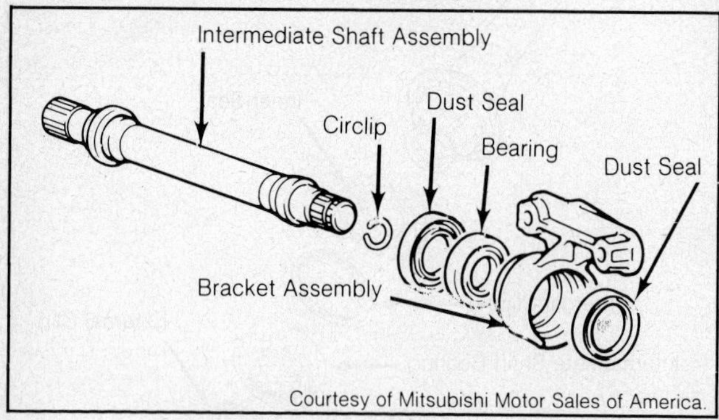

Courtesy of Mitsubishi Motor Sales of America.

Disassembly & Reassembly (Chrysler Motors & Mitsubishi)

Remove axle shaft from intermediate shaft. See AXLE SHAFTS under REMOVAL, DISASSEMBLY, REASSEMBLY & INSTALLATION in this article. Press intermediate shaft out of bearing. Remove outer oil seal from shaft. Press bearing out of bracket assembly and remove inner seal. *See Fig. 53.* To reassemble, reverse removal procedure.

Removal & Installation (Mazda 626)

Drain fluid from transaxle. Remove axle shaft from intermediate shaft. See AXLE SHAFTS REMOVAL in this article. Remove 4 mounting bolts securing intermediate shaft and remove. Use care not to damage seal in transaxle by holding shaft horizontal during removal. To install, reverse removal procedure. *See Fig. 54.*

Disassembly & Reassembly (Mazda 626)

Remove circlip retaining shaft to bracket. Remove shaft from bracket. Remove intermediate shaft outer oil seal. Press intermediate shaft out of bearing using care not to damage shaft. Remove intermediate shaft inner seal. Press intermediate shaft bearing out of bearing bracket. To reassemble, reverse removal procedure.

Removal & Installation (Nissan)

Drain fluid from transaxle. Remove axle shaft from intermediate shaft. See AXLE SHAFTS under REMOVAL & INSTALLATION in this article. Remove 3 mounting bolts securing intermediate shaft and remove. To install, reverse removal procedure. *See Fig. 55.*

Disassembly & Reassembly (Nissan)

Remove dust shield. Pry off snap ring. Press support bearing assembly off of drive shaft. Press support bearing out of retainer assembly, replace if necessary. Remove intermediate shaft inner seal. To reassemble, reverse removal procedures.

Removal & Installation (Saab)

Drain fluid from transaxle. Remove axle shaft from intermediate shaft. See AXLE SHAFTS REMOVAL in this article. Remove 4 mounting bolts securing intermediate shaft. Install Slide Hammer (8390270) into alternator bolt hole and carefully remove bearing bracket and shaft. To install, reverse removal procedure. *See Fig. 56.*

Fig. 54: Nissan Intermediate Shaft Assembly

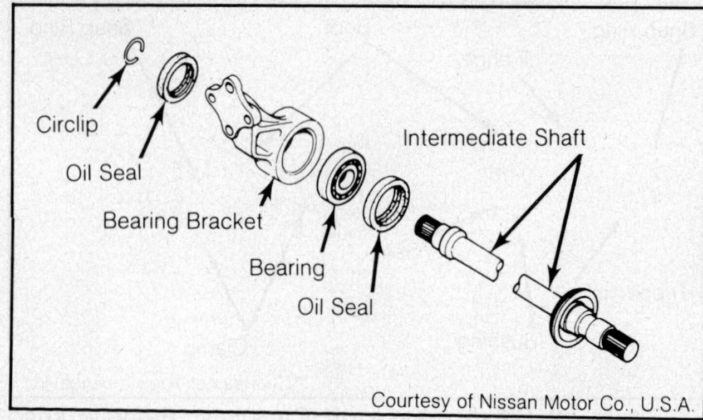

Courtesy of Nissan Motor Co., U.S.A.

Disassembly & Reassembly (Saab)

Press off intermediate drive shaft using Adapters (8790636) and (8791212), and a drift inside of tube. Remove dust seal. Remove circlip. Install 4 bolts into bearing bracket. Use press to remove intermediate shaft and dust cover from bracket. Remove inner circlip and press out bearing using Adapter (8791204). Take care not to damage shaft. To reassemble, reverse removal procedures.

Removal & Installation (Toyota)

Remove axle shaft from intermediate shaft. See AXLE SHAFTS under REMOVAL, DISASSEMBLY, REASSEMBLY & INSTALLATION in this article. Remove bolts retaining intermediate shaft bracket. *See Fig. 57.* Pull intermediate shaft out of transaxle. Replace snap ring at transaxle end of shaft. To complete installation, reverse removal procedure.

Disassembly & Reassembly (Toyota)

Remove circlip retaining shaft to bracket. Remove shaft from bracket. To reassemble, reverse disassembly procedure.

Fig. 55: Mazda Intermediate Shaft Assembly

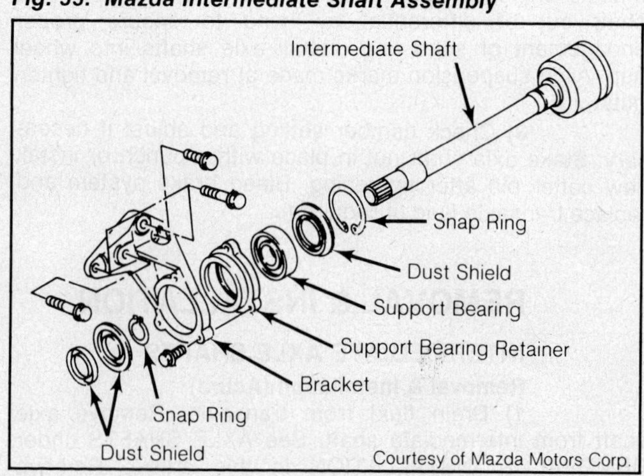

Courtesy of Mazda Motors Corp.

FWD Axle Shafts

ALL MODELS (Cont.)

Fig. 56: Saab Intermediate Shaft Assembly

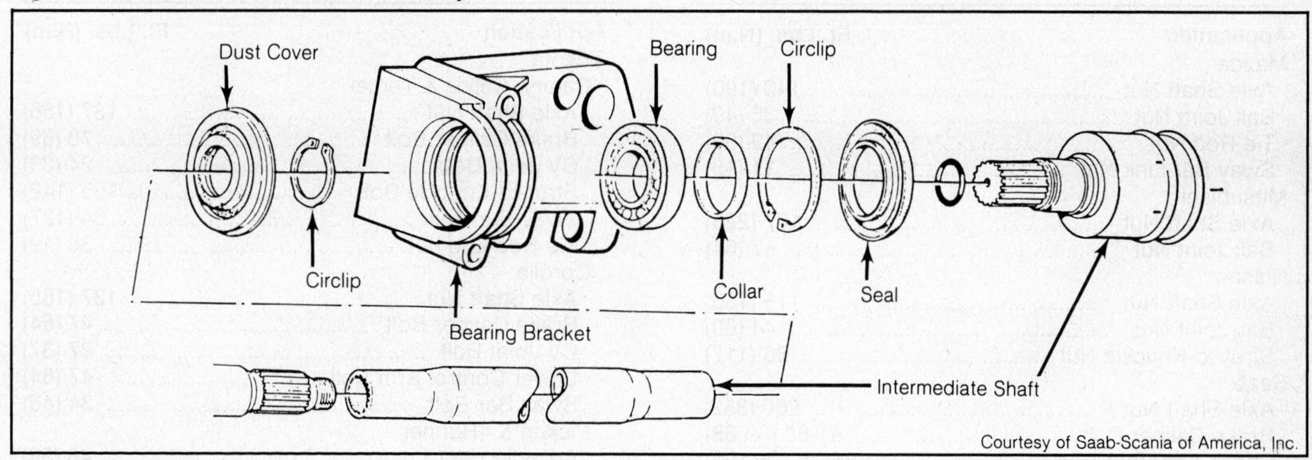

Fig. 57: Toyota Intermediate Shaft Assembly

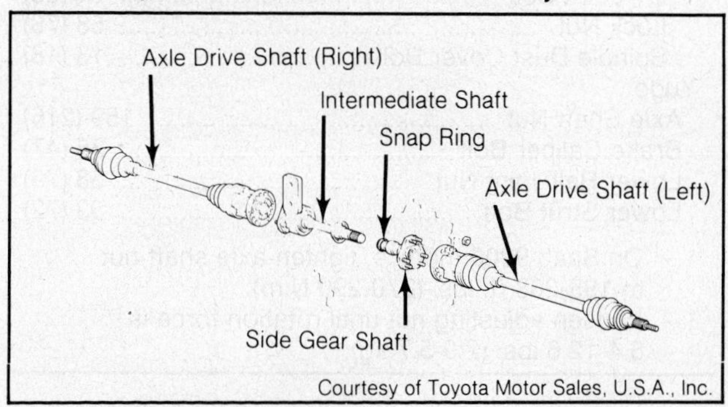

TIGHTENING SPECIFICATIONS

Application	Ft. Lbs. (N.m)
Acura	
Integra	
Axle Shaft Nut	134 (182)
Ball Joint Nut	29 (39)
Brake Caliper Bolt	53 (72)
Intermediate Shaft Bolts	29 (39)
Legend	
Axle Shaft Nut	180 (244)
Ball Joint Nut	72 (98)
Brake Caliper Bolt	24 (33)
Damper Fork Bolt	47 (64)
Damper Pinch Bolt	39 (53)
Intermediate Shaft Bolt	
8 mm	16 (22)
10 mm	28 (38)
Audi & Volkswagen	
Except 5000S	
Axle Shaft Nut	203 (275)
Ball Joint Nut	47 (64)
Brake Caliper Bolts	83 (113)
CV Joint Bolt	32 (43)
Stabilizer Bar Bolts	18 (24)
5000S	
Axle Shaft Nut	200 (271)
CV Joint Bolt	32 (43)

TIGHTENING SPECIFICATIONS (Cont.)

Application	Ft. Lbs. (N.m)
Chevrolet Spectrum	
Axle Shaft Nut	137 (186)
Ball Joint Nut	51 (69)
Stabilizer Arm Bolts	80 (108)
Wheel Lug Nut	65 (88)
Chevrolet Sprint	
Axle Shaft Nut	109-195 (148-264)
Ball Joint Nut	37-51 (50-69)
Brake Caliper Bolt	18-26 (24-35)
Stabilizer Bar Bolts	22-40 (30-55)
Tie Rod End	22-40 (30-54)
Chrysler Motors Imports	
Axle Shaft Nut	167 (226)
Ball Joint Nut	46 (62)
Stabilizer Bar Bolts	45 (61)
Ford Motor Co.	
Axle Shaft Nut	145 (197)
Ball Joint Nut	36 (49)
Lower Stabilizer Arm Bolt	47 (64)
Honda	
Axle Shaft Nut	134 (182)
Ball Joint Nut	32 (43)
Tie Rod Nut	32 (43)
Knuckle-to-Strut Nut	47 (64)
Hyundai	
Axle Shaft Nut	160 (217)
Ball Joint Nut	75 (102)
Strut Bar Bolt	75 (102)
Isuzu I-Mark	
Axle Shaft Nut	137 (186)
Knuckle-to-Strut Nut	86 (117)
Tie Rod Nut	42 (57)
Wheel Lug Nut	65 (88)
Isuzu P'UP & Trooper II	
Ball Joint-to-Lower Control Arm Bolt	51 (69)
Ball Joint-to-Knuckle Nut	75 (102)
Brake Caliper-to-Support Nut	22-25 (30-34)
Hub-to-Rotor Nut	33-40 (45-54)
Support-to-Steering Knuckle Nut	62-65 (84-88)
Strut Rod Nut	41-61 (56-83)

FWD Axle Shafts

ALL MODELS (Cont.)

TIGHTENING SPECIFICATIONS (Cont.)

Application	Ft. Lbs. (N.m)
Mazda	
Axle Shaft Nut	140 (190)
Ball Joint Nut	36 (49)
Tie Rod Nut	42 (59)
Sway Bar Link Nut	11 (15)
Mitsubishi	
Axle Shaft Nut	167 (226)
Ball Joint Nut	47 (64)
Nissan	
Axle Shaft Nut	115 (156)
Ball Joint Nut	44 (60)
Strut-to-Knuckle Nut	86 (117)
Saab	
Axle Shaft Nut [1]	260 (352)
Brake Caliper Bolt	51-65 (69-88)
Shock Absorber Bolt	56-75 (76-102)
Sterling	
Axle Shaft Nut	180 (244)
Ball Joint Nut	72 (100)
Brake Caliper Bolt	24 (33)
Damper Fork Bolt	47 (64)
Damper Pinch Bolt	39 (53)
Intermediate Shaft Bolt	28 (38)
Subaru	
Axle Shaft Nut	145 (197)
Ball Joint Nut	25 (34)
Brake Caliper	35 (47)
Strut-to-Knuckle Nut	30 (41)
Tie Rod Nut	22 (30)

TIGHTENING SPECIFICATIONS (Cont.)

Application	Ft. Lbs. (N.m)
Toyota	
Camry, Celica & Tercel	
Axle Shaft Nut	137 (186)
Brake Caliper Bolt	70 (69)
CV Joint Bolt	24 (33)
Strut-to-Knuckle Bolt	105 (142)
Sway Bar Bolt	94 (127)
Tie Rod End nut	36 (49)
Corolla	
Axle Shaft Nut	137 (185)
Brake Caliper Bolt	47 (64)
CV Joint Bolt	27 (37)
Lower Control Arm Bolt	47 (64)
Sway Bar Bolt	34 (46)
Pickup & 4Runner	
Adjusting Nut [2]	43 (58)
Brake Caliper Bolt	90 (122)
CV Joint Bolt	61 (83)
Lock Nut	58 (78)
Spindle Dust Cover Bolt	13 (18)
Yugo	
Axle Shaft Nut	159 (216)
Brake Caliper Bolt	35 (47)
Lower Ball Joint Nut	58 (78)
Lower Strut Bolt	53 (72)

[1] – On Saab 9000 models, tighten axle shaft nut to 195-208 ft. lbs. (270-290 N.m).

[2] – Loosen adjusting nut until rotation force is 6.4-12.6 lbs. (2.9-5.7 kg).

AUDI 4000CS QUATTRO, 5000CS QUATTRO & VOLKSWAGEN QUANTUM SYNCRO

NOTE: Complete information is not available from manufacturer.

DESCRIPTION

The rear axle is part of the full time 4WD system. Unlike most 4WD vehicles, this system does not use a transfer gearbox. The complete system consists of 3 differentials: front, central and rear. The front and central differentials are incorporated with the 5-speed transmission. The central and rear differential can be locked at any speed for varying road conditions.

The rear differential has a hypoid type ring and pinion gear. The drive pinion gear is supported by roller bearings and preload is maintained by a collapsible spacer between the bearings. A locking device is incorporated and consists of a shift shaft, shift fork operating sleeve and gear.

OPERATION

Power is transmitted by transmission to rear differential, through a propeller shaft. Power is also transmitted through the pinion shaft to the front axle differential.

When traction between road surface and tires is low, differential locks for both central and rear axle differentials can be engaged to improve traction. The differential locks can be engaged either when vehicle is stationary or while driving. There are 2 warning lights on the console that indicate when differentials are locked.

VACUUM SYSTEM

Central and rear differential locks are operated by a vacuum system. Center differential can be locked independently of rear differential. Rear differential can only be locked if center differential is locked. When differential locks are engaged, warning lights on console light up.

When operating knob is pulled to first position, vacuum is supplied to engagement side of center vacuum unit. When operating knob is pulled to second position, vacuum is supplied to engagement side of center and rear vacuum units.

When vacuum switch is pushed in, vacuum is transferred to the opposite side of vacuum units and differential locks are disengaged. *See Fig. 1.*

Fig. 1: Vacuum Control System

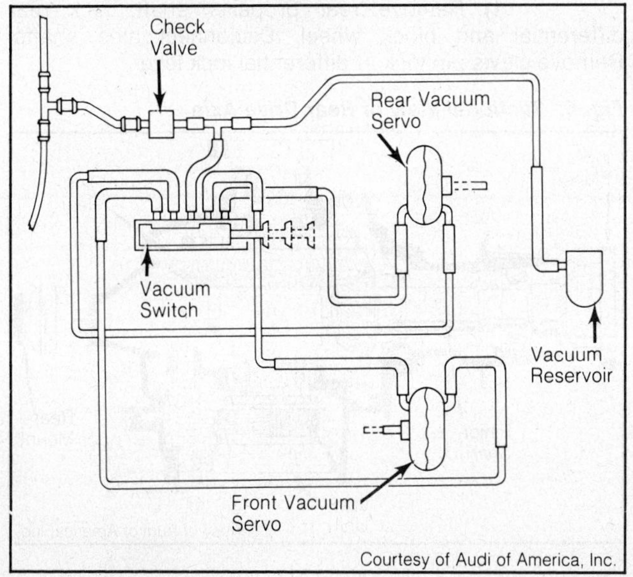

AXLE RATIO & IDENTIFICATION

The rear axle identification code is stamped under the front nose section of the drive axle. On Audi models, rear final drive code consists of code letters: WF, day, month and year of manufacture. Quantum Syncro rear final drive has identification letters AAG. All 4000CS Quattro and 5000CS Quattro models use the same final drive axle ratio of 3.89:1. Quantum Syncro final drive is 4.11:1.

ADJUSTMENTS

CENTER DIFFERENTIAL LOCK

Disengage lock. Plastic bracket on servo must be pulled in. Check that cable is located correctly at all mounting points. Pull outer cable to rear and install clip in front groove on outer cable. *See Fig. 2.*

Fig. 2: Center Differential Lock

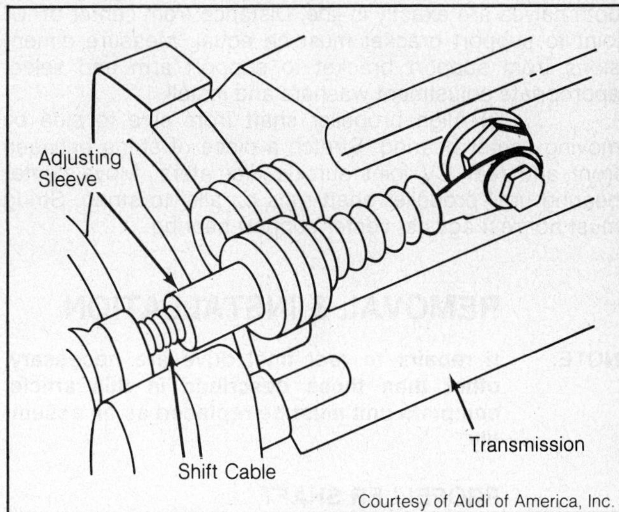

NOTE: Differential lock can only be engaged with sufficient vacuum. If necessary, run engine and check lock operation.

REAR DIFFERENTIAL LOCK

Disengage lock. Clevis pin on servo must be pressed out. Loosen clamping bolt for lever on operating shaft. Turn operating shaft clockwise to stop and pull servo clevis out. In this position, tighten clamping bolt for lever. *See Fig. 3.*

PROPELLER SHAFT

NOTE: When removing propeller shaft always replace CV joint seals.

AUDI 4000CS QUATTRO, 5000CS QUATTRO & VOLKSWAGEN QUANTUM SYNCRO (Cont.)

Fig. 3: Rear Differential Lock

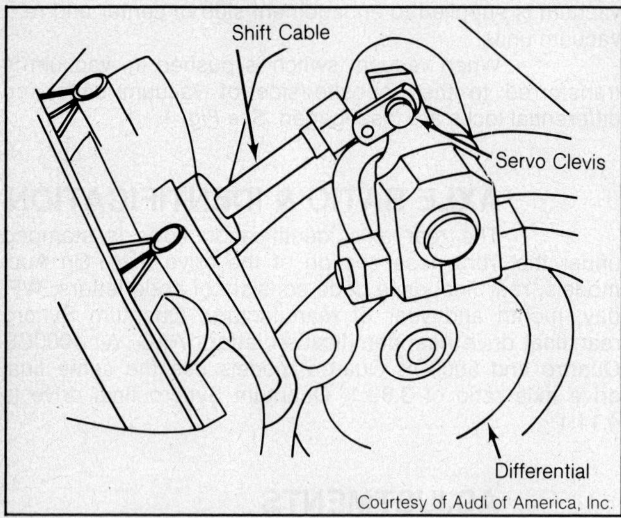

Courtesy of Audi of America, Inc.

1) Loosen center support bearing bolts. Remove adjustment washers and reinstall bolts. Check propeller shaft alignment with a straightedge approximately 47" (1194 mm) long. Be sure edge is perfectly straight. Cut recess .593" (15.08 mm) deep and 7.875" (200.03 mm) long in area of center support bearing.

2) Raise propeller shaft by tightening bolts until both halves are exactly in line. Distance from center of "U" joint to support bracket must be equal. Measure dimensions from support bracket to support arm and select appropriate adjustment washers and install.

3) Align propeller shaft from side to side by moving center bearing. Stretch a piece of string between front and rear CV joint outside diameters. Move center bearing until propeller shaft runs parallel to string. String must not rest against center support bearing.

REMOVAL & INSTALLATION

NOTE: **If repairs to rear final drive are necessary, other than those described in this article, complete unit must be replaced as an assembly.**

PROPELLER SHAFT

Removal

Detach propeller shaft from transmission output flange and support end of shaft. Disconnect propeller shaft from rear final drive flange. If necessary, engage differential lock and block wheel. Tie up shaft end. Detach center bearing from body and remove propeller shaft.

Installation

To install, reverse removal procedure. Always replace CV joint seals. Align propeller shaft after installation.

AXLE SHAFTS

NOTE: **Axle shafts are diagonally interchangeable. Left rear is identical with right front and right rear is identical with left front.**

Removal

1) Loosen wheel bolts (remove and install axle nut only with wheels on ground). Remove axle nut. Raise vehicle and remove wheel. Remove right brake backing plate.

2) Detach axle shaft from final drive flange and lay out of way. Remove ball joint clamp bolt. Detach brake hose from bracket. Pry ball joint out of hub. Move strut toward outside.

3) Press stub axle from hub. Check that there is sufficient clearance between inner CV joint and final drive housing. Remove axle assembly. *See Fig. 4*.

Fig. 4: Pressing Out Stub Axle

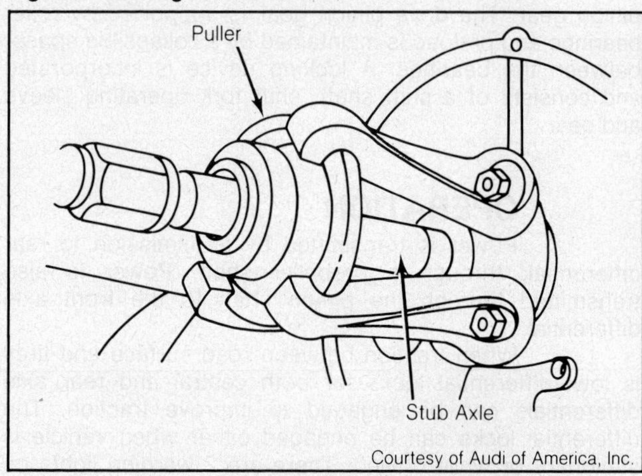

Courtesy of Audi of America, Inc.

NOTE: **Remove stub axle with mechanical or hydraulic puller only. Never heat up stub axle, as this will severely damage assembly.**

Installation

To install, reverse removal procedure. Replace gasket on inner CV joint. Ensure axle splines are free of grease and oil. Apply a bead of locking compound about .203" (5.16 mm) wide around splines. Install axle shaft.

DRIVE AXLE

Removal

1) Remove rear propeller shaft, lock rear differential and block wheel. Disconnect axle shafts. Remove clevis pin lock at differential lock lever.

Fig. 5: Sectional View of Rear Drive Axle

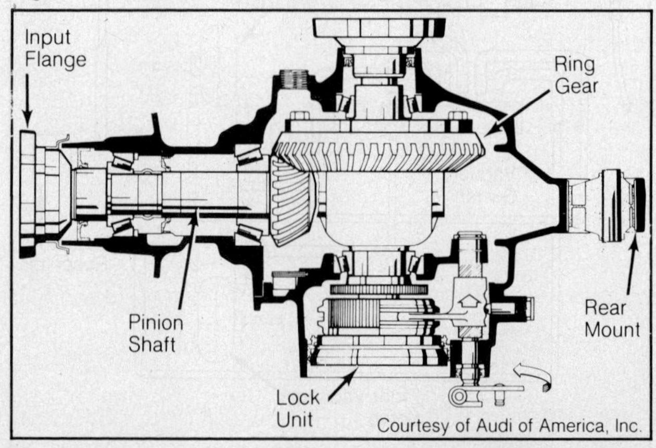

Courtesy of Audi of America, Inc.

AUDI 4000CS QUATTRO, 5000CS QUATTRO & VOLKSWAGEN QUANTUM SYNCRO (Cont.)

Fig. 6: Exploded View of Propeller Shaft

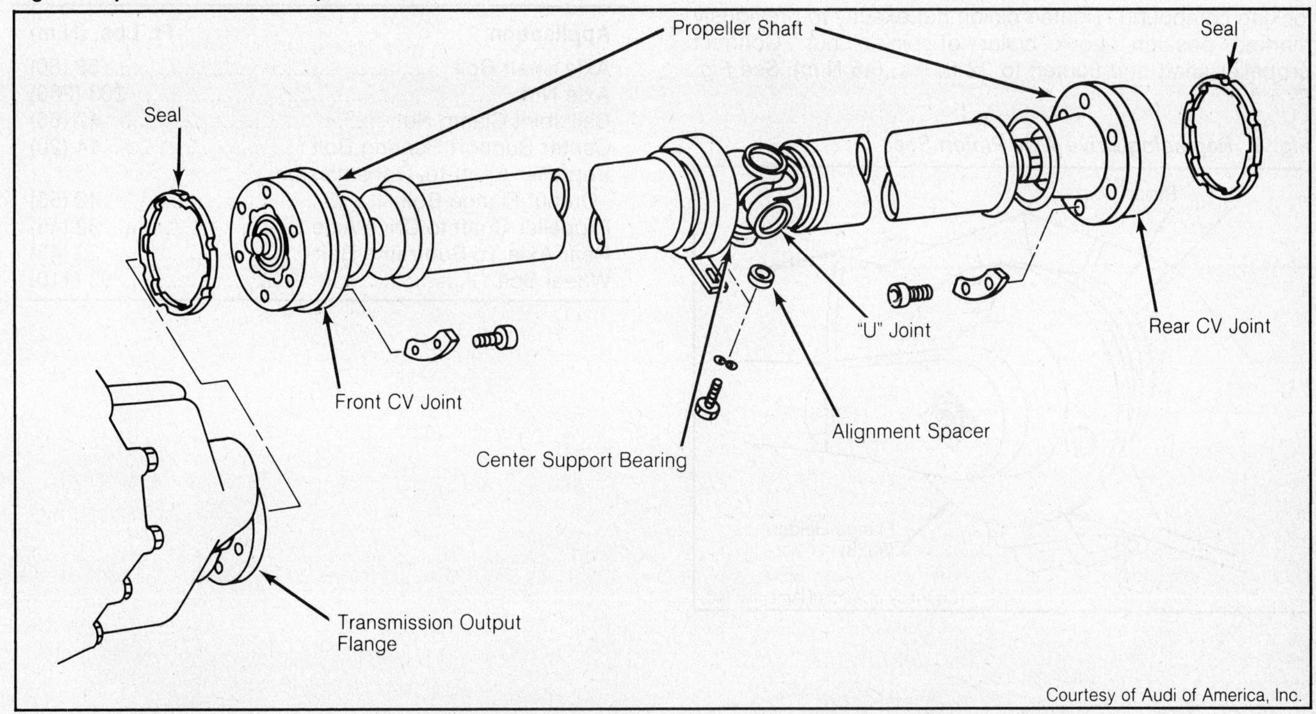

2) Remove lock pin (only possible with differential lock in off position). Remove drive axle mounting bolts. Slightly raise drive axle with jack. Push forward, then carefully lower unit.

Installation

To install, reverse removal procedure. Ensure final drive mounts are not under tension. Readjust differential lock cable.

FINAL DRIVE FLANGE OIL SEAL

Removal (Right Side)

Disconnect axle shaft. While holding flange with drift, remove drive flange bolt. Place oil drip tray in position. Pull drive flange out and remove oil seal.

Installation

To install, drive in oil seal completely. Be careful not to damage seal. Fill space between sealing lips with multipurpose grease.

Removal (Left Side)

Drain oil from drive axle. Remove axle shaft and push upward out of way. Remove left drive axle mount. Lower drive axle until flange is accessible. Remove drive flange bolt while holding flange with 2 bolts. DO NOT lose adjustment shim between flange shaft and drive axle. Using a seal puller, remove oil seal.

Installation

1) Install threaded shaft of Seal Installer (3066). Place oil seal on seal installer and tighten to stop. Remove seal installer. Fill oil seal and sealing lips with multipurpose grease. *See Fig. 7.*

2) Attach adjustment shim (with grease) on flange shaft and install. Tighten drive flange bolt to 25 ft. lbs. (34 N.m). Install left final drive mount and tighten nut to 32 ft. lbs. (45 N.m). Check drive axle oil level and top off as necessary.

Fig. 7: Installing Left Flange Seal

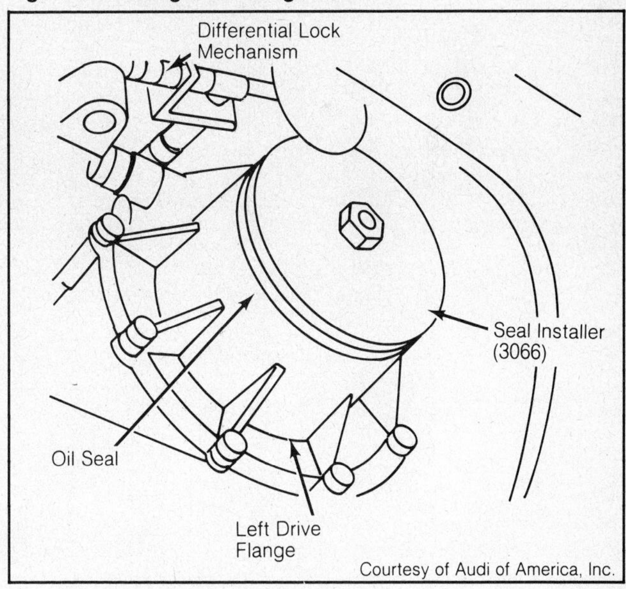

PINION SHAFT SEAL

Removal

Disconnect rear propeller shaft at drive axle. Mark position of pinion nut on pinion. Always use same pinion nut if possible. Using Flange Holder (3028), remove pinion nut. Using Puller (VW 391), remove pinion flange. Using Seal Puller (VW 691), remove oil seal.

Installation

1) Fill oil seal with multipurpose grease between sealing lips and install to stop. Install pinion flange. Clean grease and oil from threads of pinion nut and pinion shaft.

Drive Axles

AUDI 4000CS QUATTRO, 5000CS QUATTRO & VOLKSWAGEN QUANTUM SYNCRO (Cont.)

2) Coat threads of pinion nut with thin coat of locking compound. Tighten pinion nut exactly to previously marked position. Lock collar of pinion nut. Connect propeller shaft and tighten to 32 ft. lbs. (45 N.m). *See Fig. 8.*

Fig. 8: Replacing Drive Axle Pinion Seal

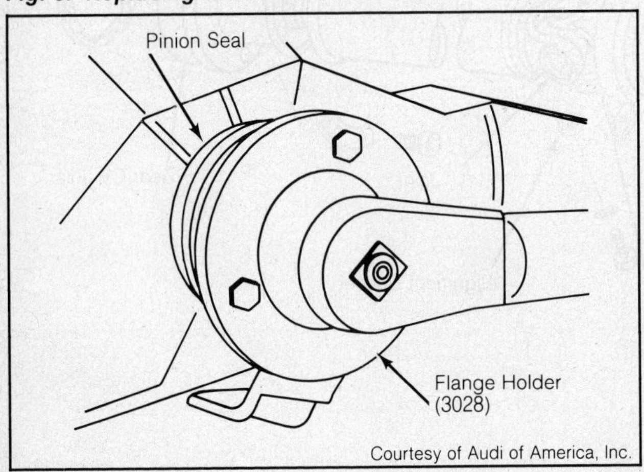

Courtesy of Audi of America, Inc.

TIGHTENING SPECIFICATIONS

Application	Ft. Lbs. (N.m)
Axle Shaft Bolt	58 (80)
Axle Nut	203 (280)
Ball Joint Clamp Nut	47 (65)
Center Support Bearing Bolt	14 (20)
Propeller Shaft-to-Transmission Output Flange Bolt	40 (55)
Propeller Shaft to Drive Axle Bolt	32 (45)
Rear Axle To Subframe Bolt	32 (45)
Wheel Bolt	80 (110)

BMW INTEGRAL CARRIER

All Models

DESCRIPTION

The final drive assembly has hypoid type ring and pinion gear. Assembly may have a multi-disc, self-locking differential (ZF DL-175). Housing has a removable rear cover. Differential carrier is retained in the sides of the housing by bearing caps and is supported by tapered roller bearings.

Shims under the bearing caps maintain proper carrier bearing preload. Drive pinion gear is supported by roller bearings and preload is maintained by a collapsible spacer between the bearings.

AXLE RATIO & IDENTIFICATION

The ring and pinion gear set with Klingelnberg tooth design can be identified by the letter "K" stamped on the drive pinion gear. Gleason teeth are noted by an "H" stamping. Letter "S" indicates a self-locking differential.

To determine axle ratio, divide number of ring gear teeth by number of drive pinion gear teeth. The number of teeth on ring and drive pinion gears is stamped on forward right side of differential housing.

AXLE RATIO SPECIFICATION

Application	Ratio:1
325, 325e & 325es	2.79 or 2.93
325i & 325is	3.73
528e	2.93
535i & 535is	3.25
635CSi	3.46
735i & L7	3.46

REMOVAL & INSTALLATION

CONSTANT VELOCITY JOINT

Removal

Remove cover from joint housing. Remove snap ring from end of drive shaft. Remove clamps from boot. Press drive shaft from joint and note position of thrust washer (if equipped). Remove dust boot.

Installation

To install, reverse removal procedure. Convex side of thrust washer faces joint (if equipped). When repacking CV joints, use only Moly-type grease.

DRIVE AXLES & BEARINGS

Removal

1) Raise and support vehicle. Remove wheel and brake drum assembly. Remove drive shaft. Loosen castellated nut (6-cyl. models) securing flange to drive axle. Using a puller, remove flange.

2) On all models, install castellated nut on axle shaft and drive out drive axle using a soft-headed mallet. Remove bearings and seals. Remove spacer sleeve and shim (if equipped).

Installation

1) To install, reverse removal procedure. Install inner bearing. Determine distance between outer races of inner and outer bearings.

Fig. 1: Sectional View of Axle Shaft Assembly

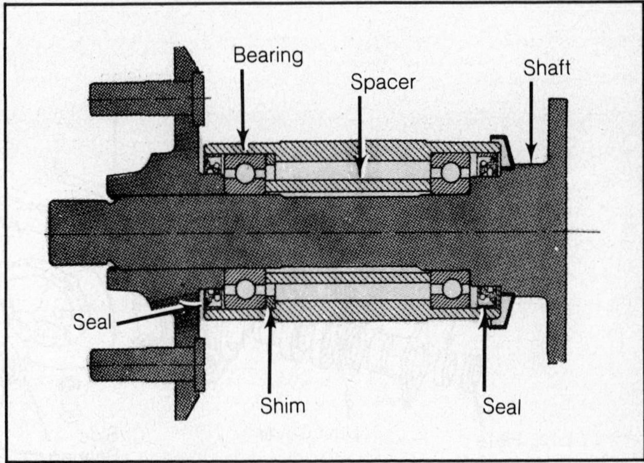

Courtesy of BMW of North America, Inc.

2) Measure spacer and shim. Install spacer and shim that will obtain specified axle shaft end play. Pack bearings and hub with grease. Complete installation procedure, using new seals.

DRIVE PINION COMPANION FLANGE OIL SEAL

Removal

1) Remove final drive assembly and mount on holding fixture. Remove lock washer. Using a pin punch, mark installed position of companion flange. Using an INCH lb. torque wrench, measure and record pinion gear preload.

2) Hold flange stationary and remove lock nut. Pull off companion flange. Check bearing surface of flange. Replace flange if deeply scored. Pull out seal and discard.

Installation

1) Dip new seal in gear oil. Drive seal into case until flush. Press companion flange onto pinion gear, aligning punch marks made during removal.

2) Loosely install lock nut. Using INCH lb. torque wrench, tighten lock nut. Tighten lock nut to pinion gear preload value measured during removal, PLUS 2 INCH lbs. (.23 N.m) for new seal.

3) If lock nut can not be tightened to specified torque value or if preload value (measured during removal) is exceeded, removal and installation of drive pinion is required (always replace "Crush" sleeve). If preload value is obtained, install lock washer.

AXLE FLANGE & OIL SEAL

Removal

With final drive assembly mounted in holding fixture, pry off drive flanges. Mark flanges for installation in original positions. Check flanges for scored bearing or seal surfaces. Replace if damaged. Remove and discard flange snap ring. Remove seal with puller.

Installation

Dip seal in gear oil. Drive seal into case until it rests against stop. Insert new snap ring into recessed groove in case. Replace drive flange. Ensure snap ring is fully locked in groove.

BMW INTEGRAL CARRIER (Cont.)

Fig. 2: Exploded View of BMW Integral Carrier Assembly

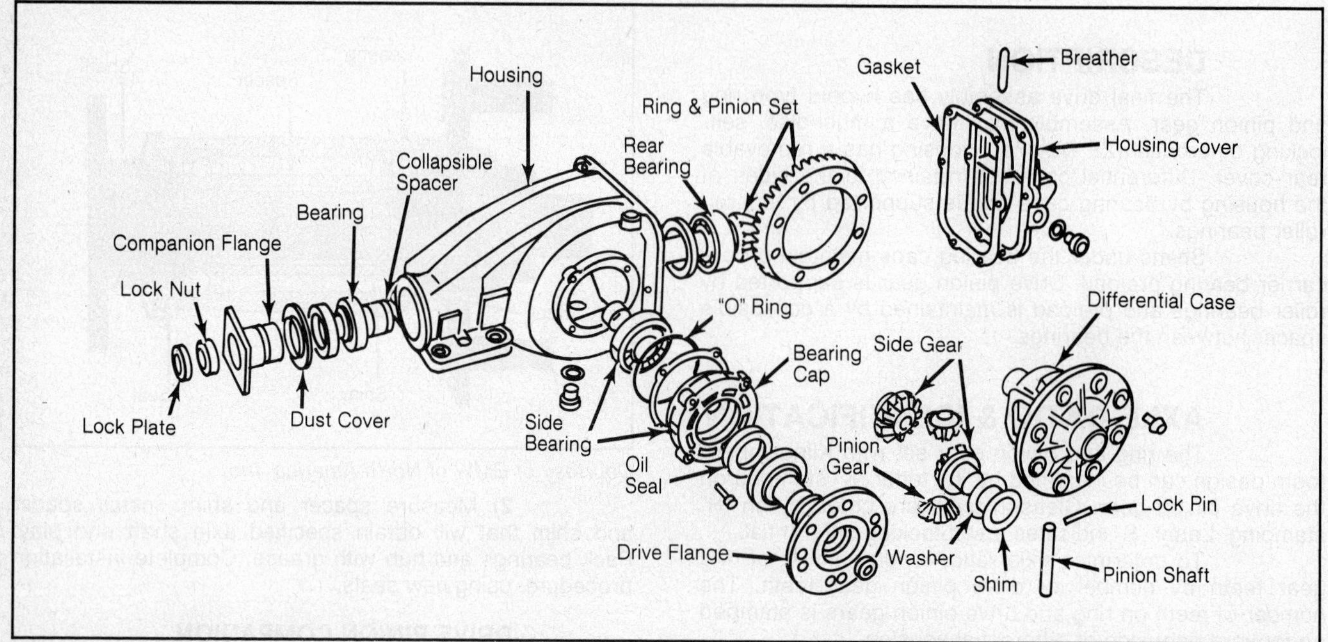

DIFFERENTIAL ASSEMBLY

Removal

Disconnect propeller shaft and drive shafts from final drive. Suspend shafts out of way. Detach self-aligning support at final drive. Remove electrical connectors. Support final drive on jack and remove final drive mounting bolts. Lower jack and remove final drive assembly.

Installation

To install, reverse removal procedure. Install new self-locking nuts on propeller shaft. Ensure that assembly is stress-free when tightened to specification.

OVERHAUL

DISASSEMBLY

Differential Housing (Conventional)

1) Remove final drive assembly and mount in holding fixture. Using an INCH lb. torque wrench, measure and record preload of pinion gear and differential gears.

2) Drain oil and remove rear cover plate. Discard gasket. Remove drive flanges as previously described. Remove both bearing caps, keeping right and left parts separated. Record number and location of shims located under bearing caps. Remove differential case assembly from housing.

3) Remove multi-tab pulse ring. Remove side bearings, using a puller. Remove ring gear mounting bolts and ring gear. Drive out pinion shaft lock pin. Remove pinion shaft and gears. Remove side gears, shims and thrust washers.

Differential Housing (Limited Slip)

1) With differential removed from housing, remove 8 retainer plate bolts. Turn case upside down and allow plate assembly to slide out. Remove thrust washer, diaphragm spring, outer and inner plates.

2) Lift off pressure member and remove pinion side gear. Remove pinion gears with shaft. Check and replace any components that show scoring, easy movement or being worn. Keep all components in order for reassembly.

Drive Pinion Gear

1) Remove lock washer. Using a punch, mark installed position of companion flange. Using an INCH lb. torque wrench, measure and record pinion gear preload.

2) Hold flange stationary and remove lock nut. Pull off companion flange. Check bearing surface of flange. Replace flange if deeply scored. Pull out seal and discard. Press drive pinion from housing. Remove collapsible spacer. Using Puller Set (33 1 350 and 33 1 371), remove front housing bearing.

3) Remove drive pinion shaft oil seal. Using Puller Set (33 1 350, 33 1 356, 33 1 362 and 33 1 363), remove pinion inner bearing race from case. Note shim "X" thickness under bearing race. *See Fig. 3.*

REASSEMBLY & ADJUSTMENT

Drive Pinion Gear

1) Using bearing race installer, install front and rear bearing races in housing. *See Fig. 4.* Press rear bearing onto drive pinion. Note any deviations ("+" or "–") stamped on drive pinion. This amount must be added (if "+") or subtracted (if "–") from measurement "C". *See Fig. 5.*

2) Heat ring gear to 176-212°F (80-100°C) if necessary. If original ring and pinion gear set is being installed, install drive pinion gear using original shim and new collapsible spacer. If new ring and pinion gear set is being installed, install new shim that is same thickness as original shim.

Drive Pinion Bearing Preload

1) Install shim and drive pinion gear. Using Bearing Installers (23 1 300 and 23 2 150), install front drive pinion gear bearing. DO NOT install collapsible

BMW INTEGRAL CARRIER (Cont.)

Fig. 3: Sectional View of Drive Pinion Gear Assembly

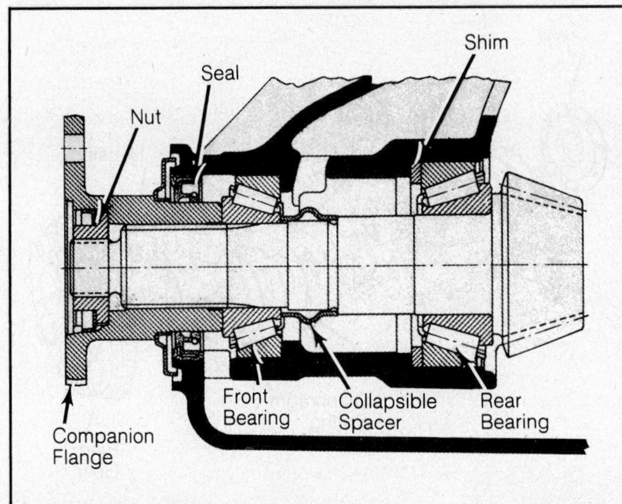

Courtesy of BMW of North America, Inc.

Fig. 4: Installing Bearing Outer Races

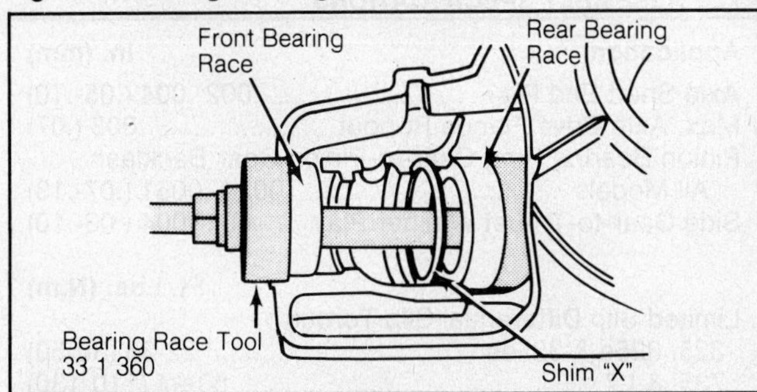

Courtesy of BMW of North America, Inc.

Fig. 5: Pinion Shim Measuring Points

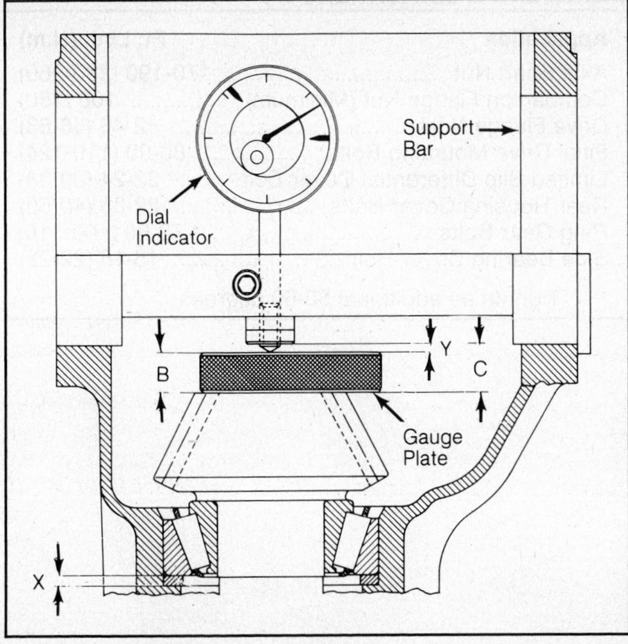

Courtesy of BMW of North America, Inc.

spacer or seal. Install companion flange. Loosely install lock nut. Using an INCH lb. torque wrench, tighten lock nut to obtain preload.

2) Mount dial indicator on Support Bar (33 1 381). Place support bar and dial indicator over Gauge Plate (33 1 382). Zero dial indicator with .157" (4 mm) preload. Place gauge plate on drive pinion in housing. Place support bar with dial indicator in housing. Measure distance between support bar and gauge plate (dimension "Y").

3) Basic setting adjustment is .453" (11.50 mm) on all models except 735i. On 735i models, adjustment setting is .728" (18.50 mm). Using dimensions, determine required shim thickness "X" by using sample calculation chart. *See Fig. 5.*

SAMPLE PINION BEARING PRELOAD CALCULATION

Dimension	In. (mm)
"C" (Basic Setting)	[1] .453" (11.50)
PLUS or MINUS Deviation	- .012" (.30)
"C" Target	.441" (11.20)
Measured Value "Y"	.063" (1.60)
Sum "B" (Gauge Plate)	.374" (9.50)
PLUS Measured Value "Y"	+ 1.063" (27.00)
"C" Actual	.437" (11.10)
"C" Target	.441" (11.20)
"C" Actual	[2] - .437" (11.10)
Difference =	.004" (.10)
Installed Shim Thickness	.163" (4.14)
PLUS or MINUS Difference	- .004" (.10)
Shim "X" Thickness =	.159" (4.04)

[1] – Calculations are for 528e.

[2] – If "C" target is greater than "C" actual, difference is subtracted from shim thickness. If "C" target is smaller than "C" actual, difference is added to shim thickness.

4) Remove gauge, companion flange and drive pinion gear. Install shims of calculated thickness. Shims are available in .0004-.0012" (.01-.03 mm) thicknesses.

5) Install shims, drive pinion gear, collapsible spacer and seal. Install companion flange and tighten lock nut to obtain specified pinion gear bearing preload. If preload is exceeded, new collapsible spacer must be installed and procedure repeated.

Differential Housing (Conventional)

1) Press on side bearings. Install both differential side gears with thrust washers and shims. Ensure concave side of thrust washers face gears. Using drive flanges, center side gears.

2) Mount differential assembly in vise. Install Spreader (33 1 430). *See Fig. 6.* Spread side gears by tightening spindle until drive flange can just be turned. Remove drive flange and install pinion gears. Remove spreader. Install pinion shaft, lock pin, drive flanges and center side gears.

3) Install side gear gauge plate and spindle. Hand tighten spindle. Mount dial indicator on differential case. Zero dial indicator. Tighten spindle until thrust washer is pressed flat.

4) Loosen spindle. Turn side gear and repeat measurement at various points. Repeat procedure on opposite side gear. Adjust specified clearance by installing thicker or thinner shims.

BMW INTEGRAL CARRIER (Cont.)

5) Shims are available in .002" (.05 mm) increments. Remove gauge plate and spindle, pinion shaft, pinion gears and side gears. Install shims of calculated thickness and repeat procedure.

NOTE: Ring gear tooth pattern has priority over backlash and preload adjustments. After setting backlash and preload, perform tooth contact pattern check and adjust shims accordingly.

Fig. 6: Spreading Differential Side Gears

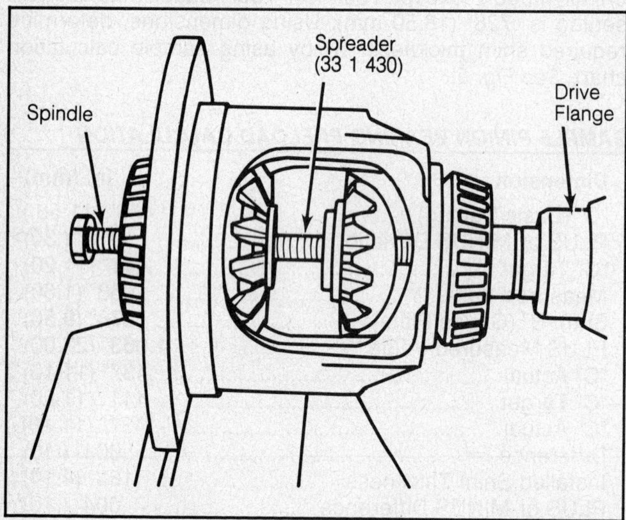

Courtesy of BMW of North America, Inc.

Differential Bearing Preload

1) Install INCH lb. torque wrench on companion flange lock nut. Measure total preload of drive pinion gear and ring gear, with seals installed. Compare preload reading with that measured during disassembly. Add 2 INCH lbs. (.23 N.m) for new drive pinion gear seal.

2) Preload should be within specification. If not, perform tooth contact pattern check and adjust total shim thickness. After final adjustments or changing shim thickness or positions, always verify adjustments with tooth contact pattern check. Install new rear cover gasket, cover and fill with lube oil. See GEAR TOOTH PATTERNS article in this section.

Limited Slip Differential

1) To reassemble, reverse disassembly procedure. Place diaphragm spring and thrust washer in case. Oil grooves of thrust washer should face up. Install in order; diaphragm spring, outer plate, inner plate, pressure ring and differential side gear in case. *See Fig. 7.*

2) Install drive flanges. Check slip torque while holding one differential side gear and driving the other. See AXLE ASSEMBLY SPECIFICATIONS table in this article. Slip torque is adjusted with outer plates which are available in 3 different thicknesses.

Fig. 7: Limited Slip Plate Assembly

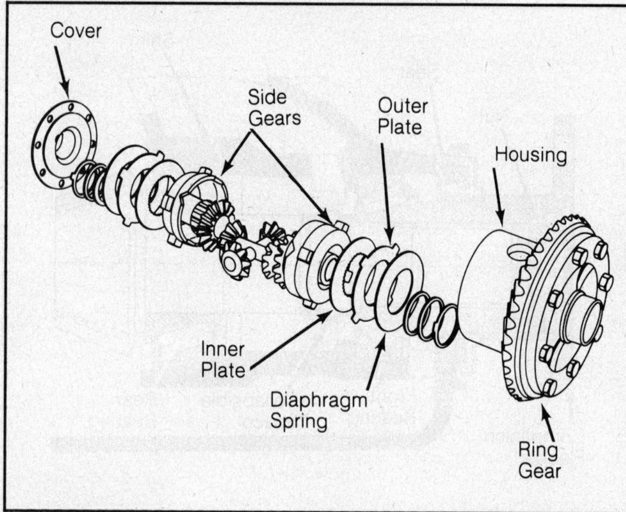

Courtesy of BMW of North America, Inc.

AXLE ASSEMBLY SPECIFICATIONS

Application	In. (mm)
Axle Shaft End Play	.002-.004 (.05-.10)
Max. Axle Drive Flange Runout	.003 (.07)
Pinion Bearing Ring Gear-to-Pinion Gear Backlash	
All Models	.0024-.0051 (.07-.13)
Side Gear-to-Thrust Washer Play	.001-.004 (.03-.10)
	Ft. Lbs. (N.m)
Limited Slip Differential Slip Torque	
325, 325e & 325es	22-36 (30-50)
735i & L7	80-94 (110-130)
All Other Models	36-54 (50-75)

TIGHTENING SPECIFICATIONS

Application	Ft. Lbs. (N.m)
Axle Shaft Nut	170-190 (230-260)
Companion Flange Nut (Minimum)	108 (150)
Drive Flange Nuts	42-46 (58-63)
Final Drive Mounting Bolts	80-90 (110-124)
Limited Slip Differential Cover Bolt	22-24 (30-33)
Rear Housing Cover Bolts	29-36 (40-50)
Ring Gear Bolts	[1] 72-80 (100-110)
Side Bearing Cover Bolt	16-18 (22-25)

[1] – Tighten an additional 50-60 degrees.

Drive Axles

CHRYSLER MOTORS & MITSUBISHI INTEGRAL HOUSING

Chrysler Motors: Colt Vista 4WD, Conquest;
Mitsubishi: Starion

DESCRIPTION

Rear axle features an integral housing. Differential consists of hypoid reduction gears and straight bevel differential gears. Limited slip differential is available on some models.

AXLE RATIO & IDENTIFICATION

Ratio is determined by dividing number of ring gear teeth by number of drive pinion teeth.

AXLE RATIO SPECIFICATIONS

Application	Ratio
Colt Vista	3.91
Conquest & Starion	3.55

TESTING

LIMITED SLIP DIFFERENTIAL PRELOAD

1) Place transmission or transaxle in Neutral. Block front wheels. Raise one rear wheel free of ground and remove wheel. On Colt Vista models, ensure 4WD control switch is in the "OFF" position.

2) Use Adapter (MB990767) for Colt Vista or (MB990241-01) for Conquest and Starion models. Install adapter on wheel studs. Release parking brake.

3) Using torque wrench, measure starting torque on Conquest and Straion models when rotating wheel in forward direction. On Colt Vista models, measure rotating torque. This measurement is read once axle is turning. Differential must be repaired if torque is less than specification. See TESTING SPECIFICATIONS table.

TESTING SPECIFICATIONS

Application	Ft. Lbs. (N.m)
Colt Vista	5.1 (7)
Conquest & Starion	[1] 28 (39)

[1] – Includes 3 ft. lbs (4 N.m) for disc brake drag.

AXLE SHAFT END PLAY

Using dial indicator, check axle shaft end play. End play must not exceed .031" (.78 mm). If not within specification, check companion flange nut tightness. If tight, bearings must be replaced.

AXLE TOTAL BACKLASH

1) Raise and support rear axle. Place transmission or transaxle in Neutral. Apply parking brake. Rotate drive shaft clockwise. Place reference marks on companion flange dust cover and torque tube or housing.

2) Rotate drive shaft counterclockwise and measure distance between reference marks. Differential must be removed and backlash adjusted if distance exceeds .2" (5 mm).

REMOVAL & INSTALLATION

DRIVE AXLES

Removal (Colt Vista)

Remove drive axle companion flange-to-axle shaft retaining bolts. Using screwdriver, pry drive axle from differential carrier. Use care not to damage oil seal. Pry oil seal from differential carrier if replacement is required.

CAUTION: Always replace circlip on inboard side of drive axle.

Installation

1) Using Seal Installer (MB991115) and Handle (MB990938), install oil seal in differential. Coat seal lip with grease.

2) Install new circlip on drive axle. Install drive axle in differential carrier. Install companion flange bolts. Tighten to specification. See TIGHTENING SPECIFICATIONS table at end of article.

Removal (Conquest & Starion)

Raise and support vehicle. Remove rear wheels. Remove retaining bolts and separate drive shaft from companion flange. Using slide hammer, remove drive axle shaft. Use care not to damage oil seal. Remove differential oil seal (if necessary).

CAUTION: Always replace circlip on inboard side of drive axle.

Installation

1) Using Oil Seal Installer (MB990727-01) and Handle (MIT304180), install oil seal in differential (if removed). Apply grease to seal lip. Install drive axle into differential. Using slide hammer, drive axle into differential.

2) Ensure axle is locked in position. Install companion flange bolts and nuts. Tighten to specification. See TIGHTENING SPECIFICATIONS table at end of article.

AXLE HOUSING ASSEMBLY

Removal (Conquest & Starion)

1) Disconnect parking brake cable from rear brake caliper. Remove brake caliper, leaving hydraulic line connected. Remove brake disc. Remove drive axle companion flange retaining bolts.

2) Remove axle housing from lower control arm. Remove strut assembly-to-axle housing retaining bolts. Separate axle housing from strut assembly. Remove axle housing.

Installation

Reverse removal procedure. Tighten all fasteners to specification.

INNER ARM

Removal

1) Raise and support vehicle. Remove wheel and tire assembly. Disconnect drive axle companion flange-to-axle shaft retaining bolts. Support inner arm with jack.

2) Remove shock absorber retaining bolt. Mark position of upper end of outer arm and crossmember body installation bracket. Remove inner and outer arm coupling bolts. Remove coupling bolt from inner arm and crossmember. Remove inner arm.

CHRYSLER MOTORS & MITSUBISHI INTEGRAL HOUSING (Cont.)

Installation

Reverse removal procedures. Tighten bolts to specification. Check toe-in on axle.

TORQUE TUBE

Removal (Conquest & Starion)

1) Remove retaining bolts and propeller shaft. Loosen differential companion flange nut if disassembly is required. DO NOT remove.

2) Remove torque tube-to-differential carrier bolts. Remove torque tube-to-front support bolts. Using slide hammer, separate extension shaft from spline coupling. Remove torque tube assembly.

CAUTION: DO NOT hit torque flange or bracket when installing torque tube.

Installation

1) Apply grease to pocket and spline of differential side of extension shaft. Install torque tube assembly onto differential carrier and front support.

2) Using slide hammer, drive extension shaft onto differential spline coupling. Ensure torque tube flange fully contacts surface of differential carrier flange. If clearance exists, torque tube is assembled incorrectly.

3) Install torque tube-to-differential carrier bolts. Tighten to specification. Coat torque tube-to-front support bolts with oil and install. Tighten to specification.

4) Install companion flange with mating marks aligned (if removed). Hold extension shaft by applying parking brake. Companion flange retaining nut must always be replaced. Install and tighten to specification. See TIGHTENING SPECIFICATIONS table at end of article.

5) Using dial indicator, measure companion flange runout. If runout exceeds .004" (.10 mm), change the phase of companion flange and extension shaft. Remeasure runout again. If runout is excessive, replace defective parts. Install propeller shaft. Tighten to specification.

DIFFERENTIAL CARRIER

Removal (Colt Vista)

1) Drain gear oil from differential housing. Remove drive axles. Mark propeller shaft flange-to-pinion flange on differential. Remove propeller shaft.

2) Support differential carrier. Remove differential carrier-to-rear support bolts. Remove differential carrier front mount bolt. Remove differential carrier.

Installation

1) When installing vent plug, apply semi-drying sealant to mating surfaces of vent plug and cover. Reverse removal procedures for remaining components. Tighten bolts to specification.

2) Fill differential with gear lube. Use Mopar Gear Lube (3744994) in conventional axles. On limited slip axles, use Mopar Gear Lube (4318058) and Mopar Friction Modifier (4318060).

Removal (Conquest & Starion)

1) Drain gear oil from differential housing. Remove drive axles, torque tube, and propeller shaft as previously described. Remove rear support insulator-to-rear crossmember nuts.

2) Remove insulator-to-rear support nuts. Raise differential carrier. Disconnect differential carrier from rear support insulators. Remove rear supports, cover, and gasket.

Installation

1) Apply sealant to differential carrier, gasket, and cover surfaces. Install cover. Tighten to specification. When installing vent plug, apply semi-drying sealant to mating surfaces of vent plug and cover.

2) Reverse removal procedures for remaining components. Tighten bolts to specification. Fill differential with gear oil. Use SAE 90W gear oil with API classification GL-5 in conventional axles.

3) On limited slip axles, use Mitsubishi Gear Lube (8149630EX) or Mopar Gear Lube (4318058) and Mopar Friction Modifier (4318060).

Fig. 1: Exploded View of Limited Slip Differential (Conquest & Starion)

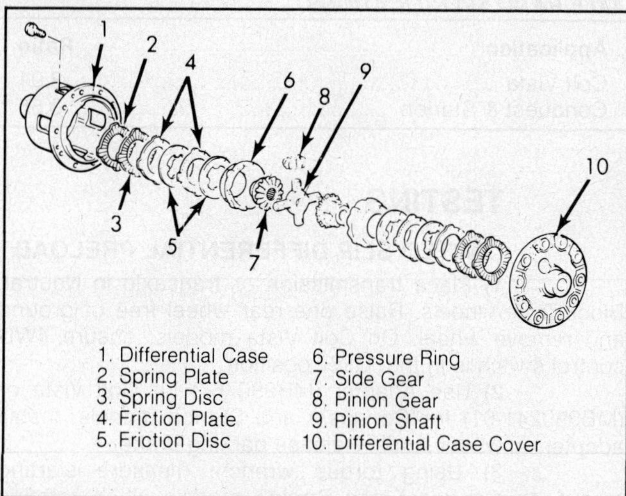

Courtesy of Chrysler Motors.

OVERHAUL

DRIVE AXLES & BEARINGS

NOTE: References to BJ refer to Birfield Joint and DOJ to Double Off-Set Joint.

Disassembly

1) Remove boot protector and bands. Remove circlip from DOJ outer race. Separate drive shaft from DOJ outer race. *See Fig. 3.* Remove balls from DOJ cage. Remove DOJ cage from DOJ inner race in direction of BJ.

2) Remove snap ring from drive axle shaft. Remove DOJ inner race from shaft. Remove circlip from shaft. Wrap tape around splines of shaft to prevent boot damage during removal.

3) Remove DOJ boot protector and boot. Drive axle and BJ are serviced as a unit. Remove BJ boot if damaged.

CAUTION: Drive axle and BJ are serviced as a unit. DO NOT disassemble BJ and drive axle.

Inspection

1) Inspect BJ for rust, dirt, water, or damage to balls and races. Inspect shaft for bend or spline damage. Inspect boots for cracks or wear.

CHRYSLER MOTORS & MITSUBISHI INTEGRAL HOUSING (Cont.)

Fig. 2: Exploded View of Conventional Differential

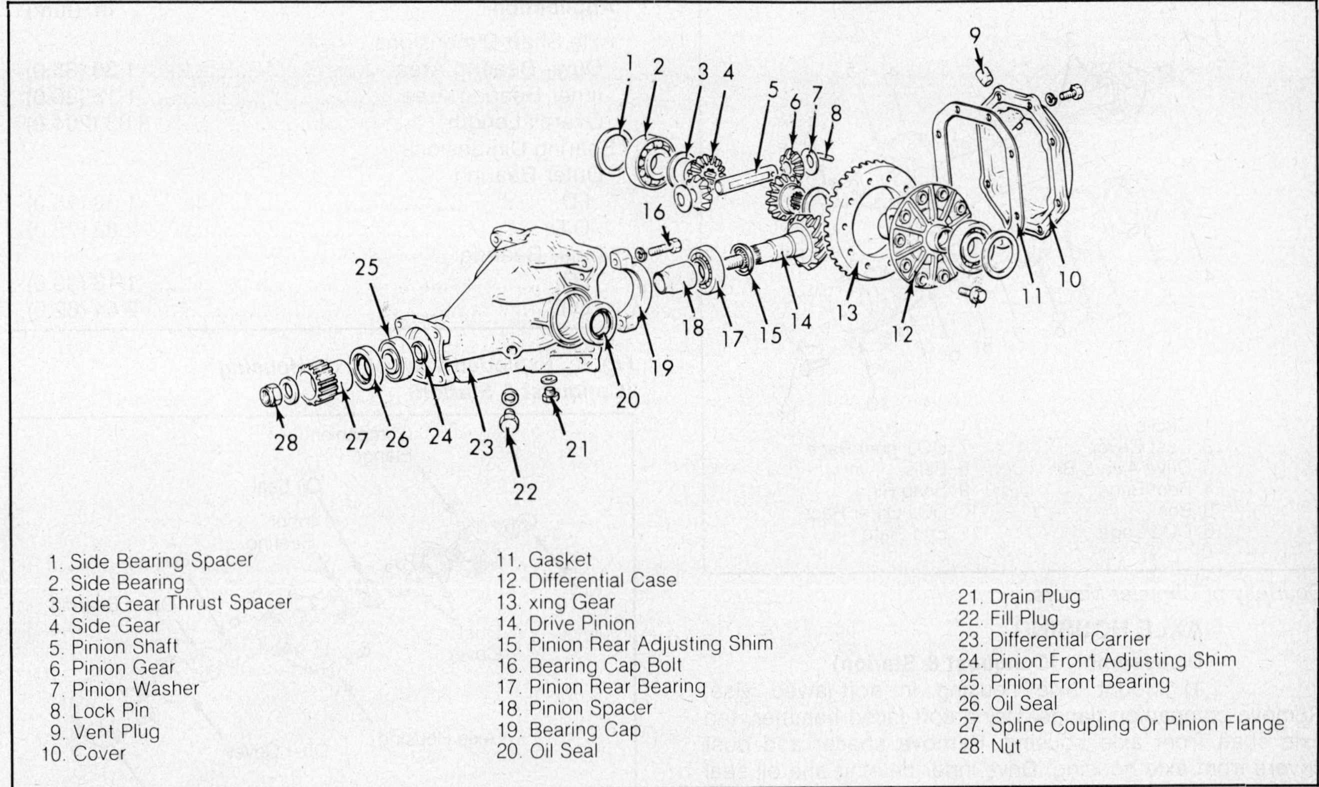

Courtesy of Chrysler Motors.

2) Inspect DOJ inner and outer races for wear or damage. Check DOJ cage and balls for rust, dirt, or wear damage.

Reassembly

1) Apply light coat of grease to drive axle shaft. Wrap tape around splines of shaft. Install BJ boot, new boot bands, and DOJ boot on shaft. Pack proper amount of grease in BJ boot. See GREASE APPLICATION table.

NOTE: BJ and DOJ boots are different in size and shape.

GREASE APPLICATION

Application	Ozs. (g)
Colt Vista	
BJ Boot	3.9 (110)
DOJ Outer Race	3.9 (110)
Conquest & Starion	
BJ Boot	
Conventional Axle	2.8-3.5 (80-100)
Limited Slip Axle	3.4-4.1 (95-115)
DOJ Outer Race	
Before Installing Shaft	
Conventional Axle	2.1-2.5 (60-70)
Limited Slip Axle	2.3-2.6 (65-75)
After Installing Shaft	
Conventional Axle	1.2-1.6 (35-45)
Limited Slip Axle	1.6-1.9 (45-55)

2) Place DOJ cage on shaft with smaller diameter installed first. Install circlip, DOJ inner race, and snap ring on shaft. Apply grease to DOJ inner race and cage. Install balls into cage.

3) Apply proper amount of grease to outer DOJ race. Install shaft into DOJ outer race. Apply proper amount of grease to DOJ outer race and install circlip. See GREASE APPLICATION table.

4) Place DOJ boot over DOJ outer race. Install boot bands. Adjust DOJ boot bands to specification. See BOOT BAND SPECIFICATIONS table. Proper distance must be maintained between centerline of boot bands. This distance is necessary to control air in DOJ boot. Tighten boot bands.

BOOT BAND SPECIFICATIONS

Application	In. (mm)
Colt Vista	3.15-3.39 (80.0-86.1)
Conquest & Starion	3.0-3.2 (76-81)

CHRYSLER MOTORS & MITSUBISHI INTEGRAL HOUSING (Cont.)

Fig. 3: Exploded View of Drive Axle

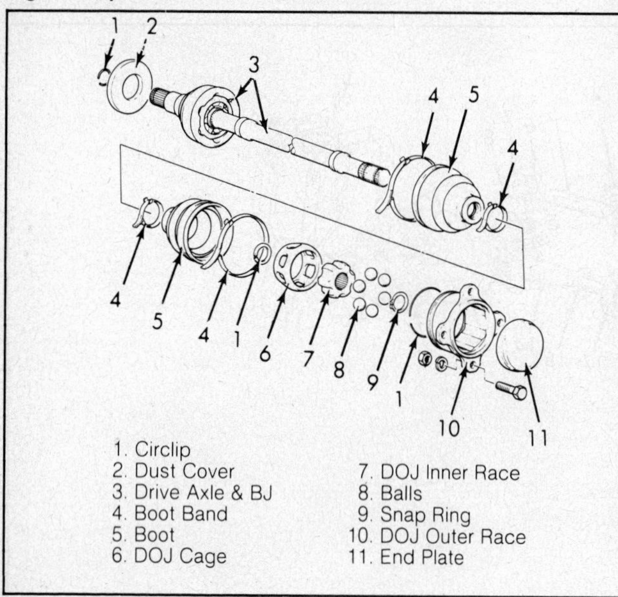

Courtesy of Chrysler Motors.

AXLE HOUSING

Disassembly (Conquest & Starion)

1) Mount axle housing in soft-jawed vise. Remove companion flange. Using soft-faced hammer, tap axle shaft from axle housing. Remove spacer and dust covers from axle housing. Drive inner bearing and oil seal from axle housing (if necessary).

CAUTION: DO NOT remove inner and outer bearings unless replacement is required.

2) If outer bearing requires replacement, cut bearing retainer in 3 places with chisel. Insert claws of Bearing Remover (MB990918) in 3 places and rotate 90 degrees. Tighten claws in body of bearing remover. Pull bearing from shaft. *See Fig. 5.*

Inspection

1) Inspect companion flange and dust cover for wear or damage. Check oil seal for damage. Measure axle shaft O.D. in bearing areas. Inspect axle housing for signs of bearing movement.

2) Inspect bearings for roughness or damage. Measure bearing I.D. and O.D. Inspect axle shafts for wear or damage. Replace components not within specification. See AXLE HOUSING SPECIFICATIONS table.

AXLE HOUSING SPECIFICATIONS

Application	In. (mm)
Axle Shaft Dimensions	
Outer Bearing Area	1.38 (35.0)
Inner Bearing Area	1.18 (30.0)
Overall Length	8.03 (204.0)
Bearing Dimensions	
Outer Bearing	
I.D.	1.38 (35.0)
O.D.	2.83 (72.0)
Inner Bearing	
I.D.	1.18 (30.0)
O.D.	2.44 (62.0)

Fig. 5: Exploded View of Axle Housing (Conquest & Starion)

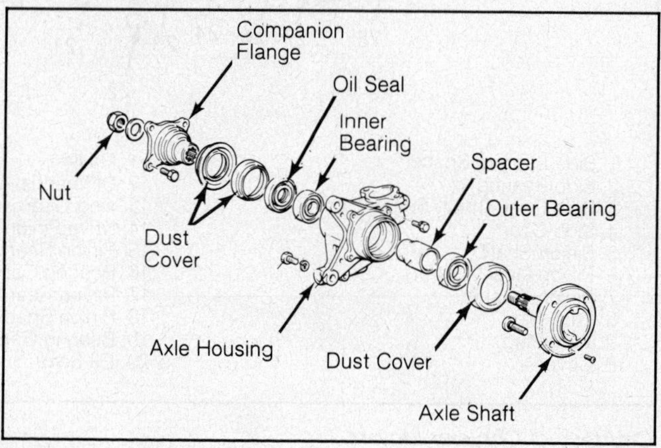

Courtesy of Chrysler Motors.

Reassembly

1) Press outer bearing on axle shaft (if removed). Ensure seal side of outer bearing faces axle flange. Apply grease to inner surface of axle housing.

2) Using Bearing Installer (MB990932-01) and Handle (MB990938-01), install inner bearing with seal side facing companion flange (if removed). Lubricate axle housing seal area with grease.

3) Using Seal Installer (MB990727-01) and Handle (MIT304180), install seal until it bottoms on axle housing. Install dust cover on axle housing. Apply grease to oil seal lip.

4) Install axle shaft and spacer into axle housing. Install companion flange. Install new companion flange nut. Tighten to specification. Ensure axle shaft turns freely.

Fig. 4: Removing Outer Axle Bearing

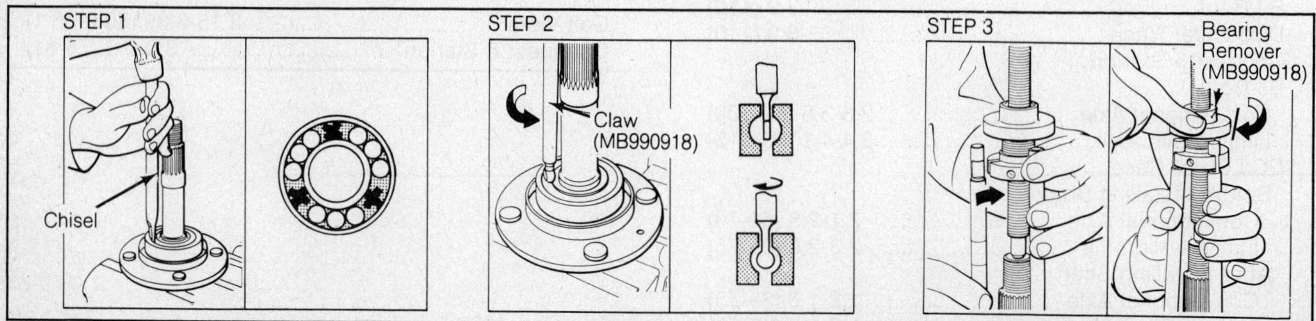

Courtesy of Chrysler Motors.

CHRYSLER MOTORS & MITSUBISHI INTEGRAL HOUSING (Cont.)

INNER ARM & AXLE SHAFT

Disassembly (Colt Vista)

1) Remove brake drum. Remove drive axle from axle shaft companion flange. Using Axle Holder (MB990767), hold axle shaft and remove companion flange retaining nut and companion flange. *See Fig. 6.*

2) Using slide hammer, remove axle shaft. Using Bearing Puller (MB990560) and hydraulic press, remove outer wheel bearing from axle shaft. Remove dust cover. Inner arm may require removal for access of inner bearing.

3) Remove dust cover and oil seal from inside of inner arm. Using Bearing Remover (MB990927) and Handle (MB990938), remove inner bearing from arm.

Fig. 6: Exploded View of Inner Arm & Axle Shaft (Colt Vista)

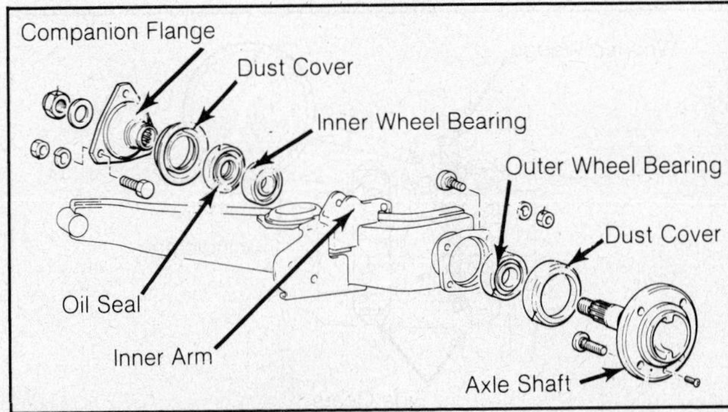

Courtesy of Chrysler Motors.

Inspection

1) Inspect companion flange and dust cover for wear or damage. Check oil seal for damage. Measure axle shaft O.D. in bearing areas. Inspect inner arm for signs of bearing movement.

2) Inspect bearings for roughness or damage. Measure bearing I.D. and O.D. Inspect axle shafts for wear or damage. Replace components not within specification. See AXLE SHAFT SPECIFICATIONS table.

AXLE SHAFT SPECIFICATIONS

Application	In. (mm)
Axle Shaft Dimensions	
Outer Bearing Area	1.38 (35.0)
Inner Bearing Area	1.10 (27.9)
Overall Length	8.46 (214.9)
Bearing Dimensions	
Outer Bearing	
I.D.	1.38 (35.0)
O.D.	2.83 (72.0)
Inner Bearing	
I.D.	1.10 (27.9)
O.D.	2.28 (57.9)

Reassembly

1) Using Bearing Installer (MB990931) and Handle (MB990938), install inner bearing in arm. Using Seal Installer (MB990799), install seal in inner arm with concave side facing outward.

2) Coat seal lip with light coat of grease. Install dust cover. If backing plate was removed, apply semi-drying sealant to flange area of inner arm. Install backing plate. Tighten bolts to specification.

3) Using Dust Cover Installer (MB990799), install dust cover on axle shaft. Concave side of dust cover must face splined end of axle shaft. Using bearing installer and press, install bearing on axle shaft with seal surface facing toward flange side of axle shaft.

4) Install axle shaft in inner arm. Install companion flange and new retaining nut. Using axle holder, tighten nut to specification. Check axle shaft end play.

TORQUE TUBE

Disassembly (Conquest & Starion)

Scribe mating marks on extension shaft and companion flange. Remove companion flange. Using soft-faced hammer, drive extension shaft from tube. Remove bearing retaining snap ring. Using slide hammer, remove bearing from torque tube. *See Fig. 7.*

Inspection

Inspect bearing for roughness or damage. Inspect torque tube for cracks or bent flange. Inspect extension shaft for damaged splines or threads.

Fig. 7: Exploded View of Torque Tube

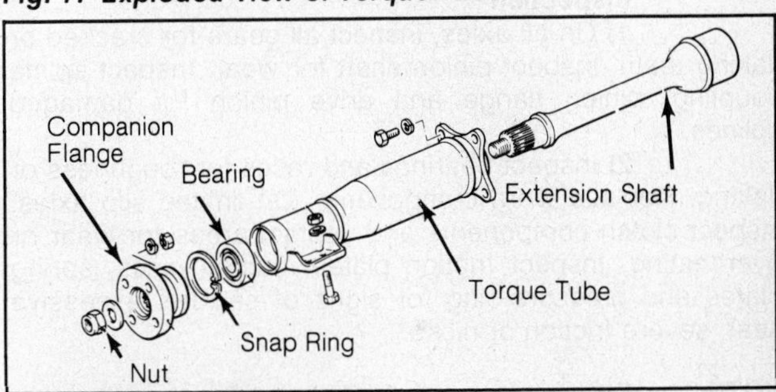

Courtesy of Chrysler Motors.

Reassembly

1) Using Bearing Installer (MB990941-01) and Handle (MIT208977), install bearing in torque tube until bearing installer contacts torque tube. Apply grease to pocket and spline of differential side of extension shaft.

2) Install bearing retaining snap ring. Install extension shaft in torque tube. Install companion flange with mating marks aligned. Install new companion flange retaining nut.

3) Temporarily tighten retaining nut. Install torque tube as previously described. Hold extension shaft by applying the parking brake. Tighten companion flange retaining nut to specification.

DIFFERENTIAL CARRIER

Disassembly

1) Remove differential carrier from vehicle. Mark bearing caps for location. Remove bearing caps. Remove case assembly from differential carrier. Mark side bearing adjusting spacers and side bearings for location.

CAUTION: Ensure adjusting spacers, bearing caps and side bearings are marked for location. Components must be installed in original location.

2) Using bearing puller, remove differential case side bearings. Place alignment marks on ring gear and differential case for reassembly. Loosen ring gear retaining bolts in diagonal sequence. Remove ring gear.

CHRYSLER MOTORS & MITSUBISHI INTEGRAL HOUSING (Cont.)

3) On conventional axles, drive pinion shaft lock pin from differential case. Remove differential pinion shaft and pinion gears. Remove pinion side gears and thrust spacers. Mark components for reassembly reference.

4) On limited slip units, mark differential case and differential case cover for reassembly reference. Remove differential case retaining screws. Separate differential case and cover. Remove components from case. *See Fig. 1.* Mark components for location.

Drive Pinion

1) On all models, remove spline coupling or pinion flange retaining nut. Use Holder (C-3281) for Colt Vista models or (MB990907-01) for Conquest and Starion models to hold coupling or flange.

2) Scribe alignment marks on drive pinion and spline coupling or pinion flange for reassembly. Using soft-faced hammer, drive out pinion. Remove front adjusting shim and spacer from pinion.

3) Using bearing puller, remove rear bearing from pinion. Remove rear adjusting shim from pinion. Remove oil seal and bearing races from differential carrier.

Inspection

1) On all axles, inspect all gears for cracked or flaking teeth. Inspect pinion shaft for wear. Inspect spline coupling, pinion flange and drive pinion for damaged splines.

2) Inspect bearings and races for roughness or flaking. Replace worn components. On limited slip axles, inspect clutch components and contact areas for wear or overheating. Inspect friction plates, friction discs, spring plates and pressure ring for signs of seizure, excessive heat, severe friction or nicks.

NOTE: **Outer areas of friction surfaces will wear heavier due to clutch plate and preload spring.**

3) Using dial indicator, check friction plate and friction disc for warpage. Replace if beyond specification. See FRICTION PLATE & DISC SPECIFICATIONS table.

4) Measure friction plates and disc thickness at projection areas not within wear area. Measure plate and disc thickness in friction surface.

5) Difference between thickness of projections and friction surface indicates amount of wear. Replace components if not within specification. See FRICTION PLATE & DISC SPECIFICATIONS table.

FRICTION PLATE & DISC SPECIFICATIONS

Application	In. (mm)
Warpage Limit	.003 (.08)
Wear Limit	.004 (.10)

REASSEMBLY & ADJUSTMENT

Case Assembly (Conventional)

1) Install thrust spacers, side gears, pinion washers and pinion gears in differential case.

2) Install pinion shaft without lock pin. Check pinion and side gear backlash. Install wooden wedge to lock side gears. Using dial indicator, measure gear backlash. *See Fig. 8.*

3) Backlash must be within specification. See PINION & SIDE GEAR BACKLASH SPECIFICATIONS table. Adjust backlash by using different side gear spacers. Ensure both sides are equally shimmed.

PINION & SIDE GEAR BACKLASH SPECIFICATIONS

Application	In. (mm)
Standard	.003 (.08)
Wear Limit	.008 (.20)

4) Install pinion shaft lock pin from back side of ring gear. Securely stake in 2 places. Ensure adhesive is removed from ring gear mounting bolts and gear mounting surface. Clean internal threads with tap.

Fig. 8: Checking Pinion & Side Gear Backlash

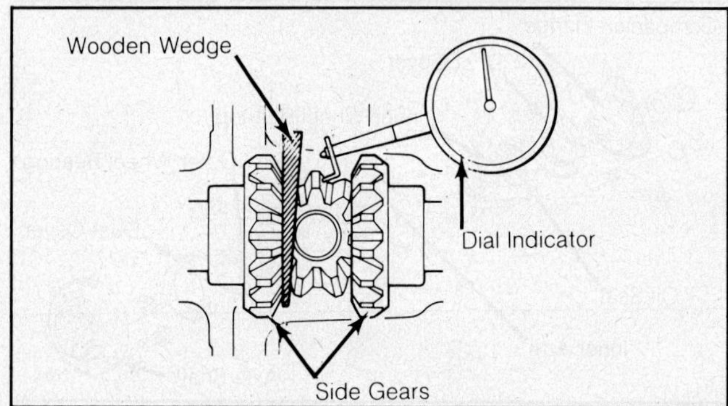

Courtesy of Chrysler Motors.

5) Install ring gear on differential case. Ensure alignment marks on differential case and ring gear are aligned. Apply Loctite 271 to bolts and install. Tighten bolts alternately in diagonal sequence to specification.

Case Assembly (Limited Slip)

1) On Conquest and Starion models, assemble friction disc and friction plates with 2 on each side. Assemble plate, disc, plate and disc. *See Fig. 11.* Measure assembly thickness. Assemble disc and plates to give standard difference of .0020" (.050 mm) between the 2 sides.

2) Assemble spring disc and spring plates with one on each side. Measure assembly thickness. Assemble disc and plates to obtain minimum difference in thickness between each assembly.

3) On Colt Vista models, assemble 2 friction discs and 3 friction plates with plate, disc, plate, disc and plate arrangement. *See Fig. 11.* Assemble disc and plates to obtain minimum difference in thickness between each assembly.

4) Assemble friction discs, friction plates and spring plates to give standard difference of .0020" (.050 mm) between the 2 sides. Adjust clutch plate combination to give correct dimension.

5) On all models, assemble clutch assemblies, pressure rings, pinion gears, side gears and pinion shaft. Measure overall width of assembly plus spring plate and spring disc. Spring disc is not used on Colt Vista models. This measurement is "C". *See Fig. 9.*

CHRYSLER MOTORS & MITSUBISHI INTEGRAL HOUSING (Cont.)

Fig. 9: Measuring Clutch Assembly Width

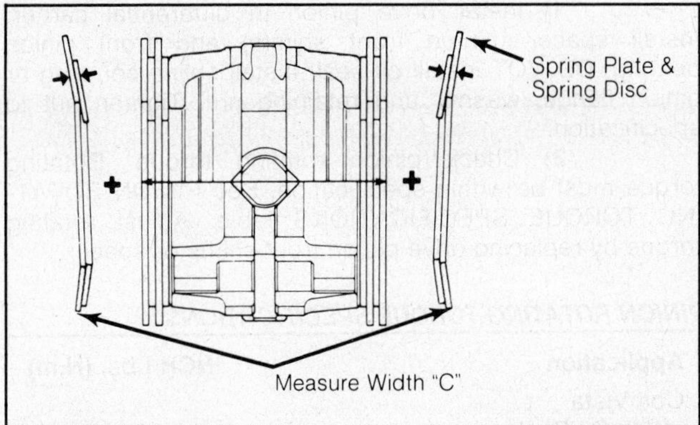

Courtesy of Chrysler Motors.

6) Determine depth "D" of differential case, using formula "D" = "E" + "F" - "G". *See Fig. 10.* Subtract measurement "C" from measurement "D" to determine spring plate-to-case clearance. Adjust spring disc thickness to obtain proper spring plate-to-case clearance. See SPRING PLATE CLEARANCE SPECIFICATIONS table.

SPRING PLATE CLEARANCE SPECIFICATIONS

Application	In. (mm)
Colt Vista	.002-.010 (.05-.25)
Conquest & Starion	.002-.008 (.05-.20)

Fig. 10: Measuring Limited Slip Case Depth

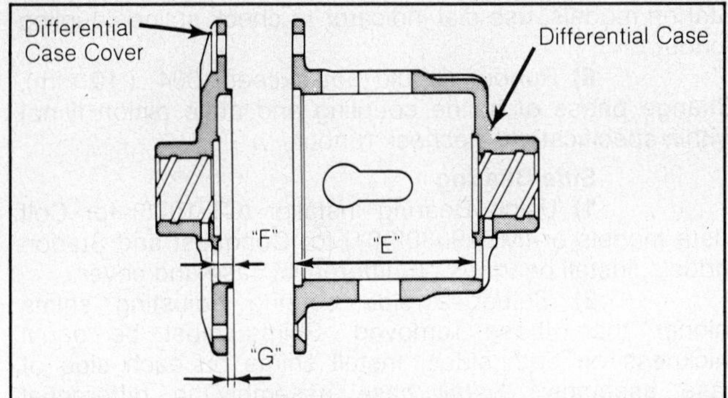

Courtesy of Chrysler Motors.

7) Apply gear oil and friction modifier to all components. Install components in differential case. Ensure assembly order and direction of spring plates. *See Fig. 11.*

8) Install differential case cover with mark aligned with differential case. Tighten screws in several steps. Ensure cases contact each other when fully assembled. Check for incorrect clutch assembly if gap exists.

9) Using Clutch Plate Preload Tool (MB990988), Shaft (MB990989) and torque wrench, measure starting torque. Slightly rotate unit before measuring starting torque. *See Fig. 12.*

10) Starting torque must be within specification. See STARTING TORQUE SPECIFICATIONS table. Ensure adhesive is removed from ring gear mounting bolts and gear mounting surface. Clean internal threads with tap.

Fig. 11: Limited Slip Differential Assembly

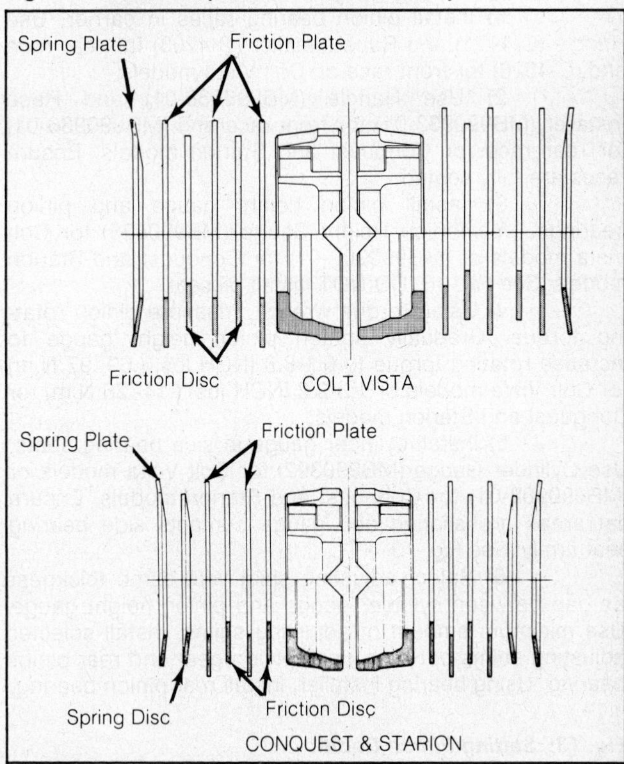

Courtesy of Chrysler Motors & Mitsubishi Motor Sales of America.

Fig. 12: Checking Differential Starting Torque

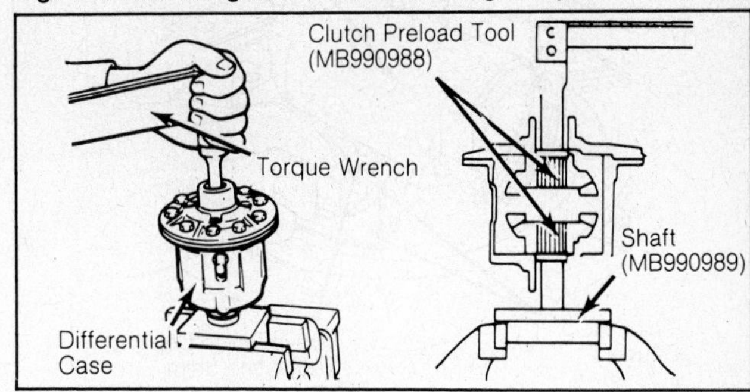

Courtesy of Chrysler Motors.

11) Install ring gear on differential case. Ensure alignment marks on differential case and ring gear are aligned. Apply Loctite 271 to bolts and install. Tighten bolts alternately in diagonal sequence to specification.

STARTING TORQUE SPECIFICATIONS

Application	Ft. Lbs. (N.m)
Colt Vista	
Used Clutch Plates	11-44 (15-60)
New Clutch Plates	25-44 (34-60)
Conquest & Starion	
Used Clutch Plates	25-58 (34-79)
New Clutch Plates	36-58 (49-79)

Drive Axles

CHRYSLER MOTORS & MITSUBISHI INTEGRAL HOUSING (Cont.)

Drive Pinion Depth

1) Install pinion bearing races in carrier. Use Handle (C-4171) and Race Installer (C-4203) for rear race and (C-4628) for front race on Colt Vista models.

2) Use Handle (MB990938-01) and Race Installer (MB990933-01) for front race and (MB990936-01) for rear race for Conquest and Starion models. Ensure races are fully seated.

3) Install pinion height gauge and pinion bearings. Use Pinion Height Gauge (MB990835) for Colt Vista models or (MB990901-01) for Conquest and Starion models. *See Fig. 13.* DO NOT install oil seal.

4) Using torque wrench, measure pinion rotating torque. Gradually tighten pinion height gauge to increase rotating torque to 6.1-8.6 INCH lbs. (.69-.97 N.m) for Colt Vista models or 1.3-2.2 INCH lbs. (.14-.25 N.m) for Conquest and Starion models.

5) Install cylinder gauge in side bearing seats. Use Cylinder Gauge (MB990392) for Colt Vista models or (MB990903-01) for Conquest and Starion models. Ensure flat areas are aligned and gauge contacts side bearing seat firmly. *See Fig. 13.*

6) Select adjusting shim with same thickness as gap between cylinder gauge and pinion height gauge. Use minimum amount of adjusting shims. Install selected adjusting shims between drive pinion gear and rear pinion bearing. Using bearing installer, install rear pinion bearing.

Fig. 13: Setting Pinion Depth

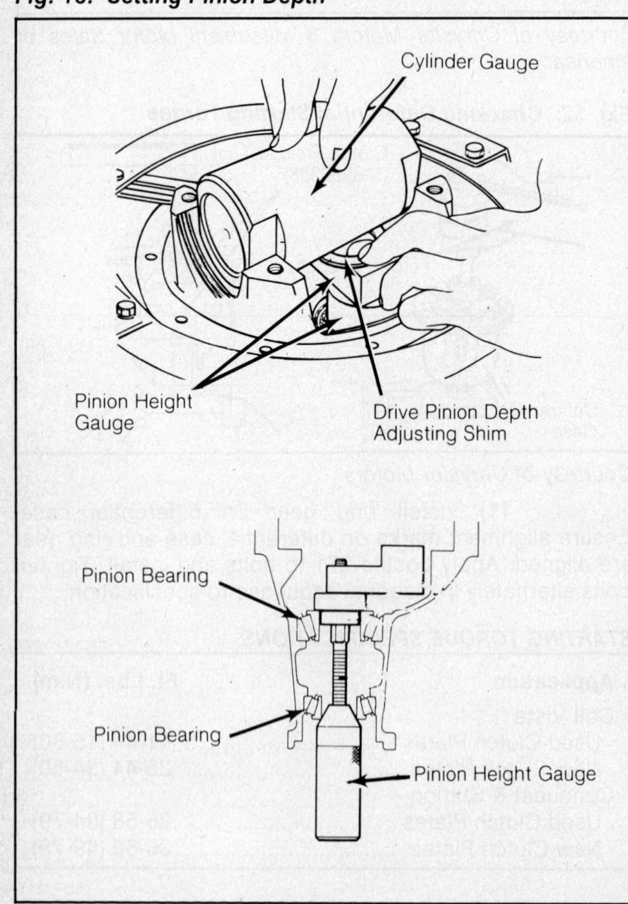

Courtesy of Chrysler Motors.

Drive Pinion Preload

1) Install drive pinion in differential carrier. Install spacer, pinion front shim(s) and front pinion bearing. DO NOT install oil seal. Install spline coupling or pinion flange, washer and retaining nut. Tighten nut to specification.

2) Check pinion rotating torque. Rotating torque must be within specification. See PINION ROTATING TORQUE SPECIFICATIONS table. Adjust rotating torque by replacing drive pinion front shims or spacer.

PINION ROTATING TORQUE SPECIFICATIONS

Application	INCH Lbs. (N.m)
Colt Vista	
With Oil Seal	8.6-11.3 (.97-1.3)
Without Oil Seal	6.1-8.6 (.69-.97)
Conquest & Starion	
With Oil Seal	
Conventional Axle	3.0-3.9 (.34-.44)
Limited Slip Axle	3.5-4.3 (.40-.48)
Without Oil Seal	1.3-2.2 (.14-.25)

3) Once correct rotating torque is obtained, install oil seal. Coat seal lip with grease. Install spline coupling or pinion flange so alignment marks are correct.

4) Apply light coat of grease to spline coupling or pinion flange washer contact area. Install new retaining nut. Tighten to specification.

5) Check pinion rotating torque. Rotating torque must be within specification. See PINION ROTATING TORQUE SPECIFICATIONS table. On Conquest and Starion models, use dial indicator to check spline coupling runout.

6) Runout should not exceed .004" (.10 mm). Change phase of spline coupling and drive pinion if not within specification. Recheck runout.

Side Bearing

1) Using Bearing Installer (CT-1075) for Colt Vista models or (MB990802-01) for Conquest and Starion models, install bearings on differential case and cover.

2) Select 2 side bearing adjusting shims thinner than those removed. Shims must be equal thickness on both sides. Install shims on each side of case assembly. Install case assembly in differential carrier.

3) Push case assembly fully to one side of carrier. Using 2 feeler gauges, measure clearance between carrier and side bearing shim at opposite sides of bearing. Remove shims from one side of differential carrier.

4) Measure thickness of shims removed. Add removed shim thickness and 1/2 of feeler gauge clearance measurement plus .002" (.05 mm). This thickness shim should be installed on each side of case. Select proper shims. Install equal shims on each side of case assembly.

NOTE: **Ensure no clearance exists between gear carrier and adjusting shim.**

5) Install side bearing shims and differential case assembly in differential carrier. Using brass drift, tap shims to fit them to side bearing outer race. Install bearing caps. Tighten bolts to specification. Check ring gear backlash.

CHRYSLER MOTORS & MITSUBISHI INTEGRAL HOUSING (Cont.)

Ring Gear Backlash

1) Lock drive pinion in place. Using dial indicator, check ring gear backlash at heel of ring gear tooth. Measure at 4 locations of ring gear. Gear backlash must be within specification. See RING GEAR BACKLASH SPECIFICATIONS table.

RING GEAR BACKLASH SPECIFICATIONS

Application	In. (mm)
Colt Vista	.004-.006 (.10-.15)
Conquest & Starion	
Conventional Axles	.004-.006 (.10-.15)
Limited Slip Axles	.005-.007 (.13-.18)

2) If not within specification, change side bearing adjusting shims and recheck backlash. If backlash is too small, install thinner shim behind ring gear and thicker shim opposite ring gear.

3) If backlash is excessive, install thicker shim behind ring gear and thinner shim opposite ring gear. Check gear tooth contact using paint impression method. See GEAR TOOTH PATTERNS article in this section.

CAUTION: Change shims so total thickness of all shims remains the same.

Ring Gear Runout

Using dial indicator, measure runout at back side of ring gear. Runout must be within .002" (.05 mm). If runout is excessive, change ring gear-to-differential case mounting position. Recheck runout.

TIGHTENING SPECIFICATIONS (CONQUEST & STARION)

Application	Ft. Lbs. (N.m)
Axle Housing-to-Control Arm Bolt	51-58 (69-79)
Axle Shaft Companion Flange Bolt	188-217 (255-294)
Axle Shaft-to-Companion Flange Bolt	40-47 (54-64)
Bearing Cap Bolt	40-47 (54-64)
Caliper Retaining Bolt	29-36 (40-49)
Cover Bolt	11-16 (15-22)
Filler Plug	29-44 (39-60)
Propeller Shaft-to-Torque Tube Bolt	36-43 (49-58)
Ring Gear Bolt	58-65 (79-88)
Spline Coupling Nut	116-159 (157-216)
Strut-to-Axle Housing Bolt	36-51 (49-69)
Support-to-Crossmember Nut	18-22 (24-30)
Torque Tube Companion Flange Bolt	116-159 (157-216)
Torque Tube-to-Differential Carrier Bolt	51-61 (69-82)
Torque Tube-to-Front Support Bolt	25-33 (34-45)

TIGHTENING SPECIFICATIONS (COLT VISTA)

Application	Ft. Lbs. (N.m)
Axle Shaft Companion Flange Nut	116-159 (157-216)
Bearing Cap Bolt	29-43 (39-58)
Brake Backing Plate Nut	36-43 (49-58)
Brake Line	10-12 (14-16)
Cover Bolt	22-30 (30-41)
Differential Mount-to-Body Bolt	43-65 (58-88)
Drive Axle Flange-to-Axle Shaft Flange Bolt	36-43 (49-58)
Front Support-to-Crossmember Bolt	87-101 (118-137)
Front Support-to-Differential Carrier Bolt	43-65 (58-88)
Inner Arm-to-Crossmember Bolt	51-65 (69-88)
Inner Arm-to-Outer Arm Bolt	58-72 (79-98)
Pinion Flange Nut	116-159 (157-216)
Propeller Shaft-to-Pinion Flange Bolt	22-25 (30-34)
Rear Support-to-Differential Carrier Bolt	43-65 (58-88)
Rear Support-to-Mount Bolt	65-94 (88-127)
Ring Gear Bolt	58-65 (79-88)

CHRYSLER MOTORS & MITSUBISHI – FRONT

Front Axles
Chrysler Motors: Raider, Ram-50 4WD;
Mitsubishi: Montero, Pickup 4WD

DESCRIPTION

Front axle assembly consists of differential carrier, housing tube, inner shaft and drive axles. Drive axles are of full-floating design. Birfield Joints (BJ) and Double Off-Set Joints (DOJ) are used at opposite ends of each drive axle along with torsion bar front suspension.

AXLE RATIO & IDENTIFICATION

Ratio is determined by dividing number of ring gear teeth by number of drive pinion teeth.

AXLE RATIO SPECIFICATIONS

Application	Ratio
Montero & Raider	4.63
Pickup & Ram-50	3.91

NOTE: References to BJ refer to Birfield Joint and DOJ to Double Off-Set Joint.

REMOVAL & INSTALLATION

DRIVE AXLES

Removal

1) Remove and support brake calipers. Place hub in freewheeling position. Remove drive hub cover, snap ring and shim from drive axle.

2) Using dial indicator, check drive axle end play. Rotate drive axle forward and rearward until maximum end play is obtained. Check end play. End play must be adjusted during reassembly if not within .008-.020" (.20-.50 mm).

3) Disconnect tie rod assembly. Support lower control arm with jack. Using Ball Joint Remover (MB990809-01) for lower ball joint and (MB990635) for upper ball joint, remove ball joints from knuckle.

CAUTION: Support lower control arm during axle shaft removal and installation.

4) Remove knuckle and front hub assembly. Remove left drive axle from differential carrier. Use care not to damage oil seal. On right drive shaft, remove drive axle-to-inner shaft retaining bolts. Remove right drive axle.

5) Remove inner shaft from differential carrier. Pry dust seal from housing tube assembly using a screwdriver if replacement is required. *See Fig. 1.* If oil seal replacement is required, remove housing tube. Using slide hammer, remove oil seals.

Fig. 1: Front Drive Axle & Suspension

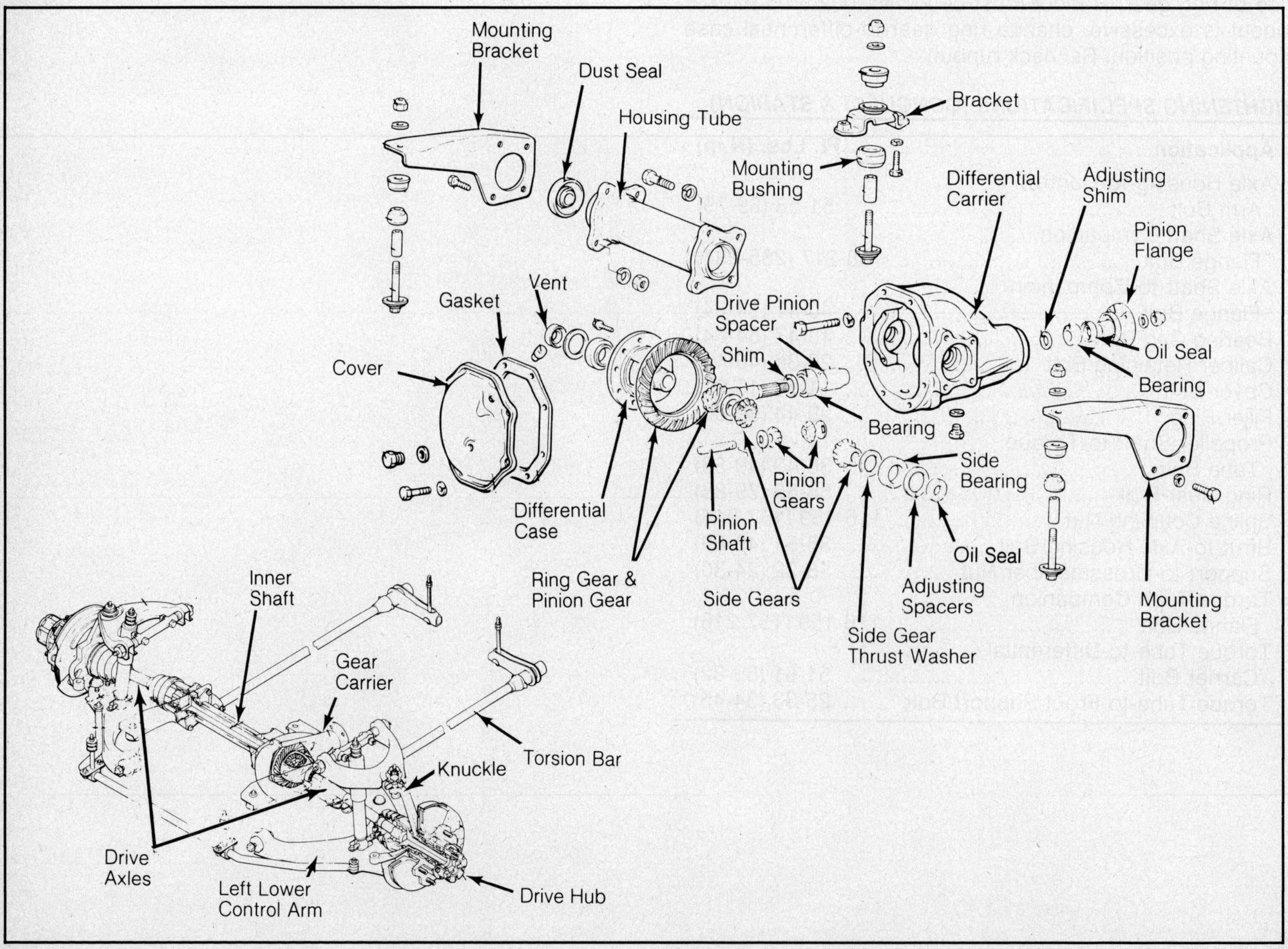

Courtesy of Chrysler Motors.

CHRYSLER MOTORS & MITSUBISHI – FRONT (Cont.)

CAUTION: Always replace circlips on BJ splines of left drive axle and splines of inner shaft.

Installation

1) Using Oil Seal Installer (MB990934-01) and Handle (MB990938-01), install oil seal in differential carrier. Coat seal lips with grease. Install housing tube. Tighten bolts to specification.

2) Using Seal Installer (MB990955) and Handle (C-4171), install new dust seal in housing tube. Dust seal must be even with housing tube. Coat seal lip with grease.

3) Install new circlip on inner shaft. Drive inner shaft into differential. Use care not to damage oil seal. Install right drive axle on inner shaft. Tighten bolts to specification. See TIGHTENING SPECIFICATIONS table at end of article.

4) Install new circlip on BJ side of left drive axle. Drive left drive axle into differential. Use care not to damage oil seal. Reinstall knuckle with front hub assembly. Tighten all fasteners to specification.

5) If axle shaft end play requires adjustment, select proper shim to obtain proper end play. Shim is located behind snap ring on end of drive axle. Install shim and recheck axle end play. Install remaining components in reverse of removal procedure.

DIFFERENTIAL CARRIER

Removal

1) Raise and support vehicle. Drain gear oil. Support differential carrier. Remove drive axles and inner shaft. Place alignment mark on propeller shaft and pinion flange for reassembly.

2) Remove propeller shaft. Remove differential mounting brackets at differential and frame. Disconnect front crossmember from frame. Remove differential carrier assembly and front crossmember. Remove differential carrier from front crossmember.

Installation

1) Reverse removal procedures. Align marks on propeller shaft and pinion flange. Tighten bolts to specification. See TIGHTENING SPECIFICATIONS table at end of article.

2) Fill assembly with Mopar Gear Oil (3744994) or SAE 80W-90 gear oil conforming to API classification GL-4 or above.

OVERHAUL

DRIVE AXLES & BEARINGS

NOTE: References to BJ refer to Birfield Joint and DOJ to Double Off-Set Joint.

Disassembly

1) Remove boot bands. Remove circlip from DOJ outer race. Separate drive shaft from DOJ outer race. Remove balls from DOJ cage. Remove DOJ cage from DOJ inner race in direction of BJ. *See Fig. 2.*

2) Remove snap ring from drive axle shaft. Remove DOJ inner race from shaft. Remove circlip from shaft. Wrap tape around splines of shaft to prevent boot damage during removal.

3) Remove DOJ boot. Note size of boot. Remove dust cover from shaft. Straighten BJ boot protector and remove protector band. Move boot protector toward BJ side of shaft and remove. Remove BJ boot.

CAUTION: Drive axle and BJ are serviced as a unit. DO NOT disassemble BJ and drive axle.

Inspection

1) Inspect BJ for rust, dirt, water, or damage to balls and races. Inspect shaft for bend or spline damage. Inspect boots for cracks or wear.

Fig. 2: Exploded View of Drive Axles

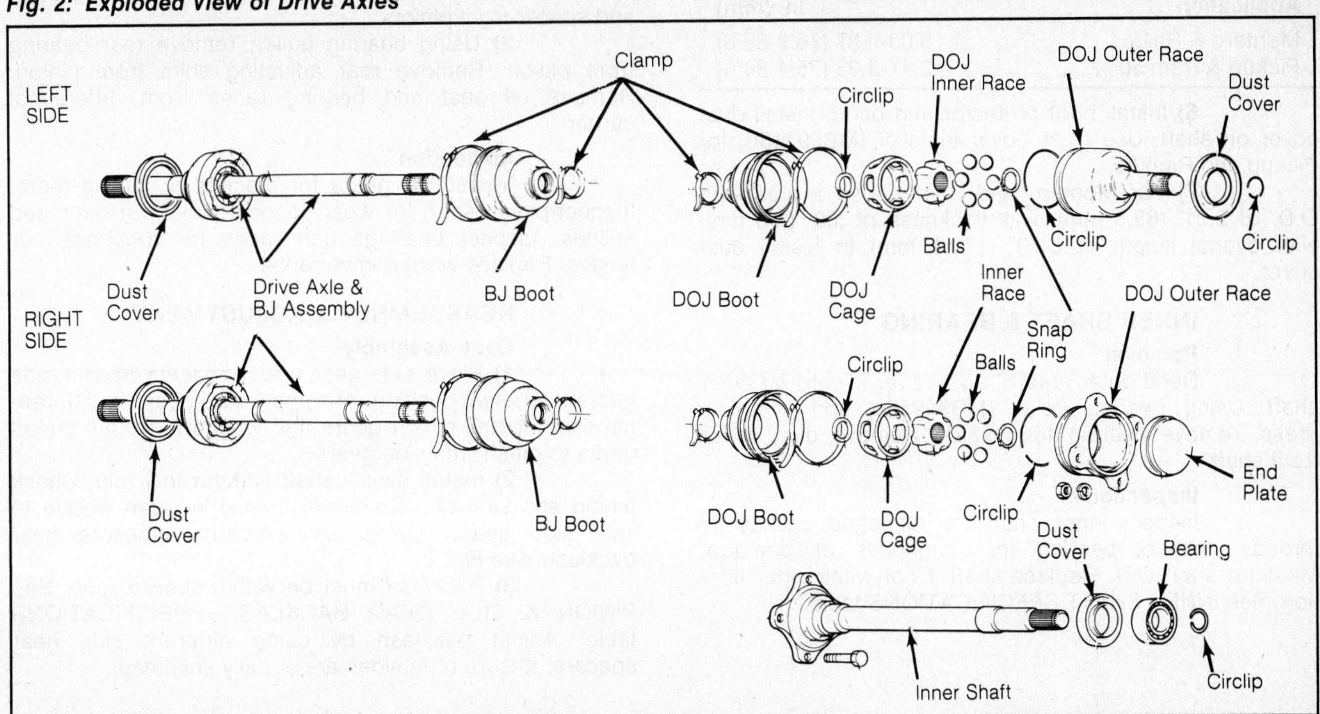

Courtesy of Chrysler Motors.

CHRYSLER MOTORS & MITSUBISHI – FRONT (Cont.)

2) Inspect DOJ inner and outer races for wear or damage. Check DOJ cage and balls for rust, dirt, or wear damage.

Reassembly

1) Coat shaft with light coat of grease. Wrap splines with tape. Install BJ boot, bands and DOJ boot on shaft. Boots are different size and must be installed in correct location.

2) Boot bands must be installed so lever is pulled toward rear of vehicle when band is tightened. Pack proper amount of grease in BJ and BJ boot. See GREASE APPLICATION table.

GREASE APPLICATION

Application	Ozs. (g)
BJ Boot	3.9 (110)
DOJ Outer Race	
Before Installing Shaft	1.9 (55)
After Installing Shaft	1.9 (55)

3) Place DOJ cage on shaft with smaller diameter installed first. Install circlip, DOJ inner race, and snap ring on shaft. Apply grease to DOJ inner race and cage. Install balls into cage.

4) Apply proper amount of grease to outer DOJ race. Install shaft into DOJ outer race. Apply proper amount of grease to DOJ outer race and install circlip. See GREASE APPLICATION table.

5) Place DOJ boot over DOJ outer race. Install boot bands so lever is pulled toward rear of vehicle when band is tightened. Adjust DOJ boot bands to have proper distance between centerline of boot bands. See BOOT BAND SPECIFICATIONS table. This distance is necessary to control air in DOJ boot. Tighten boot bands.

BOOT BAND SPECIFICATIONS

Application	In. (mm)
Montero & Raider	3.03-3.27 (76.9-83.0)
Pickup & Ram 50	2.97-3.33 (75.4-84.6)

6) Install boot protector and band. Install dust cover on shaft. Use Dust Cover Installer (MB991150) for Pickup and Ram 50.

7) For Montero and Raider, use a pipe with O.D. of 2.71" (68.3 mm), wall thickness of .09" (2.3 mm) with overall length of 6.70" (170.1 mm) to install dust cover.

INNER SHAFT & BEARING

Removal

Bend outer area of dust cover inward on inner shaft. Using Bearing Puller (MB990560) and hydraulic press, remove bearing from shaft. Remove dust cover from shaft.

Inspection

Inspect inner shaft for damaged splines or threads. Inspect bearing for roughness or damage. Measure shaft O.D. Replace shaft if not within specification. See INNER SHAFT SPECIFICATIONS table.

INNER SHAFT SPECIFICATIONS

Application	In. (mm)
Shaft O.D.	
Bearing Area	1.38 (35.0)
Center Area	1.24 (31.4)

Reassembly

Using a pipe with O.D. of 2.95" (74.3 mm), wall thickness of .16" (4 mm) with overall length of 1.97" (50.0 mm), install dust cover on shaft. Coat inside of dust cover with grease. Using bearing installer, install bearing on shaft.

DIFFERENTIAL ASSEMBLY

Disassembly

1) Remove differential carrier from vehicle. Remove cover. Mark bearing caps for location. Remove bearing caps. Remove differential case assembly from carrier.

CAUTION: Ensure adjusting spacers, bearing caps and side bearings are marked for location. Components must be installed in original location.

2) Mark side bearing adjusting spacers and side bearings for location. Using bearing puller, remove differential case side bearings. Place alignment marks on ring gear and differential case for reassembly.

3) Loosen ring gear retaining bolts in diagonal sequence. Remove ring gear. Drive pinion shaft lock pin from ring gear side. Remove pinion shaft and pinion gears. Remove side gears and thrust spacers. Mark components for reassembly reference.

Drive Pinion

1) Using Pinion Flange Holder (MB990767-01), remove pinion flange nut. Scribe alignment mark on pinion flange and pinion. Remove flange. Using soft-faced hammer, drive out pinion. Remove front adjusting shim and spacer from pinion.

2) Using bearing puller, remove rear bearing from pinion. Remove rear adjusting shim from pinion. Remove oil seal and bearing races from differential carrier.

Inspection

Inspect all gears for cracked or flaking teeth. Inspect pinion shaft for wear. Inspect pinion for damaged splines. Inspect bearings and races for roughness or flaking. Replace worn components.

REASSEMBLY & ADJUSTMENT

Case Assembly

1) Place side gear thrust spacers behind side gears in original position. Assemble side gears in differential case. Install pinion gears and washers. Rotate pinion gears to mesh with side gears.

2) Install pinion shaft without lock pin. Check pinion and side gear backlash. Install wooden wedge to lock side gears. Using dial indicator, measure gear backlash. *See Fig. 3.*

3) Backlash must be within specification. See PINION & SIDE GEAR BACKLASH SPECIFICATIONS table. Adjust backlash by using different side gear spacers. Ensure both sides are equally shimmed.

CHRYSLER MOTORS & MITSUBISHI – FRONT (Cont.)

PINION & SIDE GEAR BACKLASH SPECIFICATIONS

Application	In. (mm)
Standard	.003 (.08)
Wear Limit	.008 (.20)

Fig. 3: Checking Pinion & Side Gear Backlash

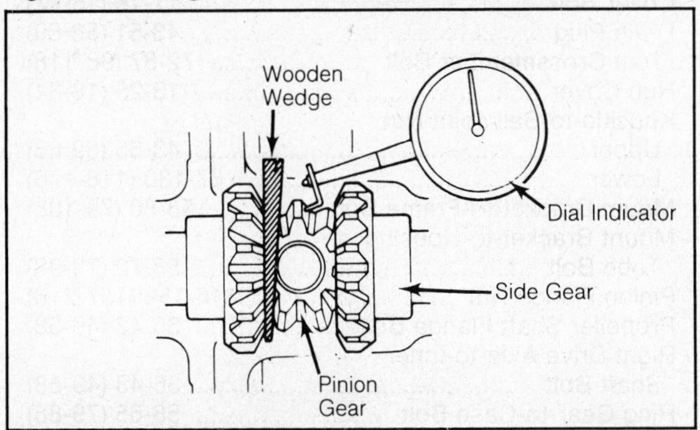

Courtesy of Chrysler Motors.

4) Install pinion shaft lock pin from back side of ring gear. Securely stake in 2 places. Ensure adhesive is removed from ring gear mounting bolts and gear mounting surface. Clean internal threads with tap.

5) Install ring gear on differential case. Ensure alignment marks on differential case and ring gear are aligned. Apply Loctite 271 to bolts and install. Tighten bolts alternately in diagonal sequence to specification.

Drive Pinion Depth

1) Install pinion bearing races in carrier. Use Handle (MB990938-01) and Race Installer (MB990933-01) for front race and (MB990936-01) for rear race. Ensure races are fully seated.

2) Install Pinion Height Gauge (MB990901-01) and pinion bearings. *See Fig. 4.* DO NOT install oil seal. Using torque wrench, measure pinion rotating torque. Gradually tighten pinion height gauge to increase rotating torque to proper specification. See PINION ROTATING TORQUE SPECIFICATIONS table.

PINION ROTATING TORQUE SPECIFICATIONS

Application	INCH Lbs. (N.m)
With Oil Seal	5.2-6.1 (.58-.69)
Without Oil Seal	
Montero & Raider	3.5-4.3 (.40-.48)
Pickup & Ram 50	3.9-4.3 (.43-.48)

3) Install Cylinder Gauge (MB990903-01) in side bearing seats. Ensure flat areas are aligned and gauge contacts side bearing seat firmly. *See Fig. 4.* Select adjusting shim with same thickness as gap between cylinder gauge and pinion height gauge. Use minimum amount of adjusting shims.

4) Install selected adjusting shims between drive pinion gear and rear pinion bearing. Using Bearing Installer (MB990802-01), install rear pinion bearing.

Drive Pinion Preload

1) Install drive pinion in differential carrier. Install spacer, pinion front shim(s) and front pinion bearing. DO NOT install oil seal. Install pinion flange, washer and retaining nut. Using Pinion Flange Holder (MB990767-01), tighten nut to specification.

Fig. 4: Setting Pinion Depth

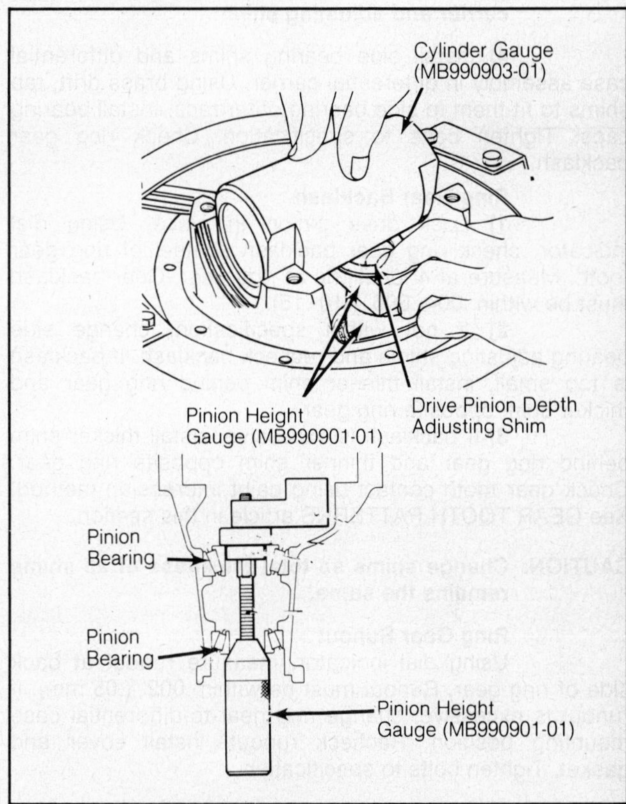

Courtesy of Chrysler Motors.

2) Check pinion rotating torque. Rotating torque must be within specification. See PINION ROTATING TORQUE SPECIFICATIONS table. Adjust rotating torque by replacing drive pinion front shims or spacer.

3) Once correct rotating torque is obtained, install oil seal using Seal Installer (MB990031-01) and Handle (MIT304180). Coat seal lip with grease.

4) Install pinion flange so alignment marks are correct. Apply light coat of grease to flange washer contact area. Install new retaining nut. Tighten to specification.

5) Check pinion rotating torque. Rotating torque must be within specification. See PINION ROTATING TORQUE SPECIFICATIONS table.

Side Bearing

1) Using Bearing Installer (MB990802-01), install bearings on differential case. Select 2 side bearing adjusting shims thinner than those removed. Shims must be equal thickness on both sides. Install shims on each side of case assembly. Install case assembly in differential carrier.

2) Push case assembly fully to one side of carrier. Using 2 feeler gauges, measure clearance between carrier and side bearing shim at opposite sides of bearing. Remove shims from one side of differential carrier.

3) Measure thickness of shims removed. Add removed shim thickness and 1/2 of feeler gauge clearance measurement plus .002" (.05 mm). This is thickness shim which should be installed on each side of case. Select proper shims. Install equal shims on each side of case assembly.

CHRYSLER MOTORS & MITSUBISHI – FRONT (Cont.)

NOTE: Ensure no clearance exists between gear carrier and adjusting shim.

4) Install side bearing shims and differential case assembly in differential carrier. Using brass drift, tap shims to fit them to side bearing outer race. Install bearing caps. Tighten bolts to specification. Check ring gear backlash.

Ring Gear Backlash

1) Lock drive pinion in place. Using dial indicator, check ring gear backlash at heel of ring gear tooth. Measure at 4 locations of ring gear. Gear backlash must be within .004-.006" (.10-.15).

2) If not within specification, change side bearing adjusting shims and recheck backlash. If backlash is too small, install thinner shim behind ring gear and thicker shim opposite ring gear.

3) If backlash is excessive, install thicker shim behind ring gear and thinner shim opposite ring gear. Check gear tooth contact using paint impression method. See GEAR TOOTH PATTERNS article in this section.

CAUTION: Change shims so total thickness of all shims remains the same.

Ring Gear Runout

Using dial indicator, measure runout at back side of ring gear. Runout must be within .002" (.05 mm). If runout is excessive, change ring gear-to-differential case mounting position. Recheck runout. Install cover and gasket. Tighten bolts to specification.

TIGHTENING SPECIFICATIONS

Application	Ft. Lbs. (N.m)
Bearing Cap Bolt	40-47 (54-64)
Caliper Bolt	58-72 (79-98)
Carrier-to-Housing	
Tube Bolt	58-72 (79-98)
Cover Bolt	11-16 (15-22)
Drain Plug	43-51 (58-69)
Front Crossmember Bolt	72-87 (98-118)
Hub Cover	13-25 (18-34)
Knuckle-to-Ball Joint Nut	
Upper	43-65 (59-88)
Lower	87-130 (118-176)
Mount Bracket-to-Frame Bolt	58-80 (79-108)
Mount Bracket-to-Housing	
Tube Bolt	58-72 (79-98)
Pinion Flange Nut	116-159 (157-216)
Propeller Shaft Flange Bolt	36-43 (49-58)
Right Drive Axle-to-Inner	
Shaft Bolt	36-43 (49-58)
Ring Gear-to-Case Bolt	58-65 (79-88)
Tie Rod-to-Knuckle Nut	33 (45)

CHRYSLER MOTORS & MITSUBISHI – REAR

Rear Axles
Chrysler Motors: Raider, Ram-50;
Mitsubishi: Montero, Pickup, Van/Wagon

DESCRIPTION

Rear axle features a rigid banjo-type housing with semi-floating axle shafts. Differential consists of hypoid reduction gears and straight bevel differential gears. Limited slip differential is available on some models.

AXLE RATIO & IDENTIFICATION

Ratio is determined by dividing number of ring gear teeth by number of drive pinion teeth.

AXLE RATIO SPECIFICATIONS

Application	Ratio
Montero & Raider	4.62
Ram 50	
2WD W/Light Suspension	
2.0L	3.91
2.6L	3.55
2WD W/Heavy Suspension	4.22
4WD	3.91
Pickup	
2WD	
2.0L	3.91
Except 2.0L	3.55
4WD	3.91
Van/Wagon	4.22

TESTING

LIMITED SLIP DIFFERENTIAL PRELOAD

1) Place transmission in Neutral. Block front wheels. Raise one rear wheel free of ground and remove wheel. Use Adapter (MB990767) for Raider and Ram 50 or (MB990241-01) for Montero and Pickup models. Install adapter on wheel studs. Release parking brake.

2) Using torque wrench, measure starting torque on Pickup and Ram 50 models when rotating wheel in forward direction. On Montero and Raider models, measure rotating torque. This measurement is read once axle is turning. Differential must be repaired if torque is less than specification. See TESTING SPECIFICATIONS table.

TESTING SPECIFICATIONS

Application	Ft. Lbs. (N.m)
Montero & Pickup	25 (34)
Raider & Ram 50	13 (18)

AXLE SHAFT END PLAY

Using dial indicator, check axle shaft end play. End play must be .0020-.0079" (.050-.200 mm). If not within specifications, change shims to obtain correct end play. See AXLE SHAFTS & BEARINGS under REMOVAL & INSTALLATION in this article.

AXLE TOTAL BACKLASH

1) Raise and support rear axle. Place transmission in Neutral. Apply parking brake. Rotate drive shaft clockwise. Place reference marks on pinion dust cover and differential housing.

2) Rotate drive shaft counterclockwise and measure distance between reference marks. Differential must be removed and backlash adjusted if distance exceeds .2" (5 mm).

REMOVAL & INSTALLATION

AXLE SHAFTS & BEARINGS

Removal

1) Block front wheels. Raise and support rear axle housing. Remove rear wheel and brake drum. Disconnect hydraulic line from wheel cylinder.

2) Disconnect parking brake cable from balancer or equalizer on all except Van/Wagon models. On Van/Wagon models, remove brake shoes and disconnect parking brake cable. On all models, remove clamps from parking brake cables.

3) Disconnect bearing case from axle housing. Using axle puller, remove backing plate, bearing case, and axle shaft as an assembly.

4) Remove "O" ring and shims. Retain shims for reassembly. Using slide hammer, remove axle shaft oil seal from housing.

Installation

1) Apply grease to lip of inner oil seal. Using seal installer, install oil seal in axle housing.

2) Ensure old sealant is removed from mating face of bearing case and housing. Insert a .04" (1.0 mm) shim and "O" ring into left side of housing.

3) Apply semi-drying sealant to mating face of bearing case. Install left side axle shaft in axle housing. Tighten bearing case retaining bolts in diagonal sequence to specification. See TIGHTENING SPECIFICATIONS table at end of article.

4) Install right axle shaft in axle housing. DO NOT use shim or "O" ring. Temporarily tighten bearing case nuts to 52 INCH lbs. (6 N.m). Using feeler gauge, measure clearance between bearing case and axle housing.

5) Measurement should not vary from vertical to horizontal position. Select shims with thickness equal to clearance measured plus .002-.008" (.05-.20 mm). Remove right axle shaft.

6) Insert selected shims and "O" ring into housing. Apply semi-drying sealant to mating face of bearing case. Install right axle shaft in housing. Tighten bearing case retaining bolts in diagonal sequence to specification.

7) Using dial indicator, check end play of axle shaft. End play must be .0020-.0079" (.050-.200 mm). If not within specifications, change shims to obtain correct end play.

8) Reverse removal procedure for remaining components. Tighten bolts to specification. Adjust parking brake and bleed brake system.

DIFFERENTIAL CARRIER

Removal

1) Raise and support vehicle. Drain gear oil. Mark propeller flange-to-pinion flange position. Remove

CHRYSLER MOTORS & MITSUBISHI – REAR (Cont.)

propeller shaft. Remove axle shafts. See AXLE SHAFTS & BEARINGS under REMOVAL & INSTALLATION.

2) Support differential carrier with jack. Remove differential carrier retaining nuts. Remove differential carrier.

Installation

1) Apply sealant to axle housing surface. Reverse removal procedures. Align marks on propeller shaft and pinion flange. Tighten bolts to specification. See TIGHTENING SPECIFICATIONS table at end of article.

2) Fill differential with gear oil. Use Mopar Gear Oil (3744994) or SAE 80W-90 gear oil conforming to API classification GL-4 or above in conventional axles. On limited slip axles, use Mopar Gear Oil (4318058) and Mopar Friction Modifier (4318060) or Mitsubishi Gear Oil (8149630EX).

OVERHAUL

AXLE SHAFTS & BEARINGS

Disassembly

1) Mount backing plate and axle shaft assembly in soft-jawed vise. Bend over axle shaft bearing lock washer. Using Lock Nut Spanner (MB990785-01), remove lock nut from axle shaft. Remove washers and reinstall lock nut on axle shaft approximately 3 turns.

2) Attach Bearing Puller (MB990787-01) to rear of backing plate to remove bearing case from axle shaft. *See Fig. 2.* Tighten puller nuts diagonally using equal pressure to avoid binding to remove bearing case. Using hammer and drift, remove bearing outer race from bearing case. *See Fig. 3.* Remove oil seal from bearing case.

Fig. 2: Removing Bearing Case From Axle Shaft

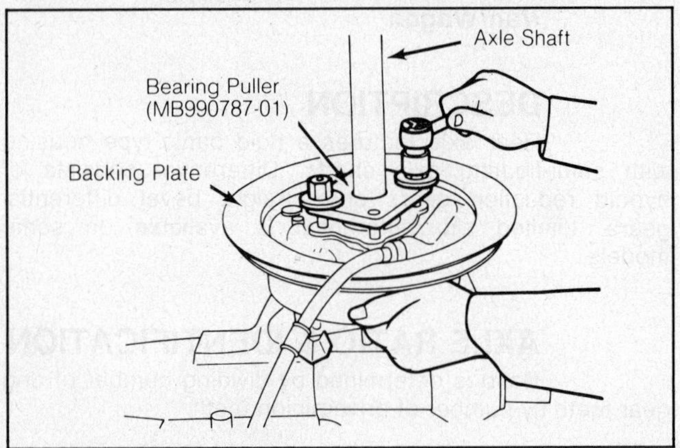

Courtesy of Chrysler Motors.

Inspection

Inspect bearings for roughness, pitting or damage. Inspect axle shaft for damaged splines or flange. Inspect bearing case for cracks or damage. Measure axle shaft O.D. in bearing area. Replace if not within specification. See AXLE SHAFT SPECIFICATIONS table.

Fig. 1: Exploded View of Rear Differential

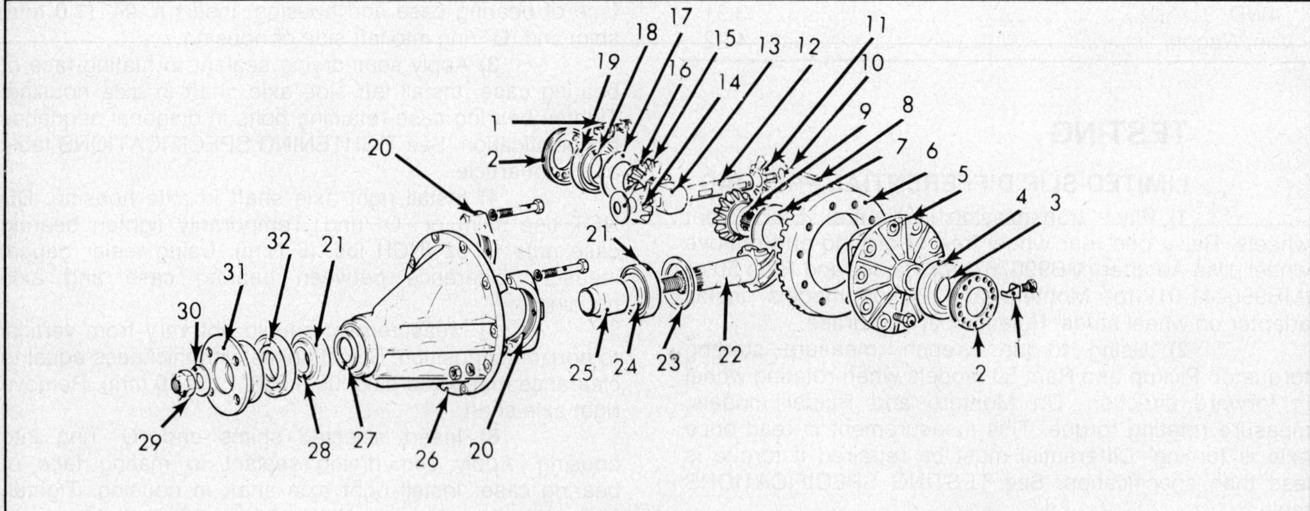

1. Lock Plate
2. Side Bearing Nut
3. Bearing
4. Bearing Race
5. Differential Case
6. Ring Gear
7. Thrust Spacer
8. Lock Pin
9. Side Gear
10. Pinion Washer
11. Pinion Gear
12. Pinion Shaft
13. Thrust Block (Some Models)
14. Pinion Gear
15. Pinion Washer
16. Side Gear
17. Thrust Spacer
18. Bearing
19. Bearing Race
20. Bearing Cap
21. Bearing Race
22. Pinion
23. Pinion Rear Shim
24. Bearing
25. Spacer
26. Differential Carrier
27. Pinion Front Shim
28. Bearing
29. Lock Nut
30. Washer
31. Pinion Flange
32. Oil Seal

Courtesy of Chrysler Motors.

CHRYSLER MOTORS & MITSUBISHI – REAR (Cont.)

AXLE SHAFT SPECIFICATIONS

Application	In. (mm)
Axle Shaft O.D.	
Van/Wagon	1.50 (38.1)
All Others	1.57 (39.8)

Fig. 3: Exploded View of Axle Shaft

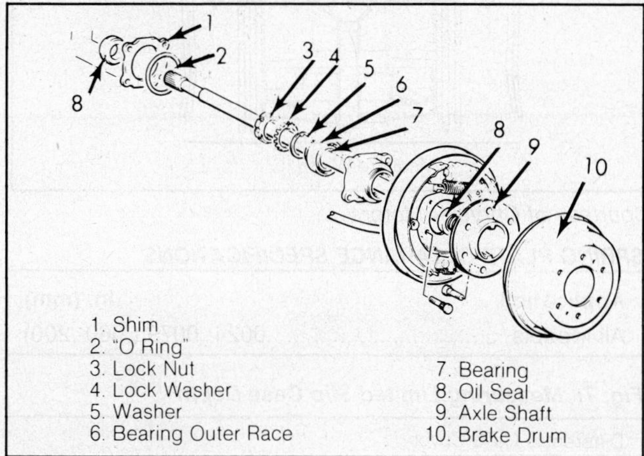

Courtesy of Chrysler Motors.

Reassembly

1) Apply grease to outer surface of bearing outer race and oil seal. Install outer race in bearing case. Use Handle (MB990938-01) and Race Installer (MB990933-01) for Van/Wagon models and (MB990937-01) for all others.

2) Install oil seal in bearing case until it is even with bearing case surface. Apply grease on bearing rollers. Install brake assembly, bearing case and bearing on axle shaft.

3) Apply grease on bearing rollers. Using Bearing Installer (MB990799-01), press inner bearing on axle shaft. Pack bearing case with grease. Coat lock nut threads with grease.

4) Install washer, lock washer, and lock nut. Lock nut must be installed with chamfered edge toward axle shaft flange. Tighten lock nut to specifications. Bend tab on lock washer into groove on lock nut.

DIFFERENTIAL ASSEMBLY

Disassembly

1) Remove differential carrier from axle housing. Remove lock plates. Using Spanner Wrench (MB990201-01), remove side bearing nuts. Mark bearing caps for location. Remove bearing caps. Remove differential case assembly from differential carrier.

CAUTION: Ensure side bearing nuts, bearing caps and side bearings are marked for location. Components must be installed in original location.

2) Using bearing puller, remove differential case side bearings. Place alignment marks on ring gear and differential case for reassembly. Loosen ring gear retaining bolts in diagonal sequence. Remove ring gear.

3) On conventional axles, drive pinion shaft lock pin from differential case. Remove differential pinion shaft and thrust block (if equipped). Remove pinion gears and washers.

4) Remove side gears and thrust spacers. Mark components for reassembly reference.

5) On limited slip units, mark differential case and differential case cover for reassembly reference. Remove differential case retaining screws. Separate differential case and cover. Remove components from case. *See Fig. 4.* Mark components for location.

Fig. 4: Exploded View of Limited Slip Differential

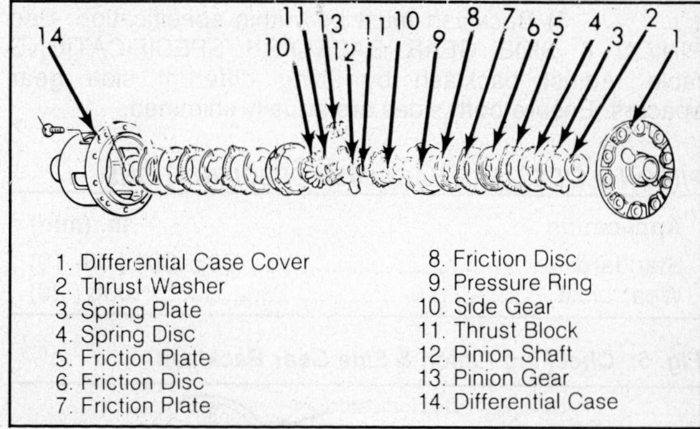

Courtesy of Chrysler Motors.

Drive Pinion

1) On all models, remove pinion flange retaining nut. Scribe alignment marks on drive pinion and pinion flange for reassembly. Using soft-faced hammer, drive out pinion. Remove front adjusting shim and spacer from pinion.

2) Using bearing puller, remove rear bearing from pinion. Remove rear adjusting shim from pinion. Remove oil seal and bearing races from differential carrier.

Inspection

1) On all axles, inspect all gears for cracked or flaking teeth. Inspect pinion shaft for wear. Inspect pinion flange and drive pinion for damaged splines.

2) Inspect bearings and races for roughness or flaking. Replace worn components. On limited slip axles, inspect clutch components and contact areas for wear or overheating. Inspect friction plates, friction discs, spring plates and pressure ring for signs of seizure, excessive heat, severe friction or nicks.

NOTE: Outer areas of friction surfaces will wear heavier due to clutch plate and preload spring.

3) Using dial indicator, check friction plate and friction disc for warpage. Replace if beyond specification. See FRICTION PLATE & DISC SPECIFICATIONS table.

4) Measure friction plates and disc thickness at projection areas not within wear area. Measure plate and disc thickness in friction surface.

5) Difference between thickness of projections and friction surface indicates amount of wear. Replace components if not within specification. See FRICTION PLATE & DISC SPECIFICATIONS table.

FRICTION PLATE & DISC SPECIFICATIONS

Application	In. (mm)
Warpage Limit	.003 (.08)
Wear Limit	.004 (.10)

CHRYSLER MOTORS & MITSUBISHI – REAR (Cont.)

REASSEMBLY & ADJUSTMENT

Case Assembly (Conventional)

1) Install thrust spacers, side gears, pinion washers and pinion gears in differential case. DO NOT install thrust block at this time.

2) Install pinion shaft without lock pin. Check pinion and side gear backlash. Install wooden wedge to lock side gears. Using dial indicator, measure gear backlash. *See Fig. 5.*

3) Backlash must be within specification. See PINION & SIDE GEAR BACKLASH SPECIFICATIONS table. Adjust backlash by using different side gear spacers. Ensure both sides are equally shimmed.

PINION & SIDE GEAR BACKLASH SPECIFICATIONS

Application	In. (mm)
Standard	.003-.004 (.08-.10)
Wear Limit	.008 (.20)

Fig. 5: Checking Pinion & Side Gear Backlash

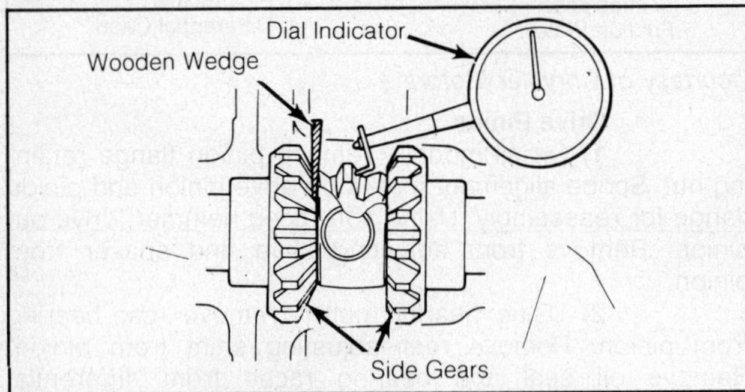

Courtesy of Chrysler Motors.

4) Install thrust block once correct backlash is obtained. Install pinion shaft lock pin from back side of ring gear. Securely stake in 2 places.

5) Ensure adhesive is removed from ring gear mounting bolts and gear mounting surface. Clean internal threads with tap. Install ring gear on differential case.

6) Ensure alignment marks on differential case and ring gear are aligned. Apply Loctite 271 to bolts and install. Tighten bolts alternately in diagonal sequence to specification.

Case Assembly (Limited Slip)

1) Assemble 2 friction disc and 2 friction plates. Assemble plate, disc, plate and disc. Measure assembly thickness. Assemble disc and plates to give standard difference of .0020" (.050 mm) between the 2 sides.

2) Assemble spring disc and spring plates with one on each side. Measure assembly thickness. Assemble disc and plates to obtain minimum difference in thickness between each assembly.

3) Assemble clutch assemblies, pressure rings, pinion gears, side gears, thrust block and pinion shaft. Measure overall width of assembly plus spring plates and spring discs. This measurement is "C". *See Fig. 6.*

4) Determine depth "D" of differential case, using formula "D" = "E" + "F" - "G". *See Fig. 7.* Subtract measurement "C" from measurement "D" to determine spring plate-to-case clearance. Adjust spring disc thickness to obtain proper spring plate-to-case clearance. See SPRING PLATE CLEARANCE SPECIFICATIONS table.

Fig. 6: Measuring Clutch Assembly Width

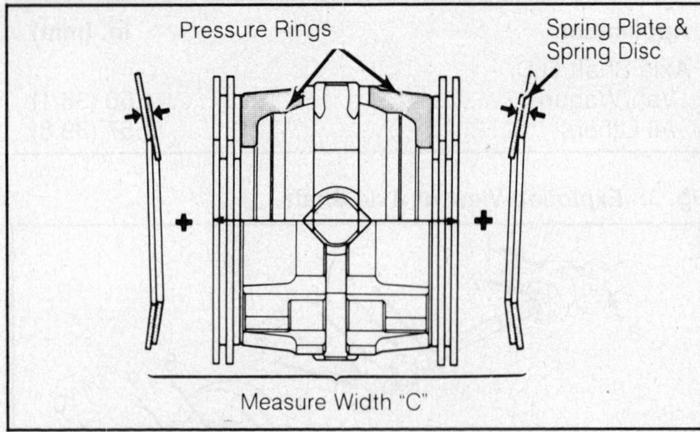

Courtesy of Chrysler Motors.

SPRING PLATE CLEARANCE SPECIFICATIONS

Application	In. (mm)
All Models	.0024-.0079 (.060-.200)

Fig. 7: Measuring Limited Slip Case Depth

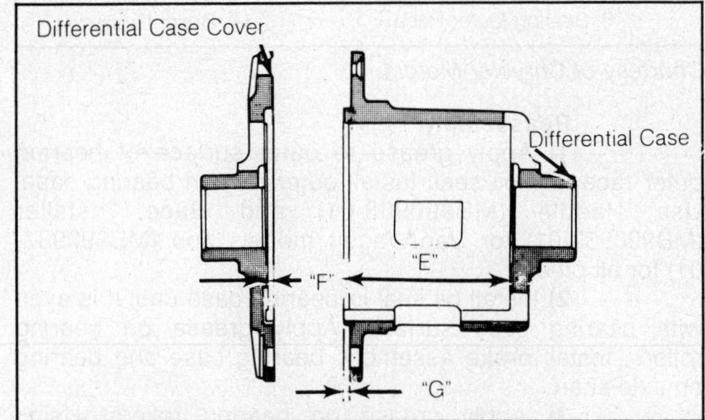

Courtesy of Chrysler Motors.

CAUTION: Do not mix clutch components for right and left sides. Mark clutch components for location.

5) Remove spring plates, spring discs, friction plates and friction disc from pressure rings. Mark components for location. Install thrust washers on each end of pressure rings. *See Fig. 8.*

6) Measure distance from end of thrust washer to rear face of pressure ring. Select proper thickness thrust washers to obtain a .0020" (.050 mm) or less difference between measurements.

7) Once correct thrust washers are determined, install thrust washers on pressure rings. Squeeze pressure rings together and measure width from end of thrust washer to remaining thrust washer. This is dimension "H". *See Fig. 8.*

8) Determine distance between thrust washer surfaces when differential case is assembled. This is dimension "I". ("I" = "J" + "K" + "L"). *See Fig. 8.* Dimension "J" is the same as dimension "D" in step **4)**.

9) Subtract dimension "H" from dimension "I". This is the clearance between thrust washer and differential case. Thrust washer must be changed to obtain correct specification. See THRUST WASHER CLEARANCE SPECIFICATIONS table.

CHRYSLER MOTORS & MITSUBISHI – REAR (Cont.)

Fig. 8: Measuring Thrust Washer Clearance

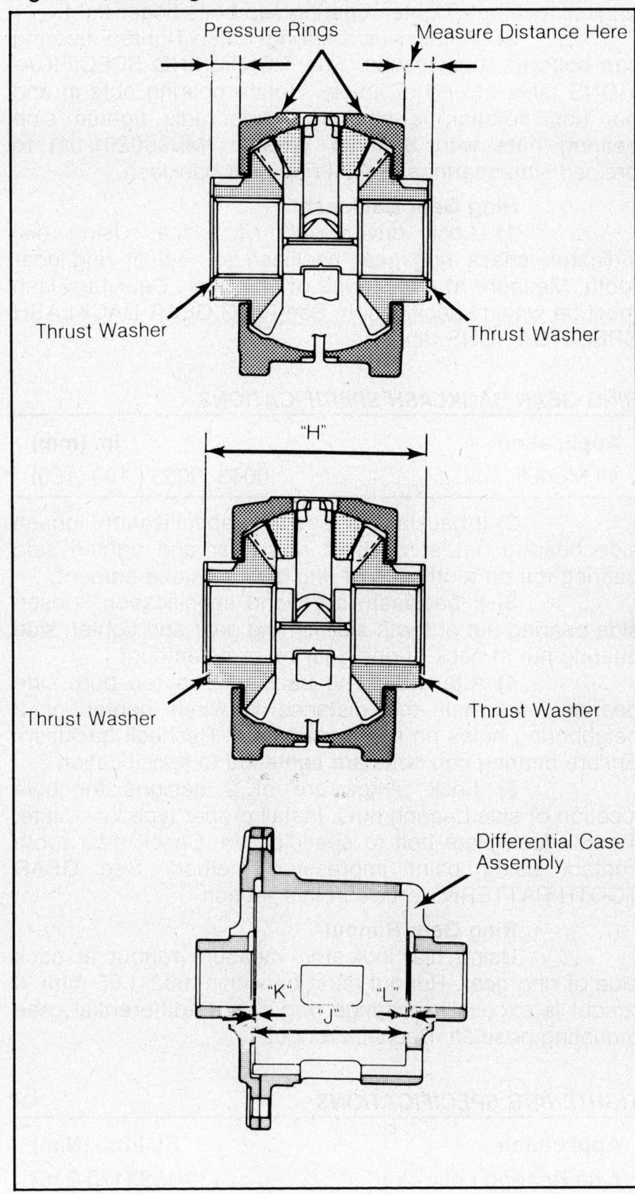

Courtesy of Chrysler Motors.

THRUST WASHER CLEARANCE SPECIFICATIONS

Application	In. (mm)
Montero & Raider	.002-.008 (.05-.20)
Pickup & Ram 50	.003-.008 (.06-.20)

10) Select thrust washers to obtain correct clearance from pressure ring face and end of thrust washer surface. Thrust washers are available in 3 sizes.

11) Apply gear oil and friction modifier to all components. Install components in differential case. Ensure assembly order and direction of clutch components. *See Fig. 9.*

12) Install differential case cover with mark aligned with differential case. Tighten screws in several steps. Ensure cases contact each other when fully assembled. Check for incorrect clutch assembly if gap exists.

Fig. 9: Limited Slip Differential Assembly

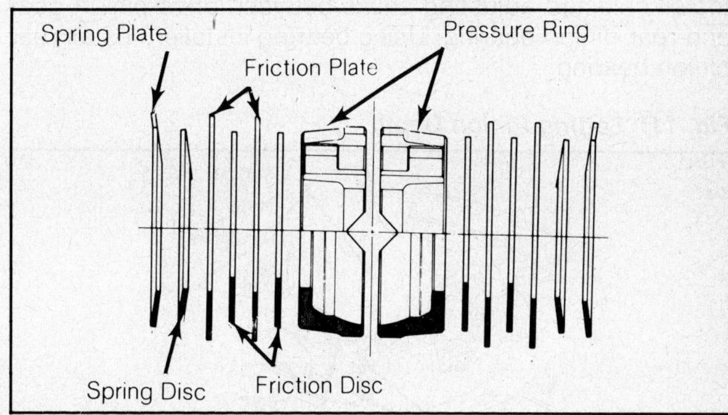

Courtesy of Chrysler Motors.

13) Using Clutch Plate Preload Tool (MB990988), Shaft (MB990989) and torque wrench, measure starting torque. Slightly rotate unit before measuring starting torque. *See Fig. 10.*

Fig. 10: Checking Differential Starting Torque

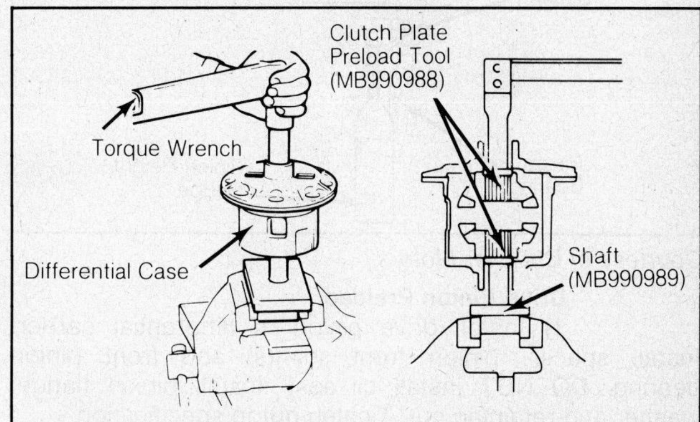

Courtesy of Chrysler Motors.

14) Starting torque must be within specification. See STARTING TORQUE SPECIFICATIONS table. Ensure adhesive is removed from ring gear mounting bolts and gear mounting surface. Clean internal threads with tap.

15) Install ring gear on differential case. Ensure alignment marks on differential case and ring gear are aligned. Apply Loctite 271 to bolts and install. Tighten bolts alternately in diagonal sequence to specification.

STARTING TORQUE SPECIFICATIONS

Application	Ft. Lbs. (N.m)
Used Clutch Plates	25-72 (34-98)
New Clutch Plates	47-72 (64-98)

Drive Pinion Depth

1) Install pinion bearing races in carrier. Ensure races are fully seated. Install pinion height gauge and pinion bearings. Use Pinion Height Gauge (C-4626) for Raider and Ram 50 models or (MB990901-01) for all others. *See Fig. 11.* DO NOT install oil seal.

2) Using torque wrench, measure pinion rotating torque. Gradually tighten pinion height gauge to increase rotating torque to 3.5-4.3 INCH lbs. (.40-.48 N.m).

3) Install cylinder gauge in side bearing seats. Ensure flat areas are aligned and gauge contacts side bearing seat firmly. *See Fig. 11.* Select adjusting shim with same thickness as gap between cylinder gauge and pinion height gauge.

CHRYSLER MOTORS & MITSUBISHI – REAR (Cont.)

4) Use minimum amount of adjusting shims. Install selected adjusting shims between drive pinion gear and rear pinion bearing. Using bearing installer, install rear pinion bearing.

Fig. 11: Setting Pinion Depth

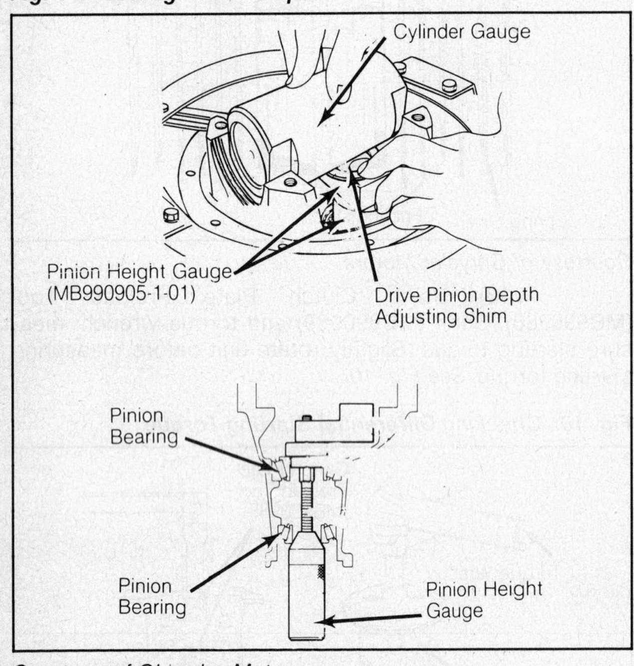

Courtesy of Chrysler Motors.

Drive Pinion Preload

1) Install drive pinion in differential carrier. Install spacer, pinion front shim(s) and front pinion bearing. DO NOT install oil seal. Install pinion flange, washer and retaining nut. Tighten nut to specification.

2) Check pinion rotating torque. Rotating torque must be within specification. See PINION ROTATING TORQUE SPECIFICATIONS table. Adjust rotating torque by replacing drive pinion front shims or spacer.

PINION ROTATING TORQUE SPECIFICATIONS

Application	INCH Lbs. (N.m)
With Oil Seal	5.6-6.5 (.63-.74)
Without Oil Seal	3.5-4.3 (.40-.48)

3) Once correct rotating torque is obtained, install oil seal. Coat seal lip with grease. Install pinion flange so alignment marks are correct.

4) Apply light coat of grease to pinion flange washer contact area. Install new retaining nut. Tighten to specification. Check pinion rotating torque.

5) Rotating torque must be within specification. See PINION ROTATING TORQUE SPECIFICATIONS table.

Side Bearing

1) Press side bearings onto differential case. Install differential carrier in housing and install outer races. Align bearing cap index marks and snug carrier cap bolts. Ensure outer races and bearing caps are installed in original location. Tighten bearing cap bolts finger tight.

2) Install side bearing nuts. Tighten bearing cap bolts to specification. See TIGHTENING SPECIFICATIONS table at end of article. Rotate bearing nuts in and out until rotation is smooth. Temporarily tighten side bearing nuts with Spanner Wrench (MB990201-01) to preload side bearings. Adjust ring gear backlash.

Ring Gear Backlash

1) Lock drive pinion in place. Using dial indicator, check ring gear backlash at heel of ring gear tooth. Measure at 4 locations of ring gear. Gear backlash must be within specification. See RING GEAR BACKLASH SPECIFICATIONS table.

RING GEAR BACKLASH SPECIFICATIONS

Application	In. (mm)
All Models	.0043-.0063 (.109-.160)

2) If backlash is less than specification, loosen side bearing nut at back of ring gear and tighten side bearing nut on tooth side of ring gear by same amount.

3) If backlash is beyond specification, loosen side bearing nut at tooth side of ring gear and tighten side bearing nut at back of ring gear by same amount.

4) After adjusting backlash, tighten both side bearing nuts half the distance between center of 2 neighboring holes on side bearing nut. Recheck backlash. Ensure bearing cap bolts are tightened to specification.

5) Lock plates are of 2 designs for hole location of side bearing nuts. Install proper type lock plate. Tighten lock plate bolt to specification. Check gear tooth contact using paint impression method. See GEAR TOOTH PATTERNS article in this section.

Ring Gear Runout

Using dial indicator, measure runout at back side of ring gear. Runout must be within .002" (.05 mm). If runout is excessive, change ring gear-to-differential case mounting position. Recheck runout.

TIGHTENING SPECIFICATIONS

Application	Ft. Lbs. (N.m)
Axle Bearing Lock Nut	130-159 (176-216)
Bearing Case-to-Axle Housing Bolt	36-43 (49-58)
Bearing Cap Bolt	40-47 (54-64)
Brake Line	10-12 (14-16)
Differential Carrier-to-Axle Housing Nut	18-22 (24-30)
Drain Plug	43-50 (58-68)
Filler Plug	29-43 (39-58)
Lock Plate Bolt	11-16 (15-22)
Pinion Flange Nut	137-181 (186-246)
Propeller Shaft-to-Pinion Flange Bolt	36-43 (49-58)
Ring Gear Bolt	58-65 (79-88)

FORD MOTOR CO. INTEGRAL CARRIER

Merkur XR4Ti

DESCRIPTION

Drive axle assembly is hypoid type with integral carrier housing. Drive axle uses 7.5" ring gear. Drive pinion bearing preload adjustment is maintained by collapsible spacer positioned between inner and outer pinion bearings.

Differential side bearing preload and ring gear backlash are adjusted by threading carrier bearings in or out of housing. Side bearing carriers are retained in place using lock plates. Drive pinion depth is adjusted by shims behind rear drive pinion bearing outer race. Stub axles are held in place using selective thickness "C" clips.

AXLE RATIO & IDENTIFICATION

There are no identification tags on rear drive axle. To determine axle ratio, divide number of ring gear teeth by number of drive pinion gear teeth.

AXLE RATIO SPECIFICATIONS

Application	Ratio
Auto. Trans.	3.36:1
Man. Trans.	3.64:1

REMOVAL & INSTALLATION

NOTE: **Differential housing is a lightweight aluminum alloy casting. Special care should be used whenever servicing to prevent damage to housing and components.**

DRIVE AXLES

Removal

1) Place transmission in Neutral. Release parking brake. Raise and support vehicle with rear wheels hanging free. Remove 6 bolts attaching drive axle to stub axle shaft. Rotate drive axle as necessary to access bolts.

2) Support outer end of drive axle to prevent damage to outer CV joint. Remove bolts attaching drive axle to drive axle flange. Remove drive axle from vehicle.

Installation

NOTE: **Drive axles are different lengths and MUST BE installed on correct side of vehicle. Longer drive axle is installed on right side of vehicle.**

Pack CV joints with grease. Support outer end of drive axle and install inner end on drive axle flange. Install outer end of drive axle on stub axle shaft. Tighten drive axle mounting bolts to 28-31 ft. lbs. (38-42 N.m).

AXLE SHAFTS & BEARINGS

Removal

1) Raise and support vehicle. Place transmission in Neutral and release parking brake. Remove wheel and tire assembly. Ensure rear suspension is hanging free. Remove brake drum.

2) Remove wheel flange lock nut and washer. Discard lock nut. Remove wheel flange using Puller (D81L-1002-A). Support backing plate. Remove bearing hub assembly. Clamp bearing hub assembly in vise. Pry inner grease seal from hub.

NOTE: **Wheel flange lock nuts are not interchangeable. Left side nut has left-hand threads and right side nut has right-hand threads.**

Fig. 1: Exploded View of Rear Drive Axle & Stub Axle Shaft

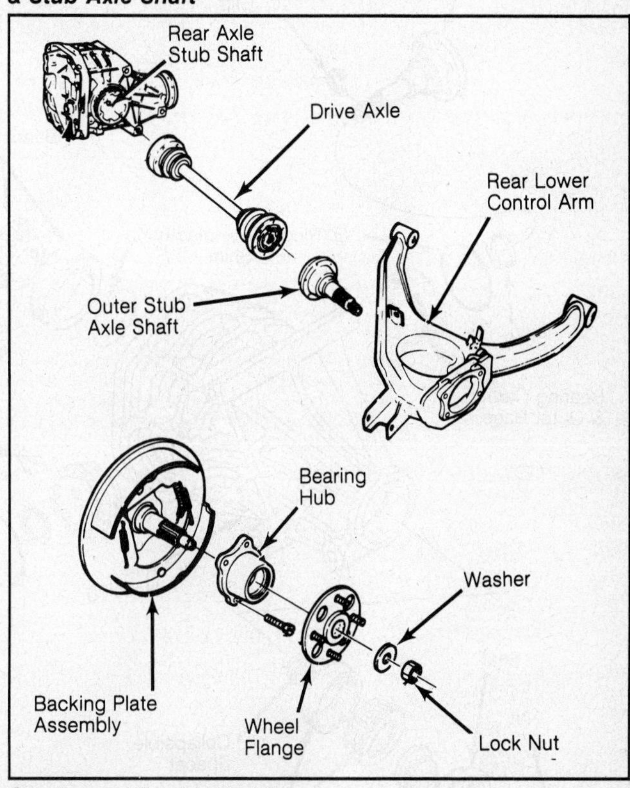

Courtesy of Ford Motor Co.

3) Remove inner bearing from hub. Remove outer seal and bearing in same manner. Remove outer bearing races from hub using Puller (T77F-1102-A) and slide hammer. Ensure puller jaws do not catch on edges inside hub.

4) Disconnect and support outer end of drive axle. From under vehicle, pull stub axle out from rear of bearing hub.

Installation

To install, reverse removal procedure. Lubricate seals before installing. Install bearing hub with rounded side up. Tighten mounting bolts and nuts to specification. Use new wheel flange lock nut.

DRIVE PINION FLANGE & PINION SEAL

Removal

Remove propeller shaft. Hold drive pinion flange with Flange Holder (T78P-4851-A) and remove nut. Remove drive pinion flange using Puller (D80L-1002-L). Remove pinion seal using pry bar or screwdriver.

CAUTION: **Remove pinion seal carefully to prevent damage to seal bore in aluminum case.**

Installation

To install, reverse removal procedure. Lubricate pinion seal before installing drive pinion flange.

FORD MOTOR CO. INTEGRAL CARRIER (Cont.)

Fig. 2: Exploded View of Rear Differential Assembly

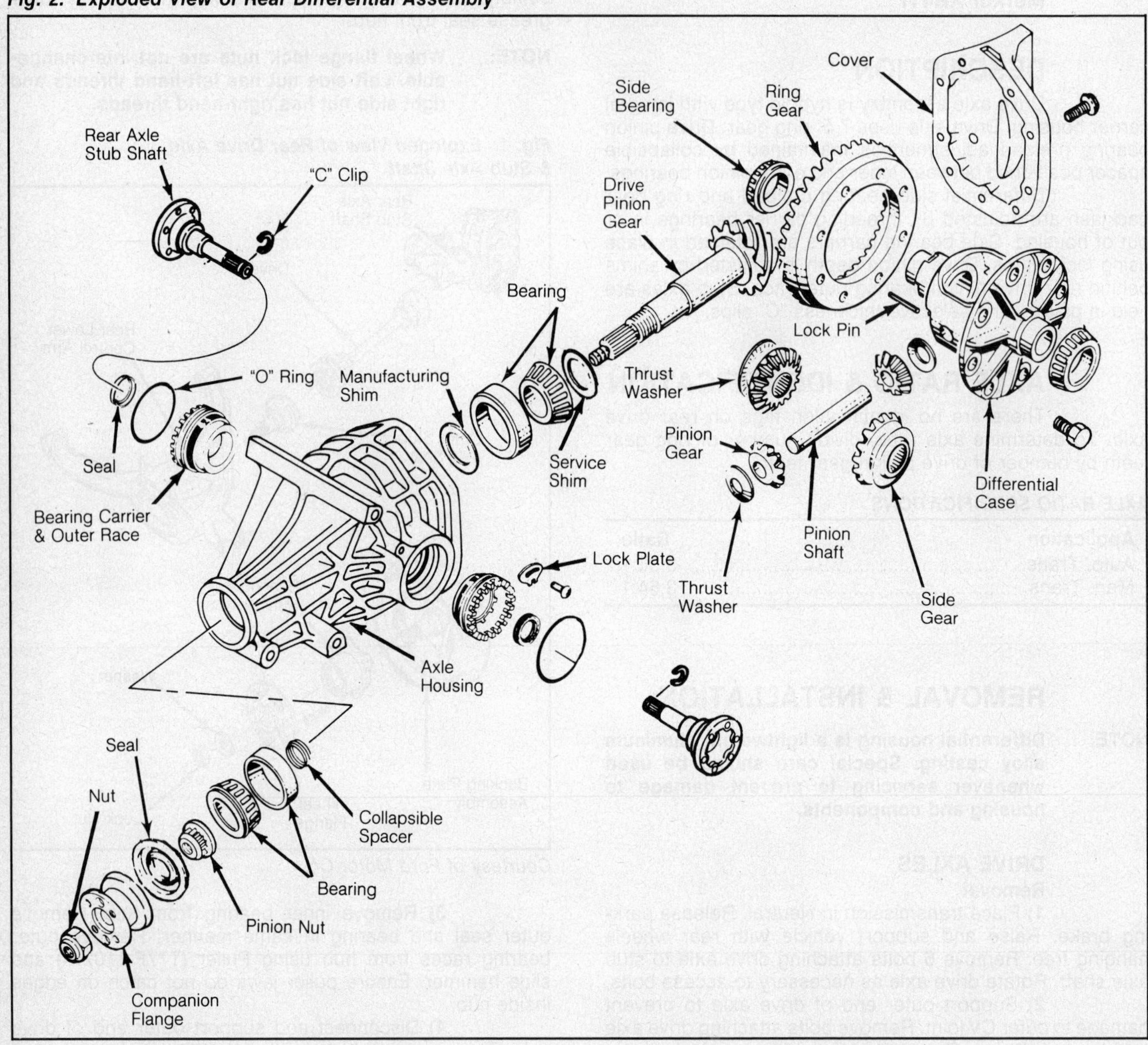

Courtesy of Ford Motor Co.

DIFFERENTIAL ASSEMBLY

Removal

1) Raise and support vehicle. Support drive axles with wire in normal position to prevent excessive CV joint angularity. Disconnect drive axles from differential. Mark propeller shaft and companion flange for reassembly reference. Remove propeller shaft.

2) Support rear axle assembly with a jack. Remove rear body mount attaching bolts. Remove 4 bolts and 2 shims (if equipped) attaching front end of housing to crossmember brackets. Remove nut and through-bolt attaching axle housing to body.

3) Lower differential assembly clear of rear suspension. Remove differential assembly. Remove rear mount from differential cover.

Installation

To install, reverse removal procedure. Tighten mounting bolts to specification. See TIGHTENING SPECIFICATIONS table in this article. Align index marks on propeller shaft and companion flange. Fill differential assembly with gear oil. Check mounting flange clearance.

MOUNTING FLANGE CLEARANCE CHECK

1) Whenever axle case, axle assembly or suspension crossmember has been replaced, mounting flange clearance must be checked. If gap is found between rear axle mounting boss and crossmember mounting flanges, selective shims must be installed to compensate for clearance.

2) Install rear mount on axle housing rear cover. Tighten mounting bolts to 37-41 ft. lbs. (50-56 N.m). Lift assembly into position between crossmember flanges. Install through-bolt and 4 axle-to-crossmember mounting bolts. DO NOT tighten bolts at this time.

3) Position axle housing rear mount against body and secure with 4 bolts. Tighten mounting bolts to

FORD MOTOR CO. INTEGRAL CARRIER (Cont.)

14-18 ft. lbs. (19-24 N.m). Tighten front lower attaching bolt to 51-66 ft. lbs. (69-89 N.m). Tighten through-bolt to 51-66 ft. lbs. (69-89 N.m).

4) Using a feeler gauge, check clearance between crossmember flanges and rear axle mounting boss. Select and install appropriate shims between crossmember and axle. Tighten mounting bolts to 51-66 ft. lbs. (69-89 N.m). *See Fig. 3.*

Fig. 3: Checking Mounting Flange Clearance

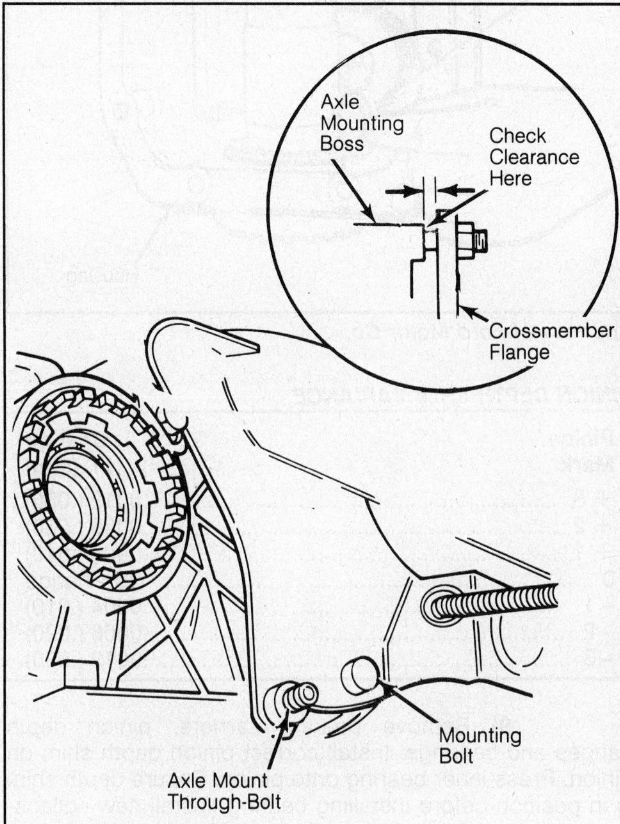

Courtesy of Ford Motor Co.

OVERHAUL

DISASSEMBLY

Differential Housing

1) Mount differential assembly in Holding Fixture (T57L-500-B). Remove cover mounting bolts using Torx Bit (No. 50). Drain lubricant. Remove stub axle shaft "C" clips. Remove stub axle shafts.

2) Mark side bearing carriers for reassembly in original locations. Remove stub axle shaft oil seals using Bearing Cup Puller (D78P-1225-B). If puller is not available, leave seals in carriers for removal after bearing carriers are removed from housing.

3) Remove bearing carrier lock plates using Torx Bit (No. 50). Remove bearing carriers using Side Bearing Adjusting Wrench (T85M-4970-A). Remove and discard "O" rings from bearing carriers. Remove differential case from housing. Remove companion flange as previously described. Carefully remove companion flange oil seal.

4) Remove staking from pinion nut using chisel. Remove and discard pinion nut using Pinion Nut Socket (T85M-4610-A) and Pinion Spline Socket (T85M-4610-B). Hold pinion nut socket stationary and rotate spline socket counterclockwise.

NOTE: Pinion nut has left-hand threads.

5) Remove drive pinion with inner bearing and collapsible spacer. Remove and discard collapsible spacer. Remove pinion outer bearing from housing. Remove drive pinion bearing outer race from one side of housing using Bearing Cup Remover (D78P-1225-B) and a puller. DO NOT remove both drive pinion bearing races at the same time.

6) One bearing race MUST remain inside housing at all times. Remove rear pinion bearing from drive pinion using a press. Remove stub axle shaft seals if not removed previously. Clean and inspect all components for wear and damage. Replace components as necessary.

Fig. 4: Removing Drive Pinion From Housing

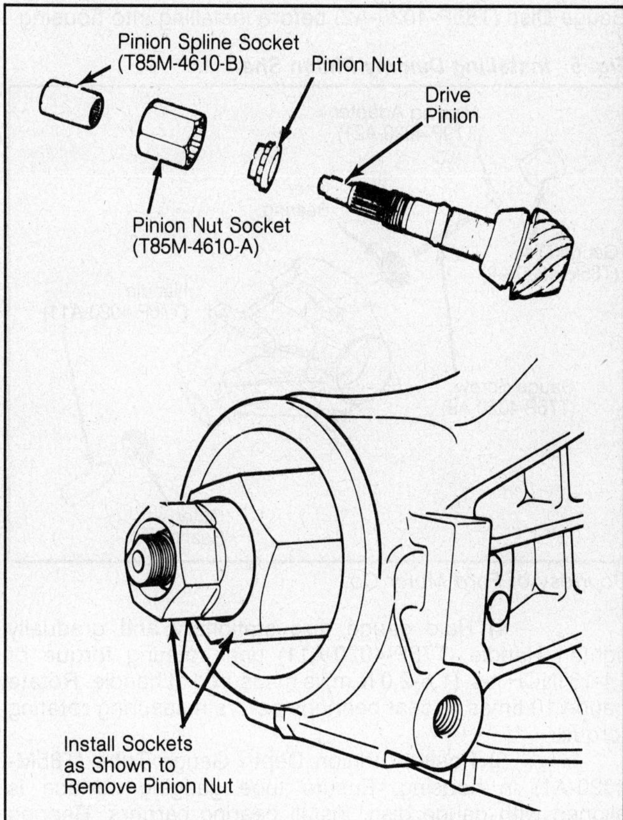

Courtesy of Ford Motor Co.

Differential Case

1) Remove side bearings from case using Bearing Puller (T77F-4220-B1) and Step Plate (T77F-4220-B2). Remove 10 ring gear mounting bolts. Using hammer and brass drift, tap ring gear off differential case.

2) Remove pinion shaft roll pin from case using a punch. Drive pinion shaft from case using a brass drift. Rotate side gears until pinion gears revolve into openings in case. Remove pinion gears, side gears and thrust washers.

REASSEMBLY & ADJUSTMENT

Differential Case

1) Install thrust washers on side gears and position into differential case. Install thrust washers on pinion gears. Mesh pinion gears with side gears, 180

FORD MOTOR CO. INTEGRAL CARRIER (Cont.)

degrees from each other. Rotate side gears to position pinion gears into case. Install pinion shaft, aligning roll pin holes in shaft and case.

2) Install roll pin. Install ring gear on carrier and install new mounting bolts. Tighten bolts in several steps using a criss-cross pattern. Tighten ring gear bolts to 55-66 ft. lbs. (75-90 N.m).

Drive Pinion Bearing Depth & Preload

1) Install axle stub shaft seals into bearing carriers. Position standard 2 mm pinion depth shim (manufacturing shim) in inner bearing outer race housing bore. Lightly oil bearing bores in housing.

2) Install inner and outer bearing outer races into housing using Pinion Bearing Cup Replacers (T85M-4616-A and T56T-4616-B2) and Drawbolt (T75T-1176-A).

3) Lubricate drive pinion bearings with gear oil. Install pinion bearings and dummy pinion shaft into housing. *See Fig. 5*. Ensure Gauge Screw (T76P-4020-A9) is tight in Gauge Disc (T85P-4020-A2) before installing into housing.

Fig. 5: Installing Dummy Pinion Shaft

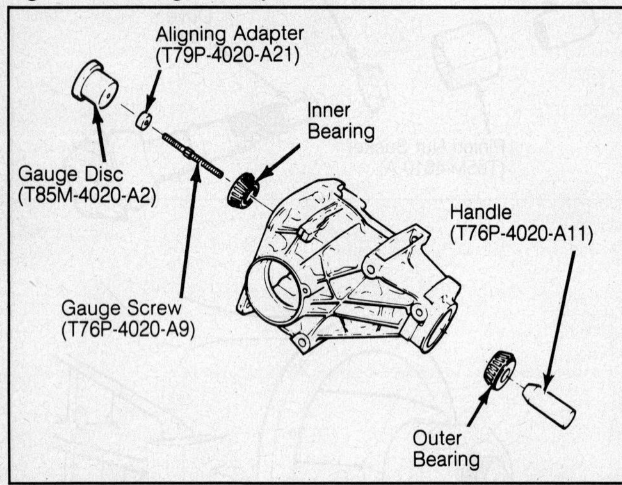

Courtesy of Ford Motor Co.

4) Hold gauge disc stationary and gradually tighten Handle (T76P-4020-A11) until rotating torque of 14-18 INCH lbs. (1.6-2.0 N.m) is measured at handle. Rotate gauge 10 times to seat bearings before measuring rotating torque.

5) Position Pinion Depth Gauge Tube (T85M-4020-A1) in housing. Ensure tube gauging surface is aligned with gauge disc. Install bearing carriers. Bearing carriers MUST BE installed in original housing bores and without "O" ring seals. Thread bearing carriers evenly into housing.

6) When carriers contact gauge tube, snug them down to remove all end play from tube. Carriers are properly installed when a moderate amount of effort is required to rotate gauge tube by hand.

7) Slide various drive pinion depth shims between gauge tube and gauge disc. Correct shim thickness is obtained when a slight drag is felt between shim and gauging surfaces. This determines pinion depth thickness for a "nominal" or "zero" variance pinion. *See Fig. 6*.

8) If pinion is marked with a plus "+" number, subtract that amount from shim thickness in step **7)**. If pinion is marked with a minus "–" number, add that amount to shim thickness obtained in step **7)**. See PINION DEPTH SHIM VARIANCE table.

Fig. 6: Setting Drive Pinion Depth

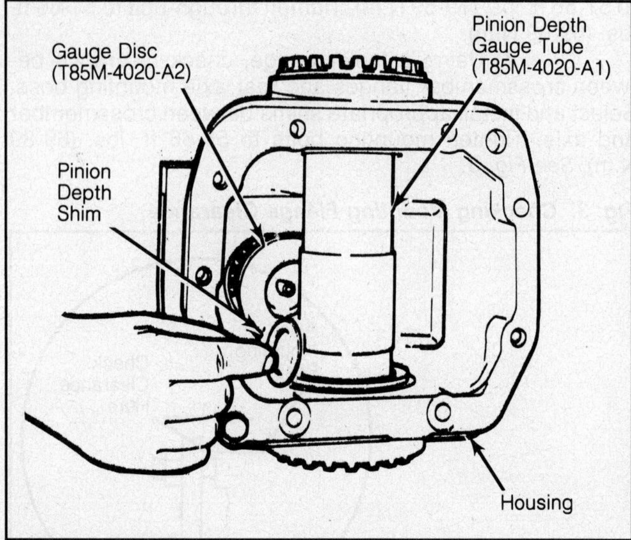

Courtesy of Ford Motor Co.

PINION DEPTH SHIM VARIANCE

Pinion Mark	Change In. (mm)
+ 3	.0012 (.030)
+ 2	.0008 (.020)
+ 1	.0004 (.010)
0	No Change
– 1	.0004 (.010)
– 2	.0008 (.020)
– 3	.0012 (.030)

9) Remove bearing carriers, pinion depth gauges and bearings. Install correct pinion depth shim on pinion. Press inner bearing onto pinion. Ensure depth shim is in position before installing bearing. Install new collapsible spacer on drive pinion.

10) Lubricate pinion bearings and install pinion into housing. Install front pinion bearing. Install new pinion nut. To preload pinion bearings, gradually tighten pinion nut using Pinion Nut Socket (T85M-4610-A) and Pinion Spline Socket (T85M-4610-B). Hold pinion nut socket stationary while turning pinion spline socket.

11) Check pinion bearing rotating torque using torque wrench and pinion spline socket. Tighten pinion nut until rotating torque of 14-18 INCH lbs. (1.6-2.0 N.m) is obtained.

12) If nut is tightened beyond specified rotating torque, install a new collapsible spacer and repeat pinion bearing preload procedure. Stake pinion nut to pinion. Lubricate and install pinion seal, using Installer (T80T-4000-C). Install pinion flange and mounting nut. Tighten mounting nut to 95-110 ft. lbs. (129-149 N.m).

Differential Housing

1) Position differential case into housing. Install new "O" rings on bearing carriers. Lubricate bearing carrier threads, "O" rings and seals. Install bearing carriers in original locations.

2) Using Side Bearing Adjuster Wrench (T85M-4970-A), rotate bearing carriers into housing until they seat lightly against differential side bearings. Position dial indicator on housing so that it contacts ring gear at right angle.

FORD MOTOR CO. INTEGRAL CARRIER (Cont.)

Fig. 7: Adjusting Pinion Bearing Preload

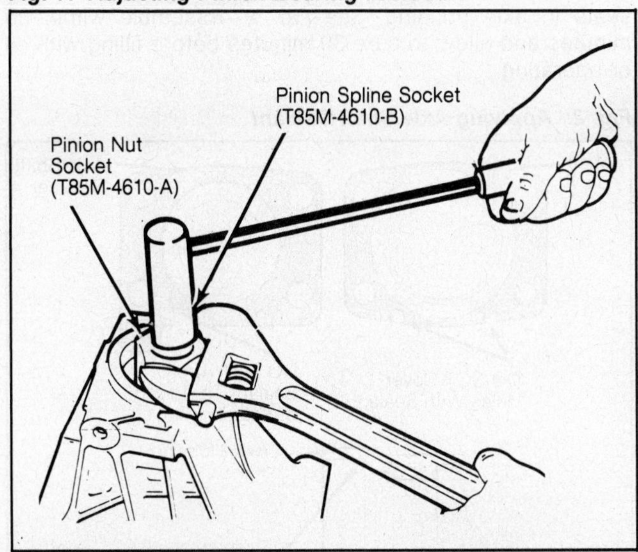

Courtesy of Ford Motor Co.

3) Measure ring gear backlash. Rotate bearing carriers into case EQUAL amounts until backlash reading is .0004" (.010 mm). After backlash is set, tighten bearing carrier on differential case side of housing an additional 4-5 teeth. Check ring gear backlash. Backlash should be .004-.007" (.10-.18 mm).

4) Install bearing carrier lock plates. Tighten lock plate bolts to 14-18 ft. lbs. (19-24 N.m) using a Torx Bit (No. 50). Install stub axle shafts. Install thickest possible "C" clip in each stub axle shaft groove. Apply Sealant (E1FZ-19562-A) to housing cover. Install housing cover and tighten mounting bolts to 33-44 ft. lbs. (45-60 N.m).

TIGHTENING SPECIFICATIONS

Application	Ft. Lbs. (N.m)
Bearing Carrier Lock Plate Bolt	14-18 (19-24)
Bearing Hub Mounting Bolts	45-48 (61-65)
Companion Flange Nut	95-110 (129-149)
Differential Mount Through-Bolt	51-66 (69-89)
Differential-to-Rear Mount Bolts	37-41 (50-56)
Drive Axle Bolts	28-31 (38-42)
Front Differential Mounting Bolts	14-18 (19-24)
Housing Cover Bolts	33-44 (45-60)
Ring Gear Bolts	55-66 (75-90)
Wheel Flange Lock Nut	185-214 (251-290)

HONDA REAR AXLE

Honda: Civic Wagon 4WD

DESCRIPTION

Rear axle features a rigid banjo-type housing with semi-floating axle shafts. Differential consists of hypoid reduction gears and bevel differential gears.

AXLE RATIO & IDENTIFICATION

Rear axle ratio is 2.53:1. Ratio is determined by dividing number of ring gear teeth by number of drive pinion teeth.

REMOVAL & INSTALLATION

AXLE SHAFT & BEARINGS

Removal

1) Raise and support vehicle. Remove rear wheel and brake drum. Disconnect and plug brake line at wheel cylinder. Remove brake shoes and parking brake cable.

2) Remove axle shaft retaining nuts. Using slide hammer, remove axle shaft from axle housing. Pry oil seal from axle housing.

3) Check bearing for roughness. Replace bearing if damaged. See AXLE SHAFTS & BEARINGS under OVERHAUL in this article.

Installation

1) Using Seal Installer (07746-0010400) and Handle (07749-0010000), install oil seal in axle housing. Coat seal lip with grease.

2) Measure and record width "A" of outer bearing race. Measure and record brake backing plate thickness "B". Measure and record depth "C" from edge of axle housing to bearing seating surface. *See Fig. 1.*

3) Add readings "B" and "C". Subtract total from reading "A" to obtain reading "X". Using dimension "X", determine shim to be used. See AXLE END PLAY SHIM SPECIFICATIONS table. Shims are available in 2 thicknesses.

4) Apply a thin coat of Sealant (08740-99986) to backing plate mating surface of shim and shim contact surface of axle shaft retainer. Ensure sealant does not cover designated areas. *See Fig. 2.*

5) Apply sealant to axle housing where bearing seats in axle housing. *See Fig. 2.* Assemble within 20 minutes and allow to cure 30 minutes before filling with oil or operating.

Fig. 2: Applying Axle Shaft Sealant

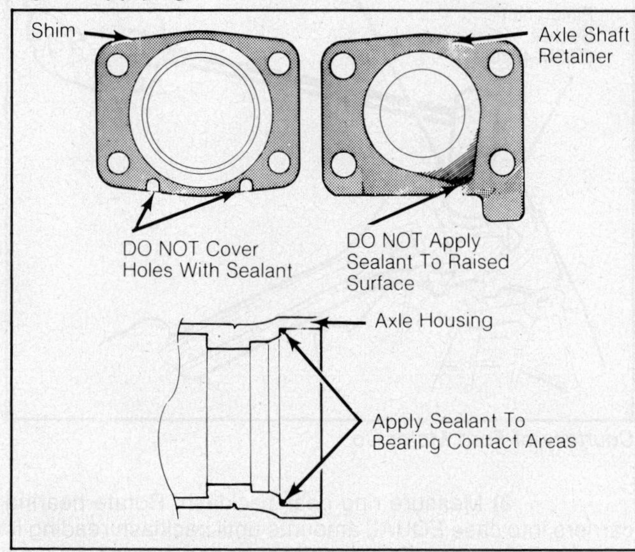

Courtesy of American Honda Motor Co., Inc.

6) Install axle shaft. Align axle splines. Using slide hammer, drive axle shaft into housing. Install axle retainer mounting nuts. Tighten to specification.

7) Reverse removal procedure for remaining components. Tighten bolts to specification. Bleed and adjust brakes.

DIFFERENTIAL CARRIER

Removal

1) Raise and support vehicle. Drain gear oil. Remove tire and wheel assembly. Remove brake drum. Remove drive axles.

AXLE END PLAY SHIM SPECIFICATIONS

Dimension "X" In. (mm)	Shim Required In. (mm)
-.0063-.0039 (-.160-.099)	None
.0039-.0098 (.099-.248)	.039 (.10)
.0098-.0157 (.248-.398)	.098 (.25)

Fig. 1: Determining Axle Shaft End Play Shim Thickness

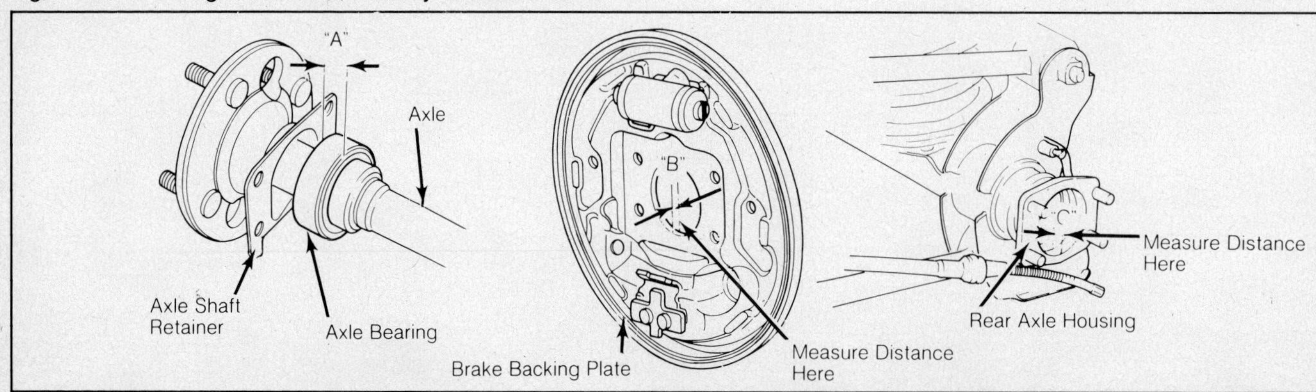

Courtesy of American Honda Motor Co., Inc.

HONDA REAR AXLE (Cont.)

2) Scribe an index mark on propeller shaft and companion flange. Remove propeller shaft. Support differential carrier with jack. Remove differential carrier retaining bolts. Remove differential carrier from axle housing.

Installation

1) Apply Sealant (08740-99986) to carrier mating flange and bolt threads. Reverse removal procedures. Align marks on propeller shaft and companion flange. Tighten bolts to specification. See TIGHTENING SPECIFICATIONS table at end of article.

2) Fill differential with Hypoid Gear Oil conforming to API classification GL-5. Use SAE 90W above 41°F (5°C) or SAE 80W below 41°F (5°C).

OVERHAUL

AXLE SHAFTS & BEARINGS

Disassembly

Grind bearing retainer until it is approximately .02" (.5 mm) thick. *See Fig. 3.* Using chisel, remove bearing retainer. Using bearing remover and press, remove bearing from axle shaft.

Fig. 3: Exploded View of Axle Shaft Assembly

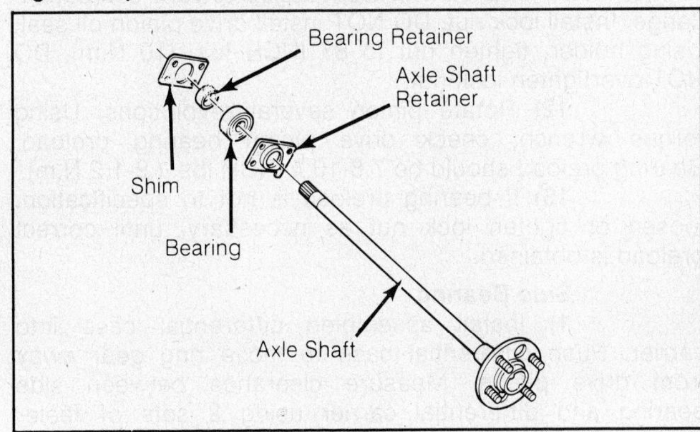

Courtesy of American Honda Motor Co., Inc.

Inspection

Inspect axle shaft for damaged wheel studs, cracks or damaged splines. Check shaft runout using lathe type tool and dial indicator. Replace axle shaft if damaged or runout exceeds .04" (1.0 mm).

Reassembly

Press axle shaft retainer, bearing and retainer on axle with bearing inner race projection toward axle shaft flange.

DIFFERENTIAL ASSEMBLY

Disassembly

1) Place differential carrier assembly on a differential carrier stand. Loosen staked area of companion flange lock nut. Using Holder (07926-SD90000), remove companion flange lock nut.

2) Remove washer and companion flange. Mark bearing caps for location. Remove bearing caps. Remove differential case from differential carrier.

CAUTION: Ensure thrust shims, bearing caps and side bearings are marked for location. Components must be installed in original location.

Fig. 4: Exploded View of Differential Assembly

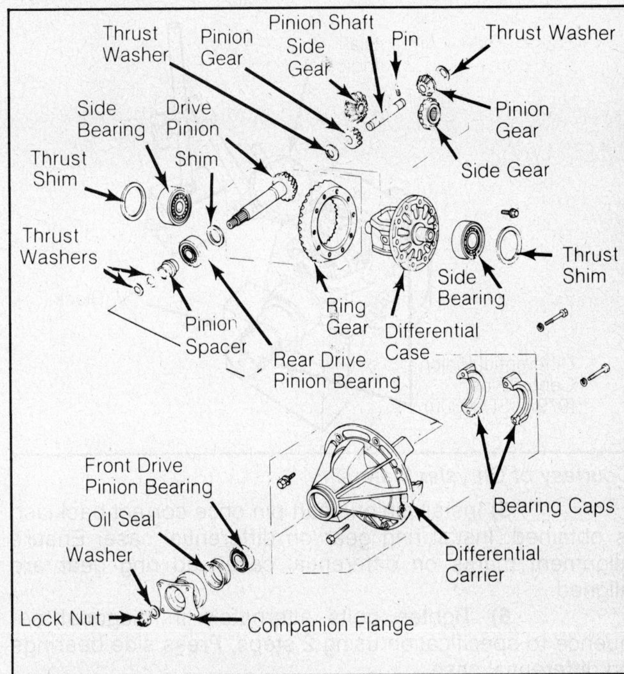

Courtesy of American Honda Motor Co., Inc.

3) Using bearing puller, remove differential case side bearings. Place alignment marks on ring gear and differential case for reassembly. Loosen ring gear retaining bolts in criss-cross pattern using 2 steps. Remove ring gear.

4) Drive pinion shaft lock pin from differential case. Remove differential pinion shaft, pinion gears, side gears and thrust washers. Mark components for reassembly reference.

Drive Pinion

Using soft-faced hammer, drive pinion from differential carrier. Remove oil seal and bearing races from differential carrier. Using bearing puller, remove rear bearing from pinion.

Inspection

1) Inspect all gears for cracked or flaking teeth. Inspect pinion shaft for wear. Inspect companion flange and drive pinion for damaged splines.

2) Inspect bearings and races for roughness or flaking. Replace worn components.

REASSEMBLY & ADJUSTMENT

Case Assembly

1) Install side gears in differential case. Install Differential Center Pins (07973-SD90300) through case and into side gears. *See Fig. 5.*

2) Install thrust washers and pinion gears in differential case. Install pinion shaft without lock pin.

3) Install assembly in "V" blocks. Using dial indicator, check pinion and side gear backlash. *See Fig. 5.*

4) Backlash must be within .002-.006" (.05-.15 mm). Adjust backlash by using different pinion gear thrust washers. Thrust washers are available in thickness from .70-1.00 mm in .05 mm increments. Ensure both sides are equally shimmed.

HONDA REAR AXLE (Cont.)

Fig. 5: Checking Pinion & Side Gear Backlash

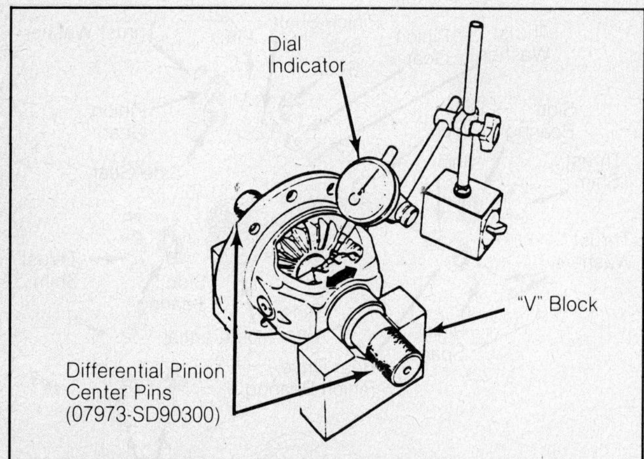

Courtesy of Chrysler Motors.

5) Install pinion shaft pin once correct backlash is obtained. Install ring gear on differential case. Ensure alignment marks on differential case and ring gear are aligned.

6) Tighten bolts alternately in diagonal sequence to specification using 2 steps. Press side bearings on differential case.

Drive Pinion Depth & Preload

1) Install pinion bearing races in carrier. Use Driver (07749-0010000) and Race Installer (07746-0010600) for rear race and (07947-SD90100) for front race. Ensure races are fully seated.

2) Install rear bearing on Collar "A" (07973-SD9060A). *See Fig. 6.* Install collar and bearing on Dummy Pinion Shaft (07973-SD9090A). Install dummy pinion shaft in differential carrier.

3) Install front pinion bearing and Collar "B" (07973-SD9070A) on dummy shaft. Install washer and lock nut.

4) Secure dummy shaft from turning and tighten lock nut to 84 INCH lbs. (10 N.m). DO NOT overtighten lock nut. Rotate pinion several revolutions. Using torque wrench, measure drive pinion preload.

5) Preload should be 7.8-10.4 INCH lbs. (.9-1.2 N.m). If preload is not within specification, loosen or tighten lock nut as necessary.

6) Position Pinion Height Gauge Arbor (07973-SD9110A) and Height Gauge Discs (07973-SD9100A) on a flat surface. Install dial indicator so tip extends .866-.905" (21.99-22.98 mm) from end of indicator housing.

7) Adjust indicator needle to zero. Position pinion height gauge assembly in differential carrier with dial indicator resting on dummy pinion shaft. Install bearing cap bolts and tighten to 36-43 ft. lbs. (49-58 N.m). *See Fig. 6.*

8) Rotate height gauge assembly slightly to measure pinion height. Note lowest reading. Calculate shim thickness needed as follows.

9) If number etched on gear end of pinion is a plus (+) number, subtract that amount from reading obtained in step **8)**. If number etched on pinion is a minus (-) number, add that amount to reading obtained in step **8)**. Select proper thickness shim. Shims are available in thickness range from .030-.047" (.76-1.19 mm).

10) Remove dial indicator, pinion height gauge assembly and dummy pinion shaft from carrier. Position selected shim on drive pinion. Using Driver (07946-

Fig. 6: Installing Pinion Height Gauge Assembly & Dummy Pinion Shaft

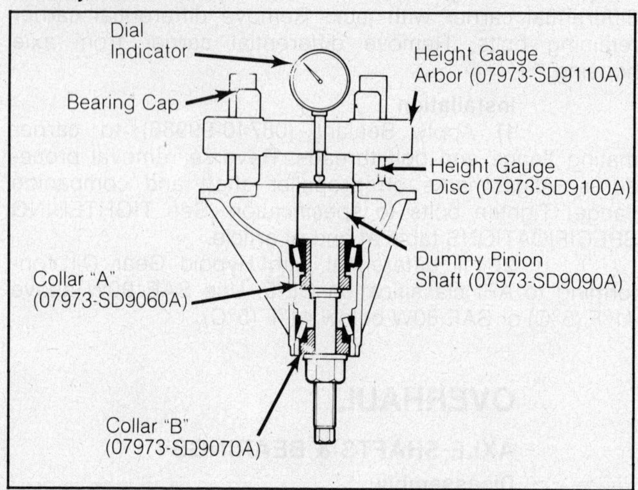

Courtesy of American Honda Motor Co., Inc.

MB00000), install rear bearing on drive pinion. Install drive pinion assembly in carrier.

11) Install front pinion bearing and companion flange. Install washer with dished side toward companion flange. Install lock nut. DO NOT install drive pinion oil seal. Using holder, tighten nut to 87 INCH lbs. (10 N.m). DO NOT overtighten lock nut.

12) Rotate pinion several revolutions. Using torque wrench, check drive pinion bearing preload. Bearing preload should be 7.8-10.4 INCH lbs. (.9-1.2 N.m).

13) If bearing preload is not to specification, loosen or tighten lock nut as necessary, until correct preload is obtained.

Side Bearing

1) Install assembled differential case into carrier. Push differential case to move ring gear away from drive pinion. Measure clearance between side bearing and differential carrier using 2 sets of feeler gauges. *See Fig. 7.*

2) To determine correct shim thickness, add .001-.002" (.03-.06 mm) to measured clearance, then divide by 2. This is thickness shim to be used. Variable shims are available in thickness range of .087 to .113" (2.20-2.86 mm).

3) Install equal thickness shims between side bearing and carrier on each side. Install bearing caps, aligning mating marks. Tighten bearing cap bolts to 40 ft. lbs. (54 N.m).

4) Lock drive pinion in place. Using dial indicator, check ring gear backlash at heel of ring gear tooth. Measure at 4 locations on ring gear. Gear backlash must be within .0043-.0063" (.109-.160 mm).

5) If backlash is excessive, move ring gear toward drive pinion by decreasing shim thickness on one side and increasing shim thickness on the remaining side. If backlash is less than specification, move ring gear away from drive pinion in same manner.

NOTE: Total shim thickness must still be equal to calculation in step 2).

6) After correct backlash is obtained, check total bearing preload using torque wrench. Total pinion

Drive Axles

HONDA REAR AXLE (Cont.)

Fig. 7: Measuring Differential Side Bearing Clearance

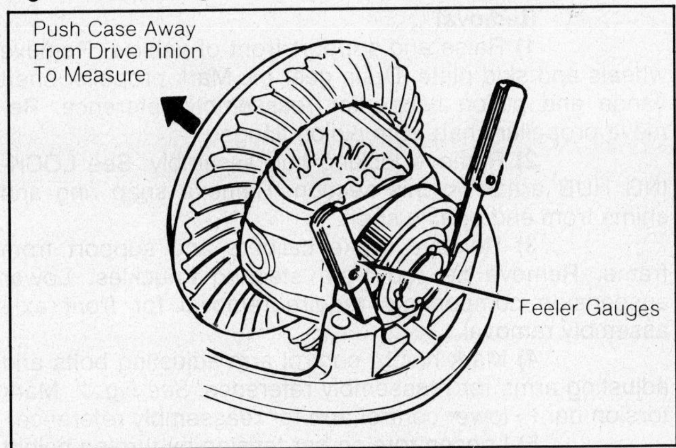

Courtesy of American Honda Motor Co., Inc.

preload and differential housing preload should be 11.2-15.6 INCH lbs. (1.26-1.77 N.m).

7) If preload is not within specification, change differential case shims. Backlash must remain within specification. Check ring gear and drive pinion tooth contact. See GEAR TOOTH PATTERNS article in this section.

Final Assembly

1) Once correct settings are obtained, remove differential case from carrier. Remove lock nut, washer, companion flange, dummy drive pinion and front drive pinion bearing.

2) Lubricate rear drive pinion bearing. Install drive pinion into carrier using new pinion spacer and thrust washers. Lubricate and install front pinion bearing.

3) Using Driver (07749-0010000) and Seal Installer (07965-SB00100), install oil seal. Lubricate seal lips with grease. Install companion flange and washer. Install washer with dished side toward companion flange.

4) Install new lock nut. Using companion flange holder, tighten lock nut to specification. Rotate pinion several revolutions.

5) Using torque wrench, check pinion bearing preload. Pinion bearing preload should be 10-13 INCH lbs. (1.1-1.5 N.m). If preload is not within specification, replace pinion spacer. DO NOT loosen or tighten lock nut beyond specification to adjust preload.

CAUTION: DO NOT loosen lock nut to obtain preload. Replace spacer if preload is excessive.

6) Stake lock nut. Install differential case in carrier. Tighten bearing cap bolts to specification. Check gear tooth contact. Check total preload. Total pinion preload and differential housing preload should be 13.4-18.2 INCH lbs. (1.51-2.05 N.m).

TIGHTENING SPECIFICATIONS

Application	Ft. Lbs. (N.m)
Axle Retainer Nut	30 (41)
Differential Bearing Cap Bolt	40 (54)
Differential Carrier Bolt	16 (22)
Drain Plug	33 (45)
Filler Plug	33 (45)
Pinion Lock Nut	86-166 (117-225)
Ring Gear Bolt	74 (100)

ISUZU FRONT AXLE

Isuzu: P'UP, Trooper II 4WD

DESCRIPTION

Front axle uses hypoid type gears with constant velocity joint type axles shafts.

AXLE RATIO & IDENTIFICATION

Ratio is determined by dividing number of ring gear teeth by number of drive pinion teeth.

AXLE RATIO SPECIFICATIONS

Application	Ratio
P'UP	4.10
Trooper II	
Diesel	4.10
Gas	4.55

REMOVAL & INSTALLATION

AXLE SHAFTS & BEARINGS

Front axle assembly requires removal prior to removal of axle shafts and bearings. See FRONT AXLE ASSEMBLY under REMOVAL & INSTALLATION.

Fig. 1: Exploded View of Axle Shaft Assembly

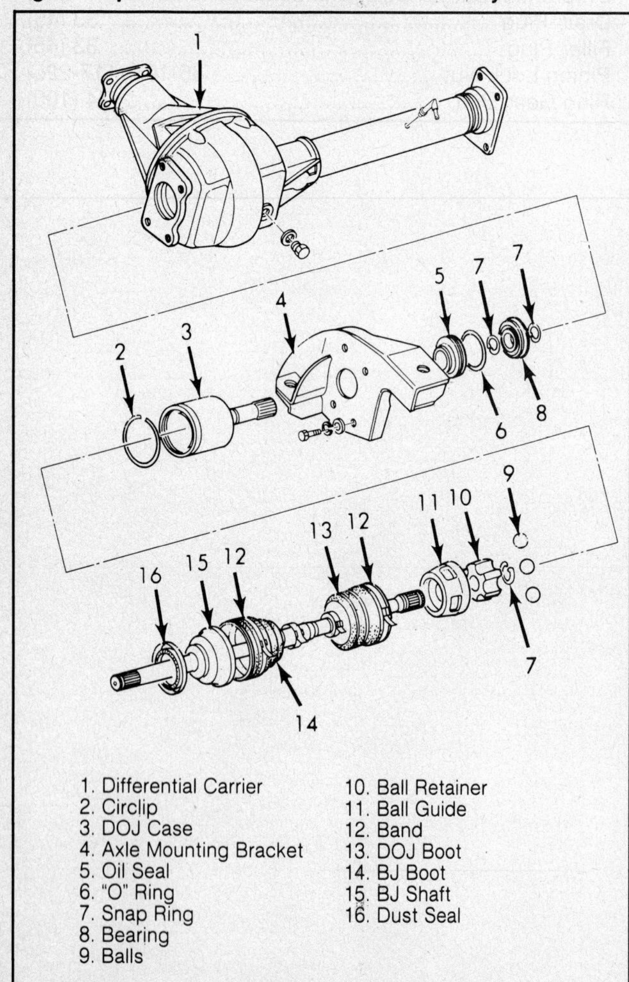

Courtesy of Isuzu Motor Co.

FRONT AXLE ASSEMBLY

Removal

1) Raise and support front of vehicle. Remove wheels and skid plate. Drain gear oil. Mark propeller shaft flange and pinion flange for reassembly reference. Remove propeller shaft from pinion flange.

2) Remove locking hub assembly. See LOCKING HUB article in this section. Remove snap ring and shims from end of axle shaft.

3) Remove brake calipers and support from frame. Remove tie rod from steering knuckles. Lower suspension components require removal for front axle assembly removal.

4) Mark height control arm adjusting bolts and adjusting arms for reassembly reference. *See Fig. 2.* Mark torsion bar to lower control arm for reassembly reference.

5) Loosen torsion bar tension by turning height control arm adjusting bolts. Disconnect stabilizer bar from lower control arm.

6) On models with strut rod, mark length of strut rod prior to removal. Remove strut rods from lower control arm. *See Fig. 2.*

7) On all models, support lower control arm with jack. Remove upper and lower ball joint-to-knuckle nuts. Separate ball joints from knuckle. Remove knuckle assembly.

8) Remove shock absorber-to-lower control arm bolts. Remove lower control arms. Support front axle assembly. Remove axle housing mounting bolts. Remove front axle assembly. DO NOT damage axle shaft boots.

9) Remove axle mounting bracket-to-differential carrier bolts. *See Fig. 1.* Remove axle shafts from differential carrier.

Fig. 2: P'UP Front Suspension Components

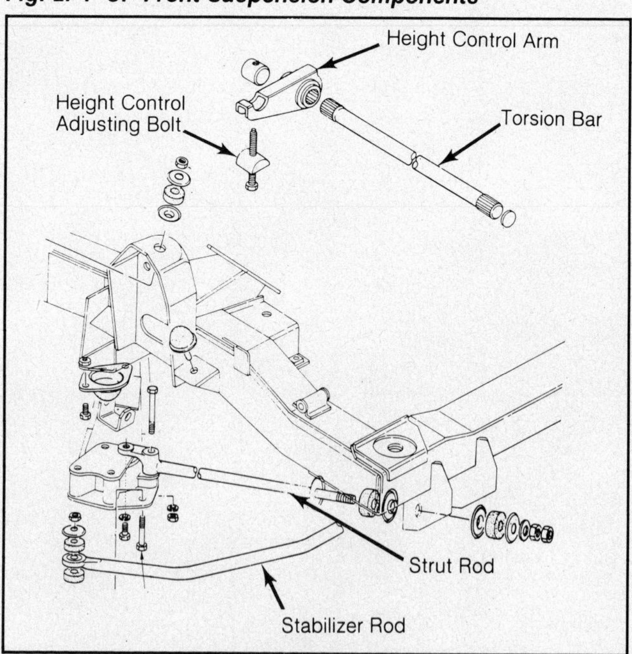

Courtesy of Isuzu Motor Co.

Installation

1) Reverse removal procedures. Tighten bolts to specification. See TIGHTENING SPECIFICATIONS table at end of article. Coat height control arm with grease in bracket contact area.

ISUZU FRONT AXLE (Cont.)

2) Adjust strut rod to original length to ensure proper caster adjustment. Adjust height control arm to original location.

3) Special procedures must be used for locking hub installation. See LOCKING HUB article in this section.

4) Install propeller shaft aligning index marks. Bleed hydraulic brake system (if required).

5) Fill front differential with with gear oil conforming to GL-5 classification. Use proper viscosity oil depending on ambient temperature. See GEAR OIL SPECIFICATIONS table.

GEAR OIL SPECIFICATIONS

Temperature	Gear Oil Viscosity
Below 50°F (10°C)	SAE 80
0° To 90°F (-18° to 32°C)	SAE 90
Above 50°F (10°C)	SAE 140

DIFFERENTIAL CARRIER

Removal & Installation

Remove front axle assembly. Remove axle shafts. Remove differential carrier retaining bolts. Remove differential carrier from axle housing. Install differential carrier in axle housing using new gasket. Tighten retaining bolts to specification.

OVERHAUL

AXLE SHAFTS & BEARINGS

NOTE: **References to BJ refer to Birfield Joint and DOJ to Double Off-Set Joint.**

Disassembly

1) Remove inner DOJ boot band. Move DOJ boot backward. Remove circlip from DOJ case. Remove BJ shaft assembly. *See Fig. 1.* Using screwdriver, remove balls from ball guide.

2) Rotate ball guide slightly to align with ball retainer projected area. Move ball guide backward toward DOJ boot. Remove ball retainer snap ring. Remove ball retainer and ball guide.

3) Remove band from BJ boot. Remove BJ boot. Remove dust seal from BJ shaft. Remove axle mounting bracket from axle housing if not previously removed.

4) Remove snap ring from end of DOJ case shaft. Remove bearing and snap ring. *See Fig. 1.* Remove "O" ring and oil seal from axle mounting bracket. Remove DOJ case.

Inspection

Inspect DOJ case, balls, ball guide and ball retainer for wear or damage. Inspect bearing for roughness or noise. Inspect boots and bands for cracks. Replace damaged components.

Reassembly

1) Reverse disassembly procedures. Use new oil seal and "O" ring. Coat BJ shaft with light coat of grease prior to boot installation. Install boot bands so lever is pulled away from front of vehicle when band is tightened.

2) Install ball guide with small diameter toward the shaft. With ball retainer installed, position ball guide with projected area of ball retainer.

3) Rotate ball guide 1/2 turn. Align ball guide and ball retainer. Install balls. Apply 3.05 oz. (49.9 g) of specified grease to inside of DOJ case. Install drive axle assembly in DOJ case.

4) Install DOJ case circlip with ends positioned away from ball grooves. After installing drive axle, apply 3.05 oz. (49.9 g) of specified grease to DOJ case.

5) Install DOJ boot and band. Adjust DOJ boot to have 5.80" (147.5 mm) distance from end of DOJ case to end of boot. Tighten band.

Fig. 3: Exploded View of Front Differential Assembly

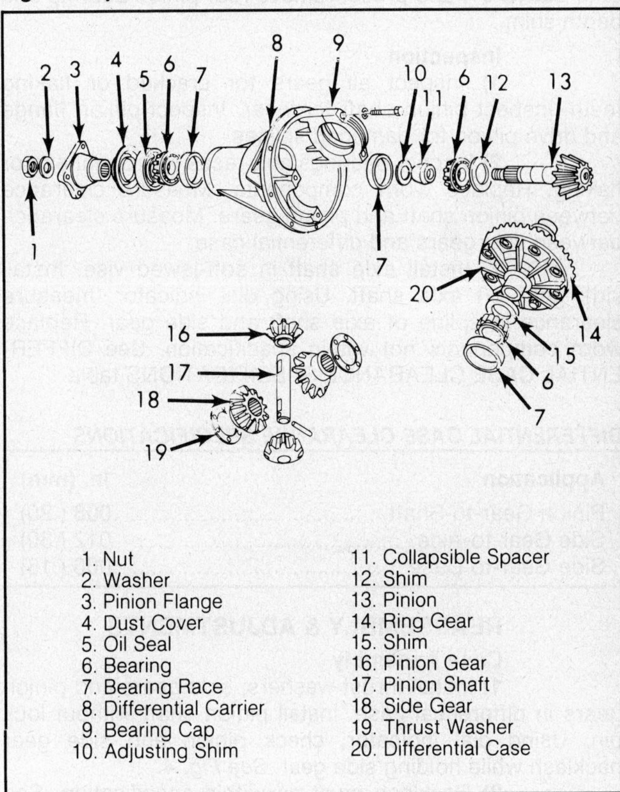

Courtesy of Isuzu Motor Co.

DIFFERENTIAL ASSEMBLY

Disassembly

1) Mark bearing caps for location. Remove bearing caps. Remove differential case assembly from carrier. Using bearing puller, remove differential case side bearings.

CAUTION: **Ensure shims, bearing caps and side bearings are marked for location. Components must be installed in original location.**

2) Mark side bearing shims and side bearings for location. Place alignment marks on ring gear and differential case for reassembly. Loosen ring gear retaining bolts in diagonal sequence. These bolts are left hand thread.

ISUZU FRONT AXLE (Cont.)

CAUTION: Ring gear retaining bolts are left hand thread.

3) Remove ring gear. Remove pinion shaft lock pin from differential case. Remove differential pinion shaft, pinion gears, side gears and thrust washers. Mark components for reassembly reference.

Drive Pinion

1) Using Flange Holder (J-8614-01), remove pinion nut and pinion flange. Using soft-faced hammer, drive out pinion. Remove collapsible spacer and adjusting shim from pinion.

2) Remove front pinion bearing and oil seal from differential carrier. Using brass drift, remove bearing inner and outer races from carrier. Using Bearing Remover (J-22912-01) and press, remove rear pinion bearing and depth shim.

Inspection

1) Inspect all gears for cracked or flaking teeth. Inspect pinion shaft for wear. Inspect pinion flange and drive pinion for damaged splines.

2) Inspect bearings and races for roughness or flaking. Replace worn components. Measure clearance between pinion shaft and pinion gears. Measure clearance between side gears and differential case.

3) Install axle shaft in soft-jawed vise. Install side gear on axle shaft. Using dial indicator, measure clearance in spline of axle shaft and side gear. Replace worn components not within specification. See DIFFERENTIAL CASE CLEARANCE SPECIFICATIONS table.

DIFFERENTIAL CASE CLEARANCE SPECIFICATIONS

Application	In. (mm)
Pinion Gear-to-Shaft	.008 (.20)
Side Gear-to-Axle	.012 (.30)
Side Gear-to-Case	.006 (.15)

REASSEMBLY & ADJUSTMENTS

Case Assembly

1) Install thrust washers, side gears and pinion gears in differential case. Install pinion shaft without lock pin. Using dial indicator, check pinion and side gear backlash while holding side gear. *See Fig. 4.*

2) Backlash must be within specification. See PINION & SIDE GEAR BACKLASH SPECIFICATIONS table. Adjust backlash by using different side gear thrust washers. Ensure both sides are equally shimmed.

PINION & SIDE GEAR BACKLASH SPECIFICATIONS

Application	In. (mm)
Standard	.001-.003 (.03-.07)

3) Once correct backlash is obtained, install pinion shaft lock pin. Stake lock pin hole to prevent movement. Install ring gear on differential case.

4) Ensure alignment marks on differential case and ring gear are aligned. Use new retaining bolts. Apply Loctite to bolts and install. Tighten bolts to specification in diagonal sequence.

5) Using Bearing Installer (J-290367) and Handle (J-8092), install side bearings on differential case. DO NOT install shims. Use Pilot (J-8107-2) to support opposite end of differential case to prevent bearing damage.

Fig. 4: Checking Pinion & Side Gear Backlash

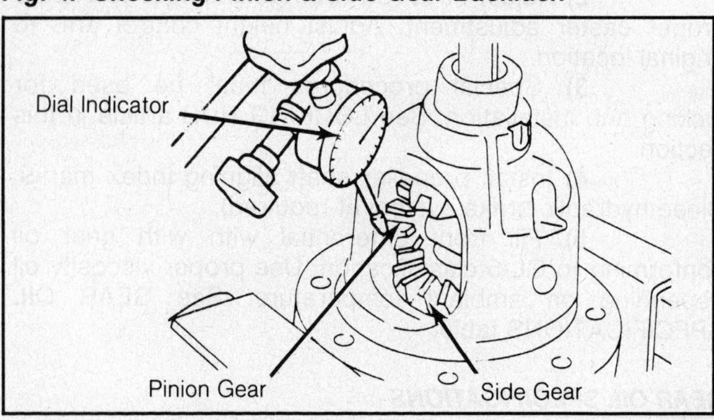

Courtesy of Isuzu Motor Co.

Drive Pinion Depth

1) Install pinion bearing races in differential carrier. Use Handle (J-8092) and Race Installer (J-29038) for front race and (J-29039) for rear race. Ensure races are fully seated.

2) Lubricate pinion bearings and install with pinion depth gauge components in differential carrier. *See Fig. 5.*

3) Rotate bearing to ensure proper seating. Tighten preload stud nut to 10 INCH lbs. (1.13 N.m) for used bearing and 20 INCH lbs. (2.26 N.m) for new bearings. Clean differential case bearing bores.

Fig. 5: Installing Pinion Depth Gauge Assembly

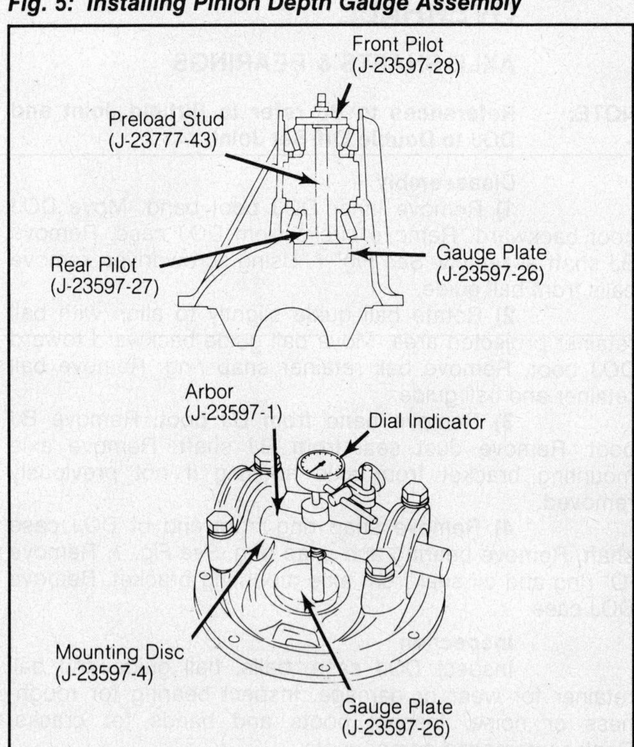

Courtesy of Isuzu Motor Co.

4) Install Mounting Discs (J-23597-4) on Arbor (J-23597-1). Install assembly in side bearing bores. Install bearing caps. Tighten bearing cap bolts to 50 ft. lbs. (68 N.m).

Drive Axles

ISUZU FRONT AXLE (Cont.)

5) Adjust dial indicator to zero. Install dial indicator on arbor post. Position stem on top surface of gauge plate. Push dial indicator downward until needle reads 1/2 turn clockwise. Tighten indicator in this position.

6) Rotate arbor back and forth until dial indicator reads maximum deflection. Adjust indicator to zero. Repeat procedure to ensure proper setting. Rotate arbor until dial indicator stem does not contact gauge plate. Record dial indicator reading. Note number etched on gear end of drive pinion.

7) Reading may be either a plus (+) or minus (-) with a numeral. If reading is 0, pinion is nominal. Using dial indicator reading and pinion marking, determine proper drive pinion shim thickness to be used. *See Fig. 6.*

8) Remove bearing caps and pinion depth components. Install selected shim pack with chamfered side toward gear side of pinion. Using Bearing Installer (J-6133-01) and press, install rear pinion bearing on drive pinion. Lubricate bearing with oil.

Pinion Bearing Preload

1) Install drive pinion, new collapsible spacer and adjusting shim in differential carrier. Install front pinion bearing. DO NOT install oil seal.

2) Install pinion flange and Dummy Nut (J-34357). Using flange holder, tighten dummy nut to 94-115 ft. lbs. (127-156 N.m). Rotate pinion to ensure bearings are seated.

3) Using torque wrench, measure drive pinion starting torque. Starting torque should be 4.3-5.1 INCH lbs. (.48-.67). Change adjusting shim thickness to obtain proper starting torque.

4) Starting torque decreases when adjusting shim thickness is increased and increases when shim thickness is decreased. Once correct starting preload is obtained, remove dummy nut.

5) Soak pinion seal in rear axle oil. Using Seal Installer (J-26234), install oil seal. Using Flange Installer (J-6403-C), install pinion flange.

6) Coat pinion threads with oil. Install new pinion flange nut. Using flange holder, tighten pinion nut to minimum specification. See TIGHTENING SPECIFICATIONS table at end of article. Rotate pinion to ensure bearings are seated.

7) Using torque wrench, measure drive pinion starting torque. Starting torque should be 5.1-9.6 INCH lbs. (.67-1.09 N.m). If starting torque is not within specification, tighten pinion nut to obtain correct starting torque. DO NOT exceed maximum tightening specification.

CAUTION: DO NOT loosen nut to decrease preload or exceed maximum tightening specification. If preload or tightening specification is exceeded, replace collapsible spacer.

Side Bearing

1) Install differential case and bearing races in axle housing. Shims should not be installed behind side bearings. Using 2 feeler gauges, install feeler gauge between each bearing outer race and axle housing to remove all end play. Ensure feeler gauge is pushed to bottom of bearing bores.

2) Lock drive pinion in place. Using dial indicator, check ring gear backlash at heel of ring gear tooth. Gear backlash must be within specification. See RING GEAR BACKLASH SPECIFICATIONS table.

RING GEAR BACKLASH SPECIFICATIONS

Application	In. (mm)
All Models	.005-.007 (.13-.18)

Fig. 6: Determining Drive Pinion Shim Thickness

Pinion Marking / Dial Indicator Reading (Inches)	+6 mm (Inches)	+4 mm (Inches)	+2 mm (Inches)	0 mm (Inches)	-2 mm (Inches)	-4 mm (Inches)	-6 mm (Inches)
0.052							1.39(0.0547)
0.053						1.39(0.0547)	1.41(0.0555)
0.054					1.39(0.0547)	1.41(0.0555)	1.43(0.0563)
0.055				1.39(0.0547)	1.41(0.0555)	1.43(0.0563)	1.45(0.0571)
0.056		1.39(0.0547)	1.41(0.0555)	1.43(0.0563)	1.45(0.0571)	1.47(0.0579)	1.49(0.0587)
0.057	1.39(0.0547)	1.41(0.0555)	1.43(0.0563)	1.45(0.0571)	1.47(0.0579)	1.49(0.0587)	1.51(0.0594)
0.058	1.41(0.0555)	1.43(0.0563)	1.45(0.0571)	1.47(0.0579)	1.49(0.0587)	1.51(0.0594)	1.53(0.0602)
0.059	1.43(0.0563)	1.45(0.0571)	1.47(0.0579)	1.49(0.0587)	1.51(0.0594)	1.53(0.0602)	1.55(0.0610)
0.060	1.47(0.0579)	1.49(0.0587)	1.51(0.0594)	1.53(0.0602)	1.55(0.0610)	1.57(0.0618)	1.59(0.0626)
0.061	1.49(0.0587)	1.51(0.0594)	1.53(0.0602)	1.55(0.0610)	1.57(0.0618)	1.59(0.0626)	1.61(0.0634)
0.062	1.51(0.0594)	1.53(0.0602)	1.55(0.0610)	1.57(0.0618)	1.59(0.0626)	1.61(0.0634)	1.63(0.0642)
0.063	1.55(0.0610)	1.57(0.0618)	1.59(0.0626)	1.61(0.0634)	1.63(0.0642)	1.65(0.0650)	1.67(0.0657)
0.064	1.57(0.0618)	1.59(0.0626)	1.61(0.0634)	1.63(0.0642)	1.65(0.0650)	1.67(0.0657)	1.69(0.0665)
0.065	1.59(0.0626)	1.61(0.0634)	1.63(0.0642)	1.65(0.0650)	1.67(0.0657)	1.69(0.0665)	1.71(0.0673)
0.066	1.61(0.0634)	1.63(0.0642)	1.65(0.0650)	1.67(0.0657)	1.69(0.0665)	1.71(0.0673)	1.73(0.0681)
0.067	1.65(0.0650)	1.67(0.0657)	1.69(0.0665)	1.71(0.0673)	1.73(0.0681)	1.75(0.0689)	1.77(0.0697)
0.068	1.67(0.0657)	1.69(0.0665)	1.71(0.0673)	1.73(0.0681)	1.75(0.0689)	1.77(0.0697)	
0.069	1.69(0.0665)	1.71(0.0673)	1.73(0.0681)	1.75(0.0689)	1.77(0.0697)		
0.070	1.71(0.0673)	1.73(0.0681)	1.75(0.0689)	1.77(0.0697)			
0.071	1.75(0.0689)	1.77(0.0697)					
0.072	1.77(0.0697)						

Courtesy of Isuzu Motor Co.

ISUZU FRONT AXLE (Cont.)

3) Adjust feeler gauge thickness on both sides to obtain ring gear backlash. With zero end play and correct backlash, remove feeler gauges.

4) Determine thickness of required shims and add .002" (.05 mm) to each shim pack to provide side bearing preload. Always use new shims. Remove differential case assembly.

5) Using bearing puller, remove side bearings. Install new shim packs on differential case. Using Bearing Installer (J-290367) and Handle (J-8092), install side bearings on differential case. Use Pilot (J-8107-2) to support opposite end of differential case to prevent bearing damage.

6) Install differential case assembly and outer bearing races in axle housing. Install bearing caps in original location. Tighten bolts to specification.

7) Using dial indicator, measure runout on back side of ring gear. If runout exceeds .002" (.05 mm), correct by cleaning or replacing parts. Check gear tooth contact using paint impression method. See GEAR TOOTH PATTERNS article in this section.

TIGHTENING SPECIFICATIONS

Application	Ft. Lbs. (N.m)
Axle Bracket-to-Body Nut	101-123 (137-167)
Axle Bracket-to-Carrier Bolt	
P'UP	40-47 (54-64)
Trooper II	55-67 (75-91)
Axle Housing-to-Bracket Bolt	40-47 (54-64)
Ball Joint Nut	72-80 (98-109)
Bearing Cap Bolt	47-54 (64-73)
Carrier-to-Axle Housing Bolt	17-20 (23-27)
Locking Hub-to-Hub Bolt	40-47 (54-64)
Lower Control Arm-to-Frame Nut	94-101 (127-137)
Pinion Flange Nut	109-145 (148-197)
Propeller Shaft-to-Pinion Flange Bolt	22-25 (30-34)
Ring Gear Bolt	51-65 (69-88)
Strut Rod Nut	58-72 (79-98)
Strut Rod-to-Lower Control Arm Bolt	50 (68)
Tie Rod Nut	39-47 (53-64)

ISUZU INTEGRAL HOUSING

Isuzu: Impulse Non-Turbo

DESCRIPTION

Axle is a semi-floating hypoid gear type axle mounted in integral housing. Integral axle shaft and drive flange are used.

AXLE RATIO & IDENTIFICATION

Rear axle ratio is 3.91:1. Ratio is determined by dividing number of ring gear teeth by number of drive pinion teeth.

REMOVAL & INSTALLATION

AXLE SHAFTS

Removal

Raise and support vehicle. Remove caliper and rotor. Remove axle shaft bearing retainer bolts. Using Slide Hammer (J-2619-01) and Adapter (J-8805-01), remove axle shaft.

Installation

Replace "O" ring located in outer race of axle bearing (if damaged). Reverse removal procedures. Tighten bolts to specification.

EXTENSION HOUSING

Removal

1) Raise and support vehicle. Disconnect rear parking brake cable from front cable. Remove parking brake cable-to-body retaining clips. Center portion of exhaust system may require removal for access.

2) Remove propeller shaft-to-companion flange retaining bolts. Remove propeller shaft. DO NOT lose spring located in transmission end of propeller shaft.

3) Support front of rear axle housing. Remove center support bracket-to-body retaining bolts. *See Fig. 1*. Remove extension housing-to-axle housing retaining bolts. Remove extension housing and center support. DO NOT lose bumper and washer located in end of extension shaft.

Installation

1) Inspect rubber washer. Replace if damaged. Install washer and bumper in end of extension shaft. Install extension shaft over spline coupling and support with a jack.

2) Install extension housing-to-axle housing retaining bolts. Tighten to specification. See TIGHTENING SPECIFICATIONS table at end of article. Install center support bracket-to-body retaining bolts. Tighten to specification.

3) Ensure spring is located in end of propeller shaft. Install propeller shaft. Tighten bolts to specification. Reverse removal procedure for remaining components. Adjust parking brake.

REAR AXLE ASSEMBLY

Removal

1) Raise vehicle and support at frame. Remove wheels. Disconnect rear parking brake cable from front cable. Remove parking brake cable-to-body retaining clips. Center portion of exhaust system may require removal for access.

Fig. 1: Exploded View of Extension Housing & Axle Housing

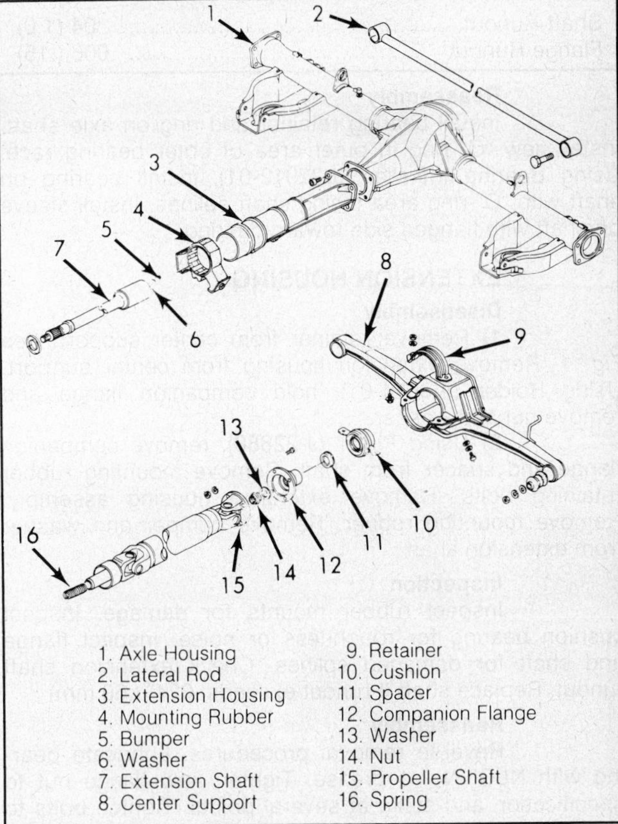

Courtesy of Isuzu Motor Co.

2) Remove propeller shaft-to-companion flange retaining bolts. Remove propeller shaft. DO NOT lose spring located in transmission end of propeller shaft.

3) Disconnect stabilizer bar at each end of axle housing. Disconnect shock absorbers. Disconnect brake line from body. Remove lateral rod at rear of axle housing.

4) Support rear axle with jack. Remove center support-to-body retaining bolts. Remove control arm-to-axle bolts. Lower axle assembly and remove coil springs and insulators. Remove axle assembly.

Installation

Reverse removal procedures. Ensure coil springs align with recessed portion of lower spring seat. Tighten bolts to specification. Bleed brake system and adjust parking brake.

OVERHAUL

AXLE SHAFTS & BEARINGS

Disassembly

Using bearing remover and press, remove sleeve and bearing from axle. Remove ring and bearing retainer from shaft.

Inspection

Inspect axle shaft for damaged splines or flange. Check runout at center of shaft and face of flange. Replace if runout exceeds specifications. See AXLE SHAFT SPECIFICATIONS table.

Drive Axles

ISUZU INTEGRAL HOUSING (Cont.)

AXLE SHAFT SPECIFICATIONS

Application	In. (mm)
Shaft Runout	.04 (1.0)
Flange Runout	.006 (.15)

Reassembly

Install bearing retainer and ring on axle shaft. Install new "O" ring in outer area of outer bearing race. Using Bearing Installer (J-22912-01), install bearing on shaft with "O" ring area facing shaft splines. Install sleeve on shaft with flanged side toward bearing.

EXTENSION HOUSING

Disassembly

1) Remove retainer from center support. *See Fig. 1.* Remove extension housing from center support. Using Holder (J-8614-01), hold companion flange and remove nut and washer.

2) Using Puller (J-22888), remove companion flange and spacer from shaft. Remove mounting rubber retaining bolts. Remove extension housing assembly. Remove mounting rubber. Remove bumper and washer from extension shaft.

Inspection

Inspect rubber mounts for damage. Inspect cushion bearing for roughness or noise. Inspect flange and shaft for damaged splines. Check extension shaft runout. Replace shaft if runout exceeds .024" (.60 mm).

Reassembly

Reverse removal procedures. Lubricate bearing with NLGI No. 1 grease. Tighten new flange nut to specification and stake at several points. Tighten bolts to specification. Install bumper and washer in end of extension shaft.

REAR AXLE

Disassembly

1) Remove lower center bolt of axle cover and drain lubricant. Remove cover. Remove axle shafts. See AXLE SHAFTS & BEARINGS under REMOVAL & INSTALLATION in this article.

2) Mark bearing caps and housing for reassembly reference. Remove bearing caps. *See Fig. 3.* Remove differential case from axle housing. Using Bearing Puller (J-22888) and Pilot (J-2241-11), remove bearings from differential case.

3) Remove shims from differential case. Mark bearings and shims for reassembly reference.

CAUTION: Ensure bearing caps, side bearings and shims are marked for location. Components must be installed in original location.

4) Mark ring gear and differential case for reassembly reference. Remove ring gear bolts in proper sequence. *See Fig. 3.* Tap ring gear from differential case.

5) Remove lock pin from pinion shaft. Remove pinion shaft, pinion gears, side gears and thrust washers. Mark components for reassembly reference.

6) Remove extension housing. See EXTENSION HOUSING under REMOVAL & INSTALLATION in this article.

Fig. 2: Ring Gear Bolt Removal & Tightening Sequence

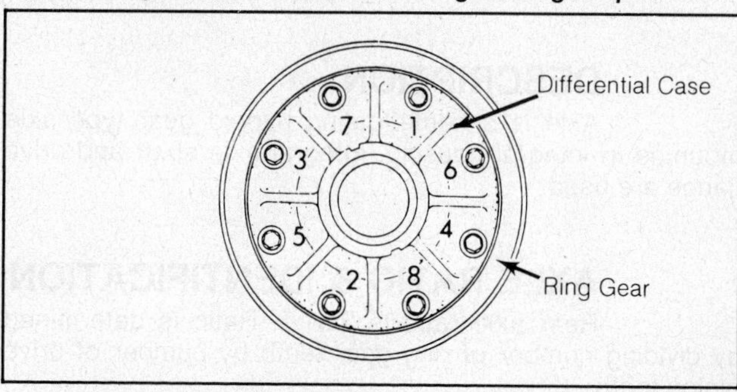

Courtesy of Isuzu Motor Co.

Drive Pinion

1) Using Spline Holder (J-22932), hold spline coupling. Remove nut and washer. Using Spline Puller (J-25599), remove spline coupling from drive pinion.

2) Tap drive pinion from axle housing. Remove bearing races from axle housing. Using Bearing Remover (J-22912-01) and press, remove rear bearing from drive pinion.

Inspection

1) Inspect all gears for cracked or flaking teeth. Inspect drive pinion for wear. Inspect spline coupling and drive pinion for damaged splines.

2) Inspect bearings and races for roughness or flaking. Measure clearance between pinion shaft and pinion gears. Measure clearance between side gears and differential case.

3) Install axle shaft in soft-jawed vise. Install side gear on axle shaft. Using dial indicator, measure clearance in spline of axle shaft and side gear. Replace worn components not within specification. See DIFFERENTIAL CASE CLEARANCE SPECIFICATIONS table.

DIFFERENTIAL CASE CLEARANCE SPECIFICATIONS

Application	In. (mm)
Pinion Gear-to-Shaft	.006 (.15)
Side Gear-to-Axle	.012 (.30)
Side Gear-to-Case	.008 (.20)

REASSEMBLY & ADJUSTMENTS

Case Assembly

1) Install thrust washers, side gears and pinion gears in differential case. Install pinion shaft without lock pin. Using dial indicator, check pinion and side gear backlash while holding side gear. *See Fig. 4.*

2) Backlash must be within specification. See PINION & SIDE GEAR BACKLASH SPECIFICATIONS table. Adjust backlash by using different side gear thrust washers. Thrust washers are available in thickness from .039-.055" (1.00-1.40 mm). Ensure both sides are equally shimmed.

PINION & SIDE GEAR BACKLASH SPECIFICATIONS

Application	In. (mm)
Standard	.0012-.0031 (.030-.078)

ISUZU INTEGRAL HOUSING (Cont.)

Fig. 3: Exploded View of Rear Axle Assembly

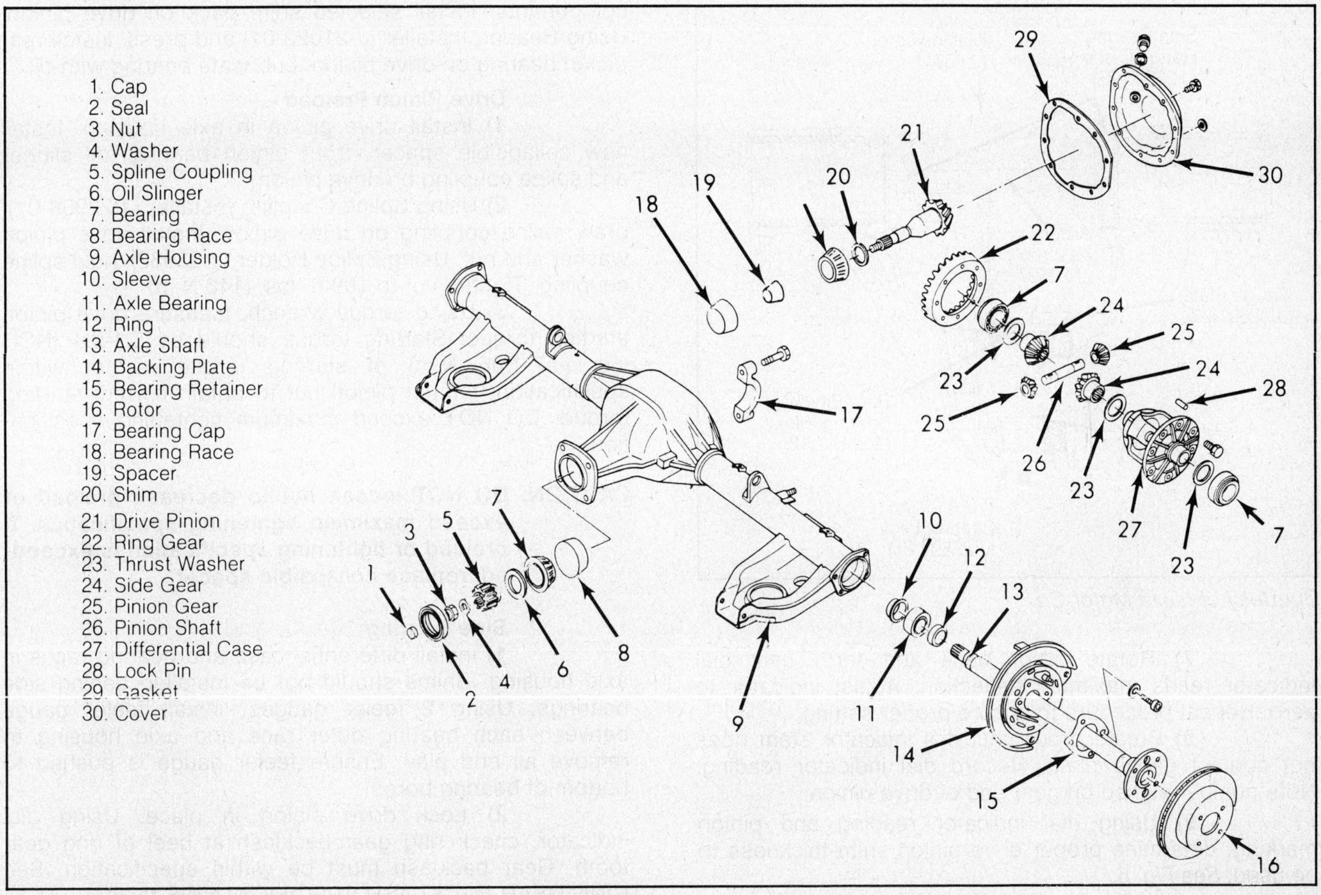

1. Cap
2. Seal
3. Nut
4. Washer
5. Spline Coupling
6. Oil Slinger
7. Bearing
8. Bearing Race
9. Axle Housing
10. Sleeve
11. Axle Bearing
12. Ring
13. Axle Shaft
14. Backing Plate
15. Bearing Retainer
16. Rotor
17. Bearing Cap
18. Bearing Race
19. Spacer
20. Shim
21. Drive Pinion
22. Ring Gear
23. Thrust Washer
24. Side Gear
25. Pinion Gear
26. Pinion Shaft
27. Differential Case
28. Lock Pin
29. Gasket
30. Cover

Courtesy of Isuzu Motor Co.

Fig. 4: Checking Pinion & Side Gear Backlash

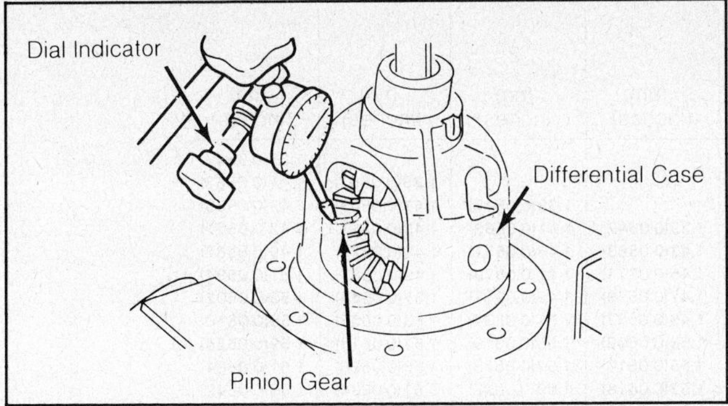

Courtesy of Chrysler Motors.

3) Once correct backlash is obtained, install pinion shaft lock pin until it bottoms in differential case. Stake lock pin hole to prevent movement. Install ring gear on differential case.

4) Ensure alignment marks on differential case and ring gear are aligned. Use new retaining bolts. Apply Loctite to bolts and install. Tighten bolts to specification in proper sequence. *See Fig. 2.*

5) Using Bearing Installer (J-22919) and Handle (J-8092), install side bearings on differential case. DO NOT install shims. Use Pilot (J-2241-11) to support opposite end of differential case to prevent bearing damage.

NOTE: **Drive pinion rear bearing shim thickness must be determined when a new axle housing, ring and pinion set, or pinion bearings and races are installed.**

Drive Pinion Depth

1) Install pinion bearing races in axle housing. Use Handle (J-8092) and Race Installer (J-7818) for front race and (J-8611-01) for rear race. Ensure races are fully seated.

2) Lubricate and install drive pinion bearings in axle housing. Install Gauge Plate (J-23597-22) and Rear Pinion Bearing Pilot (J-23597-12) on Preload Stud (J-21777-43). *See Fig. 5.*

3) Install assembly through drive pinion bearings and Front Pinion Pilot (J-23597-21). Install hex nut. Tighten nut to 15.6 INCH lbs. (1.7 N.m).

4) Rotate bearings to ensure proper seating. Install Side Bearing Discs (J-23597-23) on ends of Arbor (J-23597-1). Install arbor into axle housing ensuring discs are properly seated. *See Fig. 5.* Install side bearing caps and bolts. Tighten bolts to 33 ft. lbs. (45 N.m).

5) Adjust Dial Indicator (J-8001) to zero. Install dial indicator on mounting post of arbor. Position stem on top surface of gauge plate.

6) Push dial indicator downward until needle reads 3/4 turn clockwise. Tighten indicator in this position.

ISUZU INTEGRAL HOUSING (Cont.)

Fig. 5: Checking Drive Pinion Depth

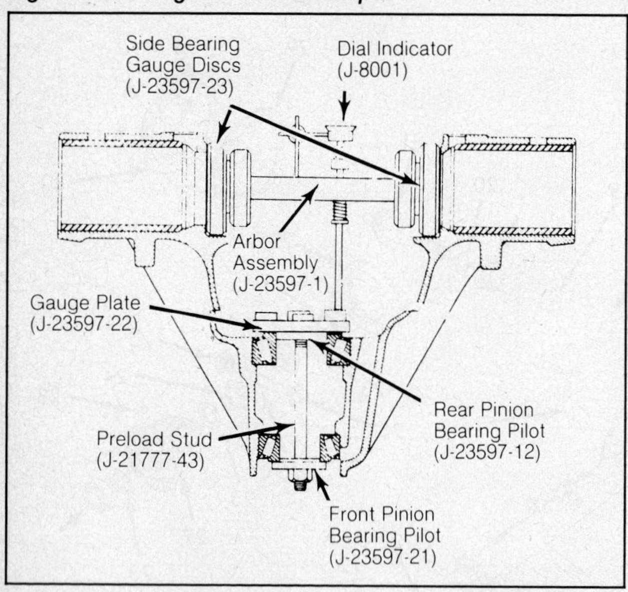

Courtesy of Isuzu Motor Co.

7) Rotate arbor back and forth until dial indicator reads maximum deflection. Adjust indicator to zero. Repeat procedure to ensure proper setting.

8) Rotate arbor until dial indicator stem does not contact gauge plate. Record dial indicator reading. Note number etched on gear end of drive pinion.

9) Using dial indicator reading and pinion marking, determine proper drive pinion shim thickness to be used. *See Fig. 6.*

10) Remove bearing caps and pinion depth components. Install selected shim pack on drive pinion. Using Bearing Installer (J-21022-01) and press, install rear pinion bearing on drive pinion. Lubricate bearing with oil.

Drive Pinion Preload

1) Install drive pinion in axle housing. Install new collapsible spacer, front pinion bearing, oil slinger and spline coupling on drive pinion.

2) Using Spline Coupling Installer (J-22938-01), draw spline coupling on drive pinion. Install drive pinion washer and nut. Using Spline Holder (J-22932), hold spline coupling. Tighten nut to 109 ft. lbs. (148 N.m).

3) Using torque wrench, measure drive pinion starting torque. Starting torque should be 5.1-9.4 INCH lbs. (.57-1.06 N.m). If starting torque is not within specification, tighten pinion nut to obtain correct starting torque. DO NOT exceed maximum tightening specification.

CAUTION: DO NOT loosen nut to decrease preload or exceed maximum tightening specification. If preload or tightening specification is exceeded, replace collapsible spacer.

Side Bearing

1) Install differential case and bearing races in axle housing. Shims should not be installed behind side bearings. Using 2 feeler gauges, install feeler gauge between each bearing outer race and axle housing to remove all end play. Ensure feeler gauge is pushed to bottom of bearing bores.

2) Lock drive pinion in place. Using dial indicator, check ring gear backlash at heel of ring gear tooth. Gear backlash must be within specification. See RING GEAR BACKLASH SPECIFICATIONS table.

Fig. 6: Determining Drive Pinion Shim Thickness

Pinion Marking / Dial Indicator Reading (Inches)	+6 mm (Inches)	+4 mm (Inches)	+2 mm (Inches)	0 mm (Inches)	-2 mm (Inches)	-4 mm (Inches)	-6 mm (Inches)
0.052							1.39(0.0547)
0.053						1.39(0.0547)	1.41(0.0563)
0.054					1.39(0.0547)	1.41(0.0563)	1.43(0.0563)
0.055				1.39(0.0547)	1.41(0.0563)	1.43(0.0563)	1.45(0.0571)
0.056		1.39(0.0547)	1.41(0.0555)	1.43(0.0563)	1.45(0.0571)	1.47(0.0579)	1.49(0.0587)
0.057	1.39(0.0547)	1.41(0.0555)	1.43(0.0563)	1.45(0.0571)	1.47(0.0579)	1.49(0.0587)	1.51(0.0594)
0.058	1.41(0.0555)	1.43(0.0563)	1.45(0.0571)	1.47(0.0579)	1.49(0.0587)	1.51(0.0594)	1.53(0.0602)
0.059	1.43(0.0563)	1.45(0.0571)	1.47(0.0579)	1.49(0.0587)	1.51(0.0594)	1.53(0.0602)	1.55(0.0610)
0.060	1.47(0.0579)	1.49(0.0587)	1.51(0.0594)	1.53(0.0602)	1.55(0.0610)	1.57(0.0618)	1.59(0.0626)
0.061	1.49(0.0587)	1.51(0.0594)	1.53(0.0602)	1.55(0.0610)	1.57(0.0618)	1.59(0.0626)	1.61(0.0634)
0.062	1.51(0.0594)	1.53(0.0602)	1.55(0.0610)	1.57(0.0618)	1.59(0.0626)	1.61(0.0634)	1.63(0.0642)
0.063	1.55(0.0610)	1.57(0.0618)	1.59(0.0626)	1.61(0.0634)	1.63(0.0642)	1.65(0.0650)	1.67(0.0657)
0.064	1.57(0.0618)	1.59(0.0626)	1.61(0.0634)	1.63(0.0642)	1.65(0.0650)	1.67(0.0657)	1.69(0.0665)
0.065	1.59(0.0626)	1.61(0.0634)	1.63(0.0642)	1.65(0.0650)	1.67(0.0657)	1.69(0.0665)	1.71(0.0673)
0.066	1.61(0.0634)	1.63(0.0642)	1.65(0.0650)	1.67(0.0657)	1.69(0.0665)	1.71(0.0673)	1.73(0.0681)
0.067	1.65(0.0650)	1.67(0.0657)	1.69(0.0665)	1.71(0.0673)	1.73(0.0681)	1.75(0.0689)	1.77(0.0697)
0.068	1.67(0.0657)	1.69(0.0665)	1.71(0.0673)	1.73(0.0681)	1.75(0.0689)	1.77(0.0697)	1.79(0.0705)
0.069	1.69(0.0665)	1.71(0.0673)	1.73(0.0681)	1.75(0.0689)	1.77(0.0697)	1.79(0.0705)	1.81(0.0713)
0.070	1.71(0.0673)	1.73(0.0681)	1.75(0.0689)	1.77(0.0697)	1.79(0.0705)	1.81(0.0713)	
0.071	1.75(0.0689)	1.77(0.0697)	1.79(0.0705)	1.81(0.0713)			
0.072	1.77(0.0697)	1.79(0.0705)	1.81(0.0713)				
0.073	1.79(0.0705)	1.81(0.0713)					
0.074	1.81(0.0713)						

Courtesy of Isuzu Motor Co.

ISUZU INTEGRAL HOUSING (Cont.)

RING GEAR BACKLASH SPECIFICATIONS

Application	In. (mm)
All Models	.005-.007 (.13-.18)

3) Adjust feeler gauge thickness on both sides to obtain ring gear backlash. *See Fig. 7.* With zero end play and correct backlash, remove feeler gauges.

Fig. 7: Adjusting Backlash

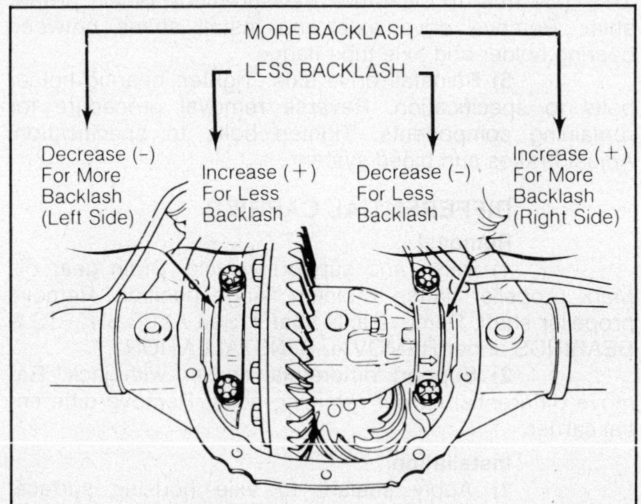

Courtesy of Isuzu Motor Co.

4) Determine thickness of required shims and add .002" (.05 mm) to each shim pack to provide side bearing preload. Always use new shims. Remove differential case assembly.

5) Using bearing puller, remove side bearings. Install new shim packs on differential case. Using Bearing Installer (J-22919) and Handle (J-8092), install side bearings on differential case. Use Pilot (J-2241-11) to support opposite end of case to prevent bearing damage.

6) Install differential case assembly and outer bearing races in axle housing. Install bearing caps in original location. Tighten bolts to specification. Rotate case assembly several times to seat bearings.

7) Using torque wrench, check ring gear starting torque using ring gear retaining bolt. Measure starting torque while moving torque wrench 180 degrees. Side bearings must be reshimmed if starting torque is not within 26-47 INCH lbs. (2.94-5.31 N.m).

8) Check gear tooth contact using paint impression method. See GEAR TOOTH PATTERNS article in this section. Soak pinion seal in rear axle oil. Using Seal Installer (J-22931), install oil seal.

9) Install axle housing cover and gasket. Apply sealant to center bolts at top and bottom of cover. Tighten bolts to specification.

TIGHTENING SPECIFICATIONS

Application	Ft. Lbs. (N.m)
Axle Bearing Retainer Bolt	27 (37)
Bearing Cap Bolt	29-36 (39-49)
Caliper Bolt	36 (49)
Center Support-to-Body Bolt	20 (27)
Companion Flange Nut	87 (118)
Control Arm-to-Axle Housing Bolt	47 (64)
Cover Bolt	
Lower Center	16 (22)
All Others	20-23 (27-31)
Extension Housing-to-Axle Housing Bolt	20 (27)
Lateral Rod Nut	47 (64)
Mounting Rubber-to-Center Support Bolt	15 (20)
Propeller Shaft-to-Companion Flange Bolt	20 (27)
Ring Gear Bolt	58-65 (79-88)
Spline Coupling Nut	109-217 (148-295)

ISUZU REAR AXLE

Isuzu: Impulse Turbo, P'UP, Trooper II

DESCRIPTION

Rear axle is banjo type housing using hypoid type gears and semi-floating drive axles. Limited slip model is available on Impulse Turbo model.

AXLE RATIO & IDENTIFICATION

Ratio is determined by dividing number of ring gear teeth by number of drive pinion teeth.

AXLE RATIO SPECIFICATIONS

Application	Ratio
Impulse Turbo	3.90
P'UP	
Diesel	
4 Speed M/T	3.42
5 Speed M/T	3.73
A/T	4.10
Gas	
4 Speed M/T	3.42
5 Speed M/T	4.10
A/T	4.10
Trooper II	
Diesel	4.10
Gas	4.55

REMOVAL & INSTALLATION

AXLES SHAFTS & BEARINGS

Removal (Impulse Turbo)

1) Raise and support vehicle. Remove wheel and tire assembly. Remove and support caliper. DO NOT disconnect brake hose from caliper. Remove brake rotor.

2) Remove bearing retainer plate bolts. Attach Adapter (J-8805-01) to wheel studs. Using Slide Hammer (J-2619-01) and adapter, remove axle shaft assembly. Remove oil seal from axle housing. Oil seal must be replaced if axle shaft is removed.

Installation

1) Using Seal Installer (J-24254), install oil seal in axle housing. Apply 2.8 oz. (80 g) of wheel bearing grease between oil seal and inner face of axle housing.

2) Reverse removal procedure for remaining components. Tighten bolts to specification. See TIGHTENING SPECIFICATIONS table at end of article.

Removal (P'UP & Trooper II)

1) Raise vehicle. Remove wheel and tire assembly. Remove brake drum. Disconnect parking brake inner cable. Disconnect and plug brake line from wheel cylinder.

2) Remove bearing holder retaining bolts. Attach Adapter (J-21579) to wheel studs. Using slide hammer and adapter, remove axle shaft assembly. Remove oil seal from axle housing. Oil seal must be replaced if axle shaft is removed.

Installation

1) Using Seal Installer (J-24254), install oil seal in axle housing. Apply 2.8 oz. (80 g) of wheel bearing grease between oil seal and inner face of axle housing.

2) If both drive axles were removed, insert a .079" (2.00 mm) shim between bearing holder and axle tube flange of one drive axle. Install drive axle. Tighten bearing holder bolts to specification. See TIGHTENING SPECIFICATIONS table at end of article.

3) Install remaining drive axle or drive axle if only one shaft was removed without shims. Install drive axle until it contacts differential thrust block. Measure clearance between bearing holder and axle tube flange.

4) Proper shim size is determined by adding .012" (.30 mm) to clearance measurement. Select proper shim. Remove drive axle and install shims between bearing holder and axle tube flange.

5) Reinstall drive axle. Tighten bearing holder bolts to specification. Reverse removal procedure for remaining components. Tighten bolts to specification. Adjust brakes and bleed system.

DIFFERENTIAL CARRIER

Removal

1) Raise and support vehicle. Drain gear oil. Mark propeller flange-to-pinion flange position. Remove propeller shaft. Remove axle shafts. See AXLE SHAFTS & BEARINGS under REMOVAL & INSTALLATION.

2) Support differential carrier with jack. Remove differential carrier retaining bolts. Remove differential carrier.

Installation

1) Apply sealant to axle housing surface. Reverse removal procedures. Align marks on propeller shaft and pinion flange. Tighten bolts to specification. See TIGHTENING SPECIFICATIONS table at end of article.

2) Fill conventional units with gear oil conforming to classification GL-5. On limited slip units, use GL-5 Limited Slip Differential gear oil. On all units, use proper viscosity oil depending on ambient temperature. See GEAR OIL SPECIFICATIONS table.

GEAR OIL SPECIFICATIONS

Temperature	Gear Oil Viscosity
Below 50°F (10°C)	SAE 80
0° To 90°F (-18° to 32°C)	SAE 90
Above 50°F (10°C)	SAE 140

OVERHAUL

AXLE SHAFTS & BEARINGS

Disassembly (Impulse Turbo)

Using Bearing Remover (J-33949) and press, remove bearing from axle shaft.

Inspection

Inspect axle shaft for damaged splines or flange. Check runout at center of shaft and face of flange. Replace if runout exceeds specifications. See AXLE SHAFT SPECIFICATIONS table.

AXLE SHAFT SPECIFICATIONS

Application	In. (mm)
Shaft Runout	.039 (.99)
Flange Runout	.003 (.07)

Drive Axles

ISUZU REAR AXLE (Cont.)

Reassembly

Install "O" ring in groove on bearing outer race. Install bearing with "O" ring toward splined end of axle shaft. Install sleeve with flanged side facing bearing. Using Bearing Installer (J-22912-01) and press, install bearing and sleeve on axle shaft

Fig. 1: Exploded View of Axle Shaft Assembly

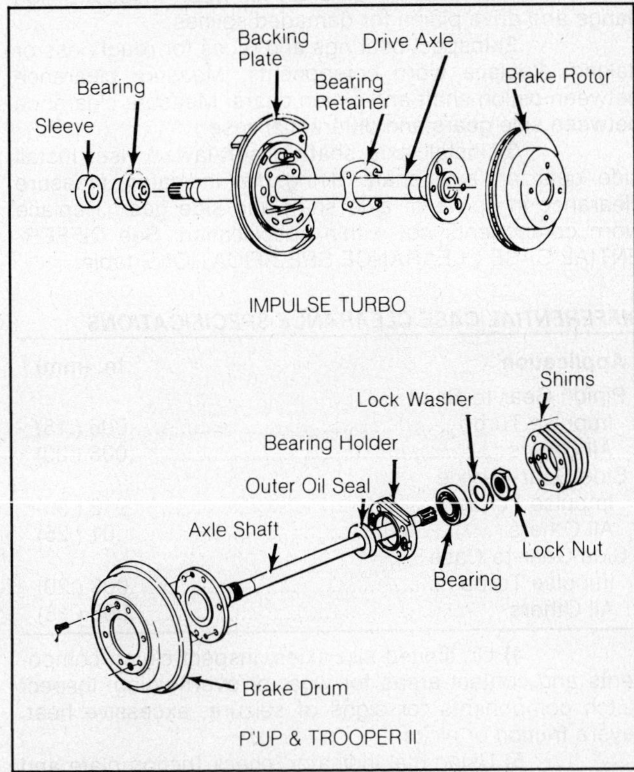

Courtesy of Isuzu Motor Co.

Disassembly (P'UP & Trooper II)

1) Flatten locking tab of lock washer. Some models may contain staked area in lock nut. Loosen stake area. Secure drive axle in soft-jawed vise with vise jaws holding lock nut.

2) Install Axle Remover/Installer (J-24246) on wheel studs. Rotate drive axle and remove lock nut and lock washer. Using press, remove bearing holder, bearing and backing plate from drive axle. Remove oil seal and bearing race from bearing holder.

Inspection

Inspect axle shaft for damaged splines or flange. Check runout at center of shaft and face of flange. Replace if runout exceeds specifications. See AXLE SHAFT SPECIFICATIONS table.

AXLE SHAFT SPECIFICATIONS

Application	In. (mm)
Shaft Runout	.039 (.99)
Flange Runout	.003 (.07)

Reassembly

1) Using Race Installer (J-24259) and Handle (J-8092), install bearing race in bearing holder. Using Seal Installer (J-24255), install oil seal in bearing holder.

2) Apply wheel bearing grease to bearing race. Install bolts into backing plate. Install bearing holder on backing plate. Ensure oil seal side of bearing holder is against backing plate.

3) Place backing plate assembly over drive axle. Using Bearing Installer (J-8609-01), press bearing into bearing holder. Install new lock washer with dished side away from bearing. Install new lock nut.

4) Secure lock nut in soft-jawed vise. Using axle remover/installer, tighten lock nut to specification. Stake lock nut in groove of axle shaft. Bend over lock washer in opposite area of locating tab.

Fig. 2: Exploded View of Differential Assembly

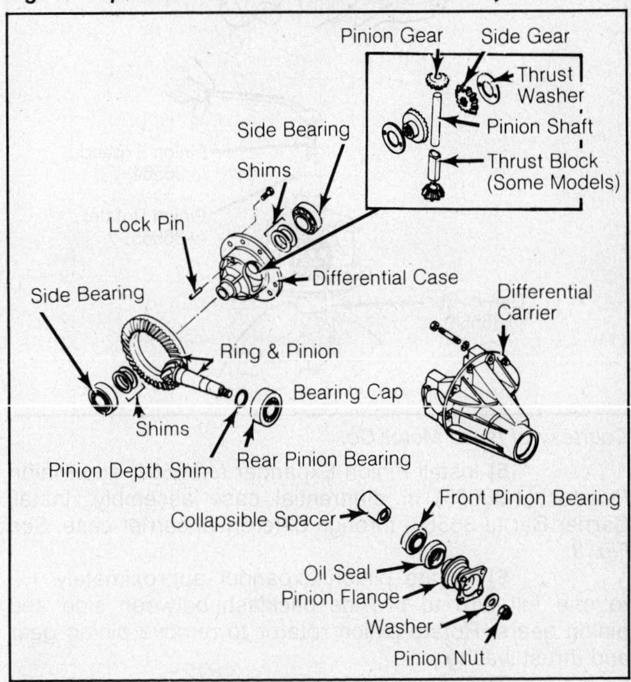

Courtesy of Isuzu Motor Co.

DIFFERENTIAL ASSEMBLY

Disassembly

1) Remove differential carrier from vehicle. Mark bearing caps for location. Remove bearing caps. Remove differential case assembly from carrier. Using bearing puller, remove differential case side bearings.

CAUTION: Ensure shims, bearing caps and side bearings are marked for location. Components must be installed in original location.

2) Mark side bearing shims and side bearings for location. Place alignment marks on ring gear and differential case for reassembly. Loosen ring gear retaining bolts in diagonal sequence. Remove ring gear.

3) On conventional axles, drive pinion shaft lock pin from differential case. Remove differential pinion shaft, thrust block (if equipped), pinion gears, side gears and thrust washers. Mark components for reassembly reference.

4) On limited slip units, remove lock pin and pinion shaft. *See Fig. 4.* Place Pinion Holder (J-36563) in soft-jawed vise. Install differential case assembly on pinion holder, aligning pinion holder with side gear. *See Fig. 3.*

ISUZU REAR AXLE (Cont.)

Fig. 3: Removing & Installing Limited Slip Differential Case Components

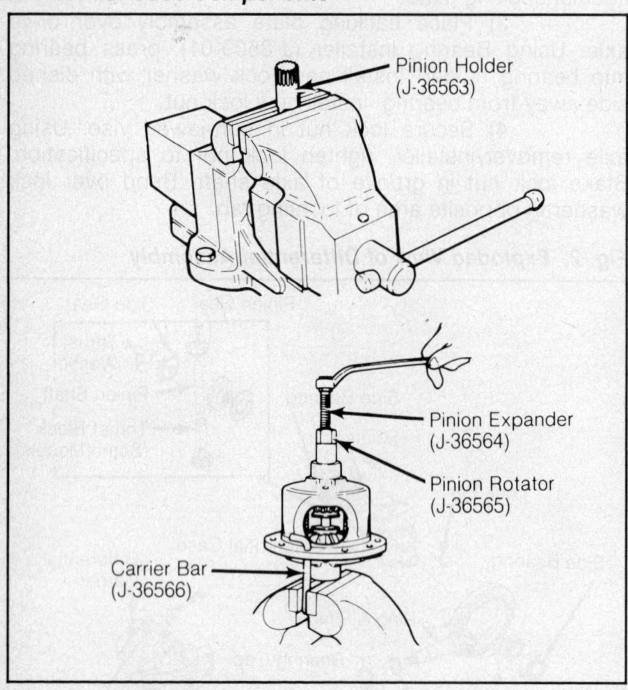

Courtesy of Isuzu Motor Co.

5) Install Pinion Expander (J-36564) and Pinion Rotator (J-36565) in differential case assembly. Install Carrier Bar (J-36566) through differential carrier case. *See Fig. 3.*

6) Rotate pinion expander approximately 1/2 to one full turn to provide backlash between side and pinion gears. Rotate pinion rotator to remove pinion gear and thrust washer.

7) Remove side gears and clutch components. Mark all components for location. *See Fig. 4.*

Fig. 4: Limited Slip Differential Case Components

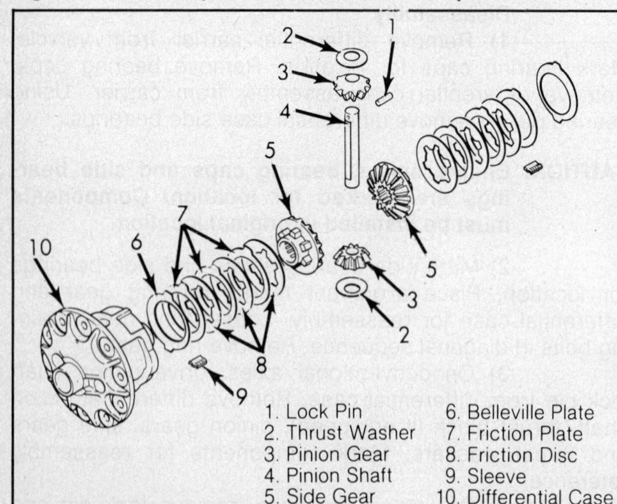

Courtesy of Isuzu Motor Co.

Drive Pinion

1) Using Flange Holder (J-8614-01), remove pinion nut and pinion flange. Using soft-faced hammer, drive out pinion. Remove collapsible spacer from pinion.

2) Remove front pinion bearing and oil seal from differential carrier. Using brass drift, remove bearing inner and outer races from carrier. Using Bearing Remover (J-22912-01) and press, remove rear pinion bearing and depth shim.

Inspection

1) On all axles, inspect all gears for cracked or flaking teeth. Inspect pinion shaft for wear. Inspect pinion flange and drive pinion for damaged splines.

2) Inspect bearings and races for roughness or flaking. Replace worn components. Measure clearance between pinion shaft and pinion gears. Measure clearance between side gears and differential case.

3) Install axle shaft in soft-jawed vise. Install side gear on axle shaft. Using dial indicator, measure clearance in spline of axle shaft and side gear. Replace worn components not within specification. See DIFFERENTIAL CASE CLEARANCE SPECIFICATIONS table.

DIFFERENTIAL CASE CLEARANCE SPECIFICATIONS

Application	In. (mm)
Pinion Gear-to-Shaft	
Impulse Turbo	.006 (.15)
All Others	.008 (.20)
Side Gear-to-Axle	
Impulse Turbo	.012 (.30)
All Others	.01 (.25)
Side Gear-to-Case	
Impulse Turbo	.008 (.20)
All Others	.006 (.15)

4) On limited slip axles, inspect clutch components and contact areas for wear or overheating. Inspect clutch components for signs of seizure, excessive heat, severe friction or nicks.

5) Using dial indicator, check friction plate and friction disc for warpage. Replace if beyond specification. See FRICTION PLATE & DISC SPECIFICATIONS table.

6) Measure friction plates and disc thickness at projection areas not within wear area. Measure plate and disc thickness in friction surface.

7) Difference between thickness of projections and friction surface indicates amount of wear. Replace components if not within specification. See FRICTION PLATE & DISC SPECIFICATIONS table.

FRICTION PLATE & DISC SPECIFICATIONS

Application	In. (mm)
Warpage Limit	.0027 (.068)
Wear Limit	.0039 (.099)

REASSEMBLY & ADJUSTMENTS

Case Assembly (Conventional)

1) Install thrust washers, side gears and pinion gears in differential case. Install pinion shaft without lock pin and thrust block (if equipped). Using dial indicator, check pinion and side gear backlash while holding side gear. *See Fig. 5.*

2) Backlash must be within specification. See PINION & SIDE GEAR BACKLASH SPECIFICATIONS table. Adjust backlash by using different side gear thrust washers.

3) Thrust washers are available in thickness from .039-.055" (1.00-1.40 mm) for Impulse Turbo models

ISUZU REAR AXLE (Cont.)

and .039-.043" (1.00-1.09 mm) for all other models. Ensure both sides are equally shimmed.

PINION & SIDE GEAR BACKLASH SPECIFICATIONS

Application	In. (mm)
Standard	.0012-.0031 (.030-.078)

Fig. 5: Checking Pinion & Side Gear Backlash

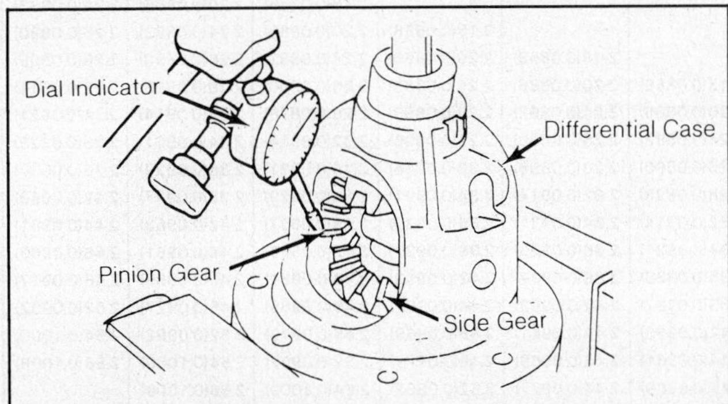

Courtesy of Isuzu Motor Co.

4) Once correct backlash is obtained, install thrust block and pinion shaft lock pin. Stake lock pin hole to prevent movement. Install ring gear on differential case.

5) Ensure alignment marks on differential case and ring gear are aligned. Use new retaining bolts. Apply Loctite to bolts and install. Tighten bolts to specification in diagonal sequence.

6) Using Bearing Installer (J-24244) and Handle (J-8092), install side bearings on differential case. DO NOT install shims. Use Pilot (J-8107-2) to support opposite end of differential case to prevent bearing damage.

Case Assembly (Limited Slip)

1) Coat friction disc and plates with GL-5 Limited Slip Differential gear oil. Install belleville plates, sleeves, friction discs, friction plates and side gears in differential case.

2) Place Pinion Holder (J-36563) in soft-jawed vise. Install differential case assembly on pinion holder, aligning pinion holder with side gear. *See Fig. 3.*

3) Install Pinion Expander (J-36564) and Pinion Rotator (J-36565) in differential case assembly. Install Carrier Bar (J-36566) through differential carrier case. *See Fig. 3.*

4) Rotate pinion expander approximately 1/2 to one full turn to provide clearance for pinion gear installation. Install pinion gears and thrust washers.

5) Rotate pinion rotator to align pinion gears and thrust washers with pinion shaft hole. Install pinion shaft and lock pin. Stake lock pin hole to prevent movement. Install ring gear on differential case.

6) Ensure alignment marks on differential case and ring gear are aligned. Use new retaining bolts. Apply Loctite to bolts and install. Tighten bolts to specification in diagonal sequence.

7) Using Bearing Installer (J-24244) and Handle (J-8092), install side bearings on differential case. DO NOT install shims. Use Pilot (J-8107-2) to support opposite end of differential case to prevent bearing damage.

Drive Pinion Depth

1) Install pinion bearing races in differential carrier. Use Handle (J-8092) and Race Installer (J-24256) for front race and (J-24252) for rear race. Ensure races are fully seated.

2) Lubricate pinion bearings and install in differential carrier. Install Gauge Plate (J-23597-7), Preload Stud (J-23597-9) and Pilot (J-21777-42) through pinion bearings. *See Fig. 6.*

3) Rotate bearing to ensure proper seating. Tighten preload stud nut to 10 INCH lbs. (1.13 N.m) for used bearing and 20 INCH lbs. (2.26 N.m) for new bearings. Clean differential case bearing bores.

Fig. 6: Installing Pinion Height Gauge Assembly

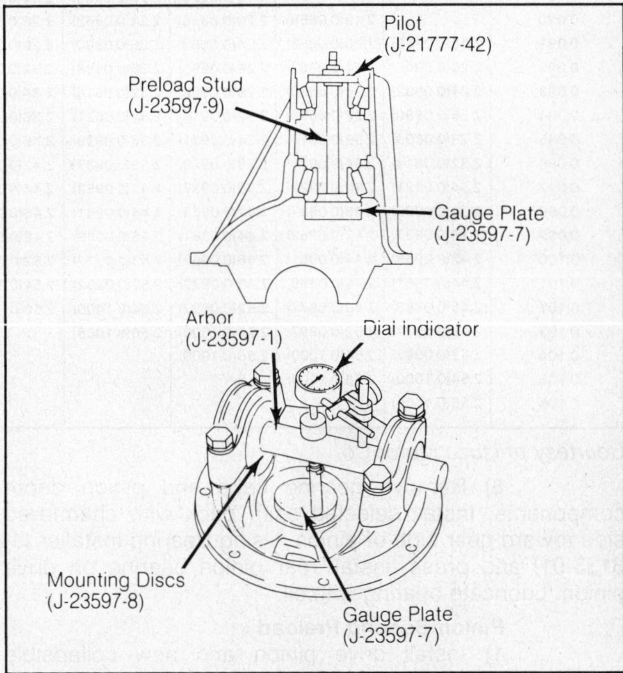

Courtesy of Isuzu Motor Co.

4) Install Mounting Discs (J-23597-8) on Arbor (J-23597-1). Install assembly in side bearing bores. Install bearing caps. Tighten bearing cap bolts to 72 ft. lbs. (98 N.m) on Impulse Turbo models or 69-76 ft. lbs (94-103 N.m) on P'UP and Trooper II models.

5) Adjust dial indicator to zero. Install dial indicator on arbor post. Position stem on top surface of gauge plate. Push dial indicator downward until needle reads 1/2 turn clockwise. Tighten indicator in this position.

6) Rotate arbor back and forth until dial indicator reads maximum deflection. Adjust indicator to zero. Repeat procedure to ensure proper setting. Rotate arbor until dial indicator stem does not contact gauge plate. Record dial indicator reading. Note number etched on gear end of drive pinion.

7) Reading may be either a plus (+) or minus (-) with a numeral. If reading is 0, pinion is nominal. Using dial indicator reading and pinion marking, determine proper drive pinion shim thickness to be used. *See Fig. 7.*

ISUZU REAR AXLE (Cont.)

Fig. 7: Determining Drive Pinion Shim Thickness

Pinion Marking / Dial Indicator Reading (Inches)	+10 mm (Inches)	+8 mm (Inches)	+6 mm (Inches)	+4 mm (Inches)	+2 mm (Inches)	0 mm (Inches)	-2 mm (Inches)	-4 mm (Inches)	-6 mm (Inches)	-8 mm (Inches)	-10 mm (Inches)
0.081											2.18(0.0858)
0.082										2.18(0.0858)	2.20(0.0866)
0.083									2.18(0.0858)	2.20(0.0866)	2.24(0.0882)
0.084								2.18(0.0858)	2.20(0.0866)	2.24(0.0882)	2.26(0.0890)
0.085							2.18(0.0858)	2.20(0.0866)	2.24(0.0882)	2.26(0.0890)	2.28(0.0898)
0.086						2.18(0.0858)	2.20(0.0866)	2.24(0.0882)	2.26(0.0890)	2.28(0.0898)	2.32(0.0914)
0.087					2.18(0.0858)	2.20(0.0866)	2.24(0.0882)	2.26(0.0890)	2.28(0.0898)	2.32(0.0914)	2.34(0.0921)
0.088				2.18(0.0858)	2.20(0.0866)	2.24(0.0882)	2.26(0.0890)	2.28(0.0898)	2.32(0.0914)	2.34(0.0921)	2.36(0.0929)
0.089			2.18(0.0858)	2.20(0.0866)	2.24(0.0882)	2.26(0.0890)	2.28(0.0898)	2.32(0.0914)	2.34(0.0921)	2.36(0.0929)	2.38(0.0937)
0.090		2.18(0.0858)	2.20(0.0866)	2.24(0.0882)	2.26(0.0890)	2.28(0.0898)	2.32(0.0914)	2.34(0.0921)	2.36(0.0929)	2.38(0.0937)	2.42(0.0953)
0.091	2.18(0.0858)	2.20(0.0866)	2.24(0.0882)	2.26(0.0890)	2.28(0.0898)	2.32(0.0914)	2.34(0.0921)	2.36(0.0929)	2.38(0.0937)	2.42(0.0953)	2.44(0.0961)
0.092	2.20(0.0866)	2.24(0.0882)	2.26(0.0890)	2.28(0.0898)	2.32(0.0914)	2.34(0.0921)	2.36(0.0929)	2.38(0.0937)	2.42(0.0953)	2.44(0.0961)	2.46(0.0969)
0.093	2.24(0.0882)	2.26(0.0890)	2.28(0.0898)	2.32(0.0914)	2.34(0.0921)	2.36(0.0929)	2.38(0.0937)	2.42(0.0953)	2.44(0.0961)	2.46(0.0969)	2.48(0.0977)
0.094	2.26(0.0890)	2.28(0.0898)	2.32(0.0914)	2.34(0.0921)	2.36(0.0929)	2.38(0.0937)	2.42(0.0953)	2.44(0.0961)	2.46(0.0969)	2.48(0.0977)	2.52(0.0992)
0.095	2.28(0.0898)	2.32(0.0914)	2.34(0.0921)	2.36(0.0929)	2.38(0.0937)	2.42(0.0953)	2.44(0.0961)	2.46(0.0969)	2.48(0.0977)	2.52(0.0992)	2.54(0.1000)
0.096	2.32(0.0914)	2.34(0.0921)	2.36(0.0929)	2.38(0.0937)	2.42(0.0953)	2.44(0.0961)	2.46(0.0969)	2.48(0.0977)	2.52(0.0992)	2.54(0.1000)	2.56(0.1008)
0.097	2.34(0.0921)	2.36(0.0929)	2.38(0.0937)	2.42(0.0953)	2.44(0.0961)	2.46(0.0969)	2.48(0.0977)	2.52(0.0992)	2.54(0.1000)	2.56(0.1008)	
0.098	2.36(0.0929)	2.38(0.0937)	2.42(0.0953)	2.44(0.0961)	2.46(0.0969)	2.48(0.0977)	2.52(0.0992)	2.54(0.1000)	2.56(0.1008)		
0.099	2.38(0.0937)	2.42(0.0953)	2.44(0.0961)	2.46(0.0969)	2.48(0.0977)	2.52(0.0992)	2.54(0.1000)	2.56(0.1008)			
0.100	2.42(0.0953)	2.44(0.0961)	2.46(0.0969)	2.48(0.0977)	2.52(0.0992)	2.54(0.1000)	2.56(0.1008)				
0.101	2.44(0.0961)	2.46(0.0969)	2.48(0.0977)	2.52(0.0992)	2.54(0.1000)	2.56(0.1008)					
0.102	2.46(0.0969)	2.48(0.0977)	2.52(0.0992)	2.54(0.1000)	2.56(0.1008)						
0.103	2.48(0.0977)	2.52(0.0992)	2.54(0.1000)	2.56(0.1008)							
0.104	2.52(0.0992)	2.54(0.1000)	2.56(0.1008)								
0.105	2.54(0.1000)	2.56(0.1008)									
0.106	2.56(0.1008)										

Courtesy of Isuzu Motor Co.

8) Remove bearing caps and pinion depth components. Install selected shim pack with chamfered side toward gear side of pinion. Using Bearing Installer (J-6133-01) and press, install rear pinion bearing on drive pinion. Lubricate bearing with oil.

Pinion Bearing Preload

1) Install drive pinion and new collapsible spacer in differential carrier. Install front pinion bearing. Soak pinion seal in rear axle oil. Using Seal Installer (J-24250), install oil seal.

2) Using Flange Installer (J-6403-C), install flange on drive pinion. Apply oil to pinion threads. Install new pinion nut and washer.

3) Using flange holder, tighten pinion nut to minimum specification. See TIGHTENING SPECIFICATIONS table at end of article. Rotate pinion to ensure bearings are seated.

4) Using torque wrench, measure drive pinion starting torque. Starting torque should be 5.6-10 INCH lbs. (.63-1.13 N.m). If starting torque is not within specification, tighten pinion nut to obtain correct starting torque. DO NOT exceed maximum tightening specification.

CAUTION: DO NOT loosen nut to decrease preload or exceed maximum tightening specification. If preload or tightening specification is exceeded, replace collapsible spacer.

Side Bearing

1) Install differential case and bearing races in axle housing. Shims should not be installed behind side bearings. Using 2 feeler gauges, install feeler gauge between each bearing outer race and axle housing to remove all end play. Ensure feeler gauge is pushed to bottom of bearing bores.

2) Lock drive pinion in place. Using dial indicator, check ring gear backlash at heel of ring gear tooth. Gear backlash must be within specification. See RING GEAR BACKLASH SPECIFICATIONS table.

RING GEAR BACKLASH SPECIFICATIONS

Application	In. (mm)
All Models	.005-.007 (.13-.18)

3) Adjust feeler gauge thickness on both sides to obtain ring gear backlash. With zero end play and correct backlash, remove feeler gauges.

4) Determine thickness of required shims and add .002" (.05 mm) to each shim pack to provide side bearing preload. Always use new shims. Remove differential case assembly.

5) Using bearing puller, remove side bearings. Install new shim packs on differential case. Using Bearing Installer (J-24244) and Handle (J-8092), install side bearings on differential case. Use Pilot (J-8107-2) to support opposite end of differential case to prevent bearing damage.

6) Install differential case assembly and outer bearing races in axle housing. Install bearing caps in original location. Tighten bolts to specification.

7) Using dial indicator, measure runout of ring gear. If runout exceeds .002" (.05 mm), correct by cleaning or replacing parts. Check gear tooth contact using paint impression method. See GEAR TOOTH PATTERNS article in this section.

ISUZU REAR AXLE (Cont.)

TIGHTENING SPECIFICATIONS (IMPULSE TURBO)

Application	Ft. Lbs. (N.m)
Axle Shaft Retainer Bolt	28 (38)
Bearing Cap Bolt	72 (98)
Caliper Bolt	36 (49)
Differential Carrier-to-Housing Bolt	18 (24)
Pinion Flange Nut	130-202 (176-274)
Propeller Shaft-to-Pinion	
Flange Bolt	24 (33)
Ring Gear Bolt	80 (109)

TIGHTENING SPECIFICATIONS (P'UP & TROOPER II)

Application	Ft. Lbs. (N.m)
Axle Bearing Lock Nut	
P'UP	188-195 (255-265)
Trooper II	170-213 (231-289)
Bearing Cap Bolt	69-76 (94-103)
Bearing Holder-to-Housing Bolt	51-58 (69-79)
Differential Carrier-to-Housing	
Bolt	17-20 (23-27)
Nut	25-30 (34-41)
Pinion Flange Nut	83-90 (113-122)
Propeller Shaft-to-Pinion	
Flange Bolt	22-25 (29-34)
Ring Gear Bolt	72-87 (98-118)

Drive Axles

JAGUAR

XJ6 III, XJS

DESCRIPTION

Differential assembly uses hypoid type gears with stub axles and half-shafts. Limited slip unit is available on some models.

AXLE RATIO & IDENTIFICATION

Limited slip differential can be identified by letters "PL" on a tag located on housing cover mounting bolt. Ratio is determined by dividing number of ring gear teeth by number of drive pinion teeth.

A 3.07 gear ratio is standard on XJ-S models and optional on XJ6-III models. A 3.31 gear ratio is standard on XJ6-III models.

REMOVAL & INSTALLATION

REAR SUSPENSION ASSEMBLY

Removal

1) Raise and support vehicle. Place jack stands forward of radius arms. Remove rear wheels. Remove rear mufflers and tail pipes from intermediate exhaust pipes. Remove intermediate pipe from front mufflers and rear of suspension unit.

2) Remove safety strap and front radius arm from body mounting. Remove roll bar link bolts from radius arms (if equipped). Disconnect and plug brake lines at body. Fully release parking brake adjustment (located under rear carpet).

3) Remove clevis pin from parking brake cable at each actuating lever. Loosen lock nut. Remove outer brake cable screw from adjuster block.

4) Remove drive shaft from differential. Remove speedometer wires from differential. Support suspension unit with jack. Remove crossmember mounts-to-frame bolts. Remove rear suspension.

Installation

To install, reverse removal procedures. Bleed brakes. Tighten radius arm nuts on lower control arm when weight of vehicle is on wheels. Tighten bolts to specification.

REAR HUB & CARRIER ASSEMBLY, HALF-SHAFT & BRAKE ROTOR

Removal

1) Support rear of vehicle on stands. Remove rear wheel. Measure and record rear hub end play before removing. If end play exceeds .005" (.12 mm), rear hub and carrier assembly must be repaired.

2) Remove bolt and pry radius arm from rear anchor point. Support outer suspension arm. Remove shocks from lower mounts. Loosen inner "U" joint shroud clip. Move shroud away from flange. Remove "U" joint-to-brake rotor nuts.

NOTE: **If necessary, remove "U" joint shields by drilling out rivets and removing clips.**

3) Tap out rotor mounting bolts and separate "U" joint from brake rotor. Remove camber adjustment shims. Mark shims for reassembly. Remove brake caliper. Remove rotor from mounting bolts.

NOTE: **DO NOT remove rotor locating shims located between differential flange and brake rotor.**

4) Remove cotter pin, nut and washer from half-shaft. Remove grease fitting from hub carrier. Fit Thread Protector (JD.1 C/7) over end of half-shaft. Using Puller (JD.1 D), pull hub and carrier from half-shaft. *See Fig. 1.*

5) Pivot hub assembly downward. Remove Bronze spacer from half-shaft. Inspect inner oil seal track. Replace track as needed.

6) Remove one nut from fulcrum shaft. Using soft-faced hammer and drift, drive fulcrum shaft out of hub and carrier assembly. Remove hub and carrier assembly. Remove half-shaft.

CAUTION: **Note shim and washer locations for reassembly reference when removing hub and carrier assembly.**

Fig. 1: Removing Hub & Carrier Assembly From Half-Shaft

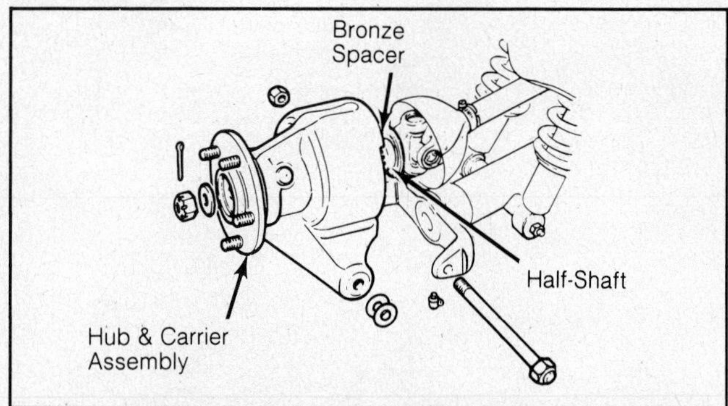

Courtesy of Jaguar Cars Inc.

Installation

1) To install, reverse removal procedures. If necessary, replace "U" joint shield. Ensure grease fitting access hole is aligned. Apply non-hardening waterproof sealant to seams in "U" joint shield.

NOTE: **Ensure camber adjustment shims are installed in original location.**

2) For rear hub installation, position hub carrier on suspension arm. Install shims and washers between hub carrier and lower suspension arm. Install outer suspension arm fulcrum shaft. Tighten fulcrum nut to specification. Install grease fitting.

3) If necessary, install oil seal track to half-shaft splined flange. Replace spacer. Thoroughly clean splines of half-shaft and bore of hub. Apply Loctite to outer half-shaft splines.

4) Assemble hub carrier to half-shaft. Install washer and tighten hub carrier assembly nut to specification. Install new cotter pin. Check and adjust rear wheel camber.

STUB AXLE, BEARINGS & OIL SEAL

Removal

1) Remove half-shaft. Remove and plug brake line from brake caliper. Remove brake caliper and rotor.

NOTE: **When removing brake rotor, note number of rotor locating shims removed from between "U" joint flange and rotor, and between rotor and stub axle flange.**

2) Remove caliper mounting bracket from differential housing. Remove stub axle, bearing housing, bearings, "O" ring and oil seal. *See Fig. 2.*

3) Clamp caliper mounting bracket in soft-jawed vise. Bend down lock washer tabs. Remove nut from stub axle.

NOTE: **Outer bearing may remain on stub axle shaft. If so, remove bearing using Bearing Remover (SL.47).**

4) Remove stub axle, inner bearing and spacer from caliper mounting bracket. Discard collapsed spacer. Remove oil seal from bracket. Remove outer bearing from bracket. Using small drift, remove bearing races from bracket.

Fig. 2: Sectional View of Stub Axle & Bearing Housing Assembly

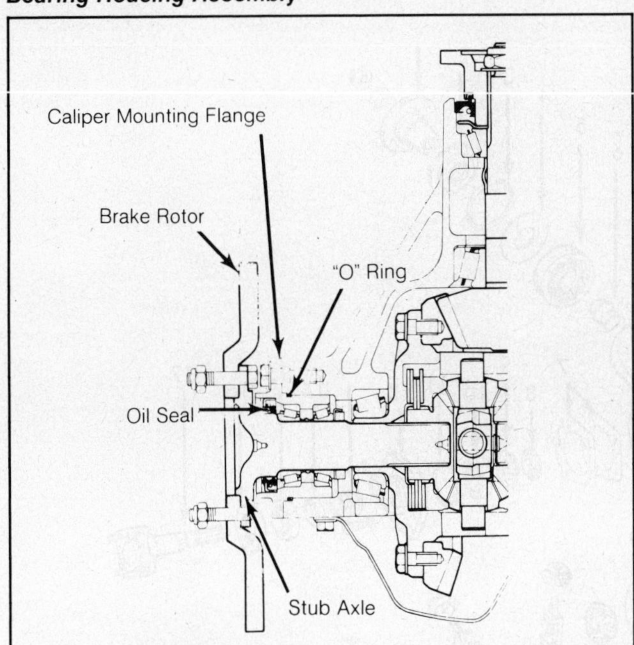

Courtesy of Jaguar Cars Inc.

Installation

1) Replace inner and outer stub axle bearings and races as a set. Install new bearing race into housing. Ensure bearing race is fully seated. Install outer bearing.

2) Lubricate oil seal lips. Install oil seal with seal lip facing bearing. Place bearing housing in soft-jawed vise. Coat seal lip with hypoid oil and pack grease between sealing edges. Ensure rotor mounting bolts are installed in stub axle flange. Install caliper mounting flange and bearing and seal assembly over stub axle.

3) Install new collapsible spacer and inner bearing on stub axle. Apply grease to locking tab washer-to-nut contact area. Install new locking tab washer and nut. Ensure bearings are fully seated against stub axle shoulder. Finger tighten nut. Using Torque Screwdriver (CBW.548) and adapter, check turning torque of stub axle.

NOTE: **Adjust Torque Screwdriver (CBW.548) to 4 INCH lbs. (.45 N.m). Increase setting progressively until shaft begins to move.**

4) Record turning torque. Tighten axle nut until bearing play is eliminated. Recheck turning torque. Torque required to turn shaft should be unchanged.

5) Tighten nut not more than 1/32 of a turn. Recheck turning torque. Turning torque should be 4.5-5.5 INCH lbs. (.51-.62 N.m) above that recorded in step **4)**. This indicates proper bearing preload.

6) Tighten nut to obtain proper turning torque. DO NOT overtighten or loosen nut.

NOTE: **DO NOT loosen nut excessively. Spacer collapses during tightening and any reversal of nut will result in improper bearing cone clamping. If turning torque is exceeded, replace collapsible spacer.**

7) If turning torque exceeds 6 INCH lbs. (.68 N.m), disassemble stub axle and bearing assembly. Replace collapsible spacer and repeat procedure.

8) Bend up lock washer tabs. Install new "O" ring into bearing housing groove. Lightly oil stub shaft splines. Install shaft in differential housing. Tighten retaining bolts to specification.

9) Install safety wire to retaining bolts. Install brake rotor and half-shaft flange. Ensure brake rotor is centered in caliper. Rotor must be centered within .010" (.25 mm) by moving shims from one side of rotor to the other.

10) Ensure to install all shims previously removed. Reverse removal procedure for remaining components. Tighten bolts to specification.

PINION FLANGE & OIL SEAL

Removal

1) Raise and support vehicle. Remove drive shaft flange from pinion flange. Using a Torque Screwdriver (CBW.548), adapter and socket, measure and record torque required to rotate pinion flange through backlash movement. Pinion flange must be rotated counterclockwise as viewed from pinion flange.

NOTE: **Set torque screwdriver gauge initially to 15 INCH lbs. (1.7 N.m). Increase setting progressively until pinion flange begins to move. Flange must be turned counterclockwise through backlash.**

2) Mark nut and pinion shaft for reassembly reference. Remove pinion flange retaining nut and washer. Using a puller, remove pinion flange. Remove oil seal from case.

Installation

1) Clean pinion flange splines. Coat seal recess with liquid sealant. Grease oil seal lip and install. Apply Loctite to pinion shaft splines. Using soft-faced hammer, install flange. Install washer and nut to alignment mark. Recheck pinion turning torque.

2) Turning torque should exceed the torque recorded during removal by specified amount. See PINION ROTATING TORQUE SPECIFICATIONS table.

JAGUAR (Cont.)

PINION ROTATING TORQUE SPECIFICATIONS

Application	INCH Lbs. (N.m)
XJ6 III	1-5 (.11-.56)
XJS	5-10 (.56-1.13)

3) If torque is below 25 INCH lbs. (2.82 N.m), continue tightening flange nut until 25-30 INCH lbs. (2.82-3.38 N.m) is obtained. If preload exceeds turning torque of 45 INCH lbs. (5.08 N.m), differential assembly requires repair. Install drive shaft. Tighten bolts to specification.

DIFFERENTIAL ASSEMBLY

NOTE: Rear suspension assembly must first be removed from vehicle.

Removal

1) Drain differential gear oil. Remove rear suspension assembly. Remove differential assembly mounting plate bolts and set screws from crossmember and inner fulcrum brackets. Remove shock absorbers and spring mounting units.

2) Remove shock absorber mounting pins. Remove spacers and tie-down brackets. Move shrouds away from "U" joints. Remove half-shaft inner "U" joint-to-brake rotor and stub shaft flange bolts.

3) Remove nut from inner suspension arm fulcrum shaft. Drive out fulcrum shaft. Remove spacers, seals and bearings for pivots. Remove half-shaft, noting shims locations.

4) Remove spacer tubes from between fulcrum bracket lugs. Disconnect and plug brake lines from calipers. Disconnect brake return springs from hand brake levers. Remove differential assembly-to-crossmember retaining bolts. Remove crossmember from differential assembly.

5) Remove set screws and fulcrum brackets from differential assembly. Note position and number of shims. Remove calipers from assembly. Remove brake rotors, noting number of shims between rotor and stub axle flange.

Fig. 3: Exploded View Of Limited Slip Differential Assembly

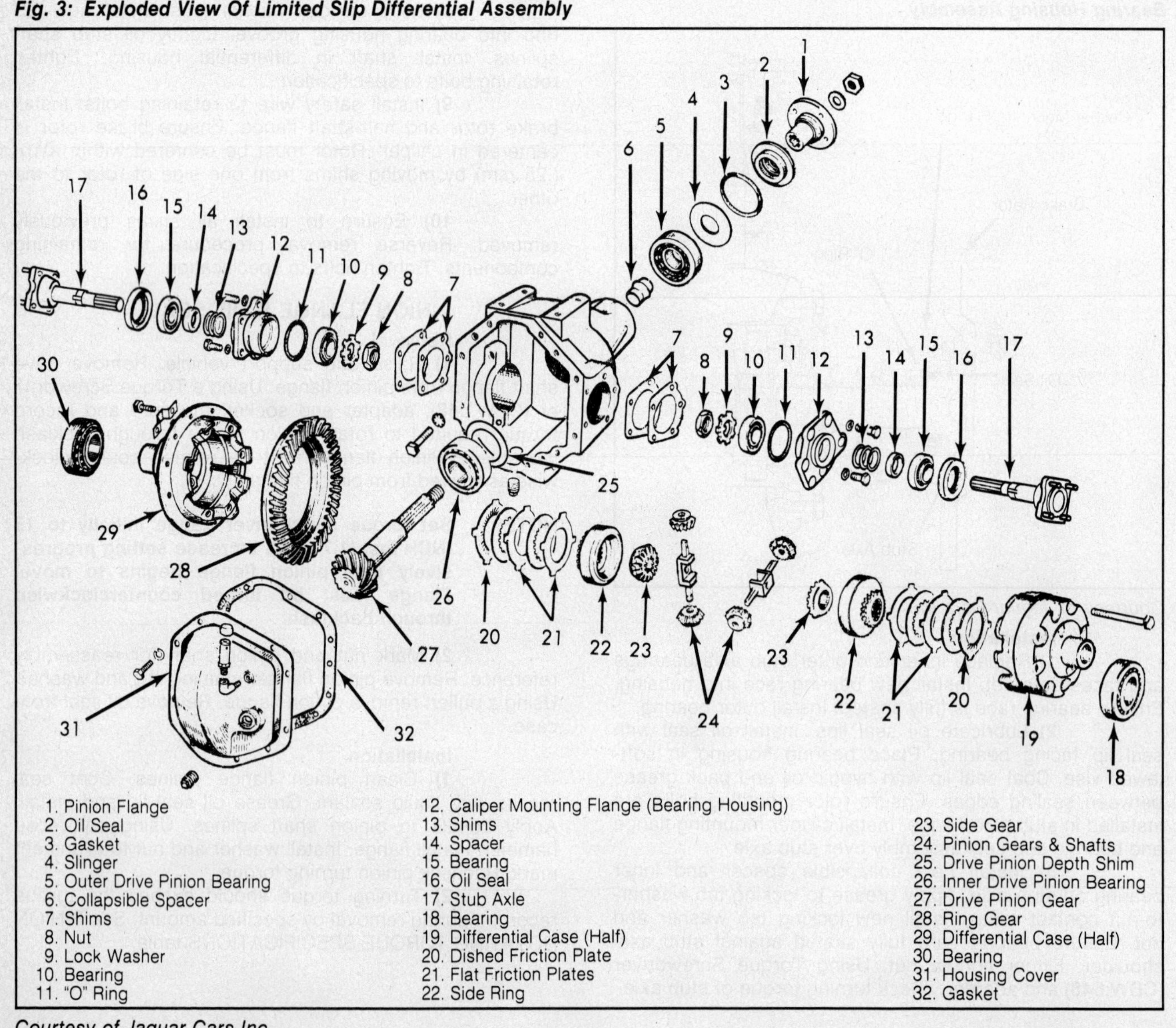

1. Pinion Flange
2. Oil Seal
3. Gasket
4. Slinger
5. Outer Drive Pinion Bearing
6. Collapsible Spacer
7. Shims
8. Nut
9. Lock Washer
10. Bearing
11. "O" Ring
12. Caliper Mounting Flange (Bearing Housing)
13. Shims
14. Spacer
15. Bearing
16. Oil Seal
17. Stub Axle
18. Bearing
19. Differential Case (Half)
20. Dished Friction Plate
21. Flat Friction Plates
22. Side Ring
23. Side Gear
24. Pinion Gears & Shafts
25. Drive Pinion Depth Shim
26. Inner Drive Pinion Bearing
27. Drive Pinion Gear
28. Ring Gear
29. Differential Case (Half)
30. Bearing
31. Housing Cover
32. Gasket

Courtesy of Jaguar Cars Inc.

JAGUAR (Cont.)

Installation

1) To install, reverse removal procedure. Ensure brake rotor is centered in caliper. Rotor must be centered within .010" (.25 mm) by transferring shims from one side of rotor to the other.

2) Tighten bolts to specification. Safety wire bolts in clockwise direction. Lubricate all thrust washers and bearings. Install new oil seals if necessary. Check rear wheel alignment and bleed brake system. Fill differential assembly with gear oil.

OVERHAUL

DIFFERENTIAL ASSEMBLY

Disassembly (Differential)

1) Remove caliper mounting brackets from differential assembly. Detach stub shafts, shims and bearing housings from each side and disassemble as necessary. *See Fig. 3.* See STUB AXLE, BEARINGS & OIL SEAL under REMOVAL & INSTALLATION in this article.

2) Remove housing cover. Mark side bearing caps for reassembly reference. Remove bearing caps. Remove differential assembly from housing.

NOTE: **Ensure bearings, races and bearing caps are marked for location.**

3) On conventional axles, grind off peened area of pinion shaft lock pin. Remove lock pin. Remove side gears, pinion gears and shafts.

4) On limited slip axles, scribe reference mark line on both halves of differential case for reassembly reference. Remove differential case retaining bolts. Separate differential case halves. Remove side gears, side rings, clutch plates, pinion gears and shafts. *See Fig. 3.*

5) On all models, remove ring gear retaining bolts. Remove ring gear from differential case. Using bearing puller, remove side bearings from differential case. Mark bearings and shims for location.

Disassembly (Drive Pinion)

1) Mark pinion flange and nut position for reassembly reference. Remove nut and washer. Using puller, remove pinion flange. Using a press, remove pinion from housing.

2) Using brass drift, tap inner bearing race from housing. Mark shims for location. Remove oil seal, oil slinger and outer bearing from housing. Remove outer bearing race.

Inspection

1) On all axles, inspect all gears for cracked or flaking teeth. Inspect pinion shaft for wear. Inspect pinion flange and drive pinion for damaged splines.

2) Inspect bearings and races for roughness or flaking. Replace worn components. On limited slip axles, inspect clutch components and contact areas for wear or overheating. Inspect clutch components for signs of seizure, excessive heat, severe friction or nicks.

NOTE: **Ensure pinion and ring gear reference numbers and letters match. The number on rear face of the case must match that on the end of pinion gear.**

REASSEMBLY & ADJUSTMENTS

Differential Case (Conventional)

1) Install pinion shaft, shims and gears into differential case. Install lock pin. Secure lock pin by peening. Install ring gear on differential case.

2) Install bolts with new tab washers. Tighten bolts to specification. Bend tab washers against bolt heads.

Differential Case (Limited Slip)

1) Install dished friction plates with convex sides against case. Install clutch plates and discs alternately into flange half of case. *See Fig. 4.*

2) Install side ring and side gear. Install pinion gears and shafts. Ensure ramps on shafts align with mating ramps of the case. Assemble differential case halves so reference marks are aligned.

3) Install retaining bolts. DO NOT tighten. Install stub axles in side gears. Tighten retaining bolts to specification with stub axles in position.

4) Check differential backlash. Hold one stub axle locked and note distance that remaining stub axle will rotate. Stub axle must not rotate more than 3/4" measured on a 6" radius. Remove stub axles. Install ring gear on differential case.

5) Install bolts with new tab washers. Tighten bolts to specification. Bend tab washers against bolt heads.

Fig. 4: Exploded View of Limited Slip Differential Assembly

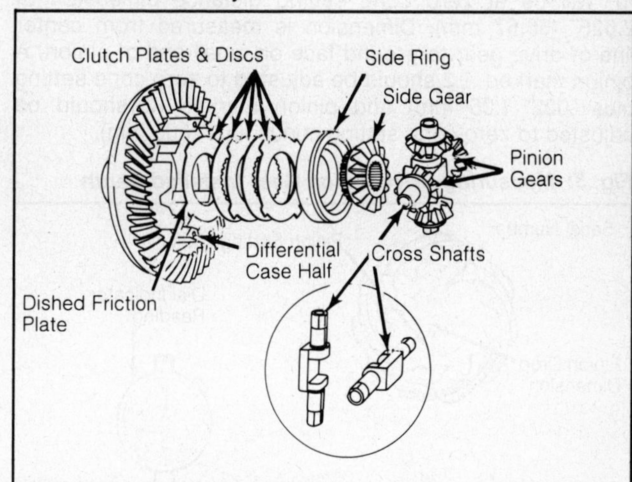

Courtesy of Jaguar Cars Inc.

Side Bearing Preload

1) Install differential side bearings. DO NOT install shims. Place differential case assembly in housing without pinion.

2) Measure total differential side bearing clearance. Add .009" (.20 mm) to reading to give total shim pack required to provide bearing preload. Remove differential assembly from housing.

Drive Pinion Depth & Preload

1) Install inner pinion bearing on pinion. Using Bearing Race Installer (SL.550-4 for XJ6 III and SL.550/8 for XJS) and Handle (550), install outer pinion bearing race. If necessary, heat case around race area to ease installation.

Drive Axles

JAGUAR (Cont.)

2) Using Bearing Race Installer (SL.550-9), install pinion inner bearing race, with adjusting shims previously removed. Install pinion and bearing assembly into housing. Support pinion and install outer pinion bearing, pinion flange, washer and nut.

NOTE: DO NOT install collapsible spacer, oil slinger and oil seal, at this time.

3) Tighten pinion nut just enough to eliminate all end play. Using Dial Indicator (SL.3), zero gauge on Setting Block (4HA). Install dial indicator with stem seated on face of pinion. Move assembly slightly to obtain minimum reading on dial. Note indicator reading to bottom of housing bearing bore. *See Fig. 5.*

4) Indicator reading shows deviation of pinion setting from zero cone setting. This value should agree with value etched on face of pinion (bottom marking). *See Fig. 5.* Note direction and amount of deviation.

NOTE: Markings on ground end of pinion are as follows: top mark is matched assembly serial number which is also marked on ring gear. Left letter mark (S) is the production code letter. Right letter and number (L1) is tolerance on offset or pinion drop dimension, also stamped on gear carrier housing cover facing, and bottom number is pinion cone setting distance (0, + or –).

5) When correctly adjusted, pinion marked with "0" will be at zero cone setting distance dimension of 2.625" (66.67 mm). Dimension is measured from center line of drive gear to ground face on small end of pinion. A pinion marked +2 should be adjusted to zero cone setting plus .002" (.05 mm) and pinion marked -2 should be adjusted to zero cone setting minus .002" (.05 mm).

Fig. 5: Measuring Drive Pinion Gear Installed Depth

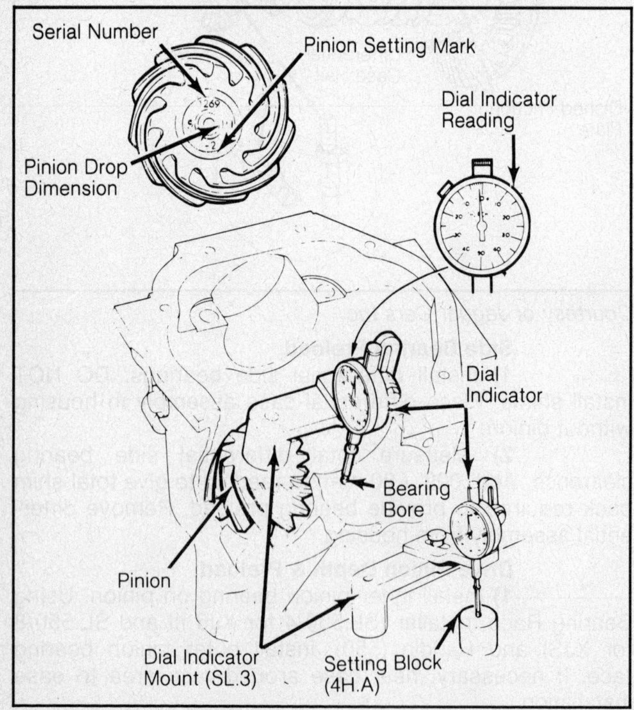

Courtesy of Jaguar Cars Inc.

6) If setting is incorrect, remove pinion. Remove pinion inner bearing race. Add or remove shims as required. Reassemble and recheck pinion depth. Shims are available in thicknesses of .0030" (.076 mm), .0050" (.127 mm) and .010" (.25 mm).

7) Remove pinion from housing when correct setting is obtained. Remove outer bearing. Install collapsible spacer on pinion. Ensure spacer seats firmly on machined shoulder of pinion. Intall pinion into housing.

8) Install outer bearing, oil slinger and oil seal. Lightly grease splines of pinion shaft and install flange. Install new washer on end of pinion with convex side facing end of shaft. Install nut. DO NOT tighten nut at this time.

9) Attach string to pinion. Using spring scale, measure pinion turning torque with oil seal and loose pinion bearings. This is the torque used to rotate pinion once shaft is turning. This reading is dimension "X".

10) Begin tightening nut in small increments to obtain proper rotating torque. Add dimension "X" to rotating torque. Rotating torque must be within specification. See PINION ROTATING TORQUE SPECIFICATIONS table. Measure rotating torque at several intervals.

PINION ROTATING TORQUE SPECIFICATIONS

Application	INCH Lbs. (N.m)
New Bearings	15-20 (1.70-2.26)
Old Bearings	25-35 (2.82-3.95)

NOTE: DO NOT loosen nut excessively. Spacer collapses during tightening and any reversal of nut will result in improper bearing cone clamping. If turning torque is exceeded, replace collapsible spacer.

Backlash Adjustment

1) Install differential case assembly without shims in housing. Tighten bearing cap bolts to specification. Install dial indicator on housing with stem on back of ring gear.

2) Pry differential case and ring gear assembly away from pinion until opposite side bearing is seated against housing. Adjust dial indicator to zero.

3) Move differential assembly towards pinion until ring gear is meshed with pinion. Note indicator reading. Subtract backlash allowance etched on ring gear for XJS models (example: B/L.007 denotes .007"). For XJ6 III models, backlash should be .006-.010" (.15-.25 mm).

4) This result will yield the thickness of shims (in inches) to be placed between differential case and side bearing on ring gear side of differential.

5) Install this thickness of shims. See SIDE BEARING PRELOAD in this article. Install balance of total shims required on opposite side of case. See EXAMPLE OF CALCULATIONS table.

6) With shims installed, install differential assembly. Install side bearing caps. Ensure bearing caps are installed in original location. Tighten cap bolts to specification. Mount dial indicator on housing with stem against back face of ring gear.

7) Turn pinion by hand and check ring gear runout. If runout exceeds .005" (.13 mm), disassemble differential. Clean all mounting surfaces and check for burrs.

Drive Axles

JAGUAR (Cont.)

EXAMPLE OF CALCULATIONS

Application	In. (mm)
Side Bearing Preload Reading	.080 (2.03)
PLUS Preload Value	.009 (.23)
Total Shim Pack	.089 (2.26)
Pinion-to-Ring Gear Clearance	.042 (1.07)
MINUS Backlash Value	.007 (.18)
Total Ring Gear Side Shims	.035 (.89)
Total Shim Pack	.089 (2.26)
MINUS Ring Gear Side Shims	.035 (.89)
Opposite Ring Gear Shim Pack	.054 (1.37)

8) Using dial indicator, check ring gear backlash at heel of ring gear tooth. Hold pinion and move ring gear and note reading. Backlash is to be within specification etched on ring gear for XJS models or .006-.010" (.15-.25 mm) for XJ6 III models. If backlash is not within specification, transfer necessary shims from one side of differential case to the other.

9) Check gear tooth contact using paint impression method. See GEAR TOOTH PATTERNS article in this section. Reverse removal procedure for remaining components. Tighten bolts to specifications.

TIGHTENING SPECIFICATIONS

Application	Ft. Lbs. (N.m)
Bearing Cap Bolt	63-70 (86-95)
Caliper Bracket-to-Differential Housing Bolt	49-55 (66-75)
Crossmember-to-Differential Assembly Bolt	70-77 (95-104)
Differential Case Bolt	43-50 (58-68)
Differential Cover Bolt	14-18 (19-24)
Exhaust Pipe Bolt	11-13 (15-18)
Fulcrum Bracket-to-Differential Set Screw	60-65 (81-88)
Fulcrum Shaft Nut	45-50 (61-68)
Half-Shaft Flange-to-Stub Shaft Flange Nut	49-55 (67-75)
Hub Carrier Assembly Nut	100-120 (136-163)
Outer Suspension Arm Fulcrum Nut	95-105 (129-142)
Pinion Flange Nut	120-130 (162-176)
Radius Arm Strap-to-Body Mounting Bolt	40-45 (54-61)
Ring Gear Bolt	70-88 (95-119)
Safety Strap-to-Body Bolt	27-32 (37-43)
Shock Absorber Mounting Nut	32-36 (43-49)
Stub Axle Nut	90-110 (122-149)

MAZDA

B2200, B2600, RX7

DESCRIPTION

Rear axle housing on B2200 and B2600 is banjo type with removable differential carrier and semi-floating drive axles. RX7 uses half-shaft type drive axles. Both models use a hypoid type ring and pinion. Centerline of pinion is set below centerline of ring gear. On RX7, an optional clutch pack Limited Slip Differential (LSD) is available.

The differential case may be either 2 pinion (normal differential) or 4 pinion (LSD differential) design. On B2200 and B2600, drive axles are retained in the housing by tapered bearings and bearing retainers at axle housing outer ends. On RX7, drive axles use CV joints to connect drive axles.

AXLE RATIO IDENTIFICATION

NOTE: **All Mazda models use one basic type of rear axle assembly. Any differences in servicing procedures will be noted where they occur.**

See AXLE RATIO table. To manually determine axle ratio, divide number of ring gear teeth by number of pinion teeth.

AXLE RATIO

Application	Ratio
B2200	3.91:1
B2600	
Auto. Trans.	3.91:1
Man. Trans.	3.73:1
RX7	
Auto. Trans.	3.9:1
Man. Trans.	4.10:1

REMOVAL & INSTALLATION

AXLE SHAFT & BEARING

Removal (B2200 & 2600)

1) Raise and support rear of vehicle. Remove rear wheels. Remove brake drum and brake shoes. Disconnect and plug brake line from wheel cylinder. Disconnect parking brake cable.

2) From inboard side of backing plate, remove nuts from the 4 axle housing through bolts. Pull drive axle, backing plate and bearing housing from axle housing. Be careful not to damage oil seal.

3) Using Bearing Nut Wrench (49 0603 635A) and Shaft holder (49 S120 645A), remove bearing lock nut from axle shaft

NOTE: **Left axle shaft lock nut is left hand threaded**

4) Remove wheel hub assembly using Rear Shaft Bearing Puller (49 S120 520). Use a round bar to tap outer race from hub.

Installation

1) Press new bearing outer race into wheel hub. Coat bearing race with grease. Tap oil seal in place until it is flush with end of axle casing. Coat oil seal lip with grease.

2) Install spacer on axle shaft with grooved surface facing backing plate. Using Press Attachment (49 S120 748) and a press, install wheel bearing on axle shaft.

3) Using Press Attachment (49 S120 748) and a press, press bearing collar on axle shaft. Standard press force is 30,379-44,121 lbs. (4200-6100 kg). If press fit force is too high or too low, replace the bearing collar or shaft.

4) Using Bearing Nut Wrench (49 0603 635A), install bearing lock nut to axle shaft and tighten to 145-217 ft. lbs. (196-245 N.m). Install one axle. Tighten backing plate bolts. Install dial indicator on backing plate and check drive axle end play. End play should be .026-.037" (.65-.95 mm), with one axle installed.

NOTE: **Adjust end play for first drive axle before inserting second drive axle. Use shims to adjust end play.**

5) To adjust end play, remove axle and insert appropriate size adjustment shim between axle hub and housing. Shims are available in sizes .004-.030" (.10-.75 mm). End play for second drive axle installed should be set to normal end play clearance of .002-.010" (.05-.25 mm), with both axles installed.

6) Tighten backing plate mounting nuts. Install parking brake cable, attaching pin and brake line. Install brake shoes and actuating hardware. Bleed brake system. Install wheel and tire.

Removal (RX7)

1) Raise rear of vehicle and support with safety stands. Remove rear wheels. Remove lock nut. Remove drive shaft flange bolts. Remove drive shaft. Disconnect caliper assembly and wire it out of the way. Remove disc plate.

2) Remove backing plate. Remove knuckle assembly. Loosen dust cover. Using Bearing Installer (49 F026 102) and a press, remove wheel hub. Using Puller (49 0636 145) and a press, remove wheel bearing inner race. Remove snap ring. Using Adapter (49 F027 007) and a press, remove wheel bearing outer race.

Installation

1) Using Bearing Installer (49 F026 102), Attachment (49 0259 748) and a press, install wheel bearing outer race. Install snap ring. Install wheel bearing inner race. Install dust cover. Using bearing installer and a press, install wheel hub.

2) Install knuckle assembly. Tighten bolts to 46-69 ft. lbs. (63-93 N.m) and then to 82-111 ft. lbs. (112-151 N.m). Install disc plate and caliper. Install drive shaft.

3) Tighten lock nut to 174-231 ft. lbs. (235-314 N.m). Measure end play. If end play exceeds .004" (.10 mm), replace wheel bearings. Crimp lock nut.

DIFFERENTIAL CARRIER

Removal

1) Raise and support vehicle with jack stands. Remove drain plug and drain lubricant. Remove tire and wheel assembly. Mark drive axles and propeller shaft positions. On B2200 and B2600, remove brake drum and drive axles. See AXLE SHAFT & BEARING in this article. On RX7, disconnect drive axles from differential assembly and wire out of the way.

2) Disconnect propeller shaft. On B2200 and B2600, remove attaching nuts and withdraw carrier from

MAZDA (Cont.)

Fig. 1: Exploded View of RX7 Drive Axle Shaft Assembly

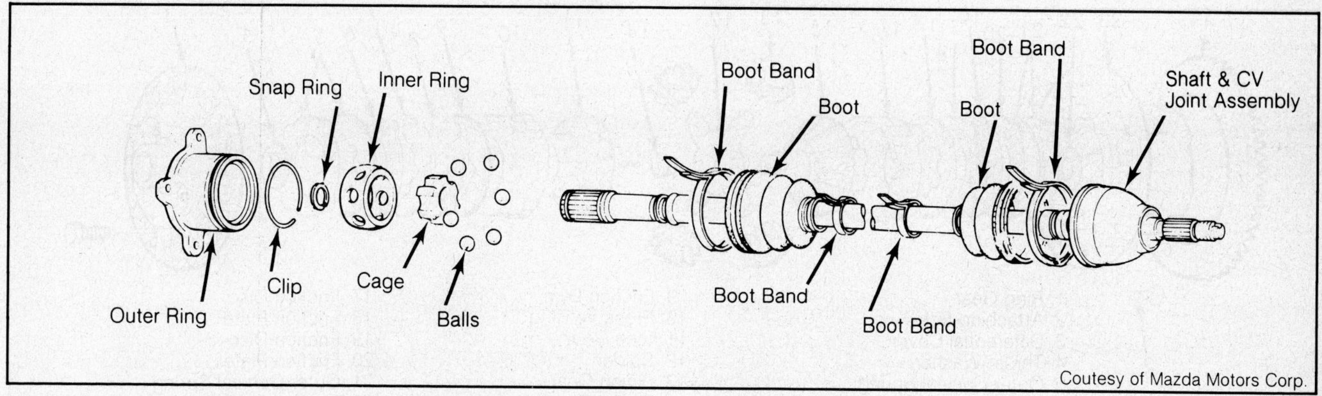

axle housing. On RX7, remove differential assembly. With differential assembly outside vehicle, remove nuts securing differential carrier. Remove differential carrier.

Installation

To install, reverse removal procedure. Apply Sealant (8527 77 739) to carrier mating flanges. Align marks made during removal. Refill axle with correct type and amount of lubricant.

OVERHAUL

AXLE SHAFT

Disassembly (RX7)

1) Remove drive shaft. Remove bands from rubber boots. *See Fig. 1.* Slide boot up on shaft. Remove clip from inside CV joint. Remove snap ring. Remove balls, inner ring and cage from shaft.

2) Rotate cage approximately 30 degrees and separate it from inner ring. Wrap tape around shaft and remove boot.

Reassembly

1) Slide new boots on shaft. Boot sizes are different. Wheel side boot has a diameter of 3.88" (98.5 mm). Differential side boot is 3.76" (95.5 mm). Install boot bands. Attach clip in shaft groove. Install inner race into cage.

2) Rotate cage approximately 30 degrees. Install balls. Apply grease to balls. Install cage to shaft. Install snap ring. Check axle shaft length. Standard length should be 24.2-25.6" (614-651 mm).

Fig. 2: Exploded View of B2200 & B2600 Rear Axle Assembly (Conventional)

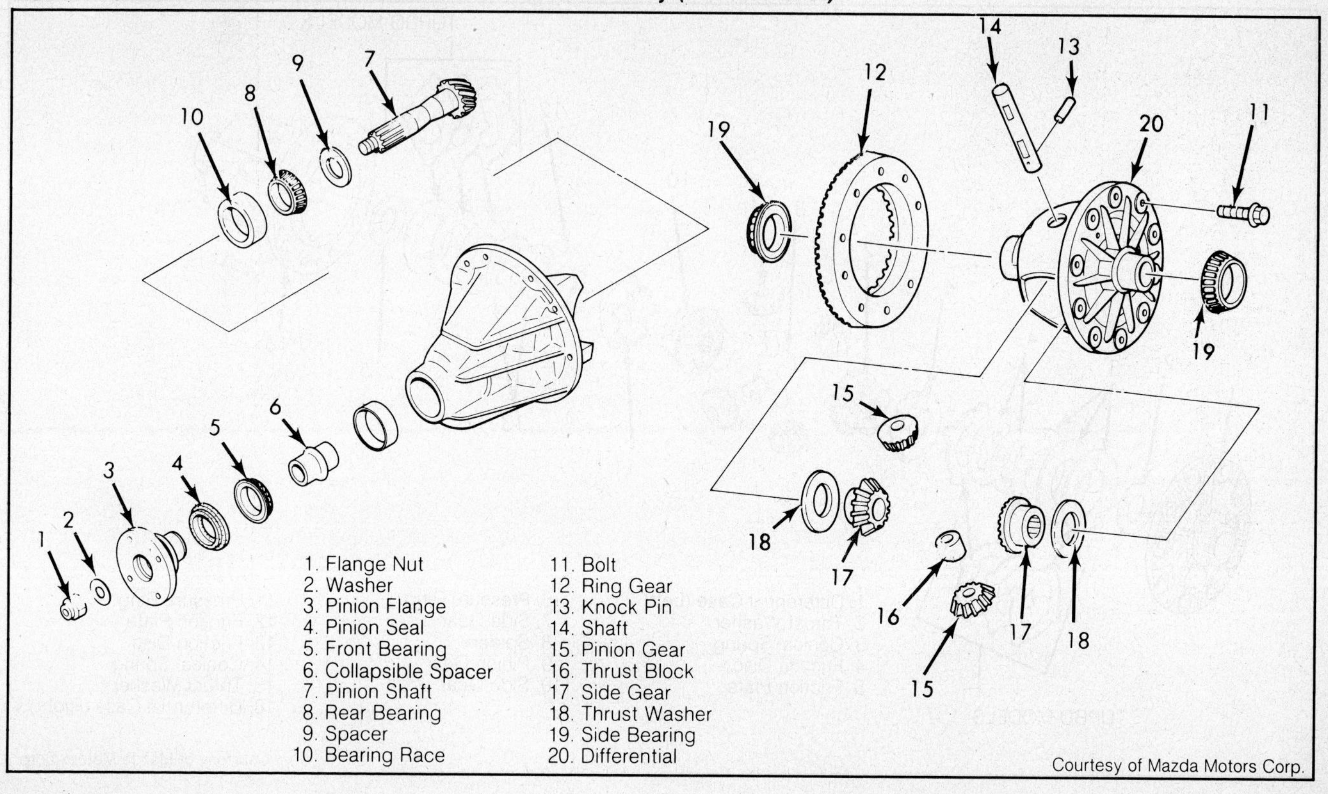

Drive Axles

MAZDA (Cont.)

Fig. 3: Exploded View of B2200 & B2600 Differential Assembly (Limited Slip)

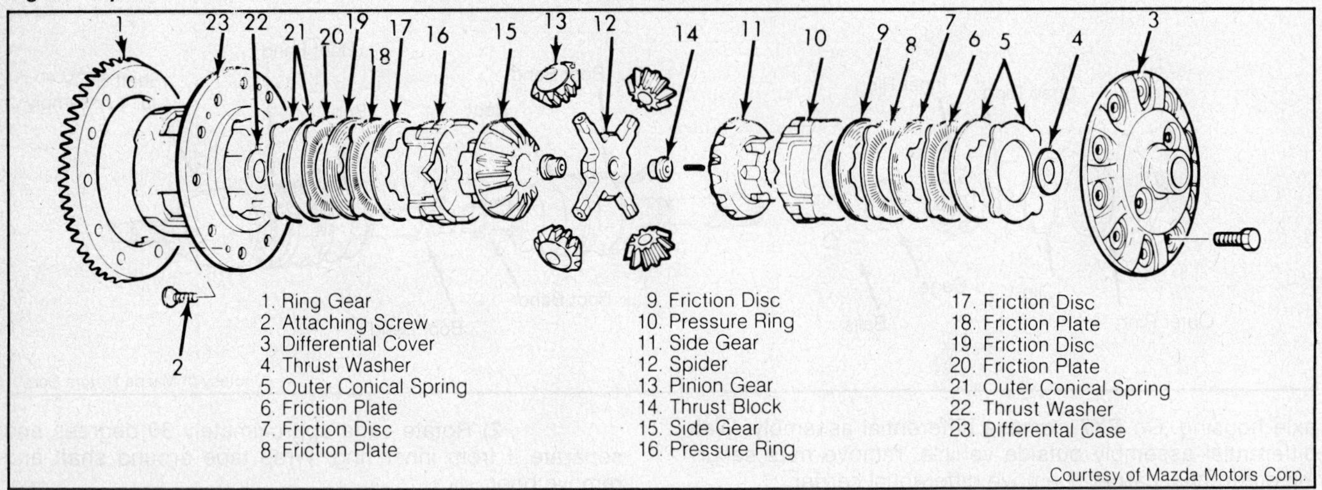

CARRIER ASSEMBLY

Disassembly

1) Mount carrier in a repair stand. Mark side bearing caps for reassembly purposes. Remove adjuster lock plates, loosen bearing cap attaching nuts or bolts, and slightly back off adjusters to relieve preload.

2) Remove bearing caps and adjusters. Withdraw differential assembly from carrier, ensuring side bearing races remain with their respective bearings.

3) Hold companion flange with Coupling Flange Holder (49 0259 710A) and remove drive pinion nut. Remove companion flange using a common gear puller of the appropriate size. Remove drive pinion, spacer, rear bearing and collapsable spacer assembly from carrier.

4) Remove oil seal and front bearing. If necessary, remove bearing outer races using a drift in slots provided on inner lip.

DIFFERENTIAL ASSEMBLY

Disassembly

1) Using Puller (49 0839 425C), remove side bearings from gear case. Ensure side bearing are marked

Fig. 4: Exploded View of RX7 Rear Axle Assembly (Limited Slip)

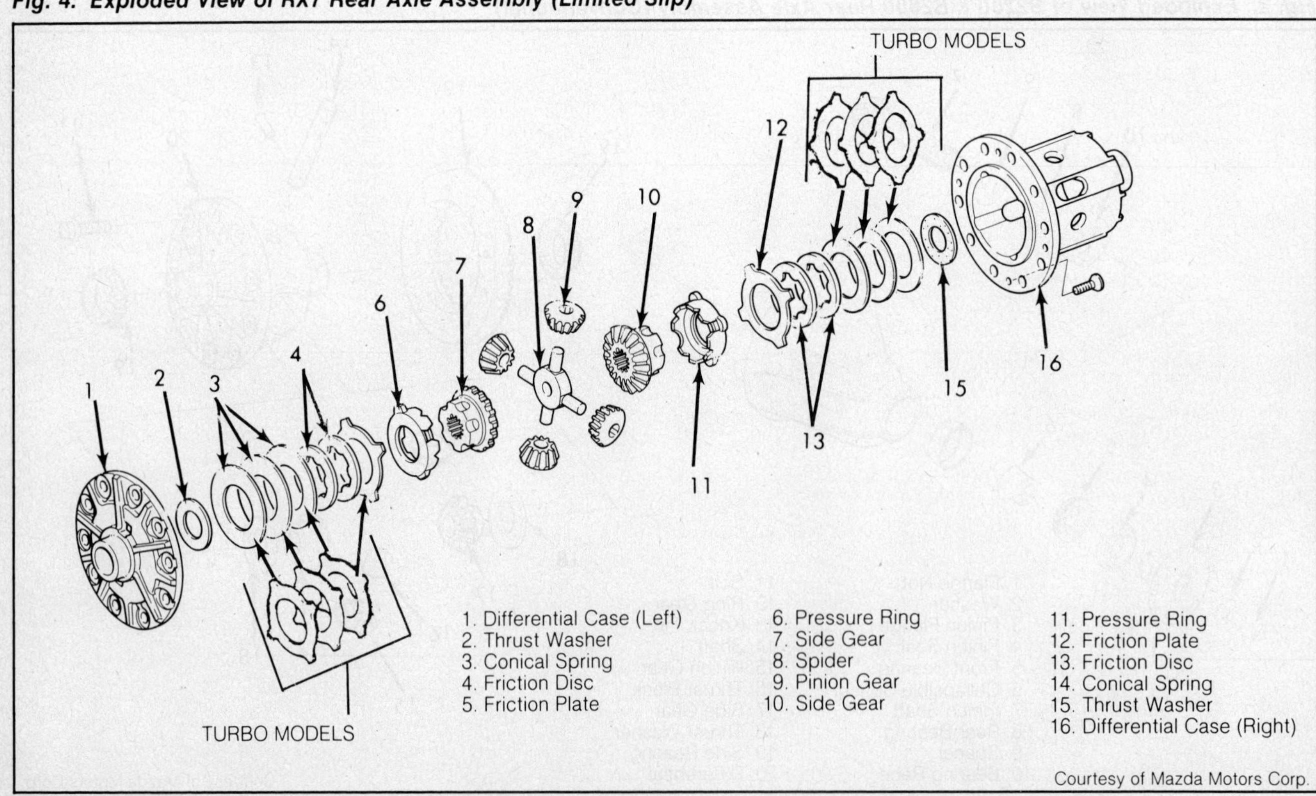

for reassembly purposes. Remove ring gear attaching bolts and separate ring gear from gear case. On limited slip differentials, gradually loosen attaching screws until distance between left and right half of differential case is about 0.12" (3 mm).

2) Mark differential halves for reassembly purposes. Carefully separate differential halves. Remove thrust washer, conical springs, friction plates, friction discs, pressure ring, side gear, pinion gear and spider. Keep parts in order for reassembly. *See Figs. 3 and 4*.

3) Drive out differential pinion shaft lock pin with a punch and remove pinion shaft. Rotate pinion gears 90 degrees and remove gears, thrust washer, thrust block (if equipped) and differential side gears.

4) Inspect all parts for chipped or worn teeth, damaged bearing journals, cracks, flaking or any damage. Replace defective parts as necessary.

Reassembly (Standard Differential)

1) Install side gears, thrust washers, thrust block, pinion gears, pinion shaft and knock pin. Stake knock pin. Using Adapter (49 G030 338) and a press, install side bearing on differential assembly. Position a dial indicator against pinion gear.

2) Secure one side gear. Check side gear and pinion gear backlash. If backlash exceeds .004" (.10 mm), replace thrust washers. Install ring gear. Tighten bolt to specifications. See TIGHTENING SPECIFICATIONS table in this article.

Reassembly
(B2200 & B2600 - LSD Differential)

1) Check friction plate, disc and thrust washer thicknesses. See B2200 & B2600 DIFFERENTIAL COMPONENT SPECIFICATIONS table in this article. Measure thickness of 4 conical springs and record measurements.

2) Measure thickness of complete clutch pack excluding conical springs. *See Fig. 5*. Subtract conical spring thickness and complete clutch pack thickness from 3.589" (91.15 mm). Difference should be .002-008" (.05-.20 mm).

3) If clearance is excessive, use oversize friction discs. Oversize friction disc thickness is .0728" (1.85 mm). Measure thickness of complete clutch pack with side gears, pressure rings, spider, pinion gears and thrust washers in place.

4) Subtract thickness from 3.7057" (94.125 mm). Difference should be .0039-.0157" (.10-.40 mm). If clearance is not as specified, install oversize thrust washers. See "B" SERIES DIFFERENTIAL COMPONENT SPECIFICATIONS table in this article.

"B" SERIES DIFFERENTIAL COMPONENT SPECIFICATIONS

Application	mm
Friction Plate Thickness	
Standard	1.73-1.77
Limit	1.65
Friction Disc Thickness	
Standard	1.73-1.77
Limit	1.65
Oversize	1.85
Thrust Washer	
Standard	1.48-1.52
Limit	1.4
Oversize	1.6 & 1.7

Fig. 5: Measuring Complete Clutch Pack Thickness

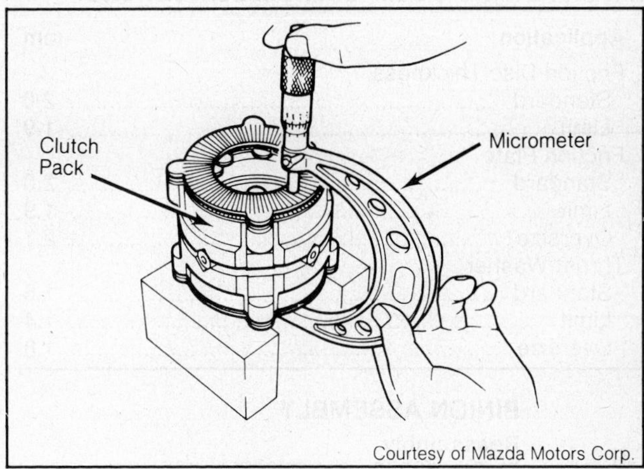

5) Coat thrust washer with grease and install in differential half. *See Fig. 3*. Install conical springs with concave side away from friction discs and plates. Install friction plates and discs in the following order: disc, plate, disc. Install pressure ring and side gear. Install pinion gear and spider assembly. Ensure spider is flat in case. Install other side gear and pressure ring.

6) Install friction plates and disc in this following order: disc, plate, disc, plate. Install conical springs with concave side away from friction discs and plates. Coat thrust washer with grease and install. Position other differential half and align marks made during disassembly. Install bolts and tighten. Apply locking compound to rear face of ring gear. Install ring gear on differential assembly.

Reassembly
(RX7 - LSD Differential)

1) Check friction plate, disc and thrust washer thicknesses. See DIFFERENTIAL COMPONENT SPECIFICATIONS table in this article. Measure thickness of 3 conical springs and record measurements.

2) Measure thickness of complete clutch pack excluding conical springs. *See Fig. 5*. Subtract conical spring thickness and complete clutch pack thickness from 3.583" (91.00 mm). Difference should be .004-010" (.10-.25 mm).

3) If clearance is excessive, use oversize friction discs. Oversize friction disc thickness is .0827" (2.10 mm). Measure thickness of side gears, pressure rings, spider, pinion gears and thrust washers in place.

4) Subtract thickness from 3.701" (94.00 mm). Difference should be .004-.016" (.10-.40 mm). If clearance is not as specified, install oversize thrust washers. See RX7 DIFFERENTIAL COMPONENT SPECIFICATIONS table in this article.

5) Install proper parts in proper order. *See Fig. 4*. Before installing thrust washers, coat with grease. When installing conical springs, ensure concave side faces side gears.

6) Align differential case and cover alignment marks. Install bolts and tighten. Apply locking compound to rear face of ring gear. Install ring gear on differential assembly.

Drive Axles

MAZDA (Cont.)

RX7 DIFFERENTIAL COMPONENT SPECIFICATIONS

Application	mm
Friction Disc Thickness	
Standard	2.0
Limit	1.9
Friction Plate	
Standard	2.0
Limit	1.9
Oversize	2.1
Thrust Washer	
Standard	1.6
Limit	1.4
Oversize	1.8

PINION ASSEMBLY

Reassembly

1) On B2200 and B2300, using press, install pinion bearing races in differential housing. Place original spacer, rear bearing and Bearing Collar (49 H027 001) onto Drive Pinion (49 8531 565). Secure collar with "O" ring. Install assembly into differential housing.

2) Place front bearing, Collar (49 U027 001), companion flange, washer and original flange nut in differential housing. *See Fig. 6*. Tighten flange nut so assembly can be turned by hand. On RX7, using press, install pinion bearing races in differential housing.

3) Install rear spacer and Drive Pinion (49 F027 001). Install center bearing, long collar, companion flange, washer and nut. Tighten flange nut enough so drive pinion can be rotated by hand.

Fig. 6: Checking Pinion Position (B2200 & B2600)

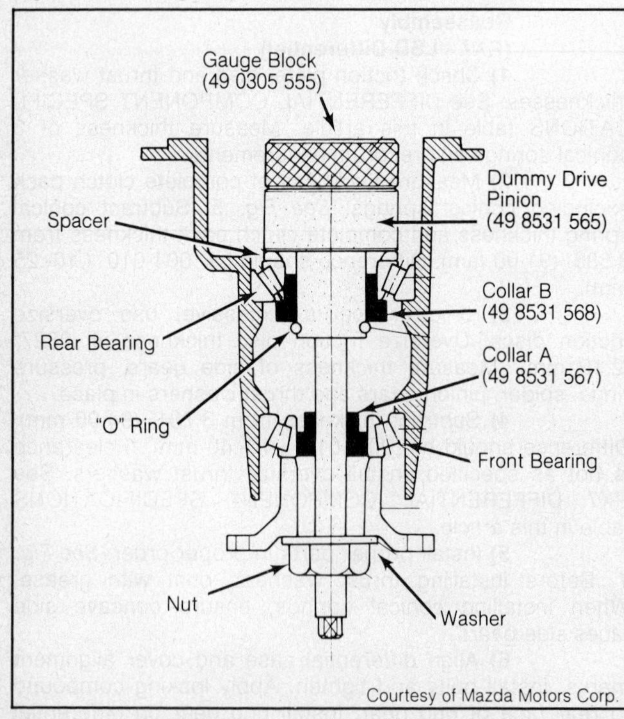

Courtesy of Mazda Motors Corp.

4) On all models, place a dial indicator on Pinion Height Gauge (49 0727 570). Place pinion height gauge on a flat surface and zero dial indicator. Position Gauge Block (49 0305 555 on RX7, 49 0660 55 on B2200 and B2600) on top of Drive Pinion (49 8531 565).

5) Set pinion height gauge on top of gauge block. Set dial indicator to measure distance to a point where side bearing sits. Measure lowest point. *See Fig. 7*. Measure both sides. Add both measurements together and divide sum by 2. Record this measurement.

6) Divide number etched on end of pinion shaft by 100. If no number is etched on end of pinion use zero. Subtract this amount from previous recorded measurement. Difference is the spacer thickness to be added to installed spacer to be used between pinion gear and rear pinion bearing. See PINION DEPTH ADJUSTING SHIMS table in this article.

PINION DEPTH ADJUSTING SHIMS

Identification Mark	Thickness In. (mm)
08	.121 (3.08)
11	.122 (3.11)
14	.124 (3.14)
17	.125 (3.17)
20	.126 (3.20)
23	.127 (3.23)
26	.128 (3.26)
29	.130 (3.29)
32	.131 (3.32)
35	.132 (3.35)
38	.133 (3.38)
41	.134 (3.41)
44	.135 (3.44)
47	.137 (3.47)

7) Remove dummy pinion shaft. Using Bearing Installer Kit (49 F401 330B), press rear pinion bearing on pinion shaft. Using press, install rear bearing. Press on bearing until pressure suddenly increases.

8) Install pinion shaft, spacer, front bearing, collapsable spacer and companion flange in differential housing. DO NOT install pinion seal at this time.

9) Tighten flange nut to 94-130 ft. lbs. (128-177 N.m). Check pinion bearing preload. Preload should be

Fig. 7: Checking Pinion Height

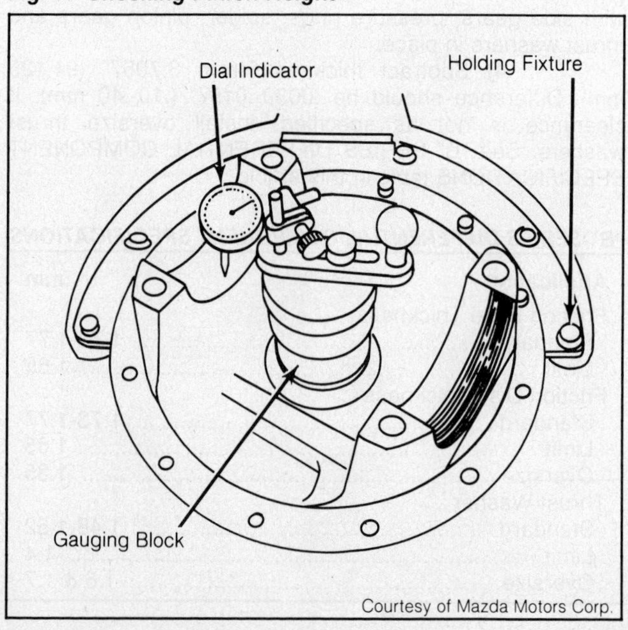

Courtesy of Mazda Motors Corp.

7.8-12.2 INCH lbs. (.9-1.4 N.m). If pinion bearing preload is not as specified, replace collapsable spacer and recheck preload.

10) Remove flange nut and companion flange. Install pinion seal, using Installer (49 M005 796). Apply oil to seal lip. Install companion flange. Using a new flange nut, tighten nut to 94-130 ft. lbs. (128-177 N.m). Recheck pinion bearing preload.

CARRIER ASSEMBLY

Reassembly

1) Install differential assembly in differential housing. Mesh pinion gear and ring gear. Position side bearing caps in differential housing. Align marks made during disassembly. Install side bearing cap bolts. DO NOT tighten at this time.

2) Using Bearing Adjuster (49 0259 720), tighten side bearing adjusters equally until adjuster contact bearing races. Mark ring gear in 4 locations, 90 degrees apart. Position a dial indicator against ring gear to check ring gear backlash.

3) Check backlash at all 4 locations. Tighten side bearing adjusters equally until backlash is .0035-.0043" (.09-.11 mm). Minimum total backlash at all 4 locations should be .002" (.05 mm). Difference between each backlash check should not exceed .0028" (.07 mm).

4) Tighten adjustment screws equally until distance between both pilot sections is 7.3004-7.3033" (185.43-185.50 mm) on RX7 and B2200. Distance on B2600 is 8.0484-7.0512" (204.42-204.50 mm). *See Fig. 8.*

5) Tighten side bearing cap bolts to specifications. See TIGHTENING SPECIFICATIONS table in this article. Check ring gear tooth patterns. SEE GEAR TOOTH PATTERNS article in this section.

Fig. 8: Checking Pilot Section Distance

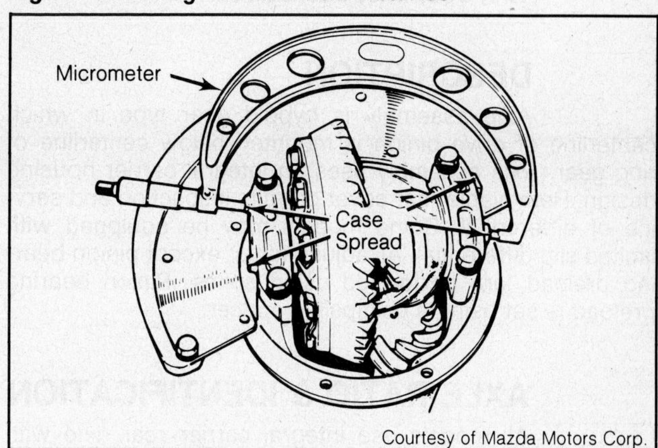

Courtesy of Mazda Motors Corp.

TIGHTENING SPECIFICATIONS

Application	Ft. Lbs. (N.m)
RX7	
Differential Case Hanger Nut	65-77 (88-105)
Differential Front Member Support Nut	54-69 (74-93)
Differential Housing Sub-Link Bolt	54-69 (74-93)
Differential Housing Support Nuts	54-69 (74-93)
Drive Axle Inner Nut	40-47 (54-64)
Drive Axle Outer Nut	174-231 (235-314)
Knuckle Assembly Mounting Bolts	
Step 1	46-69 (63-93)
Step 2	82-111 (112-151)
All Models	
Differential Housing Mounting Nuts	17-20 (23-26)
Pinion Flange Nut	94-130 (128-177)
Ring Gear-to-Differential Case Bolts	51-61 (69-83)
Side Bearing Cap Bolts	27-38 (37-52)

Drive Axles

MERCEDES-BENZ INTEGRAL CARRIER

190, 300, 420, 560 Series

DESCRIPTION

Axle assembly is hypoid gear type in which centerline of drive pinion is mounted below centerline of ring gear. Axle assembly uses an integral carrier housing design. Removable rear cover permits inspection and service of differential. Some models may be equipped with limited slip differential. All adjustments, except pinion bearing preload, are performed using shims. Pinion bearing preload is set using a collapsible spacer.

AXLE RATIO & IDENTIFICATION

All models use integral carrier rear axle with semi-trailing arm rear suspension. To determine axle ratio, divide the number of ring gear teeth by the number of pinion gear teeth.

REMOVAL & INSTALLATION

AXLE SHAFTS

Removal (190 Series)

Remove rear differential assembly from vehicle. Drain gear oil. Remove rear cover. Remove "C" lock and discard. Remove axle shaft from differential. Check sealing ring. Replace sealing ring (if necessary). Ensure compensating ring, inside flange, is firmly seated.

Installation

Install axle shaft. Install new "C" lock. Check axle shaft for end play. There should not be any end play. If there is end play, rotate "C" lock and recheck. If specification is still not correct, use a thicker "C" lock. Apply sealing compound to rear cover and install. Install rear differential assembly.

Removal (All Models Except 190 Series)

1) Drain lubricant from rear axle. Remove brake caliper and suspend with wire. Remove axle shaft-to-axle shaft flange bolt. Force axle shaft out of axle shaft flange. If additional clearance is required to aid in axle shaft removal, remove upper shock absorber mount and lower suspension arm to stop.

2) Support axle housing and remove rubber mount from body. Lower axle housing slightly. Clean housing and remove rear cover plate. Remove and discard "C" lock holding axle shaft to differential side gear. Pull shaft from gear along with spacer.

Installation

1) Face of "U" joint spider carries a stamped "R" for right or "L" for left. Ensure correct axle is used on correct side. Place old spacer ring on constant velocity joint. Slide axle shaft into differential side gear and install new "C" lock onto shaft.

2) Check end play between inner "U" joint and axle housing. There should be no end play. In addition, lock ring should still turn in groove. If necessary, install a thicker or thinner lock ring to achieve desired results.

3) Completely telescope axle shaft and install axle shaft flange. Tighten attaching nut. Mount end cover with sealing compound and tighten attaching bolts. Raise axle housing and install rubber mount to axle housing. Attach rubber mount to body.

Fig. 1: Removing Axle Shaft "C" Lock

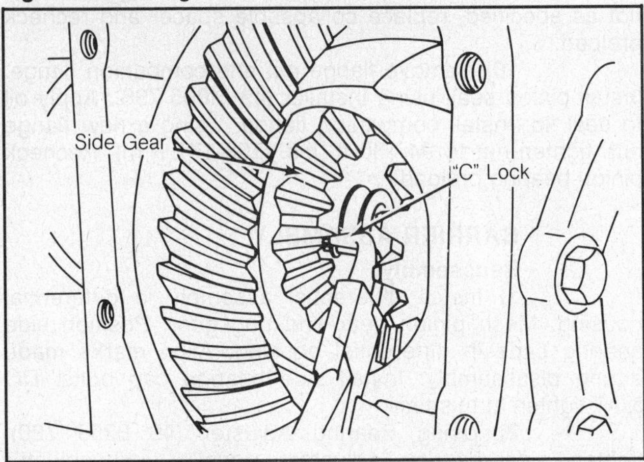

CONSTANT VELOCITY JOINT

Removal

1) Remove axle shaft. Cut stop sleeve of constant velocity (CV) joint on beaded edge and pull sleeve from spider joint. Remove spider from hub along with 6 balls. Remove locking ring from groove in axle shaft. Press spider from shaft.

2) Pull stop sleeve and rubber sleeve from shaft. Loosen hose clamps and pull second rubber sleeve across disassembled end of axle shaft. Carefully clean joint. Inspect balls and other parts for wear or damage.

Installation

1) Slide new rubber sleeve onto shaft up to bead. Place Assembly Sleeve (115 589 01 63 00) on splines to protect against damage. Place new stop sleeve on shaft and press spider onto axle shaft. Install locking ring. Assemble spider and 6 balls using magnetic ball holders for assistance.

2) Place new sealing rings on spider and attach new protective sleeve. Insert complete axle shaft into Crimper (115 589 36 63 00) and install split supporting ring. Attach beading ring and crimp edge of sleeve while tightening nuts against stop of crimper.

3) Remove axle shaft from crimper and fill CV joint with CV joint grease (supplied with rubber sleeve repair kit). Attach rubber sleeve to stop sleeve and axle shaft with new hose clamps.

AXLE SHAFT FLANGE & BEARING

Removal (190 Series)

1) Remove rear axle shaft. Remove brake caliper and wire out of the way. Remove brake rotor. Using Puller (201 589 00 61 29), remove axle shaft flange. Remove snap ring.

2) Using a puller, remove bearing. Place axle shaft flange in a soft-jawed vise. Press bearing inner race from flange. Check flange runout. See AXLE ASSEMBLY SPECIFICATIONS table at the end of this article.

Installation

Press bearing in rear axle shaft flange. Install snap ring. Ensure snap ring is seated. Install axle shaft flange. Ensure thrust washer is against bearing inner race. Install brake rotor and caliper. Install axle shaft.

Removal (All Models Except 190 Series)

1) Remove bolt and force axle shaft out of axle shaft flange. Pull axle shaft up and out of way. Support axle

MERCEDES-BENZ INTEGRAL CARRIER (Cont.)

shaft with wire. Do not allow axle shaft to hang down. Remove brake caliper and rotor. If necessary, remove parking brake shoes.

2) Hold axle shaft flange and remove slotted nut from axle shaft flange. Remove sealing rings from support housing. Knock axle shaft flange out of support housing. Remove bearing inner race along with spacer sleeve.

3) Remove outer sealing ring from support housing. Remove outer bearing outer race from support housing. Remove inner bearing outer race from support housing. Remove outer bearing inner race from axle shaft flange.

Installation

1) Ensure axle shaft flanges are installed on correct sides. Right flange is marked with "R" and left flange is marked with "L". Press outer bearing inner race onto axle shaft flange. Install both outer bearing races in support housing.

2) Coat seat for outer sealing ring on support housing with sealing compound and install seal. Ensure seal rests straight against chamfer at bottom of housing. Fill cavity between bearing races in support housing with grease.

3) Attach new spacer sleeve to axle shaft flange and install into carrier housing. Attach inner bearing inner race onto axle shaft. Fill new sealing ring with anti-friction grease and coat outer edge with sealing compound. Press inner race and sealing ring into housing. Install seal running ring and install new slot nut.

Fig. 2: Checking Axle Shaft Flange End Play

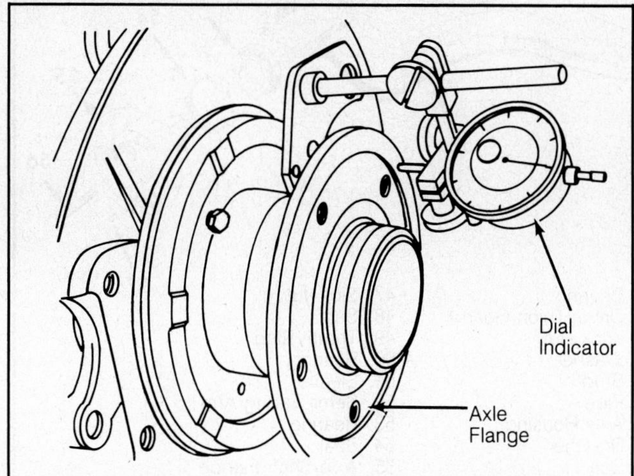

4) Attach dial indicator to support housing and adjust end play of axle shaft flange while rotating axle shaft flange back and forth. If slot nut is overtightened, reducing end play to zero, install new spacer sleeve and retighten slot nut.

5) Lock slot nut in place by bending in axle shaft flange at 2 points. Install axle shaft and brake components. Bleed brake system.

PINION FLANGE & SEAL

Removal (All Models Except 190 Series)

1) Remove exhaust system and shield (if necessary). Loosen clamping nut and unscrew propeller shaft intermediate bearing from frame. On 3-piece propeller shaft, loosen front clamping nut only. Remove propeller shaft from axle and push forward out of center support.

2) Ensure axle shafts are horizontal and that brakes are not dragging. Measure and record torque required to rotate entire rear axle assembly. Attach holding wrench to flange and remove slotted nut.

3) Pull flange from pinion using puller (if necessary). Pry seal out of housing using a screwdriver. Check running surface of seal on flange. Replace flange if surface is worn.

Installation

1) Coat outside diameter of new seal with gear oil. Install seal into axle housing using a seal installer. Attach flange and carefully tighten slotted nut until rotating torque for rear axle is the same as measured before removal. DO NOT overtighten or a new collapsible spacer will have to be installed on pinion. Peen nut if crush nut is used.

2) Reconnect propeller shaft and lightly tighten propeller shaft intermediate bearing. Fill axle housing with oil. Lower vehicle and move back and forth several times. Tighten clamping nut propeller shaft intermediate bearing. Reinstall shield and exhaust system (if removed).

Removal (190 Series)

1) Remove exhaust shield. Loosen clamping nut and unscrew propeller shaft intermediate bearing on frame floor. Remove propeller shaft from flange on rear axle and push forward from center position.

2) Tie propeller shaft with wire to frame floor. Measure and record rotating torque of entire rear axle drive. When measuring rotating torque, ensure rear axle shafts are approximately horizontal. Ensure brake pads are not rubbing against brake disks or parking brake shoes against drum.

3) Position Holding Wrench (040) on universal flange and loosen 12-point collar. Loosen, but DO NOT remove, collar nut with crush lock. Remove universal flange from drive pinion using puller.

4) Remove radial seal from rear axle housing using a screwdriver. *See Fig. 4.* Check running surface of seal on universal flange. Replace universal flange if running surface is worn out.

Installation

1) To install, reverse removal procedure. Install seal. Mount universal flange and carefully tighten with a new 12-point collar nut until measured rotating torque is attained.

2) Tighten collar nut to at least 133 ft. lbs. (180 N.m). If this minimum tightening is not attained, replace elastic spacing sleeve.

AXLE ASSEMBLY

Removal (All Models Except 190 Series)

1) Drain oil from rear axle. On vehicles without starting torque compensation, remove right brake caliper and suspend out of way. On vehicles with starting torque compensation, disconnect brake control cable. Loosen rubber bearing from frame floor and rear center piece from rear axle carrier.

2) Disconnect axle shafts from axle shaft flange on both sides. If necessary, remove exhaust system and shield (if necessary). Loosen clamping nut and unscrew propeller shaft intermediate bearing on frame.

3) On 3-piece propeller shaft, loosen front clamping nut only. Disconnect propeller shaft and push forward out of way. On models equipped with anti-lock brake system, remove RPM sensor. Support axle assembly with jack and holding fixture.

MERCEDES-BENZ INTEGRAL CARRIER (Cont.)

Fig. 3: Exploded View of Mercedes-Benz Drive Axle Assembly (All Models Except 190 Series)

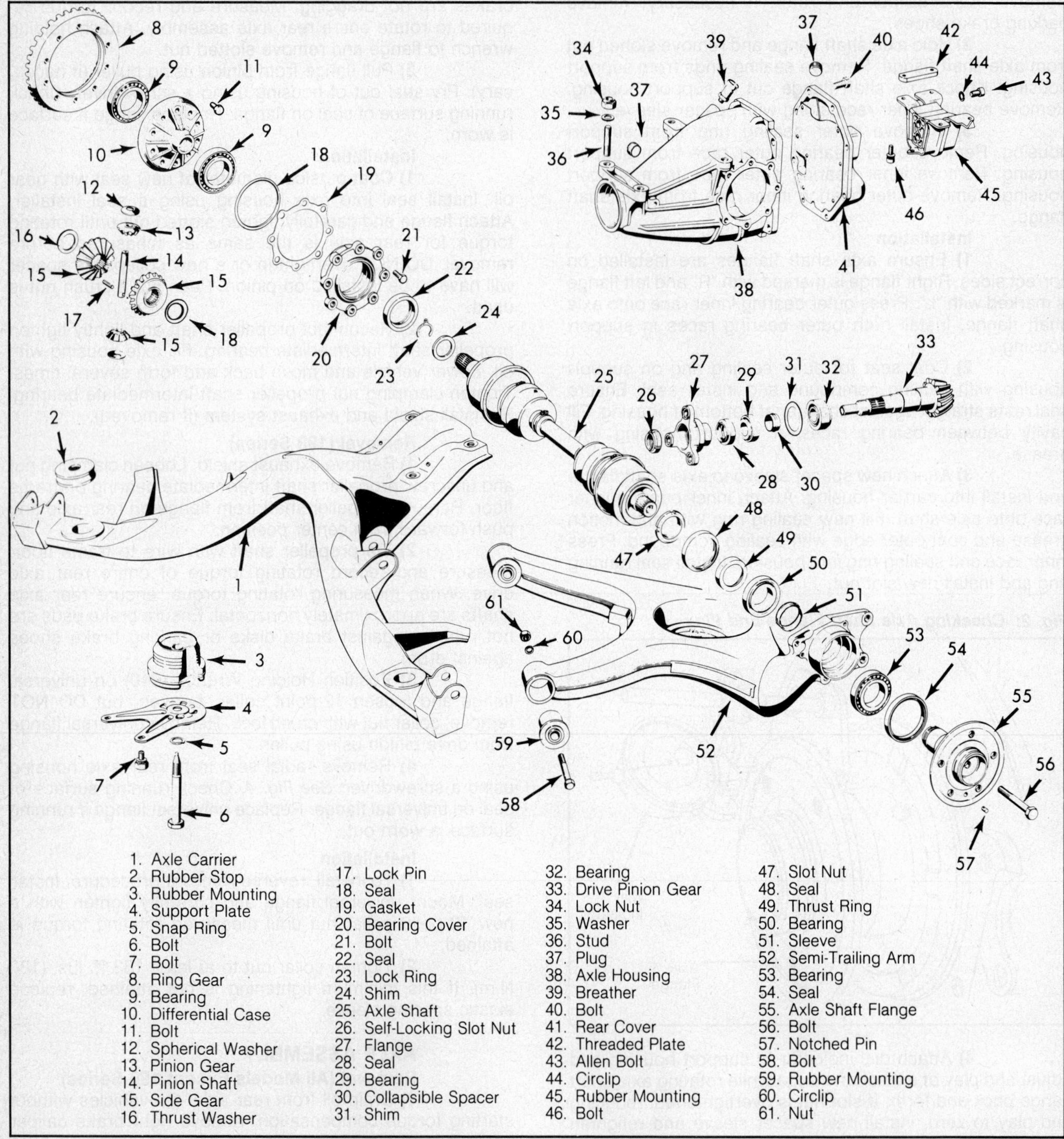

Courtesy of Mercedes-Benz of North America.

4) Unbolt rear rubber mounting on frame floor. Fold back rubber mat in trunk and remove rubber plugs. Unbolt axle housing from rear axle carrier.

5) Lower rear axle and remove along with axle drive shafts. Use care not to let axle drive shafts drop. Unbolt rubber mounting from housing and replace if worn or damaged.

Installation

1) Attach rubber mounting to axle housing. Place axle assembly on jack and holding fixture. Raise axle up under vehicle. Mount axle housing to rear axle carrier and tighten nuts. Install rubber plugs and install trunk rubber floor mat. Reattach anti-lock brake system RPM sensor. Install both axle shafts into axle shaft flanges and tighten attaching bolts.

2) Lift axle housing up to frame floor and attach rubber mounting to frame. Reconnect propeller shaft and lightly attach propeller shaft intermediate bearing. On vehicles without starting torque compensation, mount brake caliper using new lock washers.

Fig. 4: Removing Axle Flange

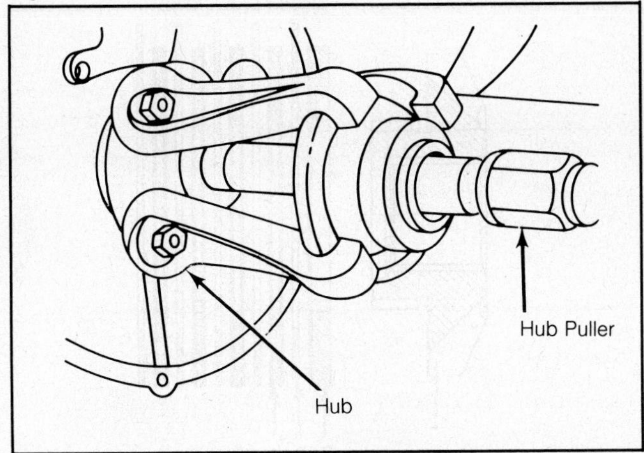

3) On vehicles with starting torque compensation, mount holding bracket for brake cable control to support housing, slide on cover and rubber sleeve, attach cable control and adjust parking brake.

4) Fill axle with oil to level of filler hole. Lower vehicle. Rock vehicle back and forth several times. Tighten clamping nut on propeller shaft and tighten propeller shaft intermediate bearing. Install exhaust system and shield (if removed).

Removal & Installation (190 Models)

1) Remove exhaust system and shields. Remove intermediate parking brake lever. Disconnect parking brake cables. Disconnect brake lines and plug. Loosen propeller shaft clamping nut. Remove propeller shaft intermediate bearing mounting bolts.

2) Disconnect rear of propeller shaft. Wire propeller shaft out of the way. Remove spring link cover. Disconnect shock absorbers. Remove rear springs and torsion bars. Remove anti-lock brake RPM sensor. Place a jack under rear axle.

3) Force water drain from rear axle. On models equipped with CIS-E fuel injection, remove fuel line. Remove rear axle assembly mounting bolts and nuts. Carefully lower rear axle assembly from vehicle. To install, reverse removal procedure.

OVERHAUL

AXLE SHAFT

Disassembly

1) Loosen boot clamps. Slide boot back and drain oil. Remove locking ring. Press synchromesh joint from rear axle shaft. Press protective sleeve from axle shaft. Mark "U" joint ring, hub and ball cage position. Disassemble joint.

2) Swivel joint and remove 6 balls. Remove joint hub. Swivel joint 90 degrees and remove cage. Check all parts for wear or damage. If parts are badly damaged, replace entire synchromesh joint.

Reassembly

To reassemble, reverse disassembly procedure. Fill synchromesh joint and rubber boot with grease.

Fig. 5: Exploded View of Axle Shaft Assembly

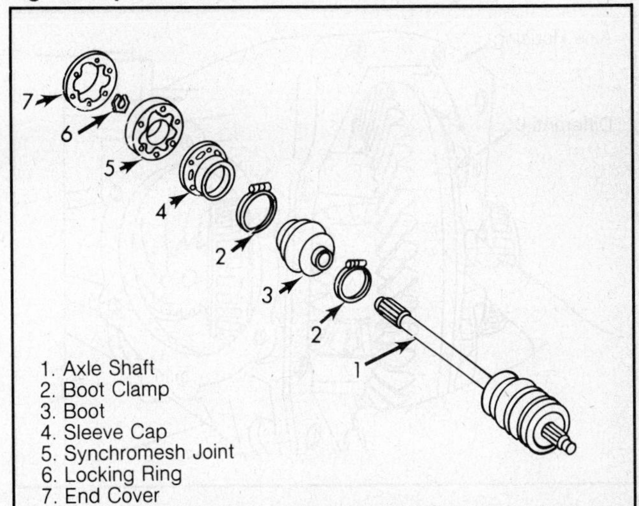

DIFFERENTIAL ASSEMBLY

Disassembly (All Models Except 190 Series)

1) Clamp axle housing in a support so that axle shafts are fully supported. Remove rear cover. Remove locking rings between inner synchromesh joints and side gears. Remove axle shafts. Remove bearing side cover bolts and push out of housing along with seal rings and shims. Mark all parts for correct left and right side reassembly reference.

2) Tilt case slightly and remove differential from housing. Mark relative position of ring gear to differential case. Remove ring gear attaching bolts and carefully remove ring gear from case. To disassemble case, remove roller bearings from case using a puller. Knock pinion shaft lock pin out of case and remove pinion shaft.

3) On limited slip differentials, insert Assembly Mandrels (115 589 04 61 00) through case and side gears. Remove pinions and spherical washers. Remove right side gear and friction discs, keeping all parts in order for reassembly. Repeat procedure for left side. On standard differentials, lift out side gears, thrust washers and spherical washers.

4) To remove drive pinion, remove flange nut and flange. Drive pinion out of housing. Pry seal out of housing with screwdriver. Remove front bearing outer race from housing using press and mandrel. Remove rear bearing outer race from case using adapter. Remove roller bearing inner race from pinion using press plate. On models equipped with anti-lock brake system, remove gear wheel.

Disassembly (190 Series)

NOTE: Mark all component locations for reassembly purposes.

1) Remove rear axle assembly. Disconnect axle shafts from axle assembly. Place rear axle center in Fixture (201 589 03 31 00). Remove rear cover. Remove "C" locks and remove axle shafts. Using a screwdriver, remove axle shaft seals.

2) Remove compensating washer. Install spreader on differential case. Position dial indicator on spreader. Preload dial indicator to 0-.12" (0-3 mm). Tighten spreader until dial indicator reads .008" (.20 mm). DO NOT exceed this amount. Remove spreader. Remove locking rings. Remove side bearing outer races.

MERCEDES-BENZ INTEGRAL CARRIER (Cont.)

Fig. 6: Removing Differential Assembly from Housing

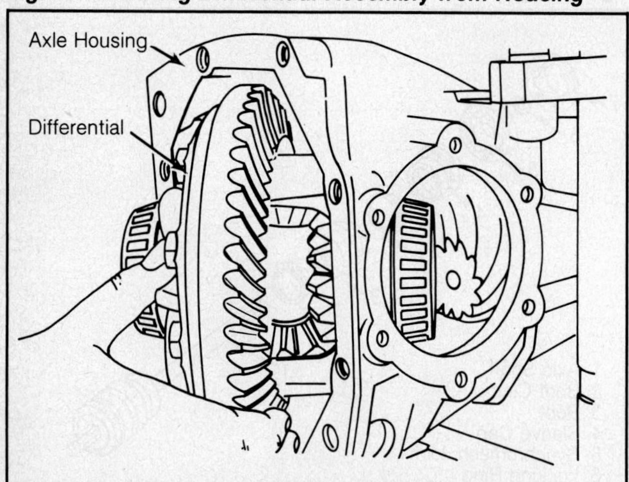

3) Remove differential assembly from housing. Remove side bearings. Remove ring gear. Check drive pinion preload. Remove drive pinion flange. Press drive pinion from housing. Using a screwdriver, remove drive pinion seal.

4) Remove bearing races. Remove spacing sleeve and thrust washers from drive pinion shaft. Remove anti-lock brake gear wheel (if equipped). Remove differential pinion shaft. Remove side gears, pinion gears and thrust washers.

REASSEMBLY & ADJUSTMENT

Case Assembly (Standard Differential)

1) Place thrust washers on side gears and insert assembled gears in case. Insert Assembly Mandrels (116 589 18 61 00) into side gears and mount both pinions along with spherical washers. Insert dummy pinion shaft into case to locate pinion gears and spherical washers.

2) Check torque required to rotate side gears. If necessary, change side gear thrust washers to obtain specified torque. When side gear preload is correct, insert pinion shaft in place of mandrel. Install new clamping sleeve and press bearing inner races on case using a mandrel.

Case Assembly (Limited Slip Differential)

1) Mount friction discs on side gears in correct order. *See Fig. 7.* Install left side gear (ring gear side) with discs and insert Assembly Mandrel (116 589 18 61 00). Ensure disc lugs align properly in case. Repeat procedure for right side gear. Install pinions with new spherical washers.

2) Insert Mandrel (116 589 07 61 00) through case, pinions and spherical washers. Check torque required to rotate side gears. If necessary, change side gear thrust washers to obtain specified torque.

3) When side gear preload is correct, insert pinion shaft in place of mandrel. Install new clamping sleeve and press bearing inner races in case using press and mandrel.

Drive Pinion Depth

1) Mount dial indicator in Measuring Device (116 589 00 23 00). Insert Gauge Block (116 589 07 21 00). Place dial indicator tip on top of gauge block. Allow dial indicator tip to depress about .08" (2 mm) on 190 series or .12" (3 mm) on gauge block and zero dial indicator. *See Fig. 9.*

Fig. 7: Installing Friction Discs

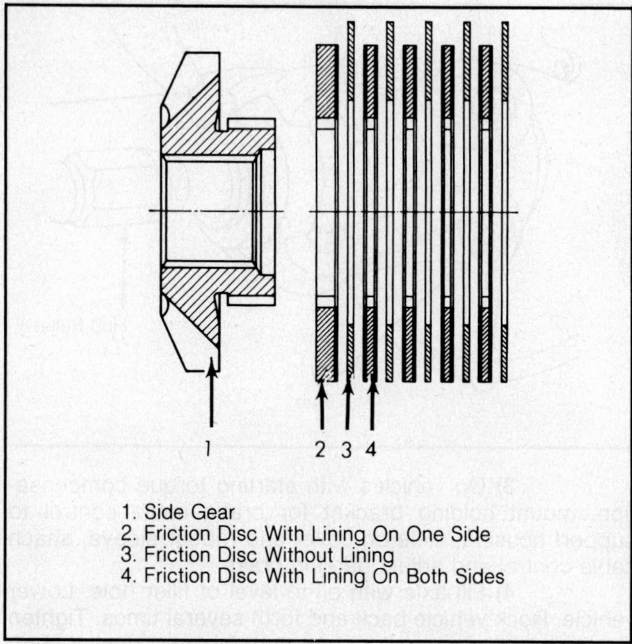

1. Side Gear
2. Friction Disc With Lining On One Side
3. Friction Disc Without Lining
4. Friction Disc With Lining On Both Sides

2) Install drive gear on models equipped with anti-lock brake systems. Press inner tapered roller bearing on drive pinion and place bearing outer race on roller cage of bearing. Insert pinion assembly into measuring device. On pinions from large center housings, place Magnetic Plate (116 589 01 21 00) on top of pinion. Place indicator stem on head of pinion and note reading.

3) Note deviation value engraved on pinion shaft in tenths of millimeters (example: + 20 = + .20 mm). From value measured above, add adjustment value if plus and subtract value if minus.

4) Insert gauge block holder into axle housing and screw on appropriate Gauge Block (116 589 07 21 00). Insert dial gauge holder into adjusting gauge and zero indicator with stem depressed about .12" (3 mm).

5) Insert adjusting gauge together with dial gauge holder into right bore of housing and screw down. Read indicator reading difference between adjusting gauge and gauge block face end.

6) If value is plus, it must be subtracted from result obtained in step **3)**, and if minus, it must be added to above result (example: If measured deviation is +.16 mm, subtract this value from 1.70 mm to obtain 1.54 mm). This result is thickness of required shim.

7) Remove all tools from axle housing. Insert shim of calculated thickness into axle housing. If necessary, a thicker washer may be ground down to required thickness. Install bearing outer races in housing. Lubricate bearings on drive pinion with hypoid gear oil and insert pinion and new collapsible spacer into housing.

8) Install front bearing inner race. Coat new seal on circumference with sealing compound and press into cover using mandrel. Coat running surface of pinion flange with molybdenum disulphide paste and slide flange on drive pinion. Ensure alignment marks are properly aligned.

Pinion Bearing Preload

1) Check that runout of pinion flange does not exceed specification. If runout is excessive, reposition flange. Hold flange and install new locking slot nut. Gradually tighten nut while turning pinion and applying light hammer blows to axle housing.

MERCEDES-BENZ INTEGRAL CARRIER (Cont.)

Fig. 8: Exploded View of Differential Assembly (190 Series)

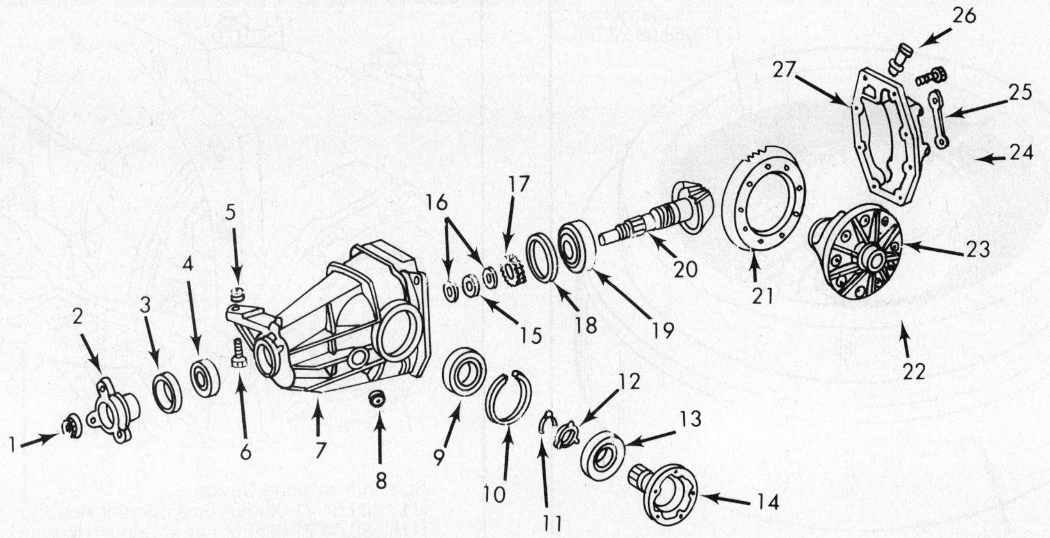

1. Drive Pinion Flange Nut
2. Drive Pinion Flange
3. Drive Pinion Seal
4. Bearing
5. Rubber Bushing
6. Bolt
7. Rear Axle Housing
8. Plug
9. Bearing
10. Snap Ring
11. "C" Lock
12. Compansating Ring
13. Seal
14. Drive Axle & Flange
15. Collapsible Spacer
16. Spacers
17. Anti-Lock Brake Gear Wheel
18. Seal
19. Bearing
20. Drive Pinion
21. Ring Gear
22. Bolt
23. Differential Assembly
24. Bolt
25. Lock Plate
26. Vent
27. Rear Cover

Fig. 9: Zeroing Dial Indicator For Pinion Depth Adjustment

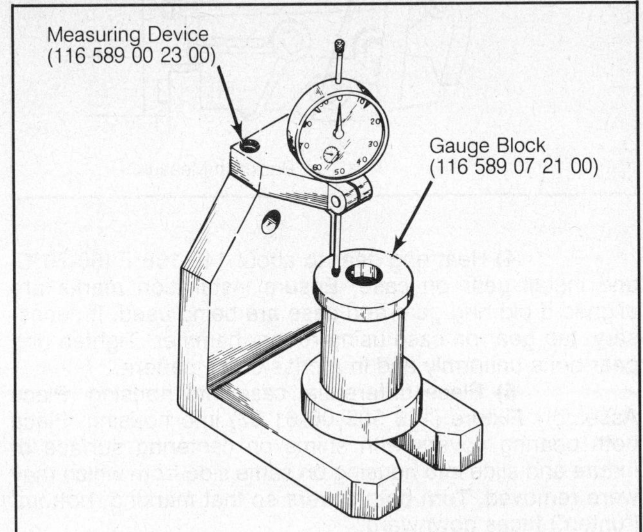

Fig. 10: Measuring Pinion Height

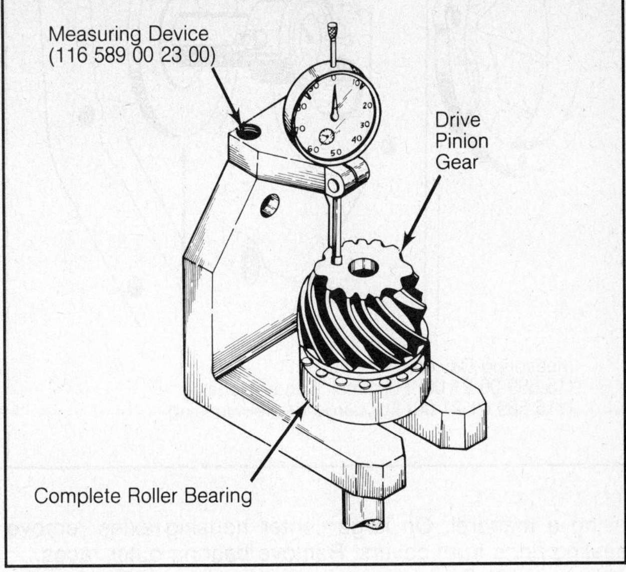

2) Continue tightening nut until specified pinion turning torque is obtained. Do not exceed specified preload. If preload is exceeded, remove pinion from housing and replace collapsible spacer.

3) Insert measuring device and dial indicator holder into right bore of housing. Place Magnetic Measuring Plate (052 C) on head of pinion. Dial indicator should read value engraved on pinion shaft. Maximum error is .0008" (.02 mm). If error is higher, disassemble pinion and install correct shim.

Backlash & Side Bearing Preload

1) On small center housing axles, press out sealing rings and outer bearing races from side covers

MERCEDES-BENZ INTEGRAL CARRIER (Cont.)

Fig. 11: Zeroing Dial Indicator

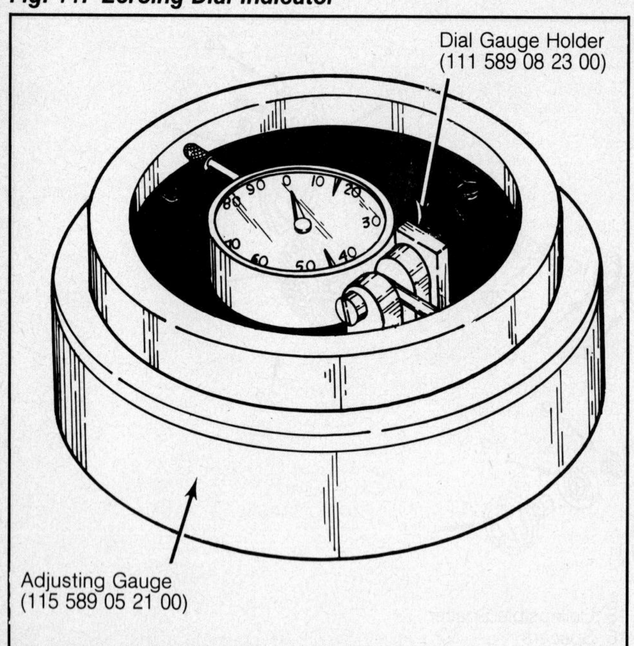

Fig. 12: Measuring Housing Depth

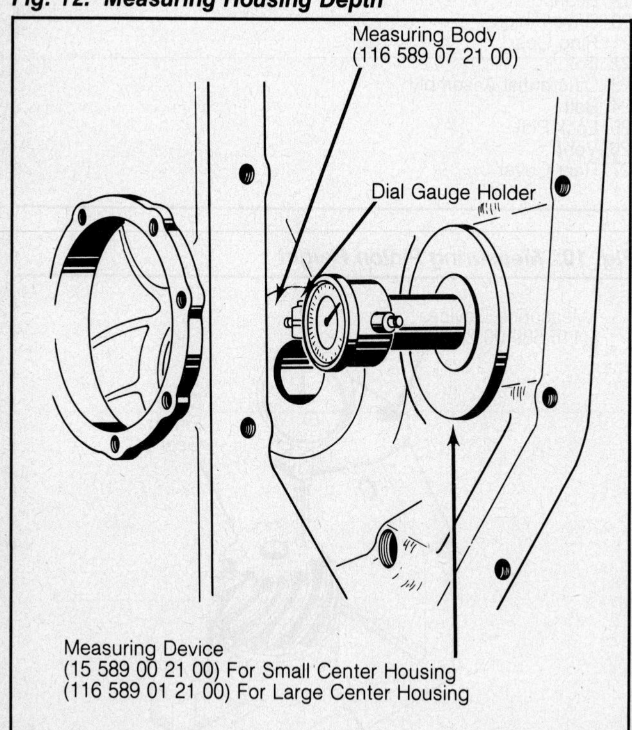

using a mandrel. On large center housing axles remove sealing rings from covers. Remove bearing outer races.

2) On all axles, press in new outer races with Sleeve (116 589 04 43 00). On small center housing, press in races with Disc (115 589 00 61 00).

3) Coat outer edge of new seals with sealing compound and press into bearing covers. Place previously used shims on bearing covers and install new sealing rings in grooves of covers. Carefully clean bore of ring gear and seat on differential case as ring gear is removed from case.

Fig. 13: Measuring Housing Spread

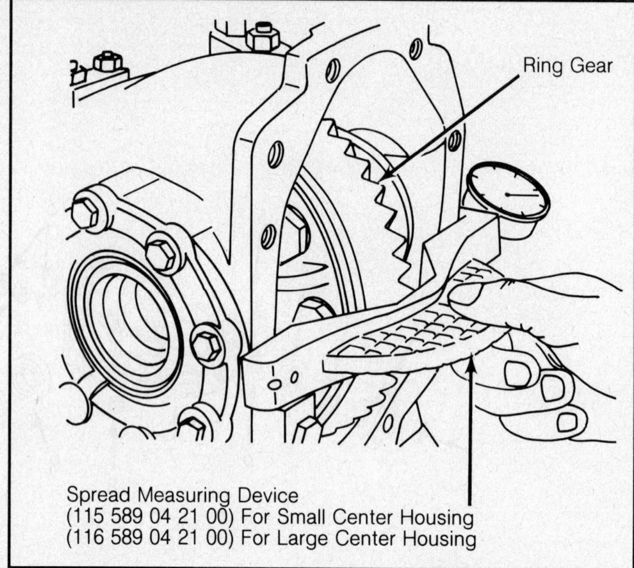

Fig. 14: Measuring Ring-to-Pinion Gear Backlash

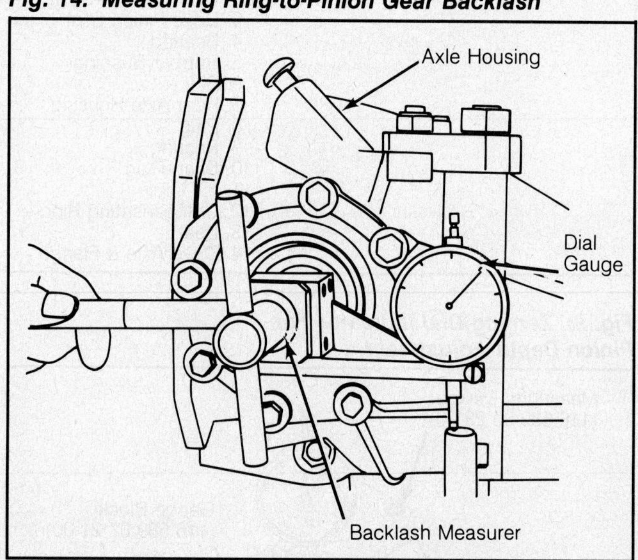

4) Heat ring gear to about 140-158°F (60-70°C) and install gear on case. Ensure installation marks are aligned if old ring gear and case are being used. If necessary, tap gear on case using rubber hammer. Tighten ring gear bolts uniformly and in a criss-cross pattern.

5) Place differential case into housing. Place Assembly Fixture (116 589 06 61 00) into housing. Place both bearing covers with shims on centering surface of fixture and slide into housing on same side from which they were removed. Turn both covers so that marking "bottom" ("unten") faces downward.

6) Remove assembly fixture and install cover attaching bolts, but do not tighten. Mount case spread measuring device and support blocks on housing. Zero dial indicator.

7) Tighten bearing cover bolts. Place spread measuring device on support blocks and measure spread of axle. Spread should not exceed specification. Adjust size of shims as necessary to obtain specified case spread.

MERCEDES-BENZ INTEGRAL CARRIER (Cont.)

Install backlash measuring device into right side bearing bore and clamp down.

8) Measure backlash at 4 points on ring gear. Adjust shims from side-to-side as necessary to obtain specified backlash. When preload and backlash are correct, install both axle drive shafts with new "C" locks. Clean end cover mating surfaces and coat with sealing compound. Install cover and tighten bolts.

AXLE ASSEMBLY SPECIFICATIONS

Application	In. (mm)
Axle Shaft Flange End Play	
190 Series	.005 (.12)
All Other Models	.0016-.0024 (.04-.06)
Axle Shaft Runout	
190 Series	
Installed	.005 (.12)
Removed	.001 (.02)
Housing Spread	
Small Center Housing	.004-.006 (.10-.15)
Large Center Housing	.006-.008 (.15-.20)
Pinion Flange Runout	.001 (.03)
Ring Gear Runout	.0008 (.02) Max.
Ring & Pinion Backlash	.0030-.0055 (.08-.14)
	Ft. Lbs. (N.m)
Side Gear Turning Torque	
Standard Differential	22-66 (30-90)
Limited Slip Diff.	59-103 (80-140)
	INCH Lbs. (N.m)
Pinion Turning Torque	
New Bearings	10.6-12.4 (1.2-1.4)
Used Bearings	4.4-8.9 (0.5-1.0)

TIGHTENING SPECIFICATIONS

Application	Ft. Lbs. (N.m)
Axle Housing-to-Axle Carrier	74 (100)
Axle Shaft-to-Drive Flange Bolts	
190 Series	51 (70)
Axle Shaft-to-Axle Shaft Flange Bolt	
190 Series	88 (120)
All Other Models	22 (30)
Bearing Cover-to-Axle Housing Bolt	15 (20)
Brake Caliper Bolt	15 (20)
Front Rubber Mount-to-Frame Nut	51 (70)
Housing Rear Cover	33 (45)
Propeller Shaft Clamping Nut	
2-Piece Shaft	22-30 (30-40)
3-Piece Shaft	
Front	22-30 (30-40)
Rear	148 (200)
Propeller Shaft-to-Flange Nut	
190 Series	29-37 (40-50)
Rear Rubber Mount-to-Frame Nut	
190 Series	51 (70)
All Other Models	18 (25)
Ring Gear Bolts	
Small Center Housing	
Standard Bolt	59 (80)
Self-Locking Bolt	74 (100)
Large Center Housing	89 (120)
Rubber Mount-to-Axle Housing Bolt	89 (120)

NISSAN FRONT AXLES

4WD Pickup & Pathfinder (R180A & R200A)

DESCRIPTION

Front axle assembly is a hypoid gear-type with integral carrier housing. Drive pinion bearing preload adjustment is made by spacer and shims. Differential side bearing preload and pinion height adjustments are also made by shims. Driving power is transmitted to axle by spline type drive shaft.

AXLE RATIO & IDENTIFICATION

Nissan does not identify axles with a particular external identification marking. See AXLE RATIO SPECIFICATIONS table to determine axle ratio.

AXLE RATIO SPECIFICATIONS

Application	Ratio
Pathfinder (4WD - Automatic Transmission)	
VG30i Engine & R200A Front Axle	
ST Models	4.375
GST Models	4.625
Pathfinder (4WD - Manual Transmission)	
VG30i Engine & R200A Front Axle	4.375
Z24i Engine & R180A Front Axle	4.625
Pickup (4WD - Automatic Transmission)	
VG30i Engine & R200A Front Axle	
ST Models	4.375
XST Models	4.625
Pickup (4WD - Manual Transmission)	
VG30i Engine & R200A Front Axle	
ST Models	4.111
XST Models	4.375
Z24i Engine & R180A Front Axle	4.375

Fig. 1: Exploded View of Nissan R180A Front Axle Assembly

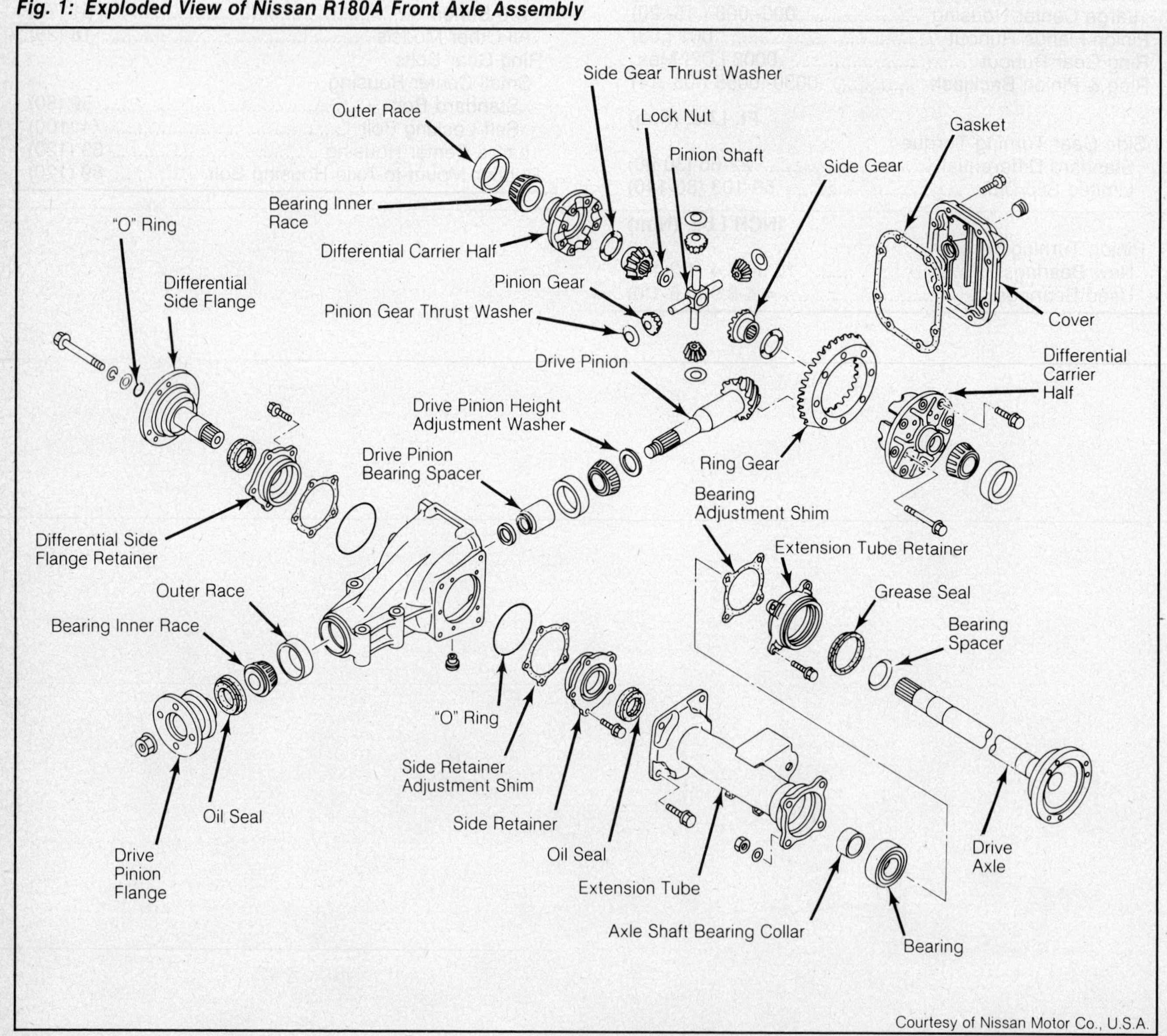

Courtesy of Nissan Motor Co., U.S.A.

NISSAN FRONT AXLES (Cont.)

REMOVAL & INSTALLATION

AXLE DRIVE SHAFTS & BEARINGS

Removal

1) Remove bolts securing axle drive shaft to extension tube. Using a slide hammer, remove axle drive shaft assembly from extension tube. Use a chisel to cut axle bearing collar.

2) Install axle drive shaft into extension tube and secure with bolts. Remove rear axle bearing by pulling axle drive shaft out of extension tube retainer. Remove grease seal and oil seal from extension tube retainer. *See Fig. 1.*

NOTE: Axle drive shaft and bearing removal and installation procedures are for axle assembly on bench. On-vehicle removal and installation procedures not available from manufacturer.

Installation

To install, reverse removal procedure. Measure axle bearing end play. End play should be .004" (.10 mm) or less. If end play is incorrect, replace adjustment shim behind extension tube retainer. *See Fig. 1.* Press axle bearing collar onto shaft.

Fig. 2: Front Axle Tightening Sequence

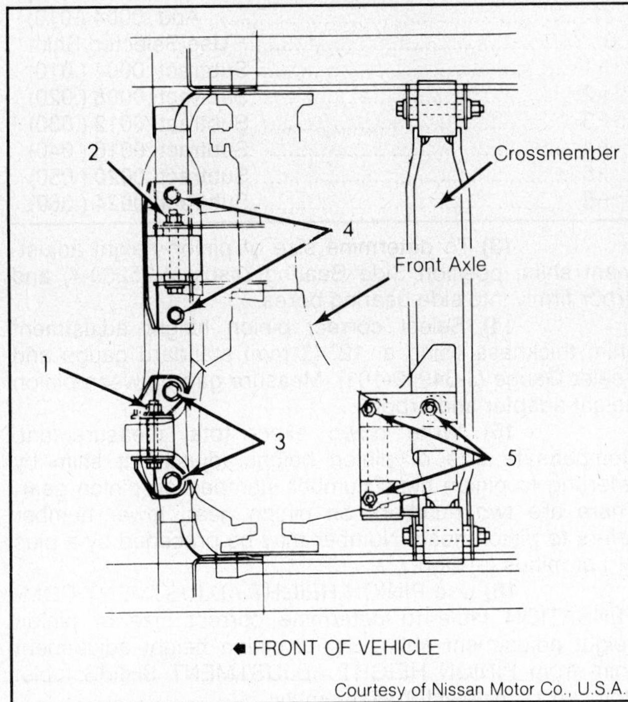

Courtesy of Nissan Motor Co., U.S.A.

PINION FLANGE & OIL SEAL

Removal

Remove propeller shaft. Using Drive Pinion Flange Wrench (J34311), loosen drive pinion nut. Remove pinion flange with puller. Remove front oil seal.

Installation

To install, reverse removal procedure. Apply grease to seal cavity at sealing lips of seal. Press fornt oil seal into place.

AXLE ASSEMBLY

Removal

Remove front propeller shaft and drive shaft. Remove engine mount bolts and raise engine. Remove front axle and crossmember.

Installation

To install, reverse removal procedure. Tighten front axle and crossmember fasteners as specified to prevent drive train vibration. *See Fig. 2.*

OVERHAUL

AXLE ASSEMBLY

Disassembly (R180A)

1) Mount axle assembly on engine stand. Turn drive pinion flange in both directions to seat bearings. Check total pinion bearing preload, ring gear-to-drive pinion backlash, ring gear runout, and gear tooth contact pattern. See AXLE ASSEMBLY SPECIFICATIONS table in this article.

2) Remove extension tube and axle shaft assembly. Remove differential side flange. Mark side retainers for reassembly reference and remove from differential case. DO NOT intermingle side retainers and shims.

3) Remove differential carrier assembly from differential case. See DIFFERENTIAL in this article if further disassembly is required. Using Puller (J25810-A), remove side bearing outer races. DO NOT mix bearing cones and races. Remove side oil seals.

4) Using Drive Pinion Flange Wrench (J34311), loosen drive pinion nut. Using puller, remove pinion flange with puller. Remove drive pinion together with pinion rear bearing inner cone, drive pinion bearing spacer, and adjustment shim.

5) Remove front oil seal and pinion front bearing inner cone. Remove pinion bearing outer races with a drift. Remove pinion rear bearing inner cone and drive pinion height adjustment shim.

Reassembly & Adjustment

1) Using Drift Handle (J25742-1) and Drifts (J25742-2 and J25742-5), press bearing outer races onto differential case. Lubricate differential carrier with Dexron automatic transmission fluid. Install differential carrier into differential case.

2) Place all original side bearing preload shims onto side bearing retainer that goes on ring gear end of carrier. Install both side bearing retainers onto differential case and tighten bolts.

3) Turn differential carrier several times to seat bearings. Using Spring Scale (J-8129), measure differential side bearing preload at a ring gear retaining bolt. Differential side bearing preload should be 7.7-8.8 lbs. (3.5-4.0 kg).

4) If side bearing preload is incorrect, establish correct side bearing preload by adding or subtracting from total amount of shim thickness. Record correct TOTAL side bearing preload shim thickness. Remove differential carrier, bearings, and set shims aside.

NOTE: Increase shim thickness to DECREASE side bearing preload. Decrease shim thickness to INCREASE side bearing preload.

NISSAN FRONT AXLES (Cont.)

Fig. 3: Pinion Gear Height & Pinion Bearing Preload Shim Selector Assembly

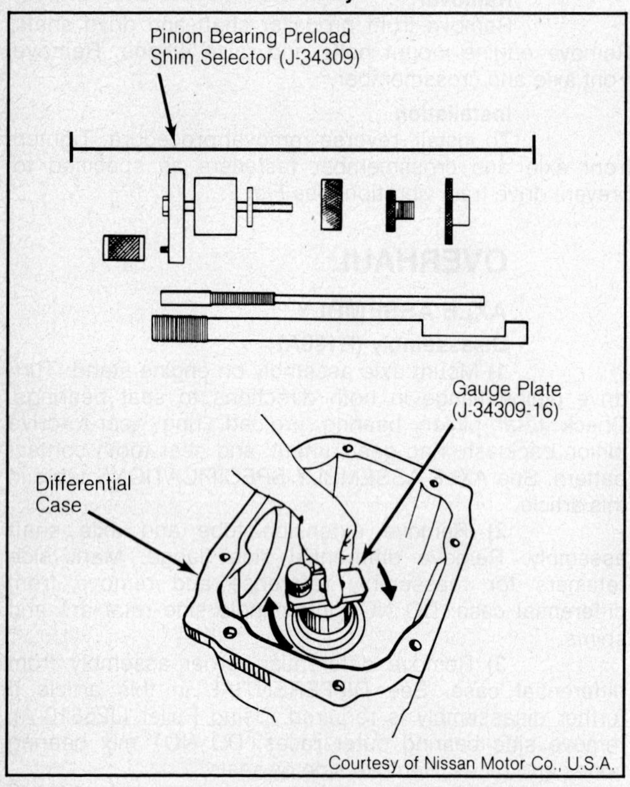

Courtesy of Nissan Motor Co., U.S.A.

5) Assemble pinion gear bearings onto Pinion Bearing Preload Shim Selector (J-34309), to determine size of pinion bearing preload shim. *See Fig. 3.*

6) On front pinion bearing, make sure that Seat (J-34309-3) is securely tightened to Gauge Anvil (J-34309-7), then turn front pinion bearing Pilot (J-34309-7) to secure bearing in its proper position.

7) On rear pinion bearing, the rear pinion bearing Pilot (J-34309-8) is used to center rear pinion bearing only. The rear pinion bearing Seat (J-34309-4) is used to lock bearing onto shim selector assembly.

8) Place Pinion Bearing Preload Shim Selector Screw (J-34309-1), with pinion rear bearing cone installed, into differential case. Install gauge anvil with front pinion bearing into case and attach to screw.

9) Attach Gauge Plate (J-34309-16) to shim selector assembly, ensure gauge plate turns a full 360 degrees, and tighten sections by hand. Turn shim selector assembly several times to seat bearings. *See Fig. 3.*

10) Measure pinion bearing turning torque at end of shim selector shaft. Turning torque should be 5.2-8.7 INCH lbs. (.6-1.0 N.m). If correct, place Pinion Height Adapter (J-34309-10 "R180A") onto gauge plate and tighten it by hand. Ensure all machined surfaces are clean.

11) Place solid pinion bearing spacer squarely into recessed portion of Gauge Anvil (J-34309-2). Select correct thickness of bearing preload adjustment shim using a .24" (6 mm) standard gauge and Feeler Gauge (J-34909-101).

12) The exact total measurement obtained with gauges is the required thickness of bearing preload adjustment shim. Select required bearing preload shim from R180A PINION BEARING PRELOAD ADJUSTMENT SHIMS table. Set selected pinion bearing preload shim aside.

R180A PINION BEARING PRELOAD ADJUSTMENT SHIMS

Thickness In. (mm)	Part No.
.2594 (6.590)	38127 01G00
.2587 (6.570)	38127 01G01
.2579 (6.550)	38127 01G02
.2571 (6.530)	38127 01G03
.2563 (6.510)	38127 01G04
.2555 (6.490)	38127 01G05
.2547 (6.470)	38127 01G06
.2539 (6.450)	38127 01G07
.2531 (6.430)	38127 01G08
.2524 (6.410)	38127 01G09
.2516 (6.390)	38127 01G10
.2508 (6.370)	38127 01G11
.2500 (6.350)	38127 01G12
.2492 (6.330)	38127 01G13
.2484 (6.310)	38127 01G14

PINION HEIGHT ADJUSTMENT COMPENSATION

Number Stamped On Pinion Head	Compensate Thickness By In. (mm)
–6	Add .0024 (.060)
–5	Add .0020 (.050)
–4	Add .0016 (.040)
–3	Add .0012 (.030)
–2	Add .0008 (.020)
–1	Add .0004 (.010)
0	Use Selected Shim
+1	Subtract .0004 (.010)
+2	Subtract .0008 (.020)
+3	Subtract .0012 (.030)
+4	Subtract .0016 (.040)
+5	Subtract .0020 (.050)
+6	Subtract .0024 (.060)

13) To determine size of pinion height adjustment shim, position Side Bearing Discs (J-25269-4) and arbor firmly into side bearing bores.

14) Select correct pinion height adjustment shim thickness using a .12" (3 mm) standard gauge and Feeler Gauge (J-34909-101). Measure gap between pinion height adapter and arbor.

15) Write down exact total measurement. Compensate size of pinion height adjustment shim by referring to pinion head number stamped on pinion gear. There are two numbers on pinion gear, lower number refers to pinion head. Number may be preceded by a plus (+) or minus (–) sign.

16) Use PINION HEIGHT ADJUSTMENT COMPENSATION table to determine correct size of pinion height adjustment shim. Select pinion height adjustment shim from PINION HEIGHT ADJUSTMENT SHIMS table. Remove shim selector assemmbly.

17) Install drive pinion height adjustment shim in drive pinion and press bearing race onto drive pinion. Install pinion front bearing inner race in differential case. Lubricate front oil seal with grease and install on case.

18) Install drive pinion bearing spacer, pinion bearing preload adjustment shim, and drive pinion in differential case. Tap pinion flange onto drive pinion and tighten pinion nut.

19) Turn drive pinion in both directions several times and measure pinion bearing preload. Pinion bearing preload should be 8-15 INCH lbs. (.9-1.7 N.m). If pinion bearing preload is incorrect, replace pinion bearing adjustment shim and spacer.

NISSAN FRONT AXLES (Cont.)

PINION HEIGHT ADJUSTMENT SHIMS

Thickness In. (mm)	Part No.
.1217 (3.090)	38154-P6017
.1228 (3.120)	38154-P6018
.1240 (3.150)	38154-P6019
.1252 (3.180)	38154-P6020
.1264 (3.210)	38154-P6021
.1276 (3.240)	38154-P6022
.1287 (3.270)	38154-P6023
.1299 (3.300)	38154-P6024
.1311 (3.330)	38154-P6025
.1323 (3.360)	38154-P6026
.1335 (3.390)	38154-P6027
.1346 (3.420)	38154-P6028
.1358 (3.450)	38154-P6029
.1370 (3.480)	38154-P6030
.1382 (3.510)	38154-P6031
.1394 (3.540)	38154-P6032
.1406 (3.570)	38154-P6033
.1417 (3.600)	38154-P6034
.1429 (3.630)	38154-P6035
.1441 (3.660)	38154-P6036

20) Press side bearing outer race into side bearing retainer. Install side oil seal and differential carrier. Install side bearing preload adjustment shims, "O" ring, and side bearing retainer. Ensure that arrows on retainer and housing are aligned.

21) Measure ring gear-to-drive pinion backlash. Backlash should be .005-.007" (.13-.18 mm). If backlash is too small, decrease thickness of right shim and increase thickness of left shim by the same amount. If backlash is too much, reverse above mentioned procedure.

NOTE: When adjusting ring gear-to-drive pinion backlash, never change the total amount of shims as it will change pinion bearing preload.

22) Turn drive pinion flange in both directions to seat bearings. Check total pinion bearing preload. Total pinion bearing preload should be 9-20 INCH Lbs. (1.0-2.3 N.m). If preload is too much, add the same amount of shims to each side. If too small, remove the same amount of shims from each side.

Fig. 4: Exploded View of Nissan R200A Front Axle Assembly

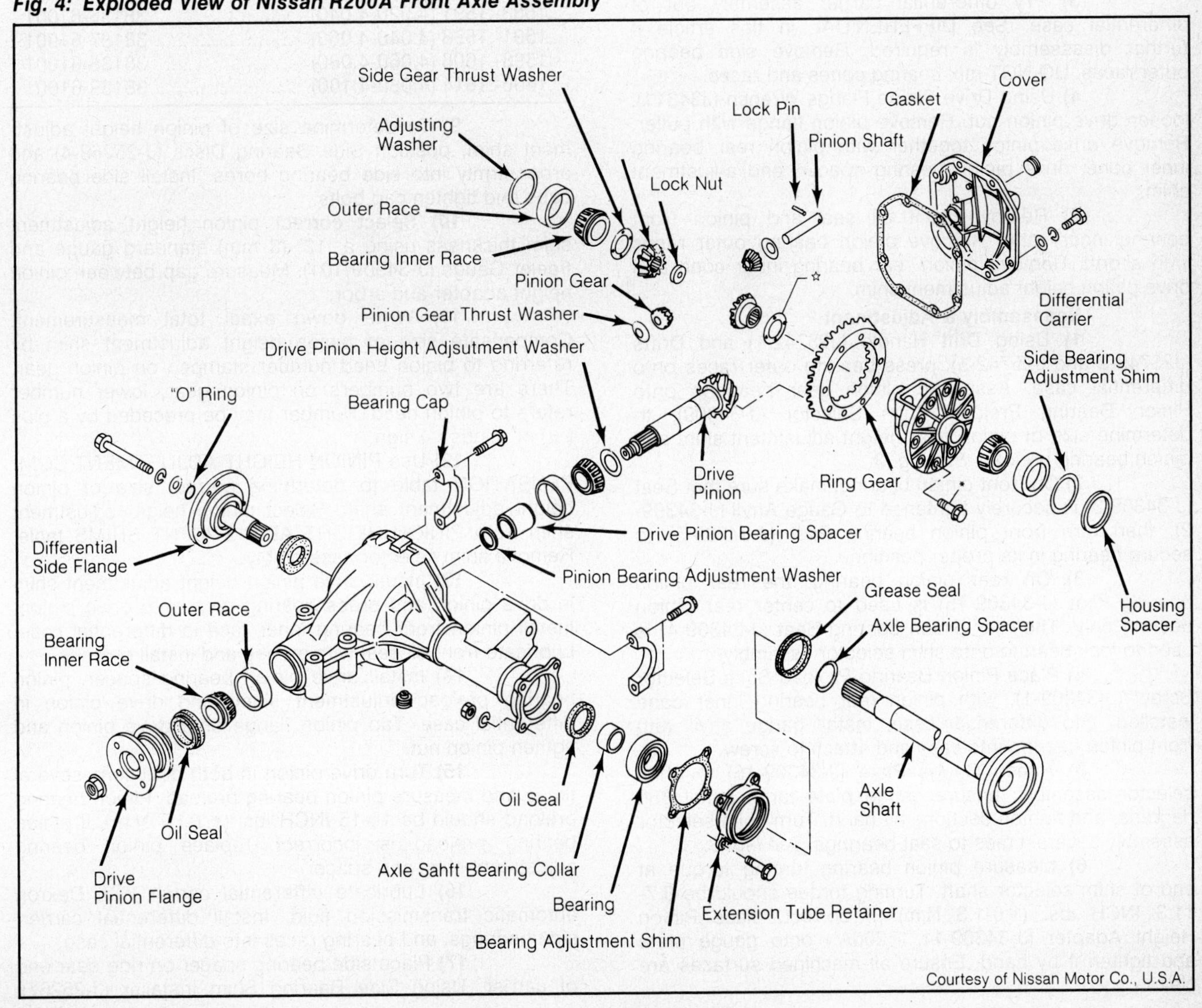

NISSAN FRONT AXLES (Cont.)

NOTE: **When adjusting total pinion bearing preload, never add or remove a different number of shims from each side as it will change ring gear-to-drive pinion backlash.**

23) Recheck ring gear-to-drive pinion backlash. If correct, check ring gear runout. Ring gear runout must not exceed .003" (.08 mm). If backlash varies excessively, foreign matter may be caught between ring gear and differential carrier.

24) If backlash varies greatly when runout of ring gear is within specification, the hypoid gear set or differential carrier should be replaced. Check gear tooth contact pattern and adjust if necessary. Install rear cover and gasket, Install extension tube and shaft assembly.

Disassembly (R200A)

1) Mount axle assembly on engine stand. Turn drive pinion flange in both directions to seat bearings. Check total pinion bearing preload, ring gear-to-drive pinion backlash, side gear-to-pinion gear backlash, ring gear runout, and gear tooth contact pattern. See AXLE ASSEMBLY SPECIFICATIONS table in this article.

2) Remove extension tube and axle shaft assembly. Remove differential side flange. Mark side bearing caps for reassembly reference and remove from differential case. DO NOT mix side bearing caps.

3) Pry differential carrier assembly out of differential case. See DIFFERENTIAL in this article if further disassembly is required. Remove side bearing outer races. DO NOT mix bearing cones and races.

4) Using Drive Pinion Flange Wrench (J34311), loosen drive pinion nut. Remove pinion flange with puller. Remove drive pinion together with pinion rear bearing inner cone, drive pinion bearing spacer, and adjustment shim.

5) Remove front oil seal and pinion front bearing inner cone. Remove pinion bearing outer races with a drift. Remove pinion rear bearing inner cone and drive pinion height adjustment shim.

Reassembly & Adjustment

1) Using Drift Handle (J25742-1) and Drifts (J25742-2 and J25742-5), press bearing outer races onto differential case. Assemble pinion gear bearings onto Pinion Bearing Preload Shim Selector (J-34309), to determine size of pinion gear height adjustment shim and pinion bearing preload. *See Fig. 3*.

2) On front pinion bearing, make sure that Seat (J-34309-3) is securely tightened to Gauge Anvil (J-34309-2), then turn front pinion bearing Pilot (J-34309-5) to secure bearing in its proper position.

3) On rear pinion bearing, the rear pinion bearing Pilot (J-34309-15) is used to center rear pinion bearing only. The rear pinion bearing Seat (J-34309-4) is used to lock bearing onto shim selector assembly.

4) Place Pinion Bearing Preload Shim Selector Screw (J-34309-1), with pinion rear bearing inner cone installed, into differential case. Install gauge anvil with front pinion bearing into case and attach to screw.

5) Attach Gauge Plate (J-34309-16) to shim selector assembly, ensure gauge plate turns a full 360 degrees, and tighten sections by hand. Turn shim selector assembly several times to seat bearings. *See Fig. 3*.

6) Measure pinion bearing turning torque at end of shim selector shaft. Turning torque should be 8.7-11.3 INCH lbs. (1.0-1.3 N.m). If correct, place Pinion Height Adapter (J-34309-11 "R200A") onto gauge plate and tighten it by hand. Ensure all machined surfaces are clean.

7) Place solid pinion bearing spacer squarely into recessed portion of Gauge Anvil (J-34309-2). Select correct thickness of bearing preload adjustment shim using a .138" (3.50 mm) standard gauge and Feeler Gauge (J-34909-101).

8) The exact total measurement obtained with gauges is the required thickness of bearing preload adjustment shim. Select required bearing preload shim from R200A PINION BEARING PRELOAD ADJUSTMENT SHIMS table. Set selected pinion bearing preload shim aside.

R200A PINION BEARING PRELOAD ADJUSTMENT SHIMS

Thickness In. (mm)	Part No.
.1496-.1504 (3.800-3.820)	38125-61001
.1504-.1512 (3.820-3.840)	38126-61001
.1512-.1520 (3.840-3.860)	38127-61001
.1520-.1528 (3.860-3.880)	38128-61001
.1528-.1535 (3.880-3.900)	38129-61001
.1535-.1543 (3.900-3.920)	38130-61001
.1543-.1551 (3.920-3.940)	38131-61001
.1551-.1559 (3.940-3.960)	38132-61001
.1559-.1567 (3.960-3.980)	38133-61001
.1567-.1575 (3.980-4.000)	38134-61001
.1575-.1583 (4.000-4.020)	38135-61001
.1583-.1591 (4.020-4.040)	38136-61001
.1591-.1598 (4.040-4.060)	38137-61001
.1598-.1606 (4.060-4.080)	38138-61001
.1606-.1614 (4.080-4.100)	38139-61001

9) To determine size of pinion height adjustment shim, position Side Bearing Discs (J-25269-4) and arbor firmly into side bearing bores. Install side bearing caps and tighten cap bolts.

10) Select correct pinion height adjustment shim thickness using a .12" (3 mm) standard gauge and Feeler Gauge (J-34909-101). Measure gap between pinion height adapter and arbor.

11) Write down exact total measurement. Compensate size of pinion height adjustment shim by referring to pinion head number stamped on pinion gear. There are two numbers on pinion gear, lower number refers to pinion head. Number may be preceded by a plus (+) or minus (–) sign.

12) Use PINION HEIGHT ADJUSTMENT COMPENSATION table to determine correct size of pinion height adjustment shim. Select pinion height adjustment shim from PINION HEIGHT ADJUSTMENT SHIMS table. Remove shim selector assemmbly.

13) Install drive pinion height adjustment shim in drive pinion and press bearing race onto drive pinion. Install pinion front bearing inner race in differential case. Lubricate front oil seal with grease and install on case.

14) Install drive pinion bearing spacer, pinion bearing preload adjustment shim, and drive pinion in differential case. Tap pinion flange onto drive pinion and tighten pinion nut.

15) Turn drive pinion in both directions several times and measure pinion bearing preload. Pinion bearing preload should be 10-15 INCH lbs. (1.1-1.7 N.m). If pinion bearing preload is incorrect, replace pinion bearing adjustment shim and spacer.

16) Lubricate differential carrier with Dexron automatic transmission fluid. Install differential carrier, side bearings, and bearing races into differential case.

17) Place side bearing spacer on ring gear end of carrier. Using Side Bearing Shim Installer (J-25267),

NISSAN FRONT AXLES (Cont.)

install both of the original side bearing preload shims (on carrier end, opposite of ring gear). Install side bearing caps and tighten bolts.

18) Turn differential carrier several times to seat bearings. Using Spring Scale (J-8129), measure differential side bearing preload at a ring gear retaining bolt. Differential side bearing preload should be 7.7-8.8 lbs. (3.5-4.0 kg).

19) If side bearing preload is incorrect, establish correct side bearing preload by adding or subtracting from total amount of shim thickness. Record correct TOTAL side bearing preload shim thickness. Remove differential carrier, bearings, and set shims aside.

20) Install differential carrier, side bearings, and bearing races into differential case. Insert selected side bearing adjustment shims between side bearings and differential case.

21) Using side bearing shim installer, install side bearing spacer on carrier end of differential carrier. Install and tighten side bearing caps. Ensure that marks made during disassembly are aligned.

22) Install side oil seal. Measure ring gear-to-drive pinion backlash. Backlash should be .005-.007" (.13-.18 mm). If backlash is too small, decrease thickness of right shim and increase thickness of left shim by the same amount. If backlash is too much, reverse above mentioned procedure.

NOTE: **When adjusting ring gear-to-drive pinion backlash, never change the total amount of shims as it will change pinion bearing preload.**

23) Turn drive pinion flange in both directions to seat bearings. Check total pinion bearing preload. Total pinion bearing preload should be 11-20 INCH Lbs. (1.2-2.3 N.m). If preload is too much, remove the same amount of shims from each side. If too small, add the same amount of shims to each side.

NOTE: **When adjusting total pinion bearing preload, never add or remove a different number of shims from each side as it will change ring gear-to-drive pinion backlash.**

24) Recheck ring gear-to-drive pinion backlash. If correct, check ring gear runout. Ring gear runout must not exceed .003" (.08 mm). If backlash varies excessively, foreign matter may be caught between ring gear and differential carrier.

25) If backlash varies greatly when runout of ring gear is within specification, the hypoid gear set or differential carrier should be replaced. Check gear tooth contact pattern and adjust if necessary. Install rear cover and gasket, Install extension tube and shaft assembly.

DIFFERENTIAL

Disassembly (R180A)

1) Using Bearing Puller (J22888 and J8107-2), remove bearing races from differential carrier. DO NOT mix left and right bearings. Loosen ring gear bolts in a criss-cross fashion. Tap ring gear off differential carrier.

2) Mark differential carrier for reassembly reference and separate halves. Check gear teeth for scoring, cracks, or chipping. If any gear is damaged, replace ring gear and drive pinion as a set.

Reassembly & Adjustment

1) Measure clearance between side gear thrust washer and differential carrier. *See Fig. 5.* Clearance should be .004-.008" (.10-.20 mm). If clearance is incorrect, replace side gear thrust washer.

2) If correct, apply gear oil to gear tooth surfaces and thrust washers. Ensure that all gears turn properly. Assemble differential carrier halves. Place differential carrier on ring gear.

3) Apply locking compound to ring gear bolts and install them. Tighten ring gear bolts in a criss-cross fashion. Using Drift (J25805-01) and Base (J8107-2), press bearing races onto differential carrier.

Fig. 5: Measuring R180A Differential Side Gear Clearance

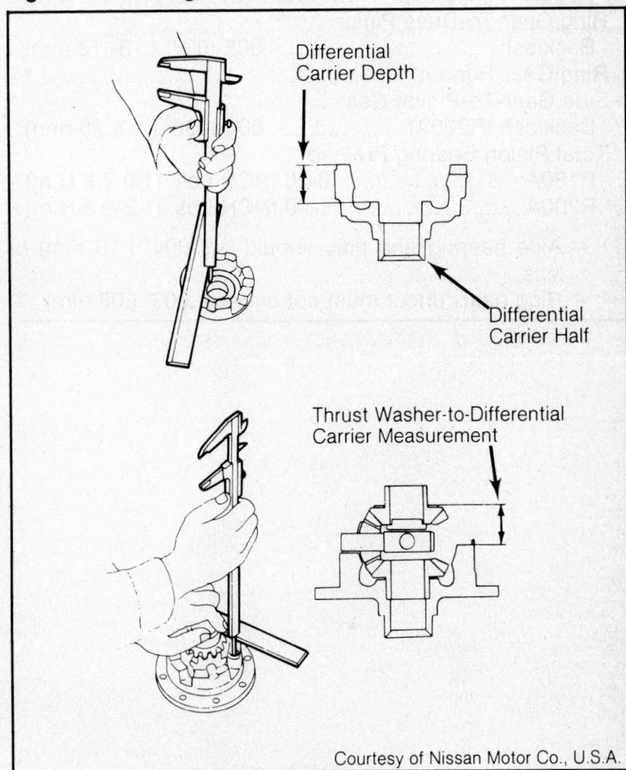

Disassembly (R200A)

Using Bearing Puller (J22888 and J8107-2), remove bearing races from differential carrier. DO NOT mix left and right bearings. Loosen ring gear bolts in a criss-cross fashion. Tap ring gear off differential carrier.

2) Use a drift punch to remove pinion shaft lock pin from ring gear side. Remove side gears, pinion gear, thrust washers and thrust block. Check gear teeth for scoring, cracks, or chipping. If any gear is damaged, replace ring gear and drive pinion as a set.

Reassembly & Adjustment

1) Install side gears, pinion gear, thrust washers, and thrust block in differential carrier. Install pinion shaft and align lock pin holes with holes in differential carrier.

2) Check clearance between rear face of side gear and thrust washer. Clearance should be .004-.008" (.10-.20 mm). If necessary, adjust clearance by changing side gear thrust washer.

3) If clearance is correct, install pinion shaft lock pin. Apply gear oil to gear tooth surfaces and thrust washers. Ensure that all gears turn properly. Tighten ring gear bolts in a criss-cross fashion. Using Drift (J25805-01) and Base (J8107-2), press bearing races onto differential carrier.

NISSAN FRONT AXLES (Cont.)

AXLE ASSEMBLY SPECIFICATIONS

Application	Specifications
Axle Bearing End Play	[1]
Differential Side	
Bearing Preload	7.7-8.8 Lbs. (3.5-4.0 kg)
Pinion Bearing Preload	
R180A	8-15 INCH lbs. (.9-1.7 N.m)
R200A	10-15 INCH lbs. (1.1-1.7 N.m)
Pinion Bearing Turning Torque	
R180A	5.2-8.7 INCH lbs. (.6-1.0 N.m)
R200A	8.7-11.3 INCH lbs. (1.0-1.3 N.m)
Ring Gear-To-Drive Pinion	
Backlash	.005-.007" (.13-.18 mm)
Ring Gear Runout	[2]
Side Gear-To-Pinion Gear	
Backlash (R200A)	.004-.008" (.10-.20 mm)
Total Pinion Bearing Preload	
R180A	9-20 INCH Lbs. (1.0-2.3 N.m)
R200A	11-20 INCH Lbs. (1.2-2.3 N.m)

[1] – Axle bearing end play should be .004" (.10 mm) or less.

[2] – Ring gear runout must not exceed .003" (.08 mm).

TIGHTENING SPECIFICATIONS

Application	Ft. Lbs. (N.m)
Axle-to-Crossmember	50-64 (68-87)
Differential Carrier Bolts (R180A)	47-54 (64-73)
Drive Flange-to-Drive Shaft	29-33 (39-45)
Drive Pinion Flange Nut	
R180A	123-145 (167-197)
R200A	137-217 (186-294)
Insulator-to-Body	50-64 (68-87)
Propeller Shaft-to-Drive Flange	29-33 (39-45)
Rear Cover Bolts	29-36 (39-49)
Rear Cover-to-Insulator	50-64 (68-87)
Ring Gear Bolts	
R180A	76-90 (103-122)
R200A	98-112 (133-152)
Differential Side Bearing	
Cap Bolts (R200A)	65-72 (88-98)
	INCH Lbs. (N.m)
Side Bearing Bolts (R180A)	80-110 (9-12)

NISSAN INTEGRAL HOUSING

200SX, 300ZX, Stanza Wagon (4WD)

DESCRIPTION

The axle assembly is a hypoid type gear with integral carrier housing. The pinion bearing preload adjustment is made with a spacer and washer between the front and rear bearing cones.

The differential side bearing preload and pinion depth adjustment are made by shims. Driving power is transmitted to the axle by spline type drive shaft with tripod joints at both ends.

AXLE RATIO & IDENTIFICATION

Nissan does not identify axles with a particular external identification marking. One basic type of axle assembly is used, with differences in ring gear diameter between model applications.

The R180 (180 mm ring gear) is used on 200SX models, rear axle on 4WD Stanza Wagon. The R200 (200 mm ring gear) is used on the 200SX Turbo and all 300ZX models. To determine axle ratio, divide the number of ring gear teeth by the number of drive pinion gear teeth.

AXLE RATIO SPECIFICATIONS

Application	Ratio
Stanza Wagon (4WD)	[1] 3.36
200SX	4.11
300ZX	
Non-Turbo	3.70
Turbo	3.55

1 - Used on rear drive axle on 4WD models only.

Fig. 1: Exploded View of Tripod-Type Rear Drive Axle

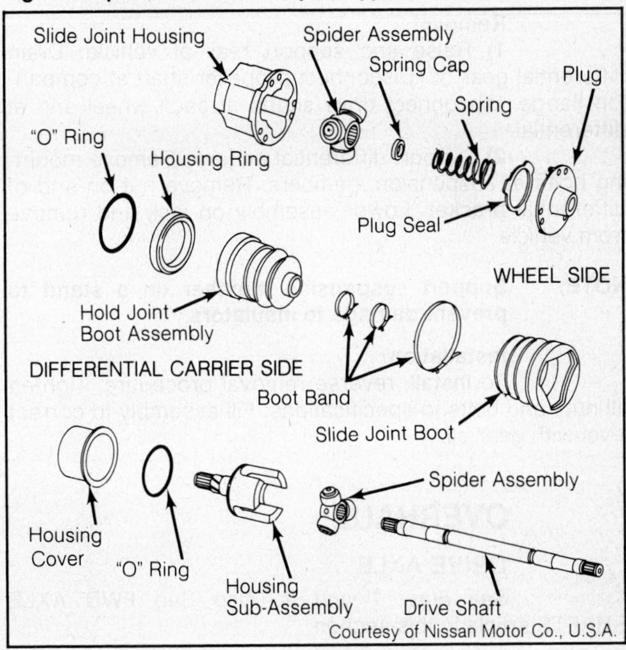

Courtesy of Nissan Motor Co., U.S.A.

Fig. 2: Exploded View of I.R.S. Rear Drive Axle

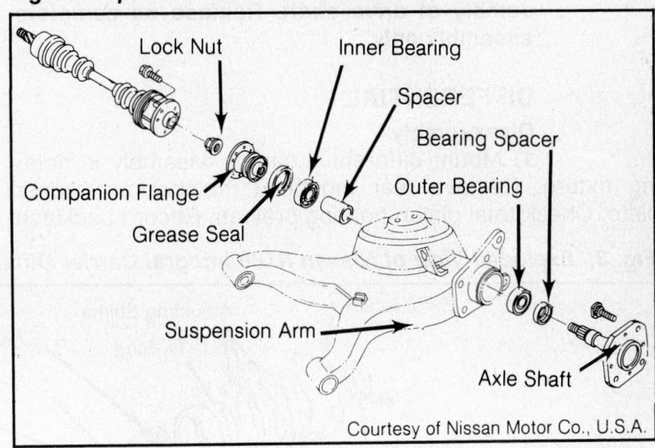

Courtesy of Nissan Motor Co., U.S.A.

REMOVAL & INSTALLATION

REAR AXLE SHAFTS & BEARINGS

Removal

1) Raise and support vehicle. Remove tire and wheel. Disconnect drive axle from axle shaft. Remove wheel bearing lock nut with parking brake engaged or brake pedal depressed. Disconnect hydraulic line at caliper and remove caliper and disc. Plug disconnected line.

2) Draw out axle shaft using adapter and slide hammer. Remove companion flange. Remove grease seal and inner bearing using a drift. Withdraw outer bearing from rear drive axle using bearing puller.

NOTE: DO NOT reuse bearing or grease seals after removal.

Installation

1) To install, reverse removal procedure. Clean and inspect all parts for wear or damage and replace as necessary. Grease wheel bearings and housing before installation.

2) When installing bearings, ensure outer bearing is installed with seal facing wheel and that inner bearing is installed with seal facing differential.

3) Axle housings are stamped with a letter. Ensure bearing spacer with same letter stamping is installed. Tighten lock nut to specification and check that drive axle end play is 0-.012" (0-.3 mm).

4) If either adjustment is not correct, replace bearing spacer and repeat procedure. Bleed and adjust brakes.

PINION FLANGE & OIL SEAL

Removal

Raise and support vehicle. Drain differential. Disconnect propeller shaft from pinion flange. Hold pinion flange and remove pinion nut. Remove flange with puller. Remove oil seal.

Installation

To install, reverse removal procedure. Apply grease between seal lips before installation. Tighten pinion nut to specifications. See TIGHTENING SPECIFICATIONS table in this article. Ensure pinion bearing preload is correctly adjusted. Fill differential to proper level with gear oil.

NISSAN INTEGRAL HOUSING (Cont.)

AXLE ASSEMBLY

Removal

1) Raise and support rear of vehicle. Drain differential gear oil. Disconnect propeller shaft at companion flange. Disconnect drive shafts at each wheel and at differential.

2) Support differential on jack. Remove mounting bolts at suspension members. Remove nut on end of differential bracket. Lower assembly on jack and remove from vehicle.

NOTE: **Support suspension member on a stand to prevent damage to insulators.**

Installation

To install, reverse removal procedure. Tighten all nuts and bolts to specifications. Fill assembly to correct level with gear oil.

OVERHAUL

DRIVE AXLE

See Figs. 1 and 2. Also See FWD AXLE SHAFTS article in this section.

NOTE: **Manufacturer does not recommend disassembly of drive shaft. Replace as complete assembly only.**

DIFFERENTIAL

Disassembly

1) Mount differential carrier assembly in holding fixture. Remove rear mounting member and cover plate. Check total pinion bearing preload. Record backlash readings at several points around ring gear for use during reassembly.

2) Check ring gear runout. Check ring and pinion gear tooth contact pattern. See GEAR TOOTH PATTERNS article in this section. On R180 differential, remove retainer bolts and pull side retainers from case with puller.

NOTE: **Retainers and shims of R180 differential must be marked for reassembly. Retainers and shims are not interchangeable.**

3) On R200 differential, pry side flange out while holding with hand to prevent shims from falling out of carrier. Remove bearing cap bolts and bearing caps. Mark carrier, caps and bearing outer races for reinstallation in original position.

4) On all models, extract differential case from carrier. On R180 differentials, remove side bearing outer races from retainers using Bearing Puller (ST33290001).

5) Hold pinion flange stationary and remove pinion nut. Remove pinion flange with puller. Press drive pinion from carrier. Using Bearing Remover (ST30031000) remove rear pinion bearing inner race, bearing spacer and adjusting washers. Remove pinion oil seal.

6) Remove pilot bearing, together with pilot bearing spacer and front bearing inner race. Press rear bearing inner race from drive pinion. Drive out front and rear bearing outer races with a drift.

NOTE: **Keep left and right side bearings separate, as they are not interchangeable.**

7) To disassemble differential case, use Side Bearing Puller (ST33051001) with Driver (ST33061000) and remove side bearings. Remove ring gear by unfolding

Fig. 3: Exploded View of Nissan R180 Integral Carrier Differential Assembly

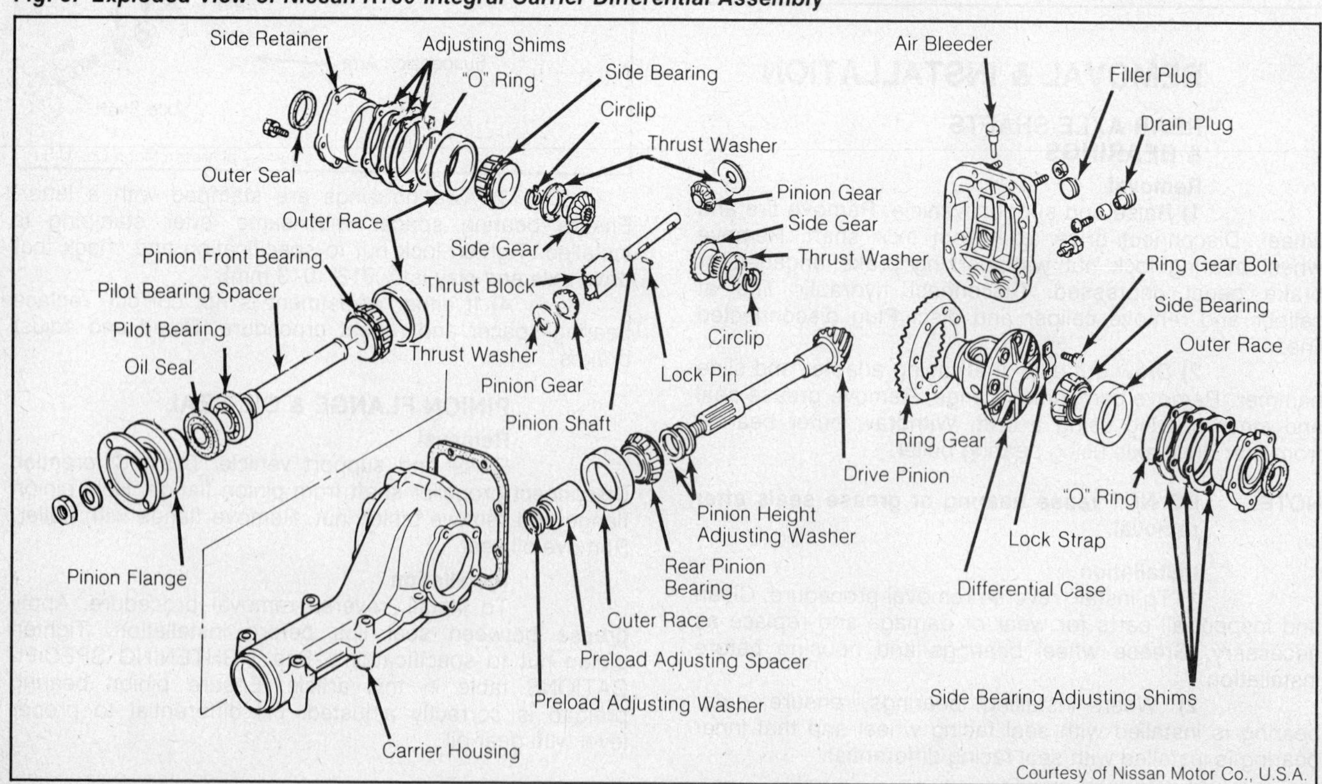

NISSAN INTEGRAL HOUSING (Cont.)

Fig. 4: Exploded View of Nissan R200 Integral Carrier Differential Assembly

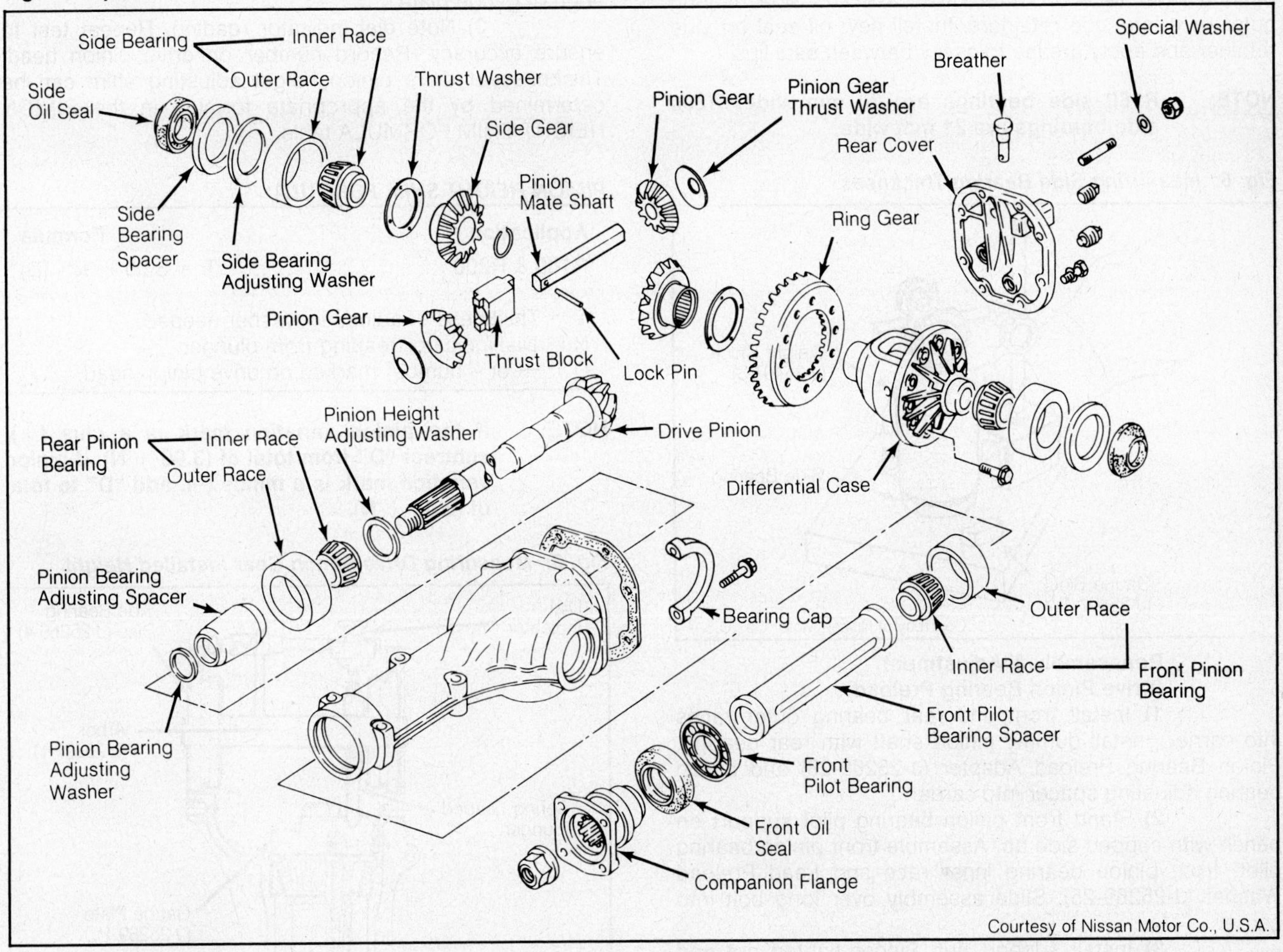

Courtesy of Nissan Motor Co., U.S.A.

lock strap and loosening bolts. Drive out pinion shaft lock pin from ring gear side.

8) Remove pinion shaft, pinion gears, side gears and thrust washers. Thoroughly clean and inspect all parts for wear or damage, and repair or replace as necessary.

NOTE: Mark gears and thrust washers for installation in their original positions.

Reassembly & Adjustment (Differential Case Assembly)

1) Assemble pinion gears, side gears and thrust washers in original positions in differential case. Fit pinion shaft to differential case so that it aligns with lock pin holes.

2) Adjust side gear-to-pinion gear backlash or adjust clearance between rear face of side gear and thrust washer. Install pinion shaft lock pin and lock in place with punch. See AXLE ASSEMBLY SPECIFICATIONS table in this article.

3) Apply gear oil to gear tooth surface and thrust surfaces. Ensure gears rotate smoothly. On R180 differentials, apply Loctite to rear face of ring gear. On R200 differentials, apply Loctite to bolt threads. On all models, install ring gear on differential case. Install bolts and new lock washers.

Fig. 5: Measuring Side Gear-to-Thrust Washer Clearance

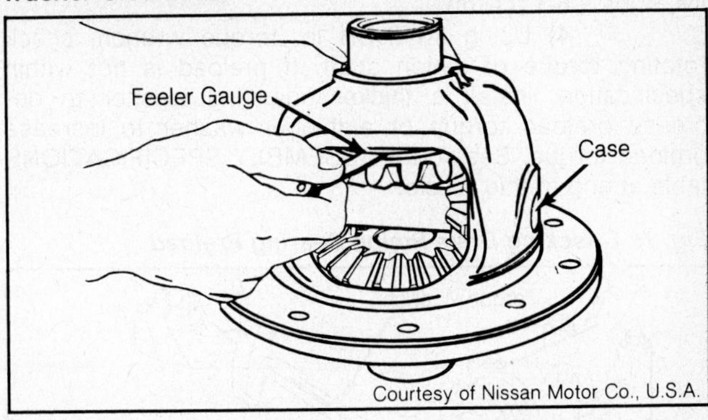

Courtesy of Nissan Motor Co., U.S.A.

NOTE: Tighten ring gear bolts diagonally, while tapping around bolt heads with hammer.

4) When replacing side bearings, measure bearing thickness with Gauge Block (J-25407-1) and Weight Block (J-25407-3) and a Base Plate (J-25407-2). Use 20 mm step of block on R180 models and 21 mm step on R200 models. Bearing thickness should be slightly smaller than gauge. *See Fig. 6*. Record left and right bearing thickness for shim selection. See SIDE BEARING SHIM FORMULAS table.

NISSAN INTEGRAL HOUSING (Cont.)

5) Using Adapter (ST33061000), press side bearing inner race on differential case and side bearing outer race into side retainers. Install new oil seal on side retainer and apply grease to cavity between seal lips.

NOTE: R180 side bearings are 20 mm wide. R200 side bearings are 21 mm wide.

Fig. 6: Measuring Side Bearing Thickness

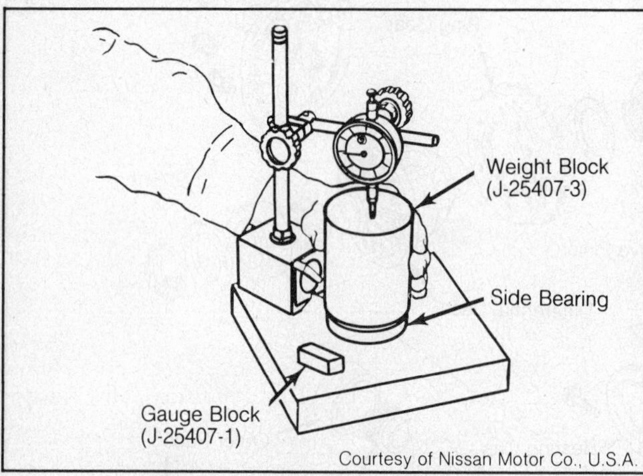

Courtesy of Nissan Motor Co., U.S.A.

Reassembly & Adjustment (Drive Pinion Bearing Preload)

1) Install front and rear bearing outer races into carrier. Install dummy pinion shaft with rear bearing, Pinion Bearing Preload Adapter (J-25269-26) and pinion bearing adjusting spacer into carrier.

2) Stand front pinion bearing pilot support on bench with cupped side up. Assemble front pinion bearing pilot, front pinion bearing inner race and Lead Preload Washer (J-25269-25). Slide assembly over long bolt into carrier.

3) Install support nut. Finger tighten nut and ensure all parts turn freely and are properly aligned. DO NOT install oil seal at this time. Tighten nut to 5.2-8.7 INCH lbs. (.6-1.0 N.m).

4) Using an INCH lb. torque wrench, check rotating torque of pinion shaft. If preload is not within specification, install a thicker adjusting washer to decrease preload torque or a thinner washer to increase preload torque. See AXLE ASSEMBLY SPECIFICATIONS table at end of this article.

Fig. 7: Checking Drive Pinion Bearing Preload

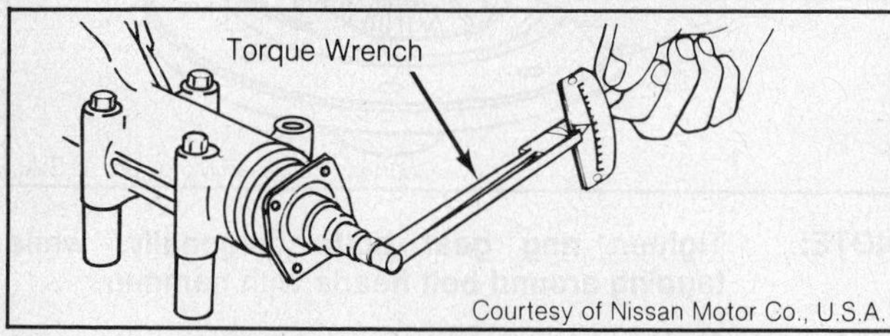

Courtesy of Nissan Motor Co., U.S.A.

Reassembly & Adjustment (Drive Pinion Gear Installed Height)

1) Leave dummy drive shaft installed and install Pinion Height and Preload Gauge Set (J-25269-B) into bearing bores of carrier. Lift spring loaded plunger and position it on face of gauge plate.

2) Install dial indicator and tighten hold-down clamp. Set dial indicator to zero. Rotate arbor plunger back and forth, and note highest deflection. Set dial indicator to zero. Rotate gauge plate until plunger falls off edge of gauge plate.

3) Note dial indicator reading. Repeat test to ensure accuracy. Record number on drive pinion head. Thickness of drive pinion height adjusting shim can be determined by the appropriate formula in the PINION HEIGHT SHIM FORMULA table.

PINION HEIGHT SHIM FORMULA

Application	Formula
R180 & R200	T = 3.00 + N - (D)

T = Thickness of adjusting washer needed.
N = Dial indicator reading from plunger.
D = + or - number marked on drive pinion head.

NOTE: If the pinion variation mark is a plus (+), subtract "D" from total of (3.00 + N). If pinion variation mark is a minus (-), add "D" to total of (3.00 + N).

Fig. 8: Measuring Drive Pinion Gear Installed Height

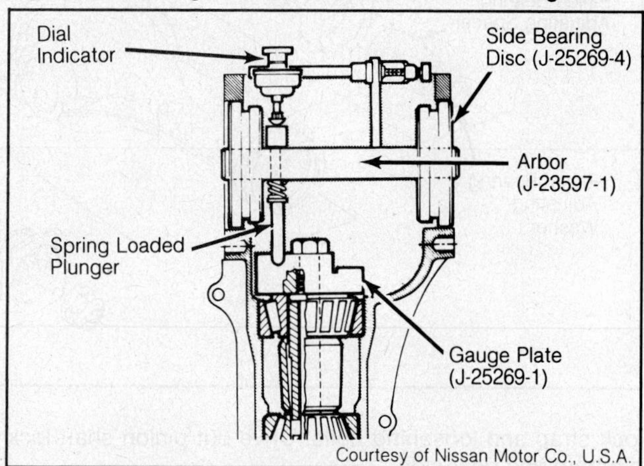

Courtesy of Nissan Motor Co., U.S.A.

4) After determining correct thickness of required pinion height adjusting washer, remove dummy shaft and height gauge. Fit correct pinion height adjusting washer on drive pinion gear, and using Adapter (ST30901000) press rear bearing inner race onto pinion gear.

5) Lubricate pinion bearings. Install drive pinion gear, pinion bearing spacer and washer, pilot bearing race, pilot bearing spacer, pilot bearing and oil seal. Install pinion flange. Tighten pinion nut to specification.

Reassembly & Adjustment (Side Bearing Preload)

1) Required thickness of left and right side retainer shims can be obtained by using the appropriate formula in the SIDE BEARING SHIM FORMULAS table.

NOTE: Formula values are given in millimeters. If value signifying A, B, C, D, G_1, and G_2 are not given, regard them as zero.

2) On R180 differentials, install differential case assembly in gear carrier in reverse order of disassembly. Fit correct shims and "O" ring seal in both side retainers in carrier. Arrow should point as shown. *See Fig. 9.*

NISSAN INTEGRAL HOUSING (Cont.)

SIDE BEARING SHIM FORMULAS

Differential Application	Formula
R180	
Left	$T_1 = A + C + G_1 - D - E + H + .76$
Right	$T_2 = B + G_2 + D - F - H + .76$
R200	
Left	$T_1 = A - C + D + E - H + 2.05$
Right	$T_2 = B - D + F + G + H + 1.95$

T_1 = Required thickness of left side retainer shim.
T_2 = Required thickness of right side retainer shim.
A & B = Figure marked on gear carrier.
C & D = Figure marked on differential case.
E & F = Difference in width of left or right bearing.
G_1 & G_2 = Figure marked on left or right retainers.
G = Standard spacer (8.10 mm) thickness difference.
H = Variation figure marked on ring gear.

3) On R200 differentials, install differential case assembly with side bearing outer races into gear carrier. Insert side bearing washers, and drive in spacer between right side washer and housing. Align marks on bearing cap and carrier and install bolts. Tighten to specification.

NOTE: Use care in installing spacer to avoid tilting side bearing outer race.

Fig. 9: Aligning Side Retainer During Installation

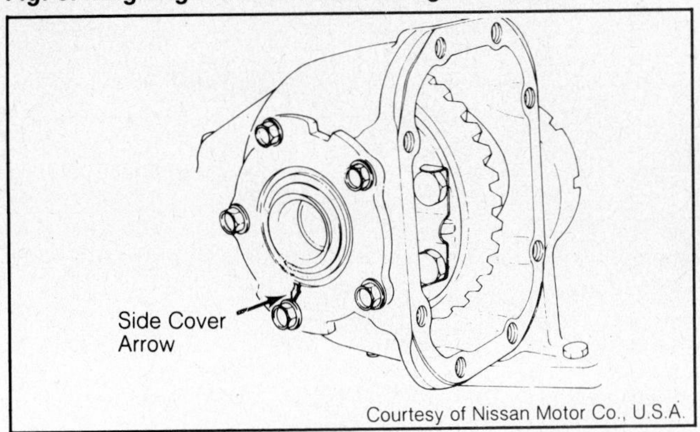

4) Using dial indicator, measure ring gear backlash and adjust if necessary. Check side bearing preload and adjust if necessary by adding or removing side retainer shims.

Fig. 11: Measuring Ring Gear Backlash

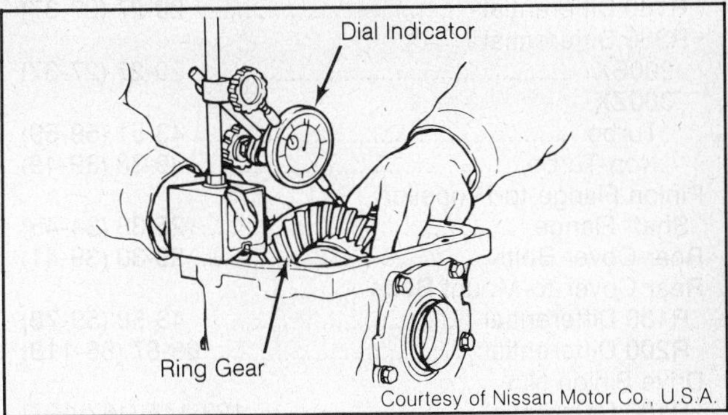

NOTE: If side bearing preload is readjusted, ring gear backlash must be checked and, if necessary, adjusted.

Final Inspection & Reassembly

1) After all adjustments are to specification, make tooth contact pattern test and make any necessary corrections. See GEAR TOOTH PATTERNS article in this section.

2) Install rear cover and tighten nuts to specification. Refill axle assembly to correct level with gear oil.

AXLE ASSEMBLY SPECIFICATIONS

Application	INCH Lbs. (N.m)
Pinion Bearing Preload	
Without Oil Seal	
All Models	9-11 (1.0-1.2)
With Oil Seal	
Pickup	8-15 (.90-1.7)
All Others	9.5-12 (1.07-1.3)
	In. (mm)
Ring Gear-to-Pinion Backlash	.005-.007 (.13-.18)
Side Gear Backlash	.004-.008 (.10-.20)

Fig. 10: Side Bearing Preload Identification Marks

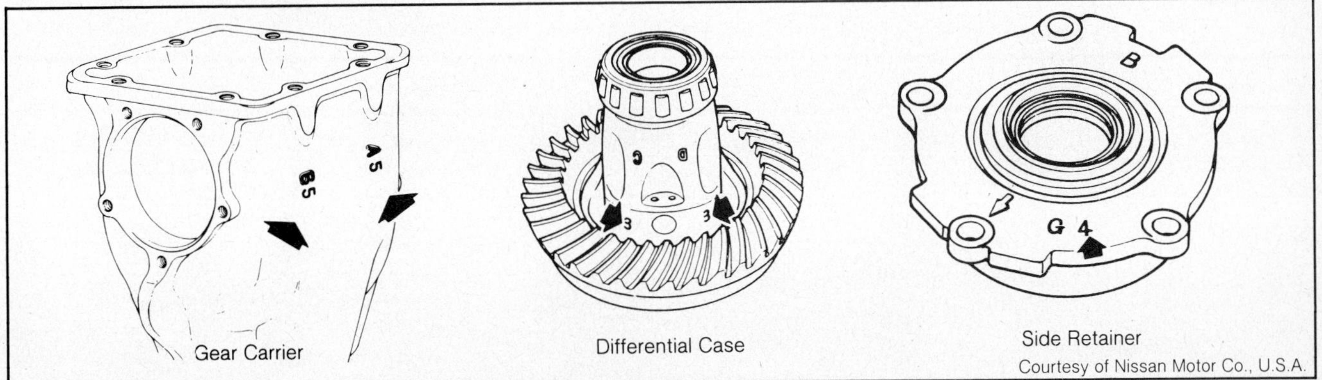

NISSAN INTEGRAL HOUSING (Cont.)

TIGHTENING SPECIFICATIONS

Application	Ft. Lbs. (N.m)
Drive Shaft Flange Bolts	
R180 Differential	20-27 (27-37)
R200 Differential	
200SX	20-27 (27-37)
300ZX	
Turbo	43-51 (59-69)
Non-Turbo	29-36 (39-49)
Pinion Flange-to-Propeller Shaft Flange	25-33 (34-45)
Rear Cover Bolts	29-30 (39-41)
Rear Cover-to-Mount Bolts	
R180 Differential	43-58 (59-78)
R200 Differential	65-87 (88-118)
Drive Pinion Nut	
R180 Differential	123-145 (167-197)
R200 Differential	137-217 (186-294)
Ring Gear Bolts [1]	
R180 Differential	65-72 (88-98)
R200 Differential	
200SX	58-72 (78-98)
300ZX	
Turbo	98-112 (132-152)
Non-Turbo	51-58 (69-78)
Side Bearing Cap Bolts	
R200 Differential	65-72 (88-98)
	INCH Lbs. (N.m)
Side Bearing Retainer Bolts	
R180 Differential	78-104 (9-12)

[1] – Apply Loctite to rear face of ring gear on R180 differentials or on bolt threads on R200 differentials.

NISSAN SEPARATE CARRIER

Pathfinder (Rear) & Pickup (Rear)
(H190A & H233B Differentials)

DESCRIPTION

Differential gear carrier assembly has a hypoid type ring and pinion gear set. The gear carrier is constructed of cast iron. The drive pinion is mounted in 2 tapered roller bearings, preloaded by a collapsible spacer. Drive pinion is aligned into position with a shim, located between shoulder on drive pinion and rear bearing.

Differential case is supported in carrier by 2 tapered roller side bearings. The side bearings are preloaded by inserting shims between bearings and differential. Case houses 2 side gears that mesh with 2 pinion gears, mounted on a lock pin. Pinion and side gears are set in front of thrust washers.

AXLE RATIO & IDENTIFICATION

Nissan does not identify rear axle with a particular outside identification marking. Both models use same basic type of removable carrier rear axle. *See Fig. 1.*

Various axle ratios are available, depending on model and whether vehicle is equipped with manual or automatic transmission. Ratio may be determined by dividing number of ring gear teeth by number of pinion gear teeth.

REMOVAL & INSTALLATION

AXLE SHAFTS & BEARINGS

Removal

1) Raise and support vehicle. Remove tire and wheel. On dual-wheel models, remove axle retaining bolts and axles. Remove wheel bearing lock nut screw, lock nut and brake drum assembly. Remove bearings from drum assembly. On all others, disconnect parking brake linkage and hydraulic line. Remove brake drum. Remove brake backing plate retaining nuts, and pull assembly from housing with a slide hammer.

2) Mount axle shaft assembly in a vise or mounting fixture and cut bearing collar with a chisel. Bend lock tabs away. Using Lock Nut Wrench (ST38020000), remove wheel bearing lock nut. Remove wheel bearing with brake backing plate using Puller (HT72480000).

NOTE: **Single-Wheel axle bearings are tapered roller type. Outer race may be removed from backing plate after removing oil seal by tapping it out with a brass drift.**

Installation

1) On dual-wheel models, reverse removal procedure and tighten bearing retainer to specification. On all other models, fit bearing outer race into position in backing plate using brass drift. Install oil seal. Pack seal lips with grease. Install bearing and new lock washers. Tighten lock nut to specification. Bend up lock tabs on washer.

2) To install, reverse removal procedure. Insert shims between backing plate and axle tube end so that measured axle shaft end play is .0008-.0060" (.020-.150 mm) on one axle.

3) If both axle bearings are serviced, end play on first axle should be .0118-.0354" (.30-.90 mm). End play on second axle should be .0008-.0060" (.020-.150 mm).

PINION FLANGE SEAL

Removal

Raise and support rear of vehicle. Drain gear oil. Scribe an index mark on propeller shaft and companion flange. Detach shaft, and wire out of way. Remove drive pinion nut and companion flange. Remove seal.

Installation

Set new oil seal into position and pack grease between seal lips. Position companion flange and flat washer on drive pinion. Tighten nut and check bearing preload.

DIFFERENTIAL CARRIER

Removal

1) Raise and support vehicle on safety stands placed under rear axle housing. Drain gear lubricant. Scribe an index mark on propeller shaft and remove. Withdraw rear axle shafts as previously described.

2) Remove nuts mounting differential gear carrier to rear axle housing and lift out gear carrier.

Installation

To install differential gear carrier, reverse removal procedure and tighten nuts to specification. See TIGHTENING SPECIFICATIONS table in this article.

OVERHAUL

DIFFERENTIAL

NOTE: **Inspection of ring gear backlash and gear tooth contact prior to disassembly can indicate where problem may exist. See GEAR TOOTH PATTERNS article in this section.**

Disassembly

1) Mount differential carrier in a holding fixture. Scribe index marks on side bearing caps and carrier. Remove bearing caps and lift out differential assembly.

2) Hold companion flange using Flange Wrench (J-25774) and remove drive pinion lock nut. Drive out drive pinion using a hammer and brass drift. Pull companion flange out by hand. Remove drive pinion together with rear bearing inner race, spacer and washer.

3) Remove oil seal and front bearing inner race. Using press and bearing plates, remove bearing from drive pinion gear. Using a drift, remove front and rear bearing races. Using puller, remove side bearings.

4) Keep right and left side components separate for reassembly reference. Bend back ring gear retaining bolt lock tabs. Remove bolts by loosening in a diagonal sequence. Using a soft hammer, tap ring gear off of gear case.

5) Drive out pinion shaft lock pin. Remove pinion shaft, pinion gears, thrust block, side gears and thrust washers. Identify gears and thrust washers for installation in original positions.

Cleaning & Inspection

Clean all disassembled parts and visually inspect for excessive wear. Check all gears for wear and

NISSAN SEPARATE CARRIER (Cont.)

Fig. 1: Exploded View of Nissan Separate Carrier Differential Assemblies

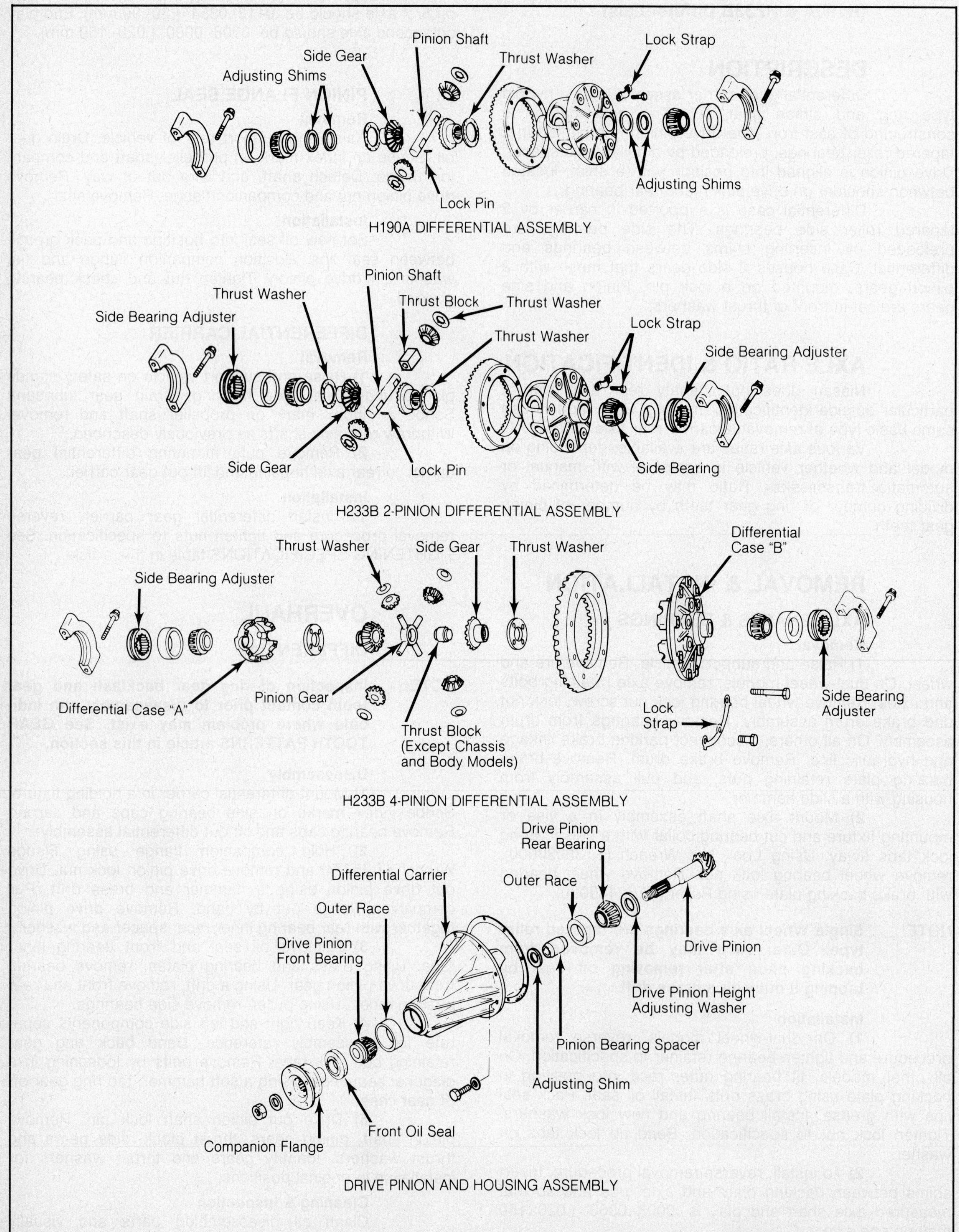

Courtesy of Nissan Motor Co., U.S.A.

NISSAN SEPARATE CARRIER (Cont.)

replace if necessary. Inspect thrust washer surfaces and be sure they are free from surface scratches.

NOTE: Drive pinion and ring gear are replaced only as a set.

Reassembly & Adjustment (Case Assembly)

1) Fit pinion, side gears, thrust washers and thrust block (if equipped) in differential case. Assemble pinion shaft to differential case so that lock pin holes align with shaft.

2) To obtain specified clearance, insert side gear thrust washers of proper thickness between rear face of side gear and thrust washer to obtain .004-.008" (.10-.20 mm) clearance. Insert pinion shaft lock pin and secure by peening with a punch.

3) Lightly oil gear tooth areas and all thrust surfaces. Ensure that gears turn freely and smoothly. Position ring gear on differential case. Tighten bolts in diagonal sequence and bend over lock tabs. See TIGHTENING SPECIFICATIONS table in this article.

Reassembly & Adjustment (Drive Pinion Height)

1) Pinion height is adjusted with drive pinion adjusting washer placed behind drive pinion gear. Ensure all parts are clean and bearings are lubricated.

2) Install rear pinion bearing on Bearing Pilot (J-34309-15) and lock in place using Locking Seat (J-3409-4). Install front pinion bearing on Gauge Anvil (J-34309-2) and lock in place using Bearing Pilot (J-3409-15).

3) With pinion bearing races installed in housing, place bearings and tool assemblies in through housing. Ensure gauge plate will rotate 360 degrees. Tighten both sections together by hand to set bearing preload. Turn assembly several times to seat bearings.

4) Turning torque at Gauge Anvil (J-34309-2) should be 9-11 INCH lbs. (1.0-1.3 N.m) on H190A models, and 4-9 INCH lbs. (3.5 7.8 N.m) on H233B models.

5) On H190A models, install Pinion Height Adapter (J-34309-14) onto gauge plate and tighten by hand. Position Arbor and Side Bearing Disc (J-25269-18) firmly into side bearing bores.

6) Install side bearing caps and torque to 36-44 (49-59 N.m). To reach standard pinion height washer thickness, measure gap between Arbor and Pinion Height Adapter (J-3409-14).

7) On H233B models, place Pinion Height Adapter (J-34309-12) onto gauge plate and tighten by hand. Place solid pinion bearing adjusting spacer squarely into recess of Gauge Anvil (J-34309-2) so end of spacer rests on Gauge Screw (J-34309-1). To reach standard pinion height washer thickness, measure gap between top of solid spacer and anvil recess.

8) On all models, check pinion head for variation mark. If mark is a plus (+) number, subtract that amount from standard pinion height washer thickness. If mark is a minus "–" number, add that amount to pinion height washer thickness. This is the correct shim thickness needed. Shims are available in increments of .03 mm.

NOTE: If pinion is unmarked or marked zero, standard pinion height washer thickness is correct pinion shim size needed. Always measure shim to verify thickness.

9) Remove assembly from housing. Select correct shim, and install on pinion shaft with beveled side toward gear. Using a press, install rear pinion bearing. Install a new washer and collapsible spacer. Lubricate pinion bearing and install into housing.

NOTE: Pinion nut, oil seal and collapsible spacer must NEVER be reused. Always use new parts during overhaul.

Reassembly & Adjustment (Drive Pinion Preload & Ring Gear Backlash)

1) After obtaining final pinion bearing height, lubricate front bearing and place into carrier. Fit new oil seal in carrier and fill space between seal lips with grease.

2) Slip new washer and collapsible spacer on drive pinion. Lubricate rear pinion bearing. Insert companion flange in oil seal, while holding flange tightly against pinion front bearing race.

3) Working from rear of carrier, insert drive pinion into companion flange. Ensure drive pinion threads and mounting nut are dirt free. Hold companion flange with Flange Wrench (J-25774) and tighten nut to specification.

4) Mount dial indicator so tip of indicator is against ring gear. Mount torque wrench on pinion nut. With the use of shims on H190A models, or rotating side bearing adjusters on H233B models, bring pinion preload and ring gear backlash into specification. *See Figs. 2 and 3.*

5) Check gear tooth contact pattern and correct any problem. See GEAR TOOTH PATTERNS article at beginning of this section.

Fig. 2: Measuring Ring Gear Backlash

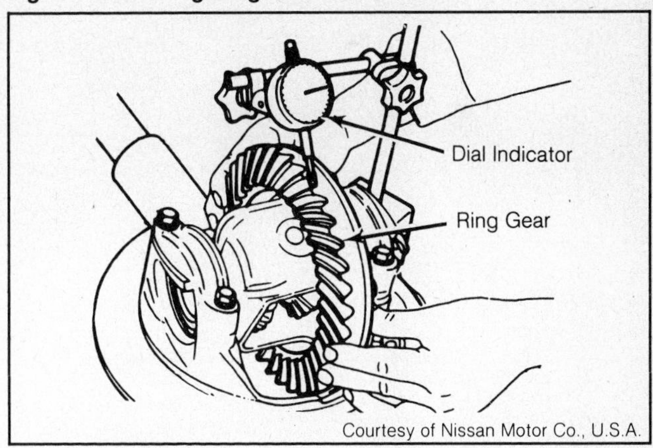

Fig. 3: Measuring Drive Pinion Preload

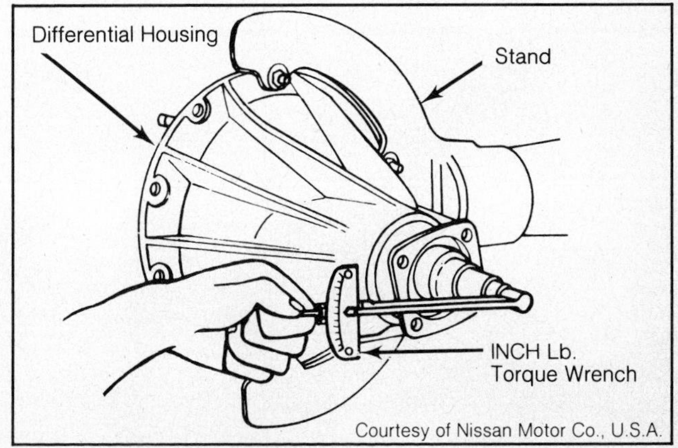

NISSAN SEPARATE CARRIER (Cont.)

AXLE ASSEMBLY SPECIFICATIONS

Application	INCH Lbs. (N.m)
Drive Pinion Total Preload	
H233B	9-17 (1.0-2.0)
H190A	10-19 (1.2-2.2)
	In. (mm)
Ring Gear-to-Pinion Backlash	
H190A	.005-.007 (.13-.18)
H233B	.006-.008 (.15-.20)
Pinion Gear-to-Side Gear Backlash	.004-.008 (.10-.20)
Ring Gear Runout	.003 (.08)

TIGHTENING SPECIFICATIONS

Application	Ft. Lbs. (N.m)
Companion Flange-to-Propeller Shaft	17-24 (24-32)
Differential Carrier-to-Axle Housing	
H190A	12-18 (17-25)
H233B	20-27 (27-37)
Dual-Wheel Bearing Retainer [1]	
Drive Pinion Nut	
H190A	94-217 (127-294)
H233B	145-181 (196-245)
Ring Gear Retaining Bolts	
H190A	
10 mm Bolts	58-72 (78-98)
12 mm Bolts	98-112 (132-152)
H233B	58-69 (78-93)
Side Bearing Cap Bolts	
H190A	36-43 (49-59)
H233B	69-76 (93-103)

[1] - After seating bearing, tighten to 35-43 INCH lbs. (4.1-4.9 N.m).

NISSAN MODEL C200 REAR AXLE

Pathfinder, Pickup 4WD, Van

DESCRIPTION

The axle assembly is a hypoid gear-type with integral carrier housing. Pinion bearing preload adjustment is made with a collapsible spacer and washer between front and rear bearing cones.

Differential side bearing preload and pinion depth adjustment are made by shims. Driving power is transmitted to axle by spline type drive shaft. Some models contain a 2 pinion gear type differential while others contain a 4 pinion type.

AXLE RATIO & IDENTIFICATION

Ratio may be determined by dividing number of ring gear teeth by the number of pinion gear teeth. See AXLE RATIO SPECIFICATIONS table.

AXLE RATIO SPECIFICATIONS

Application	Ratio
Pathfinder	4.625
Pickup	4.375
Van	
A/T	4.625
M/T	4.375

REMOVAL & INSTALLATION

AXLE DRIVE SHAFTS & BEARINGS

Removal

1) Raise and support vehicle. Remove tire and wheel. Disconnect parking brake cable and brake line. Remove axle drive shaft and backing plate retaining bolts.

2) Using slide hammer and adapter, remove axle shaft. Using screw driver, pry oil seal from axle housing. Note amount of shims installed between backing plate and axle housing.

3) On Van models, use chisel to cut bearing collar. *See Fig. 1.* Use care not to damage axle drive shaft. Using Puller (ST37110000), pull bearing and bearing collar from axle drive shaft.

Fig. 1: Exploded View of Van Axle Drive Shaft

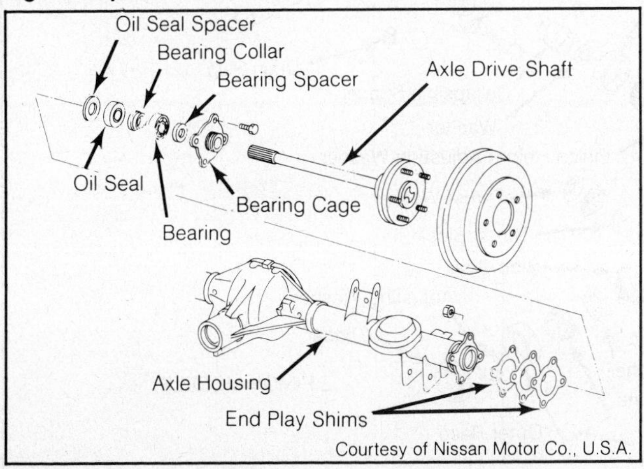

Fig. 2: Exploded View of Pathfinder & Pickup Axle Drive Shaft

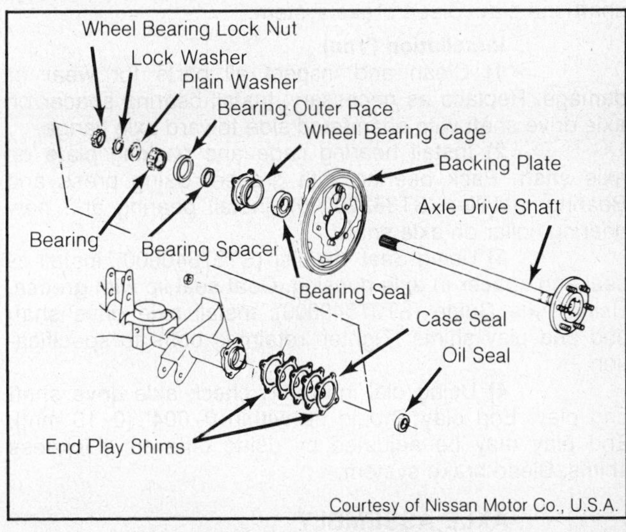

4) On Pathfinder and Pickup models, bend over wheel bearing lock washer. *See Fig. 2.* Using Bearing Nut Socket (ST38020000) and Bearing Nut Remover (KV40101000), remove wheel bearing nut.

5) Using press and Bearing Remover (J-25852-B), press bearing and backing plate from axle drive shaft. Remove grease seal and bearing race from bearing cage.

Installation (Pathfinder & Pickup)

1) Clean and inspect all parts for wear or damage. Replace as necessary. Install bearing race and new bearing oil seal in bearing cage. Lubricate oil seal lip with grease.

2) Install bearing spacer on axle drive shaft with chamfered side toward axle flange. Lubricate bearing with grease. Reverse removal procedures. Install new bearing lock washer. Using bearing nut socket, tighten wheel bearing lock nut to specification. See TIGHTENING SPECIFICATIONS table at end of article.

3) Ensure wheel bearing lock washer tab aligns with wheel bearing lock nut. Bend lock washer upward. Install new oil seal in axle housing. Lubricate seal with grease. Fill axle housing recess area with grease.

4) Lubricate axle shaft splines with grease. Install case seal and axle end play shims. End play shims should be between axle housing and case seal.

CAUTION: DO NOT install end play shims between case seal and bearing cage.

5) Using Axle Guide (ST37840000), install axle drive shaft. Tighten retaining bolts to specification. Using dial indicator, check axle drive shaft end play. End play must be adjusted to specification depending on axle drive shaft installation. See AXLE SHAFT END PLAY SPECIFICATIONS table.

AXLE SHAFT END PLAY SPECIFICATIONS

Application	In. (mm)
One Axle Only	.0008-.0059 (.020-.149)
Both Axles	
First Axle	.0118-.0354 (.299-.899)
Second Axle	.0008-.0059 (.020-.149)

NISSAN MODEL C200 REAR AXLE (Cont.)

6) Adjust end play by changing end play shims. Use care not to damage oil seal while adjusting axle drive shaft end play. Bleed brake system.

Installation (Van)

1) Clean and inspect all parts for wear or damage. Replace as necessary. Install bearing spacer on axle drive shaft with chamfered side toward axle flange.

2) Install bearing cage and backing plate on axle shaft. Pack bearing with grease. Using press and Bearing Installer (ST38220000), install bearing and new bearing collar on axle shaft.

3) Using Seal Installer (ST37840000), install oil seal and spacer in axle housing. Coat seal lip with grease. Using Axle Guide (ST37840000), install axle drive shaft and end play shims. Tighten retaining bolts to specification.

4) Using dial indicator, check axle drive shaft end play. End play should be within 0-.004" (0-.10 mm). End play may be adjusted by using different thickness shims. Bleed brake system.

AXLE ASSEMBLY

Removal (Pickup)

1) Raise and support rear of vehicle. Drain differential gear oil. Disconnect propeller shaft at companion flange. Disconnect parking brake cable. Disconnect rear brake hydraulic lines.

2) Support differential on jack. Disconnect shock absorber lower end on each side. Remove shackle nuts and shackle pins. Remove axle assembly and springs.

Installation

Reverse removal procedures. On components containing rubber bushings, tighten bolts to specification with vehicle at normal operating height. Fill differential to proper level with 80W-90 API GL-5 gear oil. Bleed brake system.

Removal (Pathfinder & Van)

1) Raise and support rear of vehicle. Drain differential gear oil. Disconnect propeller shaft at companion flange. Disconnect parking brake cable. Disconnect rear brake hydraulic lines.

2) Support differential on jack. Remove shock absorber-to-rear axle bolts. On Van models, disconnect stabilizer bar at rear axle. On Pathfinder models, disconnect stabilizer bar rods at stabilizer bar.

3) On all models, remove upper and lower support arms-to-body bolts. Remove rear support rod-to-body bolts. On Van models, remove coil spring upper mount-to-body bolts. On all models, remove rear axle assembly.

Installation

Reverse removal procedures. On all components containing rubber bushings, bolts should be tightened to specification with vehicle at normal operating height with no passengers or cargo. Fill differential to proper level with 80W-90 API GL-5 gear oil. Bleed brake system.

Fig. 3: Exploded View of C200 Differential Assembly

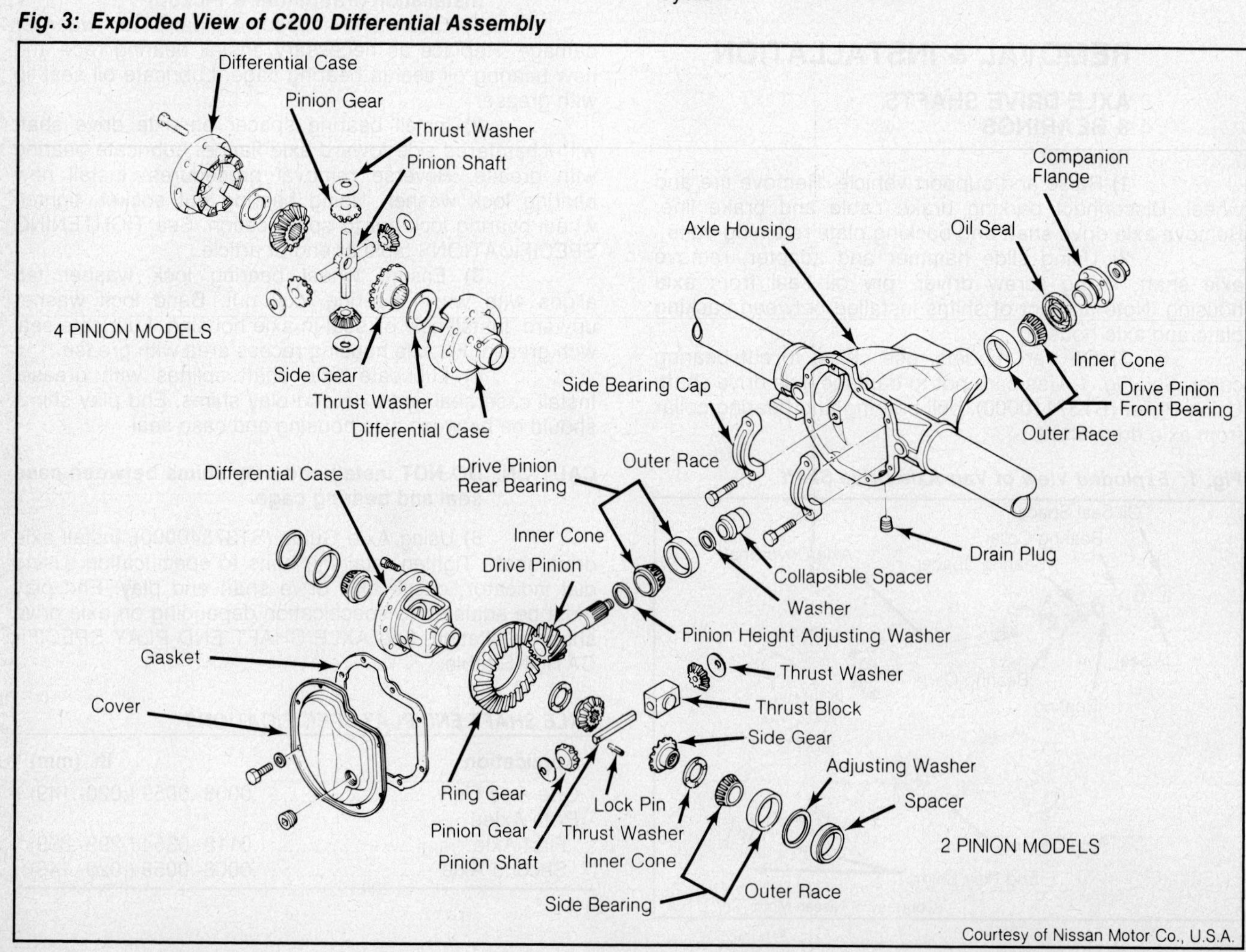

NISSAN MODEL C200 REAR AXLE (Cont.)

OVERHAUL

DIFFERENTIAL

NOTE: **Ring gear backlash, pinion total preload, ring gear runout and gear tooth contact pattern should be checked prior to disassembly.**

Disassembly

1) Mount differential assembly in holding fixture. Remove rear cover plate. Using INCH lb. torque wrench and Adapter (J25765-A), measure the total preload required to rotate the pinion and ring gear. Total preload should be 10-20 INCH lbs. (1.13-2.26 N.m).

2) Using dial indicator, check ring gear backlash while holding pinion at several locations. Ring gear backlash should be .0051-.0071" (.129-.180 mm). Using dial indicator, check ring gear runout.

3) Ring gear runout should not exceed .0031" (.078 mm). Check for damaged ring gear or differential case if runout exceeds specification.

4) Check gear tooth contact pattern. See GEAR TOOTH PATTERNS article in this section. Mark side bearing caps for location. Remove side bearing caps. Using pry bar, remove differential case assembly, bearing races, adjusting washers and spacers. Mark components for location.

CAUTION: **Side bearing caps, bearings, bearing races, adjusting washers and spacers should be marked for location. Components should be installed in original location.**

5) Using Flange Holder (J34311), hold pinion companion flange and remove pinion nut. Remove flange with puller. Using a soft-faced hammer, remove drive pinion from axle housing. Remove oil seal and pinion front bearing from axle housing.

6) Using a brass drift, remove pinion bearing outer races from axle housing. Remove collapsible spacer and washer from drive pinion. Using Bearing Remover (J-22912-01), remove rear bearing inner race and adjusting washer from drive pinion.

7) Using Side Bearing Puller (J-ST33051001) and Adapter (ST33061000), remove side bearings from differential case. Remove ring gear-to-differential case retaining bolts in a criss-cross pattern. Tap ring gear from differential case.

8) On 2 pinion models, drive out pinion shaft lock pin from ring gear side of differential case. On 4 pinion models, scribe reference mark on left and right differential cases. Remove differential case retaining bolts. Separate differential cases.

9) On all models, remove pinion shaft, pinion gears, side gears, thrust block (if equipped) and thrust washers. Mark components for location for reassembly.

CAUTION: **Mark gears and thrust washers for location. Components must be installed in original location.**

Inspection

Thoroughly clean and inspect all parts for damaged teeth or wear. Inspect pinion and ring gear for damaged thread holes. Replace damaged components.

Reassembly & Adjustment (Differential Case Assembly-2 Pinion Models)

1) Assemble pinion gears, side gears, thrust washers and thrust block in original location in differential case. Thrust block should be installed with round seat facing spacer side of assembly. *See Fig. 3.*

2) Install pinion shaft and align with lock pin hole of differential case. Using feeler gauge, check side gear clearance. *See Fig. 4.* Adjust clearance to within .0039-.0079" (.099-.200 mm) by using different thickness thrust washers.

Fig. 4: Checking Side Gear Clearance

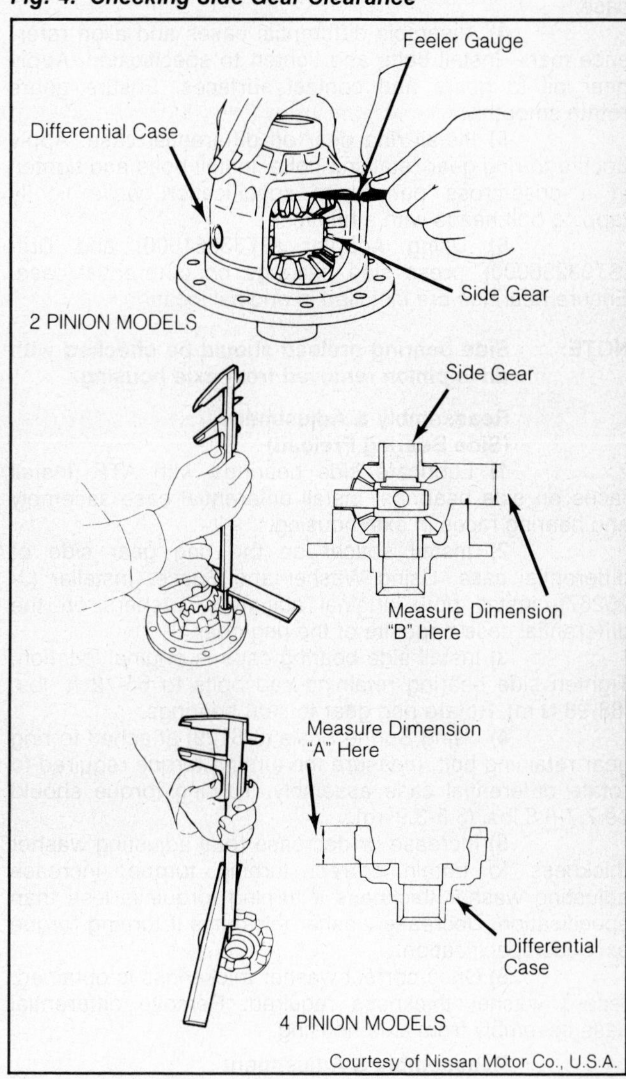

3) Once correct side clearance is obtained, install new lock pin until lock pin is even with differential case surface. Stake lock pin in place. Apply gear oil to gears and contact surfaces. Ensure gears rotate smoothly.

4) Install ring gear on differential case. Apply Loctite to ring gear retaining bolts. Install bolts and tighten in a criss-cross pattern to specification while lightly tapping bolt heads with a hammer.

5) Using Adapter (ST33061000) and Drift (ST33230000), press side bearings on differential case. Ensure bearings are installed in original location.

Reassembly & Adjustment (Differential Case Assembly-4 Pinion Models)

1) Install side gears, thrust washers and pinion shaft in differential case. Using caliper and flat edge, measure distance from upper edge of side gear to the edge of housing. *See Fig. 4.* This is dimension "B".

NISSAN MODEL C200 REAR AXLE (Cont.)

2) Measure distance from inside of differential case to the upper edge of differential case. *See Fig. 4.* This is dimension "A". Subtract dimension "B" from dimension "A". This is the side gear clearance.

3) Side clearance should be within .0039-.0079" (.099-.200 mm). Adjust clearance by using different thickness thrust washers. Assemble thrust washers, pinion shaft, pinion gears and side gears in differential case.

4) Assemble differential cases and align reference mark. Install bolts and tighten to specificaion. Apply gear oil to gears and contact surfaces. Ensure gears rotate smoothly.

5) Install ring gear on differential case. Apply Loctite to ring gear retaining bolts. Install bolts and tighten in a criss-cross pattern to specification while lightly tapping bolt heads with a hammer.

6) Using Adapter (ST33061000) and Drift (ST33230000), press side bearings on differential case. Ensure bearings are installed in original location.

NOTE: Side bearing preload should be checked with drive pinion removed from axle housing.

Reassembly & Adjustment (Side Bearing Preload)

1) Lubricate side bearings with ATF. Install races on side bearings. Install differential case assembly and bearing races in axle housing.

2) Install spacer on the ring gear side of differential case. Using Washer and Spacer Installer (J-25267), install both original adjusting washers on the differential case opposite of the ring gear.

3) Install side bearing caps in original location. Tighten side bearing retaining cap bolts to 65-72 ft. lbs. (88-98 N.m). Rotate ring gear to seat bearings.

4) Using Spring Scale (J-8129) attached to ring gear retaining bolt, measure the turning torque required to rotate differential case assembly. Turning torque should be 7.7-8.8 lbs. (3.5-3.9 kg).

5) Increase or decrease total adjusting washer thickness to obtain correct turning torque. Increase adjusting washer thickness if turning torque is less than specification. Decrease washer thickness if turning torque exceeds specification.

6) Once correct washer thickeness is obtained, record washer thickness required. Remove differential case assembly from axle housing.

Reassembly & Adjustment (Drive Pinion Installed Height & Preload)

1) Using Handle (J-25742-1) and Race Installer (J-25742-5) for pinion bearing rear outer race and (J-25742-3) for front outer race, install races in axle housing.

2) Lubricate drive pinion bearings with oil. Install drive pinion bearings on Pinion Height Gauge Assembly (J-34309). Install Gauge Screw (J-34309-1) and rear bearing in axle housing. *See Fig. 5.* DO NOT install bearing discs and arbor at this time.

3) Install front bearing assembly in axle housing. Rotate height gauge plate several times. Ensure plate will rotate 360 degress. Tighten the 2 sections of differential shim selector assembly together by hand.

4) Rotate assembly several times to seat bearings. Using Torque Wrench (J-25765A), measure turning torque required to rotate the assembly at the Gauge Anvil (J-34309-2). *See Fig. 5.* Turning torque should be 8.7-11.3 INCH lbs. (.98-1.27 N.m).

5) Ensure surfaces of height gauge plate are clean. Install Pinion Height Adapter (J-34309-13 "C200") on height gauge plate and tighten by hand. Install Bearing Discs (J-25269-4) and arbor in bearing bores. *See Fig. 5.*

Fig. 5: Determining Drive Pinion Installed Height

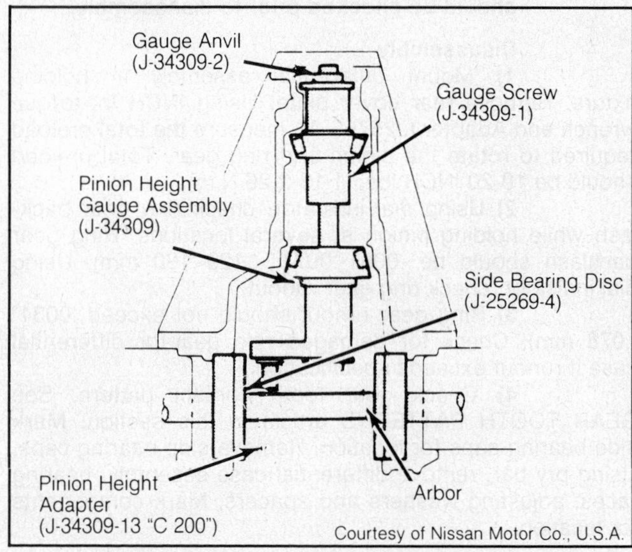

6) Install bearing caps and tighten bolts to 65-72 ft. lbs. (88-98 N.m). To determine the standard pinion height, use a .138" (3.50 mm) standard guage and Feeler Gauge (J-34309-01).

7) Measure and record clearance between end of pinion height adapter and arbor. Note pinion height head number stamped on the pinion. *See Fig. 6.*

8) Using pinion height head number, determine the amount to be added or subtracted from measurement determined in step **6)**. Determine the thickness pinion height washer to be used. *See Fig. 6.*

9) Several different thickness pinion height washers are available. Remove pinion height gauge assembly once correct height washer is determined.

10) Install pinion height adjusting washer on drive pinion with chamfered edge toward gear end of drive pinion. Using press and Adapter (ST30901000), press drive pinion rear bearing on pinion.

11) Lubricate pinion bearings. Install front pinion bearing in axle housing. Lubricate seal lip with grease. Using Seal Installer (J-25273), install oil seal in axle housing. Install washer and new collapsible spacer on pinion. Install pinion assembly.

12) Using a soft faced hammer, install companion flange on pinion. Ensure threaded end of pinion is clean. Install pinion nut. Using Flange Holder (J-34311), hold companion flange and tighten pinion nut to 94 ft. lbs. (127 N.m). Check drive pinion preload.

13) Rotate pinion several times to seat bearings. Using an INCH lb. torque wrench, check rotating torque of pinion while rotating in both directions several times. *See Fig. 7.* Preload should be 9.5-14.8 INCH lbs. (1.1-1.7 N.m).

14) Tighten pinion nut in small increments to obtain specified preload. Repeat procedure if maximum preload is obtained before minimum pinion nut torque is reached or minimum preload cannot be reached with maximum pinion nut tightened to maximum specification using a new collapsible spacer and washer.

NISSAN MODEL C200 REAR AXLE (Cont.)

Fig. 6: Determining Pinion Height Washer

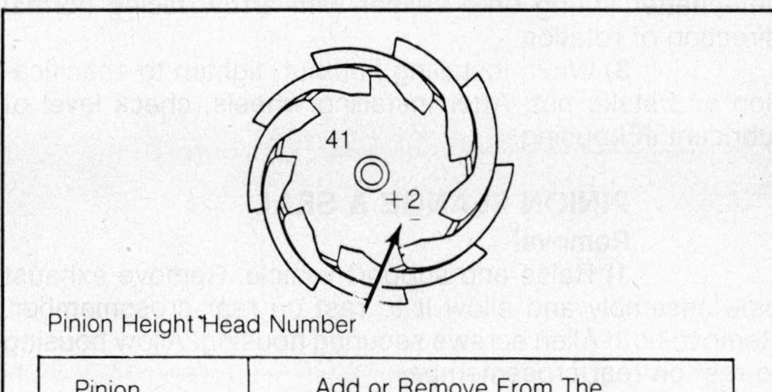

Pinion Height Head Number	Add or Remove From The Standard Pinion Height Washer Thickness Measurement
−6	Add 0.06 mm (0.0024 in)
−5	Add 0.05 mm (0.0020 in)
−4	Add 0.04 mm (0.0016 in)
−3	Add 0.03 mm (0.0012 in)
−2	Add 0.02 mm (0.0008 in)
−1	Add 0.01 mm (0.0004 in)
0	Use the selected washer thickness
+1	Subtract 0.01 mm (0.0004 in)
+2	Subtract 0.02 mm (0.0008 in)
+3	Subtract 0.03 mm (0.0012 in)
+4	Subtract 0.04 mm (0.0016 in)
+5	Subtract 0.05 mm (0.0020 in)
+6	Subtract 0.06 mm (0.0024 in)

Courtesy of Nissan Motor Co., U.S.A.

CAUTION: If pinion nut is overtightened, a new collapsible spacer and washer MUST BE installed.

Fig. 7: Checking Drive Pinion Bearing Preload

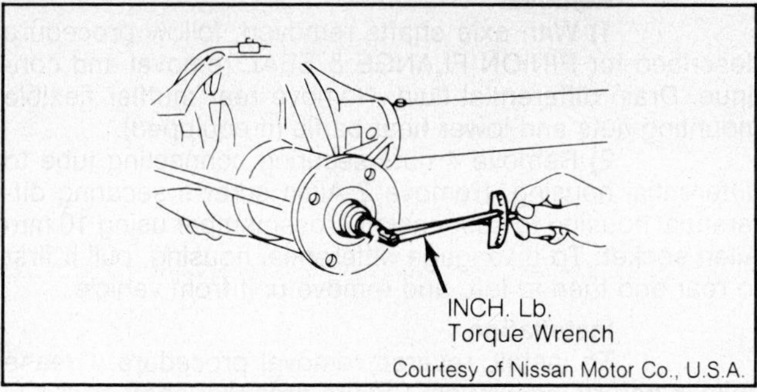

Courtesy of Nissan Motor Co., U.S.A.

Reassembly & Adjustment
(Differential Case Assembly)

1) With pinion installed, install differential case assembly and side bearing races in axle housing. Install correct adjusting washers between side bearing races and axle housing on each side.

2) Using Washer and Spacer Installer (J-25267) and hammer, install spacer on ring gear side of differential case. Install bearing caps in original location aligning reference marks. Install bearing cap bolts and tighten to specification.

3) Using dial indicator, measure ring gear-to-drive pinion backlash. *See Fig. 8.* Backlash should be .005-.007" (.13-.18 mm). If backlash is less than specification, increase adjusting washer thickness on tooth side of ring gear and decrease remaining adjusting washer thickness on the opposite side the equal amount.

Fig. 8: Measuring Ring Gear Backlash

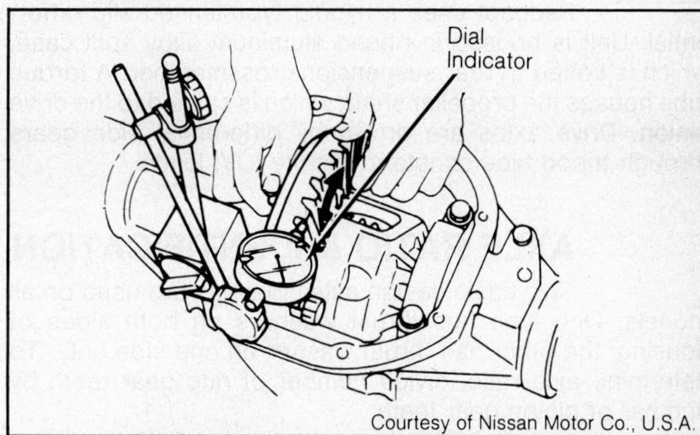

Courtesy of Nissan Motor Co., U.S.A.

4) If backlash exceeds specification, decrease adjusting washer thickness on tooth side of ring gear and increase remaining adjusting washer thickness on the opposite side the equal amount.

CAUTION: DO NOT change the total thickness of adjusting washers. Both adjusting washers must be changed the same amount to maintain side bearing preload.

Final Inspection & Reassembly

After all adjustments are to specification, make tooth contact pattern test and make any necessary corrections. See GEAR TOOTH PATTERNS article in this section. Install rear cover and tighten nuts to specification. Fill differential to proper level with 80W-90 API GL-5 gear oil.

TIGHTENING SPECIFICATIONS

Application	Ft. Lbs. (N.m)
Axle Shaft-to-Axle Housing Bolt	39-46 (53-62)
Coil Spring Mount-to-Body Bolt	
Van	10-14 (14-19)
Differential Case Bolt	47-54 (64-73)
Drain Plug	29-43 (39-58)
Pinion Nut	94-217 (127-295)
Rear Support Rod-to-Body Bolt	
Pathfinder	80-108 (109-146)
Van	80-94 (109-127)
Ring Gear Bolt	
Van	98-112 (133-152)
All Others	
10 mm Bolt	51-58 (69-79)
12 mm Bolt	98-112 (133-152)
Shackle Nut	
Pickup	37-50 (51-68)
Side Bearing Cap Bolt	65-72 (88-98)
Stabilizer Bar-to-Axle Housing Bolt	
Van	20-27 (27-37)
Stabilizer Rod Bolt	
Pathfinder	32-42 (43-57)
Upper & Lower Support Arm-to-Body Bolt	
Pathfinder	80-108 (109-146)
Van	80-94 (109-127)
Wheel Bearing Lock Nut	108-145 (146-197)
	INCH Lbs. (N.m)
Cover Bolt	
Van	96-120 (11-14)
All Others	
Bolt With Spring Washer	96-120 (11-14)
Bolt With Wave Washer	240-288 (27-33)

Drive Axles

PEUGEOT SPLIT HOUSING – I.R.S.

DESCRIPTION

Peugeot uses a hypoid type limited slip differential. Unit is housed in ribbed aluminum alloy split case, which is bolted to rear suspension crossmember. A torque tube houses the propeller shaft, which is splined to the drive pinion. Drive axles are driven by differential side gears through tripod type constant velocity (CV) joints.

AXLE RATIO & IDENTIFICATION

Two basic design axle housings are used on all models. One type has thrust washers on both sides of housing; the other has thrust washer on one side only. To determine axle ratio, divide number of ring gear teeth by number of pinion gear teeth.

REMOVAL & INSTALLATION

AXLE SHAFTS & BEARINGS

Removal

1) Raise rear of vehicle, and support under rear suspension arms. Remove rear wheels. Loosen but do not remove hub nut.

2) On disc brake models, disconnect brake line from clip on suspension arm. Remove and suspend brake caliper without distorting brake line. Mark rotor retaining screw position and remove screw. Remove the 4 axle hub bearing support-to-suspension arm bolts.

3) To remove axle, use 2 Guides (B1 and B2). Screw in until splines are fully released. Compress CV joint at differential and remove axle shaft. A universal type puller may be necessary to free axle shaft from hub. Axle hub and bearing support are removed with axle shaft. *See Fig. 1.*

Fig. 1: Removing Rear Axle Assembly

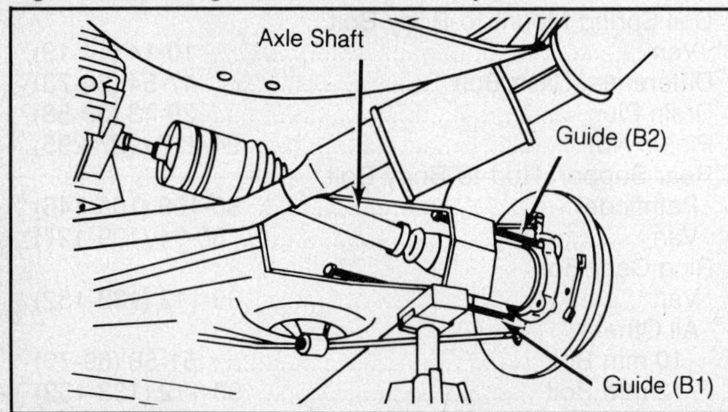

Courtesy of Peugeot Motor of America, Inc.

4) With axle assembly pressed out of control arm, remove axle assembly from rear housing without damaging housing seals. Remove axle assembly through lower control arm. With axle removed, place axle assembly in press, with adapter plate located just below hub. Remove hub nut and washer. Press axle out of hub.

Installation

1) To install, reverse removal procedure. Before assembling hub to axle bearing support, grease spline of axle stub. Before installing axle assembly into housing, ensure housing side seal is in perfect condition. Apply grease between lips of seal and to axle shaft splines.

2) Use new washer when assembling bearing support to lower control arm. Tighten bolts to specifications. Install brake caliper with new washers. Install brake anti-chatter spring onto caliper with arrow facing normal direction of rotation.

3) When installing hub nut, tighten to specification and stake nut. After installing wheels, check level of lubricant in housing.

PINION FLANGE & SEAL

Removal

1) Raise and support vehicle. Remove exhaust pipe assembly and allow it to rest on rear crossmember. Remove both Allen screws securing housing. Allow housing to rest on rear crossmember.

2) Inside vehicle, remove rear seat cushions. Loosen 3 nuts on "T" shaped metal bracket and remove first nut. Bend up "T" bracket, and remove plastic plug from guide hole. Insert Guide Pin (K1) into guide hole and tighten pin with Bar (K2).

3) Leave bar in guide pin and remove other 2 lock nuts. Lower crossmember until bar is resting on floorboard. Repeat operation on opposite side. Remove 4 nuts securing housing to propeller shaft tube. Move housing rearward and allow it to rest on wooden block.

4) Remove spring located inside propeller shaft. Remove seal support plate from front of housing. Place housing in vise. Clean front oil seal housing. Remove oil seal with pry bar. Do not damage insert deflector while removing oil seal. Damage to deflector requires replacement of complete oil seal housing.

Installation

To install, reverse removal procedure. Use all new washers and tighten all bolts to specifications. Use seal driver to seat new oil seal in housing. Drive seal inward until flush with oil seal housing. Coat new seal in engine oil and place seal housing on housing.

DIFFERENTIAL ASSEMBLY

Removal

1) With axle shafts removed, follow procedure described for PINION FLANGE & SEAL removal and continue. Drain differential fluid. Remove rear muffler flexible mounting nuts and lower heat baffle (if equipped).

2) Remove 4 nuts securing connecting tube to differential housing. Remove 2 Allen screws securing differential housing to suspension crossmember using 10 mm Allen socket. To disengage differential housing, pull it first to rear and then to left, and remove unit from vehicle.

Installation

To install, reverse removal procedure. Grease splines before installation. Ensure propeller shaft spring is placed into rear end of propeller shaft.

OVERHAUL

NOTE: **Overhaul information is not available for limited slip differential.**

REAR HUBS & HUB CARRIER BEARING & SEALS

Disassembly

1) Remove axle and hub assembly as previously outlined. With hub and axle removed, place assembly in press with adapter plate beneath hub. Remove hub nut. Press axle assembly out of hub. *See Fig. 3.*

PEUGEOT SPLIT HOUSING – I.R.S. (Cont.)

Fig. 2: Exploded View of Peugeot Independent Rear Suspension (I.R.S.) Drive Axle Assembly

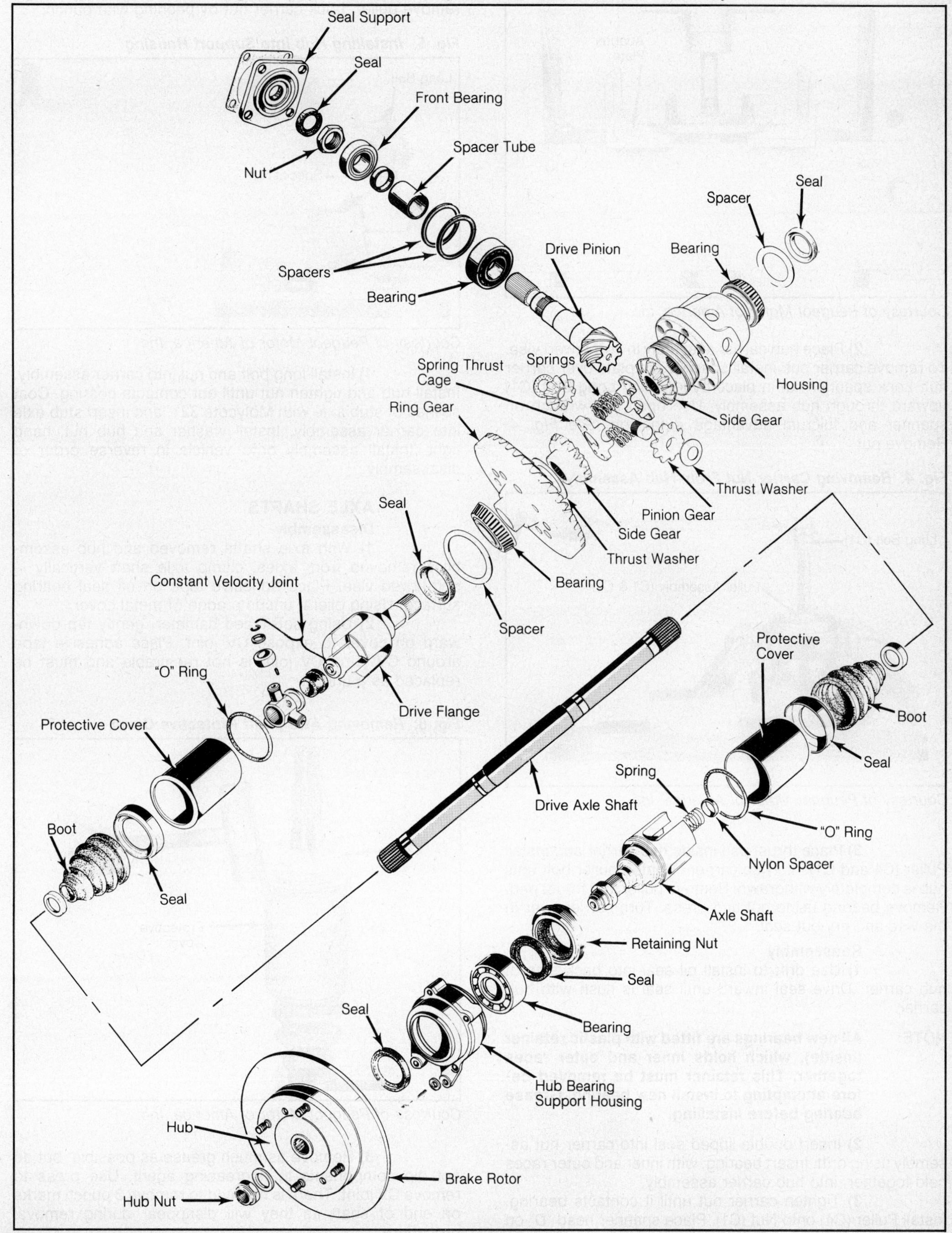

Courtesy of Peugeot Motor of America, Inc.

PEUGEOT SPLIT HOUSING – I.R.S. (Cont.)

Fig. 3: Pressing Axle Shaft From Hub Assembly

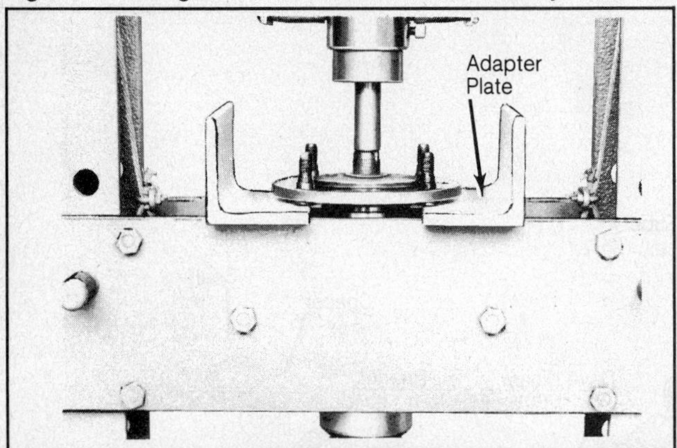

Courtesy of Peugeot Motor of America, Inc.

2) Place hub carrier assembly in soft-jawed vise. To remove carrier nut, install spanner nut plate over carrier nut. Lock spanner nut in place by inserting Long Bolt (C1) upward through hub assembly. Use open end wrench on spanner and fulcrum advantage extension. *See Fig. 4.* Remove nut.

Fig. 4: Removing Carrier Nut From Hub Assembly

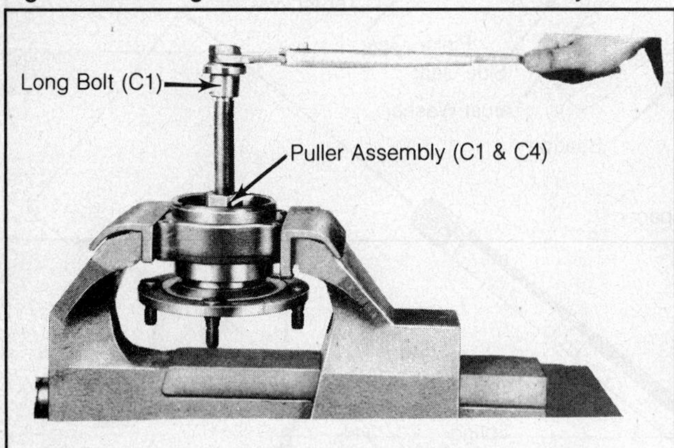

Courtesy of Peugeot Motor of America, Inc.

3) Place thrust pad inside hub carrier and install Puller (C4 and C1) into hub carrier. Tighten puller bolt until hub is completely withdrawn. Remove puller and thrust pad. Remove bearing using nut and press. Turn carrier over in the vise and pry out seal.

Reassembly

1) Use drift to install oil seal into back side of hub carrier. Drive seal inward until seal is flush with hub carrier.

NOTE: **All new bearings are fitted with plastic retainer (inside), which holds inner and outer races together. This retainer must be removed before attempting to install new bearing. Grease bearing before installing.**

2) Insert double-lipped seal into carrier nut assembly using drift. Insert bearing, with inner and outer races held together, into hub carrier assembly.

3) Tighten carrier nut until it contacts bearing. Install Puller (C4) onto Nut (C1). Place spanner head "D" on carrier nut. Insert Long Bolt (C1) fitted with Puller (C4) into hub carrier. Tighten carrier nut to 182 ft. lbs. (247 N.m) and remove puller. Lock carrier nut by peening with punch.

Fig. 5: Installing Hub Into Support Housing

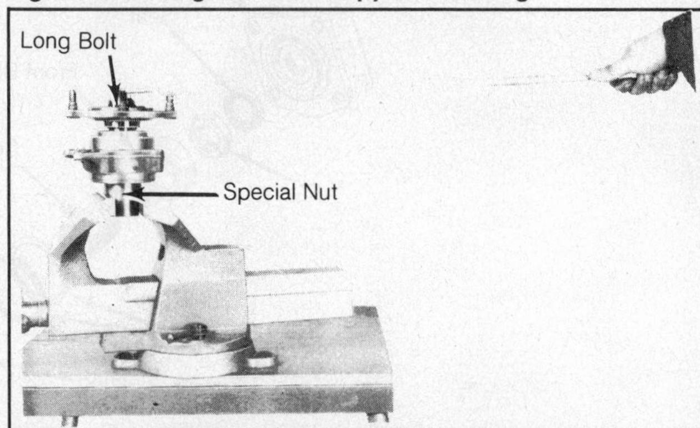

Courtesy of Peugeot Motor of America, Inc.

4) Install long bolt and nut into carrier assembly. Install hub and tighten nut until nut contacts bearing. Coat splines of stub axle with Molycote 321, and insert stub axle into carrier assembly. Install washer and hub nut, hand tight. Install assembly onto vehicle in reverse order of disassembly.

AXLE SHAFTS

Disassembly

1) With axle shafts removed and hub assemblies removed from axles, clamp axle shaft vertically in soft-jawed vise. Place adhesive tape on oil seal bearing surface. Using pliers, uncrimp edge of metal cover.

2) Using soft-faced hammer, gently tap downward on cover to expose CV joint. Place adhesive tape around CV joint. CV joint is not repairable and must be replaced as a unit.

Fig. 6: Removing Axle Shaft Protective Cover

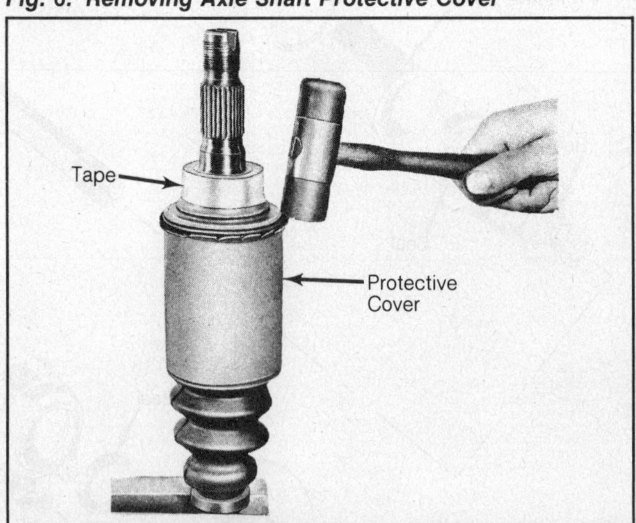

Courtesy of Peugeot Motor of America, Inc.

3) Remove as much grease as possible, but do not dip components in degreasing agent. Use press to remove CV joint. There is no need to remove 3 punch marks on end of shaft as they will disappear during removal procedure.

PEUGEOT SPLIT HOUSING – I.R.S. (Cont.)

Fig. 7: Removing Constant Velocity (CV) Joint

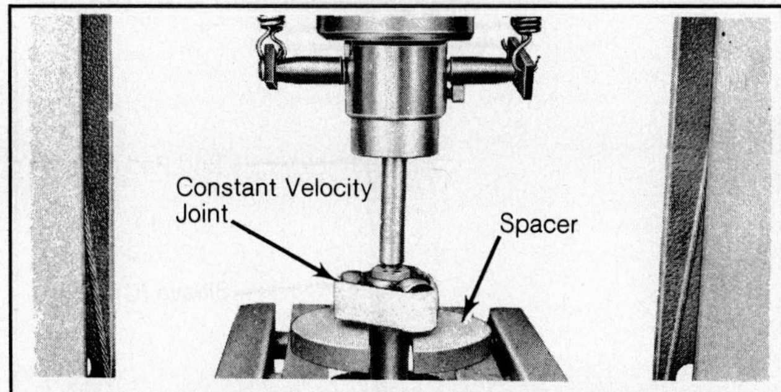

Courtesy of Peugeot Motor of America, Inc.

4) Remove protective metal cover and rubber ring. Remove other constant velocity joint in same manner as previously described. From outside joint housing, remove "O" ring. From inside, remove all grease. If nylon bushing on inside of CV joint housing is damaged, remove bushing with chisel.

5) Remove retaining washer with screwdriver. Use small stone and drill to remove any burrs in housing. When this operation is complete, clean inside of housing. Blow dry with compressed air.

Reassembly

1) To reassemble, reverse disassembly procedure. When installing metal cover, note there are 2 different sizes. The shorter one fits on differential side of axle shaft. Protective stopper must be installed on wheel side of axle shaft.

2) After installing CV joints onto respective shafts, use punch to peen shaft at 3 equally distant places on shaft end. If nylon bushing was removed, insert new bushing. Insert washer over bushing and peen washer in 3 equally distant places.

3) Before installing the cover over the CV joint housing, grease inside of housing and replace "O" ring. With cover over housing and assembly placed in press to hold tension, peen over cover. Install axle assembly as previously outlined.

Fig. 8: Disassembled View of Constant Velocity Joint Protective Covers

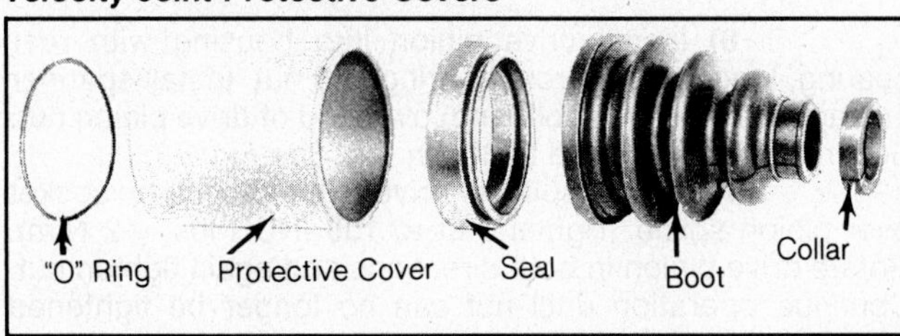

Courtesy of Peugeot Motor of America, Inc.

DIFFERENTIAL

Disassembly

1) With differential removed, remove front oil seal support plate and gasket. Install mounting plate on bottom 2 studs of housing. Place housing in vise (rear of housing up) by clamping mounting plate. Loosen all bolts and nuts on rear housing.

2) Remove front attaching screws of bearing side plates. Remove 6 bolts and 4 nuts holding housing halves together. Lift off rear half of housing. Use soft-faced mallet to assist in removing rear housing half (if necessary).

3) Loosen vise and rotate housing to allow front of housing to be in horizontal position. Install Spanner (N) and hex sleeve with bolt tang, over end of drive pinion nut. Secure spanner to front oil seal support plate stud with a nut. *See Fig. 9.*

4) Install adapter on input pinion nut and secure it to stud with a nut. Place Splined Socket (M) over pinion and then unscrew nut clockwise.

Fig. 9: Using Splined Socket to Remove Drive Pinion

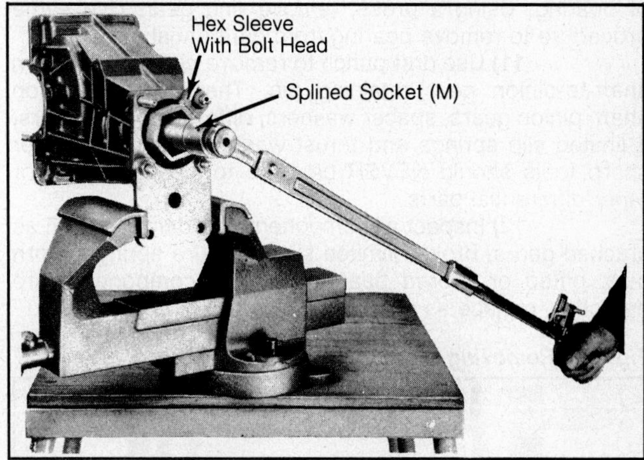

Courtesy of Peugeot Motor of America, Inc.

5) Remove housing from vise and rotate housing. Press on drive end of pinion to remove drive pinion assembly. Do not use a hammer to remove drive pinion assembly.

6) To remove drive pinion rear bearing outer race, install parts of Puller/Driver (L). Install Bolt (L1), Extractor (L4) and Support Plate (D). Turn bolt counterclockwise and remove rear outer bearing race first.

Fig. 10: Removing Pinion Rear Outer Bearing Race

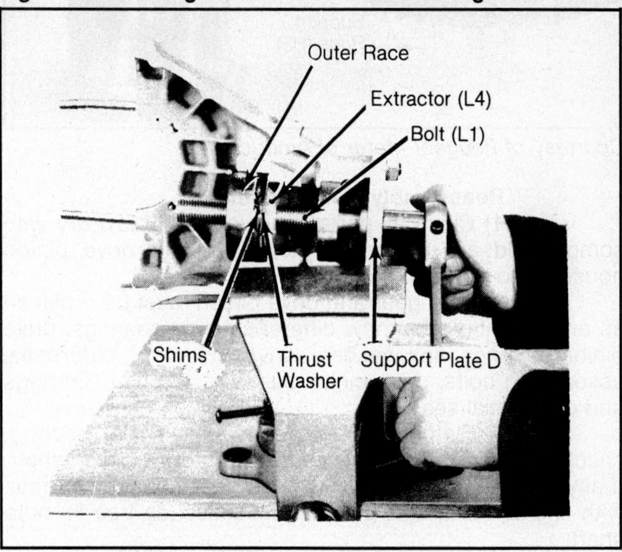

Courtesy of Peugeot Motor of America, Inc.

7) To remove drive pinion front bearing outer race, install parts of Puller/Driver (L). Install bolt and extractor. Turn bolt clockwise to remove front outer race.

8) Place drive pinion in vise and press off drive pinion rear bearing. Collar (SZ) is designed for this purpose and fits over drive pinion gear and against rear bearing shoulder.

Drive Axles

PEUGEOT SPLIT HOUSING – I.R.S. (Cont.)

CAUTION: As parts are separated in following step, catch differential side gear and thrust washer to prevent damage.

9) To disassemble differential assembly, remove ring gear-to-case bolts. Remove ring gear. Insert 4 extractor clamp Support Rods (H3) into 4 diagonally-opposed holes of ring gear. Place Adapter (H1) around bearing. *See Fig. 11.*

10) Place press Pad (H2) on ring gear, in center of bearing. Using a press, remove ring gear. Use same procedure to remove bearing from differential case.

11) Use drift punch to remove differential pinion shaft-to-pinion gear retaining pin. Then remove pinion shaft, pinion gears, spacer washers, differential side gears, 4 limited slip springs and thrust washers. Emery cloth or sharp tools should NEVER be used to clean housing or other differential parts.

12) Inspect all components for damage such as cracked gears, broken limited slip pressure springs, worn disc, pitted or scored bearings. If any components are defective, replace as necessary.

Fig. 11: Removing Differential Side Bearings

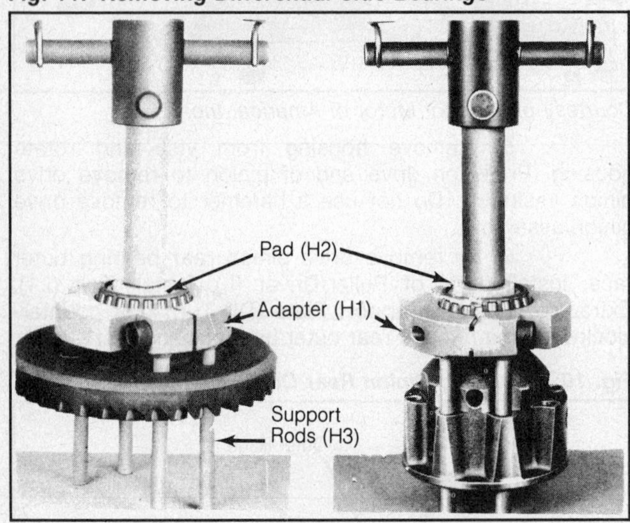

Courtesy of Peugeot Motor of America, Inc.

Reassembly & Adjustment

1) Clean all parts in solvent and blow dry with compressed air. Spray Molykote 321 into drive pinion housing. Do not heat housing.

2) Ring gear and drive pinion must be replaced as an assembly. Use new differential side bearings, drive pinion bearings, flex washers, drive pinion nut, differential assembling bolts, drive pinion seal and all other "O" rings and differential seals.

3) Before installing drive pinion rear bearing, check that front bearing slides freely on drive pinion shaft. If any difficulty is experienced, polish shaft bearing surface with fine abrasive until bearing just slides (as free fit) onto shaft.

4) Smooth front of drive pinion shaft with stone to remove any burrs. Front end of shaft serves as contact point during various adjustments. With front bearing fit correct, install pinion rear bearing by using Sleeve (C) and End Pad (H2).

5) Install mounting plate on front housing half. Place housing in vise in horizontal position. Using

Fig. 12: Installing Drive Pinion Rear Bearing

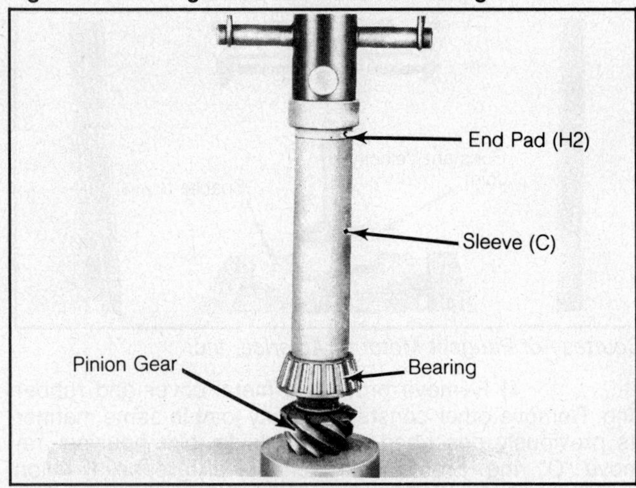

Courtesy of Peugeot Motor of America, Inc.

puller/driver, install thrust washer and outer bearing races (back-to-back) into housing. Use Bolt (L1), Thrust Plate (L2) and Nut (L5). Tighten Bolt (L1) to 101 ft. lbs. (137 N.m). Oil bearing with specified oil.

Fig. 13: Installing Drive Pinion Bearing Outer Race

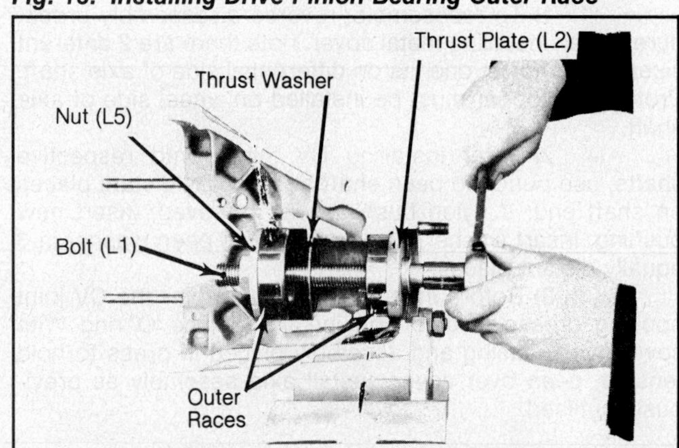

Courtesy of Peugeot Motor of America, Inc.

6) Install drive pinion into housing with rear bearing, long spacer, front bearing and nut. Install spanner (hexagon sleeve with bolt tang) over end of drive pinion nut. Secure spanner to stud bolt with nut. *See Fig. 13.*

7) Install splined drive pinion holding socket over pinion spline. Tighten nut to 108 INCH lbs. (12 N.m). Rotate drive pinion in both directions and again tighten nut. Continue operation until nut can no longer be tightened without exceeding the torque specification.

Pinion Depth Adjustment

1) Install Pinion Depth Gauge (AZ) into front half of housing. Retain in position with Bridge Clamp (A3). *See Fig. 14.* Tighten nuts of clamp to 88 INCH lbs. (10 N.m). Equalize distance between bridge pads and housing on both sides by using feeler gauges. Free Feeler Assembly (A2) and ensure there is contact with drive pinion. Equalize distance between bridge pads and housing.

2) Install dial indicator on Holder (K1). Position indicator so foot is resting on upper surface of feeler assembly. Adjust height of indicator so small hand reads "3" (for example). Zero dial indicator. Slide Holder (K1) so indicator foot contacts machined surface of Pinion Depth

PEUGEOT SPLIT HOUSING – I.R.S. (Cont.)

Fig. 14: Measuring Drive Pinion Installed Depth

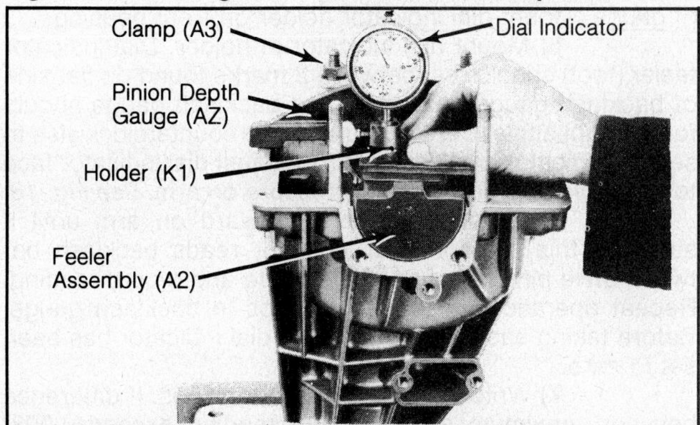

Courtesy of Peugeot Motor of America, Inc.

Gauge (AZ). Movement of dial indicator indicates depth of Feeler Assembly (A2). Record value obtained.

3) There are 2 reference marks on hypoid gear end of drive pinion. The first indicates pinion depth and second corresponds with number of ring gear (matched set). Write down reference number (bottom number). To this number, whether positive or negative, add + .012" (+ .30 mm) to find corresponding guide number.

4) Compare dial indicator reading previously obtained with guide number. The difference between 2 numbers represents thickness of shims to be installed between drive pinion rear bearing outer race and thrust washer. To find corresponding guide number and to calculate thickness of shims, use procedure outlined in SAMPLE CALCULATION 1.

SAMPLE CALCULATION 1

Dimension	Measurement
Constant Added to Determine Guide Number	.012" (.30 mm)
Number on End of Drive Pinion	- .0015" (.038 mm)
Resulting Guide Number	.010" (.25 mm)
Dial Indicator Reading from Step **2)**	.026" (.66 mm)
Subtract Guide Number (Obtained Above)	- .010" (.25 mm)
Total Shim Thickness Required	.016" (.41 mm)

Fig. 15: Identification Marks on Drive Pinion Gear

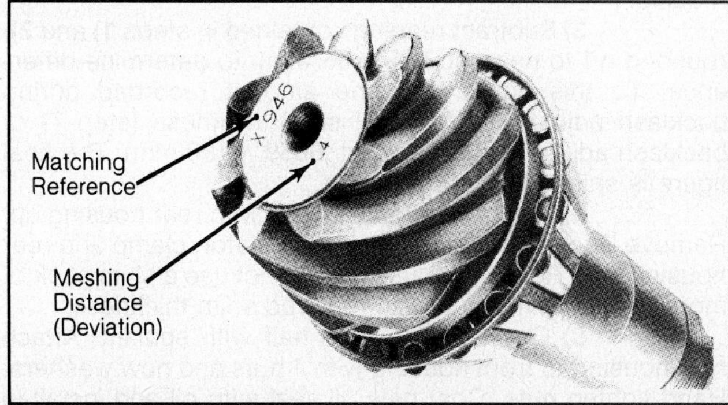

Courtesy of Peugeot Motor of America, Inc.

5) Remove pinion depth measurer and drive pinion from housing. Use puller/driver to remove drive pinion rear bearing outer race from housing. Install thrust washer and shims (previously determined). Reinstall rear bearing outer race. Tighten puller/driver to 101 ft. lbs. (137 N.m) to seat. Always replace ring and pinion gears in matched pairs.

6) Place drive pinion vertically on work bench and make colored chalk mark down full length of one spline. Install long spacer, front bearing and Nut (J). Place holding fixture over nut. Use socket to tighten pinion to 203 ft. lbs. (275 N.m).

7) Screw dial indicator onto Extension (K2). Place dial indicator on end of drive pinion. Ensure extension faces chalk mark on pinion spline and rests on machined surface of Nut (J). Move dial indicator to bring small hand to "1" and big hand to "0".

8) Remove dial indicator and lay aside, ensuring reading has not changed. Remove Nut (J) and front bearing. Place pinion into front housing with long spacer and front bearing. Tighten Nut (J) to 10 ft. lbs. (14 N.m). Rotate pinion 10 turns counterclockwise and retighten.

Fig. 16: Measuring Drive Pinion Depth

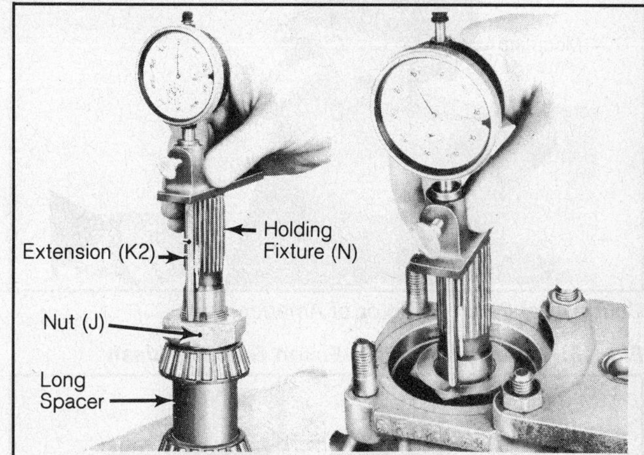

Courtesy of Peugeot Motor of America, Inc.

9) With colored chalk, mark as reference and take another reading. Place dial indicator between end of shaft and nut. Find difference between 2 readings and subtract .002" (.06 mm). The number obtained is the thickness of shims necessary between front bearing and long spacer. See SAMPLE CALCULATION 2 and 3.

10) Install pinion into housing with long spacer, adjusting shims and new nut. Torque nut to 203 ft. lbs. (275 N.m). Use speed wrench attached to Socket (C) to turn pinion by hand.

11) Use Pinion Depth Gauge (AZ), Holder (K1) and dial indicator as described in steps **1)** and **2)** to check pinion depth. Resulting number obtained should correspond to guide number, within the following tolerance: +.002" (.05 mm) or –.001" (.03 mm.) Shims are available in increments of .001" (.03 mm). Use shim closest to measurement.

Differential Backlash Adjustment

1) Install mounting plate on bottom 2 studs of front housing and mount housing in vise with rear housing up. Oil bearing housings. Install differential assembly. Install base shim of .053" (1.35 mm) behind bearing without thrust

Drive Axles

PEUGEOT SPLIT HOUSING – I.R.S. (Cont.)

SAMPLE CALCULATION 2

Measurement	Reading
On Machined Surface	.281" (7.14 mm)
In Housing	- .039" (1.00 mm)
Difference	.242" (6.15 mm)
PLUS	+ .010" (.25 mm)
Total	.252" (6.40 mm)

SAMPLE CALCULATION 3

Measurement	Reading
On Machined Surface	.287" (7.29 mm)
On Thrust Plate	- .039" (1.00 mm)
Height Of Collar	.248" (6.30 mm)

Fig. 17: Installing Clamp on Right Side

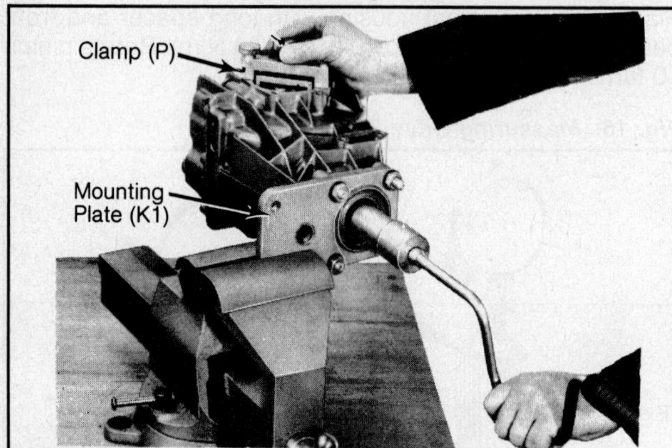

Courtesy of Peugeot Motor of America, Inc.

Fig. 18: Measuring Ring-to-Pinion Gear Backlash

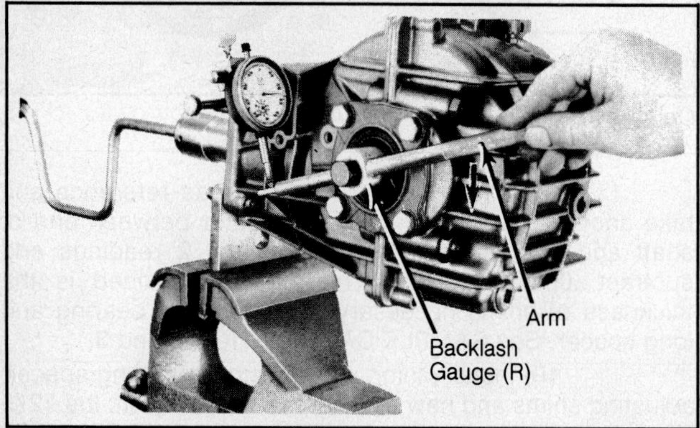

Courtesy of Peugeot Motor of America, Inc.

plate. Measure and record thickness of shim with micrometer before installation.

2) Install and hand tighten rear cover with 4 nuts and new washers. Loosen vise and install housing in vertical position with right side up. *See Fig. 17.*

3) Install Clamp (P) and hand tighten only. Rotate pinion spline 5 turns in both directions and recheck tightness of clamp. Retighten rear cover nuts to 53 INCH lbs. (6 N.m). Move assembly in vise to its normal upright position.

4) Install Backlash Gauge (R) horizontally. Ensure one radial groove in ring gear face is aligned with double quotation marks (" ") of device. Tighten central screw of gauge. Mount dial indicator holder on front housing.

5) Mount dial indicator in holder. Dial indicator feeler (foot) should rest between 2 marks found on flat side of backlash gauge and feeler and backlash gauge should form a right angle. Carefully turn pinion counterclockwise to set dial indicator small hand to "5". Adjust dial indicator face to "0", while applying upward pressure on arm. *See Fig. 18.*

6) Carefully press downward on arm until it seats. In this position, dial indicator reads backlash between drive pinion and ring gear. Note and record reading. Repeat operation at 3 different gaps in backlash gauge. Before taking each reading, ensure dial indicator has been set to zero.

7) Write down 2 extreme readings. If difference between maximum and minimum reading exceeds .003" (.08 mm), check for dirt or burrs on teeth. Record minimum backlash reading. From the BACKLASH ADJUSTMENT TABLE, determine amount to be added or subtracted from base shim.

BACKLASH ADJUSTMENT TABLE

Reading Recorded In. (mm)	Adjustment to Base Shim In. (mm)
.0070-.0086 (.178-.218)	+ .0039 (.099)
.0090-.0106 (.229-.269)	+ .0020 (.051)
.0110-.0126 (.279-.320)	0
.0129-.0138 (.328-.350)	- .0020 (.051)
.0150-.0165 (.381-.419)	- .0039 (.099)
.0169-.0185 (.429-.470)	- .0059 (.150)
.0189-.0205 (.480-.521)	- .0079 (.201)
.0209-.0224 (.531-.569)	- .0098 (.249)
.0228-.0244 (.579-.620)	- .0118 (.300)
.0248-.0264 (.630-.671)	- .0157 (.399)
.0268-.0283 (.681-.719)	- .0177 (.450)
.0287-.0303 (.729-.770)	- .0197 (.500)
.0307-.0323 (.780-.820)	- .0236 (.600)

Bearing Preload Adjustment

1) Install a .79" (20.0 mm) stem to dial indicator. Mount dial indicator on Mounting Plate (K1). Place mounting plate over thrust plate with feeler (foot) touching outer bearing surface. Set small hand of dial indicator to "5" and zero dial face.

2) Place mounting plate on flat surface of left front housing with dial indicator feeler (foot) resting on outer bearing race. Make sure mounting plate does not rest on both front and rear housings, only on front housing. Record reading.

3) Subtract readings obtained in steps **1)** and **2)**, rounded off to nearest .002" (.05 mm), to determine difference. To this figure, add the amount recorded during backlash adjustment for final shim thickness (step **7)** of backlash adjustment). Also add .0059" (.150 mm). The final figure is shim thickness required.

4) Mount assembly in vise with rear housing up. Remove Backlash Gauge (R), dial indicator, clamp and rear housing half. Remove base shim. Do not use a shim pack of more than 2 shims to obtain required shim thickness.

5) Coat rear housing half with sealant. Attach rear housing to front housing with 4 nuts and new washers. Hand tighten nuts. Coat new oil seal with oil and install in thrust plate. Install shims of calculated thickness between right bearing and housing (end opposite ring gear).

PEUGEOT SPLIT HOUSING – I.R.S. (Cont.)

6) Install new greased "O" ring between thrust plate and housing. Install thrust plate and hand tighten bolts. Tighten bolts to 53 INCH lbs. (6 N.m) in sequence. *See Fig. 19*. Rotate differential gear train in both directions. Tap housing with soft mallet to ensure mating. Tighten bolts to specification in sequence.

Fig. 19: Tightening Housing Bolts

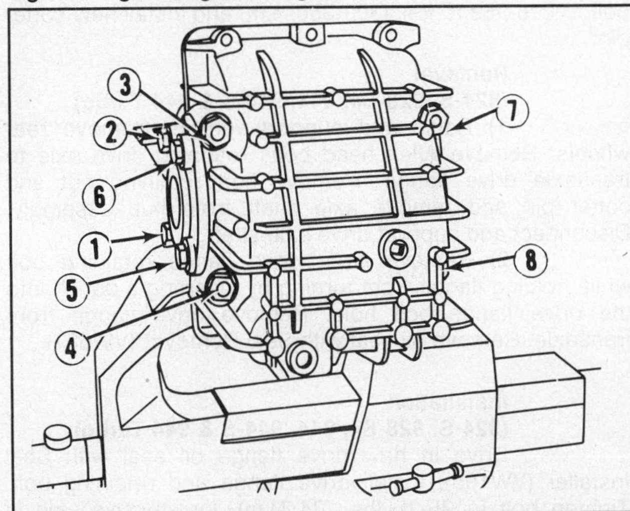

Tighten bolts to specifications in sequence.

7) As previously described, check backlash. If backlash is incorrect, repeat backlash adjustment. Install and tighten 6 housing retaining bolts.

8) Coat new oil seal with oil and install in left side of case (ring gear side). Remove mounting plate on front housing. Remove and clean oil seal plate. Remove and discard gasket and oil seal.

9) Ensure oil seal deflector is staked in position. Using a center punch, stake deflector at 3 points at 120 degree intervals. Soak new seal in oil and install. Install gasket and oil seal plate.

AXLE ASSEMBLY SPECIFICATIONS

Application	Specification
Pinion Depth	
All Models	[1] -.001" to +.002" (-.03 to +.05 mm)
Ring Gear-to-Pinion	
Gear Backlash	[2] .008" (.20 mm)

[1] – Deviation from guide used.
[2] – Maximum. With a deviation from -.0020" to +.0023" (-.05 to +.06 mm).

TIGHTENING SPECIFICATIONS

Application	Ft. Lbs. (N.m)
Hub Carrier-to-Lower Control Arm	29 (39)
Rear Caliper Retaining Bolts	31 (42)
Rear Hub Nut	203 (275)
Differential Housing-to-Subframe	
Allen Heads	27 (37)
Ring Gear-to-Differential Assembly	96 (130)
Differential Side Plate Bolts	10 (14)
Propeller Shaft (Torque Tube Nuts)	44 (60)
Body-to-Crossmember Bolts	48 (65)
Rear Housing-to-Front Housing	
Nuts	48 (65)
6 Bolts (3 Upper & 3 Lower)	10 (14)

Drive Axles

PORSCHE

911 Carrera, 911 Turbo, 924-S, 928-S4, 944, 944-S, 944 Turbo

DESCRIPTION

Axle shafts transfer power from the rear mounted transaxle to the driving wheels. All Porsche axle shafts consist of a splined shaft and 2 Constant Velocity (CV) joints, one at each end. The inner CV joint is bolted to the transaxle. The outer CV joint is splined or bolted into the hub assembly and retained by way of a spindle nut and cotter pin.

NOTE: Some disassembly may be required to obtain access to perform the following procedures.

REMOVAL & INSTALLATION

AXLE SHAFTS & TRANSAXLE DRIVE FLANGE OIL SEALS

Removal (911 Carrera & 911 Turbo)

1) Raise and support vehicle. Remove rear wheels. Remove brake line at rear caliper. If necessary, disconnect stabilizer bar at rear axle trailing arm. Remove Allen head bolts retaining drive axle to transaxle drive flange. *See Fig. 1.* Remove axle shaft-to-hub retaining castle nut and cotter pin.

2) Remove axle shaft from hub assembly. Remove rear axle shaft assembly. Remove inner drive flange retaining bolt while holding flange from turning by inserting a punch into the drive flange bolt hole. Remove drive flange from transaxle. Remove oil seal with Seal Remover (VW681).

Installation (911 Carrera & 911 Turbo)

1) Drive in new drive flange oil seal with Seal Installer (P265d) or (P265c), if side transaxle cover does not have an oil pump. Install drive flange and retaining bolt. Tighten bolt to 32 ft. lbs. (44 N.m).

2) Install drive axle in reverse order of removal to complete reassembly. Tighten axle shaft-to-transaxle Allen bolts to 30 ft. lbs. (42 N.m). Tighten axle shaft hub bolt to 216-252 ft. lbs. (300-350 N.m) and install new cotter pin.

Removal (924-S, 928-S4, 944, 944-S & 944 Turbo)

1) Raise and support vehicle. Remove rear wheels. Remove Allen head bolts retaining drive axle to transaxle drive flange. Remove hub retaining nut and cotter pin and remove axle shaft from hub assembly. Disconnect and support drive axle shaft.

2) Remove inner drive flange retaining bolt while holding flange from turning by inserting a punch into the drive flange bolt hole. Remove drive flange from transaxle. Remove oil seal with Seal Remover (VW681).

Installation (924-S, 928-S4, 944, 944-S & 944 Turbo)

Drive in new drive flange oil seal with Seal Installer (VW195). Install drive flange and retaining bolt. Tighten bolt to 25 ft. lbs. (34 N.m). Install drive axle in reverse order of removal to complete reassembly. Tighten axle shaft-to-transaxle Allen bolts to 30 ft. lbs. (42 N.m). Tighten axle shaft hub bolt to 340 ft. lbs. (460 N.m) and install new cotter pin.

Fig. 1: Exploded View of Rear Axle Shaft Assembly

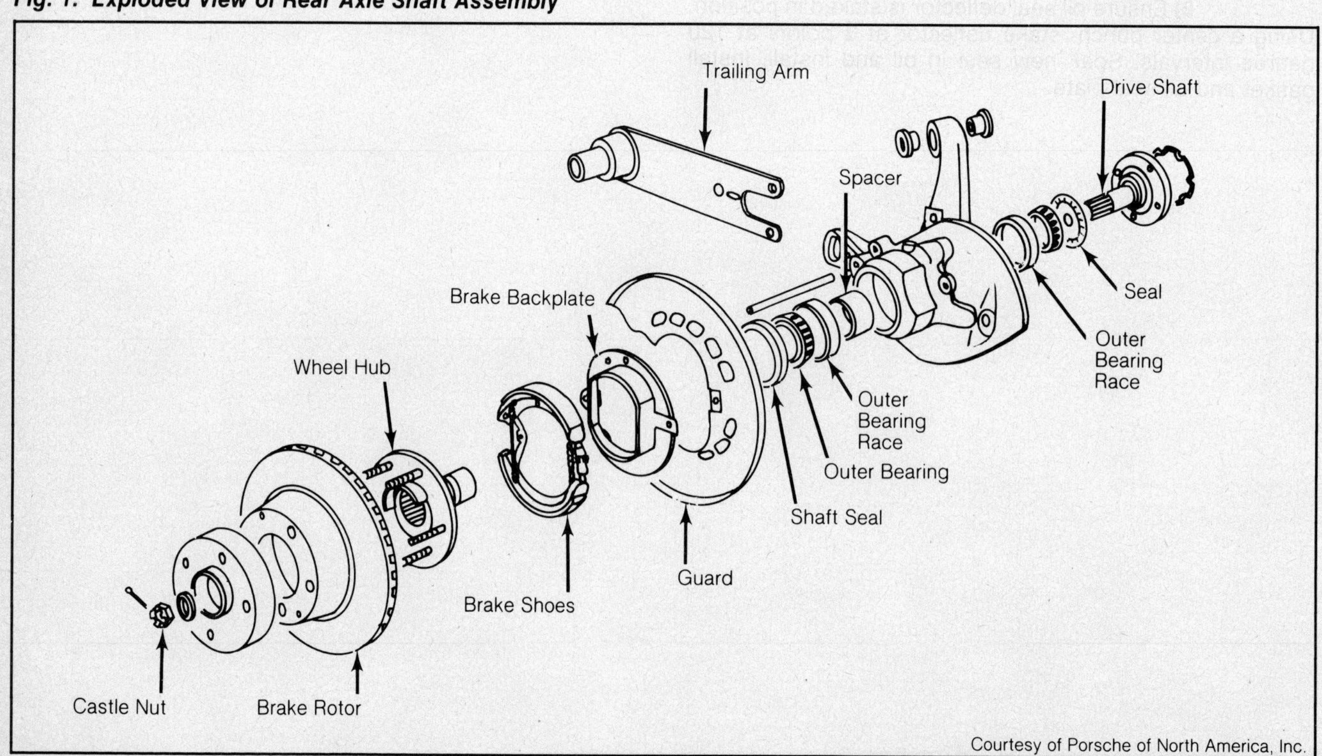

911 models are shown; others are similar.

PORSCHE (Cont.)

Fig. 2: Exploded View of 944 Rear Axle Shaft Assembly

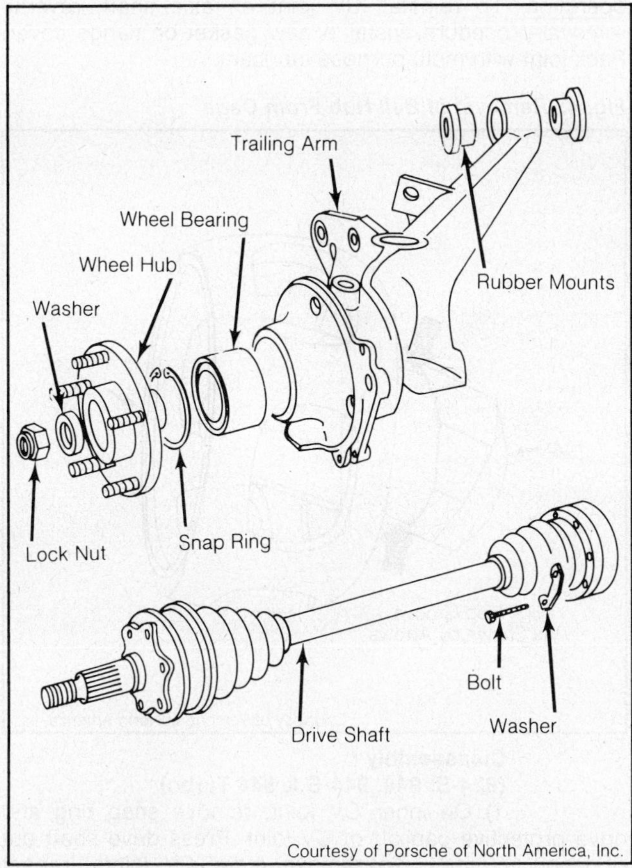

944 models are shown; others are similar.

REAR WHEEL BEARINGS

Removal & Disassembly
(911 Carrera & 911 Turbo)

1) Raise and support vehicle. Remove rear wheels. Remove drive axles as previously described. Disconnect rear stabilizer bar at trailing arm. Remove brake rotor and lift axle strut with Lifting Tool (P289). Disconnect shock absorber at trailing arm. Move parking brake cable. Remove trailing arm assembly.

2) Drive hub out of trailing arm assembly with Driver (P287a). Using a 2 or 3 jaw puller with grip ring, remove wheel bearing from hub assembly. Heat trailing arm up on a heating plate and drive outer bearing races off of trailing arm.

Reassembly & Installation
(911 Carrera & 911 Turbo)

1) Heat trailing arm assembly and insert new outer bearing races. Drive them into place with appropriate driver. Install parking brake assembly with anchor and guard onto trailing arm assembly. Install inner cross spring. Lubricate bearing surfaces of trailing arm and install outer wheel bearing. Lubricate wheel bearing.

2) Press in outer shaft seal. Using press, install hub assembly into outer wheel bearing. Install spacer. Lubricate inner wheel bearing and drive it onto wheel hub until bearing rests on spacer. Reverse removal procedure to complete installation. Adjust rear wheel bearings. Adjust parking brake. Bleed brakes if lines were opened. Tighten all bolts to specification.

STEEL TRAILING ARMS

Removal & Disassembly
(924-S, 928-S4, 944, 944-S & 944 Turbo)

1) Raise and support vehicle. Remove rear wheels. Remove drive axles as previously described. Remove trailing arm assembly.

2) Using a press or puller, remove rear wheel shaft from the trailing arm hub assembly. Pry oil seal out from trailing arm and discard. Remove snap ring and drive out bearing using an appropriate driver.

Reassembly & Installation
(924-S, 928-S4, 944, 944-S & 944 Turbo)

1) Prior to reassembly, check all parts for wear or damage and replace as necessary. Drive new wheel bearing into trailing arm using Driver (VW415a) and Adapter (VW402). Adjust bearing free play to .0019" (0.05 mm) by installing the appropriate snap ring, ranging from .0787-.0866" (2.00-2.20 mm). Measure free play with feeler gauge between back of bearing race and snap ring. Lubricate bearing surfaces and install oil seal with Driver (VW 433). Lubricate wheel bearing and housing with approximately 80 grams of lubricate.

2) Press in outer shaft seal with spacer included. Install spacer tube. Using press, install last bearing with suitable driver (if bearing has edging on one side only, it faces out). Pull in bearing seat using Puller (VW454) outer spacer and castle nut. Lubricate wheel bearing. Reverse removal procedure to complete installation. Adjust rear wheel bearings. Adjust parking brake. Bleed brakes, if lines were opened. Tighten all bolts to specification.

ALUMINUM TRAILING ARMS

Removal & Disassembly
(924-S, 928-S4, 944, 944-S & 944 Turbo)

1) Raise and support vehicle. Remove rear wheels. Remove drive axles as previously described. Disconnect brake hose and pad wear indicator from trailing arm. Remove brake caliper and rotor. Drive hub out of trailing arm assembly with Driver (P297a).

2) Remove parking brake shoes and spreader from trailing arms. Mark spring strut-to-trailing arm position for reassembly reference. Remove trailing arm after disconnecting it from the spring strut and cross tube.

3) Remove brake guard and snap ring to remove bearing from arm. Heat up trailing arm on heat plate and press out bearing using Driver (VW432) and a suitable adapter. If necessary, press inner bearing race off of hub assembly and replace.

Reassembly & Installation
(924-S, 928-S4, 944, 944-S & 944 Turbo)

1) Heat trailing arm assembly and press in new bearing using Driver (VW459). Install snap ring and press hub assembly into trailing arm. Install spreader arm and parking brake shoes. Lubricate wheel bearings.

2) Reverse removal procedure to complete installation. Adjust rear wheel bearings. Adjust parking brake. Bleed brakes if lines were opened. Tighten all bolts to specification.

CONSTANT VELOCITY JOINTS

NOTE: **Axle shafts must be removed from vehicle to service CV joints. See REMOVAL & INSTALLATION of AXLE SHAFTS & TRANSAXLE DRIVE FLANGE OIL SEALS in this article.**

Drive Axles

PORSCHE (Cont.)

Disassembly
(911 Carrera, 911 Turbo & 928-S4)

1) Clamp axle shaft in a soft-jawed vise. Remove boot clamp and push boot to center of axle. Remove snap ring and press CV joint from axle shaft using CV Joint Removers (VW401 and VW408) and a hydraulic press.

2) Swing ball and cage from joint and press in direction of the arrow *See Fig. 3.* Tilt ball hub assembly out of ball cage via the ball groove. *See Fig. 4.* Clean all components throughly and blow dry. Inspect all components for wear and/or damage.

NOTE: Ball hub and joint are a matched set. DO NOT intermix these pieces. The 6 ball bearings are also mated together for tolerance reasons and should not be mixed with each other.

Fig. 3: Ball Hub & Cage Removal

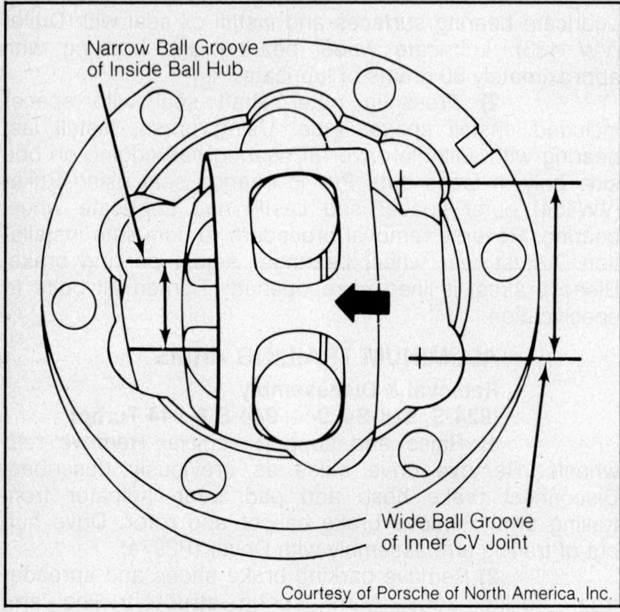

Reassembly
(911 Carrera, 911 Turbo & 928-S4)

Place ball hub in ball cage. Press balls into cage. Install hub with cage and balls into joint and swing into assembled position. Check entire rotation for smooth operation. To reinstall CV joint on axle shaft, reverse removal procedure. Install a new gasket on flange cover. Pack joint with multi-purpose lubricant.

Fig. 4: Removal of Ball Hub From Cage

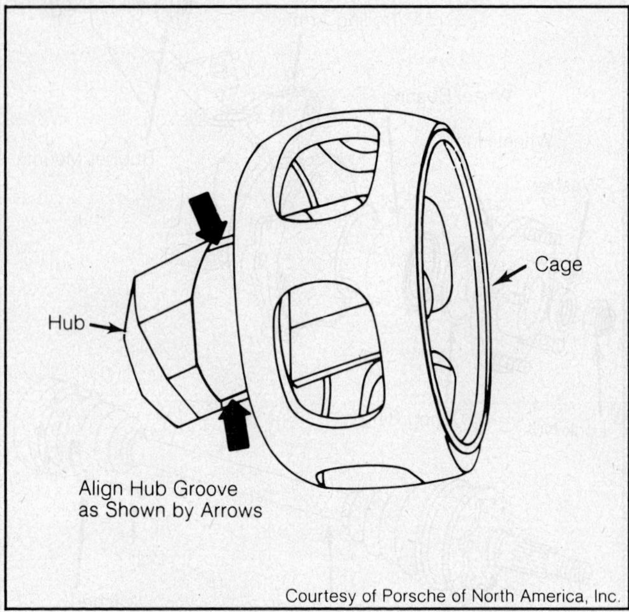

Disassembly
(924-S, 944, 944-S & 944 Turbo)

1) On inner CV joint, remove snap ring and drive protective cap off of CV joint. Press drive shaft out of inner CV joint. To remove outer CV joints, repeat procedure used for inner joints.

2) Tilt cage and hub out of CV joint to remove balls and disassemble joint. Inspect all components for wear and/or damage. Parts cannot be intermixed between joints. If any part of the joint is damaged, replacement of entire CV joint is necessary.

Reassembly
(924-S, 944, 944-S & 944 Turbo)

To reassemble, reverse disassembly procedure. Pack each side of CV joint with 1.6 oz. of mutli-purpose lubricant.

SUBARU 4WD REAR AXLE

DESCRIPTION

Rear axle assembly of all 4WD models is a hypoid type with integral carrier housing. Drive pinion is supported by 3 bearings. Pinion bearing preload adjustment is made by a selective spacer and washer.

Differential side bearing preload and pinion depth adjustments are made with shims. Driving power is transmitted to rear axle by ball spline type drive shafts with Double Offset Joint (DOJ) at inner end, and a Bell Joint (BJ) at outer end. A limited slip differential is available on all 4WD models.

AXLE RATIO & IDENTIFICATION

All 4WD models use one basic type of rear axle assembly. An identification mark is painted on top front of differential. An identification tag is attached to differential cover. To determine axle ratio, divide number of ring gear teeth by number of pinion teeth.

REAR AXLE IDENTIFICATION

Application	Mark	Ratio
Non-Turbo		
Man. Trans.	WP	3.90:1
Auto. Trans.	WL, [1] WM	3.70:1
Turbo	WL, [1] WM	3.70:1

[1] - Limited slip differential.

REMOVAL & INSTALLATION

AXLE SHAFT & BEARINGS

Removal

1) Apply parking brake. Remove wheel cap and cotter pin. Loosen castle nut and wheel nuts. Disconnect lower shock absorber bolt. Loosen cross-member outer bushing locking bolts. Raise and support vehicle. Remove wheel and tire assembly.

2) Remove castle nut and brake drum. Drive out spring pins of inner Double Offset Joint (DOJ) and outer Bell Joint (BJ) using 6 mm diameter punch. Remove outer BJ from spindle of trailing arm with trailing arm lowered fully. Remove inner DOJ from differential spindle.

Fig. 1: Exploded View of Rear Drive Axle Assembly

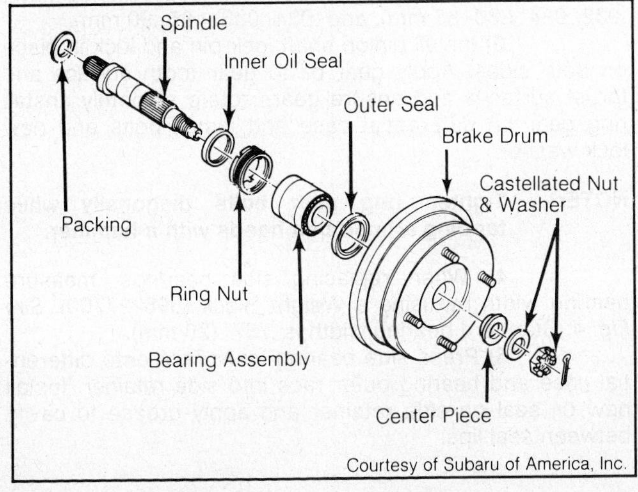

3) Remove rear exhaust pipe, muffler and covers. Disconnect brake line and plug end. Remove brake assembly from trailing arm by removing 4 bolts. Remove bolt from inner bushing of inner trailing arm. Remove 3 bolts from inner arm and outer arm. Remove inner arm. Place inner arm in vise.

4) Straighten staked portion of ring nut. Remove ring nut and remove spindle inward by tapping from outside with a soft hammer. Remove oil seal. Insert spindle from outside of housing and press outer bearing out by pushing inner race through housing. Press out inner race of spindle.

Fig. 2: Removing Double Offset Joint (DOJ) Spring Pins

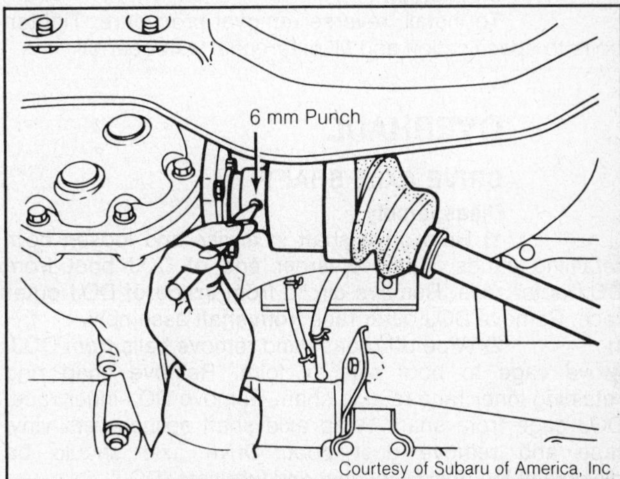

Installation

To install and reassemble, reverse removal procedure. Install new oil seal into drum until outer end of seal is flush with drum surface. Lubricate all bearings and seals. Fill hub of drum with grease. Install spacer "O" ring, spacer and inner race of inner bearing onto spindle of trailing arm.

PINION FLANGE & OIL SEAL

Removal

1) Drain gear oil from differential. Raise and support rear of vehicle. Disconnect propeller shaft from pinion flange. Measure and record rotating torque of pinion flange.

2) Hold pinion flange with Flange Wrench (398427700). Remove pinion nut. Remove pinion flange with puller. Remove oil seal using Seal Puller (398527700).

Installation

Apply grease to oil seal lip. Install oil seal using Seal Installer (398417700). Install pinion flange. Hold flange with Flange Wrench (398427700) and tighten nut to 123-145 ft. lbs. (167-196 N.m) and pinion flange rotating torque is same as recorded before removal. Stake lock nut. Install remaining components in reverse order of removal.

DIFFERENTIAL ASSEMBLY

NOTE: Dismount inner arm of trailing arm from body before removing and installing rear axle.

Removal

1) Raise and support rear of vehicle. Drain gear oil. Remove 2 upper shock mounting bolts. Remove

SUBARU 4WD REAR AXLE (Cont.)

wheel and tire assemblies. Remove spring pins from inner DOJ and outer BJ. Completely lower trailing arm assembly.

2) Remove outer BJ from spindle on trailing arm and then inner DOJ from differential. Match mark and remove drive axles. Position oil drain pan below transmission. Transmission fluid will flow from transmission when propeller shaft is removed.

3) Remove propeller shaft and plug opening in transmission. Support axle assembly with a jack. Remove 2 bolts at center of differential carrier. Remove 4 differential-to-bracket mounting bolts. Lower jack and remove axle assembly.

Installation

To install, reverse removal procedure. Tighten bolts to specification and fill differential with gear oil.

OVERHAUL

DRIVE AXLE SHAFT

Disassembly

1) Hold drive shaft in a vise and loosen boot retaining bands. Remove larger end of DOJ boot from DOJ outer race. Remove circlip from inside of DOJ outer race. Remove DOJ outer race from shaft assembly.

2) Wipe off grease and remove balls from DOJ. Move cage to boot side of joint. Remove snap ring retaining inner race to axle shaft. Remove DOJ inner race, DOJ cage from shaft. Wrap axle shaft splines with vinyl tape and remove dust boot. Drive axle should be disassembled only to inspect and lubricate (DOJ).

Inspection

Check DOJ for corrosion, damage, seizure and excessive play. Inspect drive shaft for straightness, cracks, damage and distortion. Replace drive shaft if ball spline portion is worn or damaged. Check drive shaft play at DOJ. Maximum play of DOJ is .04" (1.0 mm).

Fig. 3: Exploded View of Rear Drive Axle Shaft

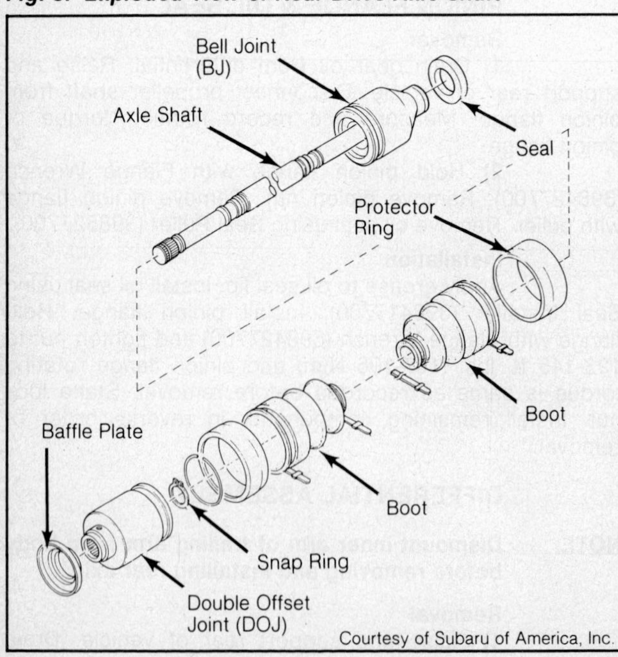

Reassembly

To reassemble, reverse disassembly procedure. Apply grease to axle splines and install DOJ. Adjust axial play to within .0008" (.020 mm) by selecting proper size snap ring. Align match marks and install axle. Be sure to install DOJ end to rear axle. Tighten all bolts. Install new drive axle spring pins.

DIFFERENTIAL CASE

NOTE: Mark side retainers for reassembly reference. Left and right retainers are not interchangeable.

Disassembly

1) Mount carrier on holding fixture. Remove rear cover and inspect differential before disassembly. Check following: tooth contact of ring and pinion and backlash. Runout of drive gear at its back surface and rotation torque of drive pinion.

2) Remove spindles using Wrench (92560000). Remove rear differential cover. Mark right and left side bearing retainer for reassembly reference. Remove side bearing retainer mounting bolts. Using puller and Adapter (398457700), remove side retainer. Remove differential case assembly from carrier.

3) Remove side bearings from differential case with puller. Pull out differential carrier. Remove ring gear by spreading lock plates and loosening bolts. Unstake pinion shaft lock pin and drive pin out from flange side.

4) Hold pinion flange stationary using Flange Wrench (398427700) and remove pinion nut. Remove pinion flange with puller. Press drive pinion from carrier and remove rear bearing inner race, bearing spacer and adjusting washer.

5) Remove pinion shaft, pinion gears, side gears and thrust washer. Keep thrust washers, pinion gears and side gears in order for reassembly reference. Thoroughly clean all parts and inspect for wear or damage. Replace as necessary.

Reassembly & Adjustment

1) Assemble pinion gears, side gears and thrust washers in original positions in differential case. Fit pinion shaft to differential case aligning lock pin holes with holes in case.

2) Adjust clearance between differential case and back of side gear to .004-.008" (.10-.20 mm) by selecting proper thrust washer. Thrust washers are available in the following sizes: .030-.032" (.75-.80 mm), .032-.034" (.80-.85 mm), and .034-.036" (.85-.90 mm).

3) Install pinion shaft lock pin and lock in place on both sides. Apply gear oil to gear tooth surface and thrust surfaces and ensure gears rotate smoothly. Install ring gear on differential case and install bolts and new lock washers.

NOTE: Tighten ring gear bolts diagonally while tapping around bolt heads with a hammer.

4) When replacing side bearings, measure bearing width by using a Weight Block (398227700). *See Fig. 4.* Standard bearing width is .787" (20 mm).

5) Press side bearing inner race onto differential case and bearing outer race into side retainer. Install new oil seal on side retainer and apply grease to cavity between seal lips.

SUBARU 4WD REAR AXLE (Cont.)

Fig. 4: Measuring Side Bearing Width

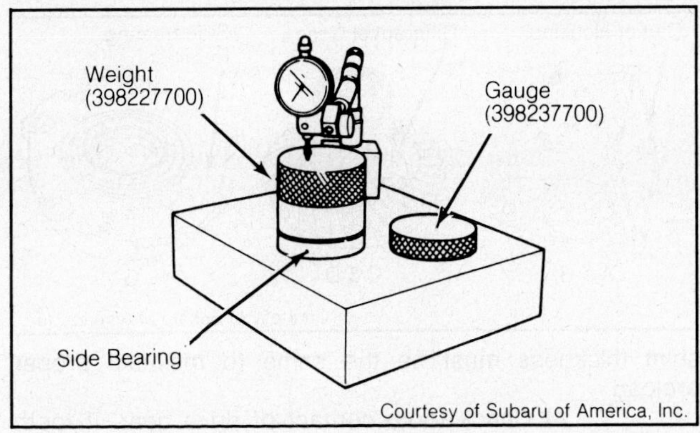

Courtesy of Subaru of America, Inc.

NOTE: Do not exceed specified preload torque during preload adjustment.

Drive Pinion Bearing Preload Adjustment

1) Press front and rear bearing outer races into carrier. Install Dummy Pinion Shaft (398507702) with rear bearing and pinion depth washer into case.

2) Install preload adjusting spacer and washer, front bearing inner race, Dummy Collar (398507703), companion flange, washer and nut onto dummy shaft. Do not install oil seal at this time. Rotate pinion by hand until it is seated.

3) Using a torque wrench, check rotating torque of pinion shaft. Tighten pinion shaft nut to specification. If preload is not within specification, install correct washer and spacer to obtain proper preload.

4) Spacers are available in lengths from 2.213" (56.21 mm) to 2.252" (57.20 mm) in increments of .008" (.20 mm). Washers are available in thicknesses from .102" (2.59 mm) to .0909" (.231 mm) in increments of .0008" (.020 mm).

Fig. 6: Installing Dummy Shaft

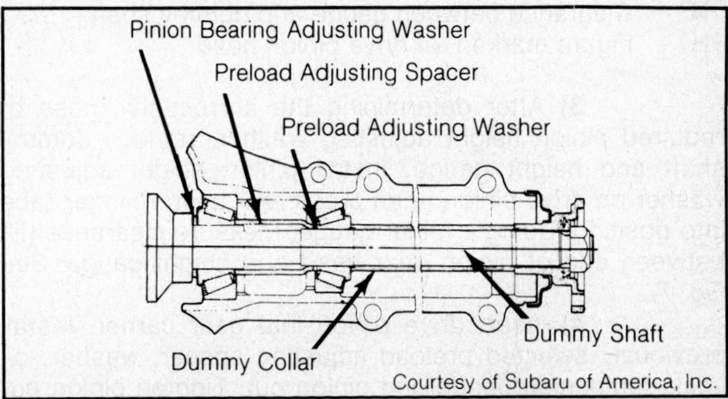

Courtesy of Subaru of America, Inc.

Drive Pinion Gear Installed Height

1) Leave dummy pinion shaft installed, and install Pinion Height Gauge (398507701). Using a feeler gauge, measure clearance between end of pinion gear head and height gauge.

Fig. 5: Exploded View of Subaru 4WD Differential Assembly

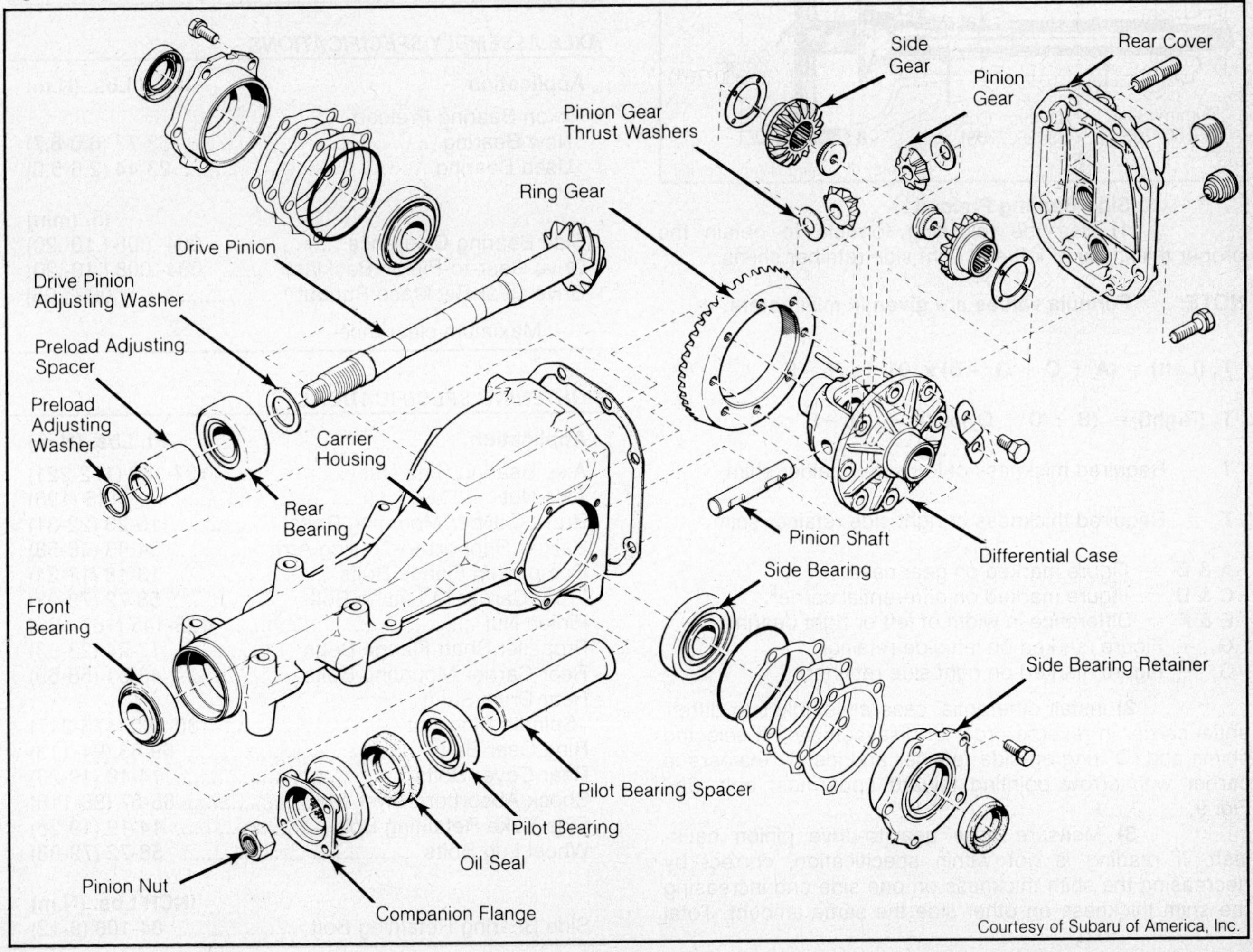

Courtesy of Subaru of America, Inc.

SUBARU 4WD REAR AXLE (Cont.)

2) Determine the thickness of the pinion height adjusting washer to be installed using the following formula.

NOTE: Formula values are given in millimeters.

T = To + N - (H x .01) - .20

T = Thickness of adjusting washer needed.
To = Thickness of washer temporarily installed.
N = Clearance between gauge and dummy shaft.
H = Figure marked on drive pinion head.

3) After determining the correct thickness of required pinion height adjusting washer, remove dummy shaft and height gauge. Install pinion height adjusting washer on drive pinion, then press rear bearing inner race into position. Using a feeler gauge, measure clearance (N) between end of pinion gear head and height gauge. *See Fig. 7.*

4) Insert drive pinion into gear carrier. Install previously selected preload adjusting spacer, washer, oil seal, companion flange and pinion nut. Tighten pinion nut to specification. If ring and pinion gear tooth contact pattern show normal pattern, reuse original washer.

Fig. 7: Measuring Drive Pinion Gear Installed Height

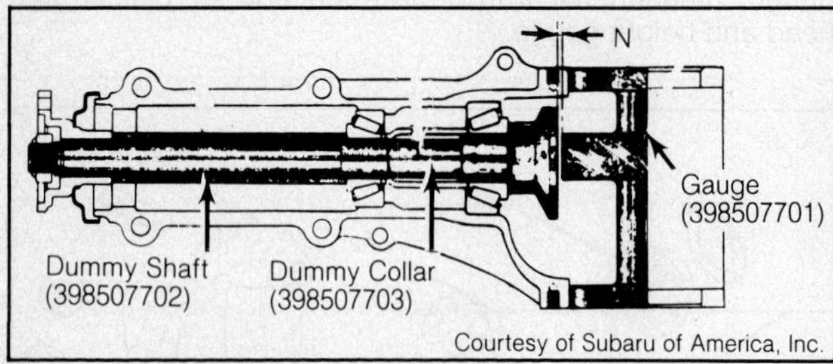

Courtesy of Subaru of America, Inc.

Side Bearing Preload

1) Use the following formula to obtain the proper thickness of left and right side retainer shims.

NOTE: Formula values are given in millimeters.

T_1 (Left) = (A + C + G_1 - D) x .01 + .76 - E

T_2 (Right) = (B + D + G_2) x .01 + .76 - F

T_1 = Required thickness of left side retainer shim.

T_2 = Required thickness of right side retainer shim.

A & B = Figure marked on gear case.
C & D = Figure marked on differential carrier.
E & F = Difference in width of left or right bearing.
G_1 = Figure marked on left side retainer.
G_2 = Figure marked on right side retainer.

2) Install differential case assembly into differential carrier in reverse order of disassembly. Fit selected shims and "O" ring on side retainer and install retainers in carrier with arrow pointing toward uppermost bolt. *See Fig. 9.*

3) Measure drive gear-to-drive pinion backlash. If reading is not within specification, correct by decreasing the shim thickness on one side and increasing the shim thickness on other side the same amount. Total shim thickness must be the same to maintain proper preload.

Fig. 8: Location of Identification Marks

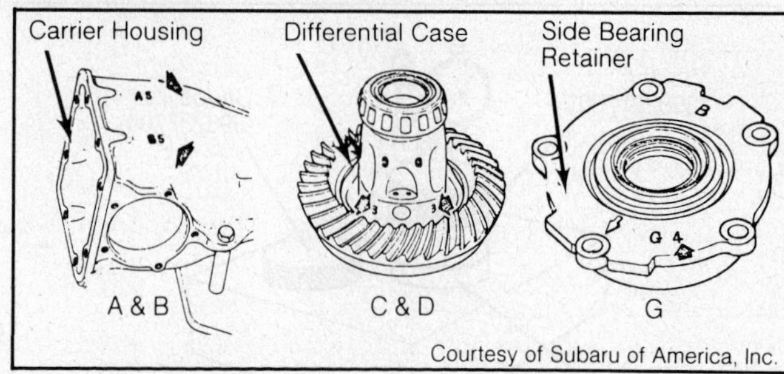

Courtesy of Subaru of America, Inc.

4) Check tooth contact of drive gear. If tooth contact is incorrect, recheck shim measurements. If the identification mark is not present, regard it as zero.

Fig. 9: Aligning Side Retainer

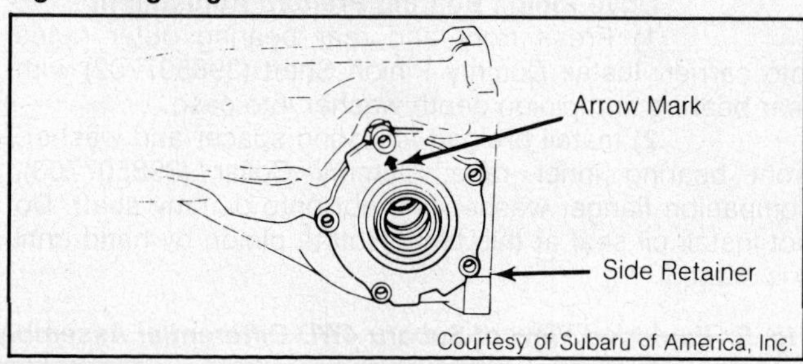

Courtesy of Subaru of America, Inc.

AXLE ASSEMBLY SPECIFICATIONS

Application	INCH Lbs. (N.m)
Pinion Bearing Preload	
New Bearing	53-77 (6.0-8.7)
Used Bearing	23-44 (2.6-5.0)
	In. (mm)
Side Bearing Clearance	.004-.008 (.10-.20)
Drive Gear-to-Pinion Backlash	.004-.008 (.10-.20)
Drive Gear Backface Runout [1]	.002 (.05)

[1] - Maximum clearance.

TIGHTENING SPECIFICATIONS

Application	Ft. Lbs. (N.m)
Axle Bearing Ring Nut	127-163 (172-221)
Axle Nut	145 (196)
Brake Caliper Mounting Bolts	16-23 (22-31)
Caliper Support-to-Trailing Arm	34-43 (46-58)
Companion Flange Bolts	13-18 (18-24)
Front Carrier Mounting Bolts	58-72 (79-98)
Pinion Nut	123-145 (167-196)
Propeller Shaft Flange Bolts	17-24 (23-33)
Rear Carrier Mounting Bolts	43-51 (58-69)
Rear Drive Shaft	
Spindle Ring Nut	130-160 (176-217)
Ring Gear Bolts	69-83 (94-113)
Rear Cover Bolts	14-19 (19-26)
Shock Absorber Lower Bolt	65-87 (88-118)
Side Yoke Retaining Bolt	14-19 (19-26)
Wheel Lug Bolts	58-72 (79-98)
	INCH Lbs. (N.m)
Side Bearing Retaining Bolt	84-108 (9-12)

Drive Axles

SUZUKI FRONT & REAR

Samurai

DESCRIPTION

Front and rear drive axles on Suzuki Samurai are identical except for the housing. Bevel gear drive is of hypoid design. Drive axles contains 8 gears: drive pinion gear, ring gear, 2 side gears and 4 pinion gears.

AXLE RATIO

Axle ratio is 3.727:1 on all models.

REMOVAL & INSTALLATION

FRONT DIFFERENTIAL ASSEMBLY

Removal & Installation

1) Remove front brake caliper with carrier. Wire caliper out of way. Using Tie Rod Remover (09913-65210), disconnect tie rod from steering knuckle. Remove 8 bolts retaining oil seal cover. Remove felt pad, oil seal and seal retainer from steering knuckle.

2) Remove 4 bolts retaining kingpins. Note kingpin position for installation purposes. Slowly remove axle shaft and spindle assembly from both sides of vehicle. Be careful not to drop lower kingpin bushings.

3) Disconnect propeller shaft from differential assembly. Remove bolts securing front differential assembly to housing. Remove front differential assembly. To install, reverse removal procedure.

REAR CARRIER ASSEMBLY

Removal & Installation

1) Using Brake Drum Remover (09943-35511) and a slide hammer, remove brake drums. Remove rear brake lines and plug. Remove backing plate. Using Rear Axle Remover (09922-66010) and a slide hammer, remove axle shafts.

2) Remove 8 bolts securing rear differential assembly in housing. Remove rear differential assembly. To install, reverse removal procedure.

OVERHAUL

DISASSEMBLY

Carrier Assembly

1) Using Flange Holder (09930-40113), remove flange nut. Mark side bearing caps for reassembly purposes. Remove carrier assembly from differential housing. *See Fig. 3*. Remove 8 bolts securing ring gear to carrier assembly. Remove ring gear.

2) Remove 8 bolts securing differential halves together. Remove right case half from left case half. Remove side gears, pinions and thrust washers from differential halves.

3) Using Bearing Puller (09913-60910) and Jig (09913-85230), remove side bearings from case. Remove pinion assembly from housing. Using a hydraulic press, remove pinion bearing from shaft.

NOTE: **If pinion or ring gear are damaged or worn, replace gear as a complete set.**

REASSEMBLY

Differential Halves

Position side gears, thrust washers and pinions in left differential half. Ensure shafts for pinions are installed properly. *See Fig. 1*. Place right differential half on left half. Install 8 bolts securing differential halves together. Tighten bolts to specified amount. See TIGHTENING SPECIFICATIONS table in this article.

Fig. 1: Correct Pinion Shaft Position

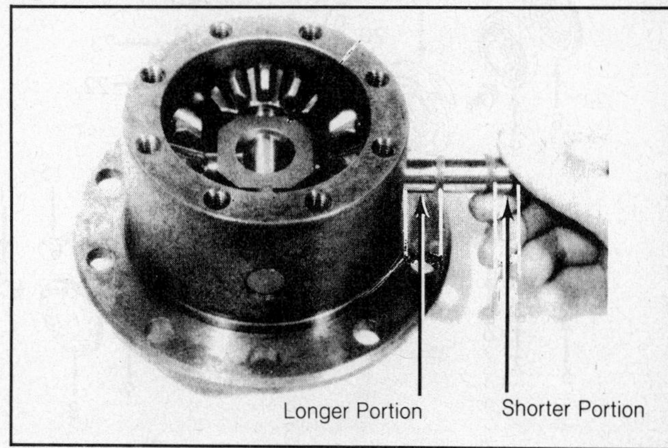

Courtesy of Suzuki of America Corp.

Side Gear Backlash

1) Position a dial indicator against differential halves. *See Fig. 2*. Check side gear backlash and thrust play. See SIDE GEAR SPECIFICATIONS table in this article.

2) If side gear backlash or side play is not as specified, replace thrust washers with proper thickness to obtain specified amount. Available thrust washers thickness are .035" (.9 mm), .039" (1.0 mm), .043" (1.1 mm) and .047" (1.2 mm).

Fig. 2: Checking Side Gear Backlash & Thrust Play

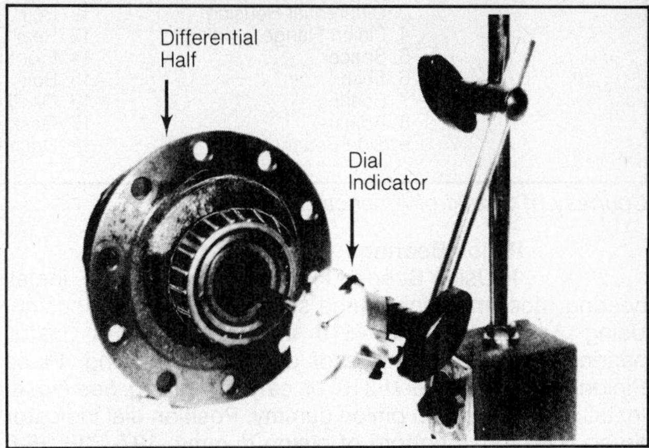

Courtesy of Suzuki of America Corp.

SIDE GEAR SPECIFICATIONS

Application	In. (mm)
Side Gear Backlash	.002-.006 (.05-.15)
Side Gear Thrust Play	.005-.014 (.12-.37)

SUZUKI FRONT & REAR (Cont.)

Fig. 3: Exploded View of Drive Axle Assembly

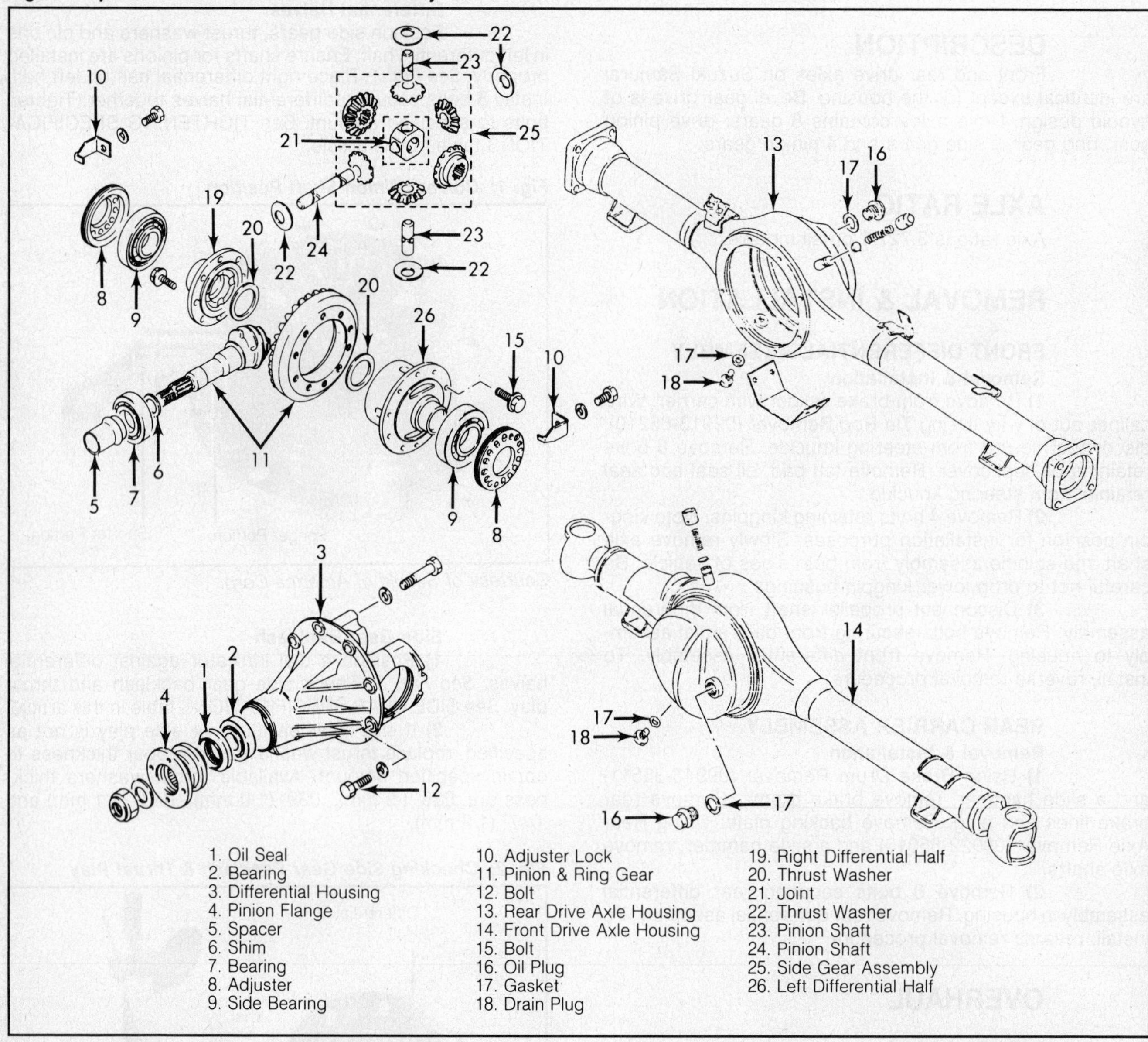

Courtesy of Suzuki of America Corp.

Pinion Bearings & Pinion Setting

1) Using Bearing Installer (09913-75510), install bearing race on pinion flange side of differential housing. Using Adapter (09924-74510 and 09926-68310), install bearing race on gear side of differential housing. Place Pinion Dummy (09926-78310) on carrier housing. *See Fig. 4*. Install dial indicator in pinion dummy. Position dial indicator tip so it protudes bottom of pinion dummy .197-.236" (5-6 mm). Place pinion dummy on an flat surface. Zero dial indicator.

2) Using Bearing Installer (09925-18010 and 09940-53111), press pinion bearing on pinion shaft. DO NOT install spacer at this time. Place pinion shaft in differential housing. Install flange and retaining nut. Install Preload Adjuster (09922-75221) on pinion flange. *See Fig. 5*.

3) Using a spring scale, check starting preload, not rotating preload. Tighten pinion nut until specified starting preload is obtained. See PINION BEARING PRELOAD SPECIFICATIONS table in this article.

PINION BEARING PRELOAD SPECIFICATIONS

Application	Lbs. (kg)
Starting Preload	4.0-7.5 (1.8-3.4)
Rotating Preload	[1]

[1] – Preload is 7.8-14.7 INCH lbs. (9.0-17.0 kg/cm^2) when not using preload adjuster.

4) Place pinion dummy in carrier housing. Measure distance "A", "B" and "C". *See Fig. 6*. "A" + "C" should equal 3.70" (94 mm). With dummy pinion secured, check dial indicator reading. Add dial indicator reading to 3.70" (94 mm).

5) Record marked value, on side of pinion shaft. Subtract sum of "A", "B" and "C" from marked valve. Difference is the shim thickness required. Shims are available from .039-.050" (1.0-1.3 mm) in .001" (.03 mm) increments. A .012" (.3 mm) shim is also available.

SUZUKI FRONT & REAR (Cont.)

Fig. 4: Installing Pinion Dummy (09926-78310)

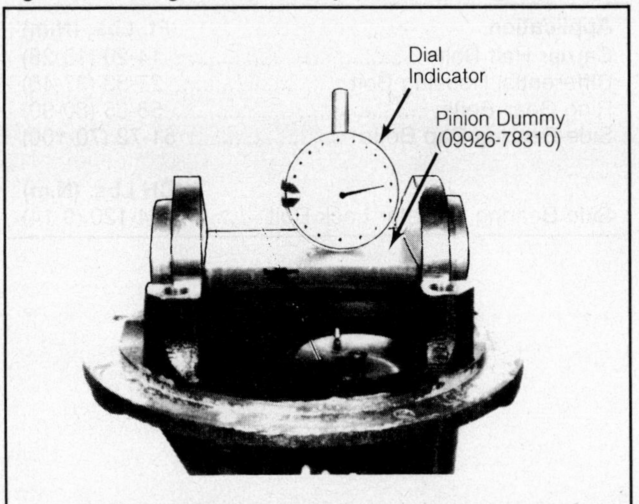

Courtesy of Suzuki of America Corp.

Fig. 5: Installing Preload Adapter (09922-75221)

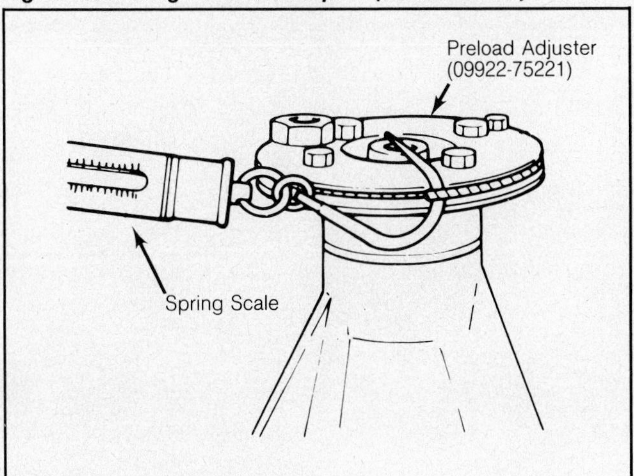

Courtesy of Suzuki of America Corp.

6) Remove pinion shaft from differential housing and install proper shims. Remove pinion dummy. Install oil seal in differential housing. Lightly oil seal and pinion bearings. Install pinion shaft with bearings, new spacer and shims.

7) Install pinion flange on pinion shaft. Hand tighten pinion nut. Install Preload Adjuster (09922-75221) on pinion flange. Rotate pinion flange a few times. Attach spring scale to preload adjuster. Check starting preload.

8) Tighten pinion nut until specified starting preload is obtained. If starting preload is exceeded, replace spacer and recheck. DO NOT loosen pinion nut to obtain correct starting preload. Caulk pinion nut.

Carrier Assembly

1) Press side bearings on differential halves. Position ring gear on differential halves. Apply Locking Cement 1333B (99000-32020) on ring gear retaining bolts.

2) Tighten bolt to specifications. See TIGHTENING SPECIFICATIONS table in this article. Place carrier assembly in differential housing. Position side bearing caps and adjusters in housing. Ensure marks made during disassembly are aligned on side bearing caps.

Fig. 6: Measuring Pinion Preload

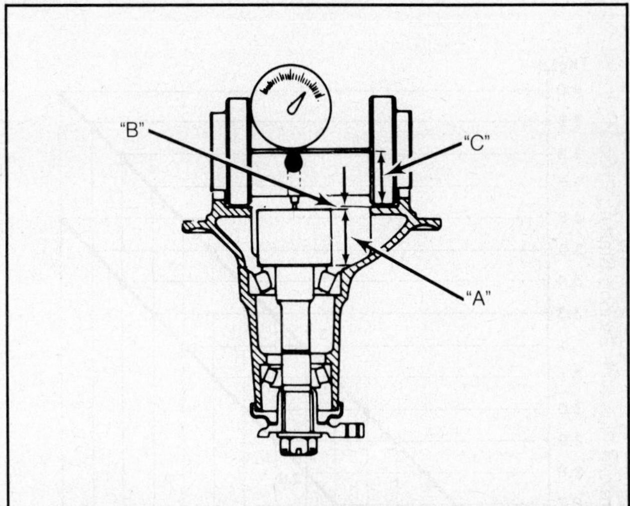

Courtesy of Suzuki of America Corp.

3) Tighten side bearing caps bolts to 90-168 INCH lbs. (10-19 N.m). Rotate adjusters until they contact side bearing races. Position a dial indicator against ring gear. *See Fig. 7.* Check ring gear backlash. See RING GEAR BACKLASH SPECIFICATIONS table in this artcile.

RING GEAR BACKLASH SPECIFICATIONS

Application	In. (mm)
All Models	.004-.006" (.10-.15 mm)

Fig. 7: Checking Ring Gear Backlash

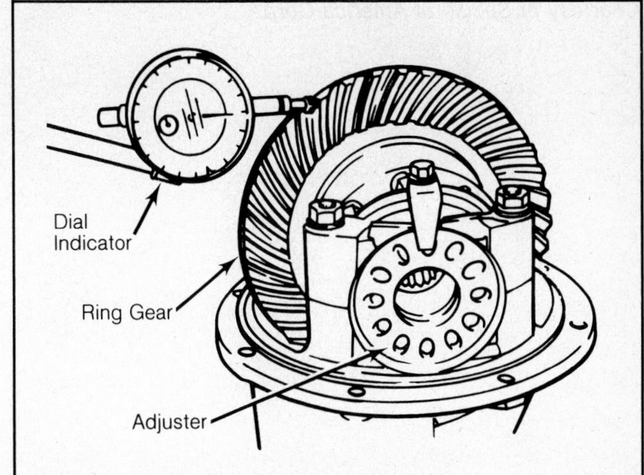

Courtesy of Suzuki of America Corp.

4) If ring gear backlash is not as specified, rotate adjusters equally, running one forward and the other backward, until correct backlash is obtained. Rotating one notch equals .002" (.05 mm) change in backlash. Attach spring scale to adapter.

5) Check total starting preload. *See Fig. 8.* If total preload is not correct, readjust ring gear preload. Tighten side bearing caps bolts to specifications. Install locks. Using Red lead paste, check contact pattern. See GEAR TOOTH PATTERNS article in this section.

Drive Axles

SUZUKI FRONT & REAR (Cont.)

Fig. 8: Total Starting Preload Chart

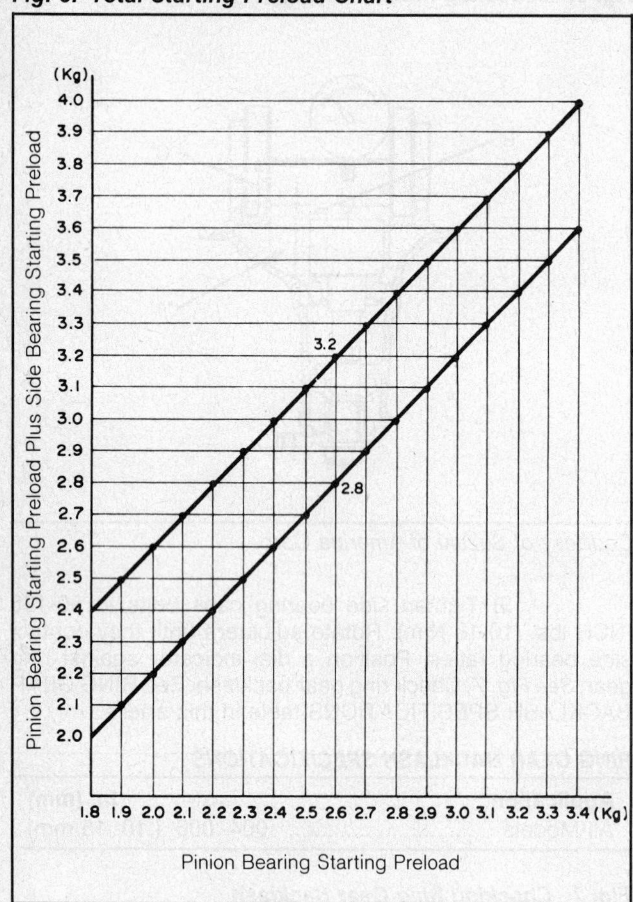

Courtesy of Suzuki of America Corp.

TIGHTENING SPECIFICATIONS

Application	Ft. Lbs. (N.m)
Carrier Half Bolt	14-20 (18-28)
Differential Housing Bolt	27-33 (37-45)
Ring Gear Bolts	58-65 (80-90)
Side Bearing Cap Bolts	51-72 (70-100)
	INCH Lbs. (N.m)
Side Bearing Adjuster Lock Bolt	84-120 (9-14)

TOYOTA INTEGRAL HOUSING – EXCEPT VAN

Cressida, Pickup (Front),
Supra, 4Runner (Front)

DESCRIPTION

Drive axle assembly is hypoid type with integral carrier housing. Drive pinion bearing preload adjustment is made with collapsible spacer between front and rear pinion bearing inner races. Differential side bearing preload and drive pinion depth adjustment are made by shims.

Driving power is transmitted to stub axles by drive axles with Constant Velocity (CV) joints at each end. Stub axles are supported in trailing arms by tapered roller bearings. A collapsible spacer sets preload on stub axle bearings. Limited Slip Differential (LSD) is available in Cressida and Supra models.

AXLE RATIO & IDENTIFICATION

Integral carrier type drive axle may be identified by inspection cover on rear of carrier housing. LSD uses 2-piece case while conventional differential uses one-piece case. To determine axle ratio, divide number of ring gear teeth by number of pinion gear teeth.

REMOVAL & INSTALLATION

FRONT WHEEL BEARINGS

NOTE: See LOCKING HUBS article in this section.

FRONT AXLE SHAFT & OIL SEAL

Removal (Pickup & 4Runner)

Remove differential assembly from vehicle. Disconnect front drive shaft from front axle shaft. Using Slide Hammer (09910-00015), remove front axle shaft. Remove differential tube. Using Puller (09308-00010), remove oil seal.

Installation

Apply grease to oil seal. Using Installer (09550-00020), install oil seal. Install differential tube. Install new snap ring on front axle shaft. Using slide hammer, install front axle shaft. Check front axle shaft runout. If runout exceeds .008" (.20 mm), replace shaft. Install differential assembly.

REAR AXLE SHAFTS & BEARINGS

Removal (Cressida)

1) Raise vehicle. Remove rear wheel. Disconnect outer CV joint from stub axle inner flange. Remove caliper and support out of way, being careful of brake line. Release parking brake fully and remove rotor.

2) Loosen staked portion of flange nut with chisel. Remove flange nut and washer. Remove inner flange and plate washer from stub axle shaft using Puller (09557-22022). *See Fig. 2.* Remove stub axle with seal and outer bearing, using puller.

Fig. 2: Removing Stub Axle Inner Flange (Cressida)

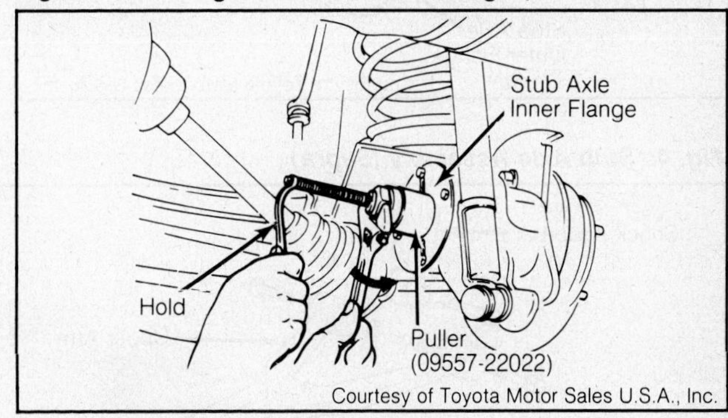

Fig. 1: Stub Axle Assembly (Cressida)

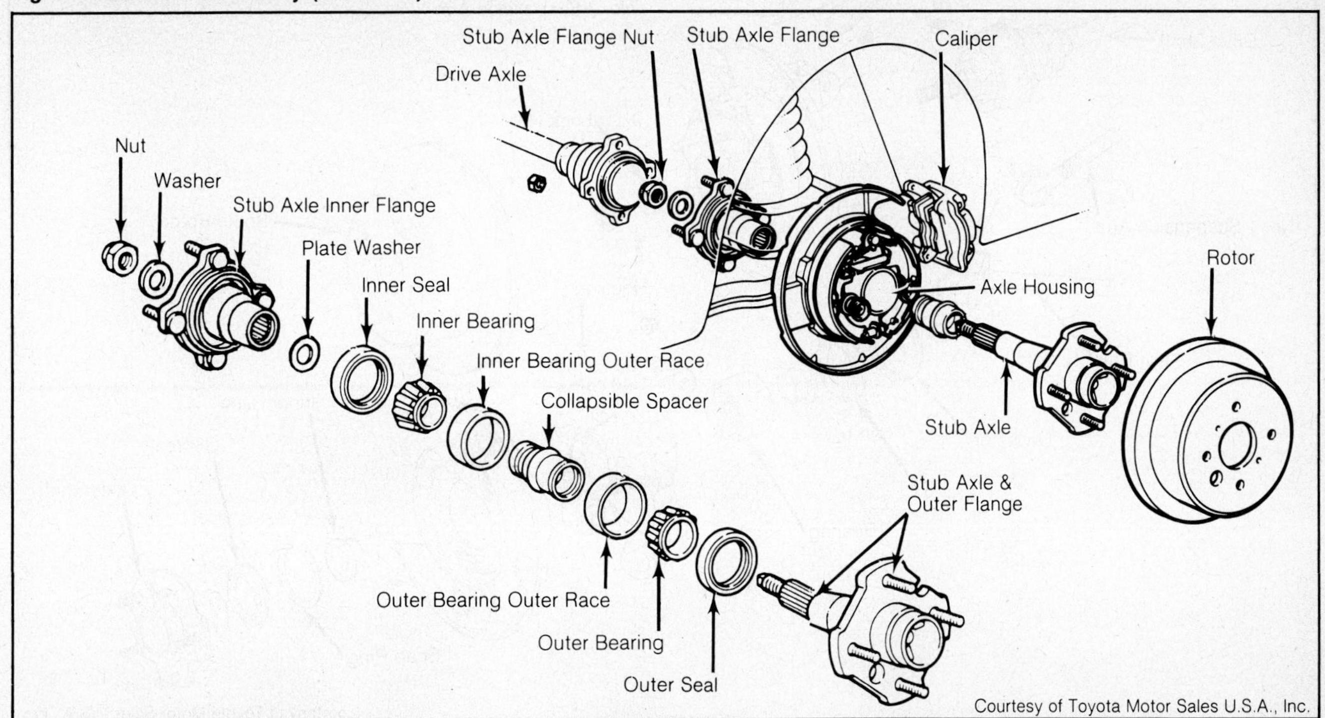

TOYOTA INTEGRAL HOUSING – EXCEPT VAN (Cont.)

3) Remove inner seal from housing and take out inner bearing. Drive stub axle bearing outer races from housing with brass drift. Press outer bearing off stub axle shaft and remove seal.

Inspection

1) Inspect stub axle shaft and outer flange for damage or wear. Measure runout of stub axle outer flange. If flange runout exceeds .004" (.10 mm), stub axle must be replaced. *See Fig. 3.*

2) Clean and dry bearings and races. Inspect for pits, scoring or heat damage. Bearing and outer race must be replaced as set if either is damaged.

Fig. 3: Checking Axle Flange Runout

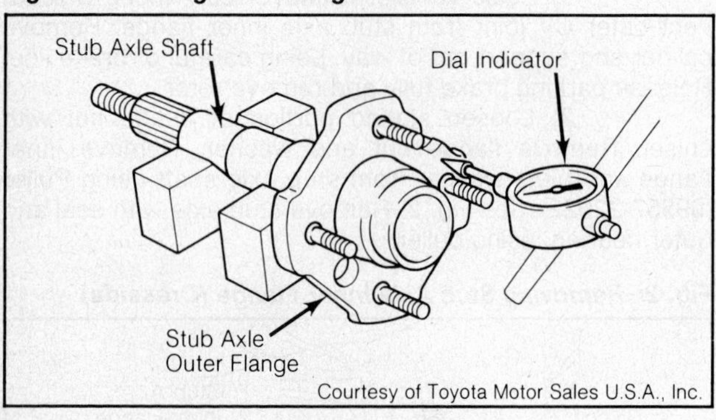

Courtesy of Toyota Motor Sales U.S.A., Inc.

Installation

1) Pack bearings with MP grease No. 2. Drive outer race of inner bearing into housing. Place inner bearing in race. Drive new inner seal into housing to correct depth. See SEAL DEPTH table in this article. Drive outer race of outer bearing into housing.

2) Pack inside of housing and coat outside of new spacer with MP grease No. 2. Install new spacer in hub. Place outer bearing in race and drive new outer seal into correct depth. Coat seal lips with No. 2 grease.

3) Install stub axle shaft in bearings. Install inner flange with plate washer in housing after lightly coating flange with grease. Use Puller (09557-22022) to align inner flange and axle shaft tip. Ensure no grease gets on shaft threads. *See. Fig. 5.*

4) Install new flange nut with washer and torque nut to 29 ft. lbs. (39 N.m). Ensure axle shaft has axial play. Rotate shaft in both directions and measure rotational resistance with torque wrench. Tighten flange nut to 58 ft. lbs. (79 N.m).

5) Check to see that rotating torque of bearings is .9-3.5 INCH lbs. (.10-.40 N.m). Turn flange one revolution per 6 seconds while measuring. If preload is too low, tighten nut 5-10 degrees at a time until specified preload is reached.

6) Maximum torque on flange nut is 145 ft. lbs. (197 N.m). If maximum torque is exceeded, new spacer must be installed and preload procedure repeated. Stake flange nut.

Fig. 4: Stub Axle Assembly (Supra)

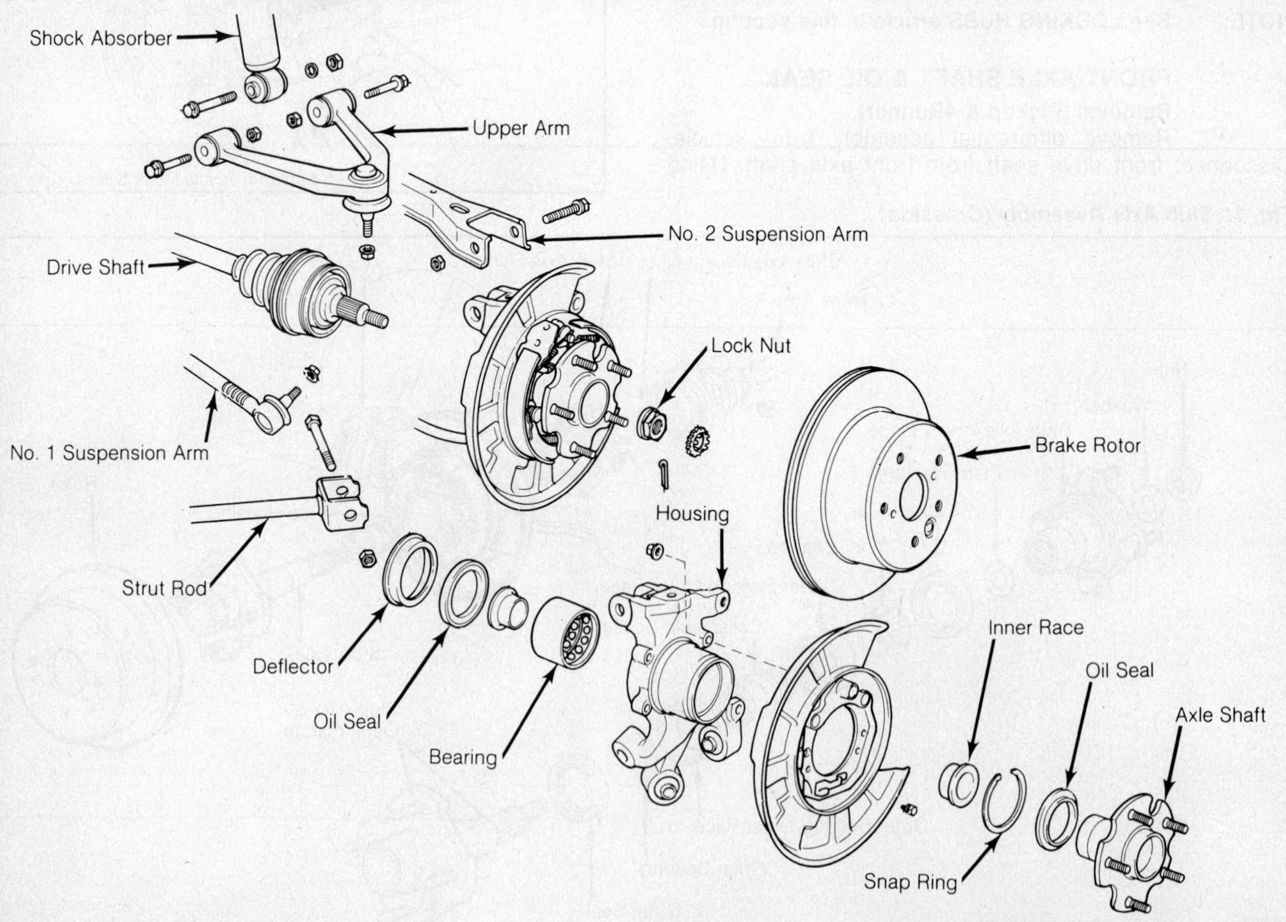

Courtesy of Toyota Motor Sales U.S.A., Inc.

TOYOTA INTEGRAL HOUSING – EXCEPT VAN (Cont.)

7) Install rotor and check parking brake adjustment. Install caliper. Attach outer CV joint to inner stub axle flange and tighten nuts to specification. Install rear wheel and tighten lug nuts.

Removal (Supra)

1) Raise vehicle. Remove rear wheel. Disconnect outer CV joint from stub axle inner flange. Remove caliper and support out of way, being careful of brake line. Release parking brake fully and remove rotor.

2) Check bearing play and axle shaft runout. Using Puller (09611 22012), disconnect No. 1 lower suspension arm from axle carrier. Remove remaining bolts attaching axle carrier. Remove axle carrier. Remove backing plate. Using Pullers (09950-00020 and 09950-20017), remove upper arm from axle carrier.

3) Remove dust cover. Remove inner oil seal. Using Puller (09950-20017) remove axle shaft from axle carrier. Using Bearing Remover (09950-20017). Remove inner bearing race. Remove outer seal. Remove snap ring. Using Adapters (09608-06020 and 09608-06100) and a press, remove bearing outer race.

Fig. 5: Aligning Axle Shaft & Inner Flange

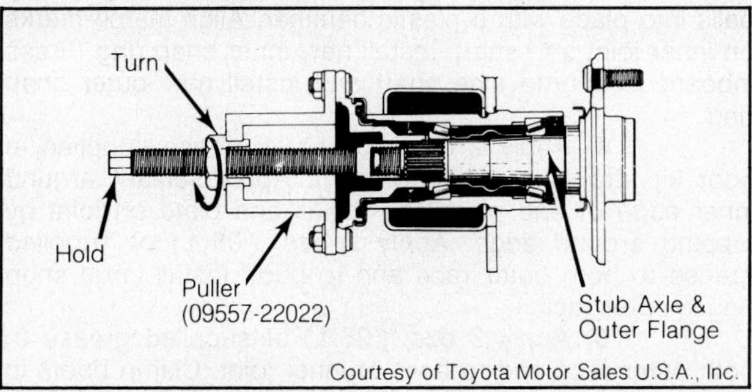

Installation

1) Using Bearing Installers (09608-32010 and 09608-35014), install new bearing outer race in axle carrier. Install snap ring. Apply grease to bearing and inside hub. Install bearing inner races. Install outer oil seal.

2) Install backing plate. Tighten bolts to 19 ft. lbs. (25 N.m). Tighten nuts to 43 ft. lbs. (59 N.m). Using Adapter (09608-35014), install axle shaft. Install inner oil seal. Install dust deflector. Reverse removal procedure to complete installation.

REAR DRIVE AXLE ASSEMBLY

NOTE: **For removal and installation information on 4Runner front drive axles, see FWD AXLE SHAFTS article in this section.**

Removal

Disconnect drive axle from differential side gear flange and from stub axle flange.

Installation

Install drive axles with narrow distance between flange and boot band at differential side. Use care to avoid damage to boots when installing drive axles. Tighten nuts to 44-57 ft. lbs. (60-77 N.m).

DRIVE PINION FLANGE & OIL SEAL

NOTE: **On Cressida, differential housing assembly must be removed from vehicle.**

Removal

1) Index propeller shaft to drive pinion flange and remove propeller shaft. Loosen staked portion of drive pinion flange nut. Remove drive pinion flange nut. Using Puller (09557-22022), remove drive pinion flange. Using Seal Remover (09308-10010), remove oil seal from housing and remove oil slinger.

2) Using Puller (09556-30010), remove front bearing from housing with puller. Remove collapsible bearing spacer and discard.

Installation

1) Install new spacer and front bearing. Install oil slinger with concave side facing front drive pinion bearing. Apply grease to seal lips. Using Installer (09554-30011), install new oil seal to correct depth. See SEAL DEPTH table at end of this article. Install flange and lightly coat drive pinion threads with grease.

2) Install flange nut and hold flange. Tighten nut to 80 ft. lbs. (108 N.m) and measure preload. See AXLE ASSEMBLY SPECIFICATIONS table at end of this article. If preload is lower than specification, tighten nut in increments of 108 INCH lbs. (12 N.m) until preload is correct. Check pinion nut torque. See TIGHTENING SPECIFICATIONS table at end of this article.

3) Check longitudinal and latitudinal runout of drive pinion flange with dial indicator. Stake drive pinion nut. Align index marks on propeller shaft and pinion flange. Tighten bolts.

DIFFERENTIAL ASSEMBLY

Removal

1) Drain gear oil. Disconnect drive axles from side gear flanges. Index propeller shaft to drive pinion flange. Disconnect propeller shaft. Remove nuts from differential assembly-to-support bolts.

2) Support differential assembly with jack. Remove through bolts holding small support member (on differential case) to large support member. Remove bolts holding case to chassis member. Lower differential carrier from vehicle.

Installation

To install, reverse removal procedure. Tighten mounting bolts to specifications. See TIGHTENING SPECIFICATIONS table in this article. Align index marks on propeller shaft and drive pinion flange. Tighten bolts. Install drain plug and fill with hypoid oil. Limited slip differentials use only LSD hypoid oil.

OVERHAUL

NOTE: **For overhaul information on front drive axle shafts, see FWD AXLE SHAFTS article in this section.**

REAR DRIVE AXLE

Disassembly (Cressida)

1) Check drive axle for excessive radial play in both outboard and inboard joints. Ensure outboard joint slides smoothly in thrust direction. Remove 4 boot clamps and slide boots to center of shaft.

2) Remove large snap ring from outer joint. Place match marks on outer race and axle shaft with paint. Do not use punch to index race and shaft. If end cover is worn or damaged, replace it.

Drive Axles

TOYOTA INTEGRAL HOUSING – EXCEPT VAN (Cont.)

Fig. 6: Exploded View of Rear Drive Axle (Cressida)

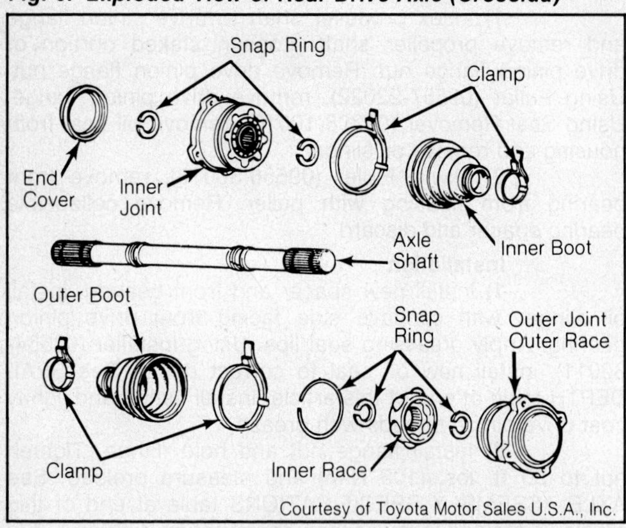

Fig. 7: Match Mark Location on Outer CV Joint

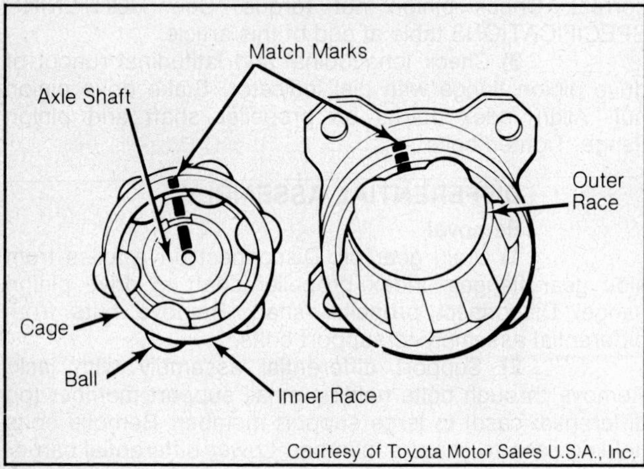

3) Remove balls from inner race of outer joint by tapping edge of cage in axial direction of shaft, using a soft hammer. Move bearing cage to center of axle shaft. Remove outer snap ring and press inner race from axle shaft. Remove inner snap ring and cage. Remove both dust boots.

4) Pry end cover from inner joint. Place match marks on inner joint and axle shaft with paint. Remove snap ring and press joint from axle shaft. Clean all parts. Check parts for cracks, wear or damage. Replace as necessary.

Reassembly

1) Wrap shaft splines with vinyl tape so as to prevent damage to boots. Assemble new clamps on boots so that straps will bend opposite to direction of rotation. Install boots and clamps on shaft. Install new inner snap rings.

2) Place cage of outer joint onto shaft with larger diameter facing outward. Align match marks and press inner race onto drive shaft. Install new outer snap ring. Coat inner race, cage and balls with grease supplied in boot kit.

3) Position cage over inner race and lightly tap balls into place with a plastic hammer. Align match marks on inner joint and shaft. Install new inner snap ring. Press inboard joint onto axle shaft and install new outer snap ring.

4) Apply 2 ozs. (.06 L) of grease supplied in boot kit into flange side of joint. Apply sealant around inner edge of end plate and install end plate on joint by tapping around edge. Apply 2 ozs. (.06 L) of supplied grease to both outer race and to boot. Install large snap ring in outer race.

5) Apply 2 ozs. (.06 L) of supplied grease to both outer race and to boot of inner joint. Clamp boots in position so that length of assembled drive axle is 17.341-17.459" (440.50-443.50 mm).

6) This distance is measured from outer face of outer joint to outer face of inner joint at ears where bolt holes are. Lock clamps with lock positioned between

Fig. 8: Exploded View of Rear Drive Axle (Supra)

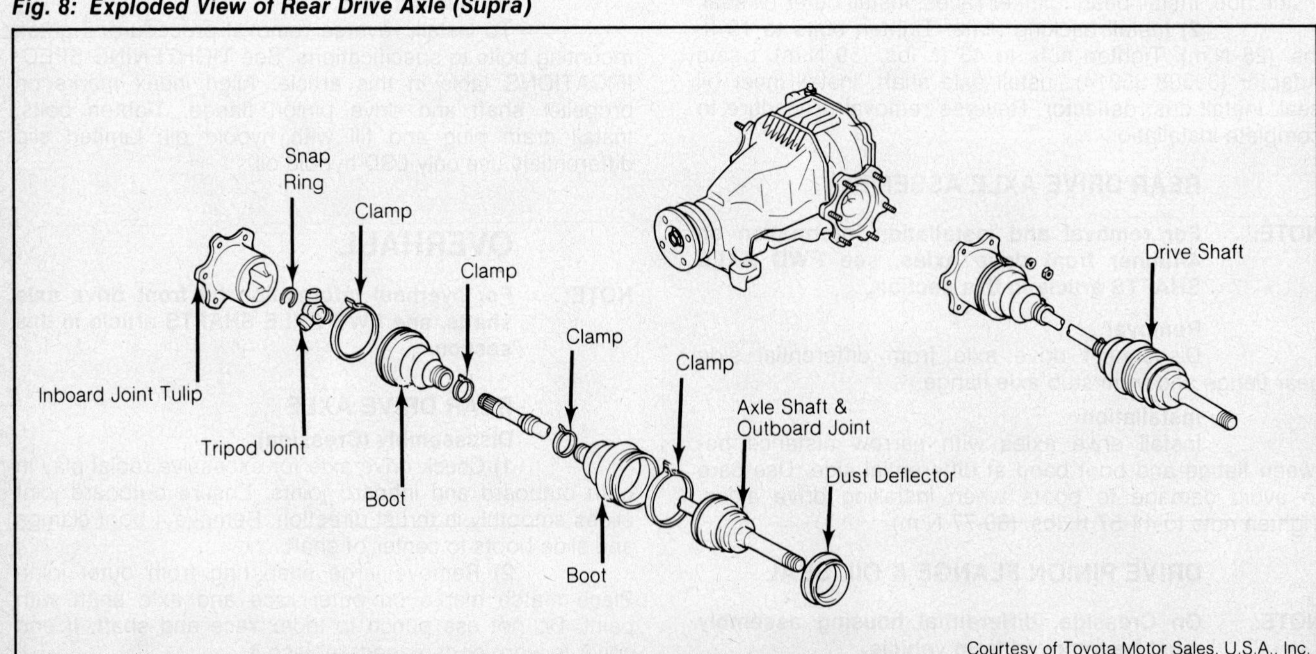

TOYOTA INTEGRAL HOUSING – EXCEPT VAN (Cont.)

flange bolt holes. Turn both joints and stretch boot to ensure that it does not deform. Install drive shaft with narrow distance between boot band and flange at differential side.

Disassembly (Supra)

1) Check for play in CV joints. Ensure CV joints slide smoothly in thrust direction. Check radial play. See AXLE ASSEMBLY SPECIFICATIONS table at end of this article. Remove inboard boot clamps. Using paint, mark inboard joint tulip and tripod. DO NOT use a punch to mark parts.

2) Remove inboard joint tulip. Remove snap ring. Mark axle shaft and tripod joint. Using a brass bar and hammer, remove tripod joint. Remove inboard boot. Remove outboard joint boot clamps. Remove dust deflector.

NOTE: **Outboard joint cannot be disassembled.**

Reassembly

1) Install dust deflector. Wrap shaft splines with tape. Temporarily install outboard and inboard joint boots. Install tripod joint on shaft. Beveled side of tripod center should be toward outboard joint. Align marks made during disassembly. Tap tripod joint on shaft.

2) Install snap ring. Apply grease and install boot and clamps. Assemble inboard tulip joint. Pack joint with grease. Align marks made during disassembly. Install boot and clamps. Check axle length. Standard length should be 21.724-21.824" (551.80-554.80 mm).

Differential Case (Conventional)

1) Remove differential carrier cover. Remove side gear shaft and oil seal. Check ring gear runout and backlash. Check gear tooth contact pattern. Check side gear backlash while holding one pinion gear toward case. Measure drive pinion preload and total preload.

2) Put alignment marks on bearing cap and differential carrier. Remove caps. Remove 2 side bearing preload adjusting plate washers. Measure plate washers and record thicknesses. Remove differential case and ring gear. Remove differential case side bearing outer races. Place reference marks on bearings, gears and thrust washers for installation in their original position.

3) Remove side bearings from case with puller. Keep side bearings with correct outer races and mark for reassembly. Put alignment marks on ring gear and differential case. Remove ring gear bolts and locking tabs. Remove ring gear by tapping on gear with a plastic hammer.

4) Using hammer and punch, drive out lock pin holding pinion shaft to case. Remove pinion shaft, pinion gears, side gears and thrust washers. Thoroughly clean and inspect all parts for wear or damage. Repair or replace parts as necessary.

Differential Case (Limited Slip)

1) Perform steps **1)** through **3)** as previously described for conventional case disassembly. Mark case cover and case for reassembly. Ensure left and right clutch member numbers match. Loosen case cover bolts in diagonal sequence.

Fig. 9: Exploded View of Toyota Conventional Differential

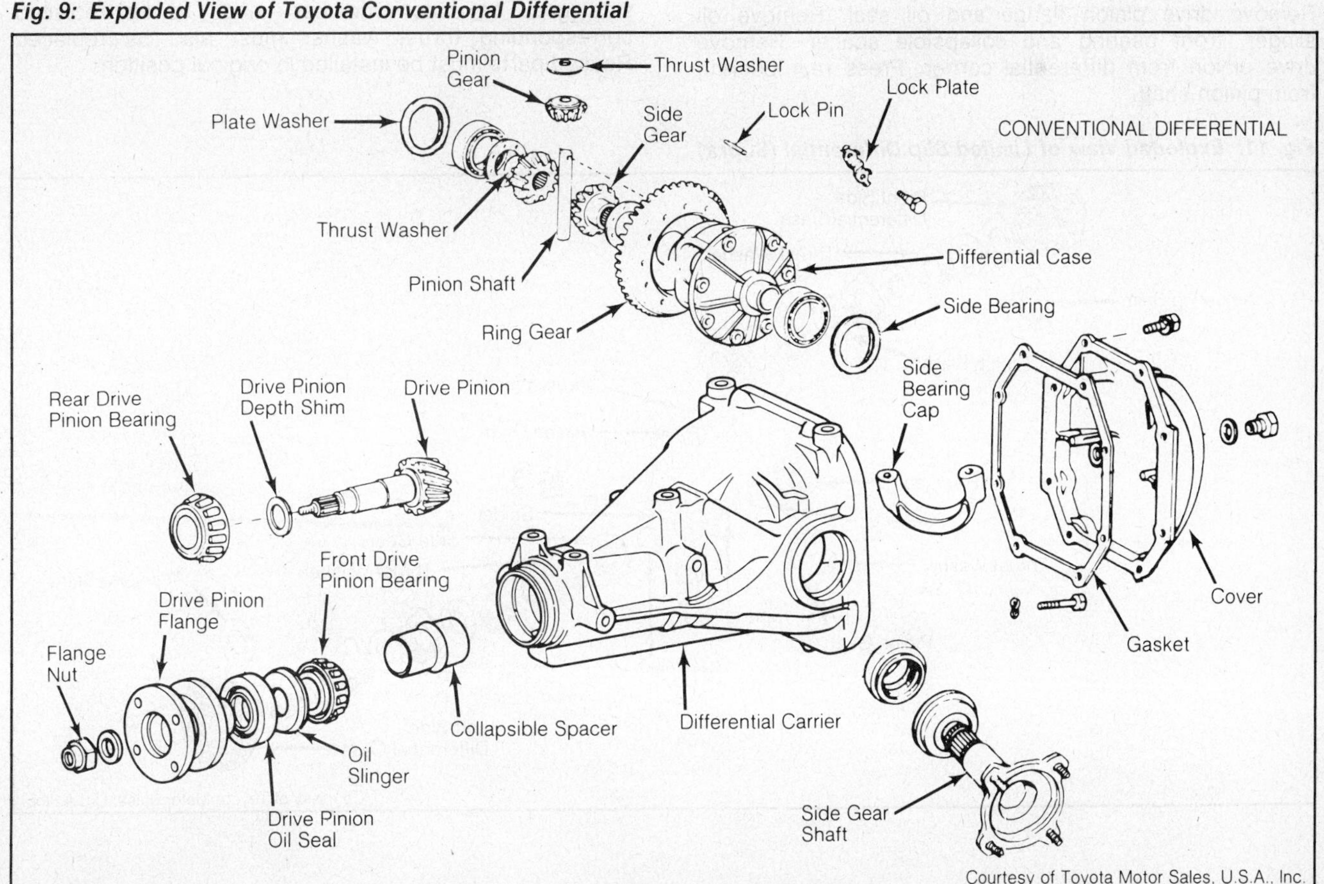

TOYOTA INTEGRAL HOUSING – EXCEPT VAN (Cont.)

Fig. 10: Exploded View of Limited Slip Differential (Cressida)

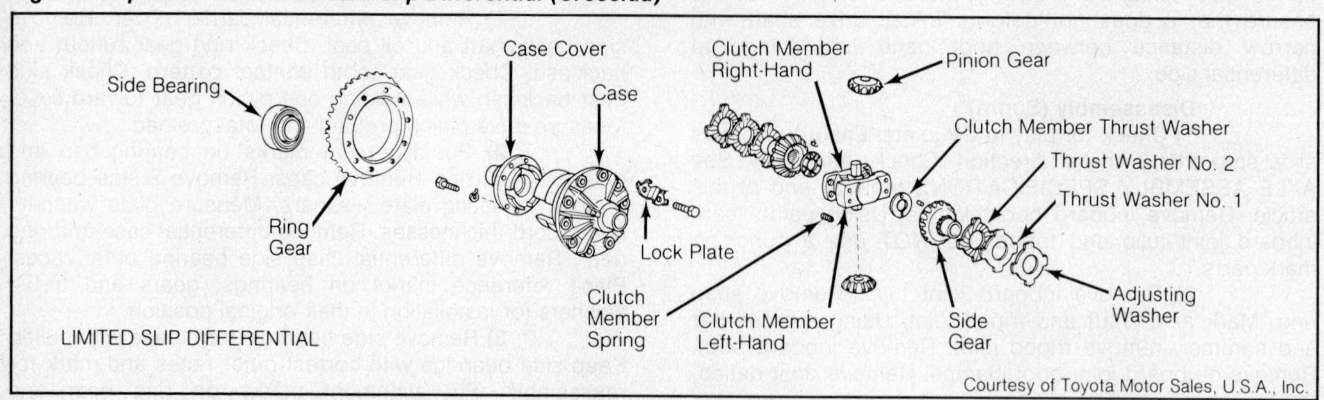

NOTE: Cover bolts are treated with retaining compound. Heating case assembly in oil bath to 302°F (150°C) makes removal of bolts easier.

2) Remove clutch member thrust washer, side gear, thrust washers (No. 1 and No. 2), and adjusting washer from cover portion of case. *See Figs. 9 and 10*. Remove right-hand clutch member with pinion gear from case.

3) Remove clutch member springs, left-hand clutch member, side gear with clutch member thrust washer, thrust washers (No. 1 and No. 2), and adjusting washer from case.

Drive Pinion

1) Hold drive pinion flange and remove nut. Remove drive pinion flange and oil seal. Remove oil slinger, front bearing and collapsible spacer. Remove drive pinion from differential carrier. Press rear bearing from pinion shaft.

2) Drive front and rear drive pinion bearing outer races from carrier. Inspect bearings, outer races and pinion shaft for wear or damage. Discard collapsible spacer. Ring gear and drive pinion must be replaced as a set.

INSPECTION

Differential (Limited Slip)

1) Check clearance between differential case and left-hand clutch member. Clearance is 0-.002" (0-.05 mm). *See Fig. 12*. Differential case opening range "B" is 1.6535-1.6545" (42.000-42.025 mm) while clutch member thickness range "A" is 1.6526-1.6535" (41.975-42.000 mm).

2) Check side gear thrust washers for heat damage or excessive wear. Check springs for tension. If side gear or clutch member needs to be replaced, corresponding thrust washer must also be replaced. Reused parts must be installed in original position.

Fig. 11: Exploded View of Limited Slip Differential (Supra)

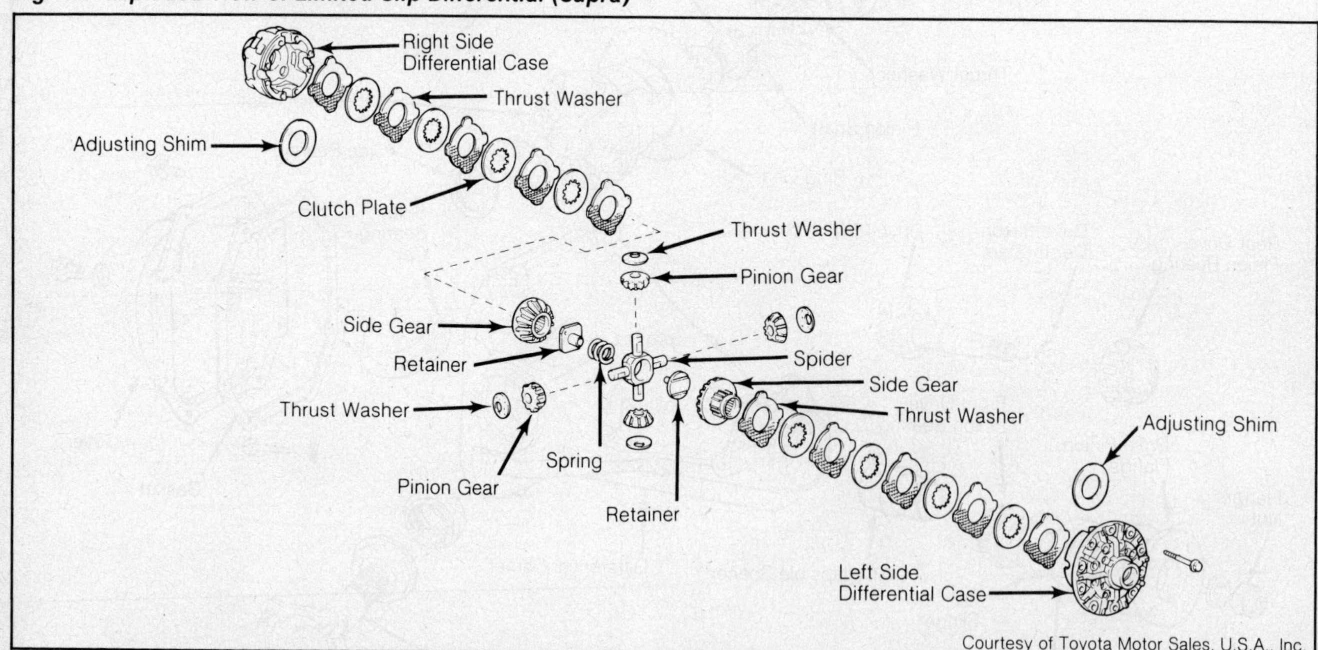

TOYOTA INTEGRAL HOUSING – EXCEPT VAN (Cont.)

Fig. 12: Measuring Clutch Member-to-Case Clearance

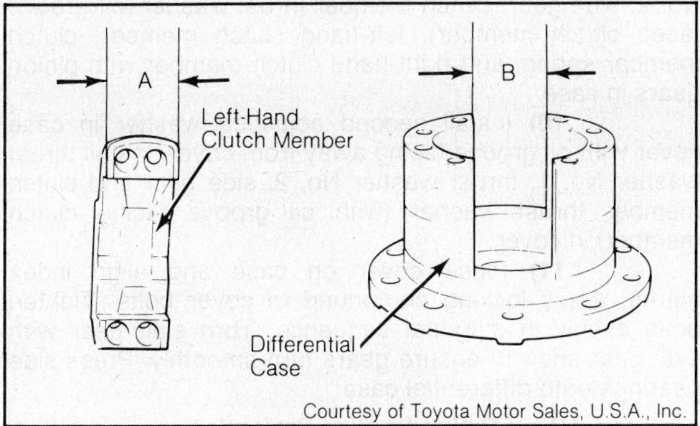

Clearance should be 0-.002" (0-.05 mm).

REASSEMBLY & ADJUSTMENT

Drive Axle

Differential Case (Conventional)

1) Install side gears and thrust washers in case. Thrust washers should be same size for both sides if possible. Install pinion gears with thrust washers and tap pinion shaft into place. Check side gear backlash while holding one pinion gear toward case.

2) If backlash is incorrect, change thickness of thrust washers until backlash is within range of .002-.008" (.05-.20 mm). Install lock pin through case and hole in pinion shaft. Stake pin to differential case. Press side bearings onto case.

3) Clean contact surfaces of differential case. Heat ring gear to 212°F (100°C) in oil bath. Clean ring gear contact surface with solvent and install on case while still hot. Align index marks on ring gear and case. Coat ring gear bolts with hypoid oil and install with lock plates.

CAUTION: Do not heat ring gear above 230°F (110°C).

4) Tighten ring gear bolts gradually in diagonal sequence. When bolts are snug, tighten to 67-75 ft. lbs. (91-102 N.m). Stake lock plates with one tab flush against flat of bolt head. Tab resting on point should be staked on tightening side of point.

5) Install case with side bearings into carrier. Snug down adjusting nut until there is no play in bearing. Check ring gear runout with a dial indicator against back of gear (opposite teeth) in 4 places.

6) Maximum allowable runout is .003" (.07 mm). If runout is excessive, rotate ring gear on case and remeasure. If runout cannot be brought within specified range, case or ring gear must be replaced.

Differential Case (Limited Slip)

1) Side gear thrust clearance (axial clearance inside case) must be determined first. Clean all parts. Set up Side Gear Thrust Washer Adjuster (09411-22011) and install parts in order. *See Fig. 13.* Do not assemble adjusting washers or clutch member springs at this time.

2) Loosen clamping nut on adjuster and hold parts with spring tension of adjuster. Measure "L" dimension with micrometer. Dimension "L" is assembled distance from outer face of left-hand thrust washer No. 1 to outer face of right-hand thrust washer No. 1.

3) Ensure parts are aligned in adjuster and measure "L" dimension several times. Take average of

Fig. 13: Selecting Side Gear Thrust Washers

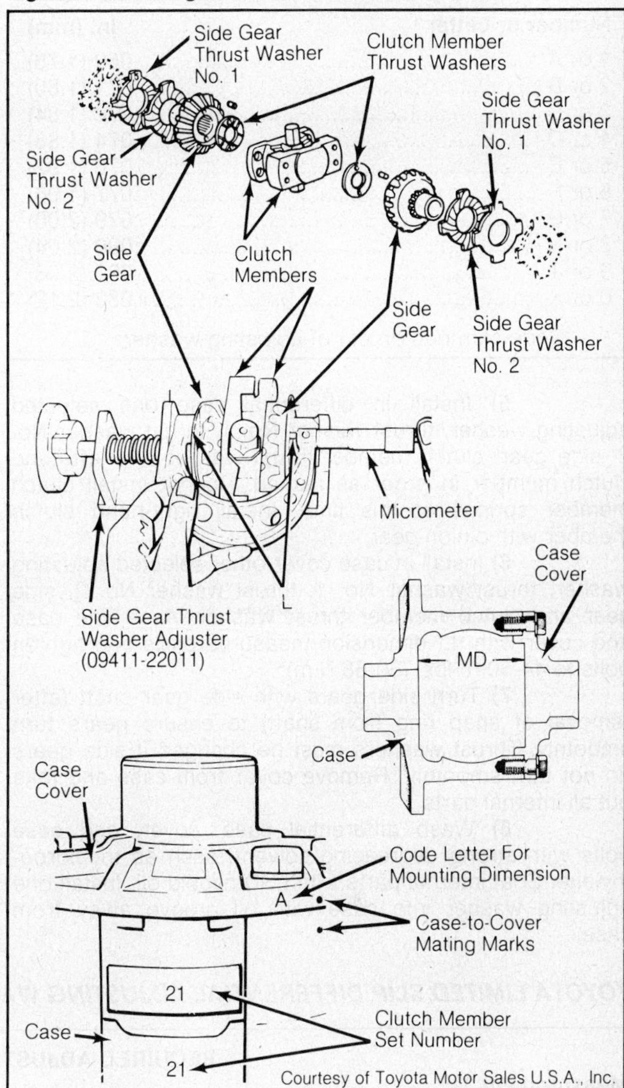

readings. Differential case mounting dimension is coded into case at time of manufacture. Code letters "A" through "E" are stamped onto edge of case cover. See CASE MOUNTING DIMENSION table.

CASE MOUNTING DIMENSION

Code Letter [1]	In. (mm)
A	2.952-2.953 (74.98-75.01)
B	2.953-2.954 (75.01-75.03)
C	2.954-2.956 (75.03-75.08)
D	2.956-2.957 (75.08-75.11)
E	2.957-2.958 (75.11-75.13)

[1] – Letter stamped in edge of case cover.

4) Adjusting washers are selected by mounting dimension (from code letter stamped on edge of case cover) and dimension "L" in table. See ADJUSTING WASHER SELECTION table. Clearance should be 0-.0063" (0-.16 mm). Adjusting washers are available in 10 thicknesses. Reference numbers or letters are stamped on one ear of washer. See ADJUSTING WASHER SIZE table.

TOYOTA INTEGRAL HOUSING – EXCEPT VAN (Cont.)

ADJUSTING WASHER SIZE

Number or Letter [1]	In. (mm)
1 or A	.069 (1.76)
2 or B	.071 (1.80)
3 or C	.072 (1.84)
4 or D	.074 (1.88)
5 or E	.076 (1.92)
6 or F	.077 (1.96)
7 or G	.079 (2.00)
8 or H	.080 (2.04)
9 or J	.082 (2.08)
0 or K	.083 (2.12)

[1] – Code stamped on ear of adjusting washer.

5) Install in differential case one selected adjusting washer, thrust washer No. 1, thrust washer No. 2, side gear, clutch member thrust washer and left-hand clutch member in order as named. Do not install clutch member springs at this time. Install right-hand clutch member with pinion gear.

6) Install in case cover other selected adjusting washer, thrust washer No. 1, thrust washer No. 2, side gear and clutch member thrust washer. Assemble case and cover with "L" dimension measured parts and tighten bolts to 44-50 ft. lbs. (60-68 N.m).

7) Turn side gears with side gear shaft (after removal of snap ring from shaft) to ensure gears turn smoothly. Thrust washers must be changed if side gears do not turn smoothly. Remove cover from case and take out all internal parts.

8) Wash differential case, cover, and case bolts with strong degreasing solvent, such as trichloroethylene. Coat internal parts with LSD hypoid oil. Install one adjusting washer into case with oil groove away from case.

9) Install thrust washer No. 1, thrust washer No. 2, side gear, clutch member thrust washer (oil groove faces clutch member), left-hand clutch member, clutch member spring, and right-hand clutch member with pinion gears in case.

10) Install second adjusting washer in case cover with oil groove facing away from cover. Install thrust washer No. 1, thrust washer No. 2, side gear and clutch member thrust washer (with oil groove facing clutch member) in cover.

11) Place cover on case and align index marks. Apply locking compound to cover bolts. Tighten bolts evenly in diagonal sequence. Turn side gear with side gear shaft to ensure gears turn smoothly. Press side bearings onto differential case.

Drive Pinion Bearing Preload

1) Install front and rear bearing outer races into carrier. Press rear drive pinion bearing onto drive pinion with depth shim under bearing. Install drive pinion into carrier. Install front bearing.

NOTE: **Drive pinion preload is set in 2 stages. Initial adjustment is made without spacer, oil slinger or oil seal installed. Final adjustment is made after differential case is installed and ring and pinion backlash have been set.**

2) Install drive pinion flange and lightly grease threads of pinion flange nut. Install flange nut and adjust drive pinion preload by slowly tightening nut. Measure preload with torque wrench. Preload range is 10.4-16.5 INCH lbs. (1.17-1.86 N.m) for new bearings and 5.2-8.7 INCH lbs. (.6-1.0 N.m) for used bearings.

CAUTION: **As there is no spacer installed at this time, tighten pinion nut slowly until desired preload is obtained. Be careful not to overtighten.**

TOYOTA LIMITED SLIP DIFFERENTIAL ADJUSTING WASHER TABLE

Measurement "L" In. (mm)	REQUIRED ADJUSTING WASHERS FOR SPECIFIC DIFFERENTIAL CASE CODE				
	A	B	C	D	E
2.7878-2.7902 (70.81-70.84)	8 + 8 or H + H	8 + 9 or H + J	9 + 9 or J + J	9 + 9 or J + J	9 + 0 or J + K
2.7894-2.7902 (70.85-70.87)	7 + 8 or G + H	8 + 8 or H + H	8 + 9 or H + J	9 + 9 or H + H	9 + 9 or H + H
2.7905-2.7913 (70.88-70.90)	7 + 8 or G + H	7 + 8 or G + H	8 + 8 or H + H	8 + 9 or H + J	9 + 9 or J + J
2.7917-2.7925 (70.91-70.93)	7 + 7 or G + G	7 + 8 or G + H	7 + 8 or G + H	8 + 8 or H + H	8 + 9 or H + J
2.7929-2.2737 (70.94-70.96)	6 + 7 or F + G	7 + 7 or G + G	7 + 8 or G + H	7 + 8 or G + H	8 + 8 or H + H
2.7941-2.7949 (70.97-70.99)	6 + 6 or F + F	6 + 7 or F + G	7 + 7 or G + G	7 + 8 or G + H	7 + 8 or G + H
2.7953-2.7961 (71.00-71.02)	6 + 6 or F + F	6 + 6 or F + F	6 + 7 or F + G	7 + 7 or G + G	7 + 8 or G + H
2.7965-2.7972 (71.03-71.05)	5 + 6 or E + F	6 + 6 or F + F	6 + 6 or F + F	6 + 7 or F + G	7 + 7 or G + G
2.7976-2.7984 (71.06-71.08)	5 + 5 or E + E	5 + 6 or E + F	6 + 6 or F + F	6 + 6 or F + F	6 + 7 or F + G
2.7988-2.7996 (71.09-71.11)	4 + 5 or D + E	5 + 5 or E + E	5 + 6 or E + F	6 + 6 or F + F	6 + 6 or F + F
2.8000-2.8008 (71.12-71.14)	4 + 5 or D + E	4 + 5 or D + E	5 + 5 or E + E	5 + 6 or E + F	6 + 6 or F + F
2.8012-2.8020 (71.15-71.17)	4 + 4 or D + D	4 + 5 or D + E	4 + 5 or D + E	5 + 5 or E + E	5 + 6 or E + F
2.8024-2.8031 (71.18-71.20)	3 + 4 or C + D	4 + 4 or D + D	4 + 5 or D + E	4 + 5 or D + E	5 + 5 or E + E
2.8035-2.8043 (71.21-71.23)	3 + 3 or C + C	3 + 4 or C + D	4 + 4 or D + D	4 + 5 or D + E	4 + 5 or D + E
2.8047-2.8055 (71.24-71.26)	3 + 3 or C + C	3 + 3 or C + C	3 + 4 or C + D	4 + 4 or D + D	4 + 5 or D + E
2.8059-2.8067 (71.27-71.29)	2 + 3 or B + C	3 + 3 or B + C	3 + 3 or B + B	3 + 4 or B + C	4 + 4 or C + C
2.8071-2.8079 (71.30-71.32)	2 + 2 or B + B	2 + 3 or B + C	3 + 3 or B + B	3 + 3 or B + B	3 + 4 or B + C
2.8083-2.8090 (71.33-71.35)	1 + 2 or A + B	2 + 2 or B + B	2 + 3 or B + C	3 + 3 or C + C	3 + 3 or C + C
2.8094-2.8102 (71.36-71.38)	1 + 2 or A + B	1 + 2 or A + B	2 + 2 or B + B	2 + 3 or B + C	3 + 3 or C + C
2.8106-2.8114 (71.39-71.41)	1 + 1 or A + A	1 + 2 or A + B	1 + 2 or A + B	2 + 2 or B + B	2 + 3 or B + C

TOYOTA INTEGRAL HOUSING – EXCEPT VAN (Cont.)

3) Install differential case and adjust ring gear-to-drive pinion backlash. See RING GEAR BACKLASH & SIDE BEARING PRELOAD procedure in this article. Remove drive pinion flange and front bearing. Install new bearing spacer, front bearing, oil slinger, and oil seal. Install drive pinion flange and tighten pinion nut.

4) Check total differential preload. Range for total preload is measured drive pinion preload plus 3.5-5.2 INCH lbs. (.40-.59 N.m). Check that drive pinion flange longitudinal and latitudinal runout do not exceed .004" (.10 mm). Stake drive pinion nut. Drive side gear shaft oil seal into carrier until flush.

5) Coat oil seal lips with grease and replace snap ring on side gear shaft. Drive side gear shaft in until it contacts pinion shaft. Measure side gear runout at flange with dial indicator. Replace side gear shaft if runout exceeds .008" (.20 mm). Install differential carrier cover with new gasket and tighten bolts.

NOTE: Since shaft cannot be checked visually on LSD models, ensure that shaft is seated by change in sound made by hammer blow after shaft bottoms out.

Ring Gear Backlash & Side Bearing Preload

1) Place bearing outer races on respective bearings and install differential case into carrier. Install plate washer only on back side of ring gear (behind teeth). Tap ring gear with plastic hammer to seat washer and bearing.

2) Install a dial indicator with plunger on tooth surface of ring gear. Apply downward pressure on side bearing boss. Measure ring gear-to-drive pinion backlash. Reference backlash should be .004" (.10 mm).

3) Select a ring gear (back side) plate washer using backlash as reference. Select a ring gear (tooth side) washer just thick enough to eliminate clearance between outer race and case. Remove plate washers and case from carrier.

4) Install plate washer into lower part of carrier. Place other plate washer on differential case with outer race. Install case assembly into carrier housing. Seat washer and bearing by tapping ring gear with plastic hammer. Measure ring gear backlash with dial indicator.

5) Backlash should be .005-.007" (.13-.18 mm) on all differentials. Adjust backlash by increasing or decreasing washers on both sides by equal amounts. There should be no clearance between plate washer and case. Ring gear backlash must exist at all times.

6) After adjustment of plate washers has been made, remove ring gear (tooth side) washer and measure thickness. Install washer .002-.004" (.05-.10 mm) thicker than washer removed.

NOTE: Select washer which can be pressed 2/3 of way in by finger.

7) Using a plastic hammer, tap washer in place. Recheck ring gear backlash. Backlash range is .005-.007" (.13-.18 mm). Adjust as necessary. Align index marks on caps and carrier. Install cap bolts and tighten to 58 ft. lbs. (78 N.m).

8) Measure total preload. Total preload must equal drive pinion preload plus 3.5-5.2 INCH lbs. (.40-.59 N.m). Coat 3 or 4 teeth at 3 different positions on ring gear with Red lead.

9) Hold companion flange firmly and rotate ring gear in both directions. Inspect gear tooth contact pattern. Adjust as necessary by changing shims on drive pinion. See GEAR TOOTH PATTERNS article in this section.

AXLE ASSEMBLY SPECIFICATIONS

Application	In. (mm)
Stub Axle Flange Runout	.008 (.20)
Drive Pinion Flange Runout	
Longitudinal	.004 (.10)
Latitudinal	.004 (.10)
Ring Gear Backlash	
Front Axle	.002-.008 (.05-.20)
Rear Axle	.005-.007 (.13-.18)
Ring Gear Runout	.003 (.07)
Side Gear Backlash	.002-.008 (.05-.20)
Side Gear Shaft Runout	.008 (.20)
	INCH Lbs. (N.m)
Drive Pinion Preload	
New Bearings	10.4-16.5 (1.2-1.9)
Used Bearings	5.2-8.7 (.6-1.0)
Assembled Preload [1]	3.5-5.2 (.40-.59)
Stub Axle Bearing Preload	.9-3.5 (.1-.4)

[1] – Add this amount to drive pinion preload to obtain total preload which is sum of drive pinion preload and side bearing preload.

SEAL DEPTH

Application	In. (mm)
Drive Pinion Seal	.06 (1.5)
Inner Stub Axle Seal	
Cressida	1.22 (31.0)
Outer Stub Axle Seal	
Cressida	.217 (5.5)
Side Gear Shaft Seal	Flush with Case

TIGHTENING SPECIFICATIONS

Application	Ft. Lbs. (N.m)
Differential Carrier Bolts	35 (47)
Drive Pinion Flange Nut	
4Runner	80 (108)
All Other Models	80-174 (108-236)
Propeller Shaft Flange Bolts	
Cressida	31 (42)
Supra	54 (74)
4Runner	54 (74)
Ring Gear Bolts	71 (97)
Side Bearing Cap Bolts	58 (78)
Stub Axle Flange Nut	51 (69)

TOYOTA INTEGRAL HOUSING – VAN

Van 4WD (Front)

DESCRIPTION

Drive axle assembly is hypoid type with integral carrier housing. Drive pinion bearing preload adjustment is made with collapsible spacer between front and rear pinion bearing inner races. Differential side bearing preload and drive pinion depth adjustment are made by shims.

Driving power is transmitted to stub axles by drive axles with Constant Velocity (CV) joints at each end. Gear shafts are supported in carrier by roller bearings.

AXLE RATIO & IDENTIFICATION

Integral carrier type drive axle may be identified by inspection cover on front of carrier housing. *See Fig. 1*. To determine axle ratio, divide number of ring gear teeth by number of pinion gear teeth.

REMOVAL & INSTALLATION

FRONT WHEEL BEARINGS

NOTE: See LOCKING HUBS article in this section.

FRONT GEAR SHAFT & OIL SEAL

Removal

Remove carrier cover. Disconnect front drive shaft from front gear shaft. Remove snap ring retaining gear shaft to differential. Remove gear shaft. Remove differential tube (if equipped). Using Puller (09308-00010), remove oil seal.

Installation

Apply grease to oil seal and install. Install differential tube (if equipped). Using slide hammer, install front gear shaft. Install new snap ring on front gear shaft.

PINION FLANGE SEAL

Removal

1) Index propeller shaft to drive pinion flange and remove propeller shaft. Remove drive pinion flange nut. Using Puller (09557-22022), remove drive pinion flange.

2) Using Seal Remover (09308-10010), remove oil seal from housing and remove oil slinger. Using Puller (09556-22010), remove rear bearing from housing. Remove collapsible bearing spacer and discard.

Installation

1) Install new spacer with large end towards differential and front bearing. Install oil slinger. Apply grease to seal lips. Using Installer (09554-22010), install new oil seal to a depth of .079" (2.0 mm). Install flange and lightly coat drive pinion threads with grease.

2) Install flange nut and hold flange. Tighten nut to 80 ft. lbs. (108 N.m) and measure preload. See AXLE ASSEMBLY SPECIFICATIONS table at end of this article. If preload is lower than specification, tighten nut in increments of 108 INCH lbs. (12 N.m) until preload is correct without exceeding maximum torque. See TIGHTENING SPECIFICATIONS table at end of this article.

3) Check longitudinal and latitudinal runout of drive pinion flange with dial indicator. Stake drive pinion nut. Align index marks on propeller shaft and pinion flange. Tighten bolts.

Fig. 1: Differential Assembly

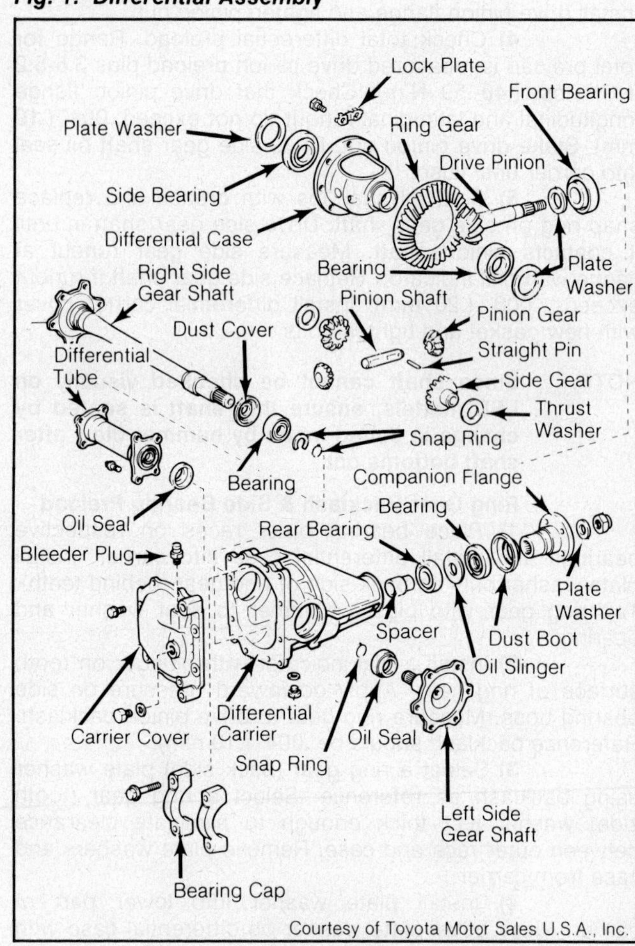

Courtesy of Toyota Motor Sales U.S.A., Inc.

DIFFERENTIAL CARRIER

Removal

Drain gear oil. Disconnect drive axles from side gear shaft flanges. Index propeller shaft to drive pinion flange. Disconnect propeller shaft. Remove engine splash shield. Remove bolts retaining differential carrier assembly to chassis supports. Lower differential carrier and crossmember from vehicle.

Installation

To install, reverse removal procedure. Tighten mounting bolts to specifications. See TIGHTENING SPECIFICATIONS table in this article. Align index marks on propeller shaft and drive pinion flange. Tighten bolts. Install drain plug and fill with hypoid oil.

OVERHAUL

NOTE: For overhaul information on 4Runner front drive axles, see FWD AXLE SHAFTS article in this section.

TOYOTA INTEGRAL HOUSING – VAN (Cont.)

NOTE: **Inspection of ring gear backlash and gear tooth contact prior to disassembly can indicate where problem may exist. See GEAR TOOTH PATTERNS article in this section.**

DISASSEMBLY

Carrier & Pinion Shaft

1) Check axle shaft deviation. Remove differential carrier cover. Remove side gear shaft and oil seal. Check ring gear runout and backlash. Check gear tooth contact pattern. Check side gear backlash while holding one pinion gear toward case. If side gear backlash is not within specification thrust washers should be replaced.

2) Measure drive pinion total preload. Put alignment marks on bearing cap and differential carrier. Remove side bearing caps. Remove side bearing preload adjusting plate washers.

3) Measure plate washers and record thicknesses. Remove differential case and ring gear. Remove differential case side bearing outer races. Place reference marks on parts for installation in their original position.

4) Hold drive pinion flange and remove pinion nut. Remove drive pinion flange and oil seal. Remove oil slinger, front bearing and collapsible spacer. Remove drive pinion from differential carrier. Press rear bearing from pinion shaft.

5) Drive front and rear drive pinion bearing outer races from carrier. Inspect bearings, outer races and pinion shaft for damage and replace if needed. Ring gear and drive pinion are a matched set, and must be replaced together. Discard collapsible spacer.

Differential

1) Remove side bearings from case with puller. Keep side bearings with correct outer races and mark for reassembly. Put alignment marks on ring gear and differential case. Remove ring gear bolts and locking tabs. Remove ring gear by tapping on gear with a plastic hammer.

2) Using hammer and punch, drive out lock pin holding pinion shaft to case. Remove pinion shaft, pinion gears, side gears and thrust washers. Thoroughly clean and inspect all parts for wear or damage. Repair or replace parts as necessary.

REASSEMBLY & ADJUSTMENT

Differential

1) Install side gears and thrust washers in differential case. Thrust washers should be same size for both sides if possible. Install pinion gears with thrust washers and tap pinion shaft into place. Check side gear backlash while holding one pinion gear toward case.

2) If backlash is incorrect, change thickness of thrust washers until backlash is within specification. See AXLE ASSEMBLY SPECIFICATION table at end of this article. Install lock pin through case and hole in pinion shaft. Stake pin to differential case. Press side bearings onto case.

3) Clean contact surfaces of differential case. Heat ring gear to 212°F (100°C) in oil bath. Clean ring gear contact surface with solvent and install on case while still hot. Align index marks on ring gear and case. Coat ring gear bolts with hypoid oil and install with lock plates.

CAUTION: Do not heat ring gear above 230°F (110°C).

4) Tighten ring gear bolts gradually in diagonal sequence. Stake lock plates with one tab flush against flat of bolt head. Tab resting on point should be staked on tightening side of point.

Carrier & Pinion Shaft

1) Install front and rear bearing outer races into carrier. Press rear drive pinion bearing onto drive pinion with depth shim under bearing. Install drive pinion into carrier. Install front bearing.

NOTE: **Drive pinion preload is set in 2 stages. Initial adjustment is made without spacer, oil slinger or oil seal installed. Final adjustment is made after differential case is installed and ring and pinion backlash have been set.**

2) Install drive pinion flange and lightly grease threads of pinion flange nut. Install flange nut and adjust drive pinion preload by slowly tightening nut. Measure preload with torque wrench. Preload range is 10-16 INCH lbs. (1.0-1.6 N.m) for new bearings and 5.2-8.7 INCH lbs. (.6-1.0 N.m) for used bearings.

3) Install differential case and adjust ring gear-to-drive pinion backlash. Remove drive pinion flange and front bearing. Install new bearing spacer with large end toward differential. Install front bearing, oil slinger, and oil seal. Install drive pinion flange and tighten pinion nut.

4) Check total differential preload and adjust if necessary. Check gear tooth pattern. See GEAR TOOTH PATTERNS article in this section. Check that drive pinion flange runout do not exceed specification. Stake drive pinion nut. Drive side gear shaft oil seal into carrier until flush.

5) Measure side gear runout at flange. Install differential carrier cover with new gasket and tighten bolts.

AXLE ASSEMBLY SPECIFICATIONS

Application	In. (mm)
Drive Pinion Flange Runout	.004 (.10)
Pinion Oil Seal Depth	.79 (2.0)
Pinion-to-Ring Gear Backlash	.005-.070 (.13-.18)
Side Gear Shaft Deviation	.004 (.10)
Side Gear Backlash	.002-.008 (.05-.20)
	INCH Lbs. (N.m)
Drive Pinion Preload	
Starting (Without Differential)	
New Bearings	9-14 (1.0-1.6)
Used Bearings	4.5-7 (.5-.8)
Total (With Differential)	
New Bearings	11.6-18 (.7-2.0)
Used Bearings	7-11 (.8-1.2)

TIGHTENING SPECIFICATIONS

Application	Ft. Lbs. (N.m)
Differential Bearing Cap Bolts	58 (79)
Differential Tube Bolts	65 (88)
Carrier Cover Bolts	34 (46)
Drive Pinion Flange Nut	80 (108)
Propeller Shaft Flange Nuts	31 (42)
Ring Gear Bolts	71 (97)
Side Bearing Cap Bolts	58 (78)
Stub Axle Flange Nuts	50 (67)

TOYOTA SEPARATE CARRIER

Corolla RWD, Cressida, Land Cruiser, Pickup (Rear), Tercel 4WD (Rear), Van, 4Runner (Rear)

NOTE: Cab and chassis models will be referred to as C & C within this article.

DESCRIPTION

The axle assembly is a hypoid gear type with a separate carrier housing. Limited slip differential is available in Corolla (RWD), Cressida and Land Cruiser models. One-piece differential cases use 2 pinion gears. Two-piece differential cases use 4 pinion gears.

Differential side bearing preload is set with adjusting nuts on all models. Pinion bearing preload can be set with either a solid spacer and adjusting shim or with a collapsible spacer.

AXLE RATIO & IDENTIFICATION

Toyota uses only one basic type of separate carrier axle assembly. Any differences in removal, installation or overhaul procedures between vehicle models will be noted where they occur. To determine axle ratio, divide number of ring gear teeth by number of pinion gear teeth.

REMOVAL & INSTALLATION

FRONT AXLE SHAFTS & BEARINGS

NOTE: On vehicles equipped with locking hubs, refer to LOCKING HUBS article in this section. Ensure locking knob is set to "FREE" position before removal.

Fig. 1: Exploded View of Front Axle Shaft Assembly (Land Cruiser)

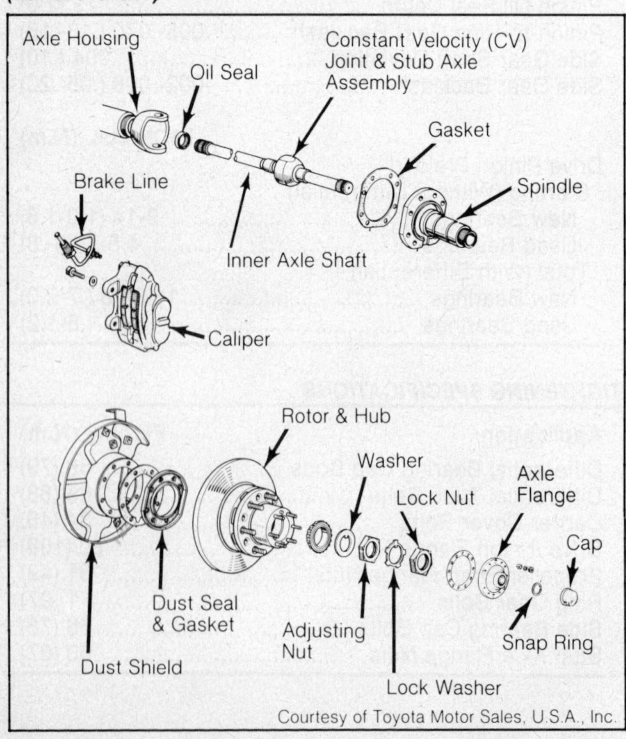

Removal (Land Cruiser)

1) Raise and support vehicle. Remove wheel and tire assembly. Disconnect brake line at brake caliper and remove caliper assembly. Remove dust cover and snap ring. *See Fig. 1.* Remove axle flange cone washers with punch.

2) Install bolts in threaded flange holes and turn bolts equally to remove axle flange. Release lock plate and remove outer lock nut. Remove lock plate and bearing adjusting nut. Remove outer bearing and thrust washer. Remove axle hub with disc.

3) To remove inner wheel bearing, pry out oil seal and remove bearing. Drive outer bearing races from hub. Replace if necessary. Remove dust shield retaining bolts. Remove dust seal, gasket and shield. Remove spindle assembly by tapping with a brass drift. Remove gasket.

NOTE: DO NOT disconnect steering knuckle. Front end alignment and knuckle bearing preload settings will be affected and require readjustment.

4) Position one flat of Constant Velocity (CV) joint so it is pointing upward. Remove axle shaft assembly. Clean assembly with solvent.

Installation

1) Install axle shaft with one flat of CV joint pointing upward. Pack steering knuckle cavity with grease to about 3/4 of knuckle volume. Install spindle on knuckle with new gasket.

2) Put dust cover, new gasket and dust seal on spindle. Tighten 8 spindle mounting bolts. Pack front hub bearings with multi-purpose grease and coat inside of hub also. Place inner bearing in hub and drive oil seal into hub. Lightly coat lips of seal with grease.

3) Install axle hub on spindle. Install outer bearing and thrust washer. Tighten adjusting nut to 43 ft. lbs. (58 N.m) with Spanner (09607-60020). Rotate hub several times in each direction. Loosen adjusting nut until hand tight. Retighten adjusting nut to 35-60 INCH lbs. (4.0-6.8 N.m).

4) Check starting preload with spring scale. If preload is within range of 6.2-12.6 lbs. (2.8-5.7 kg), install lock washer and lock nut. Tighten lock nut to 58-72 ft. lbs. (79-98 N.m) and secure by bending one tab of lock washer in and one tab out.

5) Place gasket on hub and install flange or locking hub. Install cone washers and nuts. Tighten nuts evenly. If using flange, pull stub axle shaft out of hub far enough to install snap ring. Install dust cap.

REAR AXLE SHAFTS

NOTE: Land Cruiser models with semi-floating rear axles require removal of axle housing inspection cover BEFORE attempting removal of axle shaft.

Removal (Land Cruiser – Semi-Floating)

Raise and support vehicle. Remove tire, wheel, and brake drum. Drain axle housing and remove inspection cover. *See Fig. 2.* Remove differential pinion shaft lock pin. Remove pinion shaft and spacer. Push axle shaft to center of vehicle and remove axle lock circlip. Remove axle shaft.

TOYOTA SEPARATE CARRIER (Cont.)

Fig. 2: Exploded View of Land Cruiser Semi-Floating Rear Axle Shaft Assembly

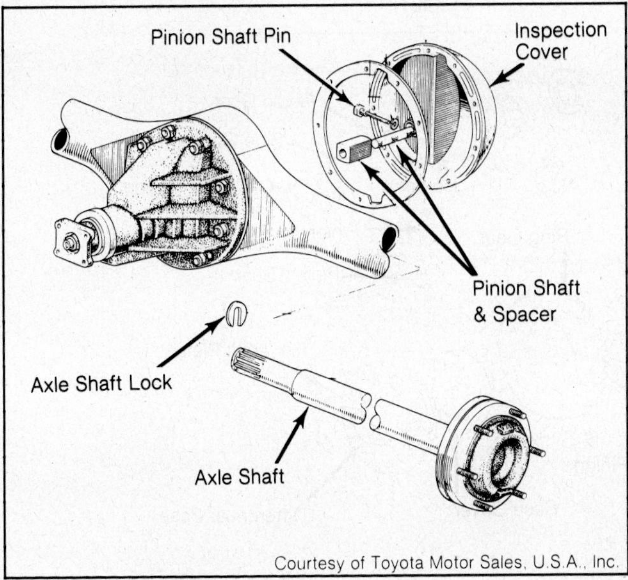

Courtesy of Toyota Motor Sales, U.S.A., Inc.

Installation

To install, reverse removal procedure. Check axle shaft end thrust clearance. Select pinion shaft spacer that gives maximum clearance of .020" (.50 mm). Fill differential with hypoid gear oil. Use limited slip additive if equipped with limited slip differential.

Removal & Installation (Land Cruiser & Pickup W/Dual Wheels – Full Floating)

Remove axle flange nuts. Using punch, remove lock washer cones. Use bolts in threaded flange holes to remove axle shaft. Remove oil seal with puller. To install, replace flange gasket and oil seal. Reverse removal procedure.

Removal (Pickup W/Single Wheel & 4Runner)

1) Raise and support vehicle. Remove tire assembly. Drain differential housing. Remove parking brake cable guide clip and clamp bolt at crossmember and frame.

2) Disconnect parking brake cable from intermediate lever on 2WD models. *See Fig. 3*. On 4WD models, remove pin and disconnect parking brake rear cable from bellcrank. Disconnect and cap brake line at wheel cylinder. Remove brake drum mounting bolts and drum.

3) Remove 4 nuts attaching backing plate to axle housing. Remove axle shaft and backing plate. Remove axle shaft snap ring. Remove and discard "O" ring. Press out axle shaft from backing plate. Remove bearing retainer.

Installation

To install, reverse removal procedure. Install new "O" ring and fill differential with gear oil. Ensure bearing retainer is installed with flat unbeveled edge toward bearing.

Removal (All Others)

1) Raise and support vehicle. Remove tire assembly and brake drum. On models with rear disc brakes, remove caliper and disc brake rotor. On all models, working through hole in axle flange, remove bearing retainer-to-axle housing bolts.

Fig. 3: Exploded View of Pickup & 4Runner Rear Axle

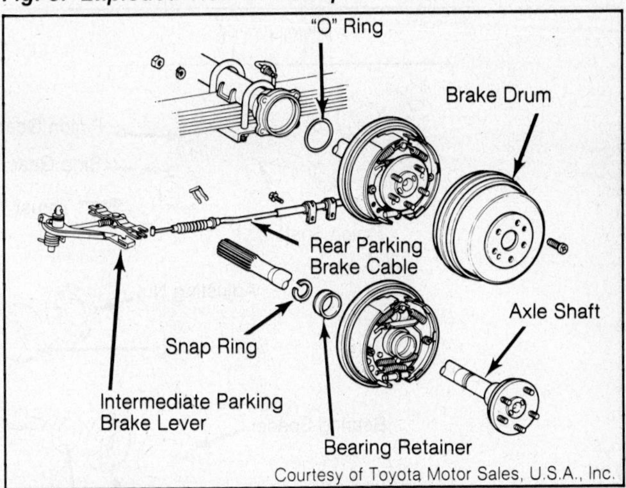

Courtesy of Toyota Motor Sales, U.S.A., Inc.

2) Using a slide hammer, remove shaft from housing, taking care not to damage axle seal. If axle housing seal is being replaced, coat sealing lip with grease before installing. See AXLE SEAL DEPTH table in this article.

Installation

To install, reverse removal procedure. *See Fig. 6*. Ensure that notches in bearing retainer and retainer gasket(s) are positioned correctly. *See Fig. 4*. Use new lock nuts for retainer and backing plate.

Fig. 4: Exploded View of Rear Axle Shaft

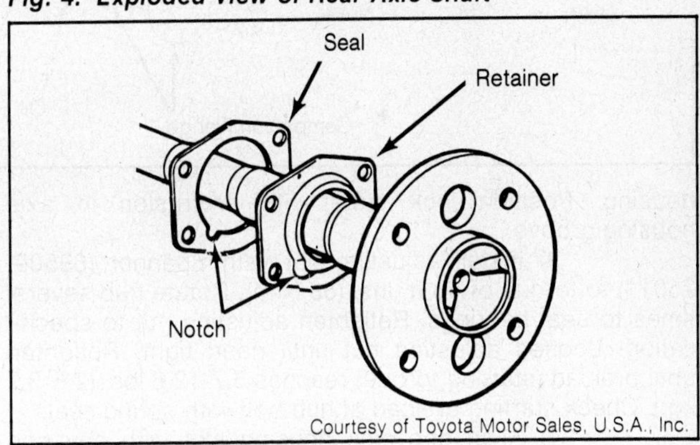

Courtesy of Toyota Motor Sales, U.S.A., Inc.

REAR AXLE BEARINGS

Removal (Pickup W/Dual Wheels & Land Cruiser)

1) Raise and support vehicle. Remove axle shafts. On models with semi-floating axles, use puller to remove axle bearing and oil seal together.

2) On models with full floating axles, remove lock screws from bearing adjusting nut. Remove adjusting nut with Spanner (09509-25011). Remove lock plate. Remove hub assembly with bearings. Remove oil seal and inner bearing. Replace bearings and seals if worn or damaged.

Installation

1) On models with semi-floating axles, drive bearing and new oil seal into housing. Coat lip of seal with grease.

2) On models with full floating axles, pack bearings and inner walls of hub with multipurpose grease. Install new seal and place hub with bearings on axle

TOYOTA SEPARATE CARRIER (Cont.)

Fig. 5: Exploded View of Toyota Conventional Rear Differential Assembly

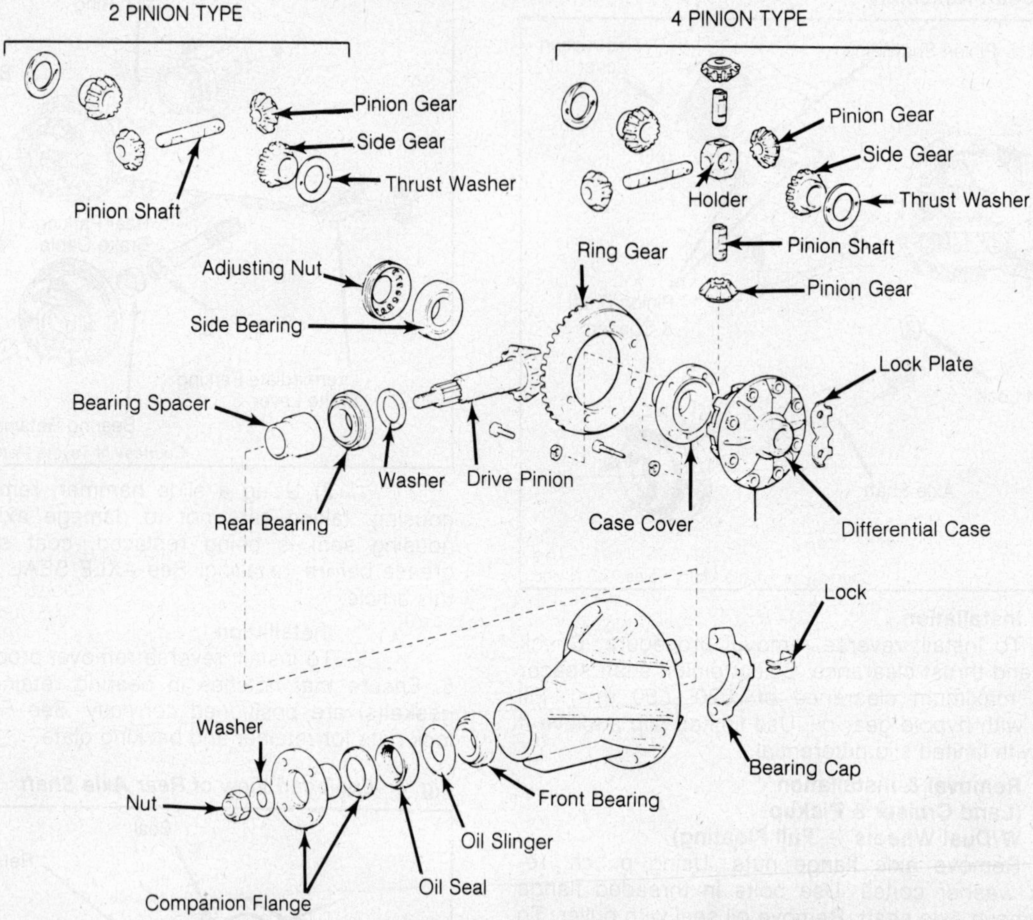

Courtesy of Toyota Motor Sales, U.S.A., Inc.

housing. Position lock plate with protrusion in axle housing groove.

3) Install adjusting nut with Spanner (09509-25011) to torque of 43 ft. lbs. (58 N.m). Rotate hub several times to seat bearings. Retighten adjusting nut to specification. Loosen adjusting nut until hand tight. Retighten until preload (starting torque) reaches 5.7-12.6 lbs. (2.6-5.7 kg.). Check starting preload at hub bolt with spring scale.

4) Align one axle housing slot with any one adjusting nut slot. Install lock screws into holes which are at right angles to aligned slots. Tighten lock screws to 35-60 INCH lbs. (4.0-6.8 N.m). Recheck starting preload. Install rear axle shaft.

Removal (Pickup W/Single Wheels & 4Runner)

Remove rear axle and brake backing plate. Press rear axle out of backing plate after removing snap ring. Remove outer oil seal. Press old bearing from backing plate.

Installation

1) Press new bearing into backing plate. Drive new oil seal into bearing case. Insert backing plate and bearing retainer on axle shaft.

2) Ensure unbeveled edge of retainer faces bearing. Press rear axle shaft into backing plate. Install snap ring. Install rear axle shaft in housing. Fill differential with gear oil.

Fig. 6: Exploded View of Rear Axle Assembly (All Models Except Pickup & 4Runner)

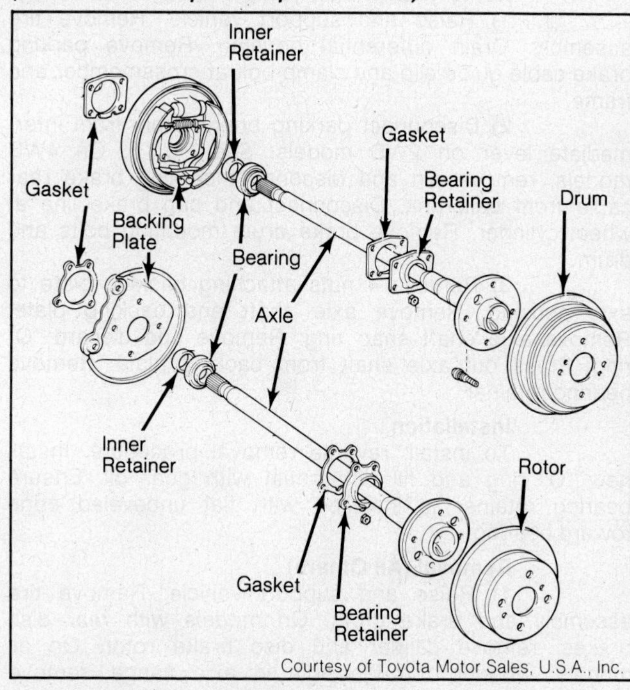

Courtesy of Toyota Motor Sales, U.S.A., Inc.

TOYOTA SEPARATE CARRIER (Cont.)

Removal & Installation (All Others)

1) To remove bearing, grind part way through bearing retainer ring, using caution not to damage axle shaft. Cut remaining portion of retaining ring off using a cold chisel. Remove split retaining ring and press bearing off shaft. Remove spacer and oil seal.

2) To install, place outer retainer and bearing onto shaft. Press bearing onto axle shaft. Heat new inner bearing retainer to about 300°F (150°C) in oil bath. Press into place with unbeveled edge of retainer toward bearing.

3) Place gasket(s) into position so when shaft is installed, gasket(s) will be between bearing retainer and backing plate. Ensure notched portion of retainer and gaskets are installed in position shown. *See Fig. 5.*

4) Coat new axle oil seal with grease and install to correct depth in housing (distance measured from outer face of seal to shoulder of housing). See AXLE SEAL DEPTH table. Install axle shaft, checking alignment of gaskets. Tighten new lock nuts.

AXLE SEAL DEPTH

Application [1]	In. (mm)
Corolla RWD	
Drum Brake	.23 (5.9)
Disc Brake	.20 (5.0)
Cressida & Van	.24 (6.0)
Pickup [2] & 4Runner	Flush
Tercel	.22 (5.6)

[1] - No seal depth given for Land Cruiser.
[2] - Single rear wheel Pickup models.

PINION SEAL REPLACEMENT (ON-VEHICLE)

Removal

1) Place reference marks on propeller shaft and drive pinion flange. Set parking brake. Disconnect propeller shaft. Loosen staked portion of pinion shaft nut. Install Spanner Wrench (09330-00021) on pinion flange and remove nut.

2) Using Puller (09557-22022), remove pinion flange. *See Fig. 7.* Remove oil seal. On Cressida and Tercel, remove oil slinger. Remove front bearing. Remove collapsible spacer.

NOTE: Toyota recommends installing new collapsible spacer whenever oil seal is replaced.

Installation

1) To install, reverse removal procedure. Apply grease to seal lip and install to proper depth. See PINION SEAL DEPTH table. Apply grease to seal lip. Install pinion flange. Install new nut after lightly greasing threads. Check and adjust pinion preload. See PINION BEARING PRELOAD and TOTAL PRELOAD SPECIFICATIONS tables in this article.

2) If preload is insufficient, gradually tighten nut in increments of 5-10 degrees, until preload is obtained. If preload is exceeded, replace bearing spacer. To complete installation, reverse removal procedure. Add lubricant as required.

Fig. 7: Removing Pinion Flange

PINION SEAL DEPTH [1]

Application	In. (mm)
Corolla RWD	
6.4" Ring Gear	0-.02 (0-0.5)
6.7" Ring Gear	.18 (.5)
Cressida	.04 (1.0)
Land Cruiser	.04 (1.0)
Pickup & 4Runner	
2WD	.06 (1.5)
1 Ton, C & C & 4WD	.04 (1.0)
Tercel & Van	.04 (1.0)

[1] - No pinion seal depth is given for Land Cruiser.

DIFFERENTIAL CARRIER

Removal

Drain oil from axle housing. Remove wheels. Index propeller shaft to pinion flange and remove propeller shaft. Remove axle shafts as previously described. Loosen bolts and remove differential carrier.

NOTE: DO NOT damage oil seal during removal of axle shaft if seal is to be reused.

Installation

To install, reverse removal procedure. Coat both sides of carrier-to-housing gasket with sealer before installation. Fill axle housing with gear oil. Use limited slip additive on models with limited slip differentials.

OVERHAUL

FRONT AXLE SHAFT & SPINDLE

Disassembly (Land Cruiser)

1) Mount spindle in vise. Remove bushing with puller. Install new bushing with press. Inspect axle shaft for wear or damage. Carefully inspect constant velocity (CV) joint for rust, dirt or excessive looseness.

2) Mount inner axle shaft in a vise with CV joint pointing upward. Place a brass drift against CV joint inner race and drive CV joint off inner shaft. Do not allow CV joint to drop. Remove snap rings from inner axle shaft. Tilt cage and inner race outward from housing.

TOYOTA SEPARATE CARRIER (Cont.)

Fig. 8: Removing & Installing CV Joint Cage & Inner Race

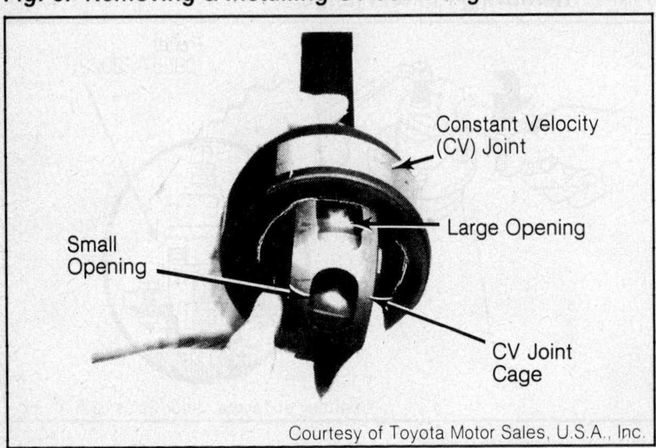

3) Remove 6 ball bearings one at a time. Turn cage and inner race 90 degrees from outer CV joint race. Align 2 larger openings of cage with 2 protrusions of outer CV joint race. Remove inner race and cage. Separate by turning inner race perpendicular to large cage openings and pulling out. *See Figs. 8 and 9.*

Fig. 9: Exploded View of CV Joint Cage & Inner Race

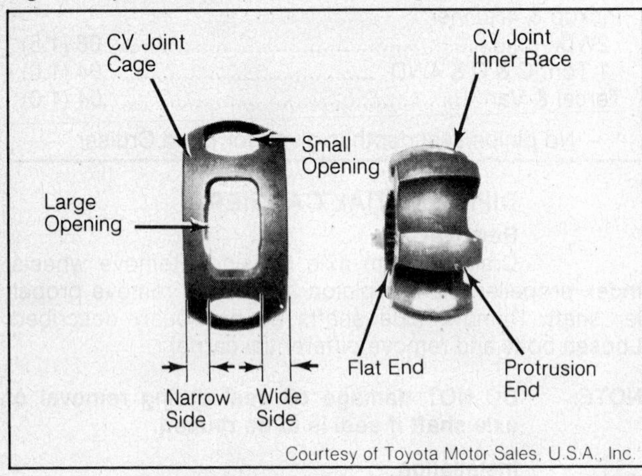

Reassembly

1) Coat inner race, cage and balls with MOS^2 grease. Reverse disassembly procedure. Ensure protruding end of inner race is covered by wide portion of cage during reassembly.

2) When installing inner race and cage into outer race, wide side of cage must face outward. Fit 6 balls into cage. After reassembly, pack stub axle end with lithium base grease.

3) Install new snap rings on axle shaft. *See Fig. 10.* Insert inner axle shaft into CV joint inner race, keeping inner snap ring compressed.

DIFFERENTIAL

NOTE: **Overhaul 4WD front differentials using same procedure as described for rear differentials.**

Case Disassembly (Conventional)

1) Mount carrier in holding fixture. Before disassembling differential, check tooth contact pattern, ring gear runout (measured at back of gear in 4 places), ring gear-to-drive pinion backlash and total drive preload. Record readings.

Fig. 10: Installing Inner Axle Shaft to CV Joint

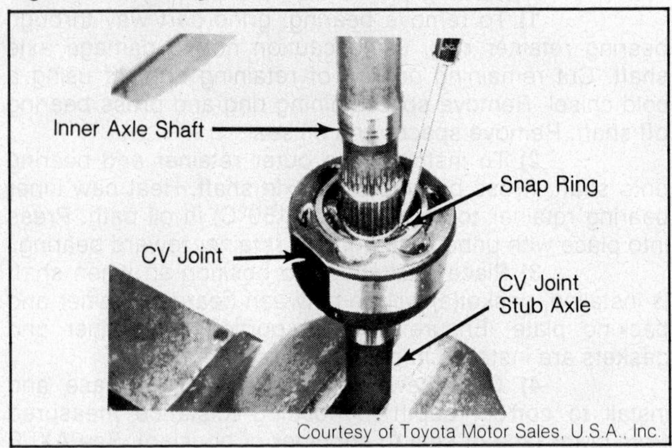

2) Loosen staked portion of pinion shaft nut. Install holder and remove nut. Using flange puller, remove pinion flange. Remove oil seal, bearing and slinger. *See Fig. 5.* Record position and number of shims removed during disassembly.

3) Mark left and right side bearing caps for reassembly reference. Remove adjusting nut lock bolts. Remove side bearing bolts, caps and adjusting nuts.

NOTE: **Mark all left and right side bearing components for reassembly reference.**

4) Remove differential case assembly with side bearings. Remove drive pinion and mount in holder. Using puller, remove rear pinion bearing. Press out front and rear pinion bearing outer races.

5) Remove side bearings from differential case. Index ring gear to case. Remove ring gear bolt lock plates and bolts. Mount case assembly in vise so ring gear teeth are pointed down.

6) Tap ring gear from case using a soft faced hammer. On 2-pinion differentials, remove pinion gear shaft retaining pin and drive out gear shaft. Remove pinion gears, side gears and thrust washers.

7) On 4-pinion differentials, index differential case cover to case. Remove cover attaching bolts. Drive out 3 pinion shafts. Remove pinion gears, pinion shaft holder, side gears and thrust washer(s).

NOTE: **Three longer differential cover bolts are used to secure pinion shafts in 4-pinion differentials.**

Case Reassembly

1) Lubricate all components with hypoid gear lubricant. On 2-pinion models, assemble side gears and pinion gears into differential case. Ensure oil groove faces towards gear (if present on side gear thrust washer).

2) On 4-pinion models, install side gears, thrust washers, differential pinions, pinion shaft holder, differential shaft and pinion shaft. Install differential case cover, aligning index marks, and tighten bolts. Note location of 3 longer bolts (pinion shaft bolts).

3) Check backlash between side gears and pinion gears. See AXLE ASSEMBLY SPECIFICATIONS table in this article. If not to specification, install selective fit thrust washers. Install equal thickness thrust washers on each side (if possible).

4) Press differential side bearings onto differential case. Heat ring gear in oil bath to approximately

TOYOTA SEPARATE CARRIER (Cont.)

Fig. 11: Installing Side Bearing On Differential Case

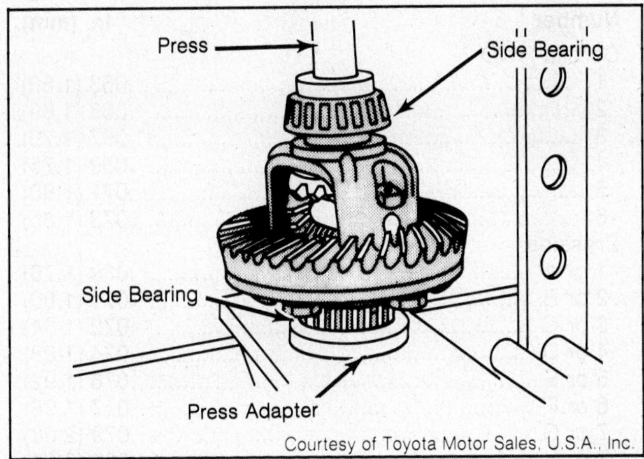

Courtesy of Toyota Motor Sales, U.S.A., Inc.

212°F (100°C). Wipe off gear and press onto differential case.

NOTE: DO NOT heat ring gear above 230°F (110°C).

5) Install and tighten bolts evenly. Bend over lock tabs. Install differential case assembly on differential carrier. Measure ring gear runout.

Case Disassembly (Limited Slip - Corolla, Cressida)

1) Index mark left and right case halves for reassembly. Loosen through bolts in diagonal sequence. Heat assembly in oil at 302°F (150°C) to ease bolt removal. Open case and remove side gears with thrust washers, clutch plates and adjusting plates. Keep left and right side components separate and mark for reassembly in same order. *See Figs. 12 and 13.*

2) Remove pinion gears and thrust washers from shafts. Remove compression springs and retainers from differential spider. Check compression spring free length. See AXLE ASSEMBLY SPECIFICATIONS table at end of this article. Measure clutch plates and side gear thrust washers for wear. The wear limit is .069" (1.74 mm) for both plates and washers.

Inspection

1) Check clearance between differential case and left-hand clutch member. *See Fig. 13*. Replace worn parts.

DIFFERENTIAL CASE DIMENSIONS

Application	In. (mm)
Corolla	
Clutch Member "A"	36.975-36.995 (1.4557-1.4565)
Differential Case "B"	37.00-37.025 (1.4567-1.4577)
Clearance	.005-.050 (.0002-.002)
Cressida	
Clutch Member "A"	41.975-42.000 (1.6526-1.6535)
Differential Case "B"	42.000-42.025 (1.6535-1.6545)
Clearance	0-.050 (0-.002)

2) Check side gear thrust washers for heat damage or excessive wear. Check springs for tension. If side gear or clutch member needs to be replaced, corresponding thrust washer must also be replaced. Reused parts must be installed in original position.

Fig. 12: Exploded View of Corolla RWD & Cressida Limited Slip Differential

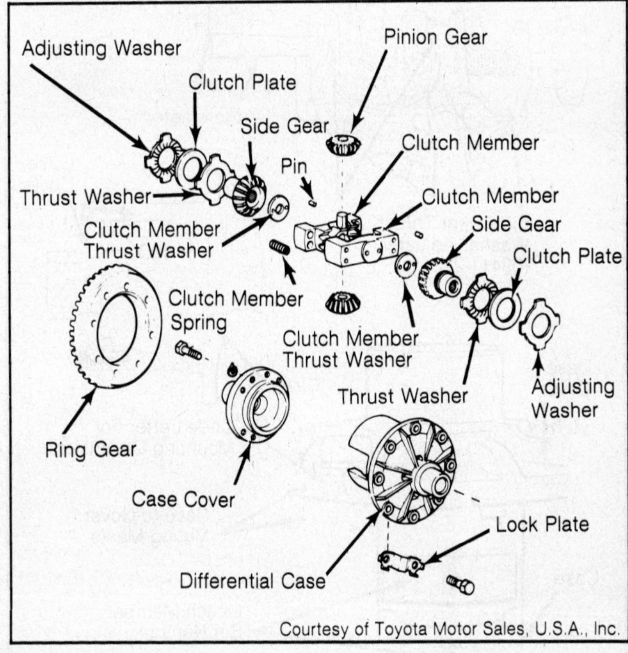

Courtesy of Toyota Motor Sales, U.S.A., Inc.

Fig. 13: Measuring Clutch Member-to-Case Clearance

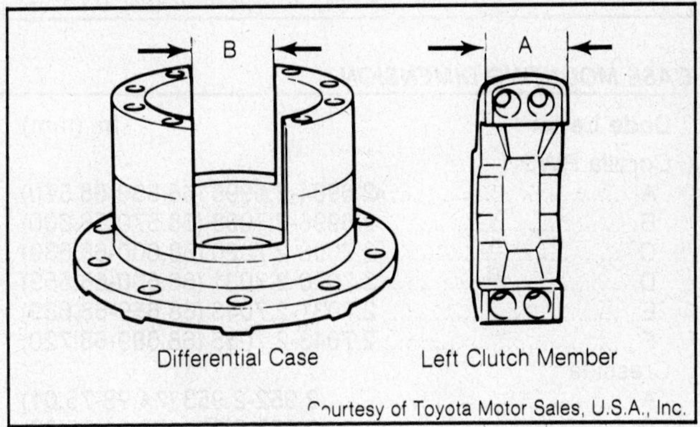

Courtesy of Toyota Motor Sales, U.S.A., Inc.

Case Reassembly

1) Side gear thrust clearance (axial clearance inside case) must be determined first. Clean all parts. Set up Side Gear Thrust Washer Adjuster (09411-22011) and install parts in order. DO NOT assemble adjusting washers or clutch member springs at this time.

2) Loosen clamping nut on adjuster and hold parts with spring tension of adjuster. Measure "L" dimension with micrometer. Dimension "L" is assembled distance from outer face of left outer thrust washer to outer face of right outer thrust washer. *See Fig. 14.*

3) Ensure parts are aligned in adjuster and measure "L" dimension several times. Take average of readings. Differential case mounting dimension is coded into case at time of manufacture. Code letters are stamped onto edge of case cover. See CASE MOUNTING DIMENSION table.

4) Adjusting washers are selected by correlating mounting dimension (from code letter stamped on edge of case cover) and dimension "L" in table. See ADJUSTING WASHER SIZE table. Clearance should be .002-.006 (.05-.15 mm). Adjusting washers are available. Reference numbers are stamped on one ear of washer. See ADJUSTING WASHER SIZE table.

TOYOTA SEPARATE CARRIER (Cont.)

Fig. 14: Selecting Side Gear Thrust Washers

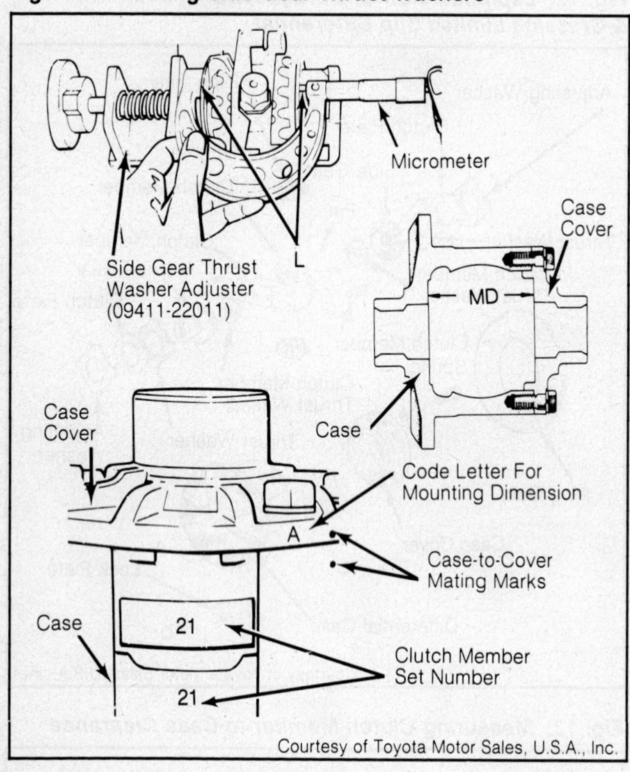

Courtesy of Toyota Motor Sales, U.S.A., Inc.

CASE MOUNTING DIMENSION

Code Letter [1]	In. (mm)
Corolla RWD	
A	2.6984-2.6996 (68.539-68.570)
B	2.6996-2.7008 (68.570-68.600)
C	2.7008-2.7020 (68.600-68.630)
D	2.7020-2.7031 (68.630-68.659)
E	2.7031-2.7043 (68.659-68.689)
F	2.7043-2.7055 (68.689-68.720)
Cressida	
A	2.952-2.953 (74.98-75.01)
B	2.953-2.954 (75.01-75.03)
C	2.954-2.956 (75.03-75.08)
D	2.956-2.957 (75.08-75.11)
E	2.957-2.958 (75.11-75.13)

[1] – Letter stamped in edge of case cover.

NOTE: **Two types of thrust washers are available. Type 1, has oil groves on one side. When installing Type 1 thrust washers, ensure oil grooves always face side gears.**
Type 2 thrust washers have oil grooves on both sides. When installing type 2 thrust washers ensure deep grooved side, faces away from side gears.

5) Wash differential case assembly. Apply LSD oil to each component. Install in differential case one selected adjusting washer, clutch plate, thrust washer, side gear, clutch member thrust washer, pin and left clutch member in order as named.

ADJUSTING WASHER SIZE

Number [1]	In. (mm)
Corolla RWD	
1	.063 (1.60)
2	.065 (1.65)
3	.067 (1.70)
4	.069 (1.75)
5	.071 (1.80)
6	.073 (1.85)
Cressida	
1 or A	.069 (1.76)
2 or B	.071 (1.80)
3 or C	.072 (1.84)
4 or D	.074 (1.88)
5 or E	.076 (1.92)
6 or F	.077 (1.96)
7 or G	.079 (2.00)
8 or H	.080 (2.04)
9 or J	.082 (2.08)
0 or K	.083 (2.12)

[1] – Number stamped on ear of adjusting washer.

6) Install clutch member springs onto left clutch member. Install right clutch member with pinion gear. Install in case cover other selected adjusting washer, clutch plate, thrust washer. Using index marks, assemble case and cover with "L" dimension measured parts.

7) Apply locking compound to cover bolts. Tighten bolts evenly in diagonal sequence to 33 ft. lbs. (44 N.m). Turn side gear with side gear shaft to ensure gears turn smoothly. Press side bearings onto differential case.

Case Disassembly (Limited Slip)

Land Cruiser

Place match marks on right and left case. Remove case bolts and seperate cases. Disassemble case, keeping parts in order for reassembly reference. *See Fig. 15.*

Inspection

Clean and check all parts for damage. Ensure contact surface of thrust washers are even and no bare metal is showing. Thrust washer thickness limit is .068" (1.74 mm). Spring free length should be 1.52" (38.6 mm). Replace parts as needed.

Case Reassembly

1) Lubricate all clutch plates and thrust washers with LSD oil. Into left differential case install following parts in following order: adjusting washer (with oil gooves facing away from case), clutch plates, side gear thrust washers, side gear spring retainer, spider with pinion gear and thrust washer. Align the holes of spider and retainer.

2) Into right case install following parts in following order: adjusting washer (with oil grooves facing away from case), clutch plates, side gear thrust washers, side gear and spring retainer.

3) Secure left side gear and measure backlash while pushing in on spring retainer.Side gear backlash should be .002-.009" (.05-.24 mm). If backlash is not within specification, adjust using different adjusting washer. See LAND CRUISER ADJUSTING WASHER THICKNESS table.

TOYOTA SEPARATE CARRIER (Cont.)

COROLLA RWD LIMITED SLIP DIFFERENTIAL ADJUSTING WASHER TABLE

Measurement "L" In. (mm)	REQUIRED ADJUSTING WASHERS FOR SPECIFIC DIFFERENTIAL CASE CODE					
	A	B	C	D	E	F
Corolla RWD						
2.5567 (64.94)	4 + 4	5 + 4	5 + 5	5 + 5	6 + 5	6 + 5
2.5571 (64.95)	4 + 4	5 + 4	5 + 4	5 + 5	5 + 5	6 + 5
2.5575-2.5579 (64.96-64.97)	4 + 4	4 + 4	5 + 4	5 + 5	5 + 5	6 + 5
2.5583 (64.98)	4 + 4	4 + 4	5 + 4	5 + 4	5 + 5	5 + 5
2.5587-2.5591 (64.99-65.00)	4 + 3	4 + 4	4 + 4	5 + 4	5 + 5	5 + 5
2.5594 (65.01)	4 + 3	4 + 4	4 + 4	5 + 4	5 + 4	5 + 5
2.5598 (65.02)	4 + 3	4 + 3	4 + 4	4 + 4	5 + 4	5 + 5
2.5602 (65.03)	3 + 3	4 + 3	4 + 4	4 + 4	5 + 4	5 + 5
2.5606 (65.04)	3 + 3	4 + 3	4 + 4	4 + 4	5 + 4	5 + 4
2.5610 (65.05)	3 + 3	4 + 3	4 + 3	4 + 4	4 + 4	5 + 4
2.5614-2.5618 (65.06-65.07)	3 + 3	3 + 3	4 + 3	4 + 4	4 + 4	5 + 4
2.5622 (65.08)	3 + 3	3 + 3	4 + 3	4 + 3	4 + 4	4 + 4
2.5626-2.5630 (65.09-65.10)	3 + 2	3 + 3	3 + 3	4 + 3	4 + 3	4 + 4
2.5634 (65.11)	3 + 2	3 + 3	3 + 3	4 + 3	4 + 3	4 + 4
2.5638 (65.12)	3 + 2	3 + 2	3 + 3	3 + 3	4 + 3	4 + 4
2.5642-2.5646 (65.13-65.14)	2 + 2	3 + 2	3 + 3	3 + 3	4 + 3	4 + 3
2.5650 (65.15)	2 + 2	3 + 2	3 + 2	3 + 3	3 + 3	4 + 3
2.5653-2.5657 (65.16-65.17)	2 + 2	2 + 2	3 + 2	3 + 3	3 + 3	4 + 3
2.5661 (65.18)	2 + 2	2 + 2	3 + 2	3 + 2	3 + 3	3 + 3
2.5665-2.5669 (65.19-65.20)	2 + 1	2 + 2	2 + 2	3 + 2	3 + 3	3 + 3
2.5673 (65.21)	2 + 1	2 + 2	2 + 2	3 + 2	3 + 2	3 + 3
2.5677 (65.22)	2 + 1	2 + 1	2 + 2	2 + 2	3 + 2	3 + 3
2.5681 (65.23)	1 + 1	2 + 1	2 + 2	2 + 2	3 + 2	3 + 3
2.5685 (65.24)	1 + 1	2 + 1	2 + 2	2 + 2	3 + 2	3 + 2
2.5689 (65.25)	1 + 1	2 + 1	2 + 1	2 + 2	2 + 2	3 + 2
2.5693-2.5697 (65.26-65.27)	1 + 1	1 + 1	2 + 1	2 + 2	2 + 2	3 + 2
2.5701 (65.28)	1 + 1	1 + 1	2 + 1	2 + 1	2 + 2	2 + 2
2.5705-2.5709 (65.29-65.30)	.....	1 + 1	1 + 1	2 + 1	2 + 2	2 + 2

CRESSIDA LIMITED SLIP DIFFERENTIAL ADJUSTING WASHER TABLE

Measurement "L" In. (mm)	REQUIRED ADJUSTING WASHERS FOR SPECIFIC DIFFERENTIAL CASE CODE				
	A	B	C	D	E
2.7878-2.7902 (70.81-70.84)	8 + 8 or H + H	8 + 9 or H + J	9 + 9 or J + J	9 + 9 or J + J	9 + 0 or J + K
2.7894-2.7902 (70.85-70.87)	7 + 8 or G + H	8 + 8 or H + H	8 + 9 or H + J	9 + 9 or H + H	9 + 9 or H + H
2.7905-2.7913 (70.88-70.90)	7 + 8 or G + H	7 + 8 or G + H	8 + 8 or H + H	8 + 9 or H + J	9 + 9 or J + J
2.7917-2.7925 (70.91-70.93)	7 + 7 or G + G	7 + 8 or G + H	7 + 8 or G + H	8 + 8 or H + H	8 + 9 or H + J
2.7929-2.2737 (70.94-70.96)	6 + 7 or F + G	7 + 7 or G + G	7 + 8 or G + H	7 + 8 or G + H	8 + 8 or H + H
2.7941-2.7949 (70.97-70.99)	6 + 6 or F + F	6 + 7 or F + G	7 + 7 or G + G	7 + 8 or G + H	7 + 8 or G + H
2.7953-2.7961 (71.00-71.02)	6 + 6 or F + F	6 + 6 or F + F	6 + 7 or F + G	7 + 7 or G + G	7 + 8 or G + H
2.7965-2.7972 (71.03-71.05)	5 + 6 or E + F	6 + 6 or F + F	6 + 6 or F + F	6 + 7 or F + G	7 + 7 or G + G
2.7976-2.7984 (71.06-71.08)	5 + 5 or E + E	5 + 6 or E + F	6 + 6 or F + F	6 + 6 or F + F	6 + 7 or F + G
2.7988-2.7996 (71.09-71.11)	4 + 5 or D + E	5 + 5 or E + E	5 + 6 or E + F	6 + 6 or F + F	6 + 6 or F + F
2.8000-2.8008 (71.12-71.14)	4 + 5 or D + E	4 + 5 or D + E	5 + 5 or E + E	5 + 6 or E + F	6 + 6 or F + F
2.8012-2.8020 (71.15-71.17)	4 + 4 or D + D	4 + 5 or D + E	4 + 5 or D + E	5 + 5 or E + E	5 + 6 or E + F
2.8024-2.8031 (71.18-71.20)	3 + 4 or C + D	4 + 4 or D + D	4 + 5 or D + E	4 + 5 or D + E	5 + 5 or E + E
2.8035-2.8043 (71.21-71.23)	3 + 3 or C + C	3 + 4 or C + D	4 + 4 or D + D	4 + 5 or D + E	4 + 5 or D + E
2.8047-2.8055 (71.24-71.26)	3 + 3 or C + C	3 + 3 or C + C	3 + 4 or C + D	4 + 4 or D + D	4 + 5 or D + E
2.8059-2.8067 (71.27-71.29)	2 + 3 or B + C	3 + 3 or B + C	3 + 3 or B + B	3 + 4 or B + C	4 + 4 or C + C
2.8071-2.8079 (71.30-71.32)	2 + 2 or B + B	2 + 3 or B + C	3 + 3 or B + B	3 + 3 or B + B	3 + 4 or B + C
2.8083-2.8090 (71.33-71.35)	1 + 2 or A + B	2 + 2 or B + B	2 + 3 or B + C	3 + 3 or C + C	3 + 3 or C + C
2.8094-2.8102 (71.36-71.38)	1 + 2 or A + B	1 + 2 or A + B	2 + 2 or B + B	2 + 3 or B + C	3 + 3 or C + C
2.8106-2.8114 (71.39-71.41)	1 + 1 or A + A	1 + 2 or A + B	1 + 2 or A + B	2 + 2 or B + B	2 + 3 or B + C

TOYOTA SEPARATE CARRIER (Cont.)

Fig. 15: Exploded View of Land Cruiser Limited Slip Differential

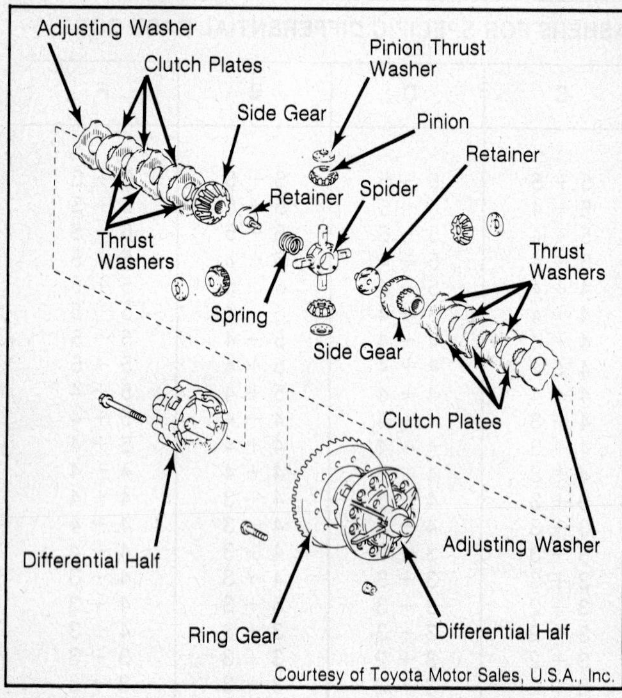

Courtesy of Toyota Motor Sales, U.S.A., Inc.

LAND CRUISER ADJUSTING WASHER THICKNESS

Code	mm
A	2.20
B	2.25
C	2.25
D	2.35
E	2.40
F	2.45
G	2.50
H	2.55
J	2.60
K	2.65
L	2.70
M	2.75
N	2.80

4) Install spring and right retainer. Using alignment marks, assemble the 2 cases while checking pinion and side gear alignment. Tighten case bolts a little at a time in a diagonal pattern, until a torque of 35 ft. lbs. (47 N.m.) is reached.

Pinion Bearing Preload

1) Install drive pinion with rear bearing and front bearing into differential carrier. Install pinion flange and nut with light coat of grease on threads. Using a torque wrench, measure pinion bearing preload.

2) Starting preload for new bearings is higher than starting preload for used bearings. See PINION BEARING PRELOAD table. Install differential in case. Install adjusting nuts. Align side bearing caps. Tighten side bearing cap bolts until spring washers are compressed.

3) Tighten adjuster on ring gear side, using Adjuster (09504-00011) until ring gear backlash is within specifications. Tighten other adjuster. Check ring gear backlash. Tighten or loosen adjusters equally until backlash is eliminated. Position a dial indicator against adjuster on ring gear side.

4) Zero dial indicator. Tighten adjuster on other side until dial indicator starts to move. Tighten adjuster an additional 1-1 1/2 turns. Check ring gear backlash. See AXLE ASSEMBLY SPECIFICATIONS table at end of this article. If backlash is not as specified, loosen one adjuster while tightening other adjuster an equal amount until backlash is as specified.

5) Tighten side bearing cap bolts. See TIGHTENING SPECIFICATIONS table at end of this article. Recheck ring gear backlash and pinion preload. Check tooth gear pattern. See GEAR TOOTH PATTERNS article in this section. If gear tooth patterns are not as specified, install correct washer behind rear bearing.

6) Washer thickness are available from .0882-.1071" (2.24-2.72 mm). Remove companion flange. Remove front bearing. Install new spacer on drive pinion. Install front bearing. Install new oil seal. See PINION SEAL REPLACEMENT (ON-VEHICLE) in REMOVAL & INSTALLATION section of this article.

7) Add pinion bearing preload for final pinion bearing preload. See TOTAL PRELOAD SPECIFICATIONS table in this article. Check pinion flange runout with a dial indicator. If longitudinal or latitudinal runout is more than .004" (.10 mm), bearings must be checked. Stake drive pinion nut. Install adjuster locks.

Fig. 16: Measuring Ring Gear Backlash

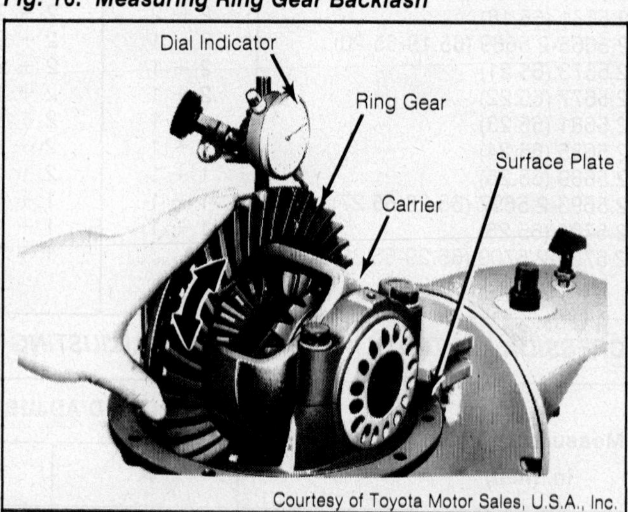

Courtesy of Toyota Motor Sales, U.S.A., Inc.

PINION BEARING PRELOAD

Application [1]	INCH Lbs. (N.m)
Corolla RWD	
New Bearings	8.7-13.9 (1.0-1.6)
Used Bearings	4.3-6.9 (.5-.8)
Pickup (1 Ton, C & C & 4WD), Land Cruiser & 4Runner	
New Bearings	16.5-22.6 (1.9-2.6)
Used Bearings	7.8-11.3 (.9-1.3)
Pickup (2WD)	
New Bearings	10.4-16.5 (1.2-1.9)
Used Bearings	5.2-8.7 (.6-1.0)
Tercel	
New Bearings	5.6-10.9 (.6-1.2)
Used Bearings	3.5-6.1 (.4-.7)
Cressida & Van	
New Bearings	13.9-19.1 (1.6-2.2)
Used Bearings	6.9-9.5 (.8-1.1)

[1] – Record torque reading.

Drive Axles

TOYOTA SEPARATE CARRIER (Cont.)

TOTAL PRELOAD SPECIFICATIONS

Application	[1] INCH Lbs. (N.m)
Corolla RWD	
6.4" Ring Gear	1.7-3.5 (.2-.4)
6.7" Ring Gear	2.6-4.3 (.3-.5)
Cressida, Land Cruiser, Pickup, Van & 4Runner	3.5-5.2 (.4-.6)
Tercel	1.7-3.5 (.2-.4)

[1] – Add this amount to pinion bearing preload to obtain total assembly preload.

AXLE ASSEMBLY SPECIFICATIONS

Application	In. (mm)
Axle Shaft Flange Runout	
Cressida, Tercel & Van	.004 (.10)
All Others	.008 (.20)
Axle Shaft Runout	
Land Cruiser	.031 (.80)
Tercel & Van	.059 (1.50)
All Others	.079 (2.00)
Drive Pinion Flange Runout (All Models)	
Longitudinal & Latitudinal	.004 (.10)
Drive Pinion-to-Ring Gear Backlash	
Land Cruiser	.006-.008 (.15-.20)
Tercel	.004-.006 (.10-.15)
All Others	.005-.007 (.13-.18)
Ring Gear Runout [1]	
Land Cruiser	.004 (.10)
All Others	.003 (.07)
Side Gear-to-Pinion Gear Backlash	
Corolla RWD	
6.38" Ring Gear	.0008-.0079 (.020-.200)
6.7" Ring Gear	.0020-.0079 (.050-.200)
Land Cruiser	
Conventional	.0008-.0094 (.020-.240)
Limited Slip	.0020-.0094 (.050-.240)
Tercel	.0008-.0060 (.020-.150)
All Others	.002-.008 (.05-.20)
	Lbs. (kg)
Axle Hub Preload Starting Torque	
Land Cruiser (Front & Rear)	.9-7.3 (.4-3.3)
Pickup W/Dual Wheels	.2-3.3 (.1-1.5)

[1] – Maximum clearance.

TIGHTENING SPECIFICATIONS

Application	Ft. Lbs. (N.m)
Adjusting Nut Lock Plates	
Tercel	[1]
All Others	[2]
Axle Retainer Flange Bolts	
Corolla RWD, Cressida & Tercel	43-54 (58-73)
Land Cruiser (Front & Rear)	21-25 (29-34)
Pickup (All) & 4Runner	44-57 (60-77)
Van	25 (34)
Carrier-to-Axle Housing	
Cressida & Tercel	23 (31)
Land Cruiser	34 (47)
Pickup (All) & 4Runner	18-22 (25-30)
Van	18-27 (25-37)
Differential Side Bearing Cap Bolts	
Corolla RWD	
6.38" Ring Gear	43 (59)
6.7" Rear Gear	58 (78)
Cressida & Land Cruiser	58 (78)
Pickup (All Models)	58 (78)
Tercel	43 (59)
Van & 4Runner	58 (78)
Differential Case Through Bolts	
Corolla RWD	
6.38" Ring Gear	23 (31)
6.7" Ring Gear	33 (44)
Land Cruiser (LSD)	35 (47)
Drive Pinion Flange Nut	
Corolla RWD & Cressida	80-174 (109-236)
Land Cruiser	181-325 (245-441)
Pickup, Van & 4Runner	
2WD	80-174 (109-236)
1 Ton, C & C & 4WD	145-253 (197-343)
Tercel	107 (145)
Van	127 (172)
Front Hub-to-Flange	
Land Cruiser	20-25 (27-34)
Front Spindle Bolts	
Land Cruiser	29-39 (39-53)
Ring Gear-to-Case Bolts	
Cressida, Pickup (All), Van, Tercel & 4Runner	71 (97)
Corolla RWD	
6.38" Ring Gear	43 (58)
6.7" Ring Gear	58 (79)
Land Cruiser	81 (110)

[1] – Specification is 48 INCH lbs. (5.4 N.m).
[2] – Specification is 108 INCH lbs. (13 N.m).

Drive Axles

VOLVO

DESCRIPTION

Axle shafts are semi-floating. Axle shaft outer bearings are pressed onto shafts and attached to axle housing by outer retainers. Axle shaft bearing clearance is not adjustable and is determined by bearing design.

Hypoid type drive pinion and ring gear set uses a 2-pinion differential with a 1-piece case. Limited slip differential is available. Limited slip cases are of 2-piece design and use 4 pinion gears mounted on a spider. Differential adjustments are made with shims.

AXLE RATIO & IDENTIFICATION

Standard (Type 1030) and heavy-duty (Type 1031) rear axles are available. Several different ratios are used. Plate attached to left front side of final drive housing gives axle ratio, part number, and serial number. Divide number of ring gear teeth by number of drive pinion gear teeth to determine axle ratio.

REMOVAL & INSTALLATION

AXLE SHAFTS & BEARINGS

NOTE: **Although axle shaft bearing end play is not adjustable, it should be checked prior to disassembly.**

Checking Procedure

1) Raise vehicle and remove rear wheel. Remove brake pads. Put steel ball in center hole of axle shaft, using small amount of grease to hold ball in place. Mount dial indicator with plunger tip against steel ball, using tip with flat surface. Plunger must be at 90 degrees to axle flange.

2) Rotate axle shaft at least one full revolution in each direction. Measure total end play. If end play exceeds specification, check axle bearing, axle housing, and outer retainer for wear or damage.

Removal

1) Remove rear wheels and collision guards (if equipped). Disconnect brake line and bracket from axle housing. Remove caliper and support to side with wire, being careful not to damage brake line. Make sure parking brake is fully released.

2) Remove brake rotor set screws. Take off rotors, tapping with soft mallet (if necessary). Remove parking brake shoes, unhooking retaining springs. Disconnect parking brake cables by driving out lock pin at lever.

3) Remove bolts for bearing retainer through holes in axle flange. Remove axle shaft using puller. Pry inner seal from housing. Press bearing and snap ring off axle shaft. Remove oil seal.

Installation

1) Pack new bearing and new seal lip groove with high temperature wheel bearing grease. Place bearing retainer and oil seal on axle shaft. Press new bearing and new snap ring onto axle shaft. Always use a new snap ring. Narrow side of taper fits into axle housing.

2) Clean axle housing and drive in new inner seal. Install axle shaft and tighten bearing retainer bolts. Install parking brake shoes and reconnect cables. Install rotors and tighten set screws.

3) Check parking brake adjustment. Install brake caliper, pads, and collision guard (if equipped). Reconnect brake line and bracket to axle housing. Install wheels and tighten lug nuts.

PINION FLANGES & SEAL

Removal

1) Disconnect propeller shaft at pinion flange. Check drive pinion and bearings for excessive play. Before new seal is installed, final drive must be removed and repaired if loose or rough.

2) Remove flange nut from drive pinion while holding flange. Remove flange using puller. Remove old oil seal and dust shield.

Installation

1) Drive new seal into housing after packing seal spring and lips with grease. Unless packed, seal spring could jump out of position. Press flange onto drive pinion.

2) Install flange washer and nut and tighten to proper torque specification. There are 3 different nuts used and torque ratings differ. Reconnect propeller shaft to drive pinion flange.

AXLE ASSEMBLY

NOTE: **On models equipped with Limited Slip Differential (LSD), rotational friction of LSD must be checked with axle assembly in vehicle.**

Checking Procedure

Raise one rear wheel and block opposite side. Place transmission in neutral and release parking brake. Remove raised wheel. Attach torque wrench to axle flange. Rotate axle flange and measure friction torque of LSD. If rotational friction is below minimum specification, friction discs and plates in LSD must be replaced.

Removal

1) Raise vehicle and remove wheels. Remove intermediate exhaust pipe. Loosen trailing arm retaining bolts so arms can pivot at front ends. Remove stabilizer bar and track (Panhard) rod. Remove collision guards (if used).

2) Disconnect ventilation hose from axle housing. Disconnect brake line brackets from axle housing. Remove calipers and hang on springs, being careful not to damage lines. Fully release parking brake and remove rotors. Remove parking brake shoes and disconnect cables from levers.

3) Disconnect propeller shaft from pinion flange. Disconnect parking brake cables from axle housing. Only remove plastic tube if axle housing is being replaced. Disconnect reaction rods at axle housing. Support axle assembly securely with transmission jack.

4) Compress springs and disconnect shock absorbers at upper mounts. Remove spring compressors. Remove bolts holding axle housing to trailing arms. Lower and remove axle assembly.

Installation

1) Move axle assembly under vehicle on transmission jack and raise into position. Connect trailing arms with stabilizer bar brackets to axle housing, leaving bolts finger tight. Compress springs and connect shock absorbers to upper mounts. Release springs.

2) Remove transmission jack. Connect reaction rods to axle housing, leaving bolts finger tight. Attach

VOLVO (Cont.)

parking brake cables to axle housing. Attach propeller shaft to pinion flange. Connect parking brake cables to levers and install parking brake shoes.

3) Install rotors and check parking brake adjustment. Install calipers and attach brake line brackets to axle housing. Attach ventilation hose to axle housing. Install collision guards (if equipped). Connect Panhard rod and stabilizer bar to axle housing and trailing arms, leaving bolts finger tight.

4) Install wheels and tighten lug nuts. Lower and rock vehicle to settle suspension. With full weight of vehicle on suspension, tighten bolts on trailing arms, reaction rods, Panhard rod, and stabilizer bar.

OVERHAUL

DISASSEMBLY

Drive Pinion & Carrier

1) Support axle assembly with pinion flange down and bottom of housing toward work stand. Remove axle shafts and inner seals. Remove inspection cover.

2) If final drive is being reconditioned because of noise, run a tooth contact pattern check before disassembly as this may assist in locating fault.

Fig. 1: Exploded View of Volvo Drive Axle Assembly

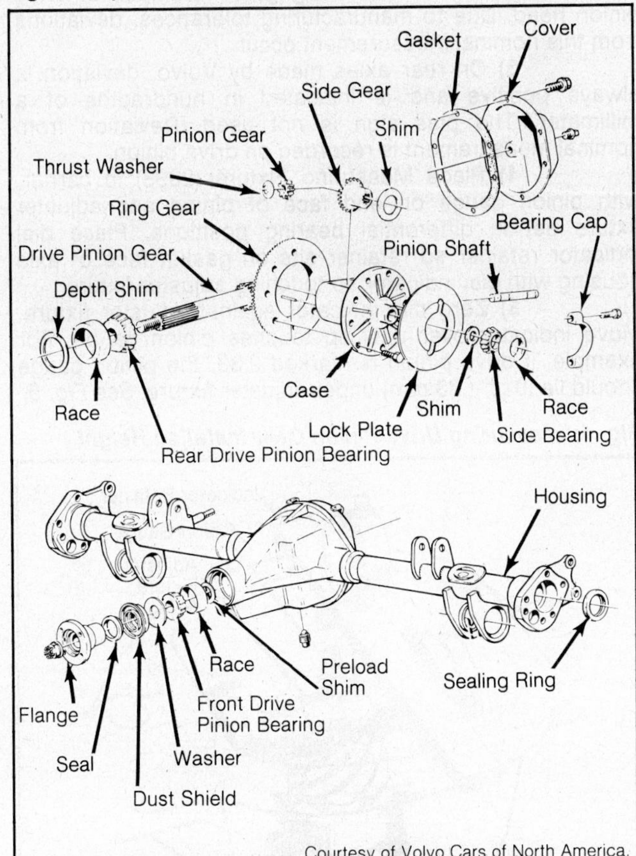

3) Check alignment markings on side bearing caps and carrier. Index caps to carrier for reassembly (if necessary). Remove side bearing caps. Attach Differential Housing Spreader (2394 and 2601) to carrier housing. Align pins on spreader with holes in housing and screw retainer bolts into housing.

4) Tighten tensioning screw until spreader fits snugly in housing. Slowly tighten tensioning screw until differential case assembly can be removed from carrier. Do not tighten screw more than 3.5 turns. Carefully pry differential assembly out of carrier.

CAUTION: Excessive or prolonged tension by spreader can distort carrier housing.

5) Remove spreader from housing. Turn axle assembly over and drain oil. Remove drive pinion flange nut, holding flange. Remove flange, using puller. Force drive pinion from carrier housing using a plastic hammer. Hold drive pinion with free hand to avoid damage.

6) Drive out front drive pinion bearing, with seal and washer, from back of housing. Drive out rear drive pinion bearing race from front of housing. Press rear drive pinion bearing off drive pinion or use Puller (5215 on Type 1030 axle assembly or 5216 and 5214 on Type 1031 axle assembly).

Case Assembly - Conventional

1) Remove side bearings with Puller (2483), taking care not to damage shims. Mark left and right bearings and shims for reassembly in correct position. Hold case assembly securely and remove lock plate over ring gear bolts.

2) Index ring gear to differential case for reassembly. Loosen bolts holding ring gear to case. Tap bolts to push ring gear from case. Discard old bolts. Drive out lock pin holding differential gear shaft.

3) Drive out differential gear shaft. Remove differential pinion gears by rolling them out of case. Remove pinion gear shims. Lift out differential side gears with shims.

Fig. 2: Exploded View of Limited Slip Differential

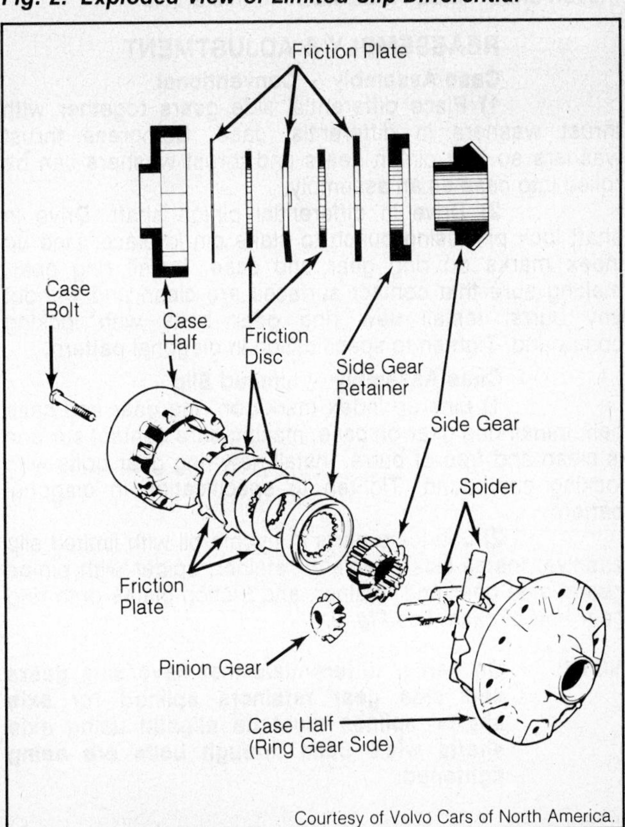

Drive Axles

VOLVO (Cont.)

Case Assembly - Limited Slip

1) Remove side bearings with Puller (2483), taking care not to damage shims. Mark left and right bearings and shims for reassembly. Index differential case halves and mark differential gear shafts for reassembly.

2) Remove bolts holding case halves together, noting that Type 1030 axle uses bolts with left-hand threads. Open differential case and remove side gears, side gear retainers, friction plates, friction discs, and pinion gears with spider.

3) Index ring gear to differential case half for reassembly. Remove and discard bolts holding ring gear to case. Remove ring gear from differential case.

INSPECTION

1) Inspect all parts for wear or damage. Bearings that have any damage from heat or scoring must be replaced. If drive pinion or ring gear show tooth damage from seizing, they must be replaced as a set.

2) If differential side or pinion gears show any damage, gears must be replaced as a complete set (2 side gears and 2 pinion gears in conventional models or 2 side gears and 4 pinion gears in LSD models).

3) Flat and thrust washers for differential gears should be replaced. Bolts holding ring gear to case must always be replaced. Pinion flange locking nut must be checked carefully as it loses locking capacity after being removed several times.

4) Replace drive pinion flange if worn or scored on sealing surface. Always use new oil seals and gaskets. Check axle housing for cracks. Check all brackets on housing for broken welds or damage.

5) On models with LSD, all friction discs should be replaced if any discs show excessive wear or heat damage. See CHECKING PROCEDURE for rotational friction under AXLE ASSEMBLY in this article.

REASSEMBLY & ADJUSTMENT

Case Assembly - Conventional

1) Place differential side gears together with thrust washers in differential case. Compress thrust washers so that pinion gears and thrust washers can be rolled into case as an assembly.

2) Drive in differential pinion shaft. Drive in shaft lock pin, using punch to stake pin in place. Line up index marks on ring gear and case. Install ring gear, making sure that contact surfaces are clean and without any burrs. Install new ring gear bolts with locking compound. Tighten to specification in diagonal pattern.

Case Assembly - Limited Slip

1) Line up index marks on ring gear and case half. Install ring gear on case, making sure contact surface is clean and free of burrs. Install new ring gear bolts with locking compound. Tighten to specification in diagonal pattern.

2) Lubricate parts in hypoid oil with limited slip additive. Install side gear and retainer, spider with pinion gears, side gear and retainer, and friction plates onto ring gear half of case. *See Fig. 2.*

NOTE: **On earlier differentials that have side gears and side gear retainers splined for axle shafts, splines must be aligned using axle shafts while case through bolts are being tightened.**

3) Align ears on friction plates and fit smaller half of case to ring gear half. Make sure index marks on case halves are aligned. Install case through bolts and torque to specification in diagonal pattern.

Drive Pinion Depth & Bearing Preload

1) Clean shoulder on drive pinion with emery cloth. Install adjusting Ring and Wrench (Type 1030 uses Ring 2685 and Wrench 2841; Type 1031 uses Ring 2840 and Wrench 2841) on drive pinion. Make sure locking screw on adjusting ring is not covered by drive pinion head. *See Figs. 3 and 4.* Place drive pinion in carrier so screw on adjusting ring faces large side of carrier.

Fig. 3: Drive Pinion Adjusting Ring & Wrench

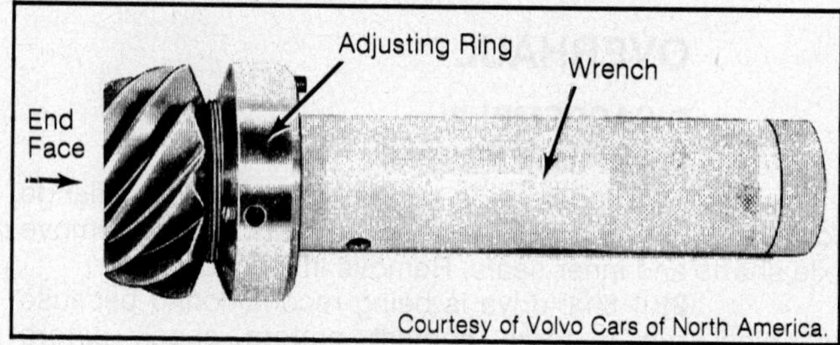

Courtesy of Volvo Cars of North America.

2) Make sure pin on adjusting ring fits into carrier recess. Drive pinion has a certain nominal measurement to center line of ring gear from face of drive pinion head. Due to manufacturing tolerances, deviations from this nominal measurement occur.

3) On rear axles made by Volvo, deviation is always positive and is indicated in hundredths of a millimeter. The plus sign is not used. Deviation from nominal measurement is recorded on drive pinion.

4) Place Measuring Fixture (2393) in carrier, with pinion gauge on end face of pinion and adjuster fixture set in differential bearing positions. Place dial indicator retainer so retainer sits on gasket face of axle housing with dial indicator tip touching adjuster fixture.

5) Zero dial indicator against adjuster fixture. Move indicator over until tip touches pinion gauge. For example, if drive pinion is marked 0.33, the pinion gauge should lie .013" (.33 mm) under adjuster fixture. *See Fig. 5.*

Fig. 4: Measuring Drive Pinion Gear Installed Height

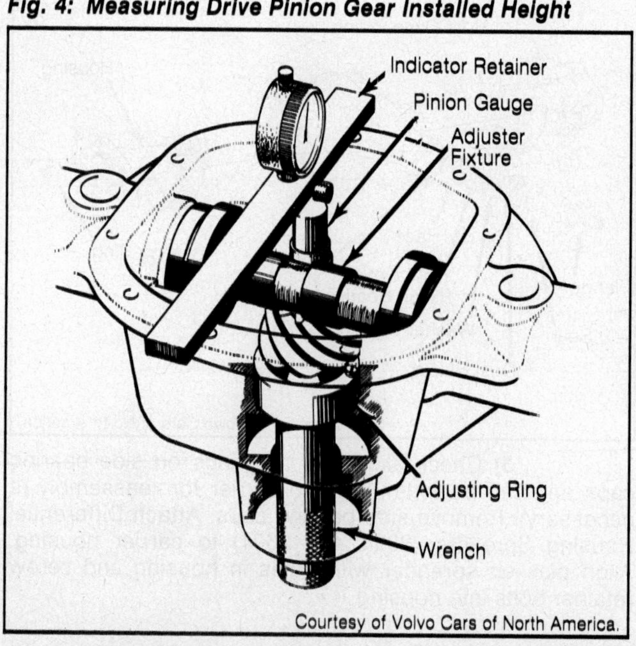

Courtesy of Volvo Cars of North America.

Drive Axles

VOLVO (Cont.)

6) Adjust indicated reading by turning wrench on drive pinion until dial indicator shows correct value. Lock wrench with set screw on adjusting ring.

7) Remove measuring fixture and drive pinion. Place complete rear pinion bearing with outer race in Measuring Fixture (2600). Assemble plate, spring, and nut with flat side of nut facing up.

Fig. 5: Dial Indicator Zeroing Location

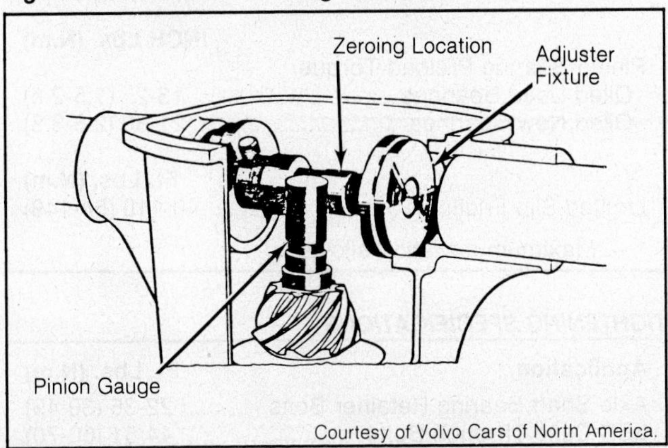

Fig. 6: Determining Pinion Depth Shim Thickness

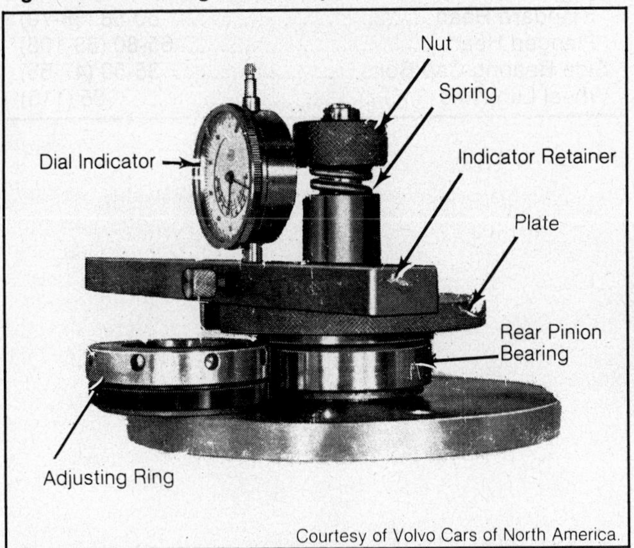

8) Rotate plate and bearing assembly several times so that rollers settle in proper position. Place Adjusting Ring (2685 or 2840) in fixture and place dial indicator tip against adjusting ring. Zero indicator. Move tip of indicator to outer race of bearing.

9) The indicator reading will now show thickness of rear drive pinion bearing shims. *See Fig. 6.* Measure shims for correct thickness with micrometer. As it is difficult to find shim of exact thickness required, shim may be .002" (.05 mm) thicker or .0008" (.020 mm) thinner than measured value.

10) Press rear bearing on drive pinion. Place measured shim in axle carrier housing. Press in outer races of rear and front drive pinion bearings.

CAUTION: The spacer washer found under rear bearing inner race during first time disassembly must not be reinstalled when overhauling.

11) Insert drive pinion in housing and install three .03" (.75 mm) thick shims and front pinion bearing. Pull pinion into housing, using Wrench (2404) and Press (1845 or 5156). Install washer and nut on pinion shaft and tighten to specifications.

Fig. 7: Measuring Installed Depth of Pinion Gear

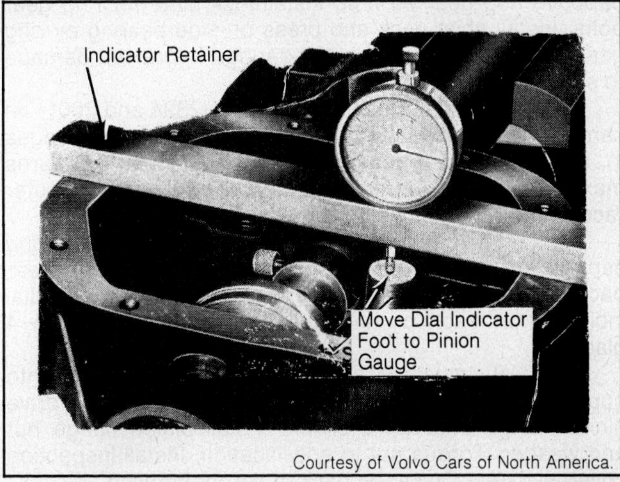

12) Install pinion gauge, dial indicator, and dial indicator retainer. *See Fig. 7.* Pull down on drive pinion while rotating it back and forth. Zero dial indicator. Press pinion up while rotating it back and forth. Record dial indicator reading.

13) Tap drive pinion from housing and remove shims equal to the dial indicator reading plus .0035" (.090 mm) for new bearings or .0028" (.071 mm) for used bearings. Install pinion with selected shim pack and front bearing. Press drive pinion in with Wrench (2404) and Press (1845 or 5156).

14) Install pinion nut with washer and torque to specification. Check drive pinion bearing preload with torque wrench. Adjust shim thickness to obtain specified torque (if required). Recheck pinion depth using measuring fixture as described in steps **4)** and **5)**.

Backlash & Side Bearing Preload

1) Lubricate inside of Adjusting Ring (2595) and install them on differential carrier. Black oxidized adjusting ring should be placed on ring gear side of differential case. Oil bearing bores in carrier. Install differential with adjusting rings in axle housing.

2) Adjust rings apart until differential is held firmly without any preload. Set dial indicator tip against ring gear tooth and adjust rings so that specified backlash is obtained. Turn both rings in same direction. Backlash range is .005-.007" (.13-.18 mm). Preferred setting is .006" (.15 mm).

NOTE: Keep bearings and shims separate so that they are installed on correct side.

3) After correct backlash is obtained, lock adjusting rings in position. Remove differential with adjusting rings. Position centering plate on Measuring Fixture (2600). Place side bearing in fixture. Install plate, spring, and nut (flat side of nut faces up). Rotate plate and bearing back and forth to settle rollers.

4) Place adjusting ring on measuring fixture. Install Retainer (2284) with dial indicator. Zero dial indicator with tip against adjusting ring. Move tip of dial indicator to inner race of side bearing. Record measurement.

5) Measure shim thickness with micrometer. Total thickness of shim(s) should be measured value plus .0028" (.071 mm). Repeat measuring procedure for opposite side bearing shim pack.

6) Install shim pack and press side bearing opposite ring gear on first. Install lock plate for ring gear bolts. Install shim pack and press on side bearing by ring gear. Use press on both side bearings to prevent damage to side bearings.

7) Install Housing Spreader (2394 and 2601) on carrier and expand until pins are flush against hole edges in carrier. Tighten tension screw additional 3.5 turns maximum. Install differential carrier with side bearing outer races in place. Remove housing spreader.

8) Check index marks and install side bearing caps. Torque cap bolts to specification. Check ring gear backlash to make sure no change has occurred. Set dial indicator on back of ring gear and check runout in 4 places.

9) Install oil slinger. Drive pinion oil seal into housing after packing seal spring with grease. Press drive pinion flange onto drive pinion. Install pinion flange nut and washer. Torque nut to specification. Install inspection cover with new gasket on back of carrier housing.

10) If inner oil seals for axle shafts were removed, drive them into housing ends after packing lips with grease. Fill space between retainer and inner race of axle bearing with grease. Reinstall axle shafts and tighten bearing retainer bolts. Fill with correct lubricant.

AXLE ASSEMBLY SPECIFICATIONS

Application	In. (mm)
Ring Gear Runout [1]	.003 (.08)
Pinion-to-Ring Gear	
Backlash Preferred	.006 (.15)
Backlash Range	.005-.007 (.13-.18)
Axle Shaft Bearing End Play [1]	.004-.014 (.10-.36)
Differential Side Bearing Preload	.005-.008 (.13-.20)
	INCH Lbs. (N.m)
Pinion Bearing Preload Torque	
Oiled Used Bearings	13-22 (1.5-2.5)
Oiled New Bearings	21-30 (2.5-3.5)
	Ft. Lbs. (N.m)
Limited Slip Friction Torque	40-110 (54-149)

[1] – Maximum deviation allowed.

TIGHTENING SPECIFICATIONS

Application	Ft. Lbs. (N.m)
Axle Shaft Bearing Retainer Bolts	22-36 (30-49)
LSD Case Through Bolts	44-51 (60-70)
Pinion Flange Nut	145-180 (197-244)
Ring Gear Bolts	
Standard Head	50-58 (68-79)
Flanged Head	65-80 (88-108)
Side Bearing Cap Bolts	35-50 (47-68)
Wheel Lug Nuts	85 (115)

Locking Hubs

ALL MANUFACTURERS

Chrysler Motors: Ram-50, Raider
Isuzu: P'UP, Trooper II
Mazda: B2600
Mitsubishi: Montero, Pickup
Nissan: Pathfinder, Pickup
Toyota: Land Cruiser, Pickup, 4Runner

DESCRIPTION

Locking hubs engage and disengage front wheels from axle shafts on 4WD vehicles. When hubs are engaged or locked, wheels and axle shafts rotate together. When hubs are disengaged or unlocked, front wheels free wheel on hub bearings and axle shafts are not turned by wheels.

Engagement is accomplished through action of gears and springs within hub. When hub is locked, hub clutch engages inner hub, which is always connected to axle shaft by inner splines of hub. Hub clutch is always connected by outer splines to hub body. Control handle applies or releases spring tension to control hub clutch position.

Automatic hubs are engaged by rotational force of axle shaft when 4WD is selected at transfer case. Automatic hubs disengage when 2WD is selected and vehicle is driven in reverse. Cams, brakes and springs are used to lock or unlock automatic hubs.

IDENTIFICATION

Several different makes of hubs are used. Manufacturer's name is on control handle of manual hubs if marked. Automatic hubs have no handle on cover. Manual hubs have control handle marked with "LOCK" and "FREE" directions. Outer edge of hub cover on manual hubs is marked with "LOCK" and "FREE" positions.

REMOVAL & INSTALLATION

MANUAL HUBS

Removal

With control knob set to "FREE" position and transfer shift lever set in "2WD" or "NEUTRAL" position, remove cover-to-body bolts and cover assembly. Remove outer snap ring and shims (if equipped) from axle shaft. Remove hub body-to-hub bolts or nuts and cone washers (if equipped). Remove hub body and inner clutch from axle shaft.

Installation

Place new gasket on axle hub and install hub body with bolts or nuts and cone washers (if equipped). Tighten fasteners. Install snap ring, making sure snap ring fits groove on axle shaft. Apply grease to splines of inner hub. Set control handle and clutch in "FREE" position. Install new gasket and cover assembly and tighten bolts. Check control handle for smooth operation.

AUTOMATIC HUBS

Removal (Chrysler Motors & Mitsubishi)

Ensure hub is in "FREE" position and transfer case lever is in "2H". Unscrew cover, remove snap ring and shims from axle shaft. Unbolt hub body from axle hub and remove hub body.

Removal (Isuzu)

Ensure hub is in "FREE" position and transfer case lever is in "2H". Remove cover-to-hub body bolts. Remove snap ring and shims from axle shaft. Unbolt hub body from axle hub and remove drive clutch and inner cam with hub body.

Removal (Nissan)

Ensure hub is in "FREE" position and transfer case lever is in "2H". Remove cover-to-hub body bolts. Remove hub assembly. Remove snap ring, washers "A" and "B" and brake "B" from axle shaft. *See Fig. 1.*

Fig. 1: Exploded View of Nissan Automatic Hub

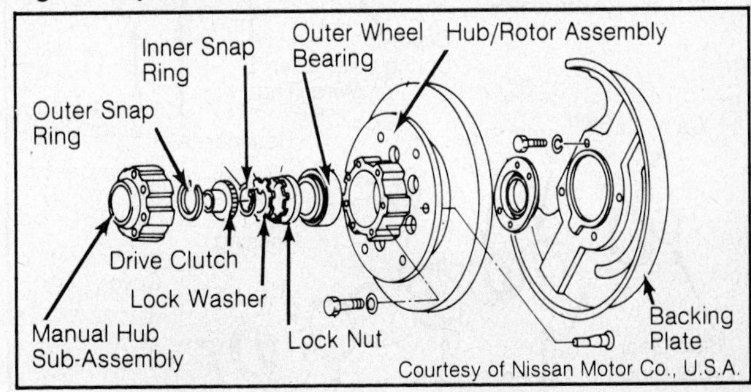

Courtesy of Nissan Motor Co., U.S.A.

Fig. 2: Exploded View of Toyota Automatic Hub

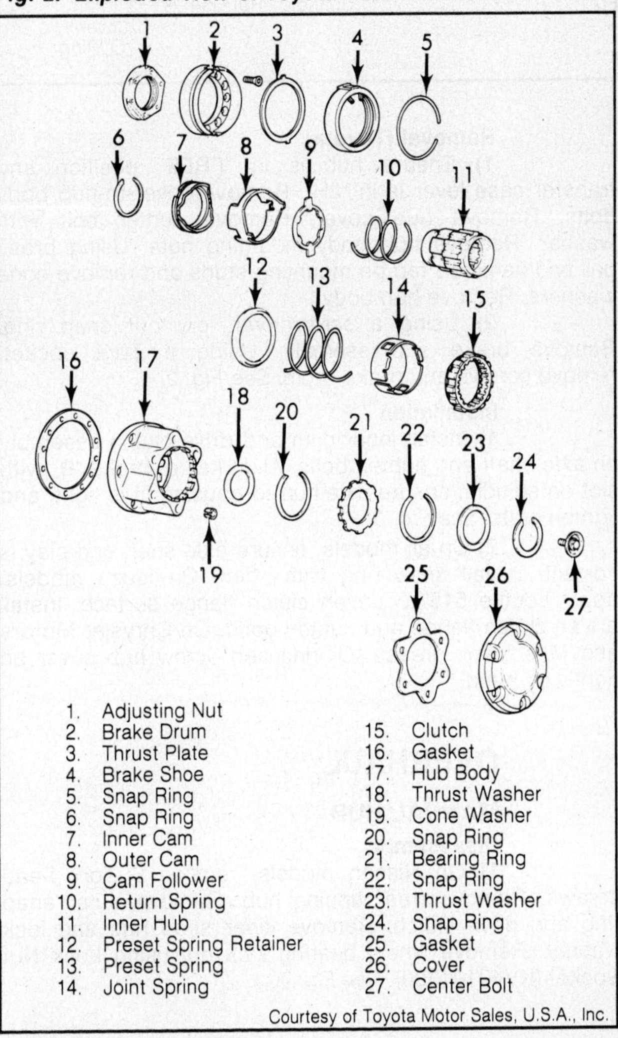

1. Adjusting Nut
2. Brake Drum
3. Thrust Plate
4. Brake Shoe
5. Snap Ring
6. Snap Ring
7. Inner Cam
8. Outer Cam
9. Cam Follower
10. Return Spring
11. Inner Hub
12. Preset Spring Retainer
13. Preset Spring
14. Joint Spring
15. Clutch
16. Gasket
17. Hub Body
18. Thrust Washer
19. Cone Washer
20. Snap Ring
21. Bearing Ring
22. Snap Ring
23. Thrust Washer
24. Snap Ring
25. Gasket
26. Cover
27. Center Bolt

Courtesy of Toyota Motor Sales, U.S.A., Inc.

Locking Hubs

ALL MANUFACTURERS (Cont.)

Fig. 3: Exploded View of Chrysler Motors, Mitsubishi & Isuzu Automatic Hubs

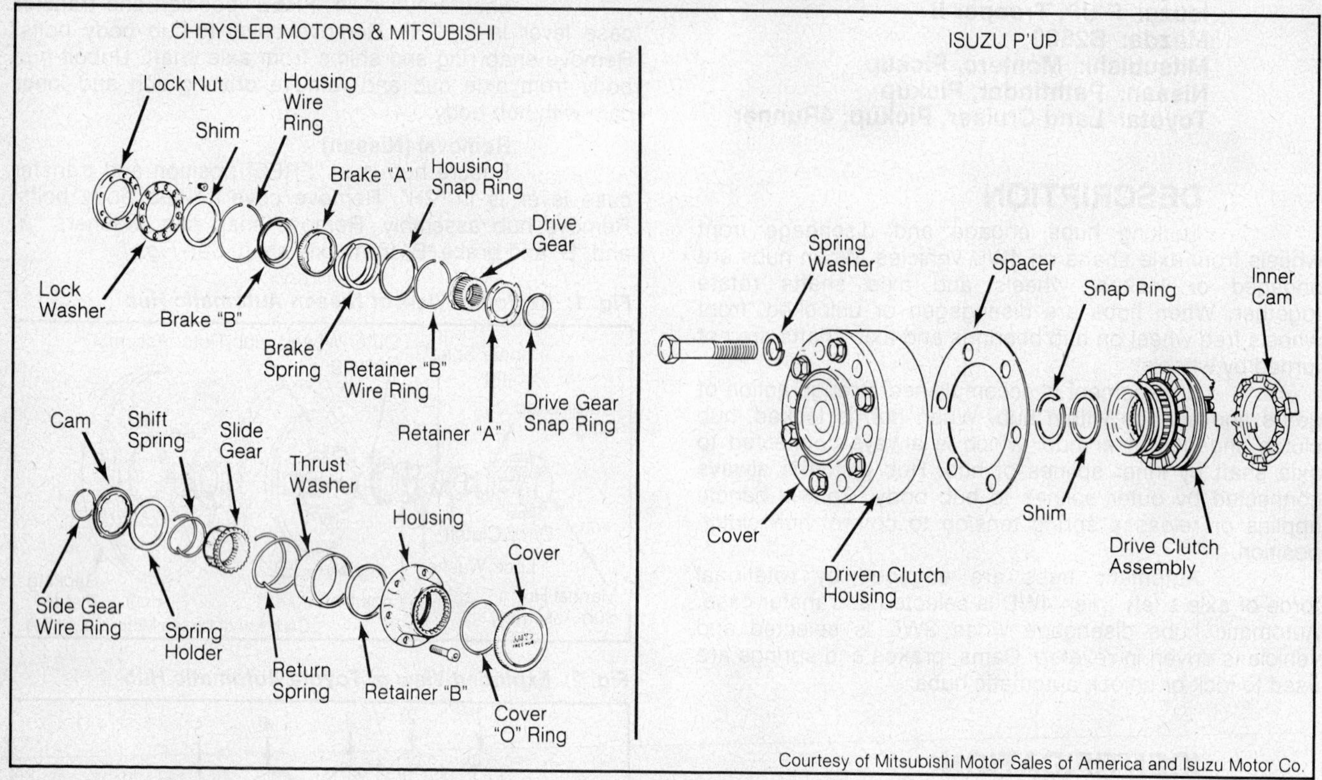

Courtesy of Mitsubishi Motor Sales of America and Isuzu Motor Co.

Removal (Toyota)

1) Ensure hub is in "FREE" position and transfer case lever is in "2H". Remove cover-to-hub body bolts. Remove hub cover. Remove center bolt with washer. Remove hub body mounting nuts. Using brass bar and hammer, tap on mounting studs and remove cone washers. Remove hub body.

2) Using a screwdriver, pry out snap ring. Remove brake sub-assembly. Using a Torx socket, remove screws and brake drum. *See Fig. 2.*

Installation

1) Install inner cam and drive clutch assembly on axle shaft and tighten bolts. Align key of brake "B" with slot on spindle, ensure axle hub-to-housing fit is tight, and tighten bolts. *See Fig. 3.*

2) On all models, ensure axle shaft end play is correct. Install snap ring with shim. On Isuzu models, apply Loctite 515 to driven clutch flange surface. Install driven clutch flange and tighten bolts. On Chrysler Motors and Mitsubishi, grease "O" ring and screw hub cover on tightly by hand.

OVERHAUL

MANUAL HUB

Disassembly

1) On Nissan models, remove 6 Torx head screws. Remove free running hub. Remove outer snap ring and drive clutch. Remove inner snap ring and lock washer. Remove wheel bearing lock nut using Lock Nut Socket (KV40104300). *See Fig. 4.*

Fig. 4: Exploded View of Nissan Manual Hub

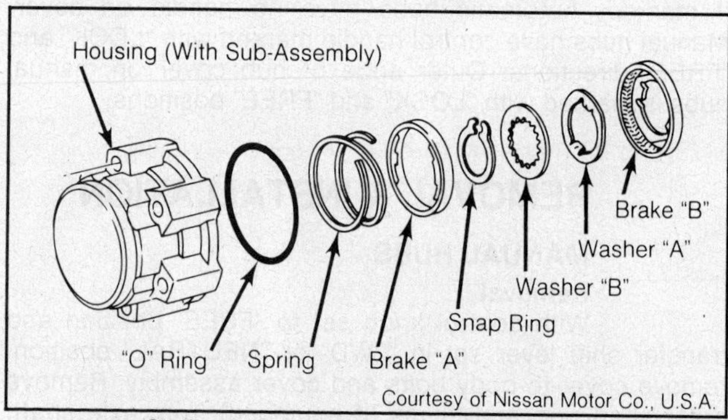

Courtesy of Nissan Motor Co., U.S.A.

2) On all other models, remove snap ring and control handle from hub cover. Remove detent ball and spring from control handle. Remove snap ring, inner hub and hub ring from body. Remove snap ring, hub ring and spacer from inner hub. *See Fig. 5.*

Inspection

1) Clean all hard parts in solvent. Inspect all parts for excessive wear or damage. Ensure control handle moves smoothly in cover. Check that clutch moves smoothly in hub body.

2) On Toyota models, measure inside diameter of hub ring at point "A" with vernier caliper. Measure outside diameter of inner hub at point "B" where hub ring rides. *See Fig. 6.* Value of "A" – "B" is oil clearance. Maximum oil clearance is .012" (.31 mm). Replace inner hub or hub ring if oil clearance is excessive.

Locking Hubs

ALL MANUFACTURERS (Cont.)

Fig. 5: Exploded View of All Other Models (Aisan) Manual Hub

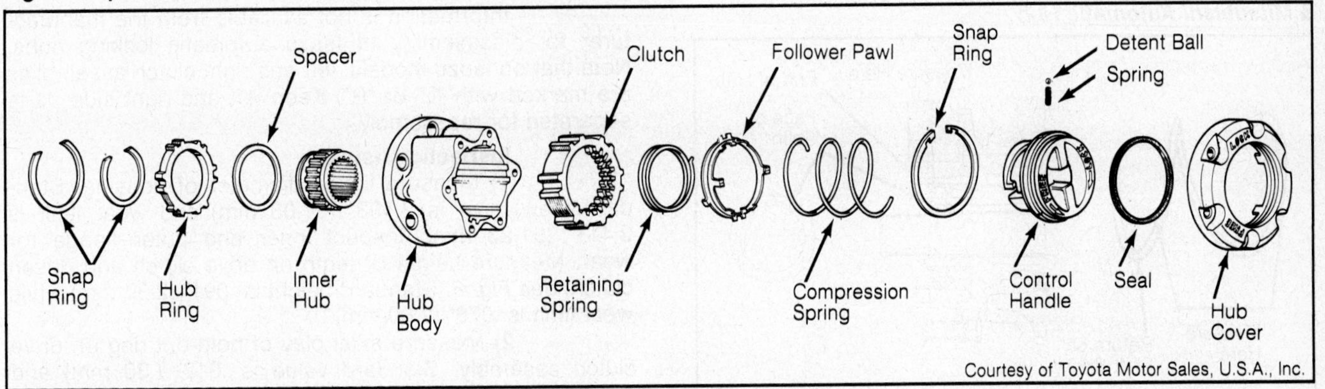

Toyota locking hub shown. Mazda locking hubs are similar.

Fig. 6: Measuring Toyota Inner Hub Oil Clearance

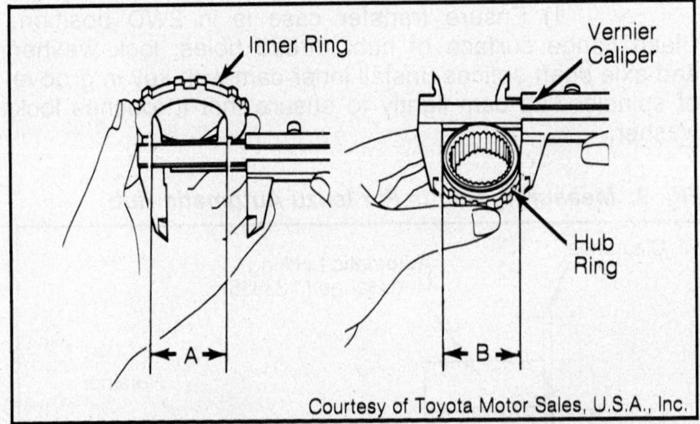

Reassembly

1) On Nissan models, reverse disassembly procedure. Lubricate free running hub. Adjust wheel bearing preload and axial play. See WHEEL BEARINGS in FRONT SUSPENSION article.

2) On all other models, apply grease to sliding surface of all parts. Install seal, detent ball and compression spring into control handle. Insert handle in cover and install snap ring. Install retaining spring in clutch with end of spring aligned with first groove cut in full width spline.

3) Install follower pawl on retaining spring with bent spring end hooked against one of large tabs on pawl. Top ring of retaining spring rides on small tabs. Place compression spring between clutch and cover with large end of spring against cover. Install clutch with pawl tab fitted to control handle.

4) Install spacer and hub ring on inner hub. Install snap ring. Insert inner hub and hub ring assembly in hub body. Install snap ring. Set control handle and clutch to "FREE" position. Install cover temporarily and ensure hub turns smoothly. Remove cover for installation procedure.

AUTOMATIC HUB

Disassembly (Chrysler Motors & Mitsubishi)

1) Pry wire ring from housing after pressing on brake "B". *See Fig. 3*. Remove brake "A", brake "B", brake spring and housing snap ring. Compress return spring by slowly pushing in on drive gear with press.

CAUTION: Use protective mat or covering under cover attaching surface before press operation is performed. Press force must not exceed 441 lbs. (200 kg).

2) Stroke of press must be more than 1.6" (41 mm) in order to compress return spring. Remove wire ring holding retainer "B". Slowly release press until return spring is fully extended. Ensure retainer "A" clears retainer "B".

3) Remove retainer "B", return spring, slide gear assembly and drive gear assembly from housing. Remove and discard snap ring on drive gear. Push down on cam and remove wire ring from slide gear.

Inspection (Chrysler Motors & Mitsubishi)

1) Check drive gear and slide gear splines for wear or damage. Check cam portion of retainer "A". Check cam, slide gear and housing teeth. Check retainer "B" and housing contact surfaces.

2) Assemble brakes "A" and "B". Set vernier caliper with jaws on both lugs of brake "A" at same time. Measure combined brake thickness. If measurement is less than .41" (10.4 mm), replace both brakes as a set.

3) Measure return spring and shift spring. *See Fig.* 7. Measure dimension shown from outside of one wire diameter to outside of other wire diameter. Return spring must be replaced if it measures less than 1.4" (36 mm). Replace shift spring if it measures less than 1.2" (30.5 mm).

Reassembly (Chrysler Motors & Mitsubishi)

1) Lightly grease mounting surfaces of all parts. Pack grooves of brake "B" and retainer "B" with grease. Grease slide gear and install return spring with smaller coil diameter toward seat. Measure starting torque of front hub assembly with spring scale.

2) If torque is outside range of 0.9-4.1 lbs. (.4-1.9 kg), adjust with lock nut setting. Measure depth of brake contact surface. *See Fig.* 7. Range of depth is .46-.48" (11.7-12.2 mm) and is adjusted by shims. Apply nonhardening sealant to hub surface.

3) Align key on brake "B" with slot in spindle and loosely install hub assembly. Check that hub surface and hub assembly face fit closely when hub assembly is pressed lightly against hub. Rotate hub until close fit is obtained. Tighten hub assembly-to-hub bolts.

Locking Hubs

ALL MANUFACTURERS (Cont.)

Fig. 7: Measuring Points for Chrysler Motors & Mitsubishi Automatic Hub

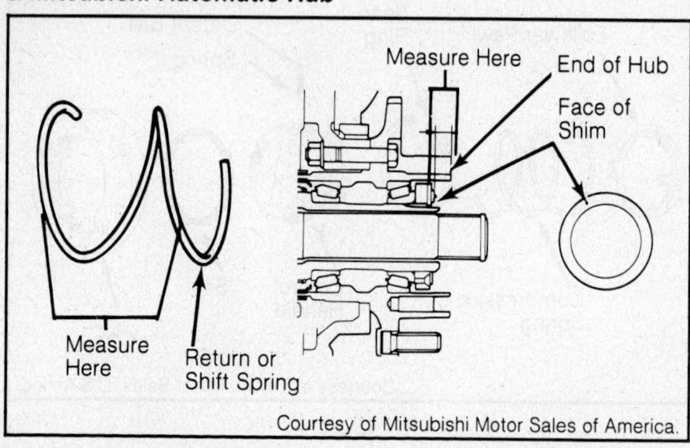

4) Install snap ring on axle shaft without shims. Mount dial indicator with tip on end of axle shaft and plunger at 90 degrees to rotor. Turn axle shaft back and forth until resistance is felt to find center of turning stroke. At this point, measure axial play (end play) of shaft. Range of .008-.020" (.20-.50 mm) is adjusted with shim.

5) Measure starting torque of hub assembly. If torque is different by 3.1 lbs. (1.4 kg) from torque of hub bearings alone, locking hub should be removed and reinstalled correctly. Apply grease to "O" ring and install in cover. Screw cover tightly onto hub by hand.

Fig. 8: Wear Point Measurements of Isuzu Automatic Hub

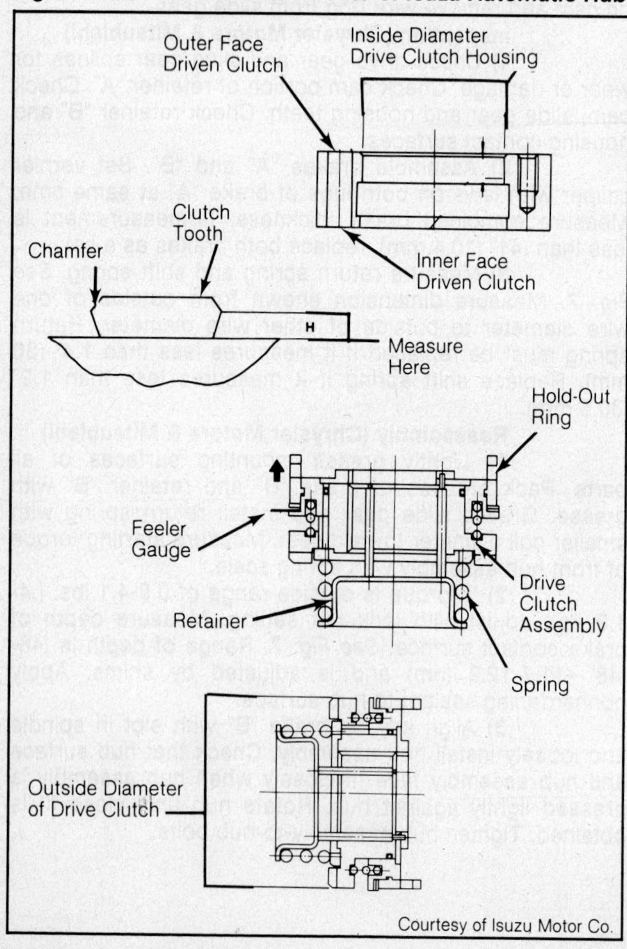

Disassembly (Isuzu)

Information is not available from the manufacturer for disassembly of Isuzu automatic locking hubs. Note that on Isuzu models, left and right clutch assemblies are marked with "L" or "R". Keep left and right side parts separated for reassembly.

Inspection (Isuzu)

1) Measure inside diameter of housing. Standard (new) size is 2.403" (61.03 mm) and wear limit is 2.411" (61.23 mm). Inspect inner and outer flange for wear. Measure height of teeth on drive clutch and driven clutch. *See Fig. 8*. Standard height is .091" (2.30 mm) while wear limit is .079" (2.00 mm).

2) Measure axial play of hold-out ring on drive clutch assembly. Standard value is .012" (.30 mm) and wear limit is .016" (.40 mm). Measure outside diameter of drive clutch assembly. Standard value is 2.39" (60.75 mm) and wear limit is 2.38" (60.45 mm).

Reassembly (Isuzu)

1) Ensure transfer case is in 2WD position. Clean flange surface of hub, thread holes, lock washer and axle shaft splines. Install inner cam with key in groove of spindle. Tap cam lightly to ensure that it touches lock washer.

Fig. 9: Measuring Points For Isuzu Automatic Hub

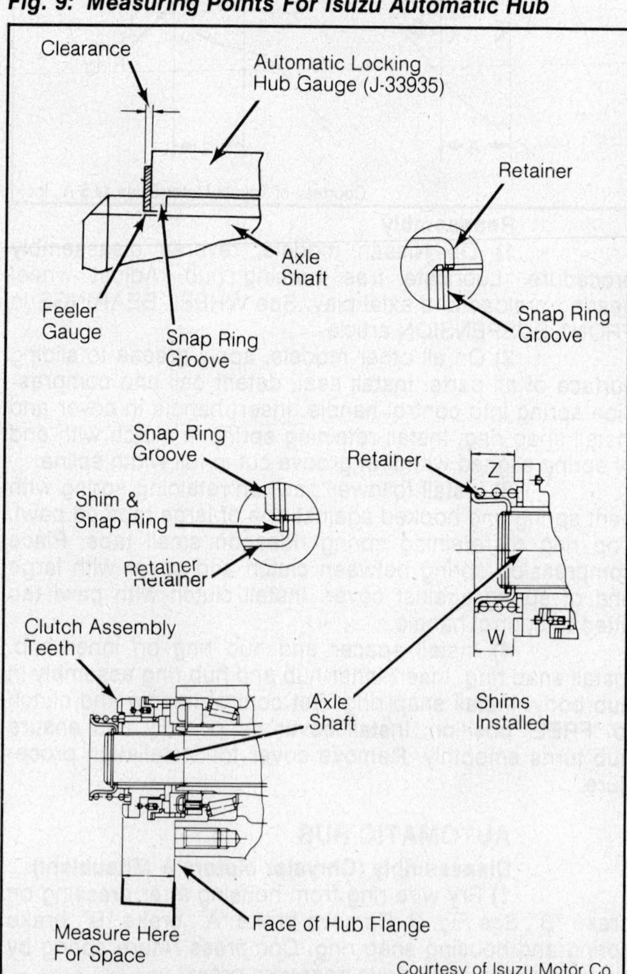

2) Hold inner cam and push stub axle of outer CV joint toward outside of wheel. Install Automatic Locking Hub Gauge (J-33935) on axle shaft so it touches

ALL MANUFACTURERS (Cont.)

lock washer. Measure clearance between outer face of gauge and outer edge of snap ring groove. *See Fig. 9.* Adjust clearance with shims to range of 0-.004" (0-.10 mm).

3) Remove gauge, making sure inner cam remains in place. Install drive clutch assembly. Check that assembly marked "L" is on left side and assembly marked "R" is on right side of vehicle. Lightly grease axle splines, inside of driven clutch, back and side grooves of drive clutch assembly.

4) Align cut portion of hold-out ring with convex part of drive clutch assembly. Align clutch assembly with inner cam and engage teeth of drive clutch with inner cam teeth. Measure distance from outer face of spring retainer on drive clutch assembly to outer face of teeth on drive clutch assembly. Record distance as "Z".

5) Using Snap Ring Installer (J-33934), install selected shims and install new snap ring. Ensure snap ring fits properly in groove of axle shaft. Measure distance from outer face of spring retainer to outer face of teeth on drive clutch assembly after installing snap ring and shims. Record distance as "W".

6) If "Z" – "W" is larger than .0028" (.7 mm), shim selection is correct. Measure distance from face of hub flange to outer face of clutch assembly teeth. *See Fig. 9.* For a distance of 1.00-1.04" (25.4-26.3 mm), no spacer is used. For a distance of 1.04-1.07" (26.3-27.2 mm), use 1 mm spacer. For a distance of 1.07-1.11" (27.3-28.1 mm), use 2 mm spacer.

7) Apply Loctite 515 to both sides of spacer and flange surface of driven clutch assembly. Install flange to driven clutch assembly. Tighten bolts. Apply Loctite 515 to flange surface of housing assembly. Install housing assembly with bolts and spring washers. Ensure housing assembly turns smoothly and tighten bolts.

Disassembly (Nissan)

Information is not available from the manufacturer for disassembly of Nissan automatic locking hubs. Keep left and right side parts separated for reassembly.

Inspection (Nissan)

Thoroughly clean and dry parts. Assemble brakes "A" and "B". Set vernier caliper with jaws on lugs of brakes "A" and "B" at same time. Measure combined brake thickness. If measurement is less than .61" (15.4 mm), replace both brakes as a set.

Reassembly (Nissan)

To reassemble, reverse order of disassembly. Ensure correct operation of hubs.

Disassembly (Toyota)

1) Using snap ring pliers, remove snap ring. remove remove inner hub sub-assembly. *See Fig. 2.* Remove outer cam. Using snap ring pliers, expand joint spring and release it from cam follower. Remove clutch with joint spring, preset spring and spring retainer.

2) Compress return spring and remove snap ring and inner cam. Remove cam follower and return spring.

Inspection (Toyota)

Remove thrust plate from brake sub-assembly. *See Fig. 2.* Without removing grease from brake drum or brake shoe and without removing spring inside of brake shoe, measure thickness of brake shoe. If measurement is less than .059" (1.5 mm), replace brake drum and shoe as an assembly.

Reassembly (Toyota)

To reassemble, reverse order of disassembly. Ensure correct operation of hubs.

TIGHTENING SPECIFICATIONS

Application	Ft. Lbs. (N.m)
Hub Body-to-Hub Bolt	
Chrysler Motors & Mitsubishi	36-43 (49-58)
Isuzu	40-47 (54-64)
Mazda	21-25 (29-34)
Toyota Land Cruiser	18-25 (24-34)
Toyota Pickup & 4Runner	21-25 (29-34)
Cover-to-Hub Body Bolt	
Chrysler Motors & Mitsubishi	7-10 (9-14)
Isuzu	17.0-22.0 (23-30)
Nissan	18-25 (24-34)
	INCH Lbs. (N.m)
Cover-to-Hub Body	
Toyota Land Cruiser	36-60 (4-7)
Toyota Pickup & 4Runner	72-96 (8-11)

SECTION 9

BRAKES

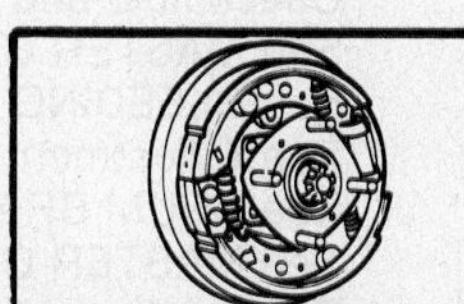

CONTENTS

TROUBLE SHOOTING **Page**

All Models 9-2

HYDRAULIC BRAKE BLEEDING

All Models 9-3

BRAKE SYSTEMS

Acura 9-4
Audi 9-14
BMW 9-22
Chrysler Motors 9-27
Ford Motor Co.
Festiva & Merkur XR4Ti 9-37
Tracer 9-44

BRAKE SYSTEMS (Cont.) **Page**

General Motors
Spectrum & Sprint 9-53
Honda 9-4
Hyundai Excel 9-58
Isuzu
I-Mark 9-53
Impulse 9-63
P'UP & Trooper II 9-68
Jaguar 9-76
Mazda 9-44
Mercedes-Benz
190, 260, 300, 420 & 560 Series 9-82
Mitsubishi
Precis 9-58
All Others 9-27
Nissan 9-86
Peugeot 9-97
Porsche 9-101
Saab
900, 900S & 900 Turbo 9-106
9000 9-110
Sterling 9-113
Subaru 9-115
Suzuki 9-121
Toyota 9-126
Volkswagen 9-142
Volvo 9-149
Yugo 9-154

ANTI-LOCK BRAKE SYSTEMS

Acura 9-157
Audi 9-163
BMW 9-176
Chrysler Motors Conquest 9-185
Jaguar 9-187
Mazda
RX7 9-192
Mercedes-Benz 9-194
Mitsubishi Starion 9-185
Peugeot 9-203
Porsche 9-209
Saab 9-222
Sterling 9-225
Toyota 9-230
Volvo 9-242

NOTE: **ALSO SEE GENERAL INDEX.**

Brakes

BRAKE SYSTEM TROUBLE SHOOTING

CONDITION	POSSIBLE CAUSE	CORRECTION
Brakes Pull Left or Right	Incorrect tire pressure	Inflate tires to proper pressure
	Front end out of alignment	See WHEEL ALIGNMENT
	Mismatched tires	Check tires sizes
	Restricted brake lines or hoses	Check hose routing
	Loose or malfunctioning caliper	See DISC BRAKES
	Bent shoe or oily linings	See DRUM BRAKES
	Malfunctioning rear brakes	See DRUM or DISC BRAKES
	Loose suspension parts	See SUSPENSION
Noises Without Brakes Applied	Front linings worn out	Replace linings
	Dust or oil on drums or rotors	See DRUM or DISC BRAKES
Noises with Brakes Applied	Insulator on outboard shoe damaged	See DISC BRAKES
	Incorrect pads or linings	Replace pads or linings
Brake Rough, Chatters or Pulsates	Excessive lateral runout	Check rotor runout
	Parallelism not to specifications	Reface or replace rotor
	Wheel bearings not adjusted	See SUSPENSION
	Rear drums out-of-round	Reface or replace drums
	Disc pad reversed, steel against rotor	Remove and reinstall pad
Excessive Pedal Effort	Malfunctioning power unit	See POWER BRAKES
	Partial system failure	Check fluid and pipes
	Worn disc pad or lining	Replace pad or lining
	Caliper piston stuck or sluggish	See DISC BRAKES
	Master cylinder piston stuck	See MASTER CYLINDERS
	Brake fade due to incorrect pads or linings	Replace pads or linings
	Linings or pads glazed	Replace pads or linings
	Worn drums	Reface or replace drums
Excessive Pedal Travel	Partial brake system failure	Check fluid and pipes
	Insufficient fluid in master cylinder	See MASTER CYLINDERS
	Air trapped in system	See BLEEDING
	Rear brakes not adjusted	See Adjustment in DRUM BRAKES
	Bent shoe or lining	See DRUM BRAKES
	Plugged master cylinder cap	See MASTER CYLINDER
	Improper brake fluid	Replace brake fluid
Pedal Travel Decreasing	Compensating port plugged	See MASTER CYLINDERS
	Swollen cup in master cylinder	See MASTER CYLINDERS
	Master cylinder piston not returning	See MASTER CYLINDERS
	Weak shoe retracting springs	See DRUM BRAKES
	Wheel cylinder piston sticking	See DRUM BRAKES
Dragging Brakes	Master cylinder pistons not returning	See MASTER CYLINDERS
	Restricted brake lines or hoses	Check line routing
	Incorrect parking brake adjustment	See DRUM BRAKES
	Parking brake cables frozen	See DRUM BRAKES
	Incorrect installation of inboard disc pad	Remove and replace correctly
	Power booster output rod too long	See POWER BRAKE UNITS
	Brake pedal not returning freely	See DISC or DRUM BRAKES
Brakes Grab or Uneven Braking Action	Malfunction of combination valve	See CONTROL VALVES
	Malfunction of power brake unit	See POWER BRAKE UNITS
	Binding brake pedal	See DISC or DRUM BRAKES
Pulsation or Roughness	Uneven pad wear caused by caliper	See DISC BRAKES
	Uneven rotor wear	See DISC BRAKES
	Drums out-of-round	Reface or replace drums

HYDRAULIC BRAKE BLEEDING

DESCRIPTION

Hydraulic system bleeding is necessary any time air has been introduced into system. Bleed brakes at all 4 wheels if master cylinder lines have been disconnected or master cylinder has run dry.

Bleeding may be done either by using pressure bleeding equipment or by manually pumping brake pedal and using bleeder tubes.

NOTE: **For vehicles equipped with Anti-Lock Brake Systems (ABS), see appropriate ANTI-LOCK BRAKE SYSTEM article in this section.**

BLEEDING PRECAUTIONS

On all models equipped with load sensing proportioning valve, bleed valve before bleeding brakes. If master cylinder is equipped with bleed screw, bleed master cylinder first.

MANUAL BLEEDING

1) On Isuzu, Jaguar and Spectrum models, start engine and run at idle. On all other models, exhaust all vacuum from power unit by depressing brake pedal several times.

2) Fill master cylinder. Install clear vinyl bleeder hose onto first bleeder valve to be serviced. See BRAKE LINE BLEEDING SEQUENCE table. Place other end of hose in clean glass jar.

3) Partially fill jar with clean brake fluid, so end of hose is submerged in fluid. Open bleeder valve 1-2 turns. Depress brake pedal slowly through its full travel.

4) Close bleeder valve, then release pedal. Pump pedal several times to push air toward wheel cylinders. Repeat procedure until flow of brake fluid is clear, and shows no signs of air bubbles. Proceed to next bleeder valve.

NOTE: **Check fluid level in master cylinder frequently during the bleeding sequence.**

PRESSURE TANK BLEEDING

1) On Isuzu, Jaguar and Spectrum models, start engine and run at idle. On all other models, exhaust all vacuum from power unit by depressing brake pedal several times.

2) Clean the master cylinder cap and surrounding area, then remove cap. With pressure tank at least 1/3 full, connect tank to the master cylinder using proper fitting adapter(s).

3) Attach bleeder hose to first bleeder valve to be serviced. See BRAKE LINE BLEEDING SEQUENCE table. Place other end of hose in clean glass jar. Partially fill jar with clean brake fluid, until end of hose is submerged in fluid.

4) Open release valve on pressure bleeder. Unscrew bleeder valve 1-2 turns, noting fluid flow. When fluid flowing into container is clear, and free of bubbles, close bleeder valve securely.

5) Bleed remaining cylinders in correct sequence and in same manner. Remove pressure tank from master cylinder and check fluid level of master cylinder reservoir.

BLEEDING SEQUENCE

See BRAKE LINE BLEEDING SEQUENCE table for proper bleeding sequence.

BRAKE LINE BLEEDING SEQUENCE

Application	Sequence
Acura & Honda	LF, RR, RF, LR
Audi & Volkswagon [1]	RR, LR, RF, LF
BMW [2]	Longest Line First
Chevrolet Spectrum [3]	LF, RR, RF, LR
Chevrolet Sprint	LR, RF, RR, LF
Chrysler Corp. Imports	
Colt & Colt Vista	LR, RF, RR, LF
Models W/Load Sensing Proportioning Valve	RR, LR, RF, LF
All Others	RR, LR, RF, LF
Ford Motor Co. Imports	
Festiva	Longest Line First
Merkur	RR, LR, Rf, LF
Tracer	Longest Line First
Hyundai	LR, RF, RR, RF
Isuzu	
I-Mark, P'UP & Trooper II [3]	LF, RR, RF, LR
Impulse	RR, LR, RF, LF
Jaguar [3]	LR, RR, Front
Mazda	Longest Line First
Mercedez-Benz	Longest Line First
Mitsubishi	
Cordia, Tredia	LR, RF, RR, LF
Precis	LR, RF, RR, LF
All Others	RR, LR, RF, LF
Nissan	LR, RR, RF, LF
Peugeot [4]	Longest Line First
Porsche [5]	LR, RR, RF, LF
Saab	LR, RF, RR, LF
Sterling	LF, RR, RF, LR
Subaru	
Justy	Longest Line First
All Others	FR, RF, RR, LF
Suzuki	LR, RF, RR, LF
Toyota	Longest Line First
Volvo [6]	
240	LF, RF, LR, RR
All Others	RR, LR, RF, LF
Yugo	RF, LF, LR, RR

[1] – Before bleeding rear brakes, push brake pressure regulator in direction of rear axle. Bleed regulator first.

[2] – If equipped with 3 bleeder valves on each front caliper, bleed lower inboard valve first, then other 2 simultaneously.

[3] – Engine running at idle speed.

[4] – If pressure tank is used, bleed all wheels simultaneously.

[5] – If equipped with inner and outer caliper bleeder valves, bleed outer valves first, then inner valves.

[6] – Raise rear wheels a few inches higher than front wheels. Front calipers have 3 bleeder valves. Bleed all 3 valves simultaneously.

ACURA & HONDA

Acura: Legend, Integra;
Honda: Accord, Civic, CRX, Prelude

DESCRIPTION

All models are equipped with front disc brakes. Legend, Integra and Prelude models are equipped with rear disc brakes. All other models are equipped with rear drum brakes. Parking brake is cable-actuated at rear wheels.

TESTING

POWER BRAKE UNIT

Functional Test

1) Start engine. Turn ignition switch to "OFF" position. Depress brake pedal several times. Depress pedal hard and hold pressure for 15 seconds. If pedal sinks, master cylinder, brake line or wheel cylinder is faulty.

2) Start engine with pedal depressed. If pedal sinks slightly, vacuum unit is working. If pedal height does not vary, booster or check valve is faulty.

Leak Test

1) Depress brake pedal with engine running. Turn ignition switch to "OFF" position. If pedal height does not vary while depressed for 30 seconds, vacuum unit is okay. If pedal rises, vacuum unit is faulty.

2) With engine stopped, depress brake pedal several times using normal pressure. Pedal should be low when first depressed. On consecutive applications, pedal height should gradually rise. If pedal height does not vary, check power brake unit check valve.

Check Valve Test

1) On Accord models, disconnect both ends of power brake booster unit vacuum hose. Check valve is inside hose and cannot be removed.

NOTE: **Mark hose ends for correct reassembly. Power unit will not function if hose ends are reversed.**

2) Use 20 psi (1.4 kg/cm²) air pressure to blow through hose. Air should flow from power unit to manifold but not from manifold to power unit. Replace check valve if air passes from manifold to power unit.

3) On all other models, disconnect power brake unit vacuum hose at booster. Start engine and allow it to idle. Ensure vacuum is available at booster end of hose. If vacuum is not available, check valve is not functioning. Replace check valve and retest.

STOPLIGHT SWITCH

1) Check continuity of stoplight switch between terminals. Using ohmmeter, place one probe on each terminal. With switch plunger pushed in, there should be no continuity.

2) With switch plunger released, there should be continuity. If there is no continuity, replace switch. If switch is replaced, check brake pedal height and readjust (if necessary).

PARKING BRAKE SWITCH

Attach one ohmmeter test probe to switch lead wire and the other to body ground. With parking brake lever pulled up, there should be continuity. With lever down, there should be no continuity. If readings are incorrect, replace switch.

ADJUSTMENTS

REAR DRUM BRAKE SHOES

Accord and Civic models rear brake shoes are self-adjusted by brake pedal action. No in-service adjustment is required.

REAR WHEEL SPINDLE NUT

1) On Prelude, tighten spindle nut to 14-22 ft. lbs. (20-30 N.m). Manually turn brake drum or rotor. Loosen spindle nut. Retighten spindle nut to 48 INCH lbs. (5 N.m).

2) Install pin holder with slots as close as possible to hole in spindle. Tighten enough to align slot with hole. Install cotter pin and hub unit cap. Check wheel bearing drag by turning rotor with spring scale attached.

NOTE: **On Prelude, loosen parking brake adjuster before checking wheel bearing drag.**

3) Standard spring scale reading is .9-4.0 lbs. (4-18 N) for drag measurement. If reading exceeds specifications, check for damaged bearing or improper spindle nut torque.

4) On all other models, check rear wheel (swing) bearing end play. Mount dial indicator on suspension arm with pointer on rear wheel hub unit cap. Standard end play is .002" (.05 mm). If adjustment is required, remove hub unit cap and loosen hub nut.

5) Remove nut staking from spindle groove (if necessary). Loosen nut. On Civic and Integra retighten nut to 134 ft. lbs. (185 N.m). On Legend tighten nut to 180 ft. lbs. (244 N.m). Stake hub unit nut shoulder against spindle groove after tightening. Install hub unit cap.

PEDAL PLAY & HEIGHT

1) Pedal height is measured from center of pedal pad to floorboard (without carpet or floormat). To adjust, loosen stoplight switch lock nut and back switch away from brake pedal arm.

2) Loosen power unit push rod lock nut and rotate push rod to adjust pedal height. On Integra, Civic Hatchback, CRX and Sedan models pedal height is 6.850" (174.0 mm). On Civic Wagon models pedal height is 6.614" (168.0 mm). On Legend pedal height is 6.717" (170.6 mm). On Prelude models, pedal height is 7.000" (176.0 mm). On Accord models, pedal height is 8.070" (205.0 mm).

3) Tighten lock nut. Adjust stoplight switch. Check for proper brake pedal free play. Brake pedal free play on all models is .040-.200" (1.0-5.0 mm).

STOPLIGHT SWITCH

1) Stoplight switch is located under dash, above brake pedal. To adjust, loosen lock nuts and turn switch until plunger is fully depressed (threaded end touching pedal arm pad).

2) Back off switch 1/2 turn and tighten lock nuts. Ensure brake lights go off when pedal is released.

PARKING BRAKE

NOTE: **When servicing drum brakes, depress brake pedal several times to set self-adjusting brakes before adjusting parking brake.**

ACURA & HONDA (Cont.)

1) With rear brakes adjusted, raise and support rear of vehicle on safety stands.

2) Loosen equalizer nut and pull brake lever up one notch. Tighten adjusting nut until rear wheels drag slightly.

3) Release brake lever. Rear wheels should rotate freely. Rear wheels should lock on Accord and Legend when lever is pulled 7-11 notches. All other models wheels lock when lever is pulled 4-8 notches.

BRAKE WARNING LIGHT

Brake warning light indicates parking brake is engaged and/or warns of low brake fluid level. To adjust parking brake light operation, turn ignition switch to "ON" position. Bend switch plate down until light comes on when parking brake lever is pulled one notch and goes out when lever is released.

PUSH ROD

NOTE: Master cylinder push rod-to-piston clearance must be checked and adjusted before installing master cylinder.

Master Cylinder

1) Using Rod Bolt Adjustment Gauge (07GAG-SE00100), mount gauge to master cylinder. Ensure top of bolt is flush with end of master cylinder piston.

2) Install rod seal of master cylinder between brake booster and rod bolt adjustment gauge. Place gauge upside down on power brake unit without disturbing adjusting bolt position. Install master cylinder nuts and tighten.

3) Connect power unit in line with vacuum gauge that will read 0-30 in. Hg to power brake unit's engine vacuum supply. Start engine and set RPM to allow reading of 20 in. Hg of vacuum.

4) Measure clearance between output rod and adjusting bolt with feeler gauge. Clearance between push rod and piston should be .016" (.40 mm) for all models. If adjustment is required, loosen star lock nut and turn adjuster in or out.

Power Brake Unit

Loosen power booster push rod lock nut. Adjust push rod length to 4.6-5.0" (117-127 mm).

REMOVAL & INSTALLATION

DISC BRAKE PADS

Removal (Front)

1) Raise and support front of vehicle. Remove wheels. Remove lower caliper guide pin and pivot caliper body out of way or remove caliper bolts.

2) Remove pads, and pad shim. Remove upper and lower anti-rattle springs, pad spring and pad retainers (if equipped). Using a vernier caliper, measure brake friction pad surfaces for wear. Measurement does not include shoe thickness. Minimum brake pad thickness is .12" (3.0 mm).

3) Thickness of each pad in a set must not vary more than .080" (2.0 mm). If lining thickness varies greatly, check caliper for free movement and adequate lubrication.

NOTE: Replace brake pads in axle sets of 4 pads. Ensure grease, brake fluid or other contaminants do not contact lining surface. Inspect, clean and resurface rotor as necessary.

Installation

1) Lubricate shim and sliding surfaces with high temperature silicone grease. Install anti-rattle springs, pad springs or pad retainers.

2) Install shim against outer pad. Install brake pads. Ensure brake pad (with pad wear indicator) is installed inside. Loosen bleeder screw and push piston into caliper bore with finger pressure.

3) Tighten bleeder screw. Ensure brake fluid does not contaminate pads. Position caliper and install lower guide pin or caliper bolts. Depress brake pedal several times to seat pads. Bleed brakes as necessary.

Removal (Rear)

1) Raise and support rear of vehicle. Remove wheels. Remove caliper shield. Detach parking brake cable by removing clip mounting cable to caliper (if necessary). Pull out lock pin from caliper to cable attachment. Remove pin from caliper.

2) Detach caliper mounting bolts. Remove caliper from bracket. Remove brake pads. Measure friction lining thickness. Service limit on all models is .063" (1.60 mm).

Installation

1) Install pad guides in caliper bracket. Install brake pads. Rotate caliper piston clockwise in caliper (if necessary). Ensure cut-out in piston aligns with tab on inner pad.

2) Avoid twisting piston boot. If boot is twisted, back out and reposition boot. Install brake caliper and parking brake cable. Install caliper shield. Tighten shield mounting bolts to 84 INCH lbs. (10 N.m). Pump brake pedal several times to seat pads. Bleed brakes as required.

DISC BRAKE CALIPER

NOTE: Front disc brake calipers are of the same basic design. Only caliper-to-bracket attachments and anti-rattle springs or clips differ between models.

Removal (Front)

1) Raise and support front of vehicle. Remove wheels. Remove banjo bolt and copper washers connecting brake line to caliper. Plug hydraulic line and caliper.

2) On all models, detach caliper guide pins or bolts and remove caliper. Avoid damage of splash guard on upper caliper bolt side during removal (if equipped). Remove disc pads, pad retainers, upper and lower anti-rattle springs and shim.

Installation

To install, reverse removal procedure. Replace copper banjo bolt washers when installing brake flex hose. Bleed brake system.

Removal (Rear)

1) Raise and support rear of vehicle. Remove wheels. Detach caliper shield mounting bolts. Remove shield. Remove parking brake cable from caliper.

2) Remove banjo bolt and copper washers connecting brake line to caliper. Plug hydraulic line and caliper. Detach caliper mounting bolts and remove caliper.

Installation

To install, reverse removal procedure. Replace copper banjo bolt washers when installing brake flex hose. Bleed brake system.

ACURA & HONDA (Cont.)

DISC BRAKE ROTOR

Removal (Front & Rear)

1) Raise and support vehicle. Remove wheels. Remove caliper assembly and suspend with wire. Check rotor runout before removal. On all rotors except Prelude rear, detach and remove two 6 mm rotor retaining screws.

2) Install two 8 x 1.25 x 12 mm bolts in existing holes. To prevent warpage, alternately turn bolts 2 turns at a time until disc can be removed from front hub. Clean rotor of all rust and inspect rotor surfaces for cracks and grooves. Resurface or replace rotor as required.

3) To remove rear rotor on Prelude models, remove dust cap. Remove cotter pin and pin retainer. Remove hub nut with hub washer and outer wheel bearing. Remove rotor from rear spindle. Inspect inner and outer wheel bearings and replace as required. Clean rotor of all rust and inspect rotor surfaces for cracks and grooves. Resurface or replace rotor as required.

4) Inspect Prelude models rear brake rotor wheel bearings and races for excessive wear, pitting or damage. If removal is necessary, drive inner and outer bearing races from rotor hub in a cross pattern to prevent cocking of bearing in bore. Clean bearing race seats thoroughly before installation of new race.

5) Drive in new races. Ensure races are completely seated in hub with Bearing Race Installer (07946-6920100) and Driver (07749-0010000). Pack multi-purpose grease in new wheel bearings. Install inner bearing and new grease seal.

Installation

1) On front rotor, reverse removal procedure to complete installation. Tighten retaining screws. Bleed hydraulic system (if necessary). On rear rotor of Prelude models, slide rotor over spindle and install outer bearing, washer and spindle nut.

2) On rear rotor of Prelude model, tighten spindle nut to 14-22 ft. lbs. (20-30 N.m) while rotating rotor by hand. Loosen spindle nut. Retighten nut to 48 INCH lbs. (5 N.m). Set pin retainer with slots as close as possible to pin hole in spindle. Tighten nut just enough to align slot and new cotter pin.

3) Check bearing drag using spring scale. Loosen parking brake adjuster before checking. Attach spring scale to rear rotor wheel stud. Turn rotor. Standard rear wheel bearing drag is .9-4.0 lbs. (4-18 N). If reading exceeds specifications recheck spindle nut torque.

BRAKE DRUM

Removal

1) Raise and support vehicle. Remove rear wheels. Pull brake drum off hub. If hub is difficult to remove, use slide hammer with hub puller attachment.

2) On all models, inspect lining friction surface of drum for grooves, excessive wear or damage. Using an inside micrometer, measure the I.D. of brake drum. Resurface drum when new linings are installed. Replace drum if specifications are exceeded.

Installation

To install, reverse removal procedure.

BRAKE SHOES

Removal

1) Raise and support rear of vehicle. Remove rear wheels and brake drums. Detach shoe retaining springs by pushing in on spring and turning tension pin 90 degrees to align with spring slot.

2) Lower brake shoe assembly to clear wheel cylinder and remove lower return spring. Note original position of all springs. *See Fig. 1*.

CAUTION: Ensure wheel cylinder rubber dust covers are not damaged during brake shoe removal.

3) Remove brake shoe assembly. Disconnect parking brake cable from parking brake lever assembly. Remove upper return spring. Separate brake shoes. Remove self-adjuster bolt, lever and spring.

4) Pry off circlip and remove washer, pivot pin and parking brake lever (if necessary). Mark parking brake lever for left or right position. Check for worn or damaged ratchet teeth.

NOTE: Inspect brake shoes for distortion, nicks or burrs, and loose, glazed, cracked or oil-soaked linings.

5) Check all springs for weakness or damage. Inspect brake linings for excessive wear or damage. Lining service limit is .080" (2.0 mm).

6) Replace linings (and springs) in axle sets only. Ensure brake drums are resurfaced when new linings are installed. New linings should be arc-ground to resurfaced or new drum I.D.

Fig. 1: Exploded View of Rear Drum Brake Assembly

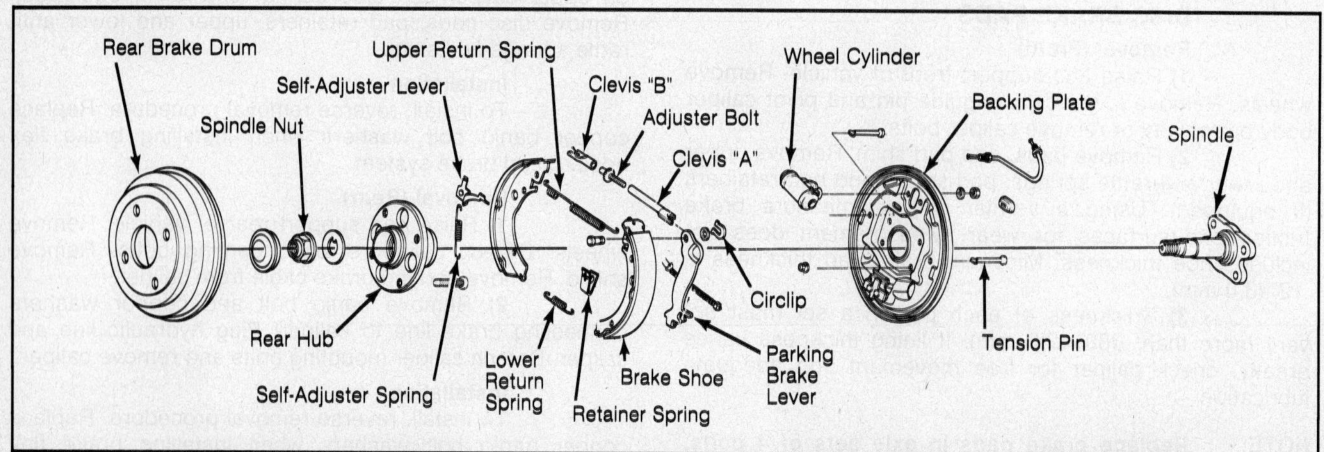

Courtesy of American Honda Motor Co., Inc.

Installation

1) Apply a light coat of high temperature grease to threads of adjuster assembly, sliding surfaces of brake shoes and metal contact areas of backing plate. Install parking brake lever to brake shoe.

2) Screw in self-adjuster bolt until it stops. Install parking brake cable on lever. To complete installation, reverse removal procedure. Adjust brakes. Bleed system as necessary.

WHEEL CYLINDER

Removal & Installation

With rear brake drum and brake shoes removed, detach and plug hydraulic fluid line at cylinder. Detach wheel cylinder mounting bolts. Remove wheel cylinder from backing plate. To install, reverse removal procedure. Bleed hydraulic system.

MASTER CYLINDER

Removal

Drain hydraulic fluid from master cylinder and disconnect hydraulic lines. Remove retaining nuts and master cylinder from power brake unit.

Installation

To install, reverse removal procedure. Bench bleed master cylinder before installation. Check push rod length. See PUSH ROD LENGTH under ADJUSTMENTS.

POWER BRAKE UNIT

Removal

1) Disconnect vacuum hose at power brake unit. Disconnect hydraulic lines at master cylinder. Remove cotter pin, and clevis pin, retaining power brake unit push rod to brake pedal.

2) Remove 4 bolts (accessible from inside vehicle) attaching power unit to firewall. Remove power brake unit and master cylinder as an assembly. Detach master cylinder.

Installation

To install, reverse removal procedure. See PUSH ROD LENGTH under ADJUSTMENTS. Tighten all bolts. Bleed hydraulic system.

REAR AXLE BEARINGS & OIL SEAL

Removal (Prelude)

1) Raise and support vehicle. Remove rear wheels. Remove dust cap, cotter pin, pin retainer, spindle nut, washer and outer wheel bearing.

2) Detach brake caliper and remove rotor. Pry grease seal from drum/rotor hub and discard. Inspect outer and inner wheel bearings. Replace wheel bearings as necessary.

Installation

To install, reverse removal procedure. Ensure hub, bearings and new seal are packed with grease. Tap in a cross pattern to avoid cocking seal in bore. Adjust rear wheel spindle nut. See ADJUSTMENTS, in this article.

NOTE: All other models use a permanently sealed bearing assembly that requires unit removal from vehicle. See appropriate article in REAR SUSPENSION section.

OVERHAUL

DISC BRAKE CALIPER

Disassembly (Front)

1) Remove piston dust boot retaining snap ring and brake pad spring (if equipped). Remove piston dust boot and 2 guide sleeve dust covers. Place shop towels around caliper and in front of piston to prevent brake fluid overspray or piston/caliper damage during removal.

CAUTION: Ensure brake fluid does not spill on painted surfaces or damage to finish will result. Do not place fingers in front of piston when air pressure is used for removal.

Fig. 2: Exploded View of Front Disc Brake Caliper Assembly (Accord, Integra & Prelude W/Fuel Injection)

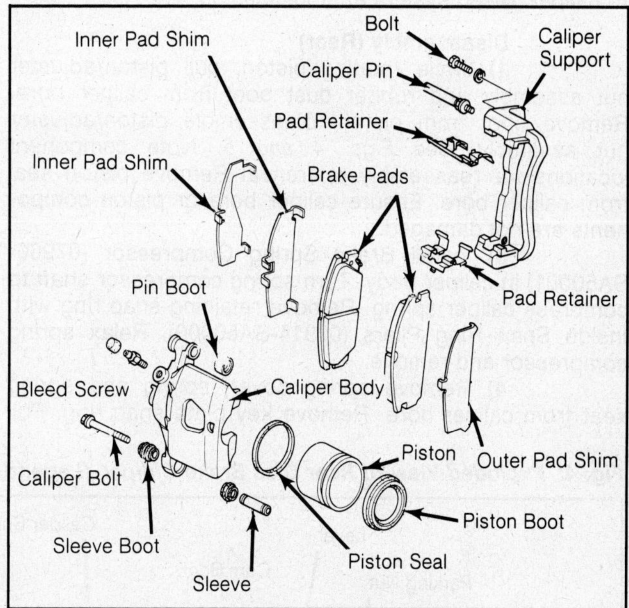

Courtesy of American Honda Motor Co., Inc.

Fig. 3: Exploded View of Front Disc Brake Caliper Assembly (All Others)

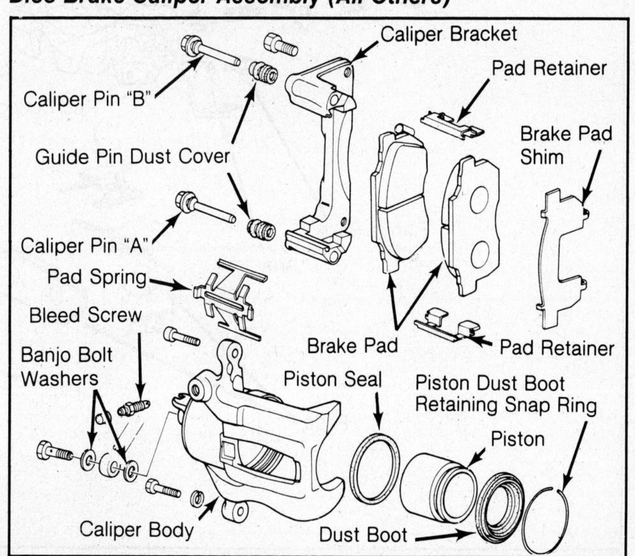

Courtesy of American Honda Motor Co., Inc.

ACURA & HONDA (Cont.)

2) Force piston out of caliper bore by slowly applying 30 psi (2.1 kg/cm²) air pressure to brake fluid inlet port. Remove piston square ring seal. Ensure caliper bore is not scored or damaged during removal of seal. Discard rubber components. *See Figs. 2 and 3.*

Reassembly

1) Apply clean brake fluid to caliper bore, piston surface and new piston seal. Install piston square ring seal in caliper bore.

2) Apply silicone grease at piston-to-dust seal ridge of piston. Install new dust boot on piston. Gently seat piston in caliper bore using finger pressure only.

3) Evenly seat outside metal edge of dust seal in caliper. Ensure dust seal outer ring is not buckled or crimped. Install new dust covers on guide sleeves (or caliper pins). Replace washers when installing brake line to caliper. Bleed system after installation.

Disassembly (Rear)

1) While rotating piston, pull piston/adjuster nut assembly and rubber dust boot from caliper bore. Remove boot from piston. Disassemble piston/adjuster nut assembly. *See Figs. 4 and 5.* Note component locations for reassembly reference. Remove piston seal from caliper bore. Ensure caliper bore or piston components are not damaged.

3) Install Brake Spring Compressor (07960-SA50001) in caliper body. Turn spring compressor shaft to compress caliper spring. Remove retaining snap ring with Inside Snap Ring Pliers (07914-SA50000). Relax spring compressor and remove.

4) Remove spring cover, spring and spring seat from caliper bore. Remove key plate snap ring. Pull out key plate, push rod, "O" ring and pin. Detach lever guide. Disconnect parking brake cable lever return spring from side of caliper (if necessary).

5) Detach nut with lock washer and remove cable lever. Pull parking brake cam from caliper bore. Remove rubber cam boot. Wash all parts in clean brake fluid. Inspect components for excessive wear or damage and replace as required. Replace all rubber components.

NOTE: **Inspect needle roller bearing in parking brake cam bore for wear or damage. Replace as required.**

Reassembly

1) Pack new parking brake cam boot with silicone grease and install in cam bore. Pack needle bearing with silicone grease. Install cam with threaded end up. Install lever, lock washer and nut. Connect return spring. Install lever guide (if removed).

2) Coat parts with silicone grease. Install new "O" ring and key plate on push rod. Position pin in push rod. Install push rod assembly in caliper piston bore and on cam. Ensure pin does not fall out.

3) Align locating lug on key plate with hole in base of caliper bore. Install snap ring over key plate. Install spring seat and spring onto push rod. Place spring cover in Rear Caliper Guide (07973-SA50000), aligning grooves in cover with slits in guide. Install assembly in bore.

4) Install brake spring compressor on spring cover/rear caliper guide assembly. Compress spring until it bottoms. Ensure caliper guide does not hang up while spring is being compressed.

Fig. 4: Exploded View of Rear Disc Brake Caliper (Legend, Integra & Prelude W/Fuel Injection)

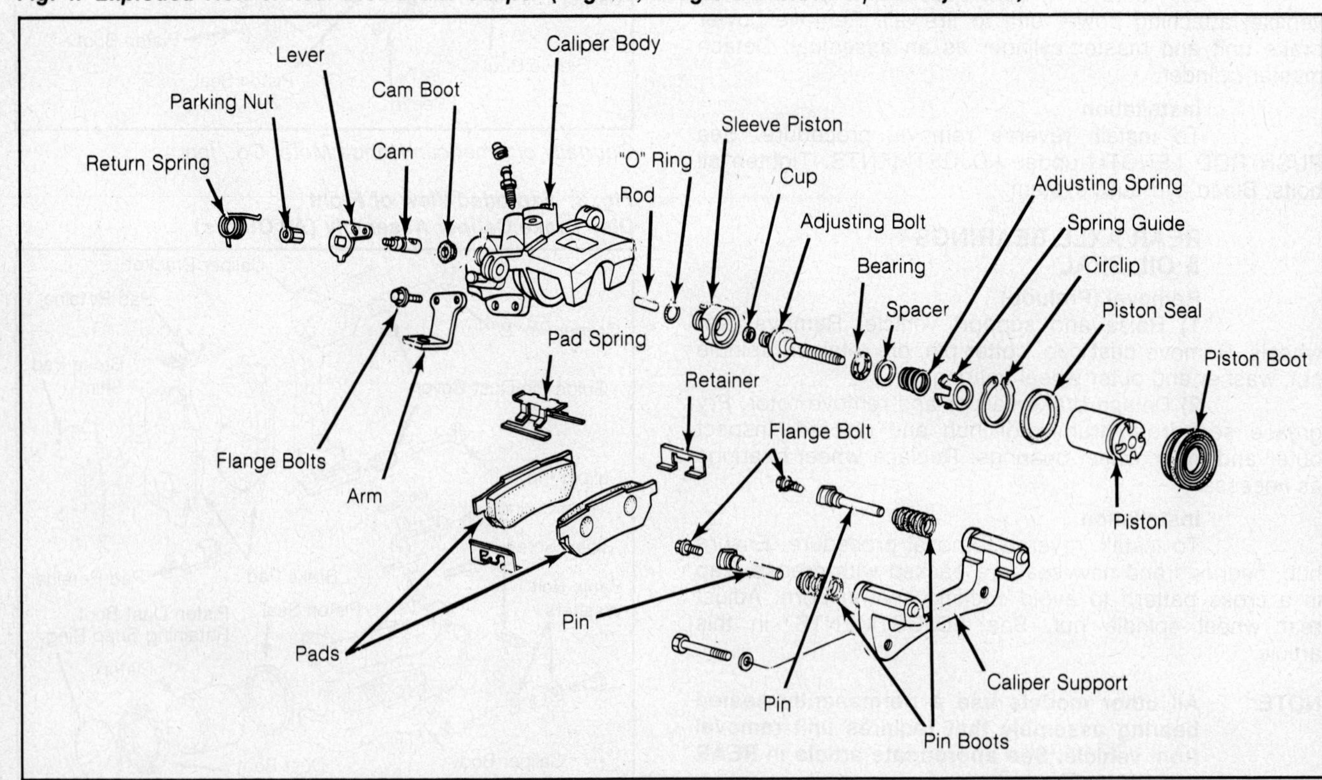

Courtesy of American Honda Motor Co., Inc.

ACURA & HONDA (Cont.)

Fig. 5: Exploded View Of Rear Disc Brake Caliper (All Others)

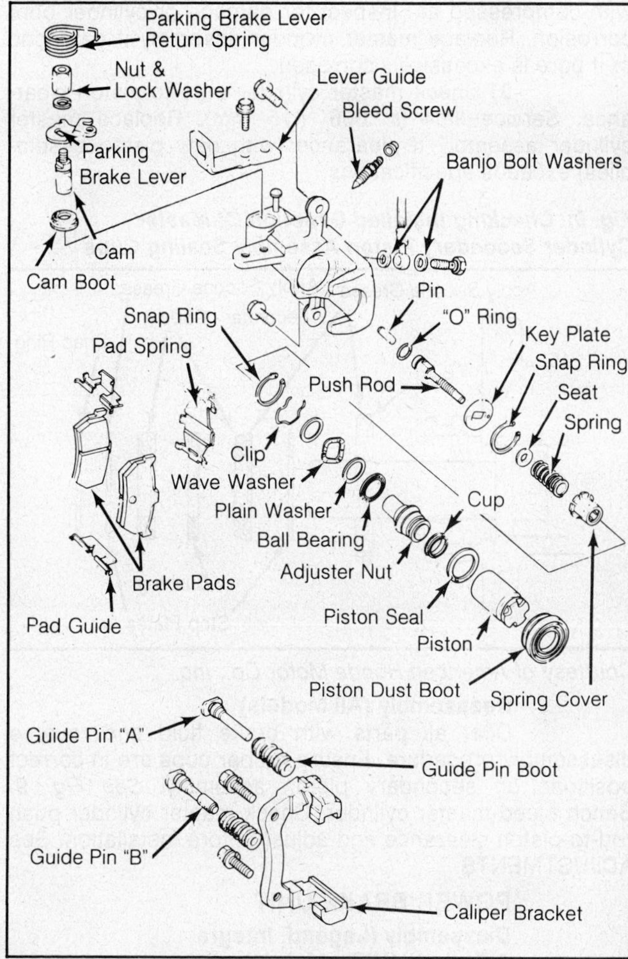

Courtesy of American Honda Motor Co., Inc.

Fig. 6: Installing Parking Brake Spring & Cover Assembly in Rear Brake Caliper Bore

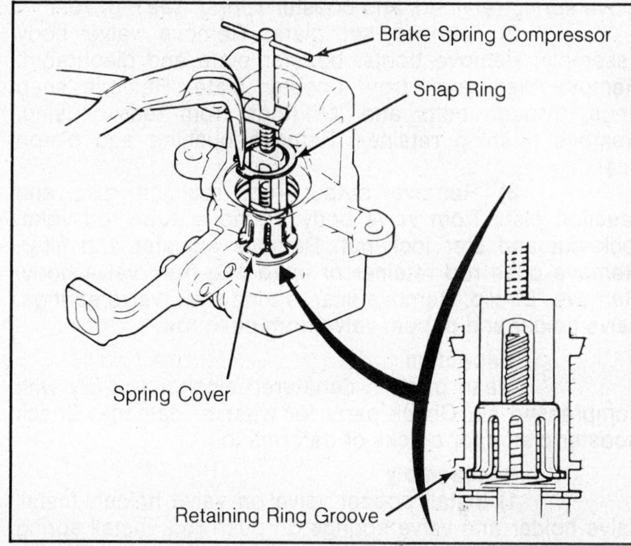

Courtesy of American Honda Motor Co., Inc.

5) Remove rear caliper guide. Ensure flared end of spring cover is below snap ring groove in caliper bore. *See Fig. 6.* Using snap ring pliers, install snap ring in groove of caliper bore. Remove spring compressor. Ensure snap ring is properly seated in groove.

6) Apply silicone grease to new piston cup. Install cup on adjuster nut with lip facing same direction as removed cup. Install ball bearing, plain washer, wave washer and adjuster nut. Slide nut in piston and secure with clip.

7) Coat new piston seal and piston boot with silicone grease and install in caliper bore. Apply grease to piston O.D. and install on push rod while turning clockwise. Ensure piston boot is not damaged during installation. Install caliper and bleed system.

WHEEL CYLINDER

Disassembly

With brake shoes detached and wheel cylinder removed from backing plate, pry dust covers off cylinder. Pull pistons and expander spring from bore. Remove rubber cylinder cups from pistons. Remove bleeder cap and screw. Discard all rubber parts.

NOTE: **Lips of piston cups must face the center of cylinder.**

Reassembly

1) If new wheel cylinder is used, apply sealant between cylinder and backing plate. Install cylinder. Reassemble brake shoes. Install drum. Bleed system.

2) If original cylinder is reused, install new cups on pistons and coat cylinder bore, pistons and cups with brake assembly fluid. Install parts in cylinder bore. Install new dust covers securely in cylinder body grooves.

3) To complete installation, reverse removal procedures. Bleed hydraulic system after installation.

MASTER CYLINDER

Disassembly (Civic, CRX & Prelude W/Carb.)

1) Remove master cylinder from power brake unit and clamp in vise. Remove reservoir cap assembly and drain brake fluid. Loosen retaining clamp and remove reservoir. Remove outer snap ring. *See Fig. 7.*

2) Remove washer, secondary cup, bushing, secondary cup, and washer. Press in on secondary piston assembly and remove stop bolt. Remove inner snap ring.

NOTE: **Ensure master cylinder bore is not damaged during inner snap ring removal.**

3) Cover open end of master cylinder with a clean shop towel. Plug stop bolt hole and secondary outlet port. Remove secondary and primary piston assemblies by applying 30 psi (2.1 kg/cm²) air pressure to primary port. Detach screw from secondary piston assembly. Disassemble secondary piston assembly. *See Fig. 7.* Remove secondary spring.

Disassembly (All Others)

1) Remove master cylinder from power brake unit and clamp in vise. Remove reservoir cap assembly and drain brake fluid. Loosen retaining clamp and remove reservoir. Remove rod seal. Remove outer snap ring. *See Fig. 8.*

ACURA & HONDA (Cont.)

Fig. 7: Exploded View of Master Cylinder (Civic, CRX & Prelude W/Carburetor)

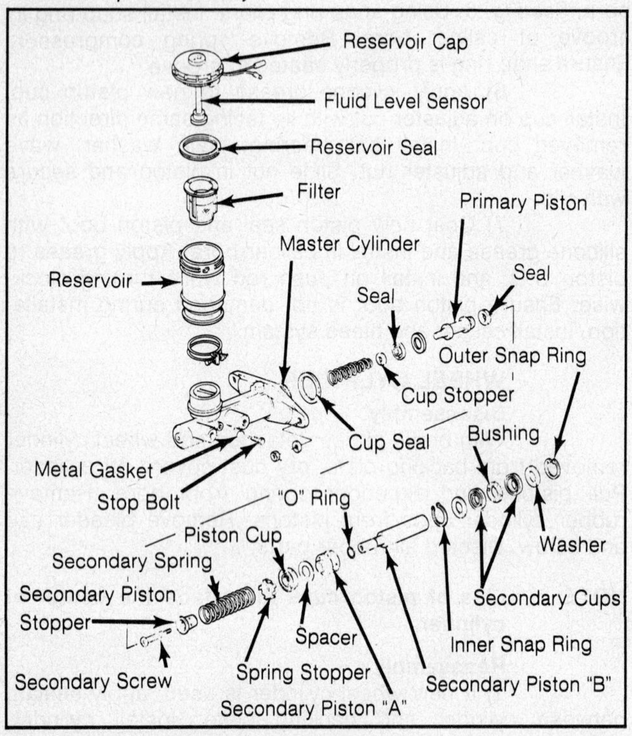

Courtesy of American Honda Motor Co., Inc.

2) Depress piston assembly and remove stop bolt. Remove primary and secondary piston assemblies. Apply low compressed air to primary outlet port if removal is difficult. Remove secondary piston screw. Disassemble secondary piston assembly.

Fig. 8: Exploded View of Master Cylinder (All Others)

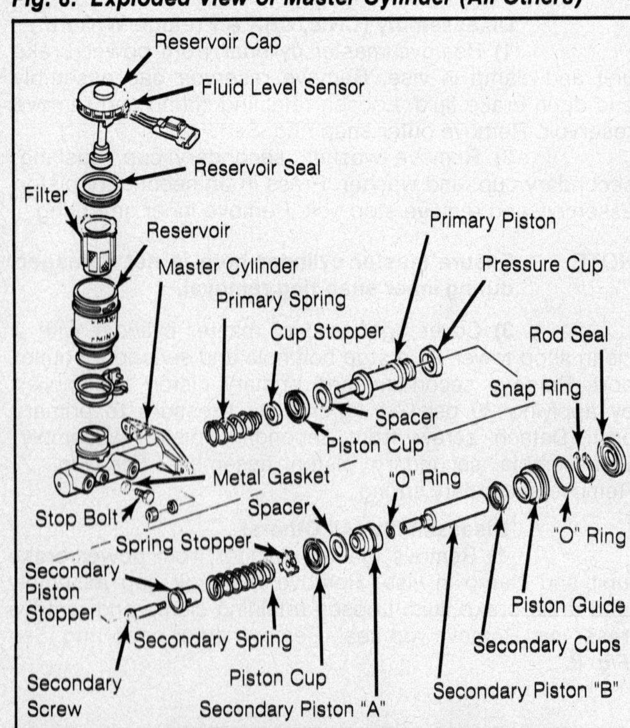

Courtesy of American Honda Motor Co. Inc.

Inspection (All Models)

1) Wash all parts in clean brake fluid. Blow dry with compressed air. Inspect for damage or cylinder bore corrosion. Replace master cylinder assembly if damaged or if bore is excessively corroded.

2) Check master cylinder bore-to-piston clearance. Service limit is .006" (.15 mm). Replace master cylinder assembly if clearance (with new piston assemblies) exceeds specifications.

Fig. 9: Checking Installed Direction Of Master Cylinder Secondary Piston Assembly Sealing Cups

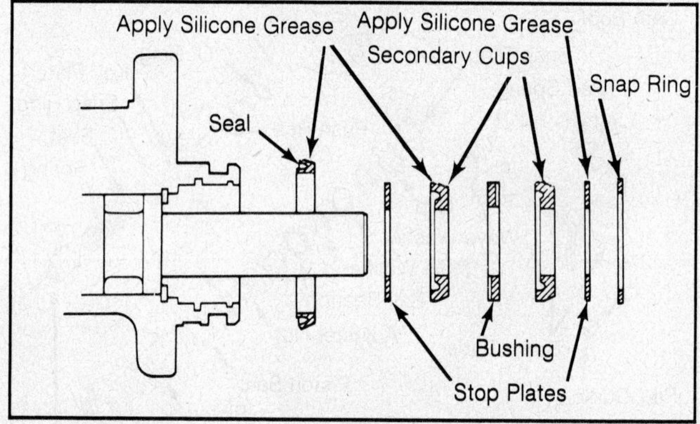

Courtesy of American Honda Motor Co., Inc.

Reassembly (All Models)

Coat all parts with brake fluid and reverse disassembly procedure. Ensure rubber cups are in correct positions on secondary piston assembly. *See Fig. 9.* Bench bleed master cylinder. Check master cylinder push rod-to-piston clearance and adjust before installation. See ADJUSTMENTS.

POWER BRAKE UNIT

Diassembly (Legend, Integra & Prelude W/Fuel Injection)

1) Mark front and rear housings for reference purposes. Remove master cylinder. Remove "E" clips. Separate front and rear housing. Remove seals and washers from spring retainer. Remove snap rings. Remove spring retainers and booster spring. *See Fig. 10*.

2) Remove set plate. Remove valve body assembly. Remove boots, booster plate and diaphragm. Remove diaphragm from booster plate. Remove snap rings, through bolts and "O" rings from rear housing. Remove bushing retainer. Remove bushing and piston seal.

3) Remove output rod, reaction disc and reaction plate from valve body. Remove push rod yoke, lock nut and star lock nut. Remove adjuster and filter. Remove push rod retainer or snap ring from valve body. Remove "E" clip. Remove filter, spring seat, valve springs, valve holder and poppet valve from push rod.

Inspection

Clean parts in denatured alcohol and dry with compressed air. Check parts for wear or damage. Check booster piston for cracks or deformation.

Reassembly

1) Install poppet valve on valve holder. Install valve holder and valve springs on push rod. Install spring seat, with short end facing filter. Install filter and "E" clip. Apply silicone grease to valve body bore (both sides) and push rod.

ACURA & HONDA (Cont.)

2) Install push rod and secure with push rod retainer or snap ring. Install filter, adjuster and star locknut. DO NOT tighten at this time. Apply silicone grease to piston seal. Install piston seal, with lip facing housing, and bushing.

3) Using Driver (07749-0010000) and Attachment (07947-6890300), position retainer .24" (6 mm) below rear housing edge. *See Fig. 11*. Install through bolts, "O" rings and snap rings. Install diaphrgam on booster plate. Install booster plate on rear housing. Ensure tabs are aligned.

4) Install boots on through bolts. Apply silicone grease to rear housing bore and valve body outer surface. Install valve body in rear housing. Install reaction plate, disc and output rod.

5) Install set plate. Install booster spring. Install spring retainers and snap rings. Install washers and seals. Align marks and install front housing onto rear housing. Check push rod length and clearance. See ADJUSTMENTS.

Fig. 10: Exploded View of Power Brake Unit (Legend, Integra & Prelude W/Fuel Injection)

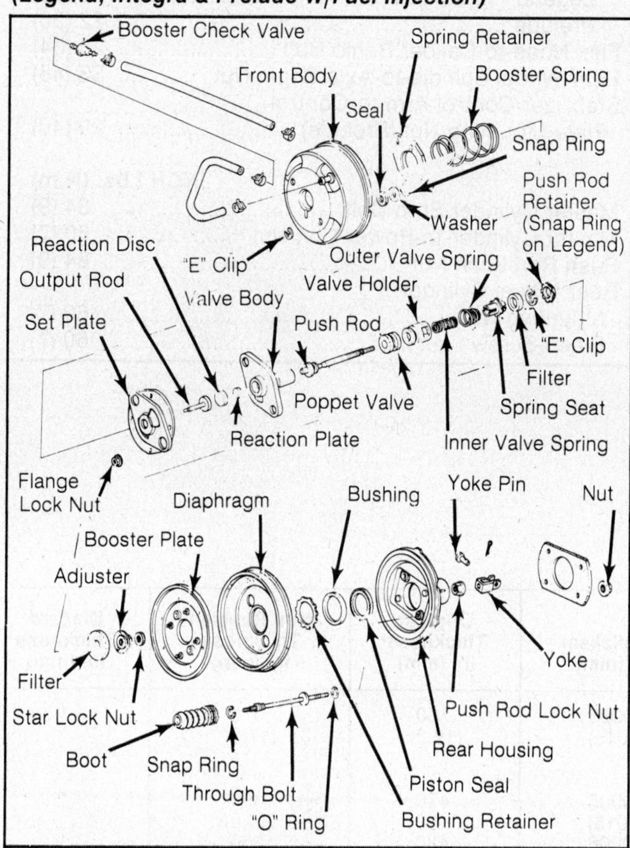

Courtesy of American Honda Motor Co., Inc.

Disassembly (All Others)

1) Remove power brake unit. Scribe an index mark across front and rear power brake unit housings for reassembly reference. Drain brake fluid. Remove master cylinder. Detach 2 "E" clips and separate front booster housing from rear booster housing.

2) Remove washers and seals from rear housing. Detach snap ring. Remove spring retainer and booster spring. Remove retainer and through bolt boots. Remove diaphragm from rear housing.

3) Remove yoke, push rod lock nut, star lock nut, adjuster and filter. Remove snap ring. Remove valve holder assembly. Remove "E" clip from valve holder assembly. Disassemble components. Note component locations for reassembly reference. *See Fig. 12.*

Fig. 11: Installing Power Brake Booster Unit Piston Seal, Bushing & Retainer

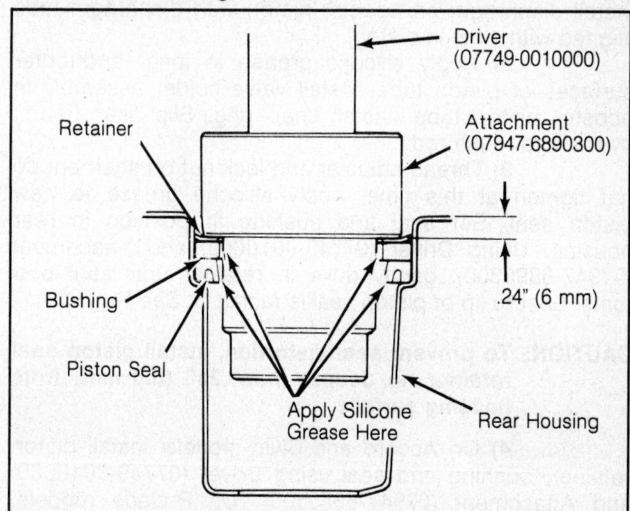

Courtesy of American Honda Motor Co., Inc.

Fig. 12: Exploded View of Vacuum Power Brake Unit

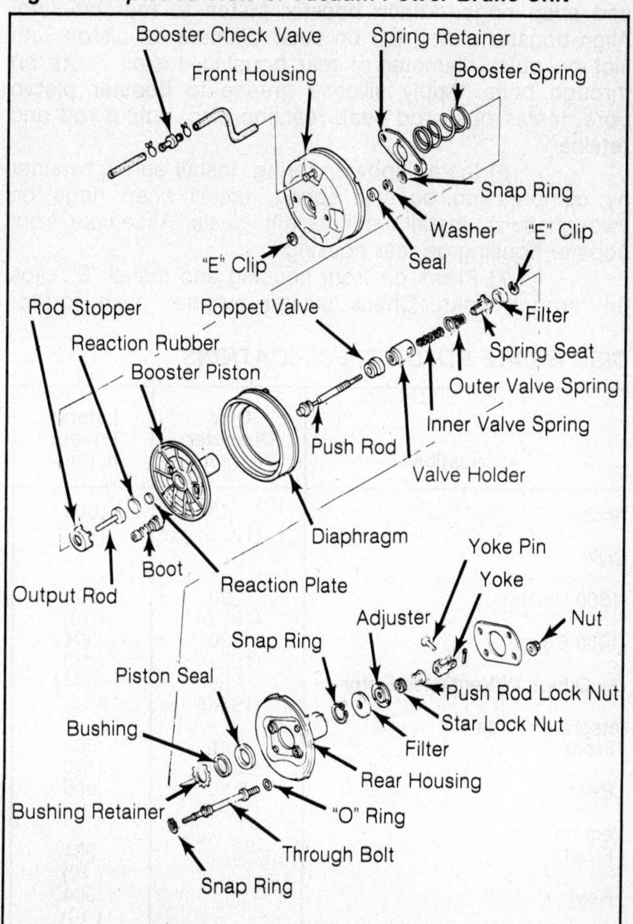

Courtesy of American Honda Motor Co., Inc.

ACURA & HONDA (Cont.)

Inspection (All Models)

Clean parts in denatured alcohol and dry with compressed air. Check parts for wear or damage. Check booster piston for cracks or deformation.

Reassembly (All Models)

1) Install poppet valve on valve holder. Reassemble valve holder assembly. Install silencer with "E" clip. Install diaphragm on booster piston with diaphragm tabs aligned with slots in piston.

2) Apply silicone grease to inner and outer surfaces of piston tube. Install valve holder assembly in booster piston tube. Install snap ring. Slip filter (foam) over end of push rod.

3) Thread adjuster and lock nut on shaft but do not tighten at this time. Apply silicone grease to new piston seal. Set seal and bushing in position in rear housing. Using Driver (07749-0010000) and Attachment (07947-6890300), gently drive in retainer until seal bottoms. Ensure lip of piston seal is facing in. *See Fig. 11.*

CAUTION: To prevent seal distortion, install piston seal retainer no deeper than .24" (6.0 mm) from housing surface.

4) On Accord and Civic models, install piston retainer, bushing and seal using Driver (07749-0010000) and Attachment (07947-6890300). On Prelude models, install retainer, bushing and seal using driver and Attachment (07947-6710100 or 07965-6920500).

5) Install 2 through bolts, using new "O" ring and snap rings. Attach booster piston to rear housing. Align booster piston tab on outer diameter of piston with slot on outer diameter of rear housing. Install boots on through bolts. Apply silicone grease to booster piston bore. Install push rod seat, reaction disc, output rod and retainer.

6) Install booster spring. Install spring retainer by compressing booster spring. Install snap rings on through bolts. Install washers and seals. Assemble front booster housing on rear housing.

7) Press on front housing and install "E" clips on through bolts. Check master cylinder push rod-to-booster piston clearance before installing master cylinder. See ADJUSTMENTS in this article.

8) Install master cylinder, fill reservoir with brake fluid and bleed hydraulic system. Check power unit for operation. See TESTING in this article.

TIGHTENING SPECIFICATIONS

Application	Ft. Lbs. (N.m)
Backing Plate Mounting Bolt	
Accord	22 (30)
Civic	33 (45)
Caliper Mount Bracket Bolt	
Front (All)	56 (76)
Integra, Legend, Prelude (Rear)	28 (39)
Caliper Guide Pin Bolt	
Front Caliper	
Accord & Integra	33 (45)
Civic & Prelude	13 (18)
Legend & Coupe	24 (33)
Rear	
Integra & Coupe	17 (23)
Legend	20 (27)
Prelude	22 (30)
Flex Hose-to-Caliper Banjo Bolt	25 (34)
Rear Wheel Spindle-to-Axle Beam Nut	33 (45)
Stabilizer Control Arm-to-Control Plate Mounting Nut (Prelude)	29 (40)
	INCH Lbs. (N.m)
Master Cylinder Stop Bolt	84 (9)
Master Cylinder-to-Power Unit Nut	60 (7)
Push Rod Lock Nut	84 (9)
Rear Wheel Cylinder	
Mounting Nut	60 (7)
Bleed Screw	60 (7)

DISC BRAKE ROTOR SPECIFICATIONS

Application	Disc Diameter In. (mm)	Lateral Runout In. (mm)	Parallelism In. (mm)	Original Thickness In. (mm)	Min. Refinish Thickness In. (mm)	Discard Thickness In. (mm)
Accord	7.60 (193.0)	.006 (.15)	.0006 (.015)	.750 (19.0)	.670 (17.0)	1
Civic						
1300 Hatchback	7.20 (182.0)	.004 (.10)	.0006 (.015)	.470 (12.0)	.390 (10.0)	1
1300 Coupe	7.20 (182.0)	.004 (.10)	.0006 (.015)	.430 (11.0)	.350 (9.0)	1
All Others W/Ventilated Rotor	7.50 (190.0)	.004 (.10)	.0006 (.015)	.670 (17.0)	.590 (15.0)	1
Integra, Prelude						
Front	9.40 (238.8)	.004 (.10)	.0006 (.015)	.750 (19.0)	.670 (17.0)	1
Rear	7.50 (190.5)	.006 (.15)	.0006 (.015)	.390 (10.0)	.310 (8.0)	1
Legend						
Front	.....	.004 (.10)	.0006 (.015)	.830 (21.0)	.750 (19.0)	1
Rear	.....	.004 (.10)	.0006 (.015)	.390 (10.0)	.310 (8.0)	1

1 - Use discard thickness stamped on rotor if different than min. refinishing thickness shown in table.

ACURA & HONDA (Cont.)

DRUM BRAKE SPECIFICATIONS

Application	Drum Diam. In. (mm)	Drum Width In. (mm)	Max. Drum Refinish Diam. In. (mm)	Wheel Cyl. Diam. In. (mm)	Master Cyl. Diam. In. (mm)
Accord, & Civic Station Wagon	7.870 (200.0)	1.400 (35.0)	[1] 7.910 (201.0)	.....	.....
Civic (All Exc. Station Wagon)	7.090 (180.0)	1.400 (35.0)	[1] 7.130 (181.0)	.....	.....

[1] - If maximum refinish diameter disagrees with specification stamped on drum, use stamped specification.

AUDI

Coupe GT, 4000S, 5000S, 5000CS Turbo 4000S Quattro, 4000CS Quattro, 5000CS Quattro

DESCRIPTION

All models have front disc brakes. On 4000CS Quattro and 5000CS Turbo and 5000CS Quattro models, rear disc brakes are used. On all other models, drum brakes are used on rear axle. Both front and rear brakes are self-adjusting.

Hydraulic system uses tandem master cylinder with either vacuum or hydraulic power assist. Tandem system on FWD models uses diagonal front and rear pairing so left front and right rear wheels form one circuit while right front and left rear wheels form the other circuit. On 4WD models, front wheels form one circuit while rear wheels form the other circuit.

Pressure regulator is used to prevent premature lock-up of rear wheels. Pressure regulator is adjustable, on all models except 4000CS Quattro. Cable-actuated parking brake mechanically applies rear brakes when handle is pulled up.

NOTE: **For information on Anti-Lock Brake Systems (ABS), see AUDI ANTI-LOCK BRAKE SYSTEM article in this section.**

ADJUSTMENTS

STOPLIGHT SWITCH

Disconnect wiring from switch. Depress brake pedal. Push switch in until it reaches stop. Pull brake pedal back up by hand.

REAR BRAKE BASIC SETTING

1) Ensure there is no tension on parking brake cable prior to adjustment. Push caliper brake lever against stop on both rear calipers. If lever of opposite caliper pulls away from stop, cable is too tight. If so, loosen adjusting nut on cable adjusting rod until both levers are resting against stops.

2) Place screwdriver into hook of pressure regulator spring so that screwdriver is between roller and rear spring hook. Using equal force each time, apply brake pedal about 40 times with vehicle stationary. Remove screwdriver from spring. Ensure both rear wheels turn without drag.

PARKING BRAKE

NOTE: **Parking brake should only need adjustment if parking brake cable, backing plate, cable adjusting rod, rear caliper or brake shoes have been replaced.**

Disc Brakes

1) Raise vehicle and support. Release parking brake lever. Check and adjust basic setting of rear brakes as necessary. Tighten adjusting nut on cable adjusting rod until both brake levers on rear calipers are just off stops.

2) Loosen adjusting nut 2 turns. Using screwdriver, push caliper lever against stop on both rear calipers. If lever of opposite side caliper is pulled off stop, cable is too tight. Loosen cable and repeat adjustment procedure until opposite lever remains on stop. *See Fig. 1.*

Fig. 1: Adjusting Parking Brake

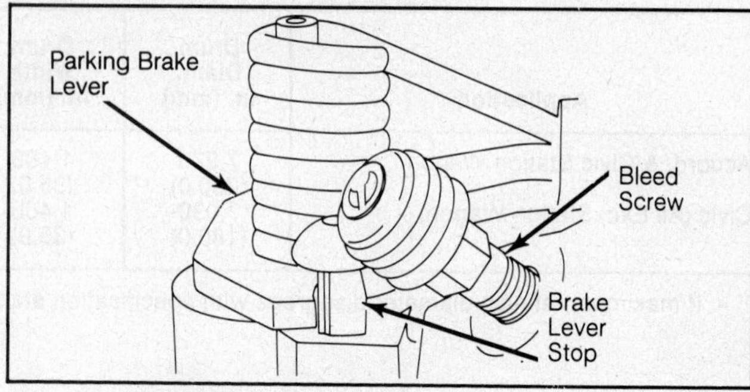

Courtesy of Audi of America, Inc.

Drum Brakes

1) Raise vehicle and support. Release parking brake lever. Loosen adjusting nut on cable adjusting rod. Firmly depress brake pedal once. Pull parking brake lever up to third notch on 5000S models or second notch on 4000CS and Coupe GT models.

2) Tighten adjusting nut at cable adjusting rod until both wheels can barely be turned by hand. Release parking brake lever. Ensure that both wheels will rotate freely. Lightly coat equalizer with multipurpose grease.

WHEEL BEARINGS

1) Tighten wheel bearing adjusting nut while turning wheel. Nut should be tightened firmly enough to seat bearings while rotating wheel so bearings do not cock or jam.

2) Back off adjusting nut until thrust washer can be moved slightly using screwdriver and no more than finger pressure. DO NOT pry or twist screwdriver in effort to move washer. When bearings are properly adjusted, install lock nut. Install grease cap.

PUSH ROD LENGTH ADJUSTMENT

Push rod must be adjusted if power booster or master cylinder is replaced. On vacuum booster models, length should be 10.59" (269 mm). On all other models, push rod length should be 9.80" (249 mm).

PRESSURE REGULATOR

Mechanical Adjustment

NOTE: **Hydraulic system fluid must be full and free of air.**

1) Brake pressure regulator is mounted on underside of body and connected to rear axle by operating spring. Adjustable regulator is on left rear side on 5000S and 5000CS Turbo and right rear side in 4000CS and Coupe GT models. Nonadjustable regulator of 4000CS Quattro is at right of brake master cylinder. 5000CS Quattro is on left rear side.

2) Step firmly on brake pedal with vehicle on ground. Release pedal rapidly. Lever on pressure regulator should move. Raise vehicle until weight is off rear suspension. Push lever of regulator toward rear of vehicle until it reaches stop.

3) Loosen lock nut holding plastic roller in place on bracket. Attach operating spring to lever and roller. Adjust roller position so that there is no play in spring and no tension on plastic roller. *See Fig. 2.* Tighten lock nut.

AUDI (Cont.)

Fig. 2: Adjusting Brake Pressure Regulator

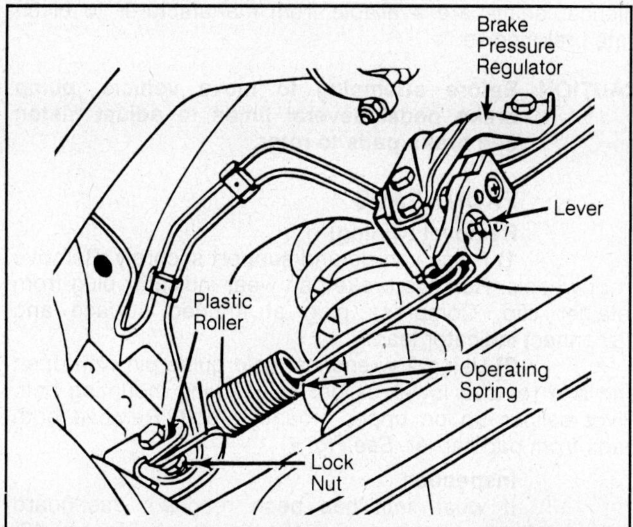

Courtesy of Audi of America, Inc.

Pressure Adjustment

NOTE: For following procedure, vehicle must be empty, have full fuel tank and be resting on wheels. The 4000CS Quattro and 5000CS Quattro has a nonadjustable regulator.

1) Disconnect parking brake cable at left rear caliper on 4000CS Quattro models. On all models except 4000CS Quattro and 5000CS connect pressure gauges at left front and right rear wheels. On 4000CS Quattro, connect gauges to left front and left rear. On 5000CS, connect gauges to rear wheels only. Bleed gauges and hoses through bleeders on gauges. Have assistant of about 165 lbs. sit in driver's seat. Bounce rear of car several times.

2) On all models except 5000CS Quattro, depress brake pedal several times until gauge at front axle shows reading of 725 psi (50 bar). On 5000CS Quattro, go to step **6)**. On 4000CS Quattro models, gauge at rear axle should show reading of 508-566 psi (32-39 bar). On 5000CS Turbo, reading should show 507-653 psi (35-45 bar). On all other models, gauge at rear axle should show reading of 471-616 psi (32.5-42.5 bar).

3) Increase pressure on brake pedal until gauge at front axle shows reading of 1450 psi (100 bar). On 4000CS Quattro models, gauge at rear axle should show reading of 841-899 psi (58-62 bar). On 5000CS Turbo, gauge should read 827-1059 psi (57-73 bar). On all other models, gauge at rear axle should show reading of 783-1037 psi (54.0-71.5 bar).

4) If pressure at rear axle is higher than specification, spring tension on brake pressure regulator is too high. If pressure at rear axle is lower than specification, spring tension on brake pressure regulator is too low. On all models except 4000CS Quattro, adjust regulator by changing spring tension.

5) Have assistant release pressure on brake pedal. Adjust tension on pressure regulator spring according to reading at rear axle. Repeat pressure test. If pressure cannot be correctly adjusted, replace brake pressure regulator. If pressure can be adjusted correctly, remove gauges. Bleed hydraulic brake system. Reconnect parking brake cable on 4000CS Quattro models.

6) On 5000CS Quattro, depress brake pedal until gauge reading on left rear wheel is 580 psi (40 bar). Reading at right rear wheel should be 217-362 psi (15-25 bar). If not, replace pressure regulator.

TESTING

CAUTION: When repairing or testing hydraulic power assist system, always relieve system pressure before opening lines to pressurized components. Press brake pedal about 20 times with engine off to relieve system pressure.

PRESSURE REGULATOR

Leakage Test

1) If leakage is suspected in pressure regulator, connect Pressure Gauges (US 1016) to left front caliper and right rear wheel cylinder. Bleed pressure gauges and hoses through bleeders on gauges. Pump brake pedal until pressure at front caliper reaches 1450 psi (100 bar).

2) Hold pressure for 5 seconds. If rear pressure reading changes by more than 145 psi (10 bar) during 5 seconds that pedal is held, pressure regulator is defective. Replace regulator. Remove gauges and bleed brake system.

HYDRAULIC SERVO

1) Drive belt tension must be correct. Ensure that there are no leaks in servo system and engine is off. Remove warning light wiring and warning switch. Remove return line at servo. If hydraulic oil leaks continuously, servo is defective and must be replaced. Relieve system pressure.

2) Using hollow banjo bolt and 2 copper washers, connect Pressure Gauge (VW 1441) to switch opening. Place thicker washer between banjo and servo and thinner washer between bolt head and banjo.

3) Start engine and let idle until reading on pressure gauge is more than 2030 psi (140 bar). If specified pressure cannot be reached, check delivery of central hydraulic pump.

Fig. 3: Location of Hydraulic Power Assist Components

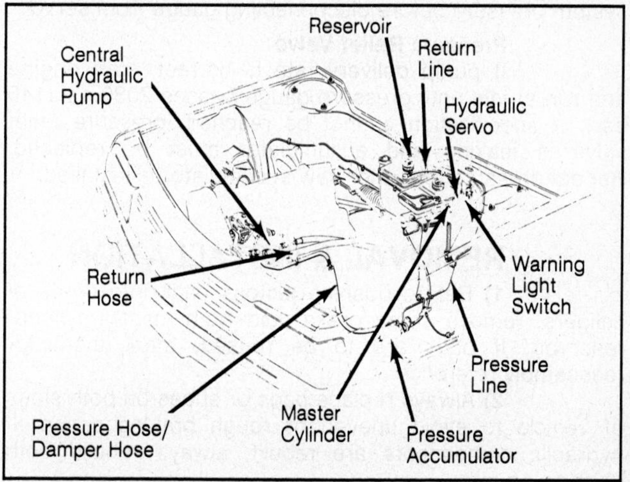

Courtesy of Audi of America, Inc.

AUDI (Cont.)

CENTRAL HYDRAULIC PUMP DELIVERY

1) Relieve system pressure. Disconnect pressure line from central hydraulic pump. Connect banjo fitting of Pressure Limiter (VW 1354) to pump, using hollow banjo bolt that was holding pressure line to pump. Remove cap off hydraulic oil reservoir. Place other end of pressure limiter hose in reservoir.

2) Start engine and run at idle until all air is bled out of pressure limiter. When no more bubbles are evident, turn engine off. Place limiter hose into measuring cup of 1 qt. (.9L) capacity. Start engine and let run at idle. Minimum delivery rate must be .3 qt./minute (.28L/minute).

3) If delivery rate is too low, replace central hydraulic pump. If delivery rate is sufficient but operating pressure reading is still too low, replace pressure accumulator. Turn engine off. After repairs are completed, start vehicle and check for leaks.

PRESSURE ACCUMULATOR

Minimum Gas Pressure

NOTE: **New accumulator will operate at 1276-1334 psi (88-92 bar) at temperature of 68°F (20°C). Minimum pressure of accumulator is 435 psi (30 bar) at temperature of 68°F (20°C).**

1) Relieve system pressure. Remove warning light switch from servo. Using hollow banjo bolt and copper washers, connect Pressure Gauge (VW 1441) to switch opening. Place thicker washer between banjo and servo and thinner washer between bolt head and banjo.

2) Start engine and run at idle until reading on pressure gauge reaches 2030 psi (140 bar). Turn engine off and pump brake pedal. Watch gauge for pressure reading from which needle drops rapidly to zero. If drop-off pressure is lower than 435 psi (30 bar), accumulator is defective and must be replaced.

Check Valve

1) If servo has no leaks, start engine and run at idle until pressure gauge reaches 2030 psi (140 bar). Turn engine off and pump brake pedal until reading on pressure gauge drops to 1957 psi (135 bar).

2) Operating pressure should not drop below 1885 psi (130 bar) within 5 minutes. If pressure drops below specification, check valve is leaking and must be replaced. If gauge is to be removed, relieve remaining system pressure before disconnecting gauge from servo.

Pressure Relief Valve

If pump delivery rate is correct, start engine and run at idle until pressure gauge passes 2030 psi (140 bar). If specification cannot be reached, pressure relief valve is leaking and accumulator must be replaced. Repeat pressure test after new accumulator is installed.

REMOVAL & INSTALLATION

1) Before pushing pistons back into bores of calipers, remove some brake fluid from master cylinder reservoir. If pads are to be reused, mark them for reassembly reference.

2) Always replace pads or shoes on both sides of vehicle to avoid uneven or rough braking action. If hydraulic components are rebuilt, always rebuild both units on an axle.

3) When replacing calipers, ensure both units on axle are of equal capacity. When machining rotors, always turn both sides at same time. Rubber coated silencer shims are available from manufacturer to eliminate brake noise.

CAUTION: **Before attemping to move vehicle, pump brake pedal several times to adjust piston and brake pads to rotor.**

FRONT PADS

Removal (Girling)

1) Raise vehicle and support securely. Remove front wheels. Remove brake pad wear indicator plug from retainer clip. Compress plug at knurled surface and disconnect indicator lead.

2) Using 2 wrenches, hold guide pin with open end and remove lower caliper self-locking mounting bolt. Pivot caliper up on upper mounting bolt. Remove both pads from pad carrier. *See Fig. 4.*

Inspection

If wear limit has been reached, dashboard indicator light should be on. New pads should be .43" (11.0 mm) thick without including thickness of backing plate. Wear limit is .276" (7.0 mm), including backing plate.

Installation

NOTE: **Always use new heat shield and self-locking bolts when replacing pads.**

1) Press piston back into caliper. Install brake pads with new heat shield between inner pad and piston. Heat shield must face piston. Swing caliper down into carrier.

2) Install new lower self-locking mounting bolt. Tighten self-locking bolt to 26 ft. lb. (35 N.m). Reconnect pad wear indicator at plug and place plug in retainer.

Fig. 4: Girling Front Disc Brake Components

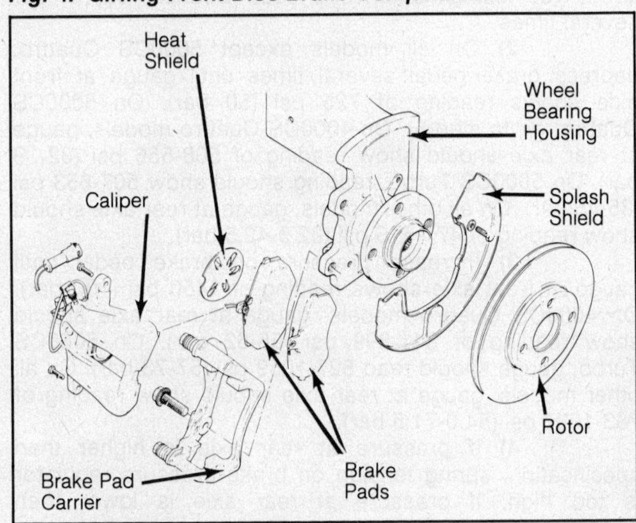

Courtesy of Audi of America, Inc.

Removal (Teves)

1) Raise and support vehicle. Remove front wheels. Remove brake pad wear indicator plug from clip. Compress plug at knurled surface and disconnect indicator lead. *See Fig. 5.*

2) Remove caps from both guide bolts. Using Allen wrench, remove guide bolts. Remove caliper from pad carrier and hang it from frame without disconnecting hose. Remove brake pads.

AUDI (Cont.)

Installation

Press piston back into caliper. Install brake pads and new heat shield. Place caliper in carrier. Tighten housing guide bolts to 18 ft. lb. (25 N.m). Reconnect pad wear indicator at plug and place plug in clip.

Fig. 5: Teves Front Disc Brake Components

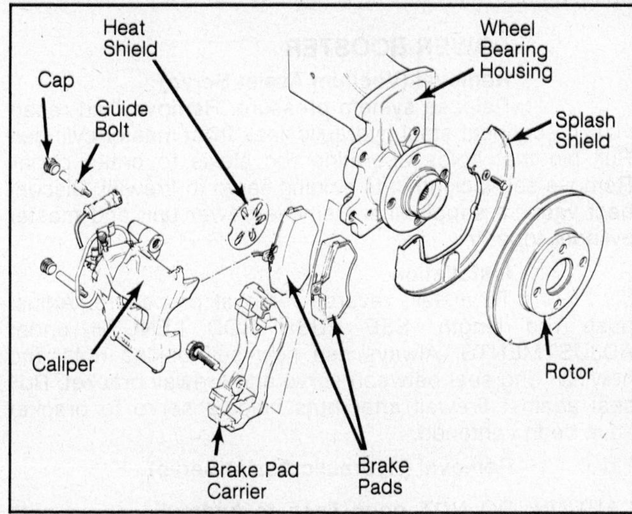

Courtesy of Audi of America, Inc.

FRONT CALIPER

Removal

Raise and support vehicle. Remove front wheels. Remove caliper guide pins (Teves) or self-locking bolts (Girling). Disconnect brake hose from caliper. Plug openings in hose end and caliper. Remove caliper from mounting frame.

Installation

To install, reverse removal procedure. Use new self-locking bolts and heat shields. Bleed complete hydraulic system.

FRONT ROTOR

Removal

NOTE: **Do not use force to remove rotor or damage to caliper mounting frame or pad carrier may occur.**

Raise and support vehicle. Remove front wheels. Remove caliper and hang from frame, leaving brake hose connected. Remove pad carrier from wheel bearing housing. Pull rotor from hub.

Installation

To install rotor assembly, reverse removal procedure.

REAR PADS

Removal

Raise and support vehicle. Remove rear wheels. Using 2 wrenches, hold guide pin with open end wrench while removing self-locking mounting bolt. Remove caliper and support from frame with wire. Do not disconnect or damage hydraulic line. Remove brake pads from carrier.

Inspection

New pads should be .430" (11.0 mm) thick without including thickness of backing plate. Wear limit is .276" (7.0 mm), including backing plate.

Installation

Using Allen wrench, turn piston clockwise while pushing it firmly into bore of caliper. Install brake pads in carrier. Install caliper using new self-locking mounting bolts. Tighten mounting bolts to 26 ft. lbs. (35 N.m). Always check basic setting of rear brakes and parking brake adjustment.

Fig. 6: Rear Disc Brake Components

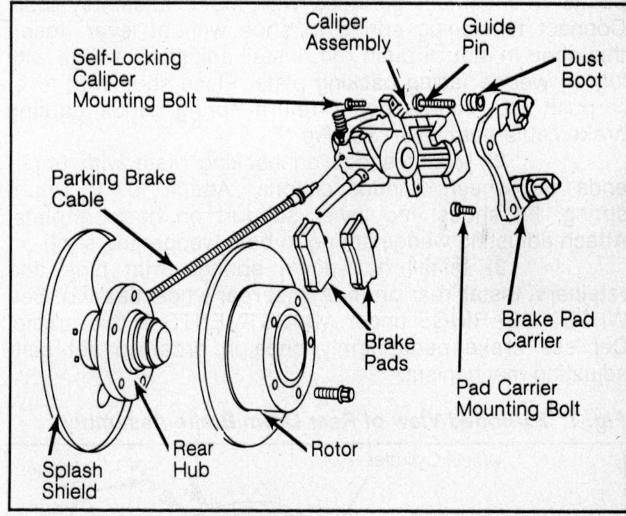

Courtesy of Audi of America, Inc.

REAR CALIPER

NOTE: **Rear caliper removal and installation procedures are the same as that used for Girling front caliper with exception of checking rear brake basic setting and parking brake adjustment. See Fig. 6.**

REAR ROTOR

NOTE: **Rear rotor removal and installation procedures are the same as that used for front rotor with Girling calipers with exception of checking rear brake basic setting and parking brake adjustment.**

REAR DRUM

Removal

Raise and support vehicle. Remove rear wheels. Insert screwdriver through wheel bolt hole and push adjusting wedge upward to back off brake shoes. Remove grease cap, cotter key, nut retainer, adjusting nut, thrust washer and outer wheel bearing. Remove drum assembly with inner bearing.

Installation

Fill hub with wheel bearing grease before installation. Repack wheel bearings. To install, reverse removal procedure. Adjust wheel bearings. See WHEEL BEARINGS under ADJUSTMENTS in this article. Depress brake pedal firmly to set self-adjusting mechanism.

Brakes

AUDI (Cont.)

REAR SHOES

Removal

1) Remove brake drum. Remove spring retainers, hold-down springs and anchor pins. Disconnect lower return spring. Remove both shoes from backing plate. Disconnect parking brake cable at lever.

2) Clamp bottom end of both shoes in vise. Disconnect adjusting wedge spring and upper return spring. Remove tensioning spring. Remove push rod, adjusting wedge and springs from shoes.

Installation

1) Lightly coat push rod and brake lever pivot points and contact surfaces with brake assembly lube. Connect tensioning spring to shoe without lever. Insert this shoe in slot of push rod. Install adjusting wedge with lug on wedge facing backing plate. Place shoe with lever in push rod. Attach upper return spring. Hook parking brake cable onto lever. *See Fig. 7.*

2) Mount shoes on backing plate with upper ends on wheel cylinder pistons. Attach lower return spring. Fit shoes into lower support on backing plate. Attach adjusting wedge spring to both wedge and shoe.

3) Install hold-down springs with pins and retainers. Install rear drum. Adjust rear wheel bearing. See WHEEL BEARINGS under ADJUSTMENTS in this article. Depress brake pedal firmly once in order to set self-adjusting mechanism.

Fig. 7: Exploded View of Rear Drum Brake Assembly

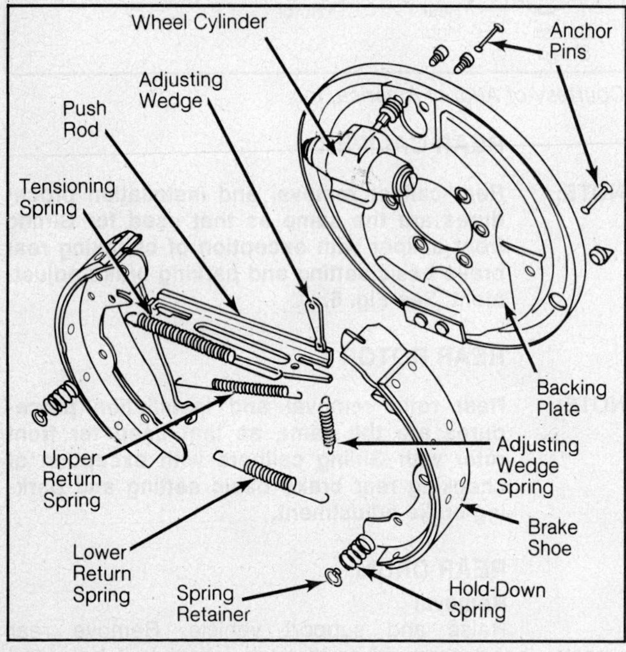

Courtesy of Audi of America, Inc.

MASTER CYLINDER

NOTE: Avoid contacting painted surfaces with brake fluid or paint can be severely damaged.

Removal

Release system pressure. Siphon brake fluid from reservoir or remove reservoir from master cylinder. Disconnect steel hydraulic lines at master cylinder. Remove mounting bolts. Separate master cylinder from power assist brake servo. Be careful not to pull out servo rod.

Installation

Always replace "O" ring between master cylinder and power assist brake servo. Reverse removal procedure. Use brake fluid to lubricate rubber grommets between reservoir and master cylinder. Bleed hydraulic system. Refill reservoir after bleeding procedure is completed.

POWER BOOSTER

Removal (Vacuum Assist Servo)

Release system pressure. Remove fluid reservoir. Disconnect steel hydraulic lines from master cylinder. Pull pin that holds operating rod clevis to brake pedal. Remove self-locking nuts holding servo to firewall. Disconnect vacuum supply line. Remove power unit and master cylinder together.

Installation

To install, reverse removal procedure. Adjust push rod length. SEE PUSH ROD LENGTH under ADJUSTMENTS. Always use new self-locking nuts and new "O" ring seal between servo and firewall bracket. Roll seal against firewall after nuts holding servo to bracket have been tightened.

Removal (Hydraulic Assist Servo)

CAUTION: DO NOT open lines to hydraulic servo until system pressure has been released. System operates at minimum pressure of 435 psi (30 bar). Never step on brake pedal when master cylinder is removed from hydraulic servo.

With engine off, pump brake pedal 20 times to relieve system pressure. Remove master cylinder from hydraulic brake servo. Disconnect pressure and return lines at servo unit. Remove push rod clevis pin. Remove self-locking mounting bolts. Remove servo unit together with gasket. *See Fig. 8.*

Fig. 8: Master Cylinder & Hydraulic Servo

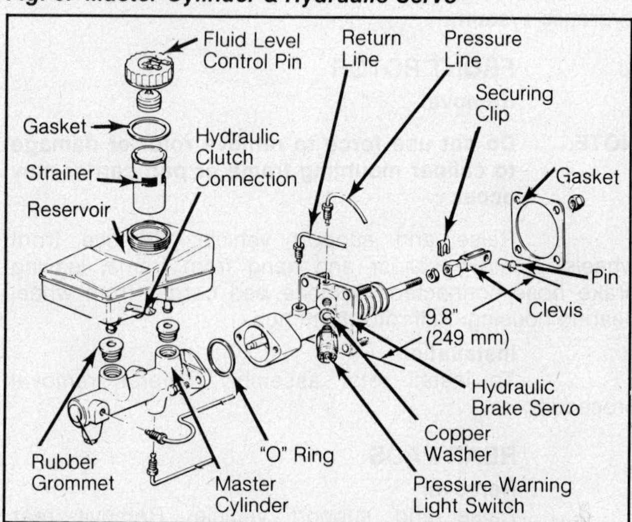

Courtesy of Audi of America, Inc.

Installation

To install, reverse removal procedure. Adjust push rod length. See PUSH ROD LENGTH under ADJUSTMENTS. Tighten clevis lock nut. Lightly grease clevis pin. Use new gasket at firewall and new self-locking nuts. Always use new clevis pin lock clip. Use new "O" ring

AUDI (Cont.)

between master cylinder and servo. Bleed brakes and check operation of system.

PRESSURE ACCUMULATOR

Removal

With engine off, pump brake pedal 20 times to relieve system pressure. Disconnect pressure/damper hose from power steering pump, pressure line from servo unit and pressure line to reservoir. Remove nuts from mounting plate. Remove pressure accumulator.

CAUTION: Drill 1/8" hole in pressure accumulator before discarding unit. Always wear safety glasses when working around high pressure system.

Installation

To install, reverse removal procedure. When damper hose is being installed, longer side of damper goes into pipe section and shorter side goes into hose section. Tighten compression nut to 18 ft. lbs. (25 N.m). Replace copper gaskets on banjo bolts.

OVERHAUL

FRONT CALIPER

Disassembly

Remove pads and clean outside surfaces of caliper. Using compressed air force piston(s) out one at a time to avoid damage to piston assemblies. Use a block of wood between piston(s) and housing to prevent damage to piston(s). Remove dust seal. Remove piston(s) seal without damaging bore or groove. *See Figs. 9 and 10.*

Fig. 9: Exploded View of Girling Front Caliper Assembly

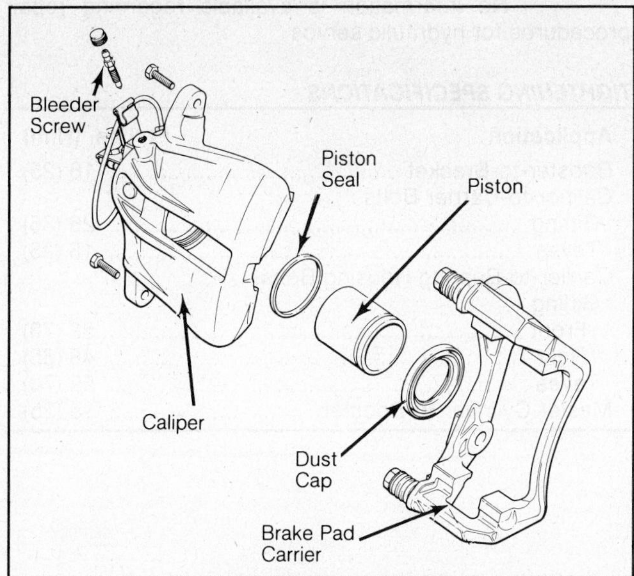

Courtesy of Audi of America, Inc.

Cleaning & Inspection

Use only alcohol or special brake parts cleaning fluid for cleaning purposes. Check cylinder bore and piston for wear or corrosion damage. Any parts not in repair kit may only be serviced by replacement.

Fig. 10: Exploded View of Double Piston Caliper

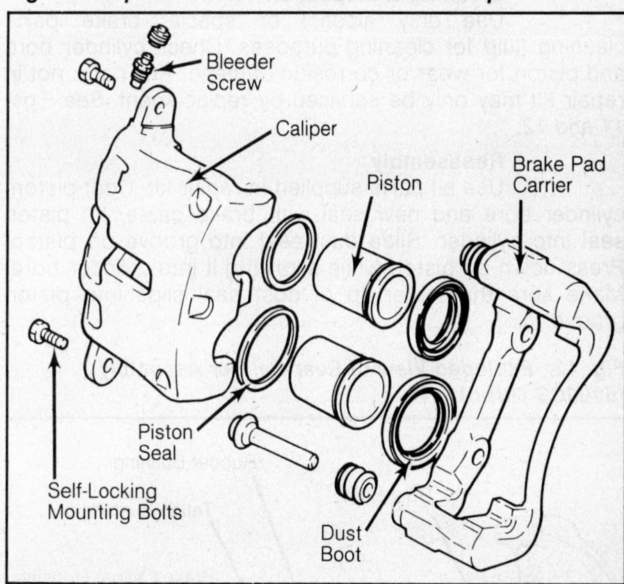

Courtesy of Audi of America, Inc.

Reassembly

1) Use all parts supplied in repair kit. Coat piston(s), cylinder bore(s) and new seal(s) with brake paste. Fit piston seal(s) into cylinder. Slide dust seal(s) onto piston(s). Slowly insert piston(s) into bore.

2) Seat inner lip of dust seal in groove on cylinder housing. Open bleeder and push piston into bore as far as possible. Fit outer lip of dust seal into piston groove.

Fig. 11: Exploded View of Rear Caliper Assembly (Quattro Models)

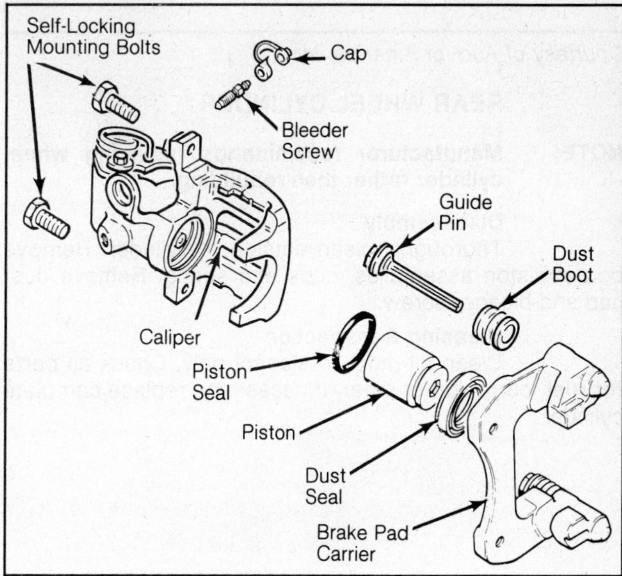

Courtesy of Audi of America, Inc.

REAR CALIPER

Disassembly

Remove pads and clean outside surfaces. Using Allen wrench, unscrew piston from caliper cylinder. Carefully remove piston seal without damaging bore or groove.

AUDI (Cont.)

Cleaning & Inspection

Use only alcohol or special brake parts cleaning fluid for cleaning purposes. Check cylinder bore and piston for wear or corrosion damage. Any parts not in repair kit may only be serviced by replacement. *See Figs. 11 and 12.*

Reassembly

Use all parts supplied in repair kit. Coat piston, cylinder bore and new seal with brake paste. Fit piston seal into cylinder. Slide dust seal into groove on piston. Press down on piston while screwing it into cylinder bore. Make sure that outer lip of dust seal slips into piston groove.

Fig. 12: Exploded View of Rear Caliper Assembly (5000CS Turbo)

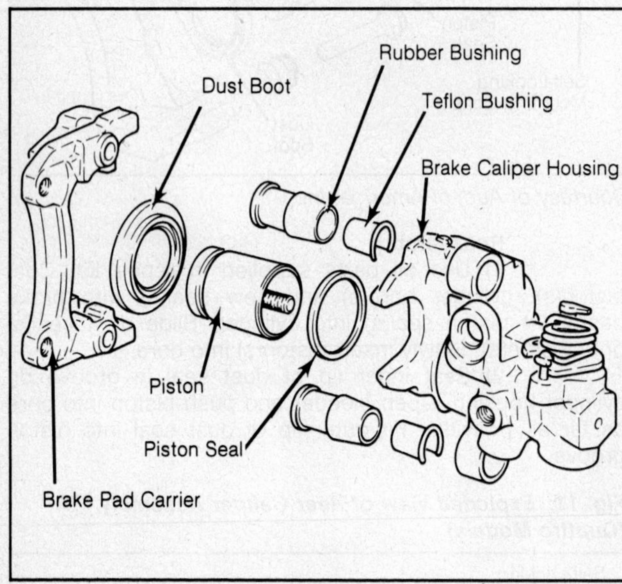

Courtesy of Audi of America, Inc.

REAR WHEEL CYLINDER

NOTE: **Manufacturer recommends replacing wheel cylinder rather than rebuilding.**

Disassembly

Thoroughly clean outside of cylinder. Remove boots, piston assemblies, cups and spring. Remove dust cap and bleeder screw.

Cleaning & Inspection

Clean all parts in alcohol only. Check all parts for rust, corrosion or wear. If necessary, replace complete cylinder.

Fig. 13: Exploded View of Rear Wheel Cylinder

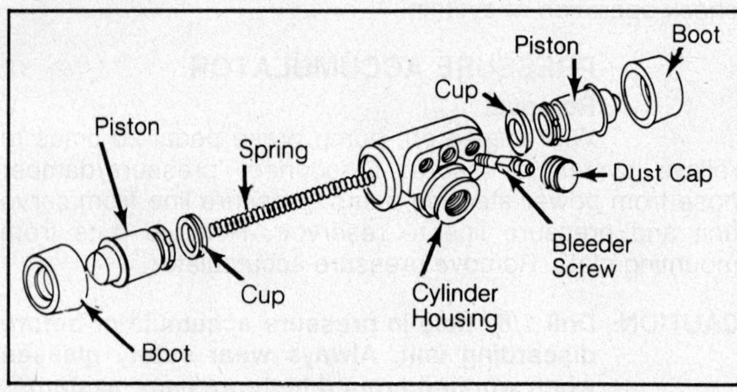

Courtesy of Audi of America, Inc.

Reassembly

Always use all parts in repair kit. Lightly coat cups, pistons and bleeder screws with brake cylinder paste before installing. To reassemble, reverse disassembly procedure. *See Fig. 13.*

MASTER CYLINDER

Vehicle manufacturer states that brake master cylinders are no longer to be repaired but are to be replaced. Master cylinders manufactured by ATE and Girling are interchangeable.

HYDRAULIC & VACUUM POWER BOOSTERS

Vehicle manufacturer states that defective power assist vacuum servos must be replaced as assemblies and not repaired. Power assist servos manufactured by different makers are interchangeable.

POWER ASSIST HYDRAULIC SERVO

No information is available regarding repair procedures for hydraulic servos.

TIGHTENING SPECIFICATIONS

Application	Ft. Lbs. (N.m)
Booster-to-Bracket	18 (25)
Caliper-to-Carrier Bolts	
Girling	26 (35)
Teves	18 (25)
Carrier-to-Bearing Housing Bolts	
Girling	
Front	52 (70)
Rear	48 (65)
Teves	52 (70)
Master Cylinder-to-Booster	18 (25)

Brakes

AUDI (Cont.)

DISC BRAKE ROTOR SPECIFICATIONS

Application	Disc Diameter In. (mm)	Lateral Runout In. (mm)	Parallelism In. (mm)	Original Thickness In. (mm)	Min. Refinish Thickness In. (mm)	Discard Thickness In. (mm)
FRONT						
Coupe GT, 4000S & 4000CS Quattro	10.079 (256.0)	.002 (.06)	.0003 (.01)	.787 (20.0)	.728 (18.5)	.709 (18.0)
5000 Series						
W/Single Piston	10.079 (256.0)	.002 (.06)	.....	.866 (22.0)	.807 (20.5)	.787 (20.0)
W/Double Piston	10.866 (276)	.001 (.03)	.0003 (.01)	.984 (25.0)	.905 (23.0)	.905 (23.0)
REAR						
4000CS Quattro, 5000CS Turbo & 5000CS Quattro	9.646 (245.0)	.002 (.06)	.0006 (.02)	.394 (10.0)	.335 (8.5)	.315 (8.0)

DRUM BRAKE SPECIFICATIONS

Application	Drum Diam. In. (mm)	Drum Width In. (mm)	Max. Drum Refinish Diam. In. (mm)	Wheel Cyl. Diam. In. (mm)	Master Cyl. Diam. In. (mm)
REAR					
Coupe GT & 4000S	7.874 (200.0)	1.575 (40.0)	7.894 (200.5)	.687 (17.46)	.81 (20.64)
5000S	9.055 (230.0)	1.575 (40.0)	9.075 (230.5)	.687 (17.46)	.....

Brakes

BMW

DESCRIPTION

Brake system is hydraulically-operated, using a tandem master cylinder and power brake unit. All models are equipped with single piston front and rear disc brake calipers.

A disc pad wear indicator light is mounted on instrument panel to indicate need for brake pad replacement. A brake pressure regulator is used to reduce fluid pressure to rear brakes. Parking brake is cable-actuated on rear parking brake models and consists of internally-mounted parking brake shoes on all rear disc brake systems.

NOTE: For information on Anti-Lock Brake Systems (ABS), see BMW ANTI-LOCK BRAKE SYSTEM article.

ADJUSTMENTS

BRAKE PEDAL HEIGHT

1) Brake pedal height (measured from firewall to pedal pad center) should be 9.252" (235 mm) on 325 series. Measurement should be 9.100" (231 mm) on 528e, 535i and 535is models. On all others, measurement should be 9.9-10.2" (251-260 mm).

2) To adjust pedal height, loosen stoplight switch lock nut and position stoplight switch out of way. Loosen brake operating rod lock nut and turn operating rod until correct pedal height is obtained. Tighten lock nut. Reposition and adjust stoplight switch. Tighten stoplight switch lock nut.

STOPLIGHT SWITCH

Stoplight switch is located under instrument panel in front of brake pedal arm. To adjust stoplight switch, loosen lock nut. Turn adjusting nut until contact plunger just touches pedal arm. Adjust length of plunger until .20-.24" (5-6 mm) is visible. Tighten lock nut.

PARKING BRAKE

NOTE: Adjustment is necessary when brake lever handle can be lifted 8 or more notches.

325 Series

1) Lift out front clamp. Pull off rubber cap. Disconnect rear clamp. Unscrew adjusting bolts. Operate brake pedal several times. Basic clearance is automatically adjusted. Listen for clicking noise at rear wheels.

2) Pull parking brake lever up to 5th tooth. Turn adjusting nuts enough so that rear wheels can just be rotated. Release lever. Check that wheels can be turned easily and that indicator light goes out with ignition on. Adjust switch, if necessary.

All Others

1) Raise and support vehicle. Ensure parking brake cables are operating freely. Remove wheel and tire assembly. Release parking brake. Insert an adjusting tool into rotor inspection hole. Turn adjuster until parking brake shoes stop rotation of rotor. Back off adjuster 4-6 notches. *See Fig. 1.*

2) From inside driver's compartment, tighten adjustment nuts on lever until parking brake holds vehicle securely before 5th ratchet stop is reached. Both rear wheels should rotate freely and evenly with parking lever released.

Fig. 1: Typical Parking Brake Components

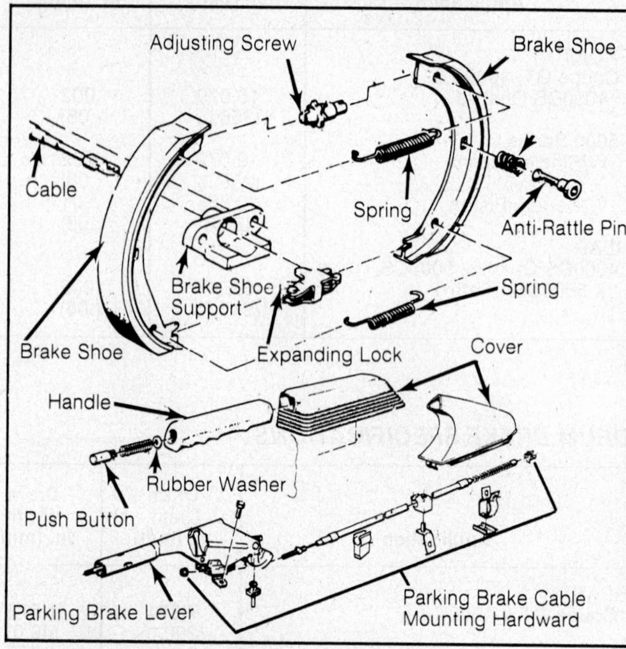

Courtesy of BMW of North America.

BRAKE WARNING LIGHT

1) A dual warning light is mounted on instrument panel. Light should glow when parking brake lever is pulled one notch (ignition on) and go off when lever is fully released.

2) To check circuit warning sensor, fully release parking brake. Ensure light is off (ignition on). Remove master cylinder filler cap. Warning light should glow. If not, check bulb or circuit connections.

TESTING

POWER BRAKE UNIT

NOTE: The following pressure test specifications are in psi and bar pressure units.

1) With engine off, pump brake pedal about 20 times with a force equal to full stop braking action (45 lbs./200 N). This will discharge pressure from hydraulic reservoir. Remove wires from warning switch. Remove warning switch.

2) Connect Brake Pressure Tester Adapter and Pressure Tester (32 4 000 and 34 3 160) to brake booster. *See Fig. 2.* Close both control valves. Start engine. Observe pressure regulator and brake booster for fluid leaks.

3) While engine is running, observe pressure gauge. Stop engine after reaching upper switching off pressure. Upper switching off pressure is 740-810 psi (52-57 bar).

4) If reservoir pressure (pressure gauge reading) drops more than 71 psi (5 bar) within 5 minutes, disconnect return line on pressure regulator. *See Fig. 2.* If fluid leaks from return line of pressure regulator, or if pressure regulator leaks, replace pressure regulator.

BMW (Cont.)

5) If there are no fluid leaks and reservoir pressure still drops, brake booster has an internal leak and must be replaced.

Fig. 2: Power Brake System Components

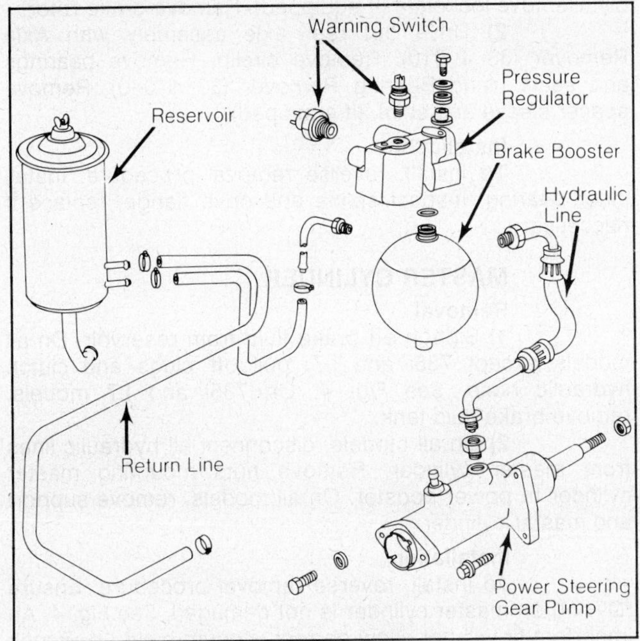

Courtesy of BMW of North America.

HYDRAULIC RESERVOIR

1) Connect brake Pressure Tester Adapter and Pressure Tester (32 4 000 and 34 3 160) to brake reservoir. *See Fig. 2.* Operate brake pedal about 20 times to reduce reservoir pressure (pressure gauge reading to "0").

2) Start engine and ensure pressure gauge reads 333-449 psi (23-31 bar). If specification is not reached or is exceeded, replace hydraulic reservoir.

PRESSURE REGULATOR

1) With Pressure Tester Adapter and Pressure Tester (32 4 000 and 34 3 160) attached to pressure regulator, start engine. Pressure should continue rising to upper switching pressure. Upper switching pressure is 740-810 psi (52-57 bar).

2) Operate brake pedal with engine running to drop reservoir pressure (pressure gauge reading) to lower switching pressure. Lower switching pressure is 512-583 psi (36-41 bar). After pressure release, pressure regulator will switch to charging reservoir (pressure rises again).

3) Replace pressure regulator if test values do not conform to specifications. Drop reservoir pressure (pressure gauge reading) to "0" by operating brake pedal about 20 times. Remove pressure gauge and check fluid level in supply tank.

BRAKE MASTER CYLINDER

1) Remove front wheel and loosen bleeder screw on caliper. Connect Brake Pressure Tester (34 3 160) to master cylinder and bleed. Install pedal force gauge on brake pedal. With engine running, apply about 100 lbs. (445 N) of pressure on 325 series models.

2) On all other models, apply about 150 lbs. (654 N) of pressure to brake pedal. The hydraulic line pressure gauge should show 710 psi (50 bar).

High Pressure Leak Test

1) Engine must be off during test. Operate brake pedal about 20 times to relieve pressure in hydraulic reservoir. Inspect both brake circuits for proper operation and leaks.

2) Unscrew bleeder screw and attach Pressure Tester (32 4 000) to one side of brake circuit. *See Fig. 3.* Bleed air from pressure tester. On 325 series models, apply 110 lbs. (489 N) force on brake pedal.

3) On all other models, apply a 150 lb. (654 N) force on brake pedal. This force will cause a rise in pressure, on pressure gauge. This pressure should be 710 psi (50 bar). After 2 minutes pressure should not drop more than 8% or 89 psi (6 bar). Repeat this test on remaining side of brake circuit.

Fig. 3: Exploded View of Single Piston Caliper

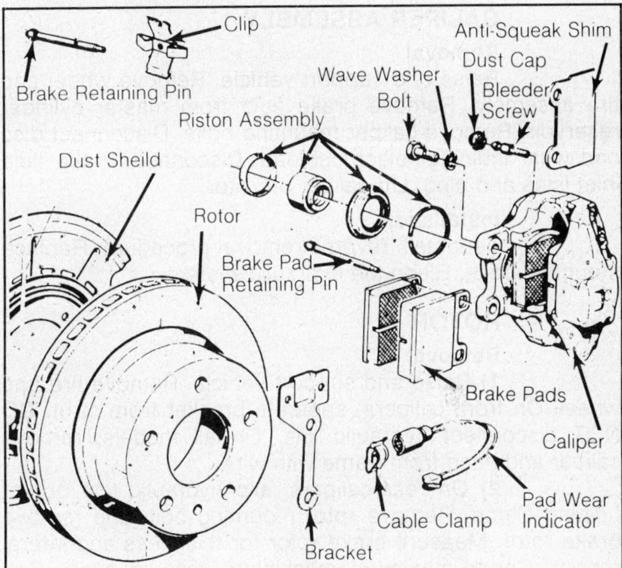

Courtesy of BMW of North America.

Low Pressure Test

1) Test both brake circuits. Set pedal force gauge to have a testing pressure of 28-70 psi (2-5 bar). Vehicle and gauges must remain still, since any motion will produce incorrect readings.

2) Pressure should remain constant for at least 5 minutes. If pressure drops considerably, check all rubber components in brake system for leakage. Bleed system after completeing test.

REMOVAL & INSTALLATION

DISC PADS

Removal (Front)

1) Raise and support vehicle. Remove wheel and tire. Disconnect pad wear sensors. Remove retaining pins. Remove cross spring.

2) Remove bottom mounting bolt and swing caliper up. Remove pads from caliper. If pad thickness has worn to .08" (2.0 mm), replace pads. Only replace pads in matched sets.

Removal (Rear)

1) On rear calipers, remove plastic caps on caliper mounting bolts and remove mounting bolts. Remove brake caliper retainer clip. Remove brake pad wear sensor from right brake pad of left wheel.

2) Pull brake caliper off toward front. Remove outer brake pad. Remove inner brake pad (inner brake pad is located in piston with a spring).

Installation (Front & Rear)

1) Using a wire brush, clean guide surface and support surface of caliper. Siphon sufficient brake fluid from master cylinder reservoir to prevent overflowing. Press pistons back into bores of calipers. Insert new brake pad wear indicator plug.

2) Replace mounting bolts and install disc pads. Be careful not to damage dust cover on brake piston when assembling. Check position of springs. After installation, depress brake pedal several times to seat pads.

CALIPER ASSEMBLY

Removal

Raise and support vehicle. Remove wheel and tire assembly. Remove brake fluid from master cylinder reservoir. Remove caliper mounting bolts. Disconnect disc pad wear indicator electrical lead. Disconnect brake fluid inlet lines and plug. Lift caliper off rotor.

Installation

To install, reverse removal procedure. Replace mounting bolts. Bleed the hydraulic system.

ROTOR

Removal

1) Raise and support vehicle. Remove tire and wheel. On front calipers, separate bracket from strut. DO NOT disconnect hydraulic line. On all models, remove caliper and hang from frame with wire.

2) On rear calipers, slip hydraulic line out of holding clamp. Remove rotor mounting bolt, and remove brake rotor. Measure brake rotor for thickness and lateral runout. Check maximum machining limits in chart. See DISC BRAKE ROTOR SPECIFICATIONS chart at the end of this article.

NOTE: **Front brake rotors are balanced. DO NOT remove or reposition balance clips. If any rotor (front or rear) must be replaced, replace rotors in axle sets.**

Installation

To install, reverse removal procedure. Ensure correct operation.

PARKING BRAKE SHOES

Removal

With rear caliper and rotor removed, disconnect upper return spring using brake spring pliers. *See Fig. 1*. Ensure that pin of spreader lock does not fall out. Using Brake Spring Removal Tool (34 4 000), turn retaining springs 90 degrees. Set spring aside. Pull brake shoes apart at bottom and lift upward.

Installation

To install, reverse removal procedure, adjust parking brake shoes and check operation. Lightly lubricate sliding surfaces of parking brake shoes and components.

REAR AXLE SEALS & BEARINGS

Removal

1) Raise and support vehicle. Remove wheel and brake drum assembly. Remove output shaft assembly. Remove lockplate (if equipped). Remove brake rotor.

2) Drive out rear axle assembly with Axle Remover (33 4 010). Remove circlip. Remove bearings and seals using Bearing Remover (33 4 040). Remove spacer sleeve and shim, (if equipped).

Installation

To install, reverse removal procedure. Install inner bearing. Inspect spline and drive flange, replace if neccessary.

MASTER CYLINDER

Removal

1) Siphon off brake fluid from reservoir. On all models except 735i and L7, pull off plugs and clutch hydraulic hose. *See Fig. 4*. On 735i and L7 models, remove brake fluid tank.

2) On all models, disconnect all hydraulic lines from master cylinder. Remove nuts mounting master cylinder to power booster. On all models, remove support and master cylinder.

Installation

To install, reverse removal procedure. Ensure "O" ring on master cylinder is not damaged. *See Fig. 4*. An imperfect fit will not allow correct vacuum build-up. Bench bleed master cylinder prior to installation.

POWER BRAKE UNIT

Removal

1) Release pressure from reservoir by operating brake pedal approximately 20 times. Siphon brake fluid from master cylinder reservoir. Remove left portion of lower instrument panel. Remove operating rod clevis pin from brake pedal arm.

2) Disconnect and plug hydraulic lines at master cylinder, including clutch hose. Remove brake fluid tank from master cylinder if necessary.

3) Disconnect vacuum hose or hydraulic lines from power brake unit. *See Fig. 2*. Remove power brake unit mounting bolts. Remove power unit/master cylinder assembly from vehicle. Separate master cylinder from power brake unit.

NOTE: **On all models except 325 series, power steering pump also supplies hydraulic pressure through hydraulic accumulator to the power brake unit. If power steering fails, there will be sufficient pressure in the hydraulic accumulator to provide a few brake applications with full power.**

Installation

To install, mount master cylinder to power brake unit and reverse removal procedure. Bleed hydraulic system after installation.

CHECK VALVE REPLACEMENT

Check valve is located in vacuum line between power unit and intake manifold. To remove, loosen hose clamps, remove vacuum lines and remove valve. To install, reverse removal procedure. Replace clamps if necessary. Ensure arrow or Black portion of valve faces intake manifold.

Brakes

BMW (Cont.)

BRAKE FORCE REGULATOR

Removal & Installation

Draw off brake fluid from reservoir. Disconnect both lines at regulator. Check codes on regulator. Ensure that pressure reduction and switching over pressures of new regulator are equivalent by matching codes. To install, reverse removal procedure.

PRESSURE FLOW REGULATOR

Removal

1) Stop engine and operate brake pedal about 20 times with a force equal to full stop braking action to discharge the hydraulic reservoir. Remove wires from brake warning switch.

2) Remove lines from regulator to tank, from regulator to steering gear, from regulator to steering pump and from regulator to brake booster. Unscrew pressure flow regulator mounting bolts and remove regulator.

NOTE: **Solid particles of dirt could impair function of pressure flow regulator, which could lead to failure of power steering assistance or brake boost. Ensure that pipes, hoses and connections are clean before installing regulator.**

Installation

To install, reverse removal procedure. Bleed air from system.

OVERHAUL

BRAKE CALIPER

Disassembly

With pads removed from caliper, remove retaining ring (if equipped) and dust boot. Insert wooden block in caliper cavity. Apply approximately 140 psi (10 bar) or less, of compressed air to fluid inlet of caliper. Remove piston seals without damaging caliper bore.

Fig. 4: Exploded View of Master Cylinder Assembly

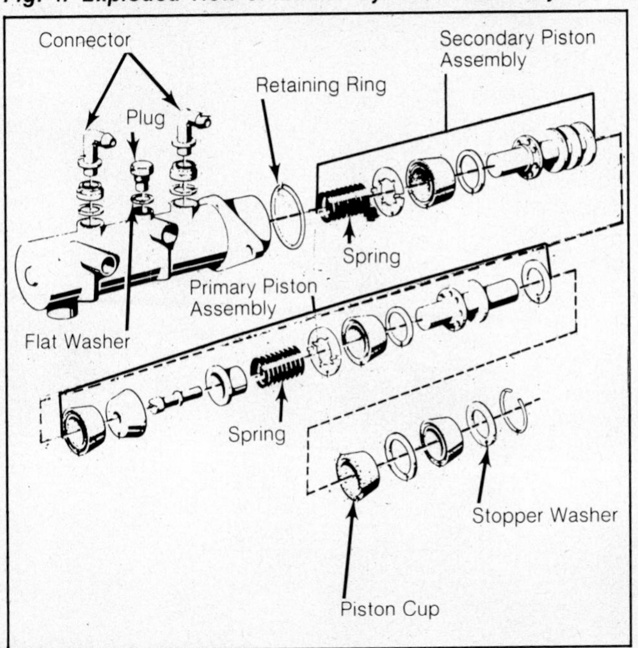

Courtesy of BMW of North America.

Cleaning & Inspection

Clean components in clean brake fluid or alcohol and blow dry. Inspect caliper bore and pistons for wear or damage. Replace caliper assembly if corroded or worn. DO NOT hone. Inspect dowel sleeves, replace if necessary. Replace piston seals and dust boots at each overhaul.

Reassembly

Coat piston and caliper bore with brake cylinder paste. Install piston seal, then install piston. Ensure piston is not tilted when inserting.

MASTER CYLINDER

Disassembly

Push in on primary piston and remove secondary piston stop screw. Remove snap ring from end of cylinder. *See Fig. 4.* Remove primary and secondary piston assemblies and stop washer. Remove return spring. Disassemble piston assemblies, noting number and position of parts used for reassembly reference.

NOTE: **Replace master cylinders with surface defects in bores. DO NOT overhaul.**

Reassembly

1) Reassemble piston assemblies using thin coating of ATE brake paste. Install piston assemblies into cylinder bore, using Guide Sleeve (34 3 000) to prevent damage to seals.

2) Install secondary piston stop screw, ensuring piston is pushed fully forward before screw is installed and tightened. *See Fig. 4.* Install retaining ring in end of master cylinder bore. Replace "O" ring between master cylinder and brake booster. Bench bleed master cylinder prior to installation.

TIGHTENING SPECIFICATIONS

Application	Ft. Lbs. (N.m)
Caliper Mounting Bolt	
325 Series	63-79 (86-107)
735i & L7	58-69 (79-94)
All Others	80-89 (109-121)
Guide Bolt	22-25 (30-34)
Master Cylinder-to-Booster	
Hydraulic Operated	18-23 (24-31)
Vacuum Operated	16-20 (22-27)

Brakes

BMW (Cont.)

DISC BRAKE ROTOR SPECIFICATIONS

Application	Disc Diameter In. (mm)	Lateral Runout In. (mm)	Parallelism In. (mm)	Original Thickness In. (mm)	Min. Refinish Thickness In. (mm)	Discard Thickness In. (mm)
FRONT						
325 Series, 528e 535i & 535is		[1] .008 (.2)	.0008 (.02)	.....	.437 (11.1)	.421 (10.7)
635CSi & L6	.....	[1] .008 (.2)	.0008 (.02)	.....	.921 (23.4)	.906 (23.0)
735i & L7	.....	[1] .008 (.2)	.0008 (.02)	.....	1.034 (26.3)	1.024 (26.0)
REAR						
All Models	.....	[1] .008 (.2)	.0008 (.02)	.....	.331 (8.4)	.315 (8.0)

[1] – Measured on vehicle. Off vehicle runout should be .002" (.05 mm).

CHRYSLER MOTORS & MITSUBISHI

All Except Precis

NOTE: **For Precis, see HYUNDAI EXCEL & MITSUBISHI PRECIS article. For information on Conquest and Starion anti-lock brake system, see CHRYSLER MOTORS & MITSUBISHI ANTI-LOCK BRAKE SYSTEM article.**

DESCRIPTION

BRAKE SYSTEM

Brake system consists of a master cylinder, vacuum power brake unit and proportioning valve. Colt Vista 2WD models, Pickup, Ram-50, Van/Wagon models have a height sensing proportioning valve. All brake systems are self-adjusting. All models are equipped with front disc brakes. Galant is equipped with rear disc or drum brakes. Conquest and Starion are equipped with rear disc brakes. All other models are equipped with rear drum brakes. Parking brake is connected to rear brakes.

ADJUSTMENTS

PEDAL HEIGHT & FREE PLAY

1) Back off stoplight switch. To adjust pedal height (distance from top of pedal to floor board) loosen lock nut, and rotate master cylinder push rod (yoke, if equipped). DO NOT depress push rod. Tighten lock nut, and ensure that brake pedal free play is .12-.31" (3-8 mm) on Galant and Van/Wagon, or .40-.60" (10-15 mm) on all other models.

PEDAL HEIGHT SPECIFICATIONS

Application	In. (mm)
Colt & Mirage	6.2-6.4 (158-163)
Colt Vista	7.1-7.3 (180-185)
Conquest, Galant & Starion	7.0-7.2 (178-183)
Cordia & Tredia	6.9-7.1 (175-180)
Montero & Raider	7.5-7.7 (191-196)
Pickup & Ram-50	6.5 (166)
Van/Wagon	7.7-7.9 (196-201)

2) After adjustment is made, start engine. Check pedal height. If clearance is not at least 3.7" (95 mm) on Montero and Raider, 3.5" (89 mm) on Cordia, Terdia and Van/Wagon or 3.1" (80 mm) on all other models, bleed system and check for misadjusted brakes.

STOPLIGHT SWITCH

On all models, loosen lock nut and adjust switch-to-pedal arm clearance to .02-.06" (.5-1.5 mm) on Van/Wagon or .02-.04" (.5-1.0 mm) on all other models. Tighten lock nut. DO NOT depress master cylinder push rod during stoplight switch adjustment.

PARKING BRAKE

NOTE: **If parking brake lever stroke is not to specifications after adjustment, automatic adjuster will malfunction.**

Colt, Colt Vista, Cordia, Galant, Mirage & Tredia

Remove console box or parking brake lever cover. Adjust the cable adjusting nut, allowing enough slack in cables to prevent brake shoe drag. Properly adjusted parking brake lever stroke should be 5-7 notches at 44 lbs. (20 kg) force. On Galant equipped with rear disc brakes, ensure clearance between parking lever and stopper is .078" (1.98 mm) or less.

Conquest & Starion

When parking brake lever is pulled with a force of 45 lbs. (20.4 kg), the lever stroke should be 4-5 notches. If not, remove accessory box or parking brake lever cover. Turn cable adjusting nut until specified number of notches is obtained.

Montero, Raider & Van/Wagon

When parking brake lever is pulled with a force of 45 lbs. (20.4 kg), the lever stroke should be 4-6 notches. If not, remove accessory box or parking brake lever cover. Turn cable adjusting nut until specified number of notches are obtained with a pull of 45 lbs. (20.4 kg) force.

Pickup & Ram-50

1) Service brake adjustment must be accurate before making parking brake adjustment. Fully release parking brake, and allow slack in rear cable to prevent brake shoe drag.

2) Adjust turnbuckle for 2WD models (turn adjusting nut on equalizer for 4WD models) to obtain a brake lever stroke of 16-17 notches with a 66 lbs. (29.9 kg) setting force.

3) On 2WD models, balancer must be parallel with center line of vehicle. On 4WD models, the equalizer and joint must be at right angles to each other.

HEIGHT SENSING PROPORTIONING VALVE

NOTE: **Remove all luggage and passengers before checking and adjusting. Ensure vehicle is parked on level surface.**

Colt Vista

Ensure lever is not against stopper bolt. Check spring length. If not 3.42-3.50" (86.9-88.9 mm), adjust cable until proper length is obtained. *See Fig. 1.*

Pickup & Ram-50

Ensure lever is not against stopper bolt. Check spring length. If not 6.85-6.93" (174.0-176.0 mm), adjust support until proper length is obtained.

Fig. 1: Measuring Height Sensing Proportioning Valve Spring (Colt Vista)

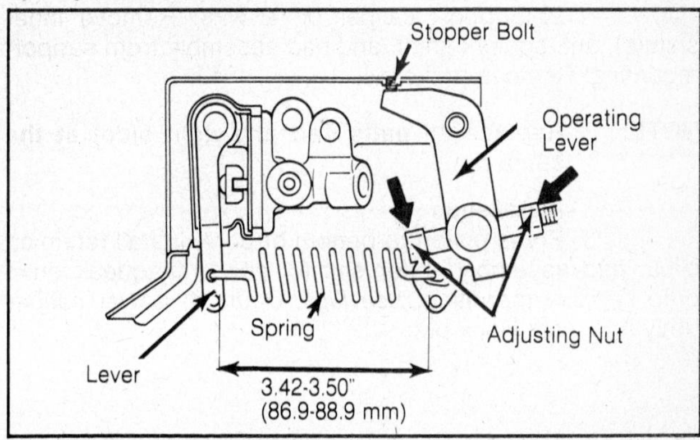

Courtesy of Chrysler Motors.

CHRYSLER MOTORS & MITSUBISHI (Cont.)

Van/Wagon

Check spring length. If not 6.93-7.05" (176.0-179.1 mm), adjust support until proper length is obtained.

REMOVAL & INSTALLATION

FRONT DISC BRAKE PADS

CAUTION: Be careful not to remove lock pin's coat of special grease or permit dirt to adhere to it.

Removal (Montero & Raider)

1) Raise and support vehicle. Remove front wheel. Remove spigot pins and pull out stopper plugs.

2) Pull caliper assembly up and down in a diagonal manner, and remove from mounting bracket. Remove inner and outer pad clips. Pull pads and anti-squeal shims from caliper support.

Installation

To install, reverse removal procedure. Press piston to bottom of caliper bore prior to pad installation. Make sure pad retaining clips are installed properly. *See Fig. 2.*

Fig. 2: Installing Montero & Raider Pad Retaining Clips

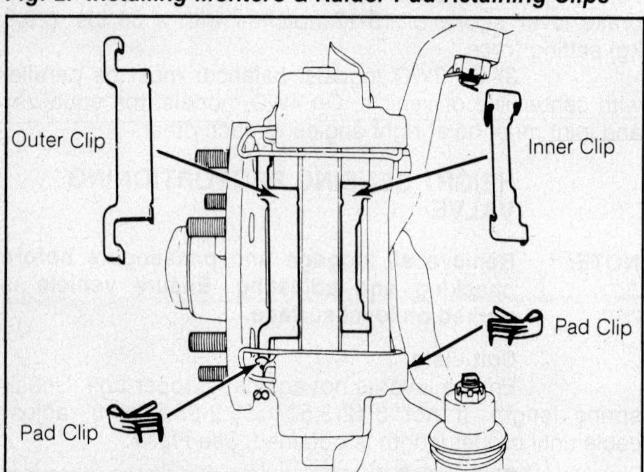

Courtesy of Mitsubishi Motor Sales of America.

Removal (All Others)

1) Raise and support vehicle. Remove front wheel. Remove lock pin or bottom sleeve bolt. Lift caliper body upward.

2) Support caliper on a wire. Remove inner shim(s), anti-squeak shim, and pad assembly from support mounting. Remove pad clips.

NOTE: Replace all pads (left and right side) at the same time.

Installation

Press piston to bottom of bore. Install retaining clips, pad assembly, inner shim(s) and anti-squeak shim onto support mounting. *See Figs. 3 and 4.* Lower caliper body and install lock pin.

Fig. 3: Exploded View of Front Disc Brake Assembly (Colt & Mirage W/1.5L)

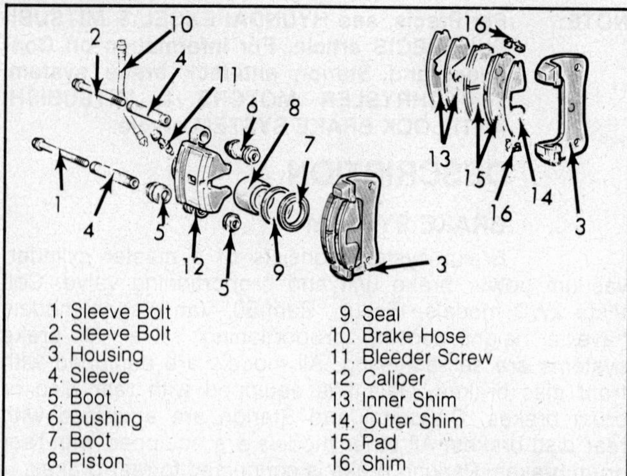

Courtesy of Chrysler Motors.

Fig. 4: Exploded View of Front Disc Brake Assembly (All Other Models)

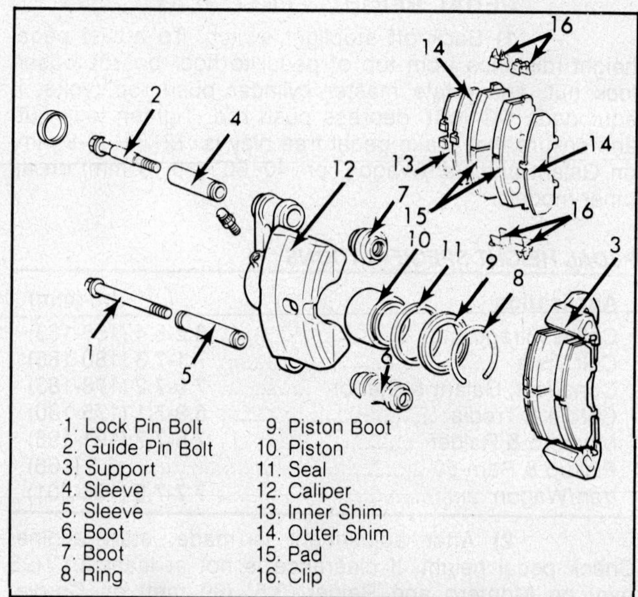

Courtesy of Chrysler Motors.

REAR DISC BRAKE PADS

Removal (Conquest, Galant & Starion)

Raise and support vehicle. Remove rear wheel. Remove lock pin bolt. Lift caliper body upward. Support caliper on a wire. Remove inner shim(s), anti-squeak shim, and pad assembly from support mounting. Remove pad clips.

NOTE: Replace all pads (left and right side) at the same time.

Installation

Using Driver (MB990652), rotate piston so stopper grooves in piston are aligned with projection on back of pads. Install retaining clips, pad assembly, inner shim(s) and anti-squeak shim onto support mounting. Lower caliper body and install lock pin.

CHRYSLER MOTORS & MITSUBISHI (Cont.)

Fig. 5: Removing Drive Shaft From Transaxle

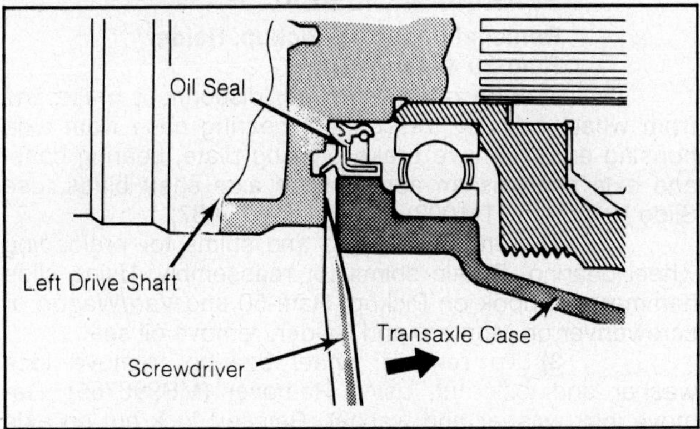

Courtesy of Mitsubishi Motor Sales of America.

FRONT DISC BRAKE CALIPER

Removal (Montero & Raider)

Remove disc pads. Pull out hose clip from strut area. Disconnect brake hose from caliper. Remove caliper.

Installation

To install, reverse removal procedure. Tighten bolts to specification and bleed brake system.

Removal (All Except Montero & Raider)

Remove disc pads. Disconnect hydraulic line, and remove bolts attaching caliper assembly to steering knuckle. Remove caliper assembly.

Installation

To install, reverse removal procedure. Tighten caliper mounting bolts to specification and bleed hydraulic system.

FRONT DISC BRAKE ROTOR

CAUTION: Place ball joint of lower arm on lower arm to prevent damage to the ball joint dust boot.

Removal (Colt, Colt Vista, Cordia, Galant, Mirage & Tredia)

1) Raise and support front of vehicle. Remove front wheels. Remove caliper. On Cordia and Tredia, disconnect stabilizer bar and strut bar. On all models, remove cotter pin, wheel bearing nut and washer. Remove lower ball joint nut. Position Puller (MB991113) to separate lower ball joint from steering knuckle.

2) Secure puller cord. DO NOT remove nut from puller. Using puller separate tie rod from steering knuckle. Disconnect stabilizer bar from lower arm. Using 2 screwdrivers, 11.4" (290 mm) in length, remove drive shaft from transaxle or center bearing. *See Fig. 5*. DO NOT use a pry bar.

3) Disconnect strut assembly from knuckle. Remove hub and knuckle assembly. Using Bracket (MB991056) and Bolt (MB990998), separate knuckle from hub. Remove rotor from hub.

Installation

1) Using Bolt (MB990998), install hub and rotor assembly into knuckle. On Colt Vista, Cordia and Tredia, tighten bolt to 144-188 ft. lbs. (196-256 N.m). Rotate hub to seat bearings. Measure hub starting torque and wheel bearing end play.

2) Starting torque should be 11 INCH lbs. (1.3 N.m) on 2WD models, or 16 INCH lbs. (1.8 N.m) on 4WD models, or greater. End play should be .008" (.20 mm) or more. If not, check for correct installation of hub. On all models, reverse removal procedure to complete installation.

Removal (Conquest & Starion)

Remove front caliper. Remove hub cap, cotter pin and nut. Remove washer and outer wheel bearing. Remove front hub assembly. Remove bolts attaching rotor to front hub.

Installation

To install, reverse removal procedure. Tighten wheel bearings in the following sequence: 14 ft. lbs. (19 N.m), loosen, then tighten to 48 INCH lbs. (5 N.m). To install cotter pin, loosen nut 15 degrees maximum.

Removal (Montero, Raider, 4WD Pickup & 4WD Ram-50)

With caliper assembly removed and supported by a wire, remove front hub assembly from the knuckle. See LOCKING HUBS article. After marking the hub and disc, disassemble the hub from the disc.

NOTE: If removal or replacement of bearings or races is necessary, see appropriate articles in FRONT SUSPENSION section.

Installation

To install, reverse removal procedures and tighten to specifications. See appropriate articles in SUSPENSION section.

Removal (Van/Wagon, 2WD Pickup & 2WD Ram-50)

Remove front caliper. Remove hub cap, cotter pin and nut. Remove washer and outer wheel bearing. Remove front hub assembly. Remove bolts attaching rotor to front hub.

Installation

To install, reverse removal procedure. Tighten wheel bearings in the following sequence: 22 ft. lbs. (30 N.m), loosen, then tighten to 72 INCH lbs. (8 N.m). To install cotter pin, loosen nut 30 degrees maximum.

REAR BRAKE DISC ROTOR

Removal (Galant)

Remove rear caliper. Remove hub cap, cotter pin, lock, nut and washer. Remove outer wheel bearing. Remove rotor and hub assembly.

Installation

To install, reverse removal procedure. Tighten wheel bearings in the following sequence; 14 ft. lbs. (19 N.m), loosen, then tighten to 84 INCH lbs. (10 N.m).

Removal & Installation (Conquest & Starion)

Remove rear caliper assembly. Disconnect parking brake cable, if necessary. Remove clip retaining rotor. Remove rotor. To install, reverse removal procedure.

REAR BRAKE SHOES

Removal (Colt Vista, Cordia, Galant & Tredia)

1) Raise and support vehicle. Remove brake drum and hold-down springs. *See Fig. 6*. Disconnect strut-

CHRYSLER MOTORS & MITSUBISHI (Cont.)

to-shoe spring and upper shoe return spring end from trailing shoe.

2) Remove shoe hold-down spring and shoe retaining spring. Remove leading shoe. Remove parking brake cable from parking brake lever. Remove trailing shoe.

Removal (Montero, Pickup, Raider, Ram-50 & Van/Wagon)

1) Raise and support vehicle. Remove brake drum. Remove shoe return spring, shoe retainer spring and shoe hold-down pin. *See Fig. 7.*

2) Remove shoe and lining assembly and shoe and lever assembly. Remove cable from parking lever. Remove brake tube from wheel cylinder and wheel cylinder from backing plate.

3) Remove backing plate together with axle shaft. DO NOT remove backing plate from axle shaft, unless absolutely necessary.

Removal (Colt & Mirage)

1) Raise and support vehicle. Remove brake drum, clip spring, shoe retainer spring, shoe-to-shoe spring and hold-down spring. *See Fig. 8.*

2) Remove shoes and adjuster as an assembly and separate. Remove parking brake cable from lever.

Installation (All Models)

1) To install, reverse removal procedure. Apply Lubriplate to all shoe contact points, adjuster assembly, wheel cylinder and parking brake lever pin.

2) Set adjustment lever all the way back. After assembling the brake shoes, install brake drum. Depress brake pedal to adjust shoe clearance. Adjust parking brake.

3) Ensure adjuster lever meshes with next tooth of adjuster when pulled, and returns to original position after wheel has moved one tooth. Adjuster assemblies differ between right and left sides.

REAR AXLE SHAFT BEARING & OIL SEAL

Removal (Montero, Pickup, Raider, Ram-50 & Van/Wagon)

1) With drum removed, disconnect brake line from wheel cylinder. Disconnect bearing case from axle housing end. Remove brake backing plate, bearing case, and axle shaft as an assembly. If axle shaft binds, use Slide Hammer (CT-1003) and Puller (CT-637).

2) Remove "O" ring and shims for preloading wheel bearing. Retain shims for reassembly. Using slide hammer and hook on Pickup, Ram-50 and Van/Wagon or screwdriver on Montero and Raider, remove oil seal.

3) To remove wheel bearing, remove lock washer and lock nut, using Remover (MB990785). Remove lock washer and washer. Reinsert lock nut on axle shaft approximately 3 turns. Install Puller (MB990787-A) to remove bearing case from axle shaft.

4) Turn nuts with equal pressure to ensure smooth removal of wheel bearing. Using a hammer and drift, drive bearing outer race from bearing case. Remove oil seal from bearing case.

Installation

1) Apply Multipurpose Grease (2525035) to oil seal. Install oil seal using Installer (C-4572). Apply grease to outside circumference of bearing outer race. Press race into bearing case.

2) Apply grease to lip of oil seal and to roller surfaces of bearing inner race. Install rear brake assembly and bearing case. Press inner bearing race onto the axle shaft.

3) Pack bearing case and axle threads with grease. Install lock washer (tab aligned with axle slot) and lock nut (chamfer toward lock washer). Tighten nut to 130-159 ft. lbs. (176-216 N.m). Bend tabs on lock washer into slots of lock nut.

4) Apply grease to oil seal area of rear axle housing. Install new oil seal into end of rear axle housing. Adjust clearance between bearing case and rear axle by

Fig. 6: Colt Vista, Cordia, Galant & Tredia Rear Brakes

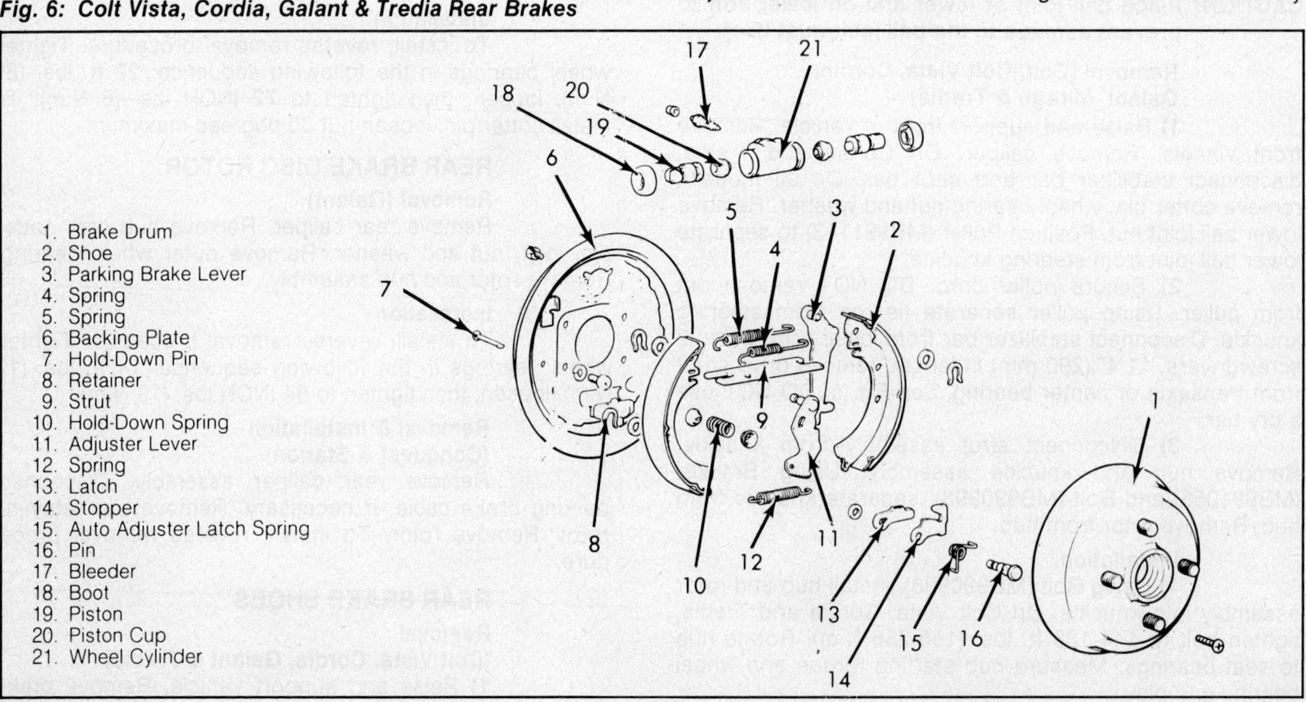

Courtesy of Mitsubishi Motor Sales of America.

CHRYSLER MOTORS & MITSUBISHI (Cont.)

Fig. 7: Exploded View of Montero, Pickup, Raider, Ram-50 & Van/Wagon Rear Brake Assembly

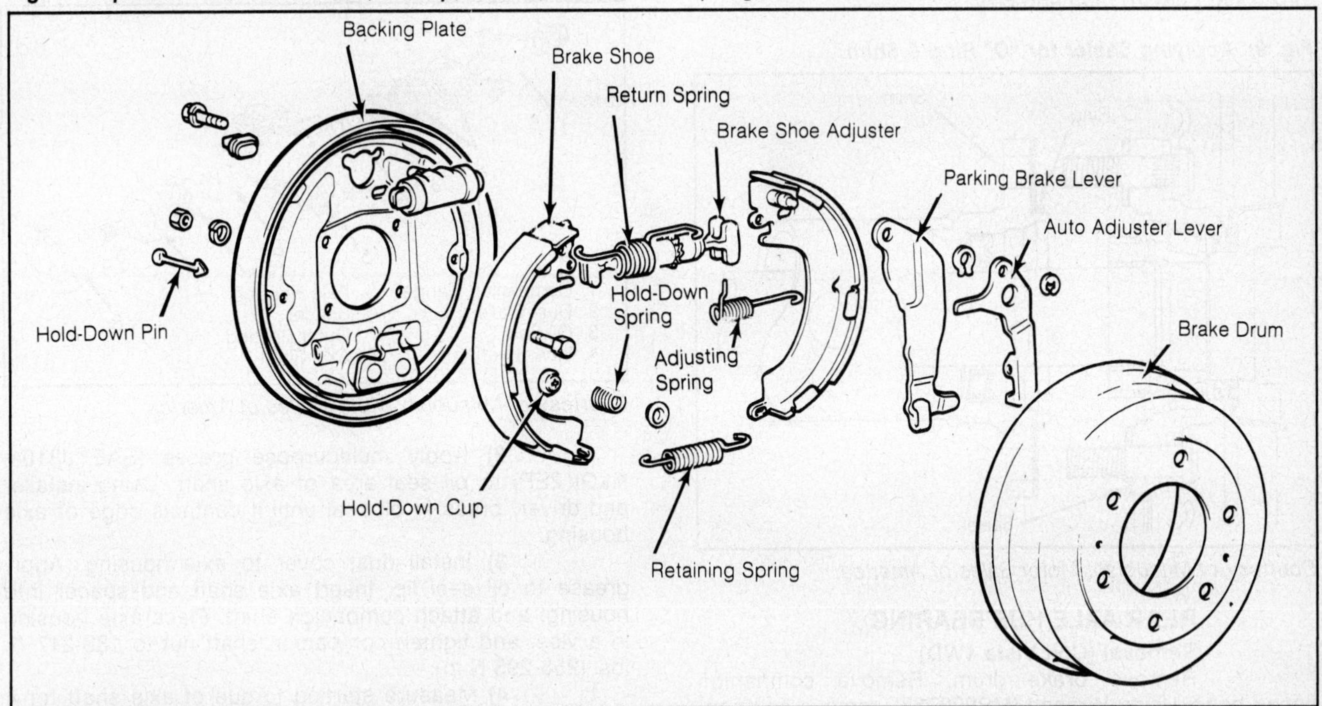

Courtesy of Mitsubishi Motor Sales of America.

inserting .04" (1.0 mm) shim and "O" ring into left rear axle housing.

5) Apply semi-drying sealant to mating surface of bearing case. Install left axle shaft into rear housing and tighten nuts diagonally to 36-43 ft. lbs. (50-58 N.m).

6) Install right axle shaft without shims and "O" ring. Temporarily tighten to about 53 INCH lbs. (6 N.m). Using a feeler gauge, measure clearance between bearing case and rear axle housing.

7) Remove right axle shaft. Install shims to equal measurement plus .002-.008" (.05-.20 mm). Install "O" ring to right rear axle housing. Apply sealant to mating surface of bearing case. *See Fig. 9.* Install axle into housing, tightening nuts diagonally to 36-43 ft. lbs. (50-58 N.m).

Fig. 8: Colt & Mirage Rear Brake Assembly

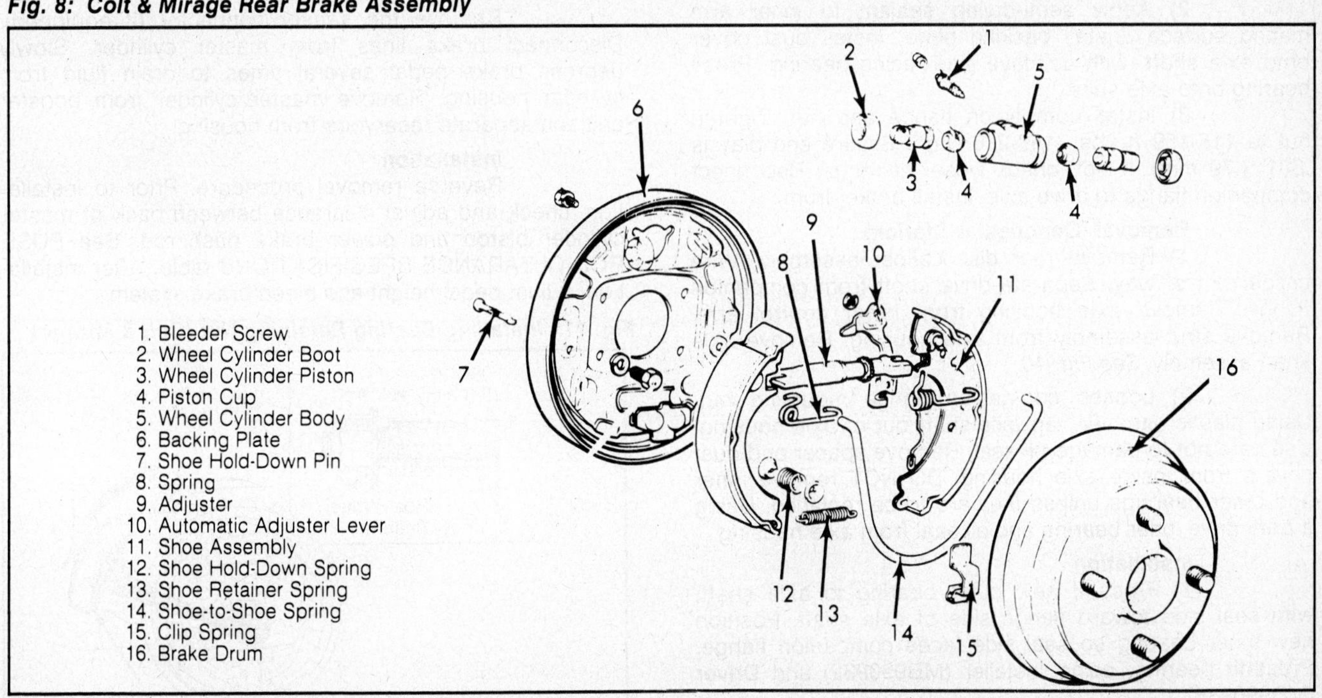

Courtesy of Mitsubishi Motor Sales of America.

CHRYSLER MOTORS & MITSUBISHI (Cont.)

8) Using dial indicator, check axle shaft for .002-.008" (.05-.20 mm) end play.

Fig. 9: Applying Sealer for "O" Ring & Shim

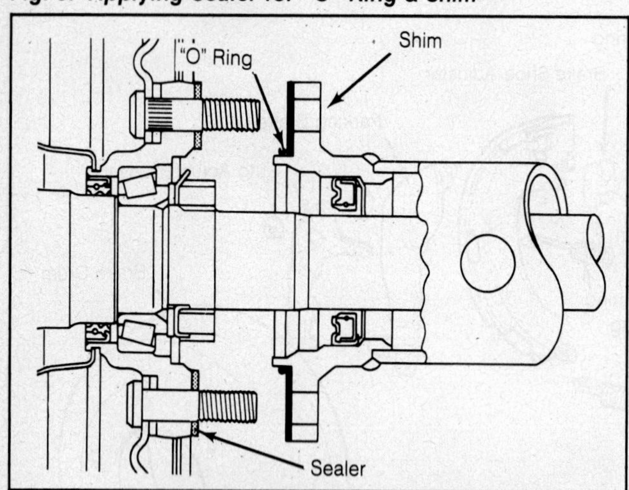

Courtesy of Mitsubishi Motor Sales of America.

REAR AXLE HUB BEARING

Removal (Colt Vista 4WD)

Remove brake drum. Remove companion flange bolts. Using Wrench (MB990767), remove companion flange nut. Remove companion flange. Using a slide hammer, remove axle shaft. Press bearing from axle shaft. Remove backing plate. Mark inner arm position. Remove inner arm bolts. Remove oil seal and bearing from inner arm.

Installation

1) Using Driver (MB9900938) and Adapter (MB990931), install bearing in inner arm. Using Driver (MB990799), install oil seal with concave surface facing outward, from rear of inner arm. Align marks and install inner arm bolts.

2) Apply semi-drying sealant to inner arm mating surface. Install backing plate. Install dust cover onto axle shaft, with concave side facing bearing. Press bearing onto axle shaft.

3) Install companion flange and nut. Tighten nut to 116-159 ft. lbs. (158-216 N.m). Ensure end play is .031" (.79 mm). If not, check wheel bearings. Reconnect companion flange to drive axle. Install brake drum.

Removal (Conquest & Starion)

1) Remove rear disc caliper assembly. Wire caliper out of way. Separate drive shaft from companion flange. Remove axle housing from lower control arm. Remove strut assembly from axle housing. Remove axle shaft assembly. *See Fig. 10.*

2) Loosen companion flange mounting nut. Using plastic hammer, tap axle shaft out of axle housing. Use care not to damage oil seal. Remove spacer and dust covers from inside axle housing. DO NOT remove inner and outer bearings unless they are to be replaced. Using a drift, drive inner bearing and oil seal from axle housing.

Installation

1) Press-fit new outer bearing to axle shaft, with seal side toward flange side of axle shaft. Position new inner bearing so seal side faces companion flange. Press-fit bearing, using Installer (MB990932) and Driver (MB990938).

Fig. 10: Exploded View of Axle Shaft Assembly

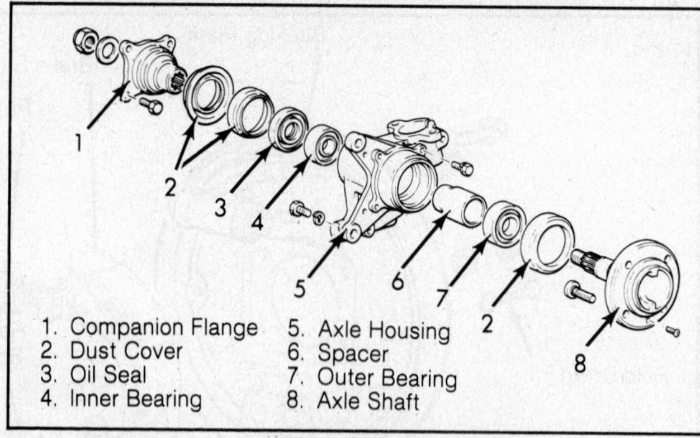

Courtesy of Mitsubishi Motor Sales of America.

2) Apply multipurpose grease (SAE J310a, NLGI 2EP) to oil seal area of axle shaft. Using installer and driver, press in oil seal until it contacts edge of axle housing.

3) Install dust cover to axle housing. Apply grease to oil seal lip. Insert axle shaft and spacer into housing, and attach companion shaft. Place axle housing in a vise, and tighten companion shaft nut to 188-217 ft. lbs. (256-295 N.m).

4) Measure starting torque of axle shaft for 4 INCH lbs. (.45 N.m) or less. If greater, replace spacer. Complete installation by installing axle housing to lower control arm and strut assembly. Using dial indicator, check axle end play for .031" (.79 mm).

MASTER CYLINDER

Removal (Van/Wagon)

Remove instrument cluster. Disconnect brake lines and reservoir hoses from master cylinder. Remove master cylinder from power booster. Remove reservoir, if necessary.

Removal (All Others)

Remove the sensor connector (if equipped). Disconnect brake lines from master cylinder. Slowly depress brake pedal several times to drain fluid from cylinder housing. Remove master cylinder from booster unit and separate reservoirs from housing.

Installation

Reverse removal procedure. Prior to installation, check and adjust clearance between back of master cylinder piston and power brake push rod. See PUSH ROD CLEARANCE SPECIFICATIONS table. After installation, adjust pedal height and bleed brake system.

Fig. 11: Installing Bearing Retaining Nut (Colt & Mirage)

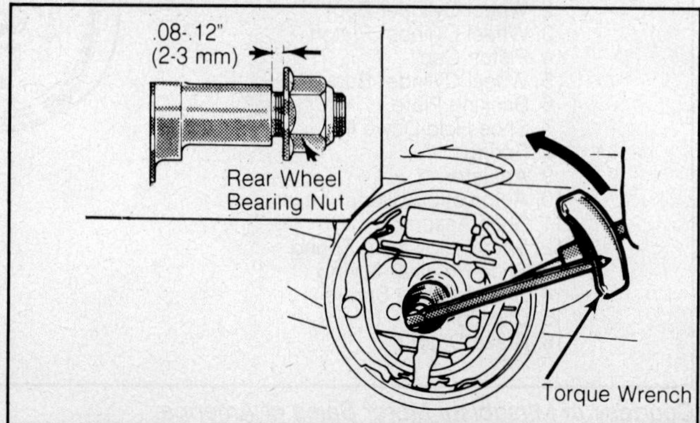

Courtesy of Chrysler Motors.

CHRYSLER MOTORS & MITSUBISHI (Cont.)

PUSH ROD CLEARANCE SPECIFICATIONS

Application	In. (mm)
Colt, Colt Vista, Cordia, Mirage, Pickup (2WD), Ram-50 (2WD) & Tredia	.016-.031 (.41-.79)
Conquest & Starion	.028-.043 (.71-1.09)
Galant & Van/Wagon	.059-.075 (1.50-1.91)
Montero & Raider	.004-.020 (.1-.5)
Pickup (4WD) & Ram-50 (4WD)	.028-.043 (.71-1.09)

POWER BRAKE UNIT CHECK VALVE REPLACEMENT

NOTE: Test check valve before removal. Pull off vacuum hose on booster side of check valve. Place finger over check valve, and crank engine. Vacuum should be felt.

Removal

Remove hose clamps from both ends of check valve. Remove check valve clamp and remove check valve.

Installation

Coat both ends of check valve with sealer and install valve with arrow (identification mark) pointing toward intake manifold side. Install check valve clamp and vacuum hoses, and secure hose clamps.

POWER BRAKE UNIT

Removal (Van/Wagon)

Remove heater duct tube. Remove steering column cover. Unplug steering column connector. Remove steering column. Disconnect vacuum hose. Remove master cylinder. Remove power brake unit and pedal assembly together. Separate power brake unit from pedal assembly.

Removal (All Others)

On Galant, remove air cleaner. On all models, remove the brake master cylinder, and disconnect vacuum hose from power brake unit. Disconnect brake pedal and operating rod of power brake unit. From inside vehicle, remove 4 nuts attaching power brake unit to firewall. Remove power brake unit.

Installation

To install, reverse removal procedure. Install master cylinder. Bleed brake system, if necessary.

OVERHAUL

FRONT DISC BRAKE CALIPER

Disassembly

Remove dust boot. Apply compressed air to fluid inlet to remove piston. Remove piston seal without damaging caliper bore or seal groove.

NOTE: Repair kits contain proper lubricants to be used during reassembly.

Reassembly

Coat piston seal with rubber grease. Slide seal into groove in cylinder bore. Slip piston into bore making sure seal is not twisted. Lightly coat dust seal groove with recommended rubber grease. Fit dust boot into place. Refit cylinder to caliper.

NOTE: Possible cause of increased pedal stroke is insufficient fit between piston and piston seal. Correct by manually levering piston to seat several times. This will create a better fit between piston and seal. Ensure brake pad is removed during this procedure.

Fig. 12: Exploded View of Front Disc Brake Caliper (Montero & Raider)

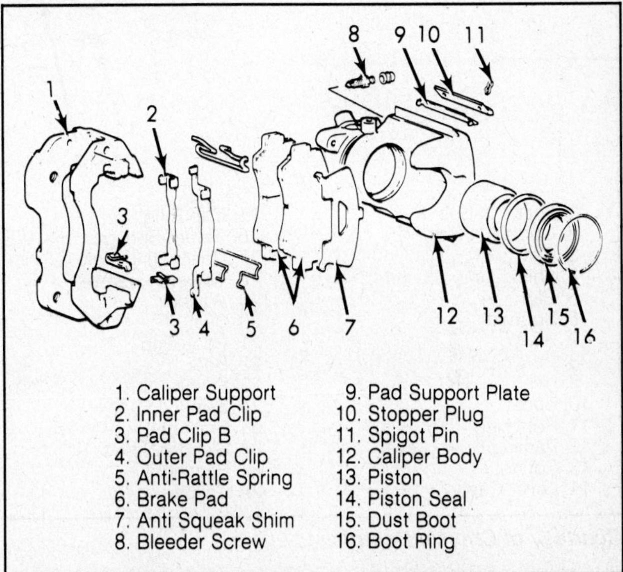

Courtesy of Mitsubishi Motor Sales of America.

REAR DISC BRAKE CALIPER

Disassembly

1) Remove cap ring and garter spring, and take off lever cap. Remove retaining ring. Pull out parking lever assembly. Unscrew automatic adjuster spindle and pull out assembly. Remove piston, piston seal and boot ring. *See Figs. 13 and 14.*

2) On Conquest and Starion, use Bearing Remover (MB990665) to press bearings from caliper. On all models, take off piston boot. Remove the guide pin and lock pin boots.

Cleaning & Inspection

Check cylinder and piston for wear, damage or rust. Replace worn parts as necessary. Always replace piston seal, adjuster seal and piston boot. Check bearings, connecting link, springs, adjuster spindle and lever assembly for wear, damage or rust. Check lever assembly for excessive play between shaft and bearing.

Reassembly

1) Lightly coat piston seal and piston with lubricant. Slide piston and seal into place, ensuring seal does not twist in groove. Lubricate boot, and slide boot into position making sure it engages groove in cylinder bore.

NOTE: Repair kit includes recommended lubricants.

2) On Conquest and Starion, use Bearing Installer (MB990665) to press in bearings until ends are flush with caliper body. Ensure mark on end of bearing faces out. Coat automatic adjuster seal with recommended grease. Fit adjuster spindle and hardware in place until spindle turns freely.

CHRYSLER MOTORS & MITSUBISHI (Cont.)

Fig. 13: Exploded View of Rear Disc Brake Caliper Assembly (Conquest & Starion)

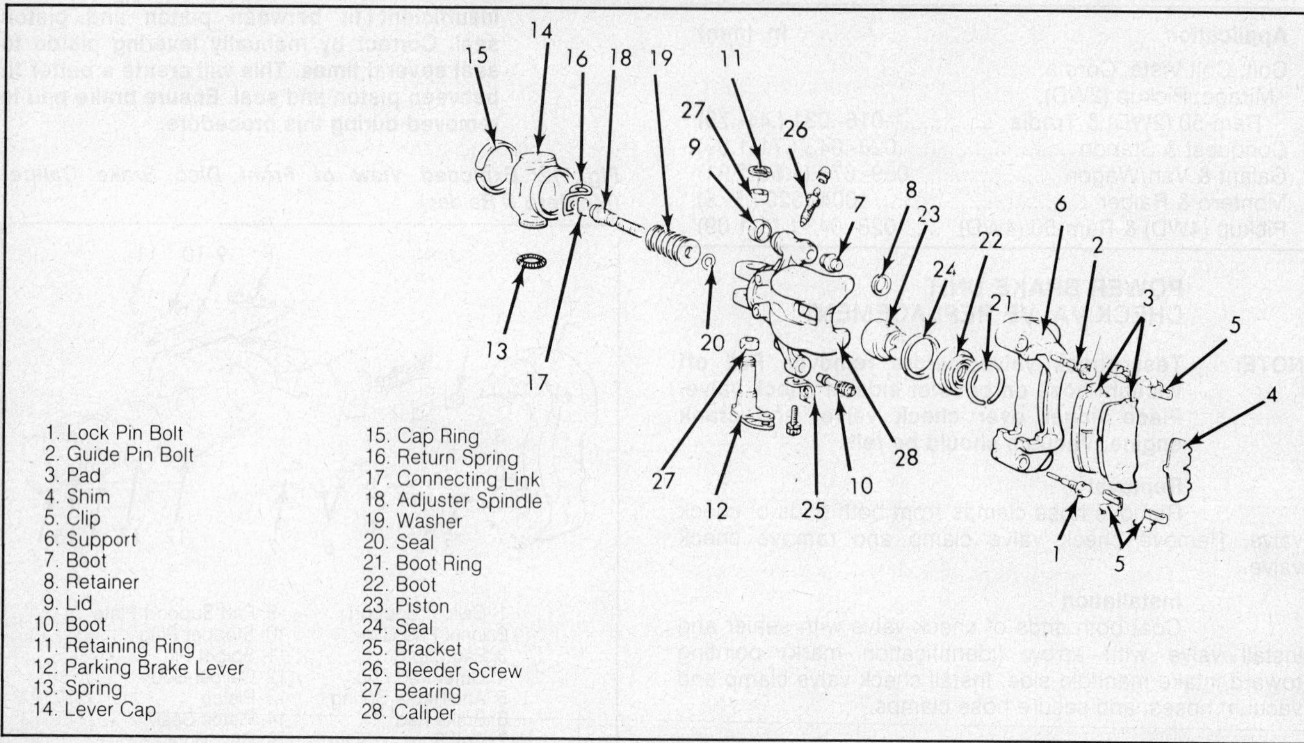

Courtesy of Chrysler Motors.

Fig. 14: Exploded View of Rear Disc Brake Caliper Assembly (Galant)

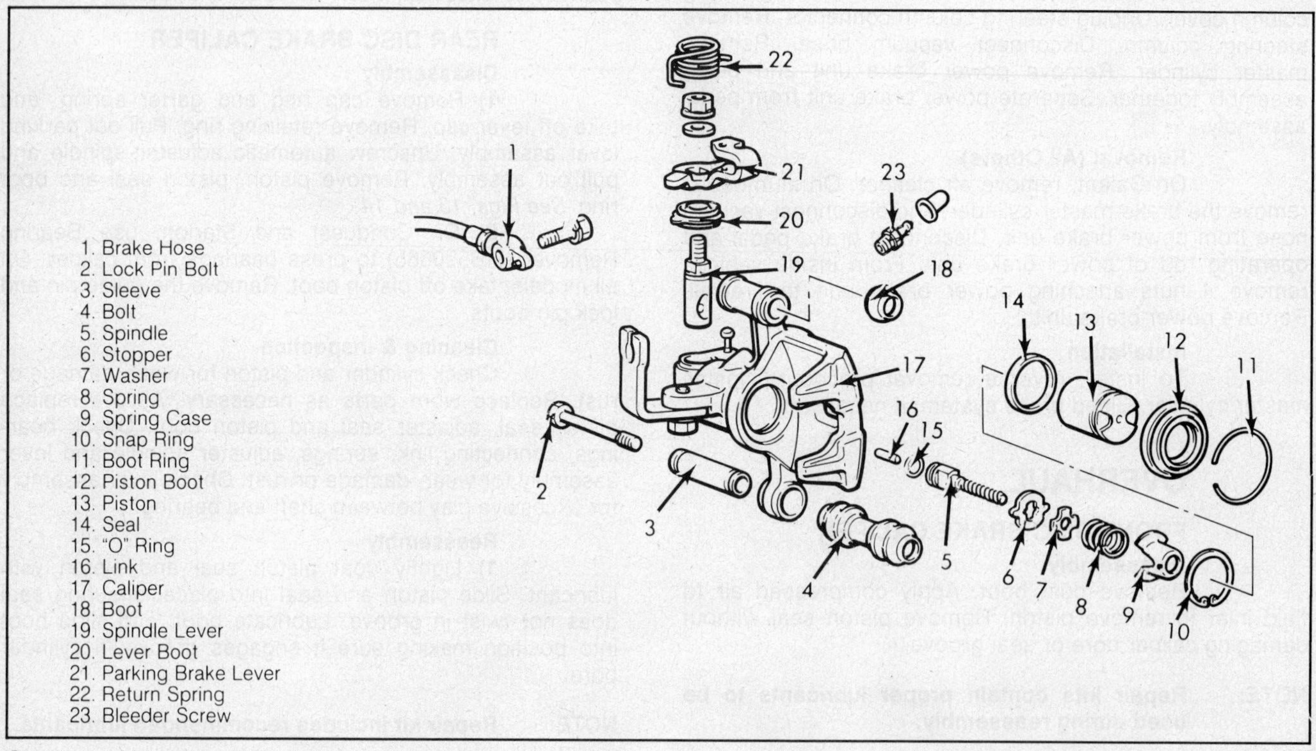

Courtesy of Mitsubishi Motor Sales of America.

CHRYSLER MOTORS & MITSUBISHI (Cont.)

3) Ensure spring faces proper direction. Press in connecting link spring washers with Installer (MB990666). *See Fig. 15.* Fit automatic adjuster spindle into place (spindle is not a press fit). Insert connecting link and lever assembly.

4) Fill lever cap with Niglube RX-2, ensuring all areas have ample grease. Lightly grease caliper sliding surface. Assembly is ready for installation.

Fig. 15: Compressing Rear Caliper Spring

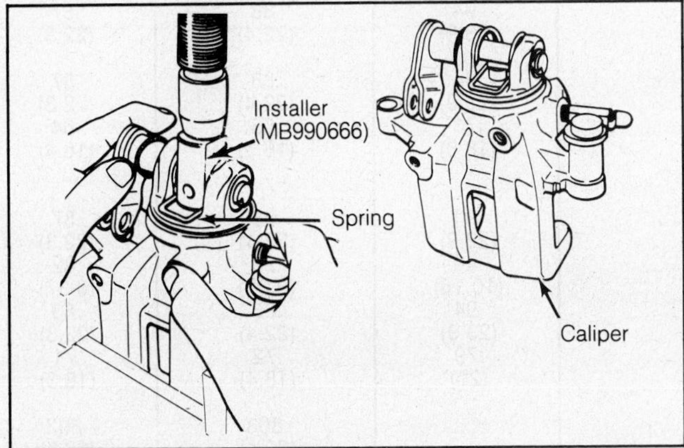

Courtesy of Chrysler Motors.

MASTER CYLINDER

Disassembly

While holding cylinder in a soft-jawed vise, remove dust boot, retaining ring, stop washer and piston stop bolt. Withdraw primary piston assembly, secondary piston assembly and secondary return spring from master cylinder. Remove check valve caps, tube seats, check valves and check valve springs. *See Fig. 16.*

NOTE: Do not disassemble primary and secondary piston assembly.

Cleaning & Inspection

Check master cylinder bore and piston for wear or other damage. Replace as necessary. Check clearance between cylinder bore and piston. If clearance exceeds .006" (.15 mm), replace master cylinder assembly.

Reassembly

Reverse disassembly procedure. Before reassembly, apply rubber grease to all parts (except boots). When assembled, check that return port is not blocked by piston cup, when piston is at return position.

Fig. 16: Disassembled View of Master Cylinder

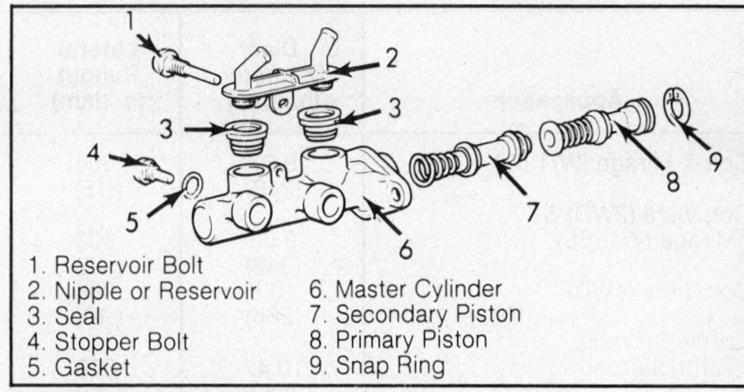

Courtesy of Mitsubishi Motor Sales of America.

TIGHTENING SPECIFICATIONS

Application	Ft. Lbs. (N.m)
Caliper Guide or Lock Pin Bolt	
Conquest & Starion	36-43 (50-58)
Pickup, Ram-50 & Van/Wagon	
Guide Pin Bolt	29-36 (40-50)
Lock Pin Bolt	23-30 (31-41)
All Other Models	16-23 (22-31)
Caliper Mounting Bolts	
Conquest, Galant & Starion	
Front	58-72 (80-100)
Rear	36-43 (50-58)
All Other Models	58-72 (80-100)
Companion Flange Nut	
Colt Vista (4WD)	116-159 (158-216)
Front Wheel Bearing Nut	
FWD Models	144-188 (196-256)
RWD Models	[1]
Rear Wheel Bearing Nut	
Colt & Mirage	72-108 (98-147)
Conquest & Starion	188-217 (256-295)
Pickup, Raider, Ram-50 & Van/Wagon	130-159 (177-216)
All Other Models	[1]
Rotor-to-Hub Bolts	
Colt Vista	43-51 (58-69)
Conquest & Starion	25-29 (34-39)
Van/Wagon	34-38 (46-52)
All Other Models	36-43 (50-58)
	INCH Lbs. (N.m)
Master Cylinder-to-Power Booster Nut	72-108 (8-12)

[1] – See text.

CHRYSLER MOTORS & MITSUBISHI (Cont.)

DISC BRAKE ROTOR SPECIFICATIONS

Application	Disc Diameter In. (mm)	Lateral Runout In. (mm)	Parallelism In. (mm)	Original Thickness In. (mm)	Min. Refinish Thickness In. (mm)	Discard Thickness In. (mm)
Colt & Mirage (W/1.5L)	9.57 (243)	.006 (.15)	.....	.51 (13.0)	.45 (11.4)	.44 (11.3)
Colt Vista (2WD) & Mirage (W/1.6L)	9.53 (242)	.006 (.15)	.....	.71 (18)	.65 (16.5)	.64 (16.4)
Colt Vista (4WD)	10.5 (266)	.004 (.10)	.....	.94 (23.9)	.88 (22.4)	.87 (22.3)
Cordia & Tredia						
Turbocharged	10.47 (265.9)	.006 (.15)	.....	.94 (23.9)	.88 (22.4)	.87 (22.3)
Non-Turbocharged	9.53 (242)	.006 (.15)	.....	.71 (18.0)	.65 (16.5)	.64 (16.4)
Galant						
W/Rear Disc Brakes						
Front	11.3 (288)	.006 (.15)	.....	.94 (23.9)	.88 (22.4)	.87 (22.3)
Rear	11.0 (279)	.012 (.30)	.....	.40 (10.16)	.33 (8.38)	.32 (8.37)
W/Rear Drum Brakes	10.5 (266)	.006 (.15)	.....	.94 (23.9)	.88 (22.4)	.83 (22.3)
Montero & Raider	10.0 (255)	.006 (.15)	.....	.79 (20)	.72 (18.4)	.71 (18.3)
Pickup & Ram-50						
2WD	10.2 (259)	.006 (.15)	.....	.....	.803 (20.4)	.802 (20.3)
4WD	10.9 (277)	.006 (.15)	.....	.....	.803 (20.4)	.802 (20.3)
Van/Wagon	10.2 (259)	.006 (.15)	.....	.....	.803 (20.4)	.802 (20.3)

DRUM BRAKE SPECIFICATIONS

Application	Drum Diam. In. (mm)	Drum Width In. (mm)	Max. Drum Refinish Diam. In. (mm)	Wheel Cyl. Diam. In. (mm)	Master Cyl. Diam. In. (mm)
Colt & Mirage	7.1 (180)	.....	7.2 (182)	.75 (19.1)	.813 (20.65)
Colt Vista (2WD), Cordia, Galant & Tredia	8.0 (203)	.....	8.1 (205)	.81 (20.6)	.875 (22.22)
Colt Vista (4WD)	9.0 (228)	.....	9.1 (230)	.75 (19.1)	.875 (22.22)
Galant	8.0 (203)	.....	8.1 (205)	.690 (17.52)	.875 (22.22)
Montero & Raider	10.0 (254)	.....	10.1 (256.5)	.81 (20.6)	.875 (22.22)
Pickup 2WD & Ram-50 2WD	10.0 (254)	.....	10.1 (256.5)	.937 (23.80)	.875 (22.22)
Pickup 4WD & Ram-50 4WD	10.0 (254)	.....	10.1 (256.5)	.875 (22.22)	.937 (23.80)
Van/Wagon	10.2 (259.1)	.....	10.1 (256.5)	.813 (20.65)	.938 (23.83)

FORD MOTOR CO. FESTIVA & MERKUR XR4Ti

Festiva, Merkur XR4Ti

NOTE: **For information on Tracer, see FORD MOTOR CO. TRACER & MAZDA article in this section.**

DESCRIPTION

All models have front disc and rear drum brakes. The parking brake mechanically operates the rear brake shoes. On Merkur XR4Ti, each of the front brake pads have a brake wear sensor.

BRAKE PRESSURE CONTROL VALVE

Merkur XR4Ti

Front-to-rear braking action is balanced by a brake pressure control valve installed in series with the master cylinder and rear wheel cylinders. The valve is located just below the master cylinder. The installation angle is critical because the deceleration rate will determine the effectiveness of the valve in controlling rear brake pressure.

Under heavy braking, the front of the vehicle will drop due to weight transfer. As the vehicle noses down, the change in body angle causes a ball weight within the valve to roll forward. As the ball changes position, its position and valves will regulate pressure from the master cylinder to the rear brakes.

ADJUSTMENTS

BRAKE PEDAL FREE PLAY & HEIGHT

Festiva

Move carpet and insulation out of way. Measure distance between brake pedal and sheet metal. Distance should be 8.03-8.23" (204-209 mm). Exhaust vacuum from power booster. Measure brake pedal free play. If free play is not .16-.28" (4-7 mm), adjust push rod.

Merkur XR4Ti

1) With engine running and parking brake released, apply pressure to the brake pedal. Measure brake pedal free height and check travel using Brake Pedal Effort Gauge (Rotunda 021-00001).

2) Insert an ice pick through carpet and sound insulator to dash panel metal. Measure distance to top center of brake pedal pad.

3) If position of brake pedal is not 7.5" (190 mm) above floor pan, check brake pedal for loose attaching bolts and missing, worn, or damaged bushings. Repair or replace components as necessary. Check that floor pan has not been distorted or that brake pedal is not bent.

4) If brake pedal free height is still out of specification, check brake pedal, booster or master cylinder to ensure components are installed correctly. Replace worn or damaged parts as necessary.

5) Hook a steel measuring tape to brake pedal. Measure and record distance from brake pedal free height position to 6 o'clock position on steering wheel rim.

6) With steel tape still hooked to brake pedal, depress brake pedal by pressing downward on brake pedal effort gauge. Apply a 25 lb. load to center of pedal. Maintain pedal load and measure distance from brake pedal to fixed reference point on steering wheel rim, parallel to centerline of steering column.

7) The difference between brake pedal free height and depressed pedal measurement under a 25 lb. load should be 2 7/32" (56 mm). If pedal travel is more than specification, make several forward and reverse stops.

8) Move vehicle backward and forward about 10 feet, then apply brakes until vehicle comes to a complete stop. This will actuate brake self-adjusters. If these stops do not bring brake pedal travel within specification, make several additional forward and reverse stops.

9) If second series of stops do not bring brake pedal travel within specification, remove brake drum and check brake self-adjusters to ensure they are functioning. Check brake linings for wear or damage. Adjust brake lining outside diameter to approximate inside diameter of brake drum with Brake Adjustment Gauge (D81L-1103A).

POWER BRAKE BOOSTER

1) Inspect all vacuum hoses and connections. All unused vacuum connectors and hoses should be capped. Hoses and their connections should be properly secured and in good condition with no holes or no collapsed areas. Inspect check valve on the power booster for damage. On Festiva, valve is located inside hose.

2) Check hydraulic system for leaks or insufficient fluid. Place transmission in Park or Neutral, stop engine and apply parking brake. Depress brake pedal several times to exhaust all vacuum in the system.

3) Depress the brake pedal and hold it in the applied position. Start engine. If vacuum system is operating properly, the brake pedal will tend to move downward under constant pressure. If no motion is felt, the power brake booster is not functioning properly.

4) Remove power brake booster vacuum hose at check valve. Manifold vacuum should be available at the check valve end of vacuum hose with engine at idle and the transmission in Neutral. Ensure that all unused vacuum outlets are properly capped, secured and in good condition. Repair or replace power brake booster as necessary.

POWER BRAKE PISTON ROD

Festiva

Remove master cylinder. Place Adjustment Gauge (T87C-2500-A) on master cylinder. Loosen set screw on gauge and place plunger against master cylinder. *See Fig. 1.* Invert gauge and position it on power booster. Check clearance between gauge and power booster. Adjust push rod until clearance is zero.

Merkur XR4Ti

The power brake booster push rod length is preset during production and is not adjustable.

PARKING BRAKE

Festiva

1) Ensure parking brake is in released position. Remove parking brake console insert. Remove locking clip from cable adjuster nut. Raise rear of vehicle and support. Tighten parking brake adjuster until slight drag is felt when rotating wheels.

2) Loosen adjuster, in small increments, until drag is eliminated. Parking brake should lock rear wheels in 11-16 notches.

FORD MOTOR CO. FESTIVA & MERKUR XR4Ti (Cont.)

Fig. 1: Measuring Push Rod Length (Festiva)

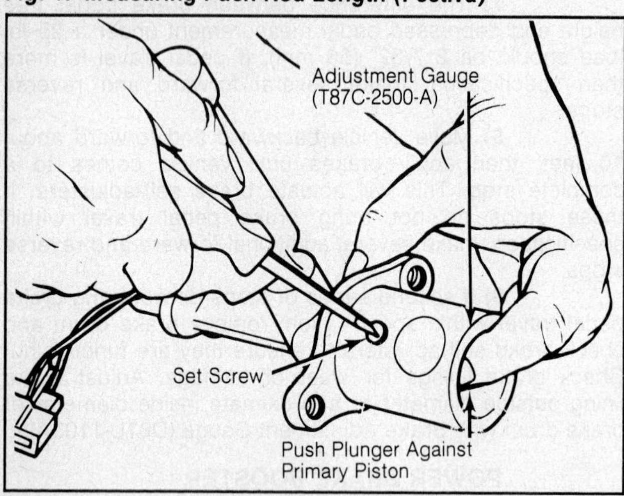

Courtesy of Ford Motor Co.

NOTE: Parking brake stop plungers are installed in both rear brake backing plates. These plungers will be used to determine correct parking brake cable adjustments.

Merkur XR4Ti

1) Ensure parking brake hand lever is in the released position. Pump brake pedal to be sure brake self-adjuster is properly set. Raise vehicle.

2) Loosen adjuster lock nut and rotate adjuster sleeve along cable casing until in and out movement can be felt at both parking brake stop plungers.

3) Both adjuster and lock nut are threaded onto cable casing. Any attempt to pry them apart will result in damage to sleeve and/or lock nut. To loosen lock nut, hold adjuster with pliers and turn lock nut counterclockwise with another set of pliers.

4) Tighten adjuster against retaining bracket until a slight movement is felt at each stop plunger. When added together, total movement of plungers should not exceed .16" (4 mm).

5) Tighten lock nut by hand against sleeve as much as possible. Tighten lock nut an additional 2 "clicks". Turn rear wheels by hand to ensure brake linings are not dragging against brake drum.

REAR AXLE BEARINGS

NOTE: On Festiva, lock nut on right side has left-hand threads. Always use new lock nut when removed.

Festiva

With bearings installed, tighten lock nut to 18-22 ft. lbs. (24-30 N.m) while rotating wheel. Slightly loosen lock nut so it can be turned by hand. Using a INCH lb. torque wrench, measure seal drag. Add this measurement to bearing preload. Tighten lock nut until bearing preload, including seal drag, is 3.5-6.5 INCH lbs. (.4-.7 N.m). Stake lock nut into notch on spindle.

REMOVAL & INSTALLATION

BRAKE CALIPER & PADS

Removal (Festiva)

Remove about 1/3 brake fluid from master cylinder. Raise front of vehicle and support. Remove wheels. Remove brake pad pin retainer. Remove anti-rattle springs and pins. Remove brake pads and shims. DO NOT discard shims from inner brake pad. *See Fig. 2.*

Installation

To install, reverse removal procedure. Ensure shims are installed behind inner brake pad.

Fig. 2: Exploded View of Front Disc Brake (Festiva)

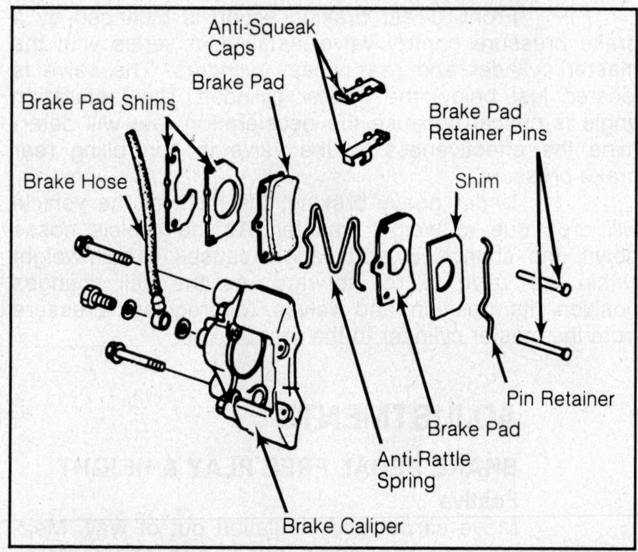

Courtesy of Ford Motor Co.

Removal (Merkur XR4Ti)

1) Remove about 1/3 of brake fluid from master cylinder reservoir. Remove wheel. Disconnect wear sensor wiring connector from harness. To separate connector, press pads on harness connector and pull apart.

Fig. 3: Exploded View of Front Disc Brake (Merkur XR4Ti)

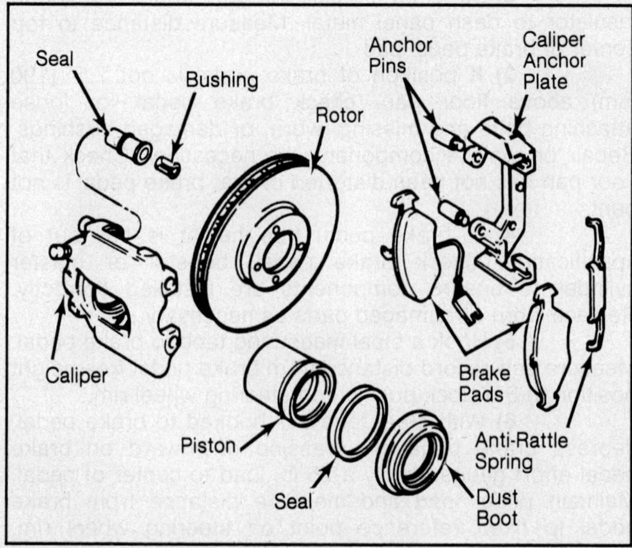

Courtesy of Ford Motor Co.

FORD MOTOR CO. FESTIVA & MERKUR XR4Ti (Cont.)

2) Remove caliper-to-anchor plate attaching pins and lift caliper assembly off rotor without disconnecting hydraulic hose.

3) When removing brake caliper, the anti-rattle spring will fall off. Remove inboard and outboard pads. Remove brake caliper from vehicle by disconnecting the hydraulic hose from brake caliper unit. *See Fig. 3.*

Installation

1) Reconnect brake caliper hose if unit is removed from vehicle. Using a "C" clamp, push piston back into caliper bore. Use care to prevent damage to piston boot. Install inboard and outboard pads. *See Fig. 4.*

Fig. 4: Retracting Brake Caliper Piston

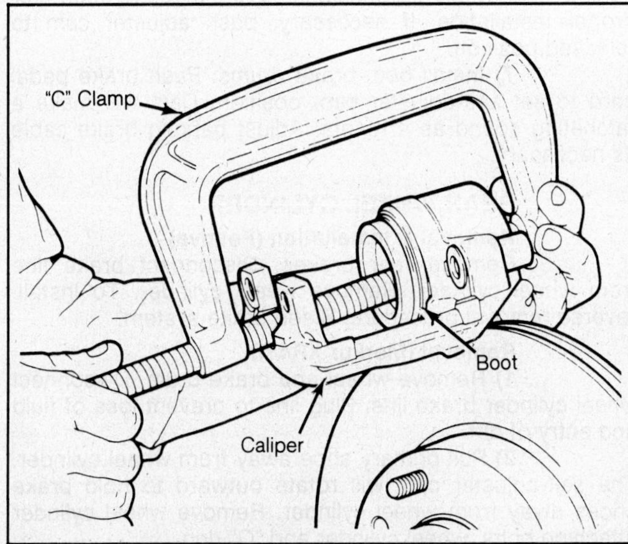

Courtesy of Ford Motor Co.

2) Position caliper over rotor. Ensure brake pads are properly engaged on anchor plate. Sensor wire must be positioned between caliper and anchor before installing caliper attaching bolts.

NOTE: **When caliper is installed, ensure brake hose has not been "kinked" by rotation of caliper. If caliper is rotated during installation, the "kinked" condition may cause the flexible hose to break.**

3) Install caliper-to-anchor attaching pins. Tighten bolt to 18-23 ft. lbs. (25-30 N.m). Install anti-rattle spring. Connect wear sensor. Ensure "O" ring is in position before making connection. To complete installation, reverse removal procedure.

DISC BRAKE ROTOR & HUB

NOTE: **On Festiva, front hub contains sealed bearings. To remove, see appropriate article in FRONT SUSPENSION section.**

Removal & Installation (Festiva)

Raise front of vehicle and support. Remove hub nut and discard. Remove caliper from rotor. Using a puller, remove rotor and hub from axle shaft. To install, reverse removal procedure. Install new hub nut.

NOTE: **Hub and rotor are a matched and balanced assembly. Before removing rotor, locate paint or etch mark that indicates proper hub-to-rotor alignment. If marks are not present, mark hub and rotor for assembly alignment. Failure to properly align hub and rotor can result in an imbalance condition.**

Removal & Installation (Merkur XR4Ti)

Remove brake caliper assembly from vehicle. Remove brake rotor retaining clip. Remove rotor from vehicle. Install rotor using balance marks for alignment reference. Position caliper over rotor and install anchor plate-to-spindle carrier attaching bolts. Tighten bolts to 43-44 ft. lbs. (51-61 N.m). Install wheel.

REAR BRAKE SHOES

Removal & Installation (Festiva)

Remove brake drum. Remove hold-down springs. Remove return springs. Remove self-adjuster. *See Fig. 5.* To install, reverse removal procedure. Apply brake grease to all shoe contact points.

Fig. 5: Exploded View of Rear Brake Assembly (Festiva)

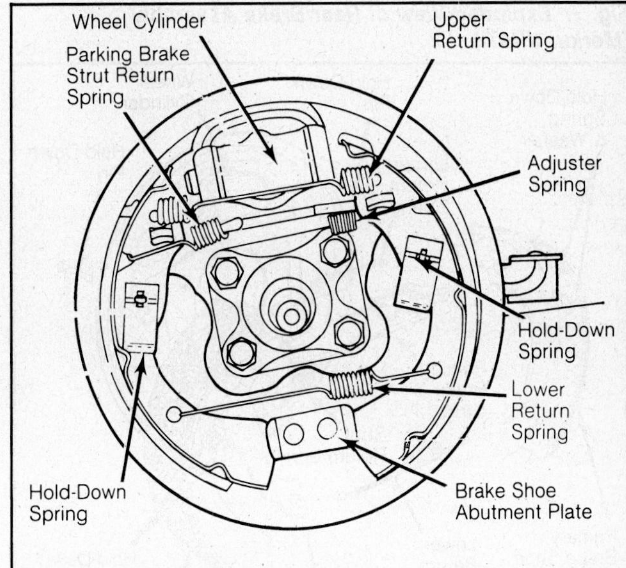

Courtesy of Ford Motor Co.

Removal (Merkur XR4Ti)

1) Remove wheel and brake drum. Discard brake drum retaining clip. If brake drum is difficult to remove, self-adjuster may be released by pushing a screwdriver against the adjustment cam. *See Fig. 6.*

2) Remove both brake shoe hold-down springs. To prevent hold-down springs from rotating during removal, hold each hold-down pin head with a finger behind backing plate. Pry lower end of primary shoe from its position against anchor.

3) Remove lower return spring. Remove shoes and strut by passing strut between wheel cylinder and hub. Pull top of primary shoe away from secondary shoe to disconnect strut from secondary shoe.

4) Disconnect parking brake cable from secondary shoe lever. Remove strut return spring from secondary shoe. Remove adjuster cam spring. Pull primary shoe away from strut while rotating cam to fully depressed position.

Fig. 6: Releasing Self-Adjuster Cam

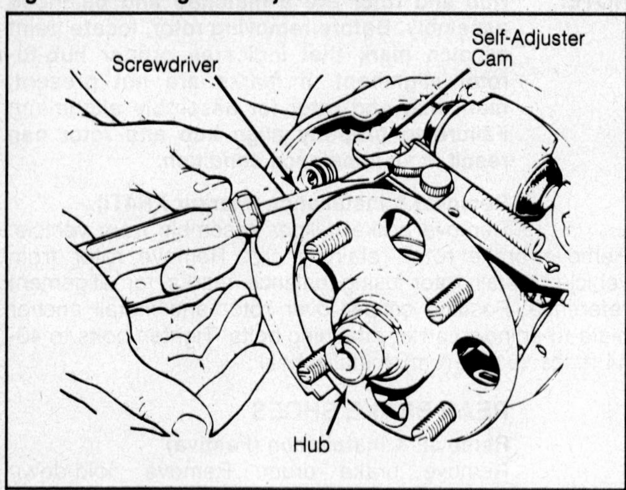

Courtesy of Ford Motor Co.

5) Remove primary shoe spring. Remove primary shoe from strut. *See Fig. 7.*

Fig. 7: Exploded View of Rear Brake Assembly (Merkur XR4Ti)

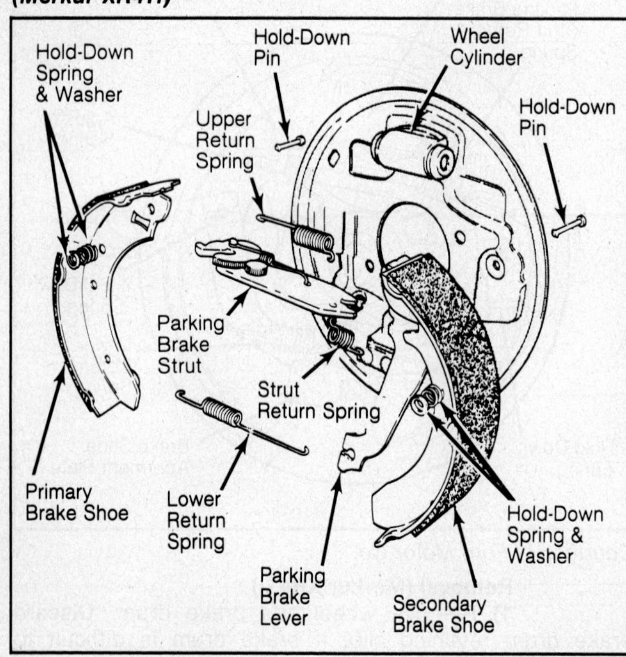

Courtesy of Ford Motor Co.

Installation

NOTE: **Before installing brake shoes, ensure wheel hub and wheel cylinder attaching bolts are tightened.**

1) Apply a light coat of grease supplied with new brake shoes to support ledges where brake shoes contact backing plate. Connect parking brake cable to secondary shoe lever.

2) To connect parking brake cable, position cable end through lever. Grip cable end with locking type pliers and push lever against spring until it can be rotated over cable. When properly installed, plastic washer will be between spring and lever.

3) Position secondary shoe and install hold-down spring. Install strut and cam assembly on primary shoe. Rotate cam to fully released position. Install adjuster cam spring.

4) Install primary shoe spring. Install strut spring in secondary shoe and then in strut. Place strut on parking brake lever and move primary shoe toward backing plate. Strut will then "click" into place over parking brake lever and secondary shoe web.

5) Install lower shoe spring with longer leg on secondary shoe. Pry lower end of primary shoe into position against anchor while holding top of shoe against backing plate. Take care not to damage the cylinder boot.

6) Install primary shoe hold-down pin, spring and washer. Ensure heel of each brake shoe is located behind anchor plate. Check each brake component for proper installation. If necessary, push adjuster cam to released position.

7) Install both brake drums. Push brake pedal hard to set self-adjuster cam position. Cam will make a ratcheting sound as it resets. Adjust parking brake cable as necessary.

REAR WHEEL CYLINDER

Removal & Installation (Festiva)

Remove rear brakes. Disconnect brake line from wheel cylinder. Remove wheel cylinder. To install, reverse removal procedure. Bleed brake system.

Removal (Merkur XR4Ti)

1) Remove wheel and brake drum. Disconnect wheel cylinder brake line. Plug line to prevent loss of fluid and entry of dirt.

2) Pull primary shoe away from wheel cylinder. The self-adjuster cam will rotate outward to hold brake shoes away from wheel cylinder. Remove wheel cylinder attaching bolts, wheel cylinder and "O" ring.

Installation

1) To install, reverse removal procedure. Install "O" ring on wheel cylinder. Position wheel cylinder and install attaching bolts. Tighten attaching bolts to 60-84 INCH lbs. (7-10 N.m).

2) Connect brake line. Using a screwdriver, push adjuster cam to released position. Install brake drum. Bleed rear brakes.

NOTE: **If pressure bleeder is used, push brake pedal to set self-adjuster cam position. The cam will make a ratcheting sound as it resets.**

MASTER BRAKE CYLINDER

Removal

Disconnect low fluid level sensor wiring. Disconnect brake lines from master cylinder. Cap lines and master cylinder ports. Remove attaching nuts and master cylinder.

Installation

To install, reverse removal procedure. Fill master cylinder to proper level and bleed hydraulic system, if necessary.

POWER BRAKE UNIT

Removal & Installation (Festiva)

Remove master cylinder. Disconnect vacuum line. Remove clevis pin at brake pedal. Remove power brake unit. To install, reverse removal procedure.

FORD MOTOR CO. FESTIVA & MERKUR XR4Ti (Cont.)

Removal (Merkur XR4Ti)

1) With engine off. Depress brake pedal several times to deplete vacuum reserve in power booster. De-pressurize EFT fuel system using a hand operated vacuum pump. Connect pump hose to fuel system pressure regulator. Apply at least 25 in. Hg of vacuum.

NOTE: Fuel supply lines will remain pressurized for some period of time after engine is shut off. System pressure must be relieved before disconnecting any fuel lines.

2) Disconnect fuel inlet hose at pulse damper. Disconnect fuel return line using Quick Connect Remover (T82L 9500 AH). *See Fig. 8.* Disconnect low oil level sensor connector and remove engine oil level dipstick.

Fig. 8: Removing Fuel Return Line

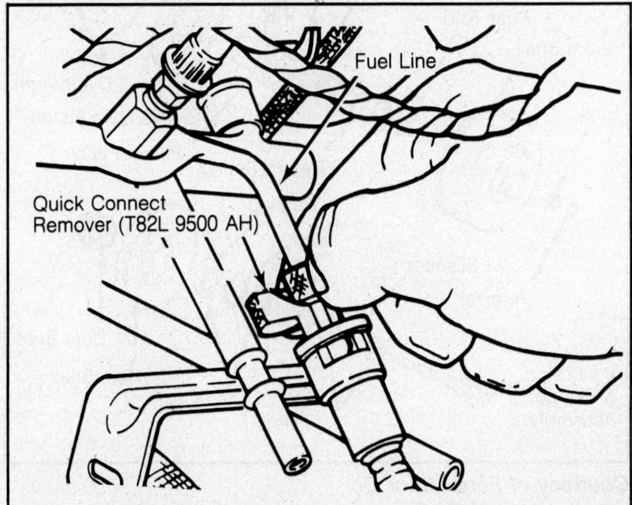

Courtesy of Ford Motor Co.

3) Remove screw attaching engine oil dipstick tube to pulse damper bracket. Remove stud nuts attaching pulse damper bracket to intake manifold. Disconnect pulse damper from fuel manifold and remove damper-/bracket assembly.

4) Disconnect source hose from vacuum "tree" and remove vacuum "tree". Disconnect low brake fluid warning connector from master cylinder reservoir cap. Pull vacuum check valve out of power booster.

5) Disconnect and plug brake lines at master cylinder. Inside vehicle, remove sound deadening panel located under instrument panel. Remove booster push rod to brake pedal retaining clip.

6) Remove booster attaching nuts. Remove power booster. Use care to prevent damage to any underhood painted surfaces (such as suspension strut tower). If necessary, tape shop cloths over these areas to prevent damage.

Installation

1) To install, reverse removal procedure. Apply a bead of Caulking Cord (D6AZ-19560-A) to rear of booster where it mates to dash panel. Ensure brake pedal bushing is on booster push rod and position booster in vehicle.

2) Apply a light coating of lubricant on bushing before installing on booster push rod. From inside vehicle, guide booster into position. A helper may be needed in engine compartment to push booster into position.

3) Install retaining clip on booster push rod and install booster attaching nuts. Install sound deadening panel. Connect brake lines at master cylinder. Position vacuum "tree" and install attaching screw.

4) Connect vacuum hose to vacuum "tree". Install vacuum check valve in power booster and connect wiring connector at master cylinder cap. Connect pulse damper to fuel rail and position bracket on intake manifold studs.

5) Install pulse damper bracket stud nuts. Install engine oil dipstick tube bracket. Connect fuel inlet line to pulse damper. Connect fuel supply line to fuel rail. Bleed hydraulic system, if necessary.

OVERHAUL

FRONT DISC BRAKE CALIPER

Disassembly

1) Remove caliper assembly and brake pads. Open bleeder screw and drain brake fluid out of caliper. Close bleeder screw.

2) Position a block of wood or a roll of shop towels between piston and caliper. To remove piston, apply air pressure through fluid inlet port. Apply only enough air pressure to ease piston out of caliper.

CAUTION: DO NOT use an excessive amount of air pressure to remove piston. Excessive pressure can force piston out with enough force to cause personal injury. NEVER attempt to catch piston by hand.

3) Remove piston seal from caliper and discard. *See Figs. 3 and 9.* Use a plastic stick or pencil to remove seal. DO NOT use a screwdriver or other metal tool. A metal tool can scratch or nick seal groove resulting in a possible seal leak. Remove bushings and seals.

Fig. 9: Exploded View of Caliper Assembly (Festiva)

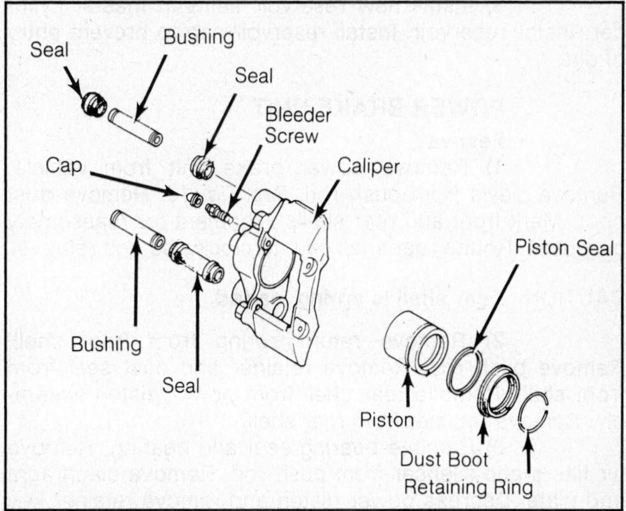

Courtesy of Ford Motor Co.

Reassembly

1) Install caliper bushings. Overlap edges of bushing slightly to fit bushing into seal. After installation,

FORD MOTOR CO. FESTIVA & MERKUR XR4Ti (Cont.)

press bushing against seal to remove overlapping. When properly installed, ends of bushing must be butted against each other.

2) Lubricate new piston seal with brake fluid and install in seal groove. Ensure seal does not become twisted but is firmly seated in groove. Install dust boot on piston.

3) Position dust boot at bottom of piston. Hold dust boot on piston and pull on seal lip until seal unfolds, allowing lip seal to extend beyond bottom of piston.

4) While holding dust boot on piston, fit seal lip in caliper bore and push piston into caliper. As piston enters bore, dust boot will refold to its original shape.

MASTER CYLINDER

Disassembly

1) Remove reservoir cap and drain master cylinder reservoir. Carefully clamp master cylinder in a vise. Pry reservoir out of master cylinder seals. Remove master cylinder seals using a thin-bladed screwdriver.

2) Remove "O" ring. Push primary piston inward and remove snap ring. Remove washer from end of primary piston (if equipped). Remove primary piston.

3) On Merkur XR4Ti, tap master cylinder on a block of wood to remove secondary piston. On Festiva, depress secondary piston and remove stop bolt. Remove secondary piston. On all models, remove seals from primary and secondary pistons.

Reassembly

NOTE: As master cylinder is reassembled, lubricate parts with brake fluid.

1) Install new seals on primary and secondary pistons. Install secondary piston. To prevent damage to seal lip, ease seal into master cylinder bore while slowly rotating and pushing.

2) On Festiva, install stop bolt. On all models, install primary piston. To prevent damage to seal lip, ease seal into master cylinder bore while slowly rotating and pushing. Push primary piston into master cylinder bore and install washer (if equipped) and snap ring.

3) Install new reservoir seals in master cylinder. Install reservoir. Install reservoir cap to prevent entry of dirt.

POWER BRAKE UNIT

Festiva

1) Remove power brake unit from vehicle. Remove clevis from push rod. *See Fig. 10.* Remove dust boot. Mark front and rear shells alignment for reassembly purposes. Rotate rear shell counterclockwise and remove.

CAUTION: Rear shell is spring loaded.

2) Remove return spring from frnot shell. Remove push rod. Remove retainer and dust seal from front shell. Remove rear shell from power piston assembly. Remove retainer from rear shell.

3) Remove bearing seal and bearing. Remove air filters and silencer from push rod. Remove diaphragm and plate. Depress power piston and remove retainer key and stopper. Disassemble power piston. Remove reaction disc from front shell.

Reassembly

1) Apply silicone grease to the following parts: reaction disc, dust seal lip, push rod, all diaphragm mating surfaces, power piston and valve plunger oil seal. Reassemble power piston. Install push rod retainer key and stopper.

2) Install air filters and silencer. Position diaphragm and plate into power piston. Ensure diaphragm is fully seated in groove. Install bearing, seal and retainer into rear shell. Install rear shell onto power piston. Using push rod, install reaction disc into power piston.

3) Install dust seal and retainer into front shell. Install push rod. Install spring. Position rear shell onto front shell. Align marks made during disassembly. Compress spring and rotate rear shell clockwise. Install dust boot. Install clevis on push rod.

Fig. 10: Exploded View of Power Brake Unit (Festiva)

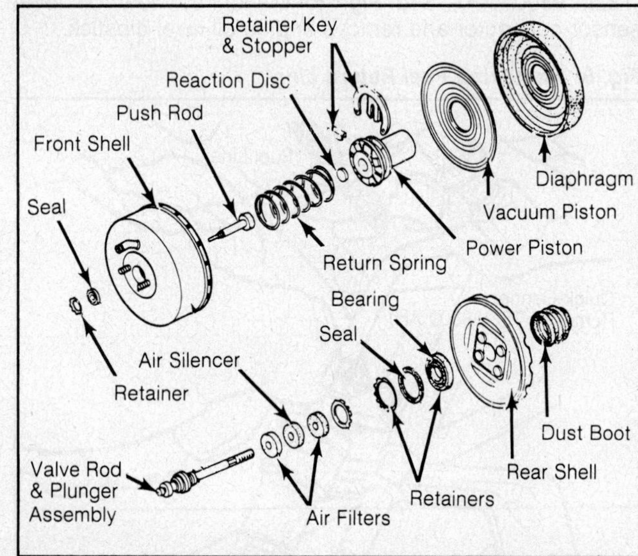

Courtesy of Ford Motor Co.

Merkur XR4Ti

Power brake unit cannot be rebuilt.

TIGHTENING SPECIFICATIONS

Application	Ft. Lbs. (N.m)
Brake Hose to Caliper	
Festiva	16-22 (22-30)
Merkur XR4Ti	15-18 (20-25)
Caliper Mounting Bolts	
Festiva	29-36 (39-49)
Merkur XR4Ti	18-23 (25-31)
Front Drive Axle Nut	
Festiva	116-174 (158-237)
Merkur XR4Ti	109-195 (150-270)
Hub-to-Rotor Bolts	
Festiva	33-40 (45-54)
Merkur XR4Ti	29-43 (39-60)
Master Cylinder-to-Booster Nuts	
Festiva	7-12 (10-16)
Merkur XR4Ti	16-20 (22-27)
Rear Axle Nut	
Festiva	[1]
Merkur XR4Ti	58-86 (80-120)
	INCH Lbs. (N.m)
Wheel Cylinder Attaching Bolts	60-84 (7-10)

[1] – See text.

FORD MOTOR CO. FESTIVA & MERKUR XR4Ti (Cont.)

DISC BRAKE ROTOR SPECIFICATIONS

Application	Disc Diameter In. (mm)	Lateral Runout In. (mm)	Parallelism In. (mm)	Original Thickness In. (mm)	Min. Refinish Thickness In. (mm)	Discard Thickness In. (mm)
Festiva	.....	.....	.....	.....	.....	[1]
Merkur XR4Ti	.....	.003 (.08)	.0004 (.010)	.95 (24)	.898 (22.8)	.762 (19.35)

[1] – Add .030" (.76 mm) to minimum thickness stamped on rotor.

DRUM BRAKE SPECIFICATIONS

Application	Drum Diam. In. (mm)	Drum Width In. (mm)	Max. Drum Refinish Diam. In. (mm)	Wheel Cyl. Diam. In. (mm)	Master Cyl. Diam. In. (mm)
Festiva	6.70 (170)	.....	6.75 (171)	.....	.....
Merkur XR4Ti	10 (254)	.....	10.06 (255.5)	.87 (22.2)	1.0 (25.4)

FORD MOTOR CO. TRACER & MAZDA

Ford Motor Co.: Tracer;
Mazda: B2200, B2600, RX7, 323, 626

NOTE: For information on Ford Festiva and Merkur XR4Ti, see FORD MOTOR CO. FESTIVA & MERKUR article. For information on anti-lock brake system, see MAZDA ANTI-LOCK BRAKE SYSTEM article.

DESCRIPTION

The brake system on all models is hydraulically-operated, using a tandem master cylinder and a power brake unit. All models have front disc brakes. Rear disc brakes are standard on the RX7 and optional on Tracer, 323 and 626. All others have rear drum brakes, with automatic adjuster. B2200 and B2600 4WD models use a load sensing "G" valve to change hydraulic pressure to rear brakes, according to vehicle load. On all other models, a proportioning valve is used to prevent premature lock-up of the rear wheels.

ADJUSTMENTS

REAR DRUM BRAKE SHOES

NOTE: Self-adjusting rear brakes require manual adjustment only after brake shoe replacement or when service operations move operating lever.

B2200 & B2600 (4WD)

1) Raise and support rear of vehicle. Release parking brake. Remove rear wheel and star wheel adjusting plugs from backing plate. Insert a flat-tipped screwdriver, and rotate star wheel until wheel is locked.

2) Remove pawl lever hole plug. Insert a flat-tipped screwdriver through hole. Push on pawl lever self-adjuster and back off star wheel adjuster 3 to 4 notches, so wheel turns freely. Repeat procedure for opposite side. Adjust parking brake and install plugs in adjusting holes.

B2200 & B2600 (2WD)

1) Raise rear of vehicle. Ensure parking brake is released. Remove plugs from rear of backing plate (one under wheel cylinder, other near outer lip of backing plate). Using a screwdriver, rotate adjuster, in direction of arrow stamped on backing plate, until wheel locks.

2) Using a drift, push pawl back from adjuster and back off adjuster 6-7 notches. Ensure wheel rotates freely. Perform same procedure on both sides. Adjust parking brake.

Tracer, 323 & 626

1) Raise and support rear of vehicle. Release parking brake. Uncrimp lock nut and remove it. Remove brake drum. Insert screwdriver between adjusting plate and quadrant. Twist screwdriver to disengage teeth.

2) Push quadrant adjusting lever toward backing plate. *See Fig. 1*. Replace drum. Install new lock nut and secure by crimping. Operate brake pedal a few times to reset adjuster. Adjust parking brake.

Fig. 1: Moving Quadrant on 626 Brake Adjuster

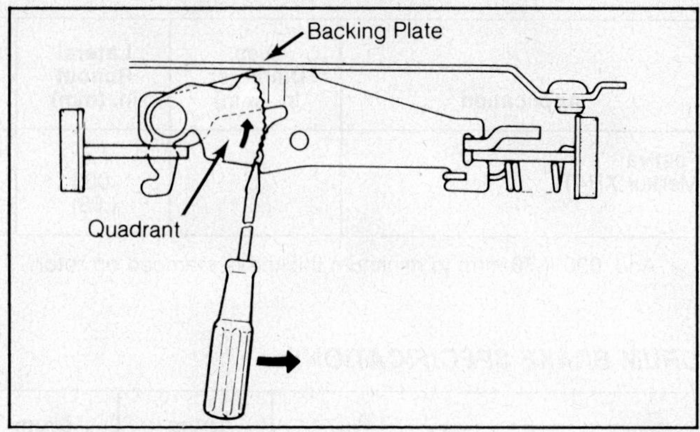

Courtesy of Mazda Motors Corp.

PEDAL FREE PLAY

Depress pedal a few times to eliminate vacuum. On 626 models, pedal free play should be .28-.35" (7-9 mm). On all other models, pedal free play should be .16-.28" (4-7 mm). Adjust play by loosening push-rod lock nut and turning push-rod until correct free play is obtained. Tighten push-rod lock nut.

PEDAL HEIGHT & STOPLIGHT SWITCH

1) Pedal height is measured from firewall to pedal pad center. On 626, remove blower duct. Loosen stoplight switch lock nut and turn switch until correct pedal height is obtained. Adjust pedal free play. Tighten stoplight switch lock nut.

2) On all other models, loosen lock nut on stoplight switch and move switch away from pedal. Loosen push rod lock nut and turn rod until correct pedal height is obtained. Adjust free play and tighten push-rod lock nut. Position stoplight switch so it contacts the pedal and turn an additional 1/2 turn. Tighten stoplight switch lock nut and connect electrical plug.

BRAKE PEDAL HEIGHT ADJUSTMENT

Application	In. (mm)
B2200 & B2600	8.2-8.4 (209-214)
RX7	7.9-8.3 (200-210)
Tracer & 323	8.6-8.8 (219-224)
626	8.4-8.6 (214-219)

PARKING BRAKE

1) Properly adjust brakes. Raise and support rear of vehicle. Remove parking brake lever boot or console, if necessary. Release brake lever. On all models except B2200 and B2600, turn adjusting screw or nut to obtain clearance. On B2200 and B2600, turn adjusting nut at front end of brake cable.

2) Pull lever with 22 lbs. (10 kg) force to obtain a stroke of 4-5 notches on RX7 and 7-9 notches on 626. Lever stroke should be 7-11 notches on Tracer and 323 models with rear drum brakes, and 9-15 notches on models with rear disc brakes.

3) On B2200 and B2600, pulling lever with 44 lbs. (20 kg), stroke should be 7-12 notches. On models equipped with rear disc brakes, ensure clearance between stopper and lever, at each caliper, is not less than .08" (2 mm).

4) Install brake lever boot or console. Remove supports and lower vehicle. Operate parking brake several times and make sure rear wheels rotate freely.

FORD MOTOR CO. TRACER & MAZDA (Cont.)

NOTE: **Ensure that rear brakes do not drag, and parking brake warning light is activated when lever is pulled one notch.**

WHEEL BEARINGS

NOTE: **For front wheel bearings on 4WD models, see LOCKING HUB article.**

Front (B2200 & B2600 2WD)

Tighten wheel bearing nut to 14-22 ft. lbs. (19-30 N.m). Rotate wheel a few times. Loosen nut. Slightly tighten wheel bearing nut. Using spring scale attached to wheel stud, measure bearing preload. Tighten nut until bearing preload is 1.3-2.4 lbs. (6-11 N). Install lock nut and cotter pin.

Front (RX7)

Tighten wheel bearing nut to 14-22 ft. lbs. (19-30 N.m). Rotate wheel a few times. Loosen nut. Slightly tighten wheel bearing nut. Using spring scale attached to wheel stud, measure bearing preload. Tighten wheel bearing nut until bearing preload is .9-2.2 lbs. (3.9-9.8 N). Install lock nut and cotter pin.

Rear (Tracer, 323 & 626)

Tighten wheel bearing nut to 18-22 ft. lbs. (24-30 N.m). Rotate wheel a few times. Loosen nut. Slightly tighten wheel bearing nut. Using spring scale attached to wheel stud, measure bearing preload. Tighten nut until bearing preload is .57-1.91 lbs. (2.6-8.5 N) on Tracer and 323. On 626, .44 lb. (2 N) or less. Stake lock nut.

TESTING

LOAD SENSING "G" VALVE (LSGV)

B2200 & B2600

1) Attach 2 pressure gauges (1422 psi) at input (from master cylinder) and output (to rear brakes) to LSGV. Gently depress brake pedal until input pressure is 356 psi (2453 kPa). Raise rear of vehicle so front end is tilted downward 15 degrees or more.

2) Rear wheels should be 2.36" (60 mm) or more above ground. Continue to depress pedal pedal until inlet pressure is 1422 psi (9807 kPa). Outlet pressure should be 519-619 psi (3581-4267 kPa). Release brake pedal. Lower vehicle.

3) Gently depress brake pedal until input pressure is 924 psi (6377 kPa). Raise rear of vehicle so front end is tilted downward 15 degrees or more. Rear wheels should be 2.36" (60 mm) or more above ground.

4) Continue to depress pedal until inlet pressure is 1422 psi (9807 kPa). Outlet pressure should be 939-1109 psi (3581-4267 kPa). If valve fails any of these test, replace LSGV.

REMOVAL & INSTALLATION

FRONT DISC BRAKE PADS

Removal & Installation (Tracer & 323)

Raise and support front of vehicle. Remove wheels. Remove slide pins and clip. Remove brake pads. *See Fig. 2*. To install, reverse removal procedure.

Fig. 2: Exploded View of Front Brake Assembly (Tracer & 323)

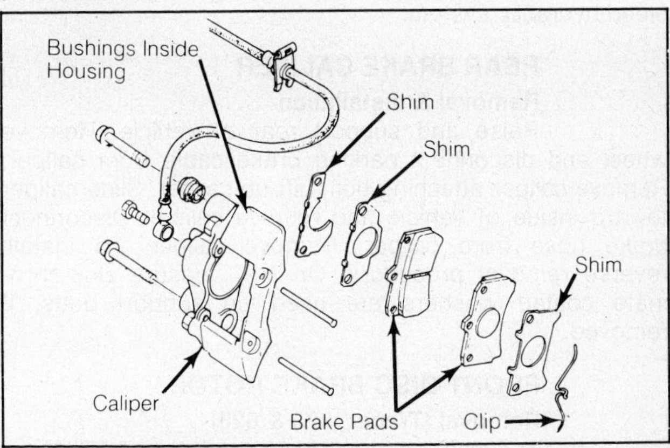

Courtesy of Mazda Motors Corp.

Removal & Installation (RX7 W/14" Wheel)

Raise front of vehicle and support. Remove wheels. Remove lower lock pin bolt. Pivot caliper upward and support. Remove brake pads. To install, reverse removal procedure.

Removal & Installation (RX7 W/15" or 16" Wheel)

Raise and support front of vehicle. Remove wheels. Remove pad clip, pins and springs. Remove brake pads. To install, reverse removal procedure.

Removal & Installation (B2200 & B2600)

Raise front of vehicle and support. Remove wheels. Remove lower lock pin bolt. Pivot caliper upward and support. Remove brake pads. To install, reverse removal procedure.

Removal & Installation (626)

1) Raise and support the front of vehicle. Remove front wheels. Remove caliper bolts. Remove caliper, but DO NOT disconnect brake line. Remove brake pads.

2) To install, reverse removal procedure. Before mounting caliper, push piston inward using the Expansion Tool (49 0221 600C).

REAR DISC BRAKE PADS

Removal

Raise and support rear of vehicle. Remove wheel. Release parking brake and disconnect parking brake cable from caliper. Remove lower caliper attaching bolt and lift caliper up off of disc. Remove brake pads.

Installation

Using Brake Piston Wrench (49 FA18 602), turn piston clockwise and fully insert piston into caliper. Position piston so that dowel on pad will seat in piston stopper groove. To complete installation, reverse removal procedure.

FRONT DISC BRAKE CALIPER

Removal

Raise and support front of vehicle. Remove wheel and disconnect brake hose. Remove brake disc pads. Remove remaining attaching bolts. Remove caliper body from vehicle.

FORD MOTOR CO. TRACER & MAZDA (Cont.)

Installation

To install, reverse removal procedure and bleed hydraulic system.

REAR BRAKE CALIPER

Removal & Installation

Raise and support rear of vehicle. Remove wheel and disconnect parking brake cable from caliper. Remove caliper attaching bolt. Lift up caliper. Slide caliper toward inside of vehicle and remove caliper. Disconnect brake hose from caliper. Remove caliper. To install, reverse removal procedure. On RX7, ensure zinc-chromate coated washers are used on support bolts, if removed.

FRONT DISC BRAKE ROTOR

Removal (Tracer, 323 & 626)

1) Raise and support front of vehicle. Remove wheel and raise lock nut tab before loosening. Apply brakes to lock hub and remove drive shaft lock nut. Loosen tie rod end nut and separate tie rod end from knuckle using Joint Puller (49 0118 850C).

2) Disconnect brake hose from shock absorber, if necessary. Remove brake caliper assembly from knuckle and support it with wire. Remove nuts and bolts which couple knuckle with ball joint and shock absorber. Remove knuckle assembly from ball joint and drive shaft.

NOTE: **If drive shaft will not separate from knuckle and hub assembly, use Bearing Puller Set (49 0839 425C)**

3) Separate knuckle from wheel hub on Tracer and 323 using Puller (49 B001 726), and on 626 using Puller (49 G030 725) and Attachment A (49 G030 727). Scribe match marks between hub and rotor assembly, detach hub bolts, and separate hub from rotor. *See Fig. 3.*

NOTE: **Place wheel hub in a vise with soft jaws to aid disassembly.**

Fig. 3: Removing Wheel Hub From Knuckle

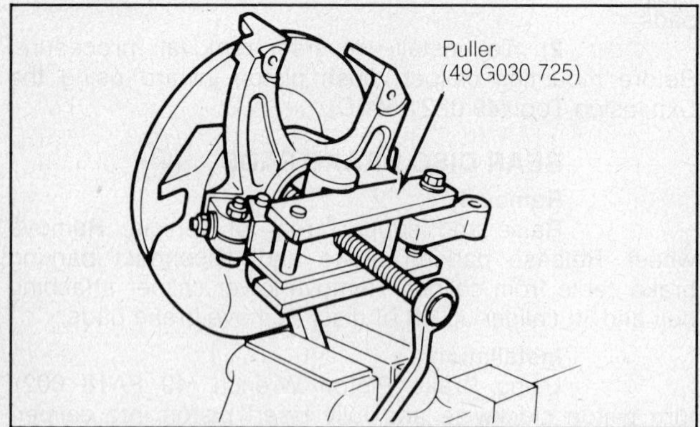

Courtesy of Mazda Motors Corp.

Installation

To install, press knuckle onto wheel hub assembly, using Spacer Selector (49 B001 727) for Tracer and 323, and Attachment B (49 G030 728) for 626. *See Fig. 4.* Reverse removal procedure to complete assembly.

Fig. 4: Assembling Wheel Hub to Knuckle (Tracer, 323 & 626)

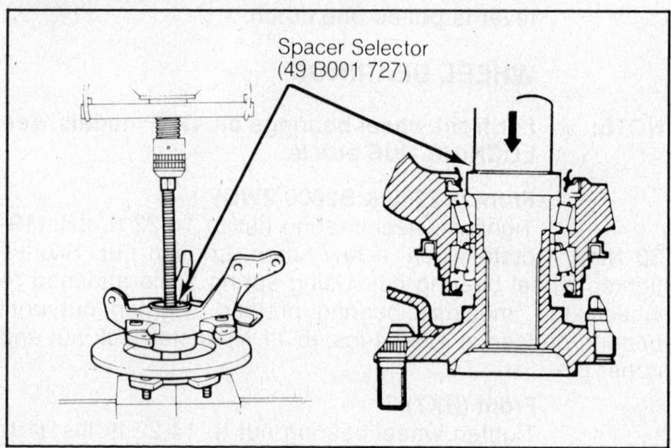

Courtesy of Mazda Motors Corp.

Removal & Installation (RX7)

Raise and support front of vehicle. Remove wheels and tires. Remove front brake caliper. Remove 2 screws retaining rotor to hub. Remove rotor. To install, reverse removal procedure.

Removal & Installation (B2200 & B2600 2WD)

1) With caliper assembly removed, remove wheel hub grease cap, cotter pin, lock plate and ring adjusting lock nut. Remove thrust washer and outer bearing from hub. Slide hub and rotor assembly from spindle.

2) Mark rotor to hub position. Separate rotor from hub. To install, reverse removal procedure and tighten bolts attaching rotor to hub evenly. Adjust wheel bearings.

Removal & Installation (B2200 & B2600 4WD)

Remove front caliper. Remove locking hub. See LOCKING HUBS article. Remove rotor and hub assembly. Mark rotor to hub position. Remove rotor from hub. To install, reverse removal procedure.

REAR DISC BRAKE ROTOR

Removal & Installation (RX7)

Rear rear brake caliper. Remove screws retaining rotor to hub. Remove rotor. To install, reverse removal procedure.

Removal (Tracer, 323 & 626)

Remove rear brake caliper. Remove hub cab. Remove brake line from shock absorber. On all models, uncrimp lock nut and remove it. Remove rear axle hub and rotor. Scribe match marks between hub and rotor assembly, detach hub bolts, and separate hub from rotor.

Installation

Install disc plate and caliper assembly. Adjust wheel bearing preload. Reverse removal procedure to complete assembly.

REAR BRAKE DRUM

Removal (Tracer, 323 & 626)

Raise and support rear of vehicle. Release parking brake. Remove wheel and grease cap. Clear staked nut's position, and remove nut and washer. Remove brake drum.

FORD MOTOR CO. TRACER & MAZDA (Cont.)

NOTE: If it is difficult to remove drum, widen clearance between shoes and drum by removing lever stop. If necessary, disconnect parking brake cable from lever, and move lever against backing plate.

Removal (B2200 & B2600)

Raise and support rear of vehicle. Release parking brake. Remove wheel and brake drum retaining screws. Thread retaining screws into tapped holes in brake drum to force brake drum off flange.

Installation

To install, reverse removal procedure. Tighten retaining screws evenly (if equipped). On Tracer, 323 and 626, adjust wheel bearings and stake lock nut. See WHEEL BEARINGS under ADJUSTMENTS in this article.

Fig. 5: Exploded View of Rear Brake Assembly (Tracer, 323 & 626)

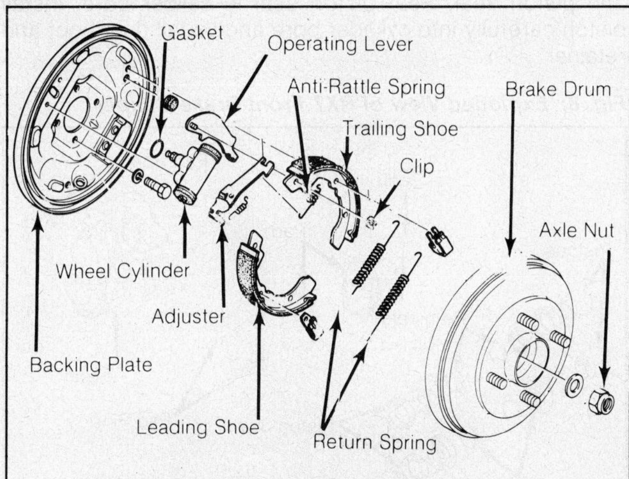

Courtesy of Mazda Motors Corp.

REAR BRAKE SHOES

Removal (Tracer, 323 & 626)

1) Remove brake drum. Remove trailing shoe hold-down spring and pin. Remove trailing shoe assembly.

2) Remove return spring, anti-rattle spring, and leading shoe hold-down spring and pin. Remove leading shoe assembly. *See Fig. 5*.

Installation

1) Apply brake grease to brake shoe contact areas on backing plate. When installing adjuster between shoes, insert a flat-tipped screwdriver between adjuster quadrant and meshing teeth on 626, or between quadrant and knurled pin on Tracer and 323. *See Fig. 1*.

2) To fully retract adjuster, move quadrant until it touches backing plate. To complete assembly, reverse removal procedure. Adjust wheel bearings and stake lock nut.

Removal (B2200 & B2600)

With brake drum removed, remove brake shoe return springs, retaining springs and guide pins. Remove brake shoes. Remove parking brake strut and disconnect parking brake cable from operating lever of secondary shoe. *See Figs. 6 and 7*.

Installation

1) Lubricate adjusting screw threads and shoe contact points on backing plate with brake grease. Install parking brake operating lever to secondary shoe and secure with clip. Engage operating lever with parking brake cable.

2) Position operating strut between slots of shoes. Mount assembly to backing plate so slots in shoes are toward adjusting screws. Install return springs and retainer springs.

Fig. 6: Exploded View of Rear Brake Assembly (B2200 & B2600 2WD)

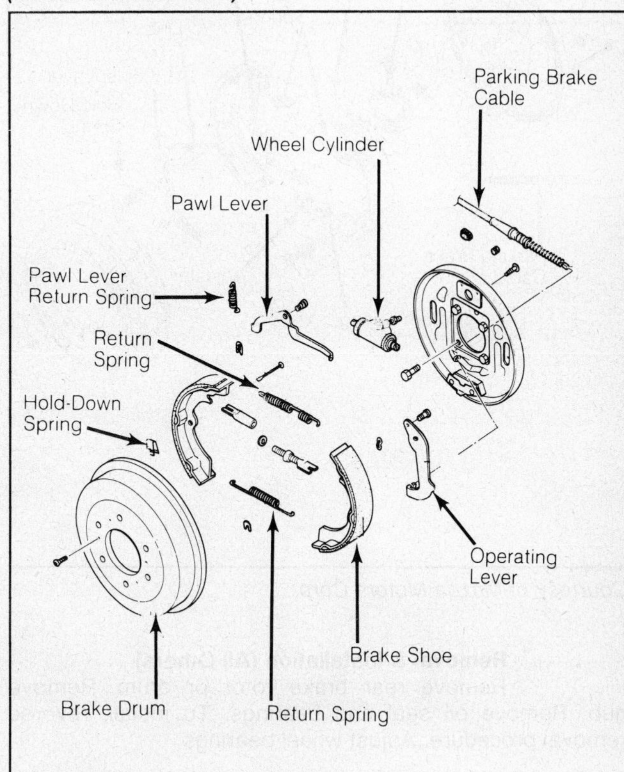

Courtesy of Mazda Motors Corp.

REAR AXLE BEARING & OIL SEAL

Removal (B2200 & B2600)

1) Remove wheel and brake drum. Disconnect parking brake cable and brake line. Remove backing plate bolts. Remove backing plate and rear axle assembly. Using Holder (49 S120 645A) and Wrench (49 0603 635A), remove axle bearing lock nut.

NOTE: Left wheel lock nut has left-hand threads.

2) Using Puller (49 S120 520A) and Adapter (49 S120 523A), remove rear axle bearings. Remove oil seal from axle housing.

Installation

1) Using Oil Seal Installer (49 U027 003), install oil seal. Using Adapter (49 F027 004), install bearing inner race. Using Bearing Installer (49 H025 001), position oil seal flush with end of axle casing. Apply multipurpose grease to oil seal lip. Install spacer with concave side facing backing plate.

2) Using Adapter (49 S120 748) and 5-ton press, install axle bearing onto axle shaft. Using wrench, install and tighten lock nut to 145-217 ft. lbs. (197-295 N.m). Install axle shaft assembly. Install backing plate. Reconnect brake line and parking brake cable. Install brake drum and wheel. Bleed brake system.

FORD MOTOR CO. TRACER & MAZDA (Cont.)

Fig. 7: Exploded View of Rear Brake Assembly (B2200 & B2600 4WD)

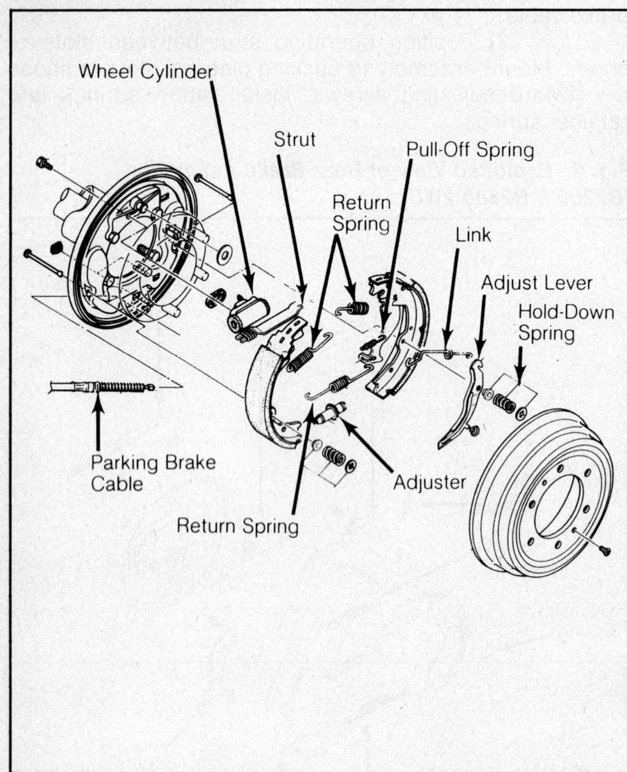

Courtesy of Mazda Motors Corp.

Removal & Installation (All Others)

Remove rear brake rotor or drum. Remove hub. Remove oil seal and bearings. To install, reverse removal procedure. Adjust wheel bearings.

MASTER CYLINDER

Removal

1) Disconnect fluid level sensor coupler (if equipped). Disconnect and plug hydraulic lines at master cylinder to prevent entry of dirt and loss of fluid.

2) Remove nuts attaching master cylinder to firewall or power brake unit. Remove master cylinder from vehicle. On RX7, remove proportioning valve by-pass bolt. To install, reverse removal procedure and bleed hydraulic system.

Installation

Place Adjustment Gauge (49 F043 001) onto master cylinder. Turn screw on adjuster gauge until it contacts piston. Remove adjuster gauge. Apply 19.7 in. Hg to power brake unit. Invert adjuster gauge and place it on power brake unit. Adjust push rod on power brake unit until there is no clearance between push rod and adjuster gauge screw. Install master cylinder.

POWER BRAKE UNIT

Removal & Installation

1) Remove master cylinder from power brake unit before removing power brake unit. Disconnect vacuum line at power brake unit. On 626, remove blower duct. From inside vehicle, remove cotter pin and clevis pin attaching push rod to brake pedal, and separate.

2) Remove nuts retaining power unit to firewall. Remove power brake unit and master cylinder as an assembly. Separate master cylinder from power brake unit. To install, reverse removal procedure and bleed hydraulic system.

OVERHAUL

FRONT DISC BRAKE CALIPER

Disassembly

Thoroughly clean exterior of caliper and remove retainer and dust boot. Place a piece of wood in front of piston(s). Apply compressed air to fluid inlet and remove piston(s). Tap caliper with plastic hammer, if required. Remove piston seal(s) without damaging caliper bore. *See Figs. 2 and 8.*

Reassembly

Apply clean brake fluid to cylinder bore, piston and piston seal. Seat piston seal in caliper bore. Install piston carefully into cylinder bore and install dust boot and retainer.

Fig. 8: Exploded View of RX7 Front Brake Caliper

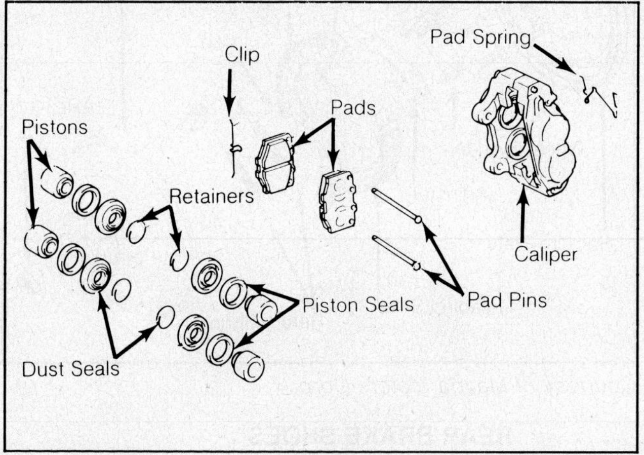

Courtesy of Mazda Motors Corp.

REAR DISC BRAKE CALIPER

Disassembly (RX7, Tracer, 323 & 626)

1) Remove retainer and dust seal. Remove piston seal and snap ring. Using Disc Brake Piston Wrench (49 FA18 602), turn piston counterclockwise and remove. Remove stopper, "O" ring, adjuster spindle and connecting link.

2) Remove guide pins and boots. Remove spring, nut, spindle lever, boot and bracket. Press needle bearing from housing. *See Fig. 9.*

Inspection

1) Clean all parts in brake fluid or alcohol. Air dry parts. Inspect caliper bore and piston for scratches, scoring or rust. Remove minor damage by polishing with crocus cloth.

CAUTION: Never use gasoline or kerosene when cleaning caliper parts.

2) Inspect needle roller bearing for or damage. Inspect boots for damage. Inspect spring for weakness or damage. Replace as necessary.

FORD MOTOR CO. TRACER & MAZDA (Cont.)

Fig. 9: Exploded View of Rear Caliper Assembly

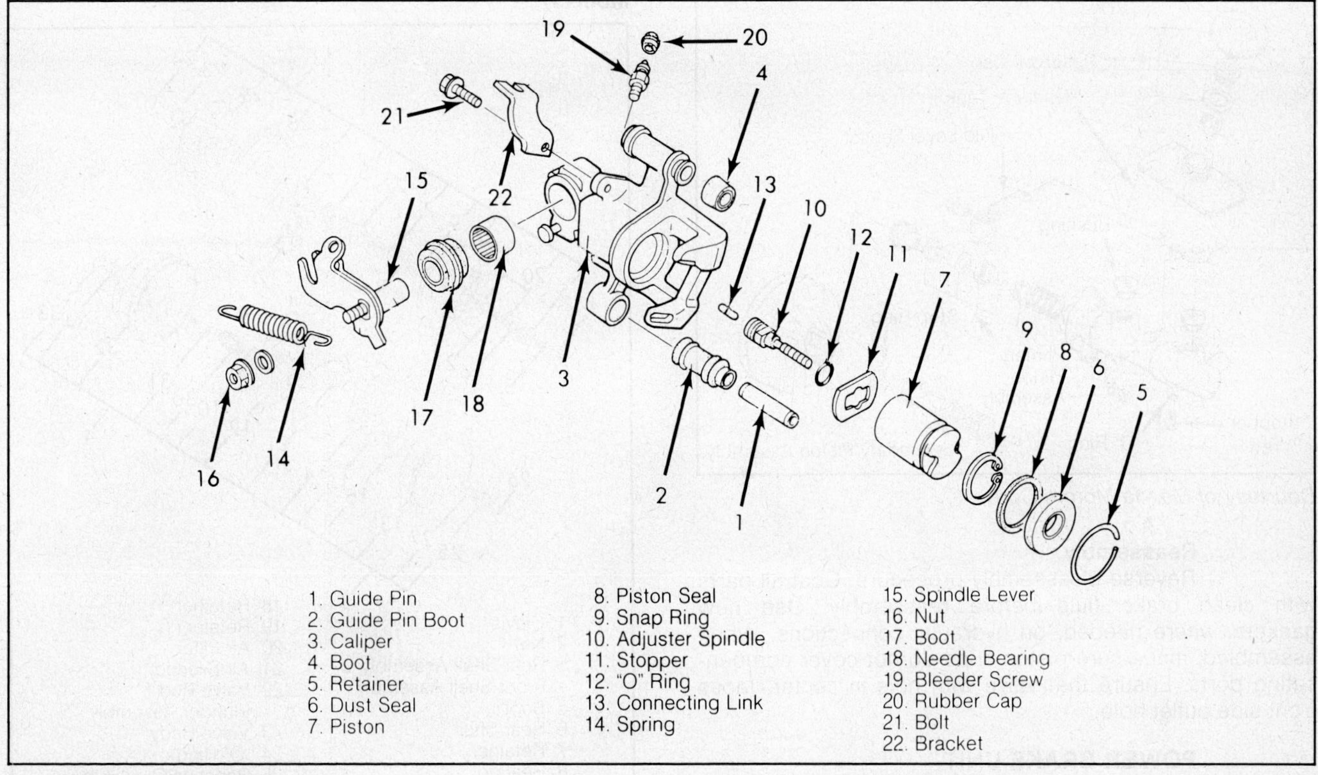

Courtesy of Mazda Motors Corp.

Reassembly

1) Assemble caliper in reverse order of disassembly. Use new piston and dust seals. Three kinds of grease contained in seal kit must be used. Use White grease on the "O" ring. Apply Red grease on piston seal.

2) Apply Orange grease on guide pins, boots, dust seal, adjuster spindle, connecting link and spindle lever. Align stopper pins with holes of caliper housing.

3) Install piston using Disc Brake Piston Wrench (49 FA18 602). Turn piston clockwise until piston is fully seated in caliper. Position piston after seating to ensure that dowel on brake pad fits in piston stopper groove.

WHEEL CYLINDERS

Disassembly

Remove dust boots. Remove pistons by pressing on cylinder cup to force out filling blocks and return spring.

Inspection

Clean all parts in alcohol or brake fluid. Check cylinder bore and pistons for scores, roughness or wear. Check clearance between cylinder bore and pistons. Replace if clearance exceeds .006" (.15 mm). Check cups for deformation. Replace as necessary.

Reassembly

Reverse disassembly procedure. Flat side of cylinder cups face outward. Coat all parts with clean brake fluid before reassembly. Ensure that flat side of cylinder cups face outward.

MASTER CYLINDER

Disassembly

1) Thoroughly clean outside of master cylinder. Remove remaining brake fluid. Remove reservoir and dust boot (if equipped). Depress primary piston assembly. *See Fig. 10.*

2) From rear of cylinder bore, remove retaining ring, washer, primary piston assembly, and return spring. Remove stopper bolt and secondary piston by blowing compressed air through outlet port. *See Fig. 10.*

3) Carefully remove the secondary piston assembly and return spring. Remove fittings, check valves and springs.

Inspection

Clean all parts in alcohol or brake fluid. Check all parts for scoring, roughness or wear. Check clearance between pistons and cylinder wall. If clearance exceeds .006" (.15 mm), replace parts as necessary. Remove all foreign matter from internal passages and recesses with compressed air. Check cylinder cups for deformation and replace as required.

FORD MOTOR CO. TRACER & MAZDA (Cont.)

Fig. 10: Exploded View of Typical Master Cylinder

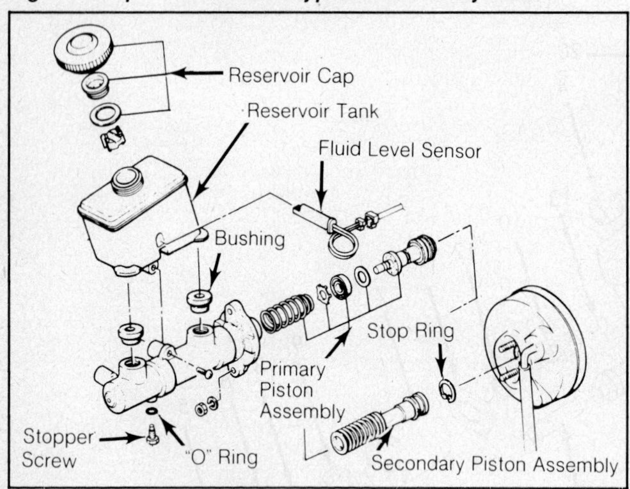

Courtesy of Mazda Motors Corp.

Reassembly

Reverse disassembly procedure. Coat all parts with clean brake fluid before reassembly. Use new gaskets, where needed, on hydraulic connections. When assembled, make sure piston cups do not cover compensating ports. Ensure that valve with hole in center, faces front side outlet hole.

POWER BRAKE UNIT

NOTE: Power brake units vary slightly between model applications. The following general overhaul procedures can be used if attention is paid to specific order of components.

Disassembly

1) Remove master cylinder and check valve from power unit. Place power unit in a vise with push rod up. Scribe alignment marks on front and rear shells to assure reassembly in original position. Remove clevis, lock nut, and dust boot from rear shell. *See Figs. 11 and 12.*

CAUTION: Separate front and rear shells carefully. Spring tension may cause rear shell to release quickly.

2) Attach a bar and plate tool to rear shell mounting studs. Press down on tool while rotating it counterclockwise to unlock rear shell. Lift rear shell assembly from power unit, remove air silencer retainer, and separate diaphragm from power piston assembly. Remove valve rod with plunger assembly from rear shell.

NOTE: Service valve rod plungers as an assembly.

3) On 4WD models, push in and rotate reaction disc hub 90 degrees. Remove valve body. After rotation, raise portion of disc hub should be aligned with notched grooves of valve body. On all models, remove lock plate and press valve rod in to remove valve retainer key.

4) Remove valve rod and plunger assembly. Remove air silencer and filter. Remove retainer and bearing. Never remove rear seal from rear shell unless seal is defective and a new one is available. Remove push rod, front seal, and support plate.

Fig. 11: Exploded View of Typical Power Brake Unit (4WD Models)

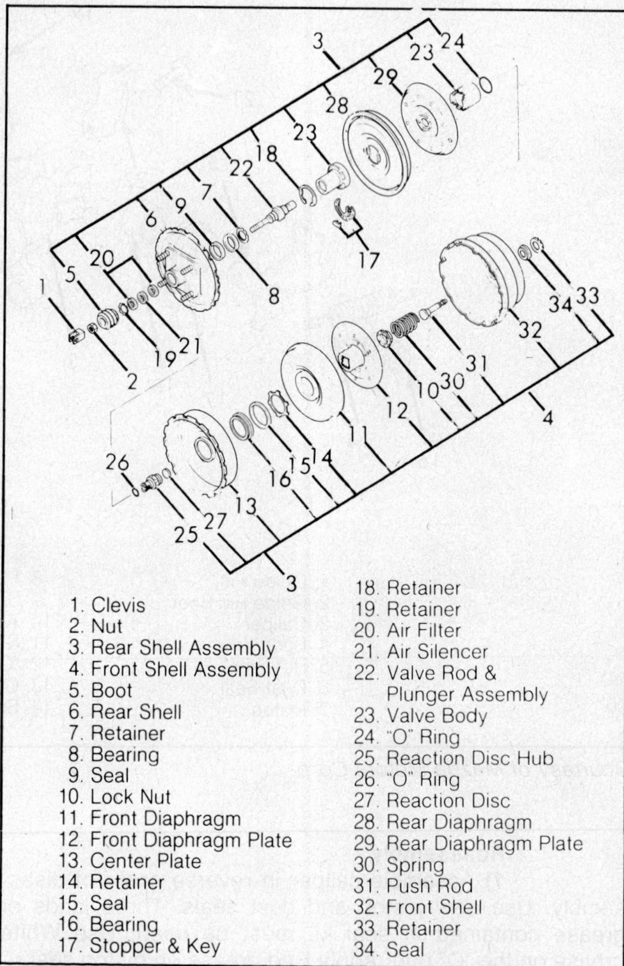

Courtesy of Mazda Motors Corp.

Fig. 12: Exploded View of Typical Power Brake Unit (All Others)

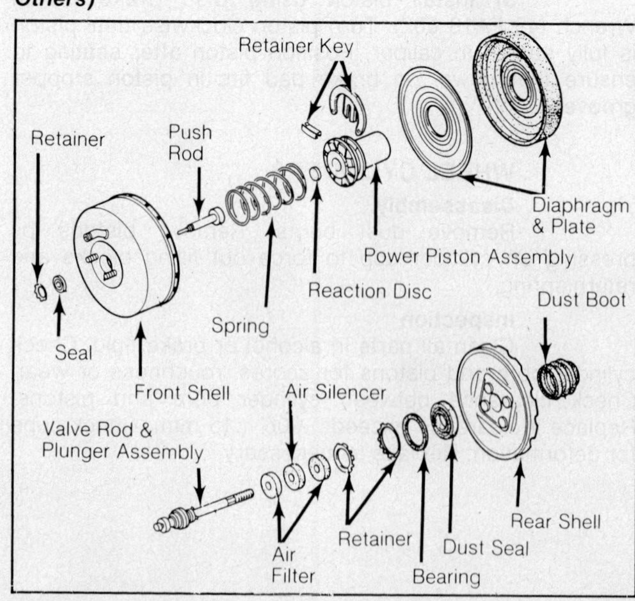

Courtesy of Mazda Motors Corp.

FORD MOTOR CO. TRACER & MAZDA (Cont.)

Inspection

Clean all parts and blow dry with compressed air. Inspect all rubber parts for cuts, nicks, deterioration or other damage. Check power piston for cracks, distortion, chipping, and damaged seats. Inspect front and rear shells for scratches, scores, pits, dents or other damage. Replace any defective parts.

Reassembly

Reverse disassembly procedure. Apply silicone grease to parts before reassembly. On 4WD models, when installing reaction disc hub, rotate it 90 degrees. Ensure raised portion of hub is properly seated in valve body. On all models, when assembling rear shell to front shell, ensure index marks are aligned.

TIGHTENING SPECIFICATIONS

Application	Ft. Lbs. (N.m)
Backing Plate (Rear)	
B2200 & B2600	
2WD	72-87 (98-118)
4WD	65-80 (88-109)
All Others	33-49 (45-67)
Caliper Mounting Bracket	
B2200 & B2600	65-80 (88-109)
Tracer & 323	
Front	29-36 (39-49)
Rear	36-51 (4969)
626	
Upper	12-18 (16-24)
Lower	15-22 (20-29)
Caliper Guide Pin or Lock Bolt	
B2200 & B2600	23-30 (31-41)
Tracer & 323 (Rear)	12-17 (16-23)
RX7	
Front (14" Wheel)	23-30 (31-41)
Rear	22-30 (30-41)
Rotor-to-Hub Bolts	
2200 & B2600	40-51 (54-69)
Tracer & 323	33-40 (45-54)
626	36-43 (49-58)
Wheel Bearing Lock Nut	
B2200 & B2600	
Front	[1]
Rear	145-217 (197-295)
Tracer, 323 & 626	
Front	116-174 (158-237)
Rear	[1]
RX7	[1]

[1] – See text.

DRUM BRAKE SPECIFICATIONS

Application	Drum Diam. In. (mm)	Drum Width In. (mm)	Max. Drum Refinish Diam. In. (mm)	Wheel Cyl. Diam. In. (mm)	Master Cyl. Diam. In. (mm)
B2200 & B2600	10.23 (260)	.....	10.31 (262)	[1] .750 (19.05)	.875 (22.2)
Tracer & 323	7.87 (200)	.....	7.91 (201)	.688 (17.5)	.875 (22.2)
626	7.87 (200)	.....	7.91 (201)	.750 (19)	.875 (22.2)

[1] – On 2WD models. On 4WD, diameter is .688" (17.5 mm).

FORD MOTOR CO. TRACER & MAZDA (Cont.)

DISC BRAKE ROTOR SPECIFICATIONS

Application	Disc Diameter In. (mm)	Lateral Runout In. (mm)	Parallelism In. (mm)	Original Thickness In. (mm)	Min. Refinish Thickness In. (mm)	Discard Thickness In. (mm)
B2200 & B2600						
2WD	10.1 (257)	.006 (.15)	.....	.79 (20)	.....	.71 (18)
4WD	10.7 (272)	.006 (.15)	.....	.87 (22)	.....	.79 (20)
RX7						
Front						
14" Wheel	8.03 (204)	.004 (.10)	.....	.87 (22)	.....	.79 (20)
15" Wheel	9.06 (230)	.004 (.10)	.....	.87 (22)		.79 (20)
Rear						
14" Wheel	8.86 (225)	.004 (.10)	.....	.394 (10)	.....	.31 (8)
15" Wheel	9.33 (237)	.004 (.10)	.....	.79 (20)	.....	.71 (18)
Tracer & 323						
Front	10.24 (260)	.004 (.10)	.....	.71 (18)	.....	.63 (16)
Rear	8.74 (222)	.004 (.10)	.....	.394 (10)	.....	.354 (9)
626						
Front	7.95 (202)	.004 (.10)	.....	.55 (14)	.....	.49 (13)
Rear	8.58 (218)	.004 (.10)	.....	.394 (10)	.....	.354 (9)

GENERAL MOTORS & ISUZU I-MARK

General Motors: Spectrum, Sprint;
Isuzu: I-Mark

DESCRIPTION

The brake system is equipped with front disc brakes and rear drum brakes. Hydraulic circuit is diagonal; left front and right rear brakes, and right front and left rear brakes. The parking brake sets the rear brakes using a cable and mechanical linkage system.

ADJUSTMENTS

PEDAL FREE PLAY

Sprint

If free play is not within .04-.32" (1-8 mm), check stoplight switch adjustment, pedal shaft bolt and master cylinder pin for looseness.

PEDAL HEIGHT

Sprint

Brake pedal height is normal if brake pedal is same height as clutch pedal. With power brake unit removed from vehicle, check distance between power brake unit mounting surface (with gasket installed) and center of brake push rod clevis pin. Correct distance is 4.94-4.98" (125.5-126.5 mm).

I-Mark & Spectrum

Check distance between level part of floor panel and top part of brake pedal. Distance should be 6.07" (154 mm). If distance is not correct, loosen lock nut on push rod. Remove clevis pin from brake pedal. Turn clevis to lengthen or shorten. Reinstall clevis pin.

PEDAL TRAVEL

Sprint

1) With engine off, pump brake pedal until all vacuum is exhausted from power brake unit. Push brake pedal with a force of 66 lbs. (30 kg). Measure distance between brake pedal face and floor. Distance must not be less than 3.35" (85 mm).

2) If distance is less than specified, check for air in lines, worn rear shoes, defective rear brake self-adjusters or improper brake pedal push rod adjustment. See PEDAL HEIGHT adjustment.

PARKING BRAKE

1) Using pulling power of 44 lbs. (20 kg) on Sprint or 66 lbs. (30 kg) on I-Mark and Spectrum, pull parking brake lever fully up and count number of notches lever travels. Adjustment is okay if lever clicks between 7-9 notches on I-Mark and Spectrum and 3-8 notches on Sprint. If not okay, first check for air in lines, worn rear shoes or seized rear self-adjusters.

2) To adjust parking brake, loosen cable adjusting nuts on Sprint or turnbuckle on I-Mark and Spectrum, at hand lever. Adjust cable(s) as necessary. On Sprint, cables must be adjusted equally. After adjustment, check for brake drag with parking brake off.

POWER BRAKE PISTON ROD

Sprint

Apply vacuum to power brake unit with engine at idle. Master cylinder primary piston-to-power brake piston rod clearance should become .004-.020" (.1-.5 mm).

STOPLIGHT SWITCH

Pull up on brake pedal and hold. Measure distance between face of brake pedal contact plate and end of stoplight switch threads. Adjust if distance is not between .004-.020" (.1-.5 mm) on I-Mark and Spectrum and .02-.04" (.5-1.0 mm) on Sprint. Tighten switch to 8-11 ft. lbs. (10-15 N.m).

REMOVAL & INSTALLATION

DISC BRAKE PADS

Removal & Installation

Hoist and support front of vehicle. Remove wheels and caliper mounting bolts. Hold inside pad while removing caliper from knuckle. Hang caliper from frame with wire. Remove outside pad, pad clips and springs. To install, reverse removal procedure. Ensure caliper slide bushings move in thrust direction and coat with silicone grease.

DISC BRAKE ROTOR & HUB

Removal (Sprint)

1) Remove caliper and pads. Remove cotter pin, castle nut and washer from end of drive axle. Measure distance between outside rotor face and outside edge of caliper mounting bracket. *See Fig. 1*. Record dimension "A" for reassembly.

Fig. 1: Measuring Rotor Position Before Removal (Sprint)

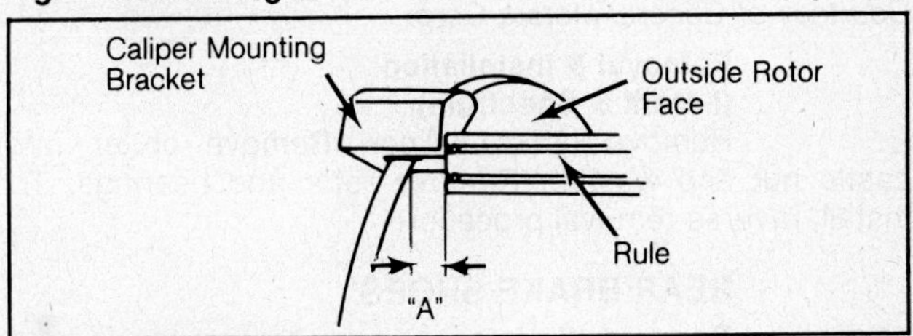

Courtesy of General Motors Corp.

2) Using Slide Hammer (J-2619-01) and Wheel Hub Remover (J-34866), remove wheel hub and rotor as an assembly. Remove rotor retaining bolts from hub and separate hub from rotor. *See Fig. 2*.

Fig. 2: Removing Hub & Rotor Assembly (Sprint)

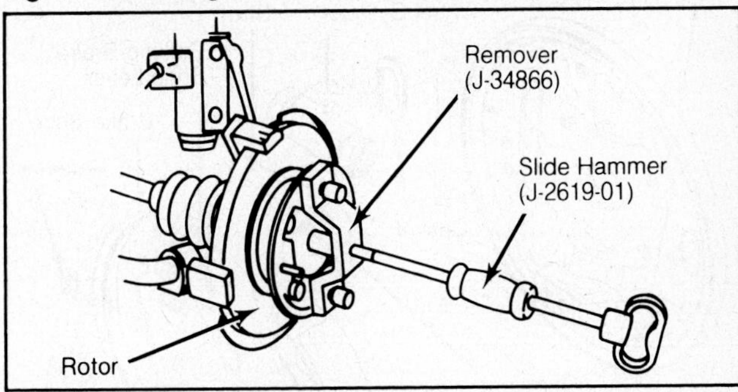

Courtesy of General Motors Corp.

Installation

1) Temporarily install rotor on hub. Insert spacer into hub. Using a plastic hammer, drive hub in until center protrudes evenly. *See Fig. 3*.

GENERAL MOTORS & ISUZU I-MARK (Cont.)

Fig. 3: Installing Spacer on Wheel Hub (Sprint)

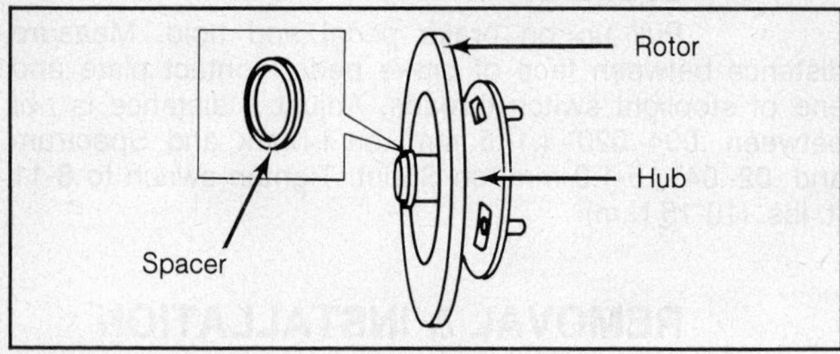

Courtesy of General Motors Corp.

2) Using Wheel Hub Installer (J-34856) and Handle (J-7079-2), drive hub and rotor assembly on drive axle until dimension "A" is reached. *See Fig. 4*.

3) Install and tighten bolts attaching hub to rotor and hub castle nut. Install cotter pin. Install pads and caliper and tighten caliper mounting bolts.

Fig. 4: Installing Front Hub Assembly

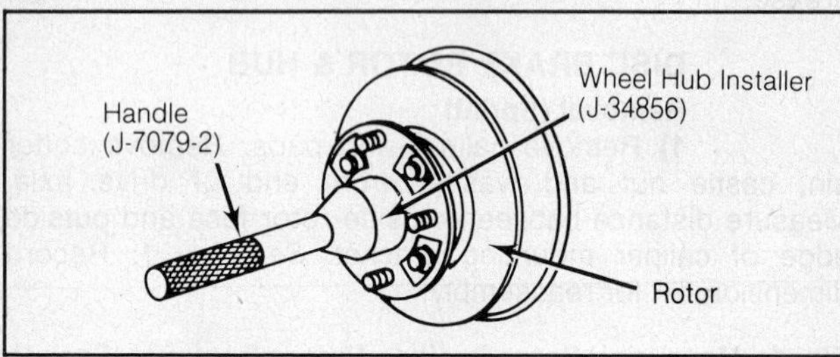

Courtesy of General Motors Corp.

Removal & Installation (I-Mark & Spectrum)

Remove brake caliper. Remove cotter pin, castle nut and washer. Remove rotor and bearings. To install, reverse removal procedure.

REAR BRAKE SHOES

Removal (Sprint)

1) Hoist rear of vehicle and support with jack stands. Remove rear wheel and dust cap. Remove cotter pin, castle nut and washer from spindle.

Fig. 5: Exploded View of Rear Brake Assembly (Sprint)

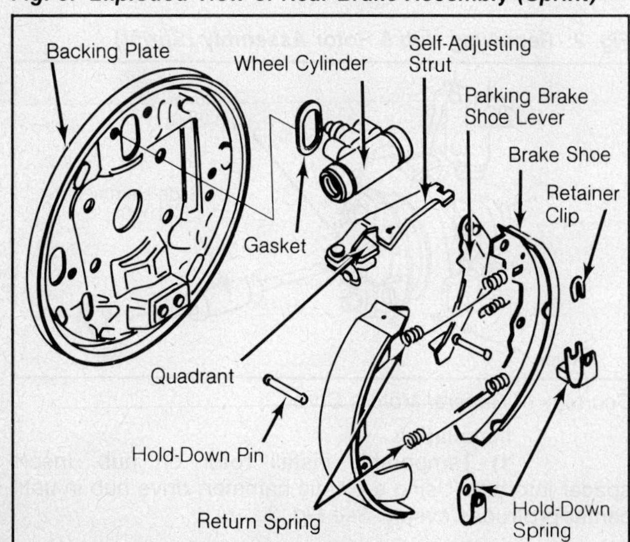

Courtesy of General Motors Corp.

2) Loosen parking brake cable adjustment nut and remove plug from backing plate. Insert screwdriver into hole and contact brake shoe hold-down spring. Push up on hold-down spring to release parking brake shoe lever from hold-down spring.

3) Remove brake drum using Slide Hammer (J-2619-01) and Remover (J-34866). *See Fig. 2* Remove hold-down springs, disconnect parking brake cable. Remove brake shoes. *See Fig. 5*.

Installation

1) Install parking brake shoe lever. Install brake strut and anti-rattle spring. Install shoes and return springs. Install parking brake cable in lever. Install hold-down spring.

2) Contract strut adjuster between shoes by pushing brake shoe away from strut while pushing quadrant against backing plate. Install rear drum, washer and castle nut. Tighten castle nut, insert cotter pin and install dust cap.

3) To adjust rear brakes, pump brake pedal 3 to 5 times with a force of 66 lbs. (30 kg). Adjust parking brake and ensure that rear brakes do not drag.

Removal (I-Mark & Spectrum)

Raise rear of vehicle and support. Remove rear wheels. Remove cotter pin, castle nut and washer. Remove rear brake drum. Remove holding pin leading shoe. Remove leading shoe and adjuster. Remove trailing shoe and attaching parts. Disconnect parking brake lever from trailing shoe.

Installation

To install, reverse removal procedure. Lubricate contact points. Adjust brake shoes so clearance between shoes and brake drum is .012" (.30 mm).

Fig. 6: Exploded View of Rear Brake Assembly (I-Mark & Spectrum)

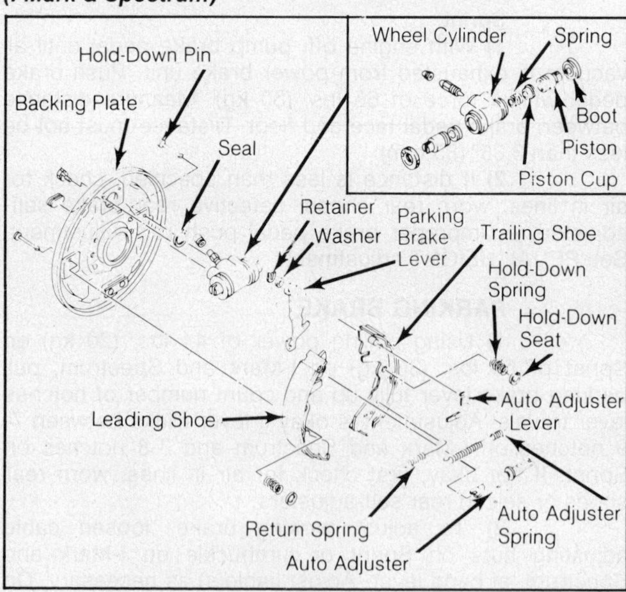

Courtesy of General Motors Corp.

MASTER CYLINDER

Removal

Clean around reservoir cap and remove fluid. Remove 2 brake lines from side of master cylinder. Remove nuts and washers attaching master cylinder to power brake unit and remove master cylinder.

GENERAL MOTORS & ISUZU I-MARK (Cont.)

Installation

Before installing master cylinder, check and adjust clearance between power brake unit piston rod and master cylinder piston. See POWER BRAKE PISTON ROD and PEDAL HEIGHT for adjustments. To complete installation, reverse removal procedure and bleed brake system.

POWER BRAKE UNIT

Removal

Remove master cylinder from power brake unit and disconnect push rod clevis from brake pedal arm. Disconnect vacuum hose from power brake unit. Remove nuts attaching unit to firewall and power brake unit.

Installation

Check and adjust clearance between power brake unit piston rod and master cylinder piston. See POWER BRAKE PISTON ROD and PEDAL HEIGHT for adjustments. To complete installation, reverse removal procedure. Check brake pedal free play.

OVERHAUL

FRONT DISC BRAKE CALIPER

Disassembly

Remove caliper from vehicle. Place block of wood between piston and caliper cavity wall. Apply a moderate amount of compressed air to force piston out of cylinder.

CAUTION: **DO NOT place fingers in front of piston when forcing piston out of cylinder.**

Reassembly

To reassemble, reverse disassembly procedure. Lubricate piston seal and cylinder with brake fluid. On Sprint, install boot with 3 grooved side facing outward and position piston in caliper so that it protrudes approximately .040" (1 mm) out of cylinder end. Install dust boot seal ring.

Fig. 7: Exploded View of Front Disc Brake Caliper (Sprint)

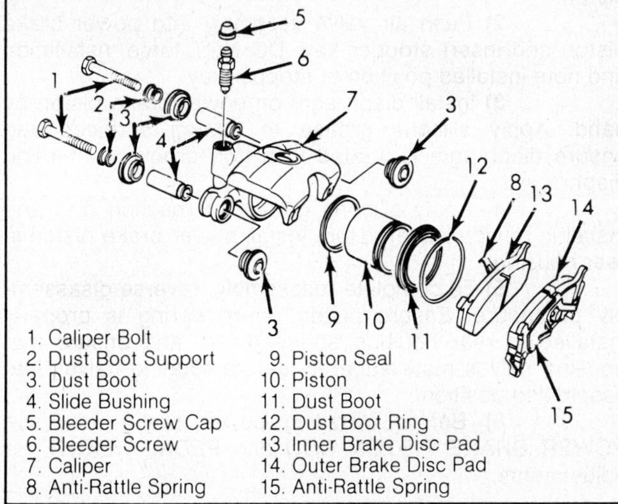

Courtesy of General Motors Corp.

Fig. 8: Exploded View of Front Disc Brake Caliper (I-Mark & Spectrum)

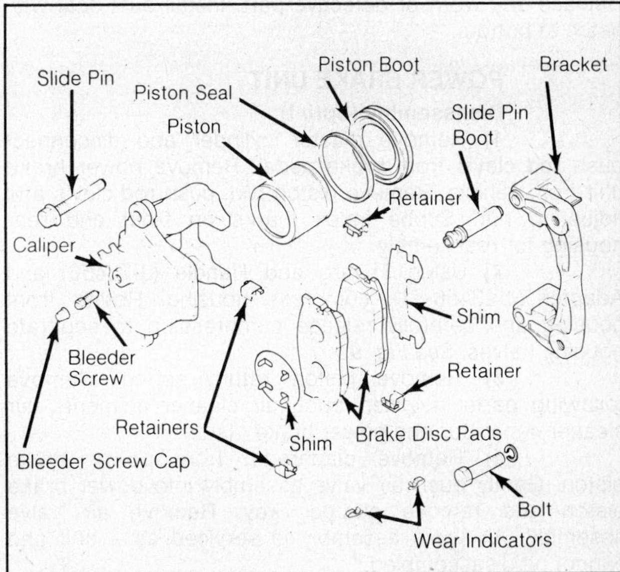

Courtesy of General Motors Corp.

MASTER CYLINDER

Disassembly (Sprint)

1) Remove circlip from end of cylinder. Apply low pressure compressed air to rear reservoir port and force out primary piston.

NOTE: **Be careful not to drop primary and secondary pistons on floor when using compressed air for removal.**

2) Remove secondary piston by removing piston stopper bolt from bottom of master cylinder and applying low pressure compressed air in stopper bolt hole.

Cleaning & Inspection

Note position of piston cups before removing. Do not reuse piston cups. Wash parts in clean brake fluid. Blow dry parts. Inspect master cylinder for scoring or corrosion. Do not attempt to polish aluminum cylinder bore. Replace if corroded.

Reassembly

1) Coat all parts with clean brake fluid. Install new piston cups on pistons. Install secondary return spring, return spring seat and secondary piston in cylinder bore.

2) Install primary return spring and primary piston in cylinder bore. Install sealing rings on primary piston stopper and install stopper in cylinder bore.

3) Depress primary piston and install snap ring in cylinder. Press primary piston into bore until seated. Install and tighten piston stopper bolt in bottom of cylinder.

4) Install reservoir on master cylinder and bench-bleed before installing in vehicle. Bleed entire brake system after installation.

Disassembly (I-Mark & Spectrum)

Remove dust seal and reservoir. Remove proportioning valves. Using a screwdriver, depress piston assembly and remove stopper bolt. Remove snap ring. Remove primary and secondary piston assemblies.

Reassembly

To install, reverse disassembly procedure. Replace any worn or defective part. Install dust seal with notch at bottom.

POWER BRAKE UNIT

Disassembly (Sprint)

1) Remove master cylinder and disconnect push rod clevis from brake pedal. Remove power brake unit from vehicle. Remove piston rod, push rod clevis and adjusting nut. Scribe index marks on front and rear housing for reassembly.

2) Using Fixture and Handle (J-23456) and Adapter (J-23456-51), compress housing. Rotate front housing and carefully release compression to separate housing halves. *See Fig. 9.*

3) Remove piston return spring. Remove following parts in order: boot, air cleaner elements, air cleaner separator and power brake piston.

4) Remove diaphragm from power brake piston. Gently push air valve assembly into power brake piston and remove stopper key. Remove air valve assembly. Air valve assembly is serviced as a unit and cannot be disassembled.

5) Using fingers only, pick reaction disc out of power brake piston. Using Fixture (J-24435-4) and Mandril (J-34874), lightly hammer oil seal out of rear housing.

Fig. 9: Exploded View of Sprint Power Brake Unit

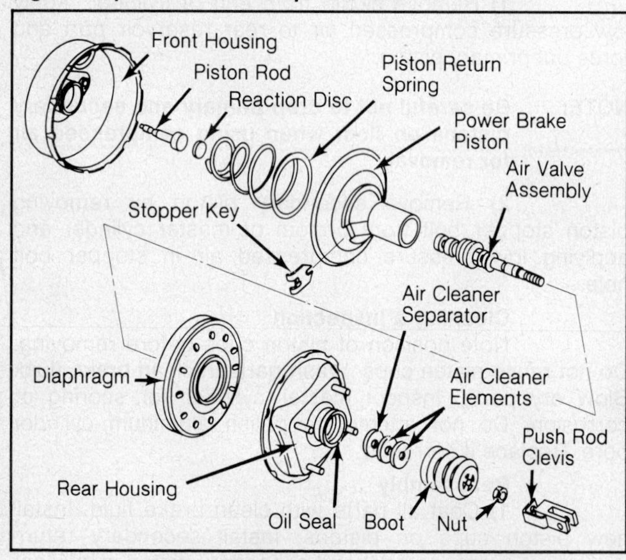

Spectrum is similar. Courtesy of General Motors Corp.

Cleaning & Inspection

Wash all metal parts in ethyl alcohol. Blow dry with compressed air. Inspect inner surface of both housings for wear or damage. Inspect all parts for cracks, nicks, distortion or other damage. Replace parts as necessary.

Reassembly

1) Apply silicone grease to rear housing oil seal and press into rear housing. Apply silicone grease to sliding surfaces of air valve assembly and install in power brake piston.

2) Push air valve assembly into power brake piston and insert stopper key. DO NOT force installation and note installed position of stopper key.

3) Install diaphragm on power brake piston by hand. Apply silicone grease to mating surfaces and ensure diaphragm is seated in piston groove by turning diaphragm.

4) Apply silicone grease to reaction disc and install in power brake piston. Install power brake piston in rear housing.

5) To complete reassembly, reverse disassembly procedure. Ensure piston return spring is properly installed in rear housing spring guide, and ensure that housing halves mate squarely before rotating halves into assembled position.

6) Before installing power brake unit in vehicle, see POWER BRAKE PISTON ROD and PEDAL HEIGHT for adjustments.

Disassembly (I-Mark & Spectrum)

1) With unit removed from vehicle, remove piston rod, push rod clevis and nut. Use screwdriver to pry out retainer. Scribe match marks between front and rear housing for reassembly.

2) Using Spanner (J-9504-01) and Holder (J-22805-01), compress housing. Rotate front housing and carefully release compression to separate housing halves.

3) Remove piston return spring, boot, air cleaner elements, air cleaner separator and power brake piston.

4) Remove diaphragm from power brake piston. Gently push air valve assembly into power brake piston and remove stopper key. Remove air valve assembly. Air valve assembly is serviced as a unit and cannot be disassembled.

5) Remove reaction disc from power brake piston. Using Spanner Wrench (J-9504-01) and Holder (J-22805-01), lightly hammer oil seal out of rear housing.

Cleaning & Inspection

Wash all metal parts in ethyl alcohol. Blow dry with compressed air. Inspect inner surface of both housings for wear or damage. Inspect all parts for cracks, nicks, distortion or other damage. Replace defective parts.

Reassembly

1) Apply silicone grease to rear housing oil seal and press into rear housing. Apply grease to sliding surfaces of air valve assembly and install in power brake piston.

2) Push air valve assembly into power brake piston and insert stopper key. DO NOT force installation and note installed position of stopper key.

3) Install diaphragm on power brake piston by hand. Apply silicone grease to mating surfaces and ensure diaphragm is seated in piston groove by turning diaphragm.

4) Apply silicone grease to reaction disc and install in power brake piston. Install power brake piston in rear housing.

5) To complete reassembly, reverse disassembly procedure. Ensure piston return spring is properly installed in rear housing spring guide, and ensure that housing halves mate squarely before rotating halves into assembled position.

6) Before installing power brake unit, see POWER BRAKE PISTON ROD and PEDAL HEIGHT for adjustments.

GENERAL MOTORS & ISUZU I-MARK (Cont.)

Fig. 10: Exploded View of I-Mark & Spectrum Power Brake Unit

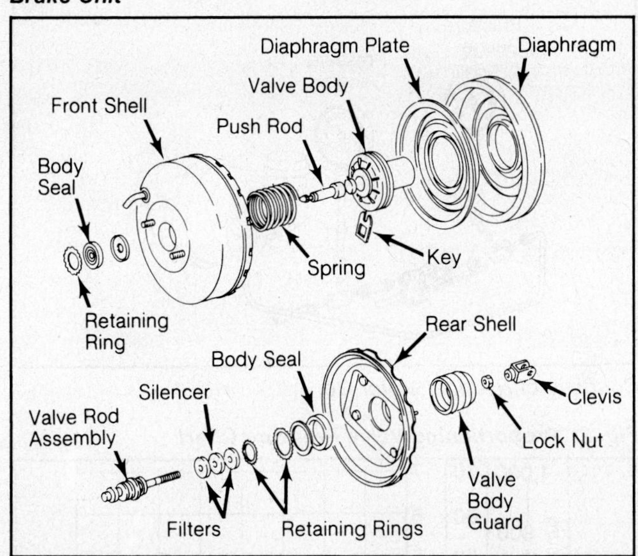

Courtesy of Isuzu Motor Co.

TIGHTENING SPECIFICATIONS

Application	Ft. Lbs. (N.m)
Brake Hose-to-Caliper	15-18 (20-24)
Brake Line Flare Nut	11-13 (14-18)
Caliper Mounting Bolts	
Sprint	18-26 (24-35)
I-Mark & Spectrum	36 (49)
Front Drive Axle Nuts	
Sprint	109-195 (148-264)
I-Mark & Spectrum	137 (186)
Hub-to-Rotor Bolts	29-43 (39-58)
Proportioning Valve	
I-Mark & Spectrum	29 (39)
Power Booster Mounting Nut	
I-Mark & Spectrum	14 (19)
Rear Axle Nuts	
Sprint	58-86 (79-117)
I-Mark & Spectrum	22 (29)
	INCH Lbs. (N.m)
Master Cylinder Mounting Nut	96-144 (10-16)
Power Booster Mounting Nut	
Sprint	96-144 (10-16)

DISC BRAKE ROTOR SPECIFICATIONS

Application	Disc Diameter In. (mm)	Lateral Runout In. (mm)	Parallelism In. (mm)	Original Thickness In. (mm)	Min. Refinish Thickness In. (mm)	Discard Thickness In. (mm)
I-Mark & Spectrum	8.94 (227)	.0059 (.150)	.0008 (.020)	.433 (11.00)	.378 (9.60)	.377 (9.58)
Sprint	.....	.0028 (.071)	.0008 (.020)	.394 (10.01)	.....	.315 (8.00)

DRUM BRAKE SPECIFICATIONS

Application	Drum Diam. In. (mm)	Drum Width In. (mm)	Max. Drum Refinish Diam. In. (mm)	Wheel Cyl. Diam. In. (mm)	Master Cyl. Diam. In. (mm)
I-Mark & Spectrum	7.09 (180)	.....	7.14 (181.4)	.690 (17.53)	.810 (20.57)
Sprint [1]	7.09 (180)	.....	7.16 (181.9)	.....	.....

[1] – Maximum runout is .0024" (.060 mm).

HYUNDAI EXCEL & MITSUBISHI PRECIS

DESCRIPTION

BRAKE SYSTEM

Brake system is hydraulically-operated using a master cylinder with a single reservoir and 2 outlets. A vacuum power brake unit is used on all models. A proportioning valve is used to control braking action. Brake system is self-adjusting.

ADJUSTMENTS

NOTE: If parking brake lever stroke is not to specification and cables at equal length after adjustment, automatic adjuster will malfunction.

PARKING BRAKE

1) Properly adjusted parking brake lever stroke should be 5-7 notches (clicks) at 44 lbs. (20 kg). If not, remove console box and release brake lever. Adjust cable adjusting nuts, allowing enough slack in cables to prevent brake shoe drag. *See Fig. 1.*

2) Loosen parking brake switch mounting bolt. Adjust switch until indicator light goes out when brake lever is fully released and light comes on when lever is pulled one notch. Ensure rear brakes do not drag with brake lever released.

Fig. 1: Parking Brake Cable Adjustment

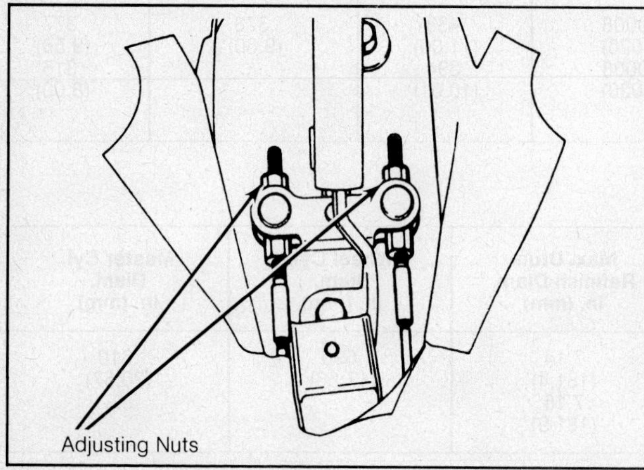

Courtesy of Hyundai Motor Co.

TESTING

PROPORTIONING VALVE FUNCTION TEST

1) Attach 2 pressure gauges that measures at least 2000 psi (140.6 kg/cm²), to the input and output side of proportioning valve. *See Fig. 2.* Measure the input and output pressure with brakes applied. Compare pressure readings with PROPORTIONING VALVE PRESSURE CHART. *See Fig. 3.*

2) If measured pressures are NOT within range, replace proportional valve. Measure both left and right pressure readings. If the difference in pressure is 60 psi (27 kg/cm²), replace proportioning valve. DO NOT disassemble proportioning valve.

Fig. 2: Testing Proportioning Valve

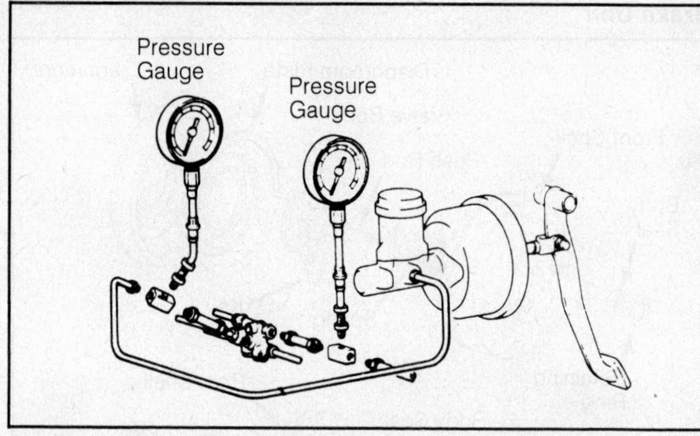

Courtesy of Hyundai Motor Co.

Fig. 3: Proportioning Valve Pressure Chart

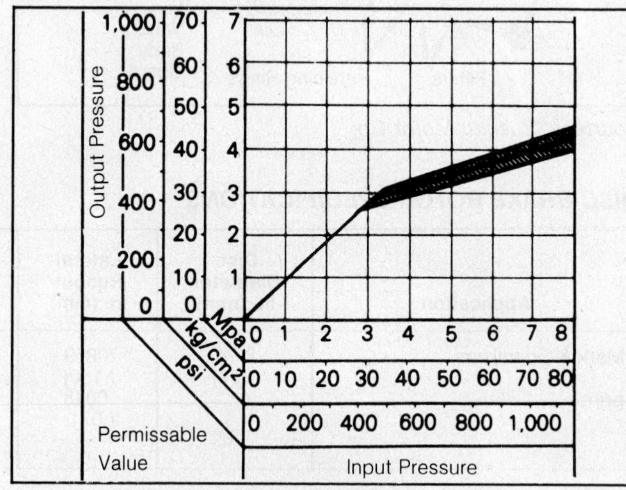

Courtesy of Hyundai Motor Co.

POWER BRAKE UNIT OPERATING TEST

Functional Test

1) Run engine for 2 minutes. Turn off engine. Step on brake pedal several times with normal pressure. If brake pedal depresses fully the first time but gradually becomes higher when depressed succeeding times, power brake unit is operating properly. If pedal height remains the same, power brake unit is defective.

2) With engine not running, step on brake pedal several times. Ensure that brake pedal height remains the same. Depress brake pedal and start engine. If pedal moves downward slightly, power brake unit is okay. If there is no change, power brake unit is defective.

3) With engine running, step on brake pedal and turn off engine. Hold pedal in depressed position for 30 seconds. If pedal height does not change, power brake unit is okay. If pedal rises, power brake unit is defective. If all 3 tests are okay, power brake unit is functioning. If one test fails, test vacuum hose, check valve or power brake unit for defects.

REMOVAL & INSTALLATION

FRONT DISC BRAKE PADS

Removal

1) Raise and support vehicle. Remove front wheel. Remove pad protector by prying up edge of clip at

HYUNDAI EXCEL & MITSUBISHI PRECIS (Cont.)

center of protector. *See Fig. 4.* Hold center of "M" clip with a screwdriver. Detach "M" clip from pad and its ends from retaining pins.

2) Remove "M" clip. Using pliers, remove "K" spring. Remove pad retaining pins. Remove pads and anti-squeak shim by gripping backing plate area of pad and shim with pliers.

CAUTION: Ensure that torque plate shaft is clean. Caliper and bushing will experience premature wear if shaft is coated with dust or mud.

Installation

Replace pads in set of 4. Press piston to bottom of bore. Install "K" spring, "M" clip, pad assembly and anti-squeak shim on support mounting. *See Fig. 5.* Lower caliper body and install retaining pin. Pad thickness wear limit is .040" (1.0 mm).

Fig. 4: Installing Pad Protector

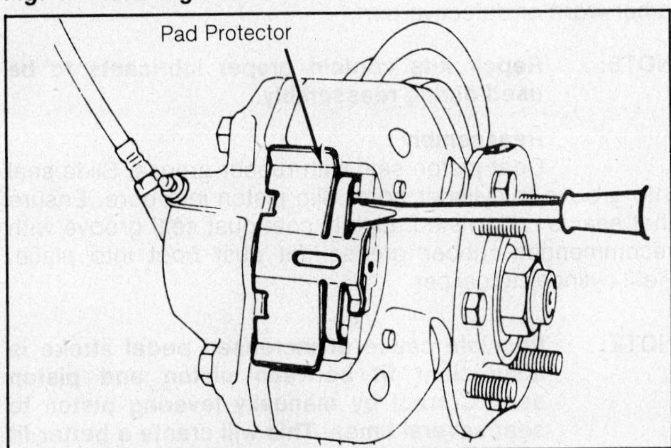

Courtesy of Hyundai Motor Co.

Fig. 5: Installing Spring & Clip on Brake Pads

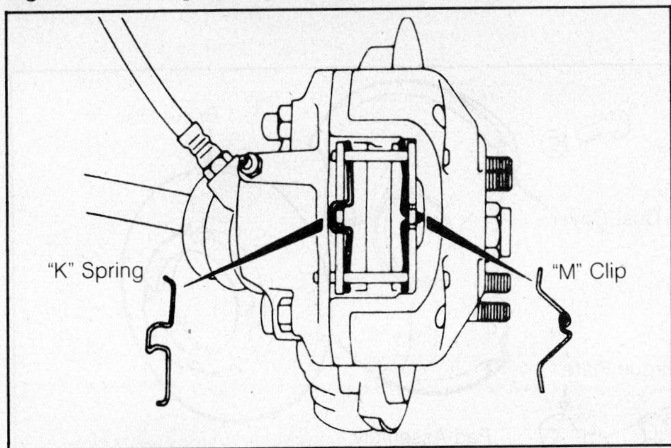

Courtesy of Hyundai Motor Co.

FRONT DISC BRAKE CALIPER

Removal & Installation

Remove disc pads. Pull out hose clip from strut area. Disconnect brake hose from caliper. Remove caliper. To install, reverse removal procedure. Tighten bolts to specification and bleed brake system.

FRONT DISC BRAKE ROTOR

Removal

1) Remove wheels. Remove undercover. Remove lower arm ball joint and strut bar from lower arm. Measure disc runout. Disc runout is .006" (.15 mm) or less. Rotor thickness is .510-.450" (13.0-11.4 mm). Remove center cap. Loosen drive shaft nut.

2) Remove caliper assembly. Remove drive shaft. Disconnect tie rod from knuckle. Remove knuckle, hub and rotor as an assembly.

3) Mount steering knuckle in a soft-jawed vise. Drive out hub and rotor assembly with a soft hammer. Remove preload adjusting spacer from hub. Remove bolts attaching rotor to hub. Remove rotor from hub assembly.

Installation

Install rotor on hub. Tighten bolts to specification. Press hub into knuckle. Install new inner oil seal. Slide drive shaft into position. Install knuckle assembly by reversing removal procedures.

REAR BRAKE SHOES

Removal

Raise and support vehicle. Remove brake drum. Remove clip springs. Disconnect shoe retainer spring, shoe-to-shoe spring and shoe hold-down spring. Remove shoes and adjuster as an assembly. Replace brake shoes if lining thickness is .04" (1.0 mm) or less.

Installation

To install, reverse removal procedure. Apply Lubriplate to all shoe contact points, adjuster assembly and parking brake attachment. Set adjustment lever all the way back. Adjust brake shoes to specification. Install brake drum. Depress brake pedal to adjust shoe clearance. Adjust parking brake and warning light to specifications, if necessary. *See Fig. 6.*

Fig. 6: Exploded View of Leading/Trailing Shoe Rear Brake Assembly

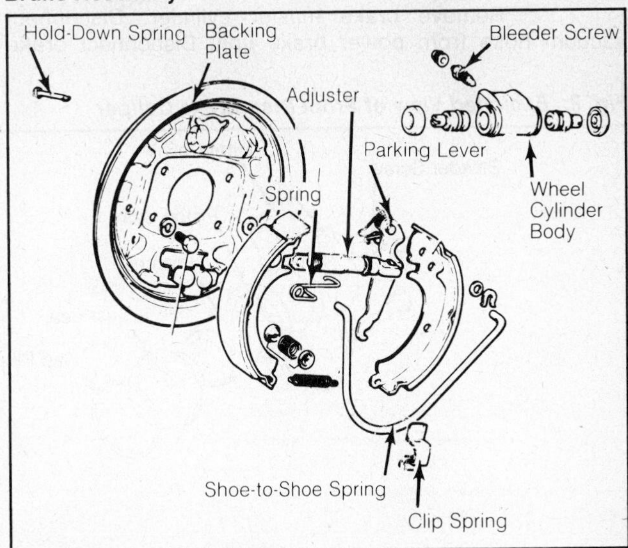

Courtesy of Hyundai Motor Co.

MASTER CYLINDER

Removal

Remove fluid level sensor harness connector. Disconnect brake lines from master cylinder. Slowly depress brake pedal several times to drain fluid from cylinder housing. Remove master cylinder from brake booster unit. Separate reservoir from housing.

HYUNDAI EXCEL & MITSUBISHI PRECIS (Cont.)

Installation

To install master cylinder, reverse removal procedure. Adjust clearance between brake booster push rod and master cylinder piston. Clearance is .016-.031" (.40-.80 mm). After installation, adjust pedal height. Bleed brake system.

POWER BRAKE UNIT CHECK VALVE REPLACEMENT

NOTE: Test check valve before removal. Disconnect vacuum hose on booster side of check valve. Place finger over check valve. Start engine. Vacuum should be felt.

Removal & Installation

Remove hose clamps from both ends of check valve. Remove check valve clamp. Remove check valve. To install, coat both ends of check valve with sealer. Install check valve with arrow pointing toward intake manifold side. Install check valve clamp and vacuum hoses. Secure hose clamps. *See Fig. 7.*

Fig. 7: Power Brake Check Valve

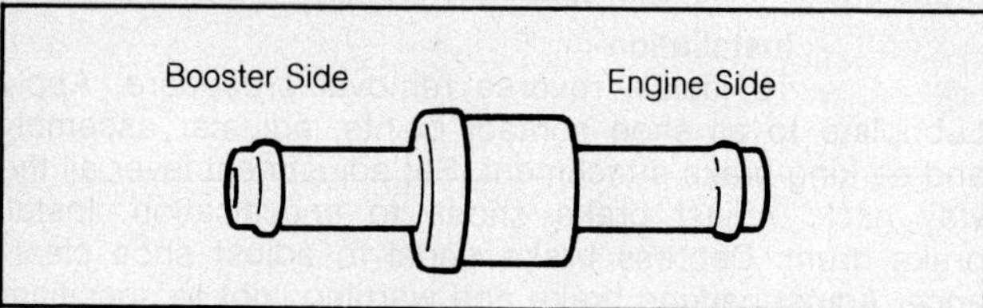

Courtesy of Hyundai Motor Co.

POWER BRAKE UNIT

Removal & Installation

Remove brake master cylinder. Disconnect vacuum hose from power brake unit. Disconnect brake pedal and operating rod of power brake unit. From inside vehicle, remove 4 nuts attaching power brake unit to firewall. Remove power brake unit. To install, reverse removal procedure. Bleed brake system.

OVERHAUL

FRONT DISC BRAKE CALIPER

Disassembly

Remove dust boot. Apply compressed air to fluid inlet to remove piston. Remove piston seal without damaging caliper bore or seal groove. *See Fig. 8.*

Cleaning & Inspection

Clean dust boot and other rubber parts in alcohol only. Clean all other parts with alcohol or brake fluid. Inspect caliper bore and piston for wear, damage or rust. Replace piston seal and dust boot. Replace any other worn or defective part.

NOTE: Repair kits contain proper lubricants to be used during reassembly.

Reassembly

Coat piston seal with rubber grease. Slide seal into groove in cylinder bore. Slip piston into bore. Ensure that seal is not twisted. Lightly coat dust seal groove with recommended rubber grease. Fit dust boot into place. Refit cylinder to caliper.

NOTE: Possible cause of increased pedal stroke is insufficient fit between piston and piston seal. Correct by manually levering piston to seat several times. This will create a better fit between piston and seal. Ensure brake pad is removed during this procedure.

Fig. 8: Exploded View of Front Disc Brake Caliper

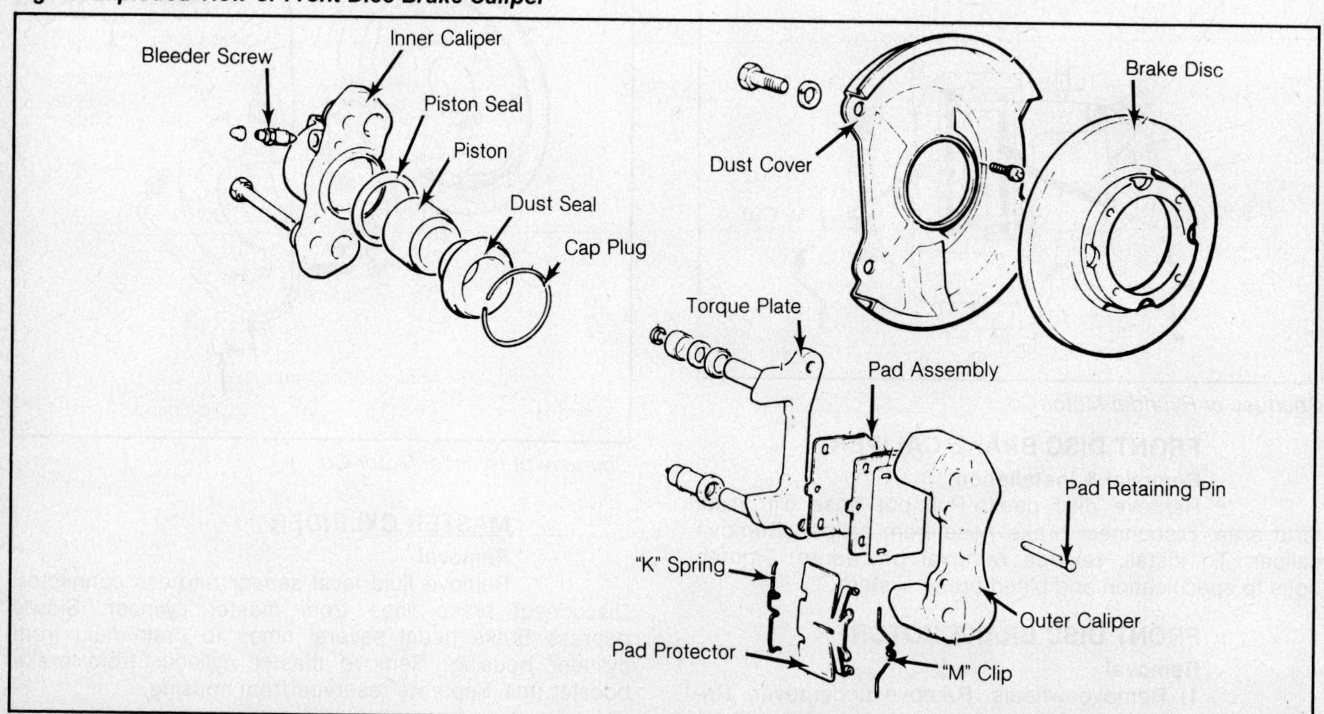

Courtesy of Hyundai Motor Co.

HYUNDAI EXCEL & MITSUBISHI PRECIS (Cont.)

MASTER CYLINDER

Disassembly

Place cylinder in a soft-jawed vise. Remove dust boot, retaining ring, stop washer and piston stop bolt. Withdraw primary piston assembly, secondary piston assembly and secondary return spring from master cylinder. Remove check valve caps, tube seats, check valves and check valve springs. *See Fig. 10.*

NOTE: Do not disassemble primary and secondary piston assembly.

Cleaning & Inspection

Inspect master cylinder bore and piston for wear or other damage. Check clearance between cylinder bore and piston. Clearance should not exceed .006" (.15 mm). If any parts are found worn or defective, replace part assembly.

Reassembly

Reverse disassembly procedure. Before reassembly, apply rubber grease to all parts (except boots). Ensure that return port is not blocked by piston cup when piston is at return position.

POWER BRAKE UNIT

Disassembly

Clean exterior of power brake unit. Install Holder (09591-21000) on power brake unit. Place unit in vise, with jaws on holder. Fabricate 2 steel pipes and attach them to Plate (09591-21100). *See Fig. 11.* Attach pipes and plate to rear shell. Turn rear shell counterclockwise. Remove rear shell. Disassemble power brake unit. *See Fig. 9.*

Inspection

Check all parts for wear and damage. Replace any worn or damaged part.

Fig. 10: Disassembled View of Master Cylinder

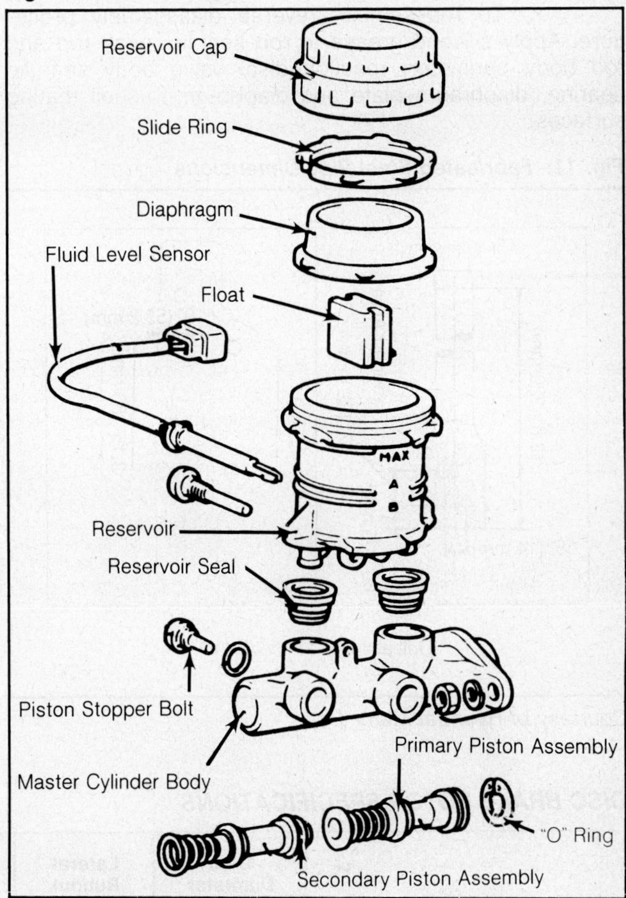

Courtesy of Hyundai Motor Co.

Fig. 9: Exploded View of Power Brake Unit

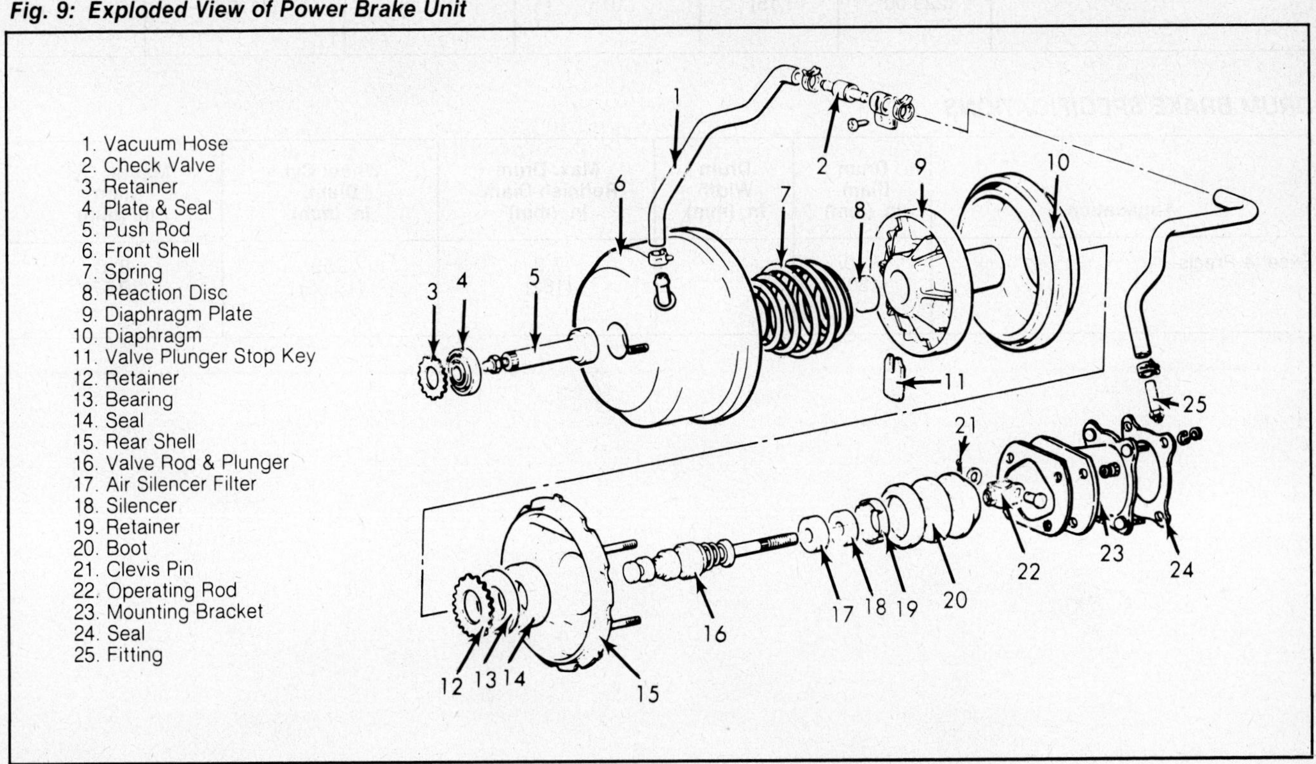

Courtesy of Hyundai Motor Co.

HYUNDAI EXCEL & MITSUBISHI PRECIS (Cont.)

Reassembly

To reassemble, reverse disassembly procedure. Apply silicone grease to rod seal lip, push rod and rod body perimeter, reaction disc, valve body seal lip bearing, diaphragm plate and diaphragm-to-shell mating surfaces.

Fig. 11: Fabricated Steel Pipe Dimensions

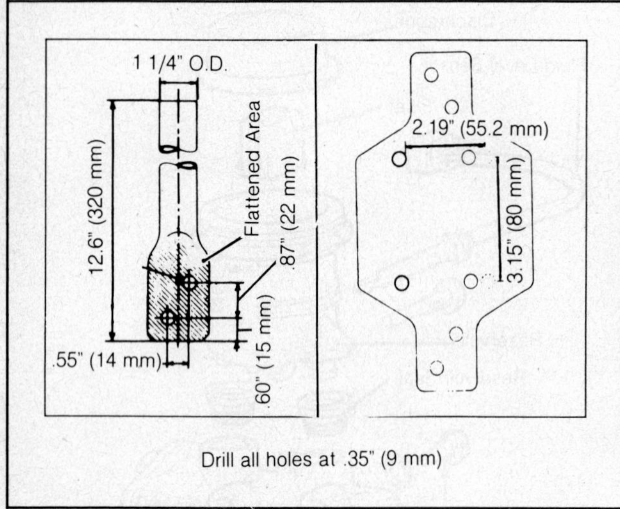

Courtesy of Hyundai Motor Co.

TIGHTENING SPECIFICATIONS

Application	Ft. Lbs. (N.m)
Backing Plate-to-Housing Bolts	22-29 (29-39)
Brake Booster Hose Fitting	11-13 (15-18)
Disc Brake	
Caliper Inner & Outer Bridge Bolts	58-69 (78-93)
Caliper Assembly-to-Knuckle Bolts	43-58 (59-78)
Disc-to-Hub Bolts	29-36 (39-49)
Master Cylinder	
Check Valve Case Bolts	29-36 (39-49)
Connector Bolts	17-25 (23-34)
Proportioning Valve Mounting Bolt	14-18 (20-25)
	INCH Lbs. (N.m)
Brake Booster-to-Spacer Bolts	72-108 (8-12)
Brake Hose	108-144 (12-16)
Brake Line Flare Nuts	108-144 (12-16)
Bleeder Screw	60-84 (7-9)
Master Cylinder	
Cylinder-to-Booster Bolts	72-108 (8-12)
Nipple Band	22-35 (2.4-3.9)
Piston Stopper	13-26 (1.5-2.9)
Reservoir-to-Master Cylinder Bolt	86-174 (9.8-19.6)
Pedal Support Bolt	72-108 (8-12)
Rear Wheel Cylinder Bolt	72-108 (8-12)
Toe Board Bolt	72-108 (8-12)

DISC BRAKE ROTOR SPECIFICATIONS

Application	Disc Diameter In. (mm)	Lateral Runout In. (mm)	Parallelism In. (mm)	Original Thickness In. (mm)	Min. Refinish Thickness In. (mm)	Discard Thickness In. (mm)
Excel & Precis	9.000 (229.00)	.006 (.15)	.0006 (.015)	.512 (13.00)	.450 (11.40)	.....

DRUM BRAKE SPECIFICATIONS

Application	Drum Diam. In. (mm)	Drum Width In. (mm)	Max. Drum Refinish Diam. In. (mm)	Wheel Cyl. Diam. In. (mm)	Master Cyl. Diam. In. (mm)
Excel & Precis	7.10 (180)	.....	7.2 (182)	.750 (19.05)	.810 (20.57)

ISUZU IMPULSE

DESCRIPTION

Brake system is equipped with vented front rotors and non-vented rear rotors. Calipers are self-adjusting, single piston, floating type on front and rear. Cable-operated parking brake (on rear wheels) is manually adjusted. Tandem diaphragm power booster unit is used on models with 4ZC1-T engine/automatic transmission combination. All other models use a single diaphragm power brake unit.

ADJUSTMENTS

PARKING BRAKE

1) Release parking brake lever. Raise and support vehicle. Adjust lining clearance by turning adjuster (through slot in backing plate) until shoe contact is felt when turning wheel. Back adjuster off 6 notches.

2) Check cable for free movement. Adjust parking brake cable where front and rear cables connect. Loosen front lock nut on front cable assembly and turn rear lock nut to adjust. Retighten lock nuts.

3) Proper brake lever travel is 11-13 notches, pulling with force of 66 lbs. (30 kg). After adjustment, check that brakes do not drag.

PEDAL HEIGHT & FREE PLAY

1) Bleed hydraulic system. Adjust power brake unit push rod to obtain 5.63" (143 mm) clearance between lower face of brake pedal and carpet. Adjust clearance between brake switch and pedal to .004" (.10 mm).

2) On all models except 4ZC1-T engine/automatic transmission combination, turn switch in 1/2 turn, then lock in position with floor-to-pedal height readjusted to 5.52" (140 mm).

3) On all models, brake pedal free play is .24-.39" (6-10 mm). Pedal stroke is 3.74" (95 mm) on models with 4ZC1-T engine/automatic transmission combination, and 3.15" (80 mm) on all other models.

WHEEL BEARING PRELOAD

Front Wheel Bearing

1) Raise and support vehicle. Remove front wheels. Detach each caliper and hang out of way with wire. Remove wheel bearing dust cap and cotter pin, then loosen castle nut.

2) Install spring scale with hook attached to wheel stud. Tighten castle nut (while pulling on scale) until scale reads preload of 1.10-3.31 lbs. (.5-1.5 kg). If rotor does not turn smoothly or preload will not adjust to specification, remove rotor and inspect wheel bearings for damage or wear.

REMOVAL & INSTALLATION

DISC BRAKE PADS

Removal (Front & Rear)

1) Raise and support vehicle. Remove wheels. To remove front pads, detach caliper support bracket sleeve bolts. *See Fig. 1.* Lift off caliper and hang out of the way with wire.

Fig. 1: Exploded View Of Front Disc Brake Assembly

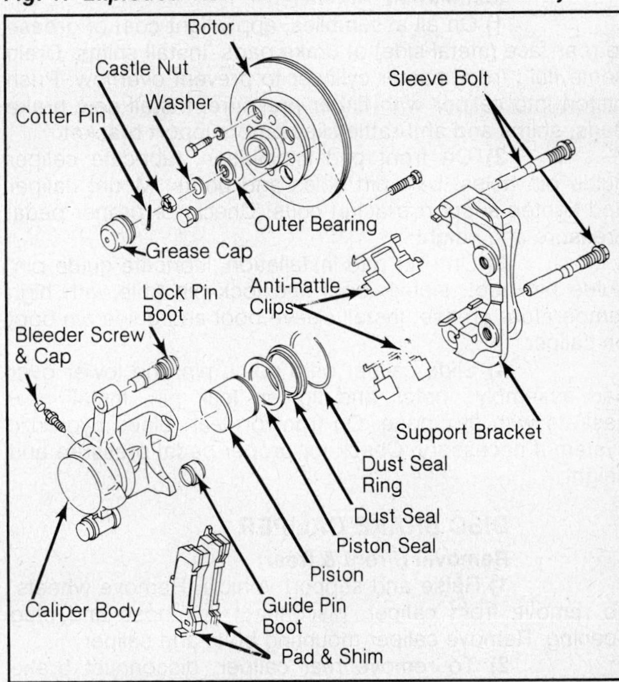

Courtesy of Isuzu Motor Co.

2) To remove rear pads, disconnect rear brake flex hose at caliper. Remove caliper lock pin, sleeve and sleeve boot. Pivot caliper up, slide off guide pin and remove guide pin boot. *See Fig. 2.*

Fig. 2: Exploded View Of Rear Brake Caliper Assembly

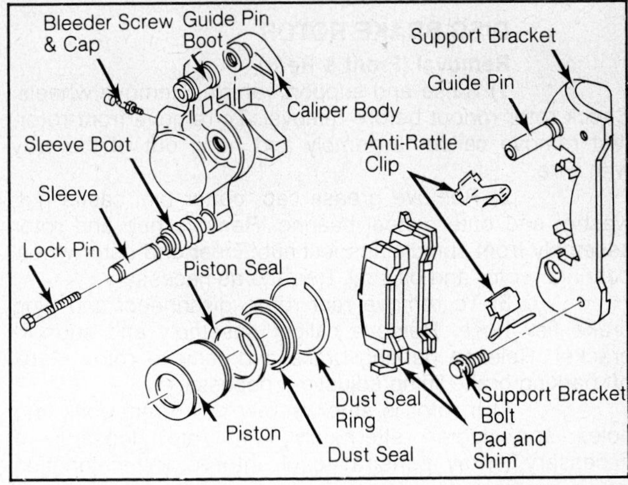

Courtesy of Isuzu Motor Co.

3) On all assemblies, remove anti-rattle clips, brake pads and shims from support bracket. Mark pads for installation, if reusable. Standard front pad thickness is .323" (8.20 mm). Standard rear pad thickness is .394" (10 mm). Minimum front and rear pad lining thickness is .04" (1.0 mm).

NOTE: **Always replace brake pads in sets of 4. Keep grease, brake fluid or other contaminants off lining surface. Check and clean rotor as necessary.**

Installation

1) On all assemblies, apply light coat of grease to rear face (metal side) of brake pads. Install shims. Drain some fluid from master cylinder to prevent overflow. Push piston into caliper with finger pressure. Install new brake pads, shims and anti-rattle clips onto support bracket.

2) On front pad installation, lubricate caliper guide pin holes, lock pin holes and boots. Mount caliper and tighten support bracket bolts. Check for proper pedal pressure and height.

3) On rear pad installation, lubricate guide pin, guide pin boot, sleeve boot and lock pin hole with high temperature grease. Install sleeve boot and guide pin boot on caliper.

4) Slide caliper onto guide pin and lower over pad assembly. Install and tighten lock pin. Install new gaskets with flex hose. On front or rear, bleed hydraulic system if necessary. Check for proper pedal pressure and height.

DISC BRAKE CALIPER

Removal (Front & Rear)

1) Raise and support vehicle. Remove wheels. To remove front caliper, disconnect flex hose and plug opening. Remove caliper mounting bolts and caliper.

2) To remove rear caliper, disconnect brake flex hose at caliper. Remove caliper lock pin, sleeve and sleeve boot. Lift up caliper, slide off guide pin and remove guide pin boot.

Installation

To install, reverse removal procedure. Install new washers on flex hose. Bleed hydraulic system. Check for proper pedal pressure and height.

DISC BRAKE ROTOR

Removal (Front & Rear)

1) Raise and support vehicle. Remove wheels. Check rotor runout before removal. To remove front rotor, first remove caliper assembly and hang out of the way with wire.

2) Remove grease cap, cotter pin, castle nut, washer and outer wheel bearing. Remove hub and rotor assembly from spindle. Inspect hub, inner and outer wheel bearings, rotor and oil seal. Replace as necessary.

3) To remove rear rotor, disconnect and plug brake flex hose. Remove caliper assembly and support bracket. Release parking brake and remove rotor. Back off parking brake lining adjuster if necessary.

4) If rotor is stuck, screw two 6 mm bolts into holes and tighten alternately until rotor loosens. If necessary, spray penetrating oil into rotor-hub junction (avoid overspray on rotor surface).

Inspection

Check rotor for wear or damage. See DISC BRAKE ROTOR SPECIFICATIONS table at end of this article. Using a micrometer, measure rotor thickness at 8 points, every 45 degrees and .39" (10 mm) in from outer edge. Replace rotor if worn less than specification.

Installation

To install, reverse removal procedure. Adjust front wheel bearings. Install the rear wheel caliper assembly and flex hose with new washers. Bleed hydraulic system.

MASTER CYLINDER

Removal

Disconnect hydraulic lines from master cylinder and plug openings. Remove 4 nuts securing master cylinder to power brake unit. Drain brake fluid. Remove master cylinder and gasket. *See Fig. 3.*

Installation

To install, reverse removal procedure. Replace gasket whenever master cylinder is removed. Tighten hydraulic lines and bleed system.

POWER BRAKE UNIT

Removal

1) Disconnect air duct connector hose and vacuum hose. Remove hydraulic lines from master cylinder and plug ends. Remove split pin and clevis pin. Separate clevis from brake pedal arm.

2) Remove power brake unit-to-dash panel retaining bolts. Lift out power brake unit and master cylinder as an assembly. *See Fig. 3.* Remove master cylinder and gasket from power brake unit.

Installation

1) To install, reverse removal procedure. Check distance from flange face of power brake unit to end of push rod. Proper distance is .709-.717" (18.0-18.2 mm). If measurement is incorrect, adjust with lock nut at end of push rod.

2) Apply sealer to dash panel face and install power brake unit. Install master cylinder (with new gasket). Bleed hydraulic system. Check and adjust brake pedal height as necessary.

Fig. 3: Master Cylinder, Power Brake Unit & Brake Pedal Bracket Assembly

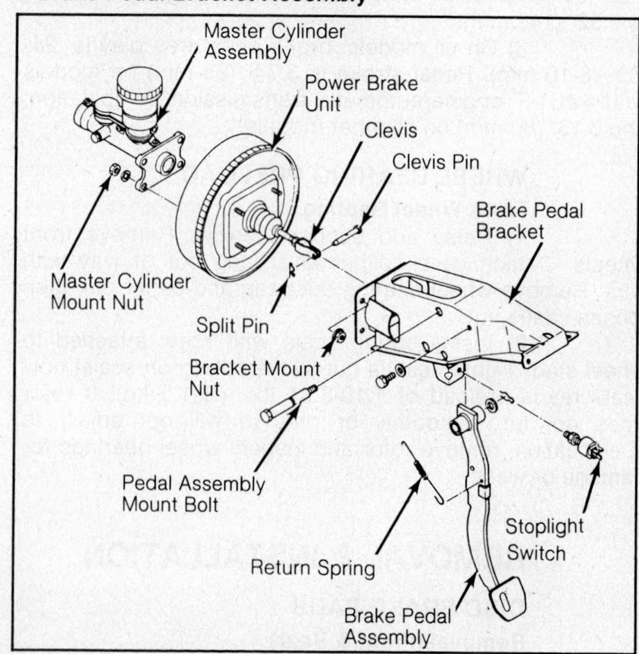

Courtesy of Isuzu Motor Co.

ISUZU IMPULSE (Cont.)

OVERHAUL

DISC BRAKE CALIPER

Disassembly (Front & Rear)

1) On all assemblies, remove caliper, pads, shims, anti-rattle clips and flex hose. On front caliper, disconnect guide pin and lock pin boots. *See Fig. 1.*

2) On rear caliper, disconnect sleeve and guide pin boots. *See Fig. 2.* On all assemblies, remove dust seal ring and dust seal. Place a block of wood between piston and caliper cavity wall. Apply compressed air to fluid inlet to force piston from caliper. Remove and discard piston square ring seal. Remove bleeder screw and cap.

Inspection

1) Clean brake parts with denatured alcohol or clean brake fluid and blow dry with compressed air. Inspect caliper body for distortion or cracking. Replace if defective. Check caliper bores and pistons for corrosion, excessive wear or scuffing.

2) Standard front brake piston O.D. is 2.12" (53.97 mm). Standard rear brake piston O.D. is 1.50" (38.1 mm). Replace caliper assembly as necessary. If caliper components are in reuseable condition, install new rubber parts and reassemble.

Reassembly

1) Apply rubber grease to new piston seal and caliper bore. Install seal in bore. Push piston into caliper bore with finger pressure. Lubricate dust seal and seal fitting face of piston. Install dust seal and dust seal ring.

2) Install anti-rattle clips. Assemble pad shims to brake pads and install into support bracket. On front caliper, lubricate lock pin boot and guide pin boot with grease and install. Lubricate lock pin and guide pin holes. Install sleeve bolts. Replace new washers on flex hose and install. Bleed hydraulic system.

3) On rear caliper, install by sliding over guide pin, then pivot down into place over pads. Lubricate lock pin hole and install lock pin. Replace new washers on flex hose and install. Bleed hydraulic system.

MASTER CYLINDER

Disassembly

1) With master cylinder and gasket removed, drain brake fluid and place cylinder in vise. Remove 3 screws retaining brake fluid reservoir. Remove reservoir and pull out dust seals and grommets. *See Fig. 4.*

2) Push in on primary and secondary pistons and remove snap ring and stopper bolt. Remove primary and secondary piston assemblies with springs. Remove piston cups (noting direction for proper installation).

Inspection

1) Wash master cylinder components in denatured alcohol or clean brake fluid only. Inspect all parts for wear or damage. Remove and replace ALL rubber parts during overhaul. Measure master cylinder bore diameter and outside diameter of primary and secondary pistons.

2) Standard bore diameter is .874" (22.20 mm). Standard clearance is .0016-.0049" (.040-.125 mm). Maximum clearance is .006" (.15 mm). Check return port for restrictions and if necessary, clean and blow away foreign matter with compressed air.

Reassembly

Lubricate master cylinder bore with rubber grease. Lubricate piston cups with clean brake fluid. Use care to avoid scratching piston cups when installing piston

Fig. 4: Exploded View Of Master Cylinder Assembly

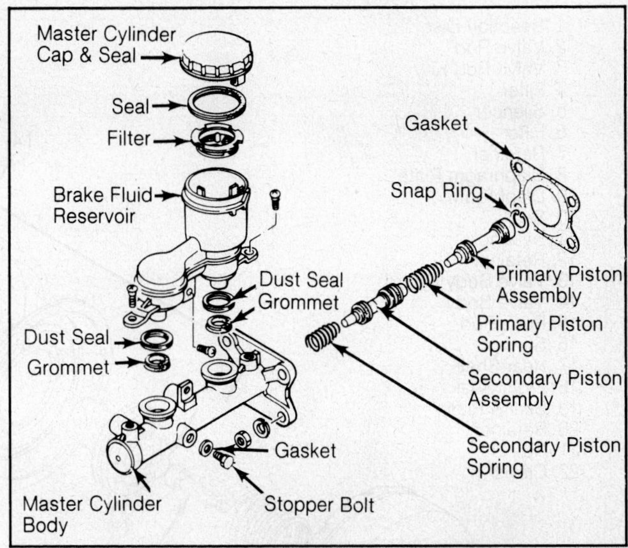

Courtesy of Isuzu Motor Co.

assemblies. To complete reassembly, reverse disassembly procedure. Bench bleed master cylinder.

POWER BRAKE UNIT

Disassembly

1) With master cylinder and power brake unit removed, drain brake fluid and separate power unit from master cylinder. Bolt power unit onto Holder (J-22805-01). Holder bolt holes may have to be altered slightly to fit. Bolt Spanner Wrench (J-9504-01) onto power unit and clamp assembly into vise with clevis yoke up.

CAUTION: Maintain pressure on spanner wrench when separating front and rear shell assemblies as rear shell is under spring pressure.

2) Index mark power unit halves for proper reassembly. Using Power Unit Spanner Wrench (J-9504-01), carefully turn rear shell counterclockwise until it disengages. Disassemble power brake unit. *See Figs. 5 and 6.*

Inspection

Remove, clean and inspect check valve and grommet. Replace worn parts as necessary. Check diaphragm plate, rotor, push rod, poppet valve and shell for weakening, distortion or damage. Replace as needed.

NOTE: Clean power brake unit components with denatured alcohol and blow dry using compressed air. Never use any cleaner containing mineral oil or damage to all rubber parts will result.

Reassembly

1) Reassemble in reverse order of disassembly. Apply silicone grease to front and rear shell fitting face of diaphragm and all sliding parts.

2) Insert diaphragm spring into front shell. Apply silicone grease to outer rim and contact faces of diaphragm plate and reaction disc. Assemble power brake unit components. *See Figs. 5 and 6.*

3) Using power unit spanner wrench, push in on rear shell and rotate clockwise until fully seated with index marks aligned.

Brakes

ISUZU IMPULSE (Cont.)

Fig. 5: Exploded View Of Single Diaphragm Power Brake Unit

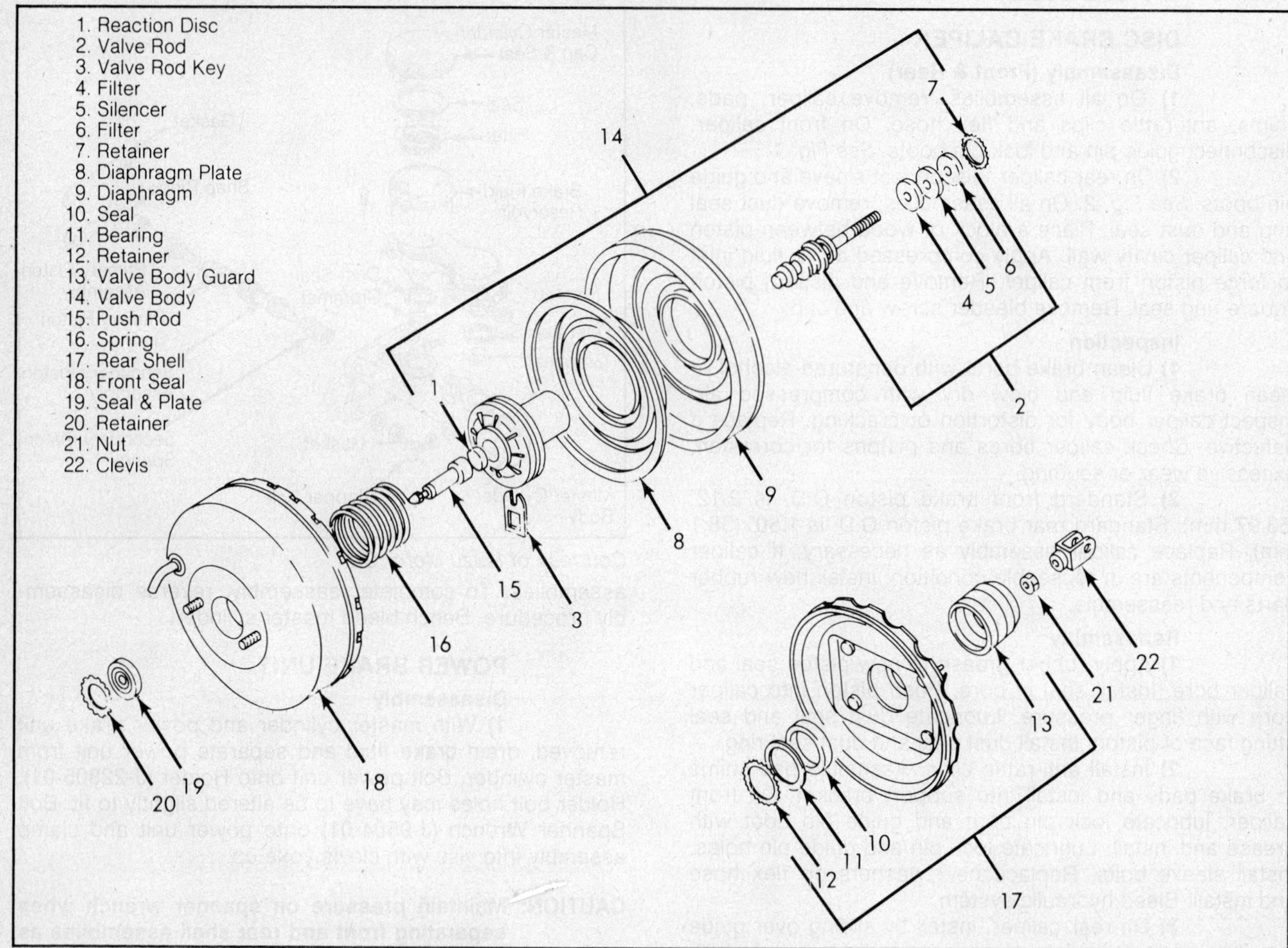

Courtesy of Isuzu Motor Co.

CAUTION: Before releasing tool, ensure rear shell is locked properly to front shell at all points.

4) Install master cylinder. See MASTER CYLINDER in REMOVAL & INSTALLATION section of this article. Install power brake unit. Check and adjust brake pedal height as necessary.

PARKING BRAKE ASSEMBLY

Disassembly

1) With rear caliper and rotor removed, check parking brake assembly for excessive brake dust. Wash off assembly with water and allow to dry.

2) Remove primary and secondary brake shoe hold-down springs and pins. Remove adjuster spring and adjuster, anchor-to-brake shoe springs and washer. Remove strut spring, strut and primary shoe assembly. *See Fig. 7.*

3) Disconnect parking brake cable from parking brake lever and remove secondary shoe assembly with lever attached. If linings are worn, remove "C" clip retainer and wave washer from lever and separate lever from shoe.

Reassembly

1) Apply high temperature grease to anchor pins, adjuster assembly and shoe sliding surfaces of backing plate. If new linings are installed, install "C" clip retainer, wave washer and parking brake lever to secondary shoe.

2) Install primary and secondary shoes to backing plate with shoe hold-down pins and springs. Connect parking brake cable to lever. Install strut and spring. Install adjuster and spring.

3) On left side, install adjuster with wheel toward front and opposite way on right side. Install primary anchor spring and washer. Install secondary anchor spring. Install rotor and adjust linings. Check parking brake cable slack and adjust as necessary.

PARKING BRAKE LININGS

Break-In

1) Parking brake linings must be burnished in periodically or whenever new linings are installed. To burnish linings, drive vehicle at 30 MPH on dry and level road.

2) With parking brake release button pushed in, pull lever with 20 lbs. (9 kg) pressure and drive for 1/4 mile. Repeat procedure 2-3 times, allow linings to cool between applications.

ISUZU IMPULSE (Cont.)

Fig. 6: Exploded View of Tandem Diaphragm Power Brake Unit

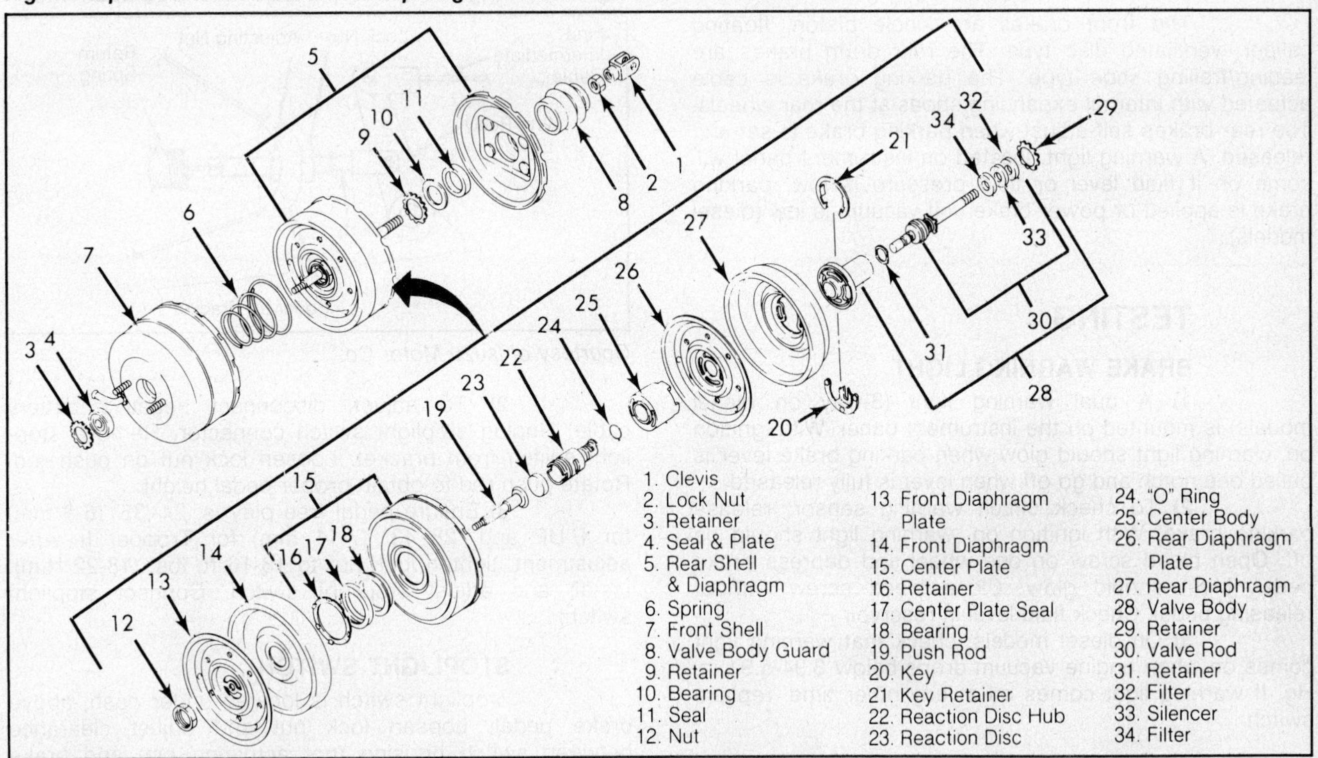

Courtesy of Isuzu Motor Co.

Fig. 7: Exploded View Of Parking Brake Assembly

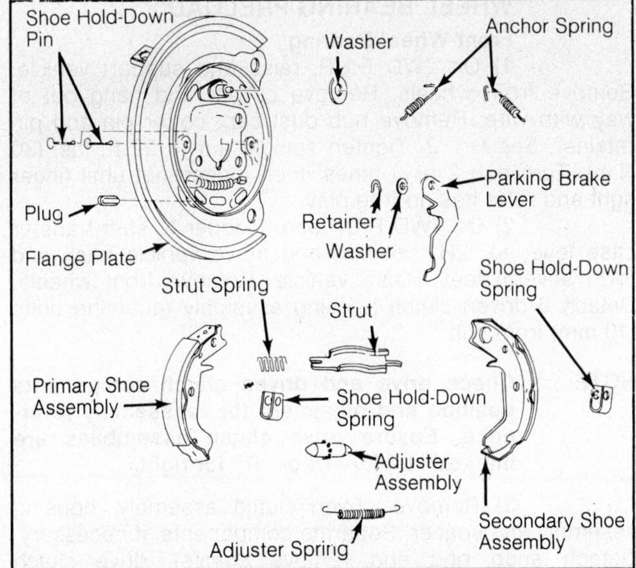

Courtesy of Isuzu Motor Co.

TIGHTENING SPECIFICATIONS

Application	Ft. Lbs. (N.m)
Brake Pedal Assembly Pivot Bolt	14-22 (19-30)
Caliper Lock Pin (Rear)	13-16 (18-22)
Hydraulic Brake Lines	
Brake Line (Front)	10-13 (14-18)
Brake Line (Rear)	10-14 (14-19)
Caliper Banjo Bolt (Front)	24-27 (33-37)
Master Cylinder	
Brake Line	10-14 (14-19)
To-Power Brake Unit Mounting Nut	10-14 (12-19)
Stopper Bolt	12-14 (16-19)
Power Brake Unit	
To-Pedal Bracket Mounting Nut	18-22 (24-30)
Push Rod Lock Nut	14-18 (19-24)
Support Bracket	
To-Knuckle Mounting Bolt	35-38 (47-52)
Sleeve Bolt (Front)	25-28 (34-38)
	INCH Lbs. (N.m)
Bleeder Screw	54-78 (6-9)

DISC BRAKE ROTOR SPECIFICATIONS

Application	Disc Diameter In. (mm)	Lateral Runout In. (mm)	Parallelism In. (mm)	Original Thickness In. (mm)	Min. Refinish Thickness In. (mm)	Discard Thickness In. (mm)
Impulse						
Front	9.84 (250)	.005 (.13)	.0006 (.015)	.709 (18)	.654 (16.6)	.....
Rear	10.47 (266)	.005 (.13)	.0006 (.015)	.709 (18)	.654 (16.6)	.....

Brakes

ISUZU P'UP & TROOPER II

DESCRIPTION

The front brakes are single piston, floating caliper, ventilated disc type. The rear drum brakes are leading/trailing shoe type. The parking brake is cable actuated with internal expanding shoes at the rear wheels. The rear brakes self-adjust when parking brake is set and released. A warning light, located on instrument panel will come on if fluid level or fluid pressure is low, parking brake is applied or power brake unit vacuum is low (diesel models).

TESTING

BRAKE WARNING LIGHT

1) A dual warning light (3-way on diesel models) is mounted on the instrument panel. With ignition on, warning light should glow when parking brake lever is pulled one notch and go off when lever is fully released.

2) To check circuit warning sensor, release parking brake. With ignition on, warning light should be off. Open bleed screw on one wheel and depress brake pedal. Light should glow. Close bleed screw without releasing pedal. Check fluid level in reservoir.

3) On diesel models, check that warning light comes on when engine vacuum drops below 3.94-5.91 in. Hg. If warning light comes on at any other time, replace switch.

ADJUSTMENTS

REAR DRUM BRAKE SHOES & PARKING BRAKE

NOTE: Adjustment must be made after changing brake linings or if adjuster setting has been changed.

1) Rear brakes are self-adjusting. If brake drum is removed, rotate adjuster so clearance between shoes and brake drum is .02" (.5 mm). Install drum.

2) Move parking brake handle to fully released position. Raise and support vehicle. Loosen second relay lever rod lock nut. While firmly holding second relay lever rod, rotate adjusting nut until all slack disappears from cable. *See Fig. 1.*

Fig. 1: Parking Brake Cable & Adjustment Components

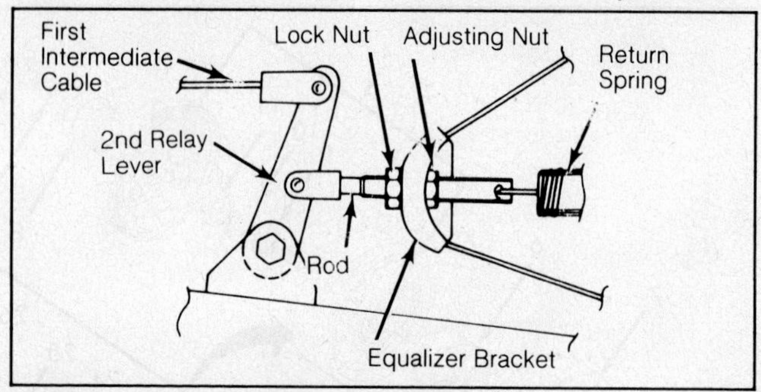

Courtesy of Isuzu Motor Co.

3) Apply 66 lbs. (30 kg) of force, 3 or 4 times, to parking brake handle to move it to fully set position. If lever is properly adjusted, travel range (between fully disengaged and fully engaged position) will be 10-12 notches on Trooper II or 12-14 notches on P'UP. Reset adjusting nut if travel range is not within limits.

PEDAL HEIGHT & FREE PLAY

NOTE: The push rod serves as the brake pedal stopper when pedal is fully released.

1) With brake pedal fully returned by spring, measure pedal height. Pedal height (measured from upper foot rest portion of pedal pad to floorboard) should be 6.5-6.9" (164-174 mm) for P'UP and 8.7-9.1" (221-231 mm) for Trooper II.

2) To adjust, disconnect negative battery cable. Unplug stoplight switch connector. Remove stoplight switch from bracket. Loosen lock nut on push rod. Rotate push rod to obtain proper pedal height.

3) Ensure pedal free play is .24-.35" (6-9 mm) for P'UP and .28-.43" (7-11 mm) for Trooper II. After adjustment, tighten lock nut to 13-16 ft. lbs. (18-22 N.m). Install and adjust stoplight switch. Connect stoplight switch.

STOPLIGHT SWITCH

Stoplight switch is located under dash, above brake pedal. Loosen lock nut and adjust clearance between switch housing (not actuating pin) and brake pedal tab to .02-.04" (.5-1.0 mm) on all models. Tighten lock nut.

WHEEL BEARING PRELOAD

Front Wheel Bearing

1) On 2WD P'UP, raise and support vehicle. Remove front wheels. Remove caliper and hang out of way with wire. Remove hub dust cap, cotter pin and pin retainer. *See Fig. 2.* Tighten spindle nut to 22 ft. lbs. (30 N.m). Turn hub 2 or 3 times, then loosen nut until finger tight and rotor has no free play.

2) On 4WD P'UP and Trooper II, shift transfer case lever to "2H" position and move vehicle back and forth several feet. Raise vehicle. Remove front wheels. Detach 6 driven clutch housing assembly mounting bolts (10 mm) from hub.

NOTE: Check drive and driven clutch components position and alignment for reassembly reference. Ensure drive clutch assemblies are marked "L" for left or "R" for right.

3) Remove driven clutch assembly, housing assembly and spacer. Separate components, if necessary. Detach snap ring and remove shim(s), drive clutch assembly, inner cam and lock washer plate. *See Fig. 2.* Using Hub Nut Wrench (J-29020-A), tighten hub nut slightly while turning rotor, to seat bearings. Loosen nut until finger tight. Ensure rotor has no free play.

4) On all models, install spring scale with hook attached to wheel stud. Tighten hub nut (while pulling on scale) until scale reads preload of no more than 3.31 lbs. (1.5 kg) for 4WD and 2.20 lbs. (1.0 kg) for 2WD.

5) If rotor does not turn smoothly or preload will not adjust to specification, remove rotor and inspect

ISUZU P'UP & TROOPER II (Cont.)

Fig. 2: Exploded View Of Front Hub, Rotor & Wheel Bearing Assemblies

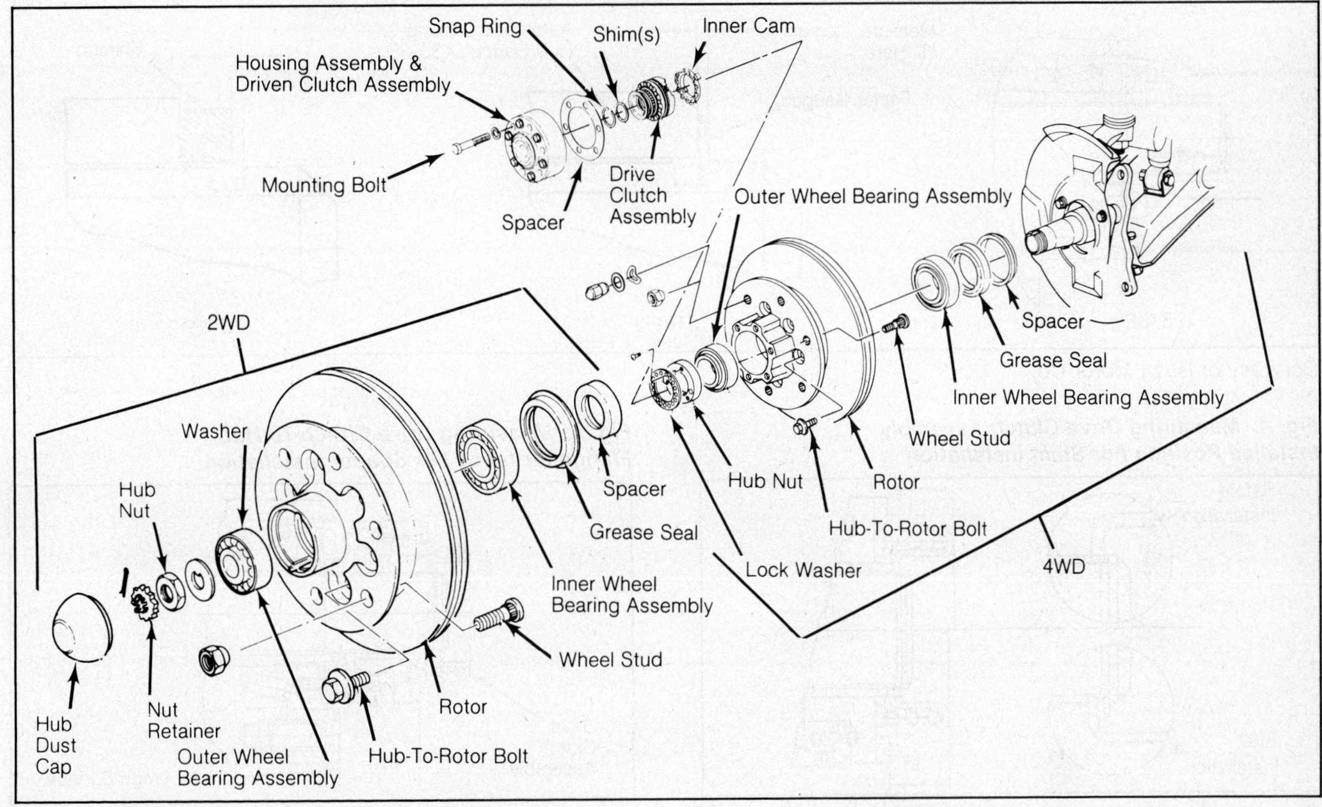

Courtesy of Isuzu Motor Co.

wheel bearings for damage or wear. Replace inner and/or outer wheel bearings and races as necessary. Recheck and adjust bearing preload if new wheel bearings are installed. On 2WD models, install nut retainer, new cotter pin and dust cap.

6) On 4WD models, when installing lock washer plate over hub nut, check that driven clutch assembly mounting bolt holes align. If not, reverse lock washer plate. If holes are still out of alignment, turn in nut only enough to obtain alignment.

7) Clean hub flange, threaded holes, lock washer plate surface and axle shaft splines. Ensure transfer case lever is in "2H" position. Install inner cam by aligning keyway of inner cam with groove in knuckle. Tap inner cam lightly with plastic hammer to ensure contact with lock washer plate.

8) Using Automatic Locking Hub Gauge (J-33935) and feeler gauge, select proper shim(s). Hold CV joint part of axle shaft and push it outward as much as possible. Hold inner cam with other hand so as not to move it. *See Fig. 3, Step 1.*

9) Install gauge onto axle shaft until it comes in contact with lock washer plate. *See Fig. 3, Step 1.* Measure clearance "T" between special tool and axle shaft snap ring groove with feeler gauge. *See Fig. 3, Step 2.*

10) If clearance "T" is larger than snap ring groove, select proper shim(s). *See Fig. 3, Step 3.* Ensure shim(s) selected allows "T" clearance of .004" (.10 mm). Remove gauge and leave inner cam in position. Apply multipurpose grease to axle shaft splines, drive clutch outer groove and inner cam face and driven clutch inner circumference.

11) Viewed from spring side, align cut part of holdout ring and cam convex part of drive clutch assembly by turning holdout ring clockwise. Align cut part of holdout ring with inner cam tab. Engage drive clutch assembly cam teeth to inner cam by turning axle shaft.

12) Measure dimension "L1" between retainer surface and clutch surface to ensure proper installation. *See Fig. 4.* Record dimension. Install selected shims and new snap ring using Snap Ring Installer (J-33934).

13) With snap ring and shim(s) installed on tool, place center projection of tool into axle shaft center hole. Tap tool by hand to force on snap ring. Do not use hammer.

14) After installing snap ring and shim(s), check fit of snap ring by measuring dimension "L2" between clutch surface and retainer surface to ensure the proper shim thickness. *See Fig. 4.* If difference between measurement "L1" and "L2" is larger than .028" (.70 mm), the shim thickness is correct.

15) Measure dimension "D" between hub flange surface and drive clutch surface. *See Fig. 5.* If "D" = 1.00-1.03" (25.4-26.2 mm), do not use a spacer. If "D" = 1.04-1.07" (26.3-27.2 mm), use a .04" (1.0 mm) thick spacer. If "D" = 1.07-1.11" (27.3-28.1 mm), use a .08" (2.0 mm) thick spacer.

NOTE: Ensure spring washers are installed on both driven clutch assembly and driven clutch housing assembly mounting bolts.

16) Apply Loctite 515 to both sides of spacer and to flange side of driven clutch assembly. If separated,

ISUZU P'UP & TROOPER II (Cont.)

Fig. 3: Automatic Locking Hub Gauge Installation & Shim Selection

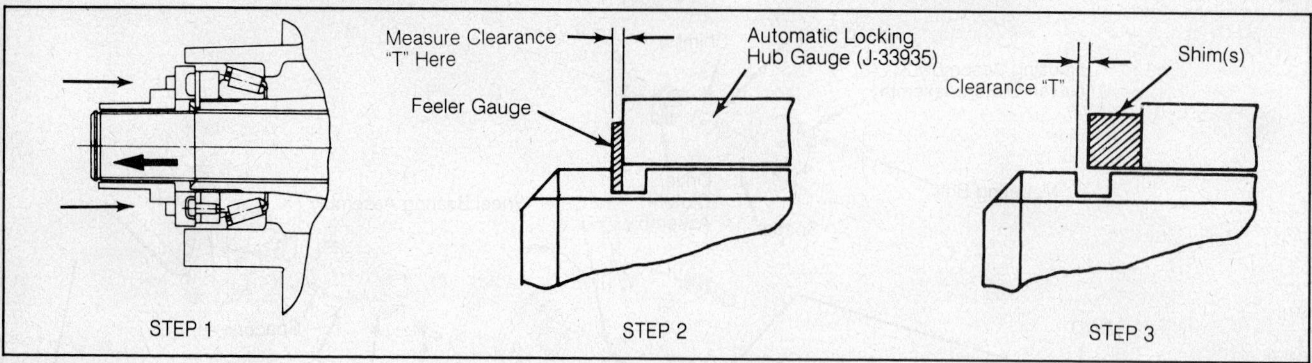

Courtesy of Isuzu Motor Co.

Fig. 4: Measuring Drive Clutch Assembly Installed Position For Shim Installation

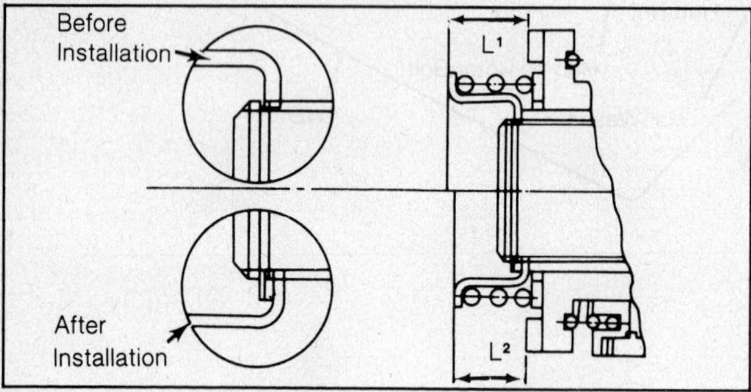

Courtesy of Isuzu Motor Co.

Fig. 5: Measuring Drive Clutch-To-Hub Flange Surfaces For Spacer Installation

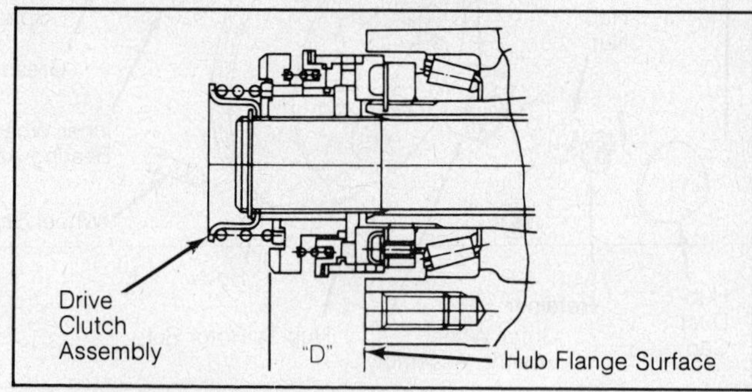

Courtesy of Isuzu Motor Co.

assemble driven clutch assembly to driven clutch housing assembly and tighten mounting bolts (8 mm) to 17-22 ft. lbs. (23-30 N.m).

17) Apply Loctite 515 to driven clutch housing assembly flange surface. Check that housing assembly turns smoothly to ensure spacer selected in step **15)** was correct. Tighten driven clutch housing assembly mounting bolts to 40-47 ft. lbs. (54-64 N.m). On all models, install calipers and wheels. Lower vehicle.

REMOVAL & INSTALLATION

DISC BRAKE PADS

Removal

1) Raise and support vehicle on safety stands. Remove front wheels. Remove lower caliper lock bolt. Rotate caliper upward on support pivot (guide pin) and hang with wire. *See Fig. 6.*

2) Remove disc pads and pad shims. Mark locations if pads are reusable. Remove disc pad clips from caliper support and discard.

Installation

1) To install, reverse removal procedure. Install new pad clips and shims. Apply high temperature brake grease to shims and caliper sliding surfaces.

2) Used pads must be installed in original position. Install pads to caliper supports with wear indicators facing LOWER SIDE of support.

Fig. 6: Exploded View Of Front Disc Brake Pads, Caliper & Support Assembly

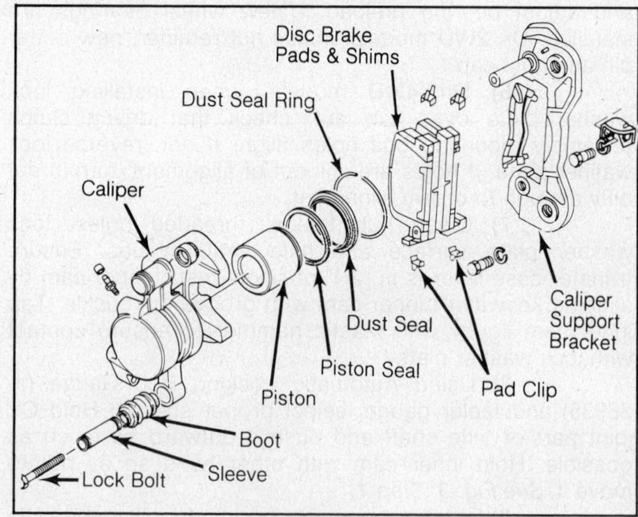

Courtesy of Isuzu Motor Co.

DISC BRAKE CALIPER

Removal

1) Raise and support vehicle. Remove front wheels. Remove lower lock bolt retaining caliper to support. Disconnect hydraulic flex hose from caliper and plug openings. Disengage guide pin dust boot from guide pin.

ISUZU P'UP & TROOPER II (Cont.)

2) Pivot caliper up and off disc pads and rotor. Remove caliper from guide pin (built into support). Replace disc pads and resurface (or replace) rotor as necessary. Inspect caliper for leakage and repair or replace as needed.

NOTE: Resurface or replace brake rotors in axle sets only (both fronts).

Installation

1) Apply rubber grease to pad shims, caliper sliding surfaces and inside rubber boots. Install sleeve dust boot on caliper and insert sleeve into dust boot.

2) Apply rubber grease into guide pin fitting hole in caliper. Install guide pin dust boot on caliper. Clean sliding surface of guide pin and lubricate with multipurpose grease. Install caliper and dust boot on guide pin.

3) Secure caliper to support by installing and tightening lock bolt. Flex hose identification stripe must follow a straight line without binding. Hose must not contact moving or vibrating parts. Install wheels. With engine running, bleed hydraulic system.

DISC BRAKE ROTOR

NOTE: Check disc brake rotor runout before removing from vehicle.

Removal

1) On 2WD models, raise and support vehicle. Remove front wheels. Detach caliper support mounting bolts. Remove caliper support with caliper. Suspend caliper and support from frame with wire. Do not hang by flexible brake hose.

2) Remove dust cap, cotter pin, nut retainer and hub nut. *See Fig. 2.* Remove hub and rotor assembly and index mark before disassembly. Separate only if replacing either component. Remove and inspect wheel bearings and grease seal. Replace components as necessary.

3) On 4WD models, shift transfer case lever to "2H" position and move vehicle back and forth several feet. Raise and support vehicle. Remove front wheels. Detach caliper support mounting bolts, then remove caliper support with caliper. Suspend caliper and support from frame with wire. DO NOT hang caliper by flexible brake hose. Detach 6 driven clutch housing assembly mounting bolts (10 mm) from hub.

NOTE: Check and mark drive and driven clutch components position and alignment for reassembly reference. Ensure drive clutch assemblies are marked "L" for left or "R" for right.

4) Remove driven clutch assembly, housing assembly and spacer. Separate components, if necessary. Detach snap ring. Remove shim(s), drive clutch assembly, inner cam and lock washer plate. *See Fig. 2.* Using Hub Nut Wrench (J-29020-A), remove hub nut. Remove outer wheel bearing. Remove hub and rotor assembly and index mark before disassembly. Separate only if replacing either component.

NOTE: Resurface or replace brake rotors in axle sets only (both fronts).

Installation

1) To install, reverse removal procedure. If rotor and hub are separated, align index mark and tighten mounting bolts.

2) On 2WD models, replace inner and outer bearing races and grease seal using hammer and drift. On 4WD models, if inner wheel bearing outer race is replaced, install race in hub using Driver (J-8092) and Bearing Race Installer (J-29016).

3) If outer wheel bearing race is replaced, install race using driver and Race Installer (J-29015). Replace grease seal using driver and Seal Installer (J-29017). Install retaining ring.

4) On all models, adjust wheel bearing preload. See ADJUSTMENTS. Install caliper and support assembly and tighten caliper support mounting bolts. If necessary, bleed hydraulic system (with engine running).

BRAKE SHOES

Removal

1) Remove brake drum. If reusable, mark linings for reassembly reference. Remove hold-down springs with cups and pins. Detach upper and lower return springs. Remove primary shoe and automatic adjuster assembly.

2) Detach parking brake cable from automatic adjuster lever. Remove secondary shoe from backing plate. Remove clip and wave washer. Separate adjuster lever components from secondary shoe. *See Fig. 7.*

Fig. 7: Exploded View Of Rear Drum Brake Assembly

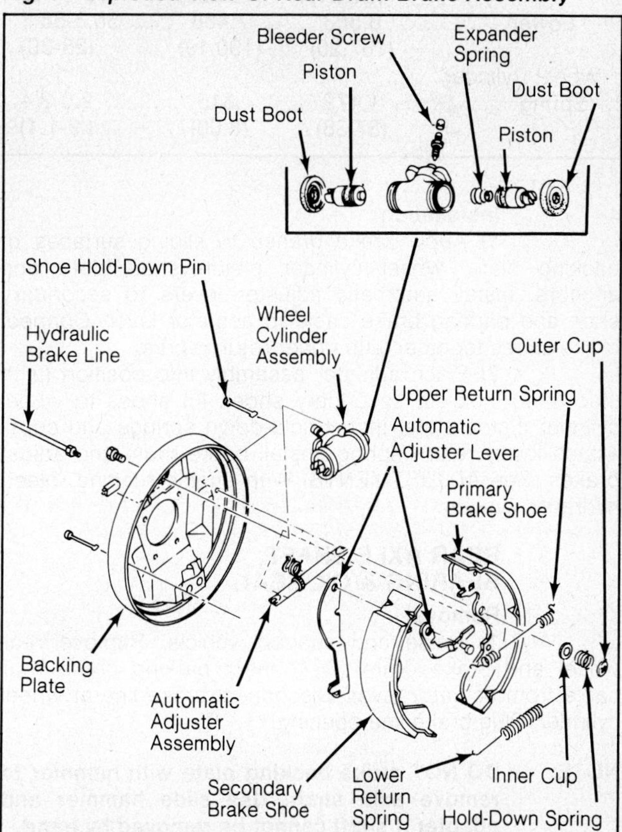

Courtesy of Isuzu Motor Co.

ISUZU P'UP & TROOPER II (Cont.)

3) Check behind wheel cylinder boots for excessive leakage. Presence of some fluid is normal and acts as piston lubricant. Repair as necessary.

Inspection

1) Inspect brake shoes for distortion, looseness, nicks or oil-soaked linings. Minimum rear brake lining thickness is .04" (1.0 mm). Repair or replace as necessary.

NOTE: **If brake linings are replaced, ensure that the new linings are arc-ground for proper lining-to-drum inner diameter contact.**

2) Check and replace tension springs if rusted or weak. Using spring scale and spring compression tester, check springs for proper tension, free length and set length. See BRAKE SPRING TENSION table. Replace as needed.

BRAKE SPRING TENSION

Application	Free Length In. (mm)	Set Length In. (mm)	Set Load lbs. (kg)
Brake Shoe Hold-Down Spring	.591 (15.0)	.441 (11.2)	20.1-24.5 (9-11)
Return Spring			
Upper	4.839 (122.91)	5.311 (134.89)	21.9-26.7 (10-12)
Lower	6.583 (167.20)	7.488 (190.19)	55.3-68.1 (25-30)
Wheel Cylinder Spring	1.472 (37.38)	.315 (8.00)	2.0-2.4 (.9-1.1)

Installation

1) Apply brake grease to sliding surfaces of backing plate, wheel cylinder piston shoe slots and anchors. Install automatic adjuster levers to secondary shoe and parking brake cable to actuator lever. Connect brake shoes together with upper return spring.

2) Place adjuster assembly into position (with star wheel nearest secondary shoe). Fit shoes to wheel cylinder piston slots. Install hold-down springs and cups. Attach lower return spring. Install brake drum and adjust brakes. See ADJUSTMENTS. With engine running, bleed hydraulic system.

REAR AXLE SHAFT, BEARING & OIL SEAL

Removal

1) Raise and support vehicle. Remove rear wheel and brake drum. Disconnect parking brake rear cable from actuator lever. Disconnect brake line at wheel cylinder. Plug brake line opening.

NOTE: **DO NOT strike backing plate with hammer to remove axle shaft. Use slide hammer and adapter if shaft cannot be removed by hand.**

2) Remove 4 nuts from bearing holder through bolts (located inside of backing plate). Using Slide Hammer (J-2619-01) and Axle Flange Adapter (J-21579), pull out axle shaft assembly (including backing plate).

3) Flatten locking tab on convex lock washer. Mount axle shaft in vise, clamping jaws around lock nut. Do not tighten excessively. Install Lock Nut Remover/Installer (J-24246) on flange studs. Lock in position with 2 wheel nuts and turn axle shaft loose from lock nut.

4) Using a hydraulic press (with light pressure), press lock nut, washer, bearing and holder and backing plate from axle shaft. Support backing plate solidly and hold axle shaft to prevent it from falling once bearing assembly is removed.

5) Remove oil seal from outboard side of bearing holder and discard. Drive off bearing outer race with a drift. Pry oil seal from axle case and discard.

Inspection

1) Install dial indicator with pointer positioned 13.78" (350 mm) from splined end. Check axle shaft for bent condition. Replace if runout exceeds .04" (1.0 mm). Never use heat to correct bent condition.

2) Check axle flange runout. Mount dial indicator (parallel to axle) with pointer (at 90 degrees to flange) at the circumference of a 6.3" (160 mm) diameter circle. Rotate axle shaft slowly while observing dial. Replace shaft if runout exceeds .003" (.08 mm).

3) Inspect axle shaft splines and replace if distorted or if step wear is noticed. Slight step wear may be corrected with pencil grinder. Check all other parts for wear, separation, cracks or seizure.

4) Wash bearing in solvent and inspect for rough rotation or damage. Replace bearing as necessary. Check threaded area of wheel stud bolts for damage and elongation. If damaged, remove stud bolts from axle flange using Stud Remover (J-6627-A).

Installation

1) Replace oil seal in axle case using Axle Case Seal Installer (J-24254). Install new bearing outer race into bearing holder using Driver (J-8092) and Axle Bearing Race Installer (J-24259). Install new grease seal into bearing holder using Bearing Holder Seal Installer (J-24255).

2) If necessary, press new wheel bolts into flange of axle shaft. Apply wheel bearing grease to bearing inner race and inner face of rear axle case. Install 4 through bolts into backing plate. With oil seal side of bearing holder against backing plate, install bearing holder to backing plate.

3) Install assembly onto axle shaft. Using Bearing Installer (J-8609-01), install bearing over axle shaft and press into holder. Install new lock washer with its dished side away from bearing. Thread lock nut onto axle shaft.

4) Secure lock nut tightly in vise. Install lock nut remover/installer onto flange studs, chamfered side first. Secure with 2 wheel nuts and tighten lock nut. Bend over portion of lock washer opposite to locating tab to prevent lock nut from loosening.

5) If only one shaft has been serviced, begin axle shaft installation with step **6)**. If both axles have been serviced, insert .08" (2.0 mm) shim between bearing holder and axle case flange. Insert axle shaft assembly into axle case.

6) Insert remaining axle shaft (assembled without shims), into axle case until it comes in contact with differential thrust block. Measure clearance between

ISUZU P'UP & TROOPER II (Cont.)

bearing holder (backing plate) and axle case flange. Proper shim size is determined by adding .012" (.30 mm) to this measurement.

7) For example, if measured clearance is .081" (2.05 mm), correct shim size is .081" + .012" = .093" (2.05 + .30 = 2.35 mm). Select shim or combination of shims of proper size.

NOTE: Axle shaft shims are available is thicknesses of .002" (.05 mm), .003" (.08 mm), .005" (.13 mm), .026" (.66 mm) and .04" (1.0 mm).

8) Remove axle. Install shim(s) between bearing holder and backing plate face. Tighten 4 through bolts to 51-58 ft. lbs. (69-79 N.m). Connect brake line. Install parking brake rear cable, brake drum and wheel. With engine running, bleed hydraulic system. Adjust rear brakes and parking brake tension. See ADJUSTMENTS.

MASTER CYLINDER

Removal

Disconnect fluid level electrical connector wires. Disconnect hydraulic lines at master cylinder and plug ends to prevent entry of dirt. Remove 2 nuts retaining cylinder to power brake unit. Remove master cylinder and gasket from power unit.

NOTE: Master cylinder should be bench-bled before installation. Once remounted, bleed hydraulic system with engine running to prevent damage to push rod seal.

Installation

To install, reverse removal procedure. With engine running, bleed hydraulic system. Monitor fluid level to prevent reservoir from running dry. Adjust pedal height if necessary. See ADJUSTMENTS.

POWER BRAKE UNIT

Removal

1) Disconnect battery ground cable. Disconnect fluid level electrical connector wires from master cylinder. Remove hydraulic lines at master cylinder, covering ends to prevent entry of dirt.

2) Detach clamp and remove vacuum hose (with check valve) from power brake unit. Note installed direction for proper check valve operation (arrow on hose label faces engine). Disconnect brake pedal return spring. Remove clip and brake pedal pin that connects push rod clevis.

3) From inside vehicle, remove 4 nuts attaching power brake unit to firewall. Remove power brake unit and master cylinder as an assembly. Remove and discard gasket(s). Detach master cylinder as necessary.

Installation

To install, reverse removal procedure. Ensure new gasket (Trooper II has 4 gaskets) is installed between power unit and firewall and sealer is applied to firewall fitting face. If master cylinder was removed, check push rod projection. See POWER BRAKE UNIT under OVERHAUL in this article. With engine running, bleed hydraulic system. If necessary, adjust pedal height.

OVERHAUL

DISC BRAKE CALIPER

Disassembly

1) Remove sleeve dust boot and guide pin dust boot. Using a blunt-pointed instrument, remove dust seal ring and dust seal. *See Fig. 6*.

2) Place wood block between piston and caliper cavity wall. Apply compressed air to force piston from caliper bore. Remove piston ring seal. Remove bleeder screw. Discard all rubber parts.

Reassembly

1) Lubricate new piston square ring seal with brake fluid or rubber grease. Insert seal into caliper bore. Carefully insert piston into caliper assembly with finger pressure.

2) Apply rubber grease to piston. Install new dust seal on piston and caliper. Fit seal ring into dust seal. Install bleeder screw. Reverse removal procedure to complete installation. With engine running, bleed hydraulic system.

WHEEL CYLINDER

Disassembly

Remove rubber dust boots from cylinder. Remove piston assemblies and expander spring. Note installed direction for each cup. Remove cups from pistons. Discard boots and cups.

Inspection

Check piston-to-cylinder bore clearance. Maximum clearance is .006" (.15 mm). If clearance is excessive, replace wheel cylinder assembly. Check spring for proper tension. See BRAKE SPRING TENSION table. Apply silicone grease (Delco Lube No. 5459912) to pistons and inner face of boots.

Reassembly

Lubricate cylinder bore with brake assembly fluid. Install spring expander. Place new piston cups on piston with flare facing center of cylinder, then install piston assemblies into cylinder. Press new boots onto cylinder.

MASTER CYLINDER

Disassembly

1) Remove fluid reservoir cap, seal and float magnet. Drain brake fluid. Place master cylinder in vise. Push primary piston in and remove stop bolt and gasket on left side of master cylinder.

2) Detach dust seal. Remove primary piston snap ring. Remove primary and secondary piston assemblies from cylinder bore. *See Fig. 8*.

NOTE: DO NOT remove reservoir assembly unless it is to be replaced.

NOTE: If fluid contamination or corrosion is found, replace all rubber parts. Use clean brake fluid to bench-bleed master cylinder. DO NOT use any cleaner containing mineral oil or damage to rubber parts will result.

ISUZU P'UP & TROOPER II (Cont.)

Fig. 8: Exploded View Of Master Cylinder Assembly

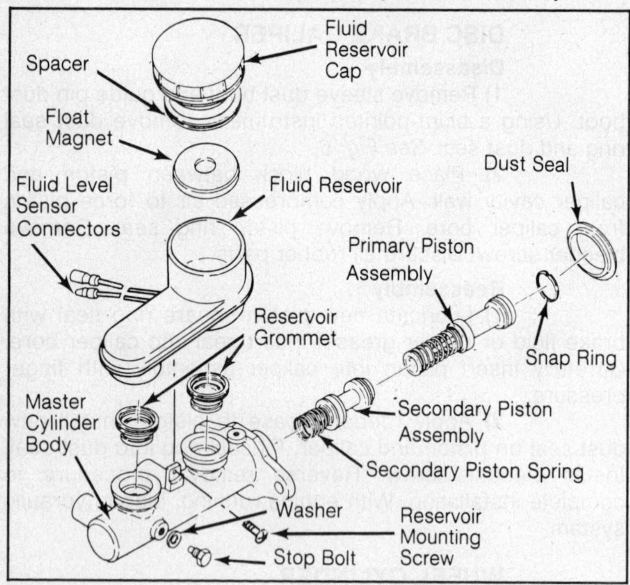

Courtesy of Isuzu Motor Co.

Inspection

Inspect cylinder bore for scoring, pitting or other damage. Check cylinder bore-to-piston clearance. Standard clearance is .0016-.0049" (.040-.125 mm). If clearance exceeds .006" (.15 mm), replace master cylinder.

Reassembly

1) Lubricate cylinder bore and parts with clean brake fluid or rubber grease. If removed, install secondary spring onto secondary piston.

2) Using a gentle twisting, rotating motion to avoid damage to new rubber seals, install secondary piston assembly, primary piston assembly and snap ring. Depress primary piston, then install piston stopper bolt with new gasket.

3) Before installing, bench bleed master cylinder. Install grommets with flared side toward cylinder body. Install cylinder body dust seal with groove turned downward. Install master cylinder on power brake unit. With engine running, bleed hydraulic system.

POWER BRAKE UNIT

Disassembly

1) Remove master cylinder reservoir cover, seal and float magnet. Drain brake fluid from reservoir. Remove 2 nuts and lock washers. Separate master cylinder from power unit front shell. Remove and discard gasket. Install Fixing Stand (J-22805-01) onto master cylinder mount studs of front shell and tighten nuts.

2) Place fixing stand in vise with power unit rear shell up. Scribe alignment marks on front and rear shells to ensure reassembly in original position. Remove push rod clevis and lock nut from valve rod assembly. Remove push rod boot from rear shell.

CAUTION: When separating front and rear shell assemblies, maintain pressure on spanner wrench as rear shell is under spring pressure.

3) Place Spanner Wrench (J-9504-01) over rear shell studs and attach mounting nuts. To separate both shells, press down on wrench, while carefully rotating rear shell counterclockwise. Detach retainer and remove rear shell from valve rod assembly.

4) Remove front shell assembly from vise and detach fixing stand. Attach Diaphragm Remover (J-34350) to front shell. Tighten diaphragm remover bolt to press diaphragm plate and diaphragm (with push rod assembly, valve body and valve rod assembly) from front shell. Separate diaphragm, plate and valve body as necessary.

5) Detach diaphragm remover from shell. Push in on valve rod assembly and detach valve rod stopper key, then remove valve rod assembly from valve body. Remove reaction disc from valve body. Remove push rod assembly and return spring from front shell. *See Fig. 9.*

Fig. 9: Exploded View Of Vacuum Power Brake Assembly

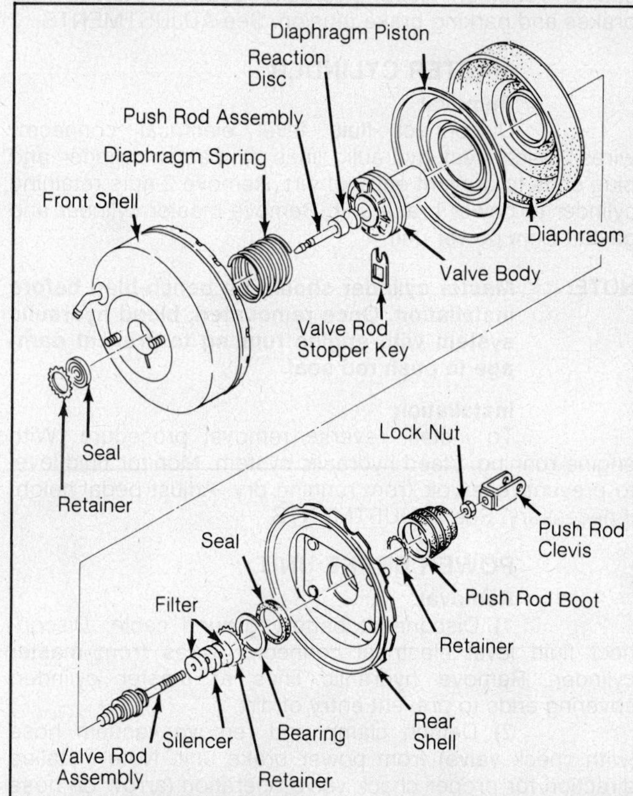

Courtesy of Isuzu Motor Co.

NOTE: DO NOT disassemble valve rod assembly. If defective, replace complete assembly.

6) Before removing seals, note installed direction and depth. To remove defective rear shell seal, pry out seal retainer. Remove bearing and seal assembly. If front shell seal is defective, pry out retainer and remove seal. If vacuum check valve is defective, remove hose and replace with a new assembly.

NOTE: Clean all parts with denatured alcohol only.

Reassembly

1) Apply silicone grease to sliding surfaces of all parts. If front shell seal was removed, apply rubber grease to new seal and seal area of shell. Install seal and retainer in shell with lip of seal facing forward.

ISUZU P'UP & TROOPER II (Cont.)

2) If rear shell seal was removed, apply rubber grease to rear shell seal area. Insert seal into rear shell with lip of seal facing forward. Install bearing and retainer. Set retainer to a depth of .508-.520" (12.90-13.20 mm) into rear shell seal area. *See Fig. 10.*

Fig. 10: Installing Power Brake Unit Rear Shell Seal, Bearing & Retainer

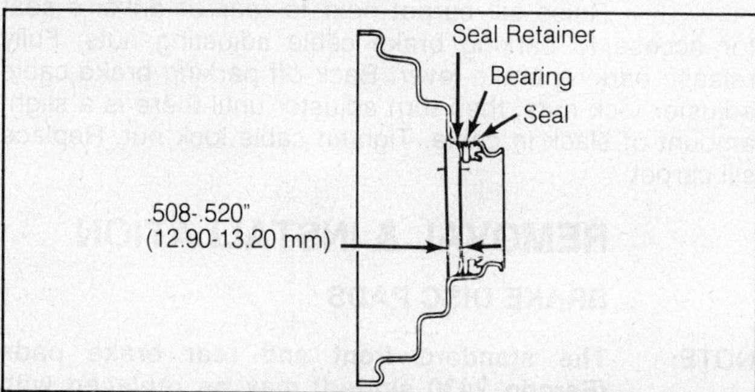

Courtesy of Isuzu Motor Co.

3) Mount fixing stand onto front shell and install assembly in vise. Using spanner wrench, compress spring and lock rear shell to front shell, ensuring marks made at disassembly are aligned.

CAUTION: Before releasing pressure on spanner wrench, ensure rear shell is locked in place at all tabs.

4) Assemble push rod boot to rear shell. Ensure boot is fully installed on retainer. Install push rod clevis lock nut and clevis. Remove assembly from vise and detach fixing stand. Position power unit in vise with push rod up (DO NOT clamp tightly). Check distance from master cylinder flange face of booster to end of push rod.

NOTE: Push rod must be bottomed in power unit before making adjustment. If necessary, apply 20 in. Hg vacuum at power unit to bottom push rod assembly.

5) Push rod end should be .709-.717" (18.00-18.20 mm) away from master cylinder mounting surface. If rod must be adjusted, hold rod at serrated portion and turn threaded end.

6) After adjustment, tighten lock nut to 13-16 ft. lbs. (18-22 N.m). Bench-bleed master cylinder, then install unit on booster. Install assembly and adjust pedal height if necessary. See ADJUSTMENTS. With engine running, bleed hydraulic system.

TIGHTENING SPECIFICATIONS

Application	Ft. Lbs. (N.m)
Brake Caliper	
Lock Bolt	22-25 (30-34)
Support Bracket Mounting Bolt	
P'UP	62-65 (84-88)
Trooper II	103-126 (140-171)
Flexible Hose-to-Caliper	24-27 (33-37)
Master Cylinder	
Push Rod Lock Nut	13-16 (18-22)
Stopper Bolt	12-14 (16-19)
Power Unit-To-Dash Panel Stud Nut	18-21 (24-29)
Rear Axle Bearing Holder	
To-Backing Plate	51-58 (69-79)
Rear Axle Bearing Lock Nut	188-195 (255-264)
Rotor-to-Hub Mounting Bolt	
P'UP	47-58 (64-79)
Trooper II	51-58 (69-79)
Wheel Lug Nut	58-80 (79-109)
	INCH Lbs. (N.m)
Brake Caliper Bleeder Screw	70-86 (8-10)
Master Cylinder Brake Line Nut	78-132 (9-15)
Master Cylinder-To-Power Brake	
Unit Mounting Nut	96-132 (11-15)
Wheel Cylinder	
To-Backing Plate Bolt	70-104 (8-12)
Brake Line Nut	120-156 (14-18)
Bleeder Screw	70-86 (8-10)

DISC BRAKE ROTOR SPECIFICATIONS

Application	Disc Diameter In. (mm)	Lateral Runout In. (mm)	Parallelism In. (mm)	Original Thickness In. (mm)	Min. Refinish Thickness In. (mm)	Discard Thickness In. (mm)
P'UP	.....	.005 (.13)	.001 (.03)	.705 (18.00)	.668 (16.97)	.654 (16.60)
Trooper II	.....	.005 (.13)	.0006 (.015)	.866 (22.0)	.826 (21.0)	.811 (20.6)

DRUM BRAKE SPECIFICATIONS

Application	Drum Diam. In. (mm)	Drum Width In. (mm)	Max. Drum Refinish Diam. In. (mm)	Wheel Cyl. Diam. In. (mm)	Master Cyl. Diam. In. (mm)
P'UP & Trooper II	10.0 (254)	.....	[1] 10.06 (255.5)	8.75 (22.22)	[2] 8.74 (22.20)

[1] – Maximum bake drum runout is .006" (.15 mm).
[2] – For P'UP only. On Trooper II, diameter is .937" (23.80 mm).

Brakes

JAGUAR

XJ6 III, XJS

DESCRIPTION

All models have 4-wheel disc brakes. Front calipers are 4-piston type. Rear calipers are 2-piston type. Parking brake is cable-actuated on rear calipers and consists of independent disc-mounted pads which act on rear rotors.

TESTING

POWER BRAKE UNIT

1) Raise front of vehicle and confirm that each wheel turns freely. Start engine, allow vacuum to build up and apply brake pedal several times. It should be possible to rotate wheel immediately after pedal is released. If brakes bind, a major defect in booster is indicated.

2) With engine running, apply brake pedal several times and check operation of pedal. If response is sluggish, check condition of vacuum hoses and unit air filter.

3) Allow vacuum to build up, switch off engine and operate brake pedal. About 2-3 applications should be vacuum assisted. Any less indicates a leaking vacuum system or inoperative check valve.

4) Turn engine off and operate brake pedal several times to evacuate vacuum in system. Hold light foot pressure on pedal and start engine. If unit is operating correctly, pedal will fall under existing foot pressure. If pedal remains stationary, a leaking vacuum system is indicated.

BRAKE WARNING LIGHT

1) With gear selector in Neutral or Park, turn ignition on. Parking brake light should be on when parking brake lever is pulled one notch. If lamp does not light, check and repair as necessary. Lamp should go off when lever is fully released.

2) If lamp remains lit, check brake fluid level and top up if needed. If lamp is still lit, check brake circuit warning sensor (pressure differential warning actuator) switch. Disconnect electrical connector at switch. If lamp is out, switch has operated.

3) If lamp remains lit, check for short in brake warning electrical circuit or sticking reservoir fluid level switch. Repair short or replace reservoir fluid level switch as necessary.

NOTE: **If pressure differential warning actuator has operated, check for major defect in hydraulic fluid system. Resetting of pressure switch is achieved automatically during bleeding of brake system.**

4) Perform switch operational check. With engine idling, fully release parking brake and ensure light is off. Apply firm pedal pressure. Open any bleed screw and light should glow.

5) Close bleed screw, then release and reapply brake pedal. Warning light should go out. If lamp fails to light under pedal pressure, replace warning switch.

ADJUSTMENTS

PARKING BRAKE

Parking Brake Caliper

Caliper is self-adjusting to compensate for pad wear. Caliper position adjustment is required only when new pads are installed or caliper is rebuilt. See PARKING BRAKE CALIPER.

CAUTION: **Parking brake cable must have slight amount of slack after adjustment or binding of caliper may result.**

Parking Brake Cable

Raise sill carpet next to rear of driver's seat for access to parking brake cable adjusting nuts. Fully release parking brake lever. Back off parking brake cable adjuster lock nuts, then turn adjuster until there is a slight amount of slack in cable. Tighten cable lock nut. Replace sill carpet.

REMOVAL & INSTALLATION

BRAKE DISC PADS

NOTE: **The standard front and rear brake pads (Ferodo 2430 slotted) may be replaced with semi-metallic pads (Ferodo 3401) in sets only. DO NOT mix semi-metallic and non-metallic pads.**

Removal (Front & Rear)

Raise and support vehicle. Remove wheels and tires. Remove pin clips, pad retaining pins, anti-chatter springs (front) and brake pads. If reuseable, mark all brake pads for proper installation.

NOTE: **Minimum pad thickness is .2" (4 mm) for front and rear brake pads.**

Fig. 1: Removing Front Disc Brake Pads

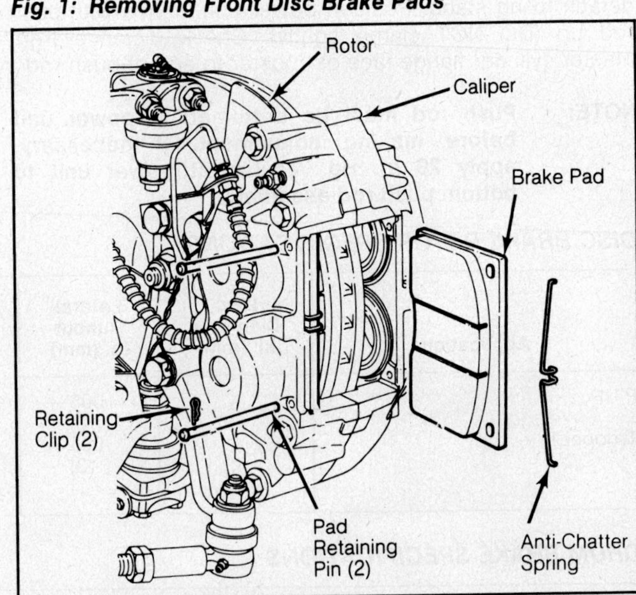

Courtesy of Jaguar Cars Inc.

Installation

1) Drain some brake fluid from reservoirs to enable caliper pistons to be pushed back into cylinders without overflow at master cylinder. Using Piston Retractor (No. 64932392), push pistons back in caliper.

NOTE: **On rear brake pads, install upper mounting pin from center of vehicle and lower mounting pin from wheel side.**

JAGUAR (Cont.)

2) Insert new pads and anti-chatter springs (front). Replace retaining pins and clips. Check pads for free movement within caliper. Check caliper-to-rotor centralization and adjust as necessary. See BRAKE CALIPER.

3) Check reservoirs for correct fluid level and add if needed. Run engine and apply brake pedal several times to relocate caliper pistons. Ensure brake pedal feels firm.

Break-In (Semi-Metallic Pads)

It is most important to properly "break-in" the semi-metallic disc pads to ensure optimum brake performance and pad/rotor service life.

1) When pads are installed and during the first 200 miles, use deliberate, frequent light applications of brakes whenever possible. Brake use is similar to that used in normal city driving.

2) If vehicle is only used on open road driving, these conditions must be simulated. If possible, do not brake from speed in excess of 60 MPH or drag brakes for any length of time. Instead, reduce speed by short applications. For example, from 50-40 MPH at intervals of about one mile.

NOTE: Proper break-in procedure will result in satisfactory brake lining/rotor conditioning and lead to optimum brake life and performance.

PARKING BRAKE DISC PADS

Removal & Installation

Parking brake caliper must be removed to replace disc pads. Remove and install parking brake disc pads according to caliper removal instructions. See PARKING BRAKE CALIPER.

PARKING BRAKE CALIPER

Removal

1) Raise and support vehicle. Ensure parking brake lever is fully released. Loosen parking brake cable adjusting lock nuts and back-off cable adjustment.

2) Remove nuts and bolts attaching rear suspension mounting plate to rear suspension unit. Remove plate from vehicle. Using a lever, move caliper arm toward center of vehicle, then disconnect parking brake cable from arm and slide back rubber sleeve. *See Fig. 2.*

Fig. 2: Removing Parking Brake Cable From Parking Brake Caliper Operating Arm

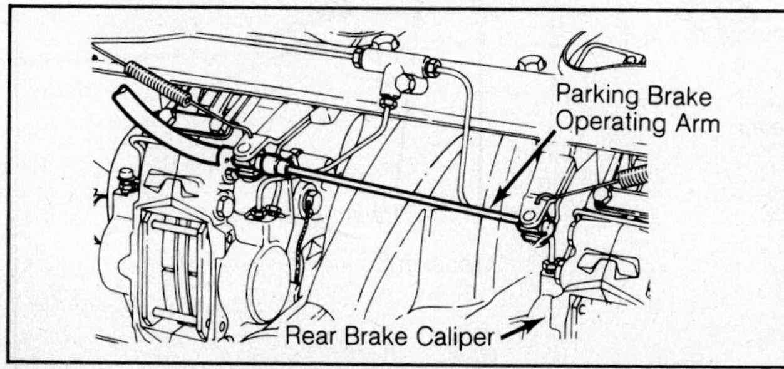

Courtesy of Jaguar Cars Inc.

3) Detach springs from caliper arms and position parking brake cable clear of calipers. Turn down lock tabs. Remove caliper mounting bolts, tab washer and retraction plate.

4) Slide caliper around rotor and remove through hole left by suspension plate. To remove disc pads, remove nut and spring washer securing pads to the pad carriers.

NOTE: Replace parking brake pads if lining thickness is .125" (3.17 mm) or less.

Fig. 3: Detail of Parking Brake Caliper

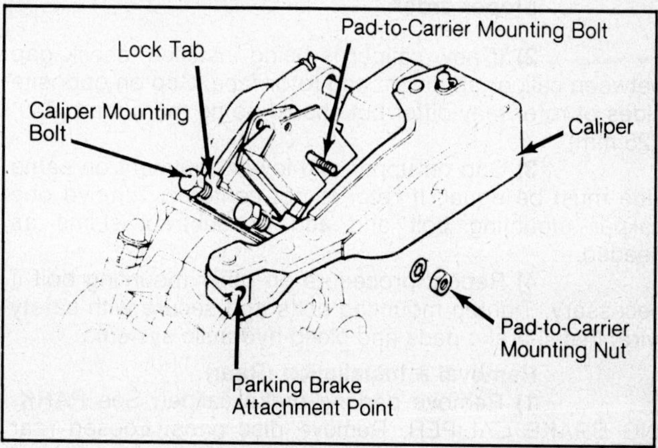

Courtesy of Jaguar Cars Inc.

Installation

1) To install, reverse removal procedure. Adjust caliper if new pads (Mintex M68/1) have been installed or if caliper has been overhauled.

2) Adjust by holding one pad carrier stationary and turning remaining carrier out 2-3 times or until there is a clearance of .75" (19 mm) between disc pad surfaces.

3) Operate caliper actuating lever until adjuster ratchet stops clicking. Install remaining components and check operation of brakes.

BRAKE CALIPER

NOTE: DO NOT separate caliper halves for repair. If a leak exists between halves, replace caliper.

Fig. 4: Removing Front Disc Brake Caliper

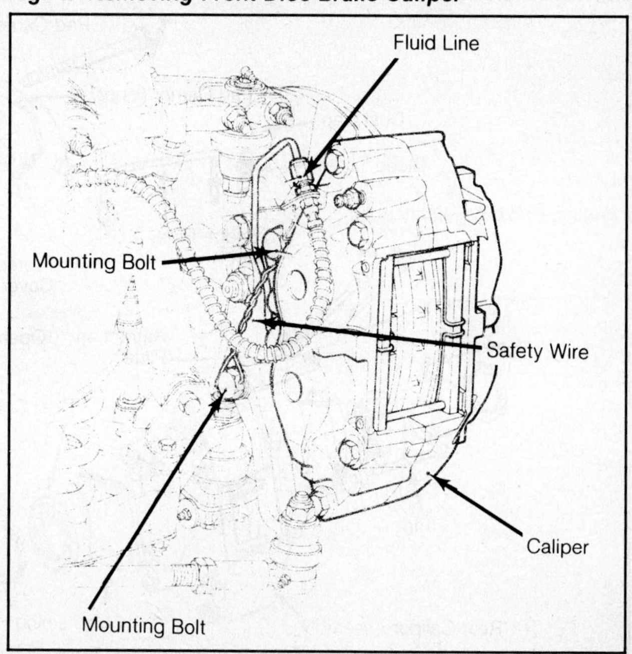

Courtesy of Jaguar Cars Inc.

JAGUAR (Cont.)

Removal & Installation (Front)

1) Raise vehicle and remove wheels. Remove disc pads. Disconnect caliper fluid line and plug. Disconnect and discard safety wire from mounting bolts. Detach mounting bolts and shims. Remove caliper from rotor.

NOTE: **Check position and number of shims between steering arm and caliper. Replace shims in proper order.**

2) If new caliper is being installed, check gap between caliper abutment and rotor face. Gap on opposite sides of rotor may differ but should be no more than .010" (.25 mm).

3) Gap on upper and lower abutment on same side must be equal. If rotor is not centered, remove one caliper mounting bolt and add or subtract shims as needed.

4) Repeat procedure on other mounting bolt if necessary. Tighten mounting bolts and secure with safety wire. Install brake pads and bleed hydraulic system.

Removal & Installation (Rear)

1) Remove parking brake caliper. See PARKING BRAKE CALIPER. Remove disc pads. Loosen rear service brake caliper fluid line at 3-way connector. Disconnect hydraulic line at caliper and position clear of work area.

2) Plug hydraulic line. Detach and discard safety wire from mounting bolts. If equipped, note shim positions and thicknesses. Remove shims and bolts. Slide caliper around brake rotor and out the hole near the left suspension plate.

NOTE: **If new caliper is installed, mount unit on bracket and check rotor/caliper centralization. Gap between caliper abutment and rotor, on both sides of caliper, must be no more than .010" (.25 mm). Adjust shims at caliper and/or rear brake rotor as necessary. See DISC BRAKE ROTOR.**

3) Place caliper and shims (if equipped) in position. Tighten mounting bolts. Install safety wire on bolts. Check rotor for centering between caliper abutments. If necessary, adjust shims between final drive flange and rotor.

4) If shim adjustment at rotor is performed, rear wheel camber must be checked. See JAGUAR WHEEL ALIGNMENT PROCEDURES in WHEEL ALIGNMENT section. To complete installation, reverse removal procedure. Bleed brakes.

DISC BRAKE ROTOR

Removal (Front)

1) Remove disc pads. Through hole in disc splash shield, detach 5 hub-to-rotor mounting bolts and washers. Remove hub dust cap, cotter pin, axle nut and washer from front axle spindle. Remove hub.

NOTE: **If water deflector must be freed, insert punch through access hole in splash shield and lightly tap on it.**

2) Remove or relocate brake caliper. See BRAKE CALIPER. If necessary, loosen steering arm-to-hub carrier mounting bolts. Remove rotor assembly by sliding it off axle spindle.

Installation

To install, reverse removal procedure. Ensure rotor/caliper centralization is correct. See BRAKE CALIPER. Pack hub and wheel bearings with grease. Adjust wheel bearings so hub end play is .002-.004" (.05-.10 mm).

Removal (Rear)

1) Remove rear brake caliper. See BRAKE CALIPER. Disconnect shock absorber from lower mount. Remove safety wire and detach radius arm locking bolt. Lever radius arm from spigot anchor point.

2) Remove lower control arm outer grease fitting. Place stands under hub assembly. Remove shock

Fig. 5: Exploded View Of Rear Brake Caliper & Parking Brake Assembly

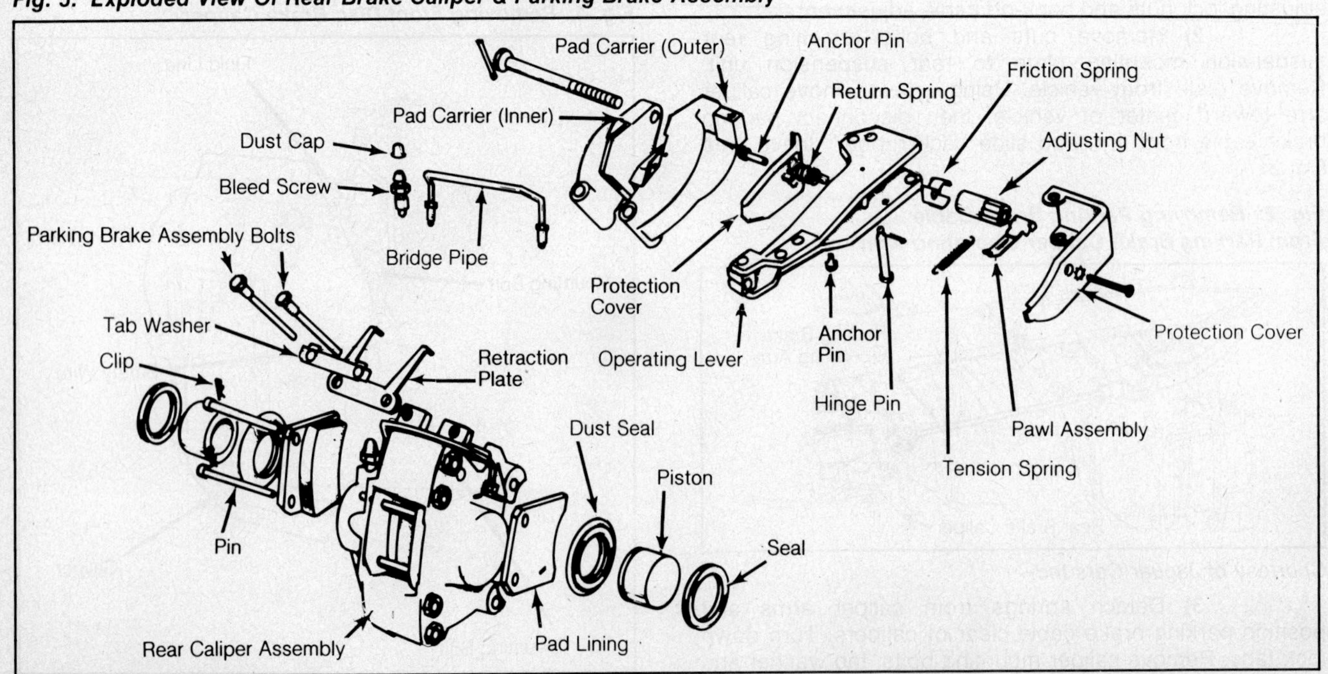

Courtesy of Jaguar Cars Inc.

absorber lower fulcrum pin. Collect spacers and towing bracket.

3) Loosen clamp and slide shroud away from inner "U" joint. Remove "U" joint-to-rotor attaching nuts. Tap rotor mounting bolts toward final drive unit. Separate "U" joint from rotor.

NOTE: DO NOT lose camber adjustment shims mounted between drive axle flange and brake rotor.

4) Remove brake rotor from mounting bolts. DO NOT disturb centralization shims between final drive flange and rotor.

Installation

1) To install, reverse removal procedure. Install brake caliper. Ensure caliper is centered on rotor. Adjust by removing caliper and rotor, then adding or removing shims from rotor mounting bolts. Note thickness of shims during this operation.

2) Reinstall rotor and caliper and recheck centralization. Caliper is centered when gap is not more than .010" (.25 mm). If shims were changed, remove half shaft inner "U" joint-to-rotor nuts and separate joint from rotor mounting bolts.

3) If shim was added to centralization shims in step 1), remove shim of same size from camber angle shims and vice versa. Reinstall removed components. Bleed system if necessary. Check rear wheel camber and adjust, if necessary. See JAGUAR WHEEL ALIGNMENT PROCEDURES in WHEEL ALIGNMENT section.

MASTER CYLINDER

NOTE: Before removing master cylinder from vacuum power brake unit, pump brake pedal several times to ensure NO vacuum exists to operate servo.

CAUTION: Operating servo with master cylinder removed will overextend mechanism and damage servo beyond repair.

Removal

1) Pull back rubber cover from brake fluid reservoir cap and disconnect electrical wires from fluid level indicator. Remove reservoir cap and filter. Using syringe, drain fluid.

2) Disconnect clips mounting hoses to cylinder adapters. Separate all hydraulic lines and plug openings. Detach nuts mounting cylinder to vacuum power brake unit studs, then remove master cylinder.

Installation

To install, reverse removal procedure. Bleed hydraulic system.

PEDAL BOX & POWER BRAKE UNIT

Removal

1) Detach bolts holding stay bar to fender and swing aside. Pry vacuum hose adapter from power brake unit and move hose aside. Detach master cylinder-to-vacuum booster mounting nuts.

2) On manual transmission equipped vehicles, detach clamps holding fluid line to clutch master cylinder. Remove line and plug openings. Disconnect and plug master cylinder lines. Remove fluid reservoir.

3) Loosen nuts holding reservoir mount bracket to pedal box and swing bracket into vertical position. Remove 4 nuts securing pedal box assembly to bulkhead. Remove master cylinder. Remove stoplight switch and brake pedal pad if necessary.

4) Maneuver pedal box and power brake unit (as an assembly) clear of bulkhead and lift from vehicle. Remove spring clip holding servo push rod clevis pin. Remove clevis pin and spring washer holding push rod to brake pedal lever.

5) Detach 4 nuts holding pedal box to power brake unit. Lay reservoir mounting bracket aside. Detach pedal box from power brake unit.

Installation

To install, reverse removal procedure and bleed hydraulic system. Bleed clutch on manual transmission equipped vehicles.

PRESSURE DIFFERENTIAL WARNING ACTUATOR (P.D.W.A) SWITCH

Removal

1) To remove switch, first disconnect battery. Pull electrical connector from air temperature sensor (if necessary). Release 2 toggle clips holding air cleaner cover, then pull cover and cleaner element from back plate.

2) Disconnect electrical lead from P.D.W.A. switch. Disconnect 4 brake fluid lines from switch and plug lines. Remove mounting bolt and detach switch.

Installation

To install new switch, reverse removal procedures. Bleed hydraulic system.

OVERHAUL

DISC BRAKE CALIPER

NOTE: DO NOT separate caliper for service. Pistons and seals may be changed without splitting caliper. If leak is detected between caliper halves, replace caliper as an assembly.

Fig. 6: Exploded View Of Front Disc Brake Caliper Assembly

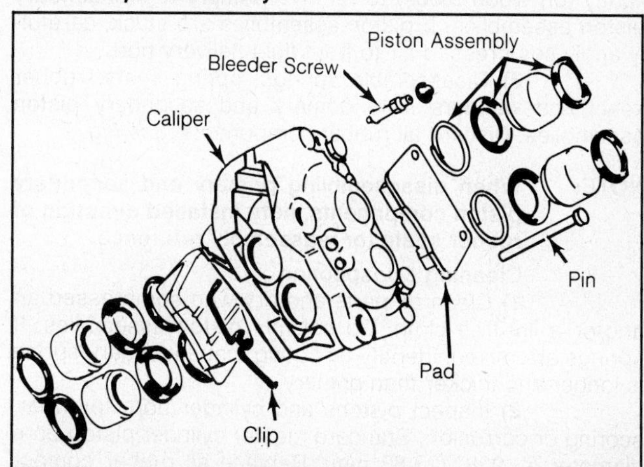

Courtesy of Jaguar Cars Inc.

Disassembly (Front & Rear)

1) With disc pads removed, thoroughly clean exterior of caliper with brake cleaner. Remove spring clamps holding piston dust covers, then remove covers.

JAGUAR (Cont.)

2) Using Piston Clamp (No. 18G 672), retain outboard piston(s), then carefully apply compressed air to fluid inlet port and dislocate inboard piston(s). Pull dust seal from piston and caliper grooves. Remove piston(s) from bore(s).

CAUTION: Inboard piston(s) must be installed before outboard piston(s) can be removed.

3) Carefully remove each piston seal from recess in cylinder bore. Do not damage piston bore during seal removal. Rebuild inboard piston(s) and caliper half, then install components and repair opposite side.

NOTE: For cleaning purposes, use only clean brake fluid or Castrol/Girling brake cleaning fluid. DO NOT use denatured alcohol. Wash all parts after cleaning and blow dry with compressed air.

Reassembly

1) Coat each cylinder bore, piston and new piston seal with brake assembly fluid before installing. Place piston seal in groove in bore. Install new dust seal over cylinder groove, then carefully insert piston through dust seal.

2) Pull dust seal into groove in piston. Using piston clamp, press piston completely into cylinder bore. Repeat procedure for other pistons and seals. Install caliper as previously outlined. Bleed hydraulic system.

PARKING BRAKE CALIPER

The manufacturer offers no overhaul procedure. If caliper assembly fails to operate properly and cleaning and adjusting does not correct problem, replace the unit.

MASTER CYLINDER

Disassembly

1) With master cylinder removed from vehicle, carefully pry hose adapters from sealing grommets and remove grommets from master cylinder. Push in on primary piston and remove secondary piston stop pin from forward grommet housing.

2) Remove circlip. Tap flange end of cylinder lightly (on wood block) to remove primary and secondary piston assemblies. If piston assemblies are stuck, carefully apply compressed air to front fluid delivery port.

3) Disassemble springs, spring seats, rubber seals and washers from primary and secondary piston assemblies. Discard all rubber components. *See Fig. 7.*

NOTE: When disassembling primary and secondary piston components, note installed direction of rubber seals for reassembly reference.

Cleaning & Inspection

1) Clean all parts and dry with compressed air and/or a lint-free cloth. Do not mix piston assemblies. If springs are mixed, identify by noting that secondary spring is longer and thicker than primary.

2) Inspect pistons and cylinder bore for wear, scoring or corrosion. Standard master cylinder piston bore diameter is .938" (23.83 mm). Replace all rubber components and any excessively worn or damaged parts.

Reassembly

1) To reassemble, reverse disassembly procedure. Lubricate all parts liberally with clean brake fluid. Install a new secondary piston inner seal in locating groove with lip facing forward.

Fig. 7: Exploded View Of Master Cylinder Assembly

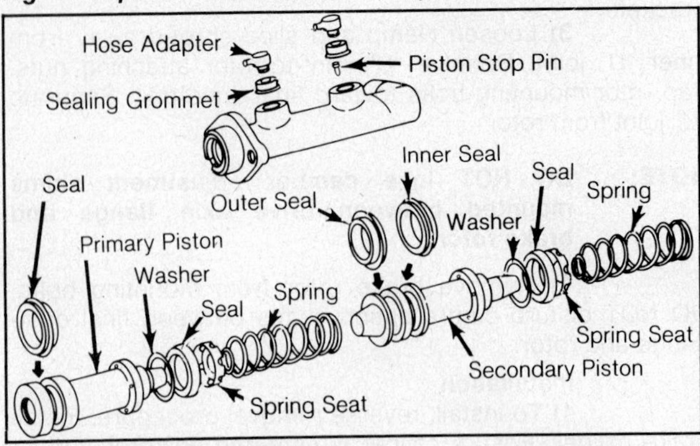

Courtesy of Jaguar Cars Inc.

2) Install remaining new secondary seal with lip facing primary piston. Install new primary piston rear seal in groove with lip facing forward (away from circlip).

3) With piston components assembled, slowly insert each piston assembly into cylinder bore with a rocking motion while rotating piston. Do not damage rubber seals during installation. Press piston into bore and install circlip.

4) Press primary piston into cylinder bore to full extent, then fit secondary piston stop pin. Fit new sealing grommets to master cylinder. Lubricate hose adapters with brake fluid and press into grommets. Install master cylinder and bleed brake system.

POWER BRAKE UNIT

The vacuum power brake unit is factory sealed and CANNOT be overhauled. Perform function checks to help determine unit condition. See TESTING. Ensure service brake system is in proper working order before performing checks. If operation of unit deteriorates to the extent that braking performance is affected and unit is determined defective, replace entire unit.

PRESSURE DIFFERENTIAL WARNING ACTUATOR SWITCH

No overhaul of the pressure differential warning actuator switch is possible. Carry out operational check as described in ADJUSTMENT. Replace component if warning lamp fails to light.

TIGHTENING SPECIFICATIONS

Application	Ft. Lbs. (N.m)
Brake Line Flare Nuts	
12 mm	12-14 (16-19)
Brake Pedal Box-to-Body Nut	11-13 (15-18)
Brake Pedal Pivot Pin	14-18 (19-24)
Caliper Mounting Bolt	
Front	55 (75)
Rear	49-55 (66-75)
Flexible Hose-to-Bracket	10-12 (14-16)
Master Cylinder-to-Power Unit Nut	15-20 (21-27)
Relay Lever Pivot	22-26 (30-35)
Wheel Lug Nut	45 (61)
	INCH Lbs. (N.m)
Brake Line Flare Nuts	
10 mm	72-120 (9-14)
Power Unit-to-Brake Pedal Box Nut	96-120 (11-14)

JAGUAR (Cont.)

DISC BRAKE ROTOR SPECIFICATIONS

Application	Disc Diameter In. (mm)	Lateral Runout In. (mm)	Parallelism In. (mm)	Original Thickness In. (mm)	Min. Refinish Thickness In. (mm)	Discard Thickness In. (mm)
XJ6 III & XJS						
Front	11.18 (283.8)	.004 (.10)	.....	.950 (24.13)	.895 (22.7)	.894 (22.6)
Rear	10.38 (263.8)	.004 (.10)	.....	.50 (12.7)	.45 (11.4)	.44 (11.3)

MERCEDES-BENZ

190, 260, 300, 420, 560 Series

DESCRIPTION

All models use a 4-wheel disc brake system. A dash panel warning light is activated when brake fluid level is low or when pressure differential between two brake circuits is caused by loss of fluid in one circuit.

Parking brakes are cable-actuated and housed in rear brake rotors. All models have brake pad wear indicator and differential pressure warning indicator. On diesel models, a vacuum pump is incorporated to supply a vacuum to the power brake unit.

NOTE: **For information on anti-lock brake system, see MERCEDES-BENZ ANTI-LOCK BRAKE SYSTEM article.**

TESTING

BRAKE WARNING LIGHT

1) Dual warning light is mounted on dash. Turn ignition on. Light should glow when parking brake lever is pulled one notch and go off when lever is fully released.

2) To check circuit warning sensor, turn ignition on, release parking brake and ensure light is off. Open bleeder screw on one wheel and depress brake pedal. Light should glow.

3) Close bleeder screw, replenish brake fluid and bleed hydraulic system. Check that light goes out after testing. If not, differential pressure pin in master cylinder must be reset.

ADJUSTMENTS

PEDAL HEIGHT & FREE PLAY

Pedal height, measured from pedal pad to pedal stop, should be 5.9" (150 mm). To adjust, loosen lock nuts and turn stop light switch until correct pedal height is obtained. Tighten lock nuts. Pedal free play should be .20-.60" (5-15 mm).

STOPLIGHT SWITCH

Stoplight switch is located under dash, above brake pedal. Loosen lock nuts and adjust switch so that contact button extends .24-.32" (6-8 mm). Tighten lock nuts.

PARKING BRAKE

1) Remove one wheel lug bolt at each rear wheel. Raise and support vehicle.

2) Rotate wheel until lug bolt hole is positioned over parking brake adjuster, approximately 45 degrees forward for diagonal swing axle and 90 degrees forward for diagonal swing axle with starting torque compensation. *See Fig. 1.*

NOTE: **Parking brake must be adjusted if brake pedal can be depressed by more than 2 steps (of 6) without any braking effect. DO NOT alter adjusting screw on parking brake intermediate lever. Screw is for balancing cable lengths only.**

Fig. 1: Adjusting Parking Brake Mechanism

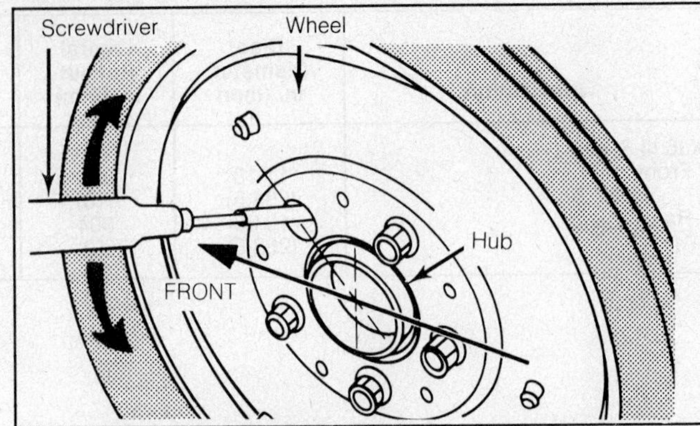

Courtesy of Mercedes-Benz of North America.

3) Using screwdriver inserted through lug bolt hole, turn adjuster until rear wheel cannot be turned. Back off adjuster until wheel can be turned without drag.

REMOVAL & INSTALLATION

DISC BRAKE PADS

Removal & Installation
(260 & 300 Series - Front)

Raise and support vehicle. Remove tire and wheel. Remove lower guide pin bolt. Loosen upper guide pin bolt. Pivot caliper upward and secure with wire. Remove pads. To install, reverse removal procedure.

Removal & Installation
(All Others - Front & Rear)

Raise vehicle and support. Remove wheels. Unplug brake pad sensor. Drive out pad pins. Remove spring clip. Remove brake pads. *See Figs. 2 and 3.* To install, reverse removal procedure.

Fig. 2: Installed View of Front Brake Caliper

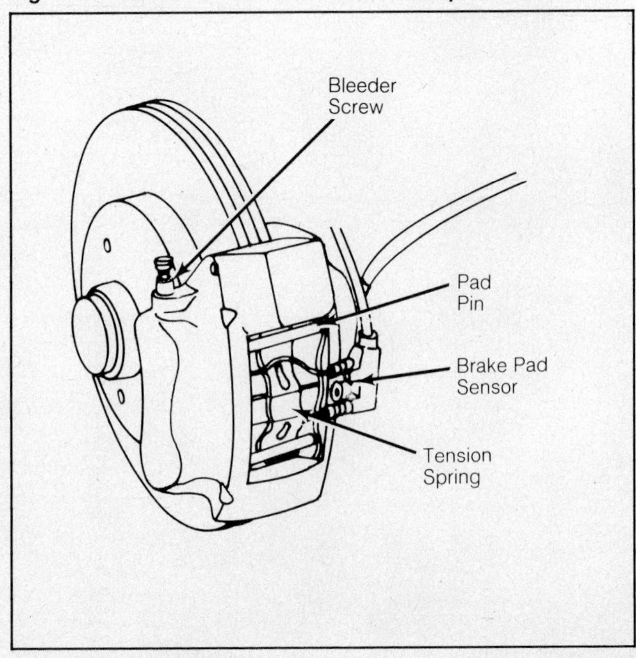

Fig. 3: Installed View of Rear Brake Caliper

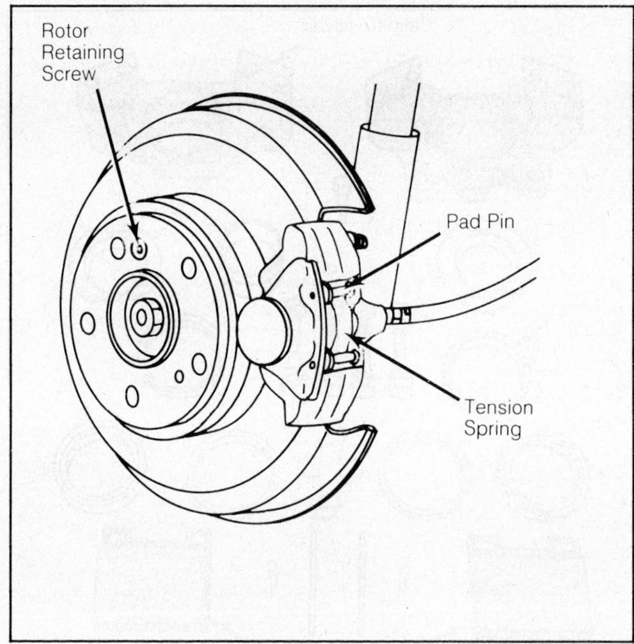

DISC BRAKE CALIPER

Removal

Raise and support vehicle. Remove wheel and tire. Open bleeder screw on caliper assembly and pump out fluid. Disconnect and plug brake lines at caliper assembly. Remove caliper attaching bolts. Remove caliper assembly from vehicle.

Installation

To install, reverse removal procedure. Replace hex head mounting bolts when installing caliper. Bleed hydraulic system. Ensure dash light goes out.

FRONT DISC BRAKE ROTOR

Removal (300 SDL, 420/560SEL & 560SEC)

1) Remove caliper assembly and hub grease cap. Remove contact spring for radio shielding. Loosen clamping nut socket screw on wheel spindle.

2) Remove clamping nut and washer. Remove wheel hub and rotor assembly. Remove bolts securing hub to rotor. Remove rotor.

Installation

To install, reverse removal procedure. Tighten all bolts and fittings evenly. Bleed hydraulic system, if necessary. Lubricate and adjust wheel bearings. See appropriate article in SUSPENSION section.

Removal & Installation (All Others)

Raise and support vehicle. Remove wheels. Remove caliper and wire out of way. Remove screws retaining rotor to hub. Remove rotor. To install, reverse removal procedure.

REAR DISC BRAKE ROTOR

Removal & Installation

Raise and support vehicle. Remove rear wheel and tire. Disconnect and plug brake lines. Remove caliper assembly. Remove screws retaining rotor to hub. Remove rotor. To install, reverse removal procedure.

REAR AXLE SEAL

Removal

1) Raise and support vehicle. Remove rear wheel and tire. Release locking plates. Remove mount bolts and caliper. Wire caliper out of the way.

2) On vehicles with starting torque compensation, disconnect brake hose holder and hang caliper assembly with wire.

3) Loosen and remove 8 mm bolt or 12 mm bolt with spacing sleeve and clamping disc at center of rear brake rotor.

4) Using rear axle shaft Assembly Tool (116 589 24 61 00) or equivalent, remove rotor from rear axle shaft flange. Pry rear axle seal from rotor at inner wheel bearing and discard.

NOTE: **If brake rotor is difficult to free from axle flange, strike outer circumference lightly with plastic hammer. Ensure parking brake is released.**

Installation

1) Coat inside of new axle seal lip and wheel bearings with grease. Install bearings and seal into rear brake rotor.

2) Coat axle splines with heat resistant lubricant and install rotor. To complete installation, reverse removal procedure.

MASTER CYLINDER

Removal

Drain master cylinder brake fluid. Disconnect and plug brake lines. Disconnect electrical wires. Remove bolts securing master cylinder to power brake unit. Remove master cylinder.

Installation

To install, reverse removal procedure. Always replace rubber "O" ring seal between master cylinder and power unit. Bleed hydraulic system and check complete system for fluid leaks. Ensure dash light is out.

PARKING BRAKE LININGS

Removal

1) Raise and support vehicle. Remove wheel and tire. Disconnect hydraulic line. Remove caliper and rotor. Turn rear axle flange until one threaded hole faces hold-down spring. Compress spring with Spring Installer (040) and turn 90 degrees.

2) Remove all retainers and hold-down springs. Detach lower return spring, opposite adjuster. Pull brake shoes apart, enough to remove over rear axle shaft flange. Detach upper return spring. Remove adjuster. *See Fig. 4*.

Cleaning & Inspection

Use brake vacuum cleaner to clear asbestos dust from assembly and check condition of linings and components.

Installation

1) Lubricate all adjuster components and sliding surfaces of backing plate with silicone brake grease. Return adjuster to home position. Install on shoes with adjusting wheel facing 45 degrees forward (diagonal swing axle) or 90 degrees forward (diagonal swing axle with starting torque compensation).

2) Attach hold-down springs, retainers and return springs. Install rotor and adjust parking brake.

Brakes

MERCEDES-BENZ (Cont.)

Fig. 4: Installed View of Parking Brake Assembly

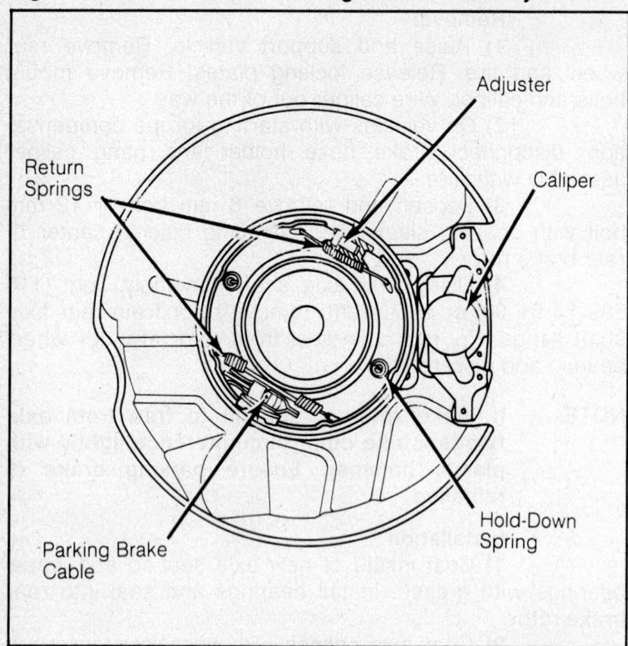

Fig. 5: Disassembled View of Dual Piston Caliper

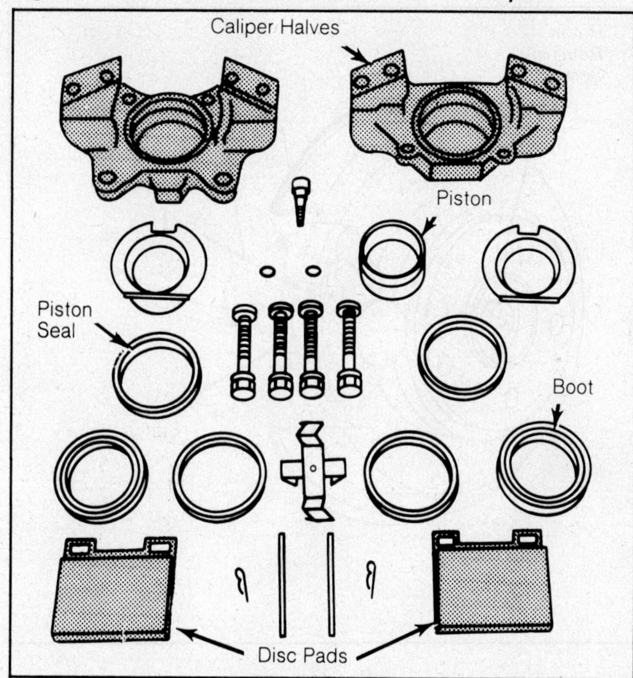

Courtesy of Mercedes-Benz of North America.

DOUBLE DIAPHRAGM VACUUM PUMP

Removal (Diesel Only)

1) Loosen upper radiator hose and drain some coolant. Remove fan, radiator shell and power steering pump "V" belt.

2) Loosen vacuum lines from pump. Remove hex head mount screws from crankcase. Remove vacuum pump with toothed intermediate sleeve and gasket.

Installation

1) Clean sealing surfaces and install pump with new gasket to crankcase. Ensure intermediate sleeve and pump locating pins are properly seated in crankcase.

2) Connect vacuum lines to pump. Install "V" belt, radiator shell, fan and hose. Check pump for proper operation.

OVERHAUL

DISC BRAKE CALIPERS

Disassembly

Remove caliper from vehicle. Place piece of wood in front of pistons. Gradually apply compressed air to fluid inlet. Remove piston. Remove dust boot from piston and piston seal from caliper bore. *See Fig. 5.*

NOTE: DO NOT separate caliper halves.

Cleaning & Inspection

Wash parts in denatured alcohol or brake fluid and air dry. Inspect caliper bore and piston for scoring, scratches or rust. Replace dust boot and piston seal when disassembling caliper. Remove small rust deposits in bore with fine emery cloth.

Reassembly

1) Install piston seal into caliper bore. Install piston and dust boot. With caliper installed on diagonal swing axle, elevation on piston faces upward. On diagonal swing axle with starting torque compensation, elevation on piston must be at bottom and project at least .004" (.10 mm) above shield.

2) Check position of piston in caliper with Piston Gauge (000 589 35 23 00). Adjust with Piston Rotating Pliers (000 589 50 37 00). Install dust boot.

MASTER CYLINDER

NOTE: Information not available from manufacturer.

POWER BRAKE UNIT

Manufacturer does not recommend disassembly of this unit. If problem is found in power brake unit, complete assembly must be replaced. DO NOT disassemble power brake unit.

NOTE: Determine whether source of problem is in power brake unit or check valve. Inspect check valve first.

TIGHTENING SPECIFICATIONS

Application	Ft. Lbs. (N.m)
Brake Pressure	
Switch-to-Master Cylinder	11-22 (15-30)
Caliper Mounting Bolts	
Front	
190, 260 & 300 Series	83 (113)
420 & 500 Series	26 (35)
Rear (All Models)	67 (90)
Hub-to-Rotor Bolts	83 (113)

MERCEDES-BENZ (Cont.)

DISC BRAKE ROTOR SPECIFICATIONS

Application	Disc Diameter In. (mm)	Lateral Runout In. (mm)	Parallelism In. (mm)	Original Thickness In. (mm)	Min. Refinish Thickness In. (mm)	Discard Thickness In. (mm)
FRONT						
190E-16	11.18 (284)	.005 (.12)	.0008 (.02)	.866 (22)	.787 (20)	.....
All Other 190	10.31 (262)	.005 (.12)	.0008 (.02)	.866 (22)	.787 (20)	.....
300SDL	11.81 (300)	.005 (.12)	.0008 (.02)	1.10 (28)	1.02 (26)	.....
All Other 300 & 560SL	11.18 (284)	.005 (.12)	.0008 (.02)	.866 (22)	.787 (20)	.....
All Others	11.81 (300)	.005 (.12)	.0008 (.02)	1.10 (28)	1.02 (26)	.....
REAR						
300D	10.16 (258)	.005 (.12)	.0008 (.02)	.394 (10.0)	.327 (8.3)	.....
All Others	11.00 (279)	.005 (.12)	.0008 (.02)	.394 (10.0)	.327 (8.3)	.....

NISSAN

Maxima, Pathfinder, Pickup, Pulsar NX, Sentra, Stanza, Van, 200SX, 300ZX

DESCRIPTION

All service brake systems are hydraulically operated using a tandem master cylinder and vacuum power unit. Maxima, 200SX and 300ZX models have 4 wheel disc brakes. All other models have front disc and rear drum brakes. Pathfinder and Pickup use a height sensing proportioning valve to regulate rear brake pressure.

ADJUSTMENTS

BRAKE PEDAL HEIGHT

1) Measure pedal height from pressure face of pedal pad to floor pan insulator, without carpet.

2) To adjust to specification shown in table, loosen brake booster input rod lock nut, and turn input rod to attain proper height. Tighten lock nut and adjust stoplight switch.

PEDAL HEIGHT SPECIFICATIONS

Application	Pedal Height In. (mm)
Maxima	7.24-7.64 (184-194)
Pathfinder & Pickup	
Auto. Trans.	8.35-8.74 (212-222)
Man. Trans.	8.23-8.62 (209-219)
Pulsar NX	
Auto. Trans.	6.54-6.93 (166-176)
Manual Trans.	6.18-6.57 (157-167)
Sentra	
Auto. Trans.	6.46-6.85 (164-174)
Man. Trans.	6.10-6.50 (155-165)
Stanza	
Sedan	7.24-7.64 (184-194)
Wagon	
Auto. Trans.	8.39-8.78 (213-223)
Man. Trans.	8.46-8.86 (215-225)
Van	6.36-6.75 (162-172)
200SX	
Auto. Trans.	7.36-7.76 (187-197)
Man. Trans.	7.28-7.68 (185-195)
300ZX	
Auto. Trans.	7.24-7.64 (184-194)
Man. Trans.	7.17-7.56 (182-192)

BRAKE PEDAL FREE PLAY

Application	In. (mm)
All Models	.04-.12 (1-3)

STOPLIGHT SWITCH & AUTOMATIC SPEED CONTROL DEVICE SWITCH

1) Both switches are located under dash panel at brake pedal. Adjust travel during pedal height adjustment. After obtaining correct pedal height, check clearance and position of switches.

2) To adjust, loosen lock nut and turn switch body. Clearance between brake pedal stopper rubber and threaded end of switch is .01-.04" (.3-1 mm) on all models. After adjustment, tighten lock nut.

PARKING BRAKE

Maxima, Sentra & Stanza (Sedan)

Remove parking brake lever cover. Raise rear of vehicle and support. Rear wheels should lock at 11-13 notches with 44 lbs. (20 kg) force applied. Loosen lock nut and rotate adjuster until properly adjusted.

Stanza Wagon

Raise rear of vehicle and support. Rear wheels should lock at 11-17 clicks, on 2WD models, or 8-9 notches on 4WD models, with 44 lbs. (20 kg) force applied. If not, rotate adjuster (2WD models) or loosen or tighten nut (4WD models), until properly adjusted.

Pulsar NX

Remove parking brake lever cover. Raise rear of vehicle and support. Rear wheels should lock at 7-11 notches with 44 lbs. (20 kg) force applied. Loosen lock nut and rotate adjuster until properly adjusted.

Pathfinder & Pickup

1) To adjust, apply parking brake with 44 lbs. (20 kg) force to obtain lever stroke of 10-12 clicks on 2WD models, 9-11 clicks on 4WD. Adjust equalizer link with adjusting nut until rear wheels are locked.

2) Release parking brake. Ensure rear wheels turn freely. After adjustment, parking brake should operate smoothly without noise or drag.

Van

To adjust parking brake, loosen adjusting rod at equalizer. Pull parking brake handle with 44 lbs. (20 kg) force. Rear wheel should lock 5-7 notches. Ensure rear wheels rotate freely when lever is released.

200SX

1) Adjust parking brake by rotating turnbuckle. Rear wheels should lock when brake lever is pulled 7-8 notches with 44 lbs. (20 kg) force.

2) After releasing lever, ensure rear wheels rotate freely, rear cables are not slack, and rear brake toggle levers are in original positions.

300ZX

Pull parking brake lever with 44 lbs. (20 kg) force. Rear wheels should lock when lever is at 8-10 notches To adjust, loosen adjusting nut at equalizer. After releasing lever, ensure rear wheels rotate freely, rear cables are not slack, and rear brake toggle levers are in original positions.

HEIGHT SENSING PROPORTIONING VALVE

NOTE: **There are two types used: adjustable and nonadjustable. *See Fig. 1*.**

Adjustable Type

1) Slowly place 221 lbs. (100 kg) of weight over center of rear axle. Attach 2 pressure gauges, one to front brake and one to rear brake. Depress brake pedal until front brake reading is 711 psi (50 kg/cm²). Rear brake reading should be 327-469 psi (23-33 kg/cm²).

2) Depress brake pedal until front reading is 1422 psi (100 kg/cm²). Rear brake reading should be 455-654 psi (32-46 kg/cm²). If readings are not correct, increase spring tension to lower rear brake reading.

NISSAN (Cont.)

Fig. 1: Height Sensing Proportioning Valve Identification

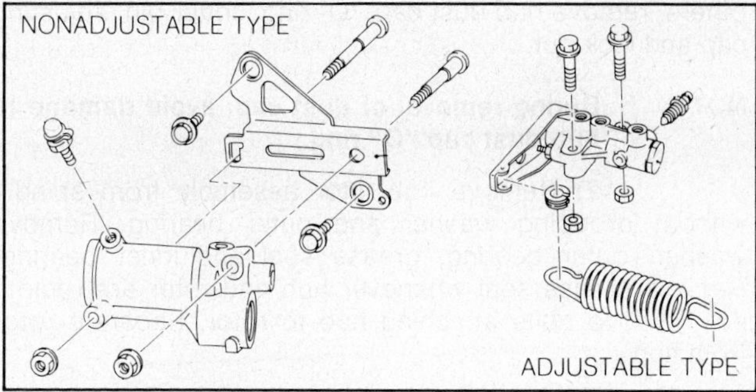

Courtesy of Nissan Motor Co., U.S.A.

REMOVAL & INSTALLATION

FRONT DISC BRAKE PADS

Removal

1) Raise and support vehicle. Remove wheel and tire. Remove bottom guide pin. Rotate caliper body upward on guide pin.

2) Remove pad retainers, shims and brake pads. Note pad condition and location for proper installation (if reusable). Minimum pad thickness is .08" (2 mm) for all models.

Installation

1) Clean piston and area around lock and guide pins. Install inner pad. Seat piston by placing lever through opening in caliper body and pushing piston into bore. Apply brake grease to pad retainer points on caliper assembly. Install outer pad and shims.

2) Install pad retainers. Rotate caliper body down into original position. Install lower lock pin. Tighten bolt, and depress brake pedal several times to seat pads.

Fig. 2: Exploded View of Dual Piston Front Brake

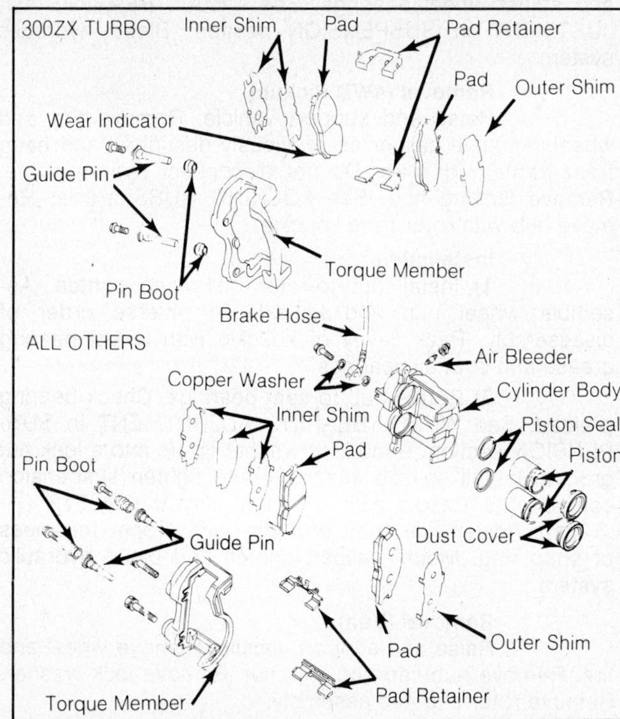

Courtesy of Nissan Motor Co., U.S.A.

Fig. 3: Exploded View Single Piston Front Brake (2WD Pickup)

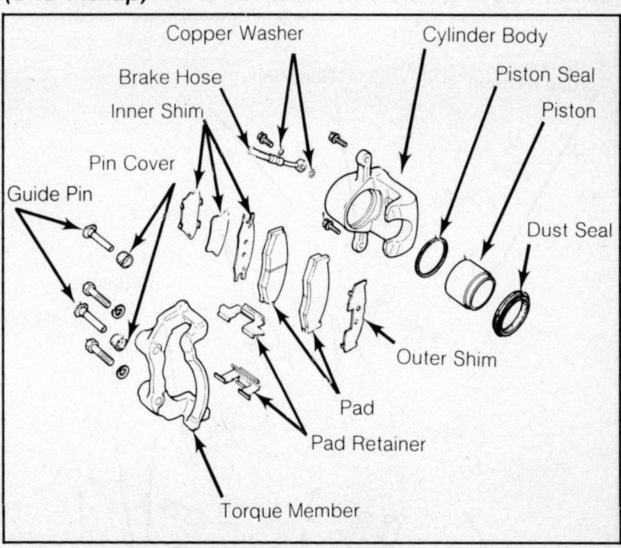

Courtesy of Nissan Motor Co., U.S.A.

Fig. 4: Exploded View Single Piston Front Brake (Sentra Sedan & Pulsar NX W/Fuel Inj.)

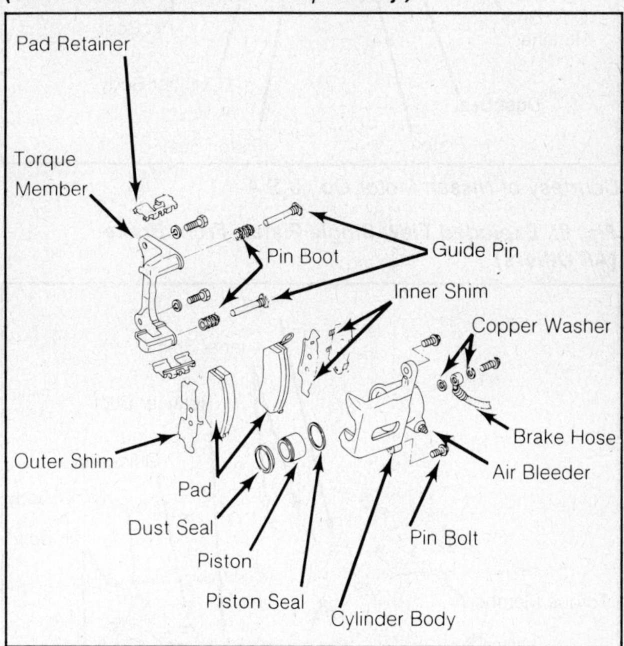

Courtesy of Nissan Motor Co., U.S.A.

FRONT DISC BRAKE CALIPER

Removal

Raise and support vehicle. Remove wheel and tire. Disconnect and plug brake line from caliper. Remove caliper mount bolts. Remove caliper assembly.

Installation

To install, reverse removal procedure. Tighten caliper mount bolts, and bleed hydraulic system.

FRONT DISC BRAKE ROTOR

NOTE: **For exploded views of hub assemblies, see NISSAN article in FRONT SUSPENSION section.**

NISSAN (Cont.)

Fig. 5: Exploded View Single Piston Front Brake (Sentra Wagon & Pulasr NX SE W/16-Valve)

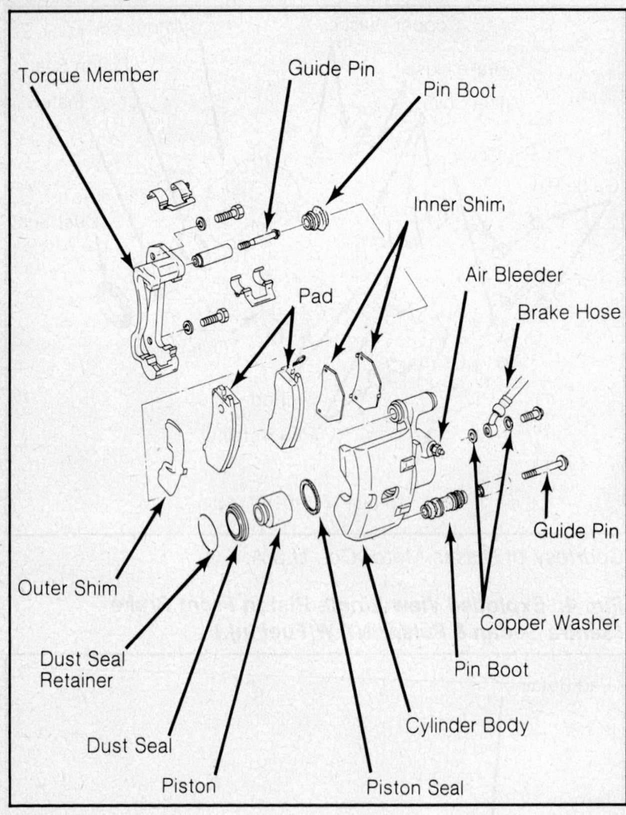

Courtesy of Nissan Motor Co., U.S.A.

Fig. 6: Exploded View Single Piston Front Brake (All Others)

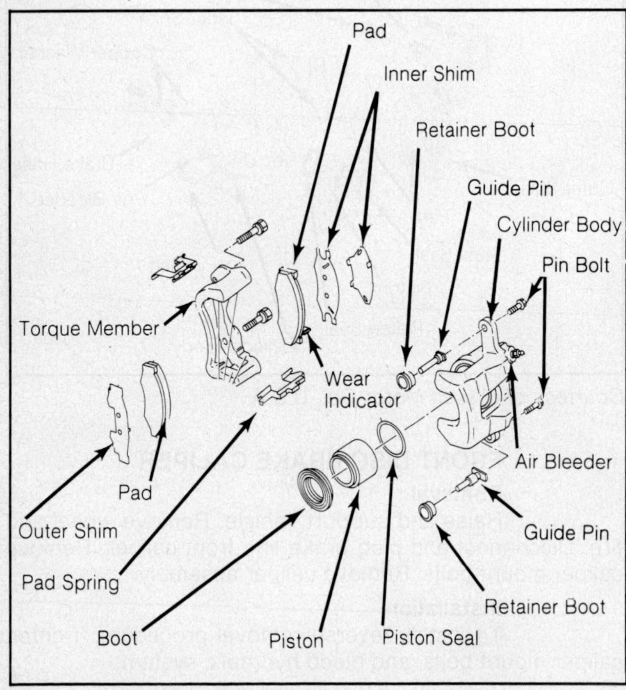

Courtesy of Nissan Motor Co., U.S.A.

Removal (Maxima, 200SX & 300ZX)

1) Remove caliper assembly as previously described, and hang assembly on frame with wire. Do not disconnect hydraulic line. On Maxima, remove rotor. All others, remove hub dust cap, "O" ring, cotter pin, adjusting cap and lock nut.

NOTE: During removal of dust cap, avoid damage to hub dust cap "O" ring.

2) Remove hub/rotor assembly from spindle without dropping washer and outer bearing. Remove washer, outer bearing, grease seal and inner bearing. Replace grease seal whenever hub and rotor are removed. Remove bolts attaching hub to rotor. Separate rotor from hub.

Installation

To install, reverse removal procedure. On 200SX and 300ZX, tighten wheel bearing lock nut to 18-22 ft. lbs. (24-30 N.m). Back nut off 60 degrees. Using a spring scale attached to a wheel stud, check bearing preload. Tighten or loosen nut until bearing preload is 1.54-3.29 lbs. (.7-1.49 kg) with new parts installed. If used parts are used, bearing preload should be .37-1.74 lbs. (.17-.79 kg).

Removal (2WD Pickup)

1) With caliper removed, remove hub dust cap, "O" ring, cotter pin, adjusting cap and lock nut. Remove hub and rotor assembly from spindle without dropping outer bearing and washer.

2) Remove washer, outer bearing, inner grease seal, inner wheel bearing and bolts attaching hub to rotor. Separate hub from rotor.

NOTE: Avoid damaging dust cap "O" ring while removing hub dust cap.

Installation

1) To install, reverse removal procedure. Coat wheel bearings and inside hub with wheel bearing grease. Install new inner grease seal.

2) Tighten bolts attaching hub to rotor evenly and adjust wheel bearings. See WHEEL BEARING ADJUSTMENT in SUSPENSION section. Bleed hydraulic system.

Removal (4WD Pickup)

Raise and support vehicle. Remove tire and wheel. Remove caliper as previously described and hang from frame with wire. Do not disconnect hydraulic line. Remove locking hub. See LOCKING HUBS article. Remove hub with rotor from knuckle.

Installation

1) Install hub-to-rotor bolts and tighten. Assemble wheel hub and knuckle in reverse order of disassembly. Pack cavity of knuckle with wheel bearing grease and coat all bearings.

2) Rotate hub to seat bearings. Check bearing preload. See WHEEL BEARING ADJUSTMENT in SUSPENSION section. Bend lock washer lip up into a lock nut groove. Install spindle assembly and tighten suspension components. Ensure axle shaft end play is .004-.012" (.1-.3 mm). Adjust axle shaft end play with proper thickness of snap ring. Mount caliper, tighten and bleed hydraulic system.

Removal (Van)

Raise and support vehicle. Remove wheel and tire. Remove hub cap and lock nut. Remove lock washer. Remove rotor and hub assembly.

Installation

To install, reverse removal procedure. Tighten lock nut to 195-260 ft. lbs. (265-354 N.m). Ensure wheel end play is 0-.002" (0-.05 mm).

Removal & Installation (Pulsar NX, Sentra & Stanza)

Raise and support vehicle. Remove tire and wheel. Remove caliper, but do not disconnect brake hose. Wire caliper out of way. Remove rotor. To install, reverse removal procedure.

REAR DISC BRAKE PADS

Removal (Maxima, 200SX & 300ZX)

1) Raise and support vehicle. Remove rear wheel and tire. Disconnect parking brake cable. Remove spring retainer. Remove pin bolts. Remove caliper and wire out of way.

2) Remove pad springs, pads and pad shim. Note location and condition of pads for proper installation (if reuseable). Minimum pad thickness is .079" (2 mm) for all models.

Installation

1) To install, reverse removal procedure. Clean area around pin bolts and piston end. Use care not to damage piston boot. Retract piston into cylinder body by turning it clockwise.

2) Apply silicone brake grease to caliper sliding surfaces and pad contact area on mounting support. Install pads, shim and pad springs. Tighten cylinder body and outer spring retainer. Connect parking brake cable.

REAR DISC BRAKE CALIPER

Removal (Maxima, 200SX & 300ZX)

Remove rear wheel and tire. Disconnect hydraulic line from caliper and plug openings. Disconnect parking brake cable. Remove 2 caliper mount bolts and remove caliper assembly. *See Fig. 7.*

Installation

To install, reverse removal procedure. Install and tighten hydraulic line and caliper mount bolts. Bleed hydraulic system.

REAR DISC BRAKE ROTOR

Removal (Maxima)

Remove caliper. Remove hub cap, adjusting cap, lock nut, washer and outer bearing. Remove rotor and hub assembly.

Fig. 7: Exploded View of Rear Disc Brake Caliper

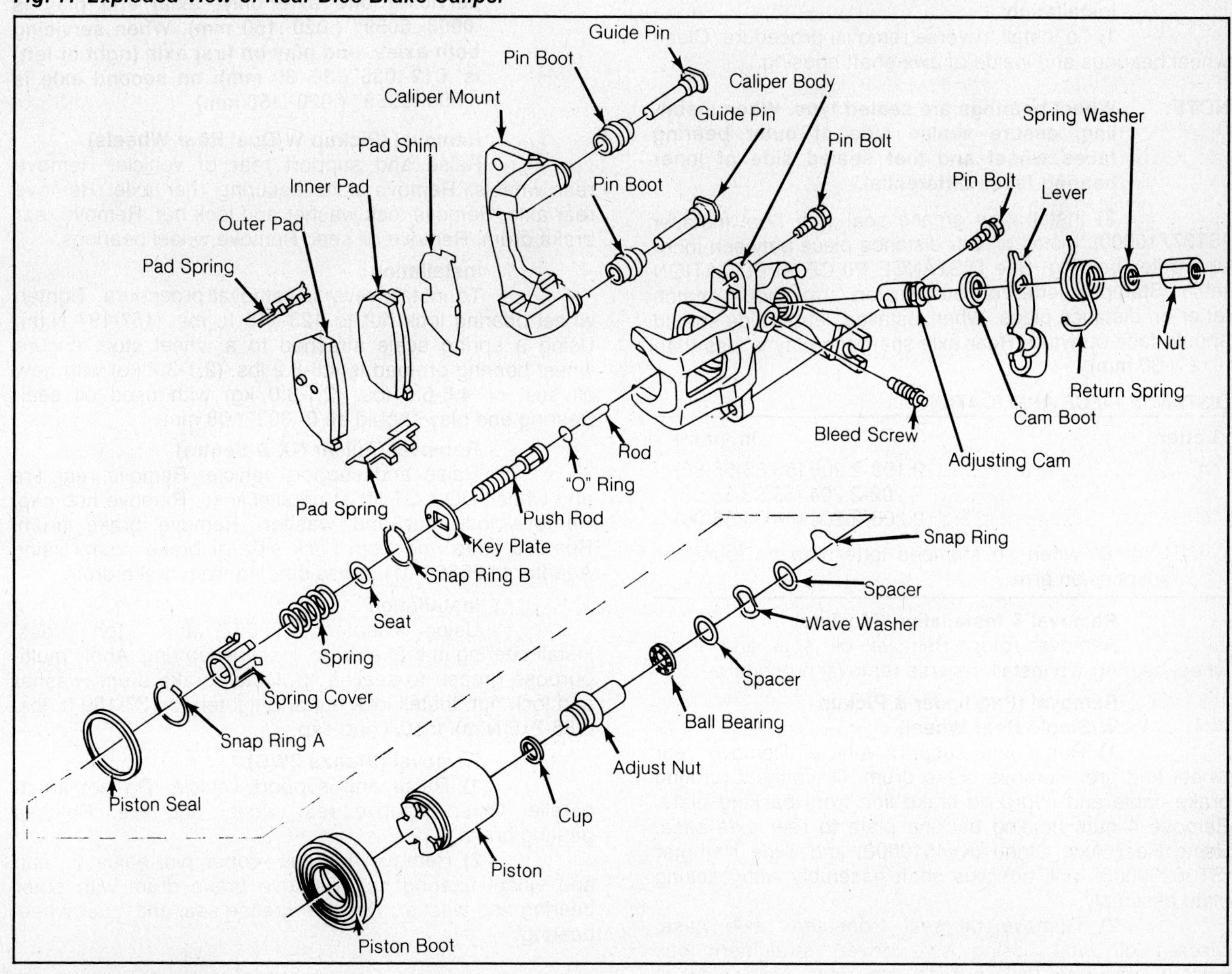

Courtesy of Nissan Motor Co., U.S.A.

Brakes

NISSAN (Cont.)

Installation

To install, reverse removal procedure. Tighten lock nut to 18-25 ft. lbs. (24-34 N.m). Loosen, then retighten to 78-104 INCH lbs. (9-12 N.m). Using a spring scale attached to a wheel stud, ensure bearing preload is less than 3.1 lbs. (1.4 kg) with new oil seal or less than 2.4 lbs. (1.1 kg) with used grease seal.

Removal (200SX & 300ZX)

With caliper removed, rotor can be removed from axle flange.

Installation

Install rotor and caliper assembly. After installation, adjust clearance between pad and rotor by depressing pedal until pedal stroke is constant.

REAR AXLE SHAFT BEARING & OIL SEAL

Removal (200SX & 300ZX)

1) Raise and support vehicle. Remove rear wheel and tire. Remove caliper assembly. Remove disc brake rotor. Disconnect drive shaft from axle shaft. Remove wheel bearing lock nut with parking brake engaged.

2) Draw out axle shaft using Slide Hammer (J-25840-A). Remove rear axle shaft. Remove companion flange and discard old grease seal.

Installation

1) To install, reverse removal procedure. Clean wheel bearings and inside of axle shaft housing.

NOTE: **Wheel bearings are sealed type. When installing, ensure sealed side of outer bearing faces wheel and that sealed side of inner bearing faces differential.**

2) Install new grease seal with Seal Installer (ST37710000). Install proper distance piece between inner and outer bearing. See DISTANCE PIECE APPLICATION table. Stamped letter on suspension arm should match letter on distance piece. When installed, larger side should should face outward. Rear axle shaft end play is less than .012" (.30 mm).

DISTANCE PIECE APPLICATION

Letter	In. (mm)
"A"	2.198-2.200 (55.83-55.88)
"B" [1]	2.202-2.204 (55.93-55.98)
"C"	2.206-2.208 (56.03-56.08)

[1] – Use "B" when no stamped letter can be found on suspension arm.

Removal & Installation (Maxima)

Remove rotor. Remove oil seal and inner wheel bearing. To install, reverse removal procedure.

Removal (Pathfinder & Pickup W/Single Rear Wheel)

1) Raise and support vehicle. Remove rear wheel and tire. Remove brake drum. Disconnect parking brake cable and hydraulic brake line from backing plate. Remove 4 nuts holding backing plate to rear axle case. Using Rear Axle Stand (KV4010000) and Slide Hammer (ST36230000), pull out axle shaft assembly with backing plate assembly.

2) Remove oil seal from rear axle case. Discard oil seal. Using screwdriver, straighten lock washer, securing lock nut on rear axle case side of backing plate. Position axle shaft in vise, using Rear Axle Stand (KV40101000).

3) Using Lock Nut Remover (ST38020000), remove bearing lock nut. Using hydraulic press and Bearing Puller (HT72480000), withdraw wheel bearing, bearing cage and backing plate. Remove oil seal in bearing cage of backing plate and discard.

Inspection

Check axle shaft for straightness, cracks, damage, wear or distortion. Check bearing for wear or damage and axial end play.

Installation

1) To install, reverse removal procedure. Install new oil seal in bearing cage, and lubricate cavity between seal lips. Be careful to place faced side of lock nut on washer side. Tighten lock nut to 108-145 ft. lbs. (147-196 N.m). Ensure washer lip fits in nut groove.

2) After installation, be sure to bend up locking tab on new bearing lock washer. Apply wheel bearing grease to wheel bearing and recess of axle case end. Apply gear oil to axle spline and grease to seal surface before installing axle shaft. When the axle shaft is installed, use Shaft Guide (ST37840000) as a guide.

NOTE: **When installing axle shaft, adjust axial end play by applying case end shims. When servicing one axle only, axial end play is .0008-.0059" (.020-.150 mm). When servicing both axles, end play on first axle (right or left) is .012-.035"(.30-.90 mm); on second axle is .0008-.0059" (.020-.150 mm).**

Removal (Pickup W/Dual Rear Wheels)

Raise and support rear of vehicle. Remove rear wheels. Remove bolts securing rear axle. Remove rear axle. Remove lock washer and lock nut. Remove rear brake drum. Remove oil seal. Remove wheel bearings.

Installation

To install, reverse removal procedure. Tighten wheel bearing lock nut to 123-145 ft. lbs. (167-197 N.m). Using a spring scale attached to a wheel stud, ensure wheel bearing preload is 4.6-8.2 lbs. (2.1-3.7 kg) with new oil seal or 4.6-6.6 lbs. (2.1-3.0 kg) with used oil seal. Bearing end play should be 0-.003" (.08 mm).

Removal (Pulsar NX & Sentra)

Raise and support vehicle. Remove rear tire and wheel. DO NOT lift at parallel links. Remove hub cap. Remove lock nut and washer. Remove brake drum. Remove snap ring from back side of brake drum. Using Adapter (J-25804-01), press bearing from brake drum.

Installation

Using Adapter (J-26082) and 3-ton press, install bearing in brake drum. Install snap ring. Apply multi-purpose grease to sealing lip. Install brake drum, washer and lock nut. Install lock nut and tighten to 137-159 ft. lbs. (186-216 N.m). Install hub cap.

Removal (Stanza 2WD)

1) Raise and support vehicle. Do not lift at parallel links. Remove rear wheel and tire. Release parking brake.

2) Remove hub cap, cotter pin, adjusting cap and wheel bearing nut. Remove brake drum with outer bearing and washer. Remove grease seal and inner wheel bearing.

NISSAN (Cont.)

Installation

1) Coat inner and outer wheel bearings with multipurpose grease, and place inner bearing in hub. Install new grease seal, coating sealing lips with grease. Install and tighten lock nut to 18-25 ft. lbs. (24-34 N.m). Loosen lock nut and retighten to 84-108 INCH lbs. (10-12 N.m), while rotating wheel.

2) Wheel bearing preload should be 3.1 lbs (1.4 kg) or less with new grease seal. With used grease seal, preload should be 2.4 lbs. (1.1 kg) or less. Install cotter pin and hub cap.

Removal (Stanza 4WD)

1) Raise rear of vehicle and support. Remove rear tire and wheel. Remove brake drum. Remove lock nut. Disconnect brake line from wheel cylinder. Disconnect parking brake cable. Using a piece of wood or brass drift and hammer, tap drive shaft to remove from knuckle.

2) Mark transverse link bolt positions for reassembly purposes. Remove all bolts. Remove rear knuckle assembly. Remove axle hub from steering knuckle. Remove backing plate and brake shoe assembly from knuckle. Remove outer bearing and grease seal. Remove inner bearing and grease seal. Remove snap rings. Remove bearing outer race.

Installation

1) Install inner snap ring. Press outer bearing race into knuckle. Install bearings and grease seals. Install backing plate and brake shoe assembly. Press hub into assembly.

2) With 5-ton pressure applied to assembly, measure bearing preload. Preload should be .4-4.0 lbs. (.2-1.8 kg). *See Fig. 8.* If not, replace bearings. To complete installation, reverse removal procedure. Tighten lock nut to 174-231 ft. lbs. (237-314 N.m).

Fig. 8: Check Bearing Preload

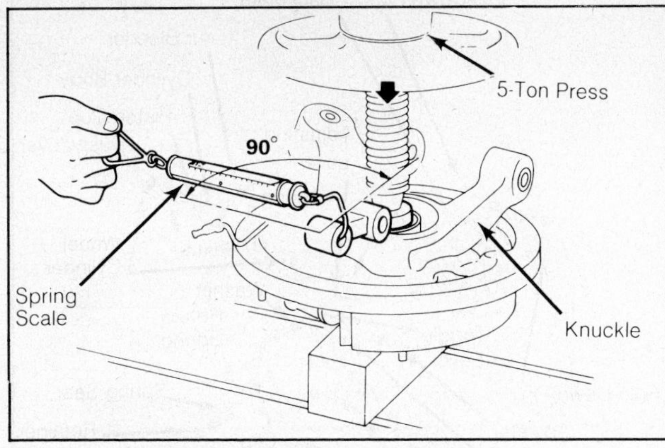

Courtesy of Nissan Motor Co., U.S.A.

Removal (Van)

1) Raise and support vehicle. Remove rear wheel and tire. Remove brake drum. Disconnect barke line from wheel cylinder. Remove backing plate bolts. Remove wheel bearing lock nut with parking brake engaged.

2) Draw out axle shaft using Slide Hammer (ST36230000). Using a screwdriver, remove oil seal. Using a cold chisel, cut collar. Using Puller (ST37110000), remove collar and wheel bearing.

Installation

Using a 5-ton press, install new wheel bearing and collar onto axle shaft. Using Installer (ST33190000), install oil seal. Install multi-purpose grease to seal lip. Install proper shim(s) and axle to obtain .004" (.1 mm) maximum axle end play. Install rear brake assembly. Bleed brake system.

MASTER CYLINDER

Removal

Disconnect electrical wiring at cylinder reservoir. Disconnect and plug hydraulic lines at master cylinder. Drain fluid from reservoir. Remove cylinder mounting nuts and master cylinder.

Installation

To install master cylinder, reverse removal procedure. Bleed hydraulic system and check pedal height.

POWER BRAKE UNIT

Removal

1) Disconnect power unit push rod from brake pedal by removing clevis pin. Disconnect hydraulic lines from master cylinder and vacuum line from power brake unit.

2) Remove master cylinder mounting nuts and master cylinder. Remove nuts attaching power brake unit to pedal bracket (Van) or firewall (all others). Remove power brake unit.

NOTE: Output rod on Sentra, Stanza (Sedan) and 200SX is nonadjustable.

Installation

1) To install, reverse removal procedure. On all models except Sentra, apply 19.7 in. Hg. Check distance output rod extends from power housing. *See Fig. 9.* Distance should be .40-.41" (10.3-10.5 mm).

Fig. 9: Measuring Distance Output Rod Length

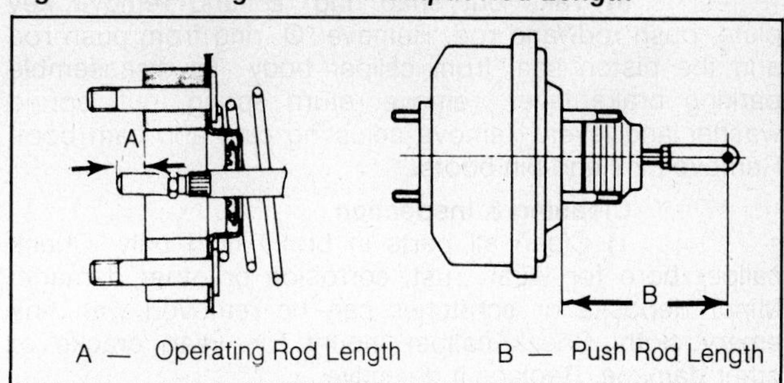

Courtesy of Nissan Motor Co., U.S.A.

CHECK VALVE REPLACEMENT

Check valve is located in vacuum line between intake manifold and power brake unit on firewall. To remove, disconnect retaining clip from firewall. Remove hose clamps, separate hoses from valve, and remove check valve. To install, reverse removal procedure.

OVERHAUL

FRONT DISC BRAKE CALIPER

Disassembly

1) Drain brake fluid from caliper body and clean exterior of caliper assembly. Remove pin bolts and separate caliper body from caliper mount.

2) Remove pad retainers and pads. Force piston(s) and dust seal(s) out of bore by applying low pressure compressed air to brake inlet.

Brakes

NISSAN (Cont.)

CAUTION: Gradually increase air pressure so piston does not fly out and cause personal injury or component damage.

Reassembly

1) Apply brake fluid to sliding portions of piston and caliper bore. Apply rubber grease to inside of dust seals. Install piston seal in bore. Install dust seal on piston and slide piston into caliper bore. Secure dust seal in piston groove and caliper groove.

2) Apply multipurpose grease to sub pin rubber bushing, main pin, and sub pin. Install seals, sub pin rubber bushing, sub pin, and main pin. Apply grease to disc pad-to-caliper mount contact portions. Install caliper mount to caliper body.

3) Install caliper assembly without pads or retainer to knuckle spindle. Install upper pin bolt. Install disc pads, shims, retainer and rotate caliper down into position. Install lower pin bolt. When caliper assembly is mounted on vehicle, turn rotor to ensure there is no excessive drag. Install front brake hose and bleed brake system.

REAR DISC BRAKE CALIPER

Disassembly

(Maxima, 200SX & 300ZX)

1) With caliper removed, remove outer spring retainer and pin bolts. Separate caliper body from caliper mount. Using long nose pliers, remove piston from bore by rotating it counterclockwise.

2) Disassemble piston by prying off retainer ring. Remove wave washer, spacers, ball bearing and adjuster nut. Remove cup from adjuster nut. To disassemble caliper body, remove snap ring "A" with snap ring pliers. Remove spring cover, spring and seat.

3) Take out snap ring "B" and remove key plate, push rod, and rod. Remove "O" ring from push rod and the piston seal from caliper body. To disassemble parking brake lever, remove return spring, nut, spring washer and lever. Remove adjusting cam and cam boot. Remove pins and pin boots.

Cleaning & Inspection

1) Clean all parts in brake fluid only. Check caliper bore for wear, rust, corrosion or other damage. Minor deposits or scratches can be removed with fine emery cloth. Check caliper mount for wear, cracks or other damage. Replace if defective.

NOTE: As piston surfaces are plated, pistons must be replaced if corroded or worn. Do not polish with emery cloth. Use DOT 3 or higher rated brake fluid in all models.

2) Check piston for rust, wear or damage. Replace if defective. Replace piston seal, dust seal, adjust nut cup and push rod "O" ring during overhaul.

Reassembly

1) Before reassembly, apply rubber grease to groove in push rod, new "O" ring, groove in adjust nut and cup, piston seal, inside of boot and sliding portions of piston and pins.

2) Install cup with lip facing center of adjust nut. Fit rod to push rod and push rod into square hole in key plate. Fit convex portion of key plate with concave portion of caliper. Install snap ring "B". Install seat, spring, spring cover and snap ring "A" with press and drift. To complete reassembly, reverse disassembly procedure.

REAR BRAKE DRUM & LININGS

Disassembly

(All Models Except Maxima, 200SX & 300ZX)

1) Raise and support vehicle. Remove rear wheel and tire. Remove brake drum. Remove parking brake rear cable. Remove retainer, anti-rattle spring, spring seat and pin from primary brake shoe. Remove return springs and primary shoe. Remove secondary brake shoe and on Stanza, remove adjuster assembly.

2) On Sentra models, remove toggle lever spring. Remove clip, washer, spacer and toggle pin. Separate toggle lever and shoe. On all models, note lining condition and location for proper installation.

NOTE: Minimum lining thickness is .059" (1.50 mm) for all models.

Reassembly

1) To install, reverse removal procedure. Using brake grease, lubricate all brake shoe sliding surfaces, adjuster nut and rod threads, shoe-to-adjuster contact points and shoe-to-wheel cylinder and anchor.

2) After installing brake shoes, set initial clearance between shoe and drum with adjuster. See INITIAL CLEARANCE SPECIFICATIONS table. After installation is complete, adjust final clearance between shoe and drum by operating parking brake several times.

INITIAL CLEARANCE SPECIFICATIONS

Application	In. (mm)
Pathfinder & Pickup	.010-.016 (.25-.41)
All Others	.014-.022 (.36-.56)

Fig. 10: Exploded View of Rear Brakes (Stanza)

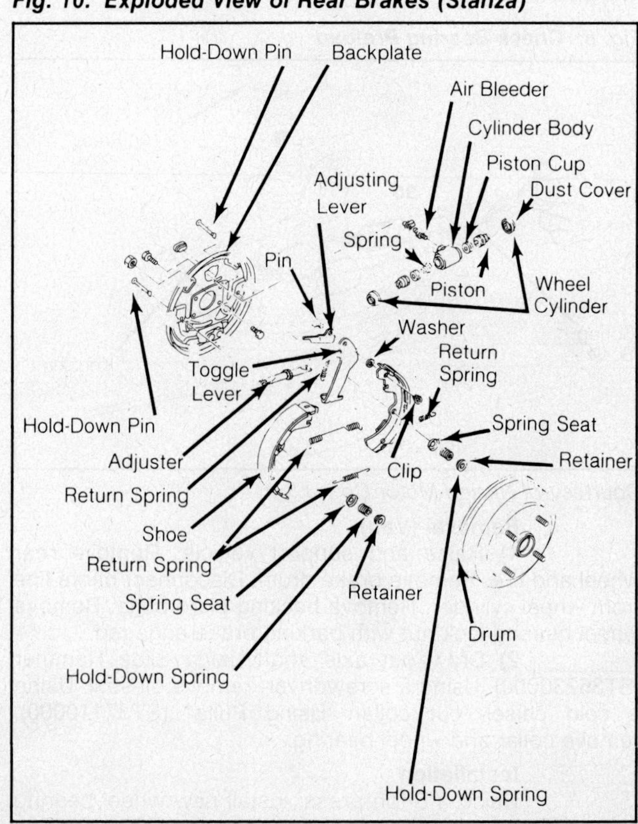

Courtesy of Nissan Motor Co., U.S.A.

NISSAN (Cont.)

Fig. 11: Exploded View of Rear Brakes (Sentra & Pulsar NX)

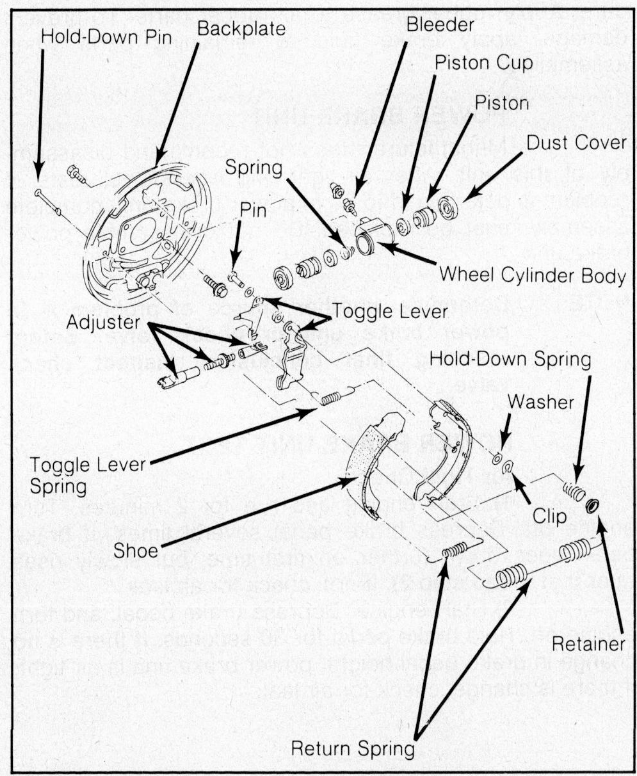

Courtesy of Nissan Motor Co., U.S.A.

REAR WHEEL CYLINDER

Disassembly
(All Models Except Maxima, 200SX & 300ZX)

With rear brake linings removed, disconnect hydraulic line and 2 mount bolts. With wheel cylinder removed, remove dust covers, pistons, cups and spring.

Cleaning & Inspection

Clean all parts in brake fluid. Check cylinder bore and pistons for excessive wear or damage. If clearance between piston and cylinder is greater than .006" (.15 mm), replace necessary parts. Replace any torn or damaged rubber parts.

NOTE: **Wheel cylinders are produced by 2 manufacturers, Nabco and Tokico. Parts are not interchangeable. Ensure repair kit matches wheel cylinder. Brake fluid must be DOT 3 or higher rated.**

Reassembly

To reassemble, reverse disassembly procedure. Apply brake fluid to cylinder bore, pistons and piston cups. Install parts using fingers only to avoid damage to rubber components.

MASTER CYLINDER

Disassembly

Remove reservoir caps and filters. Drain brake fluid from reservoir. Remove snap ring and stopper bolt. Withdraw stopper, primary piston assembly, secondary piston assembly and springs. *See Fig. 13*. Remove check valve plugs. Withdraw check valve assemblies.

Fig. 12: Installed View of Rear Brakes (All Others)

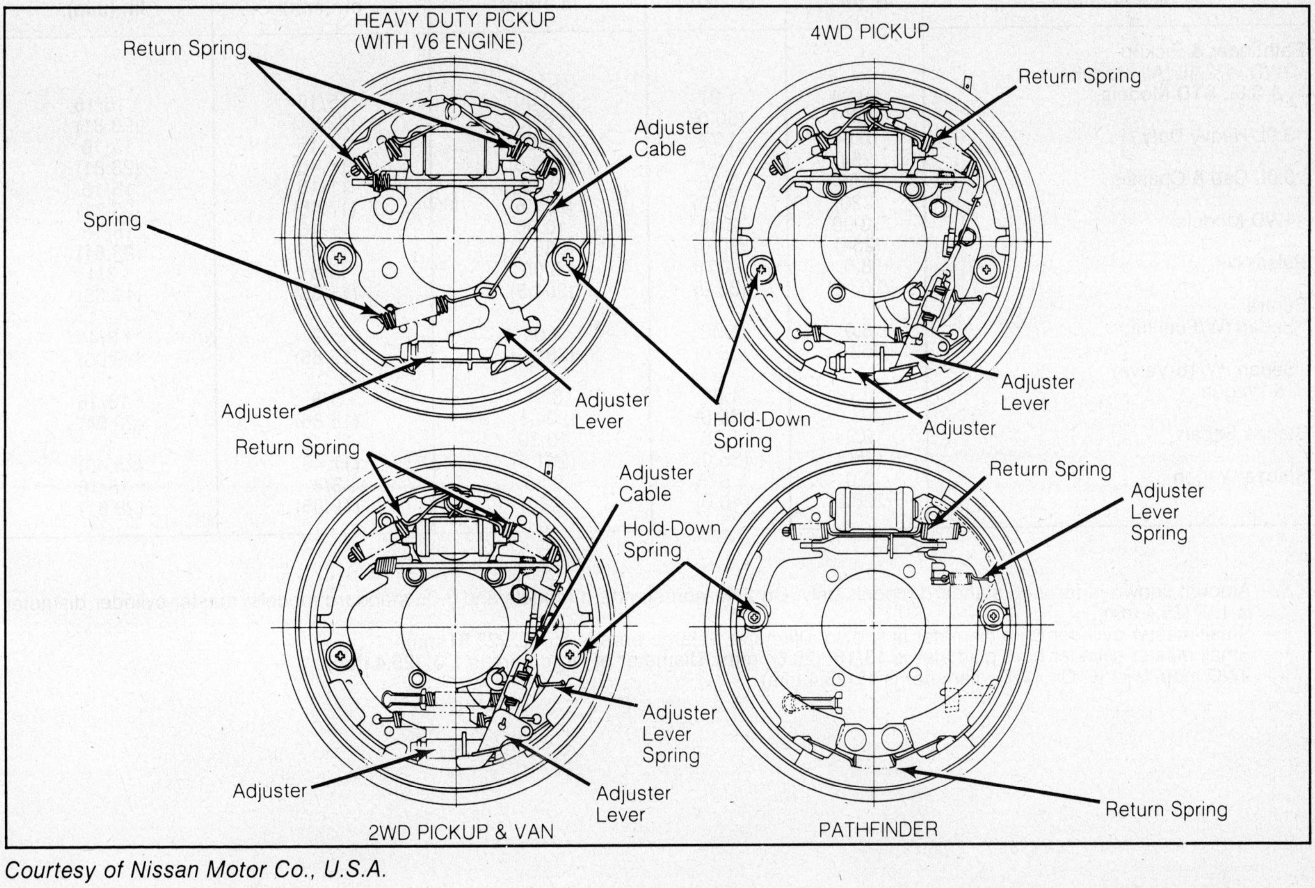

Courtesy of Nissan Motor Co., U.S.A.

Brakes

NISSAN (Cont.)

Fig. 13: Exploded View of Master Cylinder Assembly

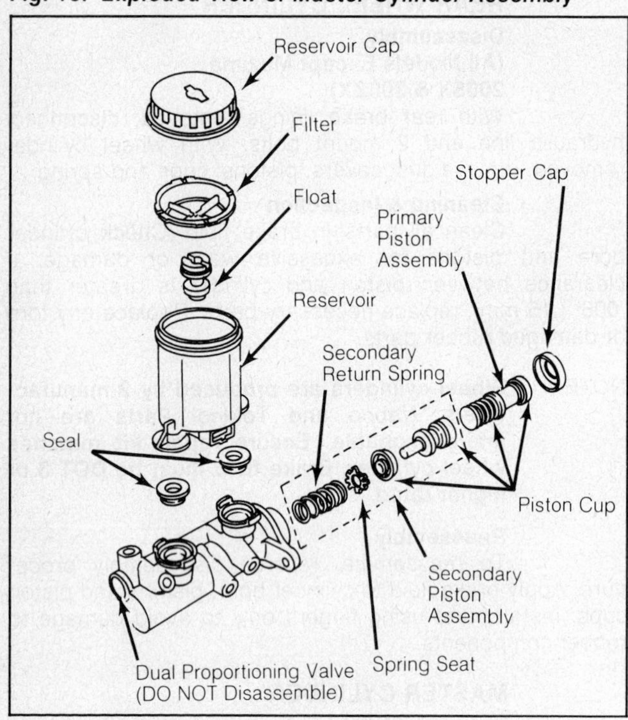

Courtesy of Nissan Motor Co., U.S.A.

Reassembly

To reassemble, reverse disassembly procedure. Apply rubber grease to all rubber parts. To prevent damage, apply brake fluid to remaining parts when assembling.

POWER BRAKE UNIT

Manufacturer does not recommend disassembly of this unit. After air-tight and operational tests, if problem is determined to be in power brake unit, complete assembly must be replaced. Do not disassemble power brake unit.

NOTE: **Determine whether source of problem is in power brake unit or check valve. Before reaching final conclusion, inspect check valve.**

POWER BRAKE UNIT TEST

Air Tight Check

1) Start engine and run for 2 minutes. Turn engine off. Depress brake pedal several times. If brake pedal goes down further on first time, but slowly rises after that, go to step **2)**. If not, check for air leak.

2) Start engine. Depress brake pedal, and turn engine off. Hold brake pedal for 30 seconds. If there is no change in brake pedal height, power brake unit is air tight. If there is change, check for air leak.

DRUM BRAKE SPECIFICATIONS

Application	Drum Diam. In. (mm)	Drum Width In. (mm)	Max. Drum Refinish Diam. In. (mm)	Wheel Cyl. Diam. In. (mm)	Master Cyl. Diam. In. (mm)
Pathfinder & Pickup					
2WD W/2.4L (All Models) & 3.0L STD Models	10.24 (260)	1.97 (50.0)	10.30 (261.5)	15/16 (23.81)	[1] 15/16 (23.81)
3.0L Heavy Duty	10.00 (254)	1.77 (45)	10.06 (255.5)	11/16 (17.46)	15/16 (23.81)
3.0L Cab & Chassis	8.66 (220)	2.36 (60.0)	8.72 (221.5)	11/16 (17.46)	15/16 (23.81)
4WD Models	10.00 (254)	2.36 (60.0)	10.06 (255.5)	11/16 (17.46)	15/16 (23.81)
Pulsar NX	8.0 (203.2)	1.378 (35.0)	8.05 (204.5)	5/8 (15.86)	[2] 3/4 (19.05)
Sentra					
Sedan (W/Fuel Inj.)	8.0 (203.2)	1.38 (35.0)	8.05 (204.5)	5/8 (15.86)	[2] 3/4 (19.05)
Sedan (W/16-Valve) & Wagon	8.0 (203.2)	1.38 (35.0)	8.05 (204.5)	5/8 (15.86)	[3] 13/16 (20.64)
Stanza Sedan	10.24 (260)	1.38 (35.0)	10.30 (261.5)	11/16 (17.46)	1 (25.40)
Stanza Wagon	9.0 (228.6)	1.575 (40.0)	9.06 (230)	3/4 (19.05)	[4] 15/16 (23.81)

[1] – Amount shown is for 2.4L standard models only. On 2.4L non-standard models and 3.0L standard models, master cylinder diameter is 1.0" (25.4 mm).
[2] – Small master cylinder bore diameter is shown. Diameter of large bore is 15/16" (23.81 mm).
[3] – Small master cylinder bore diameter is 13/16" (20.64 mm). Diameter of large bore is 1.0" (25.4 mm).
[4] – 2WD models only. On 4WD, diameter is 1" (25.4 mm).

Brakes

NISSAN (Cont.)

DISC BRAKE ROTOR SPECIFICATIONS

Application	Disc Diameter In. (mm)	Lateral Runout In. (mm)	Parallelism In. (mm)	Original Thickness In. (mm)	Min. Refinish Thickness In. (mm)	Discard Thickness In. (mm)
Maxima						
Front	10.79 (274)	.0028 (.071)	.....	.....	.787 (20.0)	.787 (20.0)
Rear	11.22 (285)	.0028 (.071)	.....	.....	.354 (9.0)	.354 (9.0)
Pathfinder & Pickup						
2WD						
4-Cyl. Engine	9.84 (250)	.0028 (.071)	.....	.....	.787 (20.0)	.787 (20.0)
V6 Engine	10.24 (260)	.0028 (.071)	.....	.....	.945 (24.0)	.945 (24.0)
4WD	10.91 (277)	.0028 (.071)	.....	.....	.945 (24.0)	.945 (24.0)
Pulsar NX	9.45 (240)	.0028 (.071)	.....	.....	.433 (11.0)	.433 (11.0)
Sentra						
Sedan W/Fuel Inj.	9.45 (240)	.0028 (.071)	.....	.....	.433 (11.0)	.433 (11.0)
Sedan W/16-Valve & Wagon	9.45 (240)	.0028 (.071)	.....	.....	.630 (16.0)	.630 (16.0)
Stanza	9.84 (250)	.0028 (.071)	.....	.....	.787 (20.0)	.787 (20.0)
Van	10.24 (260)	.0028 (.071)	.....	.....	.945 (24.0)	.945 (24.0)
200SX XE						
Front	9.84 (250)	.0028 (.071)	.....	.....	.630 (16.0)	.630 (16.0)
Rear	10.16 (258)	.0028 (.071)	.....	.....	.354 (9.0)	.354 (9.0)
200SX SE	10.79 (274)	.0028 (.071)	.....	.....	.787 (20.0)	.787 (20.0)
Rear	11.42 (290)	.0028 (.071)	.....	.....	.354 (9.0)	.354 (9.0)
300ZX						
Front						
Non-Turbo	10.79 (274)	.0028 (.071)	.....	.....	.787 (20.0)	.787 (20.0)
Turbo	11.02 (280)	.0028 (.071)	.....	.....	.945 (24.0)	.945 (24.0)
Rear	11.10 (282)	.0028 (.071)	.....	.....	.709 (18.0)	.709 (18.0)

NISSAN (Cont.)

TIGHTENING SPECIFICATIONS

Application	Ft. Lbs. (N.m)
Backing Plate Mount Nut (Drum Brakes)	
Pathfinder & Pickup	
W/Single Rear Wheels	39-46 (53-63)
W/Dual Rear Wheels	62-80 (84-109)
Pulsar NX & Sentra	25-33 (34-45)
Stanza (Sedan)	28-38 (38-52)
Stanza (Wagon) & Van	20-27 (27-37)
Booster Input Rod Lock Nut	12-16 (16-22)
Brake Line Flare Nut	11-13 (15-18)
Brake Pedal Fulcrum Bolt	
Pulsar NX & Sentra	[1]
200SX	[1]
300ZX	22-30 (30-41)
Front Disc Brake Caliper	
Maxima	
Caliper-to-Carrier Bolt	16-23 (22-31)
Carrier-to-Mount Bolt	53-72 (72-97)
Pickup	
Caliper-to-Carrier Bolt	16-23 (22-31)
Carrier-to-Mount Bolt	53-72 (72-97)
Pulsar NX	
Caliper-to-Carrier Bolt	16-23 (22-31)
Carrier-to-Mount Bolt	40-47 (54-64)
Sentra	
Caliper-to-Carrier Bolt	16-23 (22-31)
Carrier-to-Mount Bolt	40-47 (54-64)
Stanza	
Caliper-to-Carrier Bolt	16-23 (22-31)
Carrier-to-Mount Bolt	53-72 (72-97)
Van	
Caliper-to-Carrier Bolt	16-23 (22-31)
Carrier-to-Mount Bolt	80-108 (109-147)
200SX SE	
Caliper-to-Carrier Bolt	16-23 (22-31)
Carrier-to-Mount Bolt	53-72 (72-98)
200SX XE	
Caliper-to-Carrier Bolt	[2] 16-23 (22-31)
Carrier-to-Mount Bolt	53-72 (72-98)
300ZX	
Caliper-to-Carrier Bolt	16-23 (22-31)
Carrier-to-Mount Bolt	53-72 (72-98)

[1] – 72-96 INCH lbs. (8-11 N.m).
[2] – With optional caliper (without main pin), tighten to 23-30 ft. lbs. (31-41 N.m).

TIGHTENING SPECIFICATIONS (Cont.)

Application	Ft. Lbs. (N.m)
Hub-to-Rotor Bolt	
Pathfinder & Pickup	36-51 (49-69)
200SX SE (Front)	43-51 (59-69)
200SX XE (Front)	36-51 (49-69)
300ZX (Front)	43-51 (59-69)
Pickup (4WD Only)	
Drive Shaft-to-Carrier	20-27 (27-37)
Hub-to-Drive Shaft Lock Nut	108-145 (147-196)
Knuckle Arm-to-Knuckle	53-72 (72-97)
Locking Hub	18-25 (25-34)
Stabilizer Bar-to-Lower Link	12-16 (16-22)
Rear Axle Bearing Housing Nut	
Van	33-40 (45-54)
Rear Disc Brake Caliper	
Maxima, 200SX & 300ZX	
Caliper-to-Carrier Bolt	
300ZX	23-30 (31-41)
All Others	16-23 (22-31)
Carrier-to-Mount Bolt	28-38 (38-52)
Toggle Lever Nut	18-22 (25-30)
Wheel Bearing Lock Nut	
Pathfinder & Pickup (Rear)	
W/Single Rear Wheels	108-145 (147-196)
W/Dual Rear Wheels	123-145 (167-197)
Maxima (Front)	174-231 (237-314)
300ZX Rear	217-289 (294-392)
All Others (Front & Rear)	[1]
	INCH Lbs. (N.m)
3-Way Connector Mount Bolt	
Pathfinder & Pickup	60-84 (7-10)
200SX	24-36 (3-4)
300ZX	48-60 (5-7)
All Others	144-168 (16-20)

[1] – See text.

PEUGEOT

505 Series

DESCRIPTION

All models are equipped with front disc brakes. Sedan models use rear disc or drum brakes. All wagon models use rear drum brakes. Parking brake is cable activated and attched to rear brakes. Brake compensator is designed to adjust fluid pressure to rear brakes, according to vehicle load.

ADJUSTMENTS

PARKING BRAKE

Before adjusting parking brake, bleed brake system. Pump brake pedal several times with engine running.

Rear Disc Brake Models

Release parking brake. Ensure parking brake control lever, at caliper, is against nylon pad. *See Fig. 1.* Raise rear of vehicle and support. From under vehicle, loosen cable lock nuts. Equally tighten adjusting nuts until parking brake control levers are no longer against nylon pad. Loosen adjusting nut 1/2 turn. Tighten lock nut. Check that parking brake handle travel is 7-13 notches.

Rear Drum Brake Models

Release parking brake. Raise rear of vehicle and support. From under vehicle, loosen cable lock nuts. Equally tighten adjusting nuts until brake linings begin to touch brake drum. Loosen adjusting nuts 1/2 turn. Check that parking brake handle travel is 4-7 notches. Ensure rear wheels rotate freely.

Fig. 1: Checking Parking Brake Adjustment (Rear Disc Brake Models)

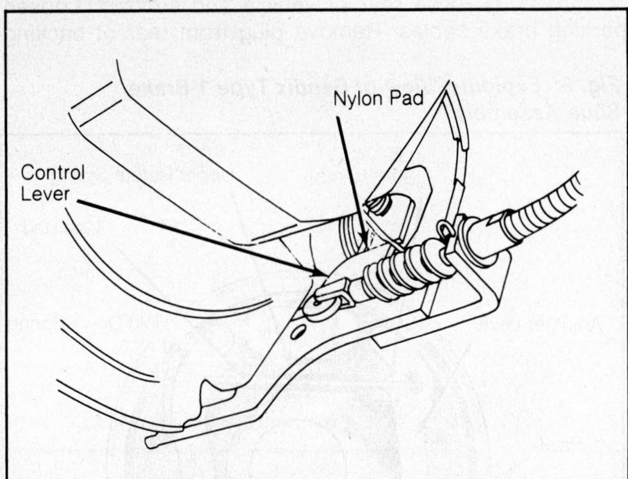

BRAKE COMPENSATOR

Feeler Gauge Method

1) Park vehicle on level surface and remove all cargo. Hang a 11 lbs. (5 kg) weight from compensator lever. Push compensator piston fully inward. Loosen lock nut. Tighten or loosen adjusting screw to obtain correct clearance.

2) On rear disc brake models, clearance should be .03" (.8 mm), with fuel tank full. On rear drum brake models, clearance should be .05-.07" (1.3-1.8 mm). With fuel tank empty, clearance should be .008" (.20 mm).

Pressure Gauge Method

1) Park vehicle on level surface and remove all cargo. Install Brake Pressure Tester (9788.69) to one front wheel and one rear wheel. Bleed tester. Depress brake pedal until front wheel pressure reading is 870 psi (60 bar). Check rear brake pressure.

2) With fuel tank empty, reading should be 609-638 psi (42-44 bar). With fuel tank full, reading should be 638-667 psi (44-46 bar). If not, move anchor point toward torque tube to increase rear pressure. Move toward compensator to decrease rear pressure. If correct pressure cannot be obtained, replace brake compensator.

REMOVAL & INSTALLATION

FRONT BRAKE PADS

NOTE: Coat back side of brake pads with anti-squeal compound.

Removal & Installation (Bendix Series IV)

Raise and support front of vehicle. Remove front wheels. Unplug brake pad sensor. Remove clip and key. *See Fig. 2.* Remove outboard pad. Remove inner pad. To install, reverse removal procedure.

Fig. 2: Installed View of Bendix Series IV Caliper Assembly

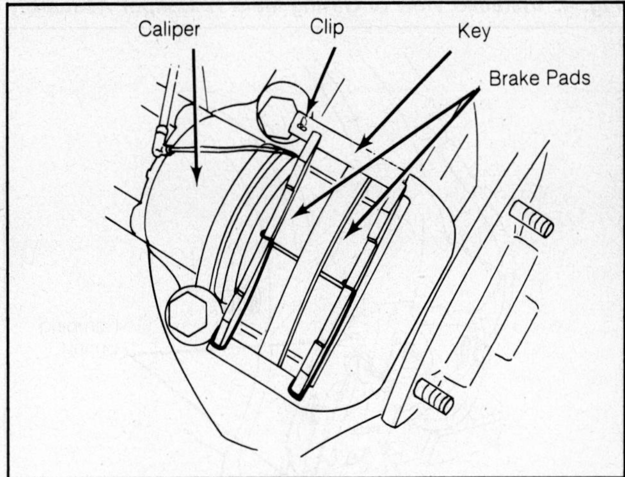

Removal & Installation (Teves)

Raise and support front of vehicle. Remove wheels. Remove retaining clip, pad pins and retaining spring. *See Fig. 3.* Unplug pad sensor. Lift sliding caliper. Remove inboard pad. Slide caliper outward and remove outboard pad. To install, reverse removal procedure.

Fig. 3: Installed View of Teves Caliper Assembly

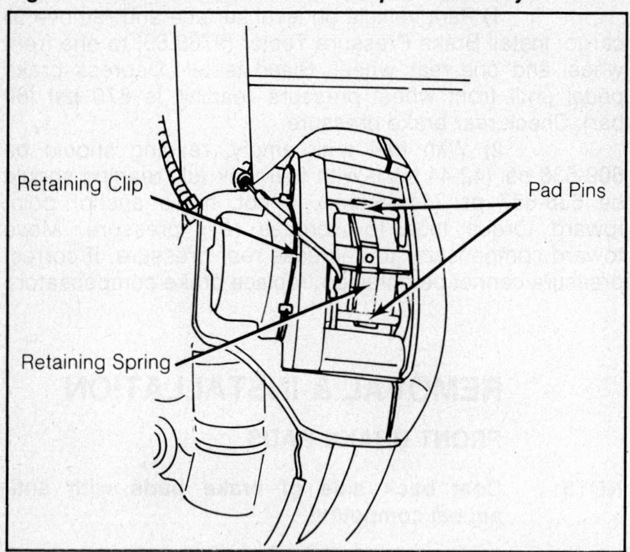

Removal & Installation (Girling Mark IV)

Raise and support front of vehicle. Remove wheels. Unplug pad sensor. Remove safety clip and retaining springs. *See Fig. 4*. Free ends of damping springs. Remove pad retaining fork. Remove spring and pads. To install, reverse removal procedure.

Fig. 4: Installed View of Girling Mark IV Caliper Assembly

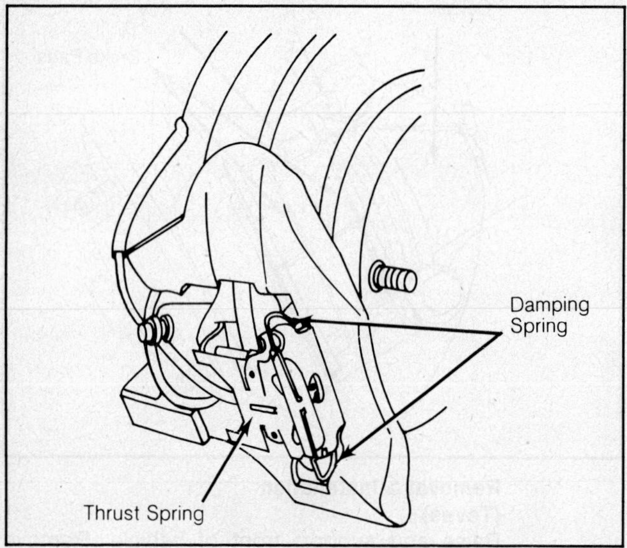

BRAKE DRUM & SHOES

Removal (Girling)

Raise and support rear of vehicle. Remove rear wheel and brake drum. Remove upper return spring. *See Fig. 5*. Secure wheel cylinder pistons. Move brake shoes outward. Remove adjuster lever and spring. Remove spacer cup and adjuster. Remove brake shoe hold-down springs. Remove brake shoes. Unhook parking brake cable from trailing shoe.

Fig. 5: Exploded View of Girling Brake Shoe Assembly

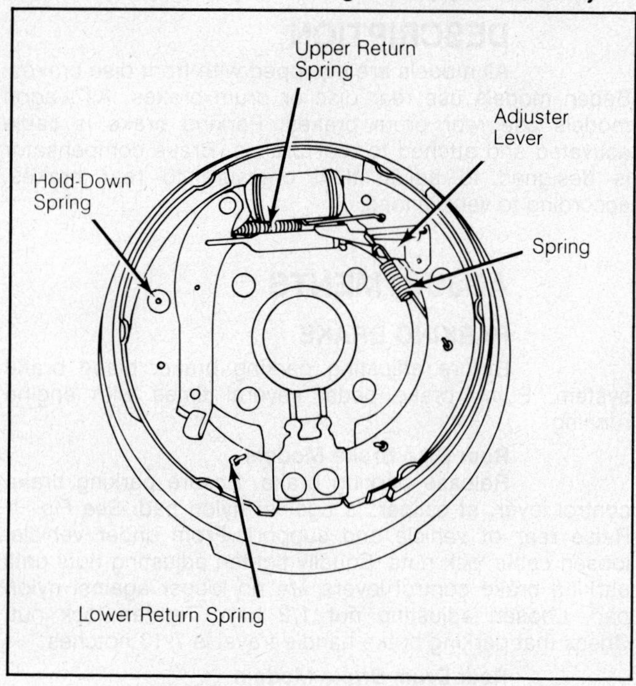

Installation

To install, reverse removal procedure. Lubricate all contact points with brake grease. Preset adjuster nut .20" (5 mm) from stop position. Adjuster on right side has left-hand threads. Other side is the opposite. After drum is installed, depress brake pedal several times to adjust brake shoes. Adjust parking brake.

Removal (Bendix Type 1)

1) Raise rear of vehicle and support. Loosen parking brake cables. Remove plug from rear of backing

Fig. 6: Exploded View of Bendix Type 1 Brake Shoe Assembly

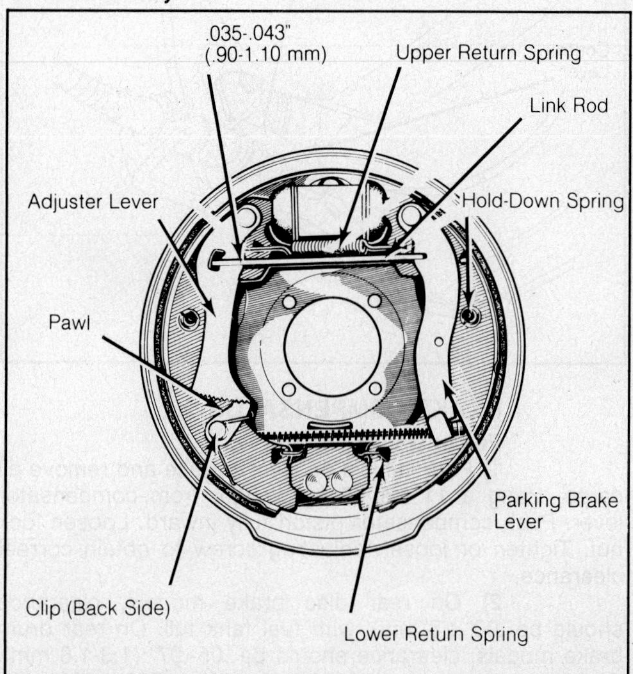

Courtesy of Peugeot Motors of America, Inc.

PEUGEOT (Cont.)

plate. Insert a screwdriver and move parking brake level outward. Install plug. Remove brake drum. Unhook lower return spring. *See Fig. 6*.

2) Check clearance between adjuster link and adjuster lever. *See Fig. 6*. If clearance is not .035-.043" (.90-1.10 mm), replace faulty part. Remove upper return spring.

3) Secure wheel cylinder pistons. Using Spring Remover (8.0803 MZ), remove shoe hold-down springs and discard. Remove brake shoes. Unhook parking brake cable from lever. Remove retainer from praking brake lever and adjuster lever and discard. Remove and discard parking brake lever clip. Check adjuster pawl pin. Replace if deformed.

Installation

To install, reverse removal procedure. Lubricate all contact points with brake grease. Place adjuster lever in rest position. After brake drum is installed, depress brake pedal several times to adjust brakes. Adjust parking brake.

Removal (Bendix Type 2)

1) Raise rear of vehicle and support. Loosen parking brake cables. Remove plug from rear of backing plate. Insert a screwdriver and move parking brake lever outward. Install plug. Remove brake drum. On sedan models, unhook lower return spring. *See Fig. 7*.

2) On all models, remove upper return spring. Secure wheel cylinder pistons. Using Spring Remover (8.0803 MZ), remove brake shoe hold-down springs. Remove leading shoe. Unhook parking brake cable from lever. Remove trailing shoe. Remove parking brake lever and adjuster from brake shoes. Discard retainers.

Installation

1) Check adjuster. Ensure bolt turns freely. Install correct new sheath. On sedan models, sheath length is .67" (17 mm). On wagon models, sheath length is .94" (24 mm). Reassemble adjuster. Apply brake grease to all contact points.

NOTE: **On some models, adjuster was fitted on inner face of brake shoe. To rectify, switch right and left side adjuster to opposite side. Mount adjuster on outside of shoe.**

2) To complete installation, reverse removal procedure. After brake drum is installed, depress brake pedal several times to adjust brake shoes. Adjust parking brake.

Fig. 7: Exploded View of Bendix Type 2 Brake Shoe Assembly

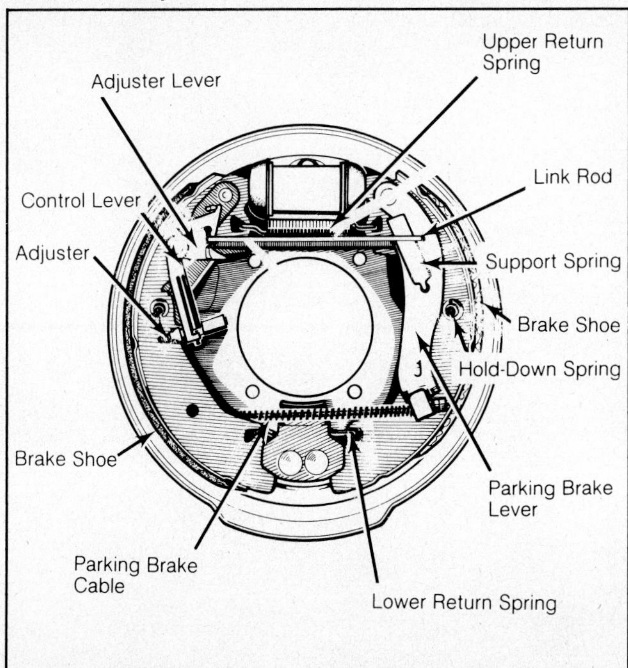

Courtesy of Peugeot Motors of America, Inc.

BRAKE DISC ROTOR

Removal (Front)

Raise front of vehicle and support. Remove bolts retaining front caliper. Remove front caliper. Remove hub nut, washer and outer bearing. Remove brake disc rotor and hub assembly. Remove brake disc rotor from hub assembly.

Installation

1) Install disc brake rotor on hub assembly. Apply Loctite to bolt threads. Install bolts, with new lock washers, retaining rotor onto hub assembly. Install hub assembly onto spindle. Install outer bearing, washer and hub nut.

2) While rotating wheel, tighten hub nut to 29 ft. lbs. (39 N.m). Loosen hub nut and retighten to 87 INCH lbs. (9.8 N.m). Install caliper. On models with Teves caliper, install new locking plate. Install Hub Adjuster (8.0616) onto hub assembly. *See Fig. 8*. DO NOT move hub nut. Rotate disc counterclockwise so hollow bolt is against slot. Tighten hub adjuster lock nut. Lock steering wheel.

3) Install Pedal Depressor (8.0804) on brake pedal. Loosen hub adjuster lock nut. Move template so hollow bolt is against other side of slot. Tighten hub adjuster lock nut. Peen hub nut. Remove hub adjuster. Ensure washer can be moved freely side-to-side in hub. Remove pedal depressor. Install wheel and lower vehicle.

Fig. 8: Adjusting Front Wheel Bearing Preload

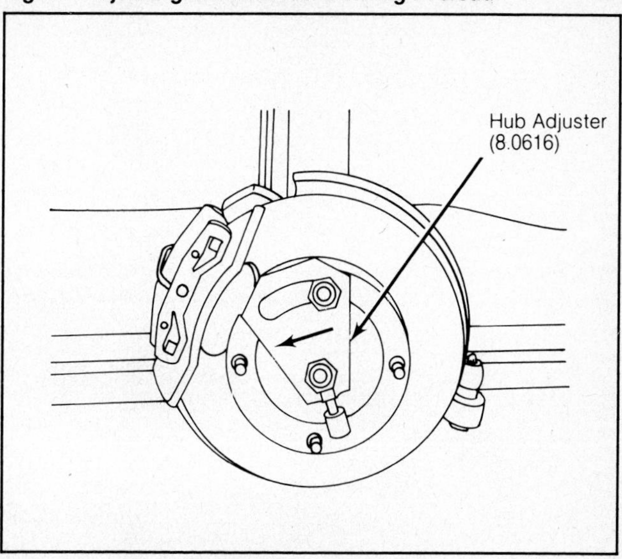

Removal (Rear)

Raise rear of vehicle and support. Remove hub nut and washer. Remove caliper and wire out of way. Remove 4 bolts securing stub axle to rear suspension

PEUGEOT (Cont.)

arm. Remove axle assembly. Place assembly in press. Remove half shaft. Using Puller (8.0521), remove hub. Mark rotor to hub position. Remove rotor from hub.

Installation

Apply Molykote to shaft splines on hub end. Apply grease to splines on differential end. Fill space between lips and seals with grease. Align rotor to hub marks. Apply Loctite to bolt threads, with new lock washers and install. Install washer and hub nut. Tighten nut to 203 ft. lbs. (276 N.m). Peen lock nut. Install hub assembly. To complete installation, reverse removal procedure.

DISC BRAKE ROTOR SPECIFICATIONS

Application	Disc Diameter In. (mm)	Lateral Runout In. (mm)	Parallelism In. (mm)	Original Thickness In. (mm)	Min. Refinish Thickness In. (mm)	Discard Thickness In. (mm)
505						
Front	.....	.002 (.05)	.0008 (.020)	.48 (12.8)	.44 (11.3)	.42 (10.8)
Rear	.....	.002 (.05)	.0008 (.020)	.47 (12.0)	.43 (11.0)	.41 (10.5)

TIGHTENING SPECIFICATIONS

Application	Ft. Lbs. (N.m)
Caliper Retaining Bolt	
Front	
Bendix	94 (128)
Teves	62 (84)
Rear	31 (42)
Rear Hub Nut	203 (276)
Stub Axle-to-Rear	
Suspension Arm Bolt	36 (49)
Wheel Lug Nut	43 (58)

PORSCHE

911 Carrera, 911 Turbo, 924-S, 928-S4, 944, 944-S, 944 Turbo

DESCRIPTION

The brake system is hydraulically-operated using a tandem master cylinder and power brake unit. All models are equipped with 4-wheel disc brakes. Rear drum parking brake is cable activated.

ADJUSTMENTS

BRAKE PEDAL TRAVEL

Pedal travel, measured from pedal pad center to point of brake application, should be 1.19-1.56" (30-40 mm). To adjust pedal travel, loosen operating rod lock nut and rotate rod. Tighten operating rod lock nut.

PEDAL FREE PLAY

Pedal free play measured from pedal pad center to floorboard should be 3/8" (10 mm), with engine off and brakes bled. To adjust, loosen operating rod lock nut and set to specification. Check pedal travel and tighten operating rod lock nut.

STOPLIGHT SWITCH

NOTE: **On 911 models and 928-S4, brake light switch is hydraulically actuated. No adjustment is necessary.**

Stoplight switch is located on bracket above brake pedal.

1) Distance "A" between stoplight switch and brake pedal, should be .197" (5 mm) when brake pedal is in neutral (off) position. *See Fig. 1.*

2) If necessary, change location of stoplight switch until specified distance is reached. Tighten and check function.

Fig. 1: Adjusting Stoplight Switch

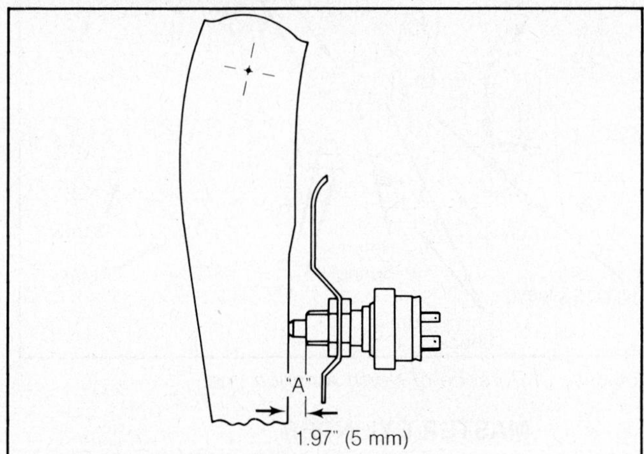

Courtesy of Porsche of North America, Inc.

PARKING BRAKE

1) Raise and support vehicle. Remove rear tire and wheel. Release parking brake lever. Push caliper pistons and pads into caliper to allow rotor to turn freely.

2) Loosen parking brake cable lock nut(s) until cable is slack. Working through access hole in parking brake drum, hand turn star wheel adjuster until rotor cannot be turned.

3) Adjust parking brake cable at rear cable end until it just begins to pull. Tighten lock nut(s). Back off star wheel adjuster until rotor turns freely without drag. Repeat operation on opposite wheel. Parking brake should lock rear wheels on 4-5 notches.

REMOVAL & INSTALLATION

DISC BRAKE PADS

NOTE: **Mark disc pads and calipers before removal. If disc pads are to be reused, they must be installed in original position. If only one pad (front or rear) needs replacing, all disc pads on same axle must be replaced.**

Removal

1) Raise and support vehicle. Remove tire and wheel. Disconnect disc pad wear indicator electrical connection (if equipped).

2) On 911 Turbo, 928-S4 and 944 Turbo, squeeze spreader spring and remove. On all other models, remove retaining pin clip, retaining pins and spreader spring (if equipped).

3) On all models, remove inner disc pad using Hazet Pad Remover (1966-2). Tab on sliding caliper frame guides outside disc pad. Push frame out away from rotor and remove outer disc pad.

CAUTION: **If fluid level is too high in reservoir, overflow will result when pistons are pushed back into calipers.**

Installation

1) Push piston back into caliper using Caliper Tool (P83) or wooden block. Remove anti-rotation locks (if equipped) and clean all parts with alcohol.

2) Inspect all parts for damage or wear. On 4 piston calipers, ensure pistons are parallel to guide surface. *See Fig. 2.* On all other calipers, ensure piston is positioned at 20 degrees, using 20 Degree Gauge (P84). *See Fig. 3.*

3) Install remaining parts in reverse order of removal, replacing parts as necessary. On 911 Turbo, 928-S4 and 944 Turbo, ensure spreader spring is installed with flat side toward brake pads.

BREAKING IN BRAKE PADS

Brand new brake pads reach their most favorable friction and wear value after a certain breaking-in time. Only then will brake pad fit correctly on disc. Intially high pedal force will go back to normal value and possible screeching should stop. Extreme braking during this period should be limited only to emergency situations.

BRAKE CALIPER

NOTE: **Some models had caliper changes during production year. Check piston sizes to ensure correct caliper will be installed.**

Brakes

PORSCHE (Cont.)

Fig. 2: Positioning Caliper Pistons (4-Piston Caliper)

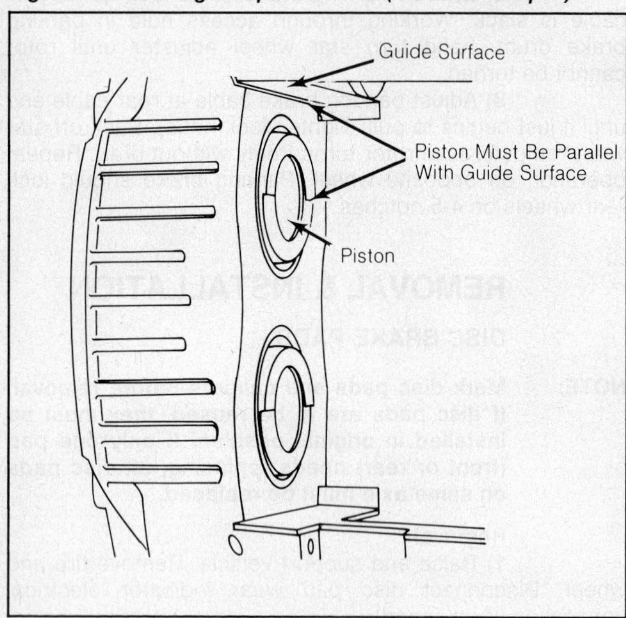

Courtesy of Porsche of North America, Inc.

Fig. 3: Positioning Caliper Piston (All Other Calipers)

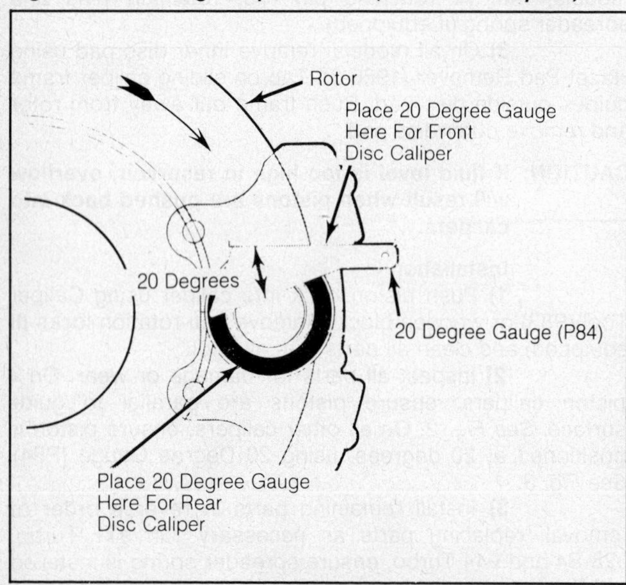

Courtesy of Porsche of North America, Inc.

Removal & Installation

Raise and support vehicle. Remove brake pads. Disconnect and plug hydraulic line. Remove caliper mounting bolts and remove caliper. To install, reverse removal procedure and bleed hydraulic system.

BRAKE ROTOR

NOTE: **Rotors must be installed in original position due to cooling holes and internal ventilation channels. These holes and channels are different for right and left sides.**

Removal

1) Remove brake caliper and wire out of way. DO NOT disconnect brake line unless caliper is being replaced. On front brake rotors, remove dust cap, loosen clamp lock screw, then remove clamp nut and thrust washer. Remove rotor and wheel bearings as an assembly, then separate.

2) On rear brake rotors, Remove spacer (if equipped). Remove rotor attaching bolts and remove rotor. Mark rotor and hub for reassembly reference. Remove hub-to-rotor bolts (if equipped) and separate hub from rotor.

NOTE: **If rear rotor cannot be removed by hand, insert two 8 mm bolts into attaching screw holes and alternately tighten bolts to press rotor from hub.**

Installation

To install, reverse removal procedure. Bleed hydraulic system and adjust front wheel bearings.

PARKING BRAKE SHOES (REAR DISC BRAKE ONLY)

Removal

Raise and support vehicle. Remove tire and wheel. Remove wheel spacer (if equipped). Turn adjuster in "loosen" direction with screwdriver applied through hole in brake disc. Detach caliper. Remove 2 screws. *See Fig. 4*. Remove brake rotor. Remove springs, adjuster and upper return spring. Remove parking brake shoes.

Installation

Lightly coat adjuster, operating lever shaft and sliding surfaces of parking brake shoes with grease. To install, reverse removal procedure. Ensure that hooks of springs engage correctly in web of brake backing plate.

Fig. 4: Exploded View of Parking Brake Assembly

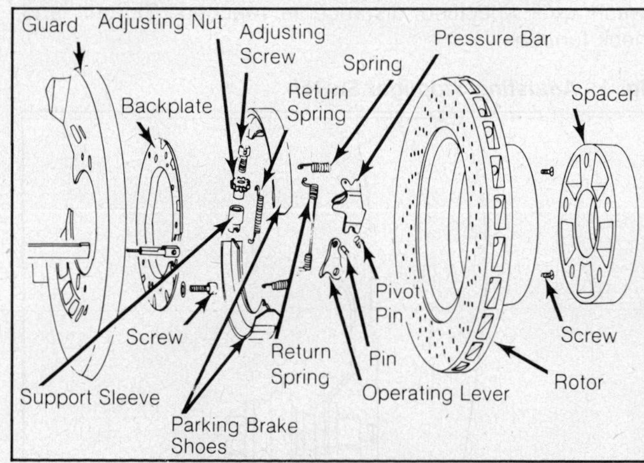

Courtesy of Porsche of North America, Inc.

MASTER CYLINDER

Removal

1) On 911 Carrera and Turbo, raise and support vehicle. Drain brake fluid from reservoir. Pull back on accelerator pedal to detach pedal from pad. Remove floor mat and floor board. Withdraw boot from master cylinder. Remove underpanel covering front axle.

PORSCHE (Cont.)

2) On all models, remove hydraulic lines, electrical connections and reservoir tubes (if equipped). Remove mounting nuts and remove master cylinder. Remove "O" ring from master cylinder (if equipped).

Fig. 5: Push Rod-to-Master Cylinder Piston Clearance on 911 Models

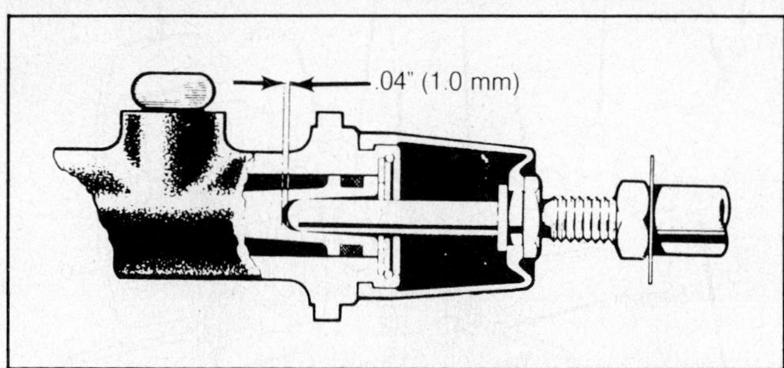

Courtesy of Porsche of North America, Inc.

Installation

1) To install, reverse removal procedure. On 911 models, be sure push rod is correctly installed and that clearance between push rod and piston is .04" (1.0 mm). *See Fig. 5.*

2) On all models, use sealing material on cylinder flange to prevent water leakage into driver's compartment. Install new "O" ring (if equipped). Bleed hydraulic system.

POWER BRAKE UNIT

Removal

1) With master cylinder removed, disconnect vacuum hose from power brake unit. On 944 models, remove oil dipstick.

2) Remove pin connecting power brake unit operating rod to brake pedal assembly, remove attaching nuts and remove power brake unit from vehicle.

Installation

To install, reverse removal procedure. Apply sealer to power brake unit mounting surface and vacuum line connections. Adjust pedal height and bleed hydraulic system. Check system for leaks.

OVERHAUL

BRAKE CALIPER

Disassembly (911 Carrera)

1) Mount caliper flange in vise. Remove dust boot retaining ring and dust boot. Install Piston Retainer (P83) to one piston and place thin wooden block between tool and piston to be removed. *See Fig. 6.*

2) Apply light air pressure to fluid inlet hole to remove piston. Remove piston seal from cylinder groove without damaging bore or groove. Repeat procedure for opposite piston after reassembly of first piston.

Separating Caliper Halves

1) Caliper halves should only be separated if "O" ring seals between caliper halves show signs of leakage.

2) To separate, remove bolts attaching caliper halves, separate caliper and discard "O" ring seals.

NOTE: **Install shorter bolts in outside holes. Tighten 2 inside bolts first, then tighten outside bolts. Bolts must be tightened in 2 stages. First to 50 percent of torque value and finally to 100 percent of torque value.**

Cleaning & Inspection

Clean all parts in alcohol or clean brake fluid. Check all parts for wear or damage and replace as necessary. If caliper piston or bore shows any signs of wear or damage, complete caliper assembly must be replaced. One side of caliper must be rebuilt, before piston from opposite side can be removed.

Fig. 6: Using Air Pressure to Remove Caliper Piston (911 Carrera)

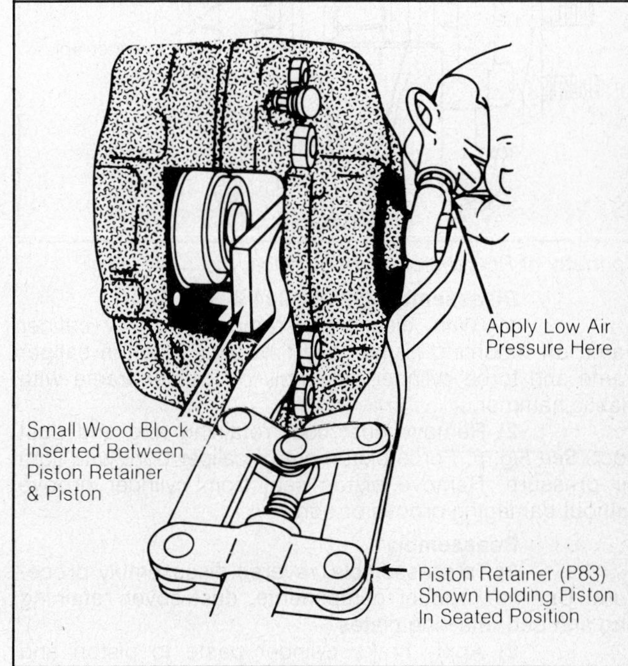

Courtesy of Porsche of North America, Inc.

Reassembly

1) To reassemble, reverse disassembly procedure. Use new rubber components, dust cover retaining ring and pad retaining plates. Apply brake cylinder paste to piston and cylinder seal.

2) Using piston installing clamp, ensure piston is straight with cylinder. Check 20 degrees position of piston with 20 Degree Gauge (P84) and correct using piston rotating pliers (if needed). Replace fluid inlet bolt and adapter seals. *See Fig. 3.*

Disassembly (911 Turbo, 928-S4 & 944 Turbo)

With brake pads removed, place a piece of wood between opposing pistons. Apply low compressed air to brake line ports to remove pistons. Remove seals.

NOTE: **DO NOT separate caliper halves. Bolts have been tighten to stretching limit.**

Reassembly

To reassemble, reverse disassembly procedure. When installed, ensure pistons are parallel to guide surface. *See Fig. 7.*

PORSCHE (Cont.)

Fig. 7: Installed View of 4-Piston Brake Caliper (911 Turbo, 928-S4 & 944 Turbo)

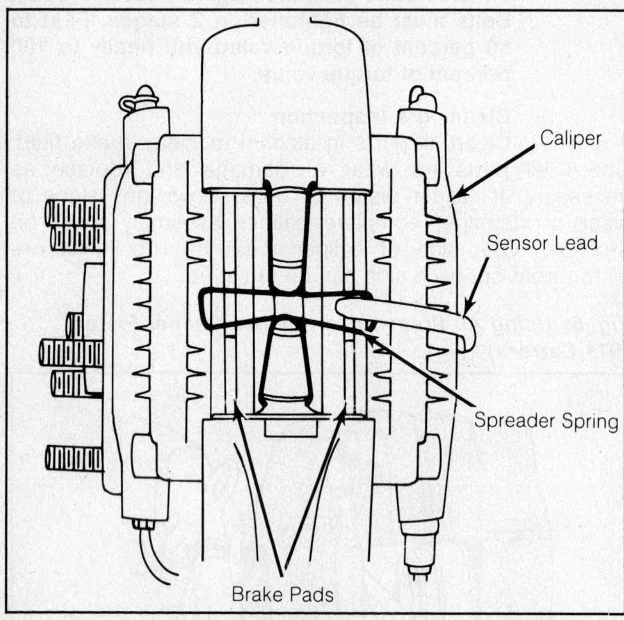

Courtesy of Porsche of North America, Inc.

Disassembly (924-S, 944 & 944-S)

1) With disc pads removed, press caliper frame off mounting frame. Insert wooden block in caliper frame and force cylinder assembly off caliper frame with plastic hammer.

2) Remove dust boot retaining ring and dust boot. *See Fig. 8.* Force piston out of caliper bore with light air pressure. Remove piston seal from cylinder groove without damaging groove or bore.

Reassembly

1) To reassemble, reverse disassembly procedure. Use new rubber components, dust cover retaining ring and pad retaining plates.

2) Apply brake cylinder paste to piston and cylinder seal. Assure piston is straight with cylinder by using piston installing clamp. Check 20 degrees position with 20 Degree Gauge (P84). *See Fig. 3.*

MASTER CYLINDER

NOTE: On models equipped with Anti-Lock Brake System (ABS), information is not available from manufacturer.

Disassembly (Non-ABS Models)

1) Push in on primary piston to remove lock ring, then remove stop plate and primary piston assembly. Remove piston stop screw. Using compressed air, remove secondary piston. Remove secondary piston support washer, spring seat and return spring.

2) To remove hydraulic warning system assembly, remove sending unit and retaining bolt from master cylinder. Using compressed air, remove pistons and springs.

Reassembly

1) To reassemble, reverse disassembly procedure. Lightly coat all parts with brake cylinder paste before installation.

Fig. 8: Exploded View of 924-S, 944 & 944-S Floating Frame Brake Caliper Assembly

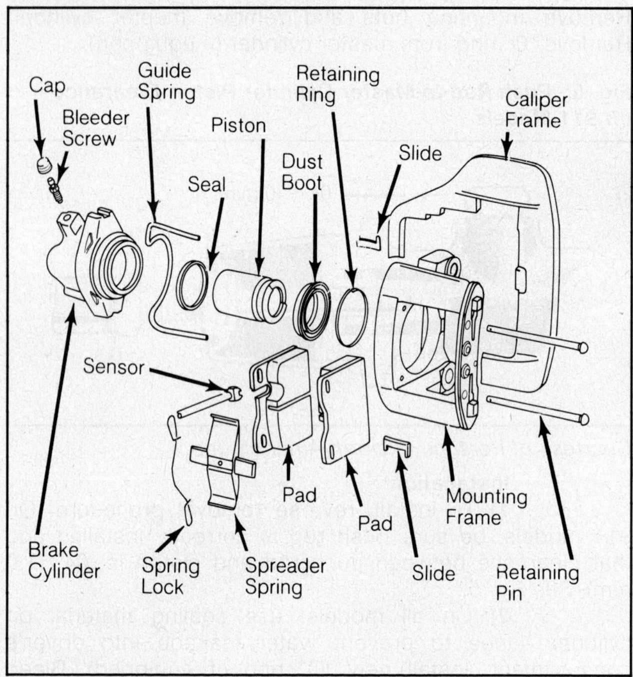

Courtesy of Porsche of North America, Inc.

2) Use new "O" ring seals on warning system sending unit and retaining bolt. Tighten all hydraulic lines and fittings. Bleed hydraulic system.

POWER BRAKE UNIT

NOTE: Manufacturer does not recommend overhaul of power brake unit. Replace as complete assembly if defective.

TIGHTENING SPECIFICATIONS

Application	Ft. Lbs. (N.m)
Brake Booster Mounting Bolt or Nut	16 (21)
Caliper Mounting Bolts	
911 Carrera	
Front	51 (70)
Rear	44 (60)
All Other Models	63 (85)
Front Caliper Housing Bolts (911 Carrera)	43 (58)
Rotor-to-Hub Screw	17 (23)
Stoplight Switch	
911 Carrera & Turbo	12 (16)
	INCH Lbs. (N.m)
Rotor-to-Hub Screw	
911 Carrera	7.3 (.8)

PORSCHE (Cont.)

DISC BRAKE ROTOR SPECIFICATIONS

Application	Disc Diameter In. (mm)	Lateral Runout In. (mm)	Parallelism In. (mm)	Original Thickness In. (mm)	Min. Refinish Thickness In. (mm)	Discard Thickness In. (mm)
911 Carrera [1]						
Front	11.12 (282.5)	.002 (.05)	.0008 (.02)	.94 (24.0)	.89 (22.6)	.87 (22)
Rear [2]	11.42 (290.0)	.002 (.05)	.0008 (.02)	.94 (24.0)	.89 (22.6)	.87 (22.0)
911 Turbo [1]						
Front	11.97 (304.0)	.002 (.05)	.0008 (.02)	1.26 (32.0)	1.20 (30.6)	1.18 (30.0)
Rear [2]	12.17 (309.0)	.002 (.05)	.0008 (.02)	1.10 (28.0)	1.05 (26.6)	1.02 (26.0)
924-S, 944 & 944-S [1]						
Front	11.12 (282.5)	.002 (.05)	.0008 (.02)	.81 (20.5)	.75 (19.1)	.72 (18.5)
Rear [2]	11.38 (289.0)	.002 (.05)	.0008 (.02)	.79 (20.0)	.76 (19.2)	.73 (18.6)
928-S4 [1]						
Front	11.97 (304.0)	.002 (.05)	.0008 (.02)	1.26 (32.0)	1.20 (30.5)	1.17 (29.7)
Rear [2]	11.77 (299.0)	.002 (.05)	.0008 (.02)	.94 (24.0)	.89 (22.6)	.87 (22.0)
944 Turbo [1]						
Front	11.73 (298.0)	.002 (.05)	.0008 (.02)	1.10 (28.0)	1.05 (26.6)	1.02 (26.0)
Rear [2]	11.77 (299.0)	.002 (.05)	.0008 (.02)	.94 (24.0)	.89 (22.6)	.87 (22.0)

[1] – Installed lateral run-out is .004" (.10 mm) maximum.
[2] – Parking brake drum diameter is 7.087" (180 mm) standard. Maximum wear limit is 7.126" (181 mm).

SAAB 900, 900S & 900 TURBO

DESCRIPTION

Front brakes have sliding-yoke Girling calipers. Rear brakes are fixed-yoke ATE units. Brake circuit is a diagonal system (right front/left rear and left front/right rear). The mechanical parking brake is self-adjusting and cable operates the FRONT caliper assemblies. Tandem master cylinder contains a level sensor. Warning light on instrument panel comes on if fluid level is low.

ADJUSTMENTS

PARKING BRAKE

NOTE: **If new cable(s) are being installed, apply parking brake several times to stretch cable(s).**

Parking Brake Lever

1) Slide seat completely forward for access to adjustment panel in shift lever tunnel. Remove console top cover, side access cover and rear ashtray as necessary.

NOTE: **Parking brake cables are crisscrossed. To adjust left brake cable, right adjusting nut must be rotated.**

2) To adjust, rotate cable adjusting nuts (under plastic cover at rear of parking brake lever). With parking brake lever released, distance between back edge of parking brake lever (on front caliper) and yoke should be .02" (.5 mm). *See Fig. 1.*

3) After parking brake lever-to-yoke adjustment, ensure clearance is the same on both sides. Parking brake lever should pull up 7-9 notches.

Fig. 1: Adjusting Parking Brake Lever-To-Yoke Position

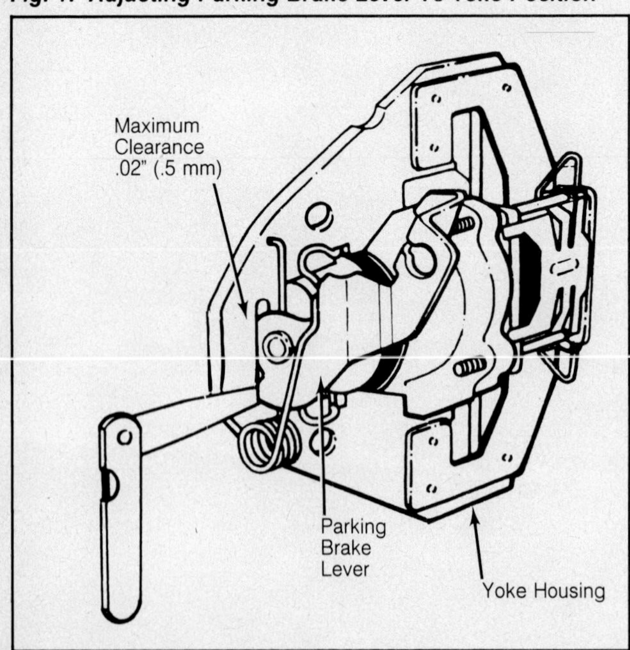

Courtesy of Saab-Scania of America, Inc.

BRAKE WARNING LIGHT

1) Brake warning lights are mounted on instrument panel. Turn ignition on. Parking brake light should glow when brake lever is pulled 2-3 notches.

2) Light should go off when lever is fully released. If light does not glow after proper lever movement, adjust the switch (located under lever) as necessary.

3) To check fluid level indicator circuit, turn ignition on. Push button on brake master cylinder downward. Warning light should glow. If not, check bulb, circuit connections and sensor.

REMOVAL & INSTALLATION

DISC BRAKE PADS

NOTE: **Ensure rotors are resurfaced or replaced each time new brake pads are installed.**

Removal (Front)

1) Raise and support vehicle. Remove wheels. Rotate disc so recess on disc edge is in-line with brake pads. Remove anti-rattle spring, damper spring and pad retaining pin.

2) If retaining pin is difficult to remove, use slide hammer and Retaining Pin Remover (89 96 175) to tap out pin. Remove brake pads. If pads are difficult to remove, use Brake Pad Extractor (89 95 771).

Inspection

1) Inspect brake pads for excessive or uneven wear. Minimum brake pad thickness is .125" (3.2 mm). Replace pads if necessary.

2) Check all components for wear and damage. Replace any damaged or worn component.

Installation

1) If necessary, siphon fluid from master cylinder to prevent overflow. Lubricate yoke sliding surfaces using Gleitmo 540 (45 30 08 612).

CAUTION: **Do not insert caliper piston excessively or piston seal will be damaged. Piston must be inserted no farther than flush with rotor side of caliper face.**

2) Rotate "direct" piston with Piston Wrench (89 96 043) as piston is pressed into cylinder. Ensure piston movement has not moved dust cover and yoke moves easily in grooves on housing. Once piston is moved back in caliper, automatic parking brake adjustment will be reset.

3) Install brake pads. Adjust parking brake cables if necessary. Pump brake pedal several times to build system pressure. Pull parking brake lever up 5 notches. Continue to pump pedal until parking brake lever operates after being pulled up to full operational position (7-9 notches).

Removal (Rear)

Raise and support vehicle. Remove wheels. Remove anti-rattle spring. Remove brake pads and shims. If pads are difficult to remove, use Brake Pad Extractor (89 95 771).

Inspection

1) Inspect brake pads for excessive or uneven wear. Minimum brake pad thickness is .125" (3.2 mm). Replace pads if necessary.

2) Inspect all components for wear and damage. Repair or replace any damaged or worn component.

SAAB 900, 900S & 900 TURBO (Cont.)

Installation

1) If necessary, siphon fluid from master cylinder to prevent overflow. Using handle of Piston Wrench (89 96 043), push pistons back no farther than is needed to install pads. Install shims and new pads. Ensure piston position is correct. *See Fig. 5.*

2) To complete installation, reverse removal procedure. Pump brake pedal several times to regain proper pedal position.

DISC BRAKE CALIPER

Removal (Front & Rear)

Raise and support vehicle. Remove wheels. Remove brake pads. On front wheel calipers, disconnect parking brake cable from lever on caliper. On all calipers, disconnect hydraulic lines and plug. Remove caliper assembly.

Inspection

Inspect front and/or rear caliper assemblies for damage, corrosion or leakage at each piston dust cover or between rear caliper halves. Rebuild or replace caliper as necessary. See OVERHAUL in this article.

NOTE: **If leakage is found between rear caliper halves, do not attempt to separate and rebuild component. Replace the rear caliper as an assembly.**

Installation

1) To install, reverse removal procedure. Lubricate front caliper-to-yoke sliding surfaces. If necessary, rotate front caliper piston with Piston Wrench (89 96 043) to move piston into cylinder.

2) Rotate rear caliper piston to proper position (if necessary) using Piston Installer (89 95 367), then check position with template. *See Fig. 5.*

3) Install brake pads. Mount caliper and install hydraulic line. Tighten mount bolts using new locking plate. Bleed hydraulic system. Adjust parking brake cables.

DISC BRAKE ROTOR

NOTE: **Before removing wheels, check for excessive wheel bearing runout. Before removing rotor, check it for excessive runout.**

Removal (Front & Rear)

1) Raise and support vehicle. Remove wheels. Remove brake pads, springs, shims and pad retaining pin.

2) Detach caliper yoke bracket mounting bolts from steering knuckle and remove caliper and bracket assembly. Detach 2 rotor-to-hub mounting screws (Phillips). Remove rotor from hub.

3) On rear wheels, remove wheel hub caps. Raise and support vehicle. Remove wheels. Remove brake pad assemblies. Detach caliper and bracket assembly mounting bolts. Detach brake line and plug openings. Hang bracket assembly out of work area with wire.

4) Detach 2 rotor-to-hub mounting screws. Pull rotor from rear hub. If rear hub must be removed, detach hub dust cap. Loosen and remove hub nut and washer, then pull hub and bearing assembly from spindle using Hub Puller (89 96 084) and 4 Extension Pieces (89 96 050).

NOTE: **Rear wheel bearings are integral with hub. If worn or damaged, components must be replaced as an assembly.**

Installation

1) Install hub assembly onto spindle. Install hub washer and hub nut. Tighten hub nut to 214-229 ft. lbs. (290-310 N.m). Using a round-nosed drift, tap nut collar into groove in spindle to lock hub nut in position. Install hub dust cap.

2) To complete front hub and rotor installation, reverse removal procedure. Recheck wheel bearing runout. Maximum hub (wheel bearing) runout is .08" (2 mm), as measured from edge of rim. Adjust parking brake cables at front calipers if necessary.

MASTER CYLINDER

Removal

1) Remove electrical lead to fluid level warning switch on master cylinder. Disconnect clutch master cylinder hose from fluid reservoir. Plug reservoir nipple to prevent fluid loss.

2) Disconnect hydraulic lines and drain fluid from master cylinder. Remove master cylinder-to-power brake unit mounting nuts. Lift off master cylinder.

Installation

To install, reverse removal procedure. Bench bleed master cylinder, then install unit and bleed hydraulic system.

POWER BRAKE UNIT

Removal

1) Remove steering column bearing cover, ashtray and lower dash panel screw (behind ashtray). Working in engine compartment, remove lower dash panel outer bolts. One bolt is located near the vacuum tank (on firewall), and other bolt is on firewall rearward of fuse block.

2) Remove center console (if equipped). Disconnect electrical leads, hydraulic and vacuum lines from master cylinder and power brake unit. Plug hydraulic lines to prevent fluid loss. Remove cotter pin from brake pedal push rod.

3) Remove 4 power brake unit mounting nuts from inside vehicle. Lift out master cylinder and power brake unit as an assembly. Detach master cylinder as necessary.

NOTE: **Power brake unit is non-serviceable. Replace as a unit. The dome nut on output push rod is set by the factory. Do not adjust.**

Installation

To install, reverse removal procedure and bleed hydraulic system.

Check Valve Replacement

Remove hose clamps and check valve from power unit. To install, reverse removal procedure.

Filter Replacement

Remove power brake unit. Remove dust boot and filter retainer. Withdraw silencer and filter from end of unit. To install, cut slit in filter and slip over push rod. Reverse removal procedure. Ensure slots in filter and silencer are 180 degrees apart.

REAR AXLE BEARINGS & SEAL

To remove rear hub or to remove axle bearing(s) and seal from rear hub, see DISC BRAKE ROTOR in this article.

SAAB 900, 900S & 900 TURBO (Cont.)

OVERHAUL

CALIPER ASSEMBLY

Disassembly (Girling Type)

1) With caliper and yoke housing assembly removed and cleaned, mount assembly in a soft-jawed vise. Remove parking brake lever return spring. Separate yoke from caliper assembly. *See Fig. 2.*

2) Remove return spring and parking brake lever from yoke. Remove dust boot retaining ring and dust boot. With compressed air, force "indirect" piston from the caliper.

3) Press out "direct" piston and push rod by hand, then remove from caliper bore. Remove "O" rings and sealing rings from caliper bore and pistons. Remove parking brake lever retainer and "O" rings from "indirect" piston bore.

Cleaning & Inspection

Wash parts, except "indirect" piston assembly, in clean brake fluid. Dry with lint-free cloth. Inspect for corrosion, damage or excessive wear. Standard front caliper bore I.D. is 2.13" (54 mm). Replace defective components and all rubber parts during overhaul.

NOTE: Do not use solvent or brake fluid to clean "indirect" piston assembly. Wipe with a clean cloth only.

Fig. 2: Exploded View of Girling Caliper

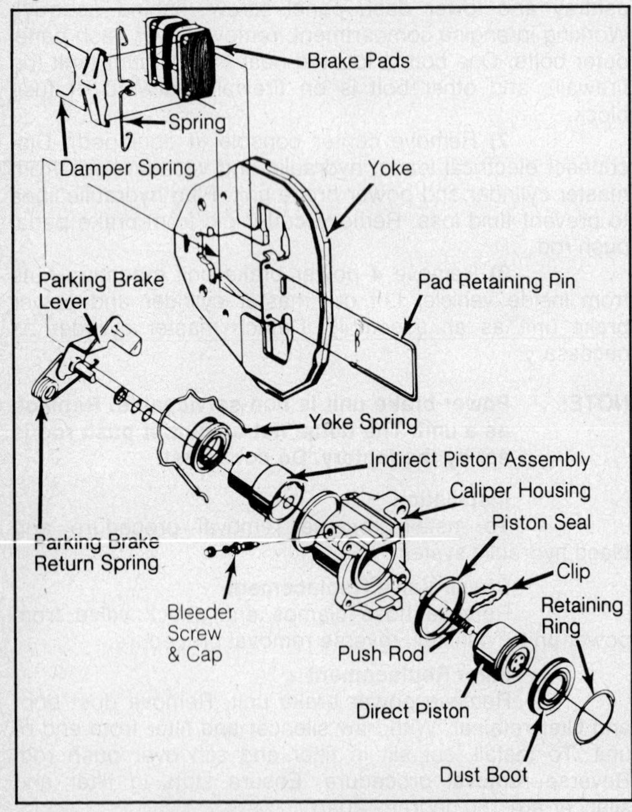

Courtesy of Saab-Scania of America, Inc.

Reassembly

1) Replace any worn, damaged or corroded parts. On "indirect" piston, replace "O" ring on push rod and "O" ring retainer at parking brake lever. Lubricate cylinder bore with brake fluid. Install new piston seals.

2) Lubricate hole for parking brake lever with brake lubricant. Install anchor plate to push rod. Install push rod into hole in "indirect" piston. Ensure recess in anchor plate comes immediately over spring in piston. Lubricate "indirect" piston and insert in caliper housing.

NOTE: When installing "indirect" piston, ensure yoke recess on piston is in-line with groove in caliper housing.

3) Push "direct" piston into cylinder. Using Piston Wrench (89 96 043), screw together piston and push rod. Push in both pistons until edges of dust cover grooves are flush with caliper. Install new dust covers and retaining rings. Install yoke spring and parking brake lever to yoke.

4) Brush Castrol-45 grease (30 08 612) on yoke sliding surfaces. Apply grease to seating surface of pad retaining disc in housing. Align yoke guide edges with grooves in caliper housing. Lift parking brake lever. Install end of axle pin into hole in "indirect" piston.

5) Ensure yoke fits correctly into recess in "indirect" piston. Install parking lever return spring. Check clearance between sliding surface of yoke and brake housing. No clearance is allowed on bleeder screw side. Opposite side must have .006-.012" (.15-.30 mm) clearance. *See Fig. 3.*

Fig. 3: Girling Caliper Clearance Measuring Points

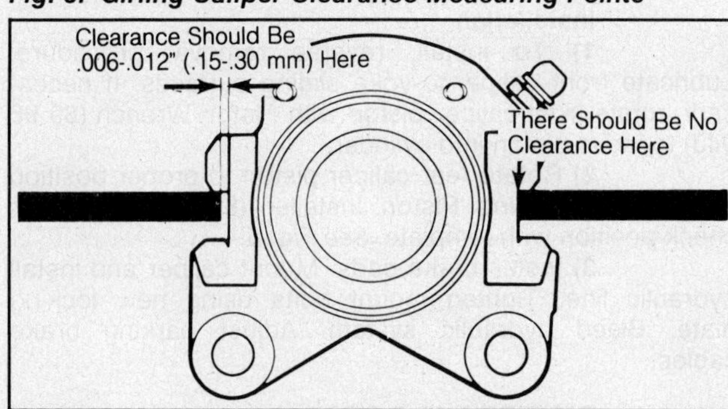

Courtesy of Saab-Scania of America, Inc.

Disassembly (ATE Type)

1) Remove caliper and brake pad assemblies. Clean caliper assembly thoroughly. Remove dust cover retaining rings and dust covers. *See Fig. 4.*

2) Insert wood block between pistons. Apply compressed air to fluid inlet port to force pistons out of cylinder bores. Remove piston seals from bores. Remove bleeder screw. Do not separate caliper halves.

Cleaning & Inspection

Wash parts in clean brake fluid. Inspect cylinder bores and pistons for corrosion, damage or excessive wear. Standard rear caliper bore I.D. is 1.18" (30 mm). Replace defective parts. All rubber parts must be replaced during overhaul.

Reassembly

1) Coat all parts with clean brake fluid. Install new piston seals in cylinder bores. Using Piston Installer (89 95 367), carefully install pistons into cylinder bores.

2) Check piston position with Template (89 95 342). Template gauge must be held against lower surface of caliper. *See Fig. 5.* Install new rubber dust boots and retainer rings. Install bleeder screw and brake pad assemblies. Ensure stamped areas of brake pads coincide with recess in pistons.

SAAB 900, 900S & 900 TURBO (Cont.)

Fig. 4: Exploded View of ATE Caliper

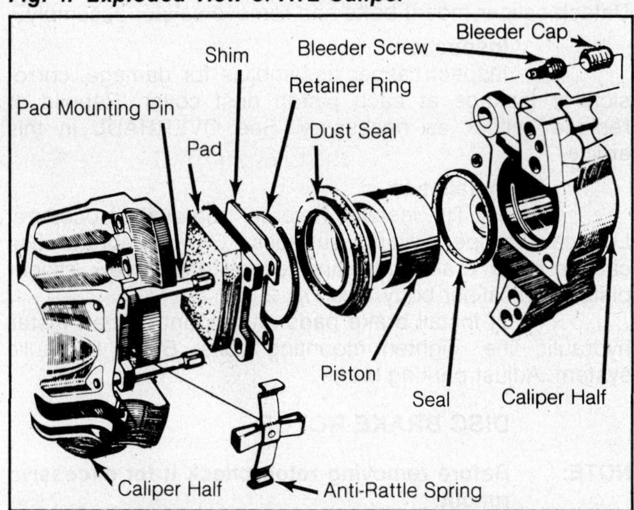

Courtesy of Saab-Scania of America, Inc.

Fig. 5: Checking ATE Caliper Piston Position

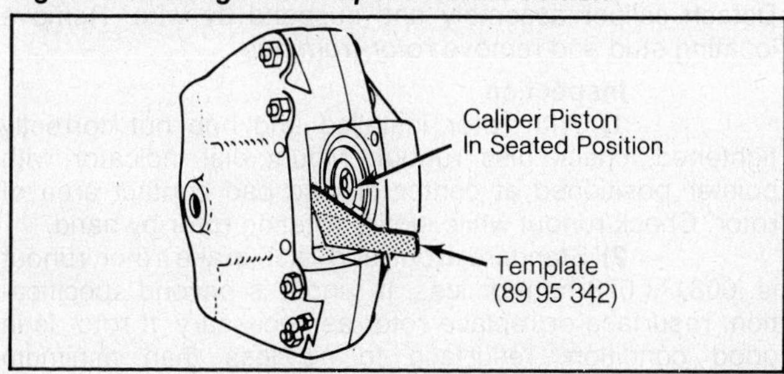

Courtesy of Saab-Scania of America, Inc.

MASTER CYLINDER

Disassembly

1) With master cylinder removed from vehicle, drain brake fluid from reservoir. Mount cylinder in a soft-jawed vise. Tap out retaining pins with drift, then separate reservoir from master cylinder.

2) Remove rubber seals from reservoir mounting holes in cylinder. Push in on primary piston. Pull secondary piston stop pin from fluid reservoir forward mounting hole. *See Fig. 6.*

3) Remove circlip. Take out primary piston assembly and spring. Remove cylinder from vise. Carefully blow with compressed air to remove secondary piston assembly and spring.

4) Remove springs and rubber sealing rings from both pistons. Note sealing rings installed direction for reassembly reference. Remove brake warning switch from

Fig. 6: Exploded View of Girling Master Cylinder

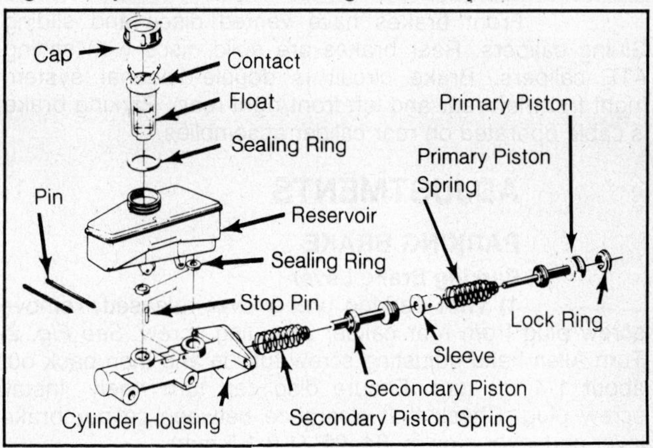

Courtesy of Saab-Scania of America, Inc.

master cylinder. Remove end plug. Lift out warning valve assembly.

NOTE: When piston seals are removed, note seal lip direction for reassembly reference.

Cleaning & Inspection

Wash all parts in clean brake fluid and dry with clean, lint-free cloth. Inspect parts for corrosion, damage or excessive wear. Standard master cylinder bore I.D. is .875" (22.23 mm). Replace defective components and all rubber parts during overhaul.

Reassembly

Reverse disassembly procedure. When installing primary and secondary pistons, coat parts with clean brake fluid. Do not damage seals during installation of pistons. Be sure seals are installed facing in the proper direction.

NOTE: When installing pistons in master cylinder bore, avoid seal damage. Rotate each spring and piston assembly with twisting motion.

TIGHTENING SPECIFICATIONS

Application	Ft. Lbs. (N.m)
Front Rotor	
Hub-to-Rotor Mounting Bolt	22-27 (30-37)
Wheel Bearing Hub Nut [1]	
Front	246-261 (340-360)
Rear	250-265 (340-360)
Wheel Lug Nut	65-80 (88-108)

[1] – Maximum hub (wheel bearing) runout is .08" (2 mm), as measured from edge of rim.

DISC BRAKE ROTOR SPECIFICATIONS

Application	Disc Diameter In. (mm)	Lateral Runout In. (mm)	Parallelism In. (mm)	Original Thickness In. (mm)	Min. Refinish Thickness In. (mm)	Discard Thickness In. (mm)
900, 900S & 900 Turbo						
Front Non Vented	10.87 (276)	.004 (.10)	.0006 (.015)	.500 (12.70)	[1] .461 (11.70)	.441 (11.20)
Front Vented	10.87 (276)	.003 (.08)	.0006 (.015)	.79 (20.0)	[1] .74 (18.9)	.72 (18.3)
Rear	10.53 (267.5)	.004 (.10)	.0006 (.015)	.413 (10.50)	[1] .374 (9.50)	.354 (9.00)

[1] – Maximum grinding depth per side is .02" (.5 mm).

SAAB 9000

DESCRIPTION

Front brakes have vented discs and sliding Girling calipers. Rear brakes are solid discs with sliding ATE calipers. Brake circuit is double-diagonal system (right front/left rear and left front/right rear). Parking brake is cable operated on rear caliper assemblies.

ADJUSTMENTS

PARKING BRAKE

Parking Brake Lever

1) With parking brake lever released, remove screw plug from rear caliper adjusting screw. *See Fig. 2.* Turn Allen head adjusting screw fully in and then back out about 1/4-1/2 turn. Ensure disc can turn freely. Install screw plug. Check that clearance between caliper brake lever and lever stop is .04-.06" (1.0-1.5 mm).

2) Apply parking brake lever several times to stretch new cables. Remove shift lever console top cover. Rotate cable adjusting nuts (under plastic cover at rear of parking brake lever) until cable slack is reduced sufficiently. Ensure disc can turn freely.

REMOVAL & INSTALLATION

DISC BRAKE PADS

Removal (Front)

Raise and support front of vehicle. Remove front wheels. Remove lower guide pin bolt. Pivot caliper up and remove pads.

Inspection

Check all components for wear and damage. Minimum thickness of friction material is .04" (1.0 mm). Check calipers for leakage or damage. Rebuild calipers, resurface rotors or replace components as necessary.

Installation

Clean surfaces between pad carrier. Fit pads and pivot caliper body back to its normal position. Refit and tighten bolt in lower guide pin. Replace wheel and lower vehicle. Pump brake pedal several times to adjust pads.

Removal (Rear)

Raise and support vehicle. Remove wheel. Release hand brake. Remove caliper hand brake retaining spring. Slide hand brake cable out of caliper lever. Remove guide pin dust caps and 7 mm Allen head guide pins. Lift off caliper body and remove pads.

Inspection

Check all components for wear and damaged. Minimum brake pad thickness is .04" (1.0 mm). Rebuild calipers, resurface rotors or replace components as necessary.

Installation

1) Remove caliper screw plug from hand brake adjusting screw and screw caliper piston into caliper body by means of the adjusting screw.

2) Install pads and caliper. Install guide pins and dust caps. Install hand brake retaining spring. Adjust hand brake and install wheel.

DISC BRAKE CALIPER

Removal (Front & Rear)

Raise and support vehicle. Remove all wheels. On rear wheel calipers, disconnect parking brake cable from lever on caliper. On all calipers, disconnect hydraulic lines. Plug lines to prevent entry of dirt or loss of fluid. Detach caliper mount bolts and remove caliper assembly.

Inspection

Inspect caliper assemblies for damage, corrosion or leakage at each piston dust cover. Rebuild or replace caliper as necessary. See OVERHAUL in this article.

Installation

1) To install, reverse removal procedure. Lubricate caliper sliding surfaces. On rear brake use caliper hand brake adjusting screw and screw caliper piston into caliper body. *See Fig. 2.*

2) Install brake pads and mount caliper. Install hydraulic line. Tighten mounting bolts. Bleed hydraulic system. Adjust parking brake.

DISC BRAKE ROTOR

NOTE: Before removing rotor, check it for excessive runout.

Removal (Front & Rear)

Raise and support vehicle. Remove wheels. Detach caliper assembly and suspend by wire. Remove locating stud and remove rotor from hub.

Inspection

1) With rotor installed and hub nut correctly tightened, check disc runout. Mount dial indicator with pointer positioned at center of disc pad contact area of rotor. Check runout while slowly rotating rotor by hand.

2) Standard front and rear brake rotor runout is .0031" (.078 mm) or less. If runout is beyond specification, resurface or replace rotor as necessary. If rotor is in good condition, resurface to no less than minimum thickness specification. Check rotor for proper thickness and parallelism.

3) Using a micrometer, measure rotor thickness at 12 points, about 30 degrees apart at center of disc pad contact area. Replace rotor if worn to more than discard specification. Ensure that when rotor thickness measurements are taken, the difference between any measurement (parallelism) is not more than .0006" (.015 mm).

CAUTION: If parallelism is more than specification, resurface rotor to no less than the minimum thickness. Ensure that the grinding depth for any one side is no more than .04" (1.0 mm) on front and .028" (.7 mm) on rear.

Installation

To install, reverse removal procedure. Adjust parking brake. Pump brake pedal to seat pads.

MASTER CYLINDER

Removal

1) Disconnect battery and remove. Disconnect fuel filter mounting bolts and push to one side. Connect a hose to front left and front right bleeder screws. Loosen bleeder screws.

2) Pump brake pedal until all fluid is removed from system. Disconnect brake hoses complete with adapters. Disconnect steel brake lines. Remove master cylinder from booster.

CAUTION: When working with brake fluid, never touch painted surfaces or steering wheel as permanent damage may result.

SAAB 9000 (Cont.)

Installation

To install, reverse removal procedure. Bench bleed master cylinder, install unit and bleed hydraulic system. Ensure brake fluid is to proper level.

POWER BRAKE UNIT

Removal

1) Remove battery. Disconnect fuel filter mounting bolts and push to one side. Remove junction box from battery shelf. Remove battery shelf. Remove master cylinder. Remove vacuum nozzle from booster.

2) Remove trim panel to provide access to foot pedal mountings. Remove pin retaining clip and clevis pin from linkage between brake pedal and push rod to servo unit. Remove 4 booster mounting nuts and booster.

Installation

To install, reverse removal procedure. Bleed brakes.

OVERHAUL

CALIPER ASSEMBLY

Disassembly (Front)

Clean caliper body. Install rag between piston head and pad retaining arms of caliper. Apply a small amount of compressed air to fluid inlet hole of caliper and remove piston. *See Fig. 1.* Pull out dust cover. Remove piston seal from bore. Inspect all parts and replace any showing damage.

Reassembly

Lubricate piston seal with brake fluid. Install new piston seal. Fit a new dust cover onto piston. Install dust cover on caliper body. Install piston being careful not to damage dust cover.

Fig. 1: Exploded View of Front Caliper

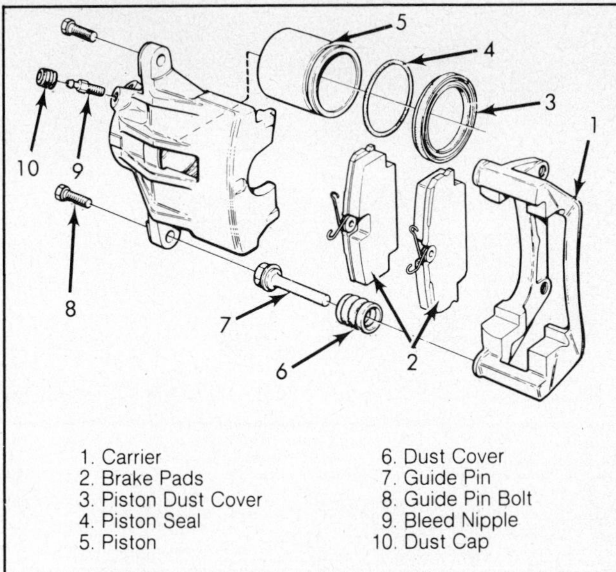

Courtesy of Saab-Scania of America, Inc.

Disassembly (Rear)

Remove dust covers. Remove spring from handbrake lever. *See Fig. 2.* Remove dust cover retainer and dust cover. Unscrew plug over piston adjusting screw. Unscrew and remove adjusting screw and piston. Remove piston seal. Inspect all components and replace any that show signs of damage.

Fig. 2: Exploded View of Rear Caliper

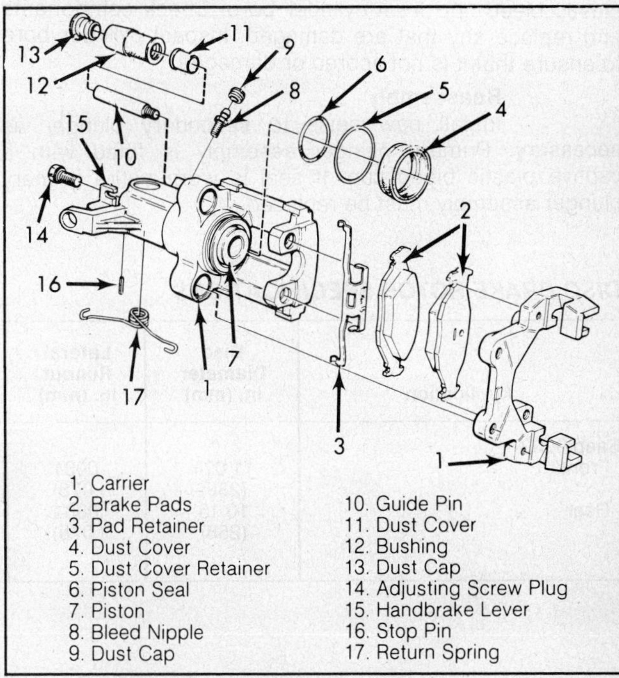

Courtesy of Saab-Scania of America, Inc.

Reassembly

Lubricate piston seal with brake fluid. Install new seal in caliper body. Install a new dust cover. Screw piston into cylinder by turning adjusting screw. Locate dust cover correctly on caliper body. Install piston and retainer. Install spring on handbrake lever. Install dust covers with bushings.

MASTER CYLINDER

Disassembly

1) With master cylinder removed, clamp master cylinder in soft-jawed vise. Remove seals from brake hose outlets. Carefully push primary plunger stop pin. *See Fig. 3.*

Fig. 3: Exploded View of Master Cylinder

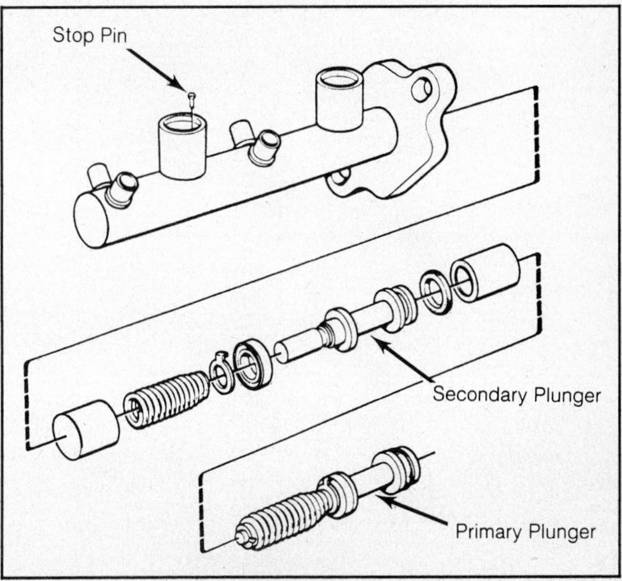

Courtesy of Saab-Scania of America, Inc.

SAAB 9000 (Cont.)

2) Withdraw plunger assemblies and the loose plastic bleed cup from cylinder bore. Check components and replace any that are damaged. Inspect cylinder bore to ensure that it is not scored or damaged.

Reassembly

Install new seals to secondary plunger as necessary. Primary plunger assembly is fitted with a captive plastic bleed cup. If seal is worn entire primary plunger assembly must be replaced.

TIGHTENING SPECIFICATIONS

Application	Ft. Lbs. (N.m)
Caliper Bolts	
Front	52-82 (70-111)
Rear	52-67 (70-90)
Wheel Bolts	76-90 (103-125)

DISC BRAKE ROTOR SPECIFICATIONS

Application	Disc Diameter In. (mm)	Lateral Runout In. (mm)	Parallelism In. (mm)	Original Thickness In. (mm)	Min. Refinish Thickness In. (mm)	Discard Thickness In. (mm)
Saab 9000						
Front	11.024 (280)	.0031 (.078)	.0006 (.015)	.858-.874 (21.79-22.19)	.787 (19.98)	.768 (19.51)
Rear	10.15 (258)	.0031 (.078)	.0006 (.015)	.35-.36 (8.9-9.1)	.295 (7.5)	.276 (7.01)

STERLING

825

DESCRIPTION

Hydraulic disc brakes are used on all 4 wheels. Cable operated parking brake system is connected to rear calipers. Vacuum assisted power brake unit reduces driver effort to stop vehicle. On models not equipped with Anti-Lock Brake System (ABS), a twin pressure conscious reducing valve is used. If there is an internal failure within the system, brake fluid will seep from plug on this valve. *See Fig. 1.*

Fig. 1: View of Twin Pressure Conscious Reducing Valve

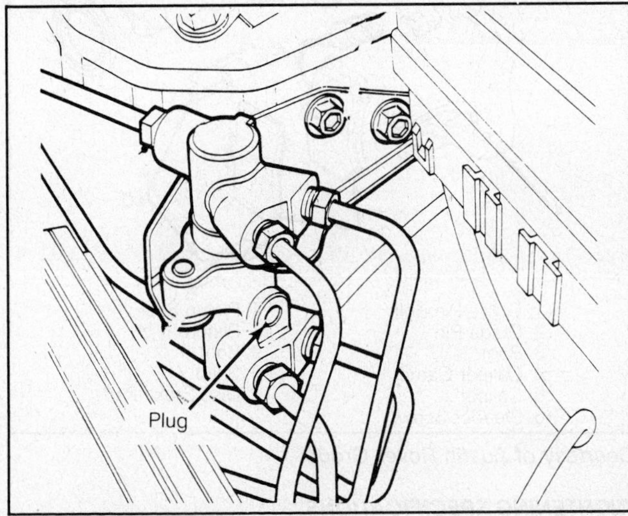

Courtesy of Austin Rover Group.

ADJUSTMENTS

PARKING BRAKE

Raise rear of vehicle and support. Release parking brake. Remove caliper cover. Measure distance between lever and stop (both sides). *See Fig. 2.* If clearance is not .020-.080" (.51-2.0 mm), remove parking brake lever cover. Turn adjusting nut until specified clearance is obtained. With parking brake applied, pump brake pedal several times.

Fig. 2: Measuring Parking Brake Cable

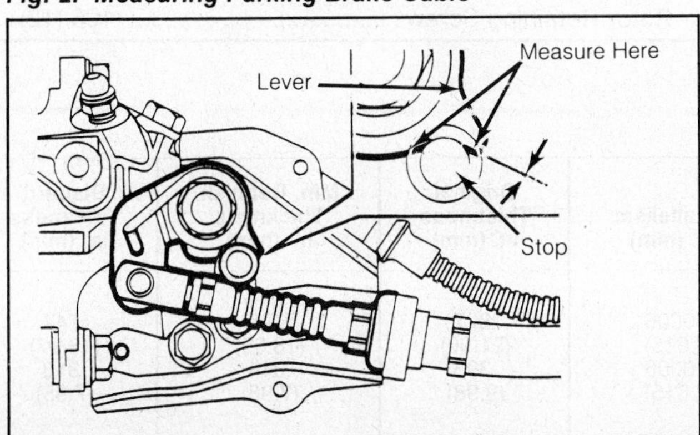

Courtesy of Austin rover Group.

REMOVAL & INSTALLATION

DISC BRAKE CALIPER & PADS

Removal (Front)

1) Raise front of vehicle and support. Unplug disc brake pad wear connector. Remove lower caliper guide pin bolt. Raise disc brake caliper upward. Remove disc brake pads and shims. Remove upper caliper guide pin bolt.

2) If only replacing pads, compress cailper piston. If removing caliper, disconnect brake lines and plug openings. Remove caliper. Check pad thickness, including backplate and excluding shims. See DISC BRAKE PAD THICKNESS table.

Installation

To install, reverse removal procedure. Bleed brake system if necessary.

DISC BRAKE PAD THICKNESS

Application	[1] In. (mm)
Front	
New	.685 (17.40)
Minimum	.322 (8.18)
Rear	
New	.570 (14.48)
Used	.283 (7.19)

[1] – Measurement should include backplate and exclude shims.

Removal (Rear)

1) Raise rear of vehicle and support. Remove rear wheel. Unplug disc brake pad wear connector. Remove rear disc brake caliper guide bolts. Remove caliper out of way. Remove disc brake pads.

2) If only replacing pads, compress caliper piston. If removing rear caliper, remove caliper cover. Remove parking brake cable clevis pin. Remove clip retaining cable. Remove brake line from caliper and plug all openings. Remove caliper from vehicle.

Installation

To install, reverse removal procedure. Bleed brake system. Adjust parking brake cable if necessary.

DISC BRAKE ROTOR

Removal & Installation

Remove disc brake pads. Remove 2 screws retaining rotor on hub. Remove disc brake rotor. To install, reverse removal procedure.

POWER BRAKE UNIT

Removal & Installation

1) Remove master cylinder. Plug all line openings. Disconnect vacuum hose fom power brake unit. Remove bolts retaining vacuum control box. Remove servo seal from closing panel on drivers side.

2) Remove clevis pin. Remove nuts retaining power brake unit. Remove power brake unit. To install, reverse removal procedure. Ensure "O" ring between master cylinder and power brake unit is replaced.

STERLING (Cont.)

OVERHAUL

FRONT DISC BRAKE CALIPER

Disassembly & Reassembly

Remove front disc brake caliper. Place a piece of wood between piston and caliper carrier. DO NOT place fingers between wood and piston. Apply low pressure air to brake line hole. Remove piston, seal and boot. To reassemble, reverse disassembly procedure. Apply clean brake fluid to piston, inside caliper bore and seal.

Fig. 3: Exploded View of Front Disc Brake Caliper

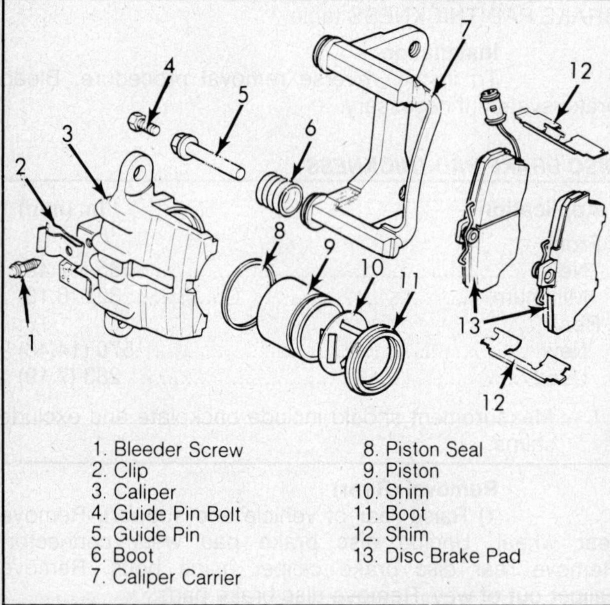

Courtesy of Austin Rover Group.

REAR DISC BRAKE CALIPER

Disassembly & Reassembly

Remove rear disc brake caliper. Wash caliper with denatured alcohol. Using Wrench (18G 1534), rotate piston countercockwise and remove from caliper. Remove seal. To reassemble, reverse disassembly procedure. Using wrench, install piston until it bottoms. Ensure boot is not pinched.

MASTER CYLINDER

Disassembly

Remove master cylinder. Remove reservoir from master cylinder. Remove snap ring. Disassemble remaining components. To reassemble, reverse disassembly procedure.

Fig. 4: Exploded View of Rear Disc Brake Caliper

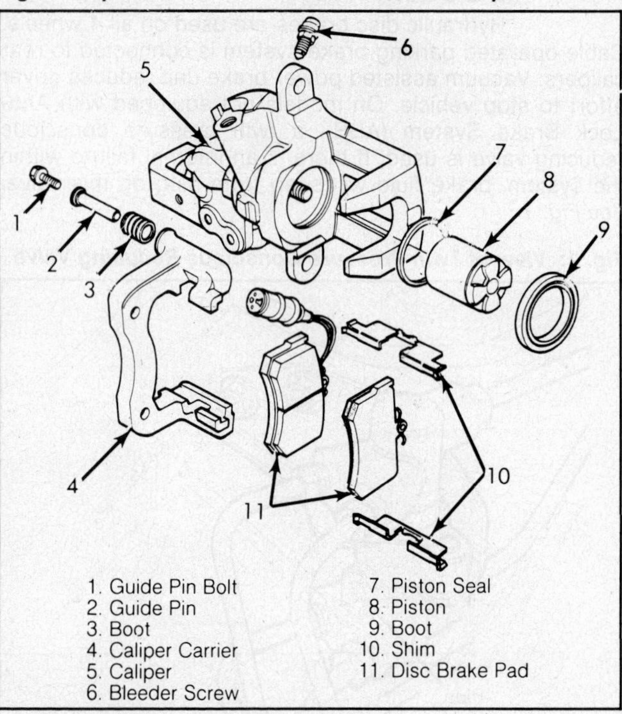

Courtesy of Austin Rover Group.

TIGHTENING SPECIFICATIONS

Application	Ft. Lbs. (N.m)
Brake Line Banjo Bolt	26 (35)
Brake Line Union Nut	
W/ABS	16 (22)
W/O ABS	10 (14)
Caliper Bracket Bolt	55 (75)
Caliper Guide Pin Bolt	24 (33)
Master Cylinder Retaining Nut	18 (25)
Power Booster Retaining Nut	18 (25)
Wheel Lug Nut	53 (72)
	INCH Lbs. (N.m)
Bleeder Screw	88 (10)
Caliper Cover Bolt	88 (10)
Rotor Retaining Screw	106 (12)

DISC BRAKE ROTOR SPECIFICATIONS

Application	Disc Diameter In. (mm)	Lateral Runout In. (mm)	Parallelism In. (mm)	Original Thickness In. (mm)	Min. Refinish Thickness In. (mm)	Discard Thickness In. (mm)
Sterling						
Front	11.22 (285)	.003 (.08)	.0006 (.015)	.827 (21.00)	.748 (18.99)	.747 (18.97)
Rear	10.23 (260)	.0006 (.015)	.0006 (.015)	.393 (9.98)	.314 (7.98)	.313 (7.95)

SUBARU

Coupe, Justy, Sedan, Station Wagon, XT Coupe

NOTE: Information on Hatchback is not available from manufacturer.

DESCRIPTION

All models are equipped with front disc brakes. Rear brakes are leading/trailing type drum or disc brakes. On all models except Justy, parking brake is mechanically actuated on FRONT brakes.

On all models except Justy and equipped with manual transaxle, Hill-Holder is incorporated into primary brake line from master cylinder. The Hill-Holder is used to permit easy starting while on a hill. Hill-Holder uses a Pressure Hold Valve (PHV) to control fluid flow to and from brakes until clutch pedal is released. PHV is linked to clutch pedal and is also controlled by gravity.

ADJUSTMENTS

REAR DRUM BRAKE SHOES

NOTE: Justy and all 4WD models rear brakes are self-adjusting.

All Except Justy & 4WD

Raise and support vehicle. Loosen adjuster lock nut and turn adjuster until wheel locks. Back off adjusting nut 180 degrees. Clearance between drum and shoes should be .004-.006" (.10-.15 mm). Wheel should be easily rotated by hand.

PEDAL HEIGHT & FREE PLAY

1) Measure brake pedal height from floorboard to pedal pad center, with brake pedal depressed. See BRAKE PEDAL HEIGHT SPECIFICATIONS table. To adjust pedal height, loosen stoplight switch lock nut and position out of way.

2) Loosen brake operating rod lock nut and turn operating rod until correct pedal height is obtained. Tighten operating rod lock nut. Adjust brake pedal free play to .20-.43" (5-11 mm) with stoplight switch. Tighten stoplight switch lock nut.

BRAKE PEDAL HEIGHT SPECIFICATIONS

Application	In. (mm)
Justy	3.35 (85)
XT Coupe	4.7 (119)
All Other Models	2.64 (67)

STOPLIGHT SWITCH

1) Stoplight switch is located under instrument panel, above brake pedal. To adjust stoplight switch, loosen lock nut and position switch so contact plunger touches pedal arm stopper.

2) Check operation of switch. Brake lights should glow when contact plunger moves .07-.13" (1.8-3.3 mm). If not, adjust switch and tighten lock nut.

PARKING BRAKE

Justy

Pull parking brake handle using 55 lbs. (25 kg) of force. Parking brake should lock wheels at 6-7 notches, or 11 maximum. If not, raise vehicle and tighten cable until correct adjustment is obtained. Ensure wheels rotate freely with parking brake released.

All Others

With service brakes properly adjusted, pull parking brake lever 3-5 times. Loosen lock nut at equalizer and turn adjusting nut until clearance is .02" (.5 mm). *See Fig. 1.* Tighten lock nut. With 55 lbs. (25 kg) applied, front wheels should lock on 3-4 notches.

Fig. 1: Location for Adjusting Parking Brake

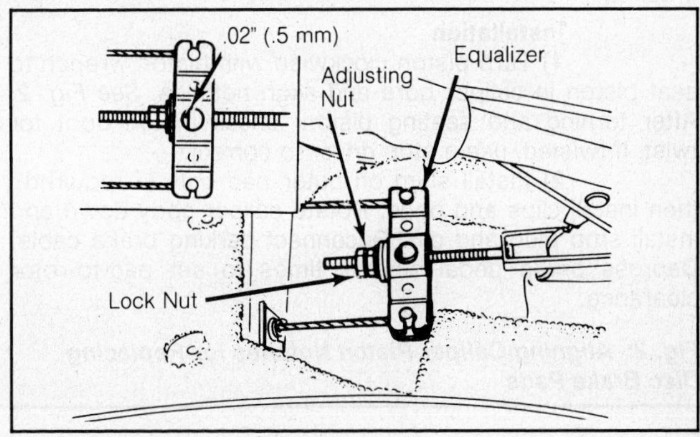

Courtesy of Subaru of America, Inc.

HILL-HOLDER

All Except Justy

1) Before adjusting Hill-Holder, ensure clutch pedal free play is within specifications. Free play at clutch pedal should be .40-.79" (10-20 mm). If not within specifications, adjust clutch by turning adjusting nut on engine side of clutch cable release fork.

2) Check stopping and starting performance by activating Hill-Holder on an uphill road with more than 3 degree inclination. If vehicle does not stop, tighten PHV cable.

NOTE: Hill-Holder may not activate on a very small hill.

3) If Hill-Holder releases too late (engine tends to stall), loosen adjusting cable at clutch release fork in small increments until smooth starting is possible. If Hill-Holder releases too early (vehicle slips backwards slightly), tighten cable in small increments until smooth starting is possible.

4) To adjust Hill-Holder to apply on a smaller hill, insert Shim (725807000) between side frame and PHV support bracket (raising front of PHV). Shims are .024" (.6 mm) thick and will increase PHV angle 1/2 degree. DO NOT raise front of PHV excessively. Never insert more than one shim at a time.

REMOVAL & INSTALLATION

FRONT DISC PADS

NOTE: Do not press on brake pedal after the pads have been removed. Do not disconnect hydraulic line.

Removal (Justy)

Raise and support vehicle. Remove caliper from support. Remove brake pads.

SUBARU (Cont.)

Installation

Depress piston by hand. If hard to depress, loosen bleeder screw when depressing. Install brake pads. Install caliper on support. Bleed brake system if necessary.

Removal (All Others)

Raise and support vehicle. Remove tire and wheel. Remove parking brake cable. Remove lower pin and stop plug. Rotate caliper body up away from disc. Remove pads, clips and shims from caliper support bracket.

Installation

1) Turn piston clockwise with piston wrench to seat piston in caliper bore and align notches. *See Fig. 2.* After turning and seating piston, check piston boot for twist. If twisted, use a strip driver to correct.

2) Install shim on outer pad only (if required), then install clips and pads. Rotate caliper body down and install stop plug and pin. Reconnect parking brake cable. Depress brake pedal several times to set pad-to-rotor clearance.

Fig. 2: Aligning Caliper Piston Notches for Replacing Disc Brake Pads

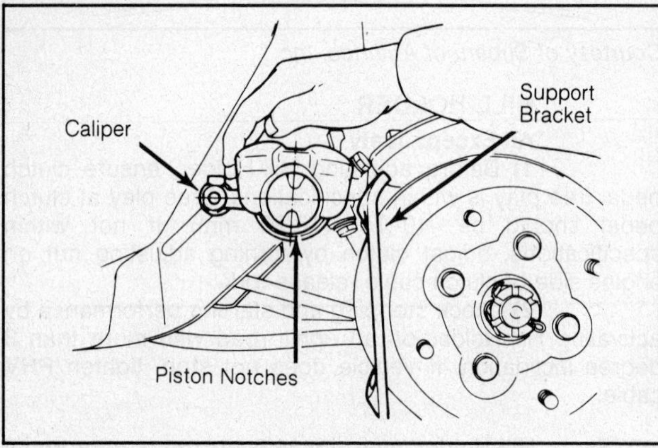

Courtesy of Subaru of America, Inc.

FRONT & REAR DISC CALIPER

Removal

Raise and support vehicle. Remove tire and wheel. Remove pads as previously described. Disconnect and plug hydraulic line at caliper and remove parking brake cable (front only). Remove caliper assembly. DO NOT remove support bracket unless rotor is being removed.

Installation

Apply silicone grease to lock pin and guide pin (front only). Install caliper assembly, pads and parking brake cable. Install hydraulic line, then bleed hydraulic system.

FRONT DISC ROTOR

Removal

1) Raise and support vehicle. Remove tire and wheel. Remove disc pads. Remove caliper assembly and hang from frame with wire. DO NOT disconnect hydraulic line. Remove caliper mounting bracket bolts and bracket.

2) Remove cotter pin and nut from axle shaft. On Justy, remove center piece with a screwdriver. Remove rotor and hub assembly. On all other models, using a puller, remove rotor and hub assembly from axle. On all models, remove bolts connecting hub to rotor and separate rotor from hub.

Installation

To install, reverse removal procedure. Tighten hub-to-rotor bolts evenly. Tighten wheel bearing nut to 130 ft. lbs. (177 N.m) on Justy, or 145 ft. lbs. (196 N.m) on all other models. Ensure conical spring is positioned correctly. Depress brake pedal several times to seat pads.

REAR DISC PADS

Removal

Raise and support vehicle. Remove caliper from support. Remove brake pads.

Installation

Depress piston by hand. If hard to depress, loosen bleeder screw when depressing. Install brake pads. Install caliper on support. Bleed brake system if necessary.

REAR BRAKE DISC & DRUM

Removal

Raise and support vehicle. Remove tire and wheel. On 2WD models, remove dust cap, nut and wheel bearing components. On 4WD models, remove cotter pin and castle nut. On Justy, loosen parking brake cable. On all models, remove brake disc or drum. Loosen brake adjustment if necessary and use puller if required to pull off brake drum.

Installation (Justy)

To install, reverse removal procedure. Tighten wheel bearing nut to 29 ft. lbs. (39 N.m). Back nut off then tighten nut until starting torque, measured with a spring scale, is 3.1-4.4 lbs. (1.4-2.0 kg).

Installation (All Others)

To install, reverse removal procedure. On 2WD models, tighten wheel bearing nut to 36 ft. lbs. (49 N.m). Back nut off approximately 1/8 turn until starting torque, using a spring scale, is 1.87-3.20 lbs. (.85-1.45 kg). On 4WD models, tighten nut to 145 ft. lbs. (196 N.m).

REAR BRAKE SHOES

Removal (Justy)

Remove brake drum. Insert a screwdriver through backplate to allow adjuster lever to pivot on strut. Remove hold-down springs. Remove and lower return springs. Remove brake shoes from vehicle.

Installation

Apply brake grease to all brake shoe contact points. Ensure adjuster is not damaged or worn. Preset adjuster to 3.78" (96 mm). *See Fig. 3.* To install, reverse removal procedure. *See Fig. 4.*

Removal (All Others)

1) With brake drum removed, remove and plug hydraulic lines from wheel cylinder. Remove backing plate bolts and backing plate assembly.

2) Separate shoes from backing plate by removing hold-down springs. Disconnect lower end first and then remove upper end from cylinder. Separate return springs from shoes. *See Figs. 5 and 6.*

Installation

To install, reverse removal procedure. On 4WD models, retract adjuster. Return springs are not interchangeable. Lower spring is larger in diameter. Adjust brakes and bleed hydraulic system.

Fig. 3: Presetting Adjuster (Justy)

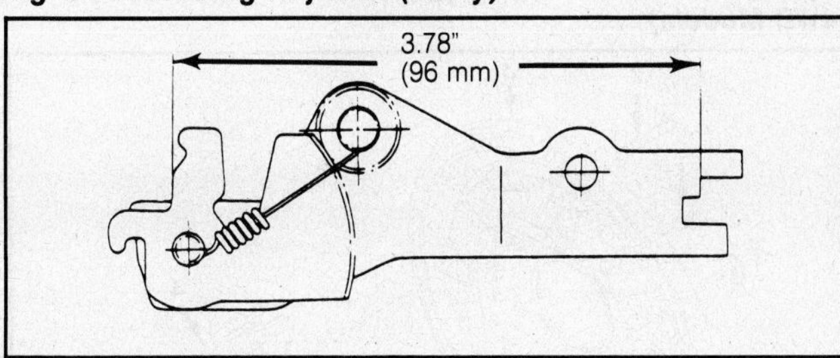

Courtesy of Subaru of America, Inc.

MASTER CYLINDER

Removal

Siphon brake fluid from reservoir. Disconnect warning light level connection. Remove hydraulic lines. Remove retaining nuts and master cylinder from power brake unit.

Installation

To install, reverse removal procedure. Bleed hydraulic system.

HILL-HOLDER (PHV)

Removal (All Except Justy)

Drain brake fluid from master cylinder. Disconnect PHV adjusting cable. Disconnect brake lines from PHV. Remove PHV from support bracket. Plug all lines and fittings.

Inspection

Inspect boots of PHV cable for damage or corrosion. Inspect return spring for damage or corrosion. Listen for check ball rolling sound when PHV valve is tilted. Inspect PHV lever for smooth rotation.

NOTE: Replace PHV as an assembly if defective. DO NOT disassemble PHV.

Installation

To install, reverse removal procedure. Apply grease to hook of return spring, cable end portion of lever and cable end portion of clutch release fork. Bleed hydraulic system.

POWER BRAKE UNIT

Removal

1) From inside vehicle, remove clevis pin and snap pin. Disconnect push rod from brake pedal. Remove power brake retaining nuts from firewall. Remove nuts connecting hydraulic lines from master cylinder.

2) Remove master cylinder retaining nuts. Disconnect vacuum hose at power brake unit and wiring harness from master cylinder. Position master cylinder to one side without damaging hydraulic lines. Remove power brake unit.

Installation

Check push rod length. On Justy, length should be .409" (10.4 mm). On all other models, length

Fig. 4: Exploded View of Rear Brake Assembly (Justy)

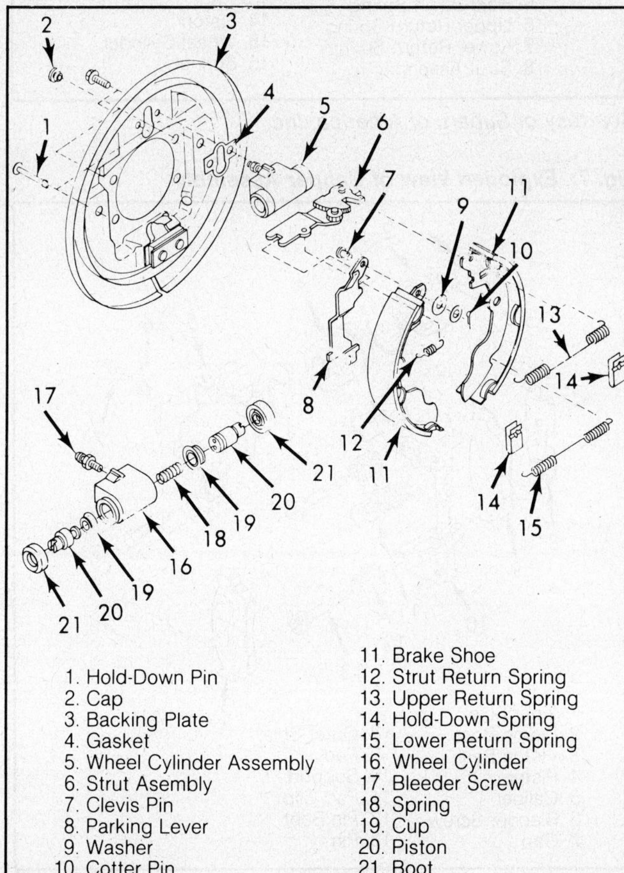

Courtesy of Subaru of America, Inc.

Fig. 5: Exploded View of Rear Drum Brake Assembly (2WD Models)

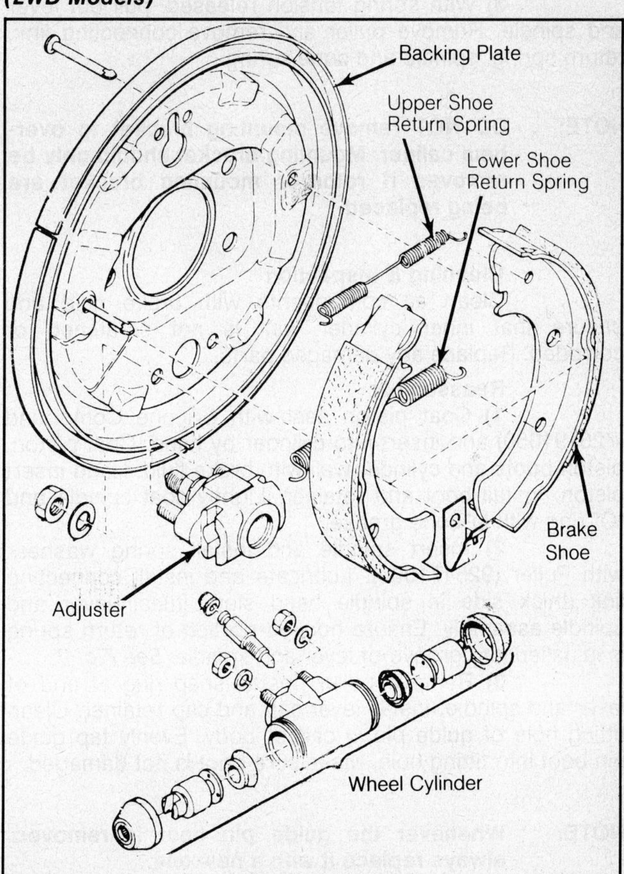

Courtesy of Subaru of America, Inc.

should be .366" (9.3 mm). To install, reverse removal procedure. Bleed hydraulic system.

OVERHAUL

FRONT CALIPER

Disassembly (Justy)

Remove caliper from vehicle. Place block of wood between piston and caliper body. Apply low compressed air to brake line port to remove piston. Remove all boots and seals. *See Fig. 7*.

Cleaning & Inspection

Clean all parts in brake fluid only. If cylinder is out of round or burred, replace as an assembly.

Reassembly

Apply rubber grease to piston seal. Wash inner wall and piston with brake fluid. Install piston by hand. Ensure piston seal and dust boot are positioned correctly.

Disassembly (All Others)

1) Thoroughly clean exterior of caliper with clean brake fluid. Remove outer pad clip and bleeder screw. Remove dust boot retainer and dust boot. Apply compressed air to fluid inlet and force piston out of caliper bore. Carefully remove guide pin boot and piston seal. *See Fig. 8*.

2) Remove parking brake lever cap ring and lever cap, then remove snap ring from lever and spindle assembly. Mount caliper assembly in soft-jawed vise and install Puller (925471000) to release spring washer tension. *See Fig. 9*.

3) With spring tension released, pull out lever and spindle. Remove puller and remove connecting link, return spring, spindle and cone spring.

NOTE: DO NOT remove mounting bracket to overhaul caliper. Mounting bracket should only be removed if rotor or mounting bracket are being replaced.

Cleaning & Inspection

Clean all components with brake fluid and ensure that inner cylinder wall is not scratched or corroded. Replace any damaged parts.

Reassembly

1) Coat piston seal with Silicone Compound (725191050) and insert into cylinder by hand. Coat piston, piston boots and cylinder wall with brake fluid. Hand insert piston. Install boot and retainer. Lightly coat spindle and "O" ring with silicone grease.

2) Insert spindle and install spring washers with Puller (925471000). Lubricate and install connecting link (thick side in spindle head slot). Install lever and spindle assembly. Ensure hooked portion of return spring is installed into groove of lever and spindle. *See Fig. 9*.

3) Remove puller. Install snap ring at end of lever and spindle. Install lever cap and cap retainer. Clean fitting hole of guide pin in caliper body. Evenly tap guide pin boot into fitting hole. Make sure boot is not damaged.

NOTE: Whenever the guide pin boot is removed, always replace it with a new one.

Fig. 6: Exploded View of Rear Drum Brake Assembly (4WD Models)

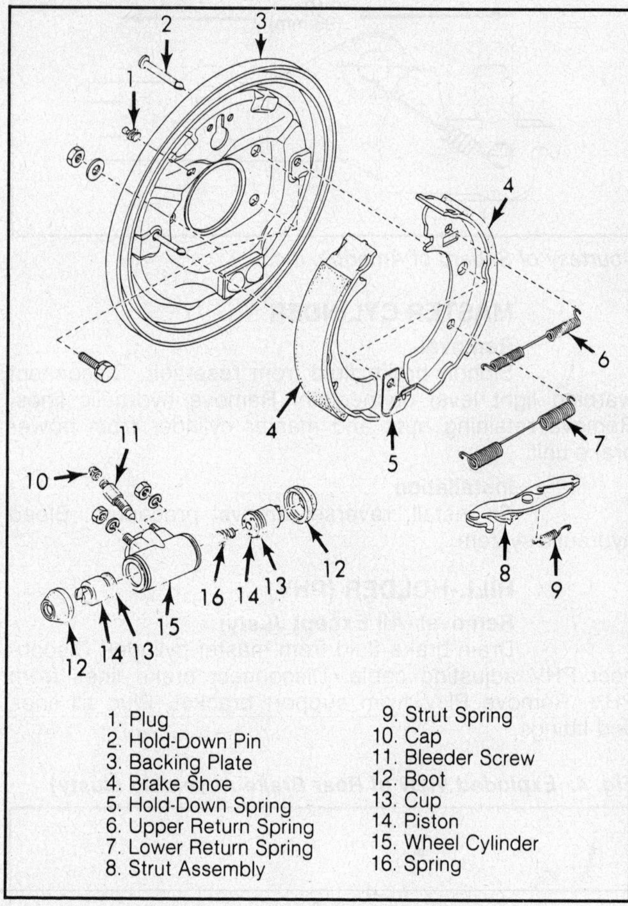

Courtesy of Subaru of America, Inc.

Fig. 7: Exploded View of Caliper Assembly

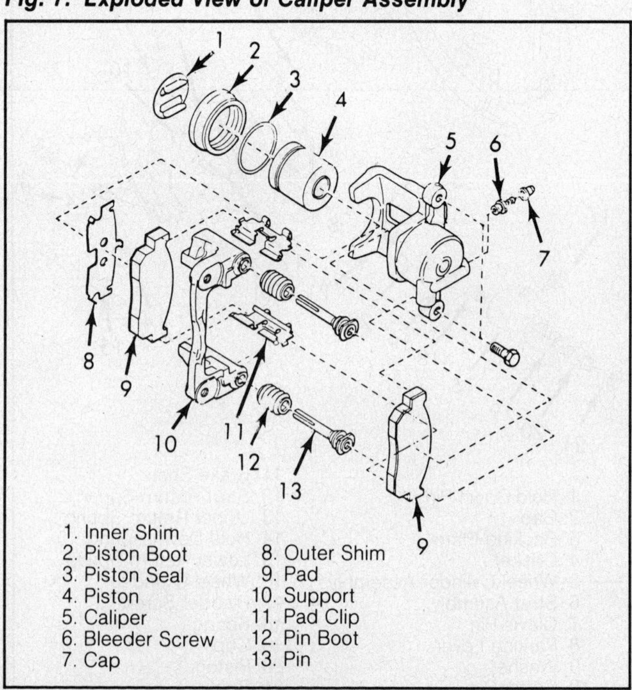

Courtesy of Subaru of America, Inc.

SUBARU (Cont.)

Fig. 8: Exploded View of Front Disc Caliper Assembly

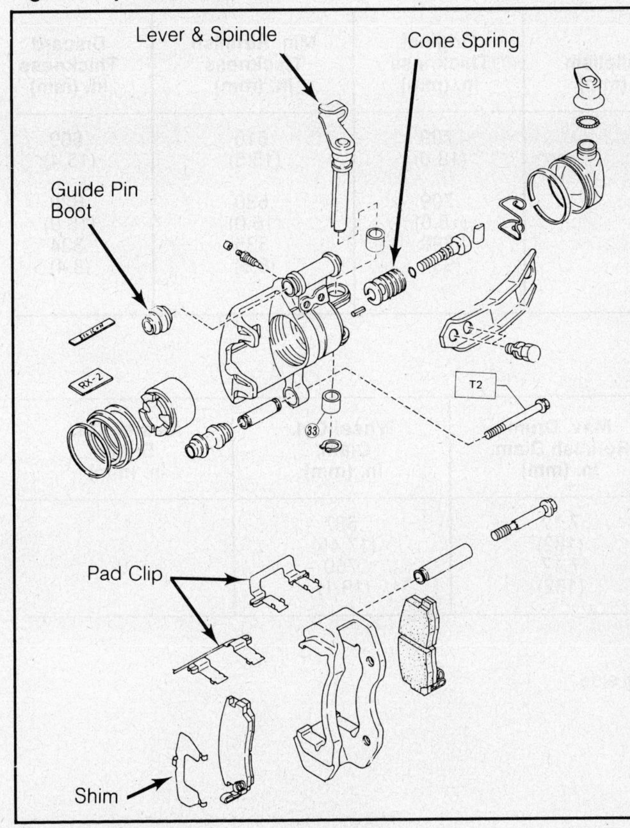

Courtesy of Subaru of America, Inc.

Fig. 9: Removal & Installation of Lever & Spindle

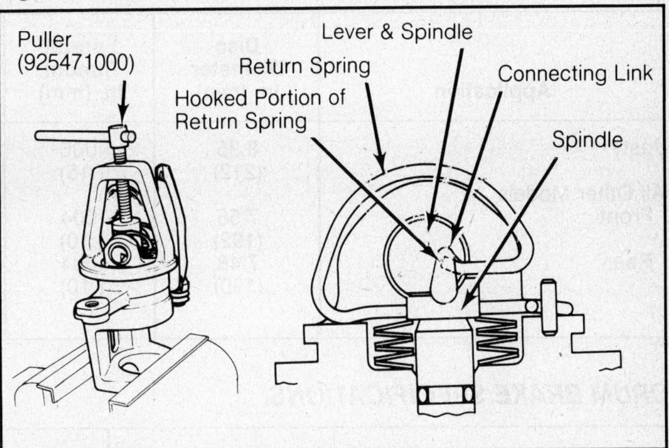

Courtesy of Subaru of America, Inc.

REAR CALIPER

Disassembly

Remove caliper from vehicle. Place block of wood between piston and caliper body. Apply low compressed air to brake line port to remove piston. Remove all boots and seals. *See Fig. 7.*

Cleaning & Inspection

Clean all parts in brake fluid only. If cylinder is out of round or burred, replace as an assembly.

Reassembly

Apply Silicone Compound (725191050) to piston seal. Wash inner wall and piston with brake fluid. Install piston by hand. Ensure piston seal and dust boot are positioned correctly.

REAR WHEEL CYLINDER

Disassembly

Remove boot and take out piston with cup. DO NOT separate cup unless replacement is available.

Cleaning & Inspection

Clean all parts in brake fluid only. If cylinder is out of round or burred, replace as an assembly. DO NOT hone.

Reassembly

To reassemble, reverse disassembly procedure. Ensure piston cup is not installed in reverse direction.

MASTER CYLINDER

Disassembly

1) Remove warning light level indicators and filters, then drain excess fluid. Push primary piston into cylinder bore and remove stop bolt and/or primary piston circlip.

2) Remove stop washer, gasket, primary and secondary piston assemblies. Remove check valve plug and valve assembly.

NOTE: Do not disassemble piston assemblies. Piston cup replacement requires replacement of piston assemblies. Removal of fluid reservoir requires installation of new reservoir.

Cleaning & Inspection

1) Clean all components in brake fluid. Inspect cylinder bore for smoothness and roundness. Replace cylinder if scored or out of round.

2) DO NOT hone cylinder. Check piston-to-cylinder clearance. Replace master cylinder if clearance is excessive or parts are worn.

Reassembly

To reassemble master cylinder, reverse disassembly procedure.

POWER BRAKE UNIT

Manufacturer does not recommend overhaul of this unit. Replace as complete assembly.

HILL-HOLDER (PHV)

Manufacturer does not recommend overhaul of this unit. Replace as complete assembly.

SUBARU (Cont.)

DISC BRAKE ROTOR SPECIFICATIONS

Application	Disc Diameter In. (mm)	Lateral Runout In. (mm)	Parallelism In. (mm)	Original Thickness In. (mm)	Min. Refinish Thickness In. (mm)	Discard Thickness In. (mm)
Justy	8.35 (212)	.006 (.15)	.....	.709 (18.0)	.610 (15.5)	.609 (15.4)
All Other Models						
Front	7.56 (192)	.004 (.10)	.....	.709 (18.0)	.630 (16.0)	.629 (15.9)
Rear	7.48 (190)	.004 (.10)	.....	.390 (9.9)	.335 (8.5)	.334 (8.4)

DRUM BRAKE SPECIFICATIONS

Application	Drum Diam. In. (mm)	Drum Width In. (mm)	Max. Drum Refinish Diam. In. (mm)	Wheel Cyl. Diam. In. (mm)	Master Cyl. Diam. In. (mm)
Station Wagon	7.09 (180)	.....	7.17 (182)	.687 (17.45)	[1]
All Other Models	7.09 (180)	.....	7.17 (182)	.750 (19.1)	[1]

[1] – Diameter is .813" (20.7 mm) on smaller side, 1.0" (25.4 mm) on larger side.

TIGHTENING SPECIFICATIONS

Application	Ft. Lbs. (N.m)
Backing Plate Mounting Bolts	
Justy	14-22 (19-30)
All Other Models	34-43 (46-58)
Booster Mounting Nut	9-17 (12-23)
Caliper Guide Pin	33-40 (45-54)
Caliper Lock Pin	23-30 (31-41)
Caliper-to-Support Bolt	
Rear	16-23 (22-31)
Hub-to-Rotor Bolt	33-42 (45-57)
Master Cylinder Mounting Nut	7-13 (10-18)
Support Bracket Mounting Bolts	
Front	36-51 (49-69)
Rear	34-43 (46-58)
Wheel Bearing Nut	
Front	
Justy	130 (177)
All Other Models	145 (196)
Rear	
2WD	[1]
4WD	145 (196)

[1] – See text.

SUZUKI

Samurai

DESCRIPTION

Brake system is hydraulically-operated using a tandem master cylinder with vacuum power assist brake booster. The vehicle uses front single piston sliding caliper disc brakes. Rear brakes are self-adjusting drum type, with a cable actuated parking brake.

ADJUSTMENTS

PARKING BRAKE

NOTE: **Before the parking brake adjustment can be performed, ensure that pedal height is oaky and brake shoes are not worn beyond limit.**

Loosen lock nut on end of brake cable. Hold cable nut with proper wrench to prevent cable from twisting and tighten adjusting nut. While pulling parking brake handle up with 44-55 lbs. (20-25 kg), brake lever stroke should be 3-8 notches.

PEDAL HEIGHT & FREE PLAY

1) Start engine. Depress brake pedal several times. Depress brake pedal with approximately 66 lbs. (30 kg) of load and measure from top of pedal pad to floorboard. Clearance must not be less than 2.95" (75 mm).

2) If clearance is less than specified, possible causes are worn out rear brake shoes, air in brake lines, malfunction of rear brake shoe adjuster or booster push rod length out of adjustment.

3) Pedal free play should be .04-.32 (1-8 mm). If out of specification, check stoplight switch for proper installation position and adjust if necessary. Also check pedal shaft bolt and master cylinder pin installation and replace if defective.

BRAKE BOOSTER PUSH ROD

Length of booster piston rod is adjusted to provide zero clearance between piston rod end and master cylinder piston. Push piston rod several times to ensure reaction disc is in place. With inside of booster at atmospheric pressure, set Booster Piston Rod Gauge (09950-98210) on master cylinder and push pin on tool until it contacts piston. Turn tool upside down and place it on booster. Adjust clearance by turning adjusting bolt of booster piston rod.

STOPLIGHT SWITCH

Loosen switch lock nut. Pull brake pedal up. Adjust switch position so clearance between end of switch thread and brake pedal contact is within .02-.04" (0.5-10 mm). Tighten lock nut.

REMOVAL & INSTALLATION

FRONT DISC BRAKE PADS

Removal & Installation

Raise and support vehicle. Remove front wheel. Remove caliper anti-rattle spring. Remove caliper guide pin caps. Remove caliper guide pins. Remove pad protectors. Pull caliper assembly up and suspend with wire. Remove brake pads. To install, reverse removal procedure.

FRONT DISC BRAKE CALIPER

Removal & Installation

1) Raise and support vehicle. Remove front wheel. Remove caliper anti-rattle spring. Remove pad protectors. Remove caliper guide pin caps. Remove caliper guide pins.

2) Pull caliper assembly up and disconnect brake line. Plug all line openings. To install, reverse removal procedure and bleed system.

FRONT ROTOR

Removal & Installation

Raise and support vehicle. Remove front wheel. Remove caliper and suspend with wire. Mount dial indicator and check rotor runout before removal. Maximum runout is .006" (.15 mm). Install two 8 mm bolts into rotor holes between wheel studs. Alternately tighten bolts and pull rotor from hub. Grind or replace rotor as necessary. To install, reverse removal procedure.

NOTE: **Ensure that brake fluid does not come in contact with painted surfaces.**

REAR DRUM

Removal

1) Remove wheel center cap. Loosen rear wheel nuts and brake drum nuts. Raise rear of vehicle. Remove rear wheel nuts and remove rear wheel. Check to ensure that parking brake lever is not pulled.

2) To increase clearance between brake shoe and drum, remove parking brake shoe lever return spring and disconnect parking brake cable joint from parking brake shoe lever. Remove parking brake shoe lever stopper plate. Remove brake drum.

NOTE: **If brake drum is difficult to remove by hand, use slide hammer and adapter.**

Installation

Ensure that grease or oil does not contaminate brake drum or brake shoes friction surface. Install brake drum. Install parking brake shoe lever stopper plate. *See Fig. 1.* Reverse remainder of removal procedure. Apply brake several times to set self-adjusting mechanism.

BRAKE SHOES

Removal & Installation

Remove brake drum. Remove shoe hold-down springs by turning shoe hold-down pins. Remove brake shoes. Remove brake shoe strut. Remove return springs. Check springs and brake shoe strut ratchet for wear or damage. Replace if necessary. To install, reverse removal procedure. Pump brake pedal several times to set automatic adjuster.

SUZUKI (Cont.)

Fig. 1: Parking Brake Shoe Lever Stopper

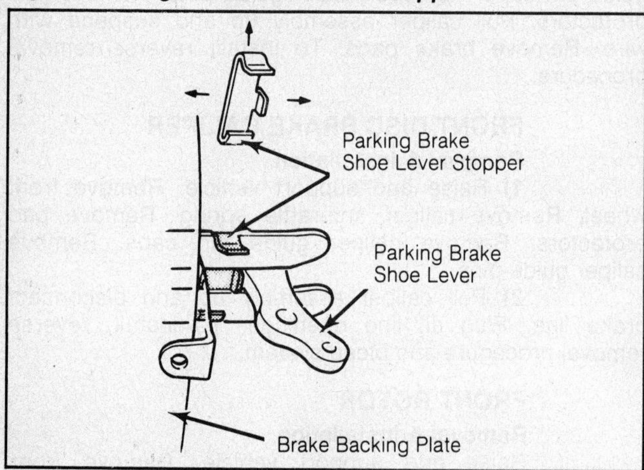

Courtesy of Suzuki of America Corp.

REAR WHEEL CYLINDER

Removal & Installation

With brake drum and shoes removed, disconnect hydraulic line from wheel cylinder. Remove mounting bolts and remove wheel cylinder. To install, reverse removal procedure.

MASTER CYLINDER

NOTE: **Ensure that brake fluid does not come in contact with painted surfaces.**

Removal & Installation

Loosen brake lines on master cylinder. Remove 2 nuts and washers attaching master cylinder to brake booster. Disconnect brake lines from master cylinder and plug outlet holes. Remove master cylinder. To install, reverse removal procedure.

POWER BRAKE BOOSTER

Removal & Installation

Remove master cylinder. Disconnect vacuum hose from booster. Disconnect push rod clevis from brake pedal arm. Remove 4 nuts attaching booster to firewall. Remove booster. To install, reverse removal procedure. Bleed hydraulic system.

OVERHAUL

FRONT CALIPER

Disassembly

Insert cloth rag between caliper piston and pad retainer arms. Apply a light amount of compressed air through brake line inlet port to remove piston. Remove piston dust seal. Remove piston seal using a thin blade. Make sure not to damage cylinder bore during seal removal. Remove bleeder screw.

Cleaning & Inspection

Clean all parts in clean brake fluid. Inspect bores and pistons for excessive wear or damage. Replace defective parts.

Reassembly

Lubricate new piston seal with brake fluid. Insert seal into piston cylinder seal groove. Carefully insert piston into cylinder using finger pressure. Apply brake fluid to piston and install new dust cover. Install bleeder screw.

Fig. 2: Exploded View of Front Brake Caliper

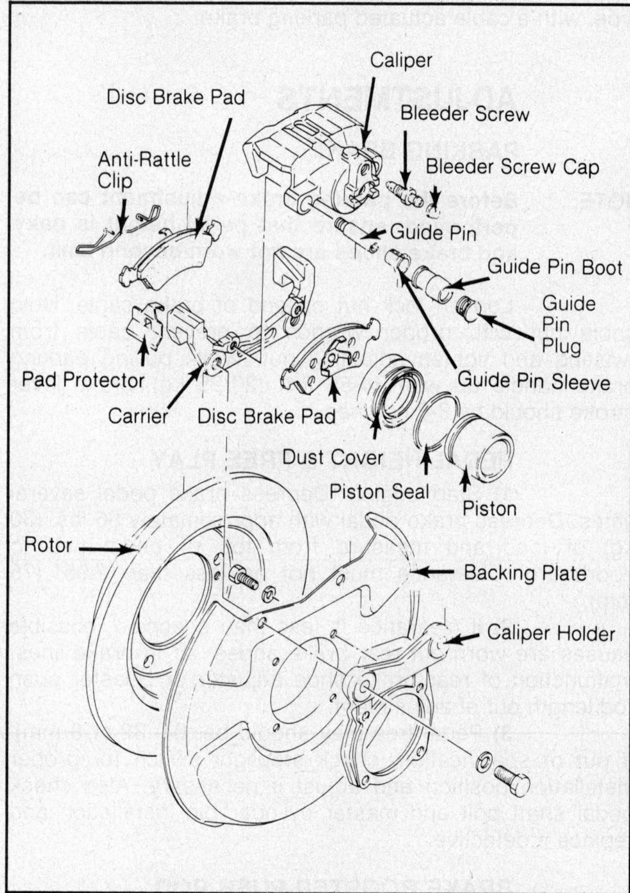

Courtesy of Suzuki of America Corp.

WHEEL CYLINDER

Disassembly

Remove rubber dust boots. Remove piston assembly and expander spring. Note installed direction for each cup. Remove cups from piston. Discard boots and cups.

Inspection

Wash all parts in clean brake fluid. Inspect cylinder bore and pistons for damage. Replace defective parts.

Reassembly

Lubricate bore with brake fluid. Install spring expander. Place new piston cups on piston with flare facing center of cylinder. Install piston assemblies into cylinder. Press new boots onto cylinder.

SUZUKI (Cont.)

Fig. 3: Exploded View of Rear Brake Assembly

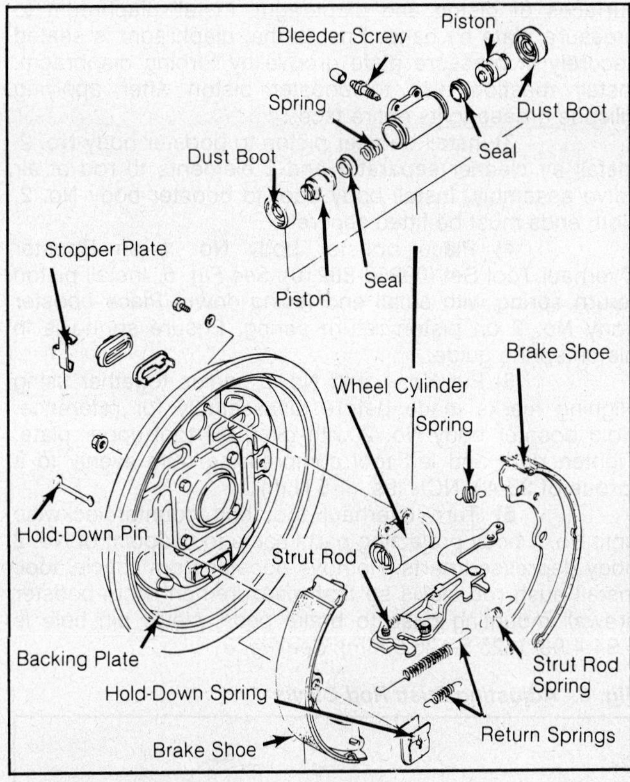

Courtesy of Suzuki of America Corp.

MASTER CYLINDER

Disassembly & Reassembly

1) Drain brake fluid from reservoir. Remove reservoir connecting screw. Remove reservoir. Remove circlip from rear of cylinder. Apply light amount of compressed air to rear reservoir fluid inlet and remove primary piston.

2) Remove piston stopper bolt on bottom side of cylinder. Apply compressed air to piston stopper bolt hole and remove secondary piston. To reassemble, reverse disassembly procedure. *See Fig. 4.*

Fig. 4: Exploded View of Master Cylinder

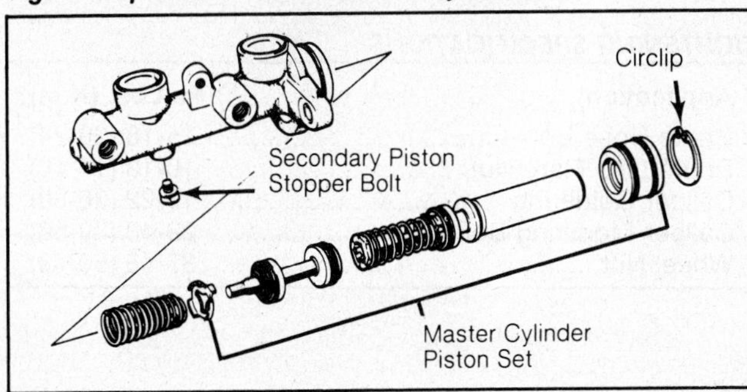

Courtesy of Suzuki of America Corp.

POWER BRAKE BOOSTER

1) Remove piston rod from booster. Remove push rod clevis and nut. Set booster in Booster Overhaul Tool (09950-88210). *See Fig. 5.* Ensure that vacuum check valve is not in contact with base of overhaul tool. Tighten 2 nuts on upper part of tool evenly to 26-43 INCH lbs. (3-5 N.m).

Fig. 5: Separating Booster Bodies

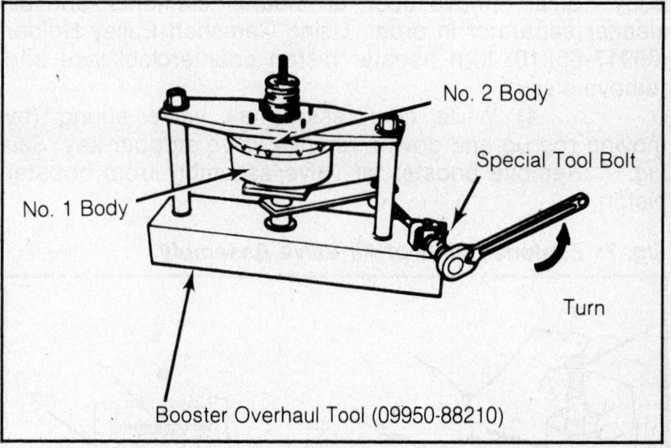

Courtesy of Suzuki of America Corp.

2) Turn overhaul tool bolt clockwise until indentations on cover No. 2 line-up with projections on body No. 1. After indentations line-up with projections. Scribe matching marks on the 2 bodies to facilitate installation. Remove booster from overhaul tool. Separate booster body No. 1 and No. 2. *See Fig. 6.*

Fig. 6: Exploded View of Power Booster

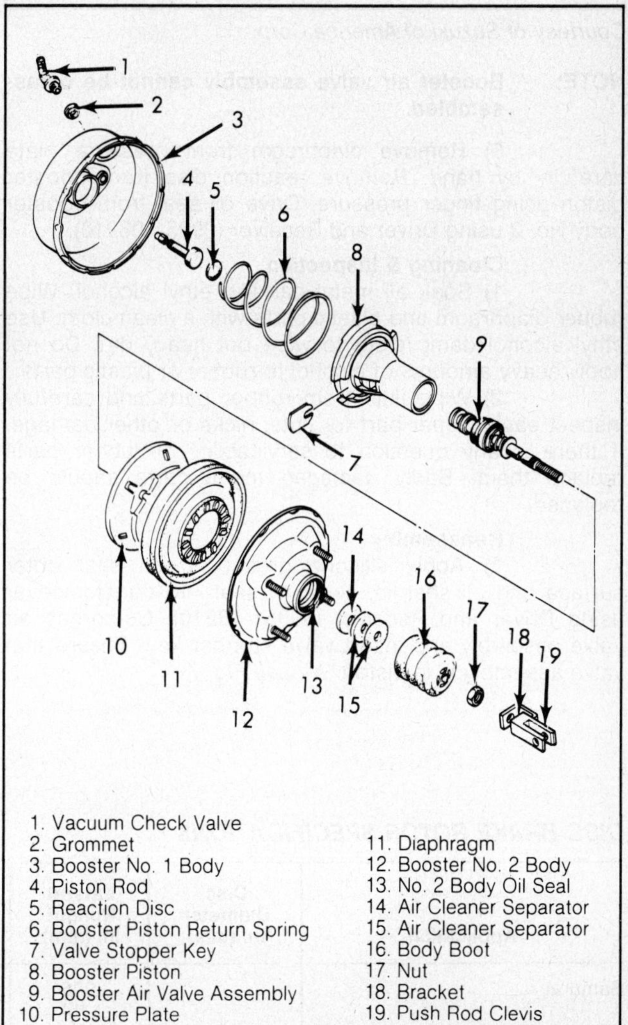

1. Vacuum Check Valve
2. Grommet
3. Booster No. 1 Body
4. Piston Rod
5. Reaction Disc
6. Booster Piston Return Spring
7. Valve Stopper Key
8. Booster Piston
9. Booster Air Valve Assembly
10. Pressure Plate
11. Diaphragm
12. Booster No. 2 Body
13. No. 2 Body Oil Seal
14. Air Cleaner Separator
15. Air Cleaner Separator
16. Body Boot
17. Nut
18. Bracket
19. Push Rod Clevis

Courtesy of Suzuki of America Corp.

SUZUKI (Cont.)

3) Remove piston return spring. From booster body No. 2, remove boot, air cleaner elements, and air cleaner separator in order. Using Camshaft Pulley Holder (09917-68210) turn booster piston counterclockwise and remove piston.

4) While compressing air valve spring (by moving rod up and down), remove valve stopper key. *See Fig. 7.* Remove booster air valve assembly from booster piston.

Fig. 7: Exploded View of Air Valve Assembly

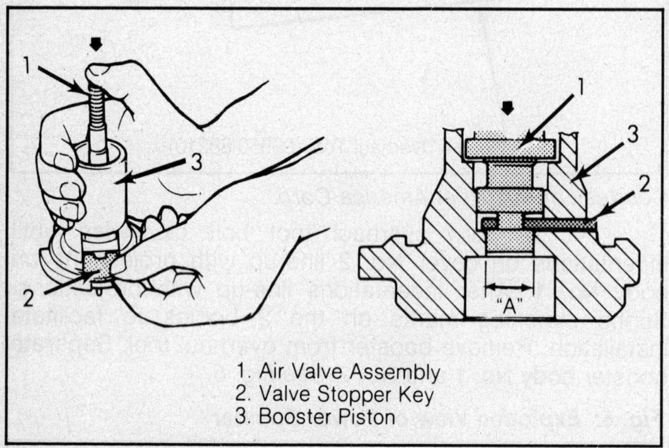

Courtesy of Suzuki of America Corp.

NOTE: Booster air valve assembly cannot be disassembled.

5) Remove diaphragm from pressure plate carefully by hand. Remove reaction disc from booster piston using finger pressure. Drive oil seal from booster body No. 2 using Driver and Receiver (09951-08210).

Cleaning & Inspection

1) Soak all metal parts in ethyl alcohol. Wipe rubber diaphragm and plastic parts with a clean cloth. Use ethyl alcohol damp cloth to wipe out heavy dirt. Do not apply heavy amounts of alcohol to rubber or plastic parts.

2) Wipe fluid from rubber parts and carefully inspect each rubber part for cuts, nicks or other damage. If there is any question to servicability of rubber parts replace them. Badly damaged metal parts should be replaced.

Reassembly

1) Apply silicone grease to oil seal outer surface and oil seal lip. Drive oil seal into booster cover using Driver and Receiver (09951-18210). Compress air valve assembly and insert valve stopper key. Ensure that valve assembly is in piston "A". *See Fig. 7* .

2) Apply silicone grease to entire mating surfaces of piston and diaphragm. Install diaphragm to pressure plate by hand. Ensure that diaphragm is seated securely in pressure plate groove by turning diaphragm. Install reaction disc to booster piston after applying silicone grease to its entire face.

3) Install booster piston to booster body No. 2. Install air cleaner separator and 2 elements to rod of air valve assembly. Install body boot to booster body No. 2. Both ends must be fitted securely.

4) Place booster body No. 1 on Booster Overhaul Tool Set (09950-88210). *See Fig. 6.* Install piston return spring with small end facing down. Place booster body No. 2 on piston return spring. Ensure spring is in piston spring guide.

5) Put No. 1 and No. 2 bodies together using aligning marks made before disassembly for reference. Hold booster body No. 2 with overhaul tool upper plate. Tighten right and left tool compressing nuts evenly to a torque of 26-43 INCH lbs. (4-5 N.m).

6) Turn overhaul tool bolt counterclockwise until No. 1 body projecting parts come to midpoint of No. 2 body depressed parts. Remove booster from special tool. Install push rod clevis so that measurement from booster firewall mounting base to brake pedal clevis pin hole is 4.94-4.98" (125.5-126.5 mm). *See Fig. 8.*

Fig. 8: Adjusting Push Rod Clevis

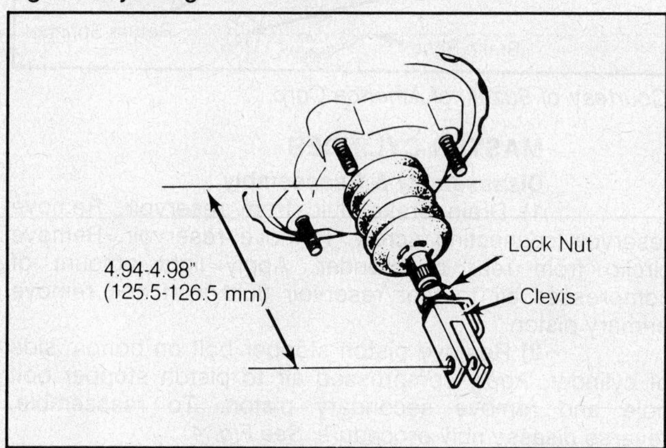

Courtesy of Suzuki of America Corp.

TIGHTENING SPECIFICATIONS

Application	Ft. Lbs. (N.m)
Brake Hose Bolt	15-18 (20-24)
Brake Line Flare Nut	10-13 (14-18)
Caliper Guide Pin	19-22 (26-30)
Caliper Mounting Bolts	29-43 (39-58)
Wheel Nut	37-58 (50-79)

DISC BRAKE ROTOR SPECIFICATIONS

Application	Disc Diameter In. (mm)	Lateral Runout In. (mm)	Parallelism In. (mm)	Original Thickness In. (mm)	Min. Refinish Thickness In. (mm)	Discard Thickness In. (mm)
Samurai	.....	.006 (.15)	.....	.394 (10)	.....	.335 (8.51)

SUZUKI (Cont.)

DRUM BRAKE SPECIFICATIONS

Application	Drum Diam. In. (mm)	Drum Width In. (mm)	Max. Drum Refinish Diam. In. (mm)	Wheel Cyl. Diam. In. (mm)	Master Cyl. Diam. In. (mm)
Samurai	8.66 (220)	.....	8.74 (222)	.....	.....

Brakes

TOYOTA

Camry, Celica, Corolla, Cressida, Land Cruiser, MR2, Pickup, Supra, Tercel, Van, 4Runner

DESCRIPTION

The hydraulic brake system uses a tandem master cylinder with a vacuum power assist servo. Cressida, Supra, MR2 and some Celica models are equipped with 4-wheel disc brakes. Corolla RWD and FX (FWD) are available with either rear drum or rear disc brakes. All other models are equipped with front disc and rear drum brakes.

A load sensing proportioning valve is used on some models to regulate brake pressure between the front and rear circuits. The rear brakes on all models are self-adjusting.

The parking brake lever mechanically activates the rear brakes. On models with rear drum brakes, a cable applies the rear shoes. On Corolla RWD and FX (FWD) models with rear disc brakes and on MR2 models, the parking brake applies the rear pads. On Celica, Cressida and Supra models, the parking brake applies 2 small shoes against the machined surface on the inside diameter of the rotor.

NOTE: **Since 4Runner and Pickup models share similar brake systems, the term Pickup will apply to all of these models unless specified otherwise.**

ADJUSTMENTS

DRUM BRAKES

Land Cruiser

Raise vehicle and support securely. Release parking brake. Ensure wheel rotates freely. Remove plug from adjustment hole in backing plate. Turn adjusting nut until shoes lock wheel. Back adjuster off about 5 notches. Wheel should turn freely or with very slight drag. Check pedal reserve distance.

All Others

All other models have self-adjusting rear drum brakes. Only adjustment possible is clearance adjustment. To adjust, measure clearance between linings and braking surface of drum. Clearance should be .024" (.60 mm). This check and adjustment is usually required only during repair or replacement of component parts.

BRAKE PEDAL HEIGHT

1) Brake pedal height is measured from face of pedal pad to asphalt sheet under carpet. To adjust clearance, loosen stoplight switch and lock nut on brake push rod. *See Fig. 1.*

2) Adjust pedal height by turning push rod. See BRAKE PEDAL HEIGHT table for correct specification. After setting pedal height, tighten lock nut on push rod. Adjust stoplight switch and tighten switch lock nut.

BRAKE PEDAL HEIGHT

Application	In. (mm)
Camry	7.0-7.4 (178-187)
Celica	6.0-6.4 (152-163)
Corolla	
FWD	5.9-6.3 (149-161)
RWD	6.3-6.7 (161-171)
Cressida	6.5-6.9 (165-176)
Land Cruiser	7.1 (180)
MR2	6.1-6.5 (154-165)
Pickup & 4Runner	
2WD & 4Runner	5.9-6.1 (149-154)
4WD	5.7-5.9 (144-149)
Supra	6.0-6.4 (152-163)
Tercel	
Sedan	5.8-6.2 (147-157)
Wagon	7.2-7.6 (183-193)
Van	5.8-6.2 (147-157)

BRAKE PEDAL FREE PLAY

1) Pedal free play is distance which pedal travels before initial resistance of power assist servo air valve is contacted by push rod. To check pedal free play, stop engine. Depress brake pedal several times to exhaust vacuum from power assist servo. Place straightedge next to brake pedal.

2) Depress pedal lightly until initial resistance is felt. *See Fig. 1.* Free play for Van models should be .04-.14" (1-3.5 mm). Free play should be .12-.24" (3-6 mm) for all other models. If free play is incorrect, adjust by turning push rod. Start engine and confirm that free play exists. Check brake pedal height if free play has been adjusted.

Fig. 1: Measuring Pedal Height & Free Play

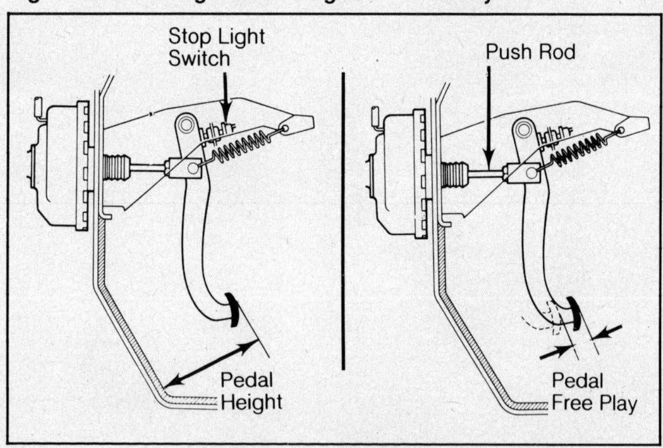

Courtesy of Toyota Motor Sales, U.S.A., Inc.

BRAKE PEDAL RESERVE DISTANCE

1) Pedal reserve distance is measured from face of pedal pad to asphalt sheet under carpet with brakes applied. Measure reserve distance with engine running and weight of 110 lbs. (50 kg) applied against pedal.

2) See BRAKE PEDAL RESERVE DISTANCE table for minimum reserve distance allowed in each model. If measured reserve distance is less than minimum distance specified in table, check braking system for problem.

TOYOTA (Cont.)

BRAKE PEDAL RESERVE DISTANCE [1]

Application	[2] In. (mm)
Camry	3.35 (85)
Celica	3.15 (80)
Cressida	2.95 (75)
MR2	3.43 (87)
Corolla	
FWD	2.56 (65)
RWD	2.95 (75)
Land Cruiser	
Front Disc	3.54 (90)
Front Drum	4.06 (103)
Pickup	
2WD	
Turbocharger	2.95 (75)
1/2 Ton	2.56 (65)
1 Ton, C & C	2.17 (55)
4WD	
Carburetor	2.17 (55)
Turbocharger	1.97 (50)
Supra	3.15 (80)
Tercel	
Sedan	2.20 (56)
Wagon	3.54 (90)
Van	2.36 (60)

[1] – Measure distance with 110.2 lbs. (50 kg) on pedal.
[2] – If less than specified, check entire brake system.

PARKING BRAKE

All Models

1) If parking brake applies brake shoes to drum or inside of rotor, clearance between brake shoes and braking surface must be correct BEFORE parking brake is adjusted. Usually clearance will only change if parts have been replaced. Wheels should be locked with parking brake applied and rotate freely when parking brake is released.

2) Pull on parking brake lever with weight of 44 lbs. (20 kg) to check parking brake adjustment. Count number of notches (clicks) until parking brake is fully applied. Compare actual count to specification in PARKING BRAKE ADJUSTMENT table. Adjust parking brake only if travel is incorrect.

Cressida

Loosen lock nuts on turnbuckle (under vehicle in right cable) and pull rod (at equalizer). Tighten cables first at turnbuckle and then at pull rod. Tighten lock nuts.

MR2

1) Pull parking brake lever up and down several times. Leave lever in released position. Pump brake pedal several times. Remove fuel tank protector. Loosen adjusting nuts at equalizer until there is slack in cable.

2) Ensure that cable bellcrank on caliper is touching stop pin. Tighten adjusting nut until cable is taut, but not so much that bellcrank is pulled off stop pin. Tighten adjusting nuts with equalizer in horizontal position. Install fuel tank protector.

Pickup

1) On 2WD models, release parking brake. Turn adjusting nut on pull rod to move equalizer bar until lever travel is correct. Pull rod is located on intermediate lever under vehicle.

2) On 4WD models, loosen lock nut on bellcrank adjuster bolt at rear of backing plate. Tighten adjuster bolt until there is no play in linkage. Loosen bolt one turn and tighten lock nut.

3) Move both adjusting nuts on intermediate lever in same direction until lever travel is correct. Tighten both adjusting nuts. Check bellcrank adjuster bolt. Bolt MUST contact backing plate when lever is released.

All Others

Remove console box or parking brake lever boot to uncover base of lever. Loosen lock nut or adjusting cap (Land Cruiser). Turn adjusting nut on cable until lever travel is correct. Tighten lock nut or adjusting cap. Install console or boot.

PARKING BRAKE ADJUSTMENT

Application	[1] Notches
Camry	5-8
Celica	4-7
Corolla	
FWD	
FX	5-8
All Others	4-7
RWD	
Disc	6-9
Drum	5-8
Cressida, MR2 & Supra	5-8
Land Cruiser	7-9
Pickup	
2WD	10-16
4WD	9-17
Tercel	
Sedan	7-9
Wagon	6-8
Van	
YR 29	6-8
All Others	7-9

[1] – Count notches with 44.1 lbs. (20 kg) applied to lever.

STOPLIGHT SWITCH

Stoplight switch is located above brake pedal. To adjust, loosen lock nuts and turn switch until its body just touches pedal stop. Tighten lock nut. Check pedal height and brake light operation.

LOAD SENSING PROPORTIONING & BY-PASS VALVE (LSP & BV or LSPV)

Camry, Land Cruiser, Pickup & Van

1) Load sensing proportioning and by-pass valve (LSP & BV or LSPV) is designed to control fluid pressures at rear brakes depending upon rear axle load. Specified weight, which includes vehicle weight, is placed on the rear axle for testing and adjusting pressures. *See Fig. 2.*

2) Test weight for rear axle load, including vehicle weight, is set at 1543 lbs. (700 kg) for Van and 1-ton 2WD Pickup models. On 1/2-ton 2WD Pickup test weight is 1764 lbs. (800 kg). Test weight for 4WD Pickup models is 1984 lbs. (900 kg). Test weight for Land Cruiser models is 2646 lbs. (1200 kg). On Camry, test weight is 200 lbs. (100 kg) above rear axle unladen weight.

3) Install Pressure Gauge Set (09709-29017) on vehicle. Connect one gauge to front caliper and one gauge to rear wheel cylinder. Bleed system. Depress brake pedal until pressure reading at front wheel is 1138

Brakes

TOYOTA (Cont.)

psi, (80 kg/cm²) on Camry, or 711 psi (50 kg/cm²) on all other models. DO NOT depress brake pedal more than once or release pedal when setting test pressure on front gauge.

Fig. 2: Exploded View Of Load Sensing Proportioning & By-Pass Valve (All Except Camry)

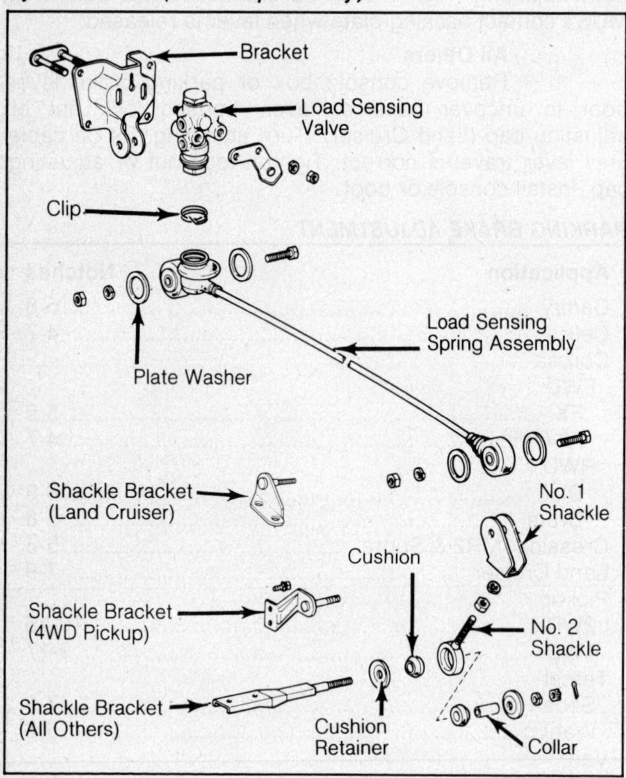

Courtesy of Toyota Motor Sales, U.S.A., Inc.

BRAKE PRESSURES

Application	Front Gauge psi (kg/cm²)	Rear Gauge psi (kg/cm²)
Camry		
1st Reading	1138 (80)	583-768 (41-54)
2nd Reading	1422 (100)	688-873 (48-61)
Land Cruiser		
1st Reading	711 (50)	498-640 (29-39)
2nd Reading	1422 (100)	725-925 (51-65)
Pickup		
2WD		
1-Ton & C & C		
1st Reading	711 (50)	455-597 (32-42)
2nd Reading	1422 (100)	696-896 (49-63)
1/2-Ton		
1st Reading	711 (50)	413-555 (29-39)
2nd Reading	1422 (100)	526-726 (37-51)
4WD		
1st Reading	711 (50)	384-526 (27-37)
2nd Reading	1422 (100)	540-740 (38-52)
Van		
1st Reading	711 (50)	341-483 (24-34)
2nd Reading	1422 (100)	384-584 (27-41)

4) Wait 2 seconds from setting of test pressure before recording pressure reading from rear gauge. Raise pressure on front gauge to 1422 psi (100 kg/cm²) and record pressure reading from rear gauge after 2 seconds. Compare recorded pressures with specified rear brake pressures. See BRAKE PRESSURES table for correct pressure ranges.

5) Adjust fluid pressure if rear pressure readings do not meet specification. On Camry, go to step **9)**. Change length of No. 2 shackle to adjust pressures. *See Fig. 3.* If rear pressure readings are low, distance "A" must be increased. If rear pressure readings are high, distance "A" must be decreased. Turn No. 2 shackle 360 degrees for pressure change of 8.5 psi (.6 kg/cm²).

Fig. 3: Adjusting Brake Fluid Pressures (All Except Camry)

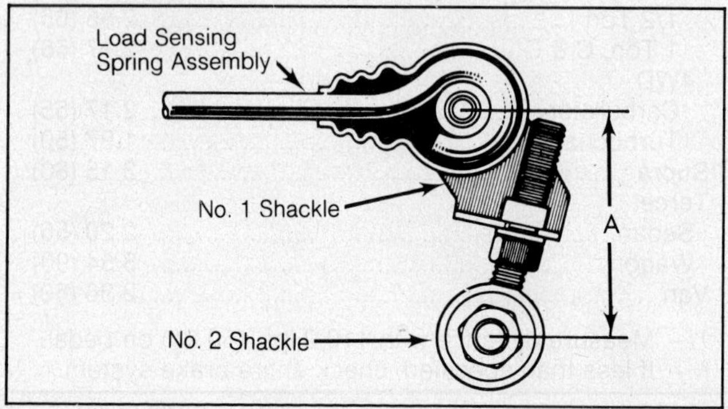

Courtesy of Toyota Motor Sales, U.S.A., Inc.

6) Repeat pressure tests after adjusting shackle length. If rear pressures do not meet specification after adjusting No. 2 shackle, reposition valve body. If rear pressures are too high, raise valve body. If rear pressures are too low, move valve body lower.

VALVE BODY ADJUSTMENT

Application	Front Gauge psi (kg/cm²)	Rear Gauge psi (kg/cm²)
Land Cruiser		
1st Reading	71 (5)	71 (5)
2nd Reading	356 (25)	148-205 (10.4-14.4)
3rd Reading	853 (60)	311-411 (21.9-28.9)
Pickups		
2WD 1-Ton/C & C		
1st Reading	71 (5)	71 (5)
2nd Reading	711 (50)	280-337 (19.7-23.7)
3rd Reading	1138 (80)	424-509 (29.8-35.8)
2WD 1/2-Ton		
1st Reading	71 (5)	71 (5)
2nd Reading	711 (50)	228-284 (16.0-20.0)
3rd Reading	1138 (80)	299-384 (21.0-27.0)
4WD		
1st Reading	71 (5)	71 (5)
2nd Reading	711 (50)	203-260 (14.3-18.3)
3rd Reading	1138 (80)	296-381 (20.8-26.8)
Van		
1st Reading	71 (5)	71 (5)
2nd Reading	356 (25)	71-128 (5-9)
3rd Reading	853 (60)	100-199 (7-14)

7) Adjust length of No. 2 shackle to standard length. Standard length of No. 2 shackle for 4WD Pickup

TOYOTA (Cont.)

models is 4.72" (120 mm) with adjusting range of 4.49-4.96" (114-126 mm). Standard length of No. 2 shackle on all other models is 3.07" (78 mm) with adjusting range of 2.83-3.31" (72-84 mm).

8) If pressures cannot be adjusted, check valve housing. Position valve body in uppermost position. Apply brakes and record rear brake pressures. See VALVE BODY ADJUSTMENT table for specified range. If measured value does not meet specification, replace valve assembly.

9) On Camry, to adjust pressure, shorten spring length to increase spring length. Standard spring length is 6.57" (166.9 mm). If pressure cannot be adjusted, raise valve body to decrease pressure.

REMOVAL & INSTALLATION

NOTE: **Different models may vary locations or numbers of anti-rattle springs, anti-squeal shims, pad support and guide plates or wear indicators. Note location of these items during removal process to assist installation process.**

FRONT PADS

NOTE: **Whenever pads are to be removed, siphon small amount of brake fluid from reservoir. Pushing piston into bore of caliper will force fluid back into master cylinder reservoir.**

Removal (Fixed Caliper)

Siphon small amount of brake fluid from reservoir. Raise vehicle and support securely. Remove wheels. Remove anti-rattle clip from retaining pins. Remove 2 retaining pins and anti-rattle spring. Pull pads from caliper. *See Fig. 4.*

Installation

Using wooden hammer handle, push pistons into caliper bores. Slide new pads into caliper. Install anti-rattle spring and 2 retaining pins. Install anti-rattle clip, making sure to fit clip into holes in end of retaining pins. Check level of fluid in reservoir.

Fig. 4: Exploded View Of Fixed Caliper Front Brake

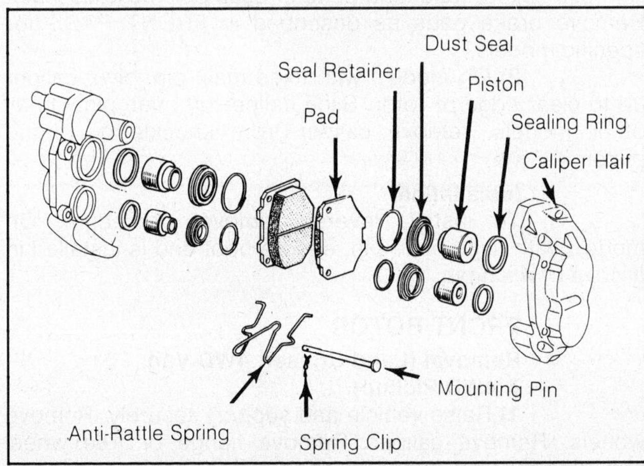

Courtesy of Toyota Motor Sales, U.S.A., Inc.

Removal (Fixed Main Pin Sliding Caliper)

Siphon small amount of brake fluid from reservoir. Raise vehicle and support. Remove wheels. Remove lower guide bolt. Pivot caliper up on upper guide bolt. Insert bolt into hole at top of torque plate to keep caliper from falling down. Remove pads and anti-squeal shim. Remove anti-rattle springs, pad guide plates and pad support plate. *See Figs. 5 and 6.*

Fig. 5: Exploded View Of Sliding Caliper With Fixed Main Pin (Supra & 2WD Van)

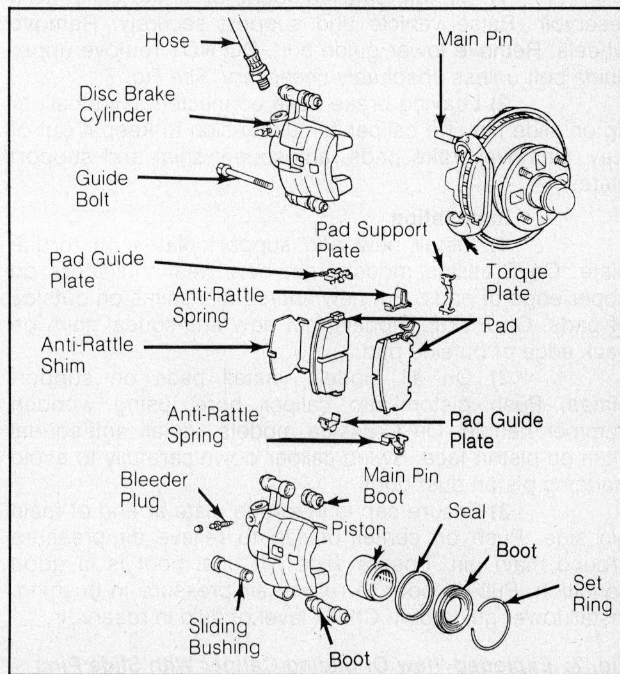

Courtesy of Toyota Motor Sales, U.S.A., Inc.

Fig. 6: Exploded View Of Sliding Caliper With Fixed Main Pin (4WD Van)

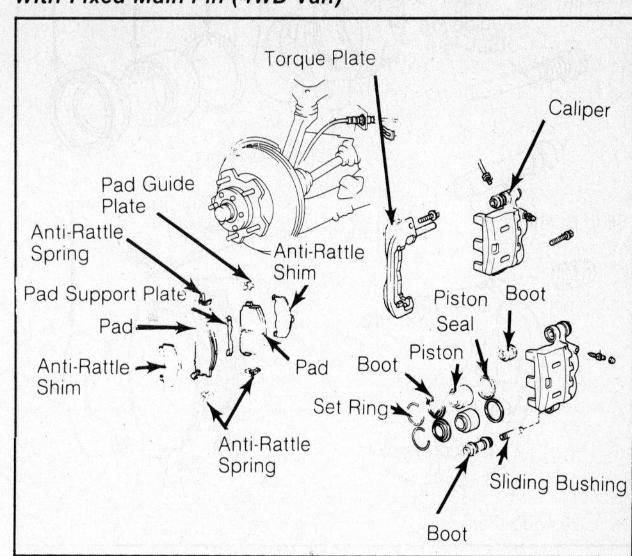

Courtesy of Toyota Motor Sales, U.S.A., Inc.

Installation

1) Install new pad support plate, pad guide plates and anti-rattle springs on torque plate. Push piston into caliper bore. Put new wear indicator on new pads. On Van models, wear indicator must be at bottom edge of outer pad. On all other models, wear indicator must be on upper edge of outer pad.

TOYOTA (Cont.)

2) Install new brake pads, using new anti-squeal shim. Anti-squeal shims must go between piston and backing plate of brake pad. Remove bolt from top of torque plate. Lower cylinder slowly. Do not let piston dust boot wedge against edge of pads. Install caliper guide bolt. Check level of fluid in reservoir.

Removal (Slide Pin Sliding Caliper)

1) Siphon small amount of brake fluid from reservoir. Raise vehicle and support securely. Remove wheels. Remove lower guide bolt. DO NOT remove upper guide bolt unless absolutely necessary. *See Fig. 7*.

2) Leaving brake hose connected, pivot caliper up on slide pin. Tie caliper to suspension to keep it out of way. Remove brake pads, anti-squeal shim and support plates.

Installation

1) Install new pad support plates on torque plate. On Cressida models, put new wear indicators on upper edge of pads. Put new anti-squeal shims on outside of pads. On Pickup models, put new anti-squeal shim on back edge of outside pad.

2) On all models, install pads on support plates. Push piston into caliper bore, using wooden hammer handle. On Cressida models, install anti-squeal shim on piston face. Swing caliper down carefully to avoid wedging piston dust boot.

3) Ensure cap is in torque plate at end of main pin side. Push on center of cap to relieve air pressure around main pin. Ensure slide pin dust boot is in good condition. Pull on boot to relieve air pressure in bushing. Install lower guide bolt. Check level of fluid in reservoir.

Fig. 7: Exploded View Of Sliding Caliper With Slide Pins

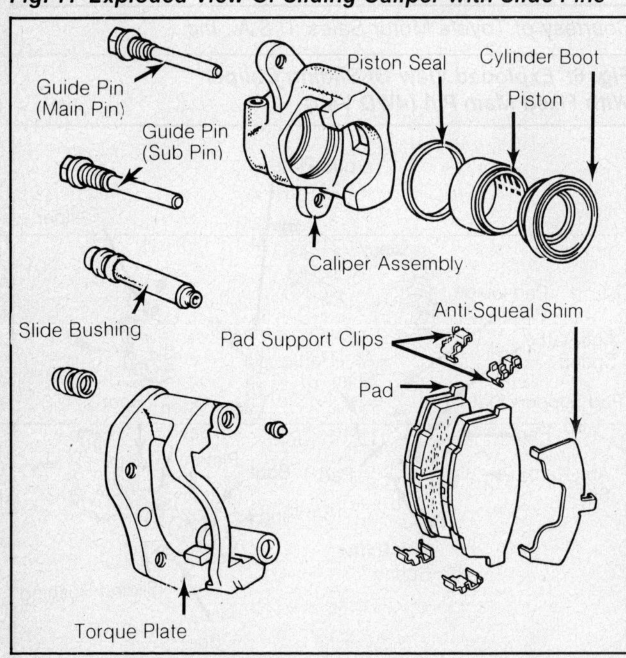

Courtesy of Toyota Motor Sales, U.S.A., Inc.

Removal (Mounting Bolts Sliding Caliper)

1) Siphon small amount of brake fluid from reservoir. Raise vehicle and support securely. Remove wheels. Hold rotor in place with lug nuts. Remove 2 guide bolts. *See Fig. 8*.

2) Leave hose connected and hang caliper from suspension so that no tension is placed on hose. Remove anti-squeal springs (if equipped), brake pads, anti-squeal shims, pad wear indicator plates and pad support plates.

Installation

1) Install new pad support plates on torque plate. Put new pad wear indicators on pads. Arrow on wear indicators must point in direction that rotor turns. Put new anti-squeal shims on pads. On MR2 models, cover both sides of No. 3 anti-squeal shim with disc brake grease.

2) On all models, install pads on support plates. Press piston into caliper with wooden hammer handle. Install caliper carefully so that piston dust boot does not wedge against brake pads. Check level of fluid in reservoir.

Fig. 8: Exploded View Of Sliding Caliper With Mounting Bolts

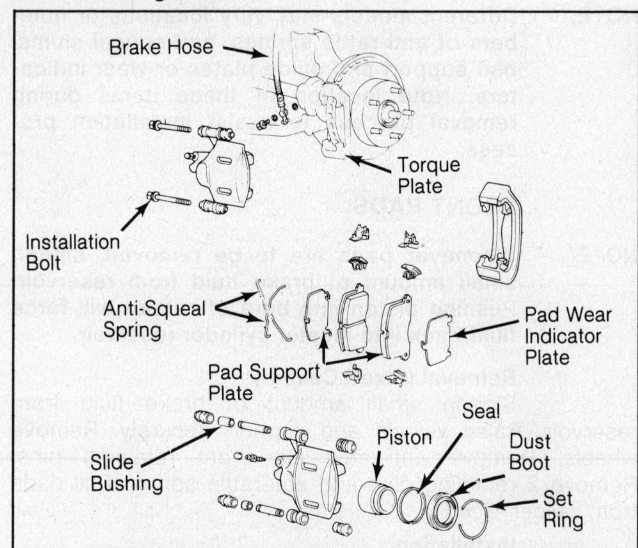

Courtesy of Toyota Motor Sales, U.S.A., Inc.

FRONT CALIPER

Removal

1) Raise vehicle and support securely. Remove tire and wheel. Disconnect hydraulic line and spring clip. Remove caliper mounting bolts or slide pins as necessary. Remove brake pads as described in FRONT PADS for specific models.

2) On models with fixed main pin, pivot caliper up to clear edge of rotor. Slide caliper off main pin. On all other models, remove caliper from knuckle or torque plate.

Installation

To install, reverse removal procedure. On models with fixed main pin, ensure boot end is installed in groove of main pin.

FRONT ROTOR

Removal (Land Cruiser, 4WD Van & 4WD Pickup)

1) Raise vehicle and support securely. Remove wheels. Remove caliper. Remove flange or free wheel hub. Use tapered punch to open slits of conical washers. Remove axle shaft snap ring.

2) Bend back tabs of outer lock washer and remove it. Using Spindle Socket (09607-60020), remove

TOYOTA (Cont.)

lock nut. Remove inner lock washer and adjusting nut. Remove thrust washer and outer bearing.

3) Remove axle hub and rotor. Remove grease seal and inner bearing. Press hub bolts out of axle hub. Remove 2 retaining bolts and separate rotor from hub.

Installation

To install, reverse removal procedure. Adjust wheel bearings. See FRONT WHEEL BEARING & OIL SEAL in this article.

Removal (Camry, Celica, Corolla FWD, MR2 & Tercel)

Remove caliper assembly with hose connected. Suspend caliper from frame without putting tension on hose. Remove torque plate from knuckle. Remove rotor from hub.

Installation

To install, reverse removal procedure.

Removal (All Others)

Remove caliper. Remove grease cap, cotter pin, washer and castellated nut. Remove thrust washer and outer wheel bearing. Remove rotor and hub assembly. Place alignment marks on rotor and hub for reassembly reference. Remove retaining bolts and separate hub from rotor.

Installation

To install, reverse removal procedure. Adjust wheel bearings. See FRONT WHEEL BEARING & OIL SEAL in this article.

FRONT DRUM

Removal & Installation (Land Cruiser)

Raise and support vehicle. Remove wheels. Remove screws retaining brake drum. Remove brake drum. To install, reverse removal procedure.

FRONT SHOES

Removal & Installation (Land Cruiser)

Remove drum. Remove front return spring. Remove hold-down springs. Remove brake shoes and rear return spring together. To install, reverse removal procedure. Apply brake grease to all brake shoe-to-backing plate contact points and adjuster. *See Fig. 10.*

Fig. 10: Exploded View of Land Cruiser Front Brake

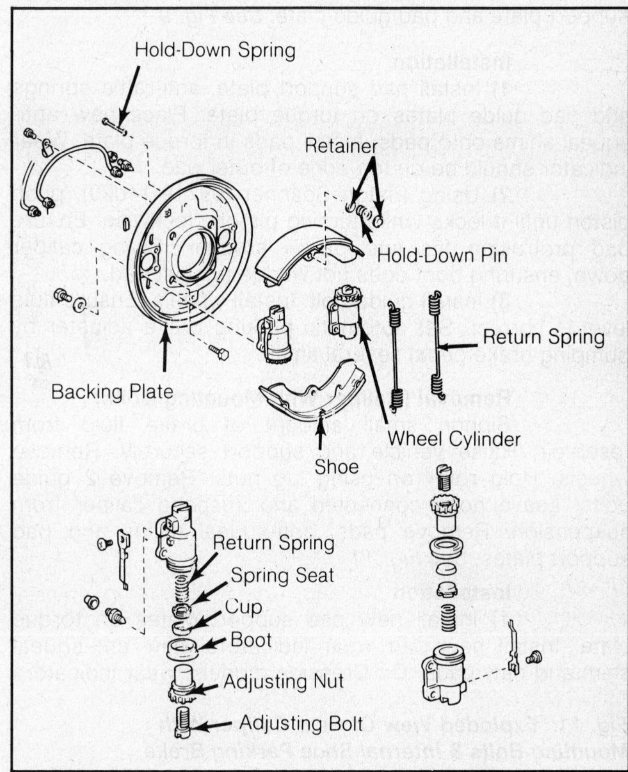

Courtesy of Toyota Motor Sales, U.S.A., Inc.

REAR PADS

NOTE: Whenever pads are to be removed, siphon small amount of brake fluid from reservoir. Pushing piston into bore of caliper will force fluid back into master cylinder reservoir.

Removal (Fixed Main Pin Caliper)

1) Siphon small amount of brake fluid from reservoir. Raise vehicle and support securely. Remove wheels. Remove guide bolt. Do not remove caliper from main pin. Leave parking brake cable connected.

2) Leaving brake hose connected, pivot caliper up on main pin. Suspend caliper at highest point. Remove

Fig. 9: Exploded View of Fixed Main Pin Rear Caliper & Integral Parking Brake

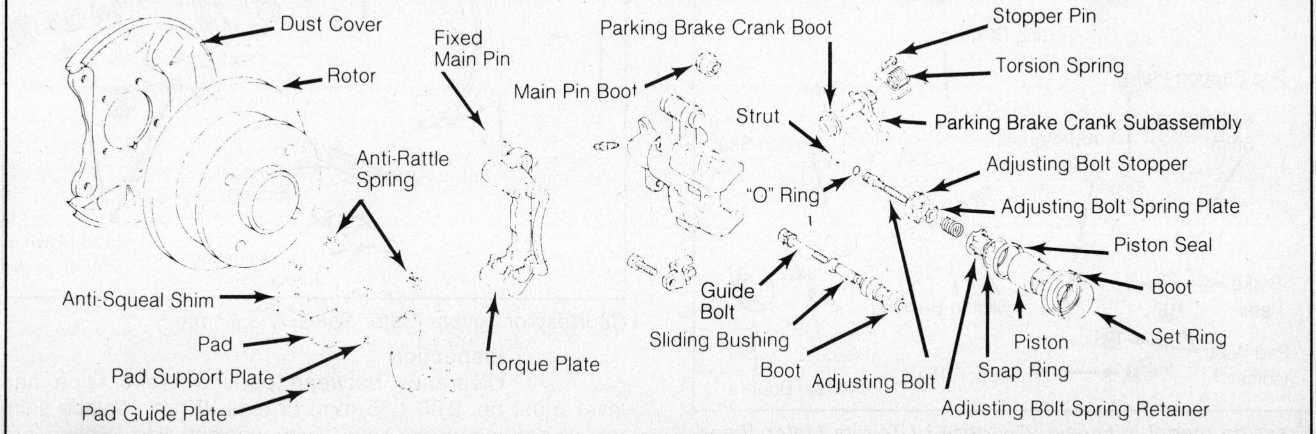

Courtesy of Toyota Motor Sales, U.S.A., Inc.

brake pads, anti-squeal shims, anti-rattle springs, pad support plate and pad guide plate. *See Fig. 9.*

Installation

1) Install pad support plate, anti-rattle springs and pad guide plates on torque plate. Place new anti-squeal shims onto pads. Install pads in torque plate. Wear indicator should be on top edge of outer pad.

2) Using Piston Spanner (09719-14020), push piston until it locks while turning piston clockwise. Ensure pad protrusion fits into piston stopper. Swing caliper down, ensuring boot does not wedge against pad.

3) Install guide bolt. Install wheels. Ensure fluid level is correct. Set automatic parking brake adjuster by pumping brake pedal several times.

Removal (Caliper With Mounting Bolts)

Siphon small amount of brake fluid from reservoir. Raise vehicle and support securely. Remove wheels. Hold rotor on using lug nuts. Remove 2 guide bolts. Leave hose connected and suspend caliper from suspension. Remove pads, anti-squeal shims and pad support plates. *See Fig. 11.*

Installation

1) Install new pad support plates on torque plate. Install new pad wear indicators, new anti-squeal shim and new pads. On Cressida models, wear indicators go on lower edge of pad. Anti-squeal shim goes at outside of pads.

2) Push piston into bore with wooden hammer handle. Put new anti-squeal shim on piston. Slide caliper onto torque plate carefully so boot does not wedge on edge of pad.

Fig. 11: Exploded View Of Rear Caliper With Mounting Bolts & Internal Shoe Parking Brake

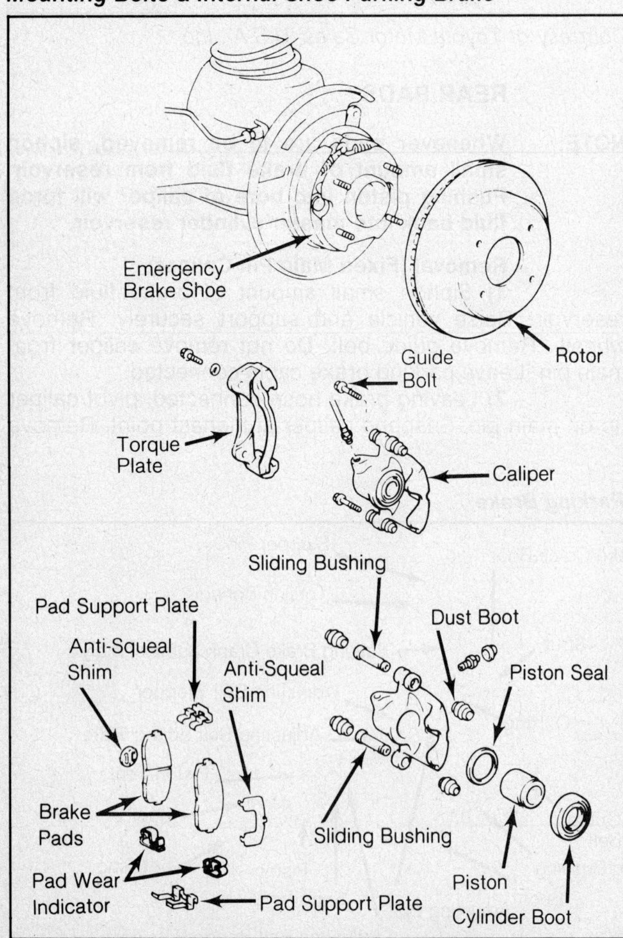

Cressida model is shown. Courtesy of Toyota Motor Sales, U.S.A., Inc.

REAR CALIPER

Removal

Disconnect brake hose. Remove mounting bolts as necessary. Disconnect parking brake cable, if attached to caliper. On fixed pin type caliper, pivot caliper up to clear rotor and slide it off main pin.

Installation

To install, reverse removal procedure. On fixed pin type caliper, ensure that boot end is installed in groove of pin. On models with integral parking brake, ensure piston stopper groove is fitted to protrusion on pad. Bleed brake system.

REAR ROTOR

Removal & Installation

Remove caliper and suspend with hose connected. Remove torque plate from backing plate. Slide rotor off axle flange. To install, reverse removal procedure.

REAR PARKING BRAKE

Removal (Internal Shoe Brake)

Remove rotor. Remove shoe return springs and shoe strut with spring. Pull out on front shoe and remove adjusting screw set. Remove front shoe and tension spring. Pull rear shoe out and disconnect parking brake cable from lever. *See Fig. 12.*

Fig. 12: Exploded View Of Internal Shoe Parking Brake Assembly

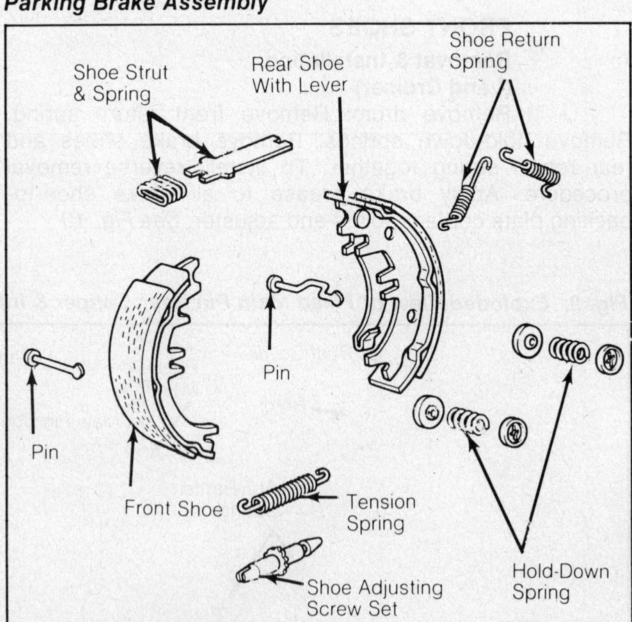

Courtesy of Toyota Motor Sales, U.S.A., Inc.

Inspection

Clearance between parking brake shoe and lever must be .014" (.35 mm) or less. If not, replace shim under parking brake lever with correct size. Shims are

TOYOTA (Cont.)

available in sizes: .008-.035" (.20-.90 mm) in .004" (.10 mm) increments. Use new "C" washer when installing lever.

Installation

1) Apply non-melting grease to both sliding surfaces of shoes and adjusting screw set. Connect parking brake lever to cable. Slide rear shoe between seat of hold-down spring and backing plate. Install tension spring on rear shoe. Connect front shoe to tension spring.

2) Slide adjusting screw set between front and rear shoes. Slide front shoe between hold-down spring and backing plate. Install front return spring. Install shoe strut and spring. Install rear return spring. Align groove of rear axle shaft flange with service hole on disc and install disc.

REAR DRUM

Removal (Tercel Sedan)

Raise and support vehicle. Remove tire and wheel. Remove grease cap, cotter pin, lock nut and bearing nut. Remove brake hub together with outer bearing and thrust washer.

Removal (All Others)

Raise and support vehicle. Remove tire and wheel. Remove set screws from brake drum (if equipped). Pull drum from axle flange. It may be necessary to loosen brake adjustment before removing drum.

Installation

1) Set brake shoe-to-drum clearance by measuring inside diameter of brake drum and diameter of brake shoes. Turn brake adjuster until difference between diameters is .02" (.6 mm). On all models except Tercel Sedan, install brake drum and adjust brakes, if required.

2) On Tercel Sedan, pack bearings and fill inside of axle hub with "MP" grease. Snug down bearing nut. Loosen until hub can be turned by hand. Tighten nut until bearing preload of 1.1-19.2 lbs. (.5-6.0 kg) is obtained. Install cotter pin.

REAR BRAKE SHOES

Removal
(Pickup With Leading/Trailing Brakes)

1) Remove return spring and adjuster. Remove front hold-down spring and pin. Remove front shoe and anchor spring. Remove rear hold-down spring, pin and rear shoe. Remove strut and spring from adjusting lever.

2) Disconnect parking brake cable from lever. Using screwdriver, remove "C" washers retaining parking brake lever and adjuster lever to rear shoe. Remove levers from shoe. See Fig. 13.

Fig. 13: Exploded View Of Rear Leading/Trailing Brake

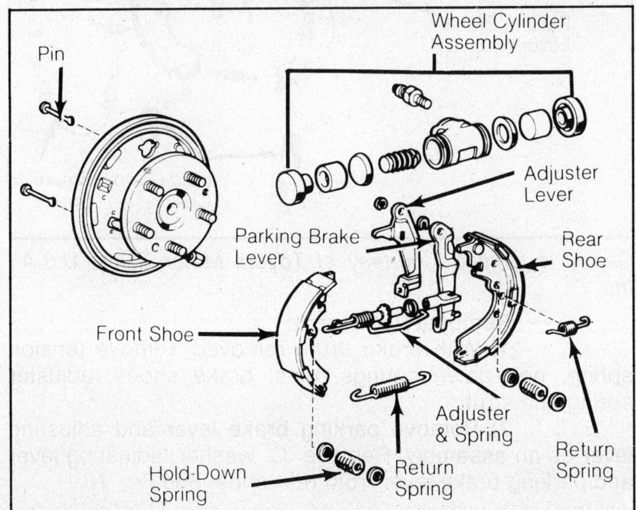

Courtesy of Toyota Motor Sales, U.S.A., Inc.

Fig. 14: Exploded View of Land Cruiser Rear Brake

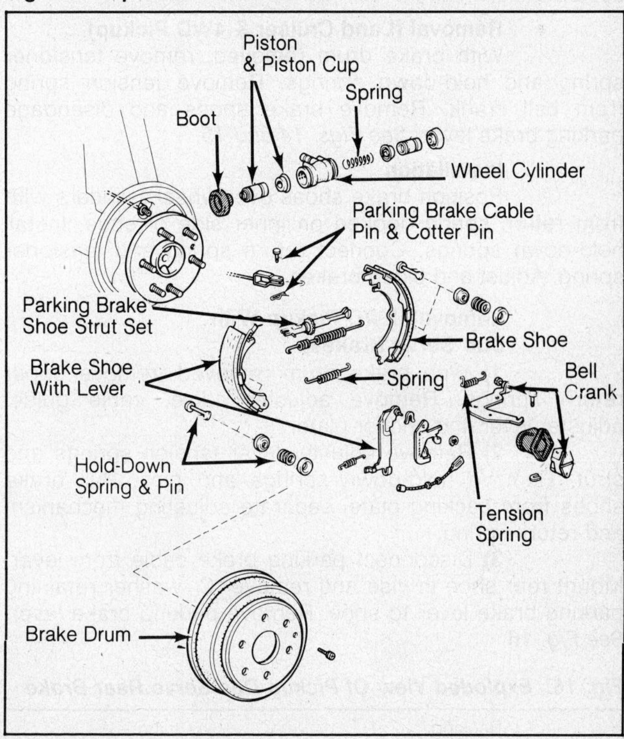

Courtesy of Toyota Motor Sales, U.S.A., Inc.

Fig. 15: Exploded View of 4WD Pickup Rear Brake

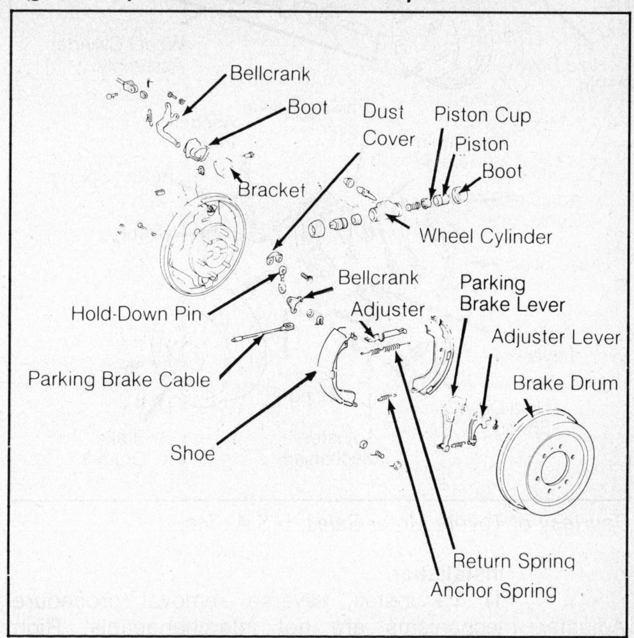

Courtesy of Toyota Motor Sales, U.S.A., Inc.

Installation

1) Install parking brake lever and adjuster lever to rear shoe with new "C" washers. When installing new

TOYOTA (Cont.)

brake shoes, coat wheel cylinder cups with rubber grease and apply non-melting grease to sliding areas of backing plate and automatic adjuster.

2) To complete installation, reverse removal procedure. After installation of brake assembly, move adjuster back and forth to ensure adjusting bolt moves. If not, check installation of brake assembly. Bleed hydraulic system.

Removal (Land Cruiser & 4WD Pickup)

With brake drum removed, remove tensioner spring and hold-down springs. Remove tension spring from bell crank. Remove brake shoes and disengage parking brake lever. *See Figs. 14 and 15.*

Installation

Position brake shoes over wheel cylinders with front return spring hooked on inner side of shoe. Install hold-down springs. Connect return spring and tensioner spring. Adjust and bleed brakes.

Removal (2WD Pickup With Duo-Servo Brakes)

1) With brake drum removed, remove upper return springs. Remove adjuster cable, cable guide, adjuster lever and anchor plate.

2) Remove adjuster lever tension springs and strut. Remove hold-down springs and pins. Pull brake shoes from backing plate, separate adjusting mechanism and return spring.

3) Disconnect parking brake cable from lever. Mount rear shoe in vise and remove "C" washer retaining parking brake lever to shoe. Remove parking brake lever. *See Fig. 16.*

Fig. 16: Exploded View Of Pickup Duo-Servo Rear Brake

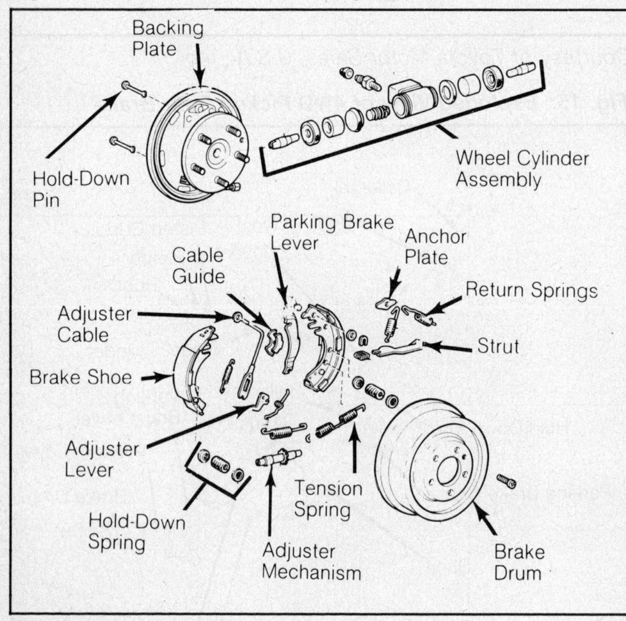

Courtesy of Toyota Motor Sales, U.S.A., Inc.

Installation

1) To install, reverse removal procedure. Adjuster mechanisms are not interchangeable. Right wheel has left-hand threads; left wheel, right-hand threads.

2) After installation of brake assembly, pull adjusting cable backward and release. Adjusting bolt should move. If not, check installation of brake assembly. Install drum and adjust brakes.

Removal (Tercel Sedan)

1) With brake drum removed, remove return spring. Remove hold-down springs and pins. Disconnect front shoe from parking brake strut and disconnect lower spring.

2) Remove front shoe. Disconnect parking brake lever return spring. Remove rear shoe from backing plate. Disconnect parking brake cable from lever.

3) Remove "C" washer, adjusting lever and parking brake lever from rear shoe. Remove "C" washer retaining parking brake lever on adjusting lever and separate levers. *See Fig. 17.*

Installation

1) Install parking brake lever onto adjusting lever with NEW "C" washer. Install lever assembly on rear shoe and retain in position temporarily with NEW "C" washer.

2) Measure clearance between adjusting lever and rear shoe. Remove "C" washer and install correct shim(s) which will give clearance of 0-.014" (0-.35 mm). Install and stake "C" washer. Ensure that lever moves.

3) Complete installation by reversing removal procedure. Adjuster mechanisms are not interchangeable. Left wheel has left-hand threads; right wheel, right-hand threads. Install drum and bleed hydraulic system.

NOTE: **Shims are available in 6 sizes: .008" (.2 mm), .012" (.3 mm), .016" (.4 mm), .020" (.5 mm), .024" (.6 mm) and .035" (.9 mm). Shims may be installed in pairs to provide proper clearance.**

Fig. 17: Exploded View Of Tercel Sedan Rear Brake

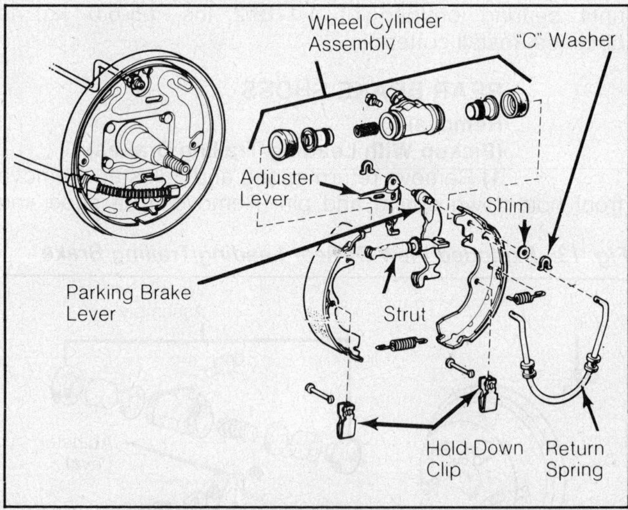

Camry is similar. Courtesy of Toyota Motor Sales, U.S.A., Inc.

Removal (All Others)

1) With brake drum removed, remove tension spring, hold-down springs, pins, brake shoes, adjuster spring and strut.

2) Remove parking brake lever and adjusting lever as an assembly. Remove "C" washer, adjusting lever and parking brake lever from rear shoe. *See Fig. 18.*

TOYOTA (Cont.)

Fig. 18: Exploded View of Rear Brake Used On Camry, Celica, Corolla, Van & Tercel FWD Wagon

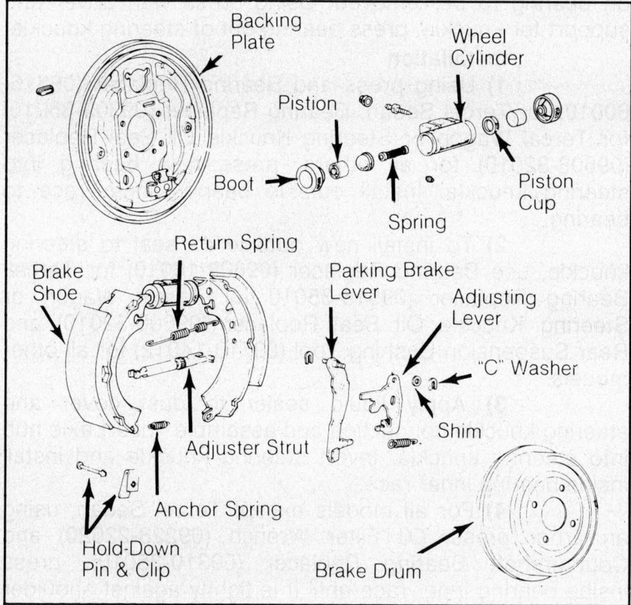

Courtesy of Toyota Motor Sales, U.S.A., Inc.

Installation

1) Install adjusting lever and parking brake lever to rear shoe with NEW "C" washer. Measure clearance between lever and shoe.

2) Remove "C" washer and install correct shim(s) which will give clearance of 0-.014" (0-.35 mm). Install and stake "C" washer. Ensure that lever moves.

3) Complete installation by reversing removal procedure. Adjuster mechanisms are not interchangeable. Left-hand thread is for right wheel and right-hand thread is for left wheel. Install drum and bleed hydraulic system.

REAR WHEEL CYLINDER

Removal

With brake drum and shoes removed, disconnect hydraulic line from wheel cylinder. Remove mounting bolts and remove wheel cylinder.

Installation

To install, reverse removal procedure. Automatic adjusting mechanisms are not interchangeable from side to side. Install adjusting mechanism at side from which it was removed.

REAR AXLE BEARING & OIL SEAL

NOTE: **This section applies to axles that have bearings lubricated by differential oil. IRS axle bearings and seals are not covered in this article.**

Removal
(Corolla RWD, 4WD Tercel & Van)

1) With wheel and brake drum removed, remove 4 backing plate mounting nuts. Using Axle Shaft Puller (09520-00031), remove axle shaft. Maximum shaft runout is .059" (1.5 mm).

2) Maximum flange runout is .004" (.1 mm). Using grinder, grind down inner bearing retainer of axle shaft and cut off with chisel and hammer.

3) Using Rear Axle Shaft Bearing Remover (09527-30010 for Corolla with disc brake or 09527-20011 for all others), press bearing from axle shaft. Use Oil Seal Puller (09308-00010) to remove oil seal from housing. Clean all parts.

Installation

1) Install outer bearing retainer and new bearing. Using press and Rear Axle Shaft Bearing Driver (09515-21010) for Corolla, Cressida and Van, Rear Axle Shaft Bearing Puller (09515-20010) for all others, press bearing onto axle shaft.

2) Heat new inner bearing retainer to about 302°F (150°C) in oil bath. While it is still hot, face non-beveled side toward bearing and press onto axle shaft, using Rear Axle Shaft Bearing Replacer (09515-21010) for Corolla, Cressida and Van, or Rear Axle Shaft Bearing Replacer (09515-20010) for all others.

NOTE: **When installing hot inner bearing retainer, make sure there is no oil or grease on axle shaft.**

3) Apply grease to lips of new oil seal. Using Rear Axle Shaft Oil Seal Replacer (09517-30010) for Corolla with disc brakes, Cressida and Van, or Rear Axle Shaft Oil Seal Replacer (09517-12010) for all others. Drive seal .079" (2.0 mm) for Corolla with disc brakes, .232" (5.9 mm) for Corolla with drum brakes, .236" (6 mm) for Cressida and Van, and .220" (5.6 mm) for all others below outer edge of housing.

4) With bearing retainer and gasket assembly on axle shaft, align and position with notches facing down. Install axle shaft into housing and tighten mounting nuts to 44-53 ft. lbs. (60-72 N.m). Complete installation by reversing removal procedures.

Removal (Land Cruiser - Semi-Floating)

1) Drain axle housing and remove inspection cover. Remove differential pinion shaft lock pin. Remove pinion shaft and spacer.

2) Push axle shaft to center of vehicle and remove axle lock circlip. Remove axle shaft, taking care not to damage bearing oil seal. Using Seal Remover (09308-00010), remove oil seal. Using Bearing Remover (09514-35011), remove rear axle bearing.

Installation

Using Bearing Installer (09608-20011), drive new bearing and oil seal into rear housing. To complete installation, reverse removal procedure.

Removal (Land Cruiser & Pickup - Full Floating)

1) Remove wheel and brake drum. Remove nuts retaining axle shaft. Remove axle shaft. Using Seal Remover (09308-00010), remove oil seal from axle shaft tube.

2) Remove lock nut. Remove outer wheel bearing and lock plate. Remove hub assembly, Using seal remover, remove oil seal from hub. Remove inner wheel bearing.

Installation

1) Install inner wheel bearing in hub. Using Seal Installer (09608-35013), install oil seal. Place hub assembly on vehicle. Install outer wheel bearing and lock plate. Install brake drum. Tighten lock nut to 43 ft. lbs. (58 N.m).

2) Rotate hub several times and recheck lock nut. Using spring scale, check bearing starting preload. Adjust lock nut to obtain .9-7.3 lbs. (.4-3.3 kg) starting preload. Align mark on lock nut with mark on axle housing.

3) Install lock bolts 90 degrees from marks. Using Seal Installer (09517-36010), install oil seal in axle shaft tube. Install axle shaft.

Removal (Pickup - Single Rear Wheel)

1) Remove wheel and brake drum. Disconnect line at wheel cylinder. Disconnect parking brake cable. Remove 4 backing plate mounting nuts. Pull out axle shaft and backing plate together. Remove snap ring from axle shaft.

2) Attach Pressing Tube (09521-25011) to rear of backing plate. Press axle shaft from backing plate. Using slide hammer with inside puller, remove outer oil seal. Support backing plate around bearing. Using press with bearing driver, press bearing out of bearing case.

3) If bearing case is worn or damaged, put nuts on serration bolts and drive bolts out with hammer. Using slide hammer with inside puller, remove inner oil seal from axle shaft. Clean all parts before reinstallation.

Installation

1) Place backing plate on new bearing case. Use 2 sockets to press serration bolts into place. Flat side of bearing case and 2 long serration bolts should be on upper side of backing plate. Using press, bearing driver and support for backing plate, press new bearing into case.

2) Using bearing driver, press new oil seal into bearing case. Install backing plate and bearing retainer onto axle shaft. Using press and supporting for backing plate and bearing case, press axle shaft into backing plate and bearing case. Install snap ring to axle shaft.

3) To install inner oil seal in rear axle housing, use bearing driver to install seal in housing. Make sure to coat lips of oil seals with grease before final installation. Install rear axle shaft in housing. Replace 4 backing plate nuts and tighten to 51 ft. lbs. (69 N.m).

4) Connect brake line to wheel cylinder. Install drum and wheel. Fill differential with gear oil. Connect parking brake cable to equalizer and install clip and clamp bolt to frame. On 4WD vehicles, also install other end of parking brake cable to bellcrank. Bleed brake system.

FRONT WHEEL BEARING & OIL SEAL

Removal (Camry, Celica, Corolla FWD & Tercel)

1) Remove cotter pin and bearing lock nut cap. Hold foot on brake pedal and loosen bearing lock nut. Remove brake caliper from steering knuckle and suspend on wire. Remove brake disc.

2) Remove cotter pin and nut from end of tie rod. Using tie rod end puller, disconnect tie rod end from steering knuckle. Place matchmarks on shock absorber lower bracket and camber adjust cam. Separate steering knuckle from shock absorber.

3) Remove 2 bolts holding ball joint to steering knuckle and separate. Using 2-jaw puller, remove axle hub from drive shaft and place steering knuckle in vise.

4) Using screwdriver, remove dust deflector. Using slide hammer with inside puller, pull oil seal out of steering knuckle. Remove snap ring from inside housing. Remove 3 bolts holding brake dust cover to steering knuckle.

5) Using 2-jaw puller, push axle hub out of steering knuckle. Remove inside bearing inner race from bearing. Using inside puller, pull oil seal out of steering knuckle.

6) Using 2-jaw puller, pull inner race of outer bearing from axle hub. Install outside bearing inner race on bearing to be removed. Using press with driver and support for knuckle, press bearing out of steering knuckle.

Installation

1) Using press and Bearing Replacer (09316-60010) for Tercel Sedan, Bearing Replacer (09309-35010) for Tercal Wagon or Steering Knuckle Oil Seal Replacer (09608-32010) for all others, press new bearing into steering knuckle. Install outside bearing inner race to bearing.

2) To install new outside oil seal to steering knuckle, use Bearing Replacer (09608-10010) for Tercel, Bearing Replacer (09515-35010 for Tercel Wagon or Steering Knuckle Oil Seal Replacer (09608-32010) and Rear Suspension Bushing Tool (09710-14012) for all other models.

3) Apply liquid sealer to dust cover and steering knuckle connection and assemble. Insert axle hub into steering knuckle. Invert steering knuckle and install inside bearing inner race.

4) For all models except Tercel Sedan, using an arbor press, Oil Filter Wrench (09228-22020) and Countershaft Bearing Replacer (09310-35010), press inside bearing inner race until it is tightly against shoulder of hub.

NOTE: DO NOT interchange inner and outer bearing races when installing.

5) Place steering knuckle in vise with hub facing down. Using snap ring pliers, install snap ring into hole of steering knuckle. Place new inside oil seal on steering knuckle hole.

6) Use Bearing Replacer (09608-10010) for Tercel Sedan, Bearing Replacer (09309-35010) for Tercel Wagon, or Steering Knuckle Oil Seal Replacer (09608-32010) and Rear Suspension Bushing Tool (09710-14012) for all other models. On Tercel Wagon, seal should be positioned .13" (3.3 mm) from end surface.

7) Using Adapter (09608-16050) for Tercel Wagon or Crankshaft Rear Oil Seal Replacer (09223-41020) for all models except Tercel, drive new dust deflector into steering knuckle. On Tercel, install bolts. On all models, install steering knuckle assembly to lower arm. Install axle hub to drive shaft.

CAUTION: Be careful not to damage oil seal lip or drive shaft boot.

8) Install steering knuckle assembly to lower stabilizer bar and install steering knuckle assembly to lower bracket of shock absorber. Insert bolts and align camber adjust cam matchmarks.

9) Install brake disc to axle hub. Install brake caliper to steering knuckle. Connect tie rod end to steering knuckle, tighten castle nut to 36 ft. lbs. (49 N.m) and secure with cotter pin. Install bearing lock nut and depress brake pedal.

10) While depressing brake pedal, tighten lock nut to 137 ft. lbs. (186 N.m). Install lock nut cap and cotter pin. Check front wheel alignment.

Removal (Land Cruiser, Van & 4WD Pickup)

1) Using flare wrench, disconnect brake line at brake caliper and remove caliper assembly. If equipped with free wheel hub, set control cover handle to "FREE".

TOYOTA (Cont.)

Remove cover bolts. Using snap ring pliers, remove snap ring from axle shaft.

2) Remove conical washers and pull hub from axle shaft. If equipped with flange, remove grease cap, bolts and snap ring. Install 2 bolts in threaded flange holes and turn bolts equally to remove axle flange.

3) Using screwdriver, open tabs on lock plate. Using spindle socket, remove outer lock nut. Remove lock plate and bearing adjusting nut. Remove outer bearing and thrust washer.

4) Remove axle hub with disc. Pry out oil seal and remove inner wheel bearing. Using brass bar, drive bearing races from hub and replace if necessary.

Installation

1) Pack front hub bearings and hub with multipurpose grease. Use bearing driver to install new races in hub. Place inside bearing inner race in hub. Drive oil seal into hub. Lightly coat lips of seal with grease.

2) Install axle hub on spindle. Install outer bearing and thrust washer. Tighten adjusting nut to 35 ft. lbs. (48 N.m) on Van without automatic locking hub or 43 ft. lbs. (58 N.m) on all other models. Rotate hub several times in each direction.

3) Loosen adjusting nut until finger tight. Retighten adjusting nut to 11 ft. lbs. (15 N.m) on Van with automatic locking hub or 35-60 INCH lbs. (4-7 N.m) all other models. Check starting preload with spring scale.

4) If preload is within range of 4.6-7.9 lbs. (2.1-3.6 kg) on Van or 6.2-12.6 lbs. (2.8-5.7 kg) on all other models, install lock plate and lock nut. Tighten lock nut to 58-72 ft. lbs. (79-98 N.m) and secure by bending 2 tabs of lock plate, one inward and one outward.

5) Place gasket on hub. Install flange or free wheel hub. Install 6 cone washers and nuts. Tighten nuts evenly to 23 ft. lbs. (31 N.m). Install bolt in axle shaft to pull shaft out of hub far enough to install snap ring.

MASTER CYLINDER

Removal (Van)

Disconnect battery cable. Remove instrument panel trim. Remove instrument panel. Remove lower panel from under steering column. Remove air ducts. Remove brake fluid from master cylinder. Remove master cylinder.

Removal (All Others)

On MR2, remove luggage compartment trim cover. On all models, unplug sensor lead (if equipped). Remove brake fluid from reservoir. Disconnect and plug hydraulic lines. Remove nuts holding master cylinder to power assist servo. Remove master cylinder.

Installation

1) ALWAYS check and adjust clearance between power assist servo push rod and master cylinder piston if either unit is replaced or overhauled. *See Fig. 19.* Place Depth Gauge (09737-00010) on master cylinder with sealing gasket installed. Loosen lock knob and lower pin of gauge until it lightly touches piston of master cylinder. Lock gauge pin in place.

2) Turn depth gauge over and set on power assist servo. Adjustment is correct if push rod just barely touches pin head of depth gauge.

NOTE: **Clearance between push rod of power assist servo and pin head of depth gauge must be zero.**

3) If not, adjust male portion of push rod with open end wrench while holding female portion of rod with pliers.

4) This adjustment will give standard operating clearance of .004-.020" (.1-.5 mm) with idle vacuum applied to servo. To install, reverse removal procedures and bleed brake system.

VACUUM PUMP

Removal (Land Cruiser)

Disconnect vacuum line from pump assembly. Disconnect and plug oil lines. Remove mounting nuts and gently pry pump off studs. Tap with plastic hammer, if necessary.

Installation

To install, reverse removal procedure. Run engine at idle speed. Loosen screw at vacuum pump outlet and check that oil is circulating.

POWER ASSIST SERVO

Removal & Installation

Remove master cylinder assembly from vehicle. On Van, remove steering column. On MR2, remove instrument panel lower trim panel. On all models, disconnect push rod clevis at brake pedal. Remove power booster attaching hardware and booster assembly from vehicle. To install, reverse removal procedure.

LOAD SENSING PROPORTIONING VALVE (LSPV)

Removal (Land Cruiser, Pickup & Van)

Raise and support vehicle. Disconnect No. 2 shackle from bracket. Disconnect and plug hydraulic lines from LSPV. Remove clip from brake hose. Remove

Fig. 19: Measuring Clearance Between Master Cylinder & Power Assist Servo

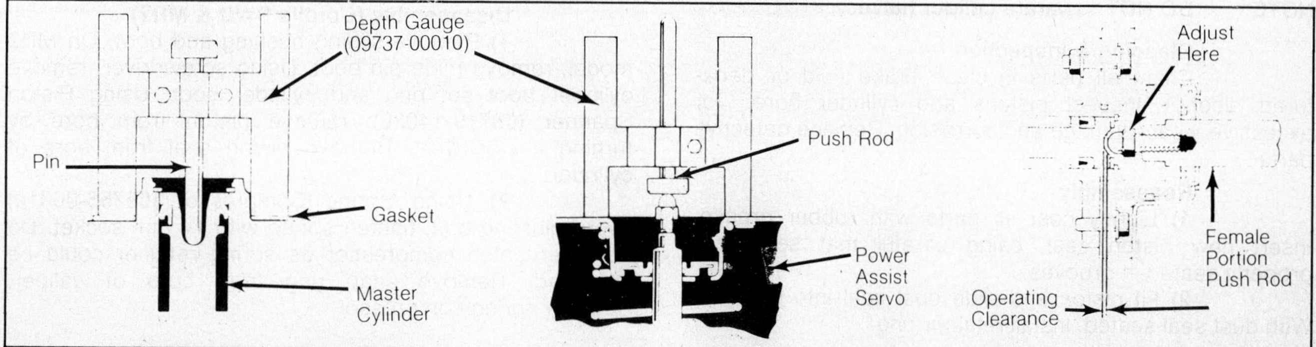

Courtesy of Toyota Motor Sales, U.S.A., Inc.

TOYOTA (Cont.)

mounting bolts from valve bracket and remove LSPV assembly. Separate valve body from bracket.

NOTE: **DO NOT disassemble valve body. If adjustments cannot be made, replace valve body.**

Installation

1) To install, reverse removal procedure. Apply rubber grease to all rubbing areas. Install new rubber plate on valve body side of spring. Adjust length of upper and lower shackle to original height.

2) DO NOT mistake valve side of load sensing spring for shackle side. After installation, position valve body so valve piston lightly contacts load sensing spring. Bleed hydraulic system and check brake pressures.

Removal & Installation (Camry)

Disconnect brake lines from LSPV. Loosen adjuster. Disconnect spring. Remove LSPV. To install, reverse removal procedure.

OVERHAUL

NOTE: **When overhauling caliper, wheel cylinder, or master cylinder assemblies, replace all soft parts. If cylinder bores are pitted or scored more than light honing will repair, replace entire assembly.**

FRONT CALIPER

Disassembly (2WD Pickup)

Remove dust boot set ring and dust boot. Insert small wooden block between pistons. Apply light air pressure to fluid inlet port to remove pistons. Remove seals without damaging bores.

Cleaning & Inspection

Clean all parts in clean brake fluid or denatured alcohol. Inspect bores and pistons for excessive wear or damage. Replace defective parts.

Reassembly

Coat piston seals, cylinder bores and pistons with rubber grease. To assemble, reverse disassembly procedure.

Disassembly (Land Cruiser & 4WD Pickup)

Remove dust seal retainer ring and seal. Insert small block of wood into cylinder cavity. Apply light air pressure to one side of cylinder to remove piston. Repeat procedure on opposite side. Remove piston seals without damaging bores.

NOTE: **DO NOT separate caliper halves.**

Cleaning & Inspection

Clean all parts in clean brake fluid or denatured alcohol. Inspect pistons and cylinder bores for excessive wear, damage and corrosion. Replace defective parts.

Reassembly

1) Lightly coat all parts with rubber grease. Insert new piston seal, being careful that seals are properly seated in grooves.

2) Fit piston and slide dust seal into position. With dust seal seated, install retainer ring.

Disassembly (All Others)

Remove retainer ring (if equipped) and boot. Apply light air pressure to fluid inlet port to remove piston from cylinder. Remove seal from cylinder without damaging bore.

Cleaning & Inspection

Clean all parts in clean brake fluid or denatured alcohol. Inspect bore and piston for excessive wear or damage. Replace defective parts.

Reassembly

Coat piston, seal and cylinder bore with rubber grease before reassembly. To reassemble, reverse disassembly procedure.

REAR CALIPER

Disassembly (Cressida)

Remove sliding bushing and dust boot. Using compressed air, remove piston from caliper. Remove cylinder boot. Remove piston seal from cylinder groove without damaging cylinder bore.

Cleaning & Inspection

Wash all parts in clean brake fluid or denatured alcohol. Inspect all parts for excessive wear, damage and corrosion. Replace defective parts.

Reassembly

Coat sliding bushing, dust boot, caliper boot, piston seal and piston with lithium soap base glycol grease. Install piston seal into caliper bore. Install piston into caliper bore. Install dust boot and sliding bushing. Make sure seal does not fold under. Make sure bushing flange faces inward into boot.

Disassembly (Celica & Supra)

Remove sliding bushing and boot. Remove main pin boot with chisel. Remove piston from caliper, using compressed air in fluid hole to force piston. DO NOT place fingers in front of piston while blowing into caliper with compressed air. Remove caliper boot and set ring from cylinder. Remove piston seal from caliper.

Cleaning & Inspection

Wash all parts in clean brake fluid or denatured alcohol. Inspect all parts for excessive wear, damage and corrosion. Replace defective parts.

Reassembly

Coat main pin boot, sliding pin and boot, piston seal, piston and dust boot with lithium soap base glycol. Install piston seal and piston into caliper. Install cylinder boot and boot set ring in caliper. Using 21 mm socket, press main pin boot in. Install dust boot and sliding bushing. Bushing flange must face toward inside of caliper.

Disassembly (Corolla RWD & MR2)

1) Remove sliding bushing and boot. On MR2 model, remove main pin boot. Using screwdriver, remove cylinder boot set ring and cylinder boot. Using Piston Spanner (09719-14020), remove piston from bore by turning it clockwise. Remove piston seal from bore of cylinder.

2) Using Spring Compressor (09756-00010) over adjusting bolt, tighten spring with 14 mm socket. Do not overtighten compressor as spring retainer could be damaged. Remove snap ring from bore of caliper. Remove spring compressor.

TOYOTA (Cont.)

CAUTION: When removing snap ring above adjusting bolt, ALWAYS use threaded spring compressor. Spring could pop out without compressor in place. This could cause physical damage to technician or inside of caliper. DO NOT overtighten spring compressor as spring retainer could be damaged.

3) Pull spring retainer, spring, spring plate and stopper out with adjusting bolt connected. DO NOT use excessive force to pry out adjusting bolt. Be very careful of "O" ring on adjusting bolt. Disassemble adjusting bolt by removing retainer, spring, spring plate and stopper. Remove "O" ring from bolt.

4) Remove strut. Remove spring from parking brake lever. Remove parking brake lever from caliper. On Corolla RWD models, turn lever so it will not catch on stop pin. Do not disassemble lever any further. If lever boot is to be replaced, remove it. Remove cable support bracket and stopper pin on MR2 models.

Reassembly

1) Put lithium soap base glycol grease on main pin, sliding bushing, strut pin, adjusting bolt, piston and all soft parts. On MR2 model, install stopper pin. Pin should be .098" (25 mm) from caliper to underside of head. Install cable support bracket.

2) On all models, install lever boot. Install lever, ensuring boot aligns with groove in lever seal. On MR2 models, ensure lever clears overlap on caliper. On all models, install spring and ensure that lever touches stopper pin. On Corolla RWD model, make sure that clearance between cable support bracket and upper side of lever is .0197-.0275" (.5-.7 mm). Use cable support bracket mount bolt to adjust clearance.

3) On all models, install strut. Ensure needle rollers do not catch on caliper hole. Install new "O" ring on adjusting bolt. Reassemble adjuster bolt with stopper, plate, spring and spring retainer. Use threaded compressor to tighten component parts of adjusting bolt assembly. Ensure that inscribed surface of stopper faces UP and notches of spring case line up with notches on stopper.

4) Install adjusting bolt assembly. Install snap ring with opening toward bleeder side. Remove threaded compressor. Pull up strongly on adjusting bolt as it should not move. Move parking brake lever by hand. Ensure adjusting bolt moves smoothly. Install piston seal in bore of cylinder.

5) Using piston spanner, slowly turn piston clockwise into caliper until it will go no further. Center of piston stopper groove must align with positioning protrusion on caliper. Place boot and set ring into caliper. On MR2 model, press main pin boot in using 21 mm socket. On all models, install dust boot and sliding bushing. Ensure seal does not fold under. Boot must be installed with flange facing inward.

MASTER CYLINDER

Disassembly

1) Remove reservoir, hose and switch. Mount cylinder in soft-jawed vise. Remove dust boot and check valves. Push pistons into cylinder bore and remove stop bolt.

2) Remove snap ring and withdraw piston assemblies. Remove unions, outlet plugs and other external components. Disassemble piston assemblies by removing springs, retainers and cups.

Cleaning & Inspection

Wash all parts in clean brake fluid or denatured alcohol. Inspect for wear, damage and corrosion. Replace defective parts as required.

Reassembly

To reassemble, reverse disassembly procedure using new soft parts. Ensure "UP" on boot is facing upward. Lubricate all components with clean brake fluid.

VACUUM PUMP

Disassembly (Land Cruiser)

Remove vacuum hose union and check valve. Drive pin down and remove end cover. Remove "O" ring. Slide rotor and blades from case.

Inspection

1) Inspect end cover and casing for damage or wear. Measure blade with calipers. Minimum width of blade is .2343" (5.95 mm). Minimum height is .543" (13.79 mm) and minimum length is 1.57" (39.88 mm).

2) Place rotor on alternator shaft and check for excessive play in direction of rotor spline rotation. Make sure check valve flows from union side to pump side. Ensure check valve does not allow flow from pump side to union side. *See Fig. 20.*

Fig. 20: Exploded View of Vacuum Pump

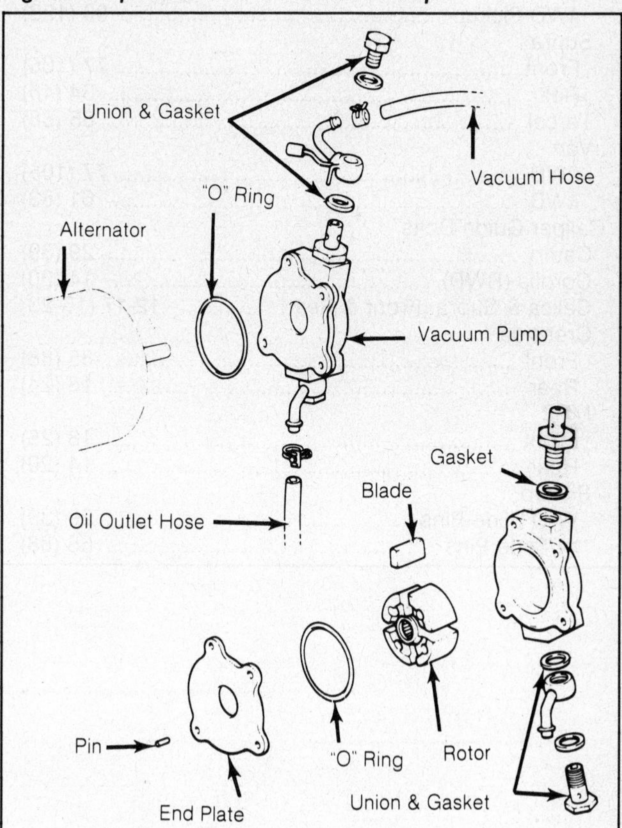

Courtesy of Toyota Motor Sales, U.S.A., Inc.

Reassembly

Install blades with rounded end out. Blade and rotor surface must be even. Lightly coat new "O" ring and insert into grooves. Place end plate on case. Align pin hole and drive in pin. Pin must protrude above cover .12" (3 mm). Install check valve with new gasket.

TOYOTA (Cont.)

POWER ASSIST SERVO

NOTE: Rebuild kits and replacement parts are available for power assist servos. No information or specifications are available for rebuilding and repair procedures.

TIGHTENING SPECIFICATIONS

Application	Ft. Lbs. (N.m)
Cable Support Bracket	34 (46)
Caliper Support Bracket Bolts	
Camry & Corolla	79 (107)
Corolla (RWD)	
Front	47 (64)
Rear	34 (46)
Celica	58-75 (77-102)
Cressida	
Front	67 (91)
Rear	34 (46)
Land Cruiser	90 (123)
MR2	
Front	65 (88)
Rear	43 (58)
Pickup	
2WD Pickup	80 (109)
4WD Pickup	90 (123)
Supra	
Front	77 (105)
Rear	34 (46)
Tercel	65 (88)
Van	
2WD	77 (105)
4WD	61 (83)
Caliper Guide Bolts	
Camry	29 (39)
Corolla (RWD)	14 (20)
Celica & Supra (Front & Rear)	12-17 (16-23)
Cressida	
Front	65 (88)
Rear	18 (24)
MR2	
Front	18 (25)
Rear	14 (20)
Pickup	
W/O Slide Pins	29 (39)
W/Slide Pins	65 (88)

TIGHTENING SPECIFICATIONS (Cont.)

Application	Ft. Lbs. (N.m)
Supra	
Front	27 (37)
Rear	14 (19)
Tercel	18 (25)
Van	
2WD	14 (19)
4WD	27 (37)
Hub-to-Rotor Bolts	
Corolla (RWD) & Pickup	47 (64)
Celica & Supra	40-54 (54-73)
Cressida	47 (64)
MR2	
Front	65 (88)
Rear	43 (58)
All Others	29-39 (39-53)
Master Cylinder Outlet Plugs	33 (44)
Parking Brake Adjusting Nuts	12 (16)
Reservoir Mounting Bolt	18 (25)
Reservoir Union Bolt	40 (54)
Lower Arm-to-Crossmember	51-65 (69-88)
Lower Arm-to Steering Knuckle	
Camry	59 (80)
Celica	94 (128)
Stabilizer Bar	66-90 (89-122)
Steering Knuckle-to-Shock	
Camry & Tercel (Sedan)	166 (226)
Celica	188 (256)
Tercel (Wagon)	105 (143)
Strut Bar	64 (87)
Tie Rod End	36 (49)
	INCH Lbs. (N.m)
Bleeder Plug	72 (8)
Brake Booster Mounting Nuts	108 (13)
Line-to-Whel Cylinder	132 (15)
Master Cylinder Brake Hoses	132 (15)
Master Cylinder Mounting Nuts	
Camry & Land Cruiser	108 (13)
Piston Stopper Bolt	84 (10)
Vacuum Pump Bolts	69 (7.8)
Wheel Cylinder Mounting Bolts	
Camry	84 (10)
Land Cruiser	
Front	156 (18)
Rear	84 (10)

TOYOTA (Cont.)

DISC BRAKE ROTOR SPECIFICATIONS

Application	Disc Diameter In. (mm)	Lateral Runout In. (mm)	Parallelism In. (mm)	Original Thickness In. (mm)	Min. Refinish Thickness In. (mm)	Discard Thickness In. (mm)
Camry						
New [1]	.....	.002 (.04)	.0002 (.002)	.984 (25)	.....	.945 (24)
Old [1]	.....	.004 (.10)	.....	.866 (22)	.....	.827 (21)
Celica						
Front	.....	.006 (.15)	.....	.866 (22)	.....	.827 (21)
Rear	.....	.006 (.15)	.....	.394 (10)	.....	.354 (9)
Corolla FWD						
Front						
FX	.....	.006 (.15)	.....	.709 (18)	.....	.669 (17)
All Others	.....	.006 (.15)	.....	.531 (13.5)	....	.492 (12.5)
Rear (FX)	.....	.006 (.15)	.....	.354 (9.0)	.....	.315 (8.0)
Corolla RWD						
Front	.....	.006 (.15)	.....	.709 (18)	.....	.669 (17)
Rear	.....	.006 (.15)	.....	.394 (10)	.....	.354 (9)
Cressida & Supra						
Front	.....	.005 (.13)	.....	.866 (22)	.....	.827 (21)
Rear	.....	.005 (.13)	.....	.709 (18)	.....	.669 (17)
MR2						
Front	.....	.005 (.13)	.....	.866 (22)	.....	.827 (21)
Rear	.....	.006 (.15)	.....	.394 (10)	.....	.354 (9)
Pickup						
2WD [2]	.....	.006 (.15)	.....	.984 (25.0)	.....	.945 (24.0)
	.....	.006 (.15)		.866 (22.0)	.....	.827 (21.0)
4WD	.....	.006 (.15)	.....	.787 (20.0)	.....	.748 (19.0)
Land Cruiser	.....	.005 (.12)	.....	.787 (20)	.....	.748 (19)
Tercel	.....	.006 (.15)	.....	.433 (11)	.....	.394 (10)
Van						
2WD	....	.006 (.15)	.....	.787 (20)	....	.748 (19)
4WD	.....	.006 (.15)	.....	.984 (25)	.....	.945 (24)

[1] – Design change during mid-year to help minimize brake pulsation. Old and new parts are NOT interchangeable.
[2] – Pickup uses 2 types of front discs. Check stamped measurement on brake rotor.

DRUM BRAKE SPECIFICATIONS

Application	Drum Diam. In. (mm)	Drum Width In. (mm)	Max. Drum Refinish Diam. In. (mm)	Wheel Cyl. Diam. In. (mm)	Master Cyl. Diam. In. (mm)
Celica, Corolla (FWD) & Tercel Wagon	7.87 (200)	.....	7.91 (201)	.....	.....
Land Cruiser (Front & Rear)	11.61 (295)	.....	11.69 (297)	.....	.....
Pickup & Van	10.00 (254)	.....	10.079 (256)	.....	.....
Tercel Sedan	7.09 (180)	.....	7.13 (181)	.....	.....
All Others	9.0 (228.6)	.....	9.079 (230.6)	.....	.....

VOLKSWAGEN

Cabriolet, Fox, Golf, GTI, Jetta, Jetta GLI, Quantum, Quantum Syncro, Scirocco, Vanagon, Vanagon Syncro

NOTE: **Information on Scirocco is not available from manufacturer.**

DESCRIPTION

GTI and Jetta GLI have 4-wheel disc brake systems. All other models have front disc brakes and self-adjusting rear drum brakes. All models are equipped with cable-actuated parking brake, which applies rear brakes.

All models use pressure regulator between front and rear brake circuits to avoid rear wheel lock-up during hard braking. Pressure regulator on Fox Coupe, and Vanagon models is nonadjustable proportioning type which is controlled by changes in operating angle of regulator.

On all other models, adjustable pressure regulators are used. Adjustable regulators vary braking pressures in direct proportion to tension placed upon operating spring. Operating spring is attached to control lever on regulator and bracket on axle. If vehicle weight transfer increases distance between lever and axle, tension on spring increases and regulator applies higher pressures to rear brakes. On Quantum Synchro, a height sensing proportioning valve is used.

ADJUSTMENTS

BRAKE PRESSURE REGULATOR

NOTE: **Adjustable pressure regulators are mounted on body and operated by spring connected to rear axle. Nonadjustable pressure regulators, which are proportioning valves, have no spring connection to axle.**

Vanagon & Vanagon Syncro

1) Raise vehicle and support securely. Attach Pressure Gauges (US 1016) to left front brake caliper and right rear wheel cylinder. Bleed pressure gauge and hoses through valve on gauges.

2) Pump brakes several times. Remove pressure regulator from studs, leaving brake lines connected. Press on brake pedal until reading on both gauges is 725 psi (50 bar).

3) Maintain pressure on pedal while tilting regulator forward. Stop tilting regulator at point where straight line between 2 mounting studs on body forms 30 degree angle with straight line between 2 mounting holes on regulator. Be careful not to kink brake lines when tilting regulator.

4) Increase pressure on brake pedal until reading on front gauge is 1450 psi (100 bar). Reading on rear pressure gauge must be 798-943 psi (55-65 bar). If reading is not within specified range, replace pressure regulator. Disconnect gauges and bleed brakes.

All Others

1) Bounce vehicle several times and allow it to settle normally. Measure distance from top of wheel rim to lower edge of fender lip (both sides) with 165 lbs. in driver's seat, full fuel tank and tires on ground. Attach spring tensioners on each side to hold axle in measured position.

2) Raise vehicle and support securely. Check measurement and adjust tensioners if necessary. Connect Pressure Gauge (US 1016) to left front caliper and right rear caliper or wheel cylinder in place of bleeder valves. Bleed hoses and gauges through bleeder valve on gauges.

3) Pump pedal several times. Depress brake pedal until front gauge shows pressure given for first reading in BRAKE PRESSURES chart. Record rear gauge reading. Increase pedal pressure until front gauge shows pressure given for second reading in BRAKE PRESSURES chart. Record rear gauge reading.

4) If pressure reading at rear gauge is too high, loosen clamp bolt and reduce spring tension. Increase spring tension if pressure reading at rear gauge is too low. Regulator must be replaced if pressures cannot be corrected by spring adjustment. Bleed hydraulic system after disconnecting gauges.

NOTE: **DO NOT adjust spring tension while pressure is applied on brake pedal.**

BRAKE PRESSURES

Application	Front Gauge psi (bar)	Rear Gauge psi (bar)
Fox		
Coupe & Sedan		
1st Reading	725 (50)	537-609 (37-42)
2nd Reading	1450 (100)	725-958 (50-66)
Wagon		
1st Reading	725 (50)	392-479 (27-33)
2nd Reading	1450 (100)	754-841 (52-58)
GLI/GTI		
1st Reading	725 (50)	450-479 (31-33)
2nd Reading	1450 (100)	754-783 (52-54)
Golf		
1st Reading	725 (50)	507-565 (35-39)
2nd Reading	1450 (100)	812-870 (56-60)
Jetta		
1st Reading	725 (50)	551-609 (38-42)
2nd Reading	1450 (100)	855-914 (59-63)
Jetta (16-Valve Engine)		
1st Reading	725 (50)	435-522 (30-36)
2nd Reading	1450 (100)	739-826 (51-57)
Quantum		
Coupe/Sedan		
1st Reading	725 (50)	508-551 (35-38)
2nd Reading	1450 (100)	812-856 (56-59)
Wagon		
1st Reading	725 (50)	580-624 (40-43)
2nd Reading	1450 (100)	885-928 (61-64)
Syncro		
1st Reading	725 (50)	508-565 (35-39)
2nd Reading	1450 (100)	841-899 (58-62)
Scirocco		
1st Reading	725 (50)	450-508 (31-35)
2nd Reading	1450 (100)	754-827 (52-57)

HEIGHT SENSING PROPORTIONING VALVE

Quantum Syncro

Height sensing proportioning valve is located on rear drive unit. Vehicle must be empty, fuel tank full and operator in driver's seat.

VOLKSWAGEN (Cont.)

1) Connect pressure gauges to left front and rear calipers. Lower vehicle and bounce several times. Depress brake pedal until front caliper pressure reading is 870 psi (60 bar). Rear caliper reading should be 595-696 psi (41-48 bar).

2) Depress brake brake until front caliper reading is 1450 psi (100 bar). Rear caliper reading should be 841-943 psi (58-65 bar). If reading is too high, release spring tension. Increase spring tension to raise pressure. Recheck pressure after adjustment.

MASTER CYLINDER PUSH ROD

NOTE: **Push rod should only need adjustment when servo is replaced.**

Vanagon & Vanagon Syncro

Loosen lock nut on push rod. Move clevis until distance from mounting face of power booster to center of clevis eye is 4 3/8" (111.5 mm). This adjustment must be made before installing pedal cluster and booster.

Quantum & Quantum Syncro

Loosen lock nut on push rod. Move clevis until distance from mounting face of power booster to center of clevis eye is 8.66" (220 mm). This adjustment must be made before brake booster is installed.

All Others

Push rod is nonadjustable.

STOPLIGHT SWITCH

NOTE: **Stoplight switches mounted on master cylinder are nonadjustable.**

Adjustable stoplight switch is located above brake pedal. Loosen lock nut. Turn switch until distance between brake pedal arm and first thread on switch body is .20-.24" (5-6 mm). Tighten lock nut. *See Fig. 1.*

Fig. 1: Stoplight Switch Adjustment

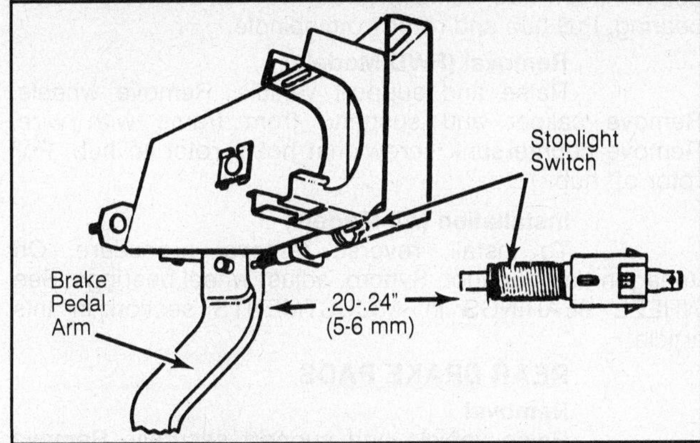

Courtesy of Volkswagen United States, Inc.

PARKING BRAKE

NOTE: **Check rear brake adjustment before adjusting parking brake.**

Vanagon & Vanagon Syncro

1) Raise vehicle and support securely. Release parking brake. Tighten self-locking adjusting nut until there is no play at brake components. Pull on cable housings to check for play. Apply and release parking brake several times.

2) Check adjustment by pulling parking brake handle up 2-4 notches. Rear wheels should be too tight to turn by hand. Release parking brake. Rear wheels should rotate freely.

Rear Disc Models

Raise vehicle and support securely. Release parking brake lever. Apply brake pedal once. Loosen lock nuts. Tighten each adjusting nut until lever on respective caliper lifts off stop. Measure gap between stop and lever. *See Fig. 2.* Do not move lever off stop more than .039" (1 mm). Tighten lock nuts.

Fig. 2: Rear Disc Parking Brake Adjustment

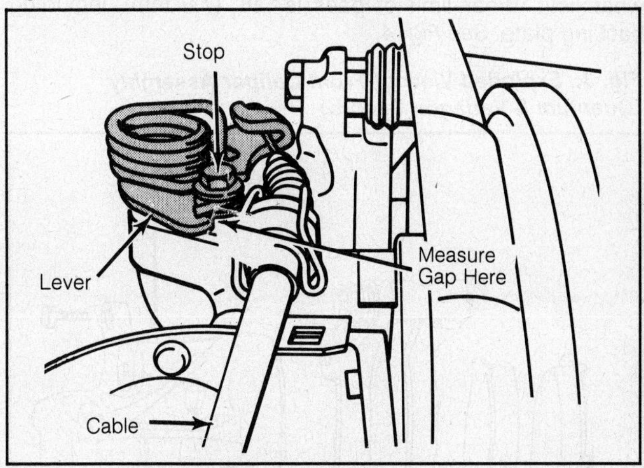

Courtesy of Volkswagen United States, Inc.

All Others

Raise vehicle and support securely. Apply brake pedal once firmly. Pull parking brake handle up 2 notches. Loosen locking nuts. Tighten each adjusting nut until respective rear wheel is locked. Release parking brake. Ensure rear wheels rotate freely. Tighten lock nuts.

WHEEL BEARINGS

NOTE: **FWD front wheel bearings and rear wheel bearings on Vanagon series, also called hub or axle bearings, are sealed units with one piece outer race. Bearings are nonadjustable.**

Rear Wheel Bearings (FWD Models)

To seat bearings, tighten adjusting nut snugly while turning drum or rotor to avoid binding of rollers. Back off and retighten nut until thrust washer can just be moved with screwdriver. Install locking cap and new cotter key. Install dust cap.

Front Wheel Bearings (Vanagon & Vanagon Syncro)

To seat bearings, tighten adjusting nut snugly while turning rotor. Back off and retighten nut slowly while checking tension on thrust washer. Wheel bearings are correctly adjusted when thrust washer can just be moved with screwdriver under finger pressure. After adjustment, peen flange of NEW hub nut into spindle axle shaft recess.

REMOVAL & INSTALLATION

FRONT PADS

Removal (Quantum & Vanagon Syncro)

Raise and support vehicle. Remove front wheels. Remove 2 self-locking bolts from hold guide pins.

VOLKSWAGEN (Cont.)

Discard hold guide pins. Remove caliper. Remove front pads. *See Fig. 3*.

Installation

To install, reverse removal procedure. Install new hold guide pins. Wear limit of pads is .28" (7.0 mm), including backing plate.

Removal (All Others)

Raise vehicle and support securely. Remove front wheels. Remove mounting bolts. Push caliper housing upward and swing out from bottom. Siphon small amount of brake fluid from reservoir. Remove pads and retaining springs from carrier. Replace pads that exceed wear limit. Wear limit of pads is .28" (7.0 mm), including backing plate. *See Fig. 4*.

Fig. 3: Exploded View of Front Caliper Assembly (Quantum & Vanagon Syncro)

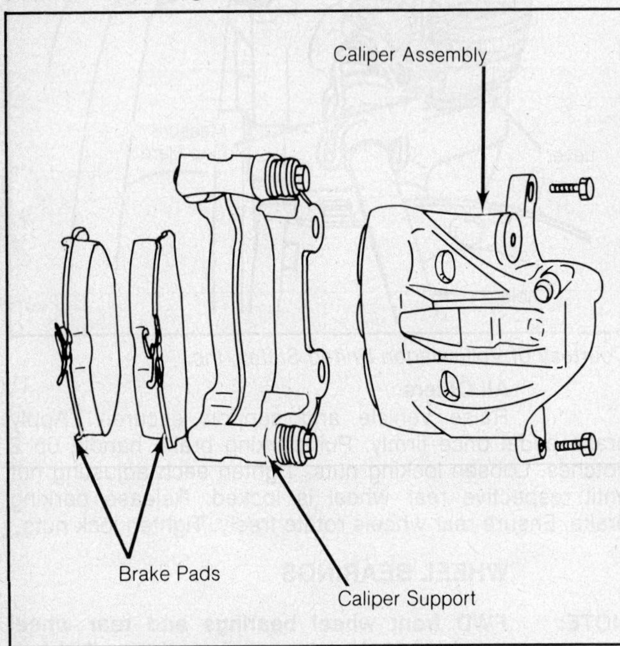

Courtesy of Volkswagen United States, Inc.

Installation

1) Seat piston fully into cylinder bore by hand or using Piston Compressor (US 1023/4). Attach retaining springs to pad carrier. Install inner pad first and then install outer pad in carrier.

2) Install caliper housing into pad carrier. DO NOT force caliper any further than necessary to start Allen head mounting bolts. Excessive force could distort springs, which would cause noises during braking. Tighten mounting bolts to 30 ft. lbs. (40 N.m) on Fox, 18 ft. lbs. (25 N.m) on all other models.

FRONT & REAR CALIPER

Removal

Raise vehicle and support securely. Remove wheels. Disconnect brake line from caliper and plug openings. Bend back locking tabs (if equipped) on mounting bolts. Remove caliper mounting bolts. Remove caliper assembly from wheel bearing housing.

Installation

To install, reverse removal procedure. Use new lock plates and mounting bolts. Bleed hydraulic brake system.

Fig. 4: Exploded View of Front Disc Brake Assembly (All Others)

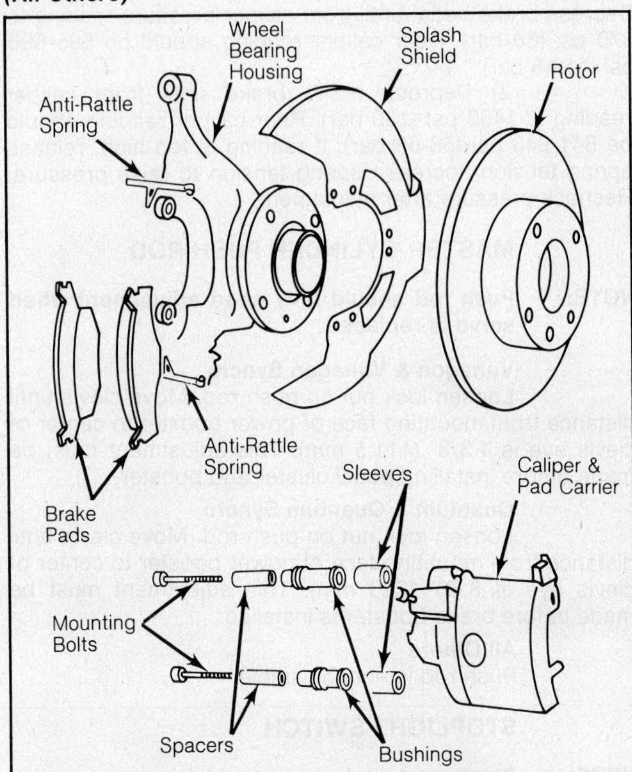

Courtesy of Volkswagen United States, Inc.

FRONT & REAR ROTOR

Removal (Vanagon & Vanagon Syncro)

Raise vehicle and support securely. Remove wheels. Remove caliper, leaving hose connected. Suspend caliper from frame with wire. Remove grease cap. Loosen peen nut. Remove thrust washer and outer wheel bearing. Pull hub and rotor from spindle.

Removal (FWD Models)

Raise and support vehicle. Remove wheels. Remove caliper and suspend from frame with wire. Remove countersunk screw that holds rotor to hub. Pull rotor off hub.

Installation (All Models)

To install, reverse removal procedure. On Vanagon and Vanagon Syncro, adjust wheel bearings. See WHEEL BEARINGS in ADJUSTMENTS section in this article.

REAR BRAKE PADS

Removal

Raise vehicle and support securely. Remove rear wheels. Disconnect parking brake cable from caliper. Using 2 wrenches, hold guide pin with open end wrench while removing upper self-locking mounting bolt. Swing caliper down on lower mounting bolt. Remove brake pads from carrier.

Inspection

New pads should be .472" (12 mm) thick without including thickness of backing plate. Wear limit is .276" (7 mm), including backing plate.

Installation

1) Place brake pads in carrier. Using Allen wrench, push piston into caliper while turning it clockwise.

VOLKSWAGEN (Cont.)

Depth of piston in bore of caliper determines clearance of outer pad to rotor.

2) Swing caliper into position and measure clearance between outer pad and rotor. When clearance is .039" (1.0 mm), brake adjustment is correct. Install NEW self-locking upper mounting bolt. Tighten bolt to 18 ft. lbs. (25 N.m). Reconnect parking brake cable and check parking brake adjustment.

REAR DRUM

CAUTION: ALWAYS loosen or tighten castellated axle nuts with wheels on ground.

Removal (Vanagon & Vanagon Syncro)

Remove dust cap and cotter pin. Loosen castellated nut. Raise and support vehicle securely. Remove wheels. Release parking brake at equalizer, and back off adjuster. Remove drum retaining screws. Attach Drum Puller (OTC 827-B) and remove drum. Ensure drum can rotate freely during removal.

Installation

To install, reverse removal procedure. Drum retaining screws must be tight. Tighten castellated axle nut to 253 ft. lbs. (350 N.m). Adjust parking brake and depress brake pedal several times to set self-adjusting mechanism.

Removal (FWD Models)

Raise and support vehicle. Remove wheels. Using screwdriver inserted through wheel bolt hole, push adjusting wedge up against stop. Remove grease cap, cotter pin, nut lock and nut. Remove thrust washer and outer bearing. Remove drum with inner bearing and grease seal.

Installation

To install, reverse removal procedure. Adjust wheel bearings. See WHEEL BEARINGS in ADJUSTMENTS section in this article. Apply brake pedal firmly several times to set self-adjusting mechanism.

BRAKE SHOES

Removal (Vanagon & Vanagon Syncro)

1) After removing drum, remove retainer clips, hold-down springs and anchor pins. Disconnect parking brake cable from lever on brake shoe. Disconnect lower return and adjuster springs. Pull brake shoes out of lower support. *See Fig. 5.*

2) Disconnect both upper return springs. Remove both brake shoes from backing plate together with adjuster lever. Ensure both pistons remain in wheel cylinder. Separate brake shoes from adjusting lever. Remove parking brake lever from rear brake shoe.

Installation

1) To install, reverse removal procedure. Adjust brake shoes so that distance from lining surface on leading shoe to lining surface on trailing shoe is 9.87" (250.7 mm).

2) Adjust parking brake at equalizer. There should be no free play between parking brake lever on brake shoe and adjusting rod. Install brake drum. Depress brake pedal several times to set self-adjusting mechanism.

Removal (FWD Models)

1) After removing drum, remove retainer clips, hold-down springs and anchor pins. Remove lower return spring. Disconnect parking brake cable from lever. *See Fig. 6.*

Fig. 5: Exploded View of Rear Brake Assembly (Vanagon & Vanagon Syncro)

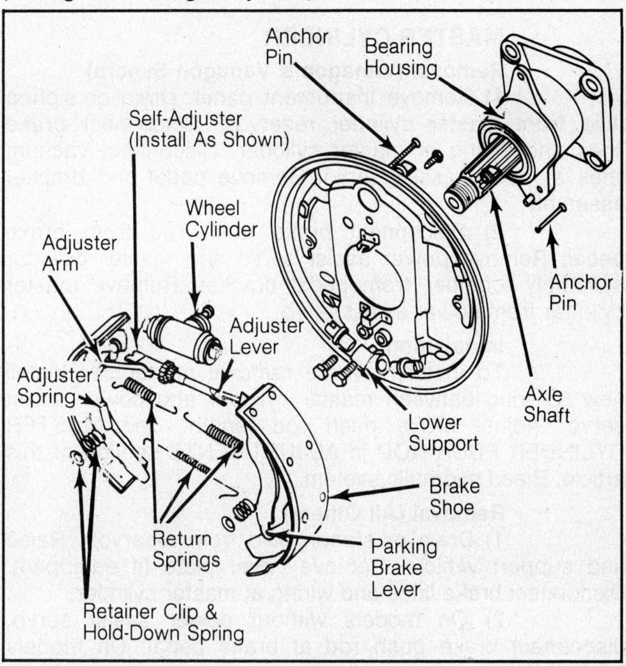

Courtesy of Volkswagen United States, Inc.

2) Disconnect adjusting wedge spring and upper return spring. Remove brake shoes together with push rod and tensioning spring. Place push rod and shoes in vise. Remove tension spring. Separate shoes from push rod.

Fig. 6: Exploded View of Rear Brake Assembly (All Others)

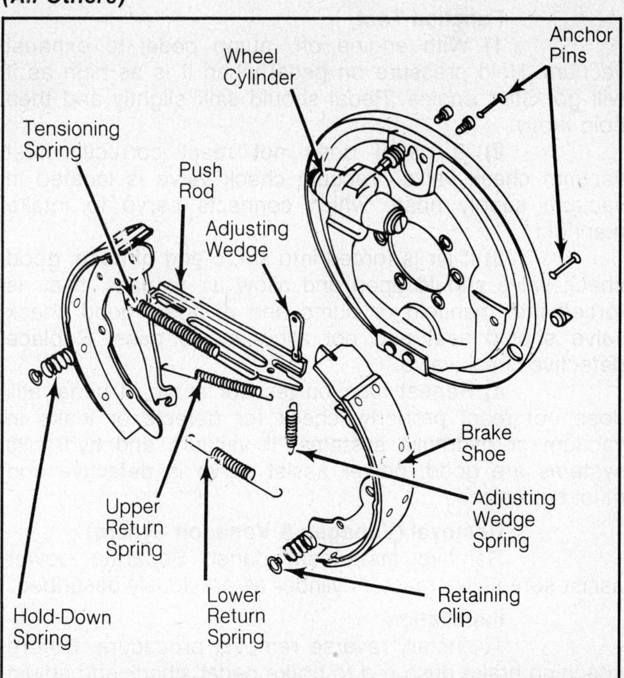

Courtesy of Volkswagen United States, Inc.

Installation

To install, reverse removal procedure. Ensure that lug on adjusting wedge faces backing plate. Adjust wheel bearings. See WHEEL BEARINGS in ADJUST-

VOLKSWAGEN (Cont.)

MENTS section of this article. Apply brake firmly to set self-adjusting mechanism.

MASTER CYLINDER

Removal (Vanagon & Vanagon Syncro)

1) Remove instrument panel. Drain or siphon fluid from master cylinder reservoir. Disconnect brake lines and wiring at master cylinder. Disconnect vacuum lines at power assist servo. Remove pedal and bracket assembly.

2) Disconnect brake push rod from brake pedal. Remove power assist servo and master cylinder assembly together from pedal bracket. Remove master cylinder from power assist servo.

Installation

To install, reverse removal procedure. Install new "O" ring between master cylinder and power assist servo. Adjust brake push rod length. See MASTER CYLINDER PUSH ROD in ADJUSTMENTS section of this article. Bleed hydraulic system.

Removal (All Others)

1) Drain or siphon fluid from reservoir. Raise and support vehicle. Remove cover plate (if equipped). Disconnect brake lines and wiring at master cylinder.

2) On models without power assist servo, disconnect brake push rod at brake pedal. On models equipped with power assist servo, remove master cylinder from servo. Be careful to keep any spacers used on attaching bolts for proper installation.

Installation

To install, reverse removal procedure. Always use new "O" ring between master cylinder and power assist servo. Bleed hydraulic system.

POWER ASSIST SERVO

Function Test

1) With engine off, pump pedal to exhaust vacuum. Hold pressure on pedal when it is as high as it will go. Start engine. Pedal should sink slightly and then hold firmly.

2) If pedal does not react correctly, test vacuum check valve. Vacuum check valve is located in vacuum supply hose, which connects servo to intake manifold.

3) If air is forced into servo end of hose, good check valve should open and allow air to pass. If air is forced into manifold or pump end of hose, good check valve should seat and not allow air to pass. Replace defective check valve.

4) Repeat function test for servo. If pedal still does not react properly, check for defects or leaks in vacuum or hydraulic systems. If vacuum and hydraulic systems are good, power assist servo is defective and must be replaced.

Removal (Vanagon & Vanagon Syncro)

Remove instrument panel. Separate power assist servo from master cylinder as previously described.

Installation

To install, reverse removal procedure. Before attaching brake push rod to brake pedal, check and adjust push rod length. See MASTER CYLINDER PUSH ROD in ADJUSTMENTS section of this article. Complete installation and bleed hydraulic system.

Removal (All Others)

1) Remove master cylinder from power assist servo as previously described. Disconnect brake push rod from brake pedal.

2) Disconnect vacuum hose from servo. Remove mounting nuts at firewall. Remove servo from vehicle.

Installation

To install, reverse removal procedure. Always replace damping ring, washer, filter and "O" ring. Slots in damping washer and filter must be offset 180 degrees.

OVERHAUL

FRONT CALIPER

Disassembly

Place caliper in soft-jawed vise. Insert wooden block in caliper. Blow compressed air into brake hose opening to force piston out of bore. Remove dust seal. Remove piston seal without damaging bore.

Cleaning & Inspection

Clean all parts in brake fluid. Check piston and caliper bore for wear or damage. Replace as necessary. Use all parts supplied in repair kit.

Reassembly

1) Install piston seal in bore. Slide dust seal onto piston. Lubricate piston and cylinder bore with brake paste. Insert piston into bore. Place inner lip of dust seal into groove of caliper bore.

2) Press piston in as far as it will go with Piston Compressor (US 1023/4). When piston is fully seated, fit outer lip of dust seal into groove on piston.

REAR CALIPER

Disassembly

Clamp caliper housing in soft-jawed vise. Use Allen wrench to remove piston from bore, turning it counterclockwise. Pry piston seal out of caliper housing bore, using care to avoid scratching surface of bore.

Fig. 7: Exploded View Of Rear Caliper

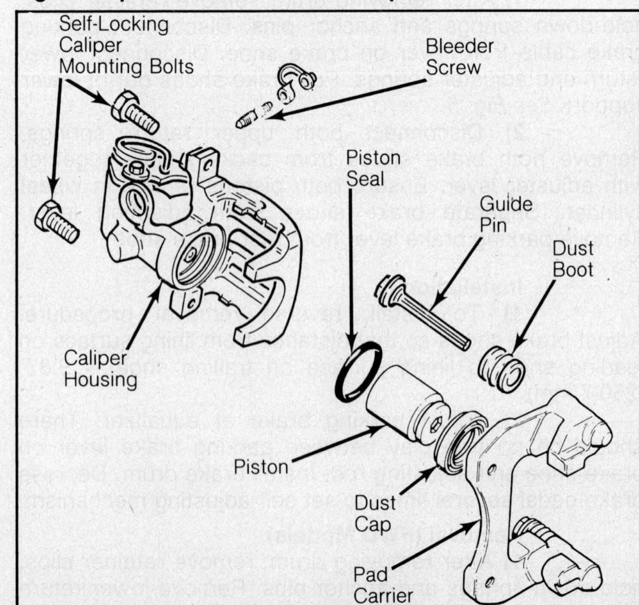

Courtesy of Volkswagen United States, Inc.

VOLKSWAGEN (Cont.)

Cleaning & Inspection

Clean all parts in brake fluid. Black staining from piston seal wear may show on caliper bore walls and piston. This staining is normal. Check piston and caliper bore for wear or corrosion damage. Replace as necessary. Replace all parts included in repair kit.

Reassembly

1) Lightly coat piston and seals with brake paste before refitting. Install piston seal in groove of caliper bore. Fit outer lip of dust cap onto piston. Inner lip of dust cap must be fitted into groove in caliper housing bore. *See Fig. 7.*

2) Press piston down into bore while turning in clockwise direction. Get piston as far as possible into bore. Outer lip of dust cap must slip into groove on piston. Check and adjust pad clearance and parking brake after installation and bleeding is completed.

MASTER CYLINDER

NOTE: **Master cylinder used on GLI and GTI models is not to be rebuilt. Complete unit must be replaced if found to be defective.**

Disassembly

1) Power assisted master cylinders differ in external design and primary piston configuration from unassisted versions. Disassembly procedure is identical for all versions. Remove dust boot (if equipped). Remove pressure valves and stoplight switches. *See Fig. 8.*

2) Move primary piston assembly slightly into bore in order to remove piston stop screw. Hold down piston assemblies against spring tension to remove circlip and washer from end of cylinder. Cover end of cylinder with rag to catch any internal parts or brake fluid that might pop out after circlip is removed.

Fig. 8: Exploded View Of Power Assist Master Cylinder

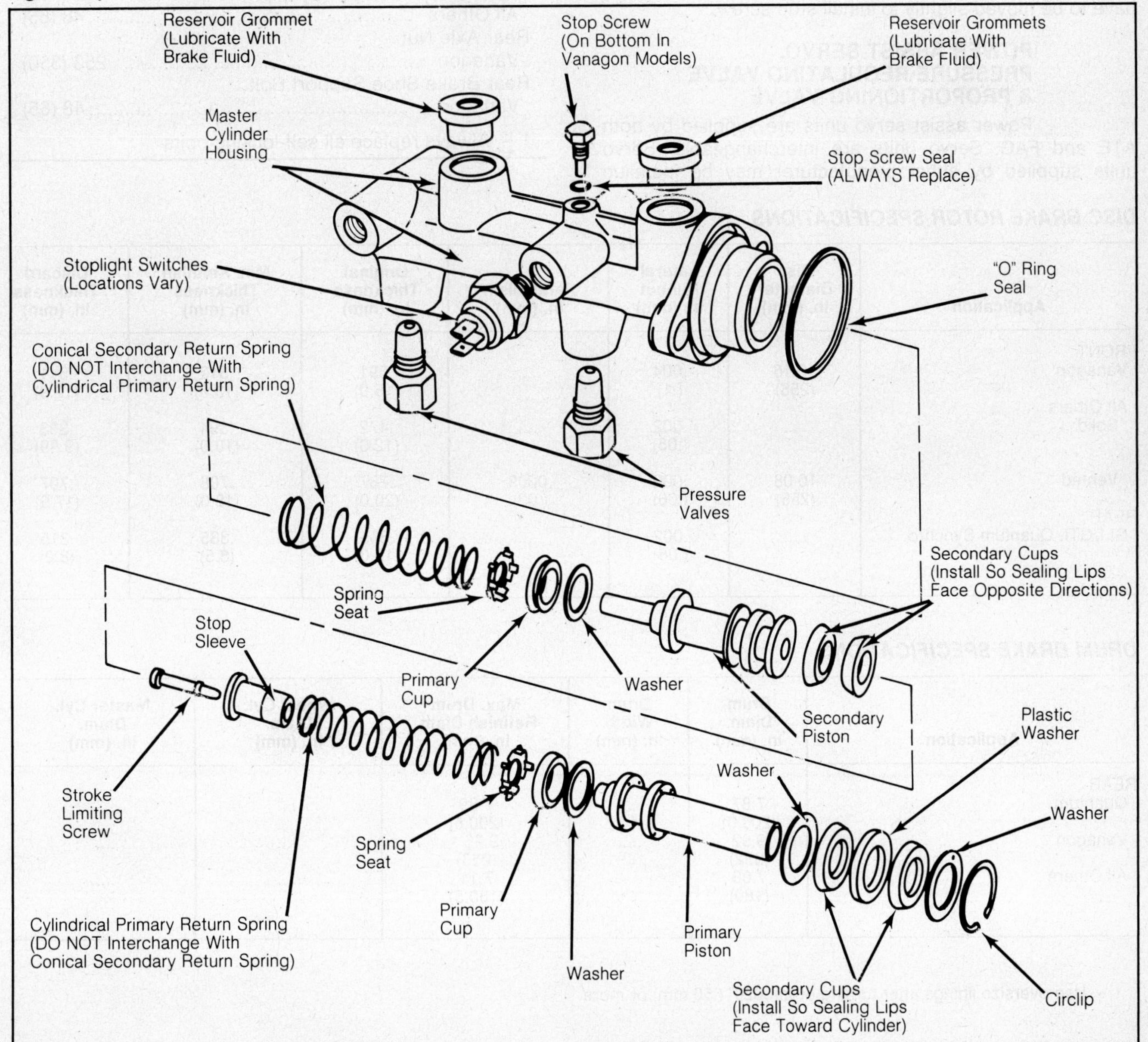

Courtesy of Volkswagen United States, Inc.

Brakes

VOLKSWAGEN (Cont.)

3) Tap open end of cylinder to remove secondary piston assembly. Note location of primary and secondary return springs and piston cups for reassembly procedure. Also note difference in size and shape between components from primary and secondary circuits. Remove all external hardware from cylinder.

Cleaning & Inspection

Clean all parts with brake fluid or denatured alcohol. Check cylinder bore and pistons for wear. Replace complete assembly if hard parts are damaged. Replace all soft parts during overhaul. ALWAYS use all parts included in repair kit.

Reassembly

To assemble, reverse disassembly procedure. Coat primary piston shaft with lubricant supplied in repair kit. Coat pistons and cups with brake paste. DO NOT interchange return springs or piston cups between primary and secondary circuits. Secondary piston may have to be moved slightly to install stop screw.

POWER ASSIST SERVO, PRESSURE REGULATING VALVE & PROPORTIONING VALVE

Power assist servo units are supplied by both ATE and FAG. Servo units are interchangeable. Servo units supplied by either manufacturer may be installed with master cylinders supplied by the other. Vehicle manufacturer states that these servos, if defective, must be replaced as complete assemblies. DO NOT disassemble power assist servo as parts are not available.

TIGHTENING SPECIFICATIONS

Application	Ft. Lbs. (N.m)
Backing Plate-to-Flange Bolt	44 (60)
Caliper Mounting Bolts [1]	
Fox	30 (41)
Quantum & Quantum Syncro	18 (25)
Vanagon & Vanagon Syncro	26 (35)
All Others	
Front	18 (25)
Rear	26 (35)
Pad Carrier Mounting Bolt	
Quantum & Quantum Syncro	52 (70)
Vanagon & Vanagon Syncro	115 (156)
All Others	48 (65)
Rear Axle Nut	
Vanagon	253 (350)
Rear Brake Shoe Support Bolt	
Vanagon	48 (65)

[1] – Always replace all self-locking bolts.

DISC BRAKE ROTOR SPECIFICATIONS

Application	Disc Diameter In. (mm)	Lateral Runout In. (mm)	Parallelism In. (mm)	Original Thickness In. (mm)	Min. Refinish Thickness In. (mm)	Discard Thickness In. (mm)
FRONT						
Vanagon	10.16 (258)	.004 (.1)	.....	.591 (15.0)	.512 (13.0)	.511 (12.9)
All Others						
Solid	.....	.002 (.06)	.....	.472 (12.0)	.394 (10.0)	.393 (9.99)
Vented	10.08 (256)	.002 (.06)	.0009 (.02)	.787 (20.0)	.708 (18.0)	.707 (17.9)
REAR						
GLI/GTI, Quantum Synchro	.....	.002 (.06)	.....	.394 (10.0)	.335 (8.5)	.315 (8.0)

DRUM BRAKE SPECIFICATIONS

Application	Drum Diam. In. (mm)	Drum Width In. (mm)	Max. Drum Refinish Diam. In. (mm)	Wheel Cyl. Diam. In. (mm)	Master Cyl. Diam. In. (mm)
REAR					
Quantum	7.87 (200.0)	.....	7.89 (200.5)	.....	.....
Vanagon	9.92 (252)	.....	9.96 [1] (253)	.....	.....
All Others	7.08 (180)	.....	7.11 (180.5)	.....	.....

[1] – Use oversize linings after turning drum .020" (.50 mm) or more.

VOLVO

240, 740, 760, 780 Series

DESCRIPTION

All models use front and rear disc brakes. Three makes of calipers are used: ATE, Bendix and Girling. Service brakes are hydraulically-operated by a tandem master cylinder and vacuum power brake unit. Each rear brake line has a pressure valve to prevent rear wheel lock-up. Parking brake is mechanically-operated on rear wheel-mounted, internal brake shoes.

NOTE: For information on anti-lock brake system, see VOLVO ANTI-LOCK BRAKE SYSTEM article.

ADJUSTMENTS

PEDAL HEIGHT

Brake pedal height should be equal to clutch pedal height. To adjust, loosen lock nut, remove cotter pin and turn push rod until pedal height is equal. Replace cotter pin and tighten lock nut. Pedal travel should be 5.9-6.7" (150-170 mm).

NOTE: Pedal travel can only be measured during brake bleeding operation. See HYDRAULIC SYSTEM BLEEDING in this section.

STOPLIGHT SWITCH

Remove soundproofing on left side of center console. Adjust switch so brake light goes on when pedal is depressed about .30-.55" (8-14 mm).

PARKING BRAKE

NOTE: Adjust parking brake when full application stroke of brake lever exceeds 10-11 notches.

240 Series

1) Remove center console rear ashtray. Working through ashtray hole, loosen parking brake cables adjusting screw until cables are slack. Raise and support rear of vehicle. Remove wheels. Align hole in parking brake drum with starwheel adjuster.

2) Tighten starwheel until drum can just be rotated by hand. Back off adjuster until drum just rotates freely. Install rear wheels. Tighten parking brake cable adjusting screw until parking brake is fully applied when lever is pulled 2-8 notches. Install ashtray and lower vehicle.

All Others

Remove cover at rear of center console. Remove adjusting screw by carefully tapping on spring sleeve with a hammer and screwdriver. Adjust cable so that parking brake is fully applied by 3-4 notches. Replace cover.

BRAKE WARNING LIGHTS

Brake Failure Light

1) This light will glow if pressure differential is exceeded or fluid level is low. Light will continue to glow until problem is corrected.

2) Check calipers, hydraulic lines, master cylinder, power brake unit and vacuum pump for defects and repair as needed.

Parking Brake Light

This light should glow when parking brake lever is pulled one notch, and go out when fully released (ignition on).

REMOVAL & INSTALLATION

DISC PADS

NOTE: Use Remover (2917) to remove brake pads, if necessary.

Removal (ATE & Girling)

Raise and support vehicle. Remove tire and wheel. Remove retaining pins. Remove spring clips. Remove brake pads.

Removal (Bendix)

Raise and support vehicle. Remove tire and wheel. Remove lower guide pin bolt. Loosen upper guide pin bolt. Pivot caliper upward and secure with wire. Remove pads.

Installation

1) Siphon small amount of fluid from master cylinder reservoir. On ATE and Girling calipers, seat pistons in caliper bore with Piston Tool (2809).

2) On ATE calipers, always use new retaining spring. On Bendix calipers, install brake pads. Check that spring is located correctly in caliper. Check rubber boots. Position brake caliper and reinstall new lower guide pin bolt.

3) On ATE rear calipers, check piston position by installing Template (2919). Piston recess should incline 20 degrees in relation to lower guide area on caliper. *See Fig. 1.* If distance from one recess to the other measurement "A" exceeds .04" (1 mm), adjust position. *See Fig. 1.*

4) Install new pads. Install intermediate plates (if equipped) or damper washers (if equipped) in original positions. On Girling calipers, install one lock pin. Install damper springs and other lock pin.

Fig. 1: Checking ATE Rear Caliper Piston Angle

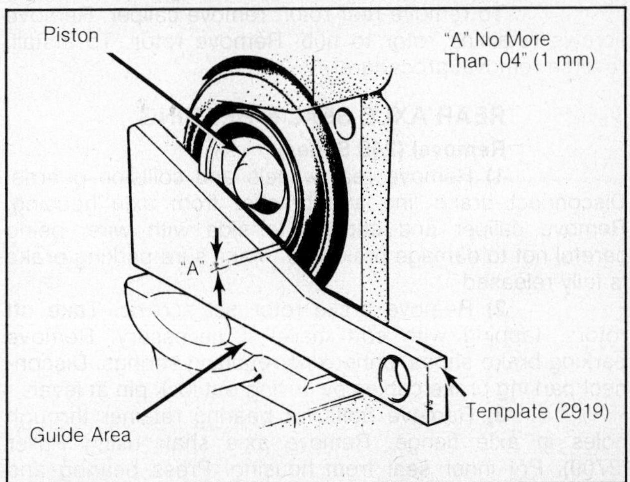

Courtesy of Volvo Cars of North America.

VOLVO (Cont.)

5) Install new lock clips on pins. On ATE calipers, tap one guide pin into position, and install new tensioning spring. Install other guide pin while holding tensioning spring in position.

NOTE: **Install the damper washers with the small contact face toward pad. DO NOT install intermediate plates in calipers equipped with damper washers.**

CALIPER ASSEMBLY

Removal

Raise and support vehicle. Remove wheel. Disconnect brake line connections at caliper. Cap lines to prevent entry of foreign matter. Remove caliper mounting bolts. Lift caliper from mounting bracket.

Installation

1) Position caliper assembly on mounting bracket, and install attaching bolts. After installing bolts, check clearance between disc pads and rotor on both sides of rotor.

2) Maximum deviation between sides should not exceed .004" (.10 mm) on front calipers or .010" (.25 mm) on rear calipers.

3) If clearance is not within specifications, correct by adding shims to caliper. Connect hydraulic lines and bleed hydraulic system.

DISC BRAKE ROTOR

Removal (240 Series)

1) With caliper assembly removed, mount a dial indicator and check rotor runout. Runout must not exceed .004" (.10 mm).

2) Measure rotor thickness through one revolution. Thickness variance must not exceed .0008" (.020 mm). Unscrew rotor lock bolts and pull rotor from hub.

Installation

To install, reverse removal procedure.

Removal & Installation (All Others)

To remove front rotor, remove caliper. Remove hub cap. Remove cotter pin, and castellated nut. Remove outer wheel bearing. Remove hub and rotor assembly. To install, reverse removal procedure. Tighten castellated nut to 42 ft. lbs. (57 N.m). Back off nut half a turn. Tighten nut to 13 INCH lbs. (1.5 N.m). Install cotter pin.

To remove rear rotor, remove caliper. Remove screws retaining rotor to hub. Remove rotor. To install, reverse removal procedure.

REAR AXLE SEAL & BEARING

Removal (240 Series)

1) Remove rear wheels and collision guards. Disconnect brake line and bracket from axle housing. Remove caliper and support to side with wire, being careful not to damage brake line. Make sure parking brake is fully released.

2) Remove brake rotor set screws. Take off rotors, tapping with soft mallet if necessary. Remove parking brake shoes, unhooking retaining springs. Disconnect parking brake cables by driving out lock pin at lever.

3) Remove bolts for bearing retainer through holes in axle flange. Remove axle shaft using Puller (2709). Pry inner seal from housing. Press bearing and snap ring off axle shaft. Remove oil seal.

Installation

1) Pack new bearing and new seal lip groove with high temperature wheel bearing grease. Place bearing retainer and oil seal on axle shaft. Press new bearing and new snap ring onto axle shaft. Always use a new snap ring. Narrow side of taper fits into axle housing.

2) Clean axle housing and drive in new inner seal. Install axle shaft and tighten bearing retainer bolts. Install parking brake shoes and reconnect cables. Install rotors and tighten set screws.

3) Check parking brake adjustment. Install brake caliper, pads, and collision guard (if used). Reconnect brake line and bracket to axle housing. Install wheels and tighten lug nuts.

Removal (All Others)

1) Remove rear wheel. Remove caliper and suspend from coil spring. Remove brake disc and pads. Remove axle shaft retaining plate. Using brake disc, fit nuts with flat side towards disc and pull out axle shaft.

2) Using long screwdriver, remove seal. Clean interior of rear axle tube. Remove bearing and lock ring.

Installation

1) Using Press Tool (5212), lift up seal and retaining plate on drive shaft so that split press plate can be installed on bearing. Place press yoke on top of press plate. Ensure that press plate opening is at 90 degree angle to press yoke opening.

2) Grease new bearing between inner and outer races until grease protrudes on other side. Grease new inner and outer seals. Fill space between seal lips with grease. Position retaining plate and seal correctly on axle shaft.

3) Install greased bearing and lock ring. Place Bearing Ring (5242) under bearing and lock ring. Position axle shaft in press. Put 2 "V" blocks under bearing ring ensuring that blocks do not touch axle shaft.

4) Use Bearing Installer (1801) to press on shaft. Using Drift (5243) and Handle (1801), install inner seal. Install and tighten axle shaft and retaining plate assembly with brake pad retaining springs.

5) Install parking brake shoes, brake disc and caliper. Ensure that disc clears parking brake shoes. Adjust parking brake cable.

PARKING BRAKE SHOES

Removal (240 Series)

1) Remove center console rear ashtray and loosen parking brake cable adjusting nut until cables are slack. Raise and support rear of vehicle and remove wheels.

2) Remove caliper (without disconnecting hydraulic line) and support out of way. Remove rotor. Remove brake shoe return springs and lift off shoes and adjuster. *See Fig. 2.*

Installation

1) To install, reverse removal procedure. Replace brake drum (rotor) if out-of-round exceeds .008" (.2 mm).

2) Apply a thin coat of heat-resistant graphite grease to brake shoe sliding surfaces and to adjusting starwheel. Adjust starwheel until wheel starts to lock. Back off starwheel 4-5 notches. Ensure wheel rotates.

Removal (All Others)

1) Remove cover at rear of center console. Remove adjusting screw by carefully tapping on spring

VOLVO (Cont.)

sleeve with a hammer and screwdriver. Unscrew adjusting screw so that cables are slackened.

2) Raise vehicle and remove rear wheels. Remove brake caliper and hang up with a steel wire on rear spring to avoid damaging brake hose. Remove brake disc. Unhook rear return spring and remove brake shoes.

Fig. 2: Exploded View of Parking Brake Assembly

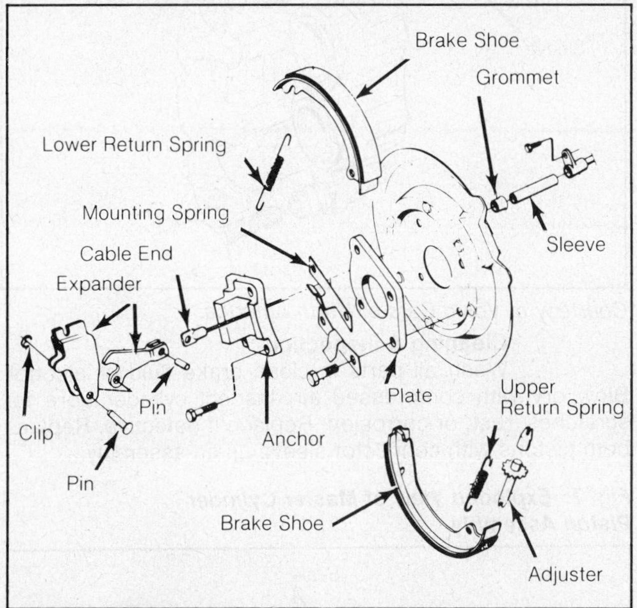

Courtesy of Volvo Cars of North America.

Installation

1) Apply thin layer of heat resistant graphite grease on brake shoe contact surfaces. Assemble brake shoes. Using new bolts, install rear return spring, brake disc and caliper.

2) Ensure that disc rotates without touching brake pads. Install wheels. Adjust parking brake cable. Lower vehicle.

MASTER CYLINDER

Removal & Installation

Disconnect hydraulic lines at master cylinder and cap openings to prevent entry of foreign matter. Remove cylinder attaching nuts. Remove cylinder assembly from vehicle. To install, reverse removal procedure. Bleed hydraulic system.

POWER BRAKE UNIT

Removal (240 Series)

Remove master cylinder. Disconnect vacuum hose. Remove soundproofing on left side of center console. Disconnect pressure rod from brake pedal. Remove 4 nuts and power brake unit.

Installation

Apply sealing compound to contact surface on firewall. Fit other types with sealing ring. Reverse removal procedure to complete installation.

Removal (All Others)

1) Disconnect master cylinder and move it aside. Leave brake pipes attached to master cylinder. Disconnect vacuum hose. Using screwdriver, pry out check valve from unit. Remove fuel filter and move it aside.

2) Disconnect vacuum pump and move it aside. Remove soundproofing on left side of center console. Disconnect push rod from brake pedal. Remove 4 nuts and power brake unit. Remove check valve seal and check for damage.

Installation

Install seal in power brake unit and ensure that it is correctly seated. Remove Sealing Ring (1272078-5) and install on new power brake unit. To complete installation, reverse removal procedure.

Check Valve Replacement

Disconnect vacuum hose from check valve. Using 2 screwdrivers, lever out check valve. Remove seal. Fit new seal ensuring that flange is properly aligned in cylinder. Smear seal with grease. Press valve carefully into place. Ensure that seal does not move out of position. Reconnect vacuum hose so that highest point is attached to valve.

OVERHAUL

BRAKE CALIPER

Disassembly

1) Remove disc pads, piston dust covers, and retaining clips. Insert wooden block into caliper housing. Apply compressed air at fluid inlet ports to force pistons out of caliper.

2) Remove piston seals from cylinder bore with blunt tool without damaging cylinder bore. Open bleeder screw.

NOTE: **DO NOT separate caliper halves.**

Cleaning & Inspection

Clean all parts in brake fluid or alcohol. Inspect cylinder bores for scoring, rust, or corrosion. Replace if defective. Replace rubber seals and dust covers during overhaul. *See Figs. 3, 4, 5 & 6.*

Fig. 3: Girling Front Caliper Assembly

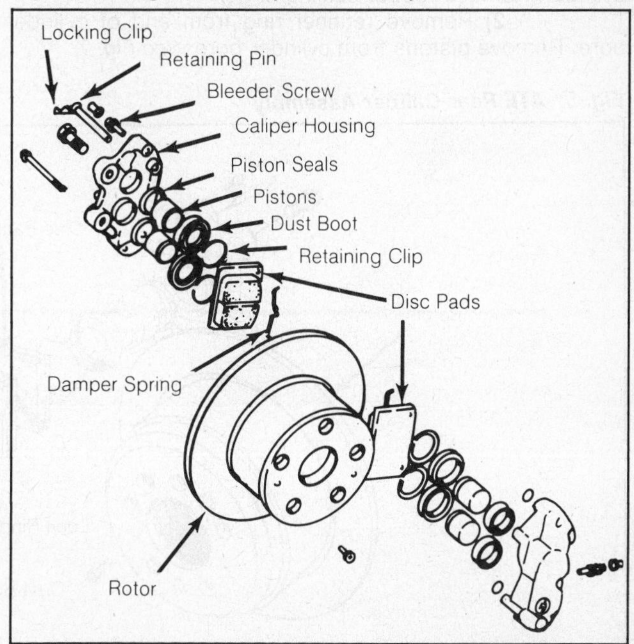

Courtesy of Volvo Cars of North America.

Fig. 4: Girling Rear Caliper Assembly

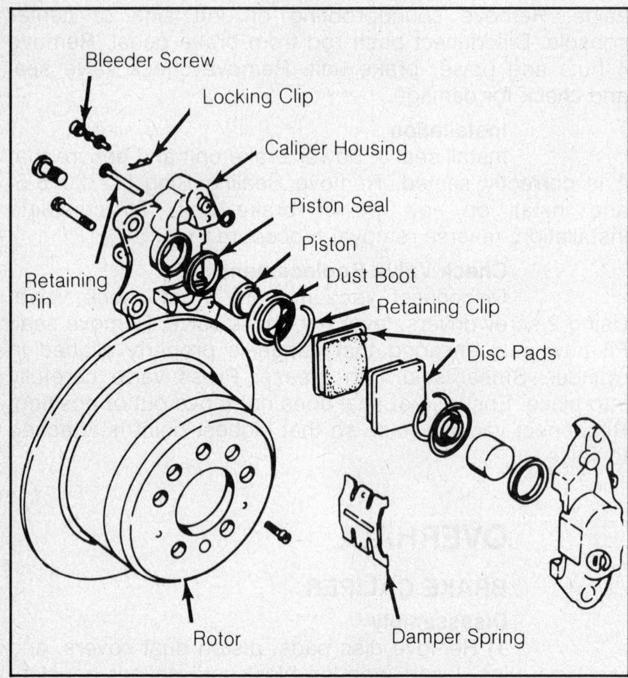

Courtesy of Volvo Cars of North America.

Reassembly

1) Coat all parts with clean brake fluid, and install new piston seals in cylinder bores. Carefully install pistons into cylinder bores.

2) On ATE rear brake calipers, check piston position. *See Fig. 1.* Install dust boots and retaining clips. Install bleeder screw and disc pads.

MASTER CYLINDER

Disassembly

1) Remove master cylinder from vehicle. Clamp mounting flange in a vise. Remove reservoir from cylinder. Remove rubber sealing rings.

2) Remove retainer ring from end of cylinder bore. Remove pistons from cylinder bore. *See Fig. 7.*

Fig. 6: Bendix Front Caliper Assembly

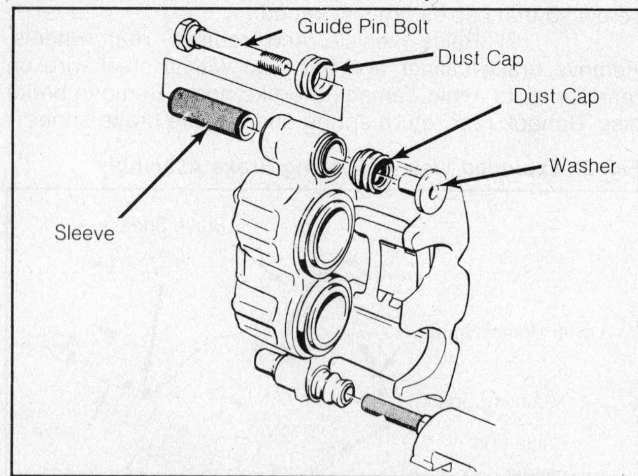

Courtesy of Volvo Cars of North America.

Cleaning & Inspection

Wash all parts in clean brake fluid or alcohol. Blow dry with compressed air. Inspect cylinder bore for scratches, rust, or corrosion. Replace if defective. Replace both pistons with connector sleeve as an assembly.

Fig. 7: Exploded View of Master Cylinder Piston Assembly

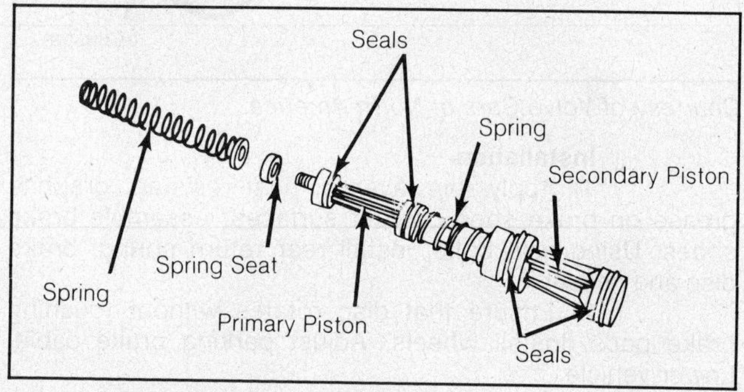

Courtesy of Volvo Cars of North America.

Fig. 5: ATE Rear Caliper Assembly

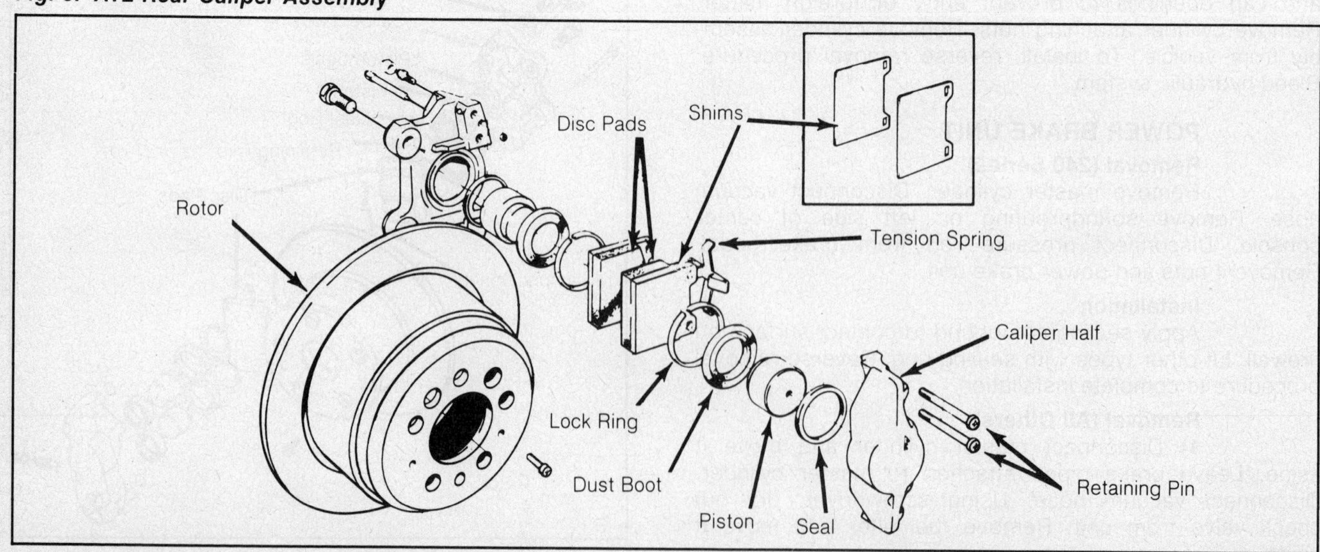

Courtesy of Volvo Cars of North America.

VOLVO (Cont.)

Reassembly

1) Lubricate all parts with clean brake fluid prior to reassembly. Position washer, seal, and back-up ring on secondary piston. Install spring thrust washer on piston. Install piston assembly into cylinder bore. Install washer, seal, and back-up ring on primary piston.

2) Install spring, with plate and sleeve on piston. Install piston assembly into cylinder bore. Push piston into cylinder bore. Install retaining ring. Install reservoir sealing rings, and install reservoir.

TIGHTENING SPECIFICATIONS

Application	Ft. Lbs. (N.m)
Axle Shaft & Retaining Plate	29 (40)
Caliper Guide Pin Bolts	
Lower	25 (34)
Upper	19 (26)
Front Caliper Mounting Bolts	74 (100)
Master Cylinder Mounting Bolts	22 (30)
Rear Caliper Mounting Bolts	43 (58)

DISC BRAKE ROTOR SPECIFICATIONS

Application	Disc Diameter In. (mm)	Lateral Runout In. (mm)	Parallelism In. (mm)	Original Thickness In. (mm)	Min. Refinish Thickness In. (mm)	Discard Thickness In. (mm)
240 Series						
Front						
Solid	10.35 (263)	.004 (.10)	.0008 (.03)	.563 (14.3)	[1] .520 (13.14)	.....
Ventilated	10.35 (263)	.004 (.10)	.0008 (.03)	.940 (23.88)	[1] .820 (20.83)	.....
Rear	11.07 (281)	.004 (.10)	.0008 (.03)	.380 (9.7)	[1] .330 (8.4)	.....
All Others						
Front						
Solid	11.02 (280)	.004 (.10)	.0008 (.03)	.551 (14.0)	[1] .443 (11.0)	.....
Ventilated	11.30 (287)	.004 (.10)	.0008 (.03)	.87 (22.10)	[1] .79 (20.07)	.....
Rear	11.07 (281)	.004 (.10)	.0008 (.03)	.378 (9.6)	[1] .330 (8.4)	.....

[1] – Minimum thickness is stamped on rotors. Always use stamped specification.

YUGO

GV

DESCRIPTION

The GV is equipped with front disc and rear drum brakes. An adjustable rear brake pressure compensator is used to regulate brake pressure between the front and rear braking circuits. The rear brakes are self-adjusting. The parking brake lever mechanically activates the rear brakes.

ADJUSTMENTS

BRAKE BOOSTER

With brake booster removed and in resting position the control rod end should protrude from the front of brake booster .032-.040" (.825-1.025 mm). If not, turn control rod adjustment screw until the specified amount of protrusion is present at the front of brake booster. *See Fig. 1.*

REAR BRAKE PRESSURE COMPENSATOR

1) Loosen compensator from its mounting studs and ensure that adjusting bar is attached to the bracket on vehicle body. Bring end of bar to within 1.165-2.559" (55-65 mm) from center of buffer mounting hole. *See Fig. 1.*

2) Raise dust boot to check contact between regulator and bar. Rotate regulator body until end of piston is in contact with end of bar. *See Fig. 1.*

Fig. 2: Internal View of Brake Booster

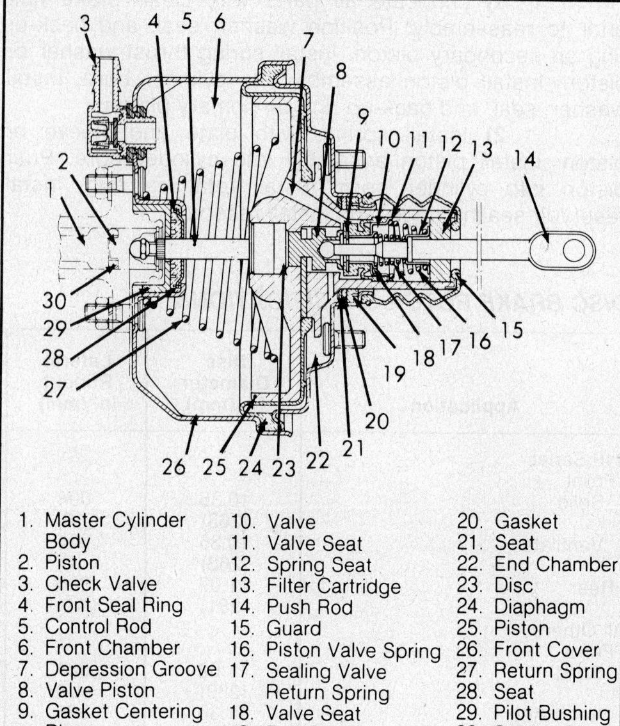

Courtesy of Yugo America, Inc.

Fig. 1: Rear Brake Compensator

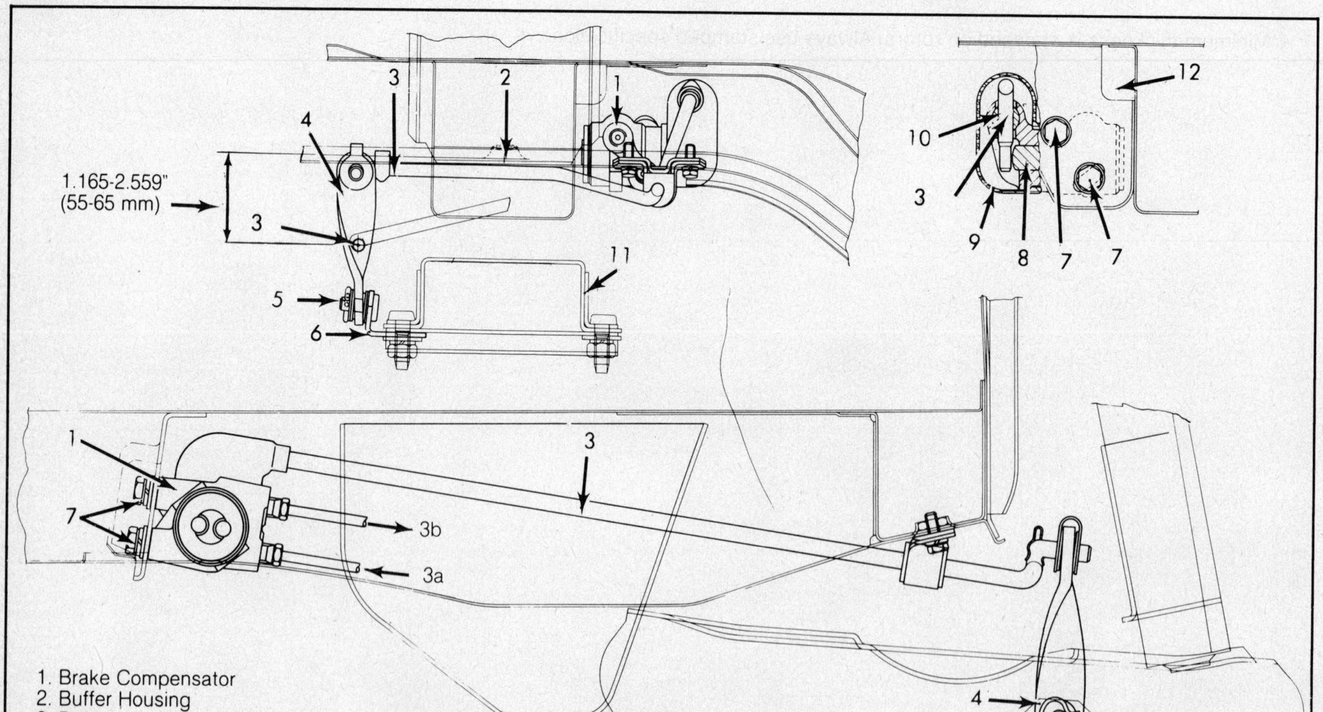

1.165-2.559" (55-65 mm)

1. Brake Compensator
2. Buffer Housing
3. Bar
3a. Compensator End of Torsion Bar
3b. Anchor Link of Torsion Bar
4. Torsion Bar Link to Control Link
5. Link Anchor Pin to Control Link
6. Link Anchor Pin Bracket
7. Brake Compensator Attaching & Adjusting Bolts
8. Compensator Piston
9. Dust Boot
10. Regulator Pin
11. Control Arm
12. Compensator Mounting Bracket

Courtesy of Yugo America, Inc.

YUGO (Cont.)

3) Tighten bolts from the bottom up. Attach torsion bar link to link pin actuator at control arm. Install spring fastener on link anchor pin to actuator. Ensure all components are tightened and road test vehicle.

PARKING BRAKE

Fully depress brake pedal several times to set pistons. Raise and support vehicle. Pull parking brake handle up 3 or 4 clicks. Loosen adjusting lock nut and tighten until wheels will not turn freely. Retighten lock nut and lower vehicle.

REMOVAL & INSTALLATION

MASTER CYLINDER

Removal & Installation

Remove retaining nuts from master cylinder mounting studs. Remove brake fluid inlet lines from master cylinder. *See Fig. 3*. Remove master cylinder from brake booster. To install, reverse removal procedure. Bench bleed master cylinder. Bleed brake system.

Fig. 3: Exploded View of Master Cylinder

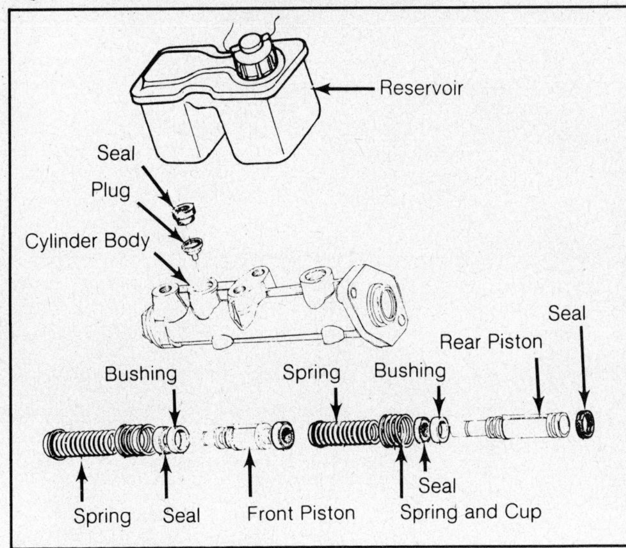

Courtesy of Yugo America, Inc.

BRAKE BOOSTER

Removal & Installation

Remove inlet brake lines from master cylinder and plug. Remove master cylinder mounting bolts. Remove master cylinder from brake booster. From inside of the driver's side compartment, remove clevis pin retaining booster push rod to brake pedal. Remove large vacuum line from booster inlet fitting. Remove booster mounting bolts and booster. To install, reverse removal procedure.

FRONT CALIPERS

Removal & Installation

1) Raise and support vehicle. Disconnect and plug inlet brake line. Remove cotter pin and slide caliper locking blocks out of retaining groove. Remove caliper and brake pads from support bracket.

2) To remove support bracket, remove mounting bolts and bracket. To install, reverse removal procedure and bleed brake system.

BRAKE ROTOR

Removal & Installation

Remove rotor retaining bolt, locator pin and plate. Install Rotor Puller/Remover (A 47210/775). Turn end bolt of puller and remove rotor. To install, reverse removal procedure.

REAR BRAKE SHOES

Removal & Installation

1) Raise and support vehicle. Remove 2 brake drum retaining bolts and remove brake drum. Install Wheel Cylinder Piston Retainer (A 72257) over wheel cylinder and remove upper and lower return springs.

2) Tilt brake shoe guide pins and lift them out along with cups and springs. Disconnect brake fluid hose from wheel cylinder and plug. Rotate hub so groove in hub will allow removal of brake shoe and self-adjusting mechanism.

3) Remove wheel cylinder mounting bolts and wheel cylinder. To install, reverse removal procedure. Adjust brake shoes and bleed air from brake system.

OVERHAUL

MASTER CYLINDER

Disassembly

Remove master cylinder from brake booster. Remove retainer holding primary and secondary pistons in bore of master cylinder. Remove reservoir from master cylinder. Remove seal, springs and cups from cylinder bore. Keep components in order for reassembly reference. *See Fig. 3*

Inspection

Clean all parts with denatured alcohol and lubricate with brake fluid.

Reassembly

Reassemble in reverse order of disassembly. Bench bleed master cylinder. Install master cylinder. Bleed brake system.

BRAKE CALIPER

CAUTION: Keep fingers clear of piston when applying compressed air.

Disassembly

1) Remove caliper from vehicle and plug fluid line. Remove dust boot. Place a protective device between caliper housing and piston. Apply low compressed air to brake line inlet hole of caliper housing.

2) Remove piston seal from bore of caliper. Remove bleeder screw and ensure inside of screw bore is clear from obstruction. Clean all parts in hot water and dry with compressed air.

Inspection

Inspect all components for signs of damage. Inspect for scoring, binding and pitting. Replace parts as necessary.

Reassembly

Lubricate all parts in in DOT 3 brake fluid. Install rubber piston seal into bore of caliper. Carefully insert piston into bore. Ensure piston seal is seated in groove. Install dust boot. Install caliper onto support bracket. Install brake hose. Fill brake fluid reservoir. Bleed air from brake system.

Brakes

YUGO (Cont.)

DISC BRAKE ROTOR SPECIFICATIONS

Application	Disc Diameter In. (mm)	Lateral Runout In. (mm)	Parallelism In. (mm)	Original Thickness In. (mm)	Min. Refinish Thickness In. (mm)	Discard Thickness In. (mm)
GV						
Front	8.937 (227)	.006 (.15)	.....	.425 (10.80)	.368 (9.35)	.354 (9)

DRUM BRAKE SPECIFICATIONS

Application	Drum Diam. In. (mm)	Drum Width In. (mm)	Max. Drum Refinish Diam. In. (mm)	Wheel Cyl. Diam. In. (mm)	Master Cyl. Diam. In. (mm)
GV					
Rear	7.298 (185.40)	.....	7.336 (186.33)	.750 (19.05)	.750 (19.05)

TIGHTENING SPECIFICATIONS

Application	Ft. Lbs. (N.m)
Brake Booster Mounting Nuts	11 (15)
Caliper Flex Line Fitting	20 (27)
Master Cylinder Mounting Nut	19 (25)
Parking Brake Lever Mounting Bolt	11 (15)
Rear Brake Compensator Bolts	19 (25)
Wheel Cylinder Flex Line Fitting	14 (20)

ACURA ANTI-LOCK BRAKE SYSTEM

Legend Coupe

DESCRIPTION

The Anti-Lock Brake System (ABS) is designed to prevent wheel lock-up during heavy braking. This effect allows driver to maintain control of the vehicle. System consists of Electronic Control Module (ECM), accumulator, power unit, 4 wheel sensors, modulator, warning light, master cylinder and power booster assembly and connecting wiring.

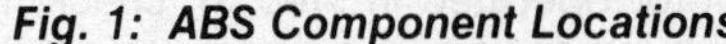

OPERATION

The ECM receives an AC signal (wheel speed) from each wheel sensor. From this information, ECM computes and electronically opens or closes the solenoids, located inside the modulator, to prevent wheel lock-up.

TROUBLE SHOOTING

"ANTILOCK" WARNING LIGHT

"ANTILOCK" warning light will come for one of the following reasons:

- Brake fluid pump runs more than 120 seconds.
- Vehicle is driven for more than 30 seconds with parking brake applied.
- Rear wheels are locked for more than specified time.
- Malfunction in anti-lock system.
- Temporarily loss of traction due to excessive cornering speed or starting from stuck condition (mud, snow or sand).
- Vehicle driven on extremely rough road.
- Low battery voltage to ECM.

If low battery voltage caused problem, recharge battery. Remove ABS fuse for 3 seconds. Reinstall fuse and check light. To reset light for all other conditions, turn ignition off. Light should reset automatically.

"ANTILOCK" WARNING LIGHT DOES NOT COME ON

If light does not come on when ignition is turn on, check bulb, Yellow wire between fuse No. 5 and instrument panel. Check Blue/Red wire from instrument panel to ECM. Check ECM self-grounding circuit.

TESTING

FUNCTION TEST

CAUTION: DO NOT operate vehicle with ABS Tester (07HAJ-SG00100). Loss of braking ability can occur.

Prelimary Procedure

Confirm "ANTILOCK" warning light is indicating a problem with system. See "ANTILOCK" WARNING LIGHT in this system. Place vehicle on level surface. Block wheels and place automatic transmission in "P" or manual transmission in "N".

Testing

1) Turn ignition off. Connect ABS Tester (07HAJ-SG00100) to 6-pin connector, located under passenger seat. Start engine. Release parking brake. Depress brake pedal. Place mode selector to "1". Push start test button. Test in progress light should come on. Within 2-4 seconds, 4 monitor light shold come on.

Fig. 1: ABS Component Locations

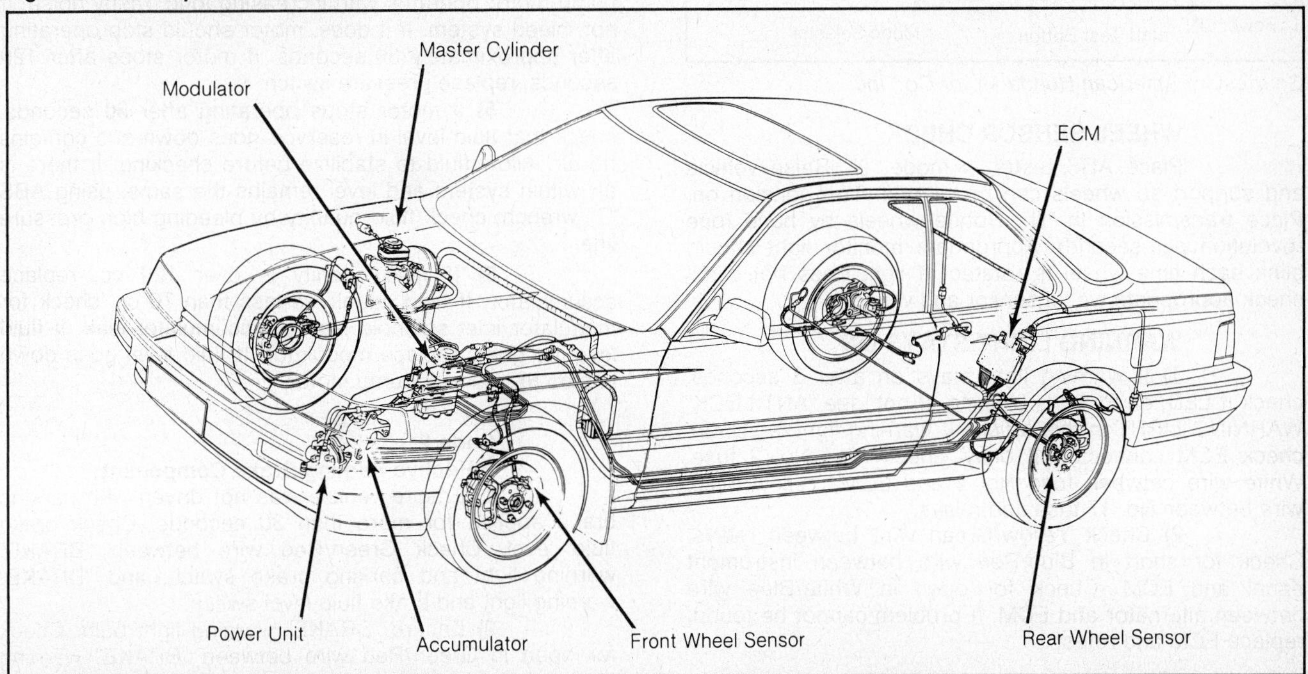

Courtesy of American Honda Motor Co., Inc.

ACURA ANTI-LOCK BRAKE SYSTEM (Cont.)

2) If "ANTILOCK" light comes on, ABS tester harness is faulty. Turn mode selector to "2". Depress brake pedal. Push start test button. "ANTILOCK" should not come on and kickback should be felt in brake pedal.

3) If light comes on or kickback is not felt, see "ANTILOCK" WARNING LIGHT in this article. Place mode selector in "3" - "6". Results should be the same as "2". If not, see "ANTILOCK" WARNING LIGHT in this article. Breakdown of testing of each mode is as follows:

Mode 1
Check self-diagnosis circuit.

Mode 2
Check lock signal to right rear wheel.

Mode 3
Check lock signal to left rear wheel.

Mode 4
Check lock signal to right front wheel.

Mode 5
Check lock signal to left rear wheel.

Mode 6
Check lock signal to both front wheels.

Perform test several times before trouble shooting other parts of the system.

Fig. 2: ABS Tester (07HAJ-SG00100)

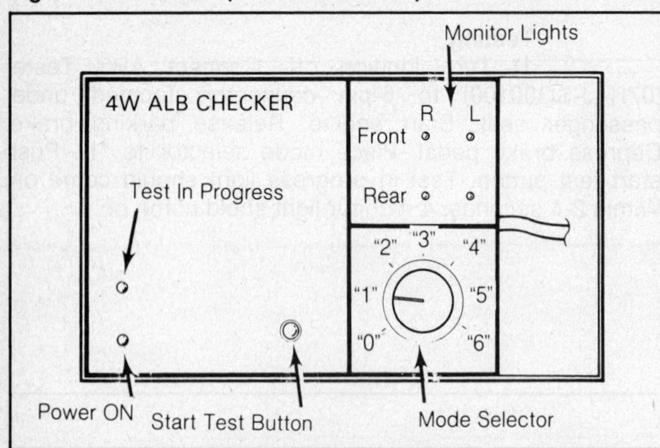

Courtesy of American Honda Motor Co., Inc.

WHEEL SENSOR CHECK

Place ABS tester in mode "0". Raise vehicle and support so wheels can be rotated. Turn ignition on. Place transmission in "N". Rotate wheels by hand (one revolution per second). Appropriate monitor light should blink each time wheel is rotated. If light does not blink, check appropriate wheel sensor and wiring.

WARNING LIGHT STAYS ON

1) If warning light stays on after 3 seconds, check if LED, on ECM, is blinking. If not, see "ANTILOCK" WARNING LIGHT in this article. If warning light is still on, check ECM connector. If okay, check ABS No. 2 fuse, White wire between fuse No. 2 and ECM, Yellow/Black wire between No. 17 fuse and relays.

2) Check Yellow/Green wire between relays. Check for short in Blue/Red wire between instrument panel and ECM. Check for open in White/Blue wire between alternator and ECM. If problem cannot be found, replace ECM and retest.

NOTE: LED will blink faintly when engine is running.

RETRIEVING CODES

Turn engine off. Turn ignition on. Ensure "ANTILOCK" light comes on. Start engine and ensure lights stay lit. Turn engine off. Turn ignition on and check LED blinking sequence. *See Fig. 3.* There should be an approximate 10 second delay before light will start blinking after ignition is turned on. A total of 3 codes can be set at one time. To recheck sequence, turn ignition off, for few seconds, then turn ignition back on.

Fig. 3: Example of LED Code

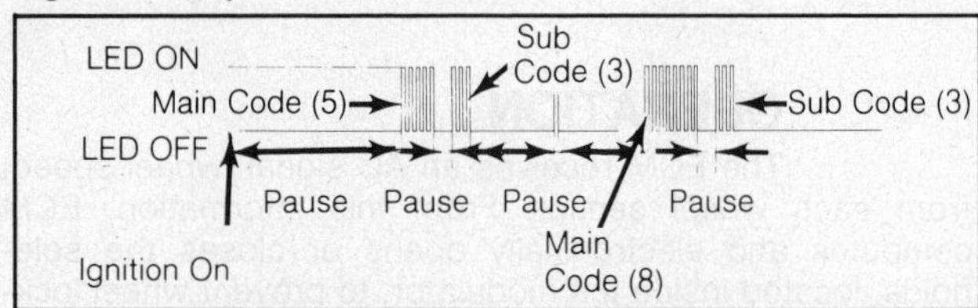

Courtesy of American Honda Motor Co., Inc.

Main Code 1
Defective Hydraulic Controlled Component

1) Check ABS fuses. Ensure brake lines are not kinked or leaking and brake fluid level is okay. Unplug pressure switch connector. Using an ohmmeter, check for continuity, If there is continuity, using ABS "T" Wrench (07HAA-SG00100), remove high pressure fluid from maintenance bleeder. *See Fig. 5.*

2) Recheck pressure switch for continuity. If there is continuity, replace pressure switch. If there was no continuity in the previous 2 tests, ensure high pressure fluid is removed. Raise vehicle and support. Start engine and place into gear.

3) With vehicle running 6 MPH or more, check pump motor operation. If pump motor does not operate, check relay. If relay is okay, connect a jumper wire between White wire and White/Blue wire on relay connector. Pump motor should run. If not, check wiring. If wiring is okay, check for short in pressure switch wiring.

4) If pump motor operated in step **3)**, check if pump motor operates with increasing loud, raspy noise. If not, bleed system. If it does, motor should stop operating after approximately 60 seconds. If motor stops after 120 seconds, replace pressure switch.

5) If motor stops operating after 60 seconds, check that fluid level in reservoir goes down and contains no air. Allow fluid to stabilize before checking. If there is air within system and level remains the same, using ABS "T" wrench, check fluid quanity by bleeding high pressure line.

6) If fluid quanity is over 120 cc, replace accumulator. If fluid quanity is less than 70 cc, check for modulator inlet solenoid leak or accumulator leak. If fluid level up goes, replace modulator. If fluid level goes down in step **5)**, recheck pump motor.

Code 2
Defective Parking Brake Component

1) Ensure vehicle was not driven with parking brake applied for more than 30 seconds. Check brake fluid level. Check Green/Red wire between "BRAKE" warning light and parking brake switch, and "BRAKE" warning light and brake fluid level switch.

2) Ensure "BRAKE" warning light bulb. Check for open in Green/Red wire between "BRAKE" warning

ACURA ANTI-LOCK BRAKE SYSTEM (Cont.)

Fig. 4: Connector Locations

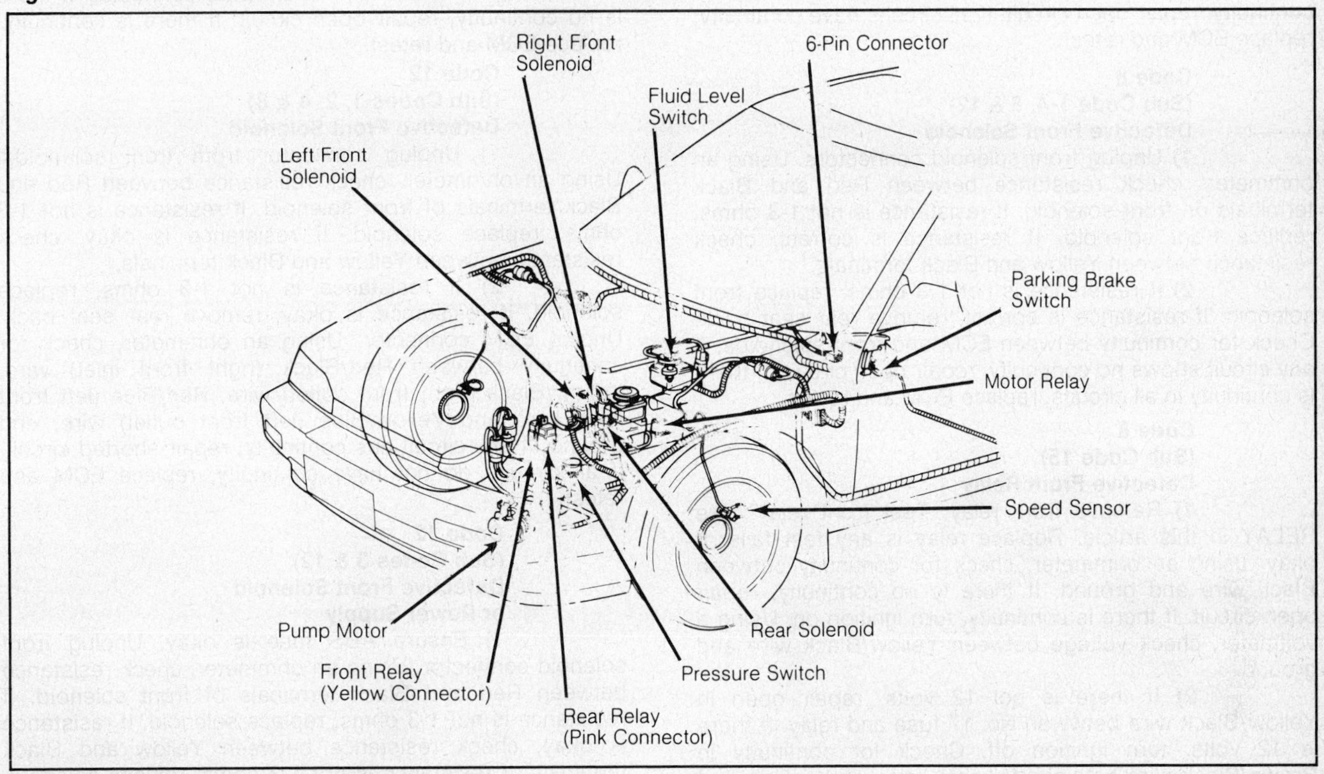

Courtesy of American Honda Motor Co., Inc.

Fig. 5: Maintenence Bleeder Location

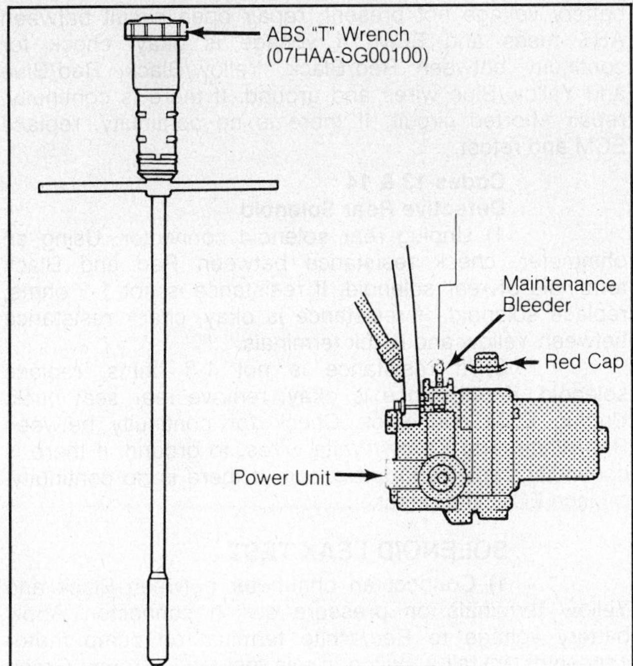

Courtesy of American Honda Motor Co., Inc.

light and parking brake, and Green/Red wire between parking brake switch and control unit. If everything is okay, all connections. If connections are okay, replace ECM and retest.

Code 3
(Sub Code 1 & 2)
Defective Relay
See RELAY in this article.

Code 3
(Sub Code 13-15)
Defective Pulser
No testing is available from manufacturer.

Code 4
(Sub Code 4, 8 & 12)
Defective Speed Sensor
or Modulator

1) Unplug wheel sensor connector. Using an ohmmeter, check resistance between wheel sensor terminals. If resistance is not 500-1000 ohms, replace wheel sensor. If resistance is correct, connect ABS tester to system. Check system with ABS tester in in modes "2" and "3". If system does not operate properly, replace modulator.

2) If system is okay, remove ABS tester. Remove rear seat back. Using an ohmmeter, check for continuity between ECM and each speed sensor. If any circuit contains no continuity, repair open circuit. If all circuits have continuity, replace ECM and retest.

Code 5, 6 or 7
(Sub Code 1, 2, 4 & 8)
Defective Speed Sensor)

Unplug wheel sensor connector. Using an ohmmeter, check resistance between wheel sensor terminals. If resistance is not 500-1000 ohms, replace wheel sensor. If resistance is correct, remove rear seat back. Using an ohmmeter, check for continuity between ECM

ACURA ANTI-LOCK BRAKE SYSTEM (Cont.)

and each speed sensor. If any circuit contains no continuity, repair open circuit. If all circuits have continuity, replace ECM and retest.

Code 8
(Sub Code 1-4, 8 & 12)
Defective Front Solenoid

1) Unplug front solenoid connectors. Using an ohmmeter, check resistance between Red and Black terminals on front solenoid. If resistance is not 1-3 ohms, replace front solenoid. If resistance is correct, check resistance between Yellow and Black terminals.

2) If resistance is not 1-3 ohms, replace front solenoid. If resistance is correct, remove rear seat back. Check for continuity between ECM and front solenoids. If any circuit shows no continuity, repair open circuit. If there is continuity in all circuits, replace ECM and retest.

Code 8
(Sub Code 15)
Defective Front Relay

1) Remove front relay. Test front relay. See RELAY in this article. Replace relay is any test fails. If okay, using an ohmmeter, check for continuity between Black wire and ground. If there is no continuity, repair open circuit. If there is continuity, turn ignition on. Using a voltmeter, check voltage between Yellow/Black wire and ground.

2) If there is not 12 volts, repair open in Yellow/Black wire betwwen No. 17 fuse and relay. If there is 12 volts, turn ignition off. Check for continuity in Brown/Black wire between fail-safe relay and solenoid. If there is no continuity, repair open circuit. If there is continuity, ensure front solenoids are connected. If not, repair as necessary. If okay, replace ECM and retest.

Code 9 & 10
Defective Rear Solenoid

1) Unplug connector from rear solenoid. Using an ohmmeter, check resistance between Red and White terminals of rear solenoid. If resistance is not 1-3 ohms, replace solenoid. If resistance is okay, check resistance between Yellow and White terminals of rear solenoid.

2) If resistance is not 1-3 ohms, replace solenoid. If okay, remove rear seat back. Unplug control unit. Check continuity of Red/White and Yellow/White wires in control unit connector. If any wire does not have continuity, repair open circuit. If all wires have continuity, replace ECM and retest.

Code 11
(Sub Codes 3, 12 & 15)
Defective Rear Fail-Safe Relay

1) Remove rear relay. Test rear relay. See RELAY in this article. Replace relay if bad. If relay is okay, using an ohmmeter, check continuity between Black wire and ground. If there is not continuity, repair open circuit. If there is continuity, turn ignition on.

2) Using a voltmeter, check voltage between Yellow/Black wire and ground. If there is not 12 volts, repair open in Yellow/Black wire between No. 17 fuse and relay. If there is 12 volts, turn ignition off. Check for continuity in Blue/Black wire between fail-safe relay and solenoid. If there is no continuity, repair open circuit.

3) If there is continuity, remove rear seat back. Check for continuity in Yellow/Green wire between relay and ECM. If there is no continuity, repair open circuit. If there is continuity, check for continuity in Red/White and Yellow/White wires in control unit wire connector. If there is no continuity, repair open circuit. If there is continuity, replace ECM and retest.

Code 12
(Sub Codes 1, 2, 4 & 8)
Defective Front Solenoid

1) Unplug connector from front solenoids. Using an ohmmeter, check resistance between Red and Black terminals of front solenoid. If resistance is not 1-3 ohms, replace solenoid. If resistance is okay, check resistance between Yellow and Black terminals.

2) If resistance is not 1-3 ohms, replace solenoid. If resistance is okay, remove rear seat back. Unplug ECM connector. Using an ohmmeter, check for continuity between Red/Black (right front inlet) wire, Yellow/Black (right front outlet) wire, Red/Blue (left front inlet) wire and Yellow/Blue (left front outlet) wire, and ground. If any circuit has continuity, repair shorted circuit. If all circuits do not have continuity, replace ECM and retest.

Code 12
(Sub Codes 3 & 12)
Defective Front Solenoid
or Power Supply

1) Ensure ABS fuse is okay. Unplug front solenoid connector. Using an ohmmeter, check resistance between Red and Black terminals of front solenoid. If resistance is not 1-3 ohms, replace solenoid. If resistance is okay, check resistance between Yellow and Black terminals. If resistance is not 1-3 ohms, replace solenoid. If resistance is okay, remove rear seat back.

2) Unplug ECM connector. Using a voltmeter, check voltage at White/Black and White/Green wires. If battery voltage not present, repair open circuit between ABS fuses and ECM. If voltage is okay, check for continuity between Red/Black, Yellow/Black, Red/Blue and Yellow/Blue wires and ground. If there is continuity, repair shorted circuit. If there is no continuity, replace ECM and retest.

Codes 13 & 14
Defective Rear Solenoid

1) Unplug rear solenoid connector. Using an ohmmeter, check resistance between Red and Black terminals of rear solenoid. If resistance is not 1-3 ohms, replace solenoid. If resistance is okay, check resistance between Yellow and Black terminals.

2) If resistance is not 1-3 ohms, replace solenoid. If resistance is okay, remove rear seat back. Unplug ECM connector. Check for continuity between Red/White, and Yellow/White wires, to ground. If there is continuity, repair shorted circuit. If there is no continuity, replace ECM and retest.

SOLENOID LEAK TEST

1) Connect an ohmmeter between Black and Yellow terminals on pressure switch connector. Apply battery voltage to Red/White terminal on pump motor connector. Install a switch in this test lead. Ground Green terminal. Turn switch on. Allow pressure to build inside accumulator. Check for continuity.

2) Once continuity is indicated, allow pump to operate 4 seconds more. Turn switch off. Check for continuity 60 seeconds after switch was turned off. If there is no continuity, check for faulty driver "O" ring or leaky solenoid. Apply 12 volts across Black (negative) and Red (positive) terminals of solenoid.

ACURA ANTI-LOCK BRAKE SYSTEM (Cont.)

3) If solenoid hisses or squeaks, replace solenoid. Ensure solenoid clicks into position. Check pressure switch for continuity within 60 seconds. If there is no continuity, replace solenoid.

RELAY

Using an ohmmeter, check for continuity between terminals No. 3 and 4. *See Fig. 7.* There should be no continuity. Apply battery voltage across terminals No. 1 and 2. There should be continuity between terminals No. 3 and 4. If relay fails any of these tests, replace relay.

Fig. 7: Relay Testing Points

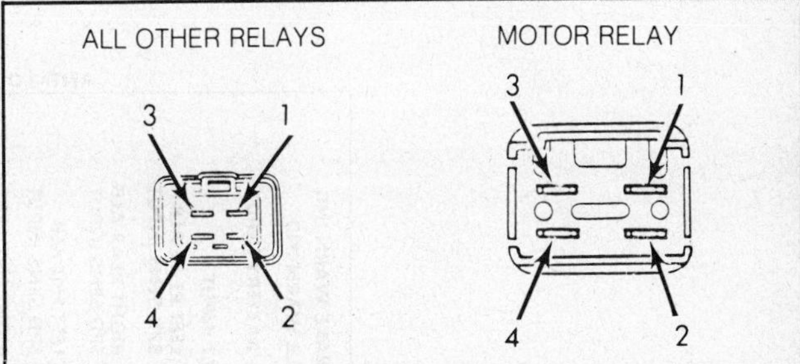

Courtesy of American Honda Motor Co., Inc.

REMOVAL & INSTALLATION

WHEEL SENSOR

Removal & Installation

Unplug wheel sensor connector. Remove wheel sensor from vehicle. To install, reverse removal procedure. Adjust wheel sensor there is .016-.039" (.40-1.0 mm) clearance between wheel sensor and sensor ring.

OVERHAUL

MASTER CYLINDER

Disassembly & Reassembly

Remove rod seal. Push in on secondary piston assembly and remove snap ring and stop bolt. Remove secondary and primary piston assembly. Disassemble pistons. *See Fig. 6.* To reassemble, reverse disassembly procedure. Replace all seals. Apply clean brake fluid to all seals before installing.

BLEEDING BRAKE SYSTEM

NOTE: **DO NOT depress brake pedal while bleeding brake system.**

1) Place vehicle on level ground. Place transmission in "P" (automatic) or "N" (manual). Block wheels. Fill master cylinder with brake fluid. Install ABS tester to 6-pin connector. Start engine. Release parking brake. Turn mode selector to "1". Press "START TEST" button. Ensure motor starts to operates and then stops.

2) Turn mode selector to "2". Press "START TEST" button. Wait until fluid in reservoir is air free (approximately 70 seconds). Turn mode selector to "6". Press "START TEST" button. Wait until fluid in reservoir is air free (approximately 70 seconds). Perform this test 2 or 3 times. Fill modulator reservoir. Check system using ABS tester.

Fig. 6: Exploded View of Master Cylinder

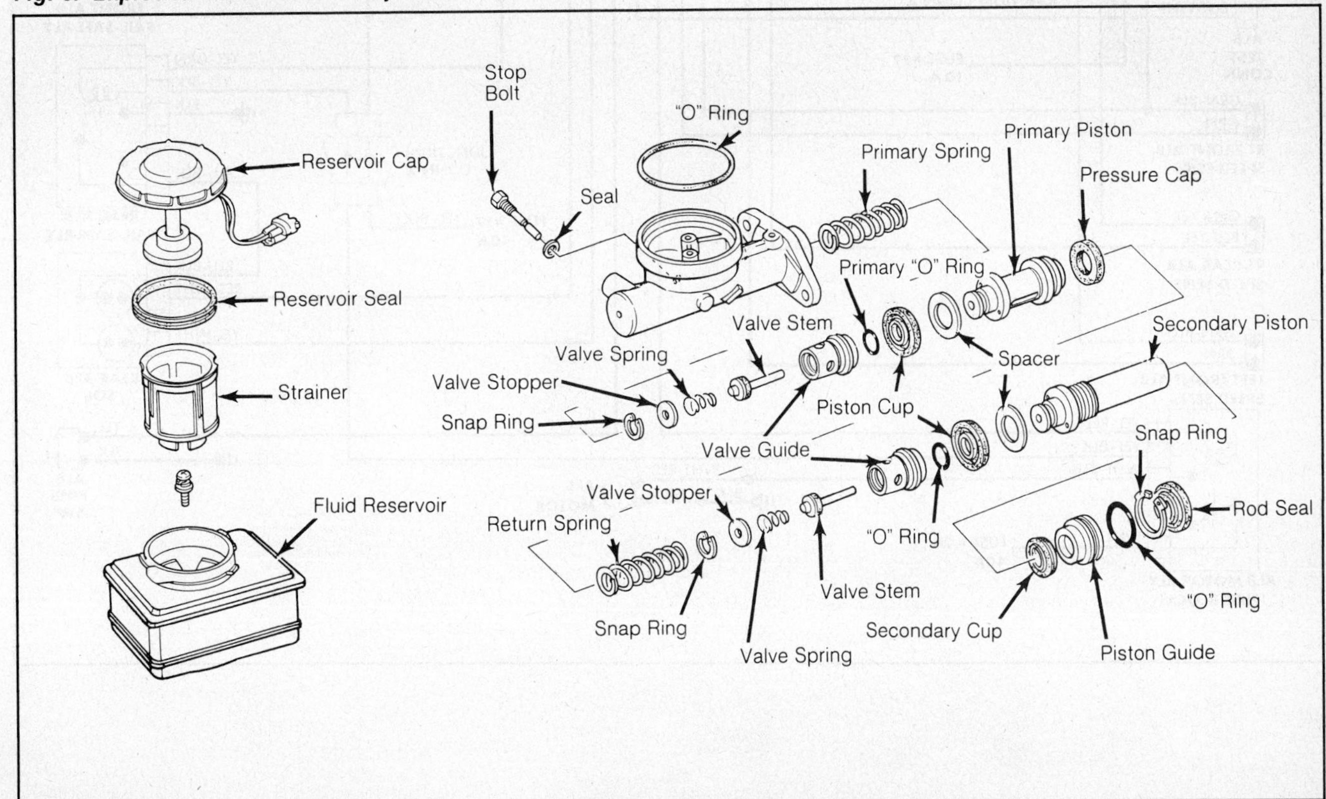

Courtesy of American Honda Motor Co., Inc.

ACURA ANTI-LOCK BRAKE SYSTEM (Cont.)

Fig. 8: Acura Anti-Lock Brake System Wiring Diagram

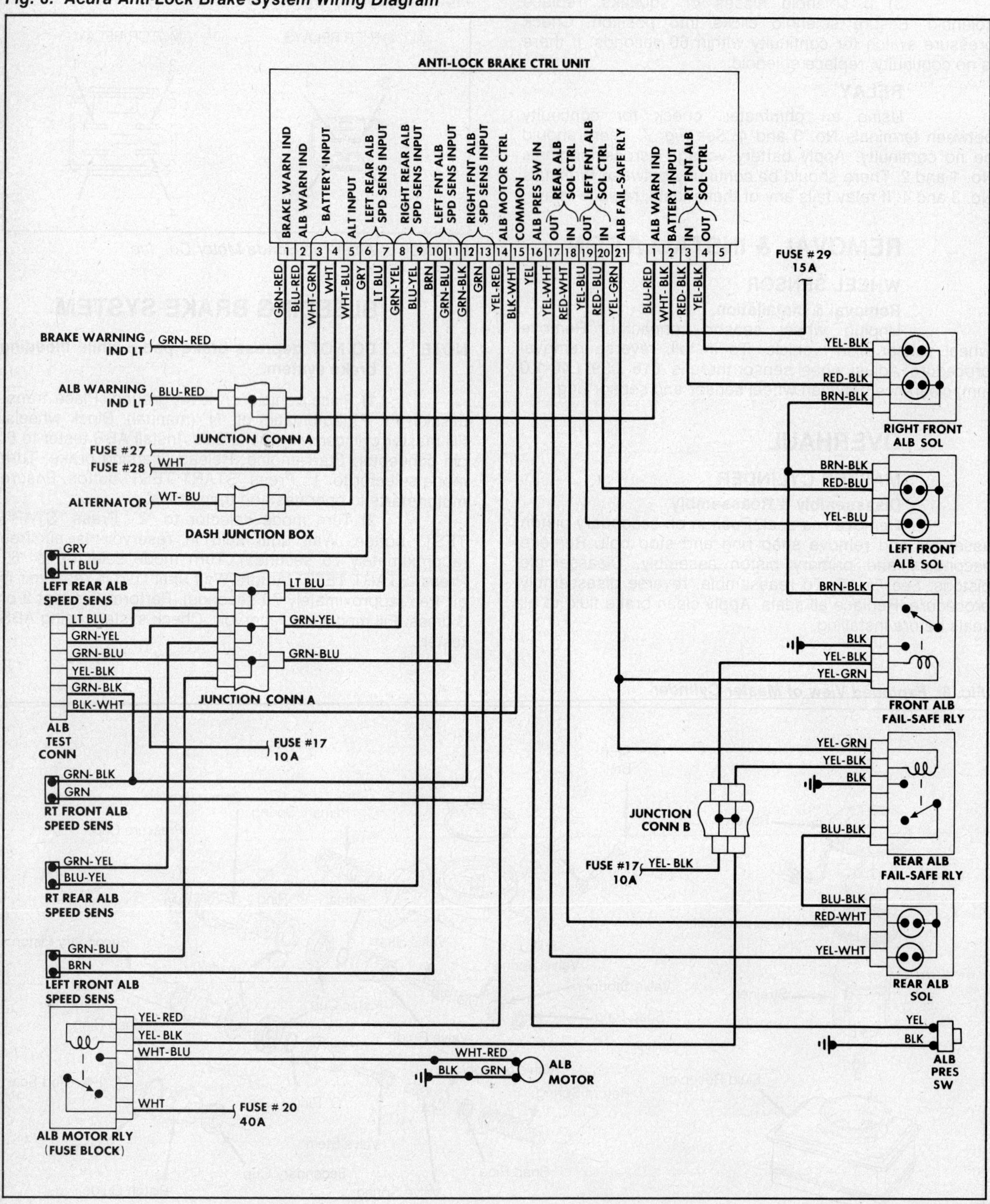

AUDI ANTI-LOCK BRAKE SYSTEM

5000S, 5000CS Quattro,
5000CS Turbo

DESCRIPTION

The Anti-Lock Brake System (ABS) consists of an ABS control unit, hydraulic modulator, system relays, speed sensors, and necessary wiring. *See Fig. 2*. An ABS defeat switch is located on the dashboard. The ABS defeat switch allows the driver to turn the system on or off as desired. If the ABS system is locked out, stopping and restarting the vehicle will automatically engage the ABS system once again.

OPERATION

ABS CONTROL UNIT

The ABS control unit, located behind rear seat, receives and interprets electrical signals from speed sensors to determine wheel braking lock-up. If one or more wheels begins to lock-up, ABS control unit automatically modulates brake pressure to prevent wheel lock-up.

SPEED SENSOR

A speed sensor is located next to hub on each axle. A speed sensor rotor is attached to each hub and rotates past the speed sensors. The rotary motion of the wheels is picked up by each sensor and an electrical signal is sent to the ABS control unit.

TESTING & DIAGNOSIS

SYSTEM WARNINGS & PRECAUTIONS

The following precautions must be followed when working on vehicles equipped with this system.

1) Disconnect ABS control unit before using welding equipment on vehicle. If vehicle is being oven dried after painting, do not expose ABS control unit to temperatures above 185°F (85°C) for more than 2 hours.

2) Never disconnect or connect ABS control unit, hydraulic modulator, or system relays with ignition on. Disconnect battery before charging battery or when replacing hydraulic modulator.

3) DO NOT drive vehicle with ABS system tester connected. Wheels and tires of matching size should only be used. Space saving (mini-spare) tires, must never be installed on vehicle.

4) The complete testing procedure must be carried out after any work is performed on the hydraulic modulator, ABS control unit, speed sensors, or system wiring.

5) If components such as brake lines or brake pressure regulators are replaced after a collision, the complete testing procedure must be carried out. If brake repairs DO NOT involve ABS system components, it is only necessary to perform OPERATIONAL TEST.

TEST EQUIPMENT

The following test equipment is required to diagnose and test system. DO NOT attempt to test this system without proper equipment. *See Fig. 1*.

- Pressure Gauge Set (VW 1310). Used to check hydraulic modulator pressures.
- ABS Tester (Bosch). The tester has program selector switches, indicator lights, and digital readouts. Tester checks the operation of the ABS control unit, system components, and wiring harness.
- ABS Tester Adapter. Adapter is used to check anti-lock power supply relay.
- Digital Multimeter (US 1119). Used to check system voltage or resistance values.

EQUIPMENT HOOK-UP

1) Use ABS tester to check anti-lock braking system, Tester is connected in series with ABS control unit and vehicle wiring harness. Tester simulates and duplicates ABS operating conditions.

2) Before connecting tester, check operation of on/off switch and the indicator light on vehicle. To do so, start engine. When engine reaches idle speed, the indicator light must go out.

3) If light does not go out, depress the anti-lock switch. If light still does not go out, check wire connection from alternator "D+" terminal to terminal No. 15 at ABS control unit.

4) If indicator light operation is correct, turn ignition off. Connect tester to vehicle. *See Fig. 1*. DO NOT drive vehicle with ABS system tester connected.

PREPARATION

Test results are dependent on the correct operation of several related non-ABS components and systems. The following areas should be checked and corrected before attempting to diagnose ABS system.

1) Ensure that fuses No. 3 and 12 are okay. Make sure anti-lock brake system is turned on and that ground connection at hydraulic modulator is tight. Check connections at hydraulic modulator for leaks.

2) Ensure brake components (pads, rotors, etc.) are okay. On 5000CS Quattro, DO NOT engage differential locks unless specified. Check that fuse on anti-lock power supply relay (located on auxiliary relay panel) is okay.

3) Ensure ignition switch is in "ON" position in all program switch positions unless told otherwise. Turn ignition off before connecting or disconnecting ABS control unit.

4) To find a fault in system, the testing procedure must be followed completely and in the specified sequence. When cause of fault is found, it should be repaired. The entire test procedure should then be repeated, starting from step one.

AUDI ANTI-LOCK BRAKE SYSTEM (Cont.)

Fig. 1: Test Equipment Hook-Up

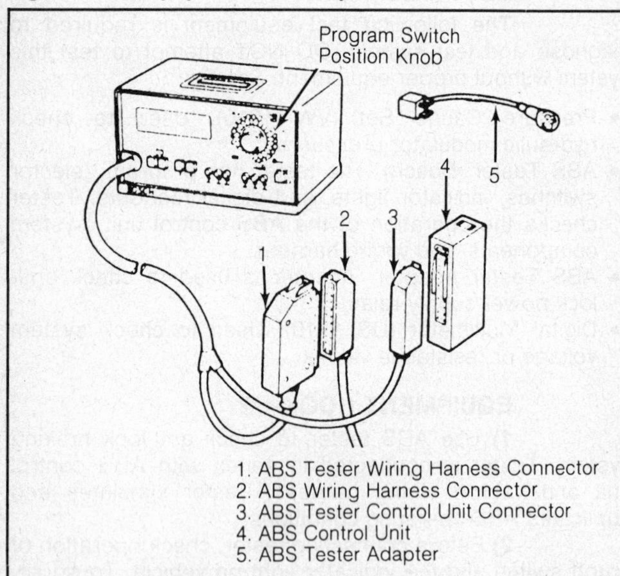

Courtesy of Audi of America, Inc.

OPERATIONAL TEST

1) This test should only be performed after repairing or replacing, brake pads, rotors, brake hoses, brake servo, master cylinder, brake cables, or parking brake components.

2) Turn ignition on. The ABS indicator light should come on. With differential locks NOT engaged (5000CS Quattro), turn ABS system on and drive vehicle above 4 miles per hour. The ABS indicator light must NOT come on. If correct, the ABS system is functional.

HYDRAULIC MODULATOR HYDRAULIC PRESSURE TEST

1) Remove one front wheel. Remove bleed screw from brake caliper. Connect and bleed Pressure Gauge Set (VW 1310). Press brake pedal until pressure gauge reads 725 psi (51 kg/cm²). If pressure drops more than 58 psi (4 kg/cm²) in 45 seconds, replace hydraulic modulator. If okay, go to next step.

2) Press brake pedal until pressure gauge reads 87 psi (6 kg/cm²). If pressure drops more than 14.5 psi (1 kg/cm²) in 3 minutes, replace hydraulic modulator.

TESTING PROCEDURES

NOTE: **If anti-lock indicator light comes on while driving and goes out again by itself after a short time, check voltage supply to ABS control unit at terminal No. 1. If anti-lock indicator light comes on while driving but ABS system is still operating (evident by pulsating brake pedal during hard stops), check voltage supply at "D+" terminal on alternator and at terminal No. 15 of ABS control unit.**

TEST 1

5000CS Quattro

1) To test voltage supply circuit, place ABS tester in program switch position No. 1 and turn ignition on. Lamp No. 1 (Green) must come on (also applies to all other program switch positions). If light comes on, go to step **7)**. Lamps No. 2 or 3 may also come on. Disregard lights No. 2 and 3 at this time.

2) If light No. 1 did not come on, check ABS control unit and tester plug connectors for tightness. If okay, remove anti-lock power supply relay from auxiliary relay panel (position No. 5).

3) Connect voltmeter between contacts No. 2 and 4, and then between contacts No. 4 and 5. Voltmeter readings should be about 12 volts. If incorrect, repair break in wiring harness. If correct, go to next step.

4) Connect voltmeter between contacts No. 4 and 8. Press and hold anti-lock switch. Voltmeter reading should be about 12 volts. If incorrect, repair break in wiring harness or replace anti-lock switch. If correct, go to next step.

5) Connect voltmeter between contacts No. 1 and 5, and then between contacts No. 3 and 5. Lock center and rear differentials (No. 1 and 2). With differentials locked, voltmeter reading should be about 12 volts.

6) With differentials unlocked, voltmeter reading should be close to zero volts. If readings are incorrect, repair wiring harness or replace differential lock switch. If readings are correct, go to next step.

NOTE: **If differential locks do not engage (warning lights do not light up), turn a wheel on front or rear axle until differential lock engages or disengages.**

7) With ABS tester in program switch position No. 1 and ignition on, light No. 1 (Green) must be on (also applies to all other program switch positions). If light is on, go to step **13)**. If not, go to next step.

8) Unclip relay socket No. 5 from auxiliary relay panel. Install anti-lock power supply relay in disconnected socket No. 5. Connect voltmeter between contacts No. 4 and 6.

9) Voltmeter reading should be about 12 volts. If reading is incorrect, check fuse and anti-lock relay or replace anti-lock power supply relay. If reading is correct, go to next step.

10) Remove anti-lock power supply relay out of socket and insert socket into auxiliary relay panel at location No. 5. Install anti-lock power supply relay. Turn ignition off.

11) Using ohmmeter, check ground wire between terminal No. 10 in ABS control unit plug and ground point under right rear seat kick panel. Ohmmeter reading must be close to zero ohms. If reading is incorrect, repair wiring harness or contact resistance. If reading is correct, go to next step.

12) Turn ignition on and connect voltmeter between terminal No. 1 and 10 in ABS control unit plug. *See Fig. 3*. Voltmeter reading should be about 12 volts. If reading is incorrect, repair wiring harness. If reading is correct, go to next step.

NOTE: **If light No. 2 comes on, battery is not fully charged or there is an excessive voltage drop at terminal No. 1 or 10 of ABS control unit plug. If light No. 2 comes on during subsequent test procedure, stop test procedure and eliminate fault. After repairs repeat entire test procedure.**

13) To test solenoid valve relay (off position), put ABS tester in program switch position No. 1 and turn

AUDI ANTI-LOCK BRAKE SYSTEM (Cont.)

Fig. 2: Anti-Lock Brake System (ABS) Components

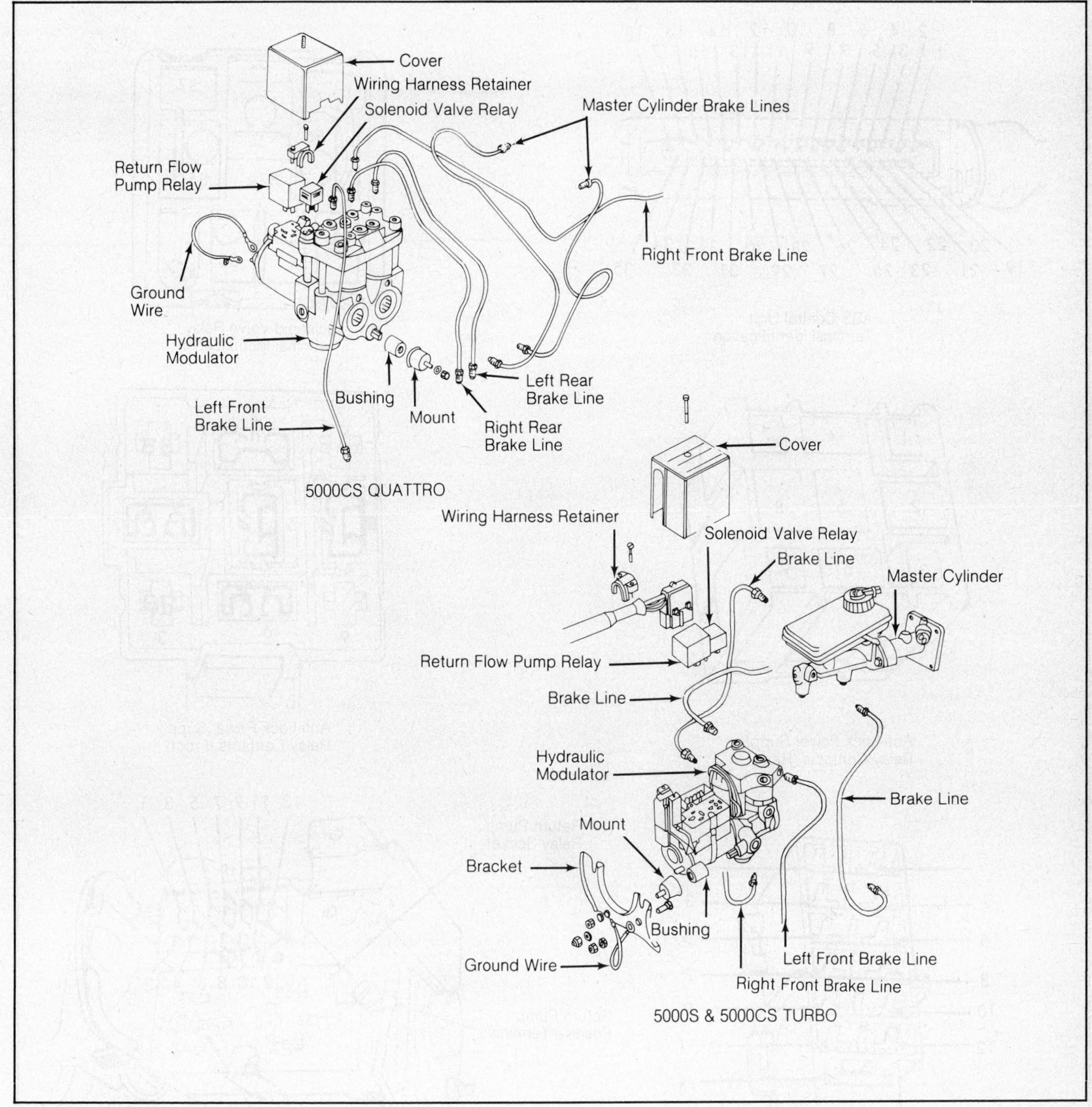

Courtesy of Audi of America, Inc.

ignition on. Lamps No. 1 and 3 (Green) must come on. If lights come on, TEST 1 is completed.

14) If light No. 4 (Red) comes on, remove relay for solenoid valves from hydraulic modulator. Use ohmmeter to test continuity between terminals No. 87A and 30. Replace relay if no continuity exists. If correct, go to next step.

15) Use ohmmeter to measure internal resistance of solenoid valve relay between terminals No. 85 and 86. Ohmmeter reading should be 70-120 ohms. If incorrect, replace solenoid valve relay. If correct, go to next step.

16) Turn ignition off and disconnect plug for hydraulic modulator. Use ohmmeter to check continuity of ground lead to terminal No. 8. If necessary, repair wiring harness. If continuity exists, go to next step.

17) Use ohmmeter to check continuity between terminal No. 8 in socket of hydraulic modulator and terminal No. 87A on relay socket for solenoid valves. *See Fig. 3.* If there is no continuity, replace hydraulic modulator. If continuity exists, go to next step.

18) Use ohmmeter to check continuity between terminal No. 12 in socket of hydraulic modulator and terminal No. 30 in socket for solenoid valves. If there is no

AUDI ANTI-LOCK BRAKE SYSTEM (Cont.)

Fig. 3: Anti-Lock Brake System (ABS) Component Contacts & Terminal Identification

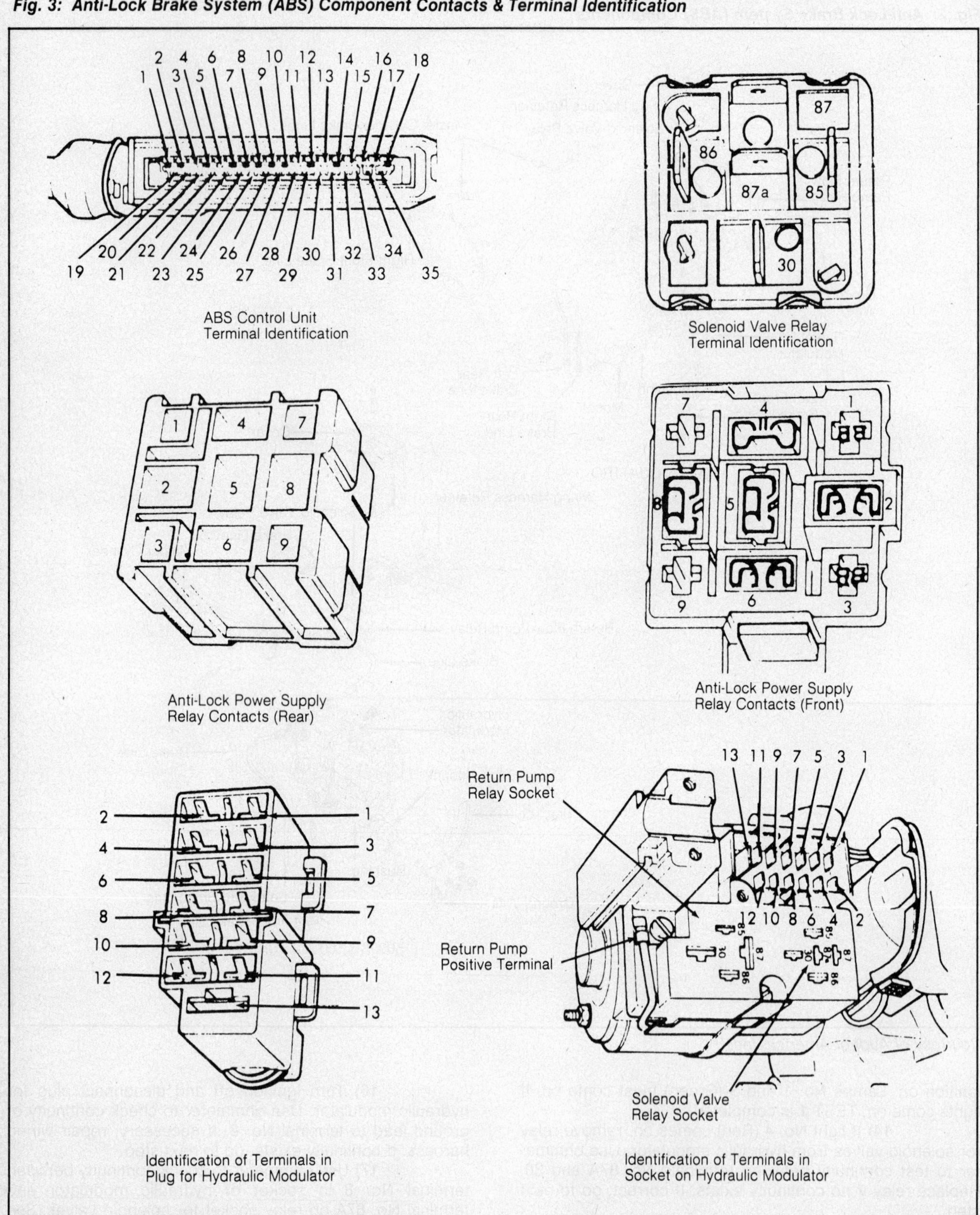

Courtesy of Audi of America, Inc.

AUDI ANTI-LOCK BRAKE SYSTEM (Cont.)

continuity, replace hydraulic modulator. If continuity exists, go to next step.

19) Use ohmmeter to check continuity between terminal No. 12 in plug for hydraulic modulator and terminal No. 32 on plug for ABS control unit. If necessary, repair wiring harness.

5000S & 5000CS Turbo

1) To test voltage supply circuit, place ABS tester in program switch position No. 1 and turn ignition on. Lamp No. 1 (Green) must come on (also applies to all other program switch positions). If light comes on, go to step **5)**. Lamps No. 2 or 3 may also come on. Disregard lights No. 2 and 3 at this time.

2) If light No. 1 did not come on, check ABS control unit and tester plug connectors for tightness. If okay, remove anti-lock power supply relay from auxiliary relay panel (position No. 1).

3) Connect voltmeter between contacts No. 2 and 4, and then between contacts No. 4 and 5. Voltmeter readings should be about 12 volts. If incorrect, repair break in wiring harness. If correct, go to next step.

4) Connect voltmeter between contacts No. 4 and 8. Press and hold anti-lock switch. Voltmeter reading should be about 12 volts. If incorrect, repair break in wiring harness or replace anti-lock switch. If correct, go to next step.

5) With ABS tester in program switch position No. 1 and ignition on, light No. 1 (Green) must be on (also applies to all other program switch positions). If light is on, go to step **11)**. If not, go to next step.

6) Unclip relay socket No. 1 from auxiliary relay panel. Install anti-lock power supply relay in disconnected socket No. 1. Connect voltmeter between contacts No. 4 and 6.

7) Voltmeter reading should be about 12 volts. If reading is incorrect, check fuse and anti-lock relay or replace anti-lock power supply relay. If reading is correct, go to next step.

8) Remove anti-lock power supply relay out of socket and insert socket into auxiliary relay panel at location No. 1. Install anti-lock power supply relay. Turn ignition off.

9) Using ohmmeter, check ground wire between terminal No. 10 in ABS control unit plug and ground point under right rear seat kick panel. Ohmmeter reading must be close to zero ohms. If reading is incorrect, repair wiring harness or contact resistance. If reading is correct, go to next step.

10) Turn ignition on and connect voltmeter between terminal No. 1 and 10 in ABS control unit plug. *See Fig. 3*. Voltmeter reading should be about 12 volts. If reading is incorrect, repair wiring harness. If reading is correct, go to next step.

NOTE: If light No. 2 comes on, battery is not fully charged or there is an excessive voltage drop at terminal No. 1 or 10 of ABS control unit plug. If light No. 2 comes on during subsequent test procedure, stop test procedure and eliminate fault. After repairs repeat entire test procedure.

11) To test solenoid valve relay (off position), put ABS tester in program switch position No. 1 and turn ignition on. Lamps No. 1 and 3 (Green) must come on. If light comes on, TEST 1 is completed.

12) If light No. 4 (Red) comes on, remove relay for solenoid valves from hydraulic modulator. Use ohmmeter to test continuity between terminals No. 87A and 30. Replace relay if no continuity exists. If correct, go to next step.

13) Use ohmmeter to measure internal resistance of solenoid valve relay between terminals No. 85 and 86. Ohmmeter reading should be 70-120 ohms. If incorrect, replace solenoid valve relay. If correct, go to next step.

14) Turn ignition off and disconnect plug for hydraulic modulator. Use ohmmeter to check continuity of ground lead to terminal No. 8. If necessary, repair wiring harness. If continuity exists, go to next step.

15) Use ohmmeter to check continuity between terminal No. 8 in socket of hydraulic modulator and terminal No. 87A on relay socket for solenoid valves. *See Fig. 3*. If there is no continuity, replace hydraulic modulator. If continuity exists, go to next step.

16) Use ohmmeter to check continuity between terminal No. 12 in socket of hydraulic modulator and terminal No. 30 in socket for solenoid valves. If there is no continuity, replace hydraulic modulator. If continuity exists, go to next step.

17) Use ohmmeter to check continuity between terminal No. 12 in plug for hydraulic modulator and terminal No. 32 on plug for ABS control unit. If necessary, repair wiring harness.

TEST 2

All Models

1) To test solenoid valve relay (on position), Turn ignition on and place ABS tester in program switch position No. 2. Lamps No. 1 and 3 (Green) must come on. If light comes on, TEST 2 is completed. If light No. 4 (Red) comes on, replace defective solenoid valve relay and go to next step.

2) Remove plug connector on hydraulic modulator. Connect voltmeter between terminal No. 4 on plug for hydraulic modulator and ground. Voltmeter reading should be about 12 volts. If reading is incorrect, repair wiring harness. If reading is correct, go to next step.

3) Use ohmmeter to check continuity between contact No. 4 in socket on hydraulic modulator and terminal No. 87 in socket for solenoid valves. If there is no continuity, replace hydraulic modulator. If continuity exists, go to next step.

4) Use ohmmeter to check continuity between terminal No. 6 in socket of hydraulic modulator and terminal No. 85 in socket for return pump relay. If there is no continuity, replace hydraulic modulator. If continuity exists, go to next step.

5) Use ohmmeter to check continuity between terminal No. 86 in socket for solenoid valves and terminal No. 86 in socket for return pump relay. *See Fig. 3*. If there is no continuity, replace hydraulic modulator. If continuity exists, go to next step.

6) Use ohmmeter to check continuity between terminal No. 86 in socket for solenoid valves and terminal No. 2 in socket on hydraulic modulator. If there is no continuity, replace hydraulic modulator. If continuity exists, go to next step.

7) Connect voltmeter between terminal No. 2 in plug for hydraulic modulator and ground. Voltmeter reading should be about 12 volts. If reading is incorrect, repair wiring harness. If reading is correct, go to next step.

8) Turn ignition off. Use ohmmeter to check continuity between terminal No. 6 in plug for hydraulic

AUDI ANTI-LOCK BRAKE SYSTEM (Cont.)

modulator and terminal No. 27 in plug for ABS control unit. If there is no continuity, repair wiring harness to restore continuity.

TEST 3

All Models

1) To test return pump relay (off position), turn ignition on and place ABS tester in program switch position No. 3. Lamps No. 1 and 3 (Green) must come on. If lights come on, TEST 3 is completed.

2) If light No. 4 (Red) comes on, replace defective return pump relay. After replacing relay, check that ground lead for hydraulic modulator is tight. If okay, turn ignition off and remove plug connector on hydraulic modulator.

3) Use ohmmeter to check continuity between terminal No. 9 in socket on hydraulic modulator and terminal No. 30 in relay socket for return pump. If there is no continuity, replace hydraulic modulator. If continuity exists, go to next step.

4) Use ohmmeter to check continuity between terminal No. 9 in socket on hydraulic modulator and positive terminal on return pump. *See Fig. 3*. If there is no continuity, replace hydraulic modulator. If continuity exists, go to next step.

5) Use ohmmeter to check continuity between terminal No. 9 in plug for hydraulic modulator and terminal No. 14 in plug for ABS control unit. If there is no continuity, repair wiring harness to restore continuity.

TEST 4

All Models

1) To test return pump relay (off position), turn ignition on and place ABS tester in program switch position No. 4. When button No. 5 lights up, press button. Lights No. 1 and 3 (Green) must come on and return pump must run. If light comes on and pump runs, TEST 4 is completed.

2) If light No. 4 (Red) comes on, replace defective return pump relay. After replacing relay, turn ignition off and remove plug connector from hydraulic modulator.

3) Use ohmmeter to test continuity between terminal No. 11 in socket on hydraulic modulator and terminal No. 85 in relay socket for return pump. *See Fig. 3*. If there is no continuity, replace hydraulic modulator. If continuity exists, go to next step.

4) Use ohmmeter to check continuity between terminal No. 13 in socket on hydraulic modulator and terminal No. 87 in relay socket for return pump. If there is no continuity, replace hydraulic modulator. If continuity exists, go to next step.

5) Turn ignition on. Connect voltmeter between terminal No. 13 in plug for hydraulic modulator and ground. Voltmeter reading should be about 12 volts. If reading is incorrect, repair wiring harness. If reading is correct, go to next step.

6) Turn ignition off. Use ohmmeter to check continuity between terminal No. 11 in plug for hydraulic modulator and terminal No. 28 on plug for ABS control unit. If there is no continuity, repair wiring harness to restore continuity.

NOTE: If all test results are correct but the return pump does not run when button No. 5 is pressed, replace hydraulic modulator.

TEST 5

All Models

1) To test anti-lock power supply relay, place ABS tester in program switch position No. 5. Turn ignition off. Disconnect plug for anti-lock brake tester from ABS control unit.

2) Remove anti-lock power supply relay from auxiliary relay panel. Use ABS tester adapter to connect anti-lock power supply relay from vehicle to back of ABS tester. *See Fig. 1*.

3) Install a new Anti-Lock Power Supply Relay (443 927 826) in auxiliary relay panel. Turn ignition on. When button No. 5 lights up, press button.

4) Lights No. 1 and 3 (Green) must come on. If lights come on, TEST 5 is completed. If light No. 4 (Red) comes on, repeat steps **1)** through **3)**. If light No. 4 comes on again, replace anti-lock power supply relay.

TEST 6

5000CS Quattro

1) To test left front solenoid valve, place ABS tester in program switch position No. 6. Turn ignition off. Connect anti-lock brake system tester to ABS control unit. Remove anti-lock power supply relay from ABS tester and install relay in auxiliary relay panel.

2) Turn ignition on and press button No. 8. Left front solenoid valve internal resistance should be .7-1.7 ohms. If reading is correct, go to step **5)**. If reading is incorrect, turn ignition off and remove plug connector from hydraulic modulator.

3) Use ohmmeter to measure resistance between terminals No. 3 and 12 in socket on hydraulic modulator. If reading is not .7-1.7 ohms, replace hydraulic modulator. If reading is correct, go to next step.

4) Use ohmmeter to check continuity between terminal No. 3 in plug for hydraulic modulator and terminal No. 2 in plug for ABS control unit. If there is no continuity, repair wiring harness to restore continuity.

5) To test right front solenoid valve, press button No. 9. Right front solenoid valve internal resistance should be .7-1.7 ohms. If reading is correct, go to step **8)**. If reading is incorrect, turn ignition off and remove plug connector from hydraulic modulator.

6) Use ohmmeter to measure resistance between terminals No. 5 and 12 in socket on hydraulic modulator. If reading is not .7-1.7 ohms, replace hydraulic modulator. If reading is correct, go to next step.

7) Use ohmmeter to check continuity between terminal No. 5 in plug for hydraulic modulator and terminal No. 35 in plug for ABS control unit. If there is no continuity, repair wiring harness to restore continuity.

8) To test rear solenoid valve, press button No. 10. Rear solenoid valve internal resistance should be .7-1.7 ohms. If reading is correct, TEST 6 is completed. If reading is incorrect, turn ignition off and remove plug connector from hydraulic modulator.

9) Use ohmmeter to measure resistance between terminals No. 7 and 12 in socket on hydraulic modulator. If reading is not .7-1.7 ohms, replace hydraulic modulator. If reading is correct, go to next step.

10) Use ohmmeter to check continuity between terminal No. 7 in plug for hydraulic modulator and terminal No. 18 in plug for ABS control unit. If there is no continuity, repair wiring harness to restore continuity.

AUDI ANTI-LOCK BRAKE SYSTEM (Cont.)

5000S & 5000CS Turbo

1) To test left front solenoid valve, place ABS tester in program switch position No. 6. Turn ignition off. Connect anti-lock brake system tester to ABS control unit. Remove anti-lock power supply relay from ABS tester and install relay in auxiliary relay panel.

2) Turn ignition on and press button No. 8. Left front solenoid valve internal resistance should be .7-1.7 ohms. If reading is correct, go to step **5)**. If reading is incorrect, turn ignition off and remove plug connector from hydraulic modulator.

3) Use ohmmeter to measure resistance between terminals No. 3 and 12 in socket on hydraulic modulator. If reading is not .7-1.7 ohms, replace hydraulic modulator. If reading is correct, go to next step.

4) Use ohmmeter to check continuity between terminal No. 3 in plug for hydraulic modulator and terminal No. 2 in plug for ABS control unit. If there is no continuity, repair wiring harness to restore continuity.

5) To test right front solenoid valve, press button No. 9. Right front solenoid valve internal resistance should be .7-1.7 ohms. If reading is correct, go to step **8)**. If reading is incorrect, turn ignition off and remove plug connector from hydraulic modulator.

6) Use ohmmeter to measure resistance between terminals No. 5 and 12 in socket on hydraulic modulator. If reading is not .7-1.7 ohms, replace hydraulic modulator. If reading is correct, go to next step.

7) Use ohmmeter to check continuity between terminal No. 5 in plug for hydraulic modulator and terminal No. 35 in plug for ABS control unit. If there is no continuity, repair wiring harness to restore continuity.

8) To test right rear solenoid valve, press button No. 12. Right rear solenoid valve internal resistance should be .7-1.7 ohms. If reading is correct, go to step **11)**. If reading is incorrect, turn ignition off and remove plug connector from hydraulic modulator.

9) Use ohmmeter to measure resistance between terminals No. 7 and 12 in socket on hydraulic modulator. If reading is not .7-1.7 ohms, replace hydraulic modulator. If reading is correct, go to next step.

10) Use ohmmeter to check continuity between terminal No. 7 in plug for hydraulic modulator and terminal No. 19 in plug for ABS control unit. If there is no continuity, repair wiring harness to restore continuity.

11) To test left rear solenoid valve, press button No. 11. Left rear solenoid valve internal resistance should be .7-1.7 ohms. If reading is correct, TEST 6 is completed. If reading is incorrect, turn ignition off and remove plug connector from hydraulic modulator.

12) Use ohmmeter to measure resistance between terminals No. 5 and 12 in socket on hydraulic modulator. If reading is not .7-1.7 ohms, replace hydraulic modulator. If reading is correct, go to next step.

13) Use ohmmeter to check continuity between terminal No. 5 in plug for hydraulic modulator and terminal No. 18 in plug for ABS control unit. If there is no continuity, repair wiring harness to restore continuity.

TEST 7

All Models

1) To test ABS control unit ground (terminal No. 10), place ABS tester in program switch position No. 7. When button No. 5 lights up, press button. Reading on ABS tester should be 80-300 millivolts. If correct, TEST 7 is completed.

2) If reading is incorrect, turn ignition off. Use ohmmeter to check continuity between terminal No. 10 in plug for ABS contol unit and ground. *See Fig. 5*. If there is no continuity, repair wiring harness to restore continuity.

TEST 8

All Models

1) To test ABS control unit ground (terminal No. 34), place ABS tester in program switch position No. 8. When button No. 5 lights up, press button. Reading on ABS tester should be 30-250 millivolts. If correct, TEST 8 is completed.

2) If reading is incorrect, turn ignition off. Use ohmmeter to check continuity between terminal No. 34 in plug for ABS contol unit and ground. If there is no continuity, repair wiring harness to restore continuity.

TEST 9

All Models

1) To test ABS control unit ground (terminal No. 20), place ABS tester in program switch position No. 9. When button No. 5 lights up, press button. Reading on ABS tester should be 30-250 millivolts. If correct, TEST 9 is completed.

2) If reading is incorrect, turn ignition off. Use ohmmeter to check continuity between terminal No. 20 in plug for ABS contol unit and ground. If there is no continuity, repair wiring harness to restore continuity.

TEST 10

All Models

1) To test left front wheel speed sensor, place ABS tester in program switch position No. 10. Press button No. 8. Resistance reading on ABS tester should be 800-1800 ohms. If correct, go to step **6)**.

2) If reading is incorrect, turn ignition off. Disconnect plug connector for left front wheel speed sensor. Plug is located next to left shock tower. Use ohmmeter to measure speed sensor internal resistance.

3) Speed sensor internal resistance should be 800-1800 ohms. If reading is incorrect, replace speed sensor. If resistance reading is correct, go to next step.

4) Install a jumper wire across speed sensor plug connector terminals. Use ohmmeter to check continuity between terminals No. 4 and 5 (terminals No. 4 and 22 on 5000CS Quattro) in ABS control unit plug. *See Fig. 4*.

5) If there is no continuity, repair wiring harness to restore continuity. After repairs check speed sensor plug connector for continuity. If continuity exists, go to next step.

6) To test right front wheel speed sensor, place ABS tester in program switch position No. 10 and press button No. 9. Resistance reading on ABS tester should be 800-1800 ohms. If correct, go to step **11)**.

7) If reading is incorrect, turn ignition off. Disconnect plug connector for right front wheel speed sensor. Plug is located next to right shock tower. Use ohmmeter to measure speed sensor internal resistance.

8) Speed sensor internal resistance should be 800-1800 ohms. If reading is incorrect, replace speed sensor. If resistance reading is correct, go to next step.

9) Install a jumper wire across speed sensor plug connector terminals. *See Fig. 4*. Use ohmmeter to check continuity between terminals No. 21 and 23 in plug for ABS control unit.

AUDI ANTI-LOCK BRAKE SYSTEM (Cont.)

Fig. 4: Speed Sensor & Speed Sensor Circuit Testing

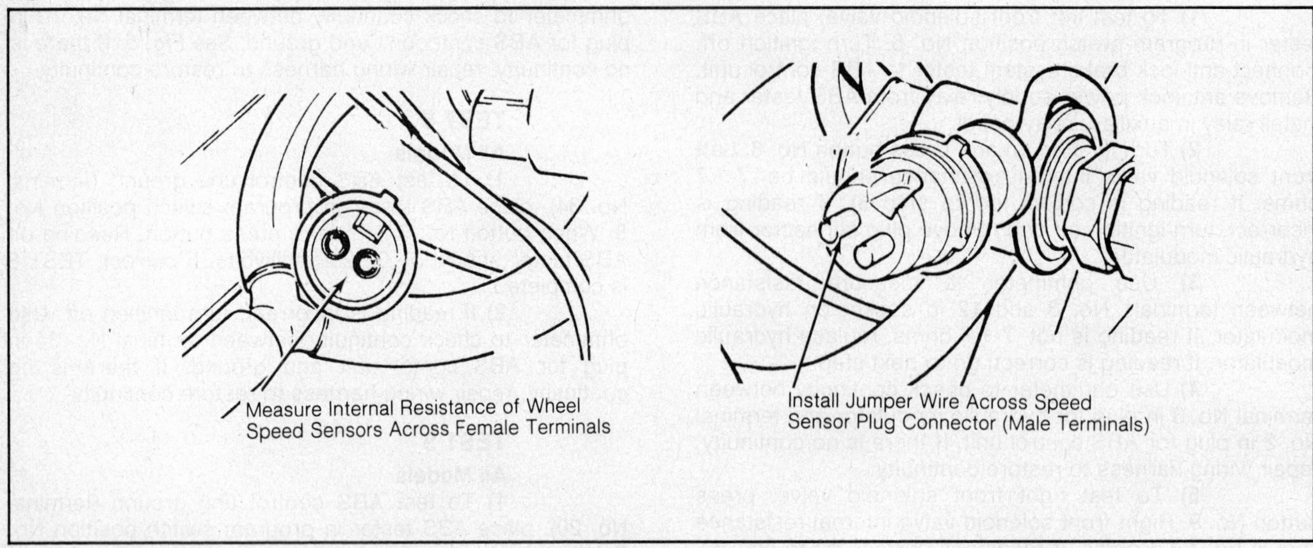
Measure Internal Resistance of Wheel
Speed Sensors Across Female Terminals
Install Jumper Wire Across Speed
Sensor Plug Connector (Male Terminals)

Courtesy of Audi of America, Inc.

10) If there is no continuity, repair wiring harness to restore continuity. After repairs check speed sensor plug connector for continuity. If continuity exists, go to next step.

11) To test left rear wheel speed sensor, place ABS tester in program switch position No. 10 and press button No. 11. Resistance reading on ABS tester should be 800-1800 ohms. If correct, go to step **16)**.

12) If reading is incorrect, turn ignition off. Disconnect plug connector for left rear wheel speed sensor. Plug is located under left rear seat. Use ohmmeter to measure speed sensor internal resistance.

13) Speed sensor internal resistance should be 800-1800 ohms. If reading is incorrect, replace speed sensor. If resistance reading is correct, go to next step.

14) Install a jumper wire across speed sensor plug connector terminals. *See Fig. 4*. Use ohmmeter to check continuity between terminals No. 7 and 9 (terminals No. 8 and 9 on 5000CS Quattro) in plug for ABS control unit.

15) If there is no continuity, repair wiring harness to restore continuity. After repairs check speed sensor plug connector for continuity. If continuity exists, go to next step.

16) To test right rear wheel speed sensor, place ABS tester in program switch position No. 10 and press button No. 12. Resistance reading on ABS tester should be 800-1800 ohms. If correct, TEST 10 is completed.

17) If reading is incorrect, turn ignition off. Disconnect plug connector for left rear wheel speed sensor. Plug is located under left rear seat. Use ohmmeter to measure speed sensor internal resistance.

18) Speed sensor internal resistance should be 800-1800 ohms. If reading is incorrect, replace speed sensor. If resistance reading is correct, go to next step.

19) Install a jumper wire across speed sensor plug connector terminals. Use ohmmeter to check continuity between terminals No. 24 and 26 in plug for ABS control unit. *See Fig. 3*.

20) If there is no continuity, repair wiring harness to restore continuity. After repairs check speed sensor plug connector for continuity.

TEST 11

All Models

1) To test left front wheel speed sensor, place ABS tester in program switch position No. 11. Press button No. 8. Resistance reading on ABS tester should be 20,000-999,000 ohms. If correct, go to step **4)**.

2) If reading is incorrect, turn ignition off. Disconnect plug connector for left front wheel speed sensor. Install a jumper wire across speed sensor plug connector terminals. *See Fig. 4*. Repeat step **1)**.

3) If resistance reading is now correct, replace speed sensor. If resistance reading is still incorrect, check wires going to terminals No. 4 and 5 (terminals No. 4 and 22 on 5000CS Quattro) in plug for ABS control unit for chafing or short to ground. After repairs, go to next step.

4) To test right front wheel speed sensor, place ABS tester in program switch position No. 11 and press button No. 9. Resistance reading on ABS tester should be 20,000-999,000 ohms. If reading is correct, go to step **7)**.

5) If reading is incorrect, turn ignition off. Disconnect plug connector for right front wheel speed sensor. Install a jumper wire across speed sensor plug connector terminals and repeat step **4)**.

6) If resistance reading is now correct, replace speed sensor. If resistance reading is still incorrect, check wires going to terminals No. 21 and 23 in plug for ABS control unit for chafing or short to ground. After repairs, go to next step.

7) To test left rear wheel speed sensor, place ABS tester in program switch position No. 11 and press button No. 11. Resistance reading on ABS tester should be 20,000-999,000 ohms. If correct, go to step **10)**.

8) If reading is incorrect, turn ignition off. Disconnect plug connector for left rear wheel speed sensor. Install a jumper wire across speed sensor plug connector terminals. *See Fig. 4*. Repeat step **7)**.

9) If resistance reading is now correct, replace speed sensor. If resistance reading is still incorrect, check wires going to terminals No. 7 and 9 (terminals No. 8 and 9 on 5000CS Quattro) in plug for ABS control unit for chafing or short to ground. After repairs, go to next step.

AUDI ANTI-LOCK BRAKE SYSTEM (Cont.)

10) To test right rear wheel speed sensor, place ABS tester in program switch position No. 11 and press button No. 12. Resistance reading on ABS tester should be 20,000-999,000 ohms. If correct, TEST 11 is completed.

11) If reading is incorrect, turn ignition off. Disconnect plug connector for right rear wheel speed sensor. Install a jumper wire across speed sensor plug connector terminals and repeat step **10)**.

12) If resistance reading is now correct, replace speed sensor. If resistance reading is still incorrect, check wires going to terminals No. 24 and 26 in plug for ABS control unit for chafing or short to ground.

TEST 12

All Models

1) To test left front wheel speed sensor, place ABS tester in program switch position No. 12. Press button No. 8. Voltage reading on ABS tester should be 0-100 millivolts. If correct, go to step **4)**.

2) If reading is incorrect, turn ignition off. Disconnect plug connector for left front wheel speed sensor. Install a jumper wire across speed sensor plug connector terminals. *See Fig. 4*. Repeat step **1)**.

3) If voltage reading is now correct, replace speed sensor. If reading is still incorrect, check wires going to terminals No. 4 and 5 (terminals No. 4 and 22 on 5000CS Quattro) in plug for ABS control unit for chafing or short to ground. After repairs, go to next step.

4) To test right front wheel speed sensor, place ABS tester in program switch position No. 12 and press button No. 9. Voltage reading on ABS tester should be 0-100 millivolts. If correct, go to step **7)**.

5) If reading is incorrect, turn ignition off. Disconnect plug connector for right front wheel speed sensor. Install a jumper wire across speed sensor plug connector terminals and repeat step **4)**.

6) If voltage reading is now correct, replace speed sensor. If reading is still incorrect, check wires going to terminals No. 21 and 23 in plug for ABS control unit for chafing or short to ground. After repairs, go to next step.

7) To test left rear wheel speed sensor, place ABS tester in program switch position No. 12 and press button No. 11. Voltage reading on ABS tester should be 0-100 millivolts. If correct, go to step **10)**.

8) If reading is incorrect, turn ignition off. Disconnect plug connector for left rear wheel speed sensor. Install a jumper wire across speed sensor plug connector terminals. *See Fig. 4*. Repeat step **7)**.

9) If voltage reading is now correct, replace speed sensor. If reading is still incorrect, check wires going to terminals No. 7 and 9 (terminals No. 8 and 9 on 5000CS Quattro) in plug for ABS control unit for chafing or short to ground. After repairs, go to next step.

10) To test right rear wheel speed sensor, place ABS tester in program switch position No. 12 and press button No. 12. Voltage reading on ABS tester should be 0-100 millivolts. If correct, TEST 12 is completed.

11) If reading is incorrect, turn ignition off. Disconnect plug connector for right rear wheel speed sensor. Install a jumper wire across speed sensor plug connector terminals and repeat step **10)**.

12) If voltage reading is now correct, replace speed sensor. If reading is still incorrect, check wires going to terminals No. 24 and 26 in plug for ABS control unit for chafing or short to ground.

TEST 13

All Models

1) To test ABS contol unit regulated voltage, place ABS tester in program switch position No. 13. When button No. 5 lights up, press button.

2) Voltage reading on ABS tester should be 4.75-5.25 volts. If correct, TEST 13 is completed. If reading is incorrect, replace control unit.

TEST 14

All Models

1) To test hydraulic modulator diode and ABS indicator light, place ABS tester in program switch position No. 14. Voltage reading on ABS tester should be .4-1.5 volts and ABS indicator light in vehicle must be on.

2) If indicator light does not come on or if voltage reading is incorrect, check indicator light and corresponding power supply wire. To do so, turn ignition off.

3) Use ohmmeter to check continuity and contact resistance between terminal No. 10 in plug for hydraulic modulator and terminal No. 29 in plug for ABS control unit. If necessary, repair wiring harness to restore continuity or eliminate contact resistance. After repairs, go to next step.

4) Use ohmmeter to measure continuity between terminals No. 10 and 12 in socket of hydraulic modulator. Note continuity on ohmmeter, and then reverse leads.

5) Ohmmeter must indicate continuity in one direction only. Replace hydraulic modulator if results are incorrect. If okay, turn ignition on and disconnect solenoid valve relay. If indicator light comes on, replace hydraulic modulator.

TEST 15

All Models

1) To test hydraulic modulator diode and ABS indicator light, place ABS tester in program switch position No. 15. Voltage reading on ABS tester should be 2.5-8.5 volts and ABS indicator light must dim slightly.

2) If indicator light does not come on or if voltage reading is incorrect, check indicator light and corresponding power supply wire. To do so, turn ignition off.

3) Use ohmmeter to check continuity and contact resistance between terminal No. 10 in plug for hydraulic modulator and terminal No. 29 in plug for ABS control unit. If necessary, repair wiring harness to restore continuity or eliminate contact resistance. After repairs, go to next step.

4) Use ohmmeter to measure continuity between terminals No. 10 and 12 in socket of hydraulic modulator. Note continuity on ohmmeter, and then reverse leads.

5) Ohmmeter must indicate continuity in one direction only. Replace hydraulic modulator if results are incorrect. If okay, turn ignition on and remove solenoid valve relay. If indicator light comes on, replace hydraulic modulator.

AUDI ANTI-LOCK BRAKE SYSTEM (Cont.)

TEST 16

All Models

1) To test ABS control unit test cycle, place ABS tester in program switch position No. 16. When button No. 5 lights up, press and hold button for at least 3 seconds.

2) When button is depressed, the anti-lock indicator light in vehicle must go out after about one second. Indicator light might flicker as return pump starts.

3) If indicator light does not go out, repeat step **1)** with engine running. If indicator light still does not go out, replace ABS control unit.

TEST 17

All Models

1) To test ABS control unit test cycle with simulated fault, place ABS tester in program switch position No. 17. When button No. 5 lights up, press and hold button for at least 3 seconds.

2) When button is depressed, the anti-lock indicator light in vehicle may flicker but must remain on when button is pressed. If indicator light does not come on, repeat step **1)** with engine running. If indicator light still does not come on, replace ABS control unit.

TEST 18

5000CS Quattro

Program switch position No. 18 (TEST 18) does not apply. Continue ABS testing procedure with TEST 19.

5000S & 5000CS Turbo

1) To test ABS control unit current for left front solenoid valve, place ABS tester in program switch position No. 18 and press button No. 8. When button No. 5 lights up, briefly press button No. 5.

2) Display on ABS tester should be 1.9-2.3 amps when pump motor starts. If correct, go to next step. If reading is incorrect, repeat step **1)** several times with engine running. If reading is still incorrect, replace ABS control unit.

3) To test ABS control unit current for right front solenoid valve, wait for digital display to zero and press button No. 9. When button No. 5 lights up, briefly press button No. 5 and then release.

4) Display on ABS tester should be 1.9-2.3 amps when pump motor starts. If correct, go to next step. If reading is incorrect, repeat step **3)** several times with engine running. If reading is still incorrect, replace ABS control unit.

5) To test ABS control unit current for left rear solenoid valve, wait for digital display to zero and press button No. 11. When button No. 5 lights up, briefly press button No. 5 and then release.

6) Display on ABS tester should be 1.9-2.3 amps when pump motor starts. If correct, go to next step. If reading is incorrect, repeat step **5)** several times with engine running. If reading is still incorrect, replace ABS control unit.

7) To test ABS control unit current for right rear solenoid valve, wait for digital display to zero and press button No. 12. When button No. 5 lights up, briefly press button No. 5 and then release.

8) Display on ABS tester should be 1.9-2.3 amps when pump motor starts. If correct, TEST 18 is completed. If reading is incorrect, repeat step **7)** several times with engine running. If reading is still incorrect, replace ABS control unit.

TEST 19

5000CS Quattro

1) To test ABS control unit control current for left front solenoid valve, place ABS tester in program switch position No. 19. Press button No. 8 and wait for button No. 5 to light up. Press button No. 5, while lit, and then release.

2) Pump motor should start up 2 times. Display on ABS tester should read 4.5-6.1 amps after a few seconds. If correct, go to next step. If incorrect, repeat step **1)** several times with engine running. If reading is still incorrect, replace ABS control unit.

3) To test ABS control unit control current for right front solenoid valve, wait for digital display to zero. Press button No. 9 and wait for button No. 5 to light up. Press button No. 5, while lit, and then release.

4) Pump motor should start up 2 times. Display on ABS tester should read 4.5-6.1 amps after a few seconds. If correct, go to next step. If incorrect, repeat step **3)** several times with engine running. If reading is still incorrect, replace ABS control unit.

5) To test ABS control unit control current for left rear solenoid valve, wait for digital display to zero. Press button No. 9 and wait for button No. 5 to light up. Press button No. 5, while lit, and then release.

6) Pump motor should start up 2 times. Display on ABS tester should read 4.5-6.1 amps after a few seconds. If correct, TEST 19 is completed. If incorrect, repeat step **5)** several times with engine running. If reading is still incorrect, replace ABS control unit.

NOTE: On 5000CS Quattro, after TEST 19 is completed, perform TEST 24. Perform TEST 24 before TEST 23.

5000S & 5000CS Turbo

1) To test ABS control unit control current for left front solenoid valve, place ABS tester in program switch position No. 19. Press button No. 8 and wait for button No. 5 to light up. Press button No. 5, while lit, and then release.

2) Pump motor should start up 2 times. Display on ABS tester should read 4.5-6.1 amps after a few seconds. If correct, go to next step. If incorrect, repeat step **1)** several times with engine running. If reading is still incorrect, replace ABS control unit.

3) To test ABS control unit control current for right front solenoid valve, wait for digital display to zero. Press button No. 9 and wait for button No. 5 to light up. Press button No. 5, while lit, and then release.

4) Pump motor should start up 2 times. Display on ABS tester should read 4.5-6.1 amps after a few seconds. If correct, go to next step. If incorrect, repeat step **3)** several times with engine running. If reading is still incorrect, replace ABS control unit.

5) To test ABS control unit control current for left rear solenoid valve, wait for digital display to zero. Press button No. 11 and wait for button No. 5 to light up. Press button No. 5, while lit, and then release.

6) Pump motor should start up 2 times. Display on ABS tester should read 4.5-6.1 amps after a few seconds. If correct, go to next step. If incorrect, repeat step **5)** several times with engine running. If reading is still incorrect, replace ABS control unit.

AUDI ANTI-LOCK BRAKE SYSTEM (Cont.)

7) To test ABS control unit control current for right rear solenoid valve, wait for digital display to zero. Press button No. 12 and wait for button No. 5 to light up. Press button No. 5, while lit, and then release.

8) Pump motor should start up 2 times. Display on ABS tester should read 4.5-6.1 amps after a few seconds. If correct, TEST 19 is completed. If incorrect, repeat step **7)** several times with engine running. If reading is still incorrect, replace ABS control unit.

NOTE: **On 5000S and 5000CS Turbo, after TEST 19 is completed, perform TEST 24. TEST 24 must be performed before TEST 23.**

TEST 20, 21 & 22

All Models

Program switch positions No. 20, 21 and 22 (TEST 20, 21 and 22) are not used.

TEST 23

All Models

1) To test left front wheel speed sensor signal, raise vehicle on hoist until all 4 wheels are free to rotate. Release parking brake. On 5000CS Quattro, disengage differential locks. On all models, place gear selector lever in Neutral.

2) Place ABS tester in program switch position No. 23. Press button No. 8. Spin left front wheel by hand at about one revolution per minute. As wheel is being rotated, note voltage reading on ABS tester.

3) Voltage reading on tester should be between 1.7-19 volts. If voltage varies, use lowest value obtained. If reading is close to 1.7 volts, check speed sensor (PVC tip) air gap. See SPEED SENSOR under REMOVAL & INSTALLATION.

4) If reading is below 1.7 volts (except zero), replace speed sensor. If voltage reading is zero volts, check speed sensor wiring for damage, open circuits, or reversed leads. *See Fig. 5, 6 or 7*.

5) If reading on ABS tester is 999 volts, wheel is being spun too fast. Rotate tire at a lower speed and repeat test. If reading is correct, go to next step.

6) To test right front wheel speed sensor signal, press button No. 9. Spin right front wheel by hand at about one revolution per minute. As wheel is being rotated, note voltage reading on ABS tester. If voltage reading is correct, go to next step. If reading is incorrect, use steps **3)** through **5)** to determine corrective action.

7) To test left rear wheel speed sensor signal, press button No. 11. Spin left rear wheel by hand at about one revolution per minute. As wheel is being rotated, note voltage reading on ABS tester. If voltage reading is correct, go to next step. If reading is incorrect, use steps **3)** through **5)** to determine corrective action.

8) To test right rear wheel speed sensor signal, press button No. 12. Spin right rear wheel by hand at about one revolution per minute. As wheel is being rotated, note voltage reading on ABS tester. If voltage reading is correct, go to FINAL CHECK. If voltage reading is incorrect, use steps **3)** through **5)** to determine corrective action.

NOTE: **If fault in ABS system has not been determined by the time TEST 23 has been carried out, replace hydraulic modulator.**

TEST 24

All Models

1) To test stoplight switch, depress brake pedal. Voltage reading on ABS tester should be 10.3-14.5 volts. If reading is incorrect, check plug connector for stoplight switch.

2) Disconnect plug connector for stoplight switch and install a jumper wire across connector. Repeat step **1)**. If voltage reading is now correct, replace stoplight switch.

3) If reading is still incorrect, check wires to stoplight switch for voltage and terminal No. 25 in ABS control unit for continuity. *See Fig. 5, 6 or 7*. Turn ignition off before disconnecting control unit. If wires are okay, replace ABS control unit.

FINAL CHECK

All Models

1) Remove test equipment and prepare ABS system for normal operation. Start engine and observe anti-lock brake system indicator light in vehicle. Indicator light must go out. While engine is running, actuate switch for ABS system. Indicator light must come on.

2) Turn ignition off and restart engine. Indicator light must go out. Drive vehicle above 20 miles per hour. Anti-lock brake system indicator light must come on.

NOTE: **On 5000CS Quattro, if the center and/or rear differential lock is engaged, the ABS indicator light must come on.**

REMOVAL & INSTALLATION

ANTI-LOCK BRAKE SYSTEM (ABS) CONTROL UNIT

Removal & Installation

Ensure ignition is off. Press spring on ABS control unit connector to release plug from unit. Remove connector from ABS control unit. Remove rear seat cushion. Unplug electrical connector. Remove bolts and ABS control unit.

HYDRAULIC MODULATOR

Removal & Installation

Disconnect brake lines from master cylinder. Disconnect hydraulic modulator from mounts. Remove wiring harness retainer and disconnect ground wire. Remove hydraulic modulator. To install, reverse removal procedure.

FRONT SPEED SENSOR

Removal & Installation

1) Remove speed sensor retaining bolt. Pull speed sensor out of wheel bearing housing. Remove wiring harness from body and unplug from nearest connector. One connector is located behind windshield washer reservoir.

2) To install, reverse removal procedure. Install new "O" ring and PVC tip on sensor. Tip ensures proper air gap between sensor and rotor. Install sensor in housing until PCV tip touches rotor.

3) Install and tighten retaining bolt to 86 INCH lbs. (10 N.m). Install rubber grommets in retainers on wheel bearing housing. Fasten wiring harness clips to body. Plug in speed sensor connector.

AUDI ANTI-LOCK BRAKE SYSTEM (Cont).

REAR SPEED SENSOR

Removal & Installation (5000CS Quattro)

1) Remove bolt securing speed sensor. Remove wiring harness from clip on lower control arm. Remove speed sensor. Remove wiring harness from body and unplug from nearest connector.

2) To install, reverse removal procedure. Install new "O" ring and PVC tip on sensor. Tip ensures proper air gap between sensor and rotor. Install sensor in housing until PCV tip touches rotor.

3) Install and tighten retaining bolt to 86 INCH lbs. (10 N.m). Fasten wiring harness clips to body. Plug in speed sensor connector.

Removal & Installation (5000S & 5000CS Turbo)

1) Press parking brake cable spacer off rear axle flange. Remove bolt securing speed sensor. Remove wiring harness from clip on lower control arm. Remove speed sensor.

2) Remove wiring harness from body and unplug from nearest connector. Let rear wheel speed sensor connector is located under rear seat. Right rear wheel speed sensor connector is located beneath central locking system pump (under rear seat).

3) To install, reverse removal procedure. Lubricate new speed sensor "O" ring with brake lubricant and install on sensor. Install PVC tip on sensor. Tip ensures proper air gap between sensor and rotor.

4) Install sensor in housing until PCV tip touches rotor. Install and tighten retaining bolt to 86 INCH lbs. (10 N.m). Fasten wiring harness to clip on lower control arm. Plug in speed sensor connector.

Fig. 5: Audi 5000S ABS Wiring Diagram

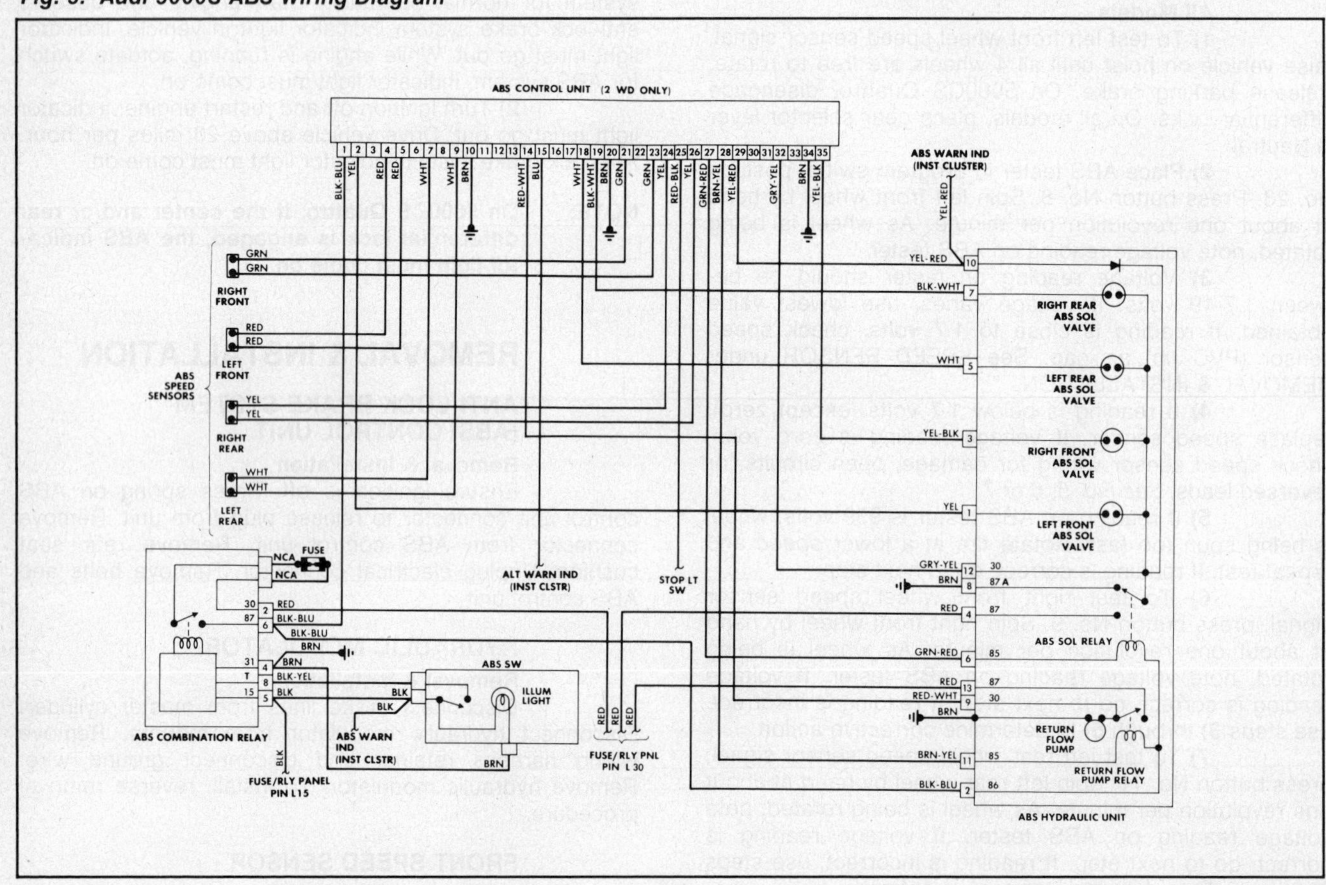

AUDI ANTI-LOCK BRAKE SYSTEM (Cont).

Fig. 6: Audi 5000CS & Quattro (Non-Turbo) ABS Wiring Diagram

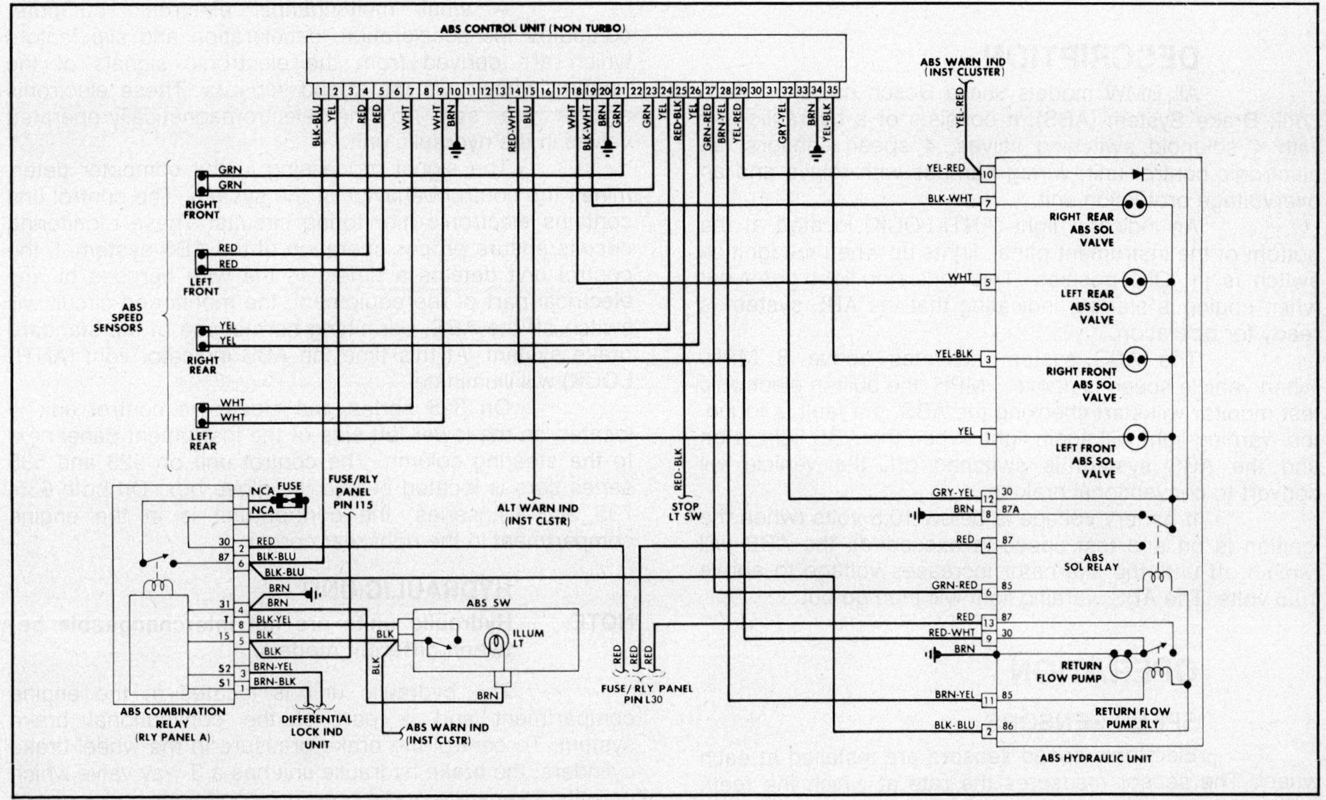

Fig. 7: Audi 5000CS & Quattro (Turbo) ABS Wiring Diagram

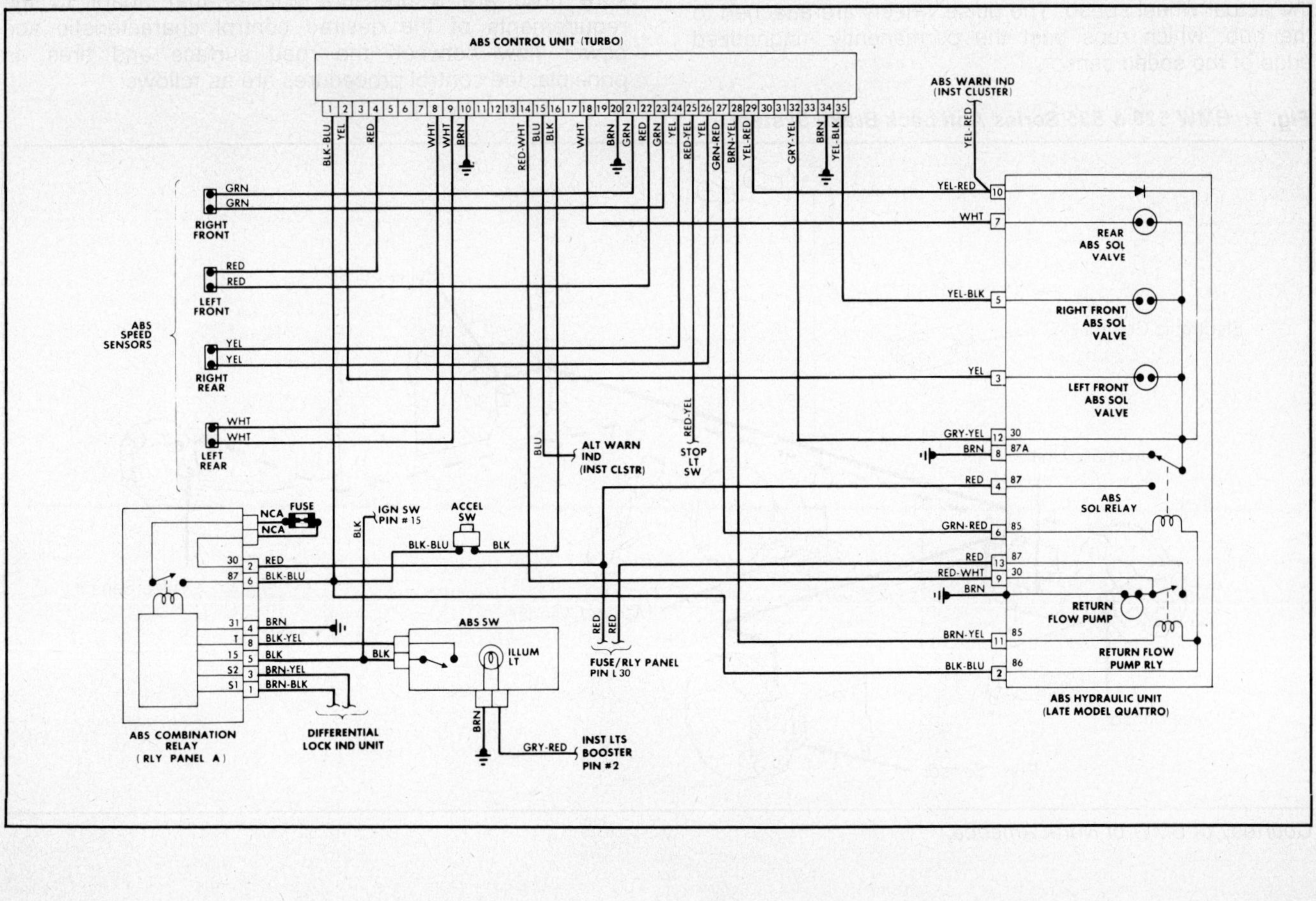

BMW ANTI-LOCK BRAKE SYSTEM

All Models

DESCRIPTION

All BMW models use a Bosch designed Anti-Lock Brake System (ABS). It consists of a hydraulic unit with 4 solenoid switching valves, 4 speed sensors, an electronic control unit, wiring harness with relays and an overvoltage protection unit.

An indicator light (ANTI-LOCK) located at the bottom of the instrument panel, lights up when the ignition switch is in "ON" position. This indicator light goes out when engine is started, indicating that the ABS system is ready for operation.

The ABS system activates above 8 MPH. When vehicle speed is above 3 MPH, the built-in electronic test monitor will start checking the ABS. If a fault is found, the warning light will again light. When the ABS light is on and the ABS system is switched off, the vehicle wil convert to conventional braking.

If battery voltage is below 10.5 volts (when the ignition is on and test speed is exceeded), the ABS will remain off until the alternator increases voltage to above 10.5 volts. The ABS warning light will then go out.

OPERATION

SPEED SENSORS

Electronic speed sensors are installed at each wheel. The sensor measures the rate at which the teeth on a pulse wheel pass before it. The sensor in turn relays this signal to the electronic control unit which computes the actual wheel speed. The pulse wheels are attached to the hub, which runs past the permanently magnetized edge of the speed sensor.

ELECTRONIC CONTROL UNIT

A small multi-channel electronic computer computes the acceleration, deceleration and slip factors which are derived from the electronic signals of the rotating wheels via the speed sensors. These electronic signals are sent to the electromagnetically-operated valves in the hydraulic unit.

The signal processing in the computer determines the control behavior of the system. The control unit contains electronic monitoring circuits. These monitoring circuits ensure proper operation of the ABS system. If the control unit detects a defect in the wire harness or any electrical part of the equipment, the monitoring circuit will switch off the ABS, permitting normal use of the standard brake system. At this time the ABS indicator light (ANTI-LOCK) will illuminate.

On 325 series, the electronic control unit is located on the lower left side of the instrument panel next to the steering column. The control unit on 528 and 535 series cars is located behind the glove box. On both 635, 735 and L7 series, the control unit is in the engine compartment in the right rear corner.

HYDRAULIC UNIT

NOTE: **Hydraulic units are not interchangeable between different models.**

The hydraulic unit is located in the engine compartment and is part of the conventional brake system. To control the brake pressure in the wheel brake cylinders, the brake hydraulic unit has a 3-way valve which permits 3 separate brake pressure conditions.

Pressure build-up, pressure holding and pressure drop are 3 pressure phases that adapt to the requirements of the desired control characteristic and power flow between the road surface and tires. In principle, the control procedures are as follows:

Fig. 1: BMW 528 & 535 Series Anti-Lock Brake System

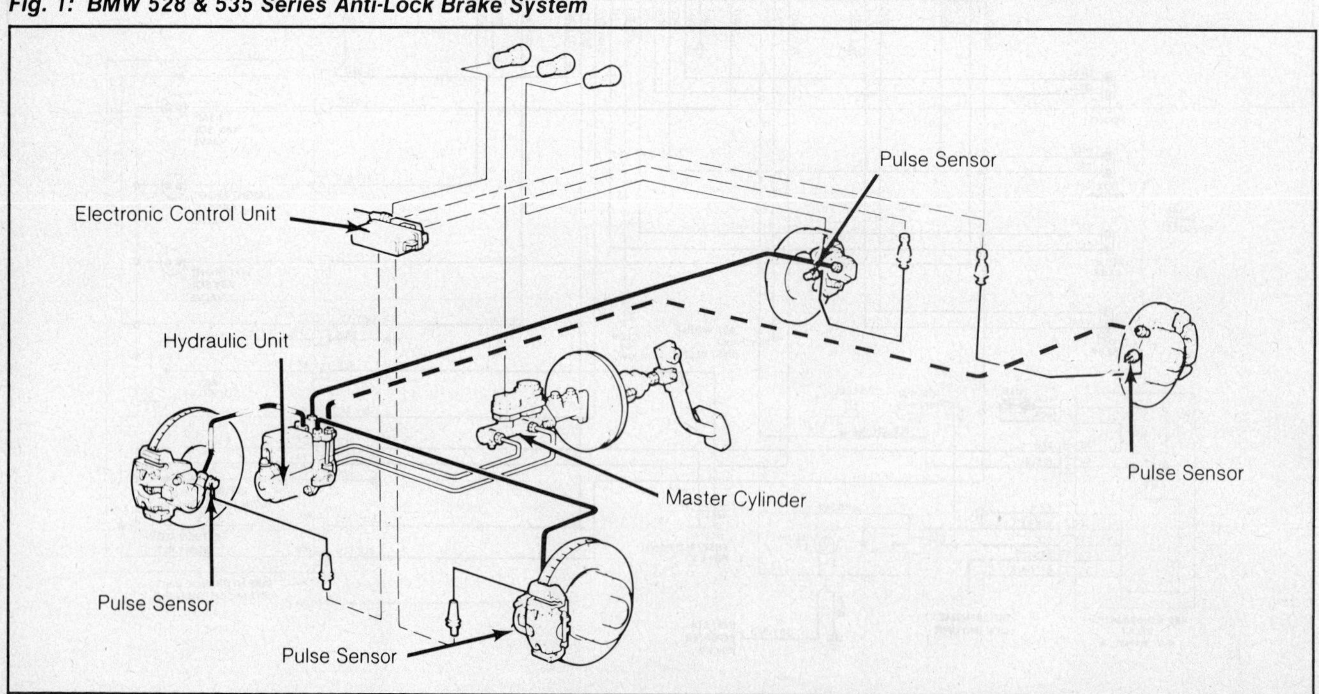

Courtesy of BMW of North America.

BMW ANTI-LOCK BRAKE SYSTEM (Cont.)

Fig. 2: BMW 735 & L7 Series Anti-Lock Brake System

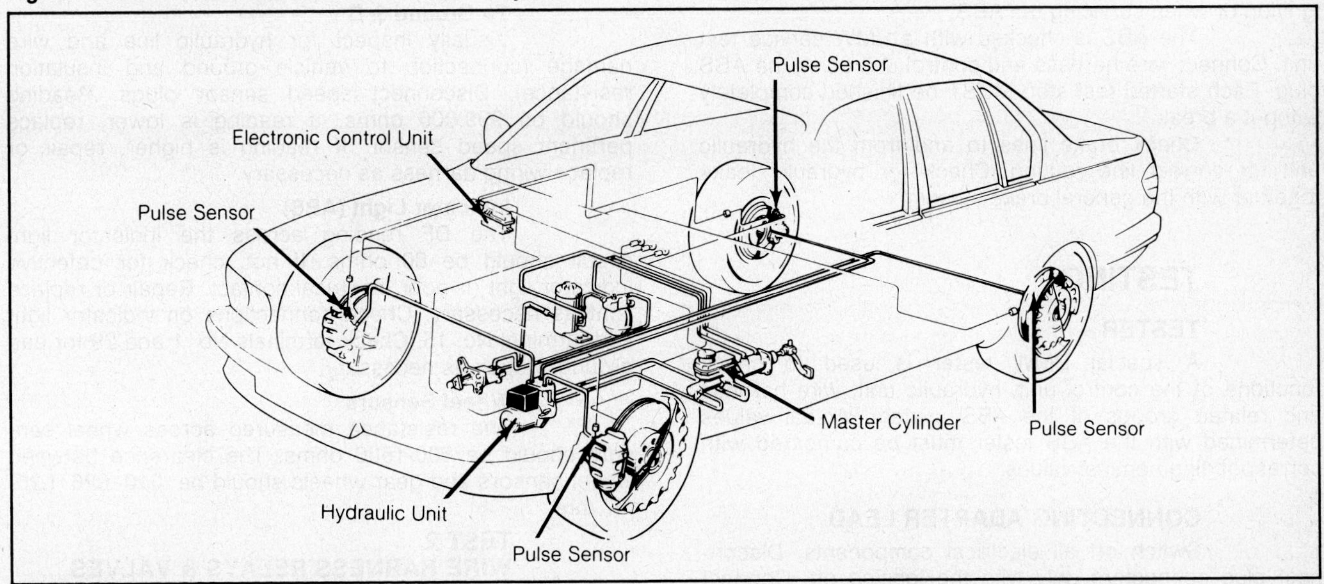

Courtesy of BMW of North America.

As soon as wheel deceleration or slip indicates the locking of a wheel, the brake pressure is first held. If the wheel still tends to lock, the pressure will be dropped as long as the wheel acceleration or the slip limit is exceeded. Afterward, the pressure is raised again and the control phases begin anew. These pressure changes occur in milliseconds.

An electrically-driven return delivery pump returns the brake fluid from the wheel brake cylinder while dropping the pressure to an appropriate brake circuit. The pump is designed as a 2 piston pump, so that the circuits of a dual brake circuit system remain fully separated.

Two relays are located under the cover of the hydraulic control unit: an engine relay and a valve relay. The engine relay is the larger of the two.

REPAIR PRECAUTIONS

Always remove plugs from electronic control unit and turn off ignition when using an electric arc welder on the vehicle. If the vehicle is painted, the electronic control unit is capable of withstanding a temperature of 185°F (85°C) for about 2 hours. Battery terminals must always be clean and tight. BMW recommends testing the ABS with a BMW service tester whenever any major repairs are performed on the brake system.

CHECKING ABS FUNCTION

An electronic circuit in the control unit constantly monitors the ABS. The ABS must be checked when the ABS indicator light does not go out, comes on

Fig. 3: BMW Anti-Lock Brake Logic System

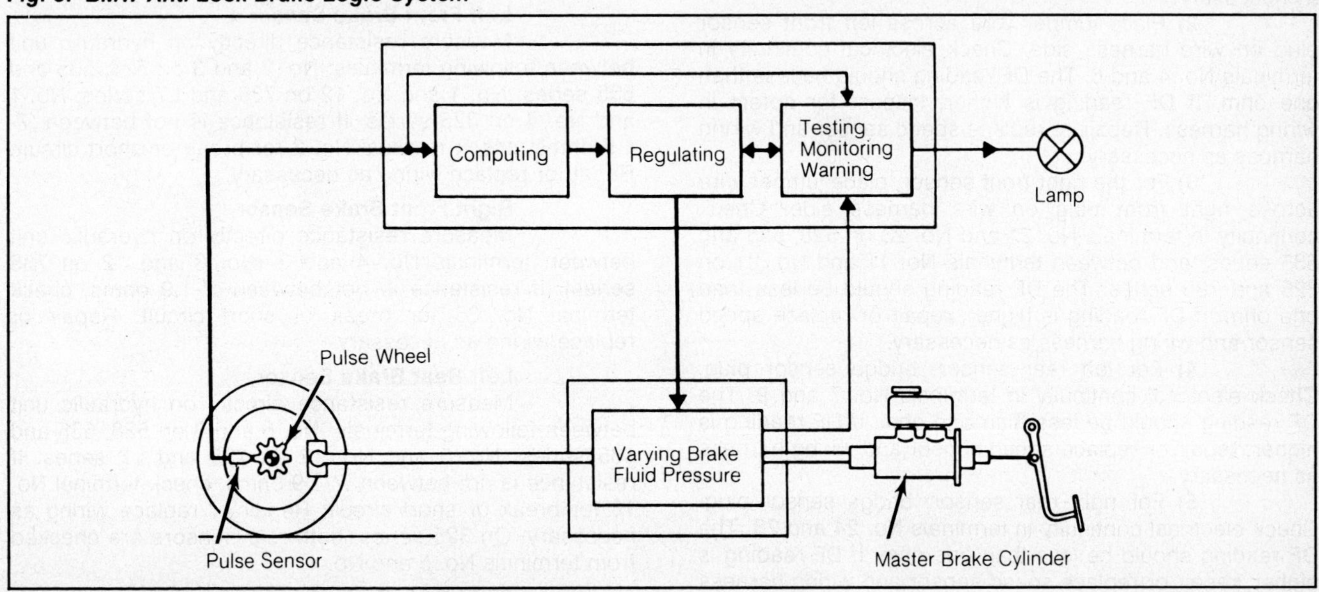

Courtesy of BMW of North America.

BMW ANTI-LOCK BRAKE SYSTEM (Cont.)

while driving, does not come on when turning on the ignition or when servicing the ABS.

The ABS is checked with a BMW service test unit. Connect wire harness and control unit using the ABS plug. Each started test step MUST be finished completely without a break.

Check brake lines to and from the hydraulic unit for correct line routing. Check for hydraulic leaks together with the general brake system.

TESTING

TESTER

A special BMW tester is used to check functions of the control unit, hydraulic unit, wire harness and related groups of the ABS system. Actual values determined with the ABS tester must be compared with corresponding nominal values.

CONNECTING ADAPTER LEAD

Switch off all electrical components. Disconnect plug connectors only with the ignition off. Connect ABS adapter between "T" plug and control unit only for TESTS 6 and 7. Note other connections and switch position for each test step. Note correct test sequence for each test step.

TEST 1
WIRE HARNESS
SPEED SENSORS

NOTE: **TESTS 8 through 10 require a Bosch ABS brake dyno. TESTS 1 through 7 can be performed without a brake dyno.**

Basic Test

1) With the control unit not connected and the ignition off, perform single test. Visually check left front plug connection. The speed sensor (DF) reading must read 999,000 ohms. If DF reading is lower, inspect for defect in wiring harness. Repair or replace wiring harness as necessary.

2) Place jumper wire across left front sensor plug on wire harness side. Check electrical continuity in terminals No. 4 and 6. The DF reading should be less than one ohm. If DF reading is higher, inspect for defect in wiring harness. Repair or replace speed sensor and wiring harness as necessary.

3) For the right front sensor, place jumper wire across right front plug on wire harness side. Check continuity in terminals No. 21 and No. 23 on 528, 535 and 635 series, and between terminals No. 11 and No. 21 on 325 and 735 series. The DF reading should be less than one ohm. If DF reading is higher, repair or replace speed sensor and wiring harness as necessary.

4) For left rear sensor, bridge sensor plug. Check electrical continuity in terminals No. 7 and 9. The DF reading should be less than one ohm. If DF reading is higher, repair or replace speed sensor and wiring harness as necessary.

5) For right rear sensor, bridge sensor plug. Check electrical continuity in terminals No. 24 and 26. The DF reading should be less than one ohm. If DF reading is higher, repair or replace speed sensor and wiring harness as necessary.

Speed Sensor Resistance To Ground & B+

Visually inspect for hydraulic line and wire damage (connection to vehicle ground and insulation resistance). Disconnect speed sensor plugs. Reading should be 999,000 ohms. If reading is lower, replace pertinent speed sensor. If reading is higher, repair or replace wiring harness as necessary.

Indicator Light (ABS)

The DF reading across the indicator light circuit should be 80 ohms. If not, check for defective indicator light or poor electrical contact. Repair or replace light as necessary. Check connections on indicator light and terminal No. 15. Check terminals No. 1 and 29 for bad ground. Repair as necessary.

Wheel Sensors

The resistance measured across wheel sensors should be 600-1600 ohms. The clearance between wheel sensors and gear wheels should be .010-.026" (.25-.67 mm).

TEST 2
WIRE HARNESS RELAYS & VALVES

NOTE: **Turn off ignition and disconnect control unit.**

Valve Relay Coil Resistance

Check plug connections on hydraulic unit (plugs and relays). If plug connectors are defective, replace as necessary. Check wiring from ignition switch terminal No. 27 to hydraulic unit. If reading is more than 100 ohms, check for break in wire to valve relay. If reading is 50 ohms or less, check for short circuit in wire to valve relay.

Motor Relay Coil Resistance

Motor coil resistance should be 34-58 ohms. If not, check plug connections on hydraulic unit. Repair or replace motor relay as necessary. Check wiring from terminal No. 28 at ignition switch to hydraulic unit. If reading is 58 ohms or more, check for break in wiring. If reading is 34 ohms or less, check for short circuit in wire to motor relay. Repair or replace wiring as necessary.

Left Front Brake Sensor

Measure resistance directly on hydraulic unit between following terminals: No. 2 and 3 on 528, 535 and 635 series; No. 1 and No. 12 on 735 and L7 series; No. 1 and No. 4 on 325 series. If resistance is not between .7-1.9 ohms, check terminal No. 2 for break or short circuit. Repair or replace wiring as necessary.

Right Front Brake Sensor

Measure resistance directly on hydraulic unit between terminals No. 4 and 3 (No. 3 and 12 on 735 series). If resistance is not between .7-1.9 ohms, check terminal No. 35 for break or short circuit. Repair or replace wiring as necessary.

Left Rear Brake Sensor

Measure resistance directly on hydraulic unit between following terminals: No. 6 and 3 on 528, 535 and 635 series; No. 5 and No. 12 on 735 and L7 series. If resistance is not between .7-1.9 ohms, check terminal No. 18 for break or short circuit. Repair or replace wiring as necessary. On 325 series, both rear sensors are checked from terminals No. 5 and No. 4.

Right Rear Brake Sensor

Measure resistance directly on hydraulic unit between following terminals: No. 8 and 3 on 528, 535 and

BMW ANTI-LOCK BRAKE SYSTEM (Cont.)

635 series; No. 7 and No. 12 on 735 series. If resistance is not between .7-1.9 ohms, check terminal No. 19 for break or short circuit. Repair or replace wiring as necessary.

TEST 3
DYNAMIC SPEED SENSOR

1) Connect "T" plug with adapter A at ABS terminal harness and control unit. Connect lead to adapter A; Red light should come on. Plug in overvoltage relay. Switch to position 3 on adapter. Raise vehicle and turn wheels at steady speed within the nominal periods (15.7-17.4 milliseconds) until 100% appears.

2) If the nominal values are not reached, check that wheel rotation is uniform. Check for dirt between pulse wheel and sensor. Check pulse wheel teeth condition. Check clearance between speed sensor and pulse wheel. Repair or replace pulse wheel as necessary.

TEST 4
DYNAMIC VOLTAGE

Voltage Between Terminals No. 1 & No. 10

Start engine. Check for proper battery voltage (11.7-13.5 volts). Check voltage between terminals No. 1 and No. 10. Reading should be above 11.5 volts. Check for voltage drop at battery positive terminal, terminal No. 15 and from ignition switch to control unit terminal No. 1. Reading should be 11.5 volts. If nominal values are not reached, check battery voltage, break or short circuit in wiring and brake switch. Repair or replace components as necessary.

Voltage Between Terminals No. 10 & No. 12

Check voltage between terminals No. 10 and No. 12. Reading should be between 4.8-5.2 volts. If nominal values are not reached, replace control unit.

Valve Relay Contact Voltage Drop

Check voltage drop between terminals No. 32 and No. 10. Reading should be 10.8 volts. If nominal value is not reached, check ground connection for excessive resistance or a break in the wiring.

Valve Relay Opening Voltage Drop

Check current in following terminals:

- On 528, 535 and 635 series, from terminal No. 7 from B+ to hydraulic unit plug. On 325, 735 and L7 series, check terminal No. 6.
- On 528, 535 and 635 series, from terminal No. 7 to valve relay terminal No. 87. On 325, 735 and L7 series, check terminal No. 6.
- On 528, 535 and 635 series, from terminal No. 5 to multiple pin plug (control unit) terminal No. 27. On 325 series, check terminal No. 2. On 735 and L7 series, check terminal No. 6.
- On 528, 535 and 635 series, from hydraulic unit terminal No. 5 to valve relay terminal No. 85. On 325 series, check terminal No. 2. On 735 and L7 series, check terminal No. 6.
- On 528, 535 and 635 series, from terminal No. 86 (valve relay) to terminal No. 86 (motor relay) and terminal No. 11. On 325 series, check terminal No. 10. On 735 and L7 series, check terminal No. 2.
- On 528, 535 and 635 series, from hydraulic unit terminal No. 11 to ignition switch terminal No. 15. On 735 and L7 series, check terminal No. 2. On 325 series, check from hydraulic unit terminal No. 10 to electronic relay terminal No. 30 or 30A.

If current is not at least 10.8 volts, replace valve relay.

Motor Relay Voltage Drop

Check ground terminals for tightness and voltage resistance. Check current in following terminals:

- From terminal B+ to plug hydraulic unit terminal No. 13.
- From multiple pin plug (control unit) terminal No. 14 to hydraulic unit plug.
- From terminal No. 10 (terminal No. 9 on 325 and 735 series) in hydraulic unit to motor relay terminal No. 30 and positive terminal on pump motor.

Voltage drop should not exceed one volt. If nominal values are not reached, replace hydraulic unit.

Safety Circuit & Indicator Light Diode

1) Check terminal No. 29 from multiple pin plug (control unit) to hydraulic unit plug terminal No. 44 for break and voltage drop. Check plug connection on indicator light. Check that valve relay is plugged in. Pull off hydraulic unit plug.

2) Test diode between terminals No. 1 and No. 3 on 528, 535 and 635 series. On 325 series, check between terminals No. 7 and No. 4. On 735 series, check between terminals No. 10 and No. 12. There should be no more than a .3-1.6 voltage drop. If nominal values are not reached, replace hydraulic unit.

TEST 5
GROUND & OVERVOLTAGE PROTECTOR

1) With engine running, check battery voltage. If okay, check connection in glove box. Check flow of multiple pin plug on wire harness (control unit) terminal No. 10 to ground connection.

2) Check ground connection in glove box. Check flow of multiple pin plug on control unit wire harness (terminal No. 20) to ground connection. Check ground connection in glove box. Check flow of multiple pin plug on the control unit wire harness (terminal No. 34) to ground connection.

3) Check ground connection on battery console. Check ground connection on return delivery pump. Check current in ground wire (no more than .7 voltage drop). Check current in multiple pin plug on the control unit wire harness (terminal No. 14) to plug on hydraulic unit and terminal No. 10 (terminal No. 9 on 325, 735 and L7 series) to terminal. Check terminal No. 87 in hydraulic unit. If there is a power flow break, replace wire harness. If current flow is okay, replace hydraulic unit.

4) If current flow is acceptable at the overvoltage protection relay, replace the control unit. If the motor relay only switches (clicks) at intervals without the pump motor running, the voltage will briefly drop excessively at the feed wires from the battery due to the high power load during switching. Repeat test with engine running. If test is not okay, replace the control unit.

TEST 6
CONTROL UNIT SIMULATION (FRONT WHEELS)

1) With engine running, check battery voltage. If battery voltage is more than 11.5 volts, check voltage between terminals No. 1 and No. 10.

2) Check left and right front solenoid pressure build-up, drop and retention (should not deviate more than .1%). If not okay, replace control unit and repeat test step.

3) If control valves do not switch or the pressure pump does not run in TESTS 8, 9 and 10, replace hydraulic unit.

BMW ANTI-LOCK BRAKE SYSTEM (Cont.)

TEST 7
CONTROL UNIT SIMULATION
(REAR WHEELS)

1) With engine running, check battery voltage. If battery voltage is more than 11.5 volts, check voltage between terminals No. 1 and No. 10.

2) Check left and right rear solenoid pressure build-up, drop and retention. Pressure drop should be no more than 4.5-5.7% and pressure retention should not deviate more than 1.9-2.3%. Due to high power draw during switching, test with engine running. If not okay, replace control unit and repeat test step.

3) If control valves do not switch or the pressure pump does not run in TESTS 8, 9 and 10, replace hydraulic unit.

TEST 8
ABS RETURN DELIVERY PUMP

NOTE: This test requires the use of a brake dyno (BPS).

1) The following connections will be needed: "T" plug with adapter A at ABS harness, lead 1 connected at ABS control unit and lead 2 connected at adapter A (Red light comes on).

2) Place front axle on BPS (dyno). Ensure tester is flashing for left front. Switch on ignition and check voltage between leads 1 and 10 (if necessary, run engine at idle speed). Voltage should be more than 11.5 volts. Switch on BPS.

3) Apply brakes until BPS reading is about 337 lbs. (1500 N) and charge axle if necessary. Maintain a steady pedal force. Press ABS test button. After about 5 seconds, valve will cut in briefly. After about 4 seconds, pressure pump cuts in briefly after display appears and brake dyno reading drops again. After about 3 seconds, terminate measurement reading by pressing test button again.

4) The display reading on the BPS should be about 337 lbs. (1500 N) for front brakes and 270 lbs. (1200 N) for rear brakes. Display for a controlled wheel will be about 67 lbs. (300 N) for front and rear brakes. After about 3 seconds, press test button. Display should be about 337 lbs. (1500 N) for front brakes and 270 lbs. (1200 N) for rear brakes.

5) If nominal values are not reached, check battery voltage and hydraulic unit. Check for mixed-up brake lines on the hydraulic unit. Replace hydraulic unit if necessary.

TEST 9
HYDRAULIC PRESSURE RELEASE

NOTE: This test requires the use of a brake dyno (BPS).

1) The following connections will be needed: "T" plug with adapter A at ABS harness, lead 1 connected at ABS control unit and lead 2 is connected at adapter A (Red light comes on).

2) Place front axle on BPS (tester should flash for left front brake). Switch on ignition. Check voltage between leads 1 and 10 (if necessary, run engine at idle speed). There should be 11.5 volts. Switch on BPS.

3) The BPS display should be about 450 lbs. (2000 N) for the front and 337 lbs. (1500 N) for the rear. There should be no more than a 45 lbs. (400 N) differential between front and rear brakes. The display reading for front brakes should drop between 90-225 lbs. (400-1000 N) and rear brakes should drop between 90-180 lbs. (300-800 N). With pedal force unchanged, the BPS display must not change by more than 67 lbs. (300 N) within 3 seconds.

4) If nominal values are not reached, check battery voltage and repeat TESTS 5, 6 and 7. Check hydraulic unit. Repair or replace components as necessary. *See Fig. 4.*

Fig. 4: Hydraulic Pressure Reduction Diagram

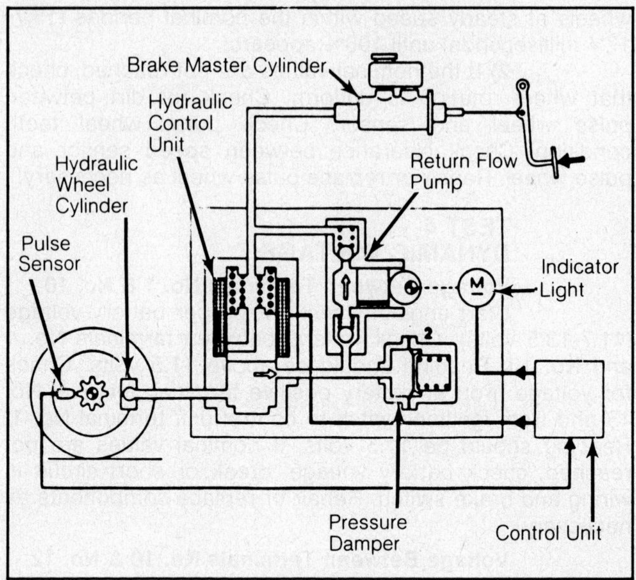

Courtesy of BMW of North America.

TEST 10
HYDRAULIC UNIT
PRESSURE BUILD-UP

1) The following connections will be needed: "T" plug with adapter A at ABS harness with lead 1 connected at ABS control unit and lead 2 connected at adapter A (Red light comes on).

Fig. 5: Hydraulic Pressure Build-Up Diagram

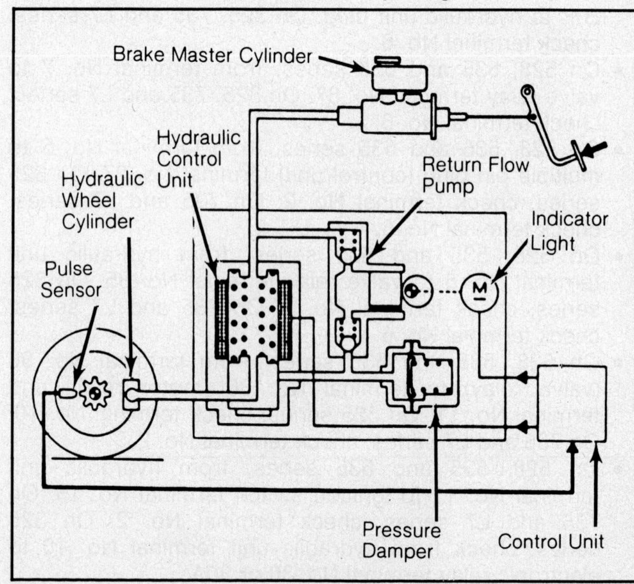

Courtesy of BMW of North America.

BMW ANTI-LOCK BRAKE SYSTEM (Cont.)

2) Place front axle on BPS. Tester should be flashing for left front brake. Switch on ignition. Check voltage between leads 1 and 10 (if necessary, run engine at idle speed). Switch on BPS.

3) Apply brakes until BPS reading is about 337 lbs. (1500 N) and maintain a steady pedal force. Press BPS test button. After about 2 seconds, hydraulic pump will come on and control valve will be opened for about 4 seconds. The control valve will then move to retention phase after a short period of pressure build-up. The display will start to run. When 5 seconds are displayed, press test button.

4) If nominal values are not reached, check battery. Check hydraulic unit. Repair or replace components as necessary. *See Fig. 5.*

REMOVAL & INSTALLATION

HYDRAULIC UNIT

Removal

1) Do not mix up brake lines when replacing hydraulic control unit. Brake lines connect to hydraulic unit as follows:

- VL – To left front brake caliper.
- VR – To right front brake caliper.
- HL – To left rear brake caliper.
- HR – To right rear brake caliper.

Connect battery ground lead. Remove coolant expansion tank on 635 series. On all series, remove left and right front, left and right rear brake lines.

2) Remove brake lines from master cylinder. Remove bolts for hydraulic unit. Pull off multiple pin plug and disconnect ground wire. Pull up front of hydraulic unit and disconnect rear. Remove hydraulic unit from vehicle.

Installation

To install hydraulic unit, reverse removal procedure. Check code number when replacing hydraulic unit. Bleed brakes. Check ABS function with test unit. See TESTING in this article.

CONTROL UNIT

NOTE: **On 325 series, the electronic control unit is located on the lower left side of the instrument panel next to the steering column. The control unit on 528 and 535 series cars is located behind the glove box. On both 635, 735 and L7 series, the control unit is in the engine compartment in the right rear corner.**

Removal

1) With ignition off, remove multiple pin cover from control unit. Push back retaining clamp and pull out multiple pin plug to the right and then disconnect to the left.

2) Detach control unit on body. When replacing control unit, check for correct connection and control unit number.

Installation

To install control unit, reverse removal procedure. First connect left side of plug and then press right side into clamp. Check ABS function. See TESTING in this article.

WIRE HARNESS

Removal

1) Disconnect battery connections. Disconnect ground lead on body. Unscrew wire clamps on body and wire clip on heater wall. Disconnect both plugs for front pulse sensor.

2) Remove hydraulic unit. Pull off multiple pin plug on hydraulic unit and disconnect ground wire.

3) Remove rear seat. Remove left "B" pillar trim. Detach left entrance for rail covers. Raise vehicle. Pull down and disconnect plugs for both pulse sensors (DO NOT damage rubber grommets).

4) Route wire inward. Detach carpet and trim on left side as necessary. Pull wire forward in vehicle. Detach left trim lower section. Disconnect harness plugs. Pull wires forward into engine compartment. Pull off cap for ABS control unit and plug.

5) Remove firewall trim. Pull wire harness through heater wall from engine compartment (fold open hydraulic unit plug for this step).

Installation

To install wire harness, reverse removal procedure. When connecting multiple pin plug, connect left side first and then press right side into clamp. Check ABS system for proper operation.

BLEEDING BRAKE SYSTEM

Connect pressure bleeder to reservoir. Attach hose to bleeder screw on right rear wheel. Depress brake pedal and open bleeder screw. Close bleeder screw and depress brake pedal. Continue this procedure 12 times per wheel. Bleed brake system in the following sequence: Right rear, left rear, right front and left front. Road test system.

BMW ANTI-LOCK BRAKE SYSTEM (Cont.)

Fig. 6: BMW 325 Series Anti-Lock Wiring Diagram

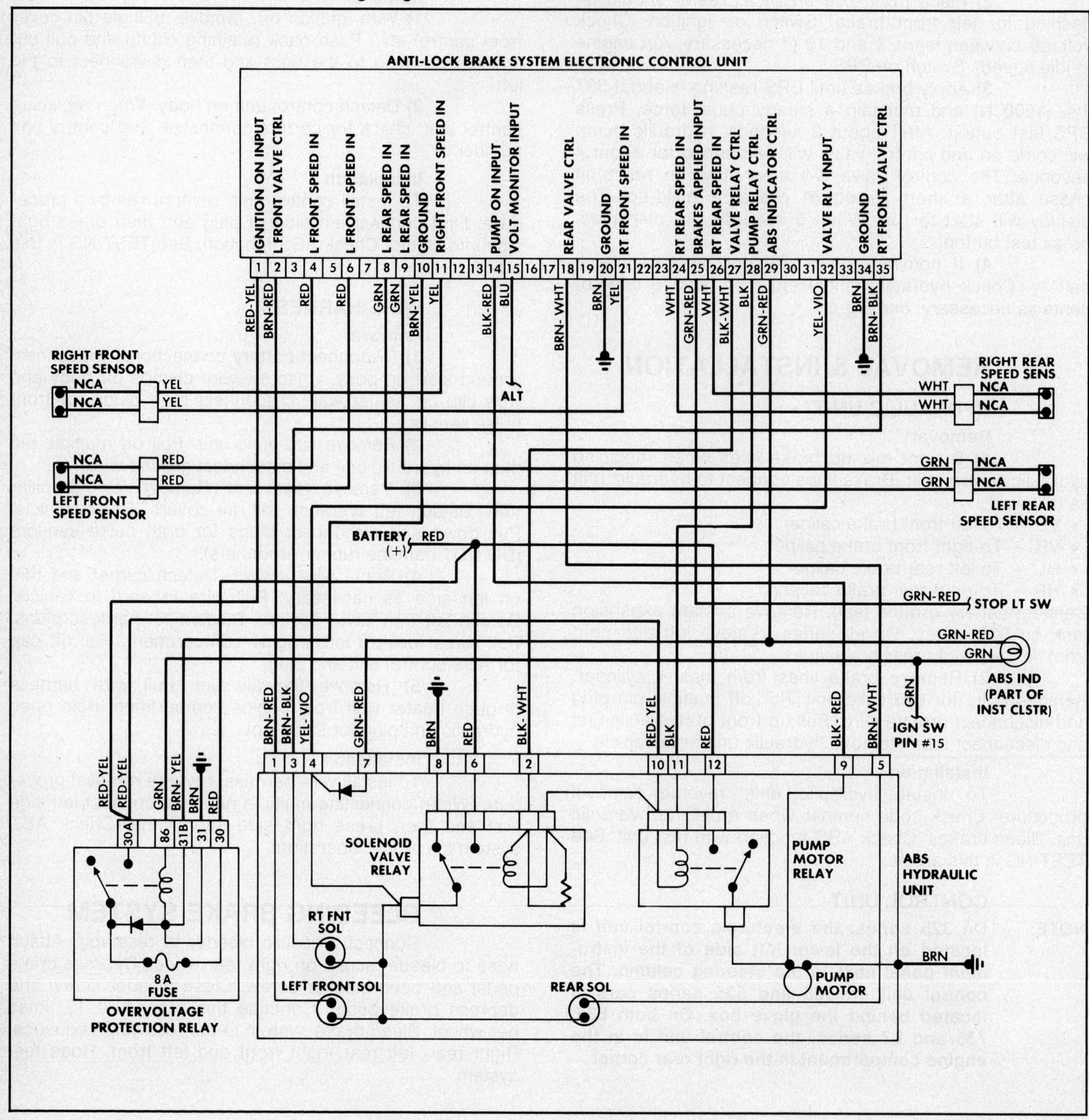

BMW ANTI-LOCK BRAKE SYSTEM (Cont.)

Fig. 7: BMW 528e & 535i Anti-Lock Wiring Diagram

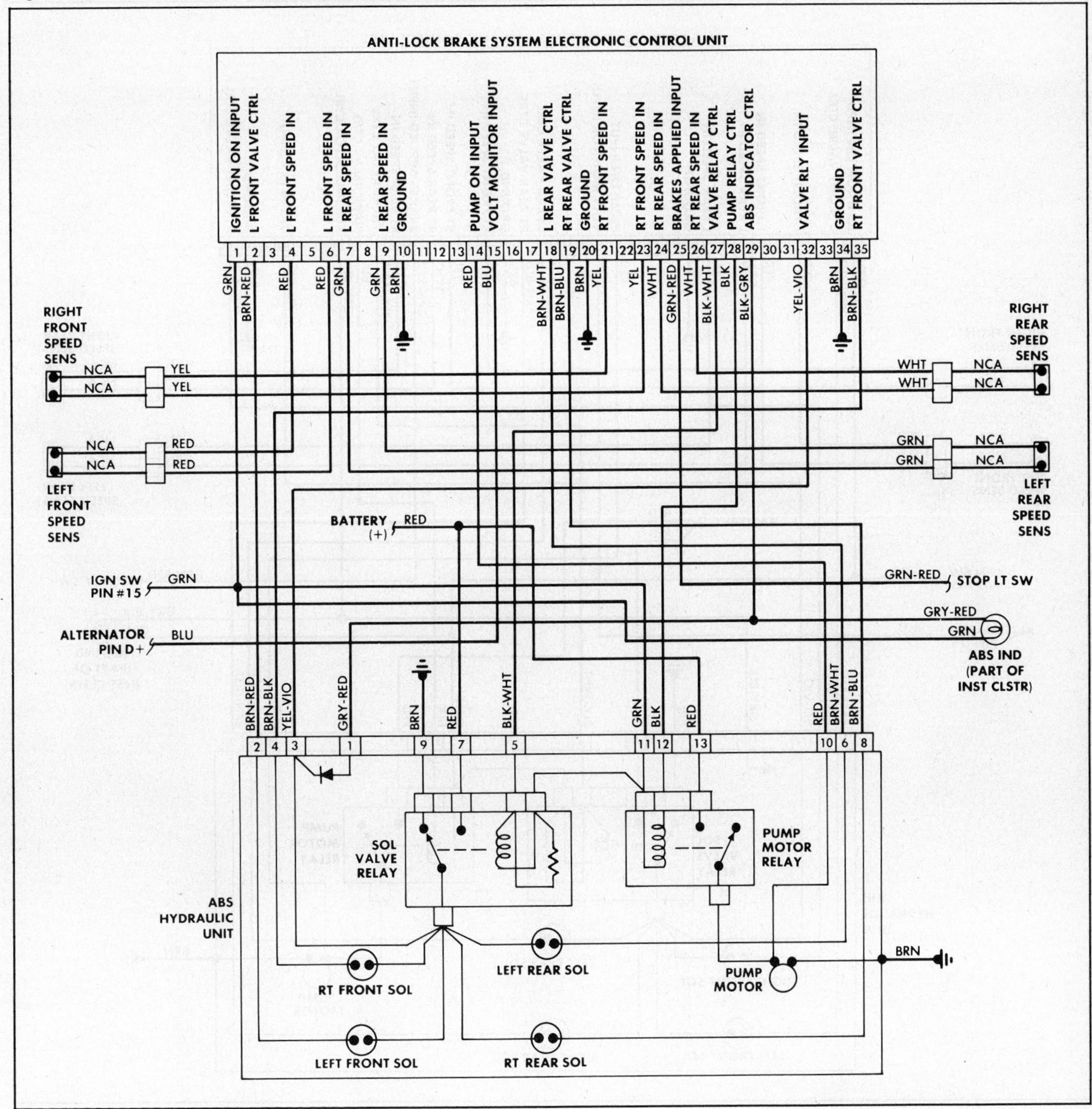

BMW ANTI-LOCK BRAKE SYSTEM (Cont.)

Fig. 8: BMW 635, 735 & L7 Series Anti-Lock Wiring Diagram

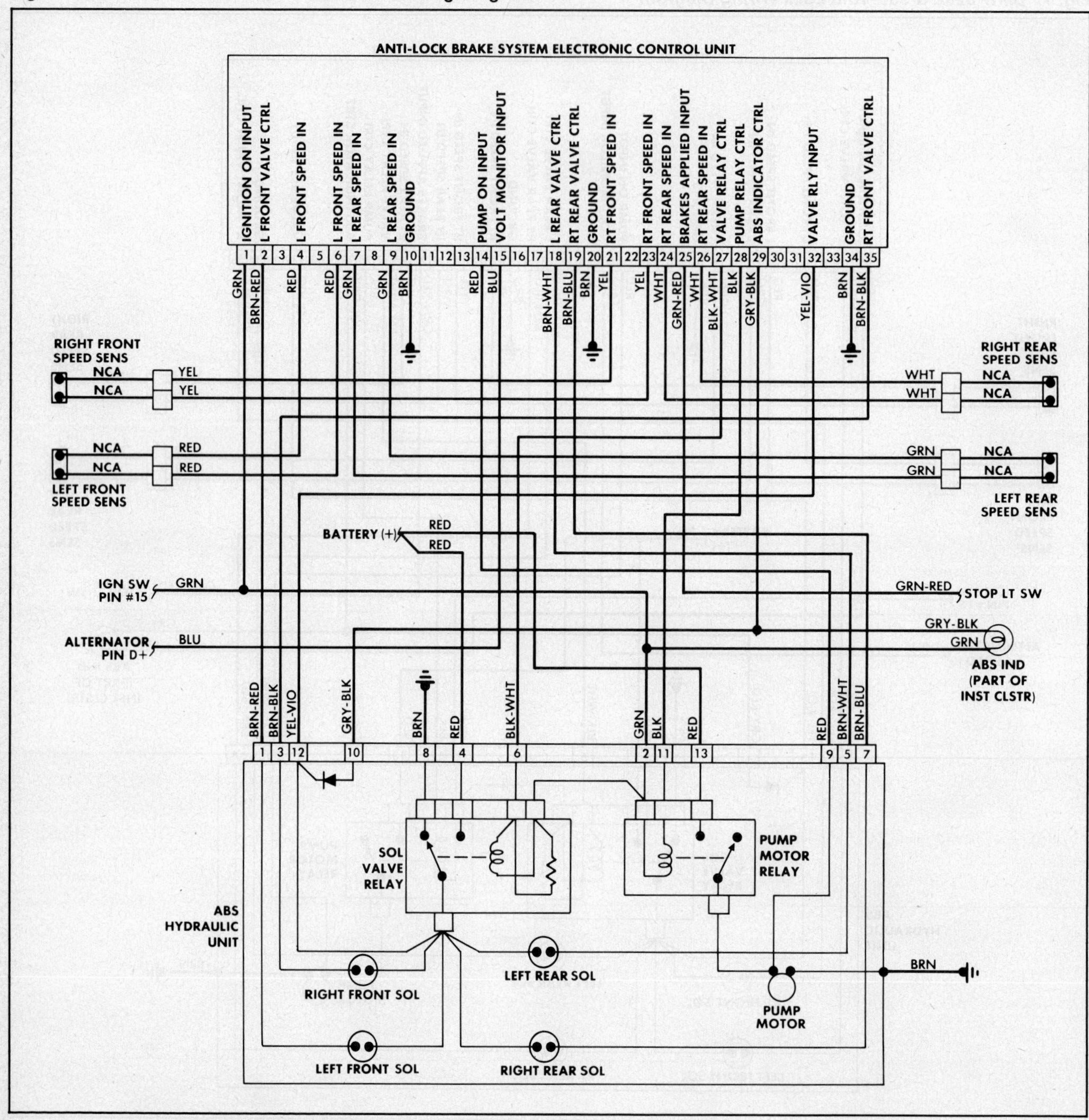

CHRYSLER MOTORS & MITSUBISHI ANTI-LOCK BRAKE SYSTEM

Chrysler Motors: Conquest;
Mitsubishi: Starion

DESCRIPTION & OPERATION

The automatic brake control system is designed to provide efficient braking for quick stops on wet or icy road surfaces, and reduce the chances of vehicle skidding. The anti-lock control system is designed for the rear wheels only. If the front wheels become locked, the automatic brake control system will not work.

PULSE GENERATOR

Pulse generator consists of a permanent magnet, a coil and a rotor. It is located on the transmission speedometer exit port. The frequency of the AC voltage, which is produced by the spinning of the rotor in combination with the coil and magnet, is proportionate to the speed of the wheels.

"G" SENSOR

The "G" sensor is composed of a differential transformer and printed circuit board. It is installed in the floor of the luggage compartment. When braking, the core of the transformer moves and produces a voltage equal to the amount of the displacement of the core, which is the speed reduction.

CONTROL UNIT

The control unit is located inside the luggage compartment. It receives signals from the pulse generator, "G" sensor, and the stoplight switch. Once the signal has been received, it sends the brake fluid pressure control signal to the modulator. It also will detect a malfunction in the control unit or modulator or an open circuit, and return the brake system to conventional operation.

MODULATOR

Located on the right fender wall of the engine compartment, the modulator consists of a pressure control section, a vacuum pressure drive section, and a solenoid valve. It receives signals from the control unit to control the brake fluid pressure for the rear brakes.

FAIL INDICATOR LIGHT

Located on the dash, the indicator light will illuminate if the control unit malfunctions.

NOTE: **Should a radio transmitter/receiver be installed in the vehicle, the following items should be noted. Install the antenna as far as possible from the control unit (preferably on the front of the vehicle). Keep the coaxial cable at least 12" away from the control unit and only cross the wiring harness at right angles. Limit transmitter output to 10W, and select a cable and an antenna which are electronically matched.**

Fig. 2: Rear Brake Lock-Up Control System

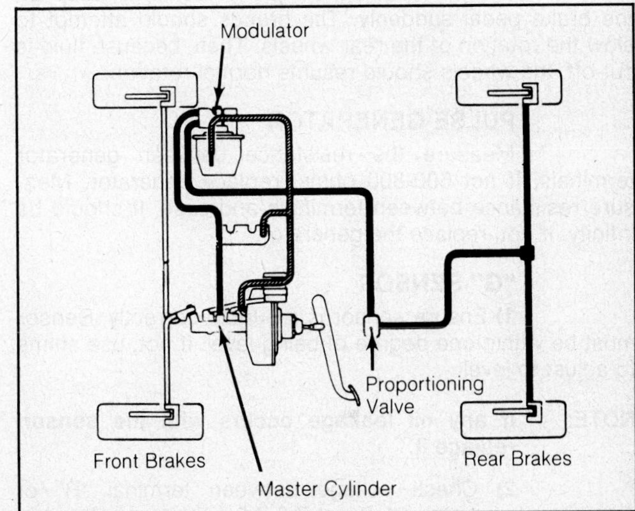

Courtesy of Chrysler Motors.

Fig. 1: Rear Brake Lock-Up Control Component Locations

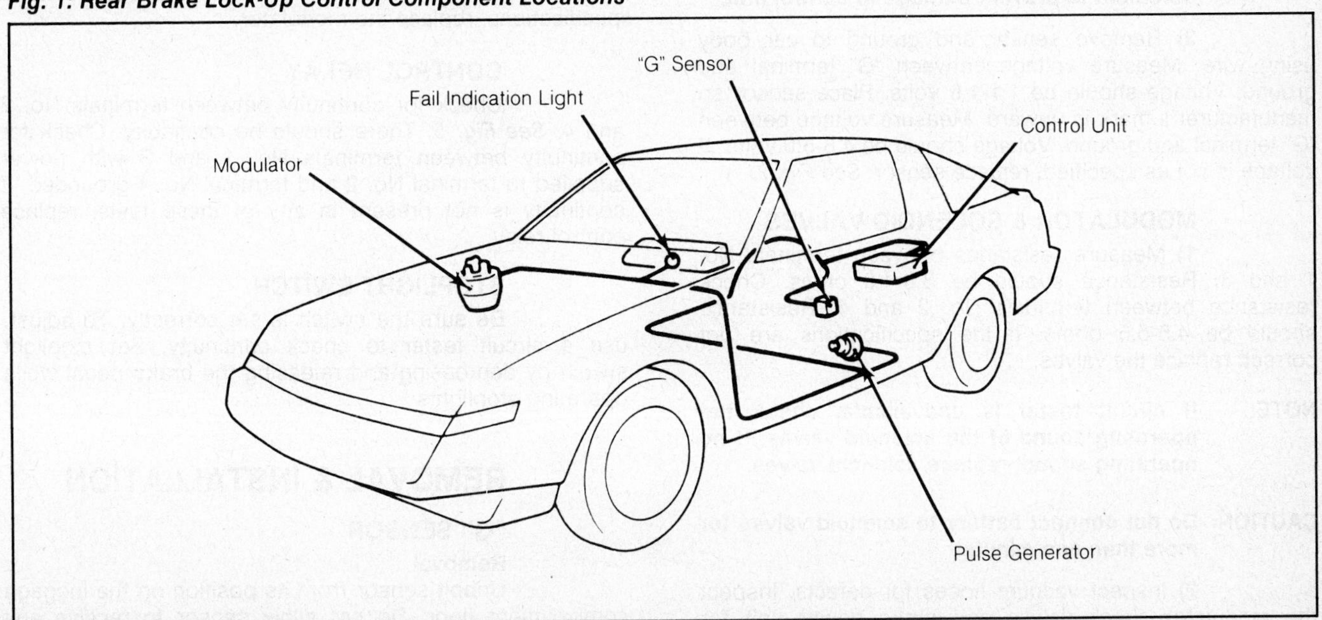

Courtesy of Chrysler Motors.

CHRYSLER MOTORS & MITSUBISHI ANTI-LOCK BRAKE SYSTEM (Cont.)

DIAGNOSIS & TESTING

REAR BRAKE CONTROL SYSTEM QUICK CHECK

NOTE: If any problem exists in the system, check all components (including wiring harness) except the control unit. If all components check out, replace the control unit

1) With vehicle stationary, operate engine for at least 5 seconds. Turn the ignition key to "LOCK" position and step on the brake pedal. Turn the ignition key to "ON" position and confirm the clicking sound of the operating modulator.

2) Raise rear of vehicle, support on stands, and block front wheels. Warm up engine and place transmission in second gear. Accelerate to a steady 19 MPH.

3) With accelerator held at 19 MPH, step on the brake pedal suddenly. The brakes should attempt to slow the rotation of the rear wheels. Then, because fluid is cut-off, the wheels should resume normal rotation.

PULSE GENERATOR

Measure the resistance between generator terminals. If not 600-800 ohms, replace generator. Measure resistance between terminals and case. It should be infinity. If not, replace the generator.

"G" SENSOR

1) Ensure sensor is mounted correctly. Sensor must be within one degree of being level. If not, use shims to adjust to level.

NOTE: If any oil leakage occurs with the sensor, replace it.

2) Check voltage between terminal "R" of control unit and ground. If not 7.0-7.5 volts, control unit is faulty.

CAUTION: Set voltmeter at correct range before measurement to prevent damage to control unit.

3) Remove sensor and ground to car body using wire. Measure voltage between "G" terminal and ground. Voltage should be 1.1-1.5 volts. Place sensor so manufacturer's mark is upward. Measure voltage between "G" terminal and ground. Voltage should be 4.6-5.0 volts. If voltage is not as specified, replace sensor. *See Fig. 7.*

MODULATOR & SOLENOID VALVES

1) Measure resistance between terminals No. 1 and 3. Resistance should be 3.8-4.8 ohms. Check resistance between terminals No. 2 and 4. Resistance should be 4.5-5.5 ohms. If the specifications are not correct, replace the valves.

NOTE: If circuit tester is unavailable, check the operating sound of the solenoid valves. If no operating sound, replace solenoid valves.

CAUTION: Do not connect battery to solenoid valves for more than one minute.

2) Inspect vacuum hoses for defects. Inspect the modulator check valves and brake power unit for clogging conditions.

3) Using 2 pressure gauges with a range of 0-2500 psi (0-175.75 kg/cm²), connect one gauge between modulator master cylinder port and master cylinder, and other to modulator rear brake port. Let engine run at idle.

Fig. 3: Modulator Pressure Gauge Test Connections

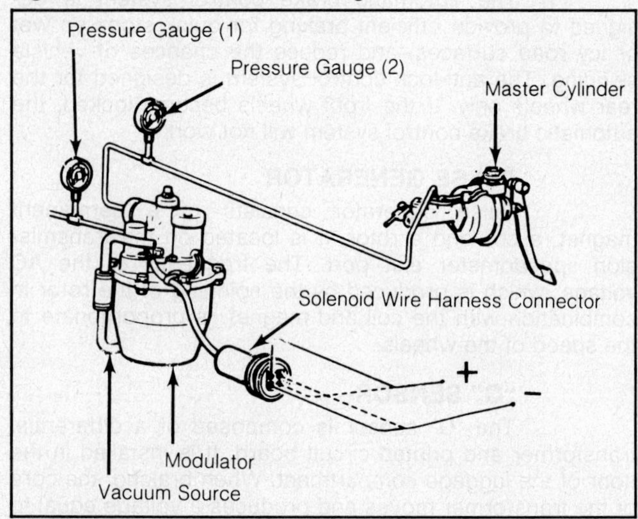

Courtesy of Chrysler Motors.

4) Depress brake pedal until 711 psi (50 kg/cm²) reads on rear brake gauge. Operate release solenoid valve. Pressure should drop to zero psi.

5) With release solenoid still operated, operate the build-up solenoid. Stop operation of release solenoid. If pressure rises to 711 psi (50 kg/cm²), the modulator is operating correctly.

6) Repeat steps **4)** and **5)**, but do not operate build-up solenoid. When release solenoid operation is cut-off, pressure should rise to 711 psi (50 kg/cm²). If so, the operation is okay.

7) Set both solenoid valves in a non-operating position. Increase pressure on master cylinder by operating brakes. Rear brake port gauge should show pressure of 1422 psi (100 kg/cm²). Master cylinder gauge should show 1707 psi (120 kg/cm²). If any test does not meet specifications, replace the modulator.

CONTROL RELAY

Check for continuity between terminals No. 2 and 4. *See Fig. 5.* There should be continuity. Check for continuity between terminals No. 1 and 3 with power supplied to terminal No. 2 and terminal No. 4 grounded. If continuity is not present in any of these tests, replace control relay.

STOPLIGHT SWITCH

Be sure the switch is set correctly. To adjust, use a circuit tester to check continuity. Set stoplight switch by depressing and releasing the brake pedal while operating stoplights.

REMOVAL & INSTALLATION

"G" SENSOR

Removal

Unbolt sensor from its position on the luggage compartment floor. Do not allow sensor to receive any impact or violent shaking.

CHRYSLER MOTORS & MITSUBISHI ANTI-LOCK BRAKE SYSTEM (Cont.)

Fig. 4: Exploded View Of Modulator

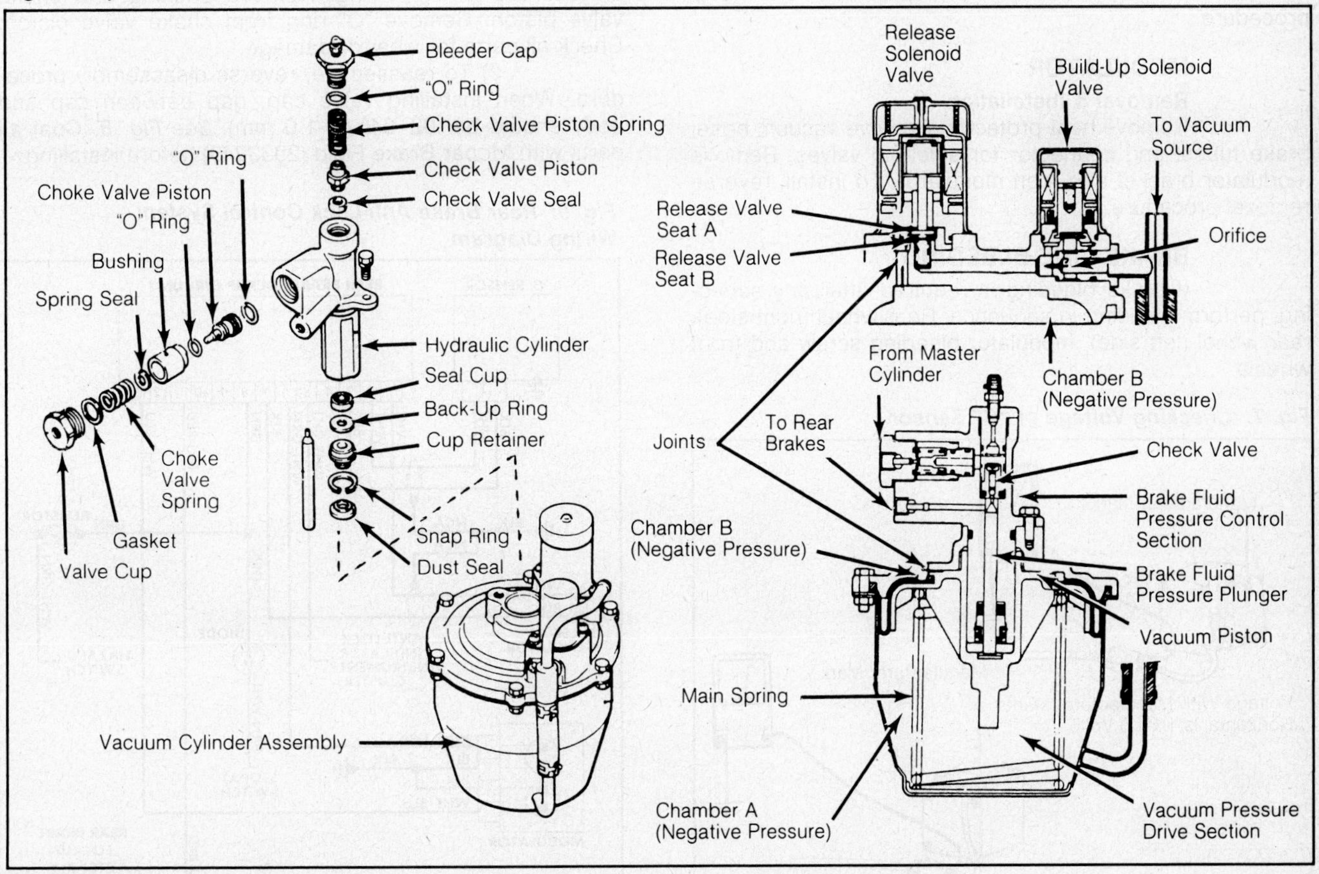

Courtesy of Chrysler Motors.

Fig. 5: Checking Control Relay

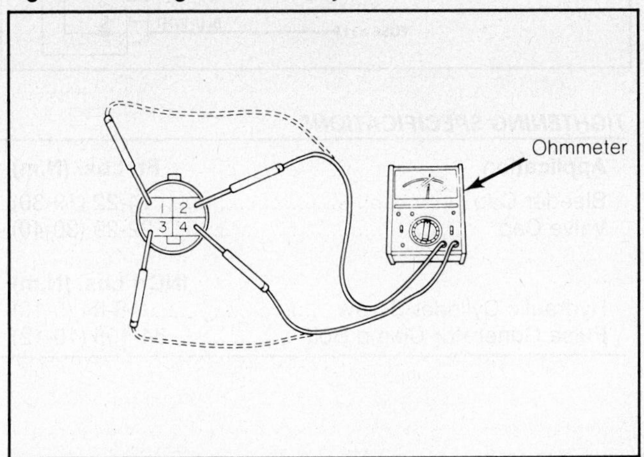

Courtesy of Chrysler Motors.

Installation

With vehicle on a level surface and unloaded, install sensor making sure it is level within one degree. Use appropriate shims to bring to correct level.

PULSE GENERATOR

Removal

Disconnect speedometer cable at pulse generator side and remove pulse generator.

Installation

Reverse removal procedure. To install on a manual transmission, count the number of speedometer driven gear teeth and select the generator sleeve mark which indicates that number of teeth. Align selected mark with reference mark on extension housing. *See Fig. 6.*

Fig. 6: Pulse Generator Alignment Marks (Manual Transmission)

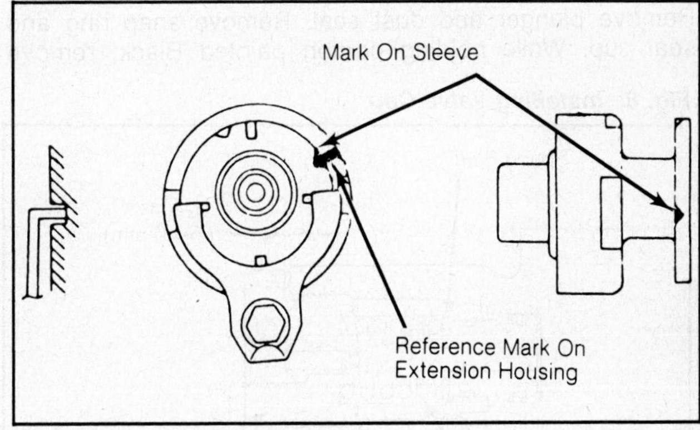

Courtesy of Chrysler Motors.

CONTROL UNIT

Removal & Installation

Remove the unit from under the high floor side panel on the right side of the luggage compartment.

CHRYSLER MOTORS & MITSUBISHI ANTI-LOCK BRAKE SYSTEM (Cont.)

Remove electrical connector. To install, reverse removal procedure.

MODULATOR

Removal & Installation

Remove heat protector. Remove vacuum hose, brake tubes, and connector for solenoid valves. Remove modulator bracket and then modulator. To install, reverse removal procedure.

BRAKE LINE BLEEDING

If brake bleeding is required after any servicing, perform bleeding in sequence: Rear wheel (right side), rear wheel (left side), modulator bleeding screw and front wheels.

Fig. 7: Checking Voltage of "G" Sensor

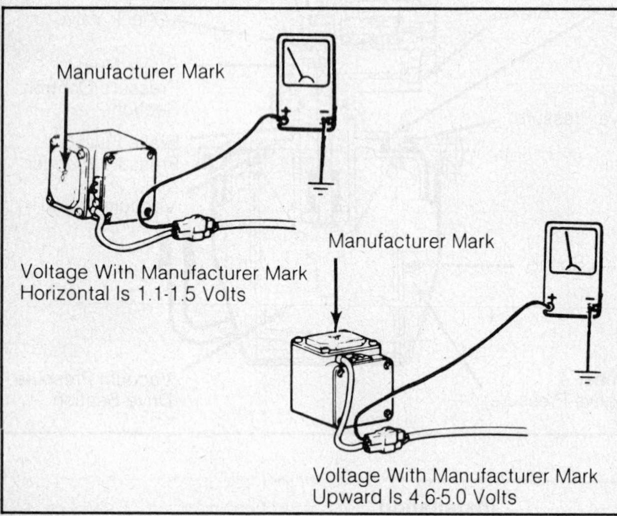

Courtesy of Chrysler Motors.

OVERHAUL

HYDRAULIC CYLINDER

Disassembly & Reassembly

1) Remove hydraulic cylinder from modulator. Remove plunger and dust seal. Remove snap ring and seal cup. While holding portion painted Black, remove bleeder cap and "O" ring. Remove bushing and choke valve piston. Remove "O" ring from choke valve piston. Check all parts for wear or damage.

2) To reassemble, reverse disassembly procedure. When installing valve cap, gap between cap and body should be .02-.04" (.5-1.0 mm). *See Fig. 8*. Coat all parts with Mopar Brake Fluid (2933249) before installing.

Fig. 8: Installing Valve Cap

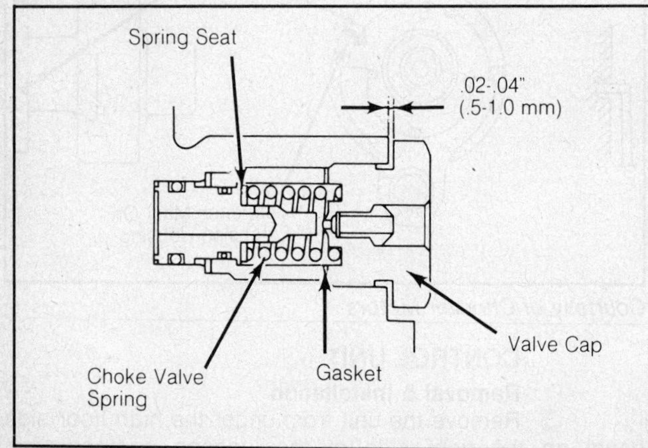

Courtesy of Chrysler Motors.

Fig. 9: Rear Brake Anti-Lock Control System Wiring Diagram

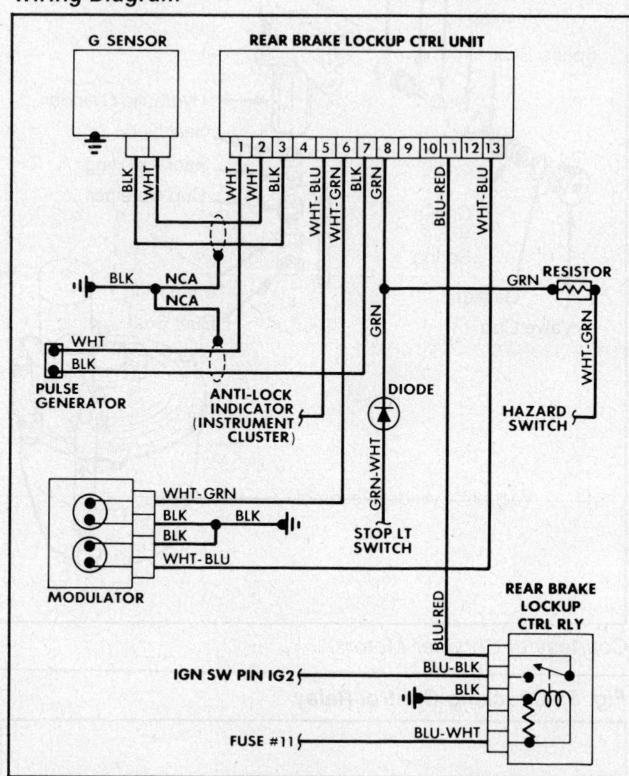

TIGHTENING SPECIFICATIONS

Application	Ft. Lbs. (N.m)
Bleeder Cap	14-22 (19-30)
Valve Cap	22-29 (30-40)
	INCH Lbs. (N.m)
Hydraulic Cylinder Screw	48-84 (5-10)
Pulse Generator Clamp Bolt	84-108 (10-12)

JAGUAR ANTI-LOCK BRAKE SYSTEM

DESCRIPTION

The Anti-Lock Brake System (ABS) eliminates wheel lock, increases vehicle stability and provides optimum deceleration during hard braking conditions even on sub-standard road surfaces. This is accomplished by regulating the amount of hydraulic pressure being sent to each brake caliper. The regulating process is controlled by the Electronic Control Unit (ECU).

As the ECU receives input signals from various sensors, it regulates hydraulic pressure to each brake caliper by means of actuating valves within the hydraulic modulator. The ABS system consists of conventional brake system components incorporated with 4 wheel speed sensors, a power assist hydraulic system, a hydraulic pump, a hydraulic modulator, associated wiring harnesses and relays. *See Fig. 1.*

Fig. 1: Components of Jaguar Anti-Lock Braking System

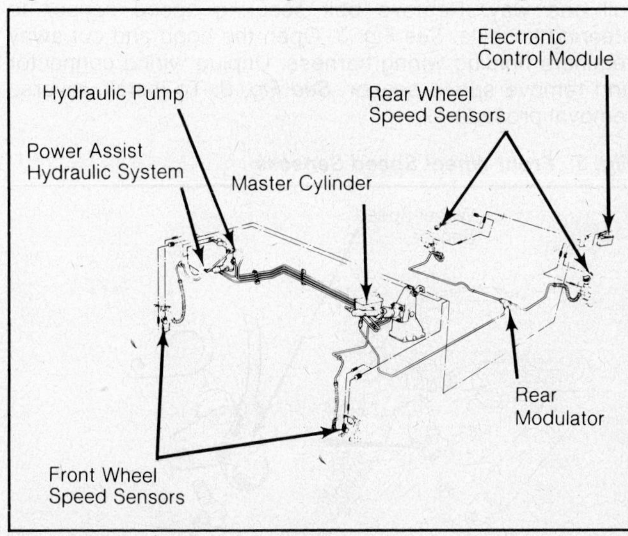

Courtesy of Jaguar Cars Ltd.

OPERATION

Each wheel speed sensor generates an AC signal to the ECU. The alternator generates a signal indicating engine speed and load. Applying the brake pedal generates a signal through the brake light simulation relay.

Signals for the hydraulic pump and modulator are obtained through a common overvoltage relay. As the ECU receives signals from these various sensors it determines needed pressure increases, pressure decreases and holding pressures. These pressure variations are applied through actuating valves within the hydraulic modulator.

Each valve inside the modulator is capable of increasing, decreasing or holding hydraulic pressure according to signals from the ECU. During pressure decrease functions, the hydraulic pump is activated by the ECU and remains in operation for 0.6 seconds after the valves close. This returns all excess fluid to the modulator and therefore repressurizes the ABS system.

TESTING

ELECTRONIC CONTROL MODULE SELF-TESTING

Testing for the Anti-Lock Brake System is a 3 phase self-testing design. The self-testing within the ECU is performed in 3 stages: Initial Tests, Low Speed Tests and Continuous Tests. All functions incorporated within the Electronic Control Unit (ECU) are monitored.

If the ECU senses a problem within its operation it illuminates a warning light on the instrument panel. Each time the vehicle ignition switch is turned from "OFF" position to the "ON" position, the self-test series begins.

Initial Tests

1) When the ECU senses the ignition swtich has been turned to the "ON" position, it sends a simulated reference signal to the wheel speed sensors as well as illuminating an ABS instrument panel light. As these signals are generated, associated sensor signals and wheel speed sensor output signals are received back to the ECU.

2) They are then checked within the ECU for correct reference voltage and response. The ECU checks battery voltage to ensure system voltage is adequate, at least 10 volts. Wheel acceleration and deceleration levels are checked for proper operation to ensure that they are set correctly. If all initial tests are completed satisfactorily, the warning light on the instrument panel is turned off.

Low Speed Tests

1) All low speed tests are initiated after the vehicle reaches 3.6 MPH (5.75 kph). After the ECU senses vehicle operation over the minimum MPH, it actuates the modulator valve. As the modulator valves begins to operate the ECU monitors their operation to ensure correct voltage flow. Next it operates the hydraulic pump and verifies correct function by voltage that is developed across the motor windings.

2) These tests are performed only on the first occasion when the vehicle reaches its minimum tesing speed of 3.6 MPH. After completeing the low speed self-tests the system resets only after the ignition switch is turned to the "OFF" position.

Continuous Tests

1) As the vehicle operates at varying speeds, the ECU constantly monitors each signal sent from the individual wheel speed sensors. It compares these readings against the values preset within the system to determine if the readings are within excepted range.

2) The ECU also constantly monitors the sensors circuitry wiring harnesses to ensure that no opens or shorts are present. If a problem is ever detected within the ABS system, the ECU will illuminate the ABS warning light on the instrument panel.

REMOVAL & INSTALLATION

CALIPER

Removal & Installation

1) Raise and support vehicle. Remove wheel and tire assembly. Open bleeder screw and compress piston back into caliper bore. Close bleeder screw. Unclip brake pad wear sensor harness connector and remove.

JAGUAR ANTI-LOCK BRAKE SYSTEM (Cont.)

2) Remove caliper lower mounting bolt. Pivot caliper upward to gain access to brake pads. Remove brake pads. Disconnect caliper brake fluid line and plug. Remove caliper guide pins and and dust boots. Remove upper mounting bolt. Remove caliper assembly. To install, reverse removal procedure and bleed air from system.

ROTOR

Removal & Installation

Loosen wheel lug nuts. Raise and support vehicle. Remove wheel and tire assembly. Remove brake pad wear sensor connector and remove. Remove caliper mounting bolts and caliper. Remove brake pads. Cut lock wire and remove caliper support bracket. Remove screw securing rotor to hub. Remove rotor. To install, reverse removal procedure.

MASTER CYLINDER

Removal & Installation

1) Disconnect electrical leads from cap of master cylinder. Remove reservoir cap and float assembly. Using a clean syringe, remove brake fluid from reservoir. Disconnect and remove brake fluid lines from master cylinder. *See Fig. 2.*

2) Remove mounting bolts and lock washers securing master cylinder. *See Fig. 2.* Remove master cylinder. To install, reverse removal procedure and bleed air from master cylinder prior to installation. Install master cylinder and bleed remainder of air from system.

Fig. 2: Typical Jaguar Master Cylinder

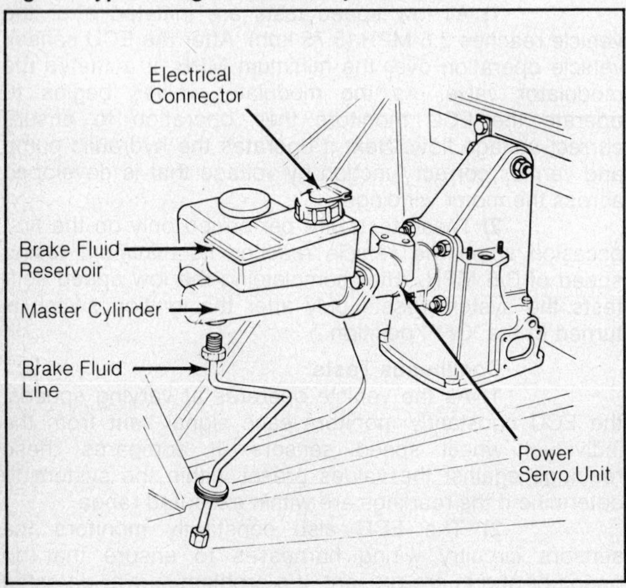

Courtesy of Jaguar Cars Ltd.

MODULATOR

Removal & Installation

Remove screw retaining modulator cover and remove cover. Remove screws securing clamp to modulator and remove. Disconnect wiring harness and move it out of working area. Remove nut retaining ground strap to mounting stud. Use a rag to catch spilled brake fluid, and disconnect brake lines from modulator. Remove modulator mounting nuts, modulator and mounting insulator. To install, reverse removal procedure and bleed air from system.

ELECTRONIC CONTROL UNIT

Removal & Installation

Open luggage compartment and remove left side liner retaining screws. Carefully remove liner for access to ECU. Remove ECU from its mounting support and lay it in the trunk compartment. Disconnect wiring harness from ECU and remove ECU. To install, reverse removal procedure.

FRONT WHEEL SPEED SENSORS

Removal & Installation

Raise and support vehicle. Turn steering wheel full one way. Remove bolt securing speed sensor to steering knuckle. *See Fig. 3.* Open the hood and cut away retainers holding wiring harness. Unplug wiring connector and remove speed sensor. *See Fig. 3.* To install, reverse removal procedure.

Fig. 3: Front Wheel Speed Sensors

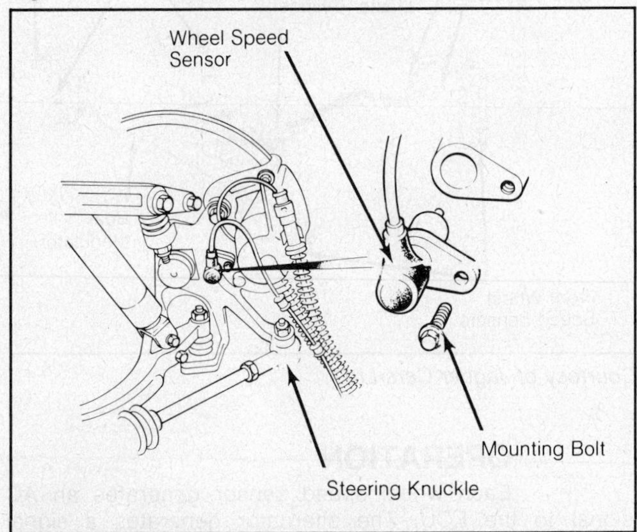

Courtesy of Jaguar Cars Ltd.

REAR WHEEL SPEED SENSORS

Removal & Installation

Open luggage compartment and remove carpeting. Remove luggage compartment liner. Cut retaining straps securing wiring harness connector. Remove speed sensor mounting bolt. Unplug connector and remove speed sensor. To install, reverse removal procedure.

OVERHAUL

NOTE: **Overhaul procedures for Anti-Lock Brake System components are not available from the manufacturer.**

JAGUAR ANTI-LOCK BRAKE SYSTEM (Cont.)

Fig. 4: Jaguar Anti-Lock Brake System Circuit Diagram

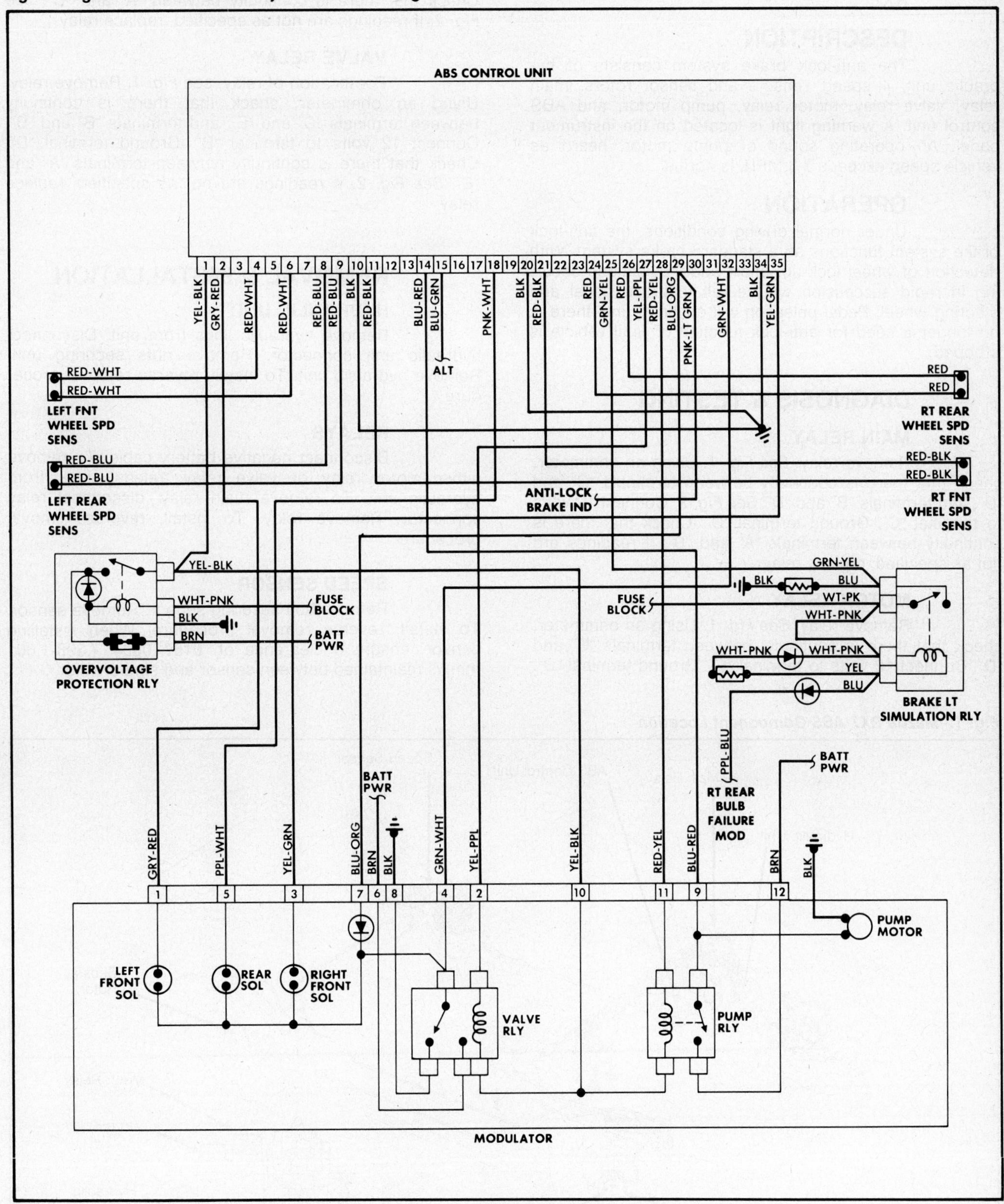

MAZDA ANTI-LOCK BRAKE SYSTEM

RX7

DESCRIPTION

The anti-lock brake system consists of hydraulic unit, 4 speed sensors and sensor rotors, main relay, valve relay, motor relay, pump motor, and ABS control unit. A warning light is located on the instrument panel. An operating sound of pump motor, heard as vehicle speed exceeds 3.8 MPH, is normal.

OPERATION

Under normal driving conditions, the anti-lock brake system functions as a standard brake system. With detection of wheel lock-up, short pedal pulsations occurring in rapid succession will be felt in brake pedal and steering wheel. Pedal pulsation will continue until there is no longer a need for anti-lock function or until vehicle is stopped.

DIAGNOSIS & TESTING

MAIN RELAY

Remove relay. *See Fig. 1*. Using an ohmmeter, check that there is continuity between terminals "C" and "D", and terminals "B" and "D". *See Fig. 2*. Connect 12 volts to terminal "C". Ground terminal "D". Check that there is continuity between terminals "A" and "B". If readings are not as specified, replace relay.

MOTOR RELAY

Remove relay. *See Fig. 1*. Using an ohmmeter, check that there is continuity between terminals "C" and "D". Connect 12 volts to terminal "C". Ground terminal "D". Check that there is continuity between "A" and "B". *See Fig. 2*. If readings are not as specified, replace relay.

VALVE RELAY

For location of relay, see *Fig. 1*. Remove relay. Using an ohmmeter, check that there is continuity between terminals "C" and "E", and terminals "B" and "D". Connect 12 volts to terminal "B". Ground terminal "D". Check that there is continuity between terminals "A" and "E". *See Fig. 2*. If readings are not as specified, replace relay.

REMOVAL & INSTALLATION

HYDRAULIC UNIT

Remove hydraulic lines from unit. Disconnect hydraulic unit connector. Remove nuts securing unit. Remove hydraulic unit. To install, reverse removal procedure.

RELAYS

Disconnect negative battery cable. To remove either motor relay or valve relay, release lock from hydraulic unit. To remove main relay, disconnect relay connector. Remove relay. To install, reverse removal procedure.

SPEED SENSOR

Remove bolt securing sensor. Remove sensor. To install, reverse removal procedure. When installing sensor, ensure a clearance of .0157-.0394" (.398-1.001 mm) is maintained between sensor and sensor rotor.

Fig. 1: Mazda RX7 ABS Component Location

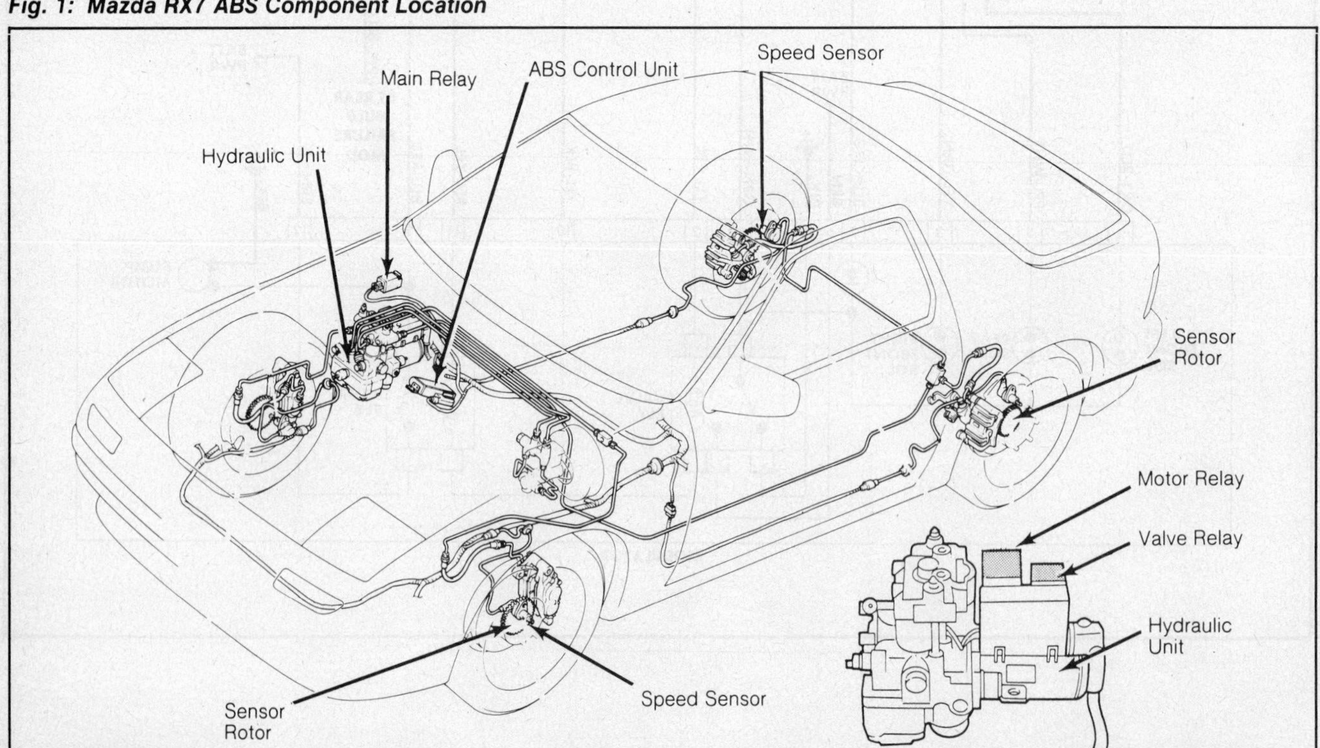

Courtesy of Mazda Motors Corp.

MAZDA ANTI-LOCK BRAKE SYSTEM (Cont.)

Fig. 2: Relay Terminal Identification

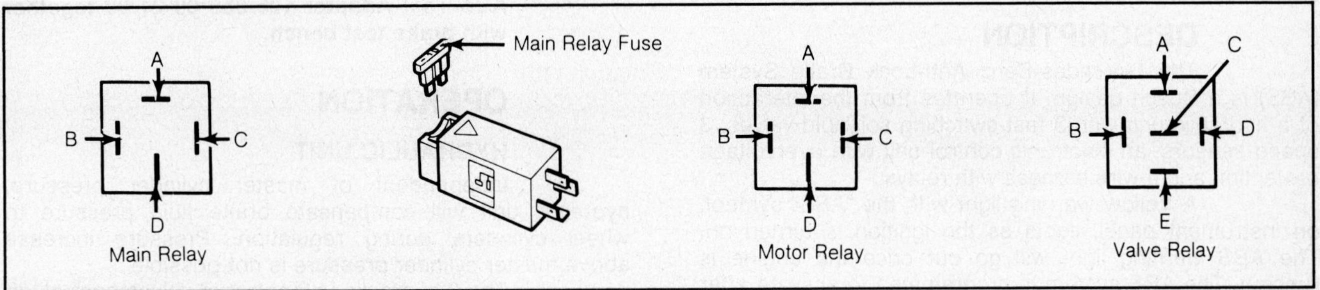

Courtesy of Mazda Motors Corp.

SENSOR ROTOR

Remove wheel hub. On rear hub, remove wheel hub from outer toe control hub using Wheel Hub Puller (49 F026 103) and Bearing Installer (49 F026 102). On front rotor, remove bolts securing rotor to hub using an Allen wrench. On rear rotor, remove screws securing rotor to hub. To install, reverse removal procedure.

Fig. 3: Mazda RX7 Anti-Lock Brake System Wiring Diagram

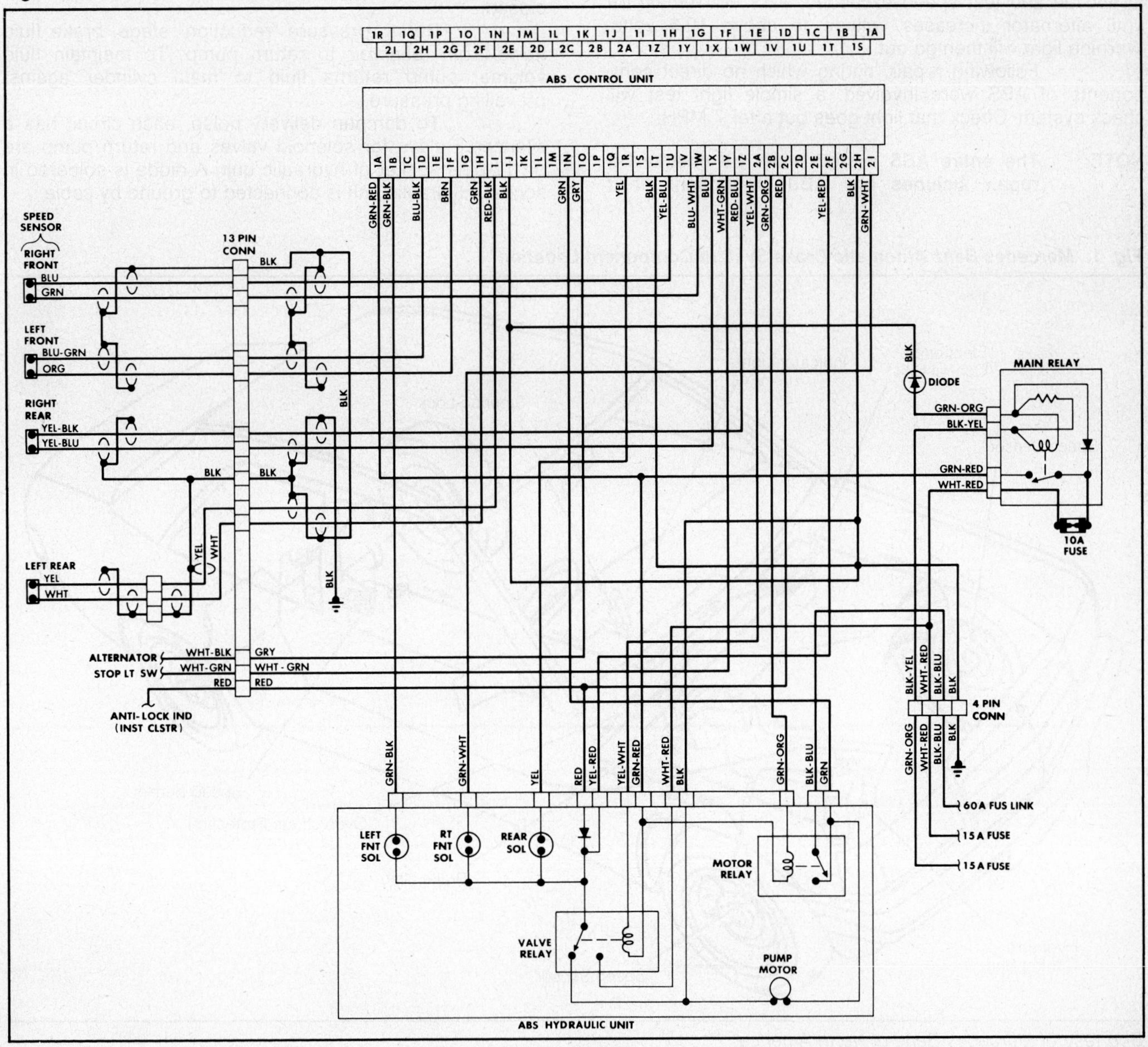

MERCEDES-BENZ ANTI-LOCK BRAKE SYSTEM

All Models

DESCRIPTION

The Mercedes-Benz Anti-Lock Brake System (ABS) is a Bosch design. It operates from the interaction of a hydraulic unit with 3 fast-switching solenoid valves, 3 speed sensors, an electronic control unit with overvoltage protection and a wire harness with relays.

A Yellow warning light with the "ABS" symbol, on instrument panel, lights as the ignition is turned on. The ABS warning light will go out once the engine is running. The ABS system is programmed to activate after 7.5 MPH.

When vehicle speed is above 3 MPH, Built-In Test Equipment (BITE) will begin check of ABS. If any fault is found, the warning light will again go on. When warning light goes on, ABS is switched off and vehicle will brake without ABS control. The conventional brake system remains operational.

If battery is below 10.5 volts, when ignition is turned on and test speed exceeded, ABS will remain off until alternator increases voltage to above 10.5 volts. Warning light will then go out.

Following repair, during which no direct components of ABS were involved, a simple light test will check system. Check that light goes out after 7 MPH.

NOTE: **The entire ABS system must be checked if repair includes any ABS component or if units are replaced following an accident. Use ABS Test Adapter 126-859-09-21-00 together with brake test bench.**

OPERATION

HYDRAULIC UNIT

Independent of master cylinder pressure, hydraulic unit will compensate brake fluid pressure to wheel cylinders during regulation. Pressure increase above master cylinder pressure is not possible.

The 3 hydraulic unit solenoid valves control left front, right front and rear brakes. By activating valves with current of varying amperage, brake fluid pressure in individual calipers may be increased, held or decreased.

In pressure "build-up" stage, pressure increases by opening intake valve to pressure supplied by master cylinder. In pressure "holding" stage, which preceeds "reduction" stage, pressure from hydraulic unit to wheels is constant. Output and input valves in solenoid valve are closed.

During pressure "reduction" stage, brake fluid flows from reservoir to return pump. To maintain fluid volume, pump returns fluid to main cylinder against prevailing pressure.

To dampen delivery noise, each circuit has a silencer. Relays for solenoid valves and return pump are on 12-pole socket of hydraulic unit. A diode is soldered in socket. Hydraulic unit is connected to ground by cable.

Fig. 1: Mercedes-Benz Automatic Brake System Component Location

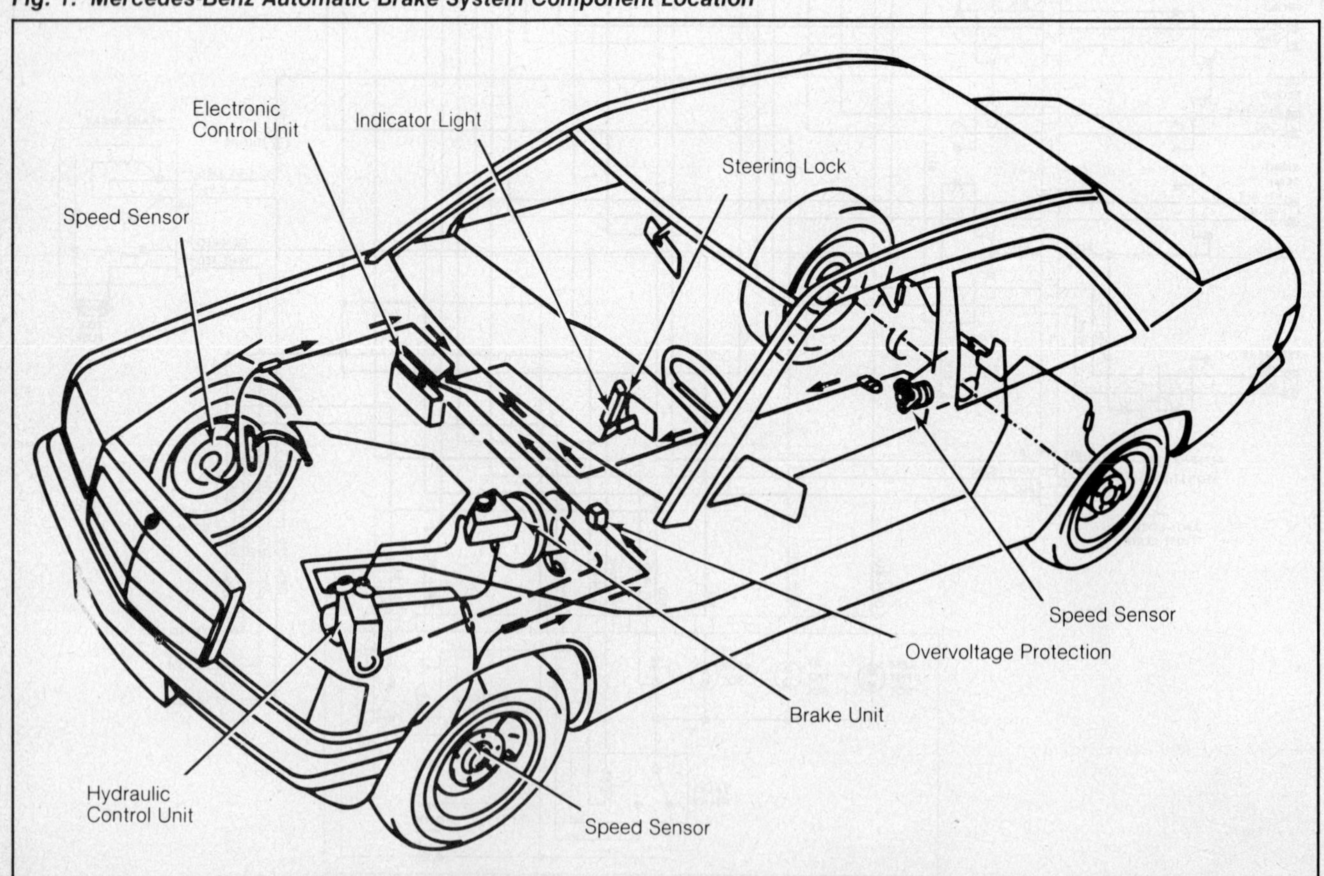

Courtesy of Mercedes-Benz of North America.

MERCEDES-BENZ ANTI-LOCK BRAKE SYSTEM (Cont.)

SPEED SENSOR

Rod shaped speed sensors (impulse transmitters) measure wheel speeds. The 3 channel system, with 3 speed sensors, separately measures wheel speed of each front wheel and both rear wheels. Speed sensors for front axle are on steering knuckles. Speed sensor for rear axle is on axle housing. Drive pinion serves to measure rear wheel speed.

Speed sensor measures wheel speeds by sensing rotor teeth movement. On front axle, rotor teeth are machined into front wheel hub. Speed sensors for front axle are double-edged with diameter of .71" (18 mm). *See Fig. 2.*

On rear axle, toothed rotor is pressed on drive pinion. Axles with different ratios have gear wheels with different number of teeth. Speed sensor for rear axle is single-edged with diameter of .59" (15 mm).

Speed sensors consist of magnetic core and coil. Rotation of rotor, set specific distance from sensor, causes alternating voltage in coil. This alternating voltage changes frequently in proportion to wheel speed and number of rotor teeth.

Fig. 2: Cutaway View Of Mercedes-Benz ABS Front Speed Sensor Assembly

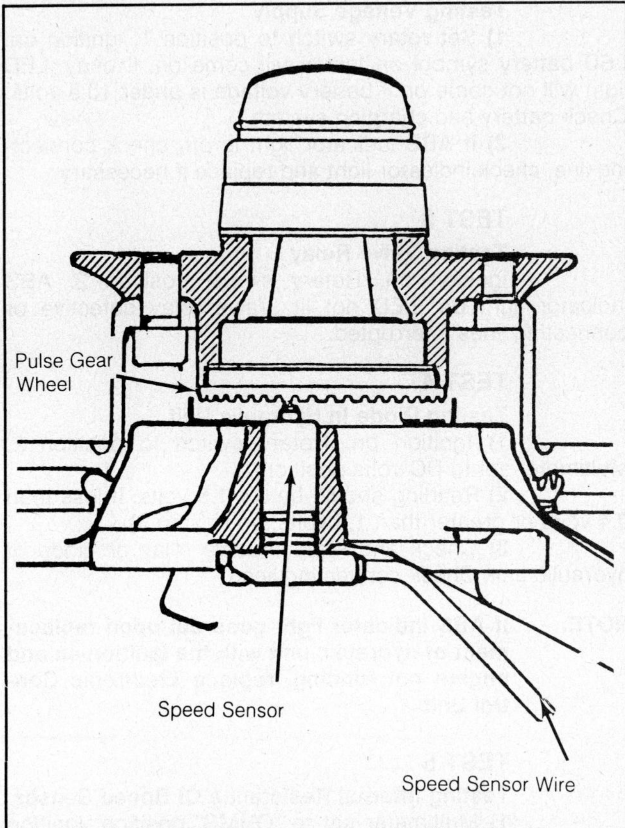

Courtesy of Mercedes-Benz of North America.

ELECTRONIC CONTROL UNIT

Electronic control unit is a 2-board design. The circuit boards are stacked inside control unit enclosed in light alloy housing. The control unit processes signals of speed sensors and contacts valves in hydraulic unit. Signal conditioning and processing is digital. The electronic control unit is subdivided by the signal conditioning section, logic section and safety circuit.

Signal Conditioning Section

In signal conditioning section, signals supplied by speed sensors are converted for logic section. While measuring wheel speed, trouble caused by production tolerances or movements in steering knuckle is prevented by filtering input signals prior to use. Deceleration and acceleration signals obtained from wheel speed signals are processed in logic section.

Logic Section

Logic section of the electronic control unit employs wheel slip, wheel speed acceleration and deceleration signals for each controlled front wheel or rear wheels. Output signals of logic section control the solenoid valves of hydraulic unit.

Safety Circuit

The safety circuit recognizes faulty signals inside and outside electronic control unit. Safety circuit intervenes in control sequence during extreme driving conditions, such as aquaplaning. When fault is recognized, system is switched off. The condition is indicated to driver by illumination of the warning light.

The safety circuit continuously monitors battery voltage. If voltage is below specified requirements, system is switched off until voltage is within specified range. In addition to the monitoring function, safety circuit also includes active test cycle section or BITE (Built In Test Equipment).

Test Cycle (BITE)

Test cycle begins when wheel speed in all 3 speed channels exceeds 3 MPH. Test cycle, which is activated by speed sensor voltage, also monitors safety circuit and logic section. The electronic control unit is given test signals to check whether correct output signals are available.

HARNESS WITH RELAY & OVERVOLTAGE PROTECTION

The ABS system includes a supplementary harness. To ensure function of ABS, power is supplied by an ignition switch activated relay. An overvoltage protection unit, between battery and relay, protects electronic control unit. The harness is connected to control unit by a 35-pole plug. The harness with 12-pole plug leads to hydraulic unit. Ground cable for hydraulic unit is mounted to inner fender well.

Front axle speed sensors connect to harness by coaxial cable. Speed sensor cable from steering knuckle-to-coaxial cable routes through tubing to bracket on firewall and on through inner front fender well.

Rear axle speed sensor connects to harness under rear seat by a cable connector. Two relays are located under hydraulic unit cover. One relay contacts return pump. The other relay flows current to solenoid valves. Diode in plug socket lights instrument panel warning lamp when multi-point plug on control unit is pulled off.

CONTROL CYCLE (ONE WHEEL)

Wheel speed measured by speed sensor provides wheel deceleration and acceleration for electronic control unit. Linking individual wheel speed provides approximate vehicle reference speed.

MERCEDES-BENZ ANTI-LOCK BRAKE SYSTEM (Cont.)

Comparison of wheel speed with reference speed supplies slip signals. If wheel locks from too much pressure in caliper, a condition recognized by wheel speed sequence (wheel slip), pressure is held constant with no additional increase possible.

If there is a tendency toward locking because constant pressure is still too high, output solenoid valve will open to lower pressure. If pressure is low enough for wheel acceleration, pressure is not lowered but instead held constant.

When re-acceleration of wheel passes a given value, pressure is increased in between by opening input valve in solenoid valve. Signals from control unit allow hydraulic unit to actuate pressure maintenance, reduction and build-up.

Control sequence is repeated during controlled braking until brake pedal is released or until just before vehicle stops.

TROUBLE SHOOTING

ABS CONTROL LIGHT

Control Lamp Lights Up Intermittently (Will Not Go Out Unless Ignition Switch Is Cycled "OFF" & "ON")

If no fault can be detected with test adapter, the problem may be an interrupted wire or loose connection on one of the speed sensor cables or the ABS wiring harness.

Perform TEST 4, 5 and 6 with test adapter and multimeter (internal resistance of speed sensors). While testing, move cable at coaxial plug at cable connector and at speed sensor. If the ohmmeter indicates a break or loose connection, replace the speed sensor and coaxial cable or tighten connections at cable connector.

Control Lamp Lights Up, ABS Operates Brake System Normally

Check altenator output. Altenator control light comes on but only very dim (hardly visible). Alternator charges but not to full capacity. When applying a load on the alternator, a humming noise can be heard.

Control Lamp Lights Up Intermittently

When switching on several electrical consumers, the battery voltage drops below 10.5 volts and the ABS control lamp lights up. If the battery voltage increases again above 10.5 volts, the control lamp goes out.

This type of failure will switch off the ABS system only during low voltage periods. Perform battery test.

Light Braking Pedal Pulsation (ABS Control Lamp Does Not Light Up)

Speed sensor or electronic control unit defective. This will cause the return pump in the hydraulic unit to operate. Check voltage signal from speed sensors. Perform test steps 4, 5 and 6 with test adapter and multimeter (Set to AC volts position).

Remove speed sensors and check for dirt accumulation (metal chips at sensor tip). If steps 1 and 2 are in order, replace electronic control unit.

TESTING

TESTING WITH ABS TESTER

NOTE: **DO NOT drive vehicle with tester connected.**

Connecting Tester

1) With ignition off, disconnect 35-pole connector of cable harness from electronic control unit.

2) Connect 35-pole connector to plug of ABS Test Adaptor (126-589-09-21-00). Make sure that all other electrical components are off before turning ignition on.

3) Connect multimeter to test adapter. This adapter permits testing the complete ABS system, except the electronic control unit.

TEST 1

Testing Relay & Valve Relay In De-Energized Position

1) Set rotary switch to position 1, ignition off. All LED's in tester should be off.

2) If LED battery symbol in tester lights up, replace relay and valve relay.

TEST 2

Testing Voltage Supply

1) Set rotary switch to position 1, ignition on. LED battery symbol on tester will come on, if okay. LED light will not come on if battery voltage is under 10.5 volts. Check battery and charging system.

2) If ABS indicator light is off, check connecting line, check indicator light and replace if necessary.

TEST 3

Testing Valve Relay

Ignition on. Rotary switch position 2. ABS indicator light on, LED not lit. Valve relay defective or connecting lines interrupted.

TEST 4

Testing Diode In Hydraulic Unit

1) Ignition on. Rotary switch to position 2. Multimeter set to DC volts position.

2) Reading should be 0.4-1.5 volts. If less than 0.4 volts or greater than 1.5 volts, go to step **3)**.

3) Check and replace valve relay or diode of hydraulic unit. Check connecting lines.

NOTE: **If ABS indicator light goes out upon replacement of hydraulic unit with the ignition on and engine not running, replace Electronic Control Unit.**

TEST 5

Testing Internal Resistance Of Speed Sensor

1) Multimeter set to "OHMS" position. Ignition on. Rotary switch moved successively to positions 4 (left front wheel), 5 (right front wheel) and 6 (rear differential).

2) Internal resistance:

- Front Wheel 1.1-2.3 kOhms.
- Rear Differential 0.6-1.6 kOhms.

3) If resistance is below or over step **2)**, check coaxial plug or cable connector and connecting lines. Replace speed sensor or adjust wheel bearing play.

MERCEDES-BENZ ANTI-LOCK BRAKE SYSTEM (Cont.)

TEST 6

Testing Insulation Resistance Of Speed Sensor

1) Follow TEST 5, step **1)**. Push ground button. Insulation resistance should be greater than 20 kOhm.

2) If not, check for grounded speed sensor, cable and line connector, or coaxial plug.

TEST 7

NOTE: **When testing speed sensor of rear differential, hold one wheel in place.**

Testing For Interchageability

1) Set multimeter to "AC VOLTS" position. Turn ignition on. Rotary switch moved successively to positions 4 (left front wheel), 5 (right front wheel) and 6 (rear differential). Spin respective wheel approximately one revolution per second.

2) Resistance should be greater than or equal to approximately 0.1 volt. If not, check coaxial plug, connecting lines, wheel bearing play adjustment or replace speed sensor.

TEST 8

Testing Internal Resistance Of Solenoid Valves

1) Set multimeter to "OHMS" position. Ignition off. Push ground button. Rotary switch moved successively to positions 8, 9 and 10.

2) Resistance should be 0.7-1.7 ohms. If internal resistance is under .07 ohms or over 1.7 ohms, go to step **3)**.

3) Check for poor contact at plug connector on hydraulic unit, interrupted connecting wires or defective hydraulic unit.

TEST 9

Testing Pressure Holding Of Solenoid Valves

1) Ignition on. Rotary switch moved successively to positions 8, 9 and 10. Spin respective wheel. Press "P" push button. Actuate brake pedal.

2) Wheel should permit turning and no brake force should build up. If not okay, go to step **3)**.

3) Check for defective motor relay, return pump, or solenoid valve. Replace as necessary.

TEST 10

Testing Pressure Reduction Of Solenoid Valve

1) Ignition on. Rotary switch moved successively to positions 8, 9 and 10. Actuate brake pedal. Press "P" button. Turn respective wheel.

2) Introduced brake force should be reducing. Return pump should be running. If not, proceed to step **3)**.

3) Check for defective motor relay, return pump, or solenoid valve. Replace as necessary.

TEST 11

NOTE: **Stoplight switch is connected to 35-pole plug at pin 25.**

Testing Overvoltage Protection Relay

Ignition on. Actuate brake pedal. LED indicator "0" should come on. If not, check connecting wires or replace stoplight switch.

REMOVAL & INSTALLATION

HYDRAULIC UNIT

Removal

With ignition off, disconnect battery. Remove lines from hydraulic unit. Plug openings. Remove hydraulic unit mounting bolt and cover. Detach ground strap from pump motor. Remove 12-pole plug socket. Remove mounting nuts and hydraulic unit.

NOTE: **DO NOT loosen sealed center bolt or 2 hex socket bolts next to cover and brake lines.**

Installation

1) To install, reverse removal procedure. Connect brake lines to hydraulic unit fittings. Brake line identification codes are as follows: Code "V" is line from master cylinder to front brake circuit. Code "H" is line from master cylinder to rear brake circuit.

2) Code "L" is line from hydraulic unit to left front brake. Code "R" is line from hydraulic unit to right front brake. Code "H" is line from unit to rear brakes. Bleed brake system. Check for leaks.

FRONT WHEEL SPEED SENSOR

Removal

1) Remove front wheel and tire. With ignition off, separate coaxial cable in engine compartment. Remove from bracket. Pull cable downward from grommet in wheelhousing.

NOTE: **When removing right speed sensor, remove windshield washer reservoir. Loosen partition in engine compartment near coaxial cable. Lift partition slightly and pull out cable.**

2) Speed sensors have different protective tubes at left and right, identified in holder by "L" or "R". Before installing, ensure NO metal is on magnetic edges of sensor. Coat sensor and steering knuckle bore with Molykote Longterm 2 lubricant.

3) Remove protective tube from cover plate. As they may be used once, remove hex head socket bolt and discard. Pull speed sensor out of steering knuckle bore.

Installation

1) Replace "O" ring on sensor. Mount unit on steering knuckle. Ensure "O" ring is not damaged. Do not force. Attach sensor to knuckle with new bolt. Tighten to 72 INCH lbs. (8 N.m).

2) Attach protective tube to cover plate. Clip cable to holder. Pull through grommet into engine compartment. Replace "O" ring. Connect coaxial cable. Mount front wheel and tire. Complete test program.

REAR AXLE SPEED SENSOR

Removal

Remove rear seat and backrest. With ignition off, remove cable at connector. Remove clips from cable to sensor. Pull cable down through grommets in frame floor and axle carrier. Remove hex head bolt and discard. Remove sensor from rear axle housing.

Installation

To install, reverse removal procedure. Replace "O" ring on sensor. Do not damage "O" ring. Insert sensor into rear axle housing. Using new bolt, attach sensor to rear axle housing and tighten.

MERCEDES-BENZ ANTI-LOCK BRAKE SYSTEM (Cont.)

Fig. 3: Rear Speed Sensor Harness Connector (Under Rear Seat)

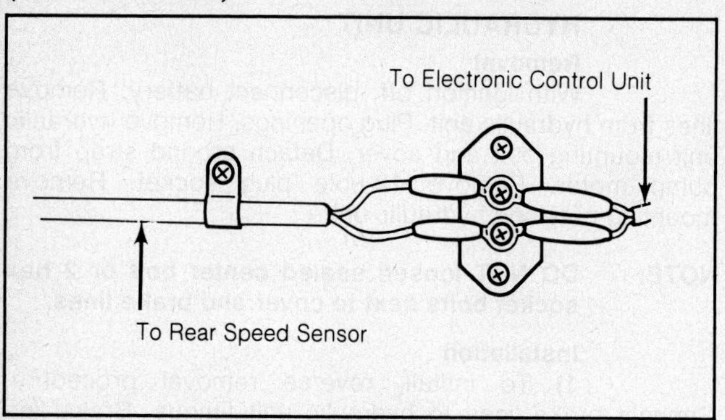

Courtesy of Mercedes-Benz of North America.

ELECTRONIC CONTROL UNIT

NOTE: Turn ignition off before removing or installing electronic control unit. Unit is located on front wall in engine compartment.

Removal & Installation

Push back holding springs. Remove electronic control unit from bracket. Actuate lock. Pull plug from unit. To install, reverse removal procedure. When mounting on unit, ensure plug engages audibly in lock.

RELAYS & OVERVOLTAGE PROTECTION

Removal & Installation

Turn ignition off. To replace ABS components, pull units from plug-in. Note location for proper installation. Engine and valve relays are mounted at hydraulic unit. Relays for electronic control unit and overvoltage protection unit are mounted at fusebox. Install relay or unit into circuit.

MERCEDES-BENZ ANTI-LOCK BRAKE SYSTEM (Cont.)

Fig. 4: Mercedes-Benz 190 Series Anti-Lock Brake System Wiring Diagram

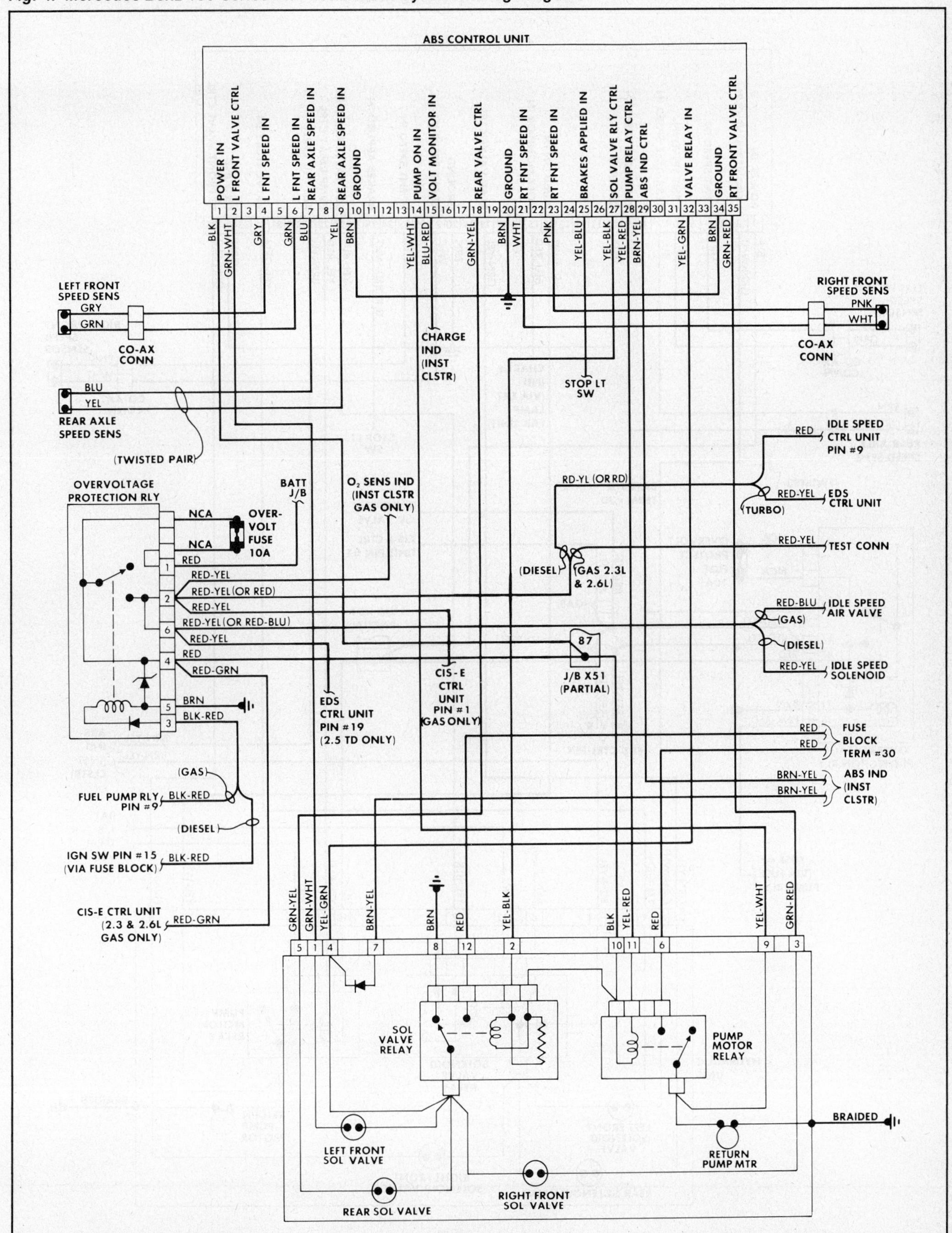

MERCEDES-BENZ ANTI-LOCK BRAKE SYSTEM (Cont.)

Fig. 5: Mercedes-Benz 300 & 260 Series Anti-Lock Brake System Wiring Diagram

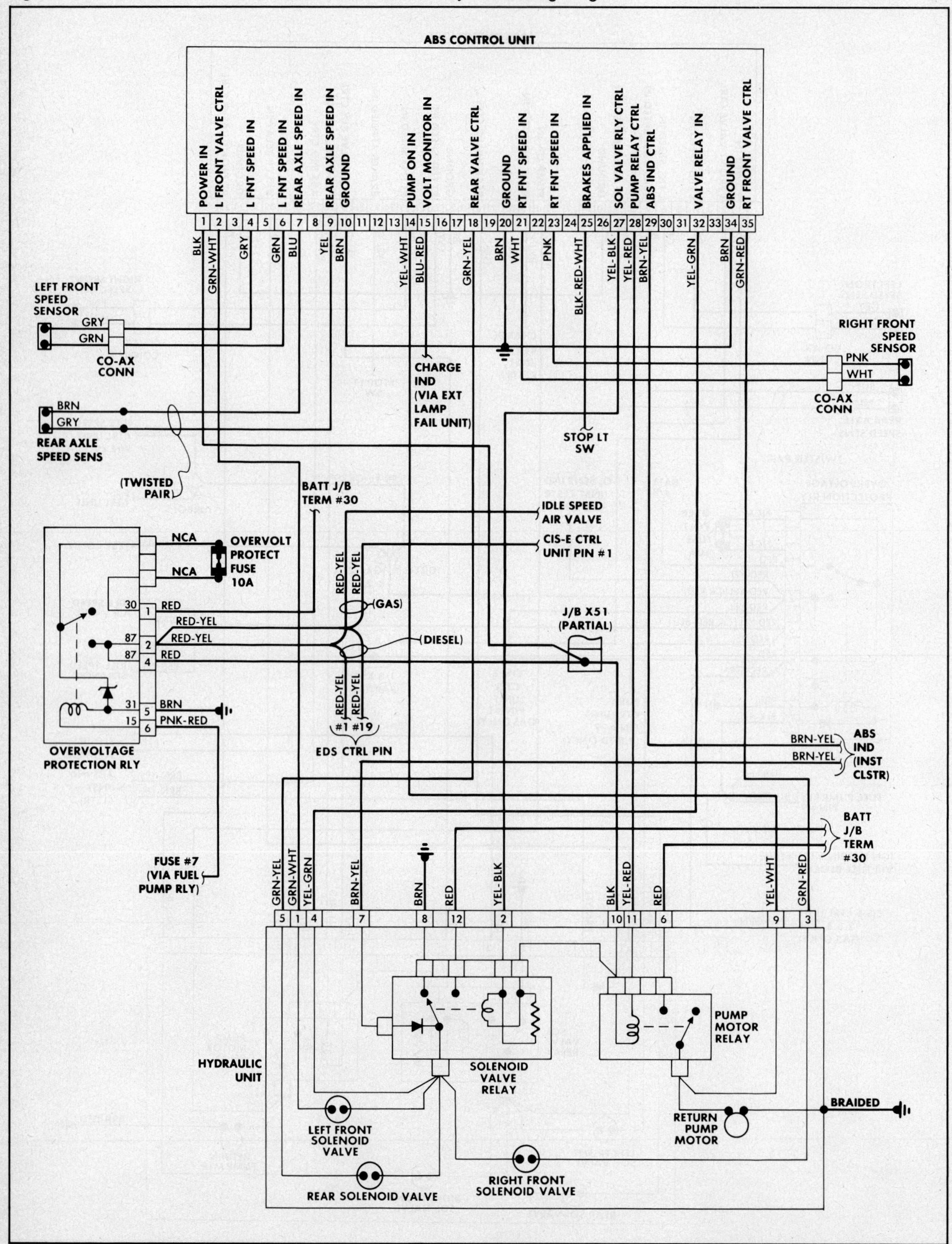

MERCEDES-BENZ ANTI-LOCK BRAKE SYSTEM (Cont.)

Fig. 6: Mercedes-Benz 300SDL, 420/560SEL & 560SEC Anti-Lock Brake System Wiring Diagram

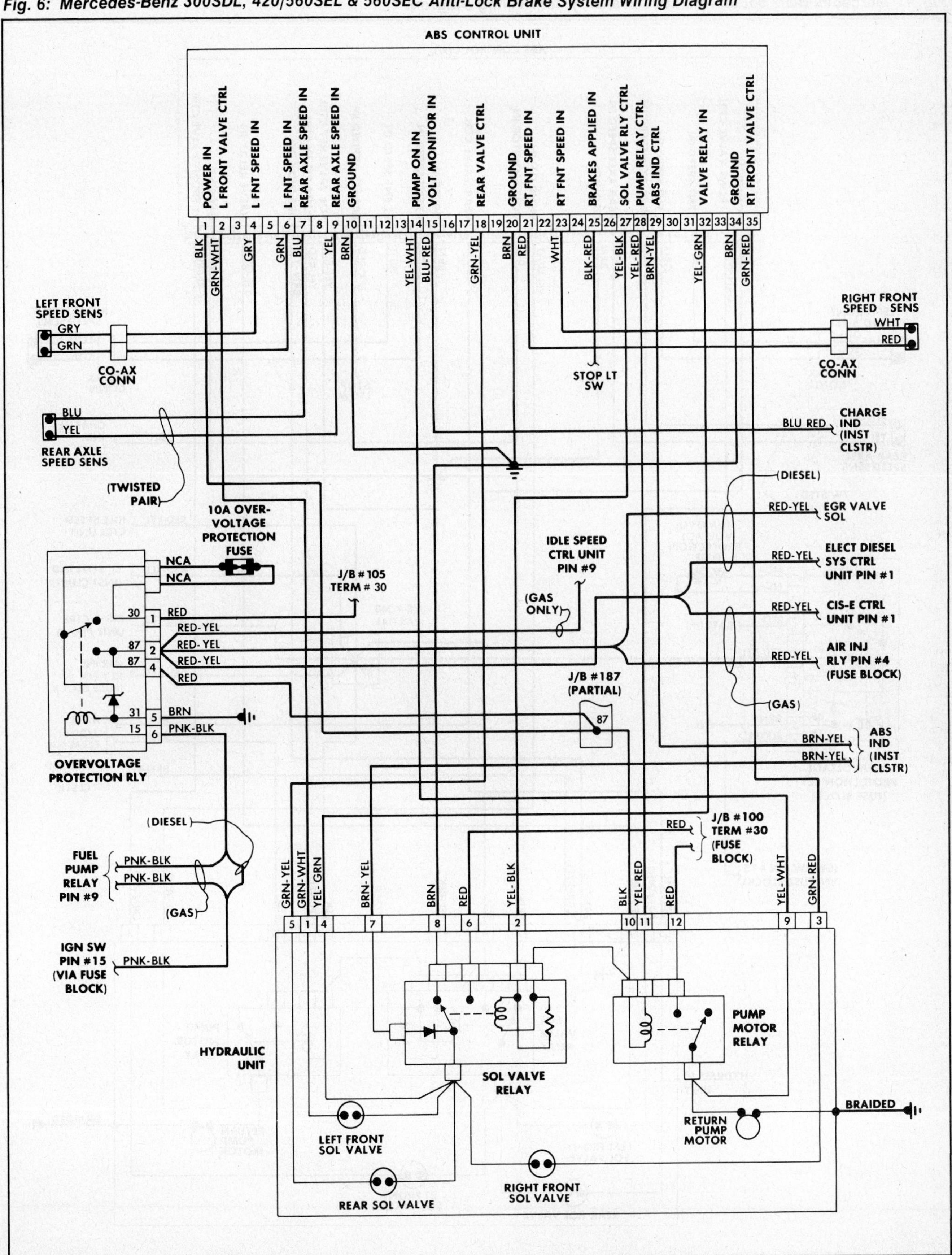

MERCEDES-BENZ ANTI-LOCK BRAKE SYSTEM (Cont.)

Fig. 7: Mercedes-Benz 560SL Anti-Lock Brake System Wiring Diagram

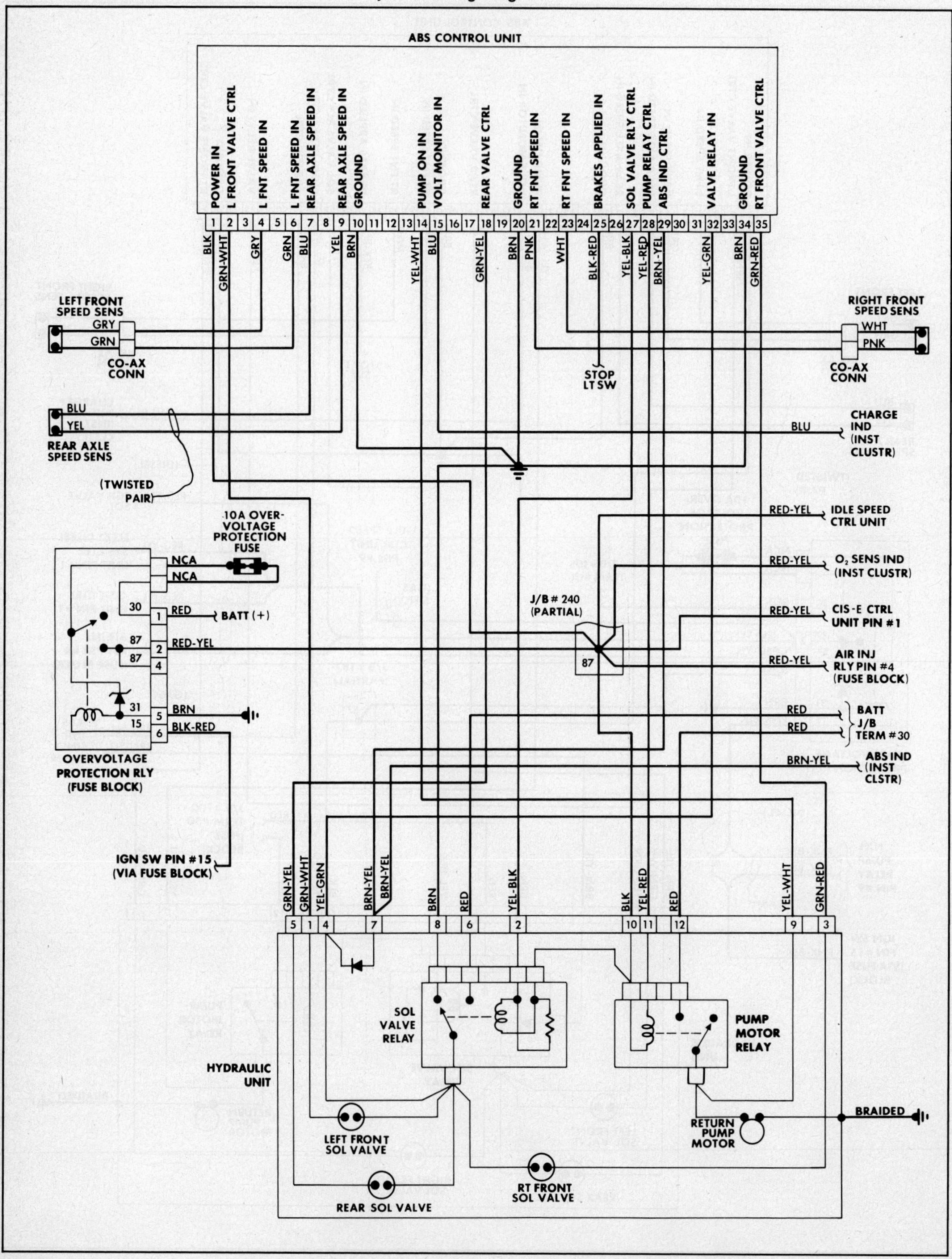

PEUGEOT ANTI-LOCK BRAKE SYSTEM

All Models

DESCRIPTION

The Anti-Lock Brake System (ABS) is designed to provide the most efficient braking ability under any road condition. The system monitors each front wheel individually, and rear wheels as a pair. During heavy braking, ABS prevents the wheels from locking up, which allows the driver to maintain steering control. It also provides the shortest stopping distance possible.

The ABS system consists of 4 wheel sensors, relays, fuses, hydraulic unit, 2 warning lights and an Electronic Control Unit (ECU). The difference between this system and other ABS systems is the brake servo unit is hydraulically operated rather than vacuum operated. Up to 12 brake pressure modulation cycles are possible per second.

OPERATION

ELECTRONIC CONTROL UNIT (ECU)

The ECU is located behind passenger's floor panel. It receives signals from each wheel sensor. From the information it receives, it controls the solenoid valves. This increases or decreases hydraulic pressure to each wheel to prevent lock-up.

NOTE: **ECU must be REMOVED from vehicle when using an arc welder on vehicle or placing vehicle in an oven for painting purposes.**

WARNING LIGHTS

The "BRAKE" warning light will come on if fluid level is low. "ANTILOCK" light will come on if there is a malfunction in the ECU, inoperative wheel sensor, faulty electrovalve or ECU power failure. During this period, ABS is deactivated. Anytime both lights are on at the same time, brake fluid is low (second warning) or hydraulic pressure is too low, electrovalve functions to front wheels are deactivated.

WHEEL SENSORS

Front sensors are located at each wheel. Sensor rings are mounted on each hub. Rear sensors are located near rear drive axle. Sensor rings are mounted on

Fig. 2: Side View of Wheel Sensors

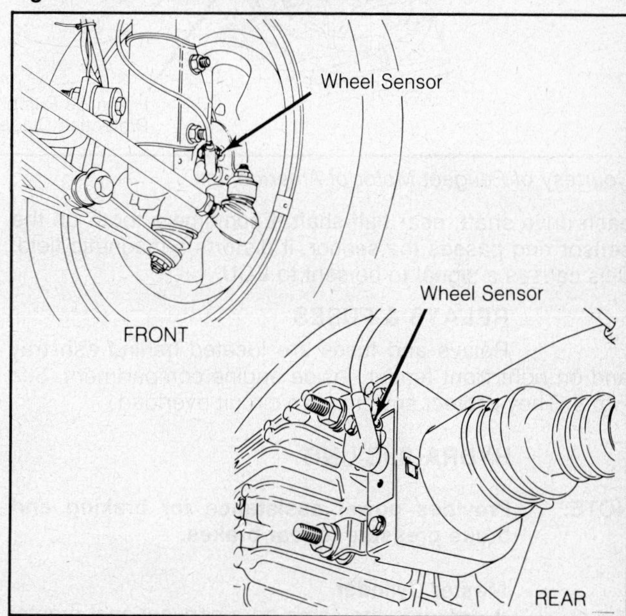

Courtesy of Peugeot Motor of America, Inc.

Fig. 1: ABS Component Locations

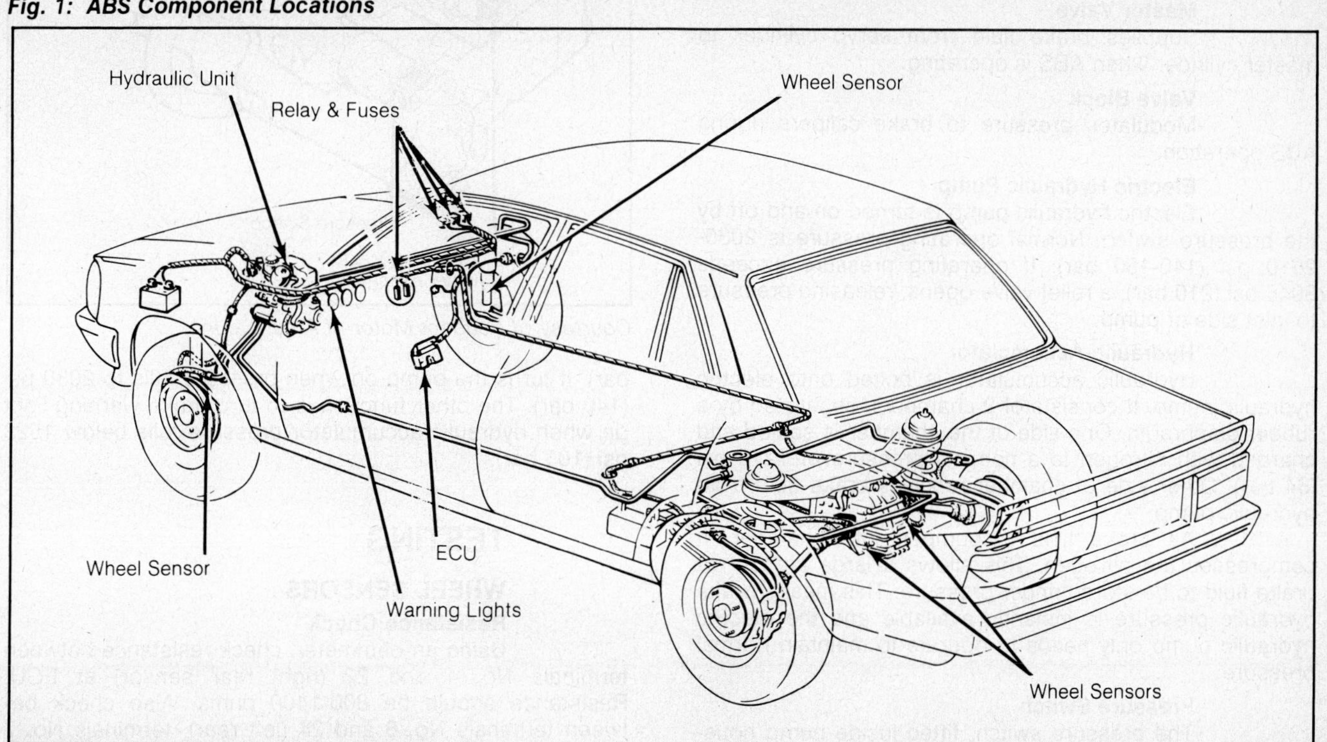

Courtesy of Peugeot Motor of America, Inc.

PEUGEOT ANTI-LOCK BRAKE SYSTEM (Cont.)

Fig. 3: Relays & Fuses Location

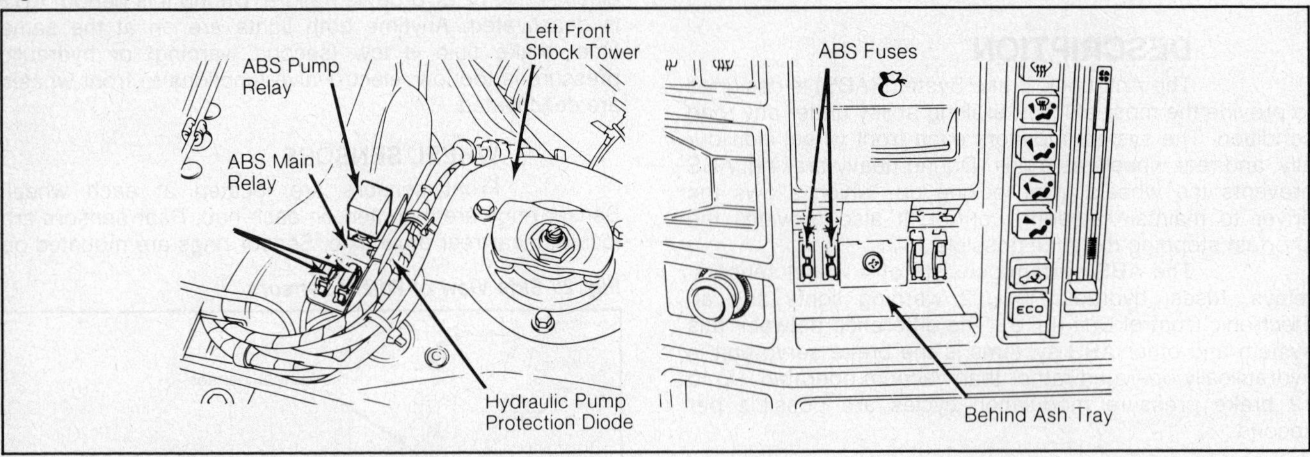

Courtesy of Peugeot Motor of America, Inc.

each drive shaft, near half-shaft. Each time a tooth on the sensor ring passes the sensor, it distorts a magnetic field. This causes a signal to be sent to ECU.

RELAYS & FUSES

Relays and fuses are located behind ash tray and on right front fender, inside engine compartment. *See Fig. 3.* They protect system from circuit overload.

HYDRAULIC UNIT

NOTE: **Provides power assistance for braking and brake pressure to rear brakes.**

Master Cylinder

It operates the same as a conventional master cylinder.

Master Valve

Supplies brake fluid from servo cylinder to master cylinder when ABS is operating.

Valve Block

Modulates pressure to brake calipers during ABS operation.

Electric Hydraulic Pump

Electric hydraulic pump is turned on and off by the pressure switch. Normal operating pressure is 2030-2610 psi (140-180 bar). If operating pressure exceeds 3045 psi (210 bar), a relief valve opens, releasing pressure to inlet side of pump.

Hydraulic Accumulator

Hydraulic accumulator is bolted onto electric hydraulic pump. It consists of 2 chambers, separated by a rubber diaphragm. One side of the chamber is sealed and charged with nitrogen to a nominal pressure of 1218 psi (84 bar). Other side of chamber receives brake fluid from hydraulic pump.

As brake fluid is pumped into chamber, it compresses the nitrogen. This allows a large amount of brake fluid to be stored under pressure. This means brake hydraulic pressure is instantly available and the electric hydraulic pump only needs to operate to maintain normal pressure.

Pressure Switch

The pressure switch, fitted inside pump housing, has 2 functions. One function is to turn the electric hydraulic pump off when pressure reaches 2610 psi (180 bar). It turns the pump on when pressure falls to 2030 psi (140 bar). The other function is to turn brake warning light on when hydraulic accumulator pressure falls below 1523 psi (105 bar).

Fig. 4: Exploded View of Hydraulic Unit

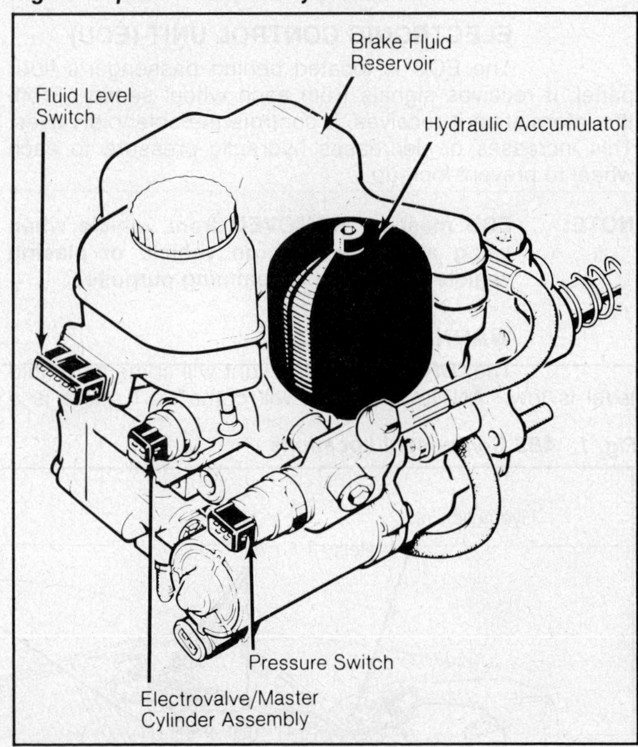

Courtesy of Peugeot Motor of America, Inc.

TESTING

WHEEL SENSORS

Resistance Check

Using an ohmmeter, check resistance between terminals No. 4 and 22 (right rear sensor) at ECU. Resistance should be 800-1400 ohms. Also check between terminals No. 6 and 24 (left rear), terminals No. 7 and 25 (right front) and terminals No. 5 and 23 (left front). If resistance is not as specified, check continuity between

PEUGEOT ANTI-LOCK BRAKE SYSTEM (Cont.)

ECU and appropriate wheel sensor. If continuity is okay, replace wheel sensor.

Voltage Check

1) Using a voltmeter, check voltage between ECU terminals No. 4 and 22 (right rear sensor) with wheel rotating approximately one revolution per second. Also check between terminals No. 6 and 24 (left rear), between terminals No. 7 and 25 (right front) and terminals No. 5 and 23 (left front).

2) Front sensor voltage should be 100-350 millivolts. Rear sensor voltage should be 100-570 millivolts. If voltage is not as specified, check air gap. Ensure sensor ring and sensor are not damaged and are installed correctly.

Cable Shielding

Using an ohmmeter, check resistance of cable shielding between ECU terminals No. 1 and 4 (right rear sensor), terminals No. 1 and 6 (left rear), terminals No. 1 and 7 (right front) and terminals No. 1 and 5 (left front). All readings should be infinity. If reading is not as specified, check cable shielding insulation.

ECU POWER SUPPLY

1) Connect a voltmeter to ECU terminals No. 1 and 2. Turn ignition on. If voltage is less than 12 volts, check wiring continuity. If voltage is okay, turn ignition off. Connect an ohmmeter to ECU terminals No. 1 and 3. If resistance is one ohm or more, check main relay and wiring continuity.

2) If resistance is okay, check resistance between ECU terminals No. 1 and 20. If resistance is one ohm or more, check wiring continuity. If resistance is okay, check resistance between ECU terminals No. 1 and 8. Resistance should be 50-100 ohms.

3) If resistance is not as specified, check main relay and wiring continuity. Connect a jumper wire between ECU terminals No. 2 and 8. Connect a voltmeter between ECU terminals No. 1 and 3. Turn ignition on. If voltage is less than 12 volts, check main relay and wiring continuity.

MAIN ELECTROVALVE

Operation

Turn ignition on. Wait until pump stops operating. Turn ignition off. Connect a jumper wire between ECU terminals No. 2 and 18. Depress brake pedal moderately. Turn ignition on. Brake pedal should become hard and force upward against foot. If not, perform RESISTANCE test.

Resistance

Using an ohmmeter, check resistance between ECU terminals No. 11 and 18. If resistance is not 2-5 ohms, check wiring continuity between ECU and electrovalve connector. If there is continuity, replace electrovalve/master cylinder assembly and retest.

CONTROL ELECTROVALVES

Operation

1) Raise vehicle and support so wheels can be rotated. Turn ignition on. Wait until pump stops operating. Turn ignition off. Connect a jumper wire between ECU terminals No. 2 and 8.

CAUTION: DO NOT energize electrovalves more than 60 seconds.

2) Connect a jumper wire between ECU terminal No. 3 and the following terminals: No. 16, 17, 33, 24 and 35, one at a time. Depress brake pedal each time jumper wire is connected. Left front wheel should be locked. Turn ignition on. Left front wheel should be free. Turn ignition off.

3) Connect jumper wire between ECU terminal No. 3 and each of the following terminals: No. 15, 16, 17, 33 and 34, one at a time. Same results from left front wheel should exist for right front wheel during this test.

4) Perform same test for rear wheels, connecting jumper wire between ECU terminal No. 3 and the following terminals: No. 17 and 33, one at a time. If system fails any of these tests, replace check continuity of wiring. If wiring is okay, replace electrovalve/master cylinder assembly and retest.

Resistance

1) Using an ohmmeter, check resistance between ECU terminals No. 1 and 11. Resistance should be less than one ohm. If resistance is one ohm or more, check continuity of wire between ECU terminal No. 11 and electrovalve. If there is continuity, check for wire grounding at electrovalve connector.

2) Check continuity between ECU terminal No. 11 and the following: Nos. 15, 16, 17, 33, 34 and 35. Resistance at each terminal should be 3-7 ohms. If continuity is not as specified, check continuity of wire between ECU and electrovalve connector. *See Fig. 8.* If wiring continuity is okay, replace electrovalve/master cylinder assembly and retest.

HYDRAULIC PUMP

Operation

Turn ignition off. Depress brake pedal approximately 25 times to depressurize brake system. Turn ignition on. Hydraulic pump should operate. If not, connect a voltmeter to hydraulic pump connector. Voltage should be 12 or more. If voltage is not as specified, check the following: Pump protection diode, relay, pressure sensor and wire continuity. If no fault can be found, replace pump motor and retest.

"ANTILOCK" LIGHT CIRCUIT

Continuity

1) Turn ignition on. Wait until pump stops operating. Turn ignition off. Using an ohmmeter, check resistance between ECU terminals No. 9 and 10. If resistance is one ohm or more, check pressure accumulator. If okay, check continuity between pins No. 1 and 2 on level switch.

2) Check between pressure switch terminals No. 3 and 5. If there is no continuity, replace defective component. If there is continuity, check for continuity between ECU terminal No. 9 and level switch pin No. 1.

3) Check between ECU terminal No. 10 and pressure switch pin No. 5, and between pressure switch pin No. 3 and level switch pin No. 2. If there is no continuity during any of these test, repair appropriate wire.

"BRAKE" LIGHT CIRCUIT

Ensure brake fluid level is okay and hand brake is released. Turn ignition on. Brake light should go off. If not, connect a jumper wire between level switch pins No. 2 and 3. Using an ohmmeter, check resistance between level switch pins No. 1 and 2. Check resistance

PEUGEOT ANTI-LOCK BRAKE SYSTEM (Cont.)

between pressure switch pins No. 1 and 2. If readings are not infinite, replace defective component.

HYDRAULIC ACCUMULATOR & PRESSURE SWITCH

CAUTION: Depress brake pedal approximately 25 times to depressurize hydraulic system before servicing system.

1) Install pressure gauge to hydraulic system. *See Fig. 5*. Turn ignition on. Pressure gauge should read 580-1305 psi (4000-9000 kPa). If not, replace hydraulic accumulator and retest. If pressure is okay, turn ignition off.

2) Depress brake pedal 25 times to depressurize system. Turn ignition on. Check pump motor operating time. If pump motor operates more than 60 seconds, check hydraulic system and reservoir filter. If okay, turn ignition off. Depressurized system. Turn ignition on.

3) Check pressure reading when pump stops operating. Pressure should be 2320-2755 psi (16,000-19,000 kPa). Pump brake pedal and check reading when pump starts operating. Reading should be 1885-2175 psi (13,000-15,000 kPa). If pressure readings are not as specified, check pressure switch. If pressure switch is okay, replace hydraulic accumulator.

Fig. 5: Hydraulic Pressure Test Point

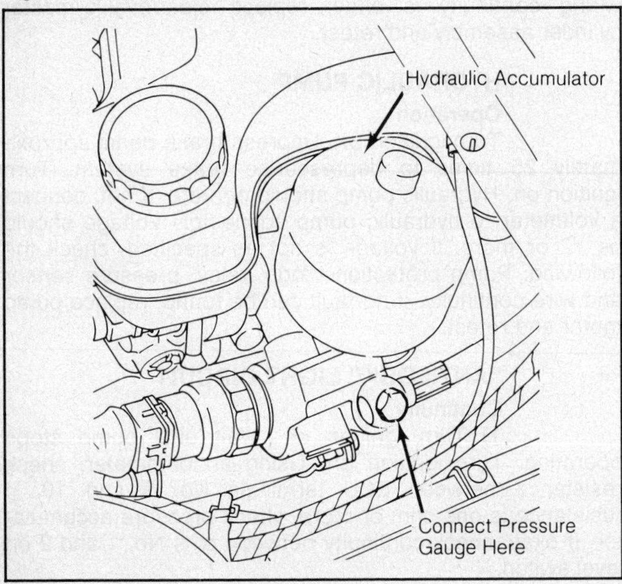

Courtesy of Peugeot Motor of America, Inc.

INTERNAL LEAK TEST

1) Turn ignition on. Wait for pump to stop operating and then wait an additional 3 minutes for system to stabilize. If system pressure drops more than 145 psi (1000 kPa) in 5 minutes, check for external leaks. If no leaks can be found, replace electrovalve/master cylinder assembly and retest.

2) Turn ignition off. Depress brake pedal approximately 25 times to depressurize system. Install pressure gauges on both front wheels. Depress brake pedal and adjust front wheel pressure to 1450 psi (10,000 kPa). *See Fig. 6*.

3) Turn ignition on. Wait for pump to stop operating. If pressure drops more than 72.5 psi (500 kPa) on front wheels or 145 psi (1000 kPa) on entire system, check for external leaks. If no leaks can be found, replace electrovalve/master cylinder assembly and retest.

Fig. 6: Adjusting Hydraulic Pressure

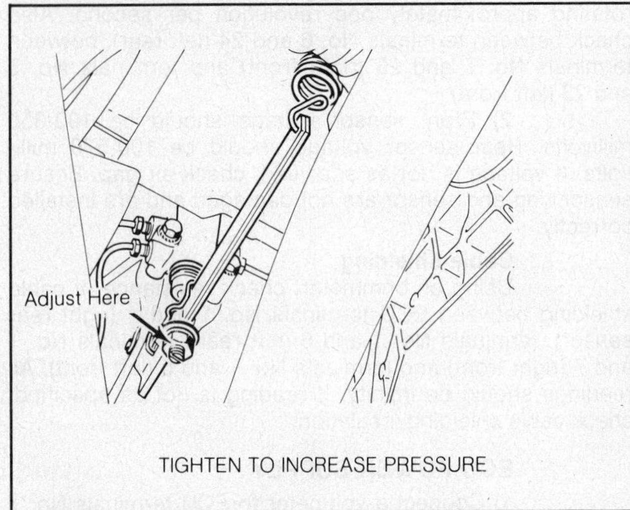

Courtesy of Peugeot Motor of America, Inc.

REMOVAL & INSTALLTION

CAUTION: When removing any ABS hydraulic brake component, depress brake pedal approximately 25 times, with engine off, to depressurize brake system.

HYDRAULIC UNIT

Removal & Installation

Unplug all connectors from hydraulic unit. Drain brake fluid from reservoir. Disconnect all brake lines from hydraulic unit and plug openings. Remove coil and ignition module. Remove panels from under dash board. Remove clevis pin. Secure push rod to brake pedal. Remove 4 nuts and hydraulic unit from vehicle. To install, reverse removal procedure. Install new gasket between hydraulic unit and firewall.

WHEEL SENSORS

Removal & Installation (Front)

1) Unplug wheel sensor connector, located in wheelwell. Remove bolt and wheel sensor. To install, clean wheel sensor thoroughly. Position support end even with rear face of wheel sensor. Tighten screw. Install wheel sensor assembly and bolt.

2) Loosen screw and move wheel sensor so it just touches sensor ring. Tighten screw to 24 INCH lbs. (2.7 N.m). Measure distance "A". *See Fig. 7*. Loosen screw and adjust wheel sensor .037" (.95 mm) less than distance "A". Tighten screw to 24 INCH lbs. (2.7 N.m). Reinstall wheel sensor assembly.

3) Apply Loctite to bolt threads. Install bolt and tighten to 84 INCH lbs. (9.5 N.m). Raise vehicle so wheel can be rotated. Connect Test Harness (.0806) to wheel sensor connector. Connect a voltmeter (A.C. scale) to test harness leads. Rotate wheel approximately one revolution per second. If voltage is not 100-350 millivolts, adjust air gap until specified voltage is obtained. Apply dab of paint to screw when proper setting is obtained.

PEUGEOT ANTI-LOCK BRAKE SYSTEM (Cont.)

Fig. 7: Checking Wheel Sensor Position

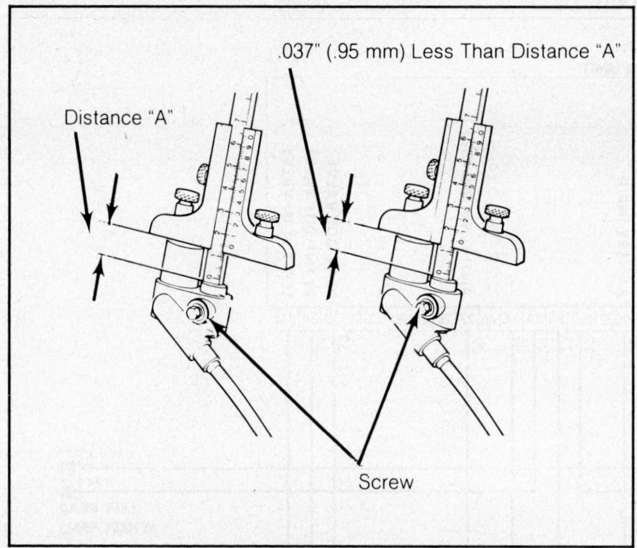

Courtesy of Peugeot Motor of America, Inc.

Removal & Installation (Rear)

1) Remove rear seat cushion. Unplug wheel sensor connector. Remove bolt and wheel sensor. To install, clean wheel sensor throughly. Position support end even with rear face of wheel sensor. Tighten screw. Raise rear of vehicle and support.

2) Install Support (.0703.J1), Adapter (.0703.J2) and dial indicator on vehicle. Rotate half-shaft until dial indicator reverses direction. Mark corresponding half-shaft position. Zero dial indicator. Rotate wheel one complete turn. Record dial indicator reading. Rotate half-shaft until reading is 1/2 of the previous reading.

3) Keep half-shaft at this position for adjustments. Install wheel sensor assembly. Apply Loctite to bolt threads before installing. Loosen screw. Insert a .037" (.95 mm) thick shim between wheel sensor and sensor ring. Tighten screw to 24 INCH lbs. (2.7 N.m).

4) Connect Test Harness (.0806) to wheel sensor connector. Connect a voltmeter (A.C. scale) to test harness leads. Rotate wheel approximately one revolution per second. If voltage is not 100-550 millivolts, adjust air gap until specified voltage is obtained. Apply dab of paint to screw when proper setting is obtained.

BLEEDING BRAKE SYSTEM

NOTE: **Always use a hose and container that can handle extreme high pressure.**

1) Fill brake system. Open left front wheel bleeder screw and depress brake pedal. tighten bleeder screw. DO NOT pump brake pedal. Continue this procedure until fluid contains no air. Bleed right front wheel using the same method.

2) Depress brake pedal approximately 25 times to depressurize brake system. Connect bleed hose to left rear wheel. With brake pedal depressed, turn ignition on. DO NOT release brake pedal. This will activate electric hydraulic pump. When brake fluid from left rear wheel contains no air, tighten bleeder. Turn ignition off. Depressurize brake system and bleed right rear wheel in the same matter.

TIGHTENING SPECIFICATIONS

Application	Ft. Lbs. (N.m)
Brake Lines-to-Hydraulic Unit	
Front Brakes	11 (15)
Rear Brakes	13 (18)
Hydraulic Accumulator	30 (41)
Pressure Switch	15 (20)
	INCH Lbs. (N.m)
Brake Fluid Reservoir Bolt	36 (4)
Wheel Sensor	
Bolt	84 (9.5)
Screw	24 (2.7)

PEUGEOT ANTI-LOCK BRAKE SYSTEM (Cont.)

Fig. 8: Peugeot 505 Series Anti-Lock Brake System Wiring Diagram

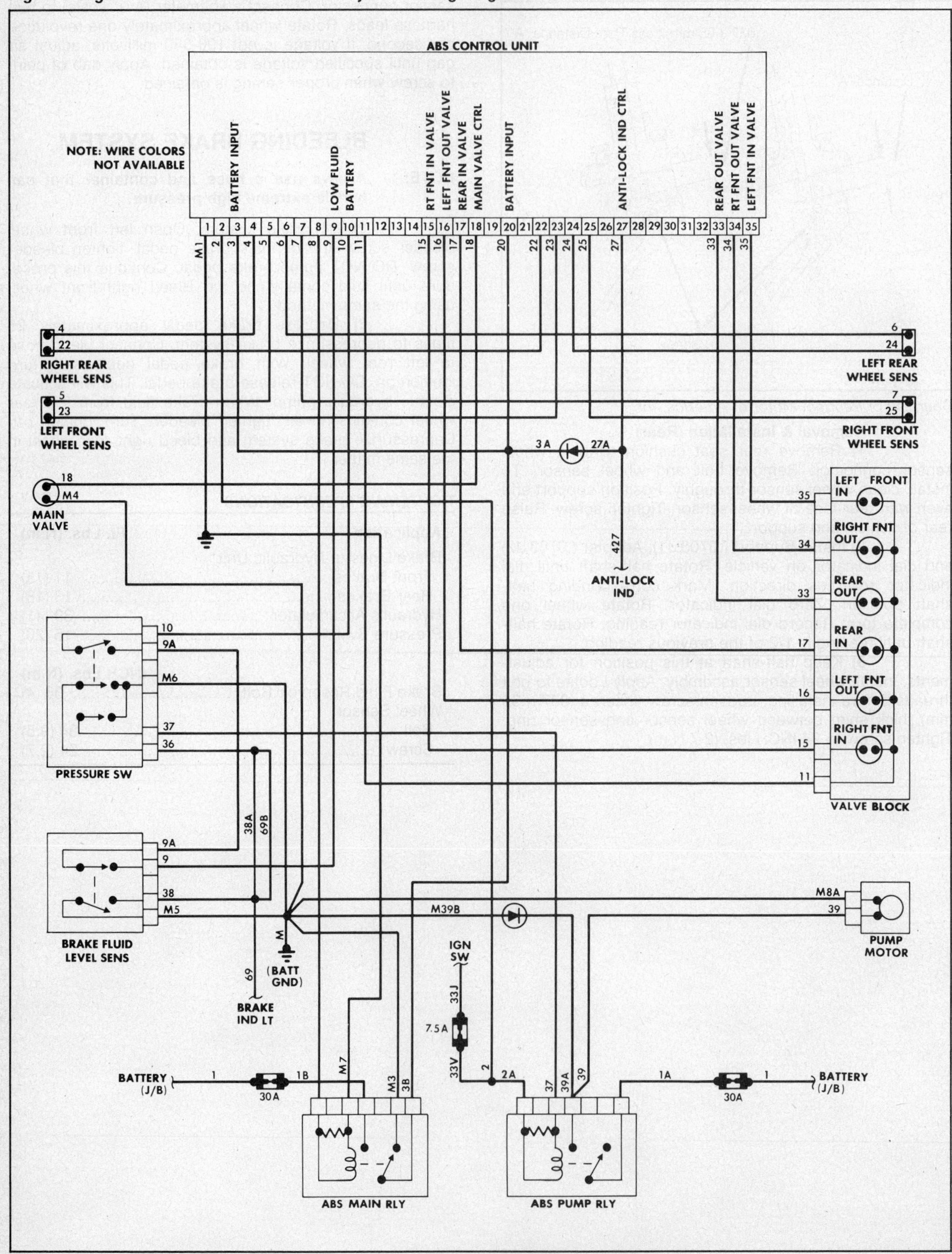

PORSCHE ANTI-LOCK BRAKE SYSTEM

928S, 944, 944S, 944 Turbo

DESCRIPTION

The Porsche Anti-Lock Brake System (ABS) consists of a hydraulic unit with 4 solenoid switching valves, 4 speed sensors and an electronic control unit. The system contains a network of wire harnesses, relays and an overvoltage protection unit. This system functions as a supplement to conventional braking. The ABS equipped vehicles require different disc rotors and master cylinders than standard brakes.

An indicator light ("ANTILOCK" on 928S; "ABS" on 944 series) is located on the instrument panel and illuminates when the ignition is turned on. This indicator light normally goes out after the engine is started, to indicate the ABS system is ready for operation.

The ABS system is activated above 8 MPH. When vehicle speed is above 3 MPH, built-in test equipment will start checking the ABS. If a fault is found, the warning light will again illuminate. When the "ANTI-LOCK" light is on, ABS is deactivated and the vehicle will convert to conventional braking.

If battery voltage drops below 10.5 volts when the ignition is on and test speed is exceeded, the ABS will remain off and warning light will illuminate. When alternator voltage increases above 10.5 volts, warning light will go out.

NOTE: **Entire ABS system must be checked if repair includes any ABS component or if units are replaced following an accident. Use Bosch Tester (016.00) and Adapter Lead (1684 460 120) together with brake test bench.**

OPERATION

HYDRAULIC UNIT

The hydraulic unit consists of 3 electric solenoid valves and a return delivery pump. Each of the electric solenoid valves are for left and right front electric solenoid valves and the mutually regulated rear solenoid valves.

The hydraulic unit can change hydraulic pressure to each of the brakes, independently of the pressure in the brake master cylinder. However, a higher brake master cylinder pressure is not possible.

Depending on amperage, the hydraulic pressure in each wheel cylinder can be as follows: increased (pressure building up phase), maintained (pressure holding phase) or reduced (pressure dropping phase).

The hydraulic unit on the 928S is located on a bracket in an opening on the inner left front wheelwell. Brake line connections are accessible from the engine compartment. On the 944 series, the hydraulic unit in the back of the right front wheelhouse. It is mounted on a bracket with a protective cover.

Pressure Building Phase

Electric solenoid valves are without electric power in the pressure building up phase. Pressure from the brake master cylinder can be effective in full amount in wheel brake cylinders.

This valve position is given for every normal brake application, when regulation is not required. If the system fails, the valve remains in this position to guarantee normal brake operation.

Pressure Holding Phase

If the braked wheel reaches the lock limit, further pressure increase in the wheel brake cylinder will be prevented.

The solenoid receives about 2 amps current. The valve piston is activated and outlet as well as inlet of solenoid valve are closed. Hydraulic pressure between hydraulic unit and wheel brake cylinder remains constant.

Fig. 1: Porsche 928S ABS Component Location

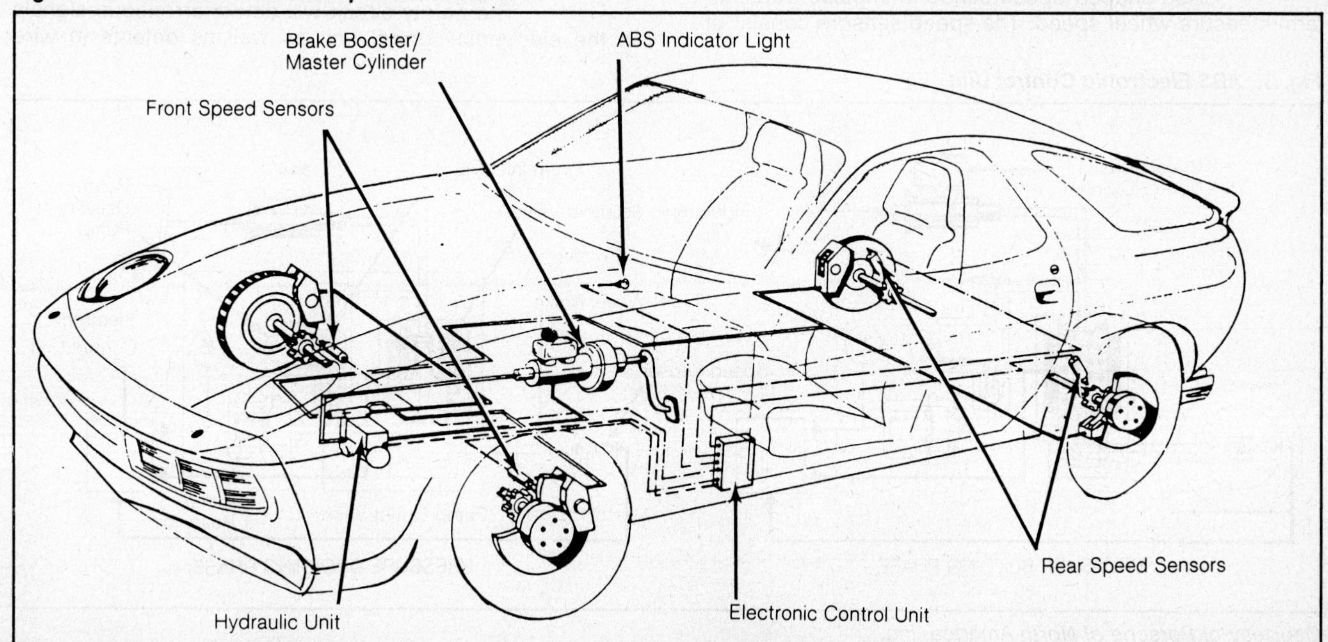

Courtesy of Porsche of North America, Inc.

PORSCHE ANTI-LOCK BRAKE SYSTEM (Cont.)

Fig. 2: Porsche 928S ABS Hydraulic Unit Assembly

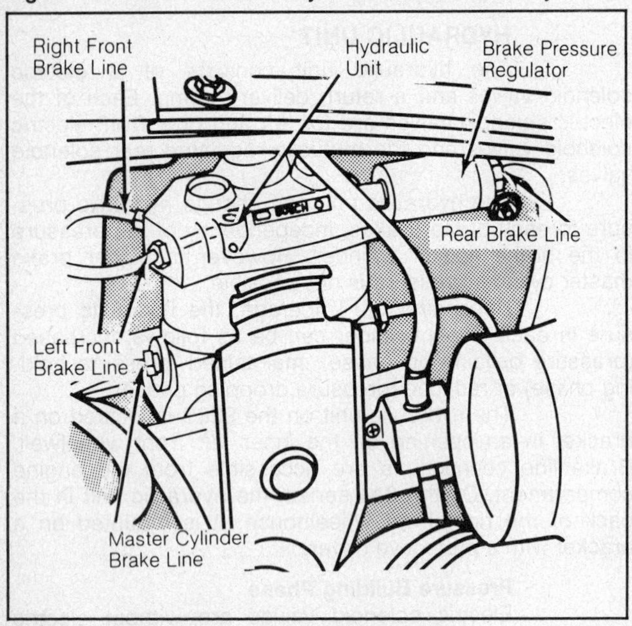

Courtesy of Porsche of North America, Inc.

Pressure Dropping Phase

If wheels still tend to lock in spite of constant hydraulic pressure because of road surface changing from dry to slippery, pressure in wheel brake cylinder must be reduced. Current higher than about 5 amps on the solenoid valve causes a greater piston stroke, which opens the outlet.

Hydraulic fluid flows to pump reservoir and return delivery pump. Return delivery pump returns brake fluid to master cylinder against existing pressure. A damper in each brake circuit stops delivery noise. The pump always runs during regulation.

SPEED SENSORS

Rod-shaped speed sensors (impulse transmitters) measure wheel speed. The speed sensors consist of a magnetic core and a coil. The pole piece is surrounded by a magnetic field. As the road wheel turns, pulse gear teeth move through this magnetic field. This changes the magnetic flux and induces alternating voltage in the coil. This alternating voltage changes its frequency according to the wheel speed. It can be used to measure wheel speed.

Front Axle Speed Sensors

The front axle uses cross pole sensors with axial tapping. They are installed in steering knuckles and secured with one socket head screw. The pulse gear wheel is pressed on front wheel hub. Pulse wheel now has 45 teeth.

Rear Axle Speed Sensors

Rear axle speed sensors have flat pole sensors with radial tappings. On 928S models, sensors are inserted in the wheel carrier. The pulse gear wheel is built directly onto the outer axle shaft. On 944 models, speed sensors are installed in trailing arms. The pulse gear is machined in end of drive axle shaft.

On all models, speed sensors must be seated against stop to give about .013" (.35 mm) clearance between sensor and pulse gear wheel.

ELECTRONIC CONTROL UNIT

The electronic control unit controls all solenoid valve functions in the hydraulic unit. On 928S models, the electronic unit is located above hood release handle on the left kick panel. On 944 models, it is located in the passenger side kick panel.

The signal processing section processes input by deriving acceleration, deceleration and wheel slip values from the speed sensor's signals. This information is sent to the logic section.

Logic Section

The logic section calculates necessary brake pressure corrections. It also commands pressure build-up, pressure holding and pressure drop.

Safety Circuit

The safety circuit will detect erroneous signals in the electronic control unit as well as defects in wire

Fig. 3: ABS Electronic Control Unit

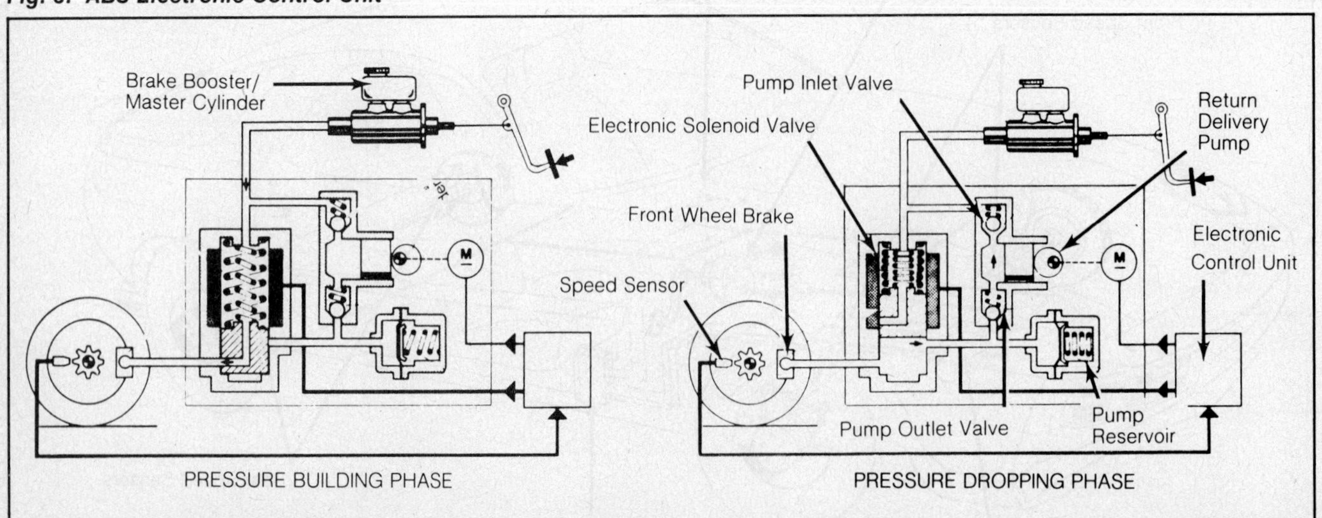

Courtesy of Porsche of North America, Inc.

PORSCHE ANTI-LOCK BRAKE SYSTEM (Cont.)

Fig. 4: Porsche ABS Speed Sensors

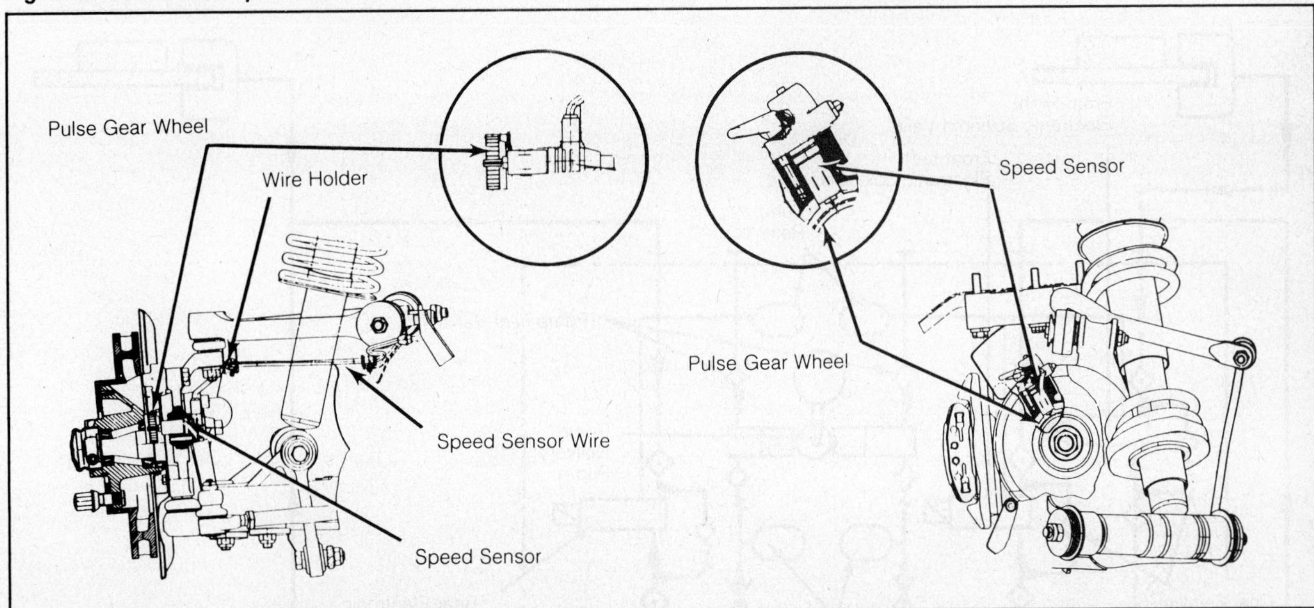

Courtesy of Porsche of North America, Inc.

harness and plug connections. The ABS is switched off when a problem occurs, indicated when indicator light comes on.

The safety circuit constantly monitors battery voltage. If voltage drops below the specified value, the ABS will be switched off until specified value is reached. The safety circuit also has an active section known as "BITE" (Built In Test Equipment).

Test Cycle

A test program runs in the control unit when ignition is switched "ON". Another test program runs at a road speed of 3 MPH. Testing at 3 MPH can be felt, since pump in hydraulic unit will run briefly. Test cycle repeats each time vehicle accelerates. Testing includes the following:

- Electronic control unit.
- Hydraulic unit.
- Speed sensors.
- Relays and wire harness.

POWER SUPPLY

Power supply for the 928S electronic control unit and pump motor relay is provided by ABS relay No. XVII on the central electric board. An overvoltage cut-out is integrated in this relay and protects the electronic control unit against overvoltage.

The power supply for the 944S and 944 Turbo is protected by ABS relay G20 on the Central Electric Board (CEB). The relay is protected a 7.5 amp fuse (No. 26) on the CEB.

BRAKE MASTER CYLINDER

A stepped brake master cylinder with 2 central valves is used.

Fig. 5: ABS Electronic Control Unit

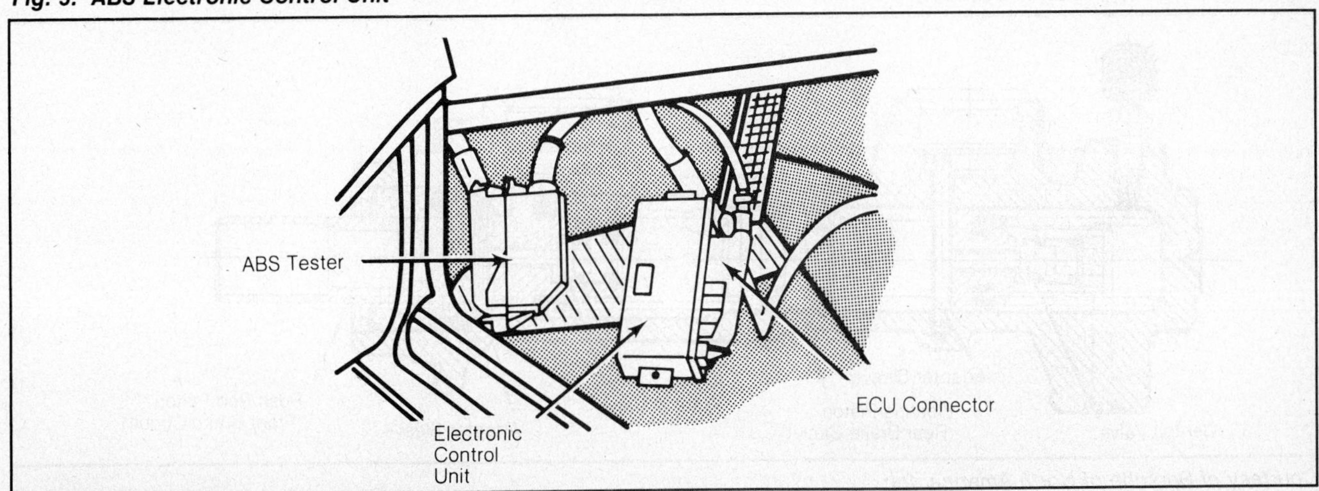

Courtesy of Porsche of North America, Inc.

PORSCHE ANTI-LOCK BRAKE SYSTEM (Cont.)

Fig. 6: Porsche ABS Circuit Diagram

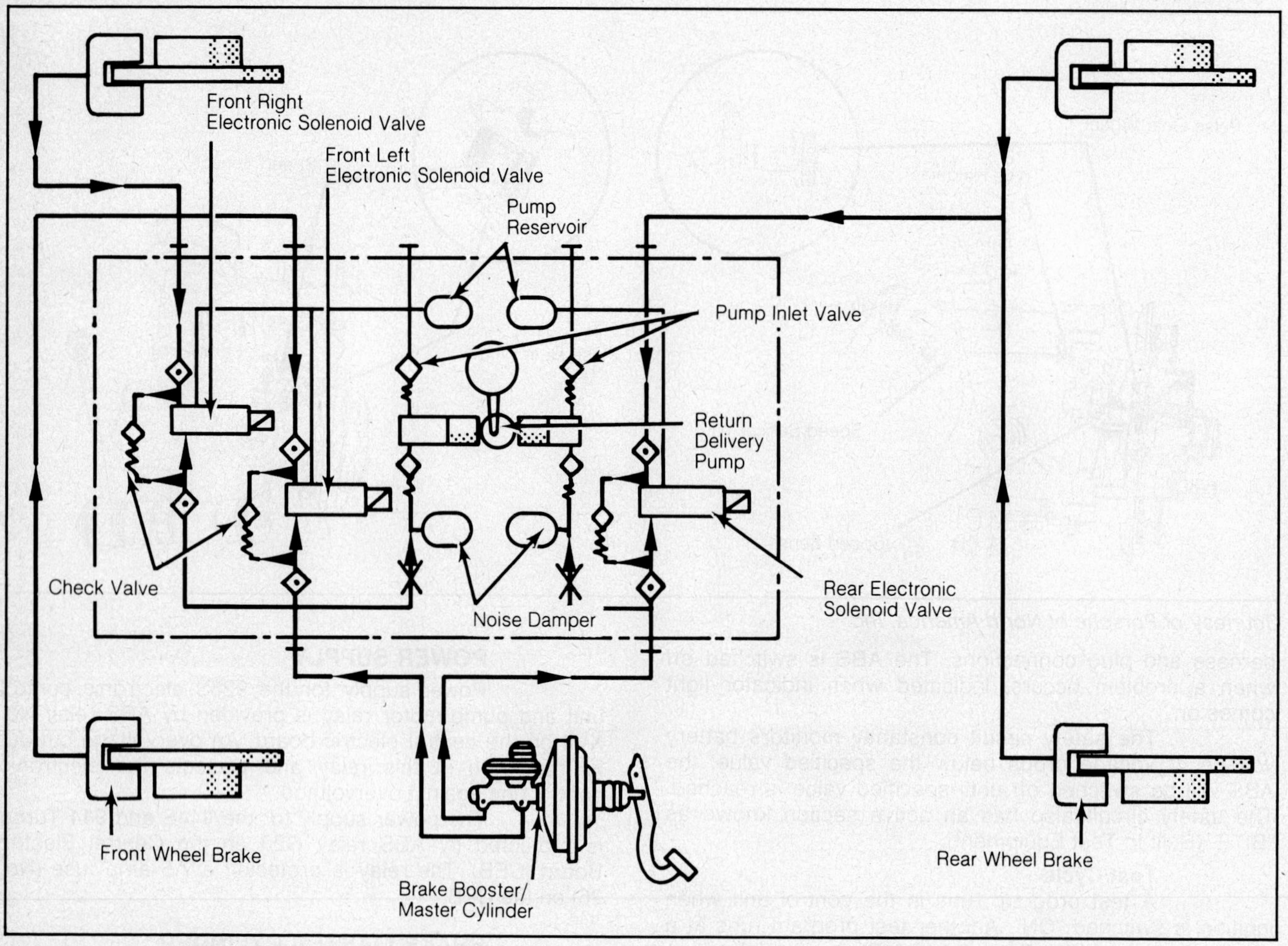

Courtesy of Porsche of North America, Inc.

Central Valves

In "OFF" position, both central valves are open through position on adapter sleeves. Brake fluid can therefore flow into system. If brakes are applied, brake master cylinder piston moves left, both central valves close and brake pressure builds.

When force is removed from brake pedal, the brake piston returns to its original position. Central valves will open after contact with adapter sleeves.

Brake Pressure Regulator

A brake pressure regulator is installed in rear wheel brake circuit at outlet of hydraulic unit. Brake pressure regulator has a fixed switching-over pressure.

Fig. 7: Porsche ABS Master Cylinder

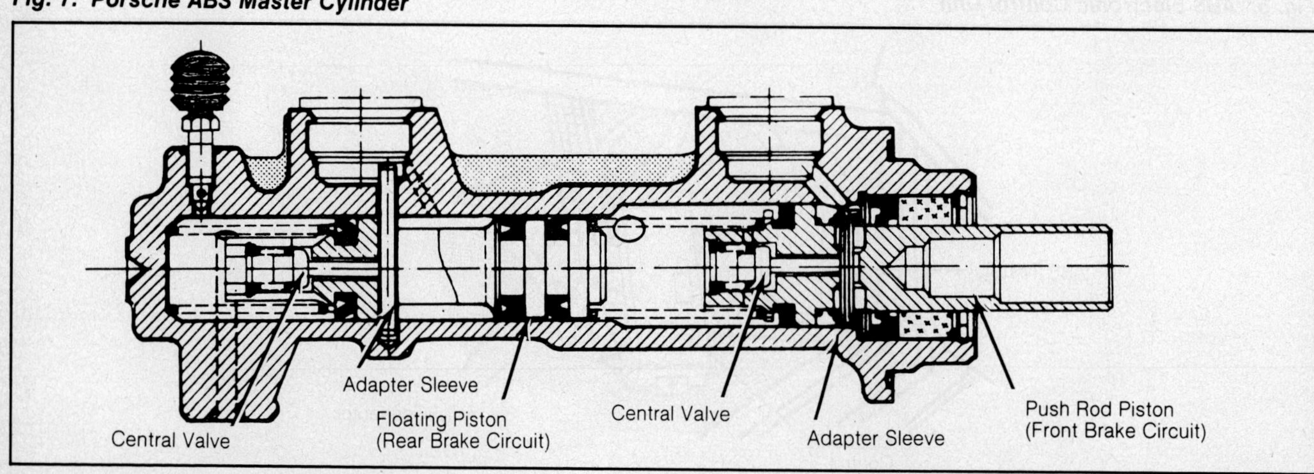

Courtesy of Porsche of North America, Inc.

PORSCHE ANTI-LOCK BRAKE SYSTEM (Cont.)

There is an equal amount of pressure on inlet and outlet sides of brake pressure regulator until switching-over pressure has been reached. As pressure increases on the inlet side, the outlet pressure will be reduced according to setting of brake pressure regulator.

The pressure regulator is located on the rear wheel brake circuit of the hydraulic circuit on 944S, 944 Turbo and 928S models. The 944 does not use a brake pressure regulator. The pressure regulators on the 944S and 944 Turbo are not interchangeable.

RELAY OPERATIONS

The ABS system has 3 relays: ABS main relay, solenoid relay and pressure pump relay.

The ABS relay has an overvoltage protection from a Zener diode. This Zener diode prevents voltage spikes over 22 volts. This diode will prevent an increase in voltage from damaging the control unit.

The solenoid relay closes when ABS control unit receives voltage from the alternator. This causes ground connection of relay terminal No. 85 by the control unit. The relay supplies battery power to solenoid valve coils. If ABS begins to regulate, control unit provides a ground to the solenoid coil of the wheel with regulated pressure.

The pressure pump relay closes when ground is provided through the control unit. The solenoid relay and pressure pump relay are located under the cover of the hydraulic control unit. The pump relay is the larger of the two.

WARNING SYSTEM

A diode is installed between terminals No. 4 and 7 of hydraulic unit connection. If electrical system of ABS control unit has a problem or control unit plug is disconnected, terminal No. 29 will become ground. This will cause problem to go on. If solenoid valve relay is malfunctioning, the indicator/warning lights will also be switched on.

STOPLIGHT SWITCH

The vehicle stoplight switch is also part of the ABS electrical system. Switch must be adjusted so that distance between brake pedal and shoulder of switch is .2" (5 mm).

ABS REPAIR PRECAUTIONS

Observe following precautions when performing repair operations outside of the ABS unit:

- Pull off plug on electronic control unit when welding with an arc welder.
- NEVER subject the electronic control unit to temperatures above 180°F (82°C) when painting a vehicle.
- Disconnect battery before charging with a fast charger. If battery has been removed, make sure wire terminals are tight on both connections after installation of battery. NEVER use a fast charger to start engine.
- NEVER disconnect or connect multiple pin plug on electronic control unit while ignition is on.

Checking Function

A simple function check can be performed following brake system service. In other words, indicator light in instrument cluster must go out after starting engine when ABS is okay. This work would include: replacing brake pads, brake hoses, brake discs, brake booster, tandem master cylinder, brake cables and parts of parking brake as well as brake lines not connected on hydraulic unit.

If work is performed on hydraulic unit, electronic control unit (replaced only), speed sensors, or wire harness or if parts are replaced because of damage through accident, function must be tested with an ABS tester.

Fig. 8: Bosch ABS Tester (016.00)

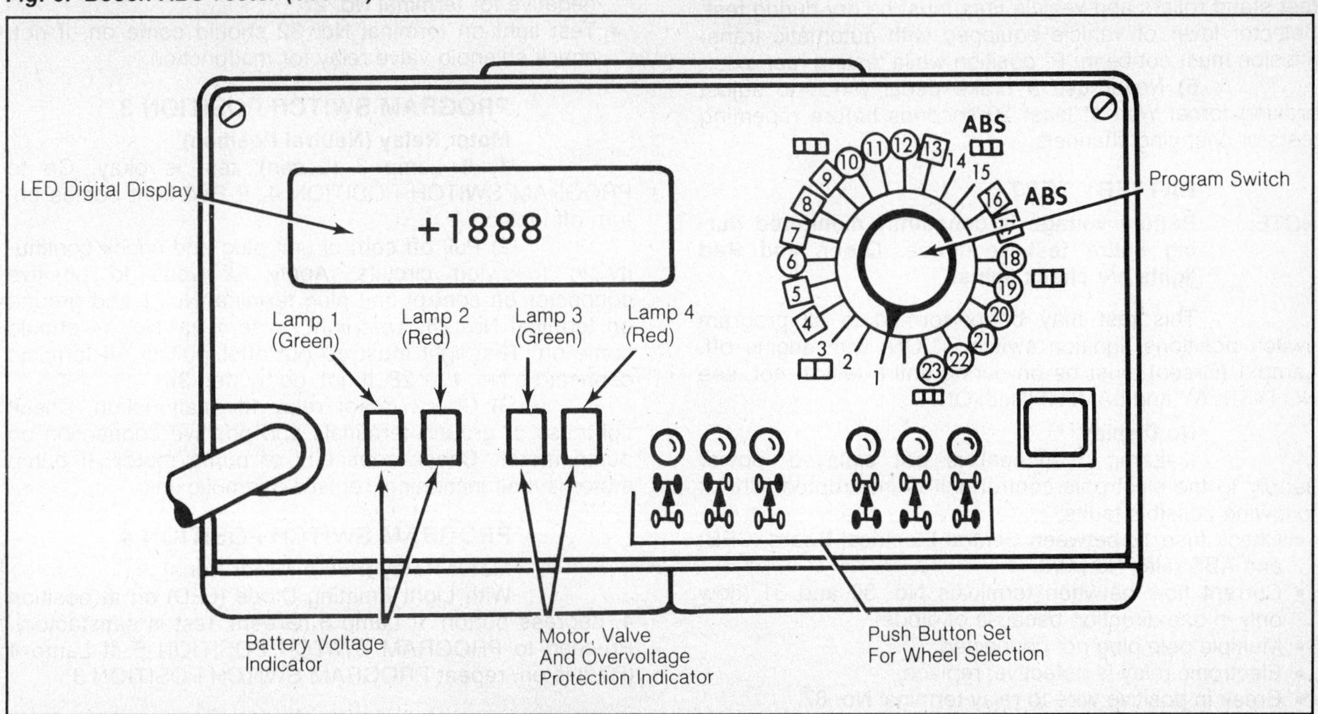

Courtesy of Porsche of North America, Inc.

PORSCHE ANTI-LOCK BRAKE SYSTEM (Cont.)

TESTING

TESTER

Bosch Tester (016.00) is used to check control unit function, hydraulic unit, wire harness and related ABS groups. Actual values determined with tester must be compared with corresponding nominal values. If actual value deviates from nominal value, see TROUBLE SHOOTING chart at end of test section.

ADAPTER LEAD

An Adapter Lead (1684 460 120) is required to connect and test electronic relay with overvoltage protection in socket on back of tester. The overvoltage protection relay supplied with Bosch Tester (016.00) MUST NOT be used.

NOTE: **It is important that adapter lead for testing electronic relay of 928S vehicles is connected correctly.**

CONNECTING TESTER

NOTE: **All test procedures will correspond with numbers on the Bosch ABS Tester.**

1) Turn off ignition and pull off multiple pin plug (35-pin) on electronic control unit. Control unit remains installed. Connect multiple pin plug of electronic control unit with plug of tester.

2) Connect tester to electronic control unit. Turn ignition on. Ensure all other electric equipment is off. NEVER operate vehicle with tester connected.

3) Always perform all tests beginning with PROGRAM SWITCH POSITION 1. PROGRAM SWITCH POSITIONS 23 and 24 must be performed prior to PROGRAM SWITCH POSITIONS 20, 21 and 22.

4) A brake test stand (chassis dyno) is required for PROGRAM SWITCH POSITIONS 20 through 23. Brake test stand rollers and vehicle tires must be dry during test. Selector lever of vehicle equipped with automatic transmission must not be in "P" position while testing rear axle.

5) Never use a brake pedal winch to adjust braking force. Wait at least 20 seconds before repeating tests or changing channels.

BATTERY TEST

NOTE: **Battery voltage is constantly monitored during entire test sequence. Green and Red lights are check lights.**

This test may be performed in all program switch positions. Ignition switch is "ON" with engine off. Lamp 1 (Green) must be on during entire test. If not, see NO DISPLAY and LAMP 2 (Red) ON.

No Display

If Lamp 1 (Green) is not diplayed, power supply to the electronic control unit is interrupted. Check following possible faults:

- Check fuse 16 between Central Electrical Board (CEB) and ABS relay No. XVII.
- Current flow between terminals No. 30 and 31 (flow only in one direction because of diode).
- Multiple pole plug not connected.
- Electronic relay is defective; replace.
- Break in positive wire to relay terminal No. 87.

Lamp 2 (Red) On

If test light illuminates during one of the following tests, stop test and eliminate cause of problem. Check the following:

- Battery insufficiently charged.
- Excessive voltage drop on ground terminals for control unit or relay for control unit including plug connections.
- Break or excessive contact resistance in ground wire to control unit terminal No. 10.
- Excessive contact resistance or open in ground connection on electronic relay.

NOTE: **All test procedures correspond with program switch position numbers on the Bosch ABS Tester. See Fig. 8.**

PROGRAM SWITCH POSITION 1

Solenoid Valve (Neutral Position)

Test is okay if Lamp 3 (Green) comes on. Go to PROGRAM SWITCH POSITION 2. If Lamp 4 (Red) indicator light comes on, check following:

- Ground connection has excessive contact resistance or an open in wiring harness.
- Turn off ignition. Pull off control unit plug and check continuity in following wires: from ground to hydraulic unit terminal No. 8 and from terminal No. 8 to control unit plug terminal No. 32.
- Solenoid valve relay malfunctioning.

PROGRAM SWITCH POSITION 2

Solenoid Valve (Function)

If Lamp 3 (Green) comes on, test is okay. Go to PROGRAM SWITCH POSITION 3. If Lamp 4 (Red) indicator light comes on, turn off ignition. Pull off control unit plug and check continuity in following wires:

- Between terminals No. 27 to 28 and between No. 27 to No. 87 on electronic relay socket.
- Positive for control unit plug terminal No. 1 and negative for terminal No. 27.
- Test light on terminal No. 32 should come on. If not, check solenoid valve relay for malfunction.

PROGRAM SWITCH POSITION 3

Motor Relay (Neutral Position)

1) If Lamp 3 (Green), test is okay. Go to PROGRAM SWITCH POSITION 4. If Red light comes on, turn off ignition.

2) Pull off control unit plug and check continuity in following circuits. Apply 12 volts to positive connector on control unit plug terminal No. 1 and ground on terminal No. 28. Test light on terminal No. 14 should come on. Test light must go out after pulling off terminal connectors No. 1 or 28. If not, go to step **3)**.

3) Check motor relay for malfunction. Check tightness of ground terminals and positive connection on pump motor. Check continuity of pump motor. If pump motor is malfunctioning, replace hydraulic unit.

PROGRAM SWITCH POSITION 4

Motor Relay (Pump Motor Runs)

With Light Emitting Diode (LED) on at position 4, depress button. If Lamp 3 (Green), test is satisfactory. Proceed to PROGRAM SWITCH POSITION 5. If Lamp 4 (Red) is on, repeat PROGRAM SWITCH POSITION 3.

PORSCHE ANTI-LOCK BRAKE SYSTEM (Cont.)

PROGRAM SWITCH POSITION 5

Electronic Relay With Overvoltage Protection For Control Unit

1) If Lamp 3 (Green) illuminates, test is acceptable. Proceed to PROGRAM SWITCH POSITION 6. If Lamp 4 (Red) light comes on, go to step **2)**.

2) Turn off ignition. Pull off plug on control unit. Pull off ABS relay XVII of CEB and connect adapter lead in test plug on back of Bosch Tester (016.00).

3) Install a new ABS relay in CEB. Turn ignition on and wait about one second. Press LED button 4. If LED comes on, test is okay. Go to PROGRAM SWITCH POSITION 6. If LED does not come on, turn off ignition, connect control unit plug again and check electronic relay connected on adapter lead for malfunction. Replace relay if necessary and repeat test.

PROGRAM SWITCH POSITION 6

Left Front Control Valve (Internal Resistance)

1) Turn ignition on. Press "VL" button. Digital display should read between .7-1.7 ohms. If okay, go to RIGHT FRONT VALVE (INTERNAL RESISTANCE) test. If not, go to step **2)**.

2) Check internal resistance and continuity between terminals No. 2 and 32 of disconnected control unit plug. Repeat test between terminals No. 4 and 1 on hydraulic unit. If test is not okay, replace hydraulic unit and repeat test.

Right Front Control Valve (Internal Resistance)

1) Press "VR" button. Digital display should read between .7-1.7 ohms. If okay, go to REAR AXLE CONTROL VALVE (INTERNAL RESISTANCE) test. If not, go to step **2)**.

2) Check internal resistance and continuity between terminals No. 35 and 32 on disconnected control unit plug. Repeat test between terminals No. 4 and 3 on hydraulic unit. If not okay, replace hydraulic unit and repeat test.

Rear Axle Control Valve (Internal Resistance)

1) Press "HA" button. Display should read between .7-1.7 ohms. If display is okay, go to PROGRAM SWITCH POSITION 7. If not, go to step **2)**.

2) Check internal resistance and continuity between terminals No. 18 and 32 on disconnected control unit plug. Repeat test between terminals No. 4 and 5 on hydraulic unit. If not okay, replace hydraulic unit and repeat test.

Wheel Speed Sensor

1) Raise and support vehicle. Wheel to be tested must rotate freely by hand. On drive axles, wheel not being tested must be held securely. Perform test sequence for each wheel in turn.

2) Set wheel selection switch to wheel to be tested. Turn wheel by hand until LED displays without flickering (about one revolution per second). Read value displayed.

3) Minimum indication is 2.0 scale divisions. There can only be a 15% difference between maximum fluctuation.

4) If LED does not light up, check for the following: speed sensor lead incorrectly connected, speed sensor lead has open circuit, speed sensor defective or pulse gear wheel is loose or missing. Speed sensor circuit should have .8-1.8 ohms resistance.

5) If test instrument indication is too low, check for the following: excessive air gap between speed sensor and pulse gear wheel, loose or missing pulse gear wheel, wrong gear wheel, or excessive wheel bearing play.

PROGRAM SWITCH POSITION 7

Ground Connection (Terminal 10)

1) Press "LED" button. Digital display should be 300 mV. If display is okay, go to PROGRAM SWITCH POSITION 8. If not, go to step **2)**.

2) Check ground terminal No. 10 for excessive contact resistance or an open in wiring. Check wire for open from steering mount ground to disconnected control unit plug terminal No. 10. Repair or replace wiring as necessary and repeat test.

PROGRAM SWITCH POSITION 8

Ground Connection (Terminal 34)

1) Press "LED" button. Digital display should read 250 mV. If display is okay, go to PROGRAM SWITCH POSITION 9. If not, go to step **2)**.

2) Check ground terminal for excessive contact resistance and open in wiring. Check wire for open from steering mount ground to disconnected control unit plug terminal No. 34. Repair or replace wiring as necessary.

PROGRAM SWITCH POSITION 9

Ground Connection (Terminal 20)

1) Press "LED" button. Digital display should read 250 mV. If okay, go to PROGRAM SWITCH POSITION 10. If not, go to step **2)**.

2) Check ground terminal for excessive contact resistance and open in wiring. Check wire for open from steering mount ground to disconnected control unit plug terminal No. 20. Repair or replace wiring as necessary.

PROGRAM SWITCH POSITION 10

Left Front Speed Sensor (Internal Resistance)

1) Press "VL" button. Digital display should read between 100-1800 ohms. If readout is okay, go to RIGHT FRONT SPEED SENSOR (INTERNAL RESISTANCE) test. If not, go to step **2)**.

2) Check internal resistance and continuity between terminals No. 4 and 6 of disconnected control unit plug. Check plug connection. If not okay, replace speed sensor.

Right Front Speed Sensor (Internal Resistance)

1) Press "VR" button. Digital display should read between 800-1800 ohms. If readout is okay, go to LEFT REAR SPEED SENSOR (INTERNAL RESISTANCE) test. If not, go to step **2)**.

2) Check internal resistance and continuity between terminals No. 21 and 23 of disconnected control unit plug. Check plug connection. If not okay, replace speed sensor.

Left Rear Speed Sensor (Internal Resistance)

1) Press "HL" button. Digital display should read between 800-1800 ohms. If readout is okay, go to

PORSCHE ANTI-LOCK BRAKE SYSTEM (Cont.)

RIGHT REAR SPEED SENSOR (INTERNAL RESISTANCE) test. If not, go to step **2)**.

2) Check internal resistance and continuity between terminals No. 8 and 9 of disconnected control unit plug. Check plug connection. If not okay, replace speed sensor.

Right Rear Speed Sensor (Internal Resistance)

1) Press "HR" button. Digital display should read between 800-1800 ohms. If readout is okay, go to PROGRAM SWITCH POSITION 11. If not, go to step **2)**.

2) Check internal resistance and continuity between terminals No. 24 and 26 of disconnected control unit plug. Check plug connection. If not okay, replace speed sensor.

PROGRAM SWITCH POSITION 11

Left Front Speed Sensor (Insulating Resistance)

1) Press "VL" button. Digital display should read 20,000 ohms. If readout is okay, go to RIGHT FRONT SPEED SENSOR (INSULATING RESISTANCE) test. If not, go to step **2)**.

2) Check plug connection. Disconnect sensor plug. Bridge coupling plug (sleeve end). Repeat test. If digital display is okay, replace speed sensor. If not, go to step **3)**.

3) Check wires from terminals No. 4 and 6 to coupling plug for malfunction. Inspect all wires for damage from rubbing. Repair or replace wiring as necessary.

Right Front Speed Sensor (Insulating Resistance)

1) Press "VR" button. Digital display should read 20,000 ohms. If readout is okay, go to LEFT REAR SPEED SENSOR (INSULATING RESISTANCE) test. If not, go to step **2)**.

2) Check plug connection. Disconnect sensor plug. Bridge coupling plug (sleeve end). Repeat test. If digital display is okay, replace speed sensor. If not, go to step **3)**.

3) Check wires from terminals No. 21 and 23 to coupling plug for malfunction. Inspect all wires for damage from rubbing. Repair or replace wiring as necessary.

Left Rear Speed Sensor (Insulating Resistance)

1) Press "HL" button. Digital display should read 20,000 ohms. If readout is okay, go to RIGHT REAR SPEED SENSOR (INSULATING RESISTANCE) test. If not, go to step **2)**.

2) Check plug connection. Disconnect sensor plug. Bridge coupling plug (sleeve end). Repeat test. If digital display is okay, replace speed sensor. If not, go to step **3)**.

3) Check wires from terminals No. 8 and 9 to coupling plug for malfunction. Inspect all wires for damage from rubbing. Repair or replace wiring as necessary.

Right Rear Speed Sensor (Insulating Resistance)

1) Press "HR" button. Digital display should read 20,000 ohms. If readout is okay, go to PROGRAM SWITCH POSITION 12. If not, go to step **2)**.

2) Check plug connection. Disconnect sensor plug. Bridge coupling plug (sleeve end). Repeat test. If digital display is okay, replace speed sensor. If not, go to step **3)**.

3) Check wires from terminals No. 24 and 26 to coupling plug for malfunction. Inspect all wires for damage from rubbing. Repair or replace wiring as necessary.

PROGRAM SWITCH POSITION 12

Left Front Speed Sensor (Direct Voltage)

1) Press "VL" button. Digital display should read 100 mV. If readout is okay, go to RIGHT FRONT SPEED SENSOR (DIRECT VOLTAGE) test. If not, go to step **2)**.

2) Disconnect sensor plug and bridge coupling plug (sleeve end). Repeat test. If okay, go to RIGHT FRONT SPEED SENSOR (DIRECT VOLTAGE) test. If not, go to step **3)**.

3) Check wires from control unit plug terminals No. 6 and 4 to coupling plug for short or open in wiring. Repair or replace wiring as necessary.

Right Front Speed Sensor (Direct Voltage)

1) Press "VR" button. Digital display should read 100 mV. If readout is okay, go to LEFT REAR SPEED SENSOR (DIRECT VOLTAGE) test. If not, go to step **2)**.

2) Disconnect sensor plug and bridge coupling plug (sleeve end). Repeat test. If okay, go to LEFT REAR SPEED SENSOR (DIRECT VOLTAGE) test. If not, go to step **3)**.

3) Check wires from control unit plug terminals No. 23 and 21 to coupling plug for short or open. Repair or replace wiring as necessary.

Left Rear Speed Sensor (Direct Voltage)

1) Press "HL" button. Digital display should read 100 mV. If readout is okay, go to RIGHT REAR SPEED SENSOR (DIRECT VOLTAGE) test. If not, go to step **2)**.

2) Disconnect sensor plug and bridge coupling plug (sleeve end). Repeat test. If okay, go to RIGHT FRONT SPEED SENSOR (DIRECT VOLTAGE) test. If not, go to step **3)**.

3) Check wires from control unit plug terminals No. 8 and 9 to coupling plug for short or open in wiring. Repair or replace wiring as necessary.

Right Rear Speed Sensor (Direct Voltage)

1) Press "HR" button. Digital display should read 100 mV. If readout is okay, go to RIGHT FRONT SPEED SENSOR (DIRECT VOLTAGE) test. If not, go to step **2)**.

2) Disconnect sensor plug and bridge coupling plug (sleeve end). Repeat test. If okay, go to RIGHT FRONT SPEED SENSOR (DIRECT VOLTAGE) test. If not, go to step **3)**.

3) Check wires from control unit plug terminals No. 24 and 26 to coupling plug for short or open in wiring. Repair or replace wiring as necessary.

PROGRAM SWITCH POSITION 13

Control Unit Power Supply

Press "LED" button. Digital display should read between 4.75-5.25 volts. If readout is okay, go to PROGRAM SWITCH POSITION 14. If not, replace control unit.

PORSCHE ANTI-LOCK BRAKE SYSTEM (Cont.)

PROGRAM SWITCH POSITION 14

Diode In Flow Direction
(ABS Indicator Lamp Not On)

1) The ABS indicator should be on and digital display should read 1.5 volts. If test is okay, go to PROGRAM SWITCH POSITION 15. If not, go to step **2)**.

2) If ABS indicator light is not on, check indicator light for burnout. Replace indicator light (if necessary). Go to step **3)**.

3) Turn ignition off. Using an ohmmeter, check for continuity of diode between terminals No. 29 and 32 on disconnected control unit plug. Display must have high resistance once and then read low ohm resistance. Go to step **4)**.

4) Pull off multiple pin plug on right side of instrument cluster. Check wires between terminals No. 29 and 32 for opens. Repair or replace wiring as necessary.

Bosch Tester
(Digital Display Deviates)

1) Turn off ignition. Check wires between terminals No. 29 and 32 of disconnected control unit plug for opens and for continuity of diode. Check wire between control unit plug terminal No. 29 and instrument cluster terminal No. 2 for open.

2) Check plug connection of indicator light, ground wire and solenoid valve relay plug connection for voltage drop. Repair or replace wiring as necessary. Replace hydraulic unit if diode is defective and wiring is okay.

PROGRAM SWITCH POSITION 15

NOTE: **The ABS indicator light will dim solenoid valve relay switches.**

Diode In Locking Direction
(ABS Indicator Light)

The digital display should be between 2.5-8.5 volts. If readout is okay, go to PROGRAM SWITCH POSITION 16. If not, check ABS indicator light and wires. Pull off solenoid valve relay. If ABS indicator light is on, replace hydraulic unit.

PROGRAM SWITCH POSITION 16

Control Unit (BITE Triggered)

1) Press "LED" button for at least 3 seconds (ABS indicator light could flash twice while pressing button). This indicates pump motor is starting. If ABS indicator light goes out within 3 seconds, test is okay. Go to PROGRAM SWITCH POSITION 17.

2) If indicator light does not go out within 3 seconds, repeat test with engine running. Replace control unit.

PROGRAM SWITCH POSITION 17

Control Unit (BITE Triggered
With Problem Simulation)

1) Press "LED" button for at least 3 seconds (ABS indicator light could flash twice while pressing button). This indicates pump motor is starting. If ABS light is on while "LED" button is pushed, test is okay. Go to PROGRAM SWITCH POSITION 18.

2) If ABS indicator light goes out while "LED" button is pushed, repeat test with engine running. If still not okay, replace control unit and repeat test.

PROGRAM SWITCH POSITION 18

Control Unit (Valve Holding Pressure)

Push "LED" button on. Press button again each time new valve is selected. If display is "0", press button again and pump motor starts. Go to LEFT FRONT CONTROL VALVE test.

Left Front Control Valve

Press "VL" and "LED" buttons. Digital display should read between 1.9-2.3 amps. If readout is okay, go to RIGHT FRONT CONTROL VALVE test. If not, repeat test with engine running. If display is still not okay, replace control unit.

Right Front Control Valve

Press "VR" and "LED" buttons. Digital display should read between 1.9-2.3 amps. If readout is okay, go to REAR AXLE CONTROL VALVE test. If not, repeat test with engine running. If digital display is still not okay, replace control unit.

Rear Axle Control Valve

Wait for "0" display. Press "HA" and "LED" buttons. Digital display should read between 1.9-2.3 amps. If readout is okay, go to RIGHT FRONT CONTROL VALVE test. If not, repeat test with engine running. If digital display is still not okay, replace control unit.

PROGRAM SWITCH POSITION 19

Control Unit Valve Flow
(Pressure Dropping)

Press "LED" button. Press button each time new valve is selected. If digital display is "0", press button again (pump motor starts twice). Go to LEFT FRONT CONTROL VALVE test.

Left Front Control Valve

Press "VL" and "LED" buttons. Digital display should be between 4.8-6.0 amps. If readout is okay, go to RIGHT FRONT CONTROL VALVE test. If not, repeat test with engine running. If digital display still not okay, replace control unit.

Right Front Control Valve

Press "VR" and "LED" buttons. Digital display should be between 4.8-6.0 amps. If readout is okay, go to REAR AXLE CONTROL VALVE test. If not, repeat test with engine running. If digital display is still not okay, replace control unit.

Rear Axle Control Valve

Press "HA" and "LED" buttons. Digital display should be between 4.8-6.0 amps. If readout is okay, go to PROGRAM SWITCH POSITION test. If not, repeat test with engine running. If digital display is still not okay, replace control unit.

NOTE: **Remaining tests are not in sequence. PROGRAM SWITCH POSITIONS 24 and 23 must be performed prior to PROGRAM SWITCH POSITIONS 20, 21 & 22.**

PROGRAM SWITCH POSITION 24

Stoplight Switch

1) Press on brake pedal. Digital display should be between 10-15 volts. A display of 0-.25 volts without operating pedal is normal. If readout is okay, go to PROGRAM SWITCH POSITION 23.

2) If there is no display, check stoplight switch including wires to switch and plugs, as well as wire from control unit plug terminal No. 25 to CEL plug S6. If display

PORSCHE ANTI-LOCK BRAKE SYSTEM (Cont.)

is less than 10 volts, eliminate contact resistance on both sides of plug and light connections or replace stoplight switch.

NOTE: The following tests require a Brake Test Bench (Chassis Dyno).

PROGRAM SWITCH POSITION 23

Speed Sensor Signal

1) Place vehicle on braking test stand (chassis dyno), front and rear wheels respectively. Switch in brake rollers of test stand separately for front and rear wheels. Separate speed sensors are selected by depressing "VR", "VL", "HL" and "HR" buttons.

2) Digital display should be 1.5. Check clearance. Use smallest value if display fluctuates. A digital display "999" means speed of test stand is too fast. If digital display between 0-1.5 is on, check the following and repair if necessary:

- Speed sensors installed on incorrect wheel (check arrangement). Speed sensor must correspond to specified wheel and control unit inlet.
- Clearance between speed sensor and gear ring excessive. Check for proper installation.
- Check bearing play of front wheels.
- Check speed sensor.

NOTE: Go to PROGRAM SWITCH POSITIONS 20, 21 & 22 only after performing PROGRAM SWITCH POSITION 23.

PROGRAM SWITCH POSITIONS 20, 21 & 22

NOTE: A brake test stand (chassis dyno) is required for PROGRAM SWITCH POSITIONS 20, 21 & 22. Brake test stand rollers and vehicle tires must be dry during test. Run engine until undervoltage occurs or brake force is not reached using foot pressure. Brake booster makes it difficult to hold 450 lbs. (2000 N) constant during test.

Additional Operations

1) Operating sequence must be maintained when performing these tests.

- Select test (program switch position).
- Select channel (wheel).
- Set brake force to 450 lbs. (2000 N) with foot.
- Press "LED" button with brief time delay (about .5 seconds).
- Press "LED" button until test stand display stops. Integral tester program runs several seconds. The Lamp 2 (Red) light should not come on during test. If it does, repeat test with engine running. Wait about 20 seconds before continuing or repeating test. Integral tester program must be run off.

2) Brake line mix-up test.

- Drive front wheels of vehicle on brake test stand.
- Select PROGRAM SWITCH POSITION 20 and press position "5.2" for front left wheel. Switch on left front brake roller.
- Operate brake pedal until brake force display on brake test stand is 450 lbs. (2000 N).
- Press "LED" button.
- Pressure must build up for left front wheel.
- Perform same test on right front wheel.
- Press "VR" button and switch on front right brake roller only.

3) Hydraulic unit front axle test.

- Parking brake applied.
- Select test.
- Select wheel (left front or right front).
- Switch on both brake rollers.
- Apply about 450 lbs. (2000 N) brake force on wheel just being tested with brake pedal and hold constant during test. NEVER use a brake pedal winch to adjust brake force.
- Deviation in brake force display between left and right must not exceed 112 lbs. (500 N).
- Press "LED" button until test stand display stops and value has been read (time is about 6 seconds).
- Check for constant brake force during test on the wheel running along. Pedal travel may change. Slight brake force change is permissible, but influences display.
- Perform PROGRAM SWITCH POSITIONS 20, 21 & 22 on both wheels separately.

4) Hydraulic unit rear axle test.

- Drive rear wheels of vehicle on brake test stand.
- Select test.
- Press rear axle button.
- Switch on both brake rollers.
- Run engine (brake force boost will be effective and makes braking easier).
- Apply 450 lbs. (2000 N) brake force on wheel just being tested with brake pedal and hold constant during test. NEVER use a brake pedal winch to adjust brake force.
- Press "LED" button until brake test stand display stops (test time about 6 seconds).

Test 20
Hydraulic Unit (Pressure Drop In Brake Lines)

If Lamp 1 (Green) is on, the test is okay. Perform TEST 21 next. If Lamp 2 (Red) test light is on, see TROUBLE SHOOTING in this article.

Test 21
Hydraulic Unit (Pressure Build-Up In Brake Lines)

After pressure drops, phase brake force display rises again to 383 lbs. (1700 N) at front axle and 405 lbs. (1800 N) at rear axle. If Lamp 1 (Green) is on, test is okay. If Lamp 2 (Red) test light is on, see TROUBLE SHOOTING in this article.

Test 22
Hydraulic Unit (Pump Delivery Rate)

After dropping pressure twice without return delivery pump, the hydraulic unit pump will switch on briefly. Brake force display must drop below 135 lbs. (600 N). Brake pedal will give slightly. If Lamp 1 (Green) is on, test is okay. This is end of test sequence. If Lamp 2 (Red) light is on, see TROUBLE SHOOTING in this article.

TROUBLE SHOOTING

With engine running, repeat proper tests. Ensure brake force is not changed during test. Charge battery and run engine. If Lamp 2 (Red) comes on, check following conventional brake system components:

- Air in brake lines.
- Brake line connections.
- Brake pads and rotors.
- Master cylinder and wheel cylinders.
- Brake fluid level and cleanliness.
- Proper installation of brake lines on hydraulic unit.

PORSCHE ANTI-LOCK BRAKE SYSTEM (Cont.)

- Recheck brake roller matching with "VL", "VR" and "HA" buttons.
- Check ground terminals on pump motor and body.
- Check positive terminal on pump motor.

NOTE: If all components are okay, but tests are not, replace hydraulic unit.

REMOVAL & INSTALLATION

HYDRAULIC UNIT

Removal

1) Remove left intake hose on air cleaner. Disconnect power steering supply tank on bracket. Ensure hoses remain connected. Pull off ignition leads on ignition coil. Remove left front wheel.

2) Disconnect brake lines and brake pressure regulators (No. 4 and 9) on hydraulic unit. Remove brake lines from holders at wheel housing (locks are opened from above).

3) Insert plugs in open brake lines and connections immediately, as dirt can enter system. If plugs are not available for brake lines, first drain tank and cover lines.

4) Remove wheel house cover and cover on pump unit. Unscrew cable release and remove 12-pin plug (No. 3).

NOTE: Both relays for pump motor or solenoid valves can be replaced.

5) Disconnect ground wire on pump motor and unscrew 2 mounting bolts. Unscrew mounting bolt and bracket for hydraulic unit. Run out hydraulic unit. Never loosen or tighten bolts marked with arrows.

Installation

1) Place brackets for hydraulic unit wheel housings and tilt down on wheel side. Move hydraulic unit into brackets from wheel side and insert 2 mounting bolts.

2) Mount hydraulic unit brackets on wheel housings (3 self-locking nuts). Mount brake pressure regulator and brake lines on hydraulic unit in correct position. If applicable, hold brake lines in brackets on wheel housings with clips and engage locks.

NOTE: Use caution to ensure brake lines are routed correctly.

3) Connect 12-pin plug and secure cable release. Mount cover on hydraulic unit. Mount wire harness on hydraulic unit bracket. Connect ground wire on pump motor.

4) Bleed brakes in order of stepped brake master cylinder, push rod brake circuit (front wheels) and intermediate piston circuit (rear wheels). Check for leaks. Bleeding procedures are same for vehicles without ABS. Check function with ABS tester.

ELECTRONIC CONTROL UNIT

Removal

1) Control unit is located on driver's side, above hood release on side panel of kick panel. Ensure ignition is off before disconnecting multiple pin plug on control unit or removing control unit.

2) Move seat back and pull up steering wheel. Press spring-loaded lock and pull plug off electronic control unit. Remove electronic control unit from bracket after unscrewing mounting nuts.

Installation

Mount electronic control unit on bracket and connect ABS tester. Plug in tester plug on electronic control unit. Ensure spring-loaded lock engages on plug. Check control unit function. See TESTING in this article.

FRONT & REAR SPEED SENSORS

Removal (Front Axle)

1) Remove front wheel. Remove intake hose on air cleaner. Turn off ignition. Pull out wire plug from holder in engine compartment and disconnect.

2) Remove front exhaust shield. Unclip wires on wheel housings and pull out rubber grommet in direction of wheel and rubber grommet for brake line.

3) Unclip wire on side member and holders on steering knuckle. Unscrew socket head screw and pull speed sensor from steering knuckle.

Removal (Rear Axle)

1) Remove wheel and turn off ignition. Remove wire plug from holder and unclip wire on rear axle carrier. Disconnect wire plug.

2) Unclip wire in holders on wheel carrier. Unscrew socket head screw and pull speed sensor out of wheel carrier.

Installation (Front & Rear Axles)

When installing, note the following:

- Rubber mounts and grommets on speed sensors are connected with wire covers in precise position.
- Ensure no foreign metal particles (burrs) are on magnetic edge of speed sensor before installing.

1) Coat speed sensor and bore in steering knuckle with Molykote Longterm 2. Replace speed sensor "O" ring. Insert speed sensor in steering knuckle without force and mount with socket head screw.

2) Clip wire in holders on wheel carrier and rear axle crossmember. Connect wire plug and insert in holder. Mount wheel. Check operation with ABS tester.

PORSCHE ANTI-LOCK BRAKE SYSTEM (Cont.)

Fig. 9: Porsche 928S Anti-Lock Brake System Wiring Diagram

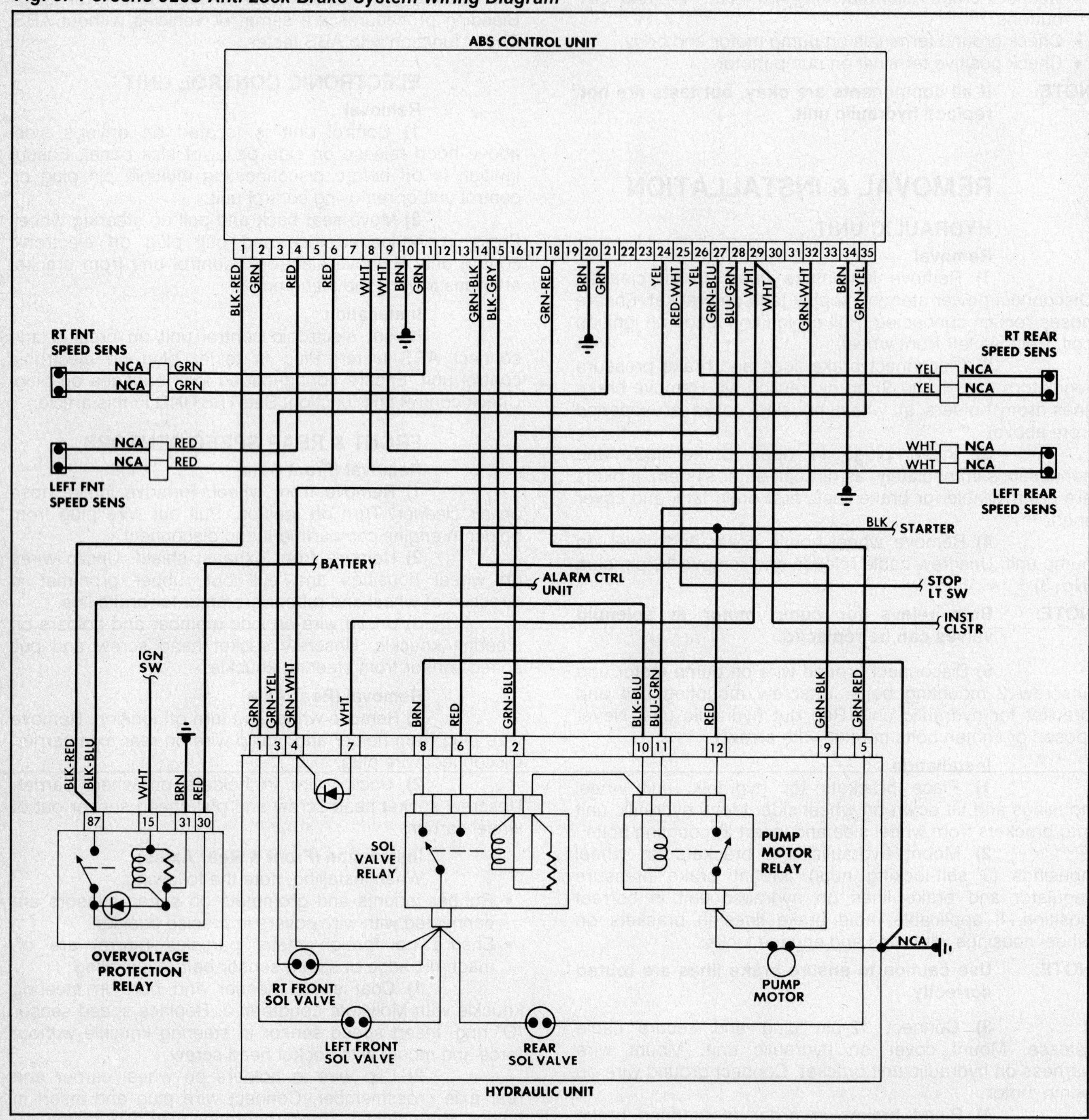

PORSCHE ANTI-LOCK BRAKE SYSTEM (Cont.)

Fig. 10: Porsche 944, 944S & 944 Turbo Anti-Lock Brake System Wiring Diagram

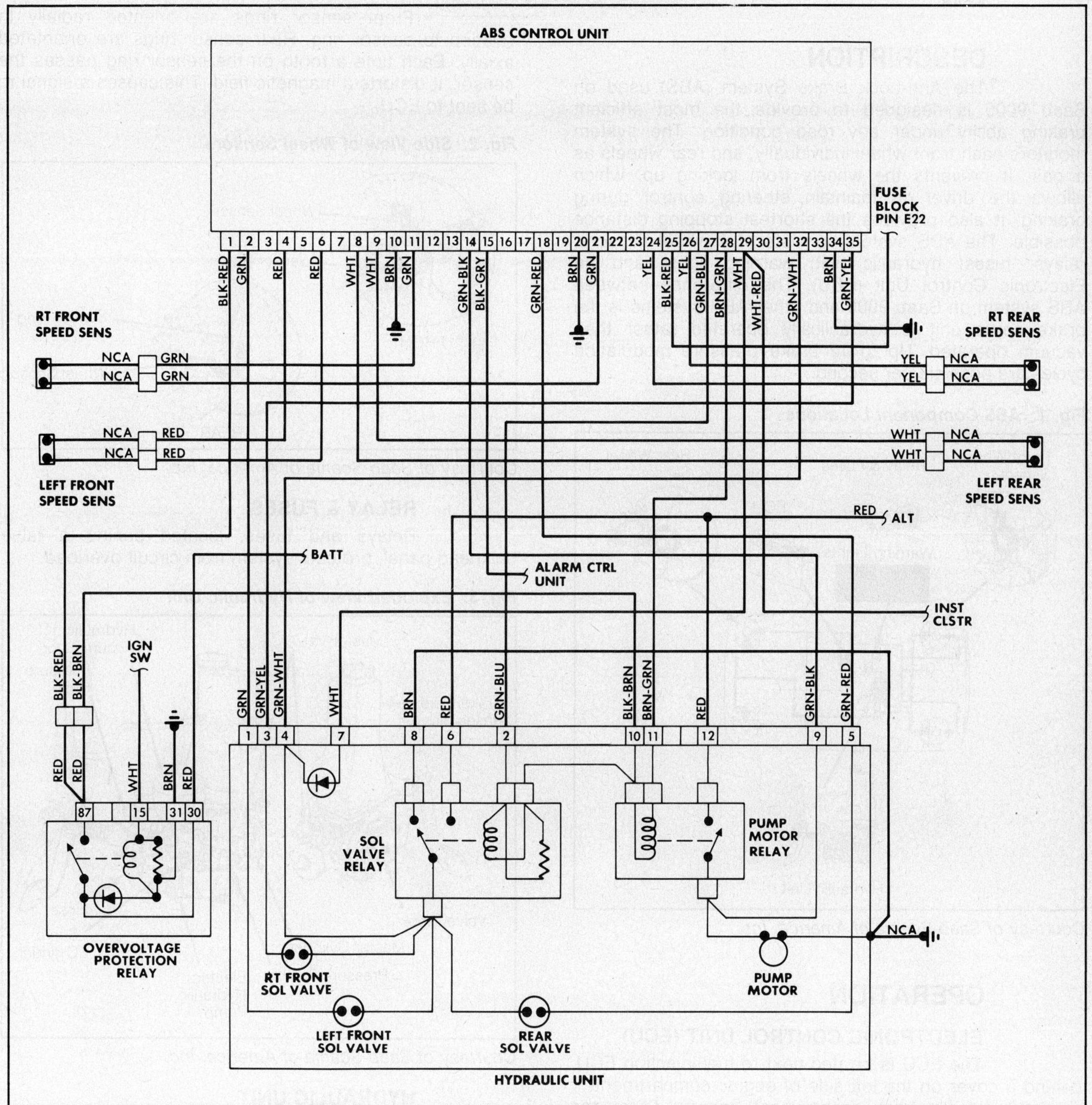

SAAB ANTI-LOCK BRAKE SYSTEM

9000

DESCRIPTION

The Anti-Lock Brake System (ABS) used on Saab 9000 is designed to provide the most efficient braking ability under any road condition. The system monitors each front wheel individually, and rear wheels as a pair. It prevents the wheels from locking up, which allows the driver to maintain steering control during braking. It also provides the shortest stopping distance possible. The ABS system consists of 4 wheel sensors, relays, fuses, hydraulic unit, warning lights and an Electronic Control Unit (ECU). The difference between ABS system on Saab 9000 and other ABS systems is the brake servo unit is hydraulically operated rather than vacuum operated. Up to 12 brake pressure modulation cycles are possible per second.

Fig. 1: ABS Component Locations

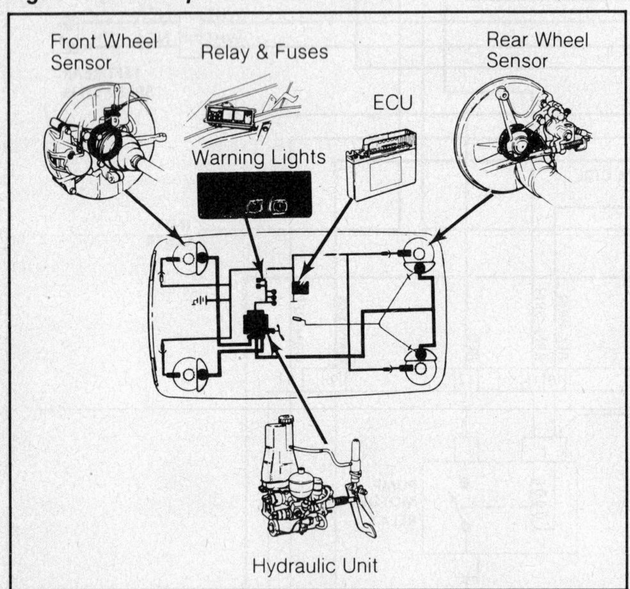

Courtesy of Saab-Scania of America, Inc.

OPERATION

ELECTRONIC CONTROL UNIT (ECU)

The ECU is located next to fuel injection ECU, behind a cover on the left side of engine compartment. It receives signals from each wheel sensor. From the information it receives, it controls the solenoid valves. This increases or decreases hydraulic pressure to each wheel to prevent lock-up.

NOTE: ECU must be REMOVED from vehicle when using an arc welder on vehicle or placing vehicle in an oven for painting purposes.

WARNING LIGHTS

The ABS warning lights will come on if brake pressure is low, fluid level is low, malfunction in the ECU, break in circuit continuity or weak signal from wheel sensor. Anytime the warning light is on, the ABS system is inoperative.

WHEEL SENSORS

Front sensor rings are oriented radially in relation to sensor ring. Rear sensor rings are orientated axially. Each time a tooth on the sensor ring passes the sensor, it distorts a magnetic fleid. This causes a signal to be sent to ECU.

Fig. 2: Side View of Wheel Sensors

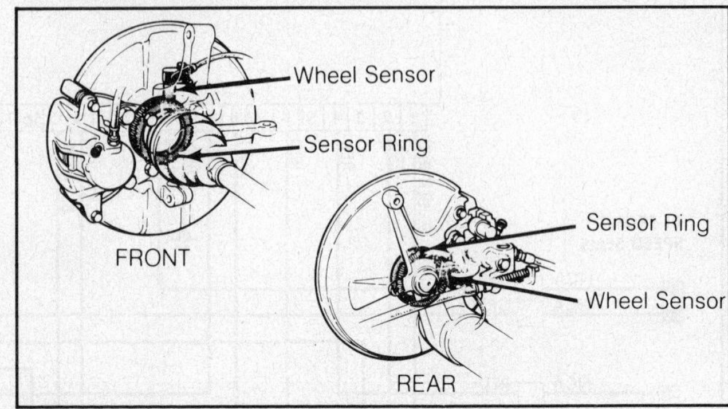

Courtesy of Saab-Scania of America, Inc.

RELAY & FUSES

Relays and fuses, located behind a false bulkhead panel, protects system from circuit overload.

Fig. 3: Exploded View of Hydraulic Unit

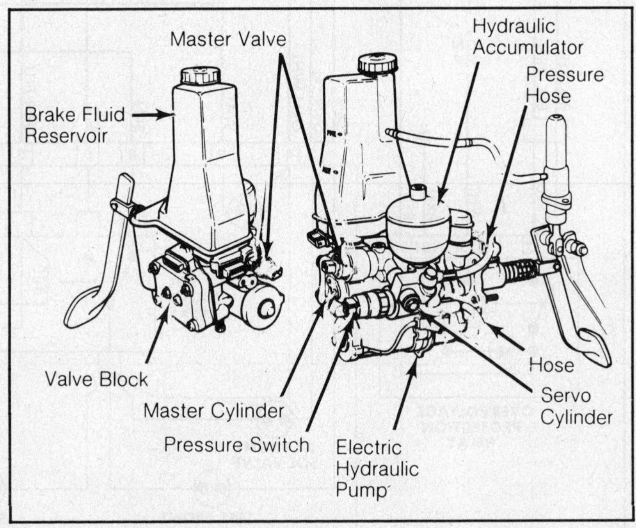

Courtesy of Saab-Scania of America, Inc.

HYDRAULIC UNIT

Servo Cylinder

Provides power assistance for braking. It also provides brake pressure to rear brakes.

Master Cylinder

It operates the same as a conventional master cylinder.

Master Valve

Supplies brake fluid from servo cylinder to master cylinder when ABS is operating.

Valve Block

Modules pressure to brake calipers during ABS operation.

SAAB ANTI-LOCK BRAKE SYSTEM (Cont.)

Electric Hydraulic Pump

Electric hydraulic pump is turned on and off by the pressure switch. Normal operating pressure is 2030-2610 psi (140-180 bar). If operating pressure exceeds 3045 psi (210 bar), a relief valve opens, releasing pressure to inlet side of pump.

Hydraulic Acummulator

Hydraulic accumulator is bolted onto electric hydraulic pump. It consists of 2 chambers, separated by a rubber diaphragm. One side of the chamber is sealed and charged with nitrogen to a nominal pressure of 1218 psi (84 bar). Other side of chamber receives brake fluid from hydraulic pump. As brake fluid is pumped into chamber, it compresses the nitrogen. This allows a large amount of brake fluid to be stored under pressure. This means brake hydraulic pressure is instantly available and the electric hydraulic pump only needs to operate to maintain normal pressure.

Pressure Switch

The pressure switch, fitted inside pump housing, has 2 functions. One function is to turn the electric hydrualic pump off when pressure reaches 2610 psi (180 bar). It turns the pump on when pressure falls to 2030 psi (140 bar). The other function is to turn brake warning light on when hydraulic accumulator pressure falls below 1523 psi (105 bar).

REMOVAL & INSTALLATION

CAUTION: When removing any ABS hydraulic brake component, depress brake pedal approximately 20 times, with engine off, to depressurize brake system.

PRESSURE SWITCH

Removal & Installation

Remove battery, battery holder and fuel filter. Unplug connectors from pressure switch, master valve, fluid level indicator and valve block. Remove brace bar from master cylinder. Disconnect ground lead. Using a 36 mm wrench, remove pressure switch. To install, reverse removal procedure. Tighten pressure switch to 15-19 ft. lbs. (20-26 N.m).

HYDRAULIC ACCUMULATOR

Removal & Installation

Remove battery. Move fuel filter to the side. Remove hydraulic accumulator. To install, reverse removal procedure. Install new "O" ring and tighten accumulator to 25-34 ft. lbs. (34-46 N.m).

HYDRAULIC UNIT

Removal & Installation

1) Remove battery. Clean outside of hydraulic system throughly. Remove trim panel. Remove clevis pin securing brake pedal to push rod. Separate junction box from battery holder. Remove fuel filter and battery holder. Remove intake rubber duct.

2) Unplug brake fluid indicator, master valve, pressure switch and valve block connectors. Remove brace bar from master cylinder. Remove ground lead. Raise and support vehicle. Remove left front wheel. Remove splash guard.

3) Unplug electric hydraulic pump connector. Clean area around brake lines throughly. Disconnect brake lines from valve block. Plug all brake lines and ports. Remove hydraulic unit from vehicle. To install, reverse removal procedure.

WHEEL SENSORS

Removal

Unplug wheel sensor connector. On front wheels, connector is located inside engine compartment. On rear wheels, connector is located under rear seat cushion. Remove retaining screw and remove sensor. Loosen set screw and remove adjusting sleeve.

Installation

1) Install new wheel sensor in adjusting sleeve. Clean end of spacer with a wire brush. Wipe clean with dry cloth. Ensure there is no trace of old fiber spacer above sensor wheel. Rotate wheel to ensure sensor ring is okay. Glue new .65 mm thick spacer onto end of sensor.

2) If necessary, a dial indicator can be used to position sensor. Tighten retaining screw. DO NOT rotate wheel before tightening retaining screw or damage to sensor will occur. Ensure set screw bottoms on adjusting sleeve, at a different point as before, to avoid incorrect setting of sensor body. Position sensor and tighten retaining screw. Press sensor body gently against sensor ring. Tighten set screw. Plug sensor connectors together.

BLEEDING BRAKE SYSTEM

NOTE: ALWAYS use DOT 4 brake fluid. DO NOT use any brake fluid with a rating less than DOT 4.

Fill brake system. Bleed left front wheel, then right front wheel. Depress brake pedal approximately 20 times to depressurize brake system. Connect bleed hose to left rear wheel. With brake pedal depressed, turn ignition on. This will activate electric hydraulic pump. When brake fluid from left rear wheel contains no air, tighten bleeder. Turn ignition off. Depressurize brake system and bleed right rear wheel in the same matter.

TIGHTENING SPECIFICATIONS

Application	Ft. Lbs. (N.m)
Hydraulic Accumulator	25-34 (34-46)
Pressure Switch	15-19 (20-26)
Pump Pressure Hose	12-18 (16-24)
	INCH Lbs. (N.m)
Brake Fluid Reservoir Bolt	36-48 (4-6)
Hydraulic Pump Bolt	60-84 (7-9)

SAAB ANTI-LOCK BRAKE SYSTEM (Cont.)

Fig. 4: Saab 9000 Anti-Lock Brake System Wiring Diagram

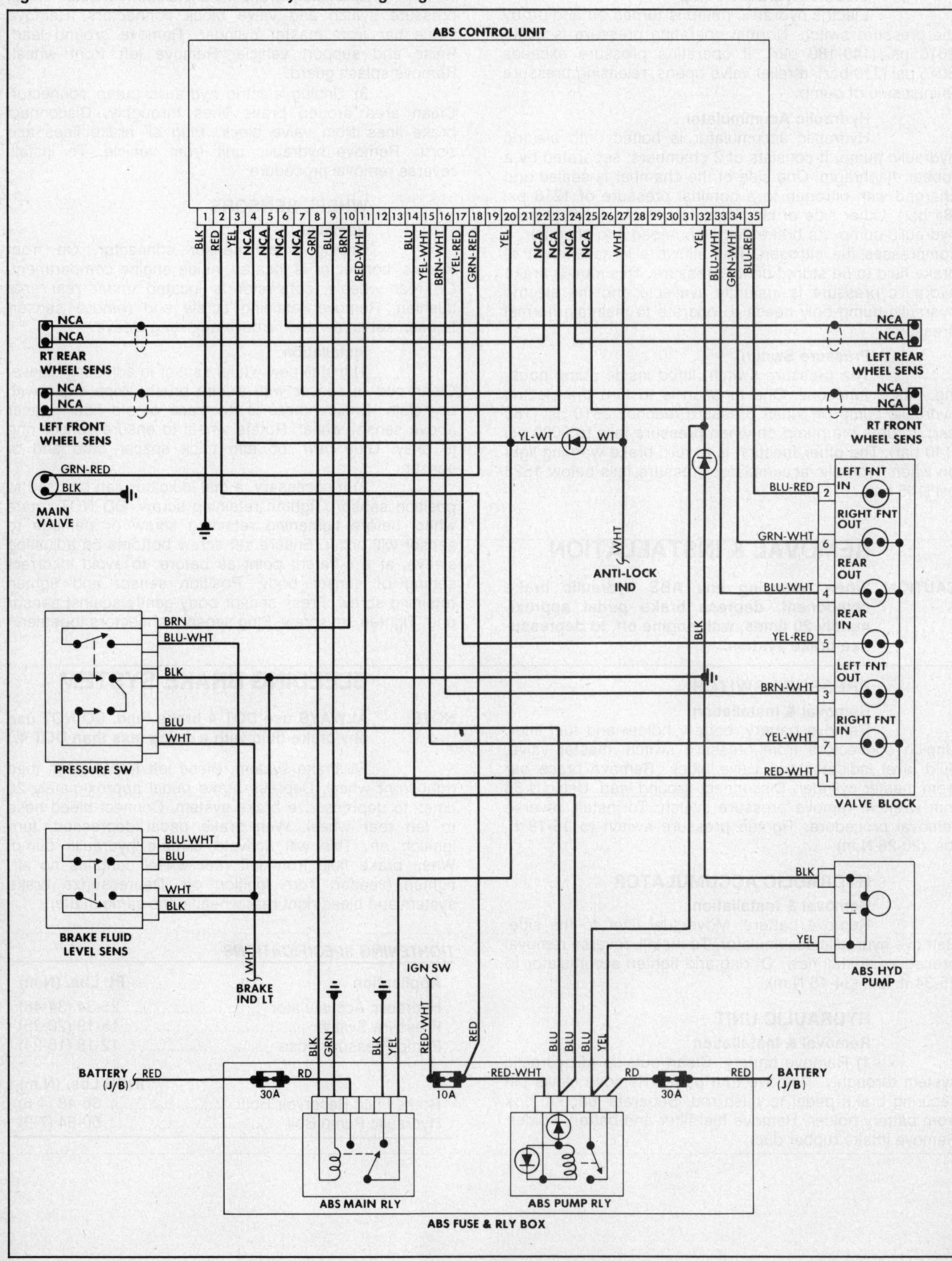

STERLING ANTI-LOCK BRAKE SYSTEM

825

DESCRIPTION

The Anti-Lock Brake System (ABS) is designed to prevent wheel lock-up during braking. This allows driver to maintain steering control of vehicle. System consists of power brake unit, master cylinder, hydraulic modulator, 3 relays, Electronic Control Unit (ECU), 4 wheel sensors and sensor rings, and a warning light.

OPERATION

ECU receives AC signal from each wheel sensor. The ECU computes wheel speed and determines correct deceleration speed of vehicle. When ECU determines that wheel lock-up is about to occur, it activates the solenoid valves to control hydraulic fluid to each wheel. This prevents wheel lock-up. System will cycle 4-10 times per second.

TESTING

ABS WARNING LIGHT ON

Warning light should come on when ignition is turned on. Light should go off after engine is started. If not, check fuse No. 14. If fuse is okay, check all ground points. If light is still on, go to ABS TEST.

ABS TEST

Turn ignition off. Unplug ECU connector. Connect ABS Tester (Fast Check) to ECU connector. Turn ignition on. If ABS tester power light does not come on, check battery and fuse. Check for continuity in circuit between cut-out relay and connector pin No. 1. If there is continuity, replace overvoltage protection relay. If there is no continuity, repair wiring. Ensure all ABS tester switches are off.

Test A
Overvoltage Protection Relay

1) Turn system test knob to "A". If system test LED comes on, go to TEST B. If not, using an ohmmeter, check for continuity between ignition switch and overvoltage protection relay (Light Green/Gray wire). If there is continuity, check fuse No. 11. If there is no continuity, repair wiring.

2) Check for continuity between battery and overvoltage protection relay (Purple/Brown wire). If there is continuity, check fuse. If there is no continuity, repair wiring. Check for continuity between overvoltage protection relay and ground (Black wire). If there is no continuity, repair wiring or replace relay.

Test B
Valve Relay

1) Turn system test knob to "B". If system test LED comes on, go to TEST C. If not, using an ohmmeter, check for continuity between battery and hydraulic modulator connector (Black/Brown wire). If there is no continuity, repair wire.

2) If there is continuity, check 30 amp fuse. If fuse is okay, check continuity between hydraulic modulator connector and ECU (Blue/Green wire). If there is no continuity, repair wire.

3) If there is continuity, check between hydraulic modulator connector and warning light (Yellow/Red wire), and warning light to ECU (Yellow/Red wire). If there is no continuity, repair wire. If there is continuity, check

Fig. 1: ABS Component Locations

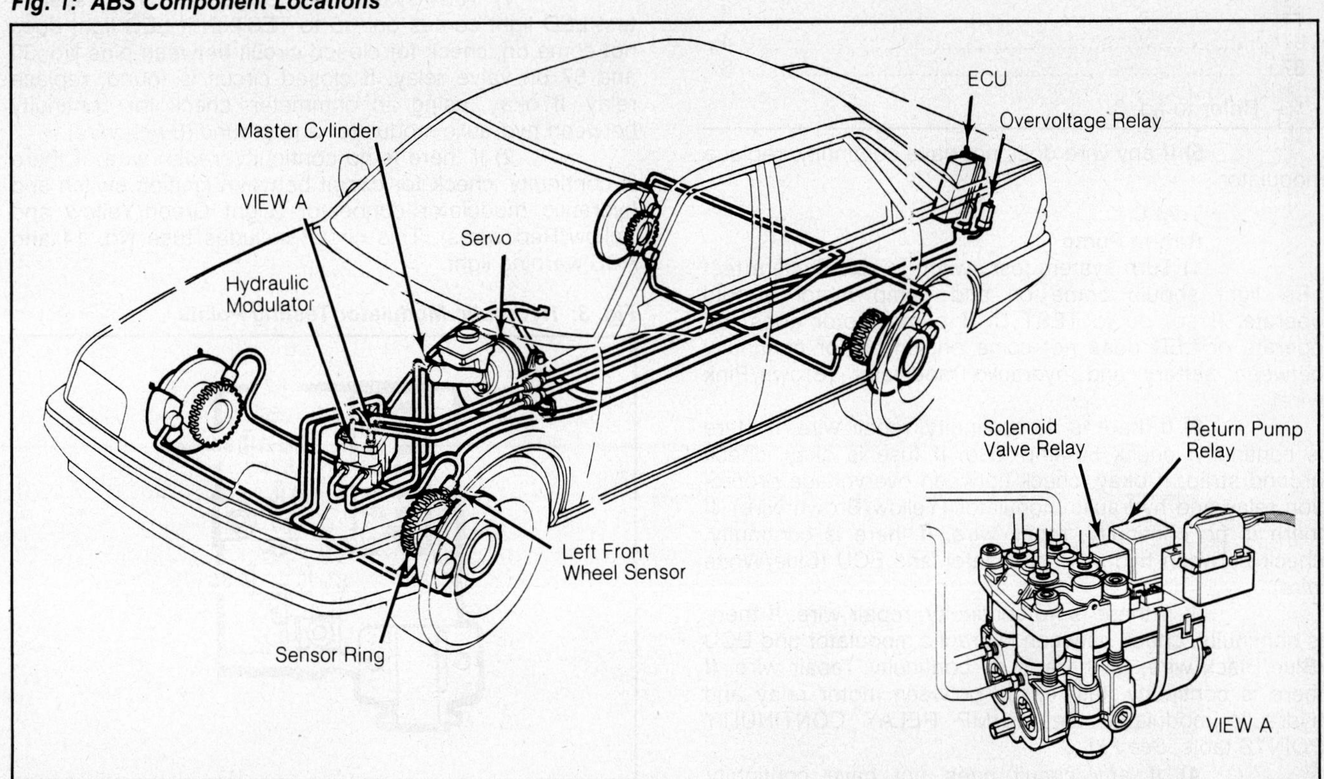

Courtesy of Austin Rover Group.

STERLING ANTI-LOCK BRAKE SYSTEM (Cont.)

Fig. 2: ABS Tester (Fast Check)

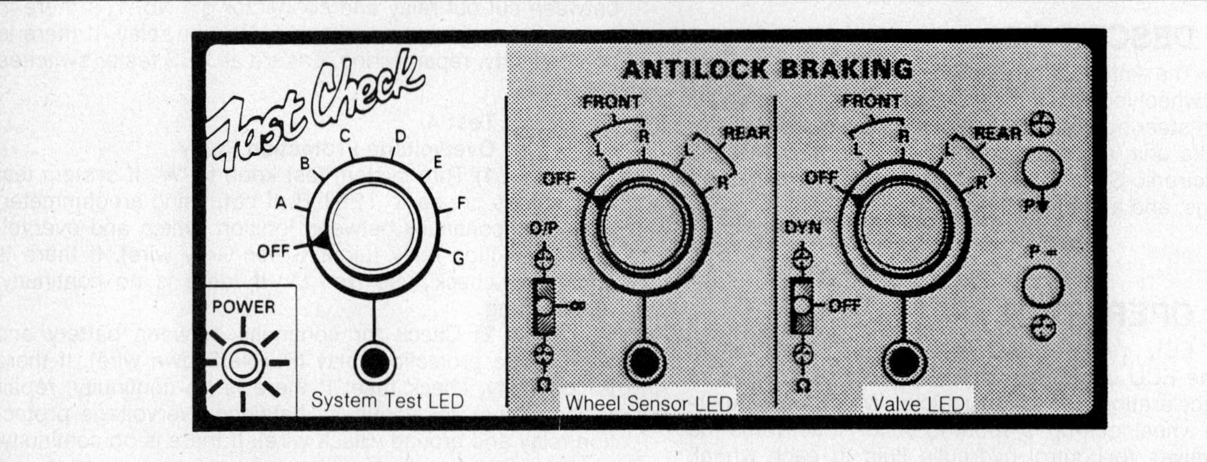

Courtesy of Austin Rover Group.

between hydraulic modulator connector and ECU (Yellow-/Green wire).

4) If there is no continuity, repair wire. If there is continuity, check between hydraulic modulator and ground (Black wire). If there is no continuity, repair wire. If there is continuity, check circuits between valve relay and hydraulic modulator. See VALVE RELAY CONTINUITY POINTS table. *See Fig. 3.* Check between valve relay pin No. 86 and motor relay pin No. 86.

VALVE RELAY CONTINUITY POINTS [1]

Valve Relay Pin No.	Modulator Pin No
30	12
85	6
87	4
87a	8

[1] – Refer to fig. 3.

5) If any wire does not have continuity, replace modulator.

Test C
Return Pump

1) Turn system test switch to "C". System test LED light should come on and pump motor should operate. If so, go to TEST D. If pump motor does not operate or LED does not come on, check for continuity between battery and hydraulic modulator (Brown/Pink wire).

2) If there is no continuity, repair wire. If there is continuity, check 50-amp fuse. If fuse is okay, check ground strap. If okay, check between overvoltage protection relay and hydraulic modulator (Yellow/Brown wire). If there is no continuity, repair wire. If there is continuity, check between hydraulic modulator and ECU (Blue/White wire).

3) If there is no continuity, repair wire. If there is continuity, check between hydraulic modulator and ECU (Blue/Black wire). If there is no continuity, repair wire. If there is continuity, test circuit between motor relay and hydraulic modulator. See PUMP RELAY CONTINUITY POINTS table. *See Fig. 3.*

4) If any circuit does not have continuity, replace hydraulic modulator.

PUMP RELAY CONTINUITY POINTS [1]

Valve Relay Pin No.	Hydraulic Modulator Pin No
30	9
85	11
86	2
87	13
86	86

[1] – Refer to fig. 3.

Test D
Diode Forward & Reverse

1) Turn system test switch to "D". If system test LED light comes on, go to TEST E. If LED light does not come on, check for closed circuit between pins No. 30 and 87 on valve relay. If closed circuit is found, replace relay. If okay, using an ohmmeter, check for continuity between hydraulic modulator and ground (Black wire).

2) If there is no continuity, repair wire. If there is continuity, check for circuit between ignition switch and hydraulic modulator connector (Light Green/Yellow and Yellow/Red wires). This circuit includes fuse No. 14 and ABS warning light.

Fig. 3: Hydraulic Modulator Testing Points

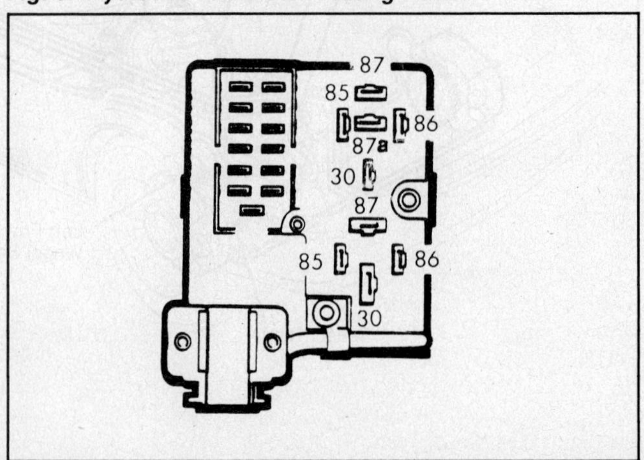

Courtesy of Austin Rover Group.

STERLING ANTI-LOCK BRAKE SYSTEM (Cont.)

3) If circuit is not okay, repair as necessary. If circuit is okay, check for continuity between hydraulic modulator and ECU (Yellow/Green wire). If no continuity is found, repair wire. If there is continuity, replace modulator.

Test E

Diode Forward & Reverse

Turn system test switch to "E". Perform same test as TEST D.

Test F

Stoplight

1) Turn system test switch to "F". Depress brake pedal. If system test LED light comes on, go to TEST G. If LED light does not come on, check for continuity between fuse block and stoplight switch (Purple wire). This includes stoplight switch and fuse.

2) If no problem can be found, check for continuity between stoplight switch and ECU (Green-/Purple wire). This includes stoplights and bulbs. If no continuity is found during any test, repair defective wire.

Test G

Alternator Output Voltage

1) Turn system test switch to "G". If system test LED light does not come on, check for continuity between alternator and ECU (Brown/Yellow wire). If there is continuity, check charging system and retest.

2) If LED light came on in step **1)**, start engine. Run engine at 2000 RPM and check LED light. If LED light goes off, go to WHEEL SENSOR TESTS. If LED light stays on, perform same test as in step **1)**.

WHEEL SENSOR TESTS

Wheel sensors can be checked using ABS Tester (Fast Check). Ensure all switches on ABS tester are in "OFF" position.

Left Front Wheel Sensor

1) Place wheel sensor selector switch to "Ω" position. Turn wheel sensor switch to "Front L". If wheel sensor LED light comes on, go to next test. If LED light does not come on, using an ohmmeter, check for continuity between Red wires at ECU.

2) If there is no continuity, unplug wheel sensor connector. Check continuity for each wire between wheel sensor and ECU. If there is no continuity, repair wire. If there is continuity, check connector. If connector is okay, replace wheel sensor.

Right Front Wheel Sensor

1) Place wheel sensor selector switch to "Ω" position. Turn wheel sensor switch to "Front R". If wheel sensor LED light comes on, go to next test.

2) If LED light does not come on, using an ohmmeter, check for continuity between Yellow wires at ECU. If there is no continuity, unplug wheel sensor connector. Check continuity for each wire between wheel sensor and ECU. If there is no continuity, repair wire. If there is continuity, check connector. If connector is okay, replace wheel sensor.

Left Rear Wheel Sensor

1) Place wheel sensor selector switch to "Ω" position. Turn wheel sensor switch to "Rear L". If wheel sensor LED light comes on, go to next test. If LED light does not come on, using an ohmmeter, check for continuity between Green wires at ECU.

2) If there is no continuity, unplug wheel sensor connector. Check continuity for each wire between wheel sensor and ECU. If there is no continuity, repair wire. If there is continuity, check connector. If connector is okay, replace wheel sensor.

Right Rear Wheel Sensor

1) Place wheel sensor selector switch to "Ω" position. Turn wheel sensor switch to "Rear R". If wheel sensor LED light comes on, go to next test. If LED light does not come on, using an ohmmeter, check for continuity between White wires at ECU.

2) If there is no continuity, unplug wheel sensor connector. Check continuity for each wire between wheel sensor and ECU. If there is no continuity, repair wire. If there is continuity, check connector. If connector is okay, replace wheel sensor.

Left Front Wheel Sensor Insulator

1) Place wheel sensor selector switch to "∞" position. Turn wheel sensor switch to "Front L". If wheel sensor LED light comes on, go to next test. If LED light does no come on, using an ohmmeter, check resistance between ECU and ground at each Red wire.

2) If resistance is 100k ohms or more, insulation is okay. If resistance is less than 100k ohms at either wire, unplug left front wheel sensor connector. Check resistance between each wheel sensor terminal and ground.

3) If resistance at either terminal is less than 100k ohms, replace wheel sensor. If resistance at both terminals was 100k ohms or more, check damaged wiring between wheel sensor and ECU.

Right Front Wheel Sensor Insulator

1) Place wheel sensor selector switch to "∞" position. Turn wheel sensor switch to "Front R". If wheel sensor LED light comes on, go to next test. If LED light does no come on, using an ohmmeter, check resistance between ECU and ground at each Yellow wire.

2) If resistance is 100k ohms or more, insulation is okay. If resistance is less than 100k ohms at either wire, unplug right front wheel sensor connector. Check resistance between each wheel sensor terminal and ground.

3) If resistance at either terminal is less than 100k ohms, replace wheel sensor. If resistance at both terminals was 100k ohms or more, check damaged wiring between wheel sensor and ECU.

Left Rear Wheel Sensor Insulator

1) Place wheel sensor selector switch to "∞" position. Turn wheel sensor switch to "Rear L". If wheel sensor LED light comes on, go to next test. If LED light does no come on, using an ohmmeter, check resistance between ECU and ground at each Green wire.

2) If resistance is 100k ohms or more, insulation is okay. If resistance is less than 100k ohms at either wire, unplug left rear wheel sensor connector. Check resistance between each wheel sensor terminal and ground.

3) If resistance at either terminal is less than 100k ohms, replace wheel sensor. If resistance at both terminals was 100k ohms or more, check damaged wiring between wheel sensor and ECU.

Right Rear Wheel Sensor Insulator

1) Place wheel sensor selector switch to "∞" position. Turn wheel sensor switch to "Rear R". If wheel sensor LED light comes on, go to next test. If LED light does no come on, using an ohmmeter, check resistance between ECU and ground at each White wire.

2) If resistance is 100k ohms or more, insulation is okay. If resistance is less than 100k ohms at

STERLING ANTI-LOCK BRAKE SYSTEM (Cont.)

either wire, unplug right rear wheel sensor connector. Check resistance between each wheel sensor terminal and ground.

3) If resistance at either terminal is less than 100k ohms, replace wheel sensor. If resistance at both terminals was 100k ohms or more, check damaged wiring between wheel sensor and ECU.

Wheel Sensor Output

1) Raise vehicle and support. Place wheel sensor selector switch to "O/P" position. Turn wheel sensor switch to "Front L". Rotate wheel by hand, so wheel spins more than one revolution per second. If wheel sensor light comes on, go to next test.

2) If LED light does not come on, check wheel sensor air gap. See WHEEL SENSOR under REMOVAL & INSTALLATION in this article. Check for loose or damaged wheel sensor, sensor ring or wheel bearings. Repair as necessary and retest. Test each wheel sensor using this method. Ensure wheel sensor switch is at proper position.

HYDRAULIC MODULATOR TEST

Hydraulic modulator sensors can be checked using ABS Tester (Fast Check). Ensure all switches on ABS tester are in "OFF" position.

Valve Internal Resistance Test

1) Place valves selector switch in "Ω" position. Turn valve switch to "Front L". If valve LED light comes on, go to next test. If LED light does not come on, using an ohmmeter, check for continuity between hydraulic modulator and ECU (Yellow/White wire).

2) If there is no continuity, repair wire. If there is continuity, replace hydraulic modulator. Perform same test in other 3 modes. If LED light does not come on in "Front R" setting, check Red/White wire. In "Rear L" mode, check Yellow/Black wire. In "Rear R" mode, check Brown/Yellow wire.

Pressure Reduction Test

1) Ensure transmission is in Neutral and parking brake released. Place valve selector switch in "DYN" position. Turn valve switch to "Front L". Depress brake pedal. Left front wheel should be locked. If not, check master cylinder, brake caliper, pads and disc. Repair as necessary.

2) With brake pedal still depressed, push and hold "P" button. Left front wheel should start to move then lock up. Pump motor should operate. Release brake pedal. Perform same test with valve switch in each position.

3) If system fails any of these tests, check hydraulic modulator ground. If ground is okay, ensure brake lines from hydraulic modulator to each wheel are positioned correctly. *See Fig. 4.* If hydraulic modulator ground and brake lines are okay, replace hydraulic modulator.

Pressurer Maintain Test

1) Ensure transmission is in Neutral and parking brake released. Turn valve switch to "Front L". Press "P=" button. Depress brake pedal. Left front wheel should turn. Release "P=" button. Left front wheel should be locked.

2) Press "P=" and release brake pedal. Left front wheel should remain locked. If not, check if brake lines are positioned correctly. If so, replace hydraulic modulator. Perform same test with valve switch in each position.

NO FAULT FOUND

After all testing procedures are performed and no problem can be found, turn ignition off to reset ECU. If code reappears, check ECU ground and all connections. If everything checks okay, replace ECU.

Fig. 4: Correct Brake Line Positions

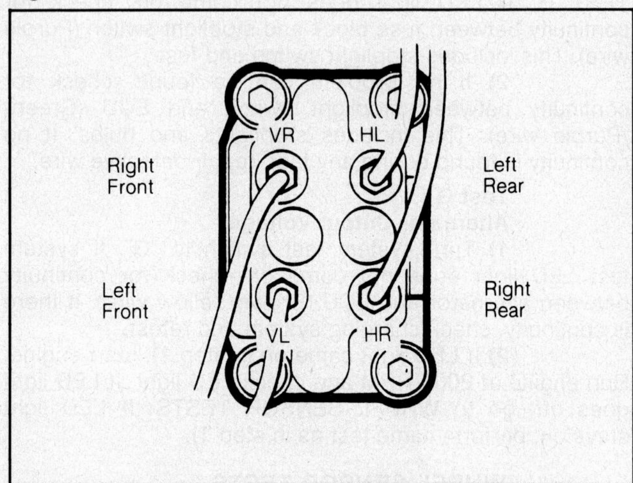

Courtesy of Austin Rover Group.

REMOVAL & INSTALLATION

WHEEL SENSORS

Removal & Installation

Raise vehicle and support. Unplug wheel sensor connector. Remove wheel sensor. To install, reverse removal procedure. Adjust air gap on front wheel sensors to .012-.040" (.30-1.02 mm). Rear wheel sensor air gap is .006-.040" (.17-1.02 mm).

BLEEDING BRAKE SYSTEM

Bleeding brake system is same as conventional system, except the sequence. Correct sequence is left front, right rear, right front and left rear.

PARKING BRAKE

Raise rear of vehicle and support. Release parking brake. Remove caliper cover. Measure distance between lever and stop (both sides). *See Fig. 2.* If clearance is not .020-.080" (.51-2.0 mm), remove parking brake lever cover. Turn adjusting nut until specified clearance is obtained. With parking brake applied, pump brake pedal several times.

STERLING ANTI-LOCK BRAKE SYSTEM (Cont.)

Fig. 5: Sterling Anti-Lock Brake System Wiring Diagram

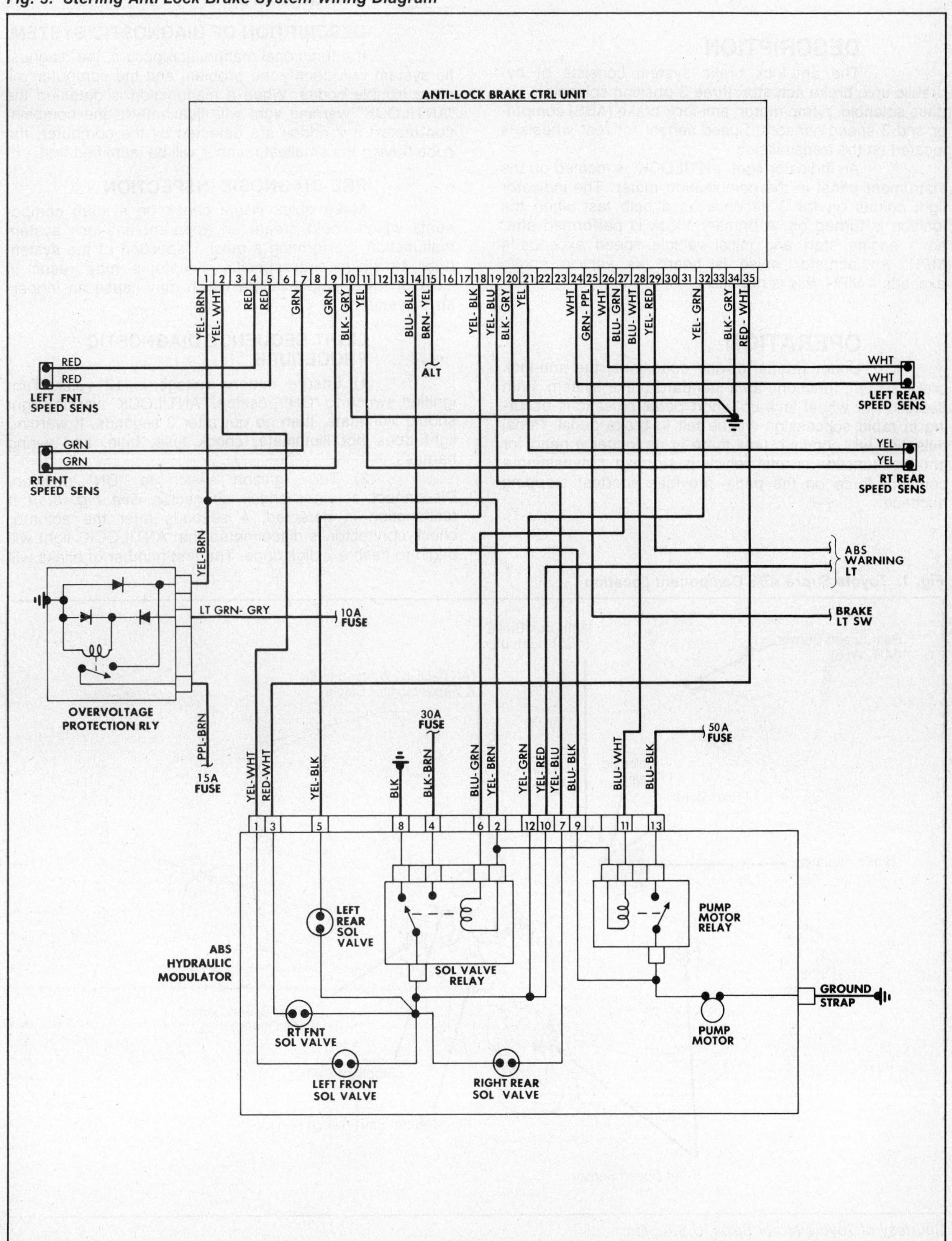

TOYOTA ANTI-LOCK BRAKE SYSTEM

Supra

DESCRIPTION

The anti-lock brake system consists of hydraulic unit, brake actuator, three 3-position solenoids, bypass solenoid, pump motor, anti-lock brake (ABS) computer and 3 speed sensors. Speed sensor for rear wheels is located on the transmission.

An indicator light "ANTILOCK" is located on the instrument panel in the combination meter. The indicator light comes on for 3 seconds as a bulb test when the ignition is turned on. A primary check is performed after each engine start and initial vehicle speed exceeds 4 MPH. An actuator noise is heard as vehicle speed exceeds 4 MPH, this is normal.

OPERATION

Under normal driving conditions, the anti-lock brake system functions as a standard brake system. With detection of wheel lock-up, short pedal pulsations occurring in rapid succession will be felt in brake pedal. Pedal pulsation will continue until there is no longer a need for anti-lock function or until vehicle is stopped. Maintaining a constant force on the pedal provides shortest stopping distance.

DIAGNOSIS

DESCRIPTION OF DIAGNOSTIC SYSTEM

If a functional malfunction occurs, the diagnostic system will identify the problem and the computer will store trouble codes. When a malfunction is detected the "ANTILOCK" warning light will illuminate in the combination meter. If 2 codes are detected by the computer, the code having the smallest number will be identified first.

PRE-DIAGNOSIS INSPECTION

Make quick visual check on system components which could create an apparent anti-lock system malfunction. Performing a quick inspection of the system prior to diagnosing specific symptoms may result in isolation of a simple failure which may cause an inoperative system.

LIGHT SEQUENCE DIAGNOSTIC PROCEDURE

1) Ensure battery voltage is 12 volts. Turn ignition switch to "ON" position. "ANTILOCK" warning light should illuminate, then go out after 3 seconds. If warning light does not illuminate, check fuse, bulb, and wiring harness.

2) Turn ignition switch to "ON" position. Disconnect actuator check connector. *See Fig. 3.* If a malfunction is detected, 4 seconds after the actuator check connector is disconneted the "ANTILOCK" light will begin to flash a 2 digit code. The first number of blinks will

Fig. 1: Toyota Supra ABS Component Location

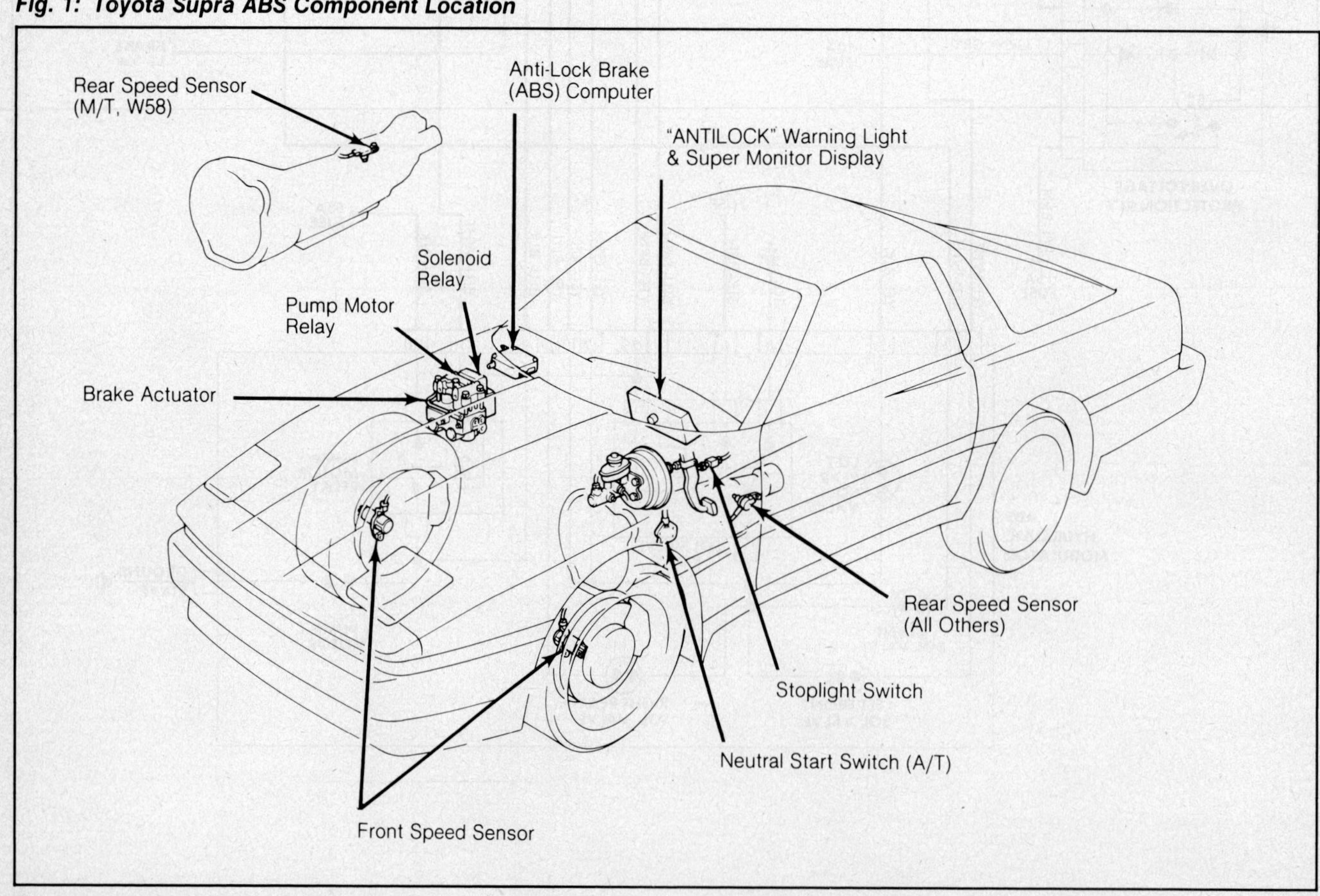

Courtesy of Toyota Motor Sales, U.S.A., Inc.

TOYOTA ANTI-LOCK BRAKE SYSTEM (Cont.)

Fig. 2: Anti-Lock Brake System Circuit Diagram

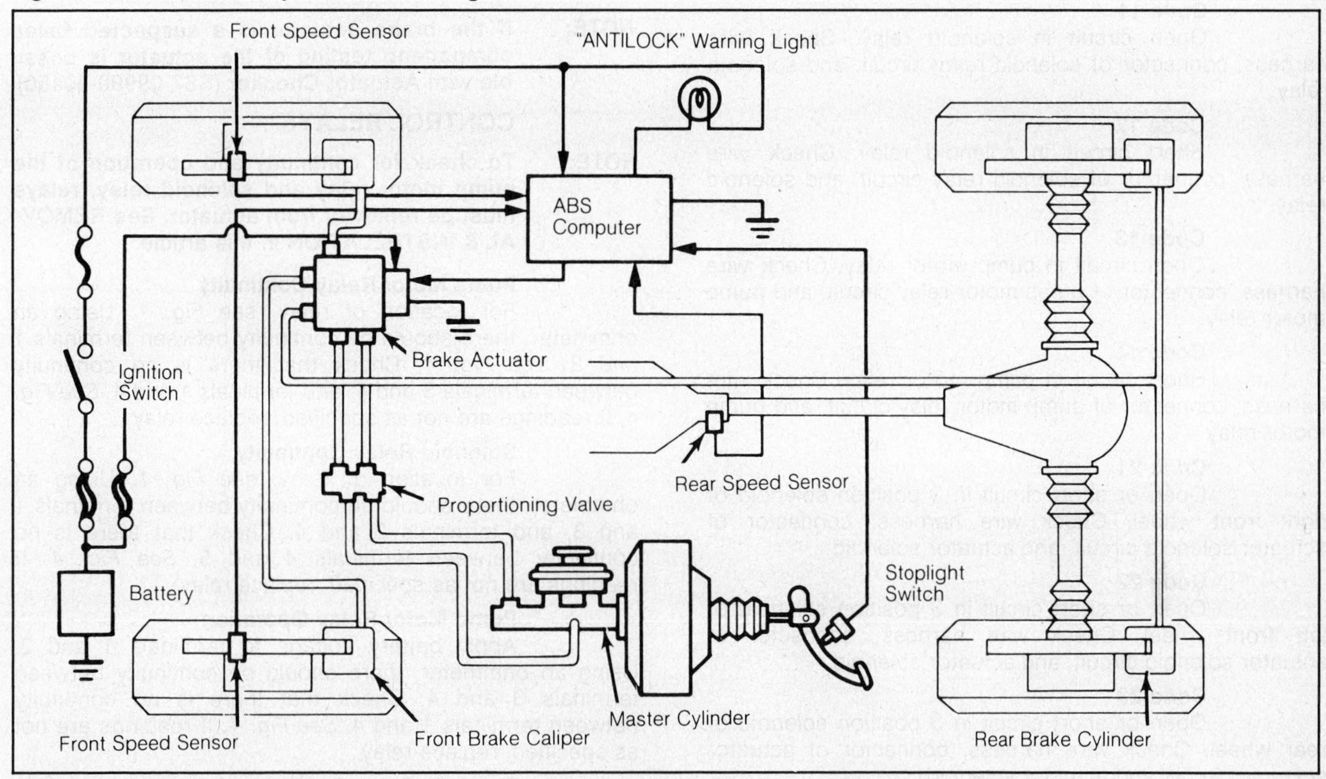

Courtesy of Toyota Motor Sales, U.S.A., Inc.

equal the first digit in a code. After a 1.5 second pause, the second number of blinks will equal the second digit in a code.

3) If two or more codes are stored, there will be a 4.5 second pause between each code. If the ABS system is functioning properly, the "ANTILOCK" light will blink once every .5 second.

Fig. 3: Actuator Check Connector Location on Brake Actuator

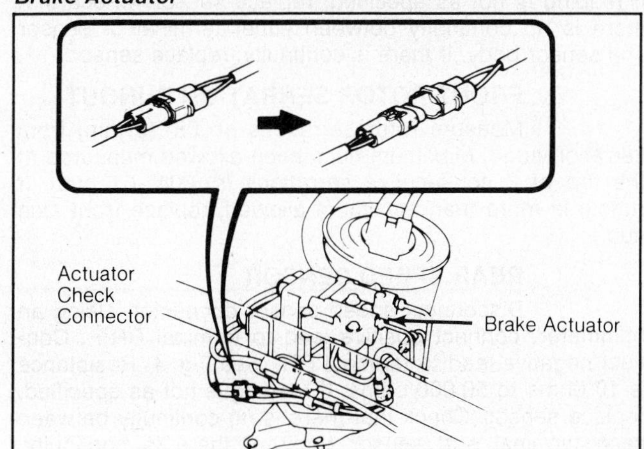

Courtesy of Toyota Motor Sales, U.S.A., Inc.

4) After repairing malfunctioning components, clear diagnostic codes. If a battery cable was disconnected during repairs, all codes will be erased. If a battery cable was not disconnected during repairs, turn ignition on. With actuator check connector disconnected and vehicle stopped, depress brake pedal 8 or more times within 3 seconds. Check that "ANTILOCK" light shows normal code (light blinking every .5 second). Connect actuator check connector. Ensure warning light is out.

SUPER MONITOR DIAGNOSTIC PROCEDURE

1) With ignition off disconnect actuator connector. *See Fig. 3.* Turn ignition switch to "ON" position. Push "SELECT" button and "INPUT" button "M" at the same time and hold in for more than 3 seconds. Release buttons. Display on super monitor should indicate "DIAG".

2) Push "SET" button and hold in for more than 3 seconds. Display will change to "ENG -". Push "SET" button twice. Display will indicate "A.B.S.". The 2 digit numbers to the right of the "A.B.S." display are diagnostic codes. If system is operating properly, super monitor will display "A.B.S.OK". If system displays "A.B.S.00", this indicates a faulty ABS computer, no ABS computer, or short or open circuit in the wiring harness between ABS computer and super monitor computer.

3) To clear diagnostic codes, push and hold in "SET" button. Then push the "INPUT" button "H". Wait for display to change to "CLEAR ?". Hold buttons in until display changes to "OK". Turn ignition off. Connect actuator check connector.

BRAKE ACTUATOR

Removal & Installation

Remove fluid from master cylinder reservoir. Disconnect 3 connectors from actuator. Disconnect 5 brake tubes from actuator. Remove 3 nuts attaching actuator to bracket. Remove actuator. Remove control relays. To install, reverse removal procedure.

TOYOTA ANTI-LOCK BRAKE SYSTEM (Cont.)

DIAGNOSTIC CODES

Code 11

Open circuit in solenoid relay. Check wire harness, connector of solenoid relay circuit, and solenoid relay.

Code 12

Short circuit in solenoid relay. Check wire harness, connector of solenoid relay circuit, and solenoid relay.

Code 13

Open circuit in pump motor relay. Check wire harness, connector of pump motor relay circuit, and pump motor relay.

Code 14

Short circuit in pump motor relay. Check wire harness, connector of pump motor relay circuit, and pump motor relay.

Code 21

Open or short circuit in 3 position solenoid of right front wheel. Check wire harness, connector of actuator solenoid circuit, and actuator solenoid.

Code 22

Open or short circuit in 3 position solenoid of left front wheel. Check wire harness, connector of actuator solenoid circuit, and actuator solenoid.

Code 23

Open or short circuit in 3 position solenoid of rear wheel. Check wire harness, connector of actuator solenoid circuit, and actuator solenoid.

Code 24

Open or short circuit in by-pass solenoid. Check wire harness, connector of actuator solenoid circuit, and actuator solenoid.

Code 31

Malfunction of right front wheel speed sensor signal. Check speed sensor, sensor rotor, and wire harness and connector of speed sensor.

Code 32

Malfunction of left front wheel speed sensor signal. Check speed sensor, sensor rotor, and wire harness and connector of speed sensor.

Code 33

Malfunction of rear wheel speed sensor signal. Check speed sensor, sensor rotor, and wire harness and connector of speed sensor.

Code 34

Open circuit in front of speed sensor. Check speed sensor, sensor rotor, and wire harness and connector of speed sensor.

Code 41

Low battery voltage of 9.5 volts or lower. Check battery and voltage regulator.

Code 42

High battery voltage of 16.2 volts or higher. Check battery and voltage regulator.

Code 51

Pump motor of actuator locked. Check battery, relay, pump motor, wire harness, connector, and ground bolt of actuator pump motor circuit.

"ANTILOCK" Light Always On

Malfunction in computer. Trouble area is computer.

TESTING

NOTE: **If the brake actuator is a suspected failed component, testing of the actuator is possible with Actuator Checker (SST 09990-00150).**

CONTROL RELAYS

NOTE: **To check for continuity and operation of the pump motor relay and solenoid relay, relays must be removed from actuator. See REMOVAL & INSTALLATION in this article.**

Pump Motor Relay Continuity

For location of relay, see *Fig. 1*. Using an ohmmeter, there should be continuity between terminals 1 and 2. *See Fig. 4*. Check that there is no continuity between terminals 3 and 4, and terminals 1 and 4. *See Fig. 4*. If readings are not as specified, replace relay.

Solenoid Relay Continuity

For location of relay, see *Fig. 1*. Using an ohmmeter, there should be continuity between terminals 1 and 3, and terminals 2 and 4. Check that there is no continuity between terminals 4 and 5. *See Fig. 4*. If readings are not as specified, replace relay.

Pump Motor Relay Operation

Apply battery voltage to terminals 1 and 2. Using an ohmmeter, there should be continuity between terminals 3 and 4. Check that there is no continuity between terminals 1 and 4. *See Fig. 4*. If readings are not as specified, replace relay.

Solenoid Relay Operation

Apply battery voltage to terminals 1 and 3. Using an ohmmeter, there should be continuity between terminals 4 and 5. Check that there is no continuity between 2 and 4. *See Fig. 4*. If readings are not as specified, replace relay.

FRONT SPEED SENSOR

Disconnect speed sensor in engine compartment. Measure resistance between terminals of sensor. *See Fig. 4*. Resistance reading should be 800-1300 ohms. If reading is not as specified, replace sensor. Check that there is no continuity between either terminal of sensor and sensor body. If there is continuity, replace sensor.

FRONT ROTOR SERRATION RUNOUT

Measure rotor serrations at .08" (2 mm) from serration edge. Maximum fluctuation allowed measured at the top of 3 consecutive serrations is .004" (.1 mm). If runout is more than maximum allowed, replace front axle hub.

REAR SPEED SENSOR

Disconnect speed sensor connector. Using an ohmmeter, connect positive lead to terminal RR+. Connect negative lead to terminal RR-. *See Fig. 4*. Resistance is 10 ohms to 50,000 ohms. If reading is not as specified, replace sensor. Check that there is no continuity between each terminal and sensor body. If there is continuity, replace sensor.

REAR ROTOR SERRATIONS

On all automatic and manual transmissions, inspect sensor rotor serrations. On manual transmission (W58) equipped vehicles, inspect reverse gear serrations. *See Fig. 5*. Inspect for scratches, cracks, missing teeth or abnormal play. If any abnormality is found replace sensor rotor or reverse gear.

Brakes

TOYOTA ANTI-LOCK BRAKE SYSTEM (Cont.)

Fig. 4: Connector Testing Points

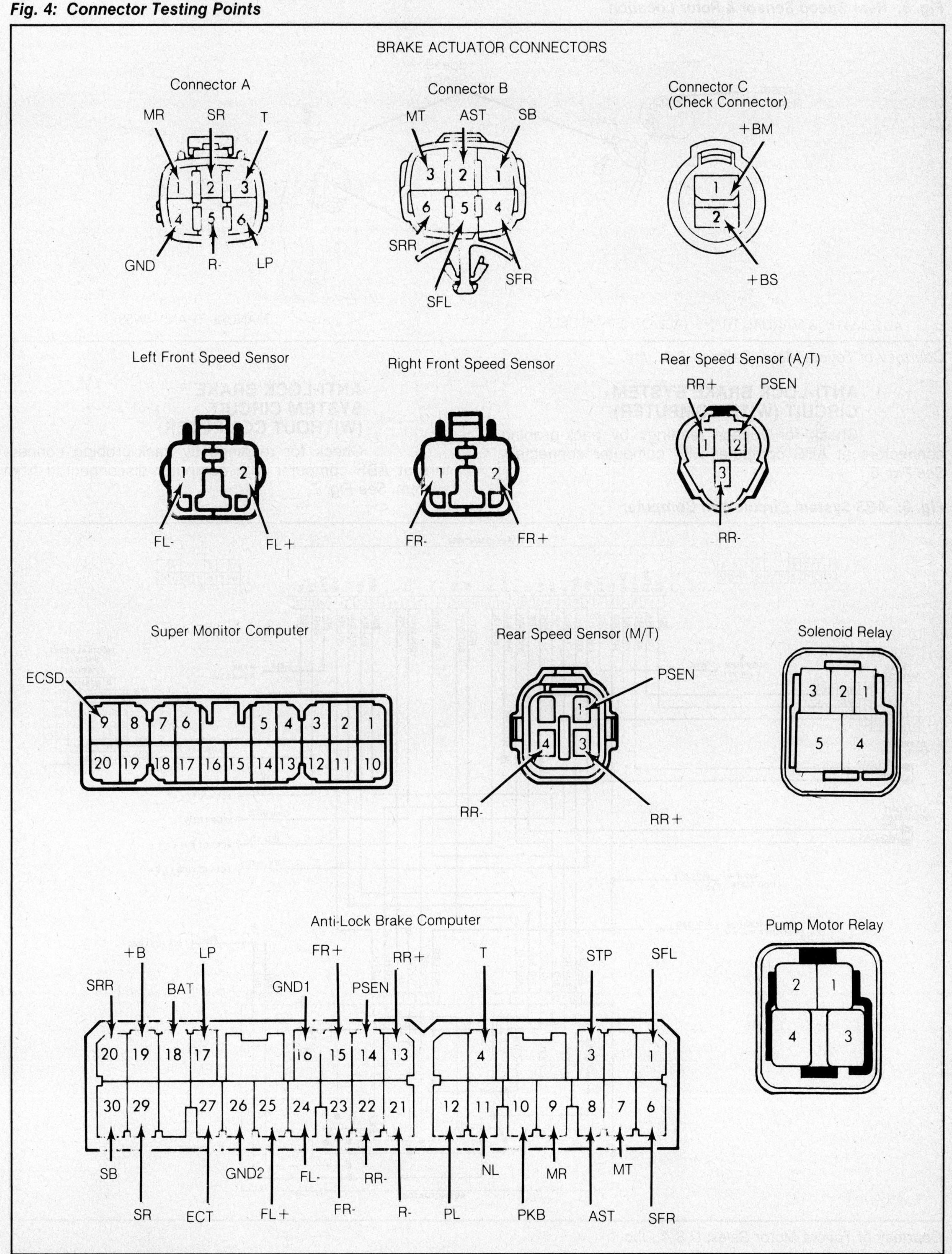

Courtesy of Toyota Motor Sales, U.S.A., Inc.

TOYOTA ANTI-LOCK BRAKE SYSTEM (Cont.)

Fig. 5: Rear Speed Sensor & Rotor Location

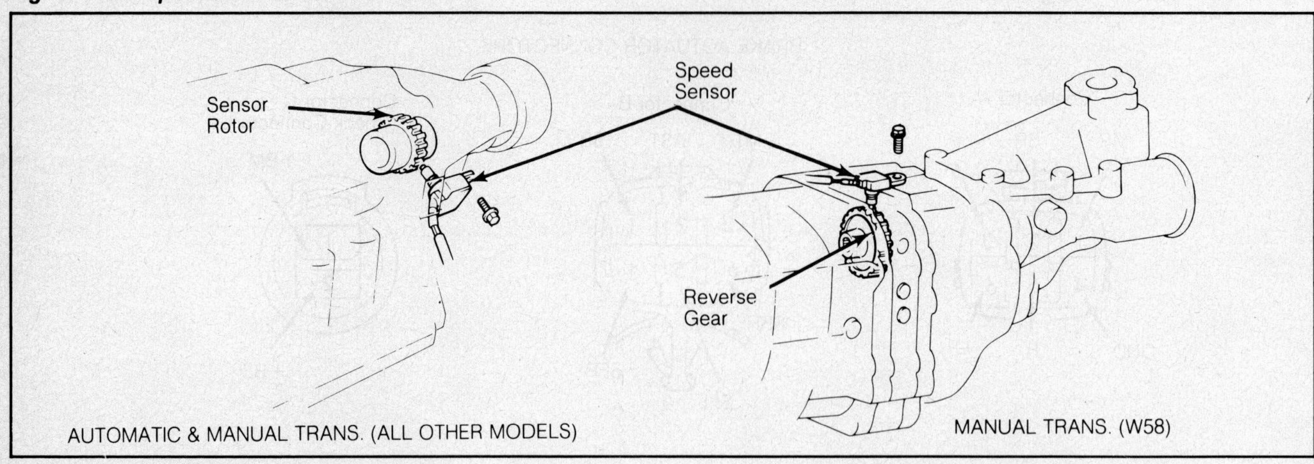

Courtesy of Toyota Motor Sales, U.S.A., Inc.

ANTI-LOCK BRAKE SYSTEM CIRCUIT (WITH COMPUTER)

Check for voltage readings by back-probing connectors at ABS computer with computer connected. *See Fig. 6.*

ANTI-LOCK BRAKE SYSTEM CIRCUIT (WITHOUT COMPUTER)

Check for readings by back-probing connectors at ABS computer with computer disconnected from system. *See Fig. 7.*

Fig. 6: ABS System Circuit With Computer

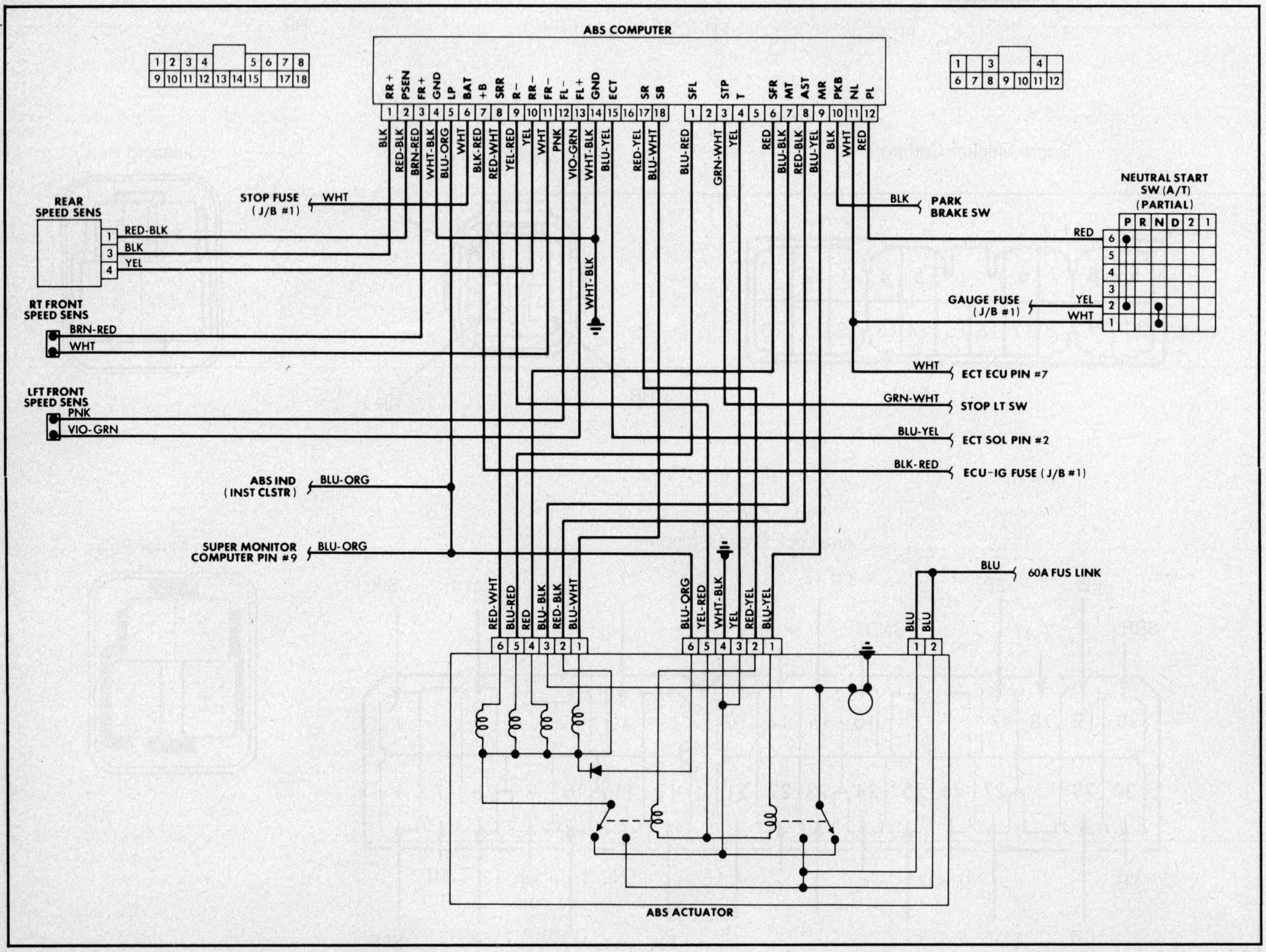

Courtesy of Toyota Motor Sales, U.S.A., Inc.

TOYOTA ANTI-LOCK BRAKE SYSTEM (Cont.)

Fig. 7: ABS System Circuit Without Computer

Tester Connection	Condition	Voltage
SFL – Body ground	Ignition switch on	Battery voltage
	Ignition switch on and "ANTILOCK" warning light goes on	About 0 V
SFR – Body ground	Ignition switch on	Battery voltage
	Ignition switch on and "ANTILOCK" warning light goes on	About 0 V
AST – Body ground	Ignition switch on	Battery voltage
	Ignition switch on and "ANTILOCK" warning light goes on	About 0 V
PESN – Body ground	Ignition switch on	Battery voltage
LP – Body ground	Ignition switch on	Battery voltage
	Ignition switch on and "ANTILOCK" warning light goes on	About 0 V
SRR – Body ground	Ignition switch on	Battery voltage
	Ignition switch on and "ANTILOCK" warning light goes on	About 0 V
SB – Body ground	Ignition switch on	Battery voltage
	Ignition switch on and "ANTILOCK" warning light goes on	About 0 V

Courtesy of Toyota Motor Sales, U.S.A., Inc.

TOYOTA ANTI-LOCK BRAKE SYSTEM (Cont.)

Fig. 8: Toyota Supra Anti-Lock Brake System Wiring Diagram

Tester Connection	Check Item	Condition	Voltage or Resistance Value
SFL – AST	Resistance	Ignition switch off	About 1 Ω
STP – Body ground	Voltage	Ignition switch off and brake pedal depressed	Battery voltage
	Continuity	Ignition switch off and brake pedal returned	Continuity
T – Body ground	Continuity	Ignition switch off	Continuity
SFR – AST	Resistance	Ignition switch off	About 1 Ω
MT – Body ground	Continuity	Ignition switch off	Continuity
AST – Body ground	Continuity	Ignition switch off	Continuity
MR – R ⊖	Resistance	Ignition switch off	50 – 80 Ω
PKB – Body ground	Voltage	Ignition switch on and PKB lever pulled	About 0 V
		Ignition switch on and PKB lever returned	Battery voltage
NL – Body ground	Voltage	Ignition switch on and shift into "N" range	Battery voltage
PL – Body ground	Voltage	Ignition switch on and shift into "P" range	Battery voltage
RR ⊕ – RR ⊖	Resistance	Ignition switch off	10 Ω – 50 kΩ
FR ⊕ – FR ⊖	Resistance	Ignition switch off	0.8 – 1.3 kΩ
GND1 – Body ground	Continuity	Ignition switch off	Continuity
BAT – Body ground	Voltage	–	Battery voltage
⊕B – Body ground	Voltage	Ignition switch on	Battery voltage
SRR – AST	Resistance	Ignition switch off	About 1 Ω
R ⊖ – Body ground	Continuity	Ignition switch off	No continuity
RR ⊖ – Body ground	Continuity	Ignition switch off	No continuity
FR ⊖ – Body ground	Continuity	Ignition switch off	No continuity
FL ⊖ – Body ground	Continuity	Ignition switch off	Continuity
FL ⊕ – FL ⊖	Resistance	Ignition switch off	0.8 – 1.3 kΩ
GND2 – Body ground	Continuity	Ignition switch off	Continuity
ECT – Body ground	Voltage	Ignition switch on and shift into "N" or "P" range	About 5 V
SR – R ⊖	Resistance	Ignition switch off	65 – 100 Ω
SB – AST	Resistance	Ignition switch off	About 2 Ω

Courtesy of Toyota Motor Sales, U.S.A., Inc.

TOYOTA ANTI-LOCK BRAKE SYSTEM (Cont.)

TROUBLE SHOOTING

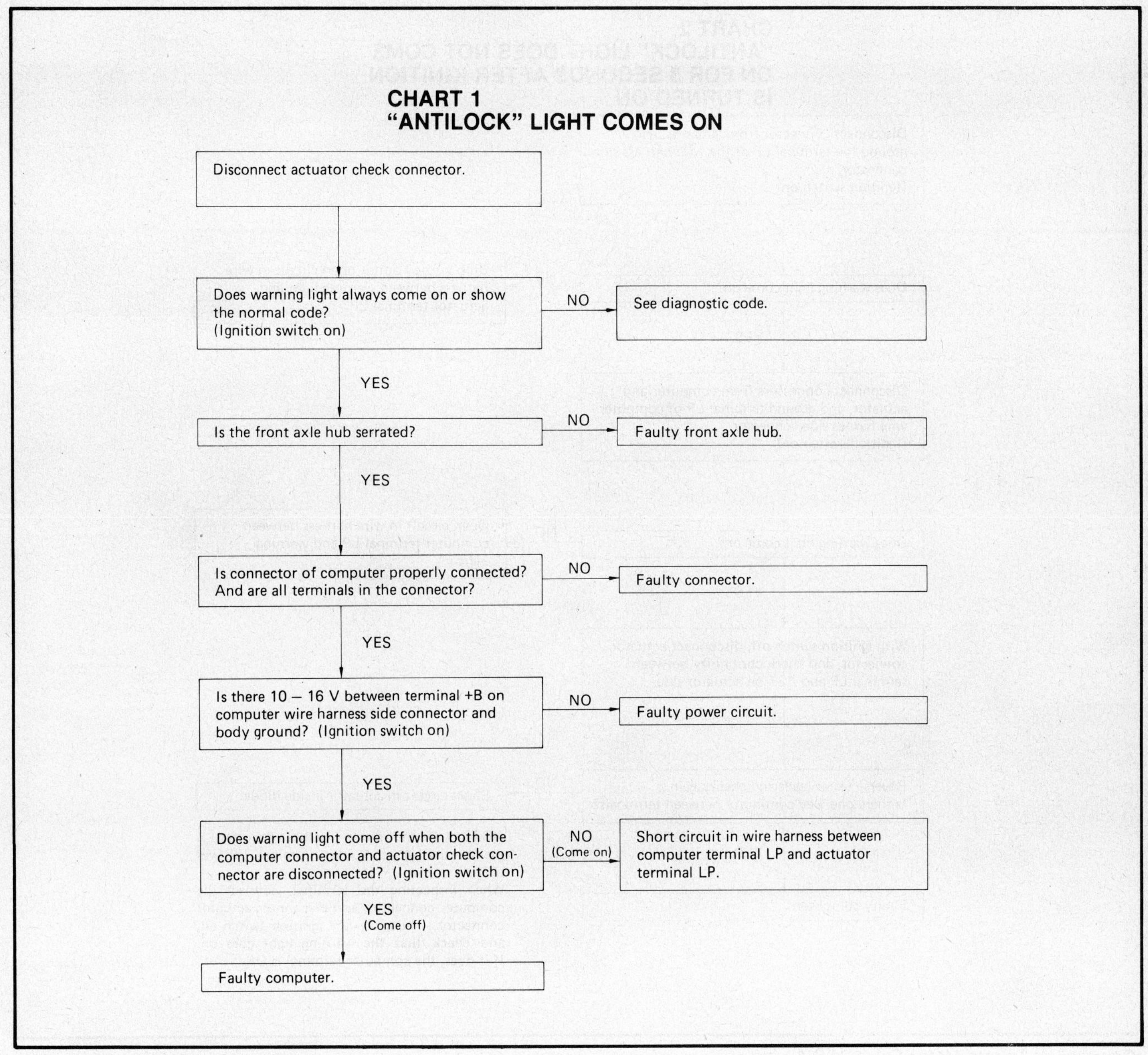
CHART 1
"ANTILOCK" LIGHT COMES ON
Disconnect actuator check connector.
Does warning light always come on or show the normal code? (Ignition switch on)
NO
See diagnostic code.
YES
Is the front axle hub serrated?
NO
Faulty front axle hub.
YES
Is connector of computer properly connected? And are all terminals in the connector?
NO
Faulty connector.
YES
Is there 10 – 16 V between terminal +B on computer wire harness side connector and body ground? (Ignition switch on)
NO
Faulty power circuit.
YES
Does warning light come off when both the computer connector and actuator check connector are disconnected? (Ignition switch on)
NO (Come on)
Short circuit in wire harness between computer terminal LP and actuator terminal LP.
YES (Come off)
Faulty computer.

Courtesy of Toyota Motor Sales, U.S.A., Inc.

TOYOTA ANTI-LOCK BRAKE SYSTEM (Cont.)

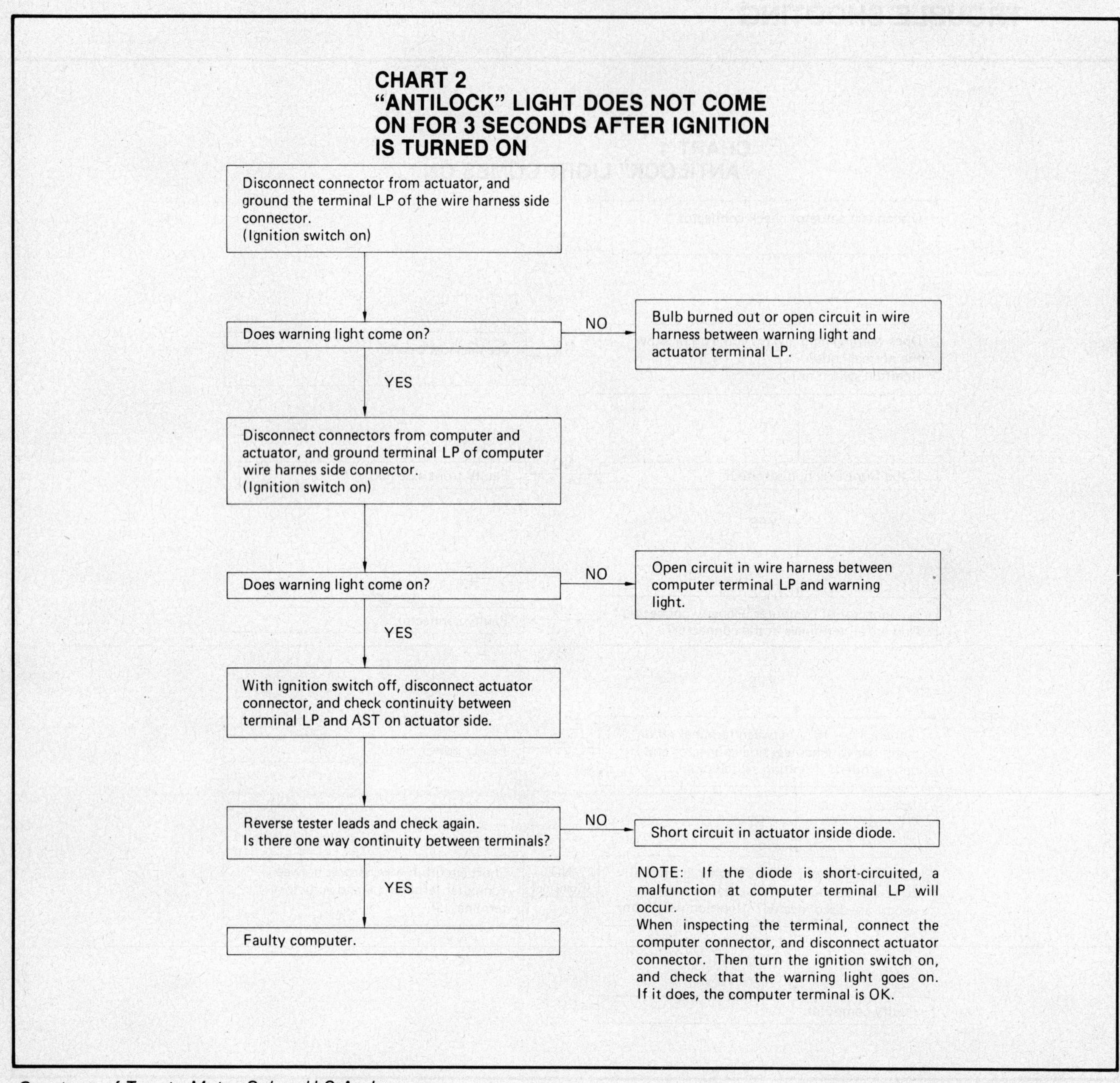

CHART 2
"ANTILOCK" LIGHT DOES NOT COME ON FOR 3 SECONDS AFTER IGNITION IS TURNED ON
Disconnect connector from actuator, and ground the terminal LP of the wire harness side connector.
(Ignition switch on)
Does warning light come on?
NO
Bulb burned out or open circuit in wire harness between warning light and actuator terminal LP.
YES
Disconnect connectors from computer and actuator, and ground terminal LP of computer wire harnes side connector.
(Ignition switch on)
Does warning light come on?
NO
Open circuit in wire harness between computer terminal LP and warning light.
YES
With ignition switch off, disconnect actuator connector, and check continuity between terminal LP and AST on actuator side.
Reverse tester leads and check again.
Is there one way continuity between terminals?
NO
Short circuit in actuator inside diode.
NOTE: If the diode is short-circuited, a malfunction at computer terminal LP will occur.
When inspecting the terminal, connect the computer connector, and disconnect actuator connector. Then turn the ignition switch on, and check that the warning light goes on. If it does, the computer terminal is OK.
YES
Faulty computer.

Courtesy of Toyota Motor Sales, U.S.A., Inc.

TOYOTA ANTI-LOCK BRAKE SYSTEM (Cont.)

CHART 3
"ANTILOCK" WARNING LIGHT COMES ON & OFF BELOW 6 MPH

- Actuator check connector is disconnected.
- Open circuit in wire harness between computer terminal T and actuator terminal T.
- Actuator terminal GND is improperly connected or open circuit in wire harness between actuator terminal GND and body ground.

Courtesy of Toyota Motor Sales, U.S.A., Inc.

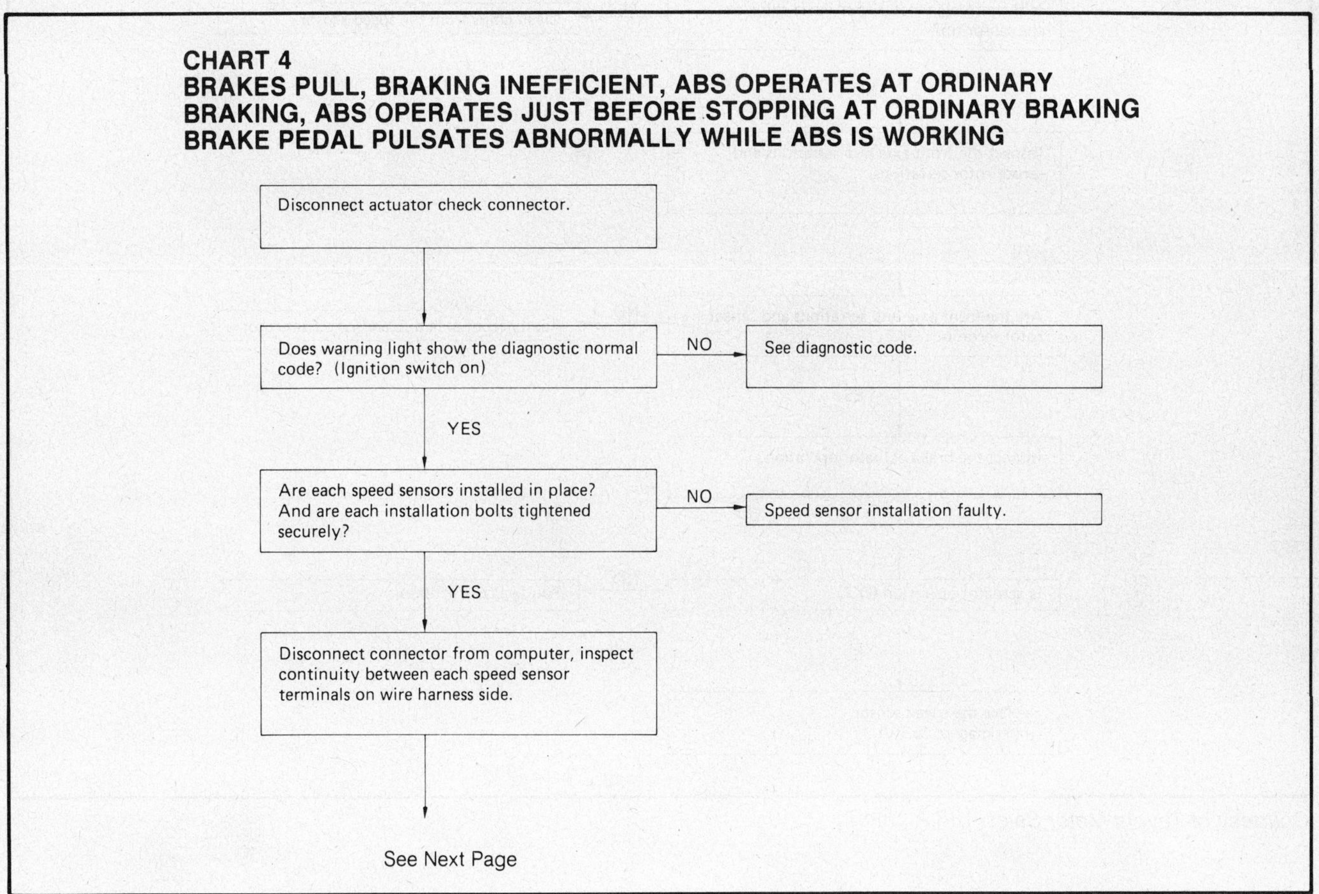

CHART 4
BRAKES PULL, BRAKING INEFFICIENT, ABS OPERATES AT ORDINARY BRAKING, ABS OPERATES JUST BEFORE STOPPING AT ORDINARY BRAKING BRAKE PEDAL PULSATES ABNORMALLY WHILE ABS IS WORKING
Disconnect actuator check connector.
Does warning light show the diagnostic normal code? (Ignition switch on)
NO
See diagnostic code.
YES
Are each speed sensors installed in place? And are each installation bolts tightened securely?
NO
Speed sensor installation faulty.
YES
Disconnect connector from computer, inspect continuity between each speed sensor terminals on wire harness side.
See Next Page

Courtesy of Toyota Motor Sales, U.S.A., Inc.

TOYOTA ANTI-LOCK BRAKE SYSTEM (Cont.)

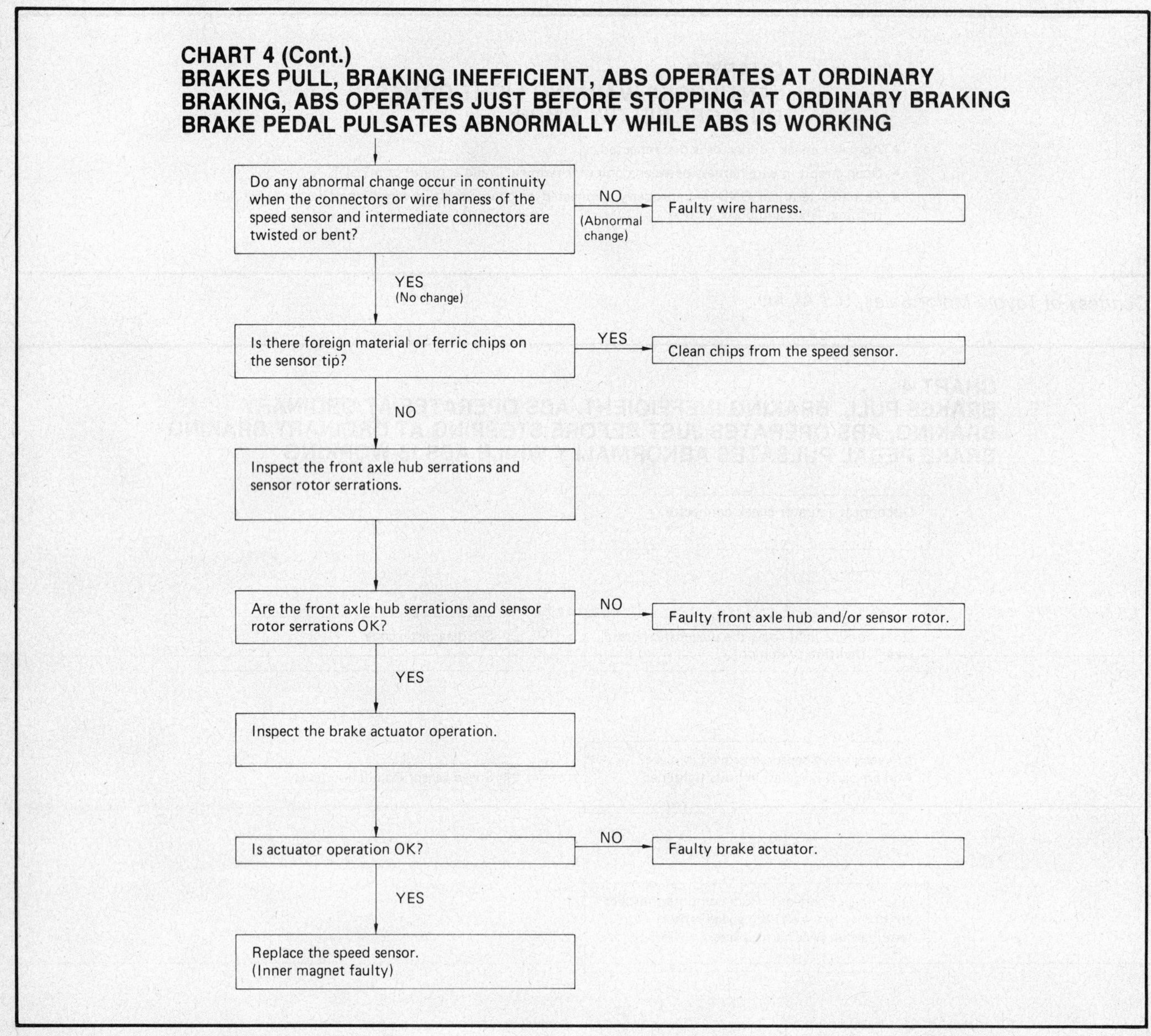

Courtesy of Toyota Motor Sales, U.S.A., Inc.

TOYOTA ANTI-LOCK BRAKE SYSTEM (Cont.)

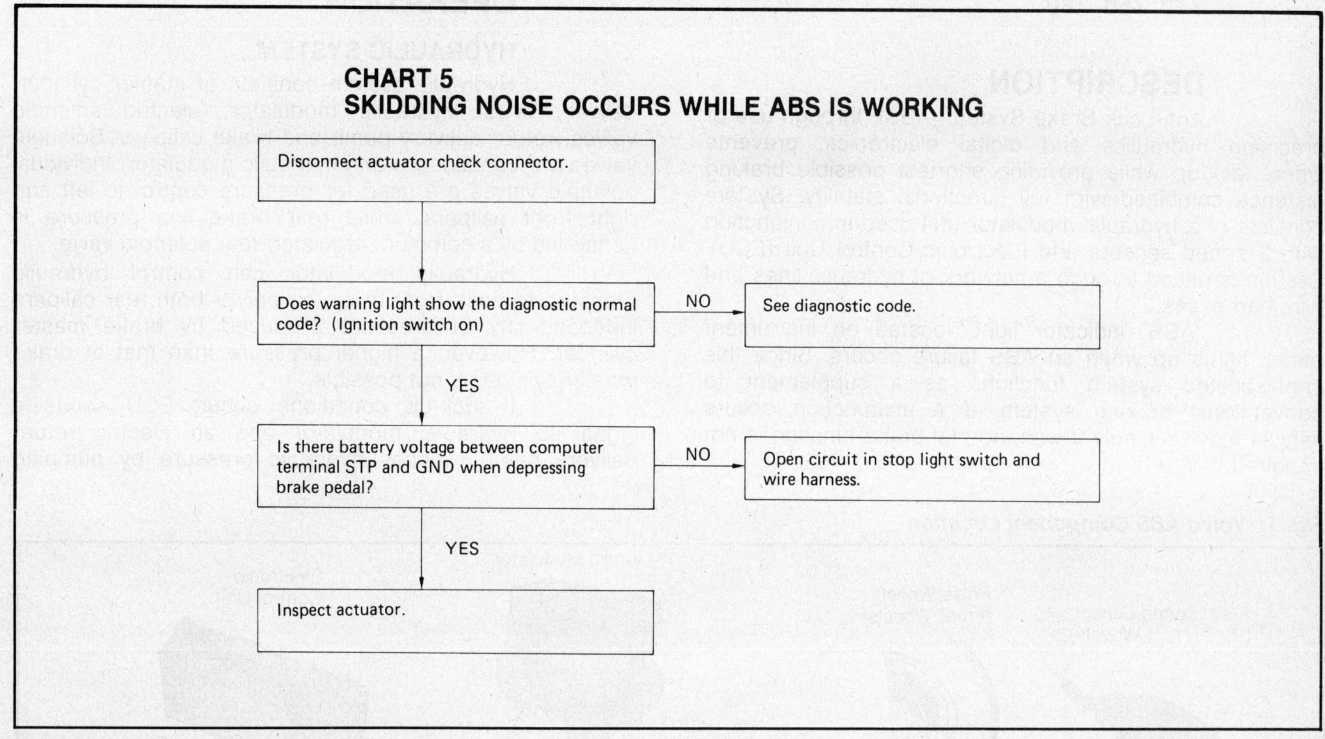
CHART 5
SKIDDING NOISE OCCURS WHILE ABS IS WORKING
Disconnect actuator check connector.
Does warning light show the diagnostic normal code? (Ignition switch on)
NO
See diagnostic code.
YES
Is there battery voltage between computer terminal STP and GND when depressing brake pedal?
NO
Open circuit in stop light switch and wire harness.
YES
Inspect actuator.

Courtesy of Toyota Motor Sales, U.S.A., Inc.

VOLVO ANTI-LOCK BRAKE SYSTEM

740, 760, 780

DESCRIPTION

Anti-Lock Brake System (ABS), through use of precision hydraulics and digital electronics, prevents wheel lock-up while providing shortest possible braking distance combined with full directional stability. System consists of a hydraulic modulator unit used in conjunction with 3 speed sensors and Electronic Control Unit (ECU). System is united through a network of hydraulic lines and wire harnesses.

"ABS" indicator light, located on instrument panel, lights up when an ABS failure occurs. Since this sophisticated system functions as a supplement to conventional braking system, if a malfunction occurs vehicle may be safely driven, normal brake function is not impaired.

OPERATION

HYDRAULIC SYSTEM

Hydraulic system consists of master cylinder, delivery lines, hydraulic modulator, electric solenoid valves, return delivery pump and brake calipers. Solenoid valves are contained within hydraulic modulator. Individual solenoid valves are used for pressure control to left and right front calipers, while rear brake line pressure is controlled by a common, regulated rear solenoid valve.

Hydraulic modulator can control hydraulic pressure to each front brake caliper or both rear calipers independently of pressure produced by brake master cylinder. However, a higher pressure than that of brake master cylinder is not possible.

If lock-up conditions occur, ECU sends a signal to hydraulic modulator and an electric return delivery pump reduces hydraulic pressure by pumping

Fig. 1: Volvo ABS Component Location

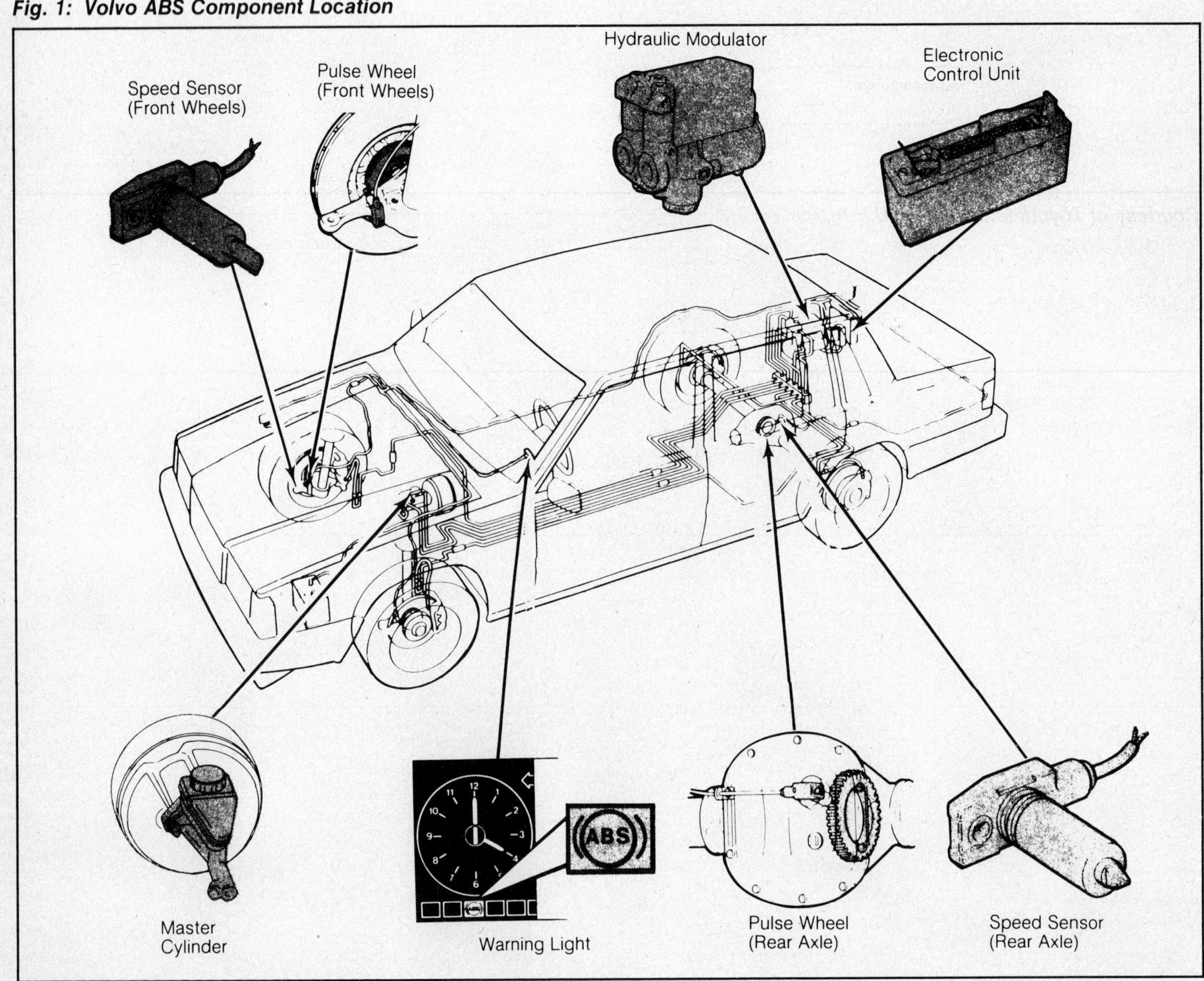

Courtesy of Volvo Cars of North America.

VOLVO ANTI-LOCK BRAKE SYSTEM (Cont.)

brake fluid from brake caliper(s) to master cylinder. This procedure is repeated at either front or both rear calipers until lock-up condition is eliminated.

The hydraulic modulator, solenoids, relays and return delivery pump are contained in a single assembly located under a cover in spare wheel well area.

Fig. 2: Volvo ABS Hydraulic Modulator Assembly

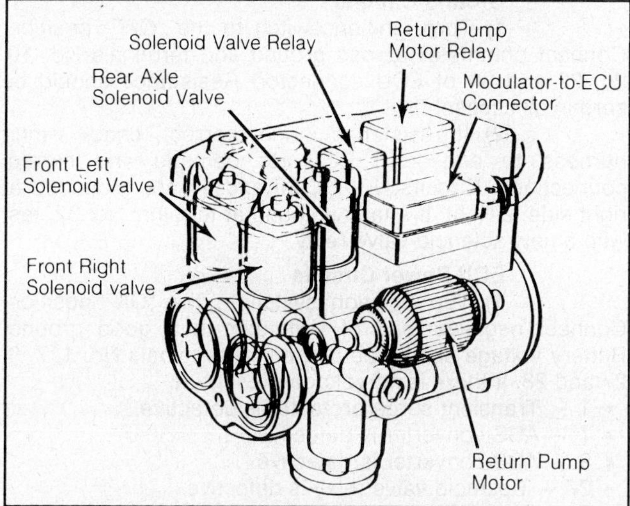

Courtesy of Volvo Cars of North America.

SPEED SENSORS

Speed sensors (impulse transmitters) are mounted behind each front wheel assembly, transmitting individual wheel speed information to ECU. An additional sensor is mounted to rear differential assembly to monitor rear wheel speed. The speed sensors consist of a magnetic core surrounded by coil windings. This pick-up coil is surrounded by a magnetic field. As wheel turns, teeth of a pulse wheel move through this magnetic field. This changes polarity of magnetic field and induces an alternating voltage in coil. This alternating voltage changes frequency according to wheel speed and can be used by ECU to measure wheel speed.

Fig. 3: Volvo ABS Front Speed Sensor

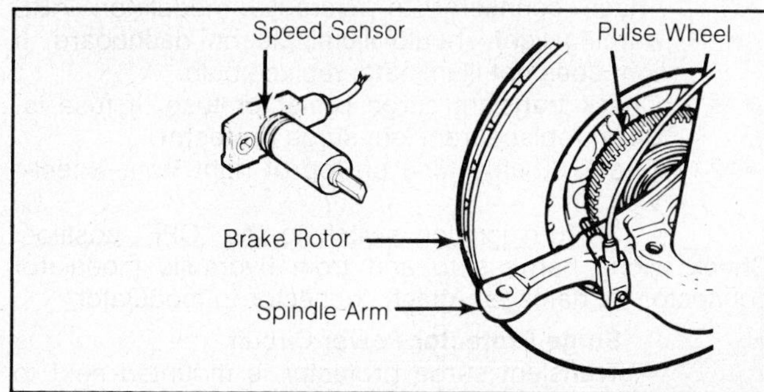

Courtesy of Volvo Cars of North America.

Front Axle Speed Sensors

The front wheels employ sensors mounted through openings in steering knuckles and secured with one socket head screw each. Pulse wheels are pressed onto front wheel hubs.

Rear Axle Speed Sensor

The speed sensor for rear wheels is inserted through an opening in rear inspection cover of differential. Sensor is secured to housing cover with a single screw. Tip of sensor is mounted approximately .0226-.0242" (.575-.615 mm) from an internally-mounted pulse wheel. The pulse wheel is mounted to right rear drive axle.

Fig. 4: Volvo ABS Rear Speed Sensor

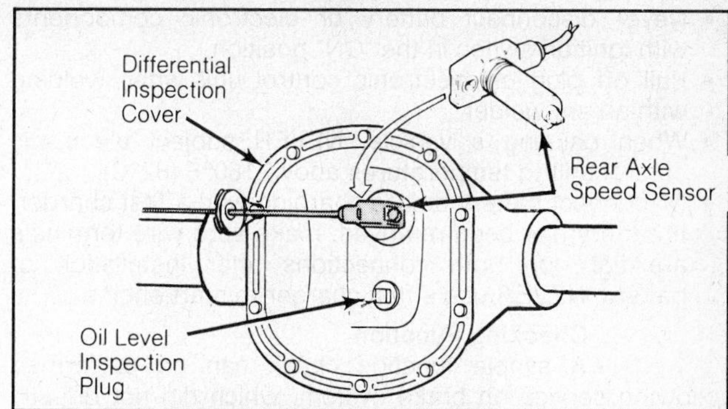

Courtesy of Volvo Cars of North America.

ELECTRONIC CONTROL UNIT

Electronic Control Unit (ECU) is located in trunk area, under the cover in right side spare wheelwell. ECU is a small, multi-channel electronic computer which computes acceleration, deceleration and slip values from electric input signals generated by speed sensors. By way of logic interconnection of these values, control commands are produced for electric solenoid valves in the hydraulic modulator.

Incorporated in ECU is a monitoring circuit which continuously performs a functional check of ABS system. If a failure is sensed "ABS" light on dash is illuminated.

POWER SUPPLY

Power supply for electronic control unit, solenoid valve relay and pump motor relay is provided through fuses No. 2 and 12 in main fuse/relay panel. An 80-amp fuse (above right wheel well) and a 10-amp transient surge fuse (located under cover in rear spare wheel well area) are used for circuit protection.

BRAKE MASTER CYLINDER

Master cylinder on ABS equipped vehicles, in contrast to non-equipped models, uses a split front and rear hydraulic system. Rear piston in master cylinder supplies brake pressure to front brakes and front piston supplies pressure for rear brakes. Fluid is pressurized in master cylinder and routed to hydraulic modulator in rear of vehicle. Under normal braking or a failure condition, fluid pressure and flow are controlled solely by master cylinder.

RELAY OPERATION

The ABS system has 2 relays, solenoid valve relay and pump motor relay. Both relays are mounted on top of hydraulic modulator. Current is supplied to both relays from battery through fuse panel. The ECU supplies a ground for relays when vehicle is running. This supplies a voltage signal from solenoid valve relay to front-control solenoids and to rear-control solenoid. Based upon speed sensor signals, ECU controls solenoid operation by supplying a ground to energize individual solenoids.

Pump motor relay closes when ground is provided through control unit. Pressure relieved by

VOLVO ANTI-LOCK BRAKE SYSTEM (Cont.)

solenoid valve operation is returned to master cylinder by return pump motor.

ABS REPAIR PRECAUTIONS

The following are precautions to observe when performing repair operations outside of ABS unit.

- Never disconnect battery or electronic components with ignition switch in the "ON" position.
- Pull off plug on electronic control unit when welding with an arc welder.
- When painting a vehicle, NEVER subject electronic control unit to temperatures above 180°F (82°C).
- Disconnect battery before charging with a fast charger. If battery has been removed, make sure wire terminals are tight on both connections after installation of battery. NEVER use a fast charger to start engine.

Checking Function

A simple function check can be performed following service on brake system, which did not directly concern ABS components. In other words, indicator lamp in instrument cluster must go out after starting engine. This would indicate system is working properly.

If work is performed on hydraulic modulator, electronic control unit, speed sensors, wire harness or if parts or equipment are replaced because of damage through accident, components can be individually tested using simple test equipment.

TESTING

NOTE: **Electronic Control Unit (ECU) for ABS system is an extremely reliable component. Prior to replacing ECU all other system components and related wiring should be tested.**
Preliminary to all testing, check fuses No. 2 and 12 in main fuse/relay panel. Check 80-amp fuse at top of right side wheel well. Check 10-amp transient surge protector fuse in right side spare wheel well area in trunk.
Check that all wires and ground connections are clean and tight. Poor contact can cause a variety of problems.

To prepare for testing, turn ignition switch to the "OFF" position. Remove cover from hydraulic modulator. Remove connector from ECU by depressing lock spring and swinging out connector. Unless otherwise stated in testing procedure, ECU connector is to remain unplugged. Consult wiring diagram while performing tests. Check ECU connector terminals through holes in side of connector using minimum force. Connector terminal numbers are molded into side of connector.

Fig. 5: Testing Volvo ECU Connector Terminals

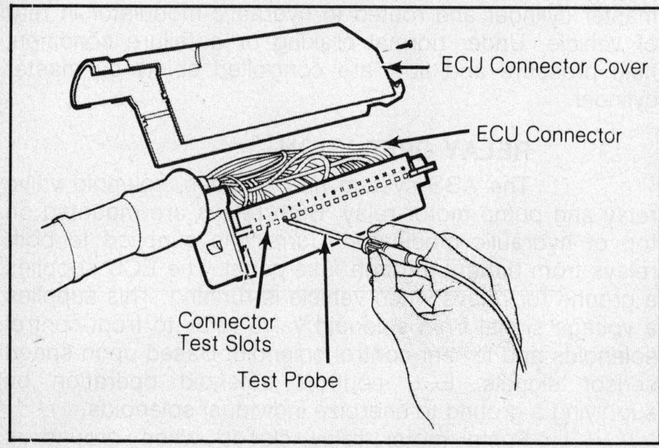

Courtesy of Volvo Cars of North America.

CIRCUIT TESTS

Ground Circuits

1) Turn ignition switch to the "OFF" position. Connect ohmmeter across ground and terminals No. 10, 20, 32 and 34 of ECU connector. Resistance should be zero in all cases.

2) If resistance is not correct, check wiring harness to and from ECU for damage and correct connections. Circuits No. 10, 20 and 34 are grounded at right side taillight. If a fault is found at terminal No. 32, test with a new solenoid valve relay.

ECU Power Circuits

1) Turn ignition switch to the "ON" position. Connect negative lead of voltmeter to a good ground. Battery voltage should be present at terminals No. 1, 7, 9, 27 and 28. If there is no voltage present at:

- 1 – Transient surge protector is defective.
- 7 – ABS converter is defective.
- 9 – ABS converter is defective.
- 27 – Solenoid valve relay is defective.
- 28 – Pump motor relay is defective.

2) If voltage at terminal No. 27 is correct (battery voltage), voltage at terminal No. 29 should be 0.5-1.0 volt. If voltage at terminal No. 29 is not correct, solenoid valve relay is defective.

3) Depress brake pedal and check terminal No. 25. Battery voltage should be present. If voltage is not correct, check stoplight switch. Replace if defective.

Hydraulic Modulator Power Circuits

1 Turn ignition switch to the "OFF" position. Disconnect hydraulic modulator connector. Turn ignition switch to the "ON" position.

2) Connect negative lead of voltmeter to a good ground. Check voltage at terminals No. 6, 7, 10 and 12. Voltmeter should indicate battery voltage. If there is no voltage present at:

- 6 – Check fuse No. 2 in main fuse/relay panel.
- 7 – Attach connector to hydraulic modulator. ABS warning light should illuminate on dashboard. If light does not illuminate, replace bulb.
- 10 – Check transient surge protector fuse. If fuse is okay, replace transient surge protector.
- 12 – Check 80-amp fuse on top of right front wheelwell.

3) Turn ignition switch to the "OFF" position. Check wiring harness to and from hydraulic modulator connector for damage. Attach connector to modulator.

Surge Protector Power Circuit

Transient surge protector is mounted next to ECU, in rear wheelwell area of trunk.

1) Check transient surge protector fuse. Turn ignition switch to the "ON" position. Check voltage at terminals No. 2, 3 and 4. Battery voltage should be present.

2) If battery voltage is not present at terminal No. 3, check wires for damage. If wires are in order, replace transient surge protector.

VOLVO ANTI-LOCK BRAKE SYSTEM (Cont.)

ABS Converter Power Circuit

ABS converter is mounted next to ECU, in rear wheel well area of trunk.

1) Turn ignition switch to the "ON" position. Using a voltmeter, check all wires for battery voltage.

2) If battery voltage is not present, check all wiring to and from ABS converter for damage. If damage is not present, replace ABS converter.

SENSORS

NOTE: All sensors are tested with ignition switch in the "OFF" position.

Front ABS Sensors

1) Using ohmmeter, check resistance between terminals No. 4 and 6 (left sensor) of ECU connector. Check resistance between terminals No. 21 and 23 (right sensor) of ECU connector. As wheels are rotated, resistance should fluctuate between 900-2200 ohms.

2) If resistance is not within specification, check resistance at sensor connectors on suspension tower in engine compartment. If resistance is now within specification, repair wiring harness to ECU. If resistance is still not within specification, replace sensor.

Rear ABS Sensor

1) Connect ohmmeter across terminals No. 7 and 9 of ECU connector. Rotate rear wheels, resistance should fluctuate between 600-1600 ohms.

2) If resistance is not within specification, check resistance of sensor at sensor connector located at fuel filler pipe in trunk. If resistance is now within specification, repair wiring harness to ECU. If resistance is still incorrect, replace sensor.

NOTE: If distance between rear speed sensor and pulse wheel is incorrect, system disengages and ABS warning light will illuminate.

SOLENOIDS

Hydraulic Modulator

Modulator pressure control solenoids are mounted inside hydraulic modulator and are not individually serviceable. Entire modulator must be replaced if solenoids are defective.

1) Turn ignition switch to the "OFF" position. Connect one lead of ohmmeter to terminal No. 32 of ECU connector. Test resistance between terminal No. 32 and terminals No. 2 (left front control solenoid), 18 (rear control solenoid) and 35 (right front control solenoid). Resistance readings should be .7-1.7 ohms.

2) If readings are not within specification, unplug modulator connector and test resistance from hydraulic modulator pin No. 4 (ground) of modulator to pins No. 1, 5 and 3. If readings are now within specification, repair ECU wiring harness to modulator.

3) If readings are still not within specification, replace hydraulic modulator.

RELAYS

Pump Motor

1) With ECU connector still unplugged, turn ignition switch to the "ON" position. Jumper terminal No. 28 of ECU connector to ground.

NOTE: Relay should not remain grounded for more than 2 seconds or damage to relay may occur.

2) Hydraulic modulator should operate while jumper is installed. If hydraulic modulator does not function, check wiring from ECU connector to modulator. If wiring is not at fault, substitute a good relay and retest.

Solenoid Valve

1) Turn ignition switch to the "ON" position. Connect voltmeter across ground and terminal No. 32 of ECU connector. Jumper terminal No. 27 of ECU connector to ground.

2) Solenoid valve relay should switch on and voltmeter should register battery voltage.

3) If fault is indicated, check wiring harness from ECU connector to hydraulic modulator. If wiring is not at fault, substitute a good relay and retest.

REMOVAL & INSTALLATION

ELECTRONIC CONTROL UNIT

Removal

1) Turn ignition switch to the "OFF" position. Fold trunk floor mat to one side and remove cover from right side spare wheelwell.

2) Remove ECU by pulling straight up. Disconnect connector by depressing lock spring and swinging out connector. Remove ECU.

Installation

To install ECU, reverse removal procedure. Ensure lock spring engages correctly.

HYDRAULIC MODULATOR

Removal

1) Turn ignition switch to the "OFF" position. Fold trunk floor mat to one side and remove cover from spare wheel well.

2) Remove hydraulic modulator cover. Remove solenoid and pump relays from modulator. Unplug modulator harness connector.

3) Disconnect ground strap from connector end of modulator.

4) Carefully clean around brake line connections on hydraulic modulator. Note position of lines on modulator. Remove nuts from rubber modulator mounts.

5) Place rags under hydraulic modulator to collect brake fluid that may flow out. Disconnect brake lines. Remove hydraulic modulator.

Installation

1) To install modulator, reverse removal procedure. Bleed brake hydraulic system.

NOTE: Bleeding an ABS system takes longer than bleeding a conventional brake system.

2) Fill brake fluid reservoir to "MAX" fluid level. Connect hoses to both bleed nipples on left front wheel. Submerge hoses in bottle containing some brake fluid. Both hoses must end below brake fluid surface.

3) Open bleed nipples. Have helper pump brake pedal 5 times, holding down on last depression stroke. There should be no air bubbles visible by last stroke. Close bleeders.

4) Bleed remaining wheels in the following order: front right wheel, rear left wheel and right rear wheel. Check brake fluid level after each open and close cycle of bleeders.

VOLVO ANTI-LOCK BRAKE SYSTEM (Cont.)

SPEED SENSORS

Removal (Front Wheel)

1) Locate sensor wires at sensor. Follow sensor wire to connector on spring tower. Disconnect sensor wires from connector. Pull wires through wheel arch and release from clamps.

2) Unbolt sensor from inboard side of spindle arm. Remove sensor.

Installation

Coat speed sensor with small amount of Grease (1161037-5). Reverse removal procedure to install sensor.

Removal (Rear)

1) Follow sensor wires from sensor to connector. Cut shrink tubing from connector (if applicable). Unplug connector. Pull sensor wiring below vehicle.

2) Unbolt sensor from differential cover. Remove sensor.

Installation

1) Remove "O" ring and shim from old sensor. Attach shim to new sensor. Remove oil level plug from differential inspection cover. Install sensor.

2) Insert .024" (.60 mm) feeler gauge between inductive tip of sensor and pulse wheel. If feeler gauge can be moved back and forth easily, increase feeler gauge thickness in .04" (1.0 mm) increments until feeler gauge sticks.

3) Note feeler gauge thickness. Subtract .024" (.60 mm) from feeler gauge thickness. Subtract this amount from original shim thickness to obtain replacement shim thickness. This will provide proper sensor-to-pulse wheel clearance. Shims are available in thicknesses of .0394-.0709" (1.000-1.800 mm) in increments of .008" (.20 mm)

Fig. 6: Checking ABS Rear Speed Sensor Clearance

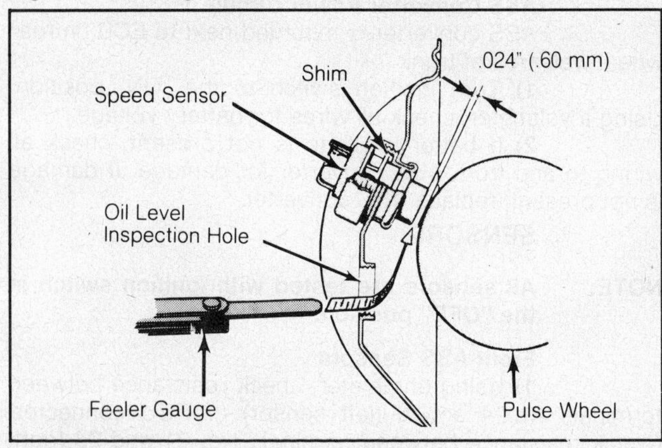

Courtesy of Volvo Cars of North America.

PULSE WHEEL

NOTE: Rear speed sensor pulse wheel is integral of differential and cannot be replaced without overhauling rear axle assembly.

Removal (Front)

1) Raise vehicle. Support with safety stands. Remove wheel assembly.

2) Remove 2 caliper retaining bolts. Remove caliper and hang out of way. Remove rotor dust cap, cotter pin, nut and outer wheel bearing. Remove brake rotor.

3) Remove inner bearing and grease seal. Remove any lock rings and spacers from rotor (if applicable). Using 2-arm universal puller, remove pulse wheel from brake rotor.

Installation

1) Press new pulse wheel onto brake rotor. Install inner wheel bearing and grease seal. Slide brake rotor onto spindle. Install outer wheel bearing and nut.

2) Torque spindle nut to 41 ft. lbs. (57 N.m) while rotating disc rotor. Loosen nut 1/2 turn and retighten finger tight. If nut recess is not lined up with hole in spindle, tighten to next recess. Install cotter pin and dust cap.

3) Install brake caliper using new attaching bolts. Torque caliper to 72 ft. lbs. (100 N.m). To complete installation, reverse removal procedure.

VOLVO ANTI-LOCK BRAKE SYSTEM (Cont.)

Fig. 7: Volvo 740, 760 & 780 Anti-Lock Brake System Wiring Diagram

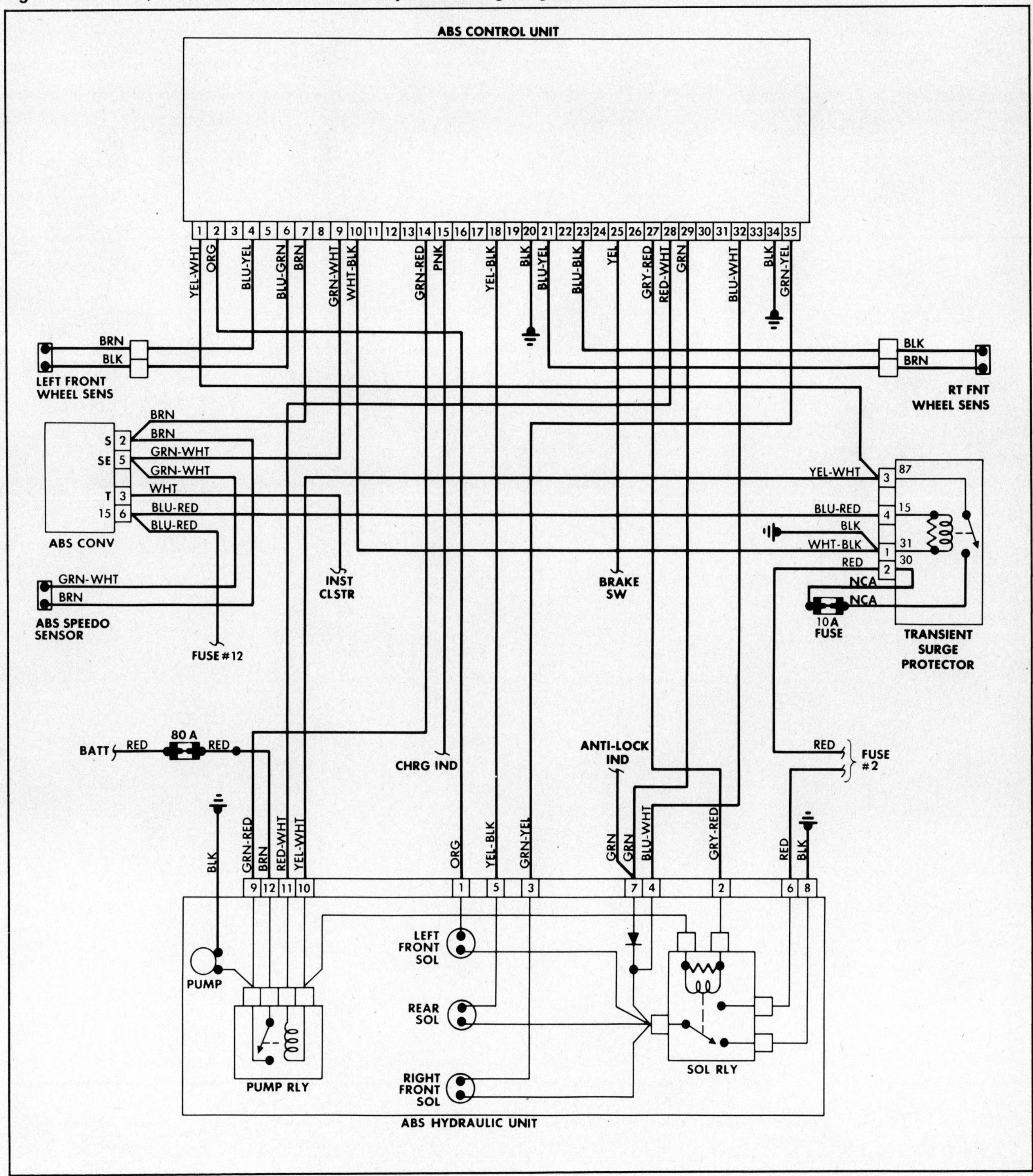

SECTION 10

WHEEL ALIGNMENT

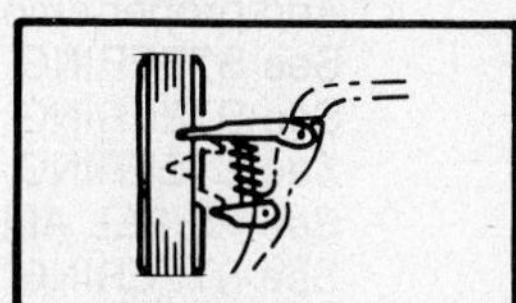

CONTENTS

TROUBLE SHOOTING — Page

All Models 10-2

RIDING HEIGHT SPECIFICATIONS

Acura-Toyota 10-3
Toyota (Cont.) 10-4

WHEEL ALIGNMENT SPECIFICATIONS

Acura 10-6
Alfa Romeo 10-6
Audi 10-6
BMW 10-6
Chevrolet 10-6
Chrysler Motors 10-6
Ford Motor Co. 10-6
Honda 10-6, 10-8

WHEEL ALIGNMENT SPECIFICATIONS (Cont.) — Page

Hyundai 10-8
Isuzu 10-8
Jaguar 10-8
Mazda 10-8
Mercedes-Benz 10-8
Mitsubishi 10-10
Nissan 10-10
Peugeot 10-10
Porsche 10-10
Saab 10-12
Sterling 10-6
Subaru 10-12
Suzuki 10-12
Toyota 10-12, 10-14
Volkswagen 10-14
Volvo 10-14
Yugo 10-14

WHEEL ALIGNMENT PROCEDURES

All Models 10-16

WHEEL LUG NUT TORQUES

All Models 10-19

JACKING & HOISTING

Acura 10-20
Alfa Romeo 10-20
Audi 10-20
BMW 10-20
Chevrolet 10-21
Chrysler Motors 10-21
Ford Motor Co. 10-21
Honda 10-22
Hyundai 10-22
Isuzu 10-22
Jaguar 10-22
Mazda 10-22
Mercedes-Benz 10-22
Mitsubishi 10-21, 10-22
Nissan 10-23
Peugeot 10-23
Porsche 10-23
Saab 10-23
Sterling 10-20
Subaru 10-24
Suzuki 10-24
Toyota 10-24
Volkswagen 10-25
Volvo 10-25

NOTE: ALSO SEE GENERAL INDEX.

Wheel Alignment

TROUBLE SHOOTING

CONDITION	POSSIBLE CAUSE	CORRECTION
Premature Tire Wear	Improper tire inflation	Check tire pressure
	Front alignment out of tolerance	See ADJUSTMENTS in WHEEL ALIGNMENT
	Suspension components worn	See SUSPENSION
	Steering system components worn	See STEERING
	Improper standing height	See RIDING HEIGHT SPECIFICATIONS
	Uneven or sagging springs	See COIL SPRINGS in SUSPENSION
	Bent wheel	See WHEEL ALIGNMENT
	Improper torsion bar adjustment	See SUSPENSION
	Loose or worn wheel bearings	See WHEEL BEARING ADJ. in SUSPENSION
	Worn or defective shock absorbers	Replace shock absorbers
	Tires out of balance	Check tire balance
Pulls to One Side	Improper tire inflation	Check tire pressure
	Brake dragging	See BRAKES
	Mismatched tires	See WHEEL ALIGNMENT
	Broken or sagging spring	See SUSPENSION
	Broken torsion bar	See SUSPENSION
	Power steering valve not centered	See STEERING
	Front alignment out of tolerance	See ADJUSTMENTS in WHEEL ALIGNMENT
	Defective wheel bearing	See WHEEL BEARINGS in SUSPENSION
	Uneven sway bar links	See SUSPENSION
	Frame bent	Check for frame damage
	Steering system bushing worn	See STEERING
	Idler arm bushing too tight	See STEERING LINKAGE
Hard Steering	Idler arm bushing too tight	See STEERING LINKAGE
	Ball joint tight or seized	SEE BALL JOINT CHECKING in SUSPENSION
	Steering linkage too tight	See STEERING LINKAGE
	Power steering fluid low	Add proper amount of fluid
	Power steering drive belt loose	See STEERING
	Power steering pump defective	See STEERING
	Steering gear out of adjustment	See STEERING
	Incorrect wheel alignment	See WHEEL ALIGNMENT
	Damaged steering gear	See STEERING
	Damaged suspension	See SUSPENSION
	Bent steering knuckle or supports	See SUSPENSION
Vehicle "Wanders"	Strut rod or control arm bushing worn	See SUSPENSION
	Loose or worn wheel bearings	See WHEEL BEARINGS in SUSPENSION
	Improper tire inflation	Check tire pressure
	Stabilizer bar missing or defective	See SUSPENSION
	Wheel alignment out of tolerance	See Adjustment in WHEEL ALIGNMENT
	Broken spring	See SUSPENSION
	Defective shock absorbers	Replace shock absorbers
	Worn steering & suspension components	See SUSPENSION
Front End Shimmy	Tire out of balance/round	Check tire balance
	Excessive wheel runout	See WHEEL ALIGNMENT
	Insufficient or improper caster	See WHEEL ALIGNMENT
	Worn suspension or steering components	See SUSPENSION
	Defective shock absorbers	Replace shock absorbers
	Wheel bearings worn or loose	See WHEEL BEARING ADJ. in SUSPENSION
	Power steering reaction bracket loose	See STEERING
	Steering gear box (rack) mounting loose	See STEERING
	Steering gear adjustment loose	See STEERING
	Worn spherical joints	See SUSPENSION
Toe-In Not Adjustable	Lower control arm bent	See SUSPENSION
	Frame bent	Check frame for damage
Camber Not Adjustable	Control arm bent	See SUSPENSION
	Frame bent	Check frame for damage
	Hub & bearing not seated properly	See SUSPENSION

RIDING HEIGHT SPECIFICATIONS – ALL MODELS

ADJUSTMENT

RIDING HEIGHT

NOTE: **On vehicles with electronic chassis controls, all systems should be functional before attempting ride height or wheel alignment adjustment.**

Before adjusting wheel alignment, check riding height. Riding height must be checked with vehicle on level floor and tires properly inflated. Bounce vehicle several times and allow suspension to settle.

Visually inspect vehicle for signs of abnormal height from front to rear or side to side. Check passenger and luggage compartments for extra heavy items and remove if present.

Measure ride height. Each model or manufacturer is tariffed in RIDING HEIGHT SPECIFICATIONS table to indicate the proper method of measuring ride height. If riding height is not within specifications listed, check, repair or replace suspension components.

NOTE: **For vehicles not listed, ride height between left and right side of vehicle should vary less than 1" (25.4 mm).**

RIDING HEIGHT SPECIFICATIONS

Application	Front In. (mm)	Rear In. (mm)
Acura		
Integra [1]		
3-Door	25.7 (645)	25.7 (645)
5-Door	25.7 (645)	25.8 (655)
Legend [1]		
All Models	25.7 (645)	25.8 (655)
Chevrolet		
Sprint [2]	10.0 (254)	13.2 (335)
Spectrum [2]	14.0 (356)	14.6 (371)
Chrysler Motors		
Colt [3]		
5-Door	9.8 (249)	12.8 (325)
Except 5-Door	10.0 (254)	13.2 (335)
Conquest [2]	14.0 (356)	14.6 (371)
Raider [4]	9.0 (229)	9.0 (229)
Ram-50 [4]	9.0 (229)	9.0 (229)
Ford Motor Co.		
Festiva	NS	NS
Merkur XR4Ti	NS	NS
Tracer	.59 (15)	.59 (15)
Honda [1]		
Accord	26.6 (675)	25.7 (637)
Civic		
Hatchback	24.8 (630)	25.8 (655)
Sedan	25.0 (635)	24.8 (630)
Wagon	25.0 (635)	25.2 (640)
Civic CRX/Si	24.8 (630)	24.7 (627)
Prelude	25.6 (650)	25.3 (643)
Hyundai		
Excel	NS	NS

[1] – Measured from fender brim to floor.
[2] – Measured from below bumper to floor.
[3] – Chassis ground clearance.
[4] – For initial rear torsion bar setting, see CHRYSLER MOTORS & MITSUBISHI FWD article in REAR SUSPENSION article.
NS – Information not supplied by manufacturer.

RIDING HEIGHT SPECIFICATIONS (Cont.)

Application	Front In. (mm)	Rear In. (mm)
Isuzu		
I-Mark [3]	6.7 (163)	6.7 (163)
P'UP		
2WD [7]		
104.3" WB	4.0 (102)	6.1 (155)
117.9" WB	4.0 (102)	7.5 (190)
4WD [7]		
104.3" WB	5.0 (127)	7.7 (195)
117.9" WB	5.0 (127)	8.8 (224)
Trooper II	5.16 (131)	1.5 (38)
Mazda		
All 323 & 626 [5]	.59 (15)	59 (15)
Mitsubishi		
Mirage [3]		
5-Door	9.8 (249)	12.8 (325)
Except 5-Door	10.0 (254)	13.2 (335)
Montero [4]	9.0 (229)	9.0 (229)
Pickup [4]	9.0 (229)	9.0 (229)
Starion [2]	14.0 (356)	14.6 (371)
Nissan		
Pickup		
2WD [7]	4.5 (113)	NS
4WD [7]	1.8 (46)	NS
Sterling [1]		
825	25.7 (645)	25.8 (655)
Subaru		
2WD [6,7]		
Wagon	9.7 (245)	11.0 (280)
XT Coupe	8.0 (204)	7.2 (183)
All Others	9.5 (240)	10.2 (260)
4WD		
Sedan	10.4 (265)	12.6 (325)
GL	10.6 (270)	12.8 (325)
Wagon	9.7 (245)	11.0 (280)
GL	10.6 (270)	13.4 (340)
DL	10.4 (265)	13.2 (335)
XT Coupe Non-Turbo	9.2 (233)	9.1 (231)
XT Coupe Turbo	10.4(265)	12.8 (325)
Suzuki [3]		
Samurai	8.1 (206)	8.1 (206)
Toyota [3]		
Camry		
165SR13	8.5 (216)	10.2 (260)
185/70SR13	8.54 (217)	10.3 (261)
Celica	7.4 (189)	9.8 (251)

[1] – Measured from fender brim to floor.
[2] – Measured from below bumper to floor.
[3] – Chassis ground clearance.
[4] – For initial rear torsion bar setting, see CHRYSLER MOTORS & MITSUBISHI FWD article in REAR SUSPENSION article.
[5] – The allowable difference in height from left to right side.
[6] – Measured from front of transverse link attaching bolt to floor.
[7] – Difference in measurements of lower link spindle center to floor and tension rod attaching bolt (bottom of spring stopper on 4WD) to floor.
NS – Information not supplied by manufacturer.

RIDING HEIGHT SPECIFICATIONS – ALL MODELS (Cont.)

RIDING HEIGHT SPECIFICATIONS (Cont.)

Application	Front In. (mm)	Rear In. (mm)
Toyota (Cont.)		
Corolla		
FWD		
155SR13	7.5 (191)	10.1 (257)
175/70SR13	7.6 (192)	10.2 (258)
175/70HR13	7.2 (183)	10.2 (259)
185/60HR14	7.1 (181)	10.1 (257)
RWD		
Exc. 196/60R14	9.2 (234)	9.3 (236)
195/60R14	9.0 (229)	9.1 (231)
Cressida		
195/70 HR14	8.8 (224)	9.7 (246)
205/60 R15	8.6 (219)	10.4 (265)
MR2	8.7 (221)	8.1 (205)
Pickup		
Std. Short Bed		
7.00x14	10.6 (269)	11.7 (279)
ER78x14	10.0 (255)	11.1 (283)
Std. Long Bed		
7.00x14	10.8 (273)	11.3 (288)
ER78x14	10.2 (259)	10.8 (274)
Long Soft-Ride	10.2 (259)	10.8 (275)
Extra Cab		
Soft Ride	9.8 (249)	10.8 (273)
Extra Cab Std.	9.8 (249)	10.7 (272)
3/4 Ton	10.7 (272)	12.4 (315)
Cab & Chassis	10.8 (275)	11.4 (290)
SR-5 Short Bed		
P195/75R14	9.8 (248)	9.6 (243)
205/70SR14	10.0 (254)	10.9 (277)
ER78x14	10.0 (254)	10.9 (276)
SR-5 Long Bed		
P195/75R14	9.9 (253)	10.8 (273)
205/70R14	10.2 (259)	10.9 (276)
ER78x14	10.1 (257)	10.8 (275)
SR-5 Extra Cab		
P195/75R14	9.8 (249)	10.7 (271)
205/70SR14	10.0 (255)	10.8 (275)
ER78x14	9.9 (253)	10.8 (273)
Supra	8.4 (213)	9.0 (229)
Tercel		
2WD		
Sedan		
145SR13	8.0 (204)	11.3 (287)
155SR13	8.2 (208)	11.5 (292)
165/70SR13	8.0 (204)	11.3 (287)
Station Wagon	8.1 (207)	12.1 (309)
4WD		
155SR13	9.2 (234)	10.7 (273)
175/70SR13	9.3 (235)	10.8 (274)
Van	9.6 (243)	10.5 (267)

Fig. 1: Acura & Honda Riding Height Measurement

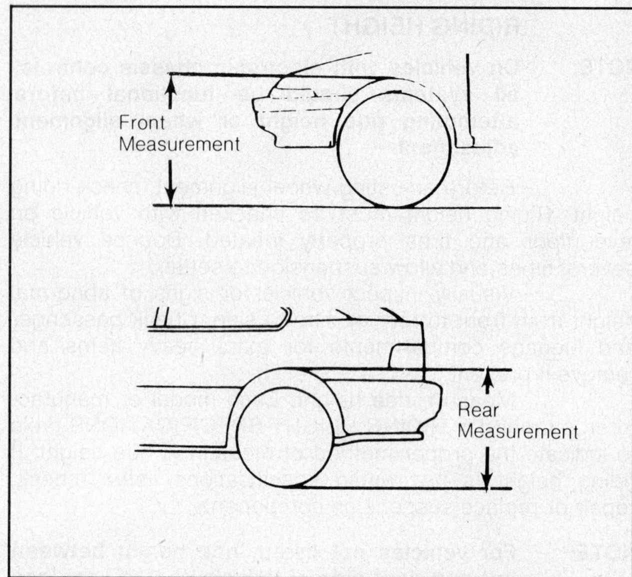

Courtesy of American Honda Motor Co., Inc.

Fig. 2: Toyota Riding Height Measurement

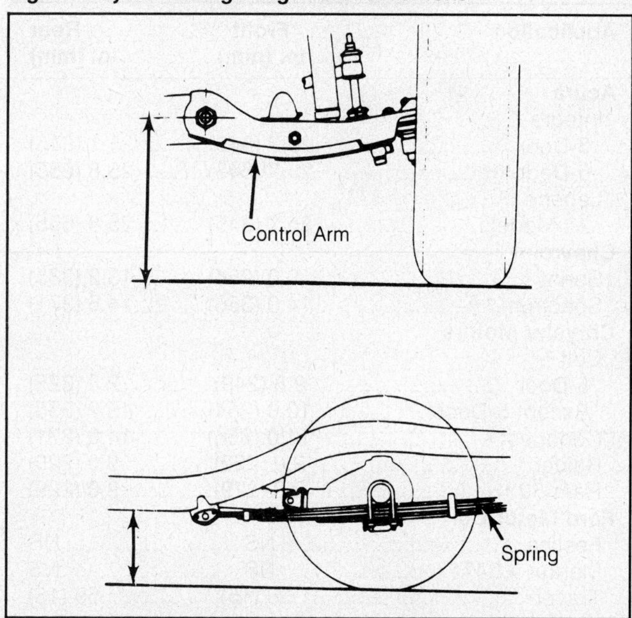

Courtesy of Toyota Motor Sales, U.S.A., Inc.

RIDING HEIGHT SPECIFICATIONS – ALL MODELS (Cont.)

Fig. 3: Nissan Front Riding Height Measurement

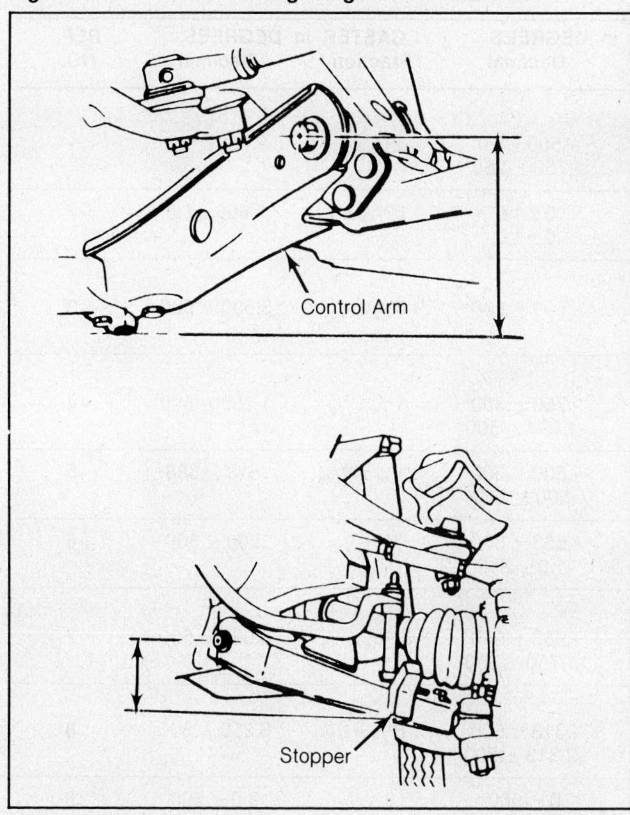

Rear height measurement is not specified. Courtesy of Nissan Motor Co., U.S.A.

Wheel Alignment

SPECIFICATIONS

WHEEL ALIGNMENT SPECIFICATIONS

MAKE & MODEL		ADJ. PROC.	CAMBER in DEGREES Fraction	CAMBER in DEGREES Decimal	CASTER in DEGREES Fraction	CASTER in DEGREES Decimal	REF. NO.
ACURA & STERLING							
Integra	Front	.....	$-\frac{1}{2} \pm 1$	$-.500 \pm 1.0$	$2\frac{1}{4} \pm 1$	2.250 ± 1.0	1
	Rear	.....	$-\frac{3}{4} \pm \frac{1}{4}$	$-.750 \pm .250$			
Legend & 825	Front	.....	0 ± 1	0 ± 1.0	$1\frac{43}{64} \pm 1$	1.666 ± 1.0	2
	Rear	.....	0 ± 1	0 ± 1.0			
ALFA ROMEO							
Milano	Front	.....	$-\frac{1}{2} \pm \frac{1}{2}$	$-.500 \pm .500$	$3\frac{1}{2} \pm \frac{1}{2}$	$3.500 \pm .500$	3
	Rear	.....	$0 \pm \frac{1}{2}$	$0 \pm .500$			
AUDI							
4000CS Quattro	Front	•	$-\frac{3}{4} \pm \frac{1}{2}$	$-.750 \pm .500$	$1\frac{1}{4} \pm \frac{1}{2}$	$1.250 \pm .500$	4
	Rear		$-1\frac{3}{32} \pm \frac{1}{2}$	$-1.094 \pm .500$			
5000 Series	Front	•, 21	$-\frac{1}{2} \pm \frac{1}{2}$	$-.500 \pm .500$	$\frac{13}{16} \pm \frac{11}{16}$	$.813 \pm .688$	5
	Rear		$\frac{1}{2} \pm \frac{5}{16}$	$.500 \pm .313$			
4000S, Coupe GT	Front	•, 9	$-\frac{9}{16} \pm \frac{1}{2}$	$-.563 \pm .500$	$\frac{1}{2} \pm \frac{1}{2}$	$.500 \pm .500$	6
	Rear	.....	$-1 \pm \frac{5}{16}$	$-1.0 \pm .313$			
BMW							
325 Series	Front	.....	$-\frac{11}{16} \pm \frac{1}{2}$	$-.688 \pm .500$	$8\frac{15}{16} \pm \frac{1}{2}$	$8.938 \pm .500$	7
	Rear	.....	$-1\frac{3}{4} \pm \frac{1}{2}$	$-1.750 \pm .500$			
528e, 535i 635CSi & L6	Front	.....	$-\frac{5}{16} \pm \frac{1}{2}$	$-.313 \pm .500$	$8\frac{1}{4} \pm \frac{1}{2}$	$8.250 \pm .500$	8
	Rear	.....	$-2\frac{5}{16} \pm \frac{1}{2}$ [1]	$-2.313 \pm .500$			
735i, L7	Front	.....	$0 \pm \frac{1}{2}$	$0 \pm .500$	$9 \pm \frac{1}{2}$	$9.0 \pm .500$	9
	Rear	.....	$-1\frac{9}{16} \pm \frac{1}{2}$	$-1.563 \pm .500$			
CHEVROLET							
Spectrum	Front	.....	$-\frac{43}{64}$ to $1\frac{11}{64}$	-.666 to 1.166	$1\frac{3}{4}$ to $2\frac{3}{4}$	1.750 to 2.750	10
Sprint	Front	.....	1	1.0	$3\frac{11}{64}$	3.166	11
CHRYSLER MOTORS							
Colt	Front	•	$0 \pm \frac{1}{2}$	$0 \pm .500$	$1 \pm \frac{1}{2}$	$1.0 \pm .500$	12
	Rear	•	$-\frac{43}{64}$	-.666			
Colt Vista (2WD)	Front	•, 2	$\frac{27}{64} \pm \frac{1}{2}$	$.416 \pm .500$	$\frac{51}{64} \pm \frac{1}{2}$	$.800 \pm .500$	13
	Rear	•, 22	$-\frac{43}{64}$	-.666			
Colt Vista (4WD)	Front	•	$\frac{55}{64} \pm \frac{1}{2}$	$.867 \pm .500$	$\frac{53}{64} \pm \frac{1}{2}$	$.833 \pm .500$	
	Rear	•, 22	0	0			
Conquest	Front	•, 2	$-\frac{1}{2}$	-.500	$5\frac{53}{64}$	5.833	14
	Rear	•, 22	$0 \pm \frac{27}{64}$	$0 \pm .416$			
Raider	Front	16, 20	$1 \pm \frac{1}{2}$	$1.0 \pm .500$	$2\frac{61}{64} \pm \frac{1}{2}$	$2.95 \pm .500$	15
Ram-50 (2WD)	Front	16, 20	$\frac{43}{64} \pm \frac{1}{2}$	$.666 \pm .500$	3 ± 1	3.0 ± 1.0	16
Ram-50 (4WD)	Front	18, 20	$1 \pm \frac{1}{2}$	$1.0 \pm .500$	2 ± 1	2.0 ± 1.0	
FORD MOTOR CO.							
Festiva	Front	•	$\frac{43}{64} \pm \frac{59}{64}$	$.666 \pm .916$	$1\frac{5}{64} \pm \frac{3}{4}$	$1.083 \pm .750$	17
Merkur XR4Ti	Front	•	$\frac{17}{32} \pm 1$	$.533 \pm 1.0$	$1\frac{31}{32} \pm 1$	1.966 ± 1.0	18
Tracer	Front	•	$\frac{53}{64} \pm \frac{3}{4}$	$.833 \pm .750$	$1\frac{37}{64} \pm \frac{3}{4}$	$1.583 \pm .750$	19
	Rear	25	$0 \pm \frac{3}{4}$	$0 \pm .750$			
HONDA							
Accord	Front	2	0 ± 1	0 ± 1.0	$\frac{1}{2} \pm 1$	$.500 \pm 1.0$	20
	Rear	11	0 ± 1	0 ± 1.0			
Civic Sedan	Front	.....	0 ± 1	0 ± 1.0	3 ± 1	3.0 ± 1.0	21
w/power steering	Front	.....	0 ± 1	0 ± 1.0	$2\frac{1}{2} \pm 1$	2.500 ± 1.0	
	Rear		$-\frac{3}{4} \pm \frac{1}{2}$	$-.750 \pm .500$			

• – Caster and rear camber are not adjustable.
* – Specification is for toe-out.
NS – Information not supplied by manufacturer.

Wheel Alignment

SPECIFICATIONS (Cont.)

WHEEL ALIGNMENT SPECIFICATIONS (Cont.)

REF. NO.	TOE-IN in INCHES Fraction	TOE-IN in INCHES Decimal	TOE-IN in DEGREES Fraction	TOE-IN in DEGREES Decimal	TOE-OUT ON TURNS Inner	TOE-OUT ON TURNS Outer	STEERING AXIS INCLINATION (SAI)
ACURA & STERLING							
1	$-\frac{3}{64} \pm \frac{7}{64}$	-.042 ± .118	$-\frac{5}{64} \pm \frac{15}{64}$	-.083 ± .236	NS	NS	$13\frac{1}{4}^\circ$
	$\frac{5}{64} \pm \frac{5}{64}$	.083 ± .083	$\frac{11}{64} \pm \frac{11}{64}$	.166 ± .166	.....	.....	.....
2	$0 \pm \frac{1}{8}$	0 ± .125	$0 \pm \frac{1}{4}$	0 ± .250	NS	NS	NS
	$0 \pm \frac{5}{64}$	0 ± .083	$0 \pm \frac{11}{64}$	0 ± .166	.....	.....	.....
ALFA ROMEO							
3	$\frac{3}{64} \pm \frac{3}{64}$	.042 ± .042	$\frac{5}{64} \pm \frac{5}{64}$	.083 ± .083	NS	30°	NS
	$0 \pm \frac{5}{64}$	0 ± .083	$0 \pm \frac{11}{64}$	0 ± .166	.....	.....	.....
AUDI							
4	$\frac{3}{32} \pm \frac{3}{32}$	.094 ± .094	$\frac{3}{16} \pm \frac{3}{16}$	.188 ± .188	NS	NS	NS
	$\frac{3}{16} \pm \frac{3}{32}$	.190 ± .094	$\frac{3}{8} \pm \frac{3}{16}$	.375 ± .188	.....	.....	.....
5	$-\frac{1}{64} \pm \frac{1}{16}$	-.016 ± .063	$-\frac{1}{32} \pm \frac{1}{8}$	-.031 ± .125	NS	NS	NS
	$\frac{1}{16} \pm \frac{1}{32}$	.063 ± .031	$\frac{1}{8} \pm \frac{1}{16}$	.125 ± .063	.....	.....	.....
6	$\frac{11}{64} \pm \frac{11}{64}$	.166 ± .166	$\frac{5}{16} \pm \frac{5}{16}$	.313 ± .313	NS	NS	NS
	$\frac{11}{64} \pm \frac{5}{16}$	.166 ± .313	$\frac{5}{16} \pm \frac{5}{8}$	.313 ± .625	.....	.....	.....
BMW							
7	$\frac{3}{32} \pm \frac{1}{64}$	.094 ± .016	$\frac{5}{16} \pm \frac{1}{32}$	.313 ± .031	$41\frac{5}{16}^\circ$	$33\frac{15}{16}^\circ$	$13\frac{15}{16}^\circ$
	$\frac{3}{32} \pm \frac{1}{32}$	.094 ± .031	$\frac{5}{16} \pm \frac{1}{16}$	.313 ± .063	.....	.....	.....
8	$\frac{3}{32} \pm \frac{1}{32}$	.094 ± .031	$\frac{3}{16} \pm \frac{1}{16}$	.188 ± .063	$43\frac{3}{4}^\circ$	33°	$12\frac{3}{16}^\circ$
	$\frac{3}{32} \pm \frac{1}{32}$	.094 ± .031	$\frac{3}{16} \pm \frac{1}{16}$	.188 ± .063	.....	.....	.....
9	$\frac{1}{32} \pm \frac{1}{32}$	.031 ± .031	$\frac{1}{16} \pm \frac{1}{16}$	.063 ± .063	$43\frac{3}{4}^\circ$	33°	$11\frac{7}{8}^\circ$
	$\frac{3}{32} \pm \frac{1}{32}$	.094 ± .031	$\frac{3}{16} \pm \frac{1}{16}$	.188 ± .063	.....	.....	.....
CHEVROLET							
10	$0 \pm \frac{1}{16}$	0 ± .063	$0 \pm \frac{1}{8}$	0 ± .125	$37\frac{11}{32}^\circ$	$32\frac{1}{2}^\circ$	$11\frac{27}{32}^\circ$
11	$\frac{1}{16} \pm \frac{1}{16}$	.063 ± .063	$\frac{1}{8} \pm \frac{1}{8}$	.125 ± .125	32°	38°	$12\frac{13}{16}^\circ$
CHRYSLER							
12	$0 \pm \frac{1}{8}$	0 ± .125	$0 \pm \frac{1}{4}$	0 ± .250	NS	NS	NS
	0	0	0	0	.....	.....	.....
13	$0 \pm \frac{1}{8}$	0 ± .125	$0 \pm \frac{11}{64}$	0 ± .166	$18\frac{21}{64}^\circ$	20°	NS
	0	0	0	0	.....	.....	.....
	$0 \pm \frac{1}{8}$	0 ± .125	$0 \pm \frac{11}{64}$	0 ± .166	20°	22°	NS
	0	0	0	0	.....	.....	.....
14	$0 \pm \frac{1}{4}$	0 ± .250	$0 \pm \frac{27}{64}$	0 ± .416	NS	NS	NS
	$0 \pm \frac{5}{64}$	0 ± .083	$0 \pm \frac{11}{64}$	0 ± .166	.....	.....	.....
15	$\frac{13}{64} \pm \frac{1}{8}$	.215 ± .135	$\frac{27}{64} \pm \frac{1}{4}$	.416 ± .250	NS	NS	NS
16	$\frac{13}{64} \pm \frac{1}{8}$	.215 ± .135	$\frac{27}{64} \pm \frac{1}{4}$	.416 ± .250	NS	NS	NS
	$\frac{13}{64} \pm \frac{1}{8}$	.215 ± .135	$\frac{27}{64} \pm \frac{1}{4}$	.416 ± .250	NS	NS	NS
FORD IMPORTS							
17	$\frac{15}{64} \pm \frac{1}{8}$	.233 ± .125	$\frac{11}{64} \pm \frac{1}{16}$	.166 ± .063	NS	NS	$14\frac{11}{64}^\circ$
18	$\frac{5}{64} \pm \frac{1}{32}$	.083 ± .032	$\frac{11}{64} \pm \frac{1}{16}$	.166 ± .063	NS	NS	NS
19	$\frac{5}{64} \pm \frac{1}{8}$	.083 ± .125	$\frac{11}{64} \pm \frac{1}{4}$	.166 ± .250	40°	33°	$12\frac{23}{64}^\circ$
	$0 \pm \frac{1}{8}$	0 ± .125	$0 \pm \frac{1}{4}$	0 ± .250			
HONDA							
20	$0 \pm \frac{1}{8}$	0 ± .125	$0 \pm \frac{1}{4}$	0 ± .250	NS	NS	NS
	$\frac{3}{32} \pm \frac{3}{32}$	.094 ± .094	$\frac{3}{16} \pm \frac{3}{16}$	.188 ± .188			
21	$0 \pm \frac{1}{8}$	0 ± .125	$0 \pm \frac{1}{4}$	0 ± .250	$41\frac{1}{2}^\circ$	$34\frac{1}{2}^\circ$	13°
	$0 \pm \frac{1}{8}$	0 ± .125	$0 \pm \frac{1}{4}$	0 ± .250	$41\frac{1}{2}^\circ$	$34\frac{1}{2}^\circ$	13°
	$\frac{5}{64} \pm \frac{5}{64}$	.079 ± .079	$\frac{5}{32} \pm \frac{5}{32}$	.158 ± .158			

• – Caster and rear camber are not adjustable.
* – Specification is for toe-out.
NS – Information not supplied by manufacturer.

Wheel Alignment

SPECIFICATIONS (Cont.)

WHEEL ALIGNMENT SPECIFICATIONS (Cont.)

MAKE & MODEL		ADJ. PROC.	CAMBER in DEGREES Fraction	CAMBER in DEGREES Decimal	CASTER in DEGREES Fraction	CASTER in DEGREES Decimal	REF. NO.
HONDA (Cont.)							
Civic Wagon (2WD)	Front	.....	0 ± 1	0 ± 1.0	2 ± 1	2.0 ± 1.0	22
	Rear	.....	-3/4 ± 1/2	-.750 ± .500			
Civic Wagon (4WD)	Front	.....	0 ± 1	0 ± 1.0	2 ± 1	2.0 ± 1.0	23
	Rear	.....					
Civic (All Others)	Front	.....	3/4 ± 1/4	.750 ± .250	3 ± 1	3.0 ± 1.0	24
	Rear	.....	-3/4 ± 1/4	-.750 ± .250			
CRX	Front	.....	0 ± 1	0 ± 1.0	2 1/2 ± 1	2.500 ± 1.0	25
	Rear	.....	-3/4 ± 1/4	-.750 ± .250			
Prelude	Front	2, 5	0 ± 1	0 ± 1.0	0 ± 1/2	0 ± .500	26
	Rear	11					
HYUNDAI							
Excel	Front	.....	1/2 ± 1/2	.500 ± .500	53/64 ± 21/64	.833 ± .333	27
ISUZU							
I-Mark	Front	.....	21/64 ± 1	.333 ± 1.0	2 1/4 ± 1/2	2.250 ± .500	28
Impulse	Front	.....	-1/2 ± 1/2	-.500 ± .500	5 ± 1 1/2	5.0 ± 1.500	29
PU'P (2WD)	Front	2, 18	1/2 ± 1/2	.500 ± .500	1/2 ± 1/2	.500 ± .500	30
PU'P (4WD)	Front	3	37/64 ± 1/2	.583 ± .500	21/64 ± 1/2	.333 ± .500	31
Trooper II	Front	3	1/2 ± 1/2	.500 ± .500	2 1/2 ± 1	2.500 ± 1.0	32
JAGUAR							
XJ6 III, XJS	Front	3	-1/2 ± 1/4	-.500 ± .250	3 1/2 ± 1/4	3.500 ± .250	33
	Rear	8	-3/4 ± 1/4	-.750 ± .250			
MAZDA							
B2200 & B2600 (2WD) w/power steering	Front	.....	1 ± 1/2	1.0 ± .500	53/64 ± 3/4 1 53/64 ± 3/4	.833 ± .750 1.833 ± .750	34
B2200 & B2600 (4WD) w/power steering	Front	.....	3/4 ± 1/2	.750 ± .500	53/64 ± 3/4 2 ± 3/4	.833 ± .750 2.0 ± .750	35
RX7	Front	14	21/64	.333	43/64	.666	36
	Rear	11	-47/64 ± 1/2	-.733 ± .500			
323	Front	24	53/64 ± 3/4	.828 ± .750	1 37/64 ± 3/4	1.583 ± .750	37
	Rear	25	0 ± 3/4	0 ± .750			
626	Front	23	21/64 ± 1/2	.333 ± .500	1 43/64 ± 3/4	1.666 ± .750	38
	Rear		NS	NS			
MERCEDES-BENZ							
190 Series	Front	17	27/64 ± 27/64	.416 ± .416	10 1/8 ± 7/8	10.125 ± .875	39
	Rear	.....	1/2 ± 1/2	.500 ± .500	.....	.....	
260E, 300D, 300E, 300TD	Front	17	0 ± 1/4	0 ± .250	10 11/64 ± 1/2	10.166 ± .500	40
	Rear	.....	-1 1/2 ± 1/2	-1.500 ± .500			
300SDL, 420SEL, 560SEC, 560SEL	Front	17	0 ± 1/4	0 ± .250	10 1/4 ± 1/2	10.250 ± .500	41
	Rear	.....	1/2 ± 11/64	.500 ± .166			
560SL	Front	17	-11/64 ± 11/64	-.166 ± .250	10 1/2 ± 1/2	10.500 ± .500	42
	Rear	.....	-1/2 ± 1/2	-.500 ± .500			

• – Caster and rear camber are not adjustable.
* – Specification is for toe-out.
NS – Information not supplied by manufacturer.

Wheel Alignment

SPECIFICATIONS (Cont.)

WHEEL ALIGNMENT SPECIFICATIONS (Cont.)

REF. NO.	TOE-IN in INCHES Fraction	TOE-IN in INCHES Decimal	TOE-IN in DEGREES Fraction	TOE-IN in DEGREES Decimal	TOE-OUT ON TURNS Inner	TOE-OUT ON TURNS Outer	STEERING AXIS INCLINATION (SAI)
HONDA (Cont.)							
22	0 ± 1/8	0 ± .125	0 ± 1/4	0 ± .250	41 1/2°	34 1/2°	12°
23	0 ± 1/8 0 ± 3/32	0 ± .125 0 ± .094	0 ± 1/4 0 ± 3/16	0 ± .250 0 ± .188	40 1/2°	33°	11 7/16°
24	0 ± 1/8 5/64 ± 5/64	0 ± .125 .083 ± .083	0 ± 1/4 5/32 ± 5/32	0 ± .250 .156 ± .156	NS	NS	NS
25	0 ± 1/8 5/64 ± 5/64	0 ± .125 .083 ± .083	0 ± 1/4 11/64 ± 11/64	0 ± .250 .166 ± .166	NS	NS	NS
26	0 ± 1/8 3/16 ± 3/16	0 ± .125 .188 ± .188	0 ± 1/4 3/8 ± 3/8	0 ± .250 .375 ± .375	38 1/2°	30°	6 7/8°
HYUNDAI							
27	3/64 ± 1/8	.042 ± .125	5/64 ± 1/4	.083 ± .250	35.6°	29.3°	12 3/4°
ISUZU							
28	0 ± 5/64	0 ± .083	0 ± 11/64	0 ± .166	NS	NS	12 1/8°
29	0 ± 1/8	0 ± .125	0 ± 1/4	0 ± .250	NS	NS	NS
30	5/64 ± 5/64	.083 ± .083	11/64 ± 11/64	.166 ± .166	NS	NS	7 1/2°
31	0 ± 5/64	0 ± .083	0 ± 11/64	0 ± .166	NS	NS	7 7/16°
32	5/64 ± 5/64	.083 ± .083	11/64 ± 11/64	.166 ± .166	NS	NS	7 3/8°
JAGUAR							
33	1/16 ± 1/16 0 ± 1/32	.063 ± .063 0 ± .032	1/8 ± 1/8 0 ± 1/16	.125 ± .125 0 ± .063	NS	NS	2°
MAZDA							
34	1/8 ± 1/8	.125 ± .125	1/4 ± 1/4	.250 ± .250	35°	33°	NS
35	1/8 ± 1/8	.125 ± .125	1/4 ± 1/4	.250 ± .250	33 1/2°	30°	NS
36	1/8 ± 1/8 0 ± 1/8	.125 ± .125 0 ± .125	1/4 ± 1/4 0 ± 1/4	.250 ± .250 0 ± .250	37°	33°	13 3/4°
37	-5/64 ± 1/8 0 ± 1/8	-.083 ± .125 0 ± .125	-11/64 ± 1/4 0 ± 1/4	-.166 ± .250 0 ± .250	40°	33°	12 1/2°
38	1/8 ± 1/8 0 ± 1/8	.125 ± .125 0 ± .125	1/4 ± 1/4 0 ± 1/4	.250 ± .250 0 ± .250	38°	31°	12 15/16°
MERCEDES-BENZ							
39	11/64 ± 5/64 13/64 ± 5/64	.166 ± .083 .208 ± .083	21/64 ± 11/64 27/64 ± 11/64	.333 ± .166 .416 ± .166	20°	19 11/16°	NS
40	11/64 ± 5/64 13/64 ± 5/64	.166 ± .083 .208 ± .083	21/64 ± 11/64 27/64 ± 11/64	.333 ± .166 .416 ± .166	20°	19 3/4°	NS
41	13/64 ± 5/64 1/4 ± 5/64	.208 ± .083 .250 ± .083	27/64 ± 11/64 1/2 ± 11/64	.416 ± .166 .500 ± .166	NS	NS	NS
42	11/64 ± 5/64 13/64 ± 11/64	.166 ± .083 .208 ± .166	21/64 ± 11/64 27/64 ± 13/64	.333 ± .166 .416 ± .208	20°	17°	NS

• – Caster and rear camber are not adjustable.
* – Specification is for toe-out.
NS – Information not supplied by manufacturer.

Wheel Alignment

SPECIFICATIONS (Cont.)

WHEEL ALIGNMENT SPECIFICATIONS (Cont.)

MAKE & MODEL	Axle	ADJ. PROC.	CAMBER in DEGREES Fraction	CAMBER in DEGREES Decimal	CASTER in DEGREES Fraction	CASTER in DEGREES Decimal	REF. NO.
MITSUBISHI							
Cordia, Tredia	Front	2	27/64 ± 1/2	.416 ± .500	51/64 ± 1/2	.800 ± .500	43
	Rear	.....	43/64	.666			
Mirage	Front	.....	0 ± 1/2	0 ± .500	1 ± 1/2	1.0 ± .500	44
	Rear	.....	-43/64	-.666			
Montero	Front	18, 20	1 ± 1/2	1.0 ± .500	2 61/64 ± 1/2	2.950 ± .500	45
Galant	Front	.....	1/2 ± 1/2	.500 ± .500	43/64 ± 1/2	.666 ± .500	46
Pickup (2WD)	Front	16, 20	43/64 ± 1/2	.666 ± .500	3 ± 1	3.0 ± 1.0	47
Pickup (4WD)	Front	18, 20	1 ± 1/2	1.0 ± .500	2 ± 1	2.0 ± 1.0	
Precis	Front	.....	1/2 ± 1/2	.500 ± .500	53/64 ± 21/64	.833 ± .333	48
Starion	Front	2	-1/2	-.500	5 53/64	5.833	49
	Rear	22	0	0			
Van	Front	.....	33/64 ± 1/2	.516 ± .500	3 9/64	3.133	50
NISSAN							
Maxima	Front	.....	21/64 ± 3/4	.333 ± .750	2 ± 3/4	2.0 ± .750	51
	Rear	.....	27/64 ± 3/4	.416 ± .750			
Pathfinder	Front	.....	43/64 ± 1/2	.666 ± .500	1 19/64 ± 1/2	1.300 ± .500	52
Pickup (2WD)	Front	.....	27/64 ± 1/2	.416 ± .500	23/64 ± 1/2	.367 ± .500	53
Pickup (4WD)							
Exc. 31x10 SR15 Tires	Front	.....	43/64 ± 1/2	.666 ± .500	1 19/64 ± 1/2	1.300 ± .500	
31x10 SR15 Tires	Front	.....	43/64 ± 1/2	.666 ± .500	1 19/64 ± 1/2	1.300 ± .500	
Pulsar NX	Front	.....	-1/2 ± 3/4	-.500 ± .750	1 59/64 ± 3/4	1.457 ± .750	54
	Rear	.....	-1 5/64 ± 3/4	-1.083 ± .750			
Sentra (Exc. Coupe)	Front	.....	-11/64 ± 3/4	-.166 ± .750	1 11/64 ± 3/4	1.166 ± .750	55
	Rear	.....	-1 ± 3/4	-1.0 ± .750			
Sentra Coupe	Front	.....	-21/64 ± 3/4	-.333 ± .750	2 ± 3/4	2.0 ± .750	
	Rear	.....	-1 5/64 ± 3/4	-1.083 ± .750			
Stanza (Exc. Wagon)	Front	.....	21/64 ± 3/4	.333 ± .750	2 ± 3/4	2.0 ± .750	56
	Rear	.....	-27/64 ± 3/4	-.416 ± .750			
Stanza Wagon (2WD)	Front	.....	1/2 ± 3/4	.500 ± .750	1 1/2 ± 3/4	1.5 ± .750	
Stanza Wagon (4WD)	Front	.....	39/64 ± 1 5/64	.616 ± 1.083	3/64 ± 3/32	.058 ± .092	
	Rear	.....	3/4 ± 3/4	.750 ± .750			
Van	Front	.....	1/4 ± 1/2	.250 ± .500	1 1/2 ± 1/2	1.5 ± .500	57
200SX	Front	.....	21/64 ± 3/4	.333 ± .750	3 1/2 ± 3/4	3.5 ± .750	58
	Rear	.....	-3/4 ± 1/2	-.750 ± .500			
300ZX	Front	.....	11/64 ± 3/4	.166 ± .750	6 37/64 ± 3/4	6.583 ± .750	59
	Rear	22	-1 11/64 ± 3/4	-1.166 ± .750			
PEUGEOT							
505	Front	.....	-1 ± 1/2	-1.0 ± .500	2 1/2 ± 1/2	2.500 ± .500	60
PORSCHE							
911 Carrera	Front	12	0 ± 3/16	0 ± .188	6 1/16 ± 3/16	6.063 ± .188	61
	Rear	10	-1 ± 3/16	-1.0 ± .188			
911 Turbo	Front	12	0 ± 3/16	0 ± .188	6 1/16 ± 3/16	6.063 ± .188	62
	Rear	10	-1/2 ± 3/16	-.500 ± .188			
924-S & 944 Series	Front	15	-5/16 ± 1/4	-.313 ± .250	2 1/2 ± 1/2	2.500 ± .500	63
	Rear	13	-7/16 ± 1/2	-.438 ± .500			

• – Caster and rear camber are not adjustable.
* – Specification is for toe-out.
NS – Information not supplied by manufacturer.

Wheel Alignment

SPECIFICATIONS (Cont.)

WHEEL ALIGNMENT SPECIFICATIONS (Cont.)

REF. NO.	TOE-IN in INCHES Fraction	TOE-IN in INCHES Decimal	TOE-IN in DEGREES Fraction	TOE-IN in DEGREES Decimal	TOE-OUT ON TURNS Inner	TOE-OUT ON TURNS Outer	STEERING AXIS INCLINATION (SAI)
MITSUBISHI							
43	0 ± 1/8	0 ± .125	0 ± 1/4	0 ± .250	NS	NS	NS
	0	0	0	0			
44	0 ± 1/8	0 ± .125	0 ± 1/4	0 ± .250	NS	NS	NS
	0	0	0	0			
45	13/64 ± 1/8	.215 ± .135	27/64 ± 1/4	.416 ± .250	NS	NS	NS
46	0	0	0	0	NS	NS	NS
47	13/64 ± 1/8	.215 ± .135	27/64 ± 1/4	.416 ± .250	NS	NS	NS
	13/64 ± 1/8	.215 ± .135	27/64 ± 1/4	.416 ± .250	NS	NS	NS
48	3/64 ± 1/8	.042 ± .125	5/64 ± 1/4	.083 ± .250	35.6°	29.3°	12 3/4°
49	0 ± 1/4	0 ± .250	0 ± 27/64	0 ± .416	NS	NS	NS
	0 ± 5/64	0 ± .083	0 ± 11/64	0 ± .166			
50	1/8 ± 1/8	.125 ± .125	1/4 ± 1/4	.250 ± .250	NS	NS	NS
NISSAN							
51	5/64 ± 3/64	.083 ± .042	3/16 ± 5/64	.183 ± .083	35 1/2 ± 1 1/2°	29 ± 2°	NS
52	5/64 ± 3/64	.083 ± .042	3/64 ± 1/8	.158 ± .075	22°	20°	8 7/64 ± 1/2°
53	1/8 ± 3/64	.125 ± .042	19/64 ± 5/64	.283 ± .083	22°	20°	9 5/64° ± 1/2°
	5/64 ± 3/64	.083 ± .042	5/32 ± 3/64	.158 ± .075	22°	20°	8 7/64° ± 1/2°
	11/64 ± 3/64	.166 ± .042	19/64 ± 3/64	.291 ± .075	22°	20°	8 7/64° ± 1/2°
54	0 ± 3/64	0 ± .042	0 ± 7/64	0 ± .109	NS	NS	NS
	1/64 ± 5/64	.021 ± .083	3/64 ± 13/64	.042 ± .208			
55	0 ± 3/64	0 ± .042	0 ± 7/64	0 ± .108	22 21/64°	20°	NS
	1/8 ± 5/64	.125 ± .083	19/64 ± 13/64	.308 ± .208			
	0 ± 3/64	0 ± .042	0 ± 7/64	0 ± .108	22 21/64°	20°	NS
	1/8 ± 5/64	.125 ± .083	19/64 ± 13/64	.308 ± .208			
56	5/64 ± 3/64	.083 ± .042	13/64 ± 7/64	.208 ± .108	NS	NS	NS
	11/64 ± 5/64 *	.166 ± .083 *	27/64 ± 13/64 *	.408 ± .208 *	NS	NS	NS
	7/64 ± 3/64	.109 ± .042	1/8 ± 1/16	.125 ± .063	NS	NS	NS
	3/64 ± 1/64	.042 ± .021	1 ± 1/16	1.0 ± .042	NS	NS	NS
	-5/64 ± 5/64	-.083 ± .083	-3/64 ± 3/64	-.042 ± .042	NS	NS	NS
57	0 ± 3/64	0 ± .042	0 ± 5/64	0 ± .083	20°	19°	NS
58	3/64 ± 1/64	.042 ± .021	5/64 ± 3/64	.083 ± .042	20°	18 3/4°	NS
	-3/64 ± 3/64	-.042 ± .042	-7/64 ± 7/64	-.10 ± .10			
59	5/64 ± 3/64	.083 ± .042	13/64 ± 5/64	.192 ± .092	22 1/2°	20°	NS
	1/64 ± 5/64	.020 ± .083	3/64 ± 11/64	.050 ± .183			
PEUGEOT							
60	1/8 ± 1/32	.125 ± .031	1/4 ± 1/16	.250 ± .063	NS	NS	9 1/2°
PORSCHE							
61	1/8 ± 1/32	.125 ± .031	1/4 ± 1/16	.250 ± .063	20°	19 1/2°	NS
	1/16 ± 1/16	.063 ± .063	1/8 ± 1/8	.125 ± .125			
62	1/8 ± 1/32	.125 ± .031	1/4 ± 1/16	.250 ± .063	NS	NS	NS
	3/32 ± 3/32	.094 ± .094	3/16 ± 3/16	.188 ± .188			
63	1/16 ± 1/32	.063 ± .031	1/8 ± 1/16	.125 ± .063	20°	8 11/16°	NS
	0 ± 1/16	0 ± .063	0 ± 1/8	0 ± .125			

• – Caster and rear camber are not adjustable.
* – Specification is for toe-out.
NS – Information not supplied by manufacturer.

Wheel Alignment

SPECIFICATIONS (Cont.)

WHEEL ALIGNMENT SPECIFICATIONS (Cont.)

MAKE & MODEL		ADJ. PROC.	CAMBER in DEGREES Fraction	CAMBER in DEGREES Decimal	CASTER in DEGREES Fraction	CASTER in DEGREES Decimal	REF. NO.
SAAB							
900, 900S	Front	3	1/2 ± 1/2	.500 ± .500	2 ± 1/2	2.0 ± .500	64
900 Turbo	Rear	.....	1/2 ± 1/4	.500 ± .250			
9000S & 9000 Turbo	Front	3	-5/8 ± 1/2	.625 ± .500	1 5/8 ± 1/2	1.625 ± .500	65
	Rear	.....	-27/64 ± 27/64	-.416 ± .416			
SUBARU							
Brat	Front	.....	2 27/64 ± 3/4	2.416 ± .750	-43/64 ± 3/4	-.666 ± .750	66
	Rear	.....	21/64 ± 3/4	.333 ± .750			
Hatchback (2WD)	Front	.....	1 1/2 ± 3/4	1.500 ± .750	-27/64 ± 3/4	-.416 ± .750	67
(4WD)	Front	.....	2 27/64 ± 3/4	2.416 ± .750	-1/2 ± 3/4	-.500 ± .750	
Justy	Front	.....	43/64 ± 1	.666 ± 1.0	2 1/2 ± 1	2.5 ± 1.0	68
	Rear	.....	1/2 ± 1/2	.500 ± .500			
Sedan & 3-Door (2WD)	Front	.....	3/4 ± 3/4	.750 ± .750	2 1/2 ± 1/2	2.500 ± .500	69
(4WD)	Front	.....	1 43/64 ± 3/4	1.666 ± .750	1 53/64 ± 3/4	1.833 ± .750	
Wagon (2WD)	Front	.....	1 ± 3/4	1.0 ± .750	2 1/8 ± 3/4	2.125 ± .750	70
(4WD)	Front	.....	1 43/64 ± 3/4	1.666 ± .750	1 37/64 ± 3/4	1.583 ± .750	
XT (2WD)	Front	.....	0 ± 3/4	0 ± .750	NS	NS	71
(4WD)	Front	.....	0 ± 3/4	0 ± .750	NS	NS	
SUZUKI							
Samurai	Front	.....	1 ± 3/4	1.0 ± .750	3 1/2 ± 1	3.500 ± 1.0	72
TOYOTA							
Camry Sedan	Front	.....	37/64 ± 1/2	.583 ± .500	1 43/64 ± 1/2	1.166 ± .500	73
	Rear	.....	-37/64 ± 3/4	-.583 ± .750			
Camry Wagon	Front	.....	1/2 ± 1/2	.500 ± .500	1 ± 1/2	1.0 ± .500	74
	Rear	.....	-37/64 ± 3/4	-.583 ± .750			
Celica	Front	.....	-11/64 ± 1/2	-.166 ± .500	1 11/64 ± 3/4	1.166 ± .750	75
	Rear	.....	-3/4 ± 3/4	-.750 ± .750			
Corolla (RWD)	Front	2	1/4 ± 3/4	.250 ± .750	2 3/4 ± 3/4	2.75 ± .750	76
w/power steering	Front	2			3 43/64 ± 3/4	3.666 ± .750	
Corolla (FWD)	Front	4	-1/4 ± 1/2	-.250 ± .500	57/64 ± 3/4	.883 ± .750	77
	Rear	22	-33/64 ± 3/4	-.515 ± .500			
Cressida Sedan	Front	19	27/64 ± 3/4	.416 ± .750	4 53/64 ± 1/2	4.833 ± .500	78
	Rear	22	-25/64 ± 1/2	-.416 ± .500			
Cressida Wagon	Front	19	27/64 ± 3/4	.416 ± .750	4 1/4 ± 3/4	4.250 ± .750	79
Land Cruiser	Front	.....	1 ± 3/4	1.0 ± .750	13/16 ± 3/4	.813 ± .750	80
MR2	Front	2, 4	1/4 ± 1/2	.250 ± .500	5 5/64 ± 1/2	5.083 ± .500	81
	Rear	4	-59/64 ± 1/2	-.916 ± .500			
Pickup (2WD) (1/2 Ton Shortbed)	Front	.....	1/2 ± 1/2	.500 ± .500	43/64 ± 1/2	.666 ± .500	82
Pickup (2WD) (1/2 Ton Longbed)	Front	.....	1/2 ± 1/2	.500 ± .500	1 11/64 ± 1/2	1.166 ± .500	83
Pickup (2WD) (1/2 Ton Extra Longbed)	Front	.....	1/2 ± 1/2	.500 ± .500	1 ± 1/2	1.0 ± .500	84

• – Caster and rear camber are not adjustable.
* – Specification is for toe-out.
NS – Information not supplied by manufacturer.

Wheel Alignment

SPECIFICATIONS (Cont.)

WHEEL ALIGNMENT SPECIFICATIONS (Cont.)

REF. NO.	TOE-IN in INCHES Fraction	TOE-IN in INCHES Decimal	TOE-IN in DEGREES Fraction	TOE-IN in DEGREES Decimal	TOE-OUT ON TURNS Inner	TOE-OUT ON TURNS Outer	STEERING AXIS INCLINATION (SAI)
SAAB							
64	3/32 ± 3/64 11/64 ± 5/64	.094 ± .046 .166 ± .083	3/16 ± 3/32 21/64 ± 11/64	.188 ± .094 .333 ± .166	NS	NS	NS
65	3/32 ± 3/64 7/64 ± 1/16	.094 ± .046 .098 ± .059	3/16 ± 3/32 13/64 ± 1/8	.188 ± .094 .208 ± .125	NS	NS	NS
SUBARU							
66	3/16 ± 1/32 0 ± 1/8	.188 ± .031 0 ± .125	3/8 ± 1/16 0 ± 1/4	.375 ± .063 0 ± .250	36 1/2°	35°	NS
67	5/16 ± 5/16 3/16 ± 1/32	.312 ± .312 .188 ± .031	1/16 ± 1/16 3/8 ± 1/16	.063 ± .063 .375 ± .063	36 1/2° 36 1/2°	35° 35°	NS NS
68	5/64 ± 3/64 0 ± 1/8	.083 ± .042 0 ± .125	11/64 ± 5/64 0 ± 1/4	.166 ± .083 0 ± .250	NS	NS	NS
69	1/32 ± 1/32 1/32 ± 1/32	.031 ± .031 .031 ± .031	1/16 ± 1/16 1/16 ± 1/16	.063 ± .063 .063 ± .063	36 1/2° 36 1/2°	35° 35°	NS NS
70	1/32 ± 1/32 1/32 ± 1/32	.031 ± .031 .031 ± .031	1/16 ± 1/16 1/16 ± 1/16	.063 ± .063 .063 ± .063	36 1/2° 36 1/3°	35° 35°	NS NS
71	0 ± 1/8 3/32 ± 1/8	0 ± .125 .09 ± .125	0 ± 1/4 3/16 ± 1/4	0 ± .250 .19 ± .250	NS NS	NS NS	NS NS
SUZUKI							
72	3/16 ± 3/32	.188 ± .094	3/8 ± 3/16	.375 ± .188	29°	26°	9°
TOYOTA							
73	3/64 ± 1/2 11/64 ± 5/64	.042 ± .083 .166 ± .083	5/64 ± 11/64 21/64 ± 11/64	.083 ± .166 .333 ± .166	22°	20°	12 3/4°
74	3/64 ± 1/2 11/64 ± 5/64	.042 ± .083 .166 ± .083	5/64 ± 11/64 21/64 ± 11/64	.083 ± .166 .333 ± .166	22°	20°	12 53/64°
75	0 ± 3/64 13/64 ± 3/64	0.0 ± .042 .208 ± .042	0 ± 5/64 27/64 ± 5/64	0.0 ± .083 .416 ± .083	21 1/2°	20°	13 1/2°
76	3/64 ± 3/64	.042 ± .042	5/64 ± 5/64	.083 ± .083	21°	20°	8 53/64°
77	3/64 ± 3/64 9/64 ± 5/64	.042 ± .042 .150 ± .083	5/64 ± 5/64 17/64 ± 11/64	.083 ± .083 .265 ± .166	21 43/64°	20°	12 27/64°
78	5/64 ± 3/64	.083 ± .042	11/64 ± 5/64	.166 ± .083	38°	38°	10 9/16°
79	5/64 ± 3/64	.083 ± .042	11/64 ± 5/64	.166 ± .083	38°	38°	10 9/16°
80	3/64 ± 11/64	.042 ± .166	5/64 ± 1/4	.083 ± .250			
81	3/64 ± 5/64 13/64 ± 5/64	.042 ± .083 .203 ± .083	5/64 ± 11/64 13/32 ± 11/64	.083 ± .166 .406 ± .166	21°	20°	12 5/64°
82	3/64 ± 3/64	.042 ± .042	5/64 ± 5/64	.083 ± .083	22 1/4°	20°	9 1/2°
83	1/8 ± 3/64	.125 ± .042	1/4 ± 5/64	.250 ± .083	22 1/4°	20°	9 1/2°
84	11/64 ± 3/64	.166 ± .042	21/64 ± 5/64	.333 ± .083	22 1/4°	20°	9 1/2°

• – Caster and rear camber are not adjustable.
* – Specification is for toe-out.
NS – Information not supplied by manufacturer.

Wheel Alignment

SPECIFICATIONS (Cont.)

WHEEL ALIGNMENT SPECIFICATIONS (Cont.)

MAKE & MODEL		ADJ. PROC.	CAMBER in DEGREES Fraction	CAMBER in DEGREES Decimal	CASTER in DEGREES Fraction	CASTER in DEGREES Decimal	REF. NO.
TOYOTA (Cont.)							
Pickup (2WD) (1 Ton)	Front	.....	1/2 ± 1/2	.500 ± .500	37/64 ± 1/2	.583 ± .500	85
Pickup (4WD)	Front	.....	43/64 ± 1/2	.666 ± .500	1 1/2 ± 1/2	1.500 ± .500	86
Supra	Front	.....	-5/64 ± 1/2	-.083 ± .500	7 1/2 ± 1/2	7.500 ± .500	87
	Rear	.....	-1/4 ± 3/4	-.250 ± .750			
Tercel exc. Wagon	Front	2	0 ± 3/4	0 ± .750	1 ± 3/4	1.0 ± .750	88
w/power steering	Front	.....			2 1/2 ± 3/4	2.500 ± .750	
Tercel Wagon (2WD)	Front	2	0 ± 3/4	0 ± .750	3/4 ± 1/2	.750 ± .500	89
w/power steering	Front	.....			2 1/4 ± 1/2	2.250 ± .500	
	Rear	.....	1/4 ± 1/2	.250 ± .500			
Tercel Wagon (4WD)	Front	2	37/64 ± 3/4	.583 ± .750	2 27/64 ± 1/2	2.416 ± .500	90
Van (2WD)	Front	2, 7	-5/64 ± 1/2	-.083 ± .500	2 1/2 ± 1/2	2.500 ± .500	91
Van (4WD)	Front	2, 7	11/64 ± 1/2	.166 ± .500	2 53/64 ± 1/2	2.833 ± .500	92
4Runner	Front	.....	43/64 ± 1/2	.666 ± .500	2 5/64 ± 1/2	2.083 ± .500	93
VOLKSWAGEN							
Cabriolet, Scirocco	Front	.....	21/64 ± 1	.333 ± 1.0	1 53/64 ± 1	1.833 ± 1.0	94
	Rear	.....	-1 1/4 ± 1 1/2	-1.250 ± 1.500			
Fox Sedan	Front	.....	-1/2 ± 21/64	.500 ± .333	2 ± 21/64	2.0 ± .333	95
	Rear	.....	1 1/2 ± 1/2	1.500 ± .500			
Fox Wagon	Front	.....	-1/2 ± 21/64	.500 ± .333	1 5/64 ± 21/64	1.083 ± .333	96
.....	Rear	.....	1 1/2 ± 1/2	1.500 ± .500			
Golf, Jetta	Front	.....	-1/2 ± 21/64	-.500 ± .333	1 1/2 ± 1/2	1.500 ± .500	97
	Rear	.....	-1 43/64 ± 21/64	-1.666 ± .333			
GTI, GLI	Front	.....	-37/64 ± 21/64	-.583 ± .333	1 37/64 ± 1/2	1.583 ± .500	98
	Rear	.....	-1 43/64 ± 21/64	-1.666 ± .333			
Quantum	Front	•, 9	-43/64 ± 1/2	-.666 ± .500	1/2 ± 1/2	.500 ± .500	99
	Rear	.....	-1 43/64 ± 21/64	-1.666 ± .333			
Quantum Syncro	Front	.....	43/64 ± 1	.333 ± 1.0	1/2 ± 11/64	.500 ± .166	100
	Rear	.....	-37/64 ± -1/2	-.583 ± -.500			
Vanagon	Front	2, 6	0 ± 1/2	0 ± .500	1/4 ± 1/4	7.250 ± .250	101
	Rear	5	-53/64 ± 1/2	-.833 ± .500			
Vanagon Syncro	Front	.....	21/64 ± 21/64	.333 ± .333	4 43/64 ± 1/4	4.666 ± .250	102
	Rear	.....	-1/4 ± 11/64	-.250 ± .166			
VOLVO							
240 Series	Front	.....	1/2 ± 1/4	.500 ± .250	NS	NS	103
740, 760 & 780 Series	Front	.....	NS	NS	NS	NS	104
YUGO							
GV & GVX	Front	.....	1 1/2 ± 1/2	1.500 ± .500	2 1/4 ± 1/2	2.250 ± .500	105
	Rear	.....	-1/2 ± 1/2	-.500 ± .500			

• – Caster and rear camber are not adjustable.
* – Specification is for toe-out.
NS – Information not supplied by manufacturer.

Wheel Alignment

SPECIFICATIONS (Cont.)

WHEEL ALIGNMENT SPECIFICATIONS (Cont.)

REF. NO.	TOE-IN in INCHES Fraction	TOE-IN in INCHES Decimal	TOE-IN in DEGREES Fraction	TOE-IN in DEGREES Decimal	TOE-OUT ON TURNS Inner	TOE-OUT ON TURNS Outer	STEERING AXIS INCLINATION (SAI)
TOYOTA (Cont.)							
85	11/64 ± 3/64	.166 ± .042	21/64 ± 5/64	.333 ± .083	22 1/4°	20°	9 1/2°
86	1/8 ± 3/64	.125 ± .042	1/4 ± 5/64	.250 ± .083	21°	20°	12°
87	0 ± 5/64 1/8 ± 5/64	0 ± .083 .125 ± .083	0 ± 11/64 1/4 ± 11/64	0 ± .166 .250 ± .166	21°	20°	10 1/2°
88	0 ± 5/64	0 ± .083	0 ± 11/64	0 ± .166	21 1/2°	20°	11 1/2°
89	-3/64 ± 3/64 0 ± 5/64	-.042 ± .042 0 ± .083	-5/64 ± 5/64 0 ± 11/64	-.083 ± .083 0 ± .166	21 1/2° 21 1/8°	20° 20°	11 3/4°
90	-3/64 ± 3/64	-.042 ± .042	-5/64 ± 5/64	-.083 ± .083	21 1/4°	20°	11 7/8°
91	0 ± 5/64	0 ± .083	0 ± 11/64	0 ± .166	22°	20°	10 1/2°
92	0 ± 5/64	0 ± .083	0 ± 11/64	0 ± .166	20 53/64°	20°	NS
93	11/64 ± 3/64	.166 ± .042	21/64 ± 5/64	.333 ± .083	21°	20°	12°
VOLKSWAGEN							
94	11/64 ± 5/64 1/4 ± 11/64	.166 ± .083 .250 ± .166	21/64 ± 13/64 1/2 ± 21/64	.333 ± .208 .500 ± .333	NS	NS	NS
95	-5/64 ± 5/64 13/64 ± 5/64	-.083 ± .083 .208 ± .083	-21/64 ± 21/64 27/64 ± 11/64	-.166 ± .166 .416 ± .166	NS	NS	NS
96	-5/64 ± 5/64 13/64 ± 5/64	-.083 ± .083 .208 ± .083	-21/64 ± 21/64 27/64 ± 11/64	-.166 ± .166 .416 ± .166	NS	NS	NS
97	0 ± 5/64 13/64 ± 1/8	0 ± .083 .208 ± .125	0 ± 11/64 27/64 ± 1/4	0 ± .166 .416 ± .250	NS	NS	NS
98	0 ± 5/64	0 ± .083	0 ± 1/8	0 ± .125	NS	NS	NS
99	5/64 ± 3/64 13/64 ± 1/8	.083 ± .042 .208 ± .125	11/64 ± 1/8 27/64 ± 1/4	.166 ± .125 .416 ± .250	NS	NS	NS
100	5/64 ± 3/64 11/64 ± 5/64	.083 ± .042 .166 ± .083	11/64 ± 5/64 21/64 ± 11/64	.166 ± .083 .333 ± .166	NS	NS	NS
101	11/64 ± 1/4 0 ± 3/32	.166 ± .250 0 ± .083	21/64 ± 1/2 0 ± 3/16	.333 ± .500 0 ± .166	NS	NS	NS
102	0 ± 11/64 5/64 ± 11/64	0 ± .166 .083 ± .166	0 ± 5/16 5/32 ± 5/16	0 ± .313 .166 ± .313	NS	NS	NS
VOLVO							
103	1/16 ± 3/64	.063 ± .042	1/8 ± 3/32	.125 ± .094	NS	NS	NS
104	3/32 ± 1/32	.094 ± .031	3/16 ± 1/16	.188 ± .063	NS	NS	NS
YUGO							
105	 3/16 ± 1/16	 .188 ± .063	 3/8 ± 1/8	 .375 ± .125	NS NS	NS NS	NS NS

• – Caster and rear camber are not adjustable.
* – Specification is for toe-out.
NS – Information not supplied by manufacturer.

ADJUSTMENT PROCEDURES – ALL MODELS

1

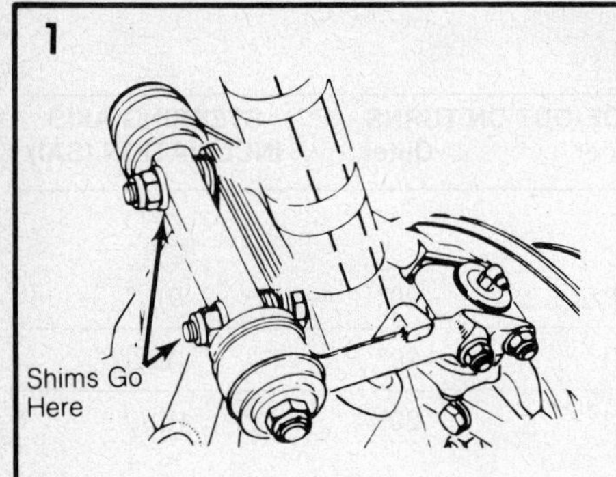

CAMBER & CASTER ADJUSTMENTS

To adjust caster, place shims from one side to the other. To adjust camber, move shims equally.

2

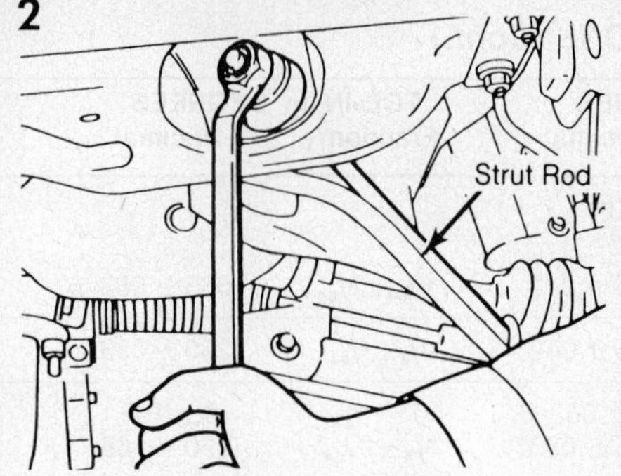

CASTER ADJUSTMENT

To adjust caster, lengthen or shorten strut rod as shown.

3

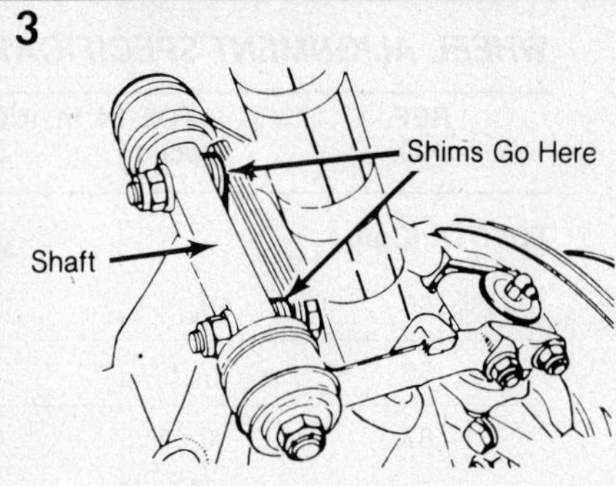

CAMBER & CASTER ADJUSTMENTS

To increase/decrease caster angle move shims from one side to the other. To adjust camber change shims equally from side to side.

4

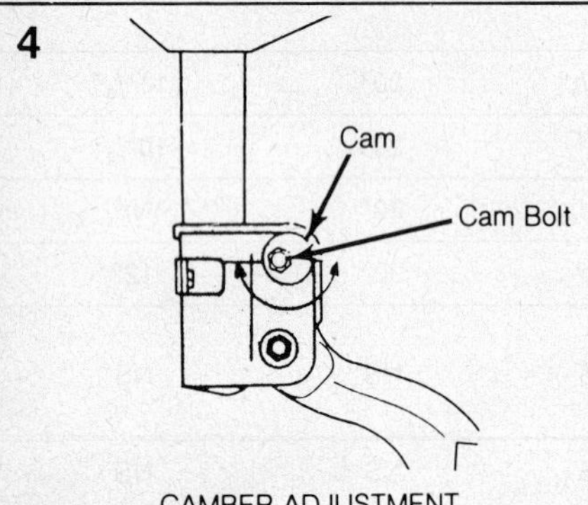

CAMBER ADJUSTMENT

Rotate eccentric cam bolt to increase or decrease camber.

5

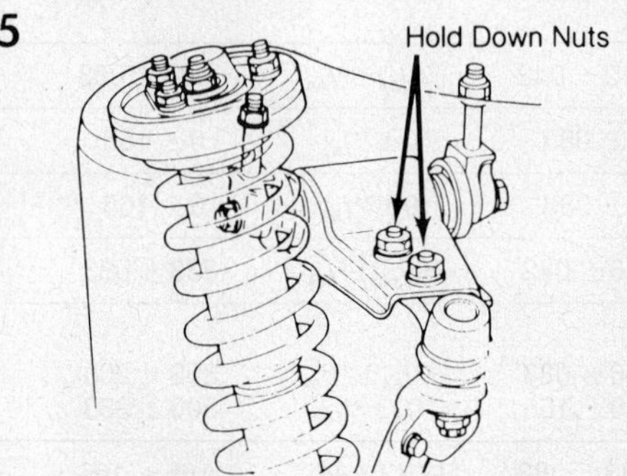

CAMBER ADJUSTMENT

Loosen hold down nuts on the control arm and position in or out to set camber.

6

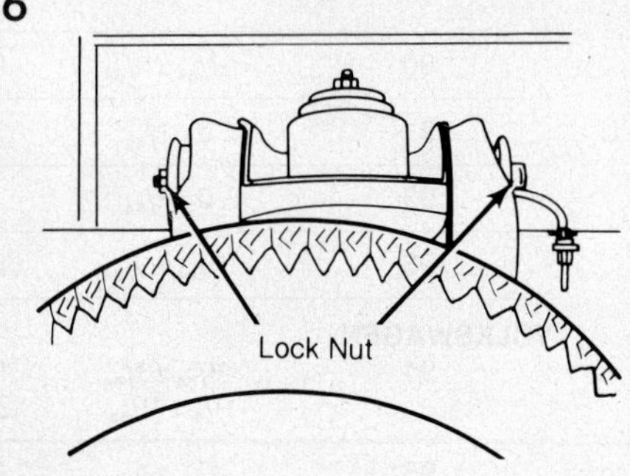

CAMBER ADJUSTMENT

Loosen lock nut on control arm and rotate to obtain correct camber setting.

7

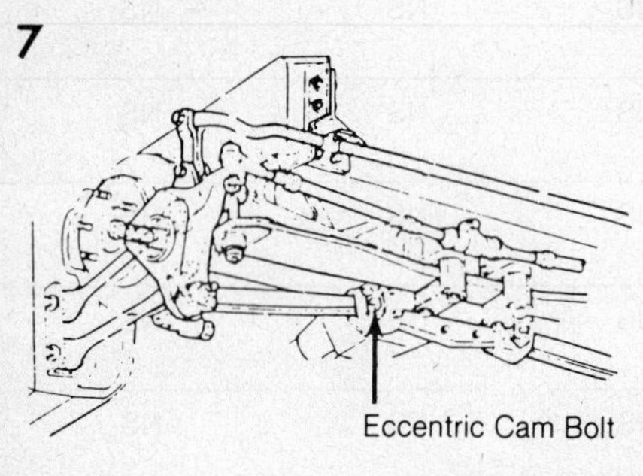

CAMBER ADJUSTMENT

To increase or decrease camber setting, turn eccentric left or right.

8

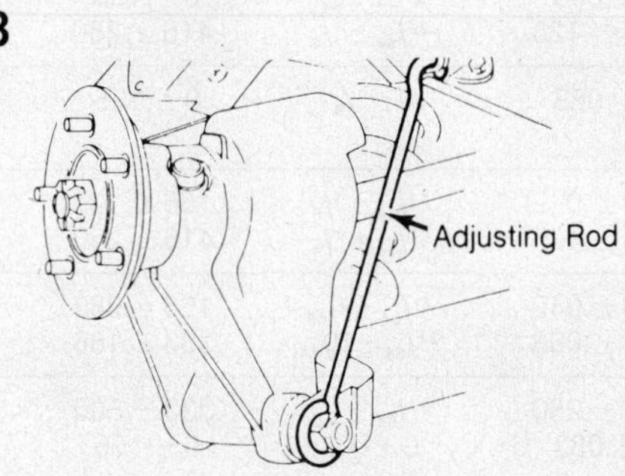

CAMBER ADJUSTMENT

To adjust, loosen or tighten as shown.

9

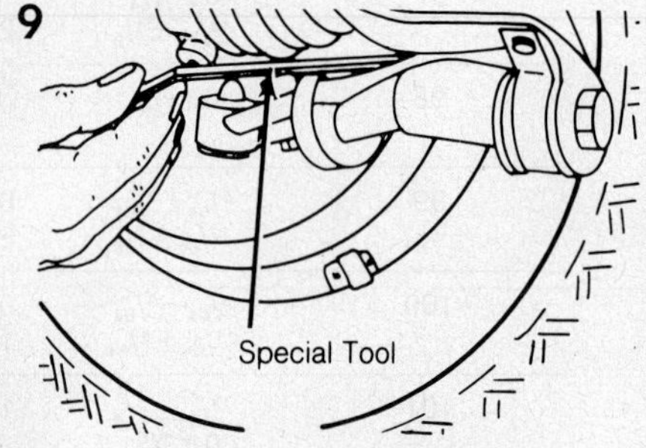

CAMBER ADJUSTMENT WITH SPECIAL TOOL

To adjust, pry lower ball joint out to increase camber.

10

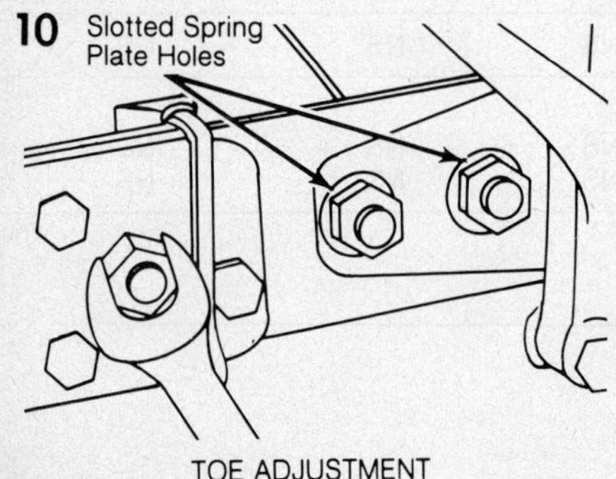

TOE ADJUSTMENT

To adjust toe, move both bolts simultaneously.

11

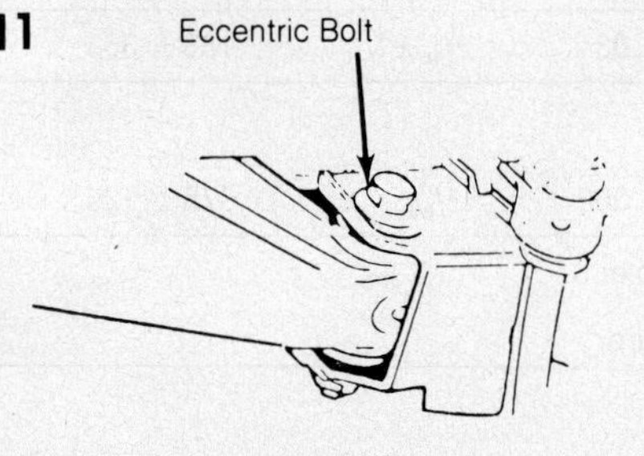

TOE ADJUSTMENT

To increase toe-in, increase eccentric width at contact point.

12

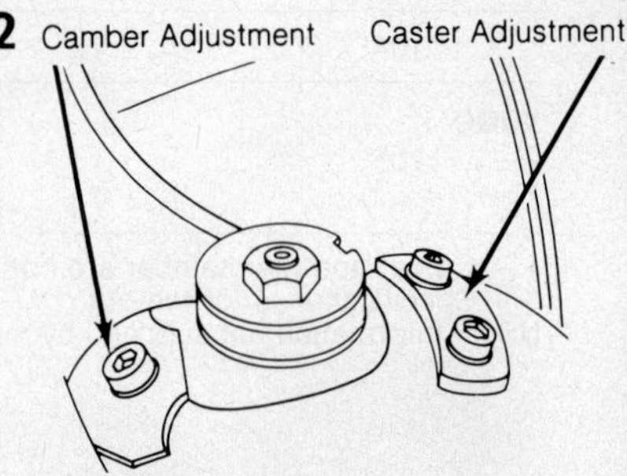

CAMBER & CASTER ADJUSTMENT

Loosen hold down bolts and move strut to adjust.

ADJUSTMENT PROCEDURES – ALL MODELS (Cont.)

13

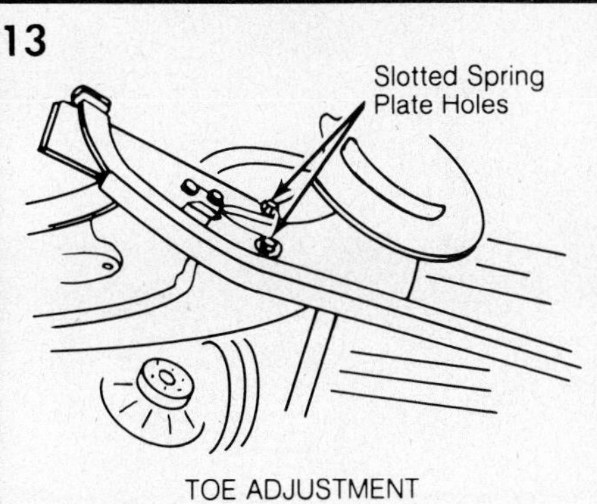

TOE ADJUSTMENT

To decrease toe-in, move arm towards front of vehicle.

14

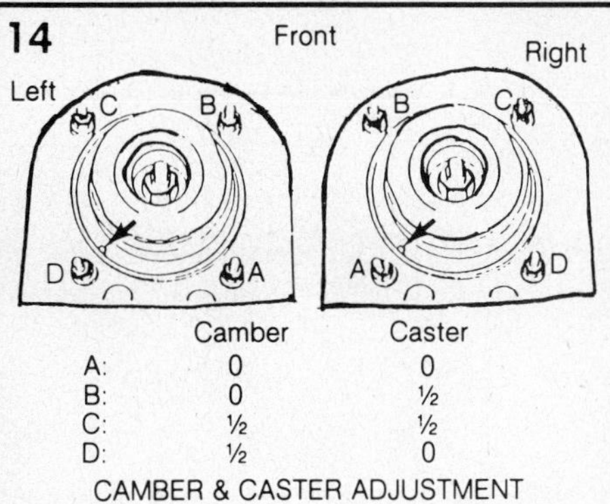

	Camber	Caster
A:	0	0
B:	0	½
C:	½	½
D:	½	0

CAMBER & CASTER ADJUSTMENT

To adjust caster and camber, remove 4 mounting bolts. Then push down and rotate block to desired position.

15

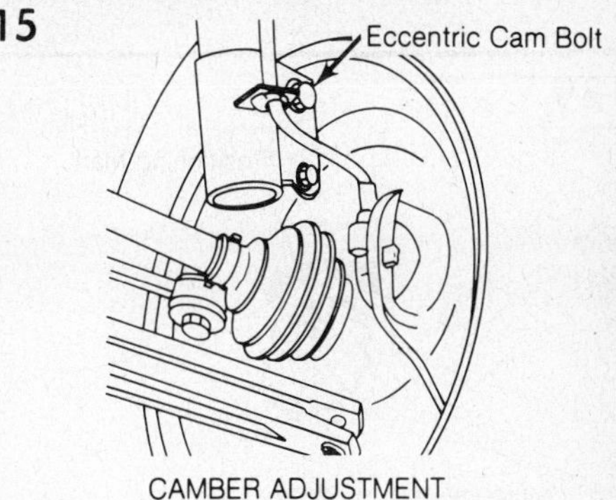

CAMBER ADJUSTMENT

To decrease camber, decrease width at eccentric contact point.

16

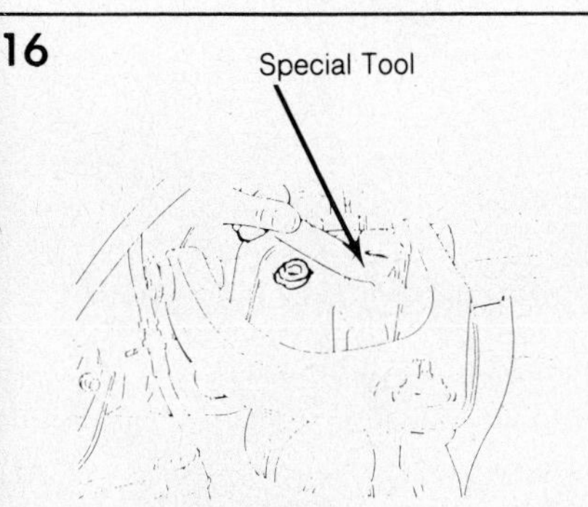

CAMBER ADJUSTMENT

Adjust caster first (turn upper shaft). Then to adjust camber change shims.

17

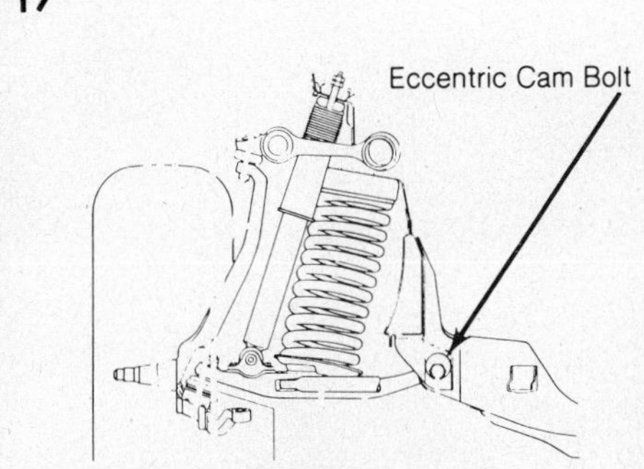

CAMBER & CASTER ADJUSTMENT

Rotate eccentric bolt to adjust camber and caster.

18

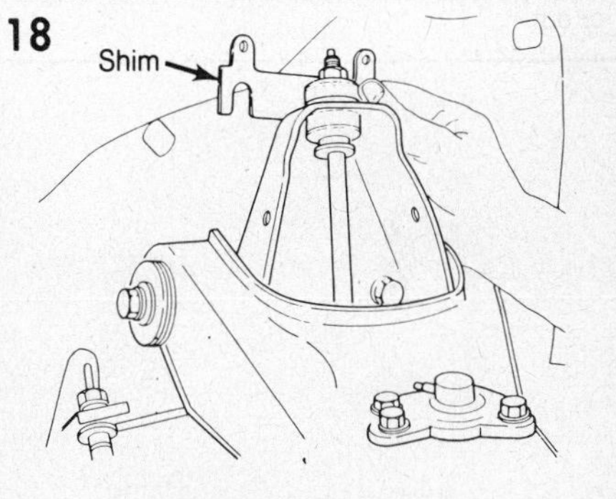

CAMBER ADJUSTMENT

Rotate pivot shaft or add shims to adjust camber angle.

19

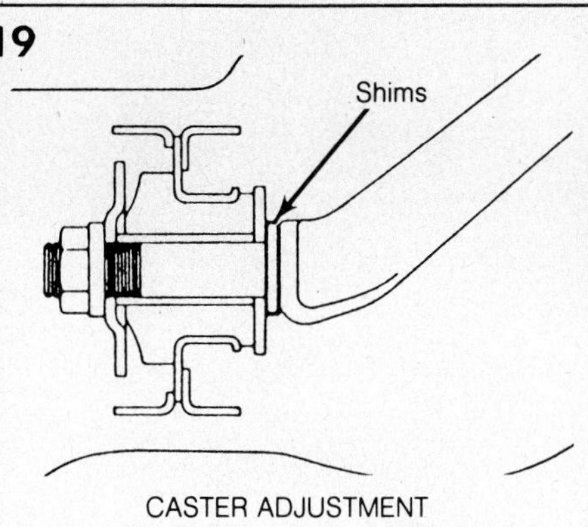

CASTER ADJUSTMENT

Change caster angle by adding/subtracting shims where shown.

20

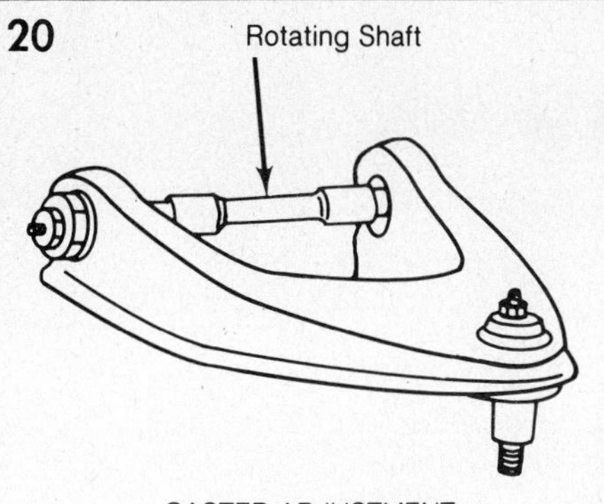

CASTER ADJUSTMENT

Disconnect upper control arm and rotate shaft to obtain desired caster adjustment.

21

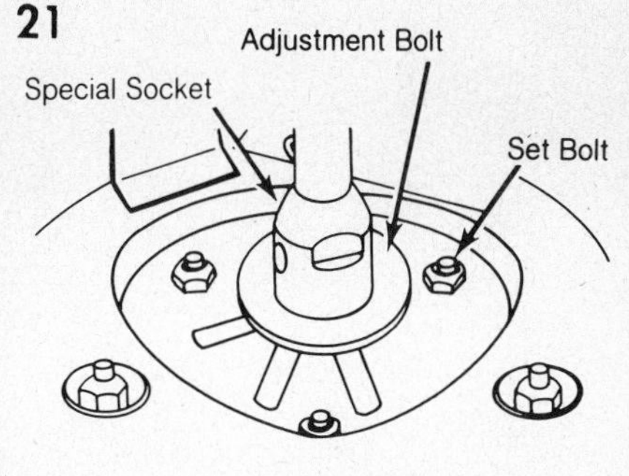

CAMBER ADJUSTMENT

Loosen set bolts, and turn center bolt with special socket to adjust camber.

22

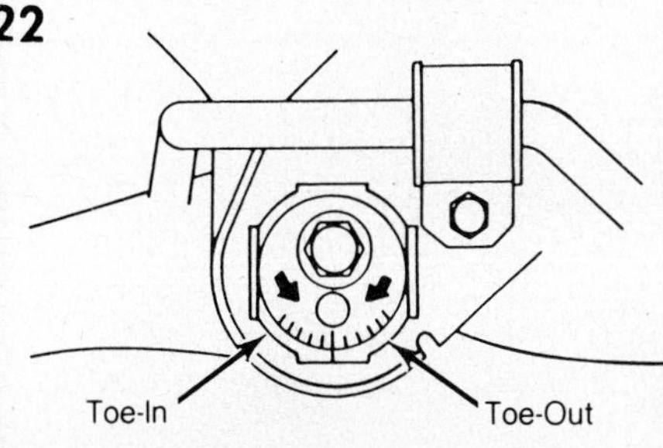

TOE ADJUSTMENT

To adjust, turn eccentric to desired setting.

23

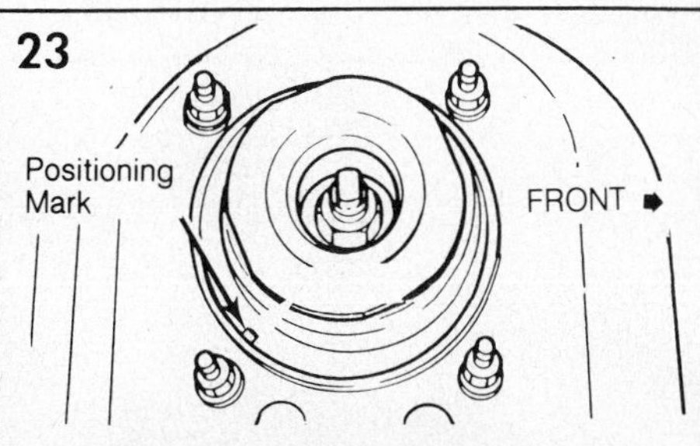

CAMBER & CASTER ADJUSTMENT

Loosen the 4 mounting bolts and turn the positioning mark to A to increase caster 5/16°, B to increase caster and camber 5/16°, and C to increase camber only 5/16°.

24

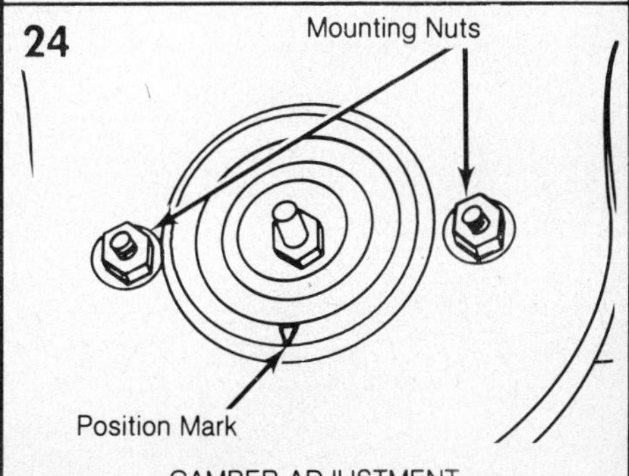

CAMBER ADJUSTMENT

To adjust, remove strut mounting nuts, press down and rotate mark.

Wheel Alignment

ADJUSTMENT PROCEDURES – ALL MODELS (Cont.)

25

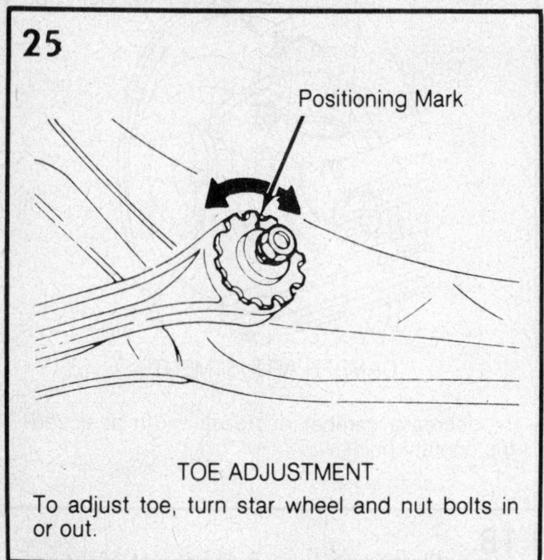

TOE ADJUSTMENT

To adjust toe, turn star wheel and nut bolts in or out.

WHEEL NUT TORQUES – ALL MODELS

WHEEL LUG NUT TIGHTENING SPECIFICATIONS

Application	Ft. Lbs. (N.m)
Acura	80 (108)
Alfa Romeo	65-79 (88-107)
Audi	
Coupe & 4000 Series	65 (88)
5000 Series	80 (108)
BMW	59-66 (80-90)
Chevrolet	
Spectrum	65 (88)
Sprint	29-51 (39-69)
Chrysler Motors Imports	
Raider	72-87 (98-118)
Ram-50	87-101 (118-137)
Colt & Conquest	65-80 (88-108)
All Other Models	
Aluminum Wheels	65-80 (88-108)
Steel Wheels	51-58 (69-79)
Ford Motor Co. Imports	
Festiva & Tracer	65-87 (88-118)
Merkur XR4Ti	72-101 (98-137)
Honda	80 (108)
Hyundai	
Aluminum Wheels	58-72 (79-98)
Steel Wheels	50-57 (68-77)
Isuzu	
I-Mark	
Aluminum Wheels	87 (118)
Steel Wheels	65 (88)
Impulse	87 (118)
P'UP	58-87 (79-118)
Trooper II	
Aluminum Wheels	80-94 (108-127)
Steel Wheels	58-87 (79-118)
Jaguar	45-65 (61-88)
Mazda	
RX7, 323 & 626	65-87 (88-118)
B2200 & B2600	
Styled Wheel	87-108 (118-146)
Exc. Styled Wheel	65-87 (88-118)
Mercedes-Benz	74 (100)
Mitsubishi	
Cordia & Tredia	
Aluminum Wheels	65-80 (88-108)
Steel Wheels	50-57 (68-77)
Galant	
Aluminum Wheels	66-81 (89-110)
Steel Wheels	50-57 (68-77)
Montero	72-87 (98-118)
Mirage & Starion	65-80 (88-108)
Pickup	51-57 (69-77)
Nissan	
Maxima, Pulsar NX, Sentra, Stanza, Stanza Wagon & 300ZX	72-87 (98-118)
200SX	87-108 (118-146)
Pickup	
Aluminum Wheels	58-72 (79-98)
Steel Wheels	
Single	87-108 (118-146)
Dual	166-202 (225-274)
All Other Models	58-72 (79-98)
Peugeot	45 (61)

WHEEL LUG NUT TIGHTENING SPECIFICATIONS (Cont.)

Application	Ft. Lbs. (N.m)
Porsche	94 (127)
Saab	
900	65-80 (88-108)
9000	76-90 (103-122)
Subaru	58-72 (79-98)
Suzuki	37-58 (50-79)
Toyota	76 (103)
Volkswagen	81 (110)
Volvo	
740 & 760 Series	63 (85)
All Other Models	72-95 (98-129)
Yugo	64 (87)

Jacking & Hoisting

ALL MANUFACTURERS

NOTE: These illustrations are not intended to represent exact structure of each vehicle's frame, underbody or body outline. They are presented only to give the mechanic some point of reference.

FRAME & UNDERBODY

The following illustrations indicate areas (parts) of the underbody and frame which may be used to raise and support the vehicle, using either floor jack or hoist. These points are indicated by shaded areas on the frame. *See Fig. 1.*

OUTERBODY

Those points designated on the outline of the body were specifically designed to facilitate the use of the vehicle's own jack. These jacking points are indicated by circular dots on the outline of the body. *See Fig. 1*. If floor jack or hoist is employed, extreme care should be exercised to avoid damaging the outer body shell.

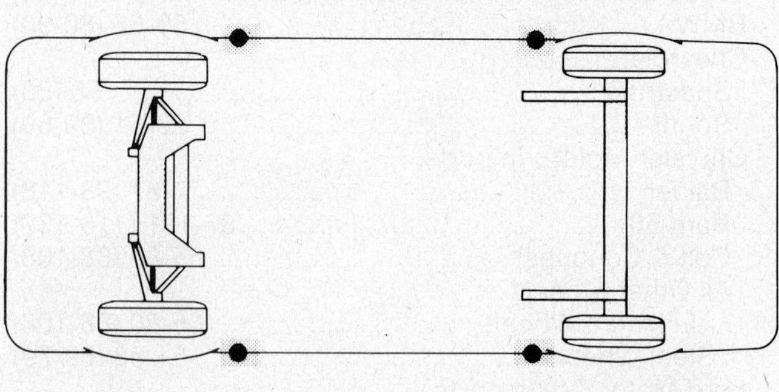

Audi

Fig. 1: Sample: Jacking & Hoisting Points (Typical Illustration)

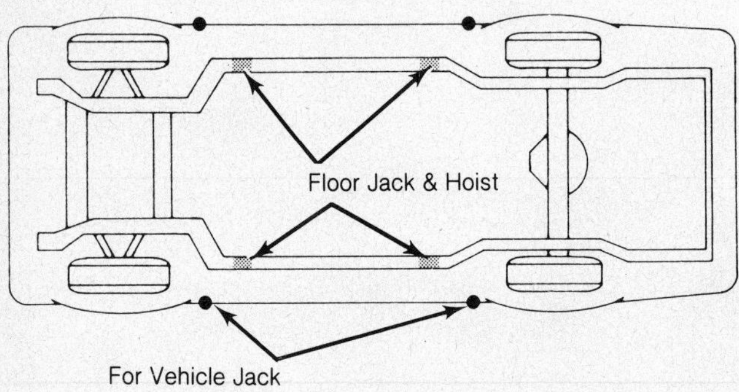

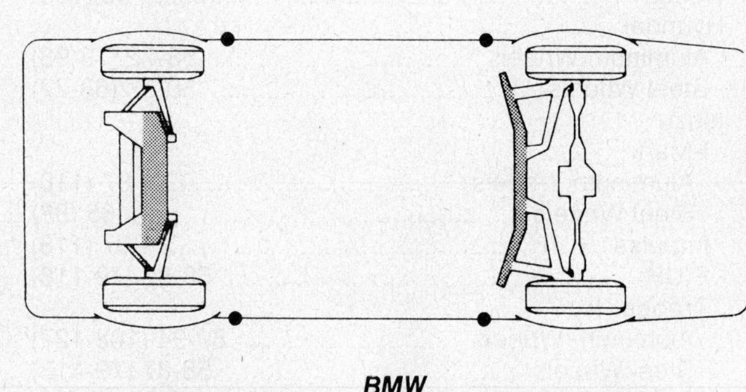

BMW

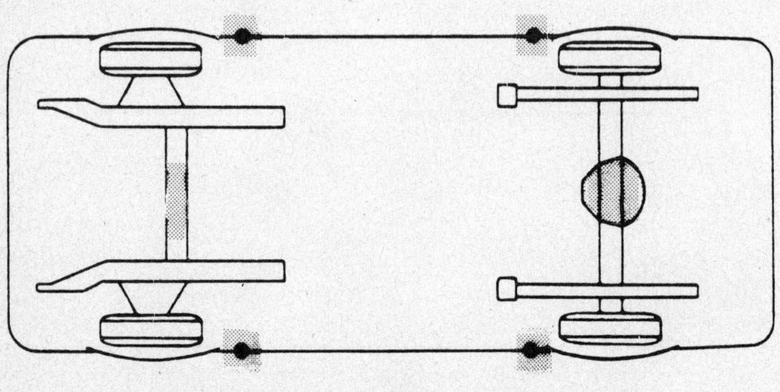

Acura & Sterling

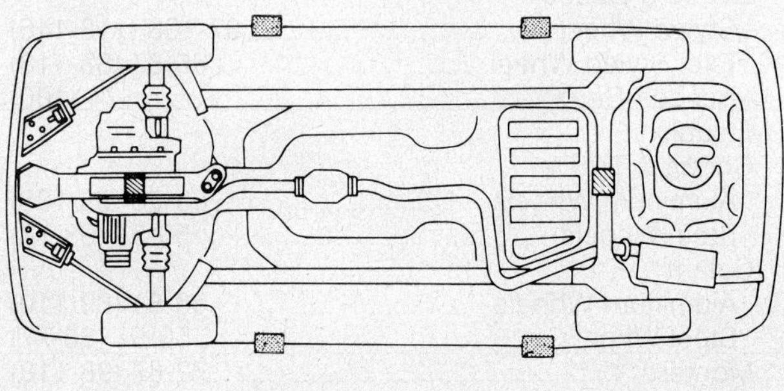

Chevrolet Spectrum

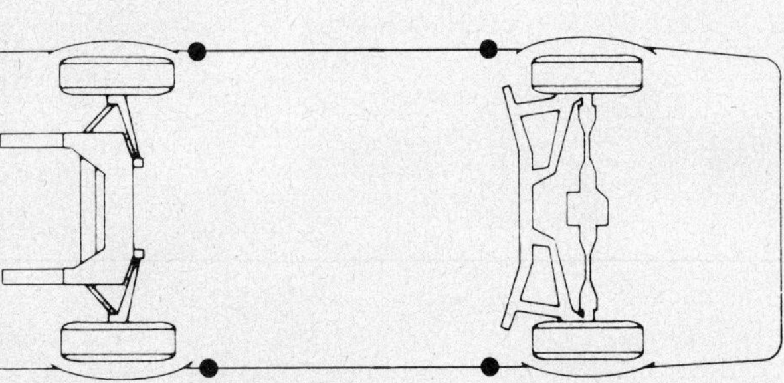

Alfa Romeo Milano

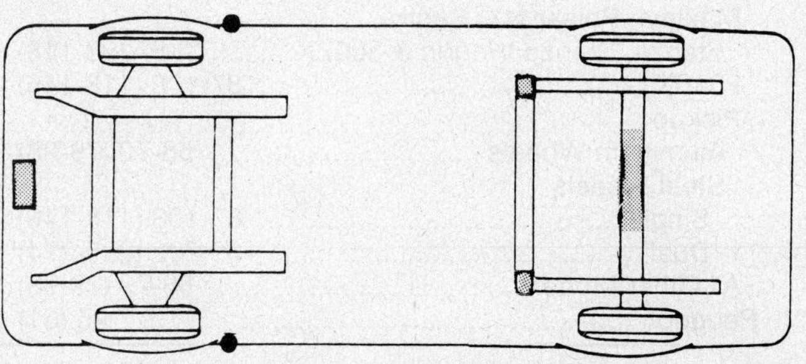

Chevrolet Sprint

ALL MANUFACTURERS (Cont.)

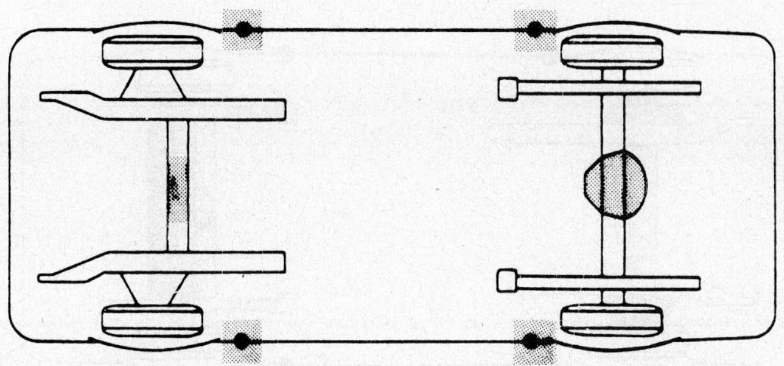
Chrysler Motors Imports Colt Vista, Conquest & Mitsubishi Starion

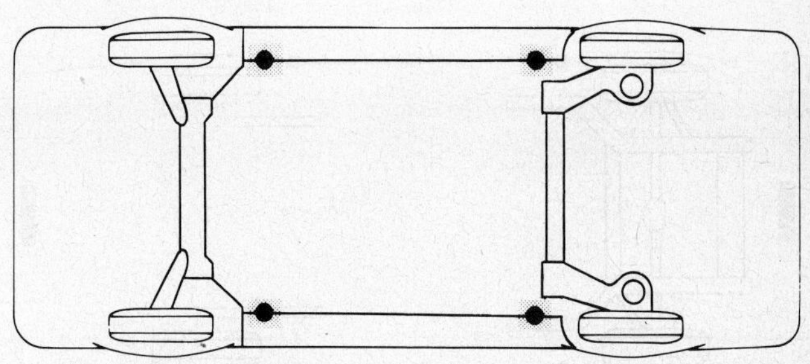
Mitsubishi Cordia & Tredia

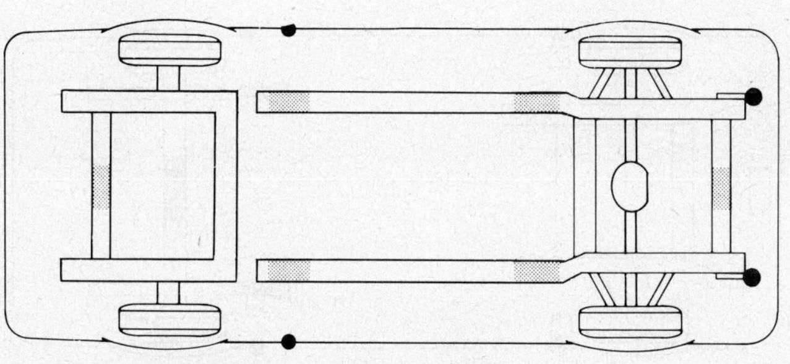
Chrysler Motors Imports Colt & Mitsubishi Mirage

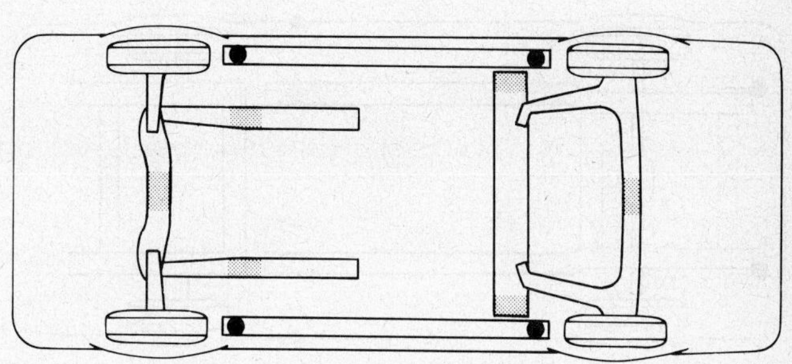
Mitsubishi Galant

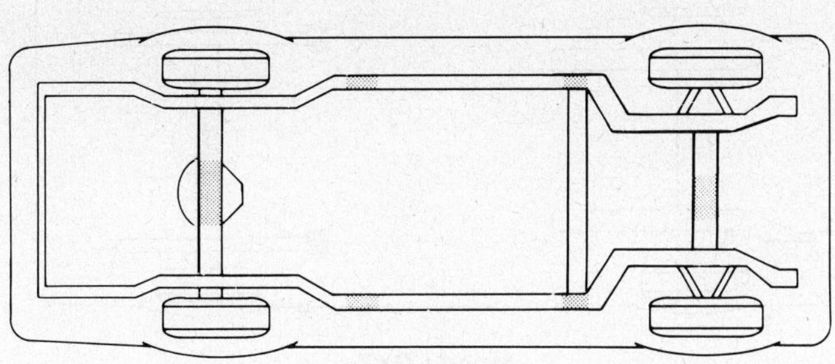
Chrysler Motors Imports Ram-50 Pickup & Mitsubishi Pickup

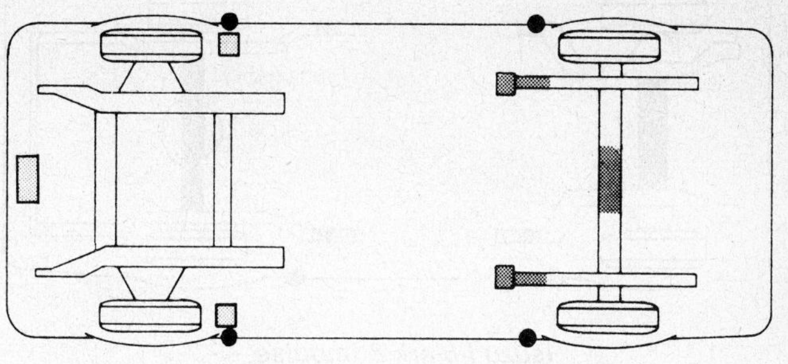
Ford Motor Co. Festiva & Tracer

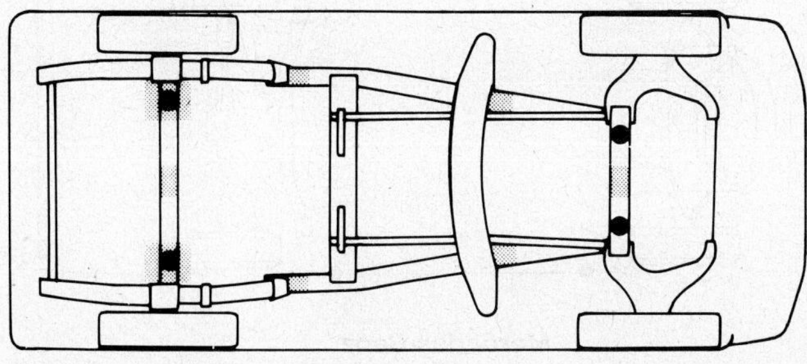
Chrysler Motors Imports Raider & Mitsubishi Montero

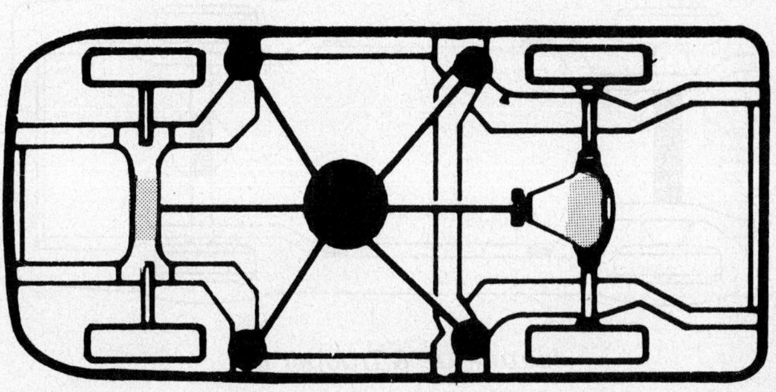
Ford Motor Co. Merkur XR4Ti

Jacking & Hoisting

ALL MANUFACTURERS (Cont.)

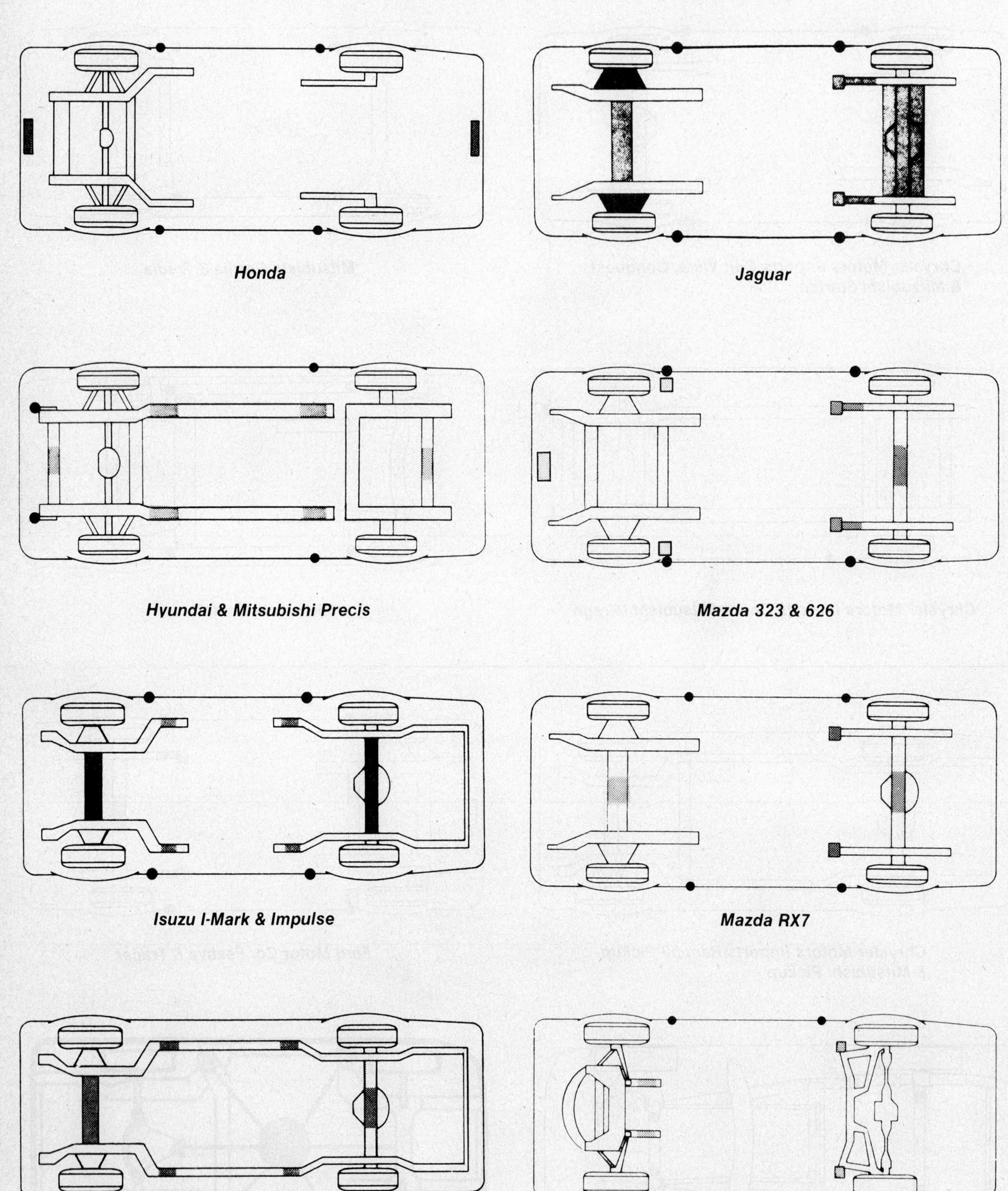

Honda

Jaguar

Hyundai & Mitsubishi Precis

Mazda 323 & 626

Isuzu I-Mark & Impulse

Mazda RX7

Isuzu P'UP & Trooper II

Mercedes-Benz

ALL MANUFACTURERS (Cont.)

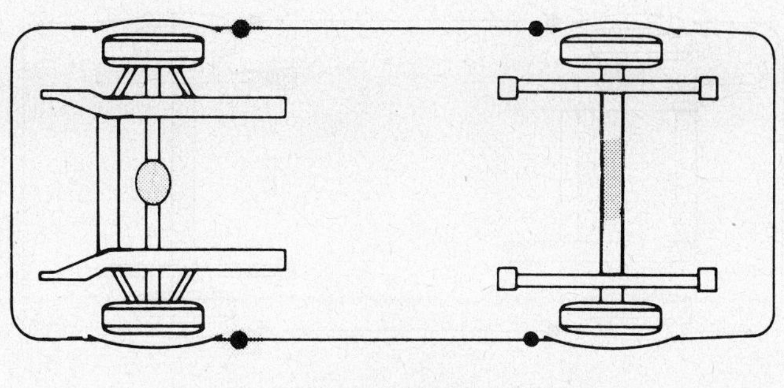
Nissan Maxima

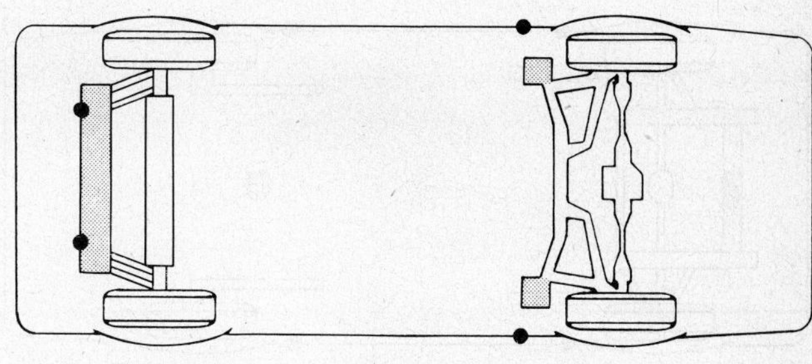
Peugeot 505

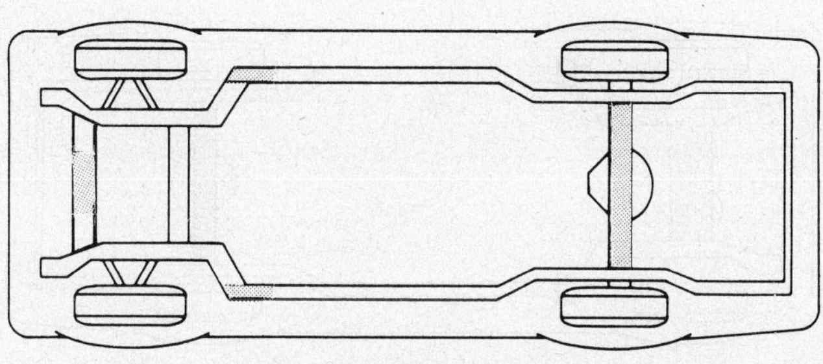
Nissan Pathfinder, Pickup & Van

Porsche 911 Series, 924S & 944 Series

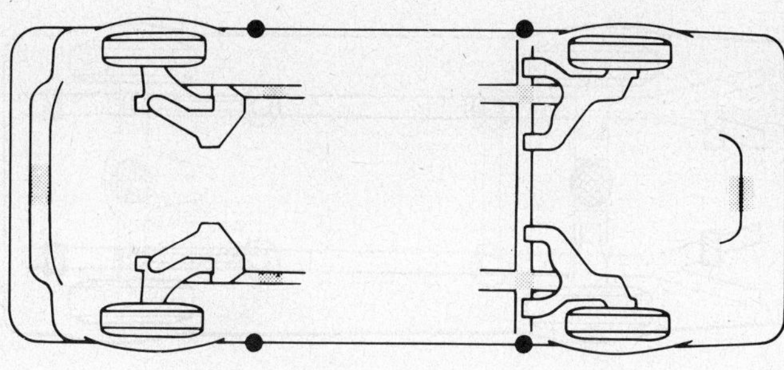
Nissan Pulsar, Sentra & Stanza

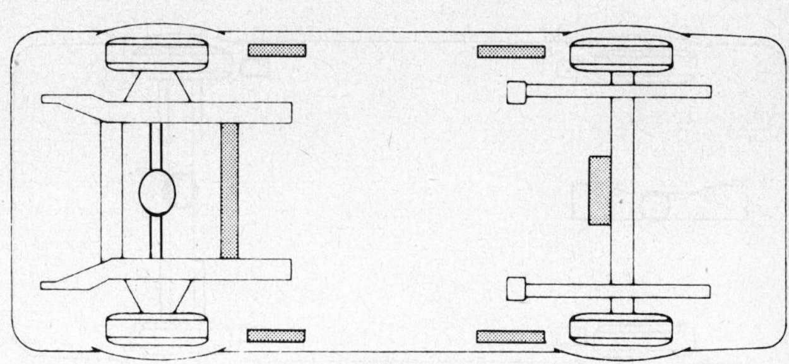
Saab 900

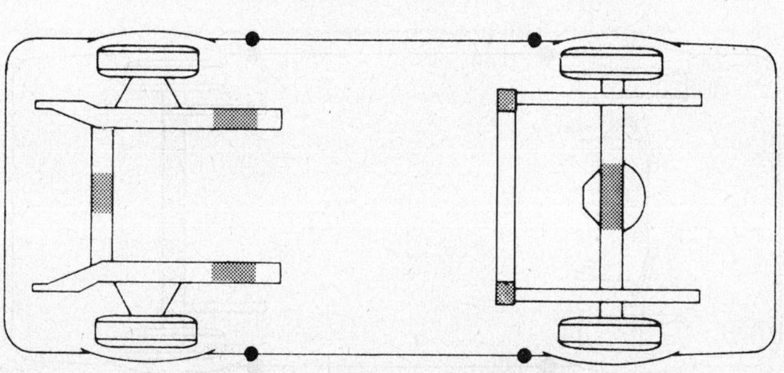
Nissan 200SX & 300ZX

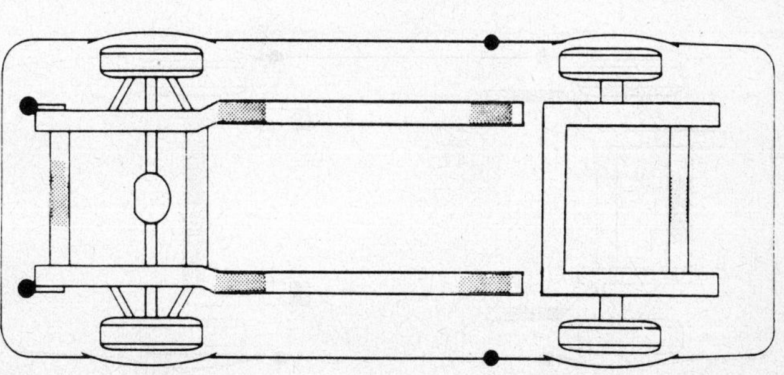
Saab 9000

Jacking & Hoisting

ALL MANUFACTURERS (Cont.)

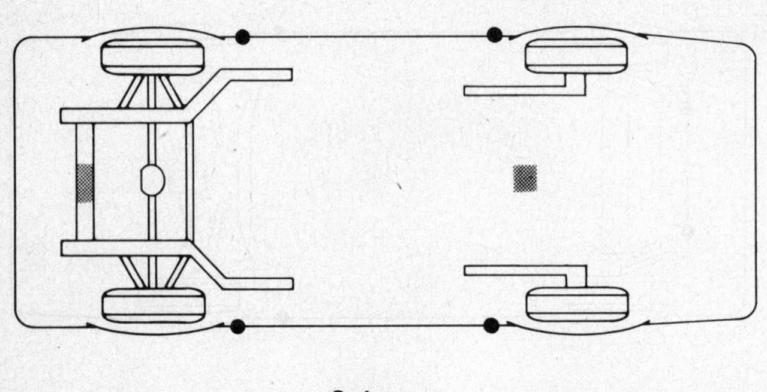

Subaru

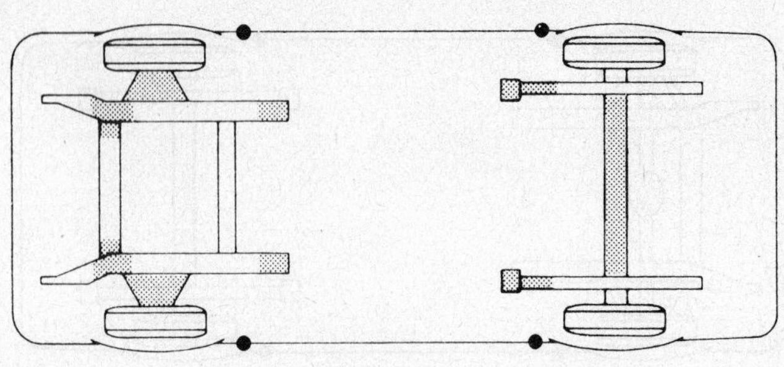

Toyota Corolla & Tercel

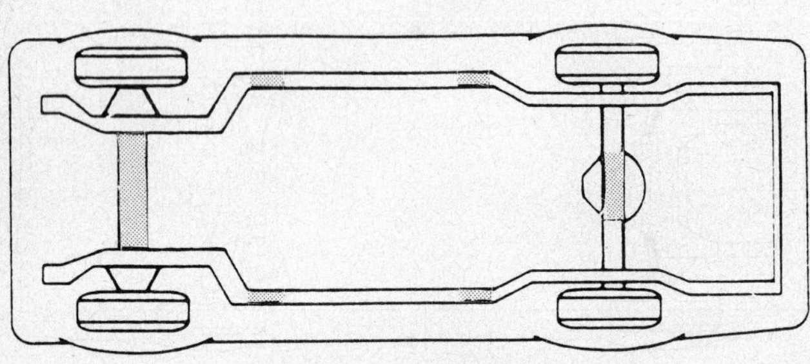

Suzuki Samurai

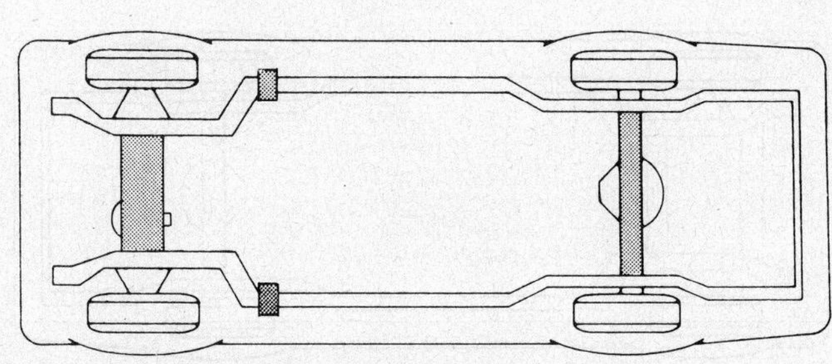

Toyota Land Cruiser, Pickup & 4Runner

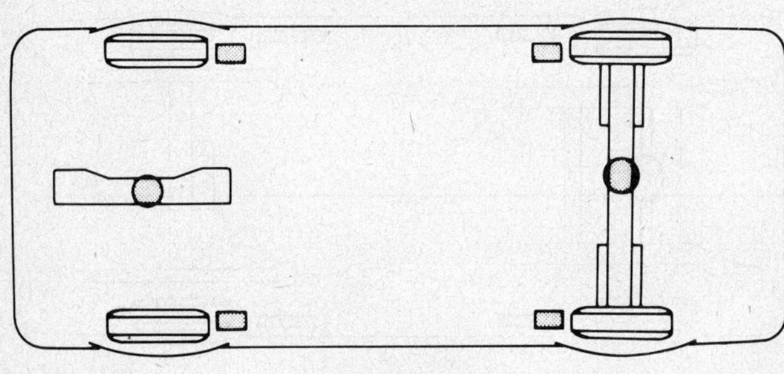

Toyota Camry

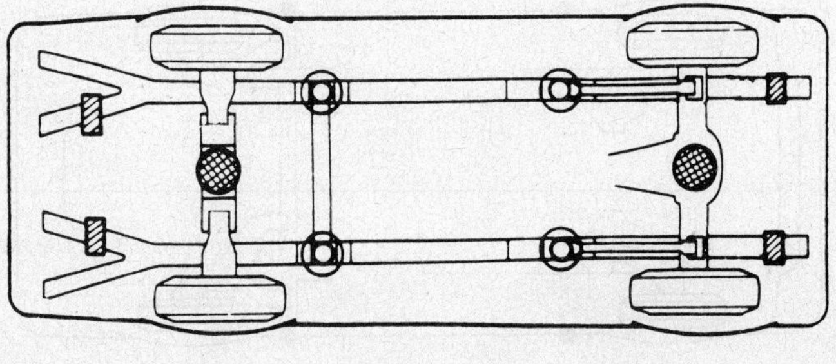

Toyota Van

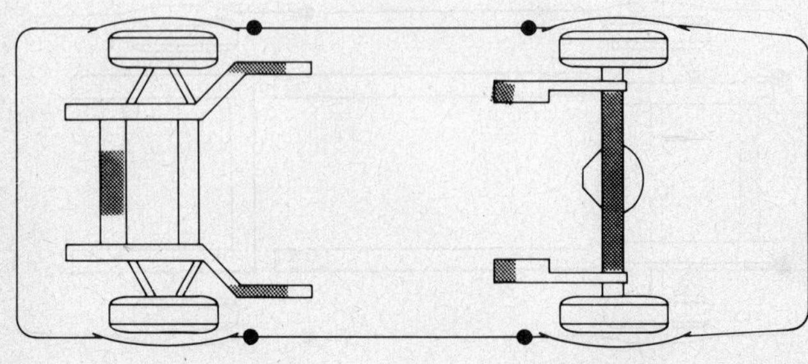

Toyota Celica, Cressida, MR2 & Supra

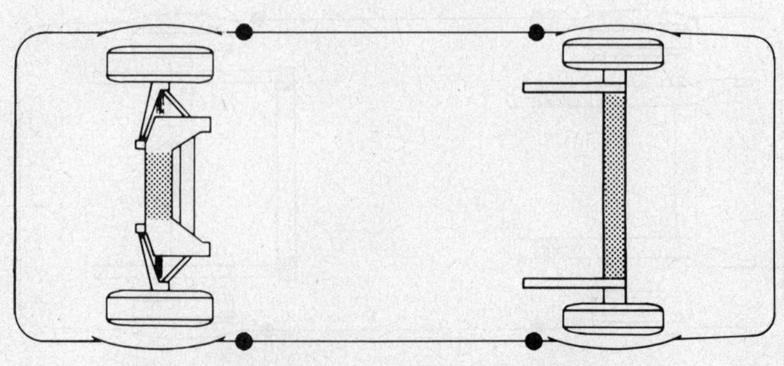

Volkswagen (Except Vanagon)

ALL MANUFACTURERS (Cont.)

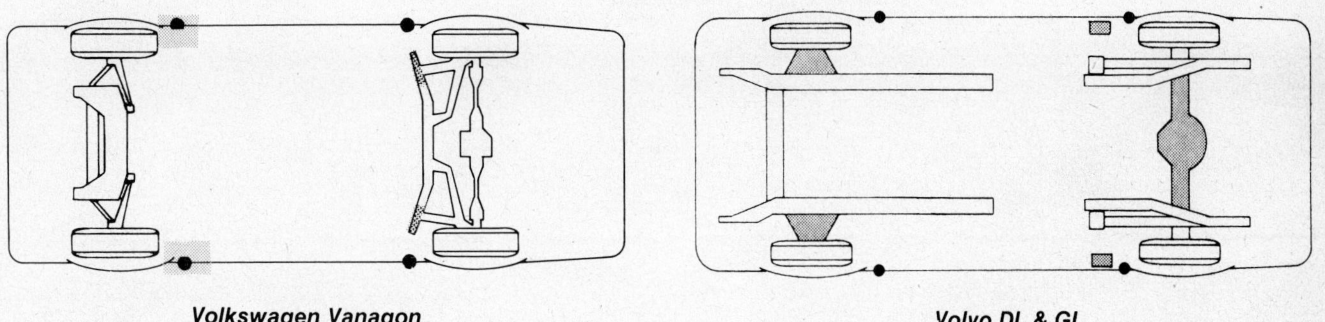

Volkswagen Vanagon

Volvo DL & GL

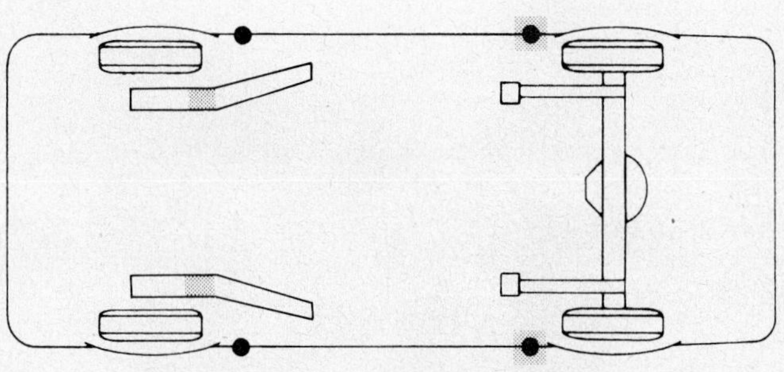

Volvo 740, 760 & 780 Series

SECTION 11

SUSPENSION

CONTENTS

TROUBLE SHOOTING

	Page
All Models	11-2

FRONT SUSPENSION

Acura	11-3
Audi	11-8
BMW	11-11
Chrysler Motors & Mitsubishi	
Colt, Colt Vista, Cordia, Mirage, Precis & Tredia	11-24
Conquest & Starion	11-14
Galant	11-74
Montero	11-18
Van/Wagon	11-77
2WD Pickup & Ram-50	11-17
4WD Pickup & Ram-50	11-18
Ford Motor Co. Festiva	11-30
Ford Motor Co. Merkur XR4Ti	11-35
Ford Motor Co. Tracer	11-39
General Motors Spectrum	11-43
General Motors Sprint	11-45
Honda	11-47
Hyundai	11-24
Isuzu I-Mark	11-43
Isuzu Impulse	11-54
Isuzu P'UP & Trooper II	11-56
Jaguar	11-62
Mazda RX7, 323 & 626	11-39
Mazda B2200 & B2600	11-65
Mercedes-Benz	
190 Series, 260E & 300 Series	11-68
300SDL, 420SEL, 560SEC, 560SEL & 560SL	11-71
Nissan	
Maxima	11-79
Pathfinder & Pickup	11-81
Pulsar NX, Sentra, Stanza & Stanza Wagon	11-87
Van	11-93
200SX & 300ZX	11-97
Peugeot	11-99
Porsche 911 Carrera & 911 Turbo	11-103
Porsche 924-S, 944, 944-S & 944 Turbo	11-101
Saab 900 Series & 9000 Series	11-105
Sterling 825	11-108
Subaru	11-112
Suzuki Samurai	11-115
Toyota	
Camry, Celica, Corolla FWD & Tercel	11-119
Corolla RWD, Cressida & Supra	11-124
MR2	11-128
2WD Pickup & Van	11-130
4WD Pickup, Van & 4Runner	11-134
Volkswagen	
Cabriolet, Golf, GTI & Jetta	11-139
Fox, Quantum & Scirocco	11-141
2WD Vanagon	11-143
4WD Vanagon	11-145
Volvo	11-148
Yugo	11-150

REAR SUSPENSION

	Page
Acura	11-152
Audi	11-157
BMW	11-160
Chrysler Motors & Mitsubishi	
Colt, Colt Vista, Cordia, Mirage, Precis & Tredia	11-165
Conquest & Starion	11-162
Galant	11-201
Ford Motor Co. Festiva	11-170
Ford Motor Co. Merkur XR4Ti	11-174
Ford Motor Co. Tracer	11-178
General Motors Spectrum	11-180
General Motors Sprint	11-182
Honda Accord, Civic (2WD) & Prelude	11-183
Honda 4WD Civic Wagon	11-188
Hyundai	11-165
Isuzu I-Mark	11-180
Isuzu Impulse	11-189
Jaguar	11-191
Mazda RX7	11-193
Mazda 323 & 626	11-174
Mercedes-Benz	
190 Series, 260E, 300 Series (Exc. 300SDL)	11-198
300SDL, 420SEL & 560 Series	11-196
Nissan	
Maxima	11-203
Pulsar NX & Sentra	11-205
Stanza	11-207
Stanza Wagon	11-210
Van	11-215
200SX & 300ZX	11-216
Peugeot	11-218
Porsche 911 Carrera & 911 Turbo	11-223
Porsche 924-S, 944, 944-S & 944 Turbo	11-221
Saab 900 Series & 9000 Series	11-225
Sterling 825	11-227
Subaru Justy	11-231
Subaru (Exc. Justy)	11-229
Toyota	
Camry, Celica, Corolla FWD & Tercel Wagon (Except 4WD)	11-238
Corolla RWD, Cressida Wagon, Tercel 4WD Wagon & Van	11-233
Cressida Sedan	11-235
MR2	11-241
Supra	11-243
Volkswagen	
Fox, Golf, GTI, Jetta, Quantum & Scirocco	11-245
Quantum Syncro	11-247
Vanagon	11-248
Volvo	11-250
Yugo	11-253

AUTOMATIC LEVEL CONTROL

Mercedes-Benz 300TD Turbo, 560SEC & 560SEL	11-255

ELECTRONIC SUSPENSION

Mazda RX7 & 626	11-258
Mazda 323	11-264
Mitsubishi Galant	11-267
Nissan Maxima & 300ZX	11-278
Subaru Sedan, Wagon & XT Coupe	11-283
Toyota Cressida & Supra	11-293

NOTE: ALSO SEE GENERAL INDEX.

Suspension

SUSPENSION TROUBLE SHOOTING

CONDITION	POSSIBLE CAUSE	CORRECTION
Front End Noise	Loose or worn wheel bearings	See Wheel Bearing Adjustment in SUSPENSION
	Worn shocks or shock mountings	Replace shocks or mountings.
	Worn struts or strut mountings	Replace struts or strut mountings
	Loose or worn lower control arm	See Lower Control Arm Removal & Installation in SUSPENSION
	Loose steering gear-to-frame bolts	See Steering Gear Removal & Installation in STEERING
	Steering knuckle contacts lower control arm wheel stop	See Steering Knuckle in STEERING or Lower Control Arm in SUSPENSION
	Worn control arm bushings	See Control Arms in SUSPENSION
	Ball joints not lubricated	Lubricate ball joints & see Ball Joint Checking in SUSPENSION
Front Wheel Shake, Shimmy or Vibration	Tires or wheels out of balance	Check tire balance
	Incorrect wheel alignment	See Adjustment in WHEEL ALIGNMENT
	Propeller shaft unbalanced	Check propeller shaft balance
	Loose or worn wheel bearings	See Wheel Bearing Adjustment in SUSPENSION
	Loose or worn tie rod ends	See Tie Rod Removal & Installation in SUSPENSION
	Worn upper ball joints	See Ball Joint Checking in SUSPENSION
	Worn shock absorbers	Replace shock absorbers
	Worn strut bushings	Replace strut bushings
Car Pulls to One Side	Mismatched or uneven tires	Check tire condition
	Broken or sagging springs	See Coil Spring Removal & Installation in SUSPENSION
	Loose or worn strut bushings	See Strut Removal & Installation in SUSPENSION
	Improper wheel alignment	See Adjustment in WHEEL ALIGNMENT
	Improper rear axle alignment	Check rear axle alignment
	Power steering gear unbalanced	See STEERING
	Front brakes dragging	See BRAKES
Abnormal Tire Wear	Unbalanced tires	Check tire balance & rotation
	Sagging or broken springs	See Coil Spring in SUSPENSION
	Incorrect front end alignment	See Adjustment in WHEEL ALIGNMENT
	Faulty shock absorbers	Replace shock absorbers
Scuffed Tires	Toe-In incorrect	See Adjustment in WHEEL ALIGNMENT
	Suspension arm bent or twisted	See appropriate SUSPENSION article
Springs Bottom or Sag	Bent or broken springs	See Coil Spring in SUSPENSION
	Leaking or worn shock absorbers	Replace shock absorbers
"Dog" Tracking	Broken leaf spring	Replace leaf spring
	Bent rear axle housing	Check rear axle housing
	Frame misalignment	Check frame for damage
Spring Noises	Loose "U" Bolts	See SUSPENSION
	Loose or worn bushings	See SUSPENSION
	Worn or missing interliners	See SUSPENSION
Shock Absorber Noise	Loose shock mountings	Check & tighten mountings
	Worn bushings	Replace bushings
	Air in system	Bleed air from system
	Undercoating on shocks	Remove undercoating
Car Leans or Sways on Corners	Loose stabilizer bar	See SUSPENSION
	Faulty shocks or mountings	Replace shocks or mountings
	Broken or sagging springs	See Coil Spring in SUSPENSION
Shock Absorbers Leaking	Worn seals or reservoir tube crimped	See SUSPENSION
Broken Springs	Loose "U" bolts	See Coil Spring in SUSPENSION
	Inoperative shock absorbers	Replace shock absorbers

Front Suspension

ACURA

DESCRIPTION

Legend uses independent wish-bone MacPherson strut front suspension. Vertically-mounted strut assembly is attached to lower control arm by a fork assembly. Steering knuckle is attached to upper and lower control arms by ball joints. A stabilizer bar is attached to lower control arm. *See Fig. 1.*

Integra uses independent torsion bar suspension. Suspension system consists of a vertically-mounted strut attached to upper steering knuckle, a lower control arm and a radius arm. Steering knuckle is attached to radius arm by a single ball joint. A stabilizer bar is attached to radius arm. *See Fig. 1.*

ADJUSTMENTS & INSPECTION

WHEEL ALIGNMENT SPECIFICATIONS & PROCEDURES

See WHEEL ALIGNMENT SPECIFICATIONS & PROCEDURES in WHEEL ALIGNMENT section.

WHEEL BEARINGS

Wheel bearings are not adjustable.

BALL JOINT CHECKING

1) Raise front of vehicle and support with safety stands. Attach dial indicator to lower control arm. Place indicator tip on steering knuckle, near ball joint. Place pry bar between lower control arm and steering knuckle.

2) Push on pry bar, and observe movement on dial indicator. Movement should not exceed .020" (0.5 mm). Replace radius arm on Integra if ball joint exceeds wear limit. Replace ball joint on Legend if ball joint exceeds wear limit. See BALL JOINT in this article.

REMOVAL & INSTALLATION

WHEEL BEARING

Removal

1) Remove steering knuckle. See STEERING KNUCKLE in this article. Remove splash guard screws. Using press, separate hub from steering knuckle. Be careful not to distort splash guard. Remove bearing retaining snap ring from knuckle. Press bearing out of knuckle.

2) Using bearing puller, remove outboard bearing from hub. Clean knuckle and hub throughly before reassembly.

Installation

1) Press new bearing into knuckle. Pressure required must not exceed 4000 lbs. (1814 kg).

2) Install snap ring in knuckle groove. Install splash guard and turn knuckle upside down.

3) Using press, install new bearing into hub. Press hub into knuckle. Pressure required must not exceed 4000 lbs. (1814 kg). Reverse steering knuckle removal procedure to complete installation.

Fig. 1: Integra & Legend Front Suspension

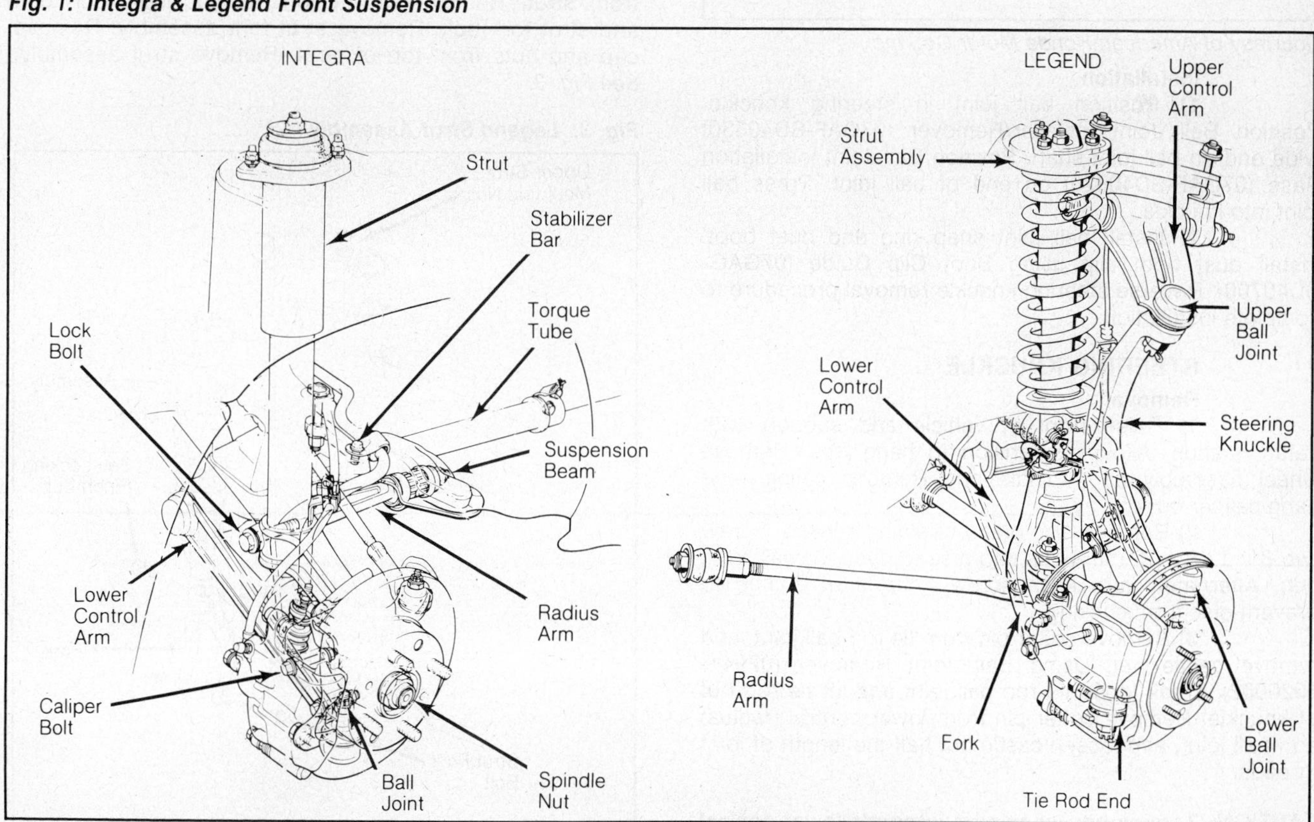

Courtesy of American Honda Motor Co., Inc.

Front Suspension

ACURA (Cont.)

BALL JOINT

Removal & Installation (Integra)

Replace radius arm and ball joint as assembly when ball joint exceeds wear limit. See RADIUS ARM in this article.

Removal (Legend)

1) Remove steering knuckle. See STEERING KNUCKLE in this article. Remove dust boot snap ring, dust boot and ball joint snap ring. Position Ball Joint Installer/Remover (07GAF-SD40330) narrow end on ball joint shaft. Install ball joint nut. Tighten ball joint nut.

2) Position Ball Joint Removal Base (07GAF-SD40310) between ball joint housing and steering knuckle and place assembly in vise. Press ball joint out of knuckle. *See Fig. 2.*

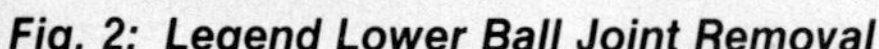

Fig. 2: Legend Lower Ball Joint Removal

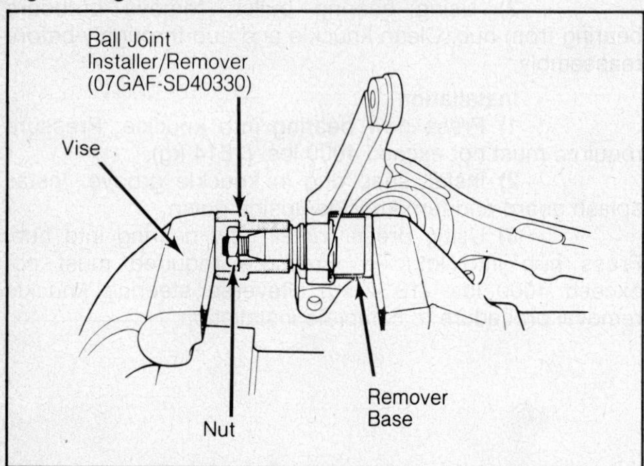

Courtesy of American Honda Motor Co., Inc.

Installation

1) Position ball joint in steering knuckle. Position Ball Joint Installer/Remover (07GAF-SD40330) wide end on ball joint shaft. Position Ball Joint Installation Base (07GAF-SD40320) on end of ball joint. Press ball joint into knuckle.

2) Install ball joint snap ring and dust boot. Install dust boot clip using Boot Clip Guide (07GAG-SD40700). Reverse steering knuckle removal procedure to complete installation.

STEERING KNUCKLE

Removal

1) Raise front of vehicle and support with safety stands. Allow suspension to hang free. Remove wheel assembly and spindle nut. Remove caliper and hang caliper out of way.

2) Remove disc brake retaining screws. Screw two 8 x 1.25 x 12 mm bolts into disc to push it away from hub. Alternately turn each screw 2 turns at a time to prevent disc from cocking.

3) Remove cotter pin from tie rod ball joint, and remove castle nut. Using Ball Joint Remover (07941-6920002), break loose tie rod ball joint and lift tie rod out of knuckle. Remove cotter pin from lower control (radius) arm ball joint, and loosen castle nut half the length of joint threads.

CAUTION: Torsion bar tension on Integra's lower control arm may cause arm to suddenly swing away from steering knuckle as ball joint is being disconnected. Use a floor jack to support lower control arm.

4) Using bearing puller, break loose lower control (radius) arm ball joint. Remove castle nut, and pull arm down until ball joint is clear of knuckle. On Integra, remove strut assembly self-locking pinch bolt, and tap knuckle down until it releases from strut.

5) On Legend, remove cotter pin from upper ball joint, and remove castle nut. Using Ball Joint Remover (07941-6920002), break loose upper ball joint.

6) Pull knuckle/hub assembly off axle. Remove splash guard screws, and press hub out of knuckle. Use care not to distort splash guard.

Installation

To install knuckle, reverse removal procedure. Tighten bolts and nuts to specification. Use new spindle nut, and stake after tightening.

STRUT ASSEMBLY

Removal (Integra)

1) Raise front of vehicle and support with safety stands. Remove wheel assembly and brake hose clamp from strut. Use a floor jack to support lower control arm.

2) Remove strut assembly self-locking pinch bolt. Gradually lower floor jack and control arm. Remove self-locking nuts from top of strut. Compress strut and remove.

Removal (Legend)

Raise front of vehicle and support with safety stands. Remove wheel assembly and brake hose clamp from strut. Remove strut-to-fork self-locking pinch bolt and strut fork bolt. Remove strut fork assembly. Remove cap and nuts from top of strut. Remove strut assembly. *See Fig. 3.*

Fig. 3: Legend Strut Assembly

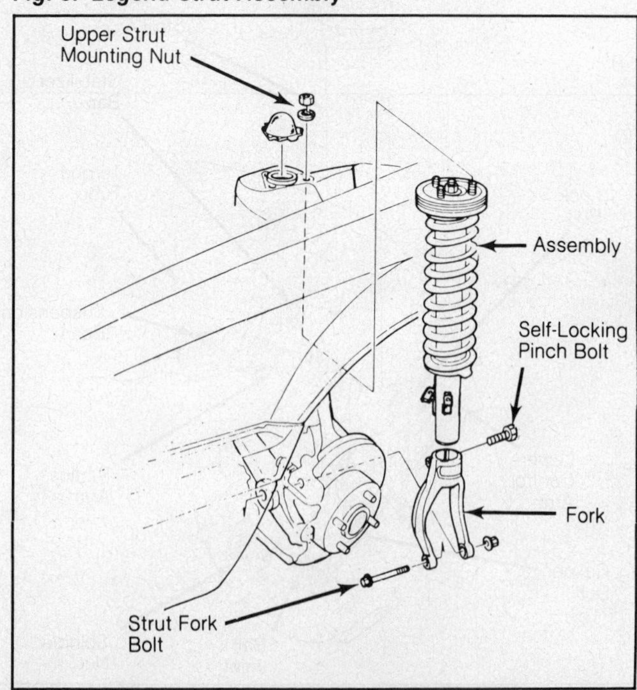

Courtesy of American Honda Motor Co., Inc.

Disassembly (All Models)

1) On Legend, use a spring compressor to compress strut assembly spring slightly to remove tension. Hold strut rod with an Allen wrench and remove spring seat nut. Slowly release spring compressor and lift spring off.

2) On Integra, hold strut rod with an Allen wrench and remove strut nut. On all models, disassemble strut assembly, noting relative position of assembled parts.

Reassembly (All Models)

1) Check spring tension, if used. Check parts for cracks, deterioration or damage. Check shock absorber for leaks and proper operation. Replace strut if when compressed, resistance is weak, uneven or jerky. Replace worn or damaged parts.

2) On Legend, position mounting base with one stud aligned with tab on strut housing. On all models, to complete reassembly, reverse disassembly procedure.

Installation (All Models)

1) On Integra, position strut assembly with tab on strut housing aligned with slot in steering knuckle. On Legend, install strut fork on lower control arm. Position strut assembly so that tab on strut housing aligns with slot in fork.

2) On all models, align upper strut studs with strut tower holes. Place jack under knuckle and raise until vehicle just lifts off safety stands. Install upper strut mount nuts. Tighten strut assembly while strut is under load. Reverse removal procedure to complete installation. Tighten nuts and bolts to specification.

LOWER CONTROL ARM

Removal (Integra)

1) Remove front fender splash shields. Remove engine lower cover. Remove torsion bar. See TORSION BAR in this article. Remove bolts and nuts securing lower control arm to radius arm. *See Fig. 4*.

2) Raise engine as necessary to gain access to lower arm. Remove power steering pump bracket and cruise control actuator (if equipped).

3) On left side of vehicle, remove alternator adapter bolt and push alternator against block. Raise engine and insert Engine Mount Spacer (07965-SB2070A) into left body mount bracket. This will raise oil pan clear of left lower arm.

4) On the right side of vehicles equipped with automatic transaxle, remove battery and battery tray. Remove transaxle mount. Raise transaxle and install Transaxle Support Bracket (07GAF-PH0010A).

5) Install Collets (07965-SB20200) into lower arm opening so they are directly opposite each other.

6) Slide Thrust Bearing (07965-SB2080A) onto Remover Shaft Bolt (07965-SB2050A) and slide bolt through Remover Shaft (07965-SB2010A). Slide assembled remover through suspension beam rear opening (torsion bar side).

7) Fit Receiver (07965-SB2030A) over bolt and lower arm. Install flat washer and nut. Hold nut stationary while turning bolt clockwise. This will pull lower arm and bushing from suspension beam.

Installation

1) Mark lower arm bushing so that it can be easily aligned with suspension beam notch and cast mark on control arm. Slide bolt and thrust washer used for installation through Pilot Assembly (07965-SB2060A), and slide through rear opening (torsion bar side) of suspension beam.

2) Slide lower arm onto bolt. Align index marks on beam and lower arm with mark on bushing.

3) Slide Installer (07965-2SB2040A), flat washer and nut onto bolt. Hold nut with wrench while turning bolt clockwise. When edge of bushing's steel outer sleeve is flush with beam end, bushing is installed to correct depth. To complete installation of remaining components, reverse removal procedure.

Fig. 4: Integra Lower Control Arm Replacement

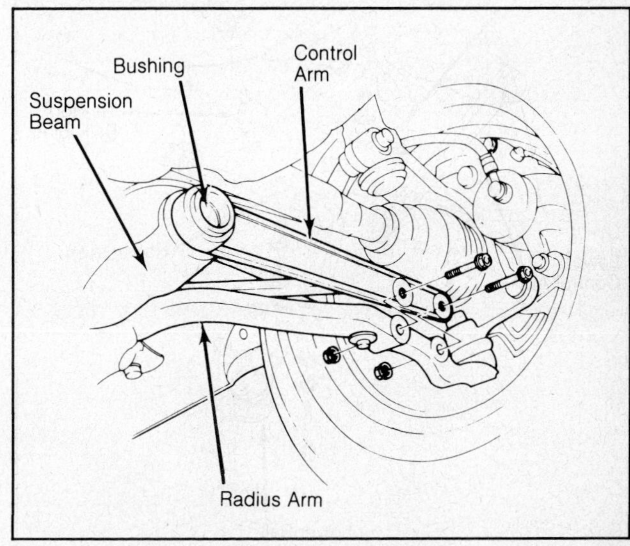

Courtesy of American Honda Motor Co., Inc.

Removal (Legend)

1) Raise front of vehicle and support with safety stands. Remove wheel assembly. Remove strut fork and strut rod (radius rod) bolts. Remove nut, bolt and bushings from stabilizer bar.

2) Remove cotter pin from lower control arm ball joint, and remove castle nut. Break loose lower control arm ball joint, and pull arm down until ball joint is clear of knuckle. Remove lower control arm pivot bolt, and remove control arm.

Installation

Check parts for deterioration or damage. Replace worn or damaged parts. Reverse removal procedure to install control arm.

RADIUS ARM

Removal (Integra Only)

1) Raise front of vehicle and support with safety stands. Remove wheel assembly. Remove self-locking nuts from radius arm. Remove self-locking nut from stabilizer bar. Remove stabilizer bolt and bushings. *See Fig. 4*.

CAUTION: Torsion bar tension on lower control arm may cause arm to suddenly swing away from steering knuckle as ball joint is being disconnected. Use a floor jack to support lower control arm.

2) Remove lower control arm-to-radius arm bolts. Remove cotter pin from radius arm ball joint, and remove castle nut. Break loose radius control arm ball

ACURA (Cont.)

joint. Use ball joint spreader if necessary. Pull radius arm down until ball joint is clear of knuckle. Remove radius arm by swinging it down, then pulling forward.

Fig. 5: Legend Lower Control Arm Assembly

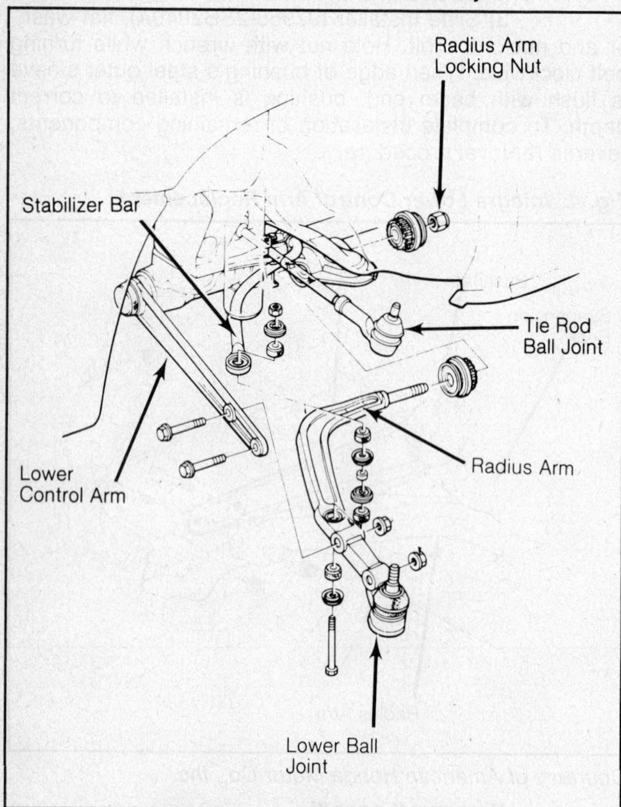

Courtesy of American Honda Motor Co., Inc.

Installation

Check parts for deterioration or damage. Replace worn or damaged parts. Reverse removal procedure to install radius arm.

UPPER CONTROL ARM

Inspection (Legend Only)

Raise front of vehicle and support with safety stands. Remove wheel assembly. Rock the upper ball joint front-to-back with a force of approximately 65 lbs. (30 kg). Replace upper arm bushings if there is any play.

Removal

1) Raise front of vehicle and support with safety stands. Remove wheel assembly. Remove cotter pin from upper ball joint, and remove castle nut.

2) Break loose upper control arm ball joint, and push arm up until ball joint is clear of knuckle. Remove anchor bolt nuts, and remove upper control arm.

Disassembly

Clamp upper control arm in vise by anchor bolts. Remove upper control arm bolt, anchor bolts and seals. Reposition upper control arm in vise, and remove upper arm collar and bushings.

Reassembly

Coat ends and insides of upper arm bushings with grease. Coat sealing lips of upper arm bushing seals with grease. Apply sealer to underside of upper control arm bolt head, threads and bolt nut. Reverse disassembly procedure, to complete reassembly.

Installation

Reverse removal procedure to install upper control arm. Check camber and adjust (if necessary).

STABILIZER BAR & SUSPENSION BEAM

Removal (Integra Only)

1) Raise front of vehicle and support with safety stands. Remove wheel assemblies. Support engine with hoist. Remove steering gearbox. Use a floor jack to support lower control arm.

2) Remove cotter pin from radius arm ball joint, and remove castle nut. Break loose radius control arm ball joint, and pull arm down until ball joint is clear of knuckle.

3) Remove torque tube holder. Remove exhaust pipe. Disconnect manual transmission shift rod and extension from transmission. Disconnect automatic transmission shift cable guide from floor and pull cable down by hand.

4) Remove engine mount bracket nuts. Use floor jacks to support suspension beam. Remove 6 suspension beam bolts and lower beam. Remove stabilizer bar bolts, brackets, and stabilizer bar. *See Fig. 6.*

Fig. 6: Integra Stabilizer Bar & Suspension Beam Removal

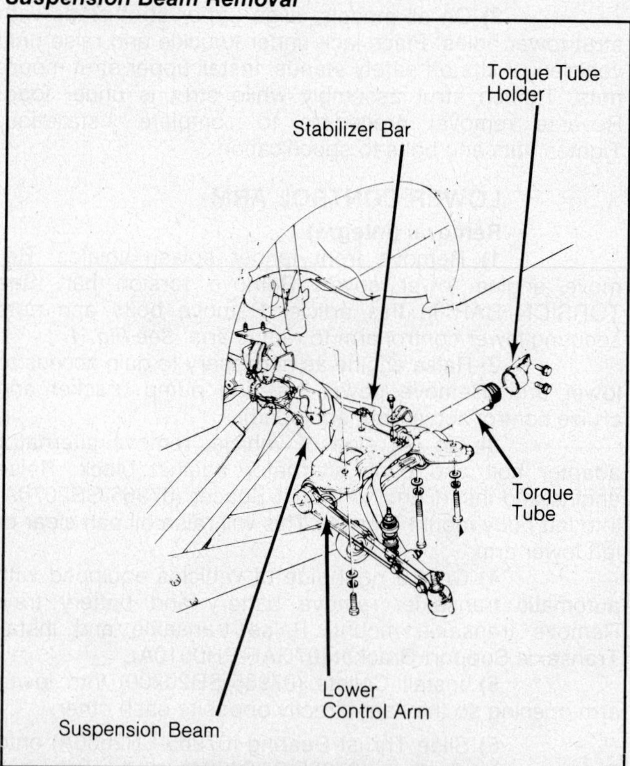

Courtesy of American Honda Motor Co., Inc.

Installation

1) If the suspension beam is being replaced, the lower bushing and sub-frame mounts must be replaced. Press new bushing into replacement beam using Bushing Driver (07965-SB40000) until outer edge of bushing is flush with end.

2) Install inner sub-frame mount with slit running parallel to torque tube. Install outer sub-frame mount with slit running parallel to suspension beam. Reuse rectangular mount, unless damaged. Reverse removal procedure to complete installation.

ACURA (Cont.)

TORSION BAR

Removal (Integra Only)

1) Raise front of vehicle and support with safety stands. Remove wheel assembly and height adjustment nut. Remove torsion bar front cap and snap ring. Remove torque tube holder, cap/bushing and rear snap ring. *See Fig. 7.*

2) Tap torsion bar forward, and remove front snap ring. Tap torsion bar backward while moving control arm up and down. Remove torsion bar and torque tube.

Fig. 7: Integra Torsion Bar Assembly

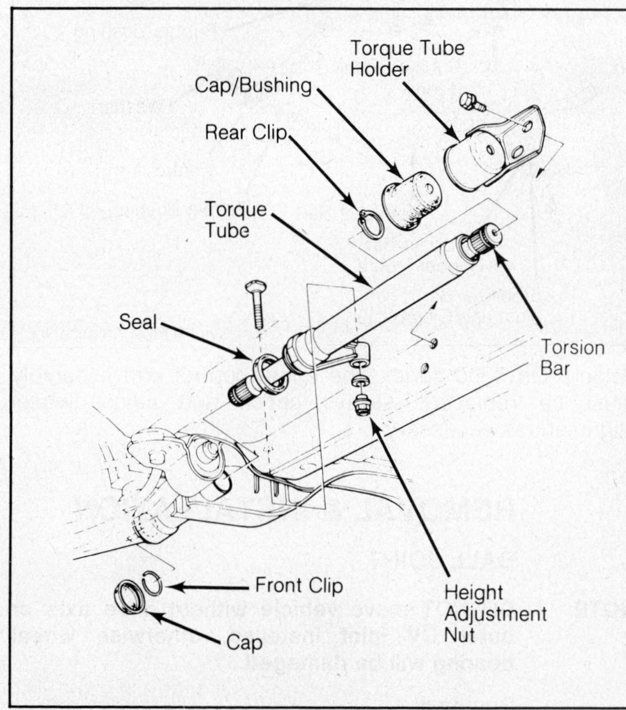

Courtesy of American Honda Motor Co., Inc.

NOTE: **Torsion bar ends are marked "L" for left and "R" for right.**

Installation

1) Inspect torsion bar for cracks or damage. Install new torque tube seal on torque tube. Coat torque tube seal and torque tube sliding surface with grease. Install on suspension beam.

2) Grease splines at each end of torsion bar, and install in torque tube from the back. Align projection on torque tube splines with cut-out in torsion bar splines.

3) Insert torsion bar about 3/8" while moving control arm up and down. Install front snap ring and cap. Install rear snap ring. Tap torsion bar forward until snap ring contacts torque tube.

4) Coat cap/bushing with grease and install on torque tube. Install torque tube holder. Coat height adjustment nut with grease and temporarily tighten. Set vehicle on ground and adjust ride height.

NOTE: **Replace self-locking nut and bolt, if nut easily threads past nylon locking inserts. Replace all self-locking nuts after removal.**

TIGHTENING SPECIFICATIONS

Application	Ft. Lbs. (N.m)
Integra	
Caliper Hold-Down Bolts	54 (75)
Caliper Pin Bolt	13 (18)
Lower Ball Joint-to-Knuckle	32 (44)
Radius Arm-to-Body Nut	60 (83)
Radius Arm-to-Control Arm	28 (39)
Spindle Nut	134 (185)
Stabilizer-to-Body	16 (22)
Stabilizer-to-Control Arm	16 (22)
Strut Assembly-to-Body (2 Nuts)	28 (39)
Strut Assembly-to-Steering Knuckle	47 (65)
Suspension Beam Bolts	54 (75)
Tie Rod End-to-Knuckle	32 (44)
Torque Tube Holder	16 (22)
Upper Strut Nut	32 (44)
Legend	
Caliper Hold-Down Bolt	56 (78)
Caliper Pin Bolt	24 (33)
Lower Ball Joint-to-Knuckle	72 (100)
Lower Control Arm Bolt	39 (55)
Spindle Nut	180 (250)
Stabilizer-to-Body	16 (22)
Stabilizer-to-Control Arm	16 (22)
Strut Assembly-to-Body (3 Nuts)	28 (39)
Strut Fork-to-Control Arm	47 (65)
Strut Rod-to-Body	32 (44)
Strut Rod-to-Control Arm	61 (85)
Tie Rod End-to-Knuckle	32 (44)
Upper Ball Joint-to-Knuckle	32 (44)
Upper Control Arm Nuts	53 (73)
Upper Fork-to-Strut Bolt	32 (44)
Upper Strut Nut	36 (50)

Front Suspension

AUDI

Coupe GT, 4000S, 4000CS Quattro, 5000S, 5000CS Turbo, 5000CS Quattro

DESCRIPTION

NOTE: The 5000S, 5000CS Turbo and 5000CS Quattro are grouped together and will be referred as the 5000 series in this article.

Front suspension is a MacPherson strut independent type suspension. The suspension consists of a strut assembly, control arm and stabilizer bar. The strut assembly attaches to inner fender panel at the top and wheel bearing housing at the bottom. *See Fig. 1.*

The 5000 series uses a control arm and ball joint combination connected to the frame by a single bushing and retaining bolt. Stabilizer bar is attached to both control arms and connected to subframe by 2 brackets. On all other models, the lower control arm is connected at the frame by 2 bushings and to the bearing housing by a replaceable ball joint. *See Fig. 2.*

Fig. 1: Exploded View of 4000 Series Front Suspension

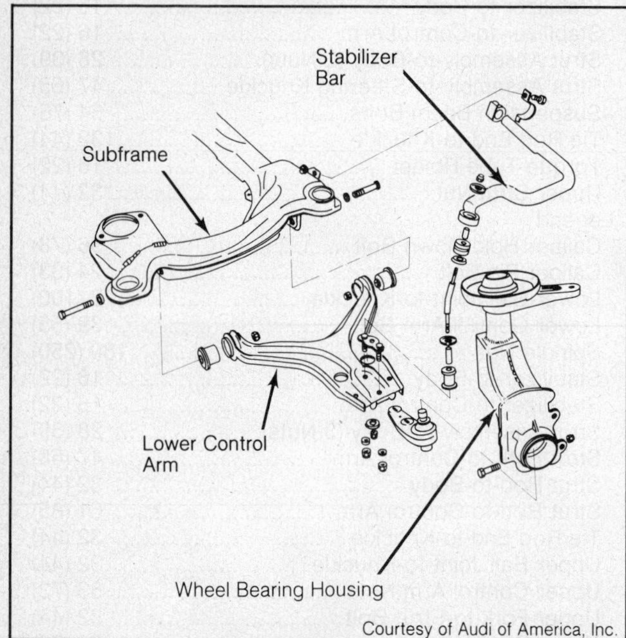

Fig. 2: Exploded View of 5000 Series Front Suspension

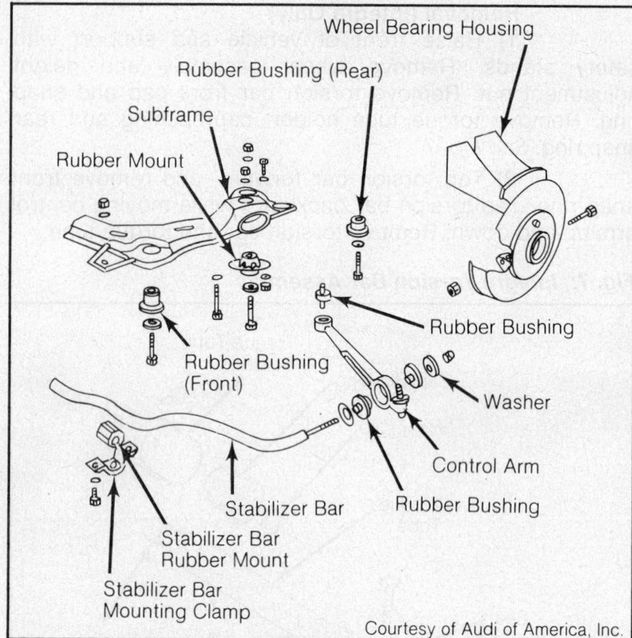

ADJUSTMENTS & INSPECTION

WHEEL ALIGNMENT SPECIFICATIONS & PROCEDURES

See WHEEL ALIGNMENT SPECIFICATIONS & PROCEDURES in WHEEL ALIGNMENT section.

WHEEL BEARING

No adjustment is required.

BALL JOINT CHECKING

Inspect ball joints for damaged rubber boots and ball joint play. Procedure and wear tolerance not available from manufacturer. When replacing ball joints on all models except 5000 series, mark the mounting position of ball joint prior to removing to avoid changing camber setting. On 5000 series, the entire control arm assembly must be replaced. Always check and adjust wheel alignment as necessary.

REMOVAL & INSTALLATION

BALL JOINT

NOTE: DO NOT move vehicle without drive axle or outer CV joint installed, otherwise wheel bearing will be damaged.

Removal

1) To remove ball joint, mark the mounting position of exisiting ball joint. Remove retaining bolt from bearing housing. Remove stabilizer bar link from control arm. Lower control arm enough for ball joint to clear bearing housing.

2) On 4000S and 4000CS Quattro models, remove 2 ball joint-to-control arm retaining bolts and remove ball joint.

3) On 5000 series, remove stabilizer bar. Remove bolt retaining control arm to frame and remove control arm. Control arm/ball joint assembly must be replaced as a unit.

Installation

To install, align ball joint bolt holes in wheel bearing housing. Drive ball joint into wheel bearing housing using Installer (VW415a). To complete installation, reverse removal procedure. Tighten all bolts and nuts to specifications. See TIGHTENING SPECIFICATIONS table in this article. Check and adjust wheel alignment as necessary.

STRUT CARTRIDGE

Removal (5000 Series Only)

1) With vehicle resting on floor at full curb weight, remove cartridge attaching nut. Punch mark mounting position and remove 3 spring strut mounting (camber adjustment) nuts and remove plate. *See Fig. 4.*

AUDI (Cont.)

2) Turn steering to center cartridge piston rod in upper spring retainer. Install a holding fixture, such as piece of wood to maintain clearance. Working through side and top of coil spring, remove washer, bump stop and boot. Install Threaded Cap Remover (2069) over cartridge shaft and remove cap. Pull cartridge through hole in strut tower.

Installation

To install, reverse removal procedure. Check and adjust wheel alignment as necessary.

STRUT ASSEMBLY

NOTE: During any removal and installation procedure, if axle nut is removed or installed, do so with vehicle resting on floor at full curb weight. Always replace axle shaft self-locking nut when removed.

Removal

1) Loosen axle nut. Raise and support vehicle. Remove wheel assembly. Without detaching brake hose or line, unbolt caliper, remove brake hose bracket and suspend caliper out of way. Remove brake rotor.

2) On 5000 series, install Spring Compressor (2070/1). Mount spring compressor retaining plate, tighten spindle and spindle nut until seated.

3) Remove stabilizer bar. Disconnect ball joint from steering knuckle. Press off tie rod end. Using puller attached to hub studs, press stub axle from hub.

4) While supporting strut assembly at bottom remove attaching nut(s) at strut tower. Remove strut assembly. *See Fig. 3.*

Fig. 3: Exploded View of 4000S Strut Assembly

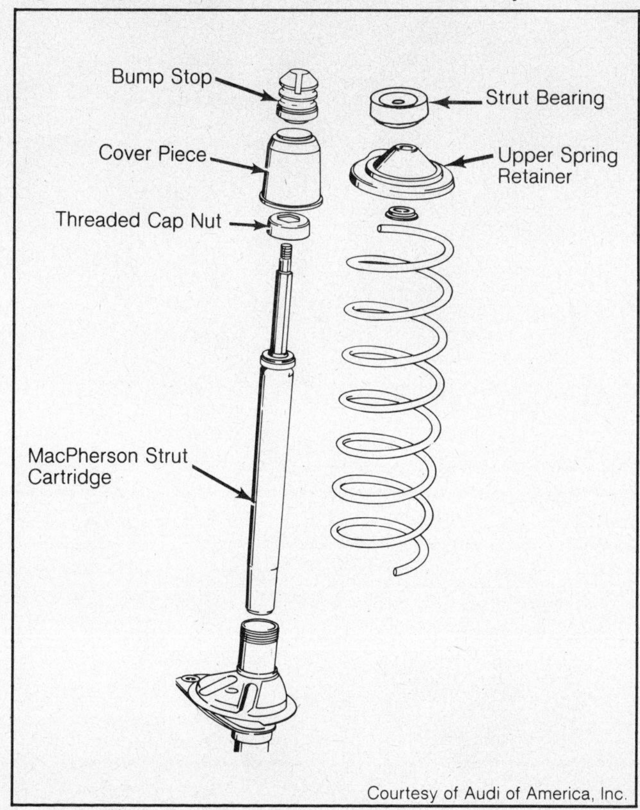

Fig. 4: Exploded View of 5000 Series Strut Assembly

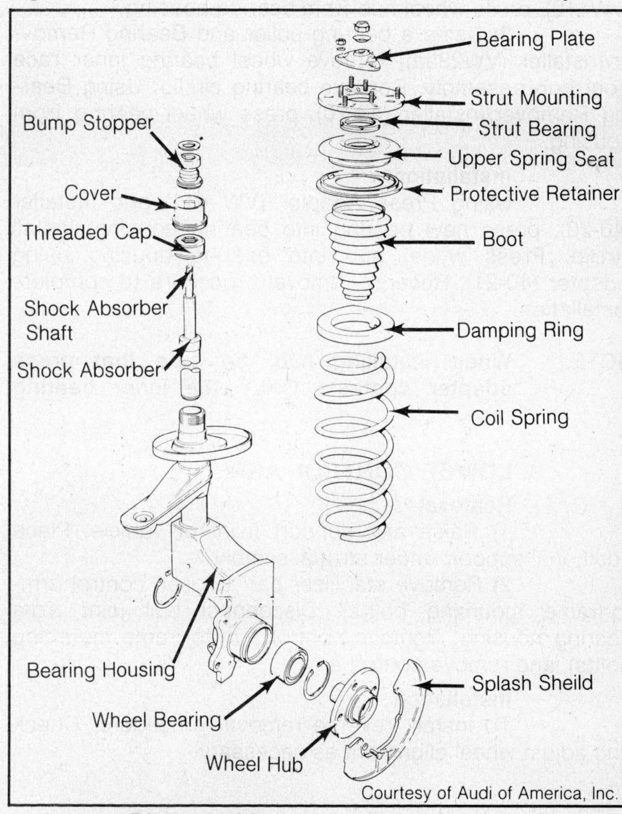

Disassembly

1) On Coupe GT, 4000S and 4000CS Quattro, place strut assembly on bench, attach spring compressor to coil spring, and compress enough to remove upper piston rod retaining nut. Remove strut bearing and upper spring seat.

2) On 5000 series, mark position of strut mounting plate in relationship to bearing plate. Place strut assembly on bench and remove spring compressor.

3) Slowly release tension from coil spring and remove spring. With Cap Remover (2069), remove threaded cap from top of strut cartridge. Remove strut cartridge.

Reassembly & Installation

1) To reassemble and install, reverse disassembly and removal procedure. On 5000 series, be sure damping ring locating tabs are mated with indentations on upper spring retainers. If suspension height of right and left sides are unequal, replacement damping ring thicknesses are available to compensate for height difference.

2) Drive axle splines must be free of oil, grease and old locking compound. Apply a narrow ring of locking compound around outer end of axle shaft splines, and allow one hour to dry before driving. Tighten drive axle nut to specification with vehicle resting on floor. Check and adjust alignment as required.

WHEEL BEARINGS

NOTE: Wheel bearing is damaged when removed: bearing MUST be replaced.

Removal

1) Remove strut assembly from vehicle. See STRUT ASSEMBLY in this article. Using Bearing Remov-

AUDI (Cont.)

er/Installer (VW 295a), Adapter (VW420) and Adapter (VW412), press wheel hub from bearing housing.

2) Using a bearing puller and Bearing Remover/Installer (VW295a), remove wheel bearing inner race from hub assembly. Remove bearing circlip. Using Bearing Remover/Installer (40-20), press wheel bearing from housing.

Installation

Using Press Adapter (VW 411) and Installer (40-20), press new bearing into bearing housing. Install circlip. Press wheel hub into bearing housing using Adapter (40-21). Reverse removal procedure to complete installation.

NOTE: When installing hub, be sure that press adapter contacts ONLY the inner bearing race.

LOWER CONTROL ARM

Removal

1) Raise and support front of vehicle. Place additional support under strut assembly.

2) Remove stabilizer bar. Loosen control arm-to-frame mounting bolt(s). Disconnect ball joint from bearing housing. Remove control arm-to-frame mounting bolt(s), and remove control arm.

Installation

To install, reverse removal procedure. Check and adjust wheel alignment as necessary.

TIGHTENING SPECIFICATIONS

Application	Ft. Lbs. (N.m)
Axle Nut [1]	
4000S & 4000CS Quattro	167 (226)
5000 Series	207 (280)
Ball Joint Bracket Nuts [1]	47 (64)
Ball Joint-to-Strut Nut [1]	
Coupe GT, 4000S & 4000CS Quattro	47 (64)
5000 Series	47 (64)
Control Arm-to-Subframe Bolts	
Coupe GT, 4000S & 4000CS Quattro	43 (58)
5000 Series	48 (65)
Suspension Strut Threaded Cap	
Coupe GT, 4000S & 4000CS Quattro	108 (146)
5000 Series	133 (180)
Strut Cartridge Shaft Nut [1]	43 (60)
Stabilizer Bar Bracket Bolts	
Coupe GT, 4000S & 4000CS Quattro	26 (35)
5000 Series Nuts	77 (105)
Stabilizer Bar-to-Control Arm	
5000 Series	81 (110)
Strut Upper Retaining Nuts	
5000 Series	22 (30)
Wheel Lug Bolts	80 (110)

[1] – Always replace nut when removed.

Front Suspension

BMW

325 Series, 528e, 535 Series
635 Series, 735 Series

DESCRIPTION

All BMW models use MacPherson strut front suspension systems. The front suspension systems consist of vertically mounted strut assemblies directly attached to steering knuckles. The steering knuckles are connected to the axle carriers (crossmembers) through lower control arms.

A stabilizer bar is used on all models. The stabilizer bar is attached to the strut assembly on 528e, 535 Series and 635 Series. The stabilizer bar is connected to the lower control arm on 325 Series and 735 Series. Strut rods are installed on all models except the 325 Series.

Fig. 1: BMW 325 Series Front Suspension Assembly

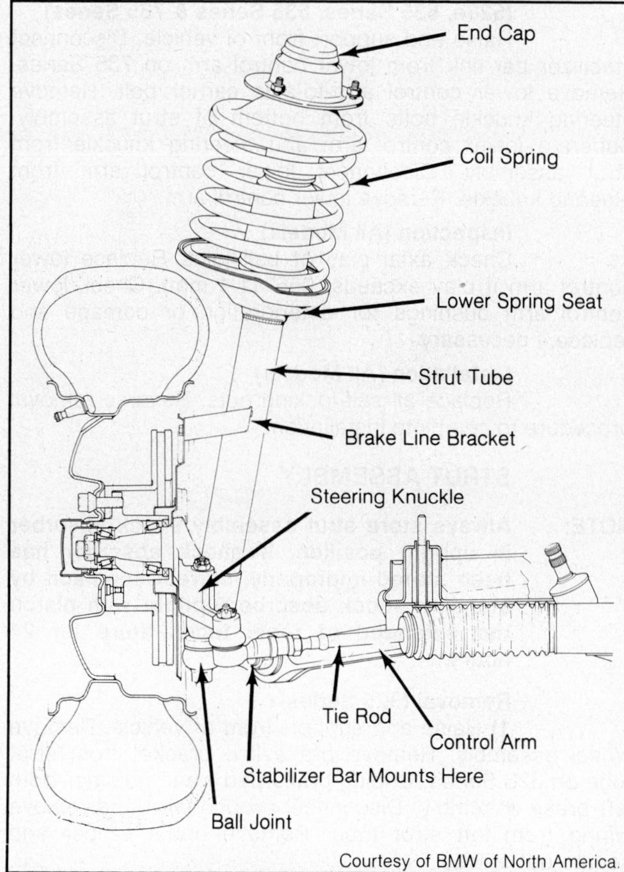

Courtesy of BMW of North America.

ADJUSTMENTS & INSPECTION

WHEEL ALIGNMENT SPECIFICATIONS & PROCEDURES

See WHEEL ALIGNMENT SPECIFICATIONS & PROCEDURES in WHEEL ALIGNMENT section.

WHEEL BEARING

735 Series

Tighten castle nut to 22-24 ft. lbs. (30-33 N.m) while rotating hub assembly. Rotate hub assembly at least 2 more times. Loosen castle nut until bearing end play is noticed. Tighten castle nut to a maximum of 24 INCH lbs. (3 N.m). If necessary, turn back (loosen) castle nut to allow cotter pin installation. Washer located between castle nut and bearing should move freely and without noticeable resistance.

BALL JOINT CHECKING

Check axial play of ball joint. Replace lower control arm if play exceeds .055" (1.4 mm).

REMOVAL & INSTALLATION

WHEEL BEARING

Removal

(325 Series, 528e, 535 Series & 635 Series)

1) Raise and support front of vehicle. Remove wheel assembly. If left brake caliper is to be removed, unplug brake pad wear indicator. Remove disc brake caliper and secure out of way. Remove hex head screw from rotor. Remove brake rotor and hub cap.

2) Unlock collar nut using a chisel and remove nut. Remove washer on 528e, 535 Series and 635 Series. Pull off hub/wheel bearing assembly. On 325 Series, if bearing inner race remains on stub axle, bend back dust guard and pull off bearing inner race.

Installation

Install new dust guard. Press hub/wheel bearing assembly on axle. Install washer on 528e, 535 Series and 635 Series. Install collar nut and lock into place. See TIGHTENING SPECIFICATIONS table in this article. Reverse removal procedure to complete installation.

Removal (735 Series)

1) Raise and support front of vehicle. Remove wheel assembly. Unplug brake pad wear indicator if left side caliper is to be removed. Disconnect brake line bracket from strut assembly. Remove disc brake caliper and secure out of way.

2) Remove hub cap, cotter pin, castle nut, washer and outer bearing. Remove hub and rotor assembly. Remove shaft seal and inner bearing. Remove bearing outer races if needed.

Installation

Press bearing outer races into hub. Pack wheel bearings. Coat hub cavity and bearing outer races with grease and install inner bearing. Coat shaft seal with grease and press in until flush. Reverse removal procedure to complete installation and adjust wheel bearings. See WHEEL BEARING ADJUSTMENT in this article.

FRONT SUSPENSION ASSEMBLY

CAUTION: Do not allow strut assemblies to tilt, sag or drop during front suspension assembly or removal, as ball joint sockets may be damaged.

Removal (325 Series)

1) Raise and support front of vehicle. Remove wheel assemblies. Disconnect ground wire and brake pad wear indicator from left brake assembly. Remove wiring from left strut tube on 325 Series. Remove brake calipers and secure out of way.

2) Remove steering gear shaft pinch bolt and disconnect steering shaft. On 325 Series, disconnect power steering lines from steering gear box and plug openings. Remove lower control arm bracket bolts. Remove heat shield from right lower control arm bracket.

3) Disconnect engine damper from axle carrier. Remove engine mount-to-axle carrier nuts. Loosen top of right engine mount on 325 Series. Attach engine sling and suspend engine with hoist. Support axle carrier with a floor jack. Remove nuts from top of strut assemblies. Remove axle carrier bolts and carefully lower front suspension assembly.

Fig. 2: BMW 528e, 535 Series & 635 Series Front Suspension

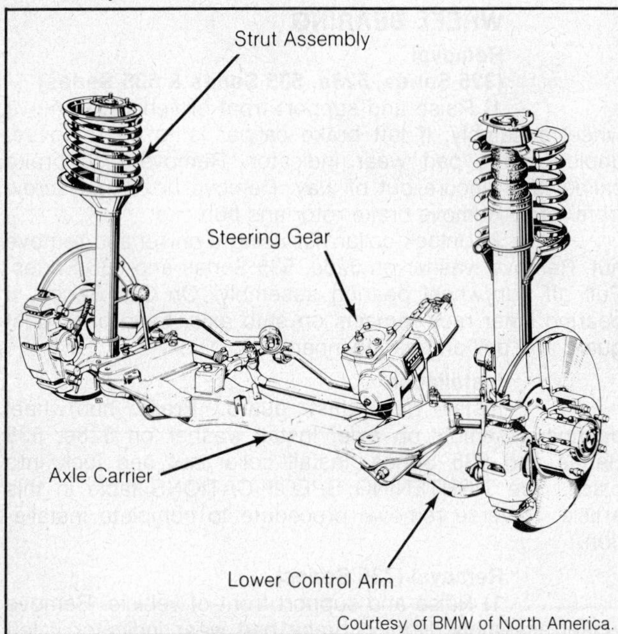

Courtesy of BMW of North America.

Removal
(528e, 535 Series, 635 Series & 735 Series)

1) Raise and support front of vehicle. Remove wheel assemblies. Remove engine splash guard on 528e, 535 Series and 635 Series. Remove brake line bracket and clamp from strut assemblies on 735 Series. Disconnect ground wire and brake pad wear indicator from left brake assembly on 735 Series. Remove brake calipers and secure out of way.

2) Disconnect ground wire and brake pad wear indicator from left brake assembly on 528e, 535 Series and 635 Series. Remove wiring from left strut tube on 528e, 535 Series and 635 Series. Disconnect steering linkage from steering gear arm. Remove steering gear mount bolts and hang steering gear.

3) Disconnect strut rods and remove stabilizer bar brackets on 528e, 535 Series and 635 Series. Remove engine mount-to-axle carrier nuts. Loosen top of right engine mount on 528e, 535 Series and 635 Series. Partially drain radiator and disconnect top radiator hose from engine on 635 Series and 735 Series.

4) Attach engine sling and suspend engine with hoist. Support axle carrier using floor jack. Remove nuts from top of strut assemblies. Remove axle carrier bolts and carefully lower front suspension assembly.

Installation (All Models)

1) Replace all self-locking nuts. Engine mount pin must engage in hole properly. Position wheels straight ahead on 325 Series. Alignment marks on steering gear housing and steering gear shaft must be aligned on 325 Series.

2) Pinch bolt must fit in groove of steering gear shaft on 325 Series. Check stabilizer bar and engine motor mounts for deterioration or damage. Bleed cooling system on 635 Series and 735 Series. Bleed power steering pump on 325 Series. Reverse removal procedure to complete installation. Check for proper wheel alignment.

LOWER CONTROL ARM

Removal (325 Series)

Raise and support front of vehicle. Remove lower control arm bracket bolts. Disconnect stabilizer bar link from stabilizer bar. Remove lower control arm ball joint nut and knock ball joint loose with a plastic hammer. Disconnect lower control arm from steering knuckle. Remove lower control arm.

Removal
(528e, 535 Series, 635 Series & 735 Series)

Raise and support front of vehicle. Disconnect stabilizer bar link from lower control arm on 735 Series. Remove lower control arm-to-axle carrier bolt. Remove steering knuckle bolts from bottom of strut assembly. Separate lower control arm and steering knuckle from strut assembly. Disconnect lower control arm from steering knuckle. Remove lower control arm.

Inspection (All Models)

Check axial play of ball joint. Replace lower control arm if play exceeds .055" (1.4 mm). Check lower control arm bushings for deterioration or damage and replace if necessary.

Installation (All Models)

Replace all self-locking nuts. Reverse removal procedure to complete installation.

STRUT ASSEMBLY

NOTE: **Always store strut assembly shock absorber in upright position. If shock absorber has been stored improperly, correct condition by standing shock absorber upright with piston rod extended at room temperature for 24 hours.**

Removal (325 Series)

1) Raise and support front of vehicle. Remove wheel assembly. Remove brake line bracket from strut tube on 325 Series. Unplug brake pad wear indicator from left brake assembly. Disconnect ground wire and remove wiring from left strut tube. Remove brake caliper and secure out of way.

2) Disconnect stabilizer bar link from stabilizer bar on 325 Series. Disconnect lower control arm and steering linkage from steering knuckle. Remove lower control arm-to-axle carrier bolt on 325 Series. Support strut assembly. Remove nuts from top of strut assembly and remove strut.

Removal
(528e, 535 Series, 635 Series & 735 Series)

1) Raise and support front of vehicle. Remove wheel assembly. Remove brake line bracket and clamp from strut tube on 735 Series. Unplug brake pad wear indicator from left brake assembly. Disconnect ground wire and remove wiring from left strut tube on 528e, 535 Series and 635 Series. Remove brake caliper and secure out of way.

BMW (Cont.)

2) Disconnect stabilizer bar link from strut tube on 528e, 535 Series and 635 Series. Disconnect stabilizer bar link from lower control arm on 735 Series. Remove steering knuckle bolts from bottom of strut assembly. Support strut assembly. Remove nuts from top of strut assembly and remove strut.

Disassembly (All Models)

1) Compress coil spring. Remove end cap, spring retainer nut and small diameter washer. Slowly release spring compressor and remove centering plate, insulator, large diameter washer, upper spring retainer, rubber ring and coil spring.

2) Remove damper washer, rubber damper and dust sleeve from shock absorber piston rod. Remove threaded ring using Ring Remover (31 3 150). Slide out shock absorber. Discard used oil.

Reassembly (All Models)

1) Replace shock absorber with same code as original, if shock absorber is to be replaced. Fill strut tube with SAE 30 oil. See SHOCK ABSORBER OIL QUANTITY table in this article.

2) Fit shock absorber into tube and tighten threaded ring. Use a rubber ring with 2 beads for coil springs with Red color code. Ends of coil spring must rest on shoulders of lower and upper spring retainers. Reverse disassembly procedure to complete reassembly.

Installation (All Models)

Replace all self-locking nuts. Reverse removal procedure to complete installation.

SHOCK ABSORBER OIL QUANTITY

Application	Oz. (cc)
325 Series	0.7-0.9 (20-25)
528e, 535 Series, 635 Series	1-1.2 (30-35)
735 Series	1.7 (50)

STABILIZER BAR

Removal (325 Series)

Raise and support front of vehicle. Disconnect stabilizer bar links and remove lower left control arm bracket bolts. Disconnect stabilizer bar from lower control arm and remove lower left control arm-to-axle carrier bolt. Remove stabilizer bar brackets and remove stabilizer bar.

Removal
(528e, 535 Series, 635 Series & 735 Series)

Raise and support front of vehicle. Disconnect stabilizer bar from stabilizer bar links on 528e, 535 Series and 635 Series. Disconnect stabilizer bar links from lower control arm on 735 Series. Remove stabilizer bar brackets and remove stabilizer bar.

Installation (All Models)

Inspect bushings for deterioration or damage and replace if necessary. Reverse removal procedure to complete installation.

STRUT ROD

Removal
(528e, 535 Series, 635 Series & 735 Series)

Raise and support front of vehicle. Remove front wheel assembly. Remove steering knuckle bolts from bottom of strut assembly. Disconnect strut rod from steering knuckle. Remove strut rod pivot bolt and remove strut rod.

Installation

Remove grease and dirt from ball joint bore. Reverse removal procedure to complete installation.

TIGHTENING SPECIFICATIONS

Application	Ft. Lbs. (N.m)
Axle Carrier-to-Body	
All Except 735 Series	31-35 (43-48)
735 Series	53-59 (73-81)
Ball Joint-to-Front Axle Carrier	
325 Series	55-69 (75-94)
Control Arm-to-Front Axle Carrier	
528e & 635 Series	52-63 (72-87)
735 Series	58-65 (80-90)
Control Arm-to-Spring Nut	
325 Series	43-51 (60-70)
Connecting Tube-to-Thrust Strut Mount	
528e & 635 Series	39-48 (54-66)
Shock Absorber Strut Threaded Ring	
All Models	87-101 (120-140)
Shock Absorber Strut-to-Mount	
All Models Except 735i	43-53 (60-73)
735 Series	56-62 (78-86)
Spring Strut Mount-to-Wheel House	
All Models	16-17 (22-24)
Strut-to-Body	
528e & 635 Series	87-103 (120-143)
Strut-to-Front Axle Carrier	
735 Series	94-105 (130-145)
Strut-to-Tie Rod Arm	
528e & 635 Series	55-69 (75-94)
Strut-to-Tie Rod Arm	
735 Series	58-65 (80-90)
Wheel Hub Shaft Nut	
325 Series	188-231 (260-320)
528e & 635 Series	166-203 (230-280)

Front Suspension

CHRYSLER MOTORS CONQUEST & MITSUBISHI STARION

DESCRIPTION

Front suspension is a MacPherson strut-type. Strut assembly and steering knuckle are integrated. Strut upper end is attached to insulator bracket in front fender wheel housing. Strut lower end is attached to steering knuckle arm, which is attached to ball joint. Ball joint is bolted to lower control arm.

ADJUSTMENTS & INSPECTION

WHEEL ALIGNMENT SPECIFICATIONS & PROCEDURES

See WHEEL ALIGNMENT SPECIFICATIONS & PROCEDURES in WHEEL ALIGNMENT section.

WHEEL BEARING

Raise front of vehicle and support. While spinning hub and rotor by hand, tighten spindle nut to 14 ft. lbs. (20 N.m) to seat bearings. Back off nut and retighten to 48 INCH lbs. (5 N.m). Install nut retainer, cotter pin and dust cap. DO NOT back off nut more than 15 degrees to accommodate cotter pin. If holes cannot be aligned within 15 degrees, repeat procedure.

Fig. 1: View of Front Suspension for Conquest & Starion

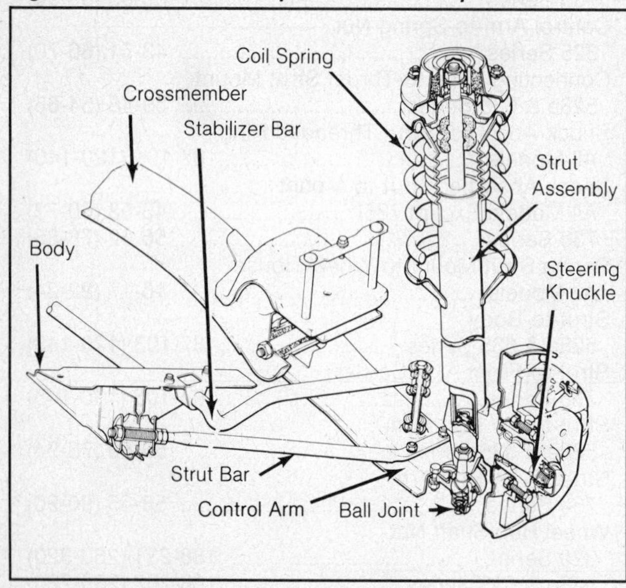

Courtesy of Chrysler Motors.

REMOVAL & INSTALLATION

WHEEL BEARINGS

Removal

1) Raise and support vehicle. Remove front wheel assembly. Remove brake caliper assembly and support out of way with wire.

2) Remove dust cap, cotter pin, nut retainer, nut and outer bearing. Remove hub and rotor assembly. Pry out inner grease seal and discard.

3) Remove inner bearing. If necessary, drive out bearing races, from inside-to-outside, by tapping uniformly around inside diameter of race lip with long drift punch.

Installation

1) To install, reverse removal procedure. For Conquest, install new bearing races by tapping into place using Bearing Driver (C-3717 for outer race and C-4171 with Handle L-4446 for inner race).

2) For Starion, use Bearing Driver (MB990927-01 for outer race and MB990931-01 for inner race with Handle MB990938-01). Ensure race is fully seated in hub.

3) Always replace inner grease seal. Apply grease to seal lip and bearing races. Pack wheel bearings with grease. Adjust according to WHEEL BEARING ADJUSTMENT procedures.

BALL JOINT

Removal

1) Remove front wheel assembly. Remove caliper support, with caliper assembly and brake hose, from disc brake adapter. Support components out of way with wire hook.

2) If necessary, disconnect stabilizer bar and strut rod from lower control arm. Disconnect tie rod end from steering knuckle arm using Puller (MB990635 for Conquest and Puller MB990778-01 for Starion). Remove bolts attaching strut-to-steering knuckle arm. Tap bolts with plastic hammer to disconnect.

3) Remove bolts attaching ball joint-to-control arm. Remove ball joint and steering knuckle arm from vehicle. Remove self-locking nut. Using Puller (MB990635 for Conquest and MB990241-01 for Starion), remove ball joint from knuckle arm.

Inspection

Check the bushings for wear or deterioration. Check the lower control arm for bend or if it is broken. Check ball joint dust cover for cracks. Check ball joint starting torque. Starting torque should be 43-69 INCH lbs. (4.8-7.8 N.m). If it exceeds upper limit, replace ball joint. Replace all deteriorated or damaged parts.

Installation

1) When installing ball joint, always use new dust cover and self-locking nut. To install, reverse removal procedure. Install stabilizer bar and strut rods.

2) Ensure strut rods are straight and identification marks are in proper positions. Left side has "L" or White mark and right side has "R" or no mark. After installation, check front end alignment.

STRUT ASSEMBLY

Removal

1) Raise and support vehicle. Remove wheel assembly. Disconnect and remove brake hose at strut and wheel house brackets. Remove caliper support, front hub with brake disc, dust cover and disc brake adapter.

2) Disconnect strut assembly from wheel house strut assembly mount bracket and steering knuckle arm. Remove strut assembly from vehicle.

Disassembly

1) Mount assembly in vise. Compress coil spring using Spring Compressor (MB990987 for Starion and L-4514 for Conquest). After removing dust cap, hold spring upper seat with Spanner Wrench (MB990899-01). Remove strut rod top nut and strut insulator. Remove spring upper seat, rubber bumper, dust cover and coil spring.

Front Suspension

CHRYSLER MOTORS CONQUEST & MITSUBISHI STARION (Cont.)

NOTE: Some strut assemblies are filled with nitrogen gas. Do not disassemble them unless necessary for replacement.

2) Before disassembly of gas type strut tube, remove dirt from outside of strut. Hold strut vertically. Drill .16" (4 mm) or less diameter hole, 2-2.4" (50-60 mm) down from top of strut to bleed nitrogen gas from housing. With Spanner Wrench (MB990899-01), remove ring nut. Remove shock absorber assembly from strut.

Fig. 2: Exploded View of Conquest & Starion Strut Assembly

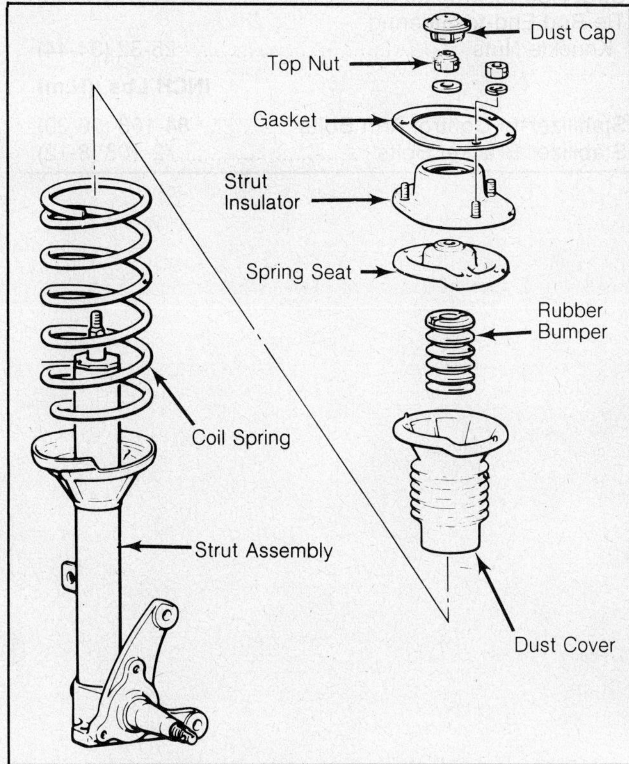

Courtesy of Chrysler Motors.

Inspection

1) Check strut insulator bearing for wear, damage or looseness. The bearing is integral with strut insulator. If defective, replace strut insulator as an assembly.

2) Check rubber components and coil spring for damage or deterioration. Inspect strut for cracks, damage, oil leakage, bent piston rod assembly and unusual noise. Minimum outer diameter of piston rod is .8642" (21.950 mm). Replace components as necessary.

Reassembly

1) Install new gas type shock absorber cartridge into strut and tighten ring nut with spanner wrench. Attach label, furnished with shock absorber, over drilled hole to prevent water entry.

NOTE: Coil springs have color marks to indicate spring identification and load classification. Ensure when springs are replaced, markings are for appropriate vehicle.

2) Install coil spring. Extend piston rod assembly and install strut components. Ensure rubber bumper is attached to spring upper seat with adhesive before installing. Align "D" shaped hole in center of spring upper seat with machined flat on piston rod shaft.

3) Align locating holes or grooves in upper and lower seats with spring locating pins. Hold seat and install insulator by attaching new self-locking nut. Remove spring compressor. Pack strut insulator bearing with grease and install dust cap.

Installation

1) Apply sealer to flanged mating surfaces of strut assembly and knuckle arm before mounting. To install, reverse removal procedure.

2) Ensure strut assembly is installed with strut insulator guide pin located in hole in strut assembly mount bracket. Tighten new top mount nuts to specification. After installation, check front end alignment.

LOWER CONTROL ARM

Removal

1) Raise and support vehicle. Remove wheel assembly. Disconnect stabilizer bar and strut rod from control arm. Using Puller (MB990635 for Conquest and Puller MB990778-01 for Starion), disconnect tie rod end from knuckle arm. Remove strut assembly from knuckle arm.

2) Remove control arm-to-crossmember bolt and remove control arm from vehicle. Remove knuckle arm from ball joint using Puller (MB990635 for Conquest and MB990241-01 for Starion).

NOTE: DO NOT remove control arm bushings unless necessary.

3) To remove lower control arm bushing, install control arm assembly on hydraulic press. Using Remover/Installer (MB990828, MB990868 and MB990799), press bushing out of control arm.

Installation

1) Press in new bushing until it contacts end surface of control arm. Install knuckle arm. Install lower control arm. Apply sealer to flange mating surfaces of strut assembly and steering knuckle arm. Install strut assembly, stabilizer bar, strut rod and remaining components.

2) Tighten control arm shaft, stabilizer bar nuts and strut rod with vehicle resting on the ground. Ensure stabilizer bar mount bolt end-to-lock nut surface distance is correct. See STABILIZER BAR & STRUT ROD in this article. After installation, check front end alignment.

STABILIZER BAR & STRUT ROD

Removal

1) Raise and support vehicle. Disconnect each end of stabilizer bar from control arms. Remove stabilizer brackets from body and bar from vehicle. Remove strut rod nut, outer end washer, collar and outer bushing from body bracket.

NOTE: Inner and outer strut rod bushings are different. Note bushing shape and location for reassembly reference. Always use new bushings and self-locking nuts.

2) Detach strut rod mount bolt from control arm and remove rod with inner bushing and end washer. Check for bent or damaged stabilizer bar and/or strut rod. Strut rod bend limit is .010" (.25 mm) or less. Check all bushings for wear and deterioration. Replace damaged parts as necessary.

Front Suspension

CHRYSLER MOTORS CONQUEST & MITSUBISHI STARION (Cont.)

Installation

1) To install, reverse removal procedure. Check strut rod identification marks before installation. Left rod mark is "L" or White mark. Right rod mark is "R" or no mark. Final tighten strut rod and stabilizer bar nuts with vehicle resting on the ground.

2) Ensure strut rod and stabilizer bar mount bolt end-to-lock nut distance is correct. Distance between stabilizer bar mount bolt end and nut is .59-.67" (15-17 mm).

3) On intercooled models, distance between strut rod end and front face of lock nut is 3.2" (81 mm). On all other models, distance should be 3.3" (83.5 mm). After installation, check front end alignment.

CROSSMEMBER

Removal

Raise and support vehicle. Remove strut rods, stabilizer bar, steering linkage and lower arms. Secure engine with engine hoist. Disconnect the engine mounts. Raise the engine slightly and remove 4 nuts, then remove crossmember.

Inspection

Check crossmember for cracks or damage. Replace crossmember if cracked or damaged.

Installation

To install, reverse removal procedure.

TIGHTENING SPECIFICATIONS

Application	Ft. Lbs. (N.m)
Ball Joint-to-Steering Knuckle Nuts	43-52 (59-70)
Control Arm-to-Crossmember Bolts	58-69 (78-94)
Control Arm-to-Ball Joint Bolts	43-52 (59-70)
Crossmember-to-Body Nuts	43-58 (59-78)
Hub-to-Rotor Bolts	25-29 (34-39)
Strut Assembly Top Nut	43-51 (59-70)
Strut Insulator-to-Body Nuts	18-25 (25-34)
Strut-to-Steering Knuckle Bolts	58-72 (78-98)
Strut Rod-to-Control Arm Bolts	43-51 (59-70)
Strut Rod-to-Bracket Bolts	54-61 (74-83)
Tie Rod End-to-Steering Knuckle Nuts	25-32 (34-44)
	INCH Lbs. (N.m)
Stabilizer-to-Control Arm Bolts	84-168 (10-20)
Stabilizer Bracket Bolts	72-108 (8-12)

Front Suspension

CHRYSLER MOTORS RAM-50 & MITSUBISHI PICKUP 2WD

DESCRIPTION

Wishbone independent front suspension with coil springs mounted between lower control arms and crossmember is used. Strut rods and stabilizer bar are mounted to lower control arms and to brackets on frame.

Fig. 1: View of 2WD Front Suspension

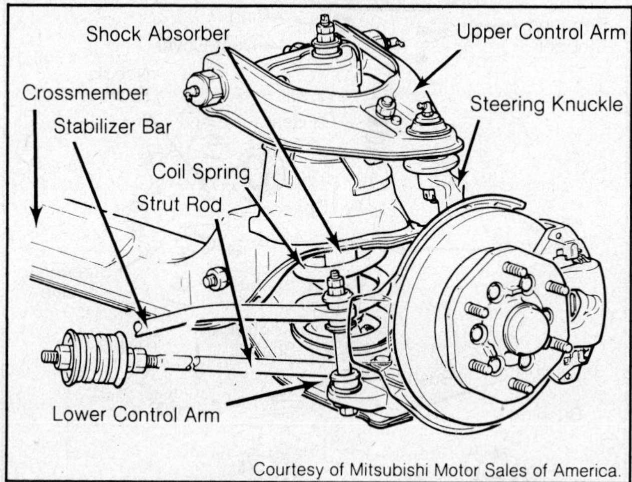

Courtesy of Mitsubishi Motor Sales of America.

ADJUSTMENTS & INSPECTION

WHEEL ALIGNMENT SPECIFICATIONS & PROCEDURES

See WHEEL ALIGNMENT SPECIFICATIONS & PROCEDURES in WHEEL ALIGNMENT section.

WHEEL BEARING

While turning hub, tighten adjusting nut to 22 ft. lbs. (29 N.m) to seat bearings. Loosen nut and retighten to 6 ft. lbs. (8 N.m). Install cotter pin, but do not loosen nut more than 30 degrees to insert cotter pin. If holes cannot be aligned within 30 degrees, repeat procedure.

REMOVAL & INSTALLATION

WHEEL BEARING

Removal

Raise and support vehicle. Remove wheel. Remove caliper assembly and support out of way. Remove dust cap, cotter pin, nut, washer and outer bearing. Remove rotor and hub assembly from spindle. Remove grease seal from back side of hub and remove inner bearing.

Installation

Clean and repack both bearings. Lightly grease lip of grease seal and install inner bearing and seal. To complete installation, reverse removal procedure.

BALL JOINT & UPPER CONTROL ARM

Removal (Lower)

1) Raise and support vehicle. Remove wheel assembly. Put tension on coil spring by raising lower control arm with a floor jack. Remove cotter pin and castle nut attaching lower ball joint to steering knuckle and separate knuckle from ball joint.

2) Lift steering knuckle from ball joint and remove dust cover retaining ring and dust cover from ball joint. Remove 3 ball joint-to-control arm bushings. Remove ball joint from vehicle.

Removal (Upper)

1) Raise and support vehicle. Remove wheel assembly. Put tension on coil spring by raising lower control arm with a floor jack. Remove upper ball joint-to-steering knuckle cotter pin and castle nut. Separate knuckle from ball joint using a ball joint separator fork.

2) Remove upper control arm shaft-to-crossmember bolts. Noting position of camber shims for reassembly, remove control arm. Remove dust cover retaining ring, dust cover and snap ring. Press ball joint from arm.

Inspection

Maximum lower ball joint vertical movement is .02" (.5 mm). Maximum upper ball joint stud rotating torque must not exceed 7-30 INCH lbs. (.8-3.4 N.m). Replace snap ring if it is loose on dust cover.

Installation (Upper & Lower)

To install components, reverse removal procedure. Align mating marks on upper ball joint and upper arm before pressing in. Embossed portion of lower ball joint dust cover must face forward.

LOWER CONTROL ARM & COIL SPRING

Removal

1) Raise and support vehicle. Remove wheel assembly. Loosen strut rod adjusting nut at frame. Disconnect stabilizer bar and strut rod from control arm. Remove shock absorber. Put tension on coil spring by raising lower control arm with a floor jack.

2) Remove lower ball joint-to-steering knuckle cotter pin and castle nut. Separate lower ball joint from knuckle. Slowly lower arm to relieve coil spring tension and remove coil spring. Remove lower arm pivot shaft, and remove arm.

Installation

To install, reverse removal procedure. Tighten lower control arm shaft nut with vehicle on ground.

STRUT ROD & STABILIZER BAR

Removal & Installation

1) Remove strut rod from bump stop on lower arm, and disconnect stabilizer bar from lower arm. Remove strut rod bracket from body with strut rod and stabilizer bar. Remove strut and stabilizer from bracket. Note position of strut rod bushings.

2) To install, reverse removal procedure. Distance from end of strut rod to front of double nuts is 2.9" (74 mm).

TIGHTENING SPECIFICATIONS

Application	Ft. Lbs. (N.m)
Shock Absorber-to-Lower Arm Bolt	6-8 (8-11)
Shock Absorber-to-Crossmember Nut	9-13 (12-17)
Lower Arm Shaft Nut	40-54 (54-73)
Ball Joint-to-Lower Arm Bolts	22-30 (30-41)
Upper Ball Joint-to-Knuckle Nut	44-65 (59-88)
Lower Ball Joint-to-Knuckle Nut	87-130 (118-176)
Upper Arm-to-Crossmember Bolt	73-86 (99-117)
Strut Bar-to-Lower Arm Bolt	51-61 (69-83)

CHRYSLER MOTORS & MITSUBISHI 4WD

Chrysler Motors: Raider, Ram-50;
Mitsubishi: Montero, Pickup

DESCRIPTION

Front suspension is an independent type consisting of upper and lower control arms, steering knuckle, torsion bar and stabilizer bar. Steering knuckle is connected to the control arms by ball joints. Torsion bars and stabilizer bar are connected to the lower control arms.

ADJUSTMENTS & INSPECTION

WHEEL ALIGNMENT SPECIFICATIONS & PROCEDURES

See WHEEL ALIGNMENT SPECIFICATIONS & PROCEDURES in WHEEL ALIGNMENT section.

WHEEL BEARING

1) Remove locking hub assembly. See LOCKING HUB under REMOVAL & INSTALLATION in this article. Remove lock washer-to-lock nut bolts and lock washer. Remove brake caliper or ensure brake pads are not contacting rotor.

2) Using Socket (MB990954) and ft. lb. torque wrench, rotate front hub and tighten lock nut to 95-145 ft. lbs. (129-197 N.m) to seat bearings. Loosen nut.

3) Retighten nut to 18 ft. lbs. (24 N.m) and loosen 30-40 degrees. Using INCH lb. torque wrench or spring scale attached to wheel stud, measure hub turning resistance.

4) Turning resistance should be 1-4 lbs. (5-18 N) using spring scale or 2.60-11.30 INCH lbs. (.3-1.3 N.m) for use with torque wrench. Using dial indicator, check front hub axial play. Axial play should be .002" (.05 mm) or less.

5) Adjust wheel bearing so turning resistance and axial play are within specification. If adjustment cannot be obtained, check wheel bearing condition and installation. Install lock washer.

6) If lock washer and lock nut holes do not align, align holes by loosening lock nut no more than 40 degrees. Install lock washer bolts to lock nut. Tighten lock washer bolts. Install locking hub.

BALL JOINT CHECKING

Upper Ball Joint

1) With ball joint disconnected from steering knuckle, place nut on ball joint stud. Using INCH lb. torque wrench, measure starting torque required to rotate ball joint stud.

2) Starting torque must be 7-30 INCH lbs. (.8-3.4 N.m). On Pickup and Ram models, replace upper control arm if starting torque is not within specification. On Montero and Raider models ball joint can be replaced.

Lower Ball Joint

1) Place ball joint in soft-jawed vise. Install dial indicator with stem resting on end of ball joint stud.

2) Measure ball joint stud end play. Replace ball joint if end play exceeds .02" (.5 mm).

Fig. 1: Exploded View of 4WD Front Suspension

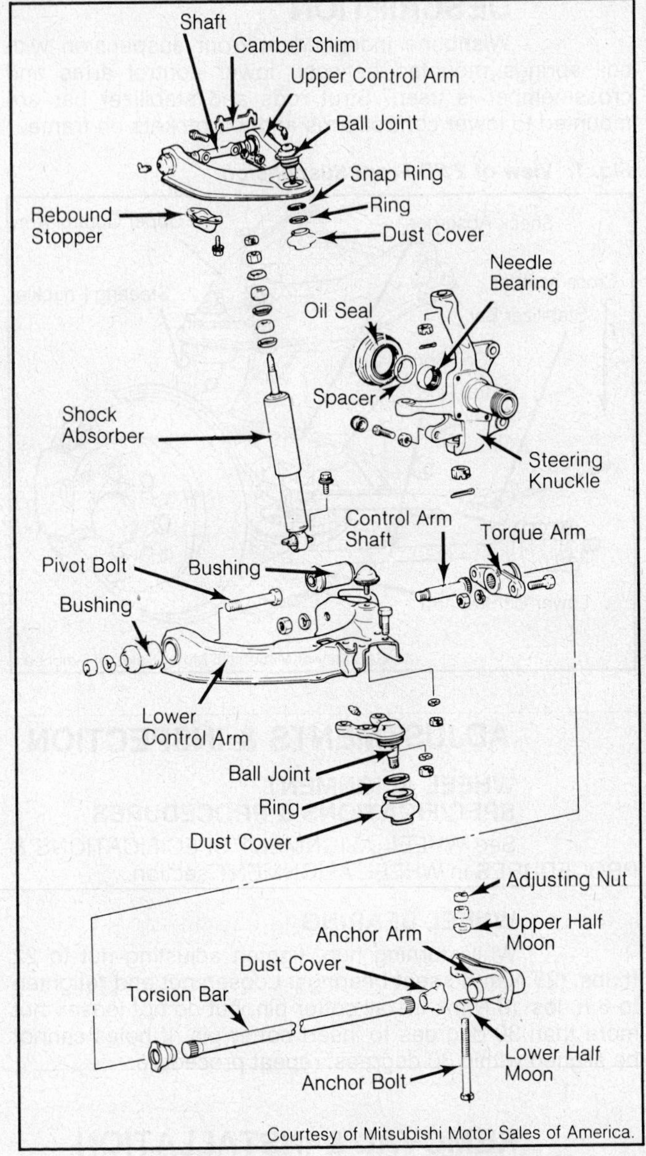

Courtesy of Mitsubishi Motor Sales of America.

REMOVAL & INSTALLATION

WHEEL BEARING

Removal

1) Raise and support vehicle. Remove wheel assembly. Remove caliper assembly. Remove locking hub. See LOCKING HUB in this article.

2) Remove lock washer. Using Socket (MB990954), remove lock nut. Remove front hub assembly from steering knuckle.

3) Remove oil seal and bearings from hub. Using brass drift and hammer, drive bearing races from hub if replacement is required.

Installation

1) Lubricate outside surfaces of bearing outer races with grease prior to installation. Install bearing outer races in hub. Ensure bearing races are fully seated.

2) Pack bearings with grease. Install inner bearing in hub. Install seal in hub. Use Seal Installer

CHRYSLER MOTORS & MITSUBISHI 4WD (Cont.)

(MB990985) for Pickup and Ram-50 models or (MB990955) for Montero and Raider models.

3) Install seal until seal is even with hub surface. Reverse removal procedures. Adjust wheel bearings. See WHEEL BEARINGS under ADJUSTMENTS & INSPECTION in this article. Tighten bolts to specification. See TIGHTENING SPECIFICATIONS table at end of article.

LOCKING HUB

NOTE: Manual and automatic locking hubs are used on Montero models while all other models use only the automatic locking hubs.

Removal (Automatic Type)

1) Hub must be placed in the free condition. This is done by placing transfer case lever in "2H" position and moving vehicle in reverse approximately 4-6 feet.

2) Remove cover from locking hub. It may be necessary to use an oil filter wrench with shop towel wrapped around cover to loosen cover. Raise and support vehicle. Remove wheel assembly.

3) Using snap ring pliers, remove snap ring and shim from end of drive axle. *See Fig. 2.* Using Socket (MD998360), remove locking hub retaining bolts. Remove locking hub assembly.

Fig. 2: Exploded View of Automatic Locking Hub

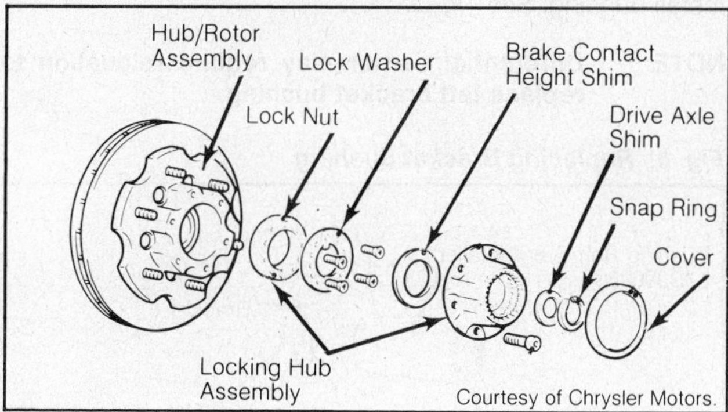

Courtesy of Chrysler Motors.

Installation

1) Using depth gauge, measure dimension "A" at 2 locations to determine brake contact surface height. *See Fig. 3.* Shims must be installed if dimension "A" is not within specification. See BRAKE CONTACT SURFACE HEIGHT SPECIFICATIONS table.

BRAKE CONTACT SURFACE HEIGHT SPECIFICATIONS

Application	In. (mm)
Pickup & Ram-50	.46-.48 (11.6-12.1)
Montero & Raider	.465-.480 (11.81-12.19)

2) Using spring scale attached to wheel stud, measure and record turning resistance required to rotate hub/rotor assembly prior to installing locking hub.

3) Apply semi-drying sealant on locking hub assembly-to-hub/rotor contact areas. Ensure no sealant exists on outer areas of hub/rotor assembly toward brake contact areas.

4) Align locking hub assembly key area with steering knuckle key way area. Loosely install locking hub assembly on hub/rotor assembly. Ensure locking hub assembly fully contacts hub/rotor asssembly.

Fig. 3: Measuring Brake Contact Surface Height

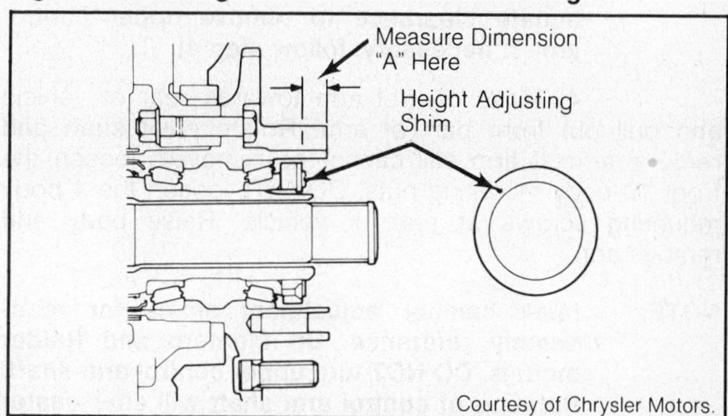

Courtesy of Chrysler Motors.

5) Install locking hub retaining bolts. Tighten to specification. Using spring scale attached to wheel stud, measure turning resistance required to rotate hub/rotor assembly.

6) Subtract reading obtained in **2)** from reading obtained in step **5)**. If reading difference exceeds 3.1 lbs. (14 N), check for incorrect installation of locking hub assembly or components.

7) Install shim and snap ring on drive axle. Rotate drive axle until maximum end play is obtained. Using dial indicator, check drive axle end play.

8) Drive axle end play should be .008-.020" (.20-.51 mm). If not within specification, adjust drive axle end play by changing axle shaft shim. Install new "O" ring and cover. Tighten cover to specification.

Removal (Manual Type)

1) Place locking hub in the "FREE" position. Remove locking hub cover and gasket. Using snap ring pliers, remove snap ring and shim from end of drive axle.

2) Remove locking hub assembly retaining bolts. Remove locking hub assembly from hub/rotor.

Installation

1) Apply semi-drying sealant on locking hub assembly-to-hub/rotor contact areas. Ensure no sealant exists on outer areas of hub/rotor assembly toward brake contact areas.

2) Install locking hub on hub/rotor. Tighten bolts to specification. Install shim and snap ring on drive axle. Rotate drive axle until maximum end play is obtained. Using dial indicator, check drive axle end play.

3) Drive axle end play should be .008-.020" (.20-.51 mm). If not within specification, adjust drive axle end play by changing axle shaft shim. Install gasket and cover. Tighten bolts to specification.

UPPER CONTROL ARM

Removal

1) Raise and support vehicle. Remove wheel assembly. Support lower control arm with jack. Loosen anchor bolt lock nut. *See Fig. 1.* Mark anchor bolt for reassembly reference. Loosen anchor bolt to release torsion bar tension. Remove upper shock absorber mount nuts.

2) Disconnect and plug brake hose at frame mount bracket. Remove cotter pin from ball joint stud. Loosen, but do not remove, ball joint-to-steering knuckle nut. Using ball joint separator, loosen ball joint from steering knuckle. Remove ball joint stud nut.

3) Remove rebound stopper from control arm. Remove upper control arm mounting bolts. Note direction of bolt installation. Remove control arm.

CHRYSLER MOTORS & MITSUBISHI 4WD (Cont.)

NOTE: On Raider models, there may not be adequate clearance to remove upper control arm. If necessary, follow step 4).

4) Move control arm towards rear of vehicle and pull out front part of arm. Rotate pivot shaft and remove arm. If arm still cannot be removed, loosen the front 10 body mounting nuts. DO NOT loosen the 4 body mounting screws at rear of vehicle. Raise body and remove arm.

NOTE: Mark camber adjustment shims for reassembly reference. On Montero and Raider models, DO NOT turn upper control arm shaft. Rotating of control arm shaft will alter caster setting.

Inspection

1) Inspect control arm for cracks or deformation. On Montero and Raider models, mount control arm in soft-jawed vise using the control arm shaft. Attach spring scale to upper end of control arm near ball joint.

2) Using spring scale, measure starting torque required to rotate control arm on the shaft. Replace control arm if starting torque exceeds 1.50 lbs. (6.8 N).

3) On all models, check ball joints. See BALL JOINT CHECKING under ADJUSTMENTS & INSPECTION in this article. Inspect ball joint dust cover for damage. Replace dust cover if damaged.

Installation

1) Reverse removal procedures. On Montero and Raider Models, ensure control arm shaft is correctly positioned prior to installation. Rotate control arm shaft to obtain correct measurement. *See Fig. 4.*

Fig. 4: Positioning Upper Control Arm Shaft (Montero & Raider)

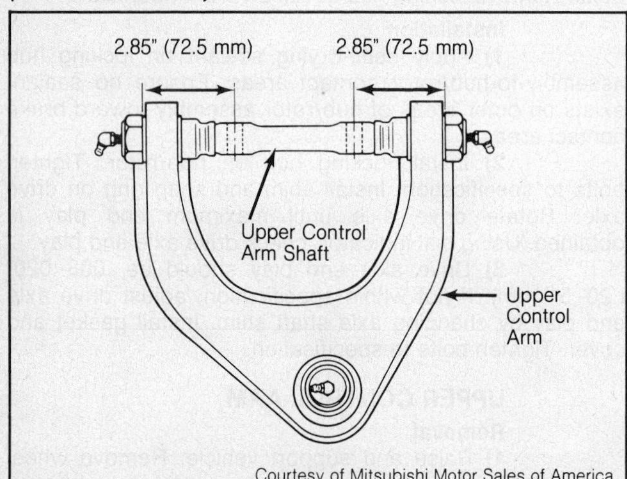

2) On Ram-50 and Pickup models, install control arm-to-crossmember bolts from the inside of crossmember with the nuts against the control arm shaft.

3) On Montero and Raider models, install control arm-to-crossmember bolts from the outside of the control arm with the nuts against the crossmember.

4) Ensure alignment shims are placed in original location. Tigthen bolts to specification. Bleed brakes. Adjust anchor bolt to proper torsion bar setting. See TORSION BAR in this article. It may be necessary to check wheel alignment if any components were changed.

LOWER CONTROL ARM

Removal

1) Raise and support vehicle. Remove wheel assembly. Remove front skid plate and undercover (if equipped). Remove torsion bar. See TORSION BAR in this article. Remove stabilizer bar bolt from control arm.

2) Remove shock absorber-to-control arm bolts. Loosen lower ball joint-to-steering knuckle nut. Using ball joint separator, separate lower ball joint from steering knuckle. Remove ball joint nut from steering knuckle.

3) Remove control arm shaft. *See Fig. 1.* Remove torque arm. Remove lower control arm pivot bolt. Remove lower control arm.

Inspection

1) Inspect control arm for cracks or deformation. Check ball joints. See BALL JOINT CHECKING under ADJUSTMENTS & INSPECTION in this article. Inspect ball joint dust covers for damage. Replace dust covers if damaged.

2) Inspect control arm bushing and frame bracket bushing for damage. Replace if necessary.

Bushing Replacement

1) For frame bracket bushing replacement, install Bushing Remove/Installer (MB990958) in bushing. *See Fig. 5.* Tighten bushing remover/installer bolt to remove bushing. Reverse bushing remover/installer to install bushing. *See Fig. 5.*

NOTE: Differential carrier may require relocation to replace left bracket bushing.

Fig. 5: Replacing Bracket Bushing

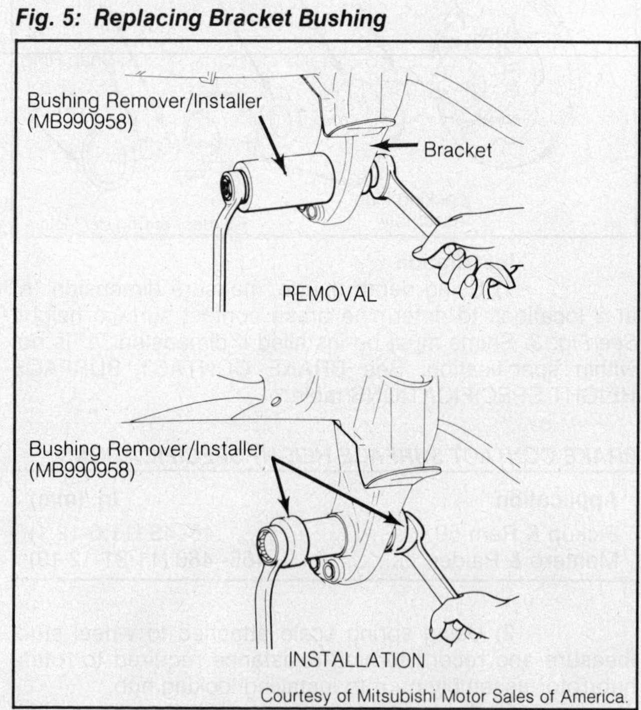

2) For control arm bushing replacement on Ram-50 and Raider models, install Bushing Remover/Installer (C-4763) in bushing. *See Fig. 6.* Tighten bushing remover/installer to remove bushing.

3) Reverse bushing remover/installer to install bushing. *See Fig. 6.* Position bushing so equal distance exists from bushing-to-control arm on both ends.

CHRYSLER MOTORS & MITSUBISHI 4WD (Cont.)

Fig. 6: Replacing Lower Control Arm Bushing

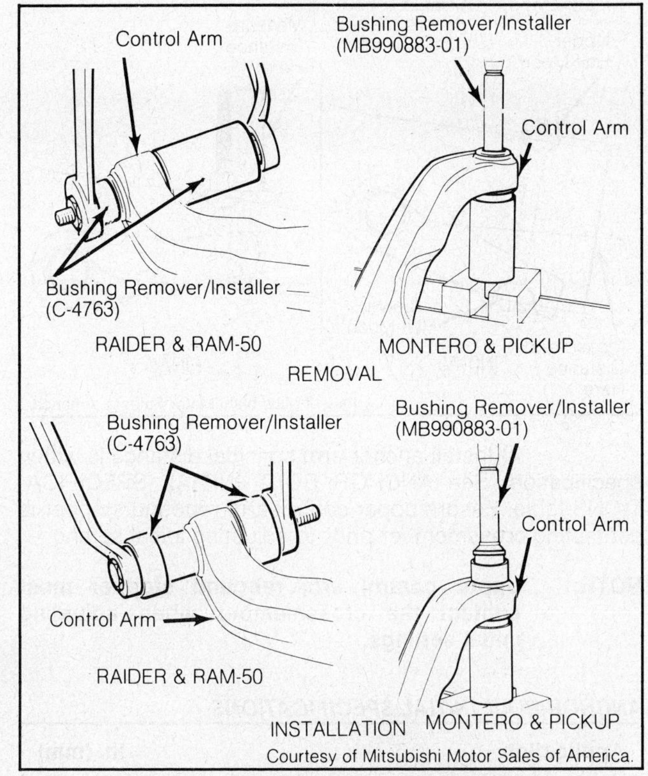

4) For control arm bushing replacement on Montero and Pickup models, use press and Bushing Remover/Installer (MB990883-01). Press bushing from control arm. *See Fig. 6.*

5) Coat bushing and control arm with soapy water. Using press and bushing remover/installer, press bushing in control arm. *See Fig. 6.* Position bushing so equal distance exists from bushing-to-control arm on both ends.

Installation

1) Reverse removal procedures. Ensure White mark located on lower mounting end of shock absorber faces outside of vehicle. Tighten bolts to specification.

2) Tighten lower control arm shaft and pivot bolt to specification with vehicle at normal operating height.

3) Install new nut on stabilizer bar-to-control arm bolt. Tighten stabilizer bar-to-control arm bolt until the distance from threaded end of the bolt to the nut is .24-.31" (6.0-7.8 mm)

CAUTION: Lower control arm shaft and pivot bolt must be tightened to specification with vehicle at normal operating height.

BALL JOINT

Removal (Lower)

1) Raise and support vehicle. Remove wheel assembly. Support lower control arm enough to release torsion bar tension. Loosen lower ball joint-to-steering knuckle nut.

2) Using ball joint separator, separate lower ball joint from steering knuckle. Remove ball joint nut from steering knuckle. Remove ball joint-to-lower control arm bolts.

3) Remove ball joint. Check ball joint for wear. See BALL JOINT CHECKING under ADJUSTMENTS & INSPECTION in this article.

Installation

1) If dust cover requires replacement, remove ring and dust cover. Lubricate ball joint with SAE J310 NLGI No. 2 grease. Apply semi-drying sealant to ball joint grooves.

2) Install new dust cover and ring. Reverse removal procedures. Tighten bolts to specification.

NOTE: On Pickup and Ram models, upper ball joints cannot be replaced. Upper control arm must

Fig. 7: Replacing Upper Ball Joint (Montero & Raider)

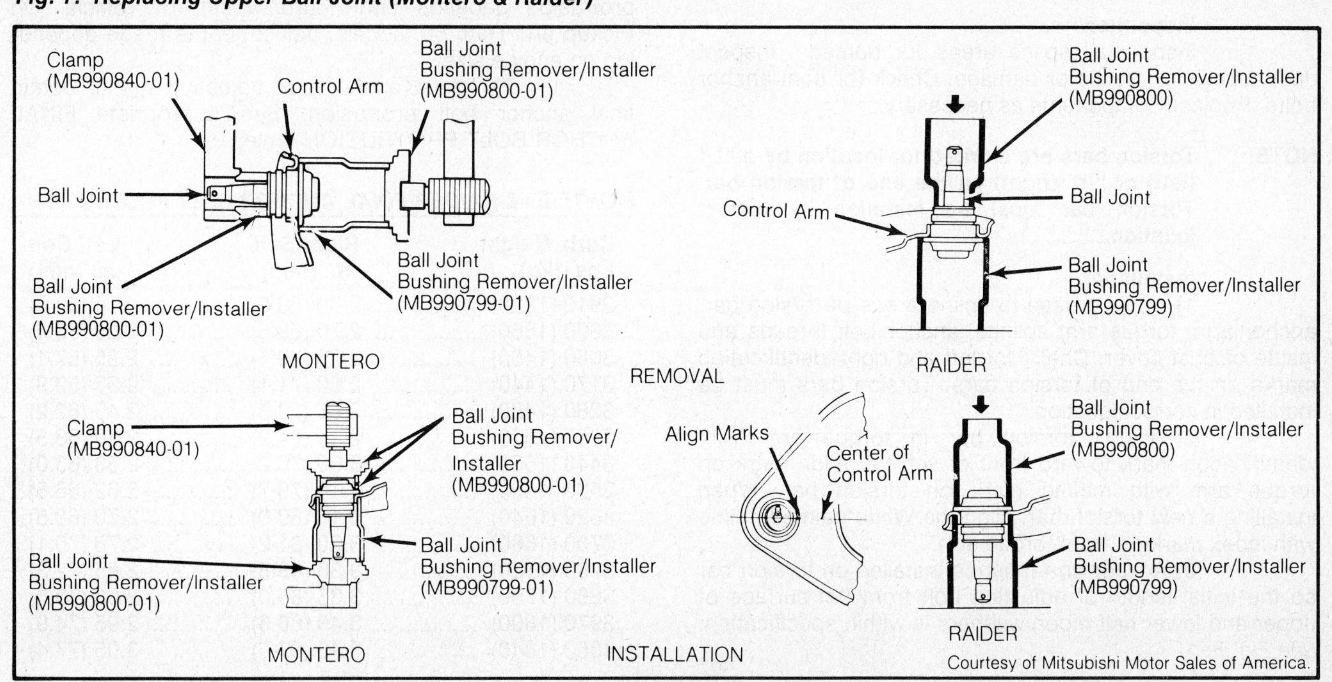

CHRYSLER MOTORS & MITSUBISHI 4WD (Cont.)

be replaced if ball joint is defective. Ball joints are replaceable on Montero and Raider models.

Removal (Upper)

1) Remove snap ring and dust cover together from ball joint. On Raider models, use press and Ball Joint Remover/Installers (MB990800) and (MB990799) to press ball joint from control arm. *See Fig. 7.*

2) On Montero models, use Ball Joint Remover/Installer (MB990799-01), Ball Joint Remover/Installer (MB990800-01) and Clamp (MB990840-01). Tighten clamp to remove ball joint. *See Fig. 7.*

Installation

1) Align reference mark on ball joint with center of control arm prior to installation. Using proper bushing remover/installers, install ball joint in control arm. *See Fig. 7.*

2) Install snap ring on ball joint. Lubricate ball joint with SAE J310 NLGI No. 2 grease. Apply semi-drying sealant to ball joint grooves. Install new dust cover and ring.

TORSION BAR

CAUTION: Mark torsion bar and anchor arm for location prior to removal. This will aid in installation if no identification marks exist on torsion bar and anchor arm.

Removal

1) Raise and support vehicle. Support lower control arm with a jack. Loosen anchor arm adjusting bolt lock nut. Loosen anchor bolt to release torsion bar tension.

2) Place reference marks on front of torsion bar, torque arm and torsion bar-to-torque arm for reassembly reference. Remove anchor arm. *See Fig. 1.*

3) Remove dust cover from end of torsion bar. On Montero and Raider models, remove heat cover (left side only) located between dust cover and torsion bar. On all models, remove torsion bar.

Inspection

Inspect all spline areas for damage. Inspect dust covers for cracks or damage. Check for bent anchor bolts. Replace components as necessary.

NOTE: Torsion bars are marked for location by a "L" (left) or "R" (right) on the end of torsion bar. Torsion bar must be installed in correct location.

Installation

1) Apply grease to spline areas of torsion bar, anchor arm, torque arm splines, anchor bolt threads and inside of dust cover. Check for left and right identification marks on the end of torsion bars. Torsion bars must be installed in correct location.

2) Install torsion bar in torque arm with identification mark toward front of vehicle. Align mark on torque arm with mating mark on torsion bar. When installing a new torsion bar, align the White painted spline with index mark on front torque arm.

3) Anchor arm must be installed on torsion bar so the initial length of adjusting bolt from flat surface of upper and lower half moon washers is within specification. *See Fig. 8.*

Fig. 8: Adjusting Anchor Arm Bolt

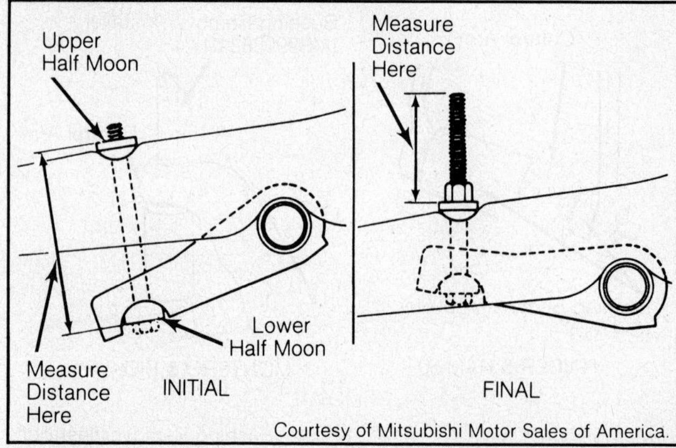

4) Install anchor arm so initial distance is within specification. See ANCHOR BOLT INITIAL SPECIFICATIONS table. Ensure upper control arm rebound stopper is contacting crossmember prior to adjusting initial setting.

NOTE: Upper control arm rebound stopper must contact the crossmember when adjusting initial settings.

ANCHOR BOLT INITIAL SPECIFICATIONS

Application	In. (mm)
Montero & Raider	
Left Side	5.323-5.638 (135.20-143.20)
Right Side	4.894-5.210 (124.30-132.33)
Pickup & Ram-50	
Left Side	5.5-5.8 (140-147)
Right Side	5.3-5.6 (134-142)

5) After initial torsion bar setting, anchor bolt adjusting nut must be tightened to obtain correct final bolt protrusion. *See Fig. 8.*

6) On Montero and Raider models, final bolt protrusion depends upon curb weight of vehicle. On Pickup and Ram-50 models, adjustment is made depending on engine size.

7) Adjust anchor bolt adjusting nut to obtain final anchor bolt protrusion. See appropriate FINAL ANCHOR BOLT PROTRUSION table.

MONTERO & RAIDER FINAL ANCHOR BOLT PROTRUSION

Curb Weight Lbs. (kg)	Right Bolt In. (mm)	Left Bolt In. (mm)
2910 (1320)	2.60 (66.0)	2.15 (54.6)
3000 (1360)	2.70 (68.5)	2.20 (55.8)
3080 (1400)	2.76 (70.1)	2.25 (57.1)
3170 (1440)	2.80 (71.1)	2.36 (59.9)
3260 (1480)	2.85 (72.3)	2.45 (62.2)
3350 (1520)	2.95 (74.9)	2.50 (63.5)
3440 (1560)	3.00 (76.2)	2.56 (65.0)
3530 (1600)	3.10 (78.7)	2.62 (66.5)
3620 (1640)	3.15 (80.0)	2.70 (68.5)
3700 (1680)	3.20 (81.2)	2.76 (70.1)
3790 (1720)	3.30 (83.8)	2.85 (72.3)
3880 (1760)	3.35 (85.0)	2.90 (73.6)
3970 (1800)	3.40 (86.3)	2.95 (74.9)
4060 (1840)	3.45 (87.6)	3.05 (77.4)

CHRYSLER MOTORS & MITSUBISHI 4WD (Cont.)

PICKUP & RAM-50 FINAL ANCHOR BOLT PROTRUSION

Application	Right Bolt In. (mm)	Left Bolt In. (mm)
2.0L	2.68 (68.1)	2.83 (71.9)
2.6L	2.68 (68.1)	3.01 (76.4)

8) Reverse removal procedures for remaining components. Tighten bolts to specification. Place vehicle in normal operating height with no load.

9) Measure clearance between lower control arm bump stop and bump stop bracket on the frame. On Montero and Raider models, clearance should be 2.8" (71 mm). On Pickup and Ram-50 models, clearance should be 3.1" (78 mm). If not within specification, adjust anchor bolt adjusting nut to obtain correct clearance.

STEERING KNUCKLE

Removal

1) Raise and support vehicle. Remove wheel assembly. Remove brake caliper. Remove hub/rotor assembly. See WHEEL BEARINGS in this article. Remove dust cover from steering knuckle.

2) Disconnect tie rod end from steering knuckle. Support lower control arm. Loosen ball joint-to-steering knuckle nuts. Using ball joint separator, separate ball joints from steering knuckle.

3) Detach upper and lower ball joints from steering knuckle. Remove steering knuckle from drive axle. Remove oil seal and spacer from steering knuckle.

Inspection

Inspect steering knuckle for cracks. Inspect needle bearing for wear or damage.

Installation

1) If needle bearing requires replacement, drive bearing from steering knuckle. Use Bearing Driver (C-4178) and Handle (C-4171) for Raider and Ram-50 models or Bearing Driver (MB990956-01) and Handle (MB9909938-01) for Montero and Pickup models.

CAUTION: Steering knuckle bearing should not be reused once removed.

2) Using bearing installer and handle, install new needle bearing until bearing is even with steering knuckle end face. Apply SAE J310 NLGI No. 2 grease on the spacer-to-steering knuckle contact areas.

3) Install spacer with chamfered side toward inside of vehicle. Using Seal Installer (MB990985-01) and Handle (MB990938-01), install seal in steering knuckle until seal is even with steering knuckle end face.

4) Apply grease to seal lip area and inside of seal. Reverse removal procedures. Tighten bolts to specification.

STABILIZER BAR

Removal

Remove skid plate (if equipped). Remove stabilizer bar bolt from lower control arm. Remove stabilizer bar clamp-to-hanger bolts. Remove stabilizer bar and bushings. Remove stabilizer bar-to-frame hangers (if necessary).

Installation

Inspect bushings for wear and stabilizer bar for deformation. Reverse removal procedures. Install stabilizer bar-to-frame hangers and stabilizer bar-to-control arm bolt using new nuts. Tighten nuts until the distance from the threaded end of the bolt to the nut is .24-.32" (6.0-8.1 mm).

TIGHTENING SPECIFICATIONS

Application	Ft. Lbs. (N.m)
Anchor Bolt Lock Nut	29-36 (39-49)
Automatic Hub Cover	13-25 (18-34)
Ball Joint Nut	
Lower	87-130 (118-176)
Upper	43-65 (58-88)
Ball Joint-to-Control Arm Bolt	39-54 (53-73)
Caliper Bolt	58-72 (79-98)
Control Arm-to-Frame Bolt	
Lower	[1] 101-116 (137-157)
Upper	72-87 (98-118)
Locking Hub-to-Hub/Rotor Bolt	36-43 (49-58)
Manual Hub Cover Bolt	10 (14)
Shock Absorber Lower Mount Bolt	
Montero & Raider	11-16 (15-22)
Pickup & Ram-50	10 (14)
Shock Absorber Shaft Nut	10-13 (14-18)
Tie Rod Nut	33 (45)
Torque Arm Bolt	69-87 (94-118)
	INCH Lbs. (N.m)
Stabilizer Bar Clamp Bolt	72-108 (8-12)

[1] – Tighten with vehicle at normal operating height.

CHRYSLER MOTORS, HYUNDAI & MITSUBISHI FWD

Chrysler Motors: Colt, Colt Vista (2WD & 4WD);
Hyundai: Excel
Mitsubishi: Cordia, Mirage, Precis, Tredia

DESCRIPTION

The independent front syspension uses a vertically-mounted sturt attached to a steering knuckle mounted on the control arm ball joint. Front suspension consists of a strut assembly, steering knuckle, control arm, stabilizer bar and strut rod (if equipped).

Fig. 1: Exploded View of Colt Vista Front Suspension

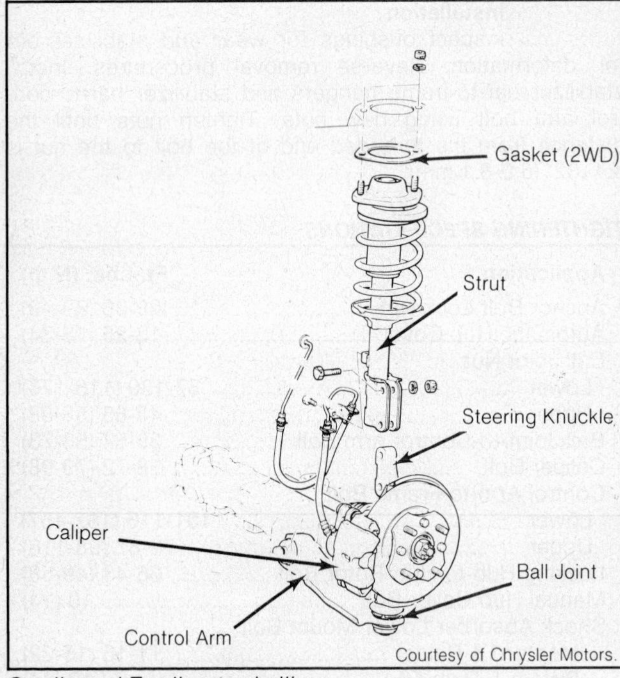

Cordia and Tredia are similiar.

Fig. 2: Exploded View of Hyundai Front Suspension

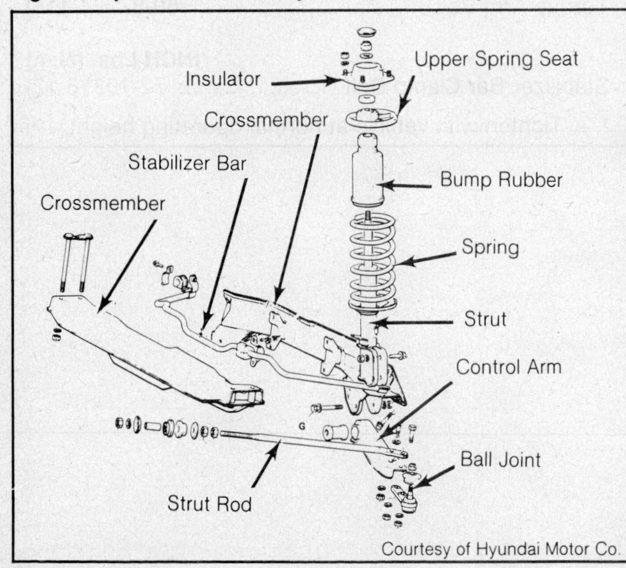

Precis is similiar.

Fig. 3: Exploded View of Mirage Front Suspension

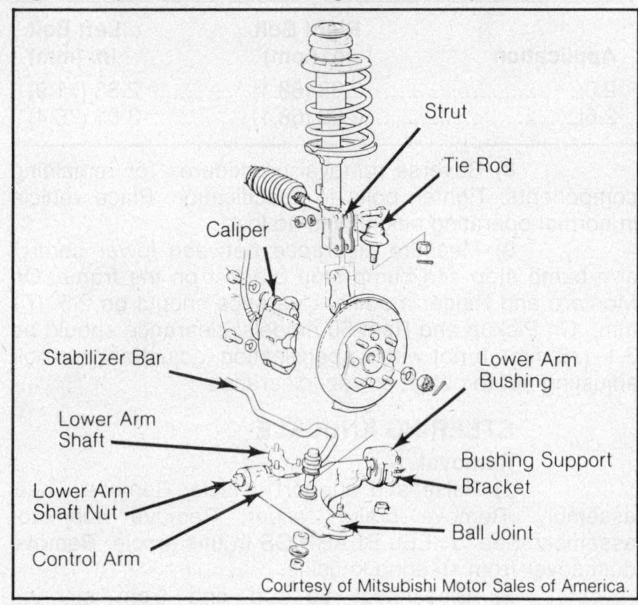

Colt is similiar.

ADJUSTMENTS & INSPECTION

WHEEL ALIGNMENT SPECIFICATIONS & PROCEDURES

See WHEEL ALIGNMENT SPECIFICATIONS & PROCEDURES in WHEEL ALIGNMENT section.

WHEEL BEARING

1) Wheel bearings are nonadjustable. Bearings or assembly procedure must be checked if axial play exceeds specification.

2) Raise and support vehicle. Remove wheel assembly. Remove caliper. On Colt Vista 4WD models, remove brake disc from hub. On all models, attach dial indicator at right angle to hub.

3) Move hub in and out and measure axial play. Check bearings or assembly procedure if movement exceeds specifications. See WHEEL BEARING AXIAL PLAY SPECIFICATIONS table.

WHEEL BEARING AXIAL PLAY SPECIFICATIONS

Application	In. (mm)
Hyundai & Precis	.0043 (.109)
All Others	.008 (.20)

BALL JOINT CHECKING

1) With ball joint disconnected from steering knuckle, install nut on ball joint stud. Move stud from side-to-side several times.

2) Using INCH lb. torque wrench, rotate ball joint stud approximately 2 revolutions per minute and note starting torque.

3) Replace ball joint or control arm if starting torque exceeds specification. See BALL JOINT STARTING TORQUE SPECIFICATIONS table. Ball joint may be used if no roughness or lack of lubrication exists or starting torque is less than minimum specification.

CHRYSLER MOTORS, HYUNDAI & MITSUBISHI FWD (Cont.)

BALL JOINT STARTING TORQUE SPECIFICATIONS

Application	INCH Lbs. (N.m)
Colt & Mirage	17-78 (2-7)
All Others	26-87 (3-10)

REMOVAL & INSTALLATION

WHEEL BEARINGS

CAUTION: Special hub remover/installer and puller must be used to separate hub from steering knuckle. Bearing damage will result if hub is removed using a hammer.

Removal (Colt Vista 4WD)

1) Remove steering knuckle. See STEERING KNUCKLE in this article. Secure steering knuckle in vise. Using Hub Remover/Installer (MB990998) and Puller (MB991056), separate hub from knuckle. *See Fig. 4.*

Fig. 4: Removing Hub from Steering Knuckle

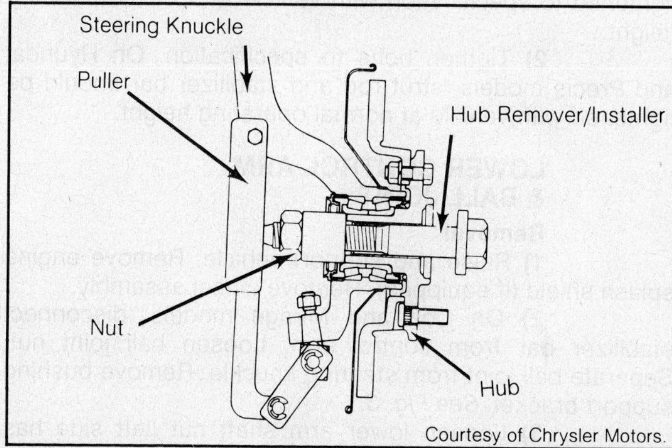

2) Using puller, remove outer bearing inner race from hub. Remove seal from the hub. Remove drive shaft seal from steering knuckle. Remove snap ring from knuckle. *See Fig. 5.*

Fig. 5: Exploded View of Steering Knuckle & Hub

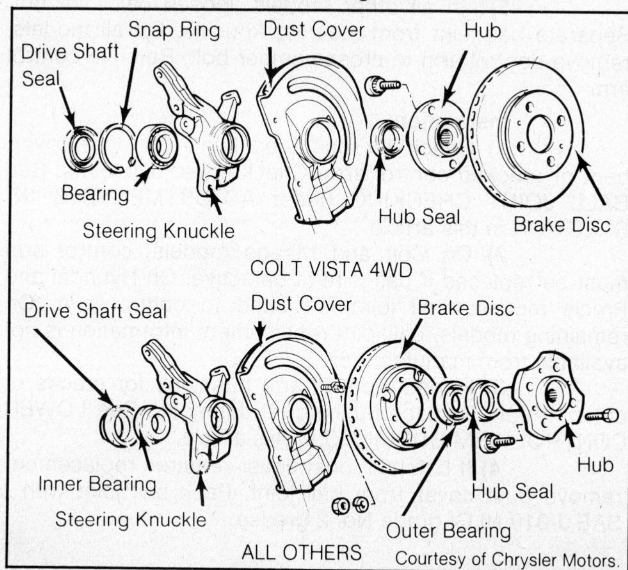

3) Using press, Bearing Remover/Installer (C-4628) and Knuckle Bridge (MB991056), remove bearing from knuckle.

CAUTION: Ensure wheel bearing inner race and ball are installed in original location if they are separated.

Installation

1) Pack bearing with grease. Coat steering knuckle and bearing contact areas with grease. Using press and bearing remover/installer, install bearing. Install snap ring.

2) Using Seal Installer (MB990985) and Handle (C-4171), install hub seal until seal is even with steering knuckle surface. Apply grease to hub seal lip.

3) Place hub on steering knuckle. Using Hub Remover/Installer (MB990998), install hub on steering knuckle. Tighten nut to 144-188 ft. lbs. (195-255 N.m). Rotate hub to seat bearing. *See Fig. 6.*

4) Using an INCH lb. torque wrench, measure bearing starting torque. *See Fig. 6.* Starting torque should be 16 INCH lbs. (1.8 N.m) or less. No roughness of rotation must be felt.

5) Install steering knuckle in vise. Install dial indicator with stem resting against hub surface. Check hub axial play. Hub axial play should not exceed .008" (.20 mm).

6) If starting torque or hub axial play are not within specifications, recheck component installation. Remove hub remover/installer.

7) Apply grease to bearing and inside of steering knuckle. Using Seal Installer (C-3972-A) and Handle (C-4171), install drive shaft seal until seal contacts snap ring. Reverse removal procedures for remaining components.

Fig. 6: Installing Hub & Checking Bearing Starting Torque

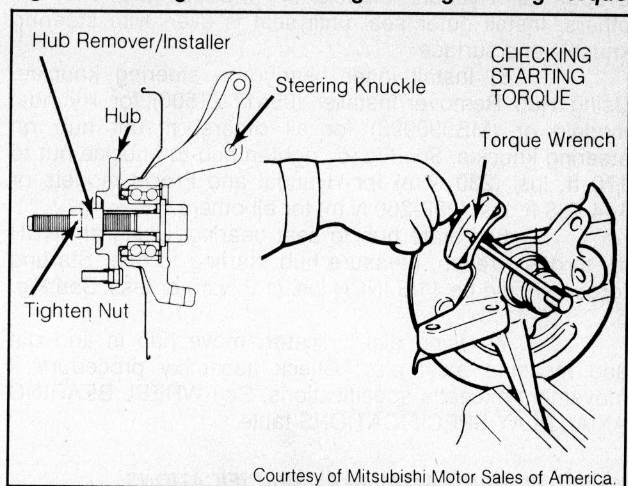

CAUTION: Special hub remover/installer and puller must be used to separate hub from steering knuckle. Bearing damage will result if hub is removed using a hammer.

Removal (All Others)

1) Remove steering knuckle and hub assembly. See STEERING KNUCKLE in this article. Install Hub Remover/Installer (09517-21500) for Hyundai and Precis

CHRYSLER MOTORS, HYUNDAI & MITSUBISHI FWD (Cont.)

models or (MB990998) for all others in hub and steering knuckle. *See Fig. 4.*

2) Install Puller (MB991056) on steering knuckle. Separate hub from steering knuckle. Remove brake disc from hub. Using bearing puller, remove bearing inner race from the hub.

3) Remove seal from steering knuckle. Using drift and hammer, remove bearing races from steering knuckle. If either race requires replacement, they must be replaced as a set.

NOTE: Verify identification marks on bearings. Bearings must be identified by the words JAPAN, KOYO or HI CAP. DO NOT use bearings which do not contain one of these identification marks.

Installation

1) Use handle and proper race installer and base. See BEARING RACE INSTALLER APPLICATION table. Install bearing races. Ensure races are fully seated.

BEARING RACE INSTALLER APPLICATION

Application	Installer	Base
Colt, Colt Vista	C-3893	MB990776-A
Hyundai	09517-21000	09517-21200
All Others	MB990933-01	MB990776-01

2) Install brake disc on the hub. Tighten bolts to specification. See TIGHTENING SPECIFICATIONS table at end of article. Pack wheel bearings with grease.

3) Install outer bearing into knuckle. Apply grease to seal lip and hub contact surface. Install outer seal in steering knuckle.

4) Use Seal Installer (09517-21000) for Hyundai models or (MB991015) for all others and Handle (09500-21000) for Hyundai models or (MB990938-01) for all others. Install outer seal until seal is even with steering knuckle end surface.

5) Install inner bearing in steering knuckle. Using Hub Remover/Installer (09517-21500) for Hyundai models or (MB990998) for all others, mount hub on steering knuckle. *See Fig. 6.* Tighten hub-to-knuckle nut to 170 ft. lbs. (230 N.m) for Hyundai and Precis models or 144-188 ft. lbs. (200-260 N.m) for all others.

6) Rotate hub to seat bearing. Using an INCH lb. torque wrench, measure hub starting torque. Starting torque should be 11.3 INCH lbs. (1.3 N.m) or less. *See Fig. 6.*

7) Using dial indicator, move hub in and out and measure axial play. Check assembly procedure if movement exceeds specifications. See WHEEL BEARING AXIAL PLAY SPECIFICATIONS table.

WHEEL BEARING AXIAL PLAY SPECIFICATIONS

Application	In. (mm)
Hyundai & Precis	.0043 (.109)
All Others	.008 (.20)

8) Use Seal Installer (09517-21000) and Handle (09500-21000) for Hyundai models or Seal Installer (MB991015) and Handle (MB990938-01) for all others for inner seal installation.

9) Install inner seal until seal contacts bearing outer race on Colt Vista, Hyundai and Precis models.

10) On all other models, install seal until seal surface projects .10" (2.5 mm) above steering knuckle surface. On all models, coat seal lip surface with grease.

STEERING KNUCKLE

Removal

1) Remove cap from hub (if equipped). Loosen drive axle nut. Raise and support vehicle. Remove wheel assembly. Remove caliper. On Colt Vista 4WD models, remove brake disc from hub. On all models, remove stabilizer bar and/or strut rod from control arm.

2) Support control arm. Disconnect lower ball joint and tie rod end from steering knuckle. Install puller on hub. Tighten puller and separate drive axle from hub.

3) Separate steering knuckle from strut. Remove steering knuckle/hub assembly from vehicle. Separate hub from steering knuckle (if required). See WHEEL BEARING in this article.

Installation

1) Reverse removal procedures. Install washer on drive axle with raised area toward axle shaft nut. On all models except Hyundai and Precis, drive axle nut must be tightened to specification with vehicle at normal operating height.

2) Tigthen bolts to specification. On Hyundai and Precis models, strut rod and stabilizer bar should be tightened with vehicle at normal operating height.

LOWER CONTROL ARM & BALL JOINT

Removal

1) Raise and support vehicle. Remove engine splash shield (if equipped). Remove wheel assembly.

2) On Colt and Mirage models, disconnect stabilizer bar from control arm. Loosen ball joint nut. Separate ball joint from steering knuckle. Remove bushing support bracket. *See Fig. 3.*

3) Loosen lower arm shaft nut (left side has left hand threads). *See Fig. 3.* Remove lower arm shaft-to-body bolts. Remove control arm.

4) On all other models, disconnect stabilizer bar and/or strut rod from control arm. On Hyundai and Precis models, remove ball joint-to-control arm retaining bolts. DO NOT separate ball joint from steering knuckle.

5) On all other models, loosen ball joint nut. Separate ball joint from steering knuckle. On all models, remove control arm-to-crossmember bolt. Remove control arm.

Inspection

1) Check for damaged ball joint dust cover, bent or cracked control arm. Check lower ball joints. See BALL JOINT CHECKING under ADJUSTMENTS & INSPECTION in this article.

2) On Colt and Mirage models, control arm must be replaced if ball joint is defective. On Hyundai and Precis models, ball joint is bolted to control arm. On remaining models, ball joint replacement information is not available from manufacturer.

3) Inspect control arm bushings for cracks or deterioration. Replace bushings if damaged. See LOWER CONTROL ARM BUSHINGS in this article.

4) If ball joint dust cover requires replacement, remove dust cover from ball joint. Pack ball joint with a SAE J-310 NLGI grade No. 2 grease.

5) Install dust cover. Use Dust Cover Installer (MB990800-01) for Mirage and Colt models, (MB990800) for Clot Vista, (MB990800-3-01) for Cordia and Tredia models or (09545-21100) for Hyundai or Precis. Drive dust cover installer on ball joint until dust cover contacts snap ring or dust cover is fully seated.

Installation

1) On Hyundai and Precis models, coat outside of control arm-to crossmember bushings with a soapy water solution. On all models, install control arm to crossmember. Ensure control arm is not twisted.

2) Install control arm bolt. Install strut rod and stabilizer bar. See STABILIZER BAR & STRUT ROD in this article. Reverse removal procedure to complete installation using new self locking nuts (if used).

3) Lower vehicle to normal operating height. Tighten all bolts to specification. See TIGHTENING SPECIFICATIONS table at end of article.

CONTROL ARM BUSHINGS

Removal & Installation (Colt & Mirage)

1) Apply soapy water solution between control arm bushing and shaft. Pry upward on bushing to remove. Apply soapy water on the control arm shaft and replacement bushing.

2) Install bushing on control arm shaft with locater pin located within 69-75 degrees of the center of control arm. *See Fig. 7.* Using press and wood block, press bushing on control arm until 0-.08" (0-2.0 mm) clearance exists between bushing and control arm. *See Fig. 7.*

CAUTION: DO NOT exceed 1100 lbs. (490 kg) when installing control arm bushing.

Fig. 7: Installing Control Arm Bushing (Colt & Mirage)

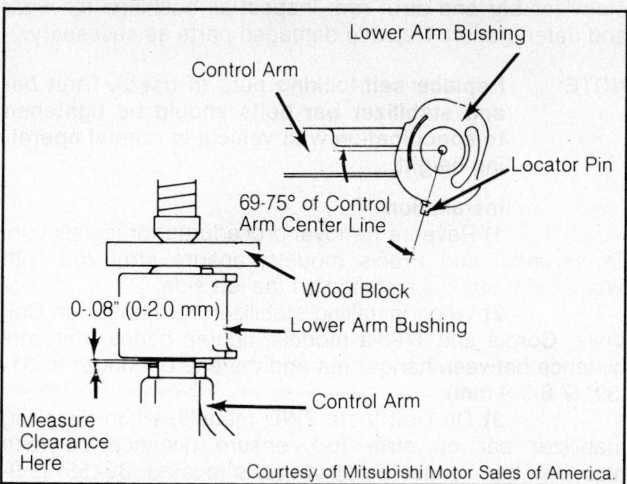

Removal & Installation (Colt Vista)

Information not available from manufacturer.

Removal (All Others)

1) On Hyundai and Precis models, apply soapy water solution to outer surface of bushing and inner surface of bushing arbor.

2) On all models, place control arm, base and ring in press. *See Fig. 8.* Use appropriate base and ring. See BASE & RING APPLICATION table.

BASE & RING APPLICATION

Application	Base	Ring
Hyundai	MB990847-01	MB990945-01
Precis	09216-21300	09216-21500
All Others	MB9901005-01	MB990997-01

3) Using press and bushing arbor, press bushing from control arm. Use Bushing Arbor (MB990947-01) for Hyundai models, (09545-21400) for Precis models or (MB990996-01) for all others. *See Fig. 8.*

Fig. 8: Typical Removal & Installation of Control Arm Bushing

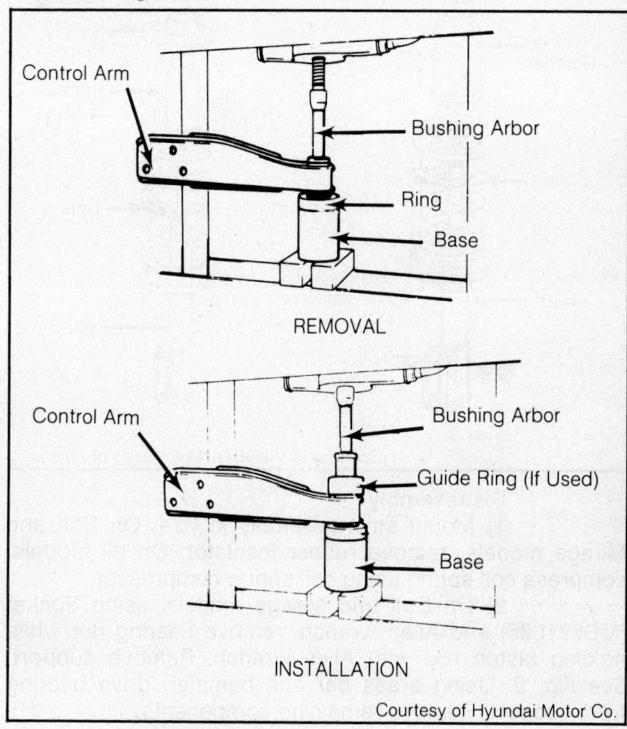

Installation

1) Apply soapy water solution to outer surface of replacement bushing, inner surface of control arm and installation tools. Place control arm, base, ring and bushing arbor in press.

2) Precis models require the use of a Guide Ring (09545-21300) between bushing arbor and bushing. *See Fig. 8.* On all models, press bushing in control arm until bushing is fully seated in control arm.

STRUT ASSEMBLY

Removal

1) Raise and support vehicle. Remove wheel assembly. Disconnect brake line bracket from strut assembly. Support control arm. Remove strut-to-steering knuckle bolts. Separate strut from steering knuckle.

2) On Colt and Mirage models, remove dust cover from top of strut. Using Socket (MB991036) and Allen wrench, remove strut-to-body nut. Allen wrench is used to hold piston shaft.

3) Remove nut, lock washer, stopper, and stopper rubber. *See Fig. 9.* On all other models, remove strut-to-body nuts. Remove strut assembly from vehicle.

CHRYSLER MOTORS, HYUNDAI & MITSUBISHI FWD (Cont.)

Fig. 9: Exploded View of Strut Assembly

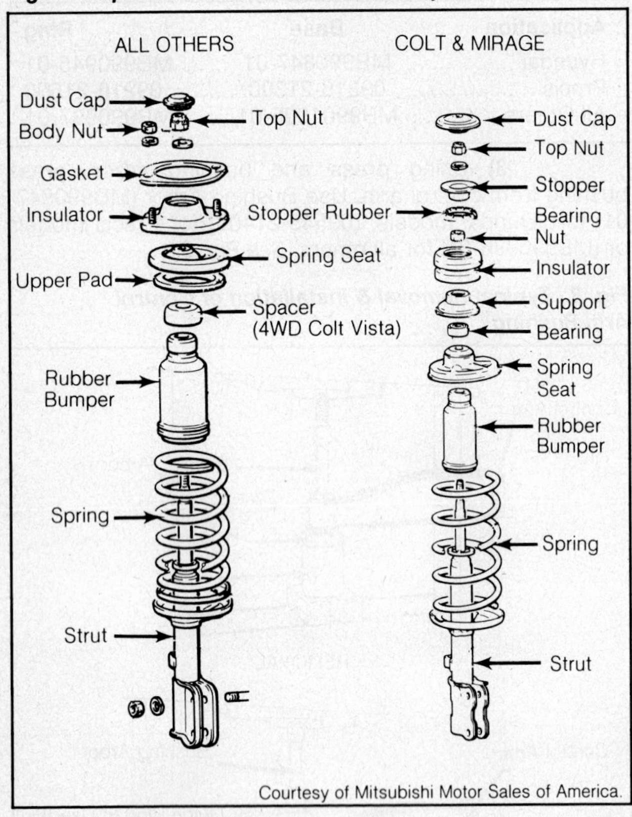

Courtesy of Mitsubishi Motor Sales of America.

Disassembly

1) Mount strut assembly in vise. On Colt and Mirage models, remove rubber insulator. On all models, compress coil spring using coil spring compressor.

2) On Colt and Mirage models, using Socket (MB991036) and Allen wrench, remove bearing nut while holding piston rod with Allen wrench. Remove support. *See Fig. 9.* Using brass bar and hammer, drive bearing from support. Remove remaining components.

3) On all other models, remove dust cover. Use Spanner Wrench (CT-1112) for Colt Vista models, (09546-21000) for Hyundai models or (MB990775-01) for all other models to hold upper spring seat. Remove self-locking top nut from strut shaft. Remove components from strut.

NOTE: On Colt Vista, Cordia and Tredia models, coil spring contains a load classification and spring identification color code mark. Ensure color mark is correct for vehicle application if spring is replaced.

Reassembly

1) Check parts for deterioration or damage. Check strut assembly for leaks and proper operation. Replace strut if fluid leakage exists. Replace worn or damaged parts.

2) Reverse disassembly procedures for reassembly. On Colt and Mirage models, install bearing in support with Black retainer side toward support. Use Bearing Installer (C-3893) for Colt models or Handle (MB990938-01) and Bushing Installer (MB990926-01) for Mirage models.

3) On Cordia, Hyundai, Precis and Tredia models, ensure D-shaped upper seat hole is aligned with notch in piston rod. On all models, align coil spring ends with grooves in spring seats.

4) On Colt Vista, Cordia and Tredia models, position of spring seats can be aligned by installation of .4" (10 mm) diameter pins into spring seat holes.

5) Using spanner wrench, tighten piston shaft top nut to specification. On all models, pack insulator bearing with grease and install dust cap. Avoid getting grease on insulators.

Installation

Reverse removal procedures for installation. Ensure strut assembly and steering knuckle mating surfaces are clean. Tighten fasteners to specification. Check front end alignment.

STABILIZER BAR & STRUT ROD

Removal

1) Raise and support vehicle. Disconnect stabilizer bar from control arms or strut rod. Note location of bushings. Remove stabilizer bar brackets or mounts from body or frame. Remove stabilizer bar.

2) Remove strut rod nut, outer end washer, collar and outer bushing from body bracket. Note location of strut rod bushings.

NOTE: Inner and outer strut rod bushings are different. Note bushing shape and location for installation reference.

3) Remove strut rod mount bolts from control arm or hanger from stabilizer bar. Remove rod with inner bushing and end washer. Note direction of strut rod projection area where it mounts to control arm.

4) On Hyundai and Precis models, left strut rod may be identified by a White paint mark on the side of strut rod.

5) On all models, check for bent or damaged stabilizer bar and strut rod. Inspect all bushings for wear and deterioration. Replace damaged parts as necessary.

NOTE: Replace self-locking nuts (if used). Strut bar and stabilizer bar bolts should be tightened to specification with vehicle in normal operating height.

Installation

1) Reverse removal procedures for installation. On Hyundai and Precis models, ensure strut rod with White paint mark is installed on the left side.

2) When installing stabilizer bar hanger on Colt Vista, Cordia and Tredia models, tighten hanger nut until distance between hanger nut and the end of hanger is .31-.39" (7.8-9.9 mm).

3) On Colt Vista 2WD models, when installing stabilizer bar on strut rod, ensure distance between stabilizer bar hanger on strut rod is located .39-.55" (9.9-13.9 mm) from the front crossmember.

4) On Colt Vista 4WD and non-turbo Cordia and Tredia models, tighten stabilizer bar-to-control arm nut until the distance from the end of the bolt to the nut is .31-.39" (7.8-9.9 mm).

5) On Colt and Mirage models, connect stabilizer bar to the control arm then to the crossmember. Tighten stabilizer bar-to-control arm nut until the distance from the end of the bolt to the nut is .83-.91" (21.0-23.1 mm).

CHRYSLER MOTORS, HYUNDAI & MITSUBISHI FWD (Cont.)

6) Prior to installing strut rod, measure the distance from the end of strut rod to the lock nut. Adjust lock nut to obtain correct distance. On Colt Vista, Cordia and Tredia models, distance should be 3.07" (78.0 mm). On Hyundai and Precis models, distance should be 3.17" (80.5 mm).

7) Tighten strut rod and stabilizer bolts and nuts to specification with vehicle on ground and suspension unloaded. Check front end alignment.

TIGHTENING SPECIFICATIONS (HYUNDAI & PRECIS)

Application	Ft. Lbs. (N.m)
Ball Joint-to-Control Arm Bolt	69-87 (93-118)
Ball Joint-to-Knuckle Nut	43-52 (58-71)
Brake Disc-to-Hub Bolt	36-43 (49-58)
Control Arm-to-Crossmember Bolt	69-87 (94-118)
Drive Axle Nut	144-188 (195-255)
Stabilizer Bar Mount To Crossmember Bolt	22-29 (30-39)
Strut Bearing Nut	25-36 (34-49)
Strut Rod-to-Control Arm Bolt	69-87 (94-118)
Strut Rod-to-Crossmember Nut	54-61 (73-83)
Strut-to-Steering Knuckle Bolt	54-65 (73-88)
Tie Rod-to-Knuckle Nut	11-25 (15-34)
	INCH Lbs. (N.m)
Strut-to-Body Nut	84-132 (10-15)

TIGHTENING SPECIFICATIONS (ALL OTHERS)

Application	Ft. Lbs. (N.m)
Ball Joint-to-Knuckle Nut	43-52 (58-71)
Brake Disc-to-Hub Bolt	36-43 (49-58)
Control Arm-to-Crossmember Bolt	
Colt Vista	
2WD	80-101 (109-137)
4WD	58-68 (79-92)
Cordia & Tredia	87-108 (118-146)
Drive Axle Nut	144-188 (195-255)
Lower Arm-Shaft Nut	
Colt & Mirage	69-87 (94-118)
Lower Arm Shaft-to-Body Bolt	
Colt & Mirage	116-137 (157-186)
Stabilizer Bar Mount To Crossmember Bolt	
Colt & Mirage	12-19 (16-26)
Stabilizer Bar-to-Strut Rod Hanger Nut	
Colt Vista	14-22 (19-30)
Cordia & Tredia (Turbo)	14-22 (19-30)
Strut Bearing Nut	
Colt, Mirage	25-36 (34-49)
All Others	43-50 (58-68)
Strut Rod-to-Control Arm Bolt	43-50 (58-68)
Strut Rod-to-Crossmember Nut	98-115 (133-156)
Strut-to-Body Nut	
Colt & Mirage	33-43 (45-58)
Colt Vista	22-29 (30-33)
Cordia & Tredia	18-25 (24-34)
Strut-to-Steering Knuckle Bolt	54-65 (73-88)
Support Bracket-to-Body Bolt	
Colt & Mirage	43-58 (58-79)
Tie Rod-to-Knuckle Nut	
Colt Vista	17-25 (23-34)
All Others	11-25 (15-34)
	INCH Lbs. (N.m)
Stabilizer Bar Hanger-to-Strut Rod Bolt	
Colt Vista, Cordia & Tredia (Turbo)	84-108 (9-12)

FORD MOTOR CO. FESTIVA

DESCRIPTION

Festiva models use MacPherson strut front suspension. The upper ends of the strut assemblies are attached to the shock towers and the lower ends are attached to the spindle carrier. A stabilizer bar is used on all models. *See Fig. 2.*

Fig. 2: Front Suspension Assembly

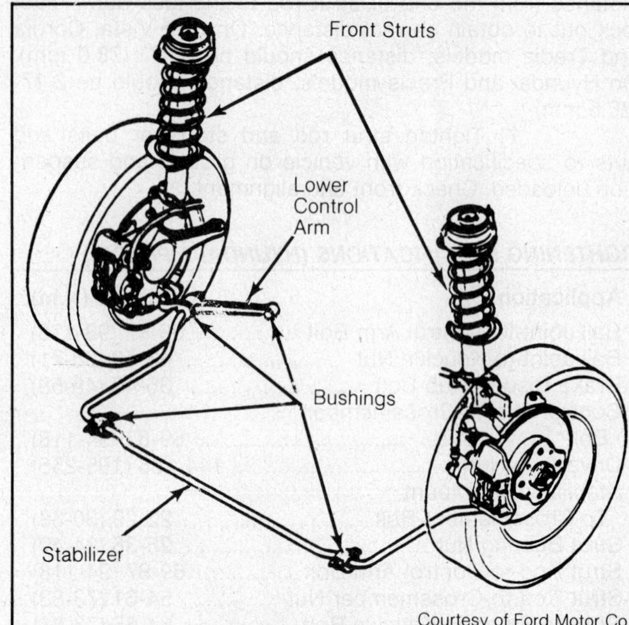

Courtesy of Ford Motor Co.

ADJUSTMENTS & INSPECTION

WHEEL ALIGNMENT SPECIFICATIONS & PROCEDURES

See WHEEL ALIGNMENT SPECIFICATIONS & PROCEDURES in WHEEL ALIGNMENT section.

WHEEL BEARING

Wheel bearing preload is maintained by a selective spacer in the steering knuckle between the inner and outer bearings and races on the hub between the inner races. *See Fig. 1.* For adjustment and inspection, see WHEEL BEARING, REMOVAL & INSTALLATION section in this article.

BALL JOINT CHECKING

1) Raise and support vehicle until tire is just off ground. Move wheel vertically and check for play. If play is present, have an assistant move wheel vertically and check for movement in lower ball joint.

Fig. 1: Exploded View of Hub Assembly

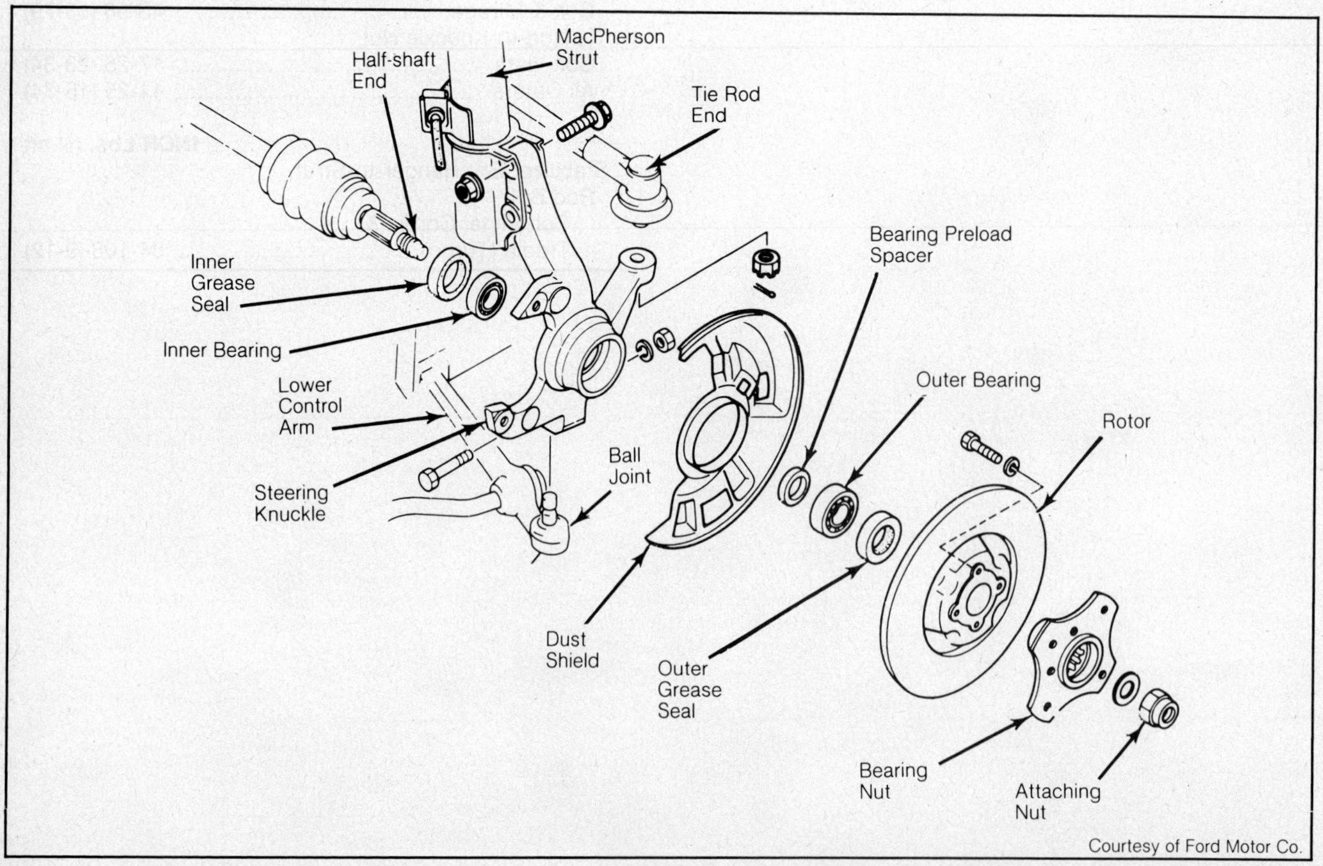

Courtesy of Ford Motor Co.

FORD MOTOR CO. FESTIVA (Cont.)

2) If play is noticed between spindle carrier and control arm, control arm assembly should be replaced. If play is present but ball joint is okay, wheel bearings should be checked for wear.

REMOVAL & INSTALLATION

WHEEL BEARING

Removal

1) Remove spindle carrier. See SPINDLE CARRIER REMOVAL. Using Knuckle Puller (T87C-1104-A), remove wheel hub/rotor assembly from steering knuckle/dust shield assembly.

NOTE: Removal of press-fitted dust shield from steering knuckle is not part of normal bearing service.

2) Remove bearing preload spacer from hub. Spacer is preselected to provide correct bearing preload. Ensure correct spacer is installed during reassembly. Install hub/rotor assembly in a vise. Scribe alignment marks on hub and rotor for reassembly reference.

3) Remove rotor attaching bolts and rotor. Using Bearing Splitter (D84L-1123-A), Shaft Protector (D80L-625-2) and a press, remove outer bearing from wheel hub. Remove and discard outer and inner grease seals. Using Bearing Puller (T77F-1102-A) and Slide Hammer (T-50T-100-A), remove races from steering knuckle. *See Fig. 3.*

Fig. 3: Outer Bearing Removal

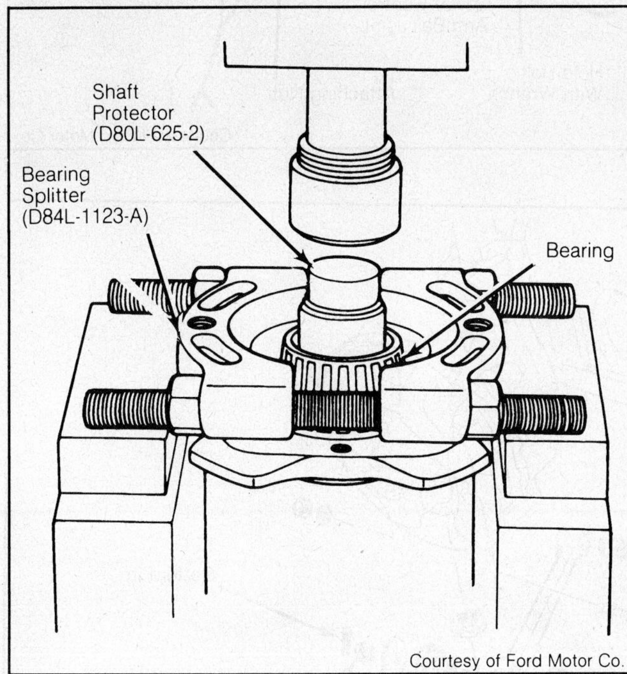

Courtesy of Ford Motor Co.

Inspection

Throughly clean all parts in solvent. Check bearings, hub, knuckle and rotor dust shield for excessive wear or damage.

Installation

1) Using Bearing Cup Replacer (D79P-1202-A) and Universal Driver Handle (T80T-4000-W), install outer bearing races in steering knuckle. Lubricate bearing races and bearing with a thin film of engine oil. Install bearings in steering knuckle. *See Fig. 4.*

Fig. 4: Bearing Race Installation

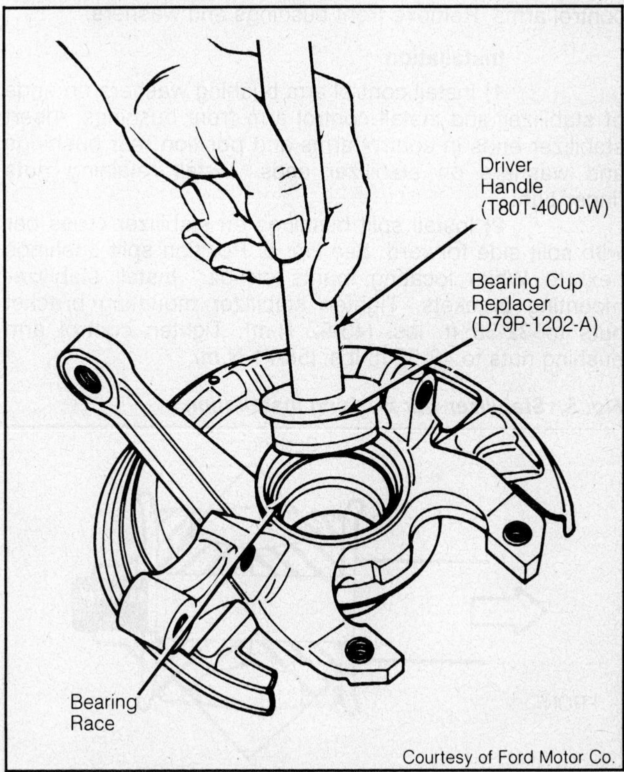

Courtesy of Ford Motor Co.

2) Install Spacer Selection Tool (T87C-1104-B) and clamp bolt head in vise. Tighten center bolt, in order, to 36, 72, 108 and finally 145 ft. lbs. (49, 98, 147 and 196 N.m). After center bolt is tightened, seat the bearings by rotating steering knuckle.

3) Remove steering knuckle from vise. Reinstall steering knuckle in vise, clamping it where shock absorber mounts. Using a torque wrench, measure torque required to rotate spacer selector tool. Ensure torque reading is taken just as wrench starts to rotate.

4) Spacer thickness is correct if torque wrench indicates 2.21-10.44 INCH lbs. (.25-1.8 N.m). If measurement indicates less than 2.21 INCH lbs. (.25 N.m), a thinner spacer must be installed. If measurement indicates more than 10.44 INCH lbs. (1.8 N.m), a thicker spacer must be installed.

5) Bearing spacers are available in 21 thicknesses, in .0016" (.040 mm) increments. Spacer No. "1" is thinnest and No. "21" is thickest. Changing spacer thickness one increment will change bearing preload 1.7-3.5 INCH lbs. (.2-.4 N.m).

6) Using Dust Shield Replacer (T87C-1175-B) and Driver Handle (T80T-4000-W), replace brake rotor dust shield. Install bearing races in steering knuckle. Pack bearings and hub area with Lubricant (C1A2-1959D-B). Position inner bearing into steering knuckle bore so it rests level. Lubricate seal lips. Using Seal Replacer (T78C-1175-A) and driver handle, drive seal into bore.

Front Suspension

FORD MOTOR CO. FESTIVA (Cont.)

STABILIZER BAR

Removal

1) Remove stabilizer mounting bracket nuts and brackets. Remove split bushings from stabilizer bar. Remove stabilizer bushing nuts at lower control arms. Remove rear dished washers and bushings.

2) Pull stabilizer bar forward to loosen from control arms. Remove front bushings and washers.

Installation

1) Install control arm bushing washers on ends of stabilizer and install control arm front bushings. Insert stabilizer ends in control arms and position rear bushings and washers on stabilizer ends. Install retaining nuts finger-tight.

2) Install split bushings on stabilizer cross bar with split side forward. *See Fig. 5.* Position split bushings next to White locating marks on bar. Install stabilizer mounting brackets. Tighten stabilizer mounting bracket nuts to 32-38 ft. lbs. (43-52 N.m). Tighten control arm bushing nuts to 43-52 ft. lbs. (58-71 N.m).

Fig. 5: Stabilizer Bar Bushing Installation

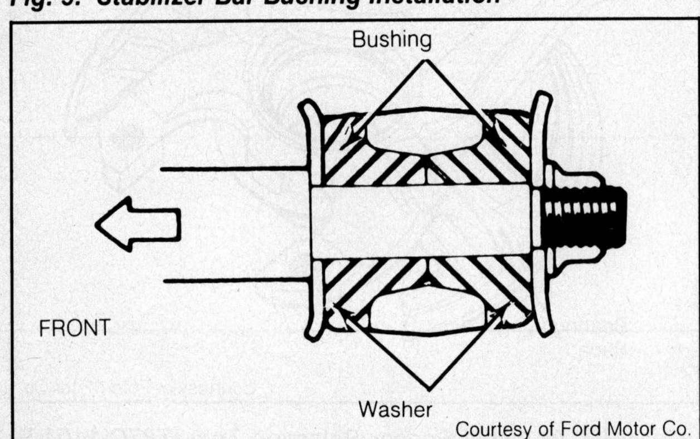

BALL JOINT & CONTROL ARM

Removal

1) Remove lower control arm pivot bolt at frame bracket. Remove ball joint clamp bolt and nut from steering knuckle assembly. Remove stabilizer bushing retaining nut from rear of control arm. Remove rear bushing washer and bushing.

Fig. 7: Control Arm Removal

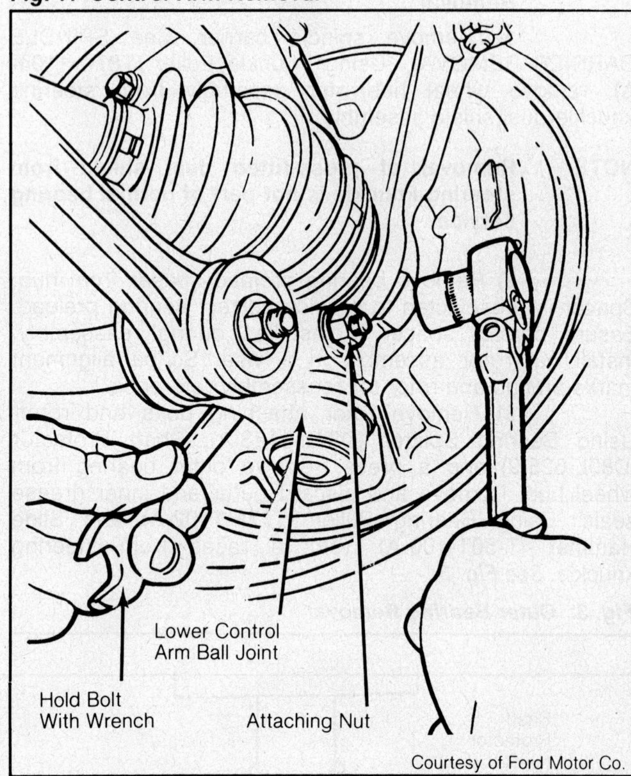

Fig. 6: Exploded View of Lower Control Arm Assembly

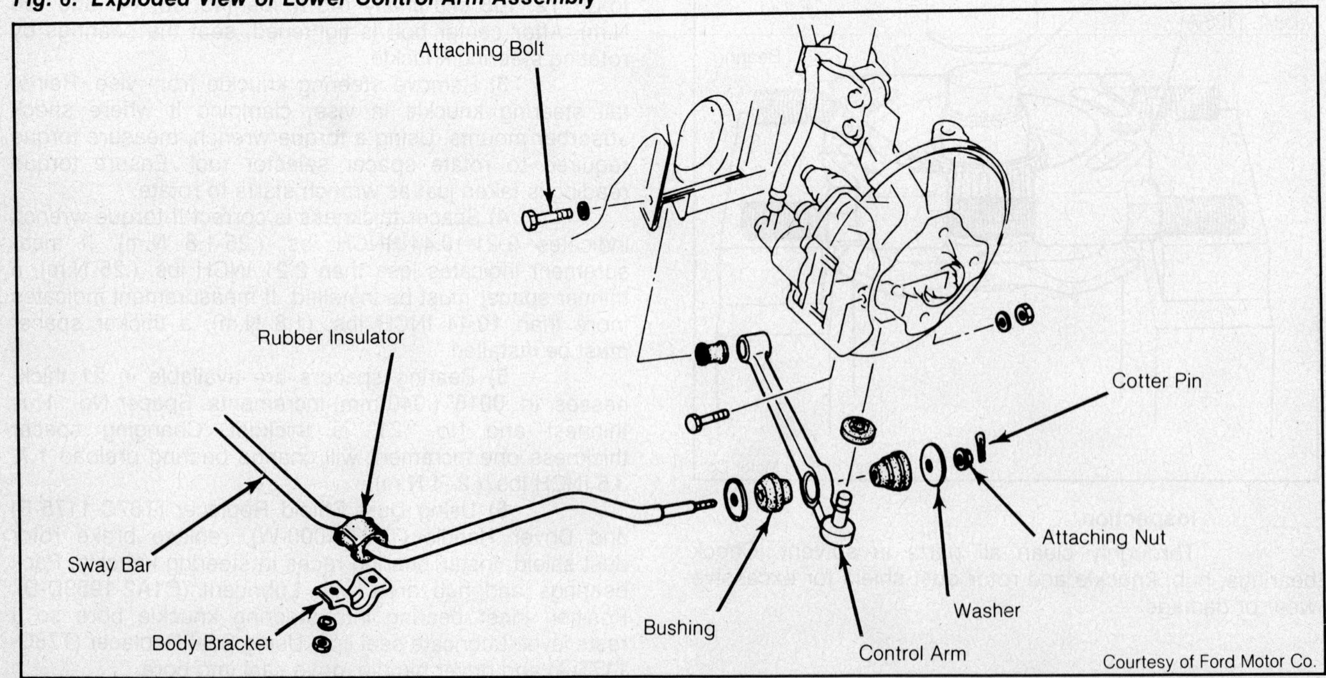

FORD MOTOR CO. FESTIVA (Cont.)

2) Lower the control arm and pry ball joint stud out of steering knuckle. Disconnect control arm from stabilizer end and remove. *See Fig. 7.*

3) Engage control arm ball joint stud with clamp bore in steering knuckle. Install clamp bolt and nut. Install stabilizer rear bushing and washer with dished side forward on stabilizer end. Tighten retaining nut to 43-52 ft. lbs. (58-71 N.m). Tighten pivot bolt at control arm frame bracket to 32-40 ft. lbs. (43-54 N.m). *See Fig. 6.*

4) Hold steering knuckle clamp bolt with a backup wrench. Tighten nut to 32-40 ft. lbs. (43-54 N.m).

Installation

1) Install front bushing washer with dished side forward. Position bushing stabilizer end and engage control arm with stabilizer. Raise control arm inner end into pivot bracket on frame. Install pivot bolt to hold it in position.

Inspection

Check control arm and pivot bushing for excessive wear or damage. Ensure ball joint stud moves freely but is not loose. Ensure ball joint rotating torque is within 16-27 INCH lbs. (1.8-3.1 N.m).

CONTROL ARM BUSHING

Removal & Installation

1) Remove control arm from vehicle. See BALL JOINT & CONTROL ARM. Use Bushing Receiver Cup (T81P-5493-B1), Bushing Pilot (T81P-5493-B2) and "C" Clamp Assembly (T74P-3044-A1) to remove control arm bushing.

2) To install, press bushing into control arm using Bushing Replacer Cup (T81P-5493-B3), bushing pilot and "C" clamp assembly.

NOTE: **Insert bushing quickly and smoothly. Bushing should only be distorted for a short time. Install control arm.**

STRUT ASSEMBLY

Removal

1) Raise and support front of vehicle so struts are fully extended. Remove front wheels. Remove brake line clip from strut lower mounting bracket and remove brake line.

Fig. 8: Exploded View of Strut Assembly

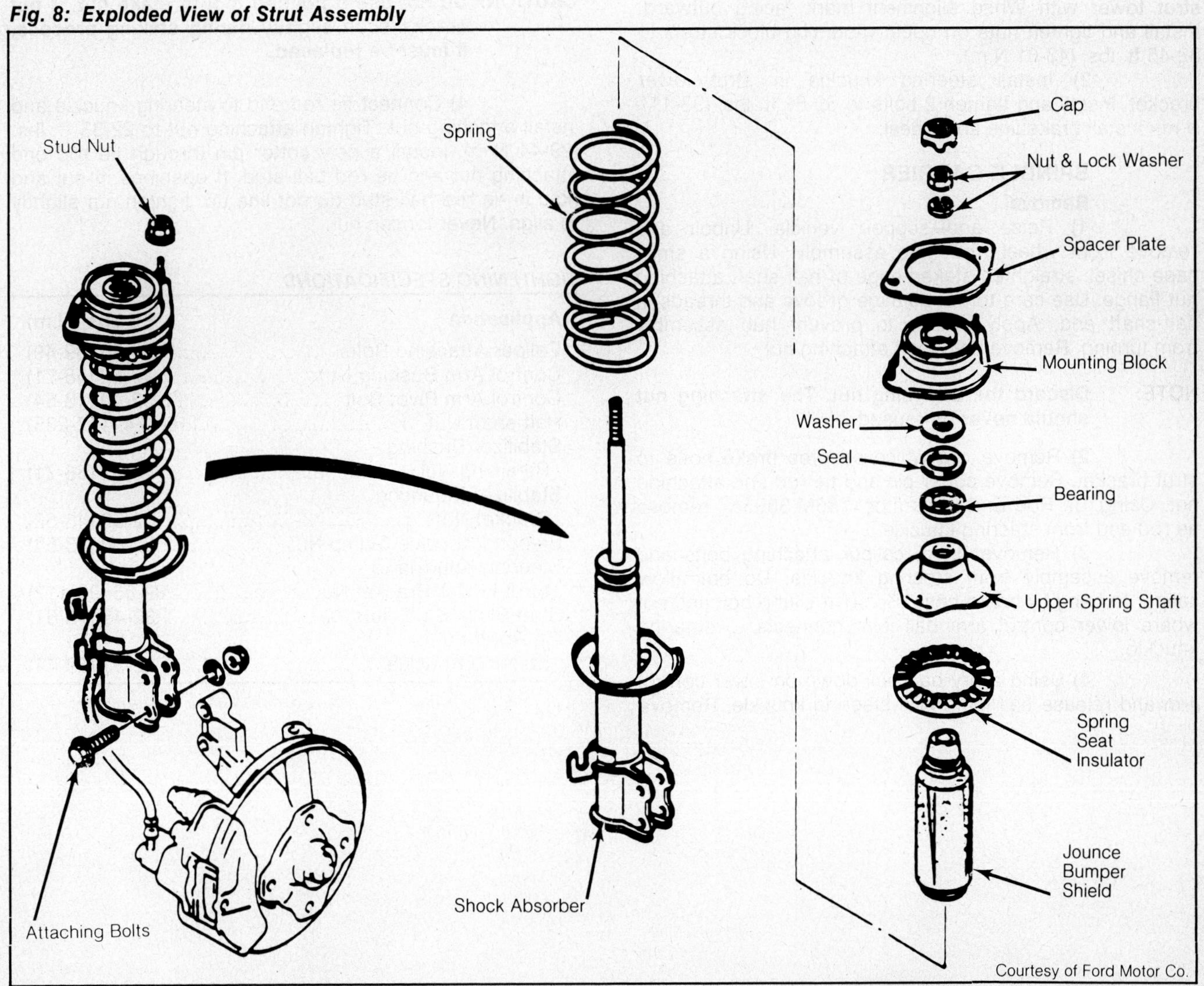

FORD MOTOR CO. FESTIVA (Cont.)

2) Remove 2 bolts which retain strut lower bracket to steering knuckle. Working inside engine compartment, remove 2 nuts which retain strut mounting block in strut tower. Disengage strut lower bracket from steering knuckle and lower strut from vehicle.

Disassembly

1) Using Spring Compressor (T81P-5310-A) or Rotunda Spring Compressor (086-00029), compress spring to unload strut. Pry out mounting blockcap and remove strut upper nut and lock washer.

2) Remove strut mounting block and spacer plate. Remove washer, bearing seal and bearing from strut rod. Remove spring upper seat, seat insulator and spring. Remove jounce bumper and shield from strut. *See Fig. 8.*

CAUTION: **During spring replacement, release spring compressor alternately to prevent spring arching. When installing a new spring, ensure compressor jaws are open wide enough to grip new spring in same position.**

Installation

1) Position strut, with spacer plate installed, in strut tower with White alignment mark facing outward. Install and tighten nuts on upper mounting block studs to 32-45 ft. lbs. (43-61 N.m).

2) Install steering knuckle in strut lower bracket. Install and tighten 2 bolts to 69-86 ft. lbs. (93-117 N.m). Install brake line and wheel.

SPINDLE CARRIER

Removal

1) Raise and support vehicle. Unbolt and remove front wheel from hub assembly. Using a small cape chisel, straighten staked edge of half-shaft attaching nut flange. Use care to not damage groove and threads in half-shaft end. Apply brakes to prevent hub assembly from turning. Remove half-shaft attaching nut.

NOTE: **Discard the attaching nut. The attaching nut should never be reused.**

2) Remove clip which secures brake hose to strut bracket. Remove cotter pin and tie rod end attaching nut. Using Tie Rod End Separator (T85M-3395A), remove tie rod end from steering knuckle.

3) Remove brake caliper attaching bolts and remove assembly from steering knuckle. Do not allow caliper to hang by brake hose. Remove clamp bolt and nut where lower control arm ball joint connects to steering knuckle.

4) Using a pry bar, pull down on lower control arm and release ball joint from steering knuckle. Remove 2 through bolts which attach steering knuckle between flanges of MacPherson strut bracket. Slide rotor/hub assembly off end of half-shaft. If binding is present or wheel hub is rusted to half-shaft, use a hub puller for removal.

Installation

1) Glide steering knuckle/rotor/hub assembly onto half-shaft and along prelubricated splines. Apply a thin coat of SAE 30 weight oil. Stop at area where uppermost arm of steering knuckle seats into MacPherson strut bracket.

2) Install strut to steering knuckle through bolts and attaching nuts. Tighten attaching nuts to 69-86 ft. lbs. (93-97 N.m). Position lower control arm ball joint in steering knuckle. Install lower control arm bolt and attaching nut. Tighten attaching nut to 32-40 ft. lbs. (43-54 N.m). Install caliper assembly on steering knuckle and install attaching bolts. Tighten caliper attaching bolts to 29-36 ft. lbs. (39-49 N.m).

3) Position caliper hose in strut routing bracket and install retaining clip. Install new half-shaft attaching nut. Tighten attaching nut to 116-174 ft. lbs. (157-235 N.m). Stake half-shaft attaching nut into shaft groove.

CAUTION: **Do not use a pointed tool to stake nut. If nut cracks even slightly during staking process, it must be replaced.**

4) Connect tie rod end to steering knuckle and install attaching nut. Tighten attaching nut to 22-33 ft. lbs. (29-44 N.m). Install a new cotter pin through tie rod end attaching nut and tie rod ball stud. If openings in nut and hold in tie rod ball stud do not line up, tighten nut slightly to align. Never loosen nut.

TIGHTENING SPECIFICATIONS

Application	Ft. Lbs (N.m)
Caliper Attaching Bolts	29-36 (39-49)
Control Arm Bushing Nuts	43-52 (58-71)
Control Arm Pivot Bolt	32-40 (43-54)
Half-shaft Nut	116-174 (157-235)
Stabilizer Bushing Retaining Nut	43-52 (58-71)
Stabilizer Mounting Bracket Nuts	32-38 (43-52)
Steering Knuckle Clamp Nut	32-40 (43-54)
Steering Knuckle-to-Strut Lower Bracket Nut	69-86 (93-117)
Strut Block Stud Nuts	32-45 (43-61)
Tie Rod End-to-Steering Knuckle	22-33 (29-44)

Front Suspension

FORD MOTOR CO. MERKUR XR4Ti

NOTE: For information on the Ford Motor Co. Tracer front suspension, see FORD MOTOR CO. TRACER & MAZDA RX7 323 & 626 article in this section.

DESCRIPTION

Merkur XR4Ti models use MacPherson strut front suspension. The upper ends of the strut assemblies are attached to the shock towers and the lower ends are attached to the spindle carrier. A stabilizer bar is used on all models. *See Fig. 1.*

ADJUSTMENTS & INSPECTION

WHEEL ALIGNMENT SPECIFICATIONS & PROCEDURES

See WHEEL ALIGNMENT SPECIFICATIONS & PROCEDURES in WHEEL ALIGNMENT section.

WHEEL BEARING

Wheel bearing preload is not adjustable.

BALL JOINT CHECKING

1) Raise and support vehicle until tire is just off ground. Move wheel vertically and check for play. If play is present, have an assistant move wheel vertically and check for movement in lower ball joint.

2) If play is noticed between spindle carrier and control arm, control arm assembly should be replaced. If play is present but ball joint is okay, wheel bearings should be checked for wear.

REMOVAL & INSTALLATION

WHEEL BEARING

Removal

1) Remove spindle carrier. See SPINDLE CARRIER REMOVAL. Install a metric nut on each wheel stud. Tighten nuts and install spindle in soft-jawed vise.

2) Vise jaws should grip wheel nuts and spindle lock nut cover plate should face upward. DO NOT overtighten spindle in vise.

NOTE: The spindle lock nut may have left-hand or right-hand threads. The left side spindle nut has right-hand threads and a Blue Nylock insert. The right side spindle nut has left-hand threads and a Yellow Nylock insert.

3) Remove spindle lock nut cover plate. Remove spindle bearing lock nut and lift spindle carrier (and bearing) from spindle shaft. Remove inner bearing and splined washer from spindle.

4) If bearings will be reused, tag bearing for reassembly reference. Clamp spindle carrier in vise and remove outer bearing seal. Remove outer bearing from spindle carrier. Tag outer bearing for reassembly reference.

5) Use Bearing Cup Remover (T77F-1102-A) and a slide hammer to remove outer bearing cup. Carefully remove inner bearing race. Bearing puller jaws MUST NOT contact bearing cup seat (in center of hub). If bearings are being reused, tag bearing races for reassembly reference.

NOTE: Use care not to create a burr on bearing race seat when pulling bearing race.

Fig. 1: Merkur XR4Ti Front Suspension Assembly

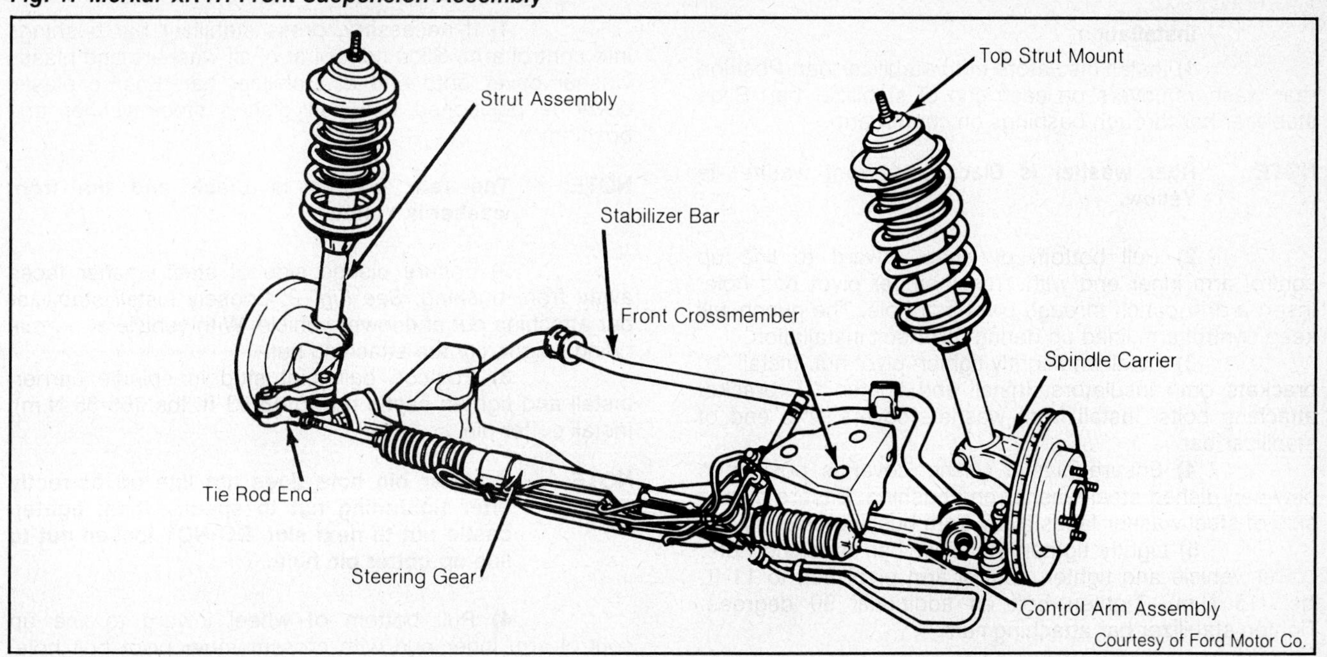

FORD MOTOR CO. MERKUR XR4Ti (Cont.)

Inspection

1) Throughly clean all parts in solvent. Blow dry all components using compressed air. Examine spindle carrier carefully for damaged caliper anchor bolt threads, damaged spindle carrier pinch bolt threads, worn bearing races and tapered or worn lower control arm or tie rod joints.

2) In addition, carrier must be checked for cracks in casting and worn or damaged suspension strut seat. Inspect carrier flange shaft for damaged or loose wheel studs, worn or scored bearing surfaces and pitted or scored seal surfaces.

NOTE: **Always replace bearings and races as a matched set.**

Installation

To install, reverse removal procedure. Before installing bearings, pack thoroughly using Lubricant (C1AZ-1959D-B, C, D or E). Do not pack grease into space between bearings.

NOTE: **When tightening spindle bearing lock nut, observe tightening specification. Over or under tightening of bearing can cause premature bearing failure. Ensure torque wrench is properly calibrated.**

STABILIZER BAR

Removal

1) Remove stabilizer bar attaching nuts and front washers. Remove "U" bracket that attaches stabilizer bar and body torque brace to body. Remove one of the control arm pivot bolts at crossmember.

2) Pull stabilizer bar out of control arms. Remove rear washers/covers from stabilizer bar ends. Remove insulators from stabilizer bar.

Installation

1) Install insulators onto stabilizer bar. Position rear washers/covers on each end of stabilizer bar. Slide stabilizer bar through bushings on control arms.

NOTE: **Rear washer is Black and front washer is Yellow.**

2) Pull bottom of wheel inward to line up control arm inner end with crossmember pivot bolt hole. Insert a drift punch through pivot bolt hole. The punch will keep control arm lined up during pivot bolt installation.

3) Install and lightly tighten pivot nut. Install "U" brackets onto insulators. Install and tighten "U" bracket attaching bolts. Install front washers/covers onto end of stabilizer bar.

4) Ensure plastic washer/cover is positioned between dished steel washer and bushing. Ensure dished side of steel washer faces away from bushing. *See Fig. 2.*

5) Lightly tighten stabilizer bar attaching nuts. Lower vehicle and tighten control arm pivot bolt to 11 ft. lbs. (15 N.m). Tighten bolt an additional 90 degrees. Tighten stabilizer bar attaching nuts.

Fig. 2: Cutaway View of Control Arm Bushing Assembly

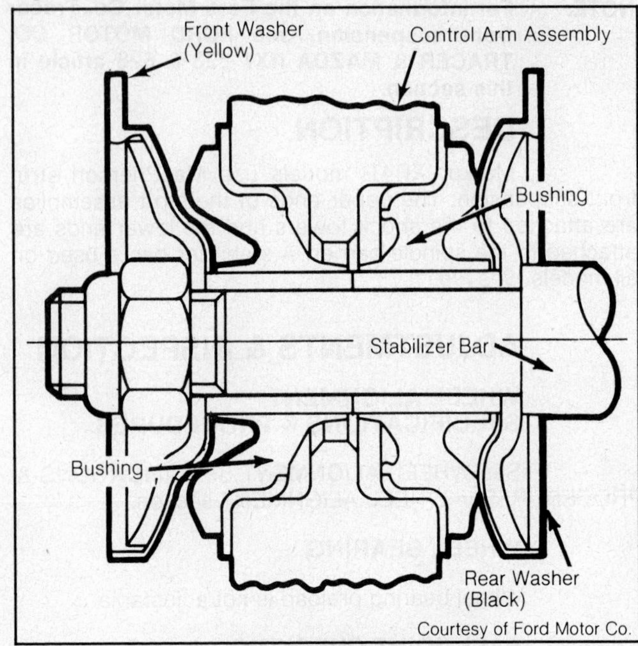

Courtesy of Ford Motor Co.

BALL JOINT & CONTROL ARM

Removal

1) Remove ball joint cotter pin and castle nut. Carefully separate control arm from spindle carrier. Remove control arm pivot bolt at crossmember.

2) Remove stabilizer bar attaching nut and front washer at control arm. Pull control arm and bushings from stabilizer bar as an assembly. If necessary, stabilizer bar bushings can be removed from control arm. See CONTROL ARM BUSHING.

Installation

1) If necessary, press stabilizer bar bushings into control arm. Slide control arm, all washers and plastic washer cover onto end of stabilizer bar. Ensure plastic cover is positioned between dished steel washer and bushing.

NOTE: **The rear washer is Black and the front washer is Yellow.**

2) Ensure dished side of steel washer faces away from bushing. *See Fig. 2.* Loosely install stabilizer bar attaching nut and lower vehicle. With vehicle at normal riding height, tighten attaching nut.

3) Position ball joint stud in spindle carrier. Install and tighten castle nut to 48-63 ft. lbs. (65-85 N.m). Install cotter pin.

NOTE: **If cotter pin hole does not line up correctly after tightening nut to specification, tighten castle nut to next slot. DO NOT loosen nut to line up cotter pin hole.**

4) Pull bottom of wheel inward to line up control arm inner end with crossmember pivot bolt hole. Insert a drift punch through pivot bolt hole. The punch will keep control arm lined up during pivot bolt installation.

FORD MOTOR CO. MERKUR XR4Ti (Cont.)

5) Slide pivot bolt through crossmember and control arm inner bushing. Lightly tighten pivot nut. Lower vehicle and tighten control arm pivot bolt to 11 ft. lbs. (15 N.m). Tighten bolt an additional 90 degrees. Tighten stabilizer bar attaching nut.

CONTROL ARM BUSHING

Removal & Installation

1) Remove control arm from vehicle. See BALL JOINT & CONTROL ARM. Use Bushing Receiver Cup (T81P-5493-B1), Bushing Pilot (T81P-5493-B2) and "C" Clamp Assembly (T74P-3044-A1) to remove control arm bushing.

2) To install, press bushing into control arm using Bushing Replacer Cup (T81P-5493-B3), bushing pilot and "C" clamp assembly.

NOTE: Insert bushing quickly and smoothly. Bushing should only be distorted for a short time. Install control arm.

STRUT ASSEMBLY

NOTE: If using a 2 post hoist to remove strut assembly, raise vehicle and install safety supports under front crossmember. After installing safety supports, lower forward post.

Removal

1) Remove front wheels. Raise and support vehicle about 4 feet from ground (the upper strut mount bolt should remain accessible). Remove strut pinch bolt from spindle carrier. The bolt is located at bottom of strut assembly. Insert Splindle Carrier Lever (T85M-3206-A) into slot in spindle carrier.

2) Rotate spindle carrier lever 90 degrees to open slot. Push rotor assembly downward just enough to release spindle carrier from strut assembly. If spindle carrier is dropped too far, brake hose may be damaged.

3) Remove protective cap from strut rod upper attaching nut. Hold strut piston (using a 6 mm Allen wrench) and loosen strut upper mounting nut. Support bottom of strut assembly. Remove and discard upper mounting nut.

Disassembly

1) Mount Strut Spring Compressor (Rotunda 086-00016) in soft-jawed vise. Adjust compressor to "START" position. Carefully compress coil spring. Hold strut piston (using a 6 mm Allen wrench) and loosen coil spring retaining nut.

2) Slowly release coil spring tension. Remove strut top mount cup, bearing, upper spring seat and dust boot. *See Fig. 3.* Slide jounce bumper from piston shaft. Remove coil spring.

Reassembly

To reassemble, reverse disassembly procedure. Tighten coil spring retaining nut.

Installation

1) Position strut upper end through shock mount. Install retainer and a new top mount attaching nut.

Fig. 3: Exploded View of Strut Assembly

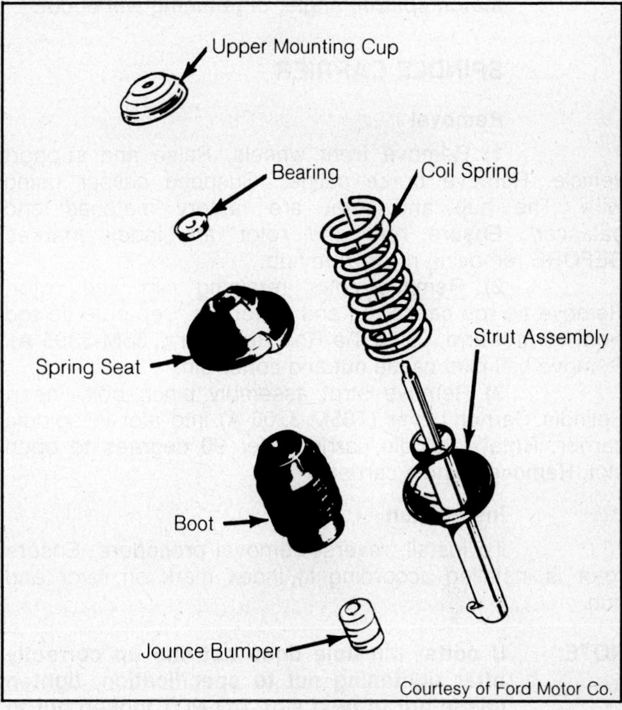

Do not tighten nut at this time. Pull bottom of strut outward and lift spindle upward using brake rotor. *See Fig. 4.*

2) Use spindle carrier lever to spread spindle carrier. This will allow strut to center in carrier. As strut moves into carrier, hold rotor and pivot spindle into position. To complete installation, reverse removal procedure.

Fig. 4: Installing Strut Assembly

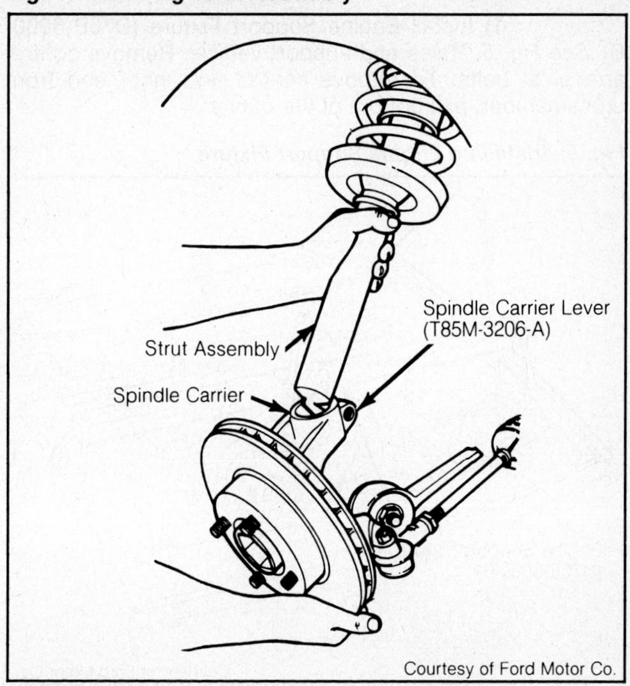

FORD MOTOR CO. MERKUR XR4Ti (Cont.)

NOTE: The spindle MUST be pulled outward to match spindle angle, or jamming will occur.

SPINDLE CARRIER

Removal

1) Remove front wheels. Raise and support vehicle. Remove brake caliper. Suspend caliper using wire. The hub and rotor are factory matched and balanced. Ensure hub and rotor are index marked BEFORE removing rotor from hub.

2) Remove rotor retaining clip and rotor. Remove tie rod castle nut and cotter pin. Separate tie rod from control arm, using Tie Rod Remover (T85M-3395-A). Remove ball joint castle nut and cotter pin.

3) Remove strut assembly pinch bolt. Insert Splindle Carrier Lever (T85M-3206-A) into slot in spindle carrier. Rotate spindle carrier lever 90 degrees to open slot. Remove spindle carrier.

Installation

To install, reverse removal procedure. Ensure rotor is installed according to index mark on rotor and hub.

NOTE: If cotter pin hole does not line up correctly after tightening nut to specification, tighten castle nut to next slot. DO NOT loosen nut to line up cotter pin hole.

CROSSMEMBER

NOTE: Set steering in straight-ahead position. Steering MUST remain in this position throughout the crossmember removal and installation procedure.

Removal

1) Install Engine Support Fixture (D76P-6000-B). *See Fig. 5.* Raise and support vehicle. Remove control arm pivot bolts. To remove control arm inner end from crossmember, pull bottom of tire outward.

Fig. 5: Installing Engine Support Fixture

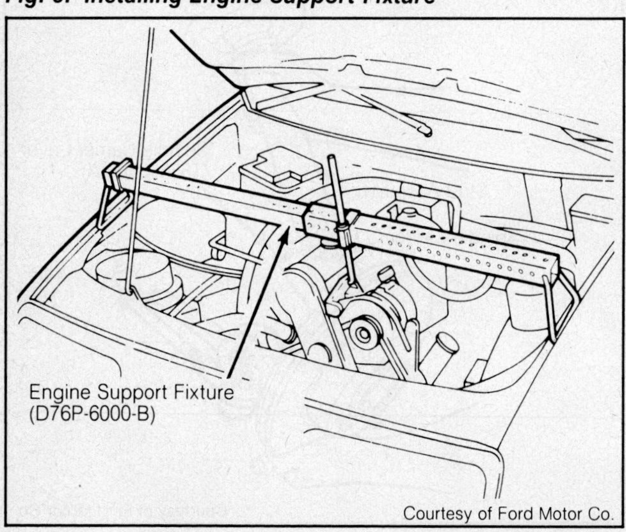

2) Remove steering column pinch bolt. *See Fig. 6.* Remove steering gear attaching bolts. Disengage steering gear from coupling. Slightly pull steering gear forward and away from crossmember.

NOTE: Use care not to damage power steering lines. Use wire to support the steering gear.

Fig. 6: Removing Steering Column Pinch Bolt

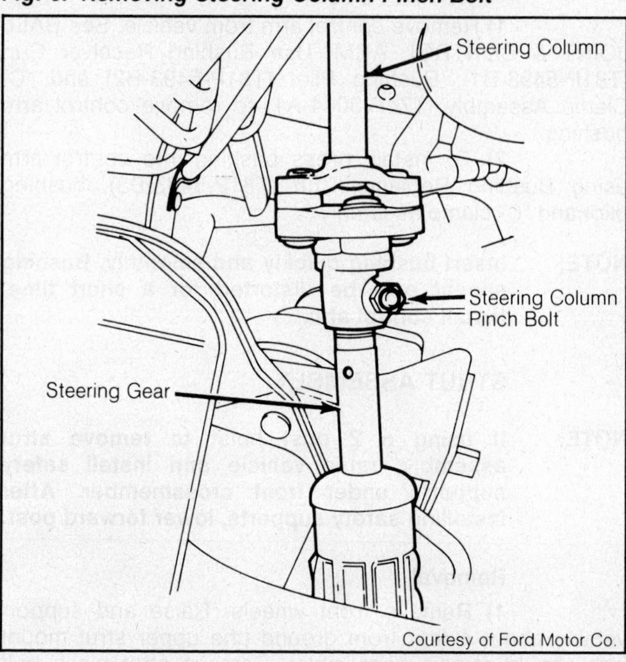

3) Remove engine mount lower stud nuts. Support crossmember using transmission jack. Remove bolts attaching crossmember to side rail. Lower crossmember from vehicle.

Installation

To install, reverse removal procedure. When installing steering gear on crossmember, ensure block splines are lined up correctly. In addition, vehicle must be at normal riding height before tightening control arm pivot bolt.

TIGHTENING SPECIFICATIONS

Application	Ft. Lbs (N.m)
Ball Joint Castle Nut	48-63 (65-85)
Coil Spring Retaining Nut	38-48 (52-65)
Control Arm Pivot Bolt [1]	11 (15)
Crossmember-to-Sidemember	
Attaching Bolts	51-66 (70-90)
Engine Mount-to-Crossmember Nut	38-47 (52-64)
Spindle Bearing Lock Nut	202-232 (274-315)
Stabilizer Bar-to-	
Control Arm	52-81 (70-110)
Body	42-52 (57-70)
Steering Coupling Pinch Bolt	18-22 (25-30)
Steering Gear Retaining Bolts [1]	11 (15)
Strut Assembly	
Pinch Bolt	59-66 (80-90)
Upper Attaching Nut	29-38 (40-52)

[1] – Tighten an additional 90 degrees.

Front Suspension

FORD MOTOR CO. TRACER & MAZDA RX7, 323 & 626

DESCRIPTION

An independent front suspension with MacPherson struts is used. Strut assemblies mount between steering knuckle and upper fender panels. Strut assemblies consist of inner shock absorbers and coil springs surrounding outside of strut tube housing.

The steering knuckle is connected to lower control arm and strut. Lower control arm pivots at crossmember and is connected by ball joint to steering knuckle. All models are equipped with a stabilizer bar which attaches to each lower control arm and frame.

ADJUSTMENTS & INSPECTION

WHEEL ALIGNMENT SPECIFICATIONS & PROCEDURES

See WHEEL ALIGNMENT SPECIFICATIONS & PROCEDURES in WHEEL ALIGNMENT section.

WHEEL BEARING

RX7

1) Raise and support vehicle. Remove brake caliper and support out of the way. Remove grease cap, cotter pin and nut lock. Loosen lock nut. Tighten to 14-22 ft. lbs. (20-29 N.m).

2) Turn wheel hub a few times to seat bearings. Loosen lock nut slightly until it can be turned by hand. Attach spring scale to hub bolt and measure preload. Note value.

3) Tighten lock nut until preload is .09-2.2 lbs. (3.9-9.8 N) more than amount measured in step **2)**. Reverse procedure to complete adjustment.

323 & Tracer

1) Raise and support vehicle. Remove wheei assembly. Remove brake caliper and wire out of way. Install a dial indicator against wheel hub and measure axial movement. Axial movement should be zero. If specification is exceeded, adjust preload or replace wheel bearing.

2) To adjust preload, remove knuckle assembly from vehicle (See WHEEL BEARING REMOVAL) and place in vise. Attach Spacer Selector (49 B001 727). Attach spring scale to caliper mounting hole and adjust preload to .53-2.55 lbs. (2.4-11.4 N) by tightening spacer selector.

3) Tighten spacer selector in steps of 36 ft. lbs. (49 N.m) to a maximum of 145 ft. lbs. (196 N.m). If preload is not within specification, change spacer to meet required preload specification.

4) Spacers are available in 21 sizes from .2474" (6.285 mm) to .2789" (7.085 mm) in increments of .0016" (.040 mm). Spacers are marked 1-21 to indicate size. Reverse procedure to complete adjustment.

NOTE: If bearing preload is too high, increase spacer thickness. If bearing preload is too low, decrease spacer thickness.

626

1) Raise and support vehicle. Remove wheel assembly. Remove brake caliper and wire out of way. Install a dial indicator against wheel hub and measure axial movement. Axial movement should not exceed .008" (.2 mm). If specification is exceeded, adjust preload or replace wheel bearing.

2) To adjust preload, loosen lock nut, then tighten by hand. Attach spring scale to hub bolt and measure preload. Note value. Reinstall brake caliper, apply brakes and tighten lock nut to 116-124 ft. lbs. (157-235 N.m).

Fig. 1: View of RX7 Front Suspension

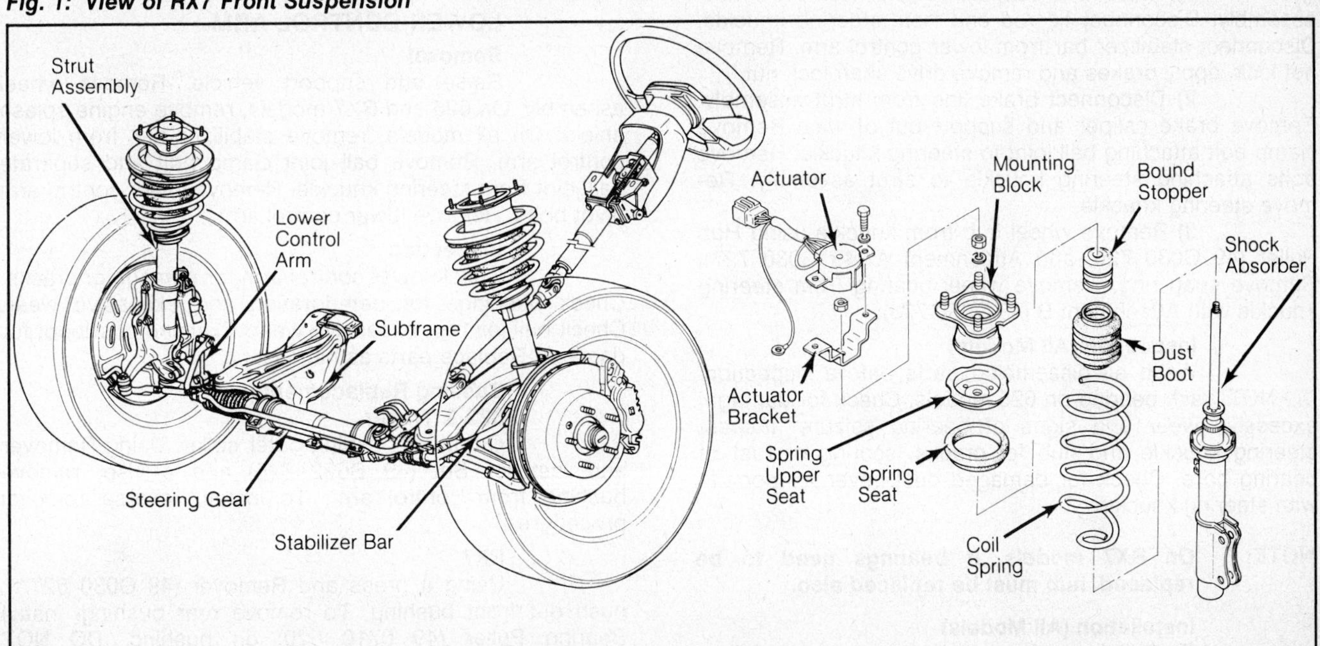

Courtesy of Mazda Motors Corp.

Front Suspension

FORD MOTOR CO. TRACER & MAZDA RX7, 323 & 626 (Cont.)

3) Remove brake caliper, attach spring scale to hub bolt and measure preload again. Preload should not exceed .44 lbs. (2.0 N) more than amount measured in step **2)**. Reverse procedure to complete adjustment.

BALL JOINT CHECKING

Remove lower control arm. Rotate ball joint stud 3-4 times. Install Preload Attachment (49 0180 510B) to ball joint stud. Measure ball joint preload using spring scale. Preload for all models is 4.4-7.7 lbs. (20-34 N).

REMOVAL & INSTALLATION

WHEEL BEARING

Removal (RX7)

Raise and support vehicle. Remove wheel assembly. Remove brake caliper and support out of way. Remove grease cap, cotter pin, nut lock and spindle nut. Remove washer and outer wheel bearing. Remove hub and rotor assembly. Remove inner oil seal and wheel bearing.

Removal (323 & Tracer)

1) Raise and support vehicle. Remove wheel assembly. Remove nut lock, apply brakes and remove drive shaft lock nut. Remove cotter pin and disconnect tie rod from steering knuckle.

2) Remove brake caliper and wire out of way. Remove ball joint clamp bolt and separate lower control arm from ball joint. Remove bolts retaining steering knuckle to strut assembly. Separate hub and knuckle from drive shaft.

3) Remove wheel hub and rotor from knuckle. Place alignment marks on rotor and wheel hub and separate. Remove dust cover. Remove bearings, oil seals, bearing outer races and spacer.

Removal (626)

1) Raise and support vehicle. Remove wheel assembly. Disconnect tie rod end from steering knuckle. Disconnect stabilizer bar from lower control arm. Remove nut lock, apply brakes and remove drive shaft lock nut.

2) Disconnect brake line from strut assembly. Remove brake caliper and support out of way. Remove clamp bolt attaching ball joint to steering knuckle. Remove bolts attaching steering knuckle to strut assembly. Remove steering knuckle.

3) Remove wheel hub from knuckle using Hub Puller (49 G030 725) and Attachment A (49 G030 727). Remove snap ring. Remove wheel bearing from steering knuckle with Attachment B (49 G030 728).

Inspection (All Models)

Wash all dissembled parts before inspection. DO NOT wash bearing on 626 models. Check for damage, excessive wear and signs of bearing seizure. Inspect steering knuckle and hub for cracks, scoring or rust of bearing bore. Check for damaged dust cover, or poor fit with steering knuckle.

NOTE: On RX7 models, if bearings need to be replaced, hub must be replaced also.

Installation (All Models)

To install, reverse removal procedure. Adjust wheel bearing preload. See WHEEL BEARING under ADJUSTMENTS & INSPECTION in this article.

Fig. 2: Exploded View of 323 & Tracer Front Suspension

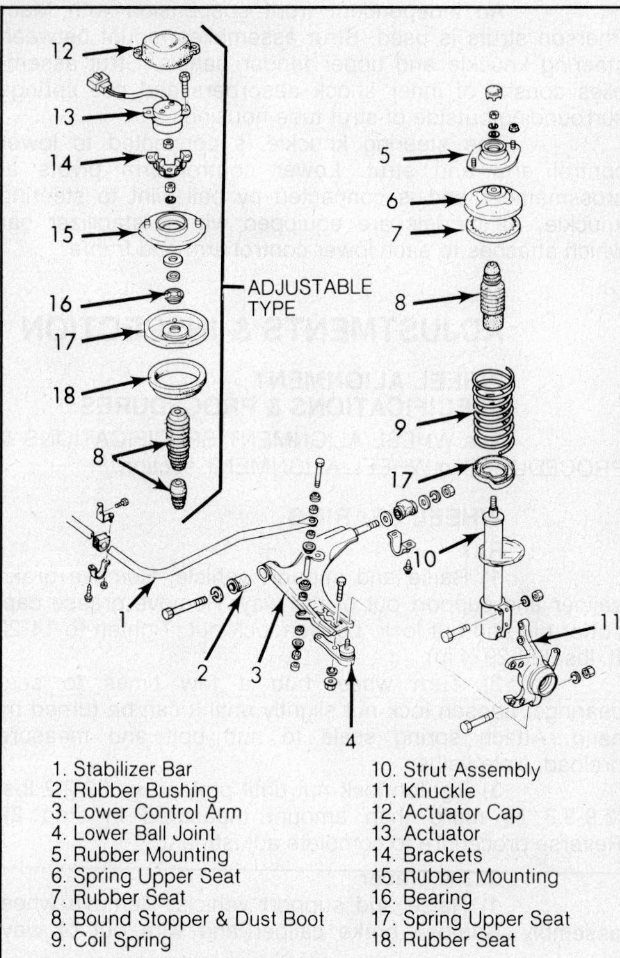

Courtesy of Mazda Motors Corp.

LOWER CONTROL ARM

Removal

Raise and support vehicle. Remove wheel assembly. On 626 and RX7 models, remove engine splash shield. On all models, remove stabilizer bar from lower control arm. Remove ball joint clamp bolt and separate ball joint from steering knuckle. Remove lower control arm pivot bolts. Remove lower control arm.

Inspection

Check lower control arm for damage or cracks. Check bushings for deterioration and excessive wear. Check ball joint for excessive wear. Examine dust boot for damage. Replace parts as necessary.

Bushing Replacement

323 & Tracer

Cut away bushing outer collar. Using Remover and Installer Set (49 B092 625) and a vise, remove bushing from control arm. To install, reverse removal procedure.

RX7

Using a press and Remover (49 G030 627A), push out front bushing. To remove rear bushing, install Bearing Puller (49 0710 520) on bushing. DO NOT overtighten bearing puller nuts or lower arm will be distorted and damaged. Use Remover (49 G030 627A) and

Front Suspension

FORD MOTOR CO. TRACER & MAZDA RX7, 323 & 626 (Cont.)

Fig. 3: View of 626 Front Suspension

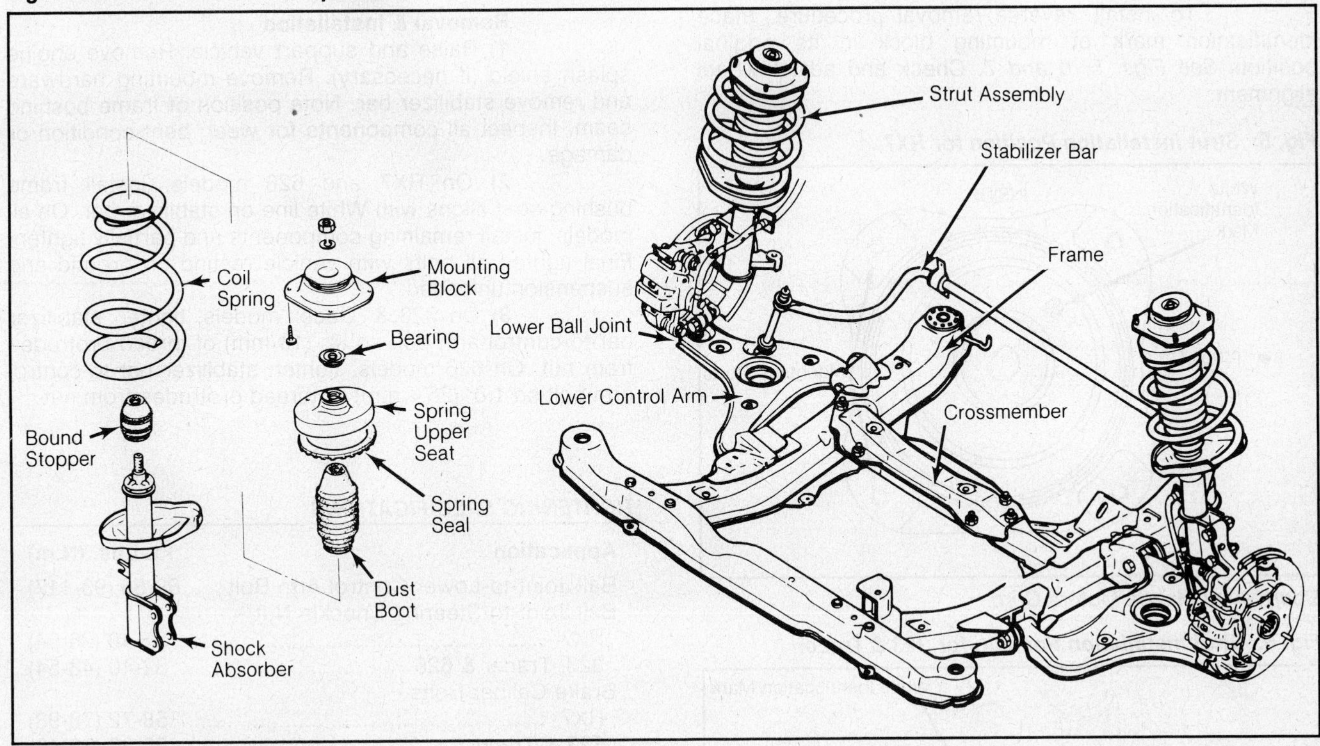

Courtesy of Mazda Motors Corp.

press to push out rear bushing. To install both bushings, use remover and Support Block (49 0823 146).

626

Cut away bushing inner collar. Using a vise, Support Block (49 G030 626A) and Remover (49 G030 627A), push out bushing. To install, apply soapy water to bushing and use Guide (49 G030 628A) and remover to press in. Always install bushing from outer side of arm. Press in bushing until collar contacts arm. *See Fig. 4*.

Installation (All Models)

To install, reverse removal procedure. Tighten lower control arm pivot bolts to specification with vehicle resting on ground and suspension unloaded.

STRUT ASSEMBLY

NOTE: **Loosen strut top mounting nut before removing strut assembly from vehicle. Prior to removing strut-to-steering knuckle bolts, make an alignment mark for reassembly reference. Note position of mounting mark on top of strut assembly before removing strut.**

Removal

1) Raise and support vehicle. Remove wheel assembly. On RX7 models, remove brake caliper and hang out of way. On all models, disconnect brake line from strut assembly. Remove bolts attaching steering knuckle arm to strut assembly.

2) Disconnect harness connector from actuator (if equipped). Remove bolts, actuator and actuator mounting bracket from upper mounting block. Remove nuts attaching upper strut assembly to body panel. Remove strut assembly.

Fig. 4: Installing Lower Control Arm Bushing on 626

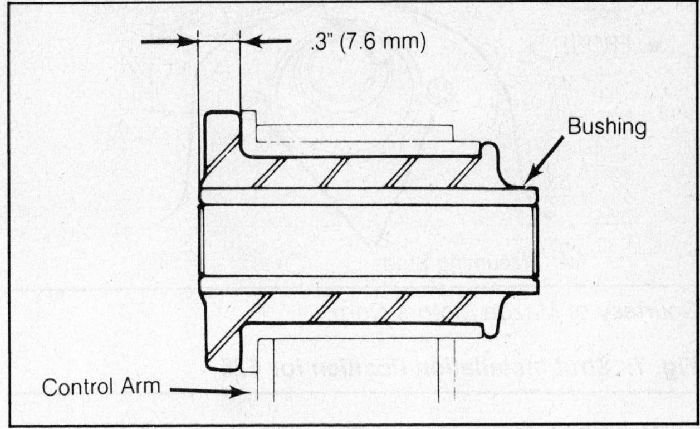

Courtesy of Mazda Motors Corp.

Disassembly

Clamp strut in vise. Compress coil spring using coil spring compressor. Remove components. Remove coil spring. Remove strut from vise.

Inspection

Check strut tube for cracks, damage, oil leakage and abnormal noise. Check rubber parts for deterioration or damage. Inspect coil spring for signs of fatigue or damage. Check control rod of strut assembly for smooth rotation (if equipped). Replace parts as needed.

Reassembly

Clamp strut in vise. Install coil spring and components in reverse order of disassembly. Ensure that coil spring is well seated in upper and lower spring seats. On 626 models, ensure upper spring seat positioning hole faces inside of vehicle.

Front Suspension

FORD MOTOR CO. TRACER & MAZDA RX7, 323 & 626 (Cont.)

Installation

To install, reverse removal procedure. Place identification mark of mounting block in its original position. *See Figs. 5, 6 and 7*. Check and adjust wheel alignment.

Fig. 5: Strut Installation Position for RX7

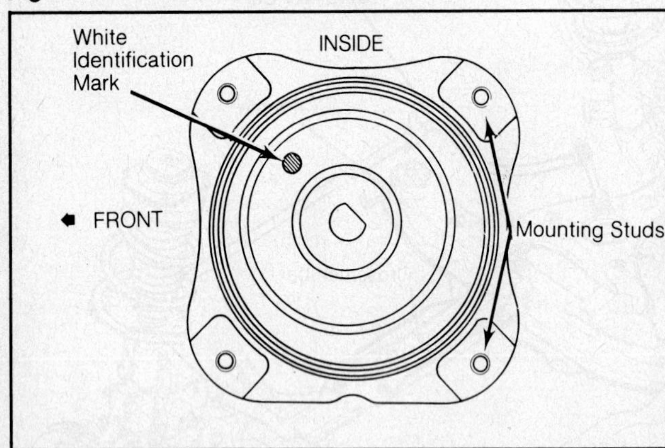

Courtesy of Mazda Motors Corp.

Fig. 6: Strut Installation Position for 323 & Tracer

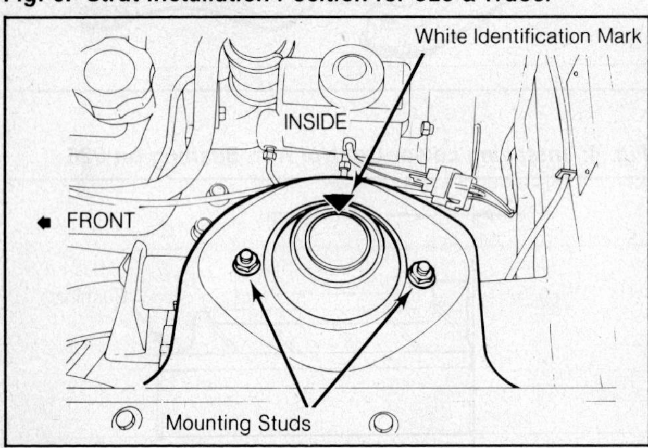

Courtesy of Mazda Motors Corp.

Fig. 7: Strut Installation Position for 626

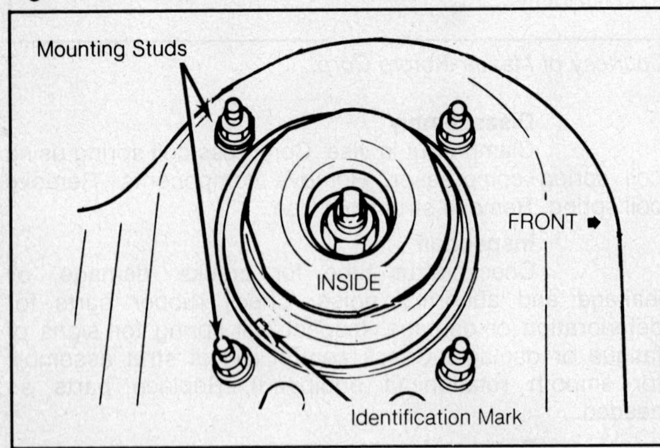

Courtesy of Mazda Motors Corp.

STABILIZER BAR

Removal & Installation

1) Raise and support vehicle. Remove engine splash shield (if necessary). Remove mounting hardware and remove stabilizer bar. Note position of frame bushing seam. Inspect all components for wear, bent condition or damage.

2) On RX7 and 626 models, install frame bushing so it aligns with White line on stabilizer bar. On all models, install remaining components and partially tighten. Final tighten all bolts with vehicle resting on ground and suspension unloaded.

3) On 323 & Tracer models, tighten stabilizer bar-to-control arm bolt so .4" (10 mm) of thread protrudes from nut. On 626 models, tighten stabilizer bar-to-control arm bolt so 1.0" (25.4 mm) of thread protrudes from nut.

TIGHTENING SPECIFICATIONS

Application	Ft. Lbs. (N.m)
Ball Joint-to-Lower Control Arm Bolt	69-86 (93-117)
Ball Joint-to-Steering Knuckle Nut	
RX7	27-40 (36-54)
323, Tracer & 626	32-40 (43-54)
Brake Caliper Bolts	
RX7	58-72 (78-98)
323 & Tracer	29-36 (39-49)
626	
Upper	12-18 (16-25)
Lower	14-22 (20-29)
Drive Axle Lock Nut	
323, Tracer & 626	116-174 (157-235)
Lower Control Arm-to-Frame	
RX7	
Front	46-69 (63-93)
Rear	43-54 (59-74)
323 & Tracer	32-40 (43-54)
626	69-86 (93-117)
Rotor-to-Hub Bolts	
323 & Tracer	33-40 (44-54)
626	36-43 (49-59)
Stabilizer Bar Bolts	
RX7	
Frame	13-20 (18-26)
Control Link	27-37 (36-50)
323 & Tracer	23-34 (32-47)
626	32-40 (43-54)
Strut Assembly-to-Body Nuts	22-27 (29-36)
Strut Assembly Lock Nut	
RX7	47-59 (64-80)
323 & Tracer	41-50 (56-69)
626	47-59 (64-80)
Strut Assembly-to-Knuckle Bolt	69-86 (93-117)
Tie Rod-to-Knuckle Nut	22-33 (29-44)

GENERAL MOTORS SPECTRUM & ISUZU I-MARK

DESCRIPTION

These models use a MacPherson independent front suspension. The upper end of the strut is connected to the vehicle body by a strut support. The strut and strut support are isolated by rubber mounts. The lower end of the strut is connected to the upper end of the steering knuckle. The lower end of the knuckle is connected to the ball joint. The ball joint is connected to the control arm.

ADJUSTMENTS & INSPECTION

WHEEL ALIGNMENT SPECIFICATIONS & PROCEDURES

See WHEEL ALIGNMENT SPECIFICATIONS & PROCEDURES in WHEEL ALIGNMENT section.

WHEEL BEARINGS

Wheel bearings are not adjustable.

REMOVAL & INSTALLATION

CONTROL ARM

Removal

Raise front of vehicle and support. Remove wheel. Remove tension rod-to-control arm bolts and lock nuts. Remove control arm mounting bolt and lock nut.

Inspection

Check control arm and bushing for distortion or cracks. Check ball joint for excessive wear. Replace worn or damaged parts.

Installation

To install, reverse removal procedure.

STRUT ASSEMBLY

Removal

Raise front of vehicle, support and remove wheel. Remove flexible brake hose clip from strut. Remove brake hose eye bolt and cap hose. Remove strut assembly nut and strut bracket bolts and lock nuts. Remove strut assembly.

NOTE: Always replace lock nuts with new nuts.

Disassembly

1) Secure strut in vise. Compress strut spring using Holding Fixture (J-3289-20) and Spring Compressor (J-34013). Compress strut about half its height after initial contact with top of strut. NEVER bottom out spring.

2) Disassemble strut, noting relative position of assembled parts. *See Fig. 1*. Inspect strut for oil leaks. Check coil springs for wear or damage. Replace worn, leaking or damaged parts.

Reassembly

Reverse disassembly procedure. Be sure that "IN" mark on inside of spring upper seat is facing inside of vehicle. Tighten strut assembly nut until shaft begins to rotate. Decrease compression force on coil spring. Tighten strut assembly nut to specifications.

Installation

To install, reverse removal procedure. DO NOT twist brake hose. Bleed brake system.

TENSION ROD

Removal & Installation

Raise front of vehicle and support. Remove stabilizer-to-tension rod bracket and insulator. Remove tension rod-to-control bolts and lock nuts. Remove tension rod-to-body nut and washer. Remove tension rod. *See Fig. 1*. To install tension rod, reverse removal procedure.

Fig. 1: Spectrum & I-Mark Front Suspension

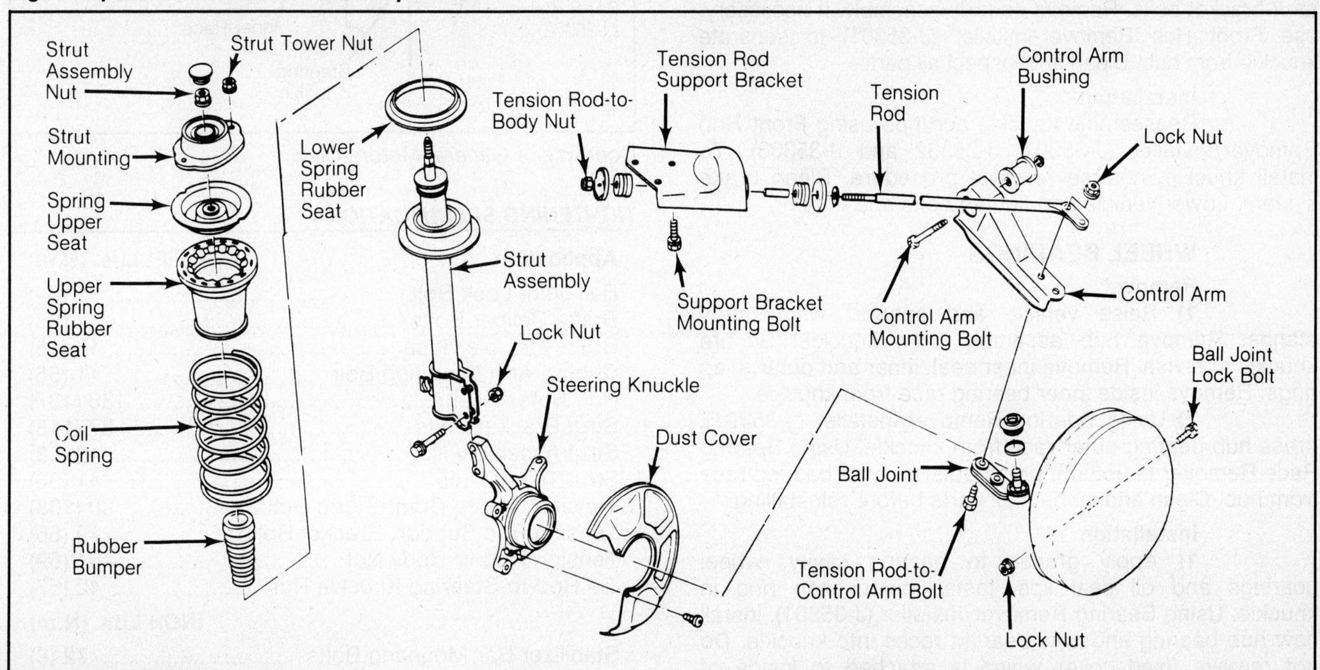

Courtesy of General Motors Corp.

Front Suspension

GENERAL MOTORS SPECTRUM & ISUZU I-MARK (Cont.)

Fig. 2: Spectrum & I-Mark Steering Knuckle & Hub

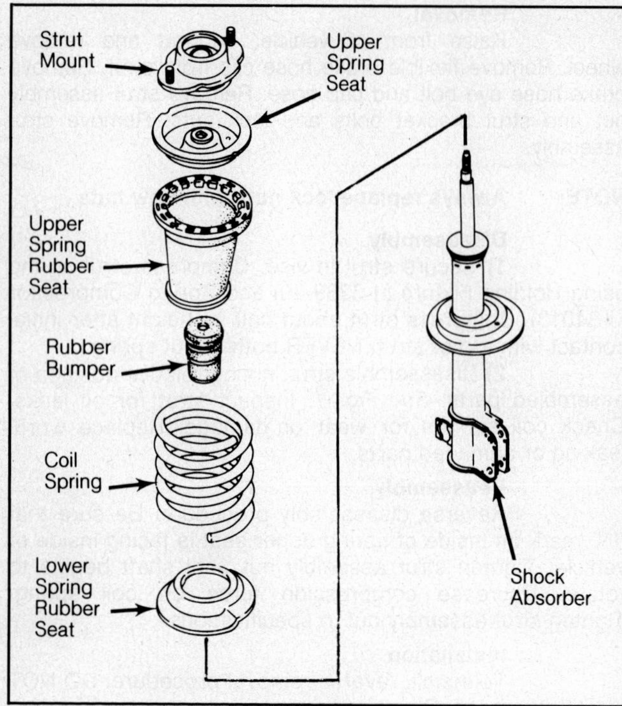

Courtesy of General Motors Corp.

STEERING KNUCKLE

Removal

1) Raise front of vehicle and remove wheel. Remove brake hose clip at strut. Disconnect hose from brake caliper and cap hose. Remove brake caliper and support with wire. Remove rotor. Remove hub using Hub Remover (J-34866 and J-2619-01). Remove splash shield.

2) Using Tie Rod Remover (J-21687-02), remove tie rod. Remove 2 tension rod-to-control arm bolts and 2 strut bracket bolts. Remove knuckle assembly. If necessary, use Front Hub Remover/Installer (J-35301) to separate knuckle from hub. Clean and inspect all parts.

Installation

Reassemble knuckle and hub using Front Hub Remover/Installer (J-35301, J-35302 and J-35303). To install knuckle, reverse removal procedure. Bleed brake system. Lower vehicle and tighten bolts and nuts.

WHEEL BEARINGS

Removal

1) Raise vehicle and support with safety stands. Remove hub assembly from knuckle. Secure knuckle in a vise. Remove inner seal, inner and outer snap rings. Remove inside inner bearing race from knuckle.

2) Using Bearing Remover/Installer (J-35301), press hub bearing outer race from knuckle. Using Bearing Race Remover (J-35893), press outside inner bearing race from hub. Clean and inspect all parts before reinstalling.

Installation

1) Apply grease to bearing cavity, wheel bearings and oil seal lips. Install outer snap ring in knuckle. Using Bearing Remover/Installer (J-35301), install new hub bearing and new bearing races into knuckle. Do not remove fixed cover which is attached to inside of bearing inner race. *See Fig. 3.*

2) Install inner snap ring in knuckle. Using Seal Installer (J-35303), install new oil seals. Using Bar Support (J-35302), install hub into bearing. Install and tighten hub nut.

NOTE: **When knuckle and hub are removed, hub bearing, inner and outer bearing races and oil seals MUST be replaced with NEW PARTS.**

Fig. 3: Spectrum & I-Mark Wheel Bearing Replacement

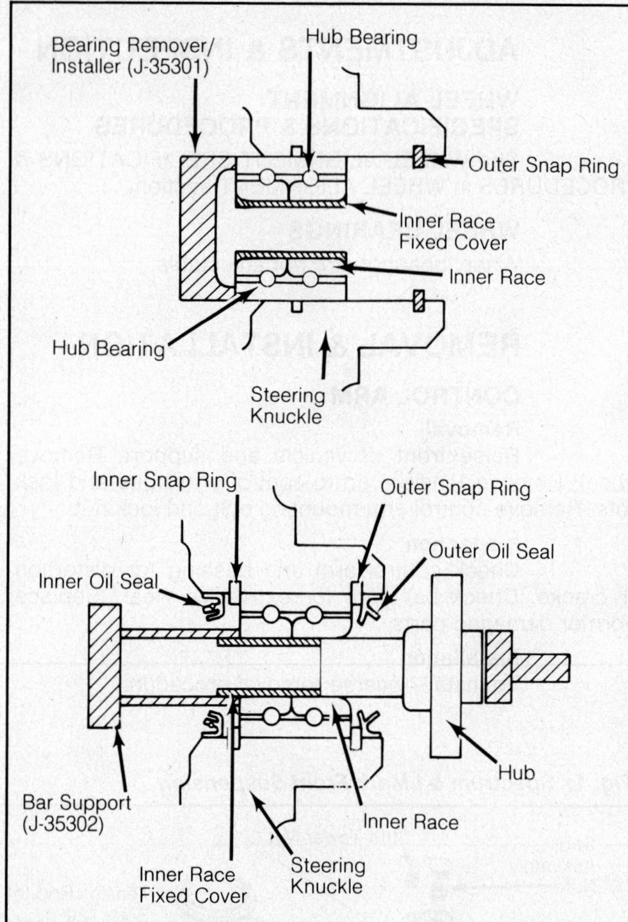

Courtesy of General Motors Corp.

TIGHTENING SPECIFICATIONS

Application	Ft.Lbs. (N.m)
Ball Joint Lock Bolt	51 (69)
Brake Caliper Bolts	41 (56)
Brake Flexible Hose	13 (18)
Control Arm Mounting Bolt	41 (56)
Hub Nuts	138 (187)
Strut Bracket Bolts	87 (118)
Strut Assembly Nut	43 (58)
Strut Tower Nuts	41 (56)
Tension Rod-to-Control Arm Bolts	80 (108)
Tension Rod Support Bracket Bolts	49 (66)
Tension Rod-to-Body Nut	51 (69)
Tie Rod-to-Steering Knuckle Nut	42 (57)
	INCH Lbs. (N.m)
Stabilizer Bar Mounting Bolts	72 (8)

GENERAL MOTORS SPRINT

DESCRIPTION

Sprint uses a MacPherson strut independent front suspension. Strut is attached to vehicle through a strut support at top. Strut and strut support are isolated by rubber mounts. Strut is connected to wheel bearing housing bottom.

Wheel bearing housing is attached to control arm by a ball joint. *See Fig. 1.*

Fig. 1: Front Suspension Assembly

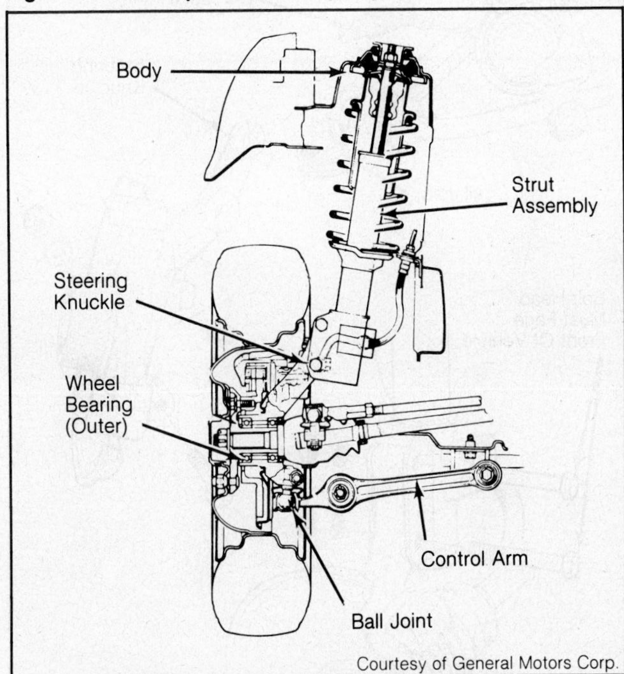

Courtesy of General Motors Corp.

ADJUSTMENTS & INSPECTION

WHEEL ALIGNMENT SPECIFICATIONS & PROCEDURES

See WHEEL ALIGNMENT SPECIFICATIONS & PROCEDURES in WHEEL ALIGNMENT section.

WHEEL BEARINGS

Wheel bearings are not adjustable. To check wheel bearing for excessive wear, raise and support vehicle. Remove wheel center cap and mount a dial indicator to wheel hub center. Grasp tire and apply force in and out. If measurement exceeds .016 in. (.4 mm), replace bearing.

REMOVAL & INSTALLATION

WHEEL BEARINGS

Removal

1) Remove wheel bearing housing. See WHEEL BEARING HOUSING in this article. Using a rod and hammer, tap outer wheel bearing out of steering knuckle. Turn knuckle over, remove spacer and tap out inner bearing.

Installation

1) Apply grease to bearing cavity, wheel bearings and oil seal lips. Using Bearing Installer (J-34856), install inner bearing with internal seal facing outward.

2) Install oil seal using Seal Installer (J-34881). Turn knuckle over and install spacer. Install outer bearing with internal seal facing outward. Ensure spacer is snug and centered between bearings. To complete installation, reverse removal procedure.

STRUT ASSEMBLY

Removal & Disassembly

1) Raise and support vehicle on safety stands. let front suspension hang free. Remove wheel assembly. Remove brake hose "E" clip and remove brake hose from bracket. Remove 2 strut bracket bolts and while holding strut by hand, remove strut support nuts. Remove strut.

2) Install strut assembly in spring compressor using Bottom Adapter (J-26584-80). Ensure strut catches on adapter and that locating pins are engaged. Install Top Adapter (J-26584-430) on strut.

3) Compress strut to about half its height, after initial contact with top of strut. Never bottom-out spring. Disassemble strut assembly, noting relative position of assembled parts. *See Fig. 2.* Clean strut bearing.

CAUTION: Strut springs are under high tension. Work with extreme care while spring is compressed.

Fig. 2: Exploded View of Strut Assembly

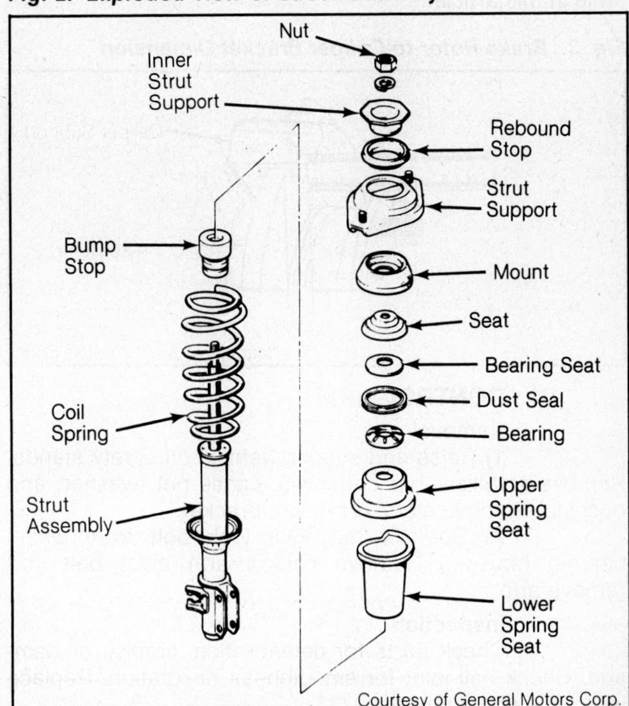

Courtesy of General Motors Corp.

Reassembly & Installation

1) Check parts for deterioration or damage. Check shock absorber for leaks and proper operation. Replace shock absorber if resistance is uneven when moved through full travel. Replace worn or damaged parts.

2) Apply grease to strut bearing and to nut and threads of strut. Check that stepped part of spring seats and spring are properly positioned. To complete assembly and installation, reverse removal and disassembly procedure.

Front Suspension

GENERAL MOTORS SPRINT (Cont.)

WHEEL BEARING HOUSING

Removal

1) Remove wheel center cap and axle shaft nut. Raise and support vehicle with safety stands. Loosen brake disc bolts about one turn. Remove caliper bolts, remove caliper and hang out of way with wire hook.

2) Measure dimension "A" and record for aid in installation. *See Fig. 3.* Pull wheel hub and rotor assembly out of wheel bearing housing using Slide Hammer (J2619-01) and Adapter (J34866). Notice spacer on inside of wheel hub. This spacer must be used for reassembly, install bevel side of spacer toward wheel.

3) Remove tie rod nut and press tie rod out using Tie Rod Remover (J21687-02). Remove 2 strut bracket bolts, ball joint clamp bolt and remove wheel bearing housing.

Installation

1) Visually check that spacer between inner and outer wheel bearings is centered. If not, move spacer to align. Install wheel hub to bearing housing and tap lightly with plastic hammer while rotating hub until center protrudes evenly. Complete installation of wheel hub by using Installer (J34856) and Handle (J7079-2) to drive in wheel hub until dimension "A" is reached.

2) Tighten brake disc attaching bolts. To complete installation, reverse removal procedure. Tighten axle shaft nut with vehicle on ground. Tighten all bolts and nuts to specification. See TIGHTENING SPECIFICATIONS table in this article.

Fig. 3. Brake Rotor-to-Caliper Bracket Dimension

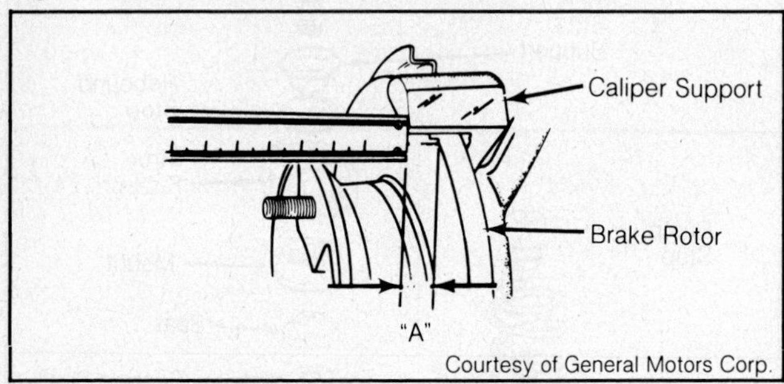

CONTROL ARM

Removal

1) Raise and support vehicle on safety stands. Remove stabilizer bar cotter pin, castle nut, washer, and bushing. Remove stabilizer mount bracket.

2) Remove ball joint lock bolt from wheel bearing housing. Remove control arm pivot bolt and remove arm.

Inspection

Check parts for deterioration, cracks, or damage. Check ball joint for smoothness of rotation. Replace worn or damaged parts.

Bushing Replacement

Press bushing out of control arm using hydraulic press and Control Arm Bushing Remover (J-34865). Lubricate control arm bushing with soapy water. Using same tool, press bushing into control arm until bushing is centered.

Installation

To install, reverse removal procedure. Tighten all bolts and nuts to specification. See TIGHTENING SPECIFICATIONS table in this article. Check and adjust toe setting.

Fig. 4: Wheel Bearing Housing

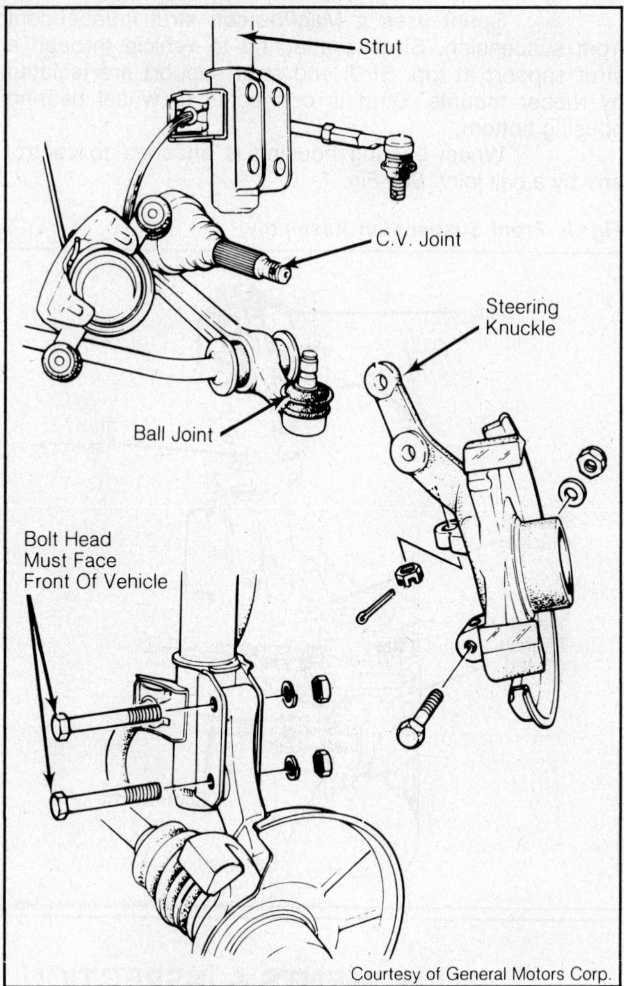

STABILIZER BAR

Removal

Raise and support vehicle with safety stands, allow suspension to hang free. Remove wheels. Remove stabilizer bar brackets and bushings. Remove cotter pin, castle nut and bushing from both sides of stabilizer bar. Remove stabilizer bar.

Installation

To install, reverse removal procedure. Check that paint on stabilizer bar aligns with bushings. Tighten all bolts and nuts to specification.

TIGHTENING SPECIFICATIONS

Application	Ft.Lbs. (N.m)
Axle Shaft Nut	150 (270)
Ball Joint Lock Bolt	37-51 (50-70)
Control Arm Pivot Bolts	37-51 (50-70)
Stabilizer Bar-to-Body Bolts	22-40 (30-55)
Stabilizer Bar-to-Control Arm Nut	29-65 (40-90)
Strut Assembly Nut	29-43 (40-60)
Strut Assembly-to-Body Nuts	14-20 (18-28)
Strut Assembly-to-Bearing Housing Bolts	51-65 (70-90)
Tie Rod-to-Steering Knuckle Nut	22-40 (30-55)
Wheel Lug Nuts	40 (55)

HONDA

Accord, Civic, Prelude

DESCRIPTION

The Accord and Prelude use an independent double wish-bone strut type suspension. The strut assembly is attached to the steering knuckle through the lower control arm. The steering knuckle is attached to upper and lower control arms by ball joints. A stabilizer bar and strut rod are attached to the lower control arm.

The Civic uses an independent torsion bar suspension. The suspension system consists of a vertically-mounted strut attached to the steering knuckle, lower control arm and a radius arm. The steering knuckle is attached to the radius arm by a single ball joint.

ADJUSTMENTS & INSPECTION

WHEEL ALIGNMENT SPECIFICATIONS & PROCEDURES

See WHEEL ALIGNMENT SPECIFICATIONS & PROCEDURES in WHEEL ALIGNMENT section.

WHEEL BEARINGS

Checking

1) Wheel bearings require no adjustment. Bearings should be checked for excessive movement. Support vehicle and remove tire.

2) Install dial indicator with stem positioned on the front hub surface. Move hub assembly inward and note reading. Movement should be 0-.002" (0-.05 mm).

Fig. 1: Civic Front Suspension

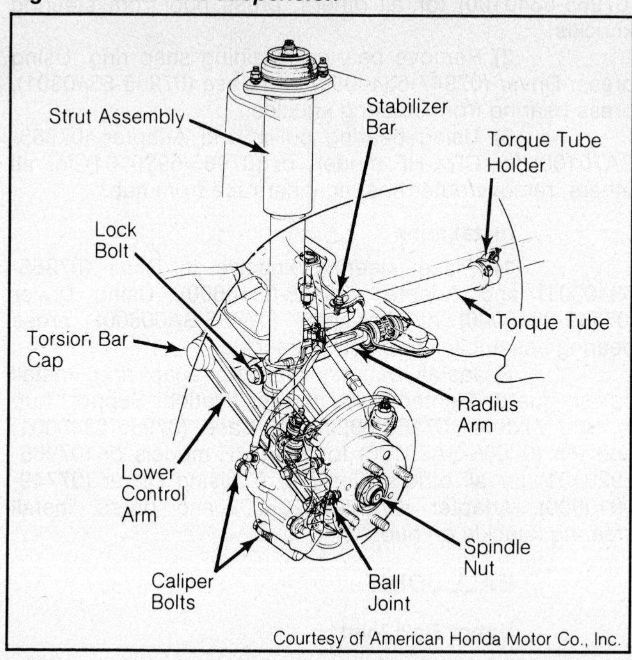

Fig. 2: Accord & Prelude Front Suspension

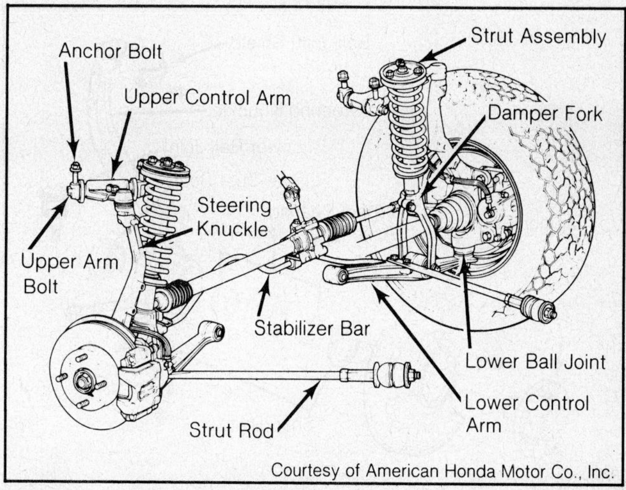

REMOVAL & INSTALLATION

WHEEL BEARING

Removal (Accord & Prelude)

1) Remove steering knuckle. See STEERING KNUCKLE in this article. Remove splash guard retaining screws. Hub must be separated from steering knuckle.

2) Using press and proper driver, separate hub from steering knuckle. Use Driver (07749-0010000) and Pin (07GAF-SE00100) for Accord models or Driver (07965-6340100) for Prelude models.

3) Remove outer seal from steering knuckle on Prelude models. *See Fig. 3.* Remove bearing retaining snap ring.

4) On Prelude models, remove outer bearing inner race and bearing. Remove inner dust seal. Remove inner bearing race and bearing. Using press, Driver (07749-0010000) and Adapter (07965-6920400), press outer bearing race from steering knuckle.

Fig. 3: Exploded View of Prelude Steering Knuckle

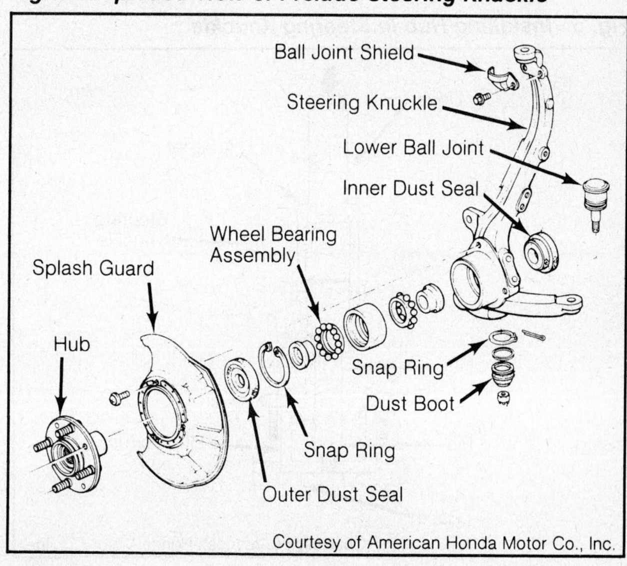

Front Suspension

HONDA (Cont.)

Fig. 4: *Exploded View of Accord Steering Knuckle*

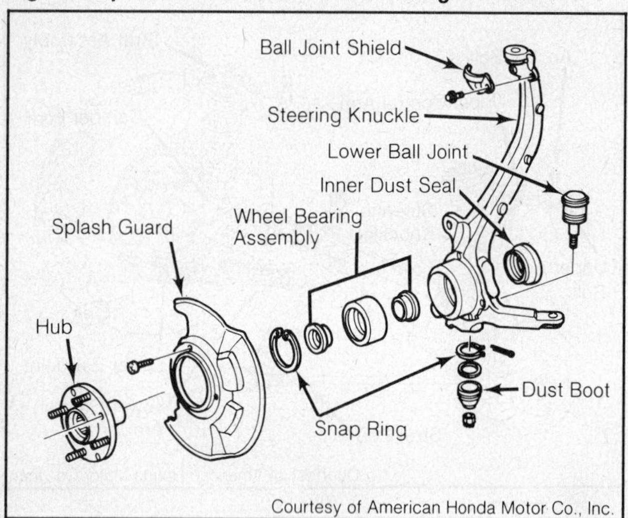

5) Using bearing puller and Adapter (07965-6920100), remove inner bearing race from the hub. Remove outer dust seal from hub.

6) On Accord models, remove wheel bearing using press, Driver (07749-0010000) and Adapter (07746-0010400). Using bearing puller and Pin (07GAF-SE00100), remove outer bearing inner race from the hub.

Installation (Accord)

1) On Accord models, install bearing in steering knuckle. Use press, Driver (07749-0010000) and Adapter (07746-0010600). Install bearing retaining snap ring. *See Fig. 4.*

2) Install splash guard on steering knuckle. Tighten bolts to specification. See TIGHTENING SPECIFICATIONS table at end of article. Support hub in Hub Fixture (07965-6920201), Base (07965-6340301) and Pin (07GAF-SE00100). *See Fig. 5.*

3) Using Driver (07749-0010000), Adapter (07GAF-SE00200) and press, install steering knuckle on hub. Install inner dust seal.

Fig. 5: *Installing Hub in Steering Knuckle*

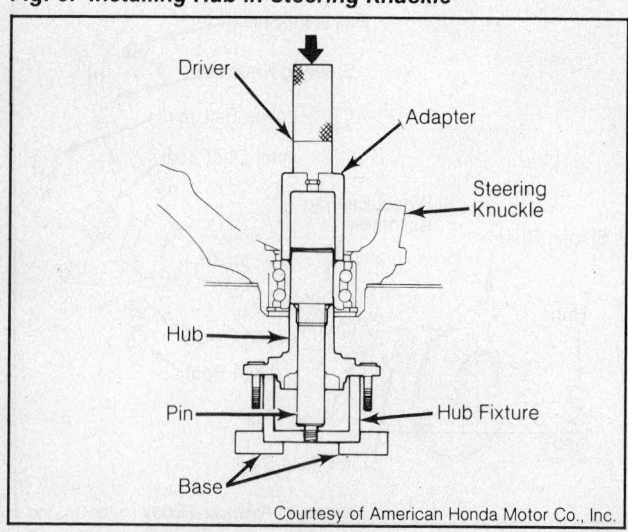

CAUTION: Press load should not exceed 4000 lbs. (1814 kg) during hub installation.

Installation (Prelude)

1) Using press, Driver (07749-0010000) and Adapter (07965-SA00600), install outer bearing race in steering knuckle.

CAUTION: Press load should not exceed 5000 lbs. (2267 kg) during bearing race installation.

2) Pack wheel bearings with grease. Apply grease to bearing races. Install outer bearing and inner race in the steering knuckle. Install bearing retaining snap ring in steering knuckle.

3) Fill outer dust seal groove of sealing lip with grease. Using Driver (07749-0010000) and Installer (07965-SA00600), install outer dust seal in steering knuckle. Seal must be even with steering knuckle surface.

4) Install splash guard. Tighten bolts to specification. Lubricate inner bearing and race with grease. Install inner bearing and race in steering knuckle.

5) Support hub in Hub Fixture (07965-6920201), Base (07965-6340301) and Pin (07965-6920100). *See Fig. 5.* Using Driver (07749-0010000), Adapter (07965-6920500) and press, install steering knuckle on hub.

6) Fill inner dust seal groove of sealing lip with grease. Using Driver (07749-0010000) and Installer (07965-SA00600), install dust seal in steering knuckle. Seal must be even with steering knuckle surface.

Removal (Civic)

1) Remove steering knuckle. See STEERING KNUCKLE in this article. Using press, Base (07965-6340301) and Pin (07965-SA70100) for CRX-HF models or (07965-6340100) for all others, press hub from steering knuckle.

2) Remove bearing retaining snap ring. Using press, Driver (07947-6340000) and Base (07965-6340301), press bearing from steering knuckle.

3) Using bearing puller and Adapter (07965-SA70100) for CRX-HF models or (07965-6920101) for all others, remove outer bearing inner race from hub.

Installation

1) Place steering knuckle in Base (07965-6340301) and Adapter (07746-0010600). Using Driver (07749-0010000) and Adapter (07965-SA00600), press bearing assembly into steering knuckle.

2) Install bearing retaining snap ring. Install splash guard. Tighten bolts to specification. Support hub in Hub Fixture (07965-6920201), Base (07965-6340301) and Pin (07965-SA70100) for CRX-HF models or (07965-6920101) for all others. *See Fig. 5.* Using Driver (07749-0010000), Adapter (07965-6920500) and press, install steering knuckle on hub.

BALL JOINT

Upper Ball Joint

Information not available from manufacturer.

Lower Ball Joint Removal (Accord & Prelude)

1) Remove steering knuckle. See STEERING KNUCKLE in this article. Remove dust boot snap ring,

HONDA (Cont.)

dust boot and ball joint snap ring. Install Ball Joint Remover/Installer (07965-SB00100) over ball joint stud. Install stud nut.

2) Position Ball Joint Base (07965-SB00300) for Accord models or (07965-SB00200) for Prelude models, between ball joint housing and steering knuckle. Place assembly in vise. Tighten vise and press ball joint from steering knuckle.

Installation

1) Position ball joint in steering knuckle. Install Ball Joint Remover/Installer (07965-SB00100) on stud end of ball joint. Position Ball Joint Base (07965-SB00200) for Accord models or (07965-SB00300) for Prelude models on end of ball joint. Press ball joint into knuckle.

2) Install ball joint snap ring and dust boot. Using Snap Ring Guide (07974-SA50700), install dust boot snap ring. Adjusting bolt in center of snap ring guide must be adjusted to give proper location for snap ring installation.

STEERING KNUCKLE

Removal

1) Pry lock tab away from spindle nut. Loosen spindle nut. Raise and support vehicle. Remove wheel assembly and spindle nut. Remove caliper assembly.

2) Remove brake disc retaining screws. Install bolts in brake disc and tighten to remove brake disc from hub. Alternate tightening bolts to prevent brake disc from binding on hub.

3) Remove cotter pin and nut from tie rod end. Separate tie rod from steering knuckle. On Civic models, support lower control arm with jack. On all models, remove cotter pin and nut from lower ball joint stud.

CAUTION: Torsion bar tension on Civic's lower control arm may cause arm to suddenly swing away from steering knuckle as ball joint is disconnected. Support lower control arm with a jack prior to disconnecting lower ball.

4) Using ball joint separator, separate lower ball joint from control arm. On Accord and Prelude models, remove upper ball joint shield. Remove upper ball joint stud nut. Using ball joint remover, separate ball joint from steering knuckle.

5) On Civic models, remove strut assembly-to-steering knuckle lock bolt. *See Fig. 1.* Using soft faced hammer, drive steering knuckle downward to clear strut assembly.

6) On all models, remove steering knuckle and hub assembly from drive shaft.

Installation

To install, reverse removal procedures. Tighten bolts to specification. See TIGHTENING SPECIFICATIONS table at end of article. Use new spindle nut, and stake after tightening to specification. Replace all self-locking bolts if nut can be easily threaded past nylon lock areas.

STRUT ASSEMBLY

Removal (Accord & Prelude)

Raise and support vehicle. Remove wheel assembly. Remove brake hose clamp from strut. Remove strut-to-damper fork bolt. Remove damper fork-to-lower control arm bolt. Remove damper fork assembly. Remove strut-to-body retaining bolts. Remove strut assembly.

Removal (Civic)

1) Raise and support vehicle. Remove wheel assembly. Remove brake hose clamp from strut. Support lower control arm with a jack.

CAUTION: Ensure floor jack is properly positioned under lower control arm. Torsion bar tension may cause steering knuckle to move when strut-to-steering knuckle lock bolt is removed.

2) Remove strut-to-steering knuckle lock bolt. *See Fig. 1.* Lower floor jack and control arm. Remove strut assembly-to-body retaining nuts. Compress strut assembly and remove.

Disassembly

1) On Accord and Prelude models, use spring compressor, compress strut assembly spring. Hold strut shaft and remove nut. Slowly release spring compressor. Remove spring and mount components. *See Fig. 6.*

2) On Civic models, hold strut rod and remove nut from damper rod. Remove washer, mount, boot and bumper stop from damper shaft.

Fig. 6: Accord & Prelude Strut Assembly

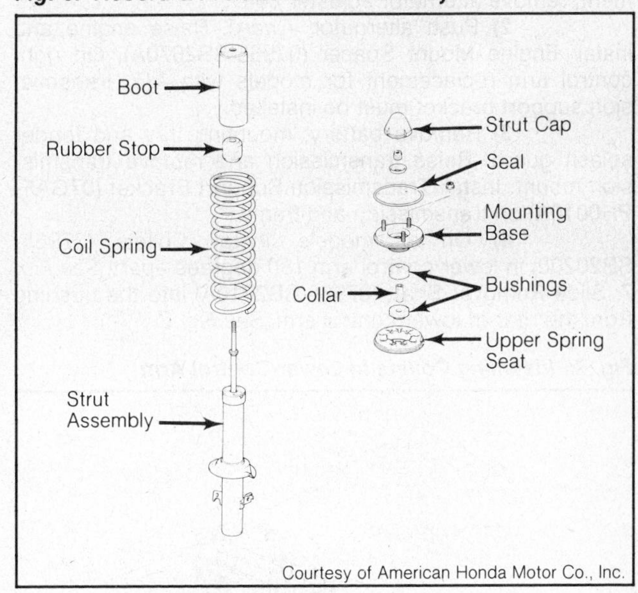

Reassembly

1) Check parts for deterioration or damage. Check strut assembly for leaks and proper operation. Replace strut if resistance is uneven or jerky. Replace worn or damaged parts.

2) On Accord and Prelude models, position mounting base so that one stud aligns with the tab on strut housing. On all models, reverse disassembly procedures using new shaft nut. Tighten strut shaft nut to specification. See TIGHTENING SPECIFICATIONS table at end of article.

Installation

1) On Accord and Prelude models, loosely install strut assembly on the body with strut housing tab

HONDA (Cont.)

facing inward. Install damper fork on lower control arm. Align damper fork with strut housing tab.

2) Place jack under steering knuckle. Raise jack until vehicle weight is placed on strut assembly. Tighten strut-to-steering knuckle bolt and damper fork bolt to specification. Tighten strut mount-to-body nuts to specification.

CAUTION: Strut mount-to-body nuts must be tightened with vehicle weight applied to strut assembly.

3) On Civic models, install strut assembly on the body. Align strut assembly with steering knuckle. Place jack under steering knuckle. Raise steering knuckle assembly.

4) Install lock bolt in steering knuckle. Install brake hose clamp bolt. Tighten bolts to specification.

LOWER CONTROL ARM

Removal (Accord & Prelude)

Information not available from manufacturer.

Removal (Civic)

1) Remove torsion bar and torque tube. See TORSION BAR in this article. Remove lower control arm-to-radius arm bolts. Raise engine as necessary to gain access to lower control arm. On left control arm replacement, remove alternator adjuster bolt.

2) Push alternator inward. Raise engine and install Engine Mount Spacer (07965-SB2070A). On right control arm replacement for models with A/T, transmission support bracket must be installed.

3) Remove battery, mounting tray and fender splash guard. Raise transmission and remove transmission mount. Install Transmission Support Bracket (07GAF-PH0010A) on transmission and frame.

4) On all models, install Collets (07965-SB20200) in lower control arm 180 degrees apart. *See Fig. 7.* Slide Remover Shaft (07965-SB2010A) into the bushing from the rear of lower control arm. *See Fig. 8.*

Fig. 7: Installing Collets in Lower Control Arm

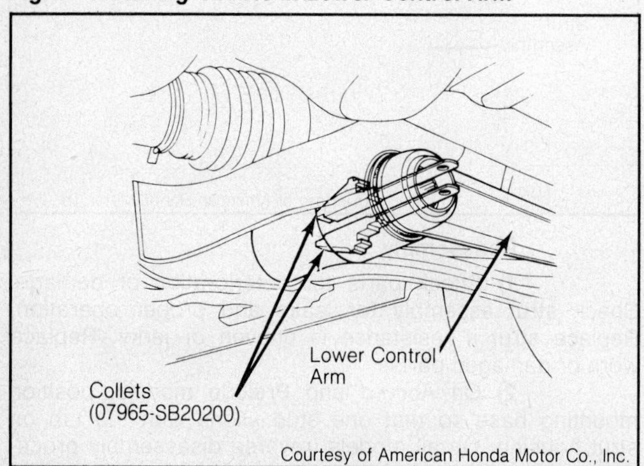

5) Install Thrust Bearing (07965-SB2080A) on Bolt (07965-SB2050A). Position bolt through the remover shaft. Install Receiver (07965-SB2030A) over bolt and lower control arm. Install flat washer and Nut (07965-SB2090A) on the bolt. *See Fig. 8.*

Fig. 8: Removing & Installing Lower Control Arm

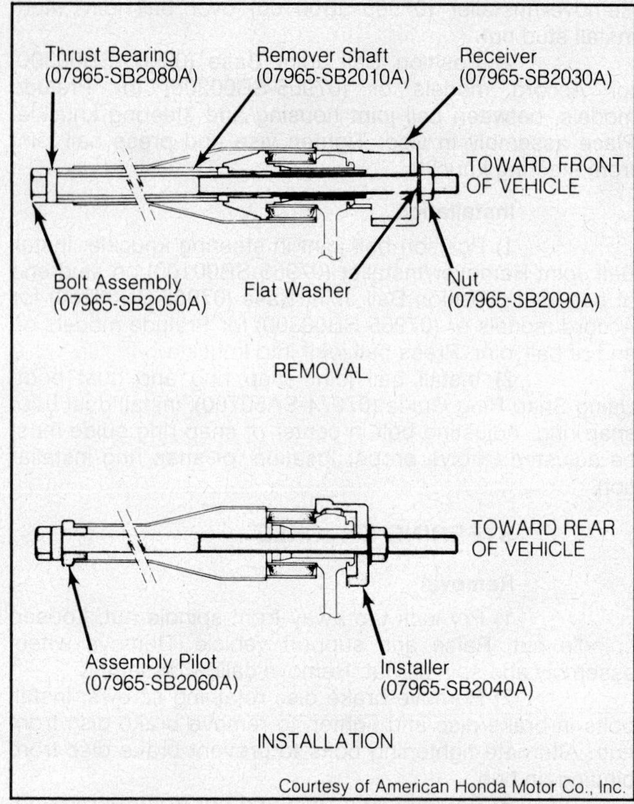

6) Hold nut and tighten bolt. Tighten bolt until lower control arm bushing is free of the beam. Remove puller assembly and bushing.

Installation

1) Mark bushing for alignment with cast lug. *See Fig. 9.* Install Assembly Pilot (07965-SB2060A), thrust bearing and flat washer on bolt. *See Fig. 8.*

2) Install bolt assembly through rear of bushing. Install lower control arm on the bolt. Align index mark on beam with mark on bushing. *See Fig. 9.*

3) Place Installer (07965-SB2040A), flat washer and nut on the bolt. Hold bolt and tighten the nut. Tigthen nut until bushing sleeve area is even with end of beam.

Fig. 9: Aligning Lower Control

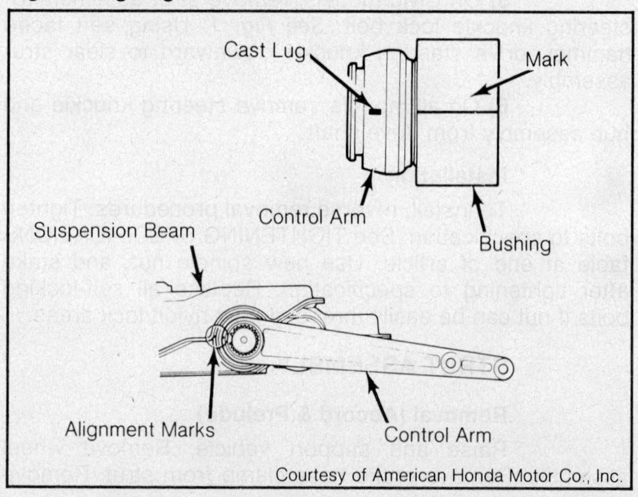

HONDA (Cont.)

4) Remove bushing installation tools. Reverse removal procedures for remaining components. Install torsion bar. Tighten bolts to specification. See TIGHTENING SPECIFICATIONS table at end of article.

RADIUS ARM

Removal (Civic)

1) Raise and support vehicle. Remove wheel assembly. Support lower control arm with a jack. Ensure jack is properly positioned. Remove ball joint stud cotter pin and nut. Separate ball joint from steering knuckle.

CAUTION: Torsion bar tension on lower control arm may cause arm to suddenly swing away from steering knuckle as ball joint is being disconnected. Use a floor jack to support lower control arm.

2) Remove radius arm-to-frame nut. Remove stabilizer bar-to-radius arm bolt. Remove lower control arm-to-radius arm bolts. Rotate radius arm downward and pull forward for removal. *See Fig. 10.*

Fig. 10: Civic Lower Control Arm & Radius Arm

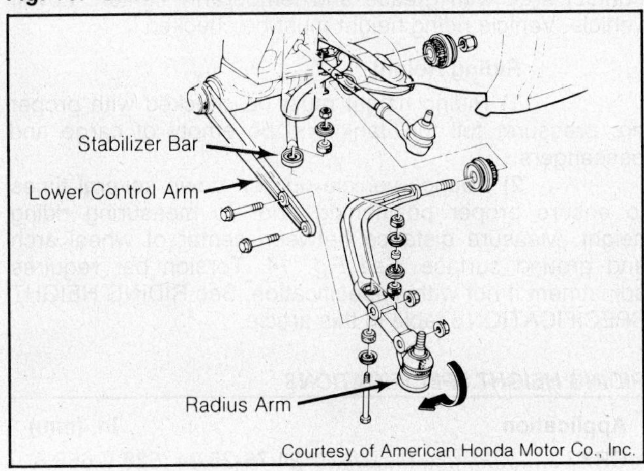

Courtesy of American Honda Motor Co., Inc.

Installation

Inspect all components for deterioration or damage. Replace all self-locking nuts. Coat radius arm bushings and stabilizer bar-to-radius arm bushings with silicone grease prior to installation. Reverse removal procedures for installation. Tighten bolts to specification.

UPPER CONTROL ARM

Inspection (Accord & Prelude)

Raise and support vehicle. Remove wheel assembly. Rock upper ball joint front-to-back with a force of approximately 65 lbs. (30 kg). Replace upper arm bushings if play exists.

Removal

1) Raise and support vehicle. Remove wheel assembly. Remove cotter pin and nut from upper ball joint stud.

2) Using ball joint remover, separate upper ball joint from steering knuckle. Remove upper control arm anchor bolts-to-body retaining nuts. *See Fig. 11.* Remove upper control arm.

Bushing Replacement

Using anchor bolts, clamp upper control arm in a soft-jawed vise. Remove upper arm bolt, anchor bolts and seals. Reposition upper control arm in vise and remove upper arm collar. Using a drift, drive bushings from upper control arm. *See Fig. 11.*

Fig. 11: Prelude Upper Control Arm Assembly

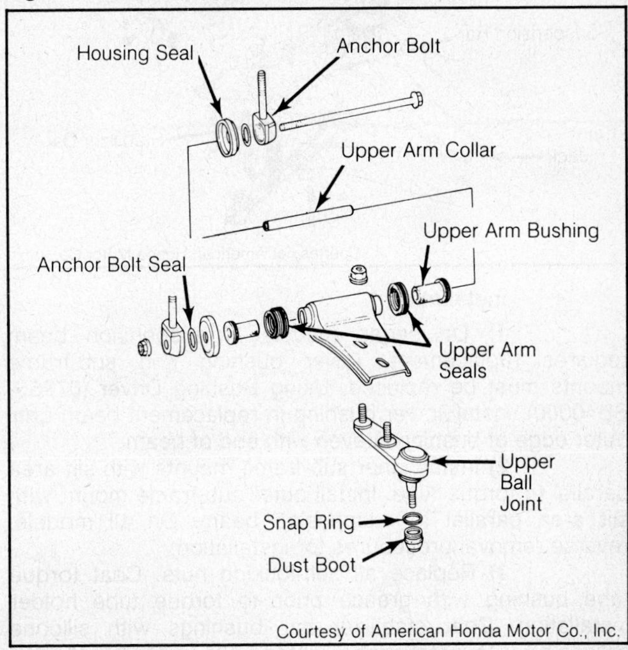

Courtesy of American Honda Motor Co., Inc.

Accord is similar.

Reassembly

Coat inner areas and the ends of upper control arm bushings with grease. Coat seal lips of bushing seals with grease. Apply thread sealant to underside of upper control arm bolt head, threads and bolt nut. Reverse disassembly procedure. Tighten bolts to specification.

Installation

Reverse removal procedures for installation. Tighten bolts to specification. Check and adjust camber.

SUSPENSION BEAM & STABILIZER BAR

Removal (Civic Only)

1) Raise and support vehicle. Remove wheel assemblies. Support engine with hoist. Remove steering gear box. Support lower control arm with a jack.

2) Remove cotter pin and nut from radius arm ball joint stud. Using ball joint remover, separate ball joint from steering knuckle.

3) Remove torque tube holder. Remove exhaust pipe. On M/T models, disconnect transmission shift rod and extension. On A/T models, disconnect transmission shift cable guide from the floor. Pull cable downward by hand.

4) On all models, remove engine mount bracket nuts. Support suspension beam with a jack. Remove suspension beam bolts and lower beam. Remove stabilizer bar bolts, brackets, and stabilizer bar. *See Fig. 12.*

Front Suspension

HONDA (Cont.)

Fig. 12: Civic Suspension Beam & Stabilizer Bar

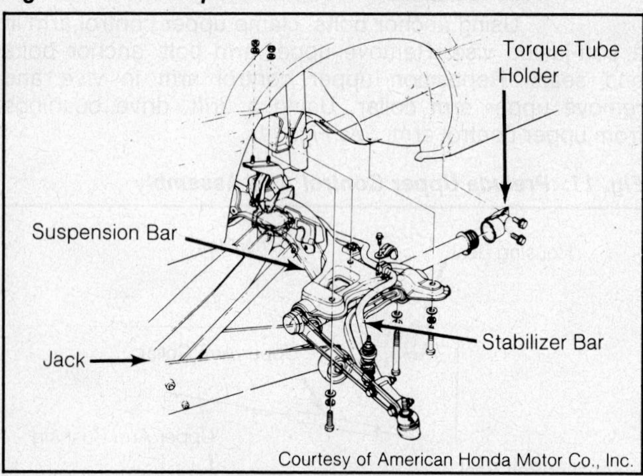

Installation

1) On sedan models, if suspension beam requires replacement, lower bushing and sub-frame mounts must be replaced. Using Bushing Driver (07965-SB40000), install lower bushing in replacement beam until outer edge of bushing is even with end of beam.

2) Install inner sub-frame mounts with slit area parallel to torque tube. Install outer sub-frame mount with slit area parallel to suspension beam. On all models, reverse removal procedures for installation.

3) Replace all self-locking nuts. Coat torque tube bushing with grease prior to torque tube holder installation. Coat stabilizer bar bushings with silicone grease prior to installation. Tighten bolts to specification.

TORSION BAR

Removal (Civic)

1) Raise and support vehicle. Remove wheel assembly and height adjustment nut. Remove torque tube holder and bushing. Remove snap ring from rear of torsion bar. *See Fig. 13.*

2) Remove cap from front of torsion bar. Tap torsion bar forward. Movement of lower control arm up and down will ease in sliding of torsion bar. Remove front snap ring from torsion bar. Tap torsion back toward rear of vehicle and remove from torque tube. Remove torque tube.

Fig. 13: Civic Torsion Bar Assembly

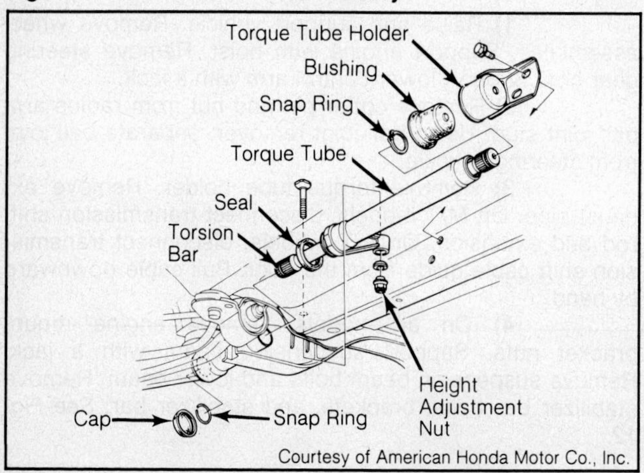

Installation

1) Inspect torsion bar for cracks or damaged splines. Install new seal on torque tube. Coat seal and torque tube sliding surfaces with grease. Install torque tube and seal on suspension beam.

2) Apply grease to spline areas of torsion bar. Install torsion bar in torque tube from the rear of torque tube. Ensure proper torsion bar is installed in correct location. Torsion bars are marked for location.

CAUTION: Torsion bars are marked "L" for left and "R" for right on the end of torsion bar. Ensure torsion bars are installed in proper location.

3) Align projection area or punch mark on torque tube splines with cutout or paint mark in torsion bar splines. Install torsion bar approximately 3/8".

4) Install torsion bar while moving lower control arm up and down. Install front snap ring and cap. Install rear snap ring. Tap torsion bar forward so no clearance exists between snap ring and torque tube.

5) Apply grease to cap bushing and install on torque tube. Install torque tube holder. Tighten bolts to specification. Coat height adjustment nut and torque tube contact area with grease and temporarily tighten. Lower vehicle. Vehicle riding height must be checked.

Riding Height

1) Riding height must be checked with proper tire pressure, full fuel tank and be empty of cargo and passengers.

2) Bounce vehicle up and down several times to ensure proper positioning prior to measuring riding height. Measure distance between center of wheel arch and ground surface. *See Fig. 14.* Torsion bar requires adjustment if not within specification. See RIDING HEIGHT SPECIFICATIONS table in this article.

RIDING HEIGHT SPECIFICATIONS

Application	In. (mm)
CRX	24.76-25.94 (628.9-658.8)
Hatchback	24.84-26.02 (630.9-660.9)
Sedan	25.04-26.22 (636.0-665.9)
Wagon	24.96-26.14 (633.9-663.9)

3) If adjustment is required, raise and support vehicle with front tires free of the ground. Allow front suspension to hang freely.

4) Rotate height adjustment nut to the right to increase or to the left to lower riding height. Height will vary .20" (5.0 mm) for each complete turn. Lower vehicle and bounce several times. Recheck riding height.

Fig. 14: Measuring Riding Height

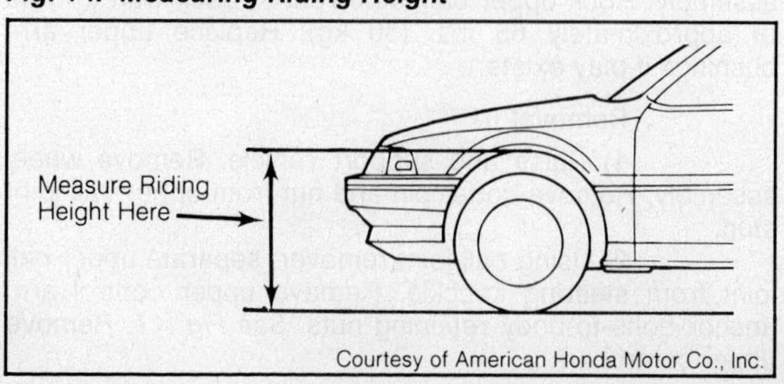

HONDA (Cont.)

TIGHTENING SPECIFICATIONS (ACCORD & PRELUDE)

Application	Ft. Lbs. (N.m)
Ball Joint Nut	
Lower	40 (54)
Upper	32 (43)
Ball Joint Shield Bolt	13 (18)
Brake Caliper Mounting Bolt	56 (76)
Control Arm Anchor Bolt-to-Body Nut	
Accord	53 (72)
Prelude	60 (81)
Damper Fork-to-Control Arm Bolt	47 (64)
Damper Fork-to-Strut Bolt	32 (43)
Lower Control Arm-to-Body Bolt	40 (54)
Spindle Nut	134 (182)
Stabilizer Bar-to-Control Arm Nut	
Accord	16 (22)
Prelude	33 (45)
Strut Shaft Nut	22 (30)
Strut-to-Body Nut	29 (39)
Strut-to-Damper Fork Bolt	32 (43)
Tie Rod Nut	32 (43)
Upper Arm Bolt	40 (54)
Wheel Lug Nut	80 (109)
	INCH Lbs. (N.m)
Splash Guard Screw	48 (5)

TIGHTENING SPECIFICATIONS (CIVIC)

Application	Ft. Lbs. (N.m)
Ball Joint Nut	32 (43)
Brake Caliper Mounting Bolt	13 (18)
Brake Line Clamp Bolt	16 (22)
Lower Control Arm-to-Radius Arm Bolt	28 (38)
Radius Arm-to-Suspension Beam Nut	60 (81)
Spindle Nut	134 (182)
Stabilizer Bar Bracket Bolt	16 (22)
Stabilizer Bar-to-Radius Arm Nut	16 (22)
Strut Shaft Nut	32 (43)
Strut-to-Body Nut	29 (39)
Strut-to-Steering Knuckle Bolt	47 (64)
Tie Rod Nut	32 (43)
Torsion Bar Holder Bolt	16 (22)
Wheel Lug Nut	80 (109)
	INCH Lbs. (N.m)
Splash Guard Screw	48 (5)

Front Suspension

ISUZU IMPULSE

DESCRIPTION

Impulse models use an independent wishbone type front suspension. The suspension system consists of a crossmember, coil springs, upper and lower control arms, upper and lower ball joints, steering knuckle and shock absorbers.

The coil spring is mounted between the crossmember and lower control arm. The shock absorber is mounted between the upper control arm and inner fender panel. A stabilizer bar and strut rod are also used to enhance stability and riding comfort.

Fig. 1: Exploded View of Impulse Front Suspension

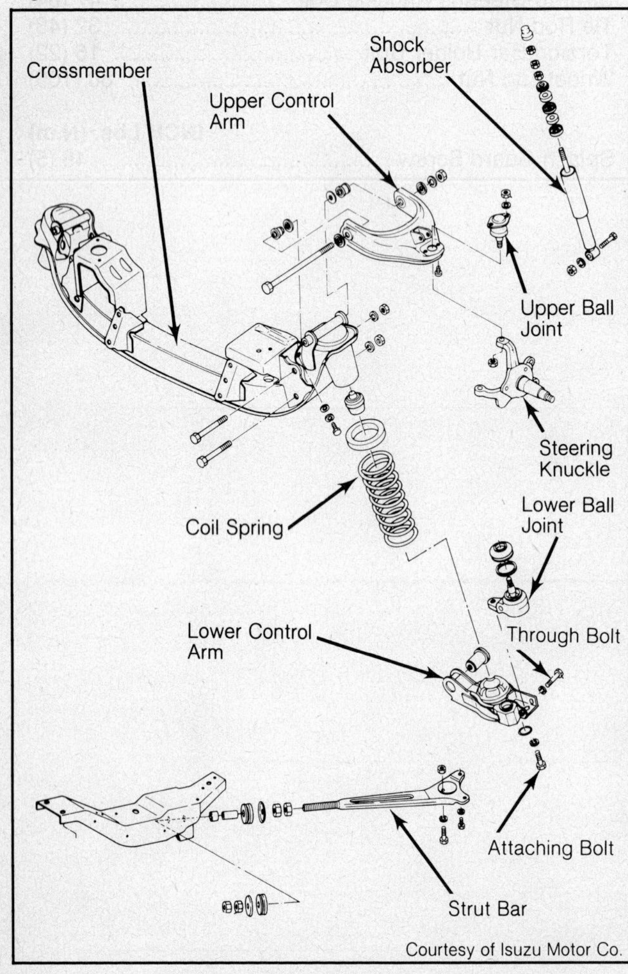

Courtesy of Isuzu Motor Co.

ADJUSTMENTS & INSPECTION

WHEEL ALIGNMENT SPECIFICATIONS & PROCEDURES

See WHEEL ALIGNMENT SPECIFICATIONS & PROCEDURES in WHEEL ALIGNMENT section.

WHEEL BEARING

1) Raise and support vehicle. Remove grease cap and cotter pin. Loosen spindle nut. Tighten spindle nut to 22 ft. lbs. (30 N.m) while rotating wheel to seat bearings. Back off spindle nut and tighten finger tight.

2) Attach a spring scale to wheel mounting stud and measure starting torque. Tighten spindle nut so that spring scale reads 1.1-3.3 lbs. (0.5-1.5 kg). Install new cotter pin.

BALL JOINT CHECKING

To check ball joint play, raise vehicle with floor jack positioned near ball joint. Grip tire at top and bottom and while applying pressure in and out on bottom of tire. If play exceeds .008" (.20 mm), replace ball joint.

REMOVAL & INSTALLATION

WHEEL BEARING

Removal

1) Raise and support vehicle. Remove wheel assembly. Remove brake caliper assembly and hang out of the way. Remove grease cap, cotter pin, hub nut and washer.

2) Remove outer wheel bearing. Remove hub/rotor assembly. Pry out inner grease seal and remove inner wheel bearing. Remove bearing races (if necessary).

Installation

To install, reverse removal procedure. Adjust wheel bearings. See ADJUSTMENTS & INSPECTION in this article.

UPPER BALL JOINT

Removal

1) Raise and support vehicle. Remove wheel assembly. Remove lower shock absorber bolt and push shock up. Remove brake caliper and hang out of the way.

2) Disconnect tie rod end from steering knuckle. Remove grease cap, cotter pin, hub nut and washer. Remove hub/rotor assembly. Remove dust plate retaining bolts and dust plate from knuckle.

3) Place a hydraulic jack under lower control arm near ball joint. Apply slight upward pressure on lower control arm with jack.

4) Loosen upper ball joint nut until nut is flush with top of ball joint stud. Using Ball Joint Remover (J-21687-02), disconnect upper ball joint from steering knuckle. Remove bolts connecting ball joint to control arm. Remove ball joint.

Installation

To install, reverse removal procedure. Install ball joint with cut-off portion facing outward. Use new locking nut on ball joint stud.

LOWER BALL JOINT

Removal

1) Raise and support vehicle. Compress coil spring and secure with safety chain. See LOWER CONTROL ARM & COIL SPRING in this article. Loosen lower ball joint nut until nut is flush with top of ball joint stud.

2) Using Ball Joint Remover (J-6627-A), disconnect lower ball joint from steering knuckle. Remove ball joint-to-lower control arm bolts. Remove ball joint.

Installation

To install, reverse removal procedure and tighten to specifications. Use new locking nut on ball joint stud.

ISUZU IMPULSE (Cont.)

SHOCK ABSORBER

Removal

Raise and support vehicle. Remove wheel assembly. Remove lower shock absorber bolt from upper control arm. Remove shock absorber nuts from inside engine compartment. Remove shock absorber.

Installation

To install, reverse removal procedure and tighten to specifications.

STEERING KNUCKLE

Removal

Raise and support vehicle. Compress coil spring and secure with safety chain. See LOWER CONTROL ARM & COIL SPRING in this article. Remove tie rod. Loosen upper and lower ball joint nuts. Using Ball Joint Remover (J-21687-02) for upper, and (J-6627-A) for lower, disconnect ball joints from knuckle. Remove steering knuckle.

Installation

To install, reverse removal procedure and tighten to specifications. Use new locking nuts on ball joint studs.

LOWER CONTROL ARM & COIL SPRING

CAUTION: To prevent personal injury, secure safety chain around upper control arm and through coil spring.

Removal

1) Raise and support vehicle. Install Spring Compressor (J-36567). See Fig. 2. Lower plate of compressor is installed in third space between coils for right side of vehicle, second space for left side of vehicle.

Fig. 2: Spring Compressor Installation

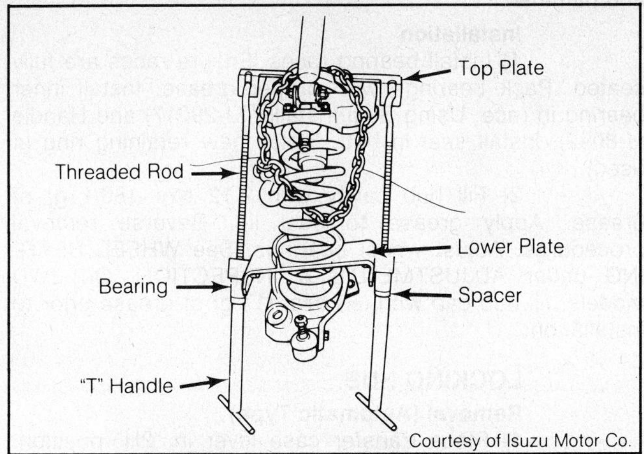

2) Install threaded rods, bearings, spacers, and "T" handles to top and lower plates. Turn "T" handles to compress spring evenly, not allowing spring to angle forward or reward.

3) Loosen lower ball joint nut until nut is flush with ball joint stud. Using Ball Joint Remover (J-6627-A), disconnect lower ball joint from steering knuckle. Press down and in on lower control arm until spring end is free of lower seat.

4) Remove lower control arm pivot bolt. Remove lower control arm. Loosen rods evenly on each side of compressor until spring is free. Remove coil spring.

Installation

To install, reverse removal procedure. Tighten control arm pivot bolt(s) to specifications with vehicle on ground. Use new locking nut on ball joint stud.

UPPER CONTROL ARM

Removal

1) Raise and support vehicle. Place a hydraulic jack under lower control arm near ball joint. Apply slight upward pressure on lower control arm with jack. Loosen upper ball joint nut until nut is flush with top of ball joint stud.

2) Using Ball Joint Remover (J-21687-02), disconnect upper ball joint from steering knuckle. Remove lower shock absorber mounting bolt. Remove upper control arm pivot bolt. Remove upper control arm.

Installation

To install, reverse removal procedure. Install control arm with large washer installed on inside of front arm and small washer installed on inside of rear arm. Tighten control arm pivot bolt to specifications with vehicle on ground. Use new locking nut on ball joint stud.

STABILIZER BAR

Removal

Raise and support vehicle. Remove engine splash guard. Remove stabilizer bar bolt and grommet assemblies from lower control arms. Remove stabilizer support clamps from body. Remove stabilizer bar.

Installation

To install, reverse removal procedure and tighten to specifications.

TIGHTENING SPECIFICATIONS

Application	Ft. Lbs. (N.m)
Ball Joint-to-Lower Control Arm Nut	
Through Bolt	76 (103)
Attaching Bolt	47 (64)
Ball Joint-to-Upper Control Arm Nut	41 (56)
Brake Caliper-to-Steering Knuckle Bolt	36 (49)
Lower Control Arm-to-Crossmember Bolt	68 (92)
Lower Ball Joint-to-Steering Knuckle Nut	58 (79)
Shock Absorber-to-Control Arm Nut	41 (56)
Tie Rod End-to-Steering Knuckle Nut	61 (83)
Upper Ball Joint-to-Steering Knuckle Nut	39 (53)
Upper Control Arm-to-Crossmember Bolt	47 (64)

ISUZU P'UP & TROOPER II

DESCRIPTION

The P'UP and Trooper II models use an independent front suspension, consisting of torsion bars, upper and lower control arms, steering knuckle, stabilizer bar and a strut bar (except Trooper II).

The steering knuckle is connected to the control arms by the use of ball joints. A stabilizer bar may be used between frame and lower control arm. A strut bar may be used on some applications. On Trooper II models, lower control arm contains 2 pivot bushings while all others contain only one bushing.

ADJUSTMENTS & INSPECTION

WHEEL ALIGNMENT SPECIFICATIONS & PROCEDURES

See WHEEL ALIGNMENT SPECIFICATIONS & PROCEDURES in WHEEL ALIGNMENT section.

WHEEL BEARING

1) Raise and support vehicle. Remove wheel assembly. Remove hub cap, grease cup, cotter pin and nut retainer on 2WD models. Remove locking hub assembly and lock washer on 4WD models. See LOCKING HUB under REMOVAL & INSTALLATION in this article.

Fig. 1: Exploded View of P'UP 2WD Front Suspension

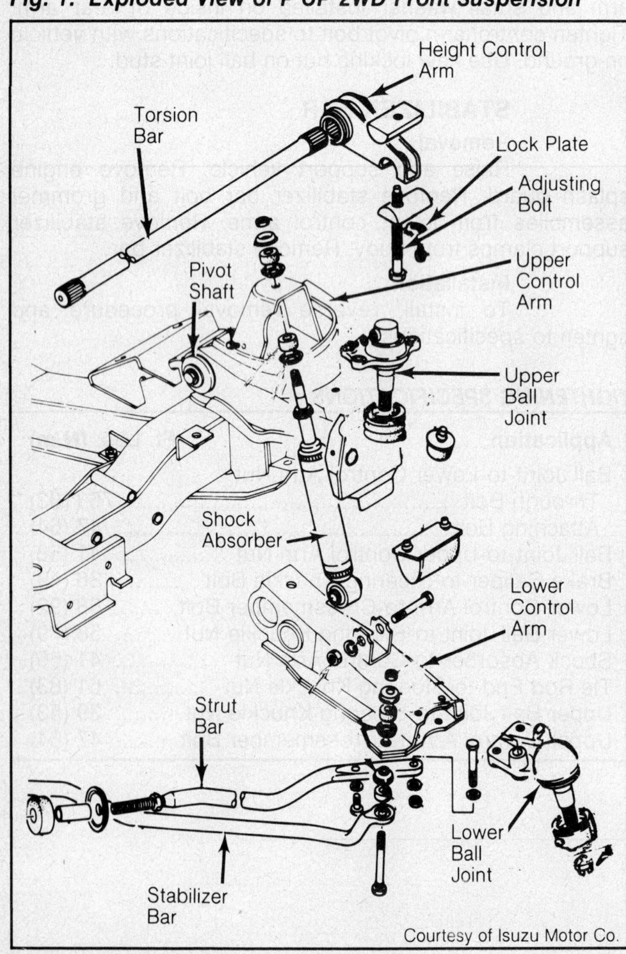

P'UP 4WD and Trooper II are similar.

2) Rotate wheel and tighten spindle nut to 22 ft. lbs. (30 N.m). Rotate wheel 2 to 3 turns and loosen spindle nut. Tighten nut finger tight until no hub free play exists.

3) Ensure brake pads are not contacting brake rotor. Using a spring scale attached to wheel stud, measure starting torque required to rotate the hub. Tighten spindle nut until spring scale reads 2.2 lbs. (1.0 kg) on 2WD models or 3.3 lbs. (1.5 kg) on 4WD models.

4) Reverse removal procedure for remaining components. On 2WD models, fill hub cap with .53 ozs. (17 g) of grease prior to installation. On 4WD models, install locking hub.

NOTE: If bolt holes on lock washer and spindle nut do not align, reverse lock washer. If holes still do not align, turn nut slightly to align holes.

REMOVAL & INSTALLATION

WHEEL BEARING

Removal (2WD)

1) Raise and support vehicle. Remove wheel assembly. Remove brake caliper. Remove hub cup, cotter pin, nut retainer, spindle nut and washer.

2) Remove hub/rotor assembly. Remove outer wheel bearing. Remove seal and inner bearing.

3) If bearing races require replacement, drive bearing races from hub using punch and hammer.

Removal (4WD)

1) Remove locking hub assembly. See LOCKING HUB in this article. Remove brake caliper. Remove spindle nut. Remove hub, outer bearing and race.

2) Remove retaining ring and seal from rear of hub. Remove inner bearing. If bearing races require replacement, drive bearing races from hub using punch and hammer.

Installation

1) Install bearing races. Ensure races are fully seated. Pack bearings with proper grease. Install inner bearing in race. Using Seal Installer (J-29017) and Handle (J-8092), install seal in hub. Install new retaining ring (if used).

2) Fill hub cavity with 2.12 ozs. (60.1 g) of grease. Apply grease to seal lip. Reverse removal procedures. Adjust wheel bearings. See WHEEL BEARING under ADJUSTMENTS & INSPECTION. On 2WD models, fill hub cap with .53 ozs. (17 g) of grease prior to installation.

LOCKING HUB

Removal (Automatic Type)

1) Place transfer case lever in "2H" position. Move vehicle back and forth approximately 3 feet or more. Raise and support vehicle. Remove wheel assembly. Remove locking hub retaining bolts.

2) Remove driven clutch assembly and housing. *See Fig. 2.* Remove spacer, snap ring and shims. Remove drive clutch assembly and inner cam.

Inspection

1) Measure O.D. of drive clutch. Measure I.D. of housing assembly at .31" (7.8 mm) below surface. *See Fig. 3.* Using feeler gauge, measure hold-out ring axial play of drive clutch assembly. *See Fig. 3.*

ISUZU P'UP & TROOPER II (Cont.)

Fig. 2: Exploded View of 4WD Automatic Locking Hub

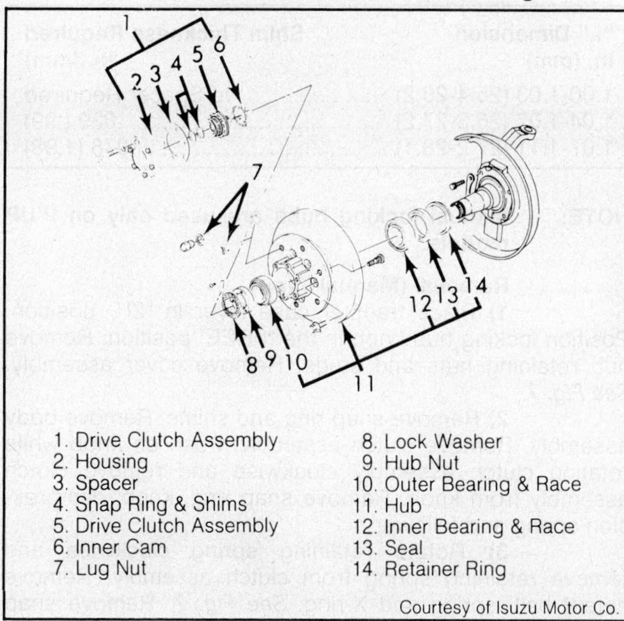

Fig. 3: Measuring Housing I.D. & Hold-Out Ring Axial Play

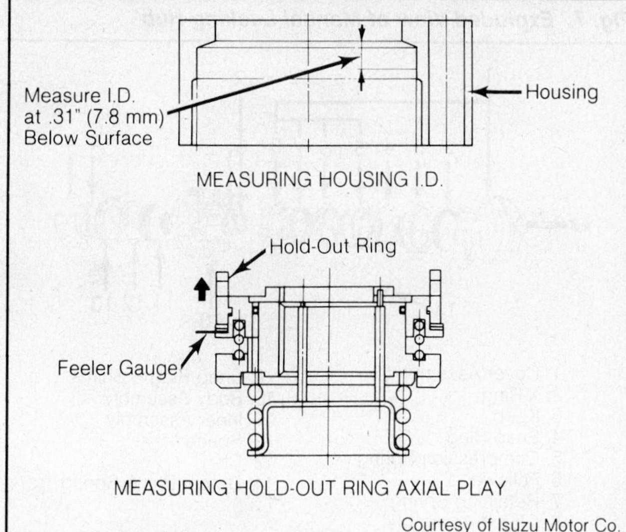

Fig. 4: Measuring Drive Clutch

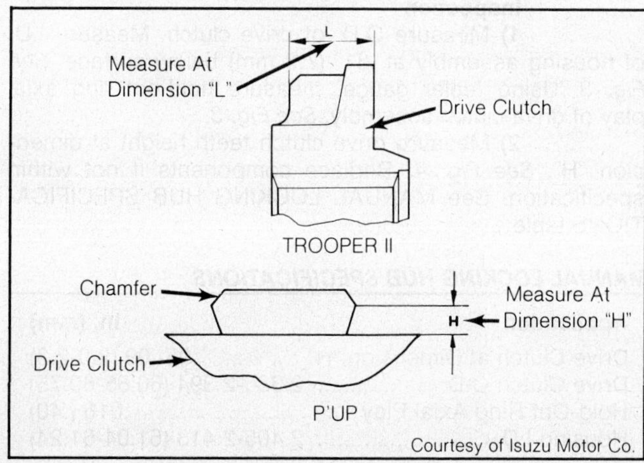

2) On P'UP models, measure driven clutch and drive clutch teeth height at dimension "H". *See Fig. 4.* On Trooper II models, measure drive clutch at dimension "L". *See Fig. 4.* Replace components if not within specification. See AUTOMATIC LOCKING HUB SPECIFICATIONS table.

AUTOMATIC LOCKING HUB SPECIFICATIONS

Application	In. (mm)
Drive Clutch at "L" or "H" Dimension	
P'UP	.0787-.0906 (1.998-2.301)
Trooper II	.307-.323 (7.79-8.20)
Drive Clutch O.D.	
P'UP	2.3839-2.3917-(60.551-60.749)
Trooper II	2.54-2.55 (64.5-64.7)
Hold-Out Ring Axial Play	
P'UP	.0157 (.398)
Trooper II	.016 (.40)
Housing I.D.	
P'UP	2.4031-2.4110 (61.038-61.239)
Trooper II	2.561-2.568 (65.05-65.23)

Installation

1) Ensure transfer case lever is in "2H" position. Ensure hub flange, lock washer and axle splines are clean. Install inner cam so cam keyway aligns with steering knuckle groove.

2) Using plastic hammer, lightly tap inner cam to ensure cam is seated against lock washer. Push axle shaft toward tire while holding inner cam. Install Gauge (J-33935) over end of axle shaft until gauge contacts lock washer.

3) Using feeler gauge, measure clearance between gauge and snap ring groove. If clearance exceeds snap ring groove distance, shims must be installed.

4) Select shims to obtain a clearance of 0-.0039" (0-.099 mm). Remove gauge. DO NOT remove inner cam. On P'UP models, note identification mark "L" (left) or "R" (right) on drive clutch assembly for proper installation.

5) On all models, apply grease to axle shaft splines. Apply grease to proper areas of drive clutch assembly and housing. *See Fig. 5.* Apply proper amount of grease to designated areas. See HUB LUBRICATION SPECIFICATIONS table.

Fig. 5: Hub Lubrication Areas

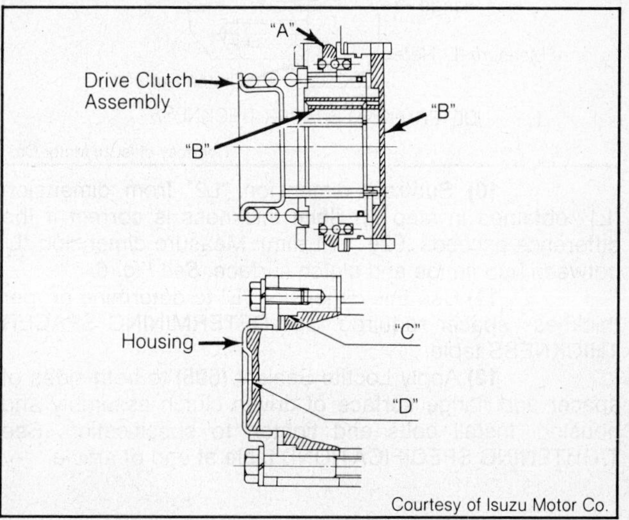

ISUZU P'UP & TROOPER II (Cont.)

HUB LUBRICATION SPECIFICATIONS

Application	Ozs. (g)
"A" Area	.25 (7.1)
"B" Area	.11 (3.1)
"C" Area	.29 (8.2)
"D" Area	.15 (4.2)

6) Align cutout area of drive clutch assembly with concave area of inner cam. Engage drive clutch teeth with inner cam by rotating axle shaft.

7) Measure and record distance "L1" between retainer surface and drive clutch surface. *See Fig. 6.* Install new snap ring on Snap Ring Installer (J-33934). Install shims on snap ring installer.

CAUTION: Always install new snap ring on axle shaft.

8) Place snap ring installer in center hole of axle shaft. Hit snap ring installer by hand while holding axle shaft toward the tire. DO NOT use hammer to install snap ring.

9) Force snap ring in position. Ensure snap ring is fully seated. Measure clearance "L2" between clutch surface and retainer surface. *See Fig. 6.*

Fig. 6: Measuring Hub Clearance

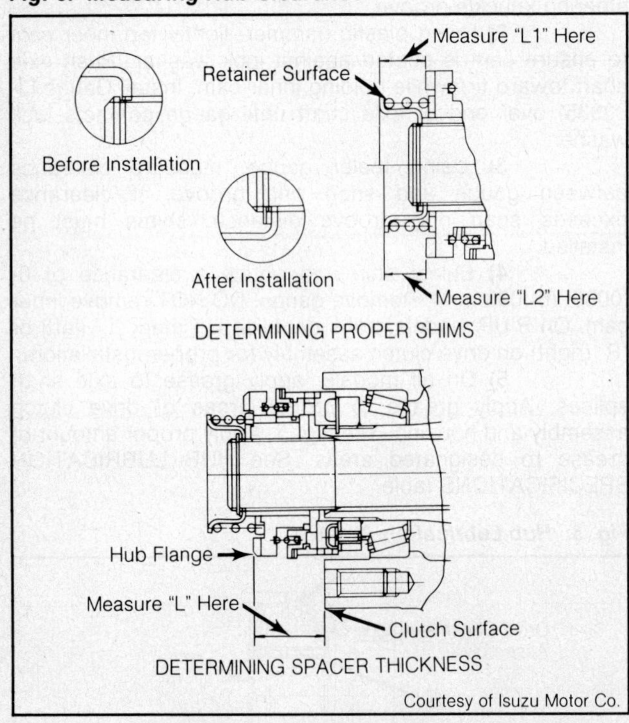

10) Subtract dimension "L2" from dimension "L1" obtained in step **7)**. Shim thickness is correct if the difference exceeds .028" (.71 mm). Measure dimension "L" between hub flange and clutch surface. *See Fig. 6.*

11) Use this dimension "L" to determine proper thickness spacer required. See DETERMINING SPACER THICKNESS table.

12) Apply Loctite Sealant (505) to both sides of spacer and flange surface of driven clutch assembly and housing. Install bolts and tighten to specification. See TIGHTENING SPECIFICATIONS table at end of article.

DETERMINING SPACER THICKNESS

"L" Dimension In. (mm)	Shim Thickness Required In. (mm)
1.00-1.03 (25.4-26.2)	No Spacer Required
1.04-1.07 (26.3-27.2)	.039 (.99)
1.07-1.11 (27.2-28.1)	.078 (1.98)

NOTE: Manual locking hubs are used only on P'UP models.

Removal (Manual Type)

1) Place transfer case lever in "2H" position. Position locking hub knob in the "FREE" position. Remove hub retaining nuts and studs. Remove cover assembly. *See Fig. 7.*

2) Remove snap ring and shims. Remove body assembly. Remove clutch assembly. Push on knob while rotating clutch assembly clockwise and remove clutch assembly from knob. Remove snap ring, knob, compression spring and follower.

3) Rotate retaining spring clockwise and remove retaining spring from clutch assembly. Remove detent ball, spring and X-ring. *See Fig. 7.* Remove snap ring and inner assembly. Remove snap ring, ring and spacer from body.

Fig. 7: Exploded View of Manual Locking Hub

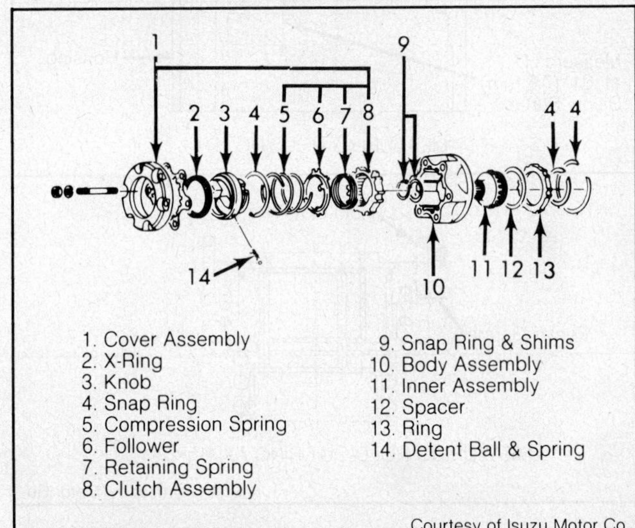

Inspection

1) Measure O.D. of drive clutch. Measure I.D. of housing assembly at .31" (7.8 mm) below surface. *See Fig. 3.* Using feeler gauge, measure hold-out ring axial play of drive clutch assembly. *See Fig. 3.*

2) Measure drive clutch teeth height at dimension "H". *See Fig. 4.* Replace components if not within specification. See MANUAL LOCKING HUB SPECIFICATIONS table.

MANUAL LOCKING HUB SPECIFICATIONS

Application	In. (mm)
Drive Clutch at Dimension "H"	.08-.09 (2.0-2.3)
Drive Clutch O.D.	2.386-2.394 (60.55-60.75)
Hold-Out Ring Axial Play	.016 (.40)
Housing I.D.	2.405-2.413 (61.04-61.24)

ISUZU P'UP & TROOPER II (Cont.)

Installation

1) Apply grease to both sides of spacer and inside of ring. Install spacer, ring and snap ring in body. Apply grease to splined area of body. Install inner assembly and snap ring.

2) Install X-ring, detent ball, spring and knob. Install knob retaining snap ring with flat side toward the knob. Install retaining spring with spring ends aligned with cut area of clutch spring groove of clutch assembly.

3) Install follower on clutch assembly with the follower projected tab positioned closest to the retaining spring. This is accomplished by aligning follower tab with outer clutch assembly teeth.

4) Hook retaining spring on spring retainer tabs of the follower. Install compression spring with smaller diameter against follower. Align follower tab with knob groove.

5) Install clutch assembly on the knob while pushing clutch assembly inward and rotating knob counterclockwise. Apply Loctite (505) to body assembly-to-hub contact area.

6) Install body. Install shims and snap ring on end of drive axle. Using feeler gauge, measure clearance between snap ring and body. Clearance should be 0-.01" (0-.3 mm). Adjust clearance to specification using different shims.

7) Apply Loctite (505) on body-to-cover contact area. Align follower tabs with grooves of body. Install cover and retaining nuts. Tighten nuts to specification.

AXLE SHAFT BEARING

Removal (4WD)

Remove steering knuckle. See STEERING KNUCKLE in this article. Remove oil seal and thrust washer from steering knuckle. *See Fig. 11.* Using Axle Shaft Bearing Puller (J-23907), remove axle shaft bearing.

Installation

1) Lubricate bearing with grease. Using Handle (J-8092) and Axle Shaft Bearing Installer (J-29019), install bearing in steering knuckle.

2) Install thrust washer. Using Handle (J-8092) and Seal Installer (J-33161), install oil seal. Lubricate seal lip with grease.

UPPER CONTROL ARM

Removal

1) Raise and support vehicle. Remove wheel assembly. Support lower control arm with jack. Remove upper ball joint cotter pin nut. Separate ball upper ball joint from steering knuckle.

2) Note number and placement of shims between upper control arm pivot shaft and frame (if equipped). Remove pivot shaft bolts. Remove shock absorber from upper support and compress (if required). Remove upper control arm.

Inspection

Inspect upper control arm and pivot shaft for cracks, distortion or thread damage. Check pivot shaft bushings for wear or damage.

Bushing Replacement

Remove bolts from ends of pivot shaft. Remove lock washer, flat washer and plate. Using Bushing Remover/Installer (J-29755), press out pivot shaft and bushings. Reverse removal procedure to install bushings. Tighten pivot shaft bolts to specification.

Installation

1) On 2WD models, install pivot shaft with smaller clearance "A" toward center of vehicle. On 4WD models, install pivot shaft with larger clearance "B" toward center of vehicle on 4WD. *See Fig. 8.*

2) Ensure shims are installed in original location. Reverse removal procedures for remaining components. Tighten bolts to specification. Check front end alignment.

Fig. 8: Upper Control Arm Installation

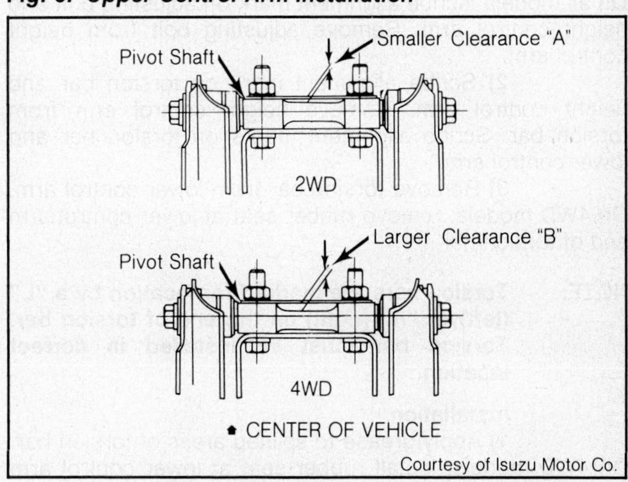

Courtesy of Isuzu Motor Co.

LOWER CONTROL ARM

Removal

1) Raise and support vehicle. Remove wheel assembly. Remove strut bar. See STRUT BAR in this article. Disconnect stabilizer bar from lower control arm. Remove torsion bar. See TORSION BAR in this article.

2) Disconnect shock absorber from lower control arm. Remove bolts attaching ball joint to lower control arm. On 2WD models, remove lower control arm pivot bolts. On 4WD models, remove bushing and pin retaining nuts. On all models, remove control arm.

Inspection

Inspect lower control arm and pivot bolt for cracks, distortion or thread damage. Check pivot bushing for wear or damage. Replace bushing (if necessary).

Installation

Reverse removal procedures for installation. Tighten bolts to specification.

SHOCK ABSORBER

Removal

Raise and support vehicle. On 2WD models, remove shock absorber dust cover. On all models, remove nut, bushing and washer from shock absorber shaft. Remove shock absorber-to-lower control arm bolt. Remove shock absorber.

Installation

Reverse removal procedures. Tighten bolts to specification.

STABILIZER BAR

Removal

Raise and support vehicle. Remove stabilizer bar-to-hanger bolts. Remove stabilizer bar-to-lower control arm bolt. Remove stabilizer bar and brackets.

ISUZU P'UP & TROOPER II (Cont.)

Installation

Inspect grommets and bushings for wear or damage. Replace grommets or bushings (if necessary). Reverse removal procedures. Tighten bolts to specification.

TORSION BAR

Removal

1) Raise and support vehicle. On 2WD models, remove lock plate from adjustment control bolt. *See Fig. 1.* On all models, scribe alignment mark on adjusting bolt and height control arm. Remove adjusting bolt from height control arm.

2) Scribe alignment mark on torsion bar and height control arm. Remove height control arm from torsion bar. Scribe alignment marks on torsion bar and lower control arm.

3) Remove torsion bar from lower control arm. On 4WD models, remove rubber seat at lower control arm end of torsion bar.

NOTE: Torsion bars are marked for location by a "L" (left) or "R" (right) on the end of torsion bar. Torsion bar must be installed in correct location.

Installation

1) Apply grease to splined areas of torsion bar. On 4WD models, install rubber seat at lower control arm end of torsion bar. On all models, install torsion bar in lower control arm. Ensure torsion bar is installed in proper location by identification mark on end of shaft.

2) Apply grease to height control arm-to-bracket contact areas. Install height control arm on torsion bar so scribe marks are aligned. Install adjusting bolt.

3) Rotate adjusting bolt until reference marks are aligned on adjusting bolt and height control arm. Check riding height. On 2WD models, install lock plate.

Riding Height

1) Riding height must be checked with proper tire pressure and vehicle empty of cargo and passengers.

2) Bounce vehicle up and down several times to ensure proper positioning prior to measuring riding height. On P'UP models, loosen front strut bar nuts only. DO NOT loosen rear adjusting nuts.

3) On P'UP models, measure the distance from upper bolt of crossmember to the ground. This is dimension "A". Measure distance from tip of lower ball joint stud to the ground. This is dimension "B". *See Fig. 9.*

4) Subtract dimension "B" from dimension "A". This is dimension "Z" or riding height. On Trooper II models, measure distance from the center of the headlights to the ground.

5) On all models, riding height must be adjusted if not within specification. See RIDING HEIGHT SPECIFICATIONS table. Adjust riding height by rotating adjusting bolt.

RIDING HEIGHT SPECIFICATIONS

Application	In. (mm)
P'UP	
2WD	4.0 (102)
4WD	5.0 (127)
Trooper II	33-34 (850-880)

Fig. 9: Measuring Riding Height & Strut Bar Location on P'UP Models

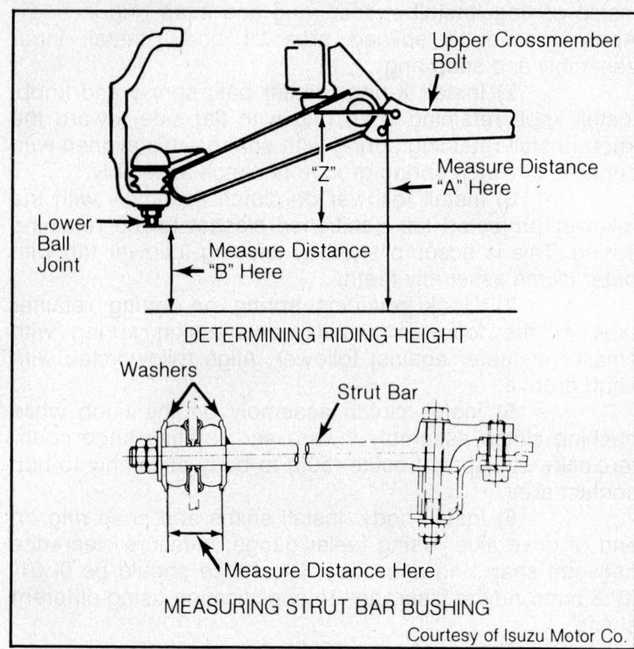

6) On P'UP models, tighten strut bar nuts to specification. Measure strut bar bushing distance between washers located at each end of rubber bushings of stabilizer bar. *See Fig. 9.* Distance must be within specification. See STRUT BAR BUSHING SPECIFICATIONS table.

STRUT BAR BUSHING SPECIFICATIONS

Application	In. (mm)
2WD	1.20-1.28 (30.5-32.5)
4WD	1.417-1.496 (35.99-37.99)

STRUT BAR

NOTE: Wheel alignment should be checked on 2WD models if strut bar nuts are moved from original location. The strut bar location is used to adjust the wheel caster.

Removal

Raise and support vehicle. Remove nuts, washers and rubber bushing from front side of strut bar. Remove strut bar-to-lower control arm bolts. Remove strut bar.

Installation

1) Reverse removal procedures. On all models, tighten strut bar nuts to specification.

2) On P'UP models, measure strut bar bushing distance between washers located at each end of rubber bushings of stabilizer bar. *See Fig. 9.* Distance must be within specification. See STRUT BAR BUSHING SPECIFICATIONS table. Check front wheel alignment on 2WD models.

STEERING KNUCKLE

Removal

1) Raise and support vehicle. Remove wheel assembly. Remove brake caliper. On 4WD models,

ISUZU P'UP & TROOPER II (Cont.)

Fig. 10: Steering Knuckle & Control Arms (2WD)

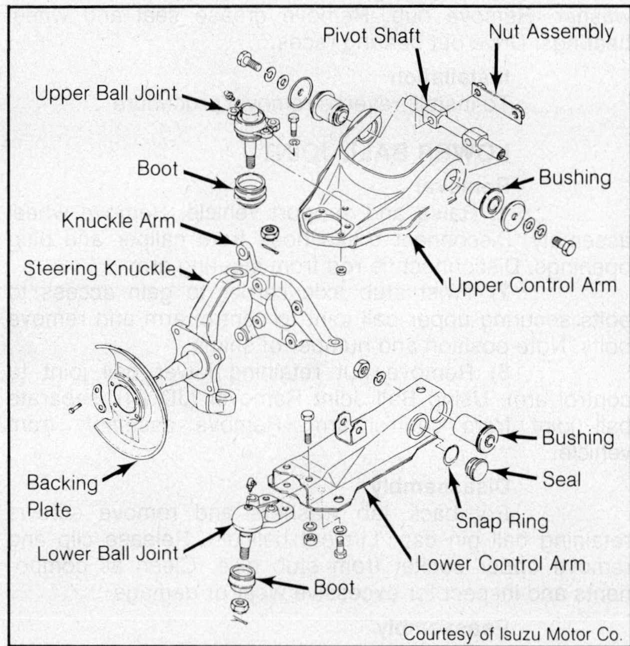

Courtesy of Isuzu Motor Co.

Fig. 11: Steering Knuckle & Control Arms (4WD)

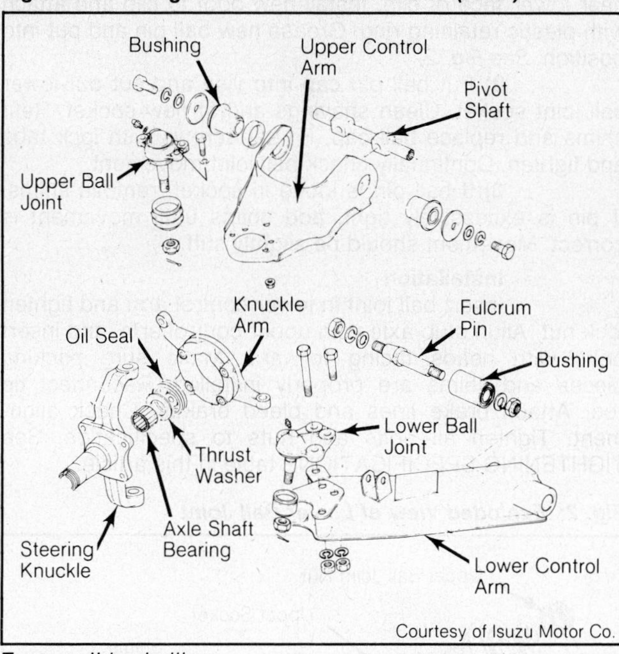

Courtesy of Isuzu Motor Co.

Trooper II is similiar.

remove locking hub. See LOCKING HUB in this article. On all models, remove hub and rotor assembly. Remove tie rod from knuckle arm.

2) Remove backing plate from steering knuckle. Separate knuckle arm from steering knuckle. *See Figs. 10 and 11.* On 4WD models, remove dust shield from knuckle arm. *See Fig. 11.*

3) On all models, support lower control arm. Remove cotter pin and nut from upper and lower ball joints. Separate ball joints from steering knuckle. Remove steering knuckle.

Installation

Reverse removal procedures. Tighten bolts to specification. Adjust wheel bearings. See WHEEL BEARINGS under ADJUSTMENTS & INSPECTION in this article.

TIGHTENING SPECIFICATIONS

Application	Ft. Lbs. (N.m)
Ball Joint Nut	75 (102)
Ball Joint-to-Control Arm Bolt	
Lower	51 (69)
Upper	19 (26)
Caliper Mounting Bolt	22-25 (30-34)
Locking Hubs	
Automatic Hub	
Driven Clutch-to-Housing Bolt	17-21 (23-29)
Housing-to-Hub Bolt	39-47 (53-64)
Manual Hub	
Cover-to-Hub Nut	40-47 (54-64)
Lower Control Arm-to-Crossmember Nut	
2WD	90 (122)
Lower Control Arm-to-Frame Nut	
4WD	97 (132)
Shock Mount	
Lower Bolt	45 (61)
Upper Nut	14 (19)
Strut Bar-to-Control Arm Bolt	51 (69)
Strut Bar-to-Frame Nut	
2WD	58-72 (79-98)
4WD	
Inner	14 (19)
Outer	43-61 (58-83)
Upper Control Arm	
Bushing Bolt	87 (118)
Upper Control Arm Pivot	
Shaft-to-Frame Bolt	75 (102)
	INCH Lbs. (N.m)
Stabilizer Bar-to-Control Arm Bolt	84 (9)

JAGUAR

XJ6 III, XJS HE

DESCRIPTION

Front suspension consists of upper and lower control arms, double acting hydraulic shock absorbers, coil springs, stabilizer bar and steering knuckles. Coil springs are mounted between lower control arms and crossmember. Shock absorbers are attached at bottom of lower control arms and at the top to body. Stabilizer bar is attached to the lower control arms and crossmember.

Fig. 1: Sectional View of Front Suspension Assembly

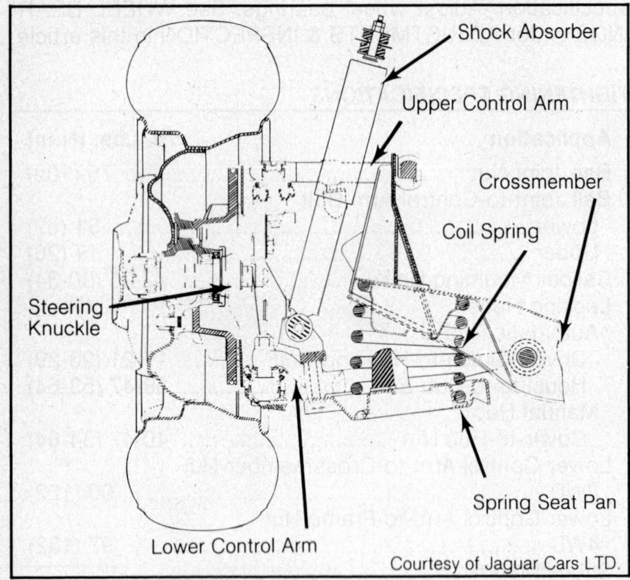

ADJUSTMENT & INSPECTION

WHEEL ALIGNMENT SPECIFICATIONS & PROCEDURES

See WHEEL ALIGNMENT SPECIFICATIONS & PROCEDURES in WHEEL ALIGNMENT section.

WHEEL BEARING

While rotating hub, tighten nut until no end play is evident. Loosen nut slightly to line up cotter pin and install new pin. Check end play with dial indicator. If end play is not .0020-.0050" (.050-.127 mm), adjust hub nut until correct end play is obtained.

BALL JOINT CHECKING

Inspect ball joints for any signs of excessive wear or damage. Replace as needed. Lower ball joint can be adjusted with shims. These shims are not to be used to compensate for worn ball joints, and are designed to provide adjustment during overhaul reassembly only.

REMOVAL & INSTALLATION

WHEEL BEARING

Removal

1) Raise and support vehicle. Remove wheel assembly. Mark hub and rotor for reassembly. Remove hub to rotor attaching bolts through holes in hub.

2) Remove grease cap, cotter pin, hub nut and washer. Remove hub. Remove grease seal and wheel bearings. Drive out bearing races.

Installation

To install, reverse removal procedure.

LOWER BALL JOINT

Removal

1) Raise and support vehicle. Remove wheel assembly. Disconnect brake hose from caliper and plug openings. Disconnect tie rod from steering arm.

2) Twist stub axle carrier to gain access to bolts securing upper ball joint to control arm and remove bolts. Note position and number of shims.

3) Remove nut retaining lower ball joint to control arm. Using Ball Joint Remover (JD 24), separate ball joint from control arm. Remove assembly from vehicle.

Disassembly

Pry back tab washers and remove screws retaining ball pin cap. Lift out ball pin. Release clip and remove upper socket from stub axle. Clean all components and inspect for excessive wear or damage.

Reassembly

1) Install new upper socket to stub axle carrier. Fit lip of boot clip in recess in ball joint socket. Lip must be near lower face of clip. Install new boot to clip and attach with plastic retaining ring. Grease new ball pin and put into position. *See Fig. 2.*

2) Put ball pin cap into vise and cut out lower ball joint socket. Clean shavings and fit new socket. Refit shims and replace ball cap. Fit set screws with lock tabs and tighten. Continually check ball joint movement.

3) If ball pin is loose in socket, remove shims. If pin is excessively tight, add shims until movement is correct. Movement should be slightly stiff.

Installation

Insert ball joint in lower control arm and tighten lock nut. Align stub axle with upper control arm, and insert bolts with heads facing forward. Make sure packing pieces and shims are properly installed. Reconnect tie rod. Attach brake lines and bleed brakes. Check alignment. Tighten all bolts and nuts to specification. See TIGHTENING SPECIFICATIONS table in this article.

Fig. 2: Exploded View of Lower Ball Joint

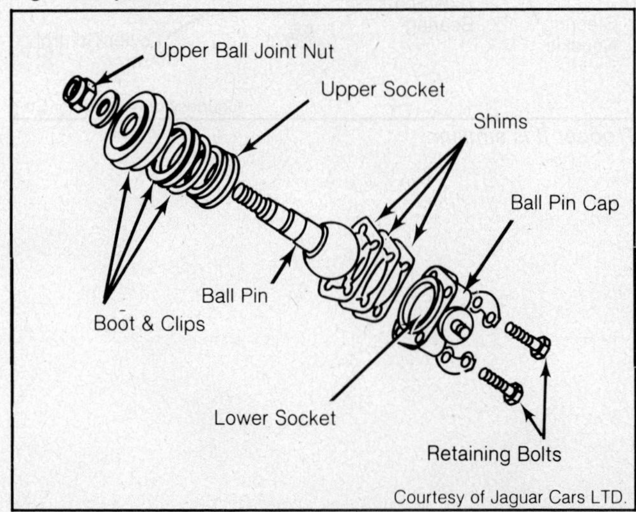

JAGUAR (Cont.)

UPPER BALL JOINT

NOTE: Upper control arm ball joint cannot be overhauled. If ball joint is excessively worn, assembly must be replaced.

Removal

1) Raise vehicle and place on safety stands. Remove wheel assembly. Turn steering to full lock position. Wire stub axle to crossmember to prevent tension on brake hose when ball joint is separated.

2) Remove bolt retaining upper ball joint to control arm. Note number of shims and position of packing pieces. Remove ball joint lock nut. Using Ball Joint Remover (JD 24), separate ball joint from control arm. Remove assembly from vehicle. Remove ball joint from stub axle.

Installation

Apply grease to replacement ball joint and position in stub axle. Hold ball joint against taper fit washer and tighten retaining nut. Refit upper control arm retaining bolts and caster shims, with bolt heads facing forward. Check wheel alignment.

FRONT SUSPENSION ASSEMBLY

Removal

1) Disconnect battery and remove air cleaners. Disconnect upper end of shock absorber. Drain power steering fluid, and disconnect and plug power steering inlet and outlet hoses.

2) Remove nuts securing engine mounts to brackets on frame crossmember, and lift engine weight off crossmember. Disconnect rear crossmember retaining bolts, and separate stabilizer bar from link. Turn steering column until pinch bolt holding lower "U" joint to pinion shaft is accessible. Remove pinch bolt.

3) Return steering to straight ahead position. Set ignition to "LOCK" position and remove key. Separate lower steering column from upper universal joint, and separate from pinion shaft.

4) Raise and support vehicle. Remove front wheel assembly. Disconnect brake hoses and lines. Detach ground strap from engine. Remove suspension retaining bolts. Collect and note location of all washers, spacers and bushings. Remove suspension assembly from vehicle.

Installation

1) To install, reverse removal procedure. Ensure brake lines and hoses are properly routed without bends or kinks. It may be helpful to remove protective heat shield covering boot on rack and pinion steering before positioning suspension in place.

2) Be sure power steering reservoir is full before starting engine after installation. If additional information is required on steering column installation, see appropriate article in STEERING section. Bleed brake system.

SHOCK ABSORBERS

Removal

Detach upper shock absorber retaining bolts. Raise and support vehicle. If necessary, remove wheel assembly for access to lower mounting. Remove lower shock absorber retaining bolts and remove from vehicle.

Installation

To install, reverse removal procedure.

COIL SPRINGS

Removal

1) Raise and support vehicle. Remove wheel assembly. Fit Spring Compressor (JD 6D) and Adapter (JD 6D 1) and collapse coil spring enough to relieve load on pan seat.

2) Remove hardware mounting spring pan to lower control arm. Slightly loosen spring compressor and remove complete assembly.

NOTE: Be sure to note number and location of any packing shims.

Installation

To install, reverse removal procedures. Place floor jack under lower ball joint to aid in aligning spring pan bolt. A maximum of 3 packing pieces may be placed in spring pan, and no more than 2 can be fitted on crossmember.

LOWER CONTROL ARM

Removal

1) Remove complete suspension assembly as previously described. With assembly on bench, detach tie rod ball joints from steering knuckle. Detach and remove steering rack from crossmember.

2) Use spring compressor to remove coil spring. Separate upper ball joint, noting location of all caster shims. Detach lower ball joint.

3) Remove stabilizer bar support bracket and shock absorber lower retaining bolts. Remove cotter pin and pivot shaft nut. Drive pivot shaft from crossmember and collect spacers. Remove lower control arm.

Installation

To install, reverse removal procedure. Do not tighten pivot shaft nut until vehicle is resting on floor at full curb weight.

UPPER CONTROL ARM

Removal

1) Raise and support vehicle. Remove wheel assembly. Detach upper ball joint from control arm. Note number and location of all caster adjusting shims.

2) Wire steering knuckle to coil spring and remove bolts holding upper control arm pivot shaft to vehicle. Note number and location of camber adjusting shims. Remove control arm from vehicle. *See Fig. 3.*

Fig. 3: Upper Control Arm Mounting Points

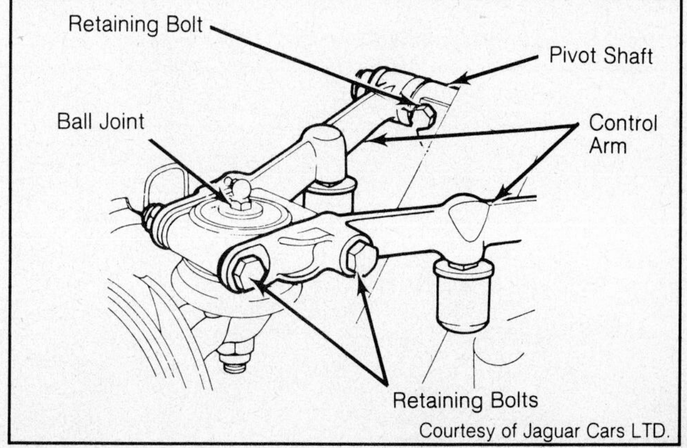

Courtesy of Jaguar Cars LTD.

Front Suspension

JAGUAR (Cont.)

Installation

To install, reverse removal procedure. Check wheel alignment.

STABILIZER BAR

Removal

Raise and support vehicle. Remove wheel assemblies. Detach both ends of stabilizer bar from links. Remove both brackets from frame. Remove all bushings from bar. Detach one tie rod end from steering knuckle and remove stabilizer from vehicle.

Installation

To install, reverse removal procedure. Fully tighten stabilizer bar nuts after vehicle is resting on floor.

TIGHTENING SPECIFICATIONS

Application	Ft. Lbs. (N.m)
Hub-to-Rotor Bolts	30-36 (40-49)
Lower Shock Absorber	45-50 (61-68)
Pivot Shaft-to-Lower Arm	32-50 (44-68)
Pivot Shaft-to-Upper Arm	45-55 (61-75)
Spring Pan Nuts	27-32 (37-44)
Stabilizer-to-Link Nuts	14-18 (19-24)
Tie Rod Nut	35-50 (48-68)
Upper Ball Joint-to-Arm	26-32 (35-44)
Upper Pivot Shaft-to-Crossmember	49-55 (67-75)
Upper Shock Absorber	27-32 (37-44)
Wheel Lug Nut	
Steel Wheel	65 (85)
Alloy Wheel	88 (102)

NOTE: Inspect all nylock nuts for damage. Replace nut if necessary to ensure locking ability

Front Suspension

MAZDA B2200 & B2600 PICKUP

DESCRIPTION

An independent double wishbone type suspension with torsion bars is used. Upper and lower control arms pivot on shafts connected to the frame. Torsion bars are mounted to torque arms which are attached to lower arms. On B2200 and 2WD B2600 models, strut rods are mounted to frame and between lower arms to provide caster adjustment. A stabilizer bar is mounted to the frame and connected to the lower arms by bushings and links.

Fig. 1: View of B2200 & B2600 (2WD) Suspension

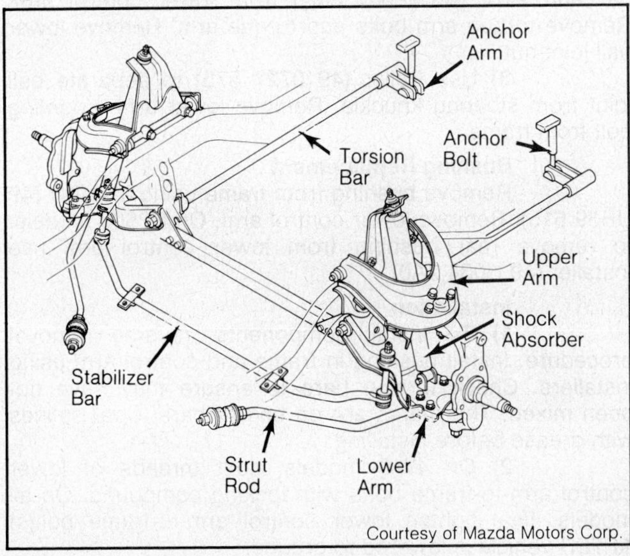

Fig. 2: View of B2600 (4WD) Suspension

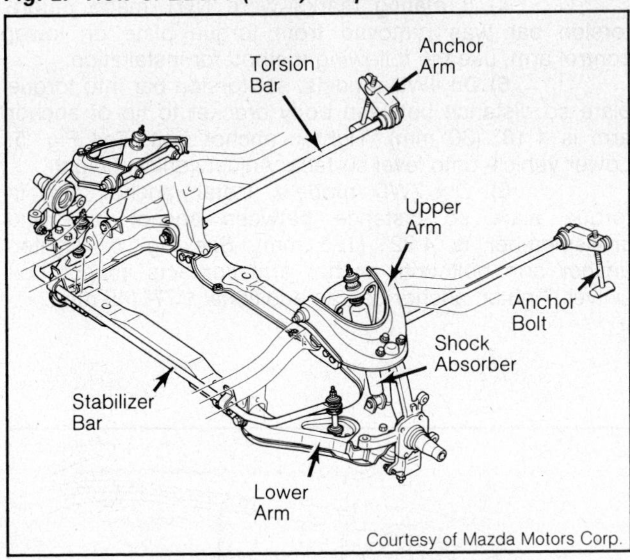

ADJUSTMENTS & INSPECTION

WHEEL ALIGNMENT SPECIFICATIONS & PROCEDURES

See WHEEL ALIGNMENT SPECIFICATIONS & PROCEDURES in WHEEL ALIGNMENT section.

WHEEL BEARING

1) Raise and support vehicle. Remove wheel assembly. Remove disc brake caliper assembly and secure out of way. Remove grease cap, cotter pin and nut lock.

2) On 4WD B2600 models, set hubs to "FREE" position. Remove freewheel hub retainer bolts and lift off hub. Remove the snap ring and spacer. Remove set bolts and bearing set plate.

3) On all models, tighten spindle nut to 14-22 ft. lbs. (20-29 N.m). Rotate hub a few times to seat bearing. Loosen adjusting nut slightly until hub can be turned by hand.

4) Using a spring tension gauge on one of the hub studs, tighten nut until preload is 1.3-2.5 lbs. (6-11 N). Replace cotter pin and reinstall components to complete adjustment.

BALL JOINT CHECKING

1) Check turning torque of ball joint using spring tension gauge and Preload Attachment (49 0180 510B). *See Fig. 3*. Move ball joint from side-to-side before measurement is made. Ball joint turning torque is 4.4-7.7 lbs. (20-34 N) on upper or lower control arms (2WD and 4WD).

2) Check for damage to dust boot. If replacement is needed, use a chisel to remove. Use Dust Boot Installer (49 S120 785) to replace dust boot.

Fig. 3: Checking Ball Joint Turning Torque

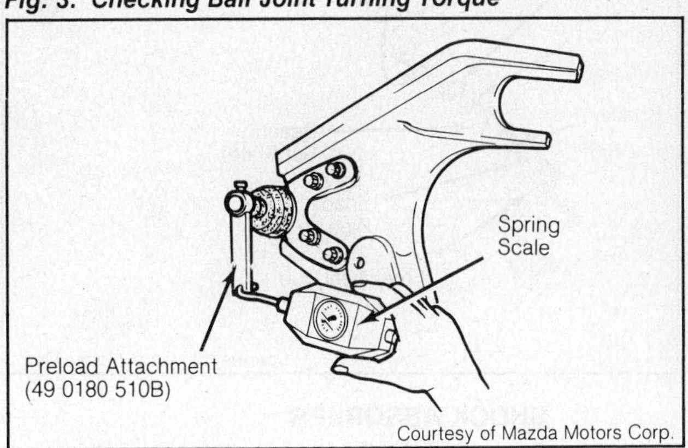

REMOVAL & INSTALLATION

WHEEL BEARING

Removal & Installation (2WD)

1) Raise and support vehicle. Remove wheel assembly. Remove brake caliper and support out of way. Remove grease cap, cotter pin, nut lock and hub nut.

2) Remove rotor and hub. Using round bar and hammer, lightly tap outer bearing and remove.

3) To install wheel bearing, reverse removal procedure. Install oil seal until flush with hub end surface. Adjust wheel bearing preload.

CAUTION: Always replace inner and outer bearings as a set.

Removal (4WD)

1) Raise and support vehicle. Remove wheel. Remove brake caliper and support out of way. Set the freewheel hub in "FREE" position.

MAZDA B2200 & B2600 PICKUP (Cont.)

2) Remove freewheel hub retainer bolts and lift off hub. Remove the snap ring and spacer. Remove set bolts and bearing set plate.

3) Remove bearing lock nut. *See Fig. 4*. Remove the hub and rotor assembly. Drive wheel bearing races out of hub using a drift and hammer.

Installation

1) Press new inner and outer races into hub. Press inner grease seal in until it is flush with hub end surface.

2) To install hub and rotor assembly, reverse removal procedure. Adjust wheel bearings as previously described.

Fig. 4: Exploded View of B2600 (4WD) Front Hub & Rotor Assembly

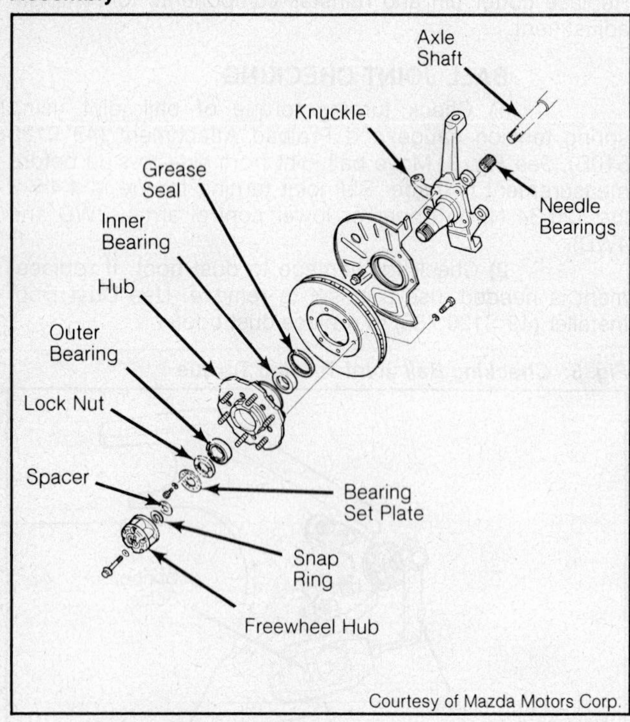

SHOCK ABSORBER

Removal & Installation

Remove nuts, rubber bushings and washers attaching upper end of shock absorber to frame tower. Remove shock absorber lower bolt from lower control arm. Remove shock absorber. To install, reverse removal procedure. The distance from tip of shock stem to top of lock nut should be .24-.32" (6.0-8.0 mm).

LOWER CONTROL ARM & TORSION BAR

Removal

1) Raise and support vehicle. Remove wheels. Remove caliper assembly and support out of way. Place alignment marks on anchor bolt threads, torsion bar to anchor arm, and torsion bar to torque plate on lower control arm. Remove anchor arm bolt and anchor arm.

2) Remove torsion bar. Disconnect stabilizer bar and strut rod (2WD only) from lower control arm. Remove torque arm bolts and torque arm. Remove lower ball joint nut.

3) Use Puller (49 0727 575) to separate ball joint from steering knuckle. Remove lower arm mounting bolt from frame.

Bushing Replacement

Remove bushing from frame using Installer (49 UB39 615). Remove lower control arm. On B2600 models, to remove rear bushing from lower control arm use Installer (49 U034 2A0).

Installation

1) To install components, reverse removal procedure. Install bushing in frame and control arm using installers. Check torsion bars to ensure they have not been mixed. The marks are on end of bars. Coat splines with grease before installing.

2) On 4WD models, coat threads of lower control arm-to-frame bolts with locking compound. On all models, final tighten lower control arm-to-frame bolt(s) AFTER vehicle is lowered to ground.

3) On all models, adjust vehicle height.

4) If mating marks were NOT made before torsion bar was removed from torque plate on lower control arm, use the following method for installation.

5) On 4WD models, set torsion bar into torque plate so distance between body bracket to tip of anchor arm is 1.18" (30 mm). Tighten anchor bolt. *See Fig. 5*. Lower vehicle onto level surface. Adjust vehicle height.

6) On 2WD models, install anchor arm in torque plate so distance between anchor arm and crossmember is 4.92" (125 mm). *See Fig. 5*. Tighten anchor arm bolt until anchor arm contacts anchor bolt swivel. Tighten anchor bolt an additional 1.77" (45 mm).

Fig. 5: Setting Torsion Bar Anchor Arm Distance

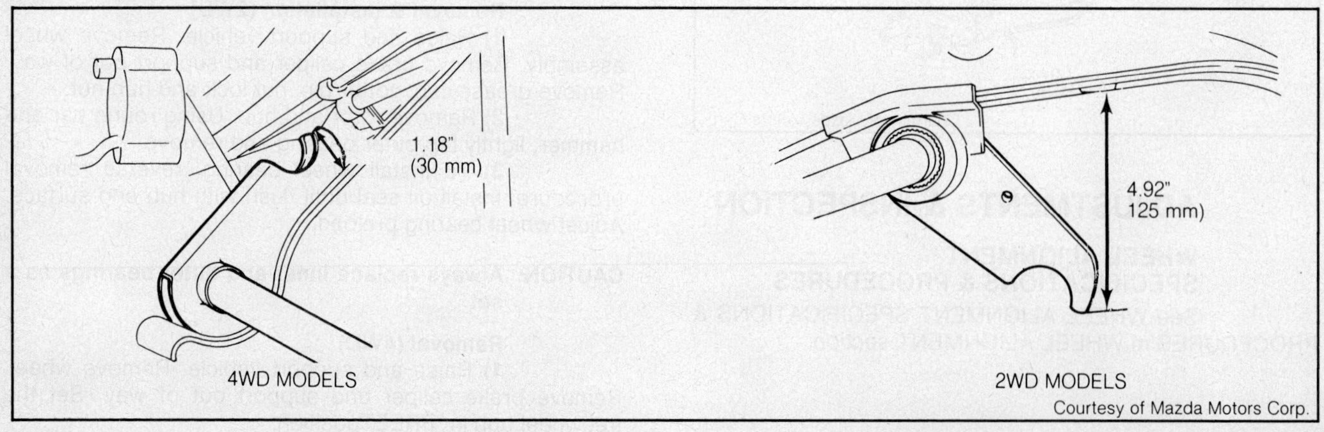

MAZDA B2200 & B2600 PICKUP (Cont.)

ADJUSTING VEHICLE HEIGHT

4WD

1) Use torsion bar anchor bolt to adjust vehicle height. With vehicle on level ground and unloaded, ensure front and rear tire pressures are correct.

2) Distance between center of wheel to fender brim should be as specified. See VEHICLE HEIGHT SPECIFICATIONS table. *See Fig. 6.*

VEHICLE HEIGHT SPECIFICATIONS

Body Style	Height In. (mm)
Short Bed	17.01 (432)
Long Bed	16.85 (428)

3) Use anchor bolt to adjust vehicle height. Side-to-side height difference should be less than .4" (10 mm).

Fig. 6: Measuring Vehicle Height

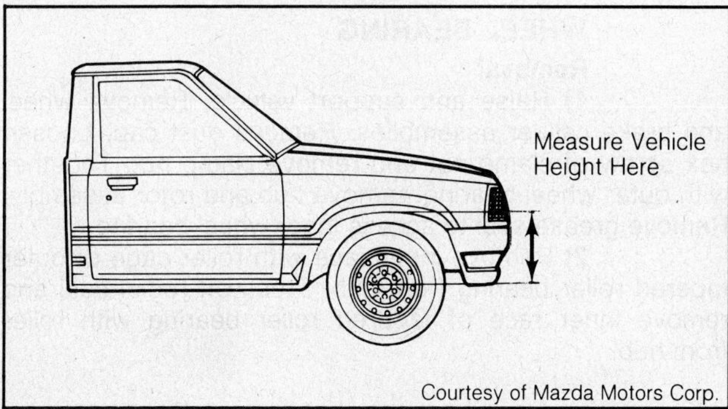

Courtesy of Mazda Motors Corp.

2WD

Information on vehicle ride height is not available from manufacturer. Side-to-side height difference should be less than .4" (10 mm). *See Fig. 6.*

UPPER CONTROL ARM

Removal & Installation

1) Raise vehicle and support. Remove wheel assembly. Disconnect upper ball joint from steering knuckle with Puller (49 0727 575).

NOTE: **Before removing upper control arm, count number and position of alignment shims.**

2) Remove nuts and bolts attaching upper arm shaft to frame tower. Remove upper control arm. To install upper control arm, reverse removal procedure. Check wheel alignment.

STRUT ROD

Removal & Installation (2WD Models)

Remove mounting nut for front bushing. Remove bolts attached to lower arm. Pull out strut rod. To install strut rod, reverse removal procedure. Distance from the end of strut rod to front edge of double nuts should be 3.88" (98.5 mm). Check alignment.

CAUTION: **Do not change position of double nut at rear of strut rod bushing except to change caster.**

STABILIZER BAR

Removal & Installation

Remove nuts attaching stabilizer to lower arm. Remove bolts to frame brackets. Remove stabilizer bar. To install, reverse removal procedure. Install bushing so seam is at front. Tighten nut on lower arm until end of bolt projects .55" (14 mm) from edge of lock nut. Check wheel alignment.

TIGHTENING SPECIFICATIONS

Application	Ft. Lbs. (N.m)
Disc Brake Freewheel Hub Bolts	22-25 (29-34)
Disc Brake Rotor-to-Hub Bolts	40-51 (54-69)
Lower Ball Joint-to-Knuckle	87-115 (118-157)
Lower Control Arm-to-Frame Bolt	
B2200	87-115 (118-157)
B2600	
Front Side	87-115 (118-157)
Rear Side	115-145 (157-210)
Shock Absorber Lower Bolt	40-59 (55-80)
Stabilizer Bracket-to-Frame	16-20 (22-26)
Strut Rod-to-Lower Arm	69-85 (93-117)
Strut Rod-to-Frame Nut	68-93 (92-127)
Torque Arm-to-Lower Arm	55-69 (75-93)
Upper Arm Shaft-to-Frame	54-69 (74-93)
Upper Ball Joint-to-Knuckle	22-37 (29-57)
Wheel Lug Nut Torque	
Standard Wheel	65-87 (90-120)
Styled Wheel	87-108 (120-150)

Front Suspension

MERCEDES-BENZ STRUT TYPE

190D, 190E, 260E,
300D Turbo, 300E, 300TD Turbo

DESCRIPTION

Mercedes-Benz uses independent front suspension, consisting of lower control arms, coil springs, shock absorbers, steering knuckles and a stabilizer bar. Steering knuckle is connected at bottom by ball joints.

ADJUSTMENTS & INSPECTION

WHEEL ALIGNMENT SPECIFICATIONS & PROCEDURES

See WHEEL ALIGNMENT SPECIFICATIONS & PROCEDURES in WHEEL ALIGNMENT section.

WHEEL BEARING

1) Jack up vehicle and remove wheel. Force brake pads away from brake disc. Remove upper mounting bolt for brake caliper. Swing brake caliper out of way.

2) Remove grease cap off of hub. Remove contact spring for radio interference. Loosen hex head bolt of bushing clamp. Tighten clamping nut while simultanously turning hub. Tighten until hub can barely be turned.

3) Loosen clamping nut about 1/3 turn and relieve tension by striking stub axle with a plastic hammer. Install dial indicator on front hub. Adjust dial indicator with a preload of .08" (2.0 mm).

4) Check end play of hub by pulling and pushing hard on hub flange. Turn wheel several times before each measurement. During measurement wheel hub must not turn.

5) Tighten hex head bolt on hub clamp and check end play. When end play of wheel bearings is correctly adjusted, washer between outer tapered roller bearing and clamping nut must just be able to turn under finger pressure.

6) Reassemble front hub and brake unit. Ensure front hub is filled with high temperature bearing grease.

BALL JOINT CHECKING

Ball joints are maintenance free (no grease fitting). Check ball joint for lateral and vertical movement. If any measureable lateral movement is observed, replace ball joint.

REMOVAL & INSTALLATION

WHEEL BEARING

Removal

1) Raise and support vehicle. Remove wheel and brake caliper assemblies. Remove dust cap. Loosen hex screw of clamp nut and remove clamp nut. Together with outer wheel bearing, remove hub and rotor assembly. Remove grease seal to access inner wheel bearing.

2) Remove inner race with roller cage of outer tapered roller bearing from hub. Press off radial seal and remove inner race of tapered roller bearing with roller from hub.

Fig. 1: Exploded View of Mercedes-Benz 190 Series & 300E Front Suspension

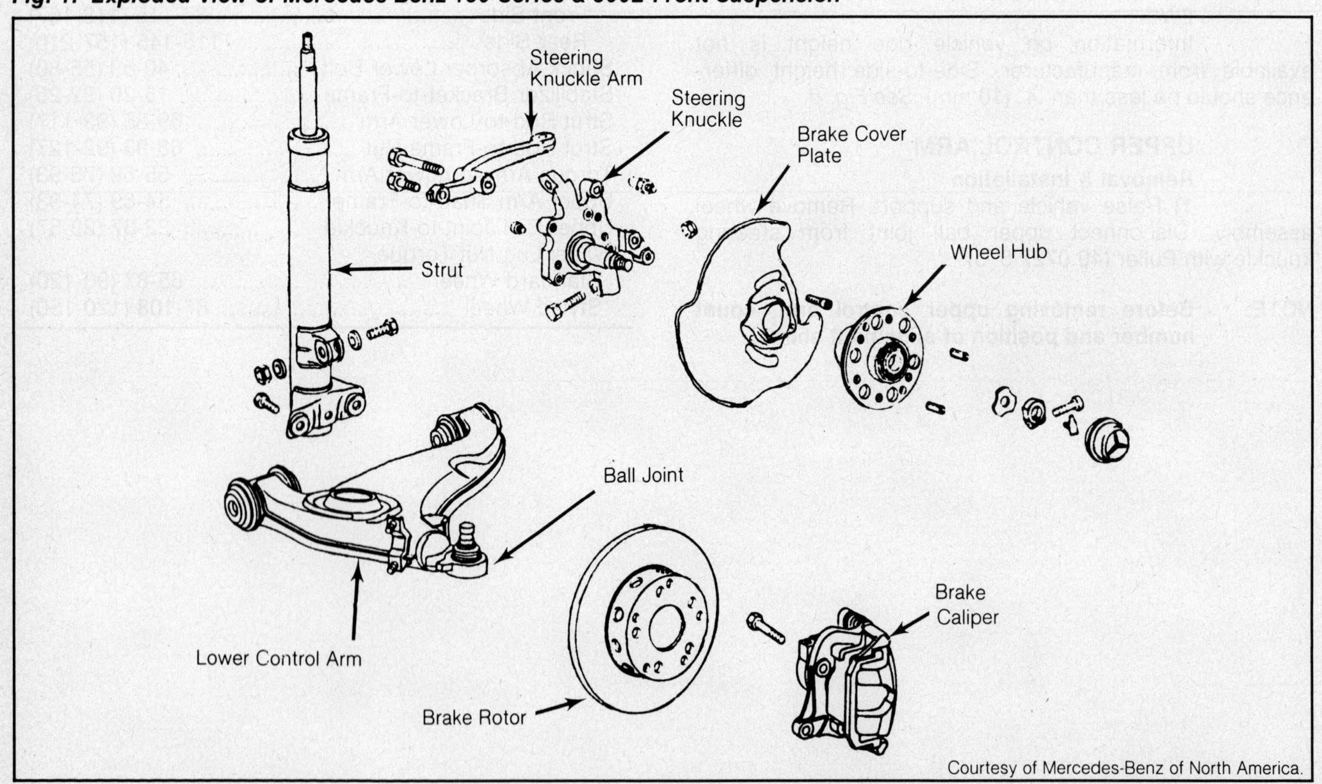

MERCEDES-BENZ STRUT TYPE (Cont.)

3) Remove outer race of inside tapered roller bearing. Knock out outer race of outer tapered roller bearing with a drift.

Installation

1) Using Installer (201 589 01 43 00), press outer races of tapered roller bearings together into wheel hub. Always ensure that thrust washers are seated correctly.

2) Pack roller cage of inside tapered roller bearing with high temperature grease. Insert inner race with roller cage into hub and grease end faces of rollers.

3) Fill radial seal between sealing lip and dust lip with specified grease and press in using Installer (201 589 01 43 00). To complete reassembly, reverse disassembly procedure.

STEERING KNUCKLE

Removal

1) With vehicle on jack stands, remove front wheel. Remove brake caliper and tie out of way. Remove brake disc and hub assembly. Remove speed sensor for ABS after releasing bolts on steering knuckle.

2) Remove brake cover plate from steering knuckle. Install spring compressor for front spring and compress spring until lower control arm is relieved of pressure. Remove hex head bolts holding steering knuckle arm to steering knuckle.

3) Remove shock absorber strut at steering knuckle. Remove clamping joint between steering knuckle and ball joint. Remove steering knuckle from ball joint.

4) If steering knuckle cannot be removed from ball joint because of corrosion, clamping joint will have to be released by widening slot in steering knuckle with Spreader (201 589 08 31 00).

Inspection

Check ball joint in lower control arm. If rubber boot was damaged when removed, replace rubber boot. If a damaged rubber boot is found in a used joint, replace complete joint assembly.

Installation

1) Install steering knuckle into ball joint. Install and tighten bolt using a new self-locking nut. Install steering knuckle arm with new bolts and tighten.

2) Install shock absorber strut to steering knuckle. Install but do not tighten mounting bolts. Press steering knuckle up against shock absorber strut. Install and slightly tighten upper bolt with washers.

3) Ensure that surface of steering knuckle contacts shock absorber strut at inside of mounting. Always use new self-locking bolts and nuts. Tighten 2 lower bolts and then upper clamping joint bolt.

4) Release tension on spring compressor and remove. Install brake cover plate using new self-locking nuts. Install ABS speed sensor in steering knuckle.

5) Install hub and brake disc assembly. Adjust wheel bearing play. Install brake caliper. Check wheel alignment. If wheel alignment is not within specifications, disassemble front strut and check for misalignment of components.

STEERING KNUCKLE ARM

Removal

1) Raise front of vehicle. Remove front wheel. Remove tie rod nut at steering knuckle. Press off tie rod ball joint using Remover (201 589 08 33 00).

2) Unscrew steering knuckle bolts and move steering knuckle to rear. Remove steering knuckle arm from vehicle.

Installation

1) Check for any damage or misalignment. Clean mating surface for steering knuckle arm at steering knuckle. If new steering knuckle arm is installed, ensure that surface contacts for steering knuckle are free of paint.

2) Bolt steering knuckle arm to steering knuckle using new bolts. Check rubber boot on tie rod ball joint. If defective, replace ball joint.

3) Reinstall tie rod to steering knuckle arm while holding knuckle pin in place. To complete installation, reverse removal procedure.

NOTE: **Always check for correct installation of components as this may alter front end alignment.**

COIL SPRING

Removal

1) Disconnect upper shock mount. Raise and support vehicle. Remove wheel assembly and attach coil spring compressor.

2) Tighten spring compressor while raising floor jack under lower control arm to assist in compressing spring. Slowly lower floor jack and remove the coil spring and rubber mounting.

Installation

Position rubber mount on coil spring. With coil spring compressed, position in vehicle. Slowly release spring, being sure it rests in mounting groove. Install wheel assembly and lower vehicle to floor. Attach upper shock absorber mount.

LOWER CONTROL ARM

Removal

1) Remove bottom engine cover (if equipped). Raise front of vehicle and remove front wheels. Remove bushing of torsion bar at lower control arm.

2) Remove front spring. Mark position of adjustment eccentric pins in relationship to frame. Remove nuts for eccentric pins and remove eccentric pins. Lower lower control arm.

3) Remove bolt from clamping joint between steering knuckle and ball joint. Remove lower control arm from steering knuckle. If ball joint cannot be removed from steering knuckle because of corrosion, release clamping joint by widening the slot in the steering knuckle using a spreader.

Installation

1) Check ball joint in lower control arm. If rubber boot on lower control arm was damaged upon removal, it will be necessary to replace the rubber boot. If a damaged boot is found in a used joint, the complete ball joint will have to be replaced.

2) Install lower control arm at clamping joint between ball joint and steering knuckle. Insert eccentric pin of lower control arm bushing at front. Do not tighten new self-locking nuts at this time.

3) To help with installation of torsion bar, raise lower control arm on opposite side with jack. Install front spring and wheel. Place eccentric pins for camber and caster setting at positions marked beforehand and tighten nuts.

Front Suspension

MERCEDES-BENZ STRUT TYPE (Cont.)

NOTE: **If position of eccentric pin was marked upon removal, move eccentric pin to center position for preliminary adjustment.**

4) Check vehicle level at front axle. Check wheel alignment and also headlight setting.

LOWER CONTROL ARM BUSHING

Removal

1) Check rubber bushing for firm seat in housing. Check inner bushing for a tight fit with its rubber sheath.

2) With lower control arm removed from vehicle, place lower control arm in a vise. Using a counter sink drill bit, sink flange of clamping sleeve. Using a drift, knock out rubber mount out of lower control arm.

Installation

1) Thoroughly clean mounting bore for front bearing in lower control arm. If necessary, clean with fine emery cloth. Apply a rubber lubricant to rubber mount around circumference and to mounting bore in lower control arm.

2) Press rubber mounts into lower control arm, ensuring that knobs of rubber mount are located in cut-out of thrust piece.

NOTE: **When installing rubber mounts, ensure flat surface of front bushings (on 190 Series) are horizontal to torsion bar. On rear bushings (all models), ensure flat surface is vertical to torsion bar. Do not use oil or grease as a lubricant for any rubber component.**

3) Insert clamping sleeve. Position Bushing Installer (201 589 06 33 00) so that unflanged side of clamping sleeve points toward housing. When screwing in bushing, install bushing so that clamping sleeve is flanged simultaneously. Check rubber mount and clamping sleeve for satisfactory seat at contact surfaces.

BALL JOINT

Removal

With lower control arm removed from vehicle, remove ball joint boot. Clamp Ball Joint Press (011) in vice. Using Sleeves (011a) and (011b), press ball joint from lower control arm.

Installation

Slip Support (011c) onto press. Insert ball joint into lower control arm so that alignment mark on ball joint aligns with middle of lower control arm boss. Place Thrust Piece (011d) on ball joint and press ball joint into lower control arm.

STRUT ASSEMBLY

NOTE: **Front strut assembly serves as a deflection stop for front wheels. For this reason loosen strut assembly only when vehicle is on the ground or when a coil spring compressor is in place.**

Removal

1) Jack up front of vehicle and remove front wheel. Insert Coil Spring Compressor (201 589 00 31 00) by inserting tensioning plates of spring compressor with an offset of 90 degrees. Tighten spring compressor until lower control arm is free of loading.

CAUTION: **Webs of spring compressor and guide sleeve must be correctly seated in grooves of 2 tensioning plates.**

2) With lower control arm supported, loosen upper suspension of strut assembly. When loosening strut assembly, pay attention to following items: Apply counterhold to shock piston rod. Do not use a impact wrench. Do not unscrew hex nut with axle fully unsprung. Control arm is fully supported.

3) Remove lower strut assembly nuts on steering knuckle. Remove strut assembly in a downward direction. To keep steering knuckle from tilting, use a wire hook on upper steering knuckle mounting hole and fastened to upper body member. Do not place any strain on brake hose, ABS sensor wire or brake lining wear sensor wire. Remove strut assembly from vehicle.

Installation

1) Use all new mounting hardware to install components. Before installing strut assembly, connect rubber sleeve on 2 short collars of rubber mount.

2) Install steering knuckle and strut together in longitudinal direction (caster) using centering bolt. Install lower strut assembly. Mount strut assembly up against steering knuckle. Tighten mounting bolts slightly, with knuckle resting against strut assembly. Tighten lower mounting bolts first.

3) Using a floor jack, lift front axle half into upper mounting position. Install mounting nuts. Loosen spring compressor while guiding spring into rubber mounts. Remove spring compressor. To complete installation, reverse removal procedure.

SUSPENSION ASSEMBLY

Removal

1) Disconnect upper shock mount. Raise vehicle and support with safety stands under outer edge of lower control arms. Remove wheel assembly. Remove coil spring, as previously outlined. Use separator fork to remove tie rod end from steering knuckle arm.

2) Detach flexible brake hose from brake line at connection on fender well. Loosen plug connection for ABS sensor wire and brake lining wear indicator on caliper. Remove bolts holding brake support to frame.

3) Support front axle half. Mark position of lower control arm. Remove eccentric bolt. Remove lower control arm. Remove complete suspension assembly.

Installation

To install, reverse removal procedure. Place eccentric bolt of camber adjustment to original position and tighten. Check vehicle riding height and wheel alignment.

TIGHTENING SPECIFICATIONS

Application	Ft. Lbs. (N.m)
Lower Ball Joint	92 (125)
Steering Knuckle Arm Bolts	80 (108)
Strut Lower Bolt W/Nut	75 (101)
Strut Lower Bolts W/Washer	100 (135)
Strut Upper Bolts	60 (81)
Tie-Rod Ball Joint	35 (47)
Torsion Bar Bracket Bolts	120 (162)
Lower Control Arm Eccentric Bolts	120 (162)

MERCEDES-BENZ – EXCEPT STRUT TYPE

300SDL, 420SEL,
560SEC, 560SEL, 560SL

DESCRIPTION

Mercedes-Benz uses independent front suspension, consisting of lower control arms, coil springs, shock absorbers, steering knuckles and a stabilizer bar. Steering knuckle is connected at bottom by ball joints.

ADJUSTMENTS & INSPECTION

WHEEL ALIGNMENT SPECIFICATIONS & PROCEDURES

See WHEEL ALIGNMENT SPECIFICATIONS & PROCEDURES in WHEEL ALIGNMENT section.

WHEEL BEARING

1) Jack up vehicle and remove wheel. Force brake pads away from brake disc. Remove upper mounting bolt for brake caliper. Swing brake caliper out of way.

2) Remove grease cap off of hub. Remove contact spring for radio interference. Loosen hex head bolt of bushing clamp. Tighten clamping nut while simultanously turning hub. Tighten until hub can barely be turned.

3) Loosen clamping nut about 1/3 turn and relieve tension by striking stub axle with a plastic hammer. Install dial indicator on front hub. Adjust dial indicator with a preload of .08" (2.0 mm).

4) Check end play of hub by pulling and pushing hard on hub flange. Turn wheel several times before each measurement. During measurement wheel hub must not turn.

5) Tighten hex head bolt on hub clamp and check end play. End play is .0004-.0008 (.01-.02 mm). Reassemble front hub and brake unit. Ensure front hub is filled with high temperature bearing grease.

Fig. 1: Sectional View of Mercedes-Benz Front Suspension

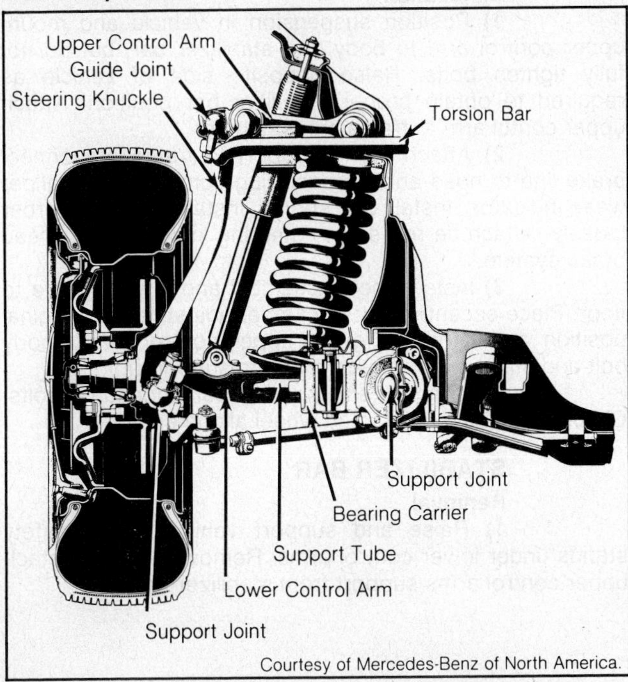

Courtesy of Mercedes-Benz of North America.

BALL JOINT CHECKING

Ball joints are maintenance free (no grease fitting). Check ball joint for lateral and vertical movement. If any measureable lateral movement is observed, replace ball joint.

REMOVAL & INSTALLATION

WHEEL BEARING

Removal

1) Raise and support vehicle. Remove wheel and brake caliper assemblies. Remove dust cap. Loosen hex screw of clamp nut and remove clamp nut. Together with outer wheel bearing, remove hub and rotor assembly. Remove grease seal to access inner wheel bearing.

2) Using Puller (001 589 36 33 00), remove inner race with roller cage of outer tapered roller bearing from hub. Remove radial seal. Remove inner race of tapered roller bearing with roller from hub.

3) Using Puller (126 589 05 33 00), remove outer race of inside tapered roller bearing. Knock out outer race of outer tapered roller bearing with a drift.

Installation

1) Using Installer (116 589 11 43 00), press outer races of tapered roller bearings together into wheel hub. Always ensure that thrust washers are seated correctly.

2) Pack roller cage of inside tapered roller bearing with high temperature grease. Insert inner race with roller cage into hub and grease end faces of rollers.

3) Fill radial seal between sealing lip and dust lip with specified grease and press in using Installer (116 589 01 43 00). To complete reassembly, reverse disassembly procedure.

STEERING KNUCKLE

Removal

1) With vehicle on jack stands, remove front wheel. Remove brake caliper and hang out of way. Remove brake disc and hub assembly. Remove speed sensor for ABS after releasing bolts on steering knuckle.

CAUTION: Loosen hex nuts on ball joints with coil spring installed ONLY WHEN SUPPORTING STANDS ARE UNDER LOWER CONTROL ARM AND NOT BODY. If jack cannot be so positioned, remove coil spring.

2) Remove hex head bolt holding steering knuckle to upper control arm. Using Remover (116 589 16 33 00), remove guide joint from upper control arm. Loosen hex head bolt for supporting joint. Swing steering knuckle outwards and remove supporting joint using Remover (116 589 09 33 00).

Installation

1) Install brake cover plate using new self-locking nuts. Install steering knuckle to lower and upper control arms. Install and tighten bolts using a new self-locking nut. Install steering knuckle arm with new bolts and tighten. Install ABS speed sensor in steering knuckle.

2) Install hub and brake disc assembly. Adjust wheel bearing play. Install brake caliper.

MERCEDES-BENZ – EXCEPT STRUT TYPE (Cont.)

STEERING KNUCKLE ARM

Removal

Raise front of vehicle. Remove front wheel. Remove tie rod nut at steering knuckle. Press off tie rod ball joint using Puller (186 589 10 33 00). Unscrew steering knuckle bolts and remove steering knuckle arm.

Installation

1) Check for any damage or misalignment. Clean mating surface for steering knuckle arm at steering knuckle. If new steering knuckle arm is installed, ensure that surface contacts for steering knuckle are free of paint.

2) Bolt steering knuckle arm to steering knuckle using new bolts. Check rubber boot on tie rod ball joint. If defective, replace ball joint.

3) Reinstall tie rod to steering knuckle arm while holding knuckle pin in place. To complete installation, reverse removal procedure.

COIL SPRING

Removal

1) Disconnect upper shock mount. Raise and support vehicle. Remove wheel assembly and attach coil spring compressor.

2) Tighten spring compressor while raising floor jack under lower control arm to assist in compressing spring. Slowly lower floor jack and remove the coil spring and rubber mounting.

Installation

Position rubber mount on coil spring. With coil spring compressed, position in vehicle. Slowly release spring, being sure it rests in mounting groove. Install wheel assembly and lower vehicle to floor. Attach upper shock absorber mount.

UPPER CONTROL ARM

Removal

1) Raise front of vehicle and support under outer edge of lower control arms. Remove front wheels.

CAUTION: Loosen hex nuts on ball joints with coil spring installed ONLY WHEN SUPPORTING STANDS ARE UNDER LOWER CONTROL ARM AND NOT BODY. If jack cannot be so positioned, remove coil spring.

2) Remove upper ball joint nut. Using Remover (116 589 16 33 00), detach ball joint from steering knuckle arm. Wire steering knuckle to frame so it will not drop.

3) Remove upper control arm support from stabilizer bar and from body. Remove upper control arm.

Installation

1) Position upper control arm in vehicle and install control arm-to-body bolt. Connect upper ball joint to steering knuckle.

2) Mount stabilizer bar support to upper control arm, attaching bolt loosely. Lower vehicle to floor and tighten all bolts to specifications.

LOWER CONTROL ARM

Removal

CAUTION: Shock absorber serves as a deflection stop for front wheel. Only release shock absorber when vehicle is resting on its wheels or the lower control arm is supported.

1) Loosen top shock absorber mount. Remove lower mount and remove shock absorber. Raise vehicle and support with safety stands under outer edge of lower contol arms.

2) Remove wheel assembly. Remove coil spring as previously outlined. Detach tie rod end from steering knuckle arm. Mark position of lower control arm eccentric bolt and bushing to crossmember for reference at reassembly.

3) Remove bolts holding brake support to frame. Remove lower control arm eccentric bolt. Detach lower ball joint from control arm. Remove lower control arm with brake support

Installation

1) Mount lower control arm to ball joint. Position control arm bushing to frame. Attach brake support to frame. Install coil spring. Loosely install shock absorber. Install wheel assembly and lower vehicle to floor.

2) Tighten shock absorber mountings. Position eccentric bolt to original position and tighten to specifications. Attach tie rod end to steering knuckle arm. Check wheel alignment.

SUSPENSION ASSEMBLY

Removal

1) Disconnect upper shock mount. Raise vehicle and support with safety stands under outer edge of lower control arms. Remove wheel assembly. Remove coil spring as previously outlined. Use separator fork to remove tie rod end from steering knuckle arm.

2) Detach flexible brake hose from brake line at connection on fender well. Loosen plug connection for ABS sensor wire and brake lining wear indicator on caliper. Remove bolts holding brake support to frame.

3) Support front axle half. Mark position of lower control arm. Remove eccentric bolt. Remove stabilizer bar support from upper control arm. Remove bolt holding upper control arm bushing to body. Remove complete suspension assembly.

Installation

1) Position suspension in vehicle and mount upper control arm to body and stabilizer bar, but do not fully tighten bolts. Raise opposite side of vehicle as required to obtain proper stabilizer bar position. Attach upper contol arm to frame crossmember.

2) Attach brake support to frame. Reconnect brake line to hose and connect plug connection of caliper wear indicator. Install coil spring. Install shock absorber loosely. Attach tie rod end to steering knuckle arm. Bleed brake system.

3) Install wheel assembly and lower vehicle to floor. Place eccentric bolt of camber adjustment to original position and tighten. Tighten upper control arm-to-body bolt and stabilizer bar-to-control arm support bolt.

4) Tighten shock absorber mounting bolts. Check axle riding height and wheel alignment.

STABILIZER BAR

Removal

1) Raise and support vehicle. Place safety stands under lower control arms. Remove wheels. Detach upper control arms support from stabilizer bar.

2) Remove master cylinder and booster. Remove heater hoses, air cleaner, regulator linkage, vacuum lines and electrical wiring as required to allow clearance for stabilizer bar removal.

3) Remove stabilizer bar mounting brackets and bushings. Remove end covers and stabilizer bar.

Fig. 2: Stabilizer Bar Mounting Location

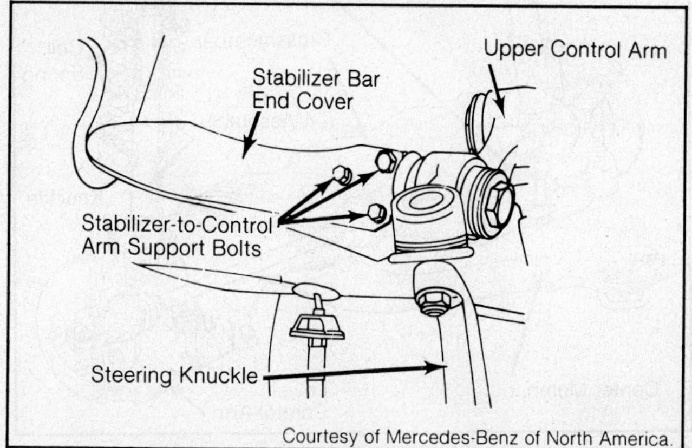

Courtesy of Mercedes-Benz of North America.

Installation

1) Position stabilizer bar in vehicle and loosely attach bar support to upper control arm. Position rubber bushings on stabilizer bar, with splits facing against frame. Install brackets loosely.

2) Attach left and right end covers and replace all hoses, linkage, wiring and brake components removed. Install wheel assemblies and lower vehicle.

3) Tighten stabilizer bar-to-control arm support bolt. Tighten mounting brackets. Check wheel alignment.

TIGHTENING SPECIFICATIONS

Application	Ft. Lbs. (N.m)
Shock Absorber Lower Mount	15 (20)
Stabilizer Bar Bracket Bolts	48 (65)
Steering Linkage Bolts	26 (35)
Steering Knuckle Arm Bolts	59 (80)
Upper Control Arm Eccentric Bolts	59 (80)
Lower Control Arm Eccentric Bolts	133 (180)
Upper Ball Joint Nut	29 (40)
Lower Ball Joint Nut	59 (80)

Front Suspension

MITSUBISHI GALANT

Mitsubishi Galant (1985-1987)

DESCRIPTION

Front suspension is a MacPherson strut type. It consists of a lower control arm, knuckle assembly, strut assembly and stabilizer bar. For testing and diagnosis information on Mitsubishi's Electronically controlled suspension, see MITSUBISHI GALANT ELECTRONIC SUSPENSION article in this section.

ADJUSTMENTS & INSPECTION

WHEEL ALIGNMENT SPECIFICATIONS & PROCEDURES

See WHEEL ALIGNMENT SPECIFICATIONS & PROCEDURES in WHEEL ALIGNMENT section.

WHEEL BEARING

NOTE: **Wheel bearing adjustment is pre-set to a specified pre-load and cannot be adjusted. Determine bearing axial play and replace damaged or worn parts as necessary.**

Inspection

Raise and support vehicle. Remove wheel assembly. Remove brake caliper and hang out of the way. Install one wheel nut so disc is kept tight to hub. Attach dial indicator at right angle to hub. Measure axial play while moving hub back and forth. Maximum axial play is .008" (.20 mm). If play exceeds limit, disassemble hub and check all parts.

REMOVAL & INSTALLATION

WHEEL BEARING

Removal

1) Remove steering knuckle and hub assembly. See KNUCKLE & HUB ASSEMBLY in this article. Separate hub from knuckle using Special Bolt (MB990998-01) and Puller (MB991056). DO NOT strike hub/knuckle assembly with hammer to separate or bearing will be damaged.

2) Remove dust cover. Remove inner race from hub using Puller (MB990810-01). Remove oil seals from hub and knuckle. Remove snap ring from knuckle. Press out bearing from knuckle using old inner race and Driver (MB990985-01).

Installation

1) Apply grease to new wheel bearing. Apply grease to knuckle bearing contact surfaces. With inner race removed, press in bearing. Install inner race into bearing. Install snap ring. Install new hub side oil seal into knuckle until flush with end surface. Apply grease to oil seal lip and hub contact surfaces.

2) Use special bolt to install hub onto knuckle. *See Fig. 2.* Tighten nut on special bolt to 144-187 ft. lbs. (200-260 N.m). Rotate hub to seat bearing. Use an INCH lb. torque wrench to measure turning torque of hub. *See Fig. 2.*

3) Turning torque should be 16 INCH lbs. (1.8 N.m) or less. Measure end play of hub. Maximum end play is .008" (.20 mm). If turning torque or end play are not within specification, recheck component installation.

Fig. 1: View of Galant Front Suspension

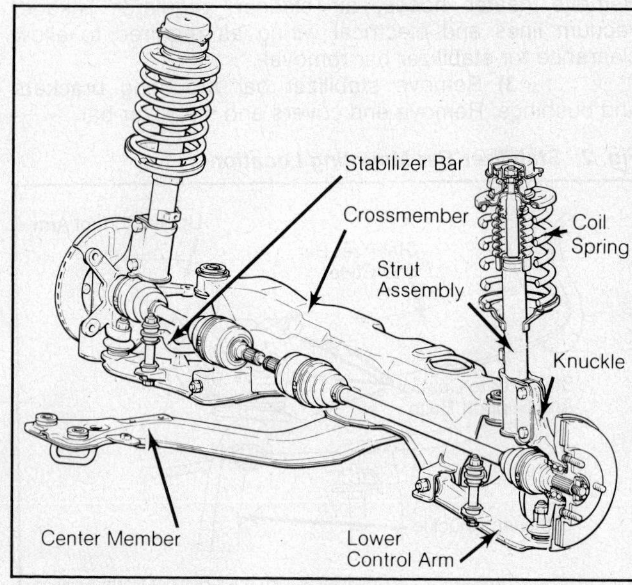

Courtesy of Mitsubishi Motor Sales of America.

4) Remove special bolt. Install new drive shaft side oil seal. Drive in seal until it contacts snap ring. Complete installation by reversing removal procedure.

Fig. 2: Checking Bearing Turning Torque

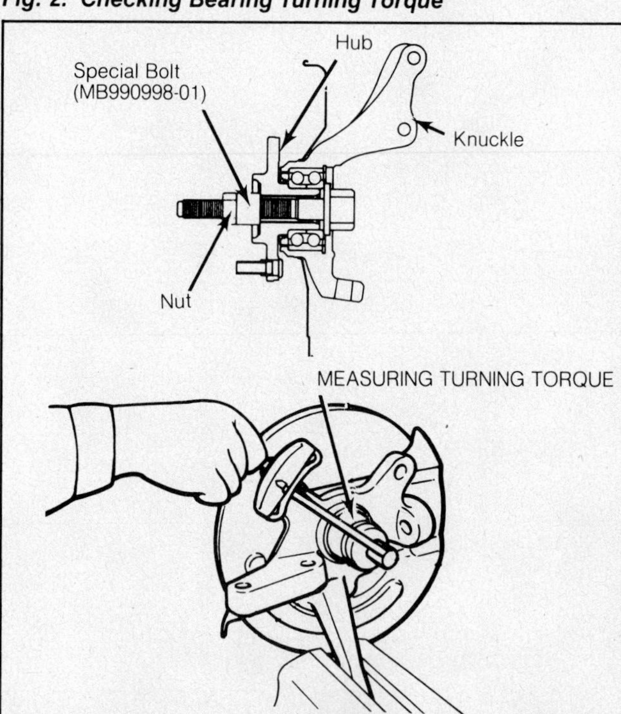

Courtesy of Mitsubishi Motor Sales of America.

LOWER CONTROL ARM

NOTE: **Always replace dust cover whenever ball joint is removed or knuckle is separated from joint.**

Removal

Raise and support vehicle. Remove wheel assembly. Disconnect stabilizer bar from lower control arm. If equipped with electronic controlled suspension, disconnect height sensor rod from lower arm (right side only). Loosen ball joint nut and disconnect ball joint from knuckle. Remove 5 bolts and remove lower arm and bushing clamp from vehicle.

Inspection

1) Check for damaged ball joint dust cover, bent or cracked lower control arm, cracks or deterioration of lower arm bushing(s), loose ball joint and proper ball joint starting torque.

2) Check ball joint starting torque using an INCH lb. torque wrench. Standard starting torque is 17-78 INCH lbs. (2-9 N.m). If starting torque exceeds standard, replace ball joint.

Installation

To install, reverse removal procedure.

STRUT ASSEMBLY

Removal & Disassembly

1) Raise and support vehicle. Remove bracket holding brake hose to strut. Remove bolts attaching strut to knuckle. Remove dust cover from top of strut assembly. While holding piston rod with an Allen wrench, use Socket (MB991036) to remove nut. Remove stopper and stopper rubber. Remove strut assembly from vehicle.

2) Compress coil spring using coil spring compressor. While holding piston rod with Allen wrench, use socket to remove piston rod lock nut. Remove all remaining components from strut. Drive out bearing from support using brass rod. *See Fig. 3.*

Inspection

Check bearing for wear. Check rubber components for damage or deterioration. Check coil spring for sagging, cracks or deterioration. Inspect strut for cracks, damage, oil leakage, bent piston rod assembly and abnormal noise.

Reassembly

NOTE: Coil springs have color marks to indicate spring identification and load classification. Ensure when springs are replaced, markings are for appropriate vehicle.

1) To reassemble strut, reverse disassembly procedure. Ensure support bearing is pressed in with Black retainer side toward support. Ensure upper seat D-shaped hole is aligned with notch in piston rod.

2) Align ends of spring with grooves in spring seats. Position of spring seats can be aligned by inserting .4" (10 mm) diameter pins into holes in seats. Pack insulator bearing with grease and install dust cap. Be careful not to get grease on insulator.

Installation

To install, reverse removal procedure. Ensure strut assembly and knuckle mating surfaces are clean to ensure tight fit. Tighten lower strut mount bolts and top mount nut to specification. After installation, check front end alignment.

Fig. 3: Exploded View of Strut Assembly

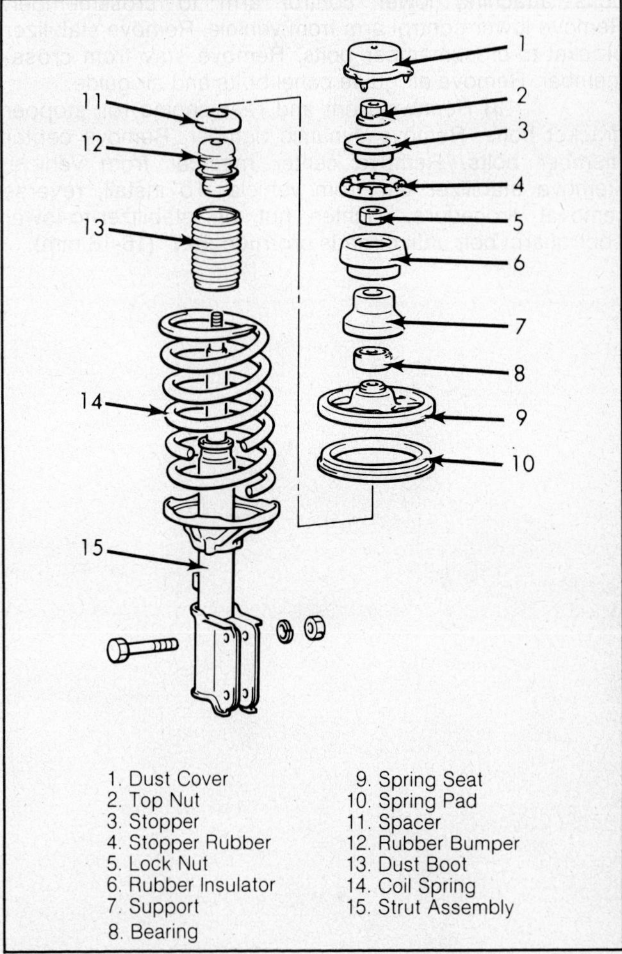

Courtesy of Mitsubishi Motor Sales of America.

KNUCKLE & HUB ASSEMBLY

Removal & Installation

1) Raise and support vehicle. Remove wheel assembly. Remove cotter pin, hub lock nut and washer. Remove brake caliper and hang out of way. Remove brake disc. Disconnect lower ball joint from knuckle. Remove stabilizer bar from lower control arm. Disconnect tie rod end from knuckle. Disconnect drive shaft from hub.

2) Disconnect strut from knuckle. Remove knuckle and hub assembly from vehicle. Separate hub from knuckle (if necessary) using Special Bolt (MB990998-01) and Puller (MB991056). DO NOT strike hub/knuckle assembly with hammer to separate or bearing will be damaged. To install, reverse removal procedure. Tighten ball joint-to-knuckle nut with vehicle on ground.

STABILIZER BAR & CENTER MEMBER

Removal & Installation

1) Raise and support vehicle. Remove wheel assembly. Raise and support engine so weight is off engine mounts. Remove front exhaust pipe. Disconnect stabilizer bar from lower control arm. Disconnect height sensor rod (if equipped).

Front Suspension

MITSUBISHI GALANT (Cont.)

2) Disconnect ball joint from knuckle. Remove bolts attaching lower control arm to crossmember. Remove lower control arm from vehicle. Remove stabilizer bracket-to-crossmember bolts. Remove stay from crossmember. Remove air guide panel bolts and air guide.

3) Remove front and rear engine roll stopper bracket bolts. Remove dynamic damper. Remove center member bolts. Remove center member from vehicle. Remove stabilizer bar from vehicle. To install, reverse removal procedure. Tighten nut on stabilizer-to-lower control arm bolt until threads protrude .6-.7" (16-18 mm).

TIGHTENING SPECIFICATIONS

Application	Ft. Lbs. (N.m)
Center Member Bolts	59-73 (80-100)
Drive Axle Lock Nut	148-192 (200-260)
Knuckle-to-Ball Joint Nut	44-53 (60-72)
Knuckle-to-Strut Bolts	66-77 (90-105)
Lower Arm Clamp-to-Body Bolt	59-73 (80-100)
Lower Arm Clamp-to-Crossmember	
Bolt	59-73 (80-100)
Nut	26-35 (35-47)
Lower Arm-to-Crossmember Bolt	70-88 (95-120)
Piston Rod Lock Nut	41-55 (55-75)
Stabilizer-to-Crossmember Bolt	22-31 (30-42)
Stay-to-Crossmember Bolts	52-59 (70-80)
Strut-to-Body Nut	37-44 (50-60)
Tie Rod-to-Knuckle Nut	18-25 (24-34)

Front Suspension

MITSUBISHI VAN/WAGON

DESCRIPTION

Front suspension consists of upper and lower control arms, torsion bars, steering knuckles, shock absorbers, strut bars and stabilizer bar. Control arms are connected to steering knuckle by ball joints. Torsion bars are mounted to upper control arms. Stabilizer bar connects to frame and lower control arms. Strut bar connects to lower control arm and body.

ADJUSTMENTS & INSPECTION

WHEEL ALIGNMENT SPECIFICATIONS & PROCEDURES

See WHEEL ALIGNMENT SPECIFICATIONS & PROCEDURES in WHEEL ALIGNMENT section.

WHEEL BEARING

Raise and support vehicle. Remove grease cap and cotter pin. Loosen nut. Tighten nut to 22 ft. lbs. (30 N.m). Loosen nut. Retighten nut to 72 INCH lbs. (8 N.m). Install cotter pin. Do not back off nut more than 30 degrees to fit cotter pin. If play exists after adjusting bearing, replace bearing.

BALL JOINT CHECKING

NOTE: Separate ball joint from control arm before checking starting torque.

Lower Ball Joint

Install nut on ball joint and twist stud 4-5 times. Measure ball joint starting torque using an INCH lb. torque wrench. Starting torque should be 9-35 INCH lbs. (1-4 N.m). If more than specification, replace ball joint. If less, ball joint is still good unless play or roughness exists.

Upper Ball Joint

Install nut on ball joint and twist stud 4-5 times. Measure ball joint starting torque using an INCH lb. torque wrench. Starting torque should be 7-30 INCH lbs. (.8-3.5 N.m). If more than specification, replace ball joint. If less, ball joint is still good unless play or roughness exists.

Fig. 1: View of Van/Wagon Front Suspension

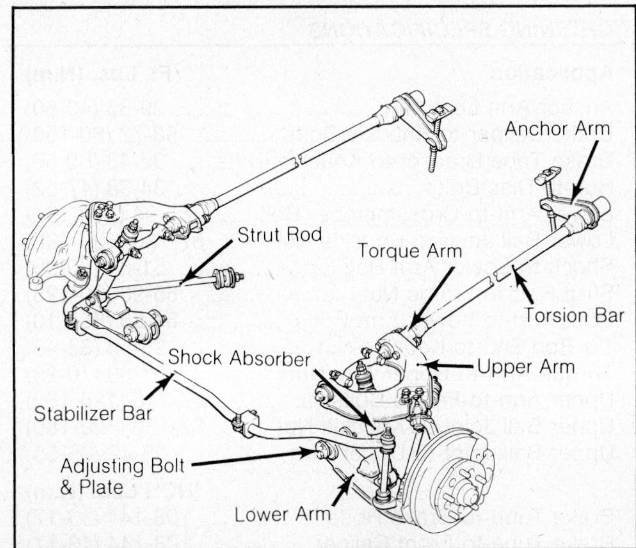

Courtesy of Mitsubishi Motor Sales of America.

REMOVAL & INSTALLATION

WHEEL BEARINGS

Removal

Raise and support vehicle. Remove wheel assembly. Remove caliper assembly and wire out of way. Remove grease cap, cotter pin and lock nut. Remove front hub assembly with washer and outer bearing. Make alignment marks for reassembly reference and separate wheel hub and brake disc (if necessary). Remove oil seal and inner and outer bearing races.

Inspection

Check oil seal for cracks and damage. Check bearings for seizure, discoloration and roughness. Always replace bearings and races as sets. Check front hub for cracks. Ensure brake disc-to-hub bolts are tight.

Installation

Using a press and Installers (MB990933-01 and MB990928-01), install inner and outer bearing races. Apply grease to oil seal lip and front hub. Apply grease to inner bearing and install. Press oil seal into hub using Installer (MB990936-01). Reverse removal procedure to complete installation. Adjust wheel bearings.

SHOCK ABSORBER & LOWER CONTROL ARM

Removal

1) Raise and support vehicle. Remove wheel assembly. Remove engine splash shield. Remove upper and lower shock absorber mounting hardware. Remove shock absorber. Disconnect strut rod and stabilizer bar from lower control arm.

2) Remove cotter pin, loosen nut and separate lower control arm ball joint from knuckle. Make alignment marks on lower control arm adjusting plate and cross-member for reassembly reference. Remove adjusting bolt and remove lower control arm from vehicle.

Inspection

Check lower control arm for cracks or deformation. Inspect rubber bushings for cracks, wear or deformation. Check shock absorbers for smoothness and abnormal noise. Check ball joint starting torque. See BALL JOINT CHECKING in this article. Check ball joint dust cover. Remove retaining ring and replace if necessary.

Installation

To install, reverse removal procedure. Ensure marks on lower control adjusting plate and crossmember are aligned. Tighten adjusting bolt with vehicle on ground and suspension unloaded. Tighten stabilizer bar nut until bolt threads protrude .4-.5" (10-12 mm). Check wheel alignment.

UPPER CONTROL ARM

Removal

1) Raise and support vehicle. Remove wheel assembly. Remove anchor arm bolt lock nut. Measure amount of anchor bolt threads protruding from adjusting nut for reassembly reference. Loosen adjusting nut. Remove rubber fenderwell shield. Disconnect upper part of shock absorber from frame.

2) Remove torque arm nuts from upper control arm. Remove cotter pin, loosen nut and disconnect upper ball joint from knuckle. Remove upper arm-to-frame bolts and remove upper control arm from vehicle.

Front Suspension

MITSUBISHI VAN/WAGON (Cont.)

Inspection

Check upper control arm for cracks or deformation. Inspect rubber bushings for cracks, wear or deformation. Check ball joint starting torque. See BALL JOINT CHECKING in this article. Check ball joint dust cover. Remove retaining ring and replace if necessary.

Installation

To install, reverse removal procedure. Check wheel alignment. Check vehicle height. With vehicle on ground and suspension unloaded, measure distance between upper arm bump stop-to-upper arm. Distance should be 2.0" (51 mm). If not to specification, adjust using anchor arm bolt.

TORSION BAR

Removal

1) Raise and support vehicle. Remove anchor arm bolt lock nut. Measure amount of anchor bolt threads protruding from adjusting nut for reassembly reference. *See Fig. 2.*

2) Remove adjusting nut, seat holding nut and anchor bolt. Remove torque arm nuts from upper arm. Remove torsion bar assembly. Slide dust covers back and mark torsion bar, torque arm and anchor arm for reassembly reference.

Inspection

Check anchor bolt for bending and damage. Check dust covers for cracks or damage. Check torsion bar for dents or other damage. Check splines on all parts for damage.

Installation

1) To install, reverse removal procedure. Ensure torsion bars are installed on proper side. Each torsion bar has an identification mark on rear end of bar. Marked end must be installed toward rear of vehicle. Apply grease to torsion bar splines, dust cover and anchor bolt threads.

2) If torsion bars are being replaced, set torsion bar and anchor arm so anchor bolt protrudes from rear arm the specified distance. *See Fig. 3.* On Van models, distance should be 1.4" (36 mm). On Wagon models, distance should be 1.2" (30 mm). On all models, install adjusting nut and tighten until bolt protrudes 2.5" (63 mm) from nut. *See Fig. 2.*

Fig. 2: Measuring Anchor Bolt Protrusion

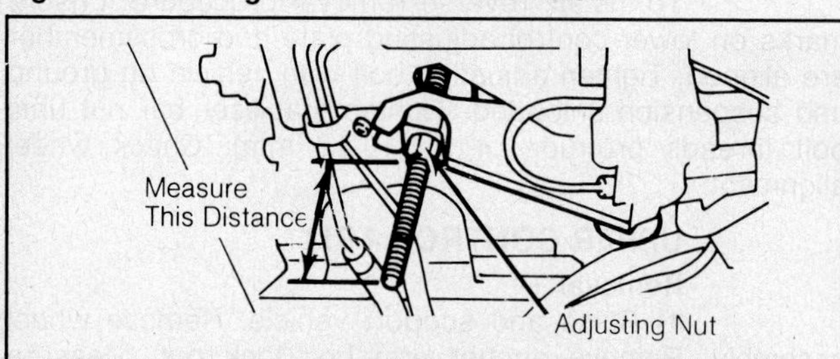

Courtesy of Mitsubishi Motor Sales of America.

STABILIZER BAR & STRUT ROD

Removal

Remove self-locking nut holding stabilizer bar to lower control arm. Remove bolts securing stabilizer bar frame brackets to frame. Remove stabilizer bar from vehicle. Remove rear strut rod nut. Remove strut rod-to-lower control arm nuts. Remove strut rod bushings noting position for reassembly reference. Remove strut rod from vehicle.

Inspection

Check both bars for bending or other damage. Check stabilizer bolts for bending or damage. Check all bushings for cracks, deterioration or damage.

Installation

To install, reverse removal procedure. Tighten stabilizer bar nut until bolt threads protrude .4-.5" (10-12 mm). Ensure strut rod bushings are installed in original position. Tighten strut rod rear nut with vehicle on ground and suspension unloaded.

Fig. 3: Adjusting Torsion Bar Anchor Arm

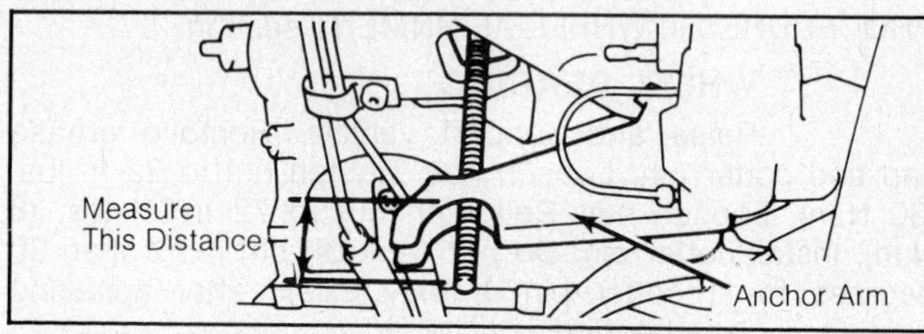

Courtesy of Mitsubishi Motor Sales of America.

KNUCKLE

Removal

1) Raise and support vehicle. Remove wheel assembly. Disconnect brake hose from brake tube. Remove caliper assembly and wire out of way. Remove grease cap, cotter pin and lock nut. Remove front hub assembly with washer and outer bearing.

2) Remove dust cover and brake line bracket bolts. Remove cotter pin, loosen nut and separate tie rod end from knuckle. Disconnect strut rod and stabilizer bar from lower control arm. Remove cotter pins, loosen nuts and separate upper and lower ball joints from knuckle. Remove knuckle from vehicle.

Inspection & Installation

Check knuckle for cracks or bends. Check knuckle spindle for wear or pounding. To install, reverse removal procedure. Bleed brakes. Adjust wheel bearings.

TIGHTENING SPECIFICATIONS

Application	Ft. Lbs. (N.m)
Anchor Arm Lock Nut	29-36 (40-50)
Brake Caliper-to-Knuckle Bolts	58-72 (80-100)
Brake Tube Bracket-to-Knuckle Bolts	36-43 (50-60)
Hub-to-Disc Bolts	34-38 (47-52)
Lower Arm-to-Crossmember Bolt	80-94 (110-130)
Lower Ball Joint-to-Knuckle Nut	87-130 (120-180)
Shock-to-Lower Arm Bolt	51-69 (70-95)
Strut Rod-to-Frame Nut	65-90 (90-125)
Strut Rod-to-Lower Arm Bolts	61-80 (85-110)
Tie Rod End-to Knuckle Nut	25-33 (35-45)
Torque Arm-to-Upper Arm Nuts	51-69 (70-95)
Upper Arm-to-Frame Bolts	87-116 (120-160)
Upper Ball Joint-to-Knuckle Nut	87-130 (120-180)
Upper Ball Joint-to-Upper Arm	25-40 (35-55)
	INCH Lbs. (N.m)
Brake Tube-to-Brake Hose	108-144 (13-17)
Brake Tube-to-Front Caliper	108-144 (13-17)
Shock-to-Frame	108-156 (13-18)
Stabilizer Bar-to-Frame Bolt	84-120 (9-14)

Front Suspension

NISSAN MAXIMA

DESCRIPTION

An electronically controlled variable shock absorber system is used on Maxima SE models. For removal, installation, testing and diagnostic procedures for these shock absorbers, see the NISSAN ELECTRONIC SUSPENSION article in this section. All models use a MacPherson strut type front suspension system.

ADJUSTMENTS & INSPECTION

WHEEL ALIGNMENT SPECIFICATIONS & PROCEDURES

See WHEEL ALIGNMENT SPECIFICATIONS & PROCEDURES in WHEEL ALIGNMENT section.

WHEEL BEARING

Loosen hub nut and tighten to specification. Measure preload with a pull scale attached to a wheel stud. Force required should be 2.2-9.9 lbs. (9.8-44.1 N).

BALL JOINT CHECKING

Check stud turning torque. Force required should be more than 4.3 INCH lbs. (.5 N.m) on a used joint and 8.7-43.4 INCH lbs. (1.0-4.9 N.m) on a new joint. Maximum stud end play is .004-.039" (.10-1.0 mm), using a force of 221 lbs. (981 N).

REMOVAL & INSTALLATION

WHEEL BEARING

Removal & Installation

1) Raise and support vehicle. Remove wheel and tire. Remove caliper assembly and wire out of way. Remove cotter pin and loosen (but do not remove) hub nut from drive shaft.

2) Remove steering knuckle. Remove bolts retaining wheel hub to rotor. Using Hub Remover (KV40101000 and ST36230000), separate rotor from hub. Remove seal.

3) Press wheel bearing from hub and remove from steering knuckle. Drive out bearing race with a brass drift fitted through notches in knuckle. To install, reverse removal procedure.

NOTE: Wheel bearings and races must be replaced as a set.

BALL JOINT

Removal & Installation

Raise and support vehicle. Remove wheel, drive shaft and ball joint stud nut. Remove ball joint-to-transverse link nuts. Using Separator (HT72520000), separate ball joint from steering knuckle. To install, reverse removal procedure.

TRANSVERSE LINK

Removal & Installation

1) Support engine mount crossmember with jack. Remove stabilizer bar bolts and transverse link-to-ball joint nuts. Remove transverse link-to-subframe bolts and transverse link.

2) Inspect transverse link and bushings for distortion or damage. To install, reverse removal procedure. Transverse link bolts must be tightened with weight of vehicle on wheels.

STEERING KNUCKLE

Removal & Installation

1) Raise and support vehicle. Remove wheel assembly. Remove brake caliper without disconnecting brake line. Remove axle nut. Using Separator (HT72520000), separate tie rod end from knuckle.

2) Using a puller, remove stub axle and brake rotor assembly from axle shaft. Disconnect ball joint and support control arm. Remove steering knuckle-to-strut bolts. Remove knuckle from vehicle. To install, reverse removal procedure.

Fig. 1: View of Front Suspension

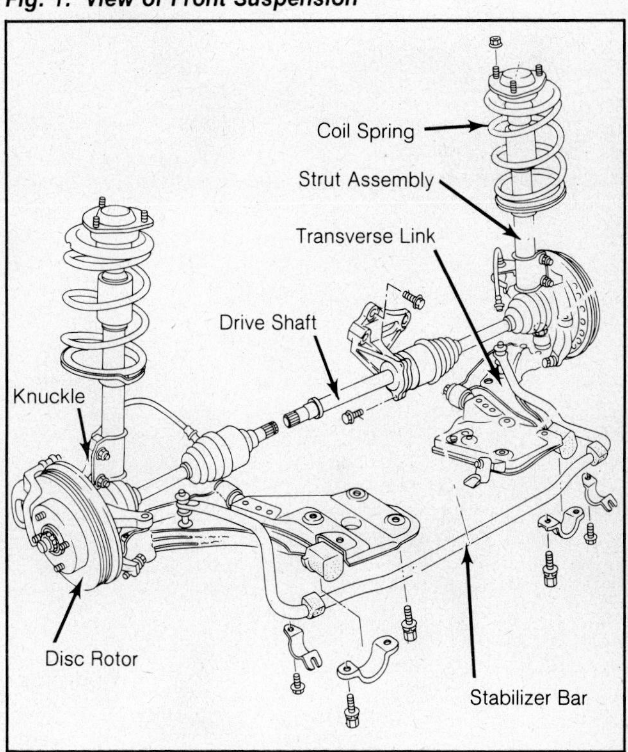

Courtesy of Nissan Motor Co., U.S.A.

STRUT ASSEMBLY

Removal

1) Raise and support vehicle. Remove wheel. Disconnect brake hose from strut. Remove brake caliper and hang out of the way with wire. Detach tie rod from steering knuckle. Position stand under transverse link for support.

2) Remove strut-to-knuckle and strut-to-body nuts. Remove strut from vehicle. With electronic controlled strut, disconnect sub-harness wiring connector and disconnect connector at top of strut. Be sure to keep water and dirt away from connector.

Disassembly

Place strut in a vise. Loosen (do not remove) piston rod nut. Using a Spring Compressor (HT71780000), slightly compress coil spring. Remove piston rod nut, strut mounting insulator case, bearing and thrust seat. Remove spring seat, coil spring, rubber bumper and dust cover.

Front Suspension

NISSAN MAXIMA (Cont.)

Reassembly

To reassemble strut, reverse disassembly procedure. Ensure flat tail of coil spring is on top. Ensure spring seat "U" mark is facing outside of vehicle.

Installation

To install, reverse removal procedure. Install a new piston rod nut, but do not tighten nut until strut is installed in vehicle.

TIGHTENING SPECIFICATIONS

Application	Ft. Lbs. (N.m)
Ball Joint Stud Nut	52-64 (71-86)
Ball Joint-to-Transverse Link	56-80 (76-109)
Caliper Retaining Bolts	53-72 (72-97)
Piston Rod Nut	43-58 (59-78)
Stabilizer Bar-to-Body Bolts	23-31 (31-42)
Stabilizer Bar-to-Link Nuts	12-16 (16-22)
Strut-to-Body Nuts	23-31 (31-42)
Strut-to-Steering Knuckle	82-91 (112-124)
Subframe-to-Body	87-108 (118-147)
Tie Rod	
Lock Nut	27-34 (37-46)
Stud Nut	22-29 (29-39)
Transverse Link-to-Subframe Bolts	87-108 (118-147)
Transverse Link-to-Subframe Nut	65-87 (88-118)
Wheel Bearing Nut	174-231 (235-314)

Front Suspension

NISSAN PATHFINDER & PICKUP

DESCRIPTION

Front suspension is an independent type with upper and lower control arms which are connected to a steering knuckle by ball joints. This suspension also incorporates a tension rod (2WD) or compression rod (4WD) which connects between lower control arm outer end and frame bracket. A double-acting shock absorber is attached to lower control arm and frame mount. A stabilizer bar is attached to each lower control arm and frame brackets.

ADJUSTMENTS & INSPECTION

WHEEL ALIGNMENT SPECIFICATIONS & PROCEDURES

See WHEEL ALIGNMENT SPECIFICATIONS & PROCEDURES in WHEEL ALIGNMENT section.

WHEEL BEARING

2WD Models

1) Tighten hub nut to 25-29 ft. lbs. (34-39 N.m). Rotate hub several times in both directions to seat bearings. Retighten hub nut. Turn hub nut back 45 degrees.

2) Install adjusting cap and loosen nut a maximum of 15 degrees to align hole for cotter pin. Install new cotter pin and measure bearing preload and axial play. Measure preload with pull gauge on one of the wheel studs.

WHEEL BEARING ADJUSTMENT SPECIFICATIONS (2WD)

Application	Specification
Bearing Preload	
New Grease Seal	2.2-6.4 lbs. (9.8-28.4 N)
Used Grease Seal	2.2-5.3 lbs. (9.8-23.5 N)
Axial Play	
All Models	Zero

Fig. 1: Exploded View of 2WD Front Suspension

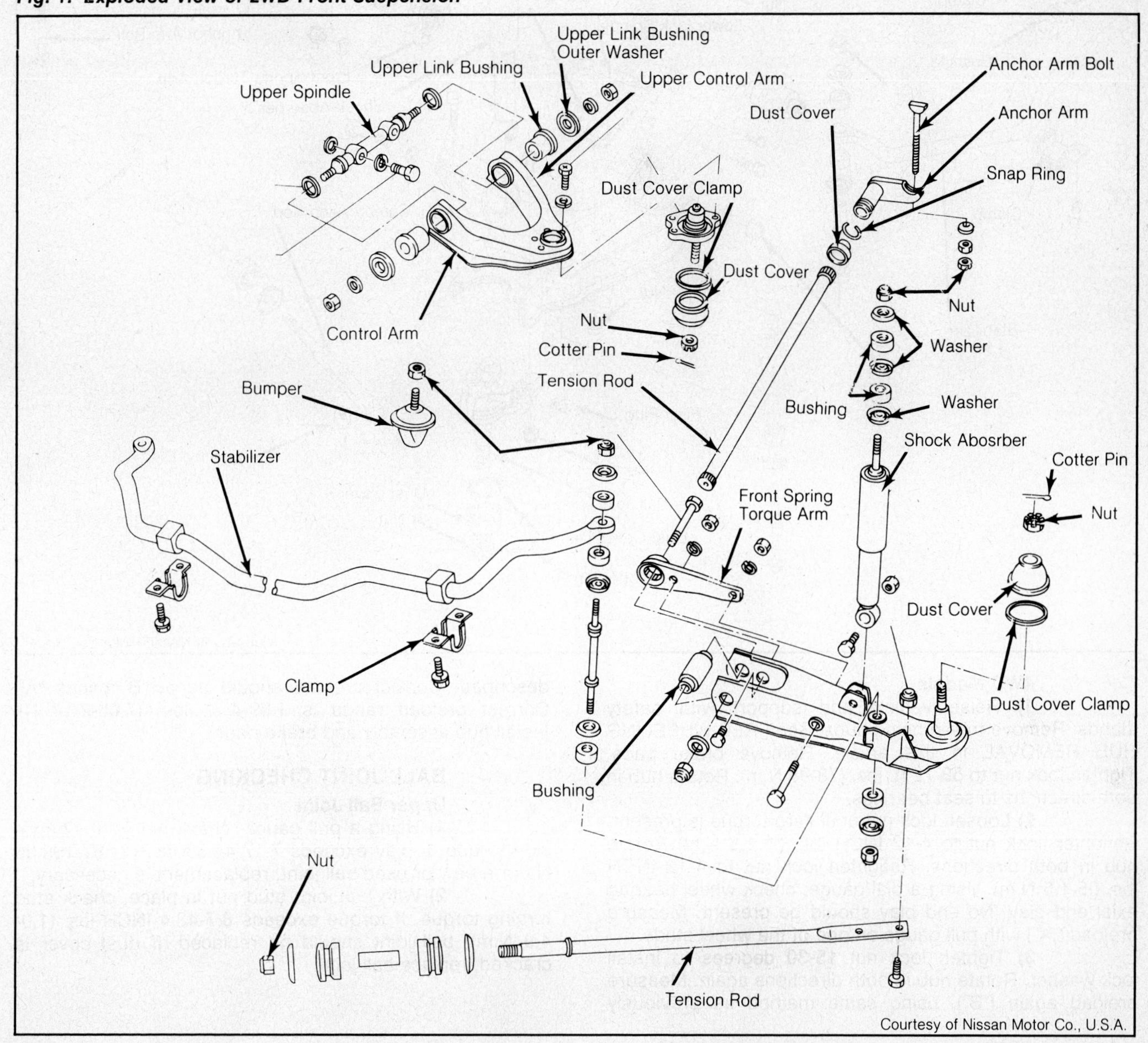

Fig. 2: Exploded View of 4WD Front Suspension

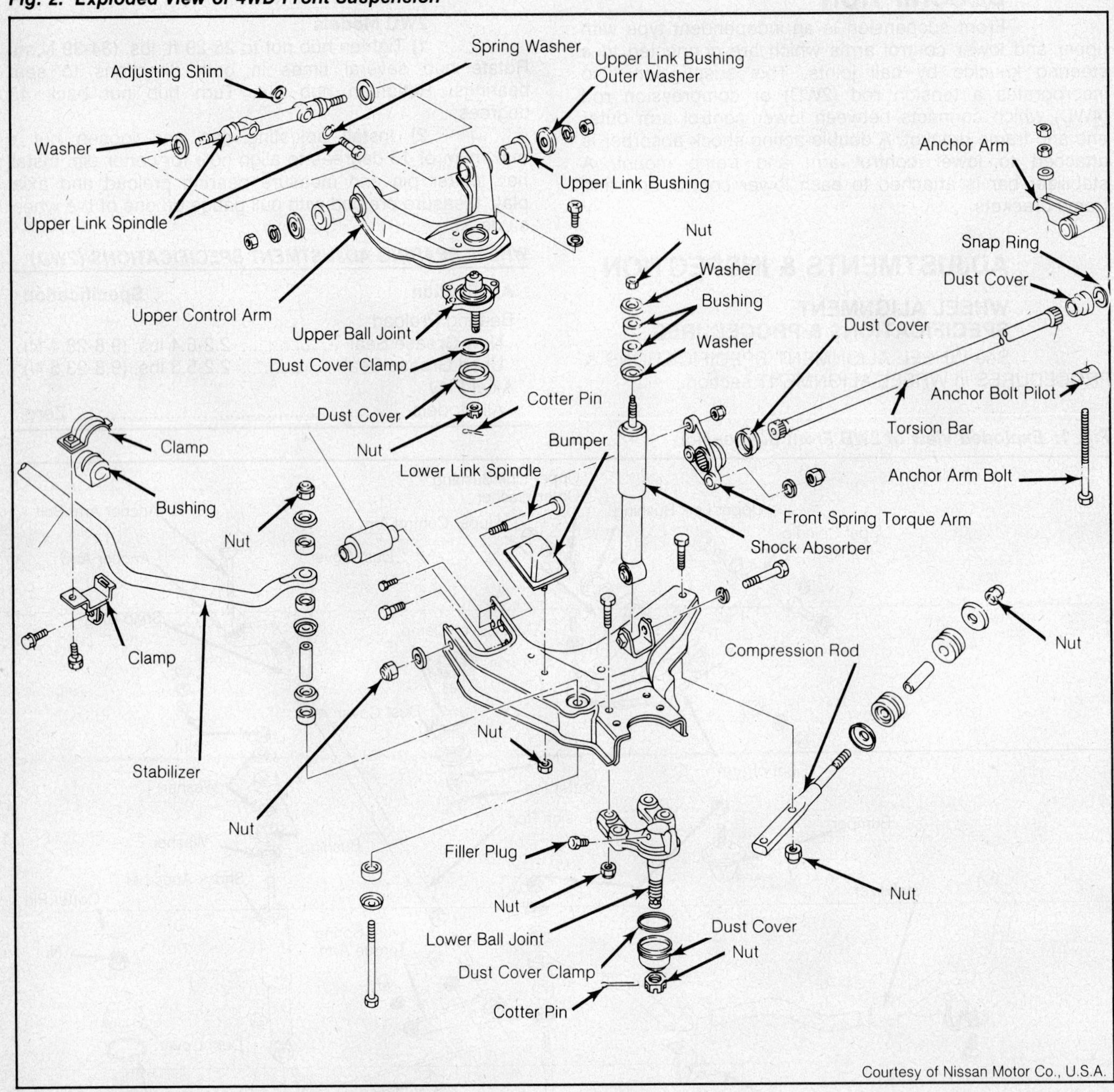

Courtesy of Nissan Motor Co., U.S.A.

4WD Models

1) Raise vehicle and support with safety stands. Remove free-running hubs. See FREE-WHEELING HUB REMOVAL in this article. Remove brake pads. Tighten lock nut to 58-72 ft. lbs. (78-98 N.m). Rotate hub in both directions to seat bearings.

2) Loosen lock nut until zero torque is present. Retighten lock nut to 4-12 INCH lbs. (.5-1.5 N.m) Rotate hub in both directions. Retighten lock nut to 4-12 INCH lbs. (.5-1.5 N.m). Using a dial gauge, check wheel bearing axial end play. No end play should be present. Measure preload ("A") with pull gauge on one of the wheel studs.

3) Tighten lock nut 15-30 degrees to install lock washer. Rotate hub in both directions again. Measure preload again ("B"), using same method as previously described. Correct preload should equal "B" minus "A". Correct preload range is 1.59-4.72 lbs. (7.06-2.14 N). Install hub assembly and brake pads.

BALL JOINT CHECKING

Upper Ball Joint

1) Using a pull gauge, check ball joint side-to-side torque. If play exceeds 7.17-44.83 lbs. (31.87-199.36 N) for a new or used ball joint, replacement is necessary.

2) With ball joint stud nut in place, check stud turning torque. If torque exceeds 8.7-43.4 INCH lbs. (1.0-4.9 N.m), ball joint should be replaced. If dust cover is cracked, replace ball joint.

NISSAN PATHFINDER & PICKUP (Cont.)

Lower Ball Joint

1) Using a pull gauge, check ball joint side-to-side torque. If play exceeds 3.06-38.28 lbs. (13.63-170.25 N) on 2WD, or 0-15.2 lbs. (0-67.7 N) on 4WD, joint should be replaced.

2) With ball joint stud nut in place, check stud turning torque. If torque exceeds 8.7-34.7 INCH lbs. (1.0-3.9 N.m) for 2WD, or 0-43 INCH lbs. (0-4.9 N.m) for 4WD, ball joint should be replaced. If dust cover is cracked, replace ball joint.

TESTING

ADJUSTABLE SHOCK ABSORBER

Terminal & Power Supply Test

1) Remove electrical connector from adjustable shock absorber. Ensure continuity is present between terminal No. 3 and body ground. *See Fig. 3.*

2) Probe voltmeter negative lead in terminal No. 3 of terminal side of shock absorber connector. Depress "SPORT" end of switch and probe terminal No. 2 with voltmeter positive lead. Battery voltage should be present. When "SPORT" switch is released, zero volts should be present.

3) With voltmeter negative lead still in terminal No. 3 of shock absorber connector, insert voltmeter positive lead into terminal No. 1. Depress "TOURING" end of switch. Battery voltage should be present. When "TOURING" switch is released, zero volts should be present.

Fig. 3: Adjustable Shock Absorber Wiring Diagram

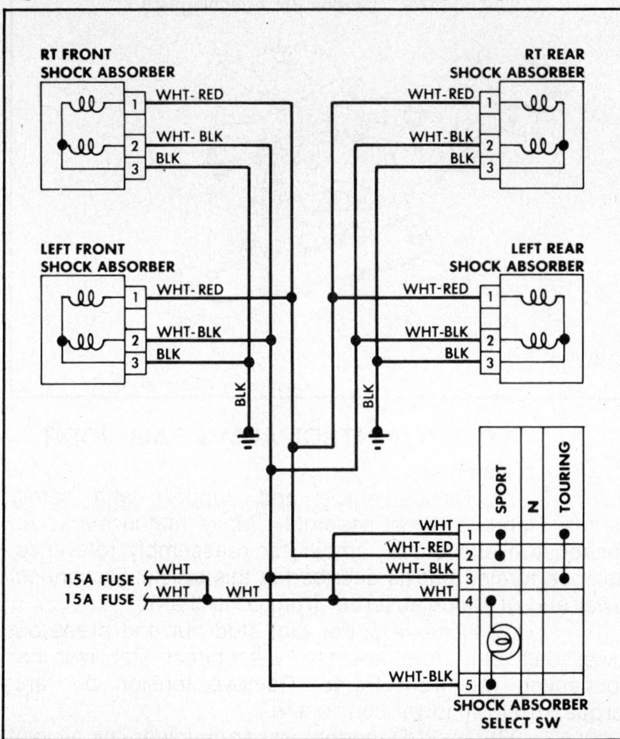

Select Switch Test

Remove connector from select switch. With switch in "SPORT" position, continuity should be present between terminals No. 1 and 2. With switch in "TOURING" position, continuity should be present between terminals No. 1 and 3. Regardless of switch position, approximately 110 ohms should be present between terminals No. 4 and 5.

Adjustable Shock Absorber Test

1) Move select switch from "SPORT" to "TOURING" position. Use a listening device and ensure actuator is operating inside shock absorber.

2) Compress shock absorber as far as possible. Apply negative battery voltage to terminal No. 3. Ensure shock absorber expansion speed varies when positive voltage is switched between "SPORT" terminal No. 1 and "TOURING" terminal No. 2. If speed changes, actuator is operating properly.

REMOVAL & INSTALLATION

FREE-WHEELING HUB

Removal

Set free-wheeling hub in "FREE" position. Depress brake pedal and remove free-wheeling hub. Remove snap ring and remove drive clutch. *See Fig. 4.*

Installation

Apply grease to drive clutch and drive shaft. Install free-running hub with hub in "FREE" position. Ensure hub operates properly after installation.

1) Raise and support vehicle. Remove wheel assembly. Remove caliper and support out of the way. On 4WD models use a block of wood and separate drive shaft from knuckle spindle by lightly tapping drive shaft end.

Fig. 4: Exploded View of Free-Running Hub Assembly

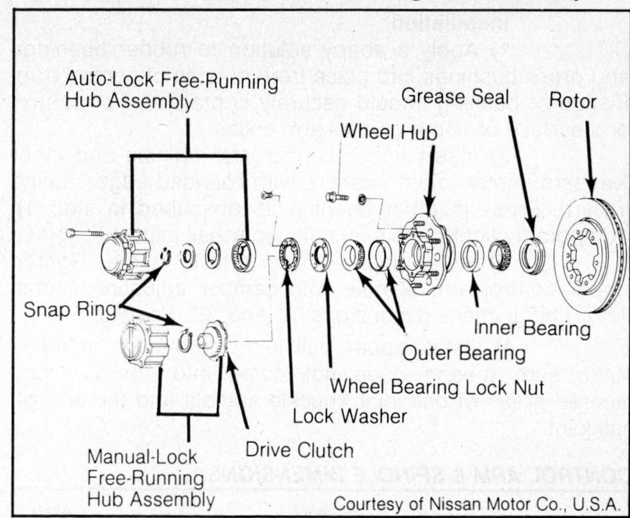

Courtesy of Nissan Motor Co., U.S.A.

WHEEL BEARING, HUB & KNUCKLE

Removal

NOTE: **To remove automatic and manual locking hubs on 4WD models, refer to LOCKING HUB article in DRIVE AXLES section.**

Front Suspension

NISSAN PATHFINDER & PICKUP (Cont.)

2) On all models, remove tie rod ends using Separator (HT72520000). Loosen (do not remove) upper and lower ball joint tightening nuts. Separate knuckle spindle from ball joints. Separate knuckle spindle from upper and lower ball joint studs.

3) Support lower control arm with a jack and remove ball joint tightening nuts. Remove knuckle spindle from upper and lower links. On 4WD models, remove lock washer from hub. On all models, remove wheel bearing lock nut. To remove wheel bearing lock nut on 4WD models, use Bearing Lock Nut Puller (KV40105400).

4) Remove wheel hub and outer bearing. Use care to not drop outer bearing. Using a brass bar, remove bearing outer races.

Installation

To install, reverse removal procedure. Ensure wheel bearings are correctly adjusted as previously described before installing complete assembly in vehicle. Ensure new lock washers, grease seals and cotter pins are used.

UPPER CONTROL ARM & BALL JOINT

Removal

1) Remove shock absorber upper nut. Support lower control arm with a jack. Remove upper ball joint nuts and upper control arm-to-frame bolts. Remove cotter pin and stud nut from upper ball joint and separate ball joint from steering knuckle.

2) Loosen bolts retaining upper ball joint to upper control arm and remove ball joint. Remove bolts retaining upper control arm spindle. Remove spindle and upper control arm. Collect all camber adjusting shims.

3) Remove nuts and washers at both ends of upper control arm spindle. Place assembly on a vise and press upper control arm spindle from one end. Remove rubber bushing. Press from other end and remove other bushing. Remove spindle from upper control arm.

Installation

1) Apply a soapy solution to rubber bushings and press bushings into place from outside of control arm. Flange of bushing should securely contact end of control end surface of upper control arm collar.

2) Insert upper control arm spindle and inner washers. Install inner washers with rounded edges facing inward. Press in other bushing as described in step **1)**. Temporarily tighten nuts. Install upper ball joint.

3) Install upper control arm to frame. Tighten upper control arm spindle with camber adjusting shims. After fitting, check dimensions "A" and "B". *See Fig. 5.*

4) Install upper ball joint to knuckle spindle. Make sure grease does not come into contact with tapered areas of ball joint knuckle spindle and threads of ball joint.

CONTROL ARM & SPINDLE DIMENSIONS [1]

Application	"A" In. (mm)	"B" In. (mm)
All Models	4.33 (110)	1.26 (32)

[1] – See Fig. 4 to measure upper control arm and spindle dimensions.

Fig. 5: Upper Control Arm & Spindle Dimensions

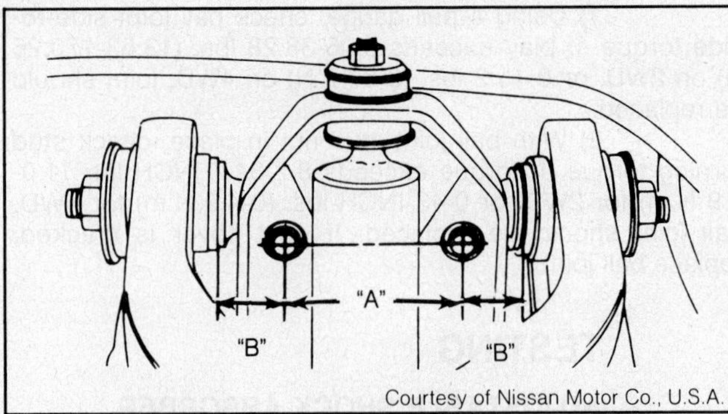

5) Install wheel assembly. Lower vehicle and check riding height "H" of lower control arm. *See Fig. 6.* Check wheel alignment. See appropriate article in WHEEL ALIGNMENT section.

Fig. 6: Unladen Vehicle Riding Height

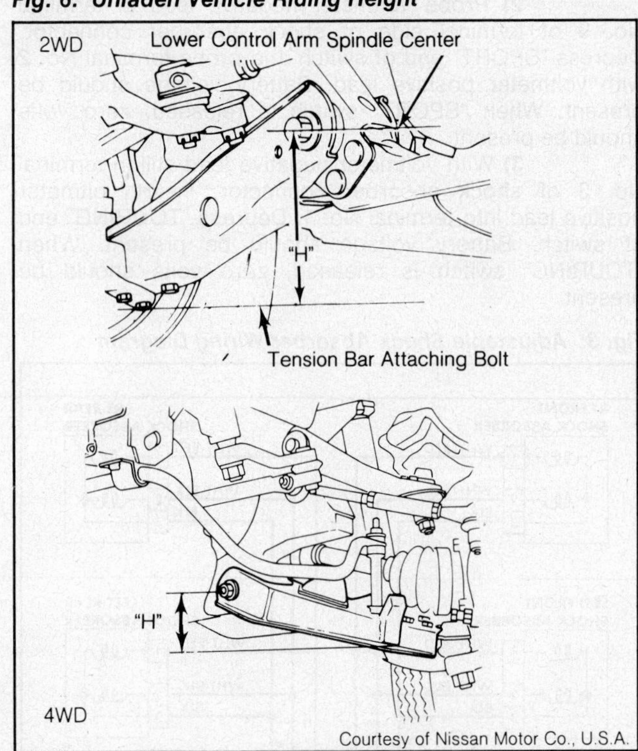

LOWER CONTROL ARM & BALL JOINT

Removal

1) Raise vehicle and support with safety stands. Remove wheel assembly. Make match marks on anchor arm and crossmember for reassembly reference. Remove torsion bar as decribed in this article. Disconnect lower end of shock absorber from control arm.

2) Remove cotter pin, stud nut and press out lower ball joint from knuckle. Disconnect stabilizer bar connecting rod from frame. Remove tension bar and torque arm from lower control arm.

3) On 2WD models, separate lower link all joint from knuckle spindle. On 4WD models, separate lower ball joint from lower link. Remove front lower link spindle bushing nut. Using a puller, remove lower link bushing from frame.

NISSAN PATHFINDER & PICKUP (Cont.)

Installation

1) To install, reverse removal procedure. Tighten nuts and bolts to specification. Ensure grease does not contact tapered area of ball joint stud or knuckle hole and does not contact ball joint threads.

2) With vehicle on floor, turn anchor bolt adjusting nut to obtain specified "H" dimension. *See Fig. 6.* Check wheel alignment. See WHEEL ALIGNMENT section.

TORSION BAR

Removal

Support lower control arm with a jack. Remove torsion bar adjusting nut. Move dust cover and remove snap ring from anchor arm. On 2WD models, pull anchor arm to the rear and withdraw torsion bar spring. Remove torque arm. On 4WD models, remove torque arm attaching nuts. Move torsion spring forward and remove with torque arm.

Installation

NOTE: Anchor arm adjusting nut is adjustable in tightening direction only. Do not attempt to adjust anchor arm by loosening adjusting nut. Torsion bars are identified by an "R" and "L" on end of bar.

1) On 2WD models, install torque arm to lower link. Coat serration of torsion bar spring with multipurpose grease. Using a jack, raise lower control arm so bumper just contacts stop.

2) On 2WD models, install torsion bar spring. On 4WD models, install torsion bar spring with torque arm. Ensure right and left torsion bar springs are installed in their proper locations.

3) Install anchor arm to serrations on torsion bar so specified dimension "A" is obtained with lower control arm in contact with rubber bumper. *See Fig. 7.* Install snap ring to anchor arm and dust cover. On 2WD models, ensure snap ring is correctly installed in anchor arm groove. On 4WD models, ensure snap ring and anchor arm are correctly installed.

Fig. 7: Measurement for Anchor Arm Dimension "A"

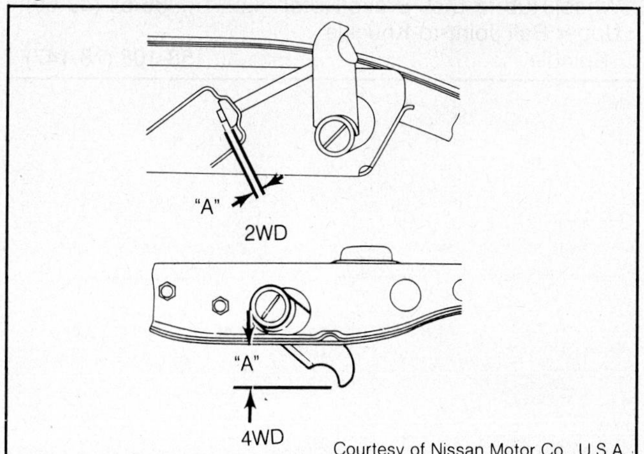

4) On all models, adjust anchor arm adjusting bolt to obtain specified dimension "B" and install lock nut. See DIMENSIONS FOR SETTING TORSION BAR table. *See Fig. 8.* On 2WD models, install snap ring and dust cover to anchor arm.

5) On all models, lower vehicle and turn anchor arm adjusting nut to obtain specified "H" dimension with vehicle unladen. *See Fig. 6.*

Fig. 8: Measurement for Anchor Arm Bolt Dimension "B"

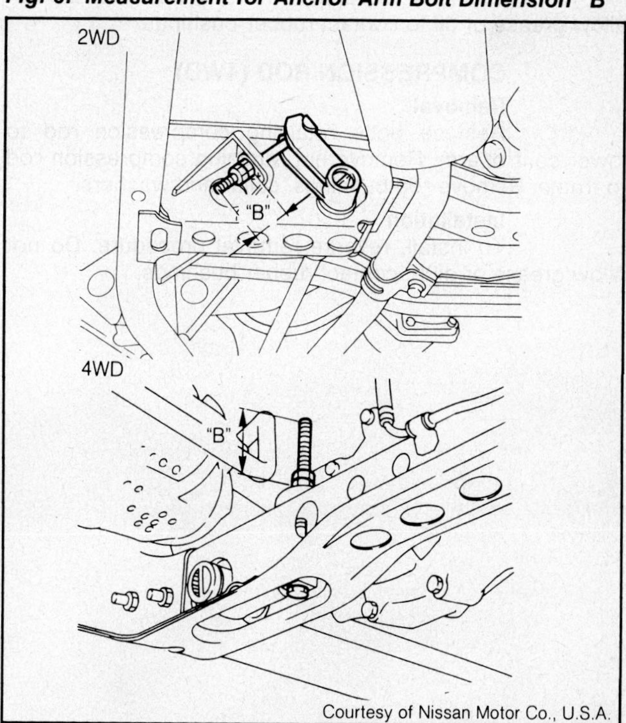

DIMENSIONS FOR SETTING TORSION BAR

Application	In. (mm)
Dimension "A"	
2WD	.24-.71 (6-18)
4WD	1.97-2.36 (50-60)
Dimension "B"	
2WD Heavy Duty,	
Cab & Chassis & STD.	1.38 (35)
All Others	1.93 (49)
4WD	3.03 (77)
Dimension "H"	
2WD	4.37-4.53 (111-115)
4WD	1.73-1.89 (44-48)

STABILIZER BAR

Removal

Remove nut retaining stabilizer connecting rod to lower control arm. Remove bolt retaining stabilizer mounting bracket to frame. Remove nut retaining stabilizer and connecting rod and remove these parts.

Installation

To install, reverse removal procedure. The White mark on stabilizer bar can be seen from both sides of the vehicle when properly installed.

TENSION ROD (2WD)

Removal

Support lower control arm with a jack. Remove bolts retaining tension rod to lower control arm and

NISSAN PATHFINDER & PICKUP (Cont.)

separate these parts. Remove nut retaining tension rod to bracket. Remove rod bushings, collar and washers.

Installation

To install, reverse removal procedure. Do not allow grease or oil to contact rubber bushings.

COMPRESSION ROD (4WD)

Removal

Remove bolts retaining compression rod to lower control arm. Remove nut retaining compression rod to frame. Remove rod bushings, collar and washers.

Installation

To install, reverse removal procedure. Do not allow grease or oil to contact rubber bushings.

TIGHTENING SPECIFICATIONS

Application	Ft. Lbs. (N.m)
Compression Rod-to-Body	87-116 (118-157)
Compression Rod-to- Lower Link	87-108 (118-147)
Drive Shaft-to-Differential Carrier	25-33 (34-44)
Knuckle Arm-to-Knuckle Spindle	53-72 (72-98)
Knuckle Arm-to-Tie Rod	40-72 (54-98)
Knuckle Spindle-to-Caliper	53-72 (72-98)
Lower Ball Joint-to-Knuckle Spindle	87-141 (118-191
Lower Ball Joint-to-Lower Link (4WD)	35-45 (47-61)
Free Running Hub-to-Wheel Hub	
Manual	18-25 (25-34)
Automatic	18-25 (25-34)
Stabilizer Bar-to-Frame	12-16 (16-22)
Stabilizer Bar-to-Lower Link	12-16 (16-22)
Steering Stopper Bolt Lock Nut	
2WD	20-27 (26-36)
4WD	56-72 (76-98)
Tension Rod-to-Frame	87-116 (118-157)
Tension Rod-to-Lower Link	36-47 (49-64)
Shock Absorber	
Lower Link	43-58 (59-78)
Upper Link	12-16 (16-22)
Torsion Bar Spring	
Anchor Adjusting Bolt	
Lock Nut	22-30 (30-40)
Torque Arm-to-Lower Link	
Inside	
2WD	37-50 (50-68)
4WD	33-44 (45-60)
Outside	
2WD	37-50 (50-68)
4WD	66-87 (89-118)
Lower Link-to-Frame	80-108 (109-147)
Upper Ball Joint-to-Upper Link	12-15 (16-21)
Upper Link Spindle-to-Frame	80-108 (109-147)
Upper Link Spindle-to-Upper Link	52-76 (71-103)
Wheel Hub Nut	87-108 (118-147)
Wheel Hub-to-Disc Brake Rotor	36-51 (49-69)
Upper Ball Joint-to-Knuckle Spindle	58-108 (78-147)

Front Suspension

NISSAN PULSAR NX, SENTRA, STANZA & STANZA WAGON

DESCRIPTION

All models use a MacPherson strut type front suspension system. Shock absorbers are built into each strut tube with a coil spring. Upper end of strut is mounted to inner fender panel. Lower end of strut is bolted to steering knuckle. Steering knuckle is attached to the transverse link by a ball joint. *See Figs. 1 and 2.* Transverse link is attached to a gusset by bushings. A stabilizer bar attaches to gusset and transverse link.

Fig. 1: Typical 2WD Front Suspension

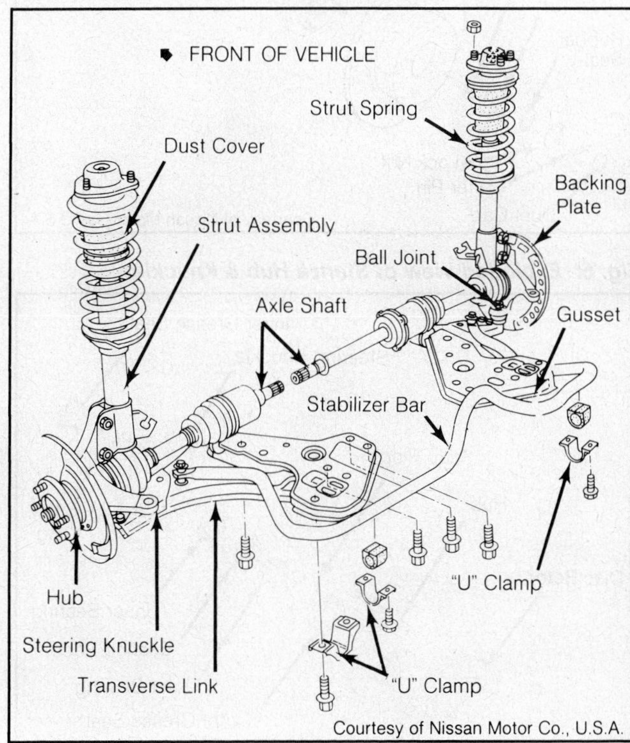

Fig. 2: Typical 4WD Front Suspension

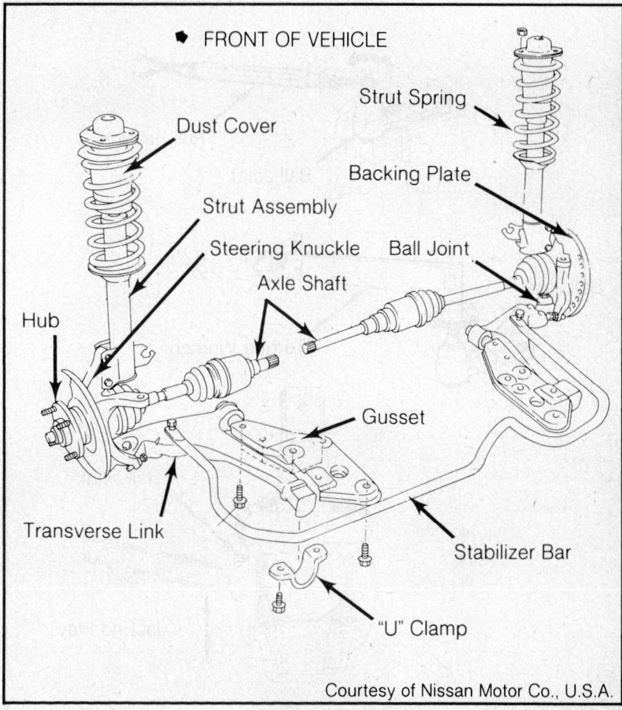

Fig. 3: Adjusting Wheel Bearing Preload

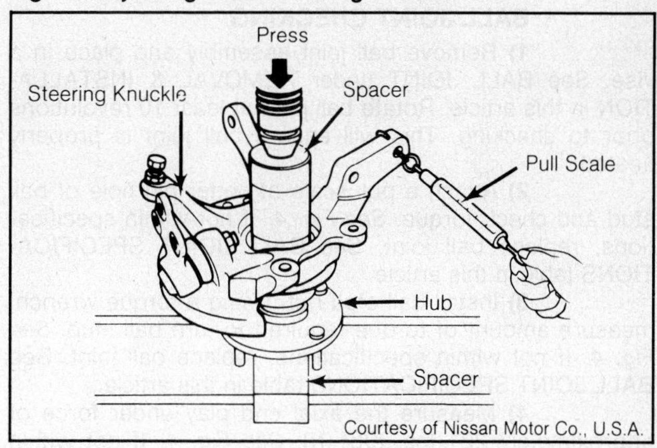

ADJUSTMENTS & INSPECTION

WHEEL ALIGNMENT SPECIFICATIONS & PROCEDURES

See WHEEL ALIGNMENT SPECIFICATIONS & PROCEDURES in WHEEL ALIGNMENT section.

WHEEL BEARING

1) Raise vehicle until front wheel are off the ground and support vehicle. Spin wheel assembly and insure bearing rotation is smooth. Check axial end play. Axial end play must not exceed .0020" (.05 mm). If axial end play is not within specifications or bearing is not smooth, hub and steering knuckle assembly must be removed. See STEERING KNUCKLE under REMOVAL & INSTALLATION in this article.

2) Bearing preload adjustment is made while pressing steering knuckle into hub assembly. Place steering knuckle and hub in a press with suitable spacers. *See Fig. 3.* Apply specified amount of pressure. See WHEEL BEARING PRELOAD SPECIFICATIONS table in this article. Spin steering knuckle several revolutions in both directions.

3) Attach a pull scale to the steering knuckle and measure amount of torque required to rotate knuckle. If bearing preload specifications can not be achieved, the bearing must be replaced as a complete set. On Pulsar and Sentra, the wheel bearing is a one piece assembly and there are no preload specifications. *See Figs. 5 and 6.*

WHEEL BEARING PRELOAD SPECIFICATIONS

Application	Pressure Ton	Preload Lbs. (N)
Stanza & Stanza Wagon	5.5	0.4-4.0 (2.0-17.7)
Pulsar NX Sentra	5.0	[1]

[1] – With specified amount of pressure applied, hub must rotate smoothly in both direction. Preload specifications not available.

Front Suspension

NISSAN PULSAR NX, SENTRA, STANZA & STANZA WAGON (Cont.)

Fig. 4: Checking Ball Joint

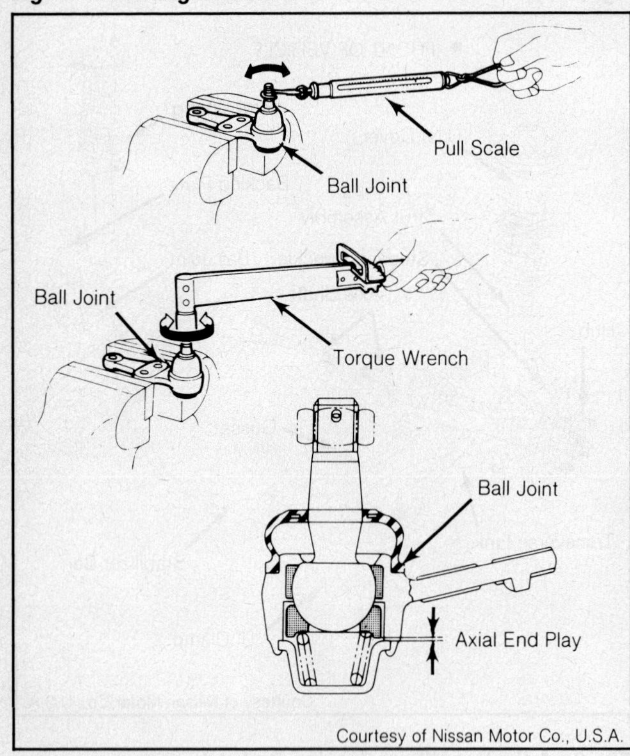

BALL JOINT CHECKING

1) Remove ball joint assembly and place in a vise. See BALL JOINT under REMOVAL & INSTALLATION in this article. Rotate ball joint at least 10 revolutions prior to checking. This will ensure ball joint is properly seated.

2) Attach a pull scale at cotter pin hole of ball stud and check torque. *See Fig. 4.* If not within specifications, replace ball joint. See BALL JOINT SPECIFICATIONS table in this article.

3) Install ball stud nut. Using a torque wrench, measure amount of torque required to turn ball stud. *See Fig. 4.* If not within specifications, replace ball joint. See BALL JOINT SPECIFICATIONS table in this article.

4) Measure the axial end play under force of approximately 221 lbs. (981 N). *See Fig. 4.* If not within specifications, replace ball joint. See BALL JOINT SPECIFICATIONS table in this article.

Fig. 5: Exploded View of Pulsar NX & Sentra Hub & Knuckle

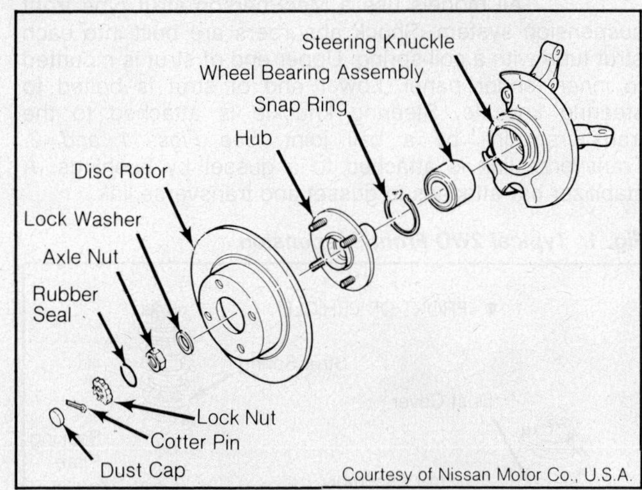

Fig. 6: Exploded View of Stanza Hub & Knuckle

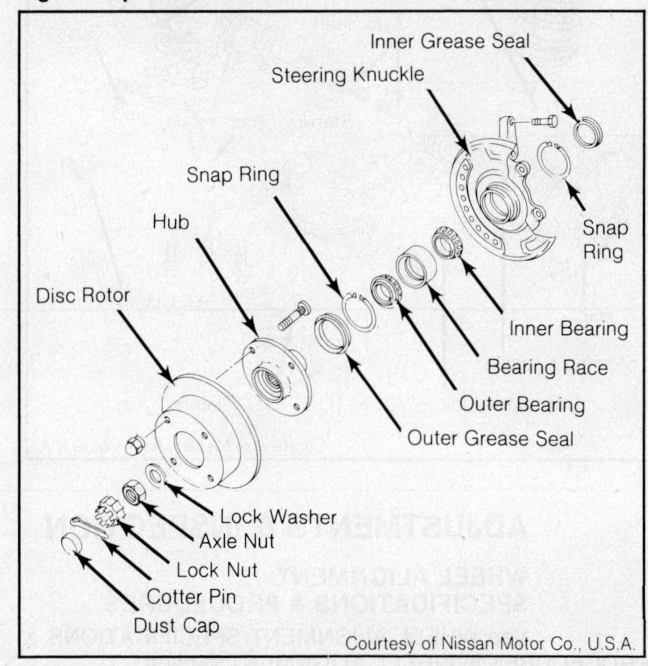

BALL JOINT SPECIFICATIONS

Application	Pull Scale Lbs. (N)	Torque Wrench INCH Lbs. (N.m)	Axial End Play In. (mm)
Stanza			
Used Part	1.8-18.1 (7.8-80.4)	4.3-43.4 (0.5-4.9)	0.004-0.039 (0.10-0.99)
New Part	5.5-18.1 (24.5-80.4)	13.0-43.4 (1.5-4.9)	0.004-0.039 (0.10-0.99)
Stanza Wagon 2WD			
Used Part	[1] 1.8 (7.8)	[1] 4.3 (0.5)	0.004-0.039 (0.10-0.99)
New Part	7.1-21.4 (31.4-95.1)	17-52 (2-6)	0.004-0.039 (0.10-0.99)
Stanza Wagon 4WD, Pulsar NX & Sentra			
Used Part	1.8-18.1 (7.8-80.4)	4.3-43.4 (0.5-4.9)	[2] 0.004-0.039 (0.10-0.99)
New Part	3.5-18.1 (15.7-80.4)	8.7-43.4 (1.0-4.9)	[2] 0.004-0.039 (0.10-0.99)

1 – Specification is at minimum.
2 – Pulsar NX and Sentra axial end play should be 0.028" or less (0.7 mm or less).

NISSAN PULSAR NX, SENTRA, STANZA & STANZA WAGON (Cont.)

REMOVAL & INSTALLATION

WHEEL BEARING

Removal (Pulsar NX & Sentra)

1) Raise and support vehicle. Remove steering knuckle and hub as an assembly. See STEERING KNUCKLE under REMOVAL & INSTALLATION in this article. Place assembly in a vise. Drive hub with inner bearing out of steering knuckle. Press outer race of inner bearing off hub.

2) Remove inner race from wheel bearing. Remove snap ring from steering knuckle. Install inner from wheel bearing in steering knuckle and press out wheel bearing assembly from steering knuckle.

NOTE: **Replace wheel bearing assembly and seals if hub and steering knuckle are separated.**

Installation

1) Press new bearing assembly into steering knuckle from the outer side of steering knuckle. DO NOT press on inner race of bearing assembly. DO NOT apply grease to wheel bearing outer surface and steering knuckle mating surface. Use care not to damage seals during pressing.

2) Install new snap ring into groove of steering knuckle. Apply multipurpose grease to lip of seals. Press hub into steering knuckle. DO NOT apply greater than 3.3 tons of pressure. Check bearing preload. See WHEEL BEARING under ADJUSTMENTS & INSPECTION in this article. To complete installation, reverse removal procedure.

Removal (Stanza & Stanza Wagon)

1) Remove hub and steering knuckle assembly. See STEERING KNUCKLE under REMOVAL & INSTALLATION in this article. Place assembly in a vise. Drive out hub (with inner bearing) from steering knuckle. *See Fig. 7.* Using a 2-jaw type puller, remove inner bearing from hub. Remove outer grease seal.

NOTE: **If replacing wheel bearing, replace complete unit as an assembly.**

Fig. 7: Separating Hub & Steering Knuckle

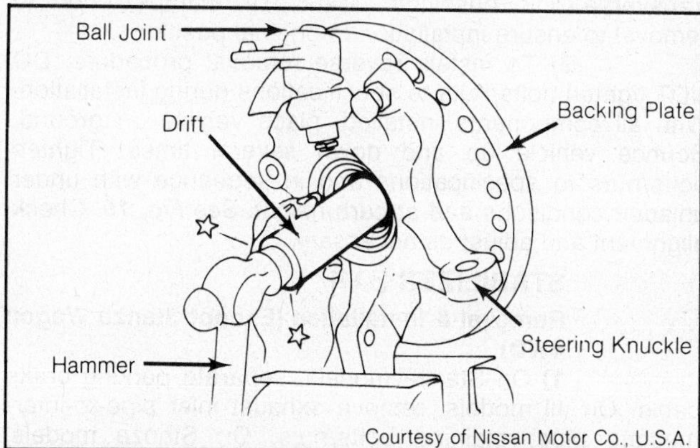

2) Remove inner grease seal from steering knuckle. Remove inner and outer snap rings with snap ring pliers. Remove outer bearing. Press bearing race out of steering knuckle (through the back side).

NOTE: **Replace wheel bearing assembly and seals if hub and steering knuckle are separated.**

Installation

1) Install outer snap ring into groove of steering knuckle. Press bearing race into steering knuckle. Coat inner and outer bearings with multipurpose grease. Install inner snap ring into groove of steering knuckle. Install inner and outer bearings.

2) Install outer grease seal. Carefully press hub into steering knuckle. DO NOT apply greater than 3.3 tons of pressure. Check wheel bearing preload. See WHEEL BEARING under ADJUSTMENTS & INSPECTION in this article. To complete installation, reverse removal procedure.

STEERING KNUCKLE

Removal & Installation

1) Raise and support vehicle. Remove wheel and tire. Apply brakes and remove axle nut. Remove brake caliper without disconnecting brake hose and suspend with wire. Remove tie rod from steering knuckle. To prevent damage, wrap shop rags around axle shaft boots and keep axle shaft straight at all times.

2) Separate axle shaft from hub by tapping on end of axle shaft with a plastic hammer. Mark position of strut-to-steering knuckle and remove strut mounting bolts. On Stanza and Stanza Wagon models, remove bolts/nuts retaining ball joint to transverse link. On Pular NX and Sentra models, separate lower ball joint from steering knuckle. On all models, remove steering knuckle and hub assembly.

3) Clamp steering knuckle in vise. Using a hammer and suitable drift, separate steering knuckle and hub. *See Fig. 7.* Remove grease seal from steering knuckle. Remove inner and outer snap rings. Press out bearing race. To install, reverse removal procedure. Tighten all bolts/nuts to specifications. Check alignment and adjust as necessary.

BALL JOINT

Removal (Pulsar NX & Sentra)

1) Raise and support vehicle. Remove tire and wheel assembly. Apply brakes and remove axle nut. To prevent damage, wrap shop rags around axle boots and keep axle shaft assembly straight at all times. Remove brake caliper. Separate tie rod end from steering knuckle.

2) Use a soft hammer and tap axle shaft loose from hub assembly. Mark strut-to-steering knuckle for installation reference. Remove strut-to-steering knuckle bolts/nuts. Pull hub and steering knuckle assembly away from axle shaft.

NOTE: **Transverse link and ball joint are removed as an assembly.**

3) Remove ball joint stud nut. Separate lower ball joint from steering knuckle with Ball Joint Remover (J25730-A). Remove hub and steering knuckle. Mark transverse link "U" clamp to ensure installation to original position. *See Fig. 8.* Remove nut, washer and spacer retaining stabilizer connecting rod to transverse link. Remove transverse link through bolt and "U" clamp. Remove transverse link and ball joint assembly.

Installation

1) Position transverse link and ball joint assembly. Install through bolt. Ensure proper position of transverse link "U" clamp and install. *See Fig. 8.* Install spacer, washer and nut retaining stabilizer connecting rod

Front Suspension

NISSAN PULSAR NX, SENTRA, STANZA & STANZA WAGON (Cont.)

Fig. 8: Transverse Link "U" Clamp Position

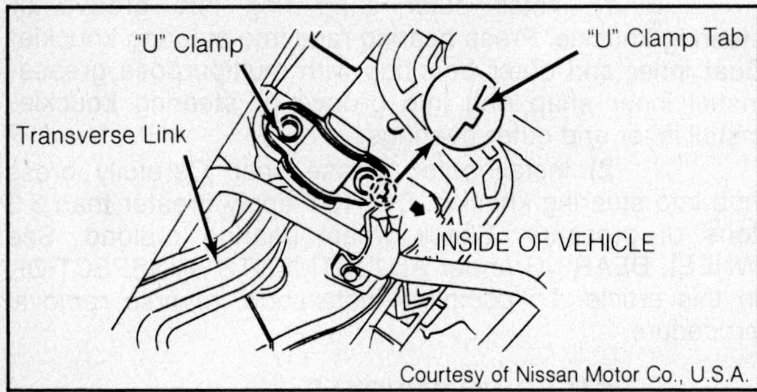

to transverse link. DO NOT tighten transverse link bolts/nuts to specifications at this time. Position hub and steering knuckle on ball joint stud and secure with nut.

2) Position axle shaft through hub. Align marks made at removal and install hub and steering knuckle assembly to strut. Tighten knuckle bolts to specifications. Install tie rod on steering knuckle and tighten to specifications. Install brake caliper. Install axle nut and tighten to specifications. Install tire and wheel assembly.

3) Place vehicle on ground. Bounce vehicle up and down several times. Final tightening must be performed with vehicle at curb weight and tires on the ground. Tighten transverse link bolts/nuts to specifications. Tighten all remaining bolts/nuts to specifications. Check wheel alignment and adjust as necessary.

Removal & Installation (Stanza & Stanza Wagon)

1) Raise and support vehicle. Remove wheel assembly. Apply brakes and remove axle shaft nut. To prevent damage, wrap axle shaft boots with shop rags and keep axle shaft straight at all times. Using a plastic hammer, tap axle shaft out of steering knuckle and hub assembly.

2) Remove nut retaining lower ball joint stud in steering knuckle. Remove bolts/nuts retaining ball joint in transverse link. Using Ball Joint Remover (J25730-A) separate ball joint from steering knuckle.

3) Perform inspection as necessary. See BALL JOINT under ADJUSTMENTS & INSPECTION in this article. To install ball joint, reverse removal procedure. Tighten all bolts/nuts to specifications.

TRANSVERSE LINK

Removal & Installation (Pulsar NX & Sentra)

For removal and installation of transverse link, see BALL JOINT under REMOVAL & INSTALLATION in this article. Ball joint and transverse link are an assembly.

Removal (Stanza & Stanza Wagon)

1) Raise and support vehicle. Remove tire and wheel. Remove stabilizer bar. See STABILIZER BAR under REMOVAL & INSTALLATION in this article. Remove 3 ball joint-to-transverse link bolts/nuts. Remove nut, washer and spacer retaining stabilizer connecting rod to transverse link.

2) On 2WD wagon models, remove 2 nuts and washers retaining front and rear bushings. Pull rear bushing out of "U" clamp. DO NOT remove "U" clamp, loosen if necessary. Remove transverse link assembly.

3) On Stanza (except 2WD wagon) models, mark "U" clamp to ensure installation to original position. Remove "U" clamp. Remove nut and washer from front bushing of transverse link. Remove transverse link assembly.

Disassembly & Reassembly

Using a press and suitable spacers, press front bushing off transverse link shaft. Avoid oil and grease on bushing. Press bushing on transverse link shaft. Ensure bushing is centered in transverse link.

Installation

1) To install, reverse removal procedure. DO NOT tighten transverse link bolts/nuts to specifications until vehicle is completely assembled, tires are on the ground and under unladen conditions. Ensure rear bushing is properly positioned in "U" clamp. *See Fig. 9.*

2) With vehicle assembled and tires on the ground, bounce vehicle up and down several times prior to final tightening. Tighten all bolts/nuts to specifications. Check alignment and adjust as necessary.

Fig. 9: Transverse Link Rear Bushing Installation

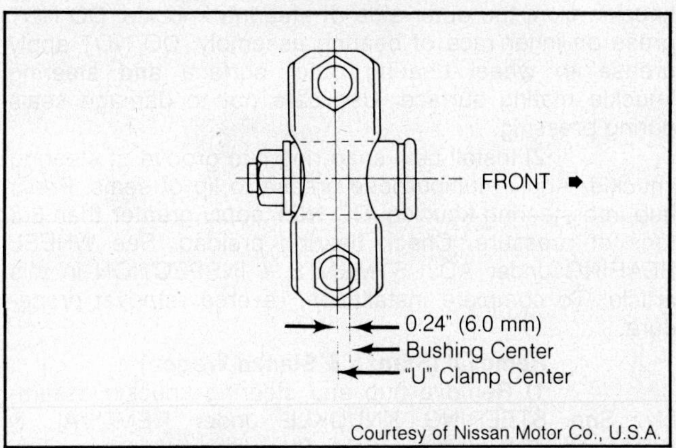

GUSSET

Removal & Installation (Stanza Wagon, 2WD & 4WD)

1) Raise and support vehicle. When removing right side gusset, support engine mounting member. On both sides, remove bolts/nuts in reverse order of tightening. *See Fig. 10.* Remove nut from front and rear transverse link bushings. Mark "U" clamps prior to removal to ensure installation to original position.

2) To install, reverse removal procedure. DO NOT tighten bolts/nuts to specifications during installation. With all components installed, place vehicle on ground. Bounce vehicle up and down several times. Tighten bolts/nuts to specifications and in sequence with under unladen conditions and at curb height. *See Fig. 10.* Check alignment and adjust as necessary.

STABILIZER BAR

Removal & Installation (Except Stanza Wagon 4WD)

1) On Stanza models, separate parking brake cable. On all models, remove exhaust inlet pipe-to-intermediate pipe retaining bolts/nuts. On Stanza models, remove insulator retaining bolt. On all models, remove nut, washer and spacer retaining stabilizer bar to transverse link by holding upper nut while removing lower nut. *See Fig. 11.*

Front Suspension

NISSAN PULSAR NX, SENTRA, STANZA & STANZA WAGON (Cont.)

NOTE: Tighten bolts/nuts to specifications after complete reassembly and with vehicle on the ground.

Fig. 10: Gusset Tightening Sequence

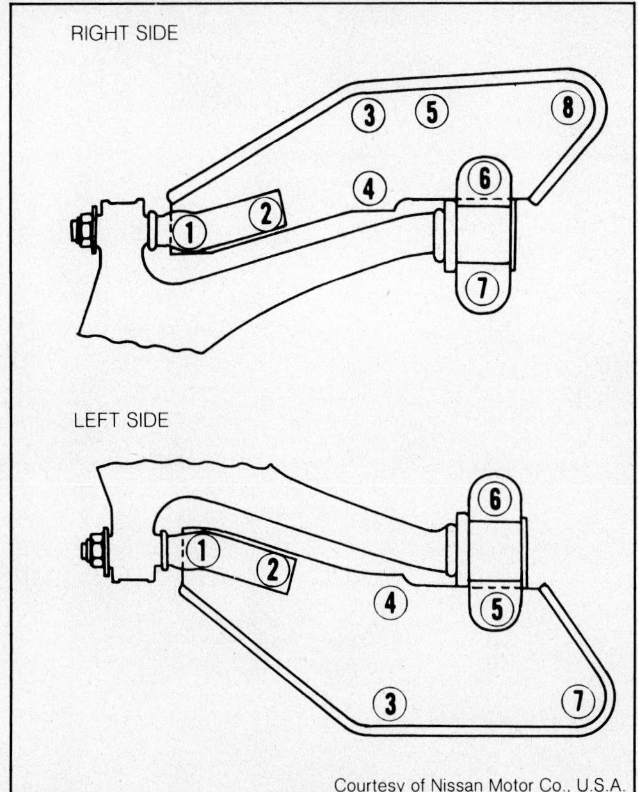

2) Mark position of "U" clamps to ensure installation to original location. Remove "U" clamps retaining stabilizer bar to gusset or frame. Remove stabilizer bar. To install, reverse removal procedure.

Fig. 11: Stabilizer Connecting Rod

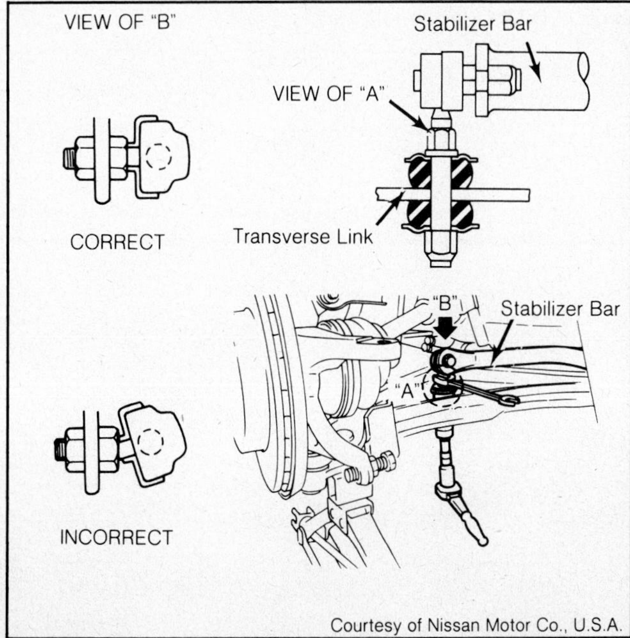

Ensure stabilizer connecting rod is positioned properly. *See Fig. 11.*

Removal & Installation (Stanza Wagon 4WD)

1) Remove transaxle support rod and control rod. *See Fig. 12.* Place matching marks on drive shaft and transfer mounting flange. Separate drive shaft. Remove exhaust inlet pipe-to-catalytic converter bolts/nuts.

Fig. 12: Support & Control Rod Location

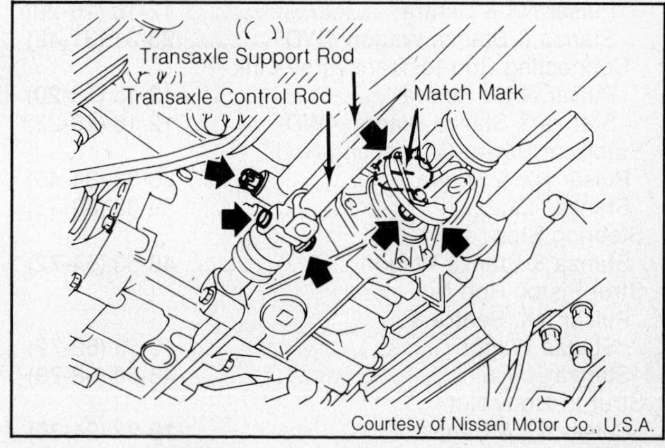

2) Remove nut, washer and spacer retaining stabilizer bar to transverse link by holding upper nut while removing lower nut. *See Fig. 11.* Mark position of "U" clamps to ensure installation to original location. Remove "U" clamps. Push down on exhaust pipe and remove stabilizer bar.

3) To install, reverse removal procedure and tighten bolts/nuts finger tight. With components reassembled, place vehicle on ground. Bounce vehicle up and down several times. Tighten all bolts/nuts to specifications. Check alignment and adjust as necessary.

STRUT ASSEMBLY

Removal & Installation

Raise and support vehicle. Remove tire and wheel assembly. Disconnect brake line from strut. Support lower control arm. Mark strut camber adjusting bolt-to-strut bracket. DO NOT remove strut piston rod lock nut until dissassembly. Remove nuts attaching upper strut to inner fender. Remove strut and coil spring assembly from vehicle. To install, reverse removal procedure.

TIGHTENING SPECIFICATIONS

Application	Ft. Lbs. (N.m)
Axle Shaft Nut	
Pulsar NX & Sentra	145-203 (197-275)
Stanza	174-231 (236-314)
Stanza Wagon	174-231 (236-314)
Ball Joint Stud Nut	
Pulsar NX & Sentra	43-54 (58-73)
Stanza & Stanza Wagon	52-64 (71-87)
Ball Joint-to-Transverse Link	
Stanza	56-80 (76-109)
Stanza Wagon	
2WD	40-47 (54-64)
4WD	56-80 (76-109)
Caliper Mounting Bolt	
Pulsar NX & Sentra	40-47 (54-64)
Stanza & Stanza Wagon	53-72 (72-98)

Front Suspension

NISSAN PULSAR NX, SENTRA, STANZA & STANZA WAGON (Cont.)

TIGHTENING SPECIFICATIONS (Cont.)

Application	Ft. Lbs. (N.m)
Engine Mount Member-to-Gusset	
Stanza & Stanza Wagon	29-36 (39-49)
Gusset-to-Body	
Stanza & Stanza Wagon	87-108 (118-146)
Stabilizer Bar	
"U" Clamp	
Pulsar NX & Sentra	12-15 (16-20)
Stanza & Stanza Wagon 4WD	23-31 (31-42)
Connecting Rod-to-Transverse Link	
Pulsar NX & Sentra	12-15 (16-20)
Stanza & Stanza Wagon 4WD	12-16 (16-22)
Stabilizer Bar-to-Connecting Rod	
Pulsar NX & Sentra	25-33 (34-45)
Stanza	29-33 (39-45)
Steering Stopper	
Stanza & Stanza Wagon	40-53 (54-72)
Strut Piston Rod Nut	
Pulsar NX, Sentra & Stanza Wagon	46-53 (62-72)
Stanza	43-58 (58-79)
Strut-to-Body Nut	
Pulsar NX & Sentra	18-22 (24-30)
Stanza & Stanza Wagon 2WD	23-31 (31-42)
Stanza Wagon 4WD	11-17 (15-23)
Strut-to-Steering Knuckle Bolt	
Pulsar NX, Sentra & Stanza Wagon	72-87 (98-118)
Stanza	82-91 (111-123)
Support Rod Bolt	
Stanza Wagon 2WD	22-24 (30-33)
Tie Rod	
Lock Nut	27-34 (37-46)
Stud Nut	22-36 (30-49)
Transverse Link Bolt	
Pulsar NX & Sentra	58-72 (79-98)
Stanza	87-108 (118-146)
Transverse Link Nut	
Pulsar NX & Sentra	72-87 (98-118)
Stanza	67-87 (91-118)
Stanza Wagon	
Front	65-87 (88-118)
Rear	72-87 (98-118)
Wheel Nut	72-87 (98-118)
	INCH Lbs. (N.m)
Control Rod Bolt	
Stanza Wagon 2WD	52-70 (6-8)
Stanza Wagon 4WD	96-120 (11-14)
Stabilizer Bar	
Connecting Rod-to-Transverse Link	
Stanza Wagon 2WD	80-104 (9-12)
"U" Clamp	
Stanza Wagon 2WD	80-104 (9-12)
Support Rod Nut	
Stanza Wagon 4WD	80-104 (9-12)

Front Suspension

NISSAN VAN

DESCRIPTION

The front suspension uses upper and lower link assemblies with ball joints. Standard shock absorbers are used along with a single leaf spring. The single leaf spring extends to both lower link assemblies under the suspension crossmember.

Compression rods attach to lower link assembly and vehicle body. A stabilizer bar mounted at front of suspension and extends from both lower link assemblies. Stabilizer bar is attached to vehicle frame by connecting rods. *See Fig. 1.*

ADJUSTMENTS & INSPECTION

WHEEL ALIGNMENT SPECIFICATIONS & PROCEDURES

See WHEEL ALIGNMENT SPECIFICATIONS & PROCEDURES in WHEEL ALIGNMENT section.

WHEEL BEARING

Raise and support vehicle. Remove tire and wheel assembly. Remove lower brake caliper mounting bolt and pivot caliper off rotor. Rotate brake rotor. Check axial end play. If end play exceeds .0020" (.051 mm) or rotation is not smooth, replace bearing assembly. Front wheel bearing is nonadjustable.

BALL JOINT CHECKING

1) Remove ball joint assembly and place in a vise. See BALL JOINT under REMOVAL & INSTALLATION in this article. Rotate ball joint at least 10 revolutions prior to checking. This will ensure ball joint is properly seated.

2) For upper ball joint, attach pull scale around ball joint stud. On lower ball joint, attach pull scale through cotter pin hole. *See Fig. 2.* Check ball joint pulling torque. If not within specifications, replace ball joint. See BALL JOINT SPECIFICATIONS table in this article.

3) Install ball stud nut. Using a torque wrench, measure amount of torque required to turn ball stud. *See*

Fig. 1: Nissan Van Front Suspension

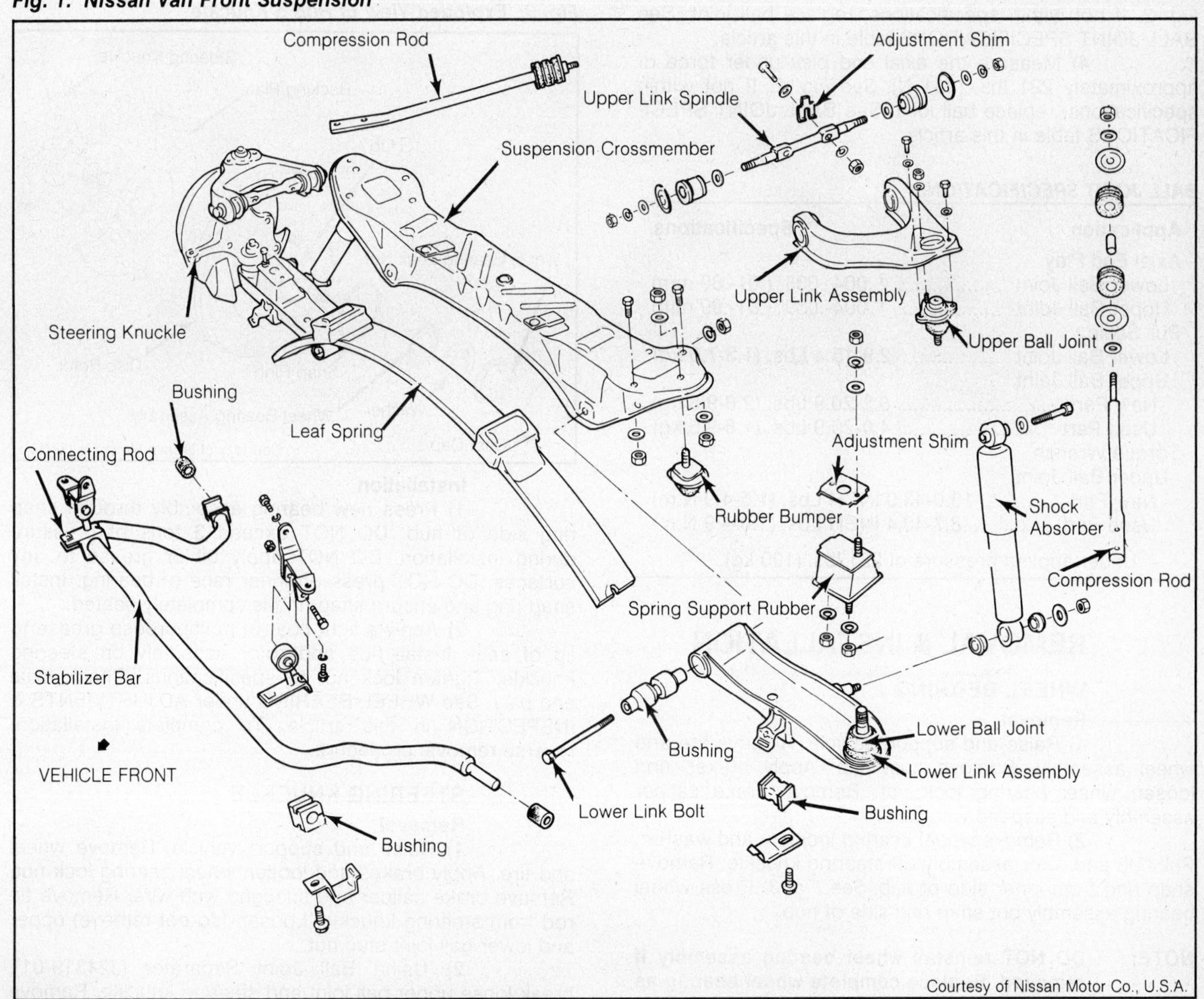

NISSAN VAN (Cont.)

Fig. 2: Checking Ball Joint

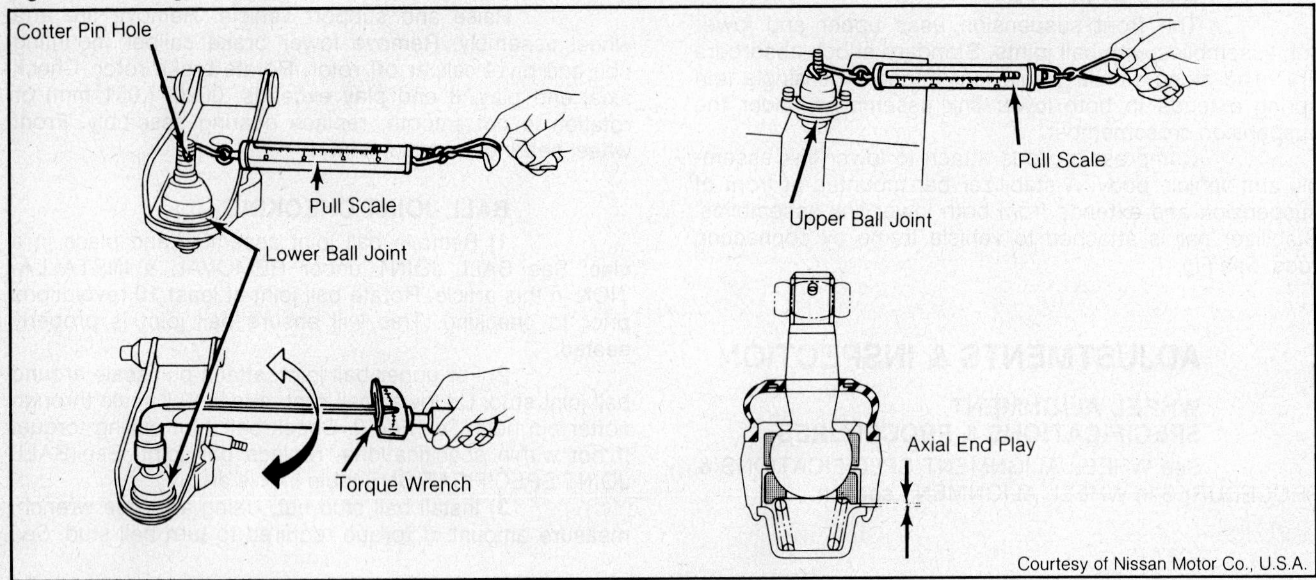

Fig. 2. If not within specifications, replace ball joint. See BALL JOINT SPECIFICATIONS table in this article.

4) Measure the axial end play under force of approximately 221 lbs. (981 N). *See Fig. 2.* If not within specifications, replace ball joint. See BALL JOINT SPECIFICATIONS table in this article.

BALL JOINT SPECIFICATIONS

Application	Specifications
Axial End Play	
Lower Ball Joint	[1] .004-.035" (.01-.89 mm)
Upper Ball Joint	[1] .004-.039" (.01-.99 mm)
Pull Scale	
Lower Ball Joint	2.9-15.4 Lbs. (1.3-7.0 kg)
Upper Ball Joint	
New Part	6.2-20.9 Lbs. (2.8-9.5 kg)
Used Part	4.0-20.9 Lbs. (1.8-9.5 kg)
Torque Wrench	
Upper Ball Joint	
New Part	13.0-43.0 INCH Lbs. (1.5-4.9 N.m)
Used Part	8.7-43.4 INCH Lbs. (1.0-4.9 N.m)

[1] – Under applied pressure of 221 lbs. (100 kg).

REMOVAL & INSTALLATION

WHEEL BEARING

Removal

1) Raise and support vehicle. Remove tire and wheel assembly. Remove dust cap. Apply brakes and loosen wheel bearing lock nut. Remove brake caliper assembly and suspend with wire.

2) Remove wheel bearing lock nut and washer. Pull hub and rotor assembly off steering knuckle. Remove snap ring from inner side of hub. *See Fig. 3.* Press wheel bearing assembly out snap ring side of hub.

NOTE: DO NOT reinstall wheel bearing assembly if removed. Replace complete wheel bearing as an assembly only.

Fig. 3: Exploded View of Hub & Knuckle

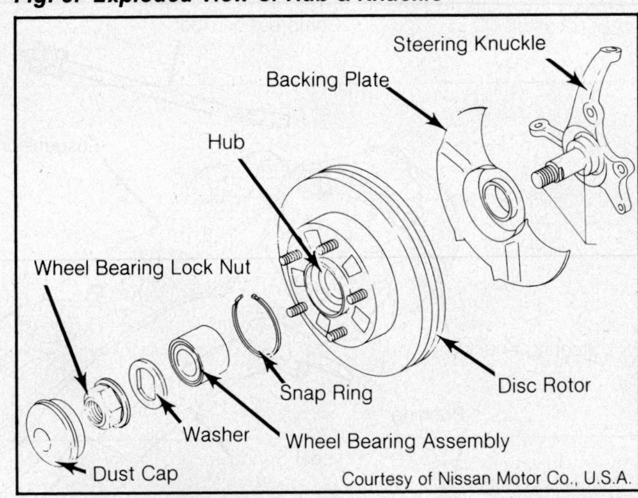

Installation

1) Press new bearing assembly through snap ring side of hub. DO NOT exceed 3 tons of pressure during installation. DO NOT apply oil or grease to any surfaces. DO NOT press on inner race of bearing. Install snap ring and ensure snap ring is completely seated.

2) Apply a light coat of multipurpose grease to lip of seal. Install hub and rotor assembly on steering knuckle. Tighten lock nut to specifications. Check axial end play. See WHEEL BEARING under ADJUSTMENTS & INSPECTION in this article. To complete installation, reverse removal procedure.

STEERING KNUCKLE

Removal

1) Raise and support vehicle. Remove wheel and tire. Apply brakes and loosen wheel bearing lock nut. Remove brake caliper and suspend with wire. Remove tie rod from steering knuckle. Loosen (do not remove) upper and lower ball joint stud nut.

2) Using Ball Joint Separator (J24319-01), break loose upper ball joint and steering knuckle. Remove

NISSAN VAN (Cont.)

separator and stud nut. Separate steering knuckle from ball joint. Install separator on lower ball joint. Reinstall upper ball joint to steering knuckle and install stud nut finger tight.

3) Break loose lower ball from steering knuckle. Remove separator. Remove upper and lower ball joint stud nuts. Remove steering knuckle assembly.

Installation

Install steering knuckle to upper and lower ball joint studs. Jack up lower link assembly. Install stud nuts on upper and lower ball joint. DO NOT use grease on threads or stud tapered areas. To complete installation, reverse removal procedure.

BALL JOINT

Removal & Installation (Upper Ball Joint)

1) Raise and support vehicle. Remove tire and wheel assembly. Loosen up ball joint stud nut. Using separator, break loose ball joint from steering knuckle. Remove separator.

2) Remove stud nut and pull steering knuckle off ball joint stud. Remove bolts and nuts retaining ball joint to upper link. Remove upper ball joint. To install, reverse removal procedure. Tighten all bolts and nuts to specifications.

NOTE: The lower ball joint and lower link are replaced as an assembly.

Removal (Lower Ball Joint)

1) Remove steering knuckle. See STEERING KNUCKLE under REMOVAL & INSTALLATION in this article. Remove stabilizer bar brackets from both lower links. Swing stabilizer bar down away from lower links.

2) Support lower link with a jack. Remove upper and lower bolt and nut retaining shock absorber and remove shock absorber. Remove compression rod assembly. See COMPRESSION ROD under REMOVAL & INSTALLATION in this article.

3) Remove nut attaching leaf spring to spring support rubber at both lower links. Gradually lower jack until no tension exists in leaf spring. Move jack and swing lower link down away from leaf spring. Jack up end of leaf spring. Remove nut attaching lower link to suspension member and remove lower link assembly.

Installation

To install lower ball joint, reverse removal procedure. Ensure washer retaining leaf spring to spring support rubber does not protrude end of leaf spring. Tighten components with vehicle unladen and tires on ground. Check and wheel alignment and adjust as necessary.

LEAF SPRING

Removal

Separate lower link and ball joint assembly on one side only. See LOWER BALL JOINT under REMOVAL & INSTALLATION in this article. Pull out leaf spring toward removed lower link side.

Installation

To install, reverse removal procedure. Ensure leaf spring pivots fit into recess of suspension member. Tighten components with vehicle unladen and tires on ground. Check and wheel alignment and adjust as necessary.

LOWER LINK BUSHING

NOTE: For removal and installation procedure, see LOWER BALL JOINT under REMOVAL & INSTALLATION in this article.

Removal & Installation

Place lower link in press. Press bushing out of lower link. Apply soap solution to bushing. Press bushing into lower link from front of vehicle side of lower link. Bushing must protrude .20-.28" (5.1-7.1 mm) beyond contact portion of lower link. *See Fig. 4.*

Fig. 4: Installation of Lower Link Bushing

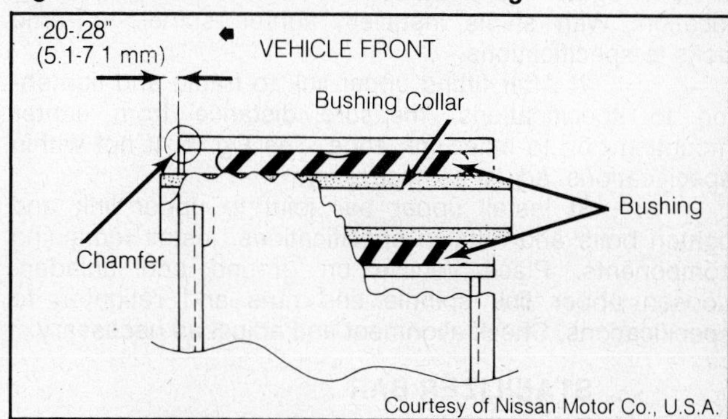

UPPER LINK

Removal

Raise and support vehicle. Support lower link with jack. Remove bolts and nuts retaining upper ball joint to upper link. Remove bolts retaining upper link spindle to frame. Mark and remove adjusting shims. Remove upper link assembly.

Fig. 5: Reassembly of Upper Link & Bushings

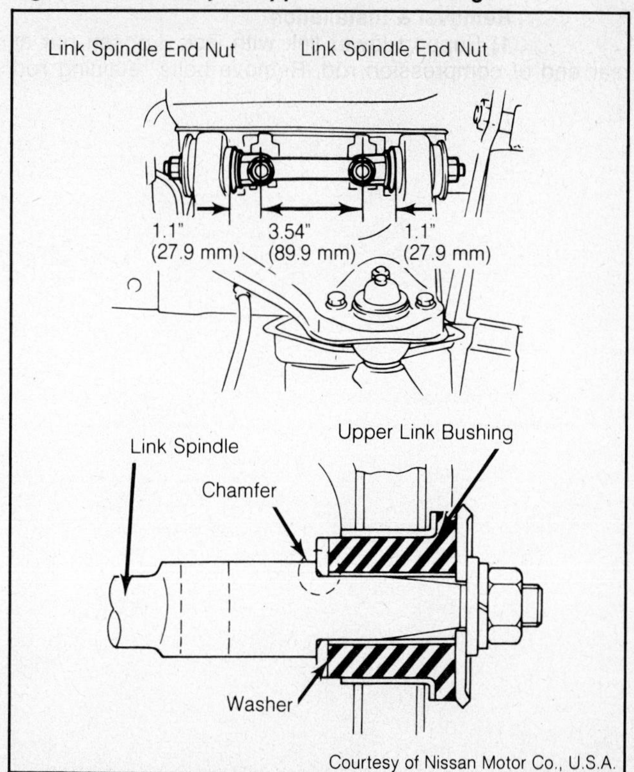

NISSAN VAN (Cont.)

Disassembly & Reassembly

1) Place upper link assembly in press. Press upper link spindle out with bushings. Apply soap solution to rubber bushing and press in one bushing until bushing flange securely contacts link collar.

2) Insert upper link spindle with inner washers. Inner washer rounded edge faces inward. *See Fig. 5.* Press in remaining bushing until bushing flange securely contacts link collar. Install and temporarily tighten spindle end nuts.

Installation

1) Position upper link to frame and install bolts without tightening. Install removed shims to original location. With shims installed, tighten spindle-to-frame bolts to specifications.

2) After fitting upper link to frame and tightening to specifications, measure distance from center mounting bolt to inner link edge. *See Fig. 5.* If not within specifications, adjust as necessary.

3) Install upper ball joint to upper link and tighten bolts and nuts to specifications. Install remaining components. Place vehicle on ground and unladen. Loosen upper link spindle end nuts and retighten to specifications. Check alignment and adjust as necessary.

STABILIZER BAR

Removal & Installation

Remove bolts retaining stabilizer bar bracket to lower links. Mark position of bushings to ensure installation of proper direction. Remove bracket bolt retaining stabilizer bar to connecting rod. Note location of bushing split to ensure installation to proper position. To install, reverse removal procedure. Tighten bolts and nuts with tires on ground and vehicle unladen.

COMPRESSION ROD

Removal & Installation

1) Support lower link with jack. Loosen nut at rear end of compression rod. Remove bolts retaining rod to lower link. Remove nut at rear end of rod. DO NOT mix washers and bushings and remove compression rod.

2) To install, reverse removal procedure. Ensure bushings and washers are installed to original position. Tighten bolts and nuts to specifications with tires on ground and vehicle unladen. Check alignment and adjust as necessary.

TIGHTENING SPECIFICATIONS

Application	Ft. Lbs. (N.m)
Brake Caliper Bolt	80-108 (109-146)
Compression Rod-to-	
Lower Link Bolt	22-30 (30-41)
Body Bolt	22-30 (30-41)
Leaf Spring-to-	
Spring Support Rubber Nut	22-27 (30-37)
Lower Ball Joint-to-	
Knuckle Nut	124-141 (168-191)
Lower Link-to-	
Suspension Member Bolt	80-101 (109-137)
Stabilizer Bar-to-	
Lower Link Bolt	23-31 (31-42)
Connecting Rod Bolt	50-58 (68-79)
Stabilizer Bar Connecting	
Rod-to-Body Bolt	23-31 (31-42)
Shock Absorber-to-	
Upper Frame Bolt	43-58 (58-79)
Lower Link Nut	22-30 (30-41)
Tie Rod-to-Knuckle Nut	40-72 (54-98)
Upper Ball Joint-to-	
Knuckle Nut	40-72 (54-98)
Upper Link Bolt	16-22 (22-30)
Upper Link-to-	
Frame Bolt	37-50 (50-68)
Upper Link End Nut	43-58 (58-79)
Wheel Bearing Lock Nut	195-260 (264-353)
Wheel Nut	72-87 (98-118)

Front Suspension

NISSAN 200SX & 300ZX

NOTE: An electronically controlled variable shock absorber system is used on 300ZX. For removal, installation, testing and diagnosis procedures for these shock absorbers, see the NISSAN ELECTRONIC SUSPENSION article in this section.

DESCRIPTION

A MacPherson strut-type suspension is used, consisting of a vertically-mounted strut, transverse link, stabilizer bar and tension rod.

ADJUSTMENTS & INSPECTION

WHEEL ALIGNMENT SPECIFICATIONS & PROCEDURES

See WHEEL ALIGNMENT SPECIFICATIONS & PROCEDURES in WHEEL ALIGNMENT section.

WHEEL BEARING

1) Tighten spindle nut to specification. Spin wheel and retighten spindle nut. Loosen nut according to specification and tighten to align cotter pin hole. Check wheel bearing for wear.

2) Install a spring scale at a upper hub bolt to measure starting torque. Starting torque should be 1.5-3.3 lb. (6.9-14.7 N) with new bearings and .4-1.8 lb. (2.0-7.8 N) with used bearings.

WHEEL BEARING ADJUSTMENT [1]

Application	Torque Ft. Lbs. (N.m)	Loosen
All Models	18-22 (25-29)	60°

[1] - Figures given are for new wheel bearings.

BALL JOINT CHECKING

1) Separate transverse link from ball joint. Attach torque gauge to top of ball joint stud nut. Measure ball joint stud turning torque. See BALL JOINT TURNING TORQUE SPECIFICATIONS table.

BALL JOINT TURNING TORQUE SPECIFICATIONS

Application	INCH Lbs. (N.m)
200SX	
New	17-65 (2.0-7.4)
Used	13 or Less (1.5)
300ZX	
New	13-43 (1.5-4.9)
Used	8.7 or Less (1.0)

2) Using a spring gauge, measure ball joint side-to-side torque. Side-to-side torque for a new ball joint should be 13-43 INCH lbs. (1.5-4.9 N). Correct side-to-side torque for a used ball joint is 8.7 INCH lbs. (1.0 N).

3) Measure axial play (up and down) movement of ball joint stud. Maximum axial play is .004-.035" (.10-.90 mm) for 300ZX and .004-.051 (.10-1.3 mm) for 200SX.

Fig. 1: Exploded View of 200SX Front Suspension

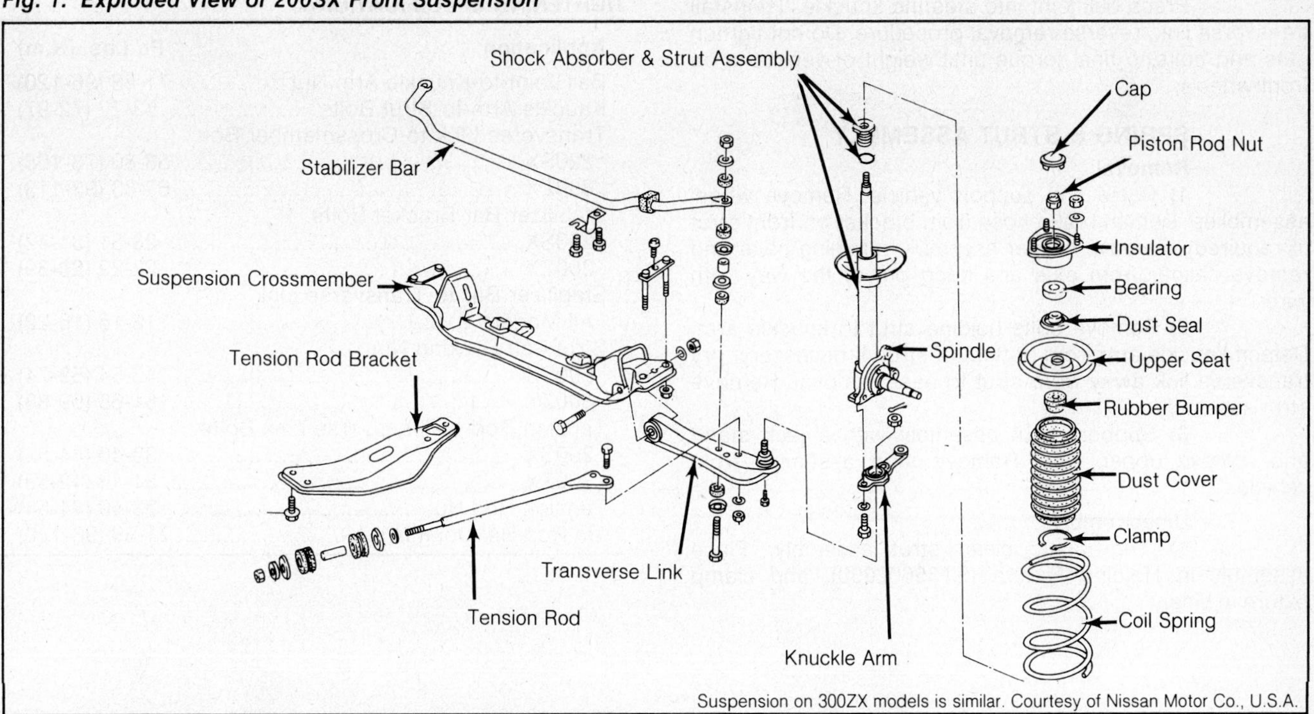

Suspension on 300ZX models is similar. Courtesy of Nissan Motor Co., U.S.A.

Front Suspension

NISSAN 200SX & 300ZX (Cont.)

REMOVAL & INSTALLATION

WHEEL BEARING

Removal

1) Raise and support vehicle. Remove wheel assembly. Remove caliper and support out of the way. Remove dust cap, cotter pin, adjusting cap and wheel bearing nut.

2) Remove wheel hub with rotor. Remove retaining bolts and separate wheel hub from rotor. Pry out wheel bearing, washers and grease seals. With a drift and hammer, drive out bearing races.

Installation

To install, reverse removal procedure. Ensure bearing races are fully seated. Pack hub, cap and bearings thoroughly with grease. Lubricate contact surface of grease seals, threaded part of spindle and bearing washer-to-bearing contact face before final assembly. Adjust wheel bearings.

TRANSVERSE LINK & BALL JOINT

Removal

1) Raise and support vehicle. Remove wheel assembly. Using Tie Rod Remover/Installer (HT72520000), detach tie rod at ball socket. Remove steering knuckle arm bolts and separate arm from bottom of strut.

2) Separate tension rod and stabilizer bar from transverse link. Remove bolt connecting transverse link to crossmember. Remove transverse link with ball joint and knuckle arm. Place steering knuckle arm in vise and press out ball joint.

Installation

Press ball joint into steering knuckle. To install transverse link, reverse removal procedure. Do not tighten nuts and bolts to final torque until weight of vehicle is on front wheels.

SPRING & STRUT ASSEMBLY

Removal

1) Raise and support vehicle. Remove wheel assemblies. Detach brake hose from bracket on front strut (if required). Remove caliper assembly retaining bolts and remove caliper from axle and hang out of the way with wire.

2) Remove bolts holding strut to knuckle arm. Detach knuckle arm from bottom of strut. If necessary, pry transverse link away from strut to ease removal. Remove strut assembly.

3) Support strut assembly with a jack stand and remove upper nuts. Remove strut assembly from vehicle.

Disassembly

1) Thoroughly clean strut assembly. Place assembly in Holding Fixture (ST35652000), and clamp fixture in vise.

2) Using a spring compressor, press spring down just far enough to permit turning of strut mounting insulator. Remove self-locking nut. Remove strut insulator, bearing, dust seal, upper spring seat, spring and rubber bumper.

Reassembly & Installation

1) Pull piston rod fully out and install rubber bumper. Place spring on lower spring seat and compress with spring compressor. Lubricate dust seal and install dust cover, spring seat, dust seal, mounting bearing and insulator.

2) Install new self-locking nut hand tight only. Tighten to specification after unit is installed in vehicle. To prevent entry of dirt, apply a thick coat of multipurpose grease around upper seal.

3) After positioning spring between upper and lower seats, release spring compressor slowly. Raise rubber bumper to upper spring seat. To install, reverse removal procedure.

STABILIZER & TENSION BARS

Removal & Installation

1) Raise vehicle and support with safety stands. Remove wheel assembly and splash guard. Back off nuts securing tension rod to mounting bracket.

2) Remove bolts attaching tension rod to transverse link. Remove nuts securing stabilizer bar to transverse link. Remove stabilizer bracket bolts and brackets. Remove stabilizer bar. To install, reverse removal procedure. Final tighten when vehicle is on the ground.

TIGHTENING SPECIFICATIONS

Application	Ft. Lbs. (N.m)
Ball Joint-to-Knuckle Arm Nut	71-88 (96-120)
Knuckle Arm-to-Strut Bolts	53-72 (72-97)
Transverse Link-to-Crossmember Bolt	
200SX	58-80 (78-108)
300ZX	69-83 (93-113)
Stabilizer Bar Bracket Bolts	
200SX	23-31 (31-42)
300ZX	22-29 (29-39)
Stabilizer Bar-to-Transverse Link	
All Models	12-16 (16-22)
Strut Self-Locking Nut	
200SX	43-54 (59-74)
300ZX	51-65 (69-88)
Tension Rod-to-Transverse Link Bolts	
200SX	33-40 (44-54)
300ZX	31-43 (42-59)
Tension Rod Nut	33-40 (44-54)
Tie Rod Ball Joint Nut	71-88 (96-120)

Front Suspension

PEUGEOT

DESCRIPTION

An independent front suspension is used, with coil spring over shock strut assemblies. The strut attaches to the inner fender at top, and to a wheel bearing housing at bottom. A lower ball joint connects the wheel bearing housing-to-lower control arm. The lower control arm pivots on the front crossmember. Attached to the lower control arms are strut rods that run forward to mounting points on front crossmember. *See Fig. 1*.

ADJUSTMENTS & INSPECTION

WHEEL ALIGNMENT SPECIFICATIONS & ADJUSTMENTS

See WHEEL ALIGNMENT SPECIFICATIONS & PROCEDURES in WHEEL ALIGNMENT section.

WHEEL BEARING

Front wheel bearings are not adjustable. Bearing is pressed into wheel bearing housing and retained by a circlip. Bearing must be replaced if removed.

Fig. 1: Front Suspension Assembly

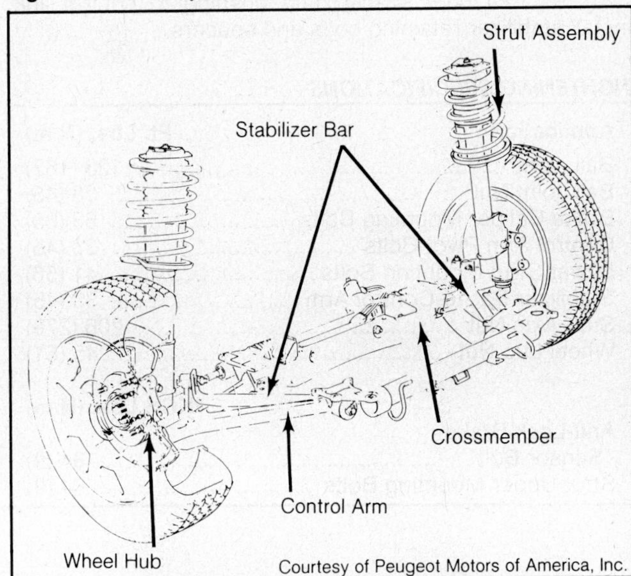

REMOVAL & INSTALLATION

WHEEL BEARING

Removal

1) Raise and support vehicle. Remove wheel assembly. Remove disc brake caliper mounting bolts and support out of way. Pry off dust cap and remove stub axle nut and washer.

NOTE: Handle wheel hub and rotor assembly carefully. Any damage to the serrated ring on the inside of the wheel hub may cause failure of the anti-lock brake system.

2) Pull wheel hub and rotor assembly off stub axle using Hub Puller (0521ZY). Using standard commercial puller, remove bearing inner race from stub axle.

3) Using hammer and drift, tap out inner seal. Remove snap ring and press out bearing using Bearing Remover (0521). Remove bearing adjusting shim.

Installation

1) Bearing installation must be precise to maintain accuracy of anti-lock brake system. Bearing adjusting shims of .004" (.10 mm), .006" (.15 mm), .008" (.20 mm) and .010" (.25 mm) are available.

2) Measure (A) depth of hub. Install snap ring and while holding snap ring tight against groove, measure (B) distance from top of snap ring-to-hub lip. Measure (C) width of snap ring. Measure (D) width of new bearing outer race. *See Fig. 2*.

Fig. 2: Measurements Required for Shim Selection

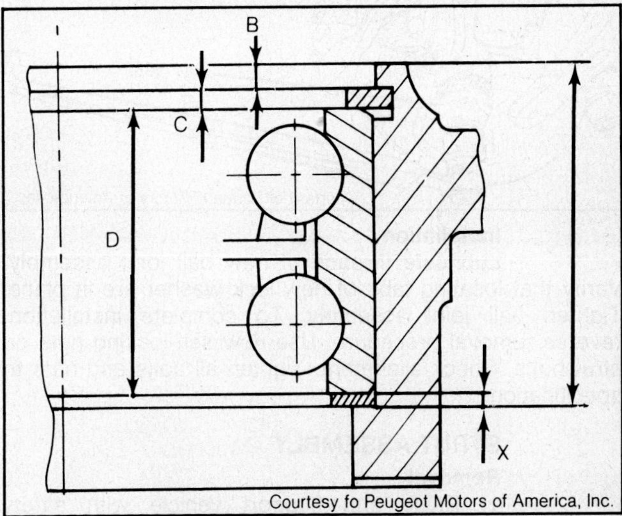

3) Add measurements B, C and D. Subtract that sum from measurement A. The difference is the thickness of bearing shim required. Use a shim with thickness just under dimension found.

4) Install the bearing shim. Pressing on outer race, install new bearing into housing. Install snap ring. Tap in new seal using Seal Installer (0521-E1) taking care not to damage hub serrations. Pack bearing with grease and install inner race.

5) Install hub and rotor assembly on stub axle. Install a new nut backwards on the stub axle and thread in all the way. Remove nut. Install washer and nut, the right way, and tighten to 206 ft. lbs. (279 N.m). Stake the nut and install dust cap.

6) To complete installation, reverse removal procedure. Tighten all bolts and nuts to specification. See TIGHTENING SPECIFICATIONS table in this article. Check anti-lock brake speed sensor gap. See PEUGEOT ANTI-LOCK BRAKE SYSTEM article in BRAKE section.

LOWER BALL JOINT

Removal

1) Ball joint must be replaced if removed. To replace ball joint, raise and support vehicle. Remove wheel assembly. Remove ball joint nut. Remove 2 lower strut mount bolts.

2) Swing wheel hub assembly out so it is 90 degrees to lower control arm. Press out ball joint from control arm using Ball Joint Press (0709).

3) Temporarily install lower bolt in wheel hub-to-strut and install leverage bar in upper bolt hole. *See Fig.*

Front Suspension

PEUGEOT (Cont.)

3. Raise and break off lock washer tabs. Using Ball Joint Socket (0616-F), remove ball joint.

Fig. 3: Removing Ball Joint

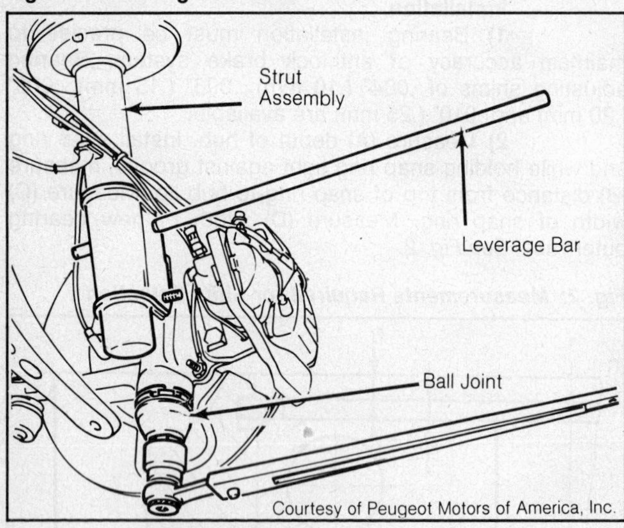

Courtesy of Peugeot Motors of America, Inc.

Installation

Lubricate threads of new ball joint assembly. Verify that locating tabs of new lock washer are in place. Tighten ball joint assembly. To complete installation, reverse removal procedure. Use new self-locking nuts on strut bolts. Check alignment. Tighten all bolts and nuts to specification.

STRUT ASSEMBLY

Removal

1) Raise and support vehicle with safety stands. Remove wheel assembly. Remove the anti-lock brake sensor wire tie. Remove 2 strut lower mounting bolts.

2) Support strut assembly by hand to prevent from falling. Remove 3 upper strut mount bolts and remove strut.

CAUTION: Coil springs are under high tension. Work carefully while compressing and disassembling strut.

Disassembly & Reassembly

1) Mount strut assembly in spring compressor. Compress coil spring. Remove strut piston rod nut and pull strut from coil spring. Remove rubber bumper from piston rod.

2) Inspect all components for wear or damage. Install rubber bumper on strut piston rod and install in coil spring. Install upper mounting hardware and tighten piston rod nut. Release tension on spring compressor.

Installation

Install strut assembly and start 3 upper bolts. Install 2 lower mounting bolts and new self-locking nuts. Tighten 3 upper bolts to 84 INCH lbs. (9 N.m). To complete installation, reverse removal procedure. Check wheel alignment. Tighten all bolts and nuts to specification.

STABILIZER BAR

Removal

With vehicle at normal riding height, remove 2 bolts retaining stabilizer bar near front crossmember. Disconnect both links mounting stabilizer bar at connecting links. Remove stabilizer bar from vehicle.

Installation

Fit cup, spacer, and bushing to control link. Install stabilizer retaining bolts and spacers.

TIGHTENING SPECIFICATIONS

Application	Ft. Lbs. (N.m)
Ball Joint	123 (167)
Ball Joint Nut	33 (45)
Brake Caliper Mounting Bolts	63 (85)
Control Arm Pivot Bolts	33 (45)
Lower Strut Mounting Bolts	41 (56)
Stabilizer Bar-to-Control Arm	33 (45)
Stub Axle Nut	206 (279)
Wheel Lug Nut	45 (61)
	INCH Lbs. (N.m)
Anti-Lock Brake Sensor Bolt	84 (9)
Strut Upper Mounting Bolts	84 (9)

PORSCHE - EXCEPT 911 SERIES

924S, 944, 944-S, 944 Turbo

DESCRIPTION

Porsche uses independent MacPherson type struts. Strut assembly top mounts are attached to the body. Lower strut assembly is attached to steering knuckle.

An alloy crossmember is used to hold the engine, steering and front control arm mounts. The back branch of the control arm mounts to frame with a "U" clamp around control arm pivot shaft. Front branch is attached to frame with bushings and pivot bolt.

ADJUSTMENTS & INSPECTION

WHEEL ALIGNMENT SPECIFICATIONS & PROCEDURES

See WHEEL ALIGNMENT SPECIFICATIONS & PROCEDURES in WHEEL ALIGNMENT section.

WHEEL BEARING

1) To seat bearings, tighten hub nut while rotating wheel. Back off nut until thrust washer can be moved sideways with light pressure from a screwdriver.

2) Hub nut should be tight enough to prevent wheel hub axial play. Tighten the pinch bolt, ensuring the hub nut does not change position.

BALL JOINT CHECKING

Using a vernier caliper, measure distance between upper edge of control arm and lower edge of steering knuckle. Place a lever under ball joint and pry upward. Measure any movement. A new ball joints should have no end play. Wear limit for a used ball joints is .10" (2.5 mm).

REMOVAL & INSTALLATION

WHEEL BEARING

Removal

1) Raise and support vehicle. Remove wheel assembly. Remove grease cap and loosen pinch bolt. Remove hub nut, washer and outer wheel bearing.

2) Remove brake caliper and secure out of way. Remove hub and rotor assembly. Pry off inner grease seal and remove inner bearing. If bearings are being replaced, drive out bearing races.

Installation

To install, reverse removal procedure. If bearing or race is bad, replace in matched sets. DO NOT use new bearings with old bearing races. Adjust wheel bearings to complete installation.

CONTROL ARM & BALL JOINT

Removal

1) Raise and support vehicle. Remove wheel assembly. Remove brake caliper and secure out of way.

Fig. 1: Exploded View of Front Suspension

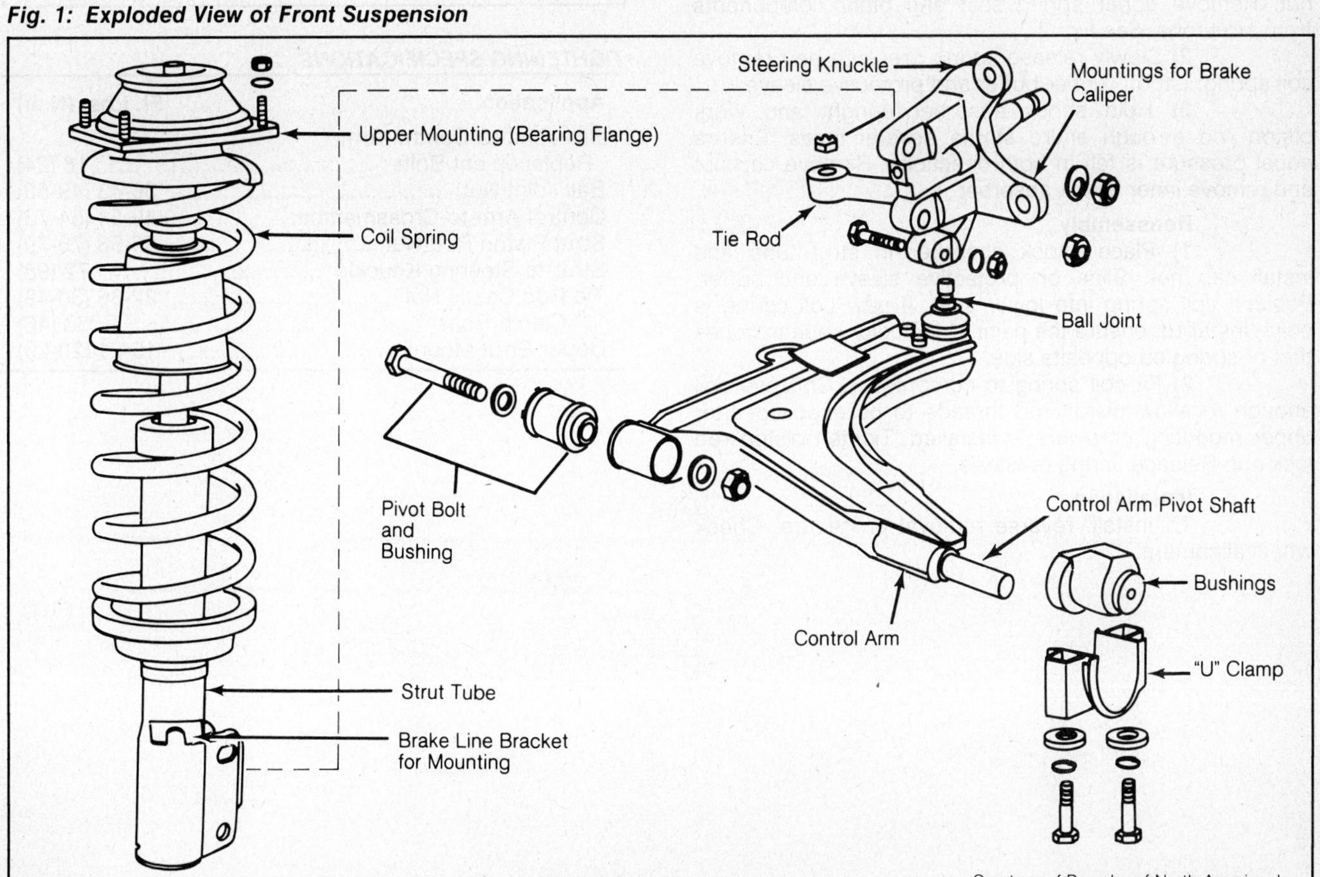

PORSCHE - EXCEPT 911 SERIES (Cont.)

Remove bolt retaining ball joint in bottom of steering knuckle. Pull ball joint out of steering knuckle.

2) If control arm is not being removed, drill through ball joint rivets with 15/64" drill bit. Chisel off rivet heads. Fit new ball joint into slot on control arm and install bolts so heads are on top of control arm.

3) If control arm is being removed, take out mounting pivot bolt and "U" clamp housing inner pivot pin. Slide out control arm. If necessary, remove ball joint.

Inspection

Check control arm bushings for excessive wear or damage. If bushings are to be replaced, press out worn bushings. Select new bushings and press into position. Ensure new bushings do not twist when seating into position.

Installation

To install, reverse removal procedure.

STRUT ASSEMBLY

Removal

1) Raise and support vehicle. Remove wheel assembly. Remove caliper and support out of way. Remove suspension strut-to-steering knuckle mounting bolts.

2) Pry strut off of steering knuckle. Support front suspension. Working inside engine compartment, remove upper strut retaining nuts. Remove strut assembly from vehicle.

Disassembly

1) Using spring compressor, slightly collapse coil spring on strut. Remove shock absorber piston rod nut. Remove upper spring seat and other components from strut tube. *See Fig. 2.*

2) Slowly release spring pressure and remove coil spring. Lift off rubber buffer and protective sleeve.

3) Hold shock absorber upright and work piston rod through entire stroke several times. Ensure equal pressure is felt in both directions. Remove cap nut and remove inner shock absorber.

Reassembly

1) Place shock absorber in strut tube and install cap nut. Slide on protective sleeve and buffer. Position coil spring into lower seat. If new coil spring is being installed, ensure the paint stripe color code matches that of spring on opposite side.

2) Fit coil spring to compressor. Collapse coil enough to allow piston rod threads to be exposed after upper mounting hardware is installed. Tighten piston rod lock nut. Release spring pressure.

Installation

To install, reverse removal procedure. Check wheel alignment.

Fig. 2: Exploded View of Suspension Strut Assembly

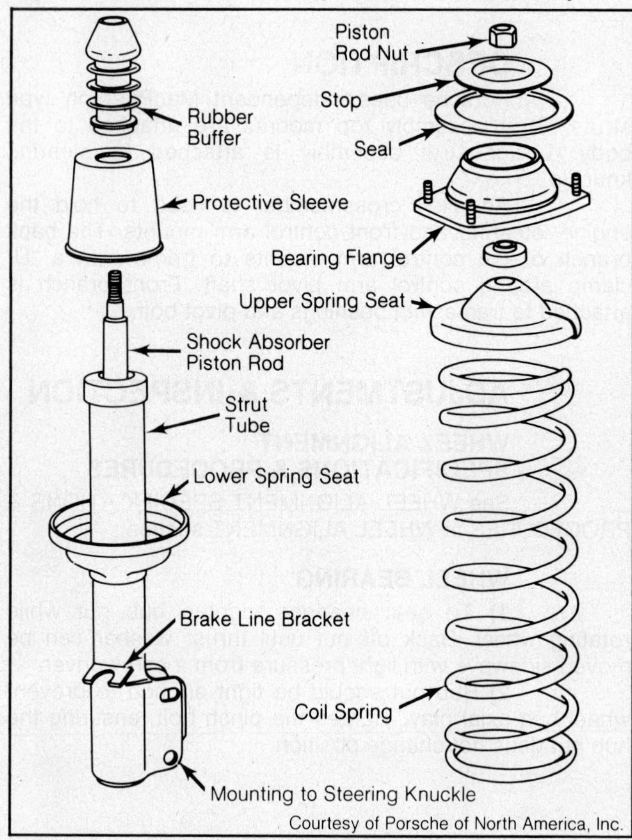

Courtesy of Porsche of North America, Inc.

TIGHTENING SPECIFICATIONS

Application	Ft. Lbs. (N.m)
Ball Joint-to-Control Arm Replacement Bolts	18 (24)
Ball Joint Nut	36-43 (49-58)
Control Arm-to-Crossmember	40-54 (54-73)
Strut Piston Rod Nut	56-58 (76-79)
Strut-to-Steering Knuckle	72 (98)
Tie Rod Castle Nut	22-36 (30-49)
"U" Clamp Bolts	33 (46)
Upper Strut Mount	15-21 (20-29)

Front Suspension

PORSCHE 911 CARRERA & 911 TURBO

DESCRIPTION

An independent MacPherson strut-type suspension with torsion bars is used. Strut assemblies are mounted to inner fender panels at top by thrust bearings. Bottom of strut assemblies are mounted to control arms by ball joints.

Steering knuckle and shock absorbers are integral with individual strut assembly. Control arms pivot in mounts connected to body at front and in mounts integral with suspension crossmember at rear. *See Fig. 1.*

ADJUSTMENTS & INSPECTION

WHEEL ALIGNMENT SPECIFICATIONS & PROCEDURES

See WHEEL ALIGNMENT SPECIFICATIONS & PROCEDURES in WHEEL ALIGNMENT section.

WHEEL BEARING

1) Tighten hub nut while rotating wheel to seat bearings. Back off nut until thrust washer can be moved sideways with light pressure from a screwdriver.

2) Spindle nut should be tight enough to prevent any wheel hub axial play. Tighten pinch bolt, making sure that hex nut does not change position.

BALL JOINT CHECKING

Check lower ball joints for any signs of unusual wear, damage or excessive play. Wear limits not available from manufacturer.

REMOVAL & INSTALLATION

WHEEL BEARING

Removal

1) Raise vehicle and support with safety stands. Remove wheel assembly. Disconnect brake line from caliper. Remove caliper. Remove grease cap, loosen hub nut pinch bolt.

2) Remove hub nut and remove wheel bearing thrust washer. Remove hub and rotor assembly from vehicle.

3) Press out outer wheel bearing. Depending on equipment used, it may be necessary to separate rotor from hub. Heat wheel hub to 250-300° F (120-150° C) and press out inner bearing and grease seal. Press out bearing races.

NOTE: Always replace bearings and races as matched sets.

Installation

To install, reverse removal procedure.

CONTROL ARM & BALL JOINT

Removal

1) Raise vehicle and support with safety stands, under body. Remove wheel assembly. Remove suspension protective cover. Remove adjusting screw from torsion bar lever and remove lever.

2) Disconnect strut assembly from control arm. Remove rear control arm retaining bolt at suspension crossmember.

3) Remove bolts securing front control arm mount to body. Slide control arm with torsion bar out of suspension crossmember.

NOTE: If both control arms are being removed, reinstall rear control arm mounting bolt in suspension crossmember before removing opposite side.

4) Secure control arm in a vise and remove ball joint retaining nut. Remove ball joint from control arm. Control arm should pivot smoothly in mounts. If control arm binds or is distorted, it must be replaced.

5) Inspect torsion bars for damaged serrations. Check sealing bellows on ball joint for damaged or cracks, (replace if necessary). Remove sealing bellows with a flat chisel and install using mandrel to press bellows on.

Fig. 1: Exploded View of Front Suspension Assembly

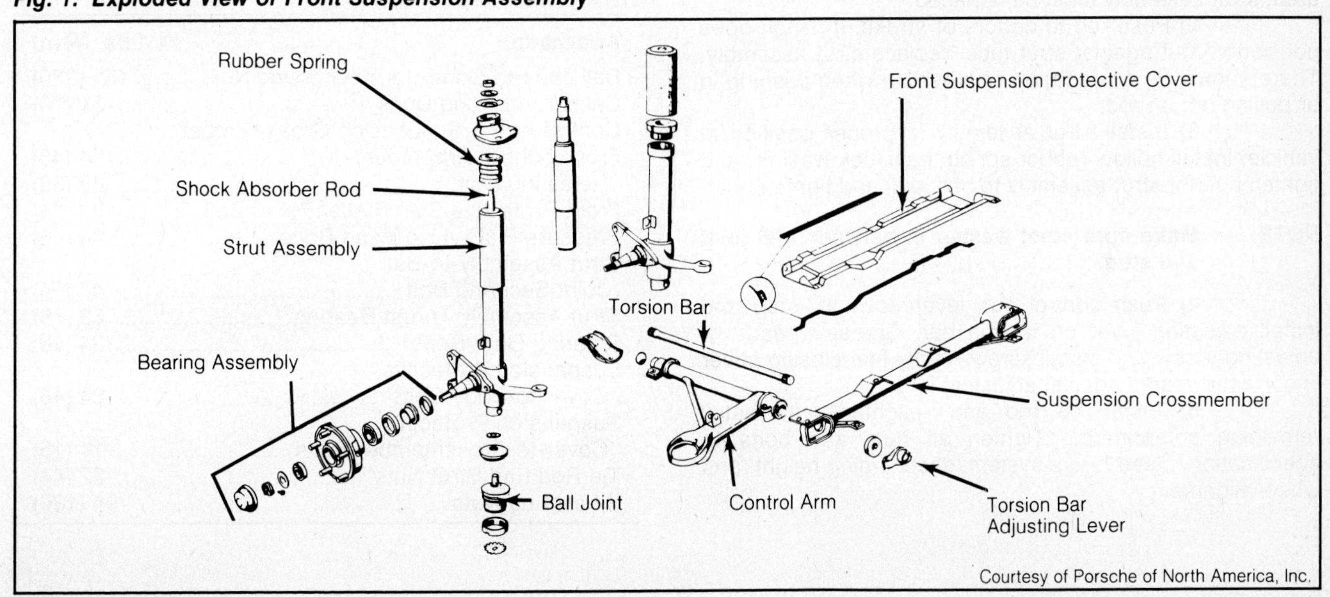

PORSCHE 911 CARRERA & 911 TURBO (Cont.)

Installation

1) Install ball joint in control arm and tighten nut. Secure nut by bending over tab on lock washer. Grease entire torsion bar and install in control arm.

2) Place control arm in proper position in vehicle and tighten retaining bolts (front to rear). Install strut assembly on ball joint and tighten retaining bolt. Push down on control arm until it contacts stops. Install torsion bar seal and adjusting lever.

3) Slide adjusting lever against torsion bar until it reaches stop. Grease adjusting bolt threads and install in lever. Verify that closing cover is correctly seated against adjusting lever.

4) Install control arm protective cover. Install wheel assembly. Lower vehicle and check riding height and wheel alignment. Tighten all bolts to specification. See TIGHTENING SPECIFICATIONS table in this article.

STRUT ASSEMBLY

Removal

1) Raise vehicle and support with safety stands. Remove wheel assembly. Remove brake caliper and rotor. Remove tie rod end strut nut and separate tie rod end from steering arm.

2) Unscrew adjusting screw from torsion bar adjusting lever and remove lever. Remove ball joint retaining bolt at bottom of strut assembly and push control arm down to separate strut assembly from ball joint.

3) From inside luggage compartment, remove center nut from upper strut assembly mount. Remove lock washer, tab washer and strut assembly.

4) Mark position of pressure plates on fender panel and remove Allen head bolts and pressure plates. Remove thrust bearing and support.

NOTE: **Thrust bearing can be removed without completely removing strut assembly by disconnecting upper mount and pulling down on control arm to separate from thrust bearing.**

Installation

1) Install thrust bearing and support. Place pressure plates in proper position and tighten Allen head bolts. Inspect strut assembly for leaks, if leak is discovered, strut assembly must be replaced.

2) Push rod to bottom of stroke. If flange does not bottom out against strut tube, replace strut assembly. There should be no variation of pressure when pushing in or pulling out on rod.

3) Install strut assembly in proper position in vehicle. Install hollow rubber spring, new lock washer, and tighten nut. Fit strut assembly to ball joint and tighten nut.

NOTE: **Make sure steel washer is between ball joint and stud.**

4) Push control arm lever down to stop and install adjusting lever on torsion bar. Grease threads of adjusting screw and install screw. Verify that closing cover is correctly seated against adjusting lever.

5) Install tie rod and retighten nut. Install remaining components. Tighten all nuts and bolts to specification, bleed brake system, check riding height, and wheel alignment.

SUSPENSION CROSSMEMBER

Removal

1) Raise vehicle and support with safety stands, under vehicle body. Remove front axle protective cover. Remove steering gear bolts from crossmember.

2) Remove rear control arm retaining bolts. Remove suspension crossmember. Place crossmember on level surface and check for distortion. Inspect crossmember for cracks or damage.

Installation

Place crossmember in vehicle and install control arm retaining bolts. Install steering gear bolts and tighten. Install front suspension protective cover. Lower vehicle. Check riding height and wheel alignment. Tighten all bolts to specification.

STABILIZER BAR

Removal

Remove stabilizer shackles. Unbolt stabilizer lever retaining nuts and extract lever. Remove stabilizer mounting cover hardware and pry cover from vehicle.

Installation

1) Check all rubber grommets for signs of wear, (replace if necessary). Coat rubber parts with lubricant. Reinstall stabilizer mounting cover, center stabilizer, and tighten attaching bolts.

2) Seat stabilizer lever in position so stabilizer protrudes approximately .118" (3 mm) beyond lever. Tighten retaining nuts to specification and install shackles.

AXLE ASSEMBLY

Removal

1) Disconnect brake hose and plug openings. Disconnect stabilizer bar at crossmember. Remove tie rod shield. Remove bolts at carrier and control arm brackets.

2) Place floor jack under crossmember. Disconnect steering shaft. Remove upper strut mounting hardware. Carefully pull front axle assembly from vehicle.

Installation

To install, reverse removal procedure. Tighten all bolts to specification.

TIGHTENING SPECIFICATIONS

Application	Ft. Lbs. (N.m)
Ball Joint-to-Control Arm Grooved Nut	181 (250)
Caliper mounting Bolts	51 (70)
Control Arm & Suspension Crossmember	
Front Control Arm Mount	34 (46)
Retaining Bolt	65 (88)
Front Protective Clamp Allen Head Bolt	32 (44)
Pressure Plate Allen Head Bolts	34 (46)
Strut Assembly-to-Ball Joint Securing Bolt	47 (64)
Strut Assembly Thrust Bearing	58 (79)
Steering Gear Bolts	34 (46)
Suspension Protective Cover-to-Body Bolts	34 (46)
Suspension Protective Cover-to-Crossmember Bolts	11 (15)
Tie Rod End Strut Nuts	32 (44)
Wheel Lug Nuts	94 (130)

SAAB

900, 900S, 9000S & 9000 Turbo

DESCRIPTION

Saab 900 series vehicles use conventional control arm front suspension with double-acting shock absorbers. Lower control arm downward travel is limited by the shock absorber. The coil spring is mounted between the upper control arm and wheel housing. The lower spring seat is attached by a rubber bushing to the upper control arm.

Fig. 1: Saab 900 Series Front Suspension

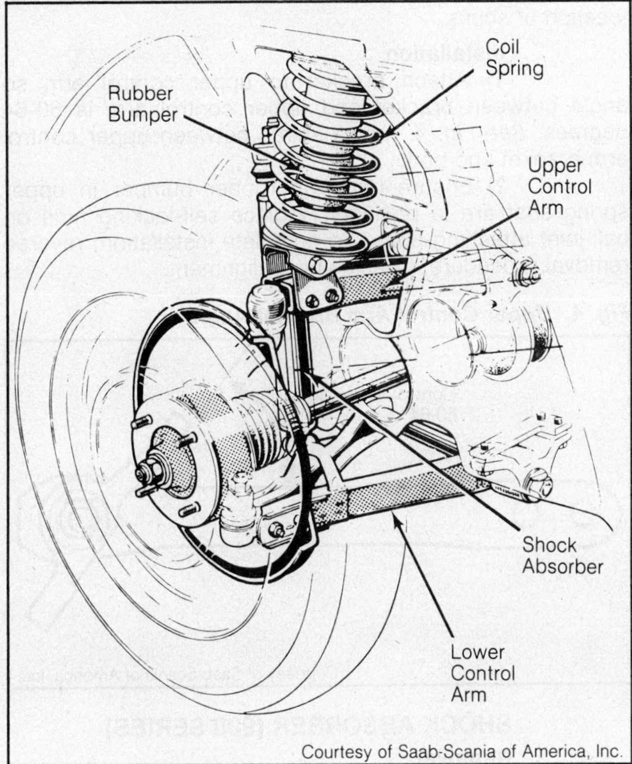

Courtesy of Saab-Scania of America, Inc.

Saab 9000 series vehicles use independent MacPherson strut type suspension with an anti-roll bar. Strut assemblies are mounted to inner fender panels at the top by 3 bolts. The bottom of the strut assemblies are mounted directly to steering knuckle with 2 bolts. The lower control arms are pressed steel and include ball joint, anti-roll bar, and frame mounting connections.

ADJUSTMENTS & INSPECTION

WHEEL ALIGNMENT SPECIFICATIONS & PROCEDURES

See WHEEL ALIGNMENT SPECIFICATIONS & PROCEDURES in WHEEL ALIGNMENT section.

WHEEL BEARING

Wheel bearings are incorporated in the wheel hub. Bearings are double row ball type which are permanently lubricated and maintenance free.

BALL JOINT CHECKING

1) On 900 series, insert Spacer (83 93 209) between upper control arm and body to release tension from upper ball joint. On all models, use a pair of channel lock pliers and compress ball joint. Check ball joint axial play. Maximum axial play is .08" (2.0 mm).

2) To check radial play, apply pressure between lower control arm and vertical link. Maximum radial play is .04" (1.0 mm). Check ball joint seals for wear or damage amd replace as necessary.

REMOVAL & INSTALLATION

WHEEL BEARING

Removal

1) On 900 series, insert Spacer (83 93 209) between upper control arm and body to release tension from upper ball joint. On all models, loosen hub nut. Raise and support vehicle. Remove wheel assembly. Align recess along rotor edge with brake pad assembly. Remove brake pads. Remove and support brake caliper. Remove disc brake rotor.

2) Using Ball Joint Remover (89 95 409), disconnect tie rod from steering knuckle assembly. Remove bolts which secure ball joint to upper and lower control arm. Remove steering knuckle assembly by pulling it off drive shaft and control arms.

3) Press hub out of steering knuckle assembly. Pull inner bearing race off hub. If no grooves are present for puller, chisel off race. Remove snap rings from steering knuckle assembly and press out bearing.

NOTE: **Pressing hub out of steering knuckle assembly damages the wheel bearing. Bearing must always be replaced.**

Fig. 2: Saab 9000 Series Front Suspension

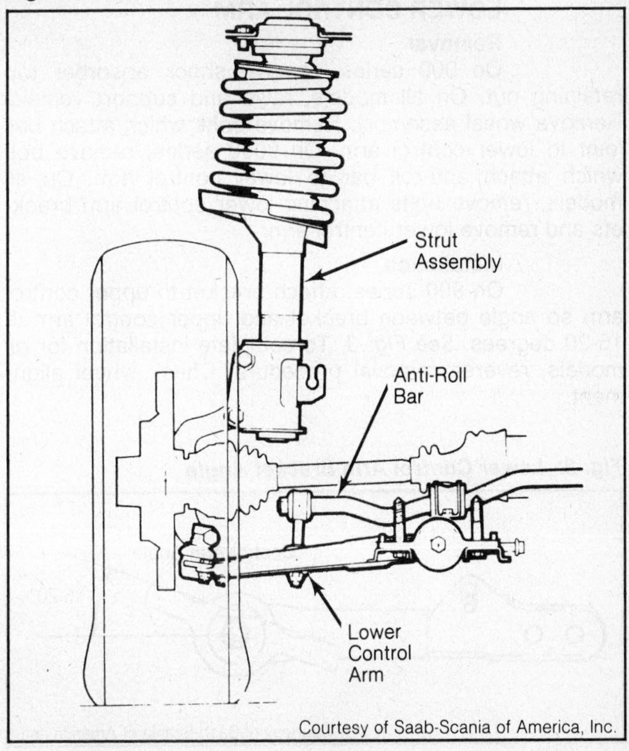

Courtesy of Saab-Scania of America, Inc.

Front Suspension

SAAB (Cont.)

Installation

1) Lubricate steering knuckle bearing recess with Molycote Paste G. Install snap ring in inner groove of steering knuckle assembly. Press bearing against snap ring.

2) Install outer snap ring and press hub into bearing. Lubricate drive shaft splines with Molycote Paste G, and insert steering knuckle assembly. To complete installation, reverse removal procedure.

BALL JOINT

Removal (900 Series)

1) Raise and support vehicle. Remove wheel assembly. Position a floor jack under lower control arm and raise arm slightly. Disconnect shock absorber from lower control arm. Lower floor jack until drive shaft is aligned with body grommet.

2) Remove ball joint nut. Using Ball Joint Remover (89 95 409), disconnect ball joint from steering knuckle. If upper ball joint is being removed, support steering knuckle to prevent damaging brake hose. Remove bolts attaching ball joint to control arm and remove ball joint.

Installation

Replace self-locking nuts on ball joint attaching bolts. To complete installation, reverse removal procedure.

Removal (9000 Series)

1) Raise and support vehicle. Remove wheel assembly. Remove bolts which secure ball joint to lower control arm.

2) Remove ball joint-to-steering knuckle bolt. Using Ball Joint Remover (89 95 409), remove ball joint from steering knuckle.

Installation

To install, reverse removal procedure.

LOWER CONTROL ARM

Removal

On 900 series, remove shock absorber top retaining nut. On all models, raise and support vehicle. Remove wheel assembly. Remove bolts which attach ball joint to lower control arm. On 9000 series, remove bolt which attach anti-roll bar to lower control arm. On all models, remove bolts attaching lower control arm brackets and remove lower control arm.

Installation

On 900 series, attach bracket to upper control arm so angle between bracket and upper control arm is 16-20 degrees. *See Fig. 3.* To complete installation for all models, reverse removal procedure. Check wheel alignment.

Fig. 3: Lower Control Arm Bracket Angle

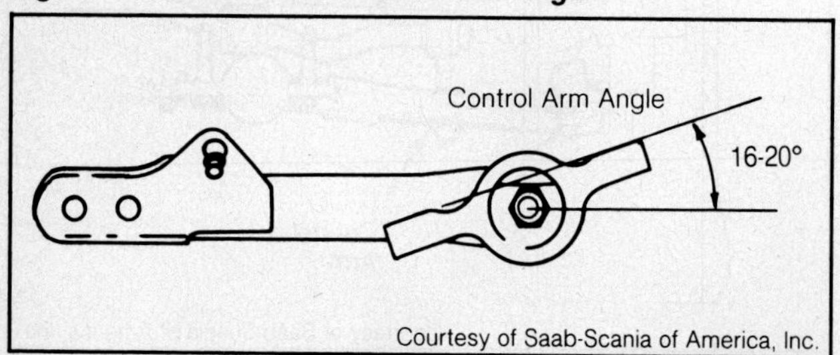

UPPER CONTROL ARM (900 SERIES)

NOTE: Engine must be removed prior to removing left upper control arm.

Removal

1) Remove shock absorber top retaining nut. Raise and support vehicle. Remove wheel assembly. Compress coil spring using Spring Compressor (89 95 839) and remove coil spring.

2) Remove bolts attaching ball joint to upper control arm. Support steering knuckle to prevent damaging brake hose. Remove bolts attaching upper control arm bracket and remove upper control arm. Note amount and location of shims.

Installation

1) Attach bracket to upper control arm so angle between bracket and upper control arm is 60-64 degrees. *See Fig. 4.* Install shims between upper control arm bracket and body.

2) Ensure ring and rubber bumper in upper spring seat are in position. Replace self-locking nuts on ball joint attaching bolts. To complete installation, reverse removal procedure. Check wheel alignment.

Fig. 4: Upper Control Arm Bracket Angle

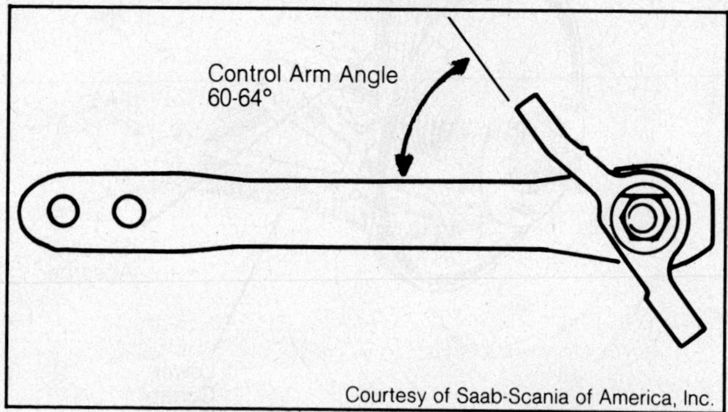

SHOCK ABSORBER (900 SERIES)

Removal

Remove shock absorber top retaining nut. Raise and support vehicle. Remove wheel assembly. Place a floor jack under lower control arm and raise arm slightly. Disconnect shock absorber from lower control arm and remove shock absorber.

NOTE: Before discarding a used gas shock absorber, drill a hole 3/8-5/8" (10-15 mm) from edge of pressure chamber. This will release pressure from shock.

Installation

Hold shock absorber in upright position and pump shock absorber for a few full strokes to bleed air from shock absorber. To complete installation, reverse removal procedure.

STRUT ASSEMBLY (9000 SERIES)

Removal

1) Raise and support vehicle. Remove wheel. Detach brake hose from clip on strut. Remove bolt attaching strut to steering swivel member.

Front Suspension

SAAB (Cont.)

2) Remove 3 bolts holding top of strut. Remove cap on center nut and lift out strut.

Installation

To install, reverse removal procedure.

TIGHTENING SPECIFICATIONS

Application	Ft. Lbs. (N.m)
Ball Joint Nut	32-41 (43-55)
Bracket-to-Lower Control Arm Nuts	70-77 (95-105)
Bracket-to-Upper Control Arm Nuts	54-66 (73-90)
Hub Nut	
900 Series	213-227 (290-310)
9000 Series	195-208 (264-281)
Lower Shock Absorber Mount	70 (95)
Steering Knuckle-to-Strut Bolts	56-75 (76-102)
Strut Nut (Top)	49-59 (66-80)
Strut Nuts (3)	22-29 (30-39)
Tie Rod End-to-Steering Knuckle	35-44 (47-60)

Front Suspension

STERLING 825

DESCRIPTION

The Sterling uses an independent double wishbone strut type suspension. The strut assembly is attached to the steering knuckle through the lower control arm. The steering knuckle is attached to upper and lower control arms by ball joints. A stabilizer bar and strut rod are attached to the lower control arm.

Fig. 1: Sterling Front Suspension

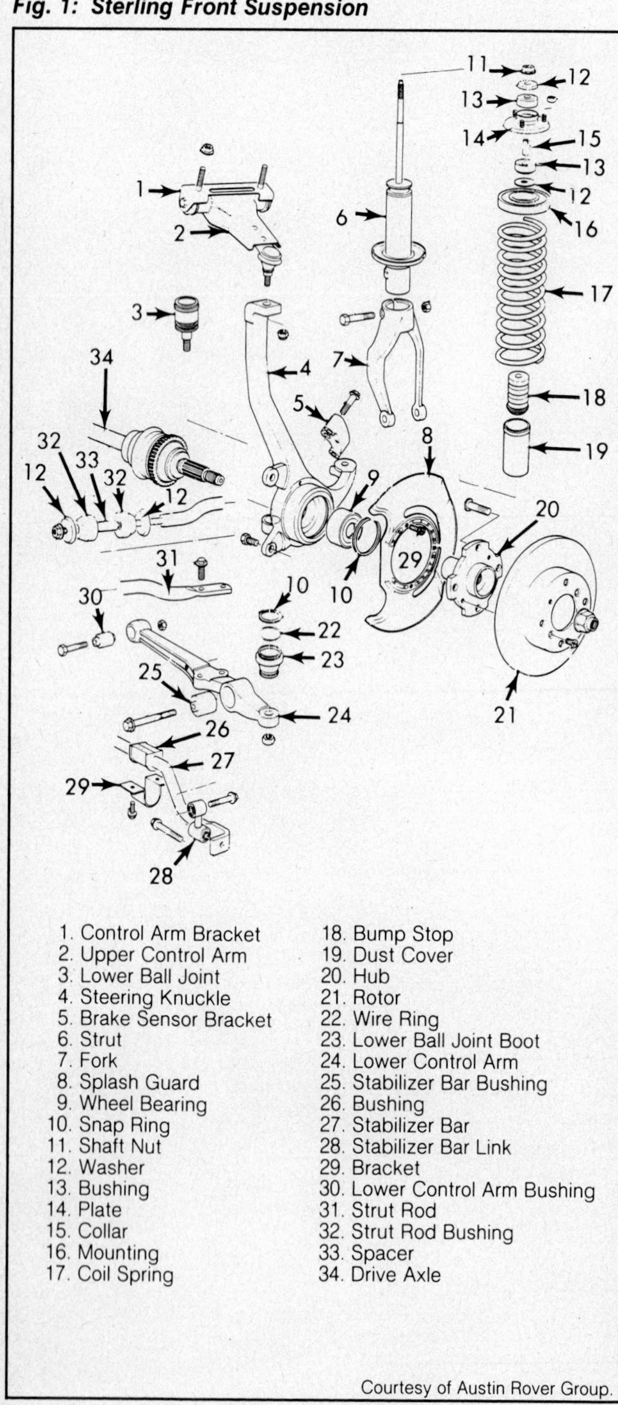

ADJUSTMENTS & INSPECTION

WHEEL ALIGNMENT SPECIFICATIONS & PROCEDURES

See WHEEL ALIGNMENT SPECIFICATIONS & PROCEDURES in WHEEL ALIGNMENT section.

WHEEL BEARING

Wheel bearings are nonadjustable.

BALL JOINT CHECKING

Information not available from manufacturer.

REMOVAL & INSTALLATION

CAUTION: Suspension may be under spring tension. Use caution when removing suspension components. All components containing bushings must have retaining bolts tightened to specification with vehicle at normal operating height.

WHEEL BEARING

Removal

1) Remove steering knuckle. See STEERING KNUCKLE in this article. Hub must be separated from steering knuckle.

2) Using press and Hub Remover (18G 1533), press hub from steering knuckle. *See Fig. 2.* Using Puller (18G 2) and Puller Ring (18G 2-1), remove bearing flange from hub. *See Fig. 3.*

Fig. 2: Removal & Installation of Hub

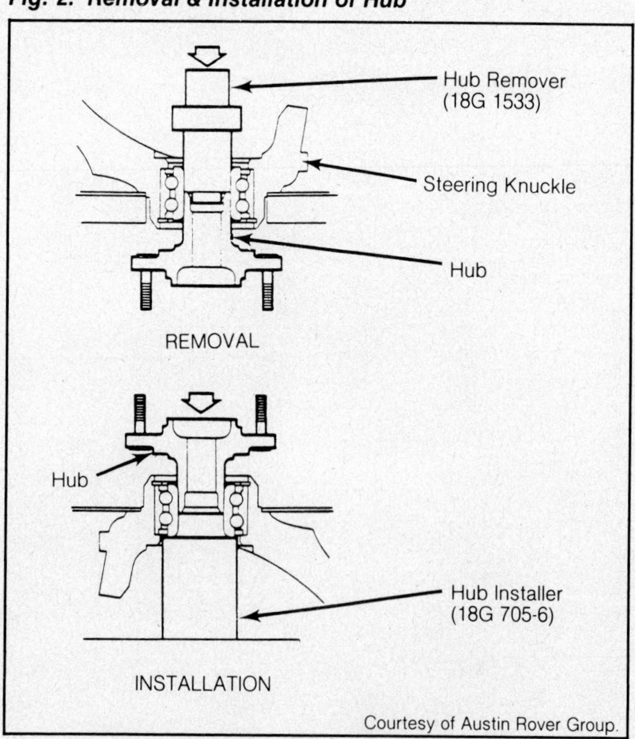

STERLING 825 (Cont.)

Fig. 3: Removing Hub Bearing Flange

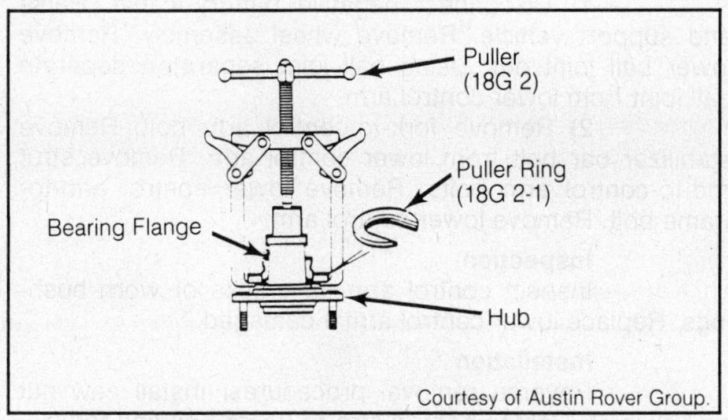

3) Remove splash guard. Remove bearing retaining snap ring from steering knuckle. Using press, Bearing Removers (18G 134) and (18G 134 BD), remove bearing from steering knuckle. *See Fig. 4.*

Fig. 4: Removal & Installation of Wheel Bearing

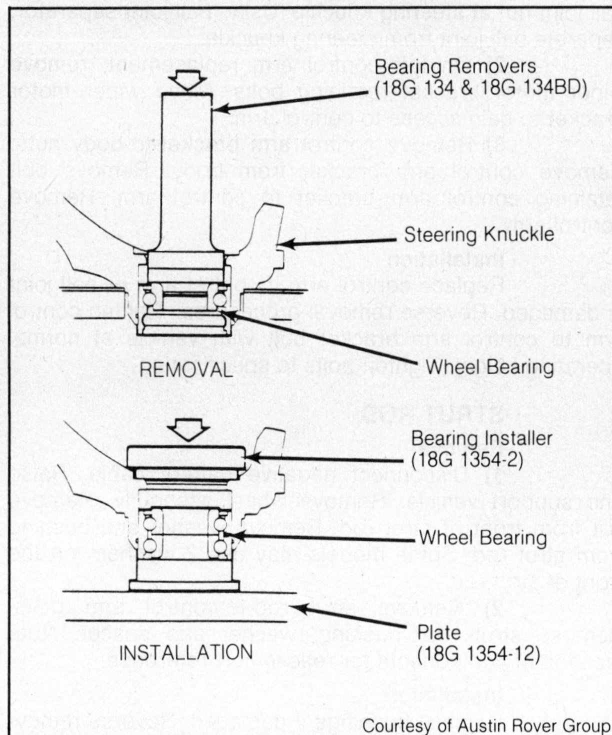

Installation

1) Lubricate wheel bearing with grease. Using press, Bearing Installer (18G 1354-2) and Plate (18G 1354-12), install wheel bearing in steering knuckle. *See Fig. 4.* Install bearing retaining snap ring.

2) Install splash guard. Install inner bearing flange on hub. Using press and Hub Installer (18G 705-6), install hub in bearing. *See Fig. 2.* Ensure hub is fully seated in wheel bearing.

BALL JOINT

Upper Ball Joint

Information not available from manufacturer.

Lower Ball Joint Removal

Remove steering knuckle. See STEERING KNUCKLE in this article. Remove snap ring from ball joint. Remove lower ball joint boot. Using vise and Ball Joint Remover/Installer (18G 1536), press ball joint from steering knuckle. *See Fig. 5.*

Fig. 5: Removal & Installation of Lower Ball Joint

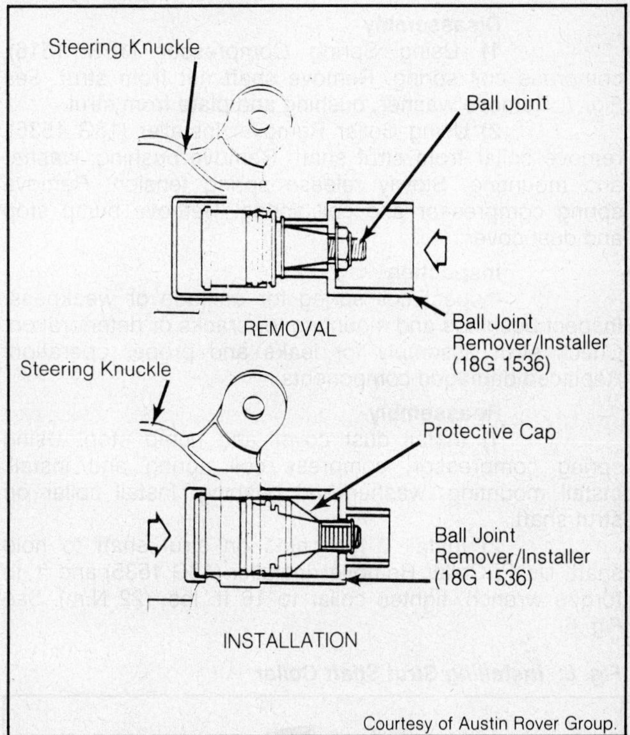

Installation

Using vise, protective cap and ball joint remover/installer, press ball joint into steering knuckle. *See Fig. 5.* Install lower ball joint boot and snap ring.

STEERING KNUCKLE

Removal

1) Disconnect negative battery cable. Raise and support vehicle. Remove wheel assembly. Remove drive axle nut. Remove brake caliper and secure away from steering knuckle.

2) Remove brake sensor bracket-to-steering knuckle bolts. Position brake sensor away from steering knuckle. Remove tie rod-to-steering knuckle nut. Disconnect tie rod from steering knuckle.

3) Support lower control arm with a jack. Remove upper and lower ball joint nuts. Using ball joint separator, separate upper and lower ball joints from steering knuckle and lower control arm. Remove steering knuckle and hub assembly from drive axle.

CAUTION: Always replace ball joint nut once removed.

Installation

Reverse removal procedures. Install new nuts on ball joints. Tighten bolts to specification. See TIGHTENING SPECIFICATIONS table at end of article. Install new drive axle nut and stake once tightened to specification.

Front Suspension

STERLING 825 (Cont.)

STRUT ASSEMBLY

Removal

1) Disconnect negative battery cable. Raise and support vehicle. Remove wheel assembly. Support lower control arm with a jack. Remove fork-to-lower control arm bolt. *See Fig. 1.* Remove fork-to-strut bolt.

2) Remove fork from strut assembly. Remove strut-to-body retaining bolts. Remove strut assembly.

Disassembly

1) Using Spring Compressor (18G 1516), compress coil spring. Remove shaft nut from strut. *See Fig. 1.* Remove washer, bushing and plate from strut.

2) Using Collar Remover/Installer (18G 1535), remove collar from strut shaft. Remove bushing, washer and mounting. Slowly release spring tension. Remove spring compressor and coil spring. Remove bump stop and dust cover.

Inspection

Inspect coil spring for damage or weakness. Inspect bushings and mounting for cracks or deterioration. Check strut assembly for leaks and proper operation. Replaced damaged components.

Reassembly

1) Install dust cover and bump stop. Using spring compressor, compress coil spring and install. Install mounting, washer and bushing. Install collar on strut shaft.

2) Install 2 lock nuts on strut shaft to hold shaft. Using Collar Remover/Installer (18G 1535) and ft. lb torque wrench, tighten collar to 16 ft. lbs. (22 N.m). *See Fig. 6.*

Fig. 6: Installing Strut Shaft Collar

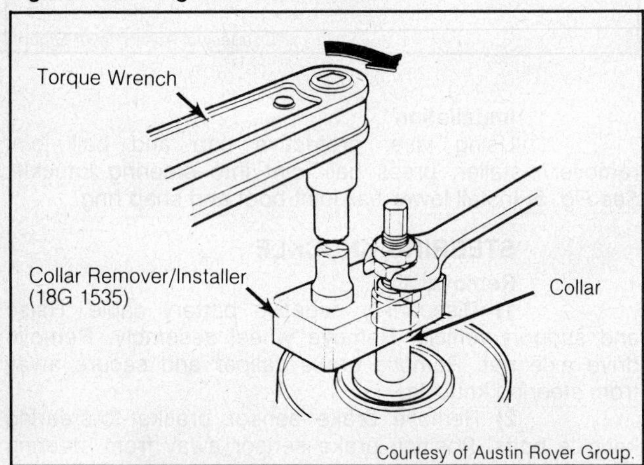

3) Reverse removal procedures. Tighten strut shaft nut to specification.

Installation

Reverse removal procedures. Tighten strut-to-body nuts and fork-to-lower control arm bolt with vehicle at normal operating height. Tighten all bolts to specification.

LOWER CONTROL ARM

CAUTION: Suspension may be under spring tension. Use caution when removing lower control arm.

Removal

1) Disconnect negative battery cable. Raise and support vehicle. Remove wheel assembly. Remove lower ball joint nut. Using ball joint separator, separate ball joint from lower control arm.

2) Remove fork-to-control arm bolt. Remove stabilizer bar bolt from lower control arm. Remove strut rod-to-control arm bolts. Remove lower control arm-to-frame bolt. Remove lower control arm.

Inspection

Inspect control arm for cracks or worn bushings. Replace lower control arm if damaged.

Installation

Reverse removal procedures. Install new nut on ball joint. Tighten control arm-to-frame bolt and fork-to-control arm bolt with vehicle at normal operating height. Tighten bolts to specification.

UPPER CONTROL ARM

Removal

1) Disconnect negative battery cable. Raise and support vehicle. Remove wheel assembly. Remove ball joint nut at steering knuckle. Using ball joint separator, separate ball joint from steering knuckle.

2) On left control arm replacement, remove wiper motor bracket retaining bolts. Move wiper motor bracket to gain access to control arm.

3) Remove control arm bracket-to-body nuts. Remove control arm bracket from body. Remove bolt retaining control arm bracket to control arm. Remove control arm.

Installation

Replace control arm if control arm or ball joint is damaged. Reverse removal procedures. Tighten control arm to control arm bracket bolt with vehicle at normal operating height. Tighten bolts to specification.

STRUT ROD

Removal

1) Disconnect negative battery cable. Raise and support vehicle. Remove wheel assembly. Remove nut from front of strut rod. Remove washer and bushing from strut rod. Some models may use 2 washers on the front of strut rod.

2) Remove strut rod-to-control arm bolts. Remove strut rod, bushing, washer and spacer. Note location of components for reassembly reference.

Installation

Replace bushings if damaged. Reverse removal procedures. Tighten sturt rod nut with vehicle at normal operating height. Tighten bolts to specification.

STABILIZER ROD

Removal

1) Disconnect negative battery cable. Raise and support vehicle. Remove wheel assembly. Remove stabilizer bar-to-lower control arm bolts. Remove stabilizer bar bracket bolts and remove brackets.

2) Remove stabilizer bar bushings. Remove stabilizer bar. Remove stabilizer bar link from stabilizer bar (if necessary).

Installation

Replace bushings if damaged. Reverse removal procedures. Tigthen bolts to specification with vehicle at normal operating height.

STERLING 825 (Cont.)

TIGHTENING SPECIFICATIONS

Application	Ft. Lbs. (N.m)
Ball Joint Nut	
Lower	66 (90)
Upper	37 (51)
Brake Caliper Bolt	55 (75)
Brake Sensor-to-Steering Knuckle Bolt	18 (24)
Control Arm Bracket-to-Body Nut	59 (80)
Control Arm Bracket-to-Control Arm Bolt	65 (88)
Drive Axle Nut	[1] 214 (290)
Fork-to-Control Arm Bolt	56 (76)
Fork-to-Strut Bolt	37 (51)
Lower Control Arm-to-Frame Bolt	37 (51)
Stabilizer Bar Bracket Bolt	16 (22)
Stabilizer Bar Link-to-Bar Bolt	36 (49)
Stabilizer Bar-to-Control Arm Bolt	36 (49)
Strut Rod Nut	66 (90)
Strut Rod-to-Control Arm Bolt	126 (171)
Strut Shaft Nut	37 (51)
Strut-to-Body Nut	19 (26)
Tie Rod Nut	33 (45)
Wheel Lug Nut	52 (70)

[1] – Stake nut after tightening to specification.

Front Suspension

SUBARU

Brat, Hatchback, Justy, Sedan, Station Wagon, XT Coupe

DESCRIPTION

Front suspension is a MacPherson strut independent type, consisting of lower control arms, leading rods, knuckle housings and a stabilizer bar. Strut is secured at top to body and at bottom to steering knuckle.

Knuckle housing pivots on ball joint attached to lower control arm. Lower control arms are attached to front crossmember. Leading rods are mounted between lower control arms and brackets on body.

Fig. 1: Exploded View of Justy Front Suspension

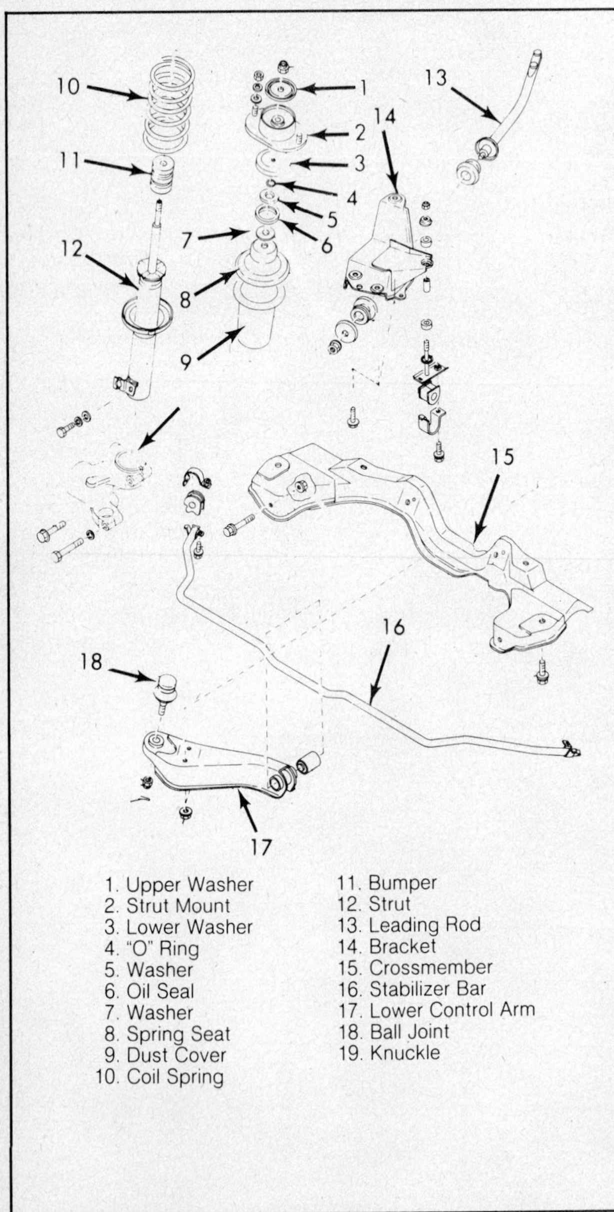

Courtesy of Subaru of America, Inc.

Fig. 2: Exploded View of Front Suspension (All Others)

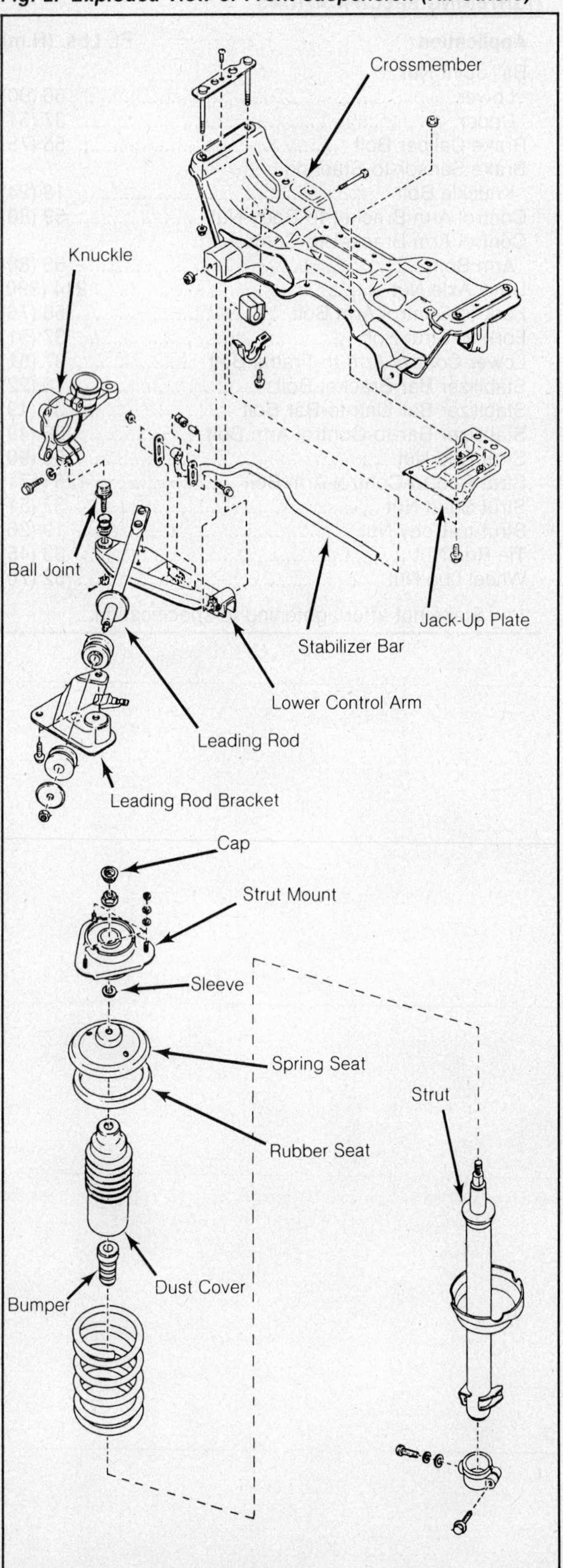

Courtesy of Subaru of America, Inc.

ADJUSTMENTS & INSPECTION

WHEEL ALIGNMENT SPECIFICATIONS & PROCEDURES

See WHEEL ALIGNMENT SPECIFICATIONS & PROCEDURES in WHEEL ALIGNMENT section.

WHEEL BEARING

Wheel bearings are not adjustable. On Justy models, tighten hub nut to 130 ft. lbs. (177 N.m). On all others, tighten hub nut to 145 ft. lbs. (197 N.m). On all models, if cotter pin hole is not aligned, tighten hub nut a maximum of 30 degrees to align hole. Install cotter pin.

BALL JOINT CHECKING

Load ball joint stud with 154 lbs. (686 N). If vertical play exceeds .012-.016" (.30-.40 mm), replace ball joint.

REMOVAL & INSTALLATION

KNUCKLE HOUSING & WHEEL BEARING

Removal

1) Raise and support vehicle. Remove wheel assembly. Remove cotter pin and loosen hub nut. On all models except Justy, pull out parking brake cable outer clip from caliper. Remove parking brake cable end from caliper lever.

2) Remove caliper assembly and hang out of way. Disconnect tie rod from knuckle housing. Disconnect strut from knuckle housing. Use a screwdriver to spread knuckle housing (if necessary). DO NOT spread housing slit more than .16" (4 mm). Be careful not to damage the CV joint boot.

3) Remove castle nut, washer spring and center piece on axle shaft. Remove hub and disc assembly. Remove the disc cover. Disconnect ball joint from knuckle housing.

4) On Justy models, separate drive shaft from differential. Remove knuckle housing with drive shaft from vehicle. Use puller to separate housing from drive shaft.

5) On all other models, use puller to separate knuckle housing from drive shaft. Remove knuckle housing from vehicle. On all models, remove bearings and oil seals from knuckle housing.

Installation

1) Press in bearings and oil seals. Be sure to install spacer between bearings. Always use new bearings and seals. Do not mix the inner and outer oil seals.

2) To install knuckle housing, reverse removal procedure. Ensure end surface of hub and disc assembly contacts ball bearings on axle shaft when installing. Ensure concave side of washer spring faces inward. Adjust wheel bearing.

FRONT SUSPENSION ASSEMBLY

Removal

1) Raise and support vehicle. Remove front wheels. Disconnect brake hose from brake pipe at fenderwell bracket. On all models except Justy, remove parking brake cable bracket from lower control arm. Remove cable clip and disconnect cable end from the caliper lever.

2) Drive out inner CV joint spring pins. On Justy models, disconnect stabilizer bar from leading rod. On all others, disconnect stabilizer bar from lower control arm. Disconnect leading rod from leading rod bracket.

3) Disconnect tie rod end from knuckle housing. Disconnect lower control arm from crossmember. Remove nuts holding strut to body. Pull CV joint from differential gear. Remove front suspension assembly from vehicle.

Installation

To install, reverse removal procedure. Use new axle shaft spring pins. Use new self-locking nuts. Tighten control arm to crossmember bolts after vehicle has been lowered to ground. Bleed brakes and align front end.

LOWER CONTROL ARM & BALL JOINT

Removal

1) Raise vehicle and support. Remove wheel assembly. Remove stabilizer bar, leading rod and parking brake cable mounting bracket (all models except Justy) from lower control arm.

2) Remove bolt and separate control arm from front crossmember. Remove ball joint pinch bolt and separate ball joint from knuckle housing. Use a screwdriver to spread knuckle housing (if necessary). DO NOT spread housing slit more than .16" (4 mm). Be careful not to damage the CV joint boot.

3) Remove control arm from vehicle. Remove ball joint nut and remove ball joint from control arm.

Installation

To install, reverse removal procedure. Check bushing for wear or damage. Replace if necessary. Tighten ball joint nut to 29 ft. lbs. (39 N.m) and continue tightening a maximum of 60 degrees until cotter pin hole is aligned. Install new cotter pin. Tighten control arm to crossmember bolt after vehicle has been lowered to ground.

STRUT ASSEMBLY

Removal

1) Raise vehicle and support. Remove wheel assembly. Disconnect brake line from caliper. Disconnect brake hose from strut bracket. Remove knuckle housing to strut retaining bolts.

2) Separate knuckle housing from strut by pushing knuckle housing down. Use a screwdriver to spread knuckle housing (if necessary). DO NOT spread housing slit more than .16" (4 mm). Be careful not to damage the CV joint boot. Remove upper strut retaining nuts. Remove strut from vehicle.

Disassembly

Compress coil spring with Compressor (926110000) until upper seat is separated from coil spring. On Justy models, hold strut rod with an Allen wrench and remove self-locking nut. On all others, use Spanner (926510000) to hold spring seat while removing self-locking nut. Remove components from strut. On Justy models, note position of thrust washers and washers for reassembly reference.

Inspection

Check all parts for wear or damage. Replace if necessary. Check rod deflection. Fully extend rod and mount a dial indicator .4" (10 mm) from end of rod. Apply a load of 4 lbs. (20 N) to end of rod and measure play. Maximum side play is .031" (.80 mm). Replace strut if play exceeds specification. Strut cannot be disassembled. Check action of rod for abnormal noise or resistance.

Front Suspension

SUBARU (Cont.)

Reassembly & Installation

1) To reassemble, reverse disassembly procedure, replacing self-locking nut with a new one.

2) On Justy models, thrust washer should be coated with grease. Ensure projection on dust cover fits into notch on upper spring seat. Ensure groove in washer for "O" ring faces up. Ensure notch in thrust washer aligns with notch in upper spring seat. Ensure notches in upper and lower spring seats are aligned.

3) On all others, ensure flat side of coil spring is up when assembling strut. To install, reverse removal procedure. Bleed brakes.

STABILIZER BAR

Removal & Installation (All Except Justy)

Raise vehicle and support with safety stands. Remove brackets securing stabilizer bar to lower control arm. Remove brackets attaching stabilizer bar to crossmember. Remove the jack-up plate of crossmember and remove stabilizer. To install, reverse removal procedure. Tighten bolts after vehicle has been lowered to ground.

CROSSMEMBER

Removal & Installation (Justy)

Raise and support vehicle. Support engine at front and rear. Remove engine splash shield. Remove center crossmember. Remove exhaust system with muffler attached. Remove the lower control arm from the crossmember. Remove engine mount nut from crossmember. Remove crossmember from vehicle. To install, reverse removal procedure.

Removal & Installation (All Others)

1) Raise and support vehicle. Remove wheels. Remove spare tire, air cleaner assembly, and pitching stopper rod. Cover the carburetor/throttle body to prevent dust from entering.

2) Remove parking brake cable bracket from lower control arm. Disconnect tie rod end from knuckle housing. Remove front exhaust pipe. Remove lower control arm from crossmember.

3) Remove nuts attaching engine mounts to crossmember. Remove nuts connecting steering torque rod and pinion shaft. Lift engine assembly .40" (10 mm). Support crossmember with jack. Remove nuts and remove crossmember along with steering box.

4) To install, reverse removal procedure. Tighten crossmember nuts and lower control arm-to-crossmember bolt with vehicle on ground and suspension unloaded.

TIGHTENING SPECIFICATIONS

Application [1]	Ft. Lbs. (N.m)
Ball Joint-to-Control Arm	29 (39)
Ball Joint-to-Knuckle	
Justy	25-40 (34-54)
All Others	28-37 (38-50)
Body-to-Crossmember	
Justy	43-51 (59-69)
All Others	39-48 (53-65)
Control Arm-to-Crossmember	
Justy	43-58 (59-78)
All Others	43-51 (59-69)
Caliper Assy.-to-Knuckle	36-51 (49-69)
Jack-Up Plate-to-Crossmember	17-31 (23-42)
Lower Strut End-to-Knuckle	
Justy	25-40 (34-54)
All Others	28-37 (38-50)
Leading Rod-to-Control Arm	
Justy	54-69 (74-93)
All Others	58-72 (78-98)
Leading Rod Nut	
Justy	40-54 (54-74)
All Others	58-72 (78-98)
Stabilizer Bracket-to-Control Arm	14-22 (20-30)
Stabilizer Bracket-to-Crossmember	
Justy	15-21 (21-28)
Stabilizer Bracket-to-Bracket Bolt	
Justy	14-22 (20-30)
Strut Piston Rod Lock Nut	
Justy	29-43 (39-59)
All Others	38-49 (51-67)
Strut Mount-to-Body Nuts	
Justy	29-43 (39-59)
All Others	20-27 (26-36)
Tie Rod End Nut	18-22 (25-30)
	INCH Lbs. (N.m)
Stabilizer Bracket-to-Leading Rod Bracket Nut (Justy)	60-96 (7-11)

[1] – Never reuse self-locking nuts. Use NEW nuts during reassembly.

Front Suspension

SUZUKI SAMURAI

DESCRIPTION

The Suzuki has a solid type axle housing which uses shock absorbers, stabilizer bar and leaf springs for the suspension system. Leaf springs are attached to axle housing using "U" bolts.

Individual steering knuckles are attached to the axle by the use of kingpins. An optional locking hub may be installed in place of drive axle flange.

ADJUSTMENTS & INSPECTION

WHEEL ALIGNMENT SPECIFICATIONS & PROCEDURES

See WHEEL ALIGNMENT SPECIFICATIONS & PROCEDURES in WHEEL ALIGNMENT section.

WHEEL BEARING

1) Raise and support vehicle. Remove wheel assembly. On models with locking hubs, remove locking hub. See LOCKING HUB under REMOVAL & INSTALLATION in this article.

2) On all other models, remove cap from drive axle flange. Remove snap ring from drive axle shaft. *See Fig. 1.* Remove drive axle flange retaining bolts. Remove drive axle flange.

3) On all models, remove brake caliper or ensure brake pads are not contacting rotor. Using spring scale attached to wheel stud, measure starting torque required to rotate the rotor.

4) Starting torque should be 2.2-6.6 lbs. (1-3 kg). If adjustment is required, bend lock washer away from lock nut. Remove bearing lock nut and lock washer.

5) Using Socket (09941-58010) and ft. lb. torque wrench, tighten bearing nut to 58 ft. lbs. (79 N.m) while spinning hub assembly.

6) Loosen bearing nut. Using INCH lb. torque wrench, tighten bearing nut to 84-120 INCH lbs. (9-13 N.m). Install lock washer and lock nut. Tighthen lock nut to 65 ft. lbs. (88 N.m). Bend tab on lock washer against lock nut.

7) Using spring scale, recheck starting torque. Starting torque should be 2.2-6.6 lbs. (1-3 kg). Reverse removal procedures. Apply Sealing Compound 366E (99000-31090) to hub and drive axle flange prior to installation (if equipped). Tighten bolts to specification.

KINGPIN

1) Raise and support vehicle. Remove wheel assembly. Remove tie rod nut at steering knuckle. Using tie rod separator, separate tie rod from steering knuckle.

2) Disconnect tie rod from steering knuckle. Remove steering knuckle oil seal. See STEERING KNUCKLE OIL SEAL under REMOVAL & INSTALLATION in this article.

3) Ensure kingpin retaining bolts are tightened to specification prior to measuring starting torque. See TIGHTENING SPECIFICATIONS table at end of article.

CAUTION: Prior to checking starting torque, steering knuckle oil seal must be removed and kingpin retaining bolts tightened to proper specification.

4) Using spring scale attached to tie rod area of steering knuckle, measure starting torque required to move steering knuckle. Starting torque should be 2.20-3.96 lbs. (1.0-1.8 kg).

5) If starting torque is not within specification, kingpin preload must be adjusted. Remove kingpin retaining bolts. *See Fig. 1.* Install a large amount of kingpin shims. Install kingpin and tighten bolts to specification.

6) Recheck kingpin starting torque. Gradually decrease shim thickness to obtain starting torque of 2.20-3.96 lbs. (1.0-1.8 kg). Check starting torque after each shim removal.

Fig. 1: Suzuki Samurai Front Suspension

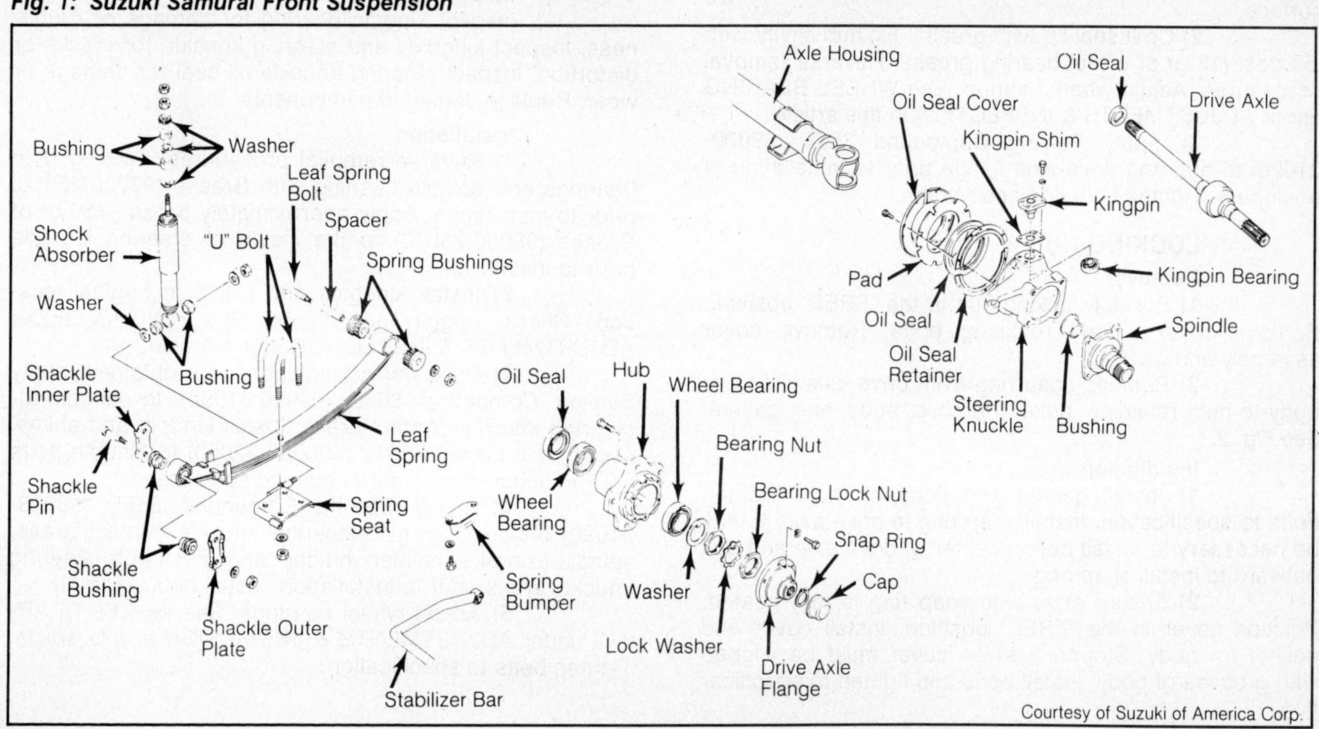

SUZUKI SAMURAI (Cont.)

7) If correct starting torque cannot be obtained when no shims are used, inspect kingpins or bearings for damage.

8) Reverse removal procedures for remaining components. Once correct starting torque is obtained, remove kingpin. Apply Sealing Compound 366E (99000-31090) to kingpin-to-steering knuckle contact areas.

9) Install kingpin. Apply Lock Cement 1342 (990000-32050) to kingpin bolts prior to installation. Tighten bolts to specification.

REMOVAL & INSTALLATION

WHEEL BEARING

Removal

1) Raise and support vehicle. Remove wheel assembly. On models with locking hubs, remove locking hub. See LOCKING HUB under in this article.

2) On all other models, remove cap from drive axle flange. Remove snap ring from drive axle shaft. *See Fig. 1.* Remove drive axle flange retaining bolts. Remove drive axle flange.

3) On all models, remove brake caliper. Remove rotor-to-hub retaining bolts. Remove rotor from hub. It may be necessary to install bolts in face of rotor to push rotor from hub.

4) Bend lock washer away from lock nut. Remove bearing lock nut and lock washer. Using Socket (09941-58010), remove bearing nut. Remove washer and hub assembly from spindle.

5) Remove oil seal from hub. Note direction of seal installation. Remove inner bearing. Using brass drift and hammer, drive bearing races from hub if replacement is required.

Installation

1) Install bearing races in hub. Ensure bearing races are fully seated. Pack wheel bearings with grease. Install inner bearing. Install seal until seal is even with hub surface.

2) Coat seal lip with grease. Fill hub cavity with .50 ozs. (15 g) of wheel bearing grease. Reverse removal procedures. Adjust wheel bearing. See WHEEL BEARING under ADJUSTMENTS & INSPECTION in this article.

3) Apply Sealing Compound 366E (99000-31090) to hub and drive axle flange prior to installation (if equipped). Tighten bolts to specification.

LOCKING HUB

Removal

1) Position locking hub in the "FREE" position. Remove cover-to-body retaining bolts. Remove cover assembly and gasket.

2) Remove snap ring from drive axle. Remove body-to-hub retaining bolts. Remove body and gasket. *See Fig. 2.*

Installation

1) Install gasket and body on hub. Tighten bolts to specification. Install snap ring in drive axle. It may be necessary to install bolt in center of drive axle and pull outward to install snap ring.

2) Ensure drive axle snap ring is fully seated. Position cover in the "FREE" position. Install cover and gasket on body. Stopper nail on cover must be aligned with grooves of body. Install bolts and tighten to specification.

Fig. 2: Exploded View of Locking Hub

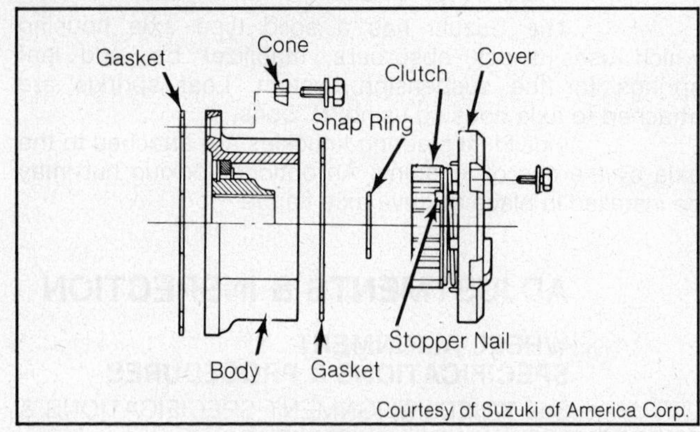

STEERING KNUCKLE

Removal

1) Remove hub and bearing. See WHEEL BEARING in this article. Loosen but DO NOT remove upper and lower kingpin retaining bolts. Remove dust cover, caliper holder and wheel spindle from axle housing. *See Fig. 1.*

2) Remove tie rod nut at steering knuckle. Using tie rod separator, separate tie rod from steering knuckle. Remove steering knuckle oil seal. See STEERING KNUCKLE OIL SEAL in this article.

CAUTION: Kingpins must be marked for location prior to removal. Kingpins and shims must be installed in original location.

3) Mark kingpins for location. Remove kingpins from steering knuckle. Note location of shims. Shims and kingpins must be installed in original location.

4) Remove steering knuckle and kingpin bearings. DO NOT allow lower kingpin bearing to drop during steering knuckle removal.

Inspection

Inspect kingpin bearing for damage or roughness. Inspect kingpins and steering knuckle for cracks or distortion. Inspect steering knuckle oil seal for damage or wear. Replace damaged components.

Installation

1) Reverse removal procedures. Pack kingpin bearings and spindle bushing with Grease (99000-25010) prior to installation. Apply approximately 5 ozs. (150 g) of Grease (99000-25010) to the inside of steering knuckle prior to installation.

2) Install kingpins and shims in original location. Check kingpin adjustment. See KINGPIN under ADJUSTMENTS & INSPECTION in this article.

3) Once correct adjustment is obtained, apply Sealing Compound 366E (99000-31090) to kingpin-to-steering knuckle contact areas. Install kingpin and shims. Apply Lock Cement 1342 (990000-32050) to kingpin bolts prior to installation. Tighten bolts to specification.

4) Apply Sealing Compound 366E (99000-31090) on dust cover-to-steering knuckle contact areas, spindle-to-brake caliper holder and spindle-to-steering knuckle areas prior to installation. Install hub assembly.

5) Adjust wheel bearings. See WHEEL BEARING under ADJUSTMENTS & INSPECTION in this article. Tighten bolts to specification.

SUZUKI SAMURAI (Cont.)

STEERING KNUCKLE OIL SEAL

NOTE: Steering knuckle oil seal is used to control steering dampening. Failure of oil seal may cause wheel shimmy. If oil leakage or wheel shimmy exists, replace oil seal.

Removal & Installation

1) Remove oil seal cover retaining bolts. *See Fig. 1.* Move oil seal cover and pad toward inside of vehicle. Remove oil seal from oil seal retainer. Note direction of seal installation.

2) Using scissors, cut oil seal and remove. Cut replacement seal and install in oil seal retainer approximately 30 degrees from top side of seal retainer area.

3) Apply Grease (99000-25120) to inside of oil seal. Apply Sealing Compound 366E (99000-31090) around entire mating surface of seal retainer to prevent water entering seal area. *See Fig. 3.*

Fig. 3: Oil Seal Grease & Sealing Compound Application Areas

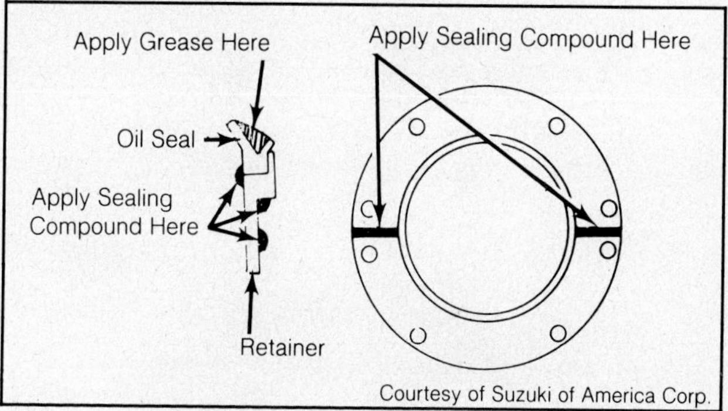

4) Reverse removal procedures for seal installation. Tigthen bolts to specification.

LEAF SPRING

Removal

1) Raise and support vehicle under chassis. Remove wheel assembly. Support axle housing with jack. Remove stabilizer bar-to-spring seat bolt. Remove shock absorber from spring seat.

2) Remove "U" bolts and spring seat. Remove leaf spring bolt and shackle pin. Note direction of bolt installation. Remove leaf spring.

Inspection

Inspect leaf spring for cracks or damage. Inspect spring and shackle bushings for damage. Replace damaged components.

Installation

1) If bushings require replacement, remove bushings from spring. Coat bushings with soapy water and install in spring. DO NOT apply oil to bushings for installation.

CAUTION: Spring bushings should only be coated with soapy water during installation. DO NOT use oil for bushing installation.

2) Reverse removal procedures. Install leaf spring bolt and shackle pins from the outside of vehicle inward.

3) Install shackle inner and outer plates with flat area toward the leaf spring. Measure distance between upper and lower shackle pins on both sides of leaf spring.

4) The distance between shackle pins should be within 0±.024" (04±.60 mm). Tighten shackle pin nut to specification with no load applied to leaf spring.

5) Ensure leaf spring center bolt is properly positioned in axle housing and spring seat. Tigthen all fasteners to specification. Tighten "U" bolts evenly to specification.

SHOCK ABSORBER

Removal & Installation

Raise and support vehicle. Remove upper mounting nut and bushings. Remove lower retaining nut and washer. Remove shock absorber and bushings. Reverse removal procedures. Tighten nuts to specification.

STABILIZER BAR

Removal

Raise and support vehicle. Note direction of bolt installation. Remove stabilizer bar-to-spring seat bolts. Remove stabilizer bushing mount brackets. Remove stabilizer bar.

Installation

1) Replace bushings if damaged. Install stabilizer bar with painted area located on right side of vehicle. *See Fig. 4.* Align stabilizer mount bushings with paint mark on stabilizer bar. *See Fig. 4.*

2) Install lock washer facing inward on stabilizer bar-to-spring seat bolt. Tighten bolts to specification with no load on suspension.

Fig. 4: Installing Stabilizer Bar

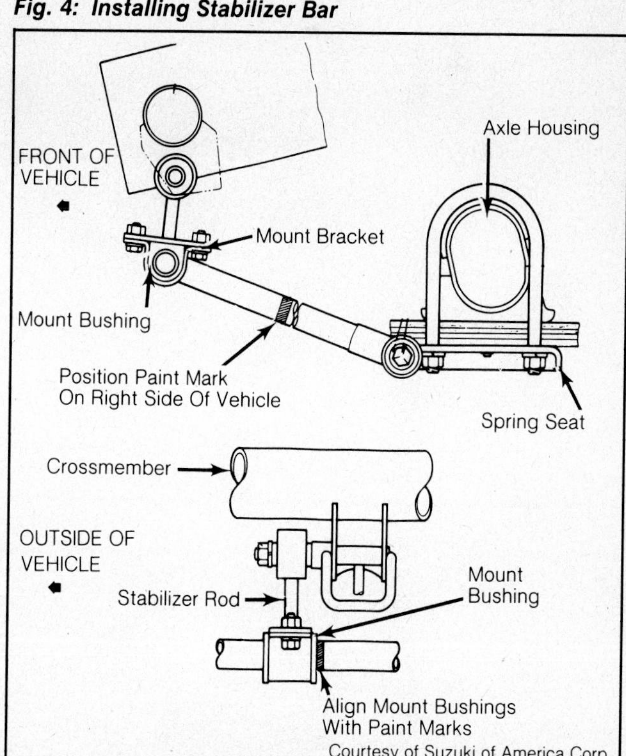

Front Suspension

SUZUKI SAMURAI (Cont.)

TIGHTENING SPECIFICATIONS

Application	Ft. Lbs. (N.m)
Caliper Guide Pin	19-22 (26-30)
Caliper Holder Bolt	29-43 (39-58)
Drive Axle Flange Bolt	15-22 (20-30)
Kingpin Bolt	15-22 (20-30)
Leaf Spring Bolt	33-51 (45-69)
Locking Hub Body-to-Hub Bolt	15-22 (20-30)
Shackle Pin Nut	22-40 (30-54)
Shock Absorber	
Lower Nut	23-40 (31-54)
Upper Nut	16-25 (22-34)
Stabilizer Bar Mount Bracket Bolt	13-20 (18-27)
Stabilizer Bar Mount To Crossmember Bolt	16-25 (22-34)
Stabilizer Bar-to-Spring Seat Bolt	51-65 (69-88)
"U" Bolt Nut	44-58 (60-79)
Wheel Bearing Lock Nut	65 (88)
Wheel Lug Nut	37-58 (51-79)
	INCH Lbs. (N.m)
Locking Hub Cover Bolt	72-102 (8-12)
Steering Knuckle Seal Retainer Bolt	72-102 (8-12)

Front Suspension

TOYOTA CAMRY, CELICA, COROLLA FWD & TERCEL

DESCRIPTION

These vehicles are equipped with front wheel drive and independent MacPherson strut front suspension. Suspension consists of vertically mounted strut assemblies, control arms and a stabilizer bar. Coil springs surround the strut tubes.

Struts are mounted between the inner fender and steering knuckle. Tie rod ends connect rack and pinion steering to steering knuckle. A ball joint connects the steering knuckle to lower control arm which attaches to frame crossmember. Stabilizer bar attaches to lower control arms and 2 points on the crossmember. On Camry and Tercel, the stabilizer bar acts as a strut rod and permits caster adjustment.

ADJUSTMENTS & INSPECTION

WHEEL ALIGNMENT SPECIFICATIONS & PROCEDURES

See WHEEL ALIGNMENT SPECIFICATIONS & PROCEDURES in WHEEL ALIGNMENT section.

WHEEL BEARING

Wheel bearings are not adjustable. Whenever bearings are removed, replace with new bearings, races, and oil seals.

BALL JOINT CHECKING

1) Raise vehicle and place a wooden block with a height of 7.09-7.87" (180.0-200.0 mm) under one front tire. Lower floor jack until there is about half the load of the vehicle on front struts. Place safety stands under vehicle.

2) Position front wheels straight ahead and block them. Use a rod to move control arm up and down. Check for vertical ball joint play. Ball joints are serviceable as a unit only. If damaged or any vertical play is found, replace ball joint.

REMOVAL & INSTALLATION

WHEEL BEARING

Removal

1) Remove cotter pin, bearing lock nut cap and bearing lock nut (apply brakes when removing lock nut). Remove brake caliper. Do not disconnect brake line. Secure caliper out of the way. Remove disc brake rotor. Remove cotter pin and castle nut from tie rod end.

2) Using Puller (09950-20016) for Camry and Corolla models, Puller (09610-20012) for Tercel models, or Puller (09628-62011) for Celica models, pull tie rod end from steering knuckle. Place reference marks on lower strut bracket and camber adjusting cam.

3) Remove bolts and nuts to separate steering knuckle and strut. On Camry and Tercel models, remove 2 bolts holding ball joint to steering knuckle and separate. On Celica and Corolla models, remove 1 bolt and 2 nuts, and separate lower arm from steering knuckle.

4) On all models, use puller to pull axle hub from drive shaft. Cover drive boot with a cloth to prevent damage. On Celica and Corolla models, use Puller (09610-55012) to remove the ball joint from the steering knuckle.

5) Place steering knuckle in a vise and remove dust deflector. Using Seal Puller (09308-00010), pull inner oil seal out of steering knuckle. Remove snap ring from steering knuckle hole.

Fig. 1: Exploded View of Tercel Front Suspension Components

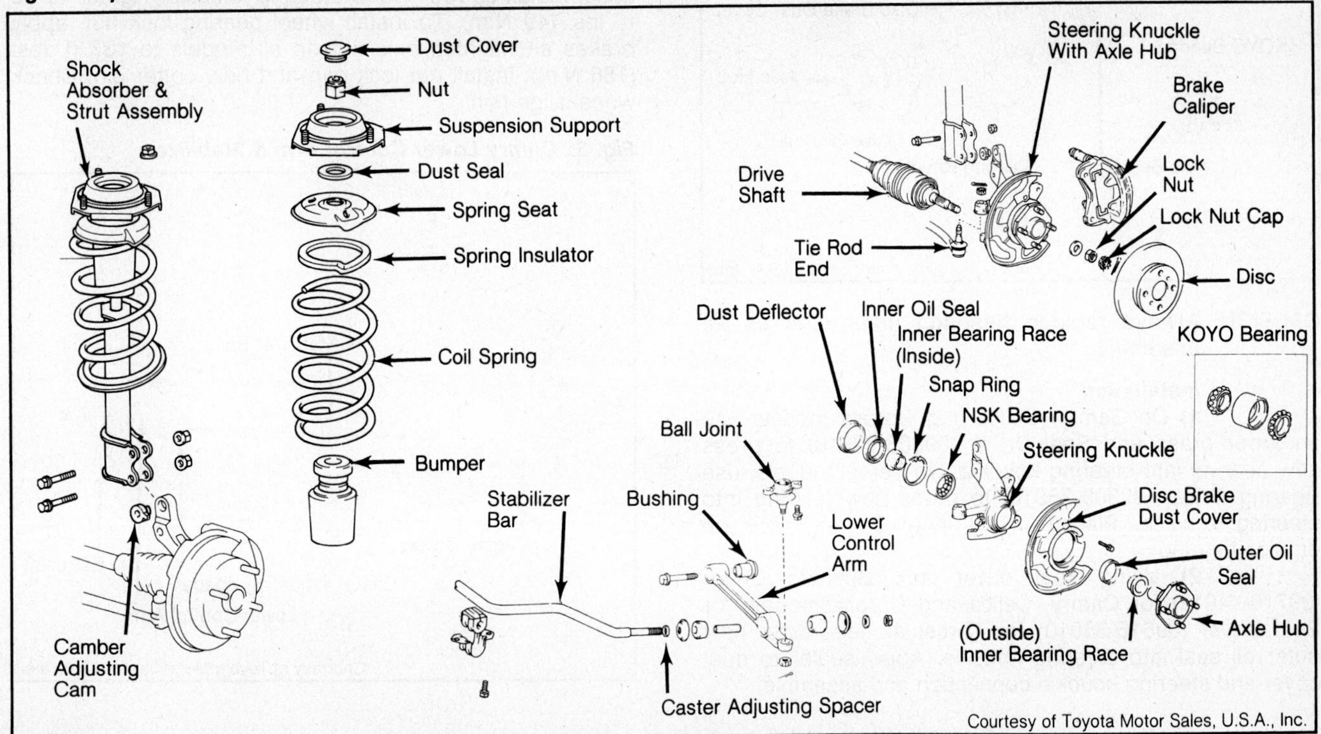

Front Suspension

TOYOTA CAMRY, CELICA, COROLLA FWD & TERCEL (Cont.)

6) Remove the 3 bolts holding the disc brake dust cover to the steering knuckle. Using puller, push axle hub from steering knuckle. Remove disc brake dust cover. Remove inside inner bearing race. Using puller, remove outside inner race from axle hub. Pull outer oil seal from steering knuckle.

7) On all models, install old outside inner race on bearing. On Tercel models, use Fixture (09228-22020) and an arbor press to remove bearing from steering knuckle. On all other models, use Driver (09605-60010) and a hammer to remove bearing.

Fig. 2: Exploded View of Camry, Celica & Corolla Axle Hub Components

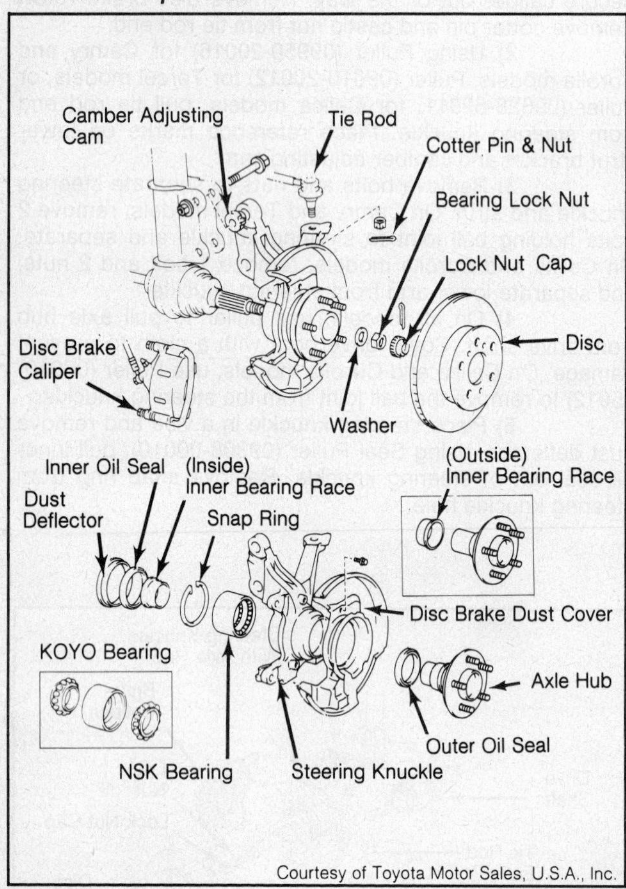

CAUTION: Always replace bearings and races as an assembly.

Installation

1) On Camry, Celica and Corolla models use an arbor press and Seal Driver (09608-32010) to press new bearing into steering knuckle. On Tercel models, use Bearing Driver (09309-35010) to press new bearing into steering knuckle. Place outside inner bearing race on outside bearing.

2) Using seal driver and Bushing Driver (09710-14012) for Camry, Celica and Corolla models, or Seal Driver (09515-35010) for Tercel models, drive new outer oil seal into steering knuckle. Appl sealer to dust cover and steering knuckle connection and assemble.

3) Use Bearing Driver (09310-35010) to press hub into steering knuckle. Do not interchange the inner and outer races on Tercel models. Install snap ring into hole of steering knuckle on all models.

4) Using seal driver and Bushing Driver (09710-14012) for Camry, Celica and Corolla models, drive new oil seal flush to the end surface of steering knuckle. On Tercel models, use Seal Driver (09309-35010) to drive inner oil seal .130" (3.3 mm) below the end surface of steering knuckle.

5) On Camry models, use Seal Driver (09223-41020) to drive new dust deflector into steering knuckle. On Tercel models, use Seal Driver (09608-16050). On Corolla models, use Seal Driver (09218-46010). On Celica models, use Seal Driver (09608-35014).

6) On Celica and Corolla models, seat ball joint to steering knuckle by tightening old nut to 14 ft. lbs. (20 N.m). Remove the nut, and install a new nut. Tighten the new nut to 82 ft. lbs. (111 N.m) on Corolla models, and 93 ft. lbs. (126 N.m) on Celica models.

7) On all models, install steering knuckle with axle hub to driveshaft with the washer and nut. Do not tighten the nut. Tighten steering knuckle-to-control arm on Camry and Tercel models to specification. Tighten ball joint-to-lower control arm on Corolla and Celica models to specification.

8) Align reference marks of camber adjusting cam-to-strut. Install steering knuckle to strut. Tighten and torque to specifications.

NOTE: Camry and Corolla model strut bolts are installed from the rear side. Celica and Tercel model strut bolts are installed from the front side.

9) Install disc rotor to axle hub. Tighten and torque brake caliper to steering knuckle bolts to specifications. Install tie rod end to steering knuckle. Tighten to 36 ft. lbs. (49 N.m). To install wheel bearing lock nut, apply brakes and tighten axle nut on all models to 137 ft. lbs. (186 N.m). Install nut lock cap and new cotter pin. Check wheel alignment.

Fig. 3: Camry Lower Control Arm & Stabilizer

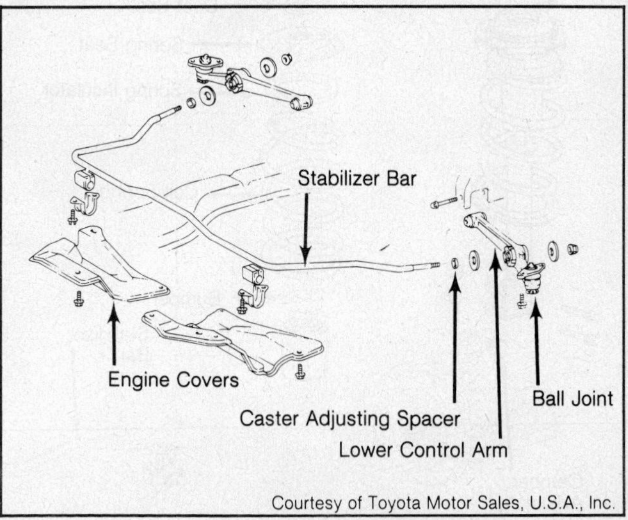

TOYOTA CAMRY, CELICA, COROLLA FWD & TERCEL (Cont.)

Fig. 4: Corolla Lower Control Arm & Stabilizer

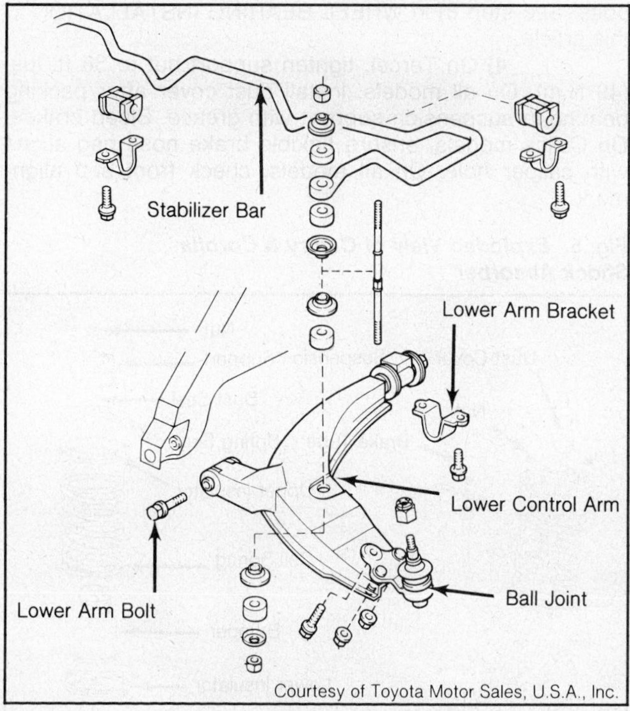

Fig. 5: Celica Lower Control Arm & Stabilizer

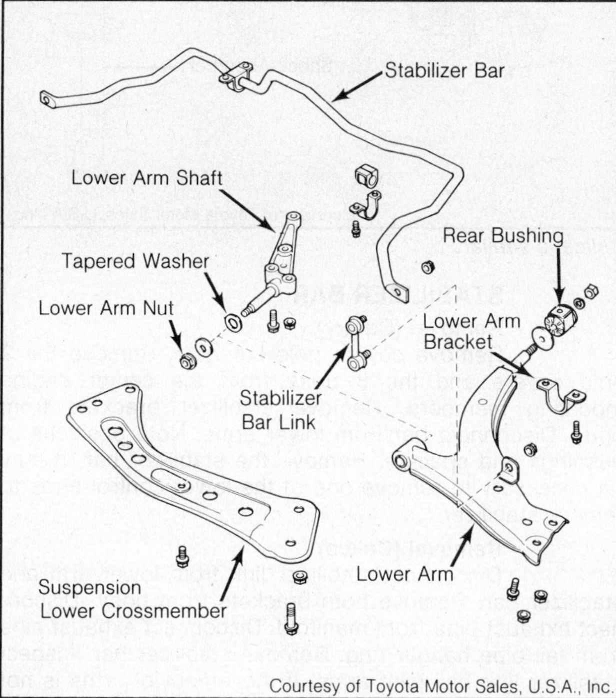

CONTROL ARM & BALL JOINT

Removal

1) Raise vehicle and support with jackstands. On Tercel and Camry models remove 2 bolts holding ball joint to steering knuckle and separate. On Celica and Corolla models remove 1 bolt and 2 nuts holding the ball joint to the control arm and separate. On Celica models, remove nut and disconnect stabilizer link from lower arm. On all other models, remove stabilizer bar nut, retainer and cushion from lower arm.

2) On Celica and Corolla models remove 2 bolts holding the lower arm rear brackets to the frame. Loosen the lower arm bolt (Corolla) or nut and washer (Celica) and remove lower arm. On Celica models only, remove suspension lower crossmember and lower arm shaft.

NOTE: **On Celica models equipped with automatic transmission, left side lower control arm must be removed together with lower arm shaft. Remove suspension lower crossmember first before removing lower arm and shaft assembly.**

3) On Camry and Tercel models, loosen the lower arm bolt. Pry on arm and pull out bolt. Disconnect lower arm from stabilizer. Be careful not to lose the caster adjusting spacer.

NOTE: **On Tercel models, jack up the opposite wheel to remove lower arm.**

4) To remove ball joint from lower arm, use ball joint puller. Temporarily install nut to prevent ball joint from falling out of control arm when removing.

Installation

1) Reverse removal procedure. Tighten ball joint nut on all models to specification. Replace cotter pin.

2) On all models except Celica, install control arm and finger tighten the bolts and the stabilizer nut. Tighten ball joint to steering knuckle on Camry and Tercel models to specification. Tighten ball joint to lower arm on Corolla models to specification.

3) On Celica models, install lower arm shaft or lower arm shaft/control arm assembly and tighten shaft nut and bolt to specification. Ensure shaft washer tapered side faces body. Install lower suspension crossmember and tighten the fasteners to specification. Tighten ball joint to lower control arm to specification. Finger tighten lower arm nut, rear bracket bolts and stabilizer bar link nut.

4) Install wheels and lower vehicle. Bounce vehicle to settle the suspension. Tighten stabilizer bar nut to specification. Tighten lower arm bolts on Camry and Tercel models to specification. Tighten Corolla lower arm rear bracket bolts and lower arm bolt to specification. Tighten Celica lower arm nut and lower arm rear bracket bolts to specification. Check alignment.

CONTROL ARM BUSHING

Removal (Camry & Tercel)

1) Before removing control arm bushing, cut off excess rubber from flange. Using a hammer and a chisel, bend bushing flange inward.

2) Using a pair of pliers, bend and break off flange. Using an arbor press and Fixture (09726-32010), press bushing from control arm.

Installation (Camry & Tercel)

When installing control arm bushing, there must be no oil or grease on bushing or arm boss. Using an arbor press and Fixture (09726-32010), press bushing into control arm boss.

Removal (Celica & Corolla)

On a vise. Remove nut, retainer and bushing from control arm.

Front Suspension

TOYOTA CAMRY, CELICA, COROLLA FWD & TERCEL (Cont.)

Installation (Celica & Corolla)

Install new bushing, retainer and nut. Tighten nut to 76 ft. lbs. (103 N.m).

STRUT ASSEMBLY

Removal

1) On Camry and Corolla models only, disconnect brake tube from flexible brake hose. Drain brake fluid into a container. Remove 2 clips and 2 "E" rings. Remove 2 bolts from the brake caliper and remove the caliper. Do not disconnect the flexible brake hose from the caliper assembly.

2) On Celica models, remove union bolt and 2 washers and disconnect brake hose from disc brake caliper. Drain fluid into a container. Remove clip from brake hose and pull off hose from bracket.

3) On all models, place reference marks on strut lower bracket and camber adjusting cam. Remove the 2 nuts and bolts and separate strut from steering knuckle.

4) Remove dust cover from top of strut. Loosen strut support nut on Tercel models only. On all models, remove 3 nuts holding top of strut to body. Remove strut from vehicle.

CAUTION: When removing strut, cover drive shaft boot with a cloth for protection.

Disassembly

1) Install a bolt and 2 nuts to the strut lower bracket to prevent distortion of strut shell when clamped. Clamp bottom of strut in a vise.

2) Using Compressor (09727-22032), compress coil spring. Hold the spring seat with Lever (09729-22031) and remove strut rod top nut. Remove suspension support, spring seat, spring, insulators and bumpers.

Inspection (Corolla)

Inspect for leaks or damage. Pull up shock absorber piston rod at a constant rate to see if tension is even throughout length of pull. Rapidly move piston up and down .20-.39" (5.0-10.0 mm) to see if there is a change in tension. If shock is defective, replace as an assembly.

Inspection (Camry, Celica & Tercel)

Inspect for leaks or damage. Push the piston rod in fully and release it. The rod should return at a constant speed throughout the stroke. Check for abnormal resistance or noise when compressing the rod. If shock is defective, replace as an assembly.

CAUTION: Be sure and discharge the gas in the shock by loosening the ring nut 2 or 3 turns before discarding. Use Shock Absorber Wrench (09720-00011) on ring nut.

Installation

1) To install, reverse removal procedure. On Celica, Corolla and Camry models, ensure "OUT" mark on spring seat faces towards the outside of the vehicle. On Celica, Corolla and Camry models, tighten support nut to 34 ft. lbs. (47 N.m). On Tercel models, install nut but do not tighten.

2) Install strut to body. Tighten and torque the 3 nuts to specifications.

3) Install strut to steering knuckle and tighten bolts. See step **8)** in WHEEL BEARING INSTALLATION in this article.

4) On Tercel, tighten support nut to 36 ft. lbs. (49 N.m). On all models, install dust cover after packing bearing in suspension support with grease. Bleed brakes. On Celica models, ensure flexible brake hose peg aligns with caliper hole. On all models, check front end alignment.

Fig. 6: Exploded View of Camry & Corolla Shock Absorber

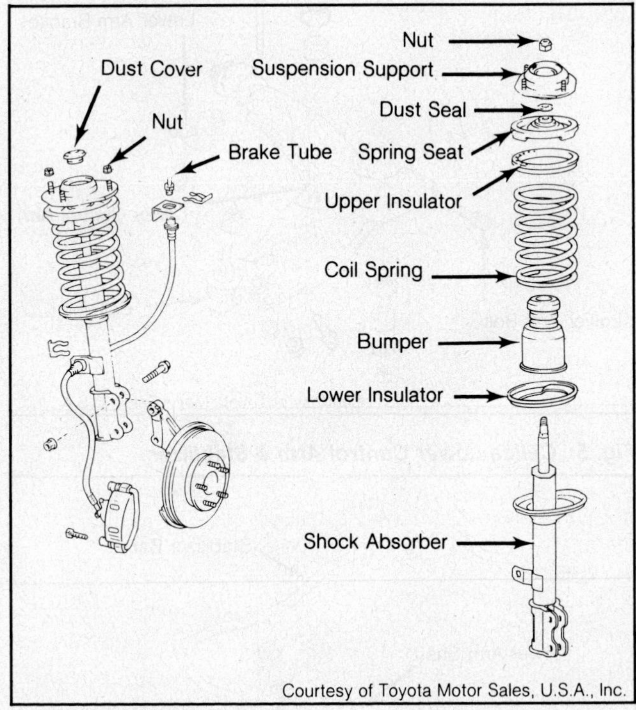

Celica is similar.

STABILIZER BAR

Removal (Camry)

Remove covers below engine. Remove the 2 hole covers and the 8 bolts from the center engine mounting members. Remove stabilizer brackets from body. Disconnect bar from lower arms. Note positions of bushings and spacers. Remove the stabilizer bar. It may be necessary to remove one of the lower control arms to remove stabilizer.

Removal (Celica)

Disconnect stabilizer link from lower arm and stabilizer bar. Remove both brackets from body. Disconnect exhaust pipe from manifold. Disconnect exhaust pipe from tail pipe hanger ring. Remove stabilizer bar. Inspect stabilizer link ball joint arms. If movement of arms is not free in all directions, replace stabilizer link.

Removal (Corolla)

Disconnect bar from lower arms. Remove brackets from body. Disconnect exhaust pipe from exhaust manifold. Remove stabilizer.

Removal (Tercel)

Remove covers below engine. Remove brackets from crossmember. Disconnect both ends from lower arms, noting positions of bushings and spacers. Remove stabilizer bar.

Front Suspension

TOYOTA CAMRY, CELICA, COROLLA FWD & TERCEL (Cont.)

Installation (All Models)

To install, reverse removal procedure. On Camry, tighten center engine mounting member bolts to 29 ft. lbs. (39 N.m). On all models, check wheel alignment.

TIGHTENING SPECIFICATIONS

Application	Ft. Lbs. (N.m)
Camry	
Axle Nut	137 (186)
Ball Joint-to-Control Arm Nut	67 (91)
Brake Caliper Bolts	86 (117)
Control Arm-to-Body Bolt	83 (113)
Control Arm-to-Steering Knuckle	83 (113)
Stabilizer-to-Control Arm Nut	86 (117)
Strut Top Support Nut	34 (47)
Stabilizer Bar Bracket Bolts	94 (127)
Steering Knuckle-to-Strut	166 (226)
Strut-to-Body Nuts	47 (64)
Tie Rod End-to-Steering Knuckle	36 (49)
Celica	
Axle Nut	137 (186)
Ball Joint-to-Knuckle Nut	82 (111)
Ball Joint-to-Lower Arm	94 (127)
Brake Caliper-to-Knuckle	70 (95)
Brake Hose-to-Caliper	22 (30)
Control Arm Bushing Nut	76 (103)
Control Arm Bracket-to-Body	72 (98)
Crossmember Bolts (4)	156 (212)
Crossmember Nuts (2)	29 (39)
Knuckle-to-Strut	188 (255)
Lower Arm Shaft-to-Body	154 (208)
Lower Arm Nut	156 (212)
Stabilizer Link-to-Lower Arm & Bar	26 (35)
Stabilizer Bracket-to-Body	14 (19)
Strut Top Support Nut	34 (47)
Strut-to-Body Nuts	47 (64)
Tie Rod-to-Knuckle	36 (49)
Corolla	
Axle Nut	137 (186)
Ball Joint-to-Steering Knuckle	82 (111)
Ball Joint-to-Control Arm	47 (64)
Brake Caliper Bolts	65 (88)
Control Arm Bracket-to-Body Bolts	64 (87)
Control Arm-to-Body Bolt	83 (113)
Control Arm Bushing Nut	76 (103)
Stabilizer Bar Nut	13 (18)
Steering Knuckle-to-Strut	105 (142)
Strut Top Support Nut	34 (47)
Strut-to-Body Nuts	23 (31)
Stabilizer Bracket Bolts	14 (19)
Tie Rod End-to-Steering Knuckle	36 (49)
Tercel	
Axle Nut	137 (186)
Ball Joint-to-Control Arm Nut	58 (78)
Brake Caliper Bolts	65-70 (88-95)
Control Arm-to-Body Bolt	59 (80)
Control Arm-to-Steering Knuckle	59 (80)
Strut Top Support Nut	34 (47)
Stabilizer Bar Bracket Bolts	32 (44)
Steering Knuckle-to-Strut	105 (142)
Strut-to-Body Nuts	23 (31)
Stabilizer-to-Control Arm Nut	78 (105)
Tie Rod End-to-Steering Knuckle	36 (49)

TOYOTA COROLLA RWD, CRESSIDA & SUPRA

DESCRIPTION

An independent MacPherson type strut suspension is used. Suspension consists of vertically mounted strut assemblies, control arms, strut rods and a stabilizer bar.

On Corolla and Cressida the strut assembly is mounted at top to inner fender and at bottom to steering knuckle arm. Steering knuckle arm is mounted to ball joint which is part of the lower control arm. *See Fig. 1.*

On Supra the strut assembly attaches to lower control arm and is not part of the steering. *See Fig. 2.*

Fig. 1: Exploded View of Corolla & Cressida Front Suspension Assembly

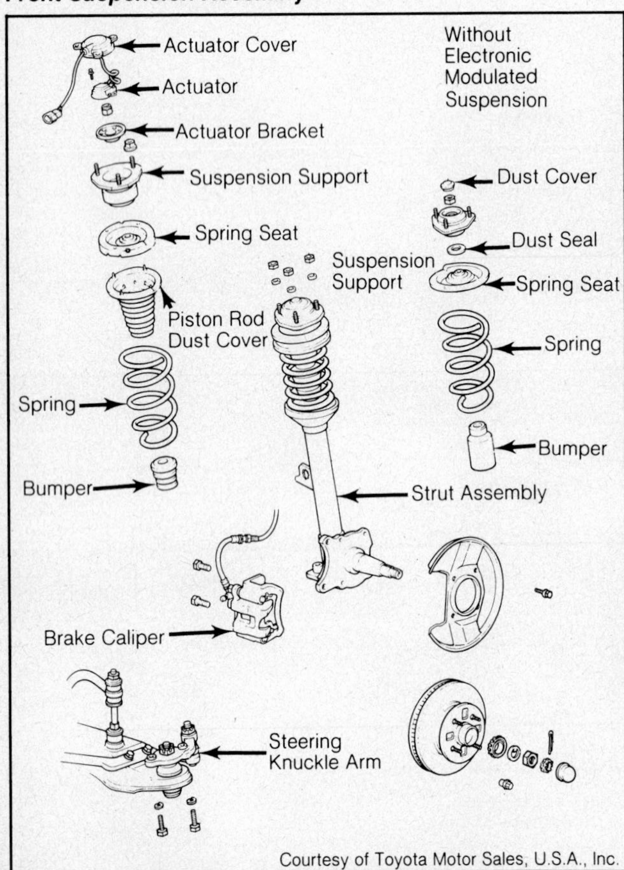

Courtesy of Toyota Motor Sales, U.S.A., Inc.

ADJUSTMENTS & INSPECTION

WHEEL ALIGNMENT SPECIFICATIONS & PROCEDURES

See WHEEL ALIGNMENT SPECIFICATIONS & PROCEDURES in WHEEL ALIGNMENT section.

WHEEL BEARING

Corolla & Cressida

Tighten nut to 21-22 ft. lbs. (28-29 N.m), while turning hub to seat bearings. Loosen hub nut until it can be turned with fingers. Tighten nut finger tight using a socket without a handle. If not aligned for cotter pin installation, tighten until installation is possible. Check hub preload by attaching a spring gauge to wheel stud and note starting preload. See BEARING PRELOAD SPECIFICATIONS table.

BEARING PRELOAD SPECIFICATIONS

Application	Lbs. (N)
Cressida	.8-1.9 (3-9)
Corolla	0-2.3 (0-10)

Supra

Wheel bearings are not adjustable. Bearings are pressed into housing and must be replaced if removed.

Fig. 2: Exploded View of Supra Front Suspension

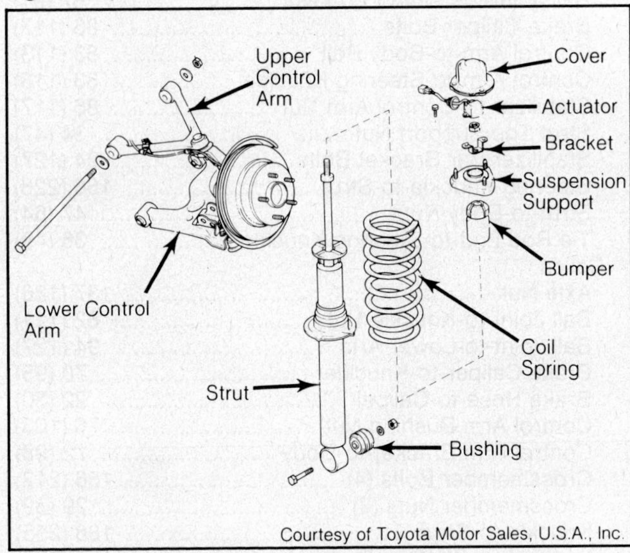

Courtesy of Toyota Motor Sales, U.S.A., Inc.

BALL JOINT CHECKING

1) Raise vehicle and support on safety stands allowing suspension to hang free. Place floor jack under control arm near ball joint. Raise control arm with jack until there is about half the load on front coil spring.

2) Using a pry bar, lift up on bottom of tire and wheel assembly and note any play. Ball joint maximum vertical play is .098" (2.5 mm).

REMOVAL & INSTALLATION

WHEEL BEARING

Removal (Corolla & Cressida)

1) Raise and support vehicle. Remove wheel assembly. Remove caliper retaining bolts. Remove caliper and support out of the way. Do not disconnect the brake hose. Remove grease cap, cotter pin, nut lock, and hub nut. Remove the hub and disc together with the outer bearing and thrust washer.

2) Using a screwdriver, remove oil seal from hub. Remove inner bearing. Using a brass drift and a hammer, drive both bearing races out of axle hub.

NOTE: Manufacturer suggests checking steering knuckle for cracks or damage by using a magnetic flaw detector and flaw detector penetrant.

Installation

1) Using Bearing Driver Set (09608-30022) for Cressida, or (09608-20012) for Corolla, drive new bearing races into place. Place grease in new bearing, inside hub and grease cap.

2) Place inside bearing in axle hub. Using Driver Set (09608-20011) for Corolla or (09608-20012) for Cressida, install oil seal.

3) To complete installation, reverse removal procedure. Adjust preload of wheel bearing. Install caliper and tighten to 47 ft. lbs. (64 N.m) for Corolla, and 67 ft. lbs. (91 N.m) for Cressida.

Removal (Supra)

1) Raise vehicle and support with safety stands. Remove wheel assembly. Remove the brake anti-lock speed sensor and brake hose bracket. Remove disc brake caliper bolts and support caliper out of way.

2) Match mark brake disc and wheel hub and remove disc. Remove tie rod end nut and press out using Ball Joint Puller (09628-10011). Remove upper ball joint nut and press out from housing using Ball Joint Puller (09628-62011). Remove lower ball joint nut and using same tool, press out ball joint from housing. Remove wheel bearing housing. *See Fig. 3.*

NOTE: Use care when handling wheel hub. The serrations on the hub trigger the anti-lock brake system.

Fig. 3: Exploded View of Supra Wheel Bearing Housing

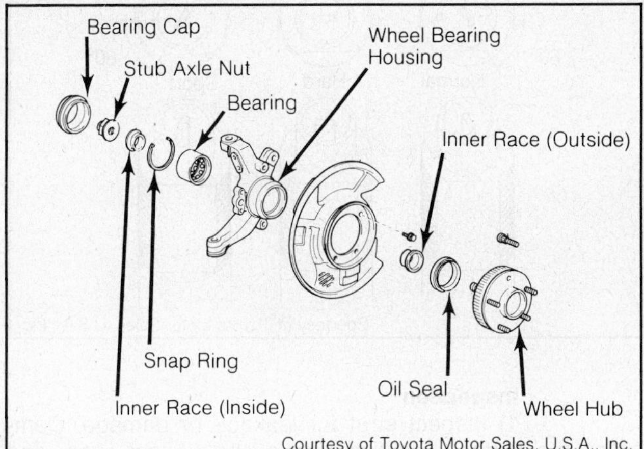

Courtesy of Toyota Motor Sales, U.S.A., Inc.

3) Remove the hub bearing cap. Using a chisel and hammer, loosen the staked part of stub axle self-locking nut and remove nut. Using a 2 jaw gear puller, remove wheel hub from bearing. Using same puller, remove inner bearing race from wheel hub.

4) Remove dust cover bolts and dust cover. Using a screwdriver pry out outer seal. Remove the bearing snap ring. Temporarily install inner race and using Bearing Replacer (09608-06100), press bearing out of housing.

Installation

1) Press new bearing in housing using Bearing Installer (09608-06120). Install snap ring. Install bearing inner race and using Seal Installer (09608-06020), drive in new seal. Install dust cover.

2) Use Press Adapter (09636-20010) to press wheel hub into housing. Install new stub axle self-locking nut and tighten to 147 ft. lbs. (199 N.m). Stake the lock nut. Install hub bearing cap.

3) To complete installation, reverse removal procedure. Upper and lower ball joints are to be initially tightened to 14 ft. lbs (20 N.m) using conventional nuts. Remove conventional nuts and install new self-locking nuts and tighten to specification. Tighten all bolts and nuts to specification. See TIGHTENING SPECIFICATIONS table in this article. Check wheel alignment.

CONTROL ARM & BALL JOINT

Removal (Corolla & Cressida)

1) Raise and support vehicle. Remove wheel assembly. Remove 2 bolts attaching steering knuckle arm to shock absorber. Push lower arm down and disconnect steering knuckle arm from shock absorber.

2) Remove cotter pin and nut holding knuckle arm to tie rod. Use Tie Rod Puller (09611-22012) to disconnect tie rod from knuckle arm for Corolla. Use Tie Rod Puller (09610-20012) for Cressida.

3) Remove nut holding stabilizer bar to lower arm and disconnect stabilizer bar. Remove nuts holding strut rod to lower arm and disconnect strut rod.

4) Remove bolt attaching control arm to crossmember. Remove control arm. Remove cotter pin and nut holding knuckle arm to ball joint. Use an arbor press to press knuckle arm from ball joint.

Disassembly

1) Use a screwdriver to remove ball joint dust cover set ring and dust cover.

NOTE: Ball joint is not serviceable separately. If worn or damaged, the ball joint and lower control arm must be replaced as a unit.

2) Using Bushing Remover (09726-12022), remove bushing from control arm.

Reassembly

1) Use Bushing Remover (09726-12022) to press new bushing into control arm. Apply ball joint grease to new dust cover.Install dust cover with escape valve facing rear of vehicle.

2) Wind wire twice around dust cover and bend wire knot down, facing to rear of ball joint. Remove plug and install grease fitting. Fill ball joint with grease. Remove fitting and install plug.

Installation

To install, reverse removal procedure. Do not tighten the lower control arm bolt to the crossmember until the vehicle has been lowered and bounced to settle the suspension. Tighten all bolts and nuts to specification. Check wheel alignment.

Removal (Supra)

1) Raise and support vehicle allowing suspension to hang free. Remove wheel assembly.

2) To remove upper control arm, Remove upper ball joint nut and press out using Ball Joint Puller (09628-62011). Remove the upper control arm mounting bolt and nut. Remove control arm.

3) To remove lower control arm, Disconnect stabilizer bar link from control arm. Remove lower ball joint nut and press out of housing using same tool as upper ball joint. Remove lower strut mounting bolt at control arm.

4) Match mark lower control arm adjusting cams. Remove nuts and adjusting cams. Remove control arm. If ball joint is to be replaced, remove attaching bolts and remove ball joint from control arm.

TOYOTA COROLLA RWD, CRESSIDA & SUPRA (Cont.)

Installation

1) To install, reverse removal procedure. Tighten upper and lower control arm bolts with vehicle on ground after bouncing vehicle to settle suspension.

2) Upper and lower ball joints are to be initially tightened to 14 ft. lbs (20 N.m) using conventional nuts. Remove conventional nuts and install new self-locking nuts and tighten to specification. Tighten all bolts and nuts to specification. Check wheel alignment.

STRUT ASSEMBLY

Removal (Corolla & Cressida)

1) Raise and support vehicle. Remove wheel assembly. Remove brake caliper mounting bolts and hang caliper out of way.

NOTE: **On Cressidas equipped with Electronic Modulated Suspension, refer to TOYOTA CRESSIDA & SUPRA ELECTRONIC SUSPENSION article at the end of this section before attempting to remove the strut assembly.**

2) Remove 3 nuts retaining top of strut assembly to inner fender. Remove 2 bolts attaching lower end of strut tube to steering knuckle arm. Push lower arm down and remove strut assembly.

Disassembly

1) Mount strut assembly in a vise. Use Spring Compressor (09727-22032) to compress coil spring. Remove the bearing dust cover. Use Seat Holding Lever (09729-22031) to hold top support of strut assembly, then remove the nut.

2) Remove suspension support, dust seal, spring seat, coil spring, and bumper. On Cressidas with Electronic Modulated Suspension remove the actuator bracket, suspension support, spring seat, piston rod dust cover, coil spring, and bumper.

Inspection

1) Inspect strut for leaks or damage. Compress piston rod. The stroke should feel even, and there should be no abnormal resistance or noise. Release piston rod, and check that it returns at a constant speed.

2) If shock absorber is defective, use Shock Absorber Wrench (09720-00011) and loosen ring nut 2 or 3 turns and allow gas to release completely. Remove ring nut and pull out shock absorber.

3) On Cressidas with Electronic Modulated Suspension, check that the control rod in the piston rod can be turned easily with needle nose pliers. With the control rod positioned as shown, check that there is a difference in damping at each position. *See Fig. 4.*

NOTE: **Before discarding the strut cartridge, the remaining gas must be released for safety. Drill a hole .079-.118" (2-3 mm) near the bottom of the cartridge to release the gas. The gas is colorless, odorless, and non-poisonous.**

Reassembly

To assemble, reverse disassembly procedure. Pack the bearing in the suspension support with grease.

Installation

To complete installation, reverse removal procedure. Tighten all bolts and nuts to specification. Check wheel alignment.

Removal (Supra)

1) Raise vehicle and support allowing suspension to hang free. Remove wheel assembly.

NOTE: **On Supras equipped with Electronic Modulated Suspension, refer to TOYOTA CRESSIDA & SUPRA ELECTRONIC SUSPENSION article at the end of this section before attempting to remove the strut assembly.**

2) Loosen strut piston rod lock nut until nut can be turned by hand. Disconnect upper control arm from body. Remove 3 upper strut retaining nuts. Remove lower strut mount bolt and remove strut.

Disassembly

1) Mount strut assembly in a vise. Use Spring Compressor (09727-22032) to compress coil spring. Remove the piston rod lock nut.

2) Remove suspension support, dust seal, spring seat, coil spring, and bumper. On Supras with Electronic Modulated Suspension remove the actuator bracket, suspension support, spring seat, piston rod dust cover, coil spring, and bumper.

Fig. 4: Control Rod Position for Cressida & Supra

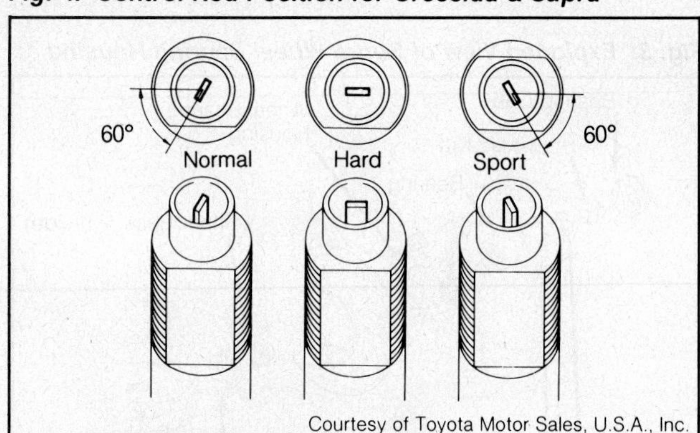

Inspection

1) Inspect strut for leakage or damage. Compress the piston rod. The stroke should feel even, and there should be no abnormal resistance or noise. Release the piston rod, and check that it returns at a constant speed. Replace if defective.

2) On Supras with Electronic Modulated Suspension, check that control rod in piston rod can be turned easily with needle nose pliers. With control rod positioned as shown, check that there is a difference in damping at each position. *See Fig. 4.*

Reassembly & Installation

To reassemble and install, reverse disassembly and removal procedures. Tighten upper control arm bolts and lower strut mounting bolt with vehicle on ground after bouncing to settle suspension. Tighten all bolts and nuts to specification. See TIGHTENING SPECIFICATIONS table in this article.

STABILIZER BAR & STRUT ROD

Removal (Cressida)

1) The strut rod and the stabilizer bar are removed together. Remove the cover under the engine.

TOYOTA COROLLA RWD, CRESSIDA & SUPRA (Cont.)

Disconnect the strut rod from the lower arm by removing the 2 nuts and bolts. Remove the front mounting nut and retainer from the body bracket. Be careful not to lose the shim on the strut rod.

2) Disconnect the stabilizer bar from the lower arm. Remove the stabilizer bracket from the strut rod body bracket. Raise the stabilizer bar and pull out the strut rod.

3) Remove the 4 bolts to the strut rod body bracket and remove the bracket with the stabilizer bar.

Removal (Corolla)

1) To remove strut rod, Remove the front strut rod nut and mounting hardware. Do not remove rear (staked) nut. Remove the nuts holding strut rod to lower control arm. Remove strut rod.

2) To remove stabilizer bar, Remove engine undercover. Disconnect stabilizer bar from lower control arms. Remove stabilizer bar chassis brackets. Remove stabilizer bar.

Installation (All Models)

1) To install, reverse removal procedure. On Corolla, check the distance between staked nut and center of bolt hole. Distance should be 14.622-14.662" (371.85-371.95 mm). *See Fig. 5.*

2) To complete installation, reverse removal procedure. Tighten all bolts and nuts to specification. Check wheel alignment.

Fig. 5: Strut Rod Adjustment

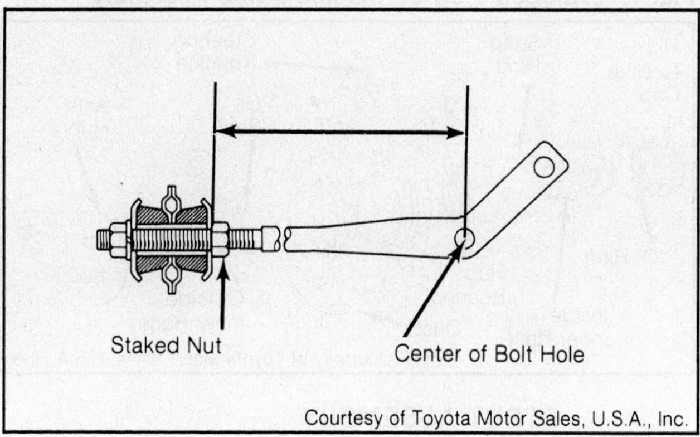

TIGHTENING SPECIFICATIONS

Application	Ft. Lbs. (N.m)
Corolla	
Ball Joint Nut	58 (78)
Brake Caliper Bolts	47 (64)
Knuckle Arm-to-Strut Bolts	58 (78)
Lower Control Arm Bolt	58 (78)
Shock Absorber Ring Nut	34 (47)
Stabilizer Bar-to-Control Arm Nut	13 (18)
Stabilizer Bar-to-Chassis Nut	10 (14)
Strut Piston Rod Nut	34 (47)
Strut Top Plate-to-Body Nut	13 (18)
Strut Rod-to-Control Arm Bolt	34 (47)
Strut Rod-to-Chassis Nut	67 (91)
Tie Rod Nut	43 (59)
Wheel Lug Nut	76 (103)
Cressida	
Ball Joint Nut	67 (91)
Brake Caliper Bolts	67 (91)
Knuckle Arm-to-Strut Bolts	80 (108)
Lower Control Arm Bolt	58 (78)
Shock Absorber Ring Nut	34 (47)
Stabilizer Bar-to-Chassis Nut	10 (14)
Stabilizer Bar-to-Control Arm Nut	13 (18)
Strut Piston Rod Nut	34 (47)
Strut Rod-to-Chassis Nut	87 (118)
Strut Rod-to-Control Arm Bolt	54 (73)
Strut Top Plate-to-Body Nut	27 (37)
Tie Rod Nut	43 (59)
Wheel Lug Nut	76 (103)
Supra	
Anti-Lock Brake	
Speed Sensor	14 (19)
Ball Joint Nut	
Lower	107 (145)
Upper	80 (108)
Ball Joint-to-Control Arm Bolt	94 (127)
Brake Caliper Bolt	77 (104)
Brake Hose Bracket	14 (19)
Control Arm-to-Chassis Bolt	
Lower	195 (265)
Upper	121 (164)
Stabilizer-to-Body Bolt	10 (14)
Stabilizer Link Nut	47 (64)
Strut Piston Rod Nut	22 (29)
Strut-to-Control Arm Bolt	106 (143)
Stub Axle Nut	147 (199)
Tie Rod Nut	36 (49)
Wheel Lug Nut	76 (103)

Front Suspension

TOYOTA MR2

DESCRIPTION

Toyota MR2 front suspension is MacPherson strut type with offset coil springs, gas shock absorbers and a spherical joint-type stabilizer bar. Lower end of strut is connected to upper end of knuckle. Lower end of knuckle connects to ball joint, which is connected to lower control arm. Stabilizer bar link is connected to strut. Strut bar is connected to lower control arm and frame and is adjustable for caster.

ADJUSTMENTS & INSPECTION

WHEEL ALIGNMENT SPECIFICATIONS & PROCEDURES

See WHEEL ALIGNMENT SPECIFICATIONS & PROCEDURES in WHEEL ALIGNMENT section.

WHEEL BEARING

Wheel bearings are not adjustable. Whenever bearings are removed, replace with new bearings, races, and oil seals. Check wheel bearing axial play with disc brake caliper and disc rotor removed. Maximum axial play is .002" (.05 mm). Replace bearing assembly if not within specification.

BALL JOINT CHECKING

1) Raise vehicle and place a 7.0-7.9" (180-200 mm) block under one front tire. Lower jack until there is half a load on front coil spring. Place safety stands under vehicle. Ensure wheels are straight ahead. Move lower arm up and down and ensure ball joint has no vertical play. Replace ball joint if vertical play is present.

2) Check turning torque of ball joint with joint removed from vehicle. Flip joint stud back and forth 5 times. Install stud nut and using an INCH lb. torque wrench, check turning torque. Turn nut one turn each 2-4 seconds and take torque reading on the fifth turn. Torque should be 7-21 INCH lbs. (.8-2.4 N.m). Replace ball joint if not within specification.

REMOVAL & INSTALLATION

WHEEL BEARING

Removal

1) Raise and support vehicle. Remove wheel assembly. Remove brake caliper and wire out of way. Remove and disassemble knuckle and hub assembly. Using Puller (09308-00010), remove oil seal from steering knuckle.

2) Remove snap ring from knuckle. Use puller to remove bearing outside inner race from hub. Drive out hub bearing from steering knuckle using Driver (09608-04060) and outside inner race.

Installation

To install, reverse removal procedure. Using Installer (09608-04070), install hub bearing in knuckle. Install new oil seal onto Installer (09608-04020) and tap into knuckle.

KNUCKLE & HUB ASSEMBLY

Removal

1) Raise and support vehicle. Remove wheel assembly. Remove brake caliper and wire out of way. Remove disc rotor. Disconnect stabilizer link from strut. Disconnect lower ball joint from lower arm.

2) Using Remover (09628-62011), remove tie rod end from knuckle. Mark strut camber adjusting cam for reassembly reference. Disconnect strut from knuckle. Remove hub and knuckle assembly.

Disassembly

Remove hub bearing cap and "O" ring. Loosen staked part of hub lock nut and remove lock nut. Remove disc brake dust cover. Using Puller (09950-20016), remove axle hub from steering knuckle.

Reassembly

To reassemble, reverse disassembly procedure. Apply grease to oil seal lip. Use Driver (09310-35010) to install axle hub into knuckle. Tighten axle hub lock nut to 90 ft. lbs. (123 N.m). Use Driver (09608-04020) to install hub cap and new "O" ring.

Installation

To install, reverse removal procedure. Ensure strut camber adjusting cam marks are aligned.

Fig. 1: Exploded View of Knuckle & Hub Assembly

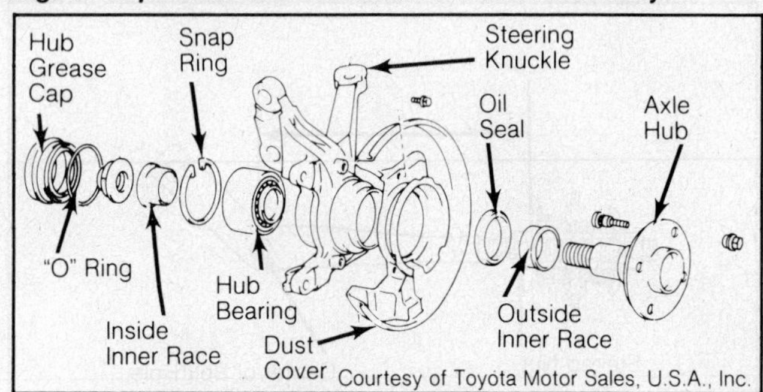

Courtesy of Toyota Motor Sales, U.S.A., Inc.

STRUT ASSEMBLY

Removal

1) Raise and support vehicle. Remove wheel assembly. Disconnect brake line from disc brake caliper. Drain fluid into container. Plug brake line. Remove clip from strut and remove brake hose. Disconnect stabilizer bar link from strut.

2) Mark strut camber adjusting cam for reassembly reference. Disconnect knuckle from strut. Remove 3 bolts holding top of strut to body. Remove strut from vehicle.

Disassembly

1) Install a bolt and 2 nuts to lower portion of strut bracket to prevent strut shell from being crushed when clamped in vise. Clamp strut in vise and use Compressor (09727-22032) to compress coil spring.

2) Use Wrench (09729-22031) to hold spring seat from turning and remove piston rod lock nut. Remove support, spring seat, coil spring, insulator and rubber bumper.

TOYOTA MR2 (Cont.)

Inspection

Check shock absorber action for abnormal noise, resistance and smoothness. If defective, replace shock absorber unit. Loosen ring nut with Spanner Wrench (09721-00071) to release gas before discarding strut.

Reassembly

To reassemble, reverse disassembly procedure. Ensure "OUT" mark on upper spring seat faces toward outside of vehicle. Tighten piston rod lock nut to 36 ft. lbs. (49 N.m).

Installation

To install, reverse removal procedure. Ensure strut camber adjusting cam marks are aligned. Ensure flexible brake hose peg aligns with hole in caliper when connecting. Bleed brakes. Check camber.

Fig. 2: Exploded View of Front Suspension Assembly

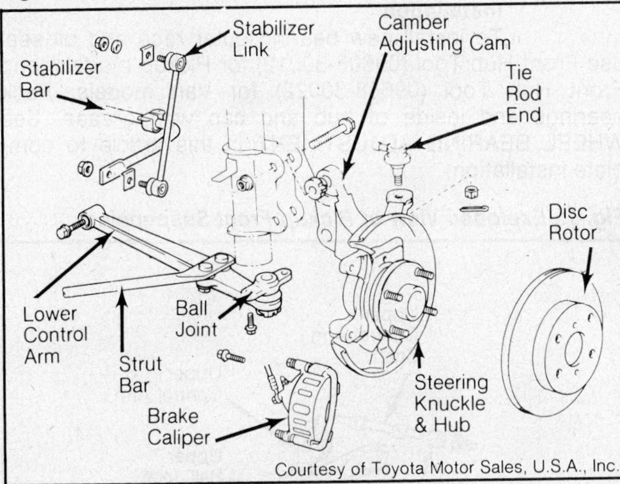

LOWER CONTROL ARM

Removal & Installation

Raise and support vehicle. Remove wheel assembly. Remove ball joint cotter pin and castle nut. Use Puller (09610-20012) to disconnect lower arm from ball joint. Disconnect strut bar from lower arm. Remove lower arm-to-frame bolt. Remove arm from vehicle. To install, reverse removal procedure. Check wheel alignment.

STABILIZER BAR

Removal

Raise and support vehicle. Remove wheel assembly. Disconnect stabilizer link from stabilizer bar. Remove stabilizer bar brackets and remove bar from vehicle. Remove stabilizer link from strut.

Inspection

Inspect stabilizer link ball joints for freedom of movement in all directions. If movement is not smooth and free, replace stabilizer link.

Installation

To install, reverse removal procedure.

STRUT BAR

Removal

Raise and support vehicle. Remove wheel assembly. Measure length "A". *See Fig. 3.* Remove front nut and cushion. Loosen rear nut. Remove nuts retaining strut bar to lower control arm. Remove arm from vehicle.

Installation

To install, reverse removal procedure. Length "A" should be 14.25-14.29" (362-363 mm). Tighten front nut to 83 ft. lbs. (113 N.m) after vehicle is lowered to ground.

Fig. 3: Measuring Strut Rod Length

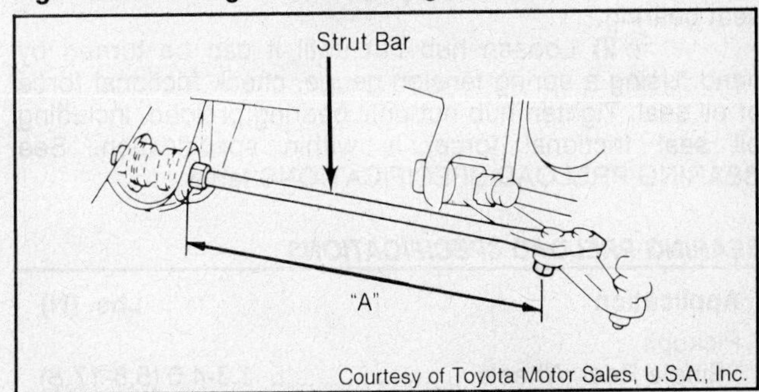

TIGHTENING SPECIFICATIONS

Application	Ft. Lbs. (N.m)
Axle Hub Lock Nut	90 (123)
Ball Joint-to-Knuckle Bolts	59 (80)
Ball Joint-to-Lower Arm Nut	58 (78)
Brake Line-to-Caliper Bolt	22 (30)
Caliper-to-Knuckle Bolts	65 (88)
Lower Arm-to-Frame Bolt	94 (127)
Stabilizer Link Nuts	47 (64)
Stabilizer Bar Bracket-to-Body	14 (19)
Strut Bar-to-Lower Arm Nuts	83 (113)
Strut Bar Front Nut	83 (113)
Strut Piston Rod Nut	36 (49)
Strut-to-Body Nuts	26 (35)
Strut-to-Knuckle Bolts	105 (142)
Tie Rod End Nut	36 (49)

Front Suspension

TOYOTA 2WD PICKUP & VAN

DESCRIPTION

Toyota 2WD Pickups and Vans have conventional type front suspension which uses torsion bars in place of coil springs. Strut bars are mounted at frame and lower control arm ends. A stabilizer bar is mounted to the frame and connected at ends to the lower control arms.

ADJUSTMENTS & INSPECTION

WHEEL ALIGNMENT SPECIFICATIONS & PROCEDURES

See WHEEL ALIGNMENT SPECIFICATIONS & PROCEDURES in WHEEL ALIGNMENT section.

WHEEL BEARING

1) Remove bolts attaching disc brake caliper and torque plate to spindle. Do not disconnect brake line. Remove and secure caliper out of way. Tighten outer bearing nut to 25 ft. lbs. (34 N.m) for Pickup and 21 ft. lbs. (28 N.m) for Van. Turn hub right and left 2 or 3 times to seat bearing.

2) Loosen hub nut until it can be turned by hand. Using a spring tension gauge, check frictional force of oil seal. Tighten hub nut until bearing preload, including oil seal frictional force, is within specification. See BEARING PRELOAD SPECIFICATIONS table.

BEARING PRELOAD SPECIFICATIONS

Application	Lbs. (N)
Pickups	
Single Rear Wheels	1.3-4.0 (5.8-17.8)
Dual Rear Wheels	0.9-2.2 (3.9-9.8)
Vans	0.8-1.9 (3.4-8.5)

3) Using a dial gauge, check hub axial play. Maximum hub axial play is .002" (.05 mm). Install nut lock, new cotter pin and dust cap. On Pickup models, install torque plate onto steering knuckle and tighten bolts to 80 ft. lbs. (108 N.m). Install disc brake caliper.

BALL JOINT INSPECTION

1) To check lower ball joint, raise and support vehicle. Ensure wheels are positioned straight ahead. Have a helper depress brake pedal. Use a sturdy rod as a lever against wheel and under lower control arm to move lower control arm up and down. Van models should have no vertical movement. On Pickup models, maximum vertical movement should not exceed .091" (2.3 mm).

2) To check upper ball joint, use a block as a fulcrum and rod as a lever under tire to move entire wheel assembly up and down. Maximum vertical movement should not exceed .091" (2.3 mm).

3) Disconnect ball joint from steering knuckle. Move ball joint stud back and forth several times, then install stud nut. Using a torque wrench, turn nut continuously about one turn every 2-4 seconds. Note torque reading on 5th turn. See BALL JOINT TURNING TORQUE SPECIFICATIONS table.

BALL JOINT TURNING TORQUE SPECIFICATIONS

Application	INCH Lbs. (N.m)
Pickup	
Lower Ball Joint	22-43 (2.5-4.9)
Upper Ball Joint	18-34 (2.0-3.9)
Van	
Lower Ball Joint	13-26 (1.5-2.9)
Upper Ball Joint	9-30 (1.0-3.4)

REMOVAL & INSTALLATION

WHEEL BEARING

Removal

1) Raise and support vehicle. Remove wheel assembly. Remove disc brake caliper. On pickup models, remove torque plate. Do not disconnect brake line. Secure caliper out of the way. Remove dust cap, cotter pin, nut lock and hub nut. Remove the hub and disc together with the outer bearing and thrust washer.

2) Using a screwdriver, remove grease seal from back of hub and inner bearing. Using a brass drift, drive inner and outer bearing races from hub and rotor assembly.

Installation

To install new bearing outer race and oil seal use Front Hub Tool (09608-30012) for Pickup models, and Front Hub Tool (09608-30022) for Van models. Pack bearings and inside of hub and cap with grease. See WHEEL BEARING ADJUSTMENT in this article to complete installation.

Fig. 1: Exploded View of Pickup Front Suspension

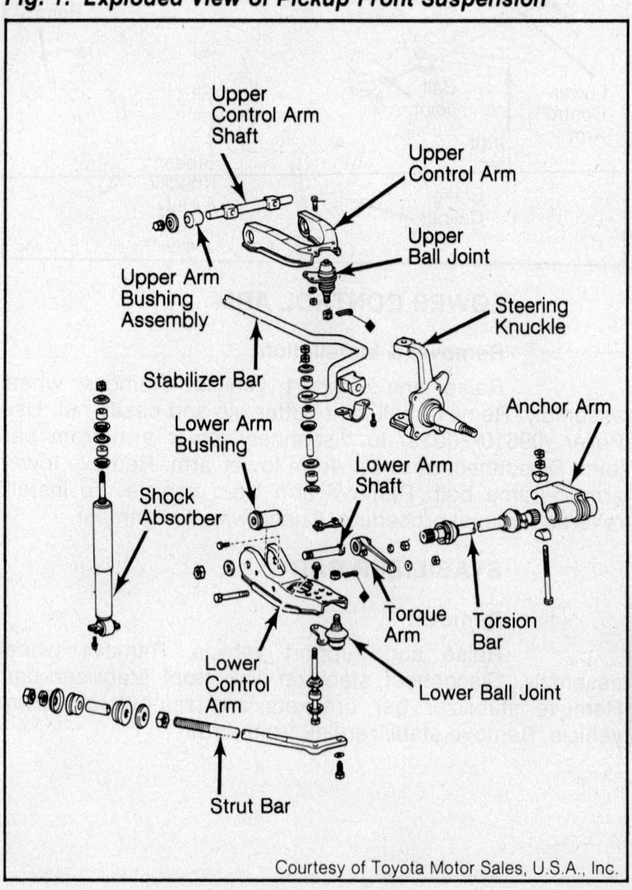

UPPER CONTROL ARM

Removal

On Van models, remove torsion bar spring and cool air intake duct. See TORSIONAL BAR removal in this

TOYOTA 2WD PICKUP & VAN (Cont.)

Fig. 2: Exploded View of Van Front Suspension

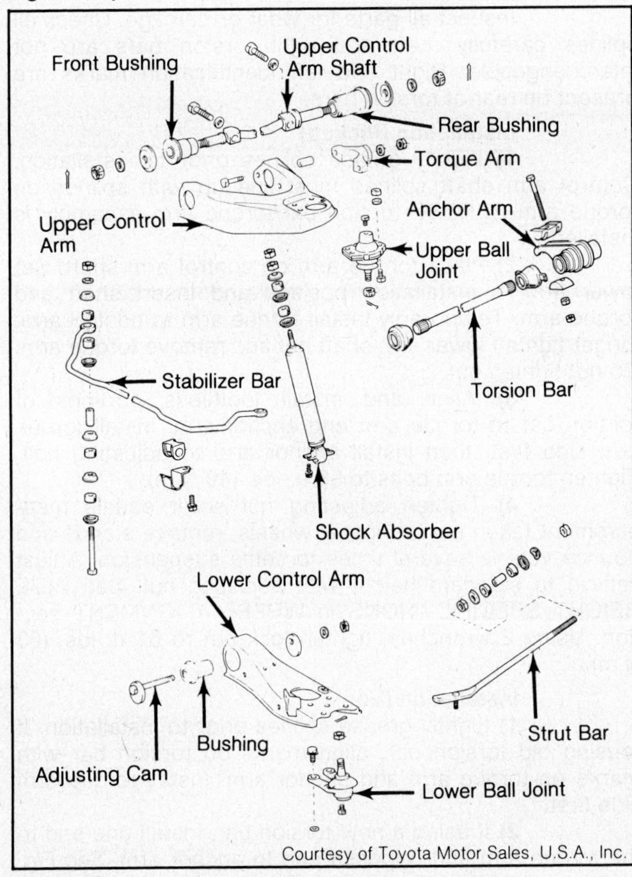

Courtesy of Toyota Motor Sales, U.S.A., Inc.

article. On all models, support lower control arm with a jack. Remove 4 ball joint-to-lower control arm bolts and disconnect upper arm. Note location of camber adjusting shims and remove upper control arm shaft bolts. Remove upper control arm.

Bushing Replacement

1) Remove bolts and washers to control arm shaft. Use an arbor press and Suspension Bushing Set (09710-30020 for Pickup, 09726-27011 for Van) to remove bushings.

2) Inspect all components for wear, cracks or distortion. Use arbor press and suspension bushing set to press bushings into upper control arm. Install bushing bolts and washers finger-tight. On Van models, install washers and nuts on shaft and position shaft so frame installation surface is at a right angle to arm. *See Fig. 3.*

NOTE: Do not apply grease or oil to the bushing.

3) On Pickup models, tighten upper arm shaft bolts to 93 ft. lbs. (126 N.m). On Van models, tighten rear shaft nuts to 71 ft. lbs. (96 N.m), then tighten front shaft nuts to 58 ft. lbs. (78 N.m). Secure with new cotter pins. Install torque arm. Tighten bolts to 35 ft. lbs. (47 N.m).

Installation (Pickup)

1) Insert camber adjusting shims in their original location. Tighten upper control arm bolts to 72 ft. lbs. (98 N.m). Raise spindle with jack and install ball joint.

2) Remove stands and lower vehicle. Bounce vehicle to stabilize suspension. Tighten upper control arm shaft bolts to 93 ft. lbs. (126 N.m). Check wheel alignment.

Fig. 3: Van Upper Arm Shaft Angle

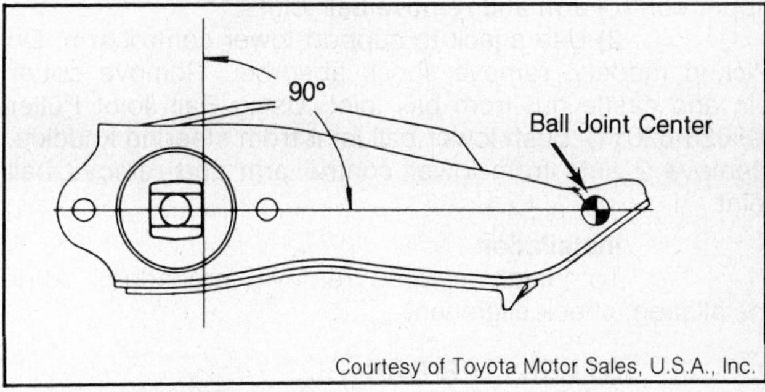

Courtesy of Toyota Motor Sales, U.S.A., Inc.

Installation (Van)

1) Tighten upper arm-to-frame bolts to 65 ft. lbs. (88 N.m) on the front side and 112 ft. lbs. (152 N.m) on the rear side.

NOTE: Tighten rear side nuts first.

2) Raise spindle with jack and install ball joint onto control arm. Install and tighten 4 ball joint-to-control arm bolts to 22 ft. lbs. (29 N.m). Install cool air intake duct and caliper assembly. Install torsion bar. Check wheel alignment.

LOWER CONTROL ARM & BUSHING

Removal

1) Raise and support vehicle. Remove wheel assembly. On Pickup models, remove torsion bar assembly. See TORSION BAR REMOVAL in this article.

2) On all models, disconnect tie rod end and remove shock absorber. Disconnect stabilizer bar and strut bar from lower control arm. Remove 3 bolts and disconnect lower ball joint from lower control arm. On Pickup models, remove lower control arm shaft nut and remove control arm. On Van, mark position of adjusting cam. Remove adjusting cam and nut and remove lower control arm.

3) To remove bushing on Pickup models cut rubber of bushing until flush with control arm. Use Lower Arm Bushing Tool (09726-27011) to remove bushing. On Van models use Spring Bushing Tool (09707-37010) and Bushing Tool Set (09726-27011) to remove bushing.

Installation

1) On Pickup, apply soapy water to bushing and install with bushing tool. On Vans, use bushing set to press bushing into control arm.

NOTE: On Vans, do not apply grease or oil to bushing. Do not press on the inside flange of the bushing.

2) On all models, complete installation by reversing removal procedure. Tighten lower arm shaft nut on Pickup and cam nut on Van to specification after vehicle has been lowered to floor and bounced to align suspension. Check wheel alignment.

BALL JOINTS

Removal

1) Remove disc brake caliper without disconnecting brake line. Secure disc brake caliper out of way. Remove cotter pin and castle nut from ball joint. Using Ball Joint Puller (09628-62011), remove ball joint from

TOYOTA 2WD PICKUP & VAN (Cont.)

steering knuckle. Remove 4 nuts holding ball joint to upper control arm and remove ball joint.

2) Use a jack to support lower control arm. On Pickup models, remove shock absorber. Remove cotter pin and castle nut from ball joint. Using Ball Joint Puller (09628-62011), push lower ball joint from steering knuckle. Remove 2 nuts from lower control arm and remove ball joint.

Installation

To install, reverse removal procedure. After installation, check alignment.

STABILIZER BAR

Removal

On Pickup models, remove one torsion bar spring. On all models, remove nuts, cushions and bolts retaining both sides of stabilizer bar to lower control arms. Remove both stabilizer bar bushings and brackets from frame. Remove stabilizer bar.

Installation

To install, reverse removal procedure. Adjust torsion bar on Pickups. See TORSION BAR in this article. Check wheel alignment.

STRUT BAR

Removal

Place reference marks on threaded portion of strut bar for reassembly reference. Remove nut from strut bar bracket. Remove bolts holding strut bar to lower control arm and remove strut bar.

Installation

To install, reverse removal procedure. Check wheel alignment.

STEERING KNUCKLE

Removal

1) Raise and support vehicle. Remove wheel assembly. Remove brake caliper without disconnecting brake line. Secure caliper out of way.

2) Remove dust cap, cotter pin and nut lock. Remove hub nut, thrust washer, outer bearing and axle hub. Remove knuckle arm and dust cover.

3) Support lower arm with jack. Remove cotter pins and castle nuts from ball joint studs. Using Ball Joint Puller (09628-62010), separate ball joints from steering knuckle. On Vans, disconnect shock at lower control arm. Remove steering knuckle.

Installation

To install, reverse removal procedure. Check wheel alignment.

TORSION BAR

Removal

1) Raise and support vehicle. Remove wheel assembly. Remove torsion bar boots. On Van models, place match marks on torsion bar, anchor arm and torque arm for correct spline alignment at reassembly.

2) On all models, remove lock nut and measure distance from end of adjuster bolt to top of adjusting nut. Record distance for use when adjusting vehicle height. Loosen adjusting nut. Remove torque arm, torsion bar and anchor arm. Do not remove torque arm on Vans.

Inspection

Inspect all parts for wear or damage. Check all splines carefully. Left and right torsion bars are not interchangeable. Right and left identification marks are present on rear of torsion bars.

Installation (Pickup)

1) Lightly grease splines prior to installation. Control arm shaft splines must line up with splines on torque arm BEFORE torsion bar/torque arm assembly is installed.

2) Place torque arm on control arm shaft. Set lower arm in installation position and insert shaft and torque arm. Temporarily install torque arm to control arm. Finger tighten lower arm shaft nut and remove torque arm. Do not tighten nut.

3) Align and install toothless portions of torsion bar to torque arm and anchor arm. Install torque arm side first, then install anchor arm to adjusting bolt. Tighten torque arm bolts to 36 ft. lbs. (49 N.m).

4) Tighten adjusting nut so it equals measurement taken earlier. Install wheels, remove stands and bounce vehicle several times to settle suspension. Adjust vehicle to standard height with adjusting nut. See RIDE HEIGHT SPECIFICATIONS in WHEEL ALIGNMENT section. Using 2 wrenches, tighten lock nut to 61 ft. lbs. (83 N.m).

Installation (Van)

1) Lightly grease splines prior to installation. If reusing old torsion bar, align marks on torsion bar with marks on torque arm and anchor arm. Install torque arm side first.

2) If using a new torsion bar, install one end to the torque arm and opposite end to anchor arm. *See Fig. 4.* Finger tighten adjusting nut. Ensure upper control arm is positioned horizontally. *See Fig. 3.*

Fig. 4: Van Anchor Arm Angle

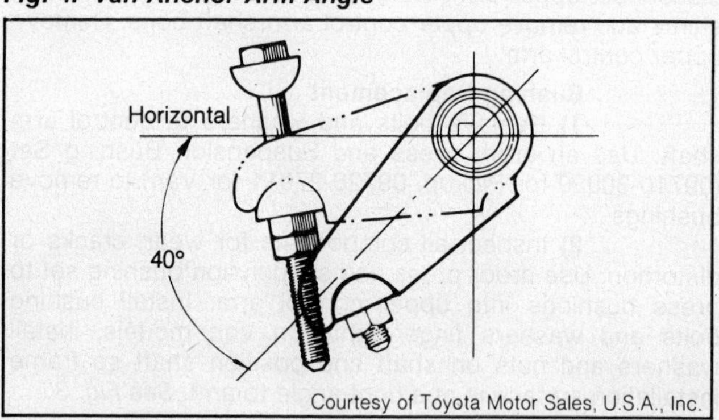

Courtesy of Toyota Motor Sales, U.S.A., Inc.

3) Tighten adjusting nut so it equals measurement taken in step **2)** of removal. Install wheels, remove stands and bounce vehicle several times to settle suspension. Adjust vehicle to standard height with adjusting nut. See RIDE HEIGHT SPECIFICATIONS in WHEEL ALIGNMENT section. Using 2 wrenches, tighten lock nut to 61 ft. lbs. (83 N.m).

SHOCK ABSORBER

Removal

1) Raise and support vehicle. Remove wheel assembly. Remove 2 nuts retaining shock absorber to bracket. Remove washers and cushions from shaft of shock absorber.

Front Suspension

TOYOTA 2WD PICKUP & VAN (Cont.)

2) Remove bolts securing shock absorber to lower control arm. Compress shock absorber and remove from vehicle.

Installation

To install, reverse removal procedure.

TIGHTENING SPECIFICATIONS

Application	Ft. Lbs. (N.m)
Pickup	
Brake Caliper Bolts	65 (88)
Lower Ball Joint-to-Arm Bolts	51 (69)
Lower Ball Joint-to-Steering Knuckle Nut	105 (142)
Lower Arm Shaft Nut	166 (226)
Lower Arm-to-Frame Bolts	199 (270)
Shock Absorber-to-Bracket Bolts	18 (25)
Shock Absorber-to-Lower Arm Bolts	13 (18)
Stabilizer-to-Lower Arm Bolts	9 (13)
Strut Bar-to-Lower Arm Bolts	70 (95)
Strut Bar Front Nut	90 (123)
Tie Rod End-to-Steering Knuckle	67 (90)
Torque Arm Lock Nut	61 (83)
Torque Arm-to-Lower Arm Bolts	36 (49)
Upper Arm Shaft-to-Frame Bolts	72 (98)
Upper Arm-to-Shaft Bolts	93 (126)
Upper Ball Joint-to-Arm Bolts	20 (26)
Upper Ball Joint-to-Steering Knuckle Nut	80 (108)

TIGHTENING SPECIFICATIONS (Cont.)

Application	Ft. Lbs. (N.m)
Van	
Adjusting Cam Nut	112 (152)
Brake Caliper Bolts	77 (104)
Lower Ball Joint-to-Arm Bolts	49 (67)
Lower Ball Joint-to-Steering Knuckle Nut	76 (103)
Lower Control Arm Adjusting Cam Nut	152 (206)
Shock Absorber-to-Lower Arm Bolts	13 (18)
Shock Absorber Upper Mounting Nut	18 (25)
Stabilizer-to-Frame Bolts	14 (19)
Strut Bar-to-Lower Arm Bolts	49 (67)
Strut Bar Rear Nut	89 (121)
Tie Rod End-to-Steering Knuckle	43 (59)
Torque Arm-to-Upper Arm Bolts	35 (47)
Upper Arm Shaft-to-Frame Bolts	
Front Side Bolts	65 (88)
Rear Side Bolts	112 (152)
Upper Arm-to-Shaft Bolts	
Front Side Nut	58 (78)
Rear Side Nut	71 (96)
Upper Arm-to-Torque Arm	35 (47)
Upper Ball Joint-to-Steering Knuckle Nut	58 (78)

Front Suspension

TOYOTA 4WD PICKUP, VAN & 4RUNNER

DESCRIPTION

An independent front suspension with upper control arm mounted torsion bars is used on all Toyota 4WD vehicles. Wheel is supported by a steering knuckle mounted between the upper and lower control arms. The torsion bars are mounted between the upper control arms and vehicle frame.

Vehicle roll is controlled by a stabilizer bar attached to each front lower control arm and frame. Shock absorbers are mounted between the lower control arm and frame.

ADJUSTMENTS & INSPECTION

WHEEL ALIGNMENT SPECIFICATIONS & PROCEDURES

See WHEEL ALIGNMENT SPECIFICATIONS & PROCEDURES in WHEEL ALIGNMENT section.

BALL JOINT

1) To inspect lower ball joint for wear, jack up front of vehicle and support with jack stands. Ensure that front wheels are in straight forward position and depress brake pedal.

2) Move lower control arm up and down, while checking for excessive play. Maximum vertical play is zero.

3) To inspect upper ball joint for wear, move upper control arm up and down. Maximum vertical play is .091" (2.3 mm). Check lower ball joints for rotation condition.

4) Using a torque wrench attached to ball joint stud, turn nut continuously one full turn each 2-4 seconds. Take torque reading on 5th turn. Torque reading for lower ball joint should be 26-52 INCH lbs. (3.0-5.9 N.m). Only lower ball joint requires this inspection.

WHEEL BEARINGS

Adjust preload by tightening adjusting nut to 43 ft. lbs. (59 N.m). Install new lock washer and lock nut. Ensure there is no bearing side play. Recheck preload using spring tension gauge attached to a wheel stud. Tension (rotating preload) on Pickup and 4Runner models should be 6.4-12.6 lbs. (28-56 N). On Van models, rotating preload should be 4.6-7.9 lbs. (21-35 N). Secure lock nut by bending one lock washer tooth outward.

REMOVAL & INSTALLATION

AUTOMATIC & FREE WHEELING HUB

Removal

Turn hub selector to "FREE" position. Remove hub cover mounting bolts and cover. Remove center bolt and washer. Remove mounting nuts and washers. Using brass bar and hammer, tap on bolt heads and remove cone washer. Remove hub body.

Installation

To install, reverse removal procedure. Tighten all nuts and bolts to specification.

WHEEL BEARING

NOTE: To check front wheel bearings, 4WD hub assembly must be removed.

Removal

1) Using Brake Tube Union Wrench (09751-36011), remove brake line from disc brake assembly. Remove disc brake caliper from steering knuckle.

2) On models with free wheeling hubs, release hub lock washer with a screwdriver. Remove lock nut and washer using Adjusting Nut Wrench (09607-60020). On all models, use same tool and remove adjusting nut. On models with free wheeling hubs, thrust washer and hub and disc assembly with outer bearing and washer. Pry out oil seal and remove inner bearing from hub.

Inspection & Replacement

Clean bearings and outer races. Inspect all components for excessive wear or damage. Using brass bar and hammer, drive out bearing outer races. Drive in new bearing races using Axle Hub and Drive Pinion Tool Kit (09608-35014).

Installation

1) Ensure all bearings are packed with multi-purpose grease. Coat inside of hub with grease. Install inner bearing into hub. Drive new oil seal into hub and coat seal lip with grease.

2) To complete installation, reverse removal procedure. Install disc brake caliper to steering knuckle and install 4WD hubs. See AUTOMATIC & FREE WHEELING HUB REMOVAL and INSTALLATION procedures in this article.

UPPER CONTROL ARM

Removal (Pickup & 4Runner)

1) Remove torsion bar spring. Remove cotter pin and nut. Disconnect upper ball joint from steering knuckle. Remove nut, cushion and retainer. Disconnect shock absorber from frame. Do not disconnect shock absorber from lower control arm.

2) Disconnect intermediate shaft from steering gear housing. Remove 2 upper control arm shaft bolts and remove upper control arm from frame.

3) To replace bushings, remove torque arm. Using a chisel and hammer, loosen and remove nut. Push out front and rear bushings.

Removal (Van)

1) Remove torsion bar spring. Remove right front seat, console box, transmission and transmission shift levers with retainers. Disconnect brake cable from brake lever. Remove brake lever assembly.

2) Disconnect brake cable from intermediate lever and remove. Remove shift cable from transmission. Remove seat floor panel, fan shroud and radiator mounting bolts and nuts. Removal of radiator is not necessary.

3) Disconnect shock absorber from frame. Do not disconnect shock absorber from lower control arm. Disconnect ball joint from steering knuckle. Remove 2 upper control arm shaft bolts and remove upper control arm from frame.

Installation

To install, reverse removal procedure. Tighten all nuts and bolts to specification.

LOWER CONTROL ARM

Removal

1) Remove shock absorber and disconnect stabilizer bar from lower control arm. Remove 4 bolts and disconnect lower control arm from lower ball joint.

2) Place match marks on front and rear adjusting cams. Remove nuts and adjusting cams. Re-

TOYOTA 4WD PICKUP, VAN & 4RUNNER (Cont.)

move lower control arm. Press out bushings from lower control arms.

Installation

To install, reverse removal procedure. Press in new bushings. Do not apply grease or oil to bushings. Inspect shock absorber. Ensure that match marks are aligned and tighten all nuts and bolts to specification. Check front wheel alignment.

BALL JOINTS

Inspection

1) To inspect lower ball joint for wear, jack up front of vehicle and support with jack stands. Ensure that front wheels are in straight forward position and depress brake pedal.

2) Move lower control arm up and down, while checking for excessive play. Maximum vertical play is zero.

3) To inspect upper ball joint for wear, move upper control arm up and down. Maximum vertical play is .091" (2.3 mm). Check lower ball joints for rotation condition.

4) Using a torque wrench attached to ball joint stud, turn nut continuously one full turn each 2-4 seconds. Take torque reading on 5th turn. Torque reading for lower ball joint should be 26-52 INCH lbs. (3.0-5.9 N.m). Only lower ball joint requires this inspection.

Fig. 1: Exploded View of 4WD Pickup & 4Runner Front Suspension

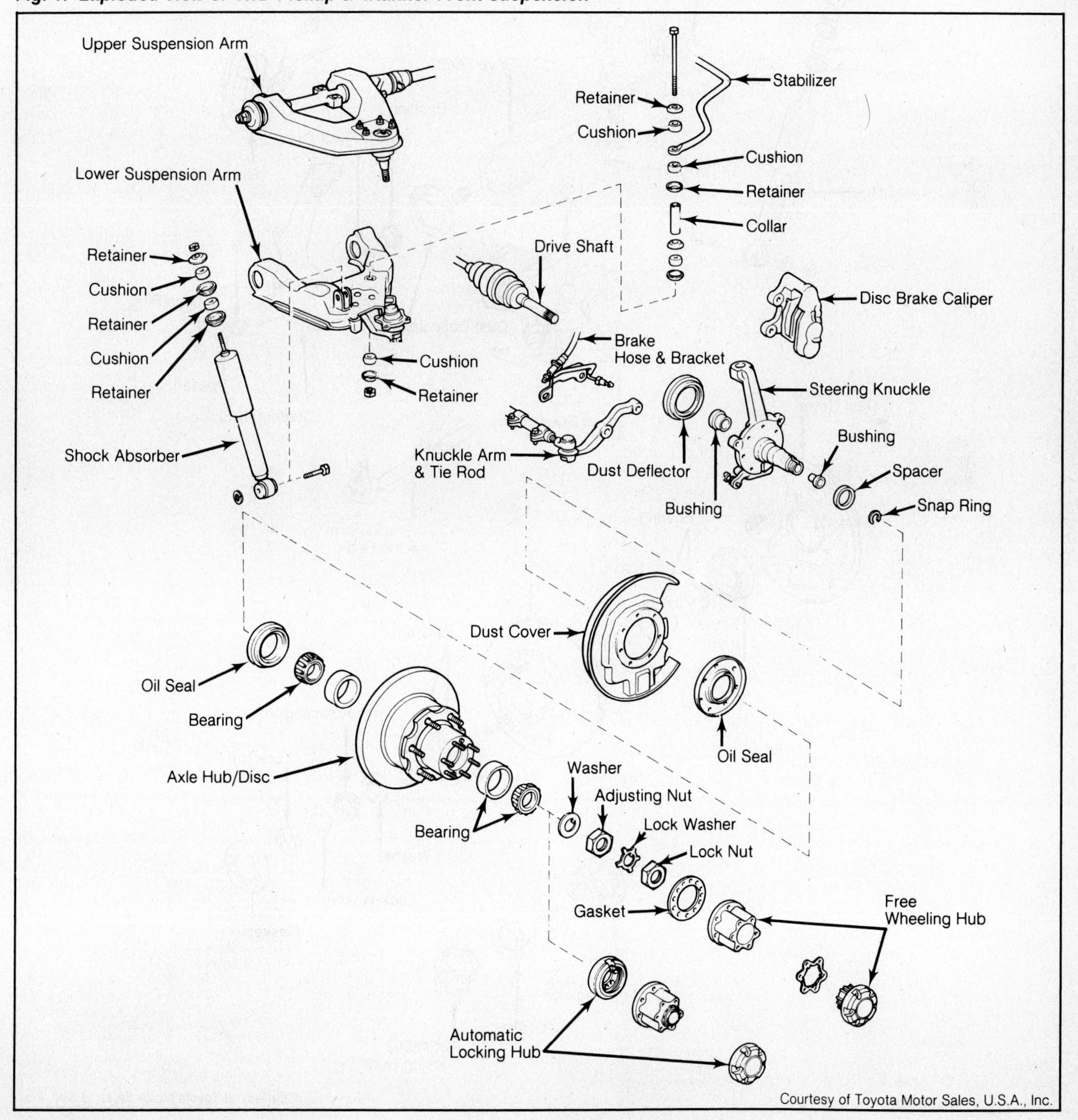

Removal

Remove steering knuckle. See STEERING KNUCKLE in this article. Remove cotter pin and nut. Remove lower ball joint from lower control arm. Remove upper ball joint from upper control arm.

Installation

To install, reverse removal procedure. Ensure all nuts and bolts are tightened to specification.

STEERING KNUCKLE

Removal

1) Remove disc brake caliper and front axle hub. Remove dust cover and oil seal. Disconnect knuckle arm from steering knuckle. Install bolt in drive shaft.

2) Using feeler gauge, measure front drive axle thrust clearance between steering knuckle outside bushing and spacer. See DRIVE AXLE THRUST CLEARANCE table.

Fig. 2: Exploded View of Van Front Suspension

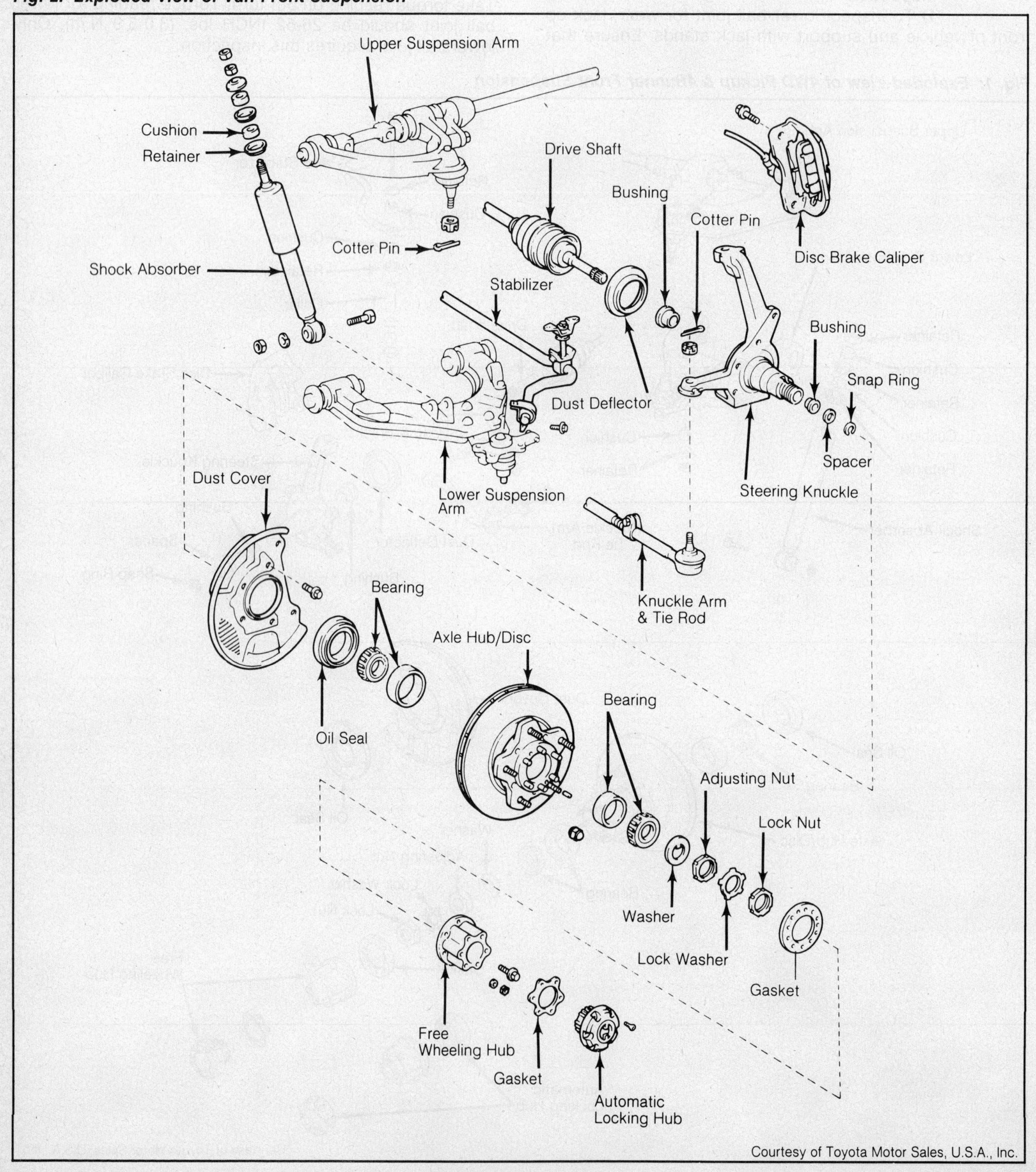

TOYOTA 4WD PICKUP, VAN & 4RUNNER (Cont.)

DRIVE AXLE THRUST CLEARANCE

Clearance	In. (mm)
Standard	.00295-.0272 (.075-.690)
Maximum	.039 (1.0)

3) If measurement is more than maximum clearance, replace steering knuckle outside and inside bushings. If measurement is within specification, go next step.

4) Disconnect front shock absorber from lower control arm. Disconnect stabilizer bar from lower control arm. Remove snap ring and spacer. Remove cotter pin and nut from upper ball joint.

5) Using Ball Joint Puller (09308-00010), disconnect steering knuckle from upper ball joint. Remove 4 bolts from lower ball joint. Disconnect steering knuckle from lower ball joint.

6) Push lower control arm down and remove steering knuckle. Using dye penetrant, check steering knuckle for cracks or excessive wear. Pry out dust deflector.

7) Using Oil Seal Puller (09308-00010), pull out steering knuckle outside bushing. Using brass bar and hammer, drive out steering knuckle inside bushing.

Installation

1) Install inside and outside bushings. On Pickup/4Runner models, use Bushing Replacer Set (09550-10012, 09252-10010 and 09555-10010). On Van models, use Bushing Replacer Set (09608-35014, 09608-06020 and 09608-06090).

NOTE: **When installing bushing in spindle, ensure that flat portion of bushing is aligned with spindle groove.**

2) Apply Molybdenum Disulphide Lithium (MDL) base grease to steering knuckle bushings. To complete installation, reverse removal procedure. Install new cotter pin. Tighten all nuts and bolts to specification.

3) Install new cotter pin. If steering knuckle bushings are replaced, recheck drive axle thrust clearance. Clearance can be altered by adding or removing spacers. Spacers are available in 2 sizes; .0709" (1.80 mm) and .0886" (2.25 mm).

TORSION BAR

Removal

Remove boots and place match marks on torsion bar spring, anchor arm and torque arm. Loosen adjusting nut. Remove anchor arm and torsion bar spring. Measure distance of protruding bolt end. Use this measurement for reference when adjusting vehicle height.

NOTE: **On rear end of torsion bar springs there are left and right indication marks. Ensure they are not interchanged when installing.**

Installation (Used Torsion Bar Spring)

Apply light coat of MDL base grease to spline of torsion bar spring. Align match marks and install torsion bar spring to torque arm. Align match marks and install anchor arm to torsion bar spring. Tighten adjusting nut so that bolt protrusion is equal to original measurement. Tighten lock nut to 61 ft. lbs. (83 N.m) and assemble boots.

Installation (New Torsion Bar Spring)

1) Remove wheel and install 2 boots to torsion bar spring. Apply light coat MDL base grease to spline of torsion bar spring.

2) Temporarily install anchor arm to small end of torsion bar spring. Place match marks on torsion bar spring and anchor arm.

NOTE: **One spline on torsion bar is larger than others. Install torsion bar spring into anchor arm. Slowly turn anchor arm until large end of spline enters matching point in anchor arm.**

3) Align match marks on torsion bar spring and anchor arm on bottom of each. Remove anchor arm from torsion bar spring. Install torsion bar spring into torque arm.

4) Align match marks and install anchor arm to torsion bar spring. On Pickup and 4Runner models, tighten adjusting nut to 3.43" (87 mm) protrusion length. On Van models, first tighten adjusting nut to 1.57" (40 mm) protrusion length. Then tighten adjusting nut to 2.48" (63 mm) length for YR31LG models and 2.40" (61 mm) length for YR32LV models.

5) On all models, temporarily install lock nut. Install wheel and remove stands. Bounce vehicle to settle suspension. Adjust chassis ground clearance by turning adjusting nut. Front chassis clearance is measured from ground to center of lower control arm front mounting bolt. See CHASSIS GROUND CLEARANCE table. On Pickup and 4Runner models, tighten lock nut to 61 ft. lbs. (83 N.m). On Van models, tighten lock nut to 58 ft. lbs. (78 N.m).

CHASSIS GROUND CLEARANCE

Vehicle Model Number	In. (mm)
RN61L-MRA	11.22 (285)
RN66L-MDA	11.38 (289)
RN66L-MDCA	11.26 (286)
RN61L-MSEA	11.14 (283)
RN66L-PDCEA	11.26 (286)
RN66L-MSCEA	11.14 (283)
RN61LG-MDEA	11.31 (287)
RN61LG-PDEA	11.31 (287)
RN61V-MDEA	11.20 (284)
RN61V-PDEA	11.47 (291)
RN61L-MBZA	11.20 (284)
RN66L-PGCZA	11.10 (282)
RN61LG-PGZA	11.34 (288)
RN61L-MDK	11.26 (286)
RN66L-MDK	11.38 (289)
RN66L-PDEK	11.38 (289)
RN66L-MSEK	11.26 (286)
RN66L-MSCEK	11.14 (283)
RN61V-MSEK	11.34 (288)
RN61V-PSEK	11.38 (289)
RN66L-PGCZK	11.10 (282)
RN61LV-PGZK	11.31 (287)
YR31LG	10.09 (256)
YR32LV	9.94 (253)

SHOCK ABSORBER

Removal

1) Raise and support vehicle. Remove wheel assembly. Remove nuts retaining shock absorber to

TOYOTA 4WD PICKUP, VAN & 4RUNNER (Cont.)

bracket. Remove washers and cushions from shaft of shock absorber.

2) Remove nuts and bolts securing shock absorber to lower control arm. Compress shock absorber and remove from vehicle.

Installation

To install, reverse removal procedure.

TIGHTENING SPECIFICATIONS

Application	Ft. Lbs. (N.m)
Automatic Hub Adjustment Preload Nut	43 (59)
Automatic Hub Cone Nut	23 (31)
Brake Line Nut	11 (15)
Disc Brake Cylinder	90 (123)
Dust Cover	13 (18)
Free Wheeling Hub Adjustment Preload Nut	35 (47)
Hub Bolt	13 (18)
Lower Ball Joint-to-Steering Knuckle Bolt	43 (58)
Lower Ball Joint-to-Lower Control Arm Nut	
Pickup & 4Runner	105 (142)
Van	113 (83)
Lower Control Arm Shaft Nut	
Pickup & 4Runner	203 (275)
Van	152 (206)
Shock Absorber-to-Lower Control Arm Nut & Bolt	
Pickup & 4Runner	101 (137)
Van	70 (95)

TIGHTENING SPECIFICATIONS (Cont.)

Application	Ft. Lbs. (N.m)
Shock Absorber-to-Frame Nut	18 (25)
Stabilizer Bar-to-Lower Suspension Arm Nut	
Pickup & 4Runner	19 (25)
Van	14 (19)
Steering Knuckle-to-Knuckle Arm	120 (163)
Tie Rod End-to-Steering Knuckle	67 (91)
Torsion Bar Lock Nut	
Pickup & 4Runner	61 (83)
Van	58 (78)
Torque Arm-to-Upper Arm Nut	70 (95)
Upper Ball Joint-to-Steering Knuckle Nut	
Pickup & 4Runner	105 (142)
Van	83 (113)
Upper Ball Joint-to-Upper Control Arm Nut	25 (33)
Upper Control Arm-to-Frame Nut	
Pickup & 4Runner	166 (226)
Van	112 (152)
	INCH Lbs. (N.m)
Hub Cover Mounting Bolt	84 (10)

VOLKSWAGEN CABRIOLET, GOLF, GTI & JETTA

DESCRIPTION

Vehicles are equipped with front wheel drive and MacPherson strut independent front suspension. Wheel bearing housings are supported by lower control arms and vertically mounted strut assemblies. Tie rods and stabilizer bar are connected to wheel bearing housing. *See Fig. 1.*

Fig. 1: Exploded View of Suspension Components

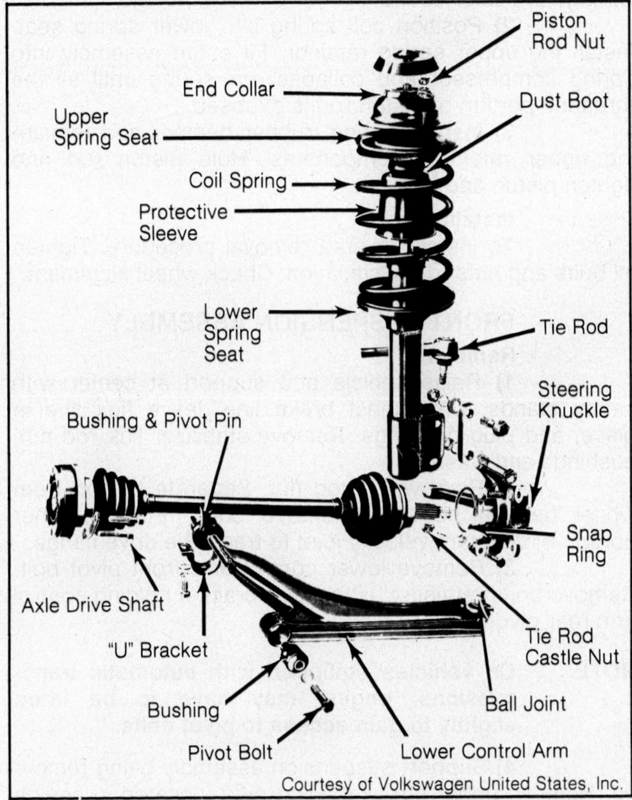

Courtesy of Volkswagen United States, Inc.

ADJUSTMENTS & INSPECTION

WHEEL ALIGNMENT SPECIFICATIONS & PROCEDURES

See WHEEL ALIGNMENT SPECIFICATIONS & PROCEDURES in WHEEL ALIGNMENT section.

WHEEL BEARING

Wheel bearings are pressed into wheel bearing housing and no adjustment is required.

BALL JOINT CHECKING

Raise vehicle and support with safety stands. Inspect ball joints for damaged rubber boots and play. Maximum tolerance for ball joint play not available from manufacturer.

REMOVAL & INSTALLATION

WHEEL BEARING

NOTE: The wheel bearing is destroyed when pressed out of the housing. Once either the wheel hub or bearing has been removed from housing, a new bearing must be installed.

Removal

1) Remove axle shaft nut. Raise and support vehicle with safety stands, allow suspension to hang free. Remove wheel assembly. Remove brake caliper attaching bolts, remove caliper and hang out of way. Remove brake disc retaining screw and remove disc.

2) Remove tie rod ball joint from wheel bearing housing. Remove nut and clamp bolt from control arm ball joint. Remove control arm ball joint from wheel bearing housing and remove housing.

3) Remove 2 circlips retaining bearing in hub. Using Hub Remover (VW 295a), press wheel hub from bearing housing. Using a bearing puller, remove wheel bearing inner race from hub assembly. Using Bearing Remover (VW433), press wheel bearing out of outboard end of bearing housing. *See Fig. 2.*

Installation

1) Press new bearing race onto hub. Using Bearing/Hub Installer (VW 472/1), press new bearing into bearing housing from outboard side. Using same adapter, press wheel hub into bearing housing. Apply a small bead approximately 1/4" of D6 locking compound to the axle splines before installing in hub.

2) To complete installation, reverse removal procedure. Always replace self-locking axle shaft nut. Tighten all bolts and nuts to specification. See TIGHTENING SPECIFICATIONS table in this article. Check wheel alignment.

NOTE: When installing hub, be sure that press adapter contacts ONLY the inner bearing race.

Fig. 2: Exploded View of Wheel Bearing Housing

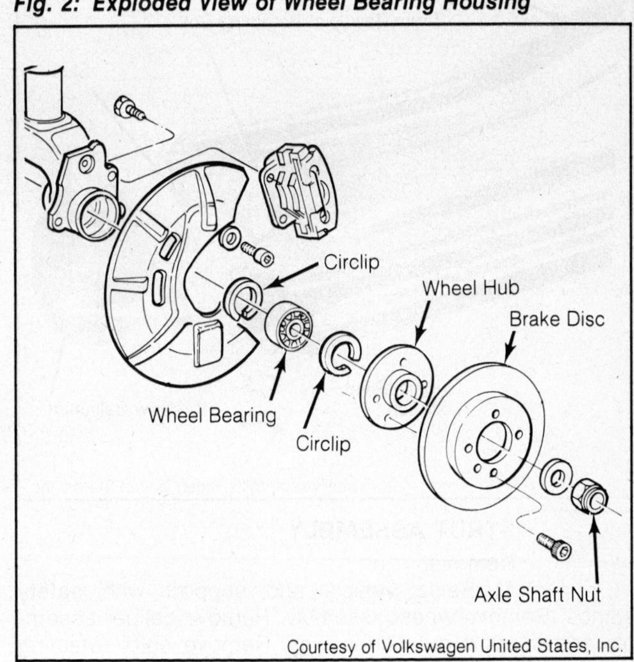

Courtesy of Volkswagen United States, Inc.

LOWER CONTROL ARM & BALL JOINT

Removal

1) Raise vehicle and support with safety stands. Remove clamp bolt retaining ball joint at wheel bearing housing. Force ball joint out of housing, (ball joint can be replaced while control arm is in vehicle). Leave control arm hanging in mounts at subframe.

VOLKSWAGEN CABRIOLET, GOLF, GTI & JETTA (Cont.)

2) If control arm is not being removed, and ball joint is riveted to control arm, drill out ball joint rivets with a 9/32" (7 mm) drill. After drilling rivets, it still may be necessary to chisel off rivet heads. Remove ball joint. *See Fig. 3.*

3) If control arm is being removed, remove stabilizer bar link rod nut, washers and bushings. Take out pivot bolt and "U" bracket housing inner pivot pin. Slide out control arm.

NOTE: **On vehicles equipped with automatic transmissions, engine may have to be lifted slightly to gain access to pivot bolts.**

Inspection

Check lower control arm bushings. Replace bushings if necessary. To replace bushings, press out worn bushing. Select new bushing and press into position. Make sure bushing does not twist when seating into place.

Installation

Slide new ball joint into slot in control arm. Install and tighten ball joint retaining bolts. Install lower control arm to subframe. Install ball joint into wheel bearing housing. To complete installation, reverse removal procedure. Tighten control arm bolts with vehicle on ground. Tighten all bolts and nuts to specification. See TIGHTENING SPECIFICATIONS table in this article. Check wheel alignment.

Fig. 3: New Ball Joint Installation on Lower Control Arm

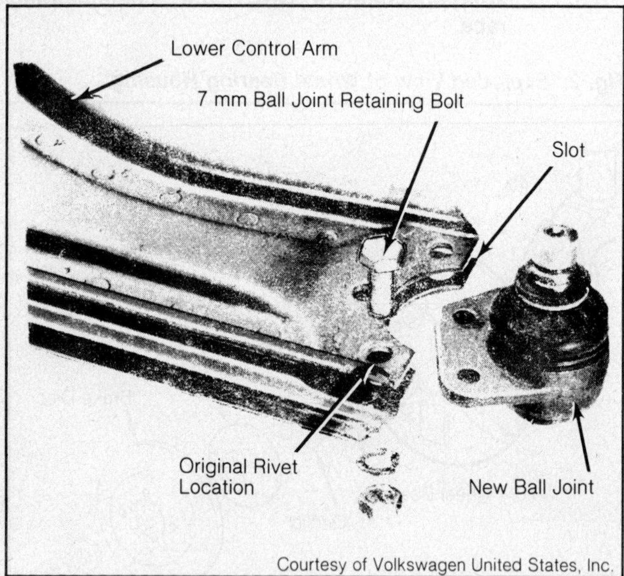

Courtesy of Volkswagen United States, Inc.

STRUT ASSEMBLY

Removal

1) Raise vehicle and support with safety stands. Remove wheel assembly. Remove caliper assembly and support out of the way. Remove bolts retaining suspension strut to wheel bearing housing. Note that top bolt is one used to adjust front wheel camber.

2) Support front suspension arm and related components. Pry or force suspension strut off wheel bearing housing. Working inside engine compartment, remove upper strut retaining nuts. Remove strut assembly.

Disassembly

Install strut in spring compressor. Slightly collapse coil spring. Remove shock absorber piston rod nut. Slowly release spring pressure. Remove upper retaining hardware and coil spring.

Reassembly

1) Install protective sleeve and buffer over piston rod. Both coil springs must be of same class. If set cannot be matched, both springs will have to be replaced. Springs are color coded.

2) Position coil spring into lower spring seat. Install the upper spring retainer. Fit entire assembly into spring compressor and collapse coil spring until all the threaded portion of piston rod is exposed.

3) Install bearing, rubber bumper and remaining upper retaining components. Hold piston rod and tighten piston and lock nut.

Installation

To install, reverse removal procedure. Tighten all bolts and nuts to specification. Check wheel alignment.

FRONT SUSPENSION ASSEMBLY

Removal

1) Raise vehicle and support at center with saftey stands. Disconnect brake line, leave flex line in place, and plug openings. Remove stabilizer link rod nut, bushings and washers.

2) Remove tie rod nut. Separate tie rod from wheel bearing housing. Remove bolts retaining inner portion of constant velocity joint to transaxle drive flange.

3) Remove lower control arm front pivot bolt. Remove bolts retaining "U" shaped bracket holding control arm rear pivot.

NOTE: **On vehicles equipped with automatic transmissions, engine may have to be lifted slightly to gain access to pivot bolts.**

4) Support suspension assembly being removed. Remove upper strut retaining nuts, (located in engine compartment). Remove suspension assembly from vehicle.

Installation

To install, reverse removal procedure. Make sure convex side of thrust washer faces pivot bolt head. Tighten all bolts and nuts to specification. Check wheel alignment.

TIGHTENING SPECIFICATIONS

Application	Ft. Lbs. (N.m)
Axle Nut	170 (230)
Axle Shaft-to-Transaxle Bolt	32 (44)
Ball Joint Clamp Bolt	37 (50)
Ball Joint-to-Control Arm Bolt	18 (24)
Caliper Pin Bolts	18 (24)
Control Arm Pivot Bolt	96 (130)
Control Arm-to-Subframe Rear Bushing Bolt	96 (130)
Strut Piston Rod Nut	44 (60)
Suspension Strut-to-Wheel Bearing Housing Bolt	59 (80)
Tie Rod Castle Nut	26 (35)
Wheel Lug Bolt	81 (110)

VOLKSWAGEN FOX, QUANTUM & SCIROCCO

DESCRIPTION

Vehicles are equipped with front wheel drive and MacPherson strut independent front suspension. Wheel bearing housings and lower strut tubes are a one piece unit, and are supported by lower control arms. Tie rods are connected to lower strut tube,and stabilizer bar are connected to lower control arm. *See Fig. 1.*

ADJUSTMENTS & INSPECTION

WHEEL ALIGNMENT SPECIFICATIONS & PROCEDURES

See WHEEL ALIGNMENT SPECIFICATIONS & PROCEDURES in WHEEL ALIGNMENT section.

WHEEL BEARING

Wheel bearings are pressed into wheel bearing housing and no adjustment is required.

BALL JOINT CHECKING

Raise vehicle and support with safety stands. Inspect ball joints for damaged rubber boots and play. Maximum tolerance for ball joint play not available from manufacturer.

Fig. 1. Exploded View of Front Suspension

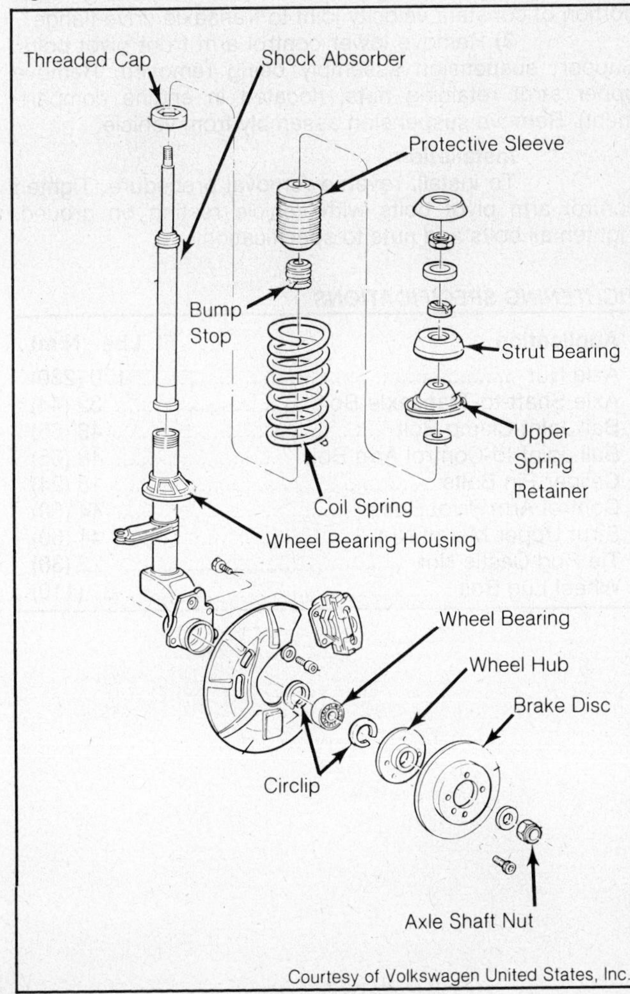

Courtesy of Volkswagen United States, Inc.

REMOVAL & INSTALLATION

WHEEL BEARING

NOTE: The wheel bearing is destroyed when pressed out of the housing. Once either the wheel hub or bearing has been removed from housing, a new bearing must be installed.

Removal

1) Remove axle shaft nut. Raise and support vehicle with safety stands and allow suspension to hang free. Remove wheel assembly. Remove brake caliper attaching bolts and brake hose bracket, remove caliper and hang out of way. Remove brake disc retaining screw and remove disc.

2) Remove tie rod ball joint from strut tube. Remove nut and clamp bolt from control arm ball joint. Remove stabilizer bracket nut from lower control arm. Remove control arm ball joint from wheel bearing housing and press out axle shaft from hub.

3) Support strut assembly to prevent it from falling. Remove upper strut mounting nut and remove wheel bearing housing and strut assembly.

4) Using Hub Remover (VW 295a), press wheel hub from bearing housing. Using a bearing puller, remove wheel bearing inner race from hub assembly. Remove circlips retaining bearing in hub. Using Bearing Remover (VW519), press wheel bearing out of outboard end of bearing housing.

Installation

1) Using Bearing Installer (40-20) and Housing Support (VW402), press new bearing into bearing housing from outboard side. Using same Housing Support and Hub Installer (VW519), press wheel hub into bearing housing. Apply a small bead approximately 1/4" of D6 locking compound to the axle splines before installing in hub. *See Fig. 2.*

NOTE: When installing hub, be sure that press adapter contacts ONLY the inner bearing race.

Fig. 2: Pressing Wheel Bearing

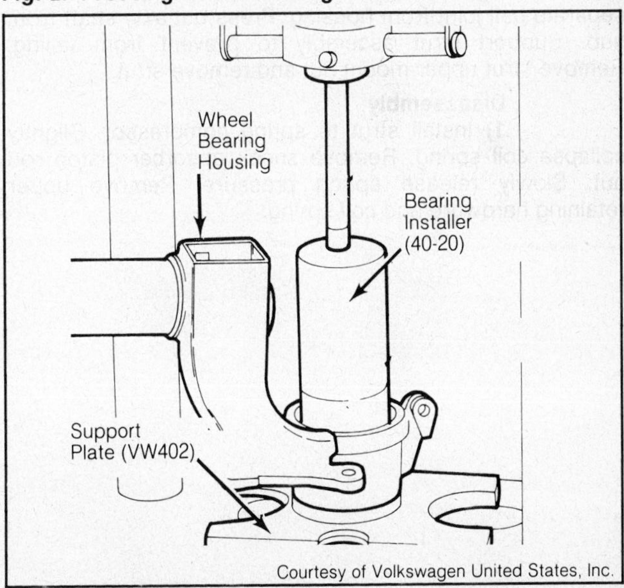

Courtesy of Volkswagen United States, Inc.

VOLKSWAGEN FOX, QUANTUM & SCIROCCO (Cont.)

2) To complete installation, reverse removal procedure. Always replace self-locking axle shaft nut. Tighten all bolts and nuts to specification. See TIGHTENING SPECIFICATIONS table in this article. Check wheel alignment.

LOWER CONTROL ARM & BALL JOINT

Removal

1) Raise vehicle and support with safety stands. Remove clamp bolt retaining ball joint to wheel bearing housing. Force ball joint out of housing, (ball joint can be replaced while control arm is in vehicle). Leave control arm hanging in mounts at subframe.

2) If control arm is not being removed, remove ball joint clamp bolt and nut and remove ball joint from wheel bearing housing by pressing down on lower control arm. Remove ball joint-to-control arm nuts and remove ball joint.

3) If control arm is being removed, remove stabilizer bar link rod nut, washers and bushings. Remove control arm pivot bolts and nuts and remove lower control arm

Installation

Slide new ball joint into slot in control arm. Install and tighten ball joint retaining bolts. Install lower control arm to subframe. Install ball joint into wheel bearing housing. To complete installation, reverse removal procedure. Tighten control arm pivot bolts with vehicle resting on ground. Tighten all bolts and nuts to specification. See TIGHTENING SPECIFICATIONS table in this article. Check wheel alignment.

STRUT ASSEMBLY & SHOCK ABSORBER

Removal

1) Remove axle shaft nut. Raise vehicle and support with safety stands allowing suspension to hang free. Remove wheel assembly. Remove caliper mounting bolts and brake hose bracket. Remove caliper and hang out of way. Remove brake disc retaining screw and remove disc.

2) Remove ball joint clamp bolt and nut from wheel bearing housing and press down on control arm to separate ball joint from housing. Press out axle shaft from hub. Support strut assembly to prevent from falling. Remove strut upper mount nut and remove strut.

Disassembly

1) Install strut to spring compressor. Slightly collapse coil spring. Remove shock absorber piston rod nut. Slowly release spring pressure. Remove upper retaining hardware and coil spring.

2) Place strut assembly in a holding fixture. Remove shock absorber threaded cap and remove shock absorber from strut tube. Drain any oil that may be in strut tube.

Reassembly

1) Install shock absorber in strut tube and install and tighten threaded cap. Install protective sleeve and bump stop over piston rod. Both coil springs must be of same class. If set cannot be matched, both springs will have to be replaced. Springs are color coded.

2) Position coil spring into lower spring seat. Install the upper spring retainer. Fit entire assembly into spring compressor and collapse coil spring until all the threaded portion of piston rod is exposed.

3) Install bearing, rubber bumper and remaining upper retaining components. Hold piston rod and tighten piston and lock nut.

Installation

To install, reverse removal procedure. Tighten all bolts and nuts to specification. Check wheel alignment.

FRONT SUSPENSION ASSEMBLY

Removal

1) Raise vehicle and support at center with safety stands. Disconnect brake line, leave flex line in place, and plug openings. Remove stabilizer link rod nut, bushings and washers.

2) Remove tie rod nut. Separate tie rod from wheel bearing housing. Remove bolts retaining inner portion of constant velocity joint to transaxle drive flange.

3) Remove lower control arm front pivot bolts. Support suspension assembly being removed. Remove upper strut retaining nuts, (located in engine compartment). Remove suspension assembly from vehicle.

Installation

To install, reverse removal procedure. Tighten control arm pivot bolts with vehicle resting on ground. Tighten all bolts and nuts to specification.

TIGHTENING SPECIFICATIONS

Application	Ft. Lbs. (N.m)
Axle Nut	170 (230)
Axle Shaft-to-Transaxle Bolt	32 (44)
Ball Joint Clamp Bolt	48 (65)
Ball Joint-to-Control Arm Bolt	48 (65)
Caliper Pin Bolts	18 (24)
Control Arm Pivot Bolts	44 (60)
Strut Upper Mount Nut	44 (60)
Tie Rod Castle Nut	22 (30)
Wheel Lug Bolt	81 (110)

Front Suspension

VOLKSWAGEN 2WD VANAGON

DESCRIPTION

Suspension is indepenent type consisting of upper and lower control arms and ball joints connected to steering knuckles. Shock absorbers are mounted inside coil springs. Coil spring tension is held by lower control arms.

Stabilizer bar is attached to body with brackets and connected to control arms using stabilizer links. *See Fig. 1.*

ADJUSTMENTS & INSPECTION

WHEEL ALIGNMENT SPECIFICATIONS & PROCEDURES

See WHEEL ALIGNMENT SPECIFICATIONS & PROCEDURES in WHEEL ALIGNMENT section.

WHEEL BEARING

Remove hub nut cover. Tighten hub nut firmly to seat bearing while turning hub. Wheel bearing is correctly adjusted when thrust washer can be moved slightly with a screwdriver and finger pressure. After adjustment, peen flange of hub nut into stub axle shaft recess.

Fig. 1: Exploded View of Front Suspension

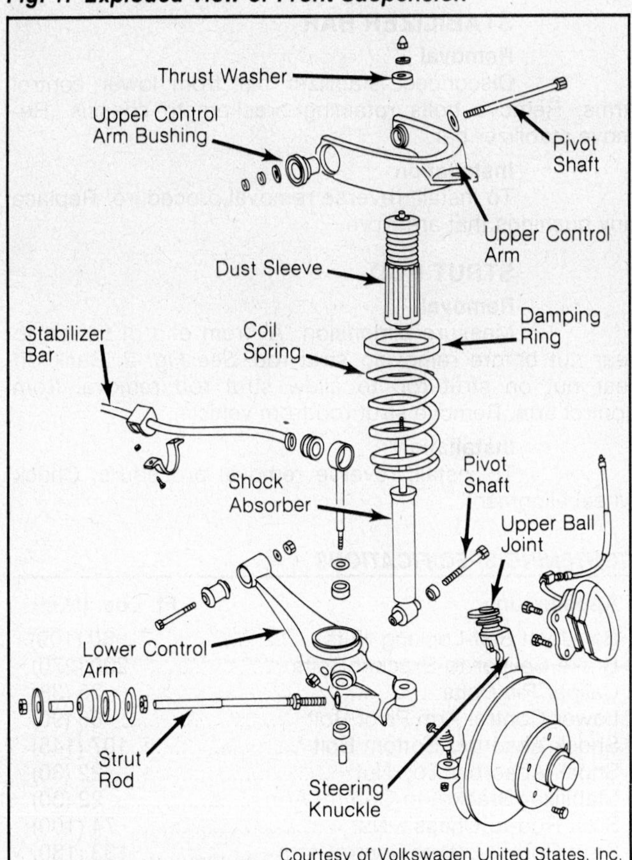

Courtesy of Volkswagen United States, Inc.

REMOVAL & INSTALLATION

WHEEL BEARING

Removal

1) Raise vehicle and support with safety stands. Remove wheel assembly. Remove dust cap. Pry flange on hub nut out of recess in shaft and loosen hub nut.

2) Remove caliper and support caliper out of the way. Remove hub nut, washer, outer bearing and hub. Remove seal and inner bearing from hub.

Installation

To install, reverse removal procedure.

BALL JOINT

Removal

1) Remove steering knuckle from vehicle. See LOWER CONTROL ARM, STEERING KNUCKLE & COIL SPRING REMOVAL in this article.

2) Remove circlip and press out lower ball joint. Remove bolts attaching upper ball joint to control arm. Remove upper ball joint.

Installation

1) Press in lower ball joint and install circlip. Install upper ball joint with attaching bolts and tighten to specifications. See TIGHTENING SPECIFICATIONS table in this article.

2) Install steering knuckle on vehicle. Tighten ball joint nuts to specifications. To complete installation, reverse removal procedure.

LOWER CONTROL ARM, STEERING KNUCKLE & COIL SPRING

Removal

1) Raise and support vehicle with safety stands. Remove wheel assembly. Detach stabilizer link from control arm.

2) Measure dimension "A" from end of thread to rear nut before removing strut rod. *See Fig. 2.* Back off rear nut on strut rod to allow strut rod removal from control arm. Remove caliper and brake hose bracket. Support caliper out of the way.

Fig. 2: Strut Rod Dimension

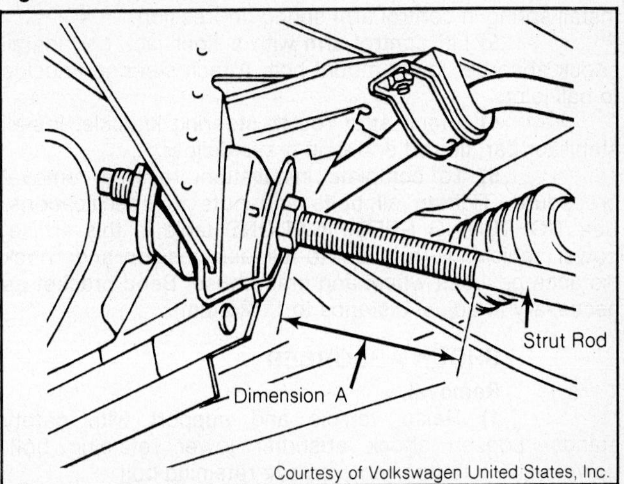

Courtesy of Volkswagen United States, Inc.

Front Suspension

VOLKSWAGEN 2WD VANAGON (Cont.)

NOTE: Strut rod length determines caster angle. If setting at body mounting is changed, caster must be readjusted.

3) Separate tie rod end from steering knuckle. Remove nuts retaining upper and lower ball joints to steering knuckle. Using Ball Joint Remover (VW 267a), separate upper and lower ball joints from steering knuckle. Detach steering knuckle from control arms. Remove steering knuckle.

NOTE: When installing replacement steering knuckle, contact could be made with the brake disc in the area indicated. (arrow). See Fig. 3. Grind down the cast on the steering knuckle 5/16-3/8" (8.0-10.0 mm) to provide clearance.

4) Loosen shock absorber lower mounting bolt. Support lower control arm with a floor jack, and pull shock absorber bolt from lower control arm.

5) Lower floor jack slowly and remove coil spring. Remove lower control arm pivot bolt and remove control arm from vehicle.

Fig. 3: Replacement Steering Knuckle

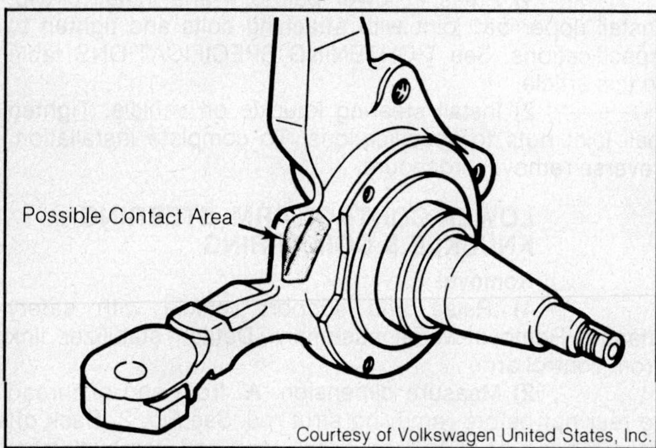

Courtesy of Volkswagen United States, Inc.

Installation

1) Install lower control arm to vehicle with pivot bolt. Position coil spring so straight end is at bottom.

2) Attach damping ring to spring with tape. Install spring in control arm spring depression.

3) Lift control arm with a floor jack and install shock absorber lower mount bolt. Attach steering knuckle to ball joints.

4) Attach strut rod to steering knuckle. Install stabilizer bar, tie rod end, and brake caliper.

5) To complete installation, reverse removal procedure. Tighten all bolts and nuts to specifications. See TIGHTENING SPECIFICATIONS table in this article. Lower vehicle. Turn wheel to full-lock position and check distance between wheel and brake hose. Bend bracket as necessary to adjust distance to 1" (25 mm).

SHOCK ABSORBER

Removal

1) Raise vehicle and support with safety stands. Loosen shock absorber lower retaining bolt. Lower vehicle to floor and remove retaining bolt.

2) Raise vehicle and remove shock absorber upper mounting hardware. Avoid damaging upper ball joint when lifting vehicle with shock absorber disconnected. Remove shock absorber from vehicle.

Installation

To install, reverse removal procedure.

UPPER CONTROL ARM

Removal

1) Raise vehicle and support with safety stands. Remove wheel assembly. Remove bolts retaining upper ball joint to upper control arm.

2) Swing steering knuckle carefully to one side. Note the position of upper control arm pivot shaft and remove from control arm. Remove control arm from vehicle.

Bushing Replacement

Note the position of and grind off spot welds retaining bushings. Using press and adapters, press out old bushing and press in replacements. Secure bushing with spot welds in noted locations. Clean up welds and paint surface to prevent rust.

Installation

Lubricate pivot shaft with grease. Install upper control arm to body and position pivot shaft as noted during removal. Install ball joint to upper control arm and tighten to specifications. To complete installation, reverse removal procedure.

STABILIZER BAR

Removal

Disconnect stabilizer bar from lower control arms. Remove bolts retaining brackets to chassis. Remove stabilizer bar.

Installation

To install, reverse removal procedure. Replace any bushings that are worn.

STRUT ROD

Removal

Measure dimension "A" from end of thread to rear nut before removing strut rod. *See Fig. 2*. Back off rear nut on strut rod to allow strut rod removal from control arm. Remove strut rod from vehicle.

Installation

To install, reverse removal procedure. Check wheel alignment.

TIGHTENING SPECIFICATIONS

Application	Ft. Lbs. (N.m)
Ball Joint Self-Locking Nuts [1]	80 (109)
Brake Caliper-to-Bracket Bolts	200 (270)
Caliper Pin Bolts	26 (35)
Lower Control Arm Pivot Bolt	66 (90)
Shock Absorber Bottom Bolt	107 (145)
Shock Absorber Top Nut	22 (30)
Stabilizer Bracket-to-Control Arm	22 (30)
Strut Rod-to-Chassis Nut	74 (100)
Strut Rod-to-Lower Control Arm	133 (180)
Tie Rod End-to-Steering Knuckle Nut	22 (30)
Upper Ball Joint-to-Control Arm Bolt	43 (58)
Upper Control Arm Pivot Bolt	54 (73)
Wheel Lug Nuts	123 (170)

[1] – Always use new self-locking nuts.

VOLKSWAGEN 4WD VANAGON

DESCRIPTION

Suspension is independent type consisting of upper and lower control arms and ball joints connected to wheel bearing housing. Shock absorbers are part of a strut assembly. Coil springs are held between an upper mount on the frame and a spring support on the lower shock strut housing. Strut rods and stabalizer bar are used for stability. *See Fig. 1*.

Fig. 1: Exploded View of Front Suspension

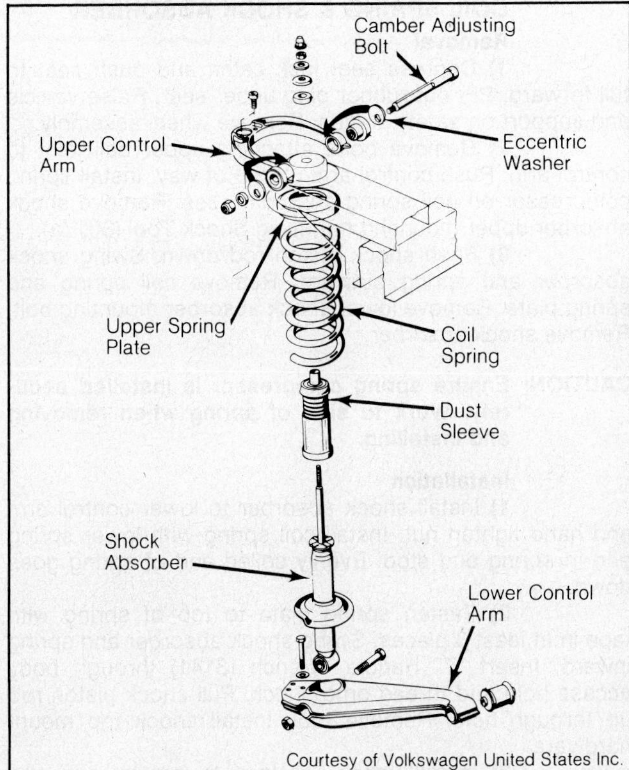

ADJUSTMENTS & INSPECTION

WHEEL ALIGNMENT SPECIFICATIONS & PROCEDURES

See WHEEL ALIGNMENT SPECIFICATIONS & PROCEDURES in WHEEL ALIGNMENT section.

WHEEL BEARING

Wheel bearing is pressed in the bearing housing with an inner and outer seal. The bearing is not adjustable and must be replaced if removed from the bearing housing.

REMOVAL & INSTALLATION

WHEEL BEARING

Removal

1) Remove bearing housing. See LOWER CONTROL ARM & BEARING HOUSING REMOVAL in this article.

2) Mount wheel bearing housing in press using Housing Support (VW 401). Press wheel hub out of bearing using Adapters (VW 408A) and (40-105). *See Fig. 2.*

NOTE: Wheel bearing is destroyed when wheel hub is pressed out.

Fig. 2: Pressing Wheel Hub

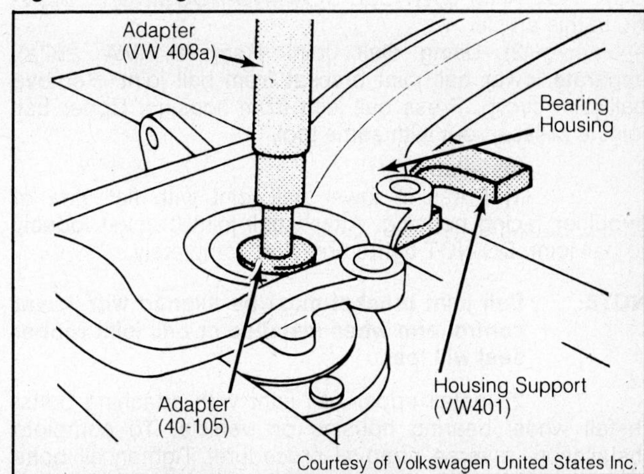

3) Remove outer seal and bearing circlip. Press wheel bearing from housing. Use Housing Supports (VW 401) and (3144) to support housing, and Adapters (VW 407) and (3074) to press bearing.

4) Remove inner bearing race from wheel hub. Use Adapter (40-105) with standard gear puller. Remove inner seal from bearing housing.

Installation

1) Press wheel bearing into housing. Use Housing Supports (VW 401) and (3144) to support housing, and Adapters (VW 412) and (3124) to press bearing. Install seals using Seal Installer (31430) and Support (3144).

2) Press wheel hub into bearing. Use Housing Supports (VW 401) and (VW 415A) to press wheel hub. To complete installation, reverse removal procedure. *See Fig. 3.*

Fig. 3: Exploded View of Wheel Bearing Housing

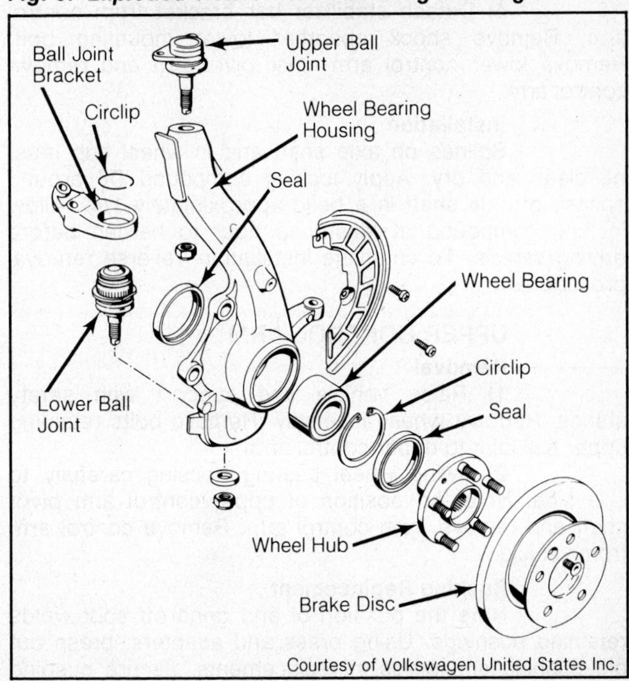

Front Suspension

VOLKSWAGEN 4WD VANAGON (Cont.)

BALL JOINT

Removal

1) Remove bearing housing. See LOWER CONTROL ARM & WHEEL BEARING HOUSING REMOVAL in this article.

2) Using Ball Joint Remover (VW 267a), separate lower ball joint bracket from ball joint. Remove ball joint circlip. Press ball joint from housing. Upper ball joint is pressed out with same tool.

Installation

1) Press in lower ball joint with flat side of shoulder facing housing. Attach ball joint bracket loosely to ball joint. DO NOT tighten bracket completely.

NOTE: Ball joint bracket must be aligned with lower control arm when installed or ball joint rubber seal will tear.

2) Install upper ball joint with attaching bolts. Install wheel bearing housing on vehicle. To complete installation, reverse removal procedure. Tighten all bolts and nuts to specification. See TIGHTENING SPECIFICATIONS table in this article.

LOWER CONTROL ARM & WHEEL BEARING HOUSING

Removal

1) Remove axle nut. Raise vehicle and support with safety stands. Remove wheel assembly. Remove brake line bracket from wheel bearing housing. Remove brake caliper and hang out of way.

2) Remove upper ball joint bolts from control arm. Remove nut from tie rod end and press out. Remove lower ball joint bracket bolts and separate strut rod, wheel bearing housing and lower control arm.

3) Press axle shaft out of wheel hub using standard puller. Remove wheel bearing housing.

NOTE: Use mechanical or hydraulic puller to press axle out of housing. DO NOT heat housing.

4) Detach stabilizer bar bracket from control arm. Remove shock absorber lower mounting bolt. Remove lower control arm inner pivot bolt and remove control arm.

Installation

Splines on axle shaft and in wheel hub must be clean and dry. Apply locking compound D6 around splines of axle shaft in a bead approximately 1/4". Allow locking compound at least one hour to harden before driving vehicle. To complete installation, reverse removal procedure.

UPPER CONTROL ARM

Removal

1) Raise vehicle and support with safety stands. Remove wheel assembly. Remove bolts retaining upper ball joint to upper control arm.

2) Swing wheel bearing housing carefully to one side. Note the position of upper control arm pivot shaft and remove from control arm. Remove control arm from vehicle.

Bushing Replacement

Note the position of and grind off spot welds retaining bushings. Using press and adapters, press out old bushing and press in replacements. Secure bushing with spot welds in noted locations. Clean up welds and paint surface to prevent rust.

Installation

Lubricate pivot shaft with grease. Install upper control arm to body and position pivot shaft as noted during removal. Install ball joint to upper control arm and tighten to specifications. See TIGHTENING SPECIFICATIONS table in this article. To complete installation, reverse removal procedure.

COIL SPRING & SHOCK ABSORBER

Removal

1) Depress seat lock catch and push seat to full forward. Pry out rubber plug under seat. Raise vehicle and support on safety stands. Remove wheel assembly.

2) Remove bolts attaching upper ball joint to control arm. Push control arm up out of way. Install spring compressor on coil spring and compress. Remove shock absorber upper mounting nut using Shock Tool (3017a).

3) Push shock piston rod down. Swing shock absorber and spring outward. Remove coil spring and spring plate. Remove lower shock absorber mounting bolt. Remove shock absorber.

CAUTION: Ensure spring compressor is installed securely. Work to side of spring when removing and installing.

Installation

1) Install shock absorber to lower control arm and hand tighten nut. Install coil spring with lower spring end in spring end stop. Evenly coiled end of spring goes down.

2) Fasten spring plate to top of spring with tape in at least 3 places. Swing shock absorber and spring inward. Insert "T" Handle Wrench (3141) through body access hole and thread onto shock. Pull shock piston rod up through hole. Remove tool. Install shock top mount hardware.

3) Install upper ball joint to control arm and tighten to specification. Lift lower control arm with hydraulic jack and remove coil spring compressor. Tighten all bolts and nuts to specifications. See TIGHTENING SPECIFICATIONS table in this article. Insert plug in access hole. push seat back. Install wheel assembly.

STABILIZER BAR

Removal

Disconnect stabilizerbar from strut rod. Remove bolts retaining brackets to chassis. Remove stabilizer bar.

Installation

To install, reverse removal procedures. Replace any bushings that are worn.

STRUT ROD

Removal

Disconnect stabilizer bar from strut rod. Remove nuts retaining strut rod, lower ball joint bracket and lower control arm together. Remove hardware mounting strut rod to chassis. Remove strut rod.

Installation

To install, reverse removal procedure. Check wheel alignment.

VOLKSWAGEN 4WD VANAGON (Cont.)

SUBFRAME

Removal

1) Remove strut rods from chassis mount. Remove stabilizer mount from strut rod. Remove lower control arm inner bolt. Remove final drive support from subframe. *See Fig. 4.*

Fig. 4: Exploded View of Subframe

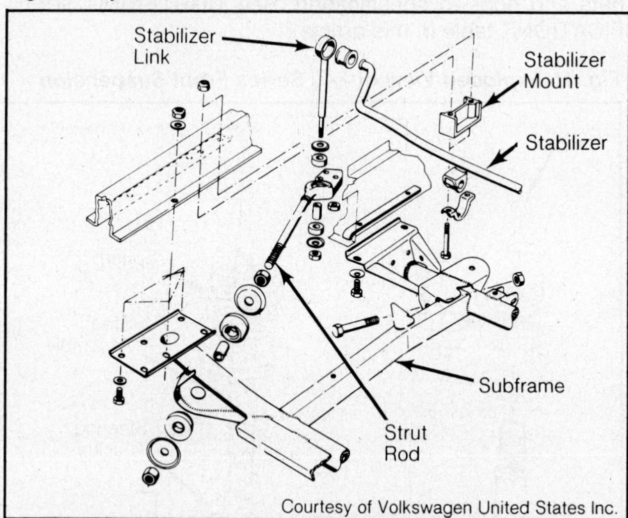

Courtesy of Volkswagen United States Inc.

2) Tie final drive support up to body. Remove protection bars and bonded rubber bushings. Tie up final drive to chassis. Use Transmission Support (V.A.G. 1383) to support subframe. Remove bolts that attach subframe to body. Carefully lower subframe and remove. *See Fig. 5.*

NOTE: **The bolts attaching the subframe-to-body are to be tightened last.**

Installation

To install, reverse removal procedure. Align vehicle after installation.

Fig. 5: Protection Bars & Bonded Bushings

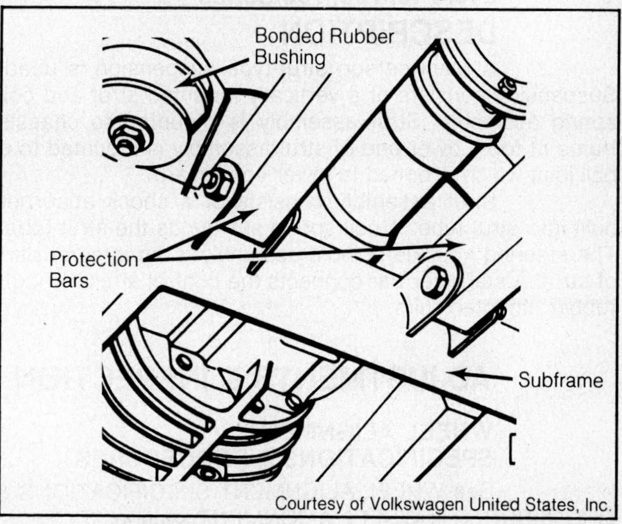

Courtesy of Volkswagen United States, Inc.

TIGHTENING SPECIFICATIONS

Application	Ft. Lbs. (N.m)
Axle Shaft Nut	236 (320)
Ball Joint Self-Locking Nuts [1]	81 (110)
Brake Caliper-to-Housing Bolts	177 (240)
Lower Control Arm Pivot Bolt	66 (90)
Shock Absorber Bottom Bolt	110 (150)
Shock Absorber Top Nut	22 (30)
Stabilizer Link-to-Strut Rod	22 (30)
Stabilizer Mount-to-Frame	18 (25)
Strut Rod-to-Chassis Nut	125 (170)
Strut Rod-to-Lower Control Arm nuts	51 (69)
Subframe-to-Body Bolts	33 (45)
Tie Rod End-to-Bearing Housing Nut	22 (30)
Upper Ball Joint-to-Control Arm Bolt	44 (60)
Upper Control Arm Pivot Bolt	54 (73)
Wheel Lug Nuts	123 (170)

[1] – Always use new self-locking nuts.

VOLVO

240, 740, 760, 780 Series

DESCRIPTION

A MacPherson strut-type suspension is used. Suspension consists of a vertically mounted strut and coil spring assembly. Strut assembly is mounted to chassis frame at top. Lower end of strut assembly is mounted to a ball joint which is bolted to lower control arm.

Strut assembly consists of a shock absorber built into strut tube. A coil spring surrounds the strut tube. The steering knuckle/spindle assembly is an integral part of strut. A stabilizer bar connects the control arms through rubber mounted links.

ADJUSTMENTS & INSPECTION

WHEEL ALIGNMENT SPECIFICATIONS & PROCEDURES

See WHEEL ALIGNMENT SPECIFICATIONS & PROCEDURES in WHEEL ALIGNMENT section.

WHEEL BEARING

While rotating hub, tighten hub nut to 42 ft. lbs. (57 N.m). Loosen nut 1/2 turn, and then tighten by hand. Verify that hub rotates freely with no end play. If necessary, loosen nut to align cotter pin holes, and install new cotter pin. Recheck end play.

BALL JOINT CHECKING

Raise and support vehicle with safety stands positioned near outer ball joint. Grasp tire and apply force up and down, maximum play is .12" (3 mm). Grasp tire and apply force in and out, maximum is .02" (.5 mm). If ball joint play is excessive, replace ball joint.

REMOVAL & INSTALLATION

WHEEL BEARING

Removal & Installation

1) Raise and support vehicle. Remove wheel assembly. Remove dust cap. Remove cotter pin and loosen hub nut. Remove caliper retaining bolts.

2) Remove and support caliper. Remove hub nut, washer, outer bearing, and hub. Remove seal and inner bearing from hub. To install, reverse removal procedure.

BALL JOINT

Removal (240 Series)

Raise and support vehicle. Remove front wheels. Remove ball joint-to-strut bolts. Remove ball joint-to-control arm nuts. Remove center ball joint retaining nut and press ball joint out of retainer.

NOTE: **Ball joints for right and left sides are different.**

Installation

Remove grease from ball joint stud. Press new ball joint into retainer and tighten center nut. Using new lock bolts, install and tighten ball joint on strut. Tighten ball joint bracket-to-control arm nuts. See TIGHTENING SPECIFICATIONS table in this article

Removal & Installation (740, 760 & 780 Series)

Raise and support vehicle. Remove front wheels. Remove sway bar-to-control arm bolt and ball joint nut. Separate ball joint from control arm. Remove ball joint-to-strut bolts and remove ball joint. Using new bolts coated with Loctite, install ball joint on strut. Tighten all nuts and bolts to specification. See TIGHTENING SPECIFICATIONS table in this article.

Fig. 1: Exploded View of 240 Series Front Suspension

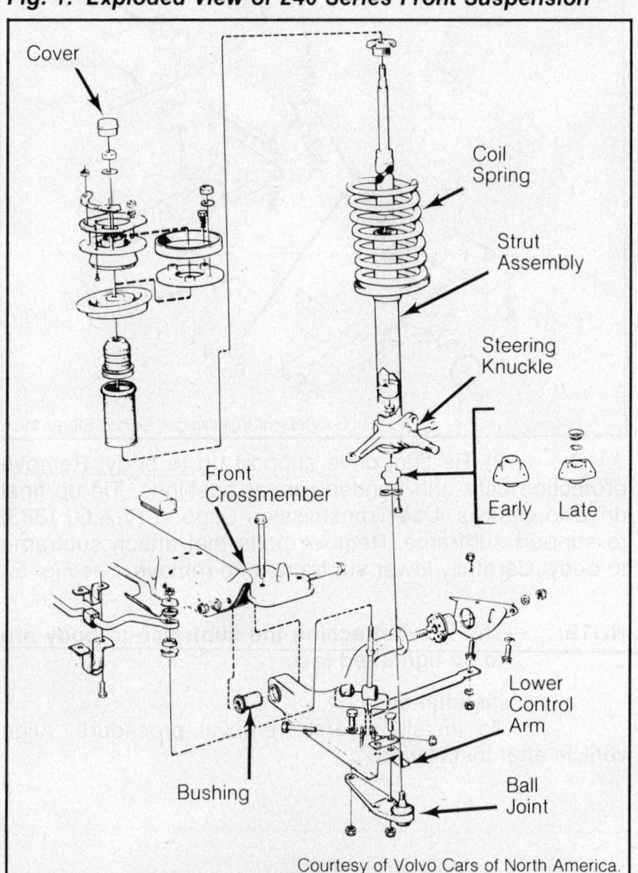

CONTROL ARM

Removal (240 Series)

1) Raise and support vehicle. Remove front wheels. Disconnect stabilizer bar from control arm. Disconnect ball joint from control arm. *See Fig. 1*. Remove front retaining bolt from control arm.

2) Remove bracket attaching rear of control arm to chassis. Remove control arm from vehicle. Separate control arm from bracket. If control arm bushing is being replaced, press out using Adapter Sleeve (5085) and Driver (5091).

Installation

1) Inspect all components for wear or damage. If necessary, use Adapter Sleeve (5085) and Driver (5084) to install new bushings. Assemble control arm to bracket. Install control arm nut finger tight.

2) Install bracket (with control arm) to chassis. Do not tighten bolts. Install front retaining bolt for control arm, but do not tighten. Install ball joint to control arm and tighten bolts.

Front Suspension

VOLVO (Cont.)

3) Position a floor jack under control arm and raise so coil spring is compressed. Connect stabilizer bar to link. Tighten control arm retaining nuts and bolts. Install wheel assembly. See TIGHTENING SPECIFICATIONS table.

Removal (740, 760 & 780 Series)

1) Raise and support vehicle. Remove front wheels. Remove ball joint stud nut, sway bar link, and control arm strut bolt from control arm.

2) Separate ball joint from control arm. *See Fig. 2.* Remove control arm from crossmember. If necessary, press out bushing.

Installation

Install control arm in crossmember. Do not tighten nut. Assemble ball joint, sway bar link, and control arm strut to control arm. Tighten all nuts and bolts. Install front wheels and lower vehicle to ground. Tighten control arm nut. See TIGHTENING SPECIFICATIONS table.

Fig. 2: 740, 760 & 780 Series Front Suspension Assembly

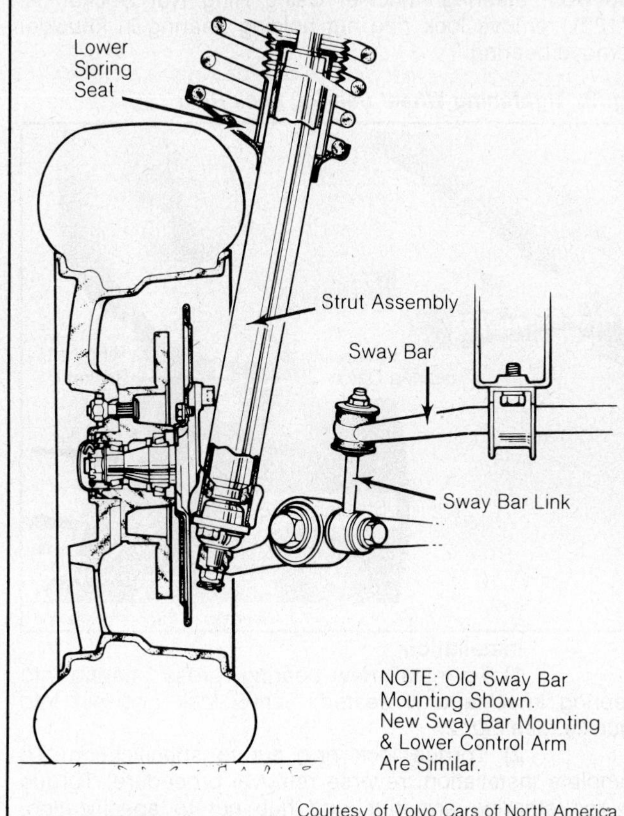

Courtesy of Volvo Cars of North America.

SHOCK ABSORBER

NOTE: **Shock absorbers are not replaceable on 780 series. Complete strut assembly must be replaced.**

Removal

1) Raise and support vehicle. Remove front wheels. Separate tie rod end from steering knuckle. Place floor jack under control arm. Remove sway bar link and brake line bracket.

2) Remove upper shock absorber cover. Loosen shock absorber nut a few turns while holding center of strut rod with Holder (5037). Mark position of upper mount to maintain wheel alignment.

3) Lower floor jack. Guide strut out of strut tower. Attach spring compressor. Remove nut and lift off upper mount, spring retainer, and bumper. Unscrew shock absorber retaining nut using Holder (5036). Hold shock with Holder (5037). Remove shock absorber.

Installation

1) Install new shock absorber and tighten nut. Install bumper, spring retainer, and upper mount. Tighten nut a few turns and remove spring compressor. Install strut in tower and tighten mounting nuts.

2) Tighten shock absorber nut. Assemble remaining suspension parts in reverse order of removal. Tighten all bolts and nuts to specification.

Fig. 3: 740 & 760 Series Shock Absorber Assembly

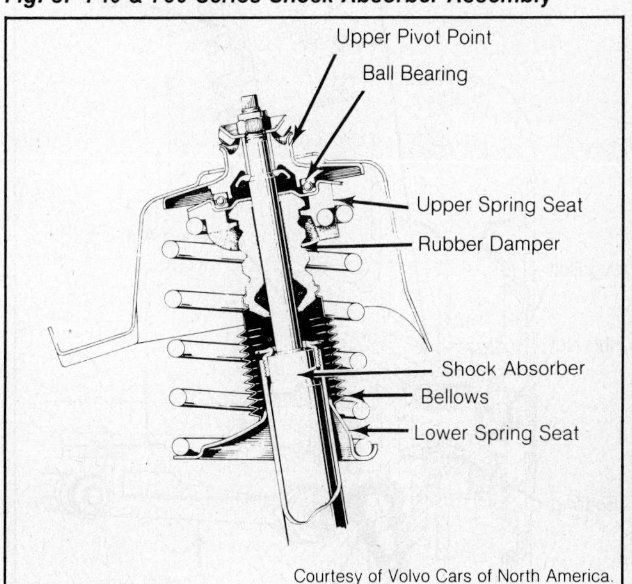

Courtesy of Volvo Cars of North America.

TIGHTENING SPECIFICATIONS

Application	Ft. Lbs. (N.m)
240 Series	
Ball Joint Stud Nut	43 (58)
Ball Joint Bracket-to-Control Arm	85 (115)
Ball Joint-to-Strut Assembly	17 (23)
Control Arm Retaining Bolts	
Front	40-70 (55-95)
Rear	37-44 (50-60)
Rear Control Arm Bracket-to-Frame	22-37 (30-50)
Shock Absorber Nut (Center)	111 (150)
Strut Assembly Nuts-to-Body	15 (20)
Wheel Lug Nuts	85 (115)
740, 760 & 780 Series	
Ball Joint Stud Nut	44 (60)
Ball Joint-to-Strut Assembly	22 (30)
Control Arm-to-Control Arm Strut	70 (95)
Shock Absorber Nut (Center)	111 (150)
Shock Absorber-to-Strut Nut	119 (160)
Wheel Lug Nuts	63 (85)

Front Suspension

YUGO

DESCRIPTION

Front suspension is MacPherson strut type, using a hydraulic shock absorber inside a strut tube. Strut tube is surrounded by coil spring. Strut is secured at top to body and at bottom to steering knuckle.

Steering knuckle pivots on ball joint attached to lower control arm. Lower control arm is attached to body with a rubber bushing, bolt and nut.

Stabilizer bar is bolted to lower control arms and attached to brackets on body with rubber bushings, bolts, washers and nuts.

Fig. 1: Front Suspension Components

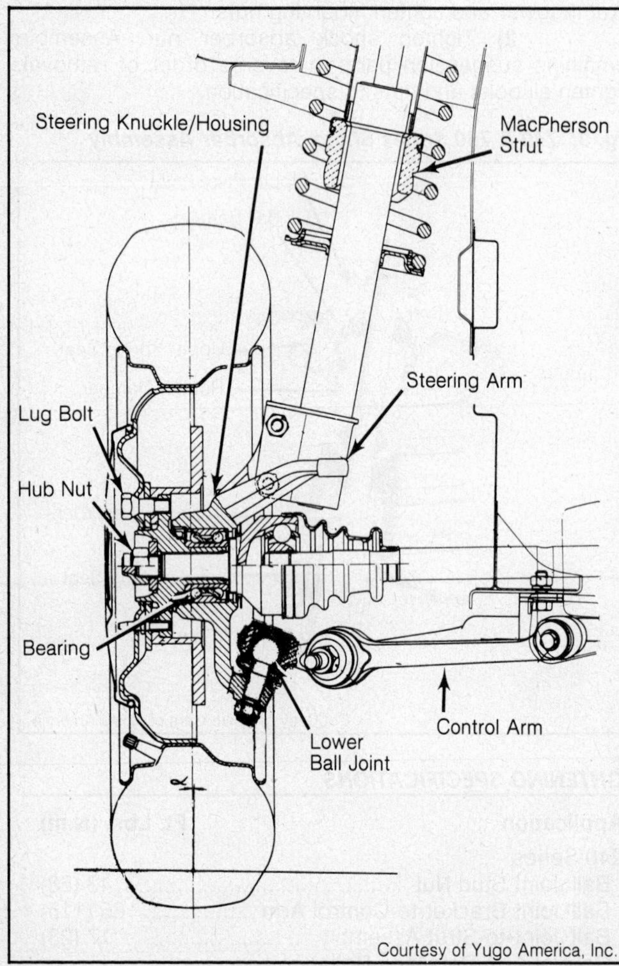

ADJUSTMENTS & INSPECTION

WHEEL BEARING

Wheel bearings are not adjustable and must be replaced each time wheel hub is disassembled.

WHEEL ALIGNMENT SPECIFICATIONS & PROCEDURES

See WHEEL ALIGNMENT SPECIFICATIONS & PROCEDURES in WHEEL ALIGNMENT section.

BALL JOINT CHECKING

Check rubber protection boots for wear, cracks or breaks that might permit moisture or dirt entry. Control arm and ball joint must be replaced as a unit.

REMOVAL & INSTALLATION

WHEEL BEARING

Removal

1) Raise vehicle and support with safety stands. Allow suspension to hang free. Remove wheel from vehicle. Remove hub nut.

2) Remove 3 bolts holding brake caliper assembly to steering knuckle. Remove and support caliper assembly out of way. Remove locating pin and bolt holding brake rotor to hub. Remove brake rotor.

3) Remove tie rod end nut. Remove tie rod end from steering arm using Puller (A. 47035). Remove ball joint nut and disconnect ball joint from steering knuckle using Puller (A. 47036).

4) Secure axle shaft to prevent it from slipping out of differential. Remove 2 bolts and nuts holding MacPherson strut assembly to steering knuckle. Slide steering knuckle off axle shaft CV joint.

5) Place steering knuckle in press and press hub from steering knuckle. Using Ring Nut Socket (A. 57123), remove lock ring nut holding bearing in knuckle. Remove bearing.

Fig. 2: Tightening Wheel Bearing Lock Ring

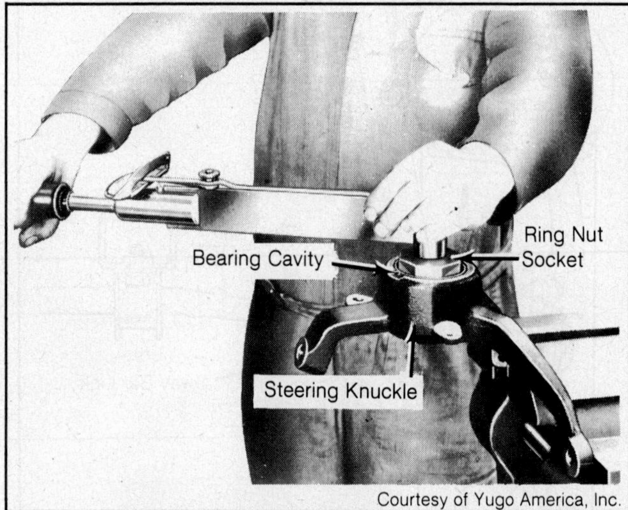

Installation

1) To install new bearing, press bearing into steering knuckle until seated. Screw lock ring nut into knuckle. *See Fig. 2.*

2) Torque lock ring nut to specification. To complete installation, reverse removal procedure. Torque tie rod steering arm nut, and hub nut to specification. Using Pliers (A. 74140/1) and Heads (A. 74141/9), stake hub nut collar in place.

LOWER CONTROL ARM & BALL JOINT

Removal

1) Raise vehicle and support with safety stands. Allow suspension to hang free. Remove wheel assembly. Remove stabilizer bar nut at control arm. Save adjustment shims on stabilizer bar for use on installation. Remove bolt and nut holding control arm to body bracket.

2) Remove nut from ball joint stud. Using Puller (A. 47036), remove ball joint from steering knuckle. Remove control arm assembly.

Front Suspension

YUGO (Cont.)

Installation

To install, reverse removal procedure. Check pivot bushing for wear or damage. Replace if necessary. Tighten nuts and bolts to specification. See TIGHTENING SPECIFICATIONS table at end of this article.

FRONT SUSPENSION ASSEMBLY

Removal

1) Raise and support vehicle. Allow suspension to hang free. Remove front wheels. Remove three bolts holding brake caliper to steering knuckle. Secure out of way.

2) Remove nut holding tie rod end to steering arm. Using Puller (A. 47035). Remove tie rod end from steering arm. Remove stabilizer bar nut at control arm. Slide stabilizer bar from control arm.

NOTE: **Save adjustment shims on stabilizer bar for use on installation.**

3) Remove control arm nut and bolt from body bracket. Secure axle shaft to prevent it from slipping out of differential. Slide suspension assembly off CV joint shaft.

4) Support front suspension and remove 3 nuts holding strut to body in engine compartment. Remove strut hub and control arm assembly.

Installation

To install, reverse removal procedure. Apply silicone grease to the stabilizer bar bushings in the control arm. Torque nuts and bolts to specification. Using Pliers (A. 74140/1) and Heads (A. 74141/9), stake hub nut collar in place.

STRUT ASSEMBLY

Removal

1) Raise vehicle and support with safety stands. Allow suspension to hang free. Remove wheel assembly. Remove 3 bolts holding caliper to steering knuckle. Hang caliper up out of way.

2) Remove two steering knuckle-to-lower strut retaining bolts and nuts. Separate steering knuckle from lower strut.

3) Remove 3 upper strut retaining nuts in engine compartment. Remove strut from vehicle.

Disassembly

1) Place strut in Spring Compressor/Holding Fixture (A. 74241) and place in horizontal position in a vise. Make sure one spring plate bolt at each end of the strut assembly is in depression used to position spring on plate of fixture. Turn handle of compressor tool until spring is compressed about one inch. *See Fig. 3.*

2) Use Spanner (A. 57020) to hold shock absorber shaft. Remove nut holding the upper mount to shock absorber. Carefully remove tension from coil spring. Remove spring from strut

Reassembly

To reassemble, reverse disassembly procedure. Replace shock absorber top mount when replacing shock absorber.

Fig. 3: Disassembling MacPherson Strut Assembly

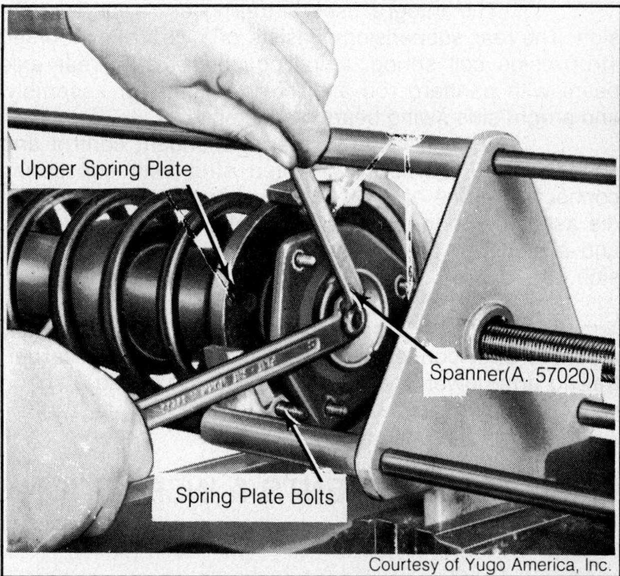

Courtesy of Yugo America, Inc.

Inspection

Check all parts for wear or damage. Inspect coil spring for cracks or distortion. Check support plate for cracks. Check shock absorber for leaks.

Installation

To install, reverse removal procedure. Torque nuts and bolts to specification.

STABILIZER BAR

Removal

Raise vehicle and support with safety stands. Remove nuts securing stabilizer bar to lower control arms. Save adjusting shims for use on installation. Remove brackets attaching stabilizer bar to crossmember. Remove stabilizer.

Installation

To install, reverse removal procedure. Apply silicone grease to stabilizer bushings in control arm.

TIGHTENING SPECIFICATIONS [1]

Application	Ft. Lbs. (N.m)
Ball Joint-to-Knuckle Nut	58 (78)
Caliper Assembly-to-Knuckle Bolt	35 (47)
Control Arm-to-Body Bolt/Nut	29 (39)
Hub Nut	159 (216)
MacPherson Strut-to-Knuckle Bolts/Nuts	53 (72)
Stabilizer Bracket Bolts/Nuts	36 (49)
Stabilizer Bar-to-Control Arm Nut	43 (59)
Tie Rod End-to-Steering Arm Nut	25 (34)
Upper Strut Cartridge Retaining Nut	18 (25)
Wheel Bearing Lock Ring Nut	159 (216)
Wheel Lug Nut	63 (86)
	Inch Lbs. (N.m)
MacPherson Strut Upper Mount Nuts	108 (12)

[1] – During final tightening of bolts and nuts, suspension should be under load equal to 4 passengers plus luggage, or 705 lbs. (320kg).

Rear Suspension

ACURA

DESCRIPTION

The Integra uses a trailing arm rear suspension. The rear suspension consists of a vertically mounted strut inside coil spring, a trailing control arm, rear axle beam with panhard rod and internal stabilizer assembly, and a right side swing bearing assembly.

Legend Coupe uses independent control arm suspension. A vertically mounted strut with coil spring connected to one of 2 lower control arms, a knuckle/spindle assembly, upper and lower control arms, trailing arm and a stabilizar bar are the components of this suspension.

Legend 4-Door also uses independent control arm suspension. Suspension consists of a vertically mounted strut connected at bottom to upper hub carrier, trailing arm, lower control arm, and a coil spring. Legend is also equipped with a rear stabilizer bar.

ADJUSTMENTS & INSPECTION

WHEEL BEARINGS

NOTE: Wheel bearings are not adjustable.

WHEEL ALIGNMENT SPECIFICATIONS & PROCEDURES

See WHEEL ALIGNMENT SPECIFICATIONS & PROCEDURES in WHEEL ALIGNMENT section.

REMOVAL & INSTALLATION

INTEGRA

Removal (Hub/Bearing Assembly)

Raise rear of vehicle and support with safety stands. Remove rear wheel. Remove caliper assembly and position out of way. Remove brake disc. Remove dust cap, nut and washer from hub/bearing assembly. Remove hub/bearing assembly. *See Fig. 1.*

Installation

To install, reverse removal procedures and stake shoulder of hub/bearing assembly nut against groove in spindle after tightening.

Removal (Swing Bearing)

1) Raise rear of vehicle and support with safety stands. Remove rear wheel. Remove caliper assembly and hang out of way. Remove dust cap, nut and washer from hub carrier assembly. Remove brake rotor. Remove backing plate bolts. Remove backing plate. Remove caliper bracket nuts and caliper.

2) Remove control arm from swing bearing. Remove spindle nuts and remove spindle/swing bearing assembly. Press wheel spindle out of swing bearing using a hydraulic press. Remove bearing inner race using bearing puller. *See Fig. 1.*

Installation

To install, reverse removal procedure.

Removal & Installation (Wheel Bearing)

1) Raise rear of vehicle and support with safety stands. Remove wheel assembly and brake caliper. Position caliper out of way. Remove brake rotor retaining bolts.

2) Remove axle shaft dust cap, spindle nut and washer. Remove brake rotor. Remove hub/bearing assembly. Replace hub/bearing assembly as a unit. To install, reverse removal procedure. *See Fig. 1.*

Removal (Stabilizer Assembly)

1) Raise rear of vehicle and support with safety stands. Remove wheel assemblies. Remove trailing arms. See TRAILING ARM in this article.

2) Remove stabilizer assembly bolts. Remove cap from left side of rear axle beam. Using a long wooden dowel and mallet, tap stabilizer assembly out of beam. *See Fig. 1.*

Installation

To install, reverse removal procedure. Tighten bushings and all rubber dampened parts with vehicle on ground. Tighten stabilizer assembly bolts last.

Removal (Trailing Arm)

1) Raise rear of vehicle and support with safety stands. Remove wheel assembly. Remove caliper assembly and position out of way. Remove dust cap, nut and washer from hub/bearing assembly. Remove brake rotor.

2) Remove backing plate bolts. Remove backing plate. Remove caliper bracket nuts. Remove caliper bracket. Remove trailing arm pivot bolt. Remove trailing arm.

Installation

To install, reverse removal procedure.

Removal (Strut Assembly)

Raise rear of vehicle and support with safety stands. Remove wheel assemblies. Use floor jack to support axle beam. Working inside luggage compartment, remove cover over strut stud. Remove self-locking nut. Gradually lower floor jack. Remove strut lower mounting bolt, spring upper seat, spring and strut. *See Fig. 1.*

Disassembly

The strut cannot be disassembled. If it does not operate smoothly, or if it makes any abnormal noises during operation, replace it.

Installation

1) Position spring seat in frame. Install strut shield on strut. Install strut spring, install lower strut bolt and loosely tighten to rear axle. Install bushing on strut rod. Raise axle beam with floor jack so that strut rod fits into hole in frame.

2) Working inside vehicle, install bushing, washer and lock nut on strut rod. Install wheel assembly and lower vehicle. Tighten strut-to-rear axle bolt and strut lock nut with vehicle on ground. Install strut cover.

LEGEND COUPE

Removal & Installation (Hub/Bearing Assembly)

1) Raise rear of vehicle and support with safety stands. Remove wheel assembly. Remove caliper and position out of way. Remove brake disc. Remove hub cap. Pry spindle nut lock tab away from spindle and loosen nut. Remove hub/bearing assembly. *See Fig. 2.*

2) To install, reverse removal procedures.

Removal (Knuckle)

1) Raise rear of vehicle and support with safety stands. Remove wheel assembly. Remove caliper and position out of way. Remove brake disc. Remove hub cap. Pry spindle nut lock tab away from spindle and loosen nut. Remove hub/bearing assembly.

ACURA (Cont.)

Fig. 1: Integra Rear Suspension

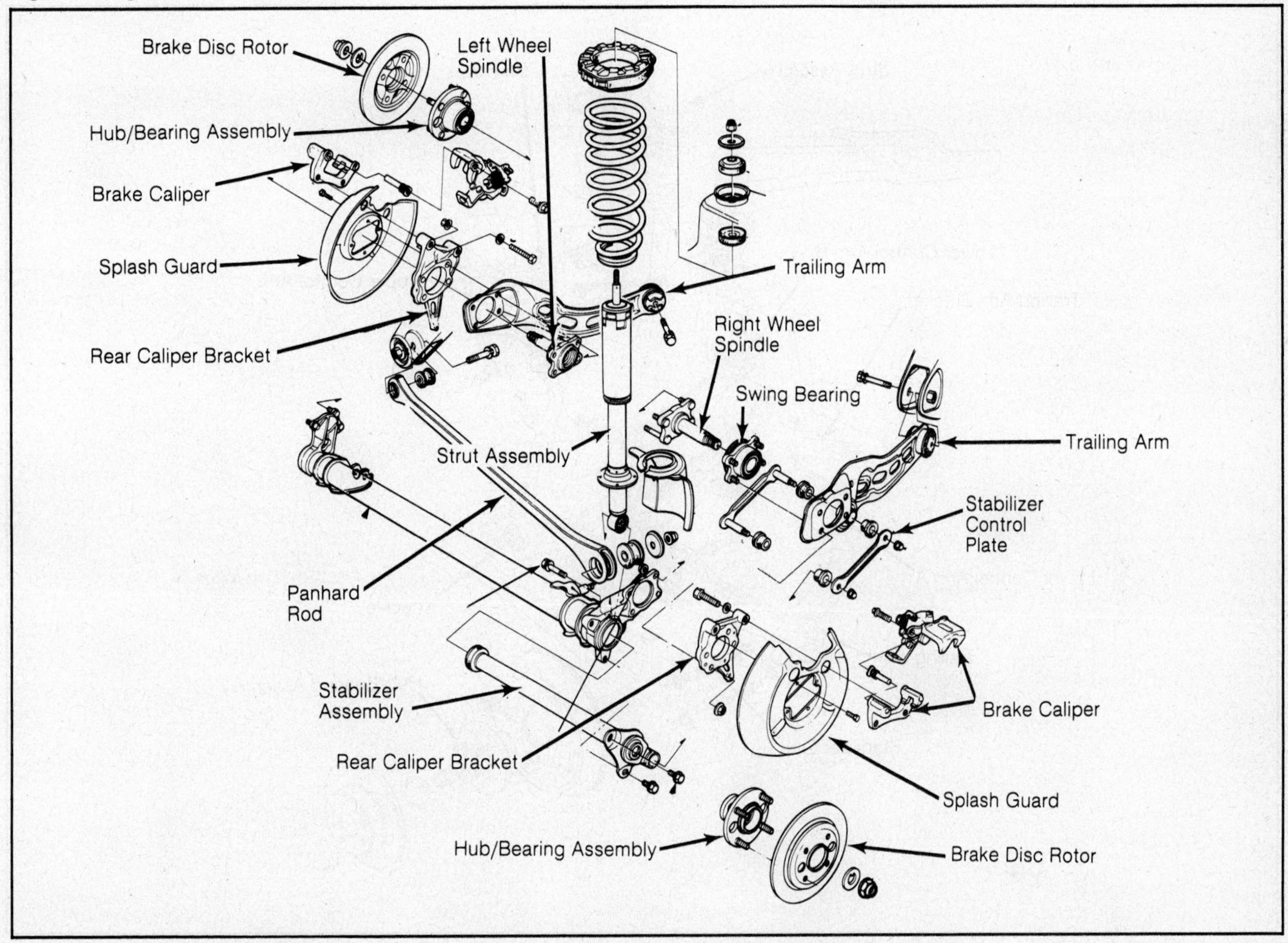

Courtesy of American Honda Motor Co., Inc.

2) Remove splash guard bolts and remove splash guard. Remove bolts attaching knuckle to trailing arm, lower control arm bracket and to upper control arm ball joint. Remove knuckle. *See Fig. 2.*

Installation

To install, reverse removal procedures.

Removal (Upper & Lower Control Arms)

1) Raise rear of vehicle and support with safety stands. Remove wheel assembly. Remove caliper and position out of way. Remove brake disc. Remove hub cap. Pry spindle nut lock tab away from spindle and loosen nut. Remove hub/bearing assembly.

2) Remove splash guard bolts and remove splash guard. Remove bolts attaching knuckle to trailing arm, lower control arm bracket and to upper control arm ball joint. Remove knuckle.

3) Remove Lower Control Arm A from trailing arm bracket and Lower Control Arm B from frame and strut assembly lower mounting bolts. Remove upper control arm attaching bolts from frame. *See Fig. 2.*

Installation

To install, reverse removal procedures.

Removal (Trailing Arm)

1) Raise rear of vehicle and support with safety stands. Remove wheel assembly. Remove caliper and position out of way. Remove brake disc. Remove hub cap. Pry spindle nut lock tab away from spindle and loosen nut. Remove hub/bearing assembly.

2) Remove splash guard bolts and remove splash guard. Remove bolts attaching knuckle to trailing arm. Remove stabilizer link bolts. Remove bolt attaching trailing arm to trailing arm bracket. Remove trailing arm. *See Fig. 2.*

Installation

To install, reverse removal procedures.

Removal (Strut Assembly)

1) Remove trunk side carpet. Remove damper mounting nuts. Remove clamp of parking brake cable from trailing arm. Remove stabilizer linkage from trailing arm.

2) Remove upper arm mounting bolts. Remove strut mounting bolts. Lower rear suspension and remove damper assembly.

Disassembly

1) Compress strut spring using a spring compressor. Do not compress spring more than necessary to remove 10 mm self-locking nut. Remove 10 mm self-locking nut from strut assembly.

2) Remove spring compressor. Note component locations and complete disassembling strut by disengaging components.

Rear Suspension

ACURA (Cont.)

Fig. 2: Legend Coupe Rear Suspension

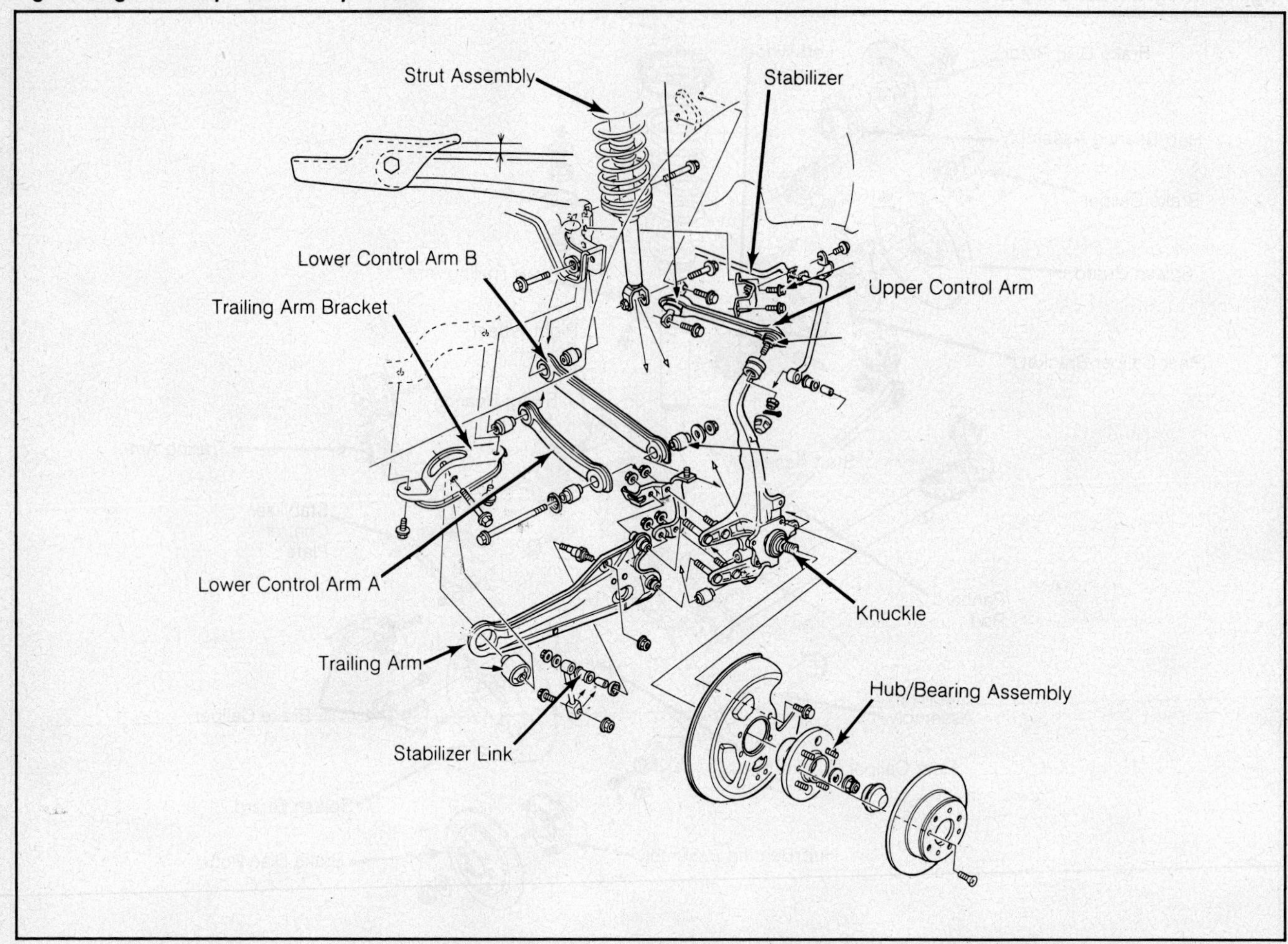

Courtesy of American Honda Motor Co., Inc.

Reassembly

To reassemble, reverse disassembly procedures.

Installation

To install, reverse removal procedures.

LEGEND 4-DOOR

Removal (Hub Carrier)

1) Raise rear of vehicle and support with safety stands. Remove wheel assembly. Remove brake caliper. Position caliper out of way. Remove spindle dust cover, spindle nut and hub washer. Support lower control arm with floor jack. Remove strut self-locking pinch bolt.

2) Remove bolt holding control arm to hub carrier. Remove hub carrier and rear axle shaft assembly. Remove splash guard bolts. If necessary, press separate rear axle shaft from hub carrier.

Installation

Align tab on strut tube with slot in hub carrier and tighten self-locking pinch bolt. Place jack under lower control arm. Place spring seat and coil spring in control arm cavity. Raise floor jack until control arm bolt can be inserted into lower hub carrier. To complete installation, reverse removal procedure.

Removal (Wheel Bearing)

1) Raise rear of vehicle and support with safety stands. Remove wheel assembly. Remove brake caliper. Hang caliper out of way. Remove spindle dust cap, nut and hub washer. Support lower control arm with floor jack. Remove strut self-locking pinch bolt.

2) Remove bolt holding lower control arm to hub carrier. Remove hub carrier and rear axle shaft assembly. Remove splash guard bolts. Using a press, separate rear axle shaft from hub carrier. Press bearing from hub carrier.

3) Remove bearing race from axle shaft using bearing remover. Wash hub carrier and axle shaft thoroughly before reassembly.

Installation

To install bearing, reverse removal procedure.

Removal (Control Arm)

1) Raise rear of vehicle and support with safety stands. Remove wheel assembly. Place floor jack under control arm. Disconnect lower stabilizer bar link at control arm.

2) Remove lower control arm bolt at hub carrier. Carefully lower floor jack. Remove coil spring and spring seat. Remove lower control arm pivot bolt. Remove lower control arm. *See Fig. 3.*

Installation

1) Install control arm pivot bolt loosely in place. Place jack under control arm. Place spring seat and spring

ACURA (Cont.)

Fig. 3: Legend 4-Door Rear Suspension

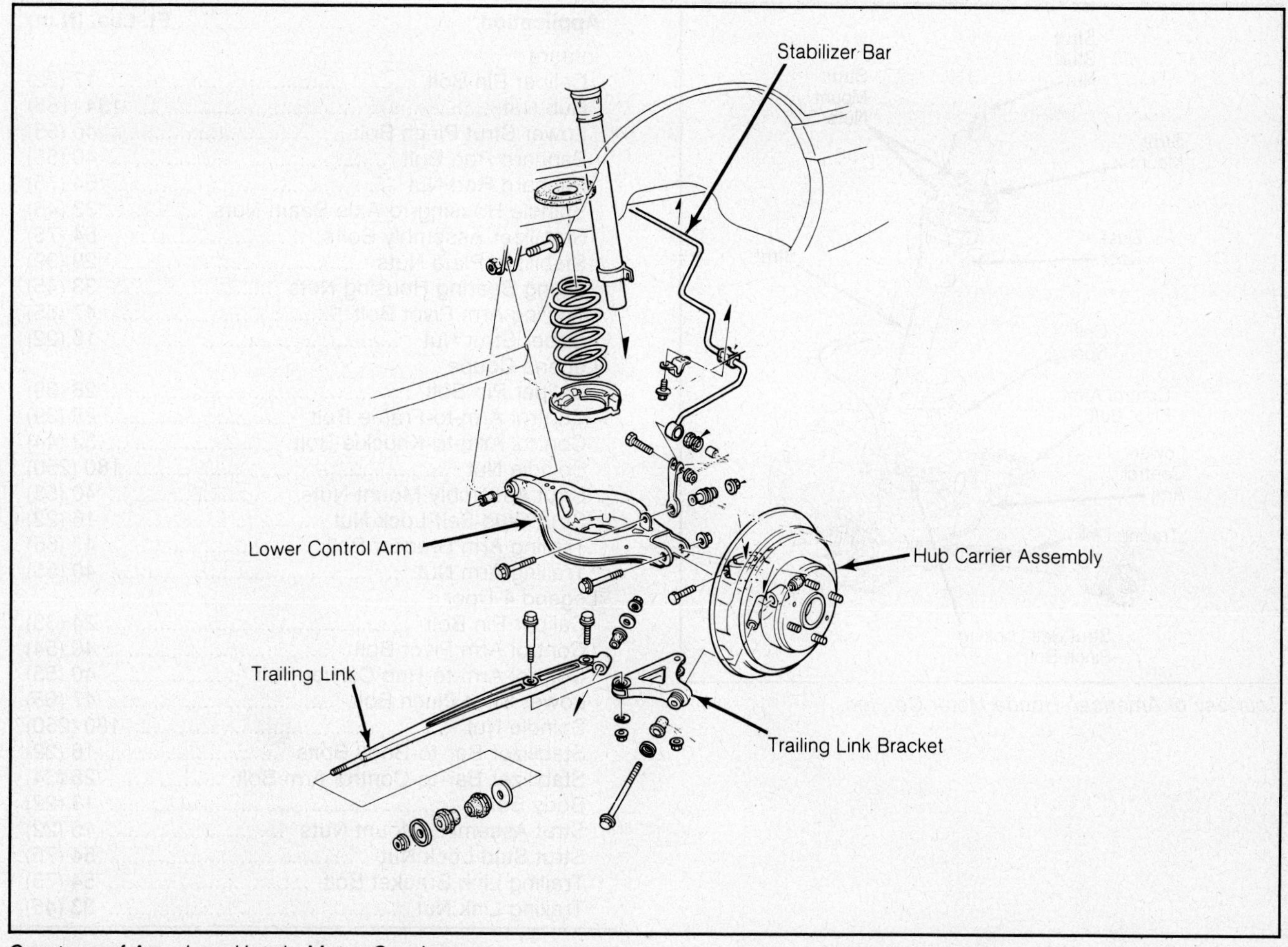

Courtesy of American Honda Motor Co., Inc.

in control arm cavity. Raise control arm until bolt can be inserted through lower hub carrier/control arm hole.

2) Tighten control arm pivot bolt and hub carrier/control arm mounting bolt. Reverse removal procedure to complete installation.

Removal (Stabilizer Bar)

Remove bolts holding stabilizer bar to lower control arm. Remove bolts attaching stabilizer bar to body. Remove stabilizer bar from vehicle. *See Fig. 3.*

Installation

Check parts for deterioration or damage. Replace worn or damaged parts. Reverse removal procedure to install.

Removal (Strut Assembly)

Raise rear of vehicle and support with safety stands. Remove wheel assembly. Jack up lower control arm slightly. Remove strut 8 mm nuts. Lower jack. Remove strut pinch bolt. Remove strut from hub carrier.

Disassembly

Using Allen wrench, hold center shaft of strut. Remove self-locking nut from strut assembly. Remove strut mount and dust cover assembly from strut. Compress and extend strut, checking for smooth operation. Replace strut if weak, uneven or jerky operation exists. *See Fig. 4.*

Reassembly

1) Check spring tension. Check parts for deterioration or damage. Check strut for leaks and proper operation. Replace worn or damaged parts.

2) To complete reassembly, reverse disassembly procedure.

Installation

Place spring seat and spring in control arm cavity. Position top of strut assembly. Loosely install strut mount nuts. Slowly raise control arm with floor jack. Align tab on strut tube with slot in hub carrier and tighten self-locking pinch bolt. Tighten strut upper mount nuts. To complete installation, reverse removal procedure.

Rear Suspension

ACURA (Cont.)

Fig. 4: Legend 4-Door Rear Strut Assembly

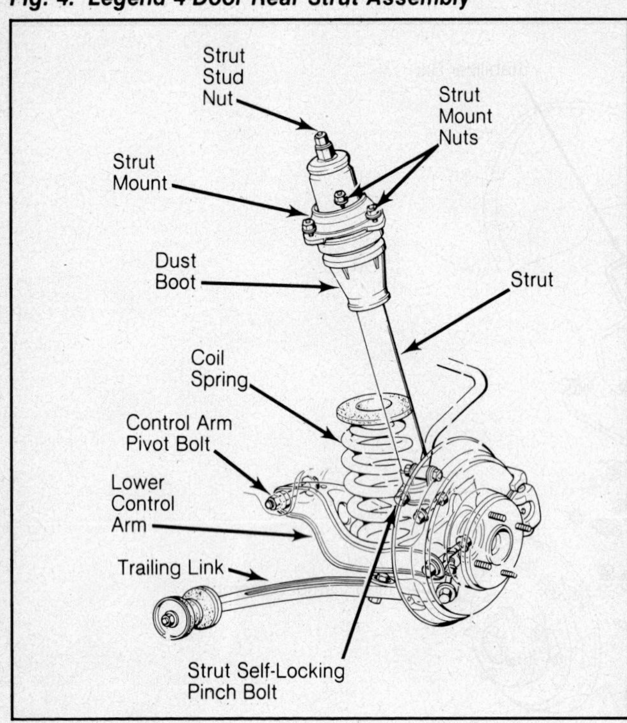

Courtesy of American Honda Motor Co., Inc.

TIGHTENING SPECIFICATIONS

Application	Ft. Lbs. (N.m)
Integra	
Caliper Pin Bolt	17 (23)
Hub Nut	134 (185)
Lower Strut Pinch Bolt	40 (55)
Panhard Rod Bolt	40 (55)
Panhard Rod Nut	54 (75)
Spindle Housing-to-Axle Beam Nuts	33 (45)
Stabilizer Assembly Bolts	54 (75)
Stabilizer Plate Nuts	29 (39)
Swing Bearing Housing Nuts	33 (45)
Trailing Arm Pivot Bolt	47 (65)
Upper Strut Nut	16 (22)
Legend Coupe	
Caliper Pin Bolt	28 (39)
Control Arm-to-Frame Bolt	28 (39)
Control Arm-to-Knuckle Bolt	32 (44)
Spindle Nut	180 (250)
Strut Assembly Mount Nuts	40 (55)
Strut Stud Self-Lock Nut	16 (22)
Trailing Arm Bracket Bolt	47 (65)
Trailing Arm Nut	40 (55)
Legend 4-Door	
Caliper Pin Bolt	24 (33)
Control Arm Pivot Bolt	40 (54)
Control Arm-to-Hub Carrier Bolt	40 (55)
Lower Strut Pinch Bolt	47 (65)
Spindle Nut	180 (250)
Stabilizer Bar-to-Body Bolts	16 (22)
Stabilizer Bar-to-Control Arm Bolt	25 (34)
Body Bolts	16 (22)
Strut Assembly Mount Nuts	16 (22)
Strut Stud Lock Nut	54 (75)
Trailing Link Bracket Bolt	54 (75)
Trailing Link Nut	33 (45)

Rear Suspension

AUDI

DESCRIPTION

Rear suspension consists of a strut assembly, transverse rod, trailing arms and stabilizer bar. Rear suspension design variations are present between all models. *See Figs. 1* and *6*.

On the 5000CS Quattro a modified reinforced crossmember with a trapezoidal control arm is used. On 4000CS Quattro, a lower control arm similar to the front suspension is used. *See Figs. 2* and *5*.

Fig. 1: Exploded View of 5000S & 5000CS Turbo Rear Suspension

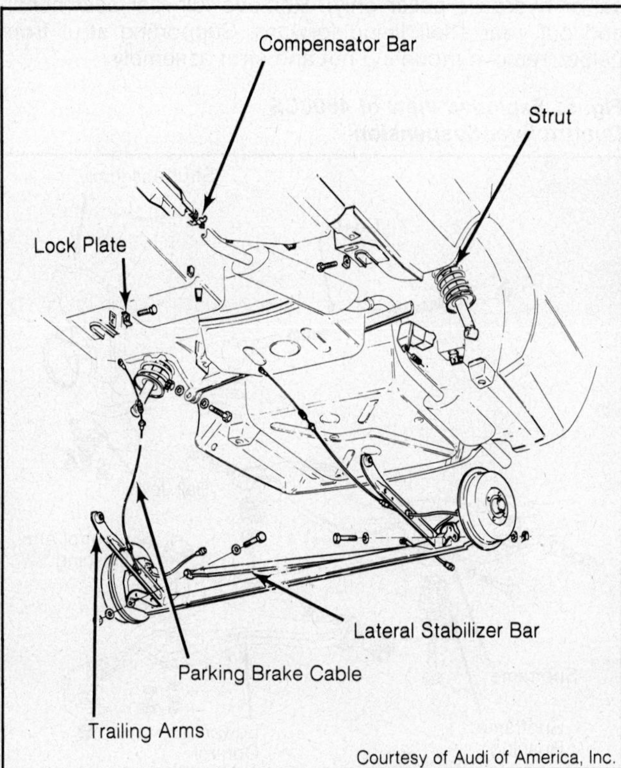

Fig. 2: Rear suspension for 5000CS Quattro

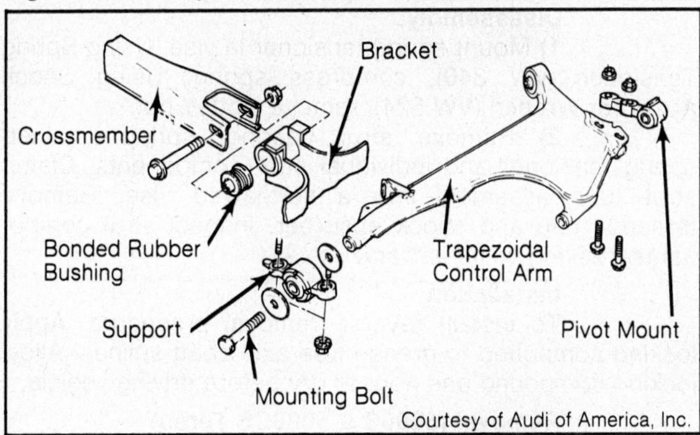

ADJUSTMENTS & INSPECTION

WHEEL ALIGNMENT SPECIFICATIONS & PROCEDURES

Rear wheel alignment is not adjustable (except 4000CS Quattro and 5000CS Quattro models). For 4000CS Quattro and 5000CS Quattro, see WHEEL ALIGNMENT SPECIFICATIONS & PROCEDURES in WHEEL ALIGNMENT section.

WHEEL BEARING

All Except Quattro

Remove grease cap, cotter pin and castle nut. While turning wheel, tighten nut firmly to seat bearing. Back nut off until washer can just be rotated using the tip of a flat tip screwdriver. Install castle nut, new cotter pin and grease cap.

Quattro

Rear wheel bearings are not adjustable, and must be replaced if removed. *See Fig. 3*.

Fig. 3: Exploded View of 4000 Quattro Wheel Bearing Housing.

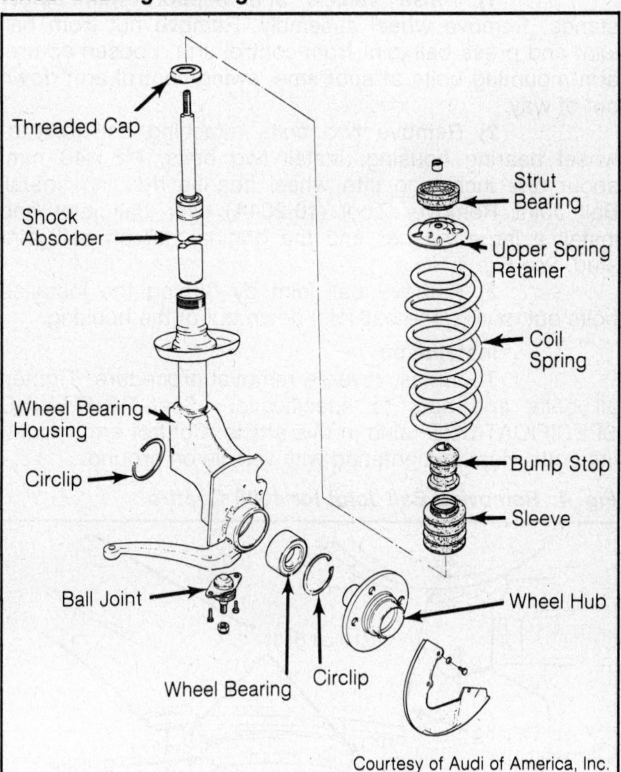

REMOVAL & INSTALLATION

WHEEL BEARING (QUATTRO)

NOTE: **Remove and install axle shaft nut with vehicle on ground. Always replace axle shaft self-locking nut.**

Removal

1) Remove axle shaft nut. Raise and support vehicle and remove wheel assembly. Remove strut assembly. See STRUT ASSEMBLY in this article.

2) Press wheel hub out of bearing using Housing Supports (VW401) and (VW402), and Adapter (VW295a). Remove wheel bearing inner race from wheel hub using a standard puller and Adapter (VW295a).

3) Remove bearing circlips and press bearing out of housing using Housing Supports (VW401) and (VW402), and Adapter (VW442).

Rear Suspension

AUDI (Cont.)

Installation

1) Lubricate bearing seat in housing using moly-paste supplied in repair kit. Press bearing into housing using same tools as removal.

2) Press wheel hub into bearing/housing using Housing Support (VW401) and Adapters (VW4120) and (VW455). To complete installation, reverse removal procedure.

NOTE: DO NOT move vehicle without drive axle or outer CV joint installed, or wheel bearing will be damaged.

BALL JOINT

Removal (4000 Quattro)

1) Raise vehicle and support with safety stands. Remove wheel assembly. Remove nut from ball joint and press ball joint from control arm. Loosen control arm mounting bolts at subframe, swing control arm down out of way.

2) Remove two bolts attaching ball joint-to-wheel bearing housing. Install two bolts, M8 x 40 mm, about one inch long into wheel bearing housing. Install Ball Joint Remover Tool (40-204A) over ball joint and install a large washer and the original nut on ball joint stud. *See Fig. 4.*

3) Remove ball joint by turning the installed bolts out, pulling the ball joint down out of the housing.

Installation

To install, reverse removal procedure. Tighten all bolts and nuts to specification. See TIGHTENING SPECIFICATIONS table in this article. Control arm mounting bolts must be tightened with vehicle on ground.

Fig. 4: Removing Ball Joint for 4000 Quattro

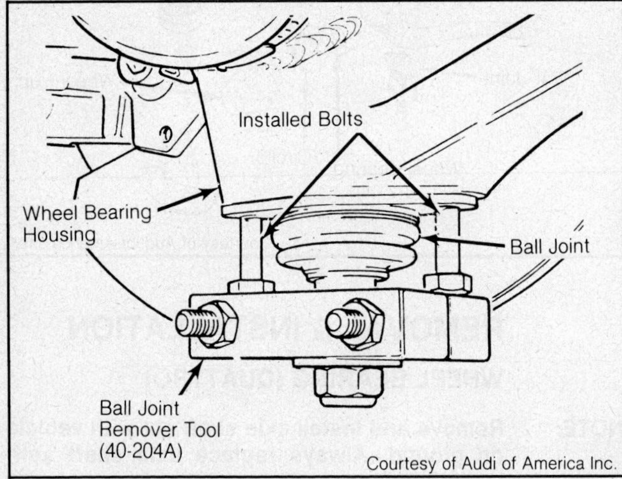

STRUT ASSEMBLY

NOTE: Remove and install shock absorbers one at a time. DO NOT allow rear axle to hang from body mounts only.

Removal (Coupe GT & 4000S)

Loosen trunk sheet metal trim, and remove shock absorber top protective cap. Remove upper mounting nut. Raise vehicle, remove lower mounting bolts and remove shock absorber.

Removal (4000CS Quattro)

1) Loosen wheel bolts slightly. Remove axle nut cover and axle shaft nut. Raise vehicle on hoist and remove wheel. Remove stabilizer tie rod retaining nut. Press tie rod end from its bore. *See Fig. 5.*

2) Remove ball joint retaining nut and press ball joint from its bore. Remove caliper and wire up out of the working area. Remove brake rotor. Loosen control arm mounting nuts. Swing control arm down and out of working area. Remove brake hose and parking brake cable.

3) Press out stub axle from hub (use mechanical or hydraulic puller only). Remove full rear seat bench and pull rear shelf lining forward. Supporting strut from below, remove mounting nut and strut assembly.

Fig. 5: Exploded View of 4000CS Quattro Rear Suspension

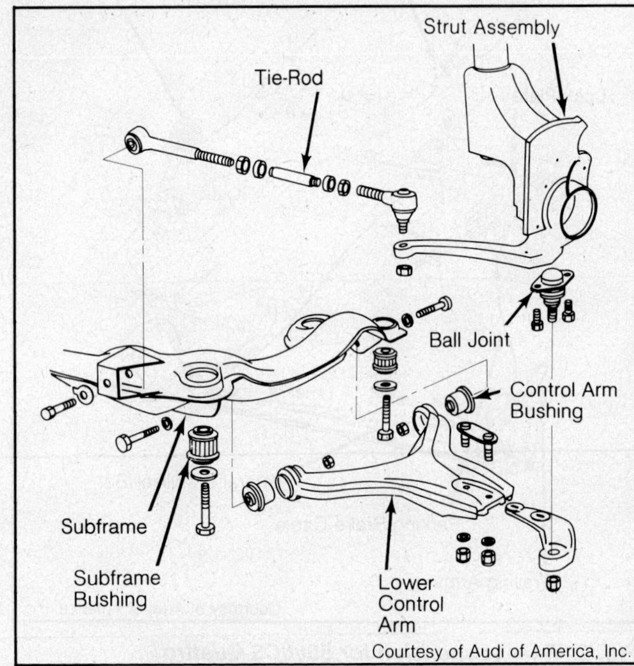

Disassembly

1) Mount spring tensioner in vise. Using Spring Tensioner (VW 340), compress spring. Using Shock Absorber Wrench (VW 524), remove slotted nut.

2) Remove strut bearing, spring retainer, spring tensioner and individual strut components. Clamp strut tube assembly into a soft-jawed vise. Remove threaded cap and shock absorber. Inspect strut components, replace as necessary.

Installation

To install, reverse removal procedure. Apply locking compound to grease free axle shaft splines. Allow locking compound one hour to dry before driving vehicle.

Removal (5000S & 5000CS Turbo)

Remove top shock absorber mounting. Remove lower mounting and shock.

Installation

To install, reverse removal procedure. Always use new self-locking nuts.

AUDI (Cont.)

REAR AXLE ASSEMBLY

Removal (Coupe GT, 4000S & 4000CS Quattro)

1) On all models, raise and support vehicle. Remove wheels. Disconnect muffler hangers. Lower and secure muffler and tailpipe.

2) Remove nut on parking brake linkage equalizer bar. Pry cable sleeves out of brackets. Remove parking brake cables from brackets. *See Fig. 6.*

Fig. 6: Exploded View of Coupe GT & 4000S Rear Suspension

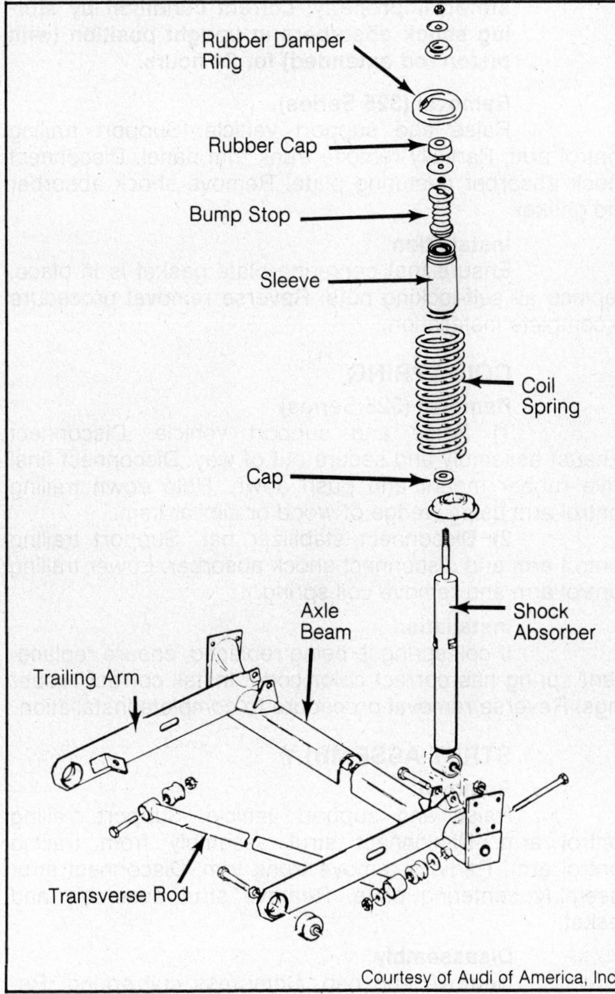

3) Disconnect brake hoses and plug lines. Remove nuts from trailing arm mounting bolts, leaving bolts in place. Disconnect spring from brake pressure regulator.

4) On 4000CS Quattro model, press out stub axle from hub. Remove stub axle with mechanical or hydraulic puller only. Remove drive shaft and angle upward, along final drive housing.

5) On all models, remove transverse rod mounting bolt, strut assembly mounting bolts and trailing arm mounting bolts. Remove rear axle assembly while guiding parking brake cable over muffler and tailpipe.

Trailing Arm Bushing Replacement

Place trailing arm in press and press bushing from arm. Reverse procedure to install new bushing. Make sure bushing slots are positioned horizontally in trailing arm.

Installation

To install, reverse removal procedure. Be sure to bleed and adjust brakes as needed.

Removal (5000S & 5000CS Turbo)

1) Raise and support vehicle. Remove wheel and tire assembly. Loosen parking brake adjusting nut. Detach right side parking brake cable.

2) Remove clips and unhook left side parking brake cable. Remove brake pressure accumulator. Leave fuel lines connected. Disconnect brake hoses and plug.

3) Detach diagonal arm retaining bolts. Remove pressure regulator spring. Support rear axle using appropriate jackstand. Remove both shock absorbers. Remove trailing arm bolts. Lower and remove axle assembly.

Bushing Replacement

Place trailing arm in press. Press bushing from arm using Bushing Removers (VW 412 and 2010). Reverse procedure to install new bushing. Align cut-outs with center axis. Larger cut-out faces front of vehicle.

Installation

To install, reverse removal procedure. Be sure to bleed brakes and adjust parking brake cable.

TRANSVERSE ROD

Removal (Except 4000CS Quattro & 5000CS Quattro)

Raise and support vehicle. Remove attaching bolts from transverse rod and remove rod. Inspect bushings and sleeves for wear. Replace as necessary.

Installation

To install, reverse removal procedure.

TIGHTENING SPECIFICATIONS

Application	Ft. Lbs. (N.m)
4000 Series	
Axle Nut [1]	203 (280)
Ball Joint Nut [1]	54 (75)
Ball Joint-to-Housing Bolts	29 (40)
Ball Joint Clamp Nut [1]	
Turbo Quattro	47 (65)
Ball Joint-to-Control Arm Nuts [1]	
Turbo Quattro	47 (65)
Brake Caliper Mounting Bolts	47 (65)
Control Arm-to-Subframe Bolts	43 (60)
Lower Shock Absorber Bolts	43 (60)
Tie Rod Nut [1]	29 (40)
Trailing Arm Bolts	72 (98)
Transverse Rod	58 (79)
Upper Shock Absorber Nut	15 (20)
5000 Series	
Lower Shock Absorber Bolt	66 (90)
Trailing Arm Bolts	69 (94)
Transverse Rod	65 (88)
Upper Shock Absorber Nut	15 (20)
Wheel Lug Bolts (All Models)	80 (110)

[1] – Always replace nut when removed.

Rear Suspension

BMW

325 Series, 528e, 535 Series
635 Series, 735 Series

DESCRIPTION

All BMW models use independent, semi-trailing control arm rear suspension systems. On 325 series, the rear suspension is controlled by telescopic shock absorbers with separate coil springs. On all other models, the rear suspension is controlled by spring/shock absorbers (strut assembly) with double-acting telescopic hydraulic dampers. A stabilizer bar is used on all models.

Fig. 1: BMW 325 Series Rear Suspension

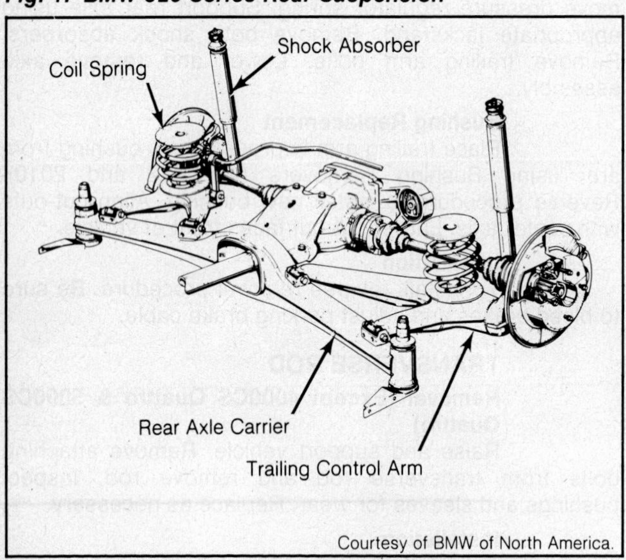

Courtesy of BMW of North America.

ADJUSTMENTS & INSPECTION

WHEEL ALIGNMENT SPECIFICATIONS

See WHEEL ALIGNMENT SPECIFICATIONS & PROCEDURES in WHEEL ALIGNMENT section.

REMOVAL & INSTALLATION

WHEEL BEARING

Removal (325 Series)

1) Raise and support vehicle. Remove wheel assembly. Remove lock plate and nut. Disconnect output shaft at drive flange and secure out of way. Press output shaft out using Output Shaft Remover (33 2 110). Remove hex head screw and remove rotor.

2) Drive out rear axle shaft using Driver (33 4 010). Remove snap ring and remove wheel bearing using puller. Remove inner bearing shell from rear axle shaft with puller, if necessary.

Removal (All Other Series)

1) Raise and support vehicle. Disconnect output shaft at drive flange and suspend out of way. Remove brake caliper bolts and brake caliper. Remove hex head screw and remove rotor.

2) Remove lock plate. Remove collar nut with Nut Remover (33 4 000). Pull off drive flange. Install collar nut flush with end of shaft. Knock shaft out using soft mallet.

3) Remove snap ring and remove wheel bearing using puller. Remove inner bearing shell from rear axle shaft using puller, if necessary.

Installation (All Models)

To install, reverse removal procedure. Tighten collar nut. Drive in lock plate with Driver (33 4 060) on 528e, 535 Series, 635 Series and 735 Series.

SHOCK ABSORBER

NOTE: Always store shock absorbers in upright position. If shock absorbers have been stored improperly, correct condition by storing shock absorbers in upright position (with piston rod extended) for 24 hours.

Removal (325 Series)

Raise and support vehicle. Support trailing control arm. Partially remove trunk trim panel. Disconnect shock absorber centering plate. Remove shock absorber and gasket.

Installation

Ensure that centering plate gasket is in place. Replace all self-locking nuts. Reverse removal procedure to complete installation.

COIL SPRING

Removal (325 Series)

1) Raise and support vehicle. Disconnect exhaust assembly and secure out of way. Disconnect final drive rubber mount and push down. Hold down trailing control arm using wedge of wood or similar item.

2) Disconnect stabilizer bar. Support trailing control arm and disconnect shock absorber. Lower trailing control arm and remove coil spring.

Installation

If coil spring is being replaced, ensure replacement spring has correct color code. Install correct rubber rings. Reverse removal procedure to complete installation.

STRUT ASSEMBLY

Removal

Raise and support vehicle. Support trailing control arm. Disconnect strut assembly from trailing control arm. Partially remove trunk trim. Disconnect strut assembly centering plate. Remove strut assembly and gasket.

Disassembly

Remove end cap. Compress coil spring. Remove spring retainer nut and washer. Slowly release spring compressor. Remove centering plate, spring, cap, snap ring, damper and dust sleeve.

Reassembly

To reassemble, reverse disassembly procedure. Before releasing spring compressor, ensure that coil spring ends are in openings provided in centering plate and lower spring retainer.

Installation

Replace all self-locking nuts. Reverse removal procedure to complete installation.

BMW (Cont.)

Fig. 2: BMW 528e Rear Suspension

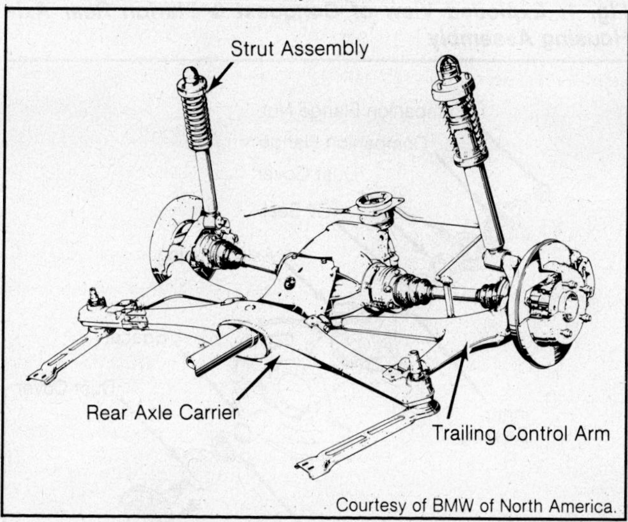

Courtesy of BMW of North America.

TRAILING CONTROL ARM

Removal

1) Raise and support vehicle. Remove wheel assembly. Apply parking brake and disconnect output shaft from drive flange. Release parking brake and remove parking brake lever.

2) Remove a small amount of brake fluid from master cylinder. Disconnect brake hose at brake line bracket. Disconnect stabilizer bar. Remove trailing arm-to-axle carrier bolts. Disconnect strut assembly and remove trailing arm.

Bushing Replacement

Press out trailing arm bushings using Bushing Remover/Installer (33 3 040). Lubricate new bushings with oil. Install bushings so that longer end of bushing sleeve faces center of vehicle.

Installation

To install, reverse removal procedure. Bleed brake system. See HYDRAULIC BRAKE BLEEDING in BRAKE section.

TIGHTENING SPECIFICATIONS

Application	Ft. Lbs. (N.m)
Axle Carrier-to-Body Bolt	101-112 (140-155)
Axle Shaft-to-Drive Flange Bolt	
528e, 635 Series & 735 Series	169-188 (234-260)
Drive Flange-to-Output Shaft Bolt	
325 Series	140-152 (195-210)
Shock Absorber-to-Trailing Arm Nut	
325 Series	52-63 (72-87)
528e, 635 Series & 735 Series	90-103 (125-143)
Spring Retainer-to-Wheel House Bolt	
528e, 635 Series & 735 Series	16-17 (22-24)
Shock Absorber-to-Body Nut	
325 Series	16-17 (22-24)
Shock Absorber-to-Rubber Mount Nut	
325 Series	9-11 (13-15)
Stabilizer-to-Trailing Arm Bolt	
325 Series	16-17 (22-24)
Trailing Arm-to-Axle Carrier Bolt	48-54 (67-75)

Rear Suspension

CHRYSLER MOTORS CONQUEST & MITSUBISHI STARION

DESCRIPTION

The rear suspension system is an independent type consisting of 2 lower control arms mounted to a rear suspension support and rear crossmember. Control arms are connected to each other by a stabilizer bar mounted to rear suspension support. Shock absorber strut assemblies are mounted to each lower control arm and upper frame bracket. Rear toe-in and camber are adjustable on these vehicles.

ADJUSTMENTS & INSPECTION

WHEEL ALIGNMENT SPECIFICATIONS & PROCEDURES

See WHEEL ALIGNMENT SPECIFICATIONS & PROCEDURES in WHEEL ALIGNMENT section.

REMOVAL & INSTALLATION

REAR AXLE SHAFT BEARING

Inspection

Place dial indicator stem on rear axle flange near lug nut. Check drive axle end play. Maximum end play should be .031" (.8 mm). Replace inner and/or outer bearing if not within specifications.

Removal

1) Raise and support vehicle on safety stands. Remove rear wheel assembly. Disconnect parking brake cable from rear brake caliper assembly. Remove rear caliper assembly, caliper support and rotor. Support caliper assembly away from work area with wire.

2) Scribe index marks on flange yoke and companion flange. Remove 4 drive axle flange yoke-to-companion flange mount bolts. Separate drive axle from flange.

3) Remove drive axle from differential carrier using Slide Hammer and Adapter (MB990211-01 and MB990906-01). Slide hammer attachment fits on outboard end of axle shaft flange.

NOTE: **Do not damage oil seal with drive axle spline during removal.**

4) Remove axle housing-to-lower control arm mounting bolts and nuts. Remove shock strut assembly from axle housing. Remove axle shaft/housing assembly.

5) Mount assembly in vise and loosen companion flange mount bolt. *See Fig. 1.*Tap axle shaft out of axle housing using a plastic hammer. Remove spacer and dust covers from inside axle housing.

CAUTION: **Do not remove inner and outer bearings unless necessary for replacement.**

6) To remove outer axle shaft bearing, cut bearing retainer in 3 places with chisel. Insert claws of Bearing Puller (MB990918) into the 3 places cut in retainer and turn tool 90 degrees to lock claws in place. Pull bearing out of housing. *See Fig. 2.*

7) To remove inner bearing and seal from axle housing, drive bearing and seal from housing using long drift and hammer.

Fig. 1: Exploded View of Conquest & Starion Rear Axle Housing Assembly

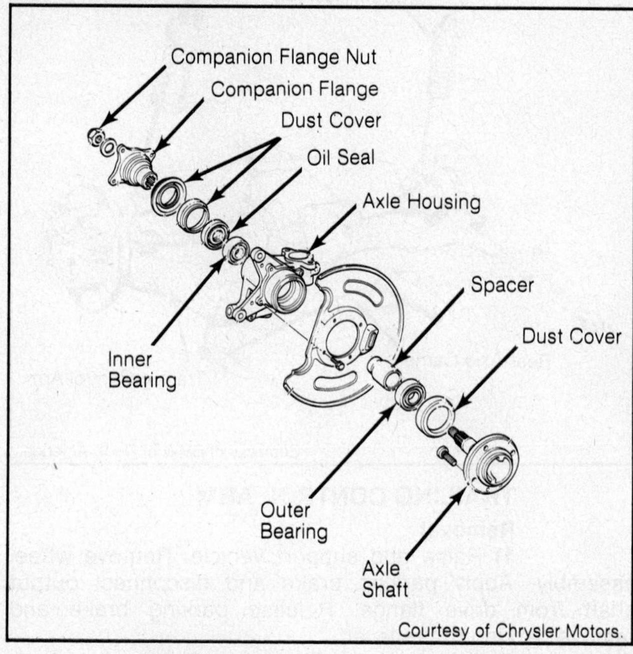

Installation

1) Press new outer bearing onto axle shaft. Ensure seal side of outer bearing faces flange side of axle shaft. Apply grease to inside surface of axle housing.

2) Position new inner bearing so seal side faces companion flange. Press bearing using Bearing Installer and Handle (MB990932-01 and MB990938-01). Apply grease to oil seal contact area of axle housing.

3) Press new oil seal into axle housing until it contacts edge of housing. Install dust cover onto axle housing. Apply grease to oil seal lip. Insert axle shaft and spacer into axle housing.

4) Attach companion flange. Mount axle housing in vise and tighten companion flange nut to 188-217 ft. lbs. (260-300 N.m).

5) Install axle housing onto lower control arm and strut assembly. Install drive shaft flange-to-companion flange mount bolts. Tighten all components to specification. Ensure axle shaft end play is within service limit.

REAR SUSPENSION ASSEMBLY

Removal & Installation

1) Raise and support vehicle a minimum of 2 feet from ground. Remove rear wheel assembly. Using rope or wire, support strut assembly to crossmember. Support rear suspension assembly with a wooden block and jack.

2) Disconnect drive shaft from torque tube. Remove center exhaust pipe and main muffler. Disconnect parking brake cable from rear disc brake and lower control arm.

3) Disconnect brake hose from rear floor. Remove strut assembly upper mount bolts located under side trim in rear hatch area. Remove crossmember mount bolts. *See Fig. 3.*

4) Detach front support mount bolts and nuts. Lower jack slowly and carefully remove suspension assembly from vehicle. Ensure all wires, cables and hoses

Rear Suspension

CHRYSLER MOTORS CONQUEST & MITSUBISHI STARION (Cont.)

Fig. 2: Removing Outer Axle Bearing

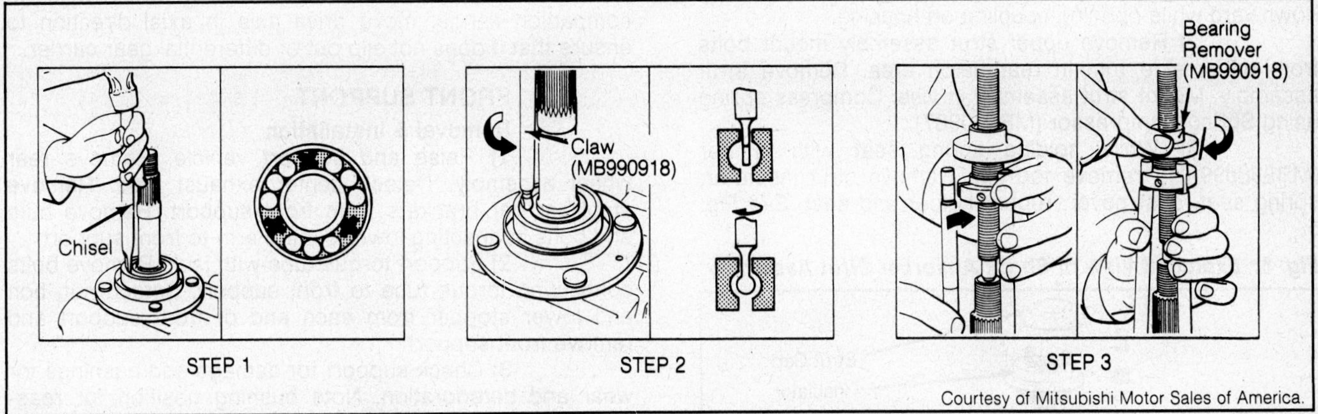

Courtesy of Mitsubishi Motor Sales of America.

are detached before removing assembly. To install rear suspension assembly, reverse removal procedure.

Fig. 3: Conquest & Starion Rear Suspension Assembly

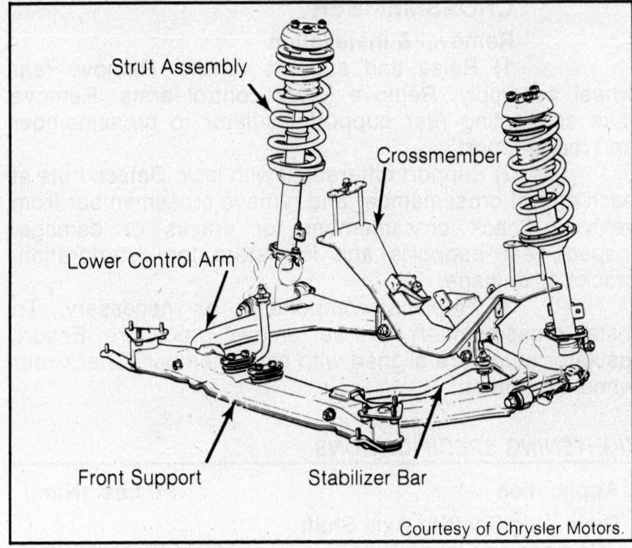

Courtesy of Chrysler Motors.

LOWER CONTROL ARM

Removal

1) Raise and support vehicle. Remove rear wheel assembly. Disconnect parking brake cable from lower control arm. Disconnect stabilizer bar. Remove lower control arm-to-axle housing nuts and bolts. *See Fig. 4.*

NOTE: Note postion of rear toe-in cam before removing lower control arm-to-crossmember bolts.

2) Remove nuts and bolts connecting lower control arm to crossmember. Detach lower control arm from crossmember and remove from vehicle. Inspect bushings for wear and deterioration. Check for bent or broken lower control arm.

Bushing Replacement

1) Press out lower control arm front bushing using Bushing Removers (MB990848-01, MB990884-01 and MB990890-01). Press out lower control arm rear bushing using Bushing Removers (MB990883-01, MB990885-01 and MB990890-01). Press out remaining bushings using Bushing Removers (MB990892-01, MB990895-01 and MB990897-01).

2) Press bushings into control arm. Do not damage control arm during assembly. Before installing, apply grease to the cut out section of the shaft connecting the lower control arm to axle housing. Do not allow grease onto bushings.

Installation

Insert shaft with reference mark on head facing down. Install remaining nuts and bolts to connect control arm assembly. When installing control arm on crossmember, ensure mark on crossmember is aligned with mark on alignment plate. After installation, check rear wheel alignment.

Fig. 4: Exploded View of Conquest & Starion Bushing Assemblies

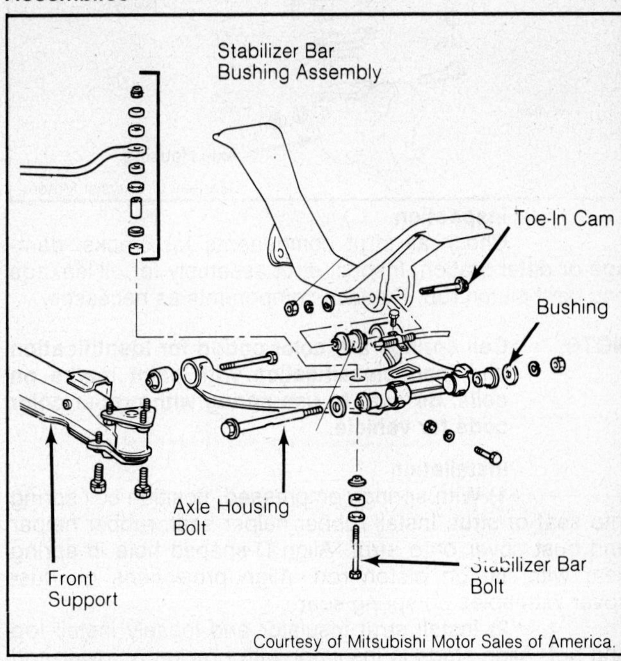

Courtesy of Mitsubishi Motor Sales of America.

STRUT ASSEMBLY

Removal

1) Raise and support vehicle. Disconnect rear brake hose at strut. Separate drive axle from companion

Rear Suspension

CHRYSLER MOTORS CONQUEST & MITSUBISHI STARION (Cont.)

flange. Remove strut assembly-to-axle housing mount bolts and separate strut from housing. Push housing downward while opening coupling on housing.

2) Remove upper strut assembly mount bolts from under side trim in rear hatch area. Remove strut assembly. Mount strut assembly in vise. Compress spring using Spring Compressor (MB990987).

3) While holding spring seat with Holder (MB990899-01), remove top nut. Remove strut insulator, spring seat, dust cover, rubber helper and seat. *See Fig. 5.*

Fig. 5: Exploded View of Shock Absorber Strut Assembly

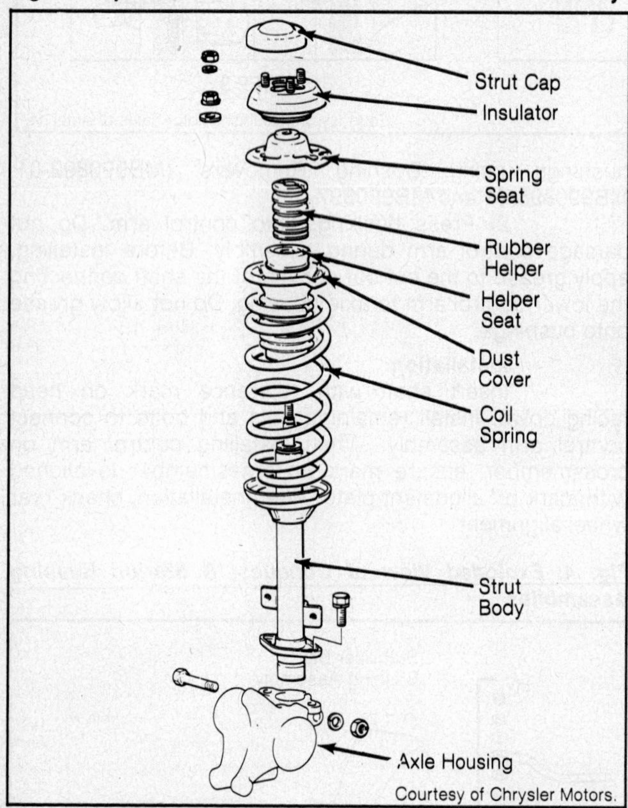

Courtesy of Chrysler Motors.

Inspection

Check all strut components for cracks, damage or deterioration. Inspect strut assembly for oil leakage and bent piston rod. Replace components as necessary.

NOTE: Coil springs are color coded for identification and load classification with paint marks on coils. Be sure to use spring with proper color code for vehicle.

Installation

1) With spring compressed, position coil spring into seat of strut. Install rubber helper seat, rubber helper and dust cover onto strut. Align D-shaped hole in spring seat with flat on piston rod. Align projections on dust cover with holes on spring seat.

2) Install strut insulator and loosely install top end nut. Align studs in insulator with bracket at lower end of strut. Hold spring seat and tighten top end nut.

3) Ensure spring is aligned in top and bottom seats. Remove spring compressor. Position rubber helper with thick sided portion up. Apply semi-drying sealant to top surface of insulator. Note that gasket is factory installed.

4) To complete installation, reverse removal procedure. Before and after coupling drive axle to companion flange, move drive axle in axial direction to ensure that it does not slip out of differential gear carrier.

FRONT SUPPORT

Removal & Installation

1) Raise and support vehicle. Remove rear wheel assembly. Detach center exhaust pipe. Remove stabilizer bar brackets from front support. Remove nuts and bolts connecting lower control arm to front support.

2) Support torque tube with jack. Remove bolts connecting torque tube to front support. Detach nut, bolt and lower stopper from each end of front support and remove front support.

3) Check support for damage and bushings for wear and deterioration. Note bushing position for reassembly reference. Replace bushing using Bushing Remover (MB990882-01). To install, reverse removal procedure. Align holes in bushing with notch in support. Check rear wheel alignment.

CROSSMEMBER

Removal & Installation

1) Raise and support vehicle. Remove rear wheel assembly. Remove lower control arms. Remove nuts connecting rear support insulator to crossmember and rear support.

2) Support differential with jack. Detach nuts at each end of crossmember and remove crossmember from vehicle. Check crossmember for cracks or damage. Inspect rear supports and insulators for deterioration, cracks or damage.

3) Replace components as necessary. To install crossmember, reverse removal procedure. Ensure insulator studs are aligned with crossmember. Check rear wheel alignment.

TIGHTENING SPECIFICATIONS

Application	Ft. Lbs. (N.m)
Drive Axle Shaft-to-Axle Shaft Companion Flange Nuts	40-47 (55-65)
Drive Shaft-to-Torque Tube Flange Bolts	36-43 (50-60)
Lower Control Arm Lock Pin Bolt	11-14 (15-20)
Lower Control Arm-to-Front Support Mount Nut	94-108 (130-150)
Lower Control Arm-to-Crossmember Mount Nut	94-108 (130-150)
Lower Control Arm-to-Axle Housing Mount Nut	80-94 (108-127)
Lower Stopper Nut	51-61 (70-85)
Lower Stopper Bolt	29-36 (40-50)
Rear Axle Shaft Companion Flange Nut	188-217 (260-300)
Stabilizer Bar Bracket Bolt	22-29 (30-40)
Strut Top Nut	18-25 (25-35)
Strut Top End Nut	51-65 (70-90)
Strut Assembly-to-Axle Housing Bolt	36-51 (50-70)
Torque Tube-to-Front Support Nuts	25-33 (35-45)
Upper Stopper Bolt	51-61 (70-85)
	INCH Lbs. (N.m)
Stabilizer Bar Mount Bolt	84-168 (10-20)

CHRYSLER MOTORS, HYUNDAI & MITSUBISHI FWD

Chrysler Motors: Colt, Colt Vista (2WD & 4WD);
Hyundai: Excel
Mitsubishi: Cordia, Mirage, Precis, Tredia

DESCRIPTION

On Colt Vista 4WD models, an independent-type suspension is used consisting of a crossmember, inner and outer arms, torsion bars, shock absorbers and extension rods.

On all other models, use an independent-type suspension consisting of an integral axle, suspension arms, shock absorbers, coil springs and stabilizer bar.

Fig. 1: Exploded View of Rear Suspension (Except Colt Vista 4WD)

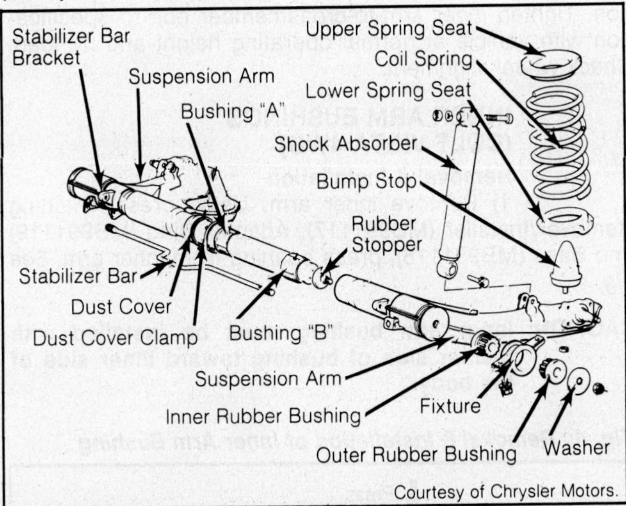

Courtesy of Chrysler Motors.

Fig. 2: Exploded View of Colt Vista (4WD) Rear Suspension

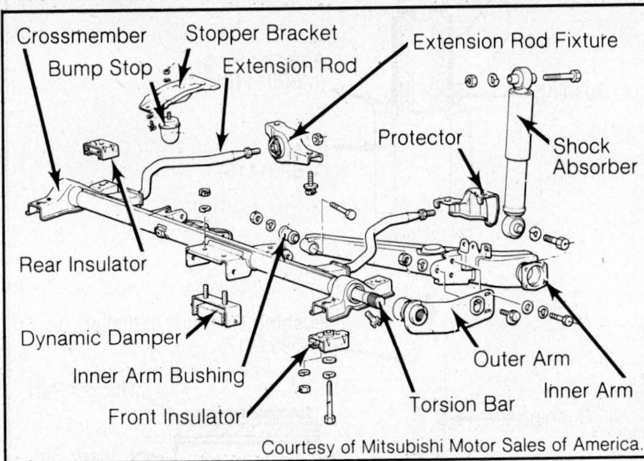

Courtesy of Mitsubishi Motor Sales of America.

ADJUSTMENTS & INSPECTION

WHEEL ALIGNMENT SPECIFICATIONS & PROCEDURES

See WHEEL ALIGNMENT SPECIFICATIONS & PROCEDURES in WHEEL ALIGNMENT section.

WHEEL BEARING

Colt Vista 4WD

1) Raise and support vehicle. Remove rear wheel and brake drum. Measure axle shaft end play with dial indicator. Maximum end play is .031" (.78 mm).

2) If end play exceeds limit, check companion flange-to-axle shaft nut torque. Replace wheel bearing if torque is within specification.

Colt & Mirage

1) Raise and support vehicle. Remove wheel. Release parking brake. Measure brake drum end play with dial indicator. Maximum end play is .008" (.20 mm).

2) If end play exceeds limit, retighten wheel bearing nut to 72-108 ft. lbs. (100-150 N.m). Recheck end play. Replace wheel bearings if end play exceeds specification.

NOTE: **To check wheel bearing nut, see REAR AXLE HUB BEARING in CHRYSLER MOTORS & MITSUBISHI brake article in BRAKES section.**

All Others

1) Raise and support vehicle. Move tire assembly and check bearings for play. If play exists, remove dust cap, cotter pin and nut retainer.

2) Loosen adjusting nut. While turning wheel or drum, tighten adjusting nut to 14 ft. lbs. (20 N.m).

3) Loosen nut and retighten to 84 INCH lbs. (10 N.m). On Hyundai and Precis models, retighten nut to 48 INCH lbs. (5 N.m). Reinstall nut retainer, cotter pin and dust cap. DO NOT back off nut more than 15 degrees to align cotter pin holes.

REMOVAL & INSTALLATION

WHEEL BEARING

Removal (Colt Vista 4WD)

1) Raise and support vehicle. Remove wheel and brake drum. Remove drive axle from axle shaft companion flange. Using Axle Holder (MB990767), hold axle shaft and remove companion flange retaining nut. Remove companion flange.

2) Using slide hammer, remove axle shaft. Using Bearing Puller/Installer (MB990560) and hydraulic press, remove outer wheel bearing and dust cover from axle shaft. Inner arm may require removal for access of inner bearing. See INNER ARM in this article.

3) Remove oil seal from inside of inner arm. Using Bearing Remover (MB990927) and Handle (MB990938), remove inner bearing from arm.

Inspection

1) Inspect companion flange and dust cover for wear or damage. Check oil seal for damage. Measure axle shaft O.D. in bearing areas. Inspect inner arm for signs of bearing movement.

2) Inspect bearings for roughness or damage. Measure bearing I.D. and O.D. Inspect axle shafts for wear or damage. Replace components not within specification. See AXLE SHAFT SPECIFICATIONS table.

Installation

1) Using Bearing Installer (MB990931) and Handle (MB990938), install inner bearing in arm. Using Seal Installer (MB990799), install seal in inner arm with concave side facing outward.

Rear Suspension

CHRYSLER MOTORS, HYUNDAI & MITSUBISHI FWD (Cont.)

AXLE SHAFT SPECIFICATIONS

Application	In. (mm)
Axle Shaft Dimensions	
Inner Bearing Area	1.10 (27.9)
Outer Bearing Area	1.38 (35.0)
Overall Length	8.46 (214.9)
Bearing Dimensions	
Inner Bearing	
I.D.	1.10 (27.9)
O.D.	2.28 (57.9)
Outer Bearing	
I.D.	1.38 (35.0)
O.D.	2.83 (72.0)

2) Coat seal lip with grease. Install dust cover. If backing plate was removed, apply semi-drying sealant to flange area of inner arm. Install backing plate. Tighten bolts to specification.

3) Using Dust Cover Installer (MB990799), install dust cover on axle shaft. Concave side of dust cover must face splined end of axle shaft. Using bearing puller/installer and press, install bearing on axle shaft with seal surface facing toward flange side of axle shaft.

4) Install axle shaft in inner arm. Install companion flange and new retaining nut. Using axle holder, tighten nut to specification. Check axle shaft end play. Reverse removal procedure for remaining components.

Removal (All Others)

1) Raise and support vehicle. Remove wheel assembly. Remove dust cap, cotter pin, nut retainer and nut. Remove brake drum, washer and outer bearing.

2) Pry grease seal from brake drum. Remove inner bearing. If bearing outer bearing races require removal, use a brass punch and hammer to remove bearing races from brake drum.

Installation

1) Install outer bearing races in brake drum. Ensure races are fully seated. Pack wheel bearings and center of brake drum with grease. Install inner bearing and grease seal. Apply grease to seal lip.

2) Install brake drum, outer bearing, washer and nut. On Colt and Mirage models, always install new wheel bearing nut. Tighten nut to specification. See TIGHTENING SPECIFICATIONS table at end of article.

3) On all other models, adjust bearing end play. See WHEEL BEARINGS under ADJUSTMENTS & INSPECTION in this article. On all models, check bearing end play. Install nut retainer, cotter pin and dust cap.

CAUTION: Always install new bearing retaining nut on Colt and Mirage models when nut is removed.

INNER ARM (COLT VISTA 4WD)

Removal

1) Raise and support vehicle. Remove wheel assembly. Remove drive axle companion flange-to-axle shaft retaining bolts. Support inner arm with jack.

2) Remove shock absorber retaining bolt. Mark position of the upper end of outer arm and crossmember body installation bracket. *See Fig. 3.* Remove inner arm-to outer arm bolts. Remove bolt from inner arm and crossmember. Remove inner arm.

Fig. 3: Marking Outer Arm for Reassembly

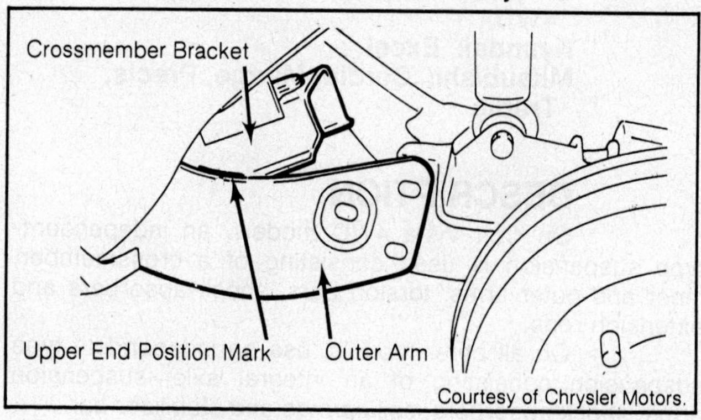

Installation

Reverse removal procedures. Align reference mark prior to tightening bolts. Tighten bolts to specification. Tighten inner arm-to-crossmember bolt to specification with vehicle at normal operating height and no load. Check wheel alignment.

INNER ARM BUSHINGS (COLT VISTA 4WD)

Removal & Installation

1) Remove inner arm. Using press, Bushing Remover/Installer (MB991117), Adapter Ring (MB991119) and Base (MB991118), press bushing from inner arm. *See Fig. 4.*

CAUTION: Inner arm bushing must be installed with thicker side of bushing toward inner side of the body.

Fig. 4: Removal & Installation of Inner Arm Bushing

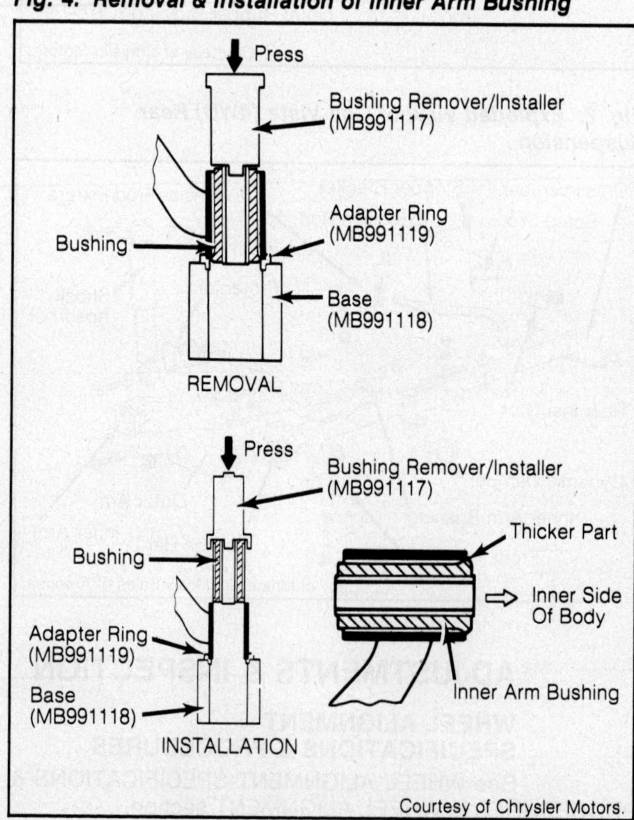

CHRYSLER MOTORS, HYUNDAI & MITSUBISHI FWD (Cont.)

2) Using press, bushing remover/installer, adapter ring and base, press bushing in inner arm with thicker side of bushing toward inner side of the body. *See Fig. 4.*

REAR SUSPENSION ASSEMBLY

Removal (Colt Vista 4WD)

1) Raise and support vehicle. Remove wheel and brake drum. Remove drive axle-to-axle shaft companion flange bolts. Using flat screwdriver, pry drive axle from differential carrer. Use care not to damage oil seal.

2) Scribe reference line on drive shaft and differential carrier companion flange. Remove drive shaft from differential carrier. Remove differential carrier mounting bolts. Remove differential carrier.

3) Disconnect brake lines, parking brake cable and mounting brackets. Remove muffler-to-inlet pipe bolts. Remove muffler supports and muffler. Raise inner arm slightly with a jack and remove shock absorbers.

4) Mark position of outer arm upper end on crossmember bracket (body side) for reassembly reference. *See Fig. 3.* Remove inner and outer arm bolts.

5) Remove protector-to-body bolts. *See Fig. 2.* Remove crossmember-to-body bolts. Remove rear suspension assembly from vehicle.

Disassembly

1) Loosen outer arm bushing retaining bolts at end of crossmember. Bolts do not require removal. Remove outer arm from torsion bar.

2) Remove torsion bar from crossmember. Note identification mark on the end of torsion bar. Torsion bar is marked for left or right location. Remove inner arm-to-crossmember bolt. Remove inner arm.

Inspection

1) Inspect crossmember, inner and outer arms and extension rod for deformation or damage. Inspect shock absorber for oil leakage or noise.

2) Inspect torsion bar and outer arm splines for wear or damage. Replace inner arm bushing if damaged. See INNER ARM BUSHINGS in this article.

Reassembly

1) Install torsion bar into outer arm. Ensure torsion bar is installed with identification mark on proper side. Torsion bar is mark on the end with an "L" (left) or "R" (right) for location. Arrow mark on end of torsion bar must be positioned toward the inner side of body.

2) Install torsion bar into the crossmember, aligning mark made previously on outer arm upper end-to-body side crossmember bracket. *See Fig. 3.* Temporarily tighten outer arm bushing retaining bolts at the end of crossmember.

3) Measure clearance between outer arm and crossmember bracket. *See Fig. 5.* Clearance should be .20-.28" (5.0-7.1 mm).

Fig. 5: Checking Outer Arm & Bracket Clearance

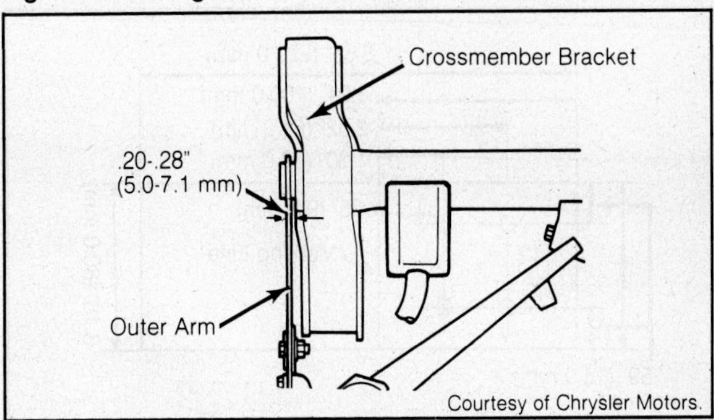

CAUTION: Clip on inner end of drive axle must always be replaced when drive alxe is removed.

Installation

1) Install new clip on inner end of drive axle. Coat seal lip with grease prior to installing drive axle. Use care not to damage oil seal when installing drive axle.

2) Reverse removal procedures. Tighten bolts to specification. Tighten inner arm-to-crossmember bolt and outer arm bushing retaining bolts to specification with vehicle at normal operating height and no load.

3) Bleed brake system. Adjust parking brake. Check vehicle height and wheel alignment. If a difference exists between left and right body heights, torsion bar may be improperly positioned.

4) Support inner arm with a jack. Remove inner and outer arm bolts. Check position of outer arm. *See Fig. 6.* Distance should be 4.00-4.11" (101.5-104.5 mm). If distance is incorrect, torsion bar must be repositioned.

5) To determine proper torsion bar positioning, a torsion bar plate must be fabricated. *See Fig. 7.* Drill holes at proper location. Bend plate 90 degree angle measured 3.94" (100.0 mm) from left edge.

6) Mark lines on plate at proper distance measured from the top of plate. *See Fig. 7.* Install plate using rear insulator bolt hole of crossmember bracket. *See Fig. 8.*

7) Correct torsion bar position is determined when marking lines on plate are at center of bolt hole for toe-in adjustment. *See Fig. 8.*

Fig. 6: Checking Outer Arm Position

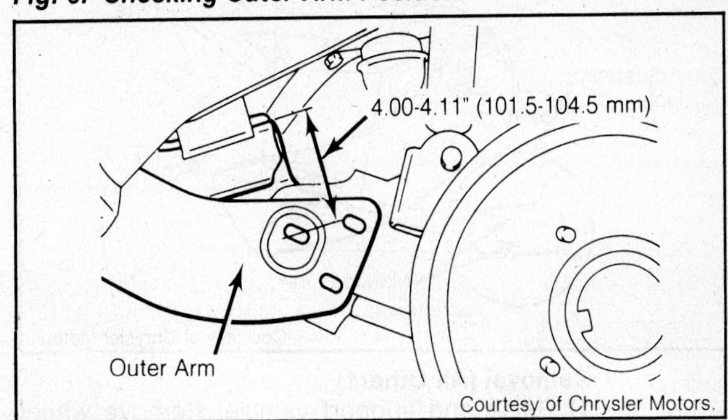

CHRYSLER MOTORS, HYUNDAI & MITSUBISHI FWD (Cont.)

Fig. 7: Fabricating Torsion Bar Plate

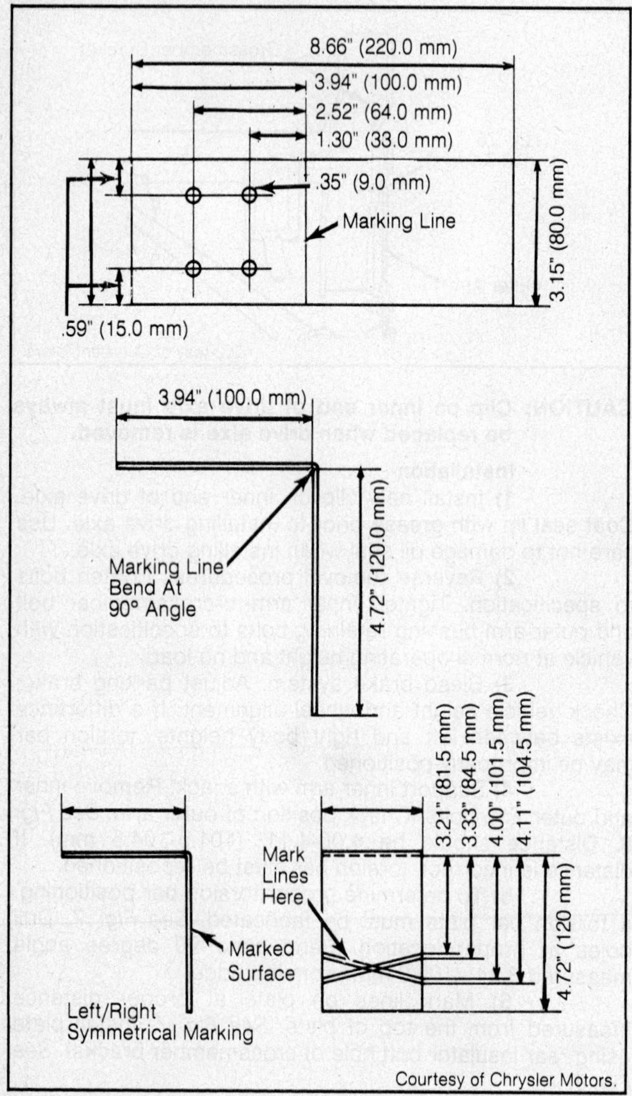

Courtesy of Chrysler Motors.

Fig. 8: Installing Torsion Bar Plate

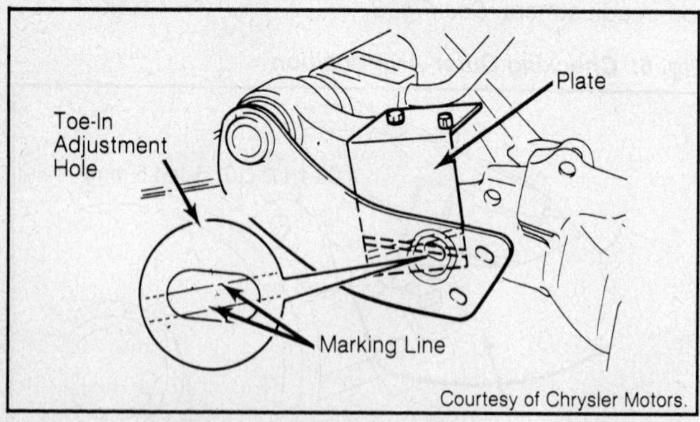

Courtesy of Chrysler Motors.

Removal (All Others)

1) Raise and support vehicle. Remove wheel assembly. Remove brake drum and wheel bearings. Disconnect brake lines and parking brake cable. Remove brake assembly. Remove muffler and pipe.

2) Raise suspension slightly with floor jack. Disconnect shock absorbers from suspension arms. Lower suspension enough to remove coil springs. Remove fixture-to-body bolts. *See Fig. 1.* Remove suspension assembly.

Disassembly

1) Scribe alignment marks on fixture-to-suspension arm position for reassembly reference. Scribe alignment mark on stabilizer bar in alignment with punch mark on stabilizer bar bracket for reassembly reference. *See Fig. 1.*

2) On Cordia and Tredia models a paint mark is located on the left side side of stabilizer bar.

3) On all models, remove fixture retaining nuts at both ends of suspension arm. Remove fixtures and rubber bushings. Note position of rubber bushings.

4) Remove dust cover clamp and slide dust cover toward right side suspension arm. DO NOT damage dust cover.

5) Separate suspension into right and left arms. Remove stabilizer bar. Remove rubber stoppers. Using a screwdriver and hammer, drive out bushing "A" from left side suspension arm. *See Fig. 1.* Drive bushing "B" from left side suspension arm.

Inspection

Check for bent, damaged suspension arm, dust cover, rubber stopper and damaged or worn bushings. Replace as necessary.

Reassembly

1) If dust cover was replaced, slide new dust cover up to stopper on right side suspension arm. Apply grease to outside of right suspension arm. Using right suspension arm, install rubber stopper into left suspension arm.

2) Apply grease to outer surfaces of bushings "A" and "B". Install bushing "B" until bushing bottoms in arm. Use Bushing Installer (0955-21100) and Handle (09555-21000) for Hyundai models or Bushing Installer (MB990780) and Handle (MB990779) for all others.

3) Using bushing installer and handle, install bushing "A". Install stabilizer bar. Slowly push suspension arms together and wipe away excess grease.

4) Ensure stabilizer bar marks align with punch mark on brackets. On Cordia and Tredia models, ensure identification mark located below spline area is installed toward the left suspension arm.

5) Install inner and outer rubber bushings, fixtures and washers. On Colt and Mirage models, bushings must be installed with projected area toward the front. DO NOT apply grease to bushings or shaft threads.

6) On Cordia, Hyundai, Precis and Tredia models, ensure toothed side of washer faces bushing. On all models, ensure cutout area of fixture faces forward. Align fixtures with suspension arm according to alignment marks and install nuts.

7) Fixture should be located approximately 30 degrees from upper flange surface and suspension arm center line on Cordia and Tredia models.

8) On Colt and Mirage models the distance from the upper flange surface to suspension arm should be approximately 1.6" (40 mm).

9) On all models, tighten nuts to specification except for Hyundai and Precis models. On Hyundai and Precis models, nuts must be tightened with vehicle at normal operating height and no load. On all models, pack dust cover with grease and secure dust cover with new clamp.

Rear Suspension

CHRYSLER MOTORS, HYUNDAI & MITSUBISHI FWD (Cont.)

Installation

1) Reverse removal procedures for installation. Check upper and lower spring seats for proper installation. Tighten bolts to specification.

2) On Hyundai and Precis models, tighten suspension arm nuts and shock absorber bolts to specification with vehicle at normal operating height and no load. Adjust wheel bearing (if required). On all models, bleed and adjust brakes.

TIGHTENING SPECIFICATIONS (4WD COLT VISTA)

Application	Ft. Lbs. (N.m)
Axle Shaft Nut	116-159 (157-216)
Drive Axle-to-Axle Shaft Flange Bolt	36-43 (49-58)
Drive Shaft-to-Differential Bolt	22-25 (30-34)
Dynamic Damper Nut	14-20 (19-27)
Extension Rod Fixture To Body Bolt	36-50 (49-68)
Extension Rod-to-Fixture Nut	72-101 (98-137)
Inner Arm-to-Backing Plate Bolt	36-43 (49-58)
Inner Arm-to-Crossmember Nut	[1] 51-65 (69-88)
Insulator-to-Body Bolt	58-87 (77-118)
Muffler-to-Pipe Bolt	22-29 (29-39)
Outer Arm Bushing Lock Bolt	16-22 (22-30)
Outer Arm-to-Inner Arm Adjusting Nut	87-101 (118-137)
Outer Arm-to-Inner Arm Bolt	58-72 (79-98)
Shock Absorber-to-Arm Bolt	58-80 (79-109)
Shock Absorber-to-Body Bolt	58-80 (79-109)
Stopper Bracket-to-Body Bolt	22-36 (30-49)
Stopper Bracket-to-Bump Stop	14-22 (19-30)
	INCH Lbs. (N.m)
Brake Line Nut	108-144 (12-16)
Insulator-to-Crossmember Bolt	84-120 (10-14)

[1] – Tighten with vehicle at normal operating height and no load.

TIGHTENING SPECIFICATIONS (2WD MODELS)

Application	Ft. Lbs. (N.m)
Backing Plate-to-Arm Bolt	
Hyundai & Precis	22-29 (30-39)
Mirage	47-58 (64-79)
All Others	36-43 (49-58)
Fixture-to-Body Bolt	
Colt Vista	87-108 (118-146)
Cordia & Tredia	
Turbo	87-108 (118-146)
Non-Turbo	51-65 (69-88)
All Others	36-51 (49-69)
Shock Absorber-to-Arm Bolt	
Colt Vista, Cordia & Tredia	58-80 (79-109)
All Others	47-58 (64-79)
Shock Absorber-to-Body Bolt	
Colt Vista	58-80 (79-109)
All Others	47-58 (64-79)
Suspension Arm End Nut	
Colt, Mirage	58-72 (79-98)
Colt Vista	94-108 (127-146)
Cordia & Tredia	
Turbo	94-108 (127-146)
Non-Turbo	58-72 (79-98)
Hyundai & Precis	36-51 (49-69)
Wheel Bearing Nut	
Colt & Mirage	72-108 (98-146)
	INCH Lbs. (N.m)
Brake Line Nut	108-144 (12-16)

Rear Suspension

FORD MOTOR CO. FESTIVA

DESCRIPTION

Festiva rear suspension is a MacPherson strut, semi-independent system. The wheels are carried on trailing arms which are rigidly connected to each other by a torsion beam. To reduce road vibration, rubber bushings are installed at the torsion beam/trailing arm body brackets. *See Fig. 1.* The rear suspension has no provision for wheel alignment.

Fig. 1: Festiva Rear Suspension

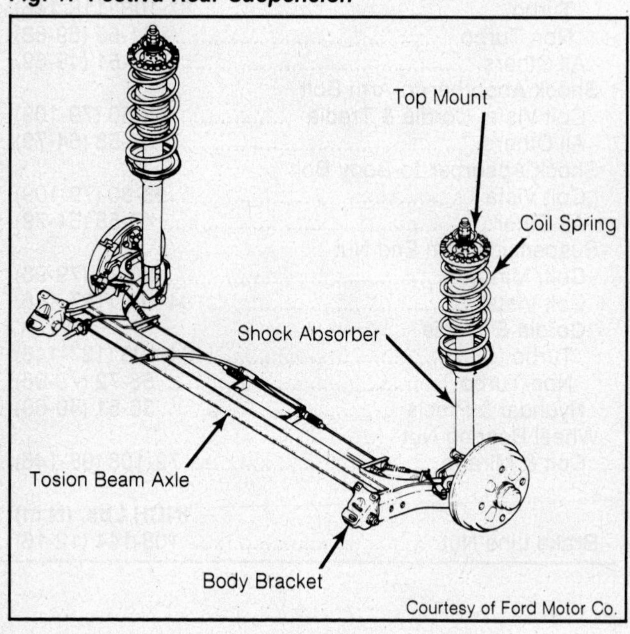

Courtesy of Ford Motor Co.

Fig. 2: Festiva Rear Hub & Bearing Assembly

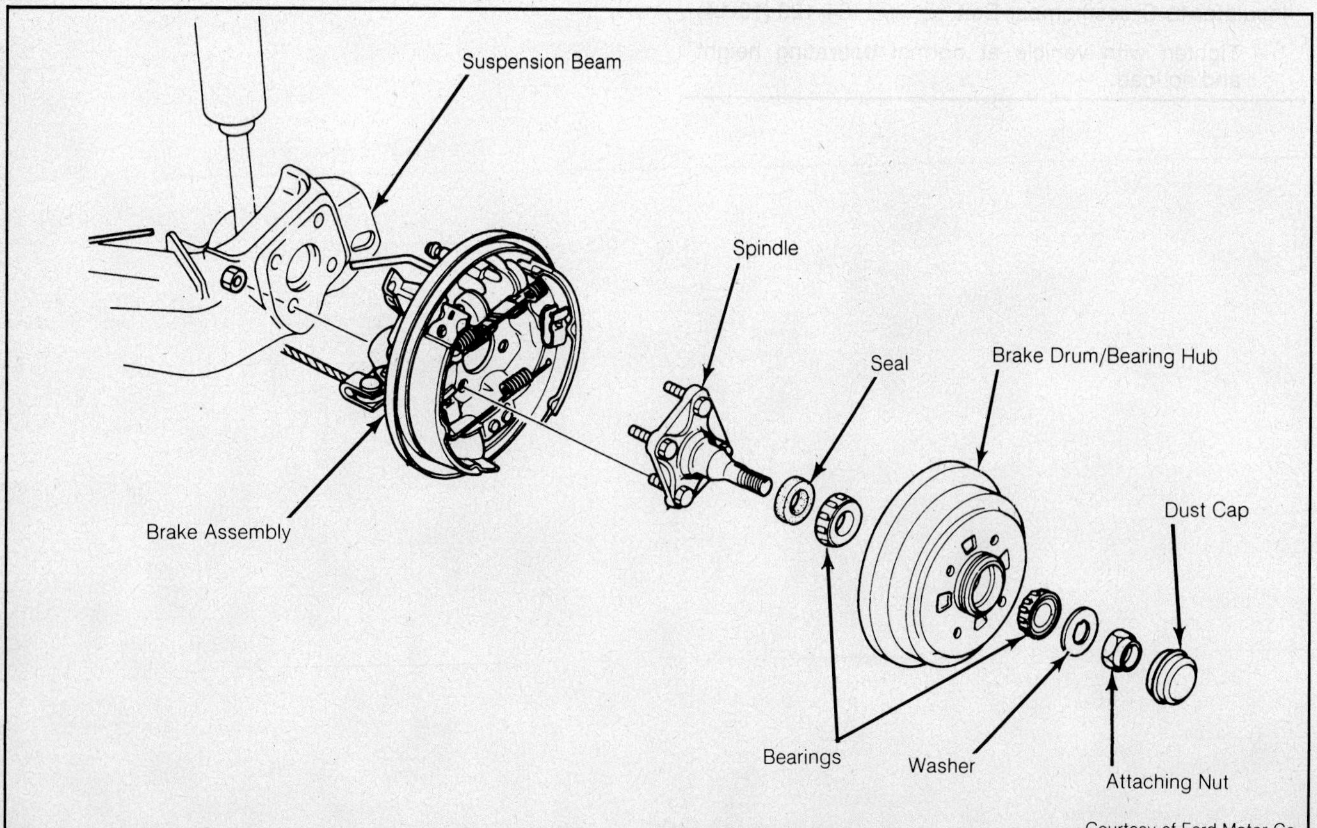

Courtesy of Ford Motor Co.

ADJUSTMENTS & INSPECTION

WHEEL BEARINGS

1) Raise and support vehicle. Ensure parking brake is fully released. Remove wheel, tire and dust cap. Rotate brake drum and ensure there is no drag. If drag is present, brakes require adjustment.

2) Using a small cape chisel, raise the staked portion of the lock nut. Remove and discard lock nut.

NOTE: **Right side lock nut has left-hand threads. Left side lock nut has right-hand threads.**

3) Install new lock nut. To seat bearings, use a torque wrench and tighten lock nut to 18-22 ft. lbs. (25-29 N.m) while rotating brake drum or rotor. After tightening, loosen lock nut until it can be turned by hand. Measure seal drag using an INCH lb. torque wrench on a lug nut at 12 o'clock position. Measure and record amount of force required to rotate brake drum.

4) To determine preload, add amount of seal drag to specified preload of 1.3-4.3 INCH lbs. (.15-.49 N.m). As an example, if seal drag measures 2.2 INCH Lbs. (.25 N.m), this amount must be added to required preload.

- 1.3 INCH lbs. (.15 N.m) + 2.2 INCH lbs. (2.2 N.m) equals 3.5 INCH lbs. (.40 N.m) minimum.
- 4.3 INCH lbs. (.49 N.m) + 2.2 INCH lbs. (.25 N.m) equals 6.5 INCH lbs. (.74 N.m) maximum.
- When seal drag is added, specified amount of preload becomes 3.5-6.5 INCH lbs. (.40-.74 N.m).

5) Tighten wheel bearing lock nut a small amount. Using an INCH lb. torque wrench on a lug nut at 12 o'clock position, measure amount of pull required to rotate brake drum. Tighten attaching nut until specified amount of preload is measured with torque wrench. Stake lock nut with a blunt chisel. Install grease cap, wheel and tire assembly.

NOTE: Nut must be replaced if it splits or cracks during staking process. Do not stake with a sharp edged tool.

REMOVAL & INSTALLATION

WHEEL BEARINGS

Removal

1) Raise and support vehicle. Ensure parking brake is fully released. Remove wheel, tire and dust cap assembly. Rotate brake drum and ensure no drag is present. If drag is present, brakes require adjustment.

2) Using a small cape chisel, raise staked portion of lock nut. Remove and discard lock nut. Remove brake drum, bearing and hub assembly from spindle. *See Fig. 2.*

NOTE: Right side lock nut has left-hand threads. Left side lock nut has right-hand threads.

3) Using a roll head pry bar, remove and discard grease seal from brake drum. Remove inner bearing from bearing hub. Bearings must be marked for reassembly reference if they are to be reused. Remove inner and outer bearing races using a Slide Hammer (T50T-100-A) and Bearing Cup Puller (T77F-1102-A).

Installation

1) Using Installer (T77F-1219-A) and Driver Handle (T80T-4000-W), install inner and outer bearing races. Pack bearings and hub area with Lubricant (C1AZ-1959D-B, C, D or E). *See Fig. 3.*

Fig. 3: Bearing Hub Lubrication Installation

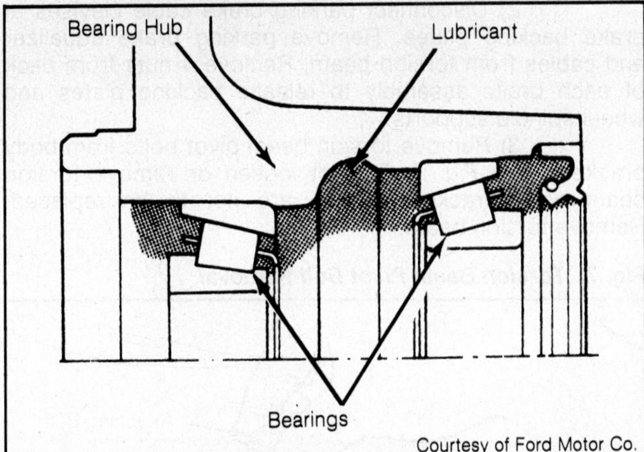

2) Position inner bearing in bearing hub. Lubricate grease seal lips and install seal. Ensure bearings and hub have sufficient lubricant. Place brake drum bearings and hub assembly on spindle. To prevent damage to grease seal and spindle threads, ensure hub is correctly centered on spindle.

3) Install outer bearing, washer and new lock nut. Stake lock nut with a blunt chisel. Adjust bearing preload as previously described in this article.

NOTE: Nut must be replaced if it splits or cracks during staking process. Do not stake with a sharp edged tool.

SPINDLE

Removal

Remove brake drum assembly as previously described in this article. Remove spindle attaching nuts located under vehicle on inboard side of torsion beam. Support backing plate with wire and remove spindle.

Installation

To install, reverse removal procedure. Tighten spindle attaching nuts to 39-45 ft. lbs. (43-61 N.m). *See Fig. 4.*

Fig. 4: Tightening Spindle Attaching Nuts

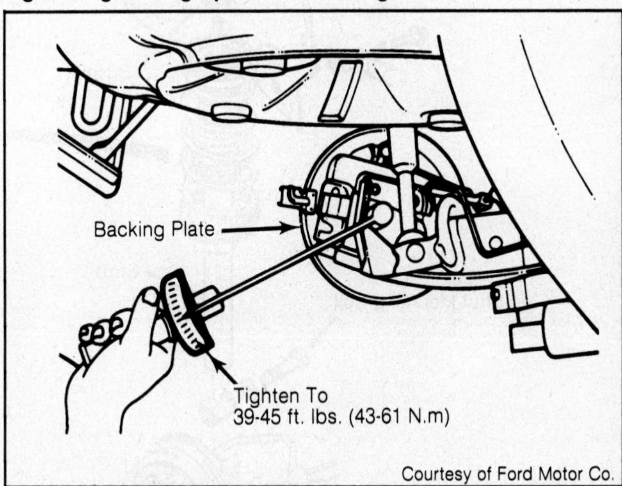

STRUTS

Removal

1) Raise and support vehicle. Remove wheel and tire assembly. Using Spring Compressor (T81P-5310-A), compress spring to unload strut. Remove rear quarter trim panel from cargo compartment.

2) Remove jam nut and flanged nut from strut rod. Remove bushing washer and upper bushing. Remove strut lower end mounting bolt from wheel support arm. Remove strut assembly and separate it from spring and seat insulator. Remove lower bushing and jounce bumper seat from strut rod. Slide jounce bumper and shield off strut. *See Fig. 5.*

Inspection

Check jounce bumper, spring seat insulator and strut rod bushings for wear or damage. Ensure strut is not leaking.

Installation

1) Slide jounce bumper and shield onto strut rod and cylinder. Install bumper seat and lower bushing on strut rod. If upper spring seat insulator has been replaced, install new insulator on spring upper end. Seat end of coil against step in insulator.

2) Place spring on strut. Ensure end of coil seats against step in strut spring seat. Install strut assembly into tower from wheel well. Guide strut rod into tower mounting hole.

3) Line up strut lower end with mounting hole in wheel support arm. Install mounting bolt to hold strut in position. Working from inside cargo compartment, install rod upper end bushing, bushing washer and flanged nut. Tighten nut to 12-18 ft. lbs. (16-24 N.m). *See Fig. 6.* Hold flanged nut while tightening jam nut to lock it in position.

FORD MOTOR CO. FESTIVA (Cont.)

Fig. 5: Exploded View of Strut Assembly

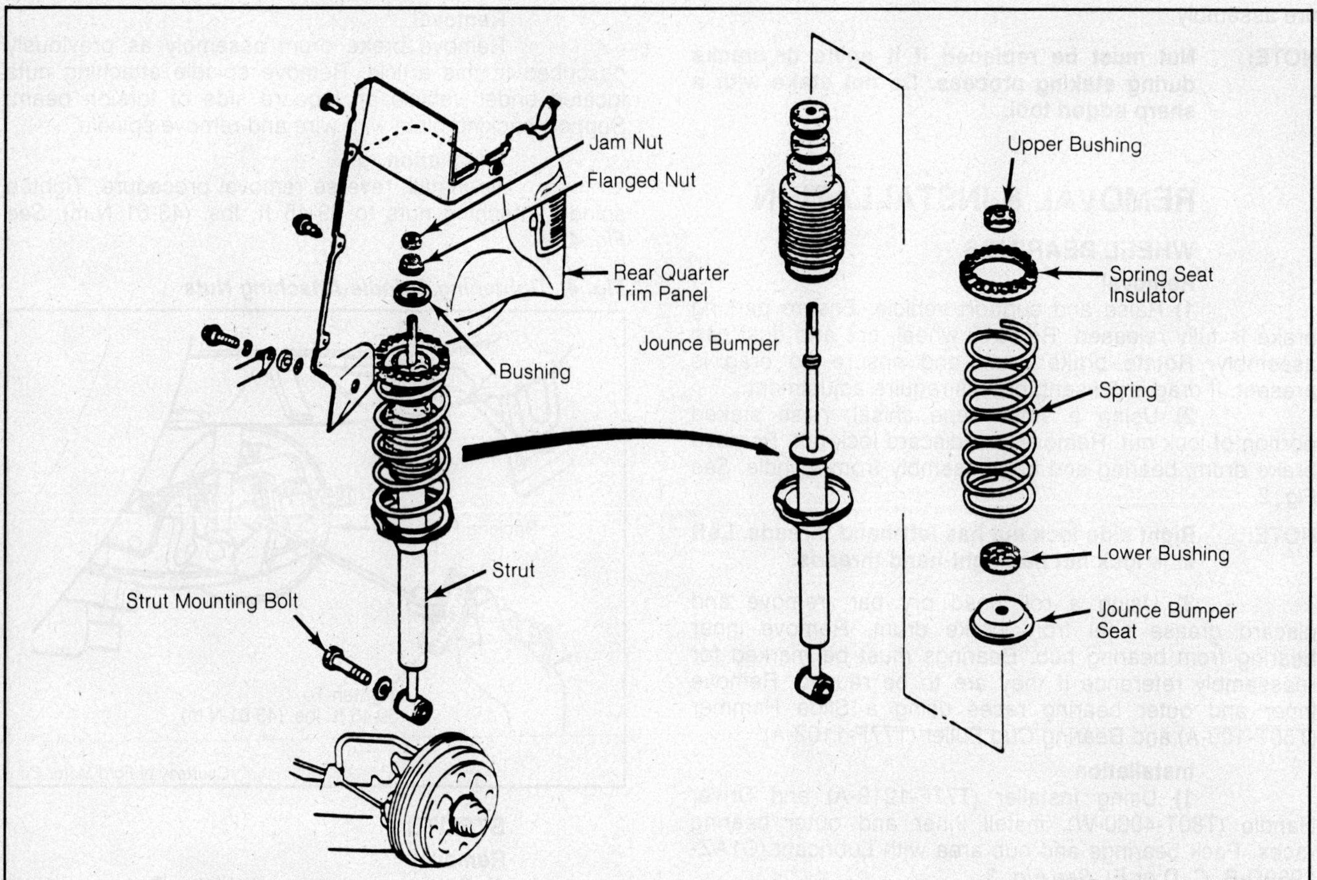

Courtesy of Ford Motor Co.

Fig. 6: Strut Flanged Nut Installation

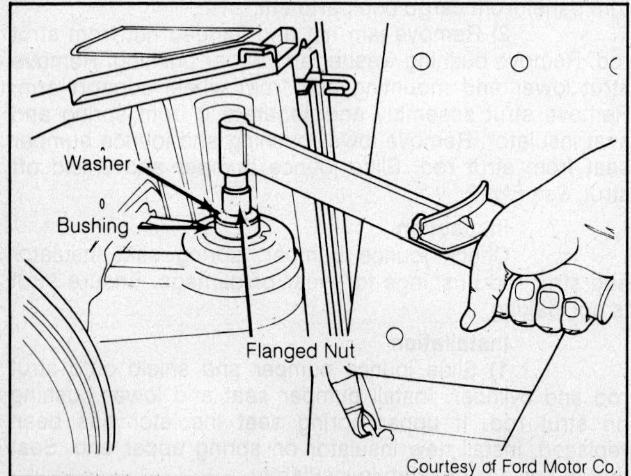

Courtesy of Ford Motor Co.

4) Tighten strut lower mounting bolt to 40-50 ft. lbs. (54-68 N.m). Remove spring compressor. Install wheel and tire assembly.

TORSION BEAM

Removal

1) Raise and support vehicle so rear struts are fully extended. Remove both wheel and tire assemblies. Remove struts and disconnect brake lines as previously described in this article.

2) Disconnect parking brake cable clevises at brake backing plates. Remove parking brake equalizer and cables from torsion beam. Remove 4 nuts from back of each brake assembly to release backing plates and wheel spindle supports.

3) Remove torsion beam pivot bolts from body brackets. *See Fig. 7.* Do not loosen or remove torsion beam body brackets if they are not to be replaced. Remove torsion beam.

Fig. 7: Torsion Beam Pivot Bolt Removal

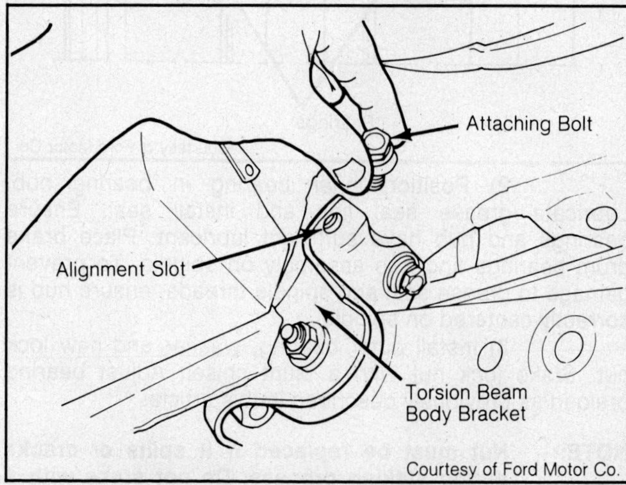

Courtesy of Ford Motor Co.

FORD MOTOR CO. FESTIVA (Cont.)

Installation

1) If removed, install torsion beam pivot brackets. Do not tighten mounting bolts at this time. If a new torsion beam is to be installed, install new pivot bushings in beam arms. See Installation - Torsion Beam Bushing in this article.

2) Install bushing flange washers and position beam arms in body brackets. Align pivot bolt holes and install bolts. Do not tighten nuts at this time. Install brake backing plates and wheel spindle support assemblies. Tighten nuts to 32-45 ft. lbs. (43-61 N.m).

3) Install parking brake equalizer assembly on torsion beam. Install cable clevises to brake levers with clevis pins and cotter pins. Clip right and left brake lines in place. Install rear suspension struts and wheel/tire assembly. Block wheels and lower vehicle to load suspension to normalize ride height. Tighten torsion beam pivot bolts at body brackets to 69-87 ft. lbs. (93-118 N.m).

4) Check rear suspension alignment. Place an alignment mark at the center of the underbody, at a point an equal distance from the right and left body bracket inboard mounting bolts. From this alignment mark, measure distance to centers of right and left strut lower mounting bolts. *See Fig. 8.*

Fig. 8: Alignment Mark Locations

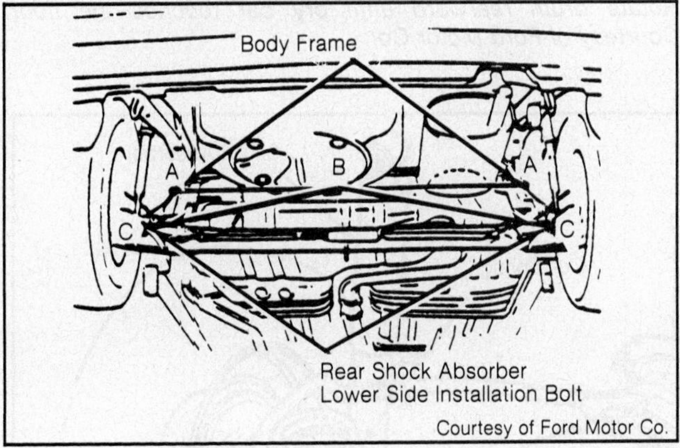

Courtesy of Ford Motor Co.

5) Both measurements must be within .20" (5 mm) of being the same. If not, shift torsion beam body brackets from side-to-side to center suspension. Once centered, tighten upper body bracket mounting bolts to 40-50 ft. lbs. (54-68 N.m) and lower bolt to 69-87 ft. lbs. (93-118 N.m). Bleed brakes.

TORSION BEAM BUSHINGS

Removal

1) Raise and support vehicle to fully extended rear struts. Remove wheel and tire assembly. Remove retaining clip at right brake line routing bracket and disconnect brake line. Remove clip from left brake line and disconnect at body crossmember.

2) Remove torsion beam pivot bolt bolts and nuts at right and left body brackets. Swing torsion beam trailing arm downward to clear body brackets. Use a piece of wood to block beam in disengaged position so bushings can be reached. *See Fig. 9.* Using a Bushing Remover/Replacer (D80L-1002-L), remove bushings from inboard side of torsion beam arm. *See Fig. 10.*

NOTE: **Bushings have "F" (front) and "R" (rear) stamped on bushing face. Ensure these marks are right side up when "F" is toward front of vehicle.**

Fig. 9: Blocking Beam in Disengaged Position

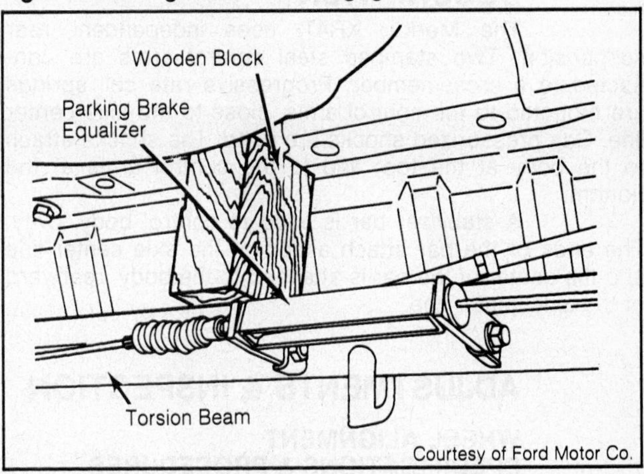

Courtesy of Ford Motor Co.

Fig. 10: Torsion Beam Bushing Removal

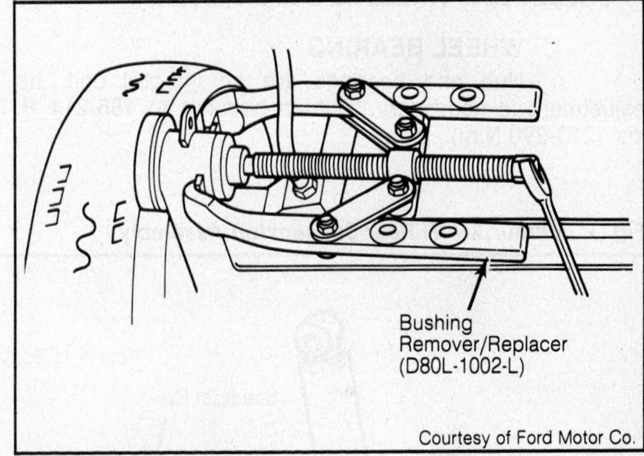

Courtesy of Ford Motor Co.

Installation

1) Place bushings on outboard sides of torsion beam arms with marks "F" and "R" aligned parallel to arm axis. To ease installation, lubricate bushings with soapy water. Press in bushings using bushing remover/installer.

2) Remove wood block holding torsion beam out of body pivot brackets. Place bushing flange washers on outboard faces of bushings. Raise torsion beam arms into brackets until pivot bolt holes align.

3) Install pivot bolts through brackets from inboard side but do not tighten nuts at this time. Connect brake lines at routing brackets. Reinstall brake line retaining clips. Reinstall wheels and tires. While lowering vehicle, block wheels until suspension is fully loaded in its normal riding position. Tighten torsion beam pivot bolt nuts to 69-87 ft. lbs. (93-118 N.m). Bleed brakes.

TIGHTENING SPECIFICATIONS

Application	Ft. Lbs. (N.m)
Brake Backing Plate & Spindle Support Bolts	32-45 (43-61)
Lower Body Bracket Mounting Bolts	69-87 (93-118)
Rod Upper End Bushing Flanged Nut	12-18 (16-24)
Spindle Lock Nut	18-22 (25-29)
Spindle Attaching Nuts	39-45 (43-61)
Strut Lower Mounting Bolt	40-50 (54-68)
Torsion Beam Pivot Bolts	69-87 (93-118)
Upper Body Bracket Mounting Bolts	40-50 (54-68)

FORD MOTOR CO. MERKUR XR4Ti

DESCRIPTION

The Merkur XR4Ti uses independent rear suspension. Two stamped steel control arms are connected to a crossmember. Progressive rate coil springs are mounted to the control arms, close to the axle center line. Gas pressurized shocks are used. The shocks attach to the body at the top, and to the control arms at the bottom.

A stabilizer bar is used to control body sway. The ends of the bar attach ahead of the axle center line and the center of the bar is attached to the body, rearward of the axle center line.

ADJUSTMENTS & INSPECTION

WHEEL ALIGNMENT SPECIFICATIONS & PROCEDURES

See WHEEL ALIGNMENT SPECIFICATIONS & PROCEDURES in WHEEL ALIGNMENT section.

WHEEL BEARING

Hub and bearings are an integral unit, no adjustment is necessary. Tighten hub nut to 185-214 ft. lbs. (250-290 N.m).

REMOVAL & INSTALLATION

WHEEL BEARINGS

Removal

NOTE: **The hub nut from left side of vehicle has left-hand threads. The hub nut from right side of vehicle has right-hand threads.**

1) Raise vehicle and remove wheel. To remove hub nut and washer, place a pry bar under one lug nut and over the other. *See Fig. 2.* Discard hub nut.

Fig. 2: Removing Hub Nut

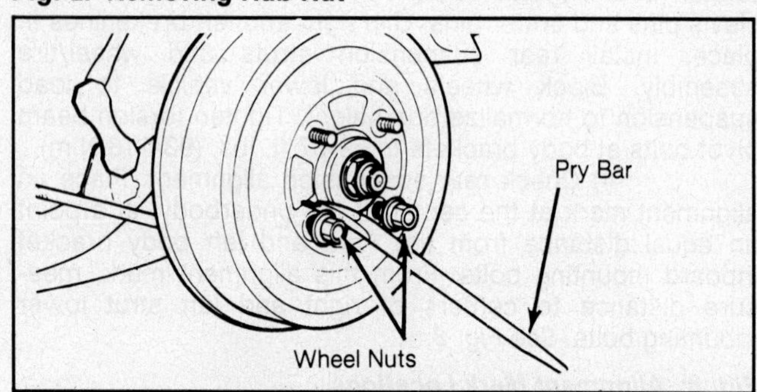

Rotate drum rearward until pry bar touches the floor. Courtesy of Ford Motor Co.

Fig. 1: Merkur XR4Ti Rear Suspension Assembly

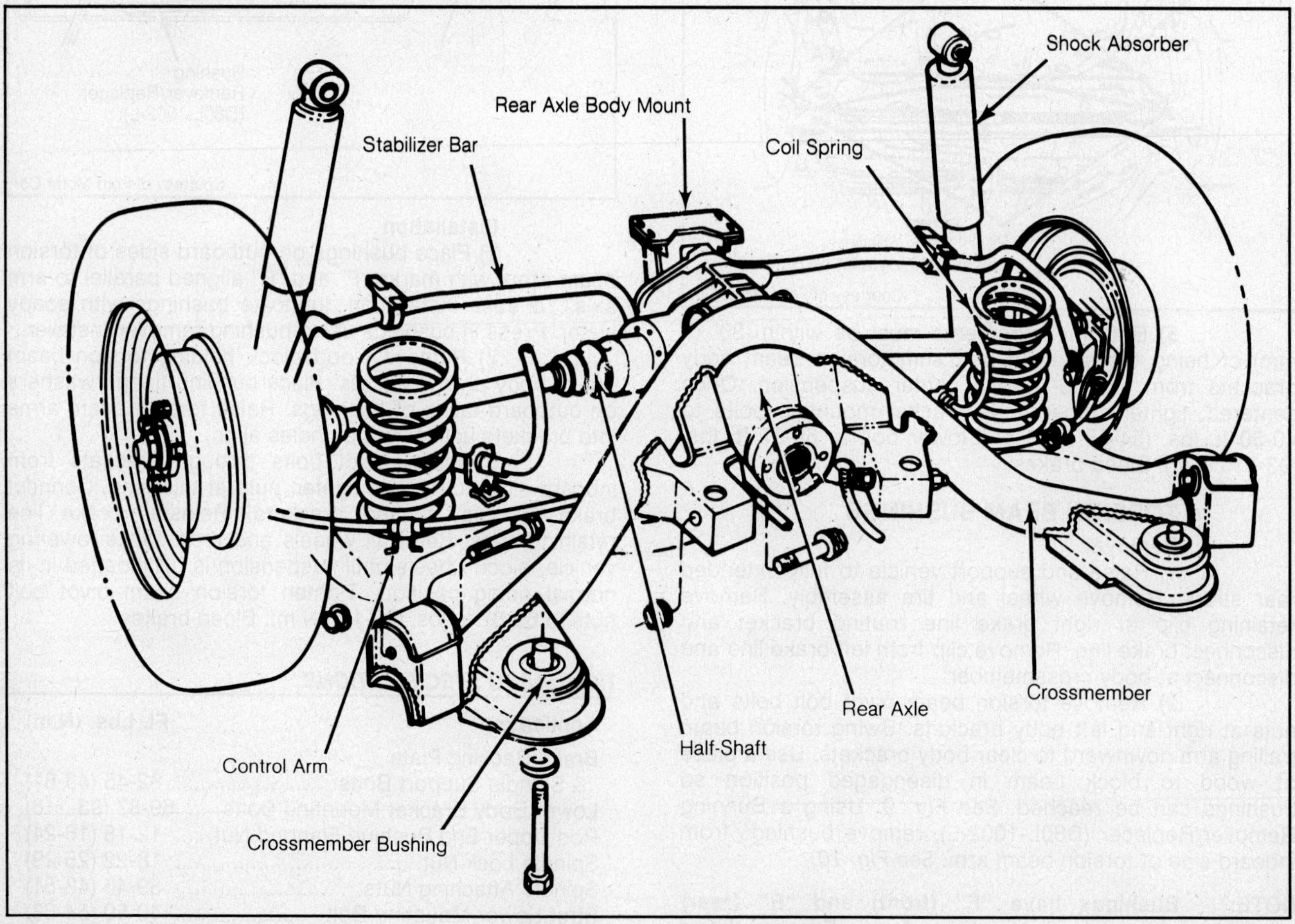

Courtesy of Ford Motor Co.

FORD MOTOR CO. MERKUR XR4Ti (Cont.)

2) Release brake shoe self-adjuster (if necessary) and remove brake drum retaining clip. Remove brake drum. Remove drive flange using Puller (D81L-1002-A). Use wire to support brake assembly. Remove 4 bearing hub attaching bolts and bearing hub.

Disassembly

1) Clamp bearing hub in vise. Remove and discard inner grease seal. Remove inner bearing from hub. Turn hub over in vise and remove outer bearing seal and bearing.

2) Use Puller (T77F-1102-A) and a slide hammer to remove outer bearing race. Use puller and slide hammer to remove inner bearing and race.

NOTE: **When removing outer bearing race, make sure that puller jaws do not contact bearing race seat. See Fig. 3.**

Fig. 3: Cutaway View of Bearing Hub

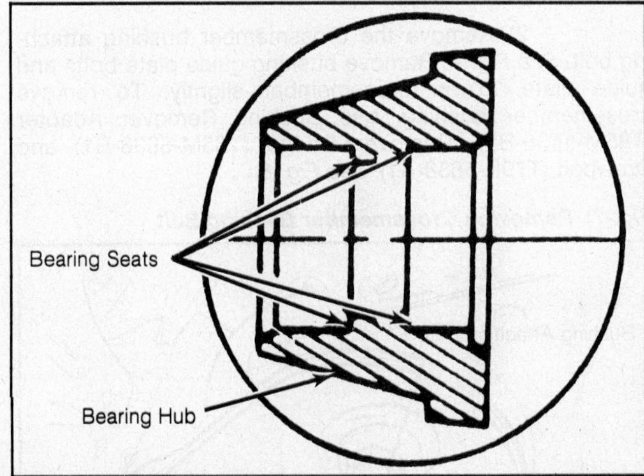

Courtesy of Ford Motor Co.

Cleaning & Inspection

1) Throughly clean all parts in solvent. Blow dry all components using compressed air. Examine bearing hub carefully for cracks, damaged grease seal seats, burrs on bearing surfaces and damaged bolt holes.

2) Inspect drive flange for damaged or loose wheel studs and damaged or worn splines. Check stub shaft for pitted or scored seal surfaces, damaged lock nut threads, and worn bearing surfaces.

Reassembly

1) Install bearing cup using Bearing Cup Replacers (T73T-1202-B and T73T-4222-B) and Threaded Drawbar (T77F-1176-A). Lubricate seal lips and pack bearings with Lubricant (CIAZ-19590-B, C, D or E).

2) Position inner bearing in hub. Install inner bearing seal using Seal Installer (T73T-1190-B). Install outer bearing and bearing seal using seal installer.

Installation

Install bearing hub with rounded edge facing upward. To complete installation, reverse removal procedure. When installing flange, it may be necessary to tap flange with plastic hammer, until shaft threads extend beyond flange hub.

SHOCK ABSORBER

Removal

1) Remove the rear parcel shelf. Remove the rear corner trim cover in the luggage compartment. Raise and support rear of vehicle, about 4 feet off the ground.

2) Position floor jack under control arm. Raise jack slightly to release coil spring tension. Remove shock absorber upper nut and bolt. Remove protector cap from bottom of shock absorber. Remove shock absorber lower nut and bolt.

Installation

To install, position shock absorber and install upper nut (hold bolt stationary). Tighten upper nut. Install and tighten lower bolt (hold nut stationary). Install protective cap. Reverse removal procedure to complete installation.

COIL SPRING

Removal

1) Raise and support rear of vehicle, under body. Rear wheels and suspension should hang free. Remove half-shaft to wheel stub shaft bolts. *See Fig. 4.*

Fig. 4: Removing Half-Shaft Bolts

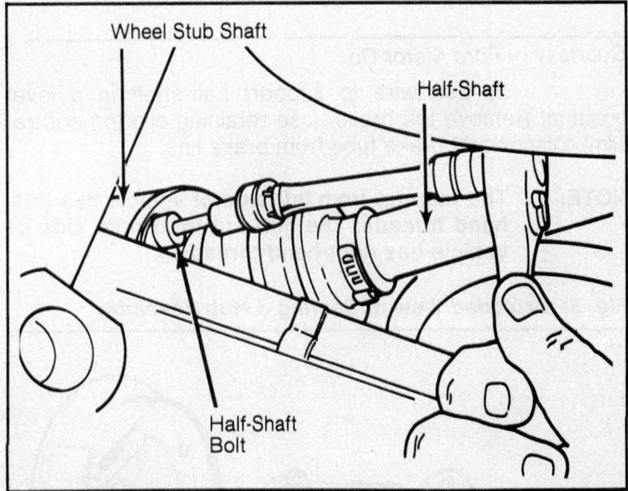

Courtesy of Ford Motor Co.

2) Use wire to support half shaft in a level position. Remove the brake hose retaining clip (on control arm). Disconnect brake tube from brake line.

3) Remove protective cap from bottom of shock absorber. Using a floor jack, raise control arm enough to release coil spring pressure. Remove shock absorber lower nut and bolt.

4) Slowly lower control arm and move floor jack to support axle housing (or support axle housing with jack stand). Remove bolts attaching rear axle mount to body, and disconnect axle vent tube. Slowly lower jack stand or floor jack until coil spring and upper seat can be removed.

Installation

To install, reverse removal procedure. When installing coil spring and upper seat, do not lubricate spring or spring seat. Ensure spring sits correctly in seat. Before installing body mount bolts, clean and apply Loctite to bolt threads.

CONTROL ARM & BUSHINGS

Removal

1) Remove coil spring. See COIL SPRING REMOVAL in this article. Use a screwdriver to release parking brake cable from clamp on control arm. Disconnect stabilizer link from control arm. *See Fig. 5.*

FORD MOTOR CO. MERKUR XR4Ti (Cont.)

Fig. 5: Removing Stabilizer Link

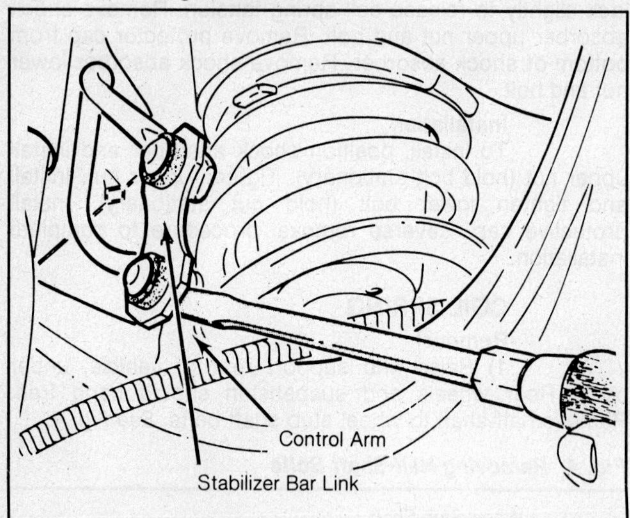

Courtesy of Ford Motor Co.

2) Use wire to support half-shaft in a level position. Remove the brake hose retaining clip (on control arm). Disconnect brake tube from brake line.

NOTE: **The hub nut from left side of vehicle has left-hand threads. The hub nut from right side of vehicle has right-hand threads.**

Fig. 6: Exploded View of Bearing & Hub Assembly

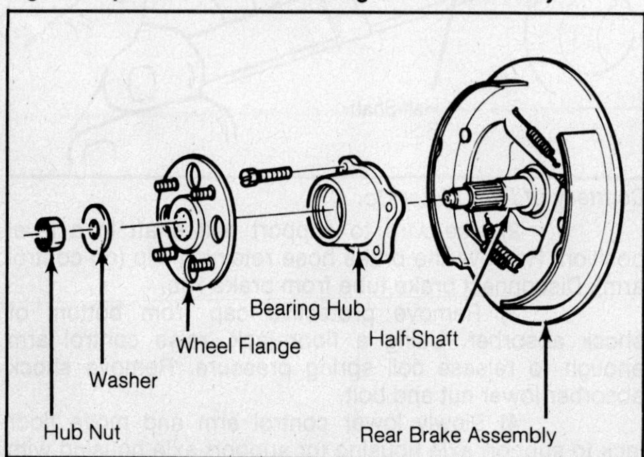

Courtesy of Ford Motor Co.

3) Working under vehicle, pull wheel stub shaft out of control arm. Remove control arm inner and outer bolts. To remove large control arm bushing, use Drawbolt (T78P-5638-A1), Receiver Cup (T85M-5638-A2) and a 7/16" nut and washer.

4) To remove small control arm bushing, use Drawbolt (T78P-5638-A1), Receiver Cup (T85M-5638-A1) and a 7/16" nut and washer.

Installation

1) If bushings were removed from control arm, install large control arm bushing using Drawbolt (T78P-5638-A1), Replacer Cup (T85M-5638-A3) and a 7/16" nut and washer. To install small control arm bushing, use Drawbolt (T78P-5638-A1), Replacer Cup (T78P-5638-A3) and a 7/16" nut and washer.

2) Position control arm and loosely install control arm bolts, washers and nuts. Install longer bolts on outboard end of control arm. Reverse removal procedure to complete installation.

NOTE: **The bolt heads MUST face inward. If the bolt threads face inward, the parking brake cable could be damaged.**

CROSSMEMBER BUSHINGS

Removal

1) Raise and support vehicle. Place jack stands under vehicle body. Tires and suspension should hang free. Raise control arm enough to eliminate coil spring pressure.

NOTE: **The control arm MUST be supported securely before removing bushing attaching bolt. If control arm is not supported, spring pressure will push the crossmember down when bushing is removed.**

2) Remove the crossmember bushing attaching bolt. *See Fig. 7.* Remove bushing guide plate bolts and guide plate. Lower crossmember slightly. To remove crossmember bushing, use Bushing Remover Adapter (T85M-5638-B2), Remover Bridge (T85M-5638-B1) and Drawbolt (T79P-5638-A1). *See Fig. 8.*

Fig. 7: Removing Crossmember Bushing Bolt

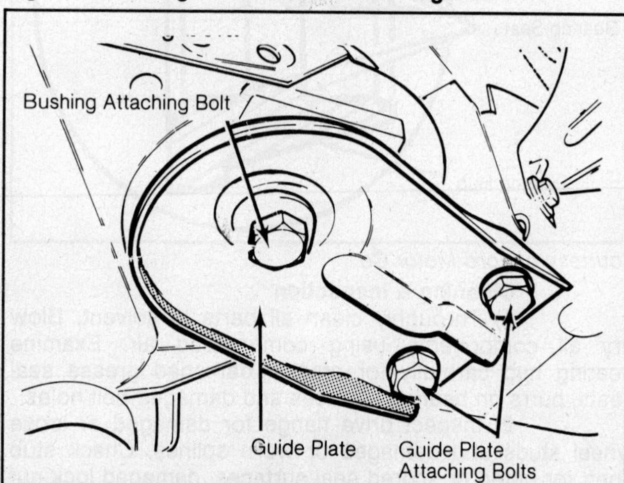

Courtesy of Ford Motor Co.

Fig. 8: Removing Crossmember Bushing

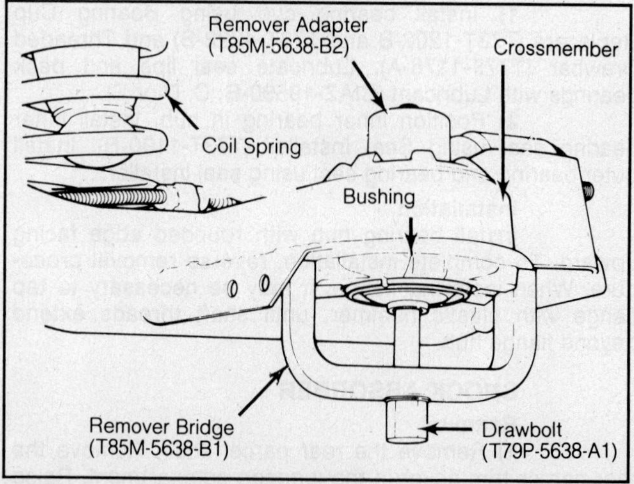

Courtesy of Ford Motor Co.

Rear Suspension

FORD MOTOR CO. MERKUR XR4Ti (Cont.)

Installation

1) Lubricate bushings with non-petroleum lubricant. Install bushing using Replacer Bridge (T85M-5638-B3), Replacer Adapter (T85M-5638-B4) and Drawbolt (T79P-5638-A1).

2) Reverse removal procedure to complete installation.

CROSSMEMBER ASSEMBLY

Removal

1) Remove coil springs. Remove drive shaft. Remove muffler and silencer assembly. Hold parking brake cable with pliers and loosen parking brake adjuster sleeve lock nut. Remove parking brake cable clip and clevis pin. *See Fig. 9.*

Fig. 9: Removing Parking Brake Clevis Pin

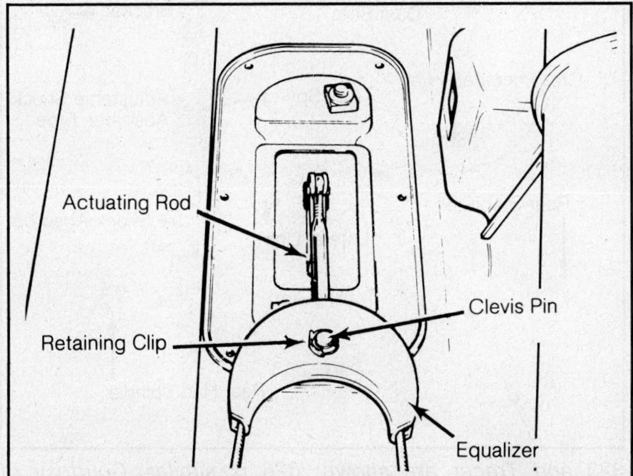

Courtesy of Ford Motor Co.

2) Disengage parking brake cable from brackets. Remove stabilizer bar "U" brackets. Place jack under rear axle. Secure axle to jack. Remove crossmember bushing attaching bolt from each side of vehicle. *See Fig. 7.*

3) Remove bolts attaching rear axle mount to body. Disconnect axle vent tube. Carefully lower crossmember from vehicle.

Installation

Raise crossmenber into position. Loosely install axle mount attaching bolts. To complete installation, reverse removal procedure. Tighten axle mount attaching bolts after installing crossmember bushing attaching bolts.

STABILIZER BAR

Removal

1) Loosen wheel nuts slightly. Raise and support rear of vehicle. Remove wheels. Disconnect stabilizer link from control arm. *See Fig. 5.*

2) Wrap tape around stabilizer bar next to "U" bracket mountings. The tape will provide reassembly reference. Remove stabilizer bar "U" bracket bolts, "U" brackets and stabilizer bar.

Installation

To install, reverse removal procedure.

TIGHTENING SPECIFICATIONS

Application	Ft. Lbs. (N.m)
Axle Body Mount Bolts	14-18 (20-25)
Bearing Hub Bolts	45-48 (52-64)
Bushing Guide Plate Bolts	30-37 (41-50)
Control Arm Attaching Nuts	63-74 (85-100)
Crossmember Bushing	
Attachment Bolt	59-74 (80-100)
Half-Shaft Attaching Bolts	28-31 (38-43)
Hub Nut	185-214 (250-290)
Lug Nut	75-101 (100-144)
Shock Absorber	
Lower Bolt [1]	30-37 (40-50)
Upper Nut [2]	30-37 (40-50)
Stabilizer Bar	
"U" Bracket Bolts	15-18 (20-25)

[1] – Hold nut in position and tighten bolt.
[2] – Hold bolt in position and tighten nut.

Rear Suspension

FORD MOTOR CO. TRACER & MAZDA 323 & 626

DESCRIPTION

Rear suspension consists of vertically mounted MacPherson type struts, crossmember, trailing arms and laterally mounted links. On 626 models, trailing arm attaches to wheel hub. On 323 and Tracer models, trailing arm attaches to strut. Lateral links attach to crossmember and wheel hub on all models. A stabilizer bar is mounted to front lateral links and crossmember. Rear wheel alignment is adjusted by turning star wheels mounted on lateral link assemblies.

NOTE: For information and testing procedures for Automatic Adjusting Suspension (AAS), see ELECTRONIC SUSPENSION article in this section.

ADJUSTMENTS &INSPECTION

WHEEL ALIGNMENT SPECIFICATIONS & PROCEDURES

See WHEEL ALIGNMENT SPECIFICATIONS & PROCEDURES in WHEEL ALIGNMENT section.

WHEEL BEARING

1) Raise vehicle and support with safety stands. Check bearing axial play by rocking wheel assembly by hand. Axial play should be zero. Remove wheel assembly. On disc brake models, remove brake caliper and hang out of way.

2) Attach spring scale to wheel stud and measure bearing preload. Ensure brakes do not drag on drum brake models. On 626 models, preload should be .88-2.19 lbs. (3.9-9.8 N). On 323 and Tracer models, preload should be .57-1.91 lbs. (2.6-8.5 N).

3) If preload is not within specification, adjust or replace wheel bearing. To adjust, tighten new bearing lock nut to 18-22 ft. lbs. (25-29 N.m.). Rotate drum or rotor 2 to 3 times to seat bearing. Loosen nut until nut can be turned by hand. Attach spring scale to wheel stud and note oil seal resistance.

4) On 323 and Tracer models, tighten axle nut until reading on scale is .57-1.91 lbs. (2.6-8.5 N) more than oil seal resistance measured in step **3)**. On 626 models, tighten axle nut until reading on scale is .88-2.19 lbs. (3.9-9.8 N) more than oil seal resistance measured in step **3)**.

REMOVAL & INSTALLATION

WHEEL BEARING

Removal

1) Raise vehicle and support with safety stands. Remove wheel assembly. Remove grease cap and lock nut. On disc brake models, disconnect brake line from strut assembly (if necessary). Disconnect parking brake cable from caliper.

2) Remove caliper assembly and hang out of way. Remove brake drum or rotor with washer and outer bearing. Remove oil seal and inner bearing. Drive out outer races from hub using brass bar (if necessary).

Inspection

Wash all parts in clean solvent. Check for wear or heat damage to bearings and races. Check for deformed grease cap. Check for rust, cracks or damage to knuckle spindle. Check for wear or rust at contact surface of spindle oil seal. Replace parts as necessary. Always replace bearings and races as a set.

Fig. 1: Exploded View of Rear Suspension & Strut Assembly

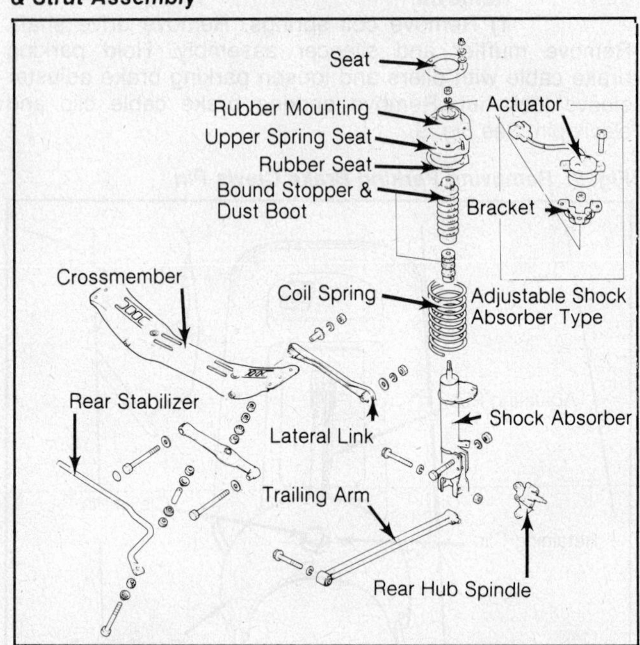

323 and Tracer are shown; 626 is similar. Courtesy of Mazda Motors Corp.

Installation

To install, reverse removal procedure. Do not use a hammer to install new oil seal, use a flat plate to press in. Adjust wheel bearing preload. See WHEEL BEARING under ADJUSTMENTS & INSPECTION in this article. Stake spindle lock nut.

STRUT ASSEMBLY

Removal & Disassembly

1) Remove rear seat and trim on 626 models. On all models, remove actuator mounting bolts (if equipped). Remove actuator. Remove piston rod upper lock nut. Remove actuator bracket. Loosen (do not remove) piston rod lower lock nut. Remove nuts retaining strut assembly to body.

2) Raise and support vehicle. Remove wheel assembly. Disconnect brake hose from strut (if necessary). Punch a alignment mark on strut housing and knuckle for reassembly reference.

3) Disconnect bolts retaining lower end of strut to knuckle assembly. On 323 and Tracer models, disconnect trailing arm from strut. On all models, disconnect bolts mounting strut to body. Remove strut assembly. Clamp strut securely in soft-jawed vise. Compress coil spring. Remove lower lock nut and washer. Remove remaining components.

Reassembly & Installation

1) To reassemble, reverse disassembly procedure. To install, reverse removal procedure. Ensure coil spring is well seated in upper and lower seats.

2) On 323 and Tracer models, ensure White mark on mounting block faces inside of vehicle. On 626 models, ensure hole in mounting block faces inside of vehicle. Also on 626 models, right side mounting block is identified with White mark on top. On all models, check rear wheel toe-in.

TRAILING ARMS & LATERAL LINKS

Removal

1) Raise and support vehicle. Remove wheel assembly. Disconnect stabilizer bar from forward lateral link. Remove adjusting bolt connecting lateral links to crossmember. Remove bolt connecting lateral links to knuckle assembly. Remove lateral links.

2) On 626 models, remove bolt attaching trailing arm to knuckle assembly. On 323 and Tracer models, remove bolt attaching trailing arm to strut. On all models, remove trailing arm-to-body bolt. Remove trailing arm.

Installation

Inspect lateral links and trailing arms for cracks or deformation. Check bushings for damage or excessive wear. Check remaining parts for deterioration or damage. Replace parts as necessary. To install, reverse removal procedure. Tighten all bolts with vehicle resting on ground and suspension unloaded. Adjust rear wheel toe-in.

TIGHTENING SPECIFICATIONS

Application	Ft. Lbs. (N.m)
Backing Plate-to-Knuckle	33-49 (45-67)
Caliper Assembly-to-Knuckle	
626	46-59 (63-82)
323 & Tracer	36-51 (49-69)
Dust Cover/Support-to-Knuckle	36-54 (49-74)
Lateral Link-to-Crossmember Bolt	69-87 (93-118)
Lateral Link-to-Knuckle Bolt	
626	69-87 (93-118)
323 & Tracer	47-55 (64-76)
Stabilizer Bar Brackets	32-40 (44-55)
Strut Assembly-to-Body Nuts	16-20 (21-26)
Strut Assembly-to-Knuckle Bolts	69-86 (93-117)
Strut Piston Rod Lock Nut	
626	41-59 (56-80)
323 & Tracer	40-47 (55-64)
Trailing Arm Bolt	
To Body	43-54 (58-74)
To Strut (323)	40-50 (55-68)
To Knuckle (626)	40-50 (55-68)

Rear Suspension

GENERAL MOTORS SPECTRUM & ISUZU I-MARK

DESCRIPTION

These models use a semi-independent rear suspension. It utilizes an axle with trailing arms and twisting cross beam, 2 coil springs, 2 shock absorbers, 2 upper spring insulators, and 2 spring compression bumpers.

ADJUSTMENTS & INSPECTION

WHEEL ALIGNMENT SPECIFICATIONS & PROCEDURES

Rear wheel alignment is not adjustable.

WHEEL BEARING

Tighten hub nut to 22 ft. lbs. (29 N.m). Rotate hub several times to seat bearings. Turn hub nut back 90 degrees and install new cotter pin. Hub nut may be tightened 15 degrees to align cotter pin hole. Preload of wheel hub must be less than 3.1 lbs. (13.7 N). If not within specifications, readjust wheel bearings.

REMOVAL & INSTALLATION

WHEEL BEARING

Removal

Raise vehicle and support with safety stands. Remove rear wheel. Remove rear hub and drum. Remove the outer bearing from hub by hand. Using Axle Seal Remover (J-26941), remove the oil seal from hub. Remove the inner bearing from hub by hand. Using a drift and hammer, tap out the inner bearing race and the outer bearing race from hub.

Inspection

Inspect all bearings and races for deterioration or damage. Replace deteriorated or damaged parts. Always replace oil seals.

Installation

1) Using Inner Bearing Race Installer (J-35307-1), install inner bearing race. Using Outer Bearing Race Installer (J-35307-2), install outer bearing race. Use a multi-purpose grease to lubricate bearings, and install inner bearing.

2) Using Seal Installer (J-35305), install new oil seal in the inner side of hub. Install hub and drum. Install outer bearing, washer, hub nut, cotter pin and dust cap. Tighten to specifications.

REAR AXLE ASSEMBLY

Removal

1) Raise and support vehicle. Remove both rear wheels. Remove brake line, retaining clip and flex hose at center of rear axle. Remove tension spring from rear axle. Disconnect parking brake cable, and parking brake cable joint.

2) Support the lower side of rear axle with a jack. Remove shock absorber from axle. Remove coil spring. Remove the fixing bolts attaching the rear axle to the body and remove rear axle.

Inspection

Check for deterioration or damage. Replace parts if worn or damaged.

Installation

To install, reverse removal procedures. Bleed brake system of air.

Fig. 1: Exploded View Of Rear Suspension

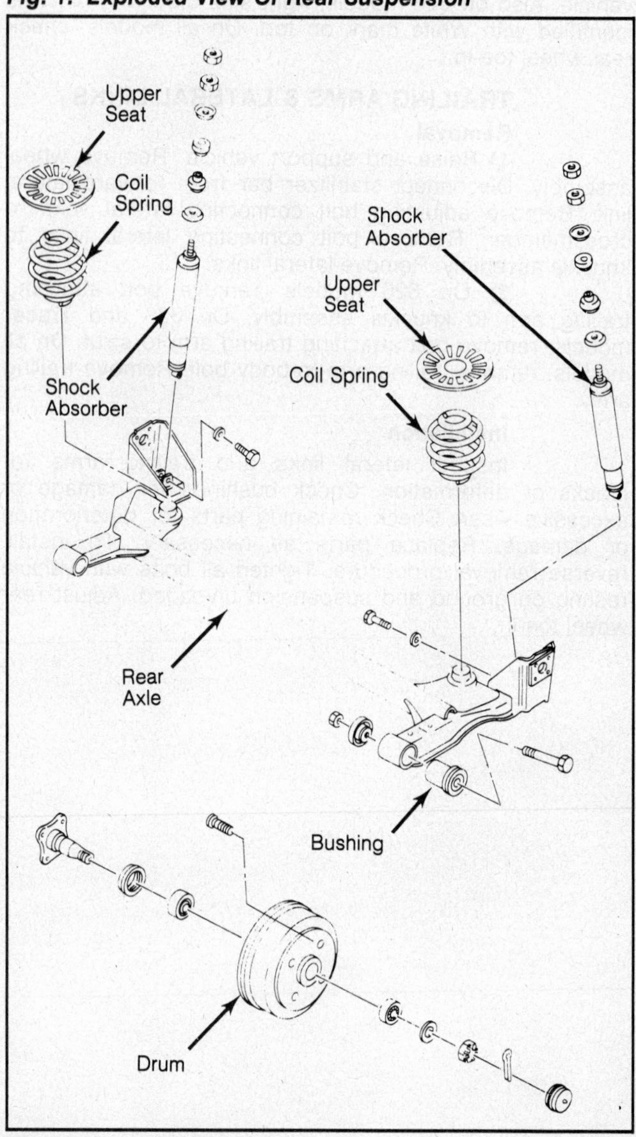

Courtesy of General Motors Corp.

SHOCK ABSORBER

Removal

Raise and support vehicle. Remove upper shock absorber nut and remove lower shock absorber bolt. Remove shock absorber from vehicle. Check for oil leaks or dampening efficiency.

Installation

To install, reverse removal procedure and tighten to specifications.

COIL SPRING

Removal & Installation

Refer to REAR AXLE ASSEMBLY in this article.

GENERAL MOTORS SPECTRUM & ISUZU I-MARK (Cont.)

HUB & DRUM ASSEMBLY

Removal

Raise and support vehicle. Remove rear wheel, dust cap, cotter pin, nut and washer. Remove hub and brake drum.

Installation

Apply multipurpose grease to inner area of hub. To install, reverse removal procedure.

TIGHTENING SPECIFICATIONS

Application	Ft. Lbs. (N.m)
Axle-to-Knuckle Bolt	41 (56)
Axle-to-Body Bolt	72 (98)
Hub Nut	22 (30)
Lower Shock Absorber Bolt	30 (40)
Lug Nut	65 (88)
Stabilizer Bolt	20 (28)
Upper Shock Absorber Nut	25 (35)

Rear Suspension

GENERAL MOTORS SPRINT

DESCRIPTION

Sprint rear suspension is a torsion beam type consisting of coil springs, rear axle, shock absorbers, lateral rod and trailing arm. *See Fig.1.*

Fig. 1. Rear Axle Assembly

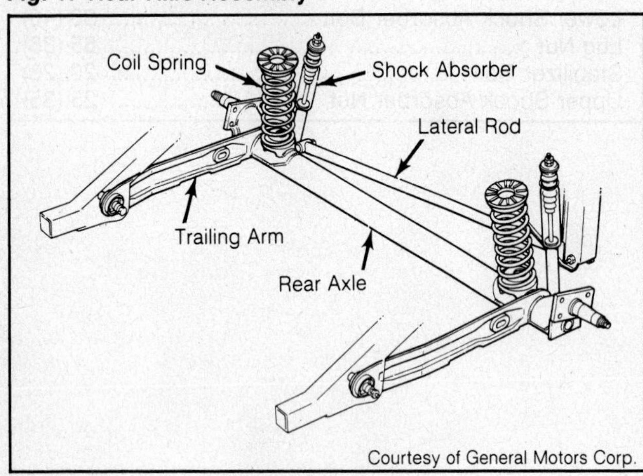

ADJUSTMENTS & INSPECTION

WHEEL BEARINGS

Wheel bearings are not adjustable. To check wheel bearing for excessive wear, raise and support vehicle. Remove wheel center cap and mount a dial indicator to brake drum center. Grasp tire and apply force in and out. If measurement exceeds .012 in. (.3mm), replace bearing.

REMOVAL & INSTALLATION

WHEEL BEARINGS

Removal

[illegible] Raise and support vehicle with safety stands and [illegible]ove wheel assembly. Remove spindle cap, spindle n[illegible]d washer. Pull brake drum and hub assembly [illegible] spindle using Slide Hammer (J2619-01) and Adapte[illegible]866).

2) [illegible]ing a rod and hammer, tap outer wheel bearing out of brake drum hub. Turn knuckle over, remove spacer and tap out inner bearing.

NOTE: **Always replace spindle nut when removed.**

Installation

1) Apply grease to bearing cavity, wheel bearings and oil seal lips. Using Bearing Installer (J-34482), install inner bearing with internal seal facing outward. Turn knuckle over and install spacer.

2) Install outer bearing with internal seal facing outward. Ensure spacer is snug and centered between bearings. To complete installation, reverse removal procedure. Tighten spindle nut to specification. See TIGHTENING SPECIFICATIONS table in this article.

SHOCK ABSORBERS

Removal & Installation

Raise and support vehicle on safety stands positioned under axle beam. Remove upper shock absorber nut, lower mount bolt and remove shock absorber. To install, reverse removal procedure. Tighten bolts and nuts to specification.

COIL SPRING & REAR AXLE

Removal

1) Raise and support vehicle on safety stands allowing rear suspension to hang free. Remove rear wheel assembly. Support rear axle with floor jack and remove lower shock absorber bolts. Remove lateral rod bolt at body mount, lower axle beam slowly until tension is off coil springs. Remove coil springs.

NOTE: **If you are replacing coil springs only, reverse procedure in step 1). Flat face of coil spring goes up, tapered face is down.**

2) Remove brake drums. See WHEEL BEARING in this article. Remove brake line "E" clips, remove brake lines from wheel cylinders and plug. Remove park brake cables from brake arms and backing plates, remove brake backing plates. Remove rear axle trailing arm bolts and lower rear axle and remove.

Installation

To install, reverse removal procedure. Apply watertight sealant to brake backing plate-to-axle mating surface, and to park brake housing-to-brake backing plate. Tighten all bolts and nuts to specification.

TIGHTENING SPECIFICATIONS

Application	Ft. Lbs. (N.m)
Brake Backing Plate Bolts	14-20 (19-27)
Lateral Rod Bolt	33-50 (45-68)
Lateral Rod Nut	33-50 (45-68)
Shock Absorber Nut	14-20 (19-27)
Shock Absorber Bolt	33-50 (45-68)
Spindle Nut	58-87 (79-118)
Trailing Arm Nut	50-65 (68-88)
Wheel Lug Nut	40 (70)

Rear Suspension

HONDA

NOTE: For information on 4WD Civic Wagon, see HONDA 4WD CIVIC WAGON article in this section.

Accord, Civic 2WD, Prelude

DESCRIPTION

The Accord and Prelude use an independent strut type suspension. The Prelude rear suspension consists of a vertically mounted strut, radius rod, lower control arm, stabilizer bar and rear hub carrier and hub. The Accord rear suspension consists of a vertically mounted strut, trailing (lower) control arm, upper and lower arms, knuckle, stabilizer bar and hub assembly.

The Civic uses an independent strut and trailing (lower) control arm type rear suspension. The rear suspension consists of a vertically mounted strut, trailing control arm, rear axle beam/stabilizer assembly and a swing bearing and hub assembly.

Fig. 1: Accord Rear Suspension

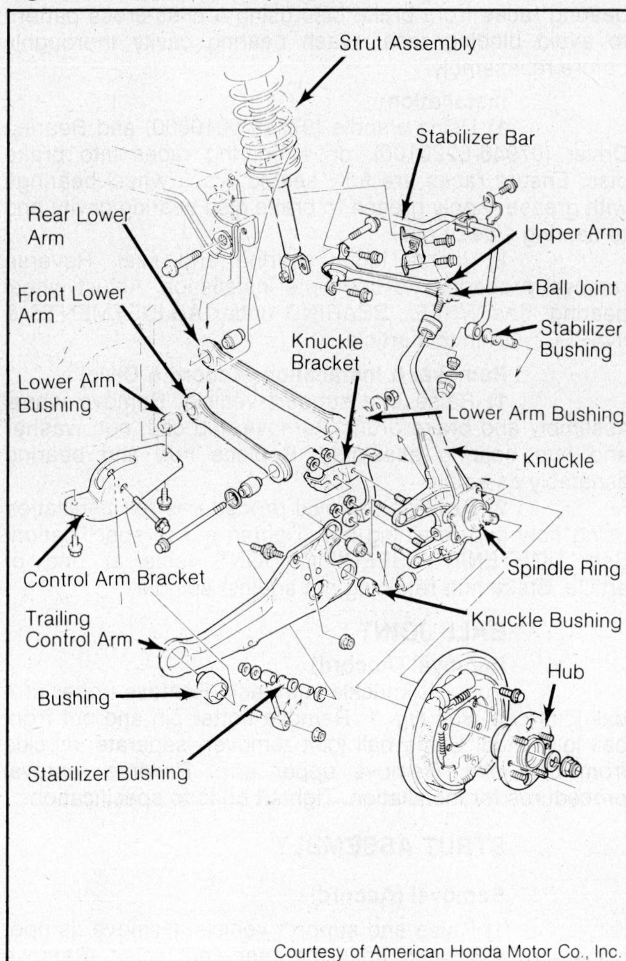

Courtesy of American Honda Motor Co., Inc.

Fig. 2: Prelude Rear Suspension

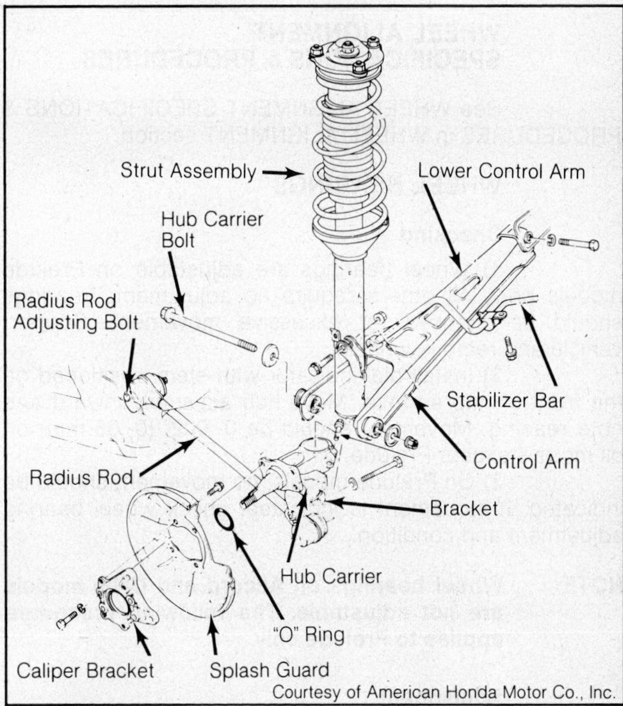

Courtesy of American Honda Motor Co., Inc.

Fig. 3: Civic 2WD Rear Suspension

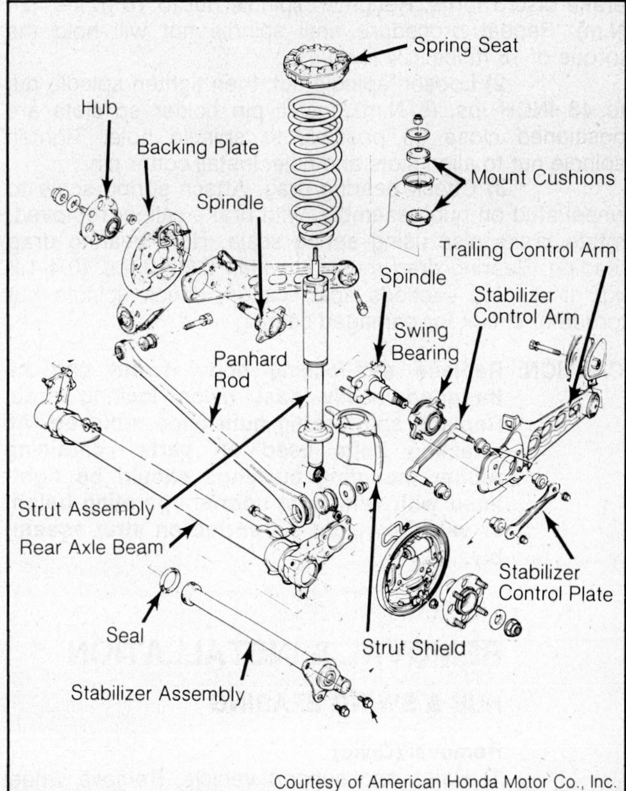

Courtesy of American Honda Motor Co., Inc.

HONDA (Cont.)

ADJUSTMENTS & INSPECTION

WHEEL ALIGNMENT SPECIFICATIONS & PROCEDURES

See WHEEL ALIGNMENT SPECIFICATIONS & PROCEDURES in WHEEL ALIGNMENT section.

WHEEL BEARINGS

Checking

1) Wheel bearings are adjustable on Prelude models only. All others require no adjustment. Bearings should be checked for excessive movement. Support vehicle and remove wheel.

2) Install dial indicator with stem positioned on the front of hub surface. Move hub assembly inward and note reading. Movement should be 0-.002" (0-.05 mm) on all models except Prelude.

3) On Prelude models, no movement should be indicated. If movement is indicated, check wheel bearing adjustment and condition.

NOTE: **Wheel bearings on Accord and Civic models are not adjustable. The following procedure applies to Prelude only.**

Adjustment

1) Apply grease to spindle nut and spindle threads. Tighten spindle nut to 18 ft. lbs. (24 N.m). Rotate brake disc 3 turns. Retighten spindle nut to 18 ft. lbs. (24 N.m). Repeat procedure until spindle nut will hold the torque of 18 ft. lbs. (24 N.m).

2) Loosen spindle nut, then tighten spindle nut to 48 INCH lbs. (5 N.m). Install pin holder so slots are positioned close as possible to spindle hole. Tighten spindle nut to align slots and hole. Install cotter pin.

3) Check bearing drag. Attach spring scale to wheel stud on hub assembly. With brake caliper removed, rotate brake disc using spring scale. Note bearing drag reading. Bearing drag must be within 0.9-4.0 lbs. (0.4-1.8 kg). If reading exceeds specification, check spindle nut torque or check for damaged bearing.

CAUTION: **Replace self-locking bolts if nut can be threaded easily past nylon locking area. Replace self-locking nuts once removed. All retaining bolts used on parts containing rubber mounting bushings should be tightened with vehicle at normal operating height or vehicle weight supported on strut assembly.**

REMOVAL & INSTALLATION

HUB & SWING BEARING

Removal (Civic)

1) Raise and support vehicle. Remove wheel and brake drum. Check wheel bearing prior to removal. See WHEEL BEARINGS under ADJUSTMENTS & INSPECTION in this article. This will indicate if bearing requires replacement.

2) Remove hub cap, nut and hub assembly. Disconnect brake line from wheel cylinder. Remove backing plate and stabilizer plate. *See Fig. 3.*

3) Remove trailing control arm from swing bearing. Remove spindle and swing bearing assembly. Using a hydraulic press, separate spindle from swing bearing. Using bearing puller, remove bearing inner race from spindle.

Installation

Reverse removal procedures for installation. Tighten bolts to specification. See TIGHTENING SPECIFICATIONS table at end of article. Bleed brake system.

WHEEL BEARINGS

Removal (Prelude)

1) Remove brake caliper. Remove cap from brake disc. Remove cotter pin and pin holder. Remove nut, washer and outer bearing. Remove brake disc. Remove inner bearing and seal from brake disc.

2) If wheel bearings require replacement, remove bearing races. Using hammer and punch, drive bearing races from brake disc using a criss-cross pattern to avoid binding race. Wash bearing cavity thoroughly before reassembly.

Installation

1) Using Handle (07749-0010000) and Bearing Driver (07946-6920100), drive bearing races into brake disc. Ensure races are fully seated. Pack wheel bearings with grease. Apply grease to brake disc bearing cavity and to bearing side of seal.

2) Install inner bearing and seal. Reverse removal procedure to complete installation. Adjust wheel bearing. See WHEEL BEARING under ADJUSTMENTS & INSPECTION in this article.

Removal & Installation (Accord & Civic)

1) Raise and support vehicle. Remove wheel assembly and brake drum. Remove hub cap, nut, washer and hub bearing assembly. Replace hub and bearing assembly as a unit.

2) Reverse removal procedures for installation using new hub retaining nut. Tighten nut to specification. See TIGHTENING SPECIFICATIONS table at end of article. Stake hub retaining nut against spindle.

BALL JOINT

Removal (Accord)

Support knuckle with jack. Remove upper arm ball joint cap. *See Fig. 1.* Remove cotter pin and nut from ball joint stud. Using ball joint remover, separate knuckle from ball joint. Remove upper arm. Reverse removal procedures for installation. Tighten bolts to specification.

STRUT ASSEMBLY

Removal (Accord)

1) Raise and support vehicle. Remove damper upper cover located near the rear seat lining. Remove stabilizer bar from lower control arm. *See Fig. 1.* Remove strut-to-body retaining nuts.

2) Place jack under lower control arm. Remove lower strut retaining bolt. Lower jack and remove strut assembly.

HONDA (Cont.)

Removal (Civic)

1) Raise and support vehicle. Remove wheel assembly. Support rear axle beam with a jack. From inside of vehicle, remove strut lid, strut lock nut, washer and mount cushion.

2) Remove strut-to-rear axle bolt. Carefully lower rear axle beam. Remove strut assembly, spring and spring seat.

Removal (Prelude)

1) Raise and support vehicle. Remove wheel assembly. Remove brake hose clamp. Disconnect stabilizer bar from lower control arm. *See Fig. 2.*

2) Loosen lower control arm pivot bolt and radius rod nut and hub carrier bolt. Remove strut assembly lock-to-hub carrier bolt. Remove strut from hub carrier. Remove upper strut mount bolts. Remove strut assembly.

Disassembly (Accord & Prelude)

Using spring compressor, compress strut assembly spring. DO NOT compress more than that required to remove shaft nut. Remove strut shaft nut. Slowly release spring compressor. Disassemble strut assembly, noting location of components. *See Figs. 4 and 5.*

Fig. 4: Accord Rear Strut Assembly

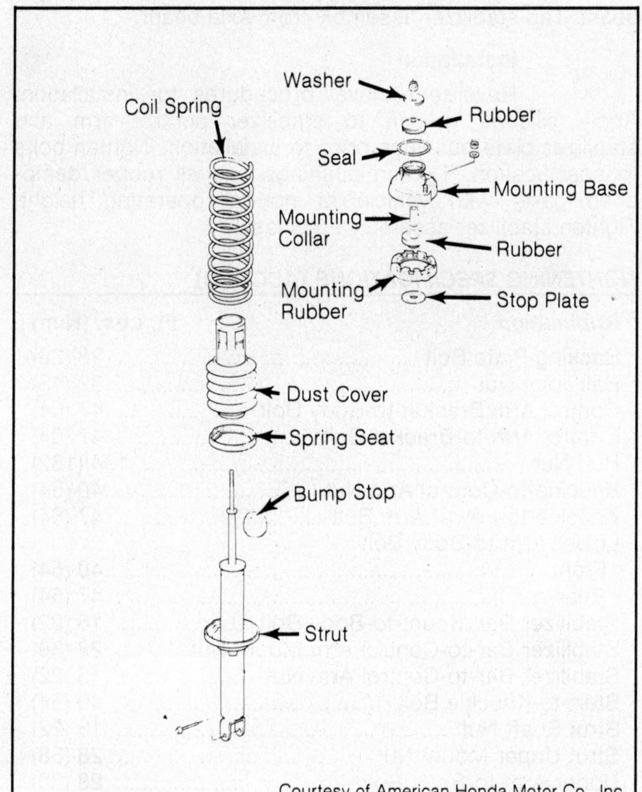

Courtesy of American Honda Motor Co., Inc.

Fig. 5: Prelude Rear Strut Assembly

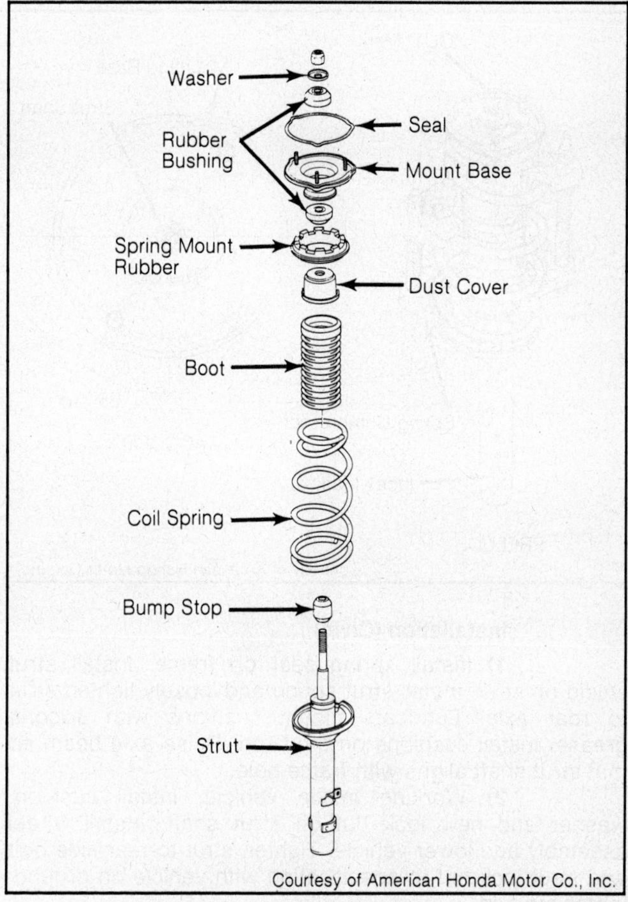

Courtesy of American Honda Motor Co., Inc.

Disassembly (Civic)

No disassembly is required. Strut assembly must be replaced if rod does not move smoothly through full travel or signs of oil leakage exists.

Reassembly (Accord & Prelude)

1) Check for weak spring tension. Inspect components for deterioration or damage. Strut assembly must be replaced if rod does not move smoothly through full travel or signs of oil leakage exists. Replace worn or damaged components.

2) On Accord models, install mounting base so bolts are within 35±3 degrees of shaft. *See Fig. 6.* On Prelude models, install strut assembly mounting base with "OUT" mark aligned with index mark on strut tube. *See Fig. 6.* Reverse disassembly procedure. Install new shaft nut. Tighten to specification.

Installation (Accord)

1) Install strut and loosely install lower strut mounting bolt. Install upper strut mounting nuts. Tighten nuts to specification. Raise rear suspension so vehicle weight is supported on strut assembly.

2) Tighten lower strut mounting bolt to specification. Reverse removal procedures for remaining components. Tighten bolts to specification.

CAUTION: Lower strut mounting bolt must be tightened to specification while vehicle weight is supported on strut assembly.

HONDA (Cont.)

Fig. 6: Aligning Strut Mounting Base

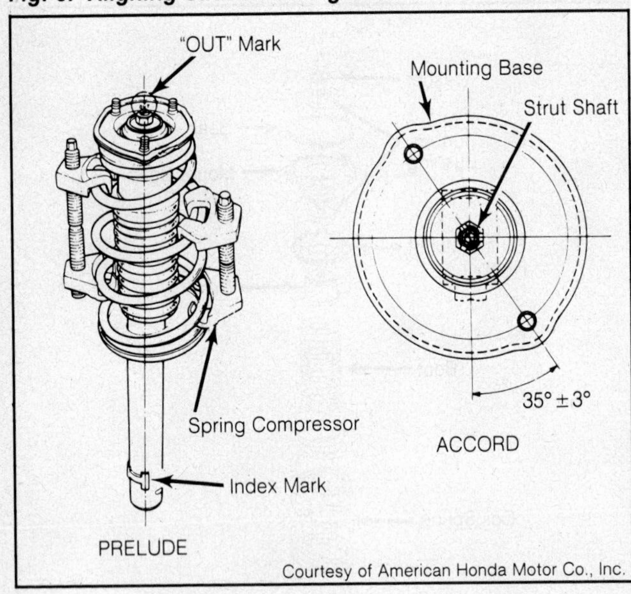

Courtesy of American Honda Motor Co., Inc.

Installation (Civic)

1) Install spring seat on frame. Install strut shield on strut. Install strut spring and loosely tighten strut to rear axle. Lubricate mount cushions with silicone grease. Install cushions on strut rod. Raise axle beam so that strut shaft aligns with frame hole.

2) Working inside vehicle, install cushion, washer and new lock nut on strut shaft. Install wheel assembly and lower vehicle. Tighten strut-to-rear axle bolt and strut lock nut to specification with vehicle on ground. Install strut lid.

Installation (Prelude)

1) Install strut assembly. Align tab on strut tube with slot in hub carrier. Tighten lock bolt to specification. Install lower control arm and radius rod bolts loosely in place.

2) Place jack under hub carrier and raise suspension until vehicle weight is supported on strut assembly. Tighten lower control arm bolt to specification. Apply silicone grease to stabilizer bushings if removed.

CAUTION: Lower control arm, radius rod bolts and stabilizer bar bolts must be tightened with vehicle weight supported on strut assembly.

3) Install stabilizer bar. Tighten bolt to specification. Tighten radius rod adjustment bolts to specification. Reverse removal procedure for remaining components. Check rear wheel alignment.

CONTROL ARM

Removal (Accord & Civic)

Information not available from manufacturer.

Removal (Prelude)

1) Raise and support vehicle. Remove wheel assembly. Remove caliper and brake disc. Remove caliper bracket and splash guard. Remove radius rod. Remove stabilizer bar-to-lower control arm.

2) Remove strut-to-hub carrier bolt. Separate hub carrier from strut. Remove hub carrier from lower control arm. Remove lower control arm pivot bolt. Remove lower control arm.

Installation

1) Reverse removal procedures for installation. Apply silicone grease to all rubber bushings. Install new "O" ring on caliper bracket.

2) Tighten lower control arm pivot bolt, radius rod bolts and stabilizer bolts to specification with jack placed under control arm and vehicle weight applied to strut assembly.

STABILIZER ASSEMBLY

Removal (Civic)

1) Raise and support vehicle. Remove wheels and brake drums. Remove cap from hub. Remove nut, washer and hub assembly. Remove backing plates.

2) Remove stabilizer plate and stabilizer control arm. *See Fig. 3.* Remove stabilizer assembly retaining bolts. *See Fig. 3.* Remove cap from left side of rear axle beam. Tap stabilizer assembly from axle beam.

Installation

Reverse removal procedures for installation. Apply silicone grease to stabilizer control arm and stabilizer plate bushings prior to installation. Tighten bolts to specification. Tighten bushings and all rubber dampened parts with vehicle at normal operating height. Tighten stabilizer assembly bolts last.

TIGHTENING SPECIFICATIONS (ACCORD)

Application	Ft. Lbs. (N.m)
Backing Plate Bolt	28 (38)
Ball Joint Nut	32 (43)
Control Arm Bracket-to-Body Bolt	47 (64)
Control Arm-to-Bracket Bolt	47 (64)
Hub Nut	134 (182)
Knuckle-to-Control Arm Nut	40 (54)
Knuckle-to-Lower Arm Bolt	47 (64)
Lower Arm-to-Body Bolt	
Front	40 (54)
Rear	47 (64)
Stabilizer Bar Mount-to-Body Bolt	16 (22)
Stabilizer Bar-to-Control Arm Mount Nut	28 (38)
Stabilizer Bar-to-Control Arm Nut	16 (22)
Sturt-to-Knuckle Bolt	40 (54)
Strut Shaft Nut	16 (22)
Strut Upper Mount Nut	28 (38)
Upper Arm-to-Body Bolt	28 (38)

Rear Suspension

HONDA (Cont.)

TIGHTENING SPECIFICATIONS (CIVIC)

Application	Ft. Lbs. (N.m)
Backing Plate Nut	33 (45)
Hub Nut	134 (182)
Panhard Rod-to-Axle Beam Bolt	54 (73)
Panhard Rod-to-Body Bolt	40 (54)
Stabilizer Assembly Bolt	54 (73)
Stabilizer Control Arm Nut	29 (39)
Strut Lower Mounting Bolt	40 (54)
Strut Upper Mounting Nut	16 (22)
Swing Bearing Retaining Nut	33 (45)
Trailing Control Arm-to-Body Bolt	47 (64)

TIGHTENING SPECIFICATIONS (PRELUDE)

Application	Ft. Lbs. (N.m)
Control Arm Pivot Bolt	40 (54)
Hub Carrier-to-Bracket Bolt	60 (81)
Hub Carrier-to-Control Arm Bolt	60 (81)
Hub Carrier-to-Radius Rod Bolt	51 (69)
Stabilizer Bar-to-Body Bolt	16 (22)
Strut Shaft Nut	40 (54)
Strut-to-Hub Carrier Bolt	40 (54)
Strut Upper Mount Nut	16 (22)
Radius Rod Adjusting Bolt	47 (64)

Rear Suspension

HONDA 4WD CIVIC WAGON

DESCRIPTION

The Honda Civic Wagon uses a solid type axle housing with a panhard rod located between the frame and axle housing. The rear suspension consists of shock absorbers, coil springs, panhard rod and upper and lower control arms.

ADJUSTMENTS & INSPECTION

WHEEL BEARING

Wheel bearings are located on axle shafts and are nonadjustable.

CAUTION: Replace self-locking bolts if nut can be threaded easily past nylon locking area. Replace self-locking nuts once removed. All rubber bushings should be coated with silicone grease prior to installation.

REMOVAL & INSTALLATION

SHOCK & COIL SPRING

Removal

1) Raise and support vehicle so rear axle can be lowered. Support rear axle with a jack. Remove shock absorber access cover. Remove cap, nuts, washer and mount rubber from shock absorber shaft. *See Fig. 1.*

Fig. 1: Exploded View of Civic Wagon 4WD Rear Suspension

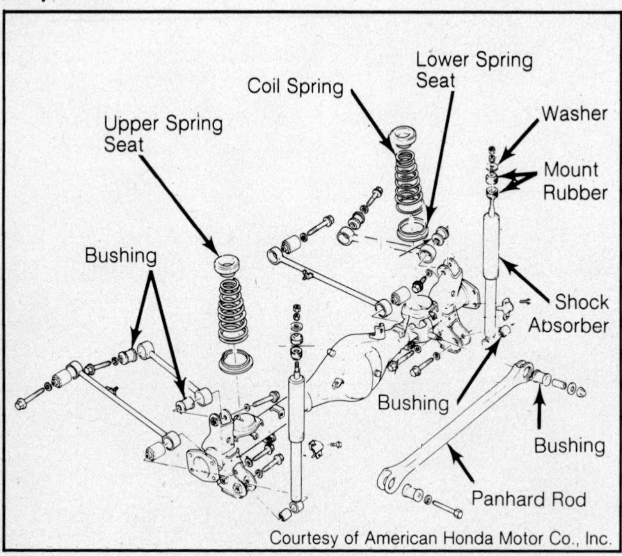

2) Slowly lower rear axle housing. Remove coil spring and upper and lower spring seats. Remove shock absorber-to-axle housing bolt. Remove shock absorber.

Installation

1) Inspect all rubber components for damage. Inspect shock absorber for smooth travel or signs of oil leakage. Replace damaged components. Install upper spring seat on frame and lower spring seat on rear axle.

2) Install coil spring on lower spring seat. Loosely install shock absorber upright on rear axle. Coat shock absorber mount rubber with silicone grease. Install mount rubber on shock absorber.

3) Raise rear axle while aligning shock absorber shaft with frame mounting hole. Ensure coil spring seats are properly located.

4) Install shock absorber upper mount rubber, washer and lower nut. Tighten shock absorber shaft lower nut to specification. See TIGHTENING SPECIFICATIONS table at end of article.

5) Install upper nut on shock absorber shaft. Tighten to specification. Install cap. Reverse removal procedure for remaining components. Tigthen bolts to specification. Tighten shock absorber-to-rear axle bolt to specification with vehicle placed on the ground at normal operating height.

CAUTION: Shock absorber-to-rear axle bolt must be tightened with vehicle at normal operating height.

TIGHTENING SPECIFICATIONS

Application	Ft. Lbs. (N.m)
Control Arm Bolt	
Lower	60 (81)
Upper	60 (81)
Panhard Rod-to-Axle Nut	54 (73)
Panhard Rod-to-Frame Bolt	40 (54)
Shock Absorber Shaft Nut	
Lower	14 (19)
Upper	16 (22)
Shock Absorber-to-Axle Bolt	60 (81)

Rear Suspension

ISUZU IMPULSE

DESCRIPTION

The rear suspension is of a 3-Link and 5-Link type and consists mainly of a track rod, control arms, coil springs, shock absorbers and a stabilizer bar.

The track rod is connected to the rear axle housing and the body. Control arms are connected to the body and rear axle housing, to control front and rear movement of the rear axle. Shock absorbers are connected to the rear wheel arch and rear axle housing.

ADJUSTMENTS

WHEEL BEARINGS

NOTE: **Wheel bearings are not adjustable.**

WHEEL ALIGNMENT SPECIFICATIONS & PROCEDURES

See WHEEL ALIGNMENT SPECIFICATIONS & PROCEDURES in WHEEL ALIGNMENT section.

REMOVAL & INSTALLATION

TRACK ROD

Removal

Raise vehicle and support with safety stands under rear axle housing. Remove bolt that attaches track rod to body. Remove nut that attaches track rod to rear axle housing. Remove track rod.

Installation

To install, reverse removal procedures. Tighten track rod bolts with vehicle on ground.

CONTROL ARMS

Removal (3-Link)

Raise vehicle and support with safety stands under rear axle housing. Remove bolts attaching control arms to rear axle housing. Remove bolts attaching control arms to body. Remove control arms.

Installation

Install control arms to body and to rear axle housing. Tighten control arm bolts with vehicle on ground.

NOTE: **Install control arms with the arrow mark pointed toward front of vehicle.**

Removal (5-Link)

1) Raise vehicle and support with safety stands under rear axle housing. Remove bolts attaching upper control arms to rear axle housing. Remove bolts attaching upper control arms to body. Remove upper control arms.

NOTE: **The upper control arms are color coded. The control arm for the right side of the vehicle is coded Red on the body end. The left control arm is coded Blue on the body end.**

2) Remove coil springs. See COIL SPRINGS in this article. Remove bolts attaching lower control arms to body. Remove bolts attaching lower control arms to axle housing. Remove lower control arms.

Fig. 1: Exploded View of 3-Link Type Rear Suspension

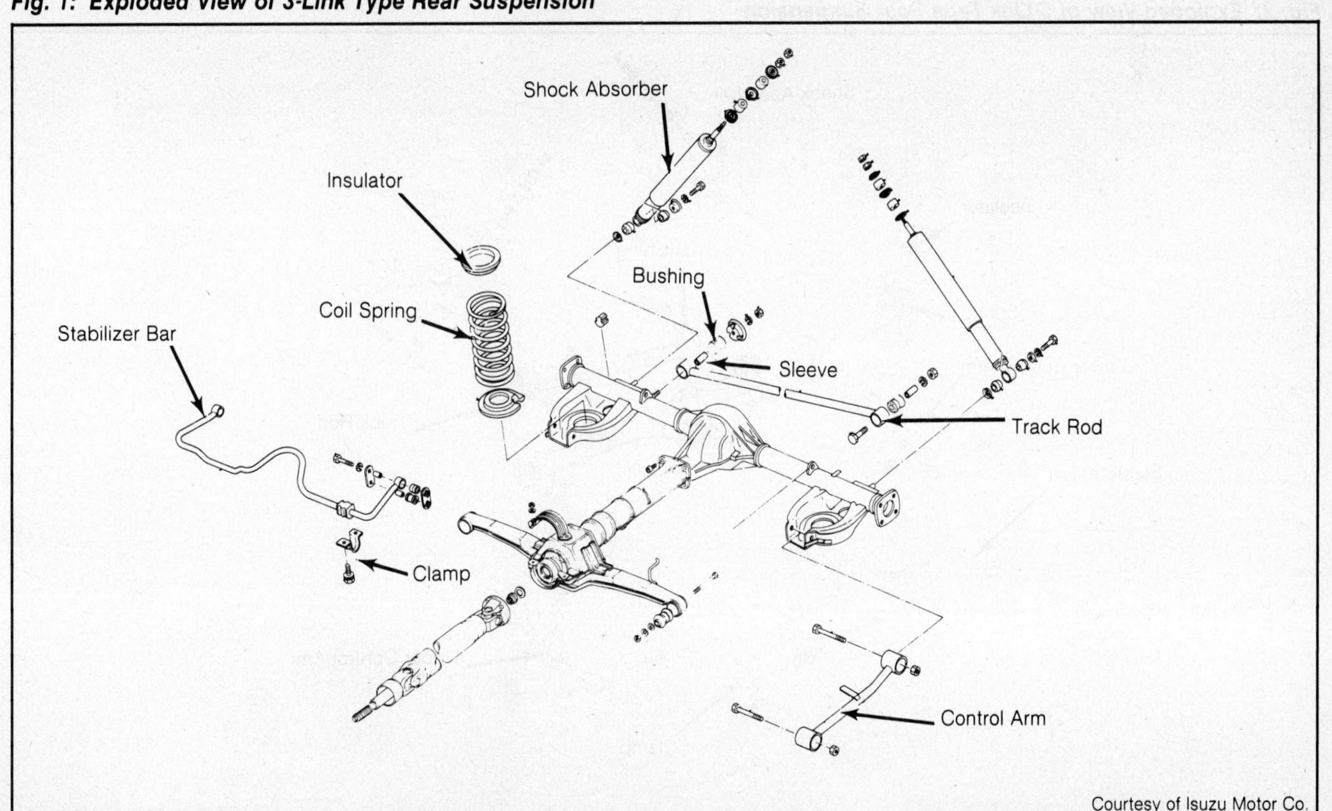

Rear Suspension

ISUZU IMPULSE (Cont.)

Installation

To install, reverse removal procedures. All control arm bolts are to be tightened to specification with vehicle on ground.

COIL SPRINGS

Removal

1) Raise vehicle and support with safety stands. Place a floor jack under rear axle housing and raise slightly to support axle housing.

2) Remove bolts retaining bottom of shock absorbers to rear axle housing. Lower axle housing until coil springs become loose enough to remove.

NOTE: **Do not stretch brake hose when lowering axle housing.**

Installation

Place spring in its proper position. Ensure that top insulator is in place. Raise axle housing until control arms and bottom of shock absorbers can be connected. Install shock absorber bolts. Tighten shock absorber bolts with vehicle on ground.

SHOCK ABSORBERS

Removal

Raise vehicle and support with safety stands under axle housing. Remove lower shock absorber bolts. Remove nuts from top of shock absorber. Remove shock absorber.

Installation

Install upper end of shock absorber. Install shock absorber nuts. Install lower shock absorber bolts. Remove support and lower vehicle.

STABILIZER BAR

Removal

Raise vehicle and support with safety stands. Remove bolts attaching stabilizer bar to axle housing brackets. Remove clamps attaching stabilizer bar to body. Remove stabilizer bar.

Installation

Install rubber bushings on stabilizer bar. Install clamps that attach stabilizer bar to body. Install bolts that attach stabilizer bar to axle housing brackets. Tighten stabilizer bar bolts with vehicle on ground.

TIGHTENING SPECIFICATIONS

Application	Ft. Lbs. (N.m)
Control Arm Bolts	
3-Link	47 (64)
5-Link	98 (133)
Shock Absorber-to-Axle Housing Nut	
3-Link	20 (27)
5-Link	20 (27)
Track Rod-to-Axle Housing Nuts	
3-Link	47 (64)
5-Link	47 (64)
Track Rod-to-Body Bolts	
3-Link	47 (64)
5-Link	47 (64)

Fig. 2: Exploded View of 5-Link Type Rear Suspension

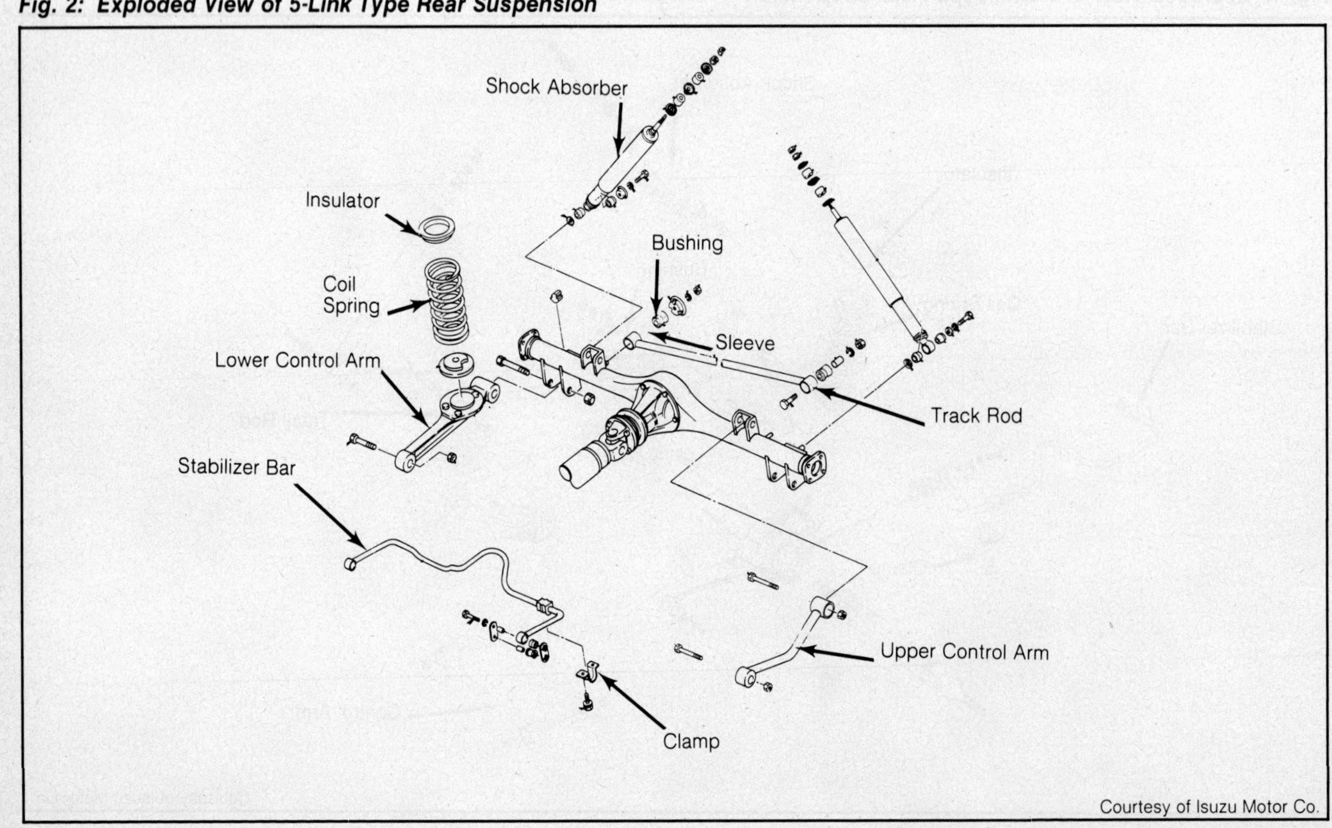

Rear Suspension

JAGUAR

XJ6 III, XJS HE

DESCRIPTION

Jaguar uses independent coil spring-type rear suspension. Outer bearing carrier and hub assembly is supported by control arms at bottom and utilizes drive axles as upper support.

Suspension is controlled by 4 coil spring/shock absorber assemblies, 2 mounted at each rear wheel. Lower control arms connect to radius arms at rear, and to chassis members at front. *See Fig. 1.*

Fig. 1: Jaguar Rear Suspension Assembly

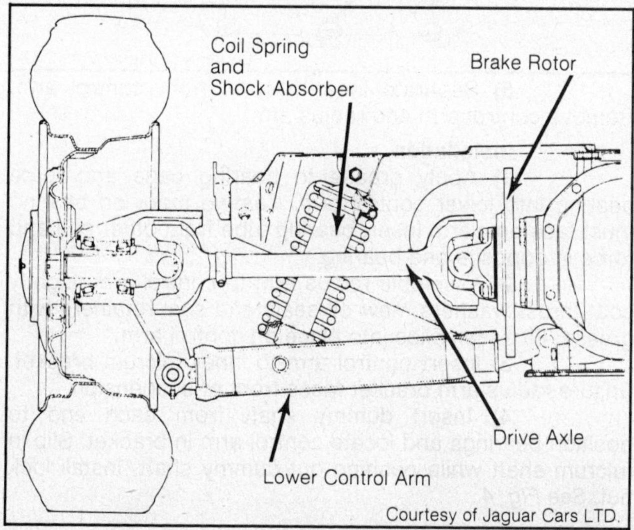

ADJUSTMENTS & INSPECTION

WHEEL ALIGNMENT SPECIFICATIONS & PROCEDURES

See WHEEL ALIGNMENT SPECIFICATIONS & PROCEDURES in WHEEL ALIGNMENT section.

WHEEL BEARING & END PLAY

Wheel bearing and end play adjustment is controlled by a spacer located next to the universal joint on the hub shaft. Spacers are available in thicknesses from .109 to .151" (2.77 to 3.84 mm) in .0030" (.076 mm) steps. End play is normally .0010-.0030" (.026-.076 mm). If it exceeds .0050" (.127 mm), change the spacer to a thicker one.

NOTE: **If vehicle is equipped with a limited slip differential, do not run engine with vehicle in gear with one wheel off floor.**

Checking

1) Raise and support vehicle. Tap hub inward toward vehicle. Clamp dial indicator mount to hub carrier web. Stylus of dial indicator must contact hub flange. Note reading of dial indicator.

2) Using 2 levers between hub and hub carrier boss, press hub outward. Take care not to damage water thrower plate. Note reading on dial indicator.

3) The difference between dial indicator readings is end play of hub bearings. If this exceeds .005" (.127 mm), install thicker spacer.

Adjustment

1) Remove cotter pin, hub nut and washer from end of axle shaft. Remove fulcrum shaft grease nipple from hub carrier. Place Thread Protector (JD 1C 7) on end of drive shaft.

2) Mount Hub Puller (JD 1D) on rear hub. Remove hub and carrier from drive shaft and remove hub puller and thread protector. Remove spacer from drive shaft and measure thickness. Select spacer(s) to obtain .0010-.0030" (.026-.076 mm) end play.

3) Clean drive shaft splines. Place selected spacer on drive shaft. Apply Loctite to outer two-thirds of drive axle splines. To complete installation, reverse removal procedure. Tighten all bolts and nuts to specification. See TIGHTENING SPECIFICATIONS table in this article.

REMOVAL & INSTALLATION

WHEEL BEARING

Removal

1) Remove cotter pin, hub nut and washer from end of axle shaft. Remove fulcrum shaft grease nipple from hub carrier. Place Thread Protector (JD 1C 7) on end of drive shaft.

2) Mount Hub Puller (JD 1D) on rear hub. Remove hub and carrier from drive shaft and remove hub puller and thread protector. Pry out oil seal retainers from fulcrum shaft housing and remove seals, bearings, distance tubes, and shims.

3) Mount hub carrier in vice and drive out bearing races from fulcrum shaft housing. Using press, remove hub assembly from carrier. Drive out inner hub bearing race with seal and bearing, from hub carrier.

4) Drive out bearing race. Using arbor press, remove outer bearing from hub. Remove oil seal track from hub shaft and clean and inspect all parts.

Installation

To install, reverse removal procedure.

COIL SPRING & SHOCK ABSORBER

Removal

1) Raise vehicle and support at lift points with safety stands. Position floor jack under control arm. Remove bolt retaining top of shock absorbers to suspension assembly crossmember.

2) Remove nuts retaining shock absorbers to lower mount. Using a drift, remove mounting piece. Remove shock absorber and coil spring assembly.

3) Using spring compressor and Adaptor (SL 14 and JD 11B), collapse spring until collets and spring seat can be removed. Release pressure and separate shock absorber from spring.

Installation

To install, reverse removal procedure.

RADIUS ARM

Removal

1) Raise vehicle and support with safety stands, forward of radius arms. Remove wheel assembly. Remove bolt and spring washer securing safety strap to body. Remove safety wire and bolt securing radius arm to body. Remove safety strap. *See Fig. 2.*

Rear Suspension

JAGUAR (Cont.)

Fig. 2: Installed Position of Radius Arm

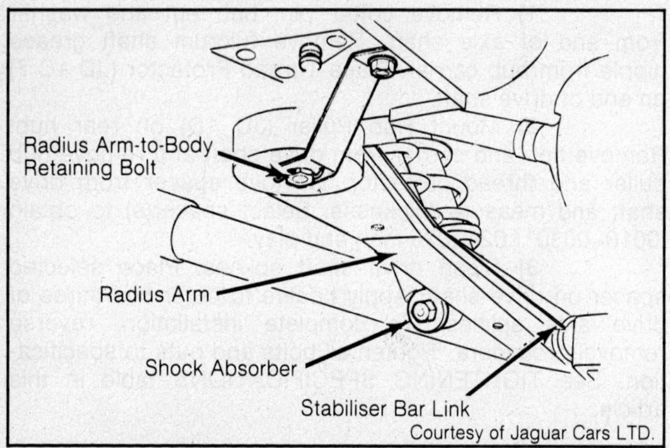

Courtesy of Jaguar Cars LTD.

2) Remove forward lower shock absorber retaining pin. Using a punch, remove pin rearward. Bend tab washer and remove bolt retaining radius arm to control arm.

Installation

Replace any damaged radius arm bushings. When pressing bushings into radius arm, bushing should protrude from each side equal amounts. To complete installation, reverse removal procedure. Tighten all bolts and nuts to specification. See TIGHTENING SPECIFICATIONS table in this article.

REAR SUSPENSION ASSEMBLY

Removal

1) Raise and support vehicle. Remove wheel assemblies. Place floor jack (with adaptor to hold suspension assembly) under rear suspension.

2) Disconnect intermediate exhaust pipes at both ends and remove. Support rear mufflers out of way. Disconnect radius arm-to-body mounting hardware.

3) Separate brake line union from body bracket. Disconnect brake lines at flexible hoses and plug. Disconnect propeller shaft at differential and lower out of way.

4) Release parking brake. Disconnect parking brake cable from junction at rear suspension assembly. Remove suspension bracket nuts. Lower suspension assembly to floor and slide from vehicle.

NOTE: Replace suspension bushings in pairs.

Installation

To install, reverse removal procedure. Bleed brake system and check wheel alignment. Tighten all bolts and nuts to specification.

LOWER CONTROL ARM

Removal

1) Raise vehicle and support with safety stands, forward of radius arms. Remove wheel assembly.

2) Remove lock nut and drive out bearing carrier fulcrum shaft. Fit dummy shaft for support. Collect shims and all seal retainers.

3) Lift bearing carrier up, clear of control arm. Keep carrier in position with heavy wire attached to the crossmember. Separate radius arm from body.

4) Remove bolts attaching support plate to the crossmember and inner fulcrum brackets. Separate shock absorber at upper mount. Drive out pivot pin. *See Fig. 3.*

Fig. 3: Bolts & Set Screws Retaining Support Plate to Crossmember & Inner Fulcrum Brackets

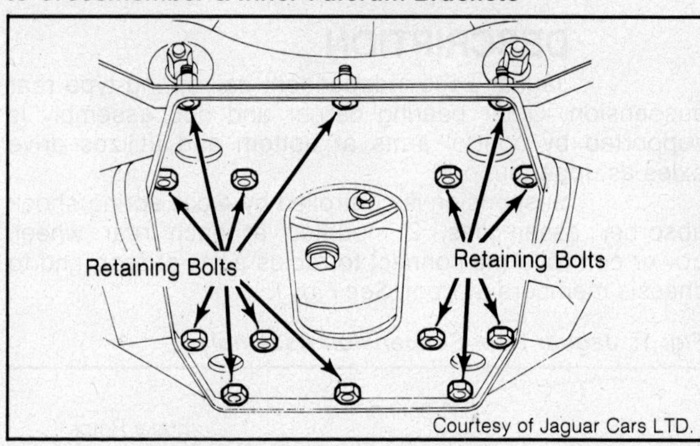

Courtesy of Jaguar Cars LTD.

5) Separate inner fulcrum from control arm. Remove control arm and radius arm.

Installation

1) Apply grease to bearing cage and force bearing into lower control arm. Casting mark on bearing must face outward. Insert bearing tube from other end and force in opposite end bearing.

2) Assemble radius arm to control arm. Lightly coat thrust washers, new oil seals and seal retainers with grease. Fit assemblies into place on control arm.

3) Insert control arm to inner fulcrum bracket. Ensure radius arm bracket faces front of suspension.

4) Insert dummy shaft from each end to position bearings and locate control arm in bracket. Slip in fulcrum shaft while pushing out dummy shaft. Install lock nut. *See Fig. 4.*

Fig. 4: Fulcrum Boss Assembly

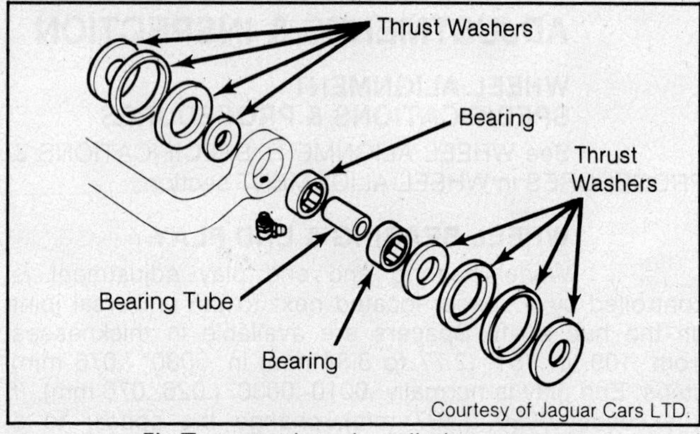

Courtesy of Jaguar Cars LTD.

5) To complete installation, reverse removal procedure. Tighten all bolts and nuts to specification.

TIGHTENING SPECIFICATIONS

Application	Ft. Lbs. (N.m)
Inner Fulcrum Shaft Nut	45-50 (61-68)
Radius Arm-to-Body Bolts	40-45 (54-61)
Radius Arm-to-Control Arm Bolts	60-70 (81-95)
Shock Absorbers	32-36 (44-49)
Stabilizer Bar Bracket-to-Body	14-18 (19-24)
Support Plate-to-Crossmember	
& Inner Fulcrum Nuts	60-65 (81-88)
Wheel Lug Nuts	
Steel Wheel	65 (88)
Alloy Wheel	88 (102)

Rear Suspension

MAZDA RX7

DESCRIPTION

Rear suspension consists of vertically mounted MacPherson type struts, trailing arms, knuckle and hub assembly, control links, sublinks and laterally mounted links. Knuckle and hub assembly attaches to trailing arm with bolts through pillow balls. Mazda calls this a triaxial floating hub. A stabilizer bar mounts to frame and trailing arms. All models are equipped with Automatic Adjusting Suspension (AAS). Rear wheel alignment is adjusted using bolt and cam plate on trailing arm.

NOTE: **For information on Auto Adjust Suspension (AAS), see MAZDA RX7 & 626 ELECTRONIC SUSPENSION article in this section.**

ADJUSTMENTS & INSPECTION

WHEEL ALIGNMENT SPECIFICATIONS & PROCEDURES

See WHEEL ALIGNMENT SPECIFICATIONS & PROCEDURES in WHEEL ALIGNMENT section.

WHEEL BEARING

Raise vehicle and support. Remove wheel assembly. Remove lower caliper slide pin and raise caliper out of way. Attach dial indicator to axle flange and measure axial play. Maximum axial play is .004" (.10 mm). If play exceeds specification, replace wheel bearing.

BALL JOINT CHECKING

Lateral Link

Remove lateral link. Rotate ball joint in socket 3-4 times before measuring preload. Attach Preload Attachment (49 0180 510B) to ball joint and measure preload of ball joint with spring scale. Spring scale should register 1.1-2.6 lbs. (5-12 N). *See Fig. 3.*

REMOVAL & INSTALLATION

WHEEL BEARING

Removal

1) Raise and support vehicle. Remove wheel assembly. Remove drive axle lock nut. Remove brake

Fig. 1: Exploded View of RX7 Rear Suspension

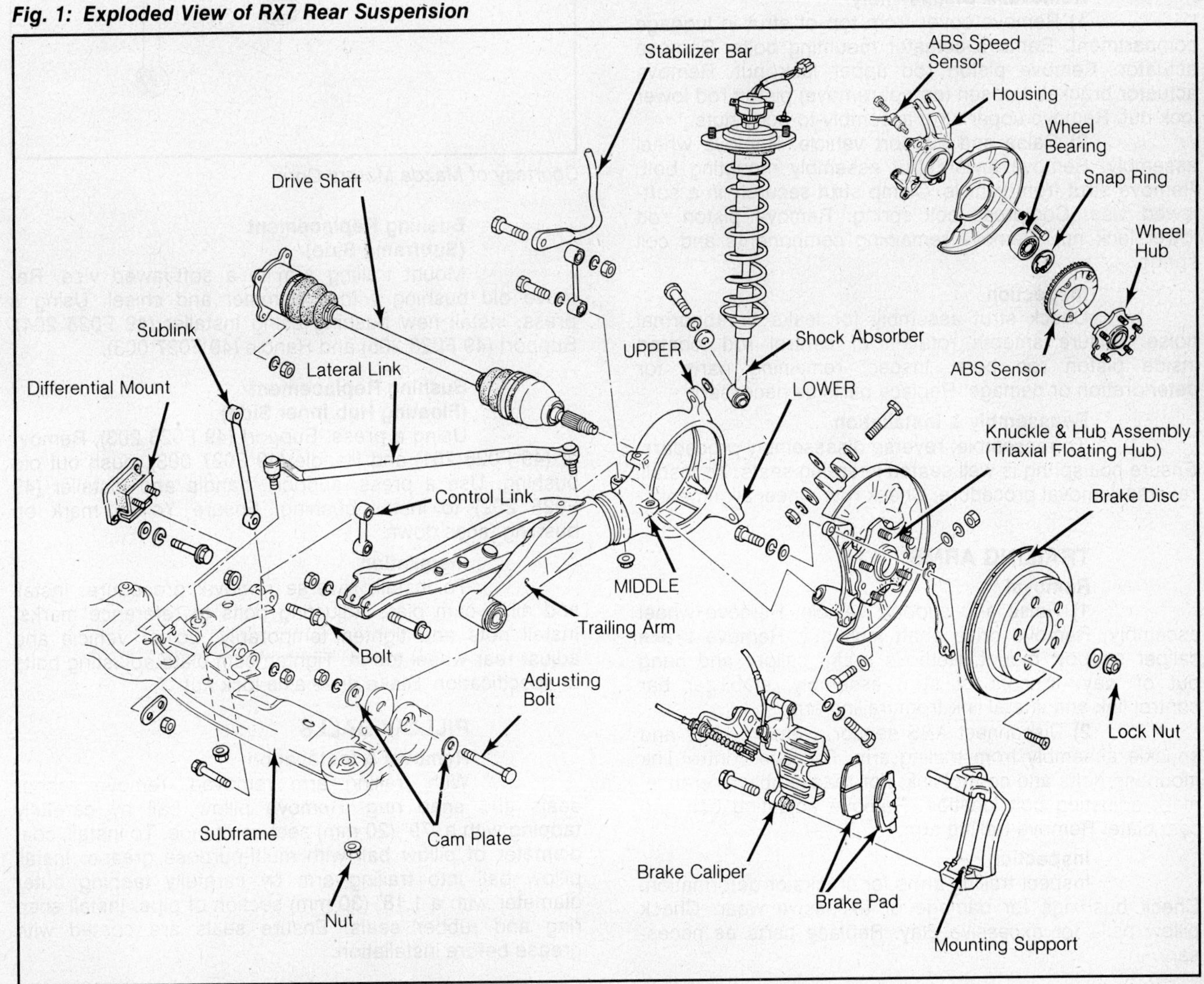

Courtesy of Mazda Motors Corp.

Rear Suspension

MAZDA RX7 (Cont.)

caliper assembly and hang out of way. Remove screws and remove rotor. Disconnect ABS speed sensor. Remove knuckle assembly from trailing arm.

2) Loosen dust cover. Using a press, Installer (49 F026 102) and Puller (49 F026 103), remove hub from knuckle. Using a press, installer and Puller (49 0636 145), remove wheel bearing inner race from hub. Remove snap ring from knuckle. Remove wheel bearing outer race from knuckle using a press and Adapter (49 F027 007).

Inspection

Check wheel hub and knuckle for cracks or damage. Check dust cover for deformation. Check bearing for excessive wear or signs of bearing seizure.

Installation

Press new wheel bearing into knuckle using installer and Adapter (49 0259 748). Press hub into knuckle using installer. To install, reverse removal procedure. Check clearance between ABS speed sensor and sensor rotor. Clearance should be .016-.039" (.40-1.00 mm). Tighten drive axle lock nut to specification. Stake drive axle lock nut. Check axial play.

STRUT ASSEMBLY

Removal & Disassembly

1) Remove cover from top of strut in luggage compartment. Remove actuator mounting bolts. Remove actuator. Remove piston rod upper lock nut. Remove actuator bracket. Loosen (do not remove) piston rod lower lock nut. Remove upper strut assembly-to-body nuts.

2) Raise and support vehicle. Remove wheel assembly. Remove lower strut assembly mounting bolt. Remove strut from vehicle. Clamp strut securely in a soft-jawed vise. Compress coil spring. Remove piston rod lower lock nut. Remove remaining components and coil spring.

Inspection

Check strut assembly for leaks or abnormal noise. Ensure smooth rotation of control rod located inside piston rod bore. Inspect remaining parts for deterioration or damage. Replace parts as necessary.

Reassembly & Installation

To rassemble, reverse disassembly procedure. Ensure coil spring is well seated in spring seats. To install, reverse removal procedure. Check rear wheel alignment.

TRAILING ARMS

Removal

1) Raise and support vehicle. Remove wheel assembly. Remove drive shaft lock nut. Remove brake caliper support mount. Remove brake caliper and hang out of way. Disconnect strut assembly, stabilizer bar control link and lateral link from trailing arm.

2) Disconnect ABS sensor. Remove rotor and knuckle assembly from trailing arm. Remove control link mounting bolts and control link. For reassembly reference, mark adjusting bolt location. Remove adjusting bolt and cam plate. Remove trailing arm.

Inspection

Inspect trailing arms for cracks or deformation. Check bushings for damage or excessive wear. Check pillow balls for excessive play. Replace parts as necessary.

Fig. 2: Exploded View of RX7 Strut Assembly

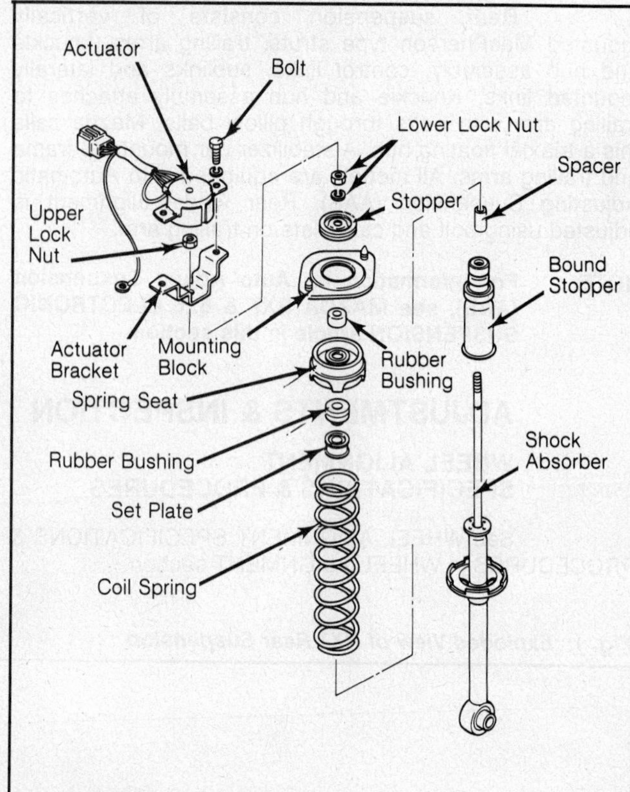

Courtesy of Mazda Motors Corp.

Bushing Replacement (Subframe Side)

Mount trailing arm in a soft-jawed vise. Remove old bushing with a hammer and chisel. Using a press, install new bushing using Installer (49 F028 204), Support (49 F028 205) and Handle (49 F027 003).

Bushing Replacement (Floating Hub Inner Side)

Using a press, Support (49 F028 203), Remover (49 F028 201) and Handle (49 F027 003), push out old bushing. Use a press, support, handle and Installer (49 F028 202) to install bushing. Ensure Yellow mark on bushing faces down.

Installation

To install, reverse removal procedure. Install and align cam plate adjusting bolts to reference marks. Install nuts and tighten temporarily. Lower vehicle and adjust rear wheel toe-in. Tighten cam plate adjusting bolts to specification. Stake drive axle lock nut.

PILLOW BALLS

Removal & Installation

With trailing arm removed, remove rubber seals and snap ring. Remove pillow ball by carefully tapping with a .79" (20 mm) section of pipe. To install, coat diameter of pillow ball with multi-purpose grease. Install pillow ball into trailing arm by carefully tapping outer diameter with a 1.18" (30 mm) section of pipe. Install snap ring and rubber seals. Ensure seals are coated with grease before installation.

MAZDA RX7 (Cont.)

LATERAL LINK

Removal & Installation

1) Raise and support vehicle. Remove nuts securing lateral link to trailing arm and subframe. Using Ball Joint Puller (49 0118 850C), separate ball joint from trailing arm. Separate ball joint from subframe. Remove lateral link.

2) Check lateral link for bend or other visible damage. Inspect dust boot for tears or damage. Replace if necessary. Remove dust boot using a chisel. Install dust boot using a press and Installer (49 F034 201).

3) Inspect ball joints. See BALL JOINT CHECKING under ADJUSTMENTS & INSPECTION in this article. To install, reverse removal procedure. Tighten to specification.

CONTROL LINK

Removal & Installation

Raise and support vehicle. Remove hardware securing control link to subframe and trailing arm. Remove control link. Check control link for bending or other damage. Inspect pillow balls for looseness or damage. Check dust boot for damage. Replace parts as necessary. To install, reverse removal procedure. Tighten to specification.

SUBLINK

Removal & Installation

Raise and support vehicle. Remove hardware securing sublink to subframe and body. Remove sublink. Check sublink for bending or other damage. Inspect bushing for looseness or damage. Replace parts as necessary. To install, reverse removal procedure. Tighten to specification.

STABILIZER BAR

Removal & Installation

1) Raise and support vehicle. Remove wheel assemblies. Remove exhaust system muffler. Remove fuel tank protector. Remove hardware securing control link to hub and stabilizer bar to frame. Remove stabilizer bar.

2) Inspect stabilizer bar, control link and bushings for damage, cracks and deterioration. To install, reverse removal procedure. Tighten all bolts to specification with vehicle resting on ground and suspension unloaded.

Fig. 3: Checking Lateral Link Ball Joint

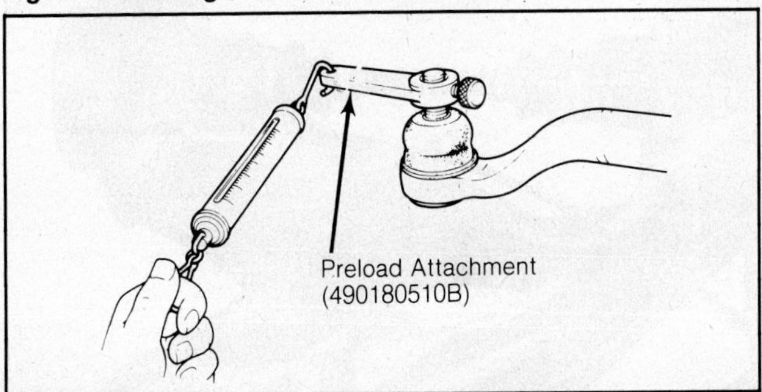

Courtesy Mazda Motors Corp.

SUBFRAME

Removal

1) Raise and support vehicle. Remove wheel assemblies. Remove exhaust pipe and drive shaft. For reassembly reference, mark trailing arm adjusting bolt location. Remove trailing arm-to-subframe bolts. Remove control link-to-subframe bolts. Disconnect lateral link and sublink from subframe.

2) Loosen left subframe-to-body nut and lower left side of subframe. Remove subframe-to-differential bracket nuts. Remove subframe-to-body nuts. Remove subframe from vehicle.

Inspection

Check subframe for deformation, cracks or damage. Check rubber mounts for damage or deterioration. Replace if necessary.

Bushing Replacement

Drill holes in rubber portion and drive out using chisel and hammer. Use a press and Installer (49 F028 206) to reinstall rubber mount in subframe. Ensure slots on rubber mount face toward front and rear of vehicle.

Installation

To install, reverse removal procedure. Do not final tighten subframe-to-body nuts until the subframe-to-differential nuts are fully tightened. Check toe-in after installation.

TIGHTENING SPECIFICATIONS

Application	Ft. Lbs. (N.m)
Control Link Bolts	27-40 (36-54)
Differential-to-Subframe Nuts	65-77 (88-105)
Drive Axle Lock Nut	174-231 (235-314)
Knuckle-to-Trailing Arm	
Upper & Lower Bolts	46-69 (63-93)
Middle Bolt	82-111 (112-151)
Lateral Link Nuts	22-33 (29-44)
Sublink Bolts	54-69 (74-93)
Subframe-to-Body Nuts	54-69 (74-93)
Stabilizer Bracket Bolts	27-40 (36-54)
Stabilizer Control Link Bolts	27-40 (36-54)
Strut-to-Body Nuts	17-22 (23-29)
Strut-to-Trailing Arm Bolt	46-69 (63-93)
Strut Piston Rod Lock Nut	25-37 (34-50)
Trailing Arm Adjusting Bolt	46-70 (63-95)

Rear Suspension

MERCEDES-BENZ TRAILING ARM TYPE

300SDL, 420SEL, 560SEC, 560SEL, 560SL

NOTE: For components not covered in this article, see AUTOMATIC LEVEL CONTROL article in this section.

DESCRIPTION

Mercedes-Benz rear suspension is independent type with coil springs and semi-trailing arms. Rear axle carrier is mounted to body at 3 points and supports rear axle assembly. Axle shafts serve as upper control arms to rear wheels.

Wheel hubs are supported by semi-trailing arms which run forward to pivot points on rear axle carrier and body. Shock absorbers are mounted inside of coil springs, attached to body on top and to semi-trailing arms on bottom. Stabilizer bar is mounted to body and to wheel hubs at ends.

ADJUSTMENTS & INSPECTION

WHEEL ALIGNMENT SPECIFICATIONS & ADJUSTMENTS

See WHEEL ALIGNMENT SPECIFICATIONS & ADJUSTMENTS in WHEEL ALIGNMENT section.

REMOVAL & INSTALLATION

SHOCK ABSORBER

CAUTION: When removing gas pressure shock absorbers while vehicle is raised and axle tension relieved, make sure that the piston rod is not rotating while loosening main strut nut. This could result in the sudden (dangerous) extension of the piston rod.

Removal

1) Rear shock absorbers simultaneously serve as a deflection stop for rear wheels. Loosen rear shock absorbers only when vehicle is on the ground. On "SL" models with removable top, remove top and open storage flap.

2) On all models, remove rear seat and backrest. On "SL" models, remove locking lever from top flap and unscrew lining. On all other models, remove nut and rubber ring of upper shock mount. Remove lower shock mount on semi-trailing arm. Remove shock absorber in a downward direction.

Installation

To install, reverse removal procedure.

COIL SPRING

Removal

1) Remove shock absorbers as previously outlined. Raise vehicle and support with safety stands. Raise semi-trailing arm until approximately level.

2) Using spring compressor, compress coil spring. Carefully lower semi-trailing arm and remove spring with rubber mounting.

Installation

To install, reverse removal procedure.

REAR SUSPENSION & AXLE

Removal

1) Raise vehicle and support with safety stands. Remove wheel assemblies. Disconnect exhaust system. Detach parking brake control cables at frame and compensating lever.

2) Loosen clamp nut and disconnect drive shaft intermediate bearing from frame. Disconnect rear of drive shaft and slide forward, out of centering position.

NOTE: On 3-piece drive shaft, loosen front clamp nut only.

Fig. 1: Rear Suspension Trailing Arm, Differential & Axle Carrier

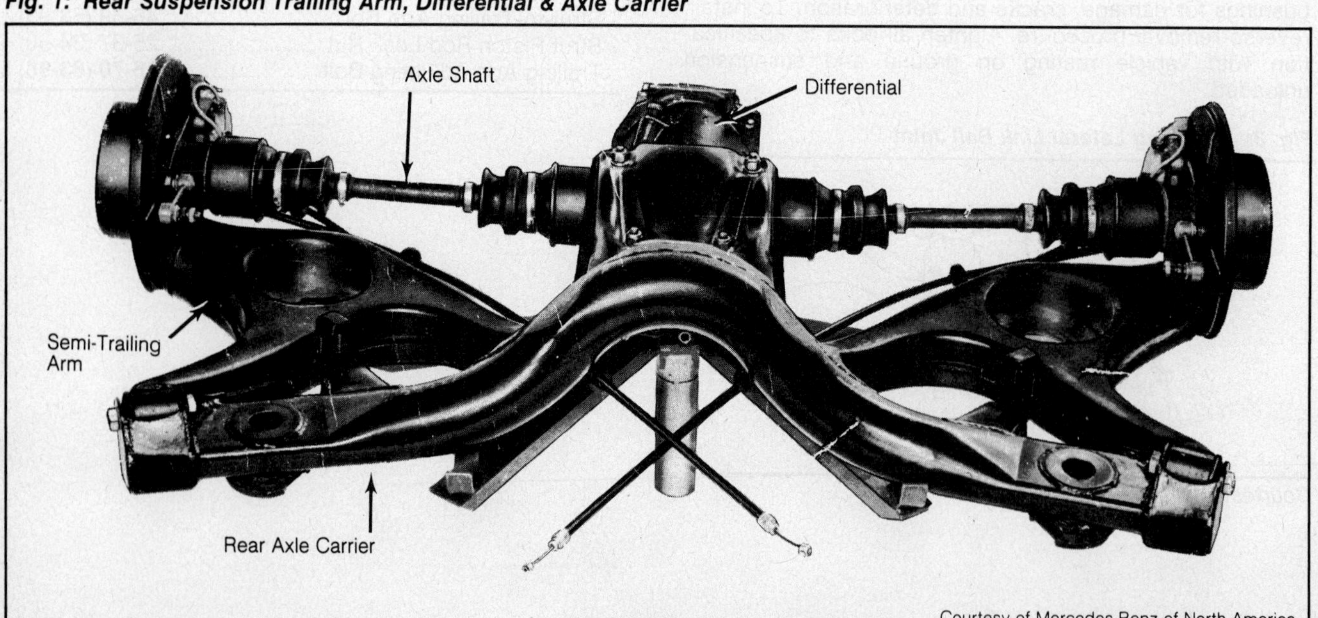

Courtesy of Mercedes-Benz of North America.

MERCEDES-BENZ TRAILING ARM TYPE (Cont.)

3) Remove shock absorber and coil spring as previously described. Detach and plug brake lines. Disconnect stabilizer bar holding clamps.

4) Place floor jack under rear suspension. Disconnect supporting plates and front and rear rubber mounts from frame. Carefully lower jack and remove rear suspension from vehicle.

5) Remove rear rubber mount from axle. When lowering and removing rear suspension, be sure cover plates of disc brakes are not damaged.

Installation

To install, reverse removal procedure. Self-locking hex head bolts with plastic coating may be used only once. Prior to screwing in self-locking bolts, refinish mounting threads with appropriate tap.

DIFFERENTIAL WITH AXLE SHAFTS

Removal

1) Drain fluid from differential. Detach brake caliper from right rotor and support out of the way. Remove axle shaft-to-flange attaching bolts (both sides) and force rear shafts out of shaft flanges.

NOTE: **It may be necessary to loosen right shock absorber upper mount and lower semi-trailing arm to deflection stop.**

2) If required, remove exhaust system. Loosen clamp nut and detach drive shaft intermediate bearing from frame. Remove drive shaft from differential and push from centering alignment.

NOTE: **On 3-piece drive shaft, loosen front clamp nut only.**

3) Support differential with floor jack and Differential Support (115 589 35 63 00). Disconnect rear rubber mount from body. Disconnect differential from rear axle carrier. Lower floor jack and remove differential with axle shaft.

CAUTION: **When moving differential with axle shafts, make sure that axle shafts are supported and do not drop down, as this might damage inner joints.**

Fig. 2: Proper Washer Placement for Rear Axle Carriers Without Spot Welds

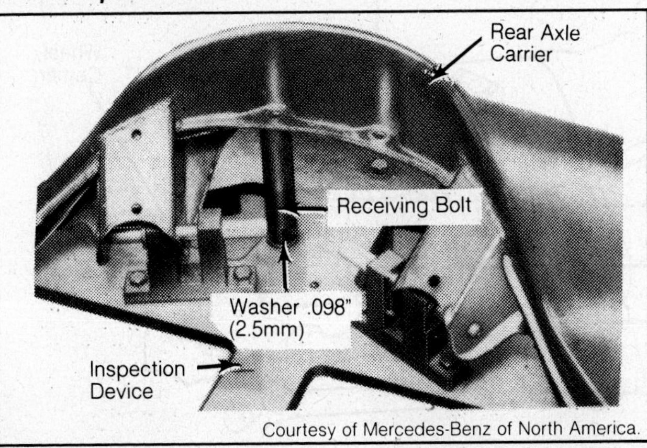

Courtesy of Mercedes-Benz of North America.

Installation

1) Check all rubber parts and replace as necessary. To install differential with rear axle shafts, reverse removal procedure.

2) Tighten down all nuts and bolts, except when connecting drive shaft to differential. These bolts must be tightened after vehicle has been rolled forward and backward to seat parts. Install exhaust system, if removed.

REAR STABILIZER BAR

Removal

1) Raise vehicle and support with safety stands. Remove wheel assemblies. Detach connecting rod from stabilizer on both sides of vehicle.

2) Remove stabilizer bar holding brackets. Loosen exhaust pipe mounts (rubber rings) and lower slightly. Remove stabilizer bar in a downward direction.

Fig. 3: Stabilizer Bar & Mounting Locations

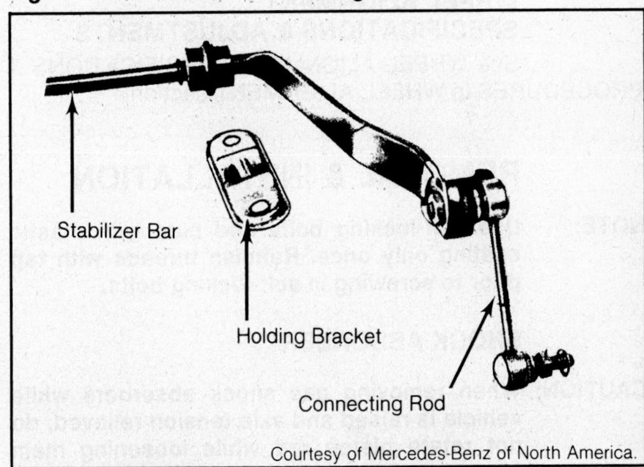

Courtesy of Mercedes-Benz of North America.

Installation

To install, reverse removal procedure.

NOTE: **When installing rear stabilizer bar, ensure that bend of bar is pointing upward.**

TIGHTENING SPECIFICATIONS

Application	Ft. Lbs. (N.m)
Axle Shaft-to-Axle Shaft Flange Bolt	69 (94)
Brake Caliper Bolts	23-29 (31-39)
Differential-to-Rear Axle Carrier Nut	72 (98)
Drive Shaft Clamp Nut	
2-Piece	22-30 (30-40)
3-Piece	
Front	22-30 (30-40)
Rear	145 (197)
Front Rubber Mounts-to-Frame	29 (39)
Rear Rubber Mount-to-End Cover	88 (120)
Rear Rubber Mount-to-Frame	18 (24)
Semi-Trailing Arm-to-Rear Axle Carrier	87 (118)
Shock Absorber Lower Mount	33 (45)
Supporting Plate-to-Frame	23-29 (31-39)
Torsion Bar Bearing Bolts	47 (64)
Torsion Bar Connecting Rod Ball Joints	33 (45)

Rear Suspension

MERCEDES-BENZ 5-LINK TYPE

190D, 190E, 260E, 300D Turbo, 300E, 300TD Turbo

NOTE: For components not covered in this article, see AUTOMATIC LEVEL CONTROL article in this section.

DESCRIPTION

Mercedes-Benz rear suspension is independent type with coil springs and 5 individual links. Shock absorbers and coil springs are mounted on rubber bushings to reduce vibration and noise. Rear axle carrier is mounted to body at 4 points and supports rear axle assembly.

ADJUSTMENTS & INSPECTION

WHEEL ALIGNMENT SPECIFICATIONS & ADJUSTMENTS

See WHEEL ALIGNMENT SPECIFICATIONS & PROCEDURES in WHEEL ALIGNMENT section.

REMOVAL & INSTALLATION

NOTE: Use self-locking bolts and nuts with plastic coating only once. Refinish threads with tap prior to screwing in self-locking bolts.

SHOCK ABSORBER

CAUTION: When removing gas shock absorbers while vehicle is raised and axle tension relieved, do not rotate piston rod while loosening main strut nut. This could result in the sudden (dangerous) extension of the piston rod.

Removal

1) Remove trunk lining. Remove nut and rubber ring of upper shock mount. Raise vehicle on rear axle.

2) Remove holding clamps on spring link and remove cover. Remove lower shock absorber mounting bolt. Pull shock absorber downward and remove from vehicle.

Installation

To install, reverse removal procedure.

COIL SPRING

Removal

1) Raise vehicle and remove rear wheel. Remove holding clamps of spring link cover and remove cover. Insert Spring Tensioner (201 589 00 31 00) with spring Tensioning Plates (201 589 00 63 00). Compress spring until spring link is free of load.

NOTE: Use extreme caution when removing gas pressurized shock absorbers.

2) Remove shock absorber as previously outlined. Remove rear spring with rubber mount.

Installation

To install, reverse removal procedure.

REAR SUSPENSION & AXLE

Removal

1) Raise vehicle and support with safety stands. Remove wheel assemblies. Disconnect exhaust system at flange connection. Remove intermediate lever of parking brake and disconnect cable controls.

2) Disconnect both brake lines and seal. Loosen clamp nut of drive shaft and intermediate bearing on frame floor and remove. Disconnect rear of drive shaft and slide forward, out of centering position. Wire drive shaft to brake cable holder.

Fig. 1: View of 190D, 190E, 260E, 300D Turbo, 300E & 300TD Turbo 300E Rear Suspension Components

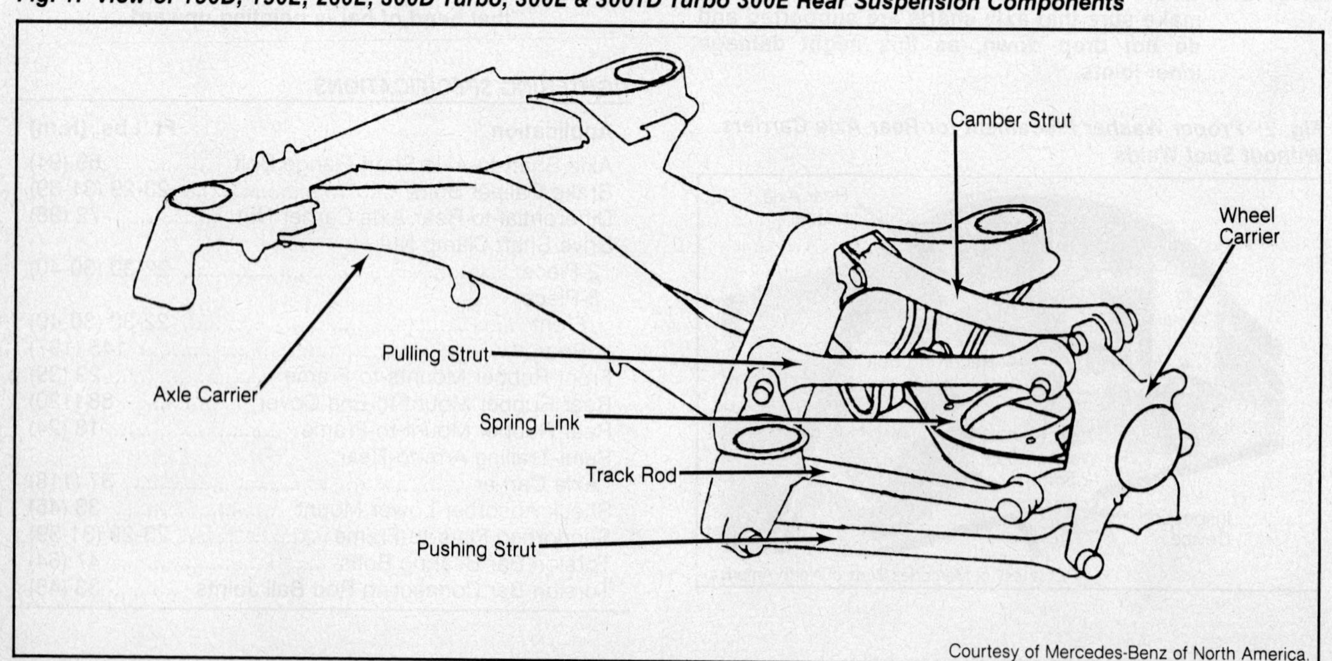

Courtesy of Mercedes-Benz of North America.

MERCEDES-BENZ 5-LINK TYPE (Cont.)

3) Remove spring link covering. Remove shock absorbers and coil springs. Loosen torsion bar connection toward rear axle and remove.

4) On vehicles with ABS, drain rear axle. Remove RPM sensor from rear axle housing. Cover magnetic edge of RPM sensor.

5) On vehicles with auxiliary heater, remove electric fuel pump and suspension plate of exhaust. Remove cable connector from rear axle crossmember. Raise rear axle assembly to lift stop. Force water drain hose out of rear axle carrier.

6) On vehicles with CIS-E fuel injection system, pinch fuel suction hose between fuel tank and fuel pump with a clamp. Loosen clamp on fuel hose to accumulator and pump. Remove fuel hose.

7) On all models, remove front and rear rubber mounts on frame floor and remove with stop plate. Lower rear axle assembly from vehicle.

Installation

To install, reverse removal procedure. Bleed brake system and adjust parking brake. Ensure differential is filled to proper level.

CAMBER STRUT

Removal

1) Raise vehicle and support with safety stands. Rubber mounts of camber strut cannot be replaced individually. If rubber mounts are damaged, replace camber strut.

2) Remove strut-to-axle carrier bolt. Remove strut-to-wheel carrier bolt. Force clamping sleeve of strut out of wheel carrier.

3) Remove camber strut at axle carrier while pulling slightly outward on wheel carrier. Remove strut in a downward direction.

Installation

To install, reverse removal procedure. Axle shaft must be horizontal prior to tightening camber strut nut.

PULLING STRUT

Removal

1) Raise vehicle and support with safety stands. Rubber mounts of pulling strut cannot be replaced individually. If rubber mounts are damaged, replace pulling strut.

2) Mark position of eccentric bolt in relation to axle carrier. Using Wrench (201 589 00 03 00), remove strut-to-axle carrier nut. Prior to pulling out eccentric bolt, push wheel carrier in forward direction to slacken.

3) Remove strut-to-wheel carrier bolt. Force clamping sleeve of pulling strut out of wheel carrier. Remove pulling strut.

Installation

To install, reverse removal procedure. Axle shaft must be horizontal prior to tightening pulling strut nut.

TRACKING ROD

Removal

1) Raise vehicle and support with safety stands. Remove rod-to-wheel carrier nut. Using Puller (201 589 01 33 00) and Thrust Piece (201 589 05 63 00), force track rod from wheel carrier.

2) Mark position of eccentic bolt in relation to axle carrier. Remove rod-to-axle carrier nut. Remove cam disk, eccentric bolt and track rod.

Installation

To install, reverse removal procedure. Clean grease from ball pin and conical seat in wheel carrier. Hold ball pin with an Allen wrench while tightening. Axle shaft must be horizontal prior to tightening tracking rod-to-axle carrier nut.

PUSHING STRUT

Removal

1) Raise vehicle and support with safety stands. Remove pushing strut cover. Rubber mounts of pushing strut cannot be replaced individually. If rubber mounts are damaged, replace pushing strut. Remove strut-to-axle carrier bolt. Remove strut-to-wheel carrier bolt with washer and contour disk.

2) Turn strut on rear axle carrier downward. Force clamping sleeve out of wheel carrier. Remove pushing strut.

Installation

To install, reverse removal procedure. Axle shaft must be horizontal prior to tightening pushing strut nuts.

SPRING LINK

Removal

1) Raise vehicle and support with safety stands. Remove spring link cover. Remove lower shock absorber bolt. Remove torsion bar from spring link. Remove coil spring as previously outlined.

2) Remove spring link-to-axle carrier bolt. Remove spring link-to-wheel carrier bolt. Remove spring link.

Installation

To install, reverse removal procedure. Axle shaft must be horizontal prior to tightening spring link nuts.

WHEEL CARRIER

Removal

1) Loosen collar nut fastening rear axle shaft prior to lifting vehicle and removing wheel. Using Remover (201 589 00 61 00), remove rear axle shaft out of rear axle shaft flange.

2) Remove brake caliper and hang out of way using a hook. Remove brake disc. Remove intermediate lever of parking brake and disengage cable control. Pull out lock on hand brake cable.

3) Remove camber strut-to-wheel carrier bolt. Force clamping sleeve of strut out of wheel carrier. Remove pulling strut-to-wheel carrier bolt. Force clamping sleeve of pulling strut out of wheel carrier.

4) Mark position of eccentric bolt of pulling strut in relation to axle carrier. Using Wrench (201 589 00 03 00), remove strut-to-axle carrier nut. Remove complete pulling strut.

5) Remove track rod-to-wheel carrier nut. Using Puller (201 589 01 33 00) and Thrust Piece (201 589 05 63 00), force track rod from wheel carrier.

6) Mark position of eccentic bolt of track rod in relation to axle carrier. Remove rod-to-axle carrier nut. Remove cam disk, eccentric bolt and complete track rod.

Rear Suspension

MERCEDES-BENZ 5-LINK TYPE (Cont.)

7) Remove nut of pushing strut on wheel carrier and remove with washer, contour disk and bolt. Force clamping sleeve out of wheel carrier.

8) Remove nut on spring link and remove from wheel carrier. Pull complete wheel carrier from rear axle shaft.

Installation

1) To install, reverse removal procedure. If position of eccentric bolts were not marked for pulling strut and track rod, position eccentric bolts in center position.

2) Prior to tightening any nuts axle shaft must be in horizontal position. Clean grease from ball pin and conical seat of track rod. Check toe-in and track angle of rear wheels.

TIGHTENING SPECIFICATIONS

Application	Ft. Lbs. (N.m)
Axle Axle Carrier-to-Frame Bolt	52 (70)
Shaft-to-Differential Bolt	52 (70)
Camber Strut-to-Axle Carrier Nut	52 (70)
Camber Strut-to-Wheel Carrier Nut	30 (40)
Drive Shaft Bearing-to-Frame Bolt	18 (25)
Drive Shaft Clamp Nut	22-30 (30-40)
Drive Shaft-to-Differential Nut	30-37 (40-50)
Front Differential-to-Axle Carrier Bolt	33 (45)
Lower Shock Absorber Nut	48 (65)
Pulling Strut-to-Axle Carrier Nut	52 (70)
Pulling Strut-to-Wheel Carrier Nut	30 (40)
Pushing Strut-to-Axle Carrier Nut	52 (70)
Pushing Strut-to-Wheel Carrier Nut	33 (45)
Rear Differential-to-Axle Carrier Bolt	37 (50)
Spring Link-to-Axle Carrier Nut	52 (70)
Spring Link-to-Wheel Carrier Nut	89 (120)
Torsion Bar-to-Spring Link Nut	15 (20)
Track Rod-to-Axle Carrier Nut	52 (70)
Track Rod-to-Wheel Carrier Nut	26 (35)

Rear Suspension

MITSUBISHI GALANT

Mitsubishi Galant (1985-1987)

DESCRIPTION

Rear suspension is a 3-link with U-shaped torsion axle beam. Torsion bar is inside axle beam and is not removable. For testing and diagnosis information on Mitsubishi's Electronically controlled suspension, see MITSUBISHI GALANT ELECTRONIC SUSPENSION article in this section.

ADJUSTMENTS & INSPECTION

WHEEL ALIGNMENT SPECIFICATIONS & PROCEDURES

See WHEEL ALIGNMENT SPECIFICATIONS & PROCEDURES in WHEEL ALIGNMENT section.

WHEEL BEARING

1) Raise and support vehicle. Remove wheel assembly. Remove grease cap, cotter pin and nut lock cap. Loosen lock nut. Tighten lock nut to 14 ft. lbs. (20 N.m). Turn hub a few times to seat bearing. Loosen lock nut.

2) On 1985 models, retighten lock nut to 48 INCH lbs. (5 N.m). On all other models, retighten lock nut to 84 INCH lbs. (10 N.m). On all models, install nut lock and cotter pin. Reposition nut lock cap to install cotter pin (if necessary). Do not back off lock nut more than 15 degrees to install cotter pin.

3) Turn hub a few times to seat bearing. Using a spring scale, measure hub turning torque. With new bearing, turning torque should be 3 lbs. (14 N) or less. With used bearing, turning torque should be 2.4 lbs. (11 N) or less.

4) If wheel hub has play or turning torque specification is exceeded, replace wheel bearings.

REMOVAL & INSTALLATION

WHEEL BEARING

Removal & Installation

1) Raise and support vehicle. Remove wheel assembly. If equipped with disc brakes, remove caliper assembly and hang out of way. Remove grease cap, cotter pin and nut lock cap.

2) Remove lock nut. Remove hub assembly with washer and outer bearing. Pry out inner oil seal and remove bearing. Remove bearing outer races using a brass bar.

3) To install, reverse removal procedure. Press in outer races using Driver (MB990926-01) for outer bearing, and Driver (MB990928-01) for inner bearing. Use Driver (MB990929-01) to install oil seal.

REAR SUSPENSION ASSEMBLY

Removal

1) Raise and support vehicle. Remove wheel assembly. Disconnect parking brake cable from rear brake assembly and torsion axle and arm. Remove brake hose bracket from torsion axle and arm assembly. Remove hub assembly. See WHEEL BEARING in this article.

2) Remove backing plate (drum brakes) or dust cover and adapter (disc brakes) and wire out of way.

Fig. 1: View of Galant Rear Suspension

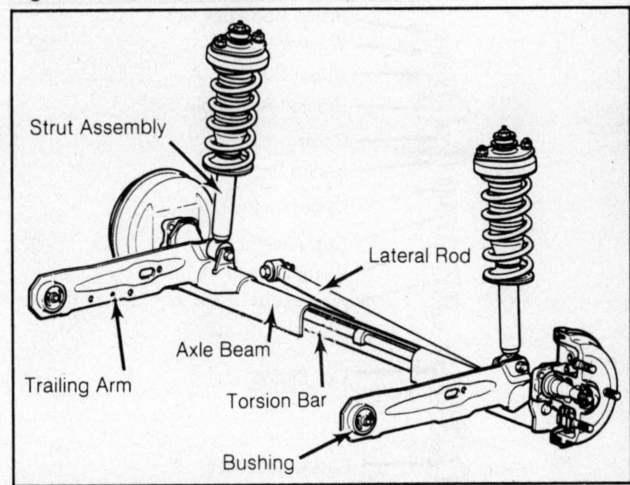

Courtesy of Mitsubishi Motor Sales of America.

Raise torsion axle and arm assembly slightly with a jack. If equipped with electronic controlled suspension, disconnect height sensor rod from lateral rod.

3) Disconnect lateral rod from body. Disconnect torsion axle and arm assembly from body. Remove rear seat. Disconnect top end of strut assembly from body. Lower jack and remove rear suspension assembly from vehicle.

Inspection

Check trailing arm and axle beam for deformation or damage. Check torsion bar for damage. Check lateral rod for deformation or damage. Check rubber bushings for deterioration, cracks or unususal wear.

Bushing Replacement

Remove arm bushing using Press (MB991045). Drive out lateral rod bushing using press and Driver (MB990947). Press in new arm bushing from beveled side of bushing housing. Ensure slots in bushing face front-to-rear. Press in new lateral rod bushing using driver. Ensure bushing protrudes equal amount from each side.

Installation

To install, reverse removal procedure. Bleed brakes. Adjust wheel bearings. Adjust parking brake.

STRUT ASSEMBLY

Removal

Remove rear seat. Raise and support vehicle. Remove wheel assembly. Raise torsion axle and arm slightly with a jack. Remove nuts and disconnect upper part of strut from body. Disconnect strut from torsion axle and arm. Lower jack and remove strut from vehicle.

Disassembly

Compress coil spring using coil spring compressor. Hold piston rod with open end wrench and remove lock nut. Remove all components from shock absorber. *See Fig. 2.*

Reassembly

To reassemble, reverse disassembly procedure. Ensure dust cover fits over cup assembly edge. Position bracket assembly so it aligns with shock absorber lower bushing and tighten piston rod lock nut. Ensure coil spring is positioned correctly in spring pad grooves.

Installation

To install, reverse removal procedure.

Rear Suspension

MITSUBISHI GALANT (Cont.)

Fig. 2: Exploded View of Strut Assembly

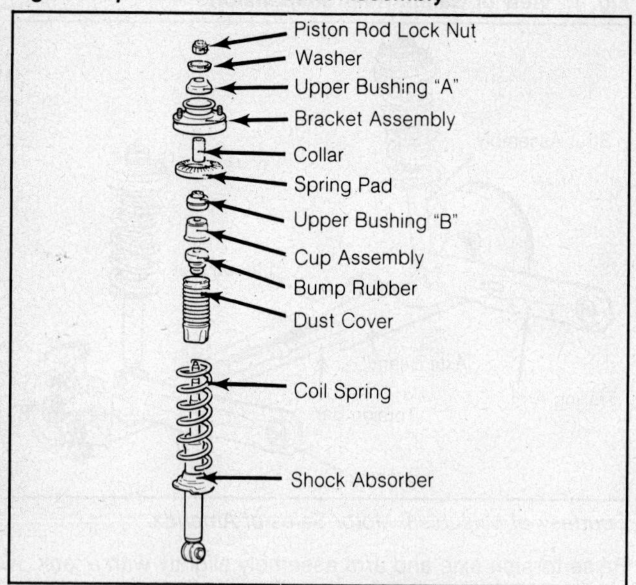

Courtesy of Mitsubishi Motor Sales of America.

NOTE: Coil springs have color marks to indicate spring identification and load classification. Ensure when springs are replaced, markings are for appropriate vehicle.

TIGHTENING SPECIFICATIONS

Application	Ft. Lbs. (N.m)
Backing Plate-to-Spindle	36-43 (50-60)
Dust Cover/Adapter-to-Spindle	36-43 (50-60)
Height Sensor Rod Bolt	12-19 (17-26)
Lateral Rod Bolts	58-72 (80-100)
Piston Rod Lock Nut	14-18 (20-25)
Strut Bracket Assembly-to-Body Nuts	18-25 (25-35)
Strut-to-Torsion Axle Assembly	58-72 (80-100)
Trailing Arm-to-Body Bolts	72-87 (100-120)

Rear Suspension

NISSAN MAXIMA

NOTE: An electronically controlled variable shock absorber system is used on Maxima SE. For removal, installation, testing and diagnostic procedures for these shock absorbers, see the NISSAN MAXIMA & 300ZX ELECTRONIC SUSPENSION article in this section.

DESCRIPTION

Rear suspension is of the MacPherson strut type. Strut is supported by parallel links, radius rod, stabilizer bar and suspension member.

ADJUSTMENTS & INSPECTION

WHEEL ALIGNMENT SPECIFICATIONS & PROCEDURES

See WHEEL ALIGNMENT SPECIFICATIONS & PROCEDURES in WHEEL ALIGNMENT section.

WHEEL BEARING

Tighten hub nut to 18-25 ft. lbs. (25-34 N.m). Rotate hub several times to seat bearings. Turn hub nut back 90 degrees and install new cotter pin. Hub nut may be tightened 15 degrees to align cotter pin hole. Turning torque measured at wheel hub bolt with new grease seal must be less than 3.1 lbs. (13.7 N). If not within specifications, readjust wheel bearings.

NOTE: When installing new grease seal, ensure White nylon guide faces spindle.

REMOVAL & INSTALLATION

WHEEL BEARING

Removal

1) Raise vehicle and remove wheels. Remove brake caliper, hub cap, hub nut and outer wheel bearing.

2) Remove hub from spindle. Remove inner wheel bearing and grease seal.

Disassembly

Clamp bearing hub in vise. Using a brass drift and hammer, remove inner and outer bearing races.

Reassembly

Using an appropriate bearing race driver (KV401021S0), reinstall inner and outer bearing races.

Installation

1) Lubricate inner and outer bearings. Install inner bearing and grease seal.

2) Place hub on spindle and install outer bearing. Adjust bearing as outlined in WHEEL BEARING ADJUSTMENT in this article. Complete installation in reverse order.

STRUT & COIL SPRING

Removal

1) Raise rear of vehicle and support with safety stands. Remove brake assembly and wheel bearing. Separate parallel links and radius rod from lower end of strut.

2) Support strut assembly with safety stand. Disconnect upper end of strut. Remove strut from vehicle.

Disassembly

For coil spring removal, mark position of shock absorber mounting insulator and lower end pin for proper reassembly. Using spring compressor, compress spring until mounting insulator can be turned by hand. Remove self-locking nut on strut shaft. Release spring compressor and remove coil spring.

Reassembly

Reverse disassembly procedure using a new self-locking nut on strut shaft.

Installation

To install, reverse removal procedure. Ensure coil spring does not touch body.

PARALLEL LINKS, RADIUS ROD, SUSPENSION MEMBER & STABILIZER BAR

Removal

1) Raise vehicle and support with safety stands. Do not jack up at parallel links or radius rods. Remove rear wheel. Mark links. Remove parallel links and radius rod. When removing front parallel link, it is necessary to remove parallel link bracket.

2) Front and rear parallel links are identified by color. Left front and right rear links are painted White. Left rear and right front links are painted Yellow.

Fig. 1: Exploded View of Rear Suspension

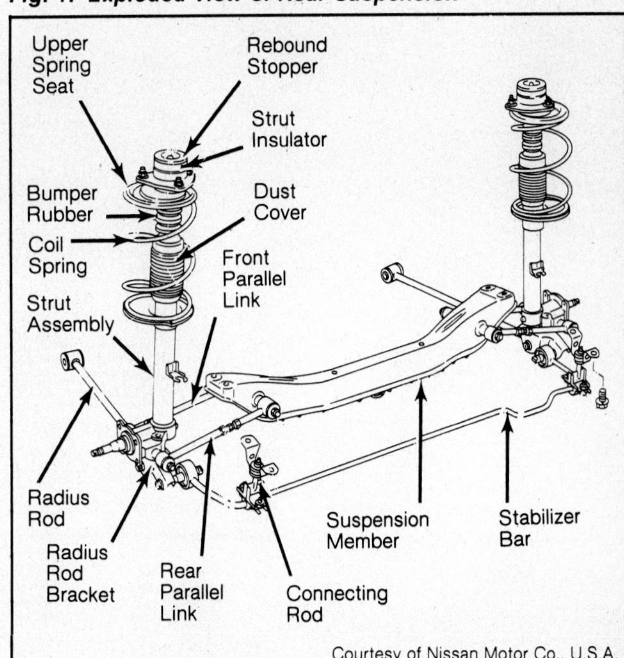

Courtesy of Nissan Motor Co., U.S.A.

Installation

To install, reverse the removal procedure. Final tightening of the bolts should be performed after vehicle is lowered to the floor. Bleed brake system and check wheel alignment.

Rear Suspension

NISSAN MAXIMA (Cont.)

TIGHTENING SPECIFICATIONS

Application	Ft. Lbs. (N.m)
Disc Brake Cover Bolt	28-38 (38-52)
Hub Nut [1]	18-25 (25-34)
Lug Nut	72-87 (98-118)
Radius Rod	
Adjuster Nut	58-72 (78-98)
Bracket to Strut	43-58 (59-78)
Nut	65-87 (88-118)
Stabilizer Bar	
End Bolt	43-58 (59-78)
"U" Clamp	23-31 (31-42)
Suspension-to-Body	65-80 (88-108)
Lower Strut Bolts	43-58 (59-78)
Upper Strut Nut	
Mounting	23-31 (31-42)
Nonadjustable	43-58 (59-78)
Adjustable	51-65 (69-88)

[1] – See WHEEL BEARING ADJUSTMENT in this article.

Rear Suspension

NISSAN PULSAR NX & SENTRA

DESCRIPTION

Rear suspension uses a front and rear parallel link which attaches to a crossmember and rear knuckle. An essentric bolt for adjusting toe is located on each inner rear parallel link. *See Fig. 1.* A radius rod is attached below the parallel links to the rear knuckles and vehicle body. Struts are attached to body and upper portion of rear knuckles.

Fig. 1: Exploded View of Rear Suspension

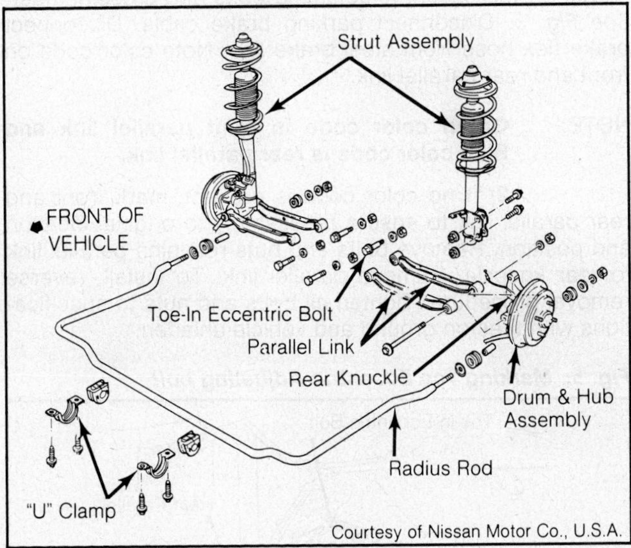

ADJUSTMENTS & INSPECTION

WHEEL ALIGNMENT SPECIFICATIONS & PROCEDURES

See WHEEL ALIGNMENT SPECIFICATIONS & PROCEDURES in WHEEL ALIGNMENT section.

WHEEL BEARING

NOTE: **See SENTRA KUNCKLE CHANGE in WHEEL BEARING under REMOVAL & INSTALLATION in this article.**

Preload of wheel bearing is not adjustable. Axial end play must be less than .002" (.05 mm). Ensure wheel bearing nut is tightened to specifications. Check axial end play. If axial end play is not within specifications or wheel bearing does not rotate smoothly, replace wheel bearing assembly. See WHEEL BEARING under REMOVAL & INSTALLATION in this article.

CAUTION: **DO NOT place jack under parallel links to raise vehicle.**

REMOVAL & INSTALLATION

NOTE: **Wheel bearing is a one piece assembly and must be replaced after removal from hub.**

WHEEL BEARING

Sentra Knuckle Change

As of August, 1986, Sentra changed the rear knuckle and wheel bearing nut assembly. The new rear knuckle has a drilled spindle for cotter pin usage. This applies to 1987 Sentra (2WD).

Removal

Raise and support vehicle. Remove tire and wheel assembly. Remove dust cover, cotter pin and lock nut. Apply brakes and remove wheel bearing nut and washer. Remove brake drum, hub and wheel bearing as an assembly. Remove snap ring retaining wheel bearing assembly in hub. Press wheel bearing and seal assembly out back side of hub and drum assembly.

Installation

1) DO NOT apply greater than 3.3 tons of pressure during installation. DO NOT apply pressure on inner race of wheel bearing assembly. DO NOT apply lubricant to outer surface of bearing or inner surface of hub.

2) Press new wheel bearing assembly into rear side of hub. Ensure grease seal faces the rear knuckle. Install new snap ring. To complete installation, reverse removal procedure. Tighten wheel bearing nut to specifications. Tighten wheel nut to specifications.

STRUT ASSEMBLY

Removal

Raise and support vehicle. Remove tire and wheel assembly. Place a jack under hub and drum assembly to prevent suspension from dropping during strut removal. DO NOT raise up on hub and drum assembly with jack. Remove 3 upper strut-to-body mounting nuts. Remove 2 lower strut bolts retaining strut to rear knuckle. Remove strut assembly.

Disassembly

Place strut assembly in vise. Loosen (DO NOT remove), piston rod nut. Install a coil spring compressor and compress spring just enough to rotate strut mounting insulator by hand. Remove piston rod nut. Remove strut mounting insulator, upper spring seat and coil spring. Remove dust cover and lower spring seat.

Reassembly

1) Install lower spring seat and dust cover. Position coil spring on strut assembly with flat side of coil spring upward. Ensure bottom side of coil spring is seated properly in lower strut. *See Fig. 2.* Compress coil spring.

2) Proper install upper spring seat and strut mounting insulator. *See Fig. 2.* To complete installation, reverse disassembly procedure. Tighten all bolts and nuts to specifications with tires on ground and vehicle unladen.

Fig. 2: Coil Spring & Mounting Insulator Position

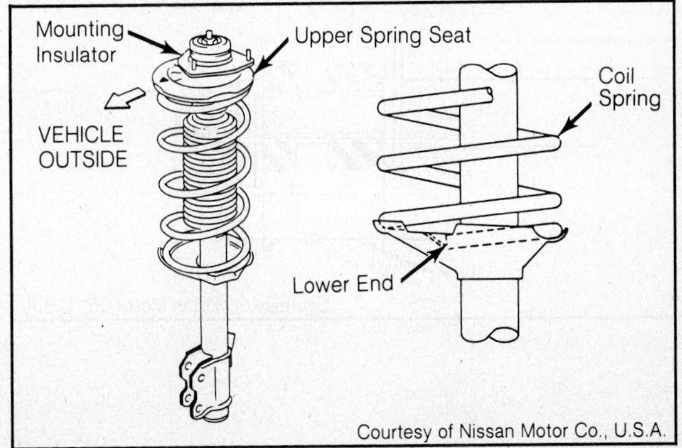

Rear Suspension

NISSAN PULSAR NX & SENTRA (Cont.)

Installation

To install strut assembly, reverse removal procedure. Check wheel alignment and adjust as necessary.

WHEEL BEARING

NOTE: **See SENTRA KNUCKLE CHANGE in WHEEL BEARING under REMOVAL & INSTALLATION in this article.**

Removal & Installation

1) Remove hub, drum and wheel bearing assembly. See WHEEL BEARING under REMOVAL & INSTALLATION in this article. Disconnect flexible brake hose from steel brake line. Disconnect parking brake. Remove backing plate assembly. Disconnect lower strut mounting bolts and nuts retaining strut to rear knuckle.

2) Remove nuts retaining radius rod to rear knuckle. Remove bolts and nuts retaining front and rear parallel links to rear knuckle. Use care not to drop rear knuckle. Remove rear knuckle. To install, reverse removal procedure. Tighten all bolts and nuts to specifications with tires on ground and vehicle unladen.

RADIUS ROD

Removal

Raise and support vehicle. Remove exhaust retaining bolts and nuts. Mark position of radius rod "U" clamps, in reference to front and rear of vehicle. "U" clamps must be installed to the proper position. *See Fig. 3.* Remove nuts retaining radius rod to rear knuckle. Pull down on exhaust pipe and remove radius rod.

Fig. 3: Radius Rod "U" Clamp Position

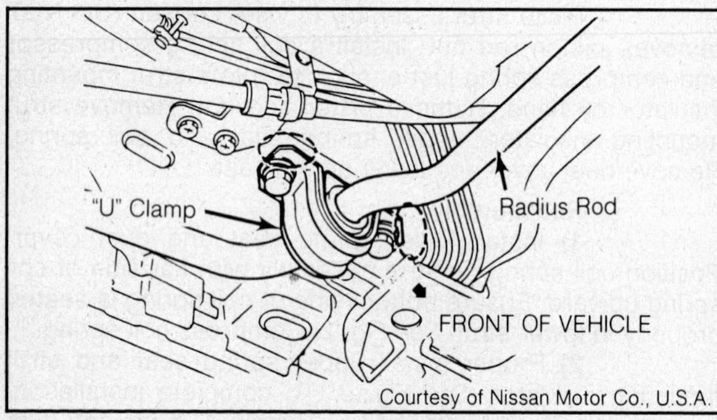

Fig. 4: Radius Rod Bushing Position

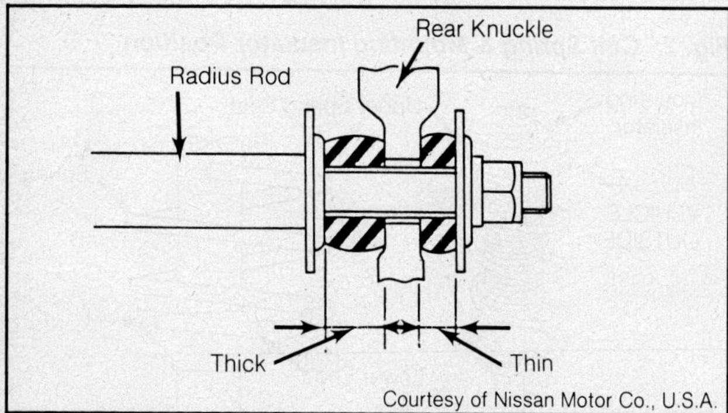

Installation

To install, reverse removal procedure. Ensure radius rod "U" clamps are installed properly. *See Fig. 3.* Ensure radius rod bushings are installed properly. *See Fig. 4.* Tighten all bolts and nuts to specifications with tires on ground and vehicle unladen.

PARALLEL LINK

Removal & Installation

1) Raise and support vehicle. Place matching marks on toe essentric adjusting bolts and crossmember. *See Fig. 5.* Disconnect parking brake cable. Disconnect brake flex hose from steel brake line. Note color code on front and rear parallel link.

NOTE: **Green color code is front parallel link and Blue color code is rear parallel link.**

2) If no color code is present, mark front and rear parallel link to ensure reassembly to original location and position. Remove bolts and nuts retaining parallel link to rear knuckle. Remove parallel link. To install, reverse removal procedure. Tighten all bolts and nuts to specifications with tires on ground and vehicle unladen.

Fig. 5: Marking Toe Eccentric Adjusting bolt

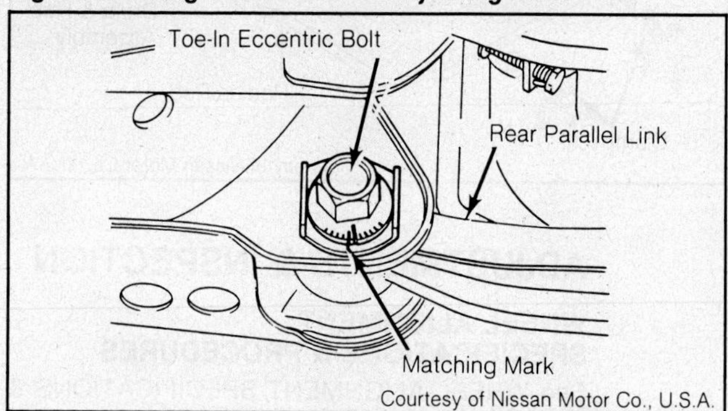

TIGHTENING SPECIFICATIONS

Application	Ft. Lbs. (N.m)
Backing Plate Bolt	25-33 (33-45)
Parallel Link-to-	
Crossmember	72-87 (98-118)
Rear Knuckle	72-87 (98-118)
Radius Rod-to-	
Body Bolt	65-80 (88-108)
Rear Knuckle Bolt	47-61 (64-83)
Strut Piston Rod Nut	46-53 (62-72)
Strut-to-Body Nut	18-22 (25-29)
Strut-to-Knuckle Bolt	72-87 (98-118)
Wheel Bearing Nut	[1] 137-159 (186-216)
Wheel Lug Nut	72-87 (98-118)

[1] – See SENTRA KNUCKLE CHANGE in WHEEL BEARING under REMOVAL & INSTALLATION in this article.

NISSAN STANZA

DESCRIPTION

Rear suspension uses MacPherson struts with rear knuckle as a one piece unit. Radius rods extend from rear knuckle toward vehicle front and attaches to vehicle body. *See Fig. 1.* Parallel links extend from front and rear side of rear knuckle and attaches to a crossmember. Rear parallel link is adjustable for setting toe. A stabilizer bar attaches to both rear knuckles across the rear of the vehicle. Stabilizer bar attaches to a connecting rod which is attached to vehicle body.

Fig. 1: Rear Suspension Assembly

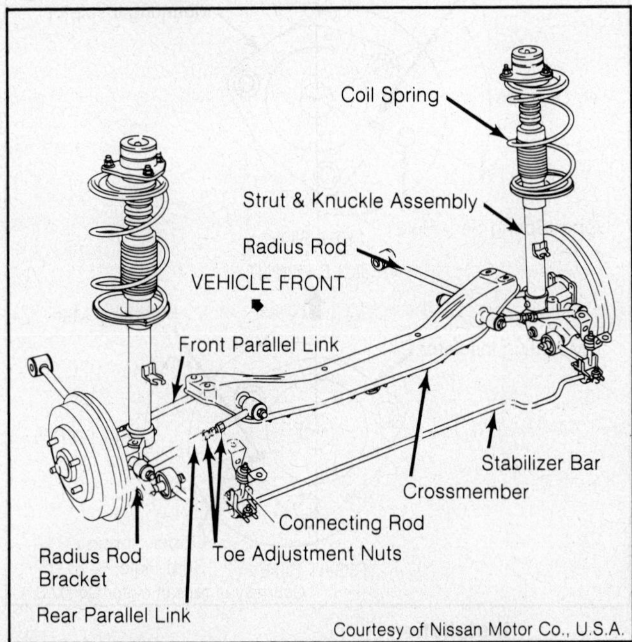

Courtesy of Nissan Motor Co., U.S.A.

ADJUSTMENTS & INSPECTION

WHEEL ALIGNMENT SPECIFICATIONS & PROCEDURES

See WHEEL ALIGNMENT SPECIFICATIONS & PROCEDURES in WHEEL ALIGNMENT section.

WHEEL BEARING

1) Tighten wheel bearing nut 18-25 ft. lbs. (25-34 N.m). Rotate hub and drum several times in both directions. Loosen wheel bearing nut just enough for zero INCH lbs. (zero N.m) preload and maintain a zero axial wheel bearing end play. Retighten wheel bearing nut to 78-105 INCH lbs. (9-12 N.m).

2) Rotate drum and hub several times in both directions. Retighten wheel bearing nut to 78-105 INCH lbs. (9-12 N.m). Install lock nut and new cotter pin. If necessary to rotate wheel bearing nut to align cotter pin hole, DO NOT loosen wheel bearing nut more than 15 degrees.

NOTE: Ensure no brake dragging resistance during measurement.

3) Rotate drum and hub several times in both directions. Attach a pull scale to wheel bolt at 12 o'clock position and measure preload rotating torque. Ensure axial end play is zero. If preload is not within specifications, repeat complete procedure until specifications are achieved. See PRELOAD SPECIFICATIONS table in this article.

PRELOAD SPECIFICATIONS

Application	Lbs. (N.)
With New Grease Seal	[1] 3.1 (13.7)
With Used Grease Seal	[1] 2.4 (10.8)

[1] – Do not exceed maximum specifications given.

REMOVAL & INSTALLATION

CAUTION: DO NOT raise vehicle with jack under parallel links.

WHEEL BEARING

Removal

Raise and support vehicle. Remove tire and wheel assembly. Remove dust cap, cotter pin and lock nut. Remove wheel bearing nut. Remove drum, hub and wheel bearings. Remove outer wheel bearing. Remove grease seal and inner wheel bearing. Using a hammer and drift, drive out inner and outer races.

Installation

To install, reverse removal procedure. Ensure White nylon guide portion of grease seal faces knuckle. Seal surface should protrude surface of hub .020" (.5 mm). Perform wheel bearing adjustment. See WHEEL BEARING under ADJUSTMENTS & INSPECTION in this article.

STRUT & KNUCKLE ASSEMBLY

Removal

1) Raise and support vehicle. Remove tire and wheel assembly. Remove drum and hub assembly. Disconnect brake hydraulic line and parking brake cable at equalizer. Remove bolts retaining backing plate to strut and knuckle assembly. Remove backing plate and brake assembly.

2) Remove bolt and nut retaining stabilizer bar to strut and knuckle assembly. Remove bolt and nut retaining front and rear parallel links to strut and knuckle assembly. Remove bolt and nut retaining radius rod to strut and knuckle assembly.

3) Remove bolts located between upper and lower cushion of rear seat and remove rear seat. Remove rear window parcel shelf. Remove 3 nuts retaining upper strut to body and remove strut and knuckle assembly.

NOTE: Perform inspection step 1) prior to disassembly.

Inspection

1) Check for oil leakage around welded portion of casing. If leakage is present, replace strut assembly. Check for oil leakage around gland packing and spring seat. If oil leakage is present, replace gland packing and "O" ring.

2) With strut assembly disassembled, use a dial indicator and check inner wall diameter. Place strut case in blocks and check for case runout. Check outer diameter of piston rod. Place piston rod in blocks and check piston rod runout. See STRUT ASSEMBLY SPECIFICATIONS table in this article. If defective components

NISSAN STANZA (Cont.)

are found, replacement kits are available. Replace complete assembly if necessary.

STRUT ASSEMBLY SPECIFICATIONS

Application	In. (mm)
Strut Case Inner Diameter	1.181-1.185 (30.00-30.10)
Strut Case Runout	[1] .008 (.20)
Piston Rod Diameter	0.79 (20.1)
Piston Rod Runout	[1] 0.004 (0.10)

[1] – Do not exceed specifications given.

Disassembly

1) Mount assembly in vise. Place match marks on mounting insulator-to-location hole on upper spring seat. Loosen (do not remove) piston rod nut. Use a coil spring compressor and compress coil spring just enough to rotate nounting insulator by hand. Remove piston rod nut.

2) Remove strut mounting insulator, upper coil spring seat, coil spring, bumper and dust cover. *See Fig. 2.* Using Gland Packing Wrench (J26083), remove gland packing and "O" ring. Push piston rod down until it bottoms in strut. Slowly withdraw piston rod from strut with piston guide. Perform inspection.

CAUTION: Avoid dirt and dust from entering gland packing portion at all time.

Fig. 2: Exploded View of Strut Assembly

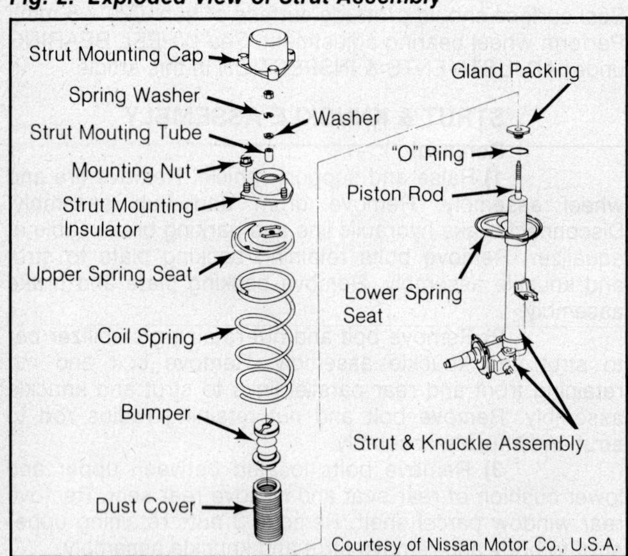

Courtesy of Nissan Motor Co., U.S.A.

Reassembly

1) Tape threads of piston rod. Insert piston guide and piston rod. Add 11.2 ozs. (.33L) of Nissan genuine strut fluid. Lubricate sealing lip of gland packing with multipurpose grease. Install gland packing.

2) Tighten gland packing with Gland Packing Wrench (J26083) to specifications. Ensure length of torque wrench being used is compensated for to achieve the proper tightening specifications.

NOTE: Bleeding procedure does not apply if strut cartridge kit is installed.

3) Bleed air from strut assembly by holding strut upward at approximately 45 degree angle. Extend piston rod completely. Place strut assembly upside down at approximately 45 degree angle and push piston rod completely in. Repeat procedure several times.

4) Install dust cover, bumper and coil spring. Ensure lower spring coil is seated properly. Align upper spring seat and mounting insulator as marked at disassembly. *See Fig. 3.* To complete reassembly, reverse disassembly procedure.

Fig. 3: Mounting Insulator & Upper Spring Seat Alignment

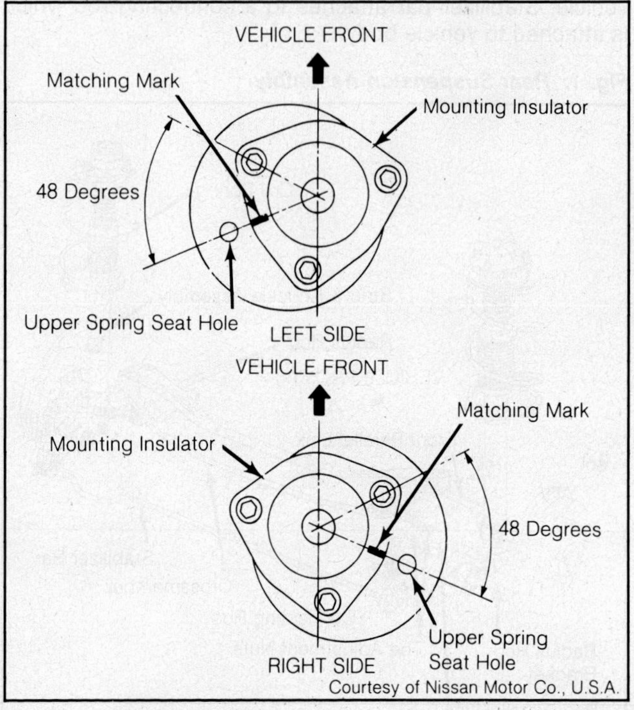

Courtesy of Nissan Motor Co., U.S.A.

Installation

To install, reverse removal procedure. Tighten bolts and nuts to specifications with all components installed, tires on ground and vehicle unladen.

RADIUS ROD

Removal

Raise and support vehicle. Remove tire and wheel. Remove bolts and nuts retaining radius rod to front of strut and knuckle assembly and vehicle body. Remove radius rod.

Installation

To install, reverse romoval procedure. Tighten bolts and nuts to specifications with all components, tires on ground and vehicle unladen.

PARALLEL LINKS

Removal

Raise and support vehicle. Remove tire and wheel. Remove bolts and nuts retaining parallel link to crossmember and strut and knuckle assembly. Remove parallel link.

Installation

To install, reverse romoval procedure. Tighten bolts and nuts to specifications with all components, tires on ground and vehicle unladen.

NISSAN STANZA (Cont.)

STABILIZER BAR

Removal

Raise and support vehicle. Remove tire and wheel. Remove bolts and nuts retaining stabilizer bar to strut and knuckle assembly. Remove bolts retaining stabilizer clamps to connecting rod. Remove stabilizer bar.

Installation

To install, reverse removal procedure. Tighten bolts and nuts to specifications with components installed, tires on ground and vehicle unladen.

CROSSMEMBER

Removal

1) Raise and support vehicle. Remove tire and wheel. Remove right side strut and knuckle assembly, parallel links and radius rod. See appropriate procedure under REMOVAL & INSTALLATION in this article.

2) Disconnect stabilizer bar from right side strut and knuckle assembly. See STABILIZER BAR under REMOVAL & INSTALLATION in this article. Remove left side strut and knuckle assembly. See STRUT & KNUCKLE ASSEMBLY under REMOVAL & INSTALLATION in this article.

3) Remove bolts retaining crossmember to body on right side and left side. Remove crossmember and left side suspension components as an assembly.

Installation

To install, reverse removal procedure. Tighten bolts and nuts to specifications with all components installed, tires on ground and vehicle unladen. Check wheel alignment and adjust as necessary.

TIGHTENING SPECIFICATIONS

Application	Ft. Lbs. (N.m)
Backing Plate Bolt	28-38 (38-52)
Crossmember Nut	65-87 (88-118)
Gland Packing	51-94 (69-127)
Parallel Link-to-	
Cross Member Bolt	65-87 (88-118)
Strut & Knuckle Bolt	65-87 (88-118)
Radius Rod-to-	
Body Bolt	65-80 (88-108)
Bracket Bolt	65-80 (88-108)
Stabilizer Bar-to-	
Connecting Rod Bolt	23-31 (31-42)
Strut & Knuckle Bolt	43-58 (59-78)
Strut & Knuckle-to-	
Body Nut	23-31 (31-42)
Strut Piston Rod Nut	43-58 (59-78)
Wheel Bearing Nut	[1]
Wheel Lug Nut	72-87 (98-118)

[1] – See WHEEL BEARING under ADJUSTMENTS & INSPECTION in this article.

Rear Suspension

NISSAN STANZA WAGON 2WD & 4WD

DESCRIPTION

The 2WD rear suspension is an independent type. It incorporates a rear arm with a torsion bar mounted inside, shock absorber, rubber bumper and stabilizer bar. *See Fig. 1.* Rear arm is mounted to frame through an anchor arm bracket and inner bushing bracket. Torsion bar is located inside of rear arm and attaches at each end to inner bushing and anchor arm sleeve.

Fig. 1: Exploded View of 2WD Rear Suspension

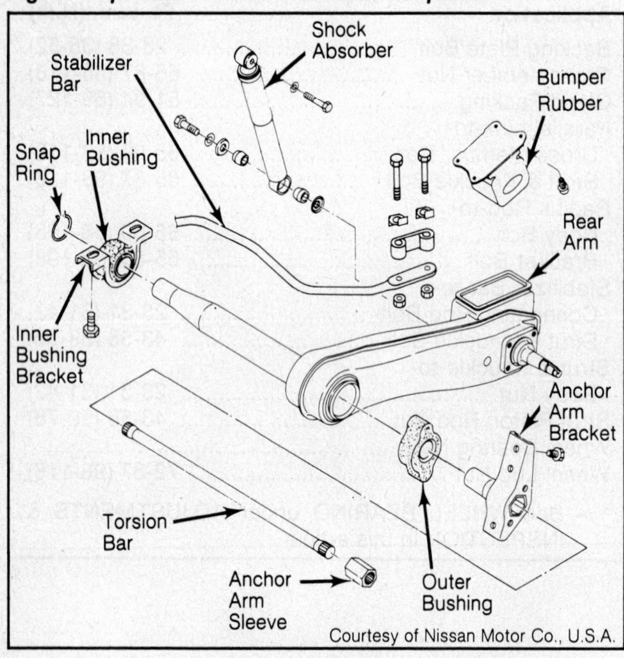

Courtesy of Nissan Motor Co., U.S.A.

The 4WD rear suspension is an independent type with MacPherson struts and a suspension member (attached to the differential). *See Fig. 2.* Transverse links are attached to the suspension member and lower portion of the rear knuckle. MacPherson struts are attached to the upper portion of the rear knuckle. A radius rod is attached to the front of the rear knuckle.

ADJUSTMENTS & INSPECTION

WHEEL ALIGNMENT SPECIFICATIONS & PROCEDURES

See WHEEL ALIGNMENT SPECIFICATIONS & PROCEDURES in WHEEL ALIGNMENT section.

WHEEL BEARING

2WD

1) Tighten wheel bearing nut to 18-25 ft. lbs. (25-34 N.m). Rotate hub in both directions to seat bearing. Loosen nut and retighten to 78-108 INCH lbs. (9-12 N.m). Rotate hub in both directions. Retighten nut again to 78-108 INCH lbs. (9-12 N.m). Install adjusting cap. Install cotter pin. If necessary, loosen lock nut a maximum of 15 degrees to align cotter pin hole.

2) Turning torque measured at wheel hub bolt with new grease seal must be less than 3.1 lbs. (13.7 N). If any axial play is present, readjust as necessary. Any wheel bearing axial play must be corrected.

4WD

1) If wheel bearing is not within specifications, replace the complete bearing assembly. Remove knuckle

Fig. 2: Exploded View of 4WD Rear Suspension

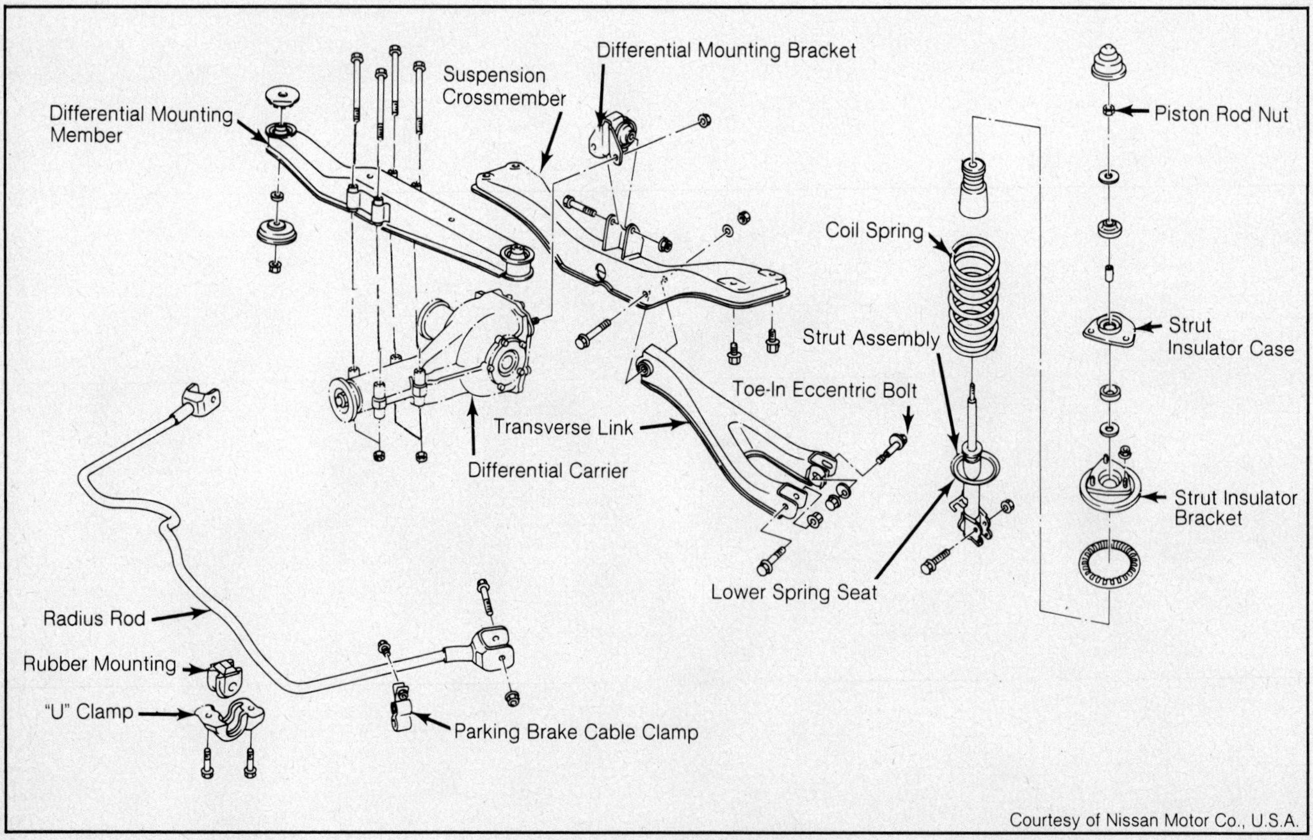

Courtesy of Nissan Motor Co., U.S.A.

NISSAN STANZA WAGON 2WD & 4WD (Cont.)

and hub assembly from vehicle. See WHEEL BEARING under REMOVAL & INSTALLATION in this article. Remove axle shaft from differential by prying axle shaft outward. Remove inner grease seal.

2) Install axle shaft in hub and knuckle assembly. Tighten axle shaft nut to specifications. Rotate hub several times in both directions. Using a torque wrench on axle shaft nut, ensure rotating torque is 2.6-22.6 INCH lbs. (0.3-2.6 N.m). Using a pull scale attached to hub bolt at 12 o'clock, ensure rotating torque is 1.1-9.9 lbs. (4.9-44.1 N).

3) If wheel bearing is being replaced, press hub into knuckle. Leave assembly in press with hub facing downward. Apply 5.5 tons of pressure to bearing. *See Fig. 3.* Rotate rear knuckle several times in both directions.

4) Attach a pull scale to the upper most strut bolt hole of rear knuckle. Rotating torque must be 0.4-4.0 lbs. (2.0-17.7 N). If not within specifications, replace wheel bearing as a complete unit. Recheck wheel bearing preload.

Fig. 3: Checking Wheel Bearing Preload

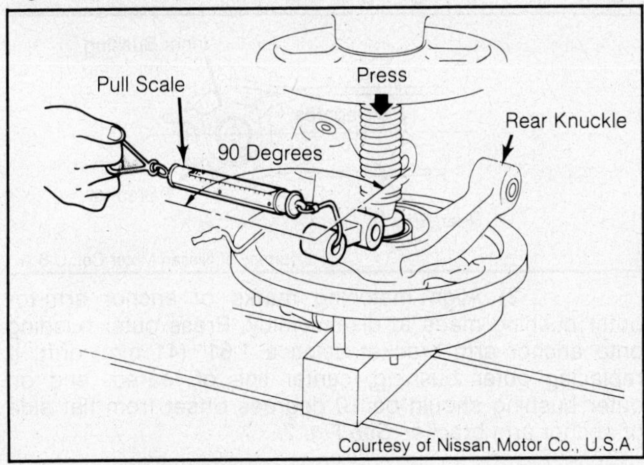

Courtesy of Nissan Motor Co., U.S.A.

REMOVAL & INSTALLATION

CAUTION: Support suspension components during removal as components are under tension.

WHEEL BEARING & 4WD REAR KNUCKLE

Removal & Installation (2WD)

1) Raise and support vehicle. Release parking brake and ensure brake drum rotates freely. Back off brakes if necessary. Remove dust cap. Remove cotter pin, lock nut, spindle nut and washer. Pull brake drum off spindle with outer bearing, using care not to drop outer bearing and remove outer bearing.

2) Pry wheel bearing grease seal from the inner side of hub and discard grease seal. Remove inner bearing. Drive out inner and outer bearing races with hammer and brass bar. To install, reverse removal procedure. Grease seal should extend .020" (.51 mm) above hub surface. Tighten spindle nut and adjust preload to specifications. See WHEEL BEARING under ADJUSTMENTS & INSPECTION in this article.

CAUTION: On 4WD models, mark toe-in adjustment essentric bolt prior to removal. See Fig. 12.

Removal (4WD)

1) Raise and support vehicle. Remove tire and wheel assembly. Remove dust cap, cotter pin, adjusting lock and insulator. Apply brakes and remove wheel bearing nut and washer. Remove brake drum from hub. Disconnect brake flex line from steel line. Disconnect parking brake cable.

NOTE: Wrap axle shaft boots with shop rags to avoid damage. Keep axle shaft assembly straight at all times.

2) Lightly tap axle shaft out of hub with a hammer and block of wood. Mark toe-in adjusting essentric bolt-to-transverse link. Remove strut-to-knuckle bolts/nuts. Disconnect radius rod and transverse link from knuckle. Remove hub, knuckle, backing plate (with rear shoes) as an assembly.

Fig. 4: Separating Hub & Rear Knuckle

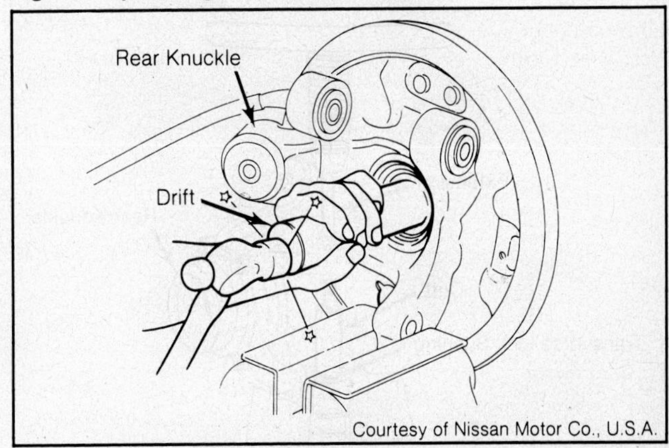

Courtesy of Nissan Motor Co., U.S.A.

3) Place assembly in a vise. Drive hub with inner bearing from knuckle using hammer and drift. *See Fig. 4.* Remove backing plate retaining bolts and remove backing plate with brake shoes attached. Using a 2-jaw type puller, remove inner bearing from hub. Remove outer grease seal from hub and discard.

4) Using a hammer and drift, remove inner bearing with inner grease seal from rear knuckle. Drive the bearing and seal out the seal side. Discard inner grease seal. Remove inner and outer snap rings. Drive bearing race out inner grease seal side of rear knuckle.

5) Remove rear knuckle radius rod bushing with a press. Apply pressure to hub side of bushing and support back side of rear knuckle with a spacer. *See Fig. 5.* Replace rear knuckle transverse link bushing with a press. Support rear knuckle portion of bushing being removed. *See Fig. 5.* Using a drift and extension, press out bushing.

CAUTION: Replace wheel bearing as a complete assembly only. DO NOT mix inner bearings and bearing race.

Installation

1) To install bushings in rear knuckle, reverese removal procedure. Install inner snap ring in rear knuckle. Press bearing race into rear knuckle. Install outer snap ring into rear knuckle. Thoroughly coat bearings and race with multipurpose grease. Install backing plate and brake shoe assembly.

2) Install outer grease seal on hub. Press hub into rear knuckle. Check and adjust bearing preload. See

NISSAN STANZA WAGON 2WD & 4WD (Cont.)

Fig. 5: Removing Radius & Transverse Link Bushing From Rear Knuckle

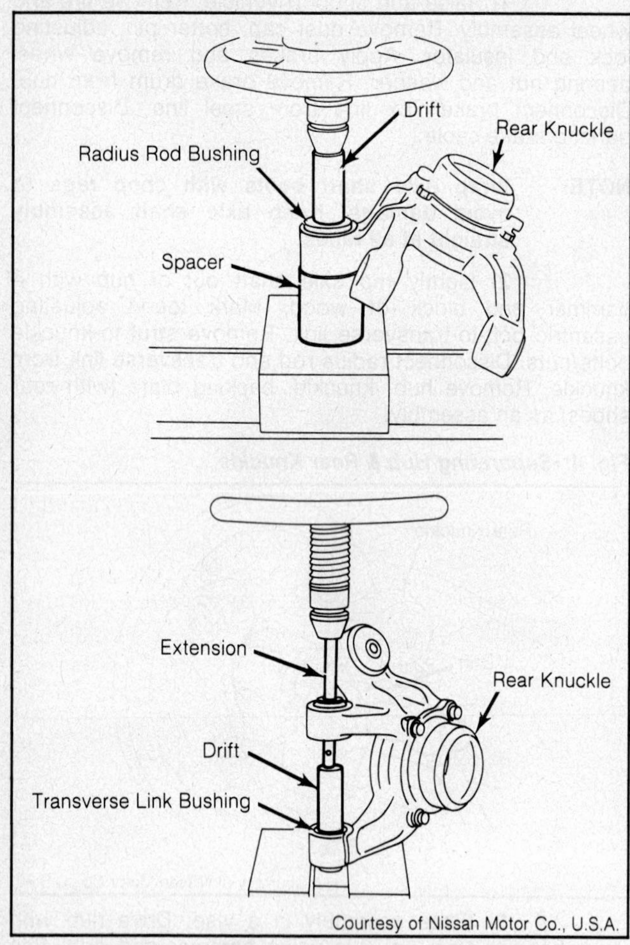

Courtesy of Nissan Motor Co., U.S.A.

WHEEL BEARING under ADJUSTMENTS & INSPECTION in this article. With bearing preload within specifications, install inner grease seal into steering knuclle. To complete installation, reverse removal procedure. Tighen all bolts/nuts to specifications.

REAR ARM

Removal (2WD)

1) Raise and support vehicle. Remove tire and wheel assembly. Remove shock absorber. Remove brake drum and wheel bearings. See WHEEL BEARING under REMOVAL & INSTALLATION in this article.

2) Disconnect and plug brake line at wheel cylinder. Disconnect parking brake cable. Remove brake shoes. Remove rear stabilizer bar bolts/nuts. Remove inner bushing clamp retaining bolts. Remove anchor arm bracket retaining bolts. *See Fig. 1.* Remove rear arm assembly.

NOTE: Match mark components for use as reference guide during reassembly.

Disassembly

1) Remove and discard snap ring from end of inner bushing bracket. Position a 1.02" (26.0 mm) diameter drift on torison bar through the inner bushing. Drive out anchor sleeve and torsion bar. Place matching marks on rear arm-to-anchor arm bracket. Pry off anchor arm bracket with the outer bushing.

2) Place matching marks at anchor arm bracket-to-outer bushing and inner bushing-to-rear arm for reassembly reference. Using a 1.42" (36.0 mm) diameter drift, press anchor arm bracket out of outer bushing.

3) Place rear arm in press with inner bushing facing upward. Press rear arm out of inner bushing.

Inspection

Check the entire rear arm spindle for evidence of cracks. Check for indications of bearing creep or damaged threads. Check for bent or cracked rear arm. Ensure anchor arm bracket is not bent or cracked. Check for twisted, bent or cracked torsion bar and anchor arm sleeve. Replace components as necessary.

Reassembly

1) Align matching marks of inner bushing-to-rear arm made at disassembly. Press inner bushing onto rear arm with a 1.61" (41 mm) drift. If inner bushing is being replaced, the mounting bracket should be approximately 5 degrees off center line of rear arm. *See Fig. 6.*

Fig. 6: Inner Bushing Alignment

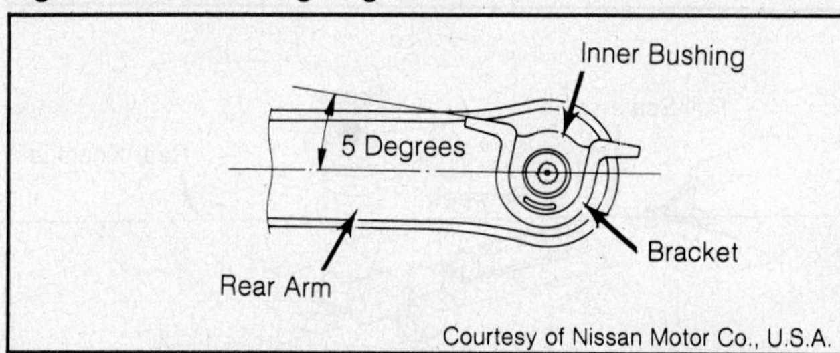

Courtesy of Nissan Motor Co., U.S.A.

2) Align matching marks of anchor arm-to-outer bushing made at disassemlby. Press outer bushing onto anchor arm bracket using a 1.61" (41 mm) drift. If replacing outer bushing, center line of "eared" end on outer bushing should be 10 degrees offset from flat side of anchor arm bracket. *See Fig. 7.*

Fig. 7: Outer Bushing & Anchor Arm Bracket Alignment

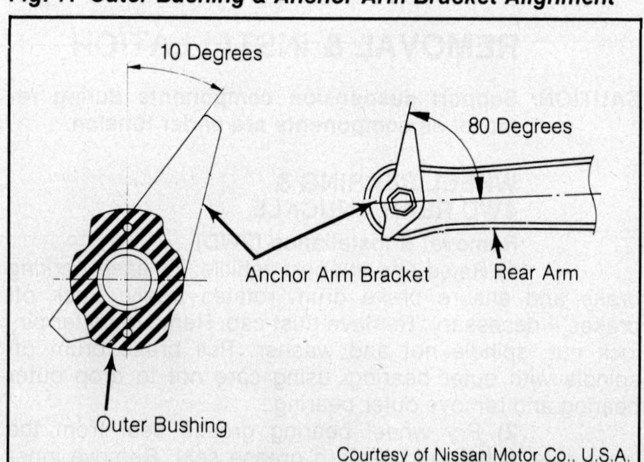

Courtesy of Nissan Motor Co., U.S.A.

3) Place anchor arm bracket and outer bushing assembly on press plate. Align match marks of rear arm-to-anchor arm bracket. Place anchor arm bracket in press and position rear arm on bracket. Press the rear arm onto anchor arm bracket. Space between anchor arm bracket face and rear arm must be .71" (18 mm) after pressing. *See Fig. 8.*

NISSAN STANZA WAGON 2WD & 4WD (Cont.)

Fig. 8: Pressing Anchor Arm Bracket & Rear Arm

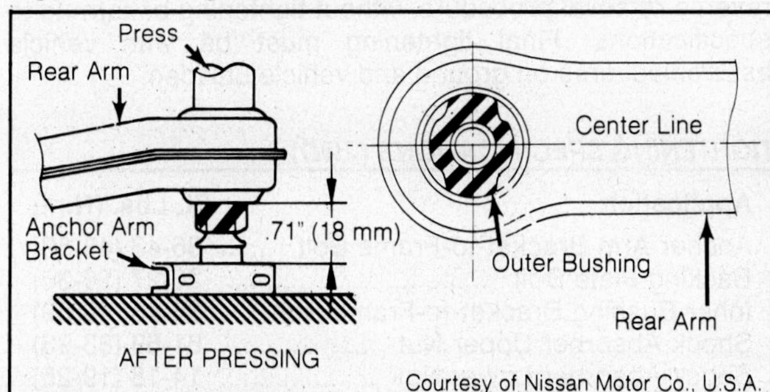

Courtesy of Nissan Motor Co., U.S.A.

4) If replacing anchor arm bracket and outer bushing, position anchor arm bracket on rear arm 80 degrees off center line of rear arm. *See Fig. 7.* The outer bushing installed position should then be aligned with center line of rear arm assembly. *See Fig. 8.*

5) Install new snap ring into inner bushing end of rear arm. Torsion bars are marked for left and right side. Ensure torsion bar is installed on the proper side. Install torsion bar and ensure rear arm center line is in alignment with torsion bar tooth. *See Fig. 9.* Insert anchor arm sleeve.

Fig. 9: Torsion Bar Position

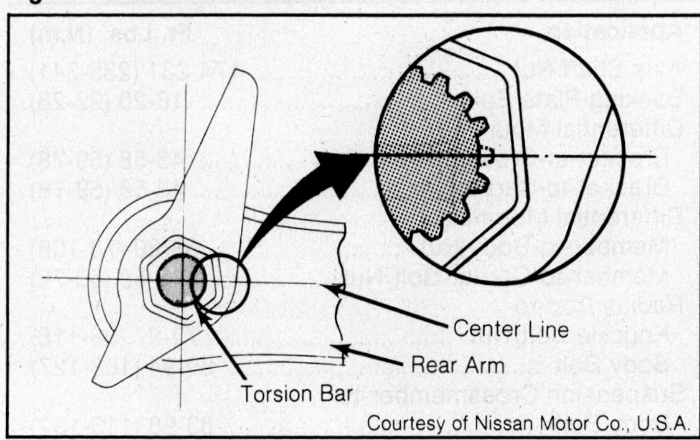

Courtesy of Nissan Motor Co., U.S.A.

Installation

1) To complete installation, reverse removal procedure. Tighten all bolts/nuts to specifications. Check and adjust vehicle unladen height. *See Fig. 10.* Vehicle height must be 13.70-14.25" (348-362 mm).

2) If not within specifications, change anchor arm sleeve. Sleeve is available in 4 sizes. Sleeve is marked with a 1, 0, M or 8. The 1 is lowest position and 8 is highest position. With vehicle height within specifications, check and adjust alignment as necessary.

Fig. 10: Measuring Vehicle Height

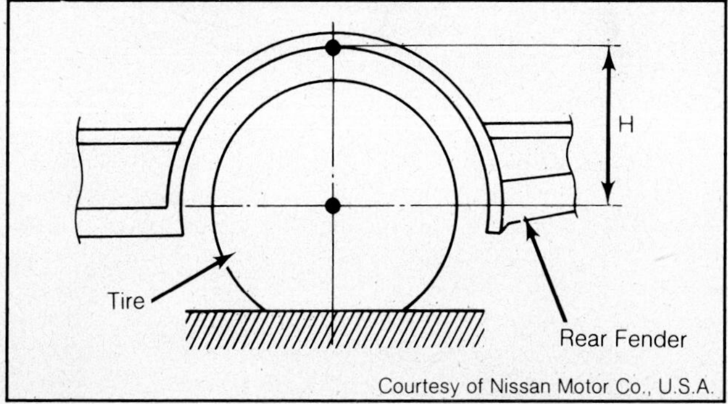

Courtesy of Nissan Motor Co., U.S.A.

STRUT ASSEMBLY

Removal (4WD)

Remove 3 upper mounting nuts. Remove brake hose. Remove 2 lower mounting bolts/nuts. Remove strut assembly from vehicle.

Disassembly

Place strut in vise. Using a coil spring compressor, compress spring just enough to permit turning of strut insulator case assembly by hand. Use care not to damage piston rod. Mark location of insulator assembly to strut for reassembly reference. Remove piston rod lock nut. Remove strut insulator case. Remove insulator bracket and spring seat. Remove coil spring.

Reassembly

Using a coil spring compressor, compress coil spring. Position lower end of coil spring on strut spring seat. Ensure contour of lower coil spring seats properly in contour of lower strut spring seat. Reassemble strut insulator. Install insulator on strut. *See Fig. 11.* Insulator must be positioned as shown. To complete reassembly, reverse disassembly procedure.

Fig. 11: Strut Mounting Insulator Position

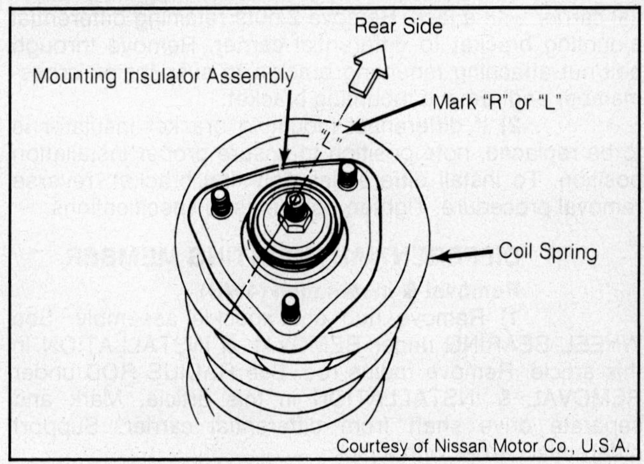

Courtesy of Nissan Motor Co., U.S.A.

Installation

To install reverse removal procedure without tightening bolts/nuts to specifications. Final tighten after complete installation, tires on ground and vehicle unladen.

TRANSVERSE LINK

Removal & Installation (4WD)

1) Raise and support vehicle. Place match marks on toe-in eccentric bolt-to-transverse link for installation reference. *See Fig. 12.* Remove bolt/nut attaching transverse link to suspension crossmember.

Fig. 12: Toe-In Eccentric Bolt

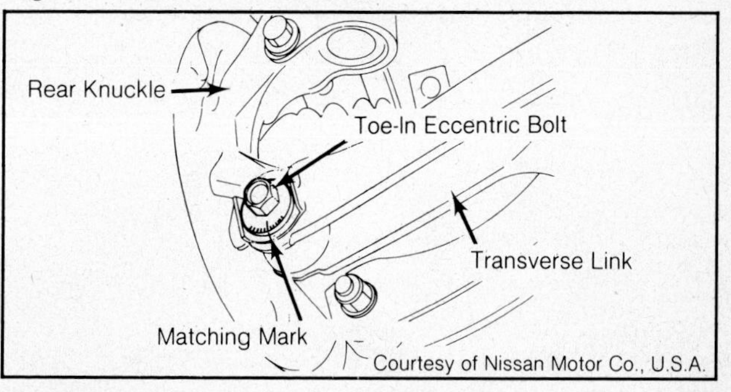

Courtesy of Nissan Motor Co., U.S.A.

NISSAN STANZA WAGON 2WD & 4WD (Cont.)

Remove both the eccentric bolt and standard bolt retaining transverse link to rear knuckle.

2) Remove transverse link. If bushings need to be replaced, replace transverse link assembly. To install, reverse removal procedure without tightening bolts/nuts to specifications. Final tightening must be with vehicle assembled, tires on ground and vehicle at curb height.

RADIUS ROD

Removal & Installation (4WD)

1) Raise and support vehicle. Separate exhaust pipe at joining point above left rear axle shaft. Remove clamps retaining parking brake cable to radius rod.

2) Remove bolts/nuts attaching radius rod to rear knuckle. Remove bolts attaching radius rod to frame and remove radius rod. To install, reverse removal procedure without tightening bolts/nuts to specifications. Final tightening must be with vehicle assembled, tires on ground and vehicle unladen.

DIFFERENTIAL MOUNTING BRACKET

Removal & Installation (4WD)

1) Raise and support vehicle. Support differential carrier with a jack. Remove 2 nuts retaining differential mounting bracket to differential carrier. Remove through bolt/nut attaching mounting bracket to suspension crossmember and remove mounting bracket.

2) If differential mounting bracket insulator is to be replaced, note position to ensure proper installation position. To install differential mounting bracket, reverse removal procedure. Tighten bolts/nuts to specifications.

DIFFERENTIAL MOUNTING MEMBER

Removal & Installation (4WD)

1) Remove hub and knuckle assembly. See WHEEL BEARING under REMOVAL & INSTALLATION in this article. Remove radius rod. See RADIUS ROD under REMOVAL & INSTALLATION in this article. Mark and separate drive shaft from differential carrier. Support differential carrier with a jack.

2) Remove differential mounting bracket. See DIFFERENTIAL MOUNTING BRACKET under REMOVAL & INSTALLATION in this article. Remove 4 differential carrier-to-differential mounting member bolts/nuts. Lower differential assembly. Remove 2 nuts retaining differential mounting member-to-frame. Remove insulators and differential mounting member assembly.

3) If replacing differential mounting member bushing, note position of old bushing to ensure proper installation of new bushing. Press bushing out. To install, reverse removal procedure without tightening bolts/nuts to specifications. Final tightening must be with vehicle assembled, tires on ground and vehicle unladen.

TIGHTENING SPECIFICATIONS (2WD)

Application	Ft. Lbs. (N.m)
Anchor Arm Bracket-to-Frame Bolt	36-43 (49-59)
Backing Plate Bolt	20-27 (26-36)
Inner Bushing Bracket-to-Frame Bolt	36-43 (49-59)
Shock Absorber Upper Nut	61-69 (83-93)
Shock Absorber Lower Nut	14-18 (19-25)
Stabilizer Bar-to-Rear Arm Bolt	65-80 (88-108)
Wheel Nut	72-87 (98-118)
	INCH Lbs. (N.m)
Axle Shaft Nut	[1] 78-104 (9-12)
Bumper Rubber Bolt	84-108 (10-12)

[1] – Final tightening specifications shown. See WHEEL BEARINGS & 4WD REAR KNUCKLE under ADJUSTMENTS & INSPECTION in this article for complete procedure.

TIGHTENING SPECIFICATIONS (4WD)

Application	Ft. Lbs. (N.m)
Axle Shaft Nut	174-231 (235-341)
Backing Plate Bolt	16-20 (22-26)
Differential Mounting	
Bracket-to-Crossmember Bolt	43-58 (59-78)
Bracket-to-CarrierNut	43-58 (59-78)
Differential Mounting	
Member-to-Body Nut	58-80 (78-108)
Member-to-Carrier Bolt/Nut	43-58 (59-78)
Radius Rod-to-	
Knuckle Bolt/Nut	72-87 (98-118)
Body Bolt	80-94 (108-127)
Suspension Crossmember-to-	
Body Bolt	83-98 (113-132)
Strut Piston Rod Nut	26-35 (35-47)
Strut-to-Body Nut	33-44 (45-60)
Strut-to-Knuckle Bolt/Nut	111-120 (151-163)
Transverse Link-to-Crossmember	69-83 (93-113)
Transverse Link-to-Knuckle	83-98 (113-132)
Wheel Nut	72-87 (98-118)
	INCH Lbs. (N.m)
Parking Brake Cable-to-	
Radius Rod Bolt	78-104 (9-12)

Rear Suspension

NISSAN VAN

DESCRIPTION

Rear suspension is 5 link type, using coil springs, upper and lower control arms, lateral rod, and stabalizer bar. Shock absorbers are mounted to axle housing and body. *See Fig. 1.*

ADJUSTMENTS & INSPECTION

WHEEL ALIGNMENT SPECIFICATIONS & PROCEDURES

Rear wheel alignment is not adjustable.

Fig. 1: Exploded View of Nissan Van Rear Suspension

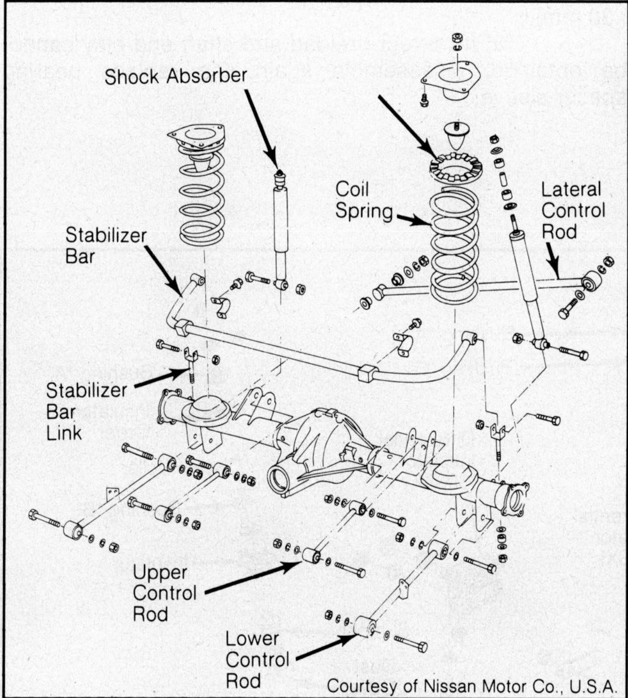

Courtesy of Nissan Motor Co., U.S.A.

REMOVAL & INSTALLATION

SHOCK ABSORBERS

Removal & Installation

1) Raise and support vehicle. Remove nut retaining shock absorber to rear axle housing. Remove nut holding shock absorber to body and remove shock absorber.

2) To install, reverse removal procedure. Tighten all bolts to specification. See TIGHTENING SPECIFICATIONS table in this article.

COIL SPRING

Removal & Installation

1) Raise and support vehicle. Using floor jack, raise axle housing. Remove nut and bolt holding shock absorber to rear axle housing. If replacing shock absorber, remove nuts, collars and cushion from shock absorber body mount.

2) Remove stabilizer bar bushing brackets from axle housing. Disconnect lateral control rod from axle housing and body.

3) Begin to lower axle housing. Lower axle housing using care not to stretch brake line or parking brake cable. Remove coil spring. Remove upper and lower insulators.

4) To install, reverse removal procedure. Lower vehicle to ground. Bounce vehicle to stabilize suspension. Tighten all bolts and nuts to specification. See TIGHTENING SPECIFICATIONS table in this article.

STABILIZER BAR

Removal & Installation

1) Raise and support vehicle. Remove stabilizer bushing brackets from rear axle housing. Remove nut, cushions and retainers from stabilizer bar end links.

2) Remove end links from brackets. Remove stabilizer bar with end links from vehicle. Remove cotter pin, nut, bolt, collar, cushions and end links from stabilizer bar.

3) To install, reverse removal procedure. Tighten all bolts to specification with vehicle on ground.

LATERAL CONTROL ROD

Removal & Installation

1) Raise and support vehicle and rear axle housing. Remove nuts, bolts, washers and bushings attaching lateral control rod to axle housing and to body. Remove lateral control rod.

2) To install, reverse removal procedure. DO NOT tighten fasteners. Lower vehicle. Bounce vehicle to stabilize suspension. Raise axle housing and tighten fasteners of lateral control rod.

UPPER & LOWER CONTROL ARMS

Removal

1) Raise and support vehicle. Support rear axle housing with floor jack. Remove nuts and bolts holding upper control arm to body and to axle housing. Remove upper control arm.

2) Remove nuts and bolts attaching lower control arm to body and to rear axle housing. Remove lower control arm.

Installation

1) To install, reverse removal procedure. DO NOT tighten fasteners. Lower vehicle to ground and bounce vehicle to stabilize suspension. Raise and support vehicle with jack stands. Raise axle housing with jack until body is free from jack stands.

2) Tighten bolts and nuts retaining control arms to body. Tighten bolts and nuts retaining control arm to axle housing. Tighten all bolts and nuts to specification.

TIGHTENING SPECIFICATION

Application	Ft. Lbs. (N.m)
Control Arms-to-Axle Bolts	80-94 (108-127)
Control Arms-to-Body Bolts	80-94 (108-127)
Lateral Control Rod-to-Axle Nut	37-49 (50-67)
Lateral Control Rod-to-Body Bolt	80-94 (108-127)
Shock Absorber Nut	
Lower	53-72 (72-97)
Upper	12-16 (16-22)
Stabilizer Bar-to-Link	20-27 (26-36)
Wheel Lug Nut	72-87 (98-118)

Rear Suspension

NISSAN 200SX & 300ZX

DESCRIPTION

NOTE: An electronically controlled variable shock absorber system is used on all 300ZX Turbo models. For removal, installation, testing and diagnosis procedures for these shock absorbers, see the NISSAN MAXIMA & 300ZX ELECTRONIC SUSPENSION article in this section.

Rear suspension is of the semi-trailing arm, independent-type. The rear wheel is supported by a coil spring and shock absorber, in addition to a semi-trailing arm. The upper end of the shock and spring are attached directly to the upper body. The lower end of the shock and spring are attached to the end of the semi-trailing arm.

The differential gear carrier is installed directly to the suspension subframe with a differential mounting bracket and insulator. The semi-trailing arm is installed on the subframe with rubber bushings and pivot bolts. The rear wheel bearing housing is welded to the end of the semi-trailing arm. The shock stay is bolted to the end of the semi-trailing arm. A stabilizer bar is used to enhance suspension control.

ADJUSTMENTS & INSPECTION

WHEEL ALIGNMENT SPECIFICATIONS & PROCEDURES

See WHEEL ALIGNMENT SPECIFICATIONS & PROCEDURES in WHEEL ALIGNMENT section.

WHEEL BEARING

1) Wheel bearings are adjusted by using a spacer sleeve between sealed wheel bearing and bearing housing. Rear wheel hub must be disassembled in order to adjust preload and rear axle shaft end play.

2) Tighten wheel bearing lock nut to 150-210 ft. lbs. (203-285 N.m). Check wheel bearing preload. Preload should be 6.1 in. lbs. (.69 N.m) maximum torque at wheel bearing lock nut. Rear axle shaft end play should be .012" (.30 mm).

3) If correct preload and shaft end play cannot be obtained, disassemble again and replace bearing spacer sleeve.

Fig. 1: Exploded View of 200SX Rear Suspension

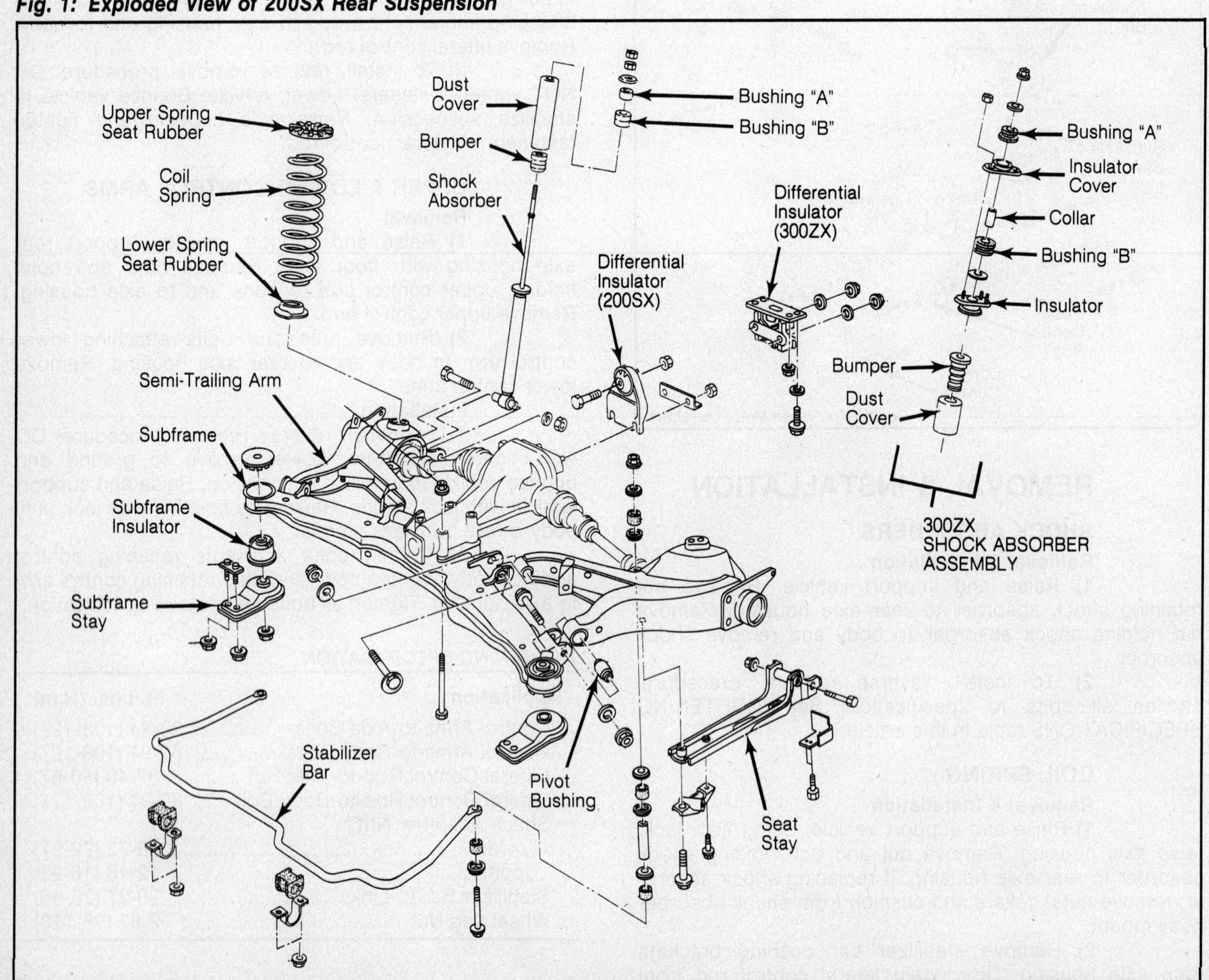

The 300ZX suspension is similar. Courtesy of Nissan Motor Co., U.S.A.

REMOVAL & INSTALLATION

WHEEL BEARING

Removal

1) Raise and support vehicle. Remove brake rotor and caliper assembly. Disconnect drive shaft from axle shaft. Remove wheel bearing lock nut using breaker bar.

2) Remove axle shaft and companion flange. Remove grease seal and inner bearing using Drift (ST37750000). Using Bearing Puller (HT72480000), remove outer bearing. Discard bearing and grease seal. *See Fig. 2.*

Installation

1) Install wheel bearings, use Bearing Drift (ST37750000) to install outer bearing. Match mark stamped on housing and on spacer sleeve and install sleeve.

NOTE: **Wheel bearings are sealed. Sealed side of outer bearing must face the wheel and sealed side of inner bearing must face differential.**

2) Install grease seal using Seal Installer (ST37710000). Tighten new bearing lock nut and measure preload and rear axle shaft end play. See WHEEL BEARING ADJUSTMENT.

Fig. 2: Exploded View of Rear Axle Bearings

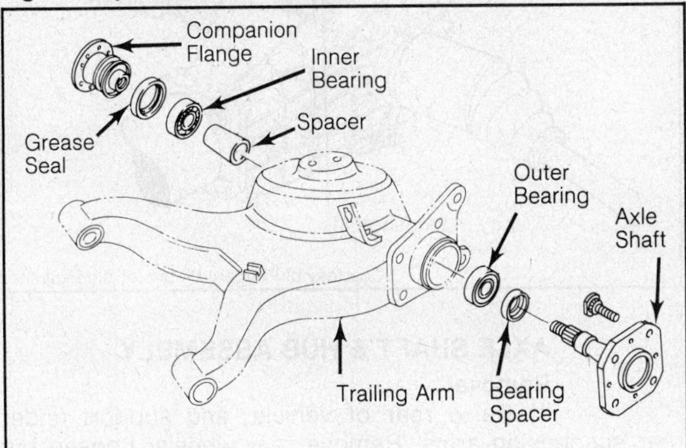

Courtesy of Nissan Motor Co., U.S.A.

SHOCK ABSORBER

Removal & Installation

Raise vehicle and support semi-trailing arm. Disconnect shock upper end nut(s) and lower end nut. Remove shock absorber. To install, reverse removal procedure. Final tightening should be done with vehicle unloaded and tires on the ground.

COIL SPRINGS

Removal & Installation

Install spring compressor. Raise and support vehicle. Remove coil spring. To install, reverse removal procedure. Verify that upper and lower spring seats do not twist or slip when installing coil spring. Ensure flat face of spring is on top.

SEMI-TRAILING ARM

Removal

1) Raise and support vehicle. Remove wheel assemblies. Disconnect brake tube from hose at semi-trailing arm and brake assembly. Remove brake line and disconnect hand brake cable from caliper. Disconnect axle shaft from stub shaft by removing flange bolts.

2) Remove stabilizer bar bolt and related hardware. Remove brake rotor and caliper assembly. Disconnect coil spring and shock from semi-trailing arm. Mark location of pivot bolts before removing. Remove pivot bolts. Remove semi-trailing arm from vehicle.

Installation

To install, reverse removal procedure. Replace all self-locking nuts. Tighten pivot bolts after installing wheels and lowering vehicle to floor. Ensure match marks made on pivot bolts are aligned. Bleed and adjust brakes.

REAR SUSPENSION ASSEMBLY

Removal

1) Raise and support vehicle with safety stands. Remove wheel assemblies. Remove heat shield from front of fuel tank. Remove rear exhaust pipe and muffler. Mark flange of propeller shaft and companion flange. Remove propeller shaft.

2) Disconnect and plug rear brake hoses at semi-trailing arm. Place a floor jack under center of suspension and differential assembly. Disconnect hand brake cables and lower shock ends.

3) Remove subframe nuts at body. Remove differential mount lock nut. Lower rear suspension assembly and remove from under vehicle.

Disassembly

Disconnect axle shafts from differential and stub shafts. Remove differential assembly from subframe. Remove pivot bolts and semi-trailing arms. Insulator bushings can be removed using Remover/Installer (ST38280000).

Reassembly & Installation

Reassemble and install in reverse order of disassembly and removal. Final tightening of semi-trailing arm pivot bolt lock nuts should be done after vehicle has been lowered to the floor. All self-locking nuts should be replaced, if they were removed.

TIGHTENING SPECIFICATIONS

Application	Ft. Lbs. (N.m)
Differential Mounting Nuts	
200SX	65-87 (88-118)
300ZX	72-87 (98-118)
Propeller Shaft-to-Flange Bolts	
200SX	20-27 (27-37)
300ZX	
Non-Turbo	29-36 (39-49)
Turbo	43-51 (59-69)
Semi-Trailing Arm Pivot Nuts	72-87 (98-118)
Shock Absorber Nut	
200SX	
Lower Nut	43-58 (59-79)
Upper Nut	11-14 (15-20)
300ZX	
Lower Nut	51-65 (69-88)
Piston Rod Nut	14-20 (20-27)
Insulator Nuts	23-31 (31-42)
Stabilizer Bar-to-Semi-Trailing Arm	12-15 (16-20)
Subframe-to-Body Bracket Nut	58-80 (79-108)
Wheel Bearing Lock Nut	150-210 (203-285)

Rear Suspension

PEUGEOT

DESCRIPTION

An independent rear suspension utilizing trailing arms and coil springs is used. The rear hub is supported by lower control arms which pivot on axle crossmember.

The coil springs are mounted between the suspension crossmember and the control arm. Hydraulic shock absorbers are located inside the coil spring. A stabilizer bar is mounted to the frame and connected to the control arms. *See Figs. 1 and 2.*

ADJUSTMENTS & INSPECTION

WHEEL ALIGNMENT SPECIFICATIONS & ADJUSTMENTS

See WHEEL ALIGNMENT SPECIFICATIONS & PROCEDURES in WHEEL ALIGNMENT section.

WHEEL BEARING

Wheel bearings are not adjustable and must be replaced if removed.

REMOVAL & INSTALLATION

WHEEL BEARINGS

Removal

1) Remove axle shaft and hub assembly. See AXLE SHAFT & HUB ASSEMBLY in this article.

2) Type 1. Remove inner seal and bearing track ring. Mount bearing hub in vice. Using Hub Nut Wrench (8.0902J), remove the hub nut. Tap out the bearing, and remove outer seal.

3) Type 2. Pry out outer seal. Remove circlip. Mount and support bearing housing in press and press bearing from housing.

Installation

1) Type 1. Install new seal and bearing. Install new inner seal and a new hub nut. Mount housing in vice and tighten new hub nut to 181 ft. lbs. (245 N.m). Install track ring.

2) Type 2. Install new outer seal in housing. Mount bearing housing in press and press in new bearing. Install circlip. Install new inner seal. Lubricate seal lips with grease.

3) To complete installation, reverse removal procedure. Tighten all bolts and nuts to specification. See TIGHTENING SPECIFICATIONS table in this article.

SHOCK ABSORBER

Removal

From inside luggage compartment, remove lock nut at top of shock absorber while holding shock to prevent it from rotating. On control arm end, remove lower pivot bolts. Remove shock absorber. Discard rubber washers and lock nut.

Installation

To install, reverse removal procedure. Use new rubber washers and lock nut. Tighten upper retaining bolt first, then tighten lower mount bolt.

Fig. 1: Assembled View of Peugeot Rear Suspension

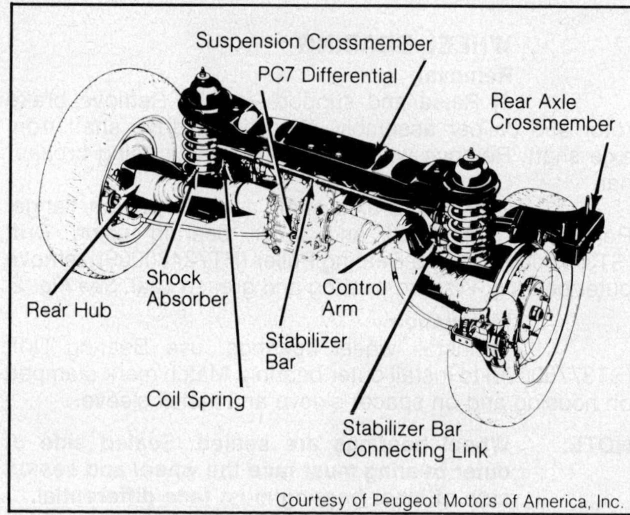

Fig. 2: Peugeot Link-Mounted PC8 Differential

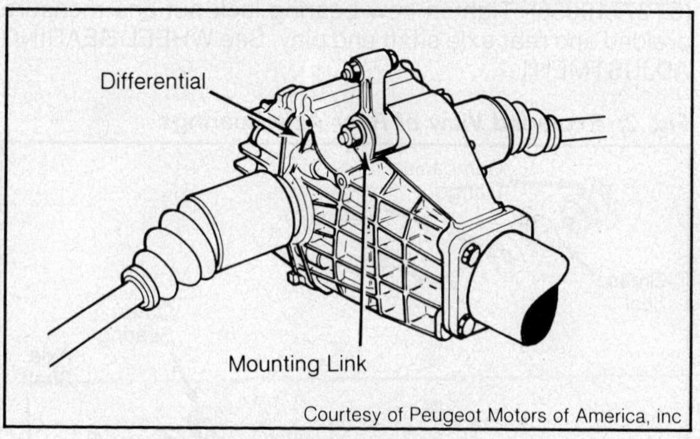

AXLE SHAFT & HUB ASSEMBLY

Removal

1) Raise rear of vehicle, and support under rear suspension arms. Remove rear wheels. Loosen but do not remove hub nut.

2) On disc brake models, disconnect brake line from clip on suspension arm. Remove brake caliper and suspend from vehicle without distorting brake line. If equipped, mark position of rotor retaining screw and remove screw. Remove 4 axle hub bearing support bolts that attach support to suspension arm.

3) Remove anti-lock brake system sensor bolt and sensor. Unclip sensor housing and swing out of way. Use extreme care with serrated ring on axle shaft. Any damage to this ring may result in improper brake operation.

4) To remove axle, use 2 Guides (B1 and B2). Screw in until splines are fully released. Compress CV joint at differential and remove axle shaft. A universal type puller may be necessary to free axle shaft from hub. *See Fig. 3.*

PEUGEOT (Cont.)

Fig. 3: Removing Rear Axle Assembly

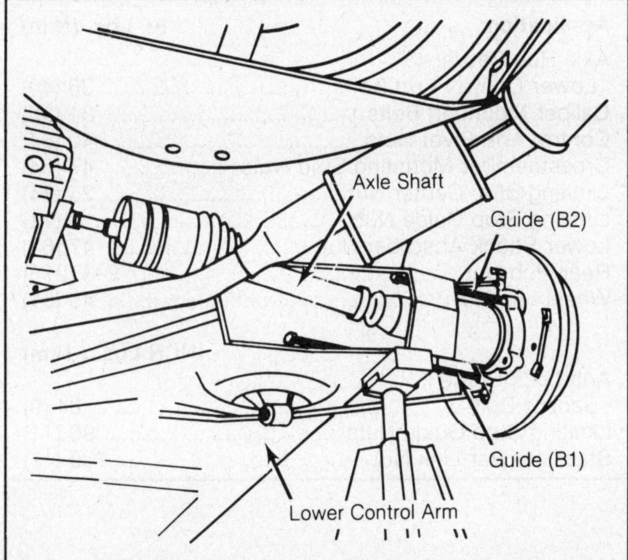

5) With axle assembly pressed out of control arm, remove axle assembly from rear housing without damaging housing seals. Remove axle assembly through lower control arm. With axle removed, place axle assembly in press, with adapter plate located just below hub. Remove hub nut and washer. Press axle out of hub.

Installation

1) To install, reverse removal procedure. Before assembling hub to axle bearing support, grease spline of axle stub. Before installing axle assembly into housing, ensure housing side seal is in perfect condition. Apply grease between lips of seal and to axle shaft splines.

2) Use new washer when assembling bearing support to lower control arm. Install brake caliper with new washers. Install brake anti-chatter spring onto caliper with arrow facing normal direction of rotation.

3) When installing hub nut, tighten to specification and stake nut. After installing wheels, check level of lubricant in housing. Tighten all bolts and nuts to specification. Check anti-lock brake speed sensor gap. See PEUGEOT ANTI-LOCK BRAKE SYSTEM article in BRAKE section.

COIL SPRING & CONTROL ARM

Removal

1) Raise and support vehicle with safety stands (under rear control arms). Remove wheel assemblies. Disconnect brake line from bracket on control arms.

2) On models with drum brakes, remove the drums. Disconnect brake line from wheel cylinder. Disconnect parking brake cable from brake assembly. Remove the axle shaft and hub assembly.

3) On models with disc brakes, remove disc brake pads. Remove calipers, retaining bolts and support calipers out of way. Remove the axle shaft and hub assembly.

4) On all models, remove shock absorber lower retaining nut and bolt. Remove the link nut, washer and bushing. Remove pivot bolt nuts and hand brake clip. Carefully lower control arm and remove spring.

5) On models equipped with PC8 link-mounted differentials, support vehicle under rear crossmember. Remove rear seat. On each side of vehicle, remove 3 nuts, sheet metal locking plate and washers securing rear crossmember to floor pan. Install Pilot Guide (8.0906 K1) in hole between 3 mounting studs on each side.

6) On PC8 differentials, lower crossmember slightly. Remove the limiter stop and guide from center of crossmember. *See Figs. 4 and 5.* On both PC7 and PC8 differentials, support control arm in horizontal position. Remove 2 pivot bolts and remove arm from vehicle.

Installation

1) Install lower control arm. Grease unthreaded parts of control arm pivot bolts, and install them with bolt heads facing each other.

2) On models with PC8 differentials, lower vehicle to refit rear crossmember. If used, remove Pilot Guide (8.0906 K1). Install flat washers, a NEW sheet metal locking plate and 3 nuts. Tighten nuts. Fold up locking plate tabs.

3) On all models with disc brakes, pass parking brake cable into control arm. On PC7 and PC8 differentials, install spring with rubber cup upward. Support control arm. Lower vehicle until lower shock bolt and link hardware can be installed. Tighten only link nut at this time.

4) Install axle shaft and hub assembly using new lock washers. On models with disc brakes, install disc brake caliper. On all models, connect brake line and parking brake cable. Secure brake line to control arm.

5) Install brake drum (if equipped). On all models, bleed brakes. Lower vehicle to ground.

6) Position a 2.36 x 2.36 x 2.36" (60 x 60 x 60 mm) wood block between control arm and rubber bumper on floor pan. Compress suspension until wood block just contacts rubber bumper.

7) With suspension compressed, tighten control arm pivot bolts and shock absorber mounting bolt. If necessary, refill differential.

8) On models with PC8 differential (equipped with a Type 1 limiting stop), install all parts without tightening fasteners. Use NEW nylon lock nuts. Ensure entire assembly moves freely. Tighten nuts. *See Fig. 4.*

9) On models with PC8 differential (equipped with Type 2 limiting stop), install all parts in place without tightening fasteners. *See Fig. 5.*

Fig. 4: Installing Type 1 Limiting Stop

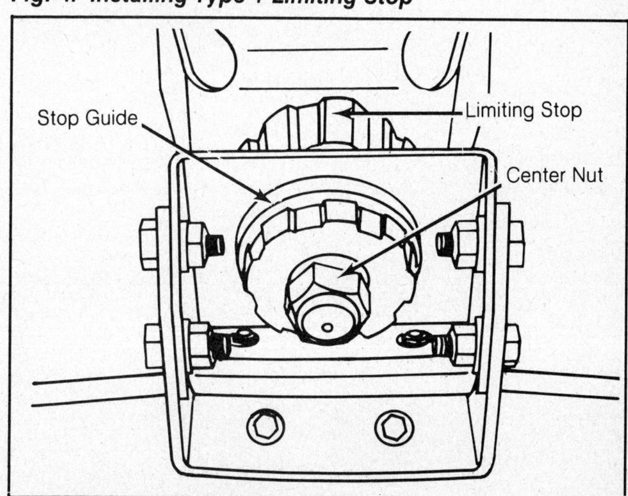

Rear Suspension

PEUGEOT (Cont.)

10) Insert a .197" (5 mm) drill bit between the limiting stop and guide. *See Fig. 5*. Holding limiting stop square with centerline of vehicle. Tighten center nut and guide nuts and bolts.

Fig. 5: Installing Type 2 Limiting Stop

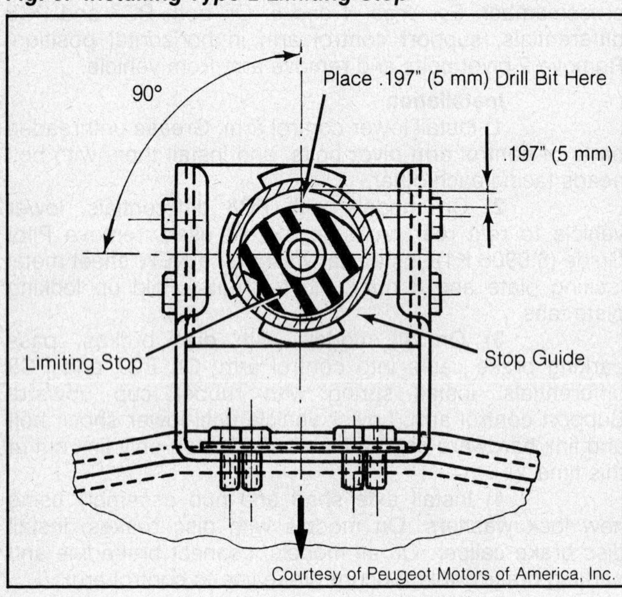

Courtesy of Peugeot Motors of America, Inc.

TIGHTENING SPECIFICATIONS

Application	Ft. Lbs. (N.m)
Axle Hub Carrier-to-Lower Control Arm Bolts	36 (49)
Caliper Mounting Bolts	31 (42)
Control Arm Pivot Nuts	40 (54)
Crossmember Mounting Stud Nuts	47 (64)
Limiting Stop Center Nut	25 (34)
Limiting Stop Guide Nuts	8 (11)
Lower Shock Absorber Nut	47 (64)
Rear Hub Nut	203 (275)
Wheel Lug Nut	45 (61)
	INCH Lbs. (N.m)
Anti-Lock Brake Sensor Bolt	84 (9)
Limiting Stop Guide Nuts	96 (11)
Stabilizer Bar Link Nut	108 (12)

Rear Suspension

PORSCHE – EXCEPT 911 SERIES

924-S, 944, 944-S, 944 Turbo

DESCRIPTION

Porsche uses independent torsion bar type rear suspension. Torsion bars mount in rear crossmember tube and anchor in center of tube by splined hub. Outer ends of torsion bar mount into splined hubs integral with spring plates.

Spring plates are bolted to control arm flange. Control arms pivot in mounts on crossmember tube and are integral with stub axle housing. Shock absorbers mount on control arm and to upper body.

ADJUSTMENTS & INSPECTION

WHEEL ALIGNMENT SPECIFICATIONS & PROCEDURES

See WHEEL ALIGNMENT SPECIFICATIONS & PROCEDURES in WHEEL ALIGNMENT section.

WHEEL BEARING

Wheel bearings are nonadjustable.

REMOVAL & INSTALLATION

SHOCK ABSORBER

Removal

Raise and support vehicle. Remove wheel assembly. Remove both bottom and top shock absorber retaining nuts and bolts. Remove shock absorber from vehicle.

Inspection & Installation

Check shock absorber for leaks and smooth operation. To install, reverse removal procedure.

CONTROL ARM

Removal

1) Remove cotter pin and loosen hub nut. Raise vehicle and support with safety stands. Remove wheel assembly and shock absorber.

2) Remove bolts retaining axle drive shaft to stub axle. Separate axle drive shaft from stub axle and wire out of way.

3) Use protective cap to cover exposed end of axle drive shaft. Remove caliper and plug brake line. Disconnect parking brake.

4) Index mark spring plate in relation to a point on control arm. Remove control arm pivot bolt and remove arm from vehicle.

Installation

To install, reverse removal procedure. Tighten pivot bolt and lock in place by staking edge to metal shoulder on bracket. Align spring plate marks with those on control arm. Bleed brake system.

CROSSMEMBER TUBE

Removal

1) Raise vehicle and support with safety stands. Remove wheel assemblies. Disconnect parking brake cable from lever and remove cable.

2) Disconnect and remove rear portion of exhaust system from catalytic converter. Remove transaxle retaining nuts. Support transaxle with a chain by attaching ends to frame.

3) Disconnect shock absorbers from control arms. Support control arms with safety stands. Remove stabilizer bar links. Mark location of spring plate on control arm. Remove camber eccentric and retaining bolts between spring plate and control arm flange.

4) Remove parking brake retaining straps from spring plates. Temporarily install shock absorbers. Remove control arm pivot bolts.

Fig. 1: Exploded View of Rear Suspension

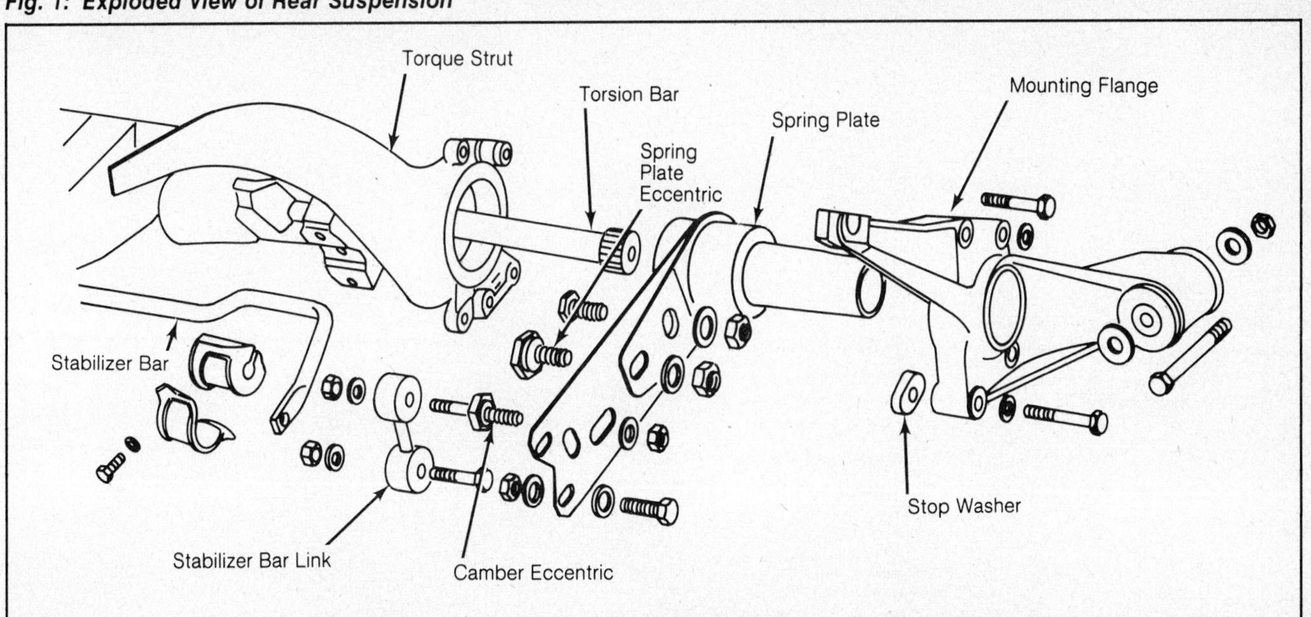

PORSCHE – EXCEPT 911 SERIES (Cont.)

5) Disconnect parking brake cable from crossmember tube. Remove crossmember lower retaining bolts. Remove torque strut bolts from upper mounts. Remove crossmember tube.

Installation

1) Apply rubber lubricant to lower mount bushings. Install crossmember tube with lower retaining bolts. Remove upper mounts from body and install on torque struts, but DO NOT tighten bolts.

2) Install control arms with pivot bolts. Disconnect shock absorber from control arm. Install control arm to spring plate, but DO NOT tighten bolts. Reinstall shock absorber to control arm.

3) Install upper retaining bolts to body approximately 2-3 threads deep. Tighten torque strut-to-mount bolts. Tighten all remaining mount bolts.

4) Lower transaxle and remove support chain. Install and tighten transaxle retaining nuts. Reinstall parking brake cables and retainers. Install wheel assemblies and lower vehicle.

5) Check and adjust rear axle alignment. After alignment, raise vehicle and remove rear wheel assemblies. Tighten all nuts and bolts to specification. Install stabilizer bar links.

TORSION BARS & SPRING PLATES

Removal

With crossmember tube removed and placed in a vise, remove mounting flange bolts and flange. Pry off spring plate. Remove spring plate and withdraw torsion bars. Left and right torsion bars are not interchangeable.

Installation

1) Position crossmember tube so that flat surface of torque strut is horizontal. Using Protractor (VW 261) and a straight edge, measure any deviation from horizontal and record that figure.

2) Add 23 degrees to recorded figure for setting spring plate angle. Set protractor at indicated angle and turn spring plate or torsion bar until bubble in level is centered.

3) Using rubber lubricant and short bolts, install mounting flange until the long bolt with stop washer can be inserted. Temporarily install mounting flange-to-torque strut bolt.

4) Compress spring plate with floor jack or Compressor (VW 655/3). Install spring plate stop washer and tighten bolt slightly. Remove compressor, allowing spring plate to position stop washer. Tighten all flange bolts.

TIGHTENING SPECIFICATIONS

Application	Ft. Lbs. (N.m)
Control Arm Camber Eccentric	65 (88)
Control Arm-to-Spring Plate	75 (102)
Shock Absorber-to-Body	44 (60)
Spring Plate Height Eccentric	177 (241)
Stabilizer Bar Link	33 (45)
Torsion Bar	
Mounting Flange-to-Body	51 (69)
Mounting Flange-to-Crossmember	33 (45)
Mounting Flange-to-Upper Mount	33 (45)
Torque Strut Mount-to-Body	33 (45)
Torque Strut Mount-to-Strut	17 (23)
Upper Mount-to-Body	33 (45)

PORSCHE 911 CARRERA & 911 TURBO

DESCRIPTION

Independent torsion bar type rear suspension is used. Torsion bars are mounted inside rear cross-member tube and anchored in center by a splined hub. Outer end of torsion bars mount into splined hubs integral with spring plates which connect at ends to control arms.

Control arms pivot in mounts integral with body and also serve as rear wheel bearing carriers. Hydraulic shock absorbers are mounted between control arms and inner fender panel. A stabilizer bar is installed on some models. *See Fig. 1.*

Fig. 1: Exploded View of Porsche Rear Suspension

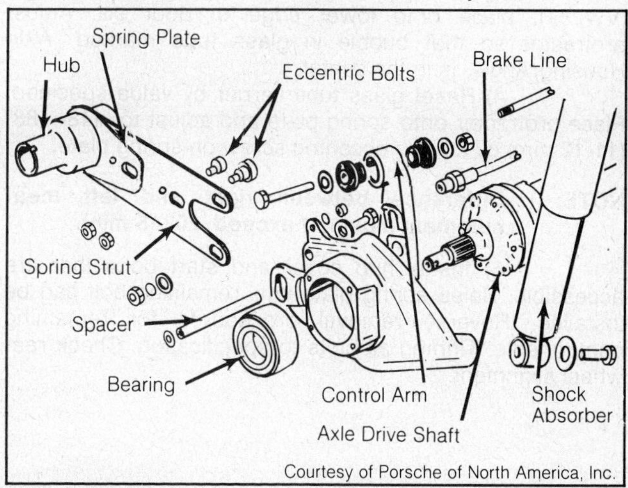

Courtesy of Porsche of North America, Inc.

REMOVAL & INSTALLATION

WHEEL BEARING

Removal

1) Remove control arm. See CONTROL ARM section in this article. Drive out wheel hub with Special Tool (P-297a). Pull wheel bearings off wheel hub grabbing bearing only at rollers.

2) Remove parking brake with anchor and gaurd. Heat bearing housing, using heating plate or oven, and drive out outer bearing races. Clean all surfaces.

Installation

1) Heat bearing housing and drive in outer bearing races. Install parking brake assembly. Fill space between outer races with grease, lubricate outer bearing and install bearing and seal.

2) Press wheel hub into outer bearing. Install bearing spacer. Lubricate inner bearing and press in until contact with spacer. To complete installation, reverse removal procedure. Tighten all bolts to specification. See TIGHTENING SPECIFICATIONS table in this article.

SHOCK ABSORBER

Removal

1) Raise vehicle and support with safety stands, in a position so weight of vehicle is still on rear wheels. Remove rubber cap from upper mount (accessible from inside engine compartment).

2) Remove nut from shock absorber. Remove bolt securing shock absorber to control arm. Remove shock absorber. Remove rod cover and rubber buffer from shock absorber.

Installation

1) Inspect rubber buffer for wear or cracking. Replace if necessary. Make sure that stop disc grooves face bottom of shock absorber when assembling.

2) Install rubber buffer and cover. Reverse removal procedure to install remaining components. Tighten upper and lower mounts to specification.

CONTROL ARM

Removal

1) Raise vehicle and support with safety stands under vehicle body. Remove wheel assemblies. Detach brake system components from rear wheel hub. See PORSCHE article in BRAKES section.

2) Remove axle hub cotter pin and nut. Remove Allen head bolts from axle shaft flanges and remove axle shafts. Using a driver, remove wheel hub from control arm.

3) Remove cotter pin and nut from parking brake cable and pull cable out toward center of vehicle. Remove bolts securing parking brake assembly to control arm and remove assembly.

4) Raise torsion bar spring plate to take tension from shock absorber. Remove lower shock absorber mount. Remove bolts securing spring plate to control arm.

5) Disconnect brake hose from bracket on control arm. Remove nut from control arm pivot bolt and drive bolt out with a punch. Remove control arm from vehicle.

Installation

To install, reverse removal procedures. Use new self-locking nuts and tighten all bolts and nuts to specification. See TIGHTENING SPECIFICATIONS table. Check riding height and wheel alignment. Bleed brake system.

TORSION BAR & SPRING PLATE

Removal

1) Raise and support vehicle. Remove wheel assembly. Raise torsion bar spring plate. Remove lower shock absorber retaining bolt. Remove bolts securing spring plate to control arm. Pull back on control arm to separate from spring plate. Remove torsion bar hub cover bolts.

2) Pry off hub cover. Remove torsion bar tensioner tool. Remove plug from body. Remove spring plate and withdraw torsion bar. If torsion bar is broken, opposite side torsion bar will have to be removed in order to drive out broken piece.

NOTE: A plastic spacer is installed on some vehicles between rear axle cross tube and spring plate to compensate for body tolerance. This prevents contact between spring plate bolts and body. Always reuse spacer if found.

Installation

1) Inspect all components for wear or damage, replace if necessary. Coat torsion bar with lithium grease before installing. Torsion bars are marked left and right.

2) Coat rubber components with glycerin paste. Install torsion bar and spring plate.

PORSCHE 911 CARRERA & 911 TURBO (Cont.)

3) To adjust torsion bars, use Protractor (VW261), place onto lower edge of door sill. Adjust protractor so that bubble in glass tube marked "Axle Housing/Angle" is in the center.

4) Reset glass tube carrier by value specified. Place protractor onto spring plate and adjust to .448-.488" (11-12 mm) by turning eccentric screw on spring plate.

NOTE: **Difference between right and left measurement must not exceed .20" (5 mm).**

5) Install hub cover and start bolts that are accessible. Raise spring plate until remaining bolt can be installed. Reverse removal procedures for remaining components. Tighten all bolts to specification. Check rear wheel alignment.

TIGHTENING SPECIFICATIONS

Application	Ft. Lbs. (N.m)
Axle Shaft Allen Head Bolts	
M8-12K	31 (42)
M10-8G	34 (46)
M10 x 55-12K	60 (82)
Axle Shaft Hub Nut	235 (320)
Lower Shock Absorber Mount	90 (125)
Spring Strut-to-Control Arm	
Eccentric Bolts	61 (85)
Mounting Bolt	87 (120)
Spring Plate-to-Spring Strut Bolts	65 (88)
Torsion Bar Hub Cover Bolts	34 (46)
Tracking Adjusting Bolt	36 (49)
Upper Shock Absorber Mount	18 (25)
Wheel Lug Nuts	96 (130)

Rear Suspension

SAAB

900, 900S, 900 Turbo
9000S, 9000 Turbo

DESCRIPTION

900, 900S & 900 Turbo

Rear axle is straight tube with a stub axle press fit into each end. Axle is mounted to body by lower control arms, which are connected at rear to the axle tube and to the body at front.

Rear links are also used, and mount rearward from stub axle assembly to body. A panhard rod is mounted on right side of axle and attaches to body support in center. Coil springs and shock absorbers are mounted between lower control arms and body.

Fig. 1: 900, 900S, 900 Turbo Rear Suspension

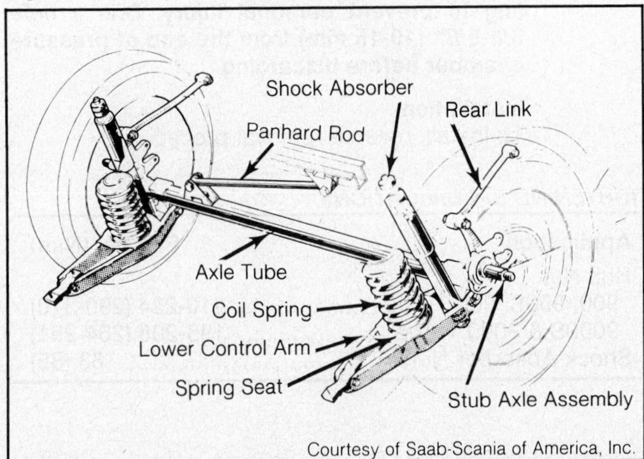

Courtesy of Saab-Scania of America, Inc.

9000S & 9000 Turbo

Rear axle is a tube with welded on mountings for spring links and welded on hub carriers. Suspension consists of a rigid axle between two spring links. A panhard rod limits lateral movement of rear axle. Two torque arms take up torsional forces.

Fig. 2: 9000S & 9000 Turbo Rear Suspension

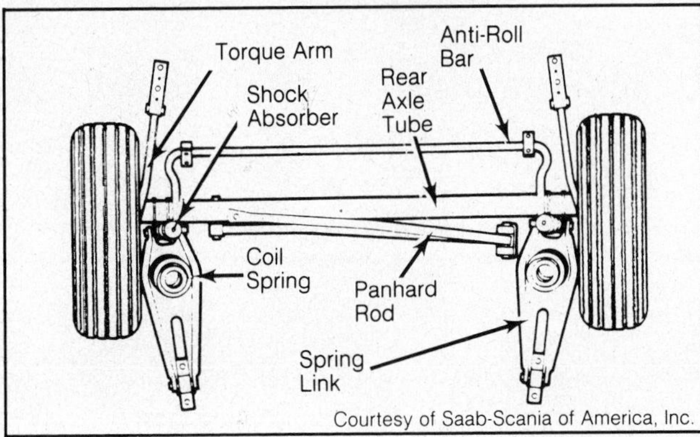

Courtesy of Saab-Scania of America, Inc.

ADJUSTMENTS & INSPECTION

WHEEL ALIGNMENT SPECIFICATIONS

See WHEEL ALIGNMENT SPECIFICATIONS in WHEEL ALIGNMENT section.

WHEEL BEARING

900, 900S & 900 Turbo

Tighten hub nut to 210-224 ft. lbs. (290-310 N.m). Lock hub nut into place by bending locking collar into slot.

9000S & 9000 Turbo

Wheel bearings are incorporated in the wheel hub. Bearings are double row ball type which are permanently lubricated and maintenance free.

REMOVAL & INSTALLATION

NOTE: Do not lift vehicle with jack applied directly to rear axle tube.

WHEEL BEARING

Removal (900, 900S, 900 Turbo)

1) Raise and support vehicle. Remove wheel assembly. Remove and support brake caliper. Remove disc brake rotor. Pry bearing dust cap off. Bend back locking collar and remove hub nut and washer.

2) Remove hub using Puller (89 96 084). Remove seal ring using a screwdriver. Remove inner bearing races. Drive out outer bearing races (if necessary).

Installation

Reverse removal procedure to complete installation. Adjust wheel bearings. See WHEEL BEARING in this article.

COIL SPRING

Removal

1) Apply hand brake and loosen wheel lug nuts. Raise and support vehicle. Remove wheel assembly. On 9000S and 9000 Turbo models, remove handbrake cable from bracket on spring link. On all models, support control arm with floor jack. Slightly raise arm and disconnect lower end of shock absorber.

2) Support rear axle with safety stand. Disconnect control arm from body. Carefully lower control arm and remove coil spring, spring support and rubber spacer.

Installation

Replace self-locking nuts that attach control arm to body. Reverse removal procedure to complete installation.

AXLE ASSEMBLY

Removal (900, 900S & 900 Turbo)

1) Raise vehicle and support with safety stands under vehicle body. Remove wheel assemblies. Disconnect rear brake hoses and plug. Lower shock absorber attachments and panhard rod.

2) Position a floor jack under rear axle. Lower axle and remove rear springs. Remove bolts from spring link rear bushings and remove axle assembly from vehicle.

Installation

1) To install, reverse removal procedure. When repositioning axle tube, do not place floor jack in center of axle tube. Either use 2 floor jacks (one at each end) or one floor jack and one safety stand.

2) Do not tighten bushings until vehicle weight is on suspension to ensure bushings are aligned correctly.

Rear Suspension

SAAB (Cont.)

Panhard rod-to-body retaining bolt must be installed with nut facing forward. Bleed brake system.

Removal (9000S & 9000 Turbo)

1) Raise vehicle and support with safety stands under vehicle body. Remove wheel assemblies. Detach handbrake cables from brackets on spring links.

2) Remove bolts for brake calipers and hang out of way. Remove brake disc. Position a floor jack under rear axle. Lift rear axle just enough to partially relieve tension on panhard rod. Remove panhard rod from axle.

3) Remove bottom bolts for shock absorbers and anti-roll bar. Carefully lower rear axle and remove springs. Unbolt front mounting for torque arm. Remove trailing-end mounting bolts for sprink link.

Installation

To install, reverse removal procedure. Position all components and leave bolts loose. Using a floor jack, lift rear axle enough to seat suspension components. Tighten bolts. DO NOT lift car with a floor jack under rear axle.

SHOCK ABSORBER

Removal (Standard Type)

Raise vehicle and support with safety stands under vehicle body. Remove wheel assembly. Disconnect shock absorber from upper and lower mounting brackets. Remove shock absorber.

Installation

Bleed air from shock absorber before installing by holding shock upright and working it through full cycle several times. Reverse removal procedure to install shock.

Removal (Gas Type)

1) Raise vehicle and support with safety stands under vehicle body. Remove wheel assembly. Support axle with safety stand to prevent sudden drop of axle.

2) Raise control arm with a floor jack placed under axle. Remove shock retaining nuts and control arm-to-rear axle mounting bolts. Lower control arm and remove shock.

3) On 9000S & 9000 Turbo models, raise vehicle and support with safety stands under rear axle at spring links. Using a floor jack, raise vehicle to relieve tension on shock absorbers and anti-roll bar.

4) Remove bolt from bottom of shock absorber. Remove panel over spare tire and fold back carpet. Remove upper nut from shock absorber and remove.

NOTE: **Used shock absorbers require special handling to prevent personal injury. Drill a hole 3/8-5/8" (10-15 mm) from the end of pressure chamber before discarding.**

Installation

To install, reverse removal procedure.

TIGHTENING SPECIFICATIONS

Application	Ft. Lbs. (N.m)
Hub Nut	
900, 900S, 900 Turbo	210-224 (290-310)
9000S & 9000 Turbo	195-208 (264-281)
Shock Absorber Nuts	63 (85)

STERLING 825

DESCRIPTION

The Sterling 825 rear suspension is an independent type suspension. Suspension consists of coil springs, shock absorbers, stabilizer bar, trailing arm, lower arm and hub carrier.

Hub carrier is attached to the shock absorber, lower arm and the trailing arm.

Fig. 1: Exploded View of Rear Suspension

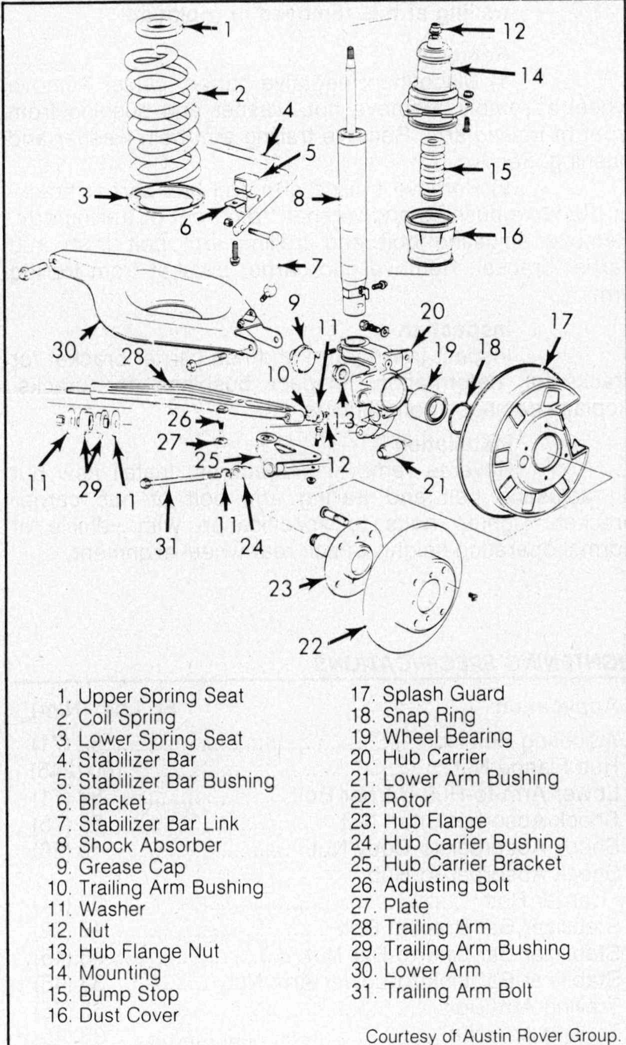

Courtesy of Austin Rover Group.

ADJUSTMENTS & INSPECTION

WHEEL ALIGNMENT SPECIFICATIONS & PROCEDURES

See WHEEL ALIGNMENT SPECIFICATIONS & PROCEDURES in WHEEL ALIGNMENT section.

WHEEL BEARING

Information not available from manufacturer.

REMOVAL & INSTALLATION

WHEEL BEARING

Removal

1) Remove hub carrier. See HUB CARRIER in this article. Remove rotor-to-hub retaining bolts. Remove rotor from hub flange. Remove grease cap. *See Fig. 1.*

2) Remove hub flange nut. Using press, remove hub flange from hub carrier. Place hub carrier in soft-jawed vise. Remove bearing retaining snap ring.

3) Using press and Bearing Remover (18G 1533), press bearing from hub carrier. *See Fig. 2.*

Fig. 2: Removal & Installation of Wheel Bearing

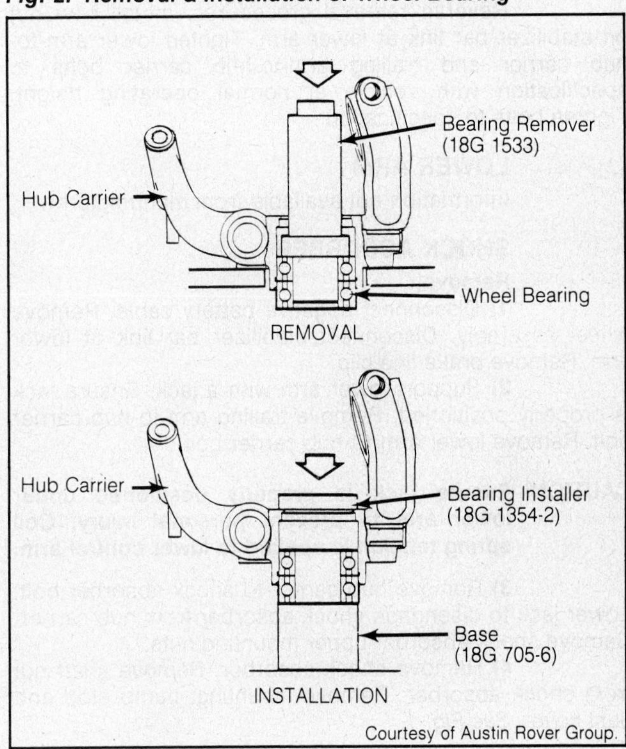

Courtesy of Austin Rover Group.

Inspection

Inspect hub flange and hub carrier for damage or cracks. Inspect bearing retaining snap ring for distortion. Replace damaged components.

Installation

1) Pack wheel bearing with grease. Using press, Bearing Installer (18G 1354-2) and Base (18G 705-6), install bearing in hub carrier. *See Fig. 2.*

2) Install bearing retaining snap ring. Using press, install hub flange in hub carrier and bearing. Install new hub flange nut. Tighten nut to specification. See TIGHTENING SPECIFICATIONS table at end of article.

3) Stake hub flange nut once tightened to specification. Install grease cap.

HUB CARRIER

Removal

1) Disconnect negative battery cable. Remove wheel assembly. Disconnect stabilizer bar link at lower arm. Remove brake caliper and move away from hub carrier.

Rear Suspension

STERLING 825 (Cont.)

2) Remove rotor-to-hub flange bolts. Remove rotor from hub flange. Support lower arm with a jack. Ensure jack is properly positioned. Remove trailing arm-to-hub carrier bolt. Remove lower arm-to-hub carrier bolt. *See Fig.1.*

CAUTION: Ensure jack is properly positioned under lower arm to prevent personal injury. Coil spring tension is applied to lower control arm.

3) Remove hub carrier-to-shock absorber bolt. Separate shock absorber from hub carrier. Remove hub carrier.

Installation

Reverse removal procedures. Install new nut on stabilizer bar link at lower arm. Tighten lower arm-to-hub carrier and trailing arm-to-hub carrier bolts to specification with vehicle at normal operating height. Tighten bolts to specification.

LOWER ARM

Information not available from manufacturer.

SHOCK ABSORBER

Removal

1) Disconnect negative battery cable. Remove wheel assembly. Disconnect stabilizer bar link at lower arm. Remove brake line clip.

2) Support lower arm with a jack. Ensure jack is properly positioned. Remove trailing arm-to-hub carrier bolt. Remove lower arm-to-hub carrier bolt.

CAUTION: Ensure jack is properly positioned under lower arm to prevent personal injury. Coil spring tension is applied to lower control arm.

3) Remove hub carrier-to-shock absorber bolt. Lower jack to disengage shock absorber from hub carrier. Remove shock absorber upper mounting nuts.

4) Remove shock absorber. Remove shaft nut from shock absorber. Remove mounting, bump stop and dust cover. *See Fig. 1.*

Inspection

Inspect shock absorber for signs of leakage. Inspect mounting, bump stop and dust cover for cracks or damage. Replace shock absorber if signs of leakage exists. Replace all damaged components.

Installation

Reverse removal procedures. Install new nut on stabilizer bar link at lower arm. Tighten lower arm-to-hub carrier and trailing arm-to-hub carrier bolts to specification with vehicle at normal operating height. Tighten bolts to specification.

STABILIZER BAR

Removal & Installation

1) Disconnect negative battery cable. Remove wheel assembly. Disconnect stabilizer bar links at lower arms. Remove stabilizer bar brackets.

2) Remove stabilizer bar. Remove stabilizer bar links and bushings from stabilizer bar. Replace bushings if damaged. Reverse removal procedures.

3) Install new nut on stabilizer bar link at lower arm. Tighten all bolts to specification with vehicle at normal operating height.

TRAILING ARM

NOTE: Rear wheel alignment must be checked once trailing arm is removed or replaced.

Removal

1) Disconnect negative battery cable. Remove wheel assembly. Remove nut, washer and bushing from front of trailing arm. Remove trailing arm bolt, washer and bushing. *See Fig. 1.*

2) Remove trailing arm and hub carrier bracket. Remove bushing and washer from front of trailing arm. Remove adjusting bolt and trailing arm bolt from hub carrier bracket. Remove hub carrier bracket from trailing arm.

Inspection

Inspect trailing arm and hub carrier bracket for cracks or deformation. Inspect bushings for cracks. Replace damaged components.

Installation

Reverse removal procedures. Install new nut on adjusting bolt and trailing arm bolt of hub carrier bracket. Tighten bolts to specification with vehicle at normal operating height. Check rear wheel alignment.

TIGHTENING SPECIFICATIONS

Application	Ft. Lbs. (N.m)
Adjusting Bolt Nut	52 (71)
Hub Flange Nut	[1] 180 (245)
Lower Arm-to-Hub Carrier Bolt	52 (71)
Shock Absorber Shaft Nut	55 (75)
Shock Absorber-to-Body Nut	19 (26)
Shock Absorber-to-Hub Carrier Bolt	52 (71)
Stabilizer Bar Bracket Bolt	16 (22)
Stabilizer Bar Link-to-Bar Nut	33 (45)
Stabilizer Bar Link-to-Lower Arm Nut	33 (45)
Trailing Arm Bolt	55 (75)
Trailing Arm Nut	33 (45)
Trailing Arm-to-Hub Carrier Bracket Bolt	52 (71)
Wheel Lug Nut	52 (71)

[1] – Stake after tightening to specification.

Rear Suspension

SUBARU – EXCEPT JUSTY

Brat, Hatchback, Sedan, Station Wagon, XT Coupe

DESCRIPTION

Rear suspension is of the semi-trailing arm independent type. Crossmember is mounted to body frame with brackets at both ends via bushings. One end of trailing arm is bolted to crossmember through a bushing, and the other end is mounted to the body through the shock absorber. An outer arm is bolted on one end to the crossmember through a bushing, and on the other end directly to the trailing arm.

ADJUSTMENTS & INSPECTION

WHEEL ALIGNMENT SPECIFICATIONS & PROCEDURES

See WHEEL ALIGNMENT SPECIFICATIONS & PROCEDURES in WHEEL ALIGNMENT section.

WHEEL BEARING

2WD Models

Tighten hub nut to 36 ft. lbs. (49 N.m). Rotate hub several times to seat bearings. Check starting torque using spring scale. Correct starting torque is 1.9-3.2 lbs. (8.3-14.2 N). Adjust starting torque by loosening nut 1/8 to 1/10 turn.

4WD Models

Wheel bearings are not adjustable. Tighten hub nut to 145 ft. lbs. (197 N.m). If cotter pin hole is not aligned, tighten further a maximum of 30 degrees to align hole. Install new cotter pin.

REMOVAL & INSTALLATION

WHEEL BEARING

Removal (2WD Models)

Raise and support vehicle. Remove wheel assembly. Remove dust cap, axle nut, lock washer and washer from axle shaft. Remove caliper assembly (if equipped). Remove drum or disc/hub and outer bearing together. Remove spacer using a puller. Remove oil seal and inner bearing. Remove "O" ring. Remove outer bearing races using a hammer and brass drift.

Installation

To install, reverse removal procedure. Press outer race of inner bearing in using Bearing Installer (925220000). Press outer race of outer bearing into drum

Fig. 1: Exploded View of 2WD & 4WD Suspension

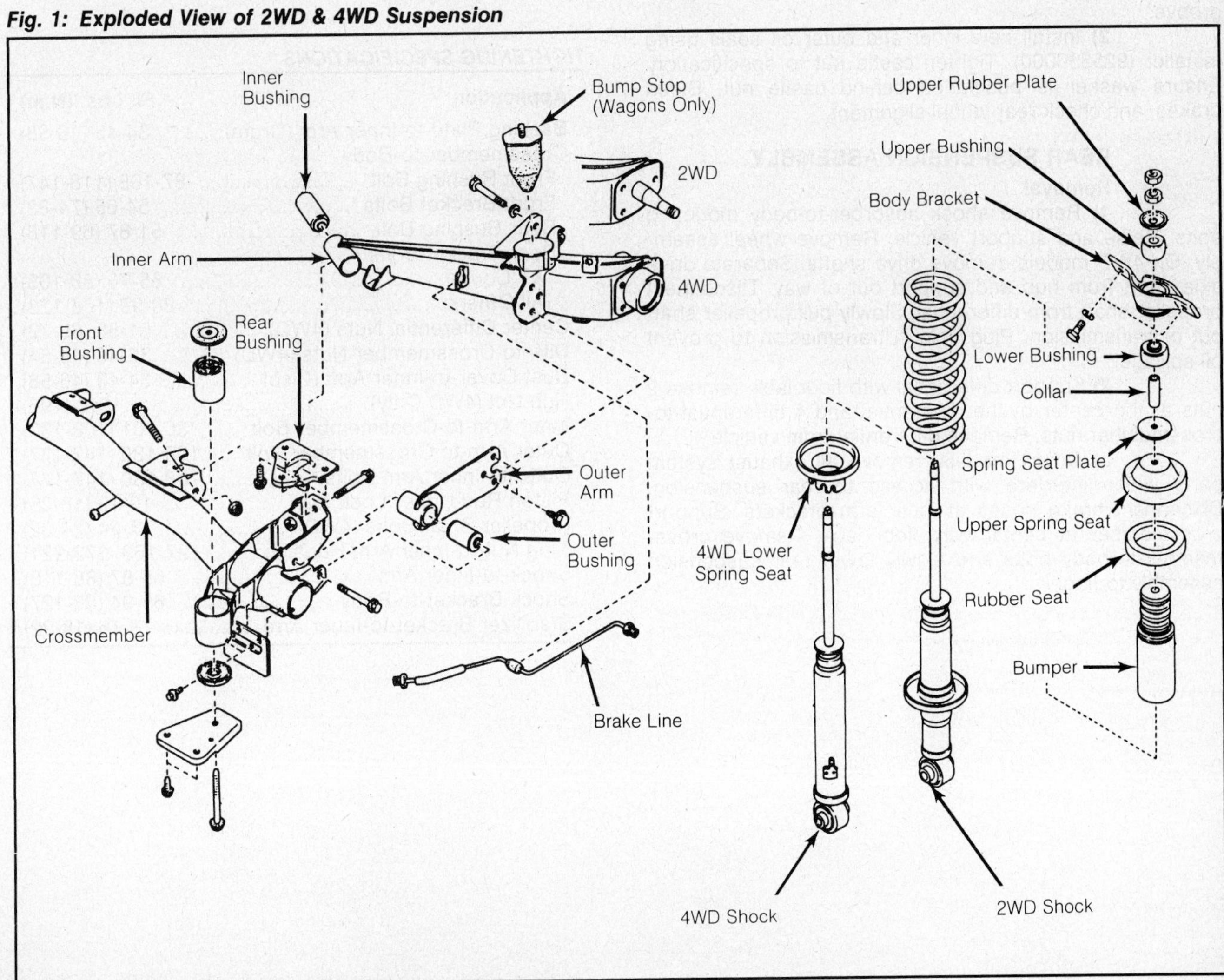

Courtesy of Subaru of America, Inc.

Rear Suspension

SUBARU – EXCEPT JUSTY (Cont.)

using Bearing Installer (921130000). Stepped surface of spacer must face toward bearing. Use new lock washer and new O-ring for dust cap.

Removal (4WD Models)

1) Apply parking brake. Remove cotter pin and loosen castle nut. Disconnect shock absorber from inner arm. Loosen lock bolts of crossmember outer bushing.

2) Raise and support vehicle. Remove rear wheels. Separate front drive axle shaft from hub and support out of way. Remove castle nut and brake drum or disc/hub assembly (if equipped).

3) Disconnect brake line from brake hose at inner arm bracket. Remove brake assembly (drum brakes) from trailing arm. Remove bolt holding inner arm bushing mount to crossmember. Remove 3 bolts connecting inner arm and outer arm. Remove inner arm.

4) Put inner arm in a vise, and straighten staked portion of ring nut. Using Socket (925550000), remove ring nut. Remove spindle by lightly tapping inward with a plastic hammer. Remove outer oil seal from inner arm housing. Using a press, remove bearings and races from housing and spindle.

Installation

1) To install, reverse removal procedure. Tighten ring nut to specification. Lock the ring nut by staking a point on the housing surface facing the ring nut groove.

2) Install new inner and outer oil seals using Installer (925530000). Tighten castle nut to specification. Ensure washer is positioned behind castle nut. Bleed brakes, and check rear wheel alignment.

REAR SUSPENSION ASSEMBLY

Removal

1) Remove shock absorber-to-body mounting bolts. Raise and support vehicle. Remove wheel assembly. On 4WD models, remove drive shafts. Separate drive axle shaft from hub and support out of way. Disconnect propeller shaft from differential. Slowly pull propeller shaft out of transmission. Plug hole in transmission to prevent oil spillage.

2) Support differential with floor jack, remove 2 nuts at the center of the differential and 4 differential-to-crossmember nuts. Remove differential from vehicle.

3) On all models, remove all exhaust system parts which interfere with access to rear suspension. Disconnect brake hoses at inner arm brackets. Support crossmember at center with floor jack. Remove crossmember-to-body bolts and slowly lower rear suspension assembly to floor.

Inspection

Check for any damage or wear to any bushings. Press out and replace if necessary. Check for any deformation or cracks on the trailing arm, outer arm and crossmember. Replace if necessary.

Installation

To install, reverse removal procedure. Tighten bolts, with bushing mounts, with vehicle in unloaded condition. Bleed brake system and check wheel alignment.

STRUT ASSEMBLY

Removal & Disassembly

Raise and support vehicle. Remove upper and lower mounting bolts and remove strut from vehicle. Compress coil spring, remove the double nuts and disassemble the shock. Note position of coil spring in relation to the upper bracket.

Inspection

Check shock absorber for oil leakage. Check the action of the piston rod for abnormal noise or resistance.

Reassembly & Installation

To reassemble, reverse removal procedure. The coil spring must be mounted with the flat end down. To install, reverse removal procedure.

TIGHTENING SPECIFICATIONS

Application	Ft. Lbs. (N.m)
Backing Plate-to-Inner Arm (Drum)	34-43 (46-58)
Crossmember-to-Body	
Front Bushing Bolt	87-108 (118-147)
Front Bracket Bolts	54-65 (74-88)
Rear Bushing Bolt	51-87 (69-118)
Rear Bracket Bolts	
XT Coupe	65-76 (88-103)
All Others	80-90 (108-123)
Center Differential Nuts (4WD)	51-58 (69-79)
Diff.-to-Crossmember Nuts (4WD)	33-40 (44-54)
Dust Cover-to-Inner Arm (Disc)	34-43 (46-58)
Hub Nut (4WD Only)	145 (196)
Inner Arm-to-Crossmember Bolt	80-101 (108-137)
Outer Arm-to-Crossmember Bolt	108-130 (147-177)
Outer-to-Inner Arm Bolts	108-130 (147-177)
Piston Rod Upper Lock Nut	13-19 (18-25)
Propeller Shaft Bolts (4WD)	17-24 (24-32)
Ring Nut-to-Inner Arm Housing	127-163 (172-221)
Shock-to-Inner Arm	65-87 (88-118)
Shock Bracket-to-Body	65-94 (88-127)
Stabilizer Bracket-to-Inner Arm	13-16 (18-22)

Rear Suspension

SUBARU JUSTY

DESCRIPTION

Rear suspension assembly consists of a crossmember, trailing links, lower control arms, strut assemblies, coil springs and spindle housings. Spindle housing is bolted to strut, trailing link and lower arm. Coil spring mounts between crossmember and lower control arm.

Fig. 1: Exploded View of Justy Rear Suspension & Strut Assembly

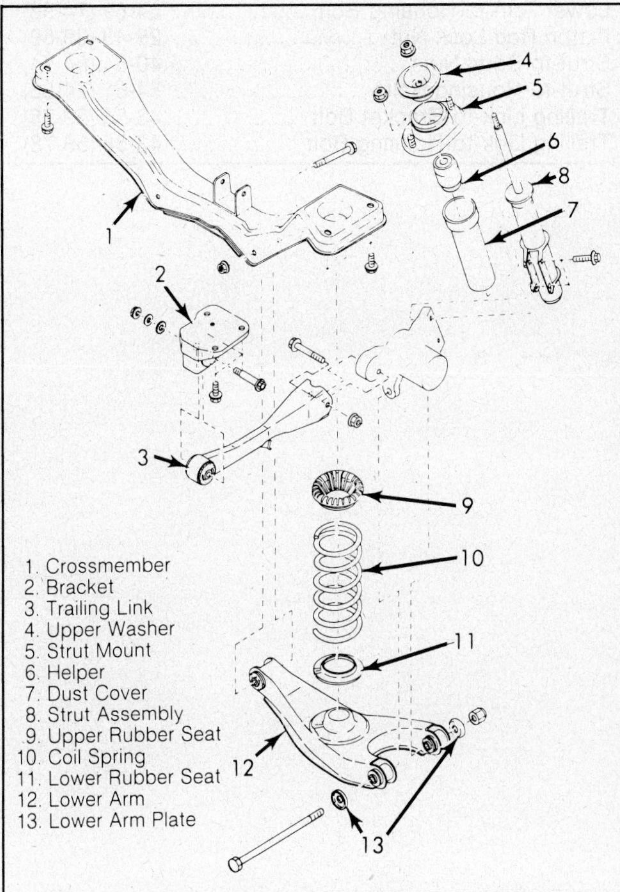

Courtesy of Subaru of America, Inc.

ADJUSTMENTS & INSPECTION

WHEEL ALIGNMENT & RIDE HEIGHT SPECIFICATIONS & PROCEDURES

See WHEEL ALIGNMENT SPECIFICATIONS & PROCEDURES in WHEEL ALIGNMENT section.

WHEEL BEARING

Tighten spindle nut to 29 ft. lbs. (39 N.m). Rotate drum several times to seat bearings. Loosen nut. Check starting torque of drum using spring scale attached to wheel lug nut. Starting torque should be 3.1-4.4 lbs. (13.7-19.6 N). Tighten spindle nut until proper starting torque is obtained.

REMOVAL & INSTALLATION

WHEEL BEARING

Removal

Raise and support vehicle. Remove wheel assembly. Remove grease cap (do not damage "O" ring), spindle nut, lock washer and washer. Remove brake drum with outer bearing. Remove spacer, oil seal and inner bearing. Drive out bearing outer races using brass bar and hammer.

Installation

1) Inspect brake drum, races and spindle for unusual wear, cracks or damage. Press bearing outer races into drum using Installer (922111000). Pack bearings with grease and install. Press oil seal in using installer.

2) To install, reverse removal procedure. Ensure spacer is installed with chamfered side facing in. Always use new lock washer. Adjust wheel bearing.

REAR SUSPENSION ASSEMBLY

Removal & Installation

1) Raise and support vehicle. Remove wheel assembly. Disconnect brake hose at frame bracket. Disconnect muffler from rear exhaust pipe. Remove rear exhaust pipe from hanger. Remove exhaust pipe heat protector rear bolt.

2) Remove equalizer at center of parking brake cable. Remove rod from support and separate inner cable. Remove clamp bolt from parking brake outer cable. Remove bolts attaching trailing link bracket to body. Remove bolt attaching lower arm to crossmember. Remove coil spring.

3) Raise and support lower arms. Remove trim cover on upper part of strut. Remove nuts attaching strut to body. Remove suspension assembly from vehicle. To install, reverse removal procedure. Always replace exhaust pipe gasket. Tighten lower arm-to-crossmember bolt with vehicle on ground and suspension unloaded.

CROSSMEMBER

Removal & Installation

Raise and support vehicle. Remove wheel assembly. Disconnect strut from spindle housing. Push lower arm down and remove coil spring. Disconnect lower arm from crossmember. Remove bolts attaching crossmember to body. Remove muffler from hanger and push down. Remove crossmember from vehicle. To install, reverse removal procedure.

STRUT ASSEMBLY & COIL SPRING

Removal & Disassembly

1) Raise and support vehicle. Remove wheel assembly. Remove trim cover on top of strut. Remove nuts attaching strut to body. Push lower arm down and pull out coil spring.

2) Remove bolts attaching strut to spindle housing. Remove strut from vehicle. Clamp strut in vise. Loosen strut rod lock nut while holding rod with Allen wrench. Remove components from strut.

SUBARU JUSTY (Cont.)

Inspection

1) Inspect strut mount for damage. Check bolt threads for damage. Inspect helper, dust cover and upper and lower coil spring seats for cracks or damage. Check strut rod for binding or unusual noise. Check strut for oil leakage, deformed outer shell or deformed or cracked bracket.

2) Check rod side play. Fully extend rod and mount a dial indicator .4" (10 mm) from end of rod. Apply a load of 4 lbs. (20 N) to end of rod and measure play. Maximum side play is .031" (.80 mm). Replace strut if play exceeds specification. Strut cannot be disassembled.

Reassembly & Installation

To reassemble, reverse disassembly procedure. Ensure helper is installed with small end up. Always use new strut rod lock nut. To install, reverse removal procedure. Ensure coil spring fits properly in upper and lower rubber seats.

TIGHTENING SPECIFICATIONS

Application	Ft. Lbs. (N.m)
Bracket-to-Body Bolts	36-51 (49-69)
Crossmember-to-Body Bolts	36-51 (49-69)
Lower Arm-to-Crossmember Bolt	43-58 (59-78)
Lower Arm-to-Housing Bolt	54-69 (74-93)
Piston Rod Lock Nut	29-43 (39-59)
Strut-to-Body Nuts	40-54 (54-74)
Strut-to-Housing Bolts	54-61 (74-83)
Trailing Link-to-Bracket Bolt	43-58 (59-78)
Trailing Link-to-Housing Bolt	43-58 (59-78)

Rear Suspension

TOYOTA COROLLA RWD, CRESSIDA WAGON, TERCEL 4WD WAGON & VAN

DESCRIPTION

Coil spring type suspension is used, utilizing upper and lower control rods as pivot supports. Coil springs are mounted between axle and chassis member.

Shock absorbers are connected to axle housing and to chassis member. A lateral control rod is mounted to rear axle housing and to mount at side of body. A stabilizer bar attaches to chassis with end links and at axle with brackets.

Fig. 1: Rear Suspension Components

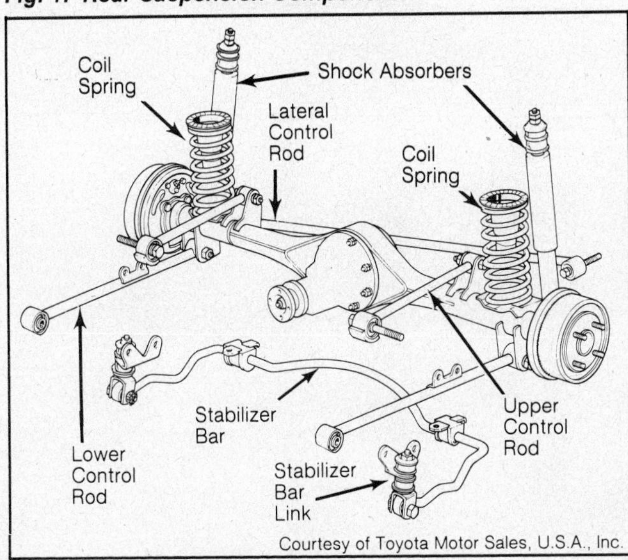

Courtesy of Toyota Motor Sales, U.S.A., Inc.

ADJUSTMENTS & INSPECTION

WHEEL ALIGNMENT SPECIFICATIONS & PROCEDURES

Rear wheel alignment is not adjustable.

REMOVAL & INSTALLATION

SHOCK ABSORBER

Removal & Installation

Raise and support vehicle. Remove nut retaining shock absorber to rear axle housing. Remove nut holding shock absorber to body and remove shock absorber. To install, reverse removal procedure. Tighten all bolts to specification. See TIGHTENING SPECIFICATIONS table in this article.

COIL SPRING

Removal & Installation

1) Raise and support vehicle. Using floor jack, raise axle housing. Remove nut and bolt holding shock absorber to rear axle housing. If replacing shock absorber, remove nuts, collars and cushion from shock absorber body mount.

2) Remove stabilizer bar bushing brackets from axle housing. Disconnect lateral control rod from axle housing and body. Begin to lower axle housing. Lower axle housing using care not to stretch brake line or parking brake cable. Remove coil spring. Remove upper and lower insulators.

3) To install, reverse removal procedure. DO NOT tighten lateral control rod fasteners. Lower vehicle to ground. Bounce vehicle to stabilize suspension. Tighten lateral control rod fasteners. Tighten all bolts and nuts to specification.

STABILIZER BAR

Removal & Installation

1) Raise and support vehicle. Remove stabilizer bushing brackets from rear axle housing. Remove nut, cushions and retainers from stabilizer bar end links.

2) Remove end links from brackets. Remove stabilizer bar with end links from vehicle. Remove cotter pin, nut, bolt, collar, cushions and end links from stabilizer bar. To install, reverse removal procedure.

LATERAL CONTROL ROD

Removal & Installation

1) Raise and support vehicle and rear axle housing. Remove nuts, bolts, washers and bushings attaching lateral control rod to axle housing and to body. Remove lateral control rod.

2) To install, reverse removal procedure. DO NOT tighten fasteners. Lower vehicle. Bounce vehicle to stabilize suspension. Raise axle housing and tighten fasteners of lateral control rod.

Bushing Replacement

Use Arbor Press and Bushing Set (09710-30020 for Van and 09710-14012 for all others) when removing or inserting bushings. Press bushings from chamfered side of lateral control rod only.

UPPER & LOWER CONTROL ARMS

Removal & Installation

1) Raise and support vehicle. Support rear axle housing with floor jack. Remove nuts and bolts holding fupper control arm to body and to axle housing.

2) Remove upper control arm. Remove nuts and bolts attaching lower control arm to body and to rear axle housing. Remove lower control arm.

Use Arbor Press and Bushing Set (09710-14012) when removing or inserting bushings. Press bushings from chamfered side of control arm only.

Bushing Replacement

Use Arbor Press and Bushing Set (09710-30020 for Van and 09710-14012 for all others) when removing or inserting bushings. Press bushings from chamfered side of lateral control rod only.

Installation

1) To install, reverse removal procedure. DO NOT tighten fasteners. Lower vehicle to ground and bounce vehicle to stabilize suspension. Raise and support vehicle with jack stands. Raise axle housing with jack until body is free from jack stands.

2) Tighten bolts and nuts retaining control arms to body. Tighten bolts and nuts retaining control arm to axle housing. Tighten all bolts and nuts to specification.

Rear Suspension

TOYOTA COROLLA RWD, CRESSIDA WAGON, TERCEL 4WD WAGON & VAN (Cont.)

TIGHTENING SPECIFICATIONS

Application	Ft. Lbs. (N.m)
Cressida & Van	
Control Arms-to-Axle Bolts	106 (143)
Control Arms-to-Body Bolts	106 (143)
Lateral Control Rod-to-Axle Nut	43 (58)
Lateral Control Rod-to-Body Bolt	
Cressida	58 (78)
Van	81 (110)
Shock Absorber Nut	
Lower	27 (37)
Upper	20 (27)
Stabilizer Bar-to-Link	19 (25)
Wheel Lug Nut	76 (103)
Corolla & Tercel	
Control Arms-to-Axle Bolts	87 (118)
Control Arms-to-Body Bolts	87 (118)
Lateral Control Rod-to-Axle Nut	47 (64)
Lateral Control Rod-to-Body Bolt	87 (118)
Shock Absorber Nut	
Lower	27 (37)
Upper	18 (25)
Stabilizer Bar-to-Link	22 (30)
Wheel Lug Nut	76 (103)

Rear Suspension

TOYOTA CRESSIDA SEDAN

NOTE: **Cressida Wagon uses a solid rear axle assembly. See appropriate article in this section.**

DESCRIPTION

Rear suspension is fully independent coil spring type. The suspension arms are mounted by bushings and pivot bolts to body and are supported by coil springs and shock absorbers. The stabilizer bar attaches to the differential support member and suspension arms.

ADJUSTMENTS & INSPECTION

WHEEL ALIGNMENT SPECIFICATIONS & PROCEDURES

See WHEEL ALIGNMENT SPECIFICATONS & PROCEDURES in WHEEL ALIGNMENT section.

WHEEL BEARING

Adjustment

Tighten hub nut to 29 ft. lbs. (39 N.m). Rotate axle back and forth to snug down. Measure preload rotation resistance. It should be .9-3.5 INCH lbs. (.1-.4 N.m). Tighten hub nut to 58 ft. lbs. (79 N.m). Check preload rotation.

Checking Preload

Turn hub flange at 10 RPM and measure preload. If preload is less than .9-3.5 INCH lbs. (.1-.4 N.m), retighten hub nut 5-10 degrees at a time until preload is reached. Maximum torque for hub nut is 145 ft. lbs. (197 N.m).

Fig. 2: Exploded View of Axle Shaft

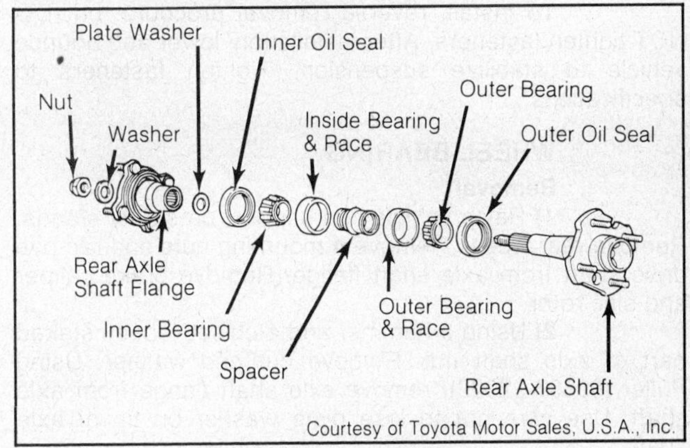

REMOVAL & INSTALLATION

SHOCK ABSORBER & COIL SPRING

Removal

1) Raise vehicle and support body with safety stands. Leave a floor jack under suspension arm. Remove brake hose clips. Disconnect nut, cushion and retainer of stabilizer bar and remove from suspension arm. Remove 4 nuts holding rear drive shaft to axle hub flange.

2) Remove lower shock absorber bolt. Disconnect shock absorber. If replacing shock absorber, use a wrench to hold shaft and remove nut retaining shock absorber to body. Remove shock absorber. Lower suspension arm using care not to stretch brake line or parking brake cable. Remove coil spring and insulators.

Fig. 1: Exploded View of Rear Suspension

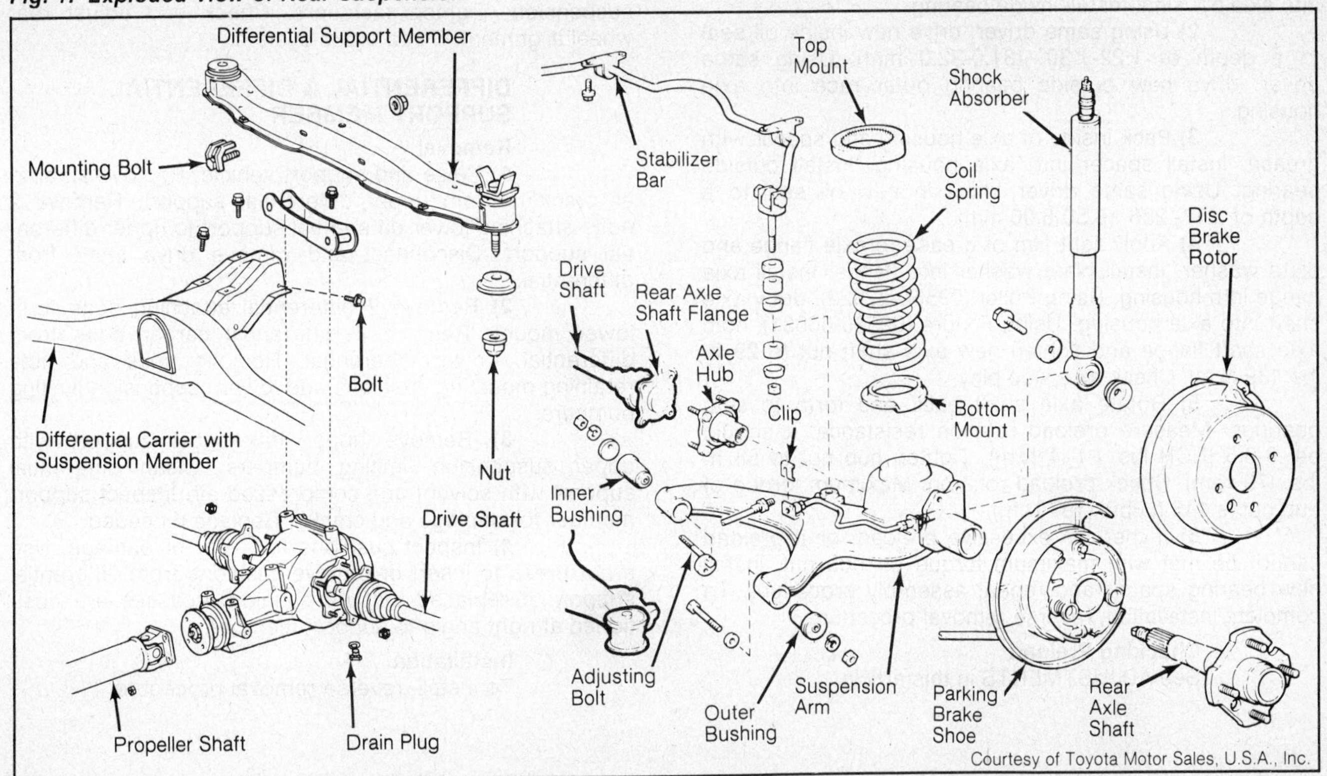

Rear Suspension

TOYOTA CRESSIDA SEDAN (Cont.)

Installation

To install, reverse removal procdure, but DO NOT tighten fasteners. After installation, lower and bounce vehicle to stabilize suspension. Tighten fasteners to specifications.

WHEEL BEARING

Removal

1) Raise vehicle and support on safety stands. Remove rear wheel. Remove 4 mounting nuts and remove drive shaft from axle shaft flange. Remove brake caliper and disc rotor.

2) Using a hammer and a chisel, loosen staked part of axle shaft nut. Remove nut and washer. Using Puller (09557-22022), remove axle shaft flange from axle shaft. Use care not to lose plate washer on tip of axle shaft.

3) Using Puller (09520-00031), remove axle shaft with oil seal and outside bearing. Using Seal Puller (09308-00010), remove inside oil seal and bearing.

4) Using a brass drift, drive inside and outside bearing outer races from axle housing. To remove bearing from axle shaft, drive a chisel between bearing and hub to provide working clearance.

5) Using Bearing Puller (09950-00020) and Adapter (09950-00030), remove outside bearing from axle shaft. Remove oil seal from axle shaft.

Inspection

Clean parts with solvent and compressed air. Using a dial micrometer and 2 "V" blocks, check axle shaft runout for damage. Maximum runout is .004" (.10 mm). Replace axle shaft if damaged or runout is greater than maximum.

Installation

1) Pack new bearings with grease. Using Driver (09550-22010), drive new inside bearing outer race into axle housing. Install inside bearing.

2) Using same driver, drive new inside oil seal to a depth of 1.22-1.30" (31.0-32.0 mm). Using same driver, drive new outside bearing outer race into axle housing.

3) Pack inside of axle housing and spacer with grease. Install spacer into axle housing. Install outside bearing. Using same driver, drive in new oil seal to a depth of .217-.236" (5.50-6.00 mm).

4) Apply light film of grease to axle flange and plate washer. Install plate washer into flange. Install axle flange into housing. Using Puller (09550-22022), draw axle shaft into axle housing. Using Fixture (09520-00031), hold axle shaft flange and tighten new axle shaft nut to 29 ft. lbs. (39 N.m). Check axle side play.

5) Rotate axle shaft back and forth to seat bearings. Measure preload rotation resistance. It should be .9-3.5 INCH lbs. (.1-.4 N.m). Tighten hub nut to 58 ft. lbs. (79 N.m). Check preload rotation. Maximum torque of hub nut is 145 ft. lbs. (197 N.m).

6) If there is excessive preload, or if preload cannot be met with maximum torque on hub nut, install new bearing spacer and repeat assembly procedure. To complete installation, reverse removal procedure.

Checking Preload

See ADJUSTMENTS in this article.

STABILIZER BAR

Removal & Installation

Remove stabilizer bar brackets from differential support member. Remove nuts, cushions and links from both sides of stabilizer bar and remove stabilizer bar. To install, reverse removal procedure.

SUSPENSION ARM

Removal

1) Disconnect stabilizer from suspension arm. Remove 4 mounting bolts and disconnect drive shaft from axle hub flange. Using Puller (09557-22022), remove rear axle hub flange. Remove parking brake cable, disc rotor and backing plate or dust cover.

2) Using Puller (09520-00031), remove axle shaft. Disconnect brake line. Disconnect shock absorber from suspension arm and remove coil spring. Place reference marks on camber adjusting cams.

3) Remove 2 mounting bolts, camber adjusting cam and suspension arm. Inspect bushings and suspension arms for wear, cracks and damage. Replace if necessary.

Bushing Replacement

1) Cut off rubber lip from flange end of bushing. Using a hammer and chisel, bend bushing flange inward. Using a pair of pliers, bend and break off flange edge.

2) Using Driver (09710-22040), press outer bushing from suspension arm, using care not to damage suspension arm flange. Using same driver, press new bushings into suspension arm.

Installation

Install camber adjusting cam to suspension arm and align to reference mark. To complete installation, reverse removal procedures but DO NOT tighten fasteners. Lower and bounce vehicle several times to align suspension. Tighten fasteners. Check and adjust rear wheel alignment. Bleed brake system.

DIFFERENTIAL & DIFFERENTIAL SUPPORT MEMBER

Removal

1) Raise and support vehicle. Remove stabilizer brackets from upper differential support. Remove 2 bolts attaching lower differential support to upper differential support. Disconnect and remove drive shaft from differential.

2) Remove 2 differential attaching bolts from lower mount. Remove 4 differential carrier bolts from differential. Lower differential. Remove bolts and nuts retaining mounting cushions and lower suspension limiting bumpers.

3) Remove upper differential support with upper suspension limiting bumpers. Clean differential support with solvent and compressed air. Inspect support member for damage and cracks. Replace if needed.

4) Inspect cushions for wear or damage. Use arbor press to insert or remove cushions from differential support. If replaced, ensure cushion recesses are positioned at right angle to support member.

Installation

To install, reverse removal procedure.

Rear Suspension

TOYOTA CRESSIDA SEDAN (Cont.)

TIGHTENING SPECIFICATIONS

Application	Ft. Lbs. (N.m)
Drive Shaft-to-	
Axle Hub Flange Bolts	44-57 (60-77)
Differential	51 (69)
Shock Absorber-to-	
Body Bolts	14-22 (19-30)
Suspension Arm Nuts	22-32 (30-43)
Stabilizer Bar-to-	
Suspension Arm Bolts	11-15 (15-20)
Suspension Arm	
Inside Bushing Bolt	73-97 (99-132)
Outside Bushing Bolt	84-108 (114-146)

Rear Suspension

TOYOTA IRS

Camry, Celica, Corolla FWD, Tercel Wagon (Exc. 4WD)

DESCRIPTION

The rear suspension system utilizes MacPherson struts, which fasten to axle carrier and wheel housing. Camry, Celica, FWD Corolla and Tercel Wagon models use a one piece axle carrier, mounted to an axle hub containing the axle bearings. The axle hub is attached to the axle carrier with 4 bolts.

Tercel Sedan and Liftback models use a 2-piece axle carrier, mounted to an axle hub containing the axle bearings. Hub is supported by axle shaft, which is mounted to the axle carrier with 4 bolts.

All models use a rear drum brake system. Celica models have an optional disc brake system. Connected to each axle carrier are 2 suspension arms, a strut rod and a stabilizer bar. Toe-in is adjusted by turning the adjusting cams, which are located in the rear suspension arms.

ADJUSTMENTS & INSPECTION

WHEEL ALIGNMENT SPECIFICATIONS & PROCEDURES

See WHEEL ALIGNMENT SPECIFICATIONS & PROCEDURES in WHEEL ALIGNMENT section.

WHEEL BEARING

NOTE: To adjust axle shaft nut for Camry, Celica, FWD Corolla and Tercel Wagon, axle hub MUST be removed from axle carrier.

1) On Camry, Celica, FWD Corolla and Tercel Wagon, adjust bearing by tightening axle shaft nut to 90 ft. lbs. (123 N.m).

2) On Tercel Sedan and Liftback models, tighten hub nut to 22 ft. lbs. (30 N.m), and turn hub several times. Loosen nut until it can be turned by hand, using ONLY a socket without a handle. Tighten axle shaft nut until preload is 0.9-2.2 lbs. (4.0-9.8 N). Adjust nut until correct preload is obtained.

NOTE: When rotating hub, there should be absolutely no brake drag.

REMOVAL & INSTALLATION

SHOCK ABSORBER & COIL SPRING

Removal

1) Raise and support vehicle. On liftback models, remove package tray, quarter vent and speaker grille. On all models, remove wheel assembly. Disconnect brake tube at wheel cylinder and at junction on shock absorber. Remove flexible brake hose at shock absorber and plug openings.

2) Loosen but DO NOT remove nut holding suspension support to shock absorber. Remove 2 bolts holding shock absorber to axle carrier. Disconnect shock absorber. On Celica models only, disconnect stabilizer bar link from shock absorber.

3) Remove 3 nuts holding shock absorber to body. Remove shock absorber. Install a bolt and 2 nuts between the bottom shock absorber mounting flanges to keep the mounting flanges from being crushed. Secure in a vise.

4) Using Spring Compressor (09727-22032), compress coil spring. Remove nut holding suspension support to shock absorber. Remove suspension support,

Fig. 1: Camry, FWD Corolla & Tercel Wagon Rear Axle Components

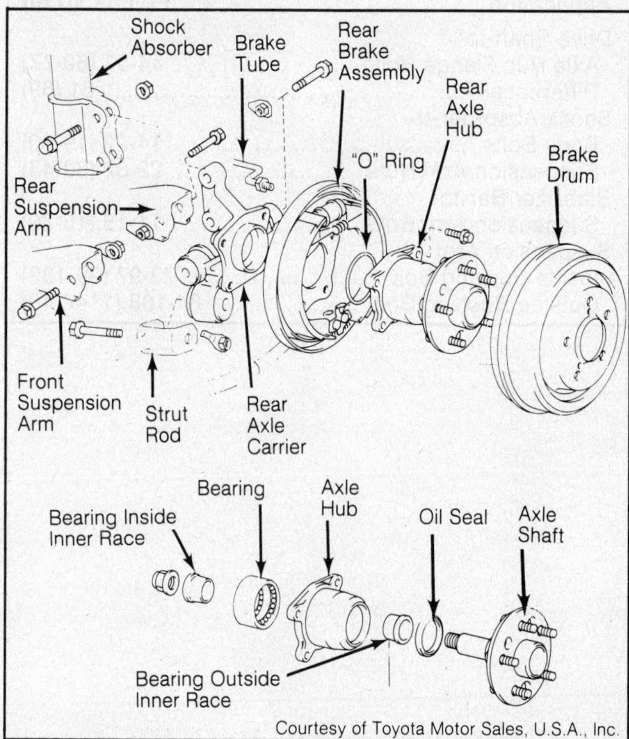

Celica is similar.

Fig. 2: Tercel Sedan & Liftback Rear Axle Components

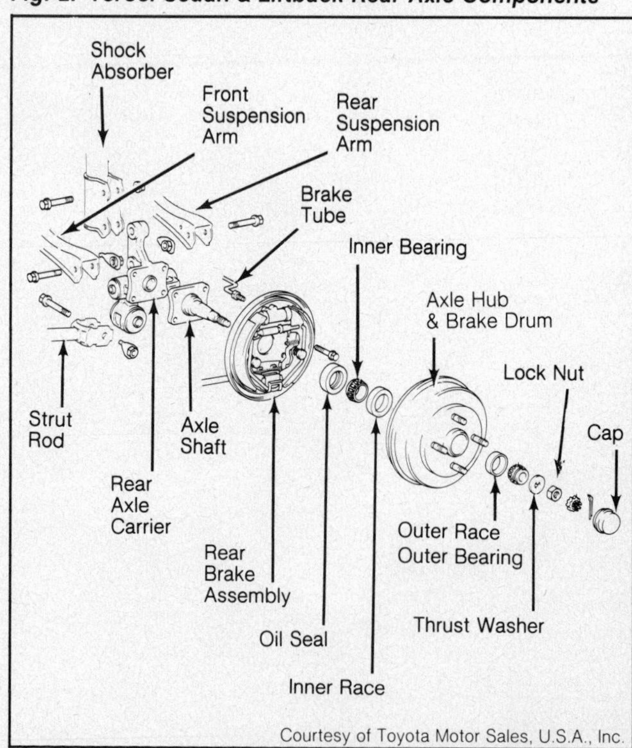

TOYOTA IRS (Cont.)

coil spring, insulator and bumper. DO NOT disassemble shock absorber.

CAUTION: When replacing a shock absorber, relieve high pressure gas by drilling a .079-.118" (2-3 mm) hole .39" (10 mm) above mounting flanges at base of shock absorber.

Installation

To install, reverse removal procedure. Align coil spring end in hollow portion of spring seat. Align suspension support with lower bracket of shock absorber. *See Fig. 3.* Bleed rear brake system. Check alignment of rear wheels.

Fig. 3: Aligning Shock Absorber Suspension Support

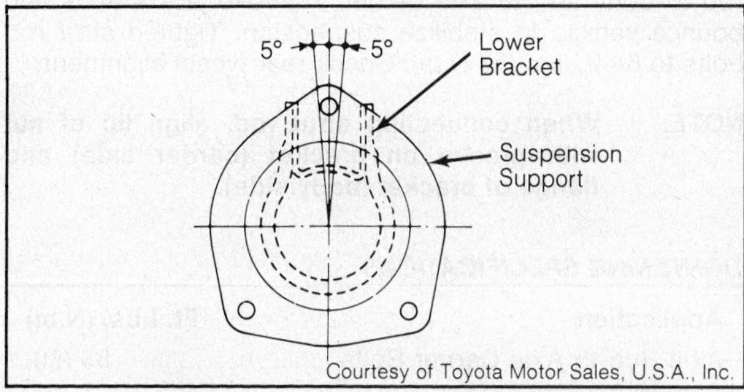

Fig. 4: Exploded View of Rear Suspension Components

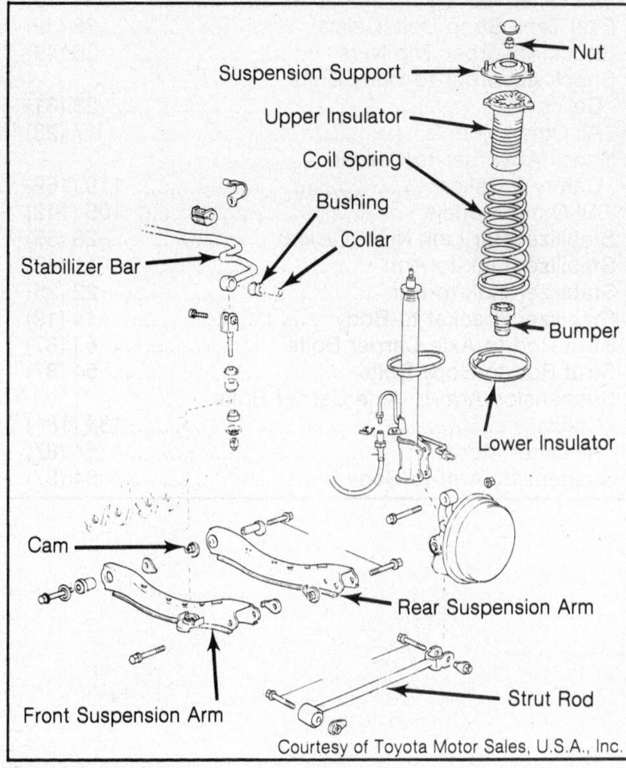

Celica is similar.

AXLE HUB, CARRIER & SHAFT

Removal

1) Raise and support vehicle. Remove rear wheel. Using a dial indicator, check bearing play in axial direction. It should be less than .002" (.05 mm). Disconnect brake tube at wheel cylinder. Plug tube openings.

2) On Tercel Sedan and Liftback models, remove grease cap, cotter pin, nut lock and axle nut. Remove thrust washer, outer bearing and brake hub/drum assembly. On Camry, Celica, FWD Corolla and Tercel Wagon, remove 4 bolts retaining axle hub to axle carrier. On Tercel Sedan and Liftback models, remove 4 bolts retaining axle shaft to axle carrier.

3) Remove axle hub on Camry, Celica, FWD Corolla and Tercel Wagon, or axle shaft on other Tercel models. On Camry, Celica, FWD Corolla and Tercel Wagon, remove "O" ring. On all models, remove nuts and bolts holding axle carrier to strut rod, shock absorber, and front and rear suspension arms. Note position of nuts on suspension arms and strut rods. Remove axle carrier.

Installation

1) On all models, place axle carrier in mounting position. Install nuts and bolts holding axle carrier to shock absorber. On Camry and Celica models, tighten nuts to 119 ft. lbs. (162 N.m). On all other models, tighten nuts to 105 ft. lbs. (142 N.m). Install but DO NOT tighten nuts and bolts to front and rear suspension arm (install lip of nut into hole on suspension arm).

2) Install but DO NOT tighten nut and bolt holding axle carrier to strut rod (insert lip of nut into groove on bracket). For Camry, Celica, FWD Corolla and Tercel Wagon, install new "O" ring to axle carrier.

3) Install axle hub assembly for Camry, Celica, FWD Corolla and Tercel Wagon or axle shaft for other Tercel models and tighten bolts to 59 ft. lbs. (80 N.m). Install brake drum and hub assembly. On Tercel Sedan and Liftback models, install outer bearing, thrust washer and nut. Adjust preload on lock nut. See ADJUSTMENTS in this article. Install cotter pin and grease cap.

4) On all models, connect brake tube to wheel cylinder. Bleed brake system. Lower vehicle to ground and bounce to stabilize suspension. With weight of vehicle on suspension, tighten axle carrier mounting bolts. Check rear wheel alignment.

WHEEL BEARINGS

Removal

1) On Tercel Sedan and Liftback models, remove rear axle hub. See AXLE HUB, CARRIER & SHAFT removal. Use screwdriver to remove oil seal and inside bearing. Using Bearing Remover (09608-16010) and Adapter (09608-20011), drive bearing races from brake drum.

2) On Camry, Celica, FWD Corolla and Tercel Wagon, use a hammer and a chisel to loosen staked part of axle nut and remove axle nut. Using Puller (09950-20015), remove axle shaft from axle hub. Using Puller (09950-20015), remove outside bearing inner race from axle shaft. Remove oil seal. Using Bearing Drivers (09228-22020 and 09636-20010), press out bearing.

Installation

1) On Camry, Celica, FWD Corolla and Tercel Wagons, use Driver (09316-60010) to press new bearing into hub. Install bearing inner races.

2) Using Driver (09310-35010), drive oil seal into axle hub. Using Adapter (09636-20010), press inner race with axle hub onto axle shaft. Tighten axle nut to 90 ft. lbs. (123 N.m) and stake axle nut.

3) On other Tercel models, use Driver (09608-16010) and Adapter (09608-20011) to drive new outer races into hub. Pack grease into new bearings, grease cap and center of hub. Place new inner bearing into hub.

Rear Suspension

TOYOTA IRS (Cont.)

Using Seal Driver (09608-20011), drive new seal into hub. Apply multipurpose grease to axle seal.

SUSPENSION ARM

Removal

1) Raise vehicle and support vehicle. Remove nut and bolt holding rear suspension arm to axle carrier. Place match marks on cam plate, rear suspension arm, and body.

2) Loosen arm retaining bolt making sure not to turn cam, so as not to disturb rear wheel alignment. Remove rear suspension arm. Remove nut and bolt retaining front suspension arm to body mounting bracket. Remove front suspension arm. If necessary, remove the stabilizer bar from the front suspension arm.

Front Arm Outside Bushing Replacement

To remove bushing from suspension arm, use Bushing Driver (09726-32010) and an arbor press to press out bushing. Use same driver to press in new bushing. Do not use a lubricant on bushing or suspension arm when pressing bushing into suspension arm.

Installation

1) To install, connect but DO NOT tighten front suspension arm to body and axle carrier with nuts and bolts. When installing front suspension arm to body, make sure lip of nut is resting on bracket flange, NOT over it. When connecting front suspension arm to axle carrier, insert lip of nut into hole on suspension arm.

2) On Celica models, front suspension arm is marked "L" and "R" respectively. Ensure arm is installed with slit side of bushing toward rear of vehicle.

3) Install but DO NOT tighten rear suspension arm to body with cam (align cam plate match mark). Install but DO NOT tighten rear suspension arm to axle carrier with nut and bolt. Be sure lip of nut is resting on bracket flange, not over it.

4) On Celica models, ensure rear arm is installed with slit side of bushing toward rear of vehicle, and Yellow paint mark toward outside of vehicle.

5) Remove jack stands and bounce vehicle to stabilize suspension. Tighten bolts with vehicle resting on suspension. Check rear wheel alignment.

STABILIZER BAR

Removal & Installation (Celica)

1) Raise vehicle and support. Remove wheels. Disconnect tail pipe from exhaust pipe. Using a jack and a wooden block, support fuel tank. Remove 2 tank band bolts from body. Disconnect stabilizer bar from stabilizer bar link.

2) Remove stabilizer bar link from shock absorber. Remove stabilizer bar brackets from body. Remove stabilizer bar from vehicle. Inspect link ball joint for free movement in all directions. Replace if necessary. To install, reverse removal procedure.

Removal & Installation (All Other Models)

Remove nuts, bolts and bushings retaining stabilizer bar to front suspension arm. Remove bolts retaining stabilizer bar to body. Remove stabilizer bar. Remove stabilizer link bolts. Using an arbor press, remove collar from stabilizer end bushing. Remove end bushing by pressing out by hand. To install, reverse removal procedure.

STRUT ROD

Removal & Installation

1) Raise vehicle and place on jack stands. Remove wheel. Remove nuts and bolts holding strut rod to axle carrier and to body. Remove strut rod.

2) To install, connect but DO NOT tighten strut rod to body and to axle carrier. Remove jack stands and bounce vehicle to stabilize suspension. Tighten strut rod bolts to 64 ft. lbs. (87 N.m). Check rear wheel alignment.

NOTE: When connecting strut rod, align lip of nut with groove on bracket (carrier side) and flange of bracket (body side).

TIGHTENING SPECIFICATIONS

Application	Ft. Lbs. (N.m)
Axle Hub-to-Axle Carrier Bolts	59 (80)
Axle Nut	
Tercel	22 (30)
All Other Models	90 (123)
Fuel Tank Strap Bolt (Celica)	29 (39)
Shock Absorber Top Nuts	36 (49)
Shock Absorber-to-Body Bolts	
Celica	23 (31)
All Other Models	17 (23)
Shock Absorber-to-Carrier	
Camry & Celica	119 (162)
All Other Models	105 (142)
Stabilizer Bar Link Nuts (Celica)	26 (35)
Stabilizer Link-to-Arm	11 (15)
Stabilizer Link-to-Bar	22 (35)
Stabilizer Bracket-to-Body	14 (19)
Strut Rod-to-Axle Carrier Bolts	64 (87)
Strut Rod-to-Body Bolts	64 (87)
Suspension Arm-to-Axle Carrier Bolts	
Celica	134 (181)
All Other Models	64 (87)
Suspension Arm-to-Body Bolts	64 (87)

Rear Suspension

TOYOTA MR2

DESCRIPTION

Rear suspension is an independent dual link with MacPherson struts, offset coil springs and gas shock absorbers. Dual links consist of a suspension arm and a lower arm. Lower end of strut is connected to upper end of axle carrier. Lower end of axle carrier is connected to ball joint, which is bolted to lower arm link. Lower arm link is connected to frame and to strut rod. Suspension arm link is connected to frame and to axle carrier and is adjustable for toe-in.

ADJUSTMENTS & INSPECTION

WHEEL ALIGNMENT SPECIFICATIONS & PROCEDURES

See WHEEL ALIGNMENT SPECIFICATIONS & PROCEDURES in WHEEL ALIGNMENT section.

WHEEL BEARING

Wheel bearings are not adjustable. Whenever bearings are removed, replace with new bearings, races, and oil seals. With bearing lock nut, brake caliper and disc rotor removed, check bearing axial play. Maximum axial play is .002" (.05 mm). Replace bearing assembly if play exceeds specification.

BALL JOINT CHECKING

1) Raise vehicle and place block with a height of 7.09-7.87" (180-200 mm) under one rear tire. Lower jack until there is half a load on rear coil spring. Place safety stands under vehicle. Move lower arm up and down and check that ball joint has zero vertical play. Replace ball joint if any vertical end play exists.

2) Check turning torque of lower arm ball joint with joint removed from vehicle. Flip joint stud back and forth 5 times. Install stud nut and using an INCH lb. torque wrench, check turning torque. Turn nut one turn each 2-4 seconds and take torque reading on the fifth turn. Torque should be 9-26 INCH lbs. (1.0-2.9 N.m). Replace ball joint if not within specification.

3) Check turning torque of suspension arm tie rod end with it removed from vehicle. Flip stud back and forth 5 times. Install stud nut and using an INCH lb. torque wrench, check turning torque. Turn nut continously one turn every 2-4 seconds and take torque reading on the fifth turn. Torque should be 7.4-30.0 INCH lbs. (0.9-3.4 N.m). Replace tie rod end if not within specification.

REMOVAL & INSTALLATION

WHEEL BEARING

Removal

1) Raise and support vehicle. Remove wheel assembly. Remove cotter pin and lock nut cap. With parking brake set, remove bearing lock nut. Remove brake caliper and wire out of way. Remove disc rotor.

2) Remove and disassemble axle carrier and hub. Remove inside inner race from bearing. Use puller to remove outside inner race from carrier. Use puller to remove outer oil seal from carrier. Place outside inner race on bearing and press out.

Installation

To install, reverse removal procedure. Use Driver (09608-32010) to press wheel bearing into carrier. Always install new grease seals. Ensure grease seals face in proper direction.

Fig. 1: Exploded View of Carrier & Hub Assembly

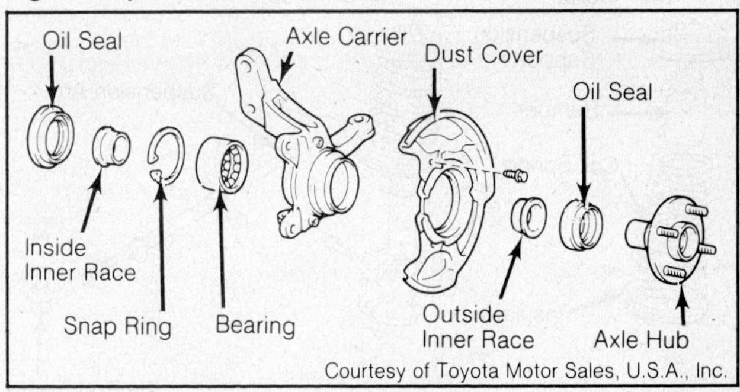

Courtesy of Toyota Motor Sales, U.S.A., Inc.

AXLE CARRIER & HUB

Removal

1) Raise and support vehicle. Remove wheel assembly. Remove cotter pin and lock nut cap. With parking brake set, remove bearing lock nut. Remove brake caliper and wire out of way. Remove disc rotor. Using Puller (09610-20012), disconnect suspension arm tie rod end from carrier.

2) Remove knuckle-to-lower control arm ball joint bolts. Mark strut camber adjusting cam for reassembly reference. Disconnect strut from carrier. Cover drive shaft boot with cloth to protect it from damage. Remove axle carrier and axle hub as a unit.

Disassembly

Using Puller (09308-00010), remove oil seal from carrier. Remove snap ring from carrier. Remove disc brake dust cover from carrier. Using Puller (09950-20016), remove axle hub from carrier.

Reassembly

To reassemble, reverse removal procedure. Use Driver (09310-35010) to press hub into carrier.

Installation

To install, reverse removal procedure. Ensure strut camber adjusting cam marks are aligned. Check wheel alignment.

STRUT ASSEMBLY

Removal

1) Raise vehicle and support. Remove wheel assembly. Disconnect brake hose from caliper. Drain fluid into container. Remove brake hose clip and disconnect hose from strut.

2) Mark strut camber adjusting cam for reassembly reference. Disconnect strut from carrier. Remove engine hood side panel. Remove strut-to-body nuts. Cover driveshaft with cloth to protect it from damage. Remove strut from vehicle.

Disassembly

1) Install a bolt and 2 nuts to lower portion of strut bracket to prevent strut shell from being crushed when clamped in vise. Clamp strut in vise and use Compressor (09727-22032) to compress coil spring.

2) Remove support cover. Clamp octagon shaped head of suspension support in vise. Remove piston rod nut. Remove suspension support, coil spring, insulator and rubber bumper.

Inspection

Check shock absorber action for abnormal noise, resistance and smoothness. If defective, replace

Rear Suspension

TOYOTA MR2 (Cont.)

Fig. 2: Exploded View of Rear Suspension Assembly

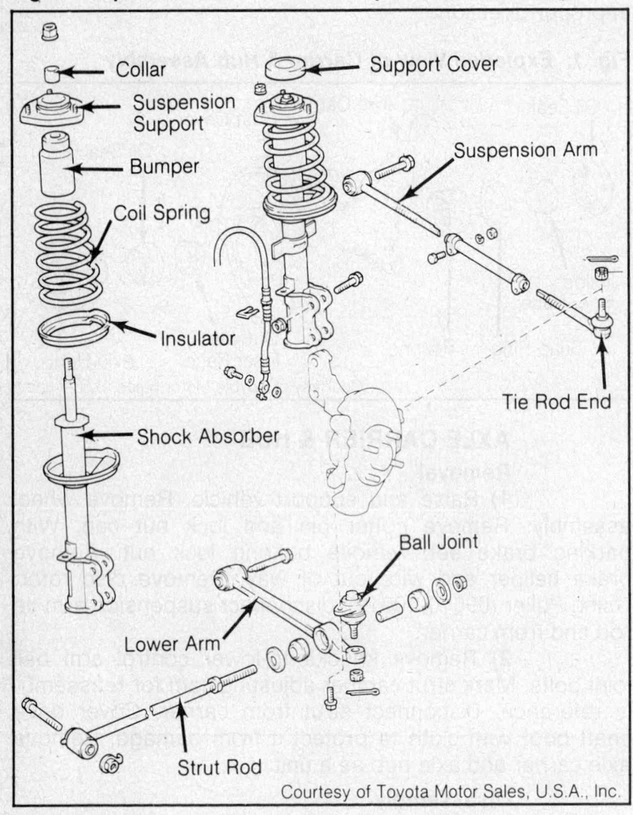

shock absorber unit. Loosen ring nut with Spanner Wrench (09721-00071) to release gas before discarding strut.

Reassembly

To reassemble, reverse disassembly procedure. Ensure notch on piston rod and suspension support are aligned. Ensure suspension support and strut lower bracket are aligned. *See Fig. 3*. Tighten piston rod lock nut to 54 ft. lbs. (73 N.m).

Installation

To install, reverse removal procedure. Ensure strut camber adjusting cam marks are aligned. Ensure flexible brake hose peg aligns with hole in caliper when connecting. Install strut-to-carrier bolts from rear side. Bleed brakes. Check alignment.

Fig. 3: Aligning Strut Suspension Support & Lower Bracket

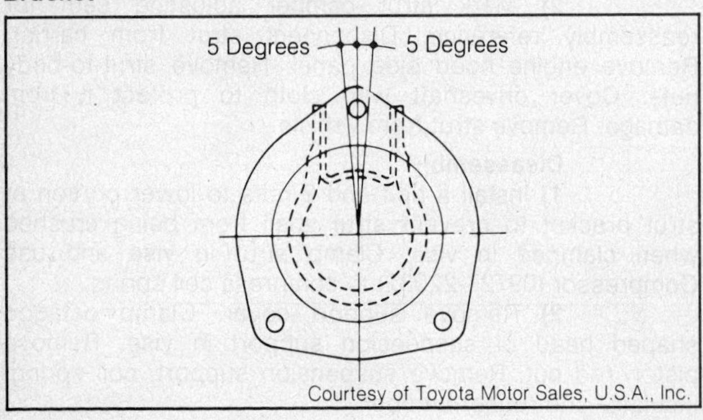

BALL JOINT

Removal & Installation

Raise vehicle and support. Remove wheel assembly. Remove cotter pin and nut from lower arm. Use Puller (09610-55012) to disconnect ball joint from lower arm. Remove bolts connecting ball joint to carrier. Remove ball joint. To install, reverse removal procedure.

LOWER ARM

Removal & Installation

1) Raise vehicle and support. Remove wheel assembly. Remove cotter pin and nut from lower arm. Use Puller (09610-55012) to disconnect ball joint from lower arm. Remove strut rod nut and retainer from lower arm. Remove lower arm-to-body bolt. Remove arm from vehicle.

2) To install, reverse removal procedure. Tighten lower arm-to-body bolt and strut rod nut after vehicle is lowered to ground. Check wheel alignment.

SUSPENSION ARM

Removal & Installation

1) Raise vehicle and support. Remove wheel assembly. Remove cotter pin and nut. Use Puller (09610-20012) to disconnect suspension arm tie rod end from carrier. Remove suspension arm-to-body bolt. Remove suspension arm from vehicle.

2) Adjust suspension arm to proper length. *See Fig. 4*. To install, reverse removal procedure. Check wheel alignment.

Fig. 4: Adjusting Suspension Arm Length

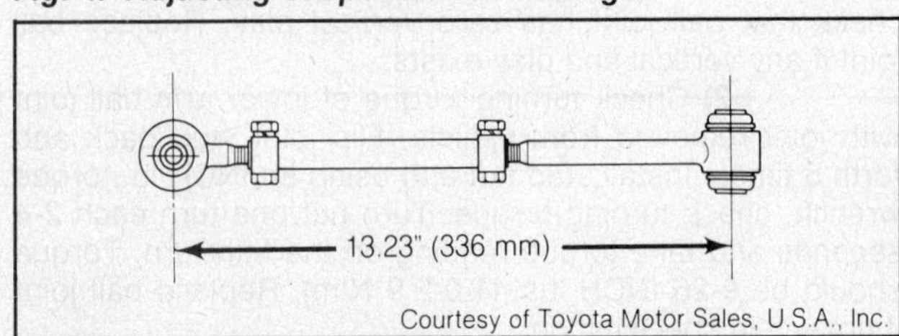

TIGHTENING SPECIFICATIONS

Application	Ft. Lbs. (N.m)
Axle Hub Nut	137 (186)
Ball Joint-to-Carrier Bolts	59 (80)
Ball Joint-to-Lower Arm Nut	67 (91)
Brake Line-to-Caliper	22 (30)
Caliper-to-Knuckle Bolts	43 (59)
Drive Shaft-to-Side Gear Shaft	27 (36)
Lower Arm-to-Body Bolt	94 (127)
Strut-to-Knuckle Bolts	105 (142)
Strut Piston Rod Nut	54 (73)
Strut-to-Body Nuts	23 (31)
Strut Rod-to-Lower Arm Nut	86 (117)
Strut Rod-to-Body Bolt	83 (113)
Suspension Arm-to-Body Bolt	64 (87)
Suspension Arm Clamp	14 (19)
Tie Rod End-to-Carrier	36 (49)

Rear Suspension

TOYOTA SUPRA

DESCRIPTION

Rear suspension is fully independent MacPherson stut type. The suspension arms are mounted by bushings and pivot bolts to body and are supported by the strut. The stabilizer bar attaches to the differential support member and suspension arms.

ADJUSTMENTS & INSPECTION

WHEEL ALIGNMENT SPECIFICATIONS & PROCEDURES

See WHEEL ALIGNMENT SPECIFICATONS & PROCEDURES in WHEEL ALIGNMENT section.

WHEEL BEARING

Wheel bearing are not adjustable. Whenever bearings, races or oil seals are removed, measure axial play when reassembled. Maximum axial play is .002" (.05 mm). Replace bearing assembly if play exceeds specification.

BALL JOINT

Ball joint inspection requires upper suspension arm removal, see REMOVAL & INSTALLATION in this article. After suspension arm removal, rotate ball joint back and forth 5 times. Install ball joint nut. Stud turning torque should be 9-30 inch lbs. (1.0-3.4 N.m). *See Fig. 3.*

Fig. 2: Exploded View of Carrier & Hub Assembly

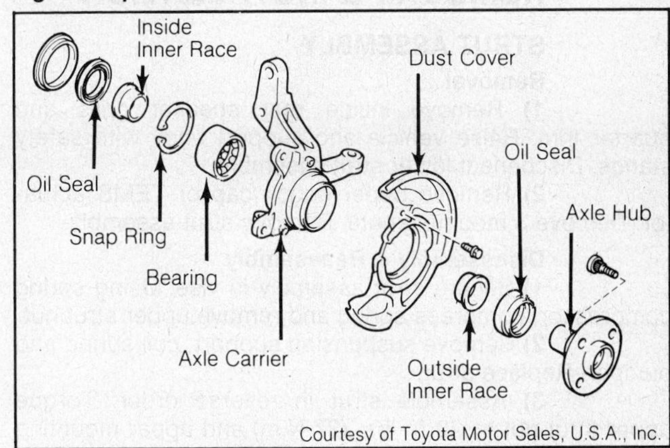

Courtesy of Toyota Motor Sales, U.S.A., Inc.

Fig. 3: Ball Joint Torque Test

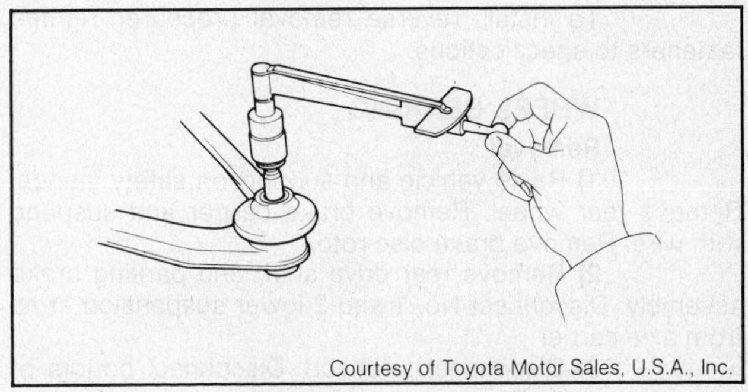

Courtesy of Toyota Motor Sales, U.S.A., Inc.

Fig. 1: Exploded View of Rear Suspension

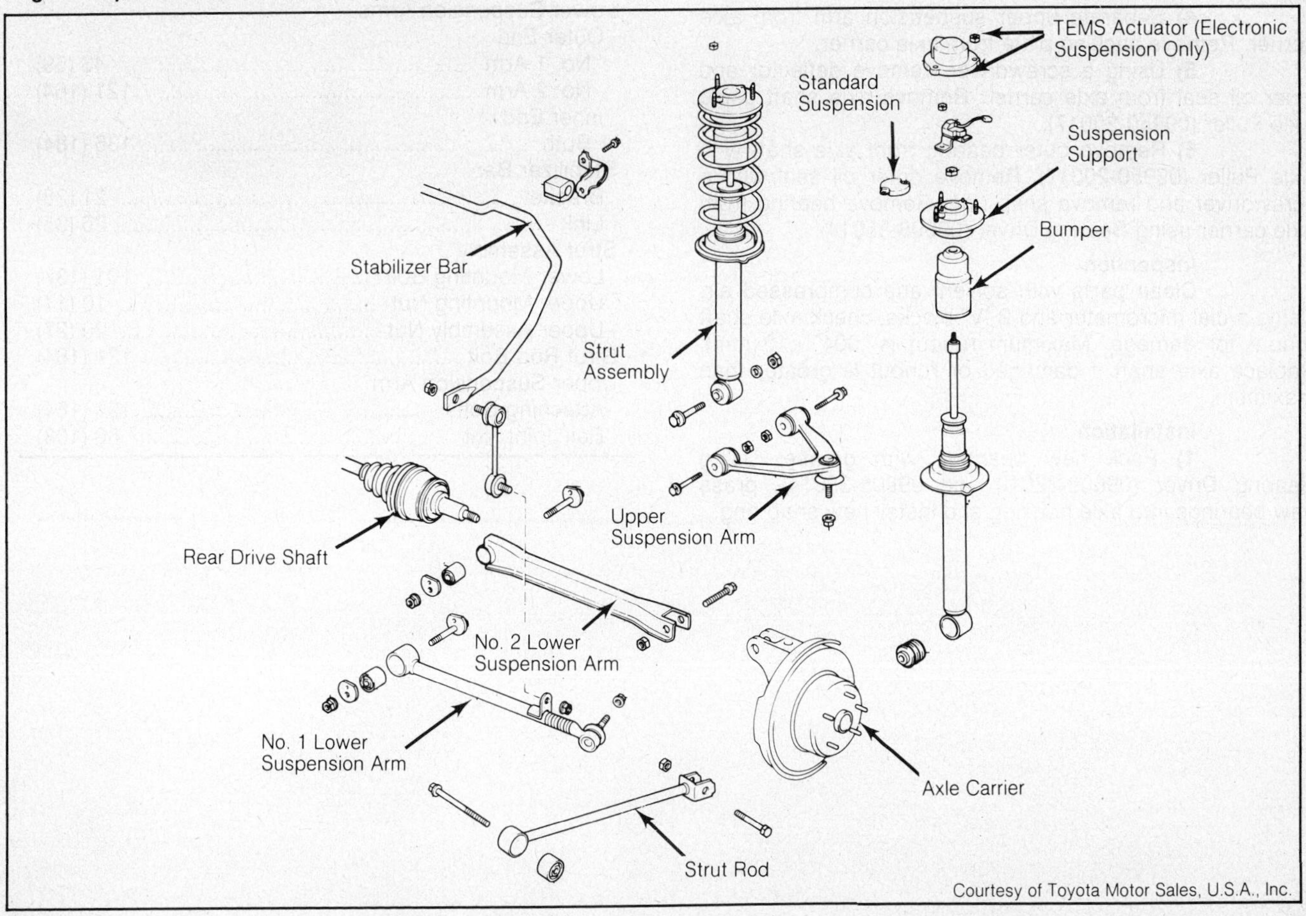

Courtesy of Toyota Motor Sales, U.S.A., Inc.

Rear Suspension

TOYOTA SUPRA (Cont.)

REMOVAL & INSTALLATION

STRUT ASSEMBLY

Removal

1) Remove inside rear speaker grills and quarter trim. Raise vehicle and support body with safety stands. Disconnect lower strut assembly.

2) Remove upper shock cap or TEMS actuator. Remove 3 mounting nuts. Remove strut assembly.

Disassembly & Reassembly

1) Secure strut assembly in vise. Using spring compressor, compress spring and remove upper strut nut.

2) Remove suspension support, coil spring and bumper. Replace strut.

3) Assemble strut in reverse order. Torque upper strut nut to 20 ft. lbs. (27 N.m) and upper mounting nut to 10 ft. lbs. (14 N.m).

Installation

To install, reverse removal procdure. Tighten fasteners to specifications.

WHEEL BEARING

Removal

1) Raise vehicle and support on safety stands. Remove rear wheel. Remove brake caliper and suspend with wire. Remove brake disc rotor.

2) Remove rear drive shaft and parking brake assembly. Disconnect No. 1 and 2 lower suspension arms from axle carrier.

3) Disconnect strut rod. Disconnect bottom of strut assembly. Disconnect upper suspension arm and remove axle carrier assembly.

4) Separate upper suspension arm from axle carrier. Remove backing plate from axle carrier.

5) Using a screwdriver, remove deflector and inner oil seal from axle carrier. Remove axle shaft using Axle Puller (09950-20017).

6) Remove outer bearing from axle shaft with Axle Puller (09950-20017). Remove outer oil seal with a screwdriver and remove snap ring. Remove bearing from axle carrier using Bearing Driver (09608-35014).

Inspection

Clean parts with solvent and compressed air. Using a dial micrometer and 2 "V" blocks, check axle shaft runout for damage. Maximum runout is .004" (.10 mm). Replace axle shaft if damaged or runout is greater than maximum.

Installation

1) Pack new bearings with grease. Using Bearing Driver (09608-32010 and 09608-35014), press new bearings into axle housing and install new snap ring.

2) Using Seal Driver (09608-32010), drive in new outer oil seal. Using Seal Driver (09223-15010), drive in new inner oil seal. Continue installation in reverse order.

STABILIZER BAR

Removal & Installation

Remove stabilizer bar brackets from differential support member. Remove nuts, cushions and links from both sides of stabilizer bar and remove stabilizer bar. To install, reverse removal procedure.

Bushing Replacement

1) Cut off rubber lip from flange end of bushing. Using a hammer and chisel, bend bushing flange inward. Using a pair of pliers, bend and break off flange edge.

2) Using Driver (09710-22040), press outer bushing from suspension arm, using care not to damage suspension arm flange. Using same driver, press new bushings into suspension arm.

Installation

Install camber adjusting cam to suspension arm and align to reference mark. To complete installation, reverse removal procedures but DO NOT tighten fasteners. Lower and bounce vehicle several times to align suspension. Tighten fasteners. Check and adjust rear wheel alignment. Bleed brake system.

TIGHTENING SPECIFICATIONS

Application	Ft. Lbs. (N.m)
Axle Shaft Nut	203 (275)
Backing Plate Nut	43 (59)
Lower Suspension Arms	
Outer End	
No. 1 Arm	43 (59)
No. 2 Arm	121 (164)
Inner End	
Both	136 (184)
Stabilizer Bar	
Bracket	21 (28)
Link	26 (35)
Strut Assembly	
Lower Mounting Bolt	101 (137)
Upper Mounting Nut	10 (14)
Upper Assembly Nut	20 (27)
Strut Rod Bolt	121 (164)
Upper Suspension Arm	
Attaching Bolts	121 (164)
Ball Joint Nut	80 (108)

Rear Suspension

VOLKSWAGEN FOX, GOLF, GTI, JETTA, QUANTUM & SCIROCCO

Fox, Golf, GTI, Jetta, Quantum, Scirocco

DESCRIPTION

Rear suspension is link type with MacPherson type suspension struts. Suspension uses control arms and axle beam for stabilization. Control arms and axle beam are combined as one unit. Brake drums or discs ride on stub axles bolted to control arms. *See Fig. 1.*

ADJUSTMENTS & INSPECTION

WHEEL ALIGNMENT SPECIFICATIONS & PROCEDURES

See WHEEL ALIGNMENT SPECIFICATIONS & PROCEDURES in WHEEL ALIGNMENT section.

WHEEL BEARING

Tighten hub nut to 7.5 ft. lbs. (10 N.m), while rotating brake drum by hand. Determine the bearing play by testing the force needed to move thrust washer. Light pressure should move thrust washer. Turn hub nut until correct pressure is obtained.

REMOVAL & INSTALLATION

STRUT ASSEMBLY

NOTE: **DO NOT remove both suspension struts at same time as this would overload bushings in axle beam.**

Fig. 1: Exploded View of Rear Suspension Components

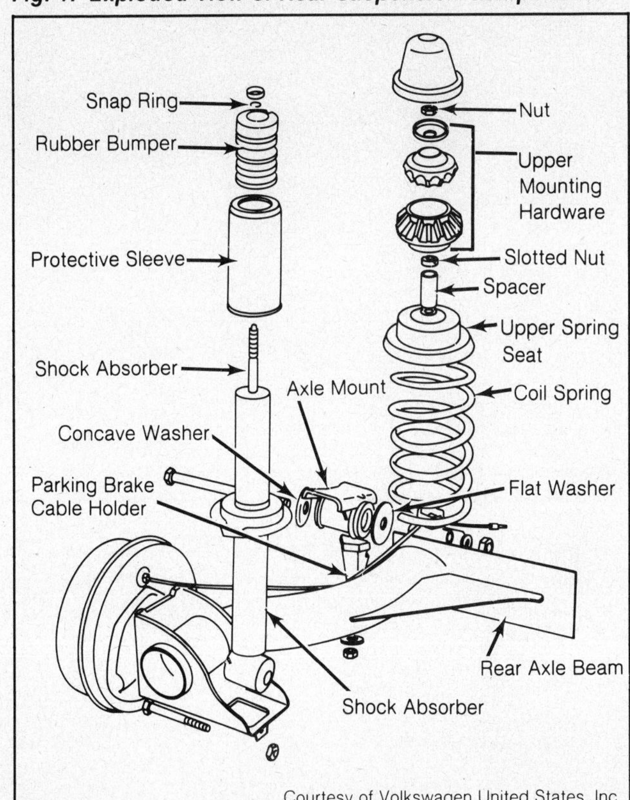

Removal

1) With vehicle on floor, take off plastic cap covering strut upper retaining nuts and remove nuts.

2) Slowly raise vehicle until weight is off spring. Remove bolt retaining lower end of strut shock absorber to axle beam mount. Raise vehicle until strut can be removed.

Disassembly

Place strut assembly in vise. Hold piston rod and remove strut retaining nut. Take off components down to slotted nut. Remove slotted nut. Take off spacer and coil spring.

NOTE: **Some models do not have the slotted nut on shock absorber shaft.**

Inspection

Hand check shock absorbers for even resistance through entire piston stroke. Worn shock absorbers cannot be overhauled. If coil spring is being replaced, ensure that paint stripe color code on replacement spring matches original spring code.

Reassembly

1) Fit protective cap and tube on shock absorber. Install rubber buffer, with small diameter end downward. Insert snap ring and washer.

2) Place spring into lower seat. Fit upper retainer with spacer sleeve. Tighten slotted nut retaining piston rod. Put on upper mounting hardware and tighten piston rod.

Installation

To install, reverse removal procedure. Tighten all bolts and nuts to specification. See TIGHTENING SPECIFICATIONS table in this article.

SUSPENSION ASSEMBLY

CAUTION: **When removing suspension assembly, add weight to rear of vehicle to prevent tipping due to change in center of gravity.**

Removal

1) With vehicle on floor, disconnect upper strut mount. Raise vehicle and support with safety stands.

2) Disconnect parking brake at holder near axle mount. Disconnect and plug brake lines. Leave flex hose attached to suspension.

3) Separate brake pressure regulator spring from axle beam (if equipped). Remove both nuts retaining axle beam on each side to body.

NOTE: **Do not install bolts and nuts coated with undercoating wax. With waxy coating on threads, true torque tightening cannot be reached. Clean or replace bolts and nuts.**

Installation

1) If axle beam mounting has been removed, adjust mounting pad. *See Fig. 2.* If pad is not correctly aligned, torsional preload of mounting bushings will be incorrect.

2) Position rear suspension on body. Install nuts retaining axle beam to body. Raise wheel and guide upper end of strut into body mount.

3) Connect parking brake cables. Connect brake lines. Lower vehicle and tighten upper strut retaining nuts. Tighten all bolts and nuts to specification. Bleed brake system.

Rear Suspension

VOLKSWAGEN FOX, GOLF, GTI, JETTA, QUANTUM & SCIROCCO (CONT.)

AXLE BEAM PIVOT BUSHING

Removal

1) This procedure is for replacing bushing with axle beam installed in vehicle. Raise vehicle and support with safety stands under vehicle body.

2) With no pressure on beam, remove nuts retaining axle beam to body and tap out pivot bolt.

Fig. 2: Correct Alignment of Axle Beam Mounting Pad

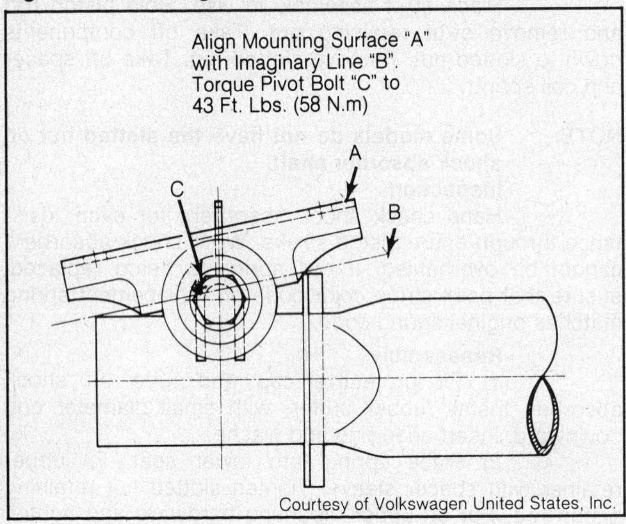
Align Mounting Surface "A"
with Imaginary Line "B".
Torque Pivot Bolt "C" to
43 Ft. Lbs. (58 N.m)
A
B
C

Courtesy of Volkswagen United States, Inc.

3) Using Bushing Remover (VW 3111), press out bushing. Select new bushing and press bushing into place.

Installation

1) Loosely install mounting pad on axle beam. On Quantum models, use Bushing Installer (VW 3111) to install bushing (with power tool if possible). Install bushing to a depth of 2.42-2.44" (61.5-62.0 mm). Concave washer and bolt head must face toward outside of vehicle. Bolt head must recess into washer.

2) Using Mounting Bracket Aligner (VW 261 or 3021), align mount. *See Fig. 2.* Tighten pivot bolt nut to specification with vehicle on ground.

TIGHTENING SPECIFICATIONS

Application	Ft. Lbs. (N.m)
Brake Caliper Bolts	48 (65)
Coil Spring Retainer-to-Piston Rod Nut	11 (15)
Rear Axle Beam Pivot Bushing Bolt	43 (58)
Rear Axle Mounting Pad-to-Body Bolts	63 (85)
Shock Absorber-to-Axle Beam Nut	52 (70)
Shock Absorber-to-Body Bolt	26 (35)
Shock Absorber Slot Nut	15 (20)
Stub Axle-to-Control Arm Bolts	44 (60)
Wheel Lug Bolts	81 (110)

Rear Suspension

VOLKSWAGEN QUANTUM SYNCRO

DESCRIPTION

Suspension is an independent system using lower control arms, strut assemblies, and a stabilizer bar. *See Fig. 1.*

ADJUSTMENTS & INSPECTION

WHEEL ALIGNMENT SPECIFICATIONS & PROCEDURES

See WHEEL ALIGNMENT SPECIFICATIONS & PROCEDURES in WHEEL ALIGNMENT section.

WHEEL BEARING

Wheel bearings are not adjustable.

REMOVAL & INSTALLATION

WHEEL BEARING

Removal

1) Remove control arm. See CONTROL ARM section in this article.

2) Remove splash shield screws and shield. Press out wheel hub using Housing Support (3110) and Press Adapters (VW-295) and (VW-295a). Using snap ring pliers, remove 2 snap rings. Press out wheel bearing using housing support and Press Adapter (40-20).

Installation

1) Install new snap ring in hub and coat bearing surface with grease. Press in new bearing using same tools as pressing out. Install snap ring. Press wheel hub into bearing using Support Plate (VW-402), Bearing Support (VW-519), and Press Adapters (VW-411) and (VW-432).

2) To complete installation, reverse removal procedure. Always replace axle shaft self-locking nut. Tighten all bolts to specification. See TIGHTENING SPECIFICATIONS table.

STRUT ASSEMBLY

Removal

1) With vehicle on floor, remove upper strut plastic cap and remove strut attaching nuts.

2) Slowly raise vehicle until weight is off spring. Remove lower strut mounting bolt. Remove strut.

Fig. 1: Quantum Syncro Rear Suspension

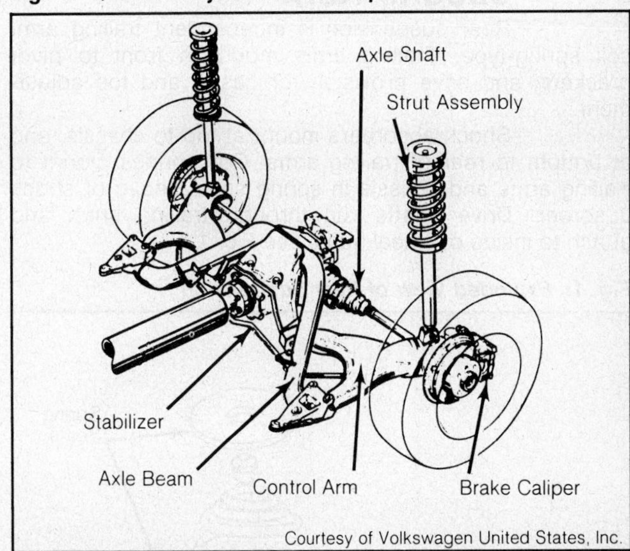

Disassembly

Place strut assembly in vice. Hold piston rod and remove nut and take off components, spacer and coil spring.

Reassembly

To assemble, reverse disassembly procedure.

Installation

To install, reverse removal procedure. Tighten all bolts to specification.

CONTROL ARM

Removal

1) Remove hub cover and axle nut. Raise and support vehicle. Remove wheel assembly, brake caliper mounting bolts and caliper. Remove brake disc.

2) Support control arm with floor jack and remove lower strut mounting bolt. Remove stabilizer bracket and 2 control arm pivot bolts. Support axle shaft and lower control arm slightly to allow control arm to be pulled off axle shaft.

Installation

To install, reverse removal procedure. Tighten axle shaft nut and control arm pivot bolts to specification with vehicle on ground. Always replace axle shaft self-locking nut.

Rear Suspension

VOLKSWAGEN VANAGON

DESCRIPTION

Rear suspension is independent trailing arm, coil spring-type. Trailing arms mount in front to pivot brackets, and have provision for caster and toe adjustment.

Shock absorbers mount at top to chassis, and at bottom to rear of trailing arms. Coil springs mount to trailing arms and chassis in spring seats ahead of shock absorber. Drive shafts run through trailing arms and attach to inside of wheel hubs. *See Fig. 1.*

Fig. 1: Exploded View of Rear Suspension

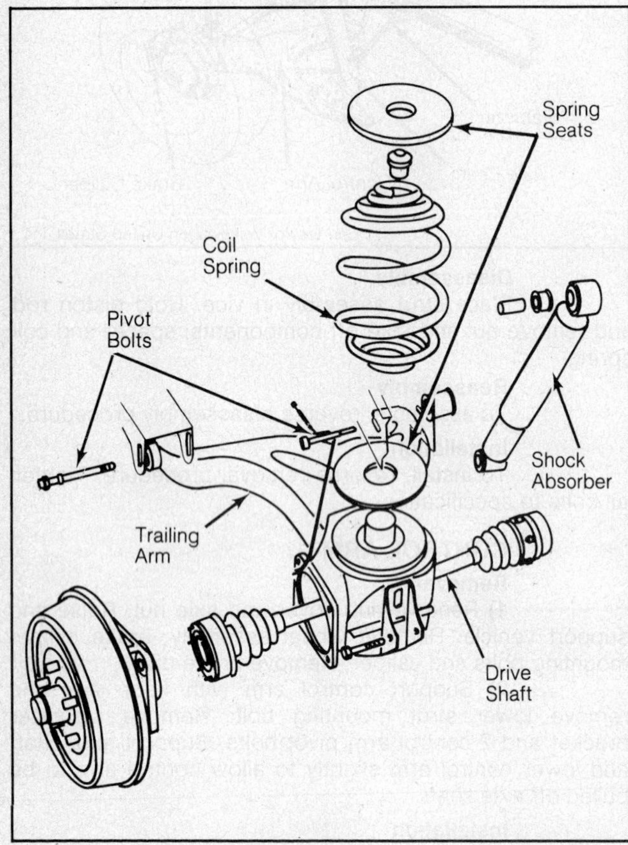

ADJUSTMENTS & INSPECTION

WHEEL ALIGNMENT SPECIFICATIONS & PROCEDURES

See WHEEL ALIGNMENT SPECIFICATIONS & PROCEDURES in WHEEL ALIGNMENT section.

REMOVAL & INSTALLATION

WHEEL BEARING

Removal

1) Remove axle nut. Raise and support vehicle. Remove wheel assembly. Remove brake line and plug. Remove brake drum and wheel hub assembly. Remove bolts attaching brake backing plate-to-wheel bearing housing. Pull backing plate off housing and support out of way.

2) Remove bolts attaching wheel bearing housing to trailing arm. Remove hex bolts at axle shaft-to-transaxle joint. Pull hub assembly and axle through trailing arm. Remove axle shaft hex bolts-to-hub and separate axle from hub. *See Fig. 2.*

3) Place bearing hub and axle shaft in press. Using Pressing Tool (VW411), press axle out of bearing housing. Remove outer grease seal. Remove inner grease seal and bearing circlip.

4) Remove inner race of outer wheel bearing. Remove spacer sleeve. Drive outer wheel bearing out with brass drift. Using Pressing Tools (VW412) and (VW244b), press inner bearing out of housing.

Installation

1) Using Support Plate (VW401) and Pressing Tools (VW407) and (VW472), Press inner bearing into housing until seated. Install bearing circlip. Press outer bearing into housing using same tools. Grease bearings and fill space between bearings with multi-purpose grease.

2) Install spacer sleeve and inner race of outer bearing. Using Seal Installer (VW240a), install outer and inner seals. Press axle shaft into bearing housing using Pressing Tools (VW412) and (30-100). To complete installation, reverse removal procedure. Tighten all bolts and nuts to specification. See TIGHTENING SPECIFICATIONS table in this article.

NOTE: During repairs on vehicles prior to VIN 25ZBH119362, install new spacer sleeve and axle nut. New nut has 10 key slots, old not has 6 key slots.

TRAILING ARMS

Removal

1) Raise and support vehicle. Remove wheel assembly and support trailing arm with a floor jack.

2) Remove nuts attaching brake drum and axle hub assembly to trailing arm. Using hex wrench, remove hex screws at axle shaft-to-transaxle joint.

3) Pull axle shaft and brake drum assembly through trailing arm and remove from vehicle. Remove shock absorber lower retaining bolt and slowly lower jack.

4) Remove coil spring and spring seats. Note relative position of trailing arm in mounting brackets. Remove pivot bolts and remove trailing arm from vehicle.

Bushing Replacement

1) Using Bushing Remover (VW 442) and Adapter (30-14), pull bushing out of trailing arm. Coat washer with oil and place between nut and tool.

2) With soapy solution, coat hole in trailing arm, Installer (3053), and bushing. Pull bushing in until sleeve contacts tool. Wait about 30 seconds before removing tool. Bushing should seat itself. If necessary, press edge of bushing out.

Installation

1) To install, reverse removal procedure. Depressions in spring seats must be aligned with ends of coil spring.

2) Align depression in lower spring seat with depression in trailing arm. Install trailing arm at noted position in bracket. Check wheel alignment.

VOLKSWAGEN VANAGON (Cont.)

Fig. 2: Exploded View of Wheel Bearing Hub

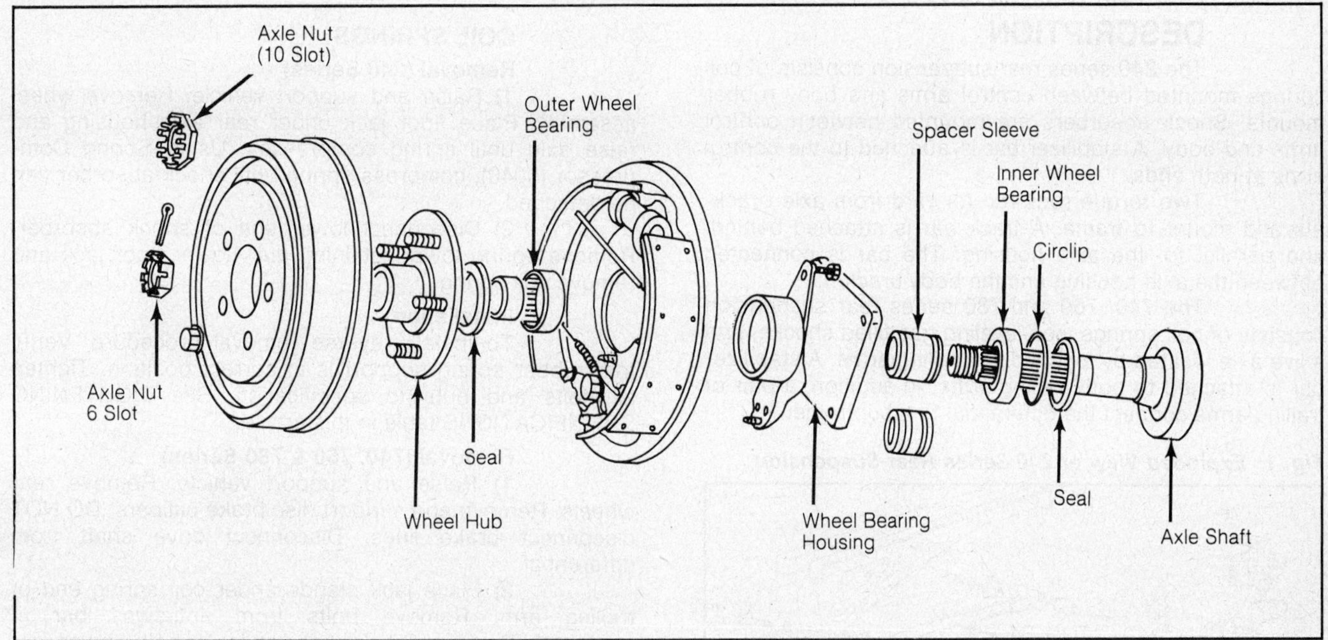

COIL SPRINGS

Removal

Raise and support vehicle. Support trailing arm with a floor jack. Remove shock absorber retaining bolts and shock absorber. Slowly lower floor jack. Remove coil spring and spring seats.

NOTE: **If only coil spring is to be removed, remove only one shock absorber mounting.**

Installation

To install, reverse removal procedure. End of the coil spring must fit in spring seat depression. Depression in lower spring seat should fit into depression in trailing arm.

TIGHTENING SPECIFICATIONS

Application	Ft. Lbs. (N.m)
Axle Nut (10 Slot)	360 (488)
Axle Nut (6 Slot)	253 (350)
Brake Backing Plate-to-Housing Lower Bolts	47 (65)
Brake Backing Plate-to-Housing Upper Bolt	14 (20)
Drive Shaft Hex Bolts	33 (45)
Housing Assembly-to-Trailing Arm	101 (137)
Shock Absorber Retaining Bolt	65 (88)
Trailing Arm Pivot Bolts	76 (103)

Rear Suspension

VOLVO

240, 740, 760, 780 Series

DESCRIPTION

The 240 series rear suspension consists of coil springs mounted between control arms and body rubber mounts. Shock absorbers are mounted between control arms and body. A stabilizer bar is attached to the control arms at both ends.

Two torque rods run forward from axle brackets and mount to frame. A track bar is attached behind, and parallel to, the axle housing. The bar is connected between the axle housing and the body bracket.

The 740, 760 and 780 series rear suspension consists of coil springs, self-leveling gas filled shocks, and a live axle located by longitudinal trailing arms. A stabilizer bar is attached to both trailing arms. In addition, a pair of trailing arms connect the differential to a subframe.

Fig. 1: Exploded View of 240 Series Rear Suspension

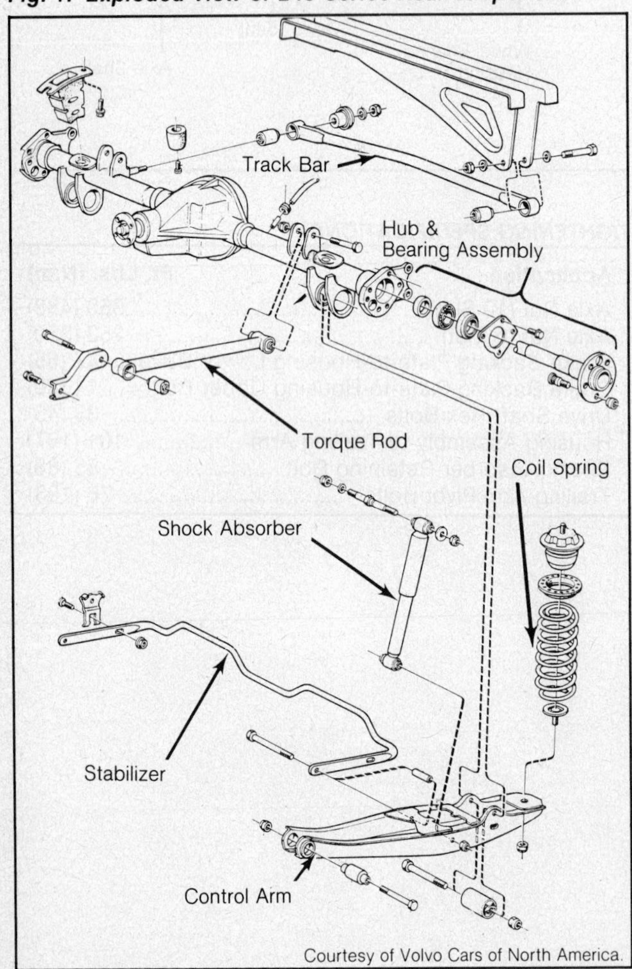

ADJUSTMENTS & INSPECTION

Wheel alignment is not adjustable. Check all bushings for wear and deterioration. Inspect torque rod and track bar for damage.

REMOVAL & INSTALLATION

COIL SPRINGS

Removal (240 Series)

1) Raise and support vehicle. Remove wheel assembly. Place floor jack under rear axle housing and raise axle until spring compresses. Using Spring Compressor (5040), compress spring until shock absorber can be detached.

2) Disconnect lower end of shock absorber. Remove spring lower retaining nut. Lower floor jack and remove coil spring.

Installation

To install, reverse removal procedure. Verify that rubber spring support is in correct position. Tighten all bolts and nuts to specification. See TIGHTENING SPECIFICATIONS table in this article.

Removal (740, 760 & 780 Series)

1) Raise and support vehicle. Remove rear wheels. Remove and support disc brake calipers. DO NOT disconnect brake lines. Disconnect drive shaft from differential.

2) Place jack stands under coil spring end of trailing arm. Remove bolts from anti-sway bar (if equipped). Remove shock absorber lower bolt. Lower rear axle slowly, to unload rear springs. Remove springs.

Installation

To install, reverse removal procedure. See TIGHTENING SPECIFICATIONS table in this article.

Fig. 2: Exploded View of Volvo 740, 760, 780 Series Rear Suspension

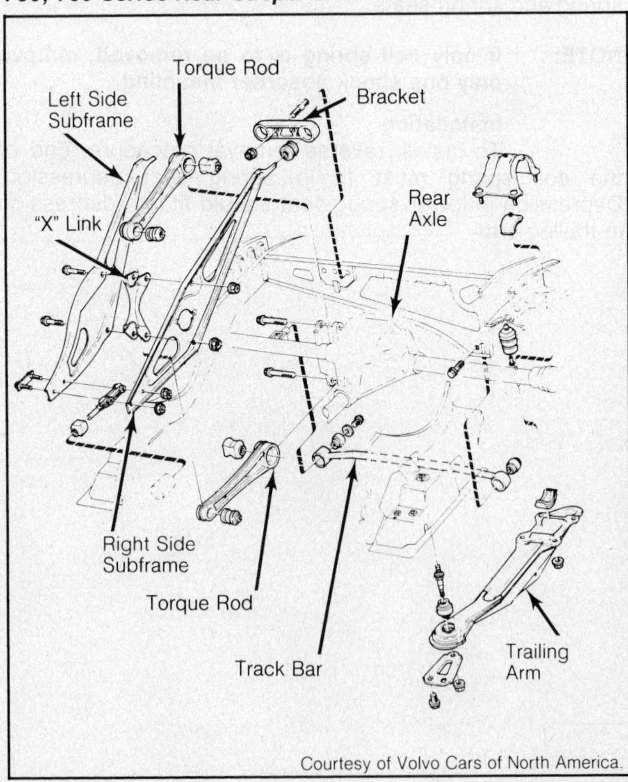

SHOCK ABSORBER

Removal

Raise and support vehicle. Remove wheel assembly. Use floor jack to raise rear axle. Using Spring Compressor (5040), compress spring until shock absorber can be detached. Remove upper and lower shock absorber retaining nuts. Remove shock absorber.

Installation

To install, reverse removal procedure. Verify that spacer sleeve is in correct position. Tighten all bolts and nuts to specification. SEE TIGHTENING SPECIFICATIONS table in this article.

CONTROL ARM

Removal (240 Series)

1) Raise and support vehicle. Position floor jack under axle and raise until spring compresses. Using Spring Compressor (5040), compress spring until shock absorber can be detached.

2) Disconnect shock absorber from control arm. Remove coil spring lower retaining nut. Remove coil spring. Remove control arm retaining bolts. Remove control arm.

Installation

1) Install retaining bolts at front. Install bolts at rear end of control arm but DO NOT tighten. Install coil spring and lower plate retaining nut.

2) Raise axle while guiding coil spring into position. Attach shock absorber lower mount. Spacer sleeve should lie on inside. Lower vehicle to floor and tighten control arm bolts. See TIGHTENING SPECIFICATIONS table in this article.

STABILIZER BAR

Removal (240 Series)

Raise vehicle and support with safety stands, under vehicle body. With a floor jack, raise axle to take load off shock absorbers. Disconnect stabilizer bar mounts and remove stabilizer bar from vehicle.

Installation

Install stabilizer bar in position on brackets (DO NOT tighten fasteners). Install lower end of shock absorber. Position stabilizer bar so it settles in bracket. Tighten fasteners.

TRAILING ARMS & BUSHINGS

Removal (740, 760 & 780 Series)

Remove coil spring. See COIL SPRINGS in this article. Remove rear trailing arm bracket and rubber support bushings. Remove front trailing arm bracket and remove trailing arm. Press front bushings out of trailing arm.

Installation

1) Press new bushings into trailing arms (tapered hole in bushing should face upward). Ensure that bushing is evenly spaced in trailing arm. Loosely install trailing arm front nuts.

2) Position rubber supports on rear axle. Coat spring ends with petroleum jelly. Guide spring into position on trailing arm. Lift trailing arm upward. Loosely install shock absorber and stabilizer.

3) Install trailing arm rear bracket and rubber support. Tighten bracket nuts. To complete installation, reverse removal procedure.

TORQUE RODS & TRACK BAR

Removal (240 Series)

Raise and support vehicle. Disconnect track bar and torque rods from body and axle mountings. Inspect bushings and sleeves for wear or damage, replace if necessary.

Installation

To install, reverse removal procedure, but do not tighten nuts. Lower car and allow suspension to settle. Tighten nuts to specification.

TORQUE RODS & BUSHINGS

Removal (740 & 760 Series)

Raise and support vehicle. Remove torque rod(s). Press bushings from torque rods.

Installation

1) Coat bushing mating surfaces with petroleum jelly. Press new bushings into torque rod. Install torque rods with longer bolt in lower position.

2) Install rear of torque rod. Install front end of torque rod. It may be necessary to remove front mount of subframe to install front of torque rod.

3) Tighten front end of torque rod. If removed, install and tighten front mount of subframe. Tighten rear of torque rod. See TIGHTENING SPECIFICATIONS table in this article.

SUBFRAME BUSHINGS

Removal (740 & 760 Series)

1) Raise and support vehicle on safety stands. Remove subframe front mount bolts. Pry out mount. Tap out front bracket using a hammer and drift. Remove torque rod front retaining bolts, "X" link, and parking brake cable clamp.

2) Insert a bolt through the front subframe mount hole. Pull subframe out of rear mounting bracket, using a "C" clamp. *See Fig. 3.* Remove rear mounting bracket from body. Use Bushing Remover (5329) to press bushings from mounting bracket.

Fig. 3: Removing Subframe from Mounting Bracket

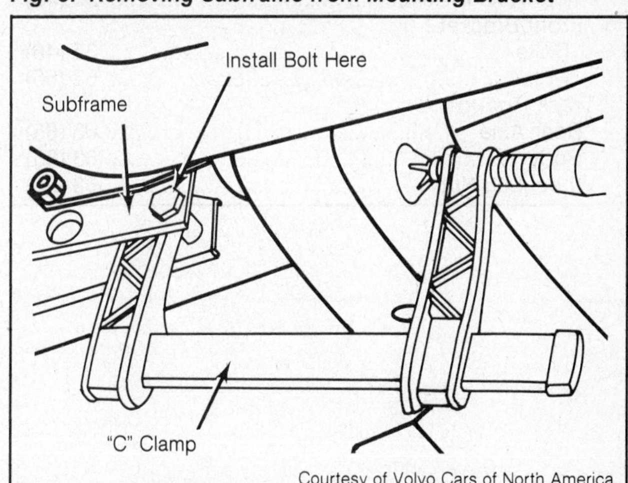

Courtesy of Volvo Cars of North America.

Installation

1) Coat bushing mating surfaces with petroleum jelly. Press new bushings into torque rod. Install torque rods with longer bolt in lower position.

Rear Suspension

VOLVO (Cont.)

2) Attach, but do not tighten, rear of torque rod. Install front end of torque rod. It may be necessary to remove front mount of subframe to install front of torque rod.

3) Tighten front end of torque rod. If removed, install and tighten front mount of subframe. Tighten rear of torque rod.

TIGHTENING SPECIFICATIONS

Application	Ft. Lbs. (N.m)
240 Series	
Bearing Retainer-to-Axle Housing	22-36 (30-49)
Control Arm-to-Body	85 (115)
Coil Spring-to-Body	30-42 (41-57)
Coil Spring-to-Control Arm	14 (19)
Control Arm-to-Rear Axle	85 (115)
Shock Absorber Bolts	62 (84)
Stabilizer Bar	
M10 Bolts	33 (45)
M12 Bolts	62 (84)
Torque Rod Bolts	65 (85)
Track Bar-to-Axle	44 (60)
Track Bar-to-Body	62 (84)
Wheel Lug Nuts	85 (115)
740, 760, 780 Series	
Brake Caliper Bolts	43 (58)
Rear Spring	
Upper Attachment	35 (48)
Rear Axle Bracket	33 (45)
Shock Absorber Nuts	
Lower	63 (85)
Upper	63 (85)
Stabilizer Bar	35 (48)
Subframe	
Front Mount	63 (85)
Rear Bushing Bracket	63 (85)
Torque Rods	
Front Bolts-to-"X" Link	103 (140)
Rear Bolts	63 (85)
Trailing Arm	
Rear Axle Bracket	33 (45)
Front Bracket	
Bolts	35 (48)
Nuts	63 (85)
Track Rod-to-	
Rear Axle	63 (85)
Body	63 (85)
Wheel Lug Nut	63 (85)

Rear Suspension

YUGO

DESCRIPTION

Rear suspension consists of stub axle with independent lower control arm, utilizing a shock absorber and single transverse mounted leaf spring. Hub and drum assembly are connected to vehicle through stub axle, shock absorber and lower control arm which is connected to body using a control arm shaft with rubber bushings. *See Fig. 1.*

ADJUSTMENTS & INSPECTION

WHEEL ALIGNMENT SPECIFICATIONS & PROCEDURES

See WHEEL ALIGNMENT SPECIFICATIONS & PROCEDURES in WHEEL ALIGNMENT section.

WHEEL BEARING

Wheel bearing is nonadjustable. When defective, bearing and hub assembly must be replaced as a unit.

REMOVAL & INSTALLATION

WHEEL BEARING

Removal

1) Raise vehicle. Support with safety stands under vehicle body. Allow suspension to hang free. Remove wheel assembly. Remove wheel centering stud and drum attaching screw. Remove brake drum. Pry bearing dust cap off.

2) Remove hub nut collar, nut and washer from stub axle. Using Hub Puller (A. 47017), remove hub and bearing assembly. Hub and bearing are not serviceable individually and must be replaced as a unit.

Installation

To install bearing/hub assembly, reverse removal procedure. Adjust hub nut to specification. Using Pliers (A. 74140/1), stake hub nut collar in place.

REAR SUSPENSION

Removal

1) Raise vehicle. Support with safety stands under vehicle body. Allow suspension to hang free. Remove rear wheels.

2) Disconnect flexible hydraulic brake line in wheelwell area. Plug brake line to eliminate fluid loss.

3) Release hand brake. Disconnect brake cable from levers on backing plates, and brake compensator bar from right control arm.

4) Place floor jack under control arm. Raise floor jack slightly to support control arm weight. Disconnect shock absorber in trunk area and lower jack. Repeat procedure for opposite side suspension. *See Fig. 2.*

Fig. 1: Yugo Rear Suspension Components

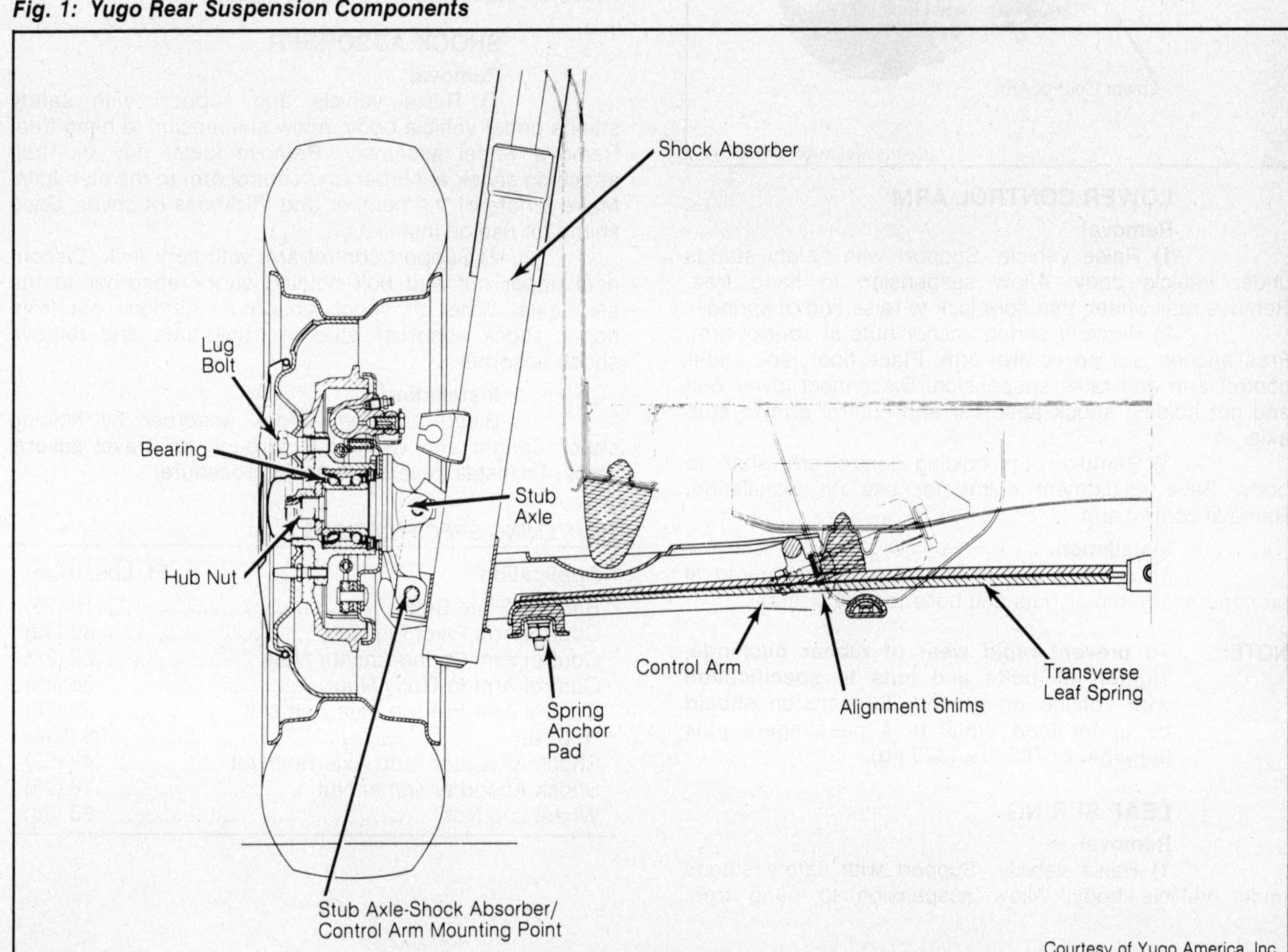

Rear Suspension

YUGO (Cont.)

5) Disconnect rubber spring anchor pad at control arm. Remove nuts holding control arm shaft to body. Save adjustment shims for use on installation. Slide off suspension assembly.

Installation

To install rear suspension, reverse removal procedure. Tighten all bolts and nuts to specification. See TIGHTENING SPECIFICATIONS table in this article.

Fig. 2: Rear Suspension Assembly

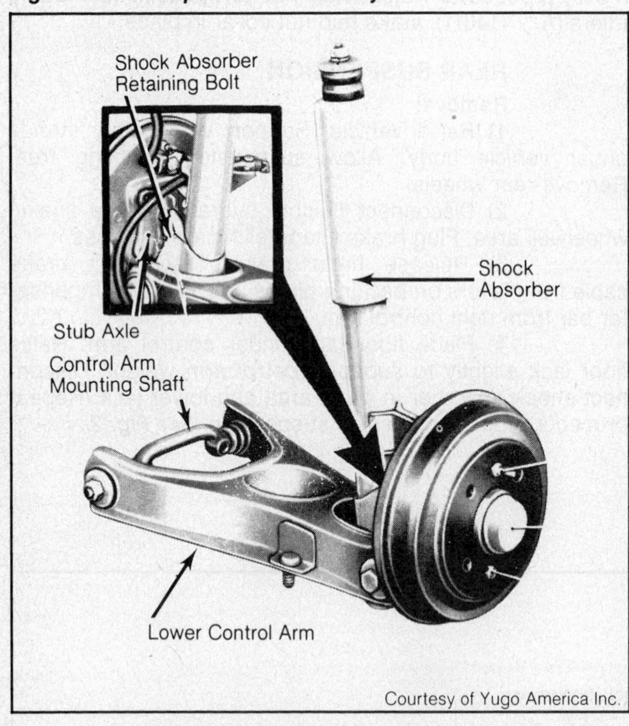

LOWER CONTROL ARM

Removal

1) Raise vehicle. Support with safety stands under vehicle body. Allow suspension to hang free. Remove rear wheel. Use floor jack to raise end of spring.

2) Remove spring anchor nuts at control arm. Free anchor pad on control arm. Place floor jack under control arm and raise suspension. Disconnect lower bolt and nut holding shock absorber and control arm to stub axle.

3) Remove nuts holding control arm shaft to body. Save adjustment shims for use on installation. Remove control arm.

Installation

To install lower control arm, reverse removal procedure. Tighten all nuts and bolts to specification.

NOTE: **To prevent rapid wear of rubber bushings, Tighten all bolts and nuts to specification with vehicle on ground. Suspension should be under load equal to 4 passengers plus luggage, or 705 lbs. (320 kg).**

LEAF SPRING

Removal

1) Raise vehicle. Support with safety stands under vehicle body. Allow suspension to hang free. Remove rear wheels. Use floor jack to raise left end of spring.

2) Remove spring anchor nuts at control arm. Free anchor pad on control arm. Repeat operation on right side of vehicle. Remove two spring guides holding spring to body. Remove spring.

Inspection & Installation

Inspect spring for cracks and distortion. Replace if necessary. To install, reverse removal procedure.

STUB AXLE ASSEMBLY

Removal

1) Raise vehicle. Support with safety stands under vehicle body. Allow suspension to hang free. Remove wheel assembly. Support control arm with jack.

2) Remove wheel centering stud, drum attaching screw and drum. Pry bearing dust cap off. Remove hub nut collar, nut and washer from stub axle. Using Hub Puller (A. 47017), remove hub and bearing assembly.

3) Remove nut and bolt holding shock absorber and control arm to stub axle. Slide off control arm.

4) Remove nut and bolt holding shock absorber to stub axle. Slide off shock absorber. Remove 4 bolts holding stub axle to backing plate. Remove stub axle.

Installation

1) To install stub axle assembly, reverse removal procedure. Tighten nuts and bolts to specification.

2) Using Pliers (A. 74140/1) and Heads (A. 74140/9), stake hub nut collar in place.

SHOCK ABSORBER

Removal

1) Raise vehicle and support with safety stands under vehicle body. Allow suspension to hang free. Remove wheel assembly. Remove lower nut and bolt attaching shock absorber and control arm to the stub axle. Make a note of the number and thickness of shims. Save shims for use on installation.

2) Support control arm with floor jack. Disconnect upper nut and bolt holding shock absorber to the stub axle. Slide off shock absorber. Remove nut from upper shock absorber stud in trunk area and remove shock absorber.

Installation

Bleed air from shock absorber by holding shock upright and working it through full travel several times. To install, reverse removal procedure.

TIGHTENING SPECIFICATIONS

Application	Ft. Lbs. (N.m)
Backing Plate Bolts	18 (25)
Control Arm Pivot Pin Nuts	36 (49)
Control Arm Spring Anchor Nuts	22 (29)
Control Arm-to-Body Nuts	36 (49)
Control Arm-to-Stub Axle Bolt/Nut	58 (78)
Hub Nut	159 (216)
Shock Absorber Stub Axle Bolt/Nut	43 (59)
Shock Absorber Upper Nut	18 (25)
Wheel Lug Nut	63 (86)

Automatic Level Control

MERCEDES-BENZ

300TD Turbo, 560SEC, 560SEL

DESCRIPTION

The Automatic Level Control system contains a hydraulic pump, reservoir, leveling valve, pressure reservoir and special combination shock absorber/suspension struts.

The leveling valve lever, which is connected to the torsion bar, has 3 positions: neutral, filling and return flow. The level valve position, which reacts to vehicle load, controls amount of fluid in the special shock absorber which raises or lowers rear of vehicle to maintain a predetermined height.

OPERATION

As rear of vehicle is lowered due to added weight, the leveling valve lever raises to the filling position. This allows fluid to flow from pump to pressure reservoir, through check valves to special shock absorbers.

This added fluid will raise the rear of the vehicle until the leveling valve lever is moved back to the neutral position. When the added weight is removed, rear of vehicle raises which moves the leveling lever to the return flow position. This allows fluid in the shock absorber to drain back to the reservoir until the leveling lever is in the neutral position and the vehicle is level.

TESTING

HYDRAULIC OIL PUMP & LEVELING VALVE

NOTE: **These tests can only be performed on a ready-to-drive vehicle. While testing, check leveling valve for leaks. In case of leaks on valve housing parting surface, install new "O" ring.**

1) Hydraulic oil must be cold before starting test. Disconnect connecting bar at leveling valve lever. Tighten leveling valve housing screws.

CAUTION: **DO NOT loosen clamping screw retaining lever on valve control shaft.**

2) Attach an oil drain line to bleed screw and release pressure in system by opening bleed screw. Remove bleed screw and attach Pressure Tester (126 589 02 21 00) and Flexible Test Line (201 589 03 63 00) directly to leveling valve via 3 or 4-way distribution fitting.

3) Push leveling valve lever up into filling position. Run engine at idle (800-1000 RPM) for a short time and observe pressure reading on tester. Pressure should read 1885 psi (132.5 bar) minimum.

NOTE: **Perform this test quickly to avoid damage to components.**

4) Turn off engine. Move leveling valve lever down to return flow position and observe base pressure reading. After a stabilization period of 5 minutes, repeat test procedure. Leave pressure tester connected at least 4 hours and observe.

NOTE: **Base pressure must not drop after the stabilization period. This also applies to extended periods, such as overnight.**

Fig. 1: Mercedes-Benz (560SEC, 560SEL) Level Control Rear Suspension System

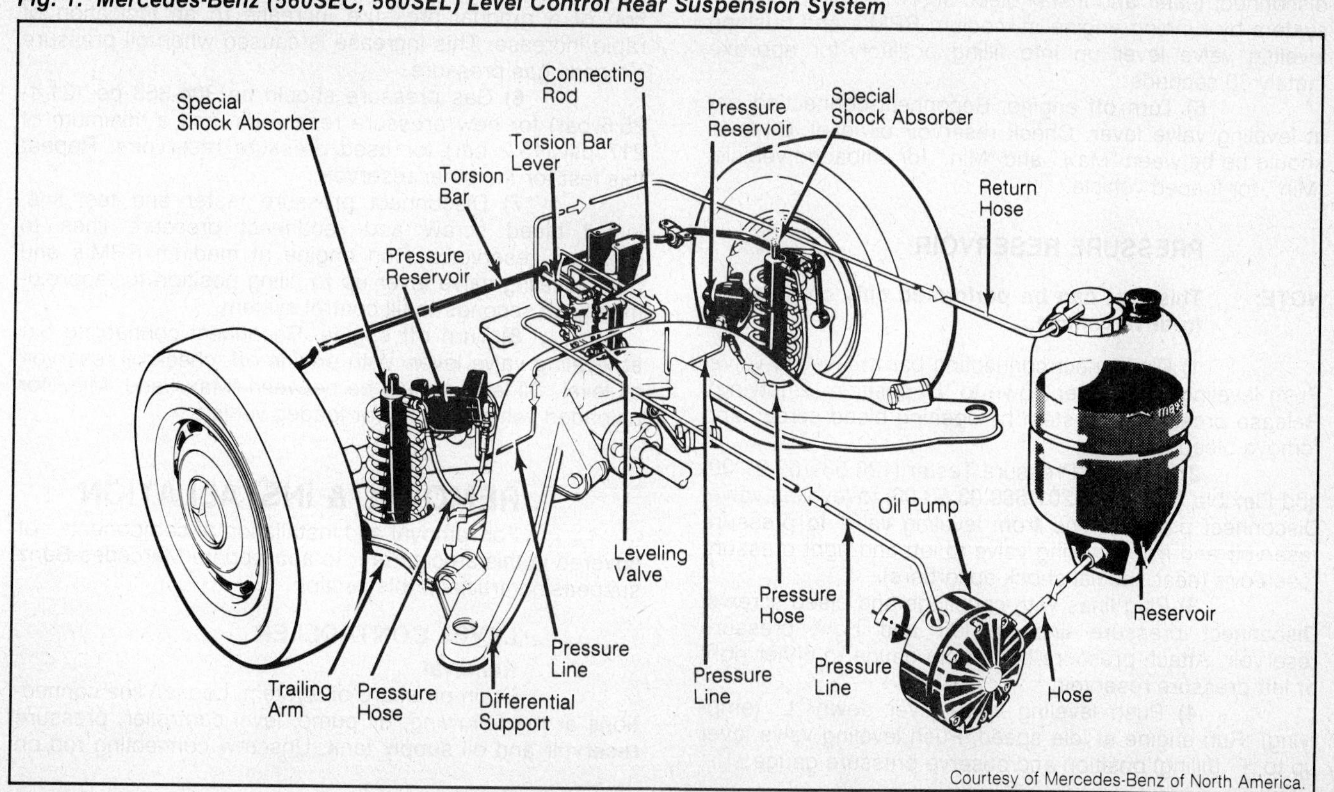

MERCEDES-BENZ (Cont.)

Fig. 2: Mercedes-Benz (300D Turbo) Level Control Rear Suspension System

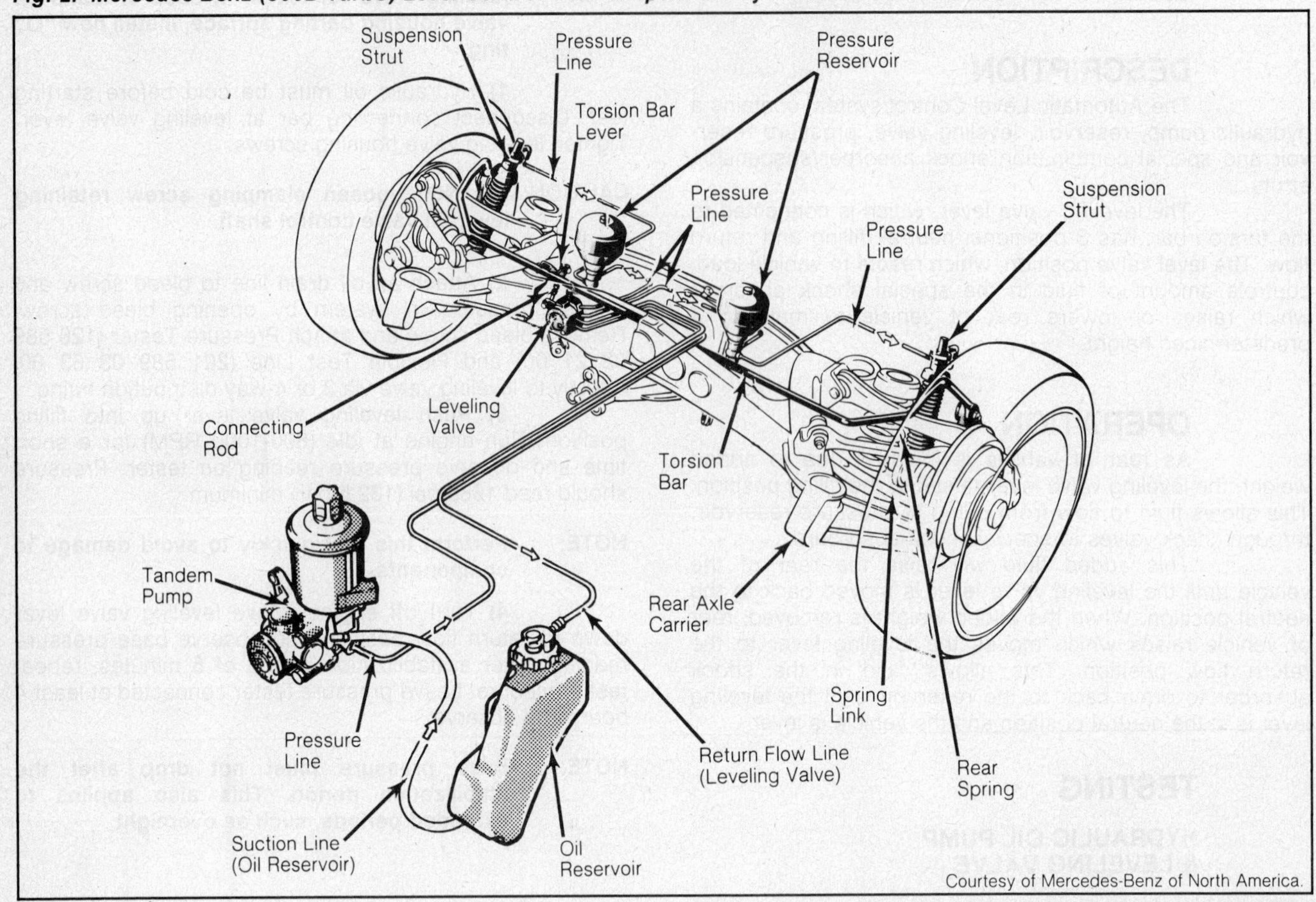

Courtesy of Mercedes-Benz of North America.

5) Bleed base pressure at bleed screw, disconnect tester and install bleed screw. Fill level control system by running engine at medium RPM's and pushing leveling valve lever up into filling position for approximately 30 seconds.

6) Turn off engine. Reconnect connecting bar at leveling valve lever. Check reservoir oil level. Oil level should be between "Max." and "Min." for unloaded vehicle, "Min." for loaded vehicle.

PRESSURE RESERVOIR

NOTE: This test can be performed only on a ready-to-drive vehicle.

1) Disconnect connecting bar at leveling valve. Push leveling valve lever down to "L" position (emptying). Release pressure in system by opening bleed screw, and remove bleed screw.

2) Connect Pressure Tester (126 589 02 21 00) and Flexible Test Line (201 589 03 63 00) to leveling valve. Disconnect pressure line from leveling valve to pressure reservoir and from leveling valve to left and right pressure reservoirs (near special shock absorbers).

3) Plug lines with couplings and bleed screws. Disconnect pressure line on left and right pressure reservoir. Attach pressure hose from gauge to either right or left pressure reservoir.

4) Push leveling valve lever down "L" (emptying). Run engine at idle speed. Push leveling valve lever up to "F" (filling) position and observe pressure gauge.

5) Gas pressure in reservoir is indicated at point where pressure gauge needle changes from indication of a gradual pressure increase to an indication of rapid increase. This increase is caused when oil pressure exceeds gas pressure.

6) Gas pressure should be 304-363 psi (21.4-25.5 bar) for new pressure reservoirs, and a minimum of 217 psi (15.2 bar) for used pressure reservoirs. Repeat this test for the other reservoir.

7) Disconnect pressure tester and test line, install bleed screw and reconnect pressure lines to pressure reservoirs. Run engine at medium RPM's and push leveling valve lever up to filling position for approximately 30 seconds to fill control system.

8) Turn off engine. Reconnect connecting bar at leveling valve lever. With engine off, check oil reservoir oil level. Oil level should be between "Max." and "Min." for unloaded vehicle, "Min." for loaded vehicle.

REMOVAL & INSTALLATION

For removal and installation of components not covered in this article, refer to appropriate Mercedes-Benz suspension article in this section.

LEVEL CONTROLLER

Removal

Drain pressure oil system. Loosen line connections at the following: oil pump, level controller, pressure reservoir and oil supply tank. Unscrew connecting rod on lever of level controller. Loosen both hex screws for attaching level controller to bracket and remove controller.

Installation

1) To install, reverse removal procedure. The 4 bolts for housing halves of level controller should be tightened when level controller is energized with oil pressure.

2) Check ball joints of connecting rod for easy operation and wear. Attach connecting rod to lever of level controller. Check vehicle level and headlights for proper adjustment.

PRESSURE PUMP

Removal

Disconnect expanding hose of pressure line and hose of suction line on pressure pump. Plug connection of suction line. Loosen pump-to-cylinder crankcase bolts or cylinder head, pull out pump and remove.

Installation

To install, reverse removal procedure. Check driver and coupling members of pump drive. Install new gasket and install pumping, making sure that driver components are correctly meshing.

SHOCK ABSORBER

Removal

1) Drain leveling control hydraulic system by opening the bleed screw. From inside storage area of vehicle, remove floor covering by turning "T" lever and lifting up. Fold down rear seat back rest. Remove screws and covering to frame crossmember. Remove cover plate from frame crossmember.

2) Disconnect pressure hose at special shock absorber. Disconnect connection fitting from shock absorber. Cap pressure hose and plug hole in shock absorber.

3) Loosen bolt of upper mount and remove with rubber bushing. Remove bolts retaining bottom of shock absorber. Remove shock absorber from bottom. Remove lower rubber bushing of upper mount.

Installation

1) To install, reverse removal procedure. Install bottom rubber bushing onto top of special shock absorber before installing into vehicle.

2) Plugged hole in shock absorber must point toward frame crossmember and mounting pin must protrude through bore in frame crossmember.

3) Verify that all bolts and fittings are tight, and that reservoir is full. Fill leveling valve by starting engine and moving leveling lever up to filling position. Check leveling suspension system for proper operation.

AUTOMATIC LEVEL CONTROL CAPACITY

Level control capacity is 2.1 qts. (2.0L). Use only Mercedes-Benz hydraulic oil. DO NOT use power steering fluid.

TIGHTENING SPECIFICATIONS

Application	Ft. Lbs. (N.m)
Ball Joint-to-Spring Strut	48 (65)
Fitting at Pressure Reservoir	32 (43)
Lower Retaining Bolt	33 (45)
Pressure Hose-to-Shock Absorber Fitting	25 (34)
Shock Absorber Fitting-to-Shock Absorber	15 (20)
Spherical Mount on Shock Absorber	48 (65)
Upper Retaining Bolt	22 (30)

Electronic Suspension

MAZDA RX7 & 626

DESCRIPTION

The Mazda Auto Adjust Suspension (AAS) is an electronically controlled, variable rate shock absorbing system. The suspension damping characteristics are selected in response to driver command issued from the AAS selection switch. With the selection switch in the "AUTO" setting, all regulation of suspension damping is assigned to the control unit.

When the "NORMAL" mode is selected, all 4 shocks are set to the "NORMAL" or soft setting. Switching to the "AUTO" mode will allow the computerized control unit to respond to driving conditions with preprogrammed adjustment. Selecting the "SPORT" mode will cause all 4 shocks to adjust to the firm setting at all speeds.

Uniquely featured are angle and speed sensors with brake and accelerator switches that constantly monitor driving conditions. As different driving situations occur, they are detected by one of the sensors or switches. This information is then sent to the control unit to override all commands and apply appropriate suspension damping immediately.

OPERATION

The AAS system uses gas-charged shock absorbers with a control rod and a selector valve built into the piston rod. An electric actuator is located on the upper end of the control rod to adjust shock damping. The control rod is connected to a selector valve that adjusts the setting by switching oil passages to alter damping. When system is operated manually, the switch by-passes the control unit, and selects the mode setting chosen.

ACTUATOR

A magnet is located in the center of the actuator surrounded by 6 coils. A shaft integrated with the magnet is attached to the control rod. As current flows through the coils, the stator becomes magnetized to attract the magnet and turn the control rod. Each turn of 60 degrees aligns one of the 3 sets of orifices in the piston rod with the rotary valve. Suspension damping characteristics are determined by the resistance of hydraulic oil flow through the orifices that the actuator selects. *See Fig. 2.*

Fig. 1: Mazda RX7 AAS Component Location

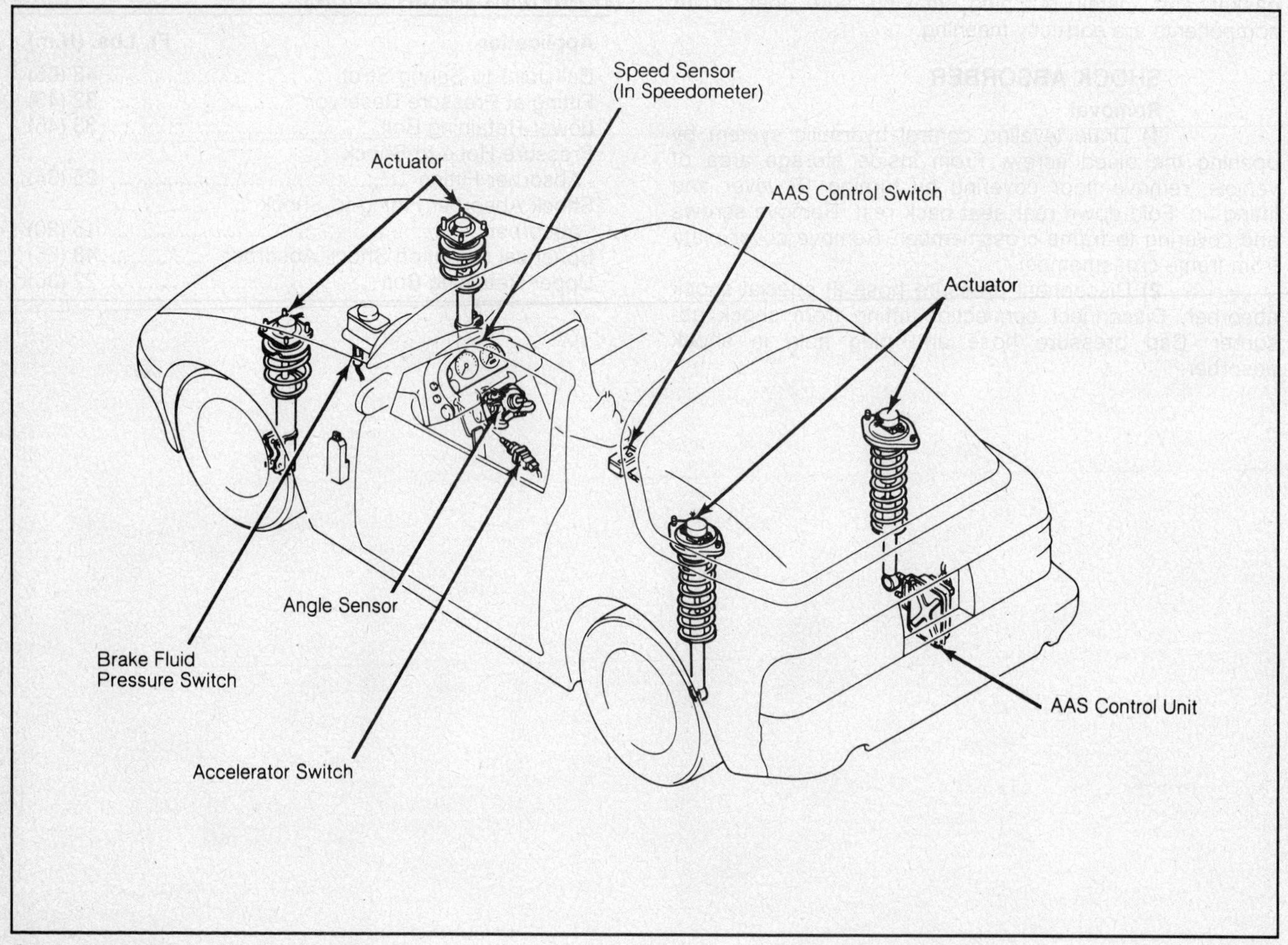

Courtesy of Mazda Motors Corp.

MAZDA RX7 & 626 (Cont.)

Fig. 2: Mazda AAS Shock Unit & Actuator Assembly

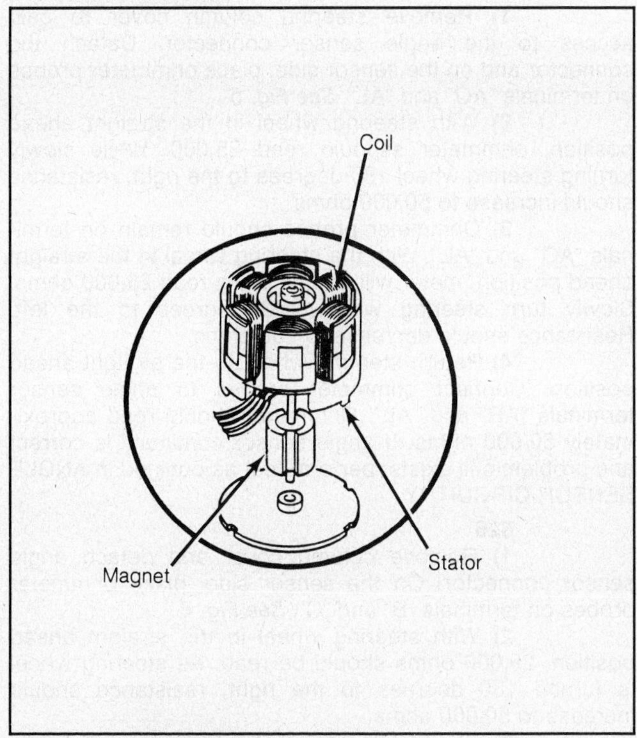

Courtesy of Mazda Motors Corp.

ACCELERATOR SWITCH

Also known as the "Kickdown" switch, this unit monitors the accelerator pedal position and reports to the control unit when approximately 83% of full throttle has been reached. Upon activation, the switch signals the control unit to respond by adjusting all shocks to the "Very Firm" position. This sequence, designed as an anti-squat function, occurs at speeds below 30 MPH regardless of selection switch position

ANGLE SENSOR

Located within the steering column, the angle sensor detects angle and movement of the steering wheel and transmits this information to the control unit. The control unit analyzes this information while calculating vehicle speed and lateral G force. These functions are designed as an anti-roll feature.

BRAKE FLUID PRESSURE SWITCH

Designed as an anti-dive function, the brake switch monitors brake fluid pressure and signals the control unit when approximately 498 psi (35 kg/cm²) has been applied to the system. As this information is received by the control unit, it overrides the selection switch and commands all actuators to switch the shock absorbers to the "Very Firm" position. The shocks will return to the position selected on the selection switch 2-4 seconds after the brake fluid pressure switch is deactivated.

SELECTION SWITCH

The AAS selection switch, designed for convenient driver accessibility, is located on the right side of the steering wheel on the console. RX7 models have 2 selections, "SPORT" and "NORMAL". The 626 AAS system has an additional "AUTO" position on the selection switch. Mode signal is sent directly to the control unit upon selection.

SPEED SENSOR

The Mazda AAS speed sensor checks speedometer cable revolution and generates electrical pulses that are sent to the control unit. These pulsations are counted by the control unit to determine vehicle speed. As an anti-roll funtion, the speed sensor works in conjunction with the angle sensor to report fast turn situations to the control unit so that the "Very Firm" mode can be activated.

TESTING & DIAGNOSIS

ACTUATOR

NOTE: Verify operation of rear actuator by listening for sound of operation. Actuator must not be disassembled during testing.

RX7

1) With ignition on, cycle the selection switch between the "SPORT" and "NORMAL" positions. Listen for operation of actuator or use an assistant to visually confirm that the control rod, viewed from the top of the actuator, is operating.

2) To test wire harness, locate defective actuator(s) and disconnect sub-harness connector. On the harness side of the connector, attach voltmeter positive lead to terminal "D" and negative lead to terminal "A". *See Fig. 3.* As "SPORT" selection is pressed, 12 volts should appear on meter for approximately one second.

Fig. 3: Strut Actuator Sub-Harness & Connector Identification

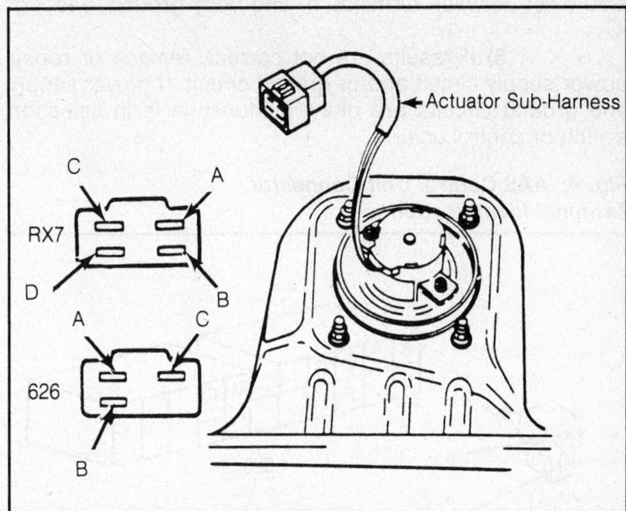

Courtesy of Mazda Motors Corp.

3) Attach voltmeter positive lead to terminal "D" and negative lead to terminal "C". As "NORMAL" selection is pressed, 12 volts should appear on meter for approximately one second. If voltage tests satisfactory, a malfunction of the actuator is indicated. Disassembly of actuator is not recommended, replace unit as an assembly.

4) If voltage readings are incorrect, disconnect control unit wire connector. Connect positive voltmeter lead to terminal "E" on the harness side of the connector.

Electronic Suspension

MAZDA RX7 & 626 (Cont.)

See Fig. 4. With ignition on, meter should read 12 volts. If not, a defective power circuit is indicated.

5) Check for ground circuit continuity by attaching voltmeter positive lead to harness connector terminal "0" and negative lead to ground. If continuity does not exist, repair ground circuit wiring. If voltage and continuity readings are correct, control unit or switch is defective.

626

1) Turn ignition switch to "ON" position. Cycle selection switch between "NORMAL" and "SPORT" positions. Verify that shaft of actuator in front and rear struts is operating.

2) If actuator operation is not verified, disconnect actuator connector and install a voltmeter. Place ignition switch in "ON" position and place selection switch in "SPORT" position. *See Fig. 3*.

3) Voltage between terminals "A" and "C" should read 1.2 volts for approximately one second. Place selection switch in "NORMAL" position. Voltage between terminals "C" and "B" should read 1.2 volts for approximately one second. *See Fig. 3*. If voltage readings are not okay, there is a defect in the actuator or in the actuator circuit.

ACTUATOR CIRCUIT

626

1) Disconnect control unit connector. Turn ignition switch to the "ON" position. Check voltage and continuity between terminals as follows. Voltage between terminal "M" and body ground should be 12 volts. *See Fig. 4*.

2) Voltage between terminal "a" and body ground should be 12 volts. Continuity should exist between teriminal "B" and body ground. Continuity should also exist between terminal "b" and body ground. *See Fig. 4*.

3) If results are not correct, replace or repair power supply circuit and/or ground circuit. If power supply and ground circuits are okay, malfunction is in selection switch or control unit.

Fig. 4: AAS Control Unit Connector Terminal Identification

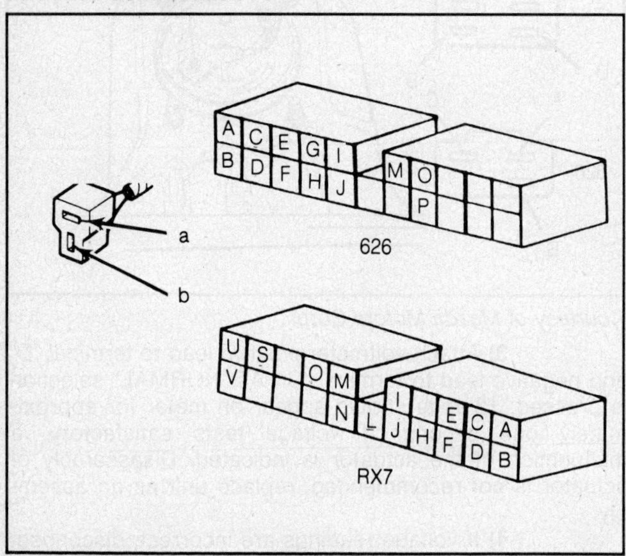

Courtesy of Mazda Motors Corp.

ANGLE SENSOR

RX7

1) Remove steering column cover to gain access to the angle sensor connector. Detach the connector and on the sensor side, place ohmmeter probes on terminals "AO" and "AL". *See Fig. 5*.

2) With steering wheel in the straight ahead position, ohmmeter sshould read 25,000. While slowly turning steering wheel 180 degrees to the right, resistance should increase to 50,000 ohms.

3) Ohmmeter probes should remain on terminals "AO" and "AL". With the steering wheel in the straight ahead position, meter will should again read 25,000 ohms. Slowly turn steering wheel 180 degrees to the left. Resistance should decrease to 200 ohms.

4) Return steering wheel to the straight ahead position. Connect ohmmeter probes to angle sensor terminals "AR" and "AL". Ohmmeter should read approximately 50,000 ohms. If angle sensor continuity is correct and problem still exists, perform test as outlined in ANGLE SENSOR CIRCUITRY.

626

1) Remove column cover and detach angle sensor connector. On the sensor side, place ohmmeter probes on terminals "B" and "C". *See Fig. 5*.

2) With steering wheel in the straight ahead position, 25,000 ohms should be read. As steering wheel is turned 180 degrees to the right, resistance should increase to 50,000 ohms.

3) Ohmmeter probes should remain on terminals "B" and "C". Return steering wheel to the straight ahead position, Meter will again read 25,000 ohms. Turn steering wheel 180 degrees to the left. Resistance should decrease to 200 ohms.

4) Position steering wheel in the straight ahead position. Connect ohmmeter probes to angle sensor terminals "A" and "C". Ohmmeter should read approximately 50,000 ohms. If angle sensor continuity is correct and malfunction still exists, proceed to ANGLE SENSOR CIRCUITRY.

Fig. 5: Angle Sensor Connector Terminal Identification

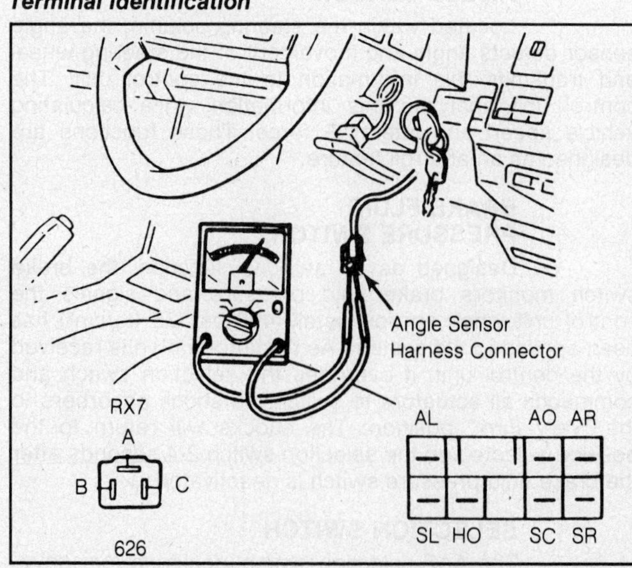

Electronic Suspension

MAZDA RX7 & 626 (Cont.)

ANGLE SENSOR CIRCUITRY

NOTE: The following test procedures are designed to isolate defects in the wiring harness. If resistances measured as outlined are incorrect, an open or short in the circuitry is indicated.

RX7

1) Remove control unit harness connector. With ignition on, use ohmmeter to measure resistance between connector terminals "I" and "J" with steering wheel straight ahead. Then, slowly turn steering wheel 180 degrees toward the right.

2) Resistance should be approximately 25,000 ohms and increase to approximately 50,000 ohms after 180 degrees turn right. Return steering wheel to straight ahead position.

3) Repeat procedure turning steering wheel 180 degrees to the left. Resistance should decrease from 25,000 ohms in straight ahead position to approximately 200 ohms after turn.

4) Return steering wheel to straight ahead position. Measure resistance between connector terminals "I" and "L". Resistance should be approximately 50,000 ohms.

626

1) Disconnect control unit wire harness connector. Position steering wheel in the straight ahead direction. Turn ignition on and use an ohmmeter to measure resistance while probing terminals "A" and "D".

2) Slowly turn steering wheel 180 degrees toward the right. Resistance should read approximately 25,000 ohms and increase to 50,000 ohms after 180 degrees turn right. Return steering wheel to straight ahead position.

3) Repeat procedure turning steering wheel 180 degrees to the left. Resistance should decrease from approximately 25,000 ohms in straight ahead position to approximately 200 ohms after 180 degrees turn left.

4) Return steering wheel to straight ahead position. Measure resistance between connector terminals "C" and "D". Resistance should read approximately 50,000 ohms.

ACCELERATOR (KICKDOWN) SWITCH

RX7

1) To verify correct operation of the accelerator switch, confirm continuity between switch terminals "B" and "D" with the tip of switch depressed .276"-315" (7-8 mm). If unit tests okay, proceed to step **2)** to test wire harness.

2) Detach control unit connector and apply ohmmeter probes between harness side terminal "N" and ground. Continuity should exist with accelerator pedal depressed 3/4 of the way down. If no continuity exists and switch tests satisfactorily, inspect wire harness for defect.

626

1) Confirm continuity between the switch terminals with the accelerator pedal depressed 3/4 of the way down. If continuity exists, switch tests okay. Proceed to step **2)** to test wire harness.

2) Detach control unit connector and place ohmmeter probes between terminal "F" and ground. *See Fig. 4.* Continuity should exist with accelerator pedal depressed 3/4 of the way down. If continuity does not exist and switch tests satisfactory, inspect wire harness for a short or open circuit.

Fig. 6: Accelerator Switch & Terminal Identification

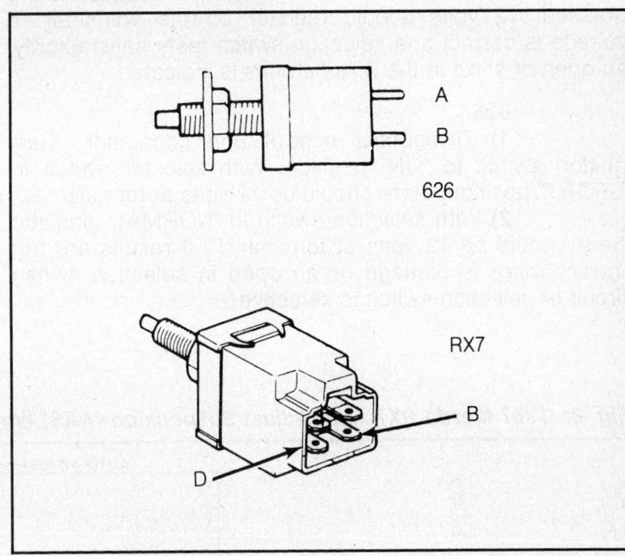

Courtesy of Mazda Motors Corp.

BRAKE FLUID PRESSURE SWITCH

1) Located below the master cylinder, the brake fluid pressure switch can be tested by confirming continuity. Detach the switch connector and apply ohmmeter probes to both terminals. Continuity should exist when brake pedal is depressed. If not, proceed to step **2)**.

2) Disconnect control unit wire connector. Apply ohmmeter probes between terminal "M" ("E" for 626) and ground. Continuity should exist when brake pedal is depressed. If no continuity exists, and switch tests satisfactory, inspect wire harness for short or open circuit.

SELECTION SWITCH

RX7

1) Separate selection switch connector and apply ohmmeter probes to terminals "A" and "D". *See Fig. 7.* If continuity exists when selection switch is in "SPORT" position, selection switch is okay. If system performance remains unacceptable, proceed to step **2)** for wire harness test.

Fig. 7: Selection Switch & Terminal Identification

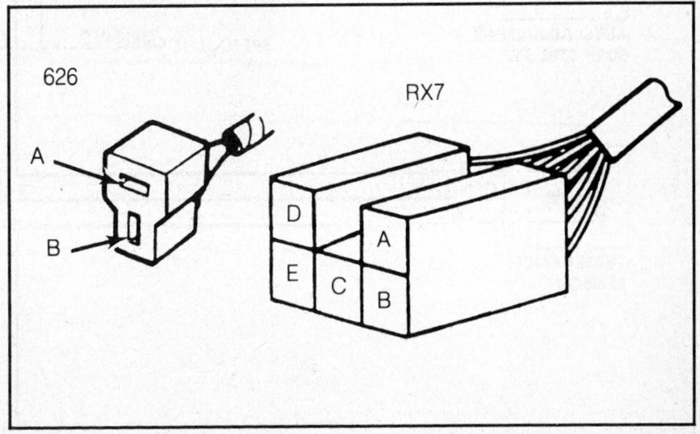

Courtesy of Mazda Motors Corp.

Electronic Suspension

MAZDA RX7 & 626 (Cont.)

2) With ignition on, disconnect the control unit wire harness connector. Attach voltmeter positive lead to terminal "F" on the harness side and negative lead to ground. *See Fig. 4.*

3) As the "SPORT" selection on the switch is pressed, 12 volts should register on the voltmeter. If voltage is correct and selection switch tests satisfactorily, an open or short in the wire harness is indicated.

626

1) Disconnect control unit connector. Turn ignition switch to "ON" position. With selector switch in "SPORT" position, there should be 12 volts at terminal "J".

2) With selection switch in "NORMAL" position there should be 12 volts at terminal "I". If results are not correct there is damage or an open in selection switch circuit or selection switch is defective.

SELECTION SWITCH UNIT

Disconnect selection switch connector. With selection switch in "SPORT" position, there should be continuity between unit terminals "B" and "D". *See Fig. 7.* With selection switch in "NORMAL" position, there should be continuity between unit terminals "D" and "F". *See Fig. 7.*

SPEED SENSOR

1) Raise and support drive axle so that wheels can be turned by hand. Disconnect the control unit wire connector. Apply ohmmeter probes between terminal "H" of the wire connector and ground.

2) Ohmmeter should oscillate continuity and non-continuity as the wheels are manually rotated. If no continuity registers, inspect wire harness for short or open circuit. If wire harness is okay, replace speed sensor and retest system.

Fig. 8: 1987 Mazda RX7 Auto Adjust Suspension (AAS) Wiring Diagram

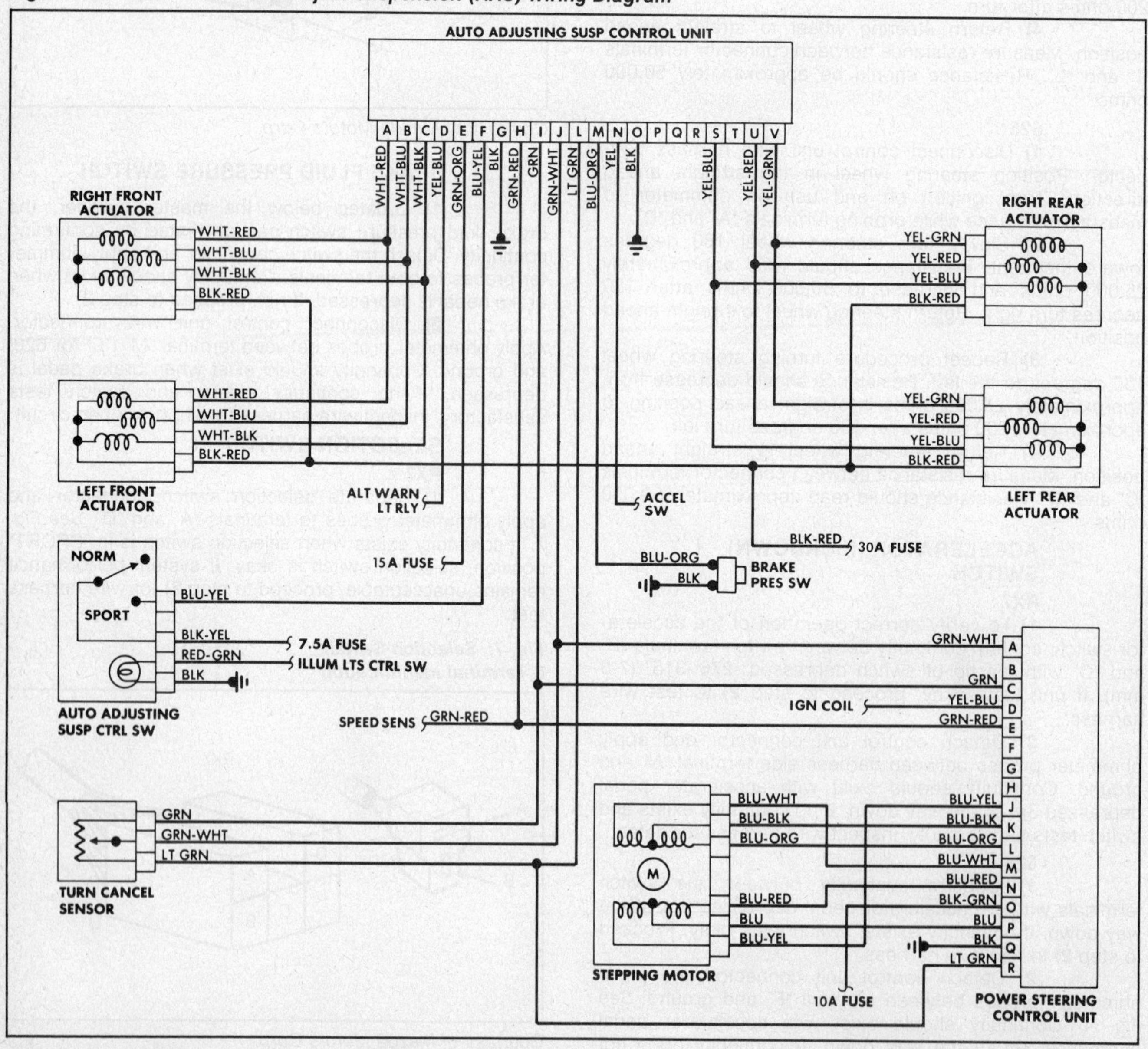

Electronic Suspension

MAZDA RX7 & 626 (Cont.)

Fig. 9: 1987 Mazda 626 Auto Adjust Suspension (AAS) Wiring Diagram

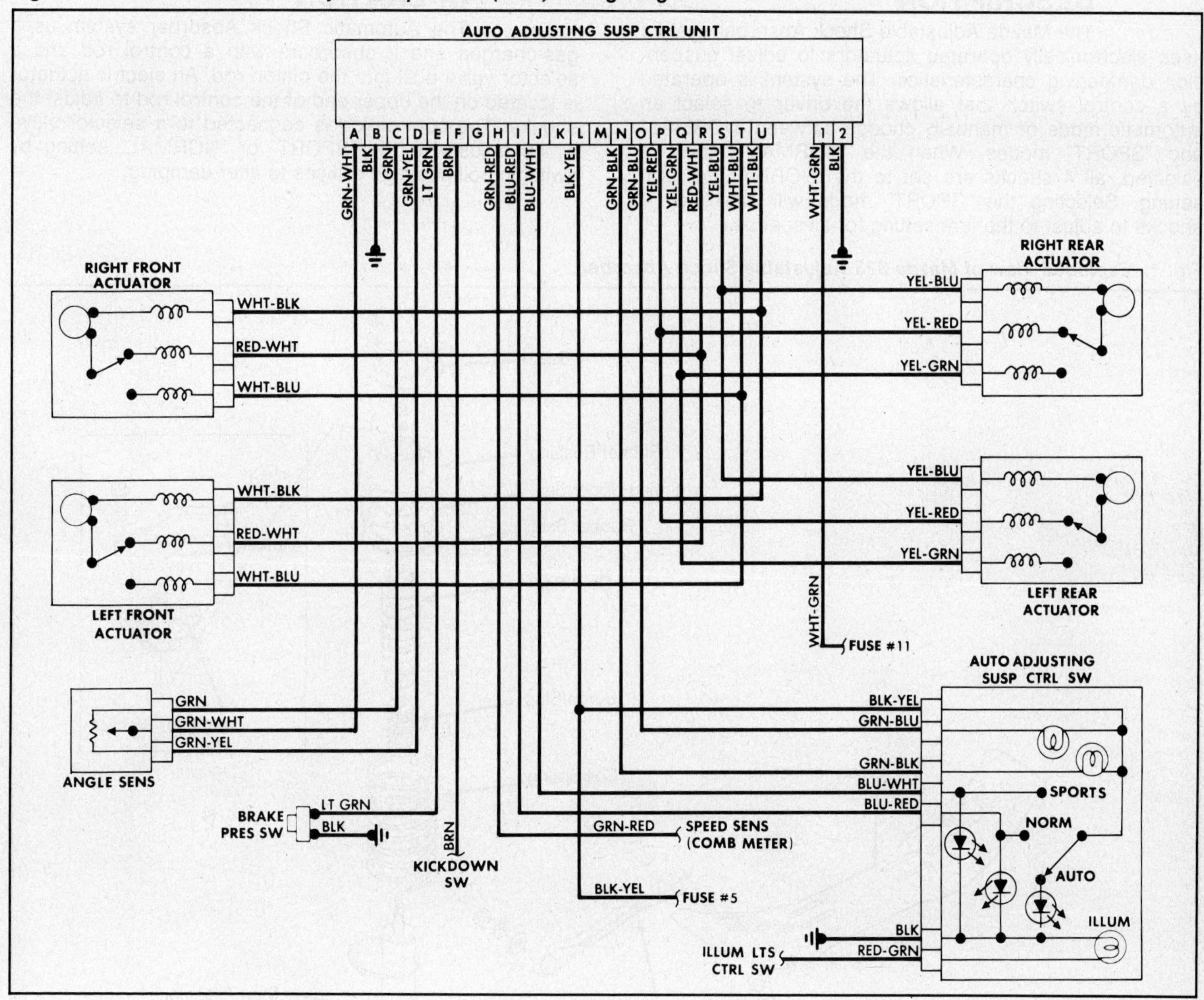

Electronic Suspension

MAZDA 323

DESCRIPTION

The Mazda Adjustable Shock Absorber system uses electronically operated actuators to adjust suspension dampening characteristics. The system is operated by a control switch that allows the driver to select an automatic mode or manually choose between "NORMAL" and "SPORT" modes. When the "NORMAL" mode is selected, all 4 shocks are set to the "NORMAL" or soft setting. Selecting the "SPORT" mode will cause all 4 shocks to adjust to the firm setting for all speeds.

OPERATION

The Automatic Shock Absorber system uses gas-charged shock absorbers with a control rod and a selector valve built into the piston rod. An electric actuator is located on the upper end of the control rod to adjust the shocks. The control rod is connected to a selector valve which adjusts to the "SPORT" or "NORMAL" setting by switching oil passage orifices to alter damping.

Fig. 1: Exploded View of Mazda 323 Adjustable Shock Absorber

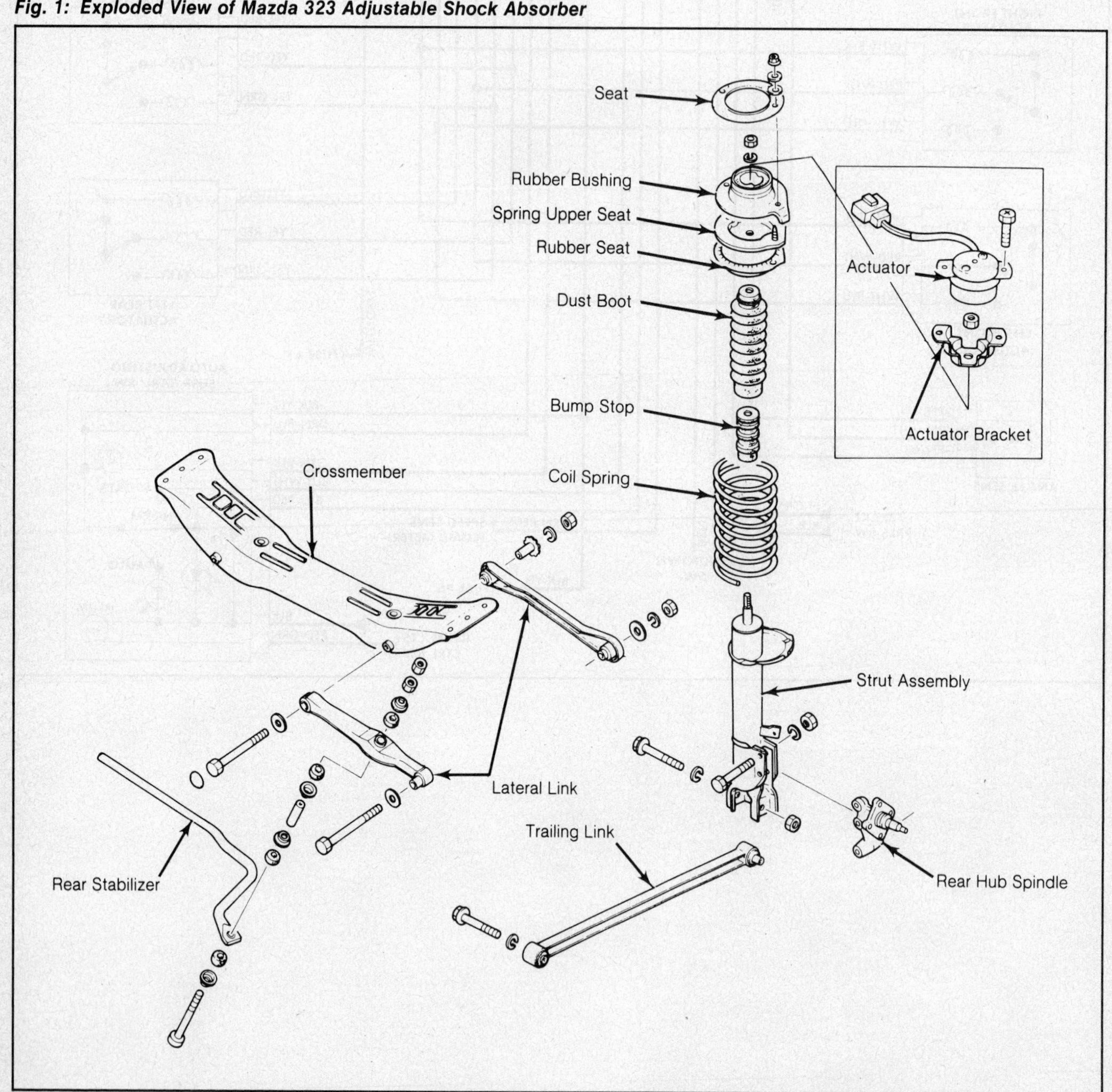

Courtesy of Mazda Motors Corp.

MAZDA 323 (Cont.)

Fig. 2: Actuator Testing & Terminal Identification

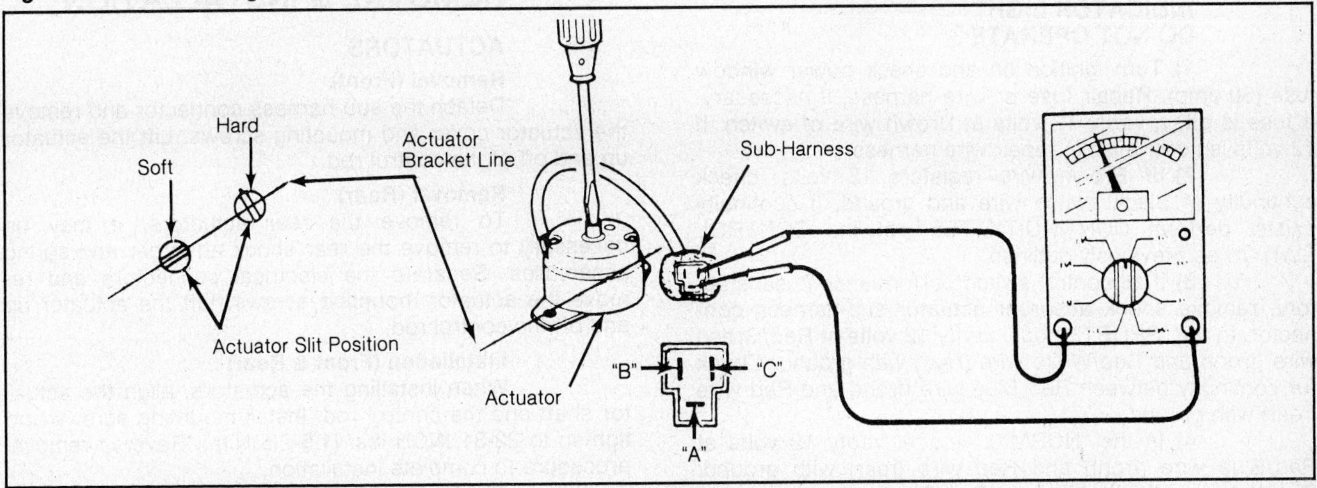

Courtesy of Mazda Motors Corp.

TESTING & DIAGNOSIS

ACTUATOR COMPONENT TESTING

NOTE: Adjustable shock absorber actuators are not serviceable and are replaced as an assembly. Observe initial installation setting of actuators to ensure position conformity. See Fig. 2.

Voltage Test

1) To confirm "NORMAL" mode actuator operation, apply 12 volts to actuator sub-harness terminal "A" and ground terminal "C". "NORMAL" mode actuator slit position is parallel with actuator bracket. *See Fig. 2.*

2) To check "SPORT" mode actuator operation, apply 12 volts to actuator sub-harness terminal "C" and ground terminal "B". "SPORT" mode actuator slit position is perpendicular (right angle) to actuator bracket.

Continuity Test

1) Actuator continuity can be tested by probing the sub-harness with an ohmmeter while turning actuator rod. *See Fig. 2.* In the "NORMAL" mode, verify continuity between terminals "A" and "C". There should be no continuity between terminals "B" and "C".

2) In the "SPORT" mode, with actuator rod perpendicular to bracket, continuity should exist between sub-harness terminals "B" and "C". Verify that no continuity exists between terminals "A" and "C".

CONTROL SWITCH

NOTE: Adjustable shock absorber control switch is not serviceable and must be replaced as an assembly.

Continuity Test

1) With the control switch in the "SPORT" position, use an ohmmeter set at the "x1000" range to confirm continuity between terminals "A", "C" and "G". *See Fig. 3.* Continuity must also exist between terminals "B", "D" and "H".

2) With the control switch in the "NORMAL" position, confirm continuity between terminals "A", "D" and "H". Continuity must also exist between terminals "B", "F" and "J".

3) Place the control switch in the "CRUISE" position to confirm continuity between terminals "A", "D" and "G". Continuity must also exist between terminals "B", "F" and "H".

Fig. 3: Control Unit Connector Identification & Bulb Replacement

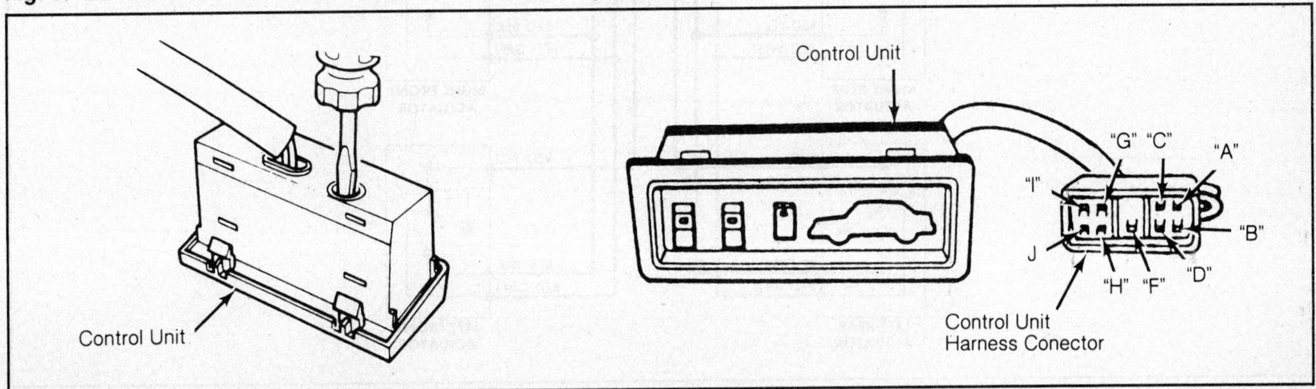

Courtesy of Mazda Motors Corp.

Electronic Suspension

MAZDA 323 (Cont.)

MODE SWITCH & INDICATOR LIGHT DO NOT OPERATE

1) Turn ignition on and check power window fuse (30 amp). Repair fuse or wire harness, if necessary. If fuse is okay, verify 12 volts at Brown wire of switch. If 12 volts is not available, repair wire harness.

2) If Brown wire registers 12 volts, check continuity of Black switch wire and ground. If continuity exists, perform CONTINUITY TEST of the CONTROL SWITCH as previously outlined.

3) If all control switch performance is satisfactory, remove shock absorber actuator sub-harness connector. In the "SPORT" mode, verify 12 volts at Red/Green wire (front) and Red/White wire (rear) with ground. Check for continuity between Red/Blue wire (front) and Red wire (rear) with ground.

4) In the "NORMAL" mode, verify 12 volts at Red/Blue wire (front) and Red wire (rear) with ground. Check for continuity between Red/Black wire (front) and Red/Yellow wire (rear) with ground.

5) If voltage or continuity values cannot be obtained, perform individual component testing to isolate defective switch, actuator or wire harness.

REMOVAL & INSTALLATION

ACTUATORS

Removal (Front)

Detach the sub-harness connector and remove the actuator cover and mounting screws. Lift the actuator up and off of the control rod.

Removal (Rear)

To remove the rear actuators, it may be necessary to remove the rear shock absorber and spring assemblies. Separate the electrical connectors and remove the actuator mounting screws. Lift the actuator up and off the control rod.

Installation (Front & Rear)

When installing the actuators, align the actuator shaft and the control rod. Install mounting screws and tighten to 22-31 INCH lbs. (1.5-2.5 N.m). Reverse removal procedure to complete installation.

CONTROL SWITCH LIGHT

With control switch removed, use a small screwdriver to push illumination light through the rear hole. *See Fig. 3.*

Fig. 4: Mazda 323 Adjustable Shock Absorber Wiring Diagram

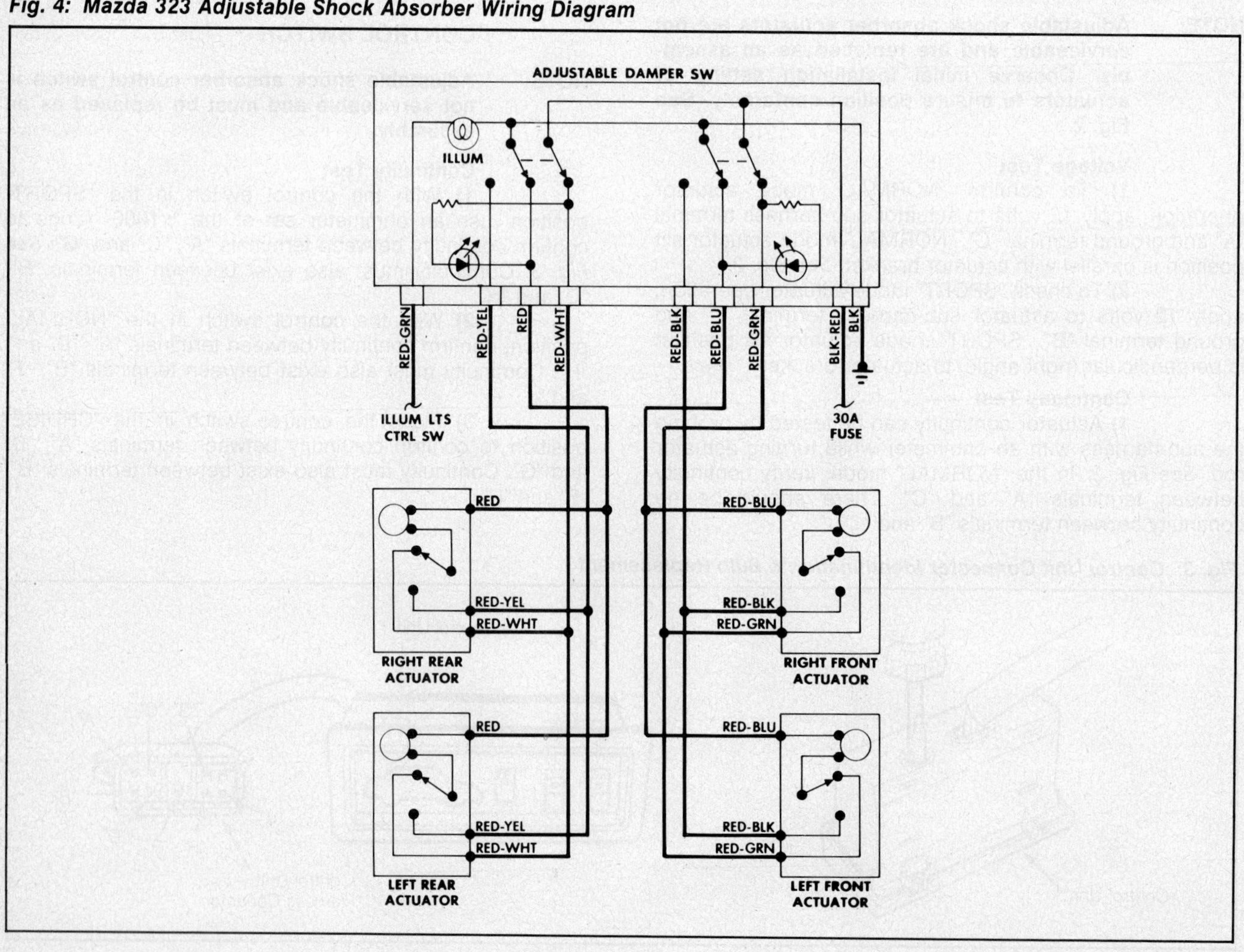

MITSUBISHI GALANT

DESCRIPTION

The Galant Electronically Controlled Suspension (ECS) uses compressed air to adjust vehicle height and rigidity. It automatically compensates for fluctuating loads and stability at high speeds.

The system has a manual override option which enables the operator to convert from soft to hard mode.

OPERATION

Airflow to the system is controlled by the air compressor, solenoids, sensors, air springs and control module. Each coil spring is reinforced by an air spring. The air suspension leveling system operates by regulating pressure in the air springs to maintain vehicle level.

The leveling system works with valving inside the strut housing to govern damping characteristics of strut assemblies. The suspension height is monitored by height sensors mounted in the front and rear. These height sensors furnish data to the control module.

AIR COMPRESSOR

A single piston air compressor is mounted to the transmission bracket on the right side of the engine compartment. When the air compressor exhaust valve is opened, vehicle is lowered.

When pressure in the reserve tank falls below specification, a signal is sent to the control unit which activates the compressor relay. After the relay is energized, the compressor will engage. A thermoswitch built into the air compressor will stop the motor if overheating occurs.

DRIER

The dual operation desiccant drier, located inside the reserve tank, removes moisture from the air as it is received from the compressor. As dry air is released by the air springs, airflow is reversed and the moisture from the desiccant is released into the atmosphere.

ELECTRONICALLY CONTROLLED SUSPENSION CONTROL UNIT

The microcomputer-based ECS control unit is located on the right side of the luggage compartment. The ECS continuously monitors the air suspension system.

If the ECS detects a malfunction in the system, an alarm light will turn on and all air system operation will stop. A self-diagnostic terminal in the glove box is provided for ECS control unit trouble shooting. *See Fig. 2.*

Fig. 2: Diagnostic Check Terminal

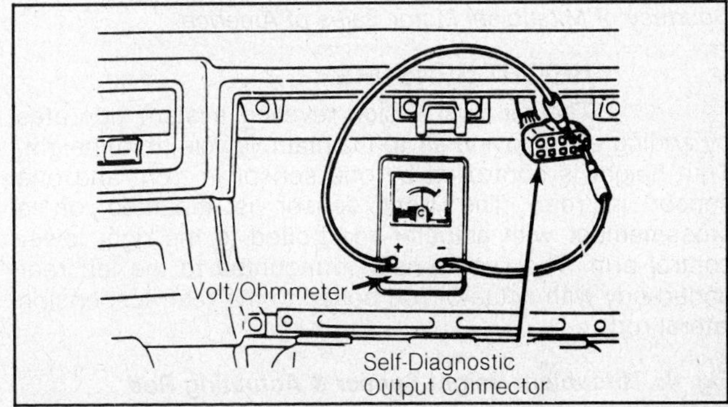

Courtesy of Mitsubishi Motor Sales of America.

ELECTRONICALLY CONTROLLED SUSPENSION INDICATOR

The ECS indicator is mounted in the console. The indicator can be checked for correct operation by verifying indicator and alarm light illumination after key is turned on. Lights should remain on for about one second after engine is started. A dimmer switch built into the system will diminish illumination of indicator lights when the taillights are switched on.

"G" SENSOR

The gravitational force "G" sensor is located below the rear console floor. As acceleration reaches .3 "G" longitudinally or .5 "G" laterally, the "G" sensor will signal the control unit to switch to hard mode. All height adjustment is suspended during "G" sensor operation. Should damage to the "G" sensor occur, the ECS will command the system to be fixed in the hard mode.

Fig. 1: Mitsubishi Electronically Controlled Suspension Component Location

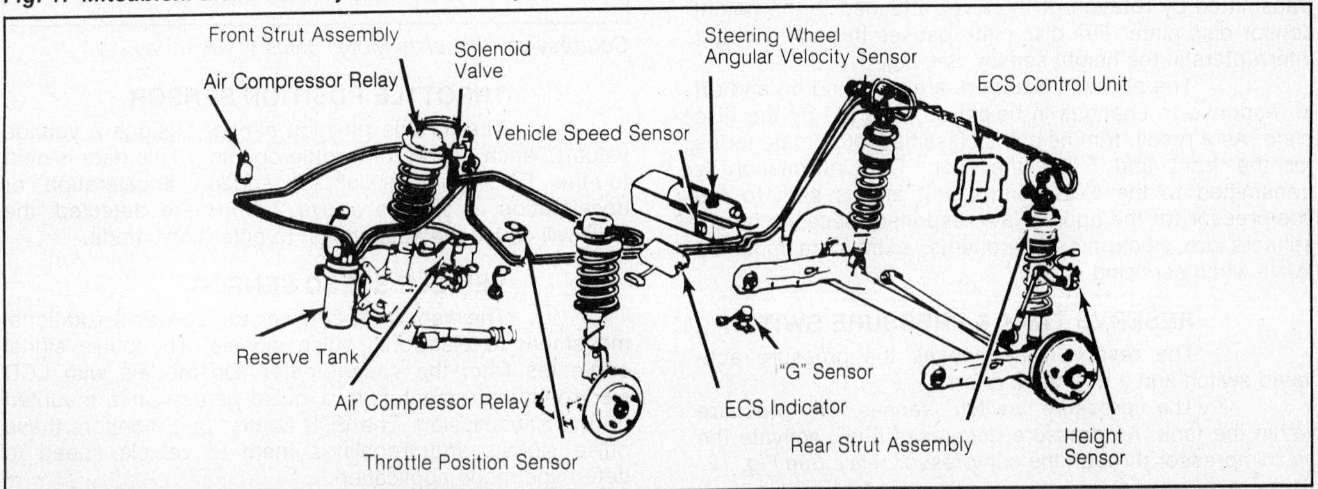

Courtesy of Mitsubishi Motor Sales of America.

Electronic Suspension

MITSUBISHI GALANT (Cont.)

Fig. 3: Mitsubishi "G" Sensor Assembly

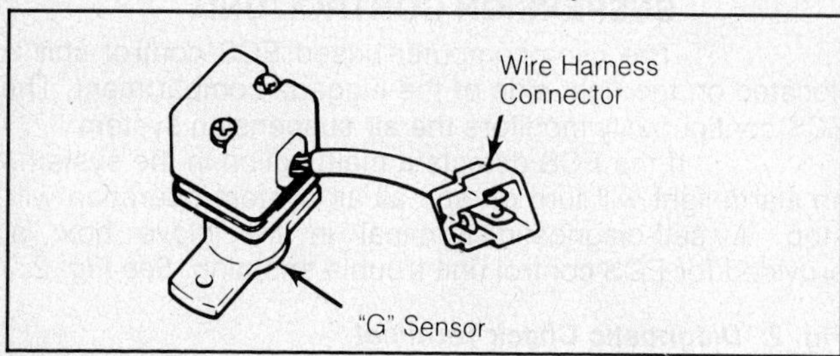

Courtesy of Mitsubishi Motor Sales of America.

HEIGHT SENSORS

The air suspension leveling system operates by adding or removing air to maintain vehicle (trim) height. Trim height is controlled by one sensor in front and one sensor in rear. The front sensor is mounted on a crossmember with actuator rod bolted to the right lower control arm. The rear sensor is mounted to the left rear underbody with actuator rod bolted to the rear suspension lateral rod.

Fig. 4: Mitsubishi Height Sensor & Actuating Rod

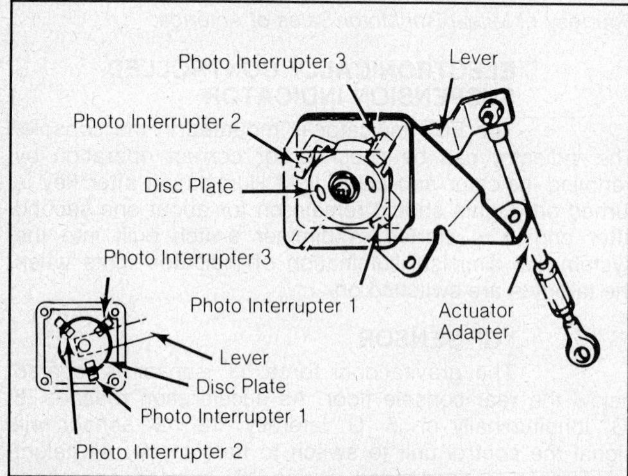

Courtesy of Mitsubishi Motor Sales of America.

HEIGHT SENSOR OPERATION

Height changes relative to suspension are transmitted by rotation of the lever attached to the height sensor disc plate. The disc plate passes through 3 photo interrupters in the height sensor. *See Fig. 5.*

The photo interrupters are switched on and off in response to changes in height as reported by the disc plate. As a result, trim height is classified into 7 categories for the front and 5 for the rear. This information is transmitted to the ECS control unit and is sent to the compressor for the appropriate response. Because height sensors are electronic components, extra care must be taken when servicing units.

RESERVE TANK & PRESSURE SWITCH

The reserve tank houses the pressure activated switch and a desiccant drier.

The pressure switch senses air pressure within the tank. As pressure decreases it will activate the air compressor through the compressor relay. *See Fig. 12.*

SOLENOID VALVES

A solenoid valve is located by each right strut assembly. Each strut assembly has a valve for height adjustment and Hard/Soft mode switching. The height control valve is operated by the ECS to either accept or discharge air from the springs. This valve will always be closed (solenoid non-continuity) during operation of the fail safe system to maintain a fixed amount of air in the springs.

The Hard/Soft mode switching valve, also managed by the control unit, will supply or discharge a compressed air signal to the actuator located on the strut tower below the dust cap. During operation of the fail-safe system, the actuator valve will open (solenoid continuity). This energizes the actuator and places the system in hard mode.

STRUT ASSEMBLY/AIR SPRING

Each air spring is made of hard rubber and is shaped like a rolling diaphragm to form an air chamber. The air springs, housed inside the strut assemblies, utilize a switching rod to perform commands received from the ECS control unit. This mechanism, located on top of each strut assembly, serves a dual function.

In addition to adding and removing air to the springs, the switching rod valving can open the compressed air chamber so all air springs share the same large volume of air pressure. This creates the soft mode. Hard mode is formed when the switching rod turns, sealing and isolating each air spring. *See Fig. 5.*

Fig. 5: Mitsubishi ECS Strut Assembly With Air Spring

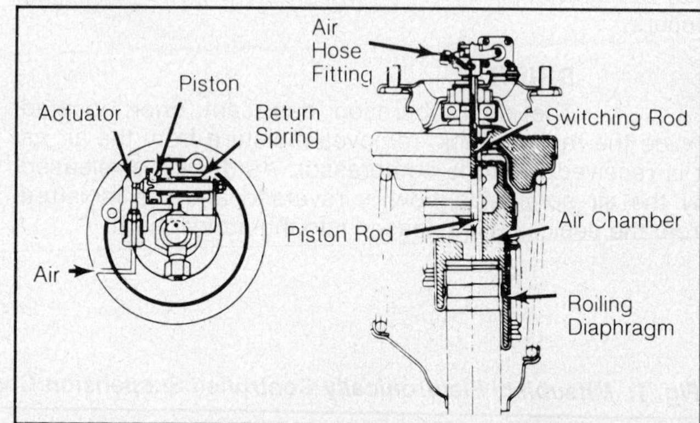

Courtesy of Mitsubishi Motor Sales of America.

THROTTLE POSITION SENSOR

The throttle position sensor assigns a voltage value to each degree of throttle opening. This data is sent to the ECS control unit. If sudden acceleration or deceleration at speeds above 2 MPH are detected, the ECS will cause the suspension to enter hard mode.

VEHICLE SPEED SENSOR

The vehicle speed sensor converts rotational movement to electronic pulse signals. The pulse signal originates from the speedometer. On models with LCD electronic instrumentation, a pulse generator is mounted on the transmission. The ECS control unit monitors these pulse signals and translates them to vehicle speed to determine mode application.

MITSUBISHI GALANT (Cont.)

ECS SELF-DIAGNOSIS

DIAGNOSTIC CODES

1) The self-diagnostic memory system stores information regarding malfunction of the Electronic Controlled Suspension (ECS). As trouble codes are received, the alarm light will illuminate.

2) Self-diagnosis is performed with ignition on. Use a volt/ohmmeter and the ECS self-diagnostic connector located inside the glove box. As voltage signals are generated to the check connector they may be read on the voltmeter as needle sweeps. The needle sweep range is zero to 12 volts. *See Fig. 6.*

Fig. 6: Normal Voltage Needle Sweep From Diagnostic Connector

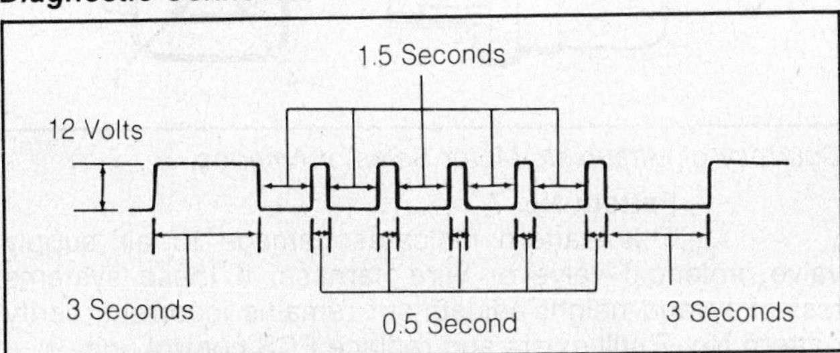

Courtesy of Mitsubishi Motor Sales of America.

3) Record the needle sweep pattern and compare with malfunction patterns on the ECS TROUBLE CODE IDENTIFICATION chart at end of article. If repair can be made without further diagnosis following identification of defective circuit, confirm normal pattern output at the diagnostic connector. If normal pattern output cannot be obtained, proceed to step **4)**.

4) If, after identifying and confirming trouble code pattern, repair cannot be made, refer to TESTING & DIAGNOSIS using self-diagnostic output patterns.

TESTING & DIAGNOSIS

Fig. 7: Wire Harness Terminal Arrangement

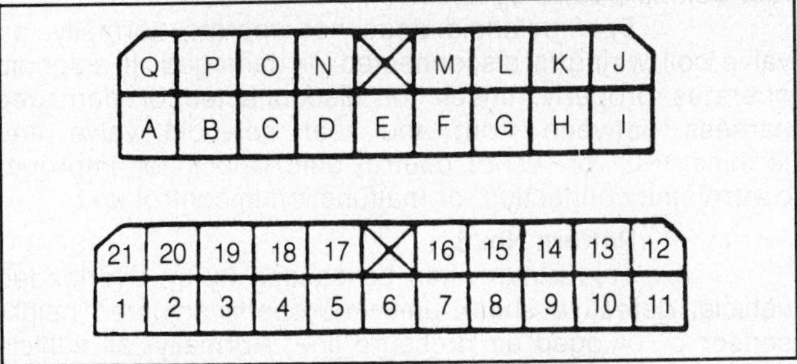

Courtesy of Mitsubishi Motor Sales of America.

TROUBLE CODE PATTERNS

Pattern No. 1

This is solenoid valve wiring damage at the Hard/Soft mode selector or in wire harness. A possible failure of output transistor may be located in electronic suspension control unit.

NOTE: **To avoid erasing ECS memory, never disconnect battery while ECS wire harness connector is separated.**

1) With 17-pin connector unplugged, check for about 20-ohms resistance between ground and terminals "M" or "F" of 17-pin connector of control unit. If resistance is about 20 ohms, go to step **4)**. If not, check for normal front and rear solenoid operation.

2) If solenoids are not operating properly, check for disconnected or damaged air valve coil wiring. If wiring is okay, replace front and/or rear solenoid.

3) If solenoids are operating properly, check for disconnected or damaged harness between front and rear solenoid valve and control unit terminals "M" or "F". Check for improper control unit connector, or malfunction of control unit.

Pattern No. 2

Loose connections or wire harness damage between "G" sensor and control unit are characteristics of internal damage to "G" sensor.

1) With ignition on and control unit connector attached, measure voltage between terminal "G" (Ground) of 17-pin connector and terminal No. 16. If a normal reading of 3.8 volts is received, go to step **2)**. If about 5 volts is received, repair "G" sensor wire harness or replace "G" sensor.

2) If normal voltage is obtained and alarm light is on, a defective electronic control unit is indicated. Replace control unit and verify system performance is correct. If alarm light is off, inspect system for poor wire connector contacts.

Pattern No. 3

Malfunction of steering wheel angular velocity sensor indicates sensor is loose or circuit is damaged.

1) With key on and electronic control unit connected, rotate steering wheel while measuring voltage between terminal "G" of 17-pin connector and terminals No. 6 and 17. A normal voltage signal will oscillate from 0-3.8 volts. If voltage reading is about 5 volts, replace angular velocity sensor or repair wire harness.

2) If voltage is normal and alarm light is on, replace electronic control unit. If alarm light is off, inspect for a faulty connector contact between angular velocity sensor and control unit.

Pattern No. 4

Abnormal condition of front height sensor indicates a loose connector, damage in wire harness between height sensor and electronic control unit or a defective height sensor.

1) With ignition on, check for about 5 volts between ground and power supply terminal (Blue wire) of front height sensor. If 5 volts are present, proceed to step **3)**. If 5 volts are not present, check for about 5 volts between "Q" terminal of 17 pin connector and ground.

2) If about 5 volts are not present, check for malfunction of control unit and replace if necessary. If about 5 volts are present, check for disconnected harness or harness damage between front height sensor and control unit terminal "Q".

3) Check for normal height sensor operation. If operation is not normal, replace sensor. If operation is normal, check for alternating 0-4.3 volts between ground and terminals No. 8, 9, 14 and/or 15 of 17-pin connector, while moving height sensor rod up and down.

4) If voltage alternates in given range, proceed to step **6)**. If voltage does not alternate and remains at zero volts, harness is shorted between front height sensor and control unit terminals No. 8, 9, 14 and/or 15. Repair harness as necessary.

Electronic Suspension

MITSUBISHI GALANT (Cont.)

5) If voltage does not alternate and remains at 4.3 volts, check for disconnected harness or damaged harness between front height sensor and control unit terminals No. 8, 9, 14, and/or 15. If alarm light is illuminated, check for malfunction of control unit and replace as necessary.

6) If alarm light is not illuminated, problem was intermittent or caused by poor contact of harness connector between front height sensor and control terminal "Q", and terminals No. 8, 9, 14 and/or 15.

Pattern No. 5

This pattern indicates abnormal signal input from rear height sensor, or malfunction of vehicle-height judgment circuit within control unit.

1) With ignition on, check for about 5 volts between ground and power supply terminal (Blue wire) of rear height sensor. If 5 volts are present, proceed to step **3)**. If not about 5 volts, check for about 5 volts between "Q" terminal of 17-pin connector and ground.

2) If not about 5 volts are present, check for malfunction of control unit and replace if necessary. If 5 volts is present, check for disconnected harness or harness damage between rear height sensor and control unit terminal "Q".

3) Check for normal height sensor operation. If operation is not normal, replace sensor. If operation is normal, check for alternating voltage of zero to about 4.3 volts between ground and terminals No. 10, 11, 12 and 13 of 17-pin connector, while moving height sensor rod up and down. If voltage alternates in given range, proceed to step **5)**.

NOTE: Terminal No. 11 is okay if it remains at zero volts during test procedure.

4) If voltage does not alternate and remains at zero volts, harness is shorted between rear height sensor and control unit terminals No. 10, 12, and/or 13. If voltage does not alternate and remains at 4.3 volts, check for disconnected harness or damaged harness between rear height sensor and control unit terminals No. 10, 11, 12, and/or 13.

5) If alarm light is illuminated, check for malfunction of control unit and replace as necessary. If alarm light is not illuminated, problem was intermittent or caused by poor contact of harness connector between rear height sensor and control terminal "Q", and terminals No. 10, 11, 12 and/or 13.

Pattern No. 6

This pattern is frequently associated with exhaust valve or air compressor relay damage. A damaged wire circuit of these components will also register this pattern. If testing proves these components are functional, ECS control unit output transistor is at fault.

1) With 17-pin connector of control unit unplugged, check for resistance of about 15 ohms between ground and terminal "E" of 17-pin connector. If resistance is about 15 ohms, go to step **3)**. If resistance is not about 15 ohms, check for normal exhaust valve operation.

2) If exhaust valve is malfunctioning, replace air compressor assembly. If exhaust valve is functioning properly, check for disconnected or damaged harness between exhaust valve and terminal "E" of control unit.

3) Check for resistance of about 100 ohms between ground and terminal "D" of 17-pin connector. If resistance is about 100 ohms, go to step **5)**. If resistance is not about 100 ohms, check for proper operation of compressor relay.

4) If compressor relay is not operating properly, replace relay. If relay is operating properly, check for disconnected or damaged harness between compressor relay and terminal "D". Check for improper control unit connection, or malfunctioning control unit.

Fig. 8: Air Compressor Relay Test Terminal Location

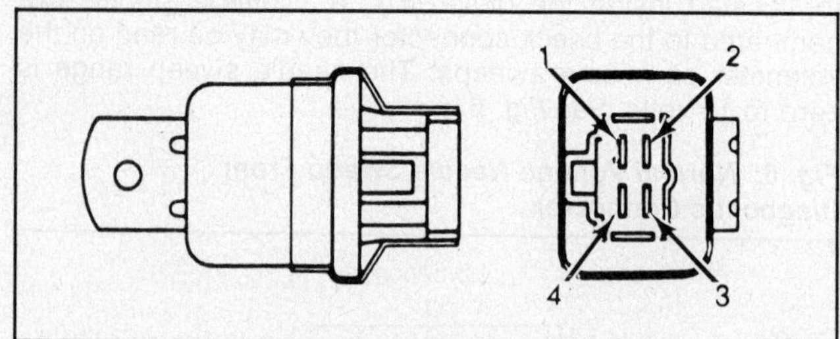

Courtesy of Mitsubishi Motor Sales of America.

Pattern No. 7

This pattern indicates damage to air supply valve, solenoid valve or wire harness. If these systems test okay and height adjustment remains incorrect, verify pattern No. 7 still exists and replace ECS control unit.

1) With 17-pin connector unplugged, turn ignition to "ON" position. Check for resistance of about 15 ohms between ground and terminal "N" of 17-pin connector.

2) If resistance is about 15 ohms go to step **4)**. If resistance is not about 15 ohms, check for proper operation of intake valve by itself. If intake valve is not operating properly, replace reserve tank.

3) If intake valve is operating properly, check for disconnected or damaged harness between intake valve and terminal "N" of control unit. Repair as necessary.

4) Check for resistance of about 20 ohms between ground and terminal "C" of 17-pin connector. If resistance is about 20 ohms, go to step **6)**. If resistance is not about 20 ohms, check for normal operation of front or rear solenoid valve by itself.

5) If solenoid does not operate normally, air valve coil wiring is disconnected or damaged. If solenoid operates properly, check for disconnected or damaged harness between front and rear solenoid valve and terminals "C" or "O" of control unit. Check for improper control unit connection, or malfunction in control unit.

Pattern No. 8

This pattern can be caused by an overloaded vehicle, defective shock unit, improperly adjusted height sensor or plugged air pressure line. Normally, all vehicle height adjustment will cease.

1) Ensure vehicle load is normal. If vehicle is overloaded, remove weight and turn ignition off. Check vehicle for height adjustment and proper height adjustment operation.

2) If vehicle load is normal, check for correct height sensor position. If sensor position is correct go to next step. If sensor position is incorrect, adjust height sensor.

3) Check for normal shock absorber rolling diaphragm. If diaphragm is not normal, repair or replace shock absorber unit. If diaphragm is normal, go to next step.

4) Check for clogged vehicle height adjustment pressure line. Repair or replace line as necessary. If pressure line is okay, control unit is malfunctioning and should be replaced.

Pattern No. 9

This pattern indicates air leakage or abnormal operating condition of air compressor.

1) Check for proper operation of air compressor. If air compressor is not operating properly, repair or replace as necessary.

2) If air compressor is operating properly, check all lines for leakage or breaks. Repair or replace as necessary.

Pattern No. 10

This pattern indicates terminal "L" of alternator has low voltage output or malfunctioning charging system. Pattern No. 10 may also indicate short in harness between control unit and terminal "L" of alternator.

1) Start engine and allow to idle. Unplug 17-pin connector. Check for about 12 volts between terminal "G" and terminal "A" (alternators terminal "L") at harness side of 17-pin connector.

2) If 12 volts is present, go to step **4)**. If 12 volts is not present, check for normal alternator output. If output is normal check for short between alternator terminal "L" and control unit terminal "A". If alternator output is not normal, check charging sytem and repair as necessary.

3) Check all connectors and wires for shorts. If connectors and wires are okay, control unit should be replaced.

Fig. 9: Air Compressor Test Connection & Terminal Identification

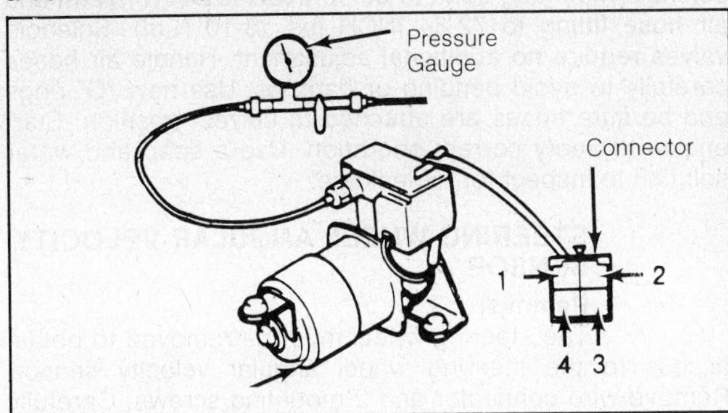

Courtesy of Mitsubishi Motor Sales of America.

REMOVAL & INSTALLATION

AIR COMPRESSOR

Removal

Remove air hose from compressor and tape openings to prevent contamination. Disconnect wire harness connector and remove compressor mounting bolts to remove air compressor.

Installation.

Reverse removal procedure to complete installation. Ensure wire connector has good contact. Apply a soap/water solution to confirm no air leakage exists.

AIR COMPRESSOR RELAY

Removal & Installation

Air compressor relay is located in the front right section of the engine compartment. The relay is secured to the inner fender by a bolt. Remove the wire harness connector and bolt to remove the air compressor relay. Reverse removal procedure to install. No adjustments are required.

AIR HOSES

Removal & Installation

When servicing air hoses, verify the part number and use a new connector and "O" ring. When replacing hose attached to front, body or control harness, leave old hose and install new hose parallel of harness. After installation, check system for correct operation. Apply soap/water solution to coupling to inspect for air leakage.

ECS CONTROL UNIT

Removal & Installation

Remove luggage compartment right side trim. Disconnect the ECS wire harness connector. Remove the ECS mounting bolts and carefully separate the control unit from the body. Use care in handling ECS unit. Do not clean with any liquid products. To install, reverse removal procedure. Ensure ventilation duct at rear of unit is securely attached. No adjustment of control unit is necessary.

ECS INDICATOR UNIT

Removal & Installation

Pry the lower part of radio panel loose and remove from console. Slide ECS indicator out of console. Light bulbs may be replaced at this time by removing 2 screws from rear cover and separating units. No replacement is available for the LED. Reverse removal procedure for installation.

"G" SENSOR

Removal & Installation

"G" sensor is located inside rear console box. Remove the inner box for accessibility to sensor. Detach wire connector and remove 2 screws holding "G" sensor to floor panel. Extreme care must be exercised in handling "G" sensor as unit is easily damaged. Reverse removal procedure for installation. Sensor is pre-set and no further adjustment is required.

HEIGHT SENSORS

Removal

1) Remove air compressor and detach front sensor actuating rod from lower control arm. Separate sensor wire connector and remove mounting screws from crossmember.

2) Disconnect rear sensor coupling and actuating rod. Disconnect wire connector and remove sensor mounting screws to separate unit from panel.

Installation & Adjustment

1) Inspect actuating rod for bending or damage. Adjustment length must conform to dimensions illustrated and dimension "A" should remain uniform. *See Fig. 10.*

MITSUBISHI GALANT (Cont.)

Fig. 10: Height Sensor Actuating Rod Adjustment

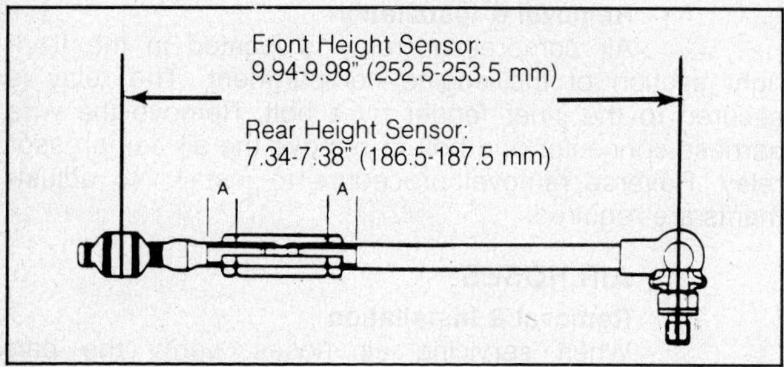

Courtesy of Mitsubishi Motor Sales of America.

2) Install height sensor with mounting screws. Tighten to specification and verify actuating rod ball joint is at rocking center. *See Fig. 11.*

3) Attach wire connector to sensor. Reverse removal procedure to complete installation. Start engine and verify system operation is correct.

Fig. 11: Height Sensor Installation & Torque Specification

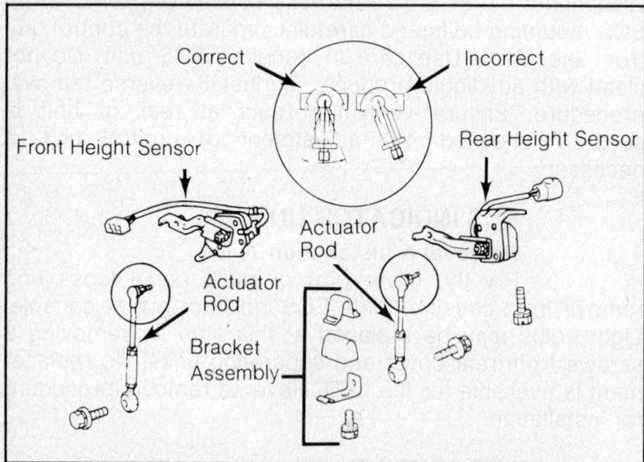

Courtesy of Mitsubishi Motor Sales of America.

RESERVE TANK & PRESSURE SWITCH

Removal

1) Remove battery and battery tray. Separate wire harness connector and air hoses. Tape air hose fittings closed to avoid contamination of the system. Ensure air hoses do not bend or contact hot surfaces.

Fig. 12: Exploded View of Reserve Tank & Pressure Switch

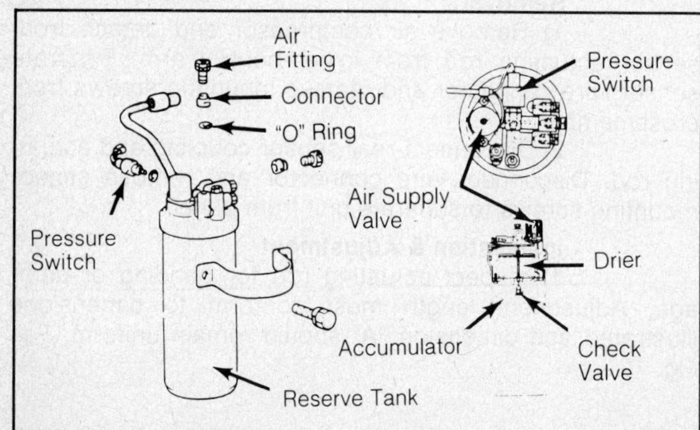

Courtesy of Mitsubishi Motor Sales of America.

2) Loosen reserve tank holder strap mounting nuts and slide tank upward to remove. If pressure switch is to be replaced, remove wire connector and turn switch counterclockwise.

Installation

If pressure switch was removed, turn clockwise to install. Lower reserve tank into mounting strap and tighten mounting nuts to 84-120 INCH lbs. (10-14 N.m). Attach wire connector and install new "O" rings on air hoses. Install air hoses and tighten to 72-84 INCH lbs. (8-10 N.m). Start engine to verify correct system operation. Use a soap and water solution on air hose connections to inspect for air leakage.

SOLENOID VALVES

Removal (Front)

Front solenoid valve is located in the engine compartment to the rear of the right strut assembly. Remove wire connector and all air hose fittings. Remove solenoid mounting bolts and remove solenoid from panel.

NOTE: Whenever air hoses are removed, tape or plug all openings to prevent contamination from entering the system.

Removal (Rear)

The rear solenoid valve is located next to the right rear strut assembly. Access can be obtained by removing the rear seat. Disconnect wire harness connector and all air hoses. Label air hoses for reassembly reference. Remove solenoid mounting bolts and separate unit from body.

Installation

To install, reverse removal procedure. Tighten solenoid mounting bolts to 60-96 INCH lbs. (7-11 N.m) and air hose fitting to 72-84 INCH lbs. (8-10 N.m). Solenoid valves require no additional adjustment. Handle air hoses carefully to avoid bending or damage. Use new "O" rings and be sure hoses are attached to correct position. Start engine to verify correct operation. Use a soap and water solution to inspect for air leakage.

STEERING WHEEL ANGULAR VELOCITY SENSOR

Removal

The steering wheel must be removed to obtain access to the steering wheel angular velocity sensor. Remove wire connector and 2 mounting screws. Carefully lift sensor out of steering column.

Installation

Because sensor is an electronic unit using photo-couplers, clean hands and work area are recommended in handling this component. Gently position sensor in steering column. Do not bend or contaminate slit plate. Install mounting screws and wire connector. Reverse removal procedure to complete installation.

STRUT ASSEMBLY

Removal

1) Lift vehicle and remove front wheels. Remove the front height sensor actuating rod from the right lower control arm. Separate brake hose bracket and remove 2 bolts at strut assembly and knuckle.

NOTE: Support steering knuckle with wire to prevent drive shaft and brake hose stress. Keep air hose connections plugged during disassembly to prevent contamination of system.

MITSUBISHI GALANT (Cont.)

2) Remove air hose and label for reassembly reference. Remove dust cap and strut assembly mounting nuts. Lower unit out of wheelhouse using caution not to damage the actuator.

Disassembly

1) Remove actuator and adapter. Use Adapter (MB991043) and spring compressor tool to compress coil spring. Pry snap ring loose and remove air hose fitting.

2) Remove actuator bracket and insulator from strut housing. Carefully loosen spring compressor tool to allow full extension of coil spring and remove adapter. Remove sub tank and coil spring with lower spring pad.

3) Inspect all components for damage or excess wear. Check coil spring for deformation and shock unit for fluid leakage. Remove "O" ring from sub tank and discard.

Reassembly

1) Lubricate "O" ring and install in sub tank. Install lower spring pad, spring, sub tank and Adapter (MB991043). Ensure all components are in correct alignment and compress coil spring.

2) Install insulator and tighten nut to 58-72 ft. lbs. (79-98 N.m). Remove adapter and apply multipurpose grease to insulator bearing channel. Align piston rod notch with "D" shape of actuator bracket. Install actuator bracket to strut housing and tighten to 29-43 ft. lbs. (39-58 N.m).

3) Lubricate and install "O" ring to piston rod. Install air hose fitting and pull piston rod upward to attach snap ring. To complete reassembly, reverse removal procedure.

Installation

To install, reverse removal procedure. Turn insulator so air hose fitting and actuator (Black and White air hose) are facing 180 degrees away from engine. Install air hoses and tighten to 72-84 INCH lbs. (8-10 N.m). Start engine to verify correct system operation. Use soap and water solution to inspect for air leakage.

Fig. 13: Exploded View of Mitsubishi ECS Strut Assembly

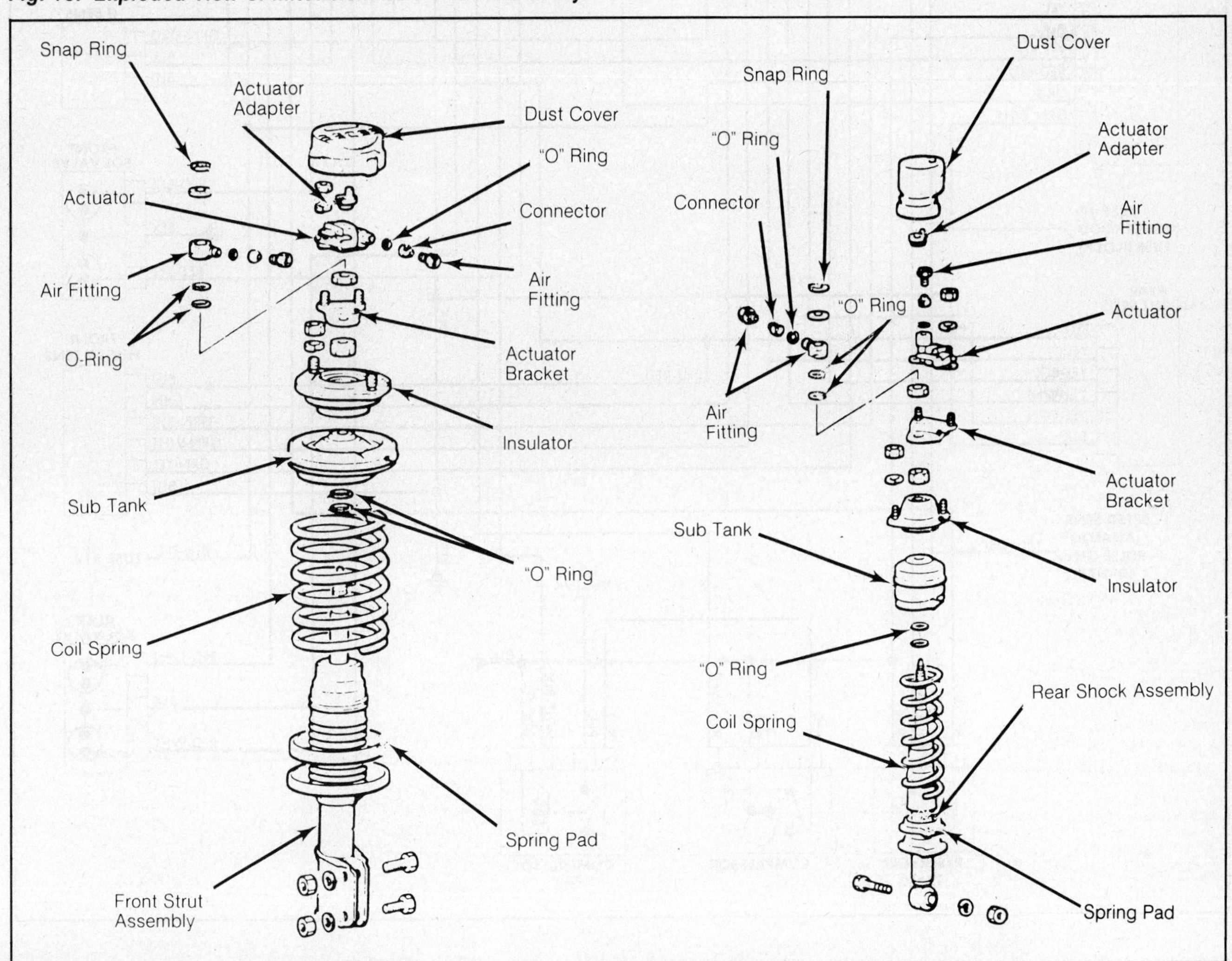

Courtesy of Mitsubishi Motor Sales of America.

Electronic Suspension

MITSUBISHI GALANT (Cont.)

Fig. 14: Mitsubishi ECS Wiring Diagram

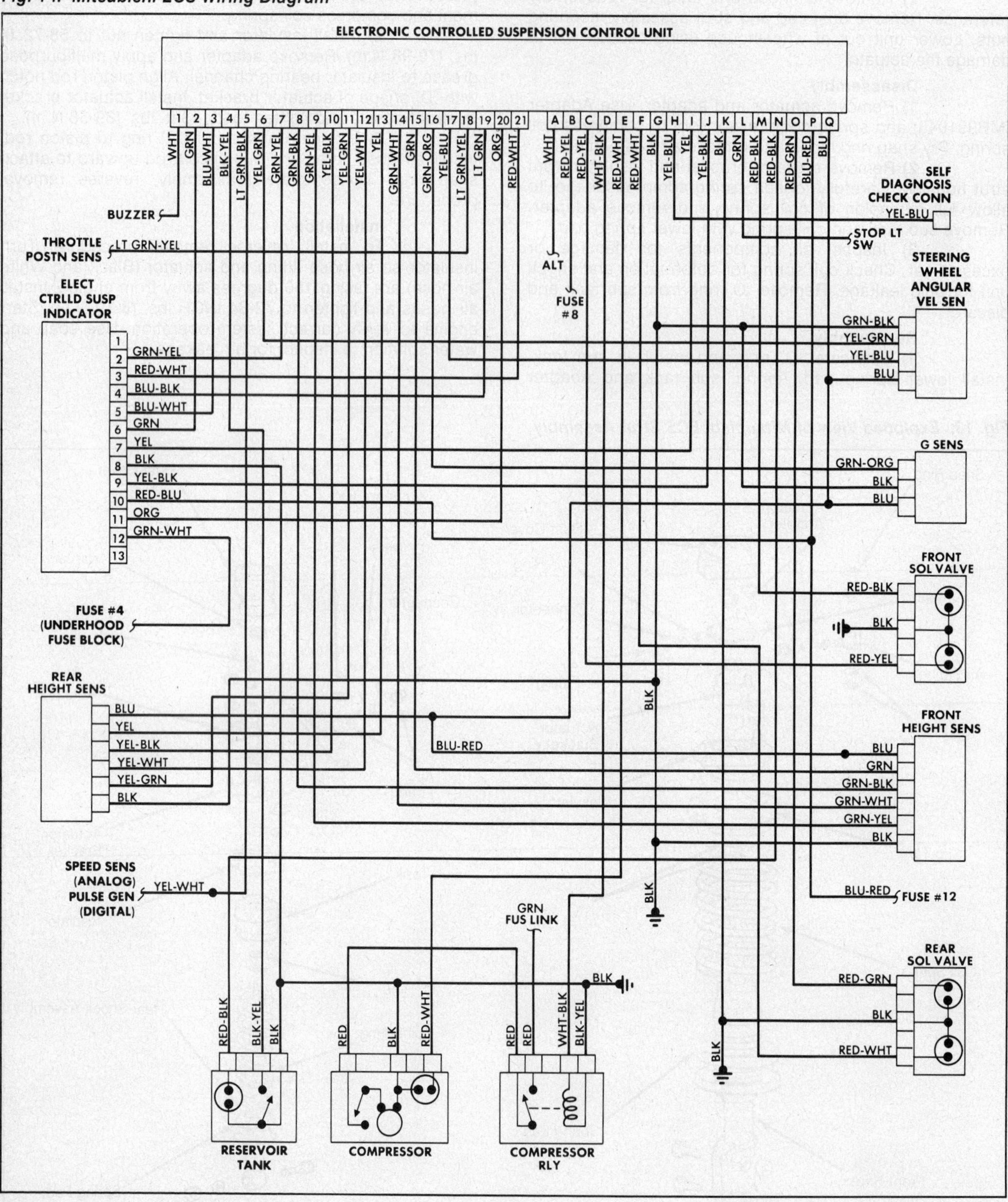

Electronic Suspension

MITSUBISHI GALANT (Cont.)

SELF-DIAGNOSIS OUTPUT PATTERN & TROUBLE SHOOTING TABLE

Mal-function No.	Self-diagnosis output pattern and output code	Problem (chassis condition)	Probable cause(s)
0	0 0 0 0 0 Repetition	Normal	—
1	0 0 0 0 1	Disconnection or damage of air-valve drive circuit for HARD/SOFT switch-over of the front or rear solenoid valve, or a short-circuit of the drive transistor within the control unit. (Alarm light illuminates and SOFT condition remains; no adjustment to HIGH vehicle height.)	· Front or rear solenoid valve connector is disconnected. · Solenoid for HARD/SOFT switchover is damaged or disconnected. · Connector disconnected or harness damaged or disconnected · Malfunction of the control unit (Malfunction of the output transistor)
2	0 0 0 1 0	G sensor input circuit is damaged or disconnected. (Alarm light illuminates; condition remains HARD.)	· Disconnection of the G sensor connector · Damage or disconnection within the G sensor · Damage or disconnection of G sensor output circuit harness, or connector is disconnected.
3	0 0 0 1 1	Steering angular-velocity sensor input circuit is damaged or disconnected, or there is a malfunction of the steering angular-velocity sensor. (Alarm light illuminates; condition remains HARD.)	· Disconnection of the steering angular-velocity sensor connector · Malfunction of the steering angular-velocity sensor connector · Damage or disconnection of the steering angular-velocity sensor output circuit harness, or disconnection of connector
4	1 0 0 0 0	Abnormal condition signal is input from front height sensor, or there is a malfunction of the vehicle-height judgment circuit within the control unit. (The alarm light illuminates, and the vehicle-height adjustment operation stops at that point.) (Note, however, that operation of the air compressor is possible.) **Caution** **Remember that approximately 32 seconds are required for malfunction judgment.**	· Disconnection of front height sensor connector · Malfunction of front height sensor · Damage or disconnection of the front height sensor circuit harness, or disconnection of the connector · Malfunction of the control unit

MITSUBISHI GALANT (Cont.)

SELF-DIAGNOSIS OUTPUT PATTERN & TROUBLE SHOOTING TABLE (Cont.)

Mal-function No.	Self-diagnosis output pattern and output code	Problem (chassis condition)	Probable cause(s)
5	1 0 0 0 1	Abnormal condition signal is input from rear height sensor, or there is a malfunction of the vehicle-height judgment circuit within the control unit. (The alarm light illuminates, and the vehicle-height adjustment operation stops at that point.) (Note, however, that operation of the air compressor is possible.) **Caution** **Remember that approximately 32 seconds are required for malfunction judgment.**	· Disconnection of rear height sensor connector · Malfunction of rear height sensor · Damage or disconnection of the rear height sensor circuit harness, or disconnection of the connector · Malfunction of the control unit
6	1 0 0 1 0	Damage or disconnection of the exhaust solenoid valve (in the compressor) or air compressor relay drive circuit, or short-circuit of drive transistor within the control unit. (Note, however, that operation of the air compressor is possible.)	· Disconnection of the exhaust solenoid valve (air compressor) connector · Disconnection of air compressor relay connector · Damaged or disconnected air compressor relay coil · Damaged or disconnected exhaust solenoid valve coil · Damaged or disconnected circuit, or disconnection of connector · Malfunction of the control unit (Malfunction of the output transistor)
7	1 0 0 1 1	Damaged or disconnected front or rear solenoid air valve for vehicle height adjustment, or intake solenoid reserve tank), or short-circuit of drive transistor within control unit (The alarm light illuminates, and the vehicle-height adjustment operation stops at that point.)	· Intake solenoid valve (reserve tank) connector is disconnected. · Intake solenoid coil is damaged or disconnected. · Solenoid coil for vehicle height adjustment is damaged or disconnected. · Circuit is damaged or disconnected, or connector is disconnected. · Malfunction of the control unit (Malfunction of the output transistor)
8	1 0 1 0 0	Even though the pressure of the reserve tank is sufficient (pressure switch is OFF), the vehicle height adjustment is not finished even though 3 minutes each or more have passed for the front and rear height adjustments. (The alarm light illuminates, and the vehicle-height adjustment operation stops at that point.)	· Overload · Improper adjustment of the front or rear height sensor · Clogging of the vehicle height adjustment air pressure line · Malfunction of the air spring of the rear shock absorber unit or front strut unit · Malfunction of the control unit (Malfunction of the output transistor)

Electronic Suspension

MITSUBISHI GALANT (Cont.)

SELF-DIAGNOSIS OUTPUT PATTERN & TROUBLE SHOOTING TABLE (Cont.)

Mal-function No.	Self-diagnosis output pattern and output code	Problem (chassis condition)	Probable cause(s)
9	1 0 1 0 1	The pressure in the reserve tank is low (pressure switch is ON), and the vehicle height adjustment is not finished even though 3 minutes each or more have passed for the front and rear height adjustments. Or, the air compressor has operated continuously for 4 minutes or more. (The alarm light illuminates, and the vehicle-height adjustment operation stops at that point.)	· Air leakage · Abnormal condition of the air compressor
10	1 0 1 1 0	The output voltage of the L terminal of the alternator is approximately 5V or less even though the ignition key is at ON and the vehicle speed is approximately 40 km/h (25 mph) or more. [The charge warning light is illuminated. Moreover, the Electronic Controlled Suspension function does not operate when the vehicle is stopped (vehicle speed of approximately 3 km/h (2 mph).] **Caution** **The Electronic Controlled Suspension alarm light does not illuminate. In addition, there is no detection of harness damage or disconnection between the alternator's L terminal and the control unit.**	· Alternator's L terminal output voltage is low (malfunction of the charging system). · The harness is short-circuited between the control unit and the alternator's L terminal.

NISSAN MAXIMA & 300ZX

DESCRIPTION

The Nissan Electronically-Controlled Variable Shock Absorber (ECVSA) system is designed to provide stability and comfort under a variety of road conditions. Selection of system firmness is accomplished with a driver-adjustable, 3 position selection switch. The system components consist of a control unit, 4 motorized strut assemblies, flexible harness circuitry and a driver selection switch. *See Fig. 2.*

OPERATION

The motors within the strut assembly adjust the dampening affects by changing the hydraulic valve position. According to the signal received from the selection switch, fluid will flow through larger orifices for a softer ride and smaller orifices for a firmer ride.

Should the system malfunction, the LED's on the selection switch will blink intermittently. However, problems found in the system are often indicated by a non-blinking LED as well. For the duration of a malfunction, the control unit will automatically direct all functioning strut assemblies to a normal setting.

TESTING & DIAGNOSIS

NOTE: **Make sure that connections are tight and correctly connected. Ensure battery is in good condition before beginning testing procedures.**

NO CONTROL LIGHTS ILLUMINATE

1) Check for a blown fuse, burnt out LED lights, open in wire harness and/or defective selection switch. If inspection shows no faults, turn ignition switch to "OFF" position and change selection switch position. Turn ignition switch to "ON" position.

2) If one or 2 lights illuminate, a defective selection switch is indicated. Replace switch and recheck system. If LED lights remain off and fuse is still good, check power supply circuit. See POWER SUPPLY CIRCUIT CHECK. If power supply circuit is okay, replace selection switch.

TWO CONTROL LIGHTS ILLUMINATE

1) If only 2 LED lights are on, inspect the harness side of the switch for a short. Also inspect selection switch for a defect. If circuit and switch are okay, turn ignition off and change selection switch position. Turn ignition switch to "ON" position and observe LED lights.

2) If lights are normal, wire circuit on switch side of harness is damaged. If lights for non-controlled positions are on, selection switch is defective or wiring circuit to selection switch is damaged.

ALL CONTROL LIGHTS ILLUMINATE

1) This condition is caused by a defective selection switch, defective control unit or a short in the selection switch wiring harness. Turn ignition switch to "OFF" position and change switch selection position. Turn ignition switch to "ON" position and observe lights.

2) If lights remain on, replace the selection switch. If lights still remain on, replace control unit. If lights for non-selected positions are on, check control unit function. See CONTROL UNIT CHECK.

ONE CONTROL LIGHT ILLUMINATE

1) Turn ignition switch to "OFF" position. Inspect for loose connections throughout the circuit. Turn ignition switch to "ON" position, check lighting condition. If no change in lighting condition, check input of control unit. See CONTROL UNIT CHECK.

2) If control unit input signal is okay, check continuity of sensor by installing a Sub-Harness Connector. *See Fig. 3.* Turn ignition switch to "OFF" position. Turn selector switch to "S" position. Turn ignition switch back to the "ON" position for 2-3 seconds. See CHECKING CONTINUITY OF SENSOR table.

Fig. 1: Maxima & 300ZX Variable Shock Absorber System

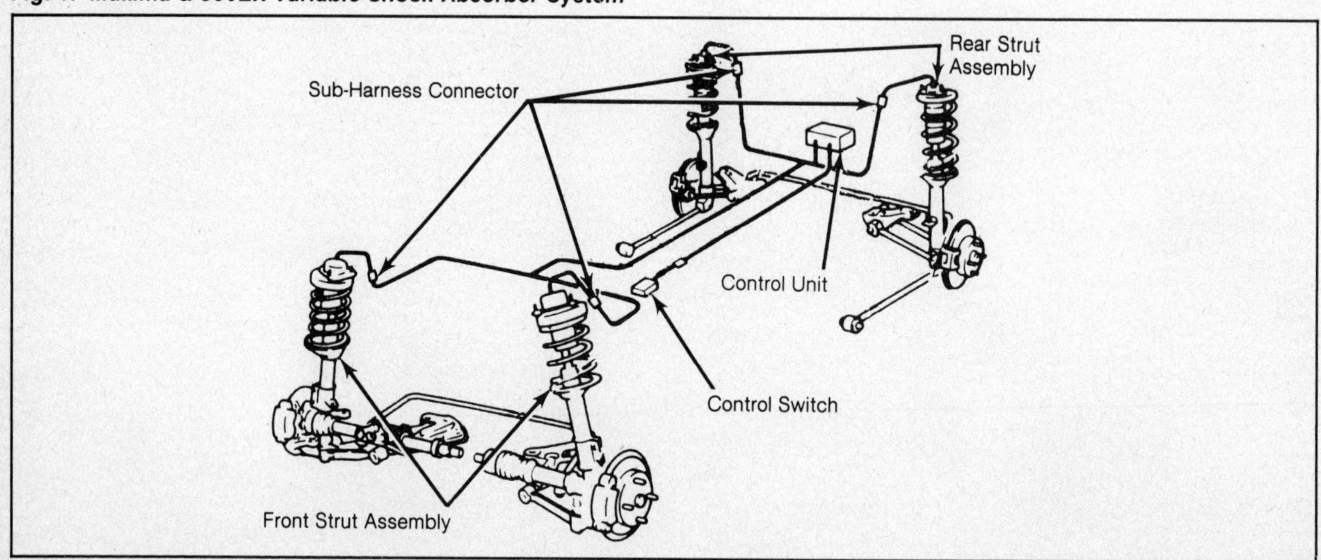

Courtesy of Nissan Motor Co., U.S.A.

NISSAN MAXIMA & 300ZX (Cont.)

Fig. 2: Exploded View of Nissan Adjustable Shock Absorber

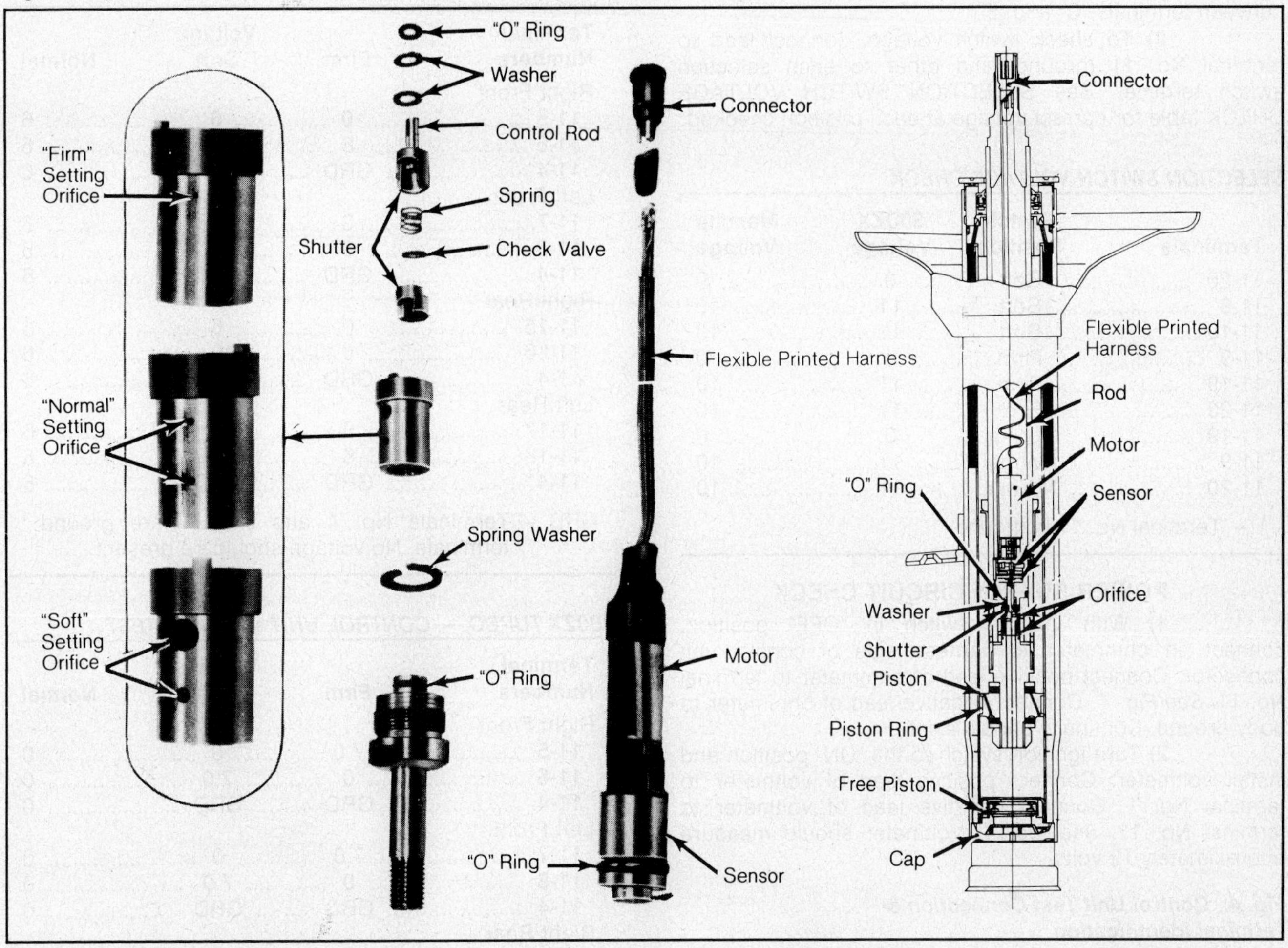

Courtesy of Nissan Motor Co., U.S.A.

NOTE: If ignition switch is turned back to "OFF" position before 2-3 seconds, or left in "ON" position more than 6 seconds, motors may not change to proper firmness setting.

3) If continuity of sensor is okay, replace control unit. If continuity is not okay, remove sub-harness connector and recheck continuity. *See Fig. 3.* If sensor continuity is okay, replace strut assembly shock absorber. If sensor continuity is not okay, replace sub-harness.

CHECKING CONTINUITY OF SENSOR

Selector Position	Continuity Terminals	No Continuity Terminals
"S"	3-5	4-5
"F"	4-5	3-5
"N"	3-5	[1] NA
"N"	4-5	[1] NA

[1] – NA is non-applicable.

SELECTION SWITCH CHECK

1) To check for continuity at each switch position, disconnect selection switch connector. Connect an ohmmeter to switch terminals and check continuity between switch positions. With selection switch in the "SOFT" position, continuity should exist between terminals "C" and "S".

2) With switch in the "NORMAL" position, continuity should exist between terminals "C" and "N". With

Fig. 3: Continuity Check of Sensor Using Sub-Harness Connector

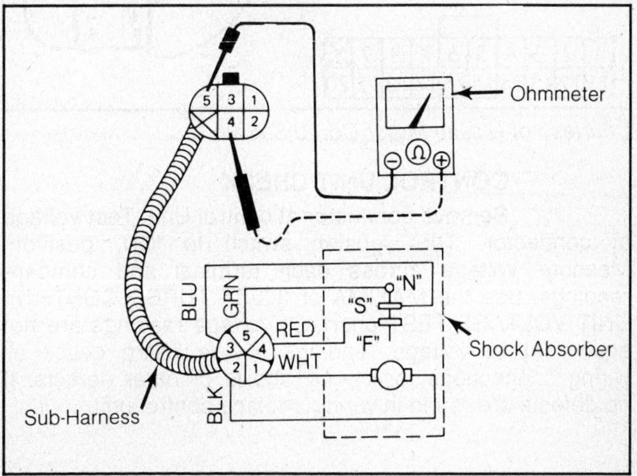

Courtesy of Nissan Motor Co., U.S.A.

Electronic Suspension

NISSAN MAXIMA & 300ZX (Cont.)

switch in the "FIRM" position, continuity should exist between terminals "C" and "F".

3) To check switch voltage, connect lead to terminal No. 11 (ground) and other to each selection switch terminal. See SELECTION SWITCH VOLTAGE CHECK table for correct voltage at each position checked.

SELECTION SWITCH VOLTAGE CHECK

Terminals [1]	Switch Position	300ZX Voltage	Maxima Voltage
11-20	Soft	0	0
11-9	Soft	11	10
11-19	Soft	11	10
11-9	Firm	0	0
11-19	Firm	11	10
11-20	Firm	11	10
11-19	Normal	0	0
11-9	Normal	11	10
11-20	Normal	11	10

[1] – Terminal No. 11 is ground.

POWER SUPPLY CIRCUIT CHECK

1) With ignition switch in "OFF" position, connect an ohmmeter to harness side of control unit connector. Connect positive lead of ohmmeter to terminal No. 11. *See Fig. 4*. Connect negative lead of ohmmeter to body ground. Continuity should exist.

2) Turn ignition switch to the "ON" position and install voltmeter. Connect positive lead of voltmeter to terminal No. 1. Connect negative lead of voltmeter to terminal No. 11. *See Fig. 4*. Voltmeter should measure approximately 12 volts.

Fig. 4: Control Unit Test Connection & Terminal Identification

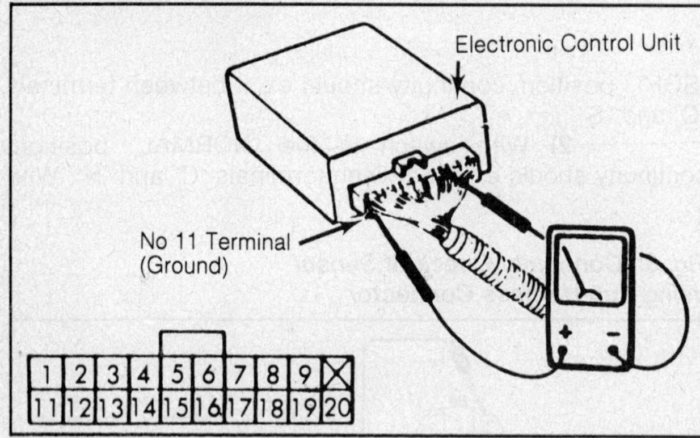

Courtesy of Nissan Motor Co., U.S.A.

CONTROL UNIT CHECK

Remove connector at control Unit. Test voltage at connector. Turn ignition switch to "ON" position. Measure voltage across each terminal and compare readings. See the MAXIMA or 300ZX TURBO CONTROL UNIT VOLTAGE TEST charts. If voltage readings are not equivalent to voltage readings of the chart, check all wiring connections for opens, shorts or other defects. If no defects are found in wiring, replace control unit.

MAXIMA – CONTROL UNIT VOLTAGE TEST

Terminal Numbers	Voltage Firm	Soft	Normal
Right Front			
11-5	0	6	6
11-6	6	0	6
11-4	GRD	GRD	6
Left Front			
11-7	0	6	6
11-8	6	0	6
11-4	GRD	GRD	6
Right Rear			
11-15	0	6	6
11-16	6	0	6
11-4	GRD	GRD	6
Left Rear			
11-17	0	6	6
11-18	6	0	6
11-4	GRD	GRD	6

GRD – Terminals No. 4 and No. 11 are ground terminals. No voltage should be present.

300ZX TURBO – CONTROL UNIT VOLTAGE TEST

Terminal Numbers	Voltage Firm	Soft	Normal
Right Front			
11-5	7.0	0	0
11-6	0	7.0	0
11-4	GRD	GRD	0
Left Front			
11-7	7.0	0	0
11-8	0	7.0	0
11-4	GRD	GRD	0
Right Rear			
11-15	7.0	0	0
11-16	0	7.0	0
11-4	GRD	GRD	0
Left Rear			
11-17	7.0	0	0
11-18	0	7.0	0
11-4	GRD	GRD	0

GRD – Terminals No. 4 and No. 11 are ground terminals. No voltage should be present.

REMOVAL & INSTALLATION

NOTE: **For removal and installation of suspension components, see appropriate front or rear suspension article in this section.**

Electronic Suspension

NISSAN MAXIMA & 300ZX (Cont.)

Fig. 5: Adjustable Strut Sub-Harness Assembly

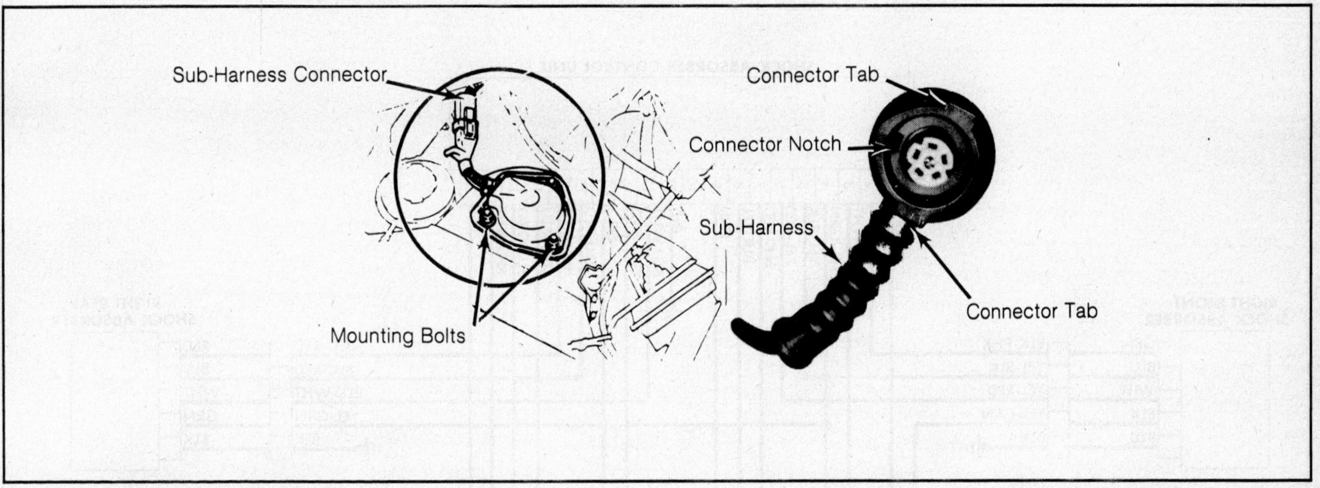

Courtesy of Nissan Motor Co., U.S.A.

Fig. 6: Maxima ECVSA Wiring Diagram

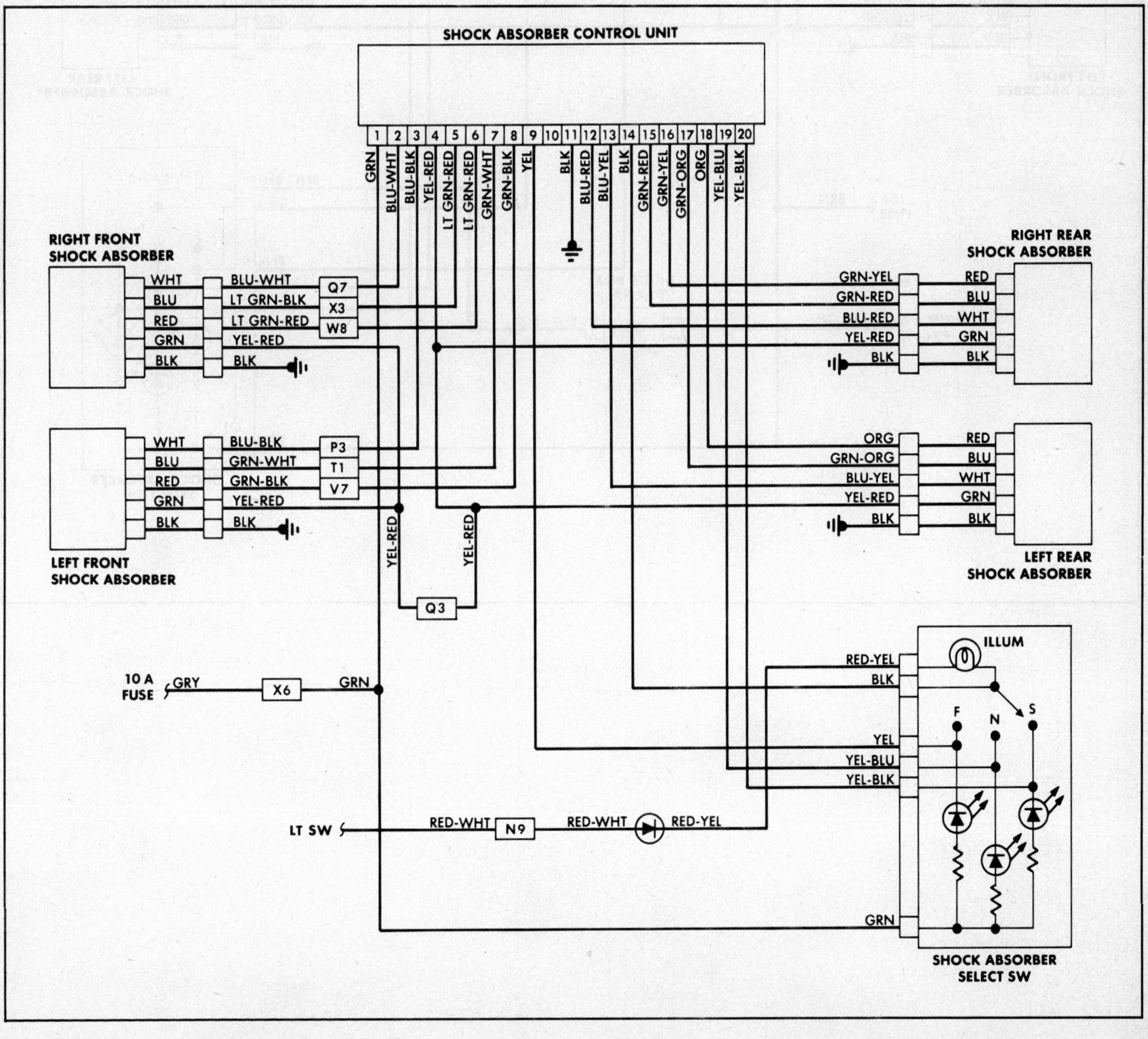

SHOCK ABSORBER CONTROL UNIT

1 GRN
2 BLU-WHT
3 BLU-BLK
4 YEL-RED
5 LT GRN-RED
6 LT GRN-RED
7 GRN-WHT
8 GRN-BLK
9 YEL
10
11 BLK
12 BLU-RED
13 BLU-YEL
14 BLK
15 GRN-RED
16 GRN-YEL
17 GRN-ORG
18 ORG
19 YEL-BLU
20 YEL-BLK

RIGHT FRONT SHOCK ABSORBER
WHT BLU-WHT Q7
BLU LT GRN-BLK X3
RED LT GRN-RED W8
GRN YEL-RED
BLK BLK

LEFT FRONT SHOCK ABSORBER
WHT BLU-BLK P3
BLU GRN-WHT T1
RED GRN-BLK V7
GRN YEL-RED
BLK BLK

RIGHT REAR SHOCK ABSORBER
GRN-YEL RED
GRN-RED BLU
BLU-RED WHT
YEL-RED GRN
BLK BLK

LEFT REAR SHOCK ABSORBER
ORG RED
GRN-ORG BLU
BLU-YEL WHT
YEL-RED GRN
BLK BLK

YEL-RED Q3 YEL-RED

10 A FUSE GRY X6 GRN

LT SW RED-WHT N9 RED-WHT RED-YEL

SHOCK ABSORBER SELECT SW
RED-YEL
BLK
YEL
YEL-BLU
YEL-BLK
GRN
ILLUM
F N S

Electronic Suspension

NISSAN MAXIMA & 300ZX (Cont.)

Fig. 7: 300ZX Turbo ECVSA Wiring Diagram

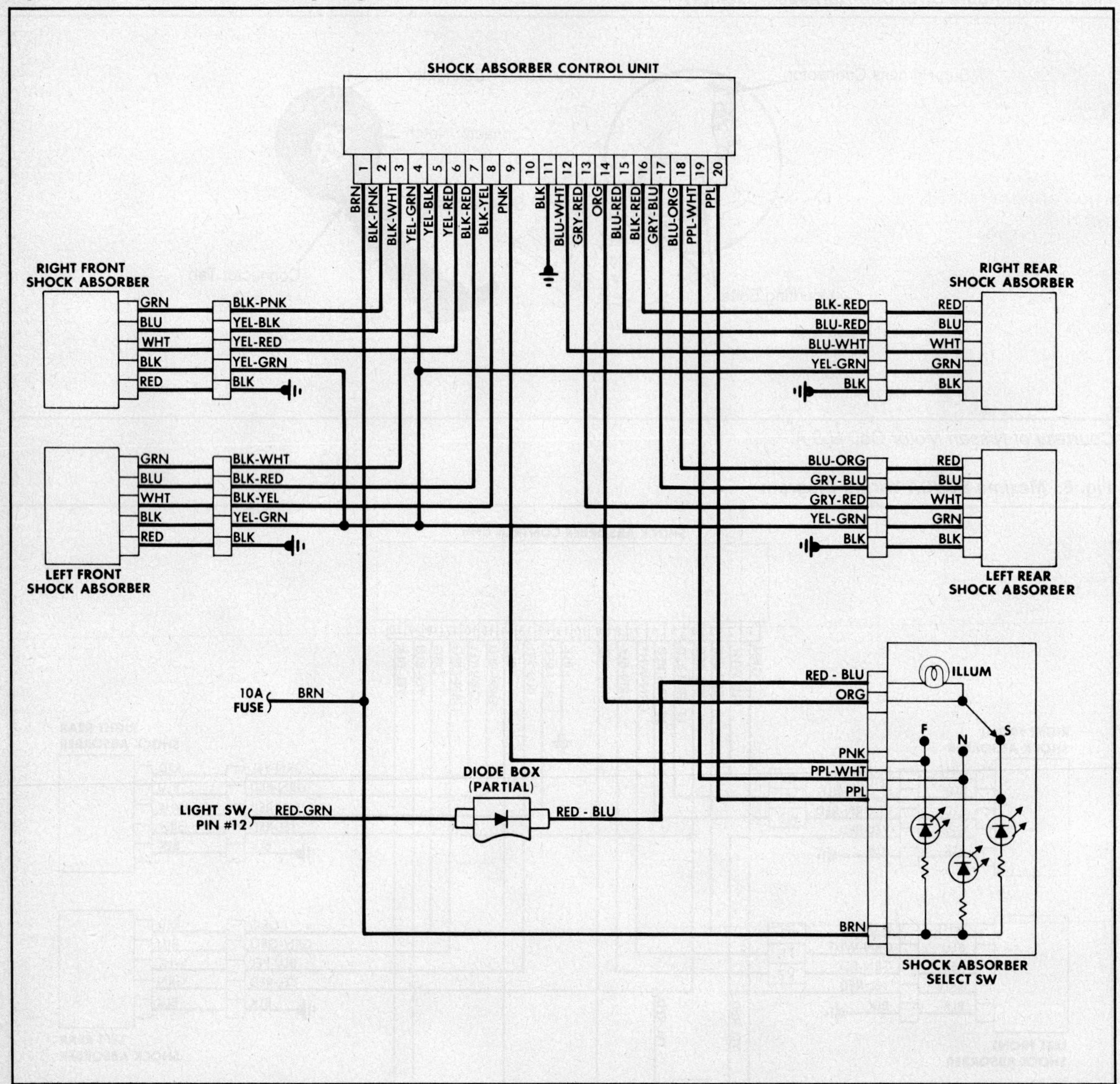

Electronic Suspension

SUBARU

Sedan, Station Wagon, 3-Door, XT Models

DESCRIPTION

The Subaru suspension system with height control consists of an air tank, air springs, pressure switch, solenoid valve, air compressor and drier. System response is from commands issued by the control switch and automatic override feature for high speed driving.

OPERATION

Vehicle height can be manually operated by the driver with the control switch located on the instrument panel. When vehicle speed exceeds 55 MPH while driving in "high ground clearance" position, ground clearance is automatically reset to "normal" position. If speed drops below 40 MPH, ground clearance is automatically reset to "high" position. When height control switch is operated while driving below 55 MPH, ground clearance is switched from "normal" to "high", or from "high" to "normal". Trim height variation is 1.18" (30 mm) for the front and 1.38" (35 mm) for the rear.

GENERAL PRECAUTIONS

1) Before raising vehicle for service, ensure vehicle is in "Normal" position with height control switch and indicator off. Disconnect battery cable to avoid accidental activation of leveling system.

2) When welding near leveling system, ensure leveling components are sufficiently protected. Never apply undercoating to leveling system components. Avoid battery electrolyte contact with air tube

TROUBLE SHOOTING

FRONT OF VEHICLE LOWERS WITH KEY OFF

NOTE: When vehicle is left inactive for an extended period of time, air pressure will bleed from the system.

1) Check for air leaks from air pipe above strut mount. Check air leakage from front solenoid valve or faulty seal. Apply compressed air to front or rear air suspension or air tank, disconnect air pipe from air joint far from above parts by using Air Pipe Remover (9265200000), and check for leaks.

Fig. 1: Air Suspension Components

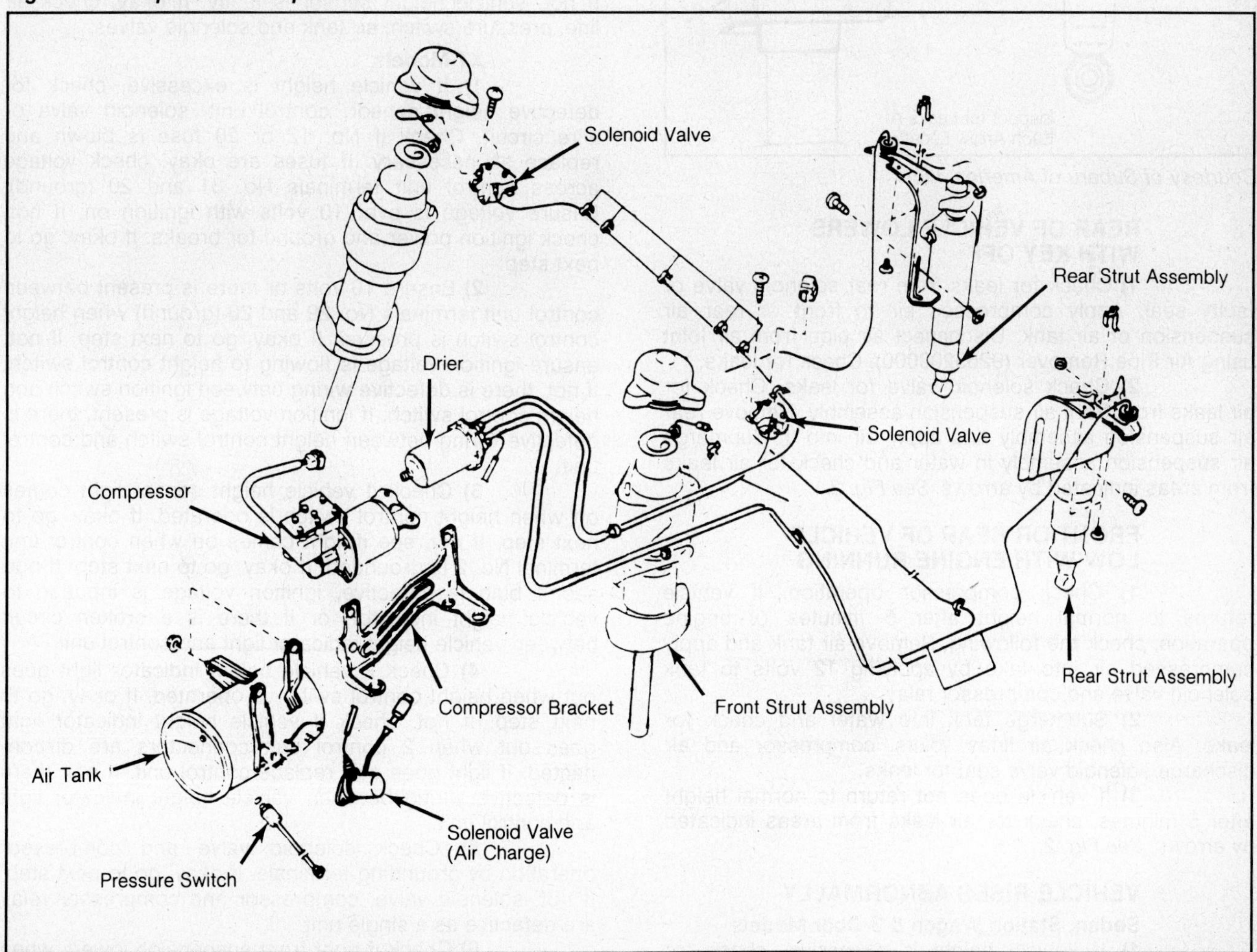

Courtesy of Subaru of America, Inc.

Electronic Suspension

SUBARU (Cont.)

2) Check solenoid valve for leaks. Check for air leaks from air suspension assembly. Remove front or rear air suspension assembly and inflate with air. Put air suspension assembly in water and check for air leaks from areas indicated by arrows. *See Fig. 2.*

Fig. 2: Air Suspension Air Leak Check

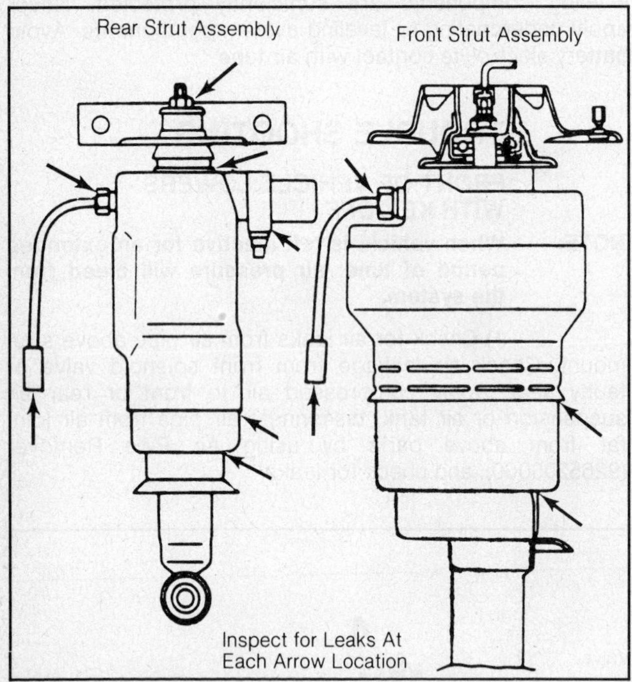

Courtesy of Subaru of America, Inc.

REAR OF VEHICLE LOWERS WITH KEY OFF

1) Check for leaks from rear solenoid valve or faulty seal. Apply compressed air to front or rear air suspension or air tank. Disconnect air pipe from air joint using Air Pipe Remover (9265200000). Check for leaks.

2) Check solenoid valve for leaks. Check for air leaks from front air suspension assembly. Remove rear air suspension assembly and apply air into it. Submerge air suspension assembly in water and check for air leaks from areas indicated by arrows. *See Fig. 2.*

FRONT OR REAR OF VEHICLE LOW WITH ENGINE RUNNING

1) Check compressor operation. If vehicle returns to normal height after 5 minutes of engine operation, check the following. Remove air tank and apply compressed air into take by applying 12 volts to tank solenoid valve and compressor relay.

2) Submerge tank into water and check for leaks. Also check air lines, joints, compressor and air discharge solenoid valve seat for leaks.

3) If vehicle does not return to normal height after 5 minutes, check for air leaks from areas indicated by arrows. *See Fig. 2.*

VEHICLE RISES ABNORMALLY

Sedan, Station Wagon & 3-Door Models

1) If vehicle height is excessive, check for defective height sensor, control unit, solenoid valve or wire circuit. Inspect for blown fuse Nos. 12 or 19. If necessary, replace fuse and/or repair circuit.

2) If fuses are not blown, check for minimum 10 volts between control unit terminals 31 (ignition) and 20 (ground). If 10 volts is not available, an open exists in circuit 31 or 20. If 10 volts is read, press height control switch. If voltage falls below 10 volts, inspect ignition power input to height control switch.

3) If no power input, repair wiring between ignition switch and height control switch. If power was input, repair wiring between height control switch and control unit. If 10 volts or more appear while pressing height control switch, proceed to step **4)**.

4) Verify height indicator light illuminates when switch is operated. If not, does light come on when control unit terminal 2 is grounded. If power is available and light bulb is not broken, replace control unit.

5) If height indicator light does not go out when switch is operated, remove 2 control unit connectors. If light remains on, repair wiring between height indicator light and control unit. If light goes out, replace control unit. Verify solenoid valves and air lines operate freely.

6) Check if 1.5 volts or less is present between terminals No. 8, 7, 5 or 4 and ground in "NORMAL" setting. Check if 1.5 volts or less is present between terminals 14, 13, 3 or 1 and ground in "HI" setting. If not, replace control unit. If voltage is present, go to next step.

7) Check for input from vehicle height sensor. If not, vehicle height sensor is faulty. If okay, check air line, pressure switch, air tank and solenoid valves.

XT Models

1) If vehicle height is excessive, check for defective height sensor, control unit, solenoid valve or wire circuit. Check if No. 12 or 20 fuse is blown and replace as necessary. If fuses are okay, check voltage across control unit terminals No. 31 and 20 (ground). Ensure voltage is over 10 volts with ignition on. If not, check ignition power and ground for breaks. If okay, go to next step.

2) Ensure 10 volts or more is present between control unit terminals No. 29 and 20 (ground) when height control switch is pressed. If okay, go to next step. If not, ensure ignition voltage is flowing to height control switch. If not, there is defective wiring between ignition switch and height control switch. If ignition voltage is present, there is defective wiring between height control switch and control unit.

3) Check if vehicle height sensor light comes on when height control switch is operated. If okay, go to next step. If not, see if light comes on when control unit terminal No. 2 is grounded. If okay, go to next step. If not, see if bulb is defective, ignition voltage is inputted to vehicle height indicator, or if there is a broken circuit between vehicle height indicator light and control unit.

4) Check if vehicle height indicator light goes out when height control switch is operated. If okay, go to next step. If not, check if vehicle height indicator light goes out when 2 control unit connectors are disconnected. If light goes out, replace control unit. If not, there is defective wiring between vehicle height indicator light and control unit.

5) Check solenoid valve and compressor operation by grounding terminals. If okay, go to next step. If not, solenoid valve, compressor and compressor relay are defective as a single unit.

6) Check if right front suspension lowers when terminals No. 18 and 11 of control unit are simultaneously grounded. Check if left front suspension lowers when

SUBARU (Cont.)

terminals No. 11 and 15 are grounded. Check if right rear suspension lowers when terminals No. 11 and 16 are grounded. Check if left rear suspension lowers when terminals No. 11 and 17 are grounded. If okay, go to step **8)**. If not, go to next step.

7) If vehicle height does not lower at any single wheel there is a faulty air discharge valve. If vehicle height does lower at some wheels, there are faulty solenoid valves or clogged air lines.

8) Remove No. 19 fuse and turn ignition on. Measure voltage across control unit terminals while raising vehicle with a jack. Push height control switch to set vehicle in "HIGH" position. Repeat voltage measurements across terminals. Measure right front suspension voltage as follows:

- Ensure voltage across terminals No. 27 and 20 ("GND") is about 5 volts.
- Ensure voltage across terminals 35 and 20 is about zero volts.
- Slowly raise vehicle with a jack until voltage across terminals No. 35 and 20 changes from zero to 5 volts.
- Ensure voltage across terminals No. 27 and 20 is about 5 volts.
- Slowly raise vehicle with a jack until voltage across terminals No. 27 and 20 changes from 5 to zero volts.
- Ensure voltage across terminals No. 35 and 20 is about 5 volts.
- Each strut must be checked in a similar manner with vehicle set from "NORMAL" to "HIGH" and from "HIGH" to "NORMAL". *See Fig. 3.* Proceed to next step.

9) If all testing indicates electrical system is okay, check air lines, pressure switch and air tank for malfunction. If complete system did not operate properly in previous test, check vehicle height sensor. If okay, replace affected strut.

INVOLUNTARY HEIGHT VARIATION

1) Inspect for defective control unit circuit, height control circuit or faulty control unit. Turn ignition on and measure voltage between control unit terminal 31 (ignition) and 20 (ground). If less than 10 volts is read, repair wiring in circuit 31 or 20.

2) If over 10 volts, measure voltage between terminal 29 and ground. If less than 10 volts is read, replace control unit. If over 10 volts, replace height control switch or wiring between switch and control unit

HEIGHT CONTROL SYSTEM INOPERATIVE

NOTE: **Height control system will remain inoperative while vehicle is turning, has one wheel off the ground or traveling over 55 MPH.**

1) Check for defective height control sensor, switch or wire harness. Test for defective control unit or solenoid valve coil. Follow procedure outlined in VEHICLE RISES ABNORMALLY.

2) Verify compressor operation and test pressure switch. Pressure switch operating pressure in "OFF" position is 137 psi (9.6 kg/cm²). In the "ON" position, operating pressure is 109 psi (7.7 kg/cm²). *See Fig. 4.*

VEHICLE DOES NOT LOWER AT 55 MPH

1) Inspect for defective speed sensor, control unit or wire harness. With vehicle stopped, operate height control switch to verify indicator light operation. If light is off, check for ground between indicator light and control unit. Repair wire harness and recheck system.

2) If light is on, test speedometer pulse input at control unit terminal No. 22. To perform this test, apply voltmeter positive lead to control unit terminal No. 22 and negative lead to ground.

3) Move vehicle 7-10 feet (2-3 m). Count each 0-12 volt oscillation of the voltmeter as a pulse. If approximately 5 pulses are read, replace control unit. If not, repair vehicle speed sensor wire circuit or replace speed sensor.

HEIGHT CHANGE WHEN KEY TURNED ON

1) Verify that B power connector for clock is attached to rear of fuse box. Check for blown No. 6 fuse. If necessary, repair wire circuit and replace fuse.

2) Apply positive voltmeter lead to control unit terminal No. 30 and negative lead to No. 20. If voltage is over 10 volts, replace control unit. If under 10 volts, repair B power circuit or ground contact.

EXCESSIVE COMPRESSOR OPERATION

Sedan, Station Wagon & 3-Door Models

1) Disconnect pressure switch. If compressor does not stop, disconnect control unit. If compressor keeps running, repair wiring between compressor relay and control unit or between compressor and compressor relay.

Fig. 3: XT Suspension Testing Procedure

Terminal combination	Right front suspension		Left front suspension		Right rear suspension		Left rear suspension	
	35↔20	27↔20	36↔20	26↔20	23↔20	25↔20	28↔20	34↔20
L (LOW)	0	5	0	5	0	5	0	5
Set height (NORMAL)	5	5	5	5	5	5	5	5
H (HIGH)	5	0	5	0	5	0	5	0

Courtesy of Subaru of America, Inc.

Electronic Suspension

SUBARU (Cont.)

2) If compressor stops running, check continuity between terminal No. 33 of control unit harness connector and ground. *See Fig 6.* If continuity exists, repair wiring between pressure switch and control unit. If not, replace control unit.

3) If compressor stops with pressure switch disconnected, place height control switch in "HI" and operate vehicle unattended for 5 minutes. If vehicle height increases, replace pressure switch.

4) If vehicle height does not increase, inspect air tank assembly for leaks or air charge valve for malfunction. Remove air tank assembly and apply 12 volts to solenoid valve and compressor relay. After tank is filled, submerge in water tank to inspect for leaks.

5) To test solenoid valve, apply 12 volts disregarding polarity. Supply air into valve and verify unrestricted air passage. If air passes through valve freely, solenoid valve is okay.

XT Models

1) Turn ignition switch to "ON" position. Check if compressor stops when 2-pole connector of pressure switch is disconnected. If it does, go to step **3)**. If not, turn ignition switch "OFF", remove fuse No. 19 and turn ignition switch "ON". If compressor does not stop there is are seized compressor relay contacts or shorted compressor circuits. If compressor does stop, go to next step.

2) Check for continunity between terminal "A" and ground. If there is, wiring between compressor relay and control unit is shorted. If not, check for continuity between terminal "B" and ground. If there is, wiring between pressure switch and control unit is shorted. If not, replace control unit.

3) Run engine. Allow vehicle to stand without getting in or out for at least 5 minutes. Set height control switch to "HIGH". See if car rises in 20 seconds. If it does, there is a faulty pressure switch. If not, there is a faulty air suction valve or solenoid valve wiring.

COMPRESSOR WILL NOT OPERATE

NOTE: This compressor has a temperature override circuit breaker, built in to stop the unit if overheating occurs. As the compressor cools, the circuit breaker will automatically reset itself and compressor operation will resume.

Sedan, Station Wagon & 3-Door Models

1) Test system for faulty compressor, pressure switch, control unit or defective electrical circuit. If vehicle height is abnormal, see VEHICLE RISES ABNORMALLY. If height is normal, disconnect pressure switch and short circuit terminal on connector side. *See Fig 4.*

2) If compressor runs, allow to operate for 3 minutes and place control switch in "HI" position. If vehicle responds to control box command, replace pressure switch. *See Fig. 8.* If not, air charge valve or wire circuit are defective.

3) If compressor does not operate with pressure switch short circuited, disconnect control unit wire harness connector. Use voltmeter to measure current at harness connector terminal No. 33 and ground. *See Fig 5.*

4) If 1.5 volts does not appear, repair wiring between pressure switch or control unit and ground. With 1.5 volts at terminal 33, check voltage at control unit terminal 12 and ground. If 1.5 volts does not appear, replace control unit. If 1.5 volts is available, proceed to step **5)**.

5) Test compressor relay by applying 12 volts to terminal B and ground terminal A. Verify continuity exists between terminals C and D. *See Fig. 8.* Remove voltage from terminal B and confirm continuity no longer present at terminals C and D. Replace relay if necessary.

6) Carefully inspect wiring system for wear, defects or disconnected leads. Test compressor by applying 12 volts directly to unit. Replace compressor if necessary.

XT Models

1) Ensure fuses No. 12 and 20 are okay and replace as necessary. If okay, ground compressor and see if it rotates. If not, wiring is faulty in compressor power circuit or compressor relay. If okay, ground compressor terminal "A". If compressor does not rotate, there is faulty wiring in compressor relay circuit. If compressor does rotate, go to next step.

Fig. 4: Air Tank Pressure Switch & Connector

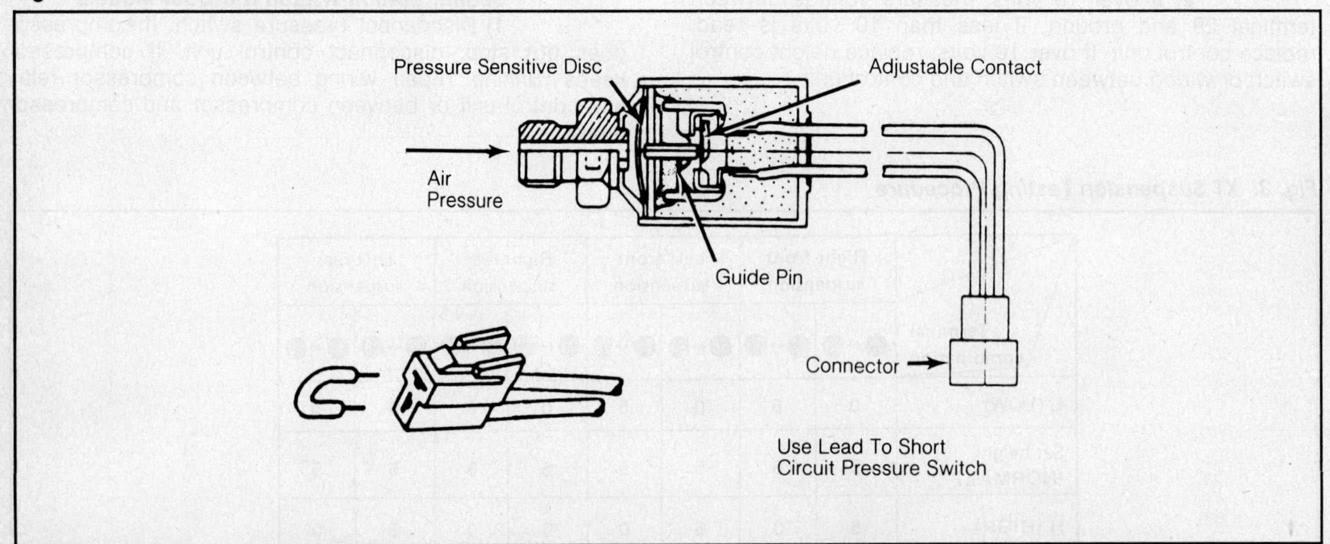

Courtesy of Subaru of America, Inc.

Electronic Suspension

SUBARU (Cont.)

Fig. 5: Wire Harness Terminal Identification

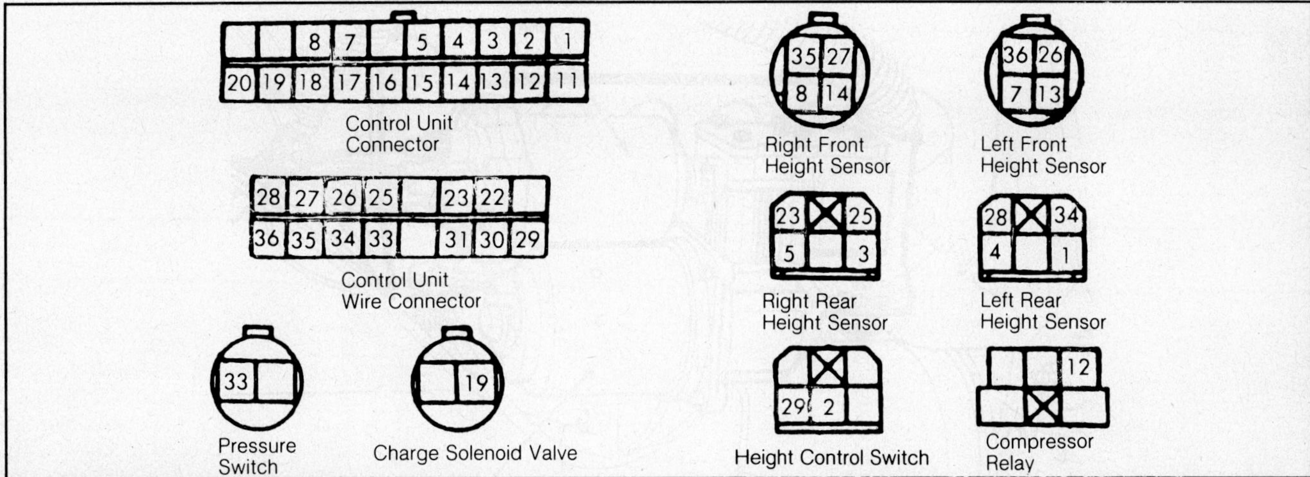

Courtesy of Subaru of America, Inc.

2) Ground control unit terminal No. 12. If compressor does not rotate, there is defective wiring in compressor power circuit, control unit ground circuit or ground wiring of compressor relay contacts. If compressor does rotate, go to next step.

3) Ground control unit terminals No. 1 and 18, 11 and 15, 11 and 16, and 11 and 17 simultaneously, and lower vehicle height. Ground terminal No. 33. Turn ignition switch "ON". Ensure compressor starts. If it does, there is a faulty pressure switch or defective wiring between control unit and pressure switch. If compressor does not start, replace control unit.

HEIGHT INDICATOR LIGHT BLINKS

Sedan, Station Wagon & 3-Door Models

1) This is an indication of height sensor or control unit failure. If light blinks beyond 10 minutes, compressor, solenoid valve or control unit are malfunctioning. Also check air tank and hoses for leaks or restrictions.

2) If vehicle height is abnormal, replace height sensor and strut assembly. Inspect height sensor circuit for defective wiring. If system appears normal, replace control unit.

3) With light blinking over 10 minutes and vehicle height normal, start engine. If compressor rotates over 8 minutes, replace control unit.

XT Models

1) If light blinks more than 10 minutes, go to step **3)**. If light blinks less than 10 minutes, disconnect right front vehicle height sensor connector while vehicle height indicator light is blinking. Turn ignition switch "OFF" and then "ON" to see if height indicator light blinks again. If not, right front vehicle height sensor is faulty and should be replaced. Repeat procedure for other height sensors. If all height sensors are okay, go to next step.

2) Remove control unit. Ensure body connector terminals of vehicle height sensors are grounded. If not, repair wire. If unit ground was okay, control unit is faulty.

3) Connect pressure gauge to system. Remove left front mudguard. Perform following tests to see if height of tested suspensions increases:

- Ground right front solenoid valve terminal No. 1 and compressor terminal No. 5.
- Ground left front solenoid valve terminal No. 2 and compressor terminal No. 5.
- Ground right rear solenoid valve terminal No. 3 and compressor terminal No. 5.
- Ground left rear solenoid valve terminal No. 4 and compressor terminal No. 5.

If suspension does not change, there is a faulty solenoid valve or clogged air line. If suspension height did change, go to next step.

Fig. 6: Compressor Relay Circuit Diagram & Terminal Identification

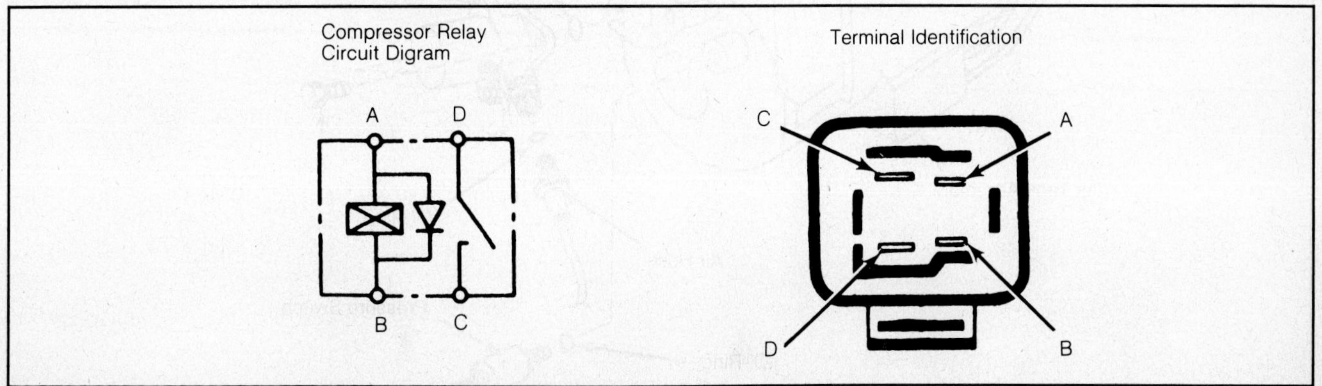

Courtesy of Subaru of America, Inc.

Electronic Suspension

SUBARU (Cont.)

Fig. 7: Air Compressor & Drier Assembly

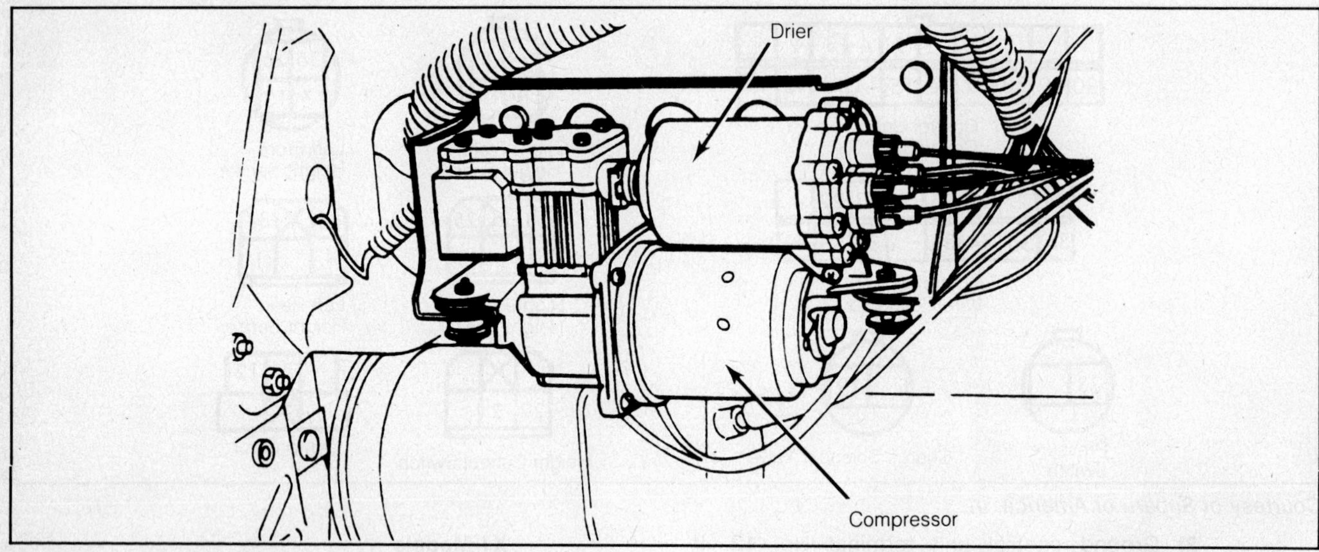

Courtesy of Subaru of America, Inc.

4) Increase air pressure to 142 psi (9.9 kg/cm²). Ground compressor terminal No. 5 and air charge solenoid valves one at a time, then disconnect. Check if pressure drop exceeds 7 psi (.5 kg/cm²) when left unattended for 10 minutes. If pressure drops, air line has leakage. If not, go to next step.

5) Check if pressure drop exceeds 7 psi when air charge solenoid valve alone is grounded. If pressure drops, there is air leaking from air tank. If not, follow trouble shooting in VEHICLE RISES ABNORMALLY, XT MODELS section.

REMOVAL & INSTALLATION

AIR COMPRESSOR & DRIER

NOTE: Air hoses may be attached to drier in any position.

Removal

1) Remove left front wheel and front half of mud guard. Use Air Hose Remover (926520000) to disconnect all 5 air hoses from drier.

2) Remove coupler and 4 compressor retainer nuts. Remove compressor and drier assembly from engine compartment as a unit.

Disassembly & Reassembly

Compressor and drier may be separated, however service is limited to unit replacement. Verify "O" rings are clean and lubricate prior to assembly.

Installation

Reverse removal procedure for installation. Ensure that all connections are clean and tight. Tighten retainer nuts to 42 INCH lbs. (.50 N.m).

Fig. 8: Air Tank Assembly

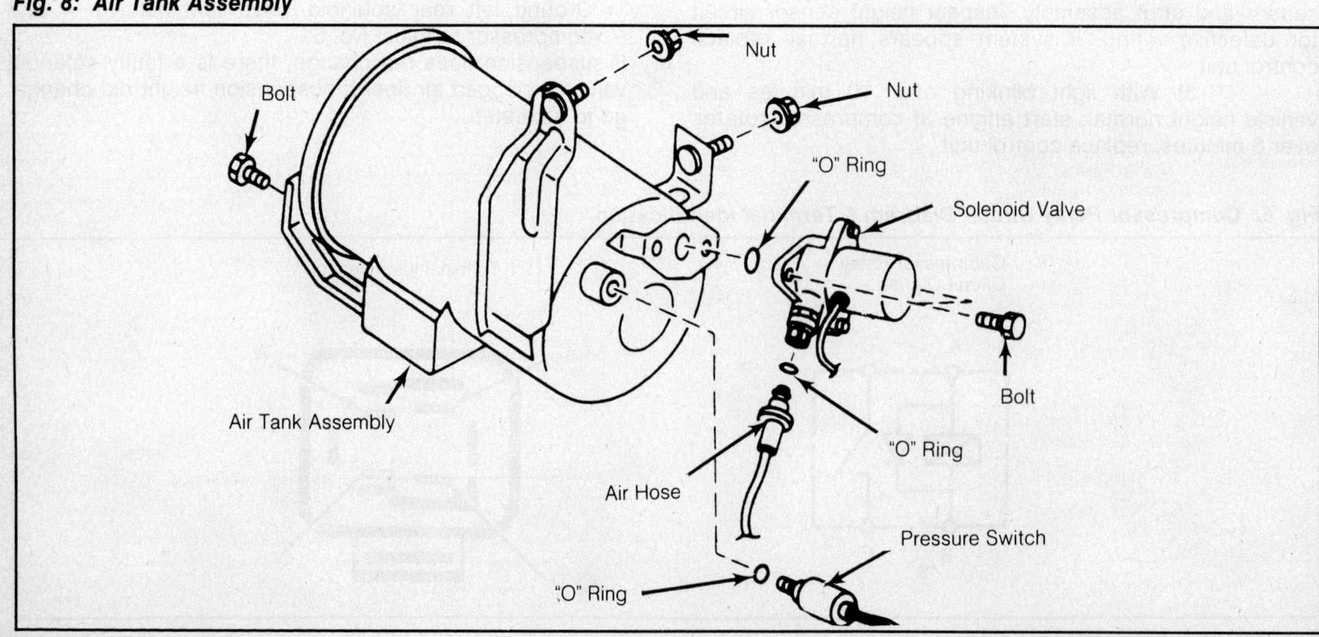

Courtesy of Subaru of America, Inc.

SUBARU (Cont.)

Fig. 9: Front Strut Disassembly

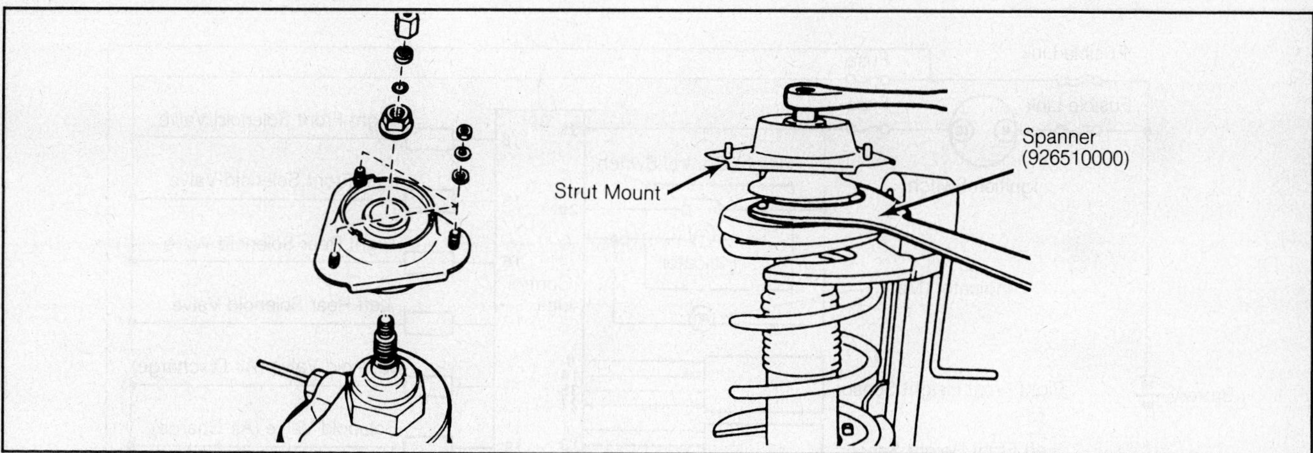

Courtesy of Subaru of America, Inc.

AIR TANK

CAUTION: Carefully discharge air pressure from tank before pressure switch or solenoid valve are removed.

Removal

1) Use Air Hose Remover to separate hoses from solenoid valve. Remove solenoid valve coupler. Remove one bolt and 2 nuts to detach air tank assembly.

2) Reverse removal procedure to complete assembly and installation. Clean and lubricate "O" rings before installation. Care must be taken in handling "O" rings to avoid damage. Apply grease to pressure switch threads and tighten to 96 INCH lbs. (11 N.m).

STRUT ASSEMBLY

Removal (Front)

1) Remove air hose and mud guard. Remove height sensor harness clip and harness coupler. Remove strut assembly as a unit and position in support tool.

2) Before removing strut mount, verify that air pressure has been removed from air spring. Place

Fig. 11: Height Sensor Wire Harness Installation Length

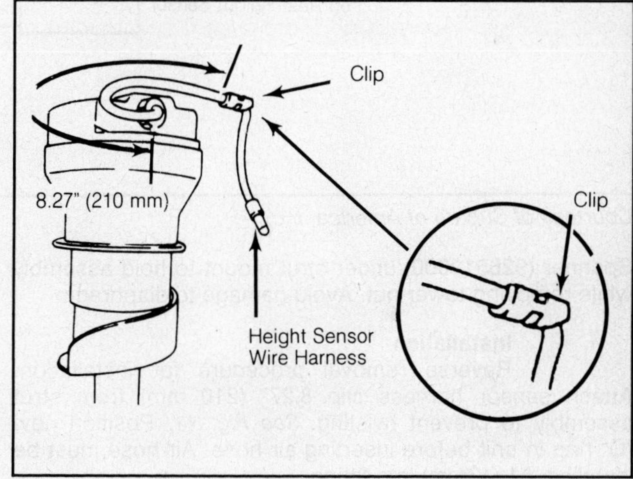

Courtesy of Subaru of America, Inc.

Fig. 10: Rear Strut Assembly Harness Arrangement

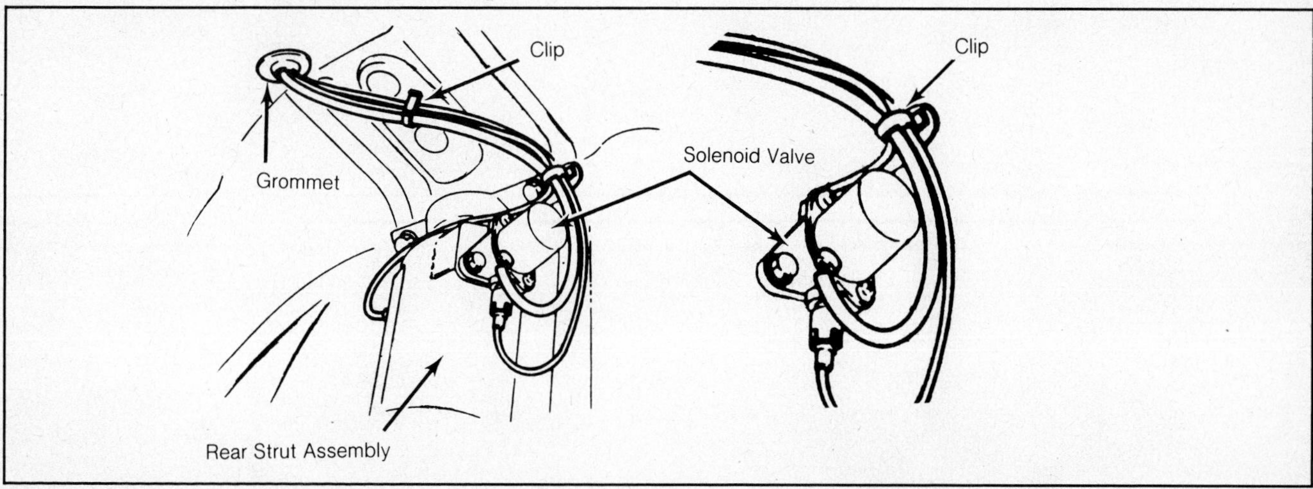

Courtesy of Subaru of America, Inc.

Electronic Suspension

SUBARU (Cont.)

Fig. 12: Height Control System Circuit Diagram

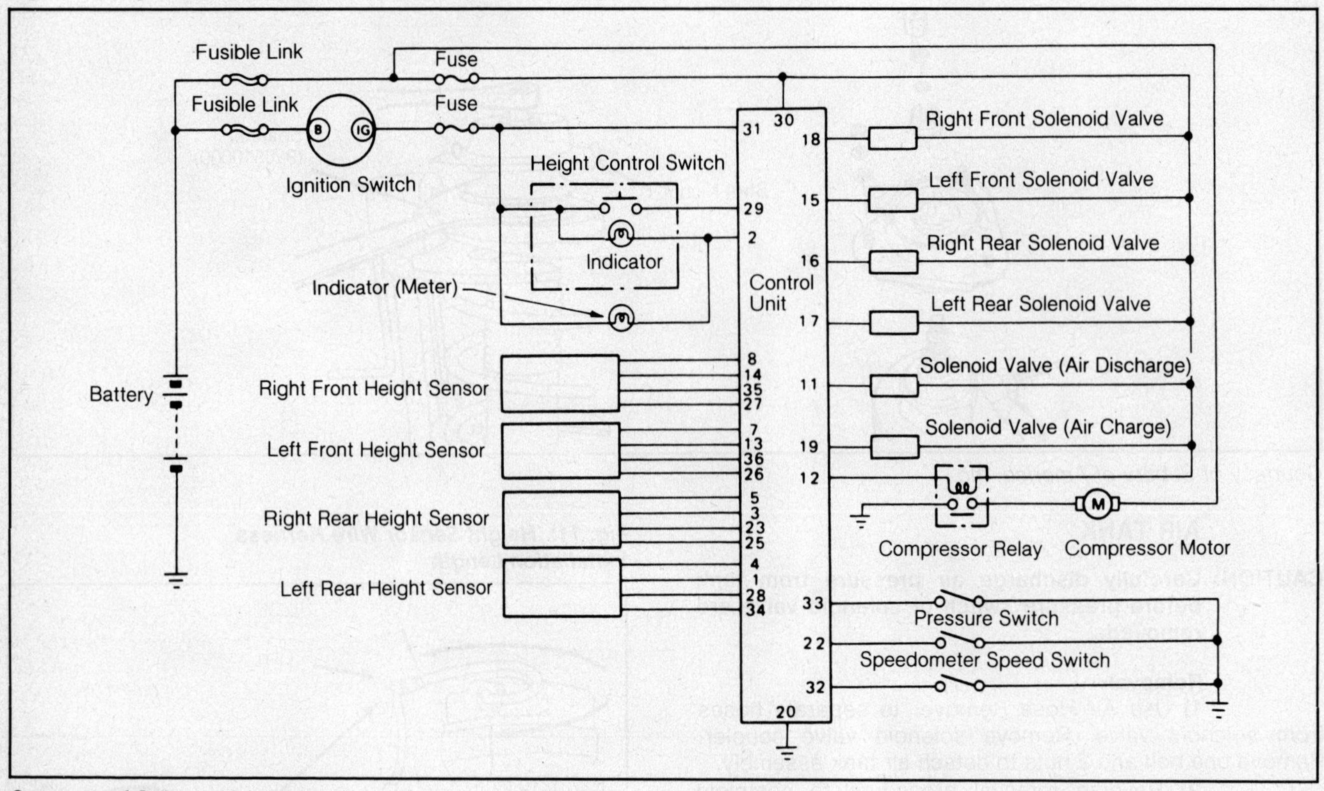

Courtesy of Subaru of America, Inc.

Spanner (926510000) under strut mount to hold assembly while removing tower nut. Avoid damage to diaphragm.

Installation

Reverse removal procedure for installation. Attach sensor harness clip 8.27" (210 mm) from strut assembly to prevent twisting. *See Fig. 11.* Position new "O" ring in unit before inserting air hose. Air hose must be installed .51 (13mm) into fitting.

Removal (Rear)

1) Remove rear apron protector. Remove rear solenoid valve and support away from work area. Remove height sensor harness from access hole in body and detach harness coupler.

2) Remove strut assembly as a unit using extreme care not to damage diaphragm discharge pressure from unit if it is to be disassembled.

Installation

Reverse removal procedure using new "O" ring to complete installation. Use same precautions as in front assembly. *See Fig. 10.*

SUBARU (Cont.)

Fig. 13: Sedan, Station Wagon & 3-Door Height Control System Wiring Diagram

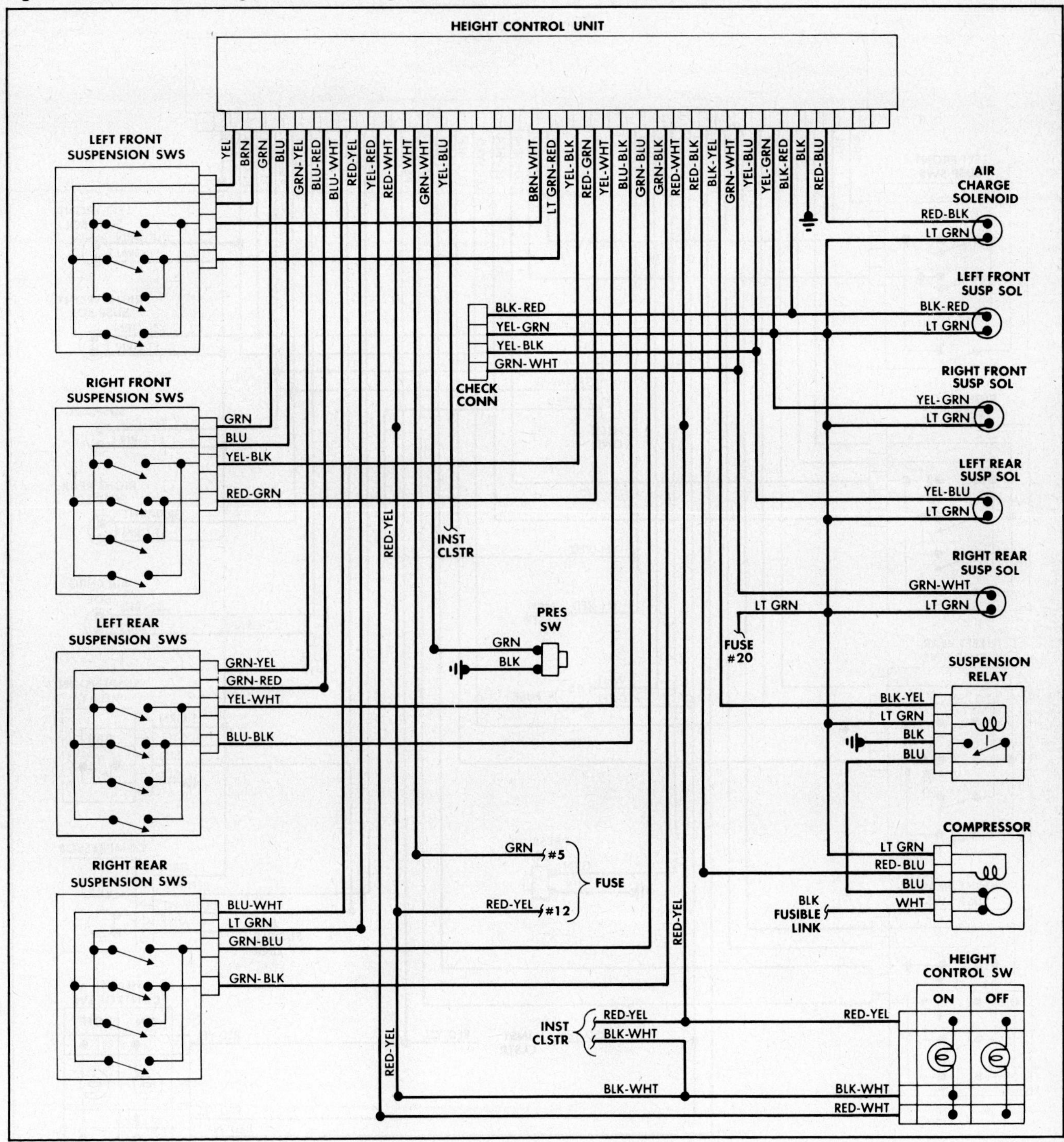

Electronic Suspension

SUBARU (Cont.)

Fig. 14: XT Coupe Height Control System Wiring Diagram

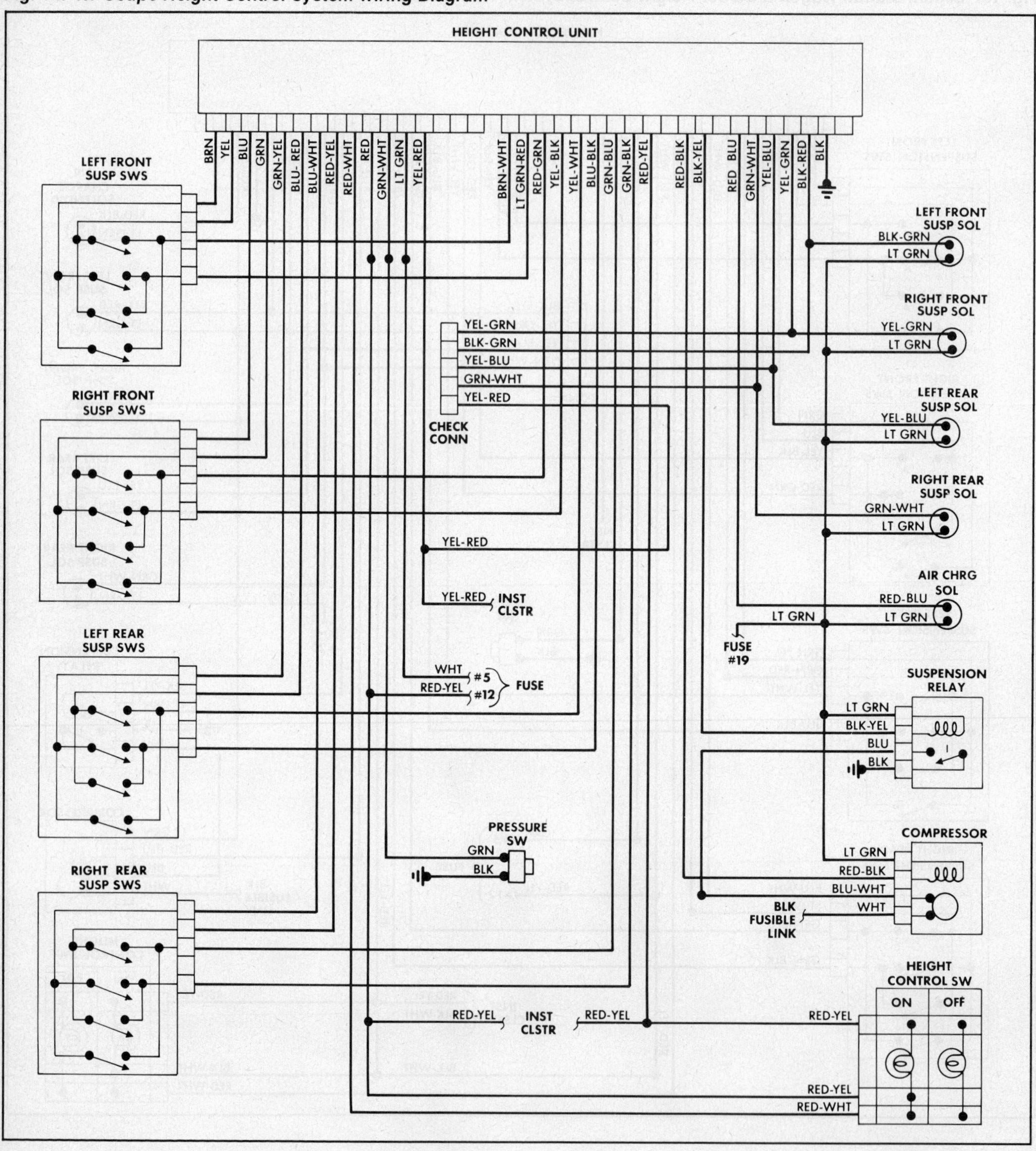

Electronic Suspension

TOYOTA CRESSIDA & SUPRA

DESCRIPTION

The Toyota Electronic Modulated Suspension (TEMS) system electronically changes shock absorber damping. The TEMS has 2 modes ("NORMAL" and "SPORT") which can be selected by the driver. On Supra, an indicator light on the instrument panel indicates the operation mode.

The TEMS computer uses information from the throttle position sensor, speed sensor, steering sensor, stoplight and neutral/start switches to determine the best setting for shock absorbers. Shock absorber firmness is accomplished by an actuator valve mounted on each shock absorber.

OPERATION

The TEMS computer receives reference signals from various sensors and switches. The computer processes this information and determines (according to mode selection) where to position the electrically operated actuator.

On top of each shock absorber is an actuator which rotates 120 degrees to vary shock stiffness. As driving conditions vary, the TEMS indicator lights will change, informing driver of the shock absorber setting.

On Cressida models, indicator lights will illuminate "M" (Medium) or "F" (Firm). On Supra, indicator lights will illuminate "S" (Soft), "M" (Medium) or "F" (Firm). *See Fig. 3.*

TESTING & DIAGNOSIS

PRELIMINARY CHECK

Perform these preliminary checks before starting test procedures.

- Check cold tire inflation pressure.
- Check for proper lubrication of suspension and steering linkage.
- Check wheel alignment and vehicle height.
- Ensure battery voltage is above 12 volts.
- Ensure all electrical connectors are clean and secure.

NOTE: **For computer test diagnosis, see appropriate COMPUTER SYSTEM CIRCUIT CHART at end of article.**

INITIAL CHECK

Cressida

1) Connect voltmeter negative terminal to terminal No. 4 of TEMS check connector located under hood. *See Fig. 2.* On automatic transmission models, position shift lever in "N" or "P". Turn ignition on. Check for battery voltage (12 volts) between terminals No. 2 and 4, and 3 and 4 of the TEMS check connector for 2 seconds. If voltage is okay, go to step **4)**. If not, go to step **3)**. If any other reading was obtained, go to next step.

2) If voltage between terminals No. 2 and 4 fluctuates between battery voltage and zero volts for 30 seconds, turn ignition off. Disconnect all 4 TEMS actuator connectors. Turn ignition on. Check for battery voltage between terminals No. 2 and 4, and 3 and 4 of TEMS check connector for 2 seconds. If voltage is okay, TEMS actuator is defective. If voltage between terminals No. 2 and 4 fluctuates between battery voltage and zero volts for 30 seconds, TEMS computer or circuit is faulty.

3) Turn ignition on. Check for battery voltage between TEMS computer terminals "+B" and "GND". If okay, TEMS computer is faulty. If not, check fuse, fusible link, battery wire harness, ignition switch and computer ground.

4) Set mode select switch to "NORM" position. Ensure there is no voltage between terminals No. 2 and 4, and 3 and 4 of the TEMS check connector. If there is, mode select switch, circuit or TEMS computer is faulty. If no voltage was indicated, go to next step.

5) Ensure there is operation noise from each actuator when mode select switch is switched from "SPORT" to "NORM" to "SPORT". If okay, go to next step. If not, disconnect actuator and check if there is above 8 volts present at connector terminals No. 1 and 2 when mode select switch is operated. If there is, TEMS actuator is defective. If not, measure resistance between terminals No. 1 and 2 (11-15 ohms) and terminals No. 3 and 4 (8-12 ohms). If okay, mode select switch or TEMS computer is faulty. If not, TEMS actuator is defective.

6) Set mode select switch to "SPORT" position while vehicle is bounced twice per second. Check if suspension becomes firmer. If it does, go to next step. If not, remove actuator from vehicle and check actuator operation. If okay, shock absorber is faulty. If not, TEMS actuator is defective.

7) Set mode select switch to "SPORT" position. Short check connector (diagnosis) terminals "Tem" and "E_2". Check if battery voltage is present between terminals No. 2 and 4, and 3 and 4 of TEMS check connector. If not, mode select switch, circuit or TEMS computer is defective. If okay, go to next step.

8) Set mode select switch to "SPORT" position. Short check connector (diagnosis) terminals "Tem" and "E_2" and bounce vehicle. Check if damping becomes even stiffer. If okay, initial check is okay. If not, go to next step.

9) Remove actuator from vehicle and check actuator operation. If okay, shock absorber is faulty. If not, TEMS actuator is defective.

Supra

1) Check TEMS indicator lights. Lights "S", "M" and "F" should illuminate for 2 seconds when ignition is turned on. If lights do not illuminate, check for 12 volts between TEMS computer terminal "B+" and ground with ignition turned on.

2) If 12 volts is not present, check for faulty fusible link, fuse, battery cable, ignition switch or ground. If 12 volts is present, check for faulty indicator bulb, indicator bulb circuit or TEMS computer.

3) If TEMS indicator lights illuminate as described in step **1)**, check for lights "M" and "F" switching off ("S" light on) when mode selector is placed in "NORMAL" position.

4) If lights do not illuminate as described in step **3)**, a faulty mode switch, mode switch circuit or TEMS computer is present. If lights illuminate, go to next step.

5) Place mode switch in "SPORT" position. Lights "S" and "M" should illuminate. If lights do not illuminate, check for faulty mode switch, mode switch circuit or TEMS computer.

6) If lights illuminate, check for operational noise from each actuator when mode switch is moved from "SPORT" to "NORMAL" to "SPORT".

Electronic Suspension

TOYOTA CRESSIDA & SUPRA (Cont.)

Fig. 1: Toyota Electronic Modulated Suspension (TEMS) Component Location

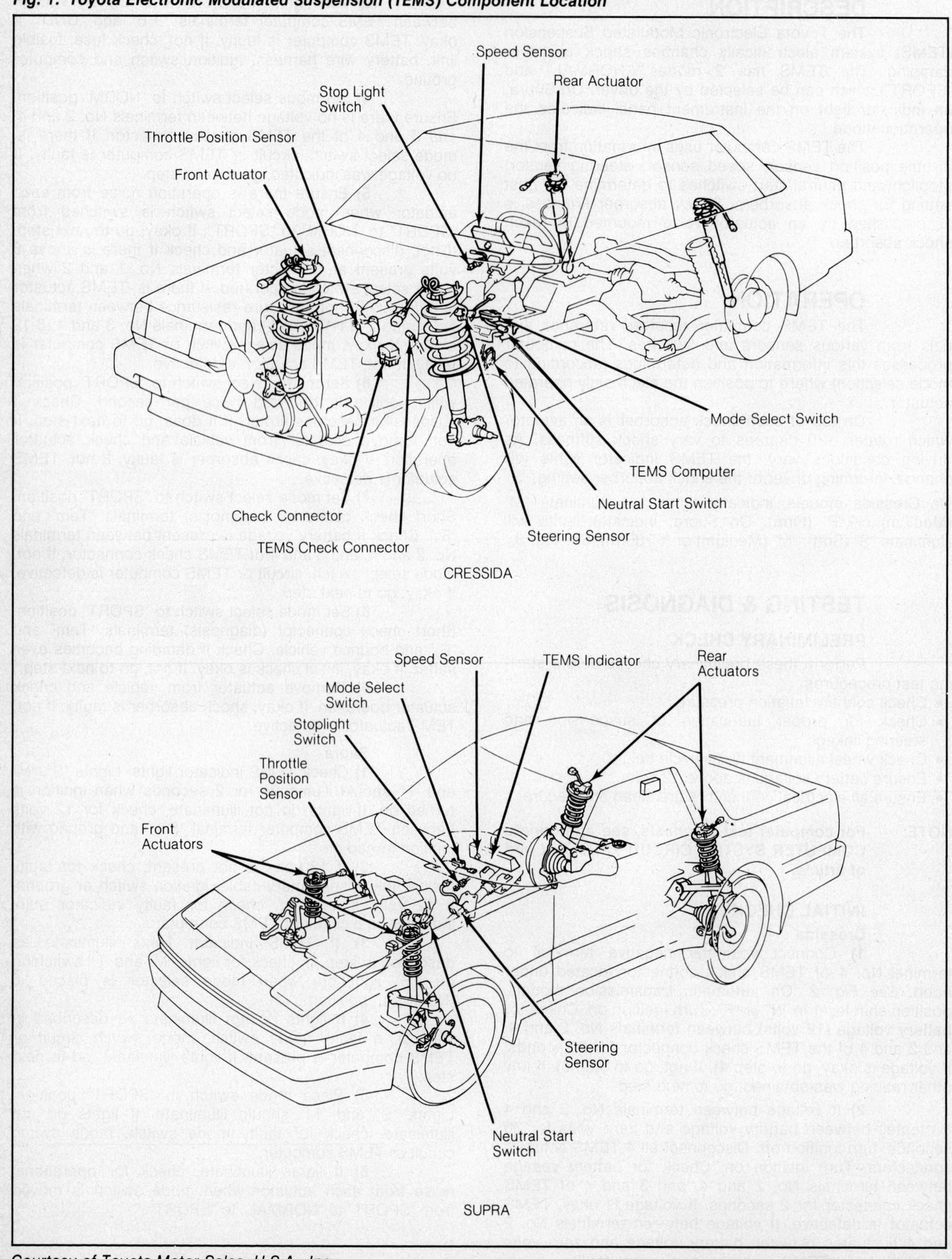

Courtesy of Toyota Motor Sales, U.S.A., Inc.

TOYOTA CRESSIDA & SUPRA (Cont.)

7) If noise is not heard, disconnect actuator and check for 8 or more volts to connector terminals (wire harness side) No. 1 and No. 2, while mode switch is operated.

8) If voltage is present, TEMS actuator is faulty. If voltage is not present as described is step **7)**, check for correct actuator terminal voltage. *See Fig. 4.* If voltage is correct, TEMS computer circuit is faulty.

Fig. 2: Cressida TEMS Connector

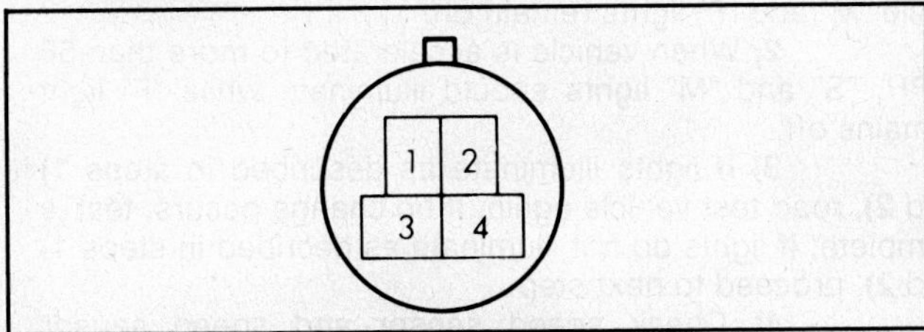

Courtesy of Toyota Motor Sales, U.S.A., Inc.

Fig. 3: Supra TEMS Indicator Lights

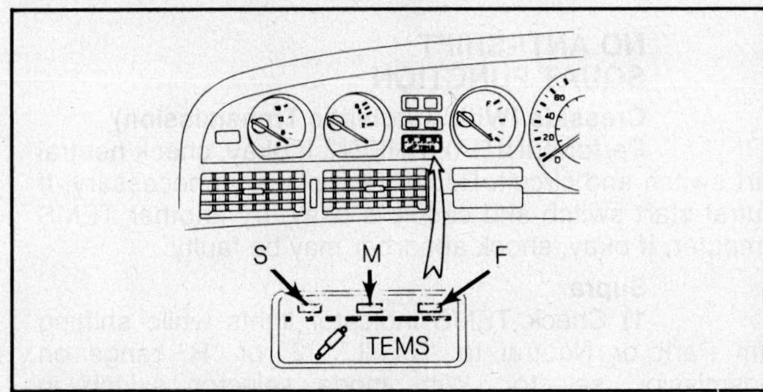

Courtesy of Toyota Motor Sales, U.S.A., Inc.

9) If noise is heard, place mode switch is "SPORT" position. Bounce vehicle twice per second. Suspension should increase in stiffness. If suspension does not increase in stiffness, remove actuator from vehicle and check for proper operation.

10) Check actuator operation by applying battery voltage to actuator terminals and note valve position. *See Fig. 4.* Replace actuator if not functioning properly. If actuator is functioning properly, replace shock absorber.

NOTE: **DO NOT apply battery voltage to actuator longer than 2 seconds. If voltage is applied longer than 2 seconds, solenoid and motor may burn out.**

11) With service connector terminal "Tem" and terminal "E_2" shorted, indicator lights should illuminate. If lights do not illuminate, mode switch, mode switch circuit or TEMS computer is faulty.

12) With mode switch in "SPORT" position, bounce vehicle and short service (check) connector terminal "Tem" and terminal "E_2". Suspension should increase in stiffness. If suspension stiffens, initial check is complete.

13) If suspension does not stiffen, remove actuator from vehicle and check for proper operation. Replace actuator if not functioning properly. If actuator is functioning properly, replace shock absorber.

Fig. 4: Actuator Valve Test Charts

+: Battery positive terminal
−: Battery negative terminal

Position \ Terminals	Motor 1	Motor 2	Solenoid 3	Solenoid 4
Firm → Medium	+	−		
Firm → Soft	−	+		
Medium → Soft	−	+		
Soft → Medium	+	−		
Medium → Firm	−	+	+	−
Soft → Firm	+	−	+	−

CRESSIDA

+: Battery positive terminal
−: Battery negative terminal

Position \ Terminals		Motor 1	Motor 2	Solenoid 3	Solenoid 4
SOFT	MEDIUM	+	−		
SOFT	FIRM	+	−	+	−
MEDIUM	SOFT	−	+		
MEDIUM	FIRM	−	+	+	−
FIRM	SOFT	−	+		
FIRM	MEDIUM	+	−		

SUPRA

Courtesy of Toyota Motor Sales, U.S.A., Inc.

NO ANTI-SQUAT FUNCTION

Cressida

Perform INITIAL CHECK. If okay, check throttle position sensor and engine Electronic Control Unit (ECU) circuit and repair as necessary. Check speed sensor and circuit and repair as necessary. Try another TEMS computer. If all are okay, shock absorber may be defective.

Supra

1) Check TEMS indicator lights under sudden acceleration (for automatic transmission "D", "2", "L" or "R" ranges). With ignition on (engine off) and mode switch in "NORMAL" position, "M" and "F" lights should remain off with "S" light on. Under sudden acceleration "S", "M" and "F" lights should illuminate.

2) With ignition on (engine off) and mode select switch in "SPORT" position, "F" light should remain off, while "S" and "M" lights illuminate. Under sudden acceleration, "S", "M" and "F" lights should illuminate.

3) If lights illuminate as described in steps **1)** and **2)**, road test vehicle again. If no change occurs, test is complete. If lights do not illuminate as decribed in steps **1)** and **2)**, proceed to next step.

4) Check Throttle Position Sensor (TPS) and engine Electronic Control Unit (ECU) circuit. If faulty, repair or replace component. If TPS and ECU are okay, check speed sensor and speed sensor circuit.

5) If speed sensor and speed sensor circuit are faulty, repair or replace as necessary. If okay, try another TEMS computer.

TOYOTA CRESSIDA & SUPRA (Cont.)

NO ANTI-ROLL FUNCTION

Cressida

Perform INITIAL CHECK. Check steering and speed sensors and circuits. Repair or replace as necessary. Try another TEMS computer. If okay, shock absorber may be defective.

Supra

1) Check TEMS indicator lights when steering wheel is turned sharply while driving at 25 MPH. With vehicle speed above 25 MPH and mode switch in "NORMAL" position, "S" light should illuminate, with "M" and "F" lights off. Under sharp turn, "S", "M" and "F" lights should illuminate.

2) With vehicle speed above 25 MPH and mode select switch in "SPORT" position, "S" and "M" lights should illuminate. With switch in same position, "F" light should remain off. Under sharp turn, "S", "M" and "F" lights should illuminate.

3) If lights illuminate as described in steps **1)** and **2)**, road test vehicle again. If no change occurs, test is complete. If lights do not illuminate as decribed in steps **1)** and **2)**, proceed to next step.

4) Check steering sensor and steering sensor circuit. If faulty, repair or replace component. If steering sensor and steering sensor circuit are okay, check speed sensor and speed sensor circuit.

5) If speed sensor and speed sensor circuit are faulty, repair or replace as necessary. If okay, try another TEMS computer.

NO ANTI-DIVE FUNCTION

Cressida

Perform INITIAL CHECK. If okay, check stoplight switch, speed sensors and circuits. Repair or replace as necessary. Try another TEMS computer. If okay, shock absorber may be defective.

Supra

1) Check TEMS indicator lights when brake is depressed while driving more than 37 MPH. With vehicle speed more than 37 MPH and mode switch in "NORMAL" position, "S" light should illuminate, while "M" and "F" lights remain off. When brake pedal is depressed "S", "M" and "F" lights should illuminate.

2) With vehicle speed more than 37 MPH and mode select switch in "SPORT" position, "S" and "M" light should illuminate. With switch in same position, "F" light should remain off. When brake pedal is depressed, "S", "M" and "F" lights should illuminate.

3) If lights illuminate as described in steps **1)** and **2)**, road test vehicle again. If no change occurs, test is complete. If lights do not illuminate as decribed in steps **1)** and **2)**, proceed to next step.

4) Check stoplight switch and stoplight switch circuit. If faulty, repair or replace. If stoplight switch and stoplight switch circuit are okay, check speed sensor and speed sensor circuit.

5) If speed sensor and speed sensor circuit are faulty, repair or replace as necessary. If okay, try another TEMS computer.

NO HIGH SPEED RESPONSE

NOTE: High speed response functions only when mode selector is in "NORMAL" position, and not in "SPORT" position.

Cressida

Perform INITIAL CHECK. If okay, check speed sensor and circuit. Repair or replace as necessary. If okay, try another TEMS computer. If okay, shock absorber may be defective.

Supra

1) Check TEMS indicator lights when vehicle is gradually accelerated from less than 43 MPH to more than 56 MPH. With vehicle speed less than 43 MPH and mode switch in "NORMAL" position, "S" light should illuminate, while "M" and "F" lights remain off.

2) When vehicle is accelerated to more than 56 MPH, "S" and "M" lights should illuminate while "F" light remains off.

3) If lights illuminate as described in steps **1)** and **2)**, road test vehicle again. If no change occurs, test is complete. If lights do not illuminate as decribed in steps **1)** and **2)**, proceed to next step.

4) Check speed sensor and speed sensor circuit. If faulty, repair or replace as necessary. If speed sensor and speed sensor circuit are okay, try another TEMS computer.

NO ANTI-SHIFT SQUAT FUNCTION

Cressida (With Automatic Transmission)

Perform INITIAL CHECK. If okay, check neutral start switch and circuit. Repair or replace as necessary. If neutral start switch and circuit is okay, try another TEMS computer. If okay, shock absorber may be faulty.

Supra

1) Check TEMS indicator lights while shifting from Park or Neutral to "D", "L", "2" or "R" range on transmission selector. With mode selector switch in "NORMAL" position, "S", "M" and "F" lights should illuminate while gear selector is in Park or Neutral.

2) When gear selector is moved from Park or Neutral to "D", "L", "2" or "R" range, "S" light should illuminate, while "M" and "F" lights remain off.

3) With mode selector in "SPORT" position, and gear selector shifted as described in step **1)**, all indicator lights should illuminate, while "F" light remains off. If indicator lights illuminate as described in steps **1)** and **2)**, road test vehicle again. If no change occurs, test is complete.

4) If lights do not illuminate as described in steps **1)** and **2)**, check neutral start switch and neutral start switch circuit. If faulty, repair or replace.

5) If neutral start switch and neutral start switch circuit are okay, try another TEMS computer.

REMOVAL & INSTALLATION

ACTUATORS

Removal

Turn ignition switch to "ON" position and mode select switch to "SPORT" position. Using a short piece of wire, jump diagnosis terminals "Tem" and "E_2". Turn ignition off and remove negative battery cable. Remove actuator connector and cover. Remove 2 actuator mounting bolts. Carefully remove actuator from shock absorber.

Inspection

Check position where shaft stops when battery voltage is applied to each actuator terminal. Do not apply voltage longer than 2 seconds. *See Fig. 4.* When switching from soft or medium to firm, run motor with solenoid on.

TOYOTA CRESSIDA & SUPRA (Cont.)

Installation

1) Ensure actuator valve and absorber control rod are faced toward firm position. *See Fig. 5.* Insert absorber control rod into groove of actuator valve. Secure actuator with bolts. Install actuator wire harness so it faces front of vehicle.

2) Install actuator cover and tighten to 10 ft. lbs. (14 N.m). Install actuator connector. Remove service wire from service connector and check TEMS operation.

Fig. 5: Actuator Valve Position

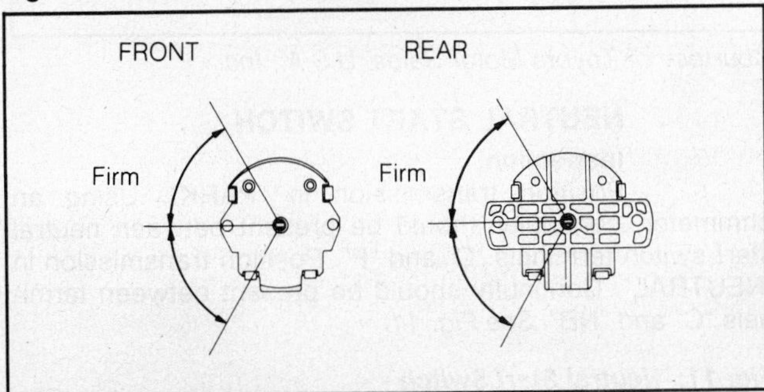

Courtesy of Toyota Motor Sales, U.S.A., Inc.

STEERING SENSOR

Inspection - Vehicles With TEMS Dash Indicator Lights

1) Put steering wheel in straight-ahead position. Put mode select switch in "NORM" position. Using a short piece of wire, jump diagnosis terminals "Tem" and "E_2". Turn ignition switch to "ON" position. Ensure indicator lights flash after 2 seconds. If not, mode select switch, service connector circuit or TEMS computer is defective.

2) Turn steering wheel 1/4 turn to the right. Ensure "F" indicator light flashes (right side) and "M" light (left side) goes out. Return steering wheel to straight ahead position, then turn 1/4 turn to the left. Ensure "M" TEMS indicator light (left side) flashes and the "F" light (right side) goes out. *See Fig. 3.* System is okay if lights flash as indicated. If not, go to next step.

3) Turn ignition on and measure voltage between steering sensor connector terminals No. 1 and 2. *See Fig. 6.* Standard voltage is 3-4 volts. While slowly turning steering wheel, measure voltage between steering sensor connector terminals No. 3, 4 and 2. Standard voltage will fluctuate between zero to 5 volts.

4) If voltage is not correct, either circuit between computer and steering sensor is shorted or steering sensor is defective. Ensure no dirt or other foreign matter is in steering sensor grooves.

Fig. 6: Testing Steering Sensor Voltage

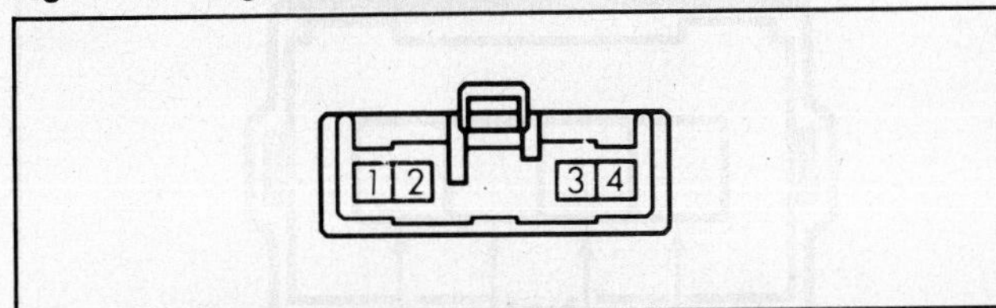

Courtesy of Toyota Motor Sales, U.S.A., Inc.

Inspection - Vehicles Without TEMS Dash Indicator Lights

1) Put steering wheel in straight-ahead position. Put mode select switch in "NORM" position. Connect voltmeters to terminals "I_2" and "I_3" of the TEMS computer and ground. Use a short piece of wire and connect check connector diagnosis terminals "Tem" and "E_2". Turn ignition switch to "ON" position. Voltmeter needles should fluctuate. *See Fig. 7.* If voltmeter needles do not fluctuate, mode select switch, connector circuit or TEMS computer is defective.

Fig. 7: Testing Steering Sensor System

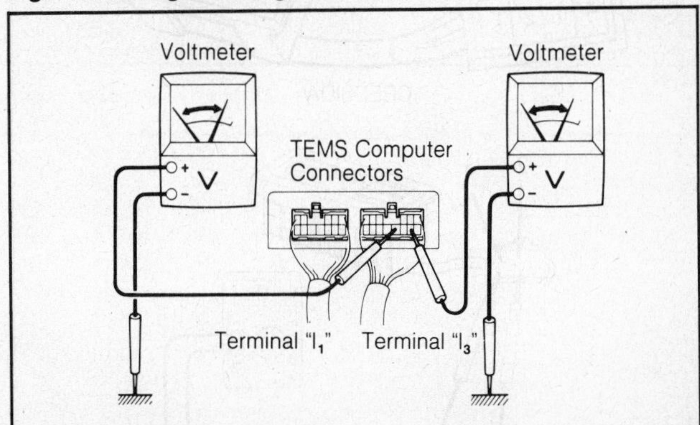

Courtesy of Toyota Motor Sales, U.S.A., Inc.

2) Turn steering wheel 1/4 turn to the right from straight-ahead position. Ensure needle of voltmeter which is connected to terminal "I_3" and ground fluctuates. Other voltmeter should show no voltage.

3) Return steering wheel to straight-ahead position, then turn 1/4 turn to the left. Ensure needle of voltmeter which is connected to terminal "I_1" and ground fluctuates. Other voltmeter should show no voltage. If not okay, go to next step.

4) Turn ignition on and measure voltage between steering sensor connector terminals No. 1 and 2. *See Fig. 6.* Standard voltage is 3.5-4.2 volts. While slowly turning steering wheel, measure voltage between steering sensor connector terminals No. 3, 4 and 2.

5) Standard voltage will fluctuate between zero to 5 volts. If voltage is not correct, either circuit between computer and steering sensor is shorted or steering sensor is defective. Ensure there is no dirt or other foreign matter in steering sensor grooves.

MODE SELECT SWITCH

Inspection

1) Remove mode select switch from center console box. Put mode select switch in "NORM" position. Use an ohmmeter to measure continuity between terminals. On Cressida, continuity should be present between terminals No. 1 and 2 when switch is in "NORM" position, and between terminals No. 1 and 2, and 3 and 4 in "SPORT" position. *See Fig. 8.*

2) On Supra, continuity should be present between terminals No. 1 and 2 in "SPORT" position. No continuity should be present between terminals No. 1 and 2 in "NORMAL" position.

SPEED SENSOR

Inspection (Cressida)

1) All Cressida models come with either an analog or digital speed sensor. On analog speed sensors, remove the combination meter. Using an ohmmeter, check continuity between terminals "SPD +" and "SPD -" while revolving the meter shaft. Ohmmeter needle should go from zero to infinity ohms. *See Fig. 9.*

TOYOTA CRESSIDA & SUPRA (Cont.)

Fig. 8: Mode Select Switch Terminal Positions

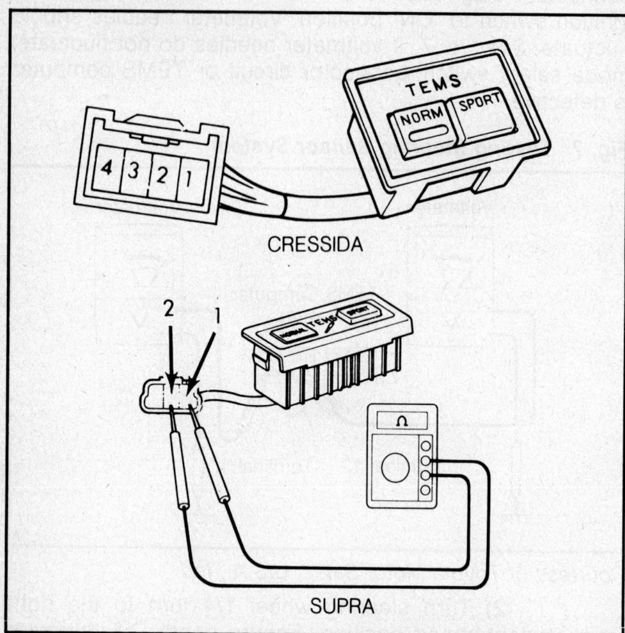

Courtesy of Toyota Motor Sales, U.S.A., Inc.

Fig. 9: Cressida Speed Sensor Checking Procedure

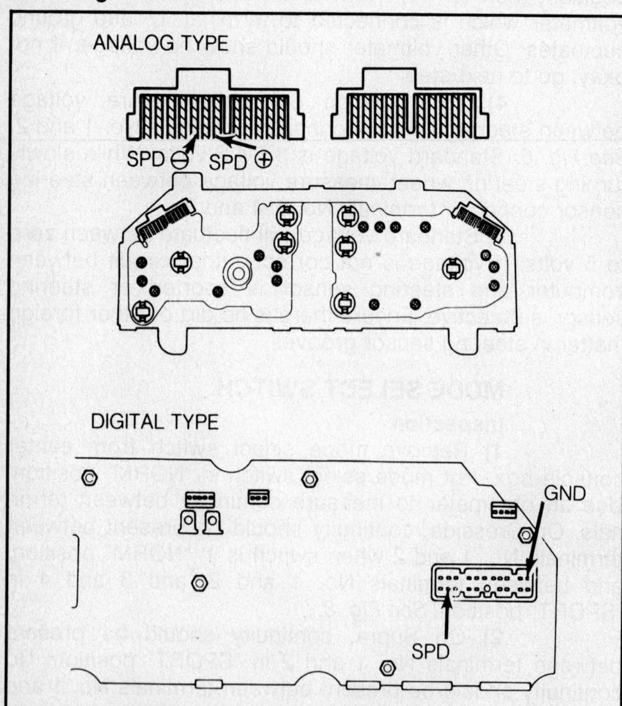

Courtesy of Toyota Motor Sales, U.S.A., Inc.

2) On digital speed sensors, remove combination meter with wire harness connected. Turn ignition switch to "ON" position. Connect a voltmeter between terminals "SPD" and "GND". Revolve meter shaft. Voltage should deflect from zero to 2 volts. *See Fig. 9.*

Inspection (Supra)

Remove combination meter. Using an ohmmeter, ensure there is continuity between terminals "SPD +" and "SPD -" 4 times per each shaft revolution. *See Fig. 10.*

Fig. 10: Supra Speed Sensor Checking Procedure

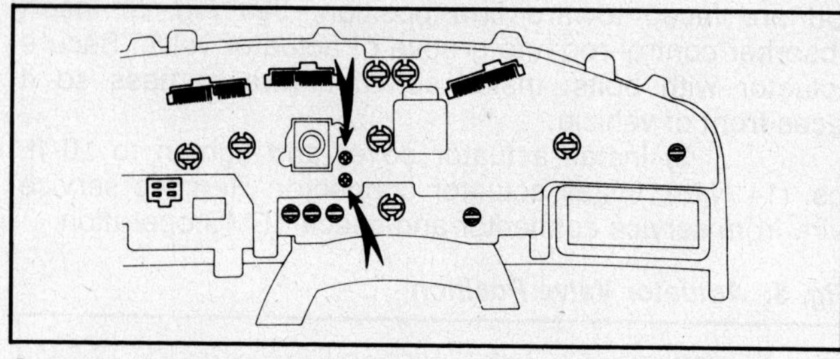

Courtesy of Toyota Motor Sales, U.S.A., Inc.

NEUTRAL START SWITCH

Inspection

Position transmission in "PARK". Using an ohmmeter, continuity should be present between neutral start switch terminals "C" and "P". Position transmission in "NEUTRAL". Continuity should be present between terminals "C" and "NB". *See Fig. 11.*

Fig. 11: Neutral Start Switch Terminal Locations

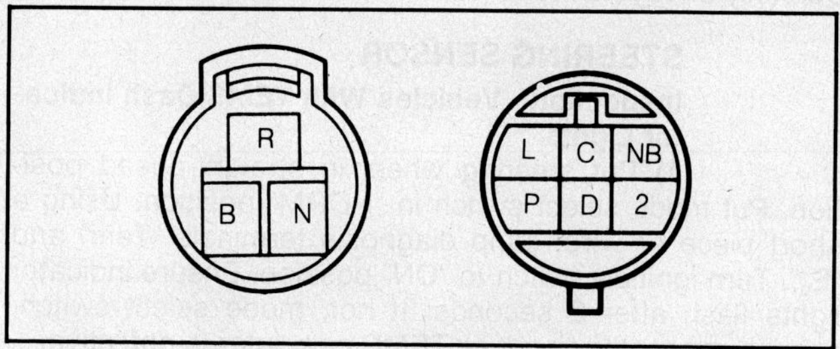

Courtesy of Toyota Motor Sales, U.S.A., Inc.

THROTTLE POSITION SENSOR

Inspection

1) Using an ohmmeter, check resistance between throttle position sensor terminals "IDL" and "E_2" with throttle valve fully closed. Resistance should be zero. Check same terminals with throttle valve open. Resistance should be infinity.

2) Check resistance between terminals "Vcc" and "E_2". Resistance should be 3-7 ohms.

3) Check resistance between terminals "Vta" and "E_2" with throttle valve fully closed. Resistance should be .2-.8 ohms. Check same terminals with throttle valve open. Resistance should be 3.3-10 ohms.

Fig. 12: Throttle Position Sensor Terminal Locations

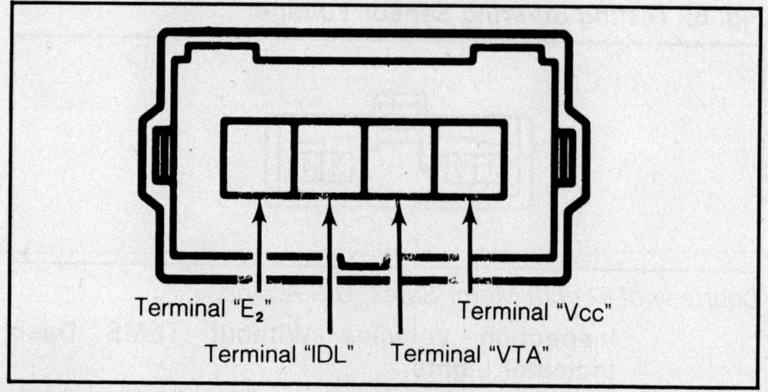

Courtesy of Toyota Motor Sales, U.S.A., Inc.

TOYOTA CRESSIDA & SUPRA (Cont.)

Fig. 13: Cressida Computer Circuit Chart

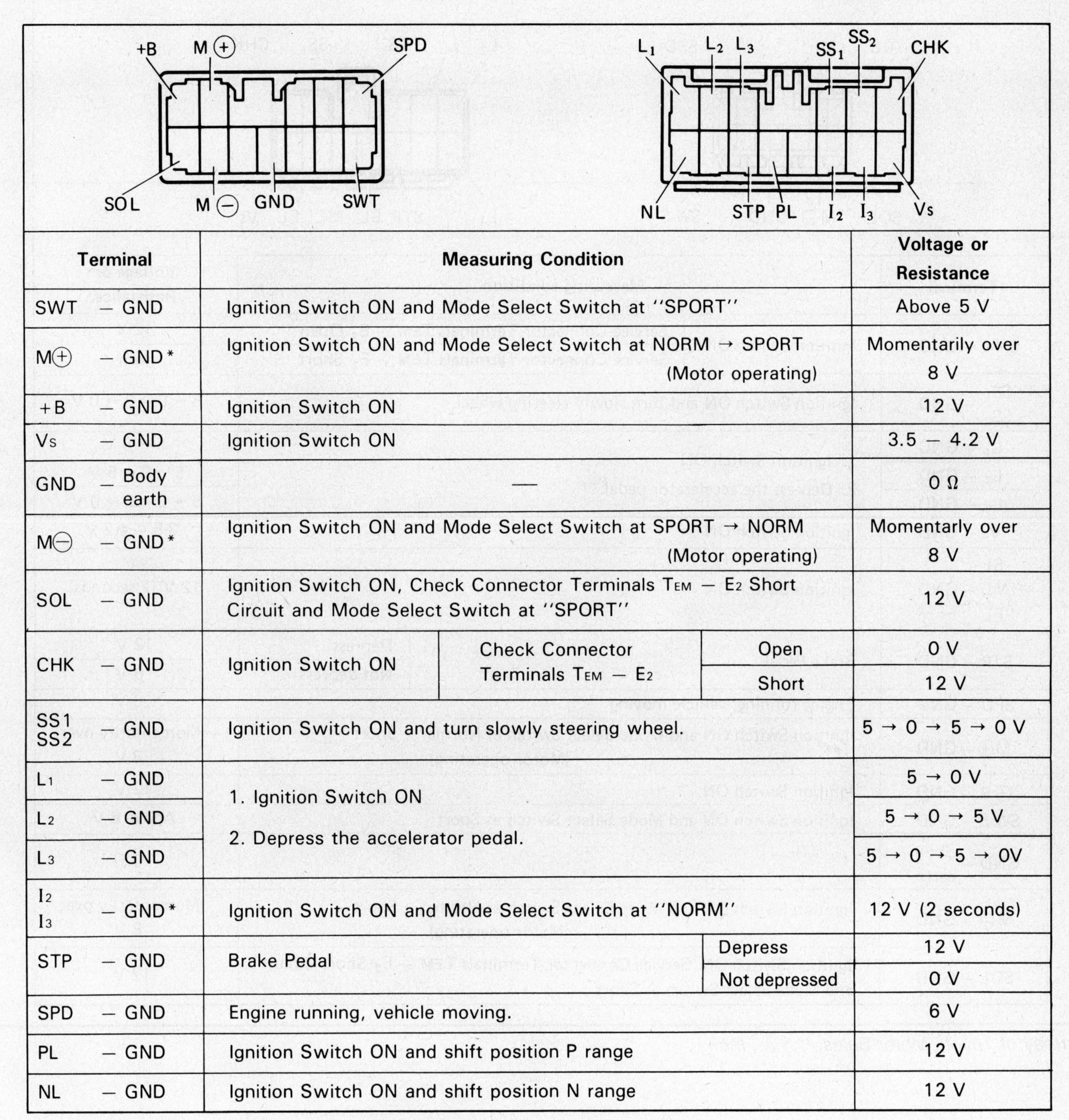

Terminal		Measuring Condition			Voltage or Resistance
SWT	– GND	Ignition Switch ON and Mode Select Switch at "SPORT"			Above 5 V
M⊕	– GND*	Ignition Switch ON and Mode Select Switch at NORM → SPORT (Motor operating)			Momentarily over 8 V
+B	– GND	Ignition Switch ON			12 V
Vs	– GND	Ignition Switch ON			3.5 – 4.2 V
GND	– Body earth	—			0 Ω
M⊖	– GND*	Ignition Switch ON and Mode Select Switch at SPORT → NORM (Motor operating)			Momentarily over 8 V
SOL	– GND	Ignition Switch ON, Check Connector Terminals T_{EM} – E_2 Short Circuit and Mode Select Switch at "SPORT"			12 V
CHK	– GND	Ignition Switch ON	Check Connector Terminals T_{EM} – E_2	Open	0 V
				Short	12 V
SS1 SS2	– GND	Ignition Switch ON and turn slowly steering wheel.			5 → 0 → 5 → 0 V
L_1	– GND	1. Ignition Switch ON 2. Depress the accelerator pedal.			5 → 0 V
L_2	– GND				5 → 0 → 5 V
L_3	– GND				5 → 0 → 5 → 0V
I_2 I_3	– GND*	Ignition Switch ON and Mode Select Switch at "NORM"			12 V (2 seconds)
STP	– GND	Brake Pedal		Depress	12 V
				Not depressed	0 V
SPD	– GND	Engine running, vehicle moving.			6 V
PL	– GND	Ignition Switch ON and shift position P range			12 V
NL	– GND	Ignition Switch ON and shift position N range			12 V

* • Check with transmission in any range except N or P. (for A/T vehicles)
• Disconnect all the TEMS actuator connectors.

Courtesy of Toyota Motor Sales, U.S.A., Inc.

Electronic Suspension

TOYOTA CRESSIDA & SUPRA (Cont.)

Fig. 14: Supra Computer Circuit Chart

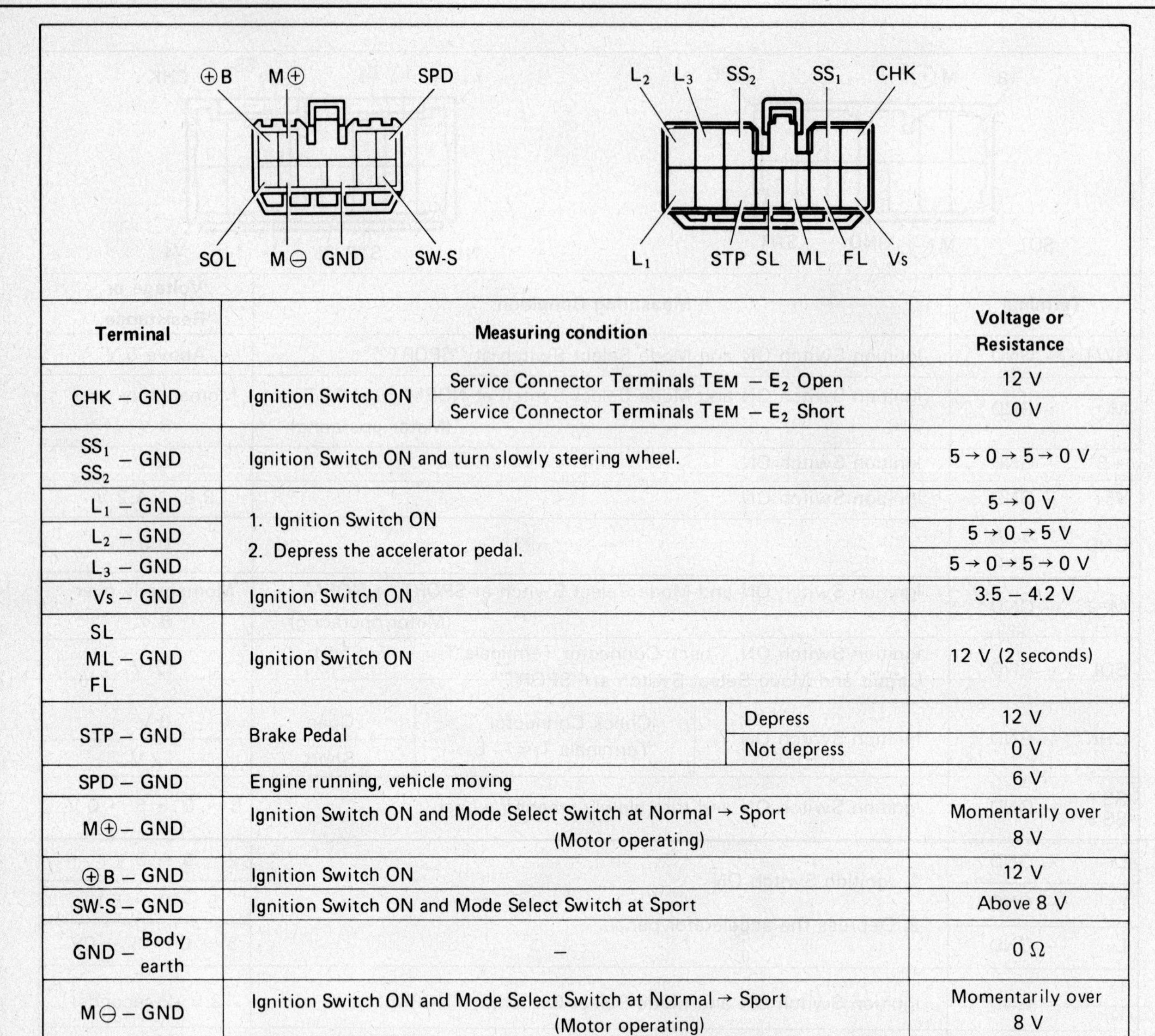

Terminal	Measuring condition		Voltage or Resistance
CHK – GND	Ignition Switch ON	Service Connector Terminals TEM – E_2 Open	12 V
		Service Connector Terminals TEM – E_2 Short	0 V
SS_1, SS_2 – GND	Ignition Switch ON and turn slowly steering wheel.		5 → 0 → 5 → 0 V
L_1 – GND	1. Ignition Switch ON 2. Depress the accelerator pedal.		5 → 0 V
L_2 – GND			5 → 0 → 5 V
L_3 – GND			5 → 0 → 5 → 0 V
Vs – GND	Ignition Switch ON		3.5 – 4.2 V
SL, ML, FL – GND	Ignition Switch ON		12 V (2 seconds)
STP – GND	Brake Pedal	Depress	12 V
		Not depress	0 V
SPD – GND	Engine running, vehicle moving		6 V
M⊕ – GND	Ignition Switch ON and Mode Select Switch at Normal → Sport (Motor operating)		Momentarily over 8 V
⊕B – GND	Ignition Switch ON		12 V
SW-S – GND	Ignition Switch ON and Mode Select Switch at Sport		Above 8 V
GND – Body earth	–		0 Ω
M⊖ – GND	Ignition Switch ON and Mode Select Switch at Normal → Sport (Motor operating)		Momentarily over 8 V
SOL – GND	Ignition Switch ON, Service Connector Terminals TEM – E_2 Short Circuit and Mode Select Switch at Sport		12 V

Courtesy of Toyota Motor Sales, U.S.A., Inc.

TOYOTA CRESSIDA & SUPRA (Cont.)

Fig. 15: Cressida TEMS Wiring Diagram

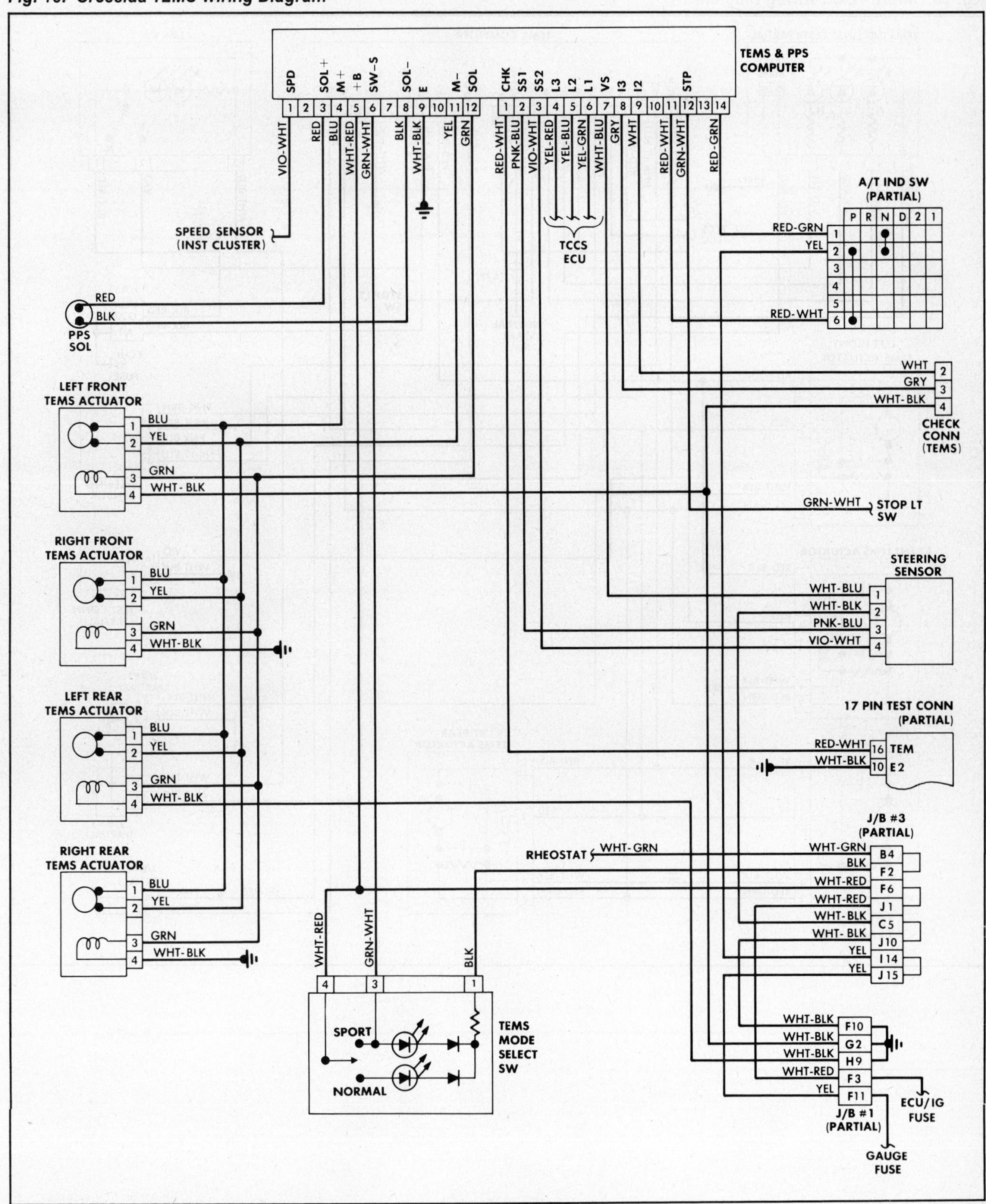

Electronic Suspension

TOYOTA CRESSIDA & SUPRA (Cont.)

Fig. 16: Supra TEMS Wiring Diagram

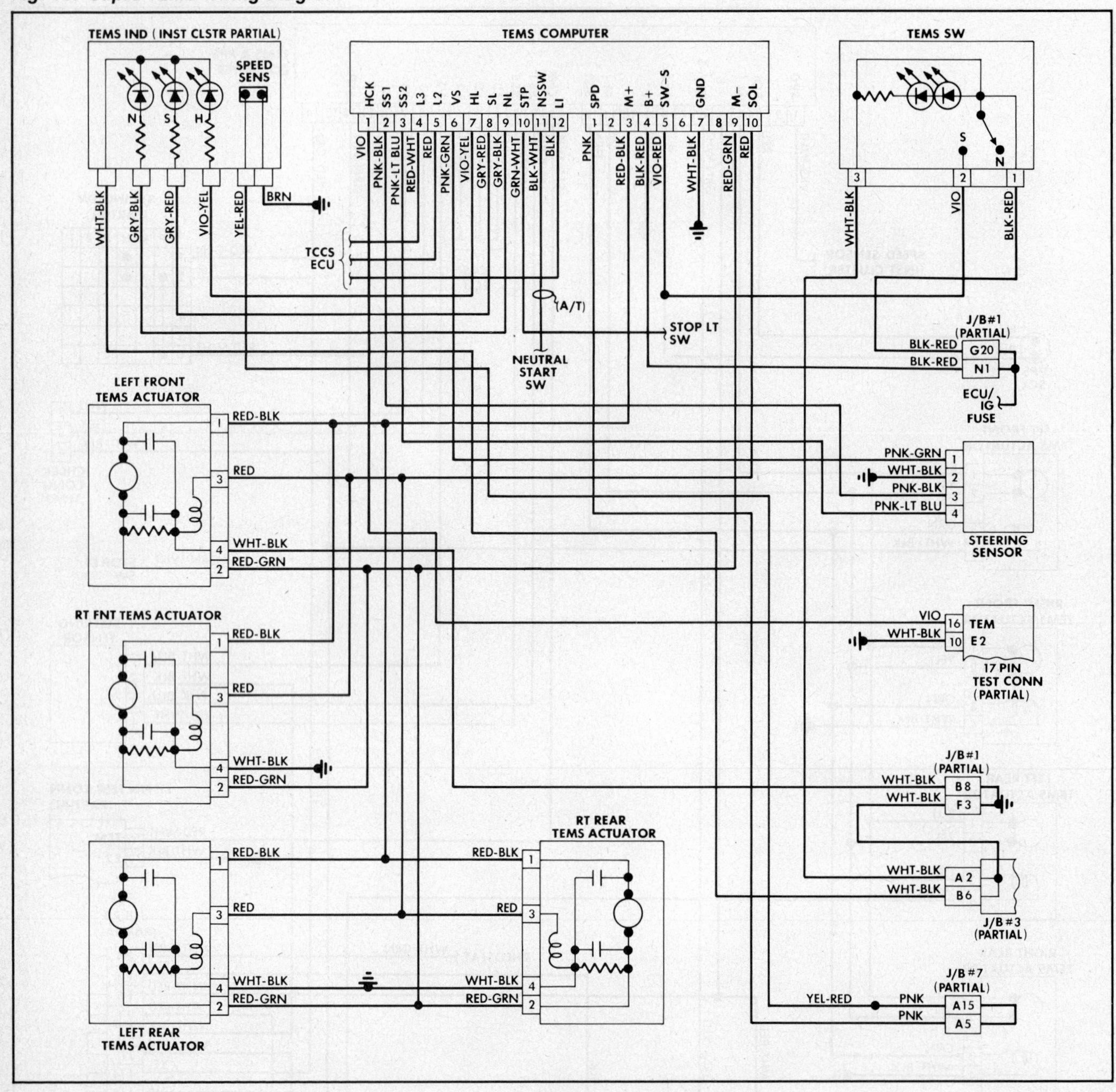

SECTION 12

STEERING

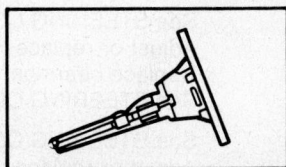

CONTENTS

TROUBLE SHOOTING — Page

All Models 12-2

STEERING WHEEL & COLUMN SWITCHES

All Models 12-6

STEERING COLUMNS

Acura 12-8
Audi 4000S, 4000CS Quattro & Coupe GT 12-10
Audi 5000S, 5000CS Turbo & 5000CS Quattro 12-11
BMW 12-13
Chevrolet 12-14
Chrysler Motors FWD 12-15
Chrysler Motors RWD 12-17
Ford Motor Co. 12-19
Honda 12-8
Hyundai 12-15
Isuzu I-Mark & Impulse 12-21
Isuzu P'UP & Trooper II 12-22
Jaguar 12-23
Mazda 12-24
Mercedes-Benz 12-26
Mitsubishi FWD 12-15
Mitsubishi RWD 12-17
Nissan 12-27
Peugeot 12-30
Porsche 12-30
Saab 900S & 9000 Turbo 12-31
Sterling 12-8
Subaru 12-32
Suzuki Samurai 12-35
Toyota – Tilt Wheel 12-36
Toyota Non-Tilt Wheel 12-41
Volkswagen Except Quantum & Vanagon 12-43
Volkswagen Quantum 12-44
Volkswagen Vanagon 12-45
Volvo 12-46
Yugo 12-47

STEERING GEARS & LINKAGE — Page

Chevrolet Rack & Pinion 12-49
Chrysler Motors (FWD) 12-50
Chrysler Motors Recirculating Ball 12-53
Ford Motor Co. (Festiva & Tracer) 12-55
Honda Rack & Pinion 12-58
Hyundai Rack & Pinion 12-50
Isuzu Rack & Pinion (I-Mark) 12-49
Isuzu P'UP Recirculating Ball 12-61
Mazda Rack & Pinion 12-55
Mazda Recirculating Ball 12-63
Mitsubishi FWD Rack & Pinion 12-50
Mitsubishi Recirculating Ball 12-53
Nissan Rack & Pinion 12-65
Nissan Pickup Recirculating Ball 12-67
Porsche Rack & Pinion 12-68
Subaru Rack & Pinion 12-69
Suzuki Recirculating Ball 12-71
Toyota Rack & Pinion 12-72
Toyota Pickup & 4Runner Recirculating Ball 12-74
Volkswagen Rack & Pinion – Except Vanagon 12-76
Volkswagen Vanagon Rack & Pinion 12-77
Yugo 12-78

POWER STEERING

Acura Rack & Pinion 12-80
Audi Power-Assisted Rack & Pinion 12-87
BMW
  Power-Assisted Rack & Pinion 12-91
  Recirculating Ball 12-91
Chevrolet Power-Assisted Rack & Pinion 12-94
Chrysler Motors
  Power-Assisted Rack & Pinion 12-98
  Power-Assisted Recirculating Ball 12-102
Ford Motor Co.
  Merkur XR4Ti 12-106
  Tracer 12-116
Honda Rack & Pinion 12-80
Hyundai Power-Assisted Rack & Pinion 12-98
Isuzu
  Power-Assisted Rack & Pinion 12-94
  Power-Assisted Recirculating Ball 12-110
Jaguar Power-Assisted Rack & Pinion 12-113
Mazda Power-Assisted Rack & Pinion 12-116
Mazda Recirculating Ball (B2200 & B2600) 12-119
Mercedes-Benz Power-Assisted
  Recirculating Ball 12-122
Mitsubishi Power-Assisted Rack & Pinion 12-98
Mitsubishi Power-Assisted Recirculating Ball 12-102
Nissan Power-Assisted Rack & Pinion 12-124
Nissan Recirculating Ball 12-135
Peugeot Power-Assisted Rack & Pinion 12-138
Porsche Power-Assisted Rack & Pinion 12-141
Saab Power-Assisted Rack & Pinion 12-143
Sterling Rack & Pinion 12-80
Subaru Power Rack & Pinion 12-146
Toyota Power-Assisted Rack & Pinion 12-151
Toyota Power-Assisted Recirculating Ball 12-159
Volkswagen Power-Assisted Rack & Pinion 12-164
Volvo Power-Assisted Rack & Pinion 12-166

ELECTRONIC POWER STEERING

Mazda RX7 & 626 12-176
Mitsubishi Galant 12-178
Toyota Cressida 12-181

NOTE: ALSO SEE GENERAL INDEX.

Steering

STANDARD STEERING COLUMN TROUBLE SHOOTING

CONDITION	POSSIBLE CAUSE	CORRECTION
Noise in Column	Coupling pulled apart	See STEERING COLUMNS
	Column not correctly aligned	See STEERING COLUMNS
	Broken lower joint	Replace joint
	Horn contact ring not lubricated	See STEERING COLUMNS
	Bearings not lubricated	See STEERING COLUMNS
	Bearing worn or broken	Replace bearing and lubricate
	Shaft snap ring not properly seated	Reseat or replace snap ring
	Plastic spherical joint not lubricated	See STEERING COLUMNS
	Shroud or housing loose	Tighten holding screws
	Lock plate retaining ring not seated	See STEERING COLUMNS
	Loose sight shield	Tighten holding screws
High Steering Shaft Effort	Column assembly misaligned	See STEERING COLUMNS
	Improperly installed dust shield	Adjust or replace
	Damaged upper or lower bearing	Replace bearings
	Tight steering universal joint	See STEERING COLUMNS
High Shift Effort	Column is out of alignment	See STEERING COLUMNS
	Improperly installed dust shield	Adjust or replace
	Seals or bearings not lubricated	See STEERING COLUMNS
	Mounting bracket screws too long	Replace with new shorter screws
	Burrs on shift tube	Remove burrs or replace tube
	Lower bowl bearing assembled wrong	See STEERING COLUMNS
	Shift tube bent or broken	Replace as necessary
	Improper adjustment of shift levers	See STEERING COLUMNS
Improper Trans. Shifting (Column Shift)	Sheared shift tube joint	Replace as necessary
	Sheared lower shaft lever weld joint	Replace as necessary
	Improper shift lever adjustment	See STEERING COLUMNS
	Improper gate plate adjustment	See STEERING COLUMNS
Excess Play in Column	Instrument panel bracket bolts loose	Tighten bolts and check bracket
	Broken weld nut on jacket	See STEERING COLUMNS
	Instrument bracket capsule sheared	See STEERING COLUMNS
	Column bracket/jacket bolts loose	Tighten bolts and check bracket
Steering Locks in Gear	Release lever mechanism damaged	See STEERING COLUMNS

TILT STEERING COLUMN TROUBLE SHOOTING

CONDITION	POSSIBLE CAUSE	CORRECTION
Steering Wheel Loose	Excess clearance in support	Check and replace if necessary
	Excess clearance in housing/pivot pin	Check and replace if necessary
	Damaged anti-lash spring in spheres	See TILT STEERING COLUMNS
	Upper bearing not seated properly	See TILT STEERING COLUMNS
	Upper bearing inner race seal missing	Replace if necessary
	Improperly adjusted tilt/telescopic lock	See STEERING COLUMNS
	Loose support screws	Tighten and check bracket
	Bearing preload spring missing/broken	Replace spring
	Housing loose on jacket	Tighten and/or replace screws
Play in Column Mount	Loose support screws	Tighten and check bracket
	Loose shoes in housing	See TILT STEERING COLUMNS
	Loose tilt head pivot pins	See TILT STEERING COLUMNS
	Loose shoe lock pin in support	See TILT STEERING COLUMNS
Housing Scraping on Bowl	Bowl bent or out of round	See TILT STEERING COLUMNS
Wheel Will Not Lock	Shoe seized on its pivot pin	See TILT STEERING COLUMNS
	Shoe may have burrs/dirt in them	Clean or replace
	Shoe lock spring weak/broken	Replace if necessary

TILT STEERING COLUMN TROUBLE SHOOTING (Cont.)

CONDITION	POSSIBLE CAUSE	CORRECTION
Wheel Fails to Return	Pivot pins are bound up	Clean or replace
	Wheel tilt spring is damaged	See TILT STEERING COLUMNS
	Turn signal switch wires too tight	Loosen and check operation
Noise When Tilting	Upper tilt bumpers worn	Replace if necessary
	Tilt spring rubbing in housing	Adjust and check operation
Hard Steering	Incorrect tire pressure	Inflate to proper pressure
	Lack of lubricant in steering linkage	Service Steering, Suspension and Linkage
	Improper front end alignment	See WHEEL ALIGNMENT
	Improper steering gear adjustment	See STEERING

MANUAL STEERING GEAR TROUBLE SHOOTING

CONDITION	POSSIBLE CAUSE	CORRECTION
Rattle or Chucking Noise in Rack and Pinion	Rack and pinion mounting bracket loose	Tighten all mounting bolts
	Lack of/or incorrect lubricant	See STEERING
	Steering gear mounting bolts loose	Tighten all mounting bolts
Excessive Play	Front wheel bearing improperly adjusted	See FRONT SUSPENSION
	Loose or worn steering linkage	See STEERING LINKAGE
	Loose or worn ball joints	See FRONT SUSPENSION
	Loose or worn steering gear shaft	See MANUAL STEERING GEARS
	Steering arm loose on gear shaft	See MANUAL STEERING GEARS
	Steering gear housing bolts loose	Tighten all mounting bolts
	Steering gear adjustment too loose	See MANUAL STEERING GEAR
	Steering arms loose on knuckles	Tighten and check steering linkage
	Rack and pinion mounting loose	Tighten all mounting bolts
	Rack and pinion out of adjustment	See adjustment in STEERING
	Tie rod end loose	Tighten and check steering linkage
	Excessive Pitman shaft-to-ball nut lash	See STEERING
Poor Returnability	Lack of lubricant in ball joint or linkage	Lubricate and service systems
	Binding in linkage or ball joints	See STEERING LINKAGE and SUSPENSION
	Improper front end alignment	See WHEEL ALIGNMENT
	Improper steering gear adjustment	See STEERING
	Improper tire pressure	Inflate to proper pressure
	Tie rod binding	See FRONT SUSPENSION
	Shaft seal rubbing shaft	See STEERING COLUMNS
Excessive Vertical Motion	Tires, wheels or rotors out of balance	Balance tires then check wheels and rotors
	Worn or faulty shock absorbers	Check and replace if necessary
	Loose tie rod ends or steering	Tighten or replace if necessary
	Loose or worn wheel bearings	See SUSPENSION
Steering Pulls to One Side	Improper tire pressure	Inflate to proper pressure
	Front tires are different sizes	Rotate or replace if necessary
	Wheel bearings not adjusted properly	See FRONT SUSPENSION
	Bent or broken suspension components	See FRONT SUSPENSION
	Improper wheel alignment	See WHEEL ALIGNMENT
	Brakes dragging	See BRAKES
Instability	Low or uneven tire pressure	Inflate to proper pressure
	Loose or worn wheel bearings	See FRONT SUSPENSION
	Loose or worn idler arm bushing	See FRONT SUSPENSION
	Loose or worn strut bushings	See FRONT SUSPENSION
	Incorrect front wheel alignment	See WHEEL ALIGNMENT
	Steering gear not centered	See MANUAL STEERING GEARS
	Springs or shock absorbers defective	Check and replace if necessary

Steering

POWER STEERING TROUBLE SHOOTING

CONDITION	POSSIBLE CAUSE	CORRECTION
Rattle or Chucking Noise in Steering	Pressure hoses touching engine parts	Adjust to proper clearance
	Loose Pitman shaft	Adjust or replace if necessary
	Tie rods ends or Pitman arm loose	Tighten and check system
	Rack and pinion mounts loose	Tighten all mounting bolts
	Free play in worm and piston assembly	See POWER STEERING GEARS
	Loose sector shaft or thrust bearing adjustment	See POWER STEERING GEARS
	Free play in pot coupling	See STEERING COLUMNS
	Worn shaft serrations	See STEERING COLUMNS
Growl in Steering Pump	Excessive pressure in hoses	Restricted hoses see POWER STEERING GEARS
	Scored pressure plates	See POWER STEERING PUMPS
	Scored thrust plates or rotor	See POWER STEERING PUMPS
	Extreme wear of cam ring	See POWER STEERING PUMPS
Rattle in Steering Pump	Vanes not installed properly	See POWER STEERING PUMPS
	Vanes sticking in rotor slots	See POWER STEERING PUMPS
Swish Noise in Pump	Defective flow control valve	See POWER STEERING PUMPS
Groan in Steering Pump	Air in fluid	See POWER STEERING PUMPS
	Poor pressure hose connection	Tighten and check, replace if necessary
Squawk When Turning	Damper "O" ring on valve spool cut	See POWER STEERING PUMPS
Moan or Whine in Pump	Pump shaft bearing scored	Replace bearing and fluid
	Air in fluid or fluid level low	See POWER STEERING PUMPS
	Hose or column grounded	Check and replace if necessary
	Cover "O" ring missing or damaged	See POWER STEERING PUMPS
	Valve cover baffle missing or damaged	See POWER STEERING PUMPS
	Interference of components in pump	See POWER STEERING PUMPS
	Loose or poor bracket alignment	Correct or replace if necessary
Hissing When Parking	Internal leakage in steering gear	Check valve assembly first
Chirp in Steering Pump	Loose or worn power steering belt	Adjust or replace if neceesary
Buzzing When Not Steering	Noisy pump	See POWER STEERING PUMPS
	Bearing loose on shaft serrations	See STEERING COLUMNS
Clicking Noise in Pump	Pump slippers too long	See POWER STEERING PUMPS
	Broken slipper springs	See POWER STEERING PUMPS
	Excessive wear or nicked rotors	See POWER STEERING PUMPS
	Damaged cam contour	See POWER STEERING PUMPS
Poor Return of Wheel	Wheel rubbing against turn signal	See STEERING WHEEL SWITCHES
	Flange rubbing steering gear adjuster	See STEERING COLUMNS
	Tight or frozen steering shaft bearing	See STEERING COLUMNS
	Steering gear out of adjustment	See Adjustment in STEERING
	Sticking or plugged spool valve	See POWER STEERING
	Improper front end alignment	See WHEEL ALIGNMENT
	Wheel bearings worn or loose	See FRONT SUSPENSION or BRAKES
	Ties rods or ball joints binding	Check and replace if necessary
	Intermediate shaft joints binding	See STEERING COLUMNS
	Kinked pressure hoses	Correct or replace if necessary
	Loose housing head spanner nut	See POWER STEERING GEARS
	Damaged valve lever	See POWER STEERING GEARS
	Sector shaft adjusted too tight	See ADJUSTMENTS in POWER STEERING GEARS
	Worm thrust bearing adjusted too tight	See ADJUSTMENTS in POWER STEERING GEARS
	Reaction ring sticking in cylinder	See POWER STEERING GEARS
	Reaction ring sticking in housing head	See POWER STEERING GEARS
	Steering pump internal leakage	See POWER STEERING PUMPS
	Steering gear-to-column misalignment	See STEERING COLUMNS
	Lack of lubrication in linkage	Service front suspension
	Lack of lubrication in ball joints	Service front suspension

Steering

POWER STEERING TROUBLE SHOOTING (Cont.)

CONDITION	POSSIBLE CAUSE	CORRECTION
Increased Effort When Turning Wheel Fast Foaming, Milky Power Steering Fluid, Low Fluid Level or Low Pressure	High internal pump leakage	See POWER STEERING PUMPS
	Power steering pump belt slipping	Adjust or replace if necessary
	Low fluid level	Check and fill to proper level
	Engine idle speed to low	Adjust to correct setting
	Air in pump fluid system	See POWER STEERING PUMPS
	Pump output low	See POWER STEERING PUMPS
	Steering gear malfunctioning	See POWER STEERING GEARS
Wheel Surges or Jerks	Low fluid level	Check and fill to proper level
	Loose fan belt	Adjust or replace if necessary
	Insufficient pump pressure	See POWER STEERING PUMPS
	Sticky flow control valve	See POWER STEERING PUMPS
	Linkage hitting oil pan at full turn	Replace bent components
Kick Back or Free Play	Air in pump fluid system	See POWER STEERING PUMPS
	Worn poppet valve in steering gear	See POWER STEERING GEARS
	Excessive over center lash	See POWER STEERING GEARS
	Thrust bearing out of adjustment	See POWER STEERING GEARS
	Steering gear coupling loose on shaft	See POWER STEERING PUMPS
	Steering disc mounting bolts loose	Tighten or replace if necessary
	Coupling loose on worm shaft	Tighten or replace if necessary
	Improper sector shaft adjustment	See POWER STEERING GEARS
	Excessive worm piston side play	See POWER STEERING GEARS
	Damaged valve lever	See POWER STEERING GEARS
	Universal joint loose	Tighten or replace if necessary
	Defective rotary valve	See POWER STEERING GEARS
No Power When Parking	Sticking flow control valve	See POWER STEERING PUMPS
	Insufficient pump pressure output	See POWER STEERING PUMPS
	Excessive internal pump leakage	See POWER STEERING PUMPS
	Excessive internal gear leakage	See POWER STEERING PUMPS
	Flange rubs against gear adjust plug	See STEERING COLUMNS
	Loose pump belt	Adjust or replace if necessary
	Low fluid level	Check and add proper amount of fluid
	Engine idle too low	Adjust to correct setting
	Steering gear-to-column misaligned	See STEERING COLUMNS
No Power, Left Turns	Left turn reaction seal "O" ring worn	See POWER STEERING GEARS
	Left turn reaction seal damaged/missing	See POWER STEERING GEARS
	Cylinder head "O" ring damaged	See POWER STEERING PUMPS
No Power, Right Turns	Column pot coupling bottomed	See STEERING COLUMNS
	Right turn reaction seal "O" ring worn	See POWER STEERING GEARS
	Right turn reaction seal damaged	See POWER STEERING GEARS
	Internal leakage through piston end plug	See POWER STEERING GEARS
	Internal leakage through side plugs	See POWER STEERING GEARS
Lack of Effort in Turning	Left and/or right reaction seal worn	Replace, see POWER STEERING GEARS
	Left and/or right reaction oil passageway not drilled	Check housing and cylinder head
	Left and/or right reaction seal sticking in cylinder head	See POWER STEERING GEARS
Wanders to One Side	Front end alignment incorrect	See WHEEL ALIGNMENT
	Unbalanced steering gear valve	See POWER STEERING GEARS
Low Pressure Due to Steering Pump	Flow control valve stuck or inoperative	See POWER STEERING
	Pressure plate not flat against cam ring	See POWER STEERING PUMPS
	Extreme wear of cam ring	Replace and check adjustments
	Scored plate, thrust plate or rotor	See POWER STEERING PUMPS
	Vanes not installed properly	See POWER STEERING PUMPS
	Vanes sticking in rotor slots	See POWER STEERING PUMPS
	Cracked/broken thrust or pressure plate	See POWER STEERING PUMPS

ALL MODELS

REMOVAL & INSTALLATION

CAUTION: When performing work on vehicles equipped with Supplement Retraint System (SRS), exercise extreme caution when working around steering wheel or column. DO NOT apply electrical power to any component on steering column without disconnecting SRS control unit (air bag system may be activated).

STEERING WHEEL & HORN

Removal

1) Disconnect battery ground cable. Remove screws attaching horn button assembly/center pad to steering wheel from behind steering wheel (if equipped).

Fig. 1: Removing Steering Wheel

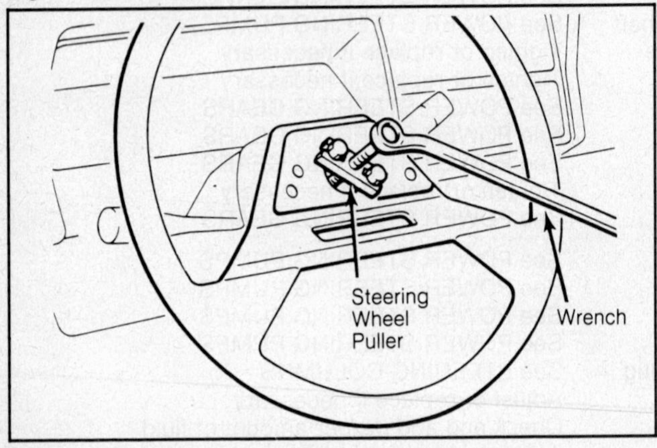

2) Pull horn button assembly/center pad from steering wheel. Use a cloth covered screwdriver to pry off horn button assembly/center pad (if necessary). Disassemble horn button assembly (if necessary).

3) Place springs, contacts, horn or cruise control harness connectors and screws in order for reassembly reference. Place wheels in a straight-ahead position.

4) Remove steering wheel retaining nut and washer. Mark steering wheel and shaft for reassembly reference. Using a steering wheel puller, remove steering wheel. *See Fig. 1.*

5) Place steering wheel, cruise control set/resume switch (if equipped), canceling cams, springs and slip rings in order for reassembly reference.

Installation

1) Coat slip ring contact surfaces with a light electrical grease. Assemble horn button assembly (if disassembled). Ensure wheels are in a straight-ahead position.

2) Aligning marks made during removal, place slip ring, springs, canceling cams, steering wheel, washer and steering wheel retaining nut on shaft.

3) Tighten nut to specification. See STEERING WHEEL TIGHTENING SPECIFICATIONS table at the end of this article. To complete reassembly, reverse removal procedure.

COMBINATION SWITCH

Removal

Remove steering wheel. Remove upper and lower steering column covers. Disconnect combination switch harness connectors. remove snap ring and washer from steering shaft (if equipped). Remove combination switch attaching screws. Remove combination switch.

Installation

To install, reverse removal procedure. Ensure all electrical connections are tight. Check canceling operation of turn signal switch.

Fig. 2: Exploded View of Typical Steering Wheel Assembly

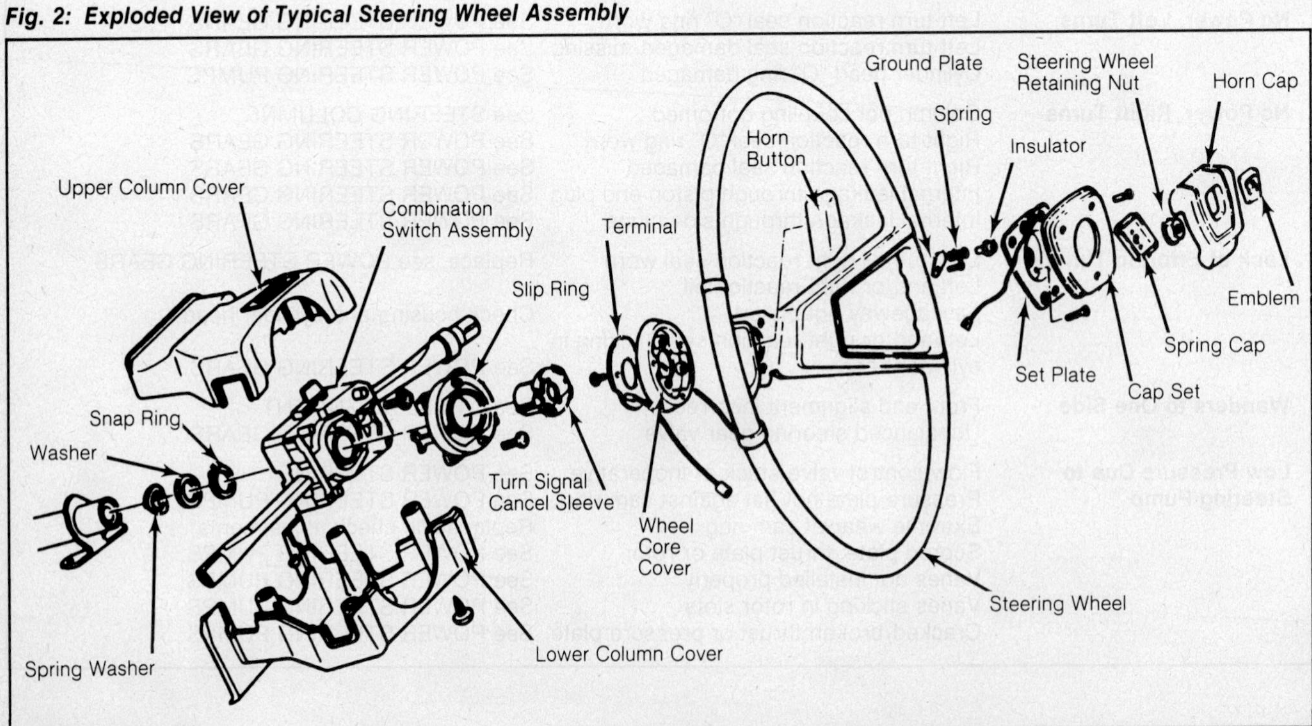

ALL MODELS (Cont.)

STEERING LOCK & IGNITION SWITCH

Removal

1) Remove steering wheel, upper and lower steering column covers and combination switch. Disconnect ignition switch harness connectors.

2) If the shear bolt studs are accessible, use a hacksaw to cut a slot into the exposed studs. Using a screwdriver, remove the studs.

3) If the shear bolt studs are recessed or hard to reach with a hacksaw, center punch studs. Using a drill bit and a screw extractor, remove studs. Remove steering lock and ignition switch.

Installation

1) To install, reverse removal procedure. Install new shear bolts. Tighten shear bolts finger tight. Ensure proper operation of steering lock and ignition switch.

2) Tighten shear bolts until heads break off. Install combination switch, upper and lower steering column covers and steering wheel.

STEERING WHEEL TIGHTENING SPECIFICATIONS

Application	Ft. Lbs (N.m)
Acura, Honda & Sterling	
All Models	37 (50)
Audi	
All Models	29 (39)
BMW	
All Models	51-61 (70-85)
Chrysler Motors, Mitsubishi & Hyundai	
All Except Van/Wagon	25-33 (34-45)
Van/Wagon	25-36 (34-49)
Ford Motor Co.	
Festiva	29-36 (39-49)
Merkur XR4Ti	33-40 (45-54)
Tracer	1
Chevrolet	
Spectrum	22 (30)
Sprint	19-28 (26-38)
Isuzu	
I-Mark & Impulse	22 (30)
P'UP &Trooper II	18-25 (24-34)

STEERING WHEEL TIGHTENING SPECIFICATIONS (Cont.)

Application	Ft. Lbs (N.m)
Jaguar	
All Models	25-32 (34-44)
Mazda	
All Models	29-36 (39-49)
Mercedes Benz	
Models With 15mm Allen Bolt	37 (50)
Models with 18mm Allen Bolt	59 (80)
Nissan	
Stanza	29-40 (39-54)
300ZX	36-43 (49-58)
All Others	22-29 (30-39)
Peugeot	
All Models	1
Porsche	
911 Carrera & 911 Turbo	54 (73)
924S & 944	37 (50)
944S & 944 Turbo	33 (45)
Saab	
All Models	26 (35)
Subaru	
All Models	22-29 (30-39)
Suzuki	
Samurai	18-29 (24-39)
Toyota	
All Models	25 (34)
Volkswagen	
All Except Quantum	37 (50)
Quantum	29 (39)
Volvo	
760GLE	21-27 (28-37)
All Others	33-55 (45-75)
Yugo	
GV	36 (49)

1 – Information not available from manufacturer.

Steering Columns

ACURA, HONDA & STERLING

Acura: Integra, Legend, Legend Coupe
Honda: Accord, Civic, CRX, Prelude
Sterling: 825

DESCRIPTION

A 2-piece safety steering column with a slip-joint flange connection is used. The steering column is supported by a column tube and a steering lock assembly.

REMOVAL & INSTALLATION

STEERING COLUMN

CAUTION: Applying excessive pressure, or causing impact to mainshaft during service, may cause the column to collapse.

Removal (Integra, Legend, Legend Coupe & 825)

1) Disconnect battery ground cable. Remove steering wheel, column covers, combination switch and ignition/lock assembly. Refer to STEERING WHEEL & COLUMN SWITCHES article in this section.

2) Remove rubber bands. Remove upper column holder. Remove steering shaft "U" joint-to-gearbox shaft bolts. Remove lower hanger retaining bolts. Remove hanger. Slide column into passenger compartment to remove.

Installation

1) Install bending plate guide on steering column. Position steering column assembly into hole in floorboard. Slide "U" joint splines onto gearbox shaft. Tighten "U" joint-to-gearbox shaft bolts.

2) Attach lower hanger bracket to engine side of firewall. Tighten lower hanger bolts. Attach steering column to underside of dashboard. Replace steering wheel, column covers, switches and ignition/lock assembly.

Removal (Accord, Civic, CRX & Prelude)

1) Remove steering wheel, upper and lower column covers, combination switch and ignition/lock assembly. Refer to STEERING WHEEL & COLUMN SWITCHES article in this section.

2) Disconnect steering joint at splines by removing clamp bolt. Detach lower dash panel. Remove harness wiring and connectors from column.

3) On Civic, CRX and Prelude, remove retaining bolts (upper bolts first). On Accord, remove column-to-mounting bracket retaining nuts (upper nuts first). Remove assembly from vehicle.

NOTE: If steering wheel has been removed, ignition switch must be in "LOCK" position to retain steering shaft during column removal.

Fig. 1: Exploded View of Integra Steering Column Assembly

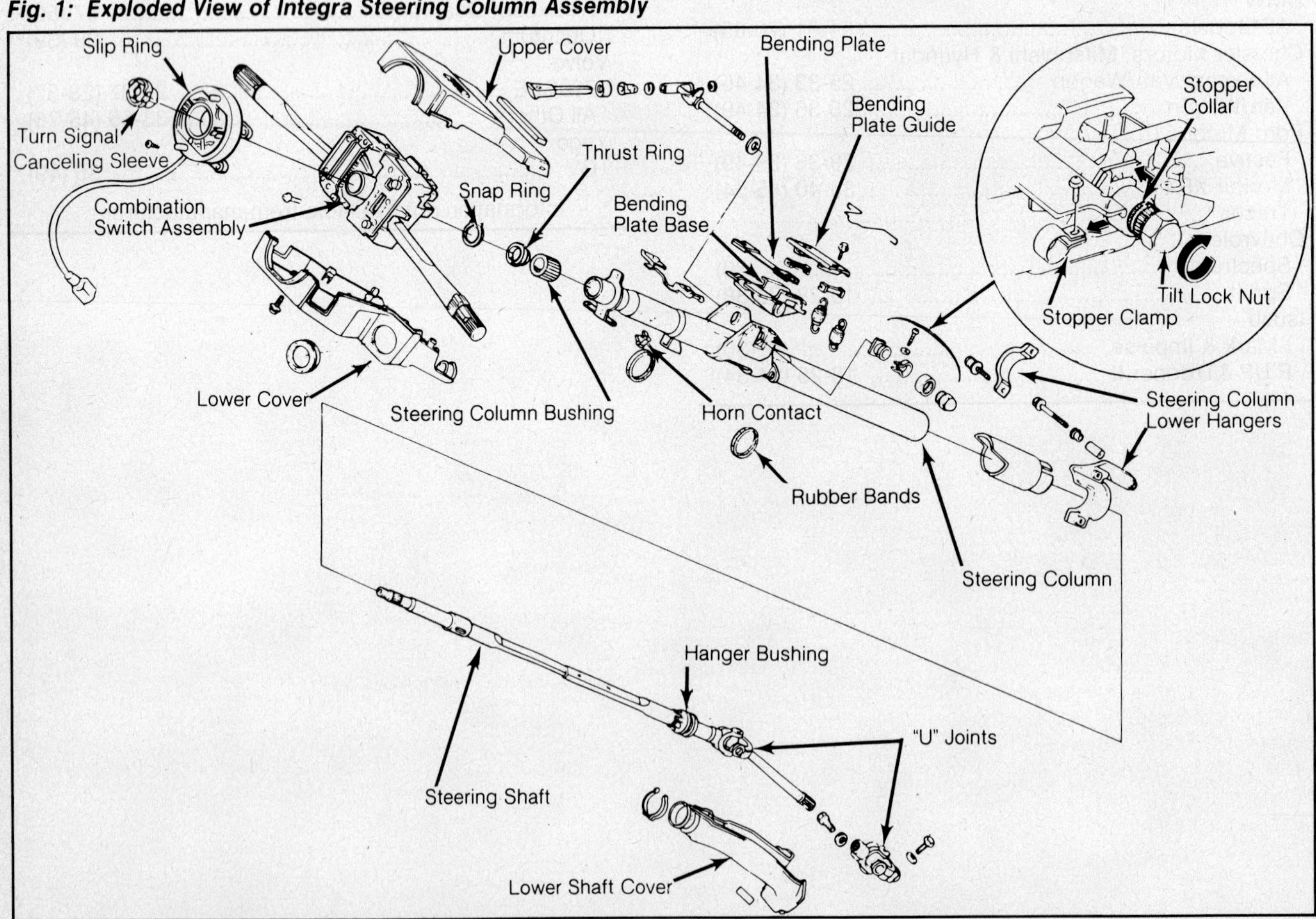

Integra is shown. Legend, Legend Coupe and 825 are similar. Courtesy of American Honda Motor Co.

ACURA, HONDA & STERLING (Cont.)

Fig. 2: Accord Steering Column Assembly

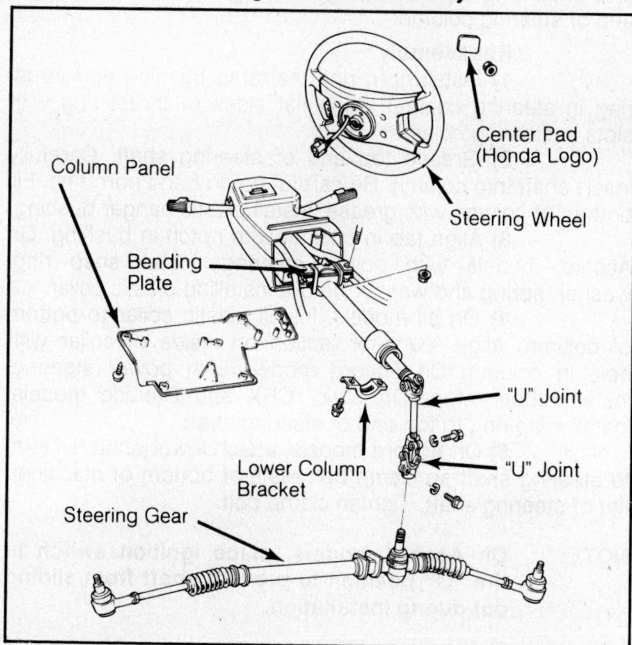

Civic, CRX and Prelude are similar.
Courtesy of American Honda Motor Co.

Installation

1) Position column in vehicle. Slide upper half of "U" joint connector onto lower shaft. Top bolt must be positioned across flat part of shaft.

2) On Accord, loosely install upper bracket retaining nuts. On Civic, CRX and Prelude, loosely install upper bracket retaining bolts.

3) Pull down on column to seat bending plate against hook. Connect lower shaft "U" joint to gear box shaft. Install and tighten bolt. Loosely install lower bracket.

4) On Accord, tighten upper and lower bracket retaining nuts. On Civic, CRX and Prelude, tighten upper and lower bracket bolts. To complete installation, reverse removal procedure.

OVERHAUL

STEERING COLUMN

Disassembly (Integra, Legend & Sterling 825)

1) Remove plastic collar. Remove stopper clip retaining screw. Slide stopper collar toward tilt lock nut side. Remove column hanger springs. Remove stopper collar. Remove pin stopper. *See Fig. 1.*

2) Remove bending plate. Remove bending plate base. Remove tilt lever lock nut. Tilt lever lock nut is a reverse thread nut. Remove tilt lever assembly.

3) Remove steering column assembly. Remove horn contact from side of column. Remove snap ring. Slide shaft from column assembly.

4) Remove column thrust ring. Remove upper bushing (if necessary). If hanger bushing is worn or damaged, replace steering shaft as an assembly.

Inspection

1) Inspect bushings for wear or scoring. Upper bushing can be replaced. Hanger bushing cannot be replaced. If hanger bushing is damaged, replace steering shaft as an assembly.

2) Inspect steering shaft for warpage. If steering shaft is bent, replace. Check "U" joints for looseness. If loose or damaged, replace.

Reassembly

1) Insert upper bushing (if removed). Install column thrust ring. Insert steering shaft from bottom of column. Place snap ring into position over steering shaft.

2) Apply electrical grease to horn contact. Snap horn contact into side of steering column. Apply grease to lower end of steering shaft and inside column. Push hanger bushing into bottom end of column as far as possible.

3) Install plastic collar over bottom end of steering column by aligning projection with hole in column. Slide plastic collar onto column until projection fits into hole.

4) Grease all tilt steering parts. Install bending plate base on steering column. With 10 mm washer on tilt lever assembly, install assembly into bending plate base. Install spin stopper on tilt lever assembly shaft. Install stopper collar over spin stopper.

5) Install column hanger springs. Install tilt lock nut (reverse thread). Tighten to 60 INCH. lbs. (7 N.m). Slide stopper collar towards tilt lock nut. If stopper collar cannot be moved toward tilt lock nut, turn tilt lock nut counterclockwise until stopper collar can slide next to tilt lock nut.

6) Place steering collar in soft-jawed vise. With tilt lever handle pulled out and using a hanging scale attached 1.38" (35 mm) from the end of the handle, measure tilt lever tension preload.

7) Preload should be between 11-19 ft. lbs. (15-26 N.m). If not within specification, slide stopper collar to spin stopper and turn tilt lock nut one spline at a time in either direction.

8) Slide stopper collar back onto tilt lock nut. Recheck preload tension. If incorrect tension is measured, continue turning tilt lock nut one spline at a time until preload tension is correct.

9) With stopper collar in place over tilt lock nut, slip stopper clip over spin stopper. Tighten clip retaining screw. Install upper column holder and bending plate on steering column with rubber bands.

Fig. 3: Exploded View of Tilt Steering Assembly

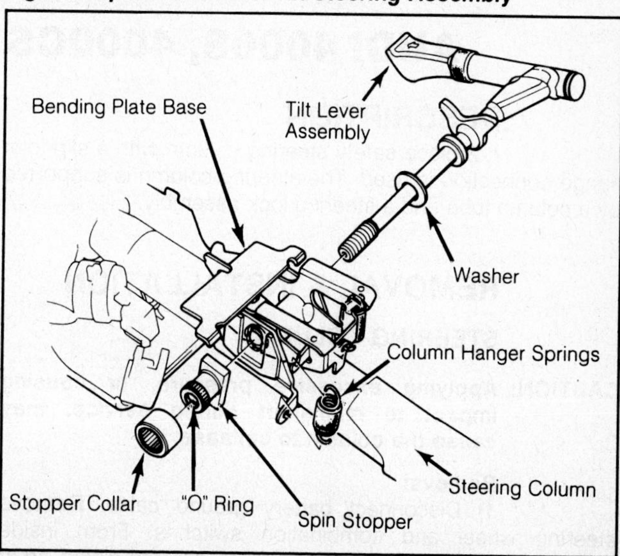

Integra is shown. All other tilt steering models are similar.
Courtesy of American Honda Motor Co.

ACURA, HONDA & STERLING (Cont.)

Fig. 4: Exploded View of Column Hanger Assembly

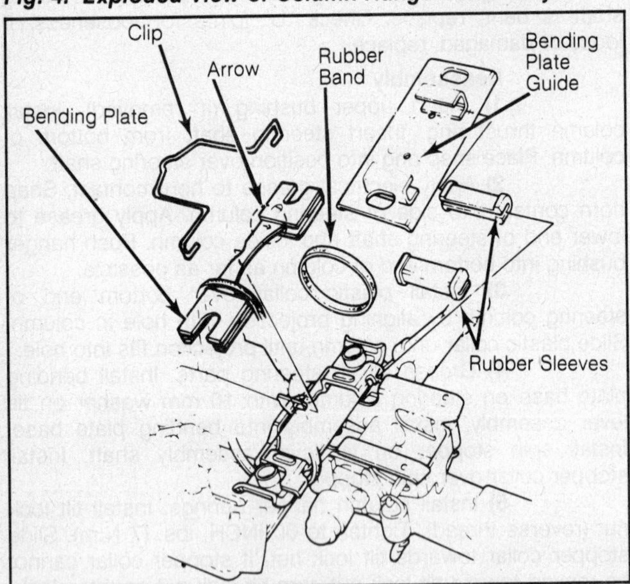

Integra is shown. All other models are similar. Courtesy of American Honda Motor Co.

Disassembly (Accord, Civic, CRX & Prelude)

1) Remove steering wheel and column switches. Remove rubber bands, bending plate and upper mounting plate. On Civic and Prelude models, remove snap ring and steering shaft washer from upper end of steering shaft.

2) Turn ignition switch to "I" position on Prelude or to "ACC" position on Accord, Civic and CRX. On all models, remove plastic collar, shaft bushing, and column hanger bushing.

3) Pull steering shaft out from bottom end of column. Remove thrust ring, bushing and horn ring from top end of column.

4) On Accord models with power steering, remove rubber stop, plastic collar, washer, spring, washer and snap ring before pulling steering shaft out of bottom end of steering column.

Reassembly

1) Install horn ring, serrated bushing and thrust ring in steering column. Align flat sides of thrust ring with slots in steering column.

2) Grease top end of steering shaft. Carefully insert shaft into column. Be careful not to bend horn ring. Fill bottom of column with grease. Install plastic hanger bushing.

3) Align tab in column with notch in bushing. On Accord models with power steering, install snap ring, washer, spring and washer before installing plastic collar.

4) On all models, install plastic collar to bottom of column. Align round projection on inside of collar with hole in column. On Accord models with power steering, install rubber stop. On Civic, CRX and Prelude models, install snap ring to top end of steering shaft.

5) On Accord models, attach lower shaft "U" joint to steering shaft so clamp bolt rests at bottom of machined flat of steering shaft. Tighten clamp bolt.

NOTE: **On Accord models, place ignition switch in the "O" position to prevent shaft from sliding out during installation.**

6) Install combination switch. Use rubber bands to assemble upper bracket and bending plate to steering column. Bending plate should fit under hook on column with arrow mark facing out and pointing down. Install upper and lower column covers.

TIGHTENING SPECIFICATIONS

Application	Ft. Lbs. (N.m)
Lower Column Bracket Bolts	16 (22)
"U" Joint Clamp Bolts	22 (30)
Steering Wheel Nut	37 (50)
	INCH Lbs. (N.m)
Upper Column Bracket Bolts	108 (12)

AUDI 4000S, 4000CS QUATTRO & COUPE GT

DESCRIPTION

A 2-piece safety steering column with a slip-joint flange connection is used. The steering column is supported by a column tube and a steering lock assembly.

REMOVAL & INSTALLATION

STEERING COLUMN

CAUTION: **Applying excessive pressure, or causing impact to mainshaft during service, may cause the column to collapse.**

Removal

1) Disconnect battery ground cable. Remove steering wheel and combination switches. From inside engine compartment, remove steering shaft-to-pinion shaft clamp bolt.

2) Remove column cover bolts. Remove column covers. Pry lock washer from steering shaft. Remove spring. Remove contact ring and steering lock assembly. Remove support ring from column tube. *See Fig. 1.*

3) Center punch and drill out column tube-to-dash shear bolt. Remove column tube-to-dash screw. From inside vehicle, pull dust boot out of floorboard. Remove steering column tube and shaft as an assembly.

Installation

1) Install assembled steering column into vehicle. Install and finger tighten shear bolt and screw. Seat dust boot into floorboard.

2) Position clamp onto steering gear pinion shaft. Place support ring into column tube. Install steering lock assembly on steering column. Install contact ring, spring and new lock washer.

3) Tighten column tube-to-dash screw. Tighten shear bolt until head snaps off. Install upper and lower column covers. Install column switches and steering wheel.

AUDI 4000S, 4000CS QUATTRO & COUPE GT (Cont.)

Fig. 1: Exploded View of Upper Steering Column

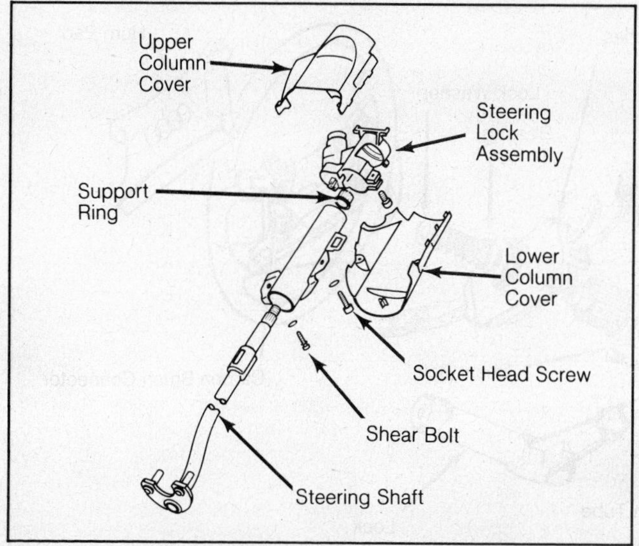

Courtesy of Audi of America, Inc.

Fig. 2: Exploded View of Lower Steering Column

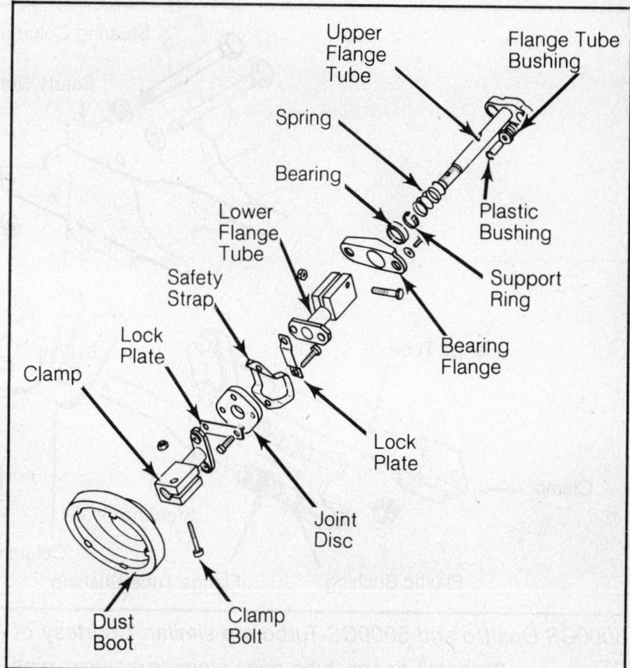

Courtesy of Audi of America, Inc.

OVERHAUL

STEERING COLUMN

Disassembly

1) On lower steering shaft, remove lower flange tube-to-upper flange tube clamp bolt. Separate flange tubes. Remove bearing flange, bearing, support ring, spring and washer. *See Fig. 2.*

2) Push upper flange tube toward steering shaft until components can be separated. Remove flange tube bushings with plastic bushings. *See Fig. 2.*

3) Remove lower flange tube-to-clamp bolts. Separate lower flange tube from clamp. Inspect joint disc, safety strap and lock plates for damage or wear.

4) Slide column tube from steering shaft. Inspect steering shaft, support ring, and steering lock assembly for wear or damage. Replace components as necessary.

Reassembly

To reassemble, reverse disassembly procedure. Press flange tube and plastic bushings in by hand.

TIGHTENING SPECIFICATIONS

Application	Ft. Lbs. (N.m)
Clamp Bolt	22 (30)
Lock Plate Bolts	18 (24)
Lower Flange Tube Bolt	22 (30)
Socket Head Screw	14 (19)
Steering Wheel Retaining Nut	29 (39)

AUDI 5000S, 5000CS TURBO & 5000CS QUATTRO

DESCRIPTION

A 2-piece collapsible steering column assembly is used. The steering shaft uses an offset slip-joint that engages the flange tube.

REMOVAL & INSTALLATION

STEERING COLUMN

CAUTION: Applying excessive pressure, or causing impact to mainshaft during service may cause the column to collapse.

Removal

1) Disconnect battery ground cable. Loosen flange tube-to-pinion shaft clamp bolt. Remove steering wheel. Insert screwdriver through access hole at bottom of switch cover to loosen clamp.

2) Remove switch assembly. Disconnect ignition switch wiring. Place ignition switch in "ON" position. Center punch steering lock retaining shear bolts.

3) Drill out shear bolts. Remove switch. Unbolt mounting flange from under dash. Remove steering column and shaft as a unit.

Installation

1) Place column assembly in vehicle. Finger tighten steering lock shear bolts. Check operation of lock. Bolt mounting flange onto bracket. Connect ignition wiring.

Steering Columns

AUDI 5000S, 5000CS TURBO & 5000CS QUATTRO (Cont.)

Fig. 1: Exploded View of Audi 5000S Steering Column

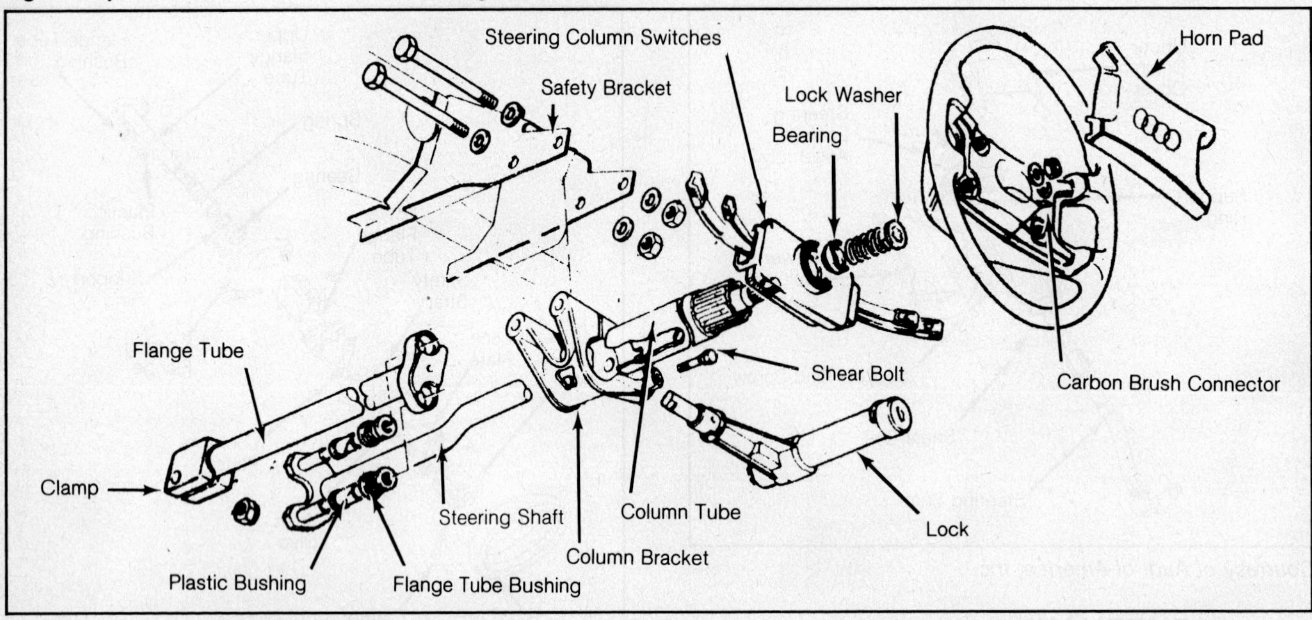

5000CS Quattro and 5000CS Turbo are similar. Courtesy of Audi of America, Inc.

2) Install flange tube over steering column pins. Press pinion shaft in place. Holding flange tube and shaft together with pliers, check length of shaft protruding from upper end of column.

3) Adjust by moving flange tube on pinion shaft until a distance of 2.56" (65 mm) is obtained. *See Fig. 2.* Tighten shear bolts until heads twist off. Install switch assembly flush with dashboard.

Fig. 2: Steering Shaft Installation Measurement

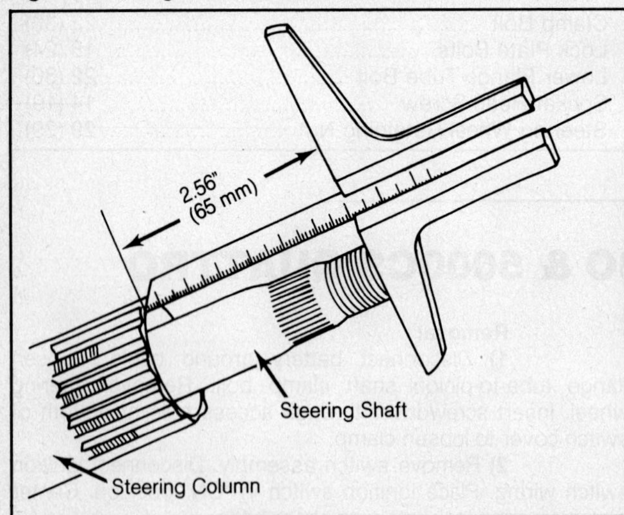

Courtesy of Audi of America, Inc.

4) With wheels in a straight-ahead position, install steering wheel. Tighten steering wheel retaining nut. Clearance between wheel and switch assembly should be .118" (3 mm). Adjust clearance (if necessary). Tighten flange tube-to-pinion shaft clamp bolt.

OVERHAUL

STEERING COLUMN

Disassembly

Remove retaining ring, spring and support ring. Pull steering shaft out of column from the bottom. Press bearing race from column (if necessary).

Reassembly

Examine bearing race. Replace bearing race if excessively worn. Slide steering shaft back into column tube. Replace support ring and spring. Use a new retaining ring to lock shaft in place.

TIGHTENING SPECIFICATIONS

Application	Ft. Lbs. (N.m)
Lock Plate Bolts	18 (24)
Lower Flange Tube Bolt	22 (30)
Socket Head Screw	14 (19)
Steering Wheel Retaining Nut	29 (39)
"U" Joint Clamp Bolt	22 (30)

BMW

DESCRIPTION

The steering column consists of a steering wheel, combination switch, upper and lower covers and an anti-theft steering column lock/ignition switch. The steering columns are telescopic.

REMOVAL & INSTALLATION

STEERING COLUMN

CAUTION: Applying excessive pressure, or causing impact to mainshaft during service, may cause the column to collapse.

Removal (735i)

1) Disconnect battery ground cable. Remove steering wheel and combination switch. Remove lower instrument panel cover and steering column housing. Disconnect harness connectors. Remove steering column harness wiring and ignition switch.

Fig. 1: Outer Tube & Clamp Bolt

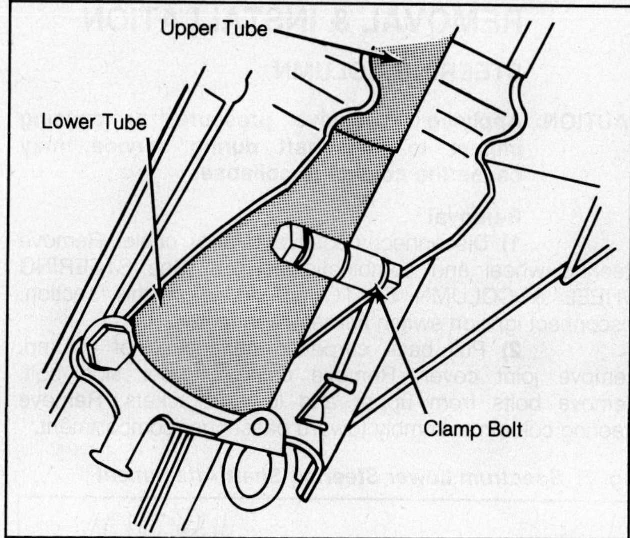

Courtesy of BMW of North America.

2) Remove lower shaft clamp bolt. Remove steering column assembly-to-dash and pedal bracket bolts. Remove upper shroud and shaft. Disconnect lower shaft from clamp in engine compartment. Pull shaft into passenger compartment.

3) Remove upper steering shaft by taking off collar, snap ring, washer, spring, and lock ring. Using screwdrivers, pry out upper bearing. Pry out lower bearing. Remove shaft. Remove snap ring, collar, ring and bearing.

Installation

To install, reverse removal procedure. Ensure wheels are in straight-ahead position. Ignition switch must be in "O" position when installed.

Removal (All Others)

1) Disconnect battery ground cable. Remove steering wheel. Remove lower half of column housing. Remove combination switch.

Fig. 2: Exploded View of Steering Column (735i)

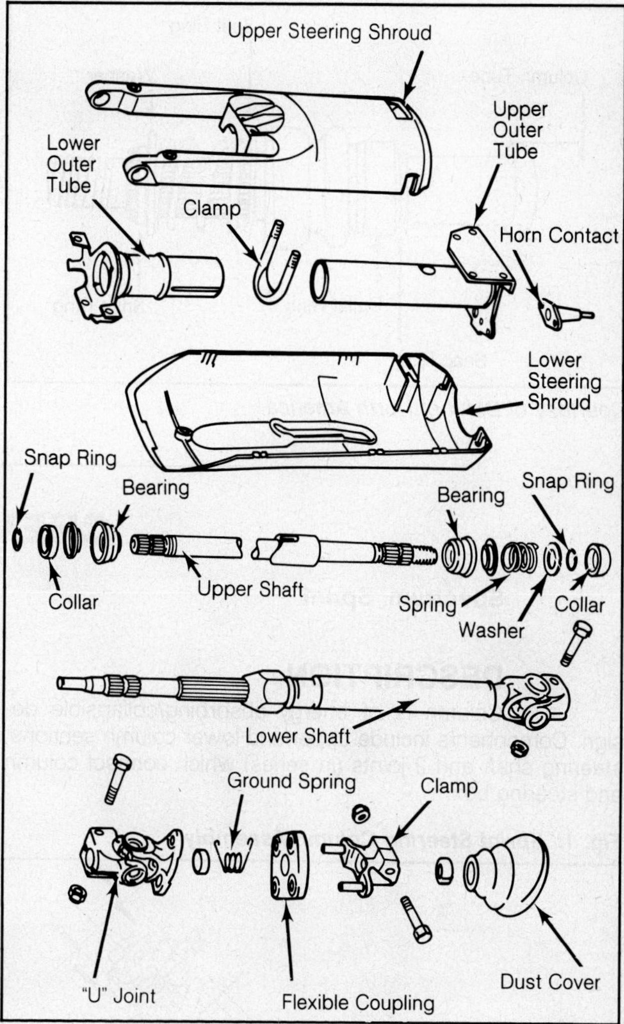

Courtesy of BMW of North America.

2) Remove steering shaft bearing holder at top of column. Loosen adjusting nut. Mark position of upper and lower shafts for reassembly reference.

3) Carefully pry steering shaft bearing from top of column. Pull shaft out from above. To remove upper outer tube, disconnect horn. Drill or chisel off switch plate shear screws.

4) Disconnect wiring harnesses. Loosen clamp bolt and support screws. Slide down lower outer tube. Lifting up outer casing, pull out outer tube.

Installation

1) To install, reverse removal procedure. Prior to tightening clamp bolt, ensure that distance from centerline of clamp bolt to end of upper outer tube is between 2.05-2.16" (52-55 mm).

2) Ensure that wheels are in a straight-ahead position. Aligning upper and lower steering shaft marks, tighten adjusting nut.

Steering Columns

BMW (Cont.)

Fig. 3: Upper Steering Shaft & Bearing (All Except 735i)

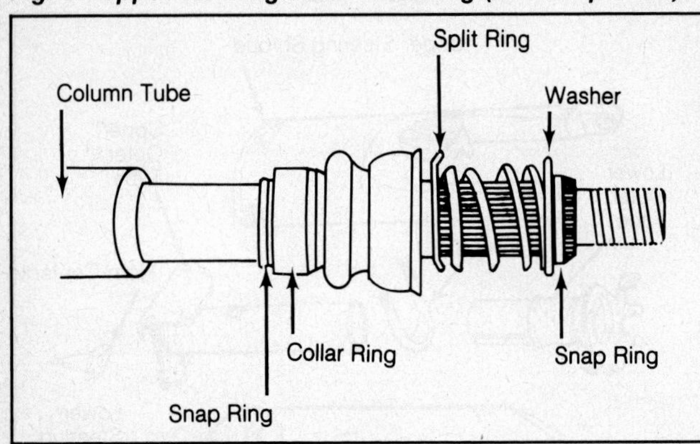

Courtesy of BMW of North America.

TIGHTENING SPECIFICATIONS

Application	Ft. Lbs. (N.m)
Casing Tube Clamp Bolt	
318i	12-14 (16-19)
325e, 524td, 528e, 535i & 635CSi	16-17 (22-23)
Column Bracket-to-Dashboard Bolts	16 (22)
Column-to-Housing Bolt	10 (14)
Lower-to-Upper Shaft Bolt (735i only)	18 (24)
Steering Wheel Nut	51-61 (70-85)
"U" Joint Clamp Bolt	18-20 (24-27)

CHEVROLET

Spectrum, Sprint

DESCRIPTION

Column is of energy absorbing/collapsible design. Components include upper and lower column sections, steering shaft and 2 joints (in series) which connect column and steering box.

Fig. 1: Sprint Steering Column Assembly

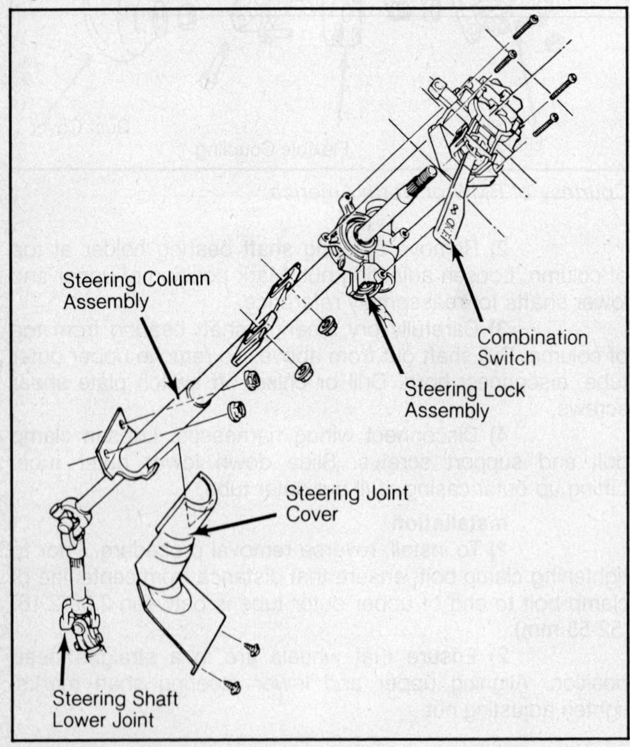

Spectrum is similar. Courtesy of General Motors Corp.

REMOVAL & INSTALLATION

STEERING COLUMN

CAUTION: Applying excessive pressure, or causing impact to mainshaft during service, may cause the column to collapse.

Removal

1) Disconnect negative battery cable. Remove steering wheel and combination switch. See STEERING WHEEL & COLUMN SWITCHES article in this section. Disconnect ignition switch harness connector.

2) Pull back carpeting near base of column. Remove joint cover. Remove column upper side bolt. Remove bolts from upper and lower brackets. Remove steering column assembly toward passenger compartment.

Fig. 2: Spectrum Lower Steering Shaft Attachment

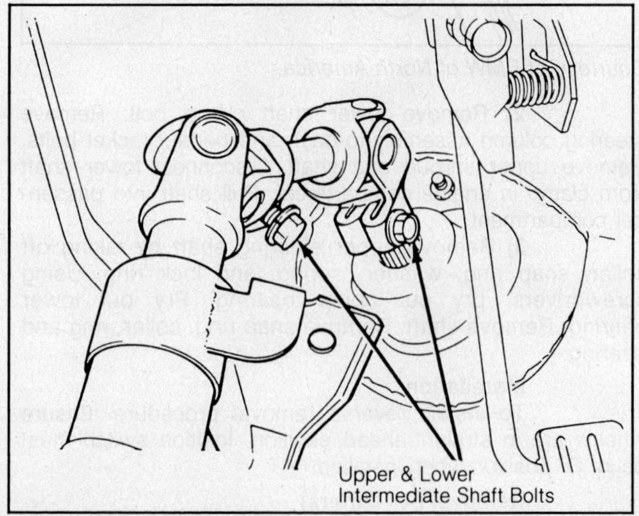

Sprint lower steering shaft attachment is similar. Courtesy of General Motors Corp.

CHEVROLET (Cont.)

Installation

1) Place wheels in a straight-ahead position. Align flat part of lower joint shaft "A" with bolt hole in upper side joint "B". Insert lower joint shaft into upper side joint. *See Fig. 3.*

Fig. 3: Installing Lower Joint

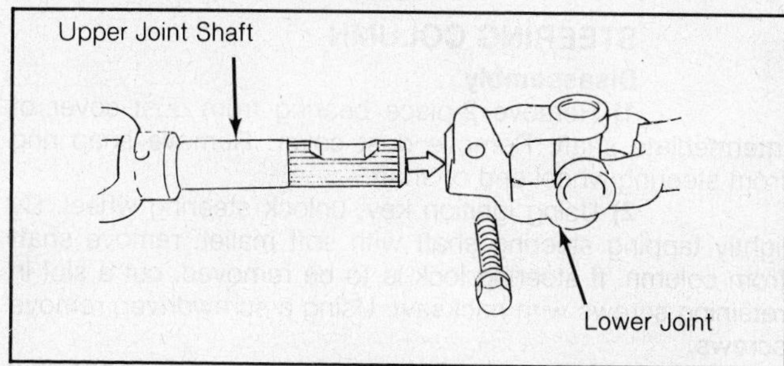

Courtesy of General Motors Corp.

2) Finger tighten joint side bolt. First tighten lower column bracket nuts and then upper column bracket nuts. Tighten joint side bolt.

3) Install combination switch and steering wheel. Connect ignition switch and combination switch harness connectors. Install joint cover.

OVERHAUL

No overhaul procedure is given by manufacturer. If steering column or shaft is defective, replace steering column as an assembly.

TIGHTENING SPECIFICATIONS

Application	Ft. Lbs. (N.m)
Upper Column Clamp Bolts	10 (14)
Shaft Joint Side Bolt	15-22 (20-30)
Steering Wheel Retaining Nut	19-29 (26-39)
	INCH Lbs. (N.m)
Lower Column Clamp Bolts	8-12 (11-17)

CHRYSLER MOTORS & MITSUBISHI (FWD) & HYUNDAI

Chrysler Motors: Colt, Colt Vista
Hyundai: Excel
Mitsubishi: Cordia, Galant, Mirage, Precis, Tredia

DESCRIPTION

The collapsible 2-piece steering system consists of an upper and lower shaft joined by a collapsible (bellows type) section. The bellows section contracts under impact, without affecting turning motion.

REMOVAL & INSTALLATION

STEERING COLUMN

CAUTION: Applying excessive pressure, or causing impact to mainshaft during service, may cause the column to collapse.

Removal

1) Remove steering wheel. Remove steering column cover. Disconnect combination switch connectors.

Fig. 1: Exploded View of Tilt & Non-Tilt Steering Columns

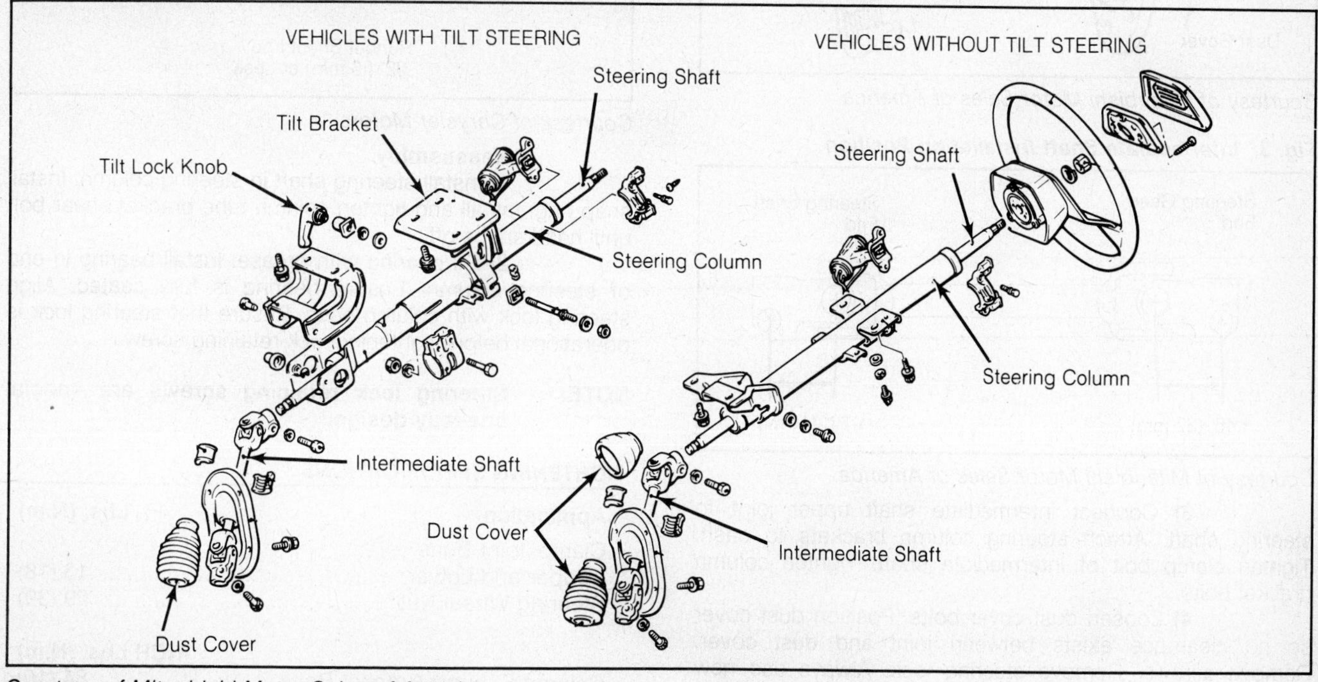

Courtesy of Mitsubishi Motor Sales of America.

Steering Columns

CHRYSLER MOTORS & MITSUBISHI (FWD) & HYUNDAI (Cont.)

Pull combination switch off steering shaft. See STEERING WHEEL & COLUMN SWITCHES article in this section.

NOTE: **When removing steering column as an assembly, leave all joining clamps intact.**

2) On vehicles without tilt steering, remove steering shaft upper coupling bolt. Remove steering column bracket-to-frame bolts. Disconnect steering shaft from coupling inside vehicle. Remove steering column assembly.

3) On vehicles with tilt steering, lower steering column assembly toward floor by removing lower bracket and tilt bracket bolts. Remove "U" joint-to-steering shaft retaining bolt. Remove steering column assembly.

4) Remove intermediate shaft lower coupling bolt at steering gear. Remove dust cover bolts. Remove intermediate shaft, with dust cover, toward inside of vehicle.

Installation

1) Install dust cover to intermediate shaft. Ensure bearing side of cover faces steering shaft side of intermediate shaft.

2) Apply grease to bearing and dust cover. Install 2-piece bearing into dust cover. *See Fig. 2.* Attach intermediate shaft lower joint to steering gear. *See Fig. 3.* Temporarily tighten dust cover bolts. Tighten lower joint clamp bolt.

Fig. 2: Dust Cover & Bearing Installation

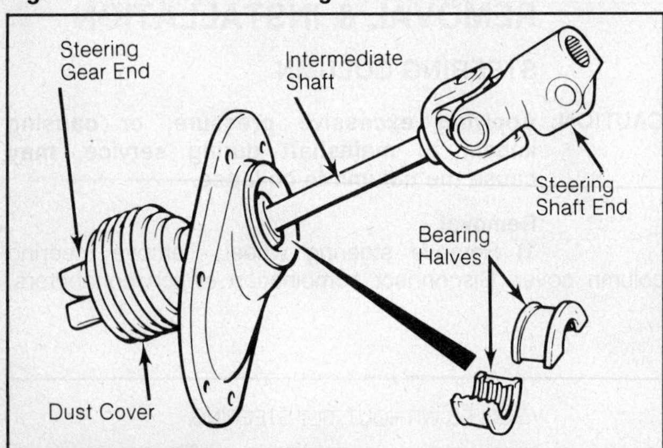

Courtesy of Mitsubishi Motor Sales of America.

Fig. 3: Intermediate Shaft Installation Position

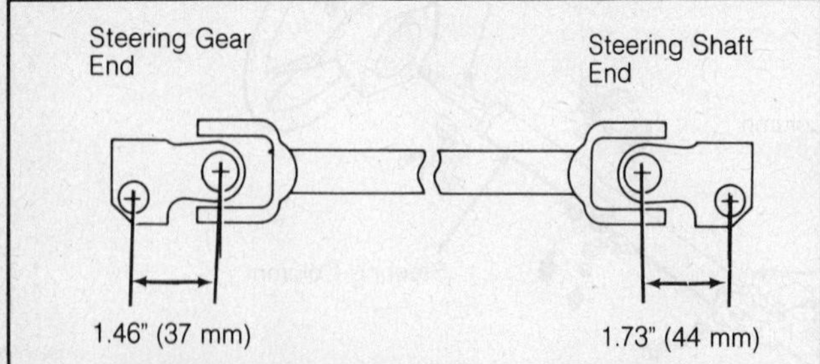

Courtesy of Mitsubishi Motor Sales of America.

3) Connect intermediate shaft upper joint to steering shaft. Attach steering column brackets to dash. Tighten clamp bolt of intermediate shaft. Tighten column bracket bolts.

4) Loosen dust cover bolts. Position dust cover so no clearance exists between joint and dust cover. Remove screws. Remove steering lock. Always use new screws and bracket when replacing steering lock.

5) If steering column bracket is removed, cut a slot in retaining bolt with hacksaw. Using a screwdriver, remove retaining bolt. Always use new bolts when installing bracket to steering column.

OVERHAUL

STEERING COLUMN

Disassembly

1) Remove 2-piece bearing from dust cover of intermediate shaft. Remove dust cover. Remove snap ring from steering wheel end of shaft.

2) Using ignition key, unlock steering wheel. By lightly tapping steering shaft with soft mallet, remove shaft from column. If steering lock is to be removed, cut a slot in retaining screws with hacksaw. Using a screwdriver, remove screws.

3) Remove steering lock. Always use new screws and bracket when replacing steering lock. If steering column bracket is removed, cut a slot in retaining bolt with hacksaw. Using a screwdriver, remove bolts. Always use new bolts to install bracket to steering column.

Inspection

1) Check steering shaft for runout. Runout should be .02" (.5 mm) or less. Check for worn or damaged bearing. On Excel and Precis, check steering shaft length.

2) Excel and Precis steering shaft length should be 23.17" (588.5 mm). If measurement is less than specification, replace steering shaft. *See Fig. 4.*

3) On intermediate shaft, check for play, noise or rough rotation in joints. Check dust cover for damage. Replace components as required.

Fig. 4: Steering Shaft Length & Runout

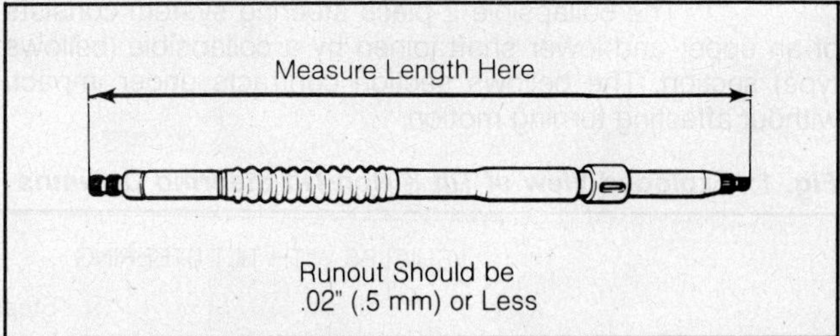

Courtesy of Chrysler Motors.

Reassembly

1) Install steering shaft in steering column. Install snap ring. Install and tighten column tube bracket shear bolt until head snaps off.

2) Fill bearing with grease. Install bearing in end of steering column. Ensure bearing is fully seated. Align steering lock with column boss. Ensure that steering lock is operational before tightening lock retaining screw.

NOTE: **Steering lock retaining screws are special one-way design.**

TIGHTENING SPECIFICATIONS

Application	Ft. Lbs. (N.m)
Clamp Joint Bolts	
Upper and Lower	13 (18)
Steering Wheel Nut	29 (39)
	INCH Lbs. (N.m)
Column Support Bracket Bolts	84 (10)

Steering Columns

CHRYSLER MOTORS & MITSUBISHI RWD

Conquest, Montero, Pickup, Raider, Ram-50, Starion

DESCRIPTION

The steering column consists of a 2-piece shaft joined by a collapsible section. This section contracts under impact without affecting turning. The upper column cover has slits, allowing it to collapse under impact.

REMOVAL & INSTALLATION

STEERING COLUMN

CAUTION: Applying excessive pressure, or causing impact to mainshaft during service may, cause the column to collapse.

Removal

1) Remove air cleaner. Unbolt steering shaft-to-gear box clamp bolt. If vehicle is equipped with A/C, this should be performed from underneath vehicle. See STEERING WHEEL & COLUMN SWITCHES article in this section.

2) On Montero, Raider, 4WD Ram-50 and 4WD Pickup, slide lower shaft boot up. Remove joint assembly-to-gear box clamp bolt. Disconnect joint assembly from steering shaft.

3) On all models, remove steering wheel. Loosen tilt lock lever or knob. Lower column. Remove column cover and floor dust cover.

4) Disconnect column switch connectors, leaving clamps intact. Pull out switch toward shaft end. On Conquest and Starion, remove column. On Pickup and Ram-50, remove tilt bracket. Remove column.

Installation

1) Insert steering shaft from inside vehicle. Connect joint assembly to steering shaft (and gear box on Montero, Raider, 4WD Ram-50 and 4WD Pickup).

2) Connect shaft to steering gear housing main shaft with bolt hole facing down. Tighten clamp bolt. Attach tilt bracket to pedal support member.

3) Apply sealer to dust cover bolt holes. Install dust cover to body. Install column switch. Route and secure wiring harness along column tube.

4) Reconnect switch connectors. Install column cover. Ensure wheels are straight and steering wheel is locked. Install steering wheel.

OVERHAUL

STEERING COLUMN

Disassembly

1) Remove clamp bolt, column tube and joint cover. Using a hacksaw, make a slit in steering lock bracket bolt and column support bolt. Remove lock and support.

2) Remove snap ring from upper shaft (upper and lower shaft snap rings on Montero, Raider, 4WD Ram-50 and 4WD Pickup). Remove shaft, with dust seal and bushing, from column tube.

3) On Conquest and Starion, slide joint cover from socket assembly. Remove retaining rings and joint pin collar. With shaft set upright, use a magnet to pull joint pins out from both sides of socket.

4) Separate column tube sections. On Pickup and Ram-50, remove yoke and rubber coupling from steering shaft lower end. Remove rubber band from dust seal.

5) Move seal to expose retainer caulking. Drill caulking. Using a drift, remove retainer. Remove rubber band, dust cover, dust seal and bushing from shaft.

NOTE: Do not remove pin from steering shaft. Do not disassemble socket.

6) On Montero, Raider, 4WD Ram-50 and 4WD Pickup, slide dust cover to lower shaft side. Separate lower and upper shafts. Remove pipe, spring and upper boot from upper shaft. Remove dust cover and lower boot from lower shaft.

Fig. 1: Exploded View of Pickup & Ram-50 Tilt Steering Column

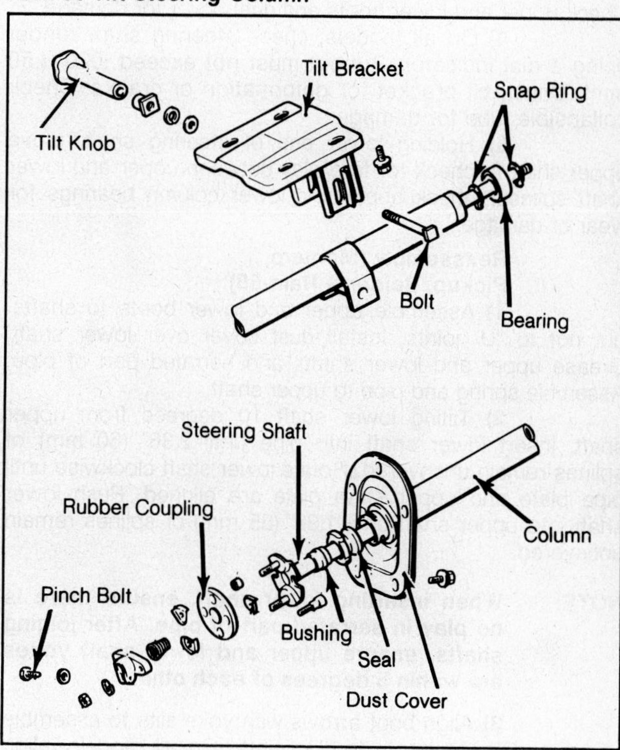

RWD is shown; 4WD is similar. Courtesy of Chrysler Motors.

Fig. 2: Exploded View of Conquest & Starion Tilt Steering Column

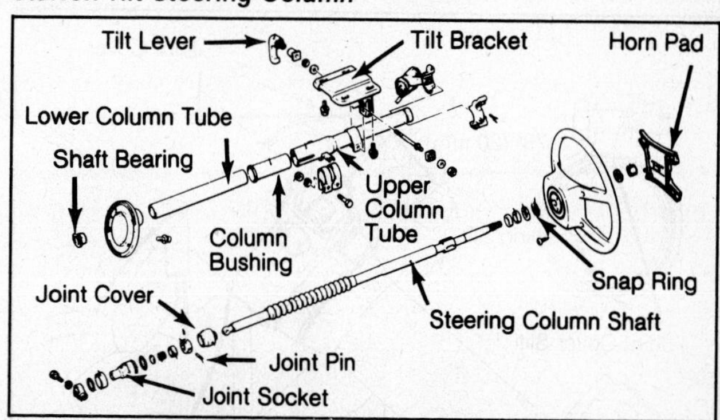

Courtesy of Chrysler Motors.

Inspection

1) Check joint cover for cracks or damage. Check shaft length. Measure length of entire shaft. See STEERING SHAFT LENGTH table.

CHRYSLER MOTORS & MITSUBISHI RWD (Cont.)

STEERING SHAFT LENGTH

Application	In. (mm)
Conquest & Starion	28.62 (727.0)
Montero & Raider	30.86-30.95 (784.0-786.0)
Pickup & Ram-50	
RWD	
Manual Steering	29.45-29.53 (748.0-750.0)
Power Steering	29.33-29.41 (745.0-747.0)
4WD,	30.86-30.95 (784.0-786.0)

2) On Pickup and Ram-50, check steering shaft-to-column bearing clearance. Clearance should be .0004-.0020" (.010-.050 mm). Check steering coupling for damage.

3) On Montero, Raider, 4WD Ram-50 and 4WD Pickup, check upper and lower "U" joints for play or sticking. Check upper and lower boots and dust cover for damage.

4) On all models, check steering shaft runout using a dial indicator. Runout must not exceed .020" (.50 mm). Check tilt bracket for deformation or cracks. Check collapsible tube for damage.

5) Holding lower end of steering shaft, move upper shaft to check for free play between upper and lower shaft splines. Check upper and lower column bearings for wear or damage.

Reassembly (Montero, Pickup, Raider & Ram-50)

1) Assemble upper and lower boots to shafts, but not to "U" joints. Install dust cover over lower shaft. Grease upper and lower shafts and serrated part of pipe. Assemble spring and pipe to upper shaft.

2) Tilting lower shaft 10 degrees from upper shaft, insert lower shaft into pipe until 2.36" (60 mm) of splines remain uncovered. Rotate lower shaft clockwise until pipe plate and upper shaft plate are aligned. Push lower shaft into upper shaft until 1.38" (35 mm) of splines remain uncovered.

NOTE: When inserting lower shaft, ensure there is no play in serrated part of pipe. After joining shafts, ensure upper and lower shaft yokes are within 5 degrees of each other.

3) Align boot arrows with yoke slits to assemble upper and lower boots to "U" joints. On all models, align column tube hole with wheel lock guide dowel. Install lock.

Fig. 3: Installing Joint Cover to Column (Montero, Pickup, Raider & Ram-50)

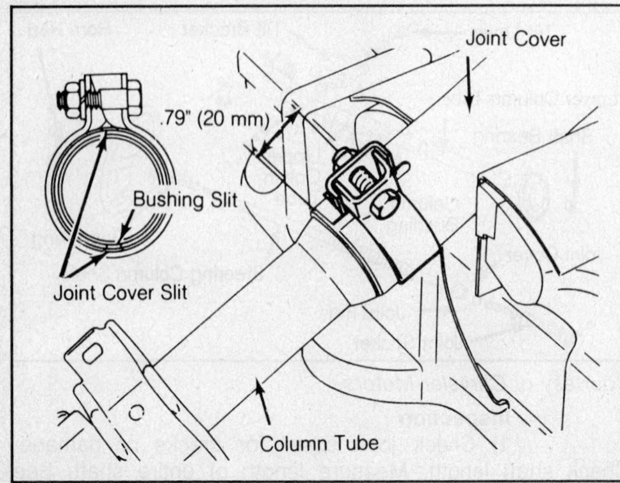

Courtesy of Chrysler Motors.

4) Using ignition key, check lock operation. Tighten lock bracket shear bolts until heads twist off.

5) Attach column support to tube. Tighten support shear bolts until heads twist off. Install joint cover to column, making sure clamp bolt faces up. *See Fig. 3.* Tighten clamp bolt.

6) Apply grease to bearing roller surfaces of column tube and inside dust cover grommet. Install steering shaft bushing, dust seal, dust cover, rubber band and retainer in order.

7) Install springs and sliders on steering shaft. Fill inside of socket with grease. Aligning punch marks, install retainer on socket. Using a punch, stake retainer at two points.

8) Fill inside of dust cover with grease. Install dust cover over socket. Install rubber band on dust cover. Apply grease to horn ground spring seats. Attach coupling and yoke to steering shaft.

Reassembly (Conquest & Starion)

1) Apply grease to inside of steering shaft bearing. Insert shaft into bearing. Apply adhesive to bearing outer contact surface. Apply grease to inside of upper bearing. Install steering shaft into column tube.

2) Install flanged bearing (with flange facing up) onto steering shaft lower end. After aligning flange bearing hole with hole in shaft lower end, insert joint pin. Fill socket with grease.

3) Insert seat, spring and spring seat into socket. Insert steering shaft lower end into socket. With the shaft upright, apply light downward pressure to insert joint pins by hand. Attach joint pin collar and retaining rings.

4) Install joint cover. Insert tilt lever screw into tilt lever until dimension "A" is .9-1.2" (23-26 mm). *See Fig. 4.* Mount tilt bracket onto column tube.

Fig. 4: Tilt Lever Screw Measurement

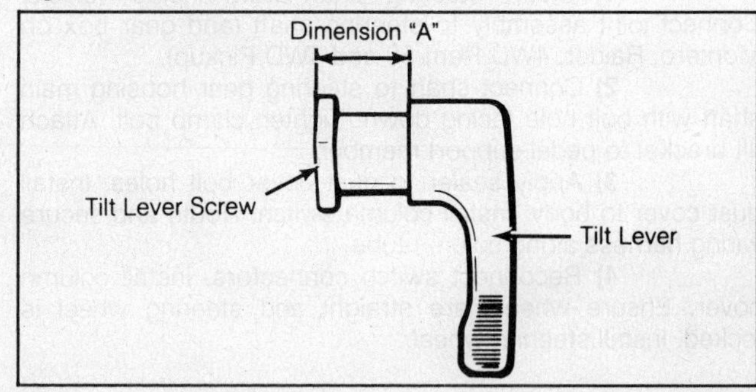

Courtesy of Chrysler Motors.

5) Insert tilt bolt. Tilt lever must be locked between vertical position and 65 degrees forward of vertical and unlocked between vertical position and 45 degrees behind of vertical. *See Fig. 5.*

6) Attach block and washer to tilt bolt. Tighten tilt nut. Check for proper lever operation. Ensure column is locked when lever is in proper position. *See Fig. 5.* Weld nut and tilt bolt together.

7) Attach column support to tube. Tighten support shear bolts until heads twist off. Install joint cover to column. Ensure clamp bolt faces up. Tighten clamp bolt.

Steering Columns

CHRYSLER MOTORS & MITSUBISHI RWD (Cont.)

Fig. 5: Installing Tilt Bracket Lever (Conquest & Starion)

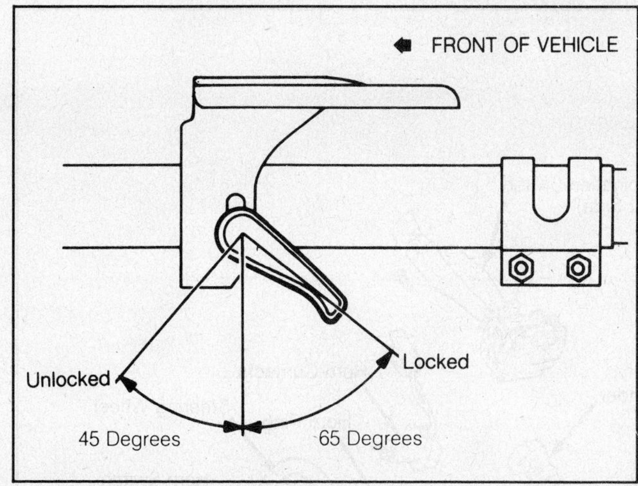

Courtesy of Chrysler Motors.

TIGHTENING SPECIFICATIONS

Application	Ft. Lbs. (N.m)
RWD	
Steering Shaft Clamp Bolt	
Conquest & Starion Only	15-18 (20-25)
Steering Wheel Retaining Nut	29 (39)
4WD	
"U" Joint-to-Gear Box Bolt	24 (33)
Steering Shaft-to-Joint Bolt	24 (33)

FORD MOTOR CO.

Festiva, Merkur XR4Ti, Tracer

DESCRIPTION

The steering column assembly consists of a shaft tube, upper and lower bearings, mounting brackets, ignition lock and 2 switch assemblies.

REMOVAL & INSTALLATION

CAUTION: Applying excessive pressure, or causing impact to mainshaft during service, may cause the column to collapse.

Removal (Festiva & Tracer)

1) Disconnect battery ground cable. Place wheels in a straight-ahead position. Remove steering wheel, upper and lower column covers, combination switch, ignition switch and harness connectors. See STEERING WHEEL & COLUMN SWITCHES article in this section.

2) Remove instrument panel brace and air duct from below steering column. Remove 2 steering column upper mounting bracket-to-instrument panel crossmember nuts.

3) Lower the upper end of column as necessary to to gain access to intermediate shaft upper "U" joint. Mark steering shaft and upper "U" joint for reassembly reference.

4) Remove "U" joint attaching bolt. Loosen 2 steering column hinge bracket-to-clutch/brake pedal support nuts. Remove steering column with upper "U" joint by pulling toward passenger compartment.

Fig. 1: Festiva Steering Column Assembly

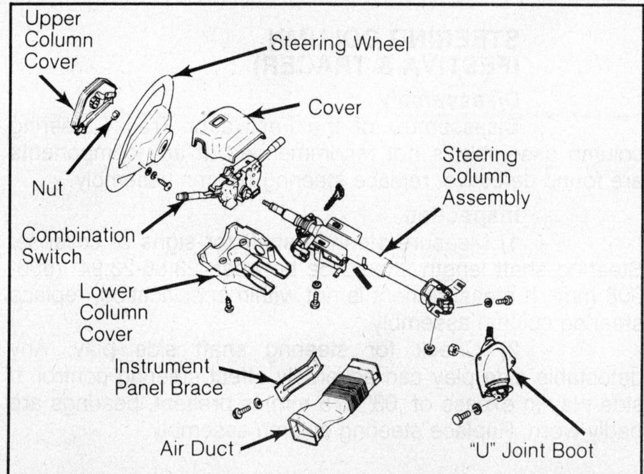

Tracer is similar. Courtesy of Ford Motor Co.

Installation

1) Aligning marks made during removal, install column with intermediate shaft upper "U" joint over intermediate shaft. Install, but do not tighten, "U" joint clamp bolt.

2) Install and tighten hinge bracket nuts. Install shim clips on column upper bracket flanges (if removed). Position upper end of steering column to instrument panel mounting studs.

3) Install upper bracket retaining nuts. Turn steering wheel lock-to-lock several times to align "U" joint splines. Tighten "U" joint clamp bolt.

4) Install air duct and instrument panel brace. Install harness connectors, ignition switch, combination switch, upper and lower column covers and steering wheel.

Removal (Merkur XR4Ti)

1) Disconnect battery ground cable. Raise vehicle. Loosen steering shaft "U" joint clamp bolt. Center steering wheel with wheels in straight-ahead position.

2) Remove steering column upper and lower covers. Remove hood release bracket attaching screw. Remove lower instrument panel. Disconnect and label wiring harness connectors.

3) Remove steering column mounting bracket nuts and washers. Pull upward on steering wheel to lift mounting bracket off mounting studs and to disengage steering shaft from "U" joint clamp. Remove steering column assembly.

Steering Columns

FORD MOTOR CO. (Cont.)

Fig. 2: Merkur XR4Ti Steering Column Assembly

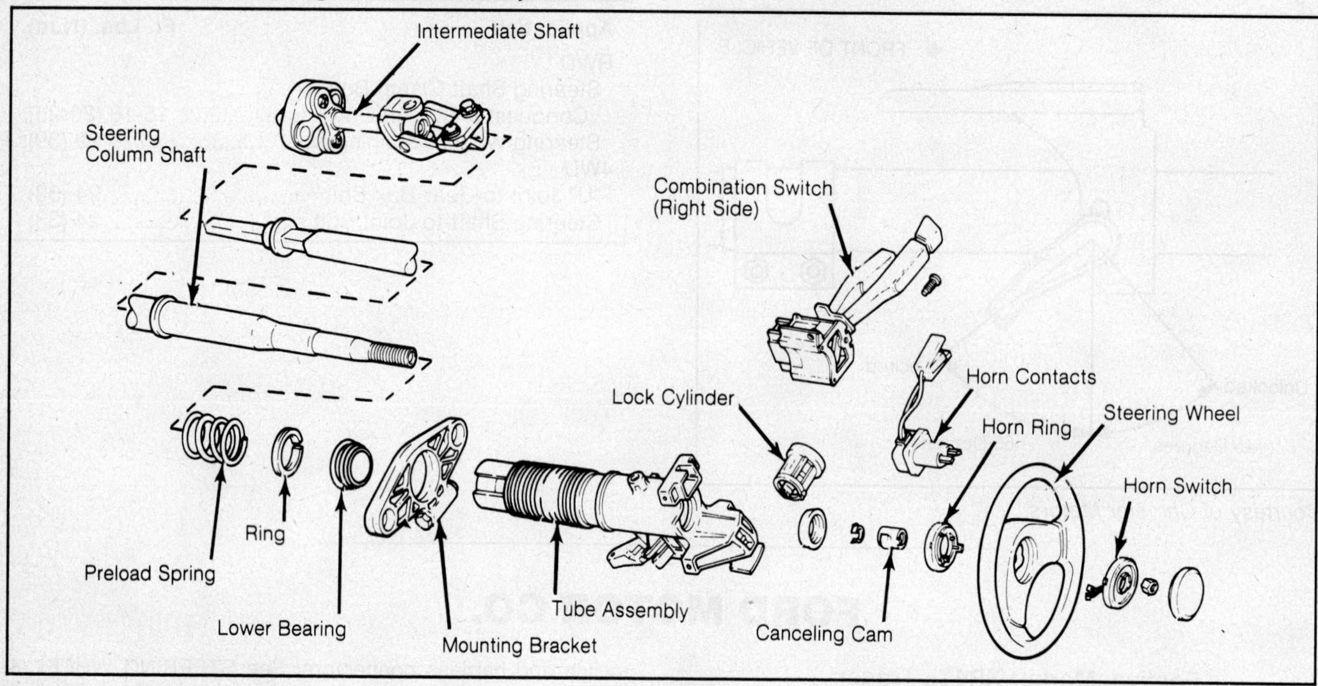

Courtesy of Ford Motor Co.

Installation

1) Install steering column assembly. Connect all wiring harness connectors. Install steering column mounting bracket washers and nuts. Tighten attaching nuts to 13-16 ft. lbs. (18-22 N.m).

2) Position lower instrument panels. Position hood release bracket. Install attaching screw. Install steering column lower and upper trim panels. Raise vehicle. Tighten steering shaft "U" joint clamp bolt to 14-19 ft. lbs. (20-25 N.m). Lower vehicle and connect battery ground cable.

OVERHAUL

TUBE ASSEMBLY (MERKUR XR4Ti)

Disassembly

1) Using a drift and mallet, remove tube assembly lower bearing. Remove mounting bracket clamp bolt. Remove screws mounting combination switches.

2) Remove left and right side combination switch. Using a screwdriver, pry horn contacts from horn contact retaining bracket. Using a screwdriver, pry upper bearing and tolerance ring from tube assembly.

3) Remove ignition switch screws. Remove ignition switch. Using key, Turn lock cylinder to "I" position. Depress lock cylinder spring clip. Remove lock cylinder.

Reassembly

1) Insert key into lock cylinder. Turn key cylinder to "I" position. Install lock cylinder into tube assembly. Using a socket and mallet, install upper bearing and tolerance ring.

2) Install horn contacts, ignition switch and combination switches. Install mounting bracket. Do not tighten mounting bracket clamp bolt. Using a socket and mallet, install lower bearing.

TILT MECHANISM (FESTIVA)

Disassembly

1) Compressing lock tabs, remove wiring harness routing clip. Remove lock lever screw and lock lever. Remove adjusting nut and clamp bolt.

2) Separate upper mounting bracket from steering column. Remove ignition switch. Using locking pliers, remove steering lock shear bolts. Remove steering lock.

Reassembly

1) Position upper mounting bracket on steering column. Install tilt lock bolt from left side. Ensure the lands under bolt head engage with the slot in the bracket.

2) Install tilt lever adjusting nut. Tighten to 88-132 INCH lbs. (10-15 N.m). Position lock lever on adjusting nut with lever against the stop.

3) Install and tighten lock lever screw to 13-19 ft. lbs. (18-26 N.m). Check that lock lever engages and disengages positively. To complete reassembly, reverse disassembly procedure.

STEERING COLUMN (FESTIVA & TRACER)

Disassembly

Disassembly of the Festiva or Tracer steering column assembly is not recommended. If any components are found defective, replace steering column assembly.

Inspection

1) Measure steering shaft for signs of collapse. Steering shaft length should be between 23.86-23.94" (606-608 mm). If measurement is not within specification, replace steering column assembly.

2) Check for steering shaft side play. Any detectable side play can adversely affect steering control. If side play in excess of .03" (.75 mm) is present, bearings are badly worn. Replace steering column assembly.

FORD MOTOR CO. (Cont.)

Fig. 3: Exploded View of Festiva Tilt Mechanism

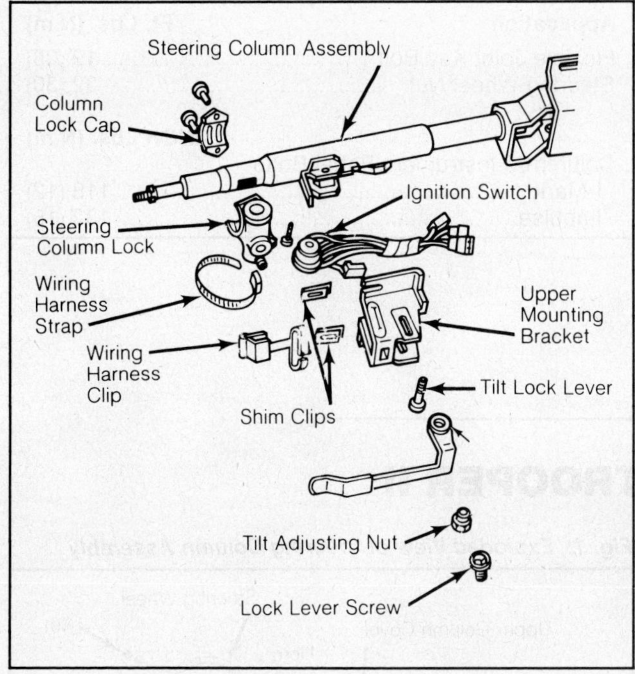

Courtesy of Ford Motor Co.

TIGHTENING SPECIFICATIONS

Application	Ft. Lbs. (N.m)
Festiva	
Lock Lever Screw	13-19 (18-26)
Merkur XR4Ti	
Steering Column	
Mounting Bracket Bolts	13-16 (18-22)
Steering Coupling Clamp Bolt	18-22 (24-30)
Steering Gear-To-	
Crossmember Bolts	11 (15)
Steering Wheel-To-Column Shaft	33-40 (45-54)
Tie Rod-To-Front Spindle Nut	15-23 (20-31)
"U" Joint Clamp Bolt	14-19 (19-26)
Tracer	[1]

[1] – No tightening specifications available for Tracer.

ISUZU I-MARK & IMPULSE

DESCRIPTION

Steering columns incorporate plastic shear pins in the steering shafts. Upon frontal impact, the plastic pins will shear off, allowing the column to collapse.

REMOVAL & INSTALLATION

STEERING COLUMN

CAUTION: Applying excessive pressure, or causing impact to mainshaft during service, may cause the column to collapse.

Fig. 1: Exploded View of Steering Column Components

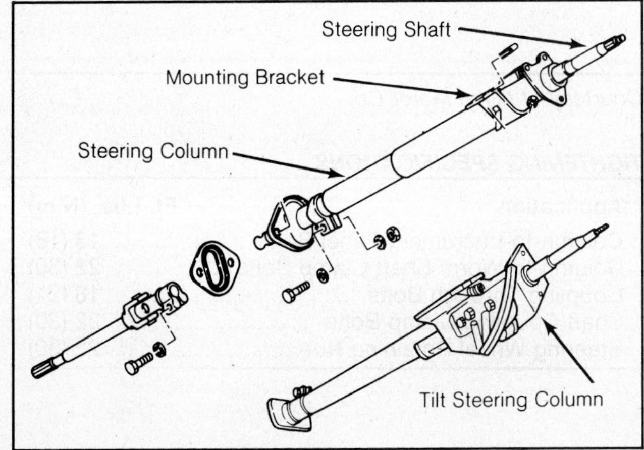

Courtesy of Isuzu Motor Co.

Removal

1) Disconnect battery ground cable. Remove steering wheel and combination switch. See STEERING WHEEL & COLUMN SWITCHES article in this section.

2) Remove flexible joint key bolt. Remove column-to-dashboard nuts. Remove column-to-instrument panel bolts. Remove steering column assembly from vehicle.

Installation

To install, reverse removal procedure. DO NOT overtighten column-to-instrument panel nuts.

OVERHAUL

STEERING COLUMN

Disassembly

Remove snap ring, washer and retaining bolts from column flange. Remove ignition lock cylinder housing. Using screwdriver, pry out lower column rubber bushing. Remove steering shaft from column.

Inspection

Measure steering shaft length. Measurement should be 30.6" (777.1 mm). Measure lower half of steering column. *See Fig. 2.* Measurement should be 8.27" (210 mm).

Reassembly

To reassemble, reverse disassembly procedure.

Steering Columns

ISUZU I-MARK & IMPULSE (Cont.)

Fig. 2: Steering Column Length Measurement Points

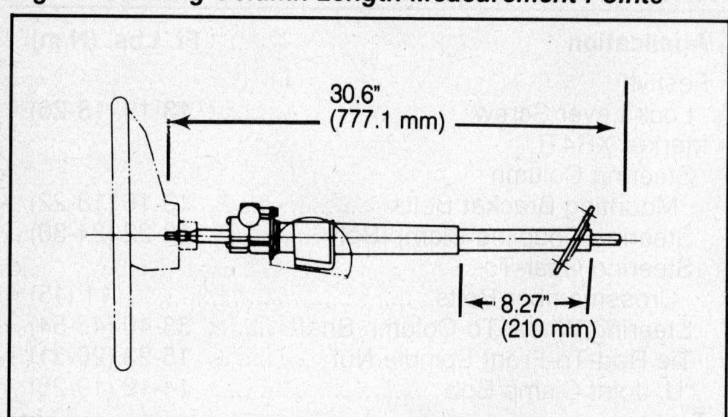

Courtesy of Isuzu Motor Co.

TIGHTENING SPECIFICATIONS

Application	Ft. Lbs. (N.m)
Flexible Joint Key Bolt	19 (26)
Steering Wheel Nut	22 (30)
	INCH Lbs. (N.m)
Column-to-Instrument Panel Bolts	
I-Mark	118 (12)
Impulse	132 (15)

ISUZU P'UP & TROOPER II

DESCRIPTION

Steering columns incorporate plastic shear pins in the steering shafts. Upon frontal impact, the plastic pins will shear off, allowing the column to collapse.

REMOVAL & INSTALLATION

CAUTION: Applying excessive pressure, or causing impact to mainshaft during service, may cause the column to collapse.

STEERING COLUMN

Removal

1) Disconnect battery ground cable. Remove horn cover and spring. Remove steering column shrouding and hazard flasher warning light switch. Remove combination switch. Remove steering wheel. See STEERING WHEEL & COLUMN SWITCHES article in this section.

2) From inside engine compartment, remove upper coupling clamp pinch bolt from steering shaft flexible coupling.

3) Mark steering shaft and coupling clamp for installation. Disconnect combination and ignition switch wiring at harness connector.

4) Remove steering column-to-instrument panel bolts. Separate rubber coupling from shaft. Pull steering column toward passenger compartment to remove.

Installation

To install, reverse removal procedure. Align reference mark on shaft to mark on coupling clamp.

FLEXIBLE COUPLING

Removal

1) Raise and support vehicle. Remove coupling through bolts and lock nuts. Remove pinch bolts on upper and lower flanges of coupling.

2) Remove column bracket retaining bolts. Pull steering column rearward about 2". Remove upper coupling flange, coupling and lower coupling flange.

Installation

Install lower coupling flange. Install coupling and upper coupling flange. To complete installation, reverse removal procedure.

Fig. 1: Exploded View of Steering Column Assembly

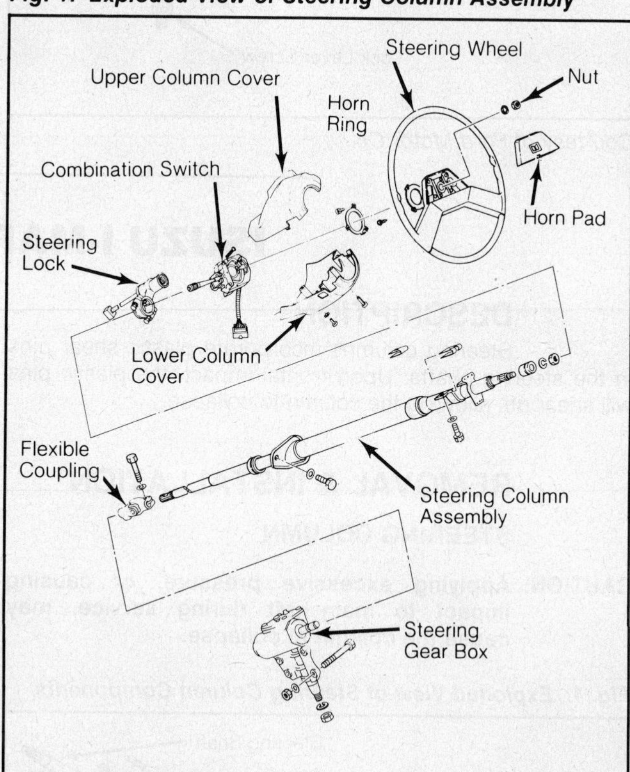

Courtesy of Isuzu Motor Co.

TIGHTENING SPECIFICATIONS

Application	Ft. Lbs. (N.m)
Column-to-Instrument Panel Bolts	13 (18)
Column-to-Worm Shaft Clamp Bolts	22 (30)
Coupling Through Bolts	18 (24)
Shaft Coupling Clamp Bolts	22 (30)
Steering Wheel Retaining Nut	22 (30)

Steering Columns

JAGUAR XJS & XJ6 III

DESCRIPTION

Upper and lower steering columns are collapsible. Nylon pins, which shear on impact, allow the shaft and columns to collapse. The upper and lower columns consist of 2 sliding shafts each. The shaft is supported by 2 prelubricated roller bearings.

REMOVAL & INSTALLATION

UPPER STEERING COLUMN

CAUTION: Applying excessive pressure, or causing impact to mainshaft during service, may cause the column to collapse.

Removal

1) Disconnect battery ground cable. Remove steering wheel. Remove speedometer casing. Unscrew knurled nut from bracket behind speedometer. Disconnect speedometer drive cable.

2) Remove trip odometer reset control cable by unscrewing knurled nut. Pressing instrument bezel, rotate speedometer clockwise until it releases. Remove headlight warning and instrument panel lights.

3) Pressing instrument bezel, rotate tachometer counterclockwise until it releases. Disconnect electrical connectors. Remove ground lead. Remove instrument light holder.

4) Remove trim panel from below the upper steering column. Disconnect switch connectors (socket and pin connectors). Detach horn contact at upper column.

5) Unscrew self-locking nut. Remove upper "U" joint-to-lower steering column pinch bolt. Loosen set screws retaining lower end of upper column.

6) Reaching through instrument openings, remove upper column retaining nuts. Remove washers, shims and nuts. Support column. Remove set screws. Remove steering column assembly from vehicle.

Inspection

1) Check column for straightness. Replace column if bent or if length is incorrect. End-to-end length without "U" joint should be 21.56-21.70" (547.7-551.1 mm).

2) Check "U" joint axial clearance. Clearance should be .375" (9.5 mm). Increase clearance by moving upper "U" joint along lower column.

Installation

Install "U" joint and/or adjusting clamp (if removed). To complete installation, reverse removal procedure. Check self-canceling operation of turn signal. Ensure that steering wheel spokes are horizontal and wheels are in a straight-ahead position.

LOWER STEERING COLUMN

Removal

1) Raise and support vehicle. Remove lower "U" joint-to-pinion shaft pinch bolt. Remove pinion shaft heat shield. Lower vehicle. Remove parcel shelf.

2) Remove both pinch bolts from upper "U" joint. Unscrew lower column retaining screws. Pull lower column from upper "U" joint. Raise vehicle. Remove lower "U" joint from pinion shaft. Remove lower steering column.

Fig. 1: Disconnecting Lower Steering Column from Pinion Shaft

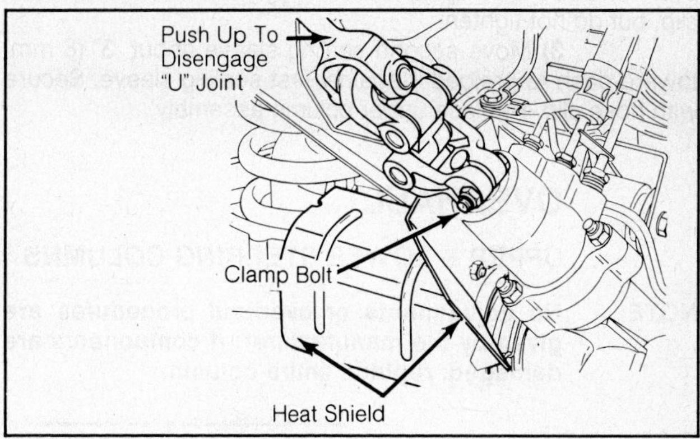

Courtesy of Jaguar Cars Ltd.

Installation

To install, reverse removal procedure. Check that a .375" (9.5 mm) clearance gap is present between lower "U" joint sections.

STEERING COLUMN ADJUSTING CLAMP

Removal

1) Remove steering wheel. Pull impact rubber from steering wheel shaft. Remove screws from beneath adjusting clamp (lock nut). Remove retaining plate.

2) Unscrew collet adapter. Remove adapter from shaft. Remove circlip from within upper side of adjuster. Remove adjuster (lock nut) and stop button. Slide split collet from shaft. *See Fig. 2.*

Fig. 2: Exploded View of Steering Column Adjusting Clamp

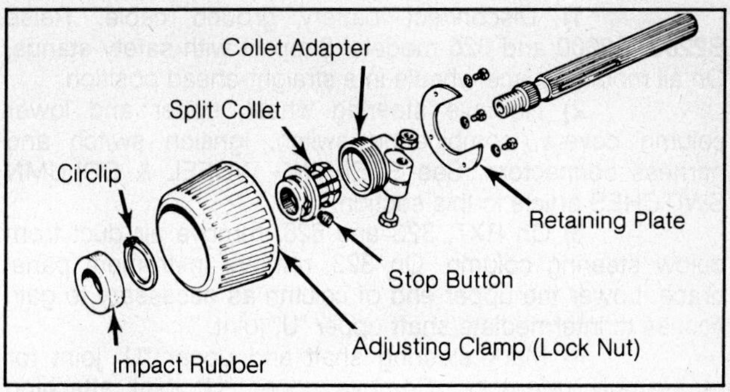

Courtesy of Jaguar Cars Ltd.

Installation

Clean parts thoroughly. Using a file, remove burrs. Lightly lubricate all enclosed metal components. To install, reverse removal procedure.

STEERING COLUMN LOWER SEAL

Removal

Remove upper steering column. Loosen hose clip attaching upper sealing sleeve to lower column. Remove clip and sleeve. Remove seal retainer-to-instrument panel screws. Slide seal, retainer and sealing sleeve up and off lower column.

Installation

1) Slide the sealing sleeve, seal and retainer over lower column end as an assembly. Insert and tighten retaining set screws.

Steering Columns

JAGUAR XJS & XJ6 III (Cont.)

2) Slide second sealing sleeve, flanged end first, over lower column up to first sealing sleeve. Position hose clip, but do not tighten.

3) Move second sealing sleeve about .3" (8 mm) toward dash to preload it against first sealing sleeve. Secure with hose clip. Replace upper column assembly.

OVERHAUL

UPPER & LOWER STEERING COLUMNS

NOTE: No adjustments or overhaul procedures are given by the manufacturer. If components are damaged, replace entire column.

TIGHTENING SPECIFICATIONS

Application	Ft. Lbs. (N.m)
Column-to-Bracket Bolts	14-18 (19-24)
Steering Wheel Nut	25-32 (34-44)
"U" Joint Bolts	14-18 (19-24)

MAZDA

DESCRIPTION

Columns use plastic shear pins to absorb collision impact. Steering shaft is connected to steering gear by a "U" joint.

REMOVAL & INSTALLATION

STEERING COLUMN

CAUTION: Applying excessive pressure, or causing impact to mainshaft during service, may cause the column to collapse.

Removal

1) Disconnect battery ground cable. Raise B2200, B2600 and 626 models. Support with safety stands. On all models, place wheels in a straight-ahead position.

2) Remove steering wheel, upper and lower column covers, combination switch, ignition switch and harness connectors. See STEERING WHEEL & COLUMN SWITCHES article in this section.

3) On RX7, 323 and 626, remove air duct from below steering column. On 323, remove instrument panel brace. Lower the upper end of column as necessary to gain access to intermediate shaft upper "U" joint.

4) Mark steering shaft and upper "U" joint for reassembly reference. Remove upper "U" joint attaching bolt. Loosen 2 steering column hinge bracket-to-clutch-/brake pedal support nuts.

5) Loosen 2 hinge bracket-to-clutch/brake pedal nuts. Remove steering column with upper "U" joint by pulling toward passenger compartment.

6) On all vehicles, remove steering column upper mounting bracket-to-instrument panel crossmember bolts. Remove column lower mounting brackets.

7) Mark steering shaft and upper "U" joint for reassembly reference. Remove upper "U" joint attaching bolt. Pull steering column assembly toward passenger compartment to remove.

Installation

1) Aligning marks made during removal, install column with intermediate shaft upper "U" joint over intermediate shaft. Install, but do not tighten, "U" joint clamp bolt.

2) On 323, install and tighten hinge bracket nuts. On all models, install shim clips on column upper bracket flanges (if removed). Position upper end of steering column to instrument panel.

3) Install upper bracket retaining nuts or bolts. Turn steering wheel lock-to-lock several times to align "U" joint splines. Tighten "U" joint clamp bolt.

4) On all except 323, install and tighten lower column mounting bracket bolts. On 323, install instrument panel brace.

5) On all models, install air duct, harness connectors and ignition switch. On 626, install angle sensor. Install combination switch, upper and lower column covers and steering wheel.

Fig. 1: RX7 Steering Column Assembly

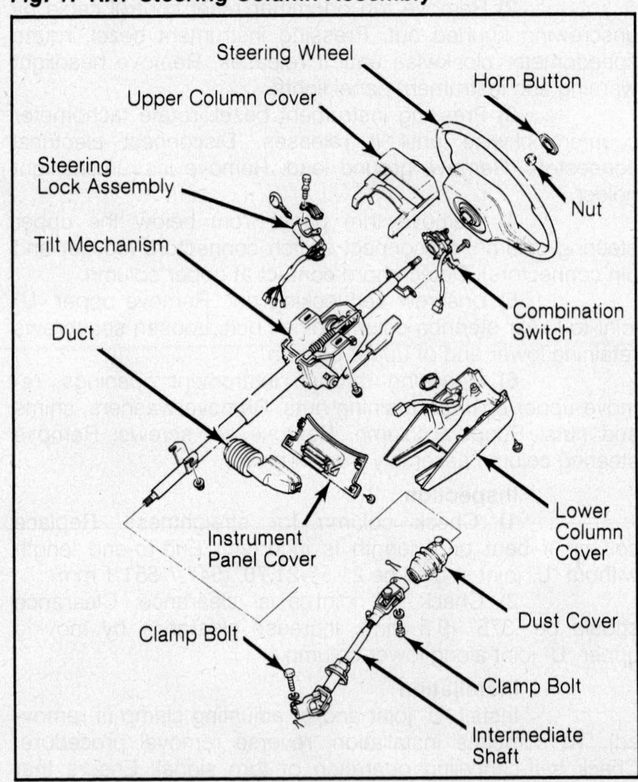

323 and 626 steering column assemblies are similar. Courtesy of Mazda Motors Corp.

MAZDA (Cont.)

Fig. 2: B2200 & B2600 Steering Column Assembly

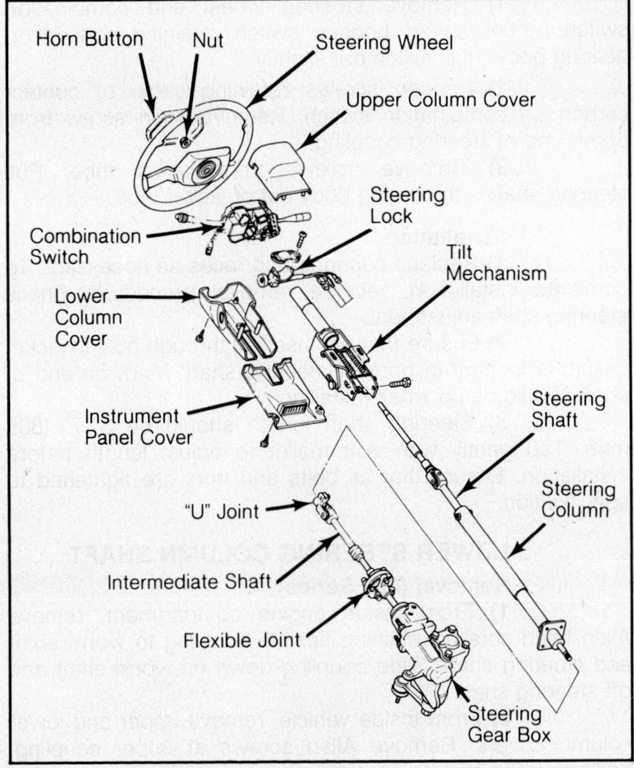

Courtesy of Mazda Motors Corp.

OVERHAUL

STEERING COLUMN

Disassembly (All Except 323)

Remove wiring and switches. Clamp column in vise. Turn steering shaft to remove. Using a chisel, make a groove in the steering lock shear screws. Using a screwdriver, remove shear screws. Remove steering lock.

Inspection & Reassembly

1) Check all components for damage or wear. Check steering shaft for bends, damage or sheared plastic pins. On 626, check for proper shaft length of 23.86-23.94" (606-608 mm). *See Fig. 3.*

Fig. 3: Measuring Steering Shaft

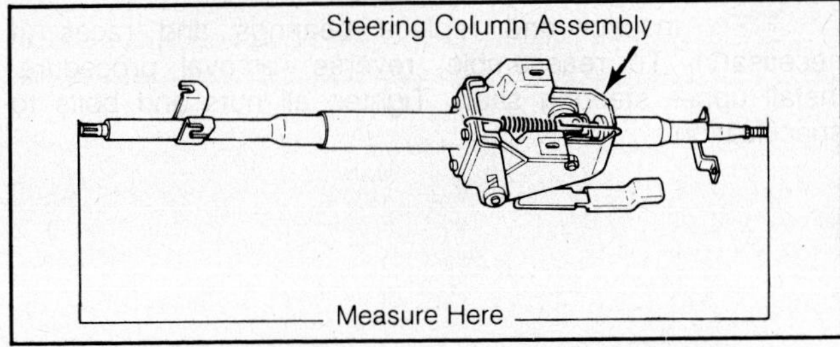

Courtesy of Mazda Motors Corp.

2) On RX7, check for proper shaft length of 32.08-32.13" (814.9-816.1 mm). On B2200 and B2600, check for proper shaft length of 32.68-32.89" (830.0-835.6 mm). Check bearings for excessive play. Replace parts as necessary.

Reassembly

To reassemble, reverse disassembly procedure. Grease steering shaft, bushings and bearings. Always use new shear screws.

Disassembly (323)

Disassembly of the 323 steering column assembly is not recommended. If any components are found defective, replace steering column assembly.

Inspection

1) Measure steering shaft for signs of collapse. Steering shaft length should be between 23.86-23.94" (606-608 mm). *See Fig. 3.* If measurement is not within specification, replace steering column assembly.

2) Check for steering shaft side play. Any detectable side play can adversely affect steering control. If side play in excess of .03" (.75 mm) is present, bearings are badly worn. Replace steering column assembly.

TILT MECHANISM

Disassembly

1) While compressing lock tabs, remove wiring harness routing clip. Remove lock lever screw and lock lever. Remove adjusting nut and clamp bolt.

2) Separate upper mounting bracket from steering column. Remove ignition switch. Using locking pliers, remove steering lock shear bolts. Remove steering lock.

Reassembly

1) Position upper mounting bracket on steering column. Install tilt lock bolt from left side. Ensure the lands under bolt head engage with slot in mounting bracket.

2) Install and tighten tilt lever adjusting nut. Position lock lever on adjusting nut with lever against stop.

3) Install and tighten tilt lever bolt. Check that tilt lever engages and disengages positively. To complete reassembly, reverse disassembly procedure.

TIGHTENING SPECIFICATIONS

Application	Ft. Lbs. (N.m)
Column Bracket Bolts	12-17 (16-23)
Steering Shaft "U" Joint Bolts	
Upper	13-20 (18-28)
Lower	24-28 (30-38)
Steering Wheel Nut	
B2200 & B2600	29-36 (39-50)
All Others	[1]
Tilt Lever Bolt	
B2200 & B2600	12-17 (16-23)
RX7, 323 & 626	13-19 (18-26)
	INCH Lbs. (N.m)
Tilt Lever Adjusting Nut	
323	88-132 (10-15)
All Others	[1]

[1] – Information not available from manufacturer.

Steering Columns

MERCEDES-BENZ

DESCRIPTION

The steering column assembly includes an impact absorbing steering wheel, upper and lower column shafts and flexible coupling. All models are available with the Supplemental Restraint System (SRS). An airbag and an Emergency Tensioning Retractor (ETR) system increases the safety of the occupants.

A corrugated tube, and a modified steering box is used in the 190 Series. The steering shaft is connected by a coupling to the steering box, which allows easier removal and installation of the steering box.

REMOVAL & INSTALLATION

STEERING COLUMN

Removal (190 Series)

1) Disconnect battery ground cable. Remove upper and lower covers from instrument panel. Disconnect all harness connectors. Remove steering wheel. See STEERING WHEEL & COLUMN SWITCHES article in this section.

CAUTION: Use extreme care when working on, or around steering wheel. If SRS is not properly disconnected, air bag could deploy.

2) Remove instrument cluster by pulling outward as far as possible and loosening tachometer, temperature and oil pressure connections.

3) Remove steering lock. Disconnect wiring connectors. Remove Allen head screw from flexible coupling Remove all nuts and screws retaining casing and column to dashboard. Remove steering column housing.

Fig. 1: 190 Series Steering Column

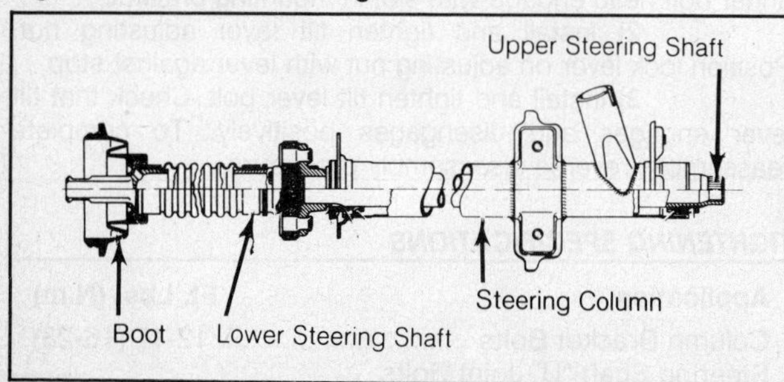

Courtesy of Mercedes-Benz of North America.

Installation

1) Always use new steering wheel Allen screws when installing steering wheel. Check that lower tube is not bent or distorted.

2) Use caution when installing jacket tube to prevent damage to shaft. To complete installation, reverse removal procedure.

Removal (All Others)

1) Remove steering wheel and combination switch rubber cover. Loosen switch retaining screws on bearing body. Pull switch out slightly.

2) Loosen screws retaining cable of contact carbon on combination switch. Remove Allen screw from upper end of steering coupling.

3) Remove screws from jacket tube. Pull steering shaft with bearing body out of jacket tube.

Installation

1) Replace bearings and races as necessary. To complete installation, reverse removal procedure. Check steering shaft adjustment.

2) Ensure that pin inserted through hole in jacket casing is located in bore of steering shaft. Mark on end of shaft should be up when installing.

3) Steering shaft length should be 31.7" (805 mm). Tap gently with soft mallet to adjust length before installation. Ensure that all bolts and nuts are tightened to specification.

LOWER STEERING COLUMN SHAFT

Removal (300 Series)

1) From inside engine compartment, remove Allen head screws retaining flexible coupling to worm shaft and steering shaft. Slide coupling down on worm shaft and off steering shaft.

2) From inside vehicle, remove upper and lower column covers. Remove Allen screws at upper coupling. Slide coupling and lower shaft off upper shaft.

Installation

Lubricate inner lips of bellows seal. Place wheels in straight-ahead position. Notch on upper shaft must face upward. To complete installation, reverse removal procedure. Tighten all nuts and bolts to specification.

DISASSEMBLY

UPPER STEERING COLUMN SHAFT

Disassembly

1) With column out of vehicle, remove combination switch. Remove jacket tube casing and spacing ring from shaft.

2) Remove gripper ring, compression spring, supporting ring and ball bearing from shaft. Using a soft mallet, knock steering shaft upward out of jacket tube.

Reassembly

Inspect and replace bearings and races (if necessary). To reassemble, reverse removal procedure. Install upper steering shaft. Tighten all nuts and bolts to specification.

MERCEDES-BENZ (Cont.)

Fig. 2: Sectional View of Mercedes-Benz Steering Column & Steering Shaft

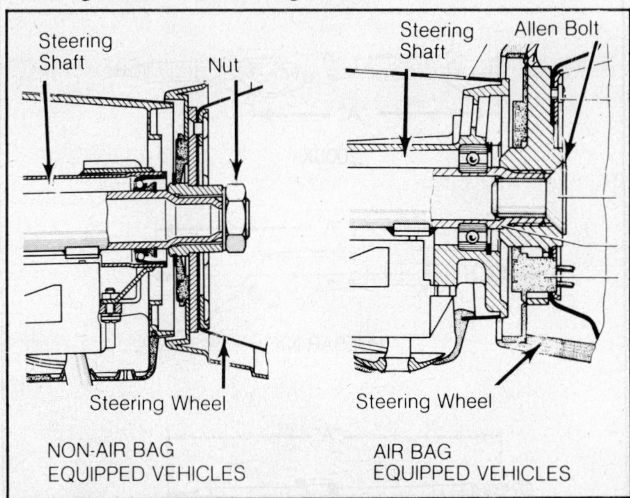

Courtesy of Mercedes-Benz of North America.

TIGHTENING SPECIFICATIONS

Application	Ft. Lbs. (N.m)
Flexible Coupling (Allen Bolt)	18 (24)
Steering Wheel	
Allen Bolt	59 (80)
Nut	37 (50)
	INCH Lbs. (N.m)
Column Support Bracket Bolts	84 (10)

NISSAN

DESCRIPTION

Steering columns are designed to be collapsible upon impact. A flexible coupling and 2 "U" joints connect steering column and gear assembly. Maxima, Pickup and Pathfinder models with tilt steering wheels also use a flexible coupling.

Fig. 1: Pulsar NX, Sentra, Stanza & 200SX Lower Steering Column Assembly

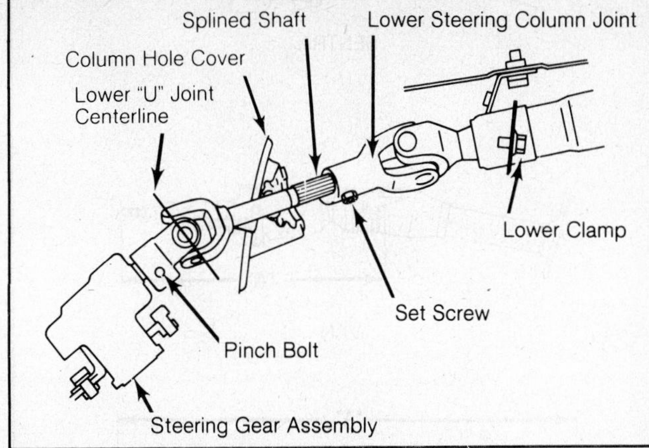

Courtesy of Nissan Motor Co., U.S.A.

REMOVAL & INSTALLATION

STEERING COLUMN

CAUTION: Applying excessive pressure, or causing impact to mainshaft during service, may cause the column to collapse.

Removal

1) Disconnect negative battery cable. Place wheels in a straight-ahead position. Remove horn pad, cruise control (if equipped) and steering wheel nut. Using a puller, remove steering wheel. See STEERING WHEEL & COLUMN SWITCHES article in this section.

2) Remove lower "U" joint clamp bolt. Remove upper and lower column covers. Remove wiring harness connectors, canceling cam, combination switch and ignition switch. Remove heater ducts, lower column bracket bolts and floor plate/dust boot bolts or nuts.

3) Mark pinion shaft to "U" joint for reassembly reference. Remove upper column bracket bolts. Carefully pull steering column toward passenger compartment to remove.

Installation

1) Place wheels in a straight-ahead position. Ensure pinion punch mark faces rear of vehicle. Insert steering column assembly through floor opening from passenger compartment side.

2) Aligning marks made during removal, connect lower "U" joint to pinion. Position steering column upper bracket, lower bracket (if equipped) and floor bracket/dust boot.

3) Finger tighten upper column bracket bolts to support column. Install and tighten lower "U" joint bolt. Tighten upper and lower column bracket bolts. See TIGHTENING SPECIFICATIONS table at end of article.

4) Install combination switch, canceling cam and ignition switch. Connect wiring harness connectors. Install heater ducts, and upper and lower column covers. Install steering wheel.

5) Tighten steering wheel nut. Install horn. Install cruise control (if equipped). Check operation of horn, ignition switch and combination switch. Turn wheel lock-to-lock to check centering and turning ease.

NISSAN (Cont.)

OVERHAUL

STEERING COLUMN

Disassembly

1) Remove snap ring from upper end of steering column. Slide steering shaft from lower end of steering column. Remove grease seals and bearings.

2) DO NOT attempt to disassemble tilt mechanism (if equipped). If damage to tilt mechanism or collapsible section in suspected, replace steering column assembly.

Inspection

Check bearings for smooth operation. If necessary, lubricate bearings with grease. Check jacket tube for deformation. Replace parts as required. If vehicle has been in a collision, check column dimension "A" in STEERING COLUMN DIMENSIONS table. *See Fig. 2 or 3.*

Fig. 2: Steering Column Measuring Points

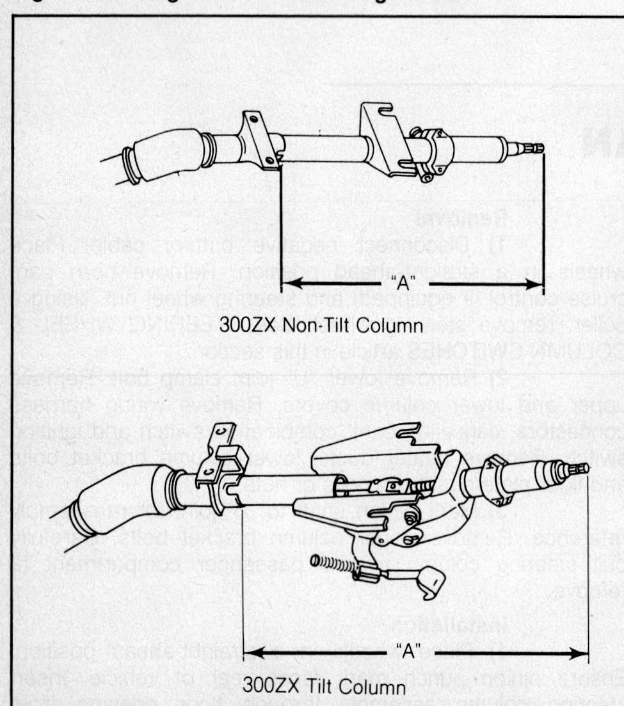

Courtesy of Nissan Motor Co., U.S.A.

STEERING COLUMN DIMENSIONS

Models	[1] Dimension "A" In. (mm)
Maxima	12.07-12.15 (306.6-308.6)
Pickup & Pathfinder	
2WD	36.38-36.44 (924-925.6)
4WD	34.89-34.95 (886.1-887.7)
Pulsar NX	23.37-23.43 (593.6-595.2)
Sentra	21.05-21.15 (534.7-537.3)
Stanza	20.41-20.48 (518.5-520.1)
Van	9.11-9.19 (231.5-233.5)
200SX	20.32-20.39 (516.2-517.8)
300ZX	18.85-18.91 (478.7-480.3)

[1] – See Fig. 2 or 3 for measuring points.

Fig. 3: Steering Column Measuring Points (Cont.)

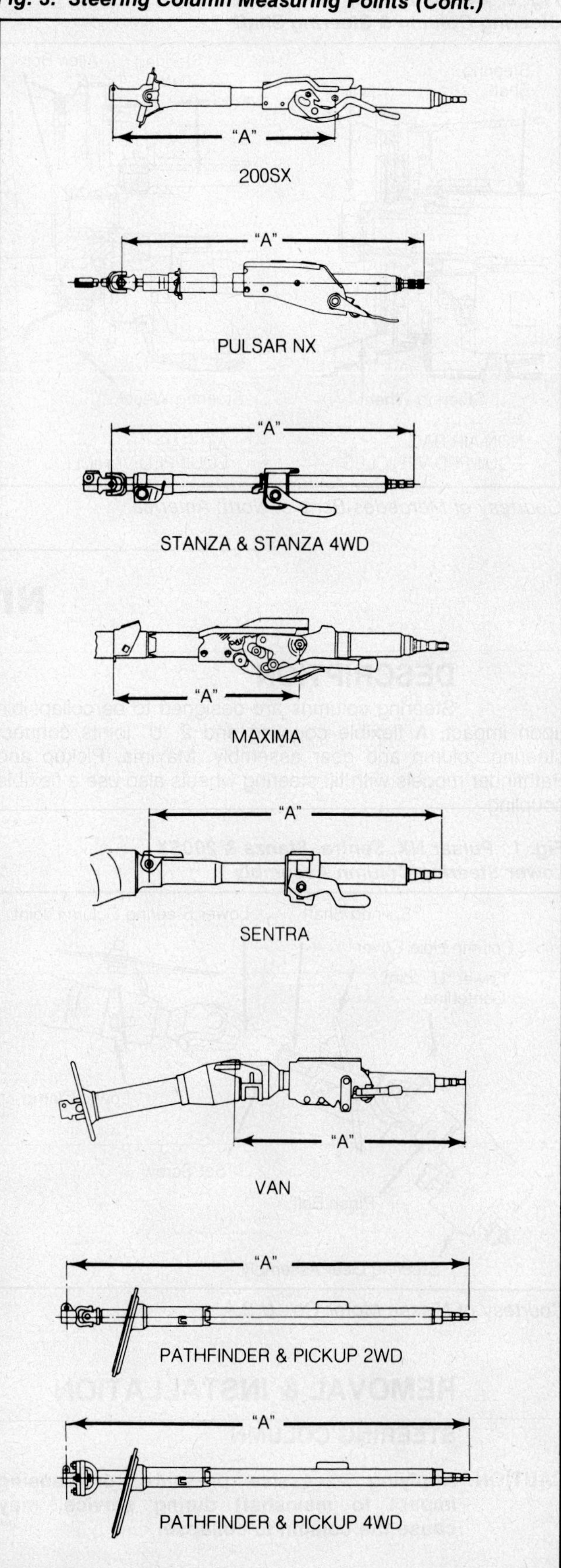

Courtesy of Nissan Motor Co., U.S.A.

NISSAN (Cont.)

Fig. 4: Exploded View of Pathfinder & Pickup Steering Column Assemblies

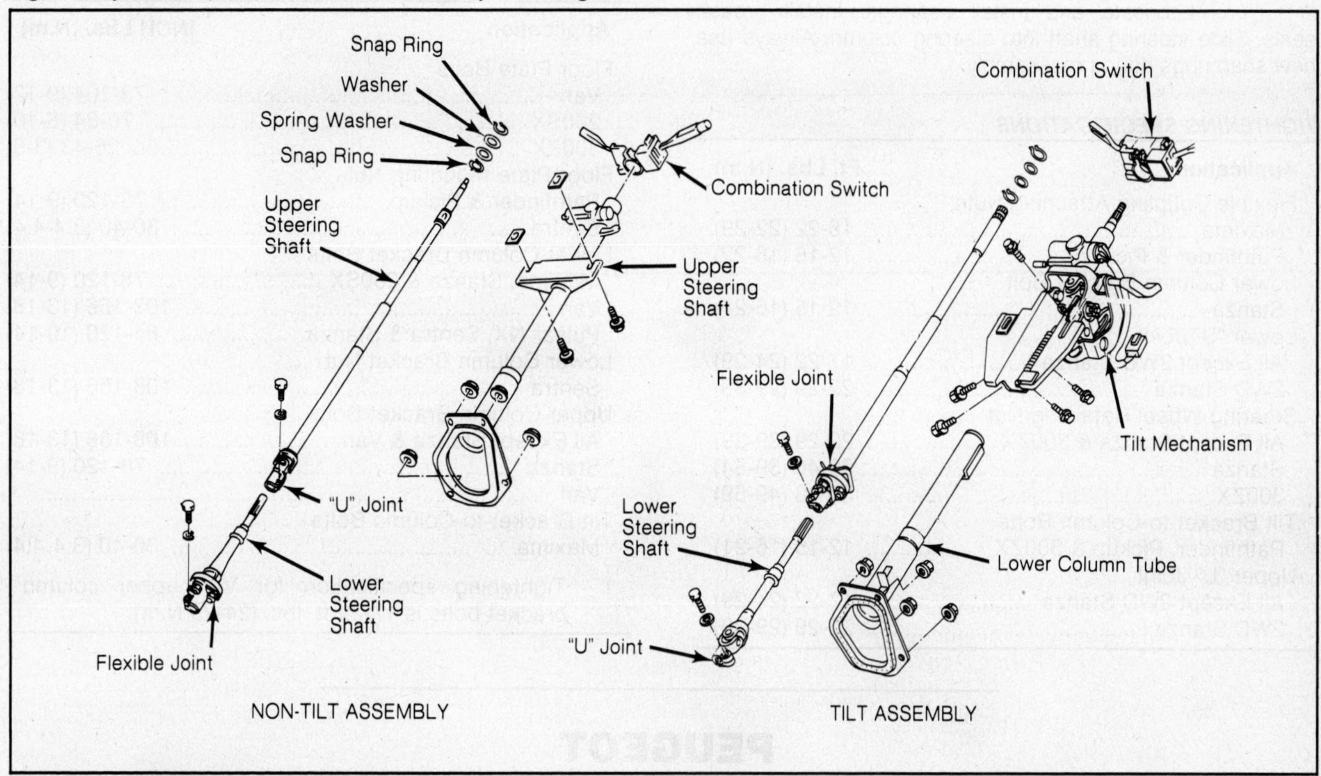

Courtesy of Nissan Motor Co., U.S.A.

Fig. 5: Exploded View of 300ZX Non-Tilt Steering Column Assembly

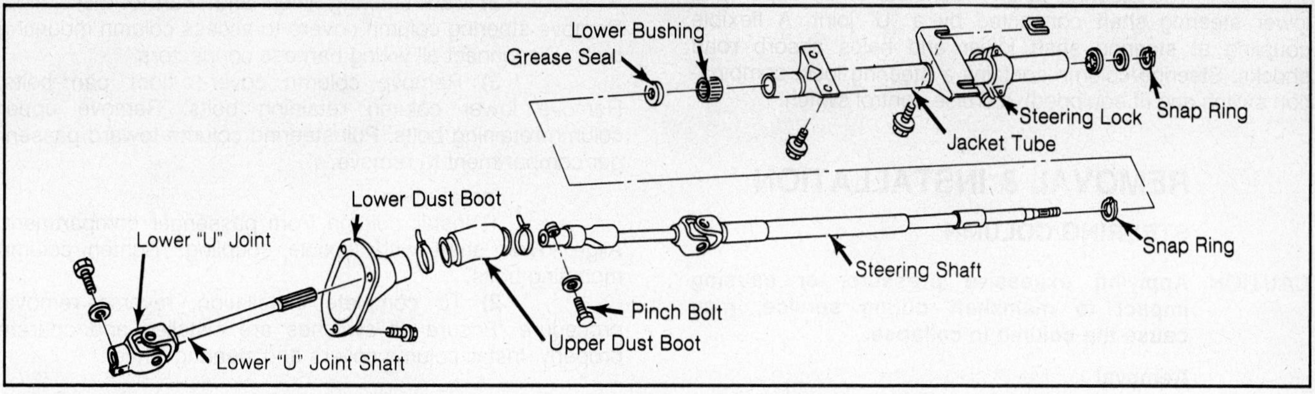

300ZX is shown. Other passenger vehicles are similar. Courtesy of Nissan Motor Co., U.S.A.

Fig. 6: Exploded View of 300ZX Tilt Steering Column Assembly

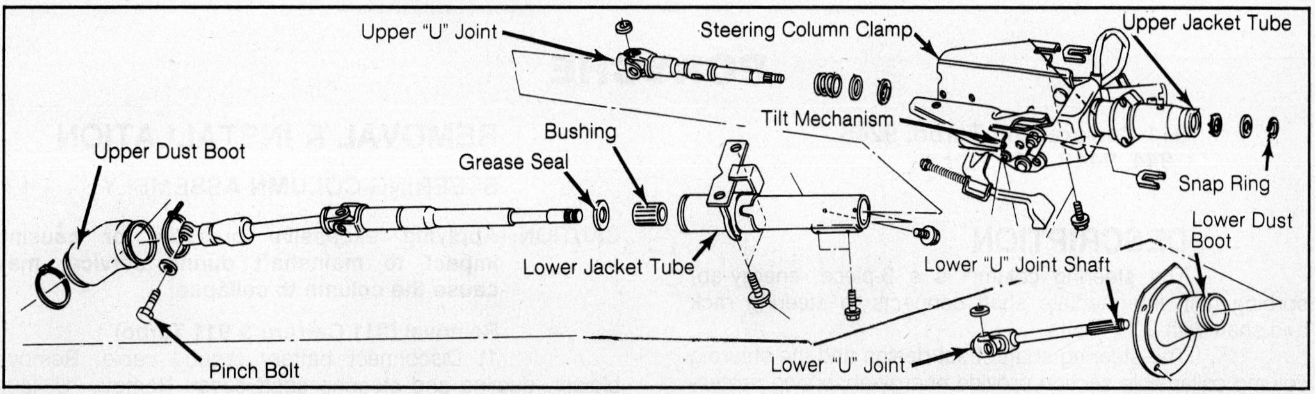

300ZX is shown. Other passsenger vehicles are similar. Courtesy of Nissan Motor Co., U.S.A.

Steering Columns

NISSAN (Cont.)

Reassembly

Lubricate and install bearings. Install grease seals. Slide steering shaft into steering column. Always use new snap rings during reassembly.

TIGHTENING SPECIFICATIONS

Application	Ft. Lbs. (N.m)
Flexible Coupling Attaching Nuts	
Maxima	16-22 (22-29)
Pathfinder & Pickup	12-16 (16-22)
Lower Column Bracket Bolt	
Stanza	12-15 (16-21)
Lower "U" Joint	
All Except 2WD Stanza	17-22 (24-29)
2WD Stanza	22-29 (29-39)
Steering Wheel Retaining Nut	
All Except Stanza & 300ZX	22-29 (29-39)
Stanza	29-40 (39-54)
300ZX	36-43 (49-59)
Tilt Bracket-to-Column Bolts	
Pathfinder, Pickup & 300ZX	12-15 (16-21)
Upper "U" Joint	
All Except 2WD Stanza	17-22 (24-29)
2WD Stanza	22-29 (29-39)

TIGHTENING SPECIFICATIONS (Cont.)

Application	INCH Lbs. (N.m)
Floor Plate Bolts	
Van	78-104 (9-12)
200SX	70-84 (8-10)
300ZX	26-43 (3-5)
Floor Plate Mounting Nuts	
Pathfinder & Pickup	78-120 (9-14)
Sentra	30-40 (3.4-4.4)
Lower Column Bracket Bolts	
Maxima, Stanza & 200SX	78-120 (9-14)
Van	108-156 (13-18)
Pulsar NX, Sentra & Stanza	84-120 (10-14)
Lower Column Bracket Nut	
Sentra	108-156 (13-18)
Upper Column Bracket Bolts	
All Except Stanza & Van	108-156 (13-18)
Stanza	78-120 (9-14)
Van	[1]
Tilt Bracket-to-Column Bolts	
Maxima	30-40 (3.4-4.4)

[1] – Tightening specification for Van upper column bracket bolts is 17-22 ft. lbs. (24-29 N.m).

PEUGEOT

DESCRIPTION

The steering column consists of an upper and lower steering shaft connected by a "U" joint. A flexible coupling at steering shaft lower end helps absorb road shocks. Steering column contains a steering lock, combination switch and (if equipped), a cruise control switch.

REMOVAL & INSTALLATION

STEERING COLUMN

CAUTION: Applying excessive pressure, or causing impact to mainshaft during service, may cause the column to collapse.

Removal

1) Place wheels in straight-ahead position. Disconnect battery ground cable. Remove bolt connecting steering shaft flexible coupling to gear box. Remove horn pad, steering wheel nut and steering wheel.

2) Mark steering wheel and shaft for installation. Remove steering column covers to access column mounting bolts. Disconnect all wiring harness connectors.

3) Remove column cover-to-floor pan bolts. Remove lower column retaining bolts. Remove upper column retaining bolts. Pull steering column toward passenger compartment to remove.

Installation

1) Install column from passenger compartment. Align lower shaft with flexible coupling. Tighten column mounting bolts.

2) To complete installation, reverse removal procedure. Ensure all switches are installed and operate properly. Install column covers and steering wheel.

PORSCHE

**911 Carrera, 911 Turbo, 924S
944, 944S, 944 Turbo**

DESCRIPTION

The steering column is a 3-piece, energy-absorbing unit. Intermediate shaft connects to steering rack and shaft with 2 "U" joints.

The steering shaft offset design and the steering column collapsible section provide energy-absorbing protection.

REMOVAL & INSTALLATION

STEERING COLUMN ASSEMBLY

CAUTION: Applying excessive pressure or causing impact to mainshaft during service, may cause the column to collapse.

Removal (911 Carrera & 911 Turbo)

1) Disconnect battery ground cable. Remove blower, ducting and steering shaft cover. Remove "U" joint retaining bolt.

PORSCHE (Cont.)

Fig. 1: Exploded View of 944 Steering Column

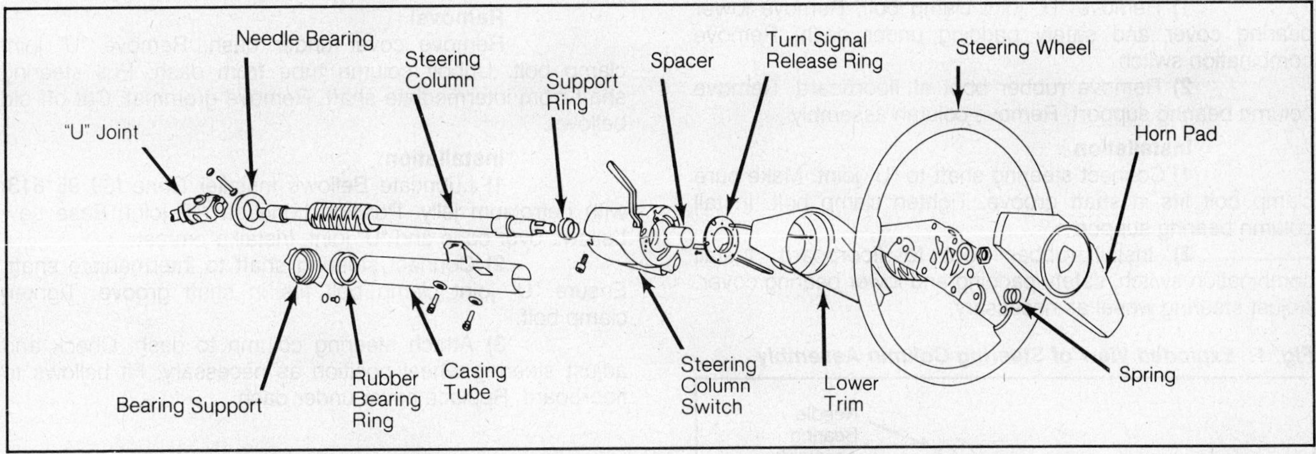

2) From driver's compartment, remove knee strip, light switch and tachometer. Drill out shear bolts retaining ignition switch/steering lock.

3) Lift off horn pad. Remove steering wheel. Detach wire connectors. Remove steering column switch assembly with steering shaft and tube.

Installation

To install, reverse removal procedure. Tighten attaching shear bolts until heads break off.

Removal (924, 944, 944S & 944 Turbo)

1) Disconnect battery ground cable. Remove horn pad. Remove steering wheel. Remove upper "U" joint retaining bolt.

2) Disconnect wiring plugs from rear of switches. Drill out casing tube shear bolts. Remove upper steering column and switches as an assembly.

Installation

1) Lubricate rubber bearing. Slide bearing support .8" (20 mm) onto casing tube. Install column switch on casing tube. Finger tighten bolts.

2) Slide casing tube with bearing support and column switch onto steering column. Install bearing support screws. Finger tighten casing tube shear bolts.

3) Drive spacer sleeve on steering column until sleeve is 1.67" (42.5 mm) from steering column face. Tighten column switch Allen bolt and bearing support mounting screws.

4) Mount lower shaft on steering gear. Make sure shaft is free of tension. Reposition casing tube if needed. Clearance between steering wheel and column should be .08-.16" (2-4 mm). Tighten shear bolts until heads break off.

OVERHAUL

STEERING COLUMN ASSEMBLY

NOTE: **Disassembly procedures for 924S, 944, 944S and 944 Turbo were not available from manufacturer.**

Disassembly (911 Carrera & 911 Turbo)

1) With column out of vehicle and switches removed from column, drive steering shaft out of tube. Remove shaft lower end circlip and lower ball bearing.

2) Press Seeger ring out of steering shaft tube top end. Remove ball bearing and contact ring.

Reassembly

1) Install ball bearing against circlip at steering column lower end, and seat bottom circlip against bearing. Circlip must seat in recessed groove.

2) Place contact ring and upper bearing together on steering shaft. Using a pipe, drive bearing into place on shaft. Pipe should contact inner race only. To complete assembly, reverse disassembly procedure.

TIGHTENING SPECIFICATIONS

Application	Ft. Lbs. (N.m)
"U" Joint Bolts	18-25 (24-34)
Steering Wheel Nut	
911 Carrera & 911 Turbo	54 (73)
924S, 944, 944S & 944 Turbo	33 (45)

SAAB 900S & 900 TURBO

DESCRIPTION

Steering column collapses upon frontal impact. Steering shaft mounts in 2 needle bearing assemblies in column support. Column support mounts to crossmember under dash. An intermediate shaft, with "U" joints at each end, connects to steering gear.

REMOVAL & INSTALLATION

STEERING COLUMN

CAUTION: **Applying excessive pressure, or causing impact to mainshaft during service, may cause the column to collapse.**

Steering Columns

SAAB 900S & 900 TURBO (Cont.)

Removal

1) Remove "U" joint clamp bolt. Remove lower bearing cover and safety padding under dash. Remove combination switch.

2) Remove rubber boot at floorboard. Remove column bearing support. Remove column assembly.

Installation

1) Connect steering shaft to "U" joint. Make sure clamp bolt fits in shaft groove. Tighten clamp bolt. Install column bearing support.

2) Install rubber boot to floorboard. Install combination switch, safety padding and lower bearing cover. Adjust steering wheel as necessary.

Fig. 1: Exploded View of Steering Column Assembly

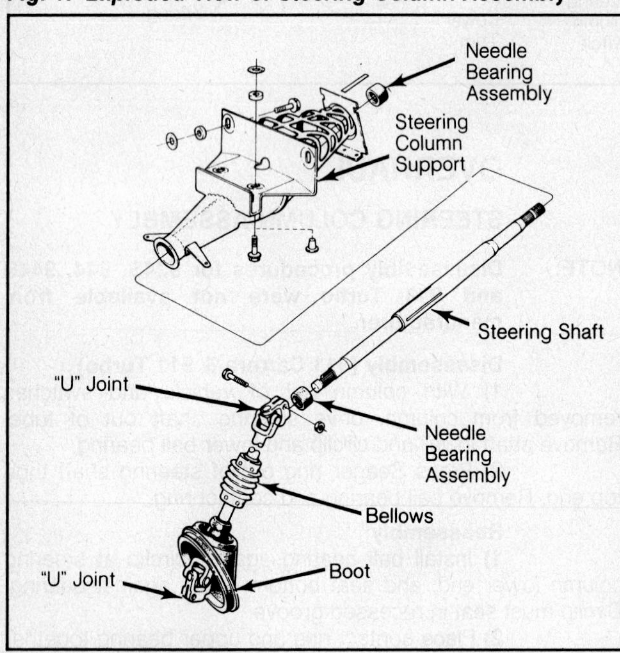

Courtesy of Saab-Scania of America, Inc.

INTERMEDIATE SHAFT BELLOWS

Removal

Remove cover under dash. Remove "U" joint clamp bolt. Unbolt column tube from dash. Pull steering shaft from intermediate shaft. Remove grommet. Cut off old bellows.

Installation

1) Lubricate Bellows Installer Cone (89 95 813) with petroleum jelly. Position cone on "U" joint. Ease new bellows over cone and "U" joint. Install grommet.

2) Connect steering shaft to intermediate shaft. Ensure "U" joint clamp bolt fits in shaft groove. Tighten clamp bolt.

3) Attach steering column to dash. Check and adjust steering wheel position as necessary. Fit bellows to floorboard. Replace cover under dash.

OVERHAUL

STEERING COLUMN

Disassembly

Remove steering wheel. Pull steering shaft out of tube. Remove rubber bushings with needle bearing assemblies.

NOTE: Replacement of needle bearing assemblies is the only overhaul procedure.

Reassembly

To reassemble steering column, reverse disassembly procedure.

TIGHTENING SPECIFICATIONS

Application	Ft. Lbs. (N.m)
"U" Joint Clamp Bolt	26-30 (35-41)
Steering Wheel Nut	20 (27)

SUBARU

Brat, Hatchback, Justy, Sedan, Station Wagon, XT Coupe

DESCRIPTION

Collapsible steering columns are used on all models. Upper and lower column sections are joined by a "U" joint. The column lower end connects to the steering gear pinion flange with a "U" joint.

REMOVAL & INSTALLATION

STEERING COLUMN

CAUTION: Applying excessive pressure, or causing impact to mainshaft during service, may cause the column to collapse.

Removal

1) Disconnect battery ground cable. Remove "U" joint clamp bolt. Remove trim panel and air duct from under instrument panel. Separate shaft from "U" joint.

2) Unplug ignition switch and combination switch connectors. Remove upper and lower bracket bolts. Remove steering column toward passenger compartment.

Installation

1) Insert column through floorboard into "U" joint. Install and tighten upper bracket bolt into instrument panel. Install air duct and trim panel.

2) Install and tighten lower column bolts. Connect electrical connectors. Tighten "U" joint clamp bolt. Check operation of steering wheel and switches.

OVERHAUL

STEERING COLUMN

Disassembly

1) Remove horn pad retaining screw (2-spoke wheel) or screws (4-spoke wheel) from behind wheel. Pull horn pad to remove. On soft-type steering wheel, lift up horn pad from front.

SUBARU (Cont.)

Fig. 1: Subaru XT Coupe Steering Column Assembly

Courtesy of Subaru of America, Inc.

2) Remove steering wheel. Remove column covers, combination switch and horn brush. Remove lower bearing screws. Pull shaft with bearing downward. Remove snap ring, washer, "O" ring and bearing.

Inspection

1) Check that "U" joint has no play in any direction. If excessive play is found in "U" joint, replace it. Flexing "U" joint, check for binding.

2) If torque required to turn "U" joint exceeds 4 INCH lbs. (.58 N.m), replace it. Check plastic washer for damage, and serration for wear.

3) Check steering shaft length. On all except XT Coupe and Justy, non-tilt column shaft length should be 20.32-20.40" (516.2-518.2 mm).

4) On all except XT Coupe and Justy, tilt column shaft length should be 11.67" (296.5 mm). On XT Coupe,

Steering Columns

SUBARU (Cont.)

shaft length should be 29.55-29.63" (750.1-752.1 mm). On Justy, shaft length should be 22.76-22.84" (578.2-580.2 mm).

5) Check shaft runout. Runout for elliptical part should be less than 1.28" (32.5 mm). Runout for upper end of shaft should be less than .047" (1.2 mm).

6) Runout for shaft collar (standard wheel) should be less than .024" (.6 mm). Replace steering shaft if not within specifications. Check bearings for damage. Replace any worn bearings.

Reassembly

1) To reassemble, reverse disassembly procedure. Lubricate shaft sliding section at lower and upper bearing and horn brush.

2) With steering wheel in place, check clearance between steering wheel and cover. If clearance exceeds .04-.12" (1.0-3.0 mm), loosen column cover screws to adjust.

Fig. 2: Subaru Justy Steering Column Assembly

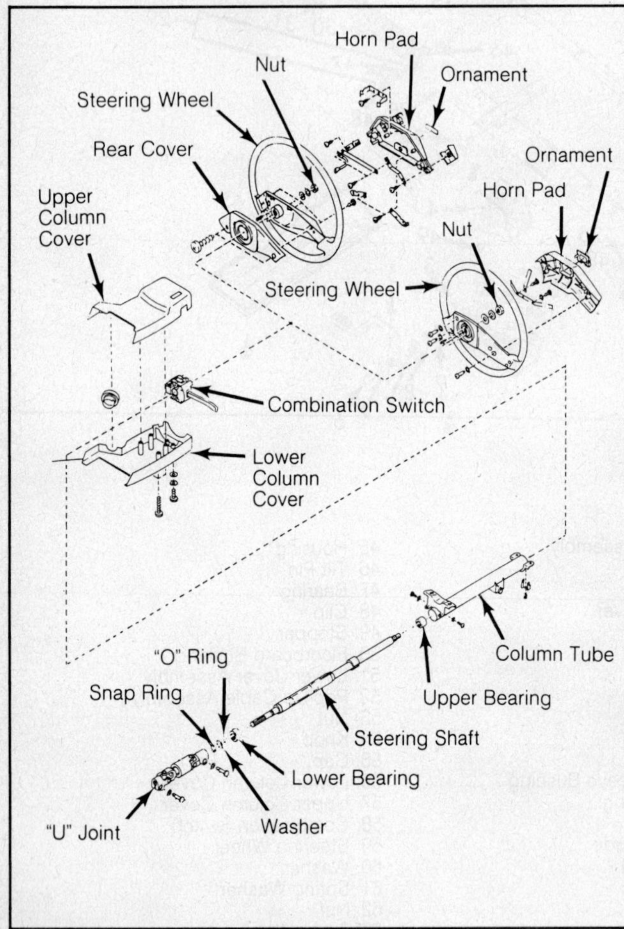

Courtesy of Subaru of America, Inc.

TILT MECHANISM

Disassembly

1) Disconnect tension cords. Place wheel in full upright position. Remove cords and balance springs. Remove "U" joint clamp bolt. Loosen lower bearing screws. Remove "U" joint shaft and bearing downward as a unit.

2) Remove snap ring, washer, "O" ring, bearing and housing from "U" joint shaft. Remove ignition switch bolts. Detach switch and "U" joint shaft from tilt bracket.

3) Using a sharp screwdriver, remove inner stop ring from ignition switch. Remove inner needle bearing and race. Remove inner spring washer.

4) Remove outer stop ring, washer, needle bearing, race and outer spring washer. Remove tilt lever spring and plate. Remove lock gear and lever as a unit.

5) Remove lever snap ring, washer and shaft. Remove tilt bracket pivot bolt and bushing. Remove tilt bracket. Remove lock gear shaft and lever shaft.

Reassembly

1) Apply grease to shaft lower bearing surface. Install bearing, "O" ring, washer and snap ring onto steering shaft. Install springs in ignition switch grooves.

2) Install inner and outer needle bearings and races into ignition switch. Install inner stop ring, outer stop ring and washer. Apply grease to inside of needle bearings.

3) Install "U" joint shaft to ignition switch. Make sure 2.29-2.30" (58.1-58.4 mm) of shaft smooth section protrudes from ignition switch. Turn shaft to check for smooth operation.

4) Apply grease to column friction surface at tilt bracket. Install wave washer and tilt bracket. Apply grease to tilt bracket bushing and shaft. Install bushing, shaft, washer and snap ring.

5) Install pivot bolt to column. Temporarily attach lock gear shaft and tilt lever shaft to column. Apply grease to both shafts. Insert lock gear guide pin into tilt lever groove. Install tilt lever and lock gear to their shafts.

6) Lubricate lock, sector gear teeth and roller surfaces. Attach spacer to lock gear. Install plate, aligning holes with pivot bolt, lock gear shaft and lever shaft.

7) Temporarily tighten pivot bolt, lock gear shaft and lever shaft. Apply grease to lever spring. Install tube on spring. Install spring to tilt lever and plate.

8) Move lever up and down. Adjust clearance between lever and plate cutout portion to .16-.31" (4-8 mm). Tighten nuts. Guide "U" joint through tilt bracket hole.

9) Install ignition switch. Install steering shaft into column tube lower end until "U" joint serration reaches tube. Aligning shaft bearing and tube holes, install lock washer and set screw. Tighten "U" joint clamp bolt.

10) Apply grease to balance springs. Install tubes on springs. Install springs and tension cords. Ensure tilt lever locks at each position during operation.

Fig. 3: Subaru XT Coupe Telescopic Mechanism

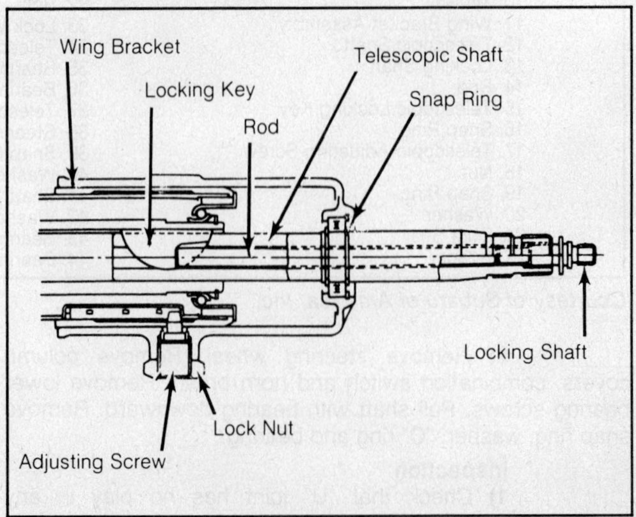

Courtesy of Subaru of America, Inc.

Steering Columns

SUBARU (Cont.)

11) Install combination switch. Clamp ignition and combination switch harnesses. Install column covers. Attach clips to column bracket. Install column to body.

TELESCOPIC MECHANISM

Disassembly (XT Coupe Only)

1) The telescopic mechanism may be disassembled without removing steering column from vehicle. Remove horn pad, steering wheel, upper and lower column covers, harness connectors and combination switch in order to gain access to telescopic mechanism.

2) Remove locking nut and adjusting screw from lower side of wing bracket. *See Fig. 3.* Slide wing bracket and telescopic shaft off column as an assembly.

3) Remove snap ring and shaft from wing bracket. Remove telescopic locking key from keyway in telescopic shaft. Remove locking shaft and rod from shaft.

Inspection

Check all sliding surfaces for excessive wear or scratches. Check for scratches on locking keyway, locking keyway mating surface and bushing.

Reassembly

1) Lubricate all sliding surfaces of telescopic assembly and inside of wing bracket. Install locking shaft and rod into shaft. Install key into keyway on telescopic shaft.

2) Insert telescopic shaft with key into locking shaft/rod assembly. Install first snap ring on telescopic shaft in groove closest to key.

3) Aligning slot in sleeve bushing with threaded opening, install sleeve bushing into wing bracket. Install bearing into wing bracket.

4) Slide wing bracket with bushing over telescopic shaft. Lock in place with 2nd snap ring. Install wing bracket assembly into tilt bracket/locking shaft assembly.

5) Ensure that slot in sleeve bushing is still aligned with threaded opening of wing bracket. Lubricate tapered end of adjusting screw.

6) Install adjusting screw and lock nut. Turn adjusting screw in until seated. Back off adjusting screw 20-30 degrees.

7) While holding adjusting screw in position, tighten lock nut to 108-144 INCH lbs. (12-16 N.m). Check for excessive play in wing bracket.

8) With telescopic shaft fully extended, install wiring harness, column covers and combination switch.

9) Install steering wheel and horn pad. Check operation of combination switch, steering wheel lock, tilt mechanism and telescopic mechanism.

TIGHTENING SPECIFICATIONS

Application	Ft. Lbs. (N.m)
Column Bracket Bolt	14-22 (19-30)
Steering Wheel Nut	
All Except Justy	22-29 (30-39)
Justy	36-43 (49-59)
"U" Joint Clamp Bolt	16-19 (22-26)
	INCH Lbs. (N.m)
Tilt Lock Nut	108-144 (12-16)

SUZUKI SAMURAI

DESCRIPTION

Collapsible steering columns are used on all models. Upper and lower column sections are joined by a "U" joint. The upper column sliding section compresses on impact. The column lower end connects to the steering gear pinion flange with a flexible coupling.

REMOVAL & INSTALLATION

STEERING COLUMN

CAUTION: Applying excessive pressure, or causing impact to mainshaft during service, may cause the column to collapse.

Removal

1) Disconnect battery ground cable. Remove "U" joint clamp bolt. Separate shaft from "U" joint. Remove steering wheel, horn pad and combination switch.

2) Unplug wiring connectors to steering column switches. Remove steering column floorboard bracket bolts. Remove steering column upper bracket bolts. Pull steering column from floorboard.

Installation

1) Insert column through floorboard into "U" joint. Install upper bracket retaining bolts. Install column-to-floorboard retaining bolts.

2) Tighten column bracket bolts. Connect all electrical connections. Tighten "U" joint clamp bolt. Tighten column-to-floorboard retaining bolts.

Fig. 1: Measuring Steering Components

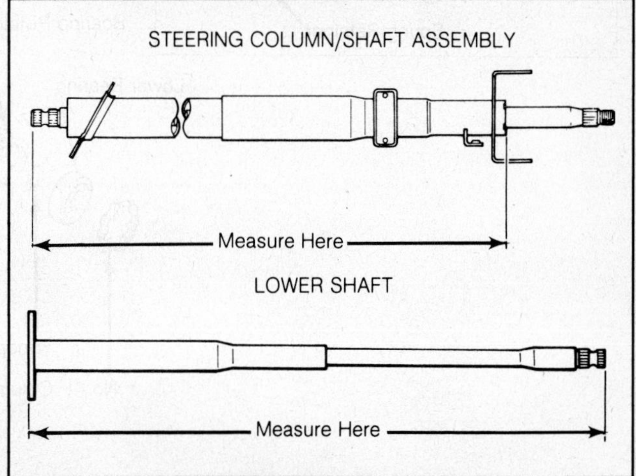

Courtesy of Suzuki of America Corp.

SUZUKI SAMURAI (Cont.)

OVERHAUL

STEERING COLUMN

Disassembly & Reassembly

It is not recommended to separate the steering column and shaft. If steering column is defective, replace as an assembly.

Inspection

Measure steering column/shaft assembly. Shaft should measure no less than 25.02" (635.5 mm). *See Fig. 1.* Measure lower shaft. Lower shaft should be between 18.98-19.05" (482-484 mm). *See Fig. 1.* If either measurement is not within specification, replace as necessary.

TOYOTA – TILT WHEEL

DESCRIPTION

Tilt steering wheels incorporate an upper steering shaft, attached by a "U" joint, with an intermediate steering shaft. These shafts are held in place by upper and lower brackets.

Brackets are pinned together so upper bracket can move up or down. Upper bracket is locked in place by pawl attached to lever. Steering columns are collapsible.

Some models of Cressida and Supra use a Progressive Power Steering (PPS) system and/or a Toyota Electronically Modulated Suspension (TEMS). the steering sensor for either system is located under the steering column near the break-away bracket.

NOTE: For models without tilt wheel steering columns, see TOYOTA NON-TILT WHEEL article in this section.

Fig. 1: Exploded View of Camry, Corolla, MR2 & Tercel Steering Column Assembly

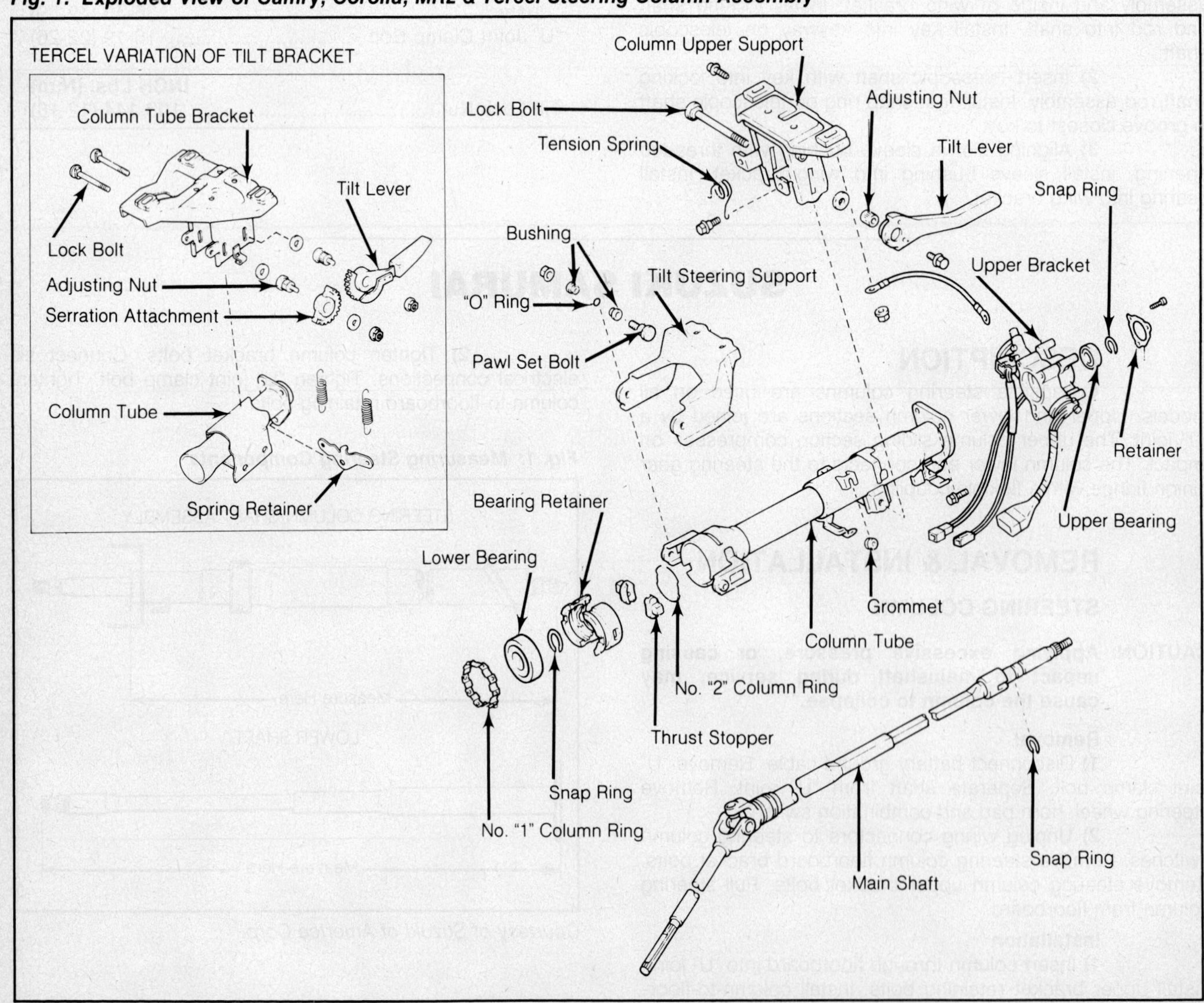

Camry is shown. Corolla, MR2 and Tercel are similar. Courtesy of Toyota Motor Sales, U.S.A., Inc.

Steering Columns

TOYOTA – TILT WHEEL (Cont.)

REMOVAL & INSTALLATION

STEERING COLUMN

Removal

1) Disconnect battery ground cable. Remove steering wheel. On Cressida, FWD Corolla, MR2 and Tercel models, remove fuse box cover, lower instrument trim panel and air duct from under steering column.

2) On all models, remove upper and lower steering column covers. Remove combination switch. Mark position of "U" joints and shaft for reassembly.

3) On models with "U" joints, remove "U" joint retaining bolt. On models with flexible joint, remove flexible joint retaining bolt.

NOTE: **Remove steering column with intermediate shaft attached on 2WD Pickup models.**

4) On all models, mark position of joint and pinion shaft for reassembly. Remove intermediate steering shaft.

5) Remove floor pan cover bolts. Remove tilt bracket-to-dashboard mounting bolts. Remove steering column toward inside of vehicle.

Installation

1) To install steering columns, reverse disassembly procedure. Grease main steering shaft and all bearings.

Fig. 2: Exploded View of Celica, Cressida & Supra Steering Column Assembly

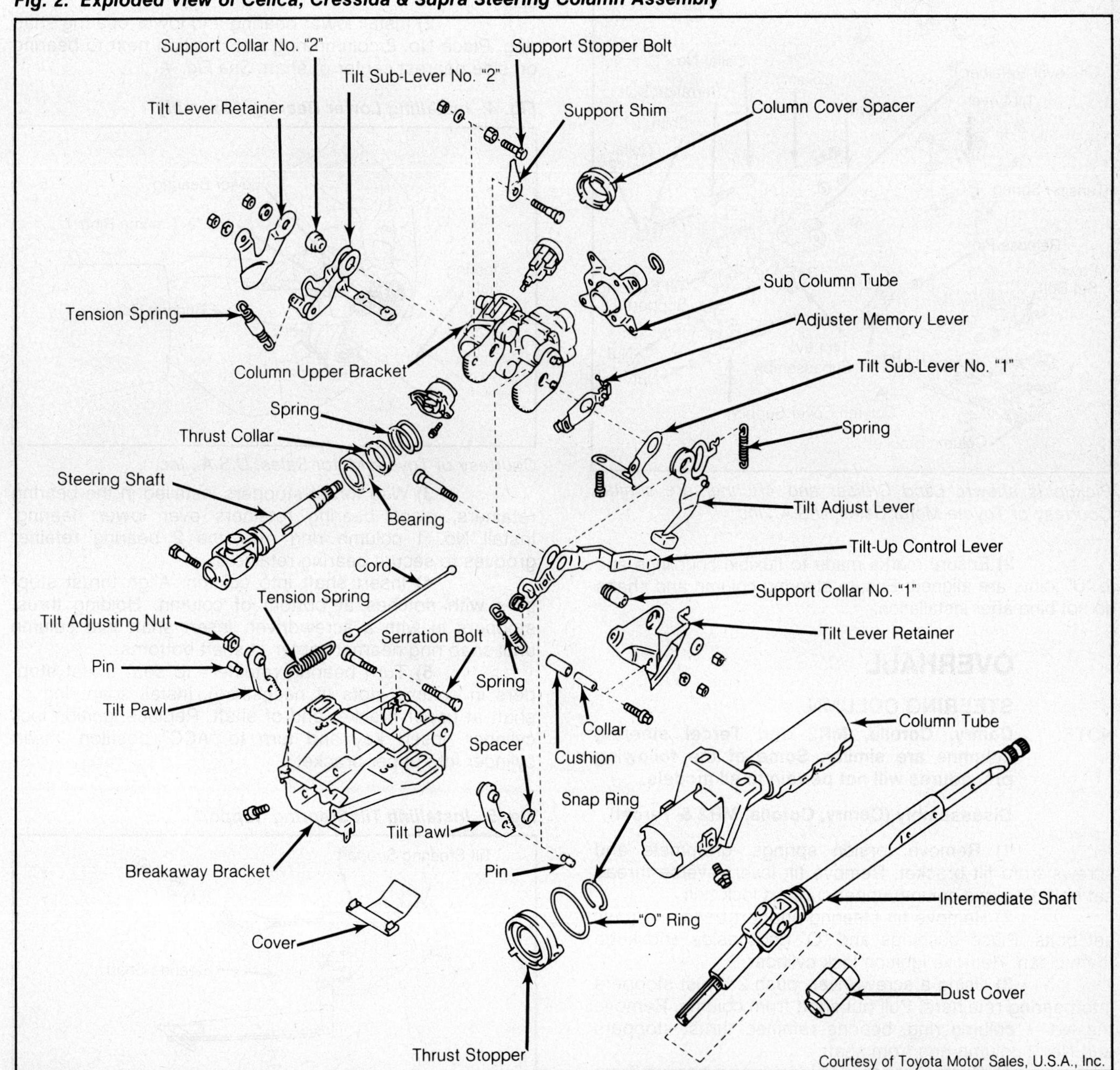

Celica is shown. Cressida and Supra are similar. Cressida and Supra have a steering sensor located at lower end of column tube.

Steering Columns

TOYOTA – TILT WHEEL (Cont.)

Fig. 3: Exploded View of Land Cruiser, Pickup, Van & 4Runner Steering Column Assembly

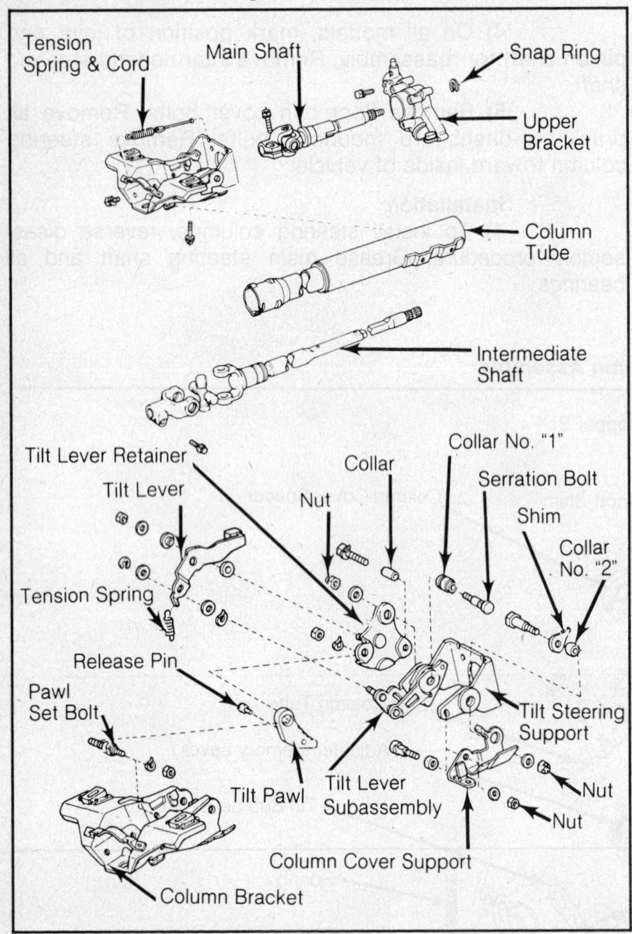

Pickup is shown. Land Cruiser and 4Runner are similar. Courtesy of Toyota Motor Sales, U.S.A., Inc.

2) Ensure marks made to flexible couplings and to "U" joints are aligned. Ensure steering column and shafts do not bind after installation.

OVERHAUL

STEERING COLUMN

NOTE: Camry, Corolla, MR2 and Tercel steering columns are similar. Some of the following procedures will not pertain to all models.

Disassembly (Camry, Corolla, MR2 & Tercel)

1) Remove torsion springs, grommets and screws from tilt bracket. Remove tilt lever reverse-thread set bolt. Remove column upper support lock bolt.

2) Remove tilt steering support bolts and pawl set bolts. Place bushings and "O" rings aside and keep them clean. Remove ignition lock cylinder.

3) Using a screwdriver, push 2 thrust stoppers into bearing retainers. Pull out shaft from column. Remove the No. 1 column ring, bearing retainer, thrust stoppers and No. 2 column ring from shaft.

4) Remove snap ring and lower bearing from shaft. Remove bearing inner snap ring. Remove upper bracket retaining bolts and ground strap. Separate upper bracket from column.

Inspection

1) Check that steering lock mechanism operates properly. Check upper bearing for smooth rotation or excessive noise. Replace upper bearing (if necessary).

2) Using Drift (09631-00020) and Adapter (09627-30010), drive bearing from upper bracket. Pack new bearing with grease. Using the same drift and adapter used in removal, drive new bearing into upper bracket.

3) Inspect lower bearing for smooth rotation or excessive noise. If lower bearing shows signs of wear or damage, replace with a new one.

Reassembly

1) Install upper bracket onto column. Install ground strap. Tighten retaining bolts to 14 ft. lbs. (19 N.m). Install inner snap ring on shaft groove nearest to center of shaft.

2) Install lower bearing and lower bearing snap ring. Place No. 2 column ring into position next to bearing on side nearest center of shaft. *See Fig. 4.*

Fig. 4: Installing Lower Bearing Assembly

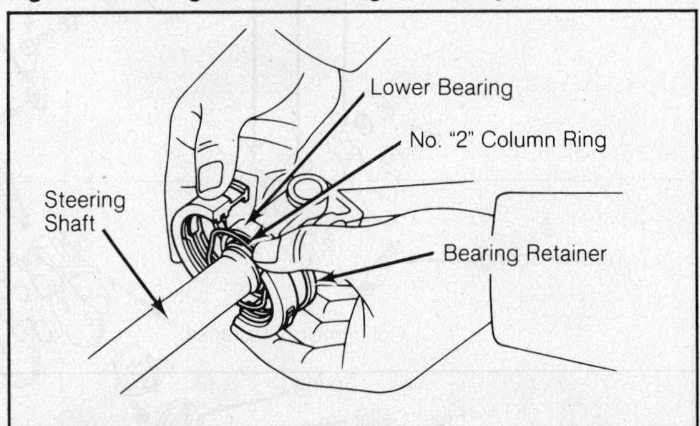

Courtesy of Toyota Motor Sales, U.S.A., Inc.

3) With thrust stoppers installed in the bearing retainers, place bearing retainers over lower bearing. Install No. 1 column ring over the 2 bearing retainer grooves to secure bearing retainers.

4) Insert shaft into column. Align thrust stoppers with notches at bottom of column. Holding thrust stoppers in with a screwdriver, insert shaft into column until snap ring nearest center of shaft bottoms.

5) Turn bearing retainers to seat thrust stoppers in column slots (if necessary). Install snap ring on shaft at upper bracket end of shaft. Replace ignition lock cylinder. Insert key and turn to "ACC" position. Insert cylinder into upper bracket.

Fig. 5: Installing Tilt Steering Support

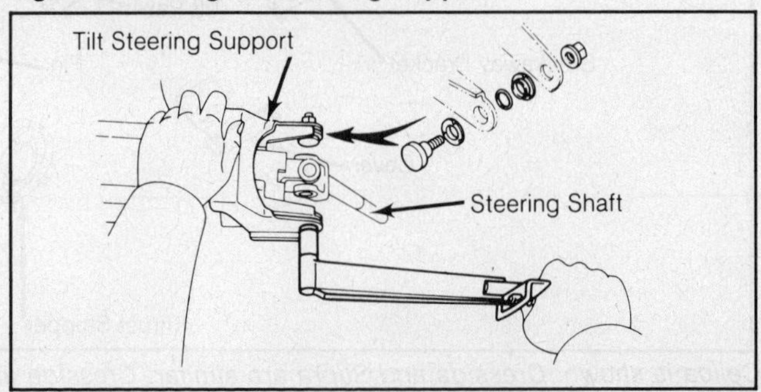

Courtesy of Toyota Motor Sales, U.S.A., Inc.

TOYOTA – TILT WHEEL (Cont.)

6) Install tilt steering support. *See Fig. 5.* Apply lithium grease to bushings and "O" rings. Install bushings to column. Install tilt steering support and pawl set bolts with bushings and "O" rings in place. Tighten nuts to 108 INCH lbs. (13 N.m).

7) Lubricate and install tilt lever lock bolt, washer and adjusting nut. *See Fig. 6.* Hand tighten adjusting nut. Adjust upper column support so that lock bolt is in center of oval and that support bracket is parallel with column, as seen from the side of upper column support.

Fig. 6: Installing Upper Column Support

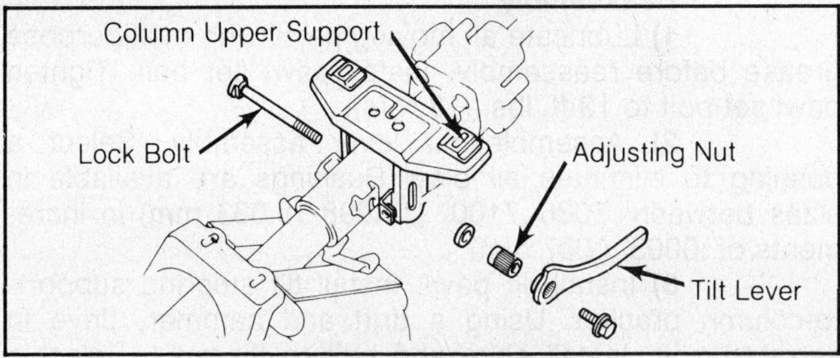

Courtesy of Toyota Motor Sales, U.S.A., Inc.

8) Tighten adjusting nut to 96 INCH lbs. (11 N.m). Install tilt lever. Tighten reverse thread set bolt to 25 ft. lbs. (33 N.m). Install 2 screws with washers to tilt bracket. Install torsion springs and grommets.

NOTE: The Celica, Cressida and Supra steering columns are similar. Some of the following procedures will not pertain to all models.

Disassembly (Celica, Cressida & Supra)

1) On Cressida and Supra, remove steering sensor cover and sensor. Keep sensor clean. On all models, remove column cover. Remove combination switch.

2) Move the tilt steering column to the full up position. Remove mainshaft retaining bolt. Remove 4 column bracket retaining bolts. Pull column with intermediate shaft from column bracket.

3) On Cressida, push two thrust stoppers into bearing retainers. Pull out intermediate shaft from column. Remove No. 1 column ring, bearing retainer, thrust stoppers and No. 2 column ring from shaft.

4) Remove snap ring, lower bearing and next snap ring from shaft. Remove dust seal from column. With the tilt bracket tilted up fully, remove springs and cords from tilt bracket with a screwdriver.

5) Using Steering Shaft Retainer (09950-20016), tighten steering mainshaft against the upper bracket. Take care not to overtighten the steering shaft retainer. Remove snap ring. Remove steering mainshaft.

6) On Celica, remove 2 thrust stopper set bolts. Remove intermediate shaft. Remove 4 tilt bracket retainer bolts. Remove column from tilt bracket.

7) With the tilt bracket tilted up fully, remove springs and cords from tilt bracket with a screwdriver. Remove snap ring. Remove mainshaft. Remove spring and collar from mainshaft.

8) On Supra, with the tilt bracket tilted up fully, remove springs and cords from tilt bracket with a screwdriver. Remove 4 tilt mechanism bolts. Separate tilt mechanism from column.

9) Remove tilt bracket support reinforcement from tilt steering support. Remove 3 bracket-to-support attaching bolts. Remove snap ring. Remove mainshaft from upper bracket.

10) On all models, Remove 2 tilt lever springs from side of column. Remove all bracket attaching nuts and bolts. Remove tilt lever retainer. Remove the release pin from the pawl.

11) Temporarily install nut on the serrated bolt to protect threads. Using a light soft mallet, drive out serrated bolt. Remove nut from serrated bolt. Remove column cover support. Remove tilt bracket nut and bolt.

12) Separate tilt bracket and upper bracket. Place in order of removal 2 bushings, tilt control lever, shim, tilt adjust lever, memory cover and memory lever.

13) Remove pawl set bolt. Remove ignition key/lock cylinder by pushing lock pin in and removing cylinder (if necessary). Using Drift (09631-00020), Adapter (09627-30010) and Sleeve (09636-20010), drive bearing from upper bracket.

14) Pack new bearing with grease. Using Bearing Collar (09527-20011) and a press, drive lower bearing from shaft.

15) Place intermediate shaft in a soft-jawed vise. Remove sensor ring from intermediate shaft. Remove bearing snap ring. Tap bearing from shaft.

Inspection

1) Check that steering lock mechanism operates properly. Check upper bearing for smooth rotation or excessive noise. Replace upper bearing (if necessary).

2) Inspect lower bearing for smooth rotation or excessive noise. If damaged, replace bearing. Check PPS sensor ring and intermediate shaft bearing for wear or damage.

Reassembly

1) Pack new bearing with grease. Place bearing over intermediate shaft. Place intermediate shaft in a soft-jawed vise with bearing at "U" joint end of shaft.

2) Using Sleeve (09612-22011) and Bearing Plates (09237-00010) and vise, drive new bearing onto shaft. Using a plastic hammer, tap the shaft toward the vise to drive the bearing onto the larger section of the shaft. Install snap ring.

3) Using a press and Collar (09515-21010), press a NEW PPS sensor ring onto shaft with lettering facing away from "U" joint.

4) Using the same drift and adapter used in removal, place upper bracket on block of wood and drive new bearing into upper bracket. Coat all moving, rubbing or sliding parts with grease.

5) Use new "O" rings where needed. Install adjuster memory cover to upper bracket. Install pawl set bolt. Tighten pawl set bolt or nut (if equipped) to 14 ft. lbs. (19 N.m). *See Fig. 2.*

6) Install tilt lever and tilt control lever over the mounting pin. Use a bushing that will eliminate all play between tilt adjust lever, tilt control lever and the mounting pin.

7) Bushings are available in sizes between .7087-.7100" (18.002-18.035 mm) in .0002" (.007 mm) increments. Install tilt steering pawl over pawl pivot pin. Aligning holes, install release pin.

8) Install tilt lever retainer. Install retainer attaching nut and bolt. Tighten to 14 ft. lbs. (19 N.m). Using a drift and hammer, drive serrated bolt into tilt bracket. Check that bolt collar is firmly installed into pivot of control lever inside plate.

9) Install nut onto serrated bolt. Tighten to 14 ft. lbs. (19 N.m). Select bushing for opposite side of tilt

TOYOTA – TILT WHEEL (Cont.)

bracket that will eliminate all play. Bushings are available in sizes between .7089-.7100" (18.005-18.035 mm) in .0005" (.015 mm) increments.

10) Select a shim or shims that will fit snugly between pivot points of upper bracket. Shims are available in sizes between .0067-.0728" (.17-1.85 mm) in increments of .011" (.30 mm).

11) Install selected bushing and shim(s) into upper bracket pivot. Install bolt with a new nut. Tighten to 14 ft. lbs. (19 N.m). Install column cover support. Install stopper bolt and a new nut. Tighten to 96 INCH lbs. (11 N.m).

12) Install 2 springs to side of tilt bracket. Install collar and spring over mainshaft. Turn ignition to "ACC" position. Insert mainshaft assembly into upper bracket.

13) Using Steering Shaft Retainer (09950-20016), tighten steering mainshaft against the upper bracket. Take care not to overtighten steering shaft retainer. Install snap ring. Remove steering shaft retainer.

14) Connect tilt bracket springs to cords. Install spring/cord assemblies into top of tilt bracket. Install dust seal to column. Install column tube to breakaway bracket. Tighten bolts to 14 ft. lbs. (19 N.m).

15) With thrust stoppers installed in the bearing retainers, place bearing retainers over lower bearing. Install No. 1 column ring over the 2 bearing retainer grooves to secure bearing retainers.

16) Insert shaft into column. Align thrust stoppers with notches at bottom of column. Holding thrust stoppers in with a screwdriver, insert intermediate shaft into column until snap ring nearest center of shaft bottoms.

17) Turn bearing retainers to seat thrust stoppers in column slots (if necessary). Connect main shaft-to-intermediate shaft "U" joint. Tighten attaching bolt to 19 ft. lbs (25 N.m).

18) On Cressida and Supra, install steering sensor to bottom of column. Check that sensor does not touch sensor ring by turning steering shaft and listening for rubbing sound. Install sensor cover.

19) On all models, check that tilt mechanism locks in all 8 positions. With mainshaft in neutral position, pull the tilt lever and check that the mainshaft rises to the uppermost position.

20) Check for smooth operation of all shafts and "U" joints. Install combination switch, steering wheel, column covers and horn pad.

Disassembly (Land Cruiser, Pickup, Van & 4Runner)

1) Remove ignition key cylinder. Mark intermediate shaft and "U" joints for reassembly reference. Remove "U" joint retaining bolts. Disconnect intermediate shaft from mainshaft.

2) Remove upper tension springs and cords. Remove bracket from column. Press in ignition cylinder retaining pin. Pull out ignition cylinder. Remove upper bracket retaining bolts. remove upper bracket.

3) Remove mainshaft retaining snap ring. Remove mainshaft from upper bracket. Remove tilt lever side tension springs, "E" clip, bushings, nut and washer.

4) Remove tilt lever retaining bolt, nuts and washers. Remove tilt lever retainer and bushing. Remove tilt lever. Remove release pin. Remove serrated bolt.

5) Remove tilt pawl. Remove column cover support nuts, bolts, bushings, washers and shims. Remove column cover support. Remove tilt steering support with tilt lever subassembly. Remove pawl set bolt.

Inspection

1) Inspect all components for wear or damage. Check bearings for smooth operation. Check steering shafts for collision damage. Check steering lock mechanism for proper operation. Inspect "U" joints for excessive play. Replace components as necessary.

2) If replacing pin and bearing blocks, make sure new bearing blocks have the small anti-rattle rubber inserts installed before assembling intermediate shaft to main steering shaft.

Reassembly

1) Lubricate all moving parts with multipurpose grease before reassembly. Install pawl set bolt. Tighten pawl set bolt to 13 ft. lbs. (18 N.m).

2) Assemble tilt lever assembly. Select a bushing to eliminate all play. Bushings are available in sizes between .7086-.7100" (17.998-18.033 mm) in increments of .0003" (.007 mm).

3) Install tilt pawl. Install tilt steering support-to-column bracket. Using a drift and hammer, drive in serrated bolt. Install shim and bolt to tilt pawl. Select a shim to eliminate all play.

4) Shims are available in thicknesses between .0078-.0711" (.193-1.805 mm) in increments of .117" (.302 mm). Install column cover support. Install release pin to tilt pawl.

5) Install tilt lever retainer attaching bolt, nuts and washers. Tighten bolt and nuts to 13 ft. lbs. (18 N.m). Install tilt lever. Install tilt lever tension spring, "E" clip, bushings, nut and washer.

6) Install mainshaft to upper bracket. Install snap ring. Install ignition switch. Install upper bracket to column bracket.

7) Apply a thread locking compound and tighten upper bracket-to-column bracket bolts to 65 INCH lbs. (7.4 N.m). Install steering column to column bracket. Tighten bolts to 14 ft. lbs. (19 N.m).

8) Aligning marks made during disassembly, connect intermediate shaft. Tighten to 19 ft. lbs. (25 N.m). Install tension springs and cords.

TIGHTENING SPECIFICATIONS

Application	Ft. Lbs. (N.m)
Column Bracket-to-Instrument Panel Bolts	19 (25)
Column Bracket-to-Instrument Panel Nuts	21 (28)
Flexible Coupling Bolts	15-22 (20-30)
Floorboard Bracket Bolts Van	14 (19)
Steering Column-to-Column Bracket Bolt	14 (19)
Steering Column-to-Tilt Bracket Bolt	13 (18)
Steering Wheel Nut	25 (34)
"U" Joint Bolts	22-33 (30-45)
	INCH Lbs. (N.m)
Column Bracket-to-Upper Bracket Bolt	65 (7.4)
Floorboard Bracket Bolts	
Pickup & 4Runner	69 (7.8)
Land Cruiser	108 (13)

TOYOTA – NON-TILT WHEEL

DESCRIPTION

Steering columns are a collapsible 2-piece design. Columns use shear pins to absorb collision impact. Steering shaft is connected directly to steering gear with either a flexible coupling or "U" joint.

NOTE: For models with tilt wheel steering columns, see TOYOTA TILT WHEEL article in this section.

REMOVAL & INSTALLATION

STEERING COLUMN

Removal

1) Disconnect battery ground cable. Remove horn pad and steering wheel. Mark steering shaft and wheel for installation. Remove steering wheel.

2) Remove dash panels and pads (if necessary). On models with A/C, remove air duct from under steering column. Remove column bracket covers.

3) Remove combination switch. Mark "U" joint and shaft for installation. On passenger vehicles, disconnect steering shaft "U" joint from steering gear in engine compartment.

4) On Land Cruiser, Pickup, Van and 4Runner models, disconnect "U" joint from lower steering shaft. Disconnect column shifter linkage (if equipped).

5) Remove bolts from column hole cover. Remove column support bracket bolts. Remove steering column from vehicle.

Installation

1) Install steering column in vehicle. Tighten column bracket bolts finger tight. Install column hole cover bolts. Tighten column bracket bolts.

2) Attach column shift linkage (if equipped). Aligning marks made during removal on "U" joints, tighten clamp bolts. Install combination switch.

3) Install bracket covers, dash panels and pads. Install air ducts (if equipped). Align marks made during removal, install steering wheel and horn pad.

OVERHAUL

STEERING COLUMN

Disassembly

Remove ignition key cylinder. Remove column shift assembly from steering column. Remove clamp bolt and lower steering shaft. Remove hole cover from column. Remove snap ring from upper steering shaft.

Inspection

Check upper bracket for damage and upper bearing for rotating smoothness. Check steering shafts for bending, damaged splines or damaged "U" joints. Check column tube for bending or other damage. Repair or replace components as necessary.

Fig. 1: Exploded View of Passenger Car Steering Column

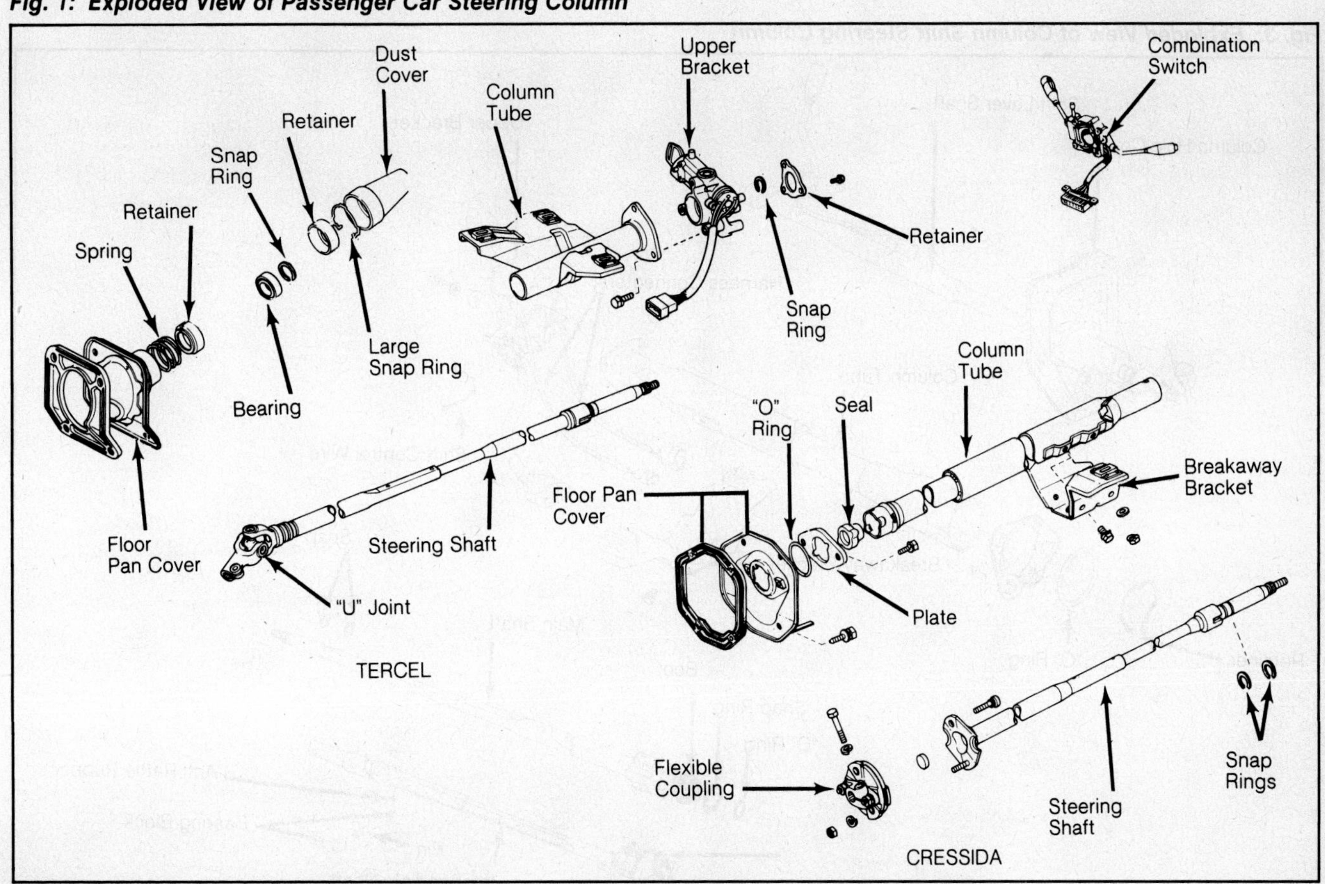

Courtesy of Toyota Motor Sales, U.S.A., Inc.

Steering Columns

TOYOTA – NON-TILT WHEEL (Cont.)

Fig. 2: Exploded View of Land Cruiser, Pickup, Van & 4 Runner Steering Column

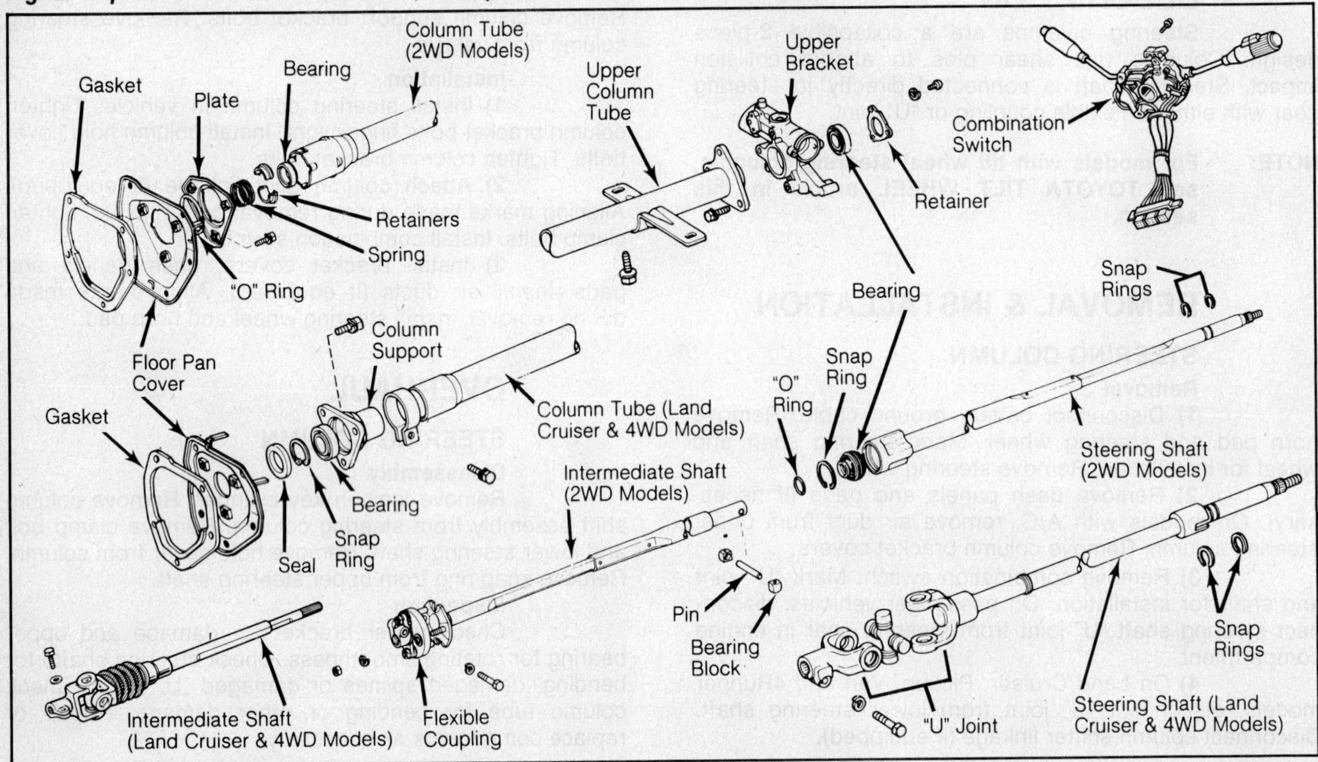

Courtesy of Toyota Motor Sales, U.S.A., Inc.

Fig. 3: Exploded View of Column Shift Steering Column

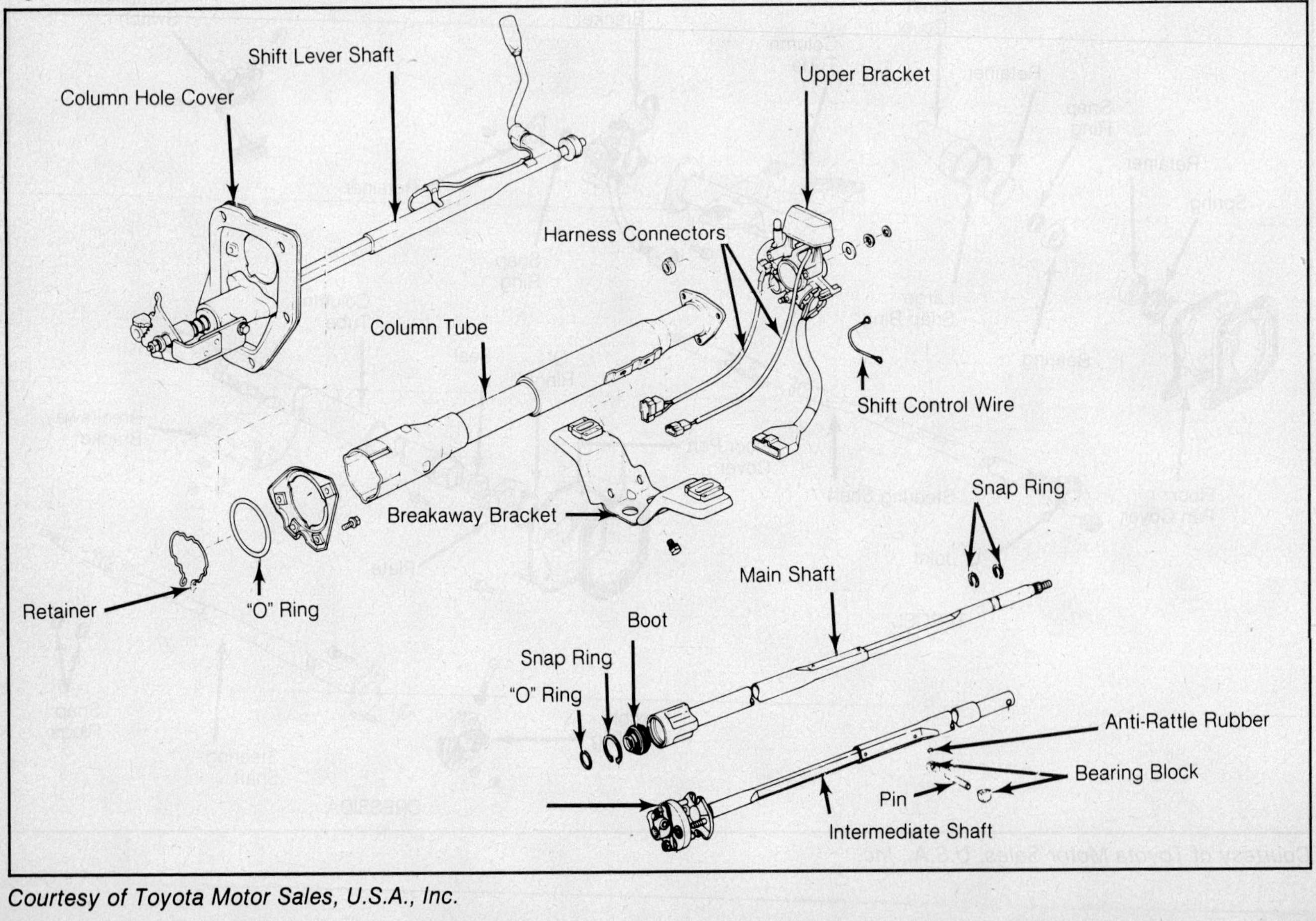

Courtesy of Toyota Motor Sales, U.S.A., Inc.

Steering Columns

TOYOTA – NON-TILT WHEEL (Cont.)

Reassembly

Reassemble in reverse order of disassembly procedures. Ensure all bushings, bearings, shims and bolts are not damaged or worn. If damaged or worn, replace with new units.

TIGHTENING SPECIFICATIONS

Application	Ft. Lbs. (N.m)
Column Bracket-to-Instrument Panel Bolts	19 (25)
Column Bracket-to-Instrument Panel Nuts	21 (28)
Flexible Coupling Bolts	15-22 (20-30)
Steering Column-to-Column Bracket Bolt	14 (19)
Steering Wheel Nut	25 (34)
"U" Joint Bolts	22-33 (30-45)
	INCH Lbs. (N.m)
Column Bracket-to-Upper Bracket Bolt	65 (7.4)
Floorboard Bracket Bolts	
Pickup & 4Runner	69 (7.8)
Land Cruiser	108 (13)

VOLKSWAGEN – ALL EXCEPT QUANTUM & VANAGON

DESCRIPTION

Swing-away steering column is held by a clamp and leaf spring. On impact, the "U" joint shaft pushes steering column against the leaf spring. The spring allows the column to disengage and swing away.

CAUTION: **Applying excessive pressure, or causing impact to mainshaft during service, may cause the column to disengage.**

REMOVAL & INSTALLATION

STEERING COLUMN

NOTE: **Do not remove steering shaft before removing column from vehicle.**

Removal

1) Disconnect battery ground cable. Remove steering wheel. Remove bolt and screw from switch housing recess. Tilt switch unit toward instrument panel. Pry spacer sleeve from column.

2) Pull up combination switch to disconnect wires. Remove combination switch. Disconnect steering shaft from "U" joint shaft. Disconnect brake pedal push rod.

3) Separate clutch pedal from clutch cable under instrument panel. Using a screwdriver, push down leaf spring retainer clip to disengage it from mounting slot.

4) Remove bolts retaining column under instrument panel. Center punch and drill out shear bolts. Remove column assembly from vehicle.

Installation

To install, reverse removal procedure. Place wheels in a straight-ahead position. Tighten pinch bolt. Install spacer. *See Fig. 1.* Install combination switch and steering wheel. Adjust brake pedal and clutch pedal height.

Fig. 1: Exploded View of Steering Column Assembly

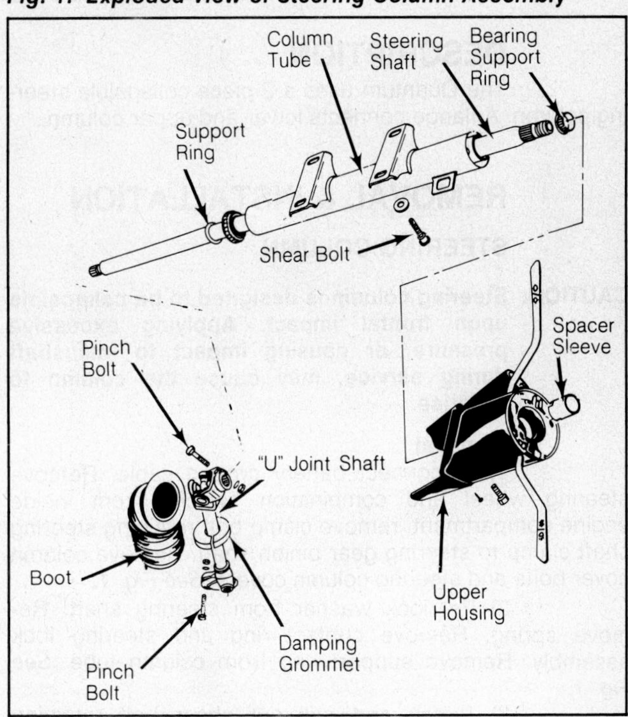

Courtesy of Volkswagen United States, Inc.

OVERHAUL

STEERING COLUMN

Disassembly

Using a press, drive steering shaft from column. Remove bearings from steering column.

Inspection

Check upper bracket for damage and upper bearing for rotating smoothness. Check shafts for signs of bending, damaged splines or damaged "U" joints. Check

VOLKSWAGEN – ALL EXCEPT QUANTUM & VANAGON (Cont.)

column tube for bending or other damage. Repair or replace components as necessary.

Reassembly

Using a press, drive in steering shaft and new bearings. DO NOT use more than 200 lbs. (90 kg) of force to press shaft and bearings into column tube.

"U" JOINT SHAFT

Disassembly

1) Remove pinch bolt connecting lower end of "U" joint shaft with steering gear pinion shaft. Separate manual gearshift linkage from steering box. Remove steering gear box-to-frame retaining nuts.

2) Pull box down to separate from lower "U" joint. Remove rubber boot from lower "U" joint. Remove upper "U" joint-to-steering shaft pinch bolt. Pull down joint and remove shaft with "U" joints.

Inspection

Inspect "U" joints for signs of excessive wear. Check for excessive play. If abnormal wear or play is noticed, replace as necessary.

Reassembly

1) Fit "U" joint to steering shaft. Align steering shaft notch with lower "U" joint slot. Install boot and damping grommet. Fit steering box to frame while guiding pinion shaft into lower "U" joint.

2) Hand tighten steering box nuts. Place wheels in a straight-ahead position. Align pinion shaft and "U" joint. Tighten pinch bolt. Tighten gear box nuts. Connect gearshift linkage to gearbox. Check linkage for smooth operation.

TIGHTENING SPECIFICATIONS

Application	Ft. Lbs. (N.m)
Pinch Bolts	22 (30)
Steering Column-to-Instrument Panel	
Retaining Bolts	15 (20)
Shear Bolts	[1]
Steering Wheel Nut	37 (50)

[1] – Tighten until bolt head snaps off.

VOLKSWAGEN QUANTUM

DESCRIPTION

The Quantum uses a 2-piece collapsible steering column. A flange connects lower and upper column.

REMOVAL & INSTALLATION

STEERING COLUMN

CAUTION: Steering column is designed to be collapsible upon frontal impact. Applying excessive pressure, or causing impact to mainshaft during service, may cause the column to collapse.

Removal

1) Disconnect battery ground cable. Remove steering wheel and combination switch. From inside engine compartment, remove clamp bolt retaining steering shaft clamp to steering gear pinion shaft. Remove column cover bolts and steering column covers. *See Fig. 1.*

2) Pry lock washer from steering shaft. Remove spring. Remove contact ring and steering lock assembly. Remove support ring from column tube. *See Fig. 1.*

3) Punch and drill out shear bolt retaining column tube to dash. Remove Allen bolt. Remove dust boot from floorboard. Remove steering column tube and shaft as an assembly.

Installation

1) Install assembled steering column into vehicle. Install shear bolt and Allen bolt finger tight. Fit dust boot into floorboard. Place clamp onto steering gear pinion shaft.

2) Place support ring into column tube. Install steering lock assembly onto steering column. Install contact ring, spring and new lock washer. Tighten Allen bolt. Tighten shear bolt until head snaps off.

3) Install upper and lower column covers. Install column switches and steering wheel.

Fig. 1: Exploded View of Upper Steering Column

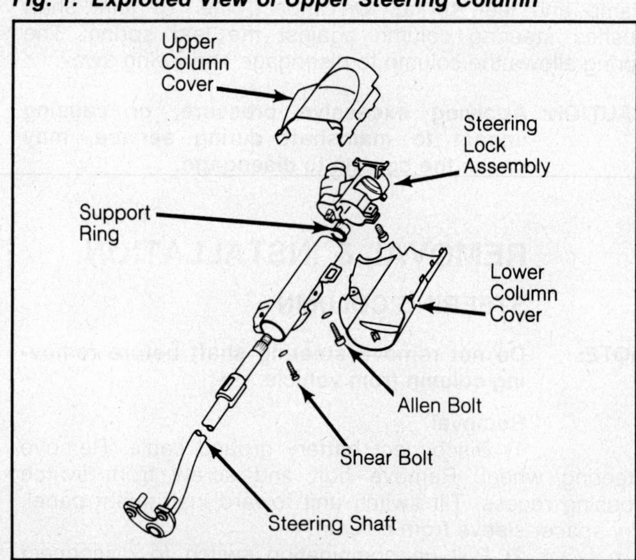

Courtesy of Volkswagen United States, Inc.

OVERHAUL

STEERING COLUMN

Disassembly

1) Remove lower flange tube clamp bolt from lower steering shaft. Separate flange tubes and remove bearing flange, bearing, support ring, spring and washer. *See Fig. 2.*

2) Push upper flange tube toward steering shaft until components can be separated. Remove flange tube bushings with plastic bushings. *See Fig. 2.* Remove joint disc bolts and pinion clamp bolt. Slide column tube from steering shaft. *See Fig. 1.*

VOLKSWAGEN QUANTUM (Cont.)

Fig. 2: Exploded View of Lower Steering Column

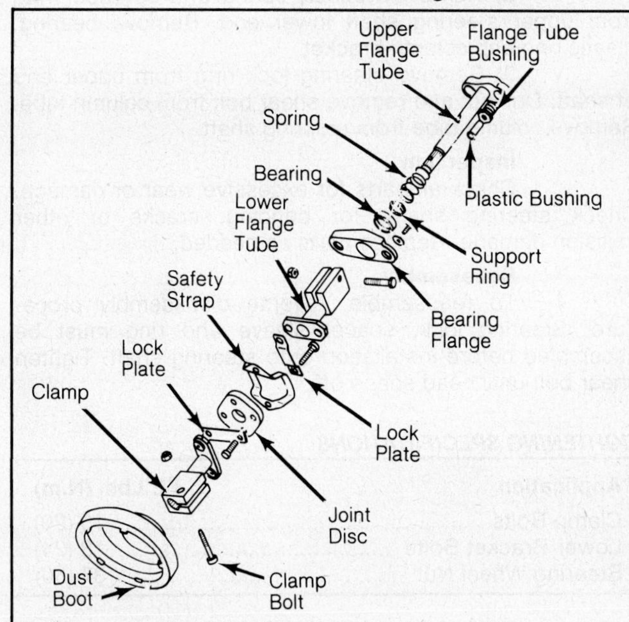

Courtesy of Volkswagen United States, Inc.

Inspection

Check joint disc, safety strap and lock plates for damage or wear. Check steering shaft, support ring and steering lock assembly for wear or damage. Replace components as necessary.

Reassembly

To reassemble steering column, reverse disassembly procedure. Press flange tube bushing and plastic bushing in by hand.

TIGHTENING SPECIFICATIONS

Application	Ft. Lbs. (N.m)
Allen Bolt	15 (20)
Clamp Bolt	22 (30)
Lock Plate Bolts	18 (24)
Lower Flange Tube Bolt	22 (30)
Steering Wheel Retaining Nut	29 (39)

VOLKSWAGEN VANAGON

DESCRIPTION

The Volkswagen Vanagon uses an energy-absorbing 2-piece steering column. The column is attached to the dash with brackets and to the floorboard with a boot flange. Lower steering shaft connects to the transfer gear with a flange.

REMOVAL & INSTALLATION

STEERING COLUMN

CAUTION: Steering column incorporates shear pins which allow the column to collapse upon frontal impact. Applying excessive pressure, or causing impact to mainshaft during service, may cause the column to collapse.

Removal

1) Remove horn pad and steering wheel. Remove column covers. Disconnect combination switch wires. Remove combination switch.

2) Using a puller, remove steering lock and spacer sleeve. Remove upper steering shaft-to-upper flange clamp bolt.

3) Remove lower column clamp bolts. Remove upper column retaining bolts. Remove upper steering shaft and column tube as an assembly.

4) Remove lower flange-to-lower steering shaft clamp bolt. Remove dust boot-to-floorboard bolts. Remove lower steering shaft.

Installation

1) To install, reverse removal procedure. Install new gasket on dust boot. Install steering shaft and column tube as an assembly.

Fig. 1: Exploded View of Steering Column

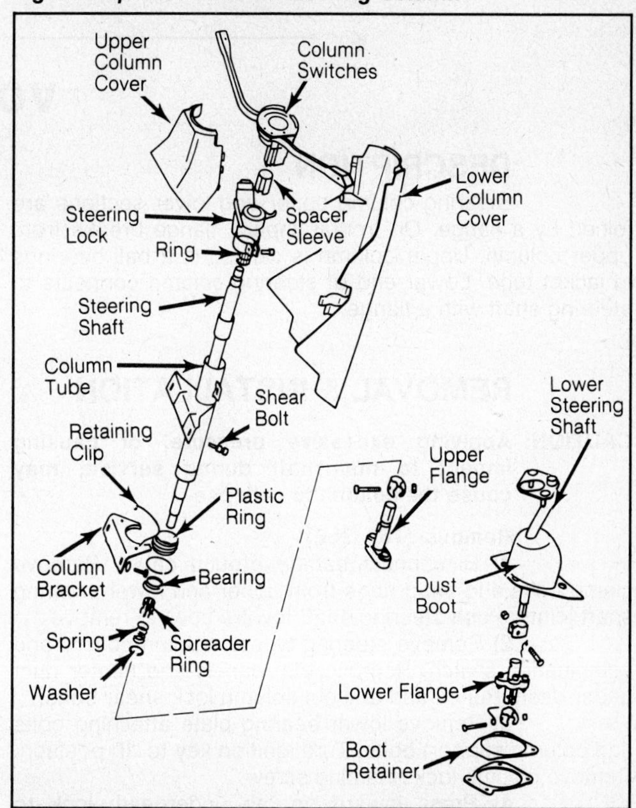

Courtesy of Volkswagen United States, Inc.

2) When installing steering lock and spacer sleeve, clamp lower steering shaft to upper flange with Clamp (VW 267a).

VOLKSWAGEN VANAGON (Cont.)

3) Ensure distance from top of column tube to top of upper steering shaft (with steering wheel and nut installed) is 1.634" (41.5 mm). Space between combination switch and steering wheel should be .079-157" (2-4 mm). *See Fig. 2.*

Fig. 2: Measurements for Installing Spacer Sleeve

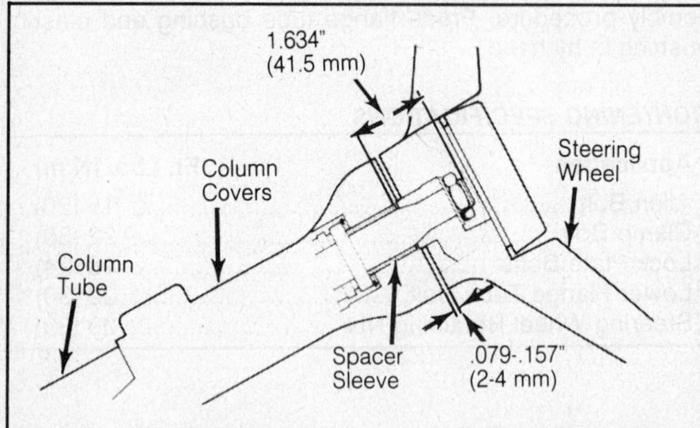

Courtesy of Volkswagen United States, Inc.

OVERHAUL

STEERING COLUMN

Disassembly

1) Remove flange from lower steering shaft. Remove clamp from flange. Remove gasket and boot retainer from dust boot.

2) Remove washer, spring and spreader ring from upper steering shaft lower end. Remove bearing, plastic ring and column bracket.

3) Remove steering lock ring from upper end of shaft. Drill out and remove shear bolt from column tube. Remove column tube from steering shaft.

Inspection

Check all parts for excessive wear or damage. Check steering shafts for bending, cracks or other collision damage. Replace parts as needed.

Reassembly

To reassemble, reverse disassembly procedure. Steering lock, spacer sleeve and ring must be assembled before installation onto steering shaft. Tighten shear bolt until head snaps off.

TIGHTENING SPECIFICATIONS

Application	Ft. Lbs. (N.m)
Clamp Bolts	15 (20)
Lower Bracket Bolts	18 (24)
Steering Wheel Nut	37 (50)

VOLVO

DESCRIPTION

Steering column upper and lower sections are joined by a flange. On frontal impact, flange breaks from upper column. Upper column is carried in 2 ball bearings in jacket tube. Lower end of steering column connects to steering shaft with a flange.

REMOVAL & INSTALLATION

CAUTION: Applying excessive pressure, or causing impact to mainshaft during service, may cause the column to collapse.

Removal (760 GLE)

1) Disconnect battery ground cable. Remove clamp bolts and snap rings from upper and lower steering shaft joints. Push steering shaft toward cowl to remove.

2) Remove steering wheel, column covers and combination switch. Remove trim panels and heater duct under dash. Punch and drill out column lock shear bolts.

3) Remove lower bearing plate attaching bolts and column support bolts. Turn ignition key to "II" position. Remove column lock retaining screw.

4) Press inward on tab underneath lock to remove lock. Remove key and wiring connector. Remove column guide from bracket. Remove column.

Installation

To install, reverse removal procedure. After installing column lock bracket and lower bearing plate, tighten new shear bolts until heads break off.

Removal (All Except 760 GLE)

1) Disconnect battery ground cable. Disconnect upper "U" joint from upper and lower steering shafts. Remove steering wheel, column covers and switches.

2) From underneath instrument panel, remove trim panel and console side panel. Disconnect connector at steering lock. Drill lock retaining screws and remove with screw extractor.

3) Remove defroster duct. Remove column lower bracket. Pull column toward seat to remove firewall seal. Remove column and lock as an assembly.

Installation

1) Install lock so upper edge is 3.8" (97 mm) from upper edge of column. *See Fig. 1.* Ensure both plastic guides and spacers are in place. Washers must face downward.

2) Insert column through firewall. Install shear bolts and column clamp finger tight. Adjust column position so lock protrudes .53-.65" (13.5-16.5 mm) from dash, measured at lock position "II".

3) Column must not contact upper attachment plastic guides. Adjust dash beam if needed. Tighten column clamp and bracket bolts. Install defroster duct and firewall seal.

VOLVO (Cont.)

4) Loosely install upper "U" joint on steering shaft. Install lower steering shaft flange to upper "U" joint. Check distance between lower steering shaft shoulder and upper "U" joint.

5) Distance should be .40-.75" (10-19 mm). If distance is incorrect, pull up lower joint cover, loosen "U" joint clamp bolts and move lower shaft up or down as necessary.

6) Check distance between steering wheel and upper column cover. If clearance is not .04-.08" (1-2 mm), pull up lower joint cover. Loosen lower "U" joint bolts. Move lower shaft up or down.

7) To complete installation, reverse removal procedure. Tighten shear bolts until heads break off. If necessary, place one or 2 flat washers between steering wheel and upper bearing spring to eliminate rattling.

OVERHAUL

STEERING COLUMN

Disassembly

1) Remove shaft from column. Clamp steering shaft in a soft-jawed vise. Using a hammer and open end wrench, remove bearing race.

2) Remove snap ring, plastic cone, bearing housing, metal cone, washer, spring and washer. Using a punch, tap out inner race first, then outer race.

Inspection

1) Check all bearing surfaces for excessive wear or scoring. Check "U" joints for excessive play. Replace worn or damaged parts as necessary.

2) Upper column length must be 28.59-28.67" (726.2-728.2 mm). If length is incorrect, replace shaft. To replace upper bearing, press bearing housing toward shaft.

Reassembly

1) Grease inside of race. Install race so that flats of race align with flats of shaft. Race should be 1.98" (50.3 mm) from shaft flat end.

2) Using Drift and Handle (2724 and 1801), install new bearing. Install washer, spring, washer and metal cone. Temporarily place 2 flat washers between upper washer and metal cone, on each side of shaft.

3) Install bearing housing and plastic cone (facing housing). Install snap ring. Remove 2 flat washers.

Fig. 1: Steering Wheel Lock Position

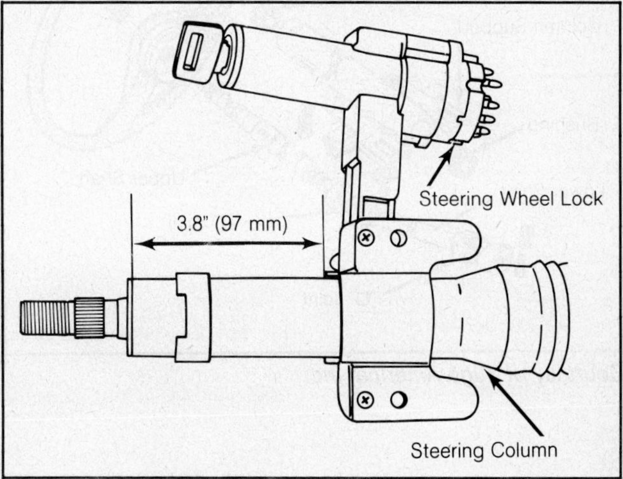

Ensure lock is properly positioned. Courtesy of Volvo Cars of North America.

TIGHTENING SPECIFICATIONS

Application	Ft. Lbs. (N.m)
Lower "U" Joint Clamp Bolt	
760 GLE	15 (20)
All Other Models	13-21 (18-28)
Steering Wheel Nut	
760 GLE	21-27 (28-37)
All Other Models	33-55 (45-75)
Upper "U" Joint Clamp Bolt	
760 GLE	15 (20)
All Other Models	14-22 (19-30)

YUGO

DESCRIPTION

Steering shaft upper and lower sections are joined by "U" joints. On frontal impact, "U" joints act to relieve direct impact force. Upper shaft is carried in 2 bushings in column tube. Lower end of steering shaft connects to pinion shaft with a "U" joint.

REMOVAL & INSTALLATION

Removal

1) Disconnect battery ground cable. Remove horn pad by squeezing top and bottom toward center of pad, and unfolding upper edge of pad. Disconnect electrical wiring. Remove steering wheel nut.

2) Remove steering wheel. Remove "U" joint-to-gearbox retaining bolt. Remove dust cover. Remove column bracket-to-dashboard bolts and nuts. Remove column and shaft toward passenger compartment.

Installation

Before installation, lubricate all moving parts. To install, reverse removal procedure.

OVERHAUL

STEERING COLUMN

Disassembly

Remove shaft from column. Remove upper-to-lower shaft "U" joint retaining bolt. Remove upper shaft from lower shaft. Remove upper and lower steering shaft bushings.

Inspection

Inspect upper and lower bushings for looseness and/or scoring. Check "U" joints for excessive play. Inspect steering shafts for bending or abnormal wear.

Steering Columns

YUGO (Cont.)

Fig. 1: Exploded View Of Yugo Steering Column Assembly

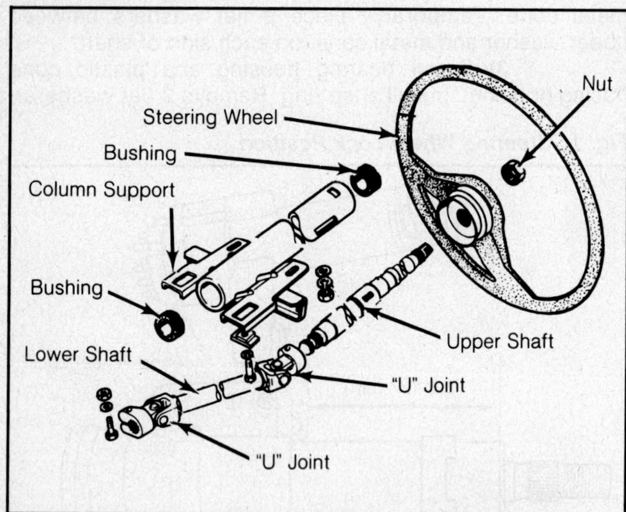

Courtesy of Yugo America, Inc.

Reassembly

Lubricate all moving parts. Replace steering shaft bushings. Attach lower steering shaft to upper steering shaft. Install shaft assembly into column.

Steering Gears & Linkage

CHEVROLET & ISUZU RACK & PINION

Chevrolet: Spectrum, Sprint
Isuzu: I-Mark

DESCRIPTION

Steering gear is a rack and pinion type. Steering gear is connected to the steering knuckles with tie rods. A flexible coupling connects pinion shaft to steering shaft.

ADJUSTMENTS

Any adjustments are made during the reassembly procedure. See OVERHAUL in this article.

REMOVAL & INSTALLATION

Removal

1) Disconnect battery ground cable. Raise and support vehicle. Remove wheels, tie rod end cotter pins and castle nuts. Using tie rod end puller, separate tie rod ends from steering knuckles.

2) Remove steering column protector. Remove flexible coupling clamp bolt. Remove steering bracket retaining nuts. Remove steering gear being careful not to damage rubber boots.

Installation

To install, reverse removal procedure. Check and adjust toe-in.

OVERHAUL

STEERING GEAR

Disassembly

1) Place steering gear in a soft-jawed vise. Loosen tie rod end lock nut. Disconnect tie rod ends from tie rods. Remove retaining clip and retaining clamp from rubber boots. Remove rubber boots.

2) Remove tie rod end lock nut. Remove adjusting plug lock nut (I-Mark and Spectrum) or cap

Fig. 1: Exploded View of I-Mark & Spectrum Rack & Pinion Steering Gear

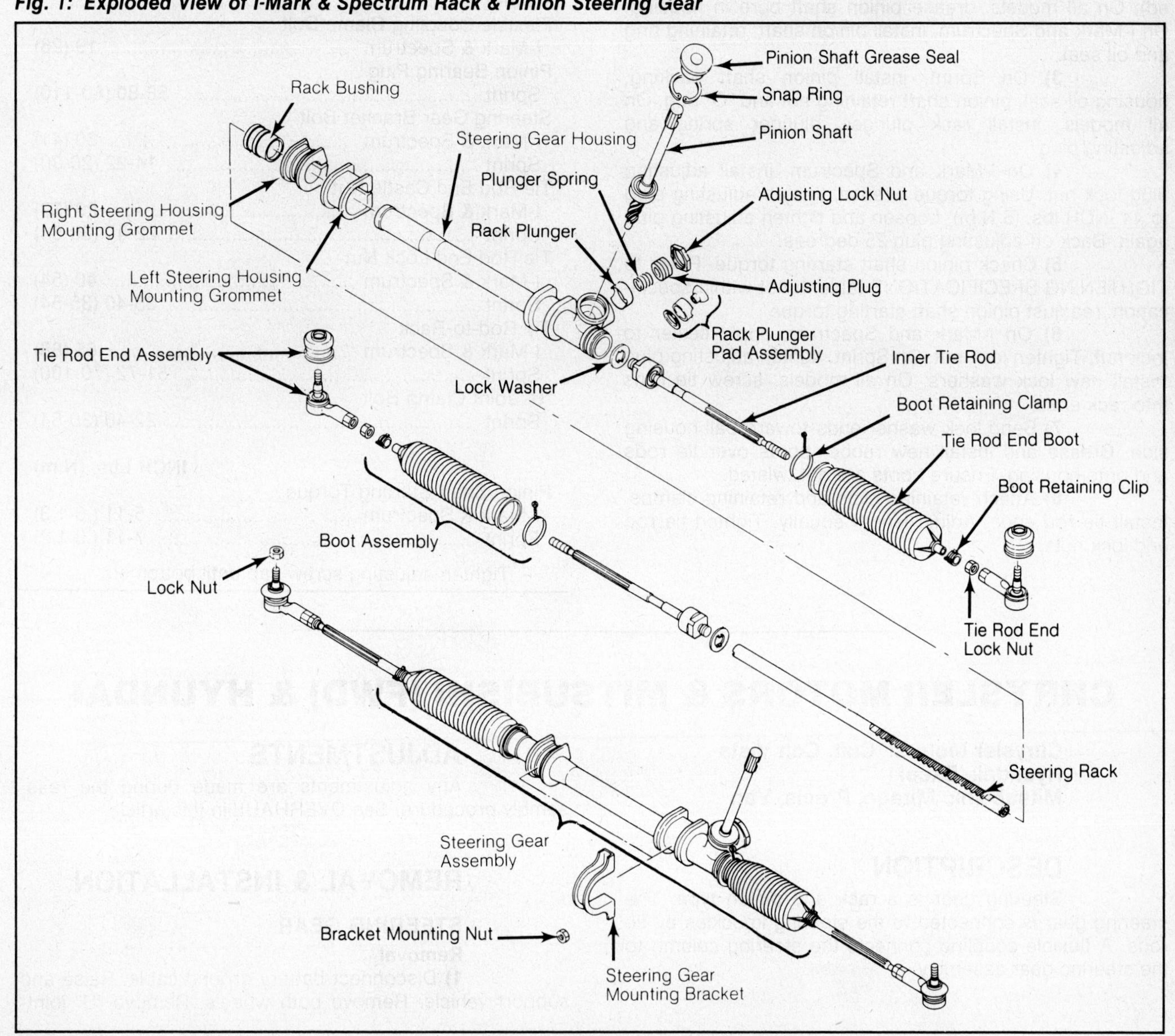

Sprint rack and pinion steering gear is similar. Courtesy of General Motors Corp.

CHEVROLET & ISUZU RACK & PINION (Cont.)

(Sprint). Remove adjusting plug, plunger spring and rack plunger from steering gear. *See Fig. 1.*

3) Remove tie rods from steering gear by turning up staked section of lock washer. Unscrew tie rod ends from rack. On I-Mark and Spectrum, remove pinion shaft grease seal and snap ring.

4) On Sprint, remove pinion shaft packing, housing oil seal, pinion shaft retaining nut and "O" ring. On all models, pull pinion shaft and steering rack from steering gear housing. On Sprint, remove pinion shaft needle bearing if loose or worn.

Inspection

Check rack for bent or damaged teeth. If pinion shaft gear or bearing is worn, replace pinion shaft and bearing as an assembly. Check tie rod assemblies for wear or damage. Replace components as necessary.

Reassembly

1) Clamp steering gear housing in a soft-jawed vise. Coat all moving parts with multipurpose grease. Insert rack into housing. Center rack in housing.

2) On Sprint, replace needle bearing (if removed). On all models, grease pinion shaft bore in housing. On I-Mark and Spectrum, install pinion shaft, retaining ring and oil seal.

3) On Sprint, install pinion shaft packing, housing oil seal, pinion shaft retaining nut and "O" ring. On all models, install rack plunger, plunger spring and adjusting plug.

4) On I-Mark and Spectrum, install adjusting plug lock nut. Using torque wrench, tighten adjusting plug to 44 INCH lbs. (5 N.m). Loosen and tighten adjusting plug again. Back off adjusting plug 25 degrees.

5) Check pinion shaft starting torque. Refer to TIGHTENING SPECIFICATIONS table. If not within specification, readjust pinion shaft starting torque.

6) On I-Mark and Spectrum, apply sealer to lock nut. Tighten lock nut. On Sprint, tighten adjusting plug Install new lock washers. On all models, screw tie rods into rack ends.

7) Bend lock washer ends toward ball housing side. Grease and install new rubber boots over tie rods and onto housing. Ensure boots are not twisted.

8) Attach retaining clips and retaining clamps. Install tie rod ends. Adjust length equally. Tighten tie rod end lock nuts.

Fig. 2: Measuring Tie Rod Length

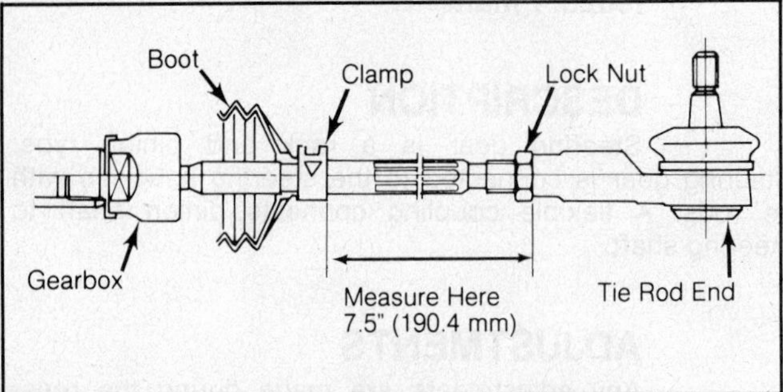

Courtesy of General Motors Corp.

TIGHTENING SPECIFICATIONS

Application	Ft. Lbs. (N.m)
Adjusting Screw Lock Nut	
I-Mark & Spectrum	49 (66)
Adjusting Screw Cap	
Sprint	[1]
Flexible Coupling Clamp Bolt	
I-Mark & Spectrum	19 (26)
Pinion Bearing Plug	
Sprint	58-80 (80-110)
Steering Gear Bracket Bolt	
I-Mark & Spectrum	30 (41)
Sprint	14-22 (20-30)
Tie Rod End Castle Nut	
I-Mark & Spectrum	29 (39)
Sprint	22-40 (30-54)
Tie Rod End Lock Nut	
I-Mark & Spectrum	40 (54)
Sprint	25-40 (35-54)
Tie Rod-to-Rack	
I-Mark & Spectrum	65 (88)
Sprint	51-72 (70-100)
"U" Joint Clamp Bolt	
Sprint	22-40 (30-54)
	INCH Lbs. (N.m)
Pinion Shaft Starting Torque	
I-Mark & Spectrum	5-11 (.6-1.3)
Sprint	7-11 (.8-1.3)

[1] – Tighten adjusting screw cap until bottomed.

CHRYSLER MOTORS & MITSUBISHI (FWD) & HYUNDAI

Chrysler Motors: Colt, Colt Vista
Hyundai: Excel
Mitsubishi: Mirage, Precis, Van

DESCRIPTION

Steering gear is a rack and pinion type. The steering gear is connected to the steering knuckles by tie rods. A flexible coupling connects the steering column to the steering gear assembly.

ADJUSTMENTS

Any adjustments are made during the reassembly procedure. See OVERHAUL in this article.

REMOVAL & INSTALLATION

STEERING GEAR

Removal

1) Disconnect battery ground cable. Raise and support vehicle. Remove both wheels. Remove "U" joint-

CHRYSLER MOTORS & MITSUBISHI (FWD) & HYUNDAI (Cont.)

Fig. 1: Exploded View of Colt Vista, Excel & Precis Rack & Pinion Steering Gear

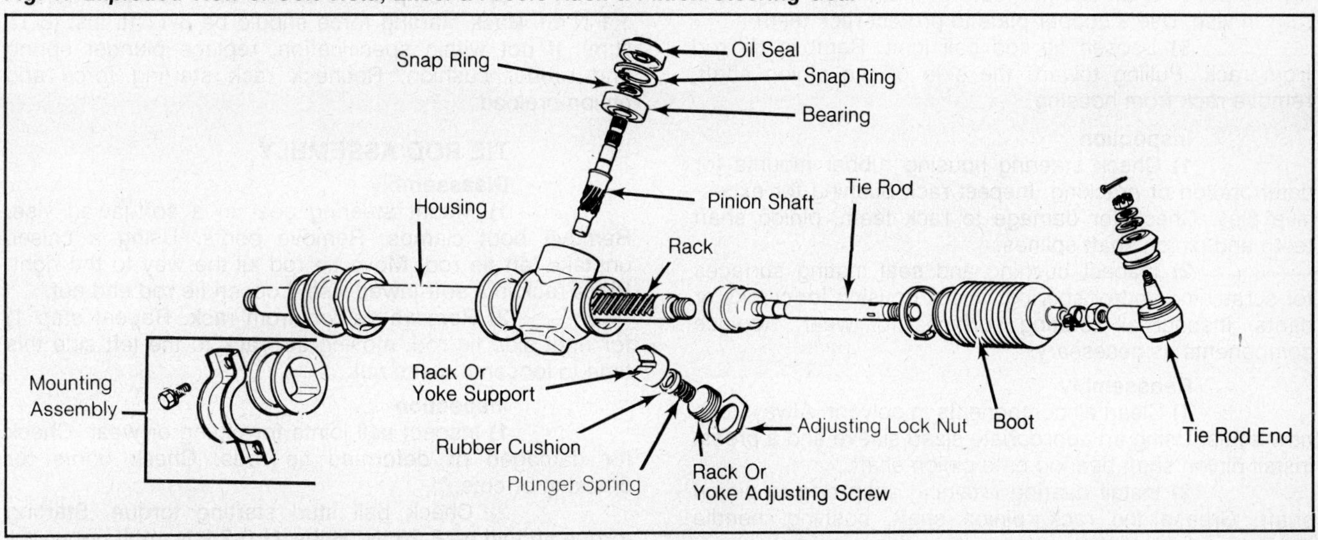

Colt Vista steering gear is shown. Excel and Precis are similar. Courtesy of Chrysler Motors.

to-pinion shaft clamp bolt. Remove tie rod end cotter pins and castle nuts.

2) Using a tie rod puller, separate tie rods from steering knuckles. Remove steering gear mounting bolts. Remove steering gear. Do not damage rubber boots.

Installation

To install, reverse removal procedure. Check and adjust toe-in.

OVERHAUL

Disassembly

1) Mount steering unit in a soft-jawed vise. Remove tie rod assemblies. Remove adjusting plug lock nut. Remove adjusting plug, plunger spring, rubber cushion and rack support from housing.

2) Using a screwdriver, pry pinion shaft oil seal from housing. Remove pinion bearing retaining snap ring from housing. Remove pinion bearing with pinion shaft.

3) Remove bearing retaining snap ring from pinion shaft. Using an appropriate sized sleeve and a press, remove bearing from pinion shaft. Remove boot retaining clamps. Remove boots.

4) Using a chisel, unstake right side (opposite pinion shaft) rack end tab washer. Move rack all the way

Fig. 3: Removing Rack From Housing

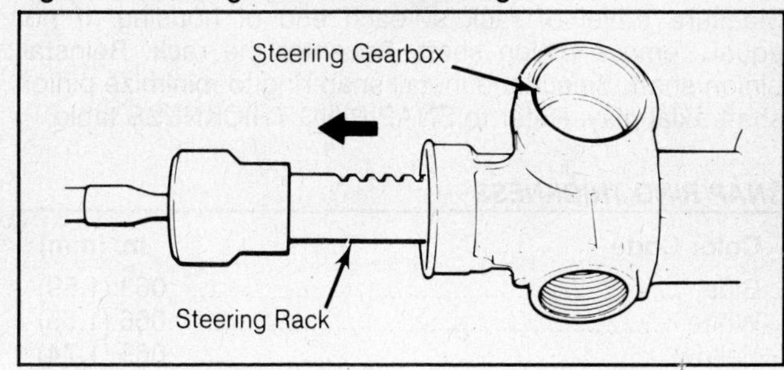

Courtesy of Chrysler Motors.

Fig. 2: Exploded View of Colt, Mirage & Van Rack & Pinion Steering Gear

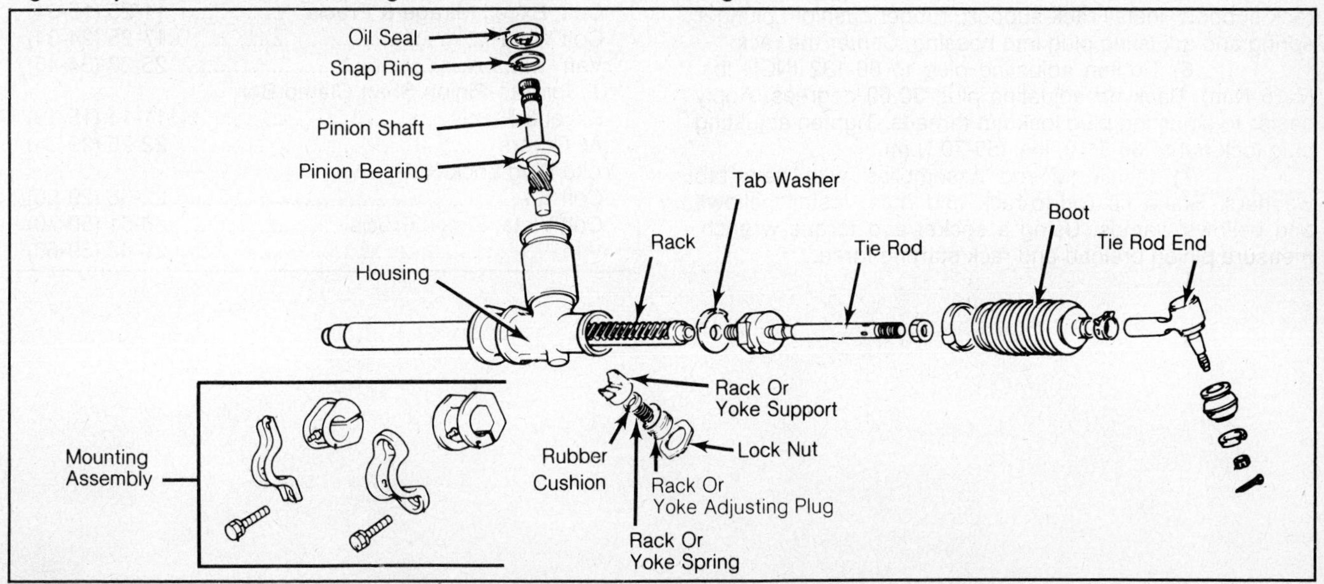

Colt rack and pinion steering gear is shown. Mirage and Van are similar. Courtesy of Chrysler Motors.

CHRYSLER MOTORS & MITSUBISHI (FWD) & HYUNDAI (Cont.)

toward pinion shaft side of housing. Place exposed end of rack in vise. Use a copper plate to protect rack teeth.

5) Loosen tie rod ball joint. Remove tie rod from rack. Pulling toward the side of the pinion shaft, remove rack from housing.

Inspection

1) Check steering housing rubber mounts for deterioration or cracking. Inspect rack bushing for excessive play. Check for damage to rack teeth, pinion shaft teeth and pinion shaft splines.

2) Inspect bushing and seal mating surfaces for scratching and/or scoring. Check housing for cracks or dents. Inspect all rotating surfaces for wear. Replace components as necessary.

Reassembly

1) Clean all components in solvent. Always use new seals. Using an appropriate sized sleeve and a press, install pinion shaft bearing onto pinion shaft.

2) Install bearing retaining snap ring to pinion shaft. Grease the rack, pinion shaft, bushing, needle bearing and other sliding surfaces.

NOTE: When lubricating components with grease, take care not to cover the air passage in the housing bushing.

3) Install rack into housing from the pinion shaft side of housing. Install pinion shaft into housing while meshing pinion shaft with rack teeth.

4) Check that rack is properly centered. Measure travel of rack at each end of housing. If not equal, remove pinion shaft. Recenter the rack. Reinstall pinion shaft. Select and install snap ring to minimize pinion shaft axial play. Refer to SNAP RING THICKNESS table.

SNAP RING THICKNESS

Color Code	In. (mm)
Blue	.063 (1.59)
White	.066 (1.66)
Yellow	.069 (1.74)

5) Grease oil seal lip and oil seal-to-housing mating surface. Install oil seal into housing. Grease the rack support. Install rack support, rubber cushion, plunger spring and adjusting plug into housing. Center the rack.

6) Tighten adjusting plug to 60-132 INCH lbs. (7-15 N.m). Back off adjusting plug 30-60 degrees. Apply sealer to adjusting plug lock nut threads. Tighten adjusting plug lock nut to 36-51 ft. lbs. (50-70 N.m).

7) Install tie rod assemblies with new tab washers. Stake tie rod-to-rack end nuts. Install bellows and bellows clamps. Using a socket and torque wrench, measure pinion preload and rack starting force.

8) Pinion preload should be 4-10 INCH lbs. (.4-1.1 N.m). Rack starting force should be 6-11 ft. lbs. (8-15 N.m). If not within specification, replace plunger spring and rubber cushion. Recheck rack starting force and pinion preload.

TIE ROD ASSEMBLY

Disassembly

1) Mount steering gear in a soft-jawed vise. Remove boot clamps. Remove boots. Using a chisel, unstake left tie rod. Move tie rod all the way to the right. Place rack in a soft-jawed vise. Loosen tie rod end nut.

2) Remove tie rod from rack. Repeat step **1)** for right side tie rod, moving the rack to the left side this time to loosen the end nut.

Inspection

1) Inspect ball joints for pitting or wear. Check for damaged or deformed tie rods. Check boots for cracking or cuts.

2) Check ball stud starting torque. Starting torque should be 8-26 INCH lbs. (1.0-2.9 N.m). If not within specifications, replace tie rod end.

3) Check for ball stud axial deflection. Deflection should be less than .06" (1.5 mm). If not within specification, replace tie rod end.

Reassembly

Install tie rod to rack. Tighten end nuts to 58-72 ft. lbs. (78-98 N.m). Install boots and boot clamps. Check and adjust toe-in.

TIGHTENING SPECIFICATIONS

Application	Ft. Lbs. (N.m)
Housing-to-Crossmember Bolt	
Colt, Colt Vista & Mirage	43-58 (60-78)
Excel & Precis	22-29 (29-39)
Van	51-65 (70-90)
Tie Rod-to-Rack	58-72 (78-98)
Tie Rod End Lock Nut	
Colt	25-36 (34-50)
Colt Vista, Excel, Mirage & Precis	36-40 (50-54)
Van	47-58 (65-78)
Tie Rod End Castle Nut	
Colt, Excel, Mirage & Precis	11-25 (15-34)
Colt Vista	17-25 (24-34)
Van	25-33 (34-45)
"U" Joint-to-Pinion Shaft Clamp Bolt	
Excel & Precis	11-14 (15-19)
All Others	22-25 (29-34)
Yoke Plug Lock Nut	
Colt	22-36 (29-50)
Colt Vista, Excel, Precis	36-51 (50-70)
Van	29-43 (39-60)

Steering Gears & Linkage
CHRYSLER MOTORS & MITSUBISHI
RECIRCULATING BALL

Chrysler Motors: Conquest,
Raider, Ram 50
Mitsubishi: Montero, Pickup, Starion

NOTE: Linkage information in this article applies to all models. Steering gear information applies only to Pickup and Ram-50 with manual steering. For information on power steering gear models, see appropriate article in POWER STEERING section.

DESCRIPTION

STEERING GEAR

Steering system is a variable ratio recirculating ball type. The variable ratio minimizes gear ratio in straight-ahead position, resulting in high on-center stability. Gear ratio increases as the wheel is turned from center, allowing easy turning.

STEERING LINKAGE

Linkage consists of an idler arm, relay rod, adjustable tie rods and steering knuckles. Components are connected by ball joints. Linkage assembly is connected to steering gear by pitman arm.

ADJUSTMENTS

Any adjustments are made during reassembly procedure. See OVERHAUL in this article.

REMOVAL & INSTALLATION

TIE ROD ASSEMBLY

Removal

1) Remove cotter pins and castle nuts from ball joints at steering knuckle and relay rod end.

2) Using Puller (C-3894-A), separate tie rod ends from knuckle and relay rod end. Unscrew tie rod ends from adjusting sleeves.

Inspection

Check tie rod ends for damage. Check ball studs for looseness. Measure ball stud starting torque. If ball joint starting torque exceeds 9-26 INCH lbs. (1-3 N.m), replace tie rod end.

Installation

1) Install "O" ring on ball socket. Grease inside of tie rod end dust cover. Coat lower edge of cup with packing sealer. Install tie rod ends to adjusting sleeves.

2) Measure center-to-center distance between tie rod studs for both tie rod assemblies. Adjust center-to-center distance to 14.82" (376.0 mm).

3) An equal number of threads should be visible on each side of adjusting sleeve. Install tie rod assemblies to knuckle and relay rod.

4) Install castle nuts and new cotter pins. Tighten castle nuts to specification. See TIGHTENING SPECIFICATIONS table at end of article. Adjust toe. See WHEEL ALIGNMENT section.

RELAY ROD

Removal

Remove tie rod ends as previously described. Remove cotter pins and castle nuts from idler arm and pitman arm. Using Puller (C-3894-A), separate relay rod from idler arm and pitman arm.

Installation

1) To install relay rod, reverse removal procedure. Ensure dust covers are well greased and that lower edge of covers are coated with packing sealer.

2) Tighten castle nuts to specification. See TIGHTENING SPECIFICATIONS table at end of article. Always use new cotter pins.

IDLER ARM

Removal

Remove lock nut from idler arm. Using Puller (C-3894-A), separate relay rod from idler arm. Remove idler arm retaining bolts. Remove idler arm from frame.

Inspection

Check idler arm bushings for damage or wear. Check ball stud on idler arm for looseness.

Installation

1) Apply soapy water to bushings and idler arm. Press bushings into idler arm. Grease shaft and inside surface of bushings. Insert shaft into idler arm.

2) Install washer (knurled side toward bushing) and a new lock nut. Position idler arm. *See Fig. 2.* Tighten lock nut to 29-43 ft. lbs. (39-58 N.m).

Fig. 1: Exploded View of Steering Linkage

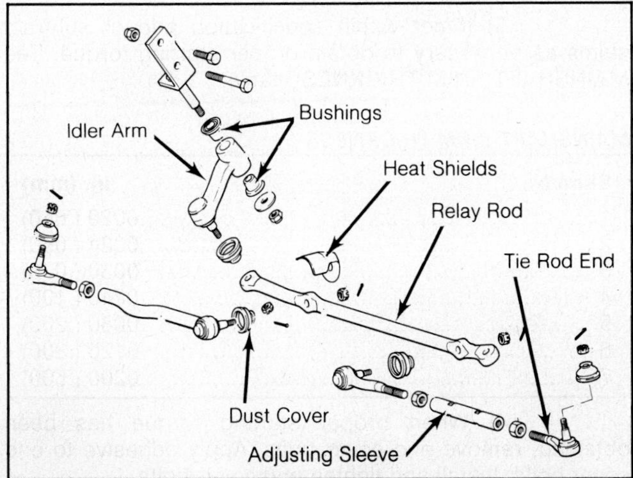

Courtesy of Chrysler Motors.

Fig. 2: Position of Idler Arm & Bracket

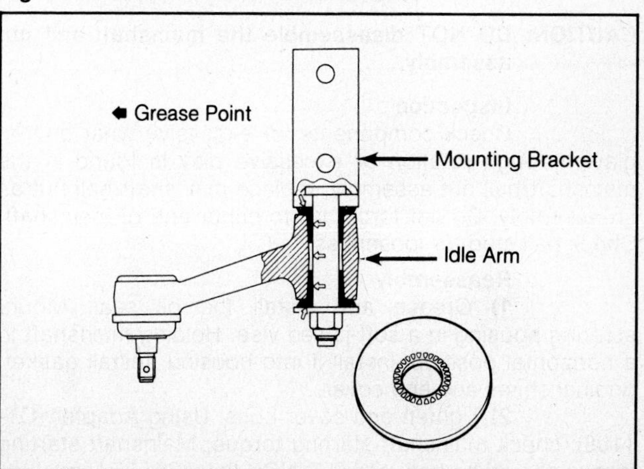

Courtesy of Chrysler Motors.

Steering Gears & Linkage
CHRYSLER MOTORS & MITSUBISHI
RECIRCULATING BALL (Cont.)

3) Place idler arm assembly in vise. Using a spring pull gauge, measure turning resistance. Turning resistance should be 84-216 INCH lbs. (9-24 N.m).

4) If not within specification, loosen or tighten lock nut to obtain proper resistance. Install idler arm to frame. Attach relay rod to idler arm.

STEERING GEAR & PITMAN ARM

Removal

1) Disconnect battery ground cable. Remove "U" joint-to-pinion shaft clamp bolt. Disconnect steering shaft from pinion shaft. Raise and support vehicle.

2) Remove pitman arm cotter pin and castle nut. Using Puller (C-3894-A), separate relay rod from pitman arm. Remove steering gear mounting bolts.

3) Remove steering gear. Remove cross shaft nut and lock washer. Mark cross shaft and pitman arm for reassembly reference. Using Puller (CT-1106), separate pitman arm from cross shaft.

Installation

1) Aligning marks made during removal, install pitman arm on cross shaft. Install and tighten lock washer and nut. Install steering shaft to pinion shaft.

2) Mount steering gear to frame. Tighten steering gear mounting bolts and "U" joint-to-pinion shaft clamp bolt. Install relay rod on pitman arm. Tighten pitman arm castle nut. Install a new cotter pin.

OVERHAUL

STEERING GEAR

Disassembly

1) Remove breather plug. Drain gear oil. Remove upper cover bolts. Loosen adjusting screw lock nut. Turn adjusting screw in 2 or 3 turns.

2) Turn cross shaft full left. Turn it back to the right, counting the number of turns to reach full right. Turn cross shaft back half the number of turns to center.

3) Using a plastic hammer, tap bottom of cross shaft to remove. Remove cross shaft and upper cover as an assembly. DO NOT damage cross shaft oil seal.

4) Place upper cover in a soft-jawed vise. Turn adjusting screw to separate upper cover from cross shaft. Keep spacer for reassembly.

5) Remove end cover and mainshaft adjusting shims. Measure and record thickness of shims. Remove mainshaft/ball nut assembly, bearings and oil seals.

CAUTION: DO NOT disassemble the mainshaft/ball nut assembly.

Inspection

Check components for excessive wear or free play. If rough rotation or excessive play is found in the mainshaft/ball nut assembly, replace mainshaft/ball nut as an assembly. Do not force ball to either end of mainshaft. Check ball stud for looseness.

Reassembly

1) Grease and install the oil seal. Mount steering housing in a soft-jawed vise. Holding mainshaft in a horizontal position, install it into housing. Install gasket, original shims and end cover.

2) Tighten end cover bolts. Using Adapter (CT-1108), check mainshaft starting torque. Mainshaft starting torque should be between 3-5 INCH lbs. (.35-.55 N.m).

Fig. 3: Exploded View of Manual Steering Gear

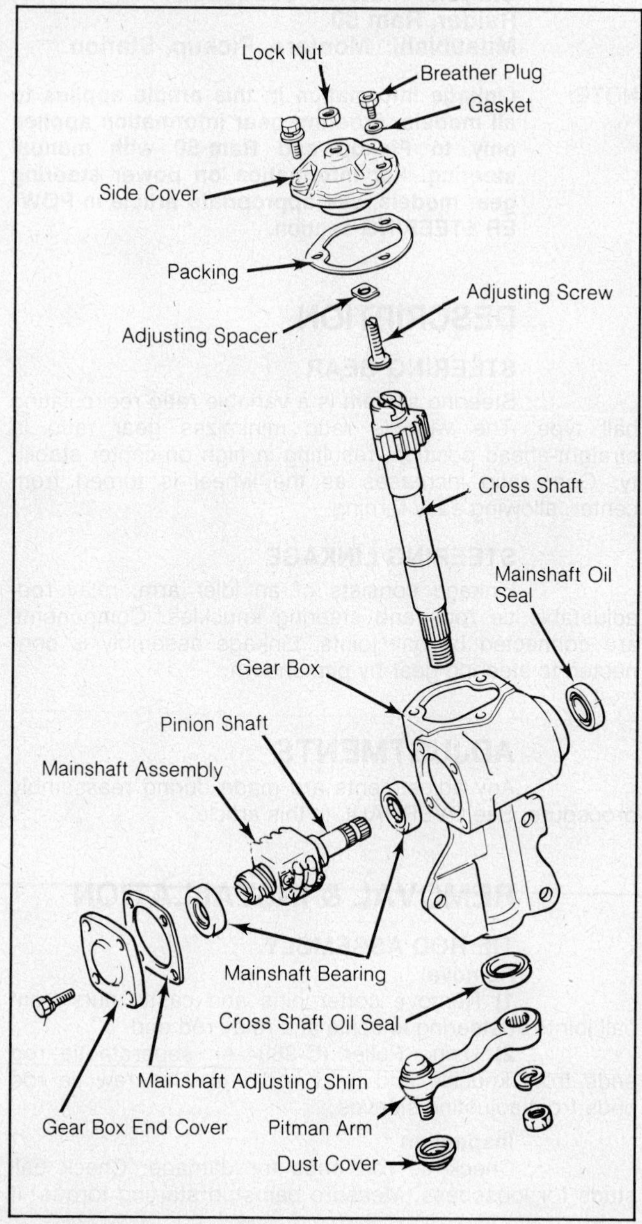

Courtesy of Chrysler Motors.

3) If not within specification add or subtract shims as necessary to obtain proper starting torque. See MAINSHAFT SHIM THICKNESS table.

MAINSHAFT SHIM THICKNESS

Shim No.	In. (mm)
1	.0020 (.050)
2	.0024 (.060)
3	.0030 (.070)
4	.0040 (.100)
5	.0080 (.200)
6.	0120 (.300)
7	.0200 (.500)

4) When proper starting torque has been obtained, remove end cover bolts. Apply adhesive to end cover bolts. Install and tighten end cover bolts.

CHRYSLER MOTORS & MITSUBISHI RECIRCULATING BALL (Cont.)

5) Install adjusting screw and original spacer on upper end of cross shaft. Use spacers to adjust axial play of cross shaft to 0-.002" (0-.05 mm). See CROSS SHAFT SPACER THICKNESS table.

CROSS SHAFT SPACER THICKNESS

Spacer No.	In. (mm)
1	.002 (.050)
2	.077 (1.95)
3	.079 (2.00)
4	.081 (2.05)
5	.083 (2.10)

6) When proper axial play of cross shaft is obtained, apply adhesive to adjusting screw. Lightly oil cross shaft. Grease the oil seal.

7) Insert cross shaft into housing so it meshes with ball nut rack. Do not damage bushing and oil seal. Position upper cover on cross shaft. Coat upper cover bolts with adhesive.

8) Install and tighten cover bolts. Install "O" ring on ball stud. Grease inside of dust cover. Install dust cover. Install pitman arm. Remove breather plug. Inject a small amount of gear oil.

9) Tighten adjusting screw until it bottoms. Move pitman arm side-to-side 3-5 times. Mount dial indicator so indicator is touching end of pitman arm.

10) Moving pitman arm by hand, measure steering gear backlash. If backlash is more than .02" (.5 mm), loosen adjusting screw to increase backlash or tighten to decrease backlash.

11) Recheck mainshaft starting torque. Mainshaft starting torque should be between 3-5 INCH lbs. (.35-.55 N.m). Adjust as necessary.

12) Fill gear box with SAE 90 gear oil. Check oil level through breather hole. Proper level from hole is 1.4" (35 mm).

TIGHTENING SPECIFICATIONS

Application	Ft. Lbs. (N.m)
Gear Box-to-Frame Bolt & Nut	
All 4WD Vehicles	40-48 (55-65)
All RWD Vehicles	26-29 (35-39)
Gear Box Lower Cover Bolts	26-33 (35-45)
Gear Box Upper Cover Bolts	11-14 (15-19)
Idler Arm Bracket-to-Frame Bolt & Nut	
All 4WD Vehicles	40-48 (55-65)
All RWD Vehicls	26-29 (35-39)
Idler Arm-to-Bracket Lock Nut	29-43 (39-58)
Pitman Arm-to-Gear Box Nut	94-108 (128-147)
Relay Rod-to-Idler Arm Nut	26-33 (35-45)
Relay Rod-to-Pitman Arm Nut	26-33 (35-45)
Tie Rod Adjusting Sleeve Lock Nuts	
All 4WD Vehicles	48-58 (65-80)
All RWD Vehicles	36-40 (50-55)
Tie Rod End Castle Nuts	
All 4WD Vehicles	33 (45)
All RWD Vehicles	26-33 (35-45)

FORD MOTOR CO. & MAZDA RACK & PINION

Ford: Festiva, Tracer;
Mazda: RX7, 323, 626

DESCRIPTION

Rack and pinion type steering is mounted by rubber insulators to crossmember. Adjustment is provided for pinion gear preload. Pinion shaft is coupled to steering shaft. Tie rods connect end of rack to steering knuckles.

ADJUSTMENTS

Any adjustments are made during reassembly procedure. See OVERHAUL in this article.

REMOVAL & INSTALLATION

STEERING GEAR

Removal

1) Raise and support vehicle. Remove front wheels. Remove cotter pins and castle nuts from tie rod ends.

2) Using tie rod puller, separate tie rod ends from steering knuckles. Remove band securing rubber boot to steering gear. Pull boot upward.

3) Remove bolt and washer securing steering shaft-to-pinion coupler. Remove steering gear bracket bolts. Remove steering gear through left tie rod hole.

Installation

To install, reverse removal procedure. Check and adjust toe-in.

OVERHAUL

STEERING GEAR

Disassembly

1) Place steering gear in a soft-jawed vise. Mark threaded portion of tie rod for reassembly. Remove tie rod ends. Remove boot band on large diameter side of gear housing.

2) Using a screwdriver, unstake washer. Using 2 wrenches, hold geared portion of rack while turning tie rod side, separating tie rod from rack.

3) On Festiva, Tracer and 323, use a small screwdriver to remove oil seal. Remove stop ring and snap ring. On RX7 and 626, remove dust cover, lock nut and rear cover/oil seal.

4) On all models, grasp pinion shaft with pliers. Pull on pinion shaft while lightly tapping on gear housing with a soft hammer. Remove pinion assembly. Remove rack from side opposite of rack bushing side of housing.

FORD MOTOR CO. & MAZDA RACK & PINION (Cont)

CAUTION: If rack is taken out of wrong side, damage to rack bushing may result.

Fig. 1: Exploded View of Festiva, Tracer & 323 Steering Gear Assembly

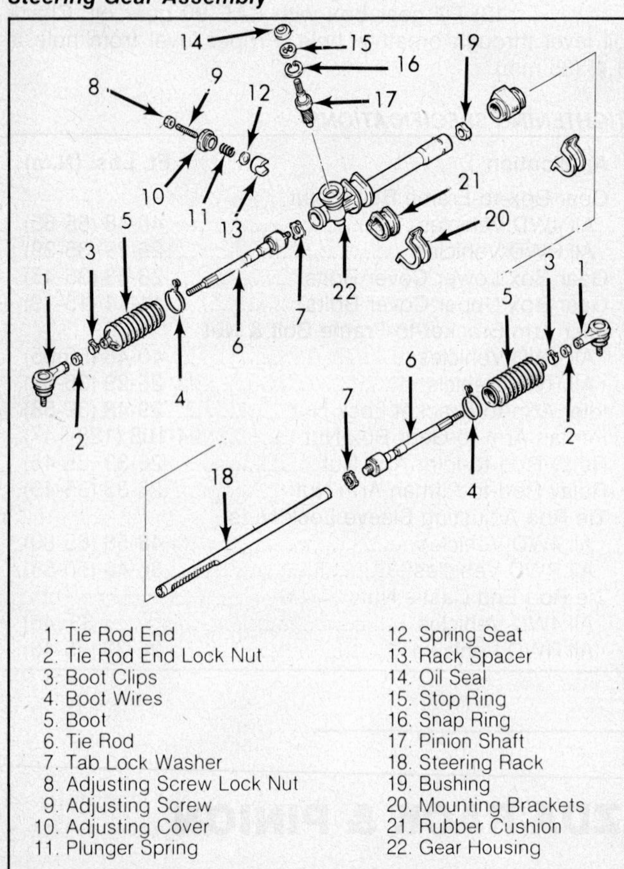

Courtesy of Mazda Motors Corp.

5) On RX7 and 626, the rack end lower bearing can be removed (if necessary). Heat the housing with hot water, about 176°F (80°C). After housing is heated, remove bearing by tapping on opposite end of housing.

Inspection

1) Check rubber boots, ball bearings and tooth surface of rack for wear or damage. Check tie rod ball joints for smooth operation. Replace parts as necessary.

2) Check sliding surface of rack support and gear housing for cracks or damage. Check rack bushing for excessive wear. Replace entire gear housing assembly if any of these parts are worn or damaged.

Reassembly (Festiva, Tracer & 323)

1) Apply lithium grease to ball bearing, roller bearing, inside of gear housing, lip of oil seal, sliding and backing surface of rack support, sliding surface of rack bushing, rack pinion teeth and ball joints.

2) Carefully insert non-toothed side of rack into pinion end of housing. Install pinion and bearing assembly. Ensure rack teeth and pinion mesh properly.

NOTE: If fit between housing and bearing is too tight, strike outer ring of bearing lightly while checking the meshing of rack and pinion.

3) Install snap ring. Install stopper with protruded portion inserted in gap of snap ring. Position a new seal in housing. Using a soft hammer, tap lightly on seal until it is flush with end surface of housing.

4) Install rack support, spring seat, spring and cover. Turn adjusting screw until tightening torque increases. Unscrew adjusting screw 0-15 degrees. Tighten lock nut. To complete reassembly, reverse disassembly procedure. To ensure correct steering position, adjust tie rod end length to .15-.55" (4-14 mm). *See Fig. 3.*

5) Using a spring scale and Adapter (49-0180-510b), measure pinion gear preload. Install adapter to gear shaft. Hook spring scale to adapter. Turn pinion at a

Fig. 2: Exploded View of RX7 & 626 Steering Gear Assembly

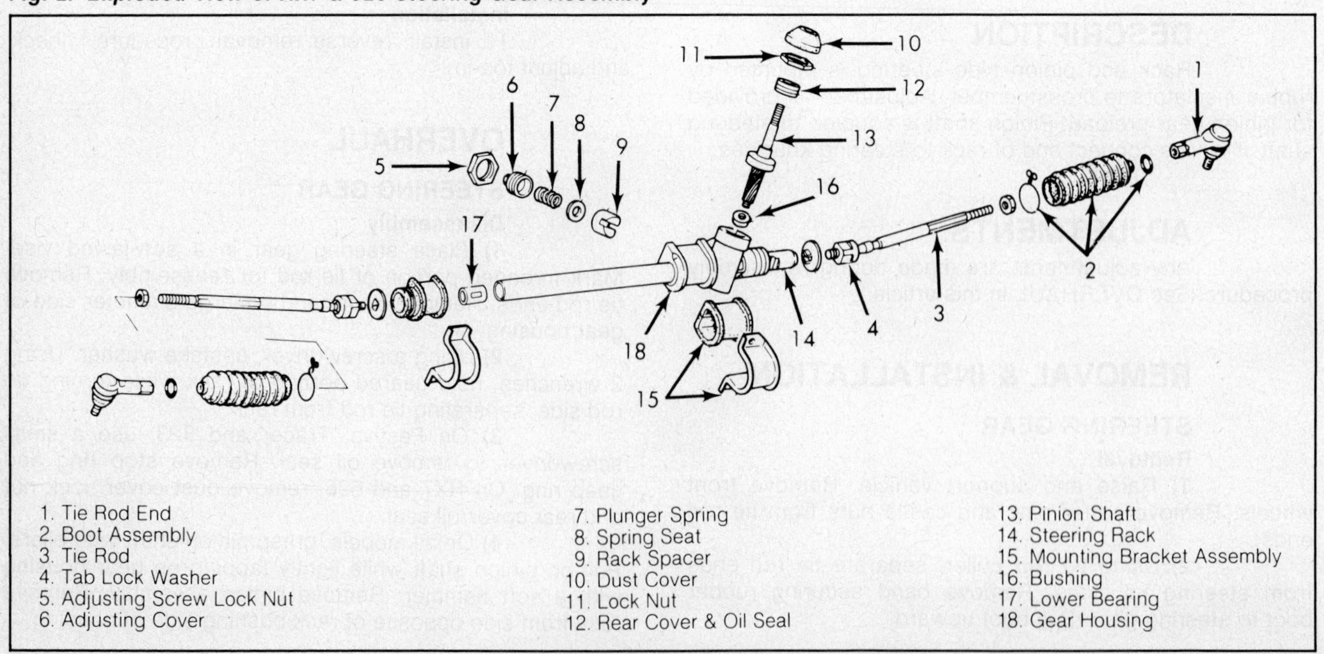

626 steering gear is shown. RX7 is similar. Courtesy of Mazda Motors Corp.

FORD MOTOR CO. & MAZDA RACK & PINION (Cont)

Fig. 3: Measuring Festiva, Tracer & 323 Tie Rod End Length

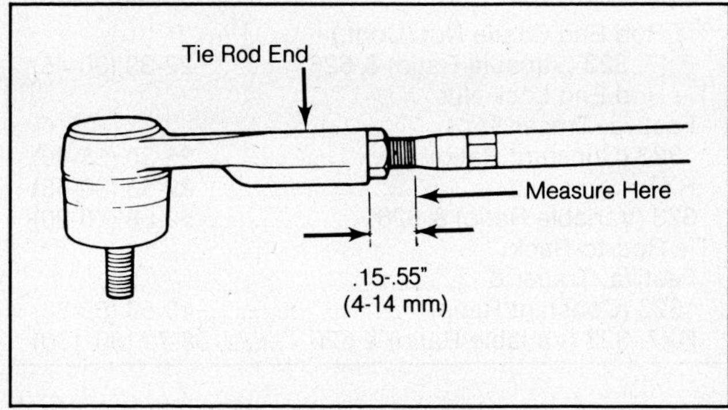

Courtesy of Mazda Motors Corp.

speed of one revolution per one to 2 seconds. Scale should read 8-11 INCH lbs. (.9-1.3 N.m).

6) If not within specification, readjust pinion preload with adjustment screw. After installation of steering gear assembly, center steering wheel. Adjust the distance from tie rod mounting hole of bracket to tie rod ball joint. *See Fig. 4.*

Fig. 4: Centering Festiva, Tracer & 323 Steering Gear

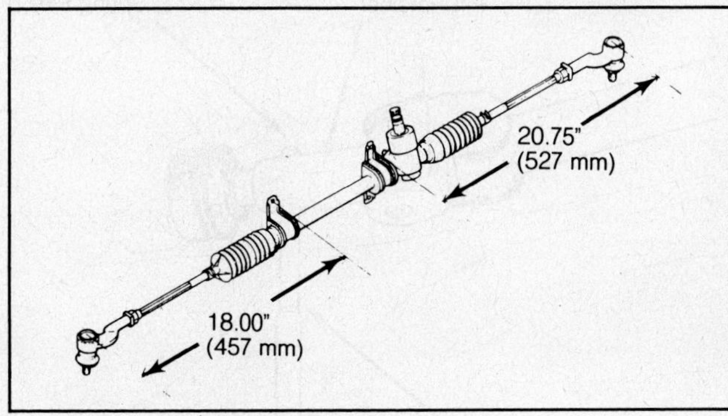

Courtesy of Mazda Motors Corp.

Reassembly (RX7 & 626)

1) Apply lithium grease to rack end lower bearing, inside of gear housing, lip of oil seal, sliding and backing surface of rack support, sliding surface of rack bushing, rack pinion teeth and ball joint of tie rods.

2) Press rack end lower bearing into place. Carefully install steering rack from pinion end of housing. Insert pinion with the notched edge of rack at central position of pinion. *See Fig. 5.*

Fig. 5: Location of Pinion on Rack

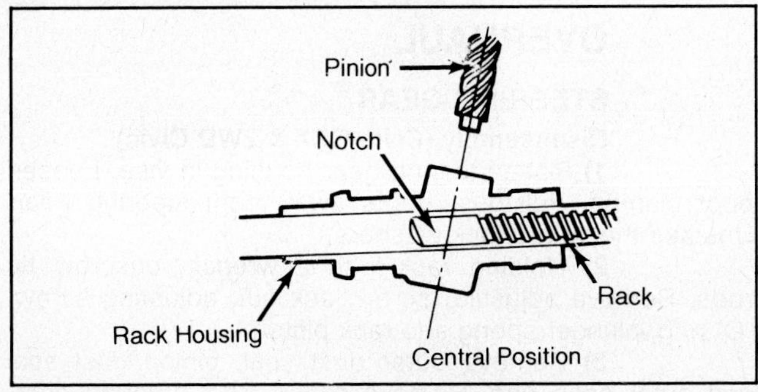

Courtesy of Mazda Motors Corp.

3) Apply grease to upper bearing and rear cover/oil seal. Install rear cover/oil seal and lock nut. Apply sealant to threaded part of lock nut.

4) Using a spring scale and Adapter (49-0180-510B), measure pinion gear preload. Install adapter to gear shaft. Scale should read 8-11 INCH lbs. (.9-1.3 N.m). Loosen rear cover. Adjust pinion torque to 1.74-2.6 INCH lbs. (.2-.3 N.m).

5) Tighten pinion shaft lock nut to 29-43 ft. lbs (39-59 N.m) for the RX7 and 51-65 ft. lbs. (69-88 N.m) for the 626. Recheck pinion torque. Readjust as necessary. Move rack so that the pinion gear is set in center position of rack gear. *See Fig. 6.*

6) Install pressure pad and spring. Coat adjustment cover with sealant. Install adjustment cover. Tighten cover to 86 INCH lbs. (10 N.m). Loosen adjustment cover. Tighten cover to 2.6 INCH lbs. (3 N.m). Back off adjustment cover 0-15 degrees.

Fig. 6: Pinion Gear Position

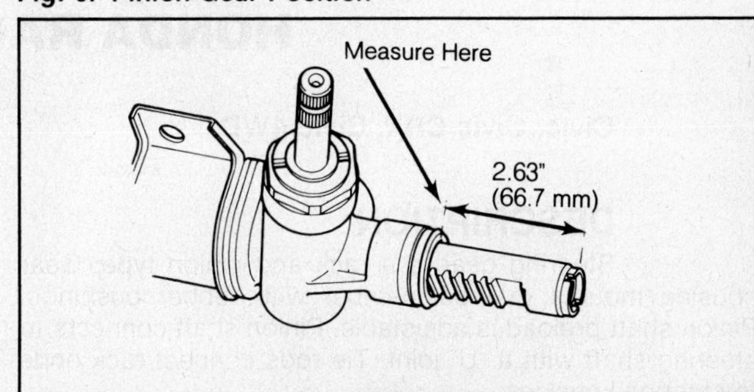

Courtesy of Mazda Motors Corp.

7) Install and tighten lock nut to 43-54 ft. lbs. (59-75 N.m). With pinion in the neutral position and using a spring scale and Adapter (49 0180 510B), measure pinion torque. Neutral pinion torque specifications should be .6-.9 INCH lbs. (.7-1 N.m). In any other position torque should be .6-1.3 INCH lbs. (.7-1.5 N.m).

8) To complete reassembly, reverse disassembly procedure. Install new oil seal and dust cover. Install and adjust tie rod ends to .047" (12 mm). *See Fig. 7.*

Fig. 7: Measuring 626 Tie Rod End Length

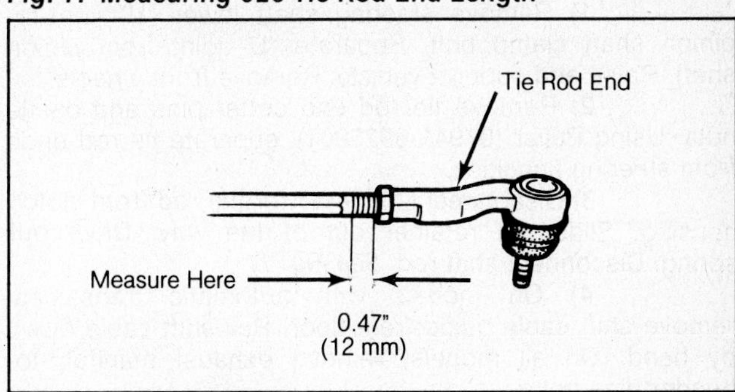

Courtesy of Mazda Motors Corp.

FORD MOTOR CO. & MAZDA RACK & PINION (Cont.)

TIGHTENING SPECIFICATIONS

Application	Ft. Lbs. (N.m)
Adjusting Screw Lock Nut	
Festiva, Tracer, RX7 & 323 (Constant Ratio)	29-43 (39-59)
323 (Variable Ratio) & 626	43-54 (59-75)
"U" Joint-to-Pinion Clamp Bolt	13-20 (18-27)
Mounting Bracket Bolt	
All Except 626	23-34 (32-47)
626	12-17 (16-23)
Pinion Shaft Lock Nut	
RX7,	29-43 (39-59)
323 (Variable Ratio) & 626	50-65 (70-88)
Tie Rod End Castle Nut	
Festiva, Tracer & 323 (Constant Ratio)	32-40 (43-54)

TIGHTENING SPECIFICATIONS (Cont.)

Application	Ft. Lbs. (N.m)
Tie Rod End Castle Nut (Cont.)	
RX7, 323 (Variable Ratio) & 626	22-33 (30-45)
Tie Rod End Lock Nut	
Festiva, Tracer & 323 (Constant Ratio)	25-30 (35-40)
RX7	22-33 (30-45)
323 (Variable Ratio) & 626	50-58 (70-80)
Tie Rod-to-Rack	
Festiva, Tracer & 323 (Constant Ratio)	43-58 (59-80)
RX7, 323 (Variable Ratio) & 626	58-72 (80-100)

HONDA RACK & PINION

Civic, Civic CRX, Civic 4WD

DESCRIPTION

Steering gear is a rack and pinion type. Gear housing mounts to crossmember with rubber bushings. Pinion shaft preload is adjustable. Pinion shaft connects to steering shaft with a "U" joint. Tie rods connect rack ends to steering knuckles.

ADJUSTMENTS

Any adjustments are made during the reassembly procedure. See OVERHAUL in this article.

REMOVAL & INSTALLATION

STEERING GEAR

Removal

1) Remove steering shaft lower "U" joint-to-pinion shaft clamp bolt. Separate "U" joint from pinion shaft. Raise and support vehicle. Remove front wheels.

2) Remove tie rod end cotter pins and castle nuts. Using Puller (07941-6920001), separate tie rod ends from steering knuckles.

3) Disconnect shift lever torque rod from clutch housing. Slide pin retainer out of the way. Drive out spring. Disconnect shift rod. *See Fig. 1*.

4) On models with automatic transaxles, remove shift cable guide from floor. Pull shift cable down by hand. On all models, remove exhaust manifold-to-header pipe bolts.

5) Push rack to extreme right (simulating a left turn). Remove steering gear mounting brackets. Lower steering gear so pinion shaft end of gear comes out of frame hole.

6) Rotate steering gear forward until pinion shaft points forward. Move steering gear to right until left tie rod clears exhaust pipe. Remove steering gear through left side of vehicle.

Fig. 1: Removal of Shift Rod

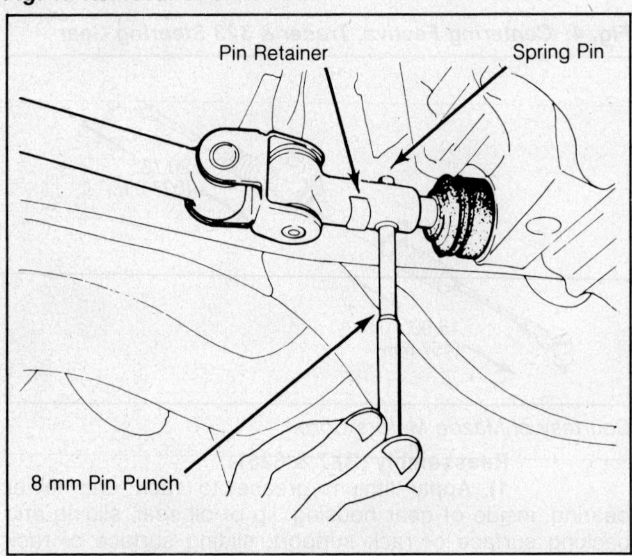

Courtesy of American Honda Motor Co., Inc.

Installation

To install, reverse removal procedure. Slide retainer into place after driving in spring pin. Check steering gear operation for smoothness.

OVERHAUL

STEERING GEAR

Disassembly (Civic CRX & 2WD Civic)

1) Place steering gear housing in vise. Loosen boot clamps. Pull dust boots away from steering gear. Unstake the tie rod lock washers.

2) Holding rack with a wrench, unscrew tie rods. Remove adjusting screw lock nut, adjusting screw, "O" ring, plunger spring and rack piston.

3) Remove outer dust seal, pinion dust seal and outer snap ring. Remove pinion from steering gear. Slide rack from steering gear. Remove small snap ring from pinion. Remove bearing from pinion.

HONDA RACK & PINION (Cont.)

Fig. 2: Exploded View of 2WD Rack & Pinion Steering Gear

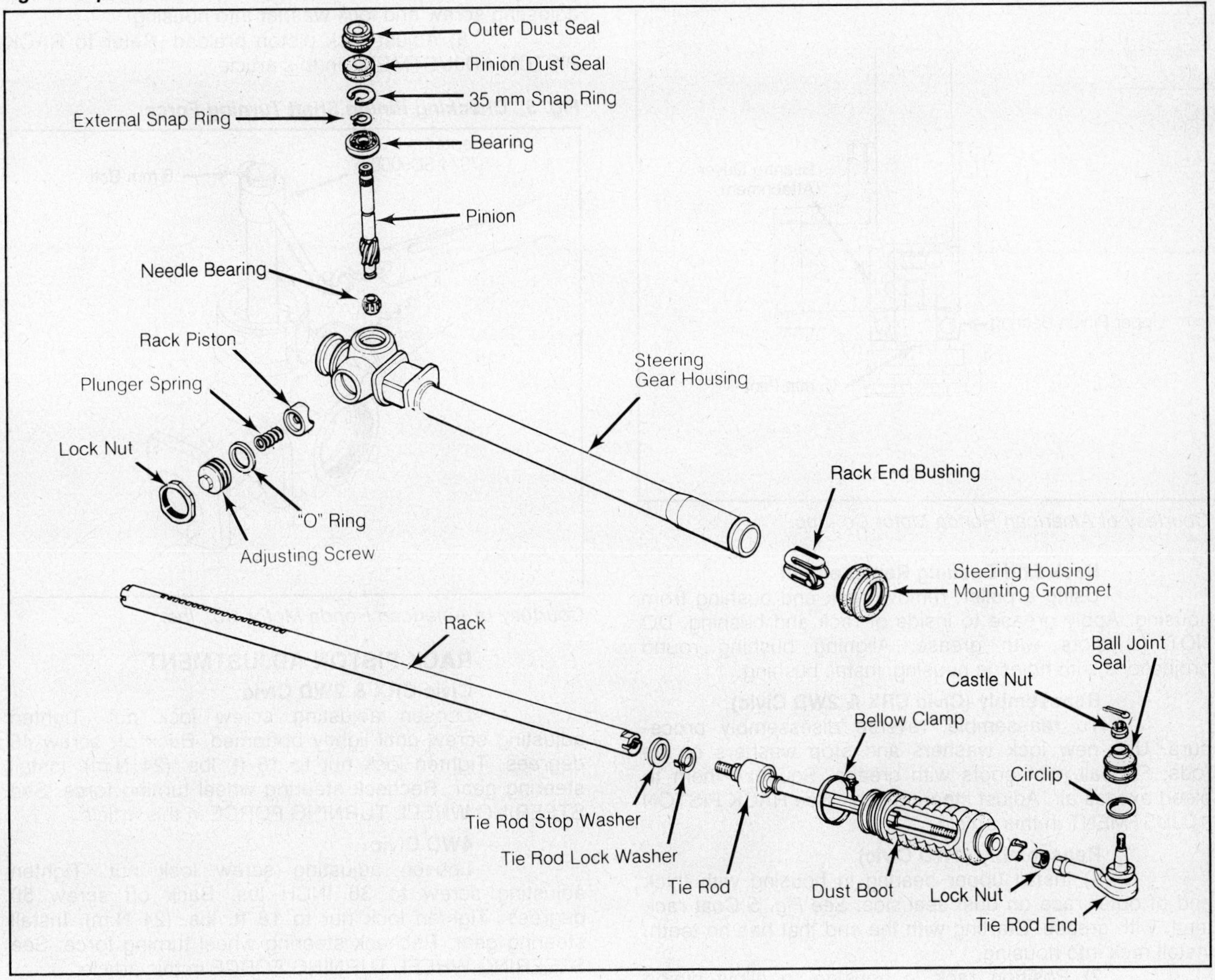

Courtesy of American Honda Motor Co., Inc.

Disassembly (4WD Civic)

1) Place steering gear housing in vise. Loosen boot clamps. Pull dust boots away from steering gear. Unstake the tie rod lock washers.

2) Holding rack with a wrench, unscrew tie rods. Remove adjusting screw lock nut, adjusting screw, "O" ring, plunger spring and rack piston.

3) Using Remover (07702-0020000), remove cover and pinion shaft lock nut. Remove pinion screw. Slide rack until its cut-out is in position to allow the pinion shaft to be removed. *See Fig. 4.*

4) Using a screwdriver, pry the ring stopper out of its groove. Slide pinion shaft down out of steering gear housing. Using a puller, remove lower pinion bearing from pinion.

5) Remove pinion dust seal. Remove upper bearing from housing by tapping on race through the 2 cut-outs. Remove dust seal holder and rack end bushing.

Inspection

Check all parts for wear or damage. Replace parts as needed

Fig. 3: Exploded View of 4WD Civic Rack & Pinion Steering Gear

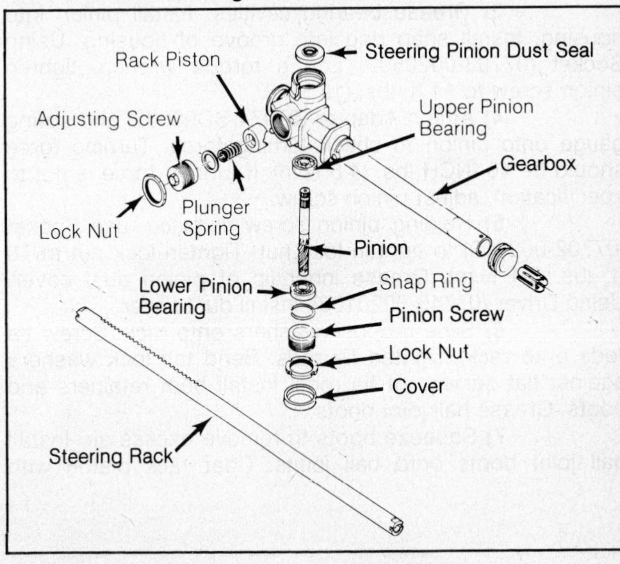

Courtesy of American Honda Motor Co., Inc.

HONDA RACK & PINION (Cont.)

Fig. 4: Cutaway View of Rack Position for 4WD Civic

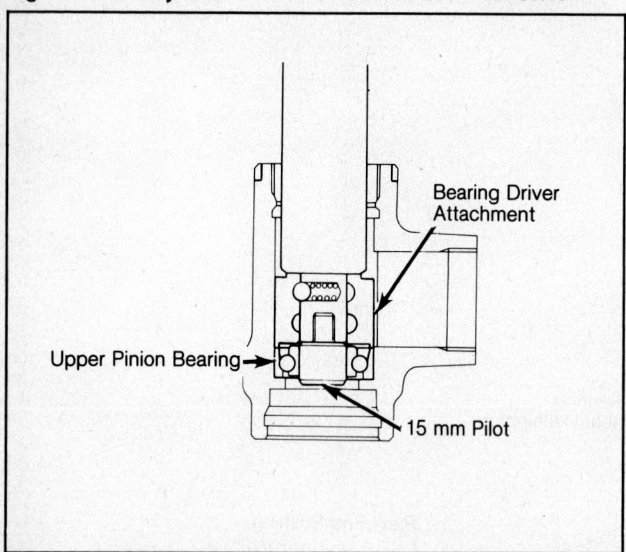

Courtesy of American Honda Motor Co., Inc.

Rack End Bushing Replacement

Using a puller, remove rack end bushing from housing. Apply grease to inside of rack end bushing. DO NOT fill slots with grease. Aligning bushing round projections with holes in housing, install bushing.

Reassembly (Civic CRX & 2WD Civic)

To reassemble, reverse disassembly procedure. Use new lock washers and stop washers on tie rods. Fill ball joint boots with grease. Squeeze them to bleed excess air. Adjust steering gear. See RACK PISTON ADJUSTMENT in this article.

Reassembly (4WD Civic)

1) Install upper bearing in housing with thick end of outer race on dust seal side. *See Fig. 5* Coat rack teeth with grease. Starting with the end that has no teeth, install rack into housing.

2) Position rack in housing to allow pinion installation. *See Fig. 4.* Using Driver (07946-SD90100), install pinion into lower pinion bearing with thick end oif outer race on gear side.

3) Grease bearing cavities. Install pinion into housing. Install snap ring into groove of housing. Using Socket (07703-0020500) and a torque wrench, tighten pinion screw to 14 ft. lbs. (19 N.m).

4) Attach Adapter (07974-SD90000) and spring gauge onto pinion to check turning force. Turning force should be 40 INCH lbs. (4.5 N.m). If turning force is not to specification, adjust pinion screw.

5) Holding pinion screw in place, use Socket (07702-002000) to tighten lock nut. Tighten lock nut to 18 ft. lbs. (24 N.m). Grease inner lip of pinion dust cover. Using Driver (07746-0020100), install dust cover.

6) Slide tab lock washers onto rack. Screw tie rods onto rack. Tighten tie rods. Bend tab lock washers against flat surface of tie rods. Install boot retainers and boots. Grease ball joint boots.

7) Squeeze boots to remove excess air. Install ball joint boots onto ball joints. Coat rack piston with grease. Install rack piston, plunger spring, "O" ring, adjusting screw and lock washer into housing.

8) Adjust rack piston preload. Refer to RACK PISTON ADJUSTMENT in this article.

Fig. 5: Checking Pinion Shaft Turning Force

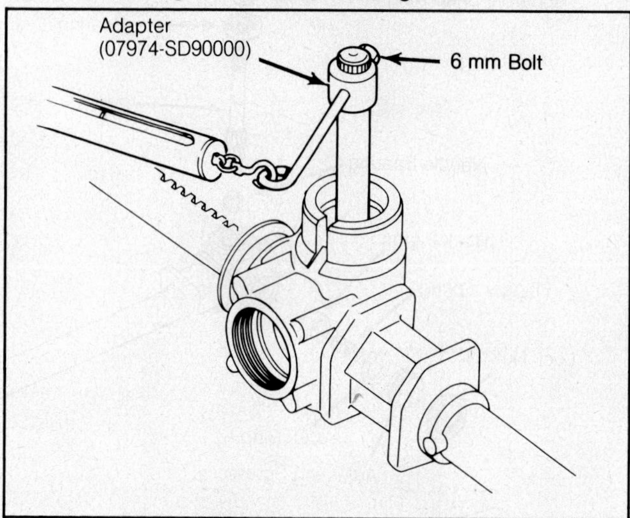

Courtesy of American Honda Motor Co., Inc.

RACK PISTON ADJUSTMENT

Civic CRX & 2WD Civic

Loosen adjusting screw lock nut. Tighten adjusting screw until lightly bottomed. Back off screw 45 degrees. Tighten lock nut to 18 ft. lbs. (24 N.m). Install steering gear. Recheck steering wheel turning force. See STEERING WHEEL TURNING FORCE in this article.

4WD Civic

Loosen adjusting screw lock nut. Tighten adjusting screw to 36 INCH lbs. Back off screw 50 degrees. Tighten lock nut to 18 ft. lbs. (24 N.m). Install steering gear. Recheck steering wheel turning force. See STEERING WHEEL TURNING FORCE in this article.

STEERING WHEEL TURNING FORCE

Install steering gear in vehicle. Install wheels. Raise and support vehicle. Attach spring gauge to spoke of steering wheel. Turn steering wheel and note reading on gauge. Steering wheel turning force should be 40 INCH lbs. (4.5 N.m). If not to specification, remove steering gear and readjust rack piston. See RACK PISTON ADJUSTMENT in this article.

TIGHTENING SPECIFICATIONS

Application	Ft. Lbs. (N.m)
Adjusting Screw Lock Nut	18 (24)
Tie Rod End Castle Nut	
Civic CRX & 2WD Civic	32 (43)
4WD Civic	29 (39)
Tie Rod-to-Rack	
Civic CRX & 2WD Civic	54 (75)
4WD Civic	38 (52)
Tie Rod End Lock Nut	32 (43)

ISUZU P'UP RECIRCULATING BALL

DESCRIPTION

STEERING GEAR

Steering gear is a recirculating ball type. A worm gear on steering shaft lower end engages with ball nut through recirculating balls. Adjustment is provided for backlash between sector gear and ball nut by a tapered sector gear. Adjustment screw is on sector shaft.

STEERING LINKAGE

A splined pitman arm from the steering gear connects to an intermediate rod. The intermediate rod attaches to the idler arm and tie rods. The idler arm pivots on a shaft that is attached to the frame by a bracket. A steering damper connects from the frame to the intermediate rod.

ADJUSTMENTS

Any adjustments are made during the reassembly procedure. See OVERHAUL in this article.

REMOVAL & INSTALLATION

STEERING LINKAGE

Removal

1) Raise and support vehicle. Remove steering damper from frame and intermediate rod. Mark the mating points of the tie rod end to tie rod and tie rod to intermediate rod, for installation reference.

Fig. 2: Exploded View of Steering Gear Assembly

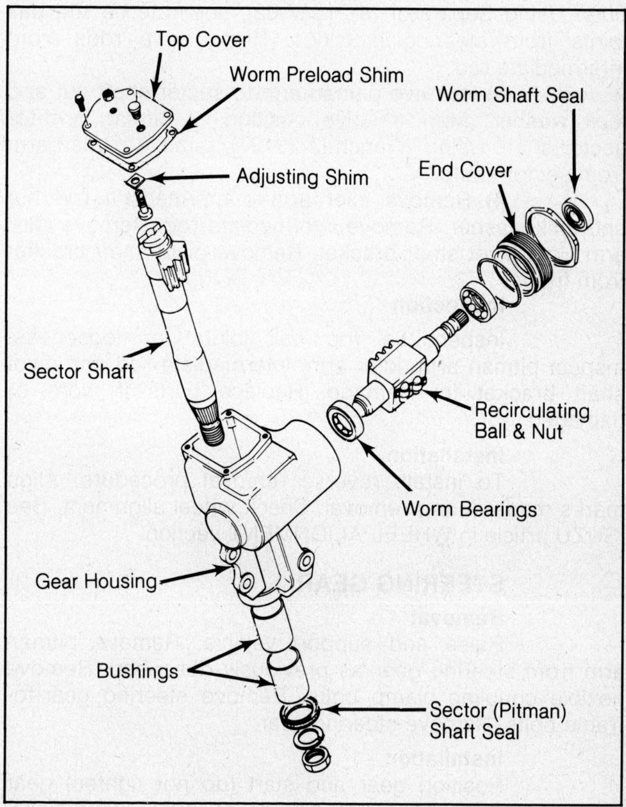

Courtesy of Isuzu Motor Co.

Fig. 1: Exploded View of Steering Linkage

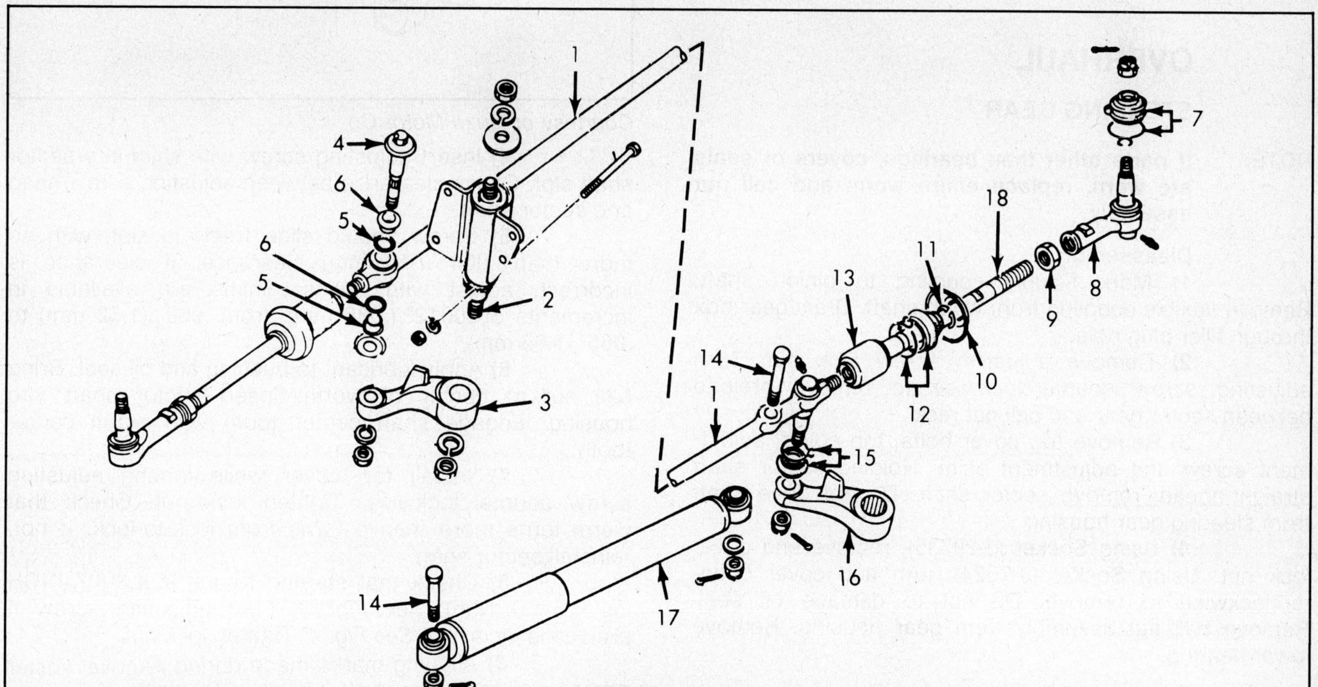

1. Intermediate Rod
2. Idler Arm Pivot Shaft
3. Idler Arm
4. Pivot Bolt
5. Bushing
6. "O" Ring
7. Boot & Wire Clip
8. Tie Rod End
9. Lock Nut
10. Cover
11. Snap Ring
12. Boot & Wire Clip
13. Inner Ball Joint
14. Steering Damper Bolt
15. Boot & Wire Clip
16. Pitman Arm
17. Steering Damper
18. Tie Rod

2WD model is shown. Courtesy of Isuzu Motor Co.

ISUZU P'UP RECIRCULATING BALL (Cont.)

2) Remove tie rod end cotter pins and castle nuts. Using Separator (J-21687-02), separate tie rod ball joints from steering knuckles. Remove tie rods from intermediate rod.

3) Remove pitman arm-to-sector shaft nut and lock washer. Mark relative position of pitman arm-to-sector shaft. Using Wrench (J-29107), remove pitman arm from sector shaft.

4) Remove idler arm-to-intermediate rod nut and lock washer. Remove intermediate rod. Remove idler arm from pivot shaft bracket. Remove pivot shaft bracket from frame.

Inspection

Inspect tie rod ball joints for looseness. Inspect pitman arm, idler arm, intermediate rod and pivot shaft bracket for damage. Replace parts if worn or damaged.

Installation

To install, reverse removal procedure. Align marks made during removal. Check wheel alignment. See ISUZU article in WHEEL ALIGNMENT section.

STEERING GEAR

Removal

Raise and support vehicle. Remove pitman arm from steering gear as previously described. Remove flexible coupling clamp bolts. Remove steering gear-to-frame bolts. Remove steering gear.

Installation

Position gear and start (do not tighten) gear box mounting bolts. Install flexible coupling clamp bolts. Tighten bolts. Tighten steering gear mounting bolts. Aligning index marks, install pitman arm to shaft.

OVERHAUL

STEERING GEAR

NOTE: **If parts other than bearings, covers or seals are worn, replace entire worm and ball nut assembly.**

Disassembly

1) Mark flexible coupling to pinion shaft. Remove flexible coupling from worm shaft. Drain gear box through filler plug hole.

2) Remove adjusting screw lock nut. Turn adjusting screw counterclockwise to remove preload between sector gear and ball nut rack.

3) Remove top cover bolts, top cover, adjustment screw and adjustment shim. Holding sector shaft straight-ahead, remove sector shaft. Do not drive shaft from steering gear housing.

4) Using Socket (J-29735), remove end cover lock nut. Using Socket (J-7624), turn end cover counterclockwise to remove. Do not to damage oil seal. Remove ball nut assembly from gear housing. Remove lower bearing.

NOTE: **Keep ball nut assembly horizontal to prevent ball nut from falling off worm.**

Inspection

1) Wash all parts in solvent. Check steering shaft for bending. Check ball nut teeth for dents and wear. Check bearings and bushings for wear or damage.

2) Check splined sections for dents or damage. Check ball nut operation on worm shaft. Check sector shaft and shaft teeth for wear or damage. Replace components as necesary.

Reassembly

1) Install lower bushings and oil seal in lower end of gear housing. Insert lower bearing into gear housing. Install worm shaft assembly in gear housing. Check lower end of worm shaft for proper fit in lower bearing.

2) Assemble upper bearing onto worm shaft. Lubricate and install "O" ring into end cover. Lubricate oil seal lip. Install cover over worm shaft. Do not damage seal.

3) Screw in end cover. Using torque wrench and Socket (J-29754), tighten end cover to 2.6-5.2 INCH lbs. (.3-.6 N.m) to set bearing preload. *See Fig. 3.* Using Socket (J-29753), install and tighten lock nut.

Fig. 3: Measuring Worm Bearing Preload

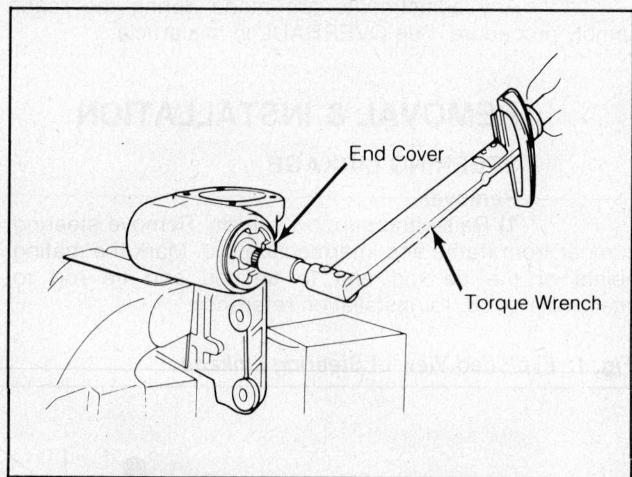

Courtesy of Isuzu Motor Co.

4) Insert adjusting screw with shim into sector shaft slot. Check clearance between adjusting screw head and sector shaft.

5) Screw should slide freely in slot, with no more than .004" (.10 mm) clearance. If clearance is incorrect, adjust with shims. Shims are available in increments of .0012" (.030 mm), from .060" (1.52 mm) to .065" (1.65 mm).

6) Apply lubricant to bushing and oil seal. Bring ball nut to center of worm. Insert sector shaft into housing. Engage shaft center tooth with worm center tooth.

7) Install top cover while turning adjusting screw counterclockwise. Tighten lock nut. Check that worm turns more than 5 turns from lock-to-lock. If not, reinstall sector shaft.

8) Check that starting torque is 4.3-8.7 INCH lbs. (.5-1.0 N.m). *See Fig. 3.* Turn adjusting screw if preload is incorrect. *See Fig. 4.* Tighten lock nut.

9) Aligning marks made during removal, install pitman arm to sector shaft. Install and tighten pitman arm nut. Install flexible coupling to worm shaft. Fill steering gear with gear lube. Install steering gear.

ISUZU P'UP RECIRCULATING BALL (Cont.)

Fig. 4: Adjusting Gear Preload

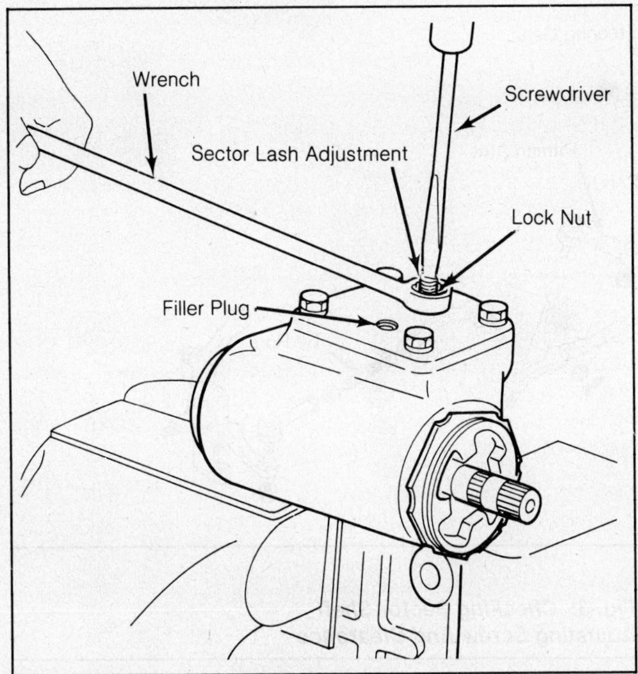

Courtesy of Isuzu Motor Co.

TIGHTENING SPECIFICATIONS

Application	Ft. Lbs. (N.m)
End Cover Lock Nut	125 (170)
Idler Arm Nut-to-Idler Arm Pivot Shaft	89 (121)
Idler Arm Nut-to-Intermediate Rod	50 (68)
Intermediate Rod End	65 (88)
Pitman Arm-to-Intermediate Rod	45 (61)
Pitman Arm Nut-to-Steering Gear	162 (220)
Steering Damper Nuts	40 (54)
Sector Shaft Lock Nut	15-22 (20-30)
Tie Rod Lock Nuts	80 (108)
	INCH Lbs. (N.m)
Total Steering Gear Preload	4.3-8.7 (.5-1.0)
Worm Bearing Preload	2.6-5.2 (.3-.6)

MAZDA RECIRCULATING BALL

B2200, B2600

DESCRIPTION

Steering gear is a recirculating ball-type with a variable ratio, depending on turning angle of sector shaft. The worm gear and steering shaft are an integral, non-separable, unit.

Steering linkage for all models include a non-adjustable center link, 2 adjustable tie rods, an idler arm assembly and pitman arm.

ADJUSTMENTS

Adjustments are performed during reassembly procedure. See OVERHAUL in this article.

REMOVAL & INSTALLATION

STEERING GEAR

Removal

Raise and support vehicle. Remove front wheels. Remove bolts from rubber coupling. Using Puller (49-0118-8505), disconnect center link from pitman arm. Remove steering gear-to-frame mounting bolts and nuts. Remove steering gear.

Installation

To install, reverse removal procedure. Ensure any shims which were removed are installed in original positions.

Fig. 1: Exploded View of B2200 & B2600 Steering Gear

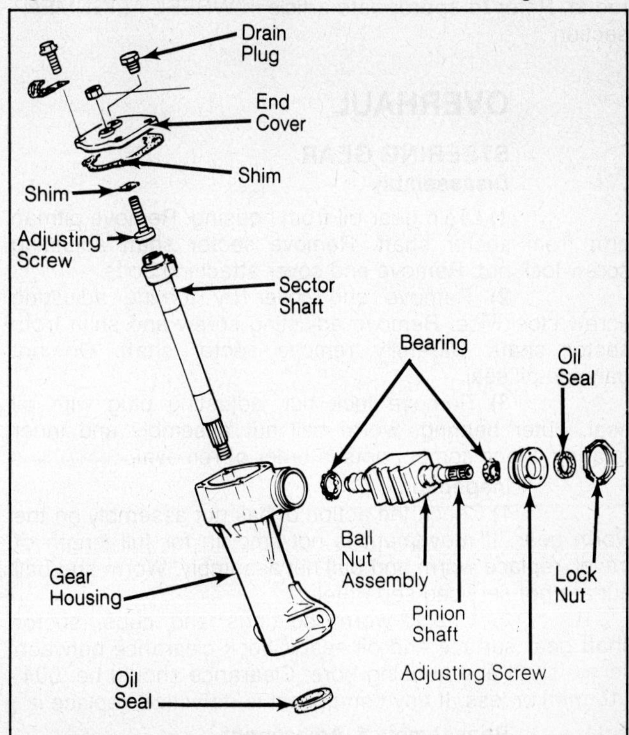

Courtesy of Mazda Motors Corp.

MAZDA RECIRCULATING BALL (Cont.)

Fig. 2: Exploded View of B2200 & B2600 Steering Linkage

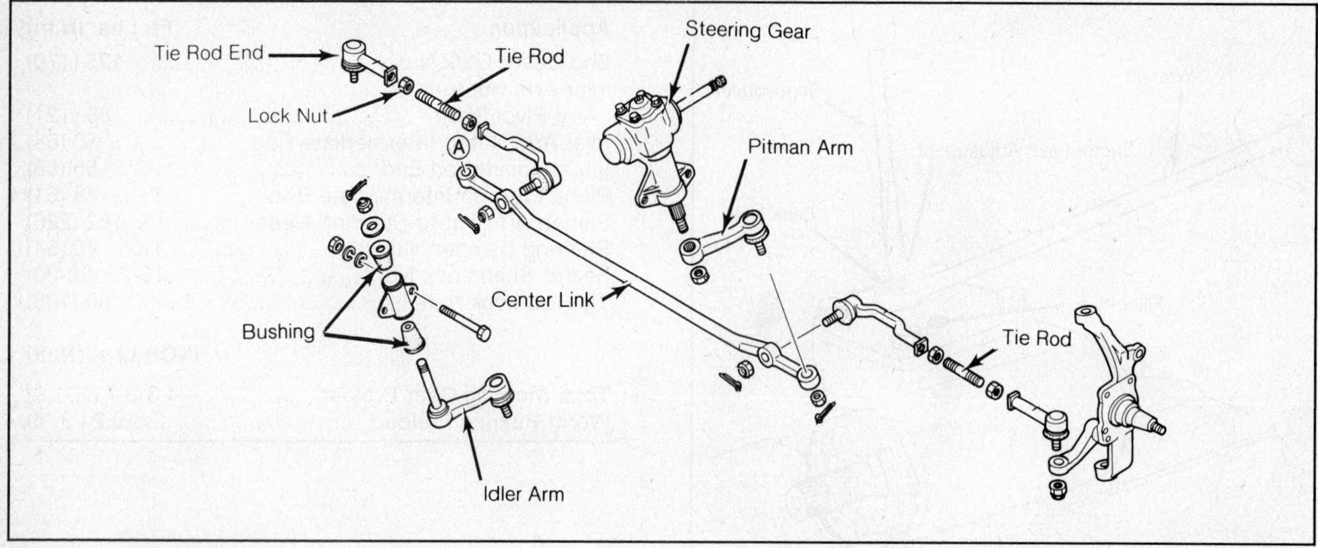

Courtesy of Mazda Motors Corp.

STEERING LINKAGE

Removal

1) Raise and support vehicle. Using Puller (49 0118 850C), separate tie rod ends from knuckles. Remove tie rods, center link and idler arm.

2) Remove idler arm bracket nuts and bolts. Remove idler arm from frame. Using Pullers (49 0118 850C) and (49 0223 695E), remove pitman arm.

Installation

To install, reverse removal procedure. Check toe-in. Refer to appropriate article in WHEEL ALIGNMENT section.

OVERHAUL

STEERING GEAR

Disassembly

1) Drain gear oil from housing. Remove pitman arm from sector shaft. Remove sector shaft adjusting screw lock nut. Remove end cover attaching bolts.

2) Remove end cover by turning adjusting screw clockwise. Remove adjusting screw and shim from sector shaft. Carefully remove sector shaft. Do not damage oil seal.

3) Remove lock nut, adjusting plug with oil seal, outer bearing, worm ball nut assembly and inner bearing. Place components in order of removal.

Inspection

1) Check the action of ball nut assembly on the worm gear. If movement is not smooth for full length of travel, replace worm and ball nut assembly. Worm and ball nut are not serviced separately.

2) Check worm bearings and cups, sector shaft gear surface and oil seal. Check clearance between sector shaft and housing bore. Clearance should be .004" (.10 mm) or less. If any component is defective, replace it.

Reassembly & Adjustment

Install bearings and oil seals (if removed). Insert worm gear ball nut assembly into gear housing. Install and tighten adjusting screw and lock nut. Check preload of worm ball nut.

Fig. 3: Checking Sector Shaft Adjusting Screw End Clearance

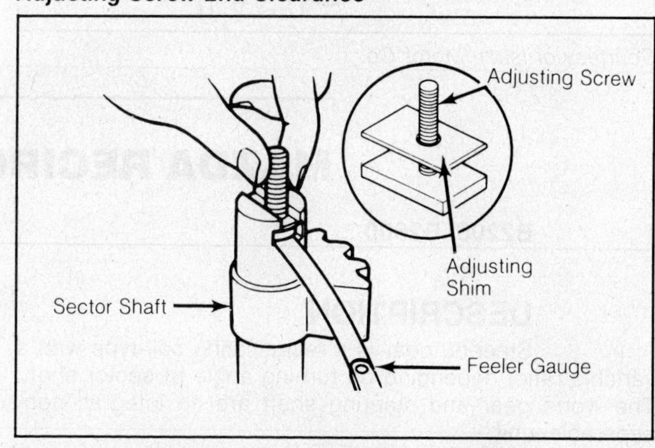

Courtesy of Mazda Motors Corp.

Worm Bearing Preload

Using a spring scale and Adapter (49-0180-510B), check worm bearing preload with sector shaft unattached. Preload reading should be 8-16 INCH lbs. (3-6 N.m). Loosen lock nut. Tighten or loosen adjusting screw as necessary to correct preload. Tighten lock nut.

Sector Shaft End Play

1) Check clearance between sector shaft adjusting screw and sector shaft. Select and install a shim that will allow a final clearance of .004" (.10 mm) or less. *See Fig. 3.* Insert sector shaft with ball nut. *See Fig. 4.*

2) Insert adjusting screw and shim in sector shaft. Place side cover and gasket over adjusting screw. Turn adjusting screw until cover is in place. Install and tighten cover bolts.

Steering Gear Backlash

1) Install pitman arm to sector shaft. Install and tighten retaining nut. Measure pitman arm backlash. Turn sector adjusting screw until zero backlash is obtained.

2) Tighten adjusting screw lock nut. Take care not to disturb backlash adjustment. Check worm shaft rotating torque.

MAZDA RECIRCULATING BALL (Cont.)

Fig. 4: Aligning Sector Shaft to Ball Nut

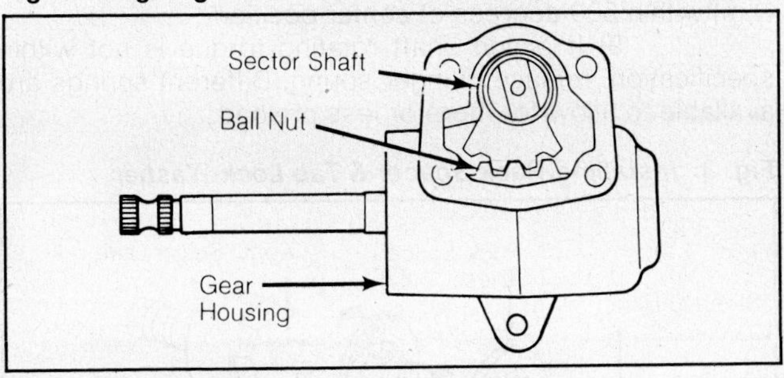

Courtesy of Mazda Motors Corp.

3) Attach an INCH lb. torque wrench to pinion shaft. Refer to TIGHTENING SPECIFICATIONS table. If not to specification, adjust as necessary. Fill gear housing with Lubricant (API GL-4 SAE 90).

TIGHTENING SPECIFICATIONS

Application	Ft. Lbs. (N.m)
End Cover Bolts	12-17 (16-23)
Flexible Coupling-to-Pinion Shaft Clamp Bolt	22-28 (30-38)
Idler Arm Bracket Nut & Bolt	46-69 (63-93)
Pitman Arm-to-Sector Shaft Nut	108-130 (147-176)
Sector Shaft Adjusting Lock Nut	23-34 (31-46)
Steering Gear-to-Frame Nut & Bolt	46-69 (63-93)
Tie Rod Adjusting Lock Nut	51-58 (69-80)
Tie Rod End Castle Nut	33-43 (44-59)
Worm Bearing Preload Lock Nut	116-144 (157-196)
	INCH Lbs. (N.m)
Final Worm Bearing Preload	8-16 (.9-1.8)
Pinion Shaft Rotating Torque	16-29 (1.8-3.3)

NISSAN RACK & PINION

Sentra

DESCRIPTION

Steering assembly is a rack and pinion type. Unit is mounted to frame by brackets with rubber grommets. Backlash is held to zero by the retainer and retainer spring. Rack preload is adjustable.

ADJUSTMENTS

Any adjustments are made during the reassembly procedure. See OVERHAUL in this article.

REMOVAL & INSTALLATION

Removal

1) Raise and support vehicle. Remove tie rod end cotter pins and castle nuts. Using tie rod end puller, separate tie rod end from steering knuckle.

2) Loosen steering gear mounting bolts. Remove steering column "U" joint-to-lower joint clamp bolt. Remove steering gear with tie rods.

Installation

To install, reverse removal procedure. Check and adjust wheel alignment. See appropriate article in WHEEL ALIGNMENT section.

OVERHAUL

STEERING GEAR

Disassembly

1) Clamp steering gear assembly in a soft-jawed vise. Remove boot wire clips and retaining bands. Pull boots away from housing. Flatten lock plates. Loosen inner joint lock nuts. Unscrew tie rods from rack.

Fig. 1: Exploded View of Sentra Rack & Pinion Steering Gear Assembly

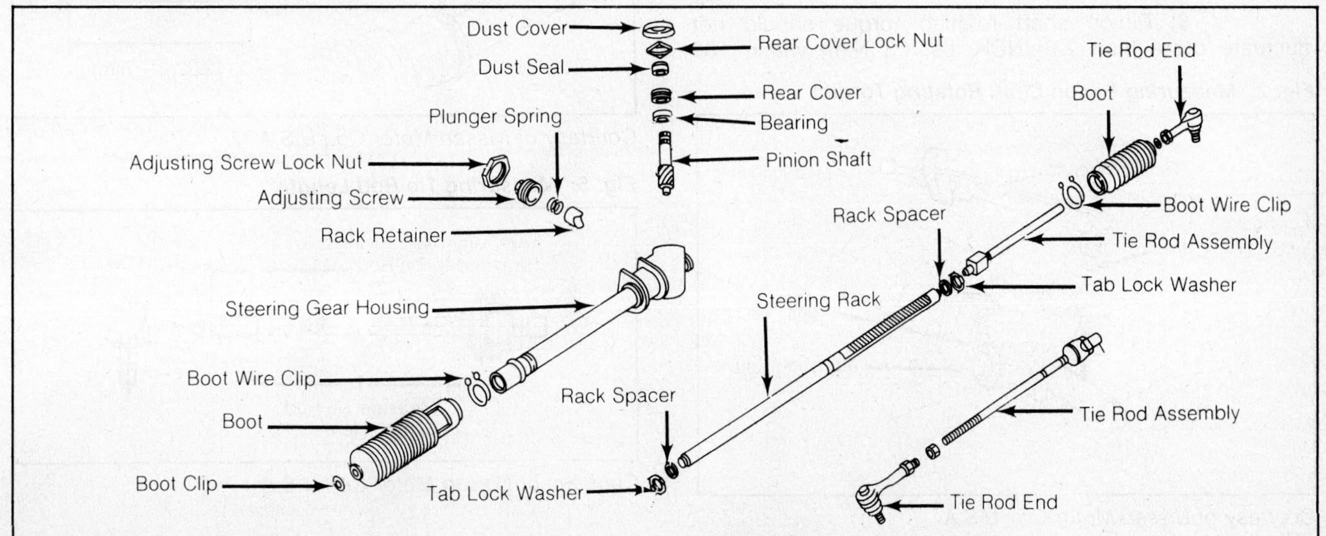

Courtesy of Nissan Motor Co., U.S.A.

NISSAN RACK & PINION (Cont.)

NOTE: Do not disassemble inner joint assembly and tie rod socket assembly.

2) Loosen adjusting screw lock nut. Remove adjusting screw. Remove plunger spring and rack retainer from housing. Remove dust cover and dust seal from top of rear cover. *See Fig. 1.*

3) Remove rear cover lock nut. Using Wrench (KV48102000), unscrew rear cover plug. Pull pinion and bearing from housing. Slide rack toward pinion end of housing to remove. Press bearing from pinion.

Inspection

Check rack and pinion gear for wear or damage. Inspect tie rod inner socket for smooth operation and for excessive looseness. Replace any parts that show signs of excessive wear or damage. Replace all oil seals.

Reassembly & Adjustment

1) Press bearing onto pinion gear. Place steering gear housing in a soft-jawed vise. Grease rack teeth and friction surfaces of rack. Install rack into housing from pinion gear side.

2) Ensure rack teeth are facing correct direction. Grease and install pinion gear and bearing. Ensure pinion teeth and rack teeth mesh properly. Ensure rack protrudes equally from each end of housing.

3) Check that guide clip on pinion shaft is in neutral position (within 6 degrees of a right angle to housing). Apply adhesive to threads of rear cover plug.

4) Using Wrench (KV48102000), install rear cover plug. Ensure pinion assembly rotates smoothly. Install rear cover lock nut. Grease inner lips of dust seal. Install dust seal and dust cover.

5) Grease the steering gear retainer. Insert gear retainer and plunger spring into housing. Tighten adjusting screw to 43 INCH lbs. (4.9 N.m). Loosen adjusting screw. Retighten adjusting screw to 1.7 INCH lbs. (.2 N.m).

6) Apply liquid sealant around lock nut. Install lock nut. Holding adjusting screw in position, tighten lock nut to 70-96 INCH lbs. (8-11 N.m). Place steering gear in a soft-jawed vise.

7) Using Socket (KV48101100) and a torque wrench, check pinion shaft rotating torque. Rotate pinion shaft 180 degrees to each side of center position. Pinion shaft rotating torque should be 6.1-10.4 INCH lbs. (.7-1.2 N.m). *See Fig. 2.*

8) Pinion shaft rotating torque should not fluctuate more than 2.6 INCH lbs. (.3 N.m) within 100 degrees of center position or more than 4.3 INCH lbs. (.5 N.m) within 500 degrees of center position.

9) If pinion shaft rotating torque is not within specification, replace plunger spring. Different springs are available to allow for more or less preload.

Fig. 2: Measuring Pinion Shaft Rotating Torque

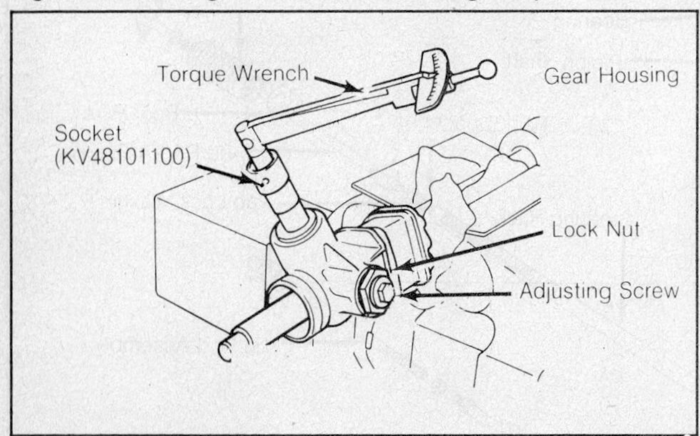

Courtesy of Nissan Motor Co., U.S.A.

Fig. 3: Installing Rack Spacer & Tab Lock Washer

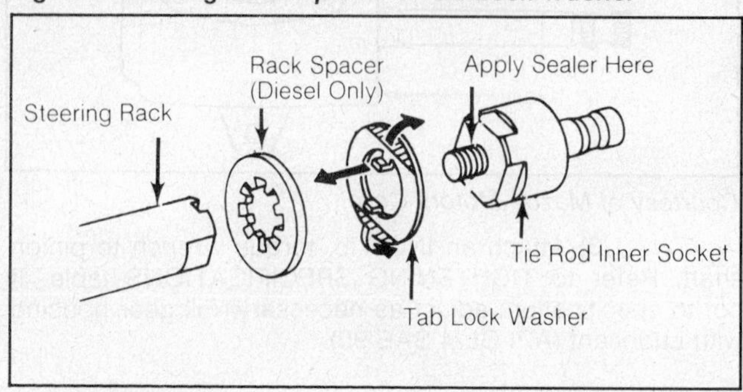

Courtesy of Nissan Motor Co., U.S.A.

10) Install rubber boot and clamp onto tie rod. Install tie rod inner socket assembly onto rack. Bend tab lock washer over at least 2 flats of inner socket.

11) Pull boot up onto gear housing. Wrap wire clip around boot 2 times and twist to install. Install boot retaining band. *See Fig. 4.* Install tie rod end lock nut onto tie rod. Install tie rod end onto tie rod.

12) Ensure that at least one inch of tie rod end is threaded onto tie rod. Tighten lock washer. Repeat procedure for opposite tie rod assembly.

13) Adjust tie rod length so that distance from outer side of lock nut to end of boot mounting groove is 6.94" 176.4 mm). *See Fig. 5.*

Fig. 4: Installing Boot Wire Clips

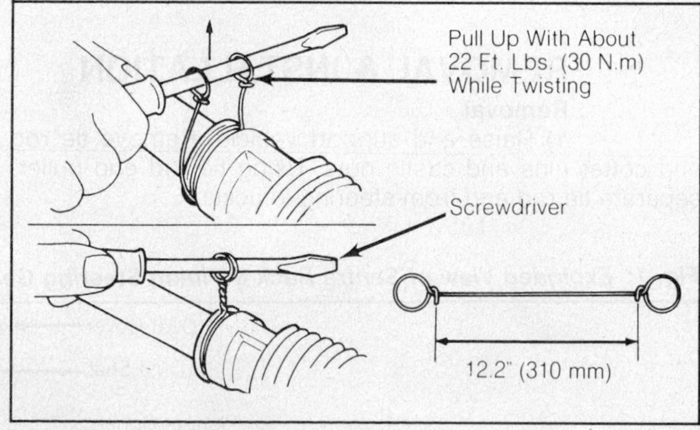

Courtesy of Nissan Motor Co., U.S.A.

Fig. 5: Measuring Tie Rod Length

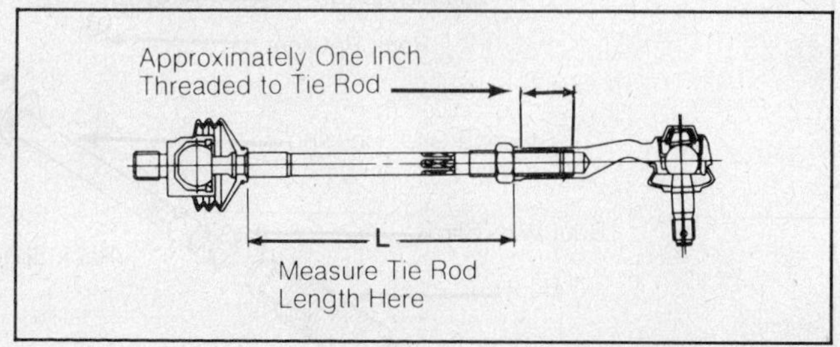

Courtesy of Nissan Motor Co., U.S.A.

NISSAN RACK & PINION (Cont.)

TIGHTENING SPECIFICATIONS

Application	Ft. Lbs. (N.m)
Gear Housing Mounting Bolt	54-72 (73-98)
Rear Cover	47-54 (64-74)
Rear Cover Lock Nut	36-51 (49-69)
Tie Rod End Castle Nut	22-29 (29-39)

TIGHTENING SPECIFICATIONS (Cont.)

Application	Ft. Lbs. (N.m)
Gear Housing Tie Rod-to-Rack	58-72 (78-98)
"U" Joint Clamp Bolts	17-22 (24-29)
	INCH Lbs. (N.m)
Pinion Adjusting Lock Nut	29-43 (4-6)

NISSAN RECIRCULATING BALL

Pickups

DESCRIPTION

The steering gear used is a recirculating ball type. The worm shaft is joined to the steering shaft by a "U" joint. The steering gear attaches by a pitman arm to one end of the center link. The other end of the center link pivots on an idler arm. The center link attaches by tie rods to the steering knuckles.

ADJUSTMENTS

Any adjustments are made during the reassembly procedure. See OVERHAUL in this article.

REMOVAL & INSTALLATION

STEERING LINKAGE

Removal

1) Raise and support front of vehicle. Remove tie rod end cotter pins and castle nuts from tie rod ends, idler arm and pitman arm. Using a tie rod puller, separate tie rod ends from steering knuckles.

2) Separate center link from idler arm and pitman arm. Remove center link and tie rods as an assembly. Idler arm bracket may be removed from frame.

Installation

1) To install, reverse removal procedure. Set tie rod end length. Tie rod end length from center of one ball joint stud to the other should be 13.54" (344 mm).

2) Check and adjust wheel alignment. See appropriate article in WHEEL ALIGNMENT section.

STEERING GEAR

Removal

Remove pitman arm cotter pin and castle nut. Using a tie rod puller, separate center link from pitman arm. Remove "U" joint-to-pinion shaft clamp bolt. Remove steering gear mounting bolts and steering gear.

Installation

To install, reverse removal procedure. Tighten bolts and nuts. See TIGHTENING SPECIFICATIONS table at end of article. Install new cotter pin.

OVERHAUL

STEERING GEAR

Disassembly

1) Drain oil from housing. Place housing in a soft-jawed vise or on a holding fixture mounted in vise. Turn pinion shaft full right. Turn pinion shaft to left. Note the number of turns to reach full left.

2) Turn back half the number of turns to center position. Remove sector shaft cover bolts. Remove sector shaft cover with sector shaft.

3) Separate cover from sector shaft. Remove oil seal (if necessary). Loosen adjusting plug lock nut and adjusting plug. Pull worm assembly from housing. Remove oil seal from adjusting plug.

CAUTION: DO NOT remove sector shaft bearings or bushings from housing. If defective, replace housing assembly. DO NOT disassemble ball

Fig. 1: Exploded View of Recirculating Ball Steering Gear Assembly

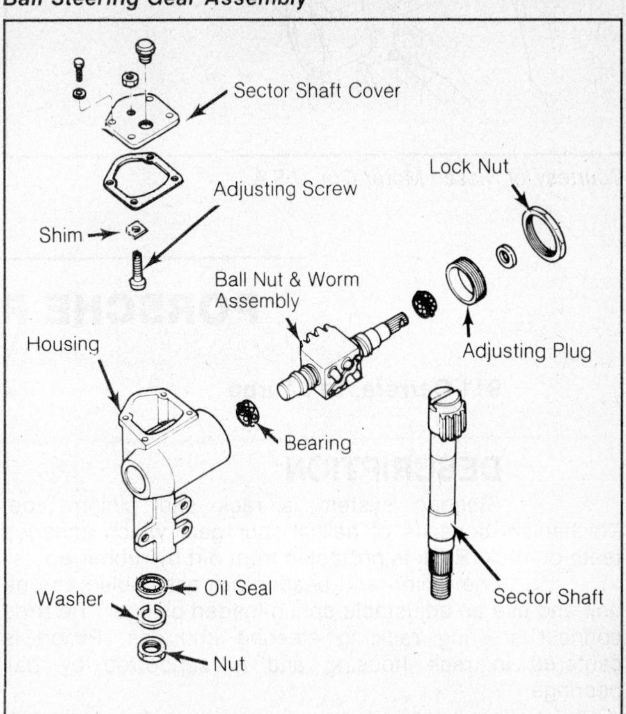

Courtesy of Nissan Motor Co., U.S.A.

NISSAN RECIRCULATING BALL (Cont.)

nut and worm assembly. Replace with new ball nut and worm assembly (if necessary). DO NOT let ball nut bottom out on either end of worm shaft, or damage to ball guides will result.

Inspection

Inspect gear teeth on sector shaft and ball nut for wear or damage; replace as necessary. Check bearings for wear and/or roughness during rotation. Ensure ball nut moves smoothly along its entire length of travel.

Reassembly & Adjustment

1) Lubricate bearings, gear and all other moving parts with gear oil. Apply grease to oil seal. Press seal into adjusting plug.

2) Fit worm gear assembly, with worm bearing, in gear housing. Install adjusting plug using Installer (KV48101400). Rotate worm shaft a few turns in both directions to seat worm bearing. Measure preload.

3) Tighten adjusting plug until preload of 1.7-5.2 INCH lbs. (.2-.6 N.m) is obtained. With preload adjusted, apply sealer to lock nut and tighten lock nut.

4) Insert adjusting screw into "T" groove of sector shaft. Adjust end play between shaft and screw head to less than .0004-.0012" (.01-.03 mm). *See Fig. 3.*

Fig. 2: Measuring Steering Gear Turning Torque

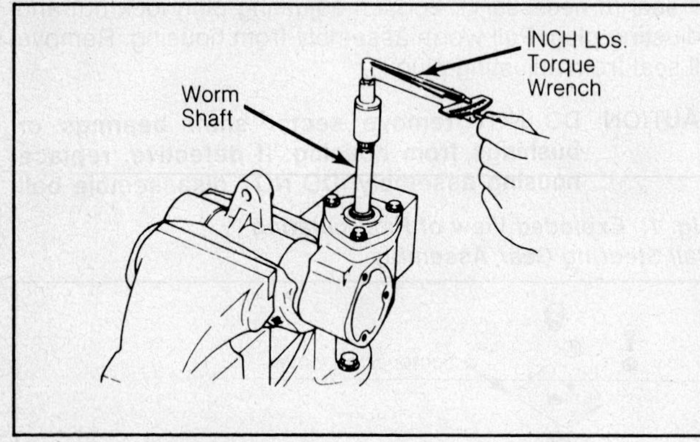

Courtesy of Nissan Motor Co., U.S.A.

Fig. 3: Measuring Sector Shaft-to-Adjusting Screw End Play

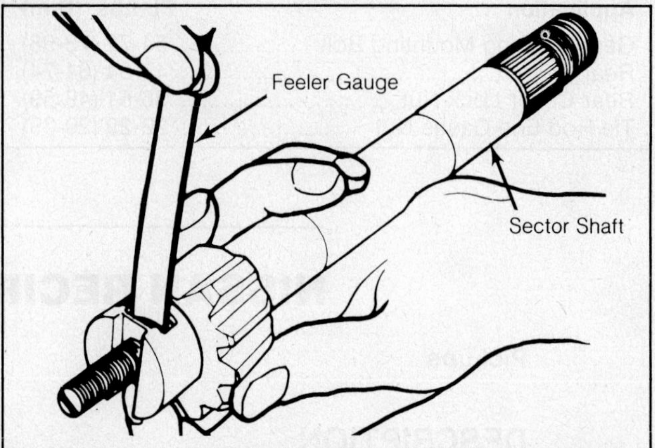

Courtesy of Nissan Motor Co., U.S.A.

5) Coat oil seal contact surface with gear oil. Press seal to steering gear housing. Install cover to sector shaft (with adjusting screw). Place worm gear in center position. Install sector gear with gasket to gear housing. Tighten bolts.

6) Fill steering gear with gear oil. Install torque wrench to worm shaft. Tighten sector shaft adjusting screw while measuring total gear turning torque (preload). Total turning torque should be less than 10.9 INCH lbs. (1.2 N.m).

NOTE: **Always adjust preload by tightening adjusting screw, never by loosening.**

TIGHTENING SPECIFICATIONS

Application	Ft. Lbs. (N.m)
Adjusting Plug Lock Nut	181-231 (246-314)
Adjusting Screw Lock Nut	22-29 (29-39)
Gear Housing-to-Frame	62-71 (84-96)
Sector Shaft	
Sector Shaft Cover Bolt	11-18 (15-25)
Sector Shaft-to-Gear Arm	94-108 (127-147)
Worm Shaft-to-Rubber Coupling	29-36 (39-49)

PORSCHE RACK & PINION

911 Carrera, 911 Turbo

DESCRIPTION

Steering system is rack and pinion type. Mechanism consists of helical spur gear which engages teeth on rack. Rack is protected from dirt by rubber boots.

The pinion and bearing are assembled as one unit and use an adjustable spring-loaded plunger. Tie rods connect steering rack to steering knuckles. Pinion is centered in rack housing and is supported by ball bearings.

ADJUSTMENTS

STEERING GEAR

NOTE: **Steering gear adjusting methods vary according to type of steering rack pressure block. Steel pressure block has a plastic contact surface and external housing dust boot seat. Plastic pressure block has no external housing dust boot seat.**

Steel Pressure Block Type

1) With housing assembly in padded vise, remove base plate. Tighten adjusting nut until it is seated. Back nut off 3 teeth.

PORSCHE RACK & PINION (Cont.)

NOTE: Base plate has integral pins which may be used as a wrench for this adjustment.

2) Using an INCH lb. torque wrench, check steering gear turning torque at pinion. Steering gear turning torque should be 3.5-7.0 INCH lbs. (.39-.80 N.m).

3) If not within specifications, loosen adjusting nut. If turning torque is correct, install base plate and gasket. If pin in plate does not fit easily between teeth of adjusting nut, move nut slightly to align.

Plastic Pressure Block Type

Remove base plate. Tighten adjusting nut until 7 INCH lbs. (.8 N.m) steering gear turning torque is obtained. Install base plate with gasket.

REMOVAL & INSTALLATION

STEERING GEAR

Removal

1) Raise and support vehicle. Place wheels in a straight-ahead position. Remove wheels. Remove "U" joint-to-pinion shaft clamp bolt.

2) Remove cotter pins and castle nuts from tie rod ends. Separate tie rod ends from steering knuckles. Remove steering housing retaining bolts. Remove steering gear from right side of vehicle.

Installation

To install, reverse removal procedure. Align indentation in pinion shaft with bolt hole in "U" joint. Check and adjust toe-in.

OVERHAUL

STEERING GEAR

Disassembly

1) Mount steering housing in a soft-jawed vise. Remove boot clamps and boots. Unscrew tie rod inner ball joint from rack. Loosen tie rod end lock nut. Remove tie rod end from tie rod.

2) Remove base plate retaining bolts. Unscrew adjusting nut (base plate may be used as wrench). Remove pressure block and plunger spring.

3) Move steering rack to either lock position. Remove castle nut. Using Puller (P 293), remove flange from pinion. Remove oil seal, lock ring and spacer.

4) Using Puller (P 282), remove pinion from pinion carrier. Make sure bearing does not bind against housing. Remove Woodruff key from pinion.

5) Press bearing off pinion. Mark position of rack for reassembly reference. Remove rack from housing. Withdraw pinion carrier.

6) Press bearing out of pinion carrier. Remove rack bushing spring retainer from end of housing. Extract support ring. Drive rack bushing out.

Inspection

Check all threaded surfaces for damage. Inspect bushing and seal mating surfaces for scoring or scratching. Check tie rod inner ball joint for wear or excessive looseness. Replace components as necessary.

Reassembly

To reassemble, reverse disassembly procedure. Coat all components with lubricant. Lubricate housing with gear lubricant using bolt hole opposite base plate. Use shims, as necessary, to adjust pinion axial play to zero.

Fig. 1: Exploded View of Steering Gear Assembly

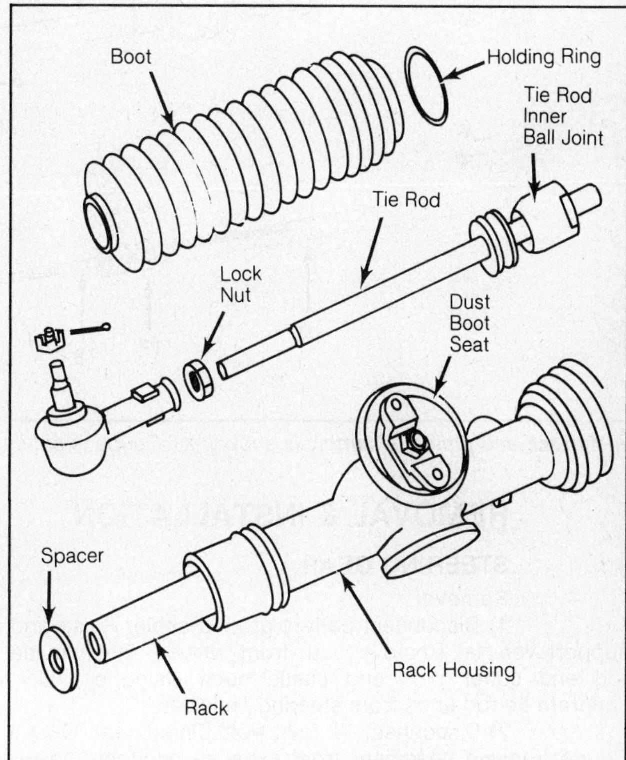

TIGHTENING SPECIFICATIONS

Application	Ft. Lbs. (N.m)
Housing-to-Crossmember Bolts	34 (46)
Tie Rod-to-Steering Knuckle Nut	33 (45)
"U" Joint Clamp Bolt	23 (31)

SUBARU RACK & PINION

Brat, XT Coupe

DESCRIPTION

Steering gear is a rack and pinion type. Rack preload is automatically adjusted. Pinion is connected to steering shaft by a flexible rubber coupling. Steering knuckles are connected to rack by tie rods which attach to ball joint studs at each end of rack.

ADJUSTMENTS

Any adjustments are made during the reassembly procedure. See OVERHAUL in this article.

SUBARU RACK & PINION (Cont.)

Fig. 1: Exploded View of Subaru Rack & Pinion Steering Gear Assembly

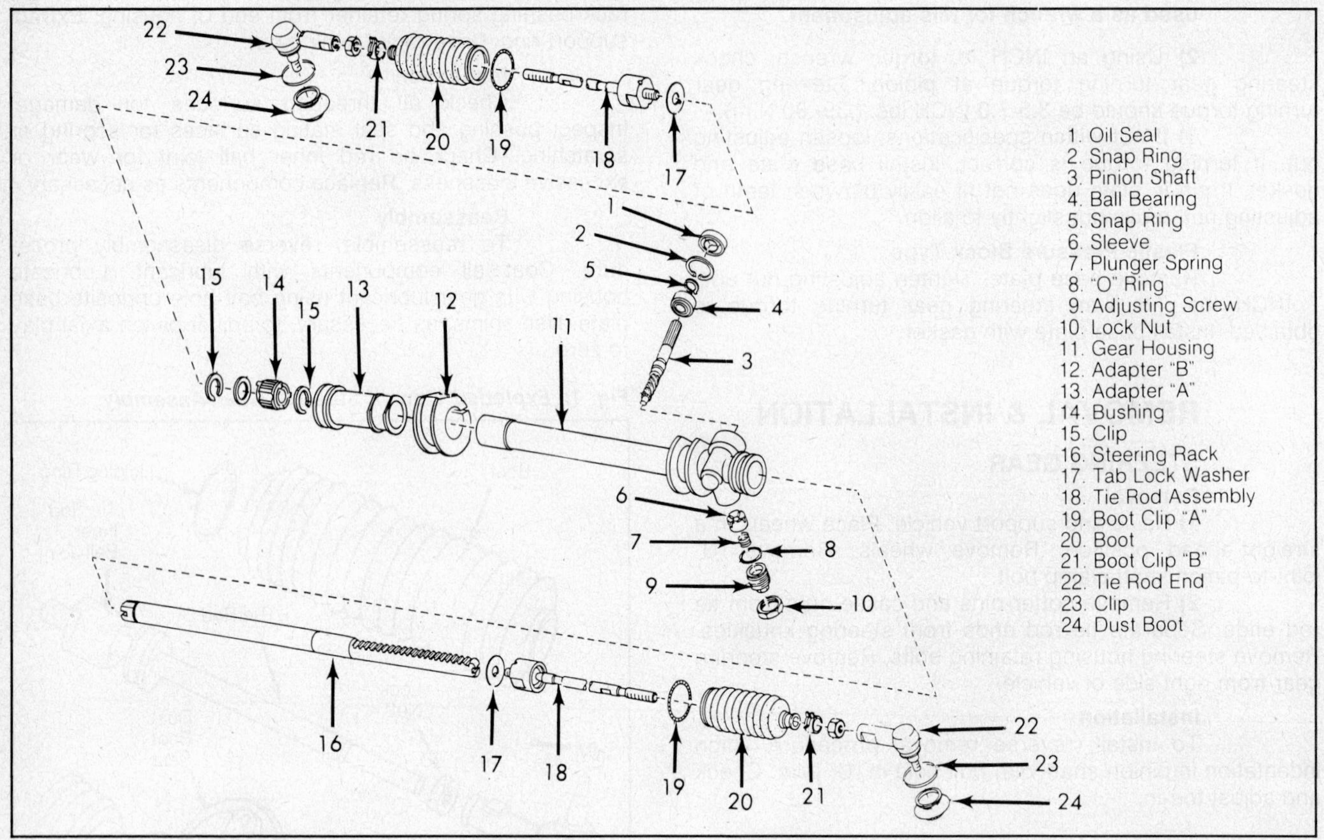

Justy rack and pinion assembly is shown; XT Coupe is similar. Courtesy of Subaru of America, Inc.

REMOVAL & INSTALLATION

STEERING GEAR

Removal

1) Disconnect battery ground cable. Raise and support vehicle. Remove both front wheels. Remove tie rod end cotter pins and castle nuts. Using a puller, separate tie rod ends from steering knuckles.

2) Disconnect "U" joint from pinion gear. On XT Coupe, remove heat riser from exhaust manifold and air cleaner. Disconnect exhaust manifold. Pull manifold down out of way. Remove pinion shaft rubber boot.

3) On all models, remove steering gear-to-crossmember bolts. Lower steering gear until pinion gear is disconnected from "U" joint. Rotate steering gear backward. Remove gear housing from left side.

Installation

To install steering gear assembly, reverse removal procedure. Tighten left steering gear mounting bracket first. Tighten all bolts and nuts to specification. Turn a maximum of 1/6 turn to align cotter pin holes. Install new cotter pins.

OVERHAUL

STEERING GEAR

Dsassembly

1) Place steering gear in a soft-jawed vise. Loosen tie rod end lock nuts. Remove ball joints from rods. Remove boot retaining clamps. Remove boots.

2) Straighten tab on inner ball joint lock washer. Remove inner ball joint from rack. Repeat procedure for other inner ball joint. Remove adjusting screw lock nut, adjusting screw, plunger spring and rack plunger.

3) Remove pinion gear oil seal from steering gear housing. Remove pinion gear large snap ring from housing. Remove pinion gear from steering gear housing.

4) Pull rack out of steering gear housing, from pinion side. Remove pinion gear small snap ring from pinion gear. Press bearing off pinion gear.

5) Remove oil seal and large snap ring. Remove clip from housing. Using an aluminum drift, remove bushing "A" from the end of housing. *See Fig. 1.*

Inspection

1) Place rack ends in "V" blocks. Attach dial indicator so plunger rests on center of rack. Rotate rack while noting deflection of gauge.

2) Maximum deflection should be less than .004" (.1 mm). If not within specification, replace rack. Check all other components for wear or damage. Replace components as necessary.

Reassembly

1) Press bushing "A" into housing. Install clip. Grease bushing "A". If pinion gear was disassembled, slide large snap ring on pinion. Install new oil seal. Press on new bearing.

2) Install small snap ring to pinion gear. Grease the toothed and sliding portions of rack. Install rack into housing from pinion side.

SUBARU RACK & PINION (Cont.)

3) On Justy, position rack so that an equal length of rack protrudes from each end of housing. On XT Coupe, position rack so that 2.99" (76.0 mm) of rack protrudes from each end of housing.

4) Grease pinion gear teeth. Install pinion into steering gear housing. Install large pinion gear snap ring to housing. Check pinion gear end play. End play should be less than .012" (.3 mm).

5) If end play is not to specification, check for worn snap rings, bearing or steering gear housing. Replace components as necessary.

6) With pinion gear end play correct, press oil seal into steering gear housing. Grease rack plunger cavity. Install rack plunger, plunger spring, adjusting screw and lock nut. Adjust rack plunger preload.

7) Turn adjusting screw in until torque increases sharply. Back adjusting screw off 15 degrees. Tighten lock nut to 22-36 ft. lbs. (29-49 N.m). Install tie rod inner ball joint lock washer to rack. Grease inner ball joint.

8) Install ball joint to rack. Tighten inner ball joint to 58 ft lbs. (79 N.m). Bend lock washer over flat area on inner ball joint. Grease inside lip of large end of rubber boot. Slide boot onto housing.

9) Install boot clamps. Install lock nuts and tie rod ends to tie rods. Ensure tie rod ends are installed on correct end of steering gear. Left ball joint is marked "LH". Right ball joint is marked "RH".

11) Make sure steering gear operates smoothly. Check pinion rotating torque at 30 degrees in each direction from straight-head position. Rotating torque should be 9.5-13 INCH lbs. for Justy and 8.4-12.0 INCH lbs. (.9-1.4 N.m) for XT Coupe.

12) If rotating torque is not within specifications, loosen lock nut. Turn adjusting screw clockwise to raise rotating torque or counterclockwise to lower it.

TIGHTENING SPECIFICATIONS

Application	Ft. Lbs. (N.m)
Tie Rod End Castle Nut	18-22 (25-29)
Steering Gear-to-Crossmember Bolt	
Justy	43-54 (59-74)
XT Coupe	35-52 (47-71)
Adjusting Screw Lock Nut	22-36 (29-49)
Tie Rod Inner Ball Joint-to-Rack	58 (79)
Tie Rod End Lock Nut	
Justy	36-47 (49-64)
XT Coupe	51-65 (69-88)
"U" Joint-to-Pinion Clamp Bolt	
Justy	16-19 (20-25)
XT Coupe	15-20 (21-26)

SUZUKI RECIRCULATING BALL

DESCRIPTION

Steering system uses steel balls in a recirculating pattern to transfer the rotary motion of the steering shaft into a linear motion in the rack gear.

The rack gear, in turn, moves the sector gear. The pitman arm is solidly attached to the sector gear and, through the tie rods, allows the vehicle to turn.

ADJUSTMENTS

PINION SHAFT STARTING TORQUE

1) Ensure oil is at proper level. Oil level should be approximately 1.4" (36 mm) from bottom of oil fill plug. Adjustment of pinion shaft starting torque is made with adjusting bolt No. 1. *See Fig. 1.*

2) Remove steering gear from vehicle. See REMOVAL & INSTALLATION in this article. Align pitman arm so that it is parallel with the pinion shaft. *See Fig. 1.*

3) Attach an INCH lb. spring scale to the outermost edge of the flexible joint by attaching a string around one of the bolts and looping it around the outermost edge of the flexible joint. *See Fig. 2.*

4) Pull on the spring scale to move the flexible joint. Note the starting torque measurement. Starting torque should be between 42-70 INCH lbs. (1.58-2.63 N.m). If not, loosen or tighten No. 1 adjusting bolt as necessary.

PINION SHAFT OPERATING TORQUE

1) Ensure oil is at proper level. Oil level should be approximately 1.4" (36 mm) from bottom of oil fill plug. Adjustment of pinion shaft operating torque is made with adjusting bolt No. 1. *See Fig. 1.*

Fig. 1: Location of Torque Adjusting Bolt

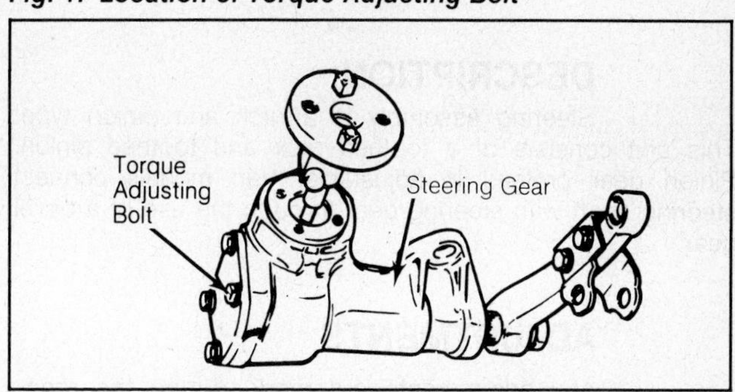

Courtesy of Suzuki of America Corp.

Fig. 2: Measuring Pinion Shaft Starting Torque

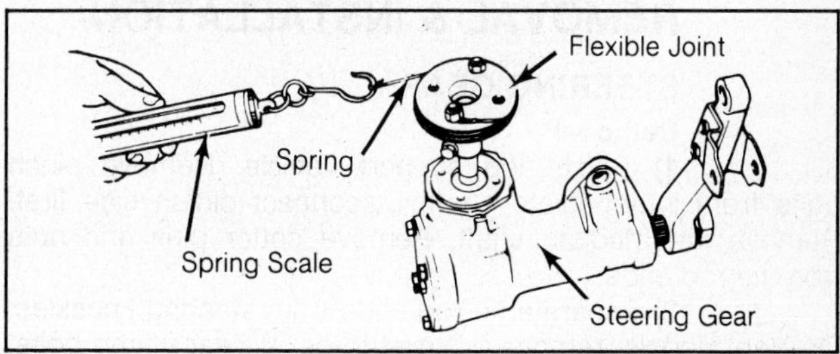

Measuring pinion shaft operating torque is done in same manner. Courtesy of Suzuki of America Corp.

2) Remove steering gear from vehicle. Align pitman arm so that it is parallel with the pinion shaft. Attach an INCH lb. spring scale to the outermost edge of the flexible joint by attaching a string, long enough for a complete turning cycle, around one of the bolts.

SUZUKI RECIRCULATING BALL (Cont.)

3) Loop the string around the outermost edge of the flexible joint. *See Fig. 2.* Pull on the spring scale to turn flexible joint through a complete turning cycle.

4) Note the operating torque measurement. Operating torque should be under 6.96 INCH lbs. (1.58-2.63 N.m). If not, loosen or tighten No. 1 adjusting bolt as necessary.

5) If pinion shaft starting torque and operating torque tests have been performed and adjustment is not possible, replace steering gear as a unit.

REMOVAL & INSTALLATION

STEERING GEAR

Removal

1) Lift and support vehicle. Remove radiator lower cover. Remove tie rod end cotter pins and castle nuts. Using Puller (09913-65210), remove tie rod ends from steering knuckles.

2) Remove steering damper-to center link attaching bolts. Remove cotter pins and castle nuts connecting center link to idler arm and pitman arm .

3) Using Puller (09913-65210), remove center link from pitman arm and idler arm. Remove flexible joint clamp bolt from pinion shaft. Remove steering gear attaching bolts and nuts. Remove steering gear.

Inspection

1) Check pinion shaft starting torque and operating torque. Refer to PINION SHAFT STARTING TORQUE and PINION SHAFT OPERATING TORQUE in ADJUSTMENTS in this article. Inspect gear box for cracks.

2) Check pinion shaft for excessive play. Check oil seals for cracking or leaking. Disassembly of the steering gear is not recommended. If any abnormalities are found, replace gear box as a unit.

Installation

To install, reverse removal procedure. Install steering gear attaching bolts from inside engine compartment. Always use new cotter pins.

TIGHTENING SPECIFICATIONS

Application	Ft. Lbs. (N.m)
Drag Rod Castle Nut	22-51 (30-70)
Flexible Coupling Pinch Bolts	11-18 (15-25)
Steering Gear Attaching Nut	51-65 (70-100)
Steering Damper Stay Nut	14-20 (19-27)
Steering Damper Attaching Nut	26-39 (35-53)
Steering Damper Pin Nut	16-25 (22-34)
Tie Rod Castle Nut	22-39 (30-55)
Tie Rod End Lock Nut	51-72 (70-100)

TOYOTA RACK & PINION

Corolla, MR2, Tercel, Van

DESCRIPTION

Steering assembly is a rack and pinion type. This unit consists of a toothed rack and toothed pinion. Pinion gear preload is adjustable. Van models connect steering shaft with steering gear through the use of a bevel gear.

ADJUSTMENTS

Any adjustments are made during the reassembly procedure. See OVERHAUL in this article.

REMOVAL & INSTALLATION

STEERING GEAR

Removal

1) Raise and support vehicle. Remove pinch bolts from intermediate shaft. Disconnect pinion side first. Remove intermediate shaft. Remove cotter pins and nuts from tie rod ends.

2) Separate tie rod ends from steering knuckles. On Van models, remove "U" joint-to-bevel gear clamp bolts. Remove bevel gear mounting bolts.

3) On all models, remove rack housing bracket bolts and brackets. Being careful not to damage rubber boots, remove steering gear.

Installation

To install, reverse removal procedure. Check toe-in. See WHEEL ALIGNMENT section. Always use new cotter pins.

Fig. 1: Exploded View of Toyota Rack & Pinion Steering Gear Assembly (All Except Van)

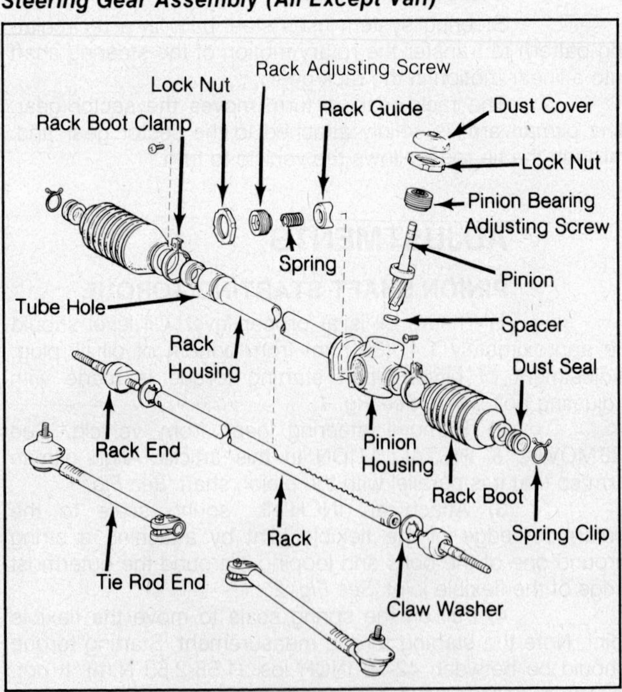

Courtesy of Toyota Motor Sales, U.S.A., Inc.

BEVEL GEAR - VAN

Removal & Installation

Remove 2 steering shaft "U" joint clamp bolts. Remove bevel gear with bracket. To Install, reverse removal procedure.

TOYOTA RACK & PINION (Cont.)

OVERHAUL

STEERING GEAR

Disassembly

1) Place steering gear in a soft-jawed vise. Mark rack end threaded areas for reassembly reference. Remove tie rod end clamp bolts and tie rod ends.

NOTE: Left and right tie rod ends, boots and rack ends are different. Mark them accordingly.

2) Remove boot spring clips, boot clamps and rack end dust seals. Remove boots. Unstake claw washers. Remove rack ends. Remove rack adjusting screw lock nut, adjusting screw and spring.

3) Using needle-nose pliers, remove rack guide. Remove pinion bearing adjusting screw lock nut and pinion bearing adjusting screw.

4) Align notched portion of rack with pinion. Pull pinion and upper pinion bearing out of pinion housing. Pull out rack toward pinion side without rotating it.

Inspection

1) Check all parts for damage or deterioration. Check for play in rack ends and tie rod end ball joints. Check pinion teeth surfaces for wear or damage.

2) If pinion oil seal must be replaced, drive it in until it protrudes .020" (.50 mm) from tip of pinion bearing adjusting screw. If pinion upper bearing must be replaced, remove with bearing puller. Drive new bearing on (seal side down).

3) If pinion lower bearing must be replaced, heat pinion housing to at least 176°F (80°C). Tap bearing out with plastic hammer. Reheat pinion housing. Drive in new bearing.

4) Check rack for runout and excessive tooth wear. Runout must not exceed .012" (.30 mm). If rack bushing must be replaced, remove with puller. Press in new bushing.

Fig. 2: Exploded View of Toyota Van Rack & Pinion Steering Gear Assembly

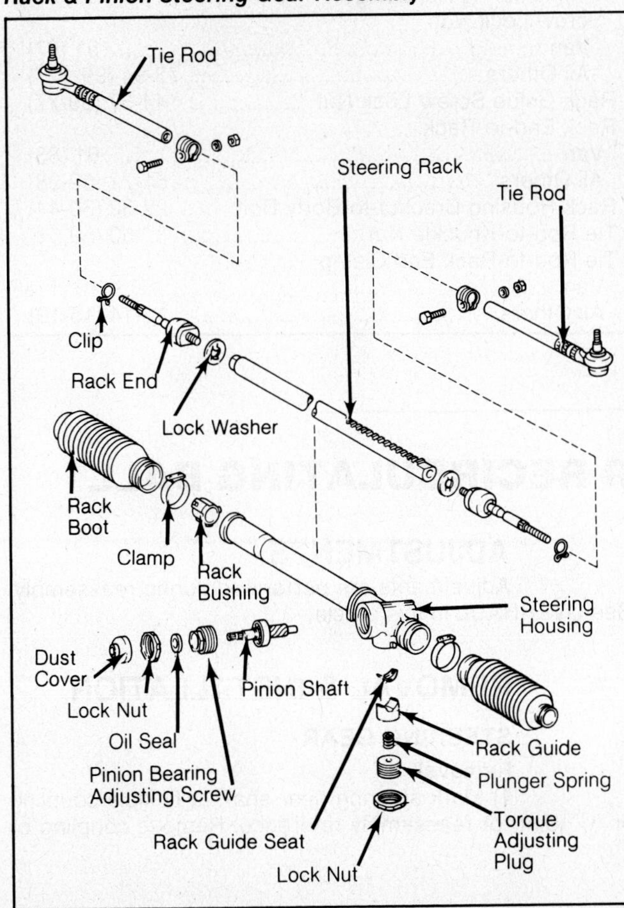

Courtesy of Toyota Motor Sales, U.S.A., Inc.

Reassembly

1) Pack pinion bearings, steering rack and pinion gear with grease. Fill rack housing about half full of grease. Insert rack from pinion housing side into the rack housing.

2) Position notched portion of rack so pinion can be inserted. On Corolla, MR2 and Tercel, insert spacer and pinion into pinion housing. On Van, insert pinion into pinion housing.

3) Pinion end must be securely positioned in pinion lower bearing. Coat oil seal with grease. Install pinion bearing adjusting screw.

4) On MR2 and Van, tighten adjusting screw until pinion turning torque is 3.2 INCH lbs. (.36 N.m). Loosen adjusting screw until pinion turning torque is 2.0-2.9 INCH lbs. (.22-.33 N.m).

5) On Corolla and Tercel models, tighten adjusting screw until pinion turning torque is 3.5 INCH lbs. (.39 N.m). Loosen adjusting screw until turning torque is 1.7-2.6 INCH lbs. (.19-.29 N.m).

6) On all models, apply liquid sealer to adjusting screw lock nut threads. Tighten lock nut to specification. Recheck pinion turning torque.

7) On MR2 and Van, turning torque should be 2.0-2.9 INCH lbs. (.22-.33 N.m). On Corolla and Tercel, turning torque should be 1.3-2.2 INCH lbs. (.15-.25 N.m).

8) Mesh rack and pinion. Coat rack guide with grease. Install rack guide, spring and rack adjusting screw. Using torque wrench, tighten adjusting screw to 18 ft. lbs. (24 N.m).

9) Loosen screw 90 degrees. Measure pinion turning torque. Adjust turning torque with adjusting screw. Turning torque should be 8.7-11.3 INCH lbs. (.98-1.27 N.m).

11) Apply adhesive to lock nut threads. Holding adjusting screw stationary, tighten lock nut to 44-57 ft. lbs. (59-77 N.m). Recheck total turning torque by turning pinion from lock-to-lock with torque wrench.

12) Apply grease to rack end ball joints. Align claw washer with rack groove. Tighten rack end into housing. Stake claw washer.

13) Coat rack end dust seal with grease. Clear rack housing tube hole of any grease. Install rack boots. Install spring clips with bends facing outward.

14) Install boot clamps. Boot clamp on pinion housing side should have a gap of .19-.24" (5-6 mm). Boot clamp on tube side should have no gap.

15) Rotate pinion while checking total rack stroke. Total rack stroke should be 4.80" (122.0 mm). Rack boots should not distort during this operation. Install tie rod ends in original position.

BEVEL GEAR (VAN ONLY)

Disassembly

1) Remove housing cover bolts. Remove dust cover, lock nut, adjusting screw, spring and spring retainer from housing. Remove No. 2 bevel gear.

TOYOTA RACK & PINION (Cont.)

Fig. 3: Exploded View of Van Bevel Gear Assembly

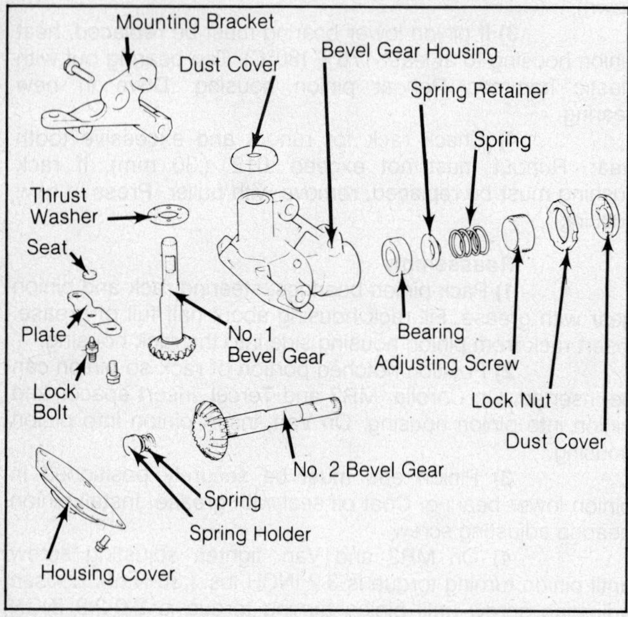

Courtesy of Toyota Motor Sales, U.S.A., Inc.

2) Remove housing cover retaining bolts and housing cover. *See Fig. 3.* Remove spring holder and spring from inside housing. Remove lock nut and adjusting screw from plate inside housing.

3) Remove plate retaining bolts, plate and seat. Remove No. 1 bevel gear dust cover. Using a drift and press, drive No. 1 bevel gear and thrust washer from bevel gear housing.

Inspection

Inspect needle roller bearing, gear teeth and contacting surfaces for wear or damage. Replace bearings and seals as necessary.

Reassembly

1) Install No. 2 bevel gear into housing. Using Press (09612-24013), install bearing into housing. Install thrust washer to No. 1 bevel gear. Install No. 1 bevel gear into housing. Ensure cutout portion of No. 1 and No. 2 bevel gear are aligned.

2) Install spring and spring holder to bevel gear No. 2. Install plate, adjusting bolt and seat. Tighten 2 plate bolts to 69 INCH lbs. (7.8 N.m). Install adjusting bolt seat. Screw in adjusting bolt until it touches seat.

3) Using a screwdriver, torque wrench and Socket (09612-10010), adjust No. 1 bevel gear preload to .7-1.3 INCH lbs. (.08-.15 N.m). Gear should have no axial play. Using a screwdriver, hold adjusting bolt and tighten lock nut to 84 INCH lbs. (10 N.m). Recheck No. 1 bevel gear preload.

4) Install spring retainer, spring and adjusting screw into housing. Coat adjusting screw with liquid sealer. Using Wrench (09616-10020) and a dial gauge, tighten adjusting screw until No. 1 and 2 bevel gear backlash is zero. Turn No. 1 bevel gear left and right 5 times to snug.

5) Using same tools, loosen adjusting screw a little at a time. Measure total preload. Total preload should be 1.3-3.5 INCH lbs. (.15-.39 N.m). When loosening adjusting screw, ensure backlash is less than .0142" (.36 mm).

6) Coat lock nut threads with liquid sealer and install. Tighten to 80 ft. lbs. (108 N.m). Recheck preload. Pack gear housing with lithium base grease. Coat contacting surface of housing cover with sealer and install. Tighten housing cover bolts to 69 INCH lbs. (7.8 N.m). Install 2 dust covers.

TIGHTENING SPECIFICATIONS

Application	Ft. Lbs. (N.m)
Dust Cover Lock Nut (Van)	83 (113)
Intermediate Shaft Pinch Bolts	22-28 (30-38)
Pinion Bearing Adjusting Screw Lock Nut	
Van	51 (67)
All Others	73-94 (99-127)
Rack Guide Screw Lock Nut	44-57 (59-77)
Rack End-to-Rack	
Van	61 (83)
All Others	51-72 (69-98)
Rack Housing Bracket-to-Body Bolt	22-32 (30-44)
Tie Rod-to-Knuckle Nut	37-50 (50-68)
Tie Rod-to-Rack End Clamp	
Van	13 (17)
All Others	11-14 (15-19)

TOYOTA PICKUP & 4RUNNER RECIRCULATING BALL

DESCRIPTION

Steering gear is a variable ratio, recirculating ball type. Ball bearings circulate within grooves in worm and nut. As worm shaft turns, ball nut moves up or down, turning the sector shaft and pitman arm.

Linkage consists of an idler arm, center relay rod, adjustable tie rods and steering knuckles. Pickups also use a steering damper attached to center relay rod. Components are connected by ball joints. Linkage assembly is connected to steering gear by a pitman arm.

ADJUSTMENTS

Adjustments are performed during reassembly. See OVERHAUL in this article.

REMOVAL & INSTALLATION

STEERING GEAR

Removal

1) Mark steering gear shaft at flexible coupling or "U" joint for reassembly reference. Remove coupling or

TOYOTA PICKUP & 4RUNNER RECIRCULATING BALL (Cont.)

Fig. 1: Exploded View of Steering Linkage

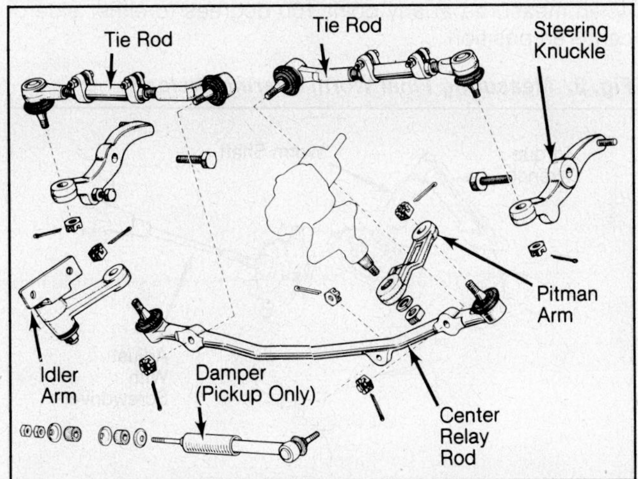

2WD steering linkage is shown; 4WD is similar.
Courtesy of Toyota Motor Sales, U.S.A., Inc.

"U" joint. Mark steering gear shaft at pitman arm. Disconnect pitman arm from steering gear.

2) Remove steering gear-to-frame retaining bolts. Separate steering gear from steering shaft while removing steering gear from vehicle.

Installation

To install steering gear, reverse removal procedure. Align marks made during removal.

STEERING LINKAGE

Removal

1) Mark pitman arm at sector shaft. Remove cotter pins and castle nuts from sector shaft, steering knuckles and idler arm. Using a puller, disconnect pitman arm from sector shaft and tie ends from steering knuckles.

2) Disconnect steering damper from cross-member (if equipped). Remove steering linkage assembly from vehicle. Remove idler arm bracket bolts. Remove idler arm.

Installation

To install steering linkage, reverse removal procedure. Align marks made during removal. Ensure tie rod lengths are to specification. Measure tie rod lengths from center-to-center of ball joints. Tie rod length should be 12.38" (314.5 mm).

OVERHAUL

STEERING GEAR

Disassembly

1) Mark pitman arm at sector shaft for reassembly reference. Remove pitman arm. Remove sector shaft adjusting screw lock nut. Remove sector shaft cover and sector shaft.

2) Be careful not to lose adjusting screw and shim. Remove worm assembly lock nut, adjusting screw and oil seal. Remove the worm assembly and bearings. *See Fig. 2.*

NOTE: Do not disassemble ball nut from worm. If recirculating ball assembly has damaged or worn components, replace entire assembly.

Fig. 2: Exploded View of Steering Gear Assembly

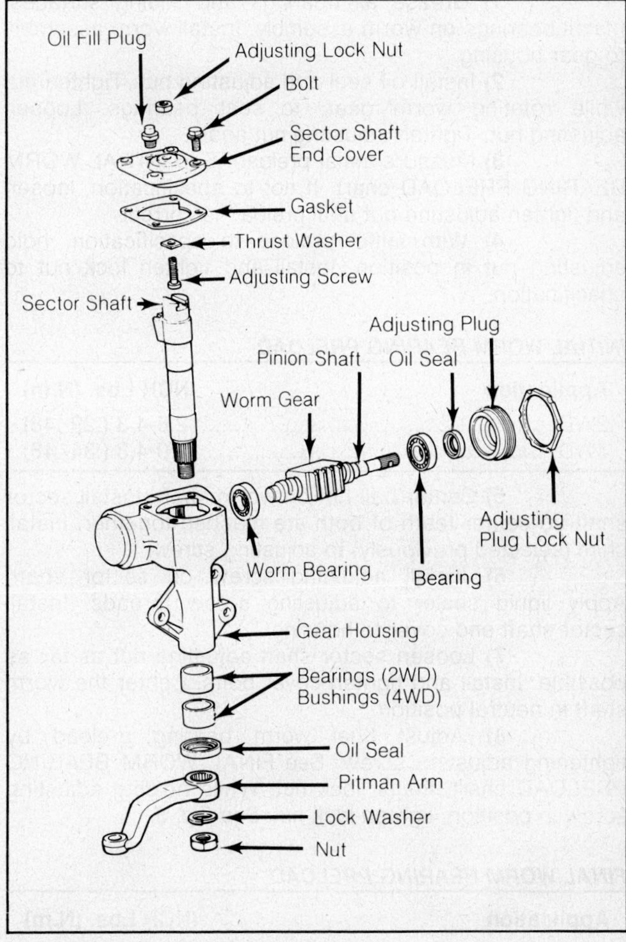

Courtesy of Toyota Motor Sales, U.S.A., Inc.

Inspection (2WD)

1) Check all components for excessive wear or damage. Measure clearance between adjusting screw (with shim installed) and sector shaft. Maximum clearance should be .002" (.05 mm).

2) If clearance is not to specification, shims are available from .0787" (2.00 mm) to .0866" (2.20 mm) in .0016" (.04 mm) increments.

3) Check worm gear and ball nut, taking care not to let ball nut bottom out on either end of worm gear. If ball nut bottoms out, damage to worm assembly will occur.

4) Check worm bearings and races for pitting and smooth operation. Replace, if damaged. Replace oil seal. Replace end cover bushing and needle bearings, if necessary.

Inspection (4WD)

1) Measure sector shaft end cover inside diameter and gear housing inside diameter. Both measurements should be 1.2598-1.2608" (32.000-32.025 mm).

2) Inspect end cover bushing for wear or damage. Standard oil clearance should be .0004-.0024" (.009-.060 mm). If not, replace bushing.

3) Check worm gear and ball nut, taking care not to let ball nut bottom out on either end of worm gear. If ball nut bottoms out, damage to worm assembly will occur.

TOYOTA PICKUP & 4RUNNER RECIRCULATING BALL (Cont.)

Reassembly & Adjustment

1) Grease all bearings and sliding surfaces. Install bearings on worm assembly. Install worm assembly to gear housing.

2) Install oil seal and adjusting nut. Tighten nut while rotating worm gear, to seat bearings. Loosen adjusting nut. Tighten adjusting nut again.

3) Measure initial preload. See INITIAL WORM BEARING PRELOAD chart. If not to specification, loosen and tighten adjusting nut until preload is correct.

4) With initial preload to specification, hold adjusting nut in position. Install and tighten lock nut to specification.

INITIAL WORM BEARING PRELOAD

Application	INCH Lbs. (N.m)
2WD	2.6-4.3 (.29-.48)
4WD	3.0-4.3 (.34-.48)

5) Center ball nut on worm shaft. Install sector shaft so center teeth of both are meshed together. Install shim (selected previously) to adjusting screw.

6) Install adjusting screw on sector shaft. Apply liquid sealer to adjusting screw threads. Install sector shaft end cover to housing.

7) Loosen sector shaft adjusting nut as far as possible. Install and tighten cover bolts. Center the worm shaft in neutral position.

8) Adjust final worm bearing preload by tightening adjusting screw. See FINAL WORM BEARING PRELOAD chart. Install lock nut. While holding adjusting screw in position, tighten lock nut. *See Fig. 3.*

FINAL WORM BEARING PRELOAD

Application	INCH Lbs. (N.m)
2WD	6.9-9.1 (.78-1.03)
4WD	6.9-9.5 (.78-1.07)

9) Aligning marks made during removal, install pitman arm and nut. Attach dial indicator so plunger touches end of pitman arm to measure backlash.

10) Sector shaft should have no backlash when measured at any point 100 degrees to either side of centered position.

Fig. 3: Measuring Final Worm Bearing Preload

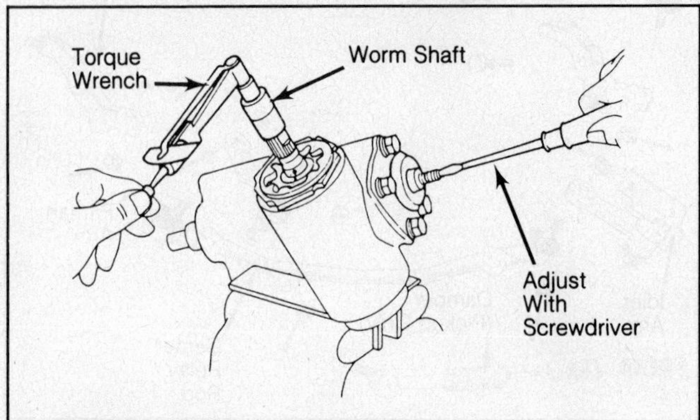

Courtesy of Toyota Motor Sales, U.S.A., Inc.

TIGHTENING SPECIFICATIONS

Application	Ft. Lbs. (N.m)
Pitman Arm-to-Sector Shaft Nut	
2WD	90 (123)
4WD	130 (177)
Sector Shaft Adjusting Screw Lock Nut	
2WD	20 (27)
4WD	33 (44)
Sector Shaft End Cover Bolts	
2WD	36 (49)
4WD	72 (98)
Steering Gear-to-Frame	
2WD	48 (65)
4WD	70 (95)
Worm Shaft Adjusting Screw Lock Nut	
2WD	177 (240)
4WD	130 (177)

VOLKSWAGEN RACK & PINION – EXCEPT VANAGON

DESCRIPTION

Steering gear is a rack and pinion type. Tie rods connect steering knuckles to ends of rack. Racks are mounted with "U" bolts and rubber bushings.

ADJUSTMENTS

RACK & TIE RODS

1) Center rack in housing so rack protrudes an equal amount from each end of rack housing.

2) If replacing the non-adjustable left tie rod with an adjustable type, adjust tie rod length "D" to 14.92" (379 mm). Screw tie rods onto rack.

3) Adjust to specified dimensions without moving rack from center position. Dimensions "B" and "C" should be 2.77" (70.5 mm) for all models.

4) When measurements are correct, secure tie rods with lock nuts. Install rubber boots. *See Fig. 1.*

Fig. 1: Installation Adjustment of Tie Rods on Rack

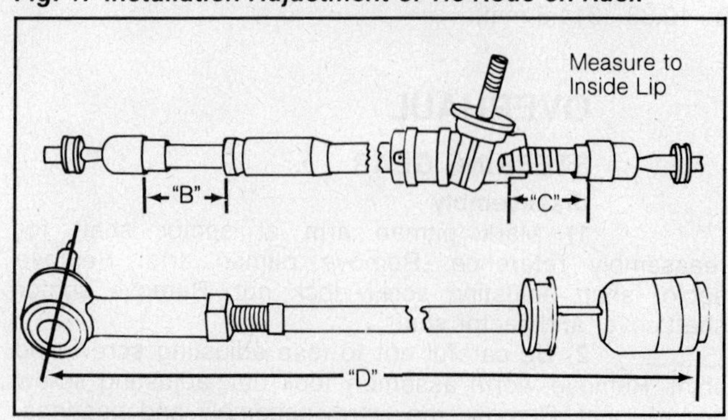

STEERING DRIVE

Loosen pinion shaft adjusting screw lock nut. Turn adjusting bolt until it just contacts thrust washer.

VOLKSWAGEN RACK & PINION – EXCEPT VANAGON (Cont.)

Tighten lock nut. Test drive vehicle. Readjust if steering is too heavy or too loose.

REMOVAL & INSTALLATION

STEERING GEAR

Removal

1) Disconnect shift linkage bearing plate from steering gear housing. Loosen lower "U" joint pinch bolt. Separate steering shaft with lower "U" joint from pinion.

2) Remove tie rod end cotter pins and castle nuts. Using a tie rod end puller, separate tie rod ends from steering knuckles. Remove steering gear clamp bolts. Remove steering gear with tie rods attached.

Installation

1) To install, reverse removal procedure. Correctly align and insert pinion shaft with steering shaft lower "U" joint before tightening steering gear clamp bolts.

2) Connect tie rod outer ends to steering knuckles. Tighten upper and lower universal joint pinch bolts. Connect and adjust shift linkage bearing plate to housing.

OVERHAUL

STEERING GEAR

Overhaul procedures for steering gear are not available from manufacturer. Replace as an assembly if damaged or worn.

TIGHTENING SPECIFICATIONS

Application	Ft. Lbs. (N.m)
Gear Box Housing-to-Frame Nuts	22 (30)
Tie Rod End Lock Nut	37 (50)
Tie Rod End Castle Nuts	26 (35)
Tie Rod-to-Rack	52 (70)
"U" Joint-to-Pinion Shaft Clamp Bolts	22 (30)

Fig. 2: Exploded View of Rack & Pinion Steering Gear Assembly

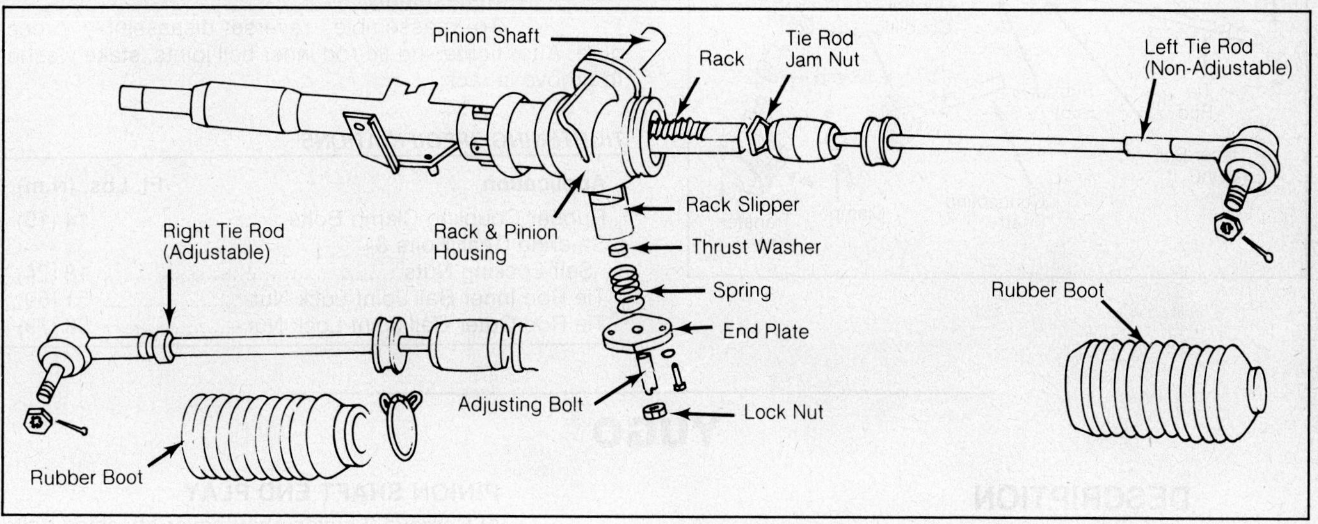

VOLKSWAGEN VANAGON RACK & PINION

DESCRIPTION

Volkswagen Vanagon models use a rack and pinion steering gear. A transfer gear is used to connect steering shaft to steering gear.

Tie rods connect the rack to the steering knuckles with ball joints. Tie rods are adjustable for toe-in.

ADJUSTMENTS

STEERING GEAR

NOTE: Steering gear is not adjustable. If gear is damaged or does not operate properly, replace as an assembly.

REMOVAL & INSTALLATION

STEERING GEAR

Removal

Remove clamp bolt retaining connecting shaft coupling to steering gear pinion shaft. Remove tie rod end cotter pins and castle nuts. Using a tie rod end puller, separate tie rod ends from steering knuckles. Remove steering gear mounting bolts. Remove steering gear from vehicle.

Installation

To install, reverse removal procedure. Tighten bolts to specification. Use NEW self-locking nuts to install steering gear.

VOLKSWAGEN VANAGON RACK & PINION (Cont.)

TRANSFER GEAR

Removal & Installation

Remove connecting shaft coupling-to-transfer gear shaft clamp bolt. Remove lower steering shaft flange-to-transfer gear shaft clamp bolt. Remove transfer gear retaining bolts. Remove transfer gear. To install, reverse removal procedure. Always use new rubber couplings.

Fig. 1: Exploded View of Steering Gear & Transfer Gear

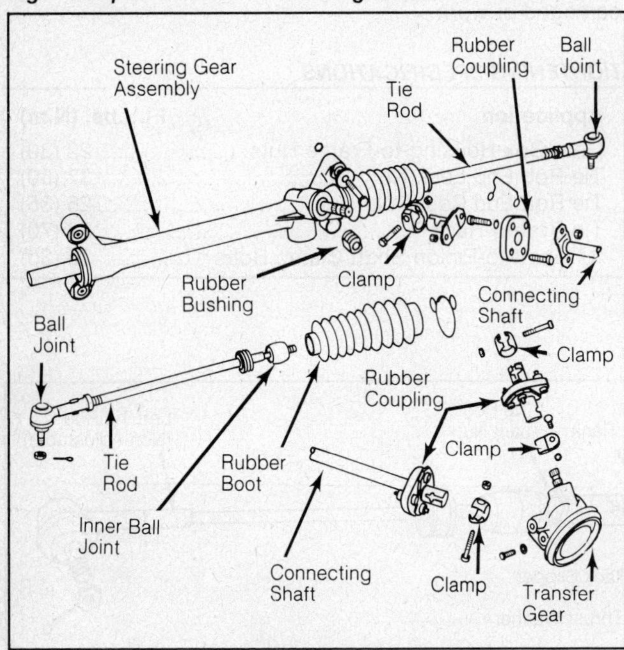

OVERHAUL

STEERING GEAR & TRANSFER GEAR

Overhaul procedures for steering gear and transfer gear are not available from manufacturer. Replace as an assembly if damaged or worn.

NOTE: Steering gear and transfer gear cannot be repaired. Replace components if damaged. Steering gear rubber boots and tie rods can be replaced.

TIE RODS & RUBBER BOOTS

Disassembly

1) Remove steering gear from vehicle. Remove boot clamps from tie rods and housing ends. Pull boots back, away from housing ends. Using a punch, unstake tie rod inner ball joint tab washer.

2) Loosen inner ball joint lock nut. Unscrew tie rods with inner ball joints and rubber boots from rack. Loosen tie rod end ball joint lock nut. Remove ball joints from tie rods.

Reassembly

To reassemble, reverse disassembly procedure. After tightening tie rod inner ball joints, stake washer to groove in rack.

TIGHTENING SPECIFICATIONS

Application	Ft. Lbs. (N.m)
Rubber Coupling Clamp Bolts	14 (19)
Steering Gear Bolts & Self-Locking Nuts	18 (24)
Tie Rod Inner Ball Joint Lock Nut	51 (69)
Tie Rod Outer Ball Joint Lock Nut	58 (79)

YUGO

DESCRIPTION

Steering gear is a rack and pinion type. Tie rods are connected to rack by a ball and socket arrangement. Tie rod ends connect directly to steering knuckle with ball joints. Tie rods are adjustable for toe-in.

ADJUSTMENTS

RACK PRELOAD

1) Center the steering rack. Remove 2 rack preload cover attaching bolts. Remove rack preload cover, shims, seal and spring.

2) While holding the preload block against the rack, turn the pinion shaft through 180 degrees of revolution to seat the rack with the pinion. Place the rack preload cover in position.

3) Using a feeler gauge, measure the gap between the cover and gear housing. Note the measurement. Select shims that will total this dimension plus an added .002-.005" (.05-.13 mm). Install spring, seal, shims and cover. Tighten cover bolts.

PINION SHAFT END PLAY

1) Remove 2 pinion shaft cover attaching bolts. Remove cover with seal, gasket and shims. Using an appropriate driver, ensure bearing is properly seated.

2) Measure the distance from top of bearing to rim of housing. Note the measurement. Select shims that will total this dimension plus an added .001-.005" (.025-.131 mm). Install shims, gasket and cover with seal. Tighten cover bolts.

REMOVAL & INSTALLATION

STEERING GEAR

Removal

1) Place wheels in a straight-ahead position. Mark steering shaft-to-pinion shaft "U" joints for reassembly reference. Remove "U" joint-to-pinion shaft clamp bolt.

2) Raise and support vehicle. Remove tie rod end cotter pin and castle nut. Using Puller (A-47035), separate tie rod end from steering knuckle. Remove steering gear mounting bolts. Remove steering gear.

Steering Gears & Linkage

YUGO (Cont.)

Fig. 1: Exploded View of Yugo Rack & Pinion Steering Assembly

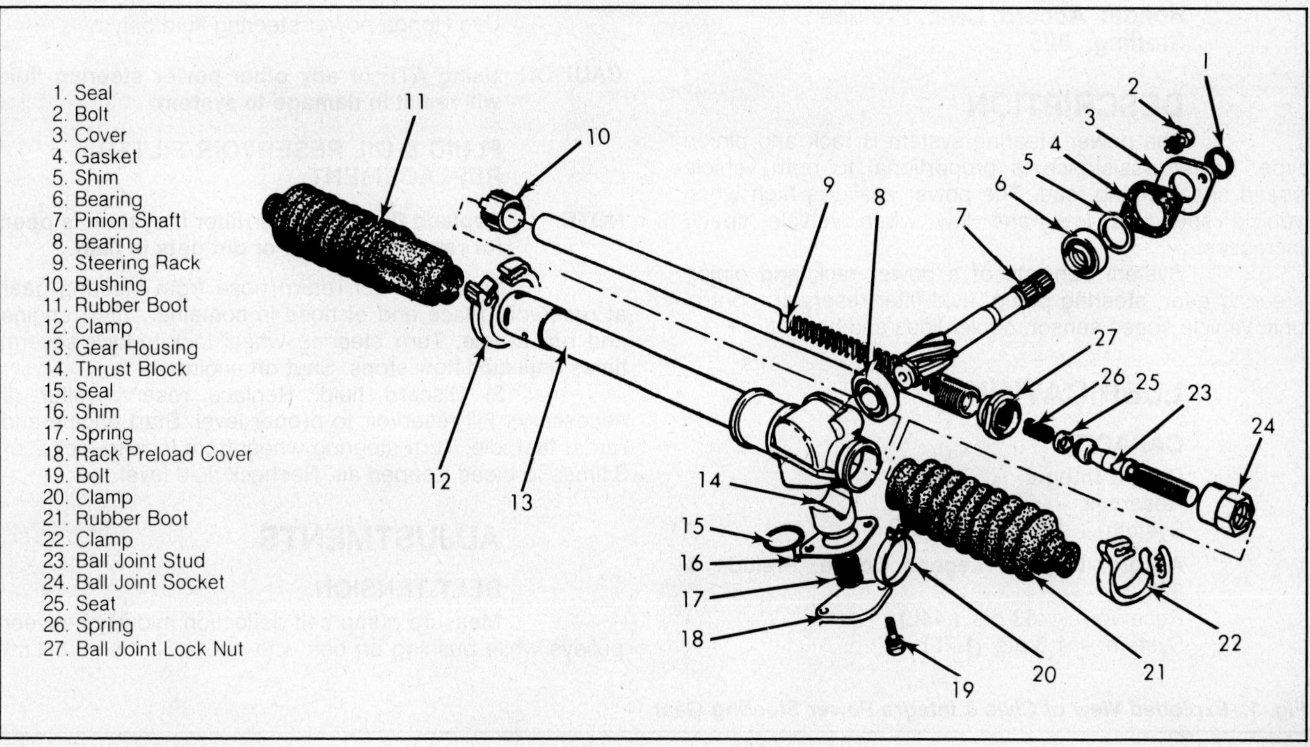

Courtesy of Yugo America, Inc.

Installation

To install steering gear, reverse removal procedure. Tighten bolts to specification. Refer to TIGHTENING SPECIFICATIONS table at end of article.

OVERHAUL

Disassembly

1) Remove 2 rack preload cover attaching bolts. Remove rack preload cover, shims, seal, spring and preload block. Remove 2 pinion shaft cover attaching bolts. Remove cover with seal, gasket and shims.

2) Remove boot clamps. Remove boots. Remove pinion shaft with bearing from gear housing. Remove tie rods from rack. Place tie rods, tie rod seats, tie rod-to-ball joint springs and tie rod lock nuts in order of removal.

3) Slide steering rack from housing. Remove bushing from steering rack. Remove pinion lower bearing from housing.

Inspection

Clean all parts before inspection. Check steering rack, pinion shaft, bearings and housing for cracks, scoring or damage. Inspect pinion shaft and steering rack teeth for chipping or abnormal wear. Replace parts as necessary.

Reassembly

1) Lubricate all parts before reassembly. To reassemble, reverse disassembly procedure. Always use new seals and boots.

2) Tighten inner ball joint socket to allow tie rod to move smoothly, but not loose enough to allow tie rods to fall under their own weight.

3) Tie rods should move approximately 60 degrees. *See Fig. 2.* Tighten bolts to specifications. Refer to TIGHTENING SPECIFICATIONS table.

Fig. 2: Tie Rod End Deflection

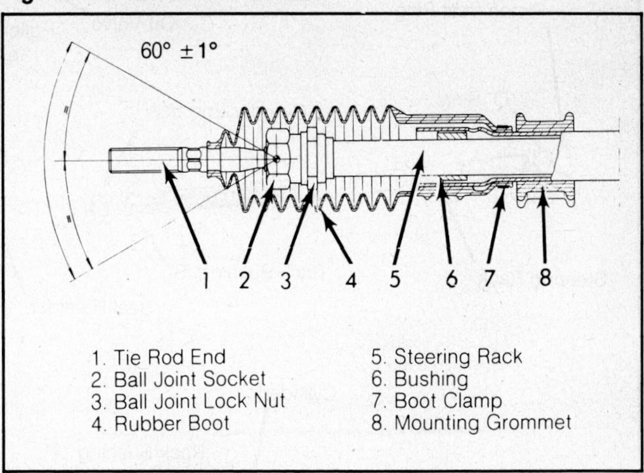

Courtesy of Yugo America, Inc.

TIGHTENING SPECIFICATIONS

Application	Ft. Lbs. (N.m)
Steering Gear Mounting Bolts	19 (26)
Tie Rod Inner Ball Joint Lock Nut	36 (49)
Tie Rod Outer Ball Joint Lock Nut	25 (34)
"U" Joint Clamp Bolts	19 (26)

ACURA, HONDA & STERLING RACK & PINION

Acura: Integra, Legend, Legend Coupe
Honda: Accord, Civic, Prelude
Sterling: 825

DESCRIPTION

The power steering system is rack and pinion type. Power assistance is proportional to both vehicle speed and steering load. The power assist is high when vehicle speed is low, and low when vehicle speed increases.

System consists of a power rack and pinion steering gear, steering pump, fluid filter/reservoir, control unit, vehicle speed sensor, cooler lines and hoses.

LUBRICATION

CAPACITY

Civic & Integra

Reservoir - .26 qts. (.25L).
System - 1.3 qts. (1.2L).

Accord, Legend, Legend Coupe, Prelude & 825

Reservoir - .53 qts. (.44L).
System - 1.8 qts. (1.7L).

FLUID TYPE

Use Honda power steering fluid only.

CAUTION: Using ATF or any other power steering fluid will result in damage to system.

FLUID & OIL RESERVOIR/FILTER REPLACEMENT

NOTE: Replace fluid reservoir/filter if system is open for repair or if water or dirt gets in fluid.

1) Disconnect return hose from steering gear at reservoir. Place end of hose in container. Start engine and run at idle. Turn steering wheel lock-to-lock several times until fluid flow stops. Shut off engine.

2) Discard fluid. Replace reservoir/filter (if necessary). Fill reservoir to proper level. Start engine and run at fast idle. Turn steering wheel from lock-to-lock 2 or 3 times to bleed trapped air. Recheck fluid level.

ADJUSTMENTS

BELT TENSION

Measure pump belt deflection midway between pulleys while pushing on belt with about 22 lbs. (30 N.m).

Fig. 1: Exploded View of Civic & Integra Power Steering Gear

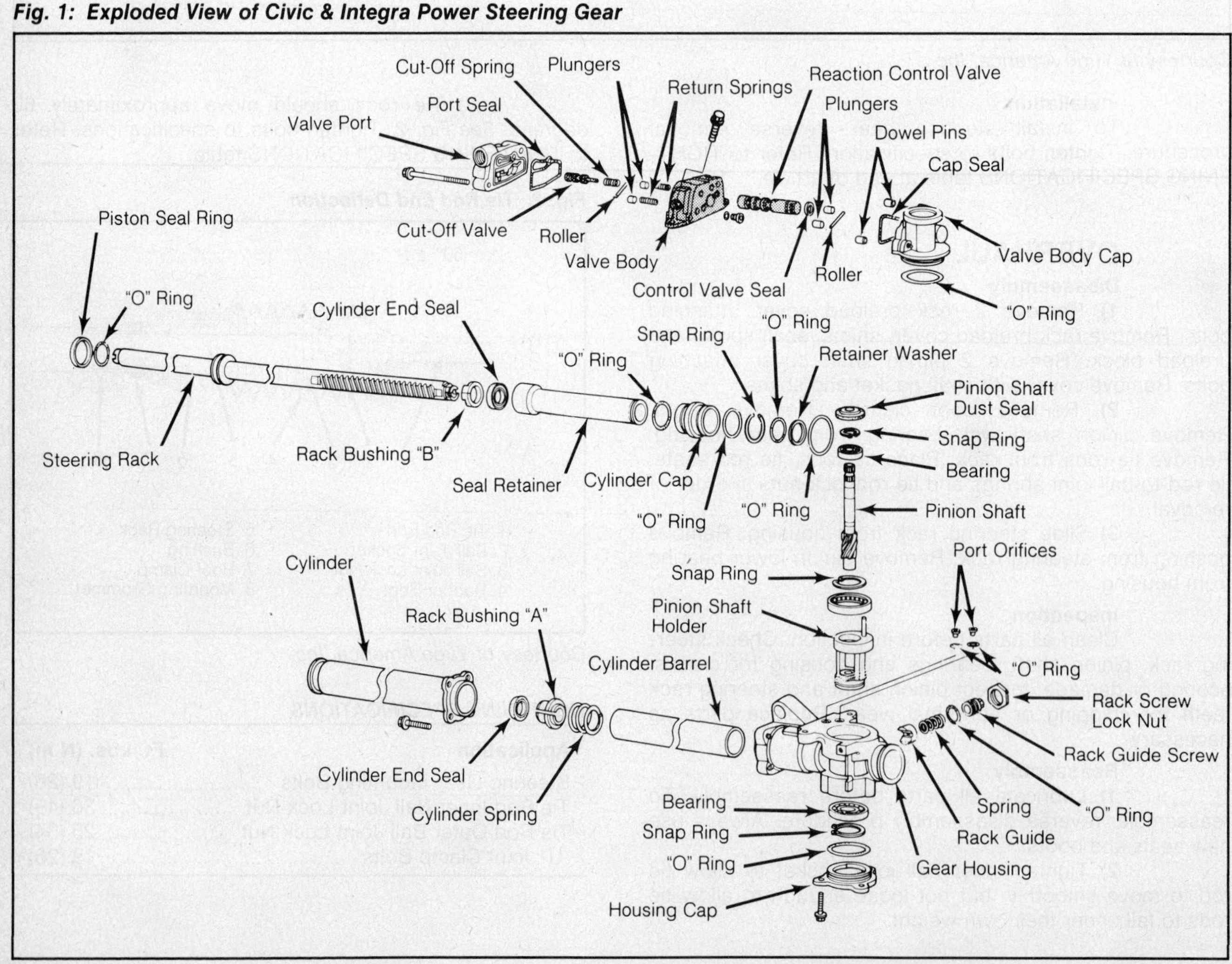

Courtesy of American Honda Motor Co., Inc.

ACURA, HONDA & STERLING RACK & PINION (Cont.)

For a new belt, deflection should be between .7-.8" (18-20 mm). For a used belt, deflection should be between .7-.9" (18-22 mm).

PUMP PRESSURE CHECK

1) Check fluid level and belt tension. Adjust as necessary. Disconnect outlet hose from pump. Install Pressure Gauge Set (07406-0010000). Fully open shut-off and pressure control valves.

2) Start engine and let idle. Turn steering wheel from lock-to-lock several times until fluid is at operating temperature. Completely close shut-off valve.

CAUTION: Do not keep shut-off valve closed for more than 5 seconds. Pump could be damaged.

3) Gradually close pressure control valve until pressure gauge needle stabilizes. Read pressure. Fully open shut-off valve. Pump pressure should be at least 1138 psi (80 kg/cm²). Replace pump if pressure is too low.

RACK ADJUSTMENT

1) Using Lock Nut Wrench (07916-SA50001), loosen lock nut. Using a 14 mm wrench, tighten rack guide screw until spring is compressed against the guide.

2) On Integra, loosen rack guide screw. Retighten to 36 INCH lbs. (4 N.m). Back off rack guide screw 1/4 turn. Holding rack guide screw in place, tighten lock nut.

3) On Legend, Legend Coupe and 825, loosen rack guide screw. Retighten to 24 INCH lbs. (3 N.m). Back off rack guide screw approximately 1/5 turn. Hole rack guide screw in place and tighten lock nut.

STEERING EFFORT

Low Speed Assist

1) Check fluid level and belt tension. Start engine and let idle. Turn steering wheel from lock-to-lock several times to warm fluid. Attach a spring tension scale to steering wheel at outer end of spoke.

Fig. 2: Exploded View of Accord, Legend, Legend Coupe, Prelude & 825 Power Steering Gear

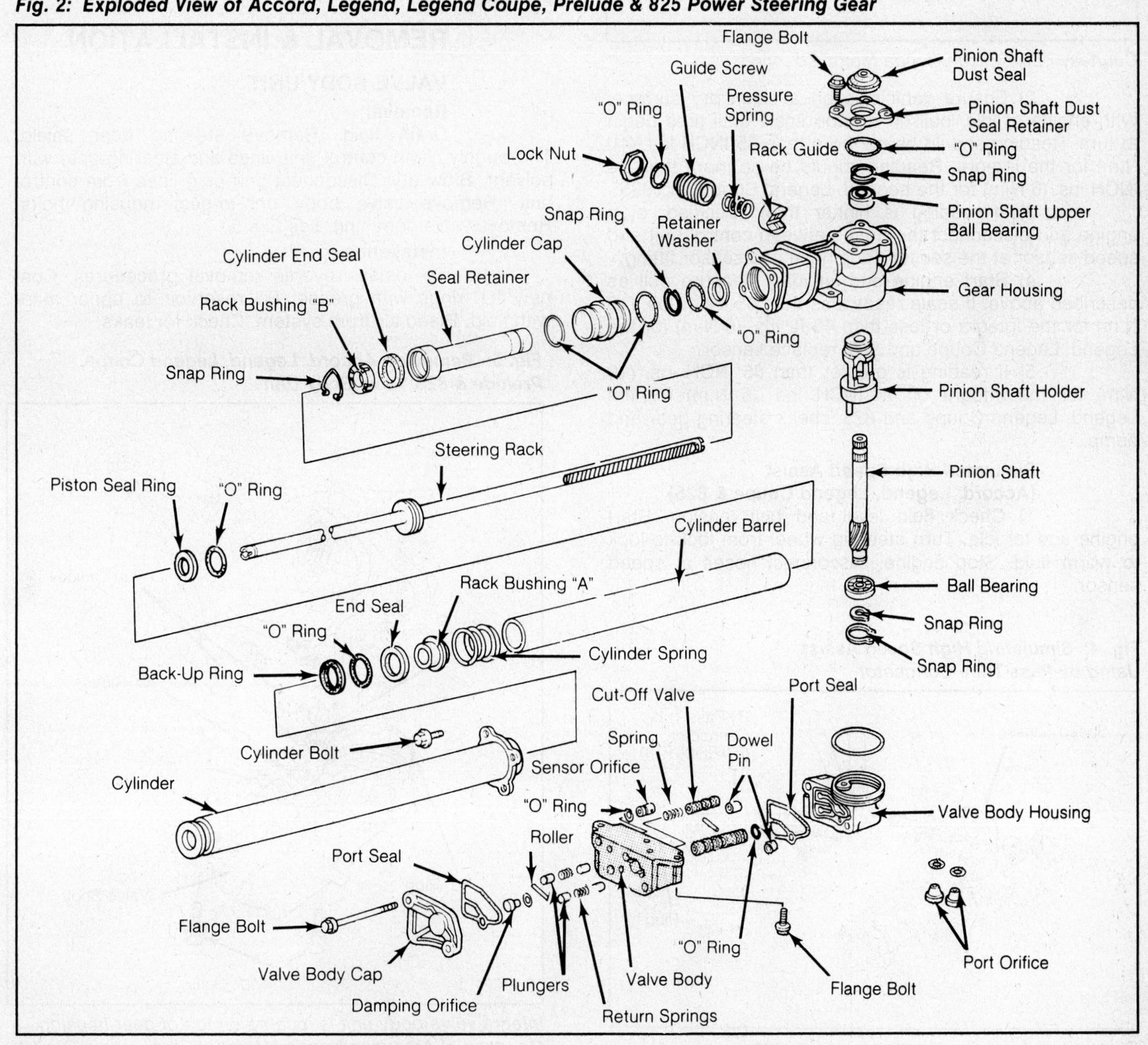

Courtesy of American Honda Motor Co., Inc.

Power Steering

ACURA, HONDA & STERLING RACK & PINION (Cont.)

Fig. 3: View of Accord, Legend, Legend Coupe & 825 Speed Sensor

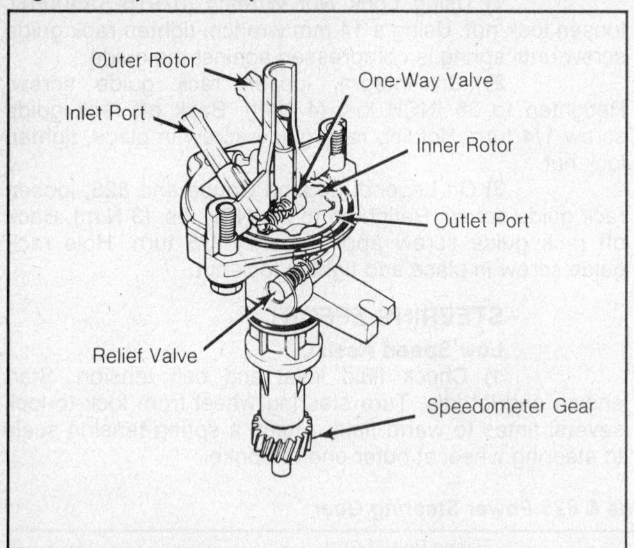

Courtesy of American Honda Motor Co., Inc.

2) Ensure vehicle is on a clean dry surface. With engine at idle, pull on tension scale until tires begin to turn. Reading should be no more than 85 INCH lbs. (10 N.m) for the Integra. Reading should be no more than 48 INCH lbs. (6 N.m) for the Legend, Legend Coupe and 825.

3) If reading is higher than specified, stop engine and disconnect the hose between control unit and speed sensor at the sensor. Plug hose and sensor fitting.

4) Start engine and let idle. Measure pull as described above. If scale reads less than 85 INCH lbs. (10 N.m) for the Integra or less than 48 ft. lbs. (6 N.m) for the Legend, Legend Coupe and 825, replace sensor.

5) If reading is greater than 85 INCH lbs. (10 N.m) for the Integra or 48 INCH lbs. (6 N.m) for the Legend, Legend Coupe and 825, check steering gear and pump.

Simulated High Speed Assist (Accord, Legend, Legend Coupe & 825)

1) Check fluid level and belt tension. Start engine and let idle. Turn steering wheel from lock-to-lock to warm fluid. Stop engine. Disconnect hoses at speed sensor.

Fig. 4: Simulating High Speed Assist Using By-Pass Tube Connector

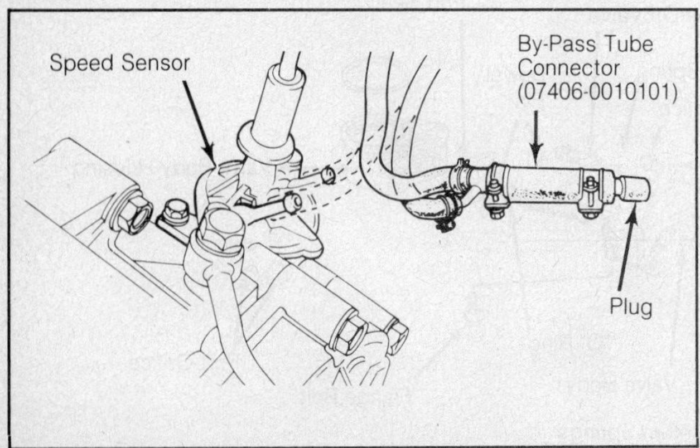

Courtesy of American Honda Motor Co., Inc.

2) Connect By-Pass Tube Connector (07406-0010101) and a plug to the hoses. *See Fig. 4.* This will connect 2 hoses from cut-off valve and control unit to reservoir hose, simulating driving speeds over 30 MPH.

3) Attach spring tension scale to outer end of spoke. With vehicle on clean dry floor, start engine and let idle. Pull on tension scale until tires begin to turn.

4) If turning force is greater than 11 lbs. (15 N.m), replace speed sensor. If turning force is less than 11 lbs. (15 N.m), speed sensor is okay.

3) Check sensor feed line for restriction. Check steering pump and steering gear for restriction.

STEERING SHAFT

1) Adjustment is necessary only when installing column. It is not necessary if steering column was lowered for gauge or wiring access, without loosening "U" joint clamp bolt.

2) For further information on steering shaft adjustment or overhaul, refer to STEERING COLUMNS section.

REMOVAL & INSTALLATION

VALVE BODY UNIT

Removal

Drain fluid. Remove steering gear shield. Thoroughly clean control unit, lines and steering gear with solvent. Blow dry. Disconnect and plug lines from control unit. Remove valve body unit-to-gear housing bolts. Remove valve body unit. *See Fig. 5.*

Installation

To install, reverse removal procedures. Coat new "O" rings with grease. Fill reservoir to upper mark with fluid. Bleed air from system. Check for leaks.

Fig. 5: Removing Accord, Legend, Legend Coupe, Prelude & 825 Valve Body Unit

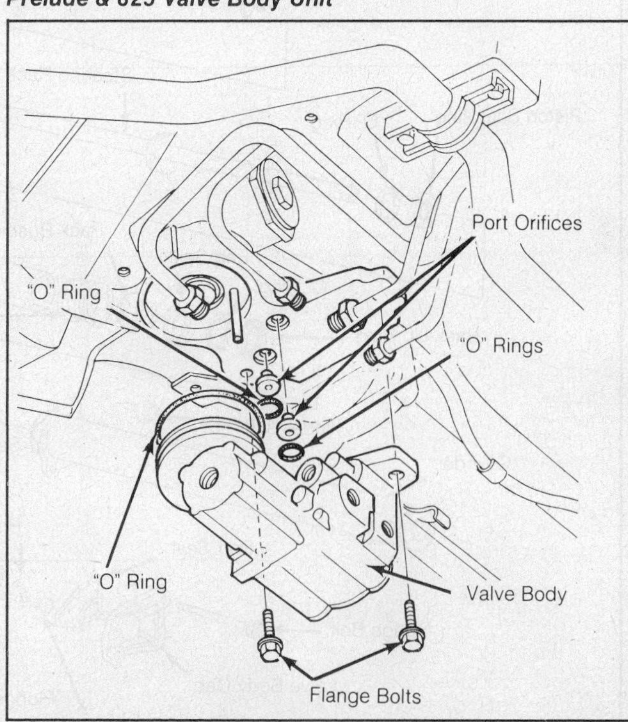

Integra valve body unit is located on top of gear housing.
Courtesy of American Honda Motor Co., Inc.

ACURA, HONDA & STERLING RACK & PINION (Cont.)

STEERING GEAR

Removal

1) Drain power steering fluid. Remove steering "U" joint cover. Remove "U" joint clamp bolts. Pull "U" joint from pinion shaft. Raise and support vehicle.

2) Remove wheels. Remove ball joint cotter pins. Partially remove castle nuts. Using Ball Joint Remover (07941-6920002), break ball joints free.

3) Remove castle nut. Drop ball joint from steering knuckle. On manual transmission models, remove shift extension from transmission case.

4) Slide shift retaining pin cover back away from transmission. Using a drift, drive shift extension retaining pin from shift extension. Remove shift extension.

5) On automatic transmission models, remove shift cable guide from floor. Pull cable down by hand. On all models, remove exhaust pipe.

6) Clean steering gear and surrounding area. On Legend, Legend Coupe and 825, remove center beam retaining bolts. Remove center beam.

7) On all models, remove steering fluid pipes (3 from Civic & Integra and 4 from all others) from housing. Remove steering gear retaining bolts.

8) Drop steering gear so that pinion shaft clears hole in frame channel. Rotate steering gear forward until pinion shaft points to rear of vehicle.

9) Slide unit to the right until the left tie rod is clear of the frame. Drop unit down and out to the left.

Installation

To install, reverse removal procedure. Use new self-locking nuts if the old ones can be easily threaded onto the bolts. Use new exhaust gaskets. Use new cotter pins when installing ball joints.

POWER STEERING PUMP

Removal

Drain fluid. On Accord, Legend, Legend Coupe, Prelude and 825, remove belt covers. On all models, disconnect inlet, outlet and return hoses at pump. Remove belt by loosening pump pivot and adjusting bolts. Remove pump retaining bolts. Remove pump. *See Figs. 6 and 7.*

Installation

To install, reverse removal procedure. Adjust belt tension. Fill reservoir with new fluid. Bleed air from system. Check for leaks.

SPEED SENSOR

Removal

Lift up speedometer cable boot. Remove retaining clip. Pull out cable. Disconnect and plug speed sensor hoses. Loosen speedometer gear set bolt. Remove speed sensor.

Installation

After replacing sensor, turn steering wheel from lock-to-lock several times, with engine idling, to bleed air from system. Check for leaks.

OVERHAUL

STEERING GEAR

Disassembly

1) Remove valve body from housing. Loosen dust boot clamps. Pull dust boots back away from cylinder barrel. Bend back the tie rod lock washer tabs. Using a 19 mm wrench to hold the rack and a 17 mm wrench on the tie rod, remove tie rod from rack.

2) Push rack into cylinder to protect rack from scratching. Using Lock Nut Wrench (07916-SA50001), loosen rack guide screw lock nut. Remove rack guide screw, spring and rack guide.

3) On Civic & Integra, remove 3 housing cap retaining bolts. Remove housing cap. Remove "O" ring from housing cap. Remove 32 mm snap ring from "U" joint side of pinion shaft. Using a drift and mallet from the bottom of housing, lightly tap pinion shaft from housing.

Fig. 6: Removing Civic & Integra Power Steering Pump

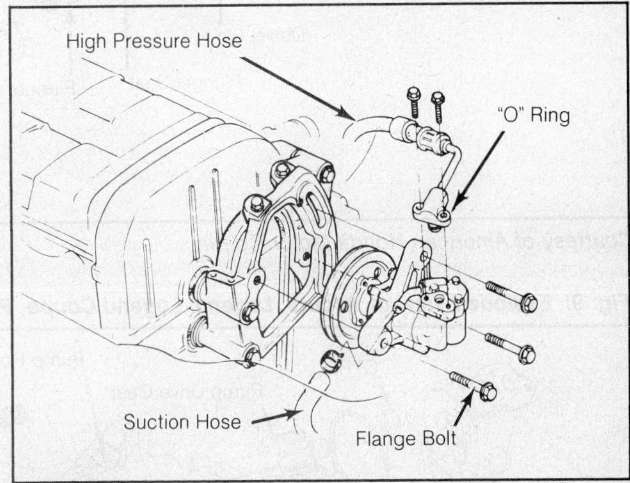

Courtesy of American Honda Motor Co., Inc.

Fig. 7: Removing Accord, Legend, Legend Coupe, Prelude & 825 Power Steering Pump

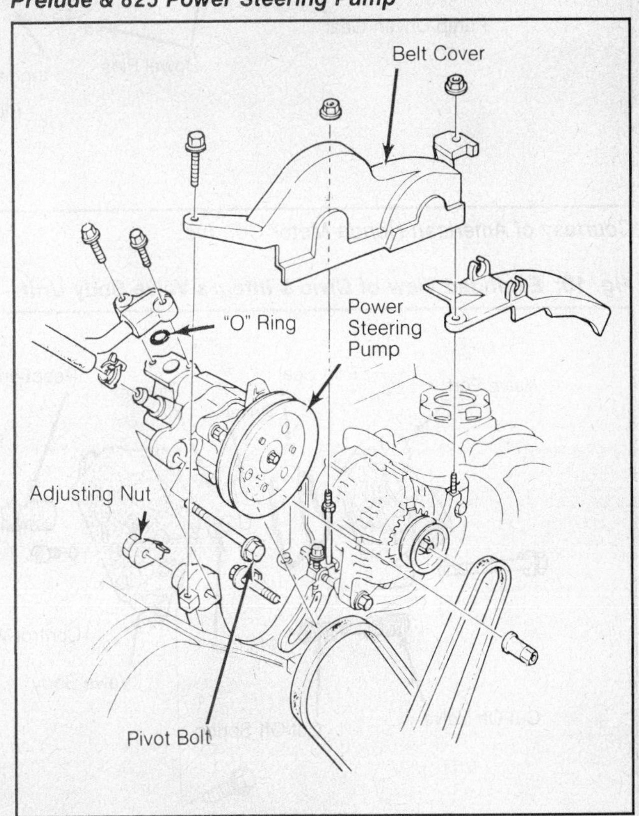

Courtesy of American Honda Motor Co., Inc.

ACURA, HONDA & STERLING RACK & PINION (Cont.)

Fig. 8: Exploded View of Civic & Integra Power Steering Pump

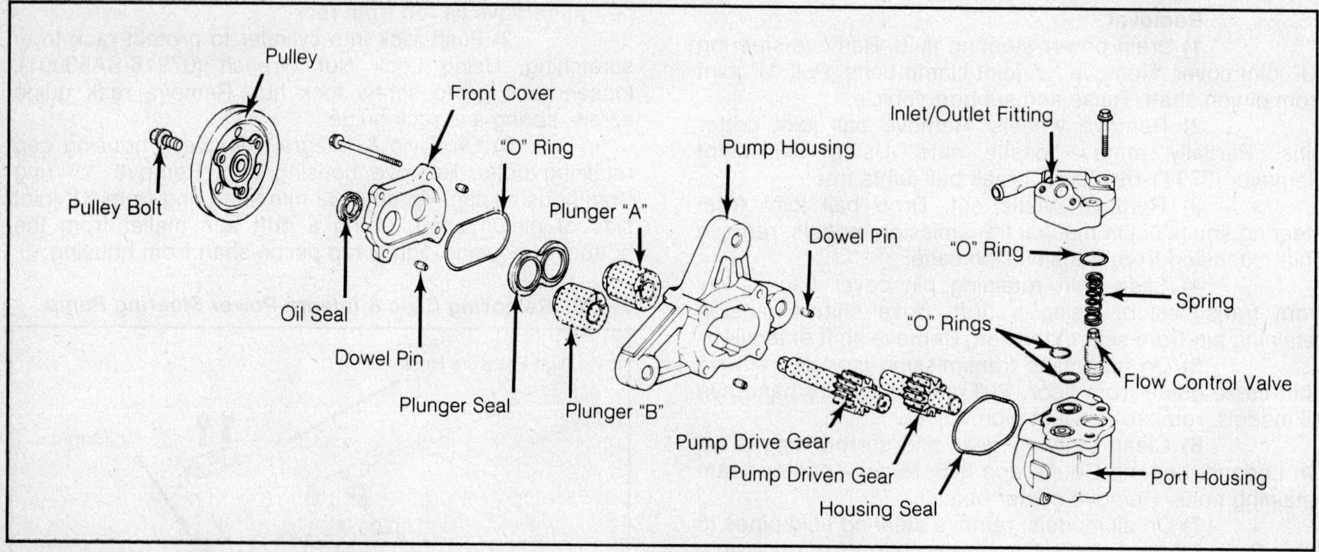

Courtesy of American Honda Motor Co., Inc.

Fig. 9: Exploded View of Accura, Legend, Legend Coupe, Prelude & 825 Power Steering Pump

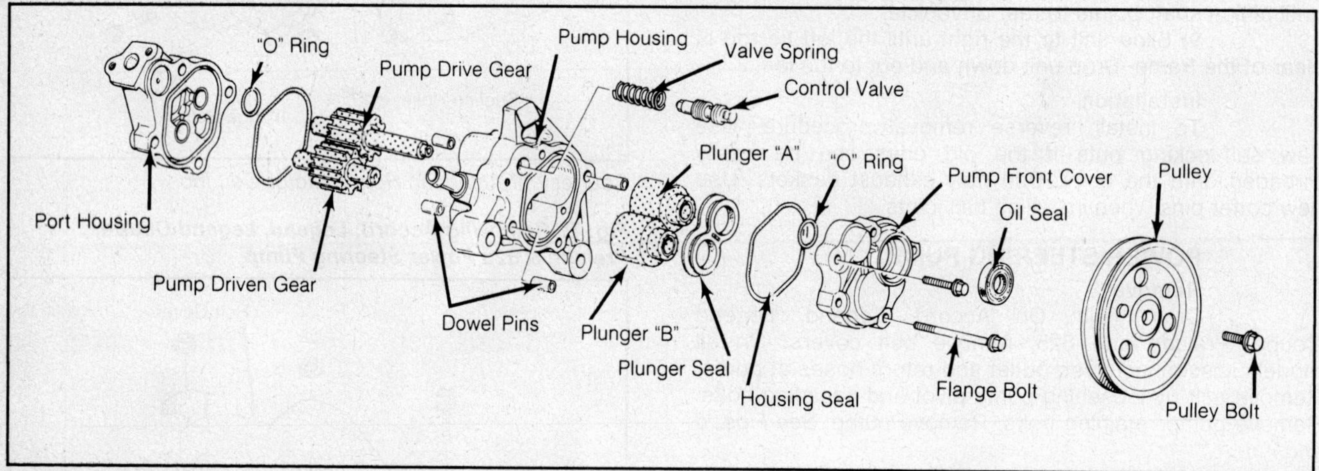

Courtesy of American Honda Motor Co., Inc.

Fig. 10: Exploded View of Civic & Integra Valve Body Unit

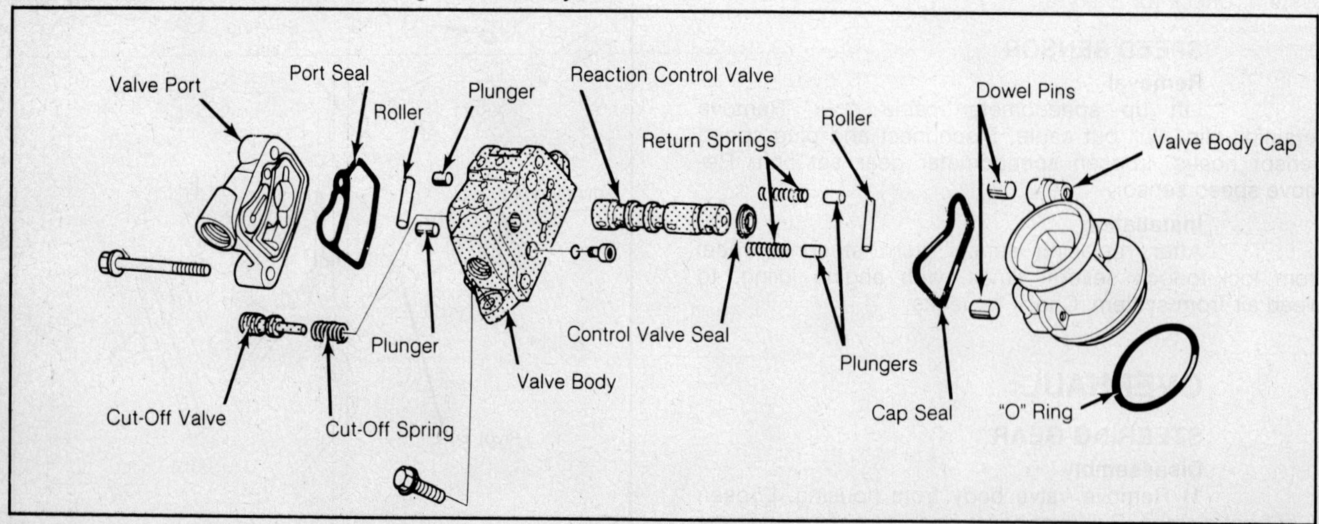

Courtesy of American Honda Motor Co., Inc.

ACURA, HONDA & STERLING RACK & PINION (Cont.)

Fig. 11: Exploded View of Accord, Legend, Legend Coupe, Prelude & 825 Valve Body Unit

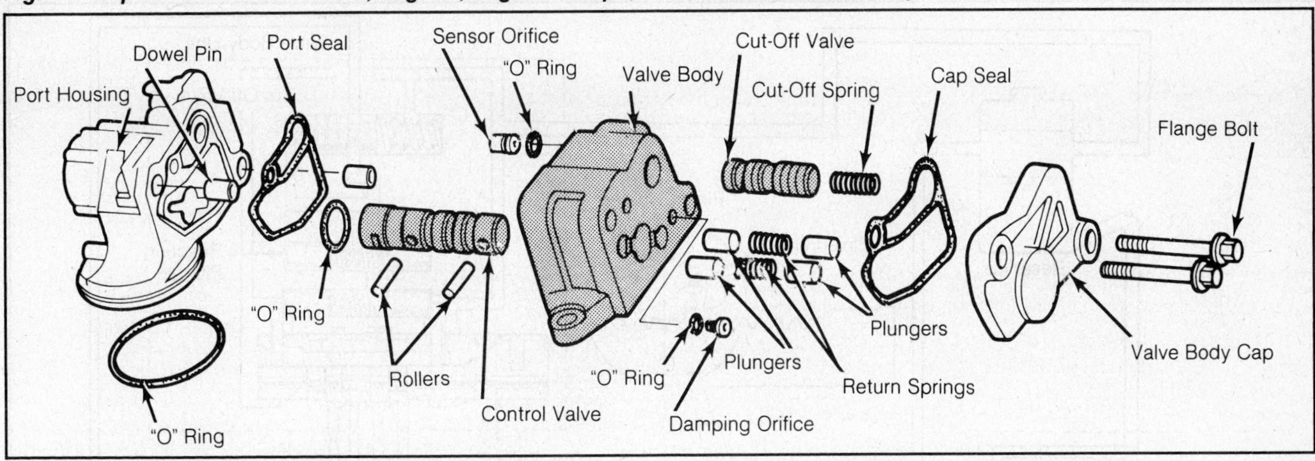

Courtesy of American Honda Motor Co., Inc.

4) On all except Civic and Integra, remove 4 dust seal cap bolts. Remove dust seal cap. Remove 28 mm snap ring from bottom of housing. Working from top of pinion shaft, use a drift and mallet and lightly tap pinion shaft from housing.

5) On all models, remove snap ring from pinion shaft. Using a bearing puller, remove bearing from pinion shaft. Remove 4 cylinder-to-gear housing bolts.

6) Remove cylinder, rack bushing and spring from housing. Pry out cylinder end seal. Remove cylinder barrel, seal retainer, cylinder cap and steering rack from housing.

7) Remove "O" ring and retainer washer from gear housing. Remove snap ring. Remove pinion holder and bearing from gear housing.

8) Remove cylinder barrel and seal retainer from steering rack. Remove "O" ring, snap ring and cylinder cap from seal retainer. Remove "O" rings from cylinder cap.

NOTE: **There are 2 types of back-up rings used in the seal retainer. The Brown back-up ring has no slit. The White back-up ring has a slit. Always replace with correct color code.**

9) Remove rack bushing "B", back-up ring and end seal from seal retainer. Using a small screwdriver, carefully pry off piston seal ring from steering rack. Remove "O" ring from steering rack.

Inspection

Check pinion holder and bearing for excessive play. Replace as necessary. Inspect needle bearings for damage. If needle bearings are damaged, replace steering gear as an assembly.

Reassembly

1) Grease all bearings and sliding surfaces before reassembly. Using Drift (07749-0010000) and Sleeve (07746-0010300), drive bearing into gear housing. *See Figs. 1 and 2.*

2) Install pinion holder into housing. Install snap ring with tapered side facing out away from housing. Align snap ring ends with flat part of pinion holder.

POWER STEERING PUMP

Front Seal Replacement Without Disassembling Pump

1) Remove pump from vehicle. Hold pulley with spanner wrench. Remove pulley nut and pulley with hub. Loosen front cover bolts in a diagonal pattern. Remove cover. Using a screwdriver, pry out seal.

2) Ensure oil passage in front cover is not clogged. Using a 19 mm socket, install new seal. Install front cover bolts. Tighten bolts diagonally to specification. Refer to TIGHTENING SPECIFICATIONS table. Reinstall pulley. Tighten nut to specification.

3) Turn pulley nut with torque wrench to measure preload. Preload should be 35 INCH lbs. (4 N.m). Install belt. Adjust as previously described. Add fluid. Bleed air from system. Check for leaks.

Disassembly

NOTE: **Overhaul of power steering pump is limited to replacement of front cover, control valve, pulley hub and seals.**

1) Remove pump from vehicle. Mount pump in vise. Hold pulley with spanner wrench. Remove nut. If pulley is damaged, separate pulley from hub. Loosen front cover bolts. Remove cover. Pry seal from front cover.

2) Remove plunger housing from pump housing. Remove plungers and gears. Separate pump housing from port housing. Remove inlet-outlet fitting from port housing. Remove "O" rings, filter, spring and control valve from port housing.

Inspection

1) Ensure oil passage in front cover is not clogged. Inspect control valve and filter. Check valve for wear, burrs or damage to edges of groove. Slip valve into bore and check for smooth movement. Replace valve (if necessary).

2) Pressure check control valve. Attach a hose to hex side of control valve. Submerge valve in steering fluid or solvent. Using no more than 3 psi (.21 kg/cm²), blow into hose and check for leakage.

3) If leak is found, disassemble and clean valve. Replace any shims found during disassembly. Retest for leakage. Replace valve if leak persists. Note if valve has an identification mark to determine correct replacement valve.

Power Steering

ACURA, HONDA & STERLING RACK & PINION (Cont.)

Fig. 12: Civic & Integra Power Steering Hydraulic Circuit Diagram

Valve Body Unit
Cut-Off Valve
Pinion Holder
Pinion Gear
Reservoir
Reaction
Plunger
Four-Way Valve
One-Way Valve
Steering Pump
Relief Valve
Steering Wheel
Power Cylinder

Courtesy of American Honda Motor Co., Inc.

Fig. 13: Accord, Legend, Legend Coupe, Prelude & 825 Power Steering Hydraulic Circuit Diagram

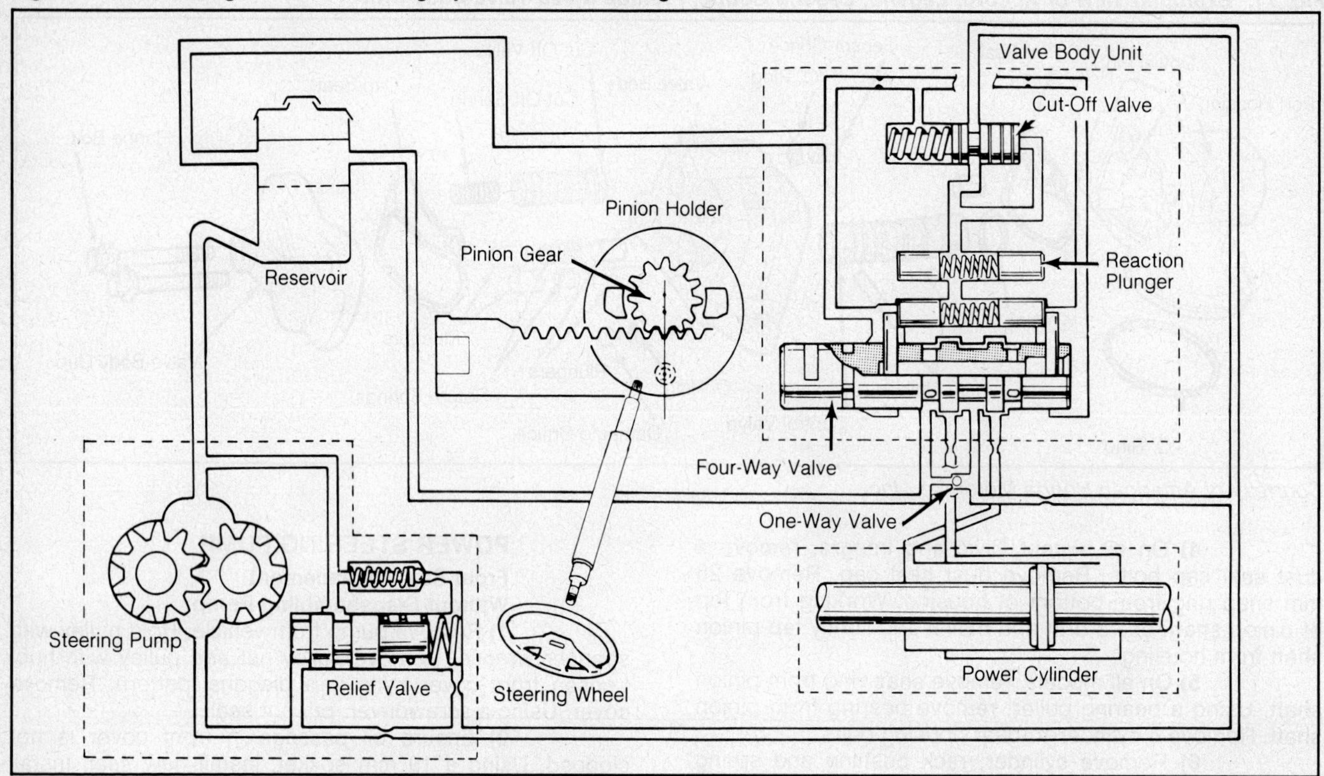

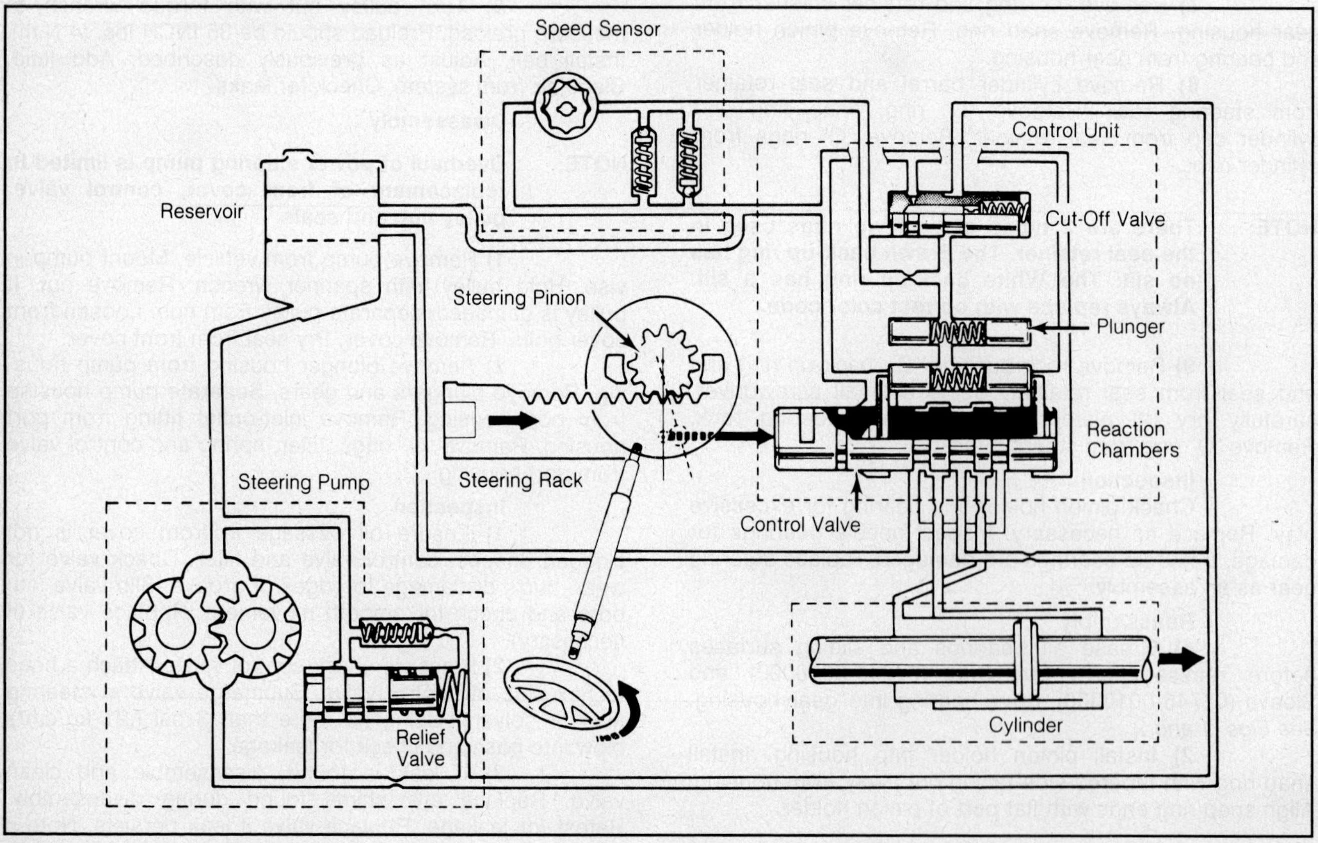

Speed Sensor
Control Unit
Reservoir
Cut-Off Valve
Steering Pinion
Plunger
Reaction
Chambers
Steering Pump
Steering Rack
Control Valve
Relief
Valve
Cylinder

Courtesy of American Honda Motor Co., Inc.

Power Steering

ACURA, HONDA & STERLING RACK & PINION (Cont.)

Reassembly

1) To reassemble, reverse disassembly procedure. Align plunger cut-outs before installing. *See Fig. 3.* Grease all "O" rings and seals before installing.

2) Lubricate gears and shafts with steering fluid. Install front cover. Tighten front cover bolts diagonally. Using a 19 mm socket, install seal into front cover.

VALVE BODY UNIT

Disassembly

NOTE: **Valve body unit on the Legend, Legend Coupe and 825 may be removed from vehicle without removing steering gear. Refer to REMOVAL & INSTALLATION in this article.**

1) Remove 2 bolts holding the valve body to the gear housing. Remove 2 small "O" rings, one large "O" ring and 2 port orifices from gear housing. Remove pinion shaft dust seal from valve body.

2) Remove 2 valve port retaining bolts. Remove valve port and seal from side of valve body. Pull cut-off valve and spring from valve body. Remove valve body cap, cap seal and dowels from valve body.

3) Pushing the reaction control valve to one side of valve body, remove roller from reaction control valve. Repeat procedure on other side of valve body to remove opposite roller. Remove control valve seal.

NOTE: **To keep plungers from falling out when removing rollers, hold plungers with fingers.**

4) On Accord, Legend, Legend Coupe and 825 models with variable assist power steering, remove sensor orifice and "O" ring from valve body. Using a 1/16" drill bit filed flat on the shank end, pry orifice from valve body.

5) Using the same drill bit used for the orifice, insert the bit through the valve body and push out the damping orifice and "O" ring from behind.

Inspection

1) Check cut-off valve for signs of scratching and/or scoring. Insert cut-off valve into valve body and check that it slides smoothly in and out. If the valve body is damaged, replace valve body and cut-off valve as a unit.

NOTE: **The cut-off valve, reaction control valve and plungers are sized to fit the valve body. If necessary to replace any of these, ensure the new part has the same identification letter.**

2) Inspect plungers for scoring or scratching. Insert plungers into valve body and check for smooth operation. If any plunger is damaged, replace. If valve body is damaged, replace valve body as a unit.

3) Check reaction control valve for scoring or scratches. Insert reaction control valve into valve body and check for smooth operation. If valve body is damaged, replace valve body as a unit.

Reassembly

1)Clean all parts before reassembly. Coat plungers, cut-off valve and reaction control valve with Honda ATF. Use new "O" rings and seals.

2) Use grease in the cap seal and port seal grooves to hold seals in place during reassembly. Use grease to hold "O" rings in place during reassembly. To complete reassembly, reverse disassembly procedure.

TIGHTENING SPECIFICATIONS

Application	Ft. Lbs. (N.m)
Cylinder Rack-to-Gear Housing Bolt	16 (22)
Steering Gear Mounting Bolts	28 (38)
Hydraulic Fittings	
14 mm	28 (38)
17 mm	20 (29)
Pump-to-Bracket Bolt	33 (45)
Pump Pulley Nut	24 (33)
Tie Rod-to-Rack	
Civic & Integra	42 (58)
All Others & 825	40 (55)
Tie Rod End Nuts	32 (44)
	INCH Lbs. (N.m)
All 6 mm Bolts	
Civic & Integra	108 (12)
All Others	84 (10)
Hydraulic Fittings	
12 mm	108 (12)
Pump Front Cover Bolt	108 (12)

AUDI POWER-ASSISTED RACK & PINION

DESCRIPTION

The steering system consists of a belt-driven vane pump, rotary piston pinion gear assembly, and an oil reservoir. The flow control valve supplies fluid to the proper side of the rack piston when the steering wheel is turned. The pump mounts on the front of the engine. The reservoir is near the firewall.

LUBRICATION

CAPACITY

Lubricant capacity is 1 qt. (.95L).

FLUID TYPE

Recommened fluid is Audi Hydraulic Fluid (G 002 000). This fluid can be mixed with Dexron ATF and Audi Hydraulic Fluid (AOE 041 020).

CAUTION: **Audi Hydraulic Fluid (G 002 000) must NOT be used in automatic transmissions.**

FLUID LEVEL CHECK

Remove reservoir cover. Start engine. Check fluid level. Fluid level should be at mark on upper inside of reservoir neck.

AUDI POWER-ASSISTED RACK & PINION (Cont.)

Fig. 1: Exploded View of Coupe GT & 4000 Series Power Steering Gear

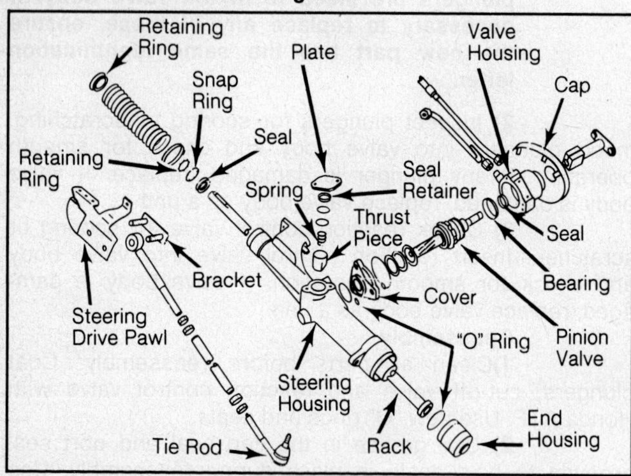

Courtesy of Audi of America, Inc.

HYDRAULIC SYSTEM BLEEDING

1) With engine at idle, check that fluid is at proper level. Turn steering wheel lock-to-lock several times quickly. Do not force wheel against locks.

NOTE: **Oil filter insert must be replaced whenever repairs are made to power steering system.**

Fig. 2: Exploded View of 5000 Series Power Steering Gear

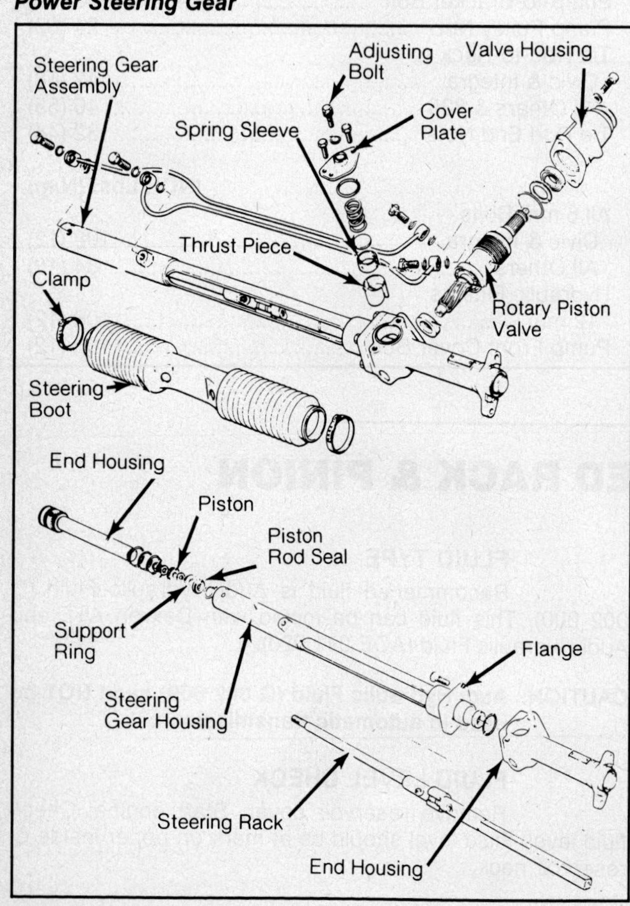

Courtesy of Audi of America, Inc.

2) Repeat step **1)** until fluid level remains at reservoir mark. Ensure no bubbles appear in reservoir when steering wheel is turned. Shut off engine. Check that oil level does not rise more than .375" (10.00 mm) above mark inside of reservoir.

OIL FILTER REPLACEMENT

Remove outer cover, gasket, and spring from reservoir. Remove inner filter cover and filter insert. Install new filter insert. Replace old filter cover, spring, gasket, and top cover. Check fluid level.

ADJUSTMENTS

PUMP BELT

Loosen pump-to-bracket mounting bolts. Turn adjusting nut on bracket until belt deflection is .375" (10 mm) at center of belt. Tighten bracket nuts.

STEERING GEAR

On 5000 series models, loosen lock nut on steering gear. Hand tighten adjusting screw until it touches thrust plate. Holding adjusting screw in position, tighten lock nut. Check adjustment with engine idling. Readjust (if necessary).

TESTING

SYSTEM PRESSURE TEST

1) Connect Pressure Gauge (US1074/2 on Coupe GT, 4000S and 4000CS Quattro; US1070 on 5000S, 5000CS Turbo and 5000CS Quattro) between pressure hose and pressure pipe of valve housing, with pressure gauge valve open. Run engine at idle.

2) Turn steering wheel lock-to-lock several times. Check pressure. Pressure should be 2103-2248 psi (148-158 kg/cm²). If pressure is not within limits, replace steering gear.

PUMP PRESSURE TEST

1) Install pressure gauge. Start engine and let it idle. Close gauge valve for a maximum of 5 seconds. Check pressure. Pressure should be 2103-2248 psi (148-158 kg/cm²).

Fig. 3: 5000 Series Steering Gear Adjustment

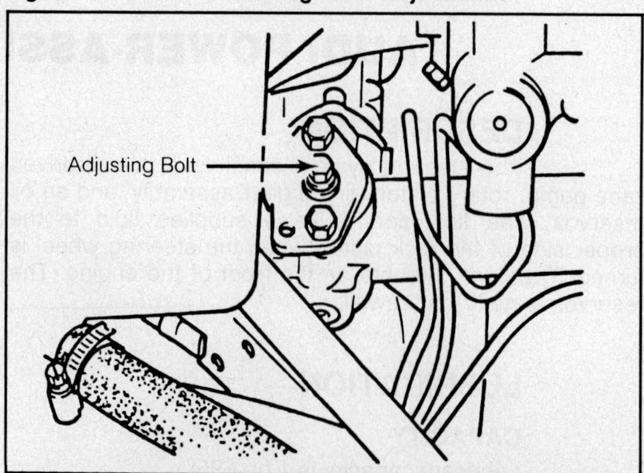

No play should be felt. Courtesy of Audi of America, Inc.

AUDI POWER-ASSISTED RACK & PINION (Cont.)

2) If pressure is not within specification, inspect bores in valve and piston for obstructions. Check that piston moves freely in housing. Install new valve (if necessary).

LEAKAGE TEST

1) With engine idling, turn steering wheel to full lock and hold. Inspect all connections. If leak shows at steering pinion, replace housing seal and both intermediate cover seals.

2) If pinion shaft seal is leaking, fluid will have entered gear housing. Check for fluid by loosening outer clamp on right steering boot while pushing boot in. If seal is leaking, replace all seals.

REMOVAL & INSTALLATION

STEERING GEAR

Removal (Coupe GT, 4000S & 4000CS Quattro)

1) Drain fluid from system. Disconnect hydraulic lines from valve housing. Disconnect lower steering shaft from pinion shaft. Move cap out of the way.

2) Remove steering drive pawl and tie rod bracket nuts. Disconnect tie rods from bracket. Remove bolts attaching gear housing to body. Remove housing.

Installation

To install, reverse removal procedure. Install one tie rod to steering gear and start bolts before installing other tie rod.

Removal (5000S, 5000CS Turbo & 5000CS Quattro)

1) Drain fluid from system. Disconnect hydraulic lines. Cap openings. Remove tie rod lock plate and both tie rod retaining bolts.

2) Separate tie rods from steering gear. Disconnect steering damper. Disconnect flange tube clamp from steering gear. Remove flange tube from steering shaft.

3) Remove steering gear retaining bolts from body. Turn wheels to right lock. Remove steering gear through opening in right wheelwell.

Installation

To install, reverse removal procedure. Replace tie rod lock plate before reinstallation. Install one tie rod to steering gear before installing other tie rod.

VANE PUMP

Removal

Remove vane pump belt. Disconnect hydraulic lines from pump. Cover openings. Remove retaining bolts from bracket. Lift pump from engine.

Installation

To install, reverse removal procedure. Adjust belt deflection to .375" (10 mm) at center. After installing hydraulic lines, start engine. Turn steering wheel to full lock. Check for leaks.

OVERHAUL

NOTE: Overhaul of 5000 series models steering gear is not recommended. Seals can be replaced if gear is removed. Check system output and pressure before removing steering gear.

NOTE: On Coupe GT, 4000S and 4000CS Quattro models, check output and system pressure before disassembling steering gear. Use all parts in Repair Kit (811 498 020). Use new self-locking nuts.

VALVE HOUSING SEAL

Disassembly (Coupe GT, 4000S & 4000CS Quattro)

1) Remove valve housing attaching bolts. Remove housing. Remove pinion gear and intermediate cover. Remove "O" rings from intermediate cover (one on each side). Clamp housing in padded vise. Drive out oil seal from the back.

2) Install new "O" rings on intermediate cover. Install new seals in valve. Ensure housing seal lip faces intermediate cover. Replace intermediate cover "O" rings.

Fig. 4: Exploded View of Vane Pump Assembly

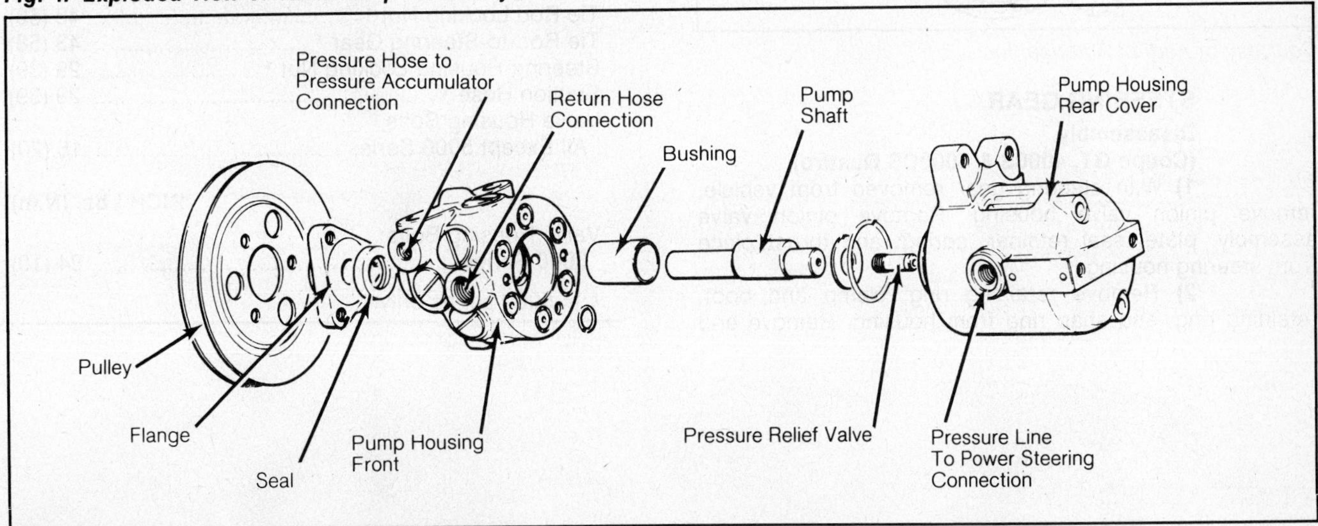

Only pressure/flow limiting valve can be replaced. Courtesy of Audi of America, Inc.

Power Steering

AUDI POWER-ASSISTED RACK & PINION (Cont.)

Reassembly

To reassemble, reverse disassembly procedure. Protect pinion teeth on shaft when replacing intermediate cover. Do not damage "O" rings.

Disassembly (5000S, 5000CS Turbo & 5000CS Quattro)

1) Remove valve housing retaining bolts. Remove housing. Remove pinion gear and intermediate cover. Remove "O" rings from intermediate cover. Drive out intermediate cover oil seal.

2) Clamp housing in padded vise. Drive out oil seal from the back. Install new seals from inside cover and housing. Ensure housing seal lip faces intermediate cover, and cover seal lip faces valve housing. Replace both intermediate cover "O" rings.

Reassembly

To Reassemble, reverse disassembly procedure. Protect pinion teeth on shaft when replacing intermediate cover. Do not damage "O" rings.

Fig. 5: 5000 Series Steering Housing Oil Seal

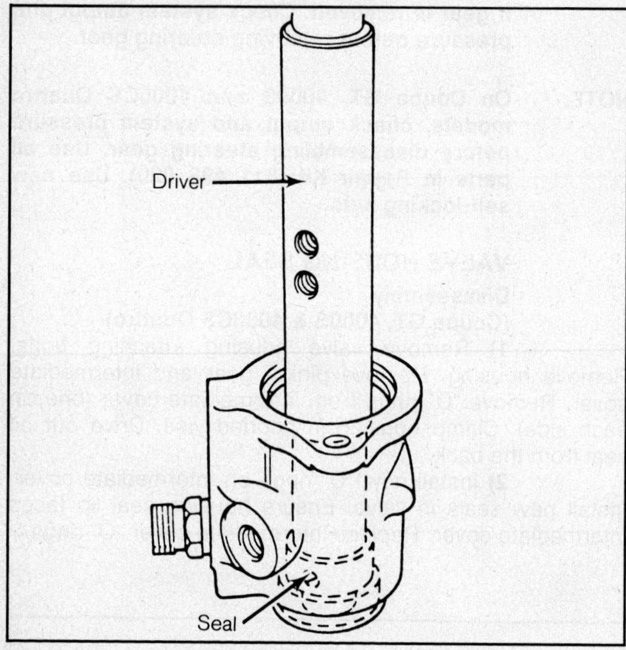

Courtesy of Audi of America, Inc.

STEERING GEAR

Disassembly
(Coupe GT, 4000S & 4000CS Quattro)

1) With steering gear removed from vehicle, remove pinion valve housing. Remove pinion valve assembly, plate, seal retainer, spring, and thrust piece from steering housing.

2) Remove retaining ring, clamp and boot, retaining ring, and snap ring from housing. Remove end housing and "O" ring from housing. Pull rack from housing. Using oil seal puller, remove oil seal from housing.

Reassembly

1) To install new oil seal in housing, place oil seal on flat surface and push sleeve (available in Repair Kit 811 498 020) into oil seal. Slide rack into housing.

2) Using Seal Installers (VW 426 and VW 416b), slide oil seal with sleeve over rack and into housing. Remove sleeve. Install snap ring and retaining ring into housing.

3) Install end housing with new "O" ring. Install thrust piece, spring, "O" ring, seal retainer, and plate. Install clamp, boot, and retaining ring. Install valve assembly as previously outlined.

STEERING HOUSING SEAL

Disassembly (5000S, 5000CS Turbo & 5000CS Quattro)

With steering gear removed from vehicle, drive out right end of steering housing with a drift. Remove seals and "O" ring. Clamp rack in a padded vise. Remove self-locking nut and piston. Insert Slide Hammer (VW771) into right side of housing. Remove oil seal and shims.

Reassembly

Using Driver (2082), install shims and seal with thin shim behind seal and seal lip facing piston. Install piston, self-locking nut, seals, "O" ring and end housing.

TIGHTENING SPECIFICATIONS

Application	Ft. Lbs. (N.m)
End Housing	37 (50)
Expansion Hose [1]	29 (39)
Flange Tube-to-Steering Gear [1]	22 (30)
Pinion Shaft Nut [1]	14 (19)
Pressure Pipe	29 (39)
Pulley-to-Pump Shaft [1]	14 (19)
Pump Retaining Bolts [1]	14 (19)
Return Pipe	
On Pump	29 (39)
On Valve Housing	22 (30)
Steering Damper [1]	29 (39)
Tie Rod Locking Nut [1]	43 (58)
Tie Rod-to-Steering Gear [1]	43 (58)
Steering Housing Locking Nut [1]	29 (39)
Suction Hose [1]	29 (39)
Valve Housing Bolts	
All Except 5000 Series	15 (20)
	INCH Lbs. (N.m)
Valve Housing Bolts	
5000 Series	84 (10)

[1] – 5000 series only.

Power Steering

BMW POWER-ASSISTED RACK & PINION

325, 325e, 325es, 325i, 325is

DESCRIPTION

A ZF power-assisted rack and pinion steering gear is used. A belt-driven vane pump draws fluid from the reservoir and supplies it to the control valve. The control valve supplies fluid to the proper side of the rack piston as the steering wheel is turned. System provides manual steering control (higher effort) if hydraulic pressure fails.

LUBRICATION

FLUID TYPE

Recommended fluid type is Dexron automatic transmission fluid (ATF).

FLUID LEVEL CHECK

Check fluid level with engine off. Fluid must be between marks on dipstick.

HYDRAULIC SYSTEM BLEEDING

Check fluid level. Start engine and let it idle. Turn steering wheel gently against each lock 2 times. Turn engine off. Operate brake pedal to discharge hydraulic accumulator. Recheck fluid level. Add fluid if needed.

TESTING

PUMP PRESSURE TEST

1) Detach steering gear pressure line. Connect Pressure Tester (32-4-000). Connect tester pressure line to gear. Close valve closest to gear pressure line.

2) Open second valve. Bleed power steering. Shut second valve for a period not to exceed 10 seconds. Pressure should read 1280-1422 psi (90-100 kg/cm²).

3) If pressure is not within limits, check drive belt tension. Recheck pump pressure. If pressure is still incorrect, replace pump.

SYSTEM PRESSURE TEST

Connect pressure tester as previously outlined. Using a spring scale, pull steering wheel against lock with a 22 lb. (10 kg) force. Read pressure. If pressure is less than previously measured pump pressure, replace steering gear.

Fig. 1: Assembled View of Power Steering Rack

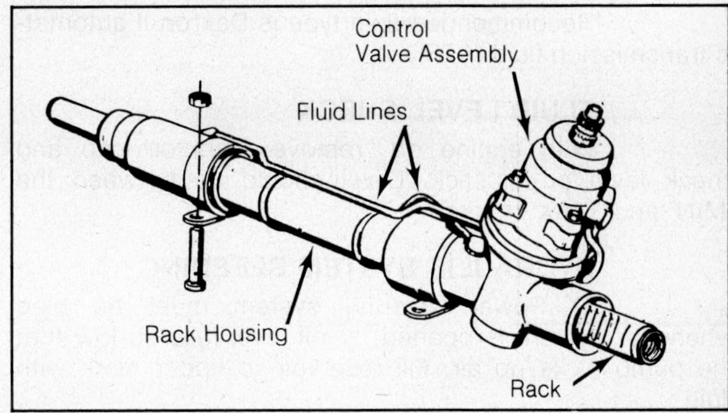

Courtesy of BMW of North America, Inc.

REMOVAL & INSTALLATION

STEERING GEAR

Removal

1) Raise and support vehicle. Remove front wheels. Remove steering shaft-to-pinion clamp bolt. Loosen steering shaft coupling clamp bolt. Press steering shaft off pinion. Remove shaft.

2) Detach fluid pressure and return lines and plug connections. Disconnect tie rod ends from knuckles. Disconnect steering gear at crossmember.

Installation

To install, reverse removal procedure. Replace fluid line connector seals. Mount gear to rear holes of crossmember. Fill and bleed system.

VANE PUMP

Removal

Disconnect fluid lines. Plug connections. Loosen adjusting bracket nut. Remove drive belt from pump. Remove pump mounting bolts. Remove pump.

Installation

To install, reverse removal procedure. Replace fluid line connector seals. Tighten drive belt. Tighten mounting bolts. Fill and bleed system.

OVERHAUL

NOTE: **Manufacturer gives no overhaul procedure for gear or pump. Replace if defective.**

BMW RECIRCULATING BALL

528e, 535i, 535is, 635CSi, 735i, L6, L7

DESCRIPTION

Power steering gear consists of a gear housing containing a sector shaft with sector gear and a power piston with gear teeth inside of piston which is in constant mesh with sector shaft teeth.

A worm shaft connects steering shaft to power piston through a universal joint coupling. The worm shaft is geared to the piston through recirculating ball contact. The steering valve is incorporated into upper end of worm gear assembly.

Power steering pump is a high pressure, belt driven, vane type pump. A fluid reservoir incorporating a filter element supplies hydraulic fluid to pump. Pump maintains hydraulic pressure to power steering gear assembly.

LUBRICATION

CAPACITY

Capacity for 528e, 535i, 535is, 635CSi and L6 is 1.25 qt. (1.2L). Capacity for 735i and L7 is 2.1 qt. (2.0L).

BMW RECIRCULATING BALL (Cont.)

FLUID TYPE

Recommended fluid type is Dexron II automatic transmission fluid (ATF).

FLUID LEVEL CHECK

With engine off, remove reservoir cap and check level on dipstick. Level should be between the "MIN" and "MAX" marks.

HYDRAULIC SYSTEM BLEEDING

1) Power steering system must be bled whenever system is opened, or oil level falls so low that the pump picks up air. Fill reservoir to upper mark with fluid.

2) Turn engine over with starter while continuing to add fluid. When oil level no longer falls, start engine and let idle.

3) Turn steering wheel rapidly from lock-to-lock and back until no further air bubbles rise in reservoir. Turn engine off.

4) Operate brake pedal to discharge hydraulic accumulator. During and after operation, fluid level must remain at upper mark.

FILTER REPLACEMENT

528e, 535i, 535is, 635CSi & L6

Remove reservoir cap. Remove spring and filter cover. Replace filter.

735i & L7

Remove reservoir cap. Remove nut, washer, spring, fine mesh filter screen and filters. Clean fine mesh filter screen. Replace filters.

ADJUSTMENTS

PUMP BELT

Loosen adjustment bolts. Shift pump to tighten belt. Adjustment is correct when it is possible to press in belt .20-.40" (5-10 mm) with the thumb.

SECTOR SHAFT

Adjustment (In-Vehicle)

1) Position wheels straight-ahead. Remove cotter pin and castle nut from tie rod end. Press off center tie-rod from steering arm. Remove BMW emblem from steering wheel.

2) Turn wheel counterclockwise one turn from center. Install torque wrench on nut, turn wheel clockwise and read frictional torque. Torque should be 2.7-3.5 INCH lbs. (.31-.40 N.m).

3) To adjust, turn steering wheel counterclockwise from center one turn. Loosen lock nut on steering gear. Turn adjusting screw clockwise until correct torque is reached when passing through center position. Tighten lock nut. Check adjustment.

Fig. 1: Cross-Sectional View of Power Steering Gear Assembly

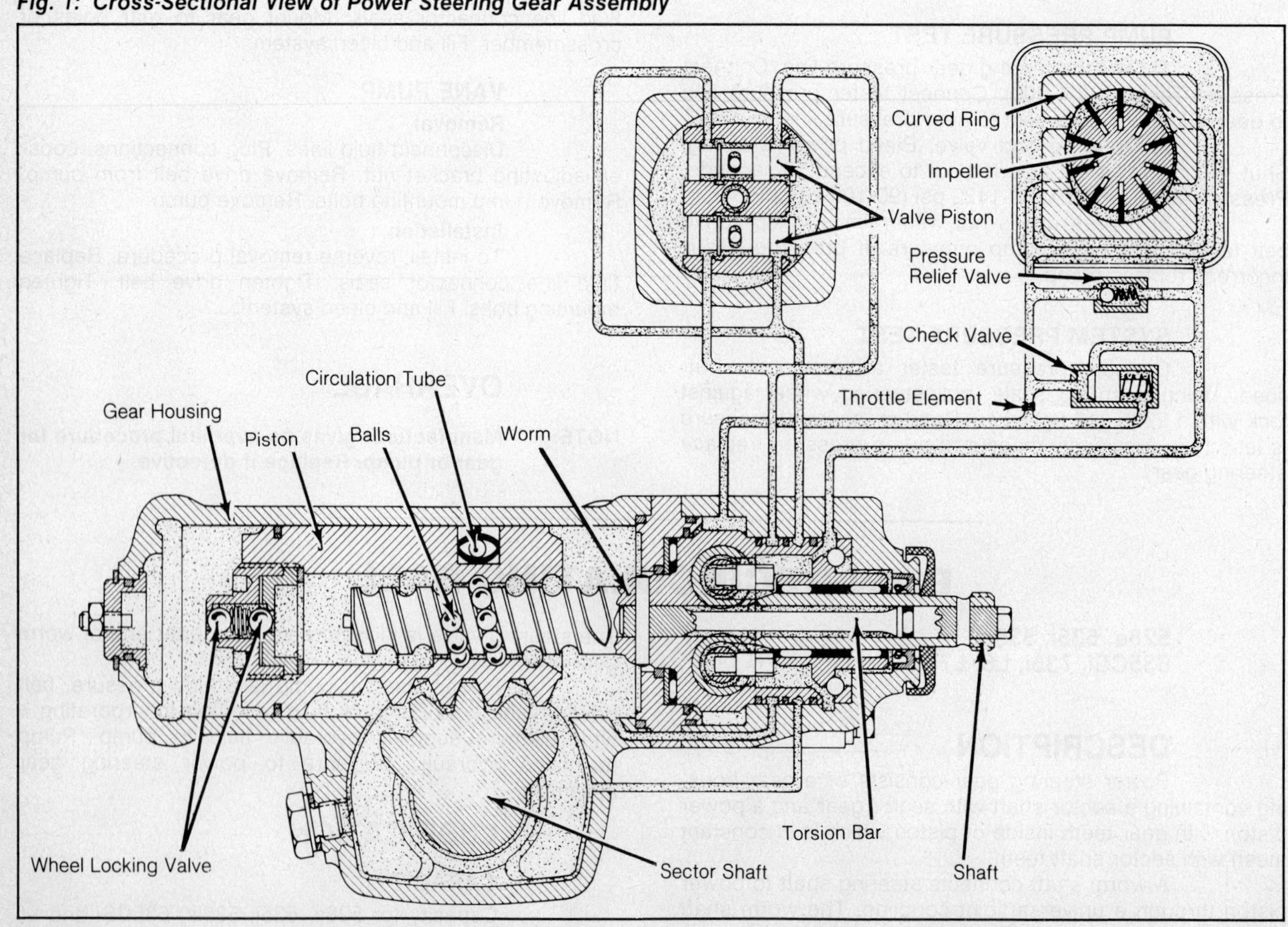

Courtesy of BMW of North America, Inc.

BMW RECIRCULATING BALL (Cont.)

TESTING

STEERING PUMP PRESSURE

1) Discharge accumulator by operating brake pedal 20 times. Disconnect pressure line from pump. Connect pump pressure line to gauge.

2) Disconnect pressure line from control regulator. Connect it to pressure gauge. Shut cut-off valve on gauge. Open shut-off valve on pressure line.

3) Bleed system with engine running at idle. Close valve in pressure line for 10 seconds maximum while reading pressure. On all models except 735i and L7, pressure should be 1422-1564 psi (100-110 kg/cm²).

4) On 735i and L7, pressure should be 1849-1991 psi (130-140 kg/cm²). If pressure is not within limits, check belt tightness. Repair or replace pump if belt adjustment does not remedy problem.

STEERING GEAR PRESSURE

NOTE: **Perform STEERING PUMP PRESSURE test before performing this test.**

1) Raise and support vehicle. Install Pressure Tester (32-4-000) as in pump pressure test. Limit steering from reaching full lock position by 1/2-3/4 turn.

2) With engine running, pull steering wheel against final lock with 22 lbs. (9.98 kg) pressure for no more than 5 seconds. Read pressure. On all models except 735i and L7, pressure should be 1422-1564 psi (100-110 kg/cm²).

3) On 735i and L7, pressure should be 1849-1991 psi (130-140 kg/cm²). Check pressure with gear at opposite lock. Steering gear must be replaced if pressure is not within specifications.

Fig. 2: Cross-Sectional View of Power Steering Pump

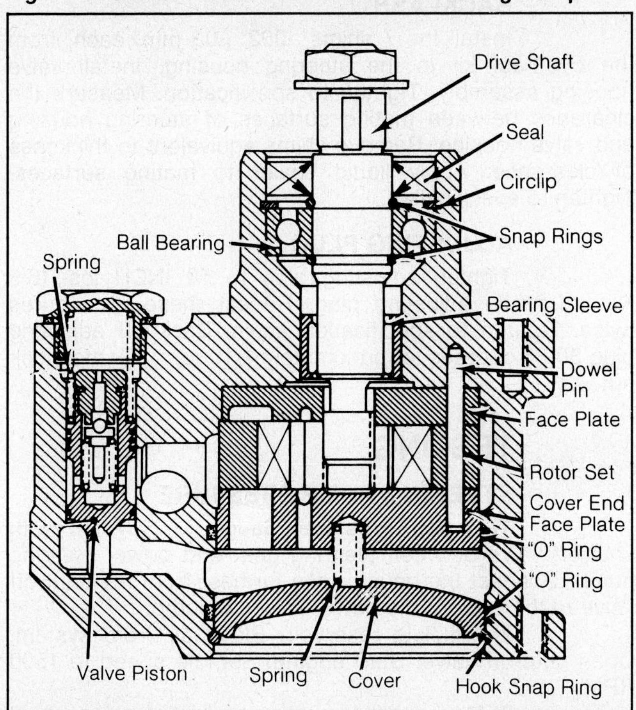

Courtesy of BMW of North America, Inc.

REMOVAL & INSTALLATION

STEERING GEAR

Removal

1) Raise and support vehicle. Turn steering to full left lock. Discharge hydraulic accumulator by depressing brake pedal 20 times. Detach hydraulic hoses from steering gear. Cap openings.

2) Remove cotter pin and castle nut from tie rod end. Separate tie rod from steering arm. Remove bolt from locking groove of steering shaft.

3) Mark steering shaft and pivot flange for reassembly reference. Push up pivot flange with steering column. Remove steering gear attaching bolts. Detach steering gear from front axle carrier.

Installation

1) To install, reverse removal procedure. Replace hose seals. Position steering wheel straight-ahead. Align marks on pivot flange with steering shaft.

2) Ensure bolt is in locking groove of steering shaft. Tighten all connections to specifications. Refer to TIGHTENING SPECIFICATIONS table. Fill system with NEW fluid. Bleed system.

STEERING PUMP

Removal

Discharge hydraulic accumulator by depressing brake pedal 20 times. Detach hoses from pump. Loosen pump retaining bolts. Remove belt. Remove pump retaining bolts and pump.

Installation

To install, reverse removal procedure. Install hoses so that they do not rub on engine carrier. Tighten to specifications. Bleed system.

OVERHAUL

STEERING GEAR

NOTE: **BMW recommends replacing the entire unit if malfunctions occur in the steering gear.**

POWER STEERING PUMP

NOTE: **Overhaul procedures are for 528e, 535i, 535is, 635CSi and L6 only. For 735i and L7, BMW recommends replacing power steering pump if malfunctions occur.**

Disassembly

1) Press cover in slightly to remove retaining ring. Remove cover, coil spring and "O" ring. Remove end plate and "O" ring, noting location of pin in one of the small holes in end plate.

2) Tilt the pump housing. Remove cam ring and rotor. Note that side of rotor with recessed hole faces drive shaft and that the rounded-off side of rotor faces cam ring. The cast-in half arrow indicates direction of rotor rotation.

3) Remove end face plate and "O" ring. Remove input shaft, pulley, shaft seal, and snap ring from housing (if necessary). Remove circlip. Remove shaft. Press ball bearing off shaft.

4) Using a mandrel, press bearing sleeve out of housing. Remove plug from pressure valve bore. Remove coil spring and valve piston. Note that threaded section on valve piston faces coil spring.

BMW RECIRCULATING BALL (Cont.)

Fig. 3: Pin Location Inside of Pump Housing

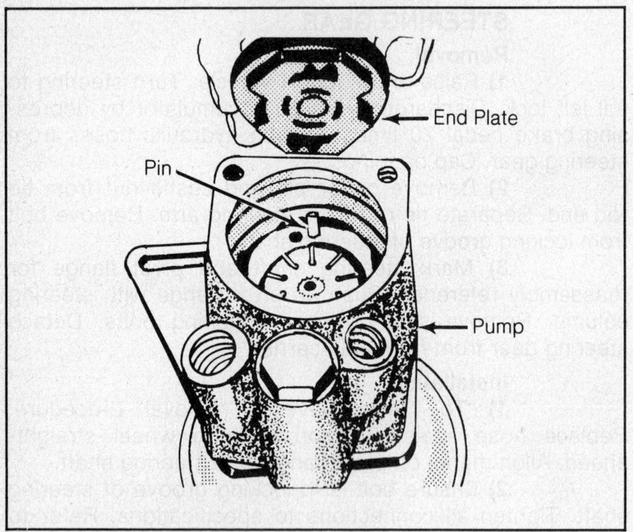

Courtesy of BMW of North America, Inc.

CAUTION: Do not alter length of coil spring or thickness of plug sealing ring.

5) The valve tolerance group ("1" or "2") is stamped into housing adjacent to pressure valve bore. Valve barrel should be scribed with one or 2 marks (lines) matching group number stamped into housing.

NOTE: If valve must be replaced, install valve of same tolerance group.

6) Clean and inspect all parts. Clean restrictor insert in pump outlet passage. Valve piston may be disassembled for cleaning. A pressure valve is located inside valve piston (flow limit valve).

CAUTION: When disassembling piston, do not clamp across sliding surfaces.

7) Thickness of washers determines cut-in range of pressure valve. Maximum pump pressure should not be more than 10 percent below value stated on plate attached to pump.

Reassembly

To reassemble, reverse disassembly procedure. Replace all seals and worn components.

TIGHTENING SPECIFICATIONS

Application	Ft. Lbs. (N.m)
Adjusting Screw Counternut	22 (30)
Hose Connections	33-37 (45-50)
Sector Shaft End Cover	
528e, 535i, 535is, 635CSi & L6	23 (31)
735i & L7	50 (68)
Steering Gear to Front Axle	33-35 (45-48)
Steering Pump Mounting	17 (23)
Worm End Cover	25 (34)

CHEVROLET & ISUZU POWER-ASSISTED RACK & PINION

Chevrolet: Spectrum
Isuzu: I-Mark, Impulse

DESCRIPTION

Power-assisted rack and pinion steering system consists of a vane pump, rotary valve assembly, and an oil reservoir.

The vane pump draws fluid from the reservoir and supplies it to the valve assembly. The rotary valve in the valve assembly supplies fluid to the proper side of the rack piston, when the steering wheel is turned.

The belt-driven pump mounts on the front of the engine. The reservoir is remote mounted, connected by hoses to the vane pump.

LUBRICATION

CAPACITY

Capacity is 1.5 pints (.7L). for I-Mark and Spectrum. Capacity for Impulse is not available from manufacturer. Refer to HYDRAULIC SYSTEM BLEEDING in this article.

FLUID TYPE

ATF Dexron.

HYDRAULIC SYSTEM BLEEDING

Fill fluid reservoir. Raise and support vehicle. Start engine. Turn steering wheel lock-to-lock 3 or 4 times. System is free of air when there is no buzz in hydraulic line. Also, fluid level should not increase with wheels in straight ahead position and engine stopped.

ADJUSTMENTS

BACKLASH

Install the 7 shims, .002" (.05 mm) each, from the overhaul kit in the steering housing. Install valve housing assembly. Tighten to specification. Measure the clearance between mating surfaces of steering housing and valve housing. Remove shims equivalent to thickness of clearance. Apply liquid sealer to mating surfaces. Tighten to specification.

ADJUSTING PLUG

Tighten adjusting plug to 58 INCH lbs. (6.5 N.m). Loosen adjusting plug. Repeat these procedures twice. Tighten to specification again. Back off adjusting plug 30-35 degrees (approximately 1/10 turn). Tighten lock nut.

TESTING

STEERING PUMP PRESSURE

1) Install Pressure Gauge (J-29877-A) with shut-off valve between steering gear and power steering pump. Connect the gauge hose furthest from the shut-off valve to the back of the power steering pump.

2) Fill fluid reservoir. Bleed air from system. Open shut-off valve. Start engine. Set idle speed to 1500 RPM.

3) Measure fluid pressure when steering wheel is turned to lock in both directions. Pressure should be 996 lbs. (70 kg/cm²) for the non-turbo Impulse.

CHEVROLET & ISUZU POWER-ASSISTED RACK & PINION (Cont.)

Fig. 1: Exploded View of Power-Assisted Rack & Pinion

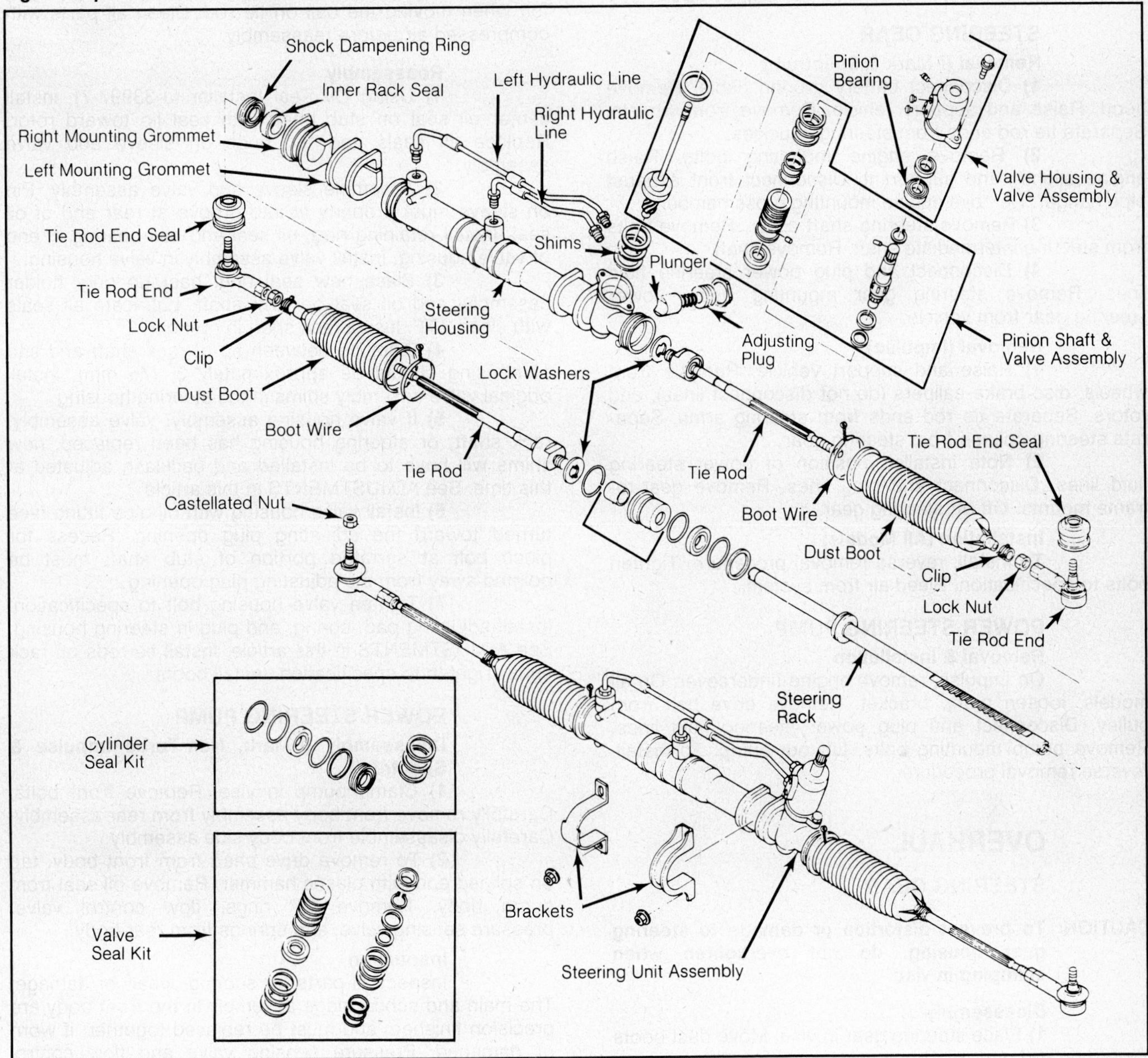

Courtesy of Isuzu Motor Co.

4) Pressure should be 925-1067 psi (65-75 kg/cm²) for all others. If pressure is higher than specified, relief valve in power steering pump is defective.

5) If pressure is lower than specified, place steering wheel in straight-ahead position. Close stop valve completely. Hold engine speed at 1500 RPM.

6) If pressure is now normal, steering gear is defective. If pressure is still low, power steering pump is defective.

POWER STEERING VALVE CLEARANCE

1) Center the steering rack. Measure between seal holder and end of rack. Measurement should be 2.5" (65.5 mm). Grease pinion gear teeth and pinion ball bearing. Using the valve adjusting kit, install all 7 shims.

2) Install pinion valve housing to steering housing. Tighten attaching bolts 1/4 turn at a time until snug. Using a feeler gauge, measure clearance between valve housing and steering housing.

3) Note the measurement. Disassemble and remove shims as necessary, to allow a maximum .002" (.50 mm) clearance when reassembled. Reassemble valve housing to gear box. Seal mating surface with RTV Sealant (1052366).

4) Center steering rack using marks made during disassembly. See DISASSEMBLY (POWER STEERING) in OVERHAUL procedure of this article. Align pinion shaft so that flat side of splines is parallel with steering rack.

5) Install rack plunger, spring, adjusting plug and lock nut. Tighten adjusting plug to 43 INCH lbs. (5 N.m). Loosen plug. Retighten plug to 43 INCH lbs. (5 N.m). Back off plug 30-35 degrees.

6) Using an INCH lb. torque wrench and socket, check pinion shaft preload. Preload should be 5-14 INCH lbs. (.6-1.6 N.m). If not within specification, loosen lock nut and reset plug preload.

CHEVROLET & ISUZU POWER-ASSISTED RACK & PINION (Cont.)

REMOVAL & INSTALLATION

STEERING GEAR

Removal (I-Mark & Spectrum)

1) Disconnect battery ground cable. Remove hood. Raise and support vehicle. Remove front wheels. Separate tie rod ends from steering knuckles.

2) Remove engine mounting bolts. Raise engine slightly and support it. Disconnect front exhaust pipe hanger. Remove engine mounting crossmember.

3) Remove steering shaft cover. Remove bolts from steering intermediate shaft. Remove shaft.

4) Disconnect and plug power steering fluid lines. Remove steering gear mounting bolts. Lower steering gear from vehicle.

Removal (Impulse)

1) Raise and support vehicle. Remove front wheels, disc brake calipers (do not disconnect lines), and rotors. Separate tie rod ends from steering arms. Separate steering column from steering gear.

2) Note installed position of power steering fluid lines. Disconnect and plug lines. Remove gear-to-frame mounts. Lift off steering gear.

Installation (All Models)

To install, reverse removal procedure. Tighten bolts to specification. Bleed air from system.

POWER STEERING PUMP

Removal & Installation

On Impulse, remove engine undercover. On all models, loosen pump bracket. Remove drive belt from pulley. Disconnect and plug power steering fluid lines. Remove pump mounting bolts. Lift out pump. To install, reverse removal procedure.

OVERHAUL

STEERING GEAR

CAUTION: To prevent distortion or damage to steering gear housing, do not overtighten when clamping in vise.

Disassembly

1) Place steering gear in vise. Move dust boots toward tie rod end. Hold rack with wrench while unscrewing tie rod. Mark position of stub shaft relative to rack shaft. Remove valve housing and valve assembly.

2) Record number of shims removed. Shims are used for adjusting backlash between rack shaft and pinion shaft if rack shaft, valve housing, and valve assembly are to be reused.

3) By inserting a pin punch into the hole at the outer circumference of steering gear housing, remove rack retaining ring. Carefully remove oil seals, rack shaft, and back-up ring. Remove seal ring from rack shaft.

4) Remove valve assembly from valve housing. Remove sleeve from stub shaft. Remove all "O" rings and seals from sleeve. Drive oil seal out of valve housing.

Inspection

1) Inspect all parts for excessive wear or damage. If the inner wall is scored or damaged, replace cylinder assembly. Sleeve and rotor are precision-machined and must be replaced as an assembly.

2) Replace the tie rod assembly if any play is felt when moving the ball on tie rod. Clean all parts with compressed air before reassembly.

Reassembly

1) Using Oil Seal Installer (J-33997-7), install center oil seal on stub shaft with seal lip toward rotor. Replace all seals and "O" rings on sleeve and valve assembly.

2) Assemble sleeve and valve assembly. Pin on sleeve must properly fit into groove at rear end of oil seal. Install retaining ring, oil seal and ball bearing in end of valve housing. Install valve assembly in valve housing.

3) Place new seal ring, back-up ring, holder assembly, and oil seal on rack shaft. Lubricate all seals with clean ATF. Install rack shaft in cylinder.

4) Distance between tip of rack shaft and end of housing should be approximately 3" (76 mm). Install original valve assembly shims in the steering housing.

5) If valve housing assembly, valve assembly, rack shaft, or steering housing has been replaced, new shims will have to be installed and backlash adjusted at this time. See ADJUSTMENTS in this article.

6) Install valve housing with oil pipe fitting face turned toward the adjusting plug opening. Recess for pinch bolt at serrated portion of stub shaft must be pointed away from the adjusting plug opening.

7) Tighten valve housing bolt to specification. Install adjusting pad, spring, and plug in steering housing. See ADJUSTMENTS in this article. Install tie rods on rack ends. Tighten to specification. Install boots.

POWER STEERING PUMP

Disassembly (I-Mark, Non-Turbo Impulse & Spectrum)

1) Clamp pump in vise. Remove front bolts. Carefully remove front body assembly from rear assembly. Carefully disassemble front body side assembly.

2) To remove drive shaft from front body, tap on splined end with plastic hammer. Remove oil seal from pump body. Remove "O" rings, flow control valve, pressure sensing valve, and springs from rear body.

Inspection

Inspect all parts for scoring, wear, or damage. The main and subcartridge assembly in the front body are precision finished, and must be replaced together, if worn or damaged. Pressure sensing valve and flow control valve must also be replaced (if defective). Check drive shaft for excessive runout.

Reassembly

1) Wash all parts in solvent. Blow dry with compressed air. Lubricate parts with ATF before reassembly. Install "O" rings, flow control valve, and pressure sensing valve in rear body.

2) Install oil seal and drive shaft with bearing into front body. Assemble front body side main and subcartridges, and side plates. Set chamfered face of main cartridge to rear body side.

3) Install front body assembly into rear body assembly. Install bolts. Tighten to specification.

Disassembly (Turbo Impulse)

1) Remove gauge cap, "O" ring, cover, "O" ring, baffle, 2 retaining rings, retaining plate and filter from reservoir. Remove reservoir mounting nut.

CHEVROLET & ISUZU POWER-ASSISTED RACK & PINION (Cont.)

Fig. 2: Exploded View of I-Mark & Spectrum Power Steering Pump

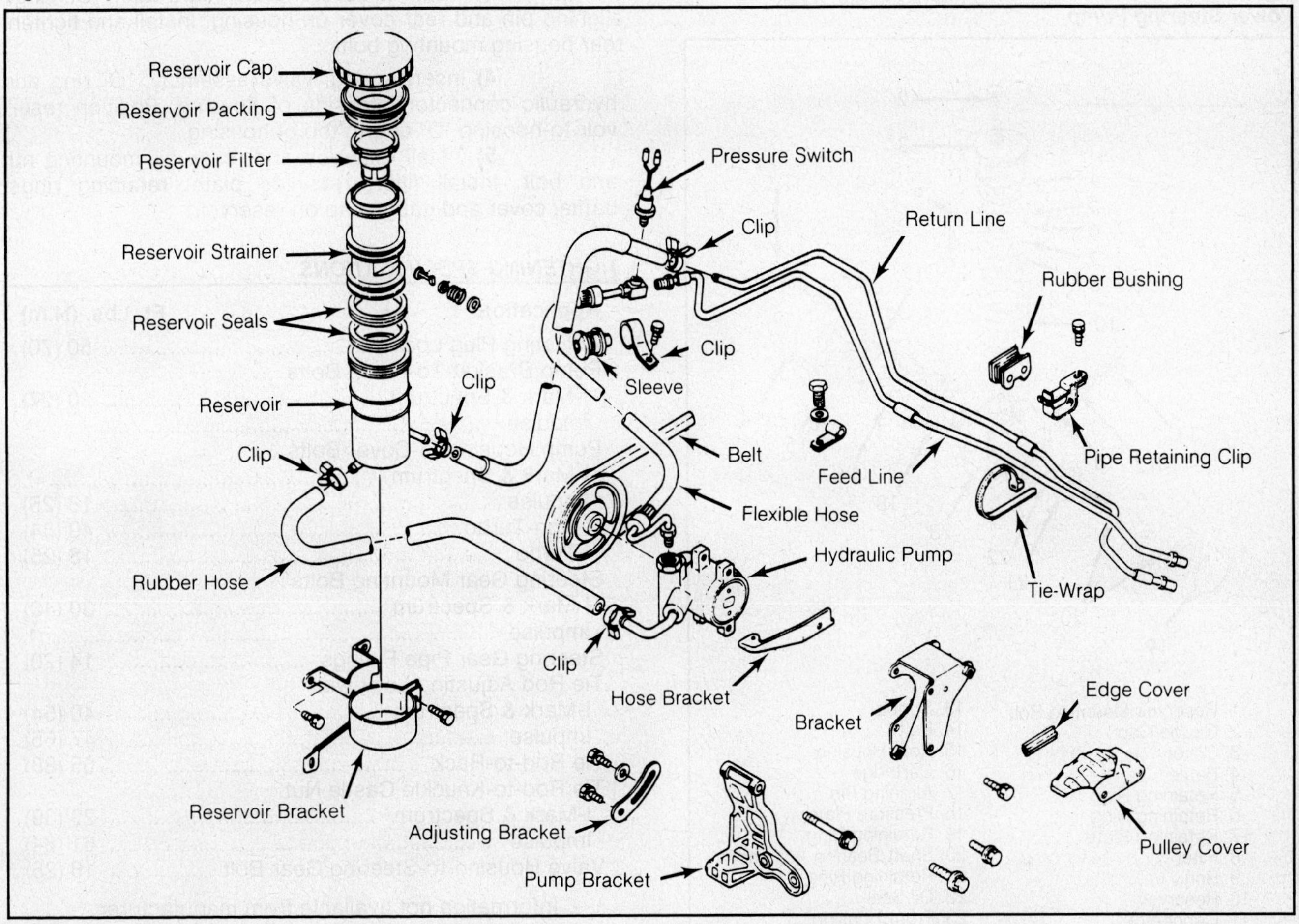

Courtesy of Isuzu Motor Co.

Fig. 3: Exploded View of Non-Turbo Impulse Power Steering Pump

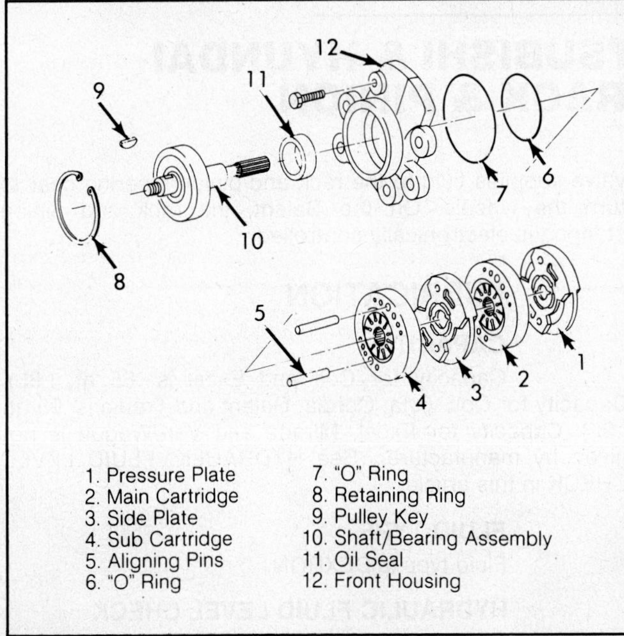

Courtesy of Isuzu Motor Co.

2) Remove reservoir mounting bolt and reservoir. Remove reservoir-to-housing "O" ring. Remove hydraulic connector, "O" ring, valve assembly and spring from housing.

3) Remove rear housing retaining bolts and rear cover. Remove "O" ring, cartridge, aligning pin, pressure polate and "O" ring from housing.

4) Remove retaining ring, ball bearing and key from shaft. Remove shaft, retaining ring and seal from housing.

Inspection

Inspect all parts for scoring, wear, or damage. The main and subcartridge assembly in the front body are precision finished, and must be replaced together, if worn or damaged. Pressure sensing valve and flow control valve must also be replaced (if defective). Check drive shaft for excessive runout. Always use new seals and "O" rings.

Reassembly

1) Wash all parts in solvent. Blow dry with compressed air. Lubricate parts with ATF before reassembly. Install seal and retaining ring into housing.

2) Install shaft into housing. Install key, ball bearing and retaining ring over shaft into housing. Position "O" ring into housing from the rear.

CHEVROLET & ISUZU POWER-ASSISTED RACK & PINION (Cont.)

Fig. 4: Exploded View of Turbo Impulse Power Steering Pump

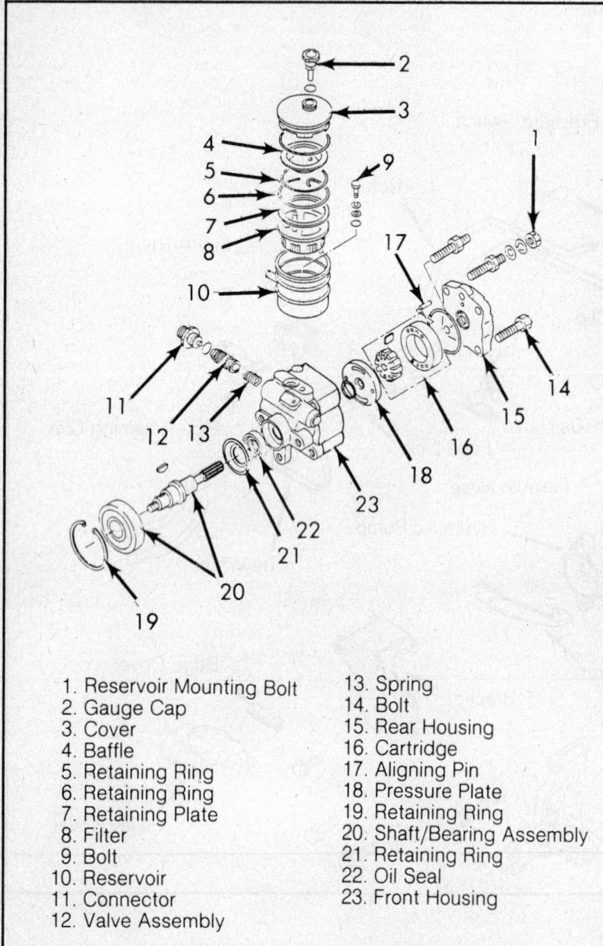

Courtesy of Isuzu Motor Co.

3) Install pressure plate, cartridge, "O" ring, aligning pin and rear cover on housing. Install and tighten rear housing mounting bolts.

4) Insert spring, valve assembly, "O" ring and hydraulic connector into side of housing. Position reservoir-to-housing "O" ring to top of housing.

5) Install reservoir and reservoir mounting nut and bolt. Install filter, retaining plate, retaining rings, baffle, cover and gauge cap on reservoir.

TIGHTENING SPECIFICATIONS

Application	Ft. Lbs. (N.m)
Adjusting Plug Lock Nut	50 (70)
Pump Bracket-To-Pump Bolts	
I-Mark & Spectrum	20 (27)
Impulse	[1]
Pump Housing-to-Cover Bolts	
I-Mark & Spectrum	[1]
Impulse	18 (25)
Non-Turbo	40 (54)
Turbo	18 (25)
Steering Gear Mounting Bolts	
I-Mark & Spectrum	30 (40)
Impulse	[1]
Steering Gear Pipe Fittings	14 (20)
Tie Rod Adjusting Lock Nut	
I-Mark & Spectrum	40 (54)
Impulse	47 (65)
Tie Rod-to-Rack	65 (88)
Tie Rod-to-Knuckle Castle Nut	
I-Mark & Spectrum	29 (39)
Impulse	61 (84)
Valve Housing-to-Steering Gear Bolt	18 (25)

[1] – Information not available from manufacturer.

CHRYSLER MOTORS, MITSUBISHI & HYUNDAI POWER-ASSISTED RACK & PINION

Chrysler: Colt, Colt Vista
Hyundai Excel
Mitsubishi: Cordia, Galant, Precis, Mirage, Tredia, Van/Wagon

NOTE: **This article covers complete power steering gear for all models except Galant. Galant information in this article includes removal and installation only. Galant electronic steering gear overhaul can be found in MITSUBISHI GALANT ELECTRONIC POWER STEERING article in this section.**

DESCRIPTION

Power-assisted rack and pinion steering system consists of a vane pump, flow control valve and an oil reservoir. The belt-driven vane pump supplies fluid through hoses to the flow control valve. The flow control valve supplies fluid to the rack and pinion steering gear to turn the wheels. On the Galant, the rack and pinion steering is electronically controlled.

LUBRICATION

CAPACITY

Capacity for Colt and Excel is .85 qt. (.8L). Capacity for Colt Vista, Cordia, Galant and Tredia is .95 qt. (.9L). Capacity for Excel, Mirage and Van/Wagon is not given by manufacturer. See HYDRAULIC FLUID LEVEL CHECK in this article.

FLUID TYPE

Fluid type is DEXRON.

HYDRAULIC FLUID LEVEL CHECK

Start engine and let it idle. Turn steering wheel several times to bring steering fluid to normal operating temperature. Turn steering wheel left and right several times while checking fluid for foaming or clouding. Fluid level should be between the "MIN" and "MAX" mark on the dipstick attached to filler cap. Fill with Dexron to the "MAX" mark.

HYDRAULIC SYSTEM BLEEDING

1) Disconnect coil high tension wire. Crank engine intermittently for 15-20 seconds while turning steering wheel left and right.

2) Connect coil high tension wire. Start engine and let it idle. Turn steering wheel left and right until there are no air bubbles in the oil reservoir.

3) Check fluid level and confirm that fluid is not milky. Turn steering wheel left and right and check to see that fluid level does not change.

4) If fluid level changes more than .2" (5 mm) or if noise is heard from pump and control valve, fill with fluid to the "MAX" mark on dipstick.

5) Repeat step **2)** until air bubbles are no longer present in fluid and fluid level ceases to fluctuate more than .2" (5 mm).

CAUTION: Do not hold steering wheel to left or right for more than 10 seconds.

ADJUSTMENTS

PINION PRELOAD

Using Adaptor (MB990228-01) and torque wrench, measure preload while turning pinion gear through one rotation. If preload is not 5-11 INCH lbs. (5-11 N.m), adjust rack support cover. Check preload again. Tighten lock nut.

TESTING

FLUID PRESSURE TESTING

1) Disconnect pressure hose from oil pump. *See Fig. 1.* Bleed air from system. Start engine and let it idle. Turn steering wheel several times until temperature reaches 122°F (50°C). Set engine idle speed to 1000 RPM.

Fig. 1: Pressure Gauge & Shut-Off Valve Connections

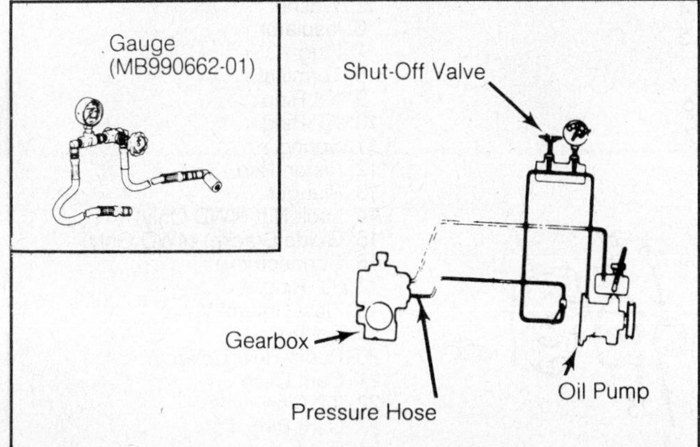

Courtesy of Chrysler Motors.

2) Close and open valve to measure oil pump pressure. If not within specifications, replace pump. See OIL PUMP PRESSURE SPECIFICATIONS table. Install pressure hose. Bleed system.

CAUTION: DO NOT leave valve on pressure gauge closed more than 10 seconds or damage to oil pump will result.

OIL PUMP PRESSURE SPECIFICATIONS

Application	psi (kg/cm²)
Colt Vista	
Valve Closed	
2WD	780-880 (55-62)
4WD	920-1000 (65-72)
Valve Open	142 (10)
Colt, Cordia, Mirage & Tredia	
Valve Closed	780-880 (55-62)
Valve Open (Maximum)	142 (10)
Excel	
Valve Closed	640-740 (45-52)
Valve Open (Maximum)	142 (10)
Galant	
Valve Closed	906-1004 (64-71)
Valve Open	100-142 (7-10)
Van/Wagon	
Valve Closed	1067-1166 (75-82)
Valve Open	114-142 (8-10)

REMOVAL & INSTALLATION

POWER STEERING PUMP

Removal

Disconnect pressure and suction hoses from pump. Drain fluid into container. On turbocharged models, remove heat insulator. On all models, remove oil pump mounting bolts, belt and oil pump. Remove reservoir retaining bolts. Remove reservoir.

Installation

To install, reverse removal procedure. Fill and bleed system.

STEERING GEAR

Removal (Colt, Excel & Mirage)

1) Raise and support front of vehicle. Remove coupling bolt from pinion shaft joint. Disconnect hydraulic lines from steering gear. Drain fluid.

2) Remove tie rod end cotter pins and castle nuts. Using Puller (MB-991113), separate tie rod ends from steering knuckles. Remove stabilizer bar mounting bolts.

3) Remove stabilizer bar. Remove steering gear-to-crossmember mounting bolts. Remove steering gear from left side of vehicle.

Removal (Colt Vista, Cordia & Tredia)

1) Raise and support front of vehicle. Remove coupling bolt from pinion shaft joint. Disconnect hydraulic lines from steering gear. Drain fluid.

2) Remove tie rod end cotter pins and castle nuts. Using Puller (MB-991113), disconnect tie rod ends from steering knuckles. Remove stabilizer bar mounting bolts.

3) Remove crossmember support bracket located on right end of crossmember. Remove fuel hose from lower fuel filter connector. Remove clips holding fuel line.

4) Secure fuel line out of way. Remove rear roll stopper stay away from engine. *See Fig. 2.* Remove steering gear toward right side of vehicle.

Power Steering

CHRYSLER MOTORS, MITSUBISHI & HYUNDAI POWER-ASSISTED RACK & PINION (Cont.)

Removal (Galant)

1) Raise and support front of vehicle. Remove coupling bolt from pinion shaft joint. Disconnect pressure and return hoses from steering gear. Drain fluid.

2) Remove center member front mounting bolt and exhaust pipe hanger from crossmember. Remove front roll stopper bolt. Disconnect front exhaust pipe. Lower exhaust pipe.

3) Remove tie rod end cotter pins and castle nuts. Using Puller (MB-991113), disconnect tie rod ends from steering knuckles. Remove left side stay.

4) Press rear of center member downward. Remove steering gear mounting bolts. Move steering gear to right to remove from crossmember. Tilting steering gear down, remove from left side of vehicle.

Fig. 2: Removing Rear Roll Stopper Stay (Colt Vista, Cordia & Tredia)

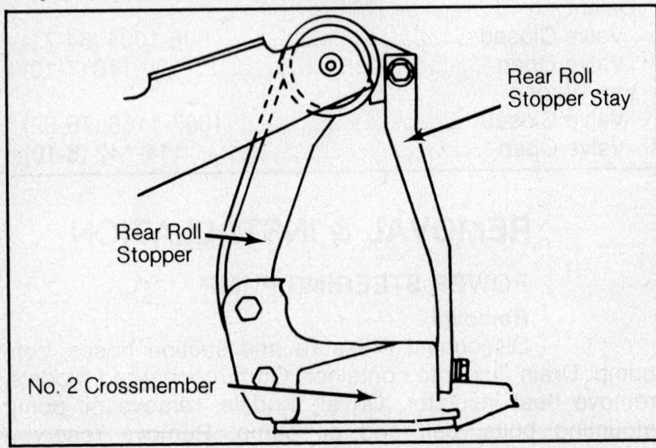

Courtesy of Chrysler Motors.

Installation

To install, reverse removal procedure. Fill and bleed system. Check wheel alignment.

OVERHAUL

POWER STEERING PUMP

Disassembly

1) Remove oil pump cover, cam ring, "O" rings and vanes from rotor. Remove snap ring from pulley assembly. Remove rotor.

2) To remove pulley assembly from pump body, tap with plastic hammer. Remove suction connector and oil seal from pump body. Remove connector, flow control valve and spring from pump body.

Inspection & Reassembly

1) Check pulley assembly, cam ring, rotor and vanes for wear. Check pump cover and pump body for abrasion. Check flow control valve for clogging.

2) Apply ATF (Dexron) fluid to "O" rings and vanes. Reassemble in reverse order of disassembly. Install oil seal into pump body with Installers (MB990925-01) and (MB990938-01). Install vanes into rotor in right direction. *See Fig. 4.*

Fig. 4: Installation of Vanes into Rotor

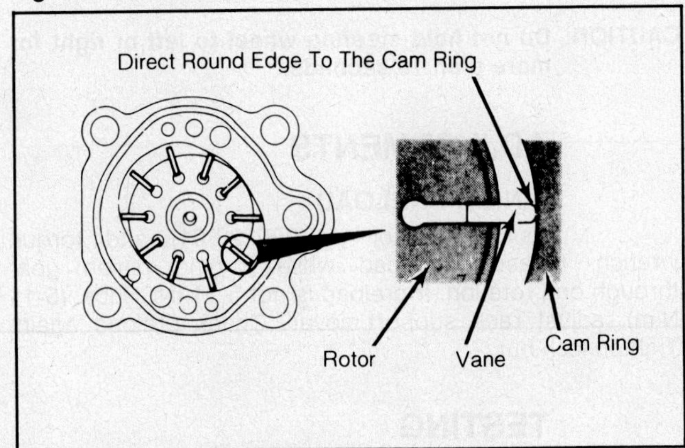

Courtesy of Chrysler Motors.

Fig. 3: Exploded View of Power Steering Pump (Colt Vista, Cordia, Galant & Tredia)

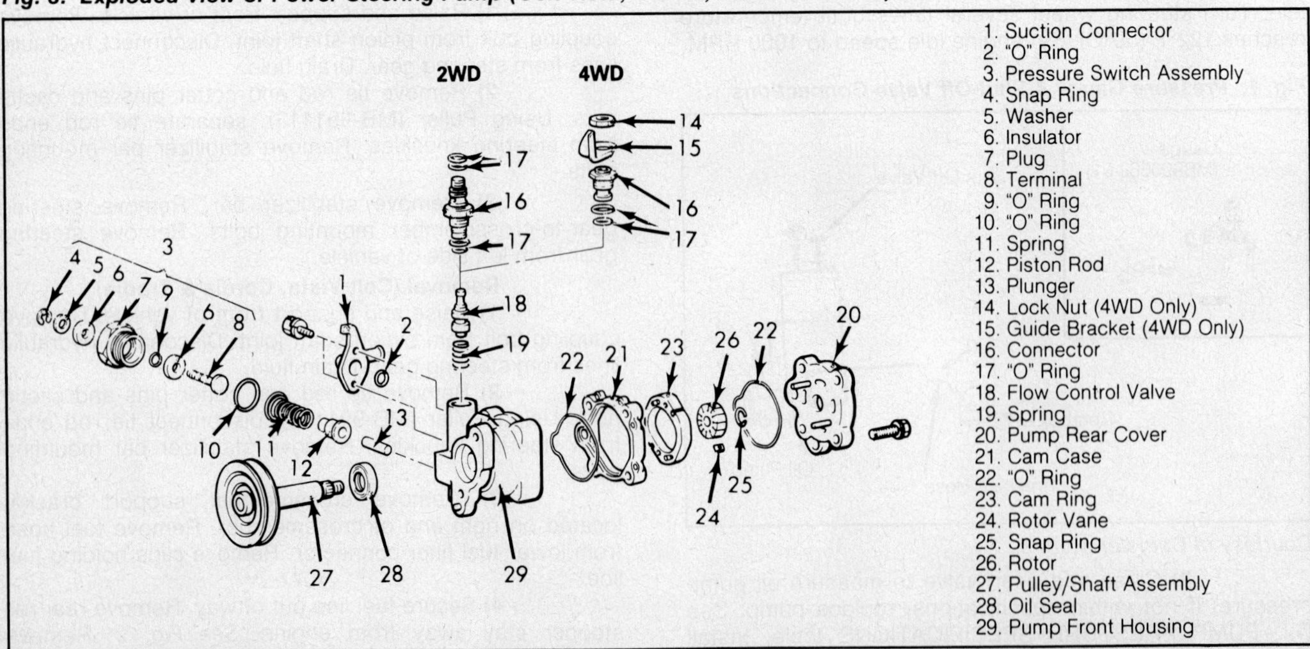

Colt, Excel, Mirage and Van/Wagon power steering pumps have no pressure switch assembly. Courtesy of Chrysler Motors.

Power Steering

CHRYSLER MOTORS, MITSUBISHI & HYUNDAI POWER-ASSISTED RACK & PINION (Cont.)

STEERING GEAR

CAUTION: On Galant, rack and pinion assembly is not to be disassembled. Replace if defective.

Disassembly (Colt, Excel, Mirage & Van/Wagon)

1) With rack and pinion assembly mounted in soft-jawed vise, remove tie rod ends, boot clamps and rubber boots. Using a chisel, remove tie rod tab washer. Remove tie rod assemblies.

2) Remove adjusting plug lock nut. Using Socket (MB990607-A), remove adjusting plug. Remove plunger spring, rubber cushion and support yoke.

3) Remove snap ring, oil seals and pinion-/valve assembly. Turn rack stopper clockwise to align circlip with slot in gear housing for removal.

4) When circlip comes out of housing, turn rack stopper counterclockwise to remove circlip. Remove rack stopper, rack bushing and rack from gear housing.

5) Remove "O" ring and oil seal from rack bushing. Use brass drift to remove ball bearing, needle bearing, and oil seal from pinion side of gear housing.

6) Use pipe to remove back washer and oil seal from rear of rack housing. Using a screwdriver, remove resin ring from pinion valve assembly.

Disassembly (Colt Vista, Cordia & Tredia)

1) With rack and pinion assembly mounted in soft-jawed vise, remove tie rod ends, boot clamps and rubber boots. Using a chisel, remove tie rod tab washer. Remove tie rod assemblies.

2) Remove adjusting plug lock nut. Using Socket (MB990607-A), remove adjusting plug. Remove plunger spring, rubber cushion and support yoke.

Inspection

Check bearings, rack bushing and rack teeth for damage and wear. On Colt and Mirage, check pinion valve assembly for damage to teeth and wear to bearing. On all models, replace all oil seals and "O" rings.

Reassembly (Colt, Excel, Mirage & Van/Wagon)

1) Apply ATF (Dexron) fluid to all "O" rings. Use multipurpose grease to lubricate rack teeth, bearings and teeth on pinion valve assembly. Reassemble in reverse order of disassembly.

2) Using Drivers (MB991097 and MB9901098), install back-up washer and oil seal in gear housing. Using Drivers (MB991100 and MB991102), install needle bearing in gear housing.

3) Using Socket (MB990607-A), install adjusting plug. Install plunger spring, rubber cushion and support yoke. Install adjusting plug lock nut.

Fig. 5: View of Colt Vista, Cordia, Galant & Tredia Power Steering Gear

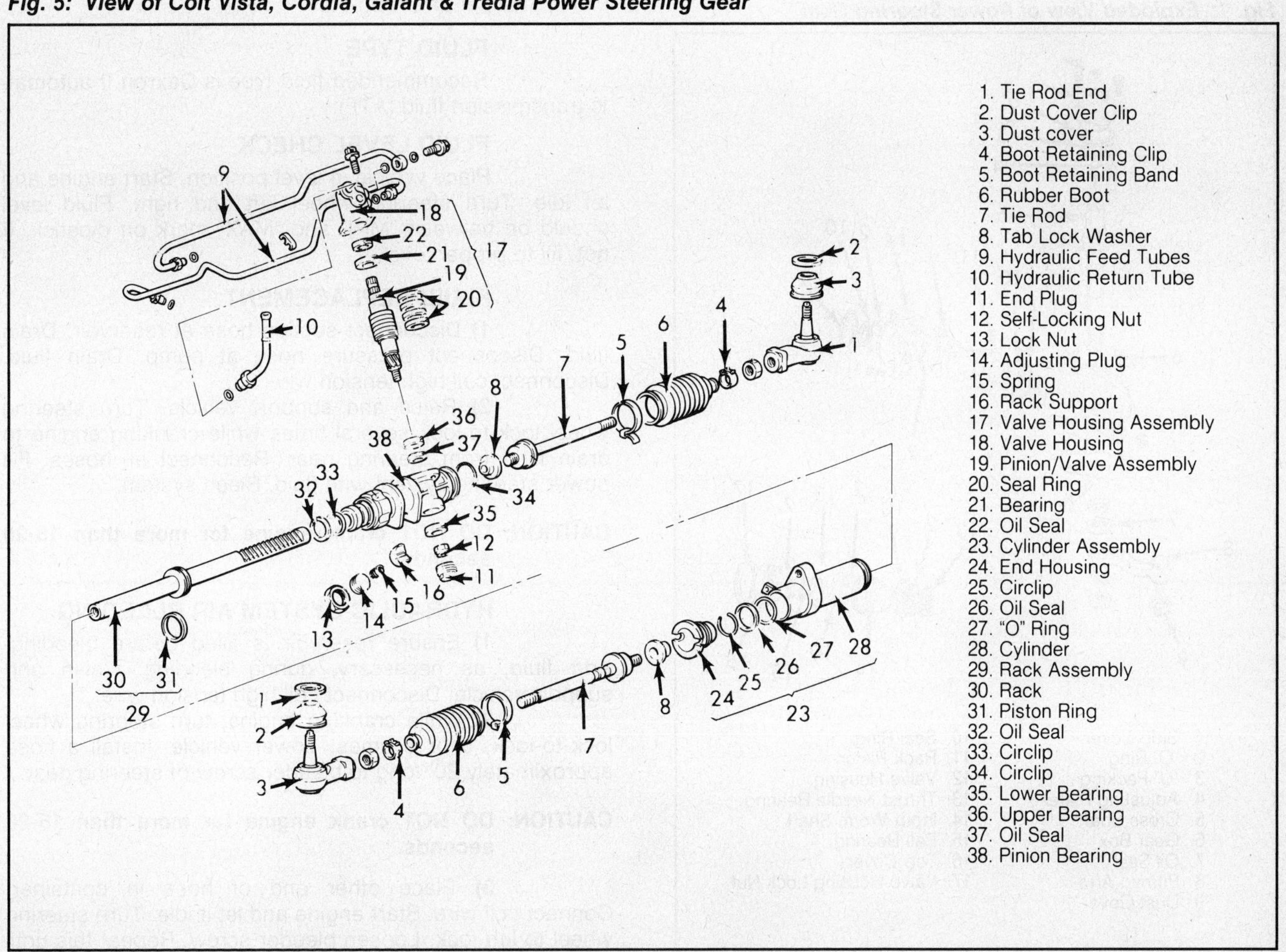

Colt, Excel, Mirage and Van/Wagon are similiar. Courtesy of Chrysler Motors.

Power Steering

CHRYSLER MOTORS, MITSUBISHI & HYUNDAI POWER-ASSISTED RACK & PINION (Cont.)

4) Using Driver (MB99100), install pinion oil seal in gear housing. Using Drivers (C-4637-1 and MB990927), install "O" ring into rack bushing. Adjust pinion preload. Refer to ADJUSTMENTS in this article.

Reassembly (Colt Vista, Cordia & Tredia)

Apply ATF (Dexron) fluid to all "O" rings. Apply multipurpose grease to rack teeth, bearings and teeth on pinion valve assembly. Reassemble in reverse order of disassembly. Adjust pinion preload. Refer to ADJUSTMENTS in this article.

TIGHTENING SPECIFICATIONS

Application	Ft. Lbs. (N.m)
Gear Box Mounting Bracket	43-58 (60-80)
Power Steering Pump Cover Bolts	13-16 (18-22)
Power Steering Pump Mounting Bolts	14-20 (19-27)
Rack Support Lock Nut	36-51 (50-70)
Tie Rod End-to-Knuckle	17-25 (24-34)
Tie Rod Lock Nut	25-40 (34-55)
Tie Rod-to-Rack	58-72 (80-100)
Valve Housing-to-Gear Housing	14-22 (20-30)

CHRYSLER MOTORS & MITSUBISHI POWER-ASSISTED RECIRCULATING BALL

Conquest, Montero, Pickup, Raider, Ram-50, Starion

DESCRIPTION

The power steering gear displaces fluid to provide hydraulic pressure assist while turning. A torsion bar helps transmit road feel to the driver. A one-piece rack piston nut is geared to the cross shaft. Backlash is adjusted with an adjusting screw.

Fig. 1: Exploded View of Power Steering Gear

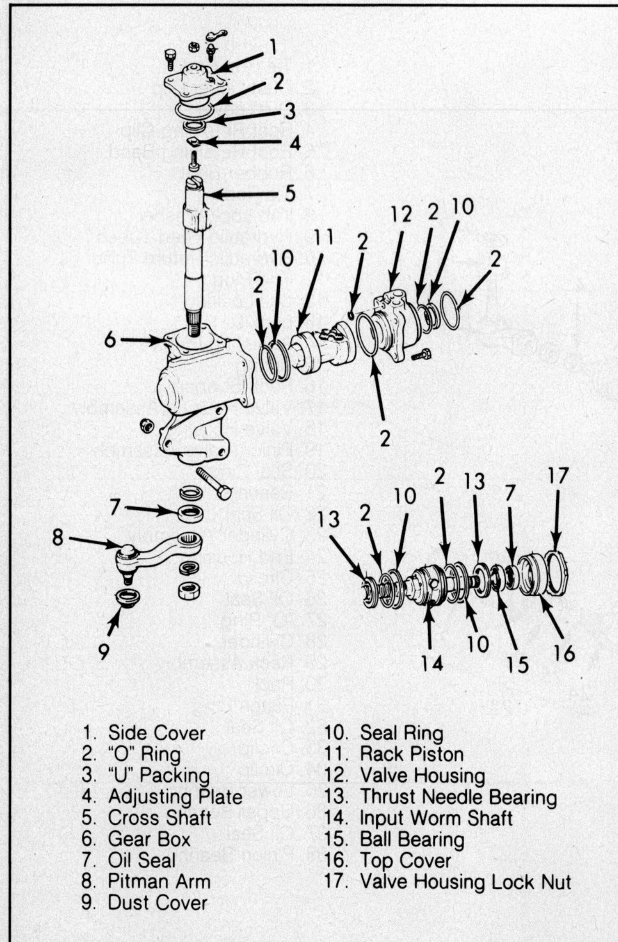

Courtesy of Chrysler Motors.

LUBRICATION

CAPACITY

Lubrication capacity is 1.2 qt. (1.1L) for Conquest and Starion. Capacity is .95 qt. (.9L) for Montero, Pickup, Raider and Ram-50.

FLUID TYPE

Recommended fluid type is Dexron II automatic transmission fluid (ATF).

FLUID LEVEL CHECK

Place vehicle in level position. Start engine and let idle. Turn steering wheel left and right. Fluid level should be between "MIN" and "MAX" mark on dipstick. If not, fill to proper level.

FLUID REPLACEMENT

1) Disconnect suction hose at reservoir. Drain fluid. Disconnect pressure hose at pump. Drain fluid. Disconnect coil high tension wire.

2) Raise and support vehicle. Turn steering wheel lock-to-lock several times while cranking engine to drain fluid from steering gear. Reconnect all hoses. Fill power steering system with fluid. Bleed system.

CAUTION: DO NOT crank engine for more than 15-20 seconds.

HYDRAULIC SYSTEM AIR BLEEDING

1) Ensure reservoir is filled before bleeding. Add fluid, as necessary, during bleeding. Raise and support vehicle. Disconnect coil high tension wire.

2) While cranking engine, turn steering wheel lock-to-lock, 5 or 6 times. Lower vehicle. Install a hose approximately 20" long to bleeder screw of steering gear.

CAUTION: DO NOT crank engine for more than 15-20 seconds.

3) Place other end of hose in container. Connect coil wire. Start engine and let it idle. Turn steering wheel to left lock. Loosen bleeder screw. Repeat this until no more bubbles appear in container.

CHRYSLER MOTORS & MITSUBISHI POWER-ASSISTED RECIRCULATING BALL (Cont.)

4) Remove hose. Tighten bleeder screw. Check fluid level. Add fluid (if necessary). Turn steering wheel lock-to-lock. Fluid level should not change more than .12-.16" (3-4 mm). If it does, repeat bleeding procedure.

ADJUSTMENTS

BELT TENSION ADJUSTMENT

With 22 lbs. (9.98 kg) applied to belt, deflection at center should be .28-.37" (7-10 mm).

STEERING WHEEL PLAY

Raise and support vehicle. Start engine and run at idle. With steering wheel in center position, ensure free play is within 1.0" (25 mm). Adjustment can be made at the steering gear adjusting bolt (if necessary).

TESTING

FLUID PRESSURE TESTING

1) Remove pressure hose from oil pump. Attach Pressure Gauge Adapter (C-3309-E). Tighten to 22-29 ft. lbs. (30-39 N.m).

2) Start engine and let idle. Place thermometer in reservoir. Close the gauge valve 3 times to bleed air from gauge. Check fluid level. Add fluid as necessary.

3) When oil temperature reaches 131°F (55°C), check pressure. Refer to OIL PUMP PRESSURE SPECIFICATIONS table. Reinstall pressure hose. Do not twist hose or let hose interfere with adjacent parts.

CAUTION: Do not keep shut-off valve closed more than 3 seconds at a time. Do not keep steering wheel turned more than 10 seconds at a time.

OIL PUMP PRESSURE SPECIFICATIONS

Application	psi (kg/cm²)
Montero & Raider	
Valve Closed	711-1138 (49-78)
Valve Open (Maximum)	142 (10)
All Others	
Valve Closed	1067-1116 (75-82)
Valve Open	142 (10)

REMOVAL & INSTALLATION

POWER STEERING GEAR

Removal

1) On Pickup and Ram 50, remove air cleaner and under cover. On all models, disconnect hydraulic lines from steering gear. Raise and support vehicle.

2) On all models, remove steering shaft-to-steering gear clamp bolt. Disconnect steering shaft from steering gear.

3) Remove cotter pin and castle nut from pitman arm. Using Puller (C-3894-A), separate tie rod and pitman arm from relay rod.

4) On pickups with automatic transmission, remove throttle linkage and shield. On pickups with manual transmission, remove starter.

5) On all models, move fuel line aside. Remove steering gear retaining bolts and lock nuts. Remove steering gear. Remove pitman arm nut. Using Puller (CT-1106), remove pitman arm from cross shaft.

Installation

1) To install, reverse removal procedure. When connecting pitman arm to cross shaft, align slit of cross shaft tip to marking on pitman arm.

2) Ensure that clearance between bolt hole at the bottom of the steering gear and pitman arm is between .73-93" (18.5-23.6 mm).

POWER STEERING PUMP

Removal

1) Loosen pump retaining bolts. Remove belt. Remove reservoir cap. Using a container to catch fluid, disconnect return hose at reservoir and drain fluid.

2) Raise and support front of vehicle. Disconnect coil high tension wire. Crank engine several times to drain fluid from system. Disconnect pressure hose from pump. Remove pulley. Remove pump bolts. Remove pump with reservoir.

Installation

To install, reverse removal procedure. Check oil pump bracket for slack. Tighten bracket (if necessary). Fill and bleed reservoir. Start engine after installation and run at 2000 RPM for 5 minutes to check for fluid leaks.

OVERHAUL

POWER STEERING GEAR

Disassembly

1) Drain fluid from steering gear. Remove adjusting lock nut. Remove side cover bolts. Screw in adjusting bolt 2 or 3 turns to separate cover.

2) With gear in neutral position, tap bottom of cross shaft with plastic hammer to remove cross shaft. Do not damage cross shaft splines and oil seal.

3) Mount valve housing in vise. Using Spanner Wrench (MB990852) to hold rack piston stationary, remove valve housing and rack piston assembly. Do not hold housing with rack pointing down as rack may slide from housing.

4) Place valve housing in vise. Move rack piston up and down to check backlash between circulator balls and rack piston gutter. Turn the rack piston fully into the valve housing.

5) Loosen 2 turns to measure backlash. Service limit is .008" (.20 mm). If backlash exceeds limit, replace ball screw unit and rack piston as an assembly.

6) Remove rack piston by turning counterclockwise. Do not lose circulator balls. Remove "O" ring, seal ring, steel balls, circulators and circulator holder from rack piston (4WD pickups use only "O" ring and seal ring).

7) Do not disconnect end cap. Using Spanner Wrench (MB990853), loosen top cover. Remove top cover and input worm shaft from valve housing.

8) Remove thrust plates, needle roller bearings, seal rings and "O" rings from input worm unit and valve housing. Screwing in adjuster bolt at tip of cross shaft, remove side cover.

9) Do not lose 33 rollers of roller bearing. Remove "O" ring, needle bearing, adjusting bolt and adjusting plate. Do not remove seal at rear of needle bearing unless fluid leaks from adjusting bolt.

Power Steering

CHRYSLER MOTORS & MITSUBISHI
POWER-ASSISTED RECIRCULATING BALL (Cont.)

Fig. 3: Measuring Backlash of Gutter & Ball

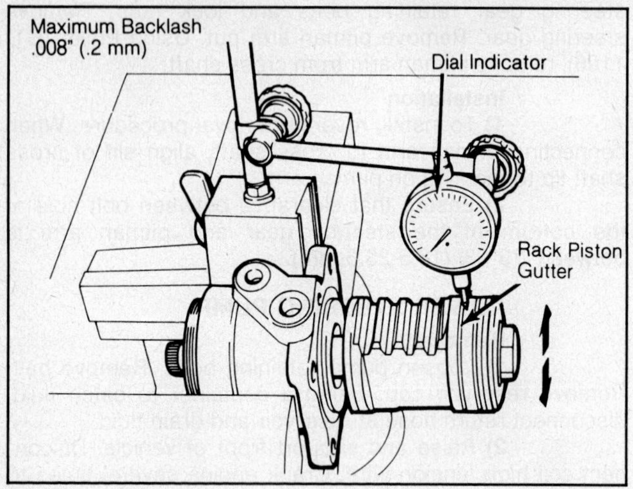

Service limit is .008" (.2 mm). Courtesy of Chrysler Motors.

10) Do not remove bleeder plug unless necessary. Remove seal ring and "O" ring from valve housing. Remove bearing and oil seal from top cover. Remove oil seal and seal ring from steering gear. Do not disassemble needle bearing.

Inspection

1) Inspect cross shaft bearing surface for peeling or pitting. Check for stepped wear of adjusting bolt shank. Inspect teeth on cross shaft and rack piston for damage.

2) Inspect for uneven wear of circulator rolling surface on rack piston. Check for damage to balls. Inspect for peeling or pitting on thrust needle roller bearing.

3) Inspect bearing surface of thrust plate of worm unit for pitting. Check ball rolling surface of worm shaft for peeling.

4) Inspect sealing surface of input shaft for damage. If thrust bearing or thrust plate is defective, replace both as a set.

5) Inspect valve housing for damage to seal ring-to-housing contact surface. Inspect "O" ring sealing surface, valve housing and side cover.

Reassembly

1) Use all new "O" rings, seal rings and oil seals. When replacing, lubricate with power steering fluid before insertion.

2) Lubricate bearing surface of side cover. Install 33 roller bearings. Apply grease to bottom of side cover. Install "O" ring to side cover.

3) Insert adjusting bolt and plate into "T" slot on top of cross shaft. Using adjusting plates, set cross shaft play to 0-.002" (0-.50 mm). See CROSS SHAFT ADJUSTING PLATE THICKNESS table.

CROSS SHAFT ADJUSTING PLATE THICKNESS

Plate No.	In. (mm)
1	.077 (1.95)
2	.079 (2.00)
3	.081 (2.05)
4	.083 (2.10)
5	.085 (2.15)

4) When installing adjusting plates, place chamfered edge of adjusting plate to contact surface of cross shaft. *See Fig. 4.* Align cross shaft with side cover.

Fig. 4: Adjusting Cross Shaft

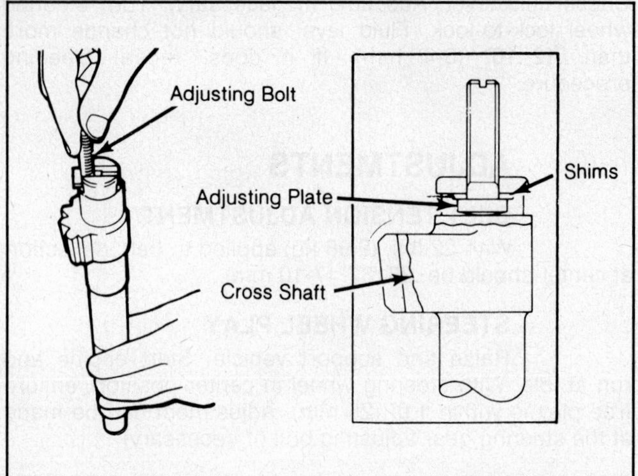

Courtesy of Chrysler Motors.

5) Tighten with adjusting bolt. Do not allow bearing to fall off or damage seal ring. Tighten lock nut temporarily. Apply grease to oil seal lip.

6) Press oil seal and ball bearing into top cover. Apply grease to "U" packing and lip of oil seal. Press into steering gear. Install "O" ring and seal ring to input worm shaft.

7) Install thrust plate, needle bearing, and thrust plate in that order onto input worm shaft. Install "O" ring and seal ring (compressed into shape) into valve housing groove.

8) Install input worm shaft to valve housing. Install thin thrust plate, needle roller bearing and thick thrust plate in that order to top cover.

9) Using Spanner Wrench (MB990853), temporarily tighten top cover to valve housing. Make sure thrust plate and needle bearing are aligned.

10) Attach spring tension gauge to spanner wrench. Tighten cover to 14-19 lbs. (6.4-8.6 kg). Loosen cover to zero. *See Fig. 5.* Check input worm shaft for uniform rotation.

11) Using Preload Socket (CT-1108) and an INCH lb. torque wrench, measure and record input worm shaft starting torque. Gradually tighten top cover until input worm shaft starting torque is 1.8-2.7 INCH lbs. (.2-.3 N.m) greater than recorded value.

12) Using Spanner Wrench (MB990852) and torque wrench, tighten valve housing nut without rotating top cover. Again measure input worm shaft starting torque while turning input worm shaft.

13) If starting torque is not 2.2-5.6 INCH lbs. (.3-.6 N.m), loosen valve housing nut and repeat steps **11)** and **12)**. Install "O" ring and seal ring to rack piston without forcing.

14) Insert rack piston into input worm shaft until piston touches worm shaft end. Rotate worm shaft while aligning ball running surface with ball insertion hole.

15) Insert 19 balls into hole by pushing lightly with a brass rod. After installation, ensure ball-to-rack piston clearance is .50" (13.0 mm). *See Fig. 6.*

16) If clearance is excessive, a ball has entered wrong groove. Remove rack piston. Reinstall balls. Insert 7 more balls with grease to keep them from falling.

NOTE: **Do not rotate input worm shaft and rack piston. Balls may enter wrong grooves.**

Power Steering
CHRYSLER MOTORS & MITSUBISHI POWER-ASSISTED RECIRCULATING BALL (Cont.)

Fig. 5: Tightening Top Cover

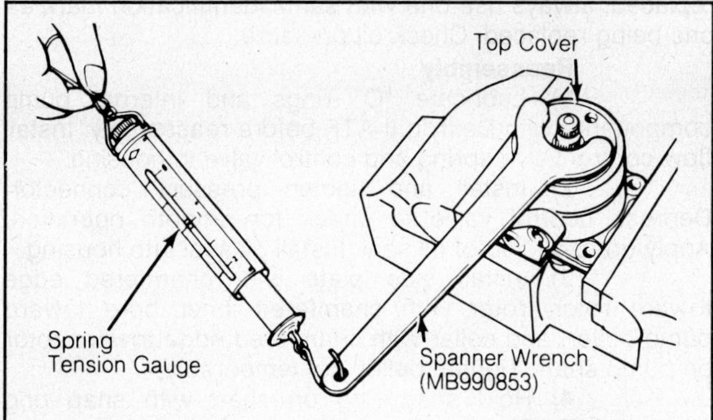

Tighten to 14-19 lbs. (6.4-8.6 kg). Courtesy of Chrysler Motors.

Fig. 6: Installing Circulator Balls to Rack Piston

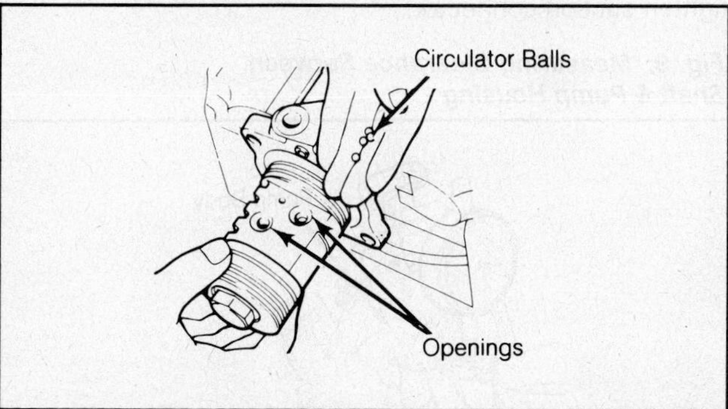

Courtesy of Chrysler Motors.

17) Insert circulator and holder to rack piston and tighten. Mount gear box in vise. Install valve housing and rack piston. Tighten valve housing. Rotate input worm shaft to move rack piston to center (neutral) position.

NOTE: **Do not force rack piston into housing. Seal ring may be damaged by edge of gear housing.**

18) Apply a thin coating of automatic transmission fluid to teeth and shaft of rack piston. Apply grease to oil seal lip. Wrap serration of cross shaft with vinyl tape to avoid damage when installing.

19) Install cross shaft and side cover to steering gear. To prevent damage to "O" ring during installation, DO NOT rotate side cover when installing.

20) Tighten side cover. Using Preload Socket (CT-1108), measure starting torque of input worm shaft. Adjust starting torque to 4.3-7.8 INCH lbs. (.5-.9 N.m) by turning cross shaft adjusting bolt.

21) Tighten lock nut. Make sure valve housing and rack piston unit operates smoothly. Connect cross shaft to pitman arm. Ensure slit on cross shaft tip aligns with groove on pitman arm.

POWER STEERING PUMP

Disassembly (Pickup & Ram 50)

1) Place pump in a soft-jawed vise. Remove pump cover retaining bolts and pump cover. Remove seal washer, cam ring and rotor. Remove vanes from rotor.

Fig. 7: Exploded View of Pickup & Ram 50 Power Steering Pump

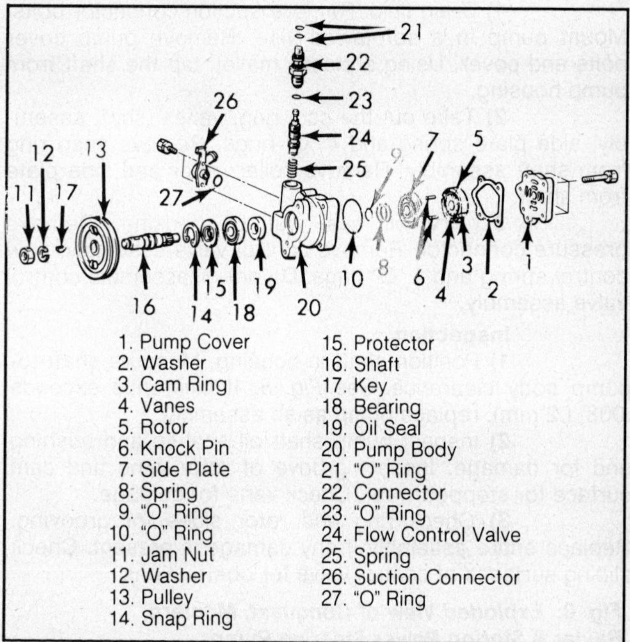

Courtesy of Chrysler Motors.

2) Remove side plate. Remove knock pins from housing. Remove 4 "O" rings. Remove pulley retaining nut, lock washer, pulley and key from shaft.

3) Remove snap ring and protector from shaft. Remove shaft, bearing and oil seal from oil pump housing. Remove "O" ring, pressure connector, "O" ring, flow control valve and spring from housing. Remove suction tube connector.

Inspection

1) Check flow control valve, rotor and ring, end plates and pump shaft for damage, scoring or excessive wear. Inspect pump housing for cracks or visual signs of damage. Check "O" ring seats for scratches or burrs.

2) Inspect pump shaft bushing in pump housing. If bushing is damaged, replace pump housing. Replace components as necessary. If any internal pump parts are damaged, flush steering gear or disassemble and clean gear.

NOTE: **Pump ring is treated and a Gray/Black finish is normal. A wave-type grain appearance inside ring is normal.**

Reassembly

1) Lubricate NEW "O" rings and internal pump components with ATF Dexron II fluid before reassembly. Install suction tube connector.

2) Install "O" ring, pressure connector, "O" ring, flow control valve and spring in housing. Install shaft, bearing and oil seal in oil pump housing.

3) Install snap ring and protector on shaft. Install key, pulley, lock washer and retaining nut on shaft. Install 4 "O" rings. Insert knock pins into housing.

4) Position side plate. Insert vanes into rotor. Position cam ring over rotor assembly. Install rotor assembly into housing. Install pump cover and cover retaining bolts.

Power Steering

CHRYSLER MOTORS & MITSUBISHI POWER-ASSISTED RECIRCULATING BALL (Cont.)

Disassembly

(All Except Pickup & Ram 50)

1) Drain fluid. Remove suction connector bolts. Mount pump in a soft-jawed vise. Remove pump cover bolts and cover. Using a plastic mallet, tap the shaft from pump housing.

2) Take out the cam ring, vanes, shaft assembly, side plate spring and 4 "O" rings. Remove snap ring from shaft assembly. Remove collar, rotor and side plate from shaft.

3) Pry oil seal out of housing. Remove pressure connector. Remove control valve assembly, flow control spring and 2 "O" rings. Do not disassemble control valve assembly.

Inspection

1) Position shaft in housing. Measure shaft-to-pump body clearance. *See Fig. 8.* If clearance exceeds .008" (.2 mm), replace pump as an assembly.

2) Inspect pump shaft oil seal lip and bushing end for damage. Inspect groove of rotor vane and cam surface for stepped wear. Check vane for damage.

3) Check ring and rotor sides for grooving. Replace entire assembly if any damage is present. Check sliding surfaces of control valve for obstructions.

Fig. 8: Exploded View of Conquest, Montero, Raider & Starion Power Steering Pump

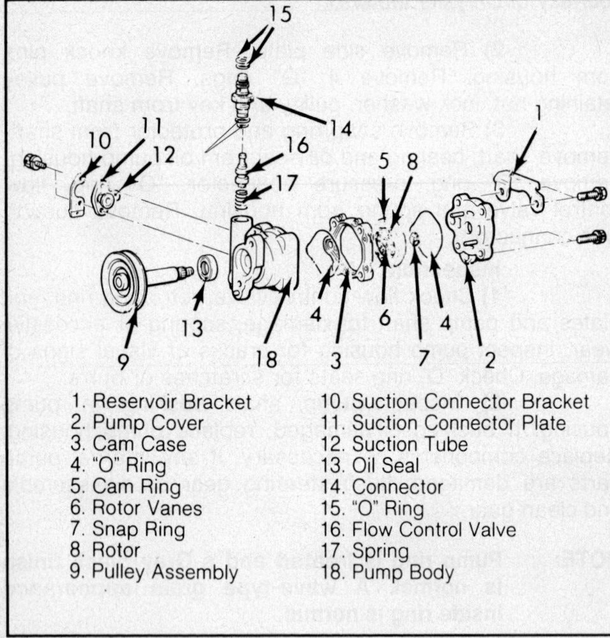

Courtesy of Chrysler Motors.

4) Replace parts as required. If control valve is replaced, always use one with same identification mark as one being replaced. Check oil pressure.

Reassembly

1) Lubricate "O" rings and internal pump components with Dexron II ATF before reassembly. Install flow control valve spring and control valve in housing.

2) Install and tighten pressure connector. Depress control valve to check for smooth operation. Apply grease to lip of oil seal. Install oil seal into housing.

3) Install side plate with chamfered edge toward rotor, rotor with chamfered inner bore toward pump cover, and collar with chamfered edge toward rotor on pump shaft. Tighten pulley nut temporarily.

4) Hold snap ring on shaft with snap ring pliers. Install "O" ring and side plate spring into housing. Install vanes with rounded edges outward onto rotor.

5) Insert shaft assembly with vanes into housing. Do not damage pump shaft seal lip. Install cam ring with chamfered edge toward side plate. Install and tighten suction connector.

Fig. 9: Measuring Clearance Between Shaft & Pump Housing

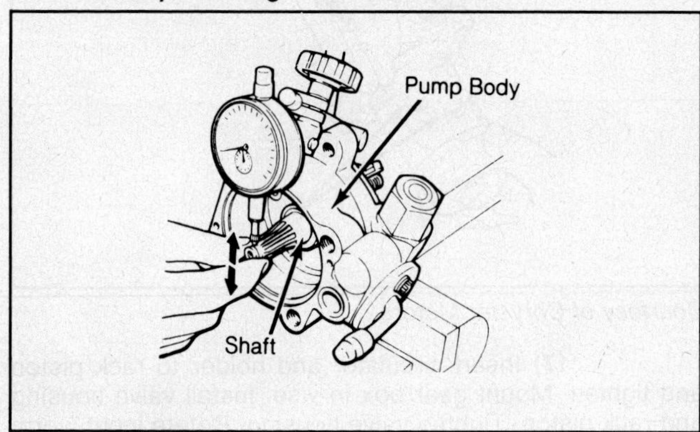

Courtesy of Chrysler Motors.

TIGHTENING SPECIFICATIONS

Application	Ft. Lbs. (N.m)
Gear-to-Frame	40-47 (54-64)
Oil Pump Cover	22-29 (30-39)
Pitman Arm-to-Cross Shaft	94-109 (128-148)
Pressure Hose	22-29 (30-39)
Suction Hose	29-36 (39-49)
Side Cover	33-40 (45-54)
Valve Housing	33-40 (45-54)
Valve Housing Lock Nut	130-166 (178-226)

FORD MOTOR CO.

Merkur XR4Ti

NOTE: **For information on Tracer power-assisted rack and pinion, refer to MAZDA & TRACER POWER-ASSISTED RACK & PINION in this section.**

DESCRIPTION

Steering system is a power-assisted rack and pinion. The system consists of a rack and pinion steering gear and power assist pump/reservoir. The steering gear and pump/reservoir are connected by flexible hoses.

FORD MOTOR CO. (Cont.)

LUBRICATION

CAPACITY

.85 quarts (.8L).

FLUID TYPE

Fluid type is DEXRON II ATF.

HYDRAULIC FLUID LEVEL CHECK

Start engine and let it idle. Turn steering wheel several times to raise fluid to normal operating temperature. Turn steering wheel left and right several times while checking fluid for foaming or clouding. If fluid is below the oil filter, fill until level is to the lower position of the filter.

HYDRAULIC SYSTEM BLEEDING

1) Disconnect coil high tension wire. Crank engine intermittently for 15-20 seconds while turning steering wheel left and right. Connect coil high tension wire Start engine. Turn steering wheel left and right until there are no air bubbles in the oil reservoir.

2) Check fluid level. Confirm that fluid is not milky. Turn steering wheel left and right while checking to see that fluid level does not change. Repeat if fluid level changes or noise is heard from pump or control valve.

ADJUSTMENTS

NOTE: **Adjustments are performed during steering gear reassembly.**

REMOVAL & INSTALLATION

Removal

1) Disconnect battery ground cable. Turn ignition to position "II". Remove cotter pins and nuts attaching tie rod ends to knuckles. Using Tie Rod Separator (T85M-3395-A), separate tie rod end from knuckle. Remove pinch bolt from flexible coupling. Rotate coupling as necessary to gain access to pinch bolt.

2) Disconnect power steering hoses from steering gear by removing routing clamp and washer-head screw, securing pump line plate assembly to gear housing. Pull assembly free. Plug housing ports to prevent entry of contaminants. Remove steering gear mounting bolts and steering gear.

Fig. 1: Exploded View of Merkur XR4Ti Power Steering Gear

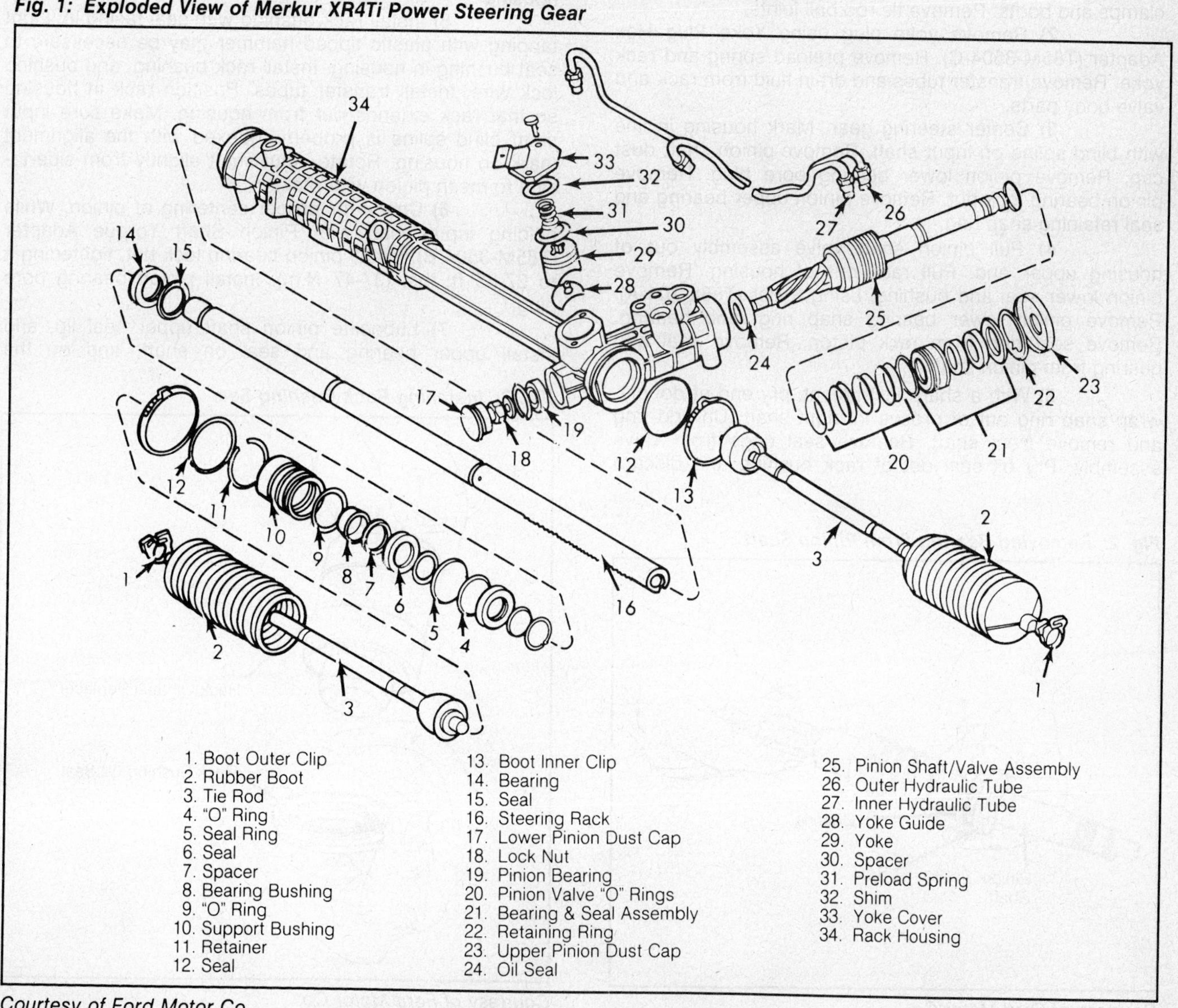

Courtesy of Ford Motor Co.

Power Steering

FORD MOTOR CO. (Cont.)

Installation

To install steering gear assembly, reverse removal procedure. Make sure splines are aligned with coupling and steering gear when installing shaft.

POWER STEERING PUMP

Removal

Using Pulley Remover (T69L-10300-B), remove pump pulley. Disconnect fluid return line. Drain fluid from pump into container. Disconnect pressure line. Remove 3 pump-to-bracket mounting bolts. Remove pump.

Installation

Reverse removal procedure to install. Using Pulley Installer (T65P-3A733-C), install pump pulley. After installation, adjust belt tension. Bleed air from steering system. Check for leaks.

OVERHAUL

STEERING GEAR

Disassembly

1) Mount steering gear in a padded vise. Remove tie rod ends and lock nuts. Remove dust boot clamps and boots. Remove tie rod ball joints.

2) Remove yoke plug using Yoke Plug Hex Adapter (T85M-3504-C). Remove preload spring and rack yoke. Remove transfer tubes and drain fluid from rack and valve body parts.

3) Center steering gear. Mark housing in line with blind spline on input shaft. Remove pinion shaft dust cap. Remove pinion lower bearing bore plug. Remove pinion bearing lock nut. Remove pinion upper bearing and seal retaining snap ring.

4) Pull pinion shaft valve assembly out of housing upper end. Pull rack out of housing. Remove pinion lower seal and bushing, using Puller (T58L-101-A). Remove pinion lower bearing snap ring, and bearing. Remove seal ring from rack piston. Remove seal and bearing from pinion shaft.

5) With a sharp instrument, pry end of double-wrap snap ring out of groove in input shaft. Unwind ring and remove from shaft. Remove seal rings from valve assembly. Pry oil seal out of rack bushing and discard seal.

Fig. 2: Removing Bearing From Pinion Shaft

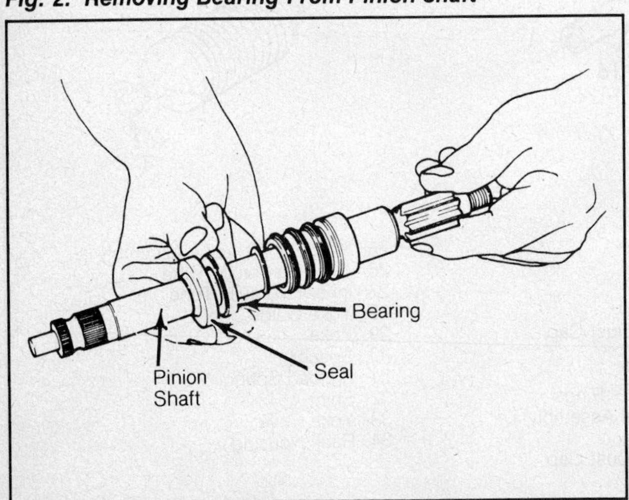

Courtesy of Ford Motor Co.

Inspection

1) Place rack ends in "V" blocks. Attach dial indicator so plunger rests on center of rack. Rotate rack. Note deflection of gauge.

2) Maximum deflection should be less than .004" (.10 mm). If not to specification, replace rack. Replace any components if worn, scored or damaged.

Reassembly & Adjustment

1) Lubricate rack piston seal with automatic transmission fluid or power steering fluid. Install seals on valve assembly.

2) Install double-wrap snap ring in its groove on input shaft. Install rack bushing seal using Rack Oil Seal Replacer (T78P-3504-K).

3) Install rack inner seal support ring in rack cylinder, using rack oil seal replacer to seat and center it (if necessary). Install pinion lower bearing using Pinion Bearing Replacer (T81P-3504-H). Install pinion bushing, lower seal, and pinion lower bearing snap ring.

4) Pack rack teeth, and coat yoke bearing surface with Lubricant (C3AZ-19578-A). Position Teflon Ring Sizing Tool (T74P-3504-H) in mouth of rack cylinder. Lubricate tool bore and push rack through sizing tool into housing.

5) Install rack bushing with seal facing in. Light tapping with plastic tipped hammer may be necessary to seat bushing in housing. Install rack bushing, and bushing lock wire. Install transfer tubes. Position rack in housing so that rack extends out from housing. Make sure input shaft blind spline is properly indexed with the alignment mark on housing. Rotate input shaft slightly from side-to-side to mesh pinion with rack.

6) Check for proper centering of pinion. While holding input shaft with Pinion Shaft Torque Adapter (T85M-3504-B), install pinion bearing lock nut, tightening it to 27-35 ft. lbs. (37-47 N.m). Install pinion bearing bore plug.

7) Lubricate pinion shaft upper seal lip, and install upper bearing and seal on shaft, and on the

Fig. 3: Installing Rack Bushing Seal

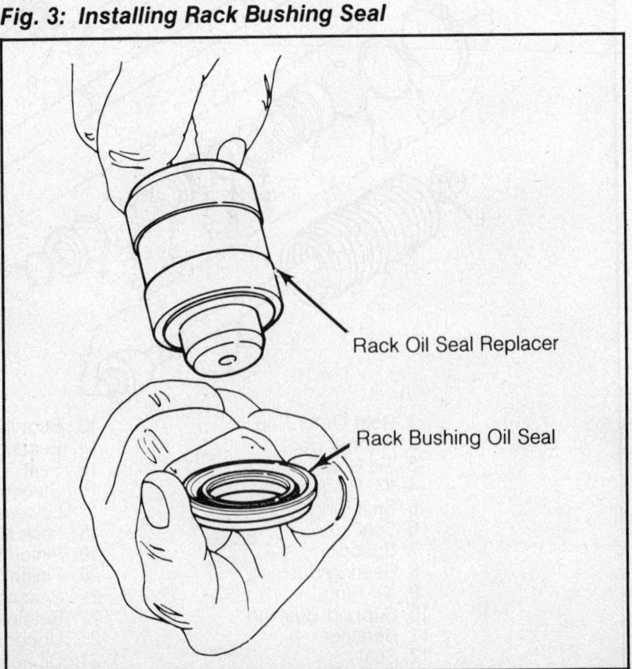

Courtesy of Ford Motor Co.

FORD MOTOR CO. (Cont.)

housing. Install pinion upper bearing and seal retaining snap ring. Install dust cover.

8) Coat rack yoke bore and rack yoke with Lubricant (C3AZ-19578-A). Install rack yoke, original shims and preload spring. Install ball joint and tie rod assemblies. Install dust boots, and tie rod ends.

POWER STEERING PUMP

Disassembly

1) Place pump in a vise. Using a screwdriver, pry shaft seal and retainer from housing. Remove the outlet fitting, pressure regulator and spring from housing. Remove pump reservoir by twisting.

2) Place Lower Support Plate (T78P-3733-A2) over shaft. Remove pump from vise. Position pump lengthwise in a "C" clamp. Place "C" clamp into the vise.

3) Tighten "C" clamp until a slight bottoming is felt. Insert a pin punch into access hole. Push in retaining ring until a screwdriver can be inserted between retaining ring and housing.

4) Pry out retaining ring. Remove pump from "C" clamp. Pull valve cover off housing. Pushing the shaft through the housing, remove upper plate, rotor assembly and dowel pins.

Fig. 4: Exploded View of the Power Steering Pump

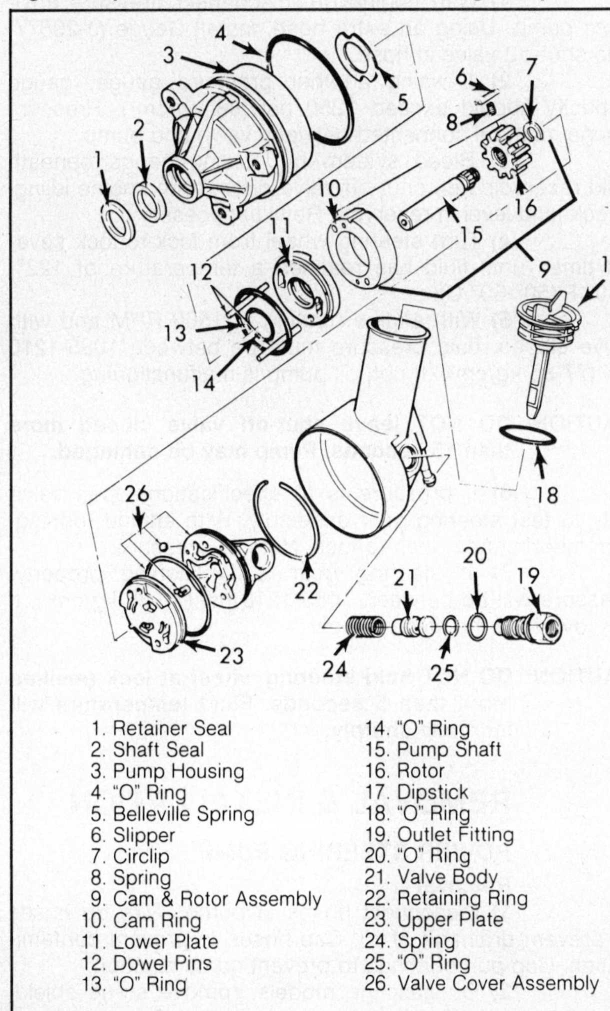

Courtesy of Ford Motor Co.

5) Tap the housing on a flat, wooden surface to remove the belleville washer and lower plate. Slide the rotor from the rotor cam. Remove the pump slippers, slipper springs, retaining ring and shaft from the rotor.

Inspection

1) Inspect all sliding surfaces for signs of wear or scoring. Check outlet fitting for signs of damage to threads. Inspect pressure regulator for nicks or burrs in the valve lands.

2) Check that pressure regulator slides freely in the bore. Check the reservoir for damage to the seal ring, cracked inlet fitting, broken or missing baffle and damaged or broken cap tabs.

3) Check rotor shaft for damaged splines or worn clip grooves. Check shaft for worn or scored thrust faces, bushing area and seal areas. Ensure that cam is not worn or that slippers and slipper springs are not bent or broken.

4) A high polish is always present on the upper and lower plates. Polish this surface if necessary, however, do not remove the phosphate coating.

5) Check the pump housing for damaged or stripped threaded holes. Using an inside micrometer, measure the shaft bushing inside diameter.

6) If the shaft bushing inside diameter measures more than .6902" (18.01 mm), replace the pump housing. Check the valve cover for nicks or burrs.

Reassembly

1) Always use new seals. Coat all parts with Dexron ATF before reassembly. Install the rotor onto the shaft. Place the cam over the rotor.

2) Extend the rotor about halfway out of the cam. Rotate the cam to align a rotor slot with a recess in the cam. Insert a slipper spring.

3) Using a slipper to compress the spring, install slipper into the rotor slot with the groove facing up. Repeat this procedure until all slippers and slipper springs have been installed.

4) Using Seal Driver (T78P-3733-A3), install the seal and seal retainer. Install the belleville washer and dowell pins in the housing. Ensure that the dished side of the washer faces up.

5) Install the lower plate "O" ring. Position the lower plate over the dowel pins with the "O" rings facing the front of the housing.

6) Using a "C" clamp and Seal Driver (T78P-3733-A3), press the lower plate into the housing until in bottoms. Remove clamp and driver. Install rotor/cam assembly into the housing.

7) Install the upper plate over dowels. Install "O" ring onto valve cover. Ensure that the plastic baffle in the valve cover is securely installed in the valve cover. If it is loose, secure it with petroleum jelly.

8) Install valve cover into housing. Ensure that the pressure channel in the valve cover aligns with the recess in the upper plate.

9) Place Lower Support Plate (T78P-3733-A2) over shaft. Position pump lengthwise in a "C" clamp. Place "C" clamp into a vise. Tighten "C" clamp until a slight bottoming is felt. Install retaining ring. Remove pump from "C" clamp.

10) Install the pump reservoir. Install the outlet fitting, pressure regulator and spring from housing. Using Driver (T78P-3733-A3), drive shaft seal and retainer into housing.

FORD MOTOR CO. (Cont.)

TIGHTENING SPECIFICATIONS

Application	Ft. Lbs. (N.m)
Pressure Line Tube Nut	10-25 (14-34)
Pump-to-Bracket Bolt	34-45 (41-61)
Steering Column	
Mounting Bracket Bolt	13-16 (18-22)
Steering Wheel-to-Shaft Nut	33-40 (45-55)
Steering Coupling Pinch Bolt	19-22 (25-30)
Steering Gear-to-Crossmember Bolt	11 (15)
Tie Rod-to-Front Spindle Nut	15-23 (20-32)
"U" Joint Clamp Bolt	15-19 (20-25)

ISUZU POWER-ASSISTED RECIRCULATING BALL

P'UP, Trooper II

DESCRIPTION

The power assisted recirculating ball steering system consists of the power steering gear assembly, hydraulic pump and hydraulic lines.

The power steering gear is an integral-type. It consists of the conventional ball/screw-type steering gear combined with a rotary and torsion bar-type control valve and power cylinder.

The oil pump is a constant delivery vane-type and is belt driven. The pump and gear assemblies are connected by hoses.

LUBRICATION

CAPACITY

1.1 qts. (1L).

FLUID TYPE

ATF Dexron.

FLUID LEVEL CHECK

1) Raise and support front of vehicle. Fill reservoir. With engine off, turn steering wheel lock-to-lock several times. Check fluid level. Refill as necessary.

2) With engine at idle, turn steering wheel lock-to-lock several times. Recheck fluid level. Add fluid (if necessary). Lower vehicle. Turn steering wheel lock-to-lock with engine at idle.

CAUTION: DO NOT hold steering wheel at full lock position for more than 10 seconds.

3) With wheels in straight-ahead position and engine off, look for fluid rising in reservoir. If fluid rises, air is trapped in system. Repeat step **2)**.

ADJUSTMENTS

BELT

On P'UP, belt deflection is .40" (10 mm) measured between pump and idler pulley. On Trooper II, belt deflection is .4" (10 mm) measured between pump and A/C compressor.

SECTOR GEAR BACKLASH

NOTE: Sector gear backlash adjustment is part of steering gear reassembly procedure.

TESTING

HYDRAULIC SYSTEM TESTING

1) With engine off, disconnect pressure hose from pump. Using an extra hose, install Gauge (J-29877) and shut-off valve in hose.

2) If using another pressure gauge, gauge capacity should exceed 1250 psi (88 kg/cm²). Pressure gauge must be connected between valve and pump.

3) Bleed system by holding gauge beneath fluid reservoir with shut-off valve open. With engine idling, check fluid level in reservoir. Refill (if necessary).

4) Turn steering wheel from lock-to-lock several times until fluid has reached a temperature of 122°-140° F (50°-60° C).

5) With engine running at 1500 RPM and with valve closed, fluid pressure must be between 1085-1210 psi (77-85 kg/cm²). If not, oil pump is malfunctioning.

CAUTION: DO NOT leave shut-off valve closed more than 15 seconds. Pump may be damaged.

6) If pressure is to specification, open valve fully to test steering gear assembly. With engine running, turn steering gear lock-to-lock. Note oil pressure.

7) If steering gear is functioning properly, pressure will be between 1085-1210 psi (77-85 kg/cm²). If not, overhaul the steering gear.

CAUTION: DO NOT hold steering wheel at lock position more than 5 seconds. Fluid temperature will increase sharply.

REMOVAL & INSTALLATION

POWER STEERING PUMP

Removal

1) Disconnect hoses at pump. Wire up hoses to prevent drainage of oil. Cap hoses to prevent contamination. Cap pump fittings to prevent contamination.

2) On gasoline models, remove stone shield. Loosen bracket-to-pump mounting bolts. Remove pump belts. Remove brackets from pump. Remove pump.

ISUZU POWER-ASSISTED RECIRCULATING BALL (Cont.)

Installation

To install pump, reverse removal procedure. Adjust belts as described under ADJUSTMENTS. Refill with fluid. Bleed system. Check for leaks.

POWER STEERING GEAR

Removal

1) Clean steering gear. Raise and support vehicle. On diesel models, remove intake air silencer and duct. Disconnect hoses at steering gear.

2) Wire up hoses to prevent drainage of fluid. Cap hoses to prevent contamination. Install plugs on gear fittings to prevent contamination.

NOTE: Before removing steering shaft coupler from stub shaft on gear assembly, mark location of coupler to shaft.

3) Remove "U" joint pinch bolt. Remove 2 steering column-to-instrument panel bolts. Disconnect "U" joint from stub shaft by pulling column and shaft approximately 2.0" (50 mm) in toward cab.

4) Remove pitman arm nut and washer. Using Puller (J-29107), separate pitman arm from shaft. Remove engine stone shield. Remove steering gear-to-frame bolts. Remove steering gear from vehicle.

Installation

To install, reverse removal procedure. Replace locking nuts and bolts. Tighten to specification. Refill system with fluid. Bleed system. Check for leaks.

Fig. 1: Exploded View of Power Steering Gear

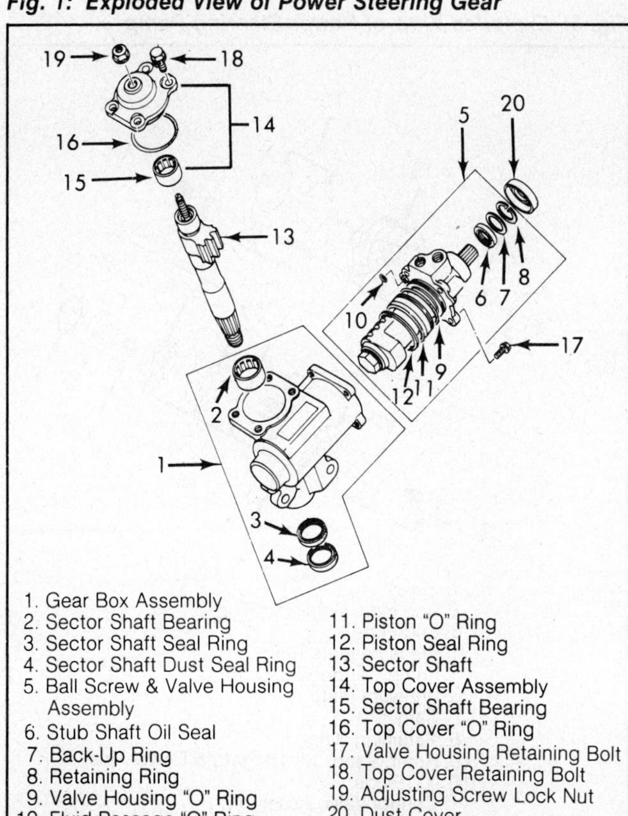

Courtesy of Isuzu Motor Co.

OVERHAUL

POWER STEERING GEAR

NOTE: Avoid clamping steering gear in vise by power cylinder portion. Internal damage to cylinder may result.

Disassembly

1) Mount steering gear in vise. *See Fig. 2.* Remove dust cover from stub shaft. Ensure clean faces of stub shaft extend outward. Remove retaining ring and back-up ring.

2) Remove stub shaft seal by plugging hose fitting on inlet side and applying compressed air through hole in outlet side. Remove adjusting screw lock nut.

3) Turn adjusting screw counterclockwise to remove the preload between sector gear and rack piston. Remove top cover bolts. Hold top cover stationary.

4) Turn adjusting screw clockwise to raise and free the top cover. Remove top cover. Ensure clean faces of sector shaft extend outward.

5) Rotate stub shaft into straight-ahead position. Remove sector shaft from housing. *See Fig. 3.* Hold sector shaft in straight-ahead position when removing it from housing.

CAUTION: DO NOT drive sector shaft out with hammer or other impact tool.

Fig. 2: Incorrect Clamping of Power Steering Gear

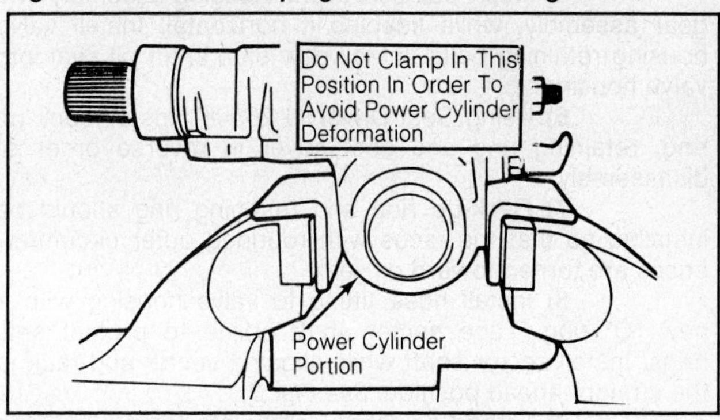

Clamp the steering gear by the sector shaft portion to prevent damage. Courtesy of Isuzu Motor Co.

Fig. 3: Removing Sector Shaft

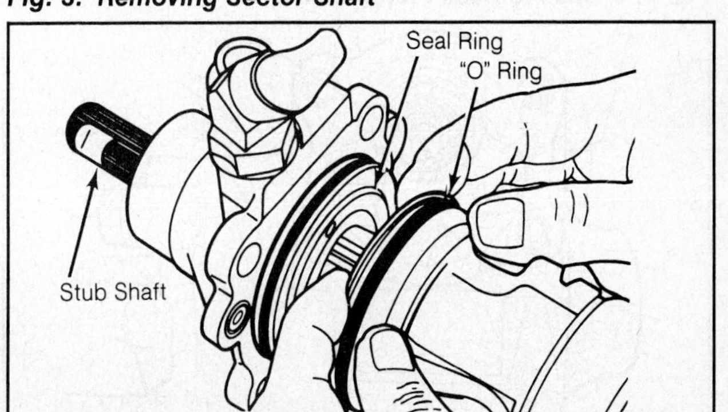

Courtesy of Isuzu Motor Co.

Power Steering

ISUZU POWER-ASSISTED RECIRCULATING BALL (Cont.)

NOTE: Always keep ball screw and valve housing assembly in a horizontal position. If held vertically, rack piston will fall off onto the end of worm, slip out, and the balls will separate.

6) Remove 4 valve housing-to-gear housing retaining bolts. Remove ball screw and valve housing with valve assembly from gear housing.

7) Remove valve housing "O" rings, piston seal ring with "O" ring and top cover "O" ring. Using a wire, remove sector shaft seals. Discard "O" rings.

Inspection

Wash all parts in solvent. Check all parts for wear, chipping or other damage. If any internal parts are damaged, entire ball screw and valve housing parts should be replaced as an assembly. Oil seal, hose fitting and dust cover may be replaced individually.

Reassembly

1) If sector shaft bearing was removed, install new bearing flush with the recessed face of housing and with name of bearing facing out toward top cover.

2) Install sector shaft seal ring and dust seal ring in housing. Apply a thin coat of grease to lip of seals and rack piston "O" ring.

3) Install "O" ring on rack piston carefully to prevent twisting. Install seal ring to rack piston over "O" ring by expanding it. *See Fig. 4.* Apply a coat of grease to entire circumference of seal ring.

4) Apply a thin coat of grease to valve housing "O" ring and top cover "O" ring. Install "O" rings in grooves carefully to prevent twisting.

5) Insert ball screw and housing assembly into gear assembly, while keeping it horizontal. Install valve housing retaining bolts. Install new stub shaft oil seal into valve housing.

6) Using Seal Driver (J-26508), install back-up ring, retaining ring and dust cover in reverse order of disassembly.

7) Back-up ring and retaining ring should be installed so that the faces with rounded outer circumferences are turned toward oil seal.

8) Install hose fitting to valve housing with a new "O" ring. Tape sector shaft spline to protect seal rings. Install sector shaft while aligning sector and rack in the straight-ahead position. *See Fig. 3.*

9) Thread adjusting screw into top cover. Turn adjusting screw counterclockwise until the top cover contacts housing. Continue for 2 more turns.

Fig. 4: Installing Rack Piston Seals

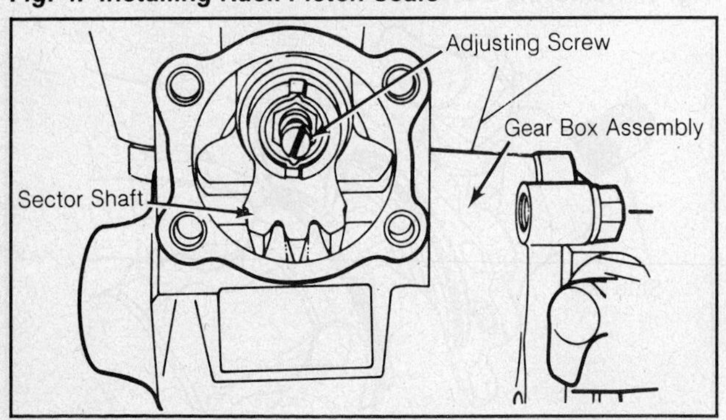

Courtesy of Isuzu Motor Co.

10) Install top cover bolts. Check if sector and rack are installed properly by turning the stub shaft lock-to-lock. Sector and rack are installed properly if stub shaft turns more than 4 turns.

11) Adjust backlash between rack piston and sector by placing relative parts in a straight-ahead position and rotating stub shaft with a torque wrench and socket.

12) Starting torque should be 62-94 INCH lbs. (.6-.9 N.m). If not, adjust with adjusting screw. To decrease backlash, turn clockwise. Install new lock nut.

POWER STEERING PUMP

Disassembly

Remove pulley, end plate retaining ring, end plate, pressure plate spring, pump cartridge and shaft. Remove pressure plate, cam, retaining ring, rotor, vane thrust plate and dowel pins. Remove "O" rings, control valve assembly, oil seal and pump housing. *See Fig. 5.*

Inspection

1) Check that groove in rotor is free from excessive wear and that vane slides smoothly. Check that sliding faces of vanes are free from wear. Check that inner face of cam has a trace of uniform contact.

2) Pump cartridge should be replaced as an entire assembly (if necessary). Check pressure plate and thrust plate sliding surfaces for ridges. Parts may be reused after lapping face.

3) Check sliding face of valve for burrs or damage. Parts with minor scores may be reused after polishing with emery cloth (No. 800 or finer). Needle bearing face must be free from abrasions and wear.

Fig. 5: Exploded View of Power Steering Pump

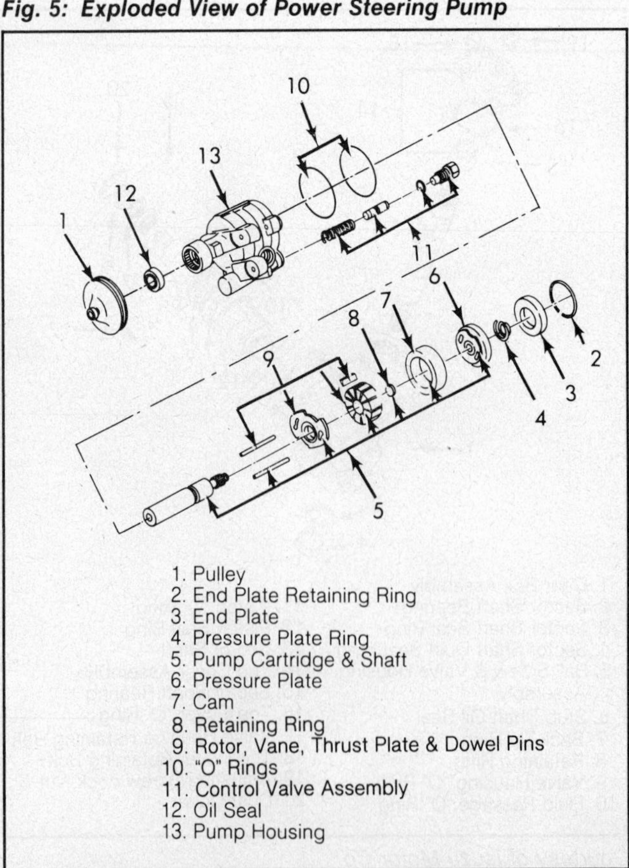

Courtesy of Isuzu Motor Co.

ISUZU POWER-ASSISTED RECIRCULATING BALL (Cont.)

Reassembly

To reassemble, reverse disassembly procedure. Install new seals. Install pulley with a press.

TIGHTENING SPECIFICATIONS

Application	Ft. Lbs. (N.m)
Pitman Arm-to-Intermediate Linkage Attaching Nut	39-47 (53-64)
Pitman Arm-to-Steering Gear Attaching Nut	145-174 (197-236)
Pump Front-to-Rear Body Bolts	36-43 (49-58)
Steering Damper Attaching Nut	39-47 (53-64)
Steering Gear Mounting Bolt	
P'UP	29-40 (39-54)
Trooper II	36-47 (49-64)
Steering Housing Cover Bolt	29-40 (39-54)
Tie Rod End-to-Spindle Nut	39-47 (53-64)
Tie Rod-to-Tie Rod End Lock Nut	80-90 (109-122)
Valve Housing Retaining Bolt	29-40 (39-54)

JAGUAR POWER-ASSISTED RACK & PINION

DESCRIPTION

Jaguar vehicles are equipped with a power-assisted rack and pinion type steering system. The system consists of the rack and pinion steering gear and the power assist pump/reservoir. The steering gear and pump/reservoir are connected by flexible fluid lines.

LUBRICATION

FLUID TYPE

ATF Dexron II.

FLUID LEVEL CHECK

1) Turn wheels to full left lock and add fluid to "COLD" level mark on dipstick. Start engine and let idle. Turn steering wheel lock-to-lock bleed. Check fluid level.

2) Straighten wheels and run engine for several minutes. Turn engine off. Check fluid level. Fluid should be up to "HOT" mark on dipstick.

ADJUSTMENTS

Any adjustments are made during reassembly. Refer to OVERHAUL in this article.

TESTING

HYDRAULIC SYSTEM

Connect a 1500 psi (100 kg/cm²) pressure gauge to pump pressure line. Start engine and let idle. Turn steering to full lock. Exert pressure on steering gear. Pressure should be 1100-1200 psi (77.5-84.4 kg/cm²).

NOTE: If pressure is below 1100 psi (77.5 kg/cm²) at idle, but rises with engine speed increase, problem is either a defective pump control valve or internal leakage in rack and pinion.

CONTROL VALVE & PINION

1) Connect a 100 psi (7 kg/cm²) pressure gauge into pump return line. Start engine and let idle. Pressure reading should be approximately 40 psi (2.8 kg/cm²). Turn steering gear left and right a small amount.

Fig. 1: Pressure Gauge & Shut-Off Valve Connections

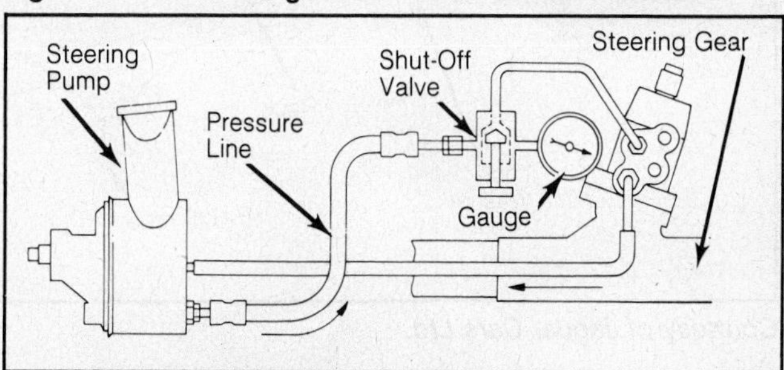

Courtesy of Jaguar Cars Ltd.

CAUTION: Excessive turning of steering gear will cause damage to pressure gauge.

2) Pressure should increase equal amounts as wheel is turned in either direction. A slight fall in pressure, occurring before rise in pressure, indicates a defective control valve. Stop and then restart engine. Check that steering does not kick to one side.

3) If system pressure readings were not to specifications, connect Shut-Off Valve (JD. 10-2) between pump and pressure gauge. This will isolate steering pump from steering gear and determine if problem is in gear or pump. *See Fig. 1.*

CAUTION: Do not keep shut-off valve closed for more than 5 seconds at a time, otherwise fluid will overheat and damage to system could occur.

4) With shut-off valve open, start engine and allow steering fluid to reach normal operating temperature. Close shut-off valve. Repeat pressure tests.

5) If pressure is to specification, fault is in steering gear. If pressure is not to specification, fault is in pump. See OVERHAUL in this article.

REMOVAL & INSTALLATION

STEERING GEAR

NOTE: Record amount and location of all washers and spacers for correct installation.

JAGUAR POWER-ASSISTED RACK & PINION (Cont.)

Fig. 2: Exploded View of Jaguar Power-Assisted Rack & Pinion Steering Gear

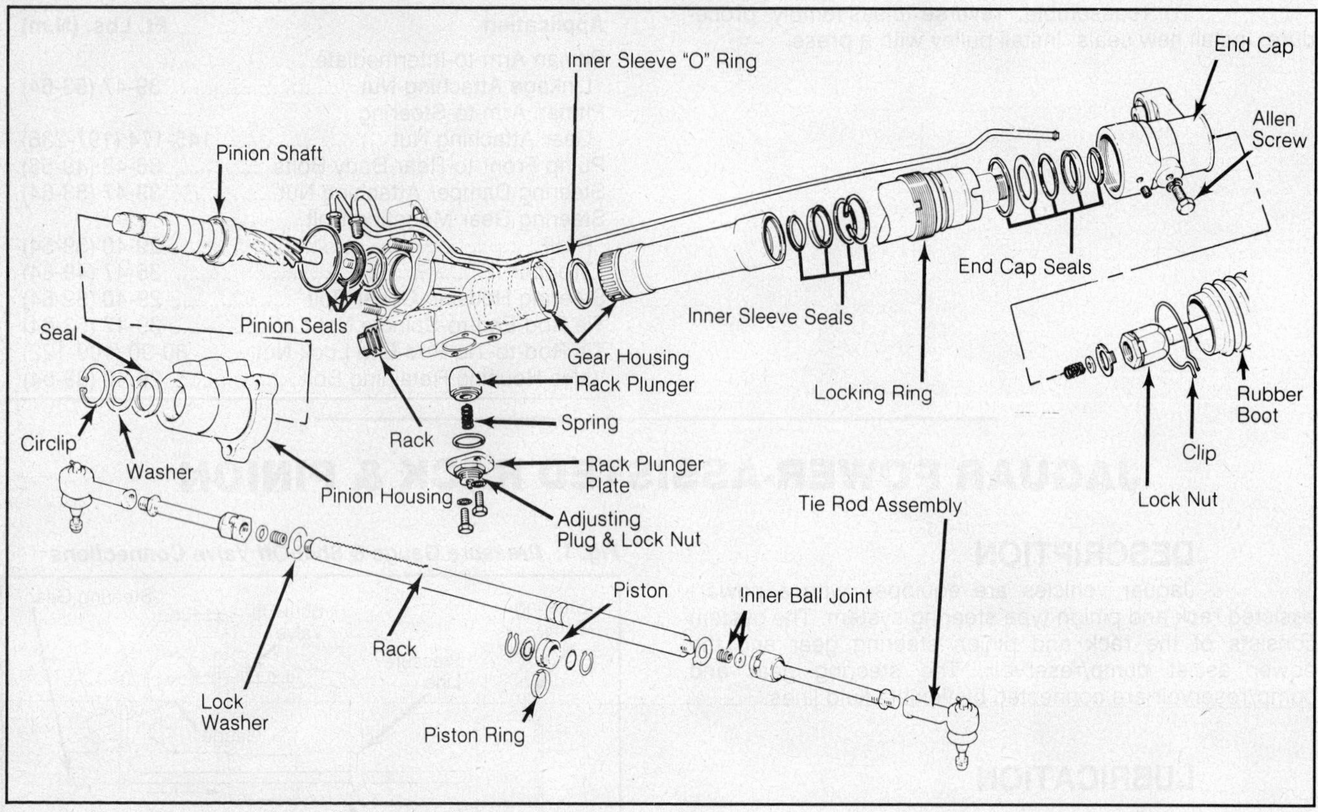

Courtesy of Jaguar Cars Ltd.

Removal

1) Remove lower steering shaft. Drain fluid from pump. Disconnect hydraulic lines. Cap openings. Disconnect ball joints from steering knuckles.

2) Remove heat shield bracket and spacers. Remove remaining bolts from rack mounting and save washers. Remove steering gear from vehicle.

Installation

1) Position rack against mounting brackets and center lugs on bracket. Insert shims between lug and bracket to ensure a gap of .05" (1.3 mm) on both sides of rack lug and mounting bracket.

2) Install bolts but do not tighten. Repeat centering procedure on upper and lower mountings on pinion side of rack. Ensure heat shield mounting bracket is located on upper mounting bolt.

3) Remove clip retaining rubber boots to rack housing. Fold bellows back to expose inner ball joints. Install attachment brackets of Alignment Tee Bar (JD.36A) over large hex head bolts on lower control arms.

4) It may be necessary to bend shields slightly to position bar correctly. *See Fig. 3.* Release locking screw. Slide collar along bar across front of suspension unit, until slot engages front weld flange of crossbeam.

5) Lock slide in this position. Rotate alignment tee bar until legs rest on tie rods. To adjust slack, loosen lock nut of single bolt mounting and raise or lower same side of rack assembly.

6) Remove tee bar. Tighten rack mounting lock nuts. Reposition boots. Secure boot clips. Reinstall tie rods and power steering hoses. Refill and bleed system. Check wheel alignment.

POWER STEERING PUMP

Removal

1) Remove air cleaner. Partially drain radiator. Remove upper radiator hose. Drain fluid from steering pump. Disconnect and cap fluid lines. Loosen nut retaining adjusting rod to timing cover.

2) Remove bolt retaining adjuster rod to pump. Swing adjuster clear of pump. Remove lower pump pivot nut. Move pump toward engine. Remove belt. Remove lower pivot bolt. Remove pump.

Fig. 3: Installing Rack & Pinion Gear

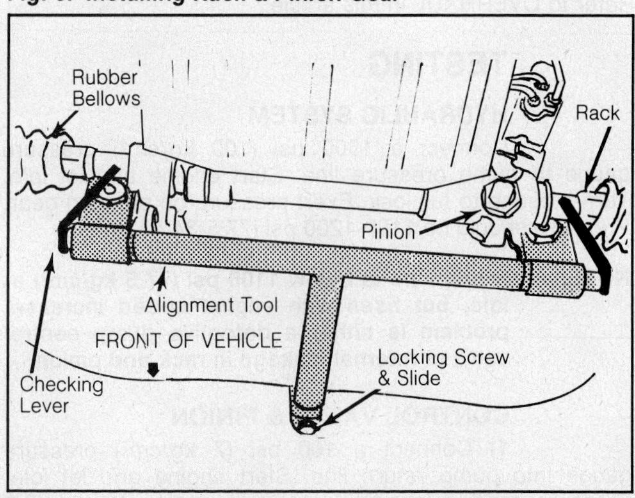

Courtesy of Jaguar Cars Ltd.

JAGUAR POWER-ASSISTED RACK & PINION (Cont.)

Installation

To install power steering pump, reverse removal procedure. After replacement, adjust belt tension and bleed system.

OVERHAUL

STEERING GEAR

Disassembly

1) Clean rack and pinion housing. Drain fluid. Remove clips attaching bellows to tie rods. Fold bellows back to expose tie rod inner ball joint.

2) Straighten lock-tab of tie rod inner ball joint. Remove tie rods from rack by loosening lock nut on inner ball joint. Note position of pinion housing-to-valve cylinder pipes. Remove pipes. Remove air transfer pipe.

3) Remove Allen screw from end cap. Remove locking ring from end housing. Remove end housing. Remove rack plunger lock nut, adjusting nut, spring and plunger. Remove pinion housing cover. Remove pinion housing from rack housing.

4) Remove pinion from pinion housing. Remove snap ring, washer and seal from pinion housing. Remove rack from rack housing. Remove porting adapter. Slide porting ring along cylinder until feed hole is exposed.

5) Using a scribe, pry seal until seal can be removed from cylinder with a hooked wire. Remove all seals, "O" rings and sleeves from rack housing.

NOTE: **Do not remove seals from pinion piston.**

Inspection

1) Clean all parts in solvent. Dry with compressed air. Check all parts for wear, scratches, nicks or scoring. Replace parts as necessary.

2) Check rack teeth and pinion teeth for chips, burrs and other damage. Always use new "O" rings and seals during reassembly. Check boots for cracks, splits or holes. Replace as necessary.

Reassembly

1) Lubricate all "O" rings, seals, sleeves and all moving parts before installation. Install seal and "O" ring to end housing.

2) Install new center feed porting adapter to porting ring. Position ring to allow conical adapter to engage with seat on cylinder. Tighten to specifications.

3) Install rack seal over rack teeth. Install anti-extrusion ring to recess in back of rack seal. Lubricate inside of rack housing and grease rack. Insert rack into rack housing with firm steady pressure until seal seats against abutment face.

4) Ensure piston ring collapses and enters rack housing without damage. Install new seal, washer and snap ring to pinion housing. Install new pinion valve seal to pinion shaft (located against pinion bearing).

5) Lubricate pinion shaft, piston seals, and bearing. Carefully install pinion shaft in pinion housing. Tap gear end of shaft lightly to properly seat.

6) Grease pinion teeth and small pinion journal. Install pinion, housing, and new gasket to rack housing. Ensure rack teeth and pinion teeth mate correctly.

7) Ensure pinion housing ports are correctly aligned so cylinder-to-valve pipes can be installed. Install seals to end housing.

8) Install end housing-to-rack housing. Screw locking ring into end housing just enough to hold mounting feet in parallel alignment.

Fig. 4: Rack End Play Adjustment

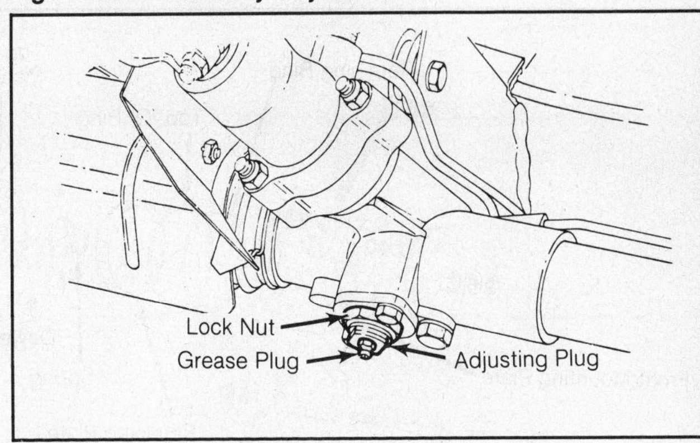

Courtesy of Jaguar Cars Ltd.

9) With end housing and mounting feet in alignment, tighten locking ring. Install rack plunger, spring, adjusting plug and lock nut. Tighten adjusting plug while moving rack through full stroke, until rack is hard to move.

10) Back off adjusting nut just enough to obtain a smooth rack movement (approximately 1/8 turn). Tighten lock nut while holding adjusting plug from turning.

11) To complete reassembly, reverse disassembly procedure. Place 1-2 oz. of grease into each bellows. Replace plug in rack plunger adjusting plug with a grease fitting. Grease rack plunger. Remove grease fitting. Install plug.

POWER STEERING PUMP

Disassembly

1) Remove rear mounting plate and pulley from pump. Remove front mounting plate from pump. Clean pump body. Remove pressure outlet union and mounting plate studs from rear of pump.

2) Tip pump to remove flow control valve and spring. Place pump in padded vise. Tap pump casing from body. Remove "O" rings from pump body and magnet from flange.

3) Using a pin punch, push retaining ring free from groove and lever from body. Remove spring retaining plate and spring. Remove "O" ring from recess in pump body.

4) Remove Woodruff key from shaft. Tap roller spindle toward body. Remove pump assembly from body. Remove "O" ring from recess in pump body. Remove dowel pins.

Cleaning & Inspection

1) Clean all parts with lint-free cloth. Replace all "O" rings and seals. Check all parts for scratches, nicks, burrs or excessive wear.

2) Replace rotor ring and vanes if excessive wear or chatter marks are present. Check flow control valve for free movement in bore. Lubricate all parts with power steering fluid before reassembly.

3) Check interference fit between pump shaft and pulley. Replace parts if interference fit is less than .001" (.025 mm) or more than .0026" (.066 mm).

Reassembly

To reassemble, reverse disassembly procedure. Refill and bleed system. Check for leaks.

JAGUAR POWER-ASSISTED RACK & PINION (Cont.)

Fig. 5: Exploded View of Power Steering Pump

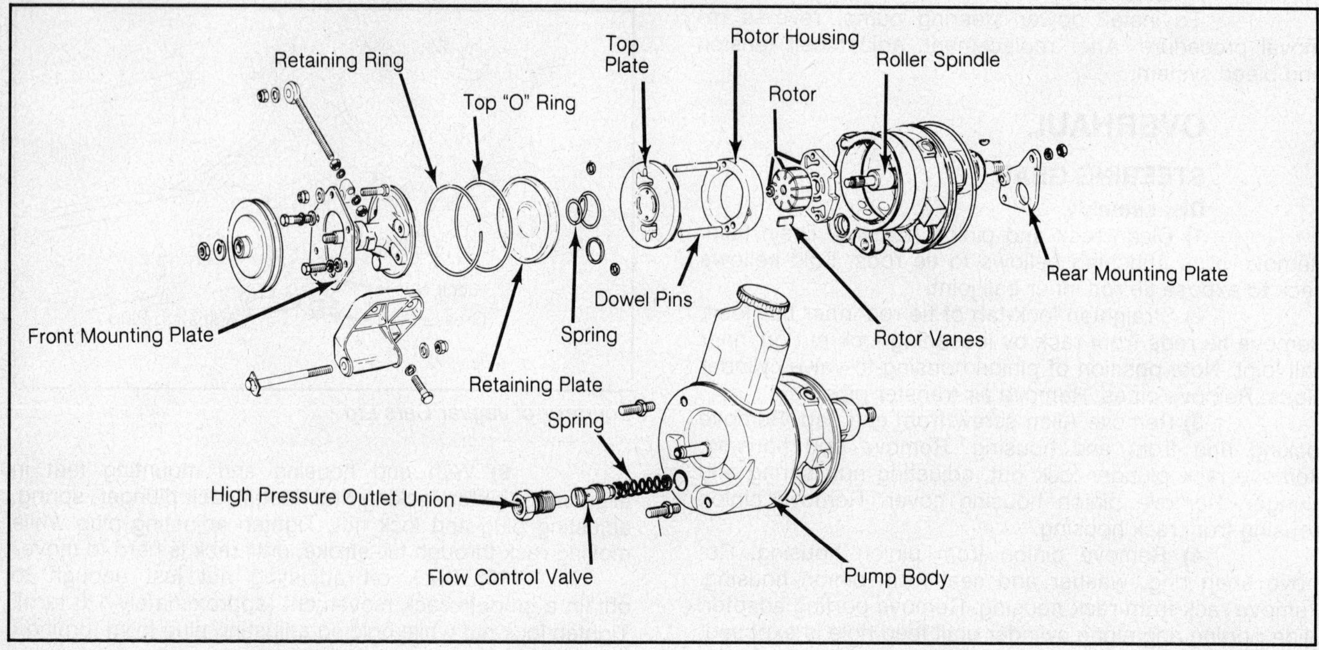

Courtesy of Jaguar Cars Ltd.

Fig. 6: Installing Vanes in Rotor Plate

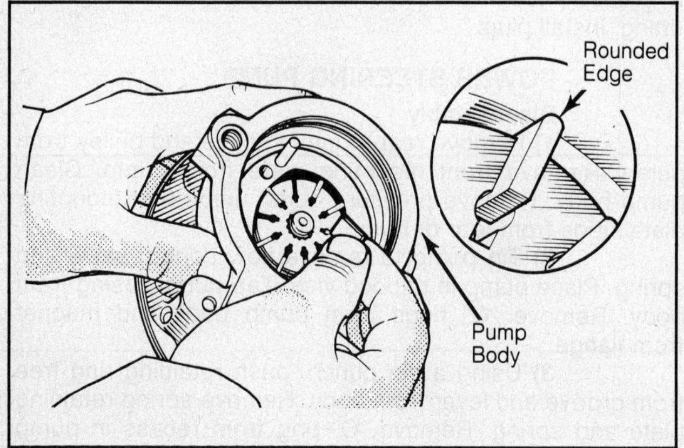

Round end of vanes face out. Courtesy of Jaguar Cars Ltd.

TIGHTENING SPECIFICATIONS

Application	Ft. Lbs. (N.m)
Center Feed Porting Adapter Ring	22-25 (30-34)
Pump High Pressure Fitting	25-40 (34-54)
Rack Housing End Plate Lock Ring	80-90 (109-122)
Rack Housing Mounting Bolts	49-55 (67-75)
Tie Rod Inner Ball Joint Lock Nut	45-55 (61-75)

MAZDA & TRACER POWER-ASSISTED RACK & PINION

Ford Motor Co.: Tracer
Mazda: RX7, 323, 626

DESCRIPTION

Steering system is a power-assisted rack and pinion. The system consists of a rack and pinion steering gear and power assist pump/reservoir. The steering gear and pump/reservoir are connected by flexible hoses.

LUBRICATION

CAPACITY

Capacity for Tracer is .63 qt. (.53L). For all other models, refer to FLUID LEVEL CHECK in this article.

FLUID TYPE

ATF Type F.

FLUID LEVEL CHECK

Fluid levels should be checked before engine is started with fluid still cool. Remove fluid level gauge on oil pump. Check fluid level. Fluid should be between the "L" and "H" marks on the level gauge dip stick. If fluid is needed, fill through the gauge tube. Recheck fluid level. DO NOT overfill.

HYDRAULIC FLUID BLEEDING

1) Raise and support front of vehicle. With ignition off, turn steering wheel completely lock-to-lock several times. Add fluid as required. Repeat this procedure until fluid level no longer decreases.

MAZDA & TRACER POWER-ASSISTED RACK & PINION (Cont.)

2) Start engine and let idle. Turn steering wheel completely lock-to-lock several times. Check fluid level. Add fluid as necessary. Continue this procedure until there is no bubbling or decrease in fluid level.

TESTING

HYDRAULIC SYSTEM PRESSURE TEST

1) Connect a pressure gauge/valve between steering pump and steering gear. *See Fig. 2.* Bleed any air from system. Open valve. Start engine and let idle.

2) Turn steering wheel lock-to-lock to increase fluid temperature. To measure pump fluid pressure, completely close the gauge valve for 15 seconds and increase engine speed to 1000-1500 RPM.

3) Pump pressure should be at least 1138 psi. (78 kg/cm²). If pump pressure is not to specification, pump overhaul is necessary.

CAUTION: Leaving gauge valve closed for more than 15 seconds can damage the pump.

4) To measure steering gear fluid pressure, open the gauge valve completely. Increase engine speed to 1000-1500 RPM. Turn steering wheel from lock-to-lock.

Fig. 2: Pressure Gauge Test Set Up

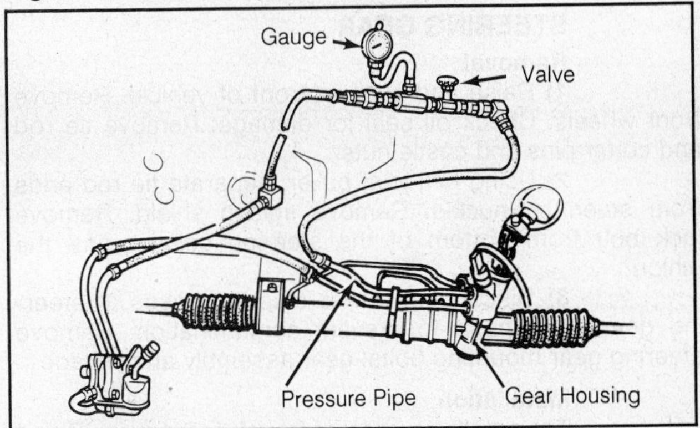

Place gauge set valve on gear housing side.
Courtesy of Mazda Motors Corp.

5) Do not keep steering wheel fully turned for more than 10 seconds. The correct gear housing fluid pressure limit is 924 psi (64 kg/cm²) at a temperature of 122-140°F (50-60°C).

6) If less than specification, steering gear is defective. If the pump is defective, replace as a complete assembly.

Fig. 1: Exploded View of Tracer & 323 Rack & Pinion Steering Gear

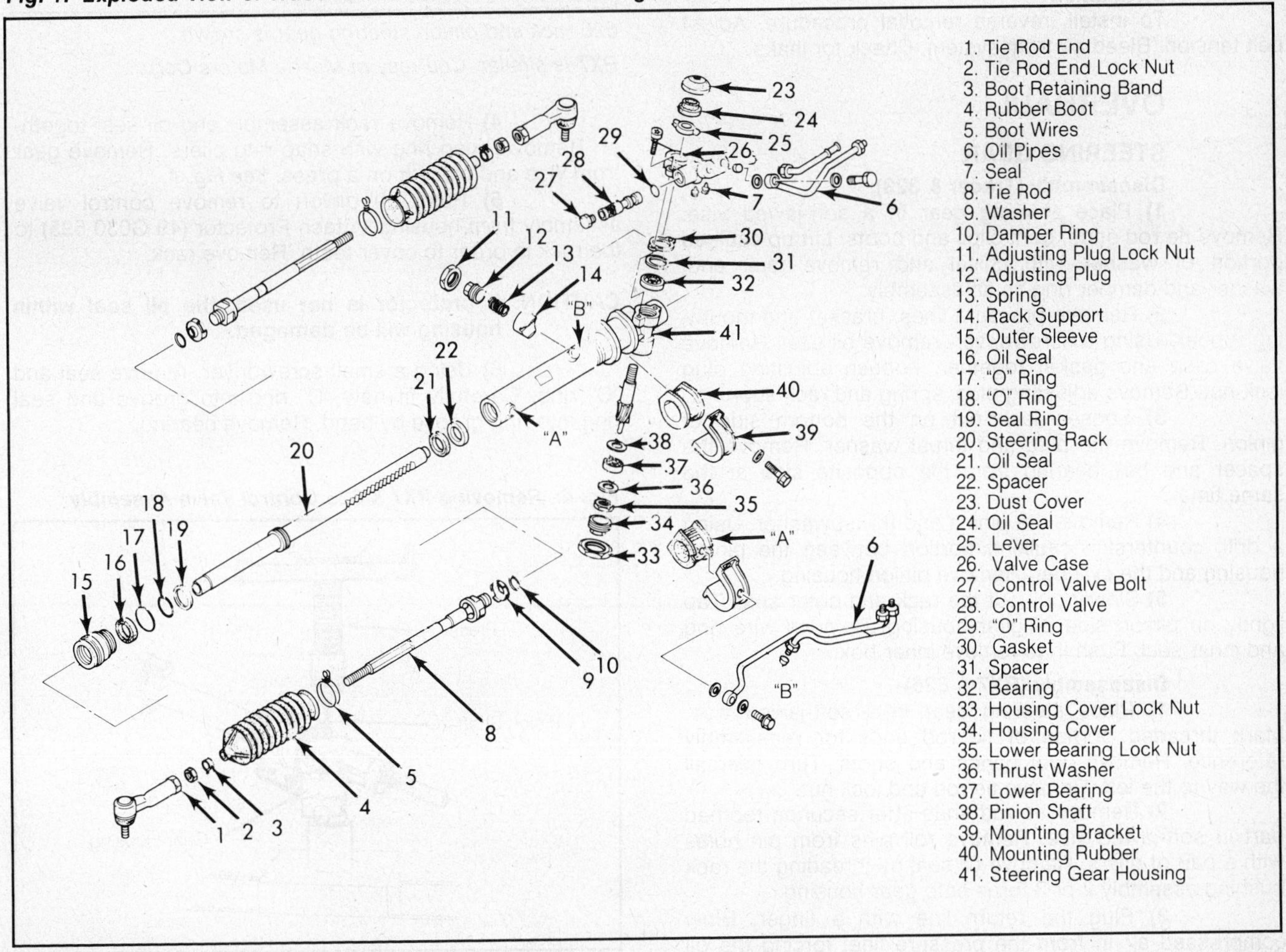

1. Tie Rod End
2. Tie Rod End Lock Nut
3. Boot Retaining Band
4. Rubber Boot
5. Boot Wires
6. Oil Pipes
7. Seal
8. Tie Rod
9. Washer
10. Damper Ring
11. Adjusting Plug Lock Nut
12. Adjusting Plug
13. Spring
14. Rack Support
15. Outer Sleeve
16. Oil Seal
17. "O" Ring
18. "O" Ring
19. Seal Ring
20. Steering Rack
21. Oil Seal
22. Spacer
23. Dust Cover
24. Oil Seal
25. Lever
26. Valve Case
27. Control Valve Bolt
28. Control Valve
29. "O" Ring
30. Gasket
31. Spacer
32. Bearing
33. Housing Cover Lock Nut
34. Housing Cover
35. Lower Bearing Lock Nut
36. Thrust Washer
37. Lower Bearing
38. Pinion Shaft
39. Mounting Bracket
40. Mounting Rubber
41. Steering Gear Housing

Courtesy of Mazda Motors Corp.

MAZDA & TRACER POWER-ASSISTED RACK & PINION (Cont.)

REMOVAL & INSTALLATION

STEERING GEAR

Removal

1) Raise and support front of vehicle. Remove front wheels. Check oil seal for damage. Remove tie rod end cotter pins and castle nuts.

2) Using ball joint puller, separate tie rod ends from steering knuckle. Remove splash shield. Remove lock bolt from bottom of the steering column and the pinion.

3) Disconnect power steering hoses at steering gear. Plug hose to prevent contamination. Remove steering gear mounting bolts, gear assembly and linkage.

Installation

To install, reverse removal procedure. Bleed air from system. Check fluid level. Check for leaks. Adjust alignment (if necessary).

POWER STEERING PUMP

Removal

1) Raise and support front of vehicle. On 626, remove right wheel and splash shield. On all models remove belt, alternator and hydraulic lines from pump.

2) On Tracer and 323, disconnect air cleaner duct and pressure switch. On all models, cap lines to prevent contamination. Remove bracket-to-pump bolts.

Installation

To install, reverse removal procedure. Adjust belt tension. Bleed air from system. Check for leaks.

OVERHAUL

STEERING GEAR

Disassembly (Tracer & 323)

1) Place steering gear in a soft-jawed vise. Remove tie rod ends, boot clips and boots. Lift up caulked portion of washer with chisel and remove rack end, washer and damper ring as an assembly.

2) Remove pressure lines, bracket and mounting rubber. Using a screwdriver, remove oil seal. Remove valve case and gasket together. Loosen adjusting plug lock nut. Remove adjusting plug, spring and rack support.

3) Loosen lock nut on the bottom side of pinion. Remove the plug and thrust washer. Remove the spacer and ball bearing from the opposite side at the same time.

4) Remove the pinion and thrust washer. Using a drill, countersink caulking portion between the pinion housing and the cylinder. Remove pinion housing.

5) Slowly pull out the rack and outer seal. Tap lightly on pinion side of gear housing. Remove wire ring and inner seal. Push in to remove inner box.

Disassembly (RX7 & 626)

1) Place steering gear in a soft-jawed vise. Mark threaded portion of tie rod ends for reassembly reference. Remove boot bands and boots. Turn gear all the way to the left. Remove tie rod end lock nut.

2) Remove tie rod ends after securing toothed part in soft-jawed vise. Remove roll pins from pin holes with a pair of pliers. Remove oil seal by threading the rack bushing assembly 2 or 3 turns onto gear housing.

3) Plug the return line with a finger. Blow compressed air in from the pressure line, forcing the oil seal to the end of rack bushing assembly.

Fig. 3: Exploded View of RX7 & 626 Rack & Pinion Steering Gear

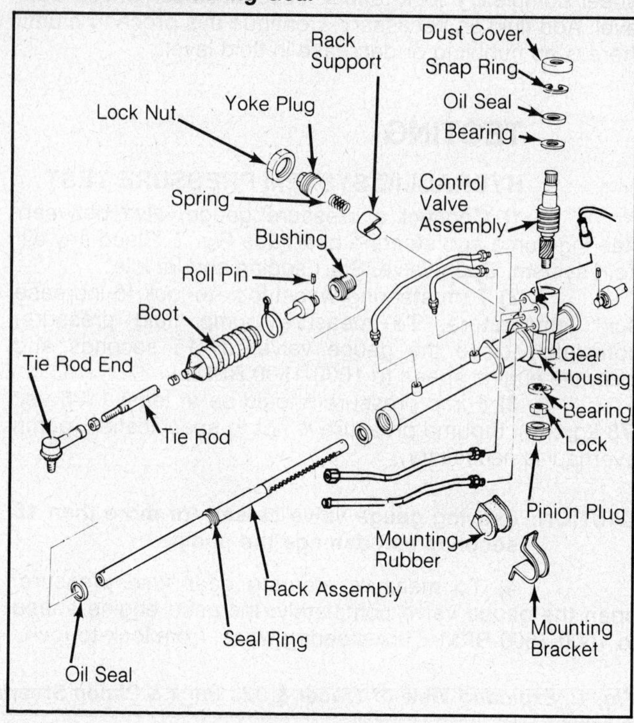

626 rack and pinion steering gear is shown; RX7 is similar. Courtesy of Mazda Motors Corp.

4) Remove rack assembly and oil seal together. Remove snap ring with snap ring pliers. Remove gear from vise and place it on a press. *See Fig. 4.*

5) Push on pinion to remove control valve assembly from housing. Attach Protector (49 G030 595) to the rack in order to cover teeth. Remove rack.

CAUTION: If protector is not used, the oil seal within housing will be damaged.

6) Using a small screwdriver, remove seal and "O" ring. Carefully fit new "O" ring into groove and seal ring into ring groove by hand. Remove bearing.

Fig. 4: Removing RX7 & 626 Control Valve Assembly

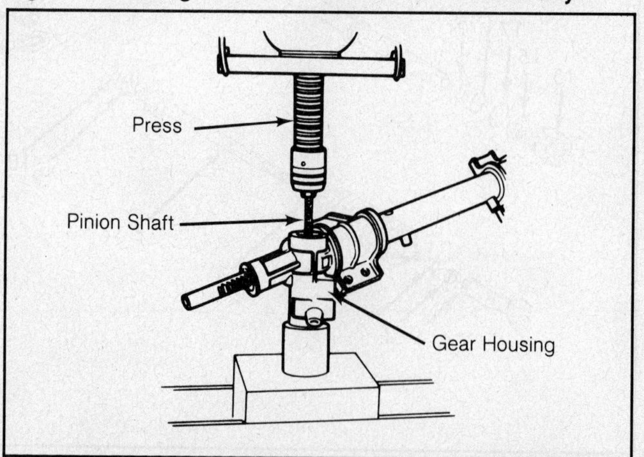

Courtesy of Mazda Motors Corp.

MAZDA & TRACER POWER-ASSISTED RACK & PINION (Cont.)

Inspection

Clean all parts. Inspect for wear or damage. Replace parts if problems are found. If any part of the gear assembly is damaged, replace as a complete gear assembly. If the teeth of the rack are worn or damaged, replace entire rack assembly as a unit.

Reassembly (Tracer & 323)

1) Before reassembly, coat (or fill) the following parts with a lithium base grease: pinion teeth, mating surface between installed pinion and gear housing, sliding parts, rear surface of rack support, rack teeth, tie rod ball joints and inside right and left boots.

2) Place steering gear in a soft-jawed vise. Install outer seal on non-tooth side of rack. Install rack in housing. Install wire ring and inner seal.

3) Install pinion, insert thrust bearing with its slide surface (Gray side) facing bearing. Position the ball bearing and spacer at opposite side.

4) Install thrust washer, lock nut and housing cover. Tighten housing cover to 29-36 ft. lbs. (40-50 N.m). Back housing cover off 10-20 degrees. Install and tighten housing cover lock nut.

5) Install rack support, spring and adjusting plug. Tighten adjusting plug to 29-36 ft. lbs. (40-50 N.m) and back off 40-60 degrees. Install and tighten lock nut.

6) Install gasket and valve case in steering gear. Lightly tap in oil seals. Check operating torque of pinion with a torque wrench.

7) Proper operating torque of pinion is 52-114 INCH lbs. (.5-1.1 N.m). Install return lines with new copper washers. Reverse removal procedure to install steering linkage.

Reassembly (RX7 & 626)

1) Before assembly, coat (or fill) the following parts with a lithium base grease: pinion teeth, mating surface between installed pinion and gear housing, sliding parts, rear surface of rack support, rack teeth, tie rod ball joints and inside right and left boots.

2) Secure gear assembly in a soft-jawed vise. Coat piston seal ring with ATF type F. Attach Protector (49 G030 595) to rack. Install rack to gear housing.

3) Install oil seal, rack and bushing assembly. Check that rack and pinion gear are correctly meshed. Coat the control valve, bearing and seal with ATF.

4) Install control valve, bearing and oil seal assembly by tapping with a piece of pipe. Using snap ring pliers, install snap ring. Finger tighten rack support, spring, yoke plug and lock nut.

5) Secure toothed end of rack in vise. Tighten tie rod to specifications. Tap in new roll pin. Install bearing. Tighten lock nut to 29-36 ft. lbs. (40-50 N.m).

6) Apply sealant to pinion plug and install. Tighten yoke plug to 48 INCH lbs. (5.5 N.m). Loosen and retighten plug. Repeat this several times. After final tightening of yoke plug, back off plug 45 degrees.

7) Using Preload Attachment (49 0180 510B) and a spring gauge, measure pinion rotating torque. Pinion rotating torque should be 9-12 INCH lbs. (1.0-1.4 N.m).

8) If pinion rotating torque is incorrect, repeat step **6)** until it is correct. Complete reassembly by installing return lines, tie rod boots and tie rods.

TIGHTENING SPECIFICATIONS

Application	Ft. Lbs. (N.m)
Mounting Bracket Bolts	23-34 (32-47)
Pinion Housing Lock Nut	
RX7 & 626	33-40 (44-54)
Tracer & 323	29-36 (39-50)
Pinion Bearing Lock Nut	29-36 (39-50)
Steering Rack-to-Tie Rod	
RX7 & 626	87 (118)
Tracer & 323	43-58 (60-80)
Tie Rod End Lock Nut	51-58 (70-80)

MAZDA POWER-ASSISTED RECIRCULATING BALL

B2200, B2600

DESCRIPTION

The power assisted recirculating ball steering system consists of the power steering gear assembly, hydraulic pump, and hydraulic lines.

The power steering gear is an integral-type. It consists of the conventional ball/screw-type steering gear combined with a valve and piston assembly.

The oil pump is a constant delivery vane-type and is belt driven. The pump and gear assemblies are connected by hoses.

LUBRICATION

FLUID TYPE

Fluid type is ATF F (M2C33-F).

FLUID LEVEL CHECK

Fluid levels should be checked before engine is started and when fluid is still cool. To check and fill, remove the fluid level gauge on oil pump assembly and check fluid level. Fluid should be between the "L" and "H" marks on the gauge dipstick. If fluid is needed, fill through the gauge tube and recheck. DO NOT overfill.

HYDRAULIC SYSTEM BLEEDING

1) Raise front of vehicle and support with safety stands. With ignition off, turn steering wheel completely to the left and right several times.

2) Add fluid as required. Repeat this process until fluid level no longer decreases. Start engine and let idle. Turn steering wheel lock-to-lock several times.

3) Check fluid level. Add fluid as necessary. Continue this process until there is no bubbling or decrease in fluid level.

ADJUSTMENTS

Any adjustments are made during the reassembly procedure. See OVERHAUL in this article.

MAZDA POWER-ASSISTED RECIRCULATING BALL (Cont.)

Fig. 1: Pressure Gauge Test Set Up

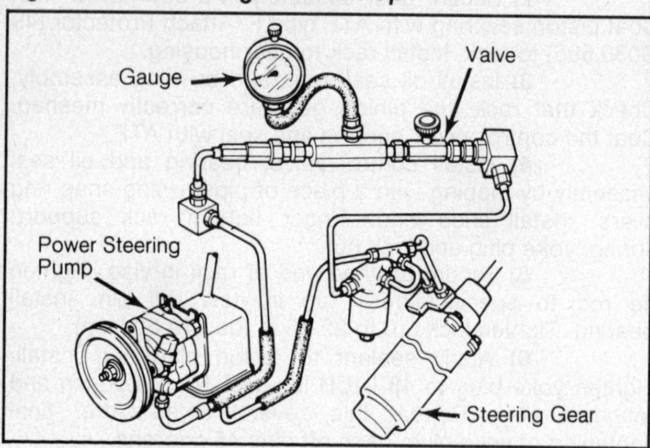

Courtesy of Mazda Motors Corp.

TESTING

HYDRAULIC SYSTEM PRESSURE TEST

1) Connect a pressure gauge between steering pump and steering gear with the valve of gauge toward the steering gear side. *See Fig. 1.*

2) Bleed air from system. Open valve. Start engine and let idle. Turn steering wheel lock-to-lock to increase fluid temperature.

3) To measure fluid pressure generated by the oil pump, completely close the gauge valve for 15 seconds and increase engine speed to 1000-1500 RPM.

NOTE: Leaving gauge valve closed for more than 15 seconds will increase fluid temperature and could damage the oil pump.

4) To measure the fluid pressure generated at the gear housing, first open the gauge valve completely, increase engine speed to 1000-1500 RPM and turn steering wheel from lock-to-lock.

4) Do not keep steering wheel fully turned for more than 10 seconds. Gear housing fluid pressure limit is 924 psi (64 kg/cm²) at 122-140°F (50-60°C). If the oil pump is defective, replaced as an assembly.

REMOVAL & INSTALLATION

POWER STEERING PUMP

Removal

Disconnect belts and power steering hoses. Remove mounting bolts and pump from bracket.

Installation

To install, reverse removal procedure. Fill and bleed system.

STEERING GEAR

Removal

Raise and support front of vehicle. Remove bolts from rubber coupling. Using Puller (49 0118 850C), separate center link from pitman arm. Disconnect hoses from steering gear. Remove steering gear-to-frame bolts and nuts. Remove steering gear.

Installation

To install, reverse removal procedure. Fill and bleed system.

STEERING LINKAGE

Removal

1) Raise and support vehicle. Remove front wheels. Remove cotter pins and castle nuts from tie rod ends, center link and idler arm.

2) Using Puller (49 0118 850C), separate and remove tie rods, center link and idler arm. Remove idler arm from frame. Using Pullers (49 0118 850C and 49 0223 695E) remove pitman arm from steering gear.

Installation

To install, reverse removal procedure. Check toe-in. See WHEEL ALIGNMENT section.

OVERHAUL

POWER STEERING PUMP

1) Secure pump in soft-jawed vise. Remove nuts and bolts holding the suction line and reservoir tank. Remove reservoir. Remove rear body bolts.

2) Remove rear body. Remove cam case, cam ring, vanes, pins, snap ring and rotor. Remove drive shaft and bolt connector from housing.

3) Remove control valve with spring. Discard all "O" rings. Carefully remove shaft seal, if damaged, to avoid damaging pump housing.

Inspection

Clean all parts in solvent. Dry thoroughly with compressed air. Check all parts for wear, burned areas and scores. Check vanes for cracks. Measure clearance between vanes and rotor grooves. Replace vanes and rotor if clearance exceeds .002" (.06 mm).

Fig. 2: Exploded View of Steering Gear

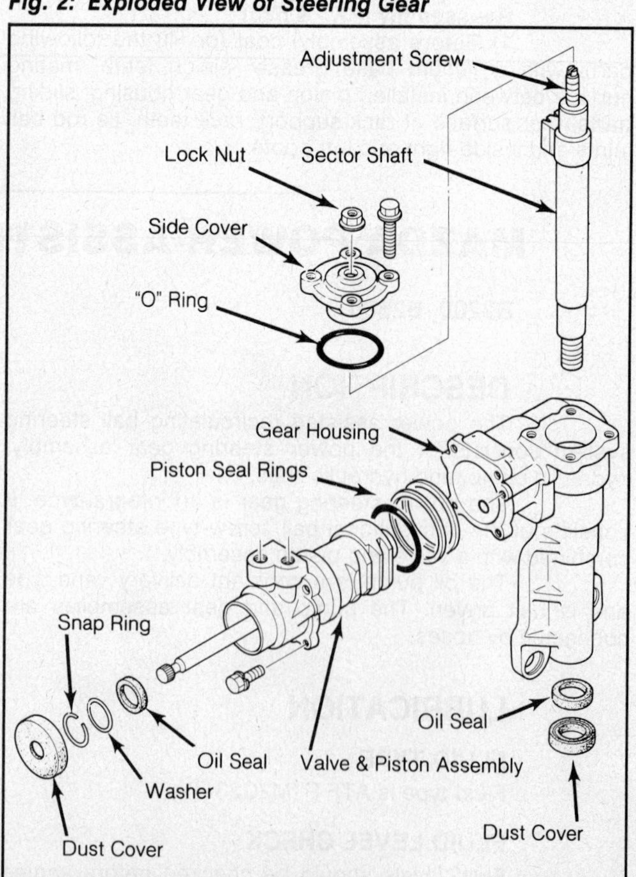

Courtesy of Mazda Motors Corp.

MAZDA POWER-ASSISTED RECIRCULATING BALL (Cont.)

Fig. 3: Exploded View of B2200 Power Steering Pump

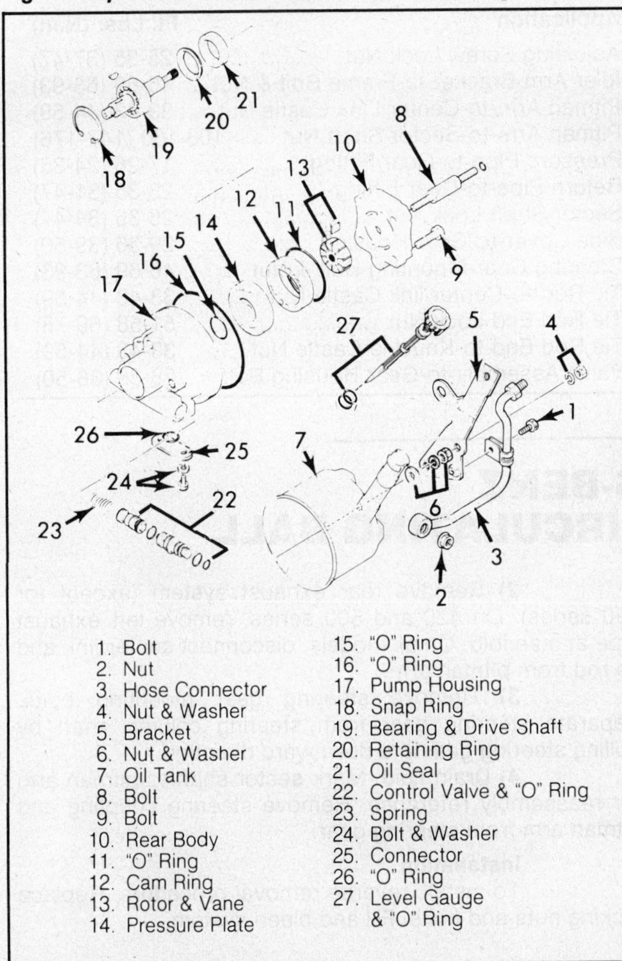

Courtesy of Mazda Motors Corp.

Fig. 4: Exploded View of B2600 Power Steering Pump

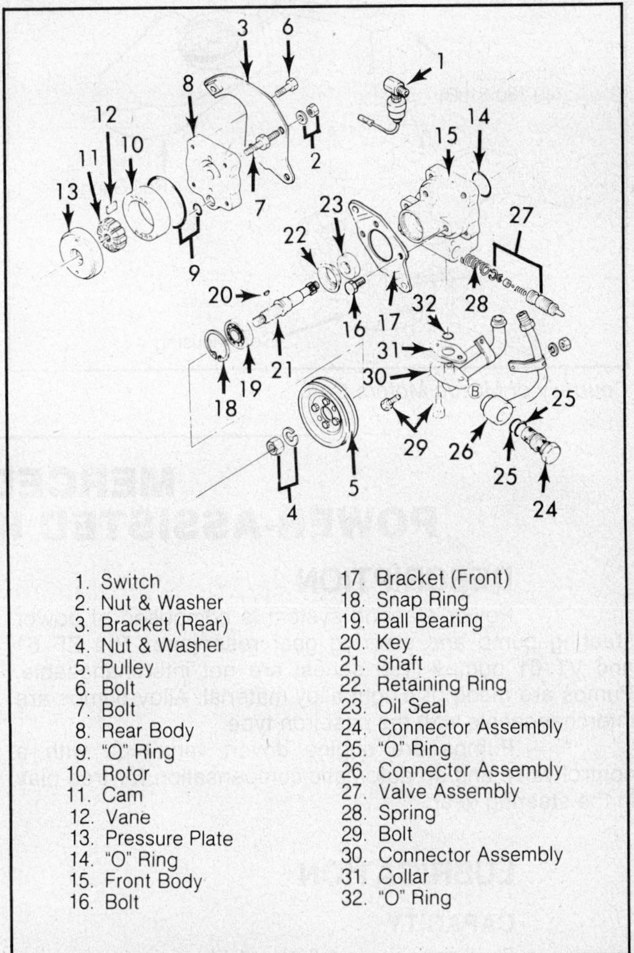

Courtesy of Mazda Motors.

Reassembly

1) Apply ATF type F fluid to vanes, rotor and control valve. Coat lip of oil seal with lithium grease. Install all new "O" rings.

2) To reassemble, reverse disassembly procedure. If replacing housing assembly and control valve, use parts bearing the same mark. Replace cam ring, rotor and vanes as a set.

STEERING GEAR

Disassembly

1) Drain oil from steering gear. Using Puller (49 0223 695E), remove pitman arm. Loosen lock nut on sector shaft. Turn worm shaft to align sector shaft with identification mark on side cover.

2) Remove side cover bolts. Using plastic hammer, tap on lower end of sector shaft to remove sector shaft with cover as an assembly.

3) Remove dust cover and oil seal from lower housing. Remove bolts and valve piston assembly from steering gear. Remove dust cover, snap ring, and needle bearing from valve and piston assembly.

4) Remove piston and valve from worm gear. DO NOT remove needle bearing from valve housing unless defective.

Inspection & Reassembly

1) Coat all parts with ATF type F fluid. Check sector shaft assembly for wear and piston ball nut assembly for scoring and replace as assemblies.

2) After reassembly, measure steering gear preload using spring gauge and Attachment (49 180 510B). *See Fig. 5.* Adjust steering gear preload to 18-35 INCH lbs. (2.0-3.9 N.m) with sector shaft adjusting screw.

3) Holding adjusting screw in position, tighten lock nut. Fill and bleed system. See HYDRAULIC SYSTEM BLEEDING in this article.

MAZDA POWER-ASSISTED RECIRCULATING BALL (Cont.)

Fig. 5: Measuring Steering Gear Preload

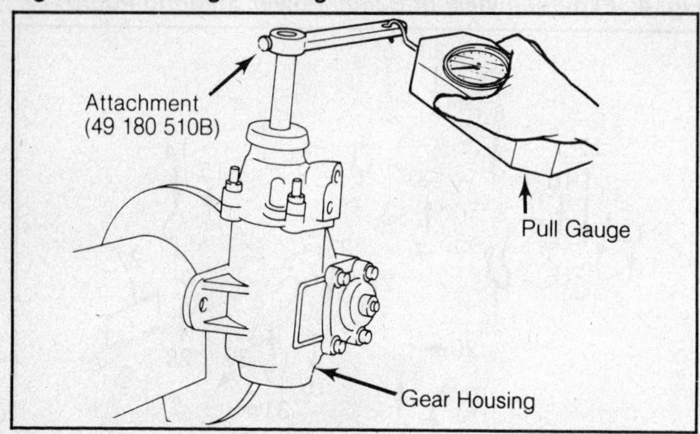

Courtesy of Mazda Motors Corp.

TIGHTENING SPECIFICATIONS

Application	Ft. Lbs. (N.m)
Adjusting Screw Lock Nut	25-35 (37-47)
Idler Arm Bracket-to-Frame Bolt & Nut	46-69 (63-93)
Pitman Arm-to-Center Link Castle Nut	33-43 (44-59)
Pitman Arm-to-Sector Shaft Nut	108-130 (147-176)
Pressure Pipe-to-Gear Fitting	17-26 (24-35)
Return Pipe-to-Gear Fitting	23-35 (31-47)
Sector Shaft Lock Nut	25-35 (34-47)
Side Cover-to-Gear Housing	29-36 (39-50)
Steering Gear Mounting Bolt & Nut	46-69 (63-93)
Tie Rod-to-Center link Castle Nut	33-43 (44-59)
Tie Rod End Lock Nut	51-58 (69-78)
Tie Rod End-to-Knuckle Castle Nut	33-43 (44-59)
Valve Assembly-to-Gear Housing Bolt	28-36 (38-50)

MERCEDES-BENZ POWER-ASSISTED RECIRCULATING BALL

DESCRIPTION

Power steering system is composed of power steering pump and steering gear reservoirs. The ZF 61 and VT 61 pumps (190 series) are not interchangeable. Pumps are made of a light alloy material. Alloy pumps are interchangeable with the cast iron type.

Pumps are engine driven vane-type with a control valve and an automatic compensation for free-play in the steering gear.

LUBRICATION

CAPACITY

Fluid capacity is 1.6 qts. (1.5L).

FLUID TYPE

Fluid type is ATF.

REMOVAL & INSTALLATION

POWER STEERING PUMP

Removal

Remove power steering tank cover, spring and damping plate. Drain tank with a syringe. Disconnect hoses. Cap openings. Loosen retaining bolts. Push pump toward engine. Remove belts. Remove retaining bolts. Remove pump with bracket.

Installation

To install, reverse removal procedure. Tighten bolts to specification. Fill and bleed system.

POWER STEERING GEAR

NOTE: The stop for the full lock position is incorporated into the housing itself. This gear can be recognized by an "A" stamped on housing.

Removal

1) Drain fluid from power steering pump. Disconnect fluid lines. Plug lines to prevent contamination. Remove steering coupling retaining bolts.

2) Remove rear exhaust system (except for 190 series). On 420 and 500 series, remove left exhaust pipe at manifold. On all models, disconnect center link and tie rod from pitman arm.

3) Remove steering gear mounting bolts. Separate steering gear from steering column shaft by pulling steering gear in a downward direction.

4) Drain fluid. Mark sector shaft-to-pitman arm for reassembly reference. Remove steering coupling and pitman arm from steering gear.

Installation

To install, reverse removal procedure. Replace locking nuts and bolts. Fill and bleed system.

OVERHAUL

POWER STEERING PUMP

Disassembly (VT 49 & VT 61 Pump)

1) Remove wing nut and cover from reservoir. Remove compression spring, 2 damping plates and filter ring. Remove Woodruff key from input shaft.

2) Install Puller (1104-7251) on input shaft. Screw bolt back on puller enough to install Clamping Shoes (11004-6304) between puller and seal. Turn clamping cone of puller to the right, up to the stop.

3) Remove seal ring from housing. Push in rear housing cover. Insert punch through hole in housing. *See Fig. 1.* Push in punch to remove circlip and cover.

4) Remove spring and "O" ring from housing. Push input shaft with pressure plate, as a unit, from cover end of housing. Remove rotor, cam ring and pressure plate assembly from rear of housing.

5) Remove pressure plate, cam ring and blades. Remove locking clip from shaft. Remove rotor and pressure plate. Remove cylinder pins from housing.

6) Using a punch, knock out locking pins in housing. *See Fig. 1.* Remove closing plug, volume control valve and compression spring from housing. Clamp volume control valve in vise. Disassemble valve.

Power Steering
MERCEDES-BENZ
POWER-ASSISTED RECIRCULATING BALL (Cont.)

Fig. 1: Removing Circlip & Locking Pin From VT49 Pump

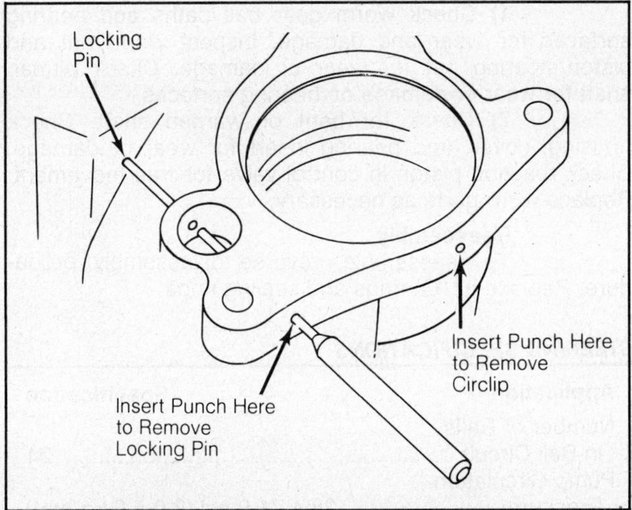

Courtesy of Mercedes-Benz of North America.

Inspection

Check spacer washer, valve cone and compression spring. Check pressure plates, input shaft, and bearing bushing for wear. Check blades for easy sliding in rotor. Check surfaces of volume control valve and bore in pump housing for wear or damage.

NOTE: **Never replace volume control valve only. Replace complete power steering pump.**

Reassembly

To reassemble power steering pump, reverse disassembly procedure.

Disassembly (ZF 61 Pump)

1) Remove Woodruff key from input shaft. Install Puller (1104-7251) on shaft. Install bolt on puller enough to install Clamping Shoes (1104-6304) between puller and seal.

2) Turn clamping core of puller right, up to the stop. Remove tool, seal and washer from housing. Remove knurled nut and cover from housing. Remove retaining and compression springs.

3) Remove upper damping plate, filter ring, and lower damping plate. Push in rear housing cover plate. Remove circlip and cover. Remove "O" ring, compression spring, and pressure plate.

4) Remove rotor with blades, "O" ring and cam ring from input shaft. Remove lock ring from forward end of shaft. Press out input shaft from rear of housing.

5) Remove circlip from shaft. Remove bearing by pressing toward rear of shaft. Remove needle bearing from housing. Remove closing plug from housing.

6) Remove compression spring and volume control valve. Clamp volume control valve in vise. Disassemble spacer washers, ball, and compression spring.

Inspection

1) Check spacer washers, ball, and compression spring. Check pressure plates, input shaft, bearing housing and bushing for wear.

2) Check blades for easy sliding in rotor. Check surfaces of volume control valve and bore in pump housing for wear or damage.

NOTE: **Never replace volume control valve only. Replace complete power steering pump.**

Reassembly

To reassemble power steering pump, reverse disassembly procedure.

POWER STEERING GEAR

Disassembly

1) Attach steering gear to Assembly Plate (116 589 01 59 00). Remove lock nut from adjusting screw. Remove copper seal ring. Remove bolts attaching pitman shaft cover to steering case.

2) With steering in center position, turn adjusting screw clockwise to force pitman shaft, with cover, from housing. Remove pitman shaft with cover.

3) Remove "O" rings from cover. Remove lock ring and seal ring. Remove lock ring from pitman shaft. Remove adjusting screw with thrust washers. *See Fig. 2.*

4) Remove bolts retaining bearing cap to steering gear housing. Turn worm gear counterclockwise until bearing cap is forced out of housing.

NOTE: **Balls will fall from ball guide if worm gear is turned too far.**

5) Remove bearing cap and worm gear with piston/steering nut from housing. Remove worm gear and bearing cap from piston/steering nut. Do not lose balls.

6) Remove "O" ring from bearing cap. Attach bearing cap to an assembly fixture. Using a hook wrench, unscrew slotted nut from bearing insert.

Fig. 2: Sectional View of Adjusting Screw

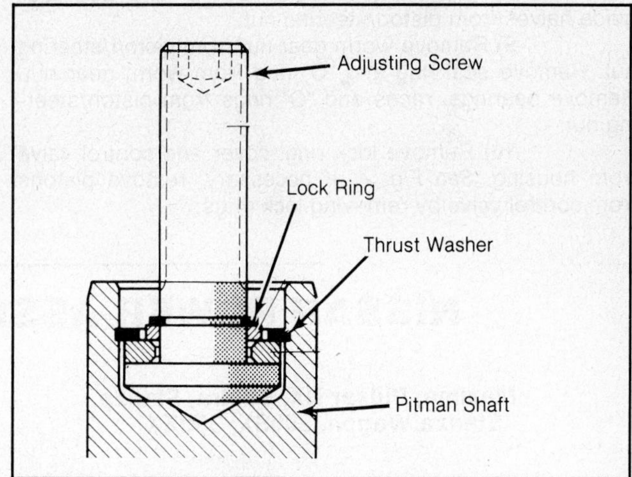

Courtesy of Mercedes-Benz of North America.

Fig. 3: Removing Bearing Insert from Bearing Cap

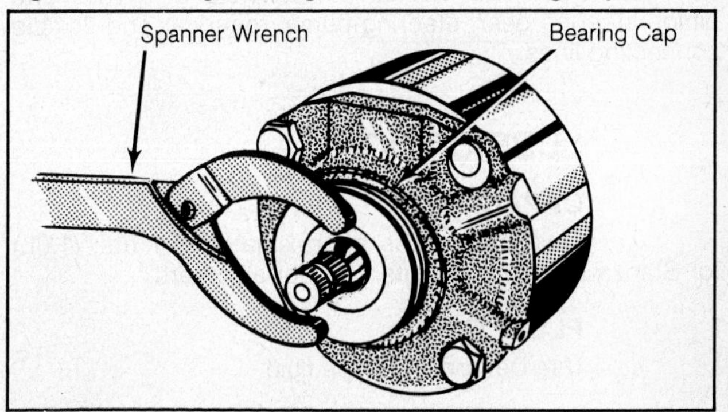

Courtesy of Mercedes-Benz of North America.

Power Steering
MERCEDES-BENZ
POWER-ASSISTED RECIRCULATING BALL (Cont.)

Fig. 4: Cross Sectional View of Steering Gear

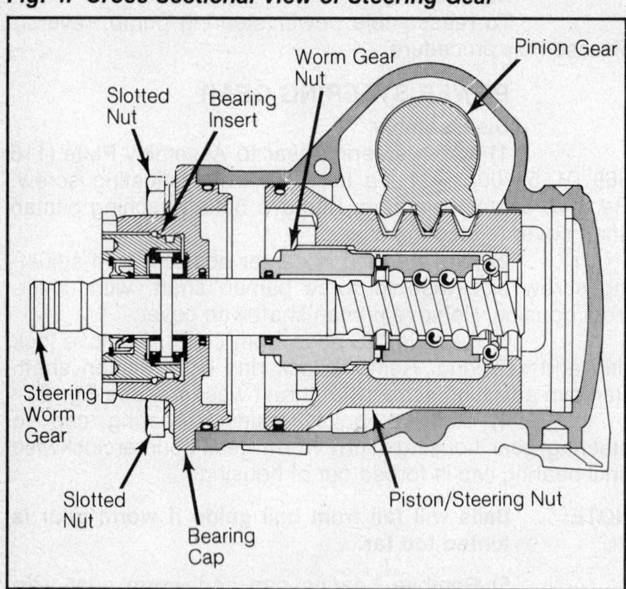

Courtesy of Mercedes-Benz of North America.

7) Using a spanner wrench, remove bearing insert from bearing cap. *See Fig. 3.* Remove steering worm and washer from bearing cap.

8) Remove roller cage from steering worm, along with seal and "O" rings. Remove bearing and disc from bearing cap. Remove bolts, clamp, and both ball guide halves from piston/steering nut.

9) Remove worm gear nut from piston/steering nut. Remove seal ring and "O" ring from worm gear nut. Remove bearings, races and "O" rings from piston/steering nut.

10) Remove lock ring, cover and control valve from housing. *See Fig. 4.* If necessary, remove pistons from control valve by removing lock rings.

Inspection

1) Check worm gear ball paths and bearing surfaces for wear and damage. Inspect worm nut and piston/steering nut for wear or damage. Check pitman shaft for wear or damage on bearing surfaces.

2) Check for bent or warped shaft. Check housing, cover, and bearing insert for wear or damage. Check reaction piston in control valve for free movement. Replace worn parts as necessary.

Reassembly

To reassemble, reverse disassembly procedure. Replace all "O" rings and sealing rings.

STEERING SPECIFICATIONS

Application	Specification
Number of Balls in Ball Circuit	24
Pump Circulation Pressure	28.4-71.0 psi (2.0-5.0 kg/cm²)
Pump Shaft End Play	
New	.028" (.71 mm) Maximum
Used	.039" (.99 mm) Maximum
Steering Wheel Free Play	1" (25 mm) Maximum

TIGHTENING SPECIFICATIONS

Application	Ft. Lbs. (N.m)
Adjusting Screw Nut	22-25 (30-34)
Pitman Arm-to-Pitman Shaft	116-145 (158-197)
Pump Housing Bolts	25-29 (34-39)
Slotted Nut-to-Bearing Cap	101-115 (137-156)
Steering Gear-to-Frame	50-57 (68-78)

NISSAN POWER-ASSISTED RACK & PINION

Maxima, Pulsar NX, Sentra, Stanza, Stanza Wagon, 200SX, 300ZX

DESCRIPTION

The power steering system is rack and pinion cam-gear type. The mechanism consists of a rack and pinion steering gear, steering pump, reservoir and flexible connecting lines.

LUBRICATION

CAPACITY

Fluid capacity is approximately 1.1 qts. (1.0L) for Stanza Wagon and 1 qts. (.9L) for all others.

FLUID TYPE

Use Dexron ATF type fluid.

FLUID LEVEL CHECK

Check fluid level when engine is cold and shut off. Remove fluid level dipstick on ATF pump reservoir. Fluid should be between "MIN" and "MAX" marks on dipstick. Add fluid through dipstick opening if needed and recheck. DO NOT overfill.

HYDRAULIC SYSTEM BLEEDING

1) Raise and support vehicle. While adding fluid, turn steering wheel quickly from lock-to-lock until fluid level no longer decreases and no bubbles exist.

2) Start engine and allow to idle and repeat step **1)**. Perform procedure until fluid level no longer decreases and no bubbles exist.

NOTE: **DO NOT hold steering wheel at or near lock position for more than 15 seconds.**

NISSAN POWER-ASSISTED RACK & PINION (Cont).

ADJUSTMENTS

BELT TENSION

With engine cold, apply 22 lbs. (10 kg) pressure on the belt at center distance between pulleys. Note amount of belt deflection. Adjust belt tension if belt deflection is not within specification. See BELT DEFLECTION SPECIFICATIONS table.

NOTE: **Belt deflection should be checked with engine cold. If engine is hot wait 30 minutes and check belt tension.**

BELT DEFLECTION SPECIFICATIONS

Model	Used Belt In. (mm)	New Belt In. (mm)
200ZX	.41-.47 (10.4-11.9)	.37-.41 (9.3-10.4)
300ZX	.55-.63 (13.9-16.0)	.47-.55 (11.9-13.9)
Maxima	.39-.47 (9.9-11.9)	.31-.39 (7.9-9.9)
Stanza	.28-.35 (7.1-8.9)	.24-.31 (6.1-7.9)
Stanza Wagon	.39-.47 (9.9-11.9)	.31-.39 (7.8-9.9)
Other Models	.28-.35 (7.1-8.9)	.26-.34 (6.6-8.6)

PINION ROTATING FORCE & RACK SLIDING FORCE

1) Install steering assembly in soft-jawed vise. DO NOT tighten vise enough to damage cylinder. Disconnect hoses from steering gear assembly. Allow fluid to drain.

2) Install Torque Adapter (J-26364) and an INCH lb. torque wrench on pinion. Measure turning force required to rotate pinion. Rotating torque should be 16 INCH lbs. (1.8 N.m) or less.

3) Attach a spring scale to tie rod end of the rack. Measure amount of force required to slide the rack from center position in both directions. Rack sliding force must be less than specification. See RACK SLIDING FORCE SPECIFICATIONS table.

RACK SLIDING FORCE SPECIFICATIONS

Application	Lbs. (kg)
Stanza Wagon (2WD)	40 (18)
All Others	55 (25)

4) If either pinion rotating force or rack sliding force is not within specification, adjust the retainer adjusting screw. Remove lock nut from adjusting screw.

5) Adjust retainer adjusting screw to obtain correct pinion rotating force and rack sliding force. Clean threads of adjusting screw and lock nut.

6) Apply thread sealant to adjusting screw and lock nut. Install lock nut. Tighten lock nut to specification. DO NOT allow adjusting screw to move.

CAUTION: **Thread sealant must be applied to adjusting screw and lock nut.**

7) On 300ZX Turbo models, rack sliding force should be checked with engine running and tie rods disconnected after installing steering gear assembly. Rack sliding force be at least 55 lbs. (25 kg).

TESTING

NOTE: **Ensure power steering belt tension and tire pressure is correct prior to performing hydraulic system pressure test.**

HYDRAULIC SYSTEM PRESSURE TEST

1) Disconnect pressure line at power steering pump. Install Pressure Gauge (J-26357) between power steering pump and steering gear. *See Fig. 1.* Open valve and bleed air from system. See HYDRAULIC SYSTEM BLEEDING under LUBRICATION in this article.

Fig. 1: Checking Hydraulic Pressure

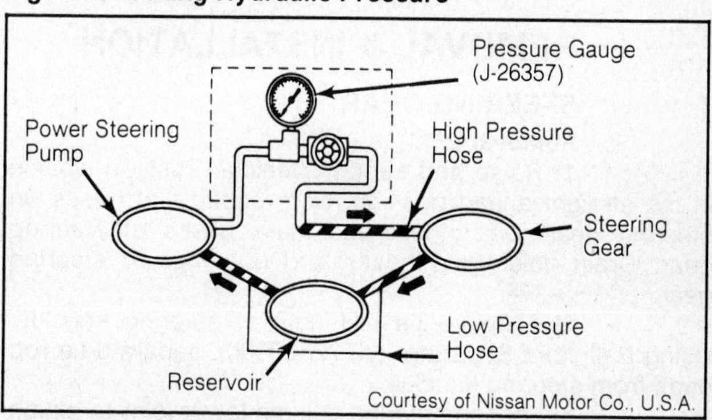

2) Check fluid level. Start and run engine, allowing fluid temperature in reservoir to reach at least 140-176°F (60-80°C).

3) Check pressure quickly with wheel turned to full lock position at both left and right positions.

NOTE: **DO NOT hold steering wheel at or near lock position for more than 15 seconds.**

4) Compare pressure to those listed. See HYDRAULIC SYSTEM PRESSURE SPECIFICATIONS table. If pressure is lower than specification, slowly close shut-off valve and note pressure. DO NOT close shuf-off valve for more than 15 seconds.

5) If pressure now reads within specification, power steering pump is okay but steering gear is defective.

6) If pressure reading is below or exceeds specification power steering pump is defective. Remove pressure gauge and bleed system.

HYDRAULIC SYSTEM PRESSURE SPECIFICATIONS

Application	psi (kg/cm²)
300ZX	967-1052 (68-74)
Pulsar NX	
DOHC Engine	924 (65)
Except DOHC	995 (70)
All Other Models	995 (70)

NOTE: **Tire pressure must be correct prior to checking steering wheel turning force.**

STEERING WHEEL TURNING FORCE

1) Park vehicle on dry, level surface. Ensure tire pressure is correct. Apply parking brake. Operate system until fluid temperature is approximately 140-176°F (60-80°C).

Power Steering

NISSAN POWER-ASSISTED RACK & PINION (Cont).

2) Attach spring scale to steering wheel. Measure steering wheel turning force after steering wheel has been turned 360 degrees from the center position.

3) Turning force should be less than 9 lbs. (4 kg). If turning force is not within specification, check pinion rotating force. See PINION ROTATING FORCE & RACK SLIDING FORCE under ADJUSTMENTS in this article.

NOTE: It may be possible to check pinion rotating force with steering gear installed in vehicle with tie rods and hoses disconnected, if adequate room exists.

REMOVAL & INSTALLATION

STEERING GEAR

Removal

1) Raise and support vehicle. Position wheels in the straight ahead position. Note position of hoses on steering gear. Disconnect and mark hoses at steering gear. Drain fluid. Plug hoses and openings in steering gear.

2) Remove tie rod nuts at steering knuckle. Using Ball Joint Separator (HT72520000), separate tie rod ends from steering knuckle.

3) Loosen steering column lower joint-to-pinion shaft retaining bolt. With wheels in straight ahead position, place punch mark on lower joint and pinion shaft for reassembly reference.

4) Remove lower joint from pinion shaft. Remove steering gear housing-to-suspension cross-member retaining bolts. Remove steering gear and linkage.

5) On some models it may be necessary to remove exhaust pipe, shift linkage for M/T models or shift cable on A/T models.

NOTE: Front wheel alignment must be checked after installation if tie rods were removed or steering gear assembly was overhauled.

Installation

1) Reverse removal procedures. Install new "O" rings on hoses (if used). Coat "O" rings with ATF prior to installation. Ensure proper sized "O" ring is installed. Align reference mark on lower joint and pinion.

2) Tighten bolts to specification. See TIGHTENING SPECIFICATIONS table at end of article. Fill system and bleed. See HYDRAULIC SYSTEM BLEEDING under LUBRICATION in this article.

STEERING PUMP

Removal

1) Loosen power steering pump pulley nut if pulley requires removal. Loosen adjusting bolts and remove pump drive belt.

2) Note angle of pressure hose installation on power steering pump. Disconnect pressure hose from power steering pump. Drain fluid.

3) Remove suction line from pump. Some models use a reservoir tank and suction hose is not used. Remove pump retaining bolts and pump.

Installation

1) Reverse removal procedures and tighten bolts. Install pressure hose using new sealing washers.

2) If suction pipe or reservoir tank was removed, install suction pipe or reservoir tank using new "O" ring. Lubricate "O" ring with ATF prior to installation.

3) Adjust belt tension. See BELT TENSION under ADJUSTMENTS in this article. Fill system and bleed. See HYDRAULIC SYSTEM BLEEDING under LUBRICATION in this article.

OVERHAUL

POWER STEERING GEAR

NOTE: Prior to disassembly, measure pinion rotating force and rack sliding force for reassembly reference. See PINION ROTATING FORCE & RACK SLIDING FORCE under ADJUSTMENTS in this article.

Disassembly (300ZX)

1) Remove breather and cylinder tube. *See Fig. 2.* Loosen lock nut and remove tie rods. Remove boot band and boot clamp. Bend over lock plate at tie rod inner socket.

2) Remove tie rod inner socket from rack. Remove retainer lock nut, adjusting screw, spring, holder and retainer. Remove rear cover cap. Using Housing Lock Nut Wrench (J-28818), remove housing lock nut. Using Rear Cover Wrench (J-28819), remove rear housing cover.

3) Remove "O" ring and oil seal from rear housing cover. Remove rear housing, bearing assembly and pinion from pinion housing. Scribe alignment marks on cylinder and pinion housing. Using End Cover Wrench (J-28822), remove end cover assembly from cylinder.

4) Using Cylinder Lock Nut Wrench (J-28820), remove cylinder lock nut. Remove cylinder from pinion housing. Remove rack assembly. Slide inner tube from rack. DO NOT loose inner tube collar.

5) Remove rack packing and back-up collar from inner tube. Using flat screwdriver, remove oil seal from pinion housing.

CAUTION: Use care not to scratch inner tube during rack packing and back-up collar removal.

Inspection

1) Clean all components in solvent. Blow dry with compressed air. Replace all oil seals, packings and "O" rings. Inspect boots for damage. Replace if damaged. Inspect all sealing surfaces for roughness.

2) Inspect tie rod and tie rod inner socket for end play. Replace tie rod or tie rod inner socket if end play exists. Inspect remaining components for wear or damage. Replace damaged components.

Reassembly

1) Apply ATF to rack. Place plastic film supplied with rebuild kit on the inside of rack packing. This is done to prevent damage to packing from rack teeth during installation.

2) Install rack packing on rack. Remove plastic film once packing is past rack teeth. Install back-up collar on inner tube. Coat teeth area of rack with grease.

3) Install rack assembly in inner tube. Lubricate rack packing with ATF. Using Rack Packing Installer (J-34264) and suitable fixture, install rack packing in inner tube. *See Fig. 3.*

NISSAN POWER-ASSISTED RACK & PINION (Cont).

Fig. 2: Exploded View of 300ZX Steering Gear

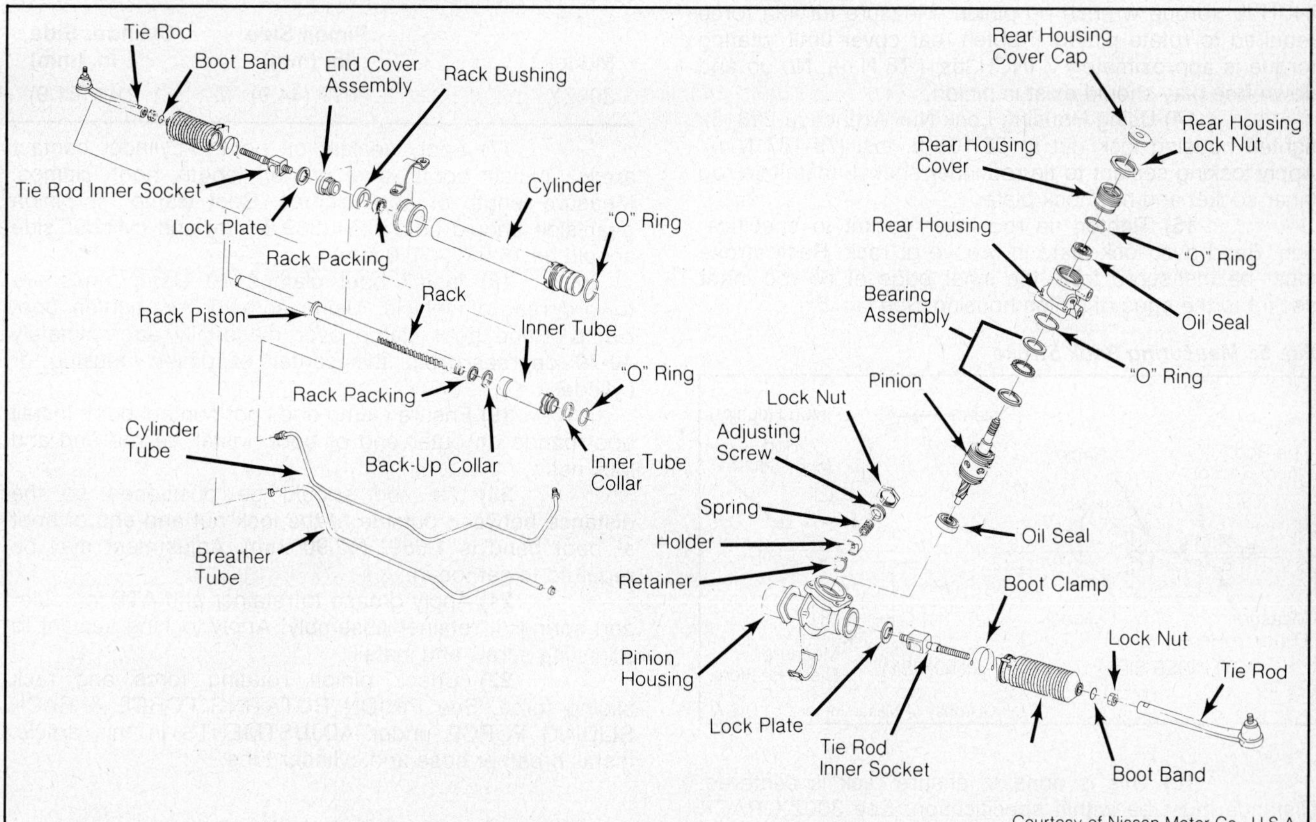

Courtesy of Nissan Motor Co., U.S.A.

Fig. 3: Installing Rack Packing In Inner Tube

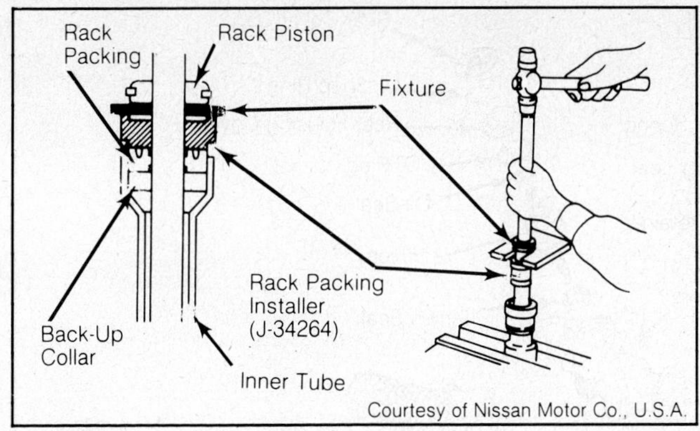

Courtesy of Nissan Motor Co., U.S.A.

Fig. 4: Positioning of Stake Area For Cylinder & End Cover Assembly

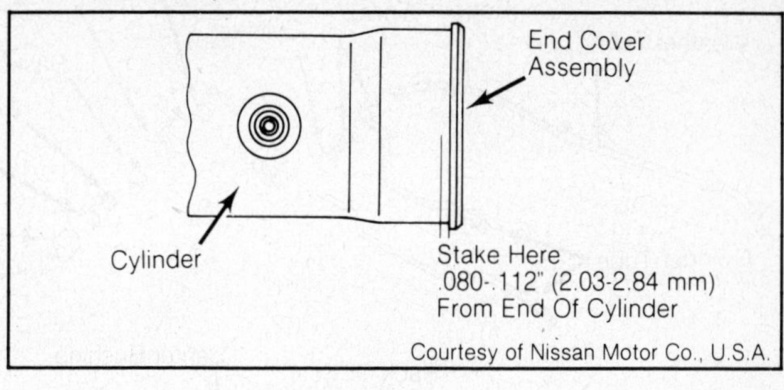

Courtesy of Nissan Motor Co., U.S.A.

4) Install new inner tube collar and "O" ring on inner tube. Install rack and inner tube in pinion housing.

5) Install cylinder on pinion housing. Align reference marks. Install cylinder lock nut. Using cylinder lock nut wrench, tighten cylinder lock nut to specification.

6) Lubricate end cover assembly with ATF. Install end cover assembly. Using end cover wrench, tighten to specification. Cylinder should be staked to retain end cover. Stake cylinder in the center approximately .080-.112" (2.03-2.84 mm) from end of cylinder. *See Fig. 4.*

7) Position rack in center position of cylinder. Lubricate pinion housing oil seal with light coat of grease. Install oil seal in pinion housing.

8) Coat pinion teeth with grease. Apply light coat of ATF to pinion sealing rings. Install pinion in pinion housing. Install new "O" ring on bottom of rear housing.

9) Coat rear housing "O" ring and inner walls with ATF. Install rear housing with line fitting areas away from cylinder area. Install housing retaining bolts and tighten to specification.

10) Lubricate pinion bearing assembly with ATF. Install bearing assembly on pinion. Lubricate rear housing cover oil seal with light coat of grease.

11) Install oil seal in rear housing cover. Lubricate rear housing cover "O" ring with ATF. Install "O" ring on rear housing cover. Wrap tape around pinion spline area. Install rear housing cover.

12) To adjust pinion preload, use Rear Cover Wrench (J-28819) and completely tighten rear cover and then loosen 180-360 degrees. Rotate pinion several times in both directions. Remove tape from pinion shaft.

NISSAN POWER-ASSISTED RACK & PINION (Cont).

13) Install Torque Adapter (J-26364) and an INCH lb. torque wrench on pinion. Measure turning force required to rotate pinion. Tighten rear cover until rotating torque is approximately 7 INCH lbs. (.78 N.m). No up and down free play should exist in pinion.

14) Using Housing Lock Nut Wrench (J-28818), tighten housing lock nut to 58-101 ft. lbs. (79-137 N.m). Apply locking sealant to tie rod inner socket. Install tie rod inner socket and new lock plate.

15) Tighten tie rod inner socket to specification. Bend over lock plate in groove or rack. Rack stroke must be measured from the inner edge of tie rod inner socket to the edge of pinion housing. *See Fig. 5.*

Fig. 5: Measuring Rack Stroke

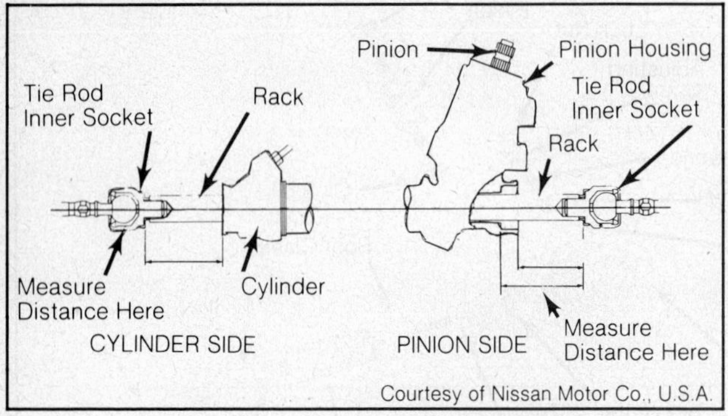

Courtesy of Nissan Motor Co., U.S.A.

16) This is done to ensure rack is centered. Distance must be within specification. See 300ZX RACK STROKE SPECIFICATIONS table.

300ZX RACK STROKE SPECIFICATIONS

Model	Pinion Side In. (mm)	Cylinder Side In. (mm)
300ZX	1.77 (44.9)	2.44 (61.9)

17) Apply sealant on boot-to-cylinder contact areas. Install boots and proper length boot clamps. Measure length of boot clamps. Boot clamp for pinion gear side should be 15.35" (389.9 mm) and cylinder side should be 16.93" (430.0 mm).

18) Install boot clamps so clamp ends are toward rear of vehicle. Using screwdriver, tighten boot clamp. Bend boot clamp over diagonally approximately 40-70 degrees from the center of pinion housing or cylinder.

19) Ensure clamp does not contact boot. Install boot bands on outer end of boot. Install tie rod end and lock nut.

20) Tie rod should be positioned so the distance between outside of the lock nut and end of boot at boot band is 1.689" (42.90 mm). Adjustment may be required to set toe-in.

21) Apply grease to retainer and ATF to holder and spring of retainer assembly. Apply locking sealant to adjusting screw and install.

22) Check pinion rotating force and rack sliding force. See PINION ROTATING FORCE & RACK SLIDING FORCE under ADJUSTMENTS in this article. Install breather hose and cylinder tube.

Fig. 6: Exploded View of Pulsar NX & Sentra Steering Gear

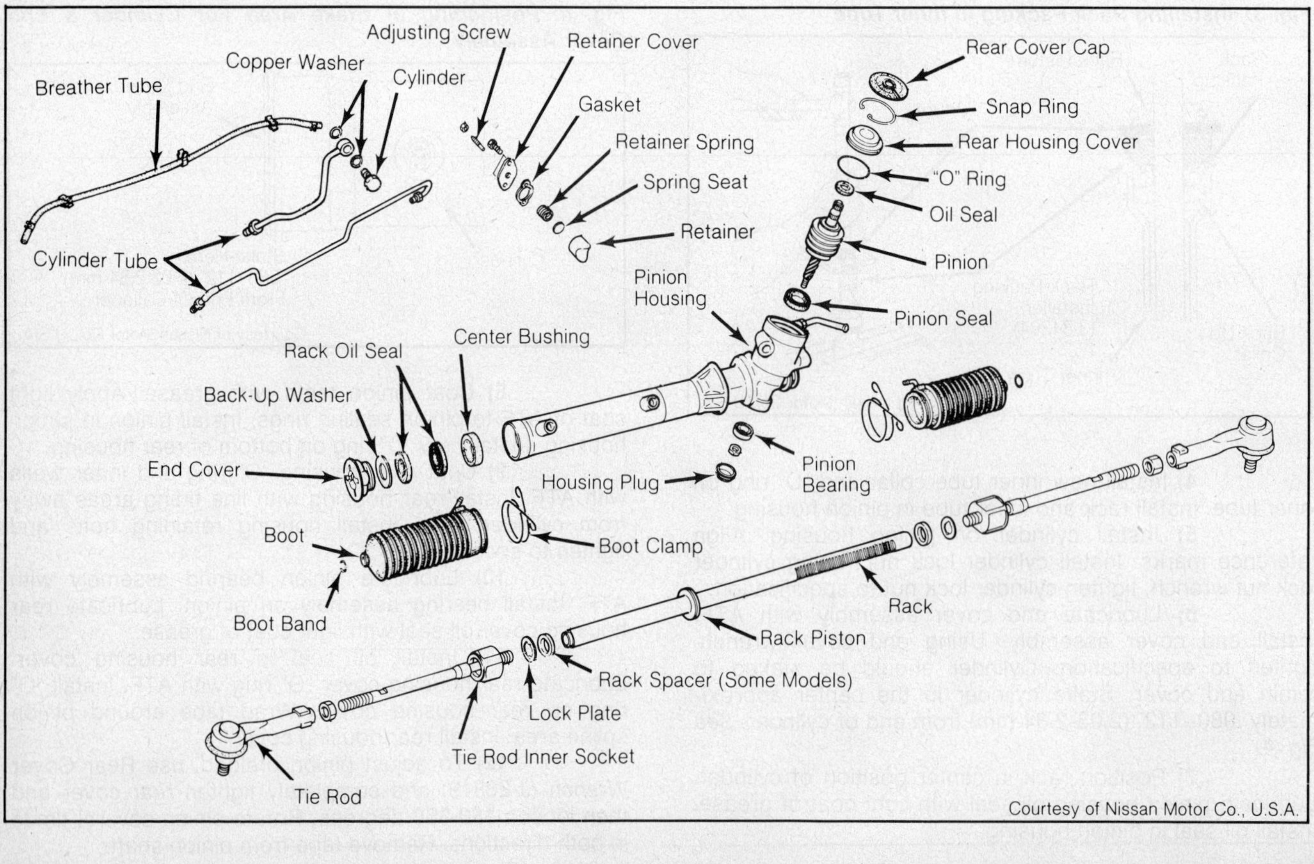

Courtesy of Nissan Motor Co., U.S.A.

NISSAN POWER-ASSISTED RACK & PINION (Cont).

NOTE: Prior to disassembly, measure pinion rotating force and rack sliding force for reassembly reference. See PINION ROTATING FORCE & RACK SLIDING FORCE under ADJUSTMENTS in this article.

Disassembly (Pulsar NX & Sentra)

1) Remove breather and cylinder tubes. *See Fig. 6.* Loosen lock nut and remove tie rods. Remove boot band and boot clamp. Bend over lock plate at tie rod inner socket.

2) Remove tie rod inner socket and rack spacer (if used) from rack. Remove retainer lock nut, adjusting screw, cover, gasket, retainer spring, spring seat and retainer.

3) Remove rear cover cap. Remove snap ring and rear housing cover, "O" ring and oil seal. Remove housing plug. Using Torque Adapter (J-26364), hold pinion and remove nut from lower end of pinion.

4) Remove pinion, pinion seal and pinion bearing from pinion housing. Using End Cover Wrench (J-28822), remove end cover and back-up washer. Remove rack from cylinder.

5) Using long extension and 19 mm socket, drive center bushing and rack oil seal from cylinder. Use care not to scratch cylinder.

Inspection

1) Clean all components in solvent. Blow dry with compressed air. Replace all oil seals, packing and "O" rings. Inspect boots for damage. Replace if damaged. Inspect all sealing surfaces and bearings for roughness.

2) Inspect tie rod and tie rod inner socket for wear or end play. Replace if end play exists.

3) Using INCH lb. torque wrench and Torque Adapter (J-25765-A), measure torque required to rotate tie rod stud. Torque should be 1.3-26.0 INCH lbs. (.1-2.9 N.m). Replace tie rod if not within specification.

4) Inspect steering gear components for damage. Replace steering gear as an assembly if steering gear components are damaged.

Reassembly

1) Lubricate rack oil seal and center bushing with ATF and install on rack. Use care not to damage seal on rack teeth during installation. Lubricate rack teeth with grease. Install rack, oil seal and center bushing in cylinder.

2) Install back-up washer and end cover. Using end cover wrench, tighten end cover to specification. Stake cylinder in the center approximately .080-.112" (2.03-2.84 mm) from end of cylinder. *See Fig. 4.*

3) Apply grease to pinion bearing and install in pinion housing. Coat pinion housing and rear housing cover oil seal lip with grease.

4) Install oil seal in pinion housing and rear cover. Wrap pinion splines with tape. Install new "O" ring on rear housing cover.

5) Install rear housing cover on pinion. Use care not to damage oil seal. Remove tape from pinion. Install pinion and rear housing cover in pinion housing.

6) Install snap ring. Install new nut on lower end of pinion. Using torque adapter, tighten pinion nut to specification. Apply thread sealant to housing plug and install. Tighten plug to specification. Stake housing plug in 3 areas.

7) Lubricate retainer with grease. Install retainer, spring seat, spring, gasket and cover. Tighten cover bolts to specification. Apply thread sealant to inner tie rod sockets.

8) Install inner tie rod sockets, new lock plates and rack spacer (if used). Tighten inner tie rod sockets to specification. Bend over lock plates. Ensure no burrs exist on lock plates or boot will be damaged.

9) Rack stroke must be measured from the inner edge of tie rod inner socket or rack spacer (if used) to the edge of pinion housing. *See Fig. 5.* This is done to ensure rack is centered. Measurements must be within specification. See PULSAR NX & SENTRA RACK STROKE SPECIFICATIONS table.

10) Apply sealant on boot-to-cylinder contact areas. Install boots and boot clamps. Install boot clamps so clamp ends are toward the rear of vehicle.

Fig. 7: Exploded View of Stanza Wagon 2WD Steering Gear

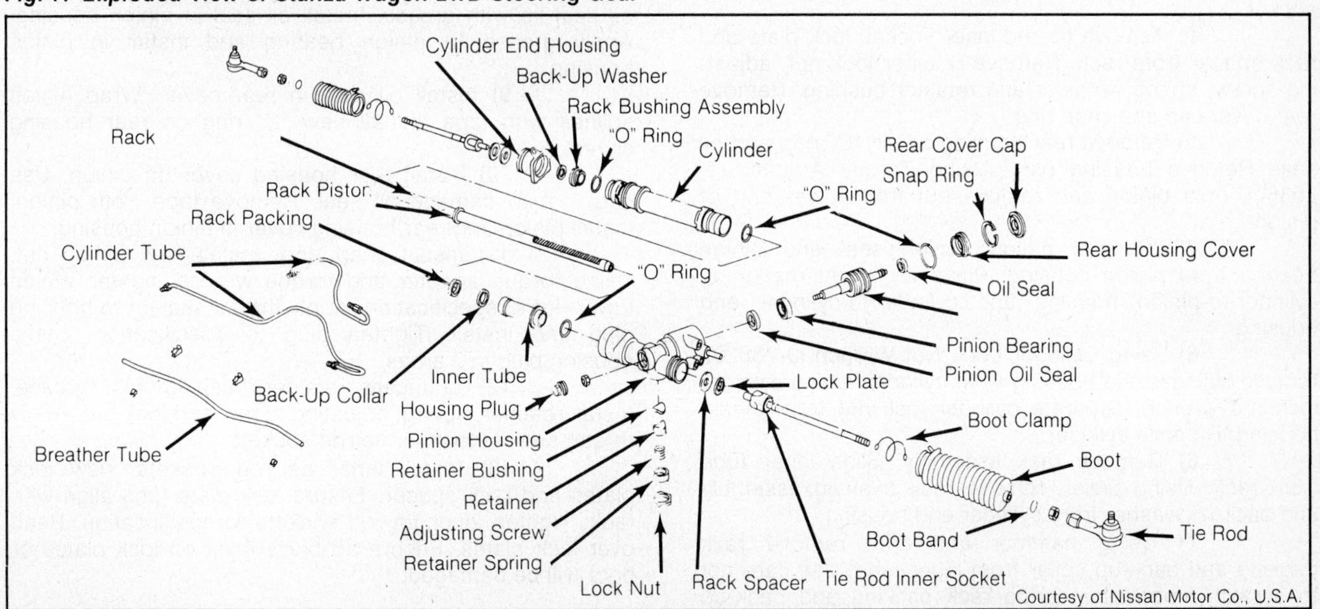

NISSAN POWER-ASSISTED RACK & PINION (Cont).

PULSAR NX & SENTRA RACK STROKE SPECIFICATIONS

Model	Pinion Side In. (mm)	Cylinder Side In. (mm)
Pulsar NX		
DOHC Engine	2.067 (52.50)	2.579 (65.50)
Except DOHC	2.244 (56.99)	2.756 (70.00)
Sentra	2.894 (73.50)	2.756 (70.00)

11) Using screwdriver, tighten boot clamp. Bend boot clamp over diagonally approximately 40-70 degrees from the center of pinion housing or cylinder. Ensure clamp does not contact boot.

12) Install boot bands on outer end of boot. Install tie rod end and lock nut. Tie rod should be positioned so that the distance between the outside of lock nut and end of boot at boot band is 6.94" (176.2 mm). Adjustment may be required to set toe-in.

13) Install rear cover cap so center indicator is toward the front of vehicle. *See Fig. 8.* Install adjusting screw. With rack in center position, tighten adjusting screw to 43 INCH lbs. (5 N.m) 2 times.

14) Loosen adjusting screw and retighten to .43-1.74 INCH lbs. (.05-.19 N.m). Apply thread sealant on adjusting screw and lock nut. Tighten lock nut to specification. DO NOT allow adjusting nut to move.

15) Using Torque Adapter (J-26364) and an INCH lb. torque wrench on pinion, measure turning force required to rotate pinion. Rotating torque should be 16 INCH lbs. (1.8 N.m) or less. Readjust screw if not within specificaiton.

NOTE: Prior to disassembly, measure pinion rotating force and rack sliding force for reassembly reference. See PINION ROTATING FORCE & RACK SLIDING FORCE under ADJUSTMENTS in this article.

Disassembly (Stanza Wagon 2WD)

1) Remove breather and cylinder tube. *See Fig. 7.* Loosen lock nut and remove tie rods. Remove boot band and boot clamp. Bend over lock plate at tie rod inner socket.

2) Remove tie rod inner socket, lock plate and rack spacer from rack. Remove retainer lock nut, adjusting screw, spring, retainer and retainer bushing. Remove rear cover cap and snap ring.

3) Remove rear housing cover, "O" ring and oil seal. Remove housing plug. Using Torque Adapter (J-26364), hold pinion and remove nut from lower end of pinion.

4) Remove pinion, pinion seal and pinion bearing from pinion housing. Place alignment marks on cylinder-to-pinion housing and cylinder-to-cylinder end housing.

5) Using Cylinder Lock Nut Wrench (J-28820), remove cylinder end housing from cylinder. Using cylinder lock nut wrench, separate cylinder lock nut from pinion housing. Remove cylinder.

6) Remove rack assembly. Slide inner tube from rack. Using puller, remove rack bushing assembly and back-up washer from cylinder end housing.

7) Using hammer and drift, remove rack packing and back-up collar from inner tube. Use care not to scratch inner tube during rack packing and back-up collar removal.

8) Remove rack bushing assembly and back-up washer from cylinder end housing. Note direction of bushing assembly installation. Using flat screwdriver, remove oil seal from pinion housing.

Inspection

1) Clean all components in solvent. Blow dry with compressed air. Replace all oil seals, packing and "O" rings. Inspect boots for damage. Replace if damaged. Inspect all sealing surfaces and bearings for roughness.

2) Inspect tie rod and tie rod inner socket for end play. Replace tie rod or tie rod inner socket if end play exists.

3) Inspect steering gear components for damage. Replace steering gear as an assembly if steering gear components are damaged.

Reassembly

1) Apply ATF to rack. Place plastic film supplied with rebuild kit on the inside of inner tube rack packing. This is done to prevent damage to packing from rack teeth during installation.

2) Install rack packing on rack. Remove plastic film once packing is past rack teeth. Install back-up collar on inner tube. Coat teeth area of rack with grease.

3) Install rack assembly in inner tube. Lubricate rack packing with ATF. Using Rack Packing Installer (J-34264) and suitable fixture, install rack packing in inner tube. *See Fig. 3.*

4) Install new "O" ring on inner tube. Lubricate "O" ring with ATF. Install rack and inner tube in pinion housing.

5) Install cylinder on pinion housing. Use care not to damage rack piston Teflon ring. Align reference marks. Install cylinder lock nut. Using cylinder lock nut wrench, tighten cylinder lock nut to specification.

6) Install back-up washer and rack bushing assembly in cylinder end housing. Wrap tape around end of rack. Install cylinder end housing on cylinder. Align reference marks.

7) Using lock nut wrench, tighten cylinder end housing lock nut to specification. Remove tape from rack. Position rack in center position.

8) Coat pinion housing and rear housing cover oil seal lip with grease. Install oil seal in pinion housing. Apply grease to pinion bearing and install in pinion housing.

9) Install oil seal in rear cover. Wrap pinion splines with tape. Install new "O" ring on rear housing cover.

10) Install rear housing cover on pinion. Use care not to damage oil seal. Remove tape from pinion. Install pinion and rear housing cover in pinion housing.

11) Install snap ring. Install new pinion nut. Using torque adapter and torque wrench, tighten pinion lower nut to specification. Apply thread sealant to housing plug and install. Tighten plug to specification. Stake housing plug in 3 areas.

12) Lubricate retainer bushing with grease. Install retainer, spring, adjusting screw and lock nut. Apply thread sealant to inner tie rod sockets.

13) Install inner tie rod sockets, new lock plates and rack spacer. Ensure lock plate tabs align with rack. Tighten inner tie rod sockets to specification. Bend over lock plates. Ensure no burrs exist on lock plates or boot will be damaged.

NISSAN POWER-ASSISTED RACK & PINION (Cont).

Fig. 8: Rear Cover Cap Installation

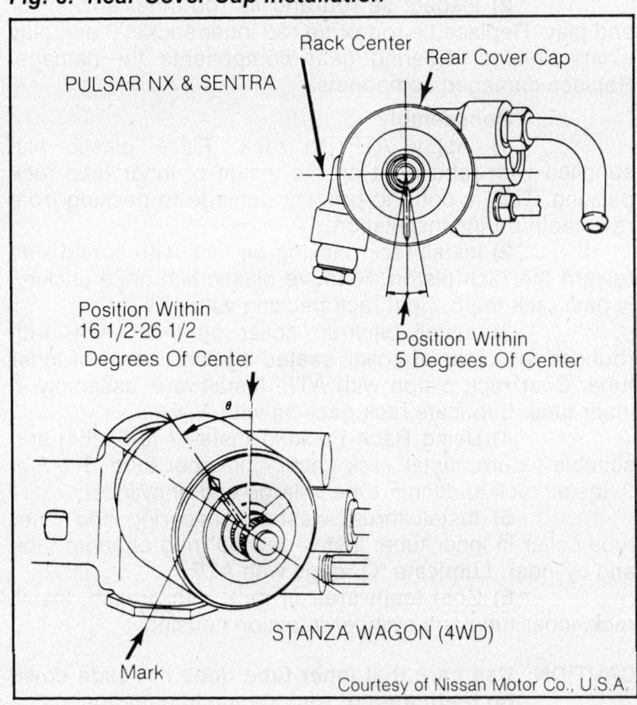

Courtesy of Nissan Motor Co., U.S.A.

14) Rack stroke must be measured from the inner edge of rack spacer to the edge of pinion housing. *See Fig. 5.* This is done to ensure rack is centered. Measurements must be within specification. See STANZA WAGON 2WD RACK STROKE SPECIFICATIONS table.

STANZA WAGON 2WD RACK STROKE SPECIFICATIONS

Model	Pinion Side In. (mm)	Cylinder Side In. (mm)
A/T	2.008 (51.00)	2.461 (62.51)
M/T	2.106 (53.49)	2.559 (64.99)

15) Apply sealant on boot-to-cylinder contact areas. Install boots and boot clamps. Measure length of boot clamps. Boot clamp for pinion gear side should be 15.35" (389.9 mm) and cylinder side should be 16.93" (430.0 mm).

16) Install boot clamps so clamp ends are toward the rear of vehicle. Using screwdriver, tighten boot clamp. Bend boot clamp over diagonally approximately 40-70 degrees from the center of pinion housing or cylinder.

17) Ensure clamp does not contact boot. Install boot bands on outer end of boot. Install tie rod end and lock nut.

18) Tie rod should be positioned so the distance between the outside of lock nut and end of boot at boot band is 6.95" (176.5 mm). Adjustment may be required to set toe-in. Install rear cover cap in neutral position. *See Fig. 8.*

19) With rack in center position, tighten adjusting screw to 43 INCH lbs. (5 N.m) 2 times. Loosen adjusting screw and retighten to .43-1.74 INCH lbs. (.05-.19 N.m). Apply thread sealant on adjusting screw and lock nut.

20) Tighten lock nut to specification. DO NOT allow adjusting nut to move. Recheck pinion rotating force and rack sliding force. See PINION ROTATING FORCE & RACK SLIDING FORCE under ADJUSTMENTS in this article.

Fig. 9: Exploded View of Steering Gear (All Others)

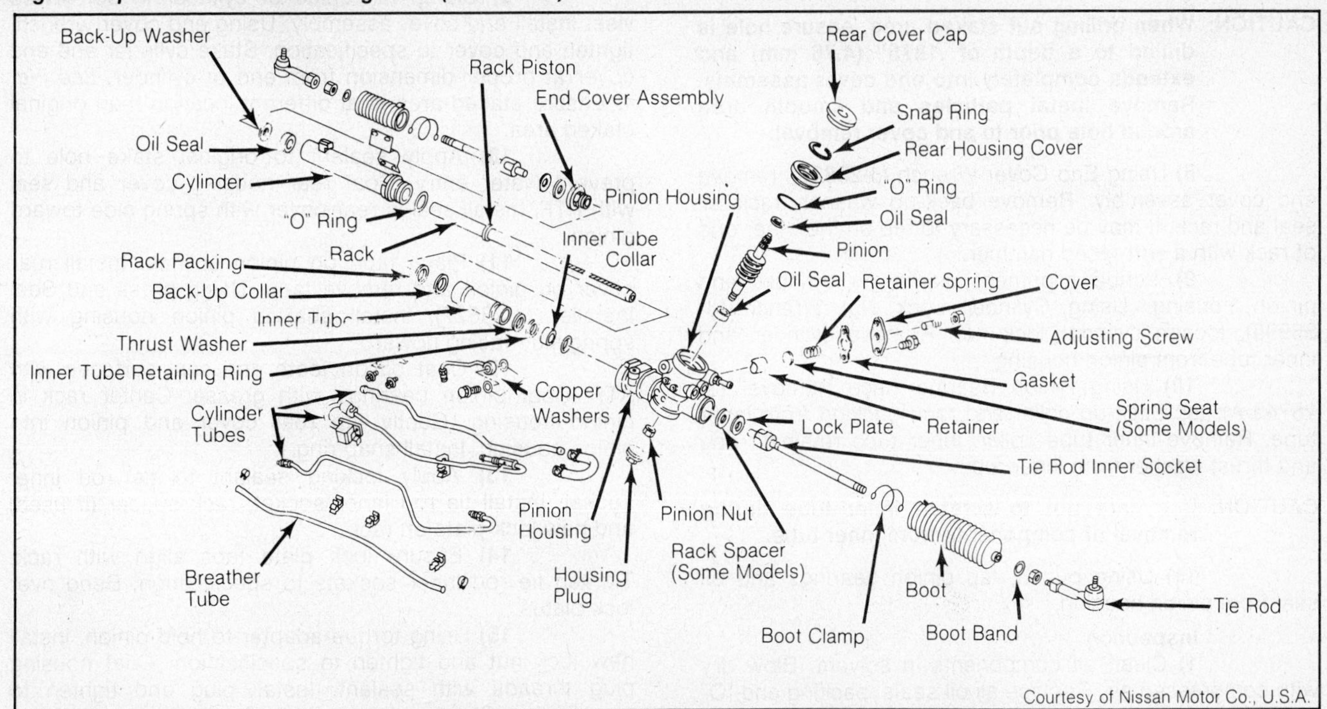

Courtesy of Nissan Motor Co., U.S.A.

Power Steering

NISSAN POWER-ASSISTED RACK & PINION (Cont).

NOTE: Prior to disassembly, measure pinion rotating force and rack sliding force for reassembly reference. See PINION ROTATING FORCE & RACK SLIDING FORCE under ADJUSTMENTS in this article.

Disassembly (All Others)

1) Remove breather and cylinder tubes. *See Fig. 9.* Remove housing plug. Using Torque Adapter (J-26364) to hold pinion, remove nut from lower end of pinion.

2) Loosen lock nut and remove tie rods. Remove boot band and boot clamp. Bend over lock plate at tie rod inner socket. Remove tie rod inner socket and rack spacers (if used) from the rack.

3) Remove retainer lock nut and adjusting screw. Remove retainer cover bolts. Remove cover gasket, retainer spring, spring seat and retainer. Remove rear cover cap and snap ring.

4) Using soft faced hammer, tap pinion and rear housing cover, "O" ring and oil seal from pinion housing.

5) Cylinder is staked to prevent end cover from loosening. Staked area must be drilled out prior to end cover removal.

CAUTION: Cylinder stake area must be drilled out prior to end cover removal.

6) Clamp cylinder in soft-jawed vise so vise jaws are located against flat areas of cylinder. DO NOT damage cylinder. Locate staked area. *See Fig. 4.* Wrap exposed end of rack with tape to prevent damage.

7) Using 3/16" drill bit, drill through staked area into end cover assembly to a depth of .1875" (4.76 mm). Ensure area is drilled completely into end cover assembly. Remove metal particles and smooth area around hole with a file.

CAUTION: When drilling out staked area, ensure hole is drilled to a depth of .1875" (4.76 mm) and extends completely into end cover assembly. Remove metal particles and smooth area around hole prior to end cover removal.

8) Using End Cover Wrench (J-28822), remove end cover assembly. Remove back-up washer, rack oil seal and rack. It may be necessary to tap on the other end of rack with a soft-faced hammer.

9) Scribe alignment marks on cylinder and pinion housing. Using Cylinder Lock Nut Wrench (J-35995), loosen cylinder lock nut. Remove cylinder and inner tube from pinion housing.

10) Using Pinion Bearing Race Remover (J-25749-A), tap back-up collar and rack packing from inner tube. Remove inner tube collar, inner tube retaining ring and thrust washer from inner tube.

CAUTION: Use care not to scratch inner tube during removal of components from inner tube.

11) Using punch, tap pinion bearings and oil seal from pinion housing.

Inspection

1) Clean all components in solvent. Blow dry with compressed air. Replace all oil seals, packing and "O" rings. Inspect boots for damage. Replace if damaged. Inspect all sealing surfaces and bearings for roughness.

2) Inspect tie rod and tie rod inner socket for end play. Replace tie rod or tie rod inner socket if end play exists. Inspect steering gear components for damage. Replace damaged componets.

Reassembly

1) Apply ATF to rack. Place plastic film supplied with rebuild kit on the inside of inner tube rack packing. This is done to prevent damage to packing from rack teeth during installation.

2) Install rack packing on rack with spring side toward the rack piston. Remove plastic film once packing is past rack teeth. Coat rack packing with ATF.

3) Install back-up collar on inner tube with rounded shoulder of collar seated against inside of inner tube. Coat rack piston with ATF. Install rack assembly in inner tube. Lubricate rack packing with ATF.

4) Using Rack Packing Installer (J-34264) and suitable fixture, install rack packing in inner tube. *See Fig. 3.* Install rack and inner tube in large end of cylinder.

5) Install thrust washer, snap ring and inner tube collar in inner tube. Install new "O" ring on inner tube and cylinder. Lubricate "O" rings with ATF.

6) Coat teeth area of rack with grease. Install rack, inner tube and cylinder in pinion housing.

CAUTION: Use care that inner tube does not slide down on teeth area of rack during installation.

7) Align reference marks on cylinder and pinion housing. Using cylinder lock nut wrench, tighten lock nut to specification. Wrap plastic film around cylinder end of rack to protect seal during installation.

8) Install rack oil seal on rack with spring side toward rack piston. Remove plactic wrap. Install new back-up washer against rack seal. Coat rack seal with ATF and tap into cylinder approximately 1" (25 mm) from end of cylinder.

9) Clamp flat sides of cylinder in soft-jawed vise. Install end cover assembly. Using end cover wrench, tighten end cover to specification. Stake cylinder and end cover at proper dimension from end of cylinder. *See Fig. 4.* Ensure staked area is at different location than original staked area.

10) Apply sealant to original stake hole to prevent water entry. Coat rear housing cover and seal with ATF. Install seal in rear cover with spring side toward pinion.

11) Place tape on pinion splines. Install rear cover on pinion and remove tape. Using press and Seal Installer (J-28527), install seal in pinion housing with spring side facing upward.

12) Coat pinion teeth and seal surfaces with ATF. Coat pinion bearings with grease. Center rack in pinion housing. Gently tap rear cover and pinion into pinion housing. Install snap ring.

13) Apply locking sealant to tie rod inner socket. Install tie rod inner socket, rack spacer (if used) and new lock plate on rack.

14) Ensure lock plate tabs align with rack. Tighten tie rod inner sockets to specification. Bend over lock plates.

15) Using torque adapter to hold pinion, install new lock nut and tighten to specification. Coat housing plug threads with sealant. Install plug and tighten to specificaion. Stake housing plug in 3 areas.

NISSAN POWER-ASSISTED RACK & PINION (Cont).

16) Rack stroke must be measured from the inner edge of tie rod inner socket to the edge of pinion housing. *See Fig. 5.* This is done to ensure rack is centered. Distance must be within specification. See RACK STROKE SPECIFICATIONS (ALL OTHERS) table.

RACK STROKE SPECIFICATIONS (ALL OTHERS)

Model	Pinion Side In. (mm)	Cylinder Side In. (mm)
Stanza Wagon 2WD	1.86 (47.4)	2.37 (60.4)
All Others	2.24 (57.0)	2.75 (70.0)

17) With rack centered, install rear cover cap so mark is positioned on drivers side of vehicle.

18) Apply sealant on boot-to-cylinder contact areas. Install boots and proper length boot clamps. Measure length of boot clamps. Boot clamp for pinion gear side should be 15.35" (389.9 mm) and cylinder side should be 16.93" (430.0 mm).

19) Install boot clamps so that clamp ends are toward the rear of vehicle. Using screwdriver, tighten boot clamp. Bend boot clamp over diagonally approximately 40-70 degrees from the center of pinion housing or cylinder.

20) Ensure clamp does not contact boot. Install boot bands on outer end of boot. Install tie rod end and lock nut. Tie rod should be positioned so that the distance between the outside of the lock nut and end of boot at boot band is within specification. See TIE ROD LOCATION SPECIFICATIONS table. Adjustment may be required to set toe-in.

TIE ROD LOCATION SPECIFICATIONS

Application	Drivers Side In. (mm)	Passengers side In. (mm)
Maxima	7.02 (178.4)	7.02 (178.4)
Stanza	7.02 (178.4)	7.05 (179.0)
Stanza Wagon	6.87 (174.7)	6.87 (174.7)
200ZX	1.68 (42.9)	1.68 (42.9)

21) Coat retainer and retainer spring contact areas with grease. Install retainer, spring seat, spring, gasket and cover. Tighten cover bolts to specification. Install adjusting screw and lock nut.

22) With rack in center position, tighten adjusting screw to 43 INCH lbs. (5 N.m) 2 times. Loosen adjusting screw and retighten to .43-1.74 INCH lbs. (.05-.19 N.m). Apply thread sealant on adjusting screw and lock nut.

23) Tighten lock nut to specification. DO NOT allow adjusting nut to move. Recheck pinion rotating force and rack sliding force. See PINION ROTATING FORCE & RACK SLIDING FORCE under ADJUSTMENTS in this article. Install cylinder and breather tubes.

POWER STEERING PUMP

NOTE: **Power steering pump should be disassembled only if oil leakage exists at pulley shaft seal, suction pipe or reservoir, housing and cam case or rear cover. Replace pump as a unit if defective.**

Disassembly

1) Ensure pump housing is cleaned prior to disassembly. Remove pulley nut and pulley. Scribe reference marks on housing, cam case (if used) and rear cover.

2) Remove suction pipe or reservoir. Remove rear cover bolts. Remove rear cover and gasket or "O" ring.

3) On Pulsar NX without DOHC engine and Sentra diesel models, remove mounting bracket from front of pump. Remove pulley shaft bearing retaining snap ring. *See Fig. 10.* Remove shaft and bearing.

CAUTION: **On all models, mark internal components for direction of installation prior to removal. Components must be installed in correct location.**

4) Mark direction of cam ring, rotor and vane installation. Remove rotor, vanes, cam ring and pins. Remove front side plate and "O" rings.

5) Remove housing spring. Remove connector, control valve and spring from housing. Remove oil seal from housing. Note directio of seal installation.

6) On all other models, remove snap ring from rear of pulley shaft. *See Fig. 11.* Remove pulley shaft. Remove cam case and "O" rings. Mark rotor and vanes for direction of installation. Remove rotor and vanes.

7) Remove connector bolts, spool connector, spool valve and spring from housing. DO NOT remove spool from inside of connector bolt. On some models spool connector is screwed into housing and retains spool valve.

Inspection

Inspect components for scoring or damage. Replace pump assembly if components are damaged.

Reassembly

1) Install new oil seals, "O" rings and gaskets. Coat "O" rings with ATF prior to installation.

2) Rotor should be installed with punch mark located on face of rotor toward housing side of pump. Install vanes with flat side toward the rotor.

3) On Pulsar NX models without DOHC engine and Sentra diesel models, install cam ring in alignment with pins. Ensure cam ring properly seats on both pins.

4) On all models, reverse removal procedures. Align reference marks. Tighten bolts to specification.

NISSAN POWER-ASSISTED RACK & PINION (Cont).

Fig. 10: Exploded View of Power Steering Pump (Pulsar NX without DOHC & Sentra Diesel Models)

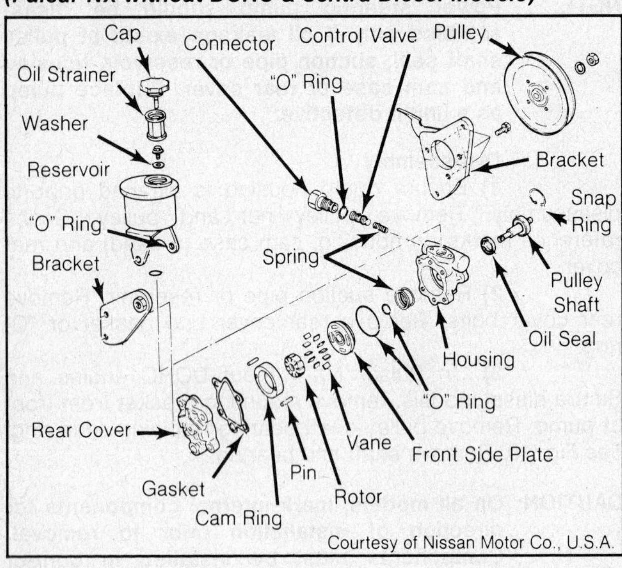

Fig. 11: Exploded View of Typical Power Steering Pump (All Others)

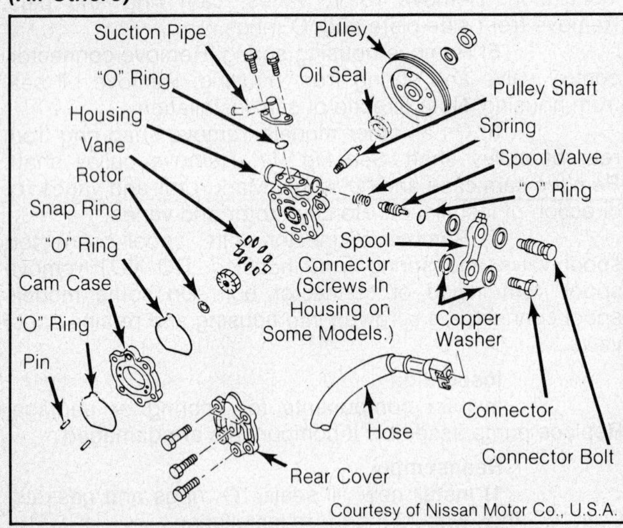

TIGHTENING SPECIFICATIONS (STEERING GEAR)

Application	Ft. Lbs. (N.m)
Adjusting Screw Lock Nut	
300ZX & Stanza Wagon 2WD	29-43 (39-58)
Cylinder End Housing Lock Nut	
Stanza Wagon 2WD	58-80 (79-109)
Cylinder Lock Nut	58-80 (79-109)
Cylinder Tube	14-20 (19-27)
End Cover	
300ZX	58-80 (79-109)
Pulsar & Sentra	47-54 (64-73)
All Others	69-80 (94-109)
Housing Plug	36-51 (49-69)
Lower Joint-to-Pinion Bolt	
Stanza Wagon	22-29 (30-39)
All Others	17-22 (23-30)
Pinion Nut	14-19 (19-26)

TIGHTENING SPECIFICATIONS (STEERING GEAR Cont.)

Application	Ft. Lbs. (N.m)
Rear Housing Lock Nut	
300ZX	58-101 (79-137)
Retainer Cover Bolt	12-15 (16-20)
Steering Gear Mount Bracket Bolt	
200SX & 300ZX	29-36 (39-49)
All Others	54-72 (73-98)
Tie Rod Inner Socket	58-72 (79-98)
Tie Rod Lock Nut	
200SX & 300ZX	58-72 (79-98)
All Others	27-34 (37-46)
Tie Rod-to-Steering Knuckle Nut	
200SX	40-72 (54-98)
All Others	22-29 (30-39)
Rear Housing Lock Nut	
300ZX	58-101 (79-137)
	INCH Lbs. (N.m)
Adjusting Screw Lock Nut	
All Except Stanza Wagon 2WD & 300ZX	84-132 (9-15)
Rear Housing-to-Pinion Housing Bolt	
300ZX	72-108 (8-12)

TIGHTENING SPECIFICATIONS (POWER STEERING PUMP)

Application	Ft. Lbs. (N.m)
Connector Bolt	
Stanza, Stanza Wagon & Maxima	51-58 (69-79)
All Others	36-51 (49-69)
Pulley Nut	
Sentra & Stanza Wagon	23-31 (31-42)
All Others	40-50 (54-68)
Rear Cover Bolt	
200SX, Stanza & 300ZX	23-31 (31-42)
Maxima & Stanza Wagon	12-15 (16-20)
Pulsar NX (Except DOHC) & Sentra (Gas Models)	28-38 (38-51)
Pulsar NX (DOHC) & Sentra (Diesel Models) [1]	
Bolt No. 1	28-38 (38-51)
Bolt No. 2	12-15 (16-20)
Bolt No. 3	23-31 (31-42)
Reservoir Tank Bolt	
Pulsar NX (Except DOHC) & Sentra (Gas Models)	12-15 (16-20)
Spool Connector	51-58 (69-79)
Suction Pipe Bolt	
Pulsar NX (Except DOHC) & Sentra (Diesel Models)	12-15 (16-20)
Stanza, Stanza Wagon & Maxima	10-13 (14-18)
	INCH Lbs. (N.m)
Suction Pipe Bolt	
200SX	72 (8)
300ZX	72-108 (8-12

[1] – See Fig. 11 for bolt reference.

NISSAN RECIRCULATING BALL

Pathfinder, Pickup & Van

DESCRIPTION

The power steering system consists of a power steering pump with separate reservoir, steering gear and connecting hoses. The power steering gear consists of an integral unit that incorporates a spool valve and power cylinder (worm, shaft, and ball nut assembly) connected to the sector shaft.

LUBRICATION

CAPACITY

Capacity is 1.0 qts. (.9L) for Pathfinder and Pickup and 1.1 qts. (1.0L) for Van.

FLUID TYPE

ATF Dexron, or Dexron II.

NOTE: Normal operating temperature of hydraulic system fluid is 140-176°F (60-80°C).

FLUID LEVEL CHECK

Fluid levels should be checked before engine is started and when fluid is still cool. Remove the fluid level dipstick on oil pump reservoir. Check fluid level. Fluid should be between the "MIN" and "MAX" marks on the dipstick. If fluid is needed, fill through the dipstick opening and recheck. DO NOT overfill.

ADJUSTMENTS

BELT TENSION

With pressure of 22 lbs. (10 kg) midway between pulleys, deflection should be .31-.47" (8-12 mm) for Pathfinder and Pickup or .35-.39 (9-10 mm) for Van.

TESTING

HYDRAULIC SYSTEM PRESSURE CHECK

1) Check fluid level. Start engine and let idle. Bring fluid to a temperature of between 140-176°F (60-80°C). Stop engine. Disconnect high pressure line at pump. Connect pressure gauge between shut-off valve and oil pump. Open shut-off valve.

2) Check fluid level. Bleed system. Run engine for about 5 seconds. Check fluid level. Restart engine and let idle. Turn steering wheel from lock-to-lock several times to expel air from system.

3) Turn wheel to full lock position while checking pressure. Pump pressure should be 1109-1194 psi (78-84 kg/cm²) for Pathfinder and Pickup or 1138 psi (80 kg/cm²) for Van.

CAUTION: Do not hold at lock position for more than 15 seconds.

4) If pressure is incorrect, slowly close shut-off valve. If pressure is too low or high after shut-off valve is closed, the pump is faulty. If pressure is now okay, steering gear is faulty.

HYDRAULIC SYSTEM BLEEDING

1) Check fluid level. Raise and support vehicle. With engine off, turn steering wheel from lock-to-lock several times. Check fluid level. Add fluid (if necessary). Start engine and run until fluid is hot. Stop engine. Recheck fluid level.

2) Run engine for 3-5 seconds. Recheck fluid level. Turn steering wheel from lock-to-lock several times. Repeat until all air is bled from system. If air cannot be completely bled, hold wheel at lock position for 5 seconds maximum. Check for leaks.

BACKLASH

In Vehicle

1) Place vehicle on level dry floor. Inflate tires to specified pressure. Ensure power steering fluid is at normal operating temperature.

2) With steering wheel in straight ahead (centered) position, turn steering wheel one complete turn. Using spring gauge attached to outer spoke of wheel, measure turning force.

3) Turning force should be 5.5-6.6 lbs. (2.3-3.0 kg) on PB48S gearbox and 9 lbs. (4.1 kg) or less on PB56S gearbox. If turning force is not to specifications, remove steering gear. Recheck turning force.

Off Vehicle

1) With steering gear removed from vehicle, attach gear Mounting Plate (KV48100301). Turn worm shaft all the way from left to right several times. Center steering gear. Turn one full turn in either direction.

2) Using torque wrench attached to worm shaft splines, measure turning force of steering gear one turn from center position. Torque should be less than 10 INCH lbs. (1.2 N.m).

3) Turn worm shaft back to center position while measuring torque. Torque at this point should be .9-3.5 INCH lbs. (.1-.4 N.m) more than torque measured one turn from center position. If not, loosen adjusting bolt lock nut.

4) Turn adjusting bolt until correct turning torque specification is obtained. If the correct turning torque cannot be obtained, replace steering gear.

REMOVAL & INSTALLATION

STEERING GEAR

Removal & Installation

1) Remove "U" joint-to-pinion shaft clamp bolt. Disconnect hydraulic lines. Wire lines up to prevent fluid spillage. Remove nut and washer from sector shaft. Using a puller, remove pitman arm from sector shaft. Remove steering gear mounting bolts. Remove steering gear.

2) To install, reverse removal procedure. Align 4 serrations in pitman arm with 4 projections of sector shaft serrations. Install and tighten lock nut.

STEERING PUMP

Removal & Installation

1) Remove air duct. Loosen pump pulley adjusting nut. Remove belt. Loosen hydraulic lines at pump. Plug fittings. Lift oil pump and reservoir. Disconnect hoses from pump. Remove clamps on crossmember. Remove hoses.

2) To install, reverse removal procedure.

NISSAN RECIRCULATING BALL (Cont.)

OVERHAUL

NOTE: **Overhaul of steering gear is limited to oil seal replacement. If any further repair is necessary, replace entire steering gear. Always check turning torque before disassembly.**

ADJUSTING SCREW SEAL REPLACEMENT

Remove adjusting screw lock nut. Remove "O" ring from lock nut. Grease new "O" ring and insert in lock nut. Replace lock nut. Adjust steering gear turning torque.

NOTE: **Always use new copper washer when adjusting screw lock nut is removed.**

SECTOR SHAFT SEAL REPLACEMENT

Disassembly

1) With steering gear assembly mounted in a vise, set sector shaft to center position. DO NOT loosen adjusting screw lock nut. Remove sector shaft cover bolts. Using a mallet, tap sector shaft out approximately .79" (20 mm).

NOTE: **Wrap a piece of stiff plastic film around the sector shaft, about the same diameter as the sector shaft and about 8" long. This will prevent bearings from falling into gear housing.**

2) Pull sector shaft from gear housing while at same time pushing plastic film into gear housing. Remove dust seal, snap ring, special large washer, and oil seal. Remove "O" ring from sector shaft cover.

Reassembly

1) Install new oil seal and special large washer. Install snap ring with rounded side of washer facing into gear housing. Press dust seal into gear housing.

2) Coat "O" ring with petroleum jelly. Install "O" ring in sector shaft cover. Ensure worm shaft and rack piston is centered. Wrap splined and threaded portions of sector shaft with tape to prevent damage to oil seal.

3) Slowly insert sector shaft into housing, pushing plastic film out and being careful not to damage oil seal. Install sector shaft. Remove plastic film. Tighten sector shaft cover bolts. Adjust steering gear turning torque.

REAR COVER SEAL REPLACEMENT

Disassembly

1) Install steering gear assembly to mounting plate. Place steering gear/mounting plate in a vise. Loosen rear cover bolts approximately .20" (5 mm). Do not remove bolts. Turn sector shaft clockwise slightly to raise intermediate cover through piston.

2) Place piston and worm shaft in center position. Remove sector shaft. See SECTOR SHAFT SEAL REPLACEMENT in this article. Remove rear cover bolts. Pull out rear cover with intermediate cover and worm gear assembly.

NOTE: **When worm assembly is removed, piston may turn and come off under its own weight. Hold piston to prevent this. Do not damage Teflon ring at piston end when removing.**

3) Turn worm assembly upside down. Lightly tap worm shaft against bench to remove rear cover. Remove rear cover oil seal. Remove large and small "O" rings from both sides of intermediate cover.

Reassembly

1) Grease the rear housing oil seal. Apply petroleum jelly on intermediate cover "O" rings. Install seal and "O" rings. Install worm assembly into rear housing then into gear housing. Do not tilt ball bearings.

CAUTION: **As worm assembly is installed, Teflon ring will be compressed. Do not damage ring on corner of sector hole.**

2) Ensure worm assembly is level. If bolts are tightened with worm assembly tilted, seals will be damaged. Tighten rear cover bolts in a diagonal pattern.

3) Install sector shaft. See SECTOR SHAFT SEAL REPLACEMENT for installation procedure. Ensure steering gear operates smoothly. Adjust turning torque.

POWER STEERING PUMP

NOTE: **Limit power steering pump overhaul to removing components listed in disassembly procedure. If damage to other components is found, replace power steering pump as a unit.**

Fig. 1: Exploded View of Nissan Power Steering Gear

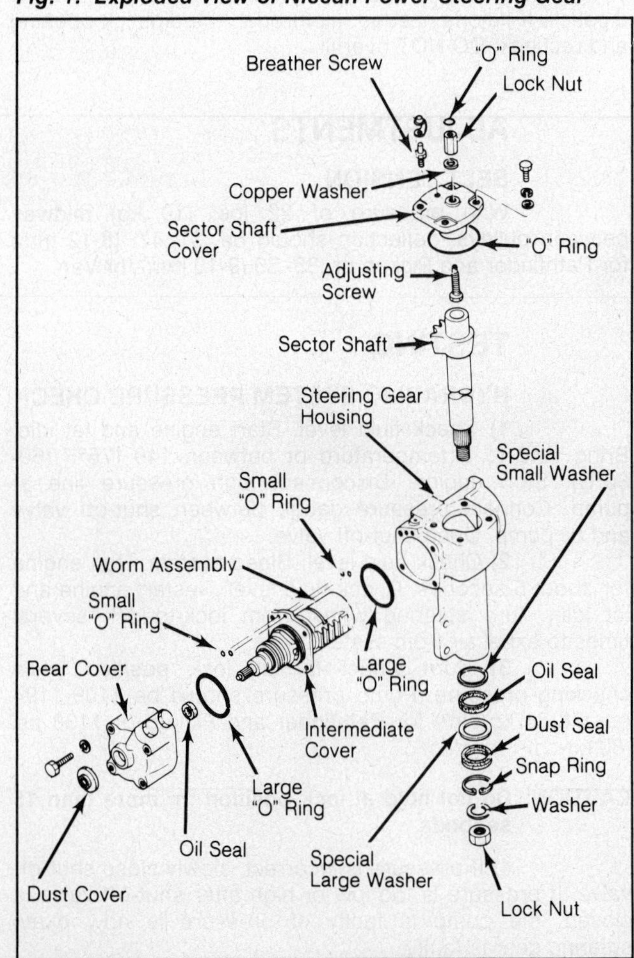

Courtesy of Nissan Motor Co. U.S.A.

NISSAN RECIRCULATING BALL (Cont.)

Disassembly (Pathfinder & Pickup)

1) Remove pulley nut and pulley. Mark rear cover, cam case and housing for reassembly reference. Separate rear cover from cam case. *See Fig. 2.*

2) Being carefull not to separate vanes from rotor, remove cam case from housing. Remove "O" ring from cam case. Remove snap ring from cam side of shaft.

3) Remove shaft from housing. Do not drop shaft. Remove rotor from housing. Remove vanes from rotor. Using a screwdriver, carefully pry oil seal from housing.

4) Remove connector, control valve and spring from housing. Remove suction pipe fitting from housing if leakage is detected. Discard all "O" rings.

Inspection

Wash all parts in solvent. Check pulley for cracks or warpage. Check pulley and shaft for worn serrations. Check housings for scratches or gouges. If housings are damaged, replace pump as a unit. If any other parts are found defective, replace as necessary.

Reassembly

Lubricate all moving parts with ATF before reassembly. To reassemble, reverse disassembly procedure. Use new "O" rings.

Disassembly (Van)

1) Remove pulley nut and pulley from shaft. Mark rear housing-to-front housing mating surface for reassembly reference. Separate rear housing from front housing. *See Fig. 3.*

2) Remove snap ring from vane side of shaft. Remove shaft from front housing. Do not drop pulley. Using a screwdriver, carefully pry out front oil seal.

3) Remove connector, "O" ring, control valve and spring from front housing. Remove suction pipe fitting and "O" ring if leaking is detected. Discard all "O" rings and gaskets.

Inspection

Wash all parts in solvent. Check pulley for cracks or warpage. Check pulley and shaft for worn serrations. Check housings for scratches or gouges. If housings are damaged, replace pump as a unit. If any other parts are found defective, replace as necessary.

Reassembly

Lubricate all moving parts with ATF before reassembly. To reassemble, reverse disassembly procedure. Use new "O" rings and gaskets.

Fig. 3: Exploded View of Van Power Steering Pump

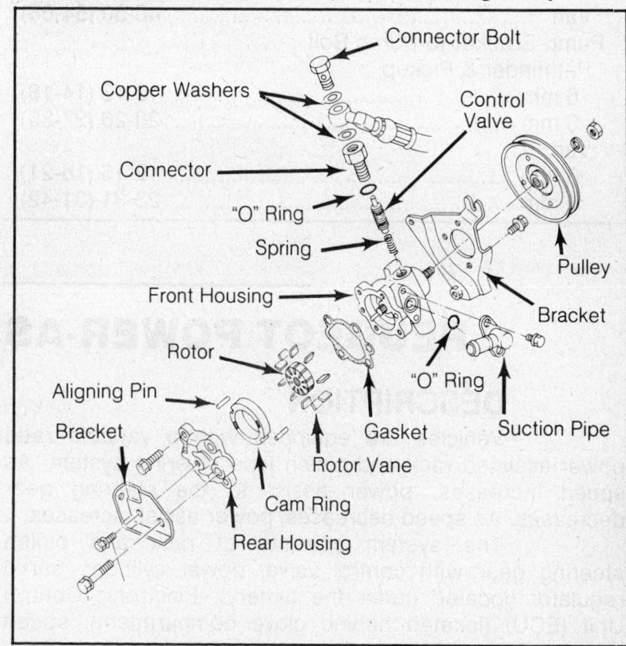

Courtesy of Nissan Motor Co. U.S.A.

Fig. 2: Exploded View of Pathfinder & Pickup Power Steering Pump

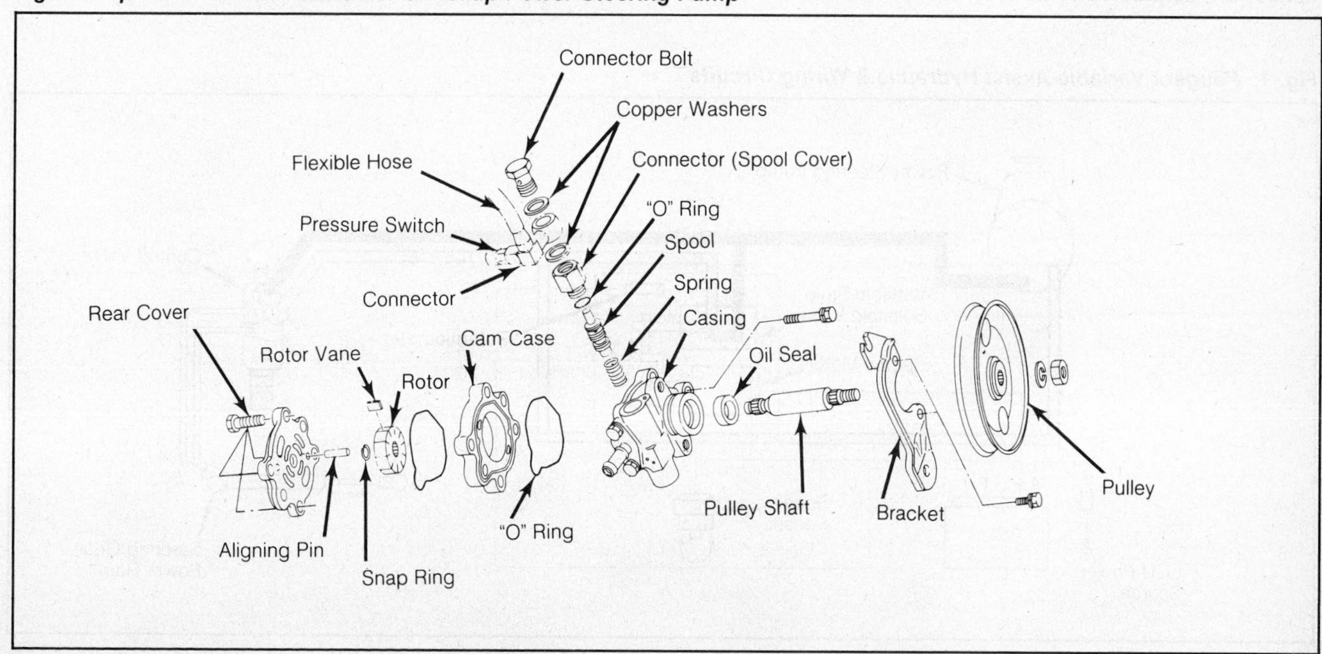

Courtesy of Nissan Motor Co. U.S.A.

NISSAN RECIRCULATING BALL (Cont.)

TIGHTENING SPECIFICATIONS

Application	Ft. Lbs. (N.m)
Adjusting Screw Lock Nut	25-30 (34-40)
Center Link-to-Idler Arm Castle Nut	40-72 (54-98)
Hydraulic Fitting-to-Steering Gear	
Pressure Line	29-36 (39-49)
Return Line	22-29 (29-39)
Idler Arm Bracket Bolt	36-51 (49-69)
Idler Arm-to-Bracket Nut	40-51 (54-69)
Pressure Fitting Banjo Bolt	36-51 (49-69)
Pump Pulley Retaining Nut	
Pathfinder & Pickup	23-31 (31-42)
Van	40-50 (54-68)
Pump Bracket-to-Pump Bolt	
Pathfinder & Pickup	
6 mm	10-13 (14-18)
8 mm	20-26 (27-35)
Van	
6 mm	12-15 (16-21)
8 mm	23-31 (31-42)

TIGHTENING SPECIFICATIONS (Cont.)

Application	Ft. Lbs. (N.m)
Pump Rear Cover-to-Housing Bolt	
Pathfinder & Pickup	28-38 (38-52)
Van	23-31 (31-42)
Sector Shaft Cover Bolts	20-24 (27-33)
Sector Shaft-to-Pitman Arm Nut	101-130 (137-177)
Steering Damper-to-Center Link Bolt	23-31 (31-42)
Steering Damper-to-Bracket Nut	12-15 (16-21)
Steering Damper	
Bracket-to-Frame Bolt	16-21 (22-29)
Steering Gear Rear Cover Bolts	20-24 (27-33)
Steering Gear-to-Frame Bolt	
Pathfinder & Pickup	62-71 (84-96)
Van	62-80 (84-108)
Suction Pipe Fitting Bolt	10-13 (14-18)
Tie Rod End-to-Knuckle Castle Nut	40-72 (54-98)
Tie Rod-to-Center Link Castle Nut	140-72 (54-98)
"U" Joint-to-Pinion Clamp Bolt	17-22 (24-29)

PEUGEOT POWER-ASSISTED RACK & PINION

DESCRIPTION

Vehicles are equipped with a variable ratio power-assisted rack and pinion type steering system. As speed increases, power assist to the steering gear decreases. As speed decreases, power assist increases.

The system consists of rack and pinion steering gear with control valve, power cylinder, servo regulator (located under the battery), Electronic Control Unit (ECU) (located behind glove compartment), speed sensor (inline with speedometer cable), and a high pressure pump with integral reservoir.

Steering gear, servo regulator and pump are connected by flexible lines. Servo regulator and speed sensor are connected to ECU by wiring harness.

LUBRICATION

FLUID TYPE

Fluid type is DEXRON II.

ADJUSTMENTS

SYSTEM BLEEDING

Fill reservoir to full mark on dipstick. Start engine and turn steering wheel from lock-to-lock several times to expel air. Recheck fluid level. Refill as necessary.

Fig. 1: Peugeot Variable-Assist Hydraulic & Wiring Circuits

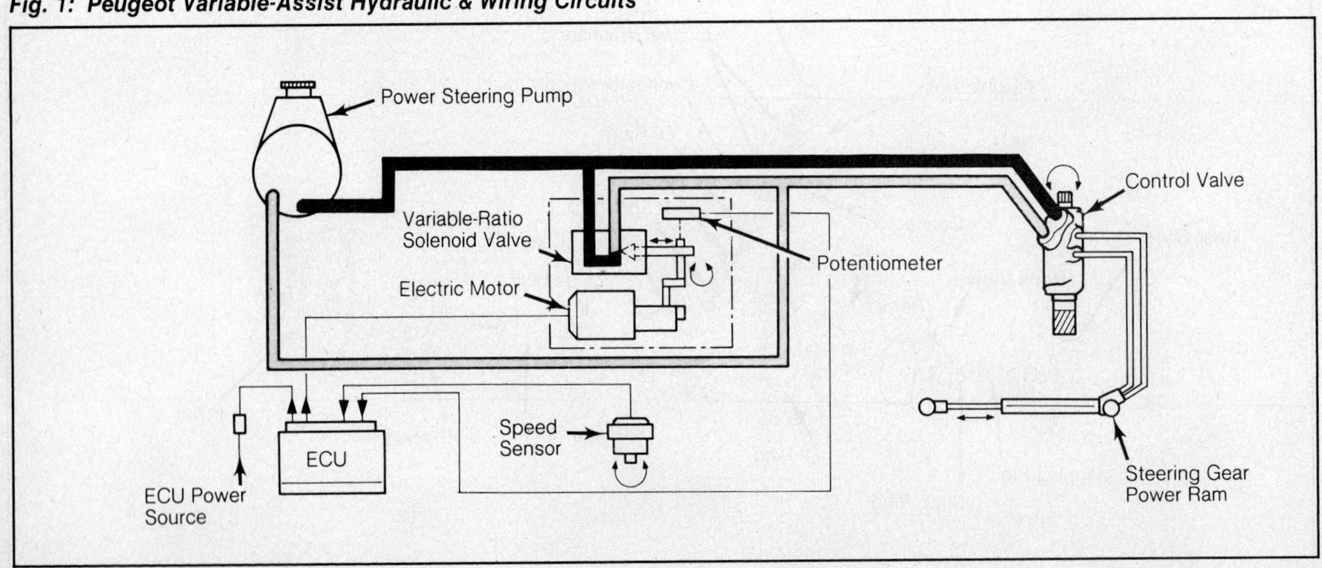

Courtesy of Peugeot Motor of America, Inc.

PEUGEOT POWER-ASSISTED RACK & PINION (Cont.)

OPERATION

The steering pump supplies pressure to the pinion shaft control valve on the steering gear. The pinion shaft control valve distributes pressurized fluid to the power cylinder to assist rack movement when turning.

The servo regulator incorporates a valve controlled by an electric motor. This valve varies the amount of pressure allowed to the pinion shaft control valve. This valve is controlled by inputs from the ECU. A potentiometer informs the ECU of the position of this valve.

The ECU also receives inputs from a speed sensor in the speedometer cable. The servo regulator consists of an electric motor, potentiometer and the electric motor controlled valve.

The system uses a diagnostic feature that allows testing with the use of only a 12-volt, 1.2 watt test lamp connected to a test lead in the engine compartment.

When the engine is not running, there is no pressure to the valve and the valve plunger is forced against it's stop by a spring. When ignition is started, electric motor pulls a piston back to it's stop and then returns it to it's initial reference position (vehicle speed below 18 MPH). *See Fig. 3.* This initial movement tests the function of the potentiometer.

When the wheels are in a straight-ahead position, regardless of speed, the pressure bleed-down at the valve is at it's maximum and very little pressure is diverted to the pinion shaft valve. In this position, the plunger is held against the cap by the spring.

When the wheels are turned at speeds below 18 MPH, the shuttle valve is in it's reference position and no fluid passes to the reservoir, allowing maximum assist.

When wheels are turned at a moderate speed greater than 18 MPH, the shuttle valve is moved to the left, this opens the orifice and allows a small amount of fluid to bleed back into the reservoir. This diminishes the assistance to the pinion shaft valve.

As speeds increase, the movement of the shuttle valve to left also increases. This uncovers the orifice more and more as the vehicle accelerates. As the orifice is uncovered further, more fluid bleeds back to the reservoir and power assist is minimal.

Fig. 2: Cross-Sectional View of Variable Assist Servo Regulator Valve

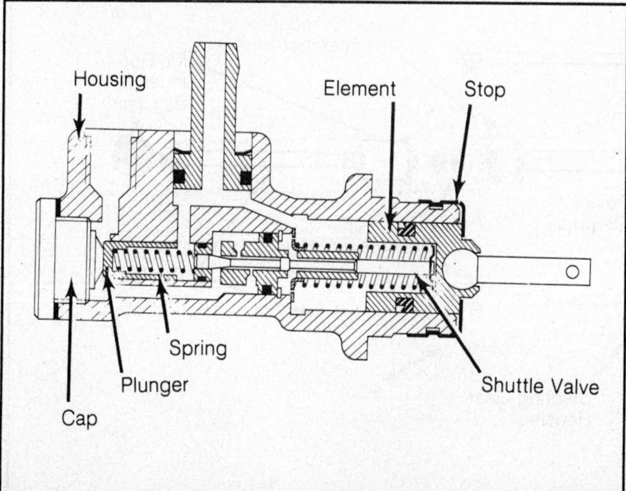

Courtesy of Peugeot Motor of America, Inc.

TESTING

VARIABLE-ASSIST CONTROLS

1) Connect a 12-volt, 1.2 watt lamp between battery positive terminal and terminal No. 12A M899 (located on inner front left fender).

2) Turn ignition to "ON" position. Check that lamp flashes. If lamp flashes 3 times, variable-assist system is working properly. If fault is still present, check hydraulic pressures. See HYDRAULIC SYSTEM PRESSURE CHECK in this article.

3) If lamp flashes 2 times, check electrical circuit between ECU and servo regulator for shorts, open circuits or loose or dirty connections.

4) If lamp flashes one time, check electrical circuit between ECU and speed sensor for shorts, open circuits or loose or dirty connections.

5) If lamp does not flash, check power circuit to ECU for shorts, open circuits or loose or dirty connections. If circuit checks satisfactory, replace ECU. Retest variable-assist system.

HYDRAULIC SYSTEM PRESSURE CHECK

1) Raise and support front of vehicle. Set parking brake. Chock rear wheels. Place transmission in "NEUTRAL" position.

2) Connect pressure gauge between pinion shaft valve and pump with a "T" fitting and valve. *See Fig. 3.* Fill with fluid and bleed air from hydraulic system.

3) Place wheels in straight-ahead position. Start engine and let idle. Regardless of engine speed, pressure should not exceed 15-73 psi (1-5.1 kg/cm²).

4) If pressure reading is greater than this at idle, valve is defective and must be replaced. If pressure is greater than specification during acceleration the regulator is malfunctioning and must be replaced.

5) Accelerate engine to a high idle speed. Turn wheels from lock-to-lock. Pressure should regulate at 1015-1160 psi (71-81 kg/cm²).

CAUTION: DO NOT keep wheels turned full lock for more than 15 seconds. Fluid temperature could rise, causing damage to system.

Fig. 3: Testing Hydraulic Pressure

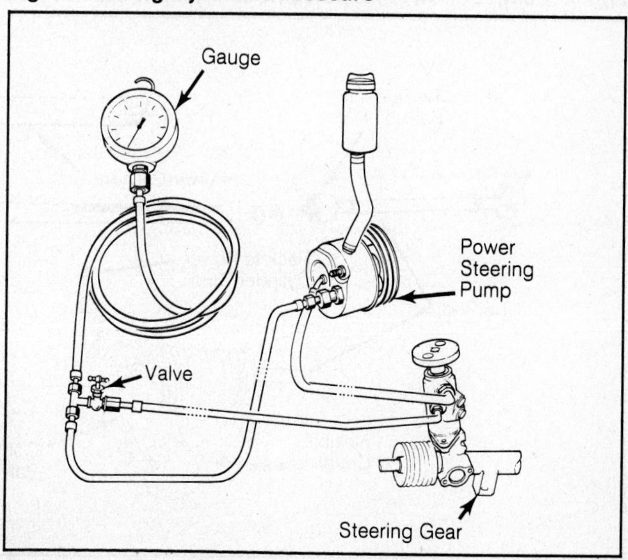

Courtesy of Peugeot Motor of America, Inc.

PEUGEOT POWER-ASSISTED RACK & PINION (Cont.)

6) If pressure is above specification, proceed to regulator check. See REGULATOR CHECK. If pressure is too low, check pump. See STEERING PUMP PRESSURE CHECK.

7) Disconnect hydraulic lines from steering gear. Attach hydraulic lines together with fittings to allow proper functioning of system with steering gear bypassed.

8) Accelerate engine to a high idle speed. Turn wheels from lock-to-lock. Pressure should regulate at 1015-1160 psi (71-81 kg/cm²).

9) If pressure is to specification now, but was too low or too high during previous testing, power cylinder or pinion shaft valve is faulty. Overhaul steering gear. If power cylinder is faulty, replace it.

REGULATOR CHECK

Eaton & Saginaw Pumps

1) On Saginaw pumps with integral reservoir, drain fluid from pump. On Saginaw pumps with remote reservoir, pinch the feed tube closed.

2) On all pumps, remove the high-pressure fitting plug, regulator piston and spring from pump (side of Eaton pumps or rear of Saginaw pumps). Check for scores or damage to galley bore.

3) Clean the screen at end of regulator piston. Ensure that oil passage is not clogged. Reinstall assembly into pump. Retest hydraulic system pressure.

REMOVAL & INSTALLATION

STEERING GEAR

Removal

1) Drain steering system. Disconnect pressure lines between pump and gear. Disconnect bolt at flexible coupling. Disconnect tie rod ball joints at steering knuckle.

2) Remove steering gear-to-crossmember mounting bolts. Remove power cylinder-to-crossmember attaching bolts. Remove steering gear from vehicle by pulling gear backwards and down.

Installation

To install, reverse removal procedure. Use new ball joint nuts. Bleed system. Check wheel alignment.

POWER STEERING PUMP

Removal

1) Remove air cleaner and connecting hoses. Remove pressure lines from pump. Loosen drive belt tensioner bolts. Remove drive belt.

2) Remove pump retaining bolts. Disconnect hose from reservoir to pump. Remove pump. Remove pulley-to-pump retaining bolts. Remove pulley.

Installation

To install, reverse removal procedure. Ensure hose connections are clean before installing. Fill system with fluid. Bleed system. See SYSTEM BLEEDING in this article. Before installing steering gear in vehicle, install spacer on power cylinder to crossmember bolt.

SERVO REGULATOR

Removal

1) Drain hydraulic system. Remove battery. On turbo models, remove alternator. Remove the low pressure hydraulic line from servo regulator.

2) Remove the high pressure line from the "T" fitting. Remove servo bracket-to-frame retaining bolts. Remove protetctive cover. Disconnect electrical connector. Remove servo regulator.

Installation

To install, reverse removal procedure. Tighten servo bracket bolts to 31 ft. lbs. (42 N.m).

OVERHAUL

POWER STEERING PUMP

Manufacturer does not recommend overhaul of power steering pump.

POWER STEERING GEAR

Disassembly

1) Clean steering gear assembly. Place steering gear assembly in a padded vise. Disconnect pressure lines from power cylinder. Plug all openings.

NOTE: **Do not disconnect pressure lines from control valve if valve is to be reused. Do not loosen lock nut on power cylinder attaching joint.**

Fig. 4: Peugeot Power-Assisted Rack & Pinion Steering Gear

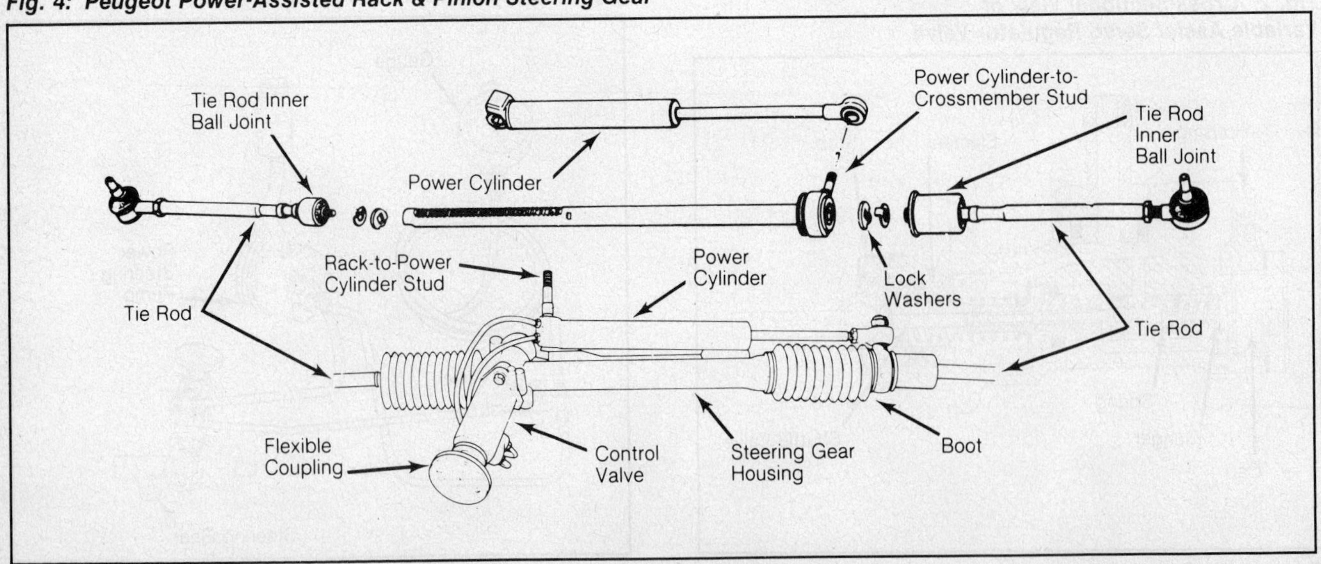

Courtesy of Peugeot Motor of America, Inc.

PEUGEOT POWER-ASSISTED RACK & PINION (Cont.)

2) Remove power cylinder-to-rack retaining nut. Remove power cylinder. Loosen lock nut on right tie rod inner ball joint. Disconnect tie rod from rack. If pinion shaft valve is to be replaced, remove pressure line connections.

NOTE: **Be careful not to bend or twist lines connecting control valve to power cylinder.**

3) Remove left boot clamp. Push boot toward steering gear. Disconnect left tie rod inner ball joint from rack. Remove rack piston cover, spring and rack piston from steering gear housing.

4) Remove pinion shaft valve bearing cap cover and nut. Remove pinion shaft valve-to-steering gear retaining bolts. Remove valve from gear housing.

5) Withdraw rack from housing. Remove snap ring. Remove pinion gear bearing. If control valve is to be rebuilt, remove flexible coupling.

6) Remove snap ring and thrust washer. Withdraw control valve piston from pinion shaft valve housing. Remove snap ring, scraper seal and oil seal from pinion shaft valve housing.

NOTE: **Do not tap on shaft to aid removal or damage to shaft will occur. Do not remove piston rotor segments from shaft.**

Inspection

Check steering gear and rack for any damage, scoring or signs of excessive wear. Check control valve housing and shaft for damage, wear or scoring. Replace components as necessary. Always use new washers, nuts, seals, and bearings.

Reassembly

1) If control valve was disassembled, install oil seal (soaked in oil) to piston/pinion gear assembly with seal lip facing pinion gear. Install piston in pinion shaft valve housing.

2) Install thrust washer and snap ring on pinion end of control valve housing. Install oil seal, scraper ring and snap ring on flexible coupling end of valve housing.

3) Install flexible coupling to control valve housing. Install new pinion gear bearing into steering gear housing. Install snap ring. Insert rack into housing.

4) Align rack teeth with pinion gear/control valve mounting hole. Align flexible coupling pinch bolt with pressure pipe holes on control valve.

5) Insert pinion shaft valve/pinion gear into steering gear housing. To ensure that pinion shaft valve is properly aligned with rack, line up pinion shaft valve flange bolt holes with housing holes.

6) Rotate control valve 90 degrees clockwise. This will properly align rack teeth with pinion teeth. While holding flexible coupling, install pinion nut. Grease bearing mating surface. Install grease cap.

7) Temporarily place plunger and spring in housing. Install rack plunger cover, upper bolt and dial indicator mount into lower bolt hole.

8) Install dial indicator on mount. Tighten cover. Using flexible coupling, turn steering rack from lock-to-lock and zero dial indicator on maximum deflection indicated.

9) Using lever, push steering rack in direction of plunger and record dial indicator reading. Remove dial indicator, rack cover and rack plunger from housing.

10) Install stop to rack plunger. Lay a straightedge over stop and plunger. Select shim pack to eliminate clearance between stop and straightedge.

11) Steering rack plunger clearance should be .002-.006" (.05-.15 mm) at maximum point along rack travel. To obtain required clearance, subtract .004" (.1 mm) from dial indicator reading obtained in step **9)**.

12) Select and install shims, stop and spring to rack plunger. Install rack plunger assembly to gear housing. Install grease nipple to cover. Install cover over rack plunger assembly. Tighten bolts.

13) Install rubber boots, with clamps, to steering gear housing. Push boots out of way when installing tie rod inner ball joints. Install stop plate and lock washer. Install tie rod inner ball joints to rack.

14) Insert bolt into power cylinder. Attach power cylinder to bolt on rack end. Tighten nut finger tight. Install pressure pipes from control valve to power cylinder.

15) Do not bend or deform pressure lines when installing and tightening connections. With pressure lines installed, tighten rack bolt nut. Install pressure lines to control valve.

TIGHTENING SPECIFICATIONS

Application	Ft. Lbs. (N.m)
Hydraulic Line-to-Steering Gear Fitting	17 (24)
Hydraulic Line-to-Pump Fitting	17 (24)
Pinion Valve Housing-to-Rack Bolt	33 (45)
Pump Mounting Bolts	26 (35)
Steering Gear-to-Crossmember Bolt	24 (33)
Steering Gear-to-Crossmember Self-Locking Nut	40 (54)
Tie Rod Inner Ball Joint-to-Rack	36 (49)
Tie Rod Adjusting Sleeve Lock Nut	33 (45)
Tie Rod End Self-Locking Nut	26 (35)
	INCH Lbs. (N.m)
Pulley Mounting Bolts	66 (7.5)

PORSCHE POWER-ASSISTED RACK & PINION

924-S, 928-S4, 944, 944-S, 944 Turbo

DESCRIPTION

Models use a power-assisted rack and pinion steering gear. The power assistance decreases as engine speed increases to provide better speed stability. System consists of a belt-driven vane pump, a remote fluid reservoir and a rotary piston pinion steering gear.

LUBRICATION

FLUID TYPE

ATF Dexron II.

FLUID LEVEL CHECK

Remove reservoir cap. Start engine and let idle. Check that fluid level is up to the top mark on the dipstick.

PORSCHE POWER-ASSISTED RACK & PINION (Cont.)

HYDRAULIC SYSTEM BLEEDING

1) Fill power steering reservoir to top mark on dipstick. Start engine and let idle for a few seconds. Turn ignition off. Check fluid level. Refill as necessary. Repeat procedure until fluid level in reservoir does not drop.

NOTE: This procedure can drop fluid level in reservoir very quickly. Oil must be added continuously to keep level at maximum mark. Reservoir must not be allowed to run dry.

2) Turn steering wheel lock-to-lock quickly to let air escape. When piston reaches end of travel, DO NOT pull harder on steering wheel than required or excessive pressure will build up in steering pump.

3) Observe oil level during bleeding. If oil level still drops, keep adding oil until level remains constant at top mark of dipstick and no more air bubbles appear.

4) When engine is turned off, oil level in must not rise by more than .39" (10.0 mm). If it does rise further than this, air is still present. Bleed system again.

SYSTEM LEAKS

With engine running, hold steering in full lock position. This produces maximum pressure in lines. Check all hose connections. Tighten connections as needed.

ADJUSTMENTS

PUMP BELT

Check belt deflection at center of belt between pump pulley and crankshaft pulley. Correct deflection is .39" (10 mm). Adjust by loosening pump mounting bolts and moving pump.

TESTING

PRESSURE CHECK

1) Unscrew bolts from stabilizer bushings. Pull stabilizer down to expose pressure line hollow bolt. Detach pressure line at steering gear. Pull down on line.

2) Attach hose about 4 1/2 feet long to pressure line with hollow bolt and adapter. Attach hose with pressure gauge between steering gear and pressure line.

3) Bleed system. Run engine at idle speed. Close pressure gauge valve. Check pressure gauge reading. Pressure should be 986-1189 psi (69-84 kg/cm²).

CAUTION: DO NOT keep valve closed for more than 5 seconds.

4) With pressure gauge valve open, turn wheel lock-to-lock and hold in lock position at a force of 22 lbs. (9.97 kg). Read pressure gauge. Pressure should be 986-1189 psi (69-84 kg/cm²).

REMOVAL & INSTALLATION

STEERING GEAR

Removal

1) Drain fluid from system. Raise and support vehicle. Remove splash shield. Using separator, remove tie rods from knuckles. Remove hose strap retaining bolt. Pull back hose and harness. Remove stabilizer bar mounting bolts.

Fig. 1: Exploded View of Power Steering Gear

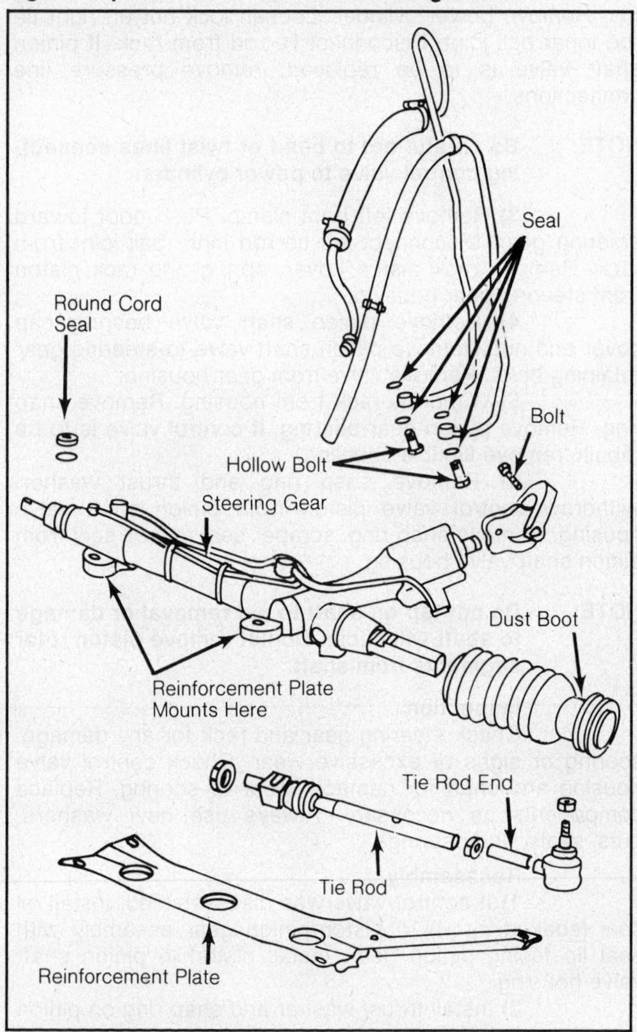

Courtesy of Porsche of North America, Inc.

2) Allow stabilizer to hang down. Disconnect hydraulic lines from steering gear. Remove reinforcement plate-to-crossmember retaining bolts. Loosen self-locking nuts on steering gear, but do not remove.

Fig. 2: Steering Intermediate Shaft Removal

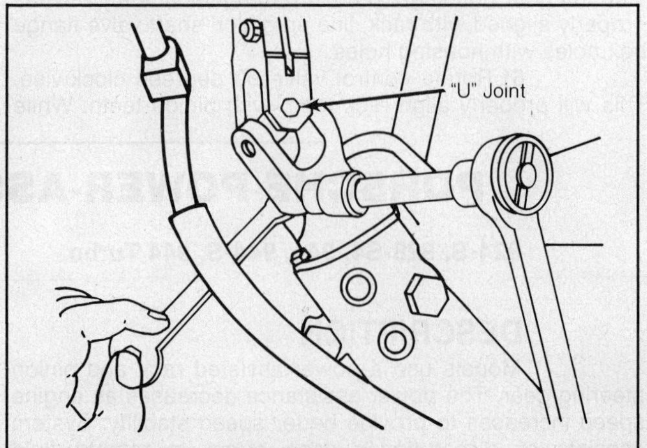

Courtesy of Porsche of North America, Inc.

PORSCHE POWER-ASSISTED RACK & PINION (Cont.)

3) Mark "U" joint and intermediate shaft for reassembly reference. Remove "U" joint-to-intermediate shaft bolt. Remove intermediate shaft. Remove steering gear lock nuts. Lower steering gear from crossmember.

Installation

To install, reverse removal procedure. Align marks made during removal. Install "U" joint-to-intermediate shaft bolt. Tighten connections and bolts. Add fluid. Bleed system. Check for leaks. Check wheel alignment.

STEERING PUMP

Removal

1) Detach intake hose from air cleaner on left side. Drain fluid from reservoir. Remove splash shield. Loosen, but DO NOT remove, front bolts on pump. Remove rear bolt from pump. Remove "V" belt.

2) Take off upper left section of belt cover. Disconnect pressure hose from pump. Loosen clip holding suction hose. Remove hose. Remove front pump attaching bolts. Remove pump.

Installation

1) To install, reverse removal procedure. Install pressure hose so that not more than 1" (25 mm) remains between inner wheel well and hose after installation.

2) If hose is too close to exhaust manifold it could slip from its holder. Adjust belt tension. Add fluid. Bleed system. Check for leaks.

OVERHAUL

NOTE: **Manufacturer does not recommend disassembly or overhaul of power steering gears or pumps.**

TIGHTENING SPECIFICATIONS

Application	Ft. Lbs. (N.m)
Pressure/Return Lines-to-Steering Rack Fittings	22 (30)
Steering Rack-to-Crossmember Bolts	33 (45)
Tie Rod End-to-Tie Rod	33 (45)
Tie Rod-to-Steering Arm Nut	61 (83)
Tie Rod-to-Steering Rack	108 (147)
"U" Joint-to-Steering Column Clamp Bolt	17 (23)

SAAB POWER-ASSISTED RACK & PINION

900, 900S, 900 Turbo, 9000S, 9000 Turbo

DESCRIPTION

System consists of a rack and pinion steering gear with a servo valve which regulates the oil flow to a servo plunger on the rack. Hydraulic pressure is generated by a belt-driven oil pump with integral reservoir. Pump contains a control valve which regulates oil pressure and flow.

LUBRICATION

FLUID TYPE

Use General Motors power steering fluid. DO NOT use ATF type fluid.

REMOVAL & INSTALLATION

POWER STEERING GEAR

Removal

1) Clean areas around hydraulic connections and disconnect return and pressure lines from steering gear. Plug lines and steering gear to prevent dirt from entering system and fluid from draining out.

2) Remove steering gear-to-intermediate shaft clamp bolt. Raise and support vehicle. Remove front wheels. Separate tie rods from steering knuckles.

3) Remove steering gear retaining bolts. Separate intermediate shaft "U" joint from steering gear. Lift steering gear to the side. Remove by guiding it diagonally downward through opening in engine compartment.

Installation

To install, reverse removal procedure. Tie rod ends are to be connected after gear assembly has been fully installed. Check wheel alignment.

OVERHAUL

POWER STEERING GEAR

Disassembly

1) With steering gear removed from vehicle, remove lock nuts and tie rod ends. Remove rubber boots and breather tube. Remove hydraulic lines from steering valve and steering housing.

2) Remove lock nut, adjusting plug, spring and piston from steering housing. Remove pinion dust cap. Using an 11/16" socket, hold pinion from rotating while removing pinion lock nut. Remove dust cover lock ring from upper pinion. *See Fig. 2.*

3) Press pinion (with spool valve) out of steering gear. The bearing, support, seal, and dust cover seal will come out with the pinion.

NOTE: **Do not use a hammer to remove pinion, or damage to pinion, spool valve and/or housing could result.**

4) Remove inner ball joint furthest from pinion. Clamp rack in a soft-jawed vise. Push plastic sleeve out of the way. Unscrew ball joint.

5) Remove lock-ring in end of hydraulic cylinder gear housing. Push rack into gear housing as far as it will go. Install Removal/Installer Sleeve (89 96 407) over rack. Tighten inner ball joint to press seal housing in.

6) Use a punch to depress wire end of lock-ring. Using 2 screwdrivers, pry out lock-ring. With ring removed, remove ball joint and special sleeve.

SAAB POWER-ASSISTED RACK & PINION (Cont.)

Fig. 1: Exploded View of Power Steering Components

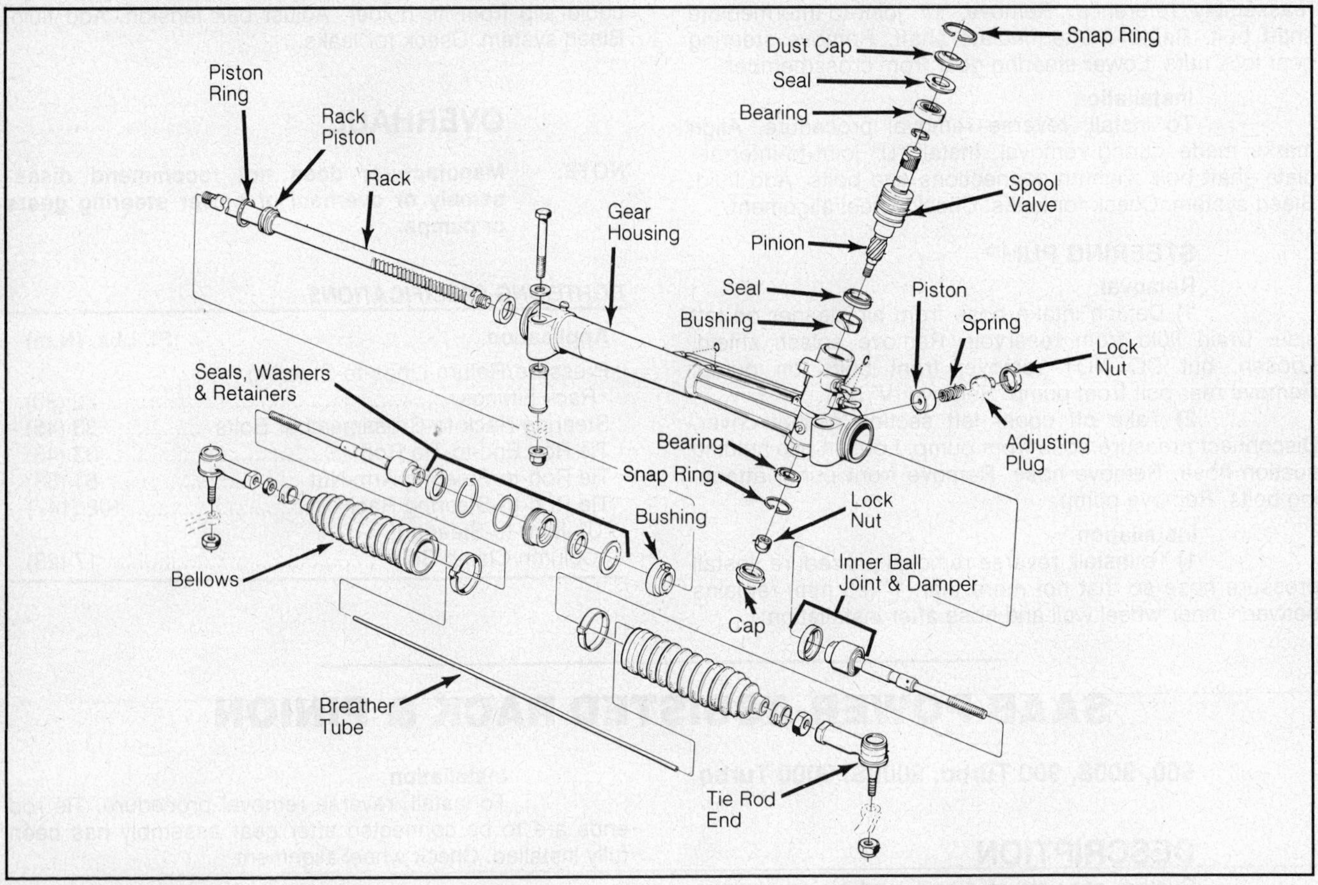

Courtesy of Saab-Scania of America, Inc.

7) Remove ball joint nearest pinion in same manner as first ball joint. Press out rack together with seal, washer and bushing. Ensure there are no burrs on rack before removing seal and bushing.

8) Using Seal Remover/Installer (89 96 399) and a long punch, remove inner rack. Insert lips of tool under seal. From opposite end of housing, insert long rod and drive out seal.

Fig. 2: Removing Pinion Lock Nut from Pinion Gear & Spool Valve

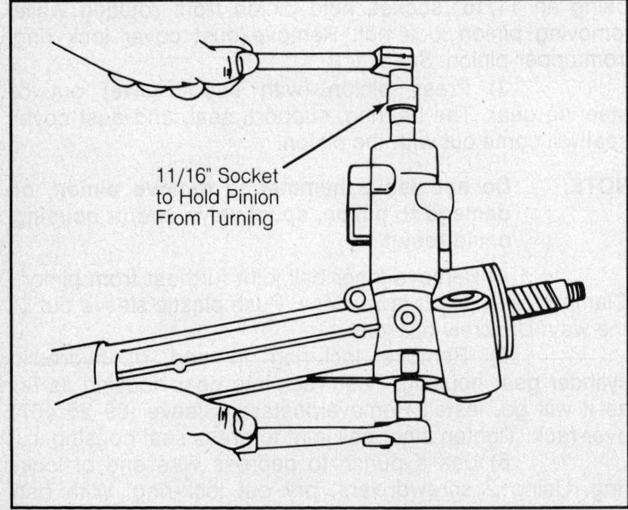

Wrap tape around serrations. Courtesy of Saab-Scania of America, Inc.

Fig. 3: Removing Wire Locking Ring from Steering Gear Housing

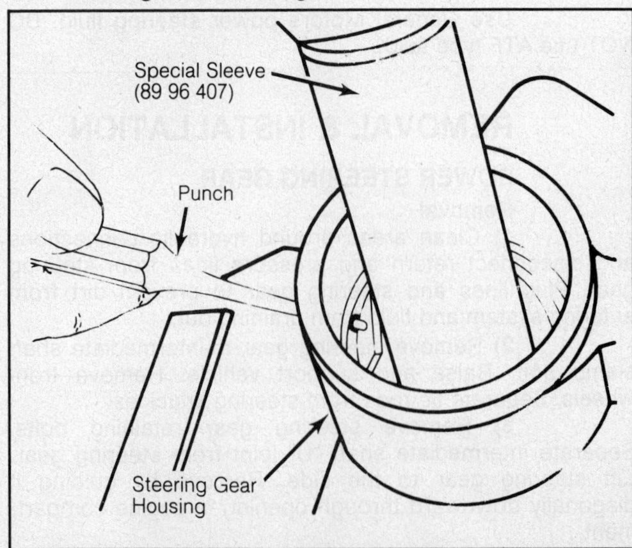

Courtesy of Saab-Scania of America, Inc.

SAAB POWER-ASSISTED RACK & PINION (Cont.)

Fig. 4: Removing Inner Rack Seal Using Remover/Installer & Long Rod

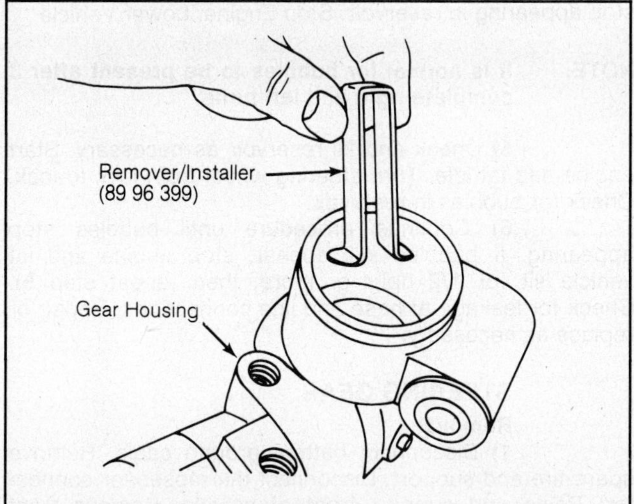

Courtesy of Saab-Scania of America, Inc.

9) Remove lock ring and lower pinion bearing. Remove sealing ring and bushing from top of housing.

Reassembly

1) Lubricate pinion gear, rack teeth, bearings and dust cover seal with lithium grease. Lubricate all hydraulic parts with power steering fluid.

2) Install lower pinion bearing (enclosed side of bearing facing downward) and lock ring (with chamfer on lock ring facing outward). Using Remover/Installer Sleeve (90 06 407), install upper pinion bushing and hydraulic seal into pinion housing of gear housing.

3) Install rack inner hydraulic seal onto rack. Use a thin plastic sheath, or metal foil to cover rack teeth to protect sealing lip of seal.

4) Install rack into housing. Install inner hydraulic seal into housing using rack piston as a press. Do not use more than 500 lbs. (226.8 kg) of force.

5) Install bushing in housing (smaller bore facing in). Install washer against bushing. Install new "O" ring on outer hydraulic seal support. Install old seal (if not damaged).

6) Slide sealing ring support carefully onto rack to avoid damaging sealing lip. Using Sleeve (83 90 148), press sealing ring support into housing. Center rack.

7) Rotate rack so that rack teeth will mesh with pinion gear teeth when it is installed. Hold pinion gear (with spool valve), so that groove in end of shaft points toward the left (9 o'clock position), when pinion teeth engage rack teeth.

8) Insert pinion. Pinion should rotate so that groove in end of pinion points toward front (12 o'clock position), with rack centered. Install pinion lock nut. Tighten lock nut. Install cover.

Fig. 5: Installing Pinion Gear & Spool Valve Into Gear Housing With Rack Installed

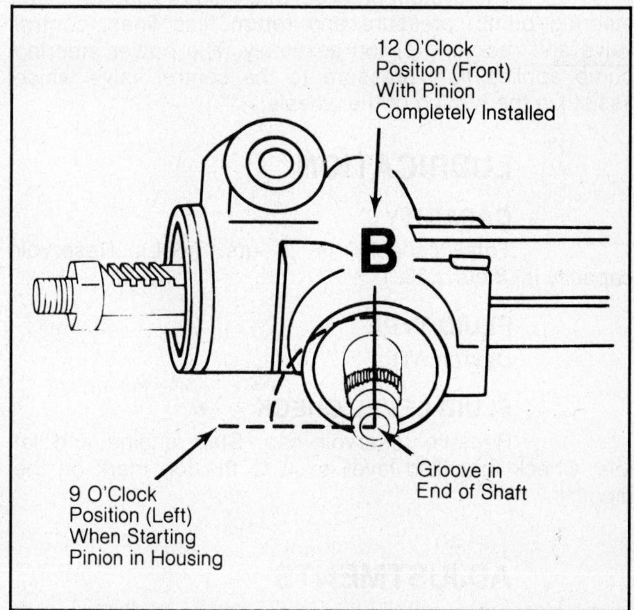

Courtesy of Saab-Scania of America, Inc.

9) Install washer, needle bearing, sealing ring, dust cover, and lock ring onto top of pinion gear (spool valve). Protect seal lips with tape or plastic sleeve over splines of pinion.

10) Install bearing piston, spring and adjusting nut in gear housing. Tighten adjusting nut until bearing piston firmly contacts rack. Back off adjusting nut 30-50 degrees. Install and tighten lock nut.

11) Install plastic sleeves (end stops) and inner ball joints, with tie rods, to rack ends. Hold rack in soft-jawed vise. Tighten ball joints. Lock inner ball joints by tapping tab on ball joint into rack. DO NOT use pinion as support when loosening or tightening ball joints.

12) Install lock ring for sealing ring support in end of gear housing. Turn pinion until inner ball joint presses against sealing ring support.

13) Press in support and, at the same time, install sealing ring in groove with a thin screwdriver. Install rubber boots, breathing tube and hydraulic lines.

TIGHTENING SPECIFICATIONS

Application	Ft. Lbs. (N.m)
Bearing Piston Lock Nut	48-55 (65-75)
Inner Ball Joint-to-Rack	59-72 (80-98)
Pinion Gear Lower Lock Nut	22-34 (30-46)
Steering Gear Clamp Bolt	44-60 (60-81)
Tie Rod End	37-44 (50-60)

SUBARU POWER RACK & PINION

DESCRIPTION

The system consists of a fluid reservoir, power steering pump, pressure and return fluid lines, control valve and rack and pinion assembly. The power steering pump applies fluid pressure to the control valve which assists in the turning of the wheels.

LUBRICATION

CAPACITY

Total capacity is .7 qts. (.66L). Reservoir capacity is .3 qts. (.28L).

FLUID TYPE

Dexron ATF.

FLUID LEVEL CHECK

Remove reservoir cap. Start engine and let idle. Check that fluid level is up to the top mark on the dipstick.

ADJUSTMENTS

RACK & PINION BACKLASH

1) Ensure sleeve is in contact with rack assembly. Tighten adjusting screw to 3.6 ft. lbs. (5 N.m). Back off screw 180 degrees. Turn adjusting screw until turning torque increases. Back off screw 15 degrees.

2) Tighten adjusting screw lock nut. Clearance should be .004" (.10 mm) or less between screw tip and sleeve. Tighten lock nut to 22-36 ft. lbs. (30-49 N.m).

REMOVAL & INSTALLATION

POWER STEERING PUMP

Removal

1) Disconnect battery ground cable. Drain fluid from reservoir. Loosen power steering pump pulley nut but do not remove at this time. Loosen drive belts.

2) Remove pulley. Using 2 wrenches, disconnect hose from side of reservoir and power steering pump. Cap hoses to prevent contamination.

3) On XT Coupe, remove hold-down clamp securing hose to reservoir. Loosen bolt holding reservoir to bracket. Remove reservoir and pump as an assembly.

4) On all others, remove 3 pump-to-bracket bolts. Remove pump and reservoir assembly. Do not remove bracket unless replacing.

5) Place assembly in a soft-jawed vise. Remove reservior from top of pump. Using 2 wrenches, remove hydraulic pipe from pump. Discard all "O" rings.

Installation

1) Install bracket on engine if removed. Using 2 wrenches, install hydraulic pipe on pump. Install a new "O" ring on reservoir. Install reservoir on pump.

2) To complete installation, reverse removal procedure. Fill reservoir with fluid. Attach ground cable to battery. Raise and support vehicle. Slowly turn steering wheel lock-to-lock.

3) Repeat procedure until bubbles stop appearing in the reservoir. Do not allow fluid level to become low at any time during this procedure.

4) Start engine and let idle. Slowly turn steering wheel from lock-to-lock. Repeat until bubbles stop appearing in reservoir. Stop Engine. Lower Vehicle.

NOTE: **It is normal for bubbles to be present after 3 complete right and left turns.**

5) Check and fill reservoir as necessary. Start engine and let idle. Turn steering wheel from lock-to-lock. Check for bubbles in reservoir.

6) Continue procedure until bubbles stop appearing. If bubbles still appear, stop engine and let vehicle sit for 1/2 hour or more, then repeat step **5)**. Check for leakage at hose and line connections. Repair or replace as necessary.

STEERING GEAR

Removal

1) Disconnect battery ground cable. Remove spare tire and support. Disconnect thermosensor connector. Raise and support front of vehicle. Remove front wheels. Remove front exhaust pipe.

2) Remove cotter pins and castle nuts. Using tie rod end remover, remove tie rod ends from steering knuckles. Remove steering gear lower plate and clamp. Remove steering gear center pipe joint.

3) Drain steering fluid by turning steering wheel lock-to-lock. Drain steering fluid from other pipes using the same procedure. Remove "U" joint lower side clamp bolt and upper side clamp bolt.

NOTE: **Mark joint and mating serration for reinstallation. Do not damage control valve pipes.**

4) Move "U" joint upward. Disconnect pump-to-valve hydraulic lines. Disconnect upper hydraulic line from control valve first, and lower hydraulic line second.

5) Remove valve-to-rack housing hydraulic pipes. Remove lower valve-to-rack housing hydraulic pipe first, and upper pipe second. Remove bolts securing steering gear to crossmember. Remove steering gear.

Inspection

1) Mount steering gear in vise and Stand (926200000). Mount dial indicator on pinion shaft. Check axial play. Dial indicator reading should be .004" (.10 mm) or less. Check pinion shaft play in radial direction. Dial indicator reading should be .007" (.18 mm).

2) Mount steering gear in vise and Stand (926200000). Using a spring scale, check sliding resistance of rack. Sliding resistance should be 55 lbs. (75 N.m).

3) Using a dial indicator, check rack shaft play in radial direction. With about 22 lbs. (30 N.m) of force applied, right turn steering radial play should be .006" (.15 mm) or less.

4) With about 22 lbs. (30 N.m) of force applied, left turn steering radial play should be .012" (.30 mm) or less from side-to-side and .006" (.15 mm) or less when moved up and down.

Installation

To install, reverse removal procedure. Check wheel alignment.

SUBARU POWER RACK & PINION (Cont.)

VALVE ASSEMBLY

Removal (XT Coupe)

1) With steering gear removed from vehicle, mount steering gear in vise and Stand (926200000). Loosen 2 bolts securing control valve assembly to rack housing.

2) Remove valve housing and pinion and valve assembly as a unit. Note shim pack amount. DO NOT remove pinion from valve assembly or dust seal will be damaged.

3) Note relative position of rack and pinion teeth. Remove pinion and valve assembly from valve housing (if necessary).

Installation

1) Clean mating surface of valve housing-to-rack housing. Attach shim(s) to stepped lip of rack housing using Fuji Bond C (004403004). Use same number of shims as removed.

2) Remove rack shaft so end of shaft protrudes 3.03" (76.9 mm) from pinion side of rack housing face. Grease pinion gear teeth and bearing. Position pinion shaft so cutout section faces sleeve boss.

3) If top of pinion tooth is in center position when viewed from sleeve side, pinion shaft is positioned correctly. If bottom of tooth is in center, turn pinion shaft 180 degrees.

4) Push valve assembly into rack housing. Position rack shaft as in step **2)**. Alternately tighten bolts to 14-22 ft. lbs. (20-29 N.m). Ensure cutout section of input shaft is facing in proper direction.

Removal (All Except XT Coupe)

1) With steering gear removed from vehicle, mount steering gear in vise and Stand (926200000). Loosen 2 bolts securing valve assembly to rack housing.

2) Carefully withdraw valve assembly with pinion shaft. Using a 1.65-1.73" (42-44 mm) diameter bar and a press, drive pinion shaft with pinion valve from valve housing (if necessary).

Fig. 1: Exploded View of Subaru XT Steering System

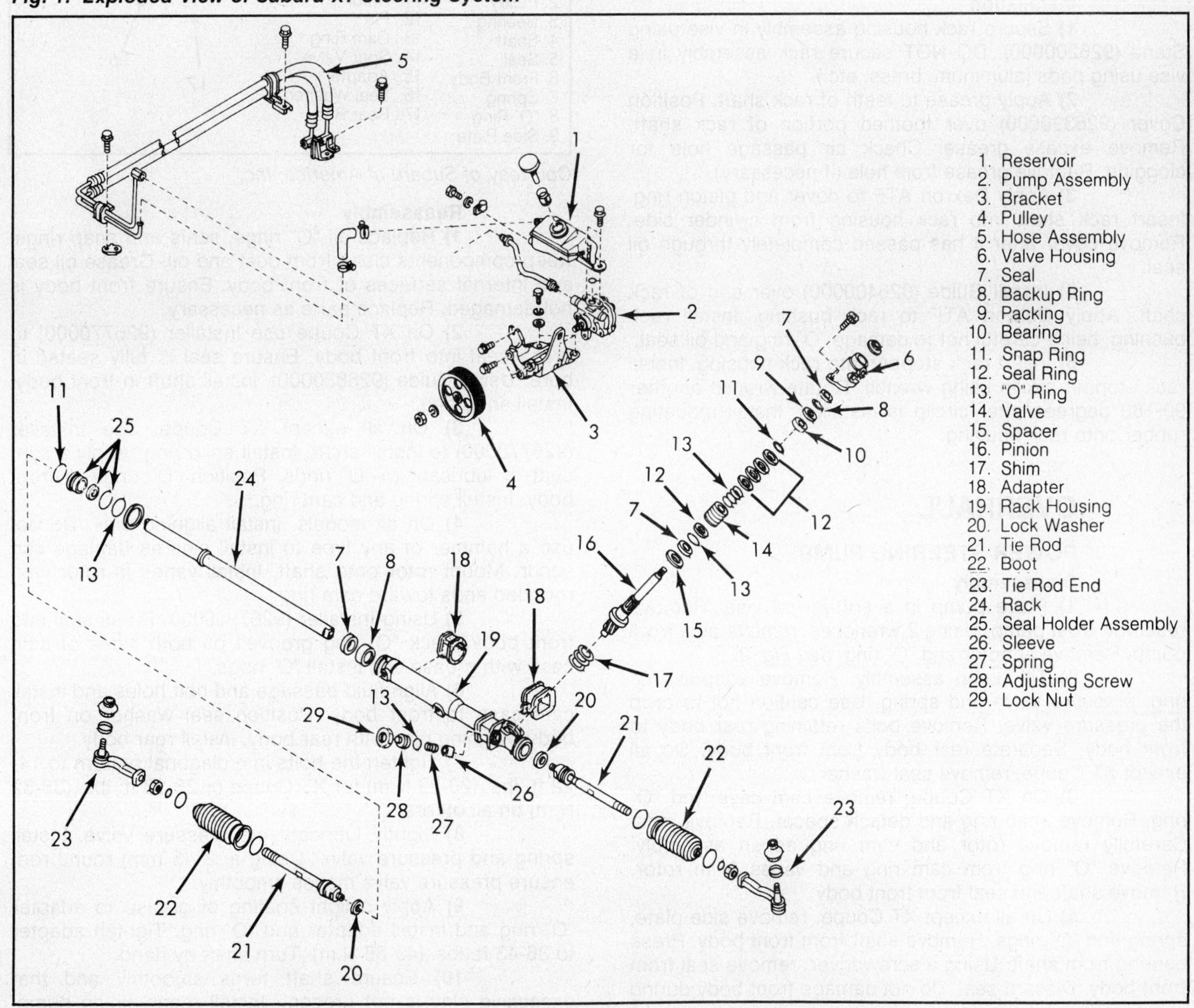

Courtesy of Subaru of America, Inc.

SUBARU POWER RACK & PINION (Cont.)

Installation

1) Apply grease to pinion gear and bearing of valve housing. Center steering rack in rack housing. If centered correctly, distance from end of rack housing to end of rack shaft will be 3". Install new packing.

2) Position valve assembly to rack housing with rack teeth facing pinion. Ensure cutout portion of pinion shaft serration faces toward adjusting screw hole. Tighten bolts alternately to 14-22 ft. lbs. (20-29 N.m).

STEERING RACK

Removal

1) With steering gear removed from vehicle, mount steering gear in vise and Stand (926200000). Slide back mounting rubber to expose slit.

2) Using Wrench (926340000), rotate rack stopper clockwise until end of circlip comes out of stopper. Rotate counterclockwise and pull out circlip.

3) Remove rack bushing assembly and rack stopper together with rack shaft from cylinder side. Ensure rack shaft does not contact inner wall of cylinder when removing. Remove rack bushing assembly and rack stopper from rack shaft. Discard rack bushing.

Installation

1) Secure rack housing assembly in vise using Stand (926200000). DO NOT secure rack assembly in a vise using pads (aluminum, brass, etc.).

2) Apply grease to teeth of rack shaft. Position Cover (926390000) over toothed portion of rack shaft. Remove excess grease. Check air passage hole for clogging. Remove grease from hole (if necessary).

3) Apply Dexron ATF to cover and piston ring. Insert rack shaft into rack housing from cylinder side. Remove cover after it has passed completely through oil seal.

4) Install Guide (926400000) over end of rack shaft. Apply Dexron ATF to rack bushing. Install rack bushing, being careful not to damage "O" ring and oil seal.

5) Insert rack stopper into rack housing. Install rack stopper circlip using wrench. Rotate wrench another 90-180 degrees after circlip is installed. Install mounting rubber onto rack housing.

OVERHAUL

POWER STEERING PUMP

Disassembly

1) Place pump in a soft-jawed vise. Remove reservoir from pump. Using 2 wrenches, remove pipe from pump. Remove adapter and "O" ring. *See Fig. 2.*

2) Tilt pump assembly. Remove adapter, "O" ring, pressure valve and spring. Use caution not to drop the pressure valve. Remove bolts retaining rear body to front body. Separate rear body from front body. On all except XT Coupe, remove seal washer.

3) On XT Coupe, remove cam case and "O" ring. Remove snap ring and detach spacer. Remove pins. Carefully remove rotor and cam ring as an assembly. Remove "O" ring from cam ring and vanes from rotor. Remove shaft and seal from front body.

4) On all except XT Coupe, remove side plate, spring and "O" rings. Remove shaft from front body. Press bearing from shaft. Using a screwdriver, remove seal from front body. Discard seal. Do not damage front body during seal removal.

Fig. 2: Exploded View of Power Steering Pump

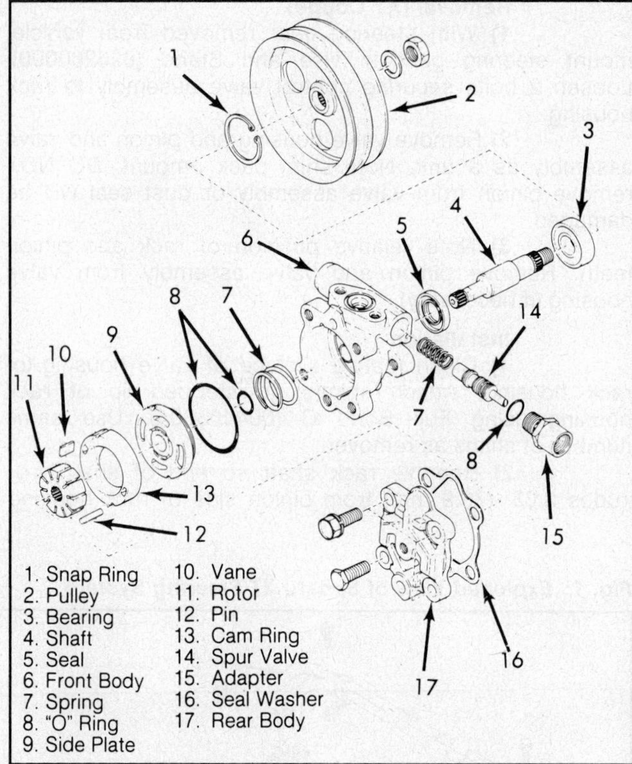

Courtesy of Subaru of America, Inc.

Reassembly

1) Replace all "O" rings, seals and snap rings. Keep components clean from dust and oil. Grease oil seal and internal surfaces of front body. Ensure front body is not damaged. Replace parts as necessary.

2) On XT Coupe use Installer (926770000) to press seal into front body. Ensure seal is fully seated in bore. Using Guide (926830000), install shaft in front body. Install snap ring.

3) On all except XT Coupe, use Installer (926770000) to install shaft. Install snap ring. Apply a light coat of lubricant to "O" rings. Position "O" rings in front body. Install spring and cam ring.

4) On all models, install aligning pins. Do not use a hammer of any type to install pins as damage can occur. Mount rotor onto shaft. Install vanes in rotor with rounded ends toward cam ring.

5) Using Installer (9267900000) Press seal into front body. Pack "O" ring grooves on both sides of cam case with grease and install "O" rings.

6) Align fluid passage and bolt holes and install cam case to front body. Position seal washer on front body. Aligning pins with rear body, install rear body.

7) Tighten the bolts in a diagonal pattern to 14-22 ft. lbs. (20-29 N.m) for XT Coupe or 28-38 ft. lbs. (38-52 N.m) on all others.

8) Lightly lubricate the pressure valve. Install spring and pressure valve. Using a .2" (5 mm) round rod, ensure pressure valve moves smoothly.

9) Apply a light coating of grease to adapter "O" ring and install adapter and "O" ring. Tighten adapter to 36-43 ft. lbs. (49-58 N.m). Turn shaft by hand.

10) Ensure shaft turns smoothly and that excessive play is not present. Install reservoir on pump. Install pipe to pump. Install pump in vehicle.

SUBARU POWER RACK & PINION (Cont.)

STEERING GEAR

Disassembly

1) Place steering gear in vise and Stand (926200000). Remove clip from boot. Move boot toward tie rod end side. Remove boot and clips.

2) Push rack into steering gear. Using chisel, straighten tie rod lock washer. Using Wrench (925700000) and Spanner (926230000), loosen ball joint.

3) Remove tie rod from rack assembly. Using spanner loosen lock nut and remove adjusting screw. Remove spring, sleeve, dust seal, and dust cover (if equipped).

Inspection

Clean all parts. Check for wear or damage. Replace any worn or damaged parts. Check for water inside of steering gear. If water is found inside of steering gear, replace boot, clips, input shaft, shaft dust seal, and adjusting screw "O" ring.

Reassembly

1) Apply Valiant (M2) grease to rack teeth, sliding portion of rack shaft, sleeve insertion hole, dust seal, and dust cover hole. Press dust seal into steering gear.

2) Maximum distance between steering gear and dust seal should be .08" (2.0 mm). Apply grease to dust cover and install cover on input shaft.

NOTE: Ensure lip of dust cover comes into contact with housing end distance of 0-.02" (0-.5 mm). If dust cover is installed too far on input shaft, steering wheel will not turn smoothly.

3) Apply grease to sliding surface of sleeve and spring seat. Insert sleeve into pinion housing. Insert spring into sleeve screw. Pack grease inside screw, and install screw.

4) Adjust backlash of rack and pinion. See ADJUSTMENTS in this article. Install new lock washer on threaded portion of rack end. Align cut portion of rack and nail of washer. Install and tighten ball joint using Wrench (925700000) and Spanner (926230000).

5) Remove steering gear from vice and Stand (926200000). Bend lock washer toward ball joint surface. Install boot clips and boot unto steering gear while holding boot flange.

6) After boot is installed, fold back boot flange so large clip cannot be seen. If tie rod end was removed, screw in lock nut and tie rod end unto threaded portion of tie rod. Tighten lock nut.

VALVE ASSEMBLY

Disassembly (XT Coupe)

Remove dust cover. Push pinion and valve assembly out of valve housing. Use a press if necessary. Do not allow serrated edges of input shaft to contact "Y" packing. Using Remover (926290000), drive dust seal, back-up ring, "Y" packing and bearing from housing.

Reassembly

1) Apply grease to inside of valve housing, back-up ring and "Y" packing. Apply grease to mating surface of Installer (926300000). Drive dust seal into place. Ensure seal faces in proper direction. Drive in "Y" packing and back up ring. Ensure "Y" packing faces in proper direction.

2) Use Remover (926290000) to press bearing into place. Fill dust seal with grease. Apply grease to Guide (926310000) and input shaft. Install guide over end of input shaft. Insert pinion and valve assembly into valve housing until lip of pinion oil seal touches valve housing. Push valve housing in until pinion and valve assembly fits.

3) Apply grease to lip of dust cover. Install cover until it butts up against graded section of input shaft. Ensure there is 0-.020" (0-.50 mm) clearance between dust cover lip and end of housing or steering wheel will not return smoothly.

Disassembly (All Except XT Coupe)

Pry off dust cover using a screwdriver. Remove snap ring. Pry off oil seal using a screwdriver. Remove snap ring and discard. Using a bar 1.46-1.50" (37.0-38.0 mm) in diameter, press out bearing with backing washer. Discard bearing. Remove and discard oil seal.

Reassembly

1) To reassemble, apply Dexron ATF to seal and press in housing using Installer (926350000). Install snap ring and dust cover. Apply Dexron ATF to outer surface of input shaft and valve body seal ring.

2) Install pinion and valve assembly into valve housing. Be careful not to damage seal. Put Installer (926360000) over pinion. Apply Dexron ATF to oil seal and installer. Insert oil seal into installer.

3) Insert oil seal into housing until installer contacts housing end face. Install backing washer. Press on bearing using Installer (926370000). Install snap ring.

RACK HOUSING

Disassembly (XT Coupe)

1) Attach Remover (926260000) to snap ring through hole in boot groove on cylinder side of rack housing. Lightly tap remover with hammer to drive out snap ring. Push on rack from valve side of housing and remove with holder assembly from opposite side.

2) Ensure rack does not contact inner wall of cylinder when removing. Insert Remover (926330000) from valve side into housing and push out back up ring and oil seal.

Inspection

Inspect rack housing needle bearing for missing or bent needle rollers. If defective, replace rack housing.

Reassembly

1) Attach rack housing to Stand (926200000). Apply grease to rack housing needle bearing. Attach oil seal to Installer (926240000). Insert installer with oil seal into rack housing from gear side. Install oil seal near piston. Install back up ring to rack housing from gear side. Ensure ring is installed in proper direction.

2) Apply grease to rack teeth grooves, sleeve sliding portion and piston sealing surface. Do not allow grease to enter vent hole in rack. Insert rack assembly into cylinder side of rack housing. Attach Guide (926250000) to exposed end of rack shaft.

3) Apply grease to rack shaft and guide. Apply grease to inner surface of holder assembly and "O" ring. Insert onto rack shaft. Attach holder assembly to rack housing. Be careful not to damage "Y" packing when installing holder assembly.

SUBARU POWER RACK & PINION (Cont.)

4) Apply grease to snap ring and install into groove to secure holder assembly. Attach Installer (926320000) to cylinder side of rack housing. Drive back up ring and oil seal into place.

Disassembly (All Except XT Coupe)

Attach unchamfered end of Remover (926410000) to rack housing from pinion housing side. Drive out oil seal and back-up washer at the same time.

Inspection

Inspect rack housing needle bearing for missing or bent needle rollers. If defective, replace rack housing.

Reassembly

Apply Dexron ATF to new oil seal. Using Installer (926380000), push in back-up washer and oil seal. Do not scratch cylinder inner wall. Ensure washer and oil seal are installed in the proper direction.

TIGHTENING SPECIFICATIONS

Application	Ft. Lbs. (N.m)
Front Pump Body-to-Rear Pump Body Bolt	
XT Coupe	14-22 (20-29)
All Except XT Coupe	28-38 (38-52)
Pulley Retaining Nut	31-46 (42-62)
Pump Adapter Bolt	
XT Coupe	36-43 (49-59)
All Except XT Coupe	51-58 (69-78)
Pump Bracket-to-Engine Bolt	13-16 (18-22)
Pump Bracket-to-Pump Bolt	22-36 (29-49)
Rack Mounting Bolts	35-52 (47-71)
Reservoir Mounting Bolt	14-22 (20-29)
Tie Rod-to-Steering Rack	58 (78)
Tie Rod End Castle Nut	18-22 (25-29)
Tie Rod End Lock Nut	58-65 (78-88)
Valve Housing Bolt	14-22 (20-29)

TOYOTA POWER-ASSISTED RACK & PINION

Camry, Celica, Corolla, Cressida, Supra, Tercel, Van

DESCRIPTION

System consists of a frame mounted rack and pinion assembly, a flow control valve, hydraulic pump and high pressure hoses. Flow control valve regulates hydraulic pressure in proportion to steering effort.

The power steering pump is a belt-driven vane-type. Pump components include an engine-driven eccentric rotor with vane plates, an eccentric cam ring, and a flow control valve to regulate amount of oil flow and maximum oil pressure.

LUBRICATION

CAPACITY

All Except Corolla .83 qt. (.80L).
Corolla .73 qt. (.70L).

FLUID TYPE

Fluid type is Dexron II ATF.

SYSTEM BLEEDING

1) Raise and support vehicle. Fill fluid to proper level in reservoir. Turn wheels fully in both directions. Recheck fluid level.

2) Start engine and let idle. Turn steering from lock-to-lock 2 or 3 times. Lower vehicle. Run engine at 1000 RPM or less. Turn wheel from lock-to-lock 2 or 3 times. Center steering wheel.

3) If fluid level does not rise and no foaming of fluid is evident, bleeding is complete. If level rises more than .20" (5.0 mm), or if foaming is evident, repeat procedure until air is released.

FLUID REPLACEMENT

1) Raise and support vehicle. Disconnect return hose. Drain fluid into container. Turn steering wheel from lock-to-lock while draining. Cap reservoir return tube.

2) Fill reservoir with fluid. Start engine and run for one to 2 seconds. Stop engine and refill reservoir. Repeat 4 or 5 times, or until no more air is in fluid. Reconnect return hose. Add fluid. Bleed system.

ADJUSTMENTS

BELT TENSION

Using a belt tension gauge, adjust belt tension to 60-100 lbs. (27-45 kg). If belt is new, adjust to 100-150 lbs. (45-68 kg).

TESTING

AIR CONTROL VALVE TESTING

Start engine. Turn steering wheel right and left. Ensure engine RPM does not decrease more than 50 RPM. Pinch air hose shut. Turn steering wheel right and left. Ensure engine RPM decreases about 200 RPM.

HYDRAULIC PRESSURE TESTING

1) On all models, disconnect pressure lines from steering gear case and vane pump. Attach pressure gauge with gauge side connected to vane pump.

2) Attach valve side of gauge to pressure line. Bleed air from system. Check fluid level. With engine at idle and with valve closed, check fluid pressure.

TOYOTA POWER-ASSISTED RACK & PINION

HYDRAULIC PRESSURE

Application	psi (kg/cm²)
Camry	1066 (75)
Celica	1024 (72)
Corolla	1066 (75)
Cressida	924 (65)
Supra	924 (65)
Tercel	782 (55)
Van	1066 (75)

NOTE: **Do not keep pressure gauge valve closed for more than 10 seconds. Fluid testing temperature should be 176°F (80°C).**

3) Open valve fully. Note pressure with engine at idle, and again at 3000 RPM. Pressure difference should be less than 71 psi (5 kg/cm²). If more, check flow control valve.

4) With steering wheel at lock position and pressure valve open, recheck pressure. Pressure should be 782 psi (55 kg/cm²) for Tercel, 1024 psi (72 kg/cm²) for Celica, 142-248 psi (10-20 kg/cm²) for Cressida, and 1066 psi (75 kg/cm²) for all other models.

5) With vehicle on flat surface, turn steering wheel to center position. With engine idling and using a spring gauge, measure steering turning force at steering wheel outer rim, in both directions.

6) Turning force should not exceed 12.1 lbs. (5.5 kg) on Corolla and Tercel, or 8.8 lbs. (4.0 kg) on all other models.

REMOVAL & INSTALLATION

POWER STEERING PUMP

Removal (Camry & Celica)

1) Raise and support vehicle on safety stands. Remove right front wheel. Remove lower crossmember. Remove air control valve vacuum hose.

2) Remove pressure and return lines, plug lines and elevate to prevent loss of fluid. Push down on drive belt and remove pulley nut. Remove 2 mounting bolts, belt and pump.

Installation

1) Loosely install pump with 2 mounting bolts. Install pulley, nut and belt. Adjust belt tension. See ADJUSTMENTS in this article. Push down on belt and tighten pulley nut to 32 ft. lbs. (43 N.m).

2) Install pressure and return lines. Tighten pressure line to 38 ft. lbs. (51 N.m) on Camry, 34 ft. lbs. (47 N.m) on Celica. Install lower crossmember and tighten 2 center bolts to 29 ft. lbs. (39 N.m), other bolts to 153 ft. lbs. (208 N.m). Fill and bleed system. See SYSTEM BLEEDING in this article.

Removal (Supra)

1) Loosen air hose clips as necessary to remove hoses from air flow meter. Disconnect electrical connector at air flow meter. Remove air flow meter bracket bolt and air cleaner box clips. Remove air flow meter.

2) Loosen 2 clamps and remove reservoir-to-pump hoses. Remove reservoir bracket bolts and reservoir. Disconnect 2 hoses from air control valve on pump. Remove adjusting strut and engine under cover.

3) Remove pressure line at pump. Remove pulley nut, belt and pulley. Remove mounting bolts and remove pump.

Installation

To install, reverse removal procedure. Tighten all bolts and nuts to specification. See TIGHTENING SPECIFICATIONS table in this article. Fill and bleed system. See SYSTEM BLEEDING in this article.

Removal (Other Models)

1) If equipped with air conditioning, fan shroud must be removed on Celica. Push down on belt and remove pulley nut. Loosen pump adjusting bolt and remove belt and pulley.

2) Using a syringe, remove oil from reservoir. Disconnect pressure and return lines at pump. Remove air control valve hoses if equipped. Remove pump mounting bolts and remove pump.

Installation

To install, reverse removal procedure. Tighten all bolts and nuts to specification. See TIGHTENING SPECIFICATIONS table in this article. Fill and bleed system. See SYSTEM BLEEDING in this article.

STEERING GEAR

Removal (FWD Models)

1) Raise and support vehicle on safety stands. Remove wheel assemblies. Remove tie rod end nuts and press out of steering arm.

2) On Tercel Sedan, remove charcoal cannister, cannister bracket, and steering column hole cover for access to bolts.

3) Match mark steering coupler "U" joint, remove bolt and disconnect. Remove pressure and return lines. Remove air control vacuum valve hose and exhaust pipe on Tercel Sedan.

4) On Camry and Corolla, remove lower engine cover. Remove engine mount bracket and center cross-members.

5) Remove steering gear mounting brackets and remove steering gear. Use care to not tear rack boots when removing from chassis.

Installation

To install, reverse removal procedure. Tighten all bolts and nuts to specification. See TIGHTENING SPECIFICATIONS table in this article.

Removal (RWD Models)

1) Raise and support vehicle on safety stands. Remove wheel assemblies. Remove tie rod end nuts and press out of steering arm.

2) Remove engine undercover if equipped. Match mark steering coupler and disconnect at "U" joint. On Corolla and Celica, remove front exhaust pipe. On Supra and Cressida, remove steering damper. Disconnect solenoid wires on Cressida.

3) On Celica remove lower crossmember, engine mounting center member and rear mount bracket.

4) Remove any line clamp bolts that may interfere with gear removal. Remove steering gear mounting brackets and remove steering gear. Use care to not tear rack boots when removing from chassis.

Power Steering

TOYOTA POWER-ASSISTED RACK & PINION (Cont.)

Fig. 1: Exploded View of Front Differential

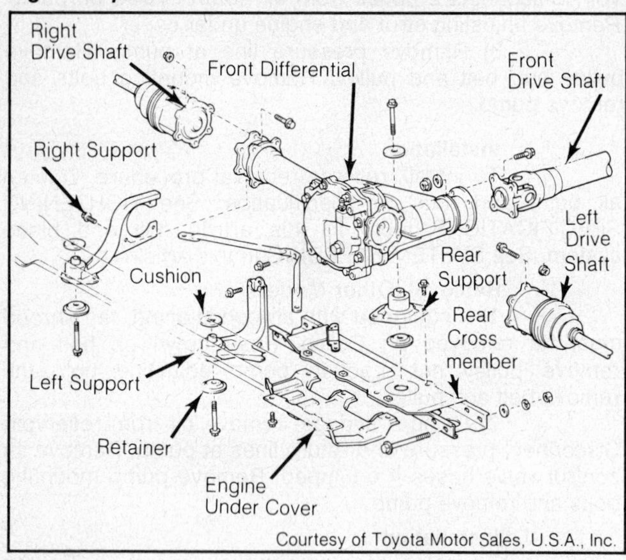

Courtesy of Toyota Motor Sales, U.S.A., Inc.

Installation

To install, reverse removal procedure. Tighten all bolts and nuts to specification. See TIGHTENING SPECIFICATIONS table in this article.

Removal (Van 2WD & 4WD Models)

1) Raise and support vehicle on safety stands. Remove wheel assemblies. Remove tie rod end nuts and press out of steering arm.

2) On 4WD Van, Remove front differential. Drain differential oil. Match mark front drive shaft and disconnect at front. Disconnect left and right drive shafts from side gear shafts and support with wire. *See Fig. 1.*

3) Remove engine under cover. Support front differential with jack. Remove air conditioner surge tank bolts. Remove crossmember rear support bolt and cushion. Remove 4 bolts and remove rear crossmember.

4) Remove the bolts, cushions and retainers holding the supports to the front crossmember. Lower jack slowly and remove differential.

5) Remove engine undercover on 2WD Van. Match mark torque shaft-to-pinion shaft coupler. Remove 3 bolts retaining bevel gear housing to chassis. Remove coupler pinch bolt and disconnect steering coupler.

6) Remove any line clamps that may interfere with gear removal. Remove pressure and return lines. Use care to not tear rack boots when removing steering gear from chassis.

Installation

1) To install steering gear, reverse removal procedure. Tighten all bolts and nuts to specification. See TIGHTENING SPECIFICATIONS table in this article.

2) To install front differential on 4WD. Raise differential assembly with jack and install right and left supports-to-front crossmember, do not tighten support bolts. Install rear crossmember,surge tank bolts, rear cushion and support bolt.

3) Tighten cushion support bolt and right and left support bolts to 50 ft. lbs. (68 N.m). Tighten rear crossmember mounting bolts to 70 ft. lbs. (95N.m).

4) Install engine under cover. Install driveshafts to side gear shafts and tighten to 50 ft. lbs. (68 N.m). Align match mark and install front driveshaft, tighten to 31 ft. lbs. (42 N.m). Fill differential with gear oil.

OVERHAUL

POWER STEERING PUMP

Disassembly (Corolla & Tercel)

1) Remove drive pulley. Place power steering pump in vise. Remove reservoir and bracket from pump. On Corolla models, remove "O" ring. On all models, remove pressure port union, flow control valve and spring. *See Fig. 2.*

Fig. 2: Exploded View of Toyota Power Steering Pump Assemblies

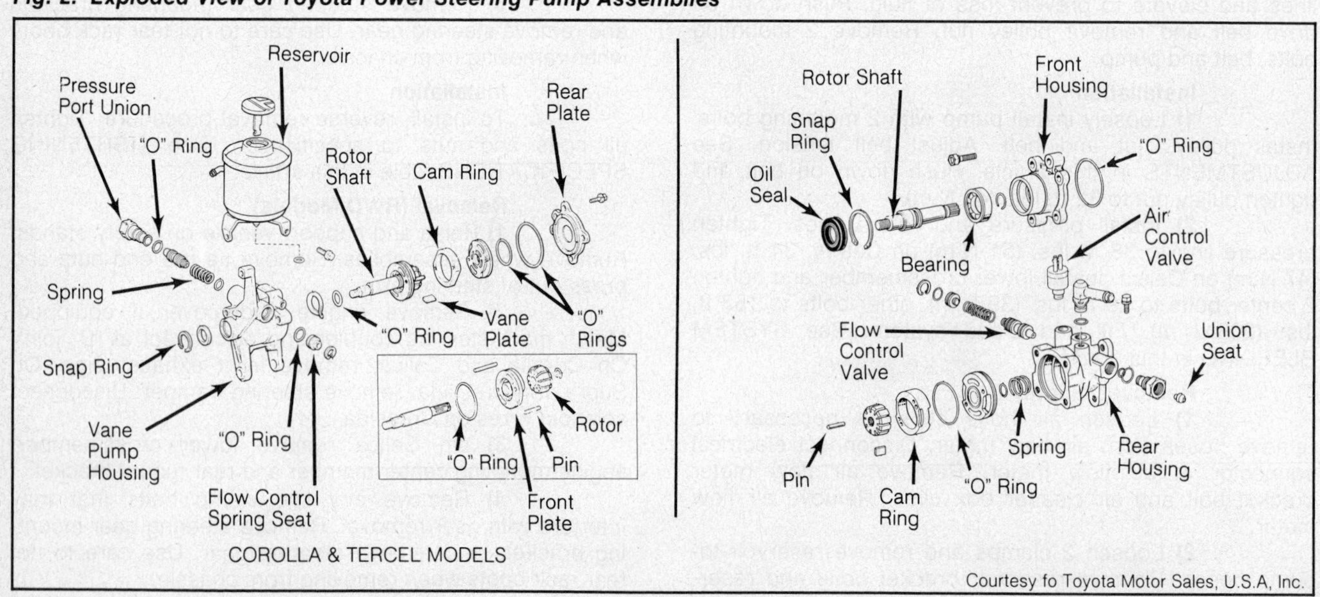

Courtesy fo Toyota Motor Sales, U.S.A, Inc.

Power Steering

TOYOTA POWER-ASSISTED RACK & PINION (Cont.)

Fig. 3: Checking Pump Housing Bushing-to-RotorShaft Clearance

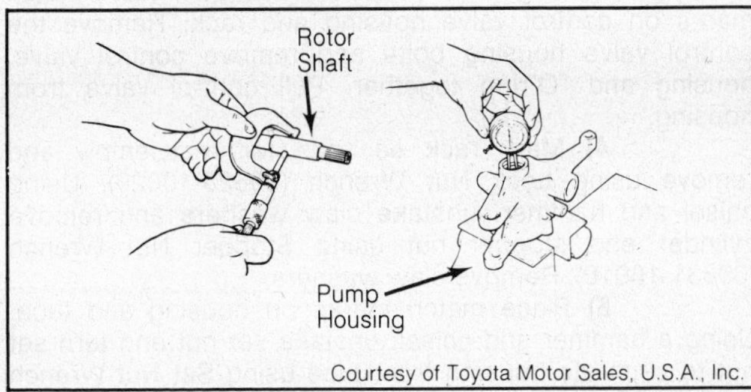

Courtesy of Toyota Motor Sales, U.S.A., Inc.

2) Remove spring seat snap ring. Install a bolt into spring seat to remove seat. Mark front and rear housings for reassembly reference. Remove rear housing. Remove rear side plate, vane plate(s) and rotor shaft assembly. Disassemble rotor, shaft and front side plate.

Disassembly (All Others)

1) Remove union from rear housing. Mark front and rear housings for reassembly reference. Remove front housing bolts. Using plastic mallet, tap off front housing.

Fig. 4: Checking Flow Control Valve

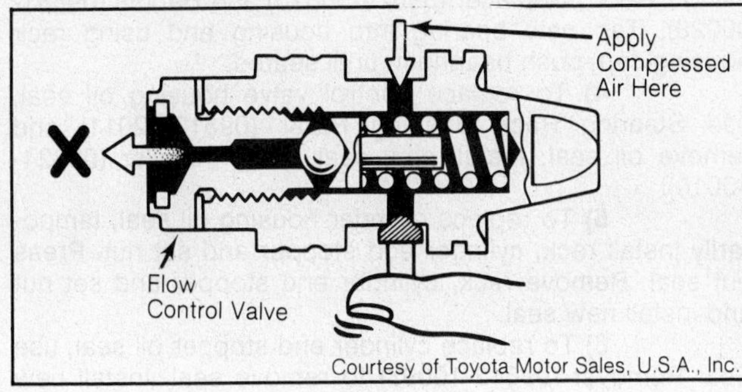

Courtesy of Toyota Motor Sales, U.S.A., Inc.

Fig. 5: View of Power Steering Pump Rotor & Cam Ring Marks

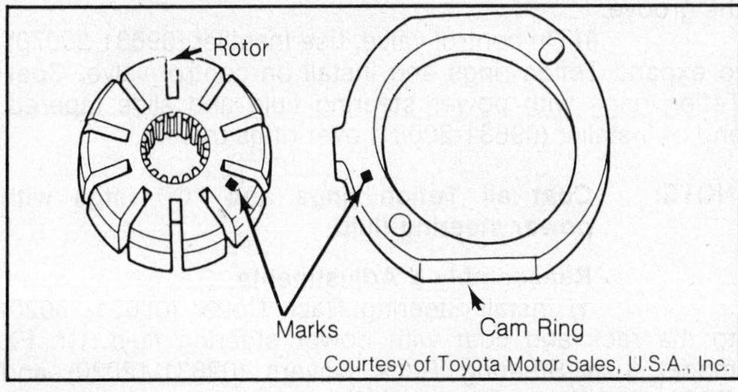

Courtesy of Toyota Motor Sales, U.S.A., Inc.

2) DO NOT let vane plates, rotor and cam plate fall out. Carefully remove cam ring, rotor and vane plates. Clamp front housing in a vise. Using chisel, pry off oil seal. Remove snap ring. Using plastic mallet, lightly tap the rotor shaft out of front housing and tap bottom of rear housing.

3) Remove rear plate and spring. Temporarily install a bolt into plug. Push in bolt. Remove snap ring. Pull out bolt with plug. Remove spring and control valve by hand. Remove pressure port union.

Inspection

1) Check all parts for wear or damage and replace as necessary. Check oil clearance between pump housing bushing and rotor shaft. *See Fig. 3.* If difference is greater than .0028" (.07 mm), replace complete pump assembly. Discard all "O" rings and replace with new ones.

2) Measure difference between cam ring and rotor. Maximum difference should be .0024" (.06 mm). Replace cam ring with one that has same letter stamped on rotor (if necessary).

3) Check vane plates for wear or damage. Celica, Supra and Van vane plate dimensions should be .589 x .307 x .067" (14.97 x 7.80 x 1.70 mm). All other models vane plate dimensions should be .590 x .319 x .070" (14.99 x 8.10 x 1.79 mm).

4) Maximum clearance between vane plate and rotor groove is .0024" (.06 mm) for Celica, Supra and Van. For all other models, clearance is .0011" (.028 mm).

5) Check flow control valve for leakage with compressed air. *See Fig. 4.* On Celica, Supra and Van models, minimum control valve spring length is 1.85" (47 mm). On all others, control valve spring length is 1.85-1.97" (47-50 mm).

Reassembly (Corolla & Tercel)

1) Coat all sliding surfaces with ATF. Install "O" rings on front side plate. Position side plate on shaft. Place rotor (with mark facing up) onto shaft. *See Fig. 5.* Secure with snap ring.

2) Grease oil seal. Install long straight pin into front housing. Using plastic hammer, tap rotor shaft into front housing. Install pin.

3) Install cam ring with mark facing outward. Install vane plates with rounded end facing outward. Install new "O" ring to rear side plate. Install plate on cam ring. Align pin holes with pins.

4) Install wave washer and new "O" ring in rear housing. Using a plastic mallet, tap rear housing into position. Install snap ring. Ensure rotor shaft operates smoothly. Install pulley nut and check rotating torque. Torque should be less than 2.4 INCH lbs. (2.7 N.m).

5) Install flow control spring seat, "O" ring and snap ring. Install spring, flow control valve, "O" rings and pressure port union. Tighten pressure port union. Install reservoir "O" ring, reservoir tank and bracket.

Reassembly (All Others)

1) Coat all sliding surfaces with ATF. Install control valve, spring, plug and snap ring to pump. Using a plastic mallet, install rotor shaft in front housing. Install snap ring to front housing.

TOYOTA POWER-ASSISTED RACK & PINION (Cont.)

2) Apply grease to oil seal lip. Using a driver and hammer, install oil seal. Install new "O" ring to front housing. Align fluid passages of cam ring and front housing. Install cam ring. Install rotor with chamfered end facing toward front housing.

3) Ensure letters on cam ring and rotor match. Install vane plates with round end facing outward. Place rear plate on cam ring with pin holes aligned with pins. Place spring on rear plate.

4) Align marks on front and rear housings. Attach housings together. Half tighten front-to-rear housing retaining bolts. Clamp rear housing in vise. Tighten housing bolts evenly in 3 or 4 stages. Lubricate and install new "O" ring to union.

5) Insert and tighten union. Install air control valve to rear housing. Ensure rotor shaft operates smoothly. Install pulley and check rotating torque. Torque should be less than 2.4 INCH lbs. (2.7 N.m).

STEERING GEAR (TERCEL WAGON, COROLLA FWD & FX)

Disassembly

1) Remove left and right turn tubes and clamp steering gear in soft jawed vice. Loosen lock nuts on tie rod ends, match mark for reassembly and remove tie rod ends. Remove outer clips, inner clamps and remove rack boots. *See Fig. 6.*

2) Remove rack guide spring cap lock nut using Lock Nut Wrench (09617-24020) and remove spring cap using Hexagon Wrench (09612-10022). Remove rack guide spring and guide.

Fig. 6. Exploded View of Tercel Wagon & Corolla (FWD) Power Rack & Pinion Steering Gear

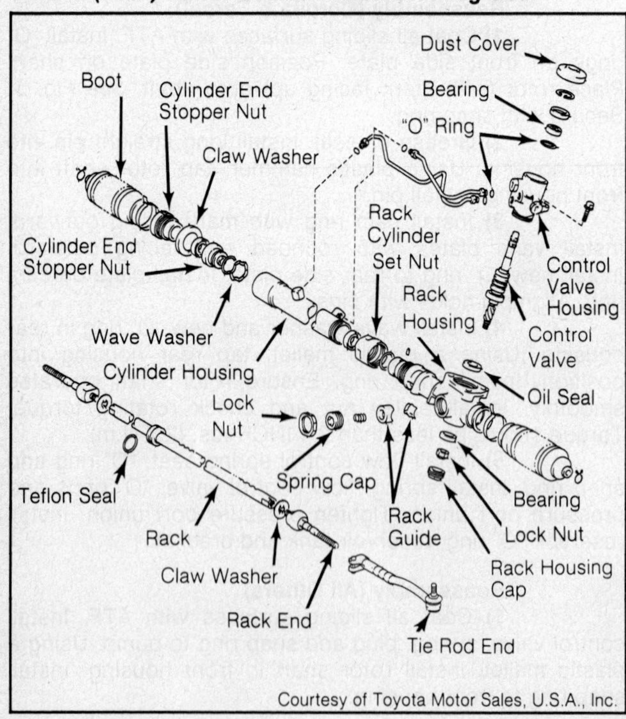

Courtesy of Toyota Motor Sales, U.S.A., Inc.

3) Remove control valve self-locking nut using Bearing Adjusting Socket (09616-00010). Place match marks on control valve housing and rack. Remove the control valve housing bolts and remove control valve, housing and "O"ring together. Pull control valve from housing.

4) Mark rack tie rods for reassembly and remove using Lock Nut Wrench (09628-10020). Using chisel and hammer, unstake claw washers and remove cylinder end stopper nut using Stopper Nut Wrench (09631-16010). Remove claw washers.

5) Place match marks on housing and tube. Using a hammer and chisel, unstake set nut and turn set nut to separate housing from tube using Set Nut Wrench (09617-16010). Set nut not used on FX model. Using a plastic-faced hammer, tap out rack and end stopper.

Inspection & Repair

1) Check all parts for damage or deterioration. Check steering rack for runout by placing the rack on "V" blocks and using a dail indicator, measure runout at center of rack. Maximum runout is .012" (.30 mm). Check all bearings and seals for damage. Always use use new "O" rings.

2) To replace control valve bearing and oil seal, remove snap ring and pry out oil seal. Press out bearing using Bearing Replacer (09515-21010) and Press Handle (09631-12020). To install, reverse procedure using same press tools.

3) To replace pinion bearing, tap out bearing using Bearing Replacer (09620-30010) and Handle (09631-00020). Tap new bearing into housing and using rack housing cap, push bearing in until seated.

4) To replace control valve housing oil seal, use Steering Rack Bushing Puller (09613-22011) and remove oil seal. Install new seal using Installer (09624-30010).

5) To replace cylinder housing oil seal, temporarily install rack, cylinder end stopper and set nut. Press out seal. Remove rack, cylinder end stopper and set nut and install new seal.

6) To replace cylinder end stopper oil seal, use Seal Remover (09612-10093) to remove seal. Install new seal using Installer (09626-30010).

7) To replace Teflon rings on rack piston and control valve, using a small screw driver remove Teflon rings. On rack, carefully expand new ring with fingers and install. Snug down the ring with fingers so it fits tightly in the groove.

8) On control valve, use Installer (09631-20070) to expand Teflon rings and install on control valve. Coat Teflon rings with power steering fluid and slide tapered end of Installer (09631-20081) over rings to seat.

NOTE: Coat all Teflon rings and "O" rings with power steering fluid.

Reassembly & Adjustments

1) Install Steering Rack Cover (09631-16020) to the rack and coat with power steering fluid. On FX model, use Steering Rack Covers (09631-12020) and (09631-12040). Insert rack into cylinder and remove rack cover. Install a new "O" ring on the end stopper and push end stopper into housing.

TOYOTA POWER-ASSISTED RACK & PINION (Cont.)

2) For all except FX, mount the housing in a soft-jawed vice. Install the pin and new "O" ring to the housing. Align the match marks and assemble the housing and cylinder with a new set nut. Tighten nut to 123 ft. lbs. (167 N.m). Using a hammer and chisel, stake the set nut at the cylinder end.

3) On FX model, perform air tightness test. Install Oil Seal Test Tool (09631-12070) and apply 15.75 in. Hg. (53.3 kPa) of vacuum for 30 seconds. If vacuum drops, recheck seals in rack housing. *See Fig. 7.*

Fig. 7: Oil Seal Test Tool

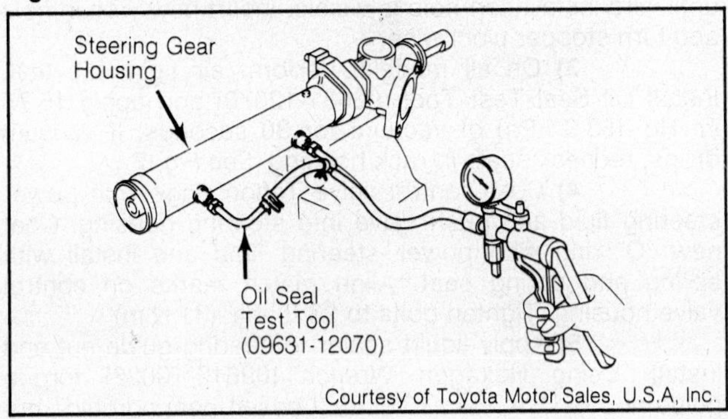

Courtesy of Toyota Motor Sales, U.S.A, Inc.

4) Insert control valve into housing. Install new "O" ring to the valve, align the match marks and install the valve and housing assembly. Tighten bolts 18 ft. lbs. (25 N.m).

5) Using Bearing Adjusting Socket (09616-00010), install new self-locking nut to bottom of control valve and tighten to 18 ft. lbs. (25 N.m), on FX model 43 ft. lbs. (59 N.m). Apply liquid sealer to a new rack housing cap, install cap and tighten to 43 ft. lbs. (59 N.m), on FX model 51 ft. lbs. (69 N.m). Stake the housing cap in 2 places.

Fig. 8: Setting Rack & Pinion Total Preload

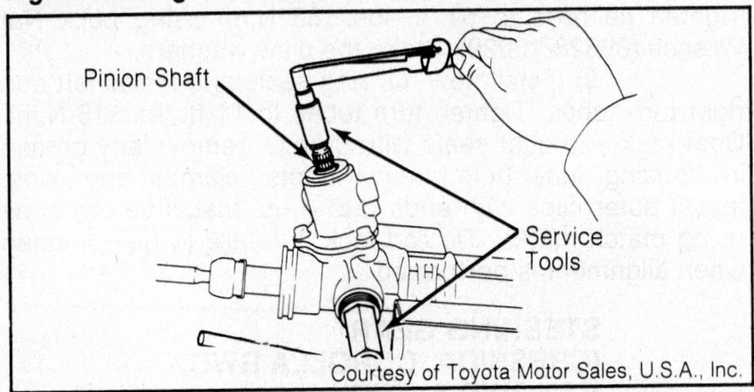

Courtesy of Toyota Motor Sales, U.S.A., Inc.

6) Install rack guide and guide spring. Apply liquid sealer to threads of rack guide spring cap, install cap using Hexagon Wrench and tighten to 18 ft. lbs. (25 N.m). Back off spring cap 12 degrees and turn control valve shaft left and right 2 times.

7) Loosen spring cap until there is no preload. Now turn the spring cap in until the turning preload is 6.9-11.3 in. lbs. (0.8-1.3 N.m). Apply liquid sealer to threads of lock nut and install. Tighten lock nut to 47 ft. lbs. (64 N.m), on FX model 33 ft. lbs. (44 N.m).

8) Align the claw of the new claw washers with the rack grove. Install the claw washer and rack tie rods. Tighten tie rods to 61 ft. lbs. (83 N.m) using Lock Nut Wrench (09628-10020). Stake the claw washers.

9) Install new "O" ring seals and install left and right turn tubes. Tighten turn tubes to 11 ft. lbs. (15 N.m). Coat rack end dust seals with grease, remove any grease in housing tube hole. Install boots, clamps and clips. Install outer clips with ends facing up. Install tie rod ends using match marks. Tie rod lock nuts are to be tightened when alignment is performed.

STEERING GEAR (TERCEL SEDAN, SUPRA, CELICA & CAMRY)

Disassembly

1) Using Rack Housing Stand (09612-00012), mount steering gear in vice and remove left and right turn tubes. On Tercel remove air control valve. Loosen lock nuts on tie rod ends, match mark for reassembly and remove tie rod ends. Remove outer clips and inner clamps and remove rack boots.

2) Remove rack guide spring cap lock nut using Lock Nut Wrench (09617-24020) and remove spring cap using Hexagon Wrench (09612-10022). Remove rack guide spring, guide and seat.

3) Remove bearing guide lock nut using Lock Nut Wrench (09617-24020) and bearing guide nut using Hexagon Wrench (09612-10022). Remove dust cover and place match marks on control valve housing and rack. Remove control valve housing bolts and remove control valve housing. Remove spool valve spring seat and spring. Pull control valve with bearing from rack.

4) Mark rack tie rods for reassembly and using chisel and hammer, unstake claw washers. Remove tie rods using Lock Nut Wrench (09628-10020) and remove claw washers.

5) Remove snap ring in end of housing. Using Bearing Replacer (09612-10061), press cylinder end stopper out until end stopper touchs press plate. Pull out rack with cylinder end stopper, spacer and oil seal.

6) On Tercel, remove cylinder end stopper using Rack Stopper Wrench (09631-10020). Turn end stopper clockwise until wire end comes out. Turn counterclockwise and remove wire. Using a brass bar and hammer, tap out rack and rack bushing. Drive out oil seal and spacer using Oil Seal Remover (09620-24010).

Inspection & Repair

1) Check all parts for damage or deterioration. Check steering rack for runout by placing rack on "V" blocks and using a dial indicator, measure runout at center of rack. Maximum runout is .012" (.30 mm). Check all bearings and seals for damage.

2) To replace control valve bearing and housing oil seal, press out oil seal with bearing using Oil Seal Remover (09620-24010) and Handle (09631-12020). Using the same tools, press in new oil seal. Using Bearing Installer (09620-24030) press in new bearing.

TOYOTA POWER-ASSISTED RACK & PINION (Cont.)

Fig. 9: Exploded View of Supra Power Rack & Pinion Steering Gear

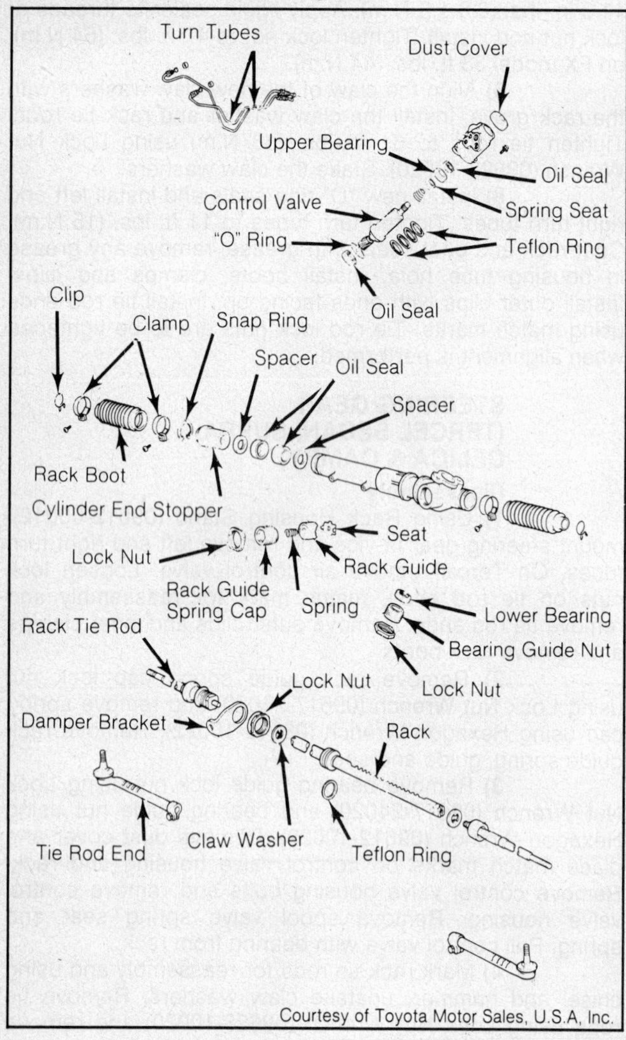

Courtesy of Toyota Motor Sales, U.S.A. Inc.

3) To replace cylinder housing oil seal, drive out spacer and oil seal using Oil Seal Remover (09631-20031). Install new oil seal and new spacer on Seal Installer (09631-20040) and drive in with plastic hammer.

4) To replace rack housing oil seal, pry out old seal. Using Seal Installer (09631-24070), drive in new seal

5) To replace Teflon rings on rack piston, using a small screw driver remove Teflon rings. Carefully expand new ring using Piston Ring Guide (09631-24020) and install ring on piston. Coat Teflon ring with power steering fluid and snug down in groove with fingers. Carefully slide tapered end of Piston Ring Tool (09631-24030) over Teflon ring to seat. On Tercel, seat piston ring with fingers.

6) To replace Teflon rings on control valve, use a small screwdriver and remove rings. Install new Teflon rings on Seal Ring Guide (09620-24040) and install rings on control valve. Coat the teflon rings with power steering fluid and slide tapered end of Installer (09620-24050) over rings to seat. On Tercel use Installer (09631-20081).

NOTE: Coat all Teflon rings and "O" rings with power steering fluid.

Reassembly & Adjustments

1) Install Steering Rack Cover (09631-16020) to rack and coat with power steering fluid. Insert rack into cylinder and remove rack cover. Wind vinyl tape on steering rack end and coat with power steering fluid. Push oil seal into cylinder, install spacer and drive in cylinder end stopper using Bearing Replacer (09612-22011). Install snap ring.

2) On Tercel only, push cylinder end stopper in until wire installation hole is visible. Insert new wire in hole and turn stopper clockwise.

3) On all models, perform air tightness test. Install Oil Seal Test Tool (09631-12070) and apply 15.75 in. Hg. (53.3 kPa) of vacuum for 30 seconds. If vacuum drops, recheck seals in rack housing. *See Fig. 7.*

4) Coat control valve Teflon rings with power steering fluid and push valve into steering housing. Coat new "O" ring with power steering fluid and install with spring and spring seat. Align match marks on control valve housing. Tighten bolts to 23 ft. lbs. (31 N.m)

5) Apply liquid sealer to bearing guide nut and install. Using Hexagon Wrench (09612-10022) torque guide nut to 11 ft. lbs. (15 N.m). Loosen bearing guide nut until a turning preload of 3.9-5.6 in. lbs. (0.4-0.6 N.m) is reached. Apply liquid sealer to bearing guide lock nut, install and tighten to 51 ft. lbs. (69 N.m) using Lock Nut Wrench (09617-24020).

6) Install rack guide, guide spring and seat. Apply liquid sealer to threads of rack guide spring cap. Install cap using Hexagon Wrench and tighten to 18 ft. lbs. (25 N.m). Back off spring cap 15 degrees and turn control valve shaft left and right 2 times.

7) Loosen spring cap until there is no preload. Now turn the spring cap in until the turning preload is 7.8-10.4 in. lbs. (0.9-1.2 N.m). Apply liquid sealer to threads of lock nut and install. Tighten lock nut to 51 ft. lbs. (69 N.m). *See Fig. 8.*

8) Align the claw of the new claw washers with the rack grove, install the claw washer and rack tie rods. Tighten tie rods to 61 ft. lbs. (83 N.m) using Lock Nut Wrench (09628-10020). Stake the claw washers.

9) Install new "O" ring seals and install left and right turn tubes. Tighten turn tubes to 11 ft. lbs. (15 N.m). Coat rack end dust seals with grease, remove any grease in housing tube hole. Install boots, clamps and clips. Install outer clips with ends facing up. Install tie rod ends using match marks. Tie rod lock nuts are to be tightened when alignment is performed.

STEERING GEAR (CRESSIDA, COROLLA RWD, VAN 2WD & 4WD)

Disassembly

1) Using Rack Housing Stand (09612-00012), mount steering gear in vice and remove left and right turn tubes. Loosen lock nuts on tie rod ends, match mark for reassembly and remove tie rod ends. Remove outer clips and inner clamps and remove rack boots.

2) Mark rack tie rods for reassembly and using chisel and hammer, unstake claw washers. Remove tie rods using Lock Nut Wrench (09617-24010) and remove

TOYOTA POWER-ASSISTED RACK & PINION (Cont.)

claw washers. On Cressida only, remove inboard rack boot and solenoid valve. Remove steering damper support, if equipped, using Lock Nut wrench (09631-22050) and remove bracket. The lock nut has left hand threads.

3) On all models, remove rack guide spring cap lock nut using Lock Nut Wrench (09617-24020) and remove spring cap using Hexagon Wrench (09612-10022). Remove rack guide spring, guide and seat.

4) Remove dust cover and place match marks on control valve housing and rack. Remove the control valve housing bolts and remove control valve and housing.

5) Remove cylinder end stopper nut using Stopper Nut Wrench (09631-20090). Using Bearing Replacer (09612-10061) press out the rack and oil seal. Pull out the steering rack, oil seal and rack end guide from the cylinder.

6) Remove dust cover. Using Bearing Guide Nut Wrench (09631-20060), remove bearing guide nut and "O" ring. Tap out control valve using a plastic hammer.

Fig 10: Exploded View of Cressida Power Rack & Pinion Steering Gear

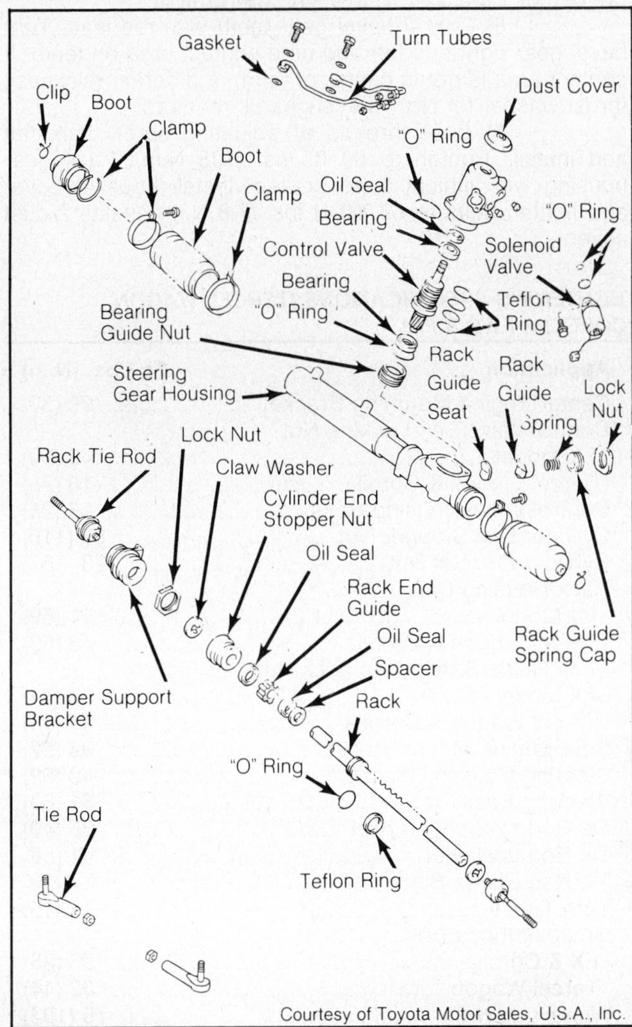

Inspection & Repair

1) Check all parts for damage or deterioration. Check steering rack for runout by placing the rack on "V" blocks and using a dial indicator, measure runout at center of rack. Maximum runout is .012" (.30 mm). Check all bearings and seals for damage.

2) To replace control valve bearing and housing oil seal, press out oil seal with bearing using Oil Seal Remover (09620-24010) and Handle (09631-12020). Using the same tools, press in new oil seal. Using Bearing Installer (09620-24030) press in new bearing.

3) To replace cylinder housing oil seal, drive out spacer and oil seal using Oil Seal Remover (09631-22040). Install new oil seal and new spacer on Seal Installer (09631-12040) and drive in with plastic hammer.

4) To replace bearing guide nut oil seal, press out old seal with a socket wrench. Using Seal Installer (09631-20040) press new seal into guide nut.

5) To replace Teflon rings on rack piston, using a small screw driver remove Teflon rings. On rack, carefully expand new ring and install ring on piston. Coat Teflon ring with power steering fluid and snug down in groove with fingers.

6) To replace Teflon rings on control valve, use a small screwdriver and remove rings. Install new Teflon rings on Seal Ring Guide (09631-20070) and install rings on control valve. Coat the Teflon rings with power steering fluid and slide tapered end of Installer (09631-20081) over rings to seat.

NOTE: **Coat all Teflon rings and "O" rings with power steering fluid.**

Reassembly & Adjustments

1) Install Steering Rack Cover (09631-20051) to the rack and coat with power steering fluid. Insert rack into cylinder and remove rack cover. Push end guide into cylinder. Wind vinyl tape around rack end and coat with power steering fluid. Coat oil seal with power steering fluid and push oil seal into cylinder. Remove vinyl tape and install end stopper nut tightening to 43 ft. lbs. (59 N.m). Stake end of stopper nut.

2) Perform air tightness test. Install Oil Seal Test Tool (09631-22030) and apply 15.75 in. Hg. (53.3 kPa) of vacuum for 30 seconds. If vacuum drops, recheck seals in rack housing. *See Fig. 7.*

3) Coat control valve Teflon rings with power steering fluid and push valve into control valve housing. Coat new "O" ring with power steering fluid and install. Install bearing guide nut and torque to 18 ft. lbs. (25 N.m) using Bearing Guide Nut Wrench (09631-20060). Stake nut and install dust cover. Align match marks on control valve housing and install. Tighten bolts to 13 ft. lbs. (18 N.m)

4) Install rack guide, guide spring and seat. Apply liquid sealer to threads of rack guide spring cap, install cap using Hexagon Wrench (09612-10022) and tighten to 18 ft. lbs. (25 N.m). Back off spring cap 30 degrees and turn control valve shaft left and right 2 times.

5) Loosen spring cap until there is no preload. Now turn the spring cap in until the turning preload is 4.3-8.7 in. lbs. (0.5-1.0 N.m). Apply liquid sealer to threads of lock nut and install. Tighten lock nut to 51 ft. lbs. (69 N.m). Using a hammer and chisel, stake lock nut. See Fig. 8.

TOYOTA POWER-ASSISTED RACK & PINION (Cont.)

6) Install steering damper lock nut and bracket to cylinder side of housing. Align the claw of the new claw washers with the rack grove, install the claw washer and rack tie rods. Tighten tie rods to 61 ft. lbs. (83 N.m) using Lock Nut Wrench (09628-10020). Stake the claw washers. Align the damper support bracket and tighten lock nut to 43 ft. lbs (59 N.m) using Lock Nut Wrench (09631-22050). Stake the lock nut.

7) Install new "O" ring seals and install left and right turn tubes. Tighten turn tubes to 18 ft. lbs. (25 N.m). Coat rack end dust seals with grease, remove any grease in housing tube hole. Install boots, clamps and clips. Install outer clips with ends facing up. Install tie rod ends using match marks. Tie rod lock nuts are to be tightened when alignment is performed.

BEVEL GEAR - VAN

Dissasembly

1) Clamp bevel gear housing bracket in vice. Remove 2 dust covers. Using Lock Nut Wrench (09617-10010) remove adjusting screw lock nut. Using Bearing Adjusting Screw Wrench (09616-10020) remove adjusting screw.

2) Remove housing cover. Loosen lock nut on No. 1 bevel gear adjusting bolt and remove bolt. Remove 2 plate bolts and remove adjusting plate. Push No. 2 bevel gear in and remove No. 1 bevel gear. Tap out No. 2 bevel gear, bearing and spring retainer. *See Fig. 11.*

Fig. 11: Exploded View of Bevel Gear Housing

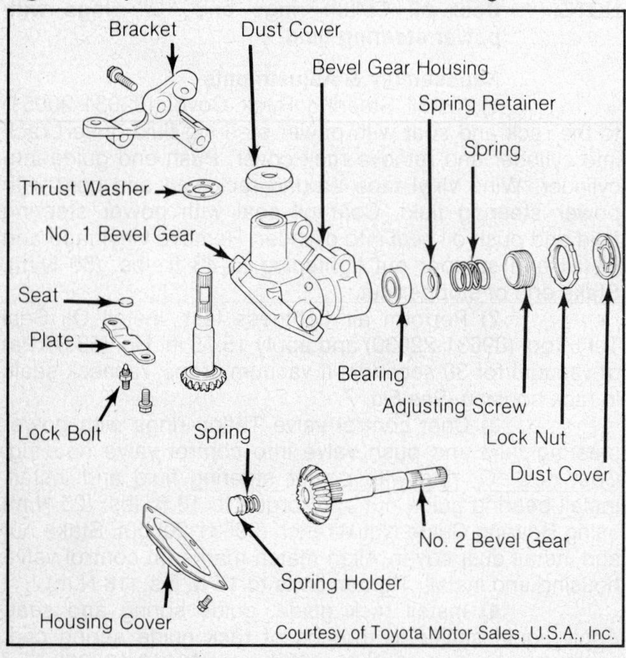

Courtesy of Toyota Motor Sales, U.S.A., Inc.

Inspection & Repair

1) Inspect No. 1 and No. 2 bevel gear for shaft and tooth wear. Inspect bearing and seals for wear or damage.

2) To replace oil seals, pry out seals. Using Seal Installer (09612-10050), drive in new seals.

Reassembly & Adjustments

1) Install No. 2 bevel gear in housing. Using Bearing Installer (09612-10061), press in bearing. Install thrust washer on No. 1 bevel gear. Align cutout portion of gears and install No. 1 bevel gear.

2) Install spring and spring holder to No. 2 bevel gear. Install adjusting plate and tighten to 69 INCH lbs. (7.8 N.m). Install adjusting bolt seat and screw in adjusting bolt until it touches seat.

3) Using screwdriver, Bearing Adjusting Socket (09616-10010) and a torque wrench, adjust No. 1 bevel gear turning preload to .7-1.3 INCH lbs. (.08-.15 N.m). Hold the adjusting bolt with a screwdriver and tighten lock nut to 84 INCH lbs. (9.5 N.m).

4) Install spring retainer in housing. Install spring to adjusting screw. Coat threads with liquid sealer and install adjusting screw in housing. Using Bearing Adjusting Wrench (09616-10020) and dial indicator, adjust screw until backlash is 0. Turn No. 1 bevel gear left and right 5 times. Loosen adjusting screw to reach a turning preload of 1.3-3.5 INCH lbs. (.15-.39 N.m).

5) Coat 2 bevel gear teeth with red lead. Turn bevel gear right and left and note contact area on teeth. If contact area is not in center of tooth, a different thickness thrust washer for No. 1 bevel gear is required.

6) Coat threads of adjusting screw lock nut and install. Tighten to 80 ft. lbs. (108 N.m). Pack gear housing with lithium base grease. Install housing cover and tighten bolts to 69 INCH lbs. (7.8 N.m). Install 2 dust covers.

TIGHTENING SPECIFICATIONS (TERCEL WAGON, COROLLA FWD & FX)

Application	Ft. Lbs. (N.m)
Center Engine Mounting Bracket	29 (39)
Control Valve Self-Locking Nut	
FX Model	43 (59)
Tercel Wagon & Corolla	18 (25)
Control Valve Housing Bolts	18 (25)
Cylinder End Stopper Nut	87 (116)
Cylinder End Set Nut	123 (167)
Rack Housing Cap	
FX Model	51 (69)
Tercel Wagon & Corolla	43 (59)
Rack Guide Spring Cap Lock Nut	
FX Model	33 (44)
Tercel Wagon & Corolla	47 (64)
Rear Engine Mount Bracket	38 (52)
Steering Gear-to-Chassis	43 (59)
Steering Rack Tie Rod	61 (83)
Tie Rod-to-Steering Arm	36 (49)
Tie Rod Lock Nut	41 (56)
Tie Rod Clamp Bolt	14 (19)
Turn Tubes	11 (15)
"U" Joint Pinch Bolt	
FX & Corolla	26 (35)
Tercel Wagon	33 (44)
Wheel Lug Nuts	76 (103)

TOYOTA POWER-ASSISTED RACK & PINION (Cont.)

TIGHTENING SPECIFICATIONS (TERCEL SEDAN, SUPRA,CELICA & CAMRY)

Application	Ft. Lbs. (N.m)
Control Valve Bearing	
Guide Lock Nut	51 (69)
Control Valve Lower Bearing	
Self-Locking Nut	18 (25)
Control Valve Housing Bolts	23 (31)
Rack Guide Spring Cap Lock Nut	
Supra Celica, & Camry	51 (69)
Tercel Sedan	29 (39)
Steering Damper	20 (26)
Steering Damper Bracket Lock Nut	61 (83)
Steering Gear-to-Chassis	
Celica, & Camry	51 (69)
Supra	56 (76)
Tercel Sedan	32 (43)
Steering Rack Tie Rod	
Supra, Celica, & Camry	61 (83)
Tercel Sedan	43 (59)
Tie Rod-to-Steering Arm Nut	36 (49)
Tie Rod Lock Nut	41 (56)
Tie Rod Clamp Bolt (Supra)	14 (19)
Turn Tubes	
Supra, Celica, & Camry	18 (25)
Tercel Sedan	10 (14)
"U" Joint Pinch Bolt	24 (32)
Wheel Lug Nuts	76 (103)

TIGHTENING SPECIFICATIONS (CRESSIDA, COROLLA RWD & VAN 2WD & 4WD)

Application	Ft. Lbs. (N.m)
Bevel Gear Housing Mount Bolts	29 (39)
Bevel Gear Adjusting Lock Nut	80 (109)
Control Valve Bearing Guide Nut	18 (25)
Control Valve Housing Bolts	13 (18)
Cylinder End Stopper Nut	
Cressida & Corolla	43 (59)
Van	58 (78)
Rack Guide Spring Cap Lock Nut	51 (69)
Steering Damper	20 (26)
Steering Damper Lock Nut	43 (59)
Steering Gear-to-Chassis	56 (76)
Steering Rack Tie Rod	
Cressida & Corolla	61 (83)
Van	76 (103)
Tie Rod Lock Nut (Cressida)	41 (56)
Tie Rod Clamp Bolt (Van & Corolla)	13 (18)
Tie Rod-to-Steering Arm Nut	43 (59)
Torque Shaft-to-Pinion Shaft Bolts	26 (35)
Turn Tubes	18 (25)
"U" Joint Pinch Bolt	26 (35)
Wheel Lug Nut	76 (103)

TOYOTA POWER-ASSISTED RECIRCULATING BALL

Land Cruiser, Pickup, 4Runner

DESCRIPTION

System consists of a belt-driven pump, variable-assist steering gear and connecting hydraulic lines. Some models are equipped with Progressive Power Steering (PPS). PPS is an electronically-controlled variable-assist steering system.

The steering gear for electronically-controlled or non-electronically-controlled controlled systems consists of 2 mechanisms. One converts steering wheel torque to cross shaft torque by means of a worm and power piston nut. The other detects hydraulic pressure and controls it in proportion to the steering effort.

LUBRICATION

CAPACITY

Refer to FLUID REPLACEMENT in this article.

FLUID TYPE

Fluid type is Dexron ATF or Dexron II.

SYSTEM BLEEDING

1) Raise and support vehicle. Fill fluid to proper level in reservoir. Turn steering wheel lock-to-lock. Recheck fluid level. Start engine and let idle. Turn steering wheel lock-to-lock 2 or 3 times. Lower vehicle.

2) Run engine at less than 1000 RPM. Turn wheel from lock-to-lock 2 or 3 times. Turn steering wheel to straight-ahead position. If fluid level does not rise and no foaming of fluid is evident, bleeding is complete. If fluid level rises, or foaming appears, repeat procedure until air is no longer present.

FLUID REPLACEMENT

1) Raise and support vehicle. Disconnect return hose. Drain fluid into container. With engine idling, turn steering wheel from lock-to-lock while draining.

2) Stop engine. Fill reservoir with fluid. Start engine and run for one to 2 seconds. Stop engine and refill reservoir. Repeat 4 or 5 times, or until air is expelled.

3) With fluid at normal operating temperature, it's level should read between the indented "HOT" mark on reservoir dipstick.

TOYOTA POWER-ASSISTED RECIRCULATING BALL (Cont.)

4) When fluid is cold, it's level should be between the indented "COLD" mark on dipstick. Reconnect return hose, add fresh fluid. Bleed system (if necessary).

ADJUSTMENTS

BELT TENSION ADJUSTMENT

1) On Land Cruiser, apply 22 lbs. (30 N.m) pressure to drive belt between idler pulley and pump pulley. Deflection should be .28-.37" (7.0-9.5 mm) for a new belt and .31-.39" (8-10 mm) for a used belt.

2) On all others, use a belt tension gauge to adjust belt tension to 60-100 lbs. (27-45 kg) for used belt; 100-150 lbs. (45-68 kg) for new belt.

OPERATION

PROGRESSIVE POWER STEERING

PPS consists of a speed sensor, Electronic Control Module (ECM), solenoid valve and connecting wiring harness. Signals from the speed sensor are used by the ECM to determine the amount and position of opening for the solenoid valve.

The amount and position of the solenoid valve opening determines the amount of hydraulic assistance to the steering gear. As the vehicle speed is increased, assistance is decreased. As the vehicle speed decreases, assistance increases. The ECM is located in the instrument panel behind the glove box.

TESTING

AIR CONTROL VALVE TESTING

(Pickup & 4Runner Only)

Start engine and let idle. Turn steering wheel right and left. Ensure engine RPM does not decrease more than 50 RPM. Pinch air hose shut. Turn steering wheel right and left. Ensure engine RPM decreases about 200 RPM.

HYDRAULIC PRESSURE TESTING

1) Disconnect pressure lines from steering gear case and vane pump. Attach Pressure Gauge (09631-22020) with gauge side connected to pump.

CAUTION: Do not keep pressure gauge valve closed for more than 10 seconds during test. Fluid testing temperature should be 176°F (80°C).

2) Attach valve side of gauge to pressure line. Bleed air from system and check fluid level. With engine at idle, check fluid pressure reading with pressure gauge valve closed. Pressure for 4WD Pickup is 924 psi (65 kg/cm²). For all others, pressure is 1067 psi (75 kg/cm²).

3) Check pressure with steering wheel at lock position and pressure valve open. Pressure for 4WD Pickup is 924 psi (65 kg/cm²). For all others, pressure is 1067 psi (75 kg/cm²).

4) Measure pressure with engine at idle and again at 3000 RPM. Pressure difference should be less than 71 psi (5 kg/cm²). If more, check flow control valve. With vehicle on flat surface, turn steering wheel to center position.

5) With engine idling, measure steering wheel turning force at steering wheel outer rim over a full rotation on both sides of center point. Turning force should not exceed 106 INCH lbs. (12 N.m).

6) On models with electronically-controlled power-assist, disconnect solenoid harness connector from harness. Apply battery voltage to solenoid.

CAUTION: Do not apply battery voltage to solenoid for more than 30 seconds. Solenoid will be damaged.

7) Measure turning force at steering wheel outer rim over a full rotation on both sides of center. Turning force should not exceed 26 lbs. (35 N.m).

PROGRESSIVE POWER STEERING PRELIMINARY CHECKS

If steering is too hard at low speeds or too sensitive at high speeds, check the following first: tire

Fig. 1: Electrical & Hydraulic Circuits of the Progressive Power Steering System

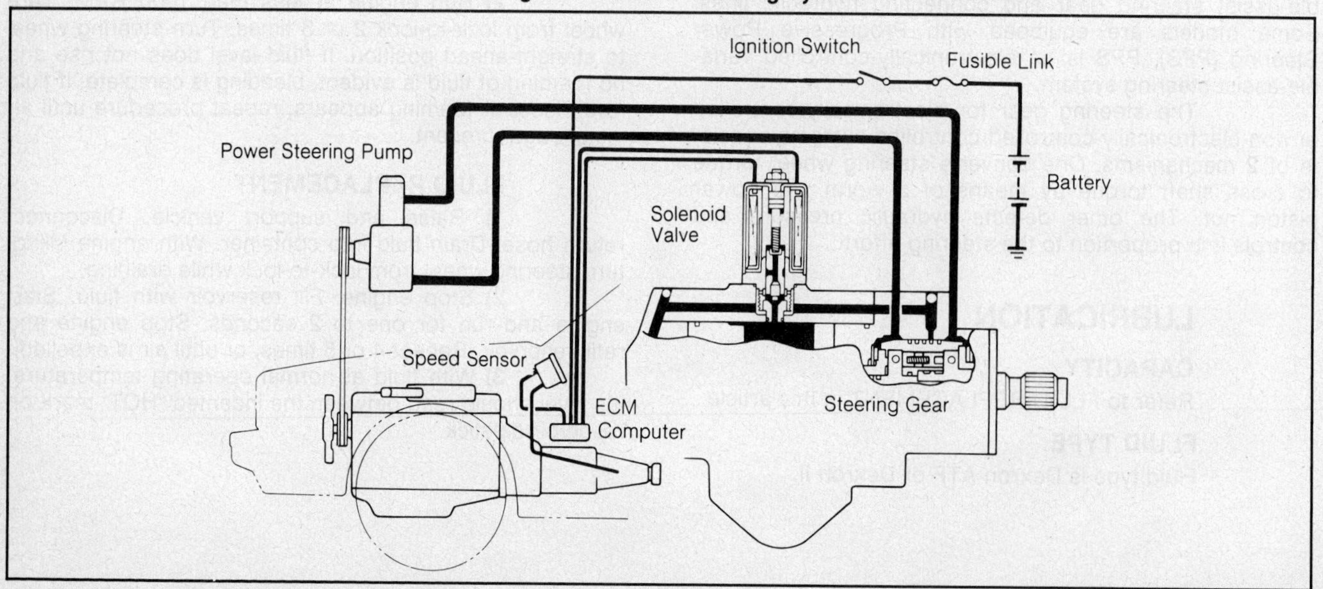

Courtesy of Toyota Motor Sales, U.S.A., Inc.

TOYOTA POWER-ASSISTED RECIRCULATING BALL (Cont.)

pressure, lubrication of suspension and steering linkage, front end alignment, ball joints too tight or steering column is bent. Also check for loose or dirty electrical connections. Check power steering pump for low fluid level.

PROGRESSIVE POWER STEERING TESTING

1) Turn ignition on. Check condition of "ENGINE" fuse. If fuse is okay, go to step **2)**. If fuse is not okay, replace it. If fuse checks satisfactory but system is still malfunctioning, check for short or open in wire harness between fuse and terminal "+B". *See. Fig. 2.*

2) Disconnect PPS connector. Check that there is battery voltage between terminal "+B" and ground. If voltage is present, proceed to step **3)**. If voltage is not present, check for open between fuse and terminal "+B".

3) Check for continuity between computer terminal "GND" and ground. If continuity is present, proceed to step **4)**. If continuity is not present, check for open between terminal "GND" and body ground.

4) Raise and support vehicle. Connect a volt/ohmmeter between computer terminals "SPD" and "GND". Spin the rear wheels and check that continuity changes from open to closed as the wheel turns.

5) If circuit opens and closes properly, proceed to step **6)**. If circuit does not open and close properly, check for open or short between the speed sensor and terminal "SPD". If circuit checks okay, proceed to step **7)** to test the speed sensor.

6) Check that there is NO continuity between connector terminal "SOL+" and "SOL-" on solenoid side connector. If there is no continuity, proceed to step **9)**. If there is continuity, check for short between terminals "SOL+" and "SOL-" or for a faulty solenoid. Proceed to step **10)**.

7) Remove combination meter from instrument panel. On models with analog meter, unplug connector "B" (middle connector). Check that there is continuity between terminals "B4" and "B7" 4 times per revolution of the wheels. If not, replace speed sensor.

8) On models with digital combination meter, connect Harness Adapter (09082-00100) to combination meter and wiring harness. Attach volt/ohmmeter to terminals "4P" and "E2" of harness adapter. If voltage does not fluctuate between zero and one volt as wheels are turned, replace speed sensor.

9) Measure resistance between terminals "SOL+" and "SOL-". Resistance should be 7.4-8.0 ohms. If resistance is correct, proceed to step **10)**. If resistance is not within specification, check for open in circuit between terminals "SOL+" and "SOL-".

Fig. 2: Progressive Power Steering ECM Connector

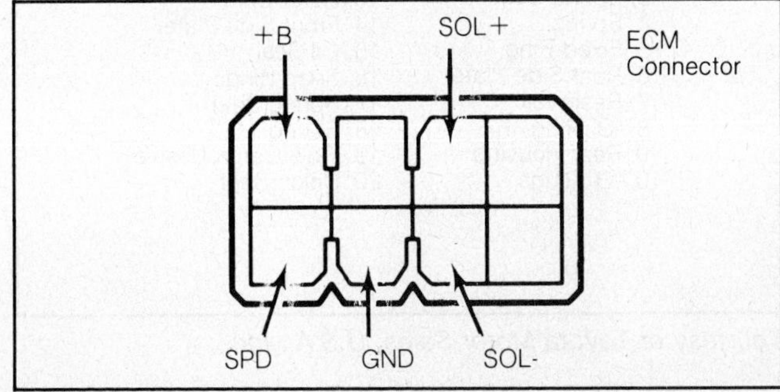

Courtesy of Toyota Motor Sales, U.S.A., Inc.

10) Check function of ECM. See ECM TESTING in this article. If ECM tests satisfactory, proceed to step **11)**. If ECM tests unsatisfactory, replace ECM.

11) Turn steering wheel to full lock position. Connect gauge to steering system as in HYDRAULIC PRESSURE TESTING. Apply battery voltage to solenoid terminals "SOL+" and "SOL-". Turn solenoid on and off by connecting and disconnecting battery voltage.

12) Fluid pressure should fluctuate as voltage is applied and removed. If fluctuation is present, steering gear is faulty. Replace steering gear.

13) If no fluctuation is present, check for clogged hydraulic lines or low fluid level. If fluid level is okay and hydraulic lines are not clogged, but system is still malfunctioning, replace solenoid.

ECM TESTING

1) Raise and support vehicle. Remove glove box. Start engine and let idle. With PPS harness connector still connected to ECM, check that there is no voltage between terminals "SOL+" and "SOL-".

2) Place transmission in a forward gear to allow a speed of about 31 MPH. Measure voltage between terminals "SOL+" and "SOL-". Voltage should be 2.1-4.1 volts. If not, replace ECM. Retest system. Turn ignition off. Install glove box. Lower vehicle.

REMOVAL & INSTALLATION

POWER STEERING PUMP

Removal

Loosen pulley retaining nut. Remove drive belt. Disconnect hoses at pump housing. Plug and elevate hydraulic lines at pump housing. Disconnect air control valve hose. Remove pump retaining bolts. Remove pump.

Installation

To install, reverse removal procedure. Adjust drive belt tension, bleed system and perform pressure test. Check for leaks.

STEERING GEAR

Removal

1) Disconnect and plug hydraulic lines at steering gear. On 4WD Pickup, remove "U" joint cover bolt. Slide "U" joint cover back out of way.

2) Mark pinion shaft to flexible coupling (2WD) or "U" joint (4WD) for reassembly reference. Disconnect flexible coupling or "U" joint from pinion shaft. Disconnect solenoid valve connector (if equipped.)

3) Mark pitman arm to sector shaft. Disconnect pitman arm. On Land Cruiser models, separate steering gear housing from heat shield. Remove steering gear retaining bolts. Remove steering gear.

Installation

To install, reverse removal procedure. Align all marks made during removal. Bleed system, perform pressure test and check for leaks.

OVERHAUL

POWER STEERING PUMP

Disassembly

1) Mount pump in a soft-jawed vise. Remove union from rear housing. Remove reservoir from pump (if

TOYOTA POWER-ASSISTED RECIRCULATING BALL (Cont.)

equipped). Mark front and rear housings for reassembly reference. Remove front housing bolts.

2) Using plastic mallet, tap off front housing. Ensure vane plates, rotor and cam plate (Pickup and 4Runner), or slippers, springs and fixed ring (Land Cruiser) do not fall out.

3) On Land Cruiser, remove slippers and springs from fixed ring. On Pickup and 4Runner, remove ring cam, rotor and vane plates.

4) Clamp front housing in vise. Using chisel, pry off oil seal. Remove snap ring. Using plastic mallet, lightly tap rotor shaft out of front housing.

5) Remove rear plate and spring. Install a bolt into plug. Push in bolt to remove snap ring. Pull out bolt to remove plug. Remove spring and control valve by hand.

Inspection

1) Check all parts for wear or damage and replace as necessary. Check oil clearance between bushing and rotor shaft. Maximum clearance is .0028" (.07 mm). Ensure bearings operate smoothly.

2) If necessary, press out old bearing and press in new bearing. Measure between cam ring and rotor. Maximum difference should be .0024" (.06 mm).

3) Dimensions of the vane plate are .589 x .307 x .067" (14.97 x 7.80 x 1.70 mm). Maximum clearance between vane plate and rotor groove is .0024" (.06 mm).

4) Check flow control valve for leakage with compressed air. Control valve spring should measure 1.85-1.97" (47-50 mm) long.

Fig. 3: Exploded View of Pickup & 4Runner Power Steering Pump

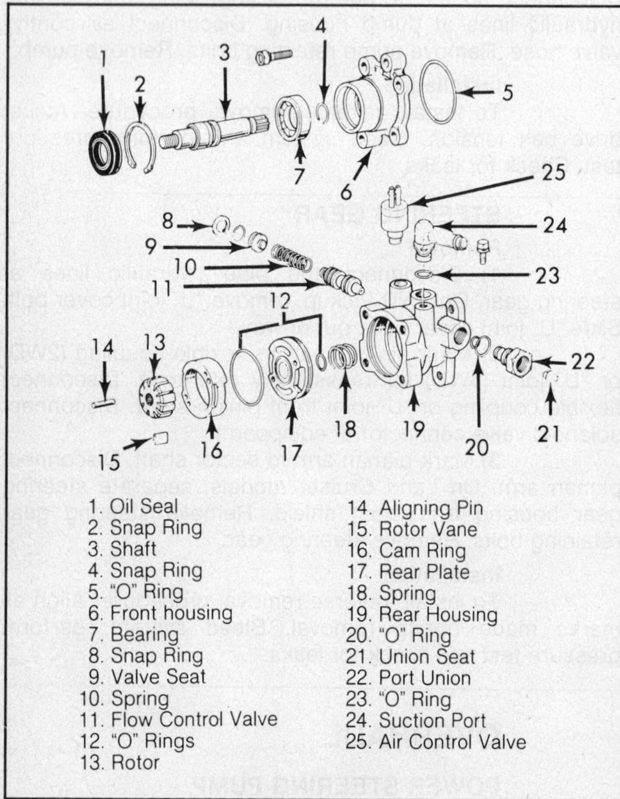

Courtesy of Toyota Motor Sales, U.S.A., Inc.

Reassembly

1) Lubricate flow control valve and spring with Dexron ATF. Install control valve, spring, plug and snap ring to pump. Lubricate rotor shaft with ATF. Using a plastic mallet, install rotor into front housing.

2) Install snap ring to front housing. Grease oil seal lip. Using a driver and hammer, install oil seal. Lubricate and install "O" ring to front housing. Align fluid passages of ring cam and front housing. Install ring cam. Lubricate rotor with ATF.

3) On Pickup and 4Runner, install cam ring. Install rotor with cut spline facing toward front housing. Ensure letters on ring cam and rotor match. Lubricate vane plates with ATF. Install vane plates with round end facing outward. Lubricate and install 2 "O" rings to rear housing.

4) On Land Cruiser, install springs and slippers into fixed ring. Holding slippers and springs in place, install shaft assembly. Install 2 "O" rings to rear housing.

5) Align pin holes with pins, place rear plate on the ring cam. Place spring on rear plate. Aligning marks on front and rear housings, install rear plate. Finger tighten front and rear housing retaining bolts. Clamp rear housing in a soft-jawed vise.

6) Tighten housing bolts evenly in 3 or 4 steps. Lubricate and install "O" ring to union. Insert and tighten union. Ensure rotor shaft operates smoothly. Install pulley nut. Check rotating torque. Torque should be less than 2.4 INCH lbs. (.3 N.m).

Fig. 4: Exploded View of Land Cruiser Power Steering Pump

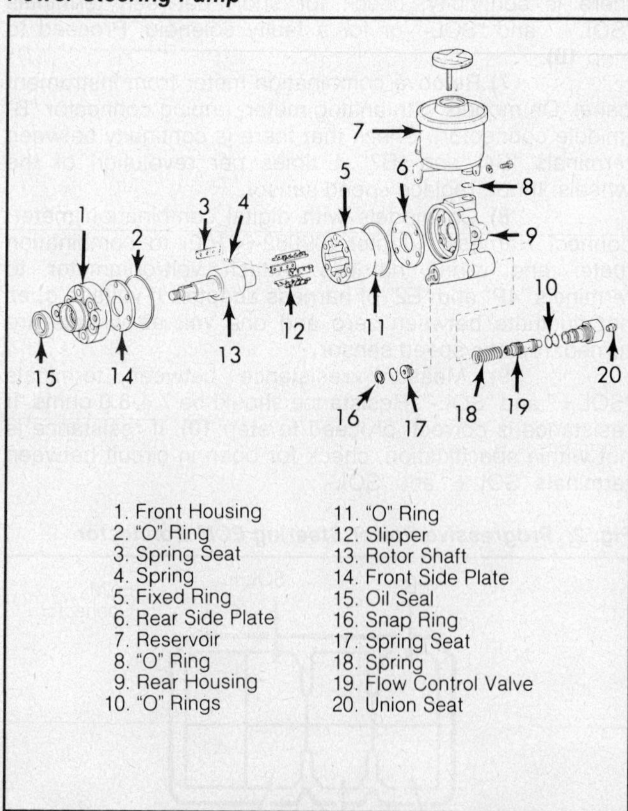

Courtesy of Toyota Motor Sales, U.S.A., Inc.

TOYOTA POWER-ASSISTED RECIRCULATING BALL (Cont.)

Fig. 5: Using Dial Indicator to Check Sector Shaft Thrust Clearance

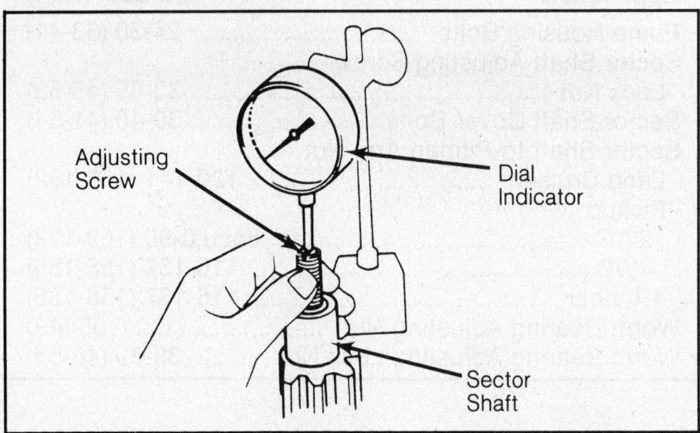

Courtesy of Toyota Motor Sales, U.S.A., Inc.

STEERING GEAR

Disassembly

1) Attach steering gear to holding fixture. Mount assembly in vise. Remove solenoid valve (if equipped). Remove sector shaft adjusting screw lock nut and cover retaining bolts.

2) Turn sector shaft adjusting screw clockwise until cover is removed. Using a mallet, remove sector shaft. Remove valve housing-to-gear housing bolts.

3) Hold power piston nut with hand while turning worm shaft clockwise. Remove valve assembly and power piston from gear housing.

CAUTION: Ensure power piston nut does not come off worm shaft. Do not disassemble valve body or remove power piston.

4) Using dial indicator, check sector shaft adjusting screw thrust clearance. Clearance should be .001-.002" (.03-.05 mm). To adjust thrust clearance, unstake adjusting nut. Turn adjusting nut as necessary.

5) Temporarily install valve assembly in gear housing. Install retaining bolts. Using lock nut tool, remove lock nut and adjusting bolt from gear assembly.

6) Remove and replace oil seal, "O" ring, and bearing assembly as necessary. Install and tighten lock nut. Remove valve assembly from gear housing.

Cleaning & Inspection

1) Clean all parts in solvent. Dry with low pressure air. Coat all sliding parts, "O" rings, and Teflon rings with Dexron ATF upon reassembly.

2) Inspect sector shaft for peeling or pitting at ball rolling surface. Check power piston nut mesh with sector shaft. Check for damaged sector shaft teeth.

3) Replace housing bearings if sector shaft bearing surfaces have been scored or pitted. Remove Teflon ring and "O" ring from gear housing. Using needle bearing removal tool, remove needle bearings.

Reassembly

1) Install needle bearings with longer edge of outer race facing outward. Ensure top end aligns with housing end surface.

2) Install lower bearing so it is positioned .93" (23.6 mm) away from housing inner end surface on Land Cruiser, or .76" (19.4 mm) on all others.

3) Install "O" ring and Teflon ring to power piston. Install large and small "O" rings to gear housing. Install power piston assembly to housing. Tighten bolts.

4) To adjust worm shaft preload, loosen lock nut. Place adjusting wrench to adjusting plug. Install torque wrench to worm shaft. Tighten adjusting plug to obtain 3.5-5.6 INCH lbs. (.4-.6 N.m) preload. While holding adjusting plug, tighten lock nut.

5) Wrap tape around splined area of sector shaft. Align sector shaft teeth with power piston teeth in the centered position. Insert sector shaft into gear housing. Do not turn sector shaft during installation, as damage to "O" ring could result.

6) Install sector shaft cover, with seal, to sector shaft adjusting screw. Turn screw counterclock-

Fig. 6: Exploded View of Power Steering Gear Assembly

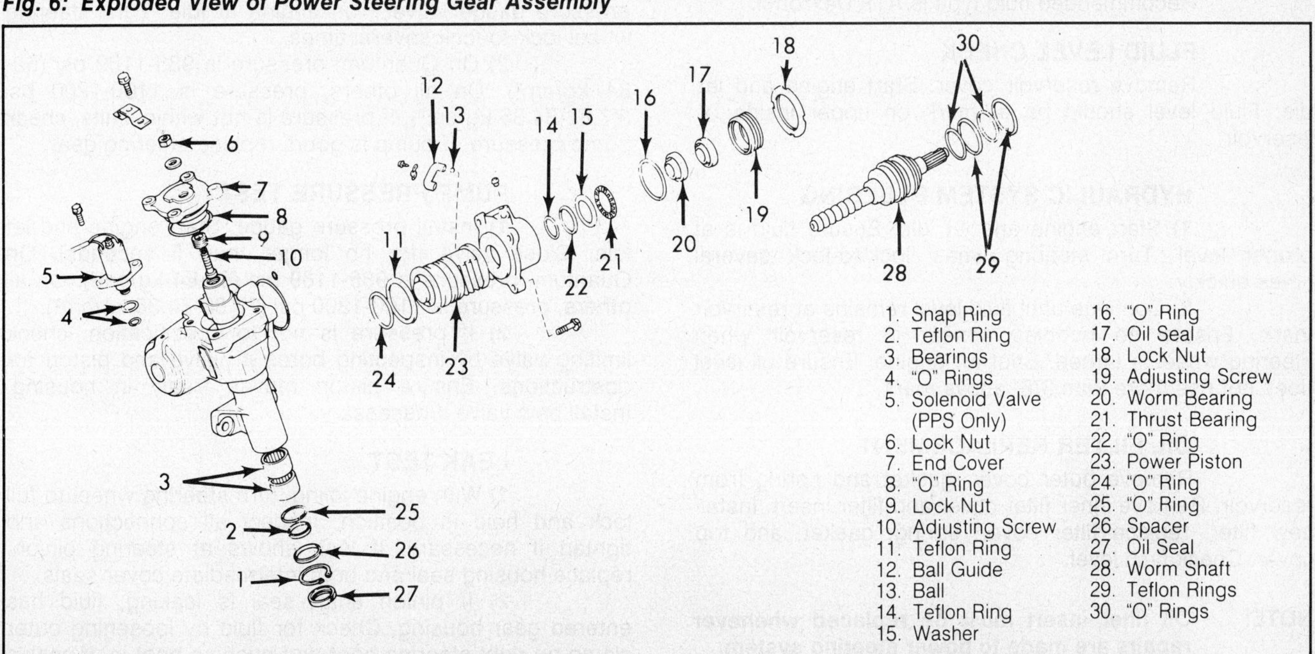

Courtesy of Toyota Motor Sales, U.S.A., Inc.

Toyota POWER-STEERING RECIRCULATING BALL (Cont.)

wise until cover will fit completely down on gear housing. Install and tighten bolts.

7) To adjust total preload of steering gear, place steering gear in center position. Attach torque wrench to worm shaft. Turn sector shaft adjusting screw until correct total preload is obtained.

8) Total preload should be the sum of worm bearing preload plus 1.7-2.6 INCH lbs. (.2-.3 N.m). Install and tighten sector shaft adjusting lock nut.

TIGHTENING SPECIFICATIONS

Application	Ft. Lbs. (N.m)
Pump Housing Bolts	24-30 (33-41)
Sector Shaft Adjusting Screw	
Lock Nut	33-39 (45-53)
Sector Shaft Cover Bolts	30-40 (41-54)
Sector Shaft-to-Pitman Arm Nut	
Land Cruiser	120-141 (163-192)
Pickup	
2WD	8acu,0-90 (109-122)
4WD	116-137 (158-186)
4Runner	116-137 (158-186)
Worm Bearing Adjusting Nut	36 (49)
Worm Bearing Adjusting Lock Nut	33-39 (45-53)

VOLKSWAGEN POWER-ASSISTED RACK & PINION

Cabriolet, Golf, GTI, Jetta, Jetta GLI, Quantum, Quantum Syncro, Scirocco, Vanagon

DESCRIPTION

The system consists of a vane pump, rotary piston pinion gear assembly and an oil reservoir. The vane pump draws fluid from the reservoir and supplies it to the flow control valve. The control valve supplies fluid to the proper side of the rack-piston.

LUBRICATION

CAPACITY

Fluid capacity is 1 qt. (.95L).

FLUID TYPE

Recommended fluid type is ATF Dexron II.

FLUID LEVEL CHECK

Remove reservoir cover. Start engine and let idle. Fluid level should be at mark on upper inside of reservoir.

HYDRAULIC SYSTEM BLEEDING

1) Start engine and let idle. Ensure fluid is at proper level. Turn steering wheel lock-to-lock several times quickly.

2) Continue until fluid level remains at reservoir mark. Ensure no bubbles appear in reservoir when steering wheel is turned. Shut off engine. Ensure oil level does not rise more than 3/8" above mark.

OIL FILTER REPLACEMENT

Remove outer cover, gasket and spring from reservoir. Remove inner filter cover and filter insert. Install new filter, replace filter cover, spring, gasket, and top cover. Check fluid level.

NOTE: Oil filter insert must be replaced whenever repairs are made to power steering system.

ADJUSTMENTS

BELT TENSION

Loosen nuts on pump mounting bracket. Turn adjusting bolt on bracket until belt deflection is 3/8" at center of belt. Tighten nuts to specification.

STEERING GEAR

With steering gear removed from vehicle, loosen lock nut on steering gear. Finger tighten adjusting screw until it just touches thrust plate. Hold adjusting screw while tightening lock nut. Rack should be able to be moved by hand without binding. Readjust if necessary.

TESTING

SYSTEM PRESSURE TEST

1) Install Pressure Gauge (US1074 B) between pressure hose and pressure pipe of valve housing. Open pressure gauge valve. Run engine at idle. Turn steering wheel lock-to-lock several times.

2) On Quantum, pressure is 986-1189 psi (69-84 kg/cm²). On all others, pressure is 1100-1200 psi (77.83-84.36 kg/cm²). If pressure is not within limits, check pump pressure. If pump is good, replace steering gear.

PUMP PRESSURE TEST

1) Install pressure gauge. Start engine and let idle. Close valve (for no longer than 5 seconds). On Quantum, pressure is 986-1189 psi (69-84 kg/cm²). On all others, pressure is 1100-1200 psi (77.83-84.36 kg/cm²).

2) If pressure is not to specification, check limiting valve by inspecting bores in valve and piston for obstructions. Ensure piston moves freely in housing. Install new valve if necessary.

LEAK TEST

1) With engine idling, turn steering wheel to full lock and hold in position. Inspect all connections and tighten if necessary. If leak shows at steering pinion, replace housing seal and both intermediate cover seals.

2) If pinion shaft seal is leaking, fluid has entered gear housing. Check for fluid by loosening outer clamp on right steering boot and pushing boot in. If seal is leaking, disassemble steering gear and replace all seals.

VOLKSWAGEN POWER-ASSISTED RACK & PINION (Cont.)

Fig. 1: Exploded View of Power Steering Gear

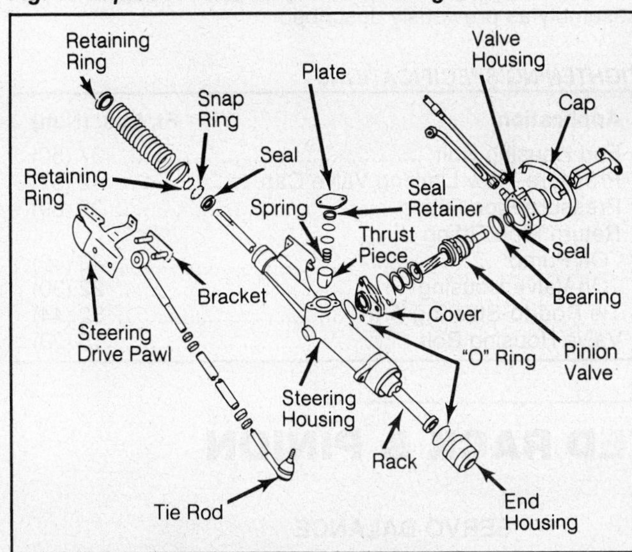

Courtesy of Volkswagen United States, Inc.

REMOVAL & INSTALLATION

STEERING GEAR

Removal

1) Drain fluid from system. Disconnect hydraulic pipes from valve housing. Disconnect lower steering shaft from pinion shaft. Disconnect tie rods from bracket.

2) Remove steering gear-to-body bolts. On all except Quantum, remove rear motor/transmission mount and exhaust pipe. Remove steering gear.

Installation

To install, reverse removal procedure. To install tie rods, install one tie rod to steering gear and tighten before installing the other tie rod.

POWER STEERING PUMP

Removal

Remove alternator and pump belts. Disconnect hydraulic lines from pump. Cap lines to prevent contamination. Remove bracket bolts. Remove pump.

Installation

To install, reverse removal procedure. Adjust belt tension. Start engine and check for leaks.

OVERHAUL

Before disassembling steering gear, check output and system pressure. When overhauling steering gear, always use all parts in Repair Kit (811 498 020). Always use new self-locking nuts and "O" rings.

On all models except Quantum and Quantum Syncro, manufacturer recommends replacement of steering gear if pinion or piston-rod seals are leaking.

PINION HOUSING SEAL

Disassembly (Quantum & Quantum Syncro)

1) Remove retaining bolts from pinion valve housing. Remove housing. Mark position of pinion gear for reassembly reference.

2) Remove pinion gear and intermediate cover. Remove "O" rings from intermediate cover. Place housing in padded vise. Drive out oil seal from back.

Inspection

Inspect seal mating surfaces for pitting or scoring. Check pinion and pinion valve surfaces for scratching or pitting. Discard old seals. Replace worn parts as necessary.

Reassembly

Install new seals. Ensure seal lip on housing seal faces intermediate cover. Replace both intermediate cover "O" rings. To complete reassembly, reverse disassembly procedure. Protect pinion teeth on shaft when replacing intermediate cover. Do not damage "O" rings during installation.

STEERING GEAR

Disassembly (Quantum & Quantum Syncro)

1) With steering gear removed from vehicle, remove pinion valve housing. Remove pinion valve assembly. Remove plate, seal retainer, spring, and thrust piece from steering gear housing.

2) Remove retaining ring, clamp and boot from steering housing. Remove retaining ring and snap ring from steering gear housing.

Fig. 2: Vane Pump Assembly

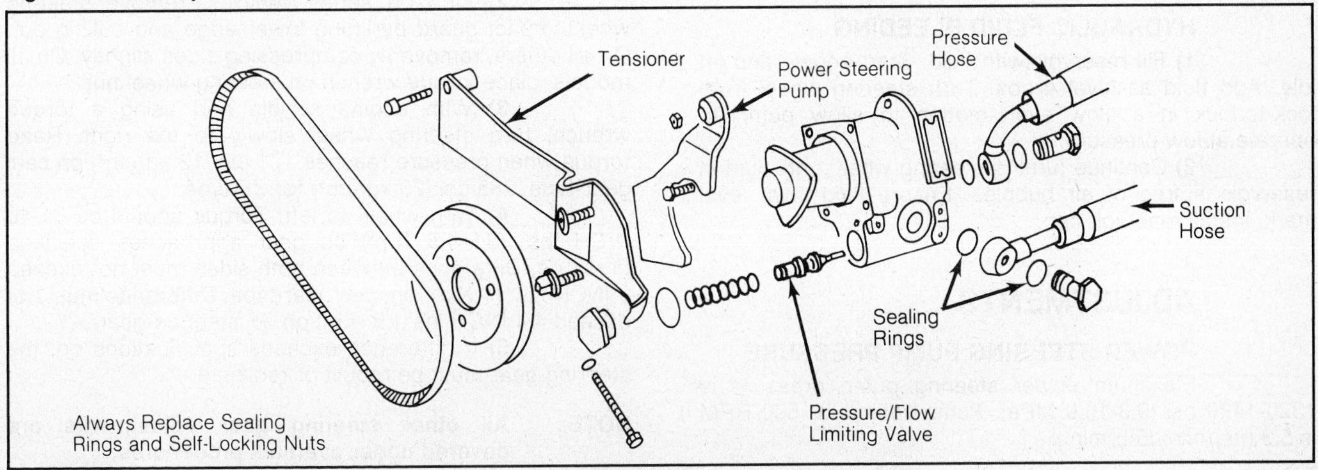

Courtesy of Volkswagen United States, Inc.

VOLKSWAGEN POWER-ASSISTED RACK & PINION (Cont.)

3) Remove end housing and "O" ring from steering gear housing. Pull rack out of housing. Using oil seal puller, remove oil seal from housing.

Reassembly

1) To install oil seal on housing, place oil seal on flat surface. Push sleeve (available in repair kit 811 498 020) into oil seal. Slide rack into housing.

2) Using Seal Installers (VW 426 and VW 4166), slide oil seal with sleeve over rack and into housing. Remove sleeve. Install snap ring and retaining ring.

3) Install end housing with new "O" ring. Lock in place with 2 punch marks 180 degrees apart. Install thrust piece, spring, "O" ring, seal retainer and plate. Install clamp, boot and retaining ring. Install pinion valve assembly as previously described.

TIGHTENING SPECIFICATIONS

Application	Ft. Lbs. (N.m)
End Housing Bolt	37 (50)
Pressure-Flow Limiting Valve Cap	42 (57)
Pressure Pipe Fitting	29 (39)
Return Pipe Fitting	
On Pump	29 (39)
On Valve Housing	22 (30)
Tie Rod-to-Steering Arm	32 (44)
Valve Housing Bolt	15 (20)

VOLVO POWER-ASSISTED RACK & PINION

DESCRIPTION

The 240 DL and GL models use either a ZF gear with a non-integral housing or a cam gear type. The 740, 760 and 780 models may be equipped with either a ZF gear with an integral housing or a cam gear steering rack.

LUBRICATION

CAPACITY

Fluid capacity is .75 qts. (.7L) for 240 series vehicles or 1 qt. (1L). for 700 series vehicles.

FLUID TYPE

System uses automatic transmission fluid (ATF).

STEERING GEAR LUBRICATION

Remove inner clamp on right rubber boot. Using a suction gun, fill gear with recommended lubricant through side of boot. Reinstall clamp. Carefully compress boot so some fluid will flow to other side.

HYDRAULIC FLUID FILLING

Fill reservoir with fluid. Start engine and let idle. Add fluid as level drops.

HYDRAULIC FLUID BLEEDING

1) Fill reservoir with fluid. Start engine and let idle. Add fluid as level drops. Turn steering wheel from lock-to-lock in a slow even motion to allow pump to operate at low pressure.

2) Continue turning steering wheel until fluid in reservoir is free of air bubbles. Ensure fluid is at level mark. Install reservoir cap.

ADJUSTMENTS

POWER STEERING PUMP PRESSURE

Maximum power steering pump pressure is 1320-1420 psi (9.3-10.0 MPa). Pump volume at 500 RPM is 5.3 qts./min. (5 L/min.).

SERVO BALANCE

1) On all models, raise front wheel off ground. Connect pressure gauge between steering pump and steering gear. *See Fig. 1.* Ensure reservoir is full. Place gauge so it can be seen from driving position.

Fig. 1: Pressure Gauge Test Set Up

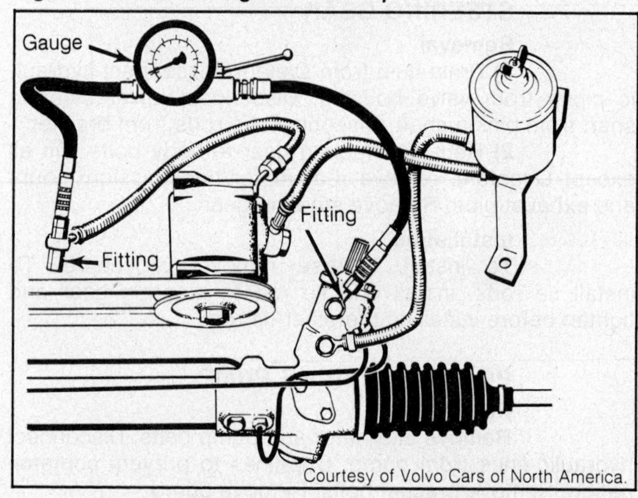

Courtesy of Volvo Cars of North America.

2) On 700 series vehicles, remove steering wheel impact guard by lifting lower edge and pulling out. On all others, remove by compressing sides slightly. On all models, place torque wrench on steering wheel nut.

3) With engine at idle and using a torque wrench, turn steering wheel slowly to the right. Read torque when pressure reaches 171 psi (12 kg/cm²) on cam gear-type, 285 psi (20 kg/cm²) for ZF-type.

4) Turn wheel to left. Torque should be 31-40 INCH lbs. (3.5-4.5 N.m) as gear approaches specified pressure. Difference between both sides must not exceed 9 INCH lbs. (1 N.m) on cam gear-type. Difference must not exceed 4.4 INCH lbs. (.5 N.m) on ZF steering gear.

5) If difference exceeds specifications on, the steering gear must be rebuilt or replaced.

NOTE: All other steering gear adjustments are covered under overhaul procedures.

VOLVO POWER-ASSISTED RACK & PINION (Cont.)

REMOVAL & INSTALLATION

STEERING GEAR

Removal

1) On 700 series vehicles, disconnect lower steering gear shaft by removing snap ring and lower clamp bolt. Loosen upper clamp bolt. Slide joint up on shaft. On all others, remove clamp screw and bend flange apart slightly to disconnect shaft from gear.

2) On all models, raise and support vehicle. Remove wheel assembies. Remove tie rod end castle nuts. Separate tie rod ends from knuckles. Remove splash guard.

3) Disconnect hoses at steering gear. Plug hose connections to prevent contamination. On 700 series vehicles, remove sway bar mounting brackets from side members. Move brackets aside. Remove steering gear attaching bolts. Lower steering gear.

4) On all others, remove steering gear boits. Pull gear down until free of steering shaft flange. Remove steering gear from left side of vehicle.

Installation

1) To install, reverse removal procedure. Ensure recess on pinion shaft is aligned toward lock bolt opening in flange. Install right side "U" bolt and flange, but do not tighten. Install and tighten left side bolts.

2) Tighten right side "U" bolt. Connect tie rods to steering gear. Ensure rods are same length. Difference should not exceed 1/16". Install lock bolt on flange. Reconnect hoses. Install splash shield and wheels.

POWER STEERING PUMP

Removal

Remove pump bracket-to-pump retaining bolts. Place a container below pump to catch fluid. Disconnect hydraulic connections at pump. Remove pump.

Installation

To install, reverse removal procedure. Fill and bleed system. Check for leaks.

OVERHAUL

STEERING GEAR

Disassembly (240 Series ZF Steering Gear)

1) Clean exterior of gear. Cut plastic clamps. Remove equalizer tube. Attach steering gear to Holding Fixture (5046). Install gear and fixture to repair stand.

2) Disconnect rubber boots. Unfold lock washer tab. Using a 27 mm spanner on ball joint and large adjustable wrench on rack, remove steering rods. *See Fig. 3.*

3) Remove pressure lines. Drain fluid. Turn rack in and out with Pinion Socket (5179) to pump out fluid. Remove preload piston by removing preload piston cover, washer, spring and piston. Remove rubber dust cover from pinion shaft.

4) Remove valve unit housing attaching bolts. Using Socket (5179) and Puller (4078), pull valve unit housing with pinion shaft off rack end housing.

5) Scratch mark center tube-to-end housing mating surfaces for reassembly reference. DO NOT use a punch to mark center tube. Using Spanner Wrench (5178), remove center tube from end housings.

CAUTION: Do not clamp center tube in vise.

6) Remove "O" rings from center tube. Remove lock ring (if lock collar is damaged and needs to be replaced). Pull out rack with spacer tube. Remove seal. If needle bearings need to be replaced, use a long punch to tap them out.

7) Remove spacer (inner) tube from rack. Remove lock rings, thrust washers and piston with Teflon ring and "O" ring. Fill lock ring grooves with grease. Slide off tube toward opposite end of rack teeth.

8) Using slide hammer and Remover (1819), remove inner spacer, seal and brass bushing. Using a screwdriver, remove "O" ring and Teflon bushing. Lock ring and thrust washer should not be removed unless they have to be replaced.

9) Remove Teflon bushing, seal and star washer out of right housing. Remove depressor and "O" ring from preload piston. Use a mallet to drive pinion from valve unit housing. Use care not to lose roller bearings.

10) Remove guide bushings from pinion shaft. Remove seal rings from guide bushing.

11) DO NOT remove small dowel pin from pinion shaft. *See Fig. 2.* Valve unit setting cannot be readjusted and valve unit must be replaced.

Fig. 2: Pinion Shaft Dowel Pin (240 Series ZF Steering Gear)

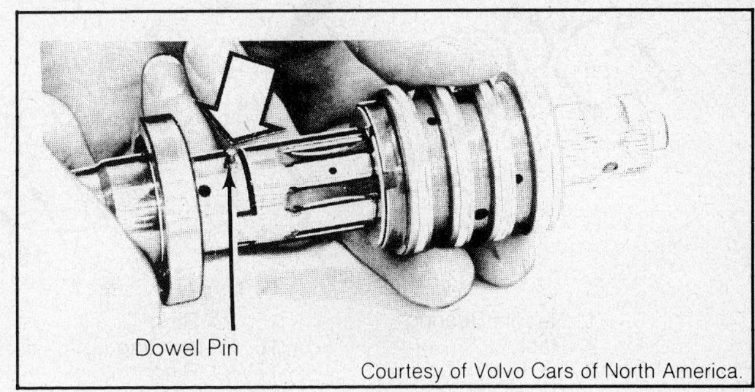

Courtesy of Volvo Cars of North America.

12) Using slide hammer and Remover (1819), pull bearing cage from valve unit housing. Using a screwdriver, remove seal from valve unit housing.

Inspection

1) Clean all parts and inspect for wear or damage. Replace as necessary. Check inner and outer ball joints for wear. Always use new seals during reassembly.

2) If any part of valve unit is defective, the valve unit and guide bushing assembly must be replaced.

Reassembly

1) If removed, lubricate needle bearing with lubricant (Part No. 1161001-1). Using a drift, install needle bearing into pinion housing so it is 2.29-2.31" (58.2-58.6 mm) from seal bottom. *See Fig. 4.*

2) Using Driver and Drift (1801 and 5184), install seal and "O" ring into pinion housing. Install bronze bushing in spacer tube with chamfered side toward inside of tube.

3) Install seal in spacer tube with lips facing away from inside of tube. Coat seal lips with lubricant.Install spacer washer, lock ring, Teflon ring and "O" ring onto spacer tube.

4) Before install spacer tube on rack, coat rack snap ring groove with wheel bearing grease. Slide spacer tube on steering rack from smooth end. Do not damage seal on snap ring grooves.

VOLVO POWER-ASSISTED RACK & PINION (Cont.)

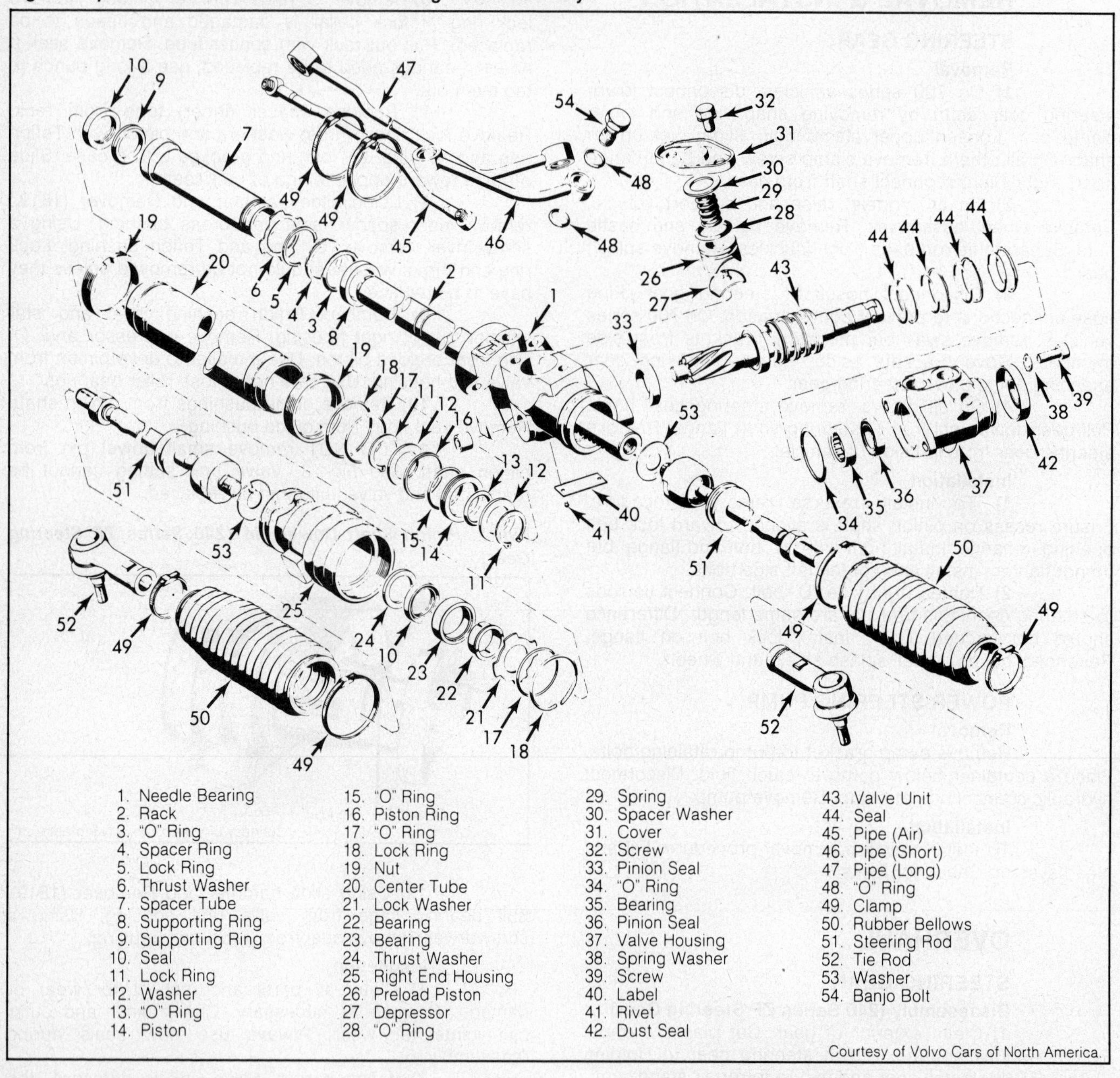

Fig. 3: Exploded View of 240 Series ZF Steering Gear Assembly

5) Install piston ring on piston. Install inner lock ring, spacer washer, "O" ring, piston with ring, spacer washer and lock ring onto rack in that order.

6) Install tube locking collars with recesses for wrench facing center of tube. Install locking rings on tube. Lubricate and install "O" rings on tube.

7) Using Drift and Driver (5184 and 1801), install seals in right side end housing. Using drift and driver, install metal bushing, Teflon bushing, and star washer in right side end housing.

8) Apply ATF to tube "O" rings. Using Spanner Wrench (5178), attach tube to right side end housing. Tighten to 88 ft. lbs. (120 N.m).

9) Coat rack teeth with lubricant (Part No. 1161001-1). Install rack with spacer assembly into pinion housing. Attach right side end housing/tube assembly to pinion housing.

10) Line up marks made during disassembly. Using Spanner Wrench (5178), tighten retaining collar to 88 ft. lbs. (120 N.m).

11) Using a sharp punch, stake right side end housing at one of the locking collar wrench recesses. Center rack so it protrudes 1 7/8" (48 mm) from pinion housing.

12) Install seal rings on guide bushing. Install guide bushing on pinion shaft. Align guide bushing with dowel pin on shaft. Using Drift (5226), drive seal into valve housing. Grease rollers (20) and install into roller cage.

VOLVO POWER-ASSISTED RACK & PINION (Cont.)

Fig. 4: Installing Needle Bearing (240 Series ZF Gear)

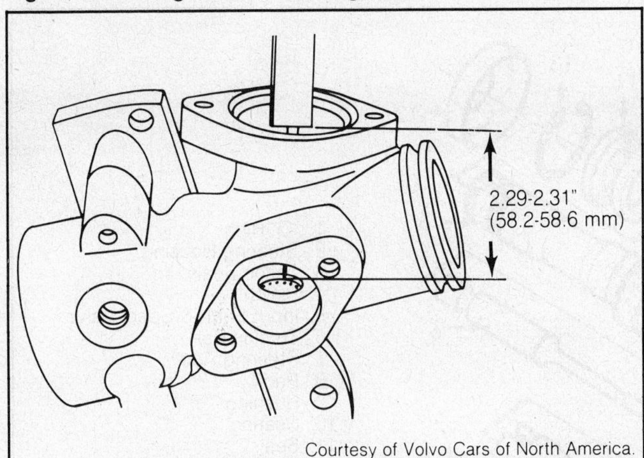

13) Using Driver and Drift (1801 and 5227), install roller bearing assembly into pinion housing. Install pinion assembly into valve housing. Large end of pinion shaft should protrude .20" (5.0 mm) from valve housing face. *See Fig. 5.*

Fig. 5: Installing Pinion Assembly in Valve Housing (240 Series ZF Gear)

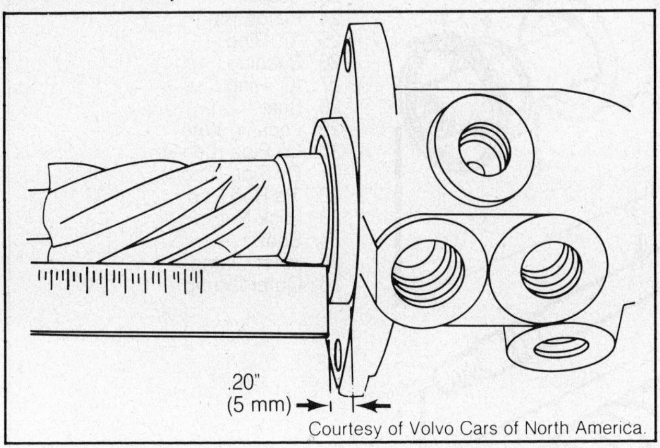

14) Install valve housing assembly to pinion housing. Flat on pinion assembly should face toward exposed rack end. Do not pinch "O" ring between valve and pinion housings. Install and tighten pinion-to-valve housing screws to 18 ft. lbs. (25 N.m). Install dust cover on pinion shaft.

15) Install preload piston with depressor but without "O" ring. Set up Preload Measuring Fixture (5865) using cover bolt hole and an 8 x 45 mm bolt. Assemble fixture with preload spring between bolt head and bolt. *See Fig. 6.* Screw in tool spindle until it tensions piston but not lock rack.

16) Use depth micrometer to measure pinion housing-to-preload piston distance. Check measurement at 3 different points on steering rack to determine piston's highest point. Subtract .004-.006" (.10-.15 mm) from smallest reading obtained. This value equals thickness of spacer washer to be installed.

17) Washers are available in thickness of 2.1-2.90 mm in increments of .05 mm. Remove measuring fixture. Lubricate "O" ring and install on preload piston.

Fig. 6: Adjusting Rack Preload

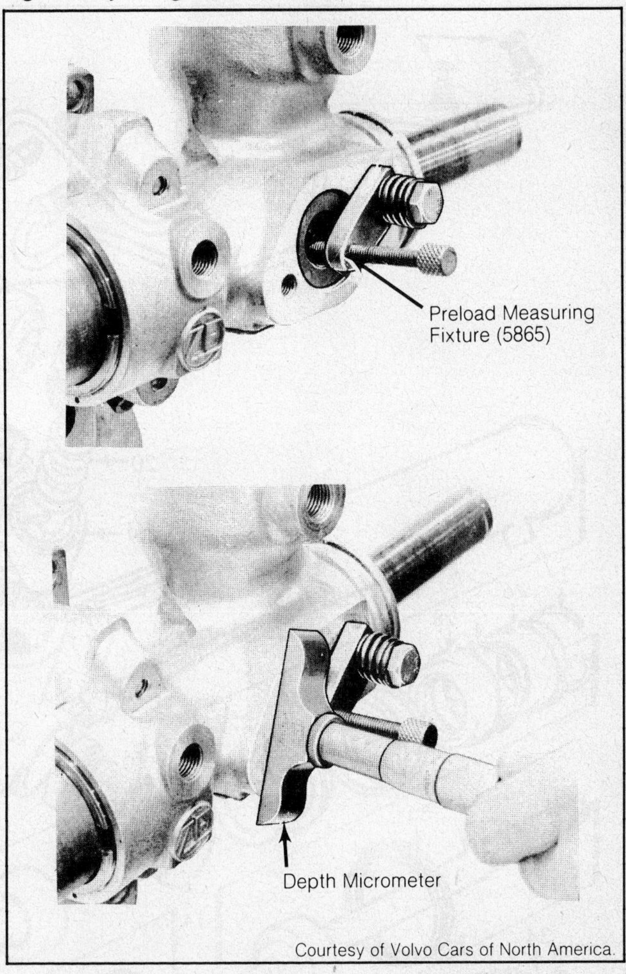

Install piston spring and spacer washer measured in step **16)**. Fill space around spring with lubricant (Part No. 111600-01).

18) Apply sealant on cover sealing surface. Install and tighten cover bolts to 16 ft. lbs. (22 N.m). Install and tighten pressure lines. Ensure "O" rings seat correctly.

19) Install tie rods. Bend back tie rod locking tabs. Install boots. Fill each boot with approximately 3/4 ounce of lubricant. Install boot clamps. Install equalizer tube and plastic clamps.

Disassembly & Reassmbly (240 Series Cam Gear Type)

Overhaul procedures are not available from manufacturer. With front end raised off ground and tie rod disconnected, turning torque of steering shaft should be 6-15 INCH lbs. (.9-1.7 N.m). *See Fig. 7.*

Disassembly (700 Series Cam Gear Type)

Two versions of the 700 Series Cam Gear are covered here - early and late versions. *See Fig. 8.* Overhaul procedures for both types are similiar.

1) Clean housing and remove oil pipes. Turn pinion back and forth to pump oil out of gear. Place rack in center position.

Power Steering

VOLVO POWER-ASSISTED RACK & PINION (Cont.)

Fig. 7: Exploded View of 240 Series Cam Gear-Type Power Steering Assembly

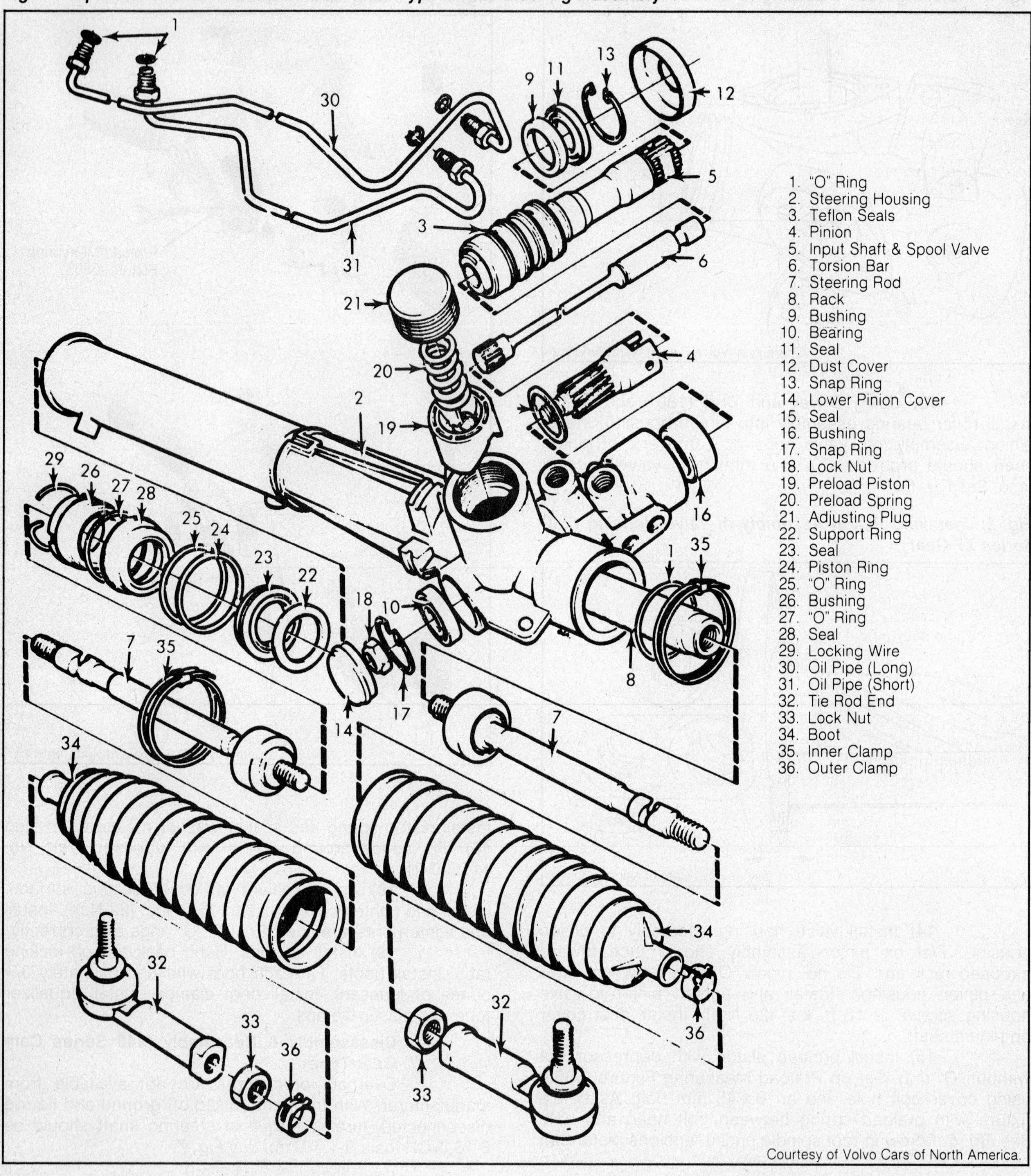

Courtesy of Volvo Cars of North America.

2) Remove clamps and boots. To prevent pinion damage, hold rack with adjustable wrench. Unscrew left steering rod completely. Loosen, but do not remove, right side steering rod. Remove right side locking wire.

3) On early version steering gears, apply compressed air through outer oil tube connector to remove lock sleeve and bushing. Remove steering rod. Remove lock sleeve, plastic ring and bushing.

4) On early and late version steering gears, remove rack preload assembly. *See Fig. 11.* Early type preload piston is held in place by shims and a cover plate.

VOLVO POWER-ASSISTED RACK & PINION (Cont.)

Fig. 8: 700 Series Rack & Pinion Steering Gears (Early & Late Versions)

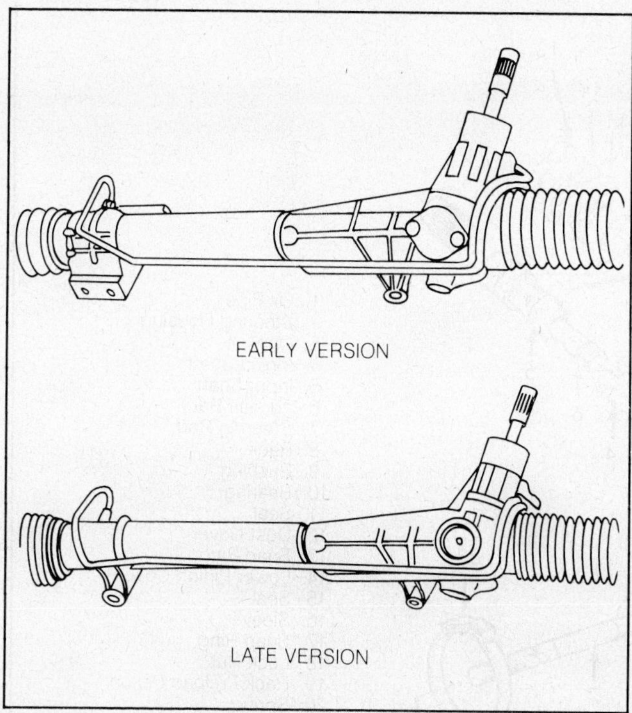

5) From top of pinion, remove dust cover and lock ring. Remove lower pinion cover and pinion nut. Lift out pinion and spool valve. Remove rack from housing.

6) Remove lock ring from lower pinion bearing and drive out bearing. From center of pinion housing, drive out pinion lower seal.

7) Tap out rack seal and spacer from inside of tube. Do not score inside of housing when removing seal. Piston seal should be replace if damaged or vehicle has been driven more than 25,000 miles.

8) Remove dust cover, lock ring, seal and upper bearing from spool valve assembly. *See Fig. 9.*

CAUTION: DO NOT remove 4 Teflon rings from spool valve assembly. Replacement rings are not sold. If rings are worn, replace entire steering gear.

Fig. 9: 700 Series Cam Gear Spool Valve Assembly (Early & Late Versions)

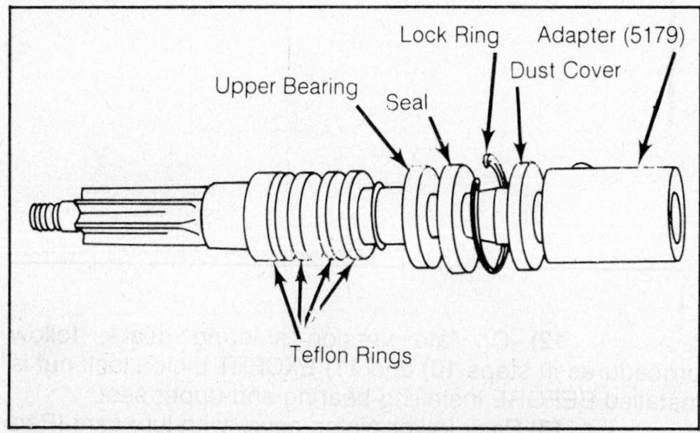

Other steering gear spool valves have similar design.

Cleaning & Inspection

Replace all seals except 4 Teflon rings on spool valve. If pinion or spool valve is damaged, replace entire steering gear. Clean and inspect rubber boots and replace if necessary.

Reassembly

1) Coat all parts with ATF before assembly. Install new "O" ring then Teflon ring on rack piston. Heat Teflon ring is difficult to install, heat it in water to about 100°F (40°C).

2) Using Seal Drive (5277) and Handle (1801), install lower pinion seal and guide sleeve in housing. Seal ring lip must face up. If seal is not centered properly, pinion will not turn easily.

3) Install lower bearing and lock ring. Wrap rack teeth with tape. Install seal with lip facing piston seal. Install tapered spacer with tapered side facing seal. Install flat spacer.

4) Press 2 spacers together. Remove tape from rack. Lube rack teeth. Install rack in housing. As rack seats, lightly push on it to seat seal and spacers.

5) To check is seal is correctly positioned, look through pressure tube opening. At least half of piston seal retainer has passed center of opening. Position rack so the end protrudes about 3/4" end of housing next to pinion housing.

6) Clean end of rack with wet fine-grit sandpaper. Clean rack and wrap one turn of tape around rack edge. Lubricate rack and tape.

7) On late type gears, install plastic spacer with beveled side facing toward seal. On early and late type gears, install lock sleeve and bushing onto rack. Use small screwdrive to lift edge of seal on end of rack.

8) Position end of lock sleeve so cut out sections face end of rack. Rack opening for locking wire must be in line with elongated hole in tube. Install locking wire. Turn bushing until wire is positioned correctly.

9) Center rack in housing and lubricate teeth with grease. Place pinion in housing with flat side in any one of 3 correct positions. *See Fig. 10*. End of rack should protrude 2.2" (55 mm).

Fig. 10: Positioning 700 Series Cam Gear Pinion Assembly (Early & Late Versions)

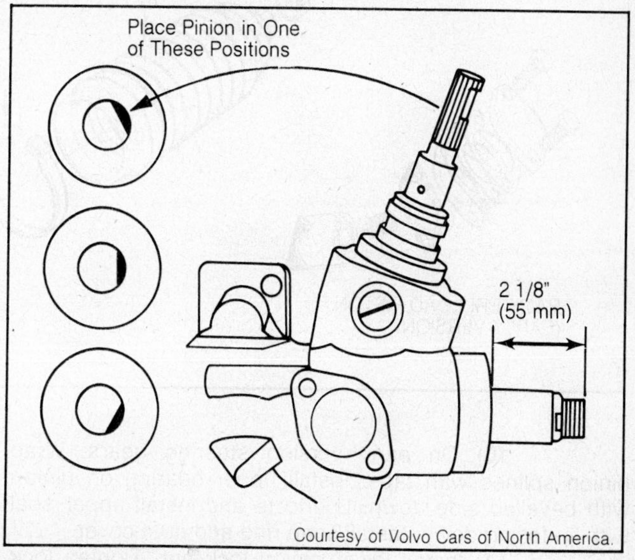

Power Steering

VOLVO POWER-ASSISTED RACK & PINION (Cont.)

Fig. 11: Exploded View of 700 Series Cam Gear (Late Version)

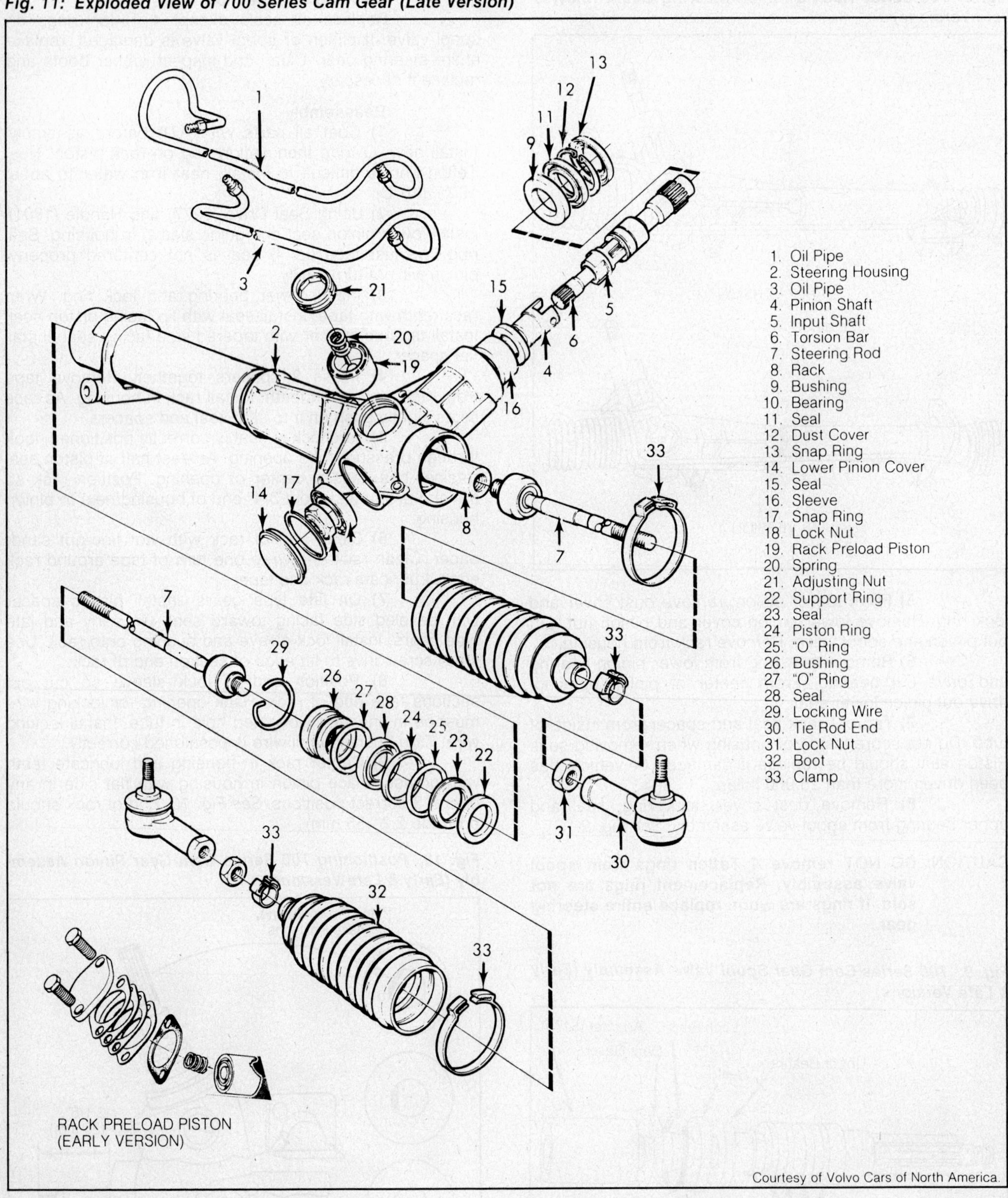

Courtesy of Volvo Cars of North America.

10) On early version steering gears, wrap pinion splines with tape. Install upper bearing on pinion with bevelled side down. Lubricate and install upper seal with lip facing down. Install snap ring and dust cover.

11) Install lower pinion lock nut. Tighten lock nut to 27 ft. lbs. (37 N.m).

12) On late version steering gears, follow procedures in steps **10)** and **11)** EXCEPT pinion lock nut is installed BEFORE installing bearing and upper seal.

13) Pack lower pinion cover with lubricant (Part No. 11 61 001-1). Install preload piston assembly in housing.

VOLVO POWER-ASSISTED RACK & PINION (Cont.)

Preload Adjustment (Early Version 700 Series Cam Gear)

1) Press piston towards rack. While sliding rack back and forth, use a feeler gauge and steel ruler to measure clearance between piston and housing.

2) To determine thickness of shim pack, add .002-.006" (.05-.15 mm) to value measured in step **1)**. Install spring, adjusting shims, gasket and cover on housing.

3) Using Adapter (5179) and Torque Gauge (9177), check turning torque of pinion shaft. Turning torque is 5-15 INCH lbs. (.6-1.7 N.m) when rack is turned from lock to lock. If torque is too high in any position, stop rack in that position. Readjust rack in high position.

Preload Adjustment (Late Version 700 Series Cam Gear)

1) Install preload piston spring and adjusting nut in housing. Place steering rack in center position. Tighten nut to 3.7-4.1 ft. lbs. (5.0-5.6 N.m) using Adapter (5296) and Torque Gauge (9177). Loosen adjusting nut 50-55°.

2) Using Adapter (5179) and Torque Gauge (9177), check turning torque of pinion shaft. Turning torque is 9-18 INCH lbs. (1.0-2.0 N.m). If torque is too high in any position, stop rack in that position. Readjust rack in high position.

3) If turning torque is still too high, install a new steering gear. If turning torque is okay, stake lock nut to valve housing with a punch.

Final Reassembly (Early & Late Version Steering Gears)

1) Install and tighten steering rods. Support rack with adjustable wrench while tightening. Use narrow punch to lock ball joints to rack recesses.

2) Fill boots with about an ounce of grease and install them on rack.

Disassembly (700 Series ZF Steering Gear)

1) Clean exterior of steering gear. Mount steering gear in vise. Remove oil tubes. Turn steering gear back and forth to pump out oil.

2) Remove clamps and boots. To prevent pinion damage, hold rack with adjustable wrench. Unscrew left and right side steering rods.

3) Remove rack piston preload piston assembly. *See Fig. 13*. Remove dust shield, lock ring and washer from upper part of pinion assembly. Remove lower pinion housing cover.

4) Secure upper pinion shaft. Remove lock nut, washer and snap ring. Withdraw pinion and spool valve assembly from housing. Remove end sleeve lock wire.

5) Slide rack and sleeve assembly from rack housing. Drive lower pinion bearing and seal out of pinion housing. DO NOT scratch inside of pinion housing surface.

6) Tap out rack seal and spacer ring from inside of steering housing. Remove "O" ring, seal, washer and bushing from rack end sleeve. Remove upper bearing housing from pinion and spool valve. Remove "O" ring and seal from upper bearing housing.

CAUTION: Only remove 4 Teflon rings from spool valve if they are damaged. Replace rack piston seal only if it is damaged or vehicle has more than 25,000 miles.

Cleaning & Inspection

Replace rubber boots if defective. Check all parts for wear, corrosion or damage. Replace as necessary. Replace entire steering gear if spool valve assembly is damaged.

Reassembly

1) Lubricate all parts with ATF prior to reassembly. Install "O" ring and Teflon ring on rack piston. Heat Teflon ring in water to 104-122°F (40-50°C) if it hard to install.

2) Install seal over rack teeth with lip facing piston. Lubricate rack piston teeth. Place spacer ring next to seal.

3) Install rack with seal and spacer ring into housing. When rack seats, gently push it in further to seat seal and spacer ring. Rack is positioned correctly when rack seal is visible in center of outlet tube hole.

4) Position rack so end protrudes about 3/4" from pinion housing end of rack housing. DO NOT push rack further into housing or seal may be damaged.

5) Install bushing, spacer washer and seal in end sleeve. Seal lips face out from end of sleeve. Drive end sleeve in housing and secure with snap ring.

6) Install "O" rings and Teflon rings (if removed) on spool valve. If necessary, heat Teflon rings in water to 104-122°F (40-50°C) to ease installation.

7) Install bearing and "O" ring in upper bearing housing. Install seal with lip facing bearing. Install lower pinion seal in pinion housing with lip facing up. Install lower pinion bearing and lock ring.

8) Install pinion and spool valve assembly in pinion housing. Install upper bearing housing, spacer washer, snap ring and dust shield. Pack bottom of dust shield with grease.

9) On bottom of pinion and spool valve assembly, install spacer washer and tighten lock nut to 11 ft. lbs. (15 N.m). Install pinion housing lower cover after filling it with grease.

10) Center steering rack in housing. Install preload spring WITHOUT "O" ring. Install spring in piston.

Fig. 12: Checking Rack Preload (700 Series ZF Steering Gear)

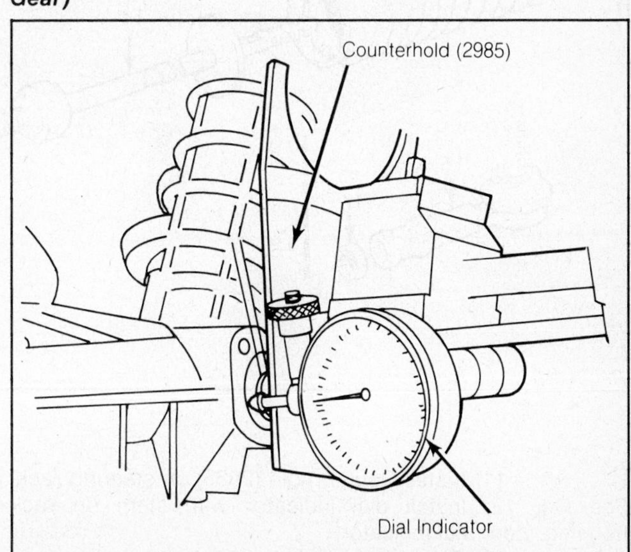

Power Steering

VOLVO POWER-ASSISTED RACK & PINION (Cont.)

Fig. 13: Exploded View of 700 Series ZF Steering Gear

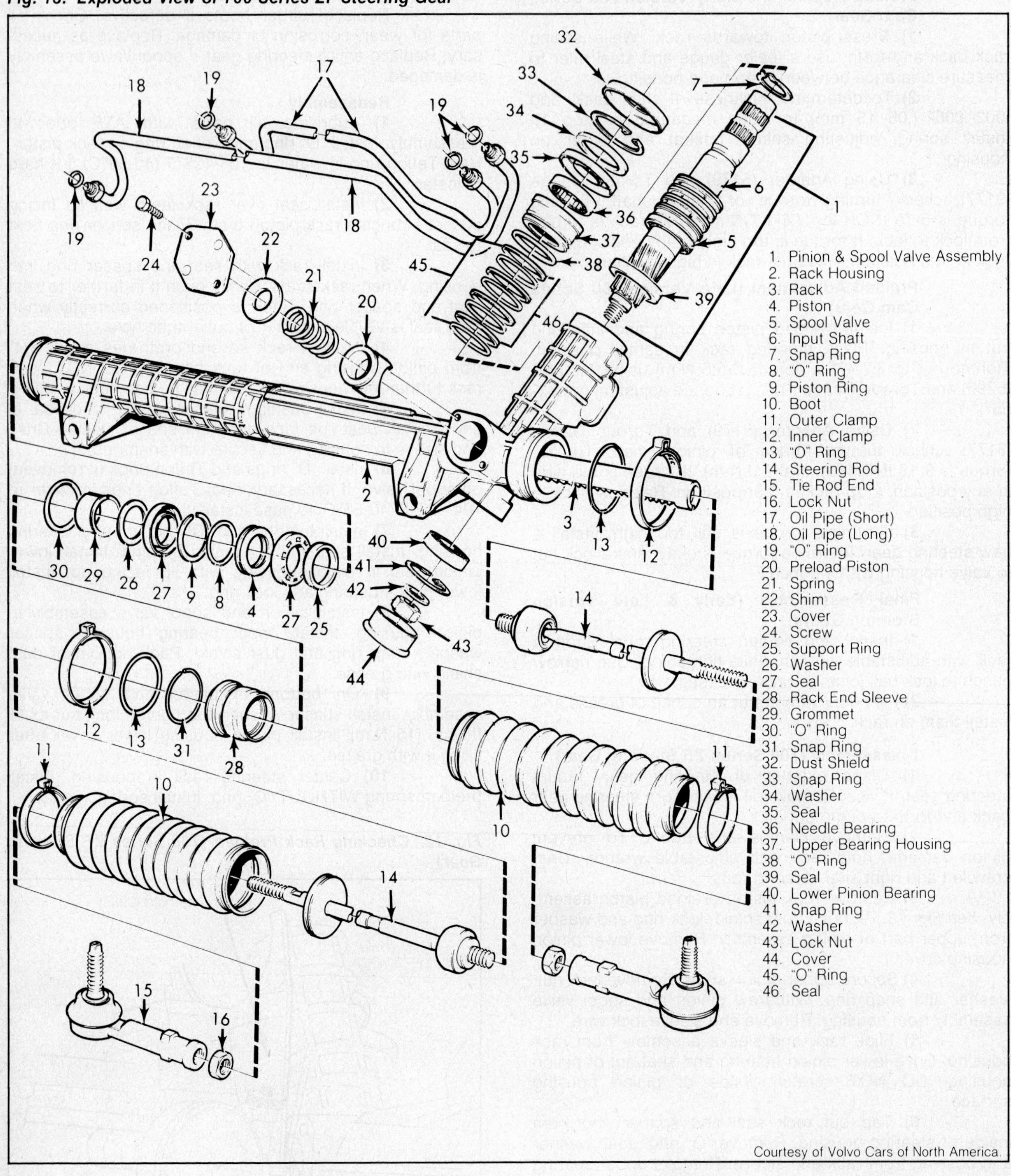

Courtesy of Volvo Cars of North America.

11) Install Counterhold (2985) on steering rack. *See Fig. 12.* Install dial indicator with stem on rack housing. Zero dial indicator.

12) Turn dial indicator so tip rests on face of preload piston. Note reading.

13) Move rack from lock to lock and note maximum indicator reading. Subtract .004" (.10 mm) from maximum indicator reading. This is total shim thickness that must be installed.

VOLVO POWER-ASSISTED RACK & PINION (Cont.)

14) Remove dial indicator and counterhold. Install "O" ring on preload piston. Install preload piston with spring and shim and cover. Tighten bolts to 79 INCH lbs. (9 N.m).

15) Install boot "O" ring and steering rods. Stake steering rods to rack to secure in position. Install boots and clamps.

TIGHTENING SPECIFICATIONS

Application	Ft. Lbs. (N.m)
240 Series ZF Steering Gear	
Oil Line Fittings	15 (20)
Preload Piston Cover	16 (22)
Tube Assembly-to-Pinion Housing	88 (120)
Valve Housing-to-Pinion Housing	18 (25)
700 Series Cam Gear Type	
Pinion Cover Bolts	12 (17)
Pinion Lower Lock Nut	27 (37)
Rack Mounting Bolts	32 (44)
	INCH Lbs. (N.m)
700 Series ZF Steering Gear	
Rack Preload Adjusting Cover Bolts	79 (9)
Rack Mounting Bolts	32 (44)

Electronic Power Steering

MAZDA RX7 & 626

DESCRIPTION

The power steering used in the RX7 is a basic hydraulically assisted rack and pinion system. This steering system changes its steering assist power according to information received from the vehicle speed sensor, turning angle sensor (steering wheel), and engine speed sensor. A control unit receives signals from all of these sensors and will regulate the proper amount of hydraulic pressure needed by rotating an electric stepping motor. This control of hydraulic pressure will provide the most appropriate steering feel under various driving conditions. *See Fig. 1*.

Control unit incorporates an audible self-diagnostic capability for all electrical steering components. It also includes a fail-safe function that if for any reason, no signal is received from vehicle speed sensor, signal from engine speed sensor would be detected, and hydraulic pressure would be regulated based upon that signal. Therefore, the appropriate steering wheel effort can be provided with the engine speed control signal alone.

DIAGNOSIS

SELF-DIAGNOSIS FUNCTION

If a malfunction occurs within the control unit or any of the various sensors, an audible buzzer will sound in different intervals, depending upon malfunction.

- If control unit receives an improper engine speed signal (short circuit or broken wire), an audible signal will buzz 2 times/pause/2 times/pause and so on.
- If control unit receives an improper stepping motor signal (broken wires or short circuit in coils or harnesses), signal will buzz 3 times/pause/3 times-/pause and so on.
- If control unit receives an improper steering sensor signal, buzzer will sound 60 seconds after broken wire or short circuit occurs to sensors or harnesses. Signal will buzz 5 times/pause/5 times/pause and so on.
- If control unit receives an improper speed sensor signal caused by a broken wire or short circuit, buzzer will sound 60 seconds after an engine speed signal of 2200 RPM continues for 18 seconds. Signal will buzz one time/pause/one time/pause and so on.
- If computer malfunctions and cannot control the system, buzzer will sound continuously. If any other circuit problems are present other than computer, signal will buzz 4 times/pause/4 times/pause and so on.

Fig. 1: Speed Sensing Power Steering Components

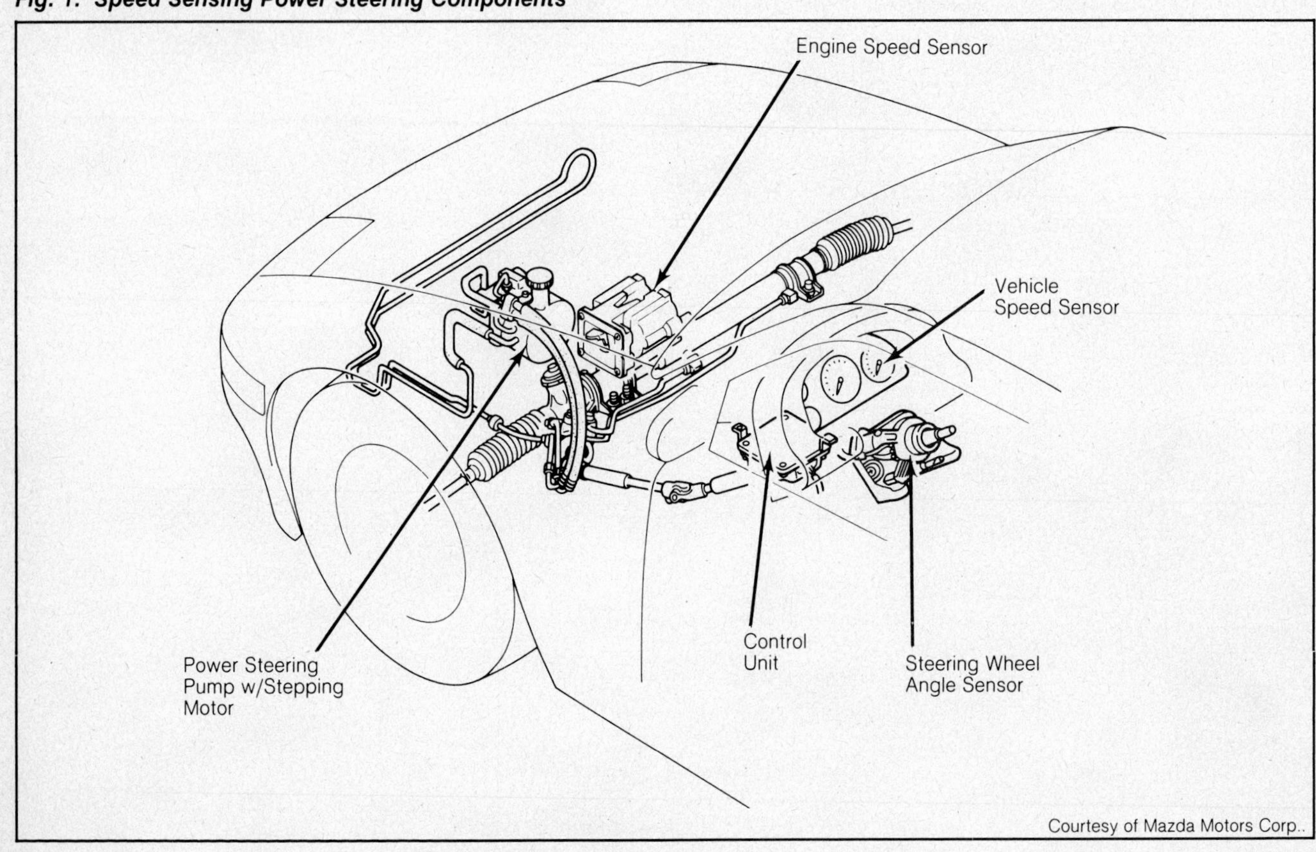

MAZDA RX7 & 626 (Cont.)

Fig. 2: Circuit Diagram of Components

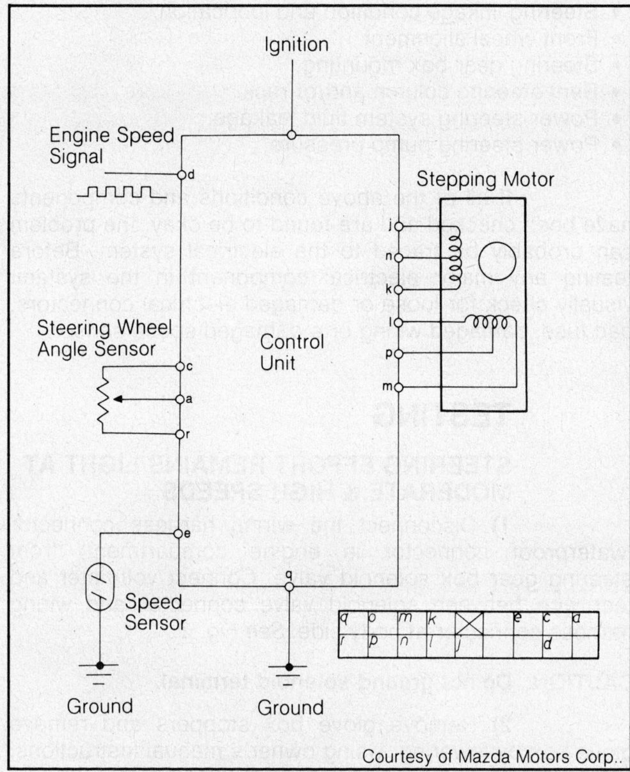

FAIL-SAFE SYSTEM

The Mazda electronically-controlled power steering system incorporates several fail-safe systems designed to maintain vehicle control under a wide variety of possible power steering malfunctions.

- If engine-speed sensor malfunctions, vehicle-speed signal will be input to computer even if engine speed signal is not. Power steering will be controlled normally.
- If vehicle-speed sensor malfunctions and vehicle speed is below 50 MPH or engine speed is above 2200 RPM, steering effort is adjusted as if vehicle speed were above 50 MPH. If vehicle speed is above 50 MPH or engine speed is less than 2200 RPM, steering effort is adjusted to speed last sensed when failure occurred.
- If steering-angle sensor malfunctions with vehicle speed more than 25 MPH and more than 35 degrees of steering angle for over 80 seconds, steering effort is slightly decreased at all speeds above 25 MPH.
- If malfunction of control unit or stepping motor output occurs, power supply to stepping motor is cancelled and steering effort is adjusted as if vehicle speed were 50 MPH.

TESTING

NOTE: Test procedures for electronic power steering is not available from manufacturer. For more information on wiring diagrams, see MAZDA RX7 & 323 ELECTRONIC SUSPENSION article in SUSPENSION section.

MITSUBISHI GALANT

DESCRIPTION

The electronically controlled power steering system is designed to provide the most appropriate steering feel for various driving conditions. This is accomplished by changing the power assist characteristics to correspond with road conditions, vehicle speed and steering force.

An electronic power steering control unit monitors signals from the engine and vehicle speed sensors. Processed information from the control unit along with the angle in which the steering wheel is turned, will electrically and mechanically control the hydraulic pressure applied to the reaction-force plunger.

Steering effort characteristics can be selected in either of two stages by using the EPS mode selector located on the floor console. Driver selects either "NORMAL" (for a normal type power steering effort), or "SPORT" (for a firmer type feel for the road). A self diagnosis check connector located under glove box opening is provided for testing using the Vehicle Speed Simulator "VSS" (MB991139). *See Fig. 1.* A fail-safe feature is also provided in the control unit to return steering mode to ordinary power steering should there be a malfunction in any of the electrical components.

Fig. 1: Vehicle Speed Simulator Test Equipment

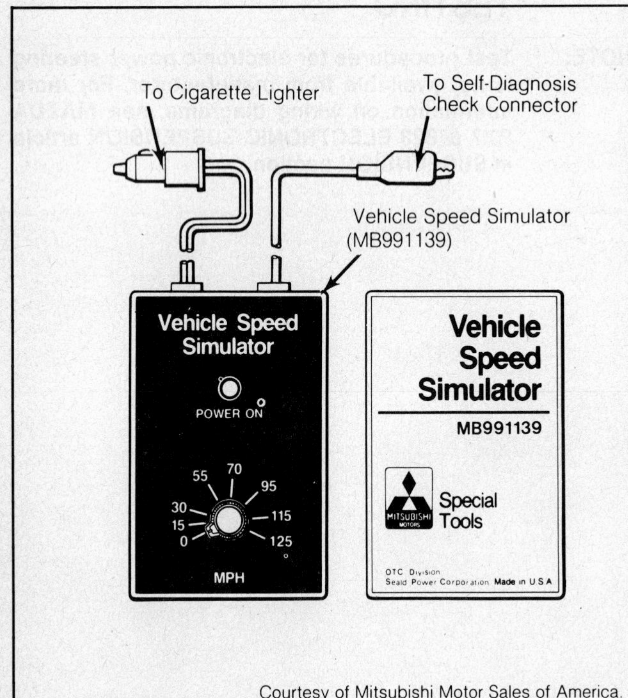

Courtesy of Mitsubishi Motor Sales of America.

TROUBLE SHOOTING

A malfunction in the electronically-controlled power steering system will usually cause hard steering at idle or low-speed driving, or too sensitive steering during high-speed driving. However, these problems do not necessarily indicate a malfunction in the electronically-controlled power steering system. Always check the following components and conditions first before trouble shooting for an electrical problem in the system.

- Loose or damaged V-belt.
- Tire condition and pressure.
- Ball joints and suspension condition.
- Steering linkage condition and lubrication.
- Front wheel alignment.
- Steering gear box mounting.
- Bent steering column and/or rack.
- Power steering system fluid leakage.
- Power steering pump pressure.

If all of the above conditions and components have been checked and are found to be okay, the problem can probably be traced to the electrical system. Before testing any major electrical component in the system, visually check for loose or damaged electrical connectors, bad fuse, damaged wiring or a damaged speed sensor.

TESTING

STEERING EFFORT REMAINS LIGHT AT MODERATE & HIGH SPEEDS

1) Disconnect the wiring harness connector (waterproof connector in engine compartment) from steering gear box solenoid valve. Connect voltmeter and test wire between solenoid valve connector and wiring harness connector at body side. *See Fig. 2.*

CAUTION: Do not ground solenoid terminal.

2) Remove glove box stoppers and remove glove box by lowering. Using owner's manual instructions, attach Vehicle Speed Simulator (MB991139) to self-diagnosis check connector (under opening of glove box). *See Fig. 3.*

3) Check solenoid current to be sure that it is between .9-1.1 amps at 0 MPH, and that current decreases as vehicle speed is increased. If current does not decrease, wiring may be damaged, connector may be disconnected or control unit may be defective. Repair or replace as needed.

NOTE: Test procedure can be performed with vehicle properly supported on hoist and wheels off the ground if VSS is not available.

Fig. 2: Testing Solenoid Valve Current

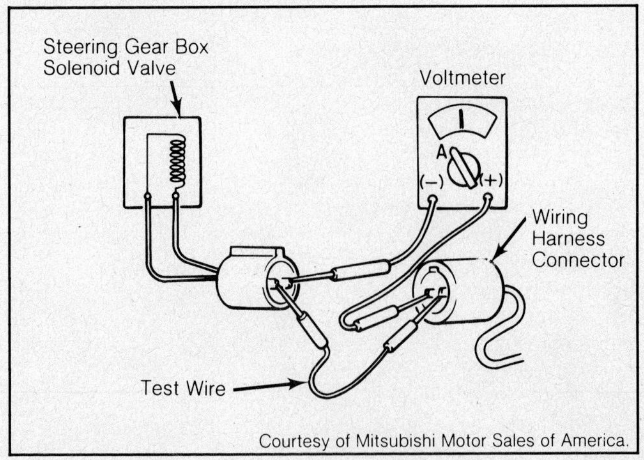

Courtesy of Mitsubishi Motor Sales of America.

MITSUBISHI GALANT (Cont.)

Fig. 3: Connecting Vehicle Speed Simulator

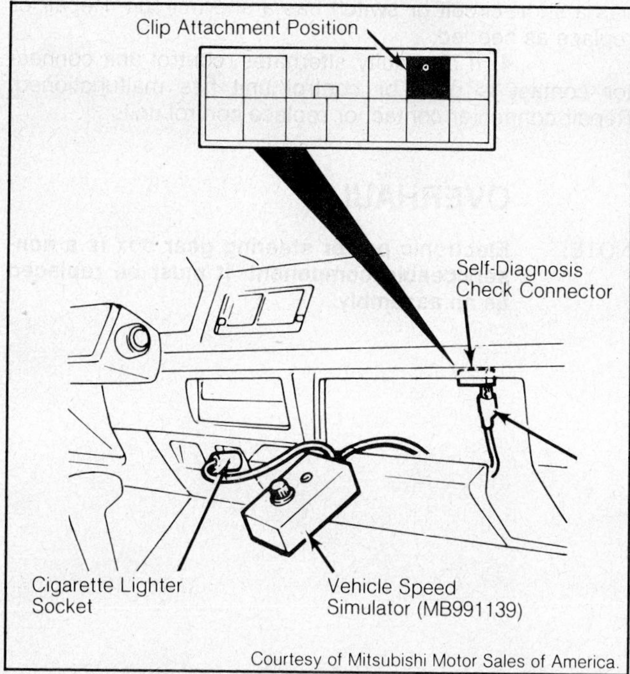

Courtesy of Mitsubishi Motor Sales of America.

Fig. 4: Electronic Power Steering Component Circuit

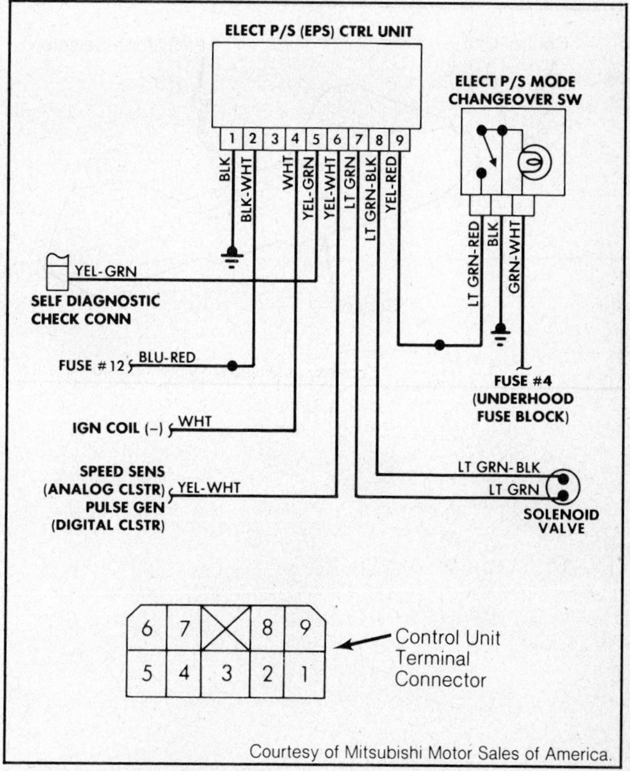

Courtesy of Mitsubishi Motor Sales of America.

NO SOLENOID CURRENT AND/OR LARGE STEERING EFFORT WITH IGNITION "ON"

NOTE: Before making the following checks, ensure that fail-safe system has not been activated by racing of the engine.

1) Check No. 12 fuse for power to control unit. If no power is present, check for a burned or damaged harness, or a short circuit in harness. Repair or replace as needed. *See Fig. 4*.

2) If power is present at No. 12 fuse, disconnect control unit harness connector. Check voltage between ground and control unit harness connector terminal No. 2 (Black/White wire) with ignition switch in the "ON" position. Voltage should read 12 volts. If not, check for damaged wiring or disconnected harness between fuse No. 12 and control unit terminal No. 2 (Black/White wire). Repair or replace as needed.

3) If voltage reads 12 volts at connector, disconnect negative battery cable. Check for continuity between control unit harness side connector terminal No. 7 (Light Green wire) and terminal No. 8 (Light Green/Black wire).

4) If continuity is present, go to step **6)**. If continuity is not present, disconnect connector for solenoid valve in engine compartment. Check for continuity between the two terminals of the connector at the steering wheel. If there is continuity, harness may be damaged between control unit and solenoid valve connector. Repair or replace harness.

5) If there is no continuity between the two terminals, wiring of solenoid valve coil may be damaged or disconnected. Replace steering gear assembly.

6) There should be approximately 5.7-7.7 ohms of resistance at 68°F (20°C) when measured between terminal No. 7 (Light Green wire) and terminal No. 8 (Light Green/Black wire). If not, there may be a poor contact at connector. Repair contact on connector.

7) If resistance is correct, control unit connector contact is poor or the control unit has malfunctioned. Repair contact or replace control unit.

NO DECREASE IN SOLENOID CURRENT WHEN DRIVING OR TESTING

1) Check for continuity between ground and control unit connector terminal No. 6 (Yellow/White wire) with ignition switch "ON" or "OFF" and front wheels jacked up and turned slowly. If there is continuity, control unit has malfunctioned. Replace control unit. If there is no continuity, go to next step.

2) Check speed-sensitive intermittent wipers (wiper system uses speed sensor) for normal operation. If normal, check for disconnected wiring harness, damage to harness between speed sensor and control unit or poor contact at connector. Correct or replace.

3) If wiper system is not normal, wiring harness has poor connection at connector, wiring harness is damaged between speed sensor and ground or speed sensor has malfunctioned. Repair wiring harness or replace speed sensor.

NO CHANGE IN STEERING EFFORT WHEN (EPS) MODE SELECTOR IS USED

1) Turn ignition switch "OFF". Disconnect connector of control unit. Check for alternating continuity and no continuity between ground and control unit harness connector ternminal No. 9 (Yellow/Red wire) by switching EPS mode switch "ON" and "OFF" repeatedly. *See Fig. 5*.

2) If there is no continuity at all, switch connector is disconnected, harness is damaged or switch has malfunctioned. Repair or replace as neeeded.

Electronic Power Steering

MITSUBISHI GALANT (Cont.)

Fig. 5: EPS Mode Selector and Control Unit

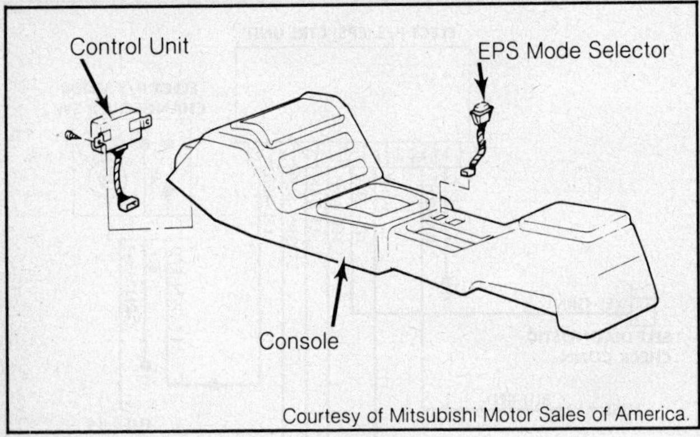

Courtesy of Mitsubishi Motor Sales of America.

3) If there is continuity all the time, harness has a short-circuit or switch has a short circuit. Repair or replace as needed.

4) If continuity alternates, control unit connector contact is poor or control unit has malfunctioned. Repair connector contact or replace control unit.

OVERHAUL

NOTE: **Electronic power steering gear box is a non-serviceable component. It must be replaced as an assembly.**

Electronic Power Steering

TOYOTA CRESSIDA

DESCRIPTION

The Toyota electronically-controlled power steering system incorporates a speed sensor, computer and a solenoid valve in addition to conventional power steering components. By electronically regulating the hydraulics, the system will reduce hydraulic pressure at high vehicle speeds (when power-assisted steering is less necessary), and increases pressure at lower speeds (when power-assistance is needed). *See Fig. 1.*

TROUBLE SHOOTING

A malfunction in the electronically-controlled power steering system will usually cause hard steering at idle or low-speed driving, or too sensitive steering during high-speed driving. However, these problems do not necessarily indicate a malfunction in the electronically-controlled power steering system. Always check following components first before trouble shooting the electronically-controlled power steering system.

- Tire Pressure.
- Suspension and steering linkage lubrication.
- Front wheel alignment.
- Steering system and suspension ball joints.
- Bent steering column.
- Power steering system leakage.
- Power steering pump pressure.

If all of the above have been checked and are found to be okay, the problem in the system can probably be traced to the electronically-controlled power steering.

TESTING

NOTE: Electrical wiring diagrams for this system can be found in the ELECTRONIC SUSPENSION section in this manual.

SYSTEM TEST

1) Turn ignition switch to "ON" position. Using voltmeter, measure voltage between computer terminal "+B" and ground "GND". *See Fig. 2.* Voltage should be 8-14 volts. If not, check battery, body ground or power circuit (fuse and/or fusible link). If voltage is okay, go to next step.

Fig. 2: Checking Voltage From Computer

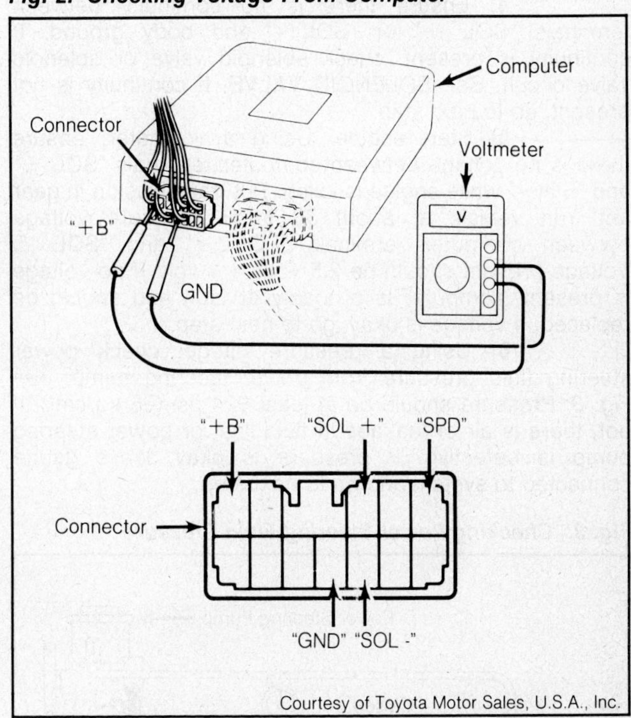

2) Raise and support vehicle. Disconnect computer connector and spin rear wheels of vehicle.

Fig. 1: Toyota Electronically-Controlled Power Steering System

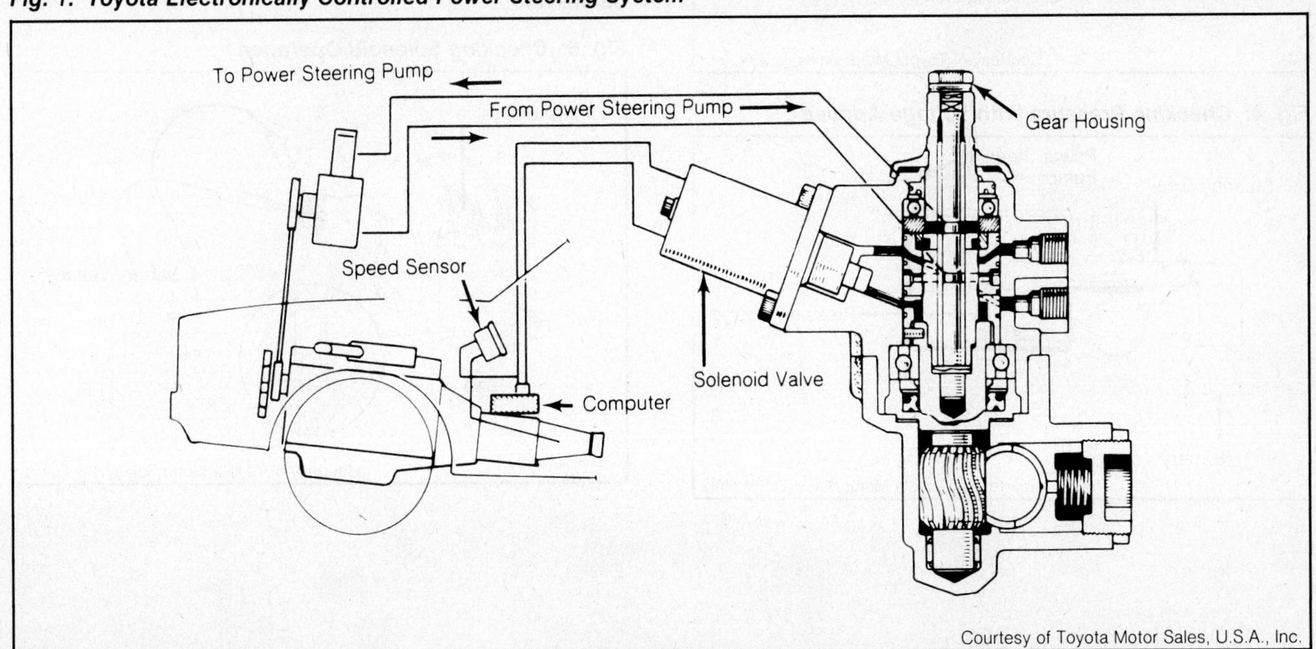

Electronic Power Steering

TOYOTA CRESSIDA (Cont.)

Using an ohmmeter, check resistance between computer connector terminals "SPD" and "GND". Resistance should be zero to infinity ohms. If not, check speed sensor and speed sensor circuit. If resistance is okay, go to next step.

3) Disconnect computer connector and check resistance between terminals "SOL +" and "SOL -". Resistance should be 7.4-8.0 ohms. If not, check solenoid valve or solenoid valve circuit. See SOLENOID VALVE. If resistance is okay, go to next step.

4) Ensure there is no continuity between terminals "SOL +" or "SOL -" and body ground. If continuity is present, check solenoid valve or solenoid valve circuit. See SOLENOID VALVE. If continuity is not present, go to next step.

5) Start engine. Using a voltmeter, ensure there is no voltage between computer terminals "SOL +" and "SOL -" while engine is idling. Put transmission in gear and run vehicle at about 30 MPH. Measure voltage between computer terminals "SOL +" and "SOL -". Voltage present should be 2.5 volts ±1 volt. If no voltage is present, computer is probably at fault and should be replaced. If voltage is okay, go to next step.

6) Using a pressure gauge, check power steering fluid pressure from power steering pump. *See Fig. 3.* Pressure should be at least 924 psi (65 kg/cm²). If not, there is air or leakage in fluid line, or power steering pump is defective. If pressure is okay, leave gauge connected to system and go to next step.

Fig. 3: Checking Power Steering Fluid Pressure

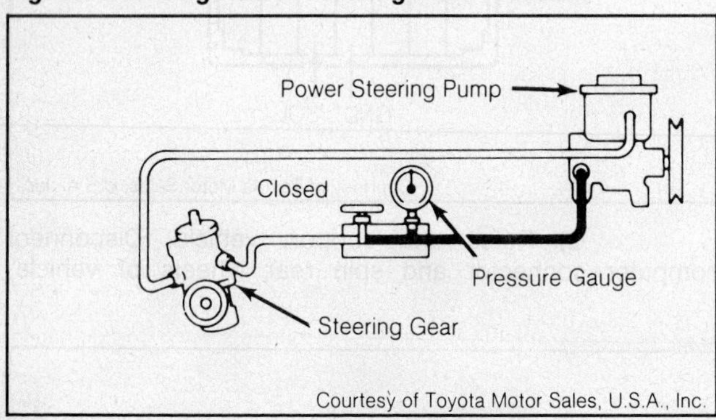

Fig. 4: Checking Pressure With Voltage Applied

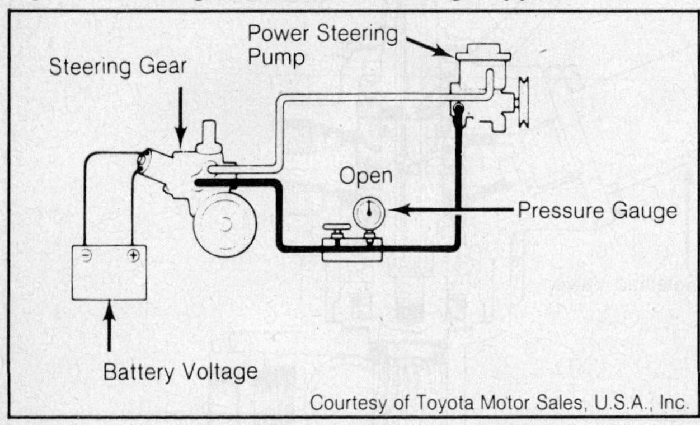

7) Apply battery voltage between terminals "SOL +" and "SOL -" on steering gear. *See Fig. 4.* Turn power steering solenoid on and off. Check for a change in gear housing fluid pressure. If there is no change in pressure, by-pass line or return line may be clogged, fluid level may be low or solenoid valve may be defective. If pressure is okay, steering gear housing is probably at fault and should be replaced.

SOLENOID VALVE

ON-VEHICLE

Remove wiring connector from solenoid valve. Using an ohmmeter, measure resistance between "SOL +" and "SOL -" terminals. *See Fig. 5.* Resistance should be 7.4-8.0 ohms. If resistance is not okay, solenoid valve is defective. Reconnect wiring connector.

Fig. 5: Checking Solenoid Resistance & Operation

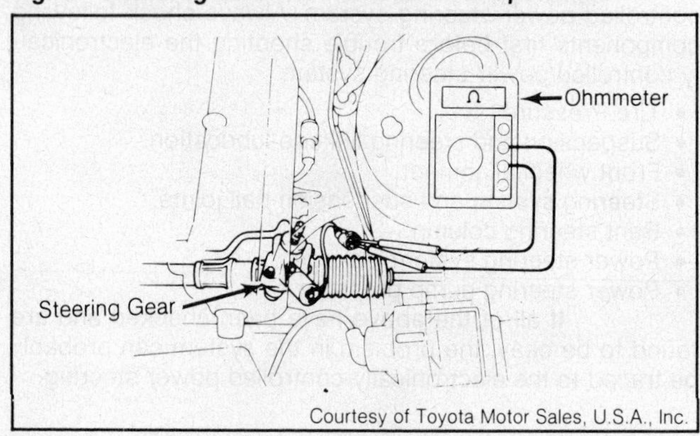

OFF-VEHICLE

Remove solenoid valve from gear housing. Connect battery positive terminal to solenoid terminal "SOL +" and battery negative terminal to solenoid terminal "SOL -". *See Fig. 6.* Ensure needle valve withdraws about .079" (2 mm). If not, solenoid valve is defective.

Fig. 6: Checking Solenoid Operation

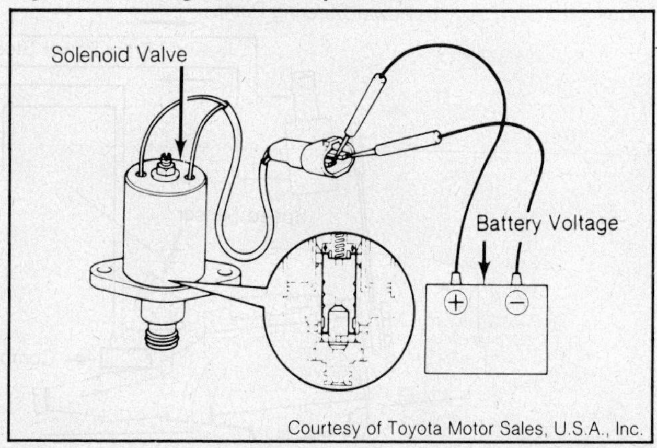

SECTION 13

TRANSMISSION SERVICING

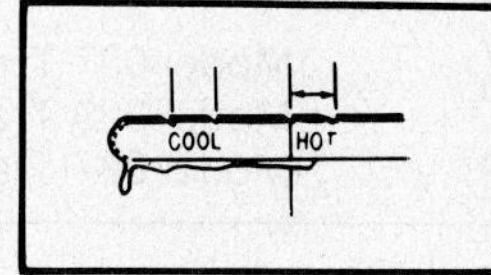

CONTENTS

AUTOMATIC TRANSMISSION APPLICATION

Page

All Models 13-2

MANUAL TRANSMISSION APPLICATION

All Models 13-5

AUTOMATIC TRANSMISSION SERVICING

Acura 13-8
Audi 13-10
BMW 13-13
Chrysler Motors 13-15
Ford Motor Co. 13-19
General Motors 13-21
Honda 13-24
Hyundai 13-26
Isuzu 13-28
Jaguar 13-30
Mazda 13-32
Mercedes-Benz 13-36
Mitsubishi 13-39
Nissan 13-44
Peugeot 13-47
Porsche 13-48
Saab 13-50
Sterling 13-52
Subaru 13-53
Toyota 13-55
Volkswagen 13-57
Volvo 13-60

MANUAL TRANSMISSION SERVICING

Page

Acura 13-62
Audi 13-62
BMW 13-64
Chrysler Motors 13-64
Ford Motor Co. 13-65
General Motors 13-66
Honda 13-67
Hyundai 13-68
Isuzu 13-68
Mazda 13-69
Mercedes-Benz 13-70
Mitsubishi 13-70
Nissan 13-71
Peugeot 13-72
Porsche 13-72
Saab 13-73
Sterling 13-74
Subaru 13-74
Suzuki 13-74
Toyota 13-75
Volkswagen 13-76
Volvo 13-79
Yugo 13-80

AUTOMATIC TRANSMISSION REMOVAL

Acura 13-81
Audi 13-81
BMW 13-82
Chevrolet 13-83
Chrysler Motors 13-83
Ford Motor Co. 13-84
Honda 13-85
Hyundai 13-85
Isuzu 13-85
Jaguar 13-86
Mazda 13-87
Mercedes-Benz 13-88
Mitsubishi 13-89
Nissan 13-90
Peugeot 13-91
Porsche 13-91
Saab 13-92
Sterling 13-92
Subaru 13-92
Toyota 13-93
Volkswagen 13-97
Volvo 13-98

MANUAL TRANSMISSION REMOVAL

For information on manual transmission removal, see CLUTCHES section.

NOTE: ALSO SEE GENERAL INDEX.

Transmission Application

AUTOMATIC TRANSMISSIONS
IMPORTED CARS & TRUCKS

MANUFACTURER & MODEL	TRANSMISSION MODEL
ACURA	
Integra	Model CA Transaxle
Legend	Model G4 Transaxle
Legend	Model L5 Transaxle
AUDI	
Coupe GT	Model 087 Transaxle
4000S, 4000CS	Model 089 Transaxle
5000S, 5000CS, 5000CS Quattro	Model 087 Transaxle
BMW	
All Models	Model ZF 4HP 22/H or 4HP 22/EH
CHRYSLER MOTORS	
Colt	Mitsubishi – Model KM171-1 Transaxle (1.5L)
	Mitsubishi – Model KM171-2 Transaxle (1.6L)
Colt Vista	Mitsubishi – Model KM172 Transaxle
Conquest	Mitsubishi – Model JM600
Raider	Mitsubishi – Model KM148
Ram-50	Aisin-Warner – AW 372 (2WD)
	Mitsubishi – Model KM148 (4WD)
FORD MOTOR CO.	
Tracer	Mazda – Model F3A Transaxle
Merkur XR4Ti	Ford – Model C-3
GENERAL MOTORS	
Spectrum	Model KF100 Transaxle
Sprint	Suzuki 3-Speed Transaxle
HONDA	
Accord	Model F4 Transaxle
Civic & Civic CRX/si	Model CA Transaxle
Prelude	Model AS Transaxle (Carb.)
	Model F4 Transaxle (Fuel Inj.)
HYUNDAI	
Excel	Mitsubishi – Model KM171-1-AP2
ISUZU	
I-Mark	Model KF100 Transaxle
Impulse	Model AW03-70 or AW03-72L
P'UP	Model AW03-55 (Diesel)
	Model AW03-75 (Gas)
JAGUAR	
XJ6	Borg-Warner – Model 66
XJS	GM Turbo Hydra-Matic Model 400
MAZDA	
B2200 & B2600	Jatco – L3N71B (4WD)
	Jatco – L4N71B (2WD)
RX7	Jatco – Model L4N71B
323	Mazda – Model F3A Transaxle
626	Mazda – Model FU06 Transaxle
MERCEDES-BENZ	
190 Series & 260E	Model W4A020
All Other Models	Model W4A040

Transmission Application

AUTOMATIC TRANSMISSIONS
IMPORTED CARS & TRUCKS (Cont.)

MANUFACTURER & MODEL	TRANSMISSION MODEL
MITSUBISHI	
Cordia & Tredia	Model KM172 Transaxle
Galant	Model KM175 Transaxle
Mirage	Model KM171-1 Transaxle (1.5L) Model KM171-2 Transaxle (1.6L)
Montero & Pickup	Aisin-Warner – Model AW 372 (2WD) Mitsubishi – Model KM148 (4WD)
Precis	Model KM171
Starion	Model JM600
Van	Model AW372L
NISSAN	
Maxima & Stanza Wagon	Jatco – Model RL4F02A Transaxle
Pickup/Pathfinder	Jatco – Model L3N71B (4WD, 6-Cyl.) Jatco – Model E4N71B (2WD, 6-Cyl.) Jatco – Model L4N71B (2WD, 4-Cyl.)
Pulsar NX & Sentra	Jatco – Model RL3F01A Transaxle
Stanza	Jatco – RL4F02A Transaxle
200SX SE & XE	Jatco – L4N71B (4-Cyl.) Jatco – E4N71B (6-Cyl.)
300ZX & 300ZX Turbo	Jatco – Model E4N71B
Van	Jatco – L4N71B
PEUGEOT	
505	Model ZF 4HP 22
PORSCHE	
924-S	Model 087 Transaxle
928-S4	Model A28/12 Transaxle
944	Model 087 Transaxle
SAAB	
900, 900S, 900 Turbo	Borg-Warner – Model 37 Transaxle
9000S	ZF – Model GAT 4102
9000T	ZF – Model GAT 4301
STERLING	
825	Acura – Model G4
SUBARU	
All Models	Gunma Transaxle
TOYOTA	
Camry	Model A140E
Celica	Model A140E or A140L Transaxle
Corolla (FWD)	Model A131L, A240E or A240L Transaxle
Corolla (RWD)	Model A42DL
Cressida	Model A340E
Land Cruiser	Model A440F or A440L
MR2	Model A240E Transaxle
Pickup & 4Runner	Model A43D (2WD) Model A340H (4WD)
Supra	Model A340E
Tercel Sedan	Model A132L Transaxle
Tercel Wagon	Model A55 (2WD) Model A55F (4WD)
Van	Model A45DL (2WD) Model A45DF (4WD)

Transmission Application

AUTOMATIC TRANSMISSIONS
IMPORTED CARS & TRUCKS (Cont.)

MANUFACTURER & MODEL	TRANSMISSION MODEL
VOLKSWAGEN	
Cabriolet, Golf, GTI, Jetta & Scirocco	Model 010 Transaxle
Quantum	Model 087 Transaxle
Vanagon	Model 090 Transaxle
VOLVO	
240 DL & GL, 740 GL & GLE (5-Door)	Aisin-Warner – Model AW70L
740 Turbo, 760 GLE, 760 Turbo, 780 GLE	Aisin-Warner – Model AW71
740 GL & GLE (4-Door)	ZF – Model 4HP 22

Transmission Application

MANUAL TRANSMISSIONS
IMPORTED CARS & TRUCKS

MANUFACTURER & MODEL	TRANSMISSION MODEL
ACURA	
Integra	5-Speed – Model CG Transaxle
Legend	5-Speed – Model C3P4 Transaxle
Legend Coupe	5-Speed – Model C3F4 Transaxle
AUDI	
Coupe GT, 4000S	5-Speed – Model 013 or 093 Transaxle
5000S, 4000CS Quattro	
5000CS Quattro	5-Speed – Model 016 Transaxle
BMW	
325 Series, 528e	5-Speed – Getrag 260/5
535i, 535is, 635CSi, 735i	5-Speed – Getrag 260/6
CHRYSLER MOTORS	
Colt	4-Speed – Model KM200 Transaxle (1.5L)
	5-Speed – Model KM201 Transaxle (1.5L)
	5-Speed – Model KM206 Transaxle (1.6L)
Colt Vista (2WD)	5-Speed – Model KM206 Transaxle
Colt Vista (4WD)	5-Speed – Model KM182 Transaxle
Conquest	5-Speed – Model KM132-B (W/O Intercooler)
	5-Speed – Model KM132-G (W/Intercooler)
Raider	5-Speed – Model KM145
Ram-50 Pickups (2WD)	5-Speed – Model KM132-I (2.6L)
	5-Speed – Model KM132-K (2.0L)
Ram-50 Pickups (4WD)	5-Speed – Model KM145
FORD MOTOR CO.	
Festiva	4 or 5-Speed Transaxle
Merkur XR4Ti	5-Speed – Hummer
Tracer	4 or 5-Speed Transaxle
GENERAL MOTORS	
Spectrum	5-Speed – Model Isuzu (76 mm) Transaxle
Sprint	5-Speed – Model MV2 Transaxle
HONDA	
Accord (Fuel Inj.)	5-Speed – Model A2Q5 Transaxle
Accord (Carb.)	5-Speed – Model A2Q6 Transaxle
Civic	4-Speed – Model GV Transaxle
	5-Speed – Model GW Transaxle
Civic (4WD)	6-Speed – Model GW-SL 4WD Transaxle
Civic CRX/Si	5-Speed – Model GW Transaxle
Prelude (Fuel Inj.)	5-Speed – Model A2K5 Transaxle
Prelude (Carb.)	5-Speed – Model A1B5 Transaxle
HYUNDAI	
Excel	4-Speed – Model KM161 Transaxle
	5-Speed – Model KM162 or KM163 Transaxle
ISUZU	
Impulse & P'UP (2WD)	4 or 5-Speed – Model MSG-4K or MSG-5K
I-Mark	5-Speed – 76 mm Transaxle
P'UP (4WD)	4-Speed – Model MSG-4
	5-Speed – Model MSG-5L
Trooper II	5-Speed – Model MSG-5

Transmission Application

MANUAL TRANSMISSIONS
IMPORTED CARS & TRUCKS (Cont.)

MANUFACTURER & MODEL	TRANSMISSION MODEL
MAZDA	
B2200	4 or 5-Speed
B2600	5-Speed
RX7	5-Speed
323	4 or 5-Speed Transaxle
626	5-Speed Transaxle
MERCEDES-BENZ	
190D	5-Speed – Model GL68/20 B-5
190E (2.3L)	5-Speed – GL68/20C-5
190E (2.6L)	5-Speed – GL76/27F-5
190E (2.3L 16V)	5-Speed – Model GL275E
260E, 300E	5-Speed – Model GL76/27A-5
MITSUBISHI	
Cordia & Tredia	5-Speed – Model KM163 Transaxle
Galant	5-Speed – KM120 Transaxle
Mirage	4-Speed – Model KM200 (1.5L) Transaxle
	5-Speed – Model KM201 (1.5L) Transaxle
	5-Speed – Model KM206 (1.6L) Transaxle
Pickup (2WD)	5-Speed – Model KM132-I (2.6L)
	5-Speed – Model KM132-K (2.0L)
Pickup (4WD) & Montero	5-Speed – Model KM145
Precis	4-Speed – Model KM161
	5-Speed – Model KM163
Starion	5-Speed – Model KM132
NISSAN	
Maxima & Stanza Wagon	5-Speed – Model RS5F50A Transaxle
Pickup/Pathfinder	
2WD & 4WD (Gas)	5-Speed – Model FS5W71C
2WD & 4WD (Diesel)	5-Speed – Model FS5R30A
Pulsar NX	5-Speed – Model RS5F31A Transaxle
Sentra	5-Speed – Model RN5F31A Transaxle
Stanza	5-Speed – Model RS5F50A Transaxle
200SX SE & XE	5-Speed – Model FS5W71C
300ZX	5-Speed – Model FS5R30A (Turbo)
	5-Speed – Model FS5W71C (Non-Turbo)
Van	5-Speed – Model RS5W71C
PEUGEOT	
505 GL, GLS & STI	5-Speed – Model BA 7/5
505 GL & STI Turbo (Sedans)	5-Speed – Model BA 10/5
505 STI & STX Non-Turbo	5-Speed – Model BA 10/5
PORSCHE	
911 Carrera	5-Speed – Model G50.01 Transaxle
911 Turbo	5-Speed – Model 930/36 Transaxle
928-S4	5-Speed – Model G28.13 Transaxle
924-S	5-Speed – Model 016J Tranaxle
944	5-Speed – Model 016K Transaxle
944-S	5-Speed – Model 083D Transaxle
944 Turbo	5-Speed – Model 016S Transaxle

Transmission Application

MANUAL TRANSMISSIONS
IMPORTED CARS & TRUCKS (Cont.)

MANUFACTURER & MODEL	TRANSMISSION MODEL
SAAB	
900 & 900 Turbo	5-Speed – Model GM 45606
900S Turbo (16 Valve)	5-Speed – Model GM 55712
9000S	5-Speed – Model GMT 5202
9000 Turbo	5-Speed – Model GMT 5401
STERLING	
825	5-Speed – Model C3P4 (Acura) Transaxle
SUBARU	
All Models	5-Speed – Gunma Transaxle
SUZUKI	
Samurai	5-Speed
TOYOTA	
Camry	5-Speed – Model S51 Transaxle
Celica	5-Speed – Model S53 Transaxle
Corolla (FWD)	5-Speed – Model C51 Transaxle
Corolla FX	5-Speed – Model C52 Transaxle
Corolla (RWD)	5-Speed – Model T50
Cressida	5-Speed – Model W58
Land Cruiser	4-Speed – Model H42
MR2	5-Speed – Model C52 Transaxle
Pickup & 4Runner (2WD)	4-Speed – Model W46 5-Speed – Model W55 or W56 (22R, 22R-E) 5-Speed – Model R150 (22R-TE)
Pickup & 4Runner (4WD)	5-Speed – Model G52 (22R) 5-Speed – Model R151F (22R-TE)
Supra	5-Speed – Model W58 (Non-Turbo) 5-Speed – Model R154 (Turbo)
Tercel Sedan	4-Speed – Model C140 or C141 Transaxle 5-Speed – Model C150 Transaxle
Tercel Wagon	5-Speed – Model Z53 Transaxle (2WD) 5-Speed – Model Z54F (4WD)
Van	5-Speed – Model G53 (2WD) 5-Speed – Model G53F (4WD)
VOLKSWAGEN	
Fox	4-Speed – Model 014
Cabriolet, Golf, GTI, Jetta & Scirocco	5-Speed – Model 020 Transaxle
Quantum	5-Speed – Model 013 or 093 Transaxle
Quantum Synchro	5-Speed – Model 016 Transaxle
Vanagon	4-Speed – Model 091/1 Transaxle 5-Speed – Model 094 (4WD) Transaxle
VOLVO	
All Except 240 DL & GL	5-Speed – Model M46
240 DL & GL	5-Speed – Model M47
YUGO	
GV	4-Speed Transaxle

ACURA

IDENTIFICATION

TRANSMISSION CODES

Application	Code
Integra	Model CA Transaxle
Legend Coupe	Model L5 Transaxle
Legend	Model G4 Transaxle

LUBRICATION

SERVICE INTERVALS

Change fluid every 30,000 miles. No filter service or band adjustment is required.

CHECKING FLUID LEVEL

1) With vehicle on level floor and at normal operating temperature, stop engine. Ensure fluid level is between "FULL" and "LOW" marks.

2) On Integra, do not screw dipstick in to check fluid level. On all models, add fluid as necessary. On Integra, do not use a wrench to secure dipstick.

RECOMMENDED FLUID

Use Dexron II ATF.

FLUID CAPACITY

TRANSMISSION REFILL CAPACITIES

Application	Refill Pts. (L)	Dry Fill Pts. (L)
Integra	6.0 (2.4)	11.4 (5.4)
Legend	6.7 (3.2)	13.7 (6.5)
Legend Coupe	6.7 (3.2)	13.7 (6.5)

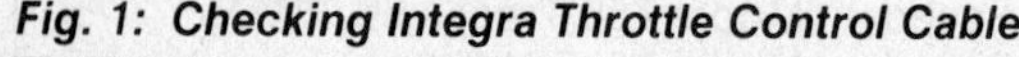

DRAINING & REFILLING

1) Ensure transaxle is at normal operating temperature. Remove transmission drain plug. Use new gasket and replace drain plug when fluid is drained.

2) Fill with about 2 qts. (1.9L) of fluid through dipstick hole and check level. Add fluid to bring to upper mark on dipstick.

ADJUSTMENTS

SHIFT CONTROL CABLE

1) Start engine. Shift to Reverse. Ensure transaxle engages in Reverse. With engine off, remove the console.

2) Shift to Drive (Integra) or Reverse (Legend and Legend Coupe). Remove lock pin from cable adjuster. Check that hole in adjuster is perfectly aligned with hole in shift cable. *See Fig. 2.*

Fig. 2: Adjusting Shift Control Cable

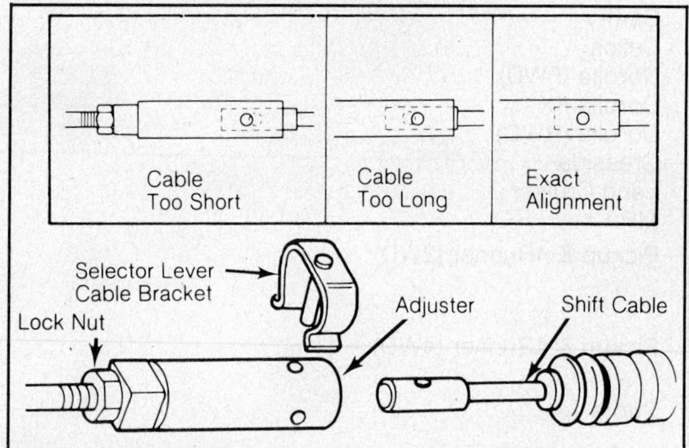

Courtesy of American Honda Motor Co., Inc.

Fig. 1: Checking Integra Throttle Control Cable

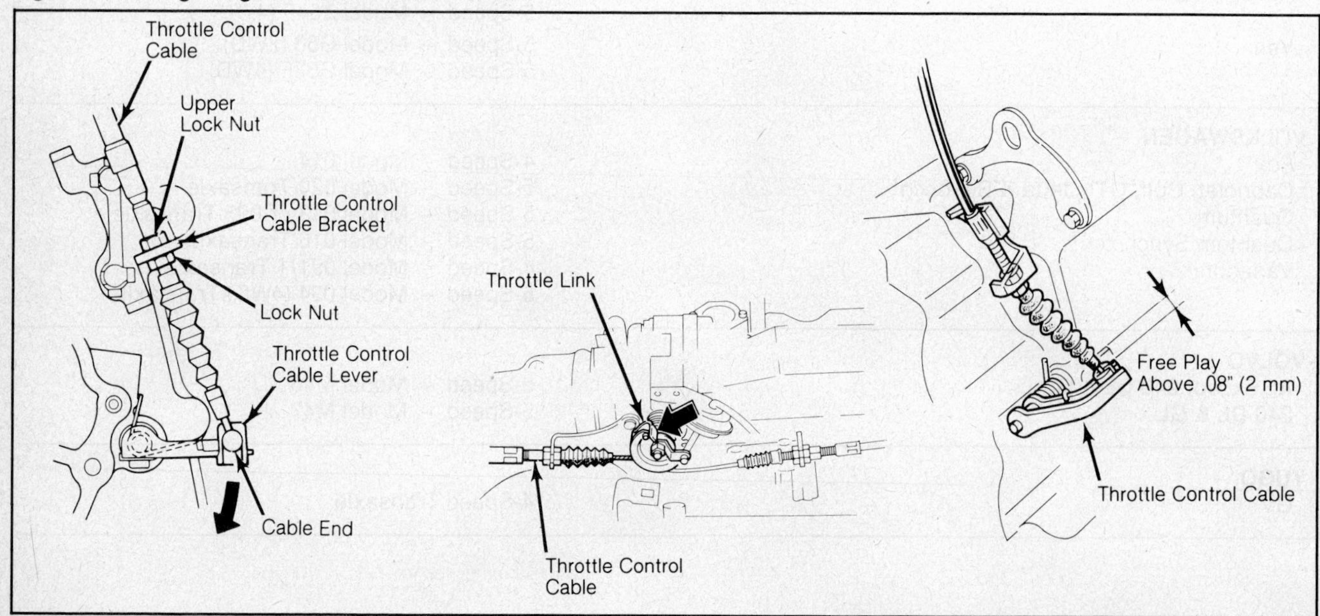

Courtesy of American Honda Motor Co., Inc.

ACURA (Cont.)

Fig. 3: Checking Legend & Legend Coupe Throttle Control Cable

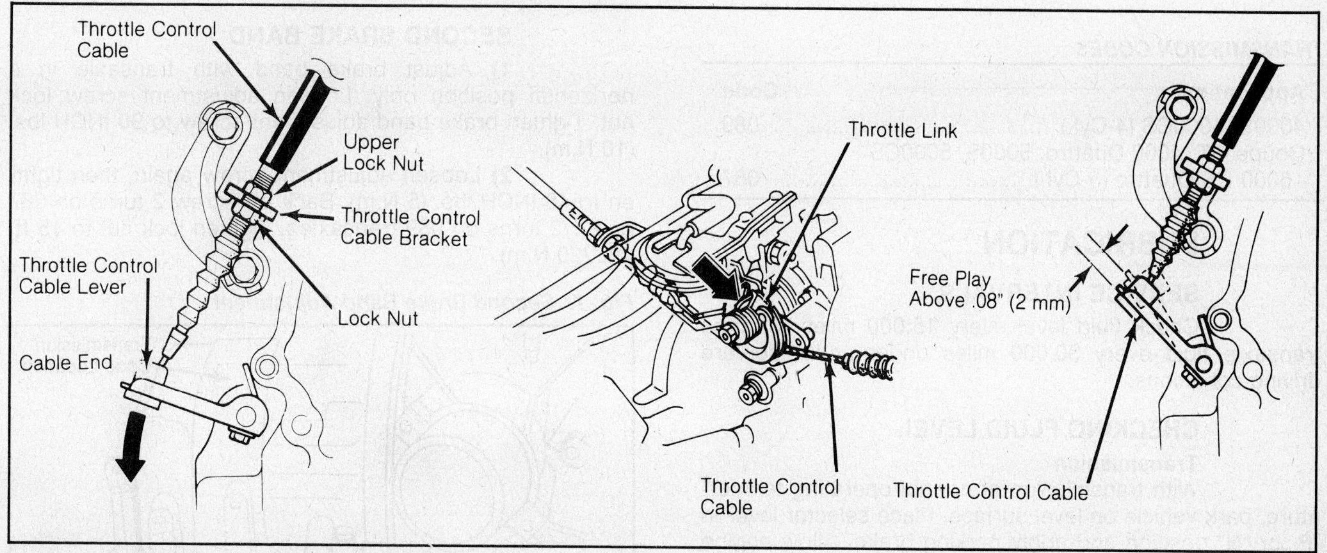

Courtesy of American Honda Motor Co., Inc.

3) The 2 holes in the end of the shift cable are positioned to allow cable adjustments in 1/4 turn increments.

4) Loosen lock nut on shift cable and adjust as required. Tighten lock nut. Install lock pin on adjuster. *See Fig. 2.*

5) Lock pin should not bind as it is installed. Start engine and check shift lever in all gears.

NEUTRAL SAFETY SWITCH

Neutral safety switch is located at bottom of shift lever under console. Ensure vehicle starts only in Park or Neutral position. If not, loosen 2 switch mounting screws and readjust.

THROTTLE CONTROL CABLE

1) Loosen lock nuts on both sides of the throttle control cable bracket. *See Fig. 1 or 3.* Press down on throttle control lever until it stops.

2) While pressing down on throttle control lever, pull on throttle link to check throttle control cable free play. Remove all free play by turning upper lock nut until it lightly seats on the throttle control cable bracket.

3) While pressing down on throttle control lever, pull open throttle link. Control lever should move at exactly same time as throttle link. Tighten other lock nut nut to secure cable adjustment. *See Fig. 1 or 3.*

4) BEFORE starting engine, depress accelerator to floor. Ensure there is at least .08" (2 mm) free play in throttle control lever. Check that cable moves freely when depressing accelerator.

5) Start engine. With shift lever in Neutral or Park, throttle control cable lever should be synchronized with engine speed by gradually depressing accelerator.

AUDI

IDENTIFICATION

TRANSMISSION CODES

Application	Code
4000S, 4000CS (4-Cyl.)	089
Coupe GT, 4000 Quattro, 5000S, 5000CS 5000 CS Quattro (5-Cyl.)	087

LUBRICATION

SERVICE INTERVALS

Check fluid level every 15,000 miles. Change transaxle fluid every 30,000 miles under under servere driving conditions.

CHECKING FLUID LEVEL

Transmission

With transmission at normal operating temperature, park vehicle on level surface. Place selector lever in "P" or "N" position and apply parking brake. Allow engine to idle. Remove dipstick, wipe clean and insert. Remove dipstick and check that fluid level is between marks on dipstick.

Final Drive

Place vehicle on level surface. Fluid level must be up to edge of fill hole on side of case. If level is too high, this may indicate fluid transfer between transmission and final drive caused by leaking seals.

NOTE: **Normal fluid color on late production vehicles is Red/Brown. This is normal.**

RECOMMENDED FLUID

Transmission

Use Dexron II ATF.

Final Drive

Use API GL-5, SAE 90.

FLUID CAPACITY

TRANSMISSION REFILL CAPACITIES

Application	Refill Qts. (L)	Dry Fill Qts. (L)
All Models		
Transmission	3.2 (3.0)	6.4 (6.0)
Final Drive		
089		.80 (.75)
087		1 (.95)

DRAINING & REFILLING

1) Remove transaxle protection plate (if equipped). Remove rear pan bolts and loosen front pan bolts. Carefully lower pan and drain as much fluid as possible. Remove oil pan and pour out remaining fluid. Remove filter. Clean oil pan in solvent and dry.

2) Install new filter and tighten screws to 27 INCH lbs. (3 N.m) on 087 transaxle or 35 INCH lbs. (4 N.m). Install oil pan, using a new gasket. Tighten oil pan bolts to 15 ft. lbs. (20 N.m). Install protection plate and tighten bolts to 18 ft. lbs. (25 N.m). Add 3.2 qts. (3.0L) of transaxle fluid and check fluid level.

ADJUSTMENTS

SECOND BRAKE BAND

1) Adjust brake band with transaxle in a horizontal position only. Loosen adjustment screw lock nut. Tighten brake band adjustment screw to 90 INCH lbs. (10 N.m).

2) Loosen adjustment screw again, then tighten to 45 INCH lbs. (5 N.m). Back off screw 2 turns on 087 or 2 1/2 turns on 089 transaxles. Tighten lock nut to 15 ft. lbs. (20 N.m).

Fig. 1: Second Brake Band Adjustment

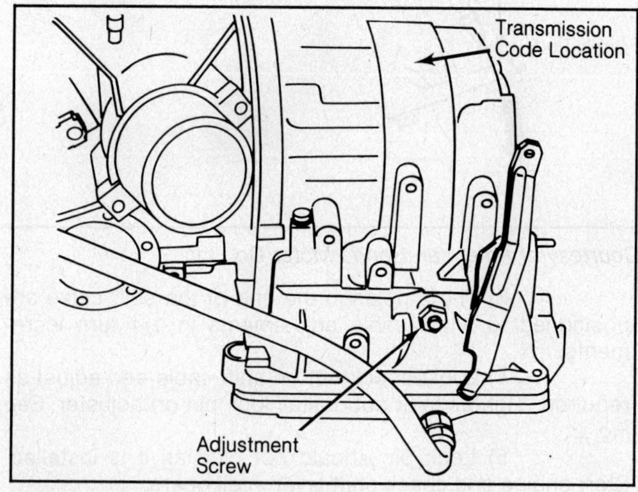

Courtesy of Audi of America, Inc.

SELECTOR LEVER CABLE

Remove center console. Place gearshift selector lever in "P". Loosen clamping nut. Place shift lever on transaxle to Park. Tighten nut on cable to 72 INCH lbs. (8 N.m).

THROTTLE CABLE

4000 Series (087 Transaxle)

1) Engine must be off at operating temperature and accelerator in idle position. Place selector lever in "P" position. Apply parking brake.

2) Loosen adjusting nut on throttle cable at transaxle. Remove retaining clips for ball sockets of push and pull rods. Pry ball sockets from relay bracket levers. *See Fig. 2.*

3) Rotate pull rod relay lever counterclockwise to stop. With relay lever against stop, loosen pull rod lock nut and turn ball socket until it fits easily on relay lever ball stud.

4) Tighten lock nut. Install push rod socket on relay lever. Install both ball socket retaining clips.

5) Loosen nut on push rod. *See Fig. 3.* Slide push rod apart so transaxle operating lever is in closed-throttle position and throttle body lever is against idle stop. Tighten nut on push rod.

NOTE: **Ensure push rod fits easily on transaxle operating lever.**

AUDI (Cont.)

Fig. 2: 4000 Series (087 Transaxle) Push & Pull Rods

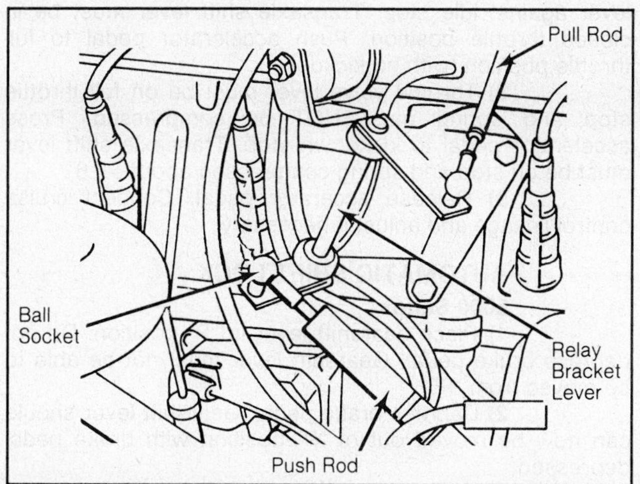

Courtesy of Audi of America, Inc.

Fig. 3: Adjusting 4000 Series (087 Transaxle) Push Rod

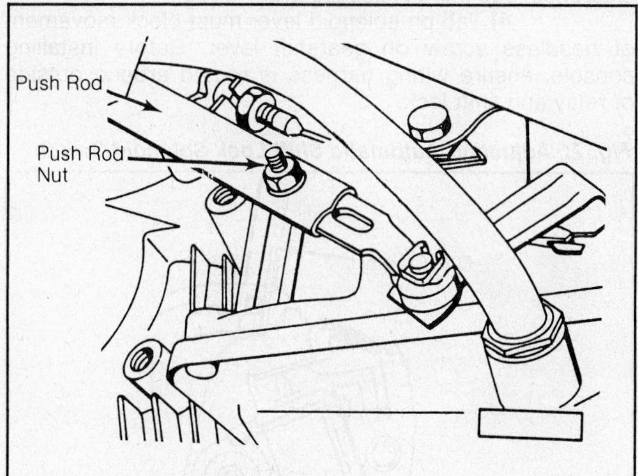

Courtesy of Audi of America, Inc.

Fig. 4: 4000 Series (087 Transaxle) Throttle Cable

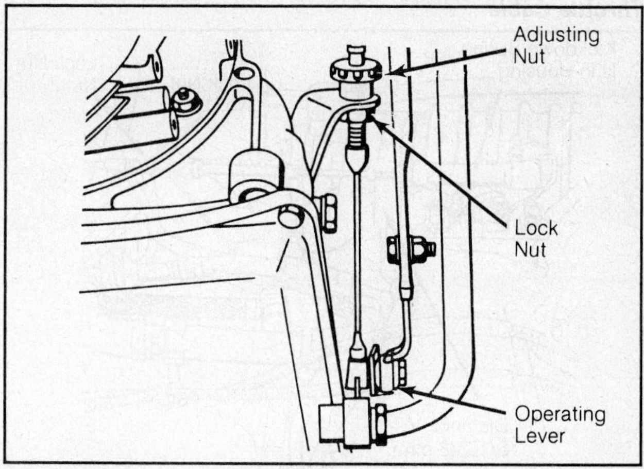

Courtesy of Audi of America, Inc.

Fig. 5: Checking 4000 Series (087 Transaxle) Push Rod Adjustment

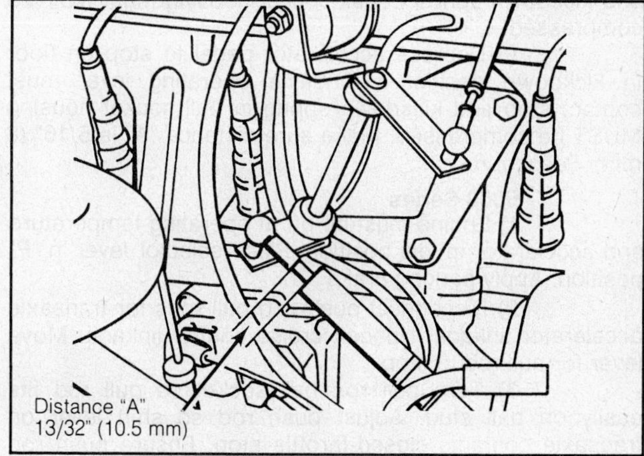

Courtesy of Audi of America, Inc.

6) Loosen lock nut located below adjusting nut on throttle cable. *See Fig. 4*. Depress accelerator pedal to stop on floor and hold.

7) Turn adjusting nut until transaxle operating lever moves, in direction of arrow, to stop. Tighten lock nut.

8) To check adjustment, push throttle lever against idle stop. Transaxle operating lever must be in closed-throttle position. Place accelerator pedal in full-throttle position, WITHOUT engaging kickdown. Throttle valve lever must contact full-throttle stop and kickdown spring in push rod must NOT be compressed.

9) Press accelerator pedal to stop (kickdown position). Transaxle operating lever must contact stop and kickdown spring in push rod must be compressed. Distance "A" on push rod must be 13/32" (10.5 mm). *See Fig. 5*.

4000 Series (089 Transaxle)

1) Engine must be off at operating temperature and accelerator in idle position. Place selector lever in "P" position. Apply parking brake.

2) Loosen throttle cable adjusting nut at transaxle. Adjusting nut is similar to the 087 transaxle. *See Fig. 4*.

3) Loosen lock nuts for throttle cable at bracket on valve cover. *See Fig. 6*. Pull sleeve on throttle cable in direction of arrow until resistance is felt.

NOTE: Throttle valve must remain closed and transaxle operating lever must be in closed-throttle position.

4) Turn adjusting nut No. 1 until it seats against bracket. Tighten lock nut No. 2 to 84 INCH lbs. (10 N.m).

5) Loosen lock nut located below throttle cable adjusting nut at transaxle end of cable. Press accelerator pedal to stop on floor and hold during adjustment.

6) Turn adjusting nut at transaxle until transaxle operating lever seats against stop. Tighten lock nut located below adjusting nut.

7) To check adjustment, push throttle lever against idle stop. Transaxle operating lever must be in closed-throttle position. Push accelerator to full throttle position (without kickdown).

AUDI (Cont.)

Fig. 6: Adjusting 4000 Series (089 Transaxle) Throttle Cable

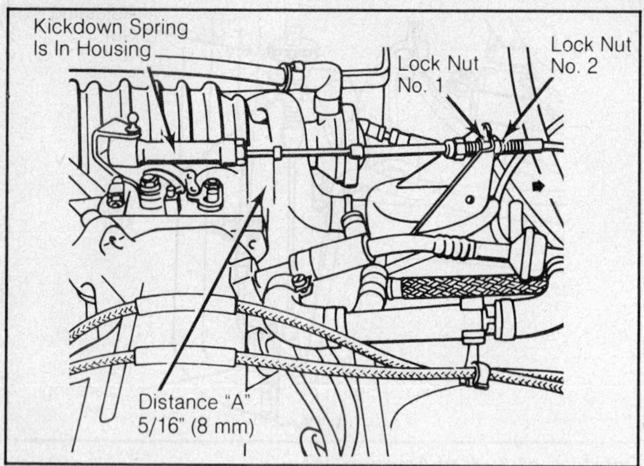

Courtesy of Audi of America, Inc.

8) Throttle lever must contact full throttle stop and kickdown spring in ball socket housing must NOT be compressed.

9) Depress accelerator pedal to stop on floor in kickdown position. Transaxle operating lever must contact stop and kickdown spring in ball socket housing MUST be compressed. Make sure distance "A" is 5/16" (8 mm). *See Fig. 6*.

5000 Series

1) Engine must be off at operating temperature and accelerator in idle position. Place selector lever in "P" position. Apply parking brake.

2) Disconnect push and pull rods for transaxle accelerator linkage. Unhook cruise control linkage. Move lever for pull rod to stop.

3) Turn pull rod ball socket so pull rod fits easily on ball stud. Adjust push rod so shift lever on transaxle contacts closed-throttle stop. Ensure push rod can be installed on transaxle without tension.

4) Remove push rod on transaxle shift lever. Press accelerator pedal to stop on floor and hold in this position during adjustment. Push transaxle shift lever against kickdown stop on transaxle.

5) Using pliers, pull accelerator cable to the end of its travel and tighten screw in clamp. Ensure transaxle shift lever is on kickdown stop.

6) If necessary, adjust accelerator pedal cable. Attach push rod to transaxle shift lever and lock in position.

7) To check adjustment, push throttle valve lever against idle stop. Transaxle shift lever must be in closed throttle position. Push accelerator pedal to full throttle position (with no kickdown).

8) Throttle valve lever must be on full throttle stop and spring must NOT be compressed. Press accelerator pedal to kickdown stop. Transaxle shift lever must be on stop and spring compressed about 5/16".

9) Release accerator pedal. Connect cruise control linkage and adjust if necessary.

AUTOMATIC SHIFT LOCK

5000 Series

1) Place gearshift lever in "P" position. Do not depress brake pedal. Gearshift lever must not be able to be moved from "P".

2) Depress brake pedal. Gearshift lever should can now be moved out of "P" position with brake pedal depressed.

3) To adjust switch, turn ignition on with engine off. Depress brake pedal. Position solenoid switch (on bottom of gearshift lever) so there is .004" (.1 mm) clearance. *See Fig. 7*. Release brake pedal.

4) Tab on solenoid lever must block movement of headless screw on gearshift lever. Before installing console, ensure wiring harness is routed around outside of relay and shift lock.

Fig. 7: Adjusting Automatic Shift Lock Solenoid Switch

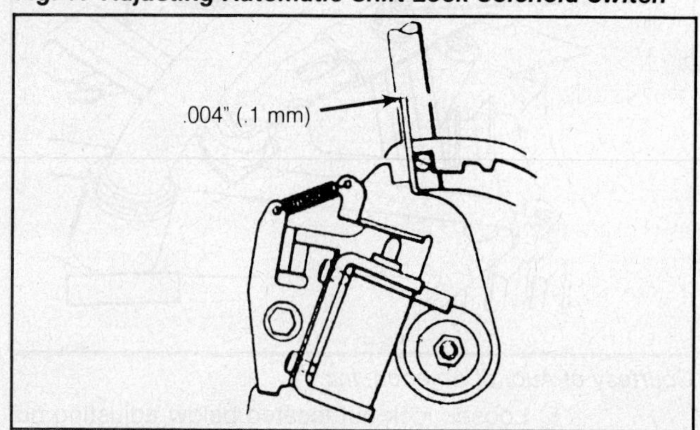

Courtesy of Audi of America, Inc.

NEUTRAL SAFETY SWITCH

Neutral safety switch is located in shift console. Remove console cover and adjust switch so that engine starts in "P" and "N" positions only.

BMW

IDENTIFICATION

TRANSMISSION CODES

Application	Code
All Models	ZF 4HP 22/H or 22/EH

LUBRICATION

SERVICE INTERVALS

Check fluid level at least at every oil change. Drain and refill transmission every 30,000 miles.

CHECKING FLUID LEVEL

Check fluid with transmission at normal operating temperature. Vehicle on level surface, engine idling and gear selector in "P". Ensure fluid level is between "MAX" and "MIN" marks on the dipstick. Distance between marks represents .42 qts. (.40L).

RECOMMENDED FLUID

Use Dexron II ATF.

FLUID CAPACITY

TRANSMISSION REFILL CAPACITES

Application	Refill Qts. (L)	Dry Qts. (L)
All Models	3.2 (3.0)	8.0 (7.5)

DRAINING & REFILLING

1) With transmission at operating temperature, remove drain plug. Remove oil pan bolts and tap on pan to break seal loose. Remove oil screen and clean or replace as necessary.

2) Clean oil pan. Reinstall filter screen and oil pan. Tighten oil pan bolts to 62-71 INCH lbs. (7-8 N.m). Tighten drain plug to 133-150 INCH lbs. (15-17 N.m). Fill with fluid.

ADJUSTMENTS

GEARSHIFT LINKAGE

325 Series

1) Place gearshift lever in "N". Disconnect selector rod from selector lever. *See Fig. 1.*

2) Make sure transmission is in Neutral. Press gearshift lever against forward stop on shift gate. Move adjusting pin so it fits easily into hole in selector lever.

3) Shorten length of selector rod by 1 turn. Secure selector rod.

All Models With Transmission Shift Cable

1) Move gearshift lever to "P". Loosen cable attaching nut on shift lever at transmission. Push transmission shift lever forward to Park and push cable rod rearward.

2) Tighten shift cable rod nut to 88-106 INCH lbs. (10-12 N.m). Check proper operation of shifter in each gear selection, readjust if necessary.

Fig. 1: Adjusting 325 Series Shift Linkage

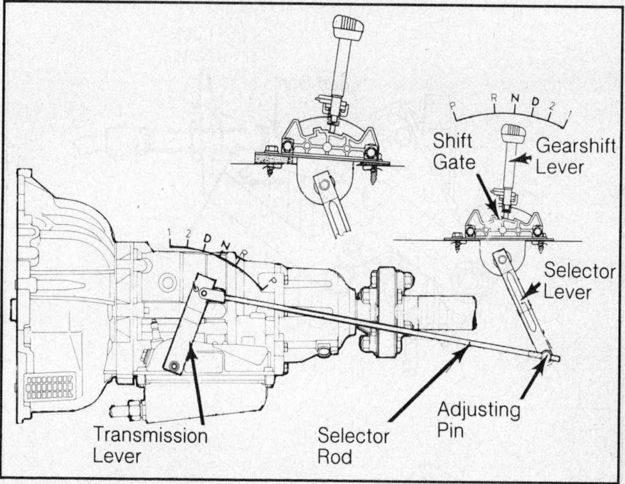

Courtesy of BMW of North America.

Fig. 2: Adjusting Gearshift Cable

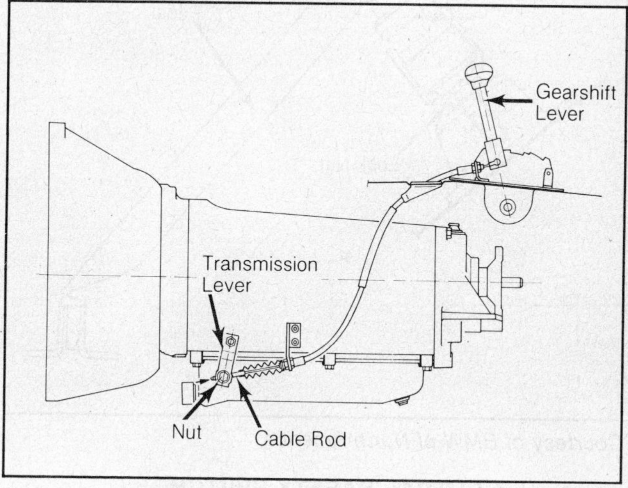

Courtesy of BMW of North America.

THROTTLE CABLE & KICKDOWN STOP

1) Throttle must be in idle position. Adjust cable play to .010-.030" (.25-.75 mm) using lock nuts. *See Fig. 3.*

2) To adjust kickdown stop, loosen lock nut and screw in kickdown stop. Push down accelerator pedal where pressure from transmission is felt.

3) With accelerator pedal in this position, unscrew kickdown stop until it contacts the accelerator pedal. Push down accelerator pedal to kickdown position.

4) Distance "S" from lead seal to end of sleeve must be at least 1.77" (45 mm) on 735i. On all others, set "S" to 1.73" (44 mm). *See Fig. 3.*

BMW (Cont.)

Fig. 3: Adjusting Throttle Cable & Kickdown Stop

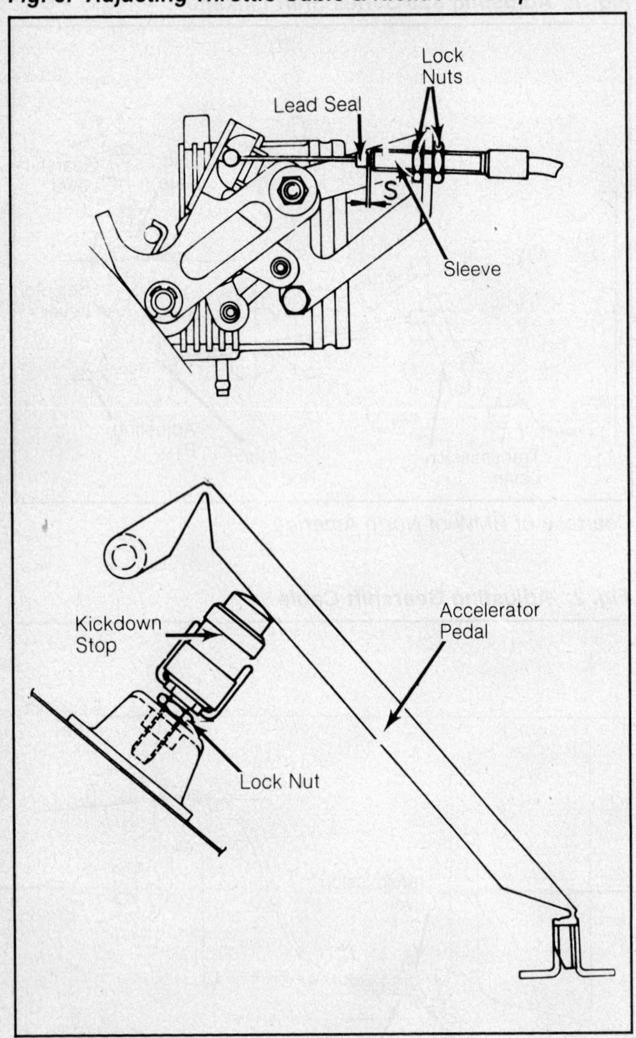

Courtesy of BMW of North America.

NEUTRAL SAFETY SWITCH

Neutral safety switch is connected with selector lever and a relay. If not operating properly, check relay and selector adjustment.

CHRYSLER MOTORS

IDENTIFICATION

TRANSMISSION CODES

Application	Code
Colt	
1.5L	KM171-1
1.6L	KM171-2
Colt Vista	KM172
Conquest	JM600
Raider	KM148
Ram-50 Pickup	
2WD	AW 372
4WD	KM148

LUBRICATION

SERVICE INTERVALS

Transmission

Change fluid and filter every 30,000 miles; if under severe usage, change more often. Adjust bands when fluid is changed. Fluid level should be checked every 6 months.

Transfer Case

On 4WD models, change transfer case fluid every 30,000 miles.

CHECKING FLUID LEVEL

Transmission

1) Park vehicle on level area. Oil must be at normal operating temperature, parking brake engaged and engine at idle. Shift transmission selector through each position, stopping briefly in each position.

2) Place selector in "N" position and clean area around dipstick tube. Ensure fluid level is between lower and upper marks, but never over upper mark in "HOT" range. Add or drain fluid as necessary.

CAUTION: If severe darkening of the fluid and a strong odor is noted, fluid and filter should be changed and bands adjusted.

Transfer Case (Raider & Ram-50)

Lubricant level should be to bottom of fill hole on side of transfer case.

Transfer Case (Colt Vista)

Transfer case is equipped with dipstick. Fluid level should be between marks on dipstick. *See Fig. 1.*

Fig. 1: Check Colt Vista Transfer Case Fluid Level

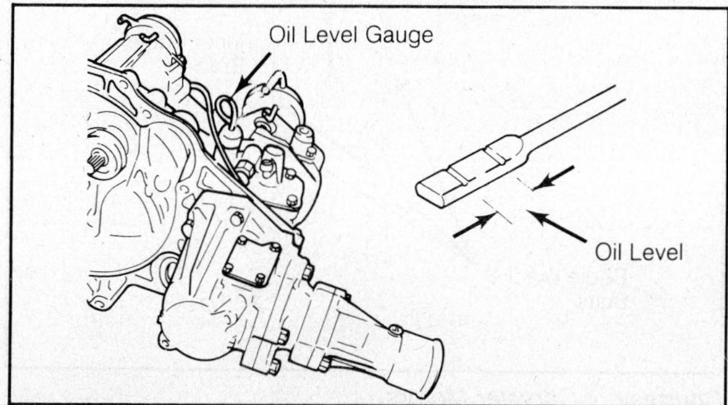

Courtesy of Chrysler Motors.

RECOMMENDED FLUID

Transmission

All transmissions use Dexron II automatic transmission fluid. Chrysler Motors does not recommend use of special additives in their transmissions.

Transfer Cases

All transfer cases use API GL-4 or GL-5, SAE 75W-85.

FLUID CAPACITY

TRANSMISSION REFILL CAPACITIES

Model	Pts. (L)
Colt	12.3 (5.8)
Colt Vista	
Transmission	
2WD	12.3 (5.8)
4WD	14.3 (6.8)
Transfer Case	1.5 (.7)
Conquest	14.8 (7.0)
Raider	15.2 (7.2)
Ram-50	
Transmission	
2WD	12.7 (6.0)
4WD	15.2 (7.2)
Transfer Case	4.7 (2.2)

DRAINING & REFILLING

CAUTION: If replacing transmission filter, note length and location of filter bolts.

Transmission (Conquest, Raider & Ram-50)

1) Carefully remove drain plug on Raider and Ram-50 models. On all models, remove oil pan and drain fluid. Install new filter on bottom of valve body.

2) Clean oil pan, replace gasket and install oil pan. Tighten bolts to 42 INCH lbs. (4.7 N.m). Pour 5.3 qts. (5.0L) of specified fluid through filler tube. Start engine and allow to idle for 2 minutes.

3) Shift transmission into each position, ending in "N" position. Check fluid level with engine running at idle and add sufficient fluid to bring level to lower mark. Recheck fluid level after transmission is at normal operating temperature.

Transaxle (Colt & Colt Vista)

1) Remove drain plug from differential and drain fluid. *See Fig. 2.* Remove bolts and lower oil pan. If necessary, install new filter on bottom of valve body. Replace pan gasket and install pan. Tighten pan bolts to 90-102 INCH lbs. (10-11 N.m).

2) Tighten differential plug to 22-25 ft. lbs. (30-34 N.m). Ensure dipstick hole area is clean and pour in about 4.2 qts. (4.0L) of Dexron II fluid.

3) Run engine for 2 minutes at idle. Shift transmission to each position, ending in "N" position. Add sufficient fluid to reach lower mark. After reaching normal operating temperature, fluid should be between upper and lower marks of "HOT" range.

Transfer Case

1) On Raider and Ram-50 models, drain plug is located on bottom of transfer case. Change drain plug gasket whenever fluid is changed. When refilling, fluid level should be up to bottom of fill hole in side of case.

CHRYSLER MOTORS (Cont.)

Fig. 2: Colt & Colt Vista Drain Plug Location

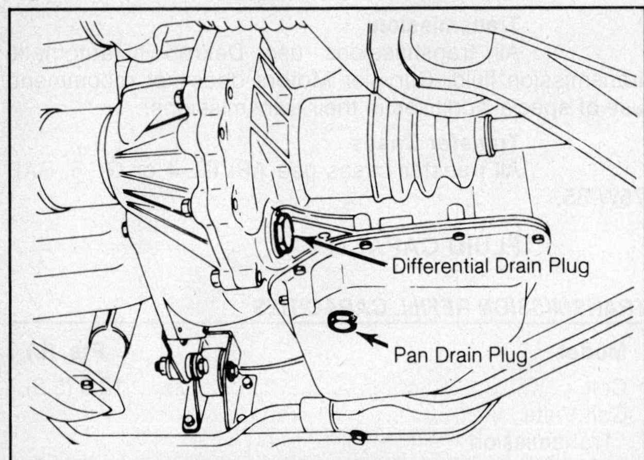

Courtesy of Chrysler Motors.

2) On Colt Vista models, drain plug is located on bottom of transfer case. Fill case through dipstick hole.

ADJUSTMENTS

BRAKE BAND

Conquest (2nd Brake Band)

Remove oil pan and drain fluid. Loosen lock nut. Tighten piston stem to 60-84 INCH lbs. (6.8-9.5 N.m). Back off adjustment screw 2 turns. Hold piston stem and tighten lock nut to 11-29 ft. lbs. (15-39 N.m). *See Fig. 3.*

Fig. 3: Adjusting 2nd Brake Band on Conquest

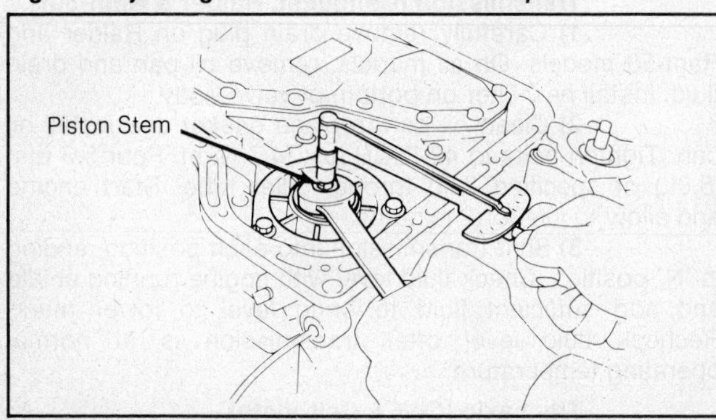

Courtesy Chrysler Motors.

Conquest (Overdrive Band)

Overdrive band is located on bottom of case in front of oil pan. Loosen lock nut. Tighten piston stem to 60-84 INCH lbs. (6.8-9.5 N.m). Back off adjustment screw 2 turns. Hold piston stem and tighten lock nut to 11-29 ft. lbs. (15-39 N.m).

TRANSMISSION THROTTLE CONTROL

Colt & Colt Vista

1) On Colt only, ensure throttle lever of carburetor is in curb idle position. Engine must be at normal operating temperature. On Colt Vista only, turn ignition key on with engine off for 15-20 seconds. Ensure throttle valve is at standard idle opening.

2) On Colt and Colt Vista, raise cover "B" of throttle cable upward to expose nipple. *See Fig. 4.* Loosen lower cable bracket mounting bolt. Move lower cable bracket until distance between nipples and top of cover "A" on throttle cable is .02-.06" (.5-1.5 mm).

3) Tighten lower cable bracket mounting bolt to 108-126 INCH lbs. (12-14 N.m). With throttle lever in wide open throttle position, pull cable upward to ensure cable still has some free play.

Fig. 4: Adjusting Throttle Cable on Colt & Colt Vista

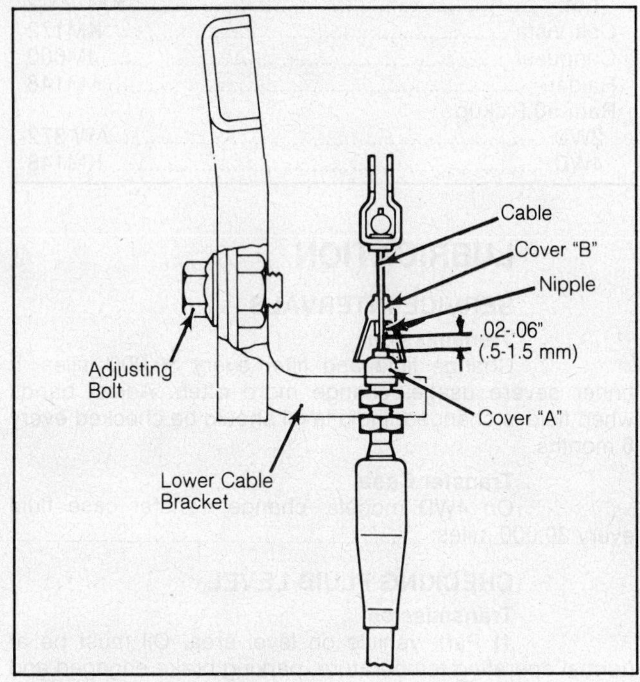

Courtesy of Chrysler Motors.

Fig. 5: Adjusting Raider & Ram-50 Throttle Cable

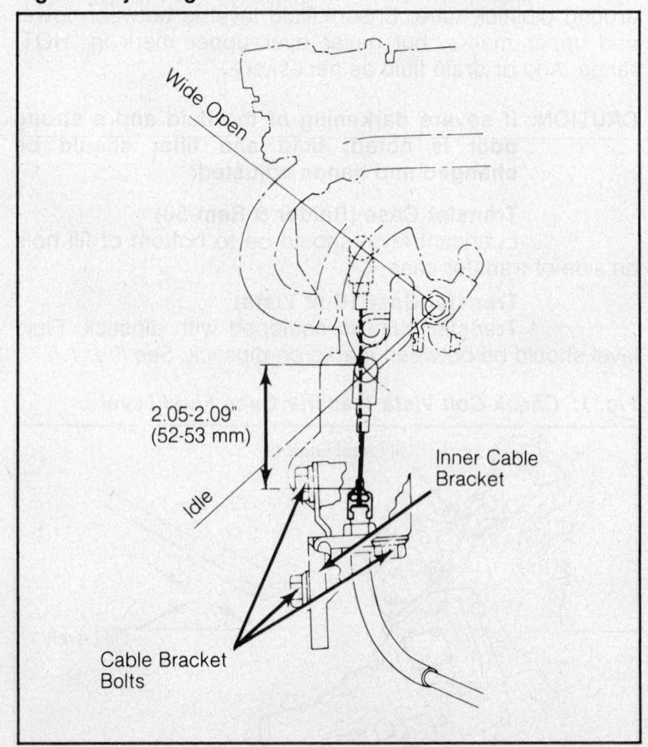

Courtesy of Chrysler Motors.

CHRYSLER MOTORS (Cont.)

CAUTION: Whenever idle is adjusted on Raider and Ram-50, always adjust throttle control cable.

Raider & Ram-50

1) Ensure engine idle is adjusted correctly. Ensure carburetor throttle lever and throttle cable bracket are not bent.

2) Measure gap between inner cable stopper and cover end with carburetor throttle valve fully open. *See Fig. 5.*

3) If gap is not 2.05-2.09" (52-53 mm), adjust inner cable bracket. Tighten cable bracket bolts to 96-112 INCH lbs. (10-14 N.m).

VACUUM DIAPHRAGM ROD

Conquest

1) Disconnect vacuum hose at vacuum diaphragm. Remove diaphragm from transmission case. Using depth gauge, measure depth "L". *See Fig. 6.*

2) Ensure vacuum throttle valve is pushed into valve body as far as possible. Select correct length rod to adjust. See VACUUM DIAPHRAGM ROD SELECTION table.

VACUUM DIAPHRAGM ROD SELECTION

Depth "L" In. (mm)	Rod Length In. (mm)	Part No.
Under 1.006 (25.55)	1.142 (29.0)	MD610614
1.010-1.026 (25.65-26.05)	1.16 (29.5)	MD610615
1.030-1.045 (26.15-26.55)	1.18 (3.0)	MD610616
1.050-1.065 (26.65-27.05)	1.20 (30.5)	MD610617
Over 1.069 (27.15)	1.22 (31.0)	MD610618

Fig. 6: Adjusting Vacuum Diaphragm Rod on Conquest

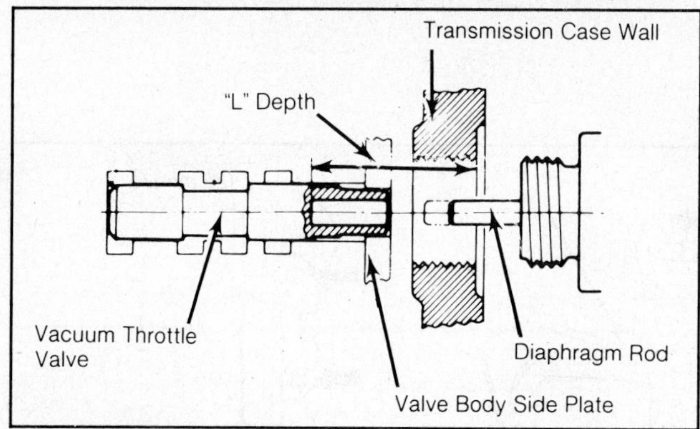

Courtesy of Chrysler Motors.

KICKDOWN SWITCH

Conquest

1) Kickdown switch is located at upper post of accelerator pedal. When pedal is fully depressed, a click should be heard just before the pedal bottoms out.

2) If click is not heard, loosen lock nut and extend switch until pedal lever makes contact with switch and switch clicks. If switch makes contact too soon, transmission will downshift on part throttle.

3) If car upshifts at 30 and 60 MPH only, the switch may be shorted internally.

SHIFT LINKAGE

Colt & Colt Vista

Shift cable is adjusted at transmission end of cable. Place shift lever in "N". Ensure transmission shift lever and neutral safety switch are in neutral position. Turn adjuster at cable end so it fits into manual lever on transmission.

Conquest

Place shift lever in "N" position. Transmission selector lever should also be in Neutral. If not, loosen lock nuts on end of cross shaft below shift lever assembly. Adjust selector rod and tighten lock nuts. *See Fig. 7.*

Fig. 7: Adjusting Conquest Shift Linkage

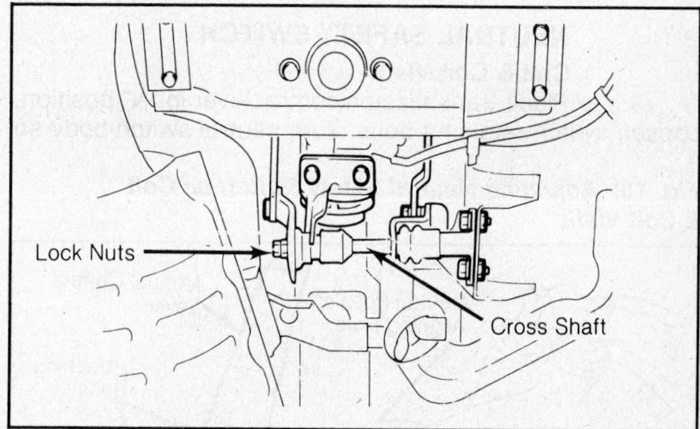

Courtesy of Chrysler Motors.

Raider

Loosen swivel nut on transmission control rod. Ensure shift lever and transmission are in Neutral. Tighten swivel nut. *See Fig. 8.*

Fig. 8: Adjusting Raider Shift Linkage

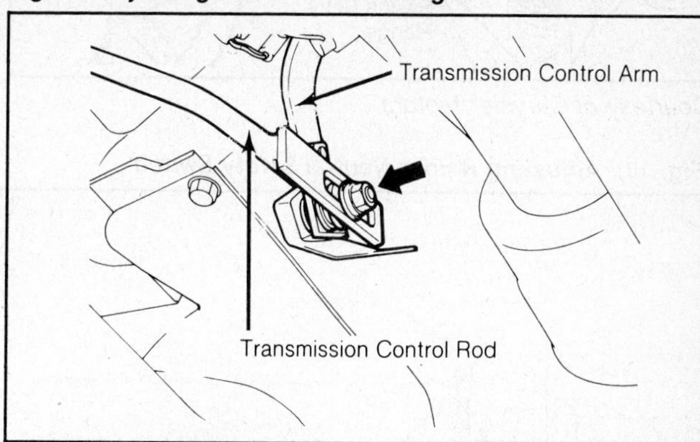

Courtesy of Chrysler Motors.

Ram-50

Disconnect shift cable at transmission. Ensure shift lever and transmission are both in Neutral. Adjust transmission end of shift cable to fit in transmission shift lever.

SHIFT LEVER SLEEVE

Colt, Colt Vista, Conquest & Raider

To adjust shift lever sleeve, remove shift handle on top of shift lever. With lever in "N" position, turn

CHRYSLER MOTORS (Cont.)

sleeve so distance between sleeve and lever end is .60-.63" (15-16 mm). *See Fig. 9.* Ensure beveled side of sleeve faces toward push button.

Fig. 9: Adjusting Selector Cam on Shift Lever

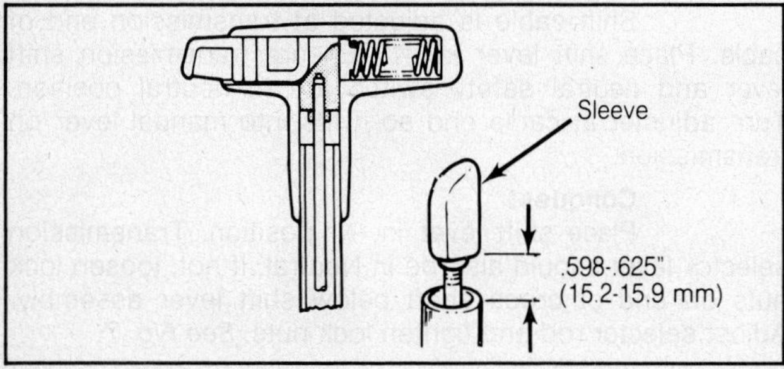

Courtesy of Chrysler Motors.

NEUTRAL SAFETY SWITCH

Colt & Colt Vista

Place transmission control lever in "N" position. Loosen switch retaining bolts. Turn neutral switch body so aligning hole end of lever overlaps switch body flange. Tighten bolts to 90-102 INCH lbs. (10-12 N.m). *See Fig. 10.*

Fig. 10: Adjusting Neutral Safety Switch on Colt & Colt Vista

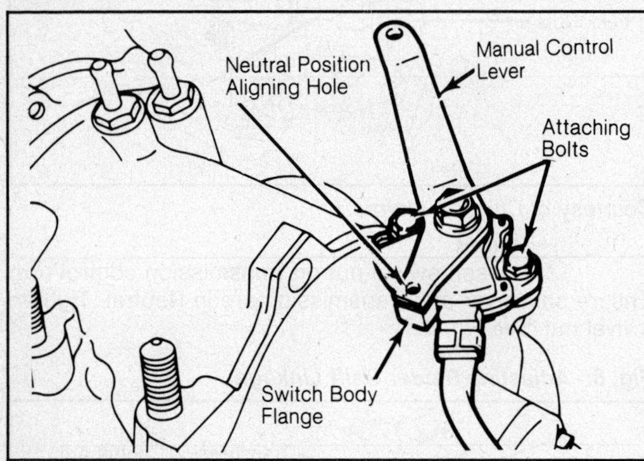

Courtesy of Chrysler Motors.

Conquest

1) Place transmission in Neutral. Remove screw on bottom of neutral safety switch at transmission. Loosen attaching bolts. *See Fig. 12.*

2) Using an .08" (2.0 mm) alignment pin, move switch until pin falls into hole in rotor. Tighten attaching bolts to 43-61 INCH lbs. (5-7 N.m).

Fig. 12: Adjusting Conquest Neutral Safety Switch

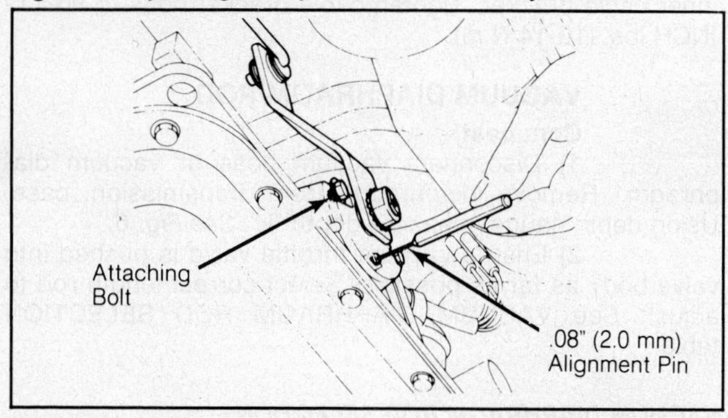

Courtesy of Chrysler Motors.

Raider

1) Neutral safety switch is located under shift lever console. Set shift lever so pin at end of rod is positioned correctly. *See Fig. 11.*

2) Using an ohmmeter, check continuity between Black/Yellow wires when neutral safety switch is moved back and forth. Mark bracket.

3) Tigthen neutral safety switch mounting screws so clearance between switch and selector lever is .1" (2.5 mm).

Ram-50

On Ram-50 models, neutral safety switch is part of ignition switch assembly.

Fig. 11: Adjusting Raider Neutral Safety Switch

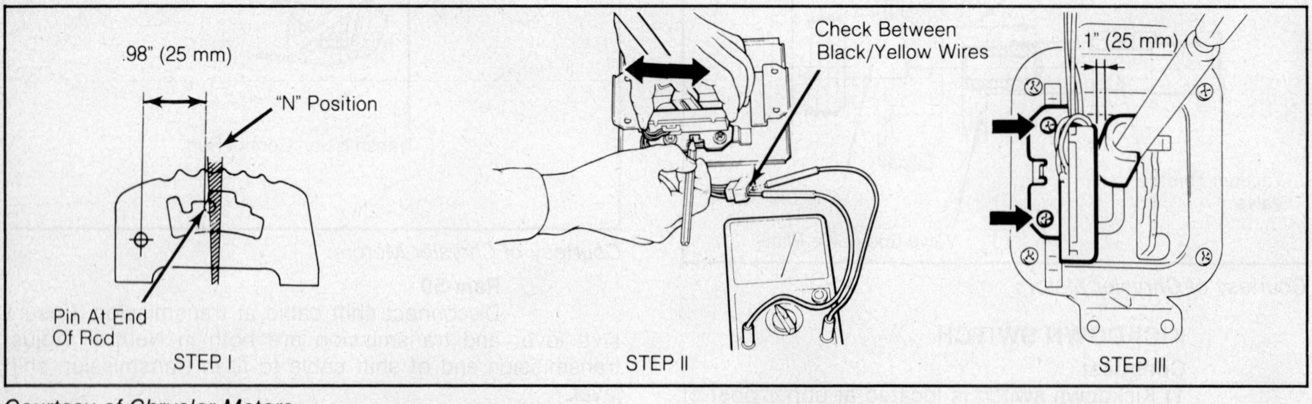

Courtesy of Chrysler Motors.

FORD MOTOR CO.

IDENTIFICATION

TRANSMISSION CODES

Application	Code
Merkur XR4Ti	C-3
Tracer	Mazda F3A Transaxle

LUBRICATION

SERVICE INTERVALS

Check fluid level at every engine oil change. Fluid, filter changes and band adjustments are not required under normal operation. Under severe service operating conditions, change fluid every 30 months or 30,000 miles. Adjust band when fluid is changed.

CHECKING FLUID LEVER

1) With transmission at normal operating temperature, place vehicle on level surface. Apply parking brake and run engine at idle. Run gearshift lever through all positions, ending in Park.

2) Fluid level should be between "ADD" and "FULL", or "F" and "L" marks. Do not overfill.

RECOMMENDED FLUID

Use Dexron II ATF in C-3 and F3A transaxles.

FLUID CAPACITY

NOTE: Capacities given are approximate. Correct fluid level should be determined by mark on dipstick.

TRANSMISSION REFILL CAPACITIES

Application	Qts. (L)
C-3	8.0 (7.6)
F3A	6.0 (5.7)

DRAINING & REFILLING

Merkur XR4Ti

1) Loosen oil pan attaching bolts and drain fluid. Remove oil pan and discard gasket. Remove filter screen. Install new filter screen and tighten to 70-79 INCH lbs. (8-11 N.m).

2) Clean oil pan. Install oil pan with new gasket. Tighten oil pan bolts to 12-17 ft. lbs. (16-23 N.m). Pour about 3 qts. of ATF in dipstick tube. Run engine and check fluid level.

Tracer

1) Remove undercover and side cover to gain access to transaxle oil pan. Remove drain plug and drain fluid. Remove oil pan and discard gasket. Clean filter screen. Replace screen if necessary. Tighten screen bolts to 23-35 INCH lbs. (3-4 N.m).

CAUTION: Do not use any type of gasket sealer or RTV on oil pan gasket. If necessary, soak oil pan gasket in clean ATF.

2) Install oil pan and tighten bolts to 44-71 INCH lbs. (5-8 N.m). Install drain with new washer. Tighten to 29-40 ft. lbs. (39-54 N.m). Install undercover and side cover. Add about 3 qts. of ATF. Do not overfill. Run engine and check fluid level.

ADJUSTMENTS

FRONT BAND

C-3 (Merkur XR4Ti)

1) Loosen and remove lock nut on adjusting screw. Tighten adjusting screw to 10 ft. lbs. (14 N.m). Back off adjusting screw exactly 2 turns. *See Fig. 1.*

2) Install a NEW lock nut, do not reuse old lock nut. Holding adjustment screw in position, tighten lock nut to 35-45 ft. lbs. (48-61 N.m).

Fig. 1: Adjusting C-3 Intermediate Band

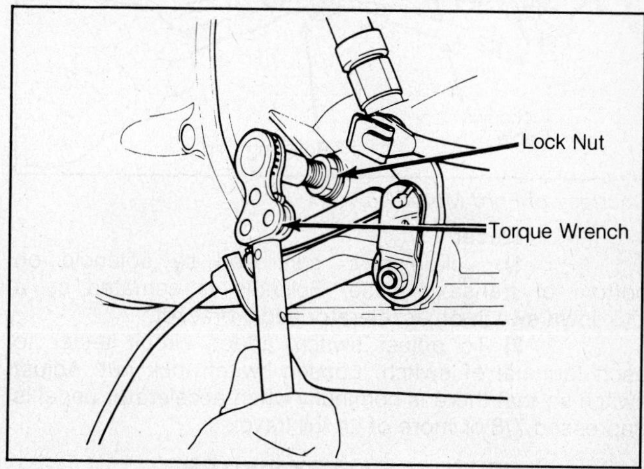

Courtesy of Ford Motor Co.

INTERMEDIATE BAND

F3A (Tracer)

1) Loosen adjuster bolt lock nut. *See Fig. 2.* Tighten adjuster bolt to 9-11 ft. lbs. (12-15 N.m). Back out adjuster bolt exacty 3 turns.

2) Holding adjuster bolt, tighten lock nut to 41-59 ft. lbs. (55-80 N.m).

NOTE: Adjuster bolt threads are coated with Sealant (E1FZ-19562-A) at factory. Ensure sealer in still on bolt after adjustment.

Fig. 2: Adjusting F3A Intermediate Band

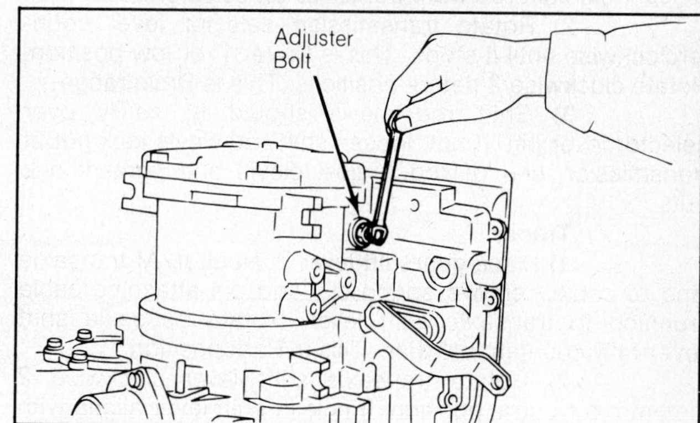

Courtesy of Ford Motor Co.

KICKDOWN CONTROL

Merkur (XR4Ti)

1) Using a pair of needle nose pliers, remove cable retaining clip near throttle body routing bracket. *See Fig. 3.* Ensure downshift lever return spring is in place on transmission.

FORD MOTOR CO. (Cont.)

2) Rotate throttle body to wide open throttle position. While holding throttle, install cable clip and release lever.

Fig. 3: Adjusting Merkur XR4Ti Kickdown Cable

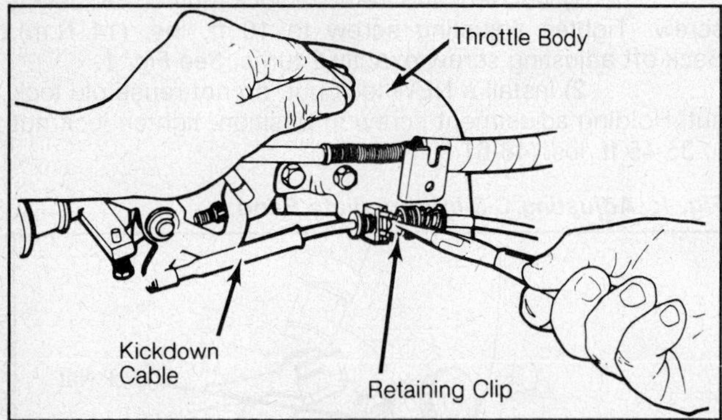

Courtesy of Ford Motor Co.

Tracer

1) Kickdown is controlled by solenoid on bottom of transaxle case. Solenoid is actuated by a kickdown switch on accelerator pedal bracket.

2) To adjust switch, attach circuit tester to each terminal of switch. Loosen switch lock nut. Adjust switch so that there is continuity when accelerator pedal is depressed 7/8 or more of its full travel.

NEUTRAL SAFETY SWITCH

Merkur XR4Ti

Neutral safety switch is screwed into left side of transmission case. There is no adjustment. Engine should only start in "N" or "P". If not, check gearshift linkage adjustment.

Tracer

Combination neutral safety switch and back-up light switch is screwed in transaxle case. No adjustments are necessary.

GEARSHIFT LINKAGE

Merkur XR4Ti

1) Place gearshift lever in "D". Raise vehicle. Disconnect shift rod from transmission selector lever.

2) Rotate transmission selector lever counterclockwise until it stops. This is Drive "1" or low position. Rotate clockwise 2 detent positions. This is Drive range.

3) Shift rod clevis should fit easily over selector lever pin. If not, loosen shift rod clevis lock nut at transmission end of rod. Adjust clevis and tighten lock nuts.

Tracer

1) Place gearshift lever in Neutral. At transaxle end of cable, remove spring clip and pin attaching cable trunnion to transaxle shift lever. Rotate transaxle shift lever fully counterclockwise. This is Park position.

2) Rotate transaxle shift lever clockwise 2 detents to Neutral position. If hole in shift lever aligns with trunnion holes, cable is adjusted properly. If not, remove gearshift lever bezel and shift quadrant.

3) Loosen adjuster nuts on shift cable. *See Fig. 4*. Place gearshift lever in Park position. If detent spring roller is centered in park detent, go to step **5)**. If not, go to step **4)**.

4) If detent spring roller is not centered in park detent, loosen attaching screws and move detent spring so it is centered. Tighten attaching screws. Go to step **5)**.

5) If detent spring roller is centered in park detent, place gearshift lever in Neutral. Thread adjuster nuts until holes in transaxle shift lever and shift cable trunnion are aligned. Tightened adjuster nuts to 69-95 INCH lbs. (8-11 N.m).

6) Check alignment of holes in cable trunnion and transaxle shift lever to ensure adjustment was not disturbed. Install attaching pin and retaining clip.

7) Ensure linkage adjustment has not affected operation of neutral safety switch. Engine must only start in Neutral or Park.

Fig. 4: Adjusting Tracer Gearshift Cable

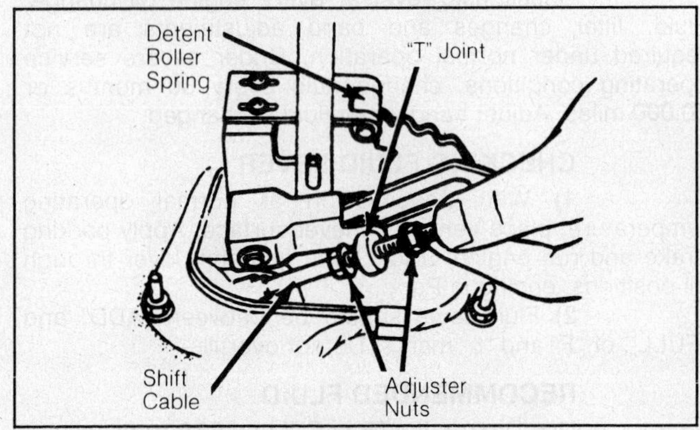

Courtesy of Ford Motor Co.

VACUUM DIAPHRAGM ROD

Tracer

Using Vacuum Diaphragm Rod Gauge (T87C-77000-A), measure dimension "N". *See Fig. 5.* See VACUUM DIAPHRAGM ROD SELECTION table.

VACUUM DIAPHRAGM ROD SELECTION

Dimension "N" In. (mm)	Rod Length In. (mm)
Below 1.000 (25.4)	1.16 (29.5)
1.000-1.020 (25.4-25.9)	1.18 (30.0)
1.020-1.039 (25.9-26.4)	1.20 (30.5)
1.039-1.059 (26.4-26.9)	1.22 (31.0)
Over 1.059 (26.9)	1.24 (31.5)

Fig. 5: Adjusting Vacuum Diaphragm Rod Length On Tracer

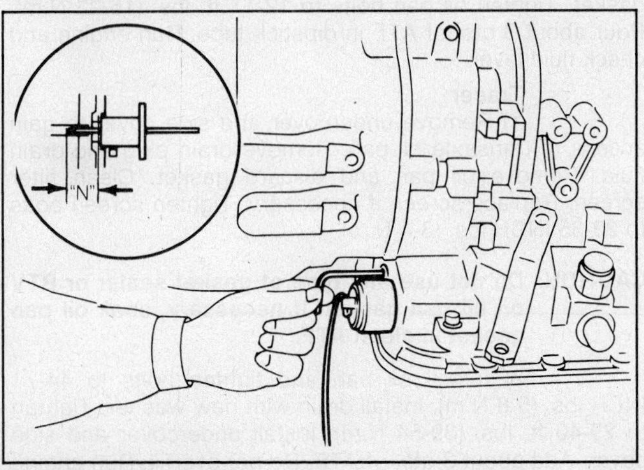

Courtesy of Mazda Motors Corp.

GENERAL MOTORS

IDENTIFICATION

TRANSMISSION CODES

Application	Code
Spectrum	KF100
Sprint	MXI

LUBRICATION

SERVICE INTERVALS

Spectrum

Check transaxle lubricant each time engine oil is changed or every 7500 miles. Replace lubricant and sump filter every 30,000 miles or 30 months under normal driving conditions. Change fluid every 15,000 miles or 15 months under severe driving conditions.

Sprint

Replace lubricant and sump filter every 100,000 miles under normal driving conditions. Change fluid every 15,000 miles or 15 months under severe driving conditions.

NOTE: **For Sprint automatic transaxle, Chevrolet recommends replacing cooler inlet and outlet hoses every 45,000 miles or 48 months.**

CHECKING FLUID LEVEL

1) Park vehicle on level surface and apply parking brake. Place selector lever in Park, start engine and allow engine to idle for 2 minutes. Apply brakes, shift through all gears and return selector lever to Park.

2) Remove dipstick and carefully touch dipstick end to determine temperature of fluid. If fluid is cool or warm, fluid level should be in "COLD" range. If fluid is too hot to touch, fluid level should be in "HOT" range.

RECOMMENDED FLUID

Use Dexron II ATF.

FLUID CAPACITY

TRANSMISSION REFILL CAPACITIES

Application	Refill Pts. (L)	Dry Fill Qts. (L)
KF100		6.1 (5.8)
Suzuki 3-Speed	3.2 (1.5)	4.8 (4.5)

DRAINING & REFILLING

CAUTION: **General Motors recommends flushing oil cooler whenever a transmission or transaxle is removed for service.**

Spectrum

1) Remove drain plug located on lower part of differential and drain lubricant. Remove oil pan and discard pan gasket. Remove (3) bolts retaining filter screen to valve body. Remove filter and discard.

2) Install new filter screen and tighten bolts to 26-35 INCH lbs. (3-4 N.m). Install oil pan using a new gasket. Tighten oil pan bolts to 60 INCH lbs. (6.8 N.m). Install drain plug, fill transaxle and check fluid level.

Sprint

Remove drain plug on bottom of oil pan and drain fluid. If filter screen is being removed, remove oil pan. Discard gasket. Remove filter screen and clean.

2) Install filter screen and tighten retaining bolts to 44-53 INCH lbs. (5-6 N.m). Install oil pan with new gasket and tighten retaining bolts to 48-72 INCH lbs. (5.4-8.1 N.m). Tighten drain plug to 14-17 ft. lbs. (18-23 N.m).

3) Add about 3 pts. of ATF (about 4 qts. after overhaul) in dipstick tube. Start engine and check fluid level.

ADJUSTMENTS

PARK LOCK CABLE

Spectrum

1) Remove console covering gearshift lever. Loosen 2 lock nuts on park lock cable bracket. Place ignition key in "LOCK" position and selector lever in "P" position.

2) Pull park cable forward at shifter bracket. Tighten forward nut until it makes contact with bracket. Tighten rear nut until it makes contact with bracket.

KICKDOWN SWITCH

Spectrum

Kickdown switch is located at top of accelerator pedal. Adjust switch so continuity exists when depressing pedal more than 7/8 of its travel.

SHIFT CONTROL CABLE

Spectrum

1) Loosen adjustment nuts at control rod link. With transaxle in Neutral detent, place gearshift lever in "N". Rotate link assembly clockwise to remove slack in cable.

2) Tighten rear adjustment nut until it makes contact with link, then tighten front adjustment nut until it makes contact with link. *See Fig. 1.* Tighten nuts.

Fig. 1: Adjusting Spectrum Shift Control Cable

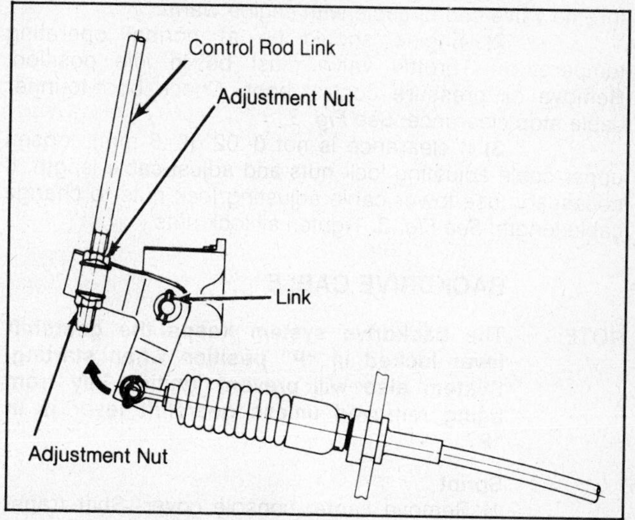

Courtesy of General Motors Corp.

Sprint

1) Move gearshift lever to Neutral. Loosen both control cable lock nuts. *See Fig. 2.* Ensure transaxle control lever to Neutral. By hand, tighten outer control

GENERAL MOTORS (Cont.)

cable lock nut until it contacts the lever joint. *See Fig. 2.*

2) Using a wrench, tighten the inner control cable lock nut. Ensure the transaxle operates in all range positions. Shift transaxle gearshift lever to Park and ensure vehicle will not move.

Fig. 2: Adjusting Sprint Shift Control Cable & Neutral Start Switch

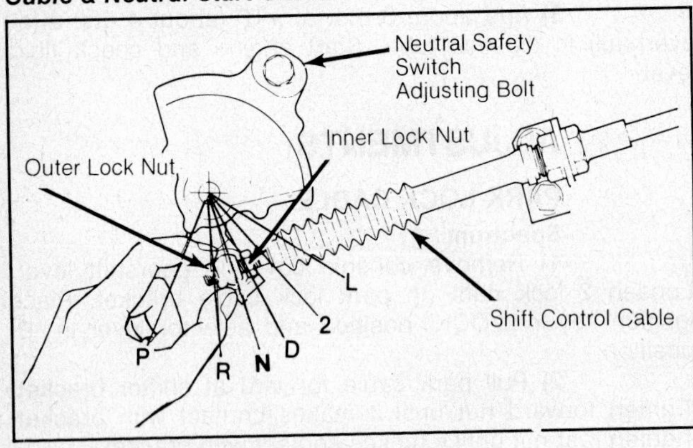

Courtesy of General Motors Corp.

NEUTRAL SAFETY SWITCH

Spectrum

Neutral safety switch is installed in side of transaxle. There is no adjustment.

Sprint

Shift transaxle gearshift lever to Neutral. Loosen adjusting bolt. *See Fig. 2.* Slide the neutral start switch back and forth until a click is heard. Tighten the adjusting bolt to 14 ft. lbs. (18 N.m). Ensure starter operates in "P" or "N" position only.

OIL PRESSURE CONTROL CABLE

Sprint

1) Ensure accelerator cable is adjusted. Accelerator cable is properly adjusted when inner cable has .12-.19" (3-5 mm). Cable slack should be measured at throttle valve end of cable with engine warm.

2) Engine should be at normal operating temperature. Throttle valve must be in idle position. Remove oil pressure control boot. Check boot-to-inner cable stop clearance. *See Fig. 3.*

3) If clearance is not 0-.02" (0-.5 mm), loosen upper cable adjusting lock nuts and adjust cable length. If necessary, use lower cable adjusting lock nuts to change cable length. *See Fig. 3.* Tighten all lock nuts.

BACKDRIVE CABLE

NOTE: The backdrive system keeps the gearshift lever locked in "P" position when starting. System also will prevent ignition key from being removed unless gearshift lever is in "P".

Sprint

1) Remove center console cover. Shift transaxle gearshift lever to "P" position. Loosen cable sheath lock nuts. Pull cable sheath forward until all slack is removed. *See Fig. 4.*

2) Hand tighten outer lock nut. Tighten inner lock nut. Check tightness of outer lock nut. Ensure ignition key will operate column lock in the "P" position.

Fig. 3: Adjusting Sprint Oil Pressure Control Cable

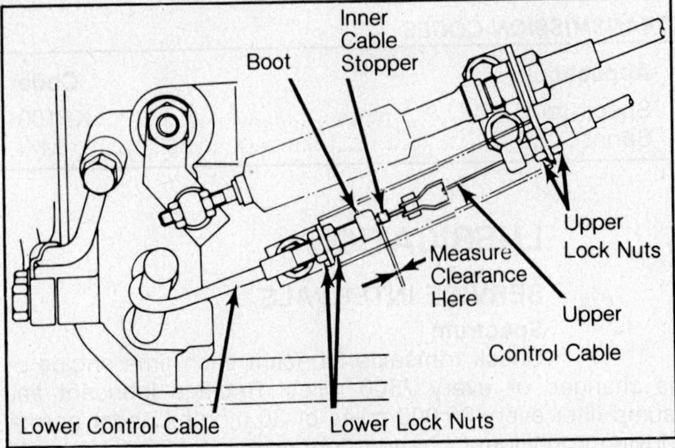

Courtesy of General Motors Corp.

3) Move transaxle gearshift lever to any other position. Ensure ignition key cannot be turned from "ACC" to "LOCK" position. If so, readjust start inhibit cable.

Fig. 4: Adjusting Sprint Backdrive Cable

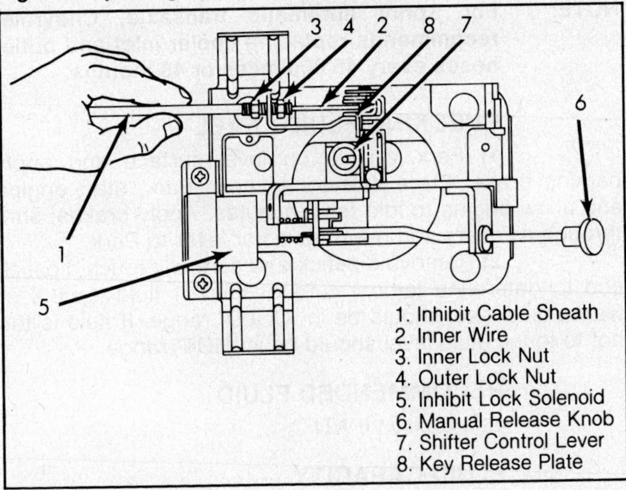

Courtesy of General Motors Corp.

BACKDRIVE SOLENOID

Sprint

1) Remove center console. Adjust solenoid so when ignition is in "OFF" (solenoid inoperative) or "ON" (solenoid operated), lock plate will be in correct position. *See Fig. 5.*

2) Clearance between lock plate and guide plate should be .04" (1.0 mm). Adjust solenoid by loosening mounting screws and moving solenoid.

3) With ignition switch in "OFF", and gearshift lever in "P", gearshift should not be able to be shifted to any other position. If manual release knob is pulled with ignition switch in "OFF", gearshift lever should move to other gear positions.

BRAKE BAND

Spectrum

1) Loosen lock nut on brake band anchor bolt. Tighten brake band anchor bolt to 10 ft. lbs. (14 N.m). *See Fig. 6.*

GENERAL MOTORS (Cont.)

Fig. 5: Checking Backdrive Solenoid Position On Sprint

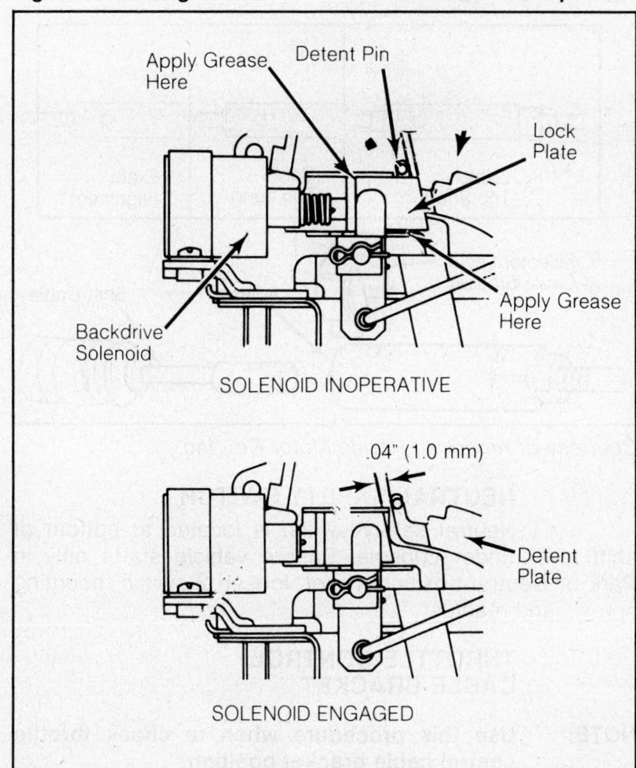

Courtesy of General Motors Corp.

2) Back off bolt 2 full turns. Hold brake band anchor bolt and tighten lock nut to 50 ft. lbs. (68 N.m).

Fig. 6: Adjusting Spectrum Brake Band

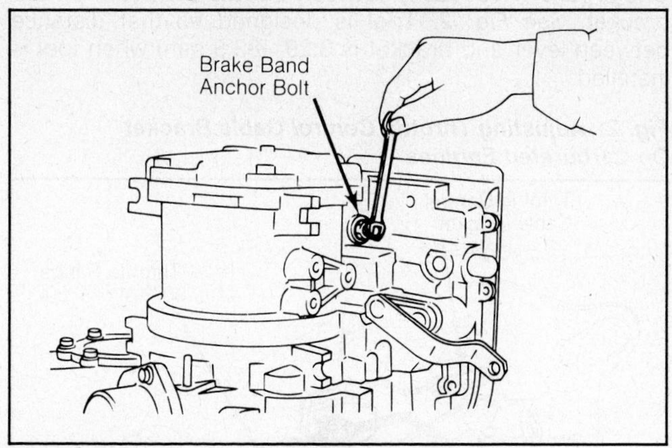

Courtesy of General Motors Corp.

VACUUM MODULATOR ROD

Spectrum

To determine correct vacuum modulator rod length, measure distance "N" at transaxle. *See Fig. 7.* See VACUUM DIAPHRAGM ROD SELECTION table for correct rod to select.

VACUUM DIAPHRAGM ROD SELECTION

Dimension "N" In. (mm)	Rod Length In. (mm)
Below 1.00 (25.4)	1.16 (29.5)
1.000-1.020 (25.4-25.9)	1.18 (30.0)
1.020-1.039 (25.9-26.4)	1.20 (30.5)
1.039-1.059 (26.4-26.9)	1.22 (31.0)
Over 1.059 (26.9)	1.24 (31.5)

Fig. 7: Adjusting Spectrum Vacuum Modulator Rod Length

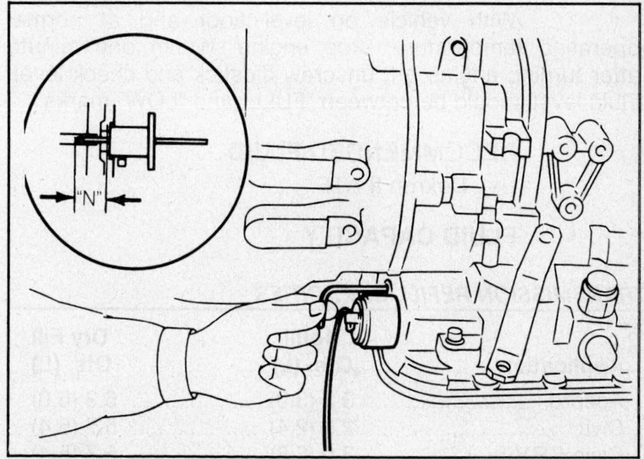

Courtesy of General Motors Corp.

HONDA

IDENTIFICATION

TRANSMISSION CODES

Application	Code
Accord	Model F4 Transaxle
Civic & Civic CRX/si	Model CA Transaxle
Prelude	
Carbureted	Model AS Transaxle
Fuel Injected	Model F4 Transaxle

LUBRICATION

SERVICE INTERVALS

Change fluid every 30,000 miles or 24 months. No filter service or band adjustment is required.

CHECKING FLUID LEVEL

With vehicle on level floor and at normal operating temperature, stop engine. Within one minute after turning engine off, unscrew dipstick and check level. Fluid level should be between "FULL" and "LOW" marks.

RECOMMENDED FLUID

Use Dexron II ATF.

FLUID CAPACITY

TRANSMISSION REFILL CAPACITIES

Application	Refill Qts. (L)	Dry Fill Qts. (L)
Accord	3.2 (3.0)	6.3 (6.0)
Civic	2.5 (2.4)	5.7 (5.4)
Civic CRX/Si	3.0 (2.8)	5.7 (5.4)
Prelude		
Carbureted	3.0 (2.8)	5.9 (5.6)
Fuel Injected	3.2 (3.0)	6.3 (6.0)

DRAINING & REFILLING

1) Ensure transaxle is at normal operating temperature. Remove transmission drain plug. Use new gasket and replace drain plug when fluid is drained.

2) Add fluid through dipstick hole and check level. Add fluid to bring to upper mark on dipstick.

ADJUSTMENTS

SHIFT CONTROL CABLE

1) Start engine. Shift to Reverse. Ensure transaxle engages in Reverse. With engine off, remove the console.

2) Shift to Drive. Remove lock pin from cable adjuster. Check that hole in adjuster is perfectly aligned with hole in shift cable. *See Fig. 1.*

3) The 2 holes in the end of the shift cable are positioned to allow cable adjustments in 1/4 turn increments.

4) Loosen lock nut on shift cable and adjust as required. Tighten lock nut. Install lock pin on adjuster. *See Fig. 1.*

5) Lock pin should not bind as it is installed. Start engine and check shift lever in all gears.

Fig. 1: Adjusting Shift Control Cable

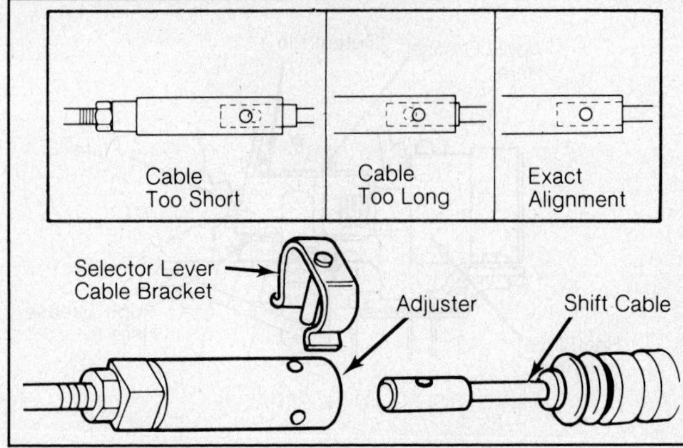

Courtesy of American Honda Motor Co., Inc.

NEUTRAL SAFETY SWITCH

Neutral safety switch is located at bottom of shift lever under console. Ensure vehicle starts only in Park or Neutral position. If not, loosen 2 switch mounting screws and readjust.

THROTTLE CONTROL CABLE BRACKET

NOTE: Use this procedure when to check throttle control cable bracket position.

Carbureted Engine Only

1) Disconnect throttle control cable from throttle control lever. Bend down lock tabs of lock plate and remove two 6 mm bolts to free bracket.

2) Install a new lock plate. Position Throttle Gauge (07974-6890300) between throttle control lever and bracket. *See Fig. 2*. Tool is designed so that distance between lever and bracket is 3.29" (83.5 mm) when tool is installed.

Fig. 2: Adjusting Throttle Control Cable Bracket On Carbureted Engines

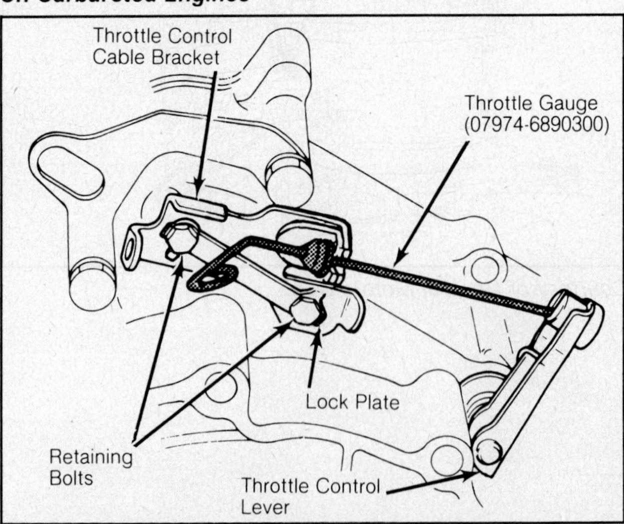

Courtesy of American Honda Motor Co., Inc.

3) Position cable bracket so there is no binding between bracket and special tool. Tighten 6 mm bolts and bend up lock tabs against bolt heads. Adjust throttle control cable.

HONDA (Cont.)

CAUTION: Make sure control lever is not pulled toward bracket side as bolts are tightened.

THROTTLE CONTROL CABLE

Carbureted Engine

1) Before adjusting transaxle throttle control cable, ensure carburetor inner throttle cable has correct free play. Check carburetor cable deflection with throttle in idle position. Inner cable deflection should be 3.16-3/8" (4-10 mm).

2) Engine should be normal operating temperature and idle speed correct. Ensure throttle control bracket is correctly adjusted. Disconnect throttle control cable from transaxle.

3) On Civic and CRX/si models only, disconnect vacuum hose from dashpot. Connect vacuum pump and apply vacuum. *See Fig. 3*. This will simulate normal running position of dashpot.

Fig. 3: Civic & CRX/si Dashpot Location

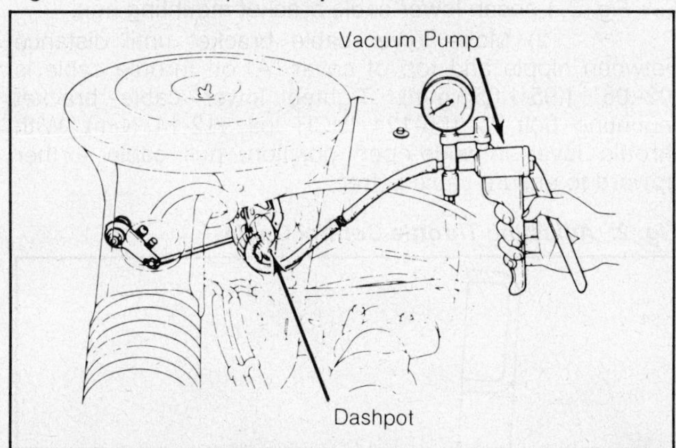

Courtesy of Honda Motor Co., Inc.

4) To adjust transaxle throttle control cable on all models, attach a weight of about 3 lbs. on accelerator pedal. Raise and release pedal. This will allow weight to remove normal free play from cable.

5) Adjust distance between cable end and lock nut "A" to 3.37" (85.5 mm). *See Fig. 4*. Keep lock nut "A" at this position.

6) Insert end of throttle control cable on transaxle. Use lock nut "B" to secure cable on bracket, keeping "A" in place. Cable must move freely after installation.

7) Remove weight on accelerator pedal. Push on accelerator pedal and make sure specified free play exists at transaxle throttle control lever. *See Fig. 5*.

8) Start engine. Press accelerator pedal and check synchronization between carburetor and throttle control cable. Transaxle throttle control cable should start to move as engine speed increases.

9) If transaxle throttle control lever moves before engine speed increases, turn cable lock nut "A" counterclockwise and tighten lock nut "B". If throttle control lever moves after engine speed increases. loosen lock nut "B". Turn lock nut "A" clockwise and tighten lock nut "B".

Fuel Injected Engine

1) Loosen lock nuts on both sides of the throttle control cable bracket. *See Fig. 5*. Press down on throttle control lever until it stops.

Fig. 4: Adjusting Throttle Control Cable End

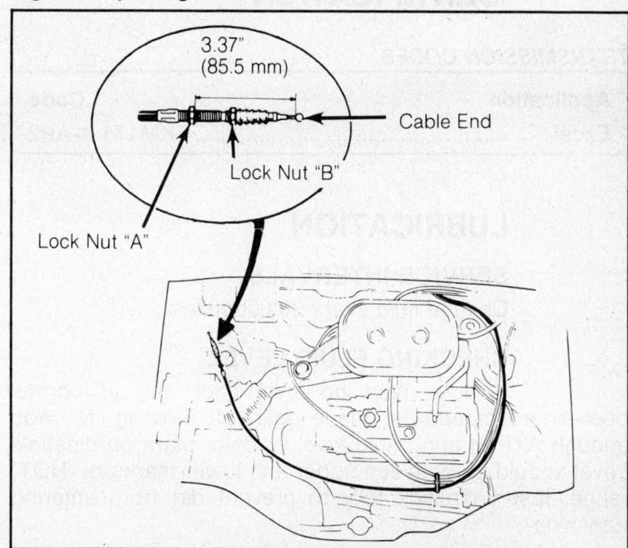

Courtesy of America Honda Motor Co., Inc.

2) While pressing down on throttle control lever, pull on throttle link to check throttle control cable free play. Remove all free play by turning upper lock nut (lock nut "A") until it lightly seats on the throttle control cable bracket.

3) While pressing down on throttle control lever, pull open throttle link. Control lever should move at exactly same time as throttle link. Tighten other lock nut (lock nut "B") to secure cable adjustment.

4) BEFORE starting engine, depress accelerator to floor. Ensure there is at least .08" (2 mm) free play in throttle control lever. Check that cable moves freely when depressing accelerator.

5) Start engine. With shift lever in Neutral or Park, throttle control cable lever should be synchronized with engine speed by gradually depressing accelerator.

Fig. 5: Adjusting Throttle Control Cable Free Play

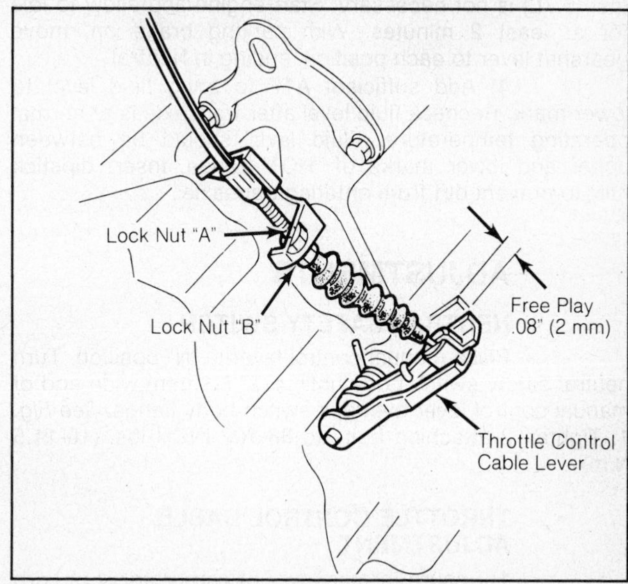

Courtesy of American Honda Motor Co., Inc.

HYUNDAI

IDENTIFICATION

TRANSMISSION CODES

Application	Code
Excel	KM171-1-AP2

LUBRICATION

SERVICE INTERVALS

Change fluid every 30,000 miles.

CHECKING FLUID LEVEL

Vehicle must be level floor and at normal operating temperature. Place gearshift lever in "N". Add enough ATF to bring fluid level to lower mark on dipstick. Level should be between upper and lower marks of "HOT" range. Insert dipstick fully to prevent dirt from entering transaxle.

RECOMMENDED FLUID

Use Dexron II ATF.

FLUID CAPACITY

TRANSMISSION REFILL CAPACITIES

Application	Pts.
Excel	12.0 (5.7)

DRAINING & REFILLING

1) Remove drain plug at differential bottom. Loosen oil pan bolts and tap pan at one corner to break it loose, allowing fluid to drain. Remove oil pan.

2) Clean gasket surfaces of transaxle case and oil pan. Install oil pan with new gasket and tighten oil pan bolts to 8-9 ft. lbs. (10-11 N.m). Install and tighten drain plug with new gasket to 22-25 ft. lbs. (30-34 N.m).

3) Pour 4.2 qts. (4.0L) of ATF into case through dipstick hole. Unless torque converter was drained, full 6.0 qts. (5.7L) is not necessary. Start engine and allow to idle for at least 2 minutes. With parking brake on, move gearshift lever to each position, ending in Neutral.

4) Add sufficient ATF to bring fluid level to lower mark. Recheck fluid level after transaxle is at normal operating temperature. Fluid level should be between upper and lower marks of "HOT" range. Insert dipstick fully to prevent dirt from entering transaxle.

ADJUSTMENTS

NEUTRAL SAFETY SWITCH

Place manual control lever in "N" position. Turn neutral safety switch body until .472" (12 mm) wide end of manual control lever overlaps switch body flange. *See Fig. 1.* Tighten 2 attaching bolts to 88-102 INCH lbs. (10-11.5 N.m)

THROTTLE CONTROL CABLE ADJUSTMENT

1) Ensure throttle lever of carburetor is in curb idle position, with engine at normal operating temperature. Raise cover "B" of throttle cable upward to expose nipple. *See Fig. 2.* Loosen lower cable bracket mounting bolt.

2) Move lower cable bracket until distance between nipple and top of cover "A" on throttle cable is .02-.06" (.95-1.05 mm). Tighten lower cable bracket mounting bolt to 106-124 INCH lbs. (12-14 N.m). With throttle lever in wide-open position, pull cable further upward to ensure cable is free.

Fig. 1: Adjusting Neutral Safety Switch

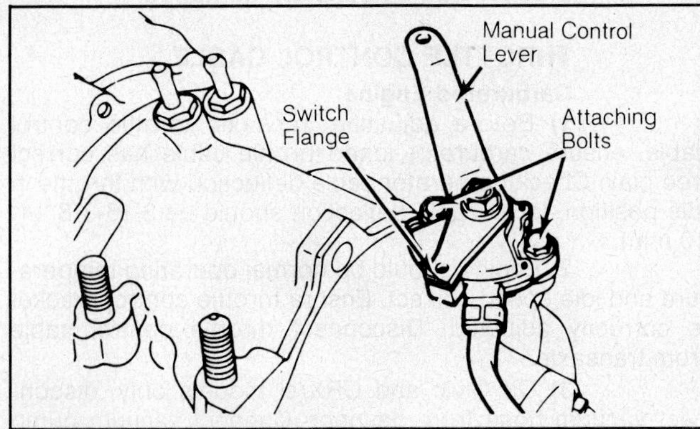

Courtesy of Hyundai Motor Co.

Fig. 2: Adjusting Throttle Control Cable

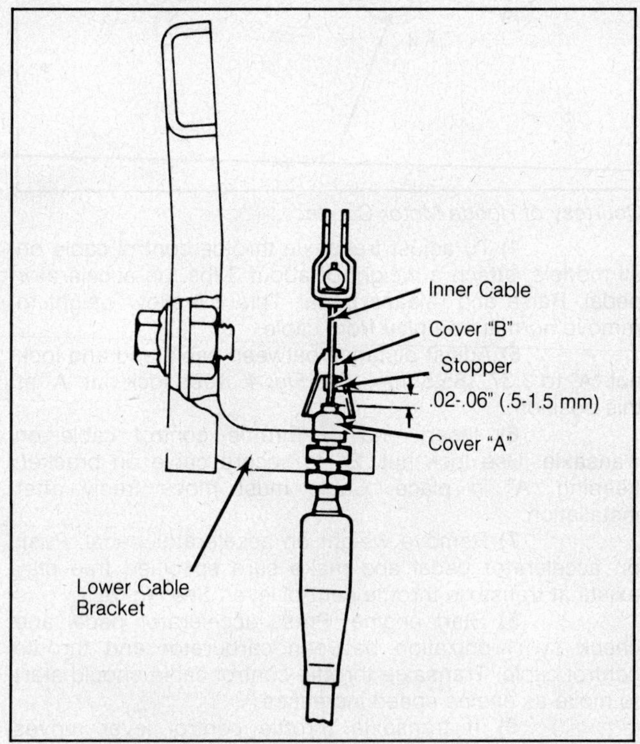

Courtesy of Hyundai Motor Co.

GEARSHIFT LINKAGE

1) Place gearshift lever in Neutral. Neutral indicator on console panel should be correctly aligned.

2) Transaxle should shift into correct gear position as gearshift lever is moved from "P" to "L". If not, gearshift cable may be adjusted at transaxle end of cable.

HYUNDAI (Cont.)

Fig. 3: Adjusting Gearshift Lever Sleeve

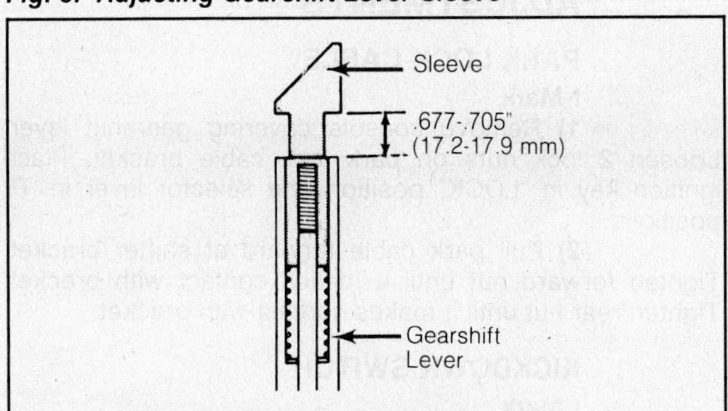

Courtesy of Hyundai Motor Co.

GEARSHIFT LEVER HANDLE

1) If shift cable is replaced, or gearshift lever does not properly lock into each position, cable sleeve may be readjusted.

2) Place gearshift lever in "N". Remove set screw and lift off gearshift lever handle. Turn sleeve so that clearance between gearshift lever end and sleeve is .677-.705" (17.2-17.9 mm). *See Fig. 3*. Apply wheel bearing grease to push button contact area of sleeve before reassembly.

ISUZU

IDENTIFICATION

TRANSMISSION CODES

Application	Code
I-Mark	KF100
P'UP	
Diesel	AW03-55
Gasoline	AW03-75
Impulse	AW03-70 or AW03-72L

LUBRICATION

SERVICE INTERVALS

Check fluid at every engine oil change. Under normal conditions, replace fluid and oil screen every 30,000 miles. Under severe conditions, change oil and screen at 15,000 mile intervals.

CHECKING FLUID LEVEL

1) Park vehicle on level surface. Place selector lever in "P" position, set parking brake and run engine to operating temperature. Apply brake pedal. Move shift lever through each gear. Place shift lever in "P" position.

2) With engine idling, clean dipstick and insert. Remove dipstick and check level reading. Fluid level should be between dimples of "HOT" range.

RECOMMENDED FLUID

Dexron II automatic transmission fluid.

FLUID CAPACITY

TRANSMISSION REFILL CAPACITIES

Application	Qts. (L)
I-Mark	6.8 (6.5)
Impulse	6.7 (6.3)
P'UP	
AW03-55	6.3 (6.0)
AW03-75	6.7 (6.3)

DRAINING & REFILLING

1) Remove drain plug and drain fluid. Remove oil pan. Remove oil screen. Clean oil pan, magnet, and oil screen in clean solvent and dry.

2) Install oil screen. Tighten bolts to 48 INCH lbs. (5.5 N.m) on Impulse and P'UP. On I-Mark, tighten bolts to 86 INCH lbs. (9.7 N.m).

3) On all models, set magnet on oil pan so that it rests directly below oil screen. Install oil pan. Tighten bolts to specification. Install filler tube clip bolt (if equipped) and tighten to 29 ft. lbs. (39 N.m).

4) Install drain plug using a new gasket. Tighten to 11-14 ft. lbs. (15-19 N.m). Add about 2.1 qts. (2.0L) of ATF. Check fluid level. Add ATF as necessary to bring fluid to proper level.

OIL PAN BOLT TIGHTENING SPECIFICATIONS

Model	INCH Lbs. (N.m)
I-Mark	60 (6.8)
Impulse	40 (4.5)
P'UP	38 (4.3)

ADJUSTMENTS

PARK LOCK CABLE

I-Mark

1) Remove console covering gearshift lever. Loosen 2 lock nuts on park lock cable bracket. Place ignition key in "LOCK" position and selector lever in "P" position.

2) Pull park cable forward at shifter bracket. Tighten forward nut until it makes contact with bracket. Tighten rear nut until it makes contact with bracket.

KICKDOWN SWITCH

I-Mark

Kickdown switch is located at top of accelerator pedal. Adjust switch so continuity exists when depressing pedal more than 7/8 of its travel.

THROTTLE VALVE CABLE

Impulse & P'UP (Gasoline Engine)

1) Loosen throttle valve cable adjusting nuts. Ensure carburetor throttle adjusting screw is in contact with idle stop.

2) Adjust setting of outer cable. On Impulse, ensure distance between upper face of rubber boot on outer cable and inner cable stopper is .032-.059" (0.8-1.5 mm). *See Fig. 1.*

3) On P'UP, pull rubber boot away from end of cable. Measure between end of cable and beginning of inner cable stopper.

Fig. 1: Throttle Valve Cable Adjustment

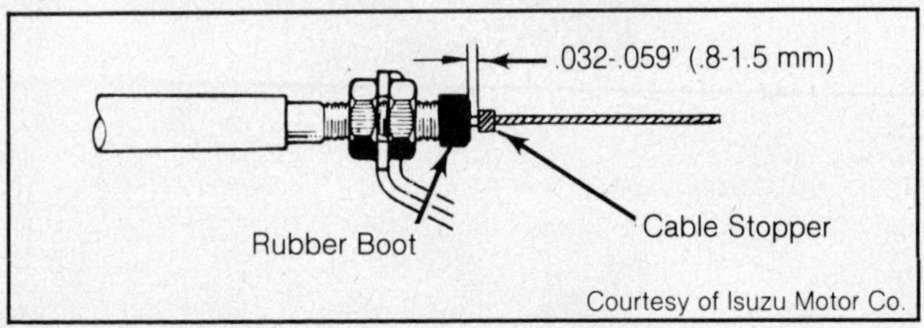

4) On all models, tighten adjusting nuts. Ensure stroke of inner cable from normal idling position to wide open throttle is 1.30-1.36" (32.0-34.5 mm).

P'UP (Diesel Engine)

1) Loosen throttle valve cable adjusting nuts. With accelerator pedal fully depressed, ensure injection pump lever is in contact with maximum speed adjust screw.

2) Hold lever in this position. Adjust setting of outer cable so distance between end of rubber boot on outer cable and inner cable stopper is .032-.059" (.8-1.5 mm). *See Fig. 1.*

3) Tighten adjusting nuts. Check that stroke of inner cable from normal idling position to wide open throttle is 1.30-1.36" (32.0-34.5 mm).

SHIFT LINKAGE

1) Loosen shift control rod adjusting nuts on transmission end of shift linkage. Turn transmission manual shaft so it is in Neutral position.

2) Ensure gearshift lever is in "N" position. Tighten adjusting nuts. Road test vehicle. Ensure shift lever moves properly and transmission operates smoothly.

ISUZU (Cont.)

NEUTRAL SAFETY SWITCH

I-Mark

Neutral safety switch is installed in side of transaxle. There is no adjustment.

Impulse & P'UP

Remove gearshift lever console. Loosen switch retaining screws (near base of gearshift lever). Place selector lever in "N". Adjust switch so vehicle will only start in "P" or "N" position. Tighten retaining screws.

BRAKE BAND

I-Mark

1) Loosen lock nut on brake band anchor bolt. Tighten brake band anchor bolt to 10 ft. lbs. (14 N.m). *See Fig. 2.*

2) Back off bolt 2 full turns. Hold brake band anchor bolt and tighten lock nut to 50 ft. lbs. (68 N.m).

Fig. 2: Adjusting I-Mark Brake Band

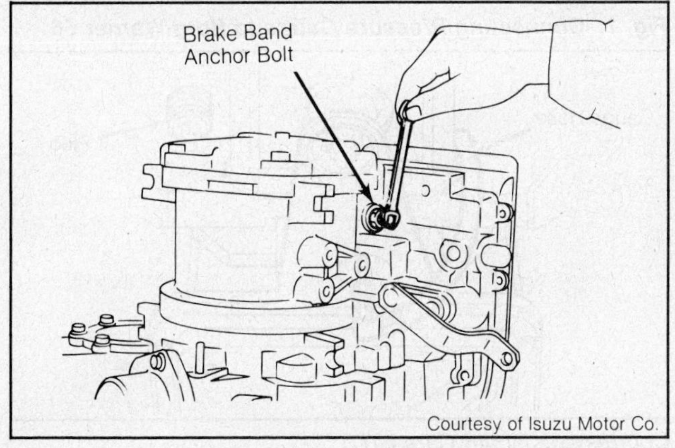

VACUUM MODULATOR ROD

I-Mark

To determine correct vacuum modulator rod length, measure distance "N" at transaxle. *See Fig. 3.* See VACUUM DIAPHRAGM ROD SELECTION table for correct rod to select.

VACUUM DIAPHRAGM ROD SELECTION

Dimension "N" In. (mm)	Rod Length In. (mm)
Below 1.00 (25.4)	1.16 (29.5)
1.000-1.020 (25.4-25.9)	1.18 (30.0)
1.020-1.039 (25.9-26.4)	1.20 (30.5)
1.039-1.059 (26.4-26.9)	1.22 (31.0)
Over 1.059 (26.9)	1.24 (31.5)

Fig. 3: Adjusting I-Mark Vacuum Modulator Rod Length

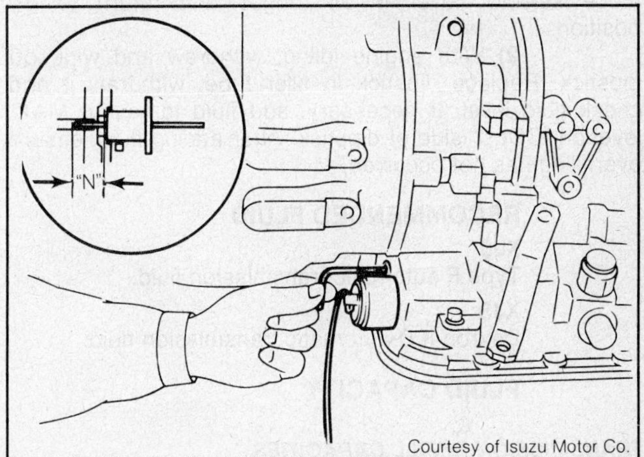

JAGUAR

IDENTIFICATION

TRANSMISSION CODES

Application	Code
XJ6	Borg-Warner 66
XJS	GM THM 400

LUBRICATION

SERVICE INTERVALS

Check fluid level at first 1,000 miles and then every 7,500 miles. Change fluid and filter at 30,000 mile intervals.

CHECKING FLUID LEVEL

1) Park vehicle on level ground. Apply hand brake and run engine at 750 RPM for several minutes. Place selector lever in all ranges and return to "P" position.

2) With engine idling, withdraw and wipe off dipstick. Replace dipstick in filler tube, withdraw it and check fluid level. If necessary, add fluid to reach "MAX" level on "COLD" side of dipstick. After adding fluid, ensure overfilling has not occurred.

RECOMMENDED FLUID

XJ6

Type F automatic transmission fluid.

XJS

Dexron II D automatic transmission fluid.

FLUID CAPACITY

TRANSMISSION REFILL CAPACITIES

Application	[1] Pts. (L)
Borg-Warner 66	16.8 (8.0)
GM THM 400	19.2 (9.1)

[1] – Dry fill.

DRAINING & REFILLING

Borg-Warner 66

1) Disconnect dipstick tube at oil pan and drain oil. Remove oil pan bolts and pan. Remove screws securing suction tube to valve body. Lower suction tube, discard gasket and remove filter.

2) Install oil filter and suction tube, using a new gasket. Clean and install oil pan. Tighten oil pan to 71 INCH lbs. (8 N.m). Connect dipstick tube, add transmission fluid and check fluid level.

GM THM 400

1) Remove vacuum modulator clamp and bolt. Disconnect capsule and drain oil. Remove oil pan bolts, carefully lower pan and drain remaining oil. Remove oil filter bolt and filter.

2) Install oil filter. Clean and install oil pan, using a new gasket. Tighten oil pan bolts to 12 ft. lbs. (16 N.m). Connect modulator, install clamp and tighten using bolt. Add transmission fluid and check fluid level.

ADJUSTMENTS

FRONT BAND

Borg-Warner 66

Remove nut securing selector lever to selector shaft and remove lever. Loosen lock nut remaining band adjustment screw and loosen screw 2 or 3 turns. Tighten screw to 60 INCH lbs. (7 N.m). Back off screw 3/4 of a turn. Tighten lock nut while holding screw in place.

REAR BAND

Borg-Warner 66

Loosen lock nut securing band adjustment screw and loosen screw 2 or 3 turns. Tighten screw to 60 INCH lbs. (7 N.m). Back off 3/4 of a turn. Tighten lock nut while holding screw in place.

DOWNSHIFT CABLE

Borg-Warner 66

1) Engine must be correctly tuned. Using Allen wrench, remove plug from transmission and connect pressure gauge to transmission with adapter. *See Fig. 1.*

Fig. 1: Connecting Pressure Gauge to Borg-Warner 66

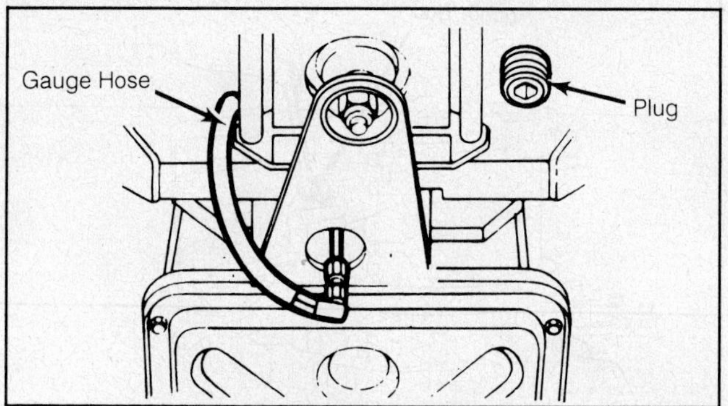

Courtesy of Jaguar Cars LTD.

2) Feed gauge hose through passenger window, keeping hose clear of exhaust pipe. Block wheels and apply hand and foot brakes. Run engine to normal operating temperature.

3) With transmission selector in "D" position, pressure gauge should read 60-75 psi (4.2-5.3 kg/cm²) at idle speed. Increase engine speed to 1200 RPM. Gauge should now read 75-115 psi (5.3-8.1 kg/cm²).

4) If correct pressures are not obtained, turn engine off and place transmission in "N". Loosen lock nut on downshift cable, and turn adjustment nut on outer cable to alter pressure. *See Fig. 2.*

5) Increasing length of cable increases pressure. Decreasing length decreases pressure. When pressures are correct, tighten cable lock nut, install plug and road test vehicle.

KICKDOWN SWITCH

GM THM 400

1) With ignition on, check that power is available at input terminal (Green wire). With one lead of test light grounded, connect other lead to output terminal (Green/White wire). *See Fig. 3.*

JAGUAR (Cont.)

2) Fully depress accelerator pedal, test light should glow. If test light fails to glow, release accelerator pedal and gently depress switch arm. If test light still does not glow, replace kickdown switch.

3) If test light glows when switch arm is depressed, loosen switch screws and move switch toward cable until at full throttle opening test light glows. Tighten switch screws and recheck.

Fig. 2: Adjusting Downshift Cable

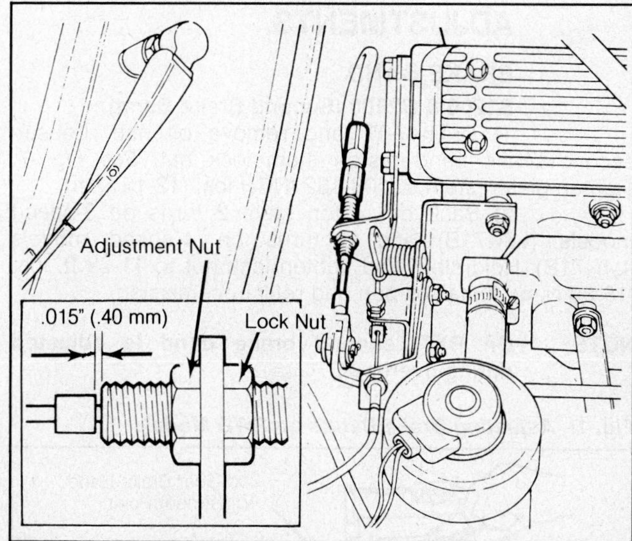

Courtesy of Jaguar Cars LTD.

Fig. 3: Adjusting Kickdown Switch

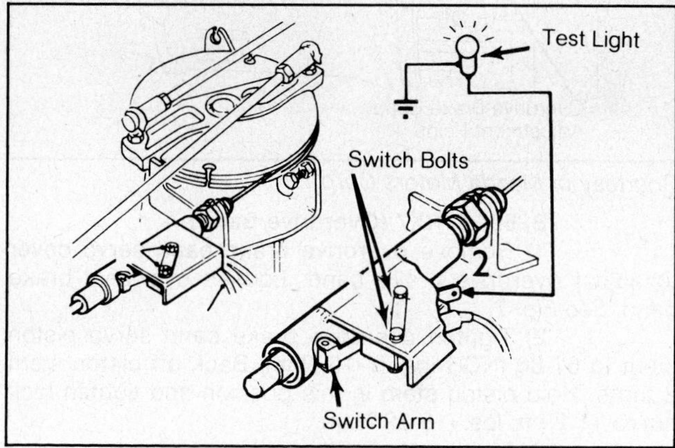

Courtesy of Jaguar Cars LTD.

SELECTOR CABLE

1) Remove console and place selector lever in "1" position on XJ6 models, and in "N" position on XJS models. Unscrew shift knob and remove indicator plate.

2) Remove cotter pin and washer retaining cable to bracket on lever. Ensure transmission lever is in "1" position on XJ6 and in "N" position on XJS models.

3) Adjust front and rear lock nuts until cable can be connected without selector or transmission lever being disturbed. Tighten lock nuts and secure cable with new cotter pin. Install selector plate and shift knob.

Fig. 4: Adjusting Selector Cable

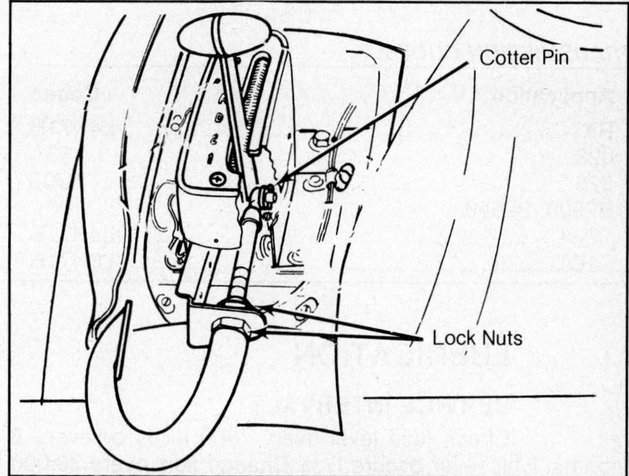

Courtesy of Jaguar Cars LTD.

NEUTRAL SAFETY SWITCH

1) Remove selector indicator and position electric window switch panel away from console. Move control panel to gain access to cigar lighter wiring and door lock switch wiring. Note position of wires and disconnect.

2) Remove control panel. Disconnect feed wire to switch and connect self-powered test light to terminal. Place selector lever in "N" position and loosen lock nuts which secure the switch. Adjust switch until test light glows. *See Fig. 5.*

3) Tighten switch lock nuts and check that light remains on with lever in "P", and goes off with lever in any driving position. Remove test light, reconnect feed wire, and install all removed parts.

Fig. 5: Adjusting Neutral Safety Switch

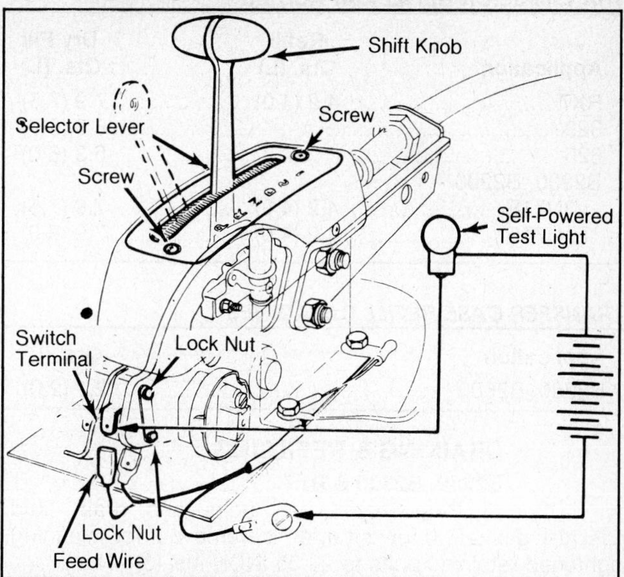

Courtesy of Jaguar Cars LTD.

MAZDA

IDENTIFICATION

TRANSMISSION CODES

Application	Codes
RX7	L4N71B
323	F3A
626	FU06
B2000, B2600	
2WD	L4N71B
4WD	L3N71B

LUBRICATION

SERVICE INTERVALS

Check fluid level every 7500 miles or every 8 months, whichever occurs first. Change fluid every 30,000 miles.

CHECKING FLUID LEVEL

Park vehicle on level ground. Apply parking brake. Bring enging to normal operating temperature. Briefly place selector lever in all gears and return to "P". Clean dipstick and insert in tube. Remove dipstick. Level should be between "L" and "F" marks. If necessary, add fluid.

RECOMMENDED FLUID

Transmission

Use Dexron II/D ATF.

Transfer Case

Use API GL-4 or 5, SAE 80W-90.

FLUID CAPACITY

TRANSMISSION REFILL CAPACITIES

Application	Refill Qts. (L)	Dry Fill Qts. (L)
RX7	4.2 (4.0)	7.9 (7.5)
323		6.0 (5.7)
626		6.3 (6.0)
B2200, B2200		
L3N71B	4.2 (4.0)	7.9 (7.5)
L4N71B	4.2 (4.0)	7.9 (7.5)

TRANSFER CASE REFILL CAPACITIES

Application	Qts. (L)
B2200, B2600	2.1 (2.0)

DRAINING & REFILLING

B2200, B2600 & RX7

1) Remove oil pan bolts and drain fluid. Discard gasket. If oil strainer is removed for cleaning, tightened retaining bolts to 26-35 INCH lbs. (3-4 N.m).

2) Clean oil pan and install, using a new gasket. Tighten oil pan bolts to 43-61 INCH lbs. (5-7 N.m). Add fluid and check fluid level. Do not overfill transmission.

323 & 626

1) Remove drain plug in oil pan. Oil pan must be removed to drain remainder of fluid. Discard old oil pan gasket. If oil strainer is removed for cleaning, tighten retaining bolts to 26-35 INCH lbs. (3-4 N.m) on 323 and 69-95 INCH lbs. (8-11 N.m) on 626.

2) Clean oil pan and install with new gasket. Tighten oil pan bolts to 43-69 INCH lbs. on 323 and 69-95 INCH lbs. (8-11 N.m) on 626. Do not overfill transaxle.

ADJUSTMENTS

BRAKE BAND

B2200 & B2600 (Second Brake Band)

1) Drain ATF and remove oil pan. Loosen second brake band piston stem lock nut. *See Fig. 1.* Tighten piston stem to 108-132 INCH lbs. (12-15 N.m).

2) Back off piston stem 2 turns on 3-speed models (L3N71B) and 3 turns on 4-speed models (L4N71B). Hold stem and tighten lock nut to 11-29 ft. lbs. (15-39 N.m). Install oil pan and refill transmission.

NOTE: On RX7, second brake band is adjusted during overhaul.

Fig. 1: Adjusting Brake Bands on RWD Models

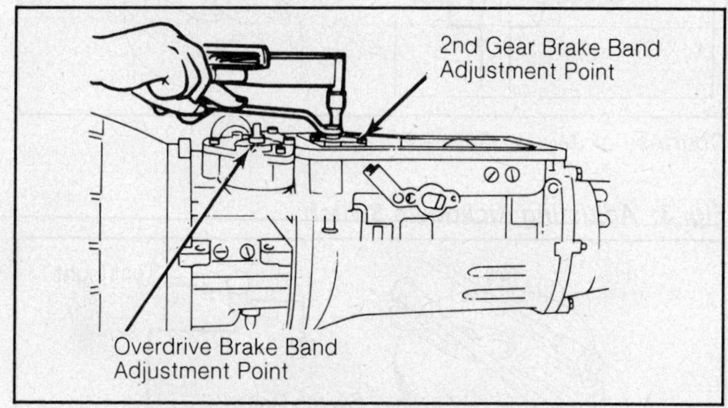

Courtesy of Mazda Motors Corp.

B2600 & RX7 (Overdrive Band)

1) Remove overdrive brake band servo cover to adjust overdrive brake band. Loosen overdrive brake band. *See Fig. 1.*

2) Tighten overdrive brake band servo piston stem to 61-86 INCH lbs. (7-10 N.m). Back off piston stem 2 turns. Hold piston stem in this position and tighten lock nut to 11-29 ft. lbs. (15-39 N.m).

3) Tighten 2nd gear brake band servo piston stem to 108-132 INCH lbs. (12-15 N.m). Back off piston stem 3 turns. Hold piston stem in this position and tighten lock nut to 11-29 ft. lbs. (15-39 N.m).

NOTE: Adjust 323 brake band with oil pump installed. Apply sealant to anchor bolt threads.

323

1) Loosen lock nut on brake band anchor bolt. Tighten brake band anchor bolt to 108-132 INCH lbs. (12-15 N.m). *See Fig. 2.*

2) Back off bolt 2 turns on carbureted models and 3 turns on fuel injected models. Hold brake band anchor bolt and tighten lock nut to 41-59 ft. lbs. (56-80 N.m).

MAZDA (Cont.)

Fig. 2: Adjusting 323 Brake Band

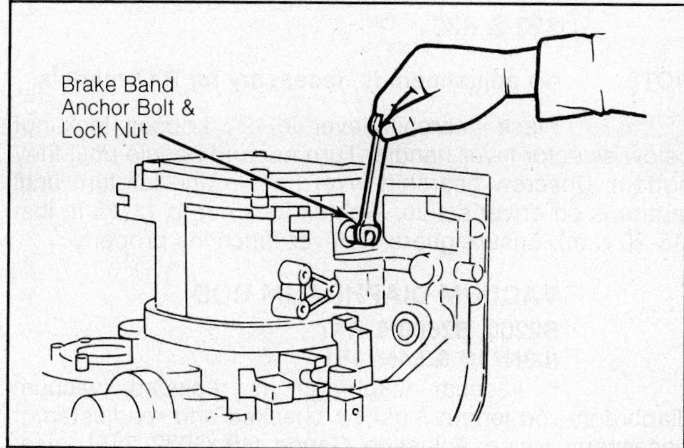

Courtesy of Mazda Motors Corp.

626

1) Brake band is usually adjusted during overhaul. If nececessary to adjust during servicing, valve body must be removed.

2) Loosen piston stem lock nut. *See Fig. 3.* Adjust piston stem so that it has a stroke of .067-.039" (1.0-1.7 mm) when compressed air is applied to apply hole. Use 57 psi (392 kPa) of air pressure.

3) Tighten lock nut to 18-29 ft. lbs. (25-40 N.m) after adjustment. Tighten valve body retaining bolts to 95-130 INCH lbs. (11-15 N.m). Install oil pan and refill transaxle.

CAUTION: When replacing valve body, ensure manual plate and manual valve are installed in correct position.

Fig. 3: Adjusting 626 Brake Band

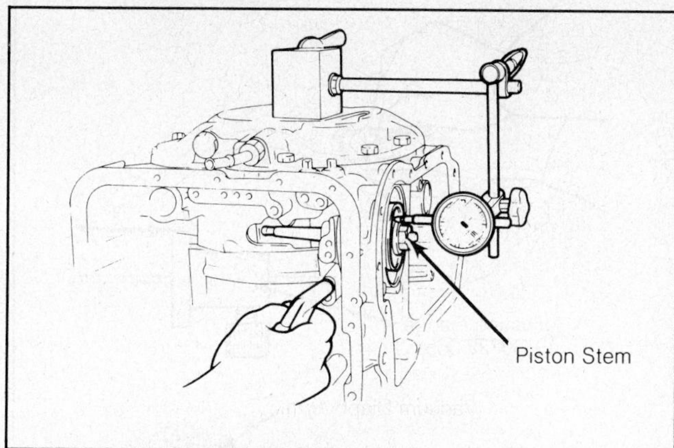

Courtesy of Mazda Motors Corp.

KICKDOWN SWITCH

B2200 & B2600

Kickdown switch is on upper part of accelerator pedal. Loosen kickdown switch lock nut. Depress accelerator pedal fully. Adjust switch so its tip is depressed and switch is on. Tighten lock nut.

323 & 626

1) Kickdown switch is located on upper part of accelerator pedal. Depress accelerator pedal to limit. Listen for a click from solenoid. Switch must operate at or after 7/8 of pedal travel.

2) If not, loosen switch retaining nut. Adjust switch to engage when pedal is 7/8 of its full travel. Tighten retaining nut and check solenoid.

GEARSHIFT LINKAGE

B2200

1) Place gearshift lever in "P" range. Loosen lock nuts on transmission end of cable. *See Fig. 4.*

2) Ensure transmission select lever is in Park range. Holding gearshift lever forward, tighten center lock nut to 69-95 INCH lbs. (7.8-11.0 N.m). Tighten forward lock nut, then rear lock nut to 69-95 INCH lbs. (7.8-11.0 N.m).

3) Remove console covering gearshift lever in cab. Move gearshift lever through "N", "D" and "P" ranges. Ensure there is clearance between guide pin on bottom of gearshift lever and detent in gearshift lever bracket. Readjust cable if necessary.

Fig. 4: Adjusting B2200 Gearshift Cable

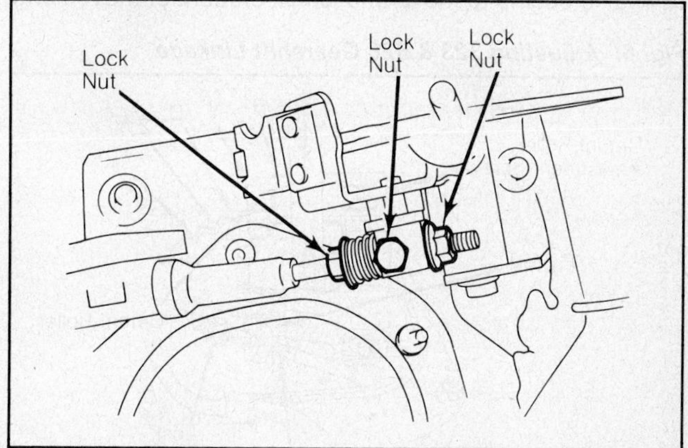

Courtesy of Mazda Motors Corp.

B2600

1) Remove console covering gearshift lever in cab. Place gearshift lever in "P". Loosen lock nuts at bottom of gearshift lever. *See Fig. 5.*

2) Ensure transmission is in Park range. There should be .039" (1 mm) clearance between the adjust lever and front lock nut. After clearance is set, tighten rear lock nut to to 69-95 INCH lbs. (7.8-11.0 N.m).

3) Move gearshift lever to "N", "D" and "P". Make sure there is clearance between guide pin on bottom of gearshift lever and detent on gearshift lever bracket. Readjust if necessary.

Fig. 5: Adjusting B2600 Gearshift Cable

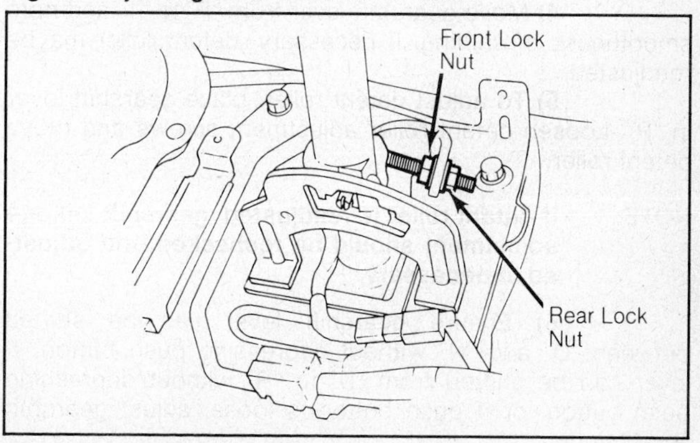

Courtest of Mazda Motors Corp.

MAZDA (Cont.)

RX7

1) Remove boot plate. Place selector lever in "P". From inside passenger compartment, loosen 2 lock nuts on connector link at bottom of gearshift lever. Move transmission selector lever to "P" position (first detent from rear of transmission).

2) Tighten front lock nut until it just touches adjust lever. Back off front lock nut one turn. Tighten rear lock nut to 69-96 INCH lbs. (7.8-11.0 N.m). Place gearshift lever in each position to ensure transmission shifts correctly.

323 & 626

1) Loosen lock nuts "A" and "B" at "T" joint. Place gearshift lever in "N". Move transaxle lever to Neutral, fourth detent position away from transaxle. *See Fig. 6*.

2) Turn lock nut "A" until it comes in contact with "T" joint. Tighten lock nut "B" to 69-95 INCH lbs. (8-11 N.m). Move gearshift lever toward "P" until lever on transaxle begins to move and check amount of movement.

Fig. 6: Adjusting 323 & 626 Gearshift Linkage

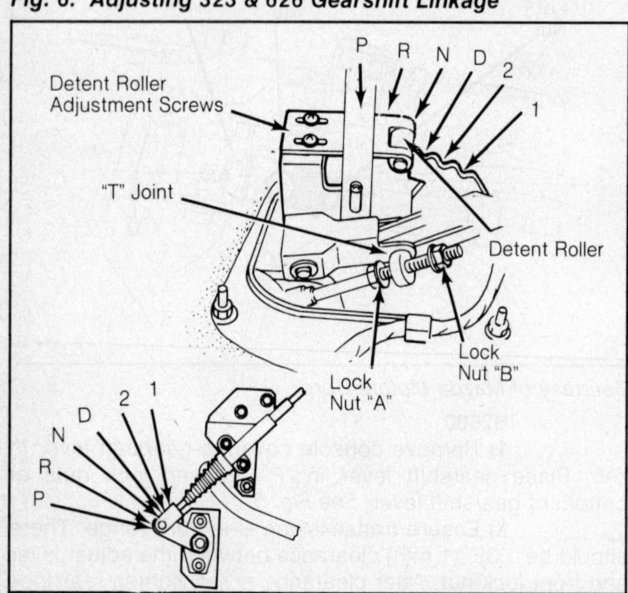

Courtesy of Mazda Motors Corp.

3) Move gearshift lever toward "D" until lever on transaxle begins to move and check amount of movement. Amount of movement should be equal. If not, adjust lock nuts so movement is equal. Ensure transmission shifts correctly.

4) Move gearshift lever from "P" to "1" and note smoothness of shifting. If necessary, detent roller maybe readjusted.

5) To adjust detent roller, place gearshift lever in "P". Loosen detent roller adjustment screws and move detent roller.

NOTE: If detent roller is readjusted, gearshift linkage adjustment should be rechecked and adjusted, if necessary.

6) Ensure gearshift lever can be shifted between "D" and "N" without depressing push button. If lever can be shifted from "D" to "R" without depressing push button, or if push button is loose, adjust gearshift lever handle.

GEARSHIFT LEVER HANDLE

323 & 626

NOTE: No adjustment is necessary for RX7 models.

Place gearshift lever in "P". Loosen lock nut below selector lever handle. Turn nut and handle until they bottom. Unscrew gearshift lever handle one full turn until button is on driver's side. Tighten lock nut to 11-15 ft. lbs. (15-20 N.m). Ensure gearshift lever functions properly.

VACUUM DIAPHRAGM ROD

B2200, B2600 & RX7
(L3N71B & L4N71B)

If vacuum diaphragm is replaced, vacuum diaphragm rod length must be checked and readjusted, if necessary. Using Adjusting Gauge (49 G032 355), measure dimension "N". *See Fig. 7*. See VACUUM DIAPHRAGM ROD SELECTION (B2200, B2600 & RX7) table.

VACUUM DIAPHRAGM ROD SELECTION (B2200, B2600 & RX7)

Dimension "N" In. (mm)	Rod Length In. (mm)
Below 1.0099 (25.65)	1.14 (29.0)
1.0099-1.0295 (25.65-26.15)	1.16 (29.5)
1.0295-1.0492 (26.15-26.65)	1.18 (30.0)
1.0492-1.0650 (26.65-27.15)	1.20 (30.5)
1.0689 Or Over (27.15)	1.22 (31.0)

Fig. 7: Adjusting Vacuum Diaphragm Rod Length on B2200, B2600 & RX7

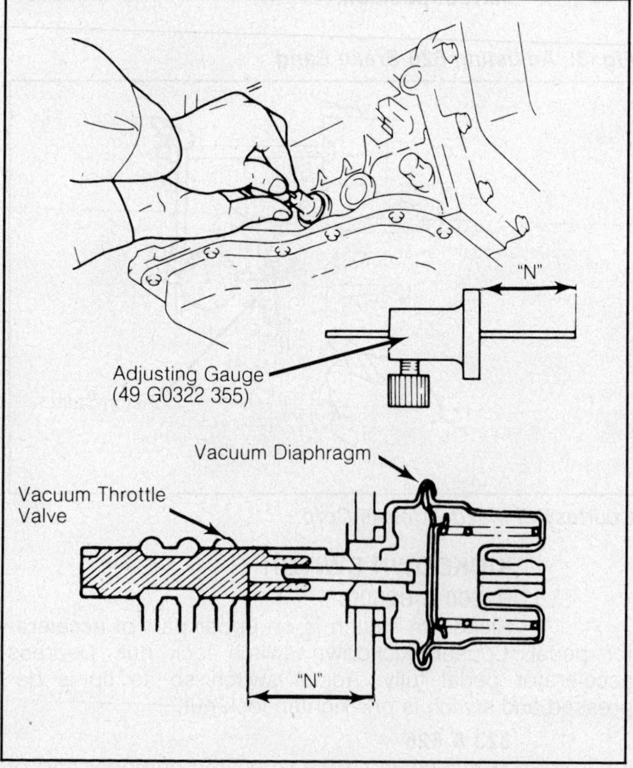

Courtesy of Mazda Motors Corp.

MAZDA (Cont.)

323

Using Adjusting Gauge (49 G032 355), measure dimension "N". *See Fig. 8.* See VACUUM DIAPHRAGM ROD SELECTION (323) table.

VACUUM DIAPHRAGM ROD SELECTION (323)

Dimension "N" In. (mm)	Rod Length In. (mm)
Below 1.000 (25.4)	1.16 (29.5)
1.000-1.020 (25.4-25.9)	1.18 (30.0)
1.020-1.039 (25.9-26.4)	1.20 (30.5)
1.039-1.059 (26.4-26.9)	1.22 (31.0)
Over 1.059 (26.9)	1.24 (31.5)

Fig. 8: Adjusting Vacuum Diaphragm Rod Length on 323

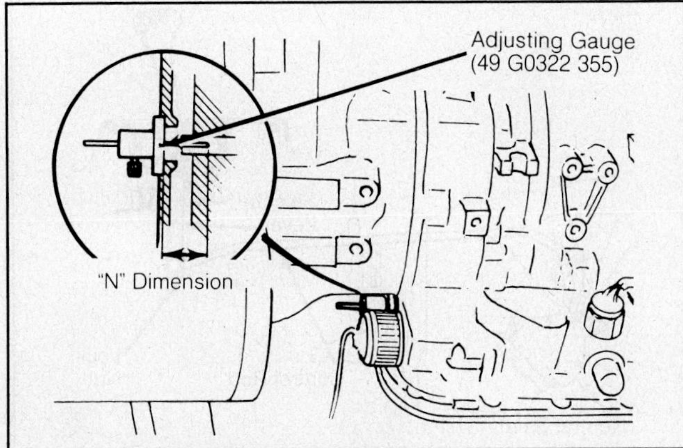

Courtesy of Mazda Motors Corp.

THROTTLE CABLE

626

1) Ensure inner and outer cables are not bent or damaged. Accelerator should operate smoothly.

2) With throttle valve fully open, distance between cable stop and end of outer cable should be 1.80-1.82" (45.8-46.2 mm). If not, readjust cable by turning lock nuts. *See Fig. 9.*

Fig. 9: Adjusting 626 Throttle Cable

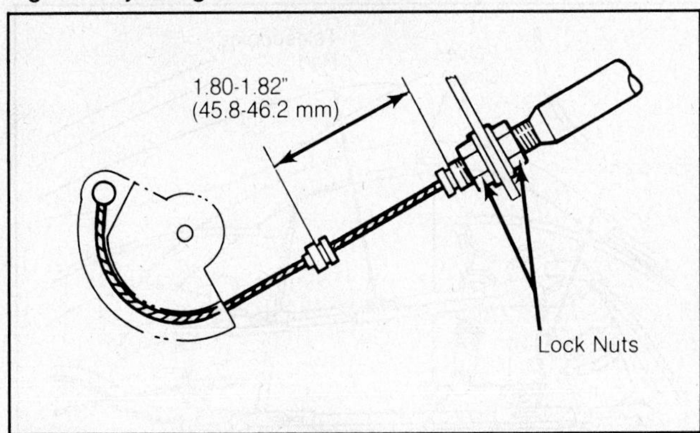

Courtesy of Mazda Motors Corp.

NEUTRAL SAFETY SWITCH

B2200, B2600, RX7 & 626

1) Place gearshift lever in Neutral. Make sure gearshift cable is adjusted correctly. Loosen neutral safety switch attaching bolts at transmission. Remove screw from alignment pin hole from bottom of switch.

2) Rotate switch and insert a .079" (2.0 mm) alignment pin through alignment holes. Tighten attaching bolts and remove alignment pin. Install alignment pin hole screw and check operation of switch. Vehicle should start in "P" and "N" positions only.

NOTE: The following instructions are for checking neutral safety switch. No adjustments are possible.

323

Ensure vehicle starts in "P" and "N", continuity should exist between terminals "A" and "B". With lever in "R", continuity should exist between terminals "C" and "D". *See Fig. 10.*

Fig. 10: Neutral Safety Switch Continuity Check

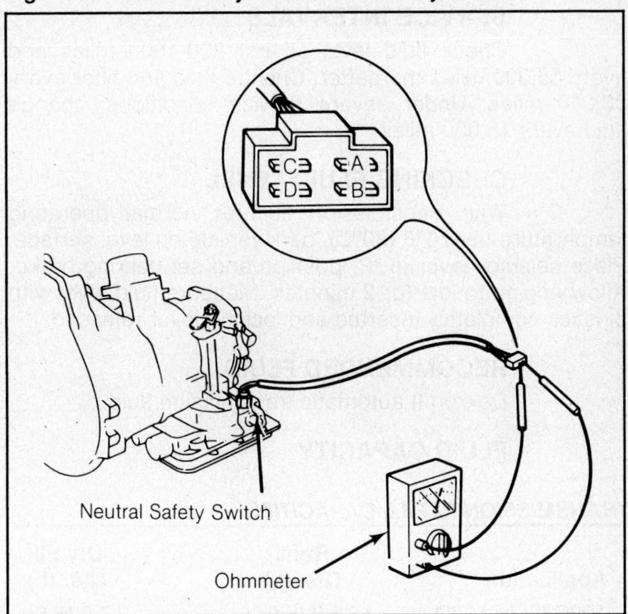

Courtesy of Mazda Motors Corp.

MERCEDES-BENZ

IDENTIFICATION

TRANSMISSION CODES

Application	Code (Model)
190E (2.3L)	722.408 (W4A020)
190E (2.6L)	722.409 (W4A020)
190D	722.414 (W4A020)
190D Turbo	722.413 (W4A020)
260E	722.409 (W4A020)
300D Turbo	722.317 (W4A040)
300E	722.320 (W4A040)
300TD Turbo	722.317 (W4A040)
300SDL	722.321 (W4A040)
420SEL	722.324 (W4A040)
560SL	722.313 (W4A040)
560SEL	722.323 (W4A040)
560SEC	722.323 (W4A040)

LUBRICATION

SERVICE INTERVALS

Check fluid level at first 800-1000 miles and every 15,000 miles thereafter. Change fluid and filter every 30,000 miles. Under severe service conditions, change fluid every 15,000 miles.

CHECKING FLUID LEVEL

With transmission fluid at normal operating temperature of 176°F (80°C), park vehicle on level surface. Place selector lever in "P" position and set parking brake. Allow engine to idle for 2 minutes. Measure fluid level with dipstick completely inserted and locking lever released.

RECOMMENDED FLUID

Dexron II automatic transmission fluid.

FLUID CAPACITY

TRANSMISSION REFILL CAPACITIES

Application	Refill Qts. (L)	Dry Fill Qts. (L)
190E (2.3), 190D	6.2 (5.9)	7.0 (6.6)
190E (2.6)	6.3 (6.0)	7.5 (7.1)
260E	6.6 (6.2)	7.6 (7.3)
300D, 300TD & 300SDL	6.3 (6.0)	7.7 (7.3)
420 & 560 Series	8.1 (7.7)	9.1 (8.6)

DRAINING & REFILLING

1) Disconnect fill tube from oil pan and drain fluid. Rotate engine until torque converter drain plug is at bottom of torque converter housing. Remove plug and drain fluid. Install plug, using a new sealing ring. Remove oil pan and filter.

2) Install filter and oil pan, using a new gasket. Attach fill tube, using new sealing rings on hollow screw. Add about 4 qts. of automatic transmission fluid.

3) Apply parking brake and start engine. Place selector lever in "P" position. Run engine at idle and gradually add fluid. Mometarily place selector lever in each gear, and then return to "P" position. Check fluid level and adjust if necessary. Do not overfill.

ADJUSTMENTS

SHIFT LINKAGE

Disconnect control rod from selector lever. Place transmission lever in "N" (vertical) position. Loosen lock nut at end of control rod and adjust rod length so that a .04" (1.0 mm) clearance exists between selector lever and "N" stop on gate plate. Connect control rod, secure and tighten lock nut. *See Fig. 1*.

Fig. 1: Adjusting Shift Linkage

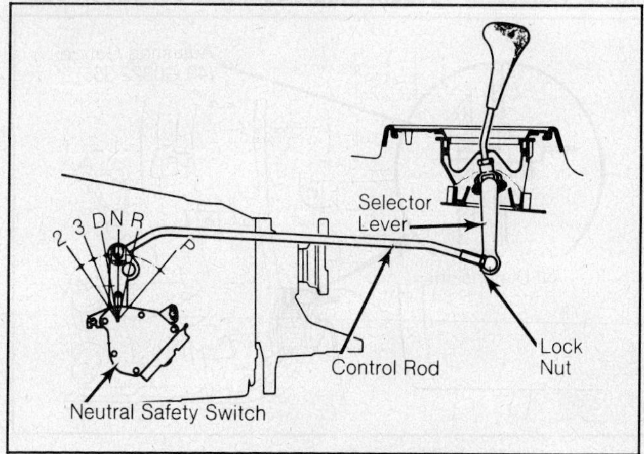

Courtesy of Mercedes-Benz of North America.

CONTROL PRESSURE CABLE

190D

Disconnect control cable at bellcrank. Extend telescoping rod to maximum length. *See Fig. 2.* Pull control cable forward until a slight resistance is felt. Hold ball socket in this position. Ball socket should fit freely into ball. Adjust rod length, if necessary.

Fig. 2: Adjusting 190D Control Pressure Cable

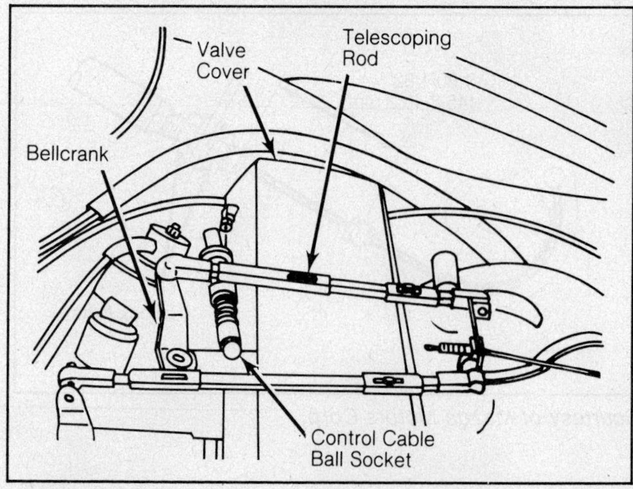

Courtesy of Mercedes-Benz of North America.

MERCEDES-BENZ (Cont.)

190E

Turn adjustment screw inward until compression nipple on spacing sleeve has a .04" (1 mm) free play. Turn adjustment screw until tip of pointer rests directly above groove of adjustment screw. *See Fig. 3.*

Fig. 3: 190E Control Pressure Cable Adjustment

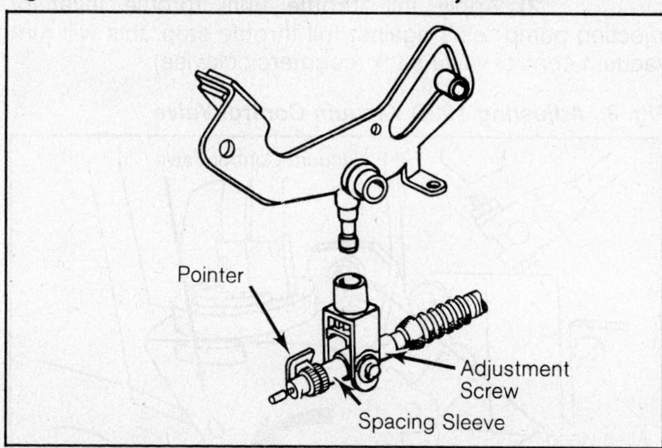

Courtesy of Mercedes-Benz of North America.

300D, 300SDL & 300TD

1) Engine throttle control must be correctly adjusted before adjusting pressure control cable. Disconnect control pressure cable at bellcrank.

2) Pull pressure control cable forward until resistance is felt. Hold ball socket in this position. Ball socket should fit freely into ball. Adjust cable length, if necessary. *See Fig. 4.*

Fig. 4: Adjusting 300D, 300SDL & 300TD Control Pressure Cable

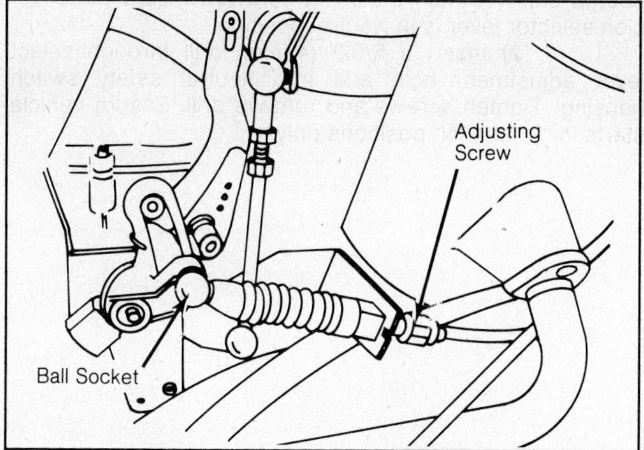

Courtesy of Mercedes-Benz of North America.

300E

1) Ensure throttle control cable is correctly adjusted. Disconnect cable ball socket. Pull control cable forward until slight resistance is felt.

2) Holding cable in this position, check if ball socket fits on ball with no tension. If not, use adjusting screw to change cable length.

Fig. 5: Adjusting 300E Control Pressure Cable

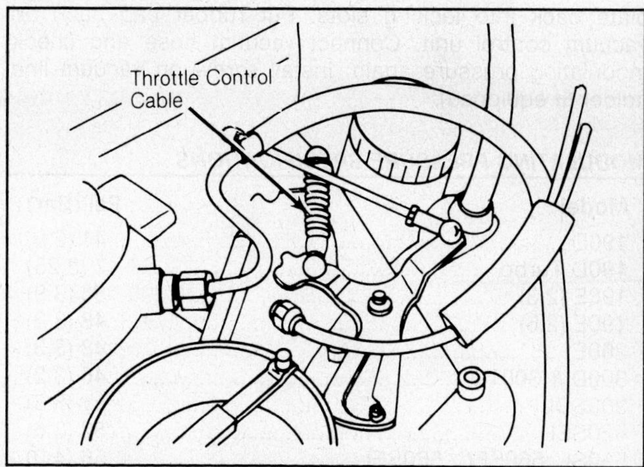

Courtesy of Mercedes-Benz of North America.

420 & 560 Series

Remove air cleaner. Loosen adjustment screw on connecting rod. *See Fig. 6.* Extend connecting rod then retract, until resistance is felt. Tighten adjustment screw and install air cleaner.

Fig. 6: Adjusting 420 & 560 Series Control Pressure Cable

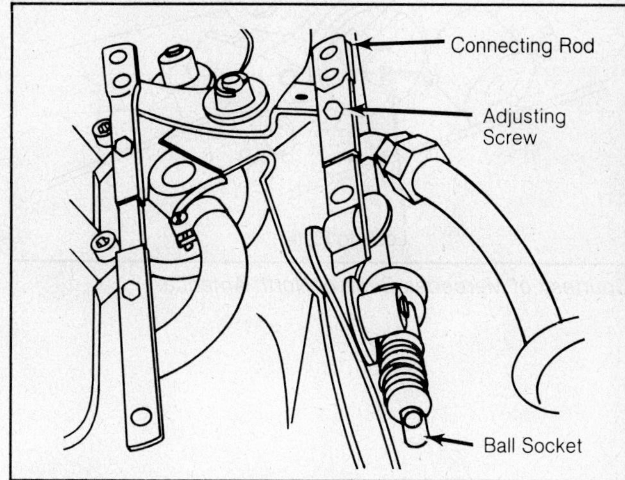

Courtesy of Mercedes-Benz of North America.

MODULATING PRESSURE

NOTE: Modulating pressure port is next to vacuum control unit at 4 o'clock position. Disconnect vacuum line and measure while driving at about 30 MPH.

1) Disconnect vacuum hose and remove rubber cap from vacuum control unit. Pull locking plate out of locking slots to permit rotation. *See Fig. 7.* Turning adjustment screw in vacuum control results in pressure change of about 6 psi (.414 Bar). Adjust to correct value. See MODULATING PRESSURE SPECIFICATIONS table.

MERCEDES-BENZ (Cont.)

3) After turning adjusting screw, push locking plate back into locking slots. Put rubber cap back on vacuum control unit. Connect vacuum hose and check modulating pressure again. Install screw on vacuum line holder (if equipped).

MODULATING PRESSURE SPECIFICATIONS

Model	Psi (Bar)
190D	41 (2.8)
190D Turbo	47 (3.25)
190E (2.3)	56 (3.9)
190E (2.6)	48 (3.3)
260E	48 (3.3)
300D & 300TD	46 (3.2)
300SDL	51 (3.5)
420SEL	52 (3.6)
560SL, 560SEC, 560SEL	58 (4.0)

Fig. 7: Adjusting Modulating Pressure

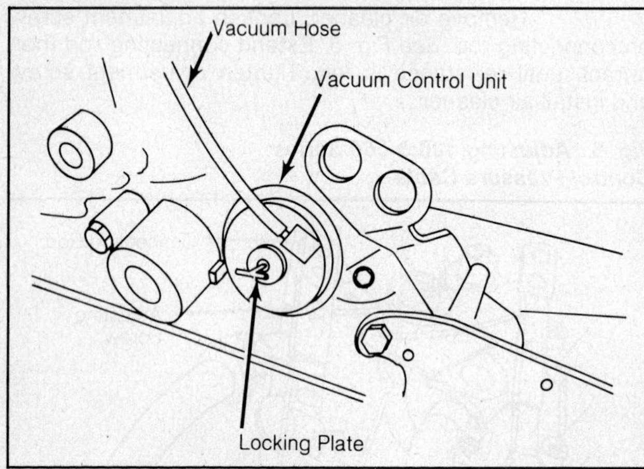

Courtesy of Mercedes-Benz of North America.

VACUUM CONTROL VALVE

190D

1) Remove air cleaner and air distributor housing. Loosen vacuum control valve Allen head screws. Turn vacuum control valve clockwise as far as possible and hold in this position. *See Fig. 8*.

2) Apply full throttle until throttle lever of injection pump rests against full throttle stop, this will turn vacuum control valve back (counterclockwise).

Fig. 8: Adjusting 190D Vacuum Control Valve

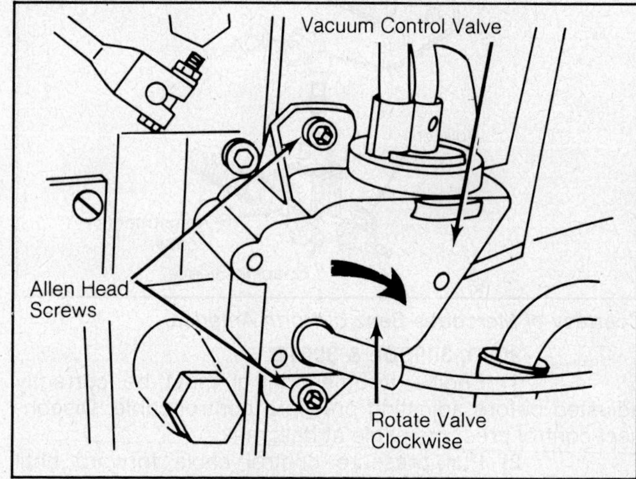

Courtesy of Mercedes-Benz of North America

NEUTRAL SAFETY SWITCH

1) Neutral safety switch is located behind transmission selector lever on transmission. Loosen neutral safety switch attaching screws. Ensure transmission selector lever is in Neutral position.

2) Insert a 5/32" (4 mm) drill through select lever adjustment hole and into neutral safety switch housing. Tighten screws and remove drill. Ensure vehicle starts in "P" and "N" positions only.

MITSUBISHI

IDENTIFICATION

TRANSMISSION CODES

Application	Codes
Cordia & Tredia	KM172
Galant	KM175
Mirage	
1.5L	KM171-1
1.6L	KM171-2
Montero & Pickup	
2WD	AW 372
4WD	KM148
Precis	KM171
Starion	JM600
Van	AW 372

LUBRICATION

SERVICE INTERVAL

Transmission

Change fluid and filter every 30,000 miles. Adjust bands (if equipped) when fluid is changed. Fluid level should be checked every 6 months.

Transfer Case

On 4WD models, change transfer case fluid every 30,000 miles.

CHECKING FLUID LEVEL

Transmission

1) Park vehicle on level area. Oil must be at normal operating temperature, parking brake engaged and engine at idle. Shift transmission selector through each position, stopping briefly in each position.

2) Place selector in "N" position and clean area around dipstick tube. Ensure fluid level is between lower and upper marks, but never over upper mark in "HOT" range. Add or drain fluid as necessary.

CAUTION: If severe darkening of the fluid and a strong odor is noted, fluid and filter should be changed and bands adjusted.

Transfer Case (Montero & Pickup)

Lubricant level should be to bottom of fill hole on side of transfer case.

FLUID CAPACITY

TRANSMISSION REFILL CAPACITIES

Application	Pts. (L)
Cordia/Tredia	12.3 (5.8)
Galant & Mirage	12.3 (5.8)
Montero	
Transmission	15.2 (7.2)
Tranfer Case	2.2 (4.7)
Pickup	
Transmission	
2WD	14.4 (6.8)
4WD	15.2 (7.2)
Transfer Case	4.7 (2.2)
Precis	12.3 (5.8)
Starion	14.8 (7.0)
Van	14.4 (6.8)

RECOMMENDED FLUID

Transmission

All transmissions use Dexron II automatic transmission fluid.

Transfer Cases

All transfer cases use API GL-4 or GL-5, SAE 75W-85.

DRAINING & REFILLING

CAUTION: If replacing transmission filter, note length and location of filter bolts.

Transmission (Montero, Pickup, Starion & Van)

1) Carefully remove drain plug on Montero, Pickup and Van models. On all models, remove oil pan and drain fluid. Install new filter on bottom of valve body.

2) Clean oil pan, replace gasket and install oil pan. Tighten bolts to 42 INCH lbs. (4.7 N.m). Pour about 5.3 qts. (5.0L) of Dexron II through filler tube or just enough fluid to bring level to lower limit of "COLD" mark on dipstick. Start engine and allow to idle for 2 minutes.

3) Shift transmission into each position, ending in "N" position. Check fluid level with engine running at idle and add sufficient fluid to bring level to lower mark. Recheck fluid level after transmission is at normal operating temperature.

Transaxle (Cordia, Galant, Mirage, Precis & Tredia)

1) Remove drain plug and drain fluid. *See Fig. 1.* Remove bolts and lower oil pan. If necessary, install new filter on bottom of valve body. Replace pan gasket and install pan. Tighten pan bolts to 90-102 INCH lbs. (10-11 N.m).

2) Tighten drain plug to 22-25 ft. lbs. (30-34 N.m). Ensure dipstick hole area is clean and pour in about 4.2 qts. (4.0L) of Dexron II.

3) Run engine for 2 minutes at idle. Shift transmission to each position, ending in "N" position. Add sufficient fluid to reach lower mark. After reaching normal operating temperature, fluid should be between upper and lower marks of "HOT" range.

Fig. 1: FWD Vehicle Drain Plug Location

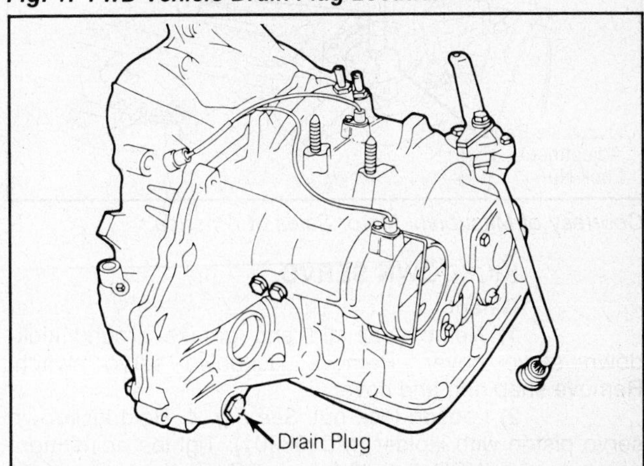

Courtesy of Mitsubishi Motor Sales of America.

Transfer Case

Drain plug is located on bottom of transfer case. Change drain plug gasket whenever fluid is

MITSUBISHI (Cont.)

changed. When refilling, fluid level should be up to bottom of fill hole in side of case.

ADJUSTMENTS

BRAKE BAND

Starion (2nd Brake Band)

Remove oil pan and drain fluid. Loosen lock nut. Tighten piston stem to 60-84 INCH lbs. (6.8-9.5 N.m). Back off adjustment screw 2 turns. Hold piston stem and tighten lock nut to 11-29 ft. lbs. (15-39 N.m). *See Fig. 2.*

Fig. 2: Adjusting 2nd Brake Band on Starion

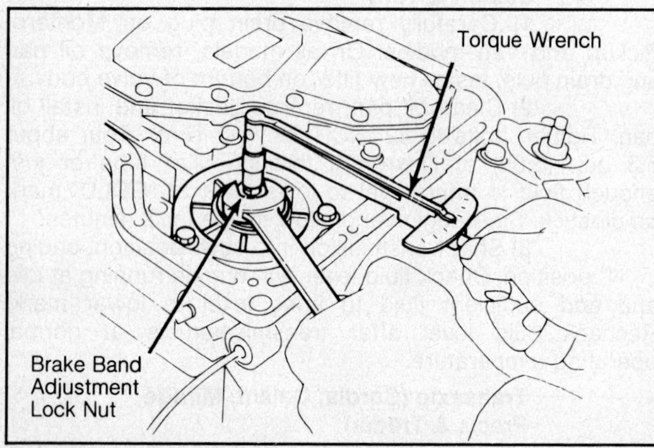

Courtesy of Mitsubishi Motor Sales of America.

Starion (Overdrive Band)

Overdrive band is located on bottom of case in front of oil pan. *See Fig. 3.* Loosen lock nut. Tighten piston stem to 60-84 INCH lbs. (6.8-9.5 N.m). Back off adjustment screw 2 turns. Hold piston stem and tighten lock nut to 11-29 ft. lbs. (15-39 N.m).

Fig. 3: Adjusting Overdrive Brake Band on Starion

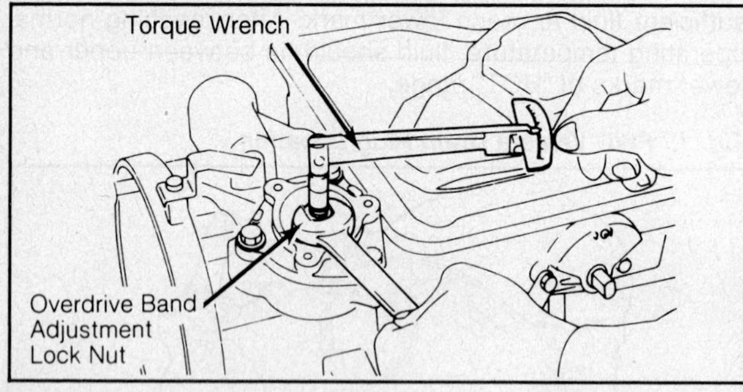

Courtesy of Mitsubishi Motor Sales of America.

KICKDOWN SERVO

Galant

1) Remove all dirt and grease around kickdown servo cover. Remove kickdown servo switch. Remove snap ring and cover.

2) Loosen lock nut. *See Fig. 4.* Hold kickdown servo piston with Holder (MD998901). Tighten adjustment screw to 86 INCH lbs. (9.8 N.m). Back out adjustment screw 2 full turns.

3) Again tighten adjustment screw to 43 INCH lbs. (4.9 N.m). Back out adjustment screw 2-2 1/4 turns. Hold kickdown servo and tighten lock nut to 18-23 ft. lbs. (25-32 N.m).

4) Install new "D" ring in groove around cover. Install cover and snap ring in case. Install kickdown switch and tighten screw to 8-12 INCH lbs. (1.0-1.4 N.m).

Fig. 4: Adjusting Kickdown Servo on Galant

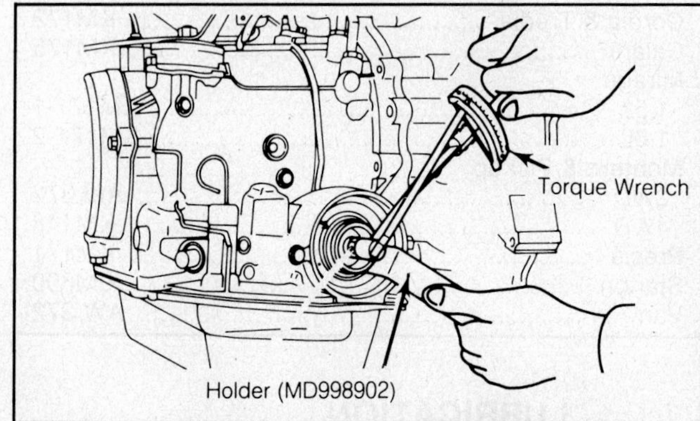

Courtesy of Mitsubishi Motor Sales of America.

TRANSMISSION THROTTLE CONTROL

Cordia, Mirage, Precis & Tredia

1) Ensure throttle lever is at curb idle position and engine is at normal operating temperature. Raise cover "B" to expose nipple. *See Fig. 5.* Loosen cable bracket mounting bolt.

2) Move lower cable bracket until distance between nipple and top cover "A" of throttle cable is adjusted to .02-.06" (.5-1.5 mm). Tighten lower cable bracket mounting bolt to 108-126 INCH lbs. (12-14 N.m).

3) With throttle lever in wide open position, pull cable upward to ensure freedom of cable movement.

Fig. 5: Adjusting Throttle Cable on Cordia, Mirage, Precis & Tredia

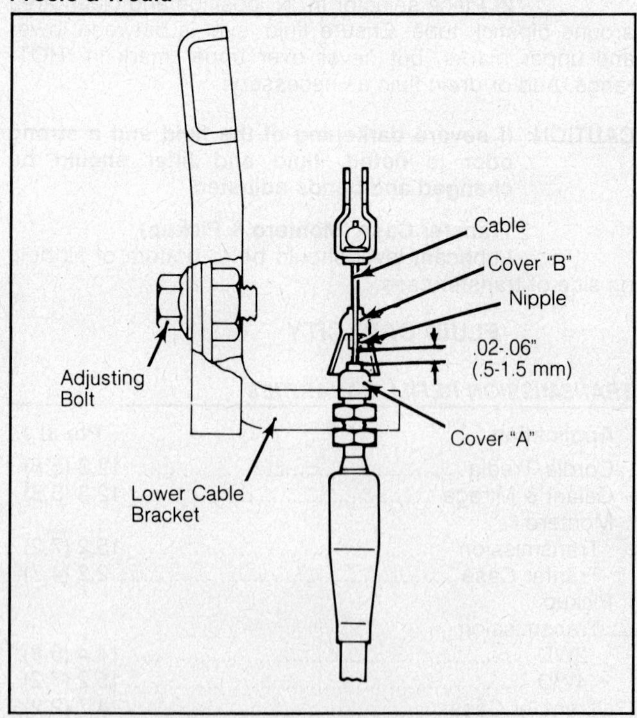

Courtesy of Mitsubishi Motor Sales of America.

MITSUBISHI (Cont.)

CAUTION: Whenever idle is adjusted on Montero and Pickup, always adjust throttle control cable.

Montero & Pickup

1) Ensure engine idle is adjusted correctly. Ensure carburetor throttle lever and throttle cable bracket are not bent.

2) Measure gap between inner cable stopper and cover end with carburetor throttle valve fully open. *See Fig. 6*.

3) If gap is not 2.05-2.09" (52-53 mm), adjust inner cable bracket. Tighten cable bracket bolts to 96-112 INCH lbs. (10-14 N.m).

Fig. 6: Adjusting Montero & Pickup Throttle Cable

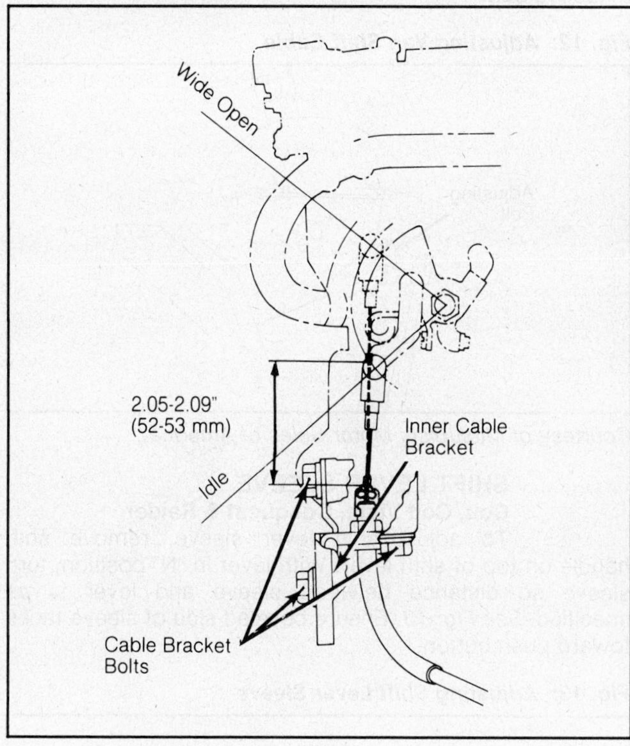

Courtesy of Mitsubishi Motor Sales of America.

Van

Ensure throttle lever and throttle cable bracket are not bent. Ensure distance between inner cable stopper end and dust cover is 0-.04" (0-1 mm). *See Fig. 7*.

Fig. 7: Adjusting Throttle Cable on Van

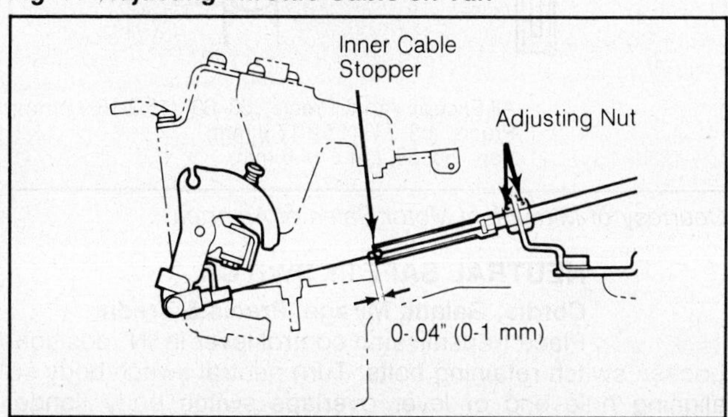

Courtesy of Mitsubishi Motor Sales of America.

VACUUM DIAPHRAGM ROD

Starion

1) Disconnect vacuum hose at vacuum diaphragm. Remove diaphragm from transmission case. Using depth gauge, measure depth "L". *See Fig. 8*.

2) Ensure vacuum throttle valve is pushed into valve body as far as possible. Select correct length rod to adjust. See VACUUM DIAPHRAGM ROD SELECTION table.

VACUUM DIAPHRAGM ROD SELECTION

Depth "L" In. (mm)	Rod Length In. (mm)	Part No.
Under 1.006 (25.55)	1.142 (29.0)	MD610614
1.010-1.026 (25.65-26.05)	1.16 (29.5)	MD610615
1.030-1.045 (26.15-26.55)	1.18 (3.0)	MD610616
1.050-1.065 (26.65-27.05)	1.20 (30.5)	MD610617
Over 1.069 (27.15)	1.22 (31.0)	MD610618

Fig. 8: Adjusting Vacuum Diaphragm Rod on Starion

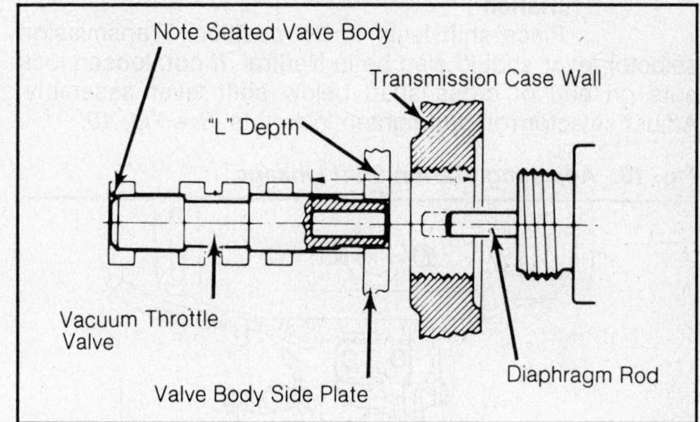

Courtesy of Mitsubishi Motors of America.

KICKDOWN SWITCH

Starion

1) Kickdown switch is located at upper post of accelerator pedal. When pedal is fully depressed, a click should be heard just before the pedal bottoms out.

2) If click is not heard, loosen lock nut and extend switch until pedal lever makes contact with switch and switch clicks. If switch makes contact too soon, transmission will downshift on part throttle.

3) If car upshifts at 30 and 60 MPH only, the switch may be shorted internally.

SHIFT LINKAGE

Cordia, Precis & Tredia

1) Shift cable is adjusted at transaxle end of cable. Place gearshift lever in "N". Ensure transaxle shift lever and neutral safety switch are in neutral position.

2) Turn adjuster at cable end so it fits into manual lever on transaxle. Turn adjusting nut so there is no slack in the cable. If cable was replaced, ensure toothed washer is positioned correctly. *See Fig. 9*.

MITSUBISHI (Cont.)

Fig. 9: Adjusting Shift Cable on Cordia, Precis & Tredia

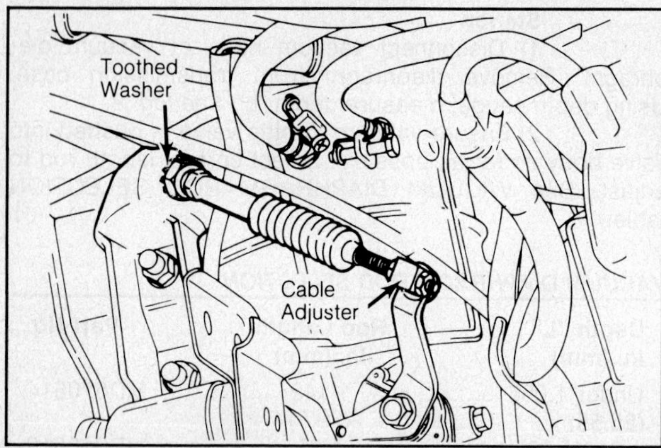

Courtesy of Mitsubishi Motor of America.

Galant & Mirage

1) Shift cable is adjusted at transaxle end of cable. Place shift lever in "N". Disconnect transaxle end of cable from transaxle. Ensure transaxle shift lever is in Neutral position.

2) Loosen adjuster lock nuts at transaxle end of cable. Ensure cable end fits into eye of transaxle shift lever. Tighten lock nuts.

Starion

Place shift lever in "N" position. Transmission selector lever should also be in Neutral. If not, loosen lock nuts on end of cross shaft below shift lever assembly. Adjust selector rod and tighten lock nuts. *See Fig. 10*.

Fig. 10: Adjusting Starion Shift Linkage

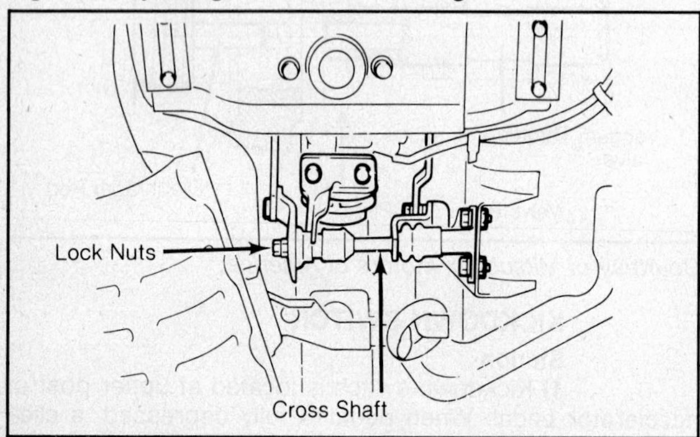

Courtesy of Mitsubishi Motor Sales of America.

Fig. 11: Adjusting Montero Shift Linkage

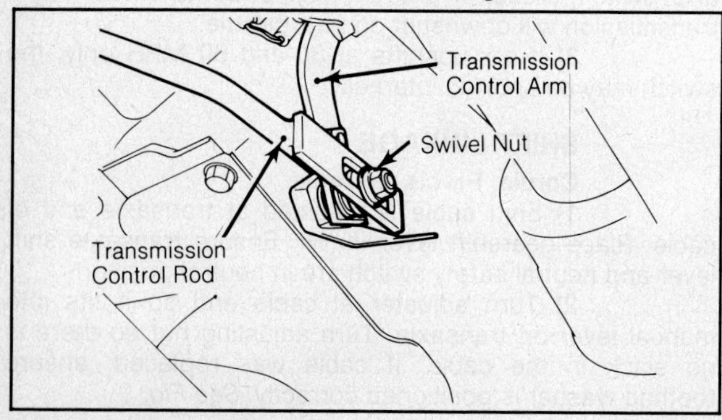

Courtesy of Mitsubishi Motor Sales of America.

Montero

Loosen swivel nut on transmission control rod. Ensure shift lever and transmission are in Neutral. Tighten swivel nut. *See Fig. 11*.

Pickup

Disconnect shift cable at transmission. Ensure shift lever and transmission are both in Neutral. Loosen lock nuts and adjust transmission end of shift cable to fit in transmission shift lever.

Van

1) Remove floor console. Place shift lever in "N". Loosen adjusting bolt. *See Fig. 12*.

2) Shift transmission into Neutral. Tighten adjusting bolt.

Fig. 12: Adjusting Van Shift Cable

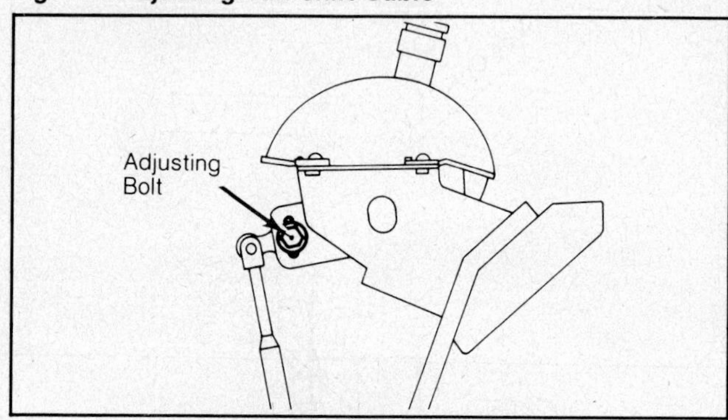

Courtesy of Mitsubishi Motor Sales of America.

SHIFT LEVER SLEEVE

Colt, Colt Vista, Conquest & Raider

To adjust shift lever sleeve, remove shift handle on top of shift lever. With lever in "N" position, turn sleeve so distance between sleeve and lever is as specified. *See Fig. 13*. Ensure beveled side of sleeve faces toward push button.

Fig. 13: Adjusting Shift Lever Sleeve

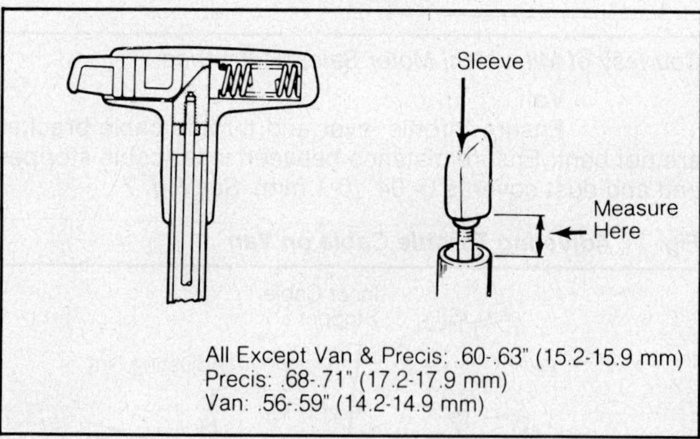

Courtesy of Mitsubishi Motor Sales of America.

NEUTRAL SAFETY SWITCH

Cordia, Galant, Mirage, Precis & Tredia

Place transmission control lever in "N" position. Loosen switch retaining bolts. Turn neutral switch body so aligning hole end of lever overlaps switch body flange. Tighten bolts to 90-102 INCH lbs. (10-12 N.m). *See Fig. 14*.

MITSUBISHI (Cont.)

Fig. 14: Adjusting Neutral Safety Switch on FWD Models

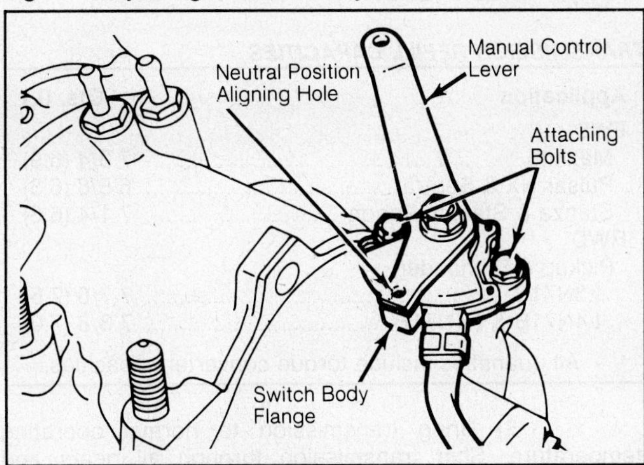

Courtesy of Mitsubishi Motor Sales of America.

Starion

1) Place transmission in Neutral. Remove screw on bottom of neutral safety switch at transmission. Loosen attaching bolts. *See Fig. 15.*

2) Using an .08" (2.0 mm) alignment pin, move switch until pin falls into hole in rotor. Tighten attaching bolts to 43-61 INCH lbs. (5-7 N.m).

Fig. 15: Adjusting Starion Neutral Safety Switch

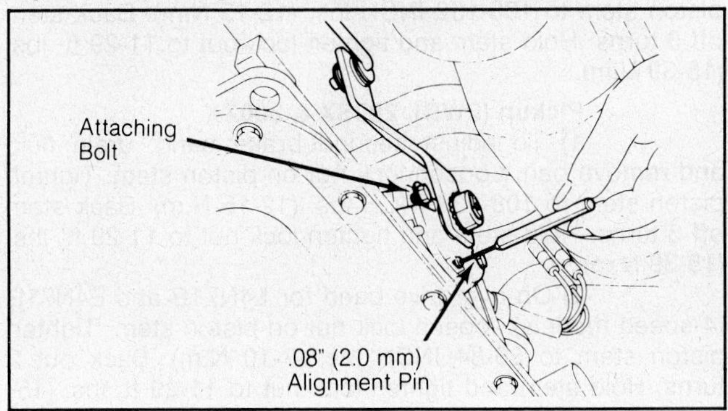

Courtesy of Mitsubishi Motor Sales of America.

Montero

1) Neutral safety switch is located under shift lever console. Set shift lever so pin at end of rod is positioned correctly. *See Fig. 16.*

2) Using an ohmmeter, check continuity between the 2 Black/Yellow wires when neutral safety switch is moved back and forth. Mark bracket.

3) Tighten neutral safety switch mounting screws so clearance between switch and selector lever is .1" (2.5 mm).

Pickup

On Pickup models, neutral safety switch is part of ignition switch assembly.

Van

Place shift lever in "N" range. Loosen switch attaching bolt. Move switch so lever and positioning boss line up. *See Fig. 17.* Tighten bolt to 36-60 INCH lbs. (4-7 N.m). Ensure vehicle only starts in "N" or "P".

Fig. 17: Adjusting Van Neutral Safety Switch

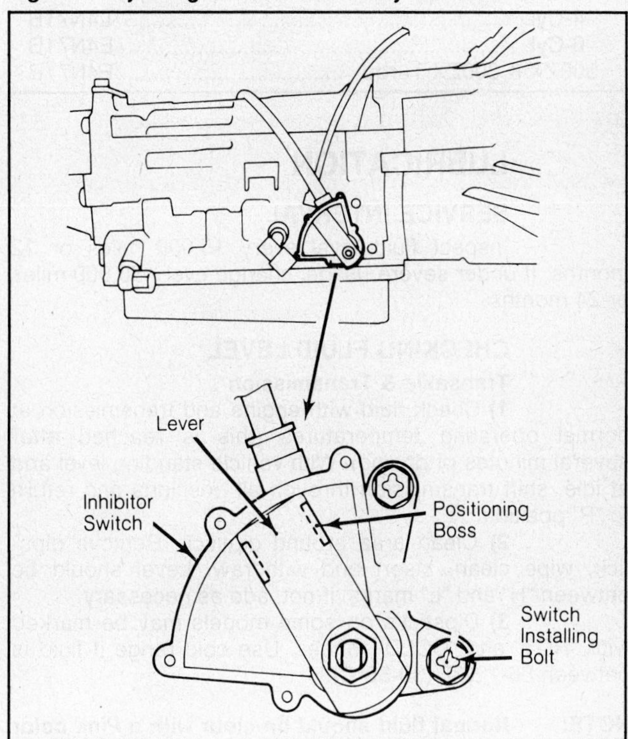

Courtesy of Mitsubishi Motor Sales of America.

Fig. 16: Adjusting Montero Neutral Safety Switch

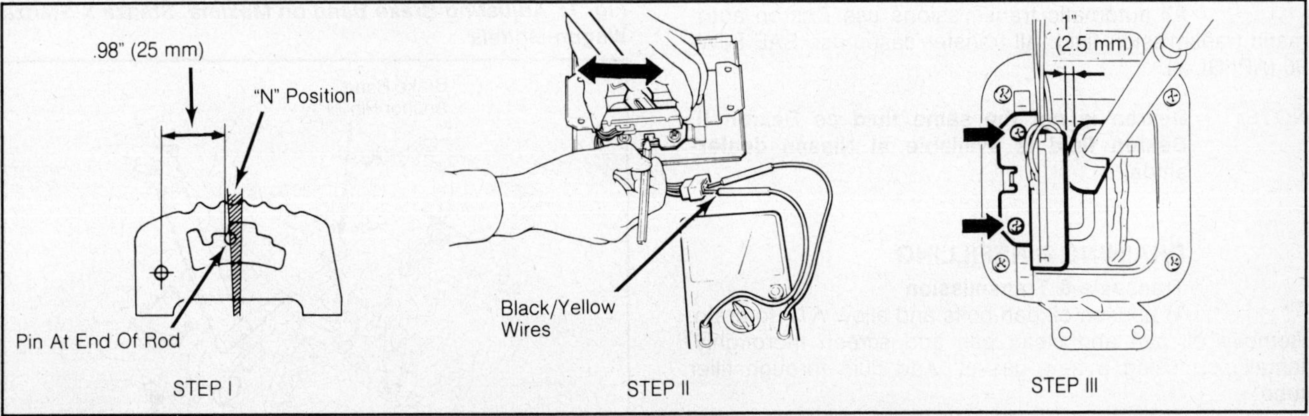

Courtesy of Mitsubishi Motor Sales of America.

NISSAN

IDENTIFICATION

TRANSMISSION CODES

Application	Code
FWD	
Maxima & Stanza Wagon	RL4F02A
Pulsar NX & Sentra	RL3F01A
Stanza	RL4F02A
RWD	
Pickup & Pathfinder	
4WD, 6-Cyl.	L3N71B
2WD, 6-Cyl.	E4N71B
2WD, 4-Cyl.	L4N71B
Van	L4N71B
200SX SE & XE	
4-Cyl.	L4N71B
6-Cyl.	E4N71B
300ZX & 300ZX Turbo	E4N71B

LUBRICATION

SERVICE INTERVAL

Inspect fluid level every 15,000 miles or 12 months. If under severe usage, change every 30,000 miles or 24 months.

CHECKING FLUID LEVEL

Transaxle & Transmission

1) Check fluid with engine and transmission at normal operating temperatures (this is reached after several minutes of driving). With vehicle standing level and at idle, shift transmission through all positions and return to "P" position.

2) Clean area around dipstick. Remove dipstick, wipe clean, insert and withdraw. Level should be between "H" and "L" marks, if not, add as necessary.

3) Dipsticks on some models may be marked with "HOT" and "COLD" ranges. Use cold range if fluid is between 86-120°F (30-50°C).

NOTE: **Normal fluid should be clear with a Pink color and should not have a strong burnt odor.**

Transfer Case

Oil level should be at bottom of fill hole.

RECOMMENDED FLUID

All automatic transmissions use Dexron automatic transmission fluid. All transfer cases use SAE 80W-90 (API GL-4).

NOTE: **Dexron is not the same fluid as Dexron II. Dexron fluid is available at Nissan dealerships.**

DRAINING & REFILLING

Transaxle & Transmission

1) Loosen oil pan bolts and allow ATF to drain. Remove oil pan and clean pan and screen thoroughly. Install pan using a new gasket. Add fluid through filler tube.

FLUID CAPACITY

TRANSMISSION REFILL CAPACITIES

Application	[1] Qts. (L)
FWD	
Maxima	7 3/4 (6.9)
Pulsar NX & Sentra	6 5/8 (6.3)
Stanza & Stanza Wagon	7 1/4 (6.8)
RWD	
Pickup & Pathfinder	
L3N71B	7 7/8 (7.5)
L4N71B & E4N71B	7 3/8 (7.0)

1 – All quantities include torque converter capacities.

2) Bring transmission to normal operating temperature. Shift transmission through all gears and return to "P" (Park). Check fluid level and add to obtain appropriate level.

ADJUSTMENTS

BRAKE BAND

Pickup & Pathfinder (4WD W/L3N71B)

To adjust second brake band, drain fluid and remove pan. Loosen lock nut on piston stem. Tighten piston stem to 108-132 INCH lbs. (12-15 N.m). Back stem off 3 turns. Hold stem and tighten lock nut to 11-29 ft. lbs. (15-39 N.m).

Pickup (2WD), 200SX & 300ZX

1) To adjust second brake band, drain fluid and remove pan. Loosen lock nut on piston stem. Tighten piston stem to 108-132 INCH lbs. (12-15 N.m). Back stem off 3 turns. Hold stem and tighten lock nut to 11-29 ft. lbs. (15-39 N.m).

2) On overdrive band for L4N71B and E4N71B (4-speed models), loosen lock nut on piston stem. Tighten piston stem to 60-84 INCH lbs. (7-10 N.m). Back out 2 turns. Hold stem and tighten lock nut to 11-29 ft. lbs. (15-39 N.m).

Pulsar NX & Sentra

Remove transmission oil pan. Loosen brake band adjuster lock nut. Tighten anchor pin to 36-48 INCH lbs. (4-6 N.m). Back off anchor pin 2 1/2 turns. Tighten lock nut (while holding anchor pin), to 12-16 ft. lbs. (16-22 N.m).

Fig. 1: Adjusting Brake Band on Maxima, Stanza & Stanza Wagon Models

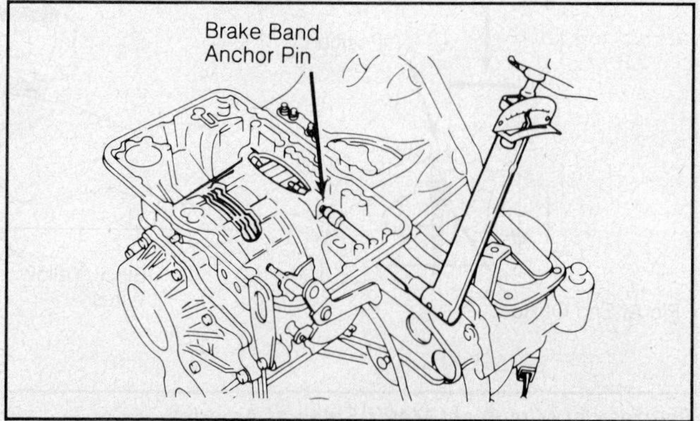

Courtesy of Nissan Motor Co., U.S.A.

NISSAN (Cont.)

Maxima, Stanza & Stanza Wagon

Remove transmission oil pan. Loosen anchor pin lock nut. Tighten anchor pin to 36-48 INCH lbs. (4-6 N.m). *See Fig. 1*. Back off anchor pin 5 1/4 turns. Tighten lock nut, while holding anchor pin, to 23-31 ft. lbs. (31-42 N.m).

SHIFT LINKAGE

Pickup (2WD With Floor Shift), 200SX & 300ZX

1) Starting in "P" position, shift through all positions to "1" position. If detents cannot be felt or pointer is improperly aligned, linkage must be adjusted.

2) Place shift lever in "P" position. Loosen lock nuts on rod. *See Fig. 2*. Tighten lock nut "X" until it touches trunnion, pulling selector lever toward "R" range side without pushing button.

3) Back off lock nut "X" one turn on Pickup models and 1/4-1/2 turn on others. Tighten lock nut "Y" to 72-96 INCH lbs. (8-11 N.m). Recheck positions, ensuring selector lever moves smoothly.

Fig. 2: Adjusting Shift Linkage on Pickup (2WD With Floor Shift), 200SX & 300ZX

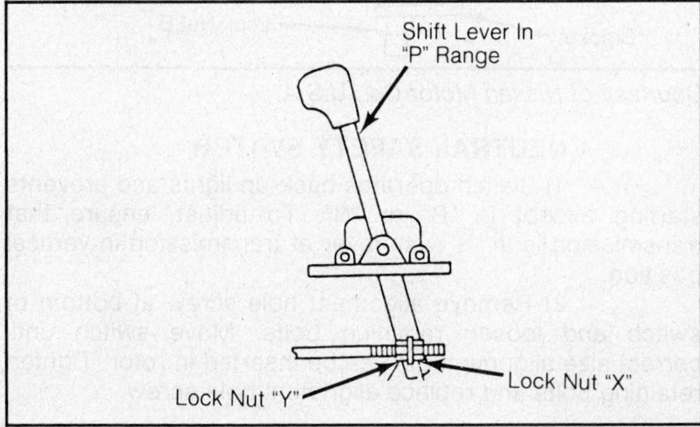

Courtesy of Nissan Motor Co., U.S.A.

Maxima, Pulsar NX, Sentra, Stanza

1) Move control lever from "P" to "1". Ensure control lever can move smoothly and without any sliding noise. If not, readjust cable.

2) Place selector lever at "P" range. Loosen lock nuts holding shift cable to shift rod. *See Fig. 3*. Ensure selector lever is in "P" range and transaxle is fully engaged in Park.

3) Turn lock nut "X" until it touches select rod end while holding select rod horizontal. Tighten lock nut "Y". Move control lever from "P" to "1" again.

4) Make sure that control lever can move smoothly and without sliding noise. Apply grease to contacting areas of selector lever and select rod.

Pickup (All With Column Shift)

1) Place selector lever in "P" range. Loosen lock nuts. *See Fig. 4*. Ensure transaxle is in Park. Tighten lock nut "A" until it touches trunnion, pulling selector lever toward "R" range side without pushing button.

2) Back off lock nut "A" 2 turns. Tighten lock nut "B" to 72-96 INCH lbs. (8-11 N.m). Ensure selector lever moves smoothly.

Fig. 3: Adjusting Shift Linkage on Maxima, Pulsar NX, Sentra & Stanza

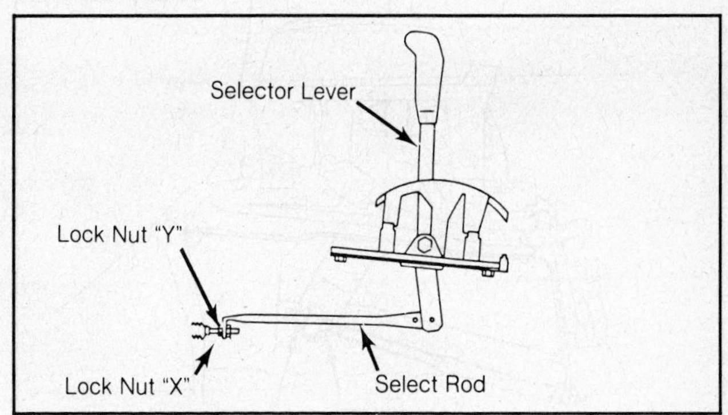

Courtesy of Nissan Motor Co., U.S.A.

Fig. 4: Adjusting Shift Linkage on Pickup With Column Shift

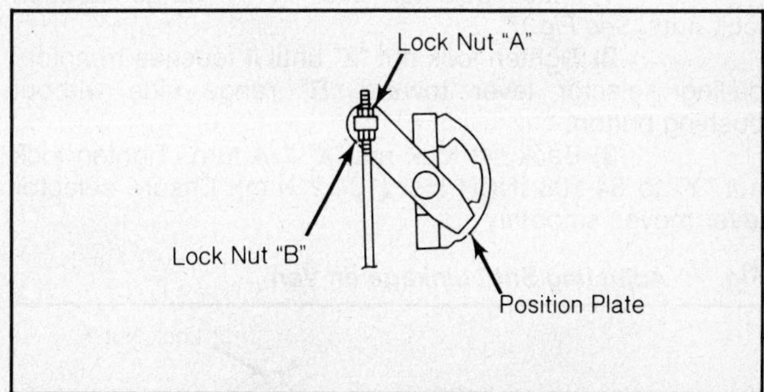

Courtesy of Nissan Motor Co., U.S.A.

Pickup (4WD With Floor Shift)

1) Place selector lever in "P" range. Loosen lock nuts. Ensure transmission is engaged in Park.

2) Tighten turn buckle until selector lever moves toward "R" range without pushing button. Back off turn buckle one turn. Tighten lock nuts to 36-48 INCH lbs. (4-6 N.m). Ensure selector moves smoothly.

Fig. 5: Adjusting Shift Linkage on 4WD Pickup Models With Floor Shift

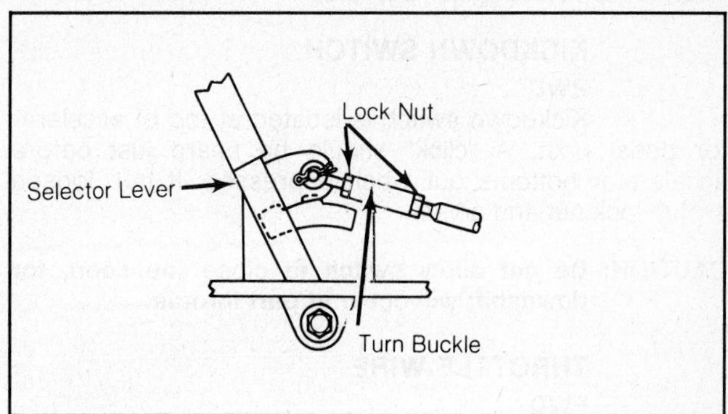

Courtesy of Nissan Motor Co., U.S.A.

Stanza Wagon

1) Remove control cable adjusting nut "A" and loosen "B". *See Fig. 6*. Place selector lever in "P". Ensure transaxle is in Park.

2) Make sure vehicle does not move. Install adjusting nut "A". Tighten nut "A" and "B" by hand. Tighten adjusting nuts to 72-96 INCH lbs. (8-11 N.m). Ensure selector lever moves smoothly.

NISSAN (Cont.)

Fig. 6: Adjusting Shift Linkage on Stanza Wagon

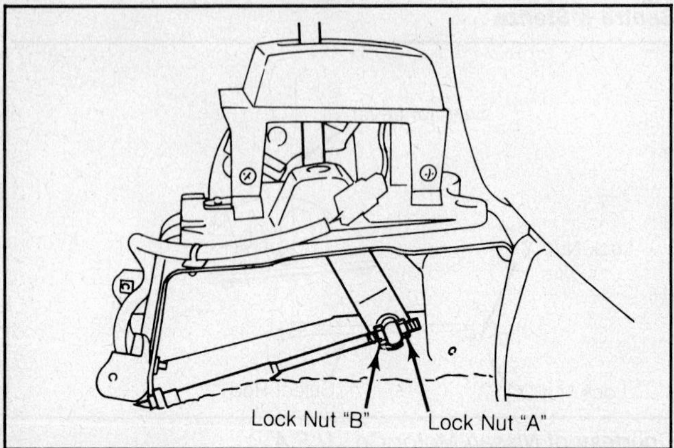

Courtesy of Nissan Motor Co., U.S.A.

Van

1) Place selector lever in "P" range. Loosen lock nuts. *See Fig. 7.*

2) Tighten lock nut "X" until it touches trunnion, pulling selector lever toward "R" range side without pushing button.

3) Back off lock nut "X" 1/4 turn. Tighten lock nut "Y" to 84-108 INCH lbs. (10-12 N.m). Ensure selector lever moves smoothly.

Fig. 7: Adjusting Shift Linkage on Van

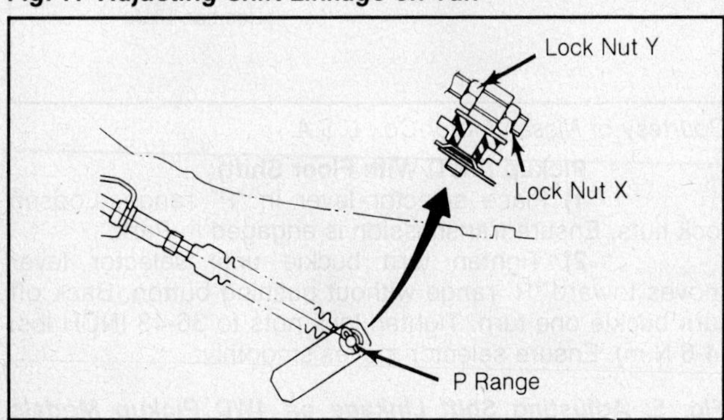

Courtesy of Nissan Motor Co., U.S.A.

KICKDOWN SWITCH

RWD

Kickdown switch is located at top of accelerator pedal post. A "click" should be heard just before accelerator bottoms out when depressed. If not, loosen switch lock nut and adjust.

CAUTION: Do not allow switch to close too soon, for downshift will occur at part throttle.

THROTTLE WIRE

FWD

1) Loosen double lock nuts on throttle plate side of cable. Move throttle plate to wide open throttle position and hold during adjustment procedure. Move cable sheath toward lock nut bracket to remove all play.

2) Turn lock nut "B" so it just contacts bracket. Turn lock nut "B" specified number of turns AWAY from bracket. *See Fig. 8.*

- Pulsar NX and Sentra - 1-1 1/2 turns.
- Maxima - 3/4-1 1/4 turns.
- Stanza & Stanza Wagon - 2 3/4-3 1/4 turns.

3) Tighten lock nut "A". Ensure throttle wire stroke "L" is within specified range between full throttle and idle. See THROTTLE WIRE STROKE SPECIFICATIONS table. Road test vehicle and note kickdown point.

THROTTLE WIRE STROKE SPECIFICATIONS

Model	Stroke In. (mm)
Pulsar NX & Sentra	1.08-1.24 (27.4-31.4)
Maxima, Stanza & Stanza Wagon	1.54-1.69 (39-43)

Fig. 8: Adjusting Throttle Wire On FWD Vehicles

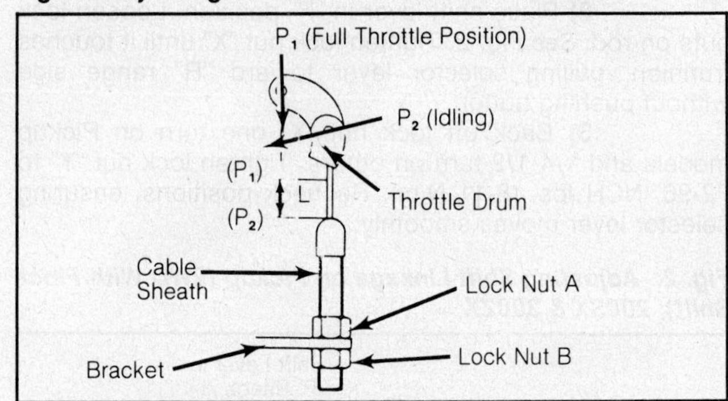

Courtesy of Nissan Motor Co., U.S.A.

NEUTRAL SAFETY SWITCH

1) Switch operates back-up lights and prevents starting except in "P" or "N". To adjust, ensure that transmission is in "N" with lever at transmission in vertical position.

2) Remove alignment hole screw at bottom of switch and loosen retaining bolts. Move switch until correct size alignment pin can be inserted in rotor. Tighten retaining bolts and replace alignment hole screw.

NEUTRAL SAFETY SWITCH ALIGNMENT PINS

Model	Pin Diameter In. (mm)
RWD	.08 (2.0)
FWD	
Pulsar NX & Sentra	.098 (2.5)
Maxima, Stanza, Stanza Wagon	.16 (4.0)

Fig. 9: Adjusting Typical RWD Neutral Safety Switch

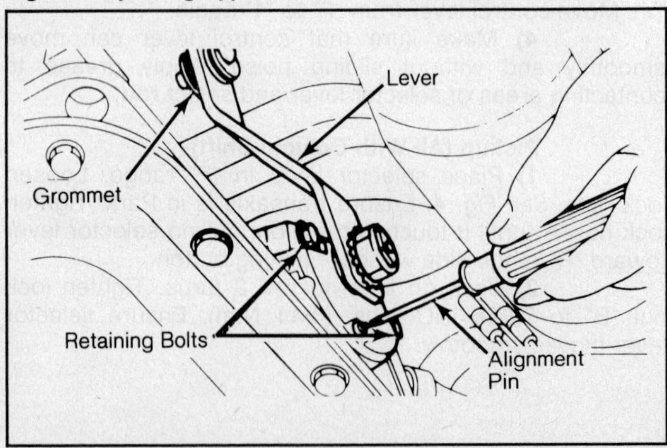

Courtesy of Nissan Motor Co., U.S.A.

Automatic Transmission Servicing

PEUGEOT

IDENTIFICATION

TRANSMISSION CODES

Application	Codes
505 Series	ZF 4HP 22

LUBRICATION

SERVICE INTERVALS

Check transmission level at every oil change. Drain and refill transmission every 30,000 miles or 2 years, whichever comes first. In severe driving conditions change fluid at 15,000 miles.

CHECKING FLUID LEVEL

1) Position vehicle on level floor and have engine at operating temperature. Apply parking brake, move selector lever through all positions ending in "P".

2) Remove dipstick and wipe with a clean lint free cloth. Reinstall dipstick and check fluid level. Top dimple mark is maximum hot level. Middle mark is minimum hot level. Bottom mark is minimum cold level.

RECOMMENDED FLUID

Use Dexron II D ATF.

FLUID CAPACITY

TRANSMISSION REFILL CAPACITIES

Application	Refill Qts. (L)	Dry Fill Qts. (L)
505 Liberte	1.7 (1.6)	5.4 (5.2)
505 Turbo Diesel	2.8 (2.6)	8.0 (7.6)
All Others	2.8 (2.6)	7.9 (7.5)

DRAINING & REFILLING

1) Have engine at normal operating temperature. Remove drain plug from transmission oil pan, allow all fluid to drain and install drain plug. Pour approximate amount of fluid as listed in TRANSMISSION REFILL CAPACITIES table.

2) Start and run engine at normal idle. Shift selector lever through all positions, check fluid level, add fluid as needed. DO NOT overfill.

ADJUSTMENTS

KICKDOWN CABLE

505 (Gasoline Engine)

With throttle control drum in normal hot idle position, adjust cable housing to give maximum clearance of .020" (.5 mm) between end of cable housing and clip on cable.

SHIFT LINKAGE

1) Place gearshift lever in Park. Raise and support vehicle. Loosen shift rod lock nut at transmission lever. Ensure transmission lever is in Park position.

2) Remove rod retaining clip and rod bushing from transmission lever. Adjust rod length so rod bushing aligns with centerline of lever stud.

3) Reassembly parts and tighten lock nut. Rod socket should be square with ball stud axis at bottom of gearshift lever.

4) Check that transmission shifts properly. Ensure vehicle only starts in "N" or "P".

NEUTRAL SAFETY SWITCH

Engine should start in "N" or "P" positions only. To adjust, install or remove shims at base of switch until proper operation is achieved. Switch is screwed into side of transmission case.

PORSCHE

IDENTIFICATION

TRANSMISSION CODES

Application	Code
924-S, 944	
944-S & 944 Turbo	087

LUBRICATION

SERVICE INTERVALS

Check fluid level every 15,000 miles. Change transaxle fluid and filter every 30,000 miles. Change final drive fluid every 60,000 miles.

CHECKING FLUID LEVEL

Transaxle

Check fluid level through transparent reservoir, located at rear end of transaxle housing. Fluid must be at operating temperature. Place vehicle on a level surface, with engine idling and selector lever in neutral. Fluid level should be between "MIN" and "MAX" marks. Do not overfill.

Final Drive

Place vehicle on level surface. Fluid level must be up to edge of fill hole on side of case. If level is too high, this may indicate fluid transfer between transaxle and final drive caused by leaking seals.

RECOMMENDED FLUID

Transaxle

All 1987 and later transaxles use only Dexron II D fluid, NOT Dexron B ATF. Approved ATF products have a 5-digit qualification number (example: D21271).

New fluid is Brown and will turn Black after short use in transaxle. Fluid also has strong odor different than that of Dexron II B. Color and odor are considered normal.

Final Drive

Use API GL-5, SAE 90.

FLUID CAPACITY

TRANSMISSION REFILL CAPACITIES

Application	Refill Qts. (L)	Dry Fill Qts. (L)
924-S & 944	2.6 (2.5)	6.3 (6.0)

FINAL DRIVE REFILL CAPACITIES

	Pts. (L)
924-S, 944	2.1 (1.0)

DRAINING & REFILLING

Transaxle

1) Unscrew oil fill tube at oil pan. Drain transaxle. Remove oil pan and filter screen.

2) Install new filter screen. Tighten retaining bolt to 31 INCH lbs. (3.5 N.m). Install oil pan and a new gasket. Tighten bolts to 15 ft. lbs. (20.5 N.m). Tighten filler tube to 59 ft. lbs. (80 N.m).

3) Add about 2.6 qts. (2.5L) of fluid. Start engine and bring to normal operating temperature. Move selector lever through all gear positions. Place selector lever in "N" and run engine at idle.

4) Check fluid level in reservoir. Add more fluid, if necessary.

Final Drive

Final drive is equipped with separate drain and fill plugs.

ADJUSTMENTS

SELECTOR LEVER

924-S & 944

1) Place selector lever in "P". From under vehicle, disconnect selector lever cable ball socket from transaxle operating lever. Place transaxle operating lever in Park position (against stop).

2) Adjust cable ball socket so it fits easily on transaxle selector lever. Use lock pin to retain ball socket on lever. Move selector through all positions with engine running to ensure correct engagement.

THROTTLE CABLE

924-S & 944

1) Adjust throttle cable sleeve on transaxle bracket so distance between end of sleeve and bracket is 1.14" (29 mm). *See Fig. 1*. Tighten lock nut to 15 ft. lbs. (20 N.m). Ensure accelerator is in idle position.

Fig. 1: Adjusting Transaxle Throttle Cable

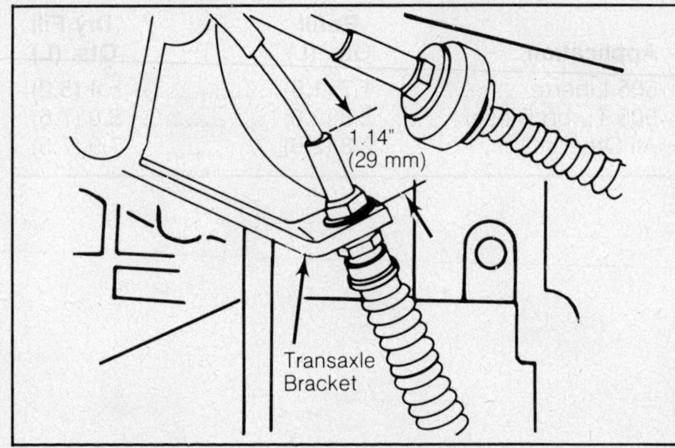

Courtesy of Porsche of North America.

2) Adjust short accelerator cable sleeve length at firewall to .31" (8 mm). *See Fig. 2*. Adjust short accelerator cable length at throttle valve cam so nipple of cable can be placed in opening of cam plate without tension.

3) Working at throttle valve end of cable, adjust long transaxle throttle control cable so it fits in cam plate without tension.

4) Cable is adjusted correctly if accerator will be in neutral position, throttle closed and transaxle operating lever is against lower stop.

5) To check full-throttle position. Press down on accelerator pedal to point where resistance is noticeable. Ensure throttle is wide open. In this position, tang in throttle cam plate slot should not be lifted off its seat and transaxle operating lever should be .45" (11.5 mm) away from final stop.

PORSCHE (Cont.)

Fig. 2: Adjusting Accelerator Cable

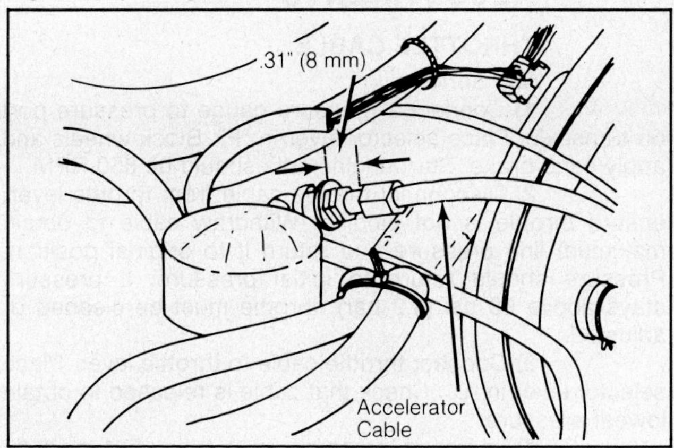

Courtesy of Porsche of North America.

Fig. 3: Checking Accelerator Cable Kickdown Position

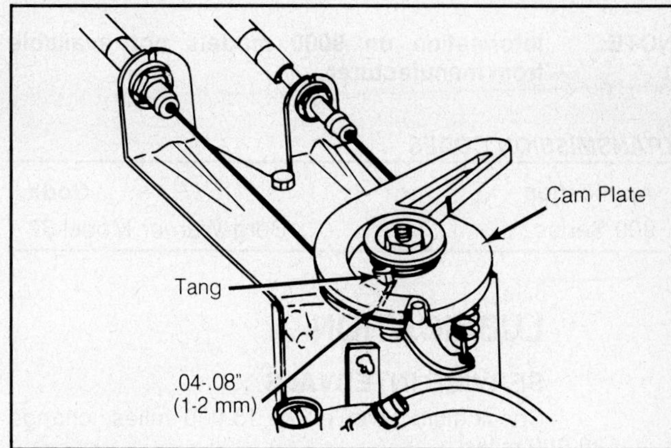

Courtesy of Porsche of North America.

6) To check kickdown position, depress accelerator pedal past full-throttle pressure point to kickdown position. Tang in cam plate will be .04-.08" (1-2 mm) away from stop. *See Fig. 3.* In kickdown position, transaxle operating lever must be 0-.04" (0-1 mm) from stop.

SECOND BRAKE BAND

Loosen lock nut on side of case. Tighten adjusting screw to 84 INCH lbs. (10 N.m). Back off adjusting screw and tighten to 48 INCH lbs. (5 N.m). Loosen adjusting screw 2 turns. Hold adjusting screw and tighten lock nut.

NEUTRAL SAFETY SWITCH

924-S & 944

Starter should operate only in "P" or "N" positions. If starter operates in any other position, remove selector lever gate and loosen retaining bolts on safety switch. Adjust switch as necessary.

SAAB

IDENTIFICATION

NOTE: Information on 9000 models not available from manufacturer.

TRANSMISSION CODES

Application	Code
900 Series	Borg-Warner Model 37

LUBRICATION

SERVICE INTERVALS

Check fluid level every 15,000 miles, change every 30,000 miles.

CHECKING FLUID LEVEL

Transaxle

1) Park vehicle on level surface and apply hand brake. Allow engine to idle. Place selector lever in all gear positions. Return to "P".

2) Remove dipstick, wipe and check fluid level. Fluid level should be between maximum and minimum marks. Use hot or cold markings on dipstick, depending on transaxle oil temperature. Do not overfill.

Final Drive

Fill plug hole is located on side of case. Fluid level should be to bottom of fill plug hole.

RECOMMENDED FLUID

Transaxle

Type F automatic transmission fluid.

Final Drive

API GL-4 or 5, SAE 80.

FLUID CAPACITY

TRANSMISSION REFILL CAPACITIES

Application	Qts. (L)
900 Series	
Transaxle	8.4 (8.0)
Final Drive	1.5 (1.4)

DRAINING & REFILLING

Transaxle

1) Remove transaxle drain plug. Remove oil pan if replacing filter and adjusting front band. Replace oil pan with new gasket. Tighten oil pan bolts to 6-9 INCH lbs. (8-12 N.m).

2) Install drain plug and tighten to 4-6 INCH lbs. (5-8 N.m). Add fluid and check fluid level. Do not overfill.

Final Drive

Final drive has separate drain and fill plugs.

ADJUSTMENTS

THROTTLE CABLE

900 Series

1) Connect a pressure gauge to pressure port on transaxle. Place selector lever in "P". Block wheels and apply hand brake. Start engine. Idle should be 850 RPM.

2) Disconnect throttle cable from throttle lever, ensure throttle is not binding. Withdraw cable to obtain maximum line pressure and return it to original position. Pressure should return to initial pressure. If pressure stays above 69 psi (4.9 bar), throttle must be cleaned or adjusted.

3) Connect throttle cable to throttle lever. Place selector lever in "D". Check that cable is released to obtain lowest pressure.

4) Increase pressure to 1.4 psi (0.1 bar) by adjusting throttle cable. Cable is adjusted at bracket in engine compartment. Place selector lever in "P". Pressure should be between 59-69 psi (4.1-4.9 bar).

SELECTOR LEVER

900 Series

1) Place selector lever in "N". Depress pawl button and move selector lever slightly back and forth, increased resistance should be felt in both directions. Hold lever midway between positions in which resistance is felt.

2) Disconnect gear selector cable from lever using an Allen wrench. Release pawl button and move lever to "N". Tighten gear selector cable set screw.

Fig. 1: Adjusting Selector Lever

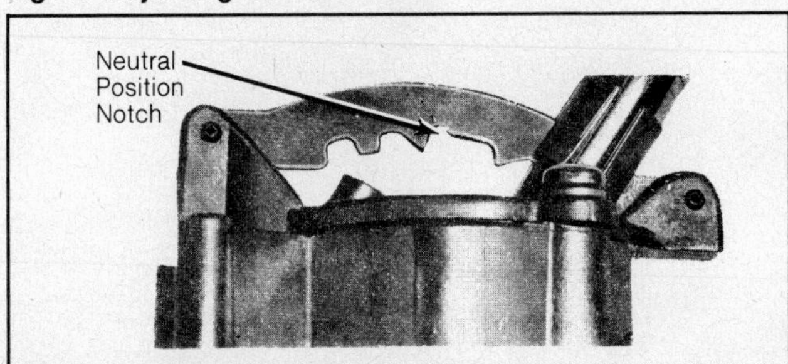

Courtesy of Saab-Scania of America.

FRONT BAND

900 Series (Up To & Including Transaxles Nos. 001-1700 & 002-2800)

1) Drain transaxle fluid and remove oil pan. Loosen lock nut.

2) Place Adjuster (87 90 073) between adjusting screw and piston rod. *See Fig. 2.* Adjuster is 1.4" (6.35 mm) thick.

3) Tighten adjusting screw to 10 INCH lbs. (1.3 N.m). Back off screw one full turn. Tighten lock nut to 15-20 ft. lbs. (20-27 N.m).

SAAB (Cont.)

NOTE: Front band on transaxles with number series 001-1700 and 002-2800 and a Borg-Warner number stamped on sheet metal plate are adjusted in same manner as later transaxles. Use following procedure.

900 Series (From Transaxles Nos. 001-1700, 002-2800, 003, 004, 005, 006 & 012)

1) Drain transaxle fluid and remove oil pan. Loosen lock nut.

2) Place Adjuster (87 91 030) between adjusting screw and piston rod. *See Fig. 2*. Adjuster is .35" (8.9 mm) thick.

3) Use Adjuster (87 91 329) for transaxle numbers 008, 009, 010 and 011. Adjuster is .31" (7.87 mm) thick.

4) On all transaxles, tighten adjusting screw to 10 INCH lbs. (1.3 N.m). Hold screw in position and tighten lock nut to 15-20 ft. lbs. (20-27 N.m). DO NOT back off adjusting screw.

REAR BAND

900 Series

Loosen lock nut (located on left side of case) a few turns and tighten adjustment screw to 114-124 INCH lbs. (13-14 N.m). Back screw off 1 1/4 turn. While holding screw in position, tighten lock nut to 29-40 ft. lbs. (40-55 N.m).

NEUTRAL SAFETY SWITCH

Place selector lever in "N". Loosen securing screws. Rotate switch housing to line up lever with mark on switch housing. Tighten securing screws.

Fig. 2: Adjusting Front Band

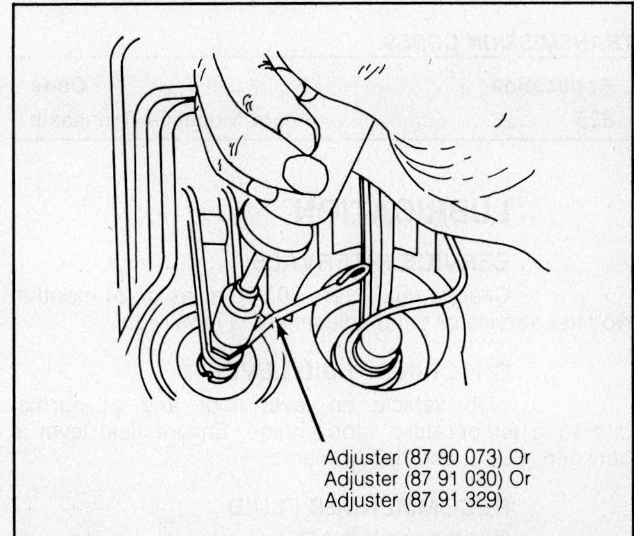

STERLING

IDENTIFICATION

TRANSMISSION CODES

Application	Code
825	Acura Model G4 Transaxle

LUBRICATION

SERVICE INTERVALS

Change fluid every 30,000 miles or 24 months. No filter service or band adjustment is required.

CHECKING FLUID LEVEL

With vehicle on level floor and at normal operating temperature, stop engine. Ensure fluid level is between "FULL" and "LOW" marks.

RECOMMENDED FLUID

Use Dexron II D ATF.

FLUID CAPACITY

TRANSMISSION REFILL CAPACITIES

Application	Refill Pts. (L)	Dry Fill Pts. (L)
825	6.7 (3.2)	13.7 (6.5)

DRAINING & REFILLING

1) Ensure transaxle is at normal operating temperature. Remove transmission drain plug. Use new gasket and replace drain plug when fluid is drained.

2) Fill with about 2 qts. (1.9L) of fluid through dipstick hole and check level. Add fluid to bring to upper mark on dipstick.

ADJUSTMENTS

SHIFT CONTROL CABLE

1) Remove center console. Place gearshift lever in "2" position (Drive low). Loosen cable nut until metal sleeve can slide through grommet. *See Fig. 1.*

2) Move metal sleeve forward to limit of travel. Tighten cable nut to 13 ft. lbs. (18 N.m). Move gearshift lever to "N".

3) Loosen cable nut again to allow shift valve to center in its detent. Tighten cable nut. Ensure transaxle shift properly through all gear positions.

NEUTRAL SAFETY SWITCH

Neutral safety switch is located at bottom of shift lever under console. Ensure vehicle starts only in Park or Neutral position. If not, loosen switch mounting screw and readjust.

Fig. 1: Adjusting Shift Control Cable

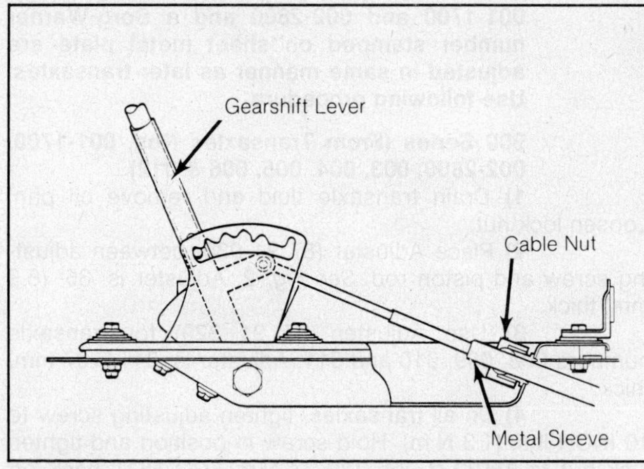

Courtesy of Austin Rover Group.

THROTTLE CONTROL CABLE

1) Loosen lock nuts on both sides of the throttle control cable bracket. *See Fig. 2.* Press down on throttle control lever until it stops.

2) While pressing down on throttle control lever, remove all free play by turning upper lock nut until it lightly seats on the throttle control cable bracket.

3) Tighten lower lock nut nut to secure cable adjustment. BEFORE starting engine, depress accelerator to floor. Ensure there is at least .08" (2 mm) free play in throttle control lever. Check that cable moves freely when depressing accelerator.

4) Start engine. With shift lever in Neutral or Park, throttle control cable lever movement should be synchronized with accelerator pedal movement.

Fig. 2: Adjusting Throttle Control Cable

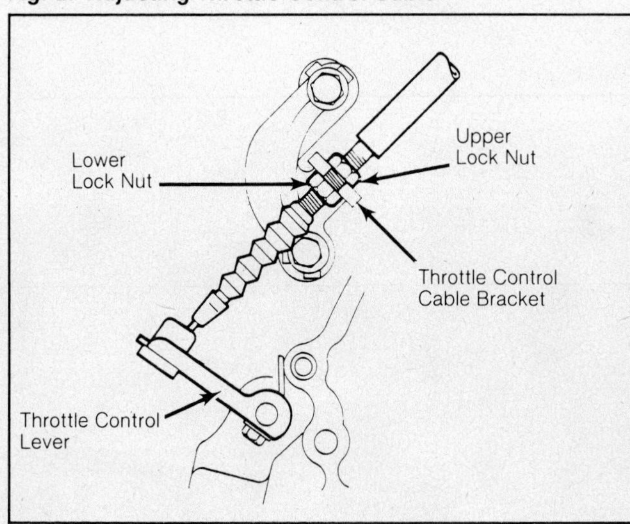

Courtesy of Austin Rover Group.

SUBARU

IDENTIFICATION

TRANSMISSION CODES

Application	Transmission (Code)
All Models	Gunma Transaxle

LUBRICATION

SERVICE INTERVALS

Check fluid level in transaxle and front differential every 5 months or 15,000 miles, whichever comes first. Transaxle fluid should be changed every 30,000 miles or 30 months and band adjusted as necessary. No oil change is necessary on front differential.

CHECKING FLUID LEVEL

Transaxle

1) Bring engine to normal operating temperature. Park vehicle on level floor. Place transaxle in all gear positions.

2) Set transmission selector lever in "P" position with engine idling. Remove dipstick and clean with lint-free cloth. Insert and remove dipstick. Note fluid level and add through dipstick hole to bring to full mark. Do not overfill.

Front Differential

Use dipstick on top of front differential to check fluid level. Level should be between "L" and "F" marks.

RECOMMENDED FLUID

Use Dexron II ATF in transaxle. Use API GL-5, SAE 80W-90 in front differential.

FLUID CAPACITY

TRANSMISSION REFILL CAPACITIES

Application	[1] Qts. (L)
XT Coupe	
2WD	9.8-10.1 (9.5-9.8)
4WD	10.0-10.4 (9.5-9.8)
All Others	
2WD	6.3-6.8 (6.0-6.4)
4WD	7.2-7.6 (6.8-7.2)

[1] – Dry fill capacities.

FRONT DIFFERENTIAL CAPACITIES

Application	Qts. (L)
XT Coupe	1.5 (1.4)
All Others	1.3 (1.2)

DRAINING & REFILLING

Transaxle

1) Remove drain plug and drain fluid. If oil screen is to be cleaned, remove oil pan. Oil screen retaining bolts should be tightened to 30-40 INCH lbs. (3.4-4.4 N.m) on XT Coupe and 53-71 INCH lbs. (6-8 N.m) on all others.

2) Replace oil pan with new gasket. Tighten oil pan bolts to 30-40 INCH lbs. (3.4-4.4 N.m). Install drain plug with new gasket. Tighten to 18 ft. lbs. (25 N.m).

3) Fill transmission with about 3 qts. ATF. Start engine and check fluid level with engine idling. Add fluid as necessary. Do not overfill.

Front Differential

Front differential has separate drain plug from transaxle if fluid needs to be changed.

ADJUSTMENTS

REAR BAND

Adjustment is made at left side of transaxle. Loosen lock nut on band adjusting screw and tighten screw to 78 INCH lbs. (9 N.m). Loosen screw 2 turns and hold in position while tightening lock nut.

KICKDOWN SWITCH & DOWNSHIFT SOLENOID

All Except XT Coupe

1) Switch ignition on and depress accelerator fully. A click should be heard just as accelerator bottoms out. Adjust switch inward or outward for proper operation.

2) If kickdown failure occurs infrequently, solenoid may be malfunctioning. Remove and clean inside of solenoid while moving pushrod. After cleaning, carefully check solenoid operation.

NOTE: **If switch operates too soon, downshift will occur at part throttle.**

SHIFT LINKAGE

All Except XT Coupe

1) Move selector lever from "P" to "1" position. Lever should set into each position with a click. At each position, check that selector dial gives proper indication of gear position.

2) If linkage is out of adjustment, set selector lever to "N" position. Loosen linkage adjusting nut at transaxle. In Neutral, transaxle selector lever should be between 2 raised bosses on case. *See Fig. 1.*

Fig. 1: Adjusting Shift Linkage on Coupe, Sedan & Station Wagon

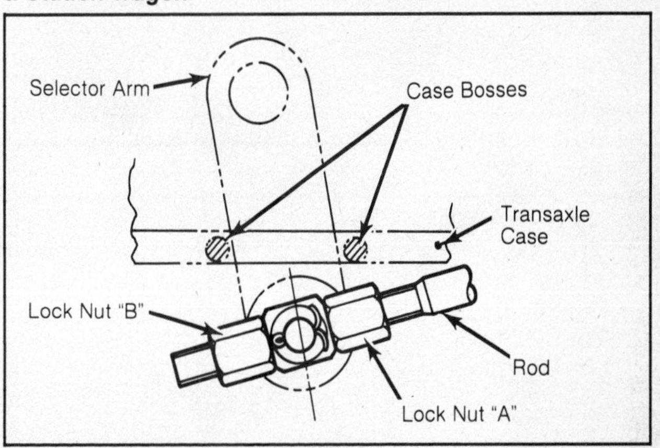

Courtesy of Subaru of America, Inc.

SUBARU (Cont.)

3) Turn lock nut "A" until it contacts selector arm. Tighten lock nut "B" to 7-13 ft. lbs. (10-18 N.m). If indicator needle is not aligned with guide plate marking, remove console box. Loosen mounting screws and adjust as required.

XT Coupe

1) Shift cable adjustment is made at bottom of gearshift lever. Set gearshift lever in "N" position. Loosen lock nuts on both sides of inner cable. *See Fig. 2.*

2) Lightly push selector lever away from lock nut "B". Tighten lock nut "A" until it contacts selector lever. Tighten lock nut "B" to 9-17 ft. lbs. (13-23 N.m).

Fig. 2: Adjusting Coupe XT Shift Cable

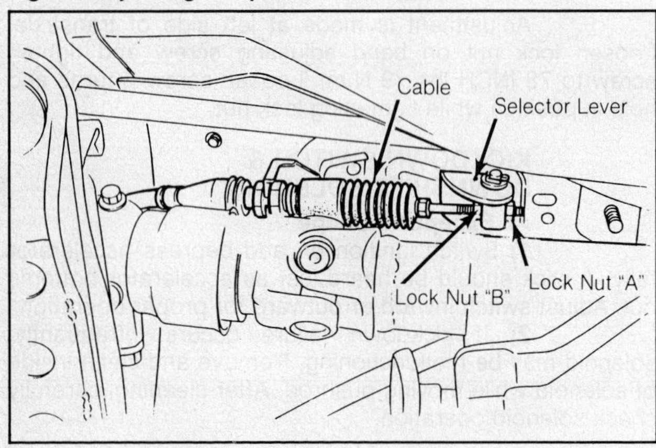

Courtesy of Subaru of America, Inc.

NEUTRAL SAFETY SWITCH

All Except XT Coupe

1) Switch is mounted on right side of selector lever plate. To adjust, remove switch from plate and insert .08" (2 mm) diameter pin in alignment hole on switch.

2) Ensure gearshift lever is in "N" position, pushed lightly toward "P". Match locator to bracket hole and moving plate pin to arm hole. Tighten retaining bolts in position. Remove alignment pin.

XT Coupe

Neutral safety switch is mounted on transaxle. Loosen 3 mounting bolts. Place gearshift lever in "N". Insert Stopper Pin (499267300) into switch alignment holes. Tighten retaining bolts. *See Fig. 4.*

Fig. 3: Adjusting Coupe, Sedan & Station Wagon Neutral Safety Switch

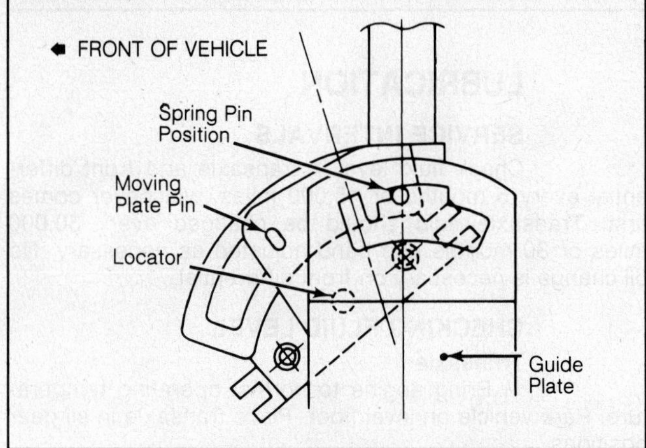

Courtesy of Subaru of America, Inc.

Fig. 4: Adjusting XT Coupe Neutral Safety Switch

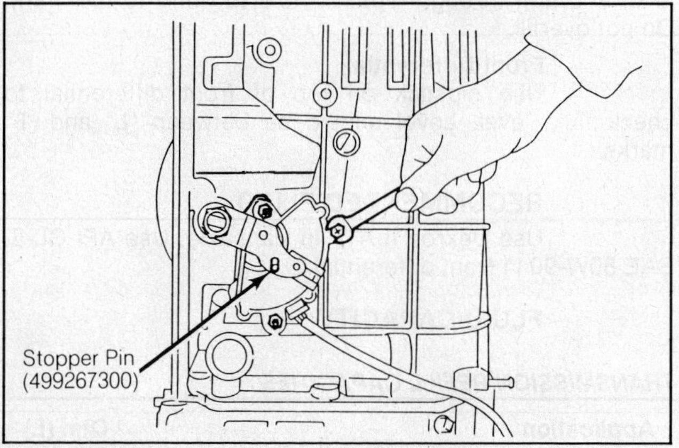

Courtesy of Subaru of America, Inc.

TOYOTA

IDENTIFICATION

TRANSMISSION CODES

Application	Code
FWD	
Camry	A140E
Celica	A140E or A140L
Corolla	A131L, A240E or A240L
Tercel Sedan	A132L
Tercel Wagon	
2WD	A55
4WD	A55F
RWD	
Corolla	A42DL
Cressida & Supra	A340E
Land Cruiser	A440F or A440L
Pickup & 4Runner	
2WD	A43D
4WD	A340H
Van	
2WD	A45DL
4WD	A45DF

LUBRICATION

SERVICE INTERVALS

Inspect fluid level every 15,000 miles. Under severe operating conditions, change ATF and filter every 15,000 miles or 24 months.

CHECKING FLUID LEVEL

Check fluid level with engine idling. Shift each gear from "P" through "L" and back to "P". Fluid level should be within "HOT" or "COLD" ranges marked on dipstick, depending on temperature of fluid. Do not overfill.

RECOMMENDED FLUID

Use Dexron II automatic transmission fluid.

DRAINING & REFILLING

1) Remove drain plug and drain fluid. If changing the transmission filter, remove the oil pan.

CAUTION: When removing the transmission filter, note different size bolt lengths for reassembly reference.

2) Replace pan (if removed) drain plug and fill transmission with approximate amount of ATF fluid. See TRANSMISSION REFILL CAPACITIES table.

3) Start engine and shift through all gears. Shift into "P" and check fluid level. Add fluid as necessary. DO NOT overfill.

Camry, Celica & Corolla (FWD)

Some FWD models have separate drain plugs for the transmission and differential. Both plugs must be removed to drain all fluid. The transaxle is filled through the dipstick tube but, the differential is filled through a separate fill plug. *See Fig. 1.* Fill differential until ATF runs out of fill hole.

FLUID CAPACITY

TRANSMISSION REFILL CAPACITIES

Application	Refill Qts. (L)	Dry Fill Qts. (L)
Camry [1]	2.5 (2.4)	6.3 (6.0)
Celica [1]	2.5 (2.4)	6.3 (6.0)
Corolla [1] (FWD)		
A131L	2.4 (2.3)	
A240L	3.3 (3.1)	
Corolla (RWD)	2.5 (2.4)	6.0 (5.7)
Cressida	1.7 (1.6)	7.3 (6.9)
Land Cruiser	5.3 (5.0)	15.9 (15.0)
MR2	2.5 (2.4)	7.6 (7.2)
Pickup		
2WD	2.5 (2.4)	6.9 (6.5)
4WD	4.8 (4.5)	10.9 (10.2)
Supra	1.7 (1.6)	7.6 (7.2)
Tercel Sedan	2.6 (2.5)	5.8 (5.5)
Tercel Wagon		
2WD	2.3 (2.2)	4.8 (4.5)
4WD	4.4 (4.2)	6.9 (6.5)
Van	2.6 (2.5)	6.9 (6.5)

[1] – Differential uses Dexron II ATF. Capacity is 1.7 qts. (1.6L).

Fig. 1: Automatic Transmission & Differential Drain Plugs For Camry, Celica & Corolla (FWD)

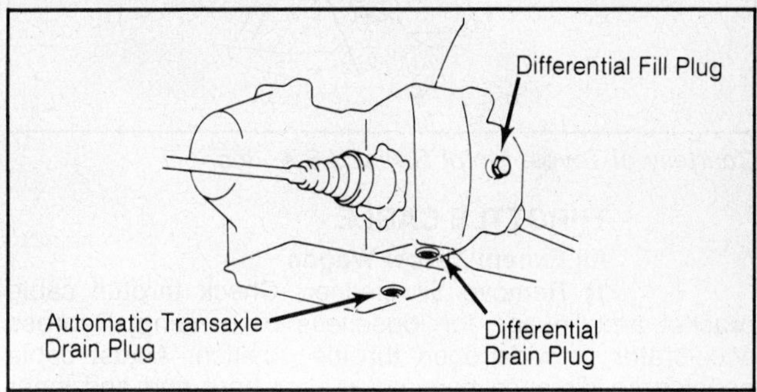

Courtesy of Toyota Motor Sales, U.S.A., Inc.

ADJUSTMENTS

SHIFT CABLE

Camry, Celica, Corolla (FWD), MR2, Tercel Sedan & Van

1) Loosen swivel nut on manual shift lever. Push manual shift lever fully toward right side of vehicle on all except Van models. On Van models, push manual lever fully rearward.

2) On all models, return lever 2 notches to Neutral position. Ensure shift lever is in "N". While holding lever lightly toward "R" range side, tighten swivel nut. *See Fig. 2.*

FLOOR SHIFT LINKAGE

Corolla (RWD), Cressida, Land Cruiser, Pickup & Tercel Wagon

1) Loosen swivel nut on connecting rod. *See Fig. 3.* Push manual shift lever fully toward rear of vehicle on all except Land Cruiser models. On Land Cruiser models, push manual lever fully toward front of vehicle.

TOYOTA (Cont.)

Fig. 2: Adjusting Shift Cable

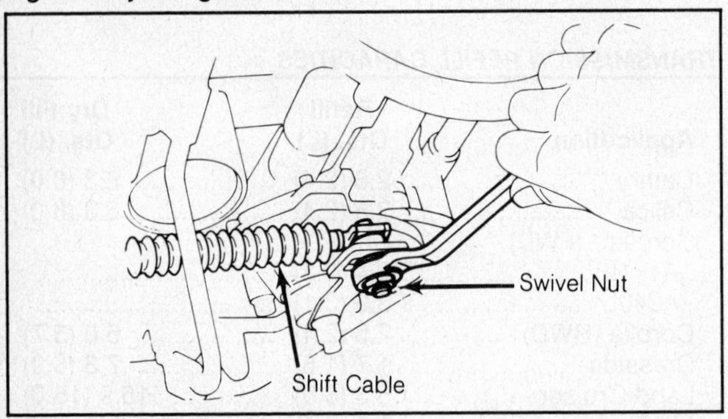

Courtesy of Toyota Motor Sales, U.S.A., Inc.

2) On all models, return lever 2 notches to Neutral position. Ensure shift lever is in "N". While holding lever lightly toward "R" range side, tighten swivel nut.

Fig. 3: Adjusting Floor Shift Linkage Assembly

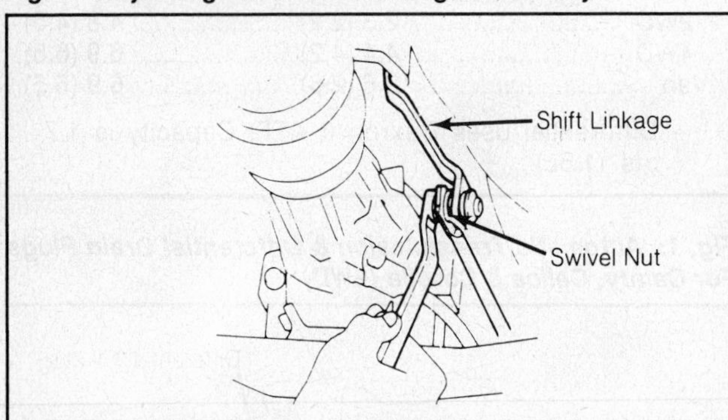

Courtesy of Toyota Motor Sales, U.S.A., Inc.

THROTTLE CABLE

All Except Tercel Wagon

1) Remove air cleaner. Check throttle cable bracket and linkage for looseness or bending. Depress accelerator to wide open throttle position. Adjust cable housing so distance between rubber boot end and inner cable stopper or paint mark is .04" (1.0 mm). Tighten lock nut. *See Fig. 4*.

Fig. 4: Adjusting Throttle Cable

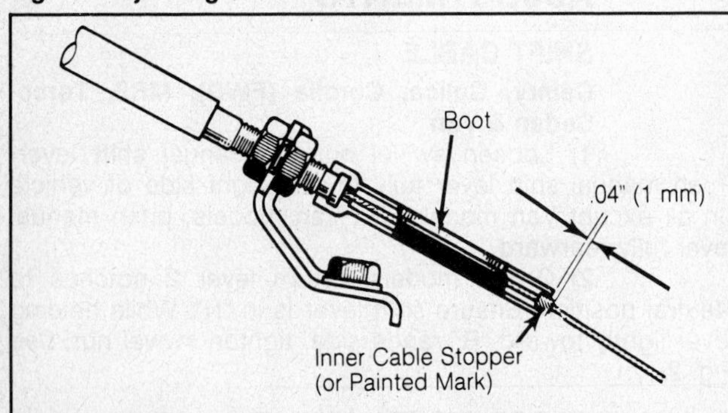

Courtesy of Toyota Motor Sales, U.S.A., Inc.

2) New throttle cables will not have a stopper or paint mark in place. With the new cable securely installed in transmission, pull inner cable slightly until resistance is felt. *See Fig. 5*. Stake new stopper or paint a mark as shown.

Fig. 5: Marking New Throttle Cable (All Except Tercel Wagons)

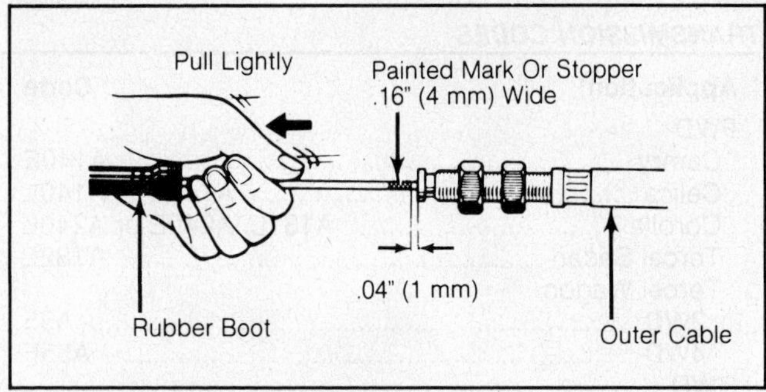

Courtesy of Toyota Motor Sales, U.S.A., Inc.

THROTTLE LINK

Tercel Wagon

1) Remove air cleaner. Check throttle cable bracket and linkage for looseness or binding. Depress accelerator to wide open throttle position, and check that throttle opens fully. If not, adjust throttle cable.

2) Fully depress accelerator pedal and hold. Adjust linkage by turning turnbuckle until throttle valve lever indicator lines up with mark on transmission case. Tighten lock nut.

Fig. 6: Adjusting Tercel Wagon Throttle Link

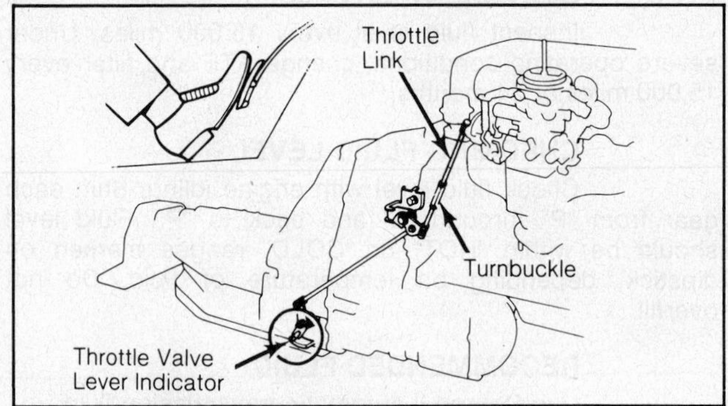

Courtesy of Toytota Motor Sales, U.S.A., Inc.

NEUTRAL SAFETY SWITCH

Loosen neutral safety switch bolts. Position shift lever in "N". Align switch shaft groove to neutral basic line. *See Fig. 7*. Tighten adjusting bolt.

Fig. 7: Adjusting FWD Neutral Safety Switch

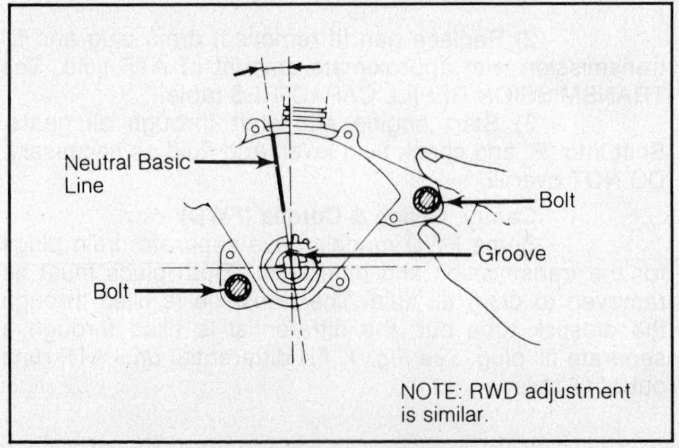

Courtesy of Toyota Motor Sales, U.S.A., Inc.

VOLKSWAGEN

IDENTIFICATION

TRANSMISSION CODES

Application	Code
Cabriolet, Golf, GTI, Jetta	010
Quantum	087
Vanagon	090

LUBRICATION

SERVICE INTERVALS

Check fluid level every 15,000 miles. Change fluid every 30,000 miles under severe driving conditions.

CHECKING FLUID LEVEL

Transmission

With transmission at normal operating temperature, park vehicle on level surface. Place selector lever in "P" or "N" position and apply parking brake. Allow engine to idle. Remove dipstick, wipe clean and insert. Remove dipstick and check that fluid level is between marks on dipstick.

Final Drive

Place vehicle on level surface. Fluid level must be up to edge of fill hole on side of case. If level is too high, this may indicate fluid transfer between transmission and final drive caused by leaking seals.

NOTE: **Normal fluid color on late production vehicles is Red/Brown. This is normal.**

RECOMMENDED FLUID

Transmission

Use Dexron II ATF.

Final Drive

Use API GL-5, SAE 90.

FLUID CAPACITY

TRANSMISSION REFILL CAPACITIES

Application	Refill Qts. (L)	Dry Fill Qts. (L)
All Models	3.2 (3.0L)	6.4 (6.0)

FINAL DRIVE REFILL CAPACITIES

Model	Qts. (L)
All Except Vanagon	.8 (.76)
Vanagon	1.3 (1.23)

DRAINING & REFILLING

1) Remove transaxle protection plate. Remove rear pan bolts and loosen front pan bolts. Carefully lower pan and drain as much fluid as possible. Remove oil pan and pour out remaining fluid. Remove filter. Clean oil pan in solvent and dry, using compressed air.

2) Install new filter and tighten screws to 27 INCH lbs. (3 N.m). Install oil pan, using new gasket. Tighten oil pan bolts to 15 ft. lbs. (20 N.m). Install protection plate, tighten bolts to 18 ft. lbs. (25 N.m). Add 3.2 qts. (3.0L) of transmission fluid and check fluid level.

ADJUSTMENTS

SECOND BRAKE BAND

1) Adjust brake band with transmission in a horizontal position only. Loosen adjustment screw lock nut. Tighten brake band adjustment screw to 90 INCH lbs. (10 N.m). *See Fig. 1.*

2) Loosen adjustment screw, then tighten to 45 INCH lbs. (5 N.m). Back off 2 turns on 5-cylinder engines or 2 1/2 turns on 4-cylinder engines. Tighten lock nut to 178 INCH lbs. (20 N.m).

Fig. 1: Adjusting Second Brake Band

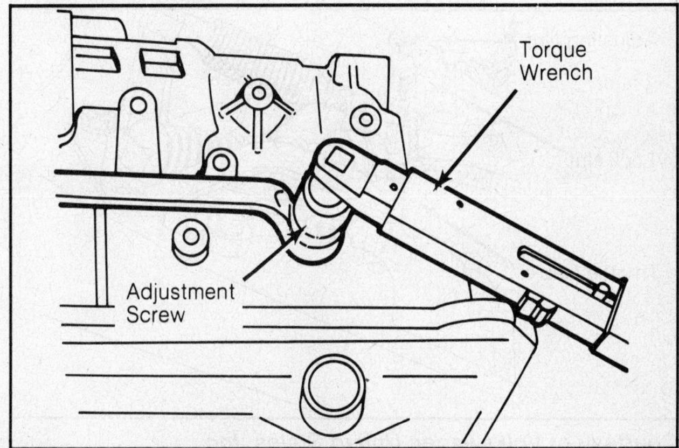

Courtesy of Volkswagen United States, Inc.

SELECTOR LEVER CABLE

Vanagon

Place transmission lever in "P" position. Loosen bolt which retains shift rod to operating lever on transaxle. *See Fig. 2.* Ensure selector lever and transaxle operating lever are in "P" position. Push shift rod to rear and tighten bolt.

Fig. 2: Adjusting Vanagon Shift Lever

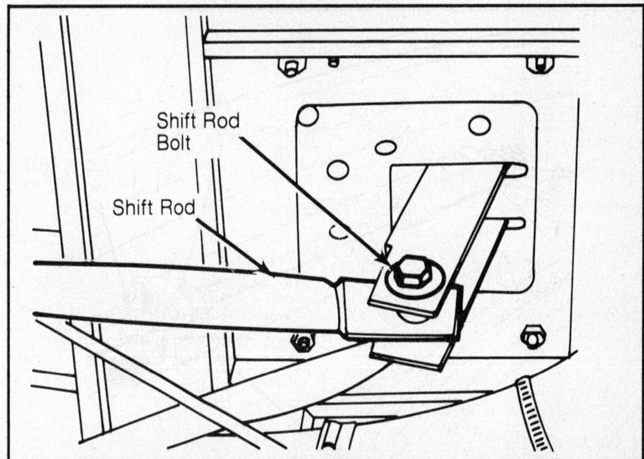

Courtesy of Volkswagen United States, Inc.

All Others

Place transmission in "P" position. Loosen nut for clamping pin which retains selector cable to operating

VOLKSWAGEN (Cont.)

lever on transaxle. Ensure selector lever and transaxle operating lever are in "P" position. Tighten cable clamping nut to 72 INCH lbs. (8 N.m).

THROTTLE CABLE

NOTE: Accelerator linkage must be adjusted so that the operating lever on transmission is against stop when throttle valve is closed.

Cabriolet, Golf, GTI, Jetta & Scirocco

1) Engine must be at operating temperature and turned off. Place gear selector in "P" position. Loosen adjusting nut and lock nut on throttle cable at transaxle. Disconnect throttle cable from transaxle. *See Fig. 3.*

Fig. 3: Transaxle Throttle Cable (All Except Quantum & Vanagon)

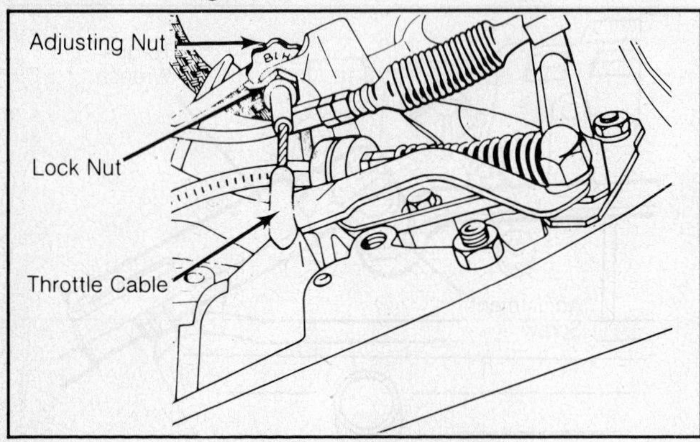

Courtesy of Volkswagen United States, Inc.

2) Loosen lock nuts on throttle cable support bracket. Push throttle cable sleeve in direction of arrow until there is no play. *See Fig. 4.*

3) Throttle valve must remain closed and accelerator/transaxle linkage must be in closed position.

4) Turn lock nut No. 1 against support bracket. Tighten lock nut No. 2. Install accelerator cable on transaxle.

Fig. 4: Adjusting Throttle Cable (All Except Quantum & Vanagon)

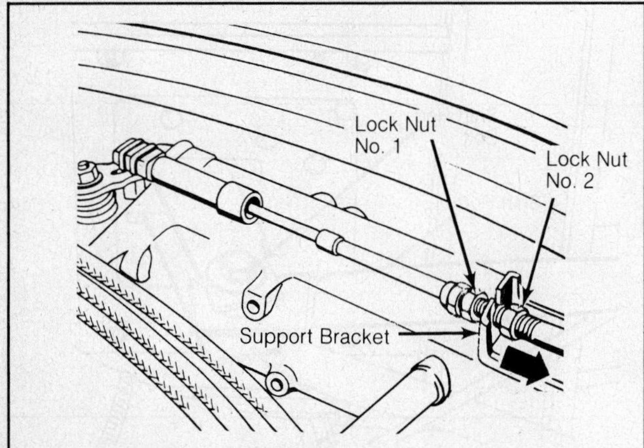

Courtesy of Volkswagen United States, Inc.

5) Depress accelerator pedal completely and hold there. Working at transaxle, push transaxle operating lever against kickdown adjusting nuts.

6) Turn adjusting nut until all slack is removed from cable. Release accelerator pedal. Ensure transaxle operating lever rests against kickdown stop. Tighten lock nut.

Quantum (087 Transaxle)

1) Engine must be at operating temperature and turned off. Place accelerator in idle position. Place selector lever in "P" position. Apply parking brake.

2) Loosen adjusting nut on throttle cable at transaxle. Remove retaining clips for ball sockets of push and pull rods. Pry ball sockets from relay bracket levers. *See Fig. 5.*

Fig. 5: Quantum Push & Pull Rods

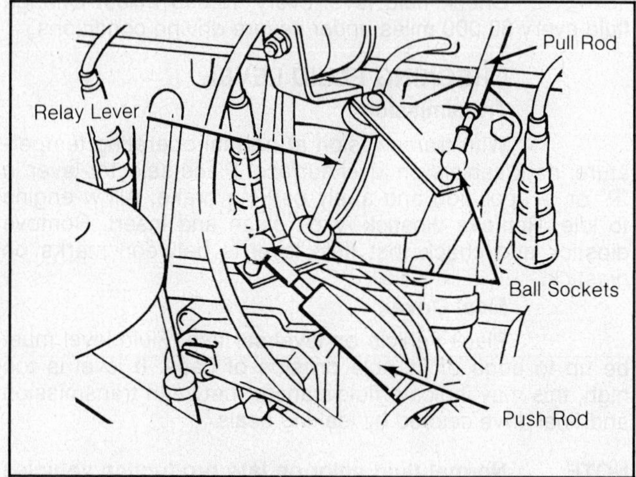

Courtesy of Volkswagen United States, Inc.

3) Rotate pull rod relay lever counterclockwise to stop. With relay lever against stop, loosen pull rod lock nut and turn ball socket until it fits easily on relay lever ball stud.

4) Tighten lock nut. Install push rod socket on relay lever. Install both ball socket retaining clips.

5) Loosen nut on push rod. *See Fig. 6.* Slide push rod apart so transaxle operating lever is in closed-throttle position and throttle body lever is against idle stop. Tighten nut on push rod.

NOTE: Ensure push rod fits easily on transmission operating lever.

Fig. 6: Adjusting Quantum Transaxle Push Rod

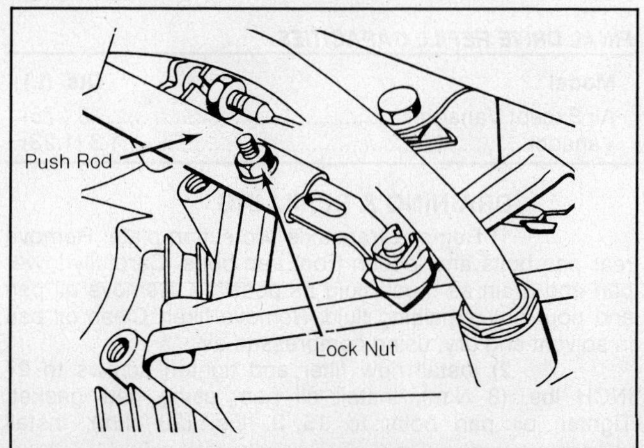

Courtesy of Volkswagen United States, Inc.

VOLKSWAGEN (Cont.)

6) Loosen lock nut located below adjusting nut on throttle cable. *See Fig. 7.* Depress accelerator pedal to stop on floor and hold.

7) Turn adjusting nut until transaxle operating lever moves, in direction of arrow, to stop. Tighten lock nut.

8) To check adjustment, push throttle lever against idle stop. Transaxle operating lever must be in closed-throttle position. Place accelerator pedal in full-throttle position, WITHOUT engaging kickdown. Throttle valve lever must contact full-throttle stop and kickdown spring in push rod must NOT be compressed.

Fig. 7: Quantum Throttle Cable

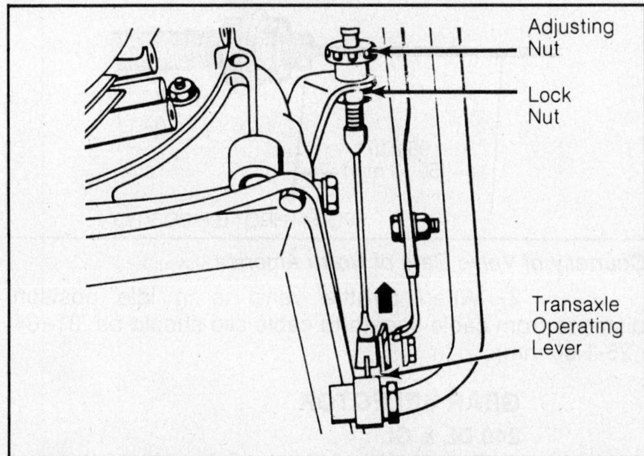

Courtesy of Volkswagen United States, Inc.

9) Press accelerator pedal to stop (kickdown position). Transaxle operating lever must contact stop and kickdown spring in push rod must be compressed. Distance "A" on push rod must be 13/32" (10.5 mm). *See Fig. 8.*

Fig. 8: Checking Quantum Push Rod Adjustment

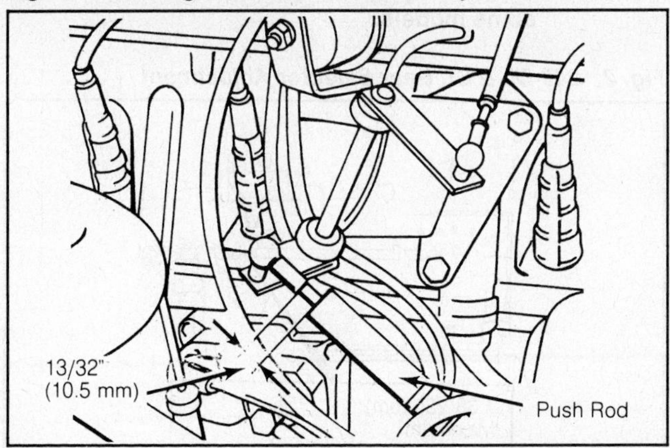

Courtesy of Volkswagen United States, Inc.

Vanagon

1) To check adjustment, place accelerator pedal in full throttle position. Throttle lever must contact stop, but kickdown lever on transaxle must NOT be in kickdown position.

2) Press accelerator pedal beyond full throttle position to floor. Override spring must be compressed and kickdown lever on transaxle must be in kickdown position. If not, readjust.

3) Loosen adjustment nut and remove override spring. *See Fig. 9.* Start engine and readjust idle speed, if necessary. Turn engine off.

4) Push accelerator rod to closed throttle position (against stop). Using a screwdriver, turn adjustment rod until it justs contacts throttle lever pivot.

5) Install overide spring, start engine and check idle speed. If necessary, adjust idle speed by turning rod. Tighten lock nut on adjustment rod.

6) Depress accelerator pedal to floor. Kickdown lever on transaxle must be in kickdown position on stop.

7) Release accelerator pedal. Kickdown lever on transaxle must return to idle position. If necessary, adjust throttle cable at clamping bolt. Clamping bolt is located at accelerator pedal end of accelerator cable.

Fig. 9: Adjusting Vanagon Accelerator Rod

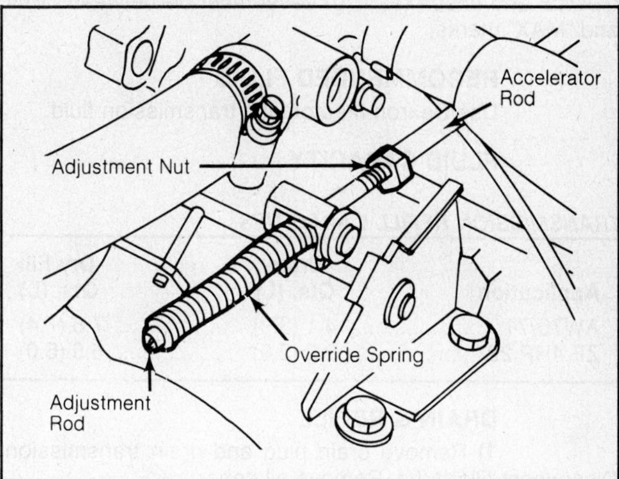

NEUTRAL SAFETY SWITCH

Neutral safety switch is located in shift console. Remove console cover and adjust switch so that engine starts in "P" and "N" positions only.

VOLVO

IDENTIFICATION

TRANSMISSION CODES

Application	Code
240 DL & GL, 740 GL & GLE (5-Door)	Aisin-Warner AW70L
740 Turbo, 760 GLE, 760 Turbo, 780 GLE	Aisin-Warner AW71
740 GL & GLE (4-Door)	ZF 4HP 22

LUBRICATION

SERVICE INTERVAL

Check fluid every 7,500 miles or twice a year. Change fluid every 20,000 miles.

CHECKING FLUID LEVEL

1) Position vehicle on level floor. Apply parking brake and shift selector lever to "P". Start engine and let idle. Shift selector lever through all gears pausing 4-5 seconds for engagement at each position.

2) Return selector lever to "P". Wait 2 minutes and remove dipstick. Wipe dipstick and insert. Withdraw dipstick and check reading. Level must be between "MIN" and "MAX" marks.

RECOMMENDED FLUID

Use Dexron II automatic transmission fluid.

FLUID CAPACITY

TRANSMISSION REFILL CAPACITIES

Application	Drain Qts. (L)	Dry Fill Qts. (L)
AW70/71	4.1 (3.9)	7.8 (7.4)
ZF 4HP 22	2.2 (2.0)	6.5 (6.0)

DRAIN & REFILL

1) Remove drain plug and drain transmission. Disconnect filler tube. Remove oil pan.

2) Remove and clean oil strainer. Install stainer. Install oil pan with new gasket. Tighten bolts to 44-88 INCH lbs. (5-10 N.m). Tighten oil filler tube to 65 ft. lbs. (90 N.m) on AW70/71 and 72 ft. lbs. (100 N.m) on ZF 4HP 22.

3) Disconnect fluid return pipe from transmission. Place end of pipe in container. Place about 3.5 qts. of fluid in transmission.

4) Start engine and let idle. Turn off engine when clean oil comes out of pipe. Connect pipe and fill transmissions.

ADJUSTMENTS

THROTTLE & KICKDOWN CABLES

AW70/71 & ZF 4HP 22 Transmissions

1) Depress accelerator pedal in passenger compartment. With pedal depressed, distance from cable sheath to clip on cable should be 1.98-2.07" (50-53 mm). *See Fig. 1.*

Fig. 1: Checking Transmission Throttle Cable

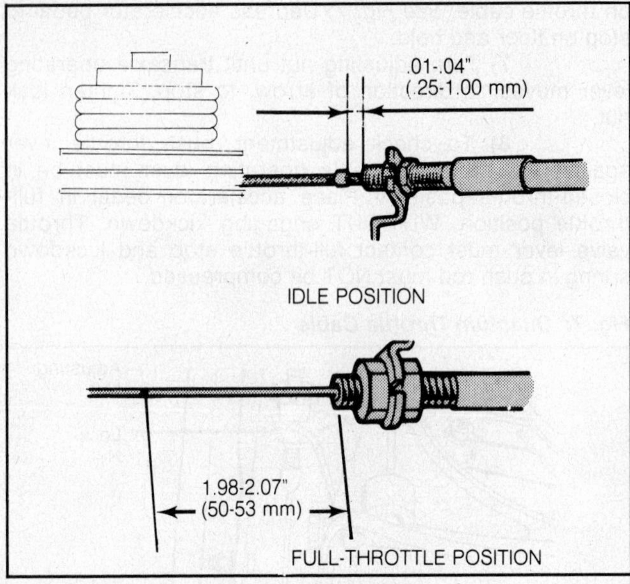

Courtesy of Volvo Cars of North America.

2) When throttle valve is in idle position, distance from cable sheath to cable clip should be .01-.04" (.25-1.00 mm).

GEAR SELECTOR

240 DL & GL

1) Ensure gear selector linkage bushings are not worn. If worn, replace.

2) Place gear selector in "D" and move lever against gate. Clearance from pin to stop in "D" should be same as clearance in "2". *See Fig. 2.* If not, go to step **3)**

3) Screw clevis in or out so maximum visible thread length is 1.38" (35 mm). Tighten lock nut.

NOTE: **Clevis may be located on front of rod on some models.**

Fig. 2: 240 DL & GL Gear Selector Adjustment

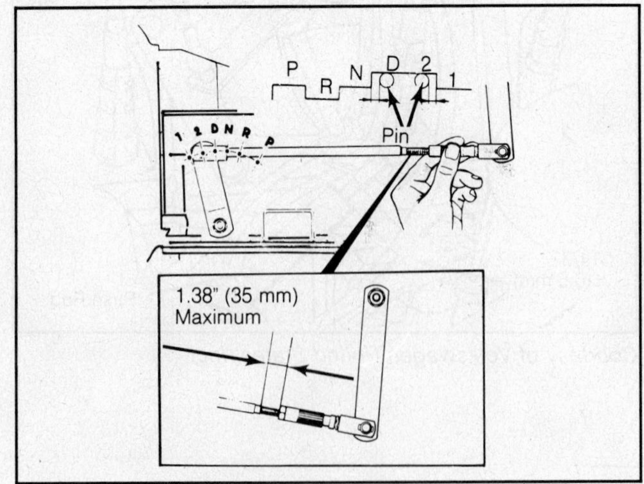

Courtesy of Volvo Cars of North America.

VOLVO (Cont.)

740, 760 & 780

1) Engine should only start is "N" or "P" positions. Back-up lights should only start in "R". Gear selector should be vertical in "P. If not, go to step **2)**.

2) Place selector lever in "P". Loosen lock nuts for actuator and selector rods. Ensure transmission is in shifted into Park. Rotate output shaft on transmission until it locks.

3) Place gear selector lever in vertical position, or slightly forward, and tighten lock nut. *See Fig. 3.* Push reaction lever lightly rearward until a slight resistance is felt. Tighten lock nut to 42 INCH lbs. (5 N.m).

NOTE: If selector lever is stiff in "D" or "2" ("3" on ZF 4HP 22), readjust reaction lever.

4) Ensure free play between pin and stop in "D" is less than or equal to play between pin and stop in "2" ("3" on ZF 4HP 22). If play is correct further tighten nut to 12-17 ft. lbs. (17-23 N.m).

5) After adjustment, ensure only starts in "N" or "P" and back-up lights come on in "R".

Fig. 3: Adjusting 740, 760 & 780 Shift Linkage

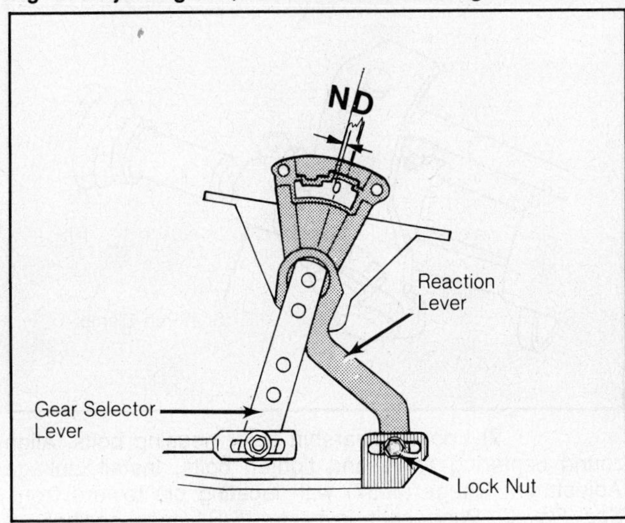

Courtesy of Volvo Cars of North America.

NEUTRAL SAFETY SWITCH

240 DL & GL

1) Switch is located at and directly controlled by shift control lever. Remove gear selector cover. Ensure "N" and "P" mark on are directly opposite selector lever in "N" and "P" positions respectively. If not, loosen 2 retaining bolts and readjust.

2) Ensure engine only starts in "N" and "P" positions. Ensure back-up lights come on in "R" position.

3) Ensure control pin does not slide out of switch lever. *See Fig. 4.*

Fig. 4: Adjusting Neutral Safety Switch

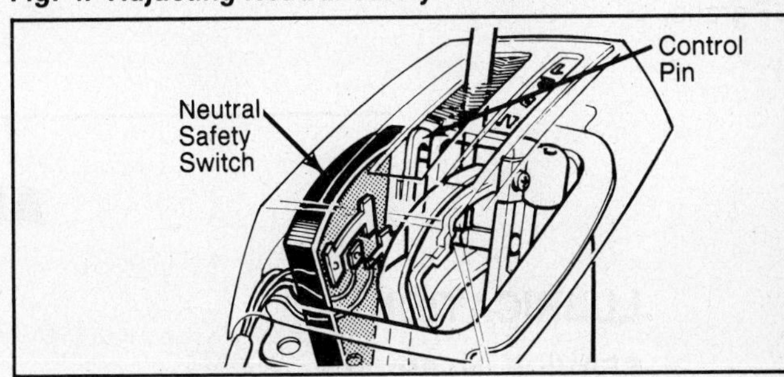

Courtesy of Volvo Cars of North America.

740, 760 & 780

Neutral safety switch is located at bottom of selector lever. No adjustments are necessary.

KICKDOWN SWITCH

740, 760 & 780

1) Kickdown switch is located on accelerator pedal. Unscrew switch to its uppermost limit. Depress accelerator pedal by hand until a resistance if felt.

2) Hold pedal in this position and screw switch down against marker on floor pan. On ZF 4HP 22 transmissions, cable clip at throttle bracket in engine compartment should be pulled out 1.651-1.69" (41-43 mm).

ACURA

LUBRICATION

SERVICE INTERVALS

Change lubricant every 30,000 miles.

CHECKING FLUID LEVEL

Ensure fluid level is at bottom of fill hole. Drain plug is located on bottom of case. Change drain plug gasket whenever fluid is changed.

RECOMMENDED FLUID

SAE 10W-30 or 10W-40 engine oil rated SE or SF grade.

FLUID CAPACITY

TRANSMISSION REFILL CAPACITIES

Application	Pts. (L)
Integra	4.8 (2.3)
Legend & Legend Coupe	4.6 (2.2)

ADJUSTMENTS

LINKAGE

No external adjustments are required.

AUDI

LUBRICATION

SERVICE INTERVALS

Check transmission lubricant level when vehicle is serviced. Lubricant never requires changing.

CHECKING FLUID LEVEL

Check fluid level at fill hole. Lubricant should be slightly below bottom of fill hole.

RECOMMENDED FLUID

Use Audi synthetic gear oil, G-50 (SAE 75W-90).

FLUID CAPACITY

TRANSMISSION REFILL CAPACITY

Application	Pts. (L)
013 (4-Cyl.)	[1] 4.2 (2.0)
093 (5-Cyl.)	[1] 5.0 (2.4)
016 (4WD)	[2] 7.0 (3.3)

[1] – Includes differential.
[2] – Includes front and center differential.

ADJUSTMENTS

GEARSHIFT LEVER

1) Place gearshift lever in 1st gear, push to left stop and release. Lever must spring back 1/4-3/8" (5-10 mm) to right. Place lever in 5th gear position, push shift lever to right stop and release. Lever must spring back 1/4-3/8" (5-10 mm) to left. Lever must spring back approximately same distance in both directions.

2) If gearshift lever does not spring back as indicated, loosen gearshift lever housing (stop plate) bolts and move housing slightly sideways in slots. If this adjustment does not correct hard shifting, perform GEARSHIFT LINKAGE ADJUSTMENT.

GEARSHIFT LINKAGE

Coupe GT & 4000S (Except 4WD)

1) Place gearshift lever in Neutral. From under vehicle, loosen shift rod clamp so shift finger slides freely on shift rod. Remove shift lever knob and rubber boot.

Fig. 1: Coupe GT & 4000S (2WD) Shift Rod Clamp

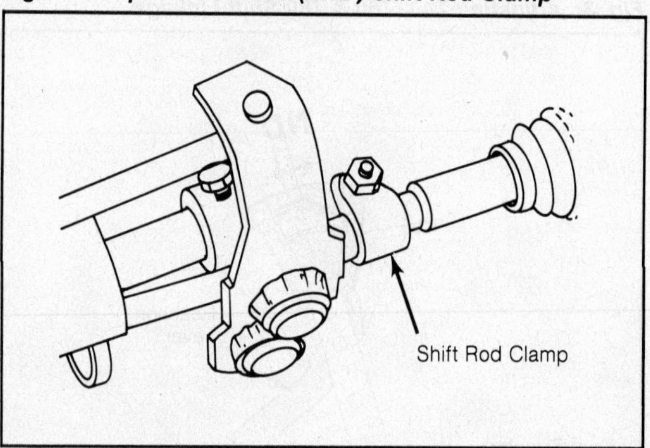

2) Loosen gearshift lever housing bolts. Align round centering holes and tighten bolts. Install Linkage Adjustment Gauge (3057) with locating pin toward front. *See Fig. 2.* Push shift lever to "5/R" gear position of gauge. Tighten lower knurled knob on gauge.

3) Move shift lever and slide to right stop. Tighten upper knurled knob on gauge. Push shift lever into "3/4" gear position of gauge. Adjust shift rod and finger. Tighten clamp nut and remove gauge.

4) Place shift lever in 1st gear, press to left stop and release. Shift lever must spring back to right. Place lever in 5th gear, push shift lever to right stop and release. Shift lever must spring back to left.

5) If gearshift lever does not spring back as indicated, move gearshift lever housing slightly sideways in slots. Ensure all gears engage easily and without jamming, particularly reverse gear stop. Install shift boot and lever knob.

NOTE: **All 4WD transaxle linkage adjustment should be performed only when gearshift lever adjustment cannot be corrected or after a repair which involved loosening shift rod clamp.**

AUDI (Cont.)

Fig. 2: Adjusting Coupe GT & 4000S (2WD) Gearshift Linkage

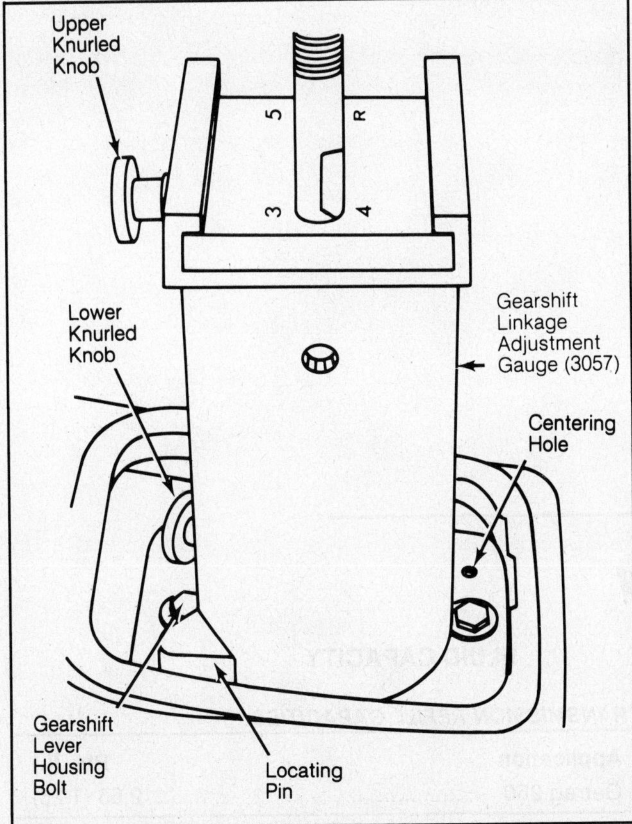

5000 Series & 4000CS Quattro (4WD)

1) Place gearshift lever in Neutral. Measure linkage rod length and adjust to 5 9/32" (134 mm), if necessary. *See Fig. 3.* Remove shift lever knob and rubber boot.

Fig. 3: Linkage Rod Adjustment Length For 5000 Series & 4000CS Quattro

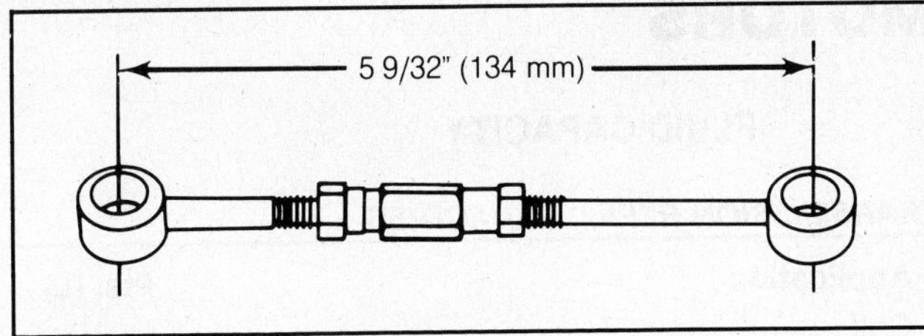

2) Working under vehicle, loosen shift rod clamp between front and rear rods, so rods move freely. In passenger compartment, loosen stop plate bolts. Align centering holes of stop plate and gearshift lever housing and tighten bolts.

3) Install Linkage Adjustment Gauge (3048) by inserting locating pins (right side pins first) into centering holes of stop plate. *See Fig. 4*.

4) Ensure gearshift lever remains in Neutral and tighten shift rod clamp. Remove adjustment gauge. When gearshift lever is placed in 1st or 5th gear, and pushed against left or right stop, it should spring back about same distance.

5) Ensure all gears engage easily and without jamming, particularly reverse gear safety catch. Adjust stop plate, if necessary. Install shift lever knob and rubber boot.

Fig. 4: Adjusting Gearshift Linkage on 5000 Series & 4000CS Quattro

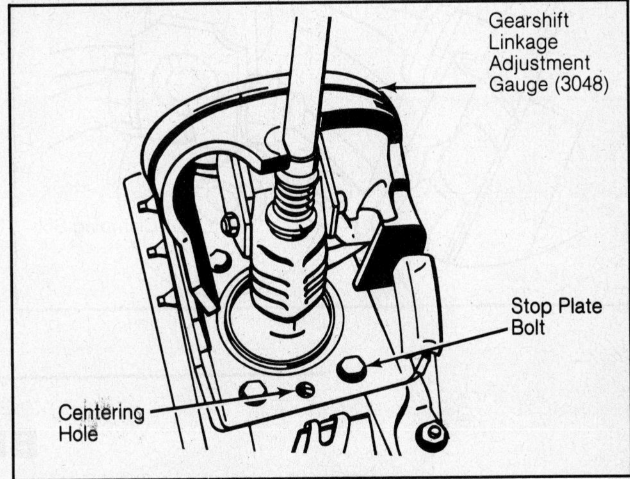

Courtesy of Audi of America, Inc.

CENTER DIFFERENTIAL LOCK

4000CS Quattro

1) Disengage differntial lock. Plastic bracket on servo must be pulled in. Remove clips on outer cable. Ensure cable is mounted correctly. *See Fig. 5*.

2) Pull outer cable to rear and transaxle shaft out to stop. Install clip No. 1 in first free groove of outer cable. Press support together and install clip No. 2 in first free groove of outer cable. Check lock operation.

Fig. 5: Adjusting Center Differential Lock On 4000CS Quattro

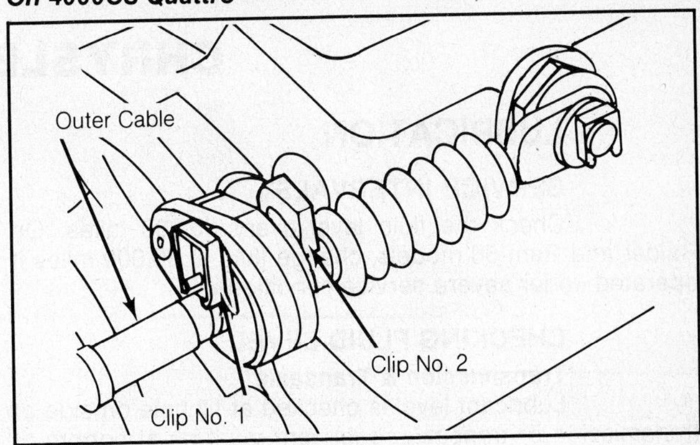

REAR DIFFERENTIAL LOCK

4000CS Quattro

1) Disengage lock. Clevis on servo must be pressed out. *See Fig. 6*. Loosen clamp bolt for lever on operating shaft.

2) Turn operating shaft clockwise to stop and pull servo clevis out. Tighten lever clamping bolt.

AUDI (Cont.)

Fig. 6: Adjusting Rear Differential Lock On 4000CS Quattro

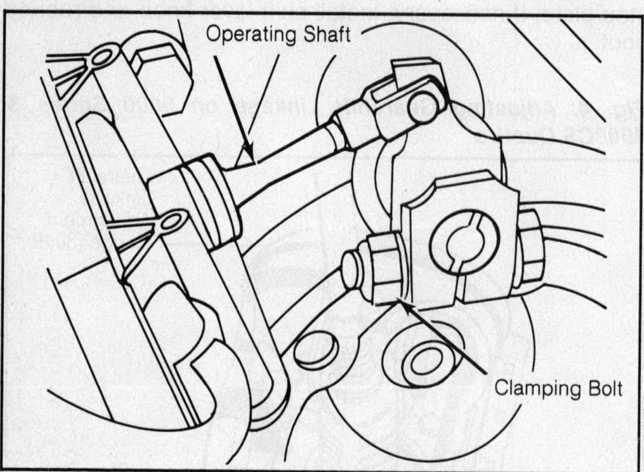

BMW

LUBRICATION

SERVICE INTERVALS

Inspect fluid level when vehicle is serviced. Change oil every 30,000 miles.

CHECKING FLUID LEVEL

Check lubricant at fill hole. Lubricant should be at bottom of fill plug hole.

RECOMMENDED FLUID

Use SAE 80W (API GL-4).

FLUID CAPACITY

TRANSMISSION REFILL CAPACITIES

Application	Pts. (L)
Getrag 260	2.65 (1.25)

ADJUSTMENTS

LINKAGE

No external adjustment is provided.

CHRYSLER MOTORS

LUBRICATION

SERVICE INTERVALS

Check the fluid level every 30,000 miles. On Raider and Ram-50 models, change fluid at 30,000 miles if operated under severe service conditions.

CHECKING FLUID LEVEL

Transmission & Transaxle

Lubricant level is checked at fill hole on side of transmission or transaxle. Lubricant must be at bottom of fill hole.

Transfer Case

Transfer case has separate drain and fill plugs. Lubricant must reach to bottom of fill hole.

RECOMMENDED FLUID

Use API GL-4 or GL-5. Use SAE 75W/85W in transaxles or SAE 90 in transmissions.

FLUID CAPACITY

TRANSMISSION REFILL CAPACITIES

Application	Pts. (L)
Colt	
1.5L	
4-Speed	3.6 (1.7)
5-Speed	3.8 (1.8)
1.6L	3.8 (1.8)
Colt Vista	
2WD	5.3 (2.5)
4WD	4.4 (2.1)
Conquest	2.4 (2.3)
Raider	4.7 (2.2)
Ram-50	
2WD	4.9 (2.3)
4WD	4.7 (2.2)

CHRYSLER MOTORS (Cont.)

ADJUSTMENTS

SELECT CABLE

Colt & Colt Vista

1) Working at transmission, place transmission shift lever in Neutral position. This will also place select lever in Neutral position. *See Fig. 1.*

Fig. 1: Colt & Colt Vista Transmission Cables

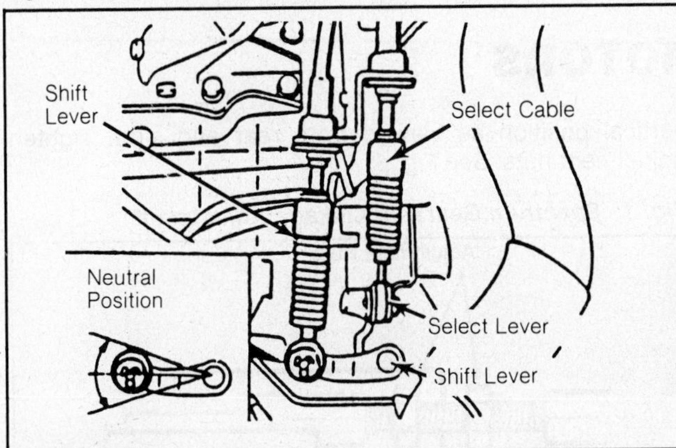

Courtesy of Chrysler Motors.

2) Disconnect shift and select cable at both ends. Ensure each operates without binding. Repair if necessary.

Fig. 2: Colt & Colt Vista Shift Lever Assembly

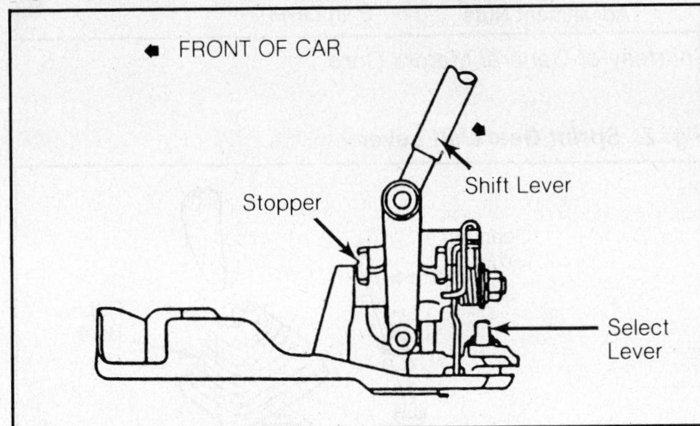

Courtesy of Chrysler Motors.

3) Reconnect both cables at transmission end. Place gearshift lever in Neutral position.

4) At gearshift lever end of select cable, adjust cable length so cable eye fits easily over select lever pin. *See Fig. 2.*

SHIFT CABLE

Colt & Colt Vista

1) Working at transmission, move shift lever to 4th gear position. It may be necessary to depress the clutch.

2) Tilt gearshift lever toward 4th gear position until it touches stopper. *See Fig. 2.* Hold lever in this position during adjustment procedure.

3) At gearshift lever end of shift cable, adjust cable length so cable eye fits easily over shift lever pin.

4) Move gearshift lever between 3rd, Neutral and 4th gear positions. Shift lever-to-stop clearances should be equal on both sides of lever. *See Fig. 3.*

5) If clearances "A" and "B" are not equal, readjust shift cable. Road test vehicle to verify smooth shifting.

Fig. 3: Adjusting Colt & Colt Vista Shift Lever Clearances

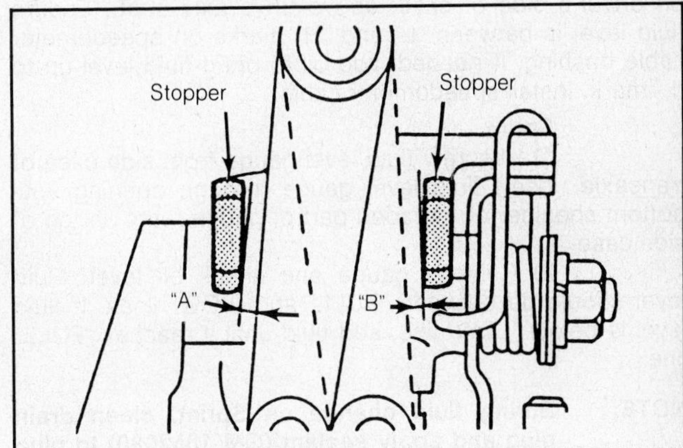

Courtesy of Chrysler Motors.

RECOMMENDED FLUID

Use API GL-4 or GL-5. Use SAE 75W-85W in transaxles or SAE 90 in transmissions.

FORD MOTOR CO.

LUBRICATION

SERVICE INTERVALS

Inspect fluid level when vehicle is serviced. No oil change interval is recommended.

CHECKING FLUID LEVEL

Merkur XR4Ti

Check lubricant at fill hole. Lubricant should be 1 INCH below bottom of fill plug hole on older units with Yellow paint square on left side of transmission case. Transmissions without Yellow paint should have fluid level to bottom of fill plug hole.

Festiva & Tracer

Place vehicle on level surface. Disconnect speedometer cable from drive gear at transaxle. Remove speedometer drive gear from transaxle. Fluid level should be to full mark on drive gear sleeve.

RECOMMENDED FLUID

Festiva & Tracer

Use Dexron II ATF.

Merkur XR4Ti

Use FORD E5RY-19C547-A (semi-synthetic oil).

FORD MOTOR CO. (Cont.)

FLUID CAPACITY

TRANSMISSION REFILL CAPACITIES

Application	Qts. (L)
Festiva	2.6 (2.5)
Merkur XR4Ti	1.4 (1.3)
Tracer	3.4 (3.2)

ADJUSTMENTS

GEARSHIFT LINKAGE

No external linkage adjustment is provided.

GENERAL MOTORS

LUBRICATION

SERVICE INTERVALS

Check fluid each time engine oil is changed or every 7500 miles. Replace every 30,000 miles. Replace at 15,000 miles if operated under severe service driving conditions.

CHECKING FLUID LEVEL

Spectrum

Remove speedometer cable assembly located on driver's side of case, above drive axle shaft. Ensure fluid level is between "L" and "H" marks on speedometer cable bushing. If needed, add oil to bring fluid level up to "L" mark. Install speedometer cable.

Sprint

1) Unscrew fluid level gauge from side case of transaxle. Insert fluid level gauge through opening until bottom shoulder of threaded part of gauge rests on top of side case.

2) Remove gauge and check oil level. Fluid level should be between "FULL" and "LOW" lines. If fluid level is below "LOW" line, add fluid until it reaches "FULL" line.

NOTE: During fluid change on Sprint, clean drain plug and apply sealant (GM 1052080) to plug threads. If transaxle is cold, tighten drain plug to 18-22 ft. lbs. (24-30 N.m). If transaxle is warm, tighten drain plug to 15-18 ft. lbs. (20-24 N.m).

RECOMMENDED FLUID

Spectrum

Use SAE 5W-30, SF rated engine oil.

Sprint

Use hypoid oil SAE 80W or 80W-90 (API GL-5).

FLUID CAPACITY

TRANSMISSION REFILL CAPACITIES

Application	Pts. (L)
Spectrum	5.6 (2.7)
Sprint	4.8 (2.3)

ADJUSTMENTS

GEARSHIFT LINKAGE

Spectrum

Place transaxle and lever in Neutral. Turn adjustment nuts, one cable at a time, until shift lever is in vertical position as viewed from rear and side. Tighten adjustment nuts. *See Fig. 1.*

Fig. 1: Spectrum Gearshift Linkage Adjustment

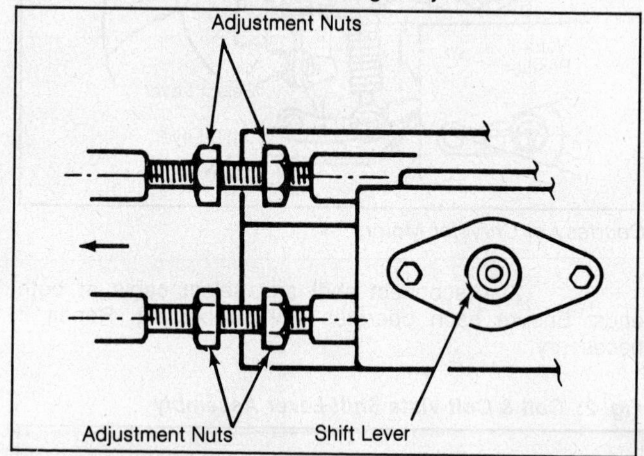

Courtesy of General Motors Corp.

Fig. 2: Sprint Gearshift Lever

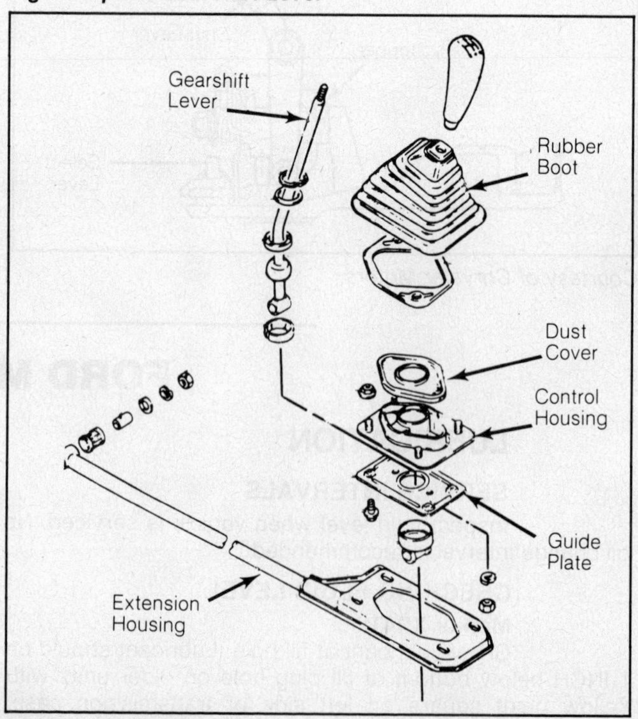

Courtesy of General Motors Corp.

GENERAL MOTORS IMPORTS (Cont.)

NOTE: Adjust Sprint gearshift if each shift stroke is short or gears do not completely mesh.

Sprint

1) Lift up gearshift lever rubber boot. Loosen gearshift control housing nuts and guide plate bolts. Adjust guide plate by moving it from front to rear so lower section of gearshift lever is in middle of guide plate and at a right angle. *See Fig. 2.*

2) With guide plate in position, tighten guide plate bolts to 72-88 INCH lbs. (8-10 N.m). Tighten left front and right rear housing nut to 11-14 ft. lbs. (15-20 N.m). Tighten right front and left rear housing nut to 27-53 INCH lbs. (3-6 N.m).

HONDA

LUBRICATION

SERVICE INTERVALS

Change lubricant every 30,000 miles or 24 months.

CHECKING FLUID LEVEL

Transaxle should be at operating temperature. Vehicle should be parked on level surface with engine off. Fluid level should be at bottom of fill hole on side of case. Use new washer on drain plug when changing fluid.

RECOMMENDED FLUID

Use SAE 10W-40 engine oil rated SE or SF.

FLUID CAPACITY

TRANSMISSION REFILL CAPACITIES

Application	Qts. (L)
Accord, Civic, CRX/Si	2.4 (2.3)
Prelude	
Carburetor	2.5 (2.4)
Fuel Injection	2.6 (2.5)

Fig. 1: Checking Selector Cable Adjustment On Civic (4WD)

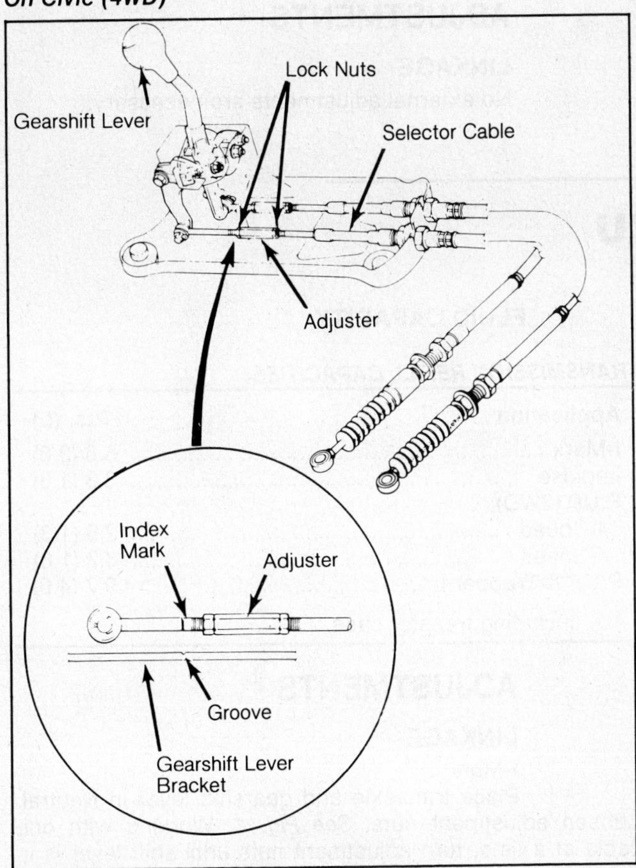

Courtesy of American Honda Motor Co., Inc.

Fig. 2: Checking Gearshift Cable Adjustment on Civic (4WD)

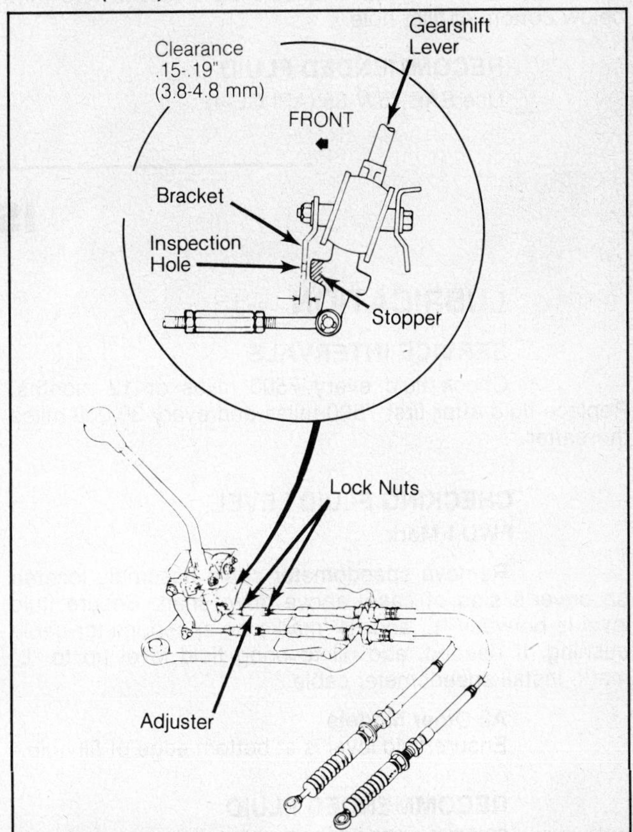

Courtesy of American Honda Motor Co., Inc.

HONDA (Cont.)

ADJUSTMENTS

GEARSHIFT LINKAGE

2WD Models

No external adjustments are required.

4WD Civic Models (Selector Cable)

1) Remove center console. Place transaxle in Neutral. Ensure groove in lever bracket is aligned with index mark on selector cable. *See Fig. 1.* If not, loosen lock nuts and turn adjuster as necessary.

NOTE: **After adjustment, check operation of gearshift lever. Threads of the cables must not extend out of cable adjuster more than 3/8".**

4WD Civic Models (Gearshift Cable)

Remove center console. Place gear selector in 4th gear. Measure clearance between gearshift lever bracket and stopper while pushing lever forward. *See Fig. 2.* If clearance is not okay, loosen lock nuts and turn adjuster until clearance is correct.

NOTE: **After adjustment, check operation of gearshift lever. Threads of the cables must not extend out of cable adjuster more than 3/8".**

HYUNDAI

LUBRICATION

SERVICE INTERVALS

Fluid should be replaced every 30,000 miles or every 24 months.

CHECKING FLUID LEVEL

Remove filler plug and inspect oil level at bottom of filler hole. Level should be within .31" (8 mm) below bottom of filler hole.

RECOMMENDED FLUID

Use SAE 75W-85 (API GL-4)

FLUID CAPACITY

TRANSMISSION REFILL CAPACITY

Application	Pts. (L)
4 & 5-Speed	4.4 (2.1)

ADJUSTMENTS

LINKAGE

No external adjustments are necessary.

ISUZU

LUBRICATION

SERVICE INTERVALS

Check fluid every 7500 miles or 12 months. Replace fluid after first 7500 miles and every 30,000 miles thereafter.

CHECKING FLUID LEVEL

FWD I-Mark

Remove speedometer cable assembly located on driver's side of case, above drive shaft. Ensure fluid level is between "L" and "H" marks on speedometer cable bushing. If needed, add oil to bring fluid level up to "L" mark. Install speedometer cable.

All Other Models

Ensure fluid level is at bottom edge of fill hole.

RECOMMENDED FLUID

0°-90°F (-18°-32°C) SAE 5W-30 engine oil.
Above 90°F (32°C) SAE 40 engine oil.

FLUID CAPACITY

TRANSMISSION REFILL CAPACITIES

Application	Pts. (L)
I-Mark	5.8 (2.8)
Impulse	3.3 (1.6)
P'UP (2WD)	
4-Speed	2.6 (1.3)
5-Speed	3.3 (1.6)
P'UP & Trooper II	[1] 9.7 (4.6)

1 – Including transfer case.

ADJUSTMENTS

LINKAGE

I-Mark

Place transaxle and gearshift lever in Neutral. Loosen adjustment nuts. *See Fig. 1.* Working with one cable at a time, turn adjustment nuts until shift lever is in vertical position as viewed from side and rear. Tighten adjustment nuts. *See Fig. 1.*

ISUZU (Cont.)

Fig. 1: Adjusting I-Mark Gearshift Linkage

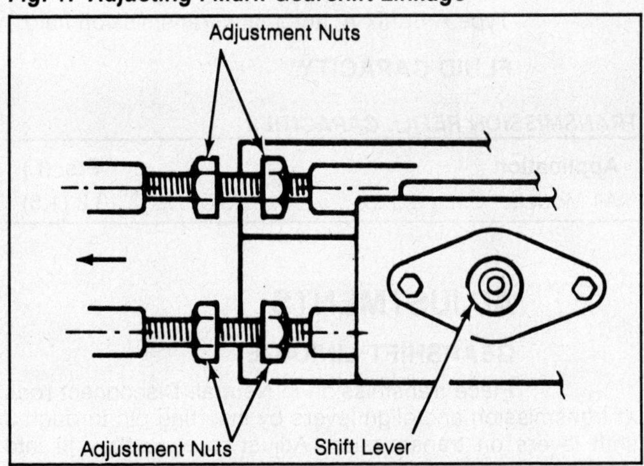

Courtesy of Isuzu Motor Co.

All Other Models

Shift linkage is integral with transmission housing and requires no external adjustment.

MAZDA

LUBRICATION

SERVICE INTERVALS

Replace fluid every 30,000 miles on transmission and transfer case.

CHECKING FLUID LEVEL

B2200, B2600 & RX7

Fluid should be up to bottom of fill hole on side of case. B2600 models have 2 drain and 2 fill plugs in transmission case. Transfer case has separate drain and fill plugs.

323 & 626

Remove speedometer cable and driven gear from transaxle case. Use "L" and "F" marks on driven gear to determine fluid level. If necessary, add oil through driven gear opening. *See Fig. 1.*

Fig. 1: Checking Oil Level on 323 & 626

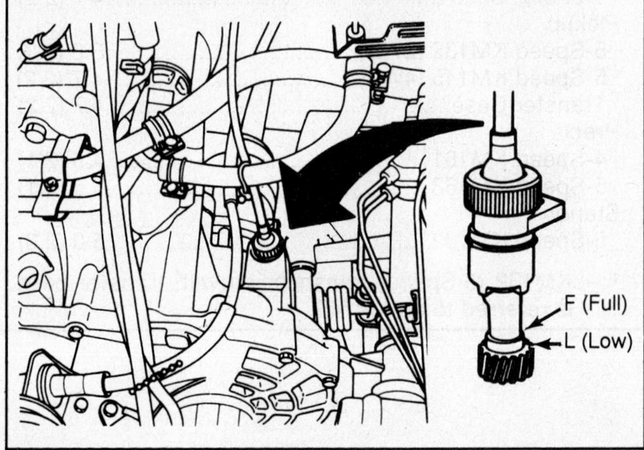

Courtesy Mazda Motors Co.

RECOMMENDED FLUID

Use Hypoid SAE 80W-90 (API GL-4 or GL-5) for transmissions, transaxles and transfer cases. On 323 and 626 models, Dexron II may be used at temperatures below 0°F (-18°C)

FLUID CAPACITY

TRANSMISSION REFILL CAPACITIES

Application	Pts. (L)
B2200	
4-Speed	3.5 (1.7)
5-Speed	4.2 (2.0)
B2600	
2WD	6.3 (3.0)
4WD	7.2 (3.4)
RX7	5.0 (2.6)
323	6.7 (3.2)
626	7.2 (3.4)

TRANSFER CASE REFILL CAPACITIES

Application	Pts. (L)
B2600	4.2 (2.0)

ADJUSTMENTS

GEARSHIFT LINKAGE

No external linkage adjustment is required.

Manual Transmission Servicing

MERCEDES-BENZ

IDENTIFICATION

TRANSMISSION CODES

Application	Code
190D	GL68/20B-5
190E (2.3)	GL68/20C-5
190E (2.3L 16V)	GL275E
190E (2.6)	GL76/27F-5
260E & 300E	GL76/27A-5

LUBRICATION

SERVICE INTERVALS

Check and correct fluid level every oil change. Change fluid every 15,000 miles.

CHECKING FLUID LEVEL

Lubricant should be level with bottom of fill hole.

RECOMMENDED FLUID

Type A Suffix A, automatic transmission fluid.

FLUID CAPACITY

TRANSMISSION REFILL CAPACITIES

Application	Pts. (L)
All Models	3.2 (1.5)

ADJUSTMENTS

GEARSHIFT LINKAGE

Place transmission in Neutral. Disconnect rods at transmission and align levers by inserting pin through 3 shift levers on transmission. Adjust rods so they fit into transmission levers freely. Install locking clips, remove centering pin and check for proper operation.

NOTE: Ensure locking clips with rounded edges are used.

MITSUBISHI

LUBRICATION

SERVICE INTERVALS

Check the fluid level every 30,000 miles. On Montero and Pickup models, change fluid at 30,000 miles if operated under severe service conditions.

CHECKING FLUID LEVEL

Transmission & Transaxle

Lubricant level is checked at fill hole on side of transmission or transaxle. Lubricant must be at bottom of fill hole.

Transfer Case

Transfer case has separate drain and fill plugs. Lubricant must reach to bottom of fill hole.

RECOMMENDED FLUID

Use API GL-4 or GL-5. Use SAE 75W-85W in transaxles or SAE 80W-90 in transmissions.

ADJUSTMENTS

LINKAGE

Transaxles

No adjustments for control rods or cables are given by manufacturer.

Transmissions

Shifter is integral with transmission housing and has no external linkage. No adjustment is required.

FLUID CAPACITY

TRANSMISSION REFILL CAPACITIES

Application	Pts. (L)
Cordia & Tredia	
5-Speed KM163	4.8 (2.3)
Galant	
5-Speed KM120	5.3 (2.5)
Mirage	
4-Speed KM200	3.6 (1.7)
5-Speed KM201 (1.5L)	3.8 (1.8)
5-Speed KM206 (1.6L)	3.8 (1.8)
Montero	
5-Speed KM145	4.7 (2.2)
Transfer Case	4.7 (2.2)
Pickup	
5-Speed KM132 (2WD)	5.0 (2.3)
5-Speed KM145 (4WD) [1]	4.7 (2.2)
Transfer Case	4.7 (2.2)
Precis	
4-Speed KM161	4.5 (2.1)
5-Speed KM163	4.5 (2.1)
Starion	
5-Speed KM132	5.0 (2.3)

[1] – KM132 (5-Speed) transmission with transfer case is referred to as KM145.

NISSAN

LUBRICATION

SERVICE INTERVALS

Inspect fluid level every 15,000 miles or 12 months. If under severe usage, change every 30,000 miles or 24 months.

CHECKING FLUID LEVEL

Fill plug is located on side of transmission or transaxle case. Lubricant level should be to bottom of fill hole.

RECOMMENDED FLUID

Hypoid SAE 80W-90 (API GL-4).

FLUID CAPACITY

TRANSMISSION REFILL CAPACITIES

Application	Pts.
Maxima, Stanza & Stanza Wagon	
5-Speed RS5F50A	10 (4.7)
Pickup & Pathfinder	
5-Speed FS5W71C	
2WD	4 1/4 (2.0)
4WD	8 1/2 (4.0)
5-Speed FS5R30A	
2WD	5 1/8 (2.4)
4WD	7 5/8 (3.6)
Transfer Case TX10	4 3/4 (2.2)
Pulsar 5-Speed RS5F31A	5 3/4 (2.5)
Sentra	
5-Speed RN5F31A	5 3/4 (2.7)
Van	
5-Speed RS5W71C	4 1/4 (2.0)
200SX	
5-Speed FS5W71C	4 1/4 (2.0)
300ZX & 300ZX Turbo	
5-Speed FS5W71C (Non-Turbo)	4 1/4 (2.0)
5-Speed FS5R30A (Turbo)	4 1/4 (2.0)

ADJUSTMENTS

LINKAGE

Select Cable (Van)

1) Select cable attaches to select lever on top of transmission. Loosen select cable adjuster lock nuts. *See Fig. 1.* Adjuster is located on shift lever end of cable.

Fig. 1: Adjuster Lock Nut Locations

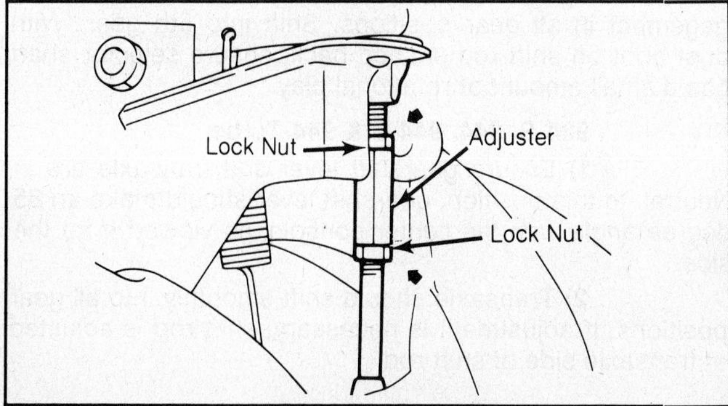

Courtesy of Nissan Motor Co., U.S.A.

2) Place shift change lever on transmission in 3rd or 4th gear position. Shift change lever is attached to cross shaft on side of transmission. Adjust length of cable with adjuster. Tighten adjuster lock nuts.

Shift Cable (Van)

1) Loosen trunnion lock nut of shift cable. *See Fig. 2.* Shift cable is attached to cross shaft on side of transmission.

2) Remove trunnion of shift cable from cross shaft. Set cross shaft in transmission to Neutral position.

Fig. 2: Shift Cable Trunnion & Lock Nut

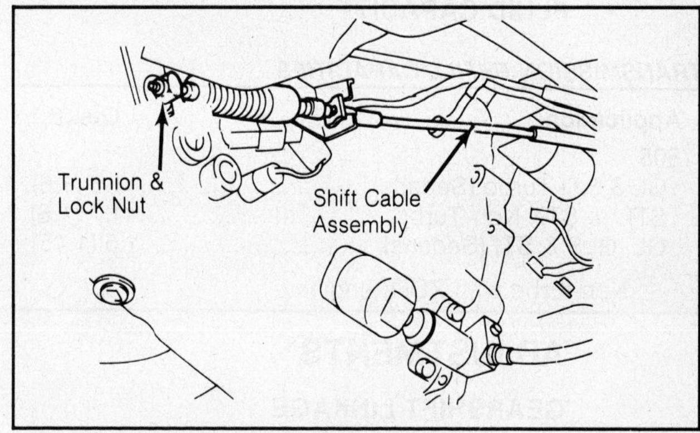

Courtesy of Nissan Motor Co., U.S.A.

3) Insert a .16" (4 mm) pin, as near horizontal as possible, into each adjustment hole in both control lever and roller bearing. *See Fig. 3.* Adjust trunnion so it will slide easily onto cross shaft. Tighten trunnion lock nut.

Fig. 3: Adjusting Van Shift Cable

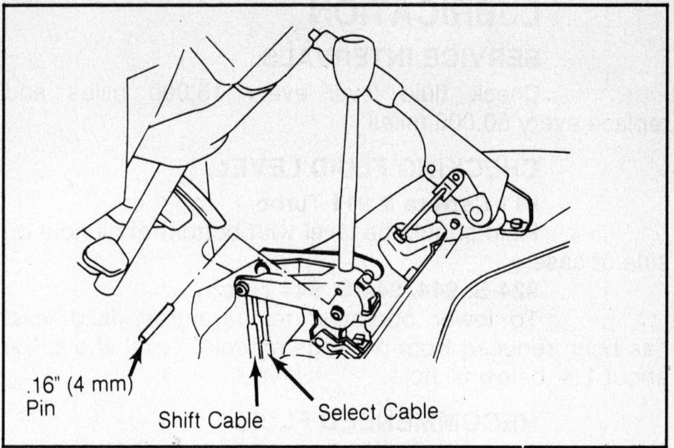

Courtesy of Nissan Motor Co., U.S.A.

NOTE: **All RWD models except Vans have floor shift mechanisms which have no external linkage and require no adjustment.**

PEUGEOT

LUBRICATION

SERVICE INTERVALS

Check oil level every 7500 miles. Change oil every 22,500 miles.

CHECKING FLUID LEVEL

Lubricant should be at bottom edge of filler hole on side of case.

RECOMMENDED FLUID

SAE 10W-40 engine oil, API grade SF.

FLUID CAPACITY

TRANSMISSION REFILL CAPACITIES

Application	Qts. (L)
505	
GL & STI Turbo (Sedans)	1.7 (1.6)
STI [1] & STX Non-Turbo	1.7 (1.6)
GL, GLS & STI (Sedans)	1.5 (1.45)

[1] – Non-turbo with ZDFL engine.

ADJUSTMENTS

GEARSHIFT LINKAGE

Lubricate ball sockets. Install shift link with center-to-center dimension of 11" (280 mm) for 5-speed. *See Fig. 1.* Adjust gate selector link with center-to-center dimension of 4.1" (105 mm). Holding ball sockets in proper directions, tighten lock nut. Install gate selector link with fixed ball socket side mounted to gearshift lever.

Fig 1: Adjusting Peugeot 5-Speed Gearshift Lever

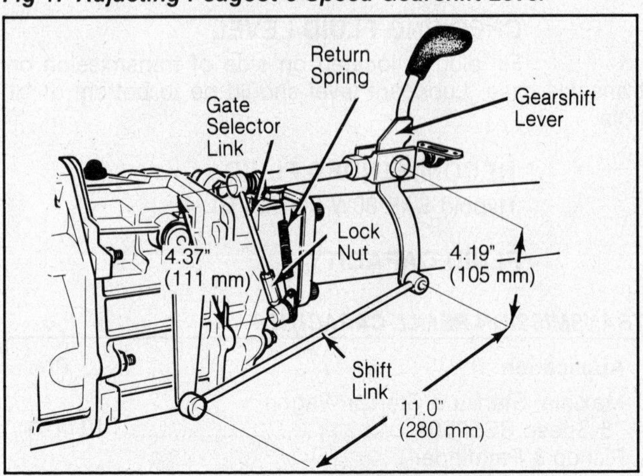

Courtesy of Peugeot Motor of America, Inc.

PORSCHE

LUBRICATION

SERVICE INTERVALS

Check fluid level every 15,000 miles and replace every 60,000 miles.

CHECKING FLUID LEVEL

911 Carrera & 911 Turbo

Fluid should be level with bottom of fill hole on side of case.

924-S, 944, 944-S, 944 Turbo

To lower operating temperatures, fluid level has been reduced from previous models. Level should be about 1/4" below fill hole.

RECOMMENDED FLUID

911

Use API GL-5, SAE 75W-90 in 911 Carrera. Use SAE 90 in 911 Turbo.

924 & 944

Use API GL-5, SAE 80W.

FLUID CAPACITY

TRANSMISSION REFILL CAPACITIES

Application	Qts. (L)
911 Carrera, 911 Turbo	10.6 (10)
924-S, 944, 944-S, 944 Turbo [1]	2.1 (2.0)

[1] – 944 Turbo transaxle with oil cooler may have slightly higher capacity.

ADJUSTMENTS

GEARSHIFT LINKAGE

911 Carrera & 911 Turbo

1) To adjust shift rod coupling at transaxle, remove carpeting or center console from tunnel between seats. Remove rear tunnel cover located in front of rear seat.

2) Place gearshift lever in Neutral. Working through rear tunnel hole, loosen shift rod clamp bolt. Rotate transaxle selector shaft to right (as viewed from driver's seat).

3) While holding selector shaft in this position, push gearshift lever to left stop in Neutral position. Ensure gearshift lever is vertical. Tighten shift rod clamp bolt to 18 ft. lbs. (25 N.m).

4) After adjustment, check for smooth engagement in all gear positions. Shift into 5th gear. With dust boot on shift rod pushed back, ensure selector shaft has a small amount of rotational play.

924-S, 944, 944-S & 944-Turbo

1) Ensure gearshift lever and transaxle are in Neutral. In this position, gearshift lever should make an 85 degree angle with the center console, as viewed from the side.

2) Transaxle should shift smoothly into all gear positions. If adjustment is necessary, shift rod is adjusted at transaxle side of shift rod.

SAAB

LUBRICATION

SERVICE INTERVALS

Check fluid level every 15,000 miles.

CHECKING FLUID LEVEL

900 Series

Check oil level with dipstick, located on right side of engine. Oil level should be between "MIN" and "MAX" marks.

9000 Series

1) The transaxle oil level is checked using the engine oil dipstick. Remove the transaxle filler plug. Insert dipstick so the notch next to the word "GEARBOX" rests against the fill plug sealing surface. Level should be between marks.

2) On 1987 1/2 and later 9000 models, method for checking fluid level has been changed. A fill plug with integral dipstick is located in transmission case (facing forward in vehicle). *See Fig. 1*.

3) Engine oil dipsticks are now similar to vehicles with automatic transmissions (without dual markings for transaxle). When checking fluid level, screw plug/dipstick completely into transaxle for accurate check. On Turbo models, it may be necessary to loosen inlet pipe to gain access to plug.

Fig. 1: Checking Fluid Level In 1987 1/2 9000 Series

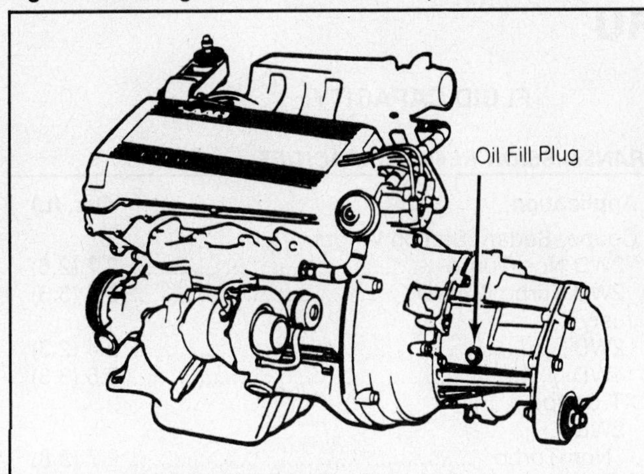

Courtesy of Saab-Scania of America.

RECOMMENDED FLUID

Use SAE 10W-30 or 10W-40 engine oil.

FLUID CAPACITY

TRANSMISSION REFILL CAPACITIES

Application	Qt. (L)
900 (5-Speed)	3.0 (3.2)
9000	2.7 (2.5)

ADJUSTMENTS

GEARSHIFT LINKAGE

900 (1986 1/2 To Present)

1) Place shift lever in 3rd gear position. Loosen pinch bolt at gear selector shaft joint on engine side of firewall. *See Fig. 2*.

2) Lock gearshift lever into 3rd gear position in gearshift housing with a .24" (6 mm) drift. It may be necessary to pry up carpeting in front of shift lever console for access to shift rod.

3) Slip Locking Device (87 91 576) into hole in shift lever input shaft and then into differential cover. *See Fig. 2*. This locks transaxle into 3rd gear. Tighten pinch bolt at gearshift joint to 22-26 ft. lbs. (20-35 N.m).

Fig. 2: Adjusting 900 Series Gearshift Linkage

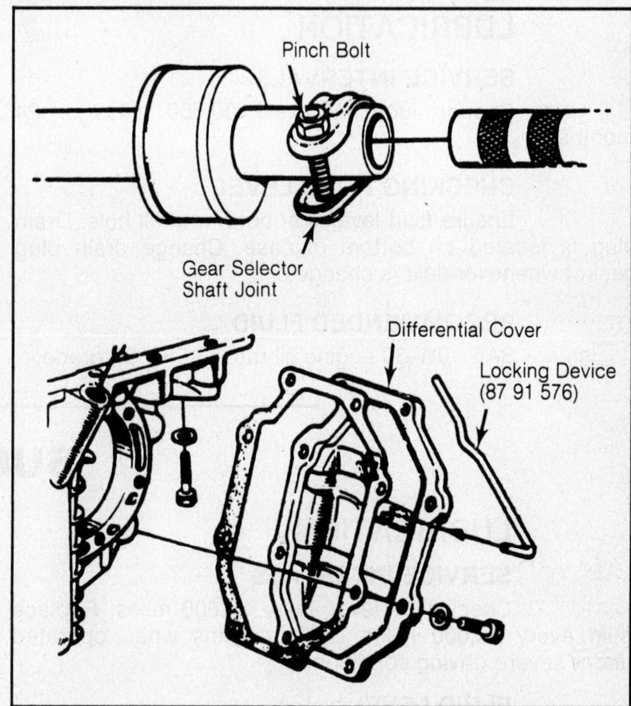

Courtesy of Saab-Scania of America.

Fig. 3: Adjusting 9000 Series Gearshift Linkage

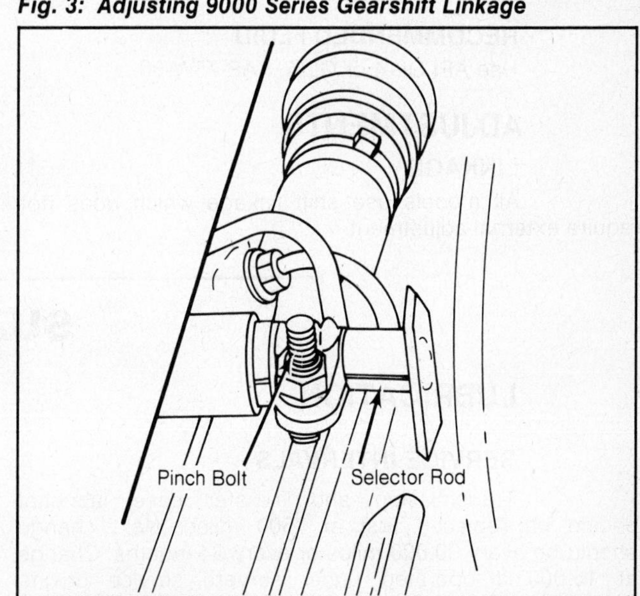

SAAB (Cont.)

9000

1) Working inside passenger compartment, pry up rubber boot around gearshift lever. Loosen the pinch bolt securing selector rod to transaxle. Pinch bolt is on engine side of firewall above steering rack. *See Fig. 3.*

2) Lock gearshift lever in reverse gear by inserting a 4 mm drill through locating holes in gearshift lever and gearshift lever housing.

3) Ensure transaxle is in Reverse. Tighten pinch bolt on selector rod. Remove drill and refit rubber boot.

STERLING

LUBRICATION

SERVICE INTERVALS

Change lubricant every 30,000 miles or 24 months.

CHECKING FLUID LEVEL

Ensure fluid level is at bottom of fill hole. Drain plug is located on bottom of case. Change drain plug gasket whenever fluid is changed.

RECOMMENDED FLUID

SAE 10W-30 engine oil rated SE or SF grade.

FLUID CAPACITY

TRANSMISSION REFILL CAPACITIES

Application	Pts. (L)
825	4.8 (2.3)

ADJUSTMENTS

LINKAGE

No external adjustments are required.

SUBARU

LUBRICATION

SERVICE INTERVALS

Check fluid level every 15,000 miles. Replace fluid every 30,000 miles or 30 months when operated under severe driving conditions.

FLUID LEVEL

Check lubricant level at dipstick located in engine compartment. Transaxle and differential are lubricated through common oil supply.

RECOMMENDED FLUID

Use API GL-4 or GL-5, SAE 75W-90.

ADJUSTMENTS

LINKAGE

All models use shift linkage which does not require external adjustment.

FLUID CAPACITY

TRANSMISSION REFILL CAPACITIES

Application	Qts. (L)
Coupe, Sedan, Station Wagon	
2WD Non-Turbo	2.7 (2.6)
2WD Turbo & 4WD	3.5 (3.3)
Justy	
2WD	2.4 (2.3)
4WD	3.5 (3.3)
XT Coupe	
2WD	
Non-Turbo	2.7 (2.8)
Turbo	3.5 (3.3)
4WD	
Selective 4WD	3.5 (3.3)
Full-Time 4WD	3.7 (3.5)

SUZUKI

LUBRICATION

SERVICE INTERVALS

Transmission and transfer case lubricant should be replaced first at 7500 miles. Next change should be every 30,000 miles or every 24 months. Change at 15,000 if operated under servere service driving conditions. Inspection should be performed every 7500 miles or every 6 months.

CHECKING FLUID LEVEL

Ensure vehicle is on level surface. Remove fill plugs from transmission and transfer case. If oil flows out of plug hole or if oil level is up to hole when level plug is removed, oil level is okay. If level is low, fill until oil level is even with plug hole.

RECOMMENDED FLUID

Use API GL-4, SAE 80W. Use SAE 75W-85 in cold climates.

SUZUKI (Cont.)

FLUID CAPACITY

TRANSMISSION REFILL CAPACITY

Application	Pts.
Transmission	2.7 (1.3)
Transfer Case	1.7 (0.8)

ADJUSTMENTS

LINKAGE

No external adjustments are necessary.

CLUTCH PEDAL HEIGHT

Adjust height of clutch pedal with clutch pedal stop bolt so clutch pedal is level with brake pedal. Tighten lock nut after adjusting.

CLUTCH PEDAL FREE PLAY

Depress clutch pedal until clutch resistance is felt. Free play should be 0.8-1.1" (20-30 mm). If free travel is out of adjustment, adjust it with clutch cable outer nuts at clutch release lever. After adjusting free travel, make sure that clutch cable end protrudes at least .20" (5 mm) from joint nut.

TOYOTA

LUBRICATION

SERVICE INTERVALS

Check lubricant level every 20,000 on all except 4WD pickups. On 4WD pickups, check every 15,000 miles. Replace fluid if vehicle is operated in severe service conditions.

CHECKING FLUID LEVEL

Transmission

Check lubricant level at fill plug hole. Lubricant should be to bottom of hole. Transmission on Tercel Wagon has 2 drain plugs on bottom of case.

Fig. 1: Tercel Wagon Transaxle & Differential Drain & Fill Plug Locations

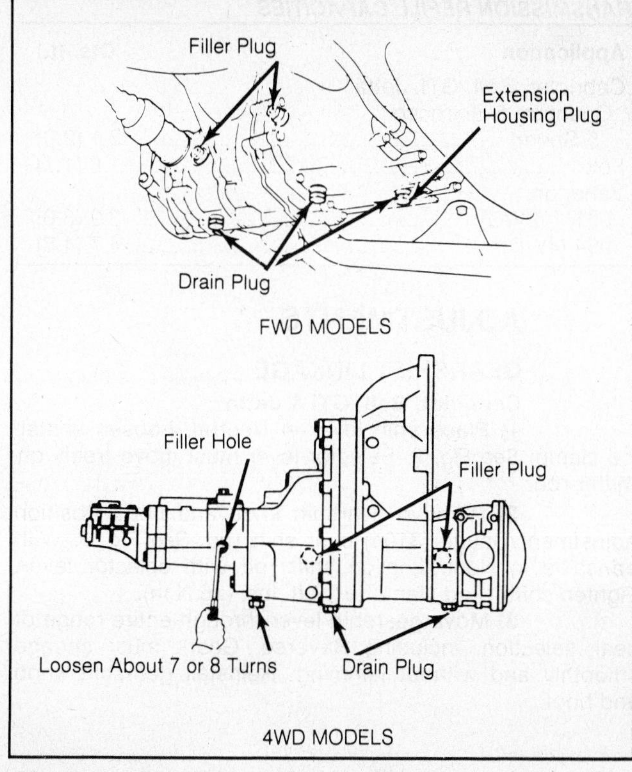

Courtesy of Toyota Motor Sales, U.S.A., Inc.

Transfer Case (Except Tercel Wagon)

Transfer cases on 4WD vehicles (except Tercel Wagon) have separate drain and fill plugs from main transmission.

Transfer Case (Tercel Wagon)

The combination differential and transaxles assembly on Tercel Wagons have separate drain and fill plugs. *See Fig. 1.* When filling with fluid, leave extension housing drain plug loose about 7 or 8 turns. After filling, tighten drain plug.

RECOMMENDED FLUID

All Except Camry & Celica

API GL-4 or GL-5, SAE 75W-90 or 80W-90W.

Camry & Celica

Dexron II ATF.

FLUID CAPACITY

TRANSMISSION REFILL CAPACITIES

Application	Qts. (L)
Camry	2.5 (2.4)
Celica	2.7 (2.6)
Cressida	2.5 (2.4)
Corolla FWD	2.6 (2.7)
Corolla RWD	1.8 (1.7)
Land Cruiser	
Transmission	3.7 (3.5)
Transfer Case	2.3 (2.2)
MR2	2.7 (2.6)
Pickup & Pathfinder	
Transmission	
2WD	
W46, 55, 56	2.5 (2.4)
R150	2.7 (2.6)
4WD	
G52	4.1 (3.9)
W56, R151F	3.2 (3.0)
Transfer Case	1.7 (1.6)
Tercel Sedan	2.5 (2.4)
Tercel Wagon	
FWD	3.6 (3.4)
4WD	4.1 (3.9)
Van	
Transmission	
2WD	2.3 (2.2)
4WD	2.7 (2.6)
Transfer Case	1.3 (1.2)

TOYOTA (Cont.)

ADJUSTMENTS

LINKAGE

Shift Lever Free Play (Camry, Celica & FWD Corolla)

1) Select a shim that allows a preload of 1.6-3.2 oz. (50-100 g) at the top of shift lever. *See Fig. 2.* Install shim in shift lever seat.

2) Shims are available from .3-1.2 mm in .1 mm increments. The .3 mm shim is marked with "A" or "3" while the .4 mm shim is marked with "B" or "4". All other shims are similarly marked up to the 1.2 mm shim ("L" or "12").

Fig. 2: Checking Shift Lever Preload on Camry, Celica & FWD Corolla

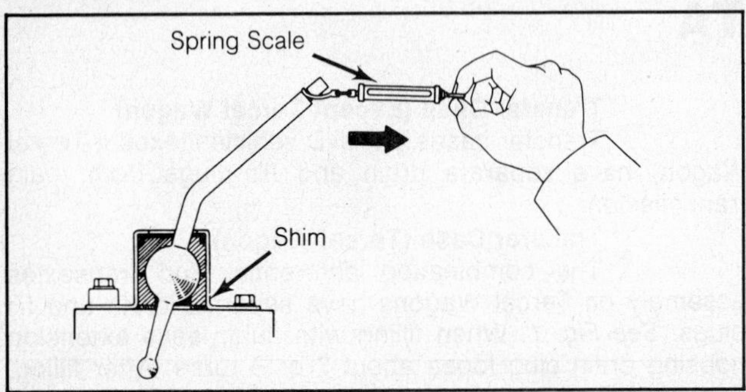

Courtesy of Toyota Motor Sales, U.S.A., Inc.

Shift Lever (Van)

1) Remove shifter console box. Ensure shift lever is in Neutral position. Check if a .24" (6 mm) diameter pin inserts easily into shift lever retainer hole and shift lever inspection hole.

2) To adjust shift lever Neutral position, loosen adjusting lock nuts on select control cable. *See Fig. 3.* Adjust length of select control cable so guide pin inserts smoothly into both holes.

3) Tighten adjusting lock nuts. Remove guide pin and install console box.

NOTE: **Models not listed do not require adjustment.**

Fig. 3: Adjusting Van Shift Lever Neutral Position

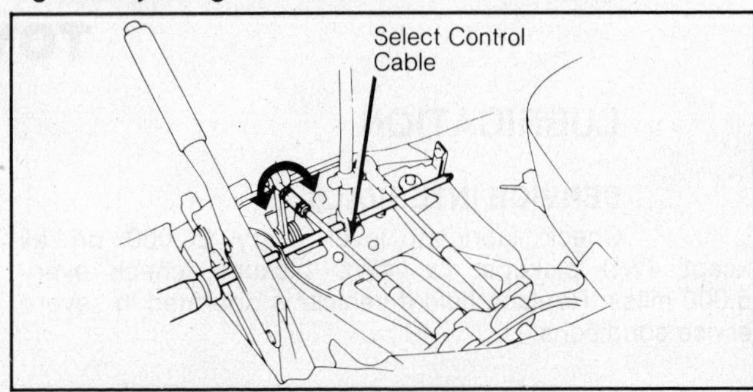

Courtesy of Toyota Motor Sales, U.S.A., Inc.

VOLKSWAGEN

LUBRICATION

SERVICE INTERVALS

No oil changes are required. Check oil every 15,000 miles.

FLUID LEVEL

All Except Cabriolet, Golf, GTI & Jetta

Check lubricant level at fill hole. Lubricant should be level with bottom of fill hole.

Cabriolet, Golf, GTI & Jetta

1) Because of transaxle mounting angle, oil will run out of checking hole even though transaxle is filled to capacity. To check oil level, place vehicle on level surface.

2) Remove oil filler plug. Allow oil to drain off until level with edge of hole. *See Fig. 1.* Remove speedometer cable at transaxle. Pour in .5 qt. (.5L) of fluid.

RECOMMENDED FLUID

Use API GL-4, SAE 80W or 80W-90.

FLUID CAPACITY

TRANSMISSION REFILL CAPACITIES

Application	Qts. (L)
Cabriolet, Golf, GTI, Jetta, Quantum & Scirocco	
5-Speed	2.1 (2.0)
Fox	1.8 (1.7)
Vanagon	
091/1 (2WD)	3.2 (3.0)
094 (4WD)	4.7 (4.5)

ADJUSTMENTS

GEARSHIFT LINKAGE

Cabriolet, Golf, GTI & Jetta

1) Place shift lever in Neutral. Loosen shifter rod clamp. *See Fig. 2.* Selector lever must move freely on shifter rod.

2) Remove gearshift knob and boot. Position Adjustment Gauge (3104) over shift rod. *See Fig. 3.* With transaxle in Neutral, align shift rod with selector lever. Tighten shifter rod clamp to 19 ft. lbs. (26 N.m).

3) Move gearshift lever through entire range of gear selection, including Reverse. Gears must engage smoothly and without jamming. Reinstall gearshift knob and boot.

VOLKSWAGEN (Cont.)

Fig. 1: Checking & Adding Fluid to Cabriolet, Golf, GTI & Jetta

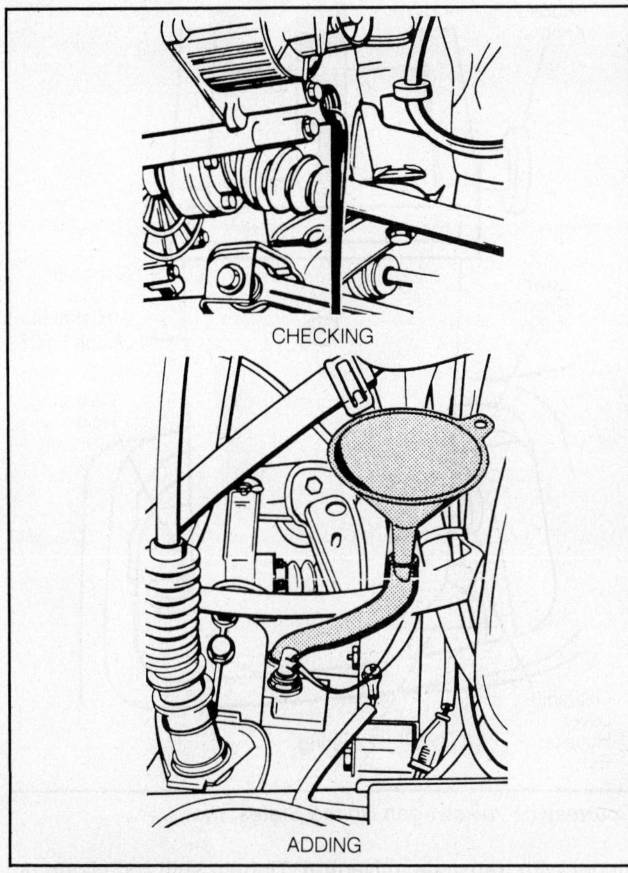

Courtesy of Volkswagen United States, Inc.

Fig. 2: Shift Rod Clamp Location (Cabriolet, Golf, GTI & Jetta

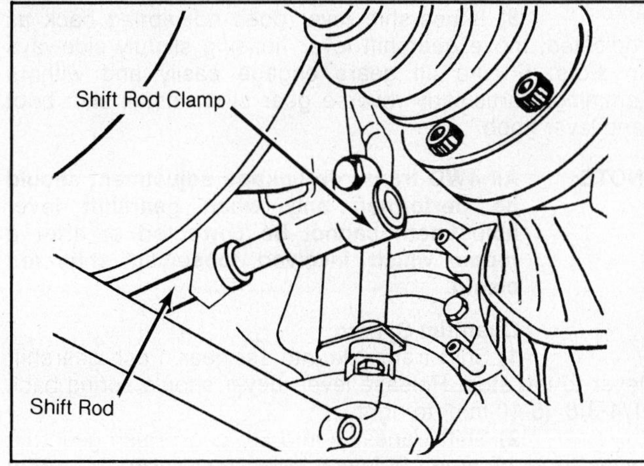

Courtesy of Volkswagen United States, Inc.

Fox

1) Shift transaxle into 1st gear. Push gearshift lever to left stop. Release lever. If lever does not spring back 1/4-3/8" (5-10 mm) to right, move gearshift lever in slots. If adjustment does not correct hard shifting, go to step **2)**.

Fig. 3: Adjustment Gauge Location

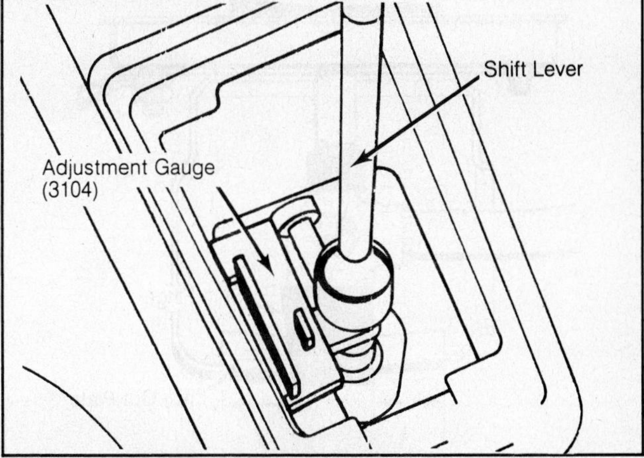

Courtesy of Volkswagen United States, Inc.

2) Place gearshift lever in Neutral. Remove gearshift lever and shift boot. Loosen shift rod clamp nut. *See Fig. 4.*

3) Ensure shift finger slides freely on shift rod. Move gearshift lever to right side, between 3rd and 4th gear positions. Gearshift lever should remain perpendicular to ball housing.

4) With inner shift lever in Neutral, and gearshift lever between 3rd and 4th gear, tighten clamp nut. Ensure transaxle shifts smoothly. If necessary, adjust gearshift lever bearing housing.

Fig. 4: Shift Rod Clamp Nut For Fox

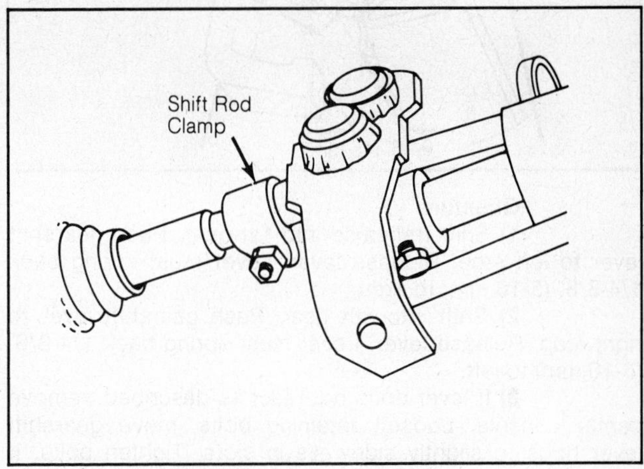

Courtesy of Volkswagen United States, Inc.

Scirocco

1) Pull boot off housing. Loosen shift rod clamp bolt so lever moves freely on shift rod. Adjust shift finger in center of lock-out plate so that an equal distance is obtained on both sides of shift finger. *See Fig. 5.*

2) Adjust shift rod end so distance "A" is 9/16" (15 mm). *See Fig. 6.* Tighten shift rod clamp to 14 ft. lbs. (20 N.m). If shift linkage is spongy or jamming after adjustment, change distance "A" to 1/2" (13 mm). If shift linkage will not stay adjusted, install a new clamp bolt and lock nut.

VOLKSWAGEN (Cont.)

Fig. 5: Adjusting Scirocco Shift Finger

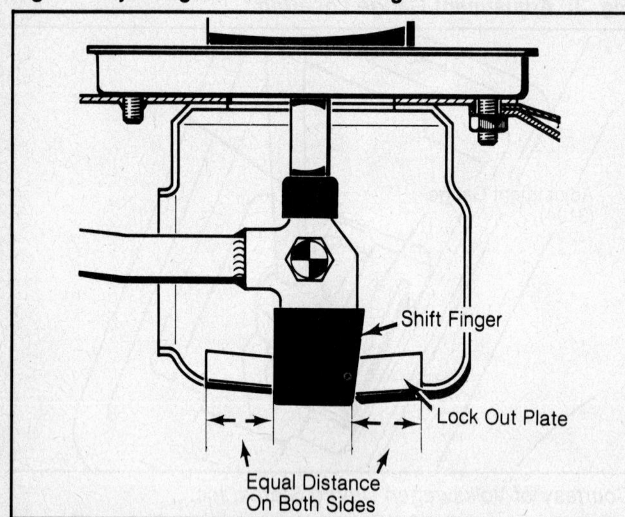

Courtesy of Volkswagen United States, Inc.

Fig. 6: Adjusting Scirocco Shift Rod End

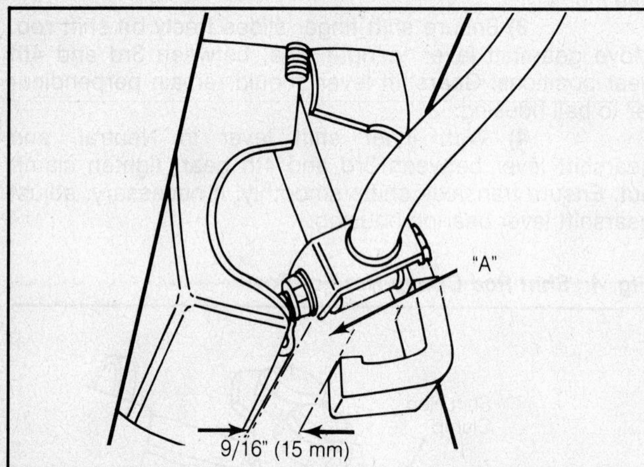

Quantum

1) Shift transaxle into 1st gear. Push gearshift lever to left stop. Release lever. Lever must spring back 1/4-3/8" (5-10 mm) to right.

2) Shift into 5th gear. Push gearshift lever to right stop. Release lever. Lever must spring back 1/4-3/8" (5-10 mm) to left.

3) If lever does not react as described, remove center console. Loosen retaining bolts, move gearshift lever housing slightly sideways in slots. Tighten bolts. If this adjustment does not correct hard shifting, proceed to step **4)**.

4) Place gearshift lever in Neutral. From under vehicle, loosen shift rod clamp nut so shift finger slides freely on shift rod. *See Fig. 4.* Remove shift lever knob and rubber boot.

5) Loosen gearshift lever housing bolts, align round centering holes and tighten bolts. Install Linkage Adjustment Gauge (3057) with locating pin toward front. *See Fig. 7.* Push shift lever to "5/R" gear position of gauge. Tighten lower knurled knob on gauge.

6) Move shift lever and slide to right stop. Tighten upper knurled knob on gauge. Push shift lever into "3/4" gear position of gauge. Adjust shift rod and

Fig. 7: Adjusting Quantum Gearshift Linkage

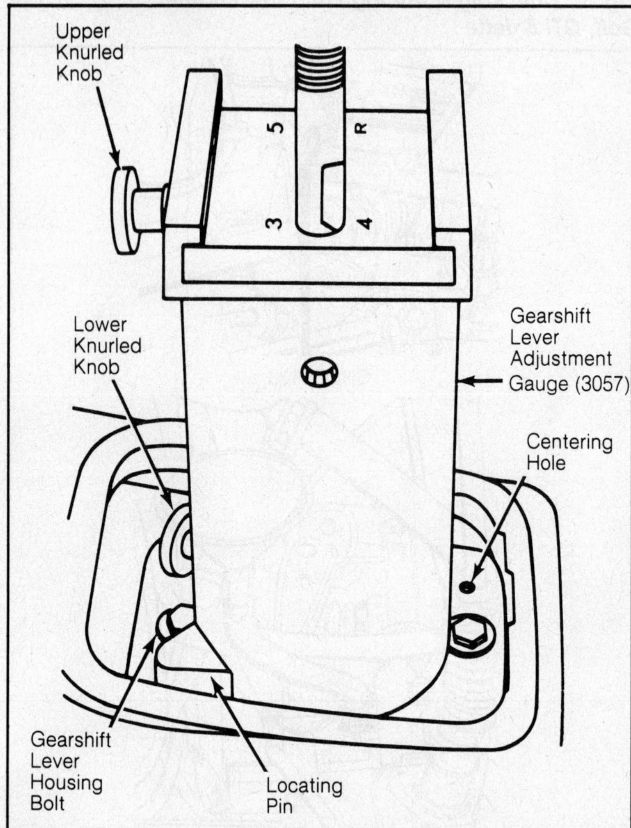

Courtesy of Volkswagen United States, Inc.

finger with transaxle in Neutral. Tighten shift rod clamp nut and remove gauge.

7) Place gearshift lever in 1st gear, press to left stop and release. Shift lever must spring back to right. Place lever in 5th gear, push shift lever to right stop and release. Shift lever must spring back to left.

8) If gearshift lever does not spring back as indicated, move gearshift lever housing slightly sideways in slots. Ensure all gears engage easily and without jamming, particularly reverse gear stop. Install shift boot and lever knob.

NOTE: **All 4WD transaxle linkage adjustment should be performed only when gearshift lever adjustment cannot be corrected or after a repair which involved loosening shift rod clamp.**

Quantum Syncro

1) Shift transaxle into 1st gear. Push gearshift lever to left stop. Release lever. Lever should spring back 1/4-3/8" (5-10 mm) to right.

2) Shift transaxle into 5th gear. Push gearshift lever to right stop. Release lever. Lever should spring back 1/4-3/8" (5-10 mm) to left.

3) If gearshift lever does not respond as described in steps **1)** and **2)**, remove shift knob. Remove lower center console.

4) Loosen 4 housing retaining bolts. *See Fig. 8.* Move gearshift lever slightly in slots. Tighten bolts.

5) If still not adjusted, place transaxle in Neutral. Loosen 4 bolts. Align centering holes of stop

VOLKSWAGEN (Cont.)

Fig. 8: Adjusting Quantum Syncro Gearshift Linkage

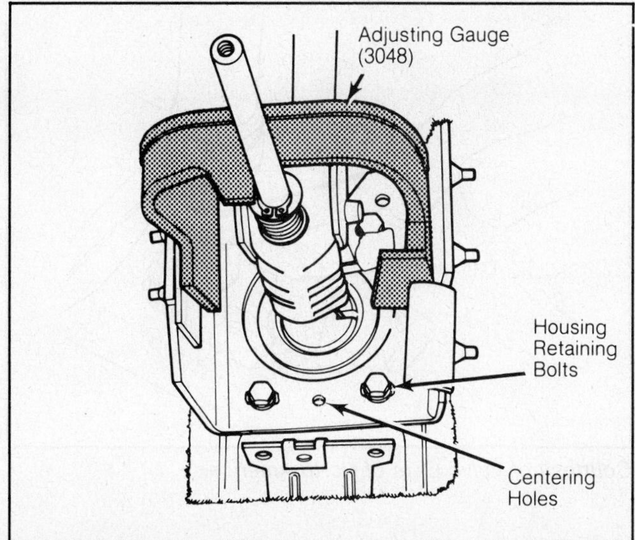

Courtesy of Volkswagen United States, Inc.

plate and bearing support. Tighten bolts. Install Adjusting Gauge (3048).

6) Loosen clamp between front and rear shift rods under vehicle. Allow rear rod to center itself. Tighten clamp nut to 11 ft. lbs. (15 N.m). Remove adjusting gauge. Ensure transaxle shifts correctly. Install console and boot.

Vanagon

1) Place gearshift lever in Neutral position. Align round centering holes of upper gearshift lever housing plate with holes in lower lever bearing plate.

2) Loosen nut on clamp that connects front and rear shift rods. Ensure joints of shift rods slide freely. Remove spare tire. Set shift lever on transaxle in vertical (Neutral) position.

3) At gearshift lever end of front shift rod, ensure stop finger of front shift rod is in center of shift mechanism housing.

4) Adjust front shift rod end so there is 29/32" (23 mm) clearance between front shift rod end and stop plate. Tighten shift rod clamp.

5) Check for proper operation. Ensure shift lever does not rub against heater pipe insulation.

Vanagon Syncro (4WD)

1) Place gearshift lever in Neutral position. Align round centering holes of upper gearshift lever housing plate with holes in lower lever bearing plate.

2) Loosen nut on clamp that connects front and rear shift rods. Ensure joints of shift rods slide freely. Remove spare tire. Set shift lever on transaxle in vertical (Neutral) position.

3) Push shift rod into transaxle until spring tension is felt (shift position for 2nd-3rd gear). Hold in this position.

4) Push shift rod to right (shift position for 1st-Reverse). Clearance between between reverse gear lock and shift rod stop should be .12" (3 mm).

5) Allow shift to spring back to left to 2nd-3rd gear shift position. Push rod slightly to right. Boot must touch inside of shift mechanism housing.

6) Making sure transaxle and gearshift lever are in Neutral positions, tighten clamp nut between front and rear shift rods. Tighten to 18 ft. lbs. (25 N.m).

7) Place gearshift lever in 2nd gear position inside passenger compartment. Distance between gearshift lever and upper edge of gearshift lever opening in console must be at least 5/8" (15 mm). If not, adjust gearshift lever bearing by sliding back in slotted holes. Ensure all gears engage smoothly.

VOLVO

LUBRICATION

SERVICE INTERVALS

Check fluid every 7500 miles.

CHECKING FLUID LEVEL

1) Fluid should be up to bottom of fill hole. When adding oil, allow sufficient time for oil to flow into overdrive unit on M46 transmission. The M46 transmission and overdrive use common fluid.

2) If fluid has to be changed on M46 transmission, overdrive unit has separate oil pan and filter. *See Fig. 1.*

3) Use Socket (2836) to remove plug. Clean strainer and magnet with solvent. Replace filter and tighten plug to 14 ft. lbs. (20 N.m). Install new gasket and tighten overdrive pan bolts to 84 INCH lbs. (10 N.m).

RECOMMENDED FLUID

Use Type F ATF. DO NOT use Dexron II. In climates where temperatures are consistently below 14°F (-10°C) or in high mileage vehicles, use Volvo Thermal Oil (1161243-9).

FLUID CAPACITY

TRANSMISSION REFILL CAPACITIES

Application	Qts.
M46 (4-Speed, Overdrive)	2.4 (2.3)
M47 (5-Speed)	1.6 (1.55)

ADJUSTMENTS

LINKAGE

No external linkage adjustment is required.

REVERSE DETENT

Place transmission in 1st gear. Clearance between detent plate and detent screw should be .02-.06" (.5-1.5 mm). Adjust by moving detent plate. *See Fig. 2.*

VOLVO (Cont.)

Fig. 1: Overdrive Filter on M46 Transmission

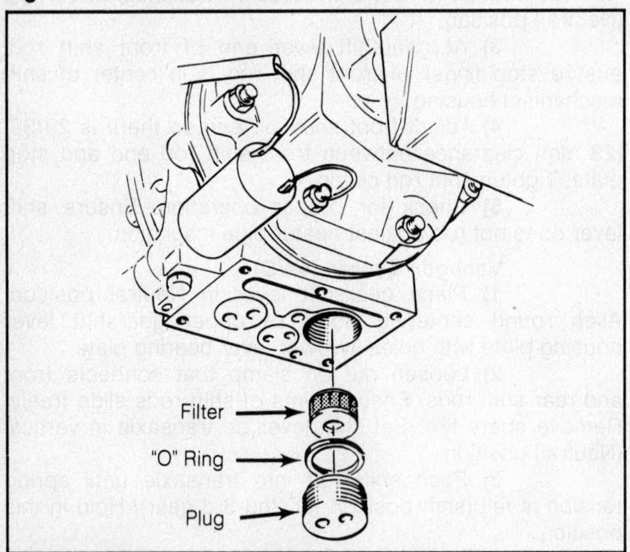

Courtesy of Volvo Cars of North America.

Fig. 2: Adjusting Reverse Detent

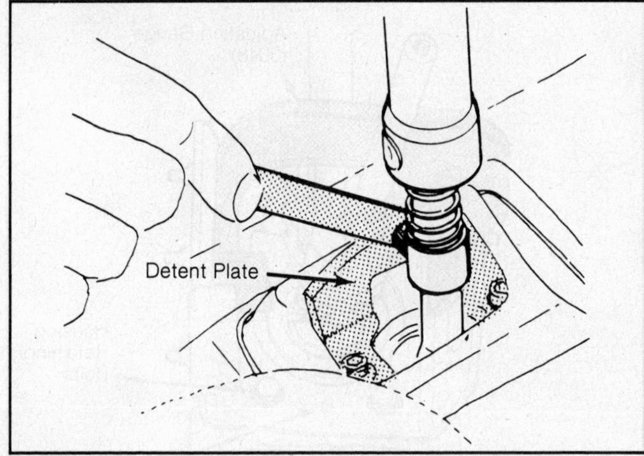

Courtesy of Volvo Cars of North America.

YUGO

LUBRICATION

SERVICE INTERVALS

Transaxle lubricant should be replaced first at 7500 miles. Replacement should be performed every 30,000 miles or every 24 months thereafter. Inspection should be performed every 7500 miles or every 6 months.

CHECKING FLUID LEVEL

Transaxle should be cool to touch. Vehicle should be on level surface. Oil should be to lower edge of fill plug hole on side of case. Drain plug is on bottom of case.

RECOMMENDED FLUID

Use low-ash detergent oil (API Service SF-CC), SAE 40.

FLUID CAPACITY

TRANSMISSION REFILL CAPACITY

Application	Quantity
GV	6.7 pts. (3.2L)

ADJUSTMENTS

GEARSHIFT LINKAGE

If transaxle slips out of gear or will not engage, readjust linkage. Gearshift lever should be in vertical position with lever in Neutral. To adjust, loosen retaining bolts and move flexible link in elongated holes.

CLUTCH PEDAL FREE PLAY

Depress clutch pedal and stop when clutch resistance is felt. Free play should be 1.0" (25 mm). If free travel is out of adjustment, adjust it with clutch cable outer nut at transaxle lever.

Fig. 1: Yugo Gearshift Linkage

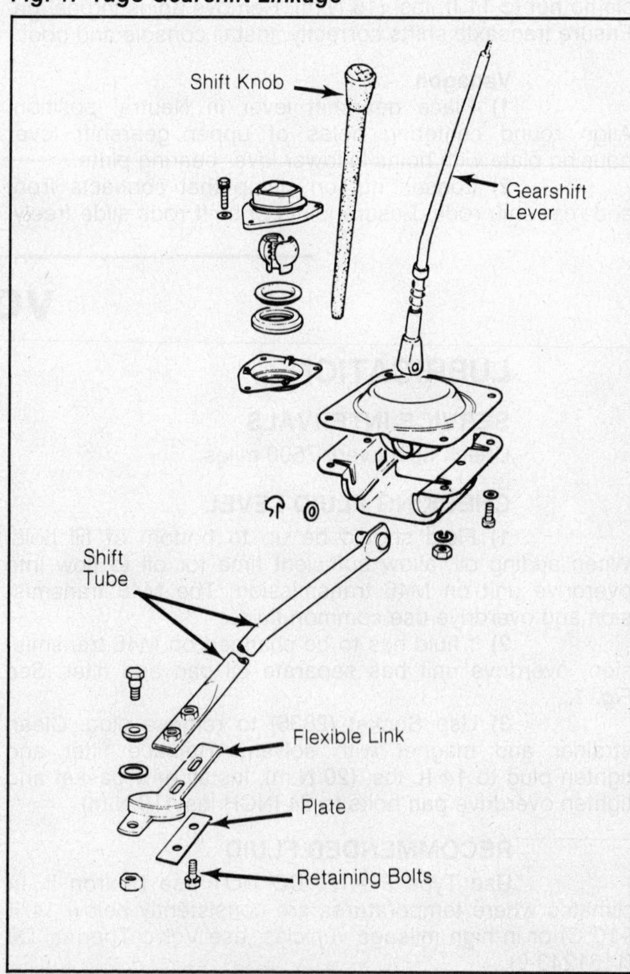

Courtesy of Yugo America, Inc.

ACURA

INTEGRA

REMOVAL

1) Disconnect ground cable at battery and transaxle. Release steering lock, and place gearshift selector lever in "N". Disconnect wiring from starter. Drain transaxle fluid. Reinstall drain plug and washer. Disconnect speedometer cable. Disconnect cooler hoses, and wire them up next to radiator, so ATF will not drain out.

2) Remove center console. Disconnect shift cable by removing adjusting pin. Unscrew cable guide bolt, and pull throttle control cable out of passenger compartment. Remove right and left drive axle shafts and intermediate shaft.

3) Screw a 10 mm bolt into cylinder head (diagonally opposite lifting eye). Attach chain hoist to bolt and other end to engine lifting eye. Lift engine slightly to unload mounts. Remove engine under cover and splash shield. Disconnect header pipe at exhaust manifold.

4) Place a jack under transaxle and raise transaxle just enough to take weight off mounts. Remove bolts from front mount at front engine bracket. Remove rear transaxle mount bracket by removing mounting bolts. Remove transaxle housing bolts from front transaxle mounting bracket.

5) Remove torque converter cover. Remove drive plate-to-converter bolts. Remove starter motor. Remove transaxle mounting bolts. Pull transaxle away from engine until it clears dowel pins, then lower on jack.

INSTALLATION

To install transaxle, reverse removal procedure. New spring clips must be used on ends of both drive axle shafts. Tighten drive plate-to-converter bolts to 108 INCH lbs. (12 N.m).

LEGEND & LEGEND COUPE

REMOVAL

1) Disconnect battery negative and positive cables from battery. Disconnect starter motor and ground cables. Drain ATF. Reinstall drain plug and washer. Remove air cleaner case complete with intake hose.

2) Remove speedometer gearbox complete with power steering speed sensor hose. Disconnect control cable at throttle body. Disconnect cooler hoses at joint pipes. Turn ends up to prevent ATF from flowing out.

3) Disconnect lock-up control solenoid valve wire connector. Remove center console, pry off adjuster pin, and disconnect control cable.

4) Remove control cable guide bolts, and pull cable out of housing. Remove right and left drive axle shafts. Remove intermediate shaft. Remove torque converter case mounting bolts from torque rod bracket.

CAUTION: Replace torque rod bolts with new ones whenever loosened or removed.

5) Attach chain hoist with 2 bolts to rear side of engine. Raise engine slight amount to unload mounts. Remove 2 front engine mount bolts from transaxle housing.

6) While holding lock nut, remove radius rod. Remove center crossmember. Remove center stopper bracket from transaxle. Remove torque converter cover. Place jack under transaxle. Raise transaxle just enough to take weight off mounts.

7) Remove 2 rear engine mount bolts from transaxle. Remove drive plate bolts. Remove starter motor. Remove remaining bolts attaching transaxle housing to engine. Lower transaxle out of vehicle.

INSTALLATION

To install transaxle, reverse removal procedure. Tighten drive plate-to-converter bolts to 96 INCH lbs. (10 N.m) on Legend and 108 INCH lbs. (12 N.m) on Legend Coupe. Tighten NEW torque rod bracket bolts to 29 ft. lbs. (39 N.m).

AUDI

COUPE GT & 4000S

REMOVAL

087 Transaxle

1) Disconnect battery ground cable. Disconnect accelerator linkage rod at accelerator. Disconnect speedometer cable. Remove upper engine-to-transaxle bolts.

2) Support engine from above. Disconnect automatic transaxle cooler lines from side of transaxle. Disconnect exhaust pipe from manifold. Disconnect exhaust pipe bracket at transaxle.

3) Unbolt exhaust pipe from catalytic converter. Remove axle shaft guard plate, then disconnect axle shafts from transaxle flanges. Wire axle shafts back out of way. Remove starter. Remove 3 bolts securing torque converter to drive plate.

4) Disconnect accelerator push rod from transaxle. Remove accelerator cable support from side of transaxle. Detach accelerator cable from operating lever.

5) Detach transaxle shift cable from transaxle. Remove front subframe mounting bolts. Support transaxle with jack and raise slightly. Remove center bolt from transaxle mount.

6) Remove lower engine-to-transaxle bolts. Separate transaxle from engine. Secure torque converter to transaxle to prevent converter from falling when removing transaxle. Lower transaxle out of vehicle.

089 Transaxle

1) Disconnect battery ground cable. Remove upper engine-to-transaxle bolts. Support engine from above. Disconnect automatic transaxle cooler lines.

AUDI (Cont.)

2) Disconnect exhaust pipe bracket at transaxle. Detach speedometer cable at transaxle. Disconnect axle shafts from transaxle flanges. Wire axle shafts back out of way. Remove starter. Remove 3 bolts securing torque converter to drive plate.

3) Separate lower ball joints from control arms. If draining ATF, remove filler tube from oil pan. Detach transaxle shift cable from transaxle. Remove accelerator cable bracket from transaxle.

4) Unhook accelerator cable from transaxle operating lever. Support transaxle with jack and raise slightly. Remove center bolt from transaxle mount.

5) Remove throttle cable bracket from side of transaxle. Remove lower engine-to-transaxle bolts. Separate transaxle from engine. Secure torque converter to transaxle to prevent converter from falling when removing transaxle. Lower transaxle out of vehicle.

INSTALLATION

087 & 089 Transaxle

To install transaxle, reverse removal procedure. Ensure torque converter is fully seated on transaxle. When fully seated, center hub of converter should be about 3/8" from engine mating surface on converter housing. Adjust accelerator and shift linkages.

AUDI 4000 TIGHTENING SPECIFICATIONS

Application	Ft. Lbs. (N.m)
Center Transaxle Mount Bolt	30 (40)
CV Joint-to-Flange Bolts	33 (45)
Front Subframe Bolts	52 (70)
Torque Converter-to-Drive Plate Bolts	22 (30)
Transaxle-to-Engine Bolts (M12)	41 (55)

5000 SERIES

REMOVAL

1) Disconnect battery ground cable. Disconnect hoses from transaxle cooler. Disconnect accelerator linkage and speedometer cable. Support engine from above. Remove upper engine-to-transaxle bolts. Remove guard plate from subframe and remove exhaust pipe.

2) Remove right guard plate at right axle drive shaft, and remove drive shaft bolts. Remove starter, selector lever cable holder and selector lever cable at transaxle lever.

3) Disconnect lower accelerator linkage rod and accelerator cable from transaxle lever. Remove right side guard plate from subframe. Remove torque converter-to-drive plate bolts.

4) Support transaxle with jack and raise slightly. Remove lower engine-to-transaxle bolts and rear subframe bolts. Position drive shafts away from transaxle. Separate transaxle from engine, secure torque converter in place and lower transaxle from vehicle.

INSTALLATION

To install, reverse removal procedure. When attaching torque converter to drive plate use new bolts and lock washers. Check and adjust accelerator cable and throttle linkage (if necessary).

AUDI 5000 TIGHTENING SPECIFICATIONS

Application	Ft. Lbs. (N.m)
C.V. Joint-to-Flange	59 (80)
Torque Converter-to-Drive Plate Bolts	22 (30)
Transaxle-to-Engine Bolts	41 (55)
Transaxle Support-to-Subframe	44 (60)
Transaxle Support-to-Transaxle	30 (40)

BMW

ALL MODELS

REMOVAL

1) Disconnect battery ground cable. Detach transmission throttle cable from accelerator cross shaft and bracket. Raise and support vehicle. Remove exhaust assembly and heat shields.

2) Disconnect joint disc from transmission output flange. Propeller shaft flanges may be left attached to joint disc. At center mount, loosen propeller shaft threaded ring several turns. Disconnect selector rod from transmission.

3) Remove bolts from center mount to body. Position propeller shaft out of way. Disconnect oil cooler lines from transmission. Drain transmission fluid. Remove oil filler tube lower end from oil pan.

4) Remove reinforcement plate below converter housing. Remove 4 torque converter-to-drive plate bolts. Support transmission with jack. Remove speed sensor and reference mark sensor from converter housing bores (if equipped).

NOTE: **Engine can not be started if speed and reference sensors positions are reversed.**

5) On EH (electronic) transmissions, disconnect wiring harness from transmission. On all models, remove transmission cross-member. Remove transmission-to-engine attaching bolts. Slide transmission back and remove.

INSTALLATION

To install, reverse removal procedure. Clean out all transmission oil cooler lines. Check for full engagement of torque converter in transmission. Adjust throttle cable and selector rod. If drive plate was removed, use NEW bolts and coat threads with Loctite No. 270.

NOTE: **BMW recommends replacing propeller shaft flange nuts and bolts. Only tighten nut, not bolts, to prevent stress in the coupling.**

BMW (Cont.)

BMW TIGHTENING SPECIFICATIONS

Application	Ft. Lbs. (N.m)
Drive Plate-to-Engine (M12)	71-81 (98-112)
Propeller Shaft Joint Disc-to-Transmission Flange	
M10 x 8.8	33 (46)
M10 x 10.9	52 (72)
M12	89 (123)
M12 (Type E32)	59 (81)
Propeller Shaft Threaded Ring	15 (20)
Torque Converter-to-Drive Plate	
M8	18-20 (25-27)
M10 [1]	34-37 (47-51)

BMW TIGHTENING SPECIFICATIONS (Cont.)

Application	Ft. Lbs. (N.m)
Transmission-to-Engine Bolts	
Hex Head Bolts	
M8	17 (24)
M10	33 (45)
M12	56-62 (78-86)
Torx Bolts [2]	
M8	15 (21)
M12	46 (63)

[1] – Always use spring washers with M10 x 16 bolts.
[2] – Torx type bolts must always use washers.

CHEVROLET

SPECTRUM

NOTE: For Spectrum information, see ISUZU I-MARK in this article.

SPRINT

REMOVAL

1) Disconnect air suction guide from air cleaner. Disconnect negative and positive cables from battery. Remove battery and tray. Disconnect negative cable at transaxle. Disconnect solenoid wire coupler and shift lever switch wire couplers. Disconnect wire harness and speedometer cable from transaxle.

2) Disconnect oil pressure control cable from accelerator cable. Disconnect accelerator cable from transaxle. Disconnect select cable from transaxle. Remove starter motor. Drain transaxle fluid.

3) Disconnect oil outlet and inlet hoses from oil pipes. After disconnecting, plug 2 oil hoses to prevent fluid in hoses and oil cooler from draining. Raise vehicle. Disconnect exhaust No. 1 pipe. Remove clutch housing lower plate.

4) Remove 6 drive plate-to-converter bolts. To lock drive plate, engage a screwdriver with drive plate gear through notch provided at underside of transaxle case. Remove left front drive axle. Detach inner CV joint of right axle from differential. Remove transaxle mounting member.

5) Securely support transaxle with a jack for removal. Disconnect transaxle left mounting. Remove bolts fastening engine and transaxle. Disconnect transaxle from engine by sliding toward left side. Carefully lower jack.

INSTALLATION

1) To install, reverse removal procedure. Before installing, apply grease around cup at center of torque converter. When installing transaxle, guide right drive axle into differential side gear as transaxle is being raised.

2) After inserting inner CV joints of right and left axles into differential side gears, push inner joints into side gears until snap rings on drive axles engage side gears. After connecting oil pressure control cable to accelerator cable, check oil pressure control cable play and adjust if necessary.

3) Tighten drive plate-to-converter bolts to 14 ft. lbs. (19 N.m). Tighten transaxle-to-engine bolts to 40 ft. lbs. (55 N.m).

CHRYSLER MOTORS

FWD MODELS

REMOVAL

1) Remove battery and battery tray. Disconnect oil cooler hoses and all external electrical connectors to transaxle. Disconnect and remove shift cable and throttle cable. Disconnect speedometer cable and wiring for starter motor. Remove starter motor.

2) Raise and support vehicle. Drain transaxle oil and remove engine under cover if necessary. Remove bellhousing cover and index mark torque converter to drive plate. Manually rotate engine and remove bolts that hold torque converter to drive plate. Push torque converter toward transaxle to ensure separation from engine.

3) Disconnect stabilizer bar, tie rod ends and lower control arm ball joint where necessary. Remove drive axle shafts and support out of the way.

4) Secure transaxle jack to transaxle and raise slightly. Remove bolts holding transaxle mount bracket to frame. Remove torque support mount (if applicable). Remove transaxle bracket from transaxle.

5) Ensure that all cables, linkage, mounts and wires have been disconnected, and that transaxle clears both drive axles. Carefully lower transaxle assembly with jack.

INSTALLATION

To install transaxle, reverse removal procedure.

CHRYSLER MOTORS (Cont.)

RWD MODELS

REMOVAL

1) Disconnect battery ground cable. On 4WD models, remove transfer case shift lever knob, dust boot and retainer plate. Disconnect transmission throttle cable at throttle lever.

2) Raise and support vehicle. Remove under carriage cover and/or skid plate. Drain transmission and transfer case (if applicable). Disconnect all external solenoids and switches at their connectors. On 4WD models, disconnect 4WD indicator lamp harness.

3) On all models, disconnect speedometer cable, shift control cable or linkage and throttle control rod (if applicable). Remove wiring for starter motor and remove starter. Remove bellhousing cover. Index mark torque converter to drive plate and remove bolts attaching torque converter to drive plate.

4) Remove exhaust pipe mounting bracket (where applicable). Disconnect transmission cooler lines and remove oil filler tube. Index mark and remove rear propeller shaft. On 4WD models, also remove front propeller shaft.

5) Secure a transmission jack under transmission/transfer case assembly and raise slightly to take weight off of mount. Remove crossmember-to-mount bolts and remove crossmember. Remove transfer case mounting bracket and mount.

6) Ensure that transmission/transfer case has been securely mounted to jack. Remove remaining transmission-to-engine mounting bolts and lower assembly with jack.

INSTALLATION

NOTE: Engine may raise slightly when transmission assembly is removed. Disconnecting front exhaust pipe from catalytic converter can help when aligning transmission with engine.

1) Inspect converter drive plate for distortion, cracks or damaged teeth. Replace if necessary. Ensure full engagement of torque converter into transmission front pump. Flush transmission cooler lines and oil cooler.

2) Before bolting transmission to engine, realign index mark (made during removal) of torque converter with mark on drive plate and ensure that transmission mounting bolt holes align with engine block guide pins. Reverse removal procedure to complete installation.

FORD MOTOR CO.

MERKUR XR4Ti

REMOVAL

1) Open hood and disconnect negative battery cable. Remove transmission dipstick. Raise and support vehicle. Remove nuts attaching catalytic converter inlet pipe to turbocharger.

2) Remove nuts attaching catalytic converter to muffler inlet flange and remove converter support bracket. Remove converter and inlet pipe as an assembly.

3) Remove propeller shaft and plug extension housing to prevent fluid leaks. Remove starter. Remove front stabilizer bar-to-body "U" brackets and body stiffener rod.

4) Position a block of wood between stabilizer bar and body side rail. Remove torque converter-to-drive plate nuts through starter opening.

CAUTION: Turn crankshaft only in clockwise direction; turning crankshaft counterclockwise may cause timing belt to jump time.

5) Support transmission with jack. Remove bolts attaching rear mount to transmission support bracket. Remove rear mount nuts and mount. Lower transmission. Disconnect speedometer cable and wiring to neutral safety switch.

6) Disconnect shift rod and cable from shift levers. Disconnect vacuum hose at modulator. Using Quick Disconnect Remover (T82L-9500-AH), disconnect transmission cooler lines.

7) Remove upper transmission-to-engine bolts. If contact with body prevents removing bolts, loosen engine mount attaching nuts until 2 or 3 threads are visible on studs ends. Place wood block against engine oil pan. Raise engine until stud nuts contact crossmember. As engine tilts downward, lower transmission. Remove bolts.

8) Remove remaining torque converter housing attaching bolts and transmission filler tube. Pull transmission rearward and lower out of vehicle.

INSTALLATION

1) To install transmission, reverse removal procedure. Ensure converter hub is fully engaged in transmission pump gear.

2) Tighten transmission-to-engine bolts to 28-38 ft. lbs. (38-51 N.m). Tighten torque converter-to-drive plate nuts to 12-16 ft. lbs. (16-22 N.m). Check and adjust shift rod and downshift cable.

TRACER

NOTE: For information on Tracer, see MAZDA 323 in this article.

HONDA

ALL MODELS

REMOVAL

1) Disconnect battery ground cable and ground strap at transaxle. Release steering lock and place selector lever in "N". Disconnect wires from starter solenoid.

2) Disconnect cooler hoses and wire them up out of way, making sure they won't drain. Remove starter mounting bolt, on transaxle side and top transaxle mounting bolt. Raise and support front of vehicle. Remove wheels.

3) Drain transaxle and reinstall plug. Remove throttle control cable from transaxle. Remove speedometer cable from transaxle. Do not remove speedometer cable holder or speedometer gear may fall into transaxle housing. Remove power steering speed sensor (if equipped).

4) On Accord and Prelude models only, remove starter side mounting bolt and remove 2 upper transaxle mounting bolts. Place a jack under transaxle and attach an engine support to engine. Remove crossbeam. Disconnect drive axle shafts from transaxle.

5) Separate right side ball joint from lower control arm. Remove starter. Remove transaxle damper bracket, located in front of torque converter cover plate, then remove cover plate. Remove center console and shift indicator. Place selector lever in "R" and remove shift cable from shift lever. Loosen nuts and pull shift cable out of transaxle housing.

6) Remove torque converter-to-drive plate bolts. Remove engine-to-transaxle mounting bolts and lower transaxle mounting bolt. Pull transaxle rearwards, then lower transaxle out of vehicle.

7) On Civic models only, remove splash shields. Remove exhaust header pipe. Separate right and left side lower ball joints and tie rod ends from lower control arms.

8) Remove drive axle shafts from transaxle. Attach chain hoist to 8 mm bolt near distributor. Place jack under transaxle. Remove bolts from front and rear engine mounts and engine torque bracket. Remove torque converter cover plate and drive plate-to-converter bolts.

9) Remove shift cable from selector lever. Remove remaining transaxle mounting bolts and pull transaxle rearward. Lower transaxle out of vehicle.

INSTALLATION

1) To install, reverse removal procedures. Always use NEW 26 mm spring clips on ends of drive axle shafts.

2) Tighten drive plate-to-converter plate bolts to 108 INCH lbs. (12 N.m) in a crisscross pattern. Tighten ball joint nut to 40 ft. lbs. (55 N.m) on Accord and Prelude, and 33 ft. lbs. (45 N.m) on Civic.

3) Fill transaxle with oil. Check shift cable and throttle control cable adjustments.

HYUNDAI

NOTE: **For Hyundai information, see MITSUBISHI in this article.**

ISUZU

I-MARK

NOTE: **This procedure also applies to Chevrolet Spectrum.**

REMOVAL

1) Disconnect negative cable at battery. Remove air intake hose from air cleaner. Disconnect shift cable from transaxle. Disconnect speedometer cable. Disconnect vacuum hose at vacuum diaphragm.

2) Disconnect engine wiring harness clamp at transaxle. Disconnect ground cable at transaxle. Disconnect kickdown solenoid wire connector at transaxle.

3) Disconnect transaxle cooler lines. Remove 3 upper transaxle-to-engine attaching bolts. Raise vehicle. Remove both front wheels. Remove splash shield at left front fender.

4) Disconnect both tie rod ends at steering knuckle. Remove tension strut from lower control arm. Disengage both drive axle shafts from transaxle. Remove drive plate dust cover. Support engine from above.

5) Remove converter-to-drive plate attaching bolts. Remove crossmember. Disconnect starter motor. Support transaxle. Remove lower transaxle-to-engine attaching bolts. Lower and remove transaxle from vehicle.

INSTALLATION

To install, reverse removal procedure. Tighten drive plate-to-converter bolts to 30 ft. lbs. (41 N.m). Adjust shift linkage. Fill transaxle with Dexron II ATF.

IMPULSE

REMOVAL

1) Drain transmission fluid. Disconnect throttle cable at engine side. Disconnect negative battery cable. Remove transmission oil dipstick and tube. Raise vehicle on hoist.

2) Remove starter attaching hardware. Remove starter by moving it toward front of vehicle. Remove propeller shaft. Disconnect shift control rod from shifter lever. Disconnect speedometer cable from transmission. Remove exhaust pipe.

3) Loosen joint nut on transmission side. Disconnect cooler by-pass pipe and wire aside to avoid

ISUZU (Cont.)

damage. Remove dust cover and under cover on front of engine. Remove 6 bolts attaching converter to drive plate. Access to bolts is obtained by rotating crankshaft pulley.

4) Remove bolt from center part of rear mounting frame bracket. Remove housing bolt. Raise engine and transmission assembly. Support rear of engine with a jack.

5) Lower transmission and engine slightly. Place jack under transmission. Remove transmission-to-engine bolts. Remove transmission from vehicle by moving it toward rear of vehicle. Do not let torque converter slip out of transmission.

INSTALLATION

1) Reverse removal procedure. Check that distance from end of converter housing to front face of converter lugs is about 1 1/4".

2) If drive plate was removed, do not reuse bolts. On 2.0L turbo engine, use slight amount of Loctite on bolt threads. Tighten drive plate bolts in a crisscross pattern to 76 ft. lbs. (103 N.m) on 1.9L, and 43 ft. lbs. (58 N.m) on 2.0L turbo.

3) Tighten drive plate-to-converter bolts to 14 ft. lbs. (19 N.m). Install propeller shaft bolts from transmission flange side and tighten to 24 ft. lbs. (33 N.m) on AW03-72L, and 20 ft. lbs. (27 N.m) on AW03-70. Fill transmission with ATF. Adjust throttle cable and shift control linkage.

P'UP

REMOVAL

1) Disconnect negative battery cable. Detach throttle valve cable from transmission. Remove air cleaner and transmission dipstick. Remove dipstick tube upper mounting bolt.

2) Raise and support vehicle. Remove dust cover from lower side of converter housing. Remove starter mounting bolts and slide starter assembly forward.

3) Mark propeller shaft for reassembly reference and remove. Disconnect speedometer cable and oil cooler lines from transmission. Disconnect shift control linkage.

4) Support transmission with jack and remove rear transmission support bolt and mount. Remove exhaust pipe bracket.

NOTE: Mark converter and flywheel for reassembly to same position.

5) Remove torque converter bolts under pan. Lower transmission until jack barely supports it and remove transmission-to-engine attaching bolts. Raise transmission to normal position. Support engine with jack. Slide transmission away from engine and lower out of vehicle.

NOTE: Use converter holder to prevent converter from sliding out of transmission during removal.

INSTALLATION

1) To install transmission, reverse removal procedure. If drive plate was removed, do not reuse bolts. Tighten new bolts to 40-47 ft. lbs. (54-64 N.m) on gasoline engines and 65-72 ft. lbs. (88-98 N.m) on diesel engines.

2) Distance from end of converter housing to drive plate lugs on converter should be at least 1 3/4" to ensure converter is seated. Tighten drive plate-to-converter bolts to 14 ft. lbs. (19 N.m).

3) Install propeller shaft bolts from transmission flange side and tighten to 18-22 ft. lbs. (24-30 N.m). After installation, adjust shift linkage and throttle cable. Fill transmission with ATF.

JAGUAR

XJS

REMOVAL

1) Disconnect negative battery cable. Remove transmission dipstick. Remove upper dipstick tube. Remove bolts securing fenders to firewall. Support the weight of the engine from above with a support bar.

2) Raise and support vehicle. Unscrew and remove nuts and bolts holding intermediate exhaust pipes, rotating flanges for access. Disconnect exhaust pipes and remove seals. Remove intermediate and rear heat shields.

3) Secure exhaust pipes aside. Remove front heat shields. Remove rear mount center nut and spacer. Put block of wood between jack and transmission rear mount. Remove rear mount bolts and spacers. Lower jack. Remove rear mounts, wooden block and jack.

4) Remove rear transmission crossmember. Remove propeller shaft and set aside. Working from above engine compartment, lower engine support slightly. From beneath vehicle, disconnect speedometer cable from transmission.

5) Unscrew nut holding selector pin to lever and disconnect cable. Unscrew bolt holding selector cable to support bracket and secure cable aside. Disconnect kick-down solenoid feed wire and remove clamp bolt holding feed wire to transmission.

6) Disconnect vacuum modulator tube. Remove modulator and drain transmission fluid. Discard modulator "O" ring.

7) Disconnect transmission cooler pipes at transmission. Remove spacer. Disconnect and plug cooler pipes. Remove access cover to torque converter.

8) Remove bolts holding converter to drive plate. Remove right side heat shield. Remove and secure catalytic converter from manifold.

9) Remove all engine-to-transmission attaching bolts except 2 lower left side bolts and lower starter attaching bolt. Remove dipstick tube and position tube/vacuum pipe mounting bracket along the vacuum pipe.

10) Support transmission weight with jack. Remove remaining transmission-to-engine bolts. Lower unit and remove transmission from beneath vehicle.

JAGUAR (Cont.)

INSTALLATION

To install transmission, reverse removal procedure. Adjust kick-down and selector cables.

XJ6 III

REMOVAL

1) Disconnect battery cable. Remove transmission dipstick from tube and bolts securing tube to manifold. Remove upper fan shroud. Disconnect kick-down cable from throttle bellcrank.

2) Raise vehicle on hoist. Remove transmission fill tube, exhaust intermediate pipe and heat shields. Place jack under transmission and raise enough to support weight of transmission.

3) Remove rear transmission support plate. Remove mount-to-transmission securing bolts and remove mount.

4) Remove drive shaft from vehicle as a unit. Lower transmission jack to position required to remove transmission, but do not remove transmission at this time. Remove rubber pad from top of transmission.

5) Support engine from above by rear lifting eye on engine. Do not damage water heater valve.

6) From transmission unit selector lever, remove nut to release ball peg on inner selector cable. Remove set screw and spring washer securing outer selector cable clamp. Disconnect speedometer cable from transmission.

7) Remove dipstick tube and cover on front of converter housing. Remove 4 bolts retaining torque converter to drive plate. Discard tab washers. Disconnect oil cooler lines from transmission case and plug lines.

8) Remove all converter housing-to-engine bolts. Move starter out of way. Separate and lower transmission from engine.

INSTALLATION

To install transmission, reverse removal procedure. Use new tab washers on torque converter-to-drive plate bolts. Readjust kick-down cable and selector cable.

MAZDA

B2200 & B2600

REMOVAL

4WD

1) From inside cab, remove shift knob, center console, transfer case shift lever plate and gearshift lever. Raise and support vehicle.

2) Remove splash shields, exhaust pipe, rear propeller shaft and front propeller shaft. Disconnect speedometer cable, "4 x 4" indicator switch connector, shift cable and vacuum diaphagm hose from transmission.

3) Remove 2 front transmission supports on converter housing. Remove lower cover plate and flex plate-to-converter bolts. Unplug neutral safety switch connector and kickdown switch connector.

4) Support transmission with jack. Remove starter and dipstick tube. Remove transmission-to-engine bolts and rear crossmember. Lower transmission from vehicle.

2WD

1) Raise and support vehicle. Disconnect speedometer cable, shift cable and vacuum hose from transmission. Remove front transmission supports from converter housing.

2) Remove flex plate-to-converter bolts. Disconnect kickdown solenoid and cooler lines from transmissions. Remove starter. Disconnect any other wiring connectors on transmission. Support transmission with jack.

3) Remove rear transmission crossmember and transmission-to-engine bolts. Lower transmission from vehicle.

INSTALLATION

2WD & 4WD

To install transmission, reverse removal procedure. Adjust shift linkage. Ensure converter is fully seated before installing transmission. Tighten flex plate-to-converter bolts to 25 ft. lbs. (N.m).

RX7

REMOVAL

1) Disconnect negative battery cable. Raise and support vehicle. Remove pipe and heat insulator. Remove propeller shaft. Disconnect vacuum hose, shift rod and speedometer cable from transmission.

2) Disconnect oil cooler pipes from transmission. Remove starter and dipstick tube. Unplug wiring harness coupler on right side of transmission.

3) Remove lower cover on converter housing. Remove flex plate-to-converter bolts. Support transmission with jack.

4) Remove transmission-to-engine bolts and rear crossmember. Slowly lower transmission out of vehicle.

INSTALLATION

Reverse removal procedure to install transmission. When installing torque converter, ensure notch in converter lines up with notch in oil pump.

Automatic Transmission Removal

MAZDA (Cont.)

323

NOTE: **This procedure also applies to the Ford Tracer.**

REMOVAL

1) Disconnect negative battery cable. Remove air cleaner. Loosen front wheel lug nuts. Disconnect speedometer cable. Disconnect selector cable from transaxle. Disconnect engine ground wire. Remove coolant pipe bracket. Remove secondary air pipe and EGR pipe bracket. Remove wire harness clip.

2) Disconnect wiring to neutral safety switch and kickdown solenoid. Disconnect body ground connector. Remove 2 upper transaxle mounting bolts. Disconnect neutral switch connector. Remove line connected to vacuum diaphragm. Loosen hose clamps, and disconnect transaxle oil cooler lines.

NOTE: **Insert a plug into hose to prevent fluid leaks.**

3) Attach Engine Support (49 E301 025A) to engine hanger and engine. Jack up vehicle and support it with safety stands at specified position. Drain out ATF. Remove front wheels. Remove under and side covers.

4) Remove lower arm ball joint and knuckle coupling bolt, pull lower arm downward, and separate lower arm from knuckle, (on left and right side of vehicle). Be careful not to damage ball joint dust boot. Separate driveshafts from transaxle by prying with bar inserted between shaft and case. Be careful not to damage oil seals.

5) Remove crossmember. Remove starter. Remove end plate. Remove torque converter bolts. Lean engine toward transaxle by loosening engine support hook bolt. Support transaxle with jack. Remove remaining transaxle mounting bolts. Slide transaxle from under vehicle.

INSTALLATION

1) To install, reverse removal procedure. Torque converter is correctly seated when distance between engine mating face of converter housing and edge of converter is about 3/4".

2) Tighten flex plate-to-torque converter bolts to 25-36 ft. lbs. (34-49 N.m). Tighten transaxle-to-engine bolts to 47-66 ft. lbs. (64-89 N.m). Before installing driveshaft, install a NEW circlip on end of shaft.

3) Tighten lower ball joint pinch bolt to 32-40 ft. lbs. (43-54 N.m). Refill transaxle with ATF.

626

REMOVAL

1) Drain fluid from transaxle (oil pan must be removed to completely drain transaxle). Remove air cleaner. Disconnect negative cable from battery. Disconnect solenoid valve, neutral safety switch, pulse generator and fluid temperature switch.

2) Disconnect throttle cable. Detach body grounds from transaxle. Disconnect selector cable and oil cooler lines from transaxle. Detach fuel filter and bracket from left shock tower.

3) Suspend engine from above with a support bar. Remove front wheels, splash shield and coolant overflow tank bracket. Remove starter. Remove left side stabilizer bar-to-lower control arm bolt.

4) Separate both lower control arms from ball joints. DO NOT damage dust boots. Separate left and right side drive axle shafts from transaxle by prying with a bar between shaft and case.

5) Remove crossmember and left side lower control arm as an assembly. Remove end plate and torque converter-to-flex plate bolts.

6) Support transaxle with jack and remove transaxle-to-engine retaining bolts. Lower transaxle assembly out of vehicle. Do not let torque converter drop.

INSTALLATION

1) To install transaxle, reverse removal procedure. Replace circlip at end of drive axle shaft with new one. When installing stabilizer bar link bolt and hardware, ensure bolt head faces down. There should be 1" of thread showing above top lock nut. Tighten nut closest to grommets to 104-156 INCH lbs. (11-18 N.m).

2) Tighten flex plate-to-converter bolts to 27-40 ft. lbs. (37-54 N.m). Tighten ball joint bolts to 32-40 ft. lbs. (43-54 N.m). Adjust shift linkage, if necessary.

MERCEDES-BENZ

190 SERIES

NOTE: **Removal procedure for 260E with W4A020 transmission is not available from manufacturer.**

REMOVAL

NOTE: **To avoid damaging firewall when transmission is lowered, place sheet metal panel between firewall and engine. Disconnect exhaust assembly at rear mounting bracket and fasten with wire.**

1) Disconnect negative cable on battery. Unscrew holder for oil filler pipe on cylinder head. Force off ball socket. Disconnect cable control for control pressure.

2) Pull out lock and loosen cable control. Raise and support vehicle. Unscrew drain plug on oil pan and torque conveter. Drain fluid. Screw back drain plugs with new seals and tighten.

3) Remove 6 torque converter bolts. Remove crossmember with rear engine mount. Remove exhaust support. Remove companion plate on universal flange of transmission.

NOTE: **Use mandrel to loosen soft companion plate installed at transmission end.**

MERCEDES-BENZ (Cont.)

4) Remove catalytic converter shielding plate. Loosen propeller shaft clamping nut at center support. Push propeller shaft together as much as possible.

5) Pull cable from kickdown solenoid valve. Loosen tachometer shaft. Disconnect control rod on floor shift. Remove fastening clip for tachometer shaft.

6) Swivel locking bracket upward and pull plug from neutal safety switch. Pull vacuum line from vacuum control unit. Pull out filler pipe in upward direction.

7) Remove oil cooler lines and clamps. Remove all transmission-to-engine mounting bolts. Slightly lift transmission with mounting. Slide transmission to the rear and remove.

INSTALLATION

1) Turn torque converter so one of 3 threaded plates is in alignment with bottom of bell housing. Lightly grease centering pin on torque converter. Connect control rod to transmission and secure.

2) Lift transmission, slide forward at until converter housing rests against engine. Tighten transmission-to-engine M10 bolts to 41 ft. lbs. (55 N.m) and M12 bolts to 48 ft. lbs. (65 N.m).

3) Continue installation in reverse of removal procedure. Use new sealing rings on oil cooler lines. tighten flex plate-to-torque converter bolts to 31 ft. lbs. (42 N.m).

4) Tighten propeller shaft clamping nut at center support to 22-29 ft. lbs. (30-40 N.m). Adjust control pressure cable. Refill transmission.

ALL EXCEPT 190 SERIES

REMOVAL

1) Disconnect negative battery cable. Remove transmission oil filler pipe clamp from cylinder head. Force off ball socket on control wire linkage pivot. Pull out wire lock and loosen control wire.

2) Raise vehicle on hoist. Remove cross yoke center body support. Remove oil pan drain plug and drain oil from transmission. Remove drain plug from torque converter and drain. Reinstall drain plugs. Remove torque converter cover plates. Remove 6 torque converter-to-drive plate bolts.

3) Place wood block between engine oil pan and front crossmember. Disconnect exhaust pipes at coupler at rear of transmission, and remove exhaust pipes. Remove rear crossmember and rear transmission mount as an assembly. Remove cable strap and unscrew kickdown solenid valve cable. Remove impulse transmitter retaining screws and remove transmitter.

4) Remove bolts attaching transmission companion flange to propeller shaft 3-arm flange. Remove exhaust shielding plate. Loosen propeller shaft clamping nut and slide propeller shaft as far rearward as possible. Turn neutral safety switch plug retainer ring in upward direction. Carefully remove plug with 2 screwdrivers.

5) Disconnect shift control rod from range selector lever. Unscrew holder and remove vacuum line from vacuum control unit. Disconnect oil cooler lines from transmission. Remove oil filler tube retainer bolt and push tube upward to remove.

6) Remove all engine-to-transmission attaching bolts except for 2 bottom bolts. Slightly raise transmission with transmission jack. Remove 2 bottom engine-to-transmission bolts.

7) Push transmission and jack toward rear of vehicle as far as possible. Remove transmission from vehicle.

INSTALLATION

1) To install, reverse removal procedure. When installing torque converter to transmission, coat converter tangs, turbine and stator shaft with assembly lubricant. Be sure that converter is fully seated in transmission before installing in vehicle.

2) Tighten transmission-to-engine M10 bolts to 41 ft. lbs. (55 N.m) and M12 bolts to 48 ft. lbs. (65 N.m). Tighten propeller shaft clamping nut to 22 ft. lbs. (30 N.m). Tighten flex plate-to-torque converter bolts to 31 ft. lbs. (42 N.m).

MITSUBISHI

NOTE: **FWD model information also includes Hyundai.**

FWD MODELS

REMOVAL

1) Remove battery and battery tray. Remove air cleaner case if necessary. On Cordia and Tredia models, remove reservoir tank, windshield washer tank and remove transaxle throttle cable at carburetor.

2) All models, disconnect control cable from transaxle. Disconnect neutral safety switch connector, oil cooler hoses and all external electrical connectors from transaxle. Disconnect speedometer cable and wiring harness for starter motor. Remove starter.

3) Remove upper transaxle-to-engine bolts. Lift vehicle and remove wheels. Drain transmission fluid and remove engine under cover. Remove strut bars and stabilizer bars from lower control arms. Remove right and left drive axle shafts from transaxle and secure them out of the way.

4) Remove transmission dust cover. Index mark torque converter to drive plate and remove bolts connecting converter with drive plate. Push torque converter away from engine into transaxle.

5) Secure transaxle with transmission jack and remove remaining transaxle-to-engine connecting bolts. Remove long bolt from transaxle insulator. On Cordia and Tredia, remove blank cap from inside right fender shield and remove bracket-to-frame bolts.

6) On all models, remove transaxle insulator and mounting brackets. Slide transaxle assembly to the right and lower to remove.

MITSUBISHI (Cont.)

INSTALLATION

Reverse removal procedures and note the following: Be sure to install torque converter first to transaxle and then to engine. Refill transaxle fluid to specified level. Adjust control cables. Ensure that Neutral safety switch harness does not contact transaxle insulator bracket.

RWD MODELS

REMOVAL

1) Disconnect battery ground cable. Disconnect and remove transmission throttle cable from bracket on top of engine (if applicable). On 4WD models, remove transfer case shift knob, dust boot and retaining plate. On Montero, remove complete 4WD floor console.

2) Raise and support vehicle. Drain transmission and (if applicable) transfer case. Disconnect all external electrical connectors from transmission and transfer case including ground cables.

3) Index mark and remove propeller shaft(s). Disconnect wiring for starter motor and remove starter. Disconnect shift control linkage/cable and throttle linkage. On Montero, remove select lever cross shaft and throttle rod.

4) Remove exhaust pipe mounting bracket and transmission front dust cover. Index mark torque converter to drive plate and remove connecting bolts. Disconnect oil cooler lines and remove oil filler tube.

5) Secure transmission jack under transmission/transfer case assembly and raise slightly taking weight off of crossmember. Remove rear engine mount and crossmember. Remove transfer case mounting bracket and mount (if applicable).

6) Ensure that all wires, linkage and brackets are cleared away from transmission and remove remaining transmission-to-engine bolts. Lower transmission assembly from vehicle.

INSTALLATION

Reverse removal procedure to install transmission. Align previously indexed marks of torque converter and drive plate before bolting torque converter to plate. Align transmission mounting bolt holes with engine dowel pins before mounting transmission assembly to engine.

NISSAN

FWD MODELS

NOTE: **On Maxima models, transaxle and engine must be removed as an assembly.**

REMOVAL

1) Remove battery and battery bracket. Remove air cleaner and airflow meter. Disconnect wiring for starter motor and remove starter. Remove throttle linkage cable or linkage, shift linkage and all external wiring connectors to transaxle. Remove transaxle cooler lines. Raise and support vehicle. Drain transaxle fluid.

2) Remove front wheels. Remove right side wheel bearing lock nut and front brake caliper assembly without disconnecting hydraulic line. Separate drive shaft from knuckle by tapping end slightly with a small wood block. Remove tie rod ball joint and remove 3 lower ball joint nuts.

3) Remove bolts holding knuckle to strut and draw out wheel hub, baffle plate and knuckle as a unit. Cover drive shaft boot with a suitable protector. Remove right side drive shaft bearing support bracket (if equipped). Remove drive shaft by prying against transaxle. Repeat drive shaft removal for other side.

4) Remove bolts securing exhaust front tube brackets (if necessary) and remove dust cover. Index mark torque converter in reference to drive plate. Rotate engine to remove each torque converter bolt.

5) Support engine under oil pan with a jack stand. Secure a transaxle jack under transaxle and remove any mounts attached to transaxle. Remove remaining bolts attaching transaxle to engine and carefully lower transaxle.

INSTALLATION

1) Measure drive plate runout with a dial indicator before installing torque converter. Runout should not exceed .020" (.5 mm). After installing torque converter into transaxle, ensure distance from edge of converter housing to converter mounting pad is within specifications. See CONVERTER TO HOUSING DISTANCE table.

CONVERTER TO HOUSING DISTANCE

Application	In. (mm)
Maxima	.709 (18)
Pulsar, Sentra	.831 (21.1)
Stanza, Stanza Wagon	.75 (19)

2) To install transaxle, reverse removal procedure. Apply sealant to torque converter bolts prior to installation. Align previously indexed marks of torque converter and drive plate before bolting torque converter to drive plate. After converter is secured to drive plate, rotate crankshaft several times to ensure free movement without binding.

RWD MODELS

REMOVAL

1) Disconnect battery ground cable. Raise and support vehicle. Drain transmission and remove propeller shaft. Remove wiring for starter motor and remove starter.

2) Remove any exhaust support brackets attached to transmission. Remove right side exhaust pipe from manifold (V6 models). Disconnect shift linkage and all

NISSAN (Cont.)

electrical and vacuum leads. Disconnect speedometer cable.

3) Remove oil filler tube from transmission and disconnect both oil cooler lines. Remove torque converter housing inspection plate and index mark torque converter to drive plate for realignment reference. Rotate engine to remove each torque converter bolt.

4) Support transmission with transmission jack. Remove rear mount and crossmember mounting bolts. Remove transmission-to-engine bolts and slowly lower transmission out of vehicle.

INSTALLATION

Reverse removal procedure to install transmission. Align previously indexed marks of torque converter and drive plate before bolting torque converter to plate. Align transmission mounting bolt holes with engine dowel pins before mounting transmission assembly to engine.

PEUGEOT

505

REMOVAL

1) Open hood as far as possible without forcing and support open with block placed under safety hook. Disconnect negative battery cable. Remove air duct between metering unit and butterfly housing. Remove 2 bolts from control pressure regulator.

2) Remove upper and lower radiator mounts and fan shroud. Place a piece of cardboard between radiator and fan to protect radiator from damage during transmission removal. Disconnect kickdown control cable at throttle linkage.

3) Remove exhaust-to-manifold nuts. Disconnect all exhaust system hangers. Remove heat shield from above muffler. Remove front seat stiffener located above muffler.

4) Remove vibration damper from propeller shaft tube. Remove extension housing bracket bolts. Disconnect differential from its mount. Mark position of lower steering column flange coupling and remove bolts.

5) On models with power steering, remove front crossmember-to-front mount bolts and replace with 2" bolts. Remove remaining crossmember bolts. Lower crossmember about 2" by unscrewing 2 bolts in crossmember. On all other models, remove steering box mounting bolts and lower steering gear without disconnecting links.

6) On all models, drain transmission fluid. Disconnect and plug cooler lines at transmission. Remove starter motor bolts. Disconnect filler tube from transmission. Remove torque converter cover plate and sensor from bellhousing. DO NOT alter sensor adjustment.

7) Remove torque converter-to-flywheel bolts. Using a retainer, secure torque converter in housing so it will not fall out during transmission removal. Place jack under transmission and remove 4 propeller shaft-to-transmission bolts.

8) Separate transmission from tube about .8" (20 mm) and install Retaining Plate (8.0403SZ) between the 2 units. Install 2 bolts to hold plate in place.

9) Pull differential and propeller shaft assembly to the rear of vehicle and allow front of tube to rest on rear crossmember. Disconnect gear shift linkage, speedometer and electrical connections from transmission. Lower and tilt transmission as far as possible.

10) Install engine lift equipment to front engine lifting eye. Lift engine far enough to gain access to upper transmission-to-engine bolts. Remove bolts and remove transmission from vehicle.

INSTALLATION

Reverse removal procedure to install. Apply grease to torque converter pilot bushing. Adjust shift and throttle linkage as needed. Fill transmission with fluid and check for leaks.

PORSCHE

924-S & 944

REMOVAL

1) Remove heat shield and rear muffler bracket. Detach axle shafts at transaxle. Suspend axle shafts in horizontal position to prevent damage to dust covers. Remove transaxle oil filter shield (if equipped). Disconnect oil cooler lines.

2) Detach selector and transaxle lever cables. Remove converter bolts through hole in torque converter housing. Support transaxle with jack and remove transaxle-to-engine bolts and transaxle mounts. Slide transaxle toward rear of vehicle and remove.

INSTALLATION

1) Reverse removal procedures to install. Ensure pump shaft and torque converter are fully seated in transaxle or damage to internal components may result during installation.

2) Use new seals on oil cooler lines. Tighten outlet hose hollow union bolt to 16 ft. lbs. (22.5 N.m). Tighten inlet union bolt to 22 ft. lbs. (30 N.m). Adjust pressure control cable.

SAAB

900

NOTE: Removal procedures for 9000 are not available from manufacturer.

REMOVAL

NOTE: Engine and transaxle must be removed as an assembly on 900 Series.

1) Disconnect negative battery terminal from battery. Drain radiator. Disconnect windshield washer hose from hood. Remove hood.

2) Label and unplug all engine and transaxle electrical connections as needed for engine removal. Remove air cleaner, preheater hose and crankcase ventilation hose. Remove radiator hose.

3) Disconnect fuel line and plug. Disconnect throttle cable, hose to expansion tank and brake servo vacuum hose. Remove clamps from drivers side inner universal joint.

4) Place Spacer (83 93 209) between upper control arm underside and frame (insert tool from engine compartment side). Spacer keeps control arm in compressed position. Raise and support vehicle.

5) Remove lower control arm-to-ball joint bolts. Pull control arm assembly from control arm and support with jack stand.

6) Remove gear selector cable screw at transaxle. Pull cable out of transaxle and slide back spring loaded sleeve, then disconnect from control lever. Disconnect speedometer cable from transaxle. Unbolt exhaust pipe from manifold.

7) Remove rear engine mounting bolts. Loosen front engine mounting nut so mount can be lifted from bracket. Attach engine lifting device on 2 engine lifting lugs, and raise engine slightly. Move engine assembly side to side to free universal joints. Lift assembly from vehicle and place on engine stand.

8) To separate transaxle from engine, drain engine oil and remove inspection cover. Remove starter. Disconnect throttle cable. Remove engine-to-transaxle bolts. Remove 4 converter-to-flex plate bolts. Turn flex plate until plate angles are horizontal, and lift engine off of transaxle.

INSTALLATION

1) To install, reverse removal procedure. Mating surfaces of transaxle and engine must be thoroughly clean. Use gasket sealer on new gasket when assembling transaxle and engine.

2) Coat flex plate-to-converter bolts with thread sealer and tighten to 24-29 ft. lbs. (33-39 N.m). Pack inner universal joints with grease, adjust shift cable if necessary and check cooling system for leaks.

STERLING

825

REMOVAL

1) Disconnect negative battery cable. Remove starter. Disconnect tranaxle cooler hoses. Disconnect kickdown cable from transaxle.

2) Raise and support vehicle. On left side of vehicle, separate top ball joint from link. Separate tie rod link.

3) Detach drive axle shafts from transaxle and support out of way. Move left side brake hoses and ABS wiring out of way so they will not interfere with transaxle removal.

4) Remove drive plate-to-torque converter bolts. Separate upper torque rod from transaxle bracket. Attach chain hoist to torque rod bracket on transaxle. Disconnect shift cable and speedometer cable from transaxle.

5) Remove lower transaxle crossmember. Support engine from above. Remove transaxle-to-engine bolts, and lower transaxle out of vehicle.

INSTALLATION

To install transaxle, reverse removal procedure.

SUBARU

COUPE, HATCHBACK, SEDAN & STATION WAGON

REMOVAL

1) Remove spare tire from engine compartment. Disconnect negative battery cable. Remove spare tire mount. Remove hill-holder cable (if equipped). Remove clutch cable.

2) Remove air duct from carbureted models. Disconnect vacuum diaphragm hose and air breather hose (4WD only). Disconnect speedometer cable from transaxle.

3) Disconnect back-up light switch connector from transaxle, ground cable from body and starter harness. Remove starter.

4) On turbo models only, remove turbo heat shields and center exhaust pipe forward of catalytic converter. On all models, remove timing hole plug. Remove 4 drive plate-to-converter bolts.

5) Disconnect and plug oil cooler hoses. Remove engine-to-transaxle mounting nut and bolt on right side. Raise and support vehicle.

6) On non-turbo models, disconnect front exhaust pipe from engine by removing all nuts except one. Disconnect front exhaust pipe from rear pipe.

SUBARU (Cont.)

7) On all models, remove torque rod connection. Disconnect dipstick tube. On 4WD models, remove propeller shaft.

8) On all models, disconnect gearshift linkage from transaxle. Disconnect stabilizer bar from lower control arm and front crossmember. Disconnect parking brake cable brake from lower control arm.

9) Remove roll pin and separate both drive axle shafts from transaxle. DO NOT reuse roll pin on reassembly; use new pin. Remove engine-to-transaxle mounting nuts. Place jack under transaxle.

10) Remove rear crossmember under transaxle. Pull transaxle away from engine and lower out of vehicle.

INSTALLATION

To install transaxle, reverse removal procedure. Always use new roll pins when installing drive axle shafts. Tighten torque converter-to-drive plate bolts to 17-20 ft. lbs. (23-27 N.m).

XT COUPE

REMOVAL

1) Disconnect battery ground cable. On turbo models, remove turbocharger heat shields.

2) On all models, raise and support vehicle. Remove exhaust system to gain access to transaxle. Disconnect speedometer cable from transaxle. Unplug all electrical harnesses from transaxle.

3) Label and disconnect all vacuum hoses from transaxle. Remove starter. Remove air intake duct. Remove timing hole plug and 4 converter-to-drive plate bolts.

4) Remove torque rod and bracket from transaxle. Support engine from above. Remove right side engine-to-transaxle mounting bolt.

5) On 4WD models, remove propeller shaft. Disconnect gearshift cable from transaxle. Separate both drive axle shafts from transaxle. Discard roll pins; new pins will be installed on installation.

6) Remove stabilizer bar from lower control arm. Remove parking brake cable from lower control arm. On both sides, remove lower control arm-to-crossmember link bolt.

7) Remove transaxle-to-engine mounting nuts. Disconnect oil cooler hoses. Secure transaxle jack under transaxle. Remove crossmember mounting nuts. Lower crossmember and transaxle from vehicle.

INSTALLATION

To install transaxle, reverse removal procedure. Always use new roll pins when installing drive axle shafts. Tighten torque converter-to-drive plate bolts to 17-20 ft. lbs. (23-27 N.m).

TOYOTA

CAMRY & CELICA

REMOVAL

1) Disconnect negative battery cable. Remove air flow meter and air cleaner. Disconnect neutral safety switch connector and all external electrical connectors. Remove ground strap.

2) Disconnect transaxle throttle valve cable at throttle linkage and remove cable from bracket. Remove transaxle case protector and disconnect speedometer cable. Disconnect shift control cable at lever and remove from bracket.

3) Disconnect oil cooler hoses and remove starter motor bolts. Remove 2 upper transaxle-to-engine bolts. Remove insulator bracket set bolt for rear engine mount. Raise and support vehicle.

4) Drain transaxle oil. Remove left front fender apron. Disconnect both axle drive shafts from transaxle. Remove lower suspension crossmember. Using pliers, remove snap ring on center axle shaft bearing bracket. Remove bearing bracket bolt and pull center axle shaft assembly out.

5) Disconnect control cable clamp and remove crossmember bolts supporting center mounts of engine. Remove crossmember. Remove stabilizer bar and left steering knuckle from lower control arm. Pull steering knuckle outward and remove left axle drive shaft.

6) Remove bellhousing cover and remove 6 bolts attaching torque converter to drive plate. Support engine with jack stand and secure transaxle jack under transaxle. Lower rear end of transaxle and remove remaining transaxle-to-engine bolts. Separate transaxle from engine and lower transaxle assembly.

INSTALLATION

1) Apply multipurpose grease to center hub of torque converter. Install one guide pin in threaded mounting pad of torque converter to aid in aligning torque converter.

2) Reverse removal procedure to complete installation of transaxle. Torque converter bolts are color coded. Install Gray bolt first, then the remaining 5 bolts. Tighten torque converter bolts to 20 ft. lbs. (27 N.m). Fill transaxle to proper capacity. Check and adjust throttle cable.

COROLLA (FWD)

REMOVAL

1) Disconnect negative battery cable and remove air cleaner. Disconnect neutral safety switch connector and solenoid valve connector. Disconnect speed sensor connector and speedometer cable.

2) Disconnect transaxle throttle valve cable from throttle linkage and remove cable and bracket. Disconnect oil cooler hoses. Remove coolant inlet bolts and remove coolant inlet.

3) Raise and support vehicle. Drain transaxle and remove engine under cover. Remove 2 dust covers from center crossmember and remove crossmember. On

TOYOTA (Cont.)

models with A240E or 4A-GE engines, remove front exhaust from manifold.

4) Remove left and right side drive axle shafts and remove starter motor. Remove bellhousing stiffener plate. Manually turn crankshaft and remove 6 torque converter bolts.

5) Support engine with jack stand and secure transaxle jack under transaxle. Remove engine rear mounting bolts and slightly lower transaxle assembly. Remove transaxle mounting bolts to separate transaxle from engine and remove transaxle from vehicle.

INSTALLATION

1) Apply multipurpose grease to center hub of torque converter. Install one guide pin in threaded mounting pad of torque converter to aid in aligning torque converter.

2) Reverse removal procedure to complete installation of transaxle. Torque converter bolts are color coded. Install the White bolt and then the 5 remaining Yellow bolts. Tighten torque converter bolts to 20 ft. lbs. (27 N.m). Fill transaxle to proper capacity. Check and adjust throttle cable.

COROLLA (RWD)

REMOVAL

1) Disconnect negative battery cable. Disconnect transmission throttle cable from carburetor linkage and remove cable from bracket. Disconnect neutral safety switch, back-up light switch and overdrive relay connectors located near starter.

2) Raise and support vehicle. Drain transmission. Index mark and remove propeller shaft. Remove exhaust pipe clamp from bellhousing and disconnect exhaust pipe from manifold. Disconnect manual shift linkage.

3) Loosen 2 nuts and remove both clamps retaining cooler lines to transmission. Disconnect both cooler lines at transmission. Remove starter and lay alongside engine.

4) Secure transmission jack under transmission. Remove ground strap and rubber exhaust hanger from crossmember. Raise transmission slightly and remove 8 bolts to remove crossmember. Disconnect speedometer cable.

5) Pry hole cover off of bellhousing cover plate. Manually turn crankshaft and remove 6 torque converter bolts. Install guide pin in one hole of torque converter.

6) Remove transmission-to-engine bolts. Pry on end of guide pin to move converter with transmission when separating from engine. Ensure that throttle cable and all electrical connectors are clear when lowering transmission.

INSTALLATION

1) Apply multipurpose grease to center hub of torque converter. Install one guide pin in threaded mounting pad of torque converter to aid in aligning torque converter.

2) Reverse removal procedure to complete installation of tranmission. Tighten torque converter bolts to 20 ft. lbs. (27 N.m). Fill transmission to proper capacity. Check and adjust throttle cable.

CRESSIDA & SUPRA

REMOVAL

1) Disconnect negative battery cable. Disconnect transmission throttle cable from throttle linkage and remove cable housing from bracket. Disconnect cable from engine rear end. On Cressida, drain coolant at radiator drain cock. Disconnect upper radiator hose and air intake connector.

2) Raise and support vehicle. Drain transmission oil. Disconnect all electrical connectors that lead to transmission (located near starter). Index mark propeller shaft flanges before removal. On Cressida, remove intermediate shaft only. On Supra, disconnect shaft at differential flange and remove both sections as one assembly with center bearing support.

3) All models, disconnect catalytic converter from tail pipe and remove rubber hangers. Remove pipe clamp from transmission housing and remove front exhaust pipe from exhaust manifold.

4) Remove oil cooler pipe clamp from transmission housing and disconnect oil cooler lines at transmission fittings. Remove oil filler tube and disconnect manual shift linkage at rear connection.

5) Disconnect speedometer cable and remove both stiffener plates. Remove bellhousing cover and manually rotate crankshaft to remove 6 torque converter bolts. Secure transmission jack under transmission and raise enough to remove weight from transmission mount.

6) Disconnect ground strap and remove crossmember and transmission mount from vehicle. Place rag between steering gear housing and engine oil pan to prevent damage. Remove starter motor and all transmission-to-engine bolts.

7) Separate transmission along with torque converter from engine. Ensure that all cables and electrical harnesses are free from snagging when lowering transmission from vehicle.

INSTALLATION

1) Apply multipurpose grease to center hub of torque converter. Install one guide pin in threaded mounting pad of torque converter to aid in aligning torque converter.

2) Reverse removal procedure to complete installation of transmission. Tighten torque converter bolts to 20 ft. lbs. (27 N.m) on Cressida, and 30 ft. lbs. (41 N.m) on Supra. Fill transaxle to proper capacity. Check and adjust throttle cable.

LAND CRUISER

REMOVAL

1) Disconnect negative battery cable. Drain coolant at radiator drain cock and disconnect upper radiator hose. Disconnect transmission throttle cable from throttle linkage and remove cable from bracket.

2) Disconnect electrical connectors located near starter. Remove transfer case shift lever knob and 4

TOYOTA (Cont.)

bolts to remove shift lever boot. Raise and support vehicle. Drain transmission oil and transfer case oil.

3) Remove transmission and transfer case undercovers. Remove clip and pin to disconnect shift rod from transfer case. Remove nut and washers to remove transfer case shift lever with control rod. Disconnect control rod from control shaft lever by removing nut on lever.

4) On models with a mechanical winch, remove shifter knob button and spring. Using an Allen wrench, remove two set screws and shift lever knob. Remove shift lever boot. Remove nut and disconnect shift rod from Power Take-Off (PTO). Remove bolt and remove shift lever with shift rod.

5) Index mark propeller shaft flanges and remove both front and rear shafts. Mark and remove PTO drive shaft (if applicable). Disconnect speedometer cable and 2 vacuum hoses from transfer case. Disconnect oil cooler tubes.

6) Remove starter and transmission oil filler tube. Pry hole cover off of bellhousing cover plate. Manually turn crankshaft and remove 6 torque converter bolts.

7) Secure a transmission jack under transmission/transfer case assembly. Remove 8 bolts and 2 nuts and remove frame crossmember. Remove flange bolts and exhaust pipe clamp to remove front pipe from tail pipe. Remove front pipe from exhaust manifold.

8) Support engine with a jack and wooden block. Lower rear of transmission/transfer case assembly. Remove 9 transmission mounting bolts. Ensure that throttle cable and all electrical harnesses are clear from snagging. Carefully draw assembly down and toward the rear when lowering.

INSTALLATION

1) Apply multipurpose grease to center hub of torque converter. Install one guide pin in threaded mounting pad of torque converter to aid in aligning torque converter.

2) Reverse removal procedure to complete installation of transmission/transfer case assembly. Tighten torque converter bolts to 21 ft. lbs. (28 N.m). Fill transmission, transfer case and PTO to proper fluid capacities.

3) Check and adjust shift control linkage for transmission and transfer case. Check and adjust PTO linkage and transfer shift control lever. Adjust throttle cable.

MR2

REMOVAL

1) Disconnect negative battery cable. Remove air flow meter and air cleaner hose. Disconnect speed sensor connector.

2) Disconnect throttle cable from throttle linkage. Remove cable from bracket and remove bracket. Remove coolant inlet bolts and disconnect ground strap. Remove transaxle mounting set bolt.

3) Raise and support vehicle. Remove left rear wheel and remove engine under cover. Disconnect speedometer cable and oil cooler hoses. Disconnect and remove shift control cable from bracket. Remove bracket.

4) Disconnect 3 electrical connectors near transaxle and remove starter motor. Remove exhaust pipe at manifold. Remove stiffener plate and engine dust cover.

5) Manually turn engine crankshaft to gain access to torque converter bolts and remove 6 bolts. Disconnect right side drive axle shaft from gear shaft and support shaft out of the way.

6) Using Pitman Arm Puller (09610-20012), disconnect left suspension arm from the rear axle carrier. Disconnect rear axle carrier from lower arm. Disconnect left drive axle shaft from side gear shaft and support with wire out of the way.

7) Support engine and transaxle with separate jacks. Remove transaxle mounting bolts and remove mounts. Remove transaxle housing-to-engine mounting bolts and remove transaxle from engine.

INSTALLATION

1) Apply multipurpose grease to center hub of torque converter. Install one guide pin in threaded mounting pad of torque converter to aid in aligning torque converter.

2) Reverse removal procedure to complete installation of transaxle. Torque converter bolts are color coded. First install Gray bolt and then 5 Black bolts. Tighten torque converter bolts to 20 ft. lbs. (27 N.m). Fill transaxle to proper capacity. Check and adjust throttle cable.

PICKUP & 4RUNNER

REMOVAL

1) Disconnect and remove negative battery cable. Remove air cleaner assembly and ducting (if necessary). Disconnect transmission throttle valve cable from carburetor linkage and remove from bracket.

2) Remove upper starter mounting nut. On 4WD and 4Runner, disconnect 5 electrical connectors. All models, raise and support vehicle. Drain transmission and disconnect all external electrical connectors. Remove starter motor and support alongside of engine.

3) Index mark and remove propeller shaft(s). Disconnect speedometer cable and manual shift linkage. Disconnect transmission oil cooler lines. On 2WD models, remove exhaust pipe support clamp, exhaust bracket and filler tube.

4) On 4WD and 4Runner, remove clips and disconnect No. 1 and No. 2 shift linkage from cross shaft. Remove cross shaft from body. Disconnect exhaust pipe from tail pipe and remove clamp from transmission case. Remove clamp holding oil cooler lines to transfer chain case and disconnect transfer case oil cooler lines.

5) All models, secure transmission jack under transmission oil pan. Raise transmission enough to remove weight from rear engine mount. Remove rear engine mount along with bracket. Remove engine undercover to gain access to crankshaft pulley.

6) On 4WD and 4Runner, remove crossmember and install a wood block between firewall and rear of cylinder head. On 2WD models, insert a piece of wood between engine oil pan and top of front crossmember.

Automatic Transmission Removal

TOYOTA (Cont.)

7) All models, pry hole covers off of bellhousing cover plate. Turn crankshaft to gain access to torque converter bolts and remove 6 bolts. Install a guide pin in one torque converter bolt hole.

8) Remove bolts attaching support braces to front of bellhousing and engine block and remove support braces. Remove all bellhousing-to-engine mounting bolts.

9) Pry on end of guide pin to begin moving torque converter and transmission from engine. Ensure that all cables and electrical harnesses are free from snagging when lowering transmission. Remove transmission from vehicle.

INSTALLATION

1) Apply multipurpose grease to center hub of torque converter and pilot hole in crankshaft. Install one guide pin in threaded mounting pad of torque converter to aid in aligning torque converter.

2) Reverse removal procedure to complete installation of transmission. Tighten torque converter bolts evenly to 20 ft. lbs. (27 N.m). Fill transmission and transfer case (if applicable) to proper capacity. Check and adjust throttle cable.

TERCEL SEDAN

REMOVAL

1) Disconnect negative battery cable. Disconnect neutral safety switch and all other electrical connectors. Disconnect speedometer cable. Disconnect transaxle throttle cable from throttle linkage and remove cable from bracket.

2) Remove wiring for starter and remove starter motor. Remove upper transaxle-to-engine bolts. Raise and support vehicle. Drain transaxle oil and drain oil from differential cavity.

3) Disconnect oil cooler hoses from pipes and remove engine under cover. Disconnect shift control cable at shift lever and remove cable from bracket. Remove both axle drive shafts.

4) Manually turn engine crankshaft and remove 6 torque converter bolts from access hole in bellhousing cover. Remove ground cable from left side engine mounting bracket.

5) Remove left side engine mount. Support engine with one jack and secure a transaxle jack under transaxle assembly. Remove 4 bolts and disconnect rear mounting bracket from body. Remove 3 bolts and remove engine rear mounting bracket.

6) Remove remaining transaxle-to-engine bolts. Ensure that all electrical harnesses and cables do not snag when lowering transaxle assembly with jack.

INSTALLATION

1) Apply multipurpose grease to center hub of torque converter. Install one guide pin in threaded mounting pad of torque converter to aid in aligning torque converter.

2) Reverse removal procedure to complete installation of transaxle. Torque converter bolts are color coded. Install Gray bolt first, then install remaining 5 Black bolts. Tighten torque converter bolts to 13 ft. lbs. (18 N.m). Fill transaxle to proper capacity. Check and adjust throttle cable.

TERCEL WAGON FWD & 4WD

REMOVAL

1) Disconnect negative battery cable. Disconnect neutral safety switch, back-up light switch and 4WD solenoid connectors from inside of engine compartment.

2) Remove air cleaner assembly and 4 upper transaxle-to-engine bolts. Remove both left and right side drive axle shafts. Raise and support vehicle.

3) Remove front exhaust pipe. Disconnect transaxle oil cooler lines. Remove throttle linkage near bellhousing and disconnect shift control rod linkage. Disconnect speedometer cable.

4) On 4WD models, disconnect fluid temperature warning switch connector. Index mark and remove propeller shaft for rear wheels. On 2WD models, remove right side stiffener plate from bellhousing and engine block.

5) Remove 3 bolts, dust cover and front bellhousing cover. Manually turn engine crankshaft to gain access to torque converter bolts. Remove 6 torque converter-to-drive plate bolts.

6) Remove transaxle lower mount bolts. Secure transaxle with transaxle jack and place a wooden block between engine and firewall. Slightly raise transaxle and remove rear engine support mount and crossmember.

7) Remove remaining transaxle-to-engine bolts. Ensure that all electrical harnesses and cables do not snag when lowering transaxle from vehicle.

INSTALLATION

1) Apply multipurpose grease to center hub of torque converter. Install one guide pin in threaded mounting pad of torque converter to aid in aligning torque converter.

2) Reverse removal procedure to complete installation of transaxle. Tighten torque converter bolts to 13 ft. lbs. (18 N.m). Fill transaxle to proper capacity. Check and adjust throttle cable.

VAN (2WD)

REMOVAL

1) Disconnect negative battery cable. Disconnect transmission throttle cable from throttle cam and remove cable from bracket. Disconnect all external electrical connectors from transmission.

2) Raise and support vehicle. Drain transmission. Index mark and remove propeller shaft. Disconnect exhaust pipe clamp from transmission bellhousing. Disconnect shift control cable, speedometer cable and ground strap.

3) Loosen nuts and remove clamps retaining cooler lines to transmission. Disconnect cooler lines. Remove mounting bolts for starter motor and secure starter alongside of engine. Secure transmission jack under transmission.

4) Remove the 2 fuel tank mount bolts and support fuel tank. Remove transmission mounting through bolt. Remove both stiffener plates and cover for access hole on bellhousing front cover.

5) Manually turn engine crankshaft to remove 6 torque converter bolts. Remove transmission-to-engine

TOYOTA (Cont.)

bolts. Remove transmission assembly ensuring that throttle cable and wiring harnesses do not entangle when lowering.

INSTALLATION

1) Apply multipurpose grease to center hub of torque converter. Install one guide pin in threaded mounting pad of torque converter to aid in aligning torque converter.

2) Reverse removal procedure to complete installation of transaxle. Torque converter bolts are color coded. Install Gray bolt first, then the other 5 bolts. Tighten torque converter bolts to 20 ft. lbs. (27 N.m). Fill transaxle to proper capacity. Check and adjust throttle cable.

VAN (4WD)

REMOVAL

1) Disconnect negative battery cable. Disconnect transmission throttle cable at throttle cam and remove cable from bracket. Disconnect 3 wiring connectors located near starter.

2) Raise and support vehicle. Drain transmission and transfer case. Disconnect ATF thermo sensor connector. Index mark and remove both front and rear propeller shafts. Remove exhaust pipe clamp from bellhousing and disconnect exhaust pipe from manifold.

3) Disconnect transmission shift control cable from transmission outer lever. Note location of vacuum hoses and remove them from vacuum actuator. Disconnect speed sensor and 4WD indicator connectors. Disconnect speedometer cable, ground strap and transfer indicator switch connector.

4) Remove 2 clamps and disconnect oil cooler lines. Remove control cable bracket from transmission bellhousing. Remove mounting bolts and secure starter alongside engine. Secure transmission jack under transmission/transfer case assembly.

5) Remove transmission mounting through bolt. Remove both stiffener plates from bellhousing. Manually turn engine crankshaft and remove 6 torque converter bolts. Remove transmission-to-engine bolts. Remove transmission ensuring that throttle cable and wiring harnesses do not entangle when lowering transmission assembly.

INSTALLATION

1) Apply multipurpose grease to center hub of torque converter. Install one guide pin in threaded mounting pad of torque converter to aid in aligning torque converter.

2) Reverse removal procedure to complete installation of transaxle. Torque converter bolts are color coded. Install Gray bolt first, then the other 5 bolts. Tighten torque converter bolts to 20 ft. lbs. (27 N.m). Fill transaxle and transfer case to proper capacity. Check and adjust throttle cable.

VOLKSWAGEN

CABRIOLET, GOLF, GTI, JETTA & SCIROCCO

REMOVAL

1) Disconnect battery ground cable. Disconnect speedometer cable from transaxle. Remove both front wheels. Remove left and right side axle shaft nuts.

2) Support engine from above. Remove left rear transaxle mount and support. Remove upper transaxle-to-engine bolts. Remove upper bolts in front engine/transaxle mount.

3) Raise and support vehicle. Remove lower bolts on front mount and remove mount. Remove protective plate from transaxle. Remove torque converter-to-drive plate bolts.

4) Disconnect accelerator and selector cables from transaxle. Remove left and right axle shaft flange bolts. Separate left and right side ball joint and wheel bearing housings. Remove axle shafts.

5) Remove left rear engine mount. Remove starter. Remove subframe mounting bolts and allow subframe to hang free. Support transaxle with jack. Remove lower mounting bolt. Lower transaxle.

INSTALLATION

1) To install transaxle, reverse removal procedure. Adjust accelerator and selector cables.

2) Tighten axle shaft-to-flange bolts to 33 ft. lbs. (45 N.m). Tighten torque converter-to-drive plate bolts to 26 ft. lbs. (35 N.m). Tighten transaxle-to-engine bolts to 55 ft. lbs. (75 N.m).

QUANTUM

REMOVAL

1) Disconnect negative battery cable. Disconnect accelerator linkage rod. Disconnect speedometer cable. Remove upper engine-to-transaxle bolts.

2) Support engine from above. Disconnect automatic transaxle cooler lines. Disconnect exhaust pipe from manifold, exhaust pipe bracket at transaxle and unbolt exhaust pipe from catalytic converter.

3) Remove axle shaft guard plate. Disconnect axle shafts from transaxle flanges. Wire axle shafts back out-of-way. Remove starter. Remove torque converter-to-drive plate bolts.

4) Disconnect coolant hoses from transaxle oil cooler. If draining ATF, disconnect filler tube from oil pan. Disconnect accelerator cable support from transaxle.

5) Remove selector cable holder and circlip, then disconnect cable and "O" ring. Remove subframe bolts. Support transaxle with jack.

6) Remove center bolt from transaxle mount. Remove lower engine-to-transaxle bolts. Separate transaxle from engine. Lower transaxle out of vehicle.

VOLKSWAGEN (Cont.)

CAUTION: Secure torque converter to transaxle to prevent converter from falling out when removing transaxle.

INSTALLATION

1) To install transaxle, reverse removal procedures. Ensure torque converter is fully seated in transaxle and all linkage is properly installed and adjusted.

2) Tighten transaxle-to-engine bolts to 41 ft. lbs. (55 N.m). Tighten converter-to-drive plate bolts to 22 ft. lbs. (30 N.m). Tighten inner CV joint flange bolts to 33 ft. lbs. (45 N.m).

VANAGON

REMOVAL

1) Disconnect battery ground cable. Remove upper engine-to-transaxle bolts. Remove dipstick and bolt for dipstick tube support bracket.

2) Remove 3 torque converter-to-drive plate bolts though hole in top of transaxle housing. Raise and support vehicle.

3) Disconnect both drive axle shafts. Remove starter. Disconnect push rod from transaxle kickdown lever. Detact accelerator cable from transaxle. Detach selector lever cable from transaxle.

4) Disconnect and clamp coolant lines from transaxle cooler. Disconnect ground strap. Remove mounting bracket bolts. Support transaxle with jack.

CAUTION: Bottom of engine must be supported when removing transaxle.

5) Remove lower transaxle-to-engine bolts. Separate engine from transaxle from engine. Lower transaxle.

INSTALLATION

1) To install transaxle, reverse removal procedure. Ensure torque converter is fully seated on one-way clutch support. Distance from engine mating surface to end of converter hub should be at least 3/8".

2) Adjust accelerator and selector cable linkages. Tighten transaxle-to-engine bolts to 41 ft. lbs. (55 N.m).

3) Tighten converter-to-drive plate bolts to 22 ft. lbs. (30 N.m). Tighten axle shaft flange bolts to 33 ft. lbs. (45 N.m).

VOLVO

240

REMOVAL

1) Disconnect kickdown cable at pulley. Disconnect negative battery cable. Remove 2 upper transmission-to-engine bolts. Remove transmission oil dipstick tube.

2) Raise and support vehicle. Remove drain plug and drain transmission fluid. Disconnect shift linkage, oil filler tube, oil cooler lines and speedometer cable.

3) Remove propeller shaft. Remove starter motor bolts and torque converter-to-flex plate bolts. Disconnect solenoid valve plug. Disconnect exhaust pipe bracket.

4) Place transmission jack under transmission. Remove rear crossmember. Remove transmission-to-engine bolts. Lower transmission.

INSTALLATION

To install, reverse removal procedure. Tighten torque converter-to-flex plate retaining bolts to 33 ft. lbs. (45 N.m). After installation, fill transmission with fluid. Adjust throttle linkage and shift control linkage.

740/760

REMOVAL

AW70 & AW71

1) Place gearshift lever in "P". Detach kickdown cable from throttle pulley. Remove negative battery cable.

2) Raise and support vehicle. Remove propeller shaft. Drain transmission fluid. Unscrew oil filler tube from transmission oil pan.

3) Disconnect reaction rod and actuator rod from transmission shift levers. Disconnect solenoid lead on AW71. Support transmission with jack. Remove rear transmission crossmember.

4) Remove starter motor bolts and cover for starter motor cutout. Remove converter housing lower cover plate. Remove torque converter-to-flex plate bolts. Disconnect oil cooler pipes.

5) Remove transmission-to-engine bolts. Slide transmission rearward and lower.

INSTALLATION

1) To install, reverse removal procedure. Tighten lower oil filler tube nut to 65 ft. lbs. (90 N.m). Tighten flex plate-to-torque converter bolts in a crisscross pattern to 32 ft. lbs. (45 N.m).

2) Adjust kickdown cable and gearshift linkage. Fill transmission with ATF.

REMOVAL

ZF 4HP 22

1) Disconnect negative battery cable. Disconnect kickdown cable from throttle pulley bracket. Place gearshift lever in "N". Raise and support vehicle.

2) Drain transmission fluid. Support transmission with jack. Remove starter motor. Disconnect oil filler tube at transmission oil pan. Disconnect oil cooler lines. Separate exhaust pipe joint.

VOLVO (Cont.)

3) Remove transmission crossmember and propeller shaft. Remove flex plate-to-torque converter bolts. Remove transmission-to-engine bolts.

INSTALLATION

1) To install, reverse removal procedure. Tighten flex plate-to-torque converter bolts to 16 ft. lbs. (22 N.m). Tighten oil filler tube bottom nut to 72 ft. lbs. (100 N.m).

2) Adjust kickdown cable and gearshift linkage. Fill transmission to proper capacity with ATF.

LATEST CHANGES & CORRECTIONS

CONTENTS

	Page
Engines	2
Drive Axles	4
Wheel Alignment	5
Suspension	6

Latest Changes & Corrections

FOR 1987 & EARLIER MODELS

NOTE: **The Latest Changes & Corrections represent a collection of last minute manual revisions and relevant technical bulletins. It may be useful to read through this section and find any changes or helpful information. Then, go to the appropriate manual and note the changes in the margins.**

ENGINES

ALFA ROMEO

1 *1986 ALFA ROMEO ENGINES: GTV-6 2.5L V6 TIGHTENING SPECIFICATIONS TABLE* – The tightening specifications table appearing on page 6-64 of the 1986 IMPORTED CARS & TRUCKS SERVICE & REPAIR manual is incomplete. This table also appears on page 6-64 of the 1986 ENGINE, CLUTCH & DRIVE AXLE SERVICE & REPAIR, IMPORTED CARS & TRUCKS supplement. Tightening specifications table should read as follows:

TIGHTENING SPECIFICATIONS

Application	Ft. Lbs (N.m)
Belt Tensioner Pulley Bolt	15 (20)
Camshaft Journal Caps	[1] 15 (20)
Camshaft Hub Nut	85 (115)
Connecting Rod Cap Bolts	[1] 36 (49)
Crankshaft Pulley Nut	[1] 174 (235)
Cylinder Head	[2] 58 (78)
Flywheel Bolts	83 (112)
Main Bearing Cap Nuts	[1] 58 (78)
Main Bearing Cap Lock Nuts	23 (17)
Propeller Shaft Coupling Bolts/Nuts	40 (55)
Propeller Shaft Central Crossmember Nuts	70 (95)
Power Steering Pump Pressure Hose	20 (27)
Power Steering Pump Return Hose	35 (47)
	INCH Lbs.
Water Pump Bolts	72-82 (8-9)

[1] – With bolts and nuts lubricated.
[2] – With engine cold and washers, nuts, and stud threads lubricated. After 600 miles loosen nuts 1 turn and retighten nuts to 65 ft. lbs. (88 N.m) with washer and nuts surfaces lubricated.

CHRYSLER MOTORS

2 *1986 2.6L ENGINE: ENGINE IDENTIFICATION* – Please change the ENGINES CODES table on page 6-3 of the 1986 IMPORTED CARS & TRUCKS SERVICE & REPAIR manual and page 6-3 of the 1986 ENGINE, CLUTCH & DRIVE AXLE SERVICE & REPAIR, IMPORTED CARS & TRUCKS supplement.

ENGINE CODES

Application	Engine Model	Engine VIN Code
2.6L		
2-Bbl.	G54B	E
Turbo	G54B	H
Turbo [2]	G54B	N

3 *1981-82 CHRYSLER MOTORS 1.4L AND 1.6L ENGINE: CYLINDER HEAD INSTALLATION PROCEDURE REVISION* – The cylinder head and intake manifold installation procedure is incomplete in the 1981 and 1982 engine overhaul article. Step **2)** under cylinder head and intake manifold installation should be changed to read as follows.

2) Tighten cylinder head bolts to initial torque of 25 ft. lbs. (34 N.m). Follow sequence in *Fig. 2*. Repeat procedure, tightening bolts to final torque of 51-54 ft. lbs. (69-73 N.m).

This cylinder head installation procedure should be changed in the following publications.

IMPORTED CARS & TRUCKS SERVICE & REPAIR manual and CHASSIS SERVICE & REPAIR, IMPORTED CARS & TRUCKS.
1981 – page 6-45.
1982 – page 6-56.

HONDA

4 *1984-86 HONDA 4-CYLINDER ENGINE: MAIN BEARING BORE DIAMETER REVISION* – Roman numeral or letter codes are stamped into the block on Civic 1.3L and 1.5L engines. Please change the explanation of these codes in the 1984-86 engine overhaul article. Use the accompanying figure to identify the bearing bore codes.

1.3L & 1.5L Honda Civic Engine Main Bearing Bore Diameter Codes

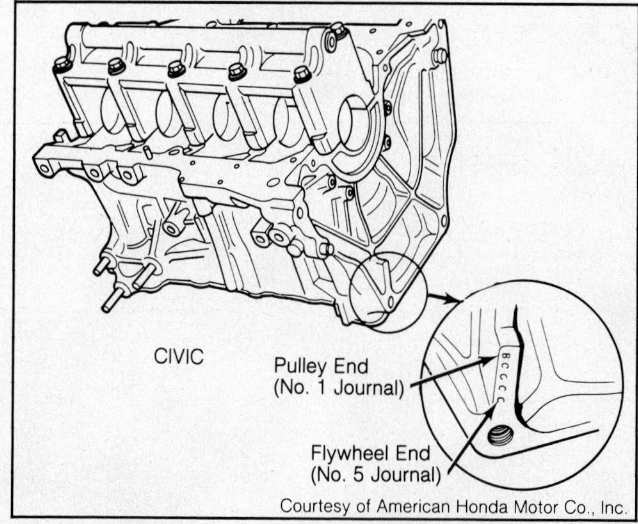

Courtesy of American Honda Motor Co., Inc.

The figure should be corrected in the following publications.

IMPORTED CARS & TRUCKS SERVICE & REPAIR manual and ENGINE, CLUTCH & DRIVE AXLE SERVICE & REPAIR, IMPORTED CARS & TRUCKS supplement.
1984 – page 6-150, Fig. 24.
1985 – page 6-119, Fig. 17.
1986 – page 6-68, Fig. 10.

Latest Changes & Corrections

FOR 1987 & EARLIER MODELS (Cont.)

5 *1984-86 HONDA CIVIC 4-CYLINDER ENGINE: REAR CRANKSHAFT OIL SEAL INSTALLATION REVISION* – Please replace the rear crankshaft oil seal replacement in the Honda engine overhaul article with the following text.

Civic

1) Remove rear crankshaft oil seal cover from rear of cylinder block. Drive seal from oil seal cover. Remove seal from oil pump. It may be necessary to remove oil screen and oil pump. See OIL PUMP in this article.

2) Coat seal lips with engine oil. Using Oil Seal Driver (07947-6340000), install front seal. Install seal until it bottoms in housing. Coat crankshaft and rear seal lip with engine oil. Using Driver (07749-0010000) and Driver Attachment (07948-SB00101), install rear seal with part number facing outward.

3) Apply non-hardening sealant to oil seal cover sealing surface of cylinder block. Sealant bead must be centered on sealing surface. Coat oil seal cover retaining bolt threads with sealant.

4) Install oil seal cover. Use care not to damage seal during installation. Tighten bolts to specification. Wait at least 30 minutes before filling engine with oil.

The revised crankshaft oil seal procedure should be added to the following manuals.

IMPORTED CARS & TRUCKS SERVICE & REPAIR manual and ENGINE, CLUTCH & DRIVE AXLE SERVICE & REPAIR, IMPORTED CARS & TRUCKS supplement.

1984 – page 6-151.
1985 – page 6-120.
1986 – page 6-68.

MAZDA

6 *1986 MAZDA 1.6L ENGINE: SERVICE MANUAL REVISION* – On page 6-222 of the 1986 IMPORTED CARS & TRUCKS SERVICE & REPAIR manual, please change the camshaft journal out-of-round wear limit in step **2)** to .002" (.05 mm).

On page 6-226, the piston ring side clearances in the PISTONS, PINS, RINGS table have been revised. The table also shows the piston pin press fit into the piston. This is incorrect. The piston pin is press fit into the connecting rod. Use the PISTONS, PINS, RINGS table in the 1987 engine overhaul article for 1986 engines.

These revisions should also be made on page 6-222 and page 6-226 in the 1986 ENGINE, CLUTCH & DRIVE AXLE SERVICE & REPAIR, IMPORTED CARS & TRUCKS supplement.

NISSAN

7 *1986 NISSAN 1.8L AND 2.0L ENGINES: CONNECTING ROD CAP TIGHTENING SPECIFICATION* – The connecting rod cap bolt torque is incorrect as shown in the 1986 engine overhaul article. Use the following corrected text. The torque is correct as shown in the original tightening specification table.

CONNECTING ROD BEARING CLEARANCE

1) Check connecting rod bearing clearance using Plastigage method. Tighten connecting rod caps to 24-27 ft. lbs. (32-36 N.m). Standard clearance is .0008-.0024" (.020-.060 mm). Maximum clearance is .004" (.10 mm) for all models.

This connecting rod cap bolt torque revision should be made on page 6-317 in the 1986 IMPORTED CARS & TRUCKS SERVICE & REPAIR manual and 1986 ENGINE, CLUTCH & DRIVE AXLE SERVICE & REPAIR, IMPORTED CARS & TRUCKS supplement.

SUBARU

8 *1986 SUBARU 1.8L 4-CYLINDER: CAMSHAFT TIMING REVISION* – On page 6-429 of the 1986 IMPORTED CARS & TRUCKS SERVICE & REPAIR manual, please disregard *Fig. 4*. The timing alignment marks illustration should be replaced with the following figure.

Subaru 1.8L OHC 4-Cylinder Timing Alignment Marks

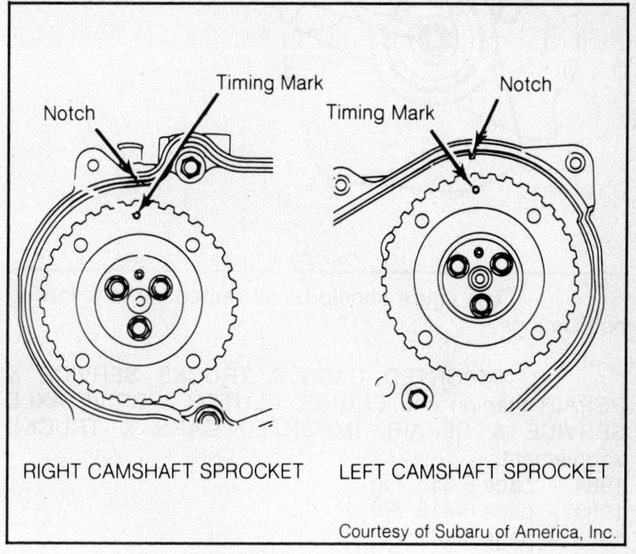

These revisions should also be made on page 6-429 in the 1986 ENGINE, CLUTCH & DRIVE AXLE SERVICE & REPAIR, IMPORTED CARS & TRUCKS supplement.

TOYOTA

9 *1986 TOYOTA COROLLA GTS AND MR2 WITH 1.6L DUAL OVERHEAD CAM 4-CYLINDER: CYLINDER HEAD REPLACEMENT PROCEDURE* – The cylinder head replacement procedure on page 6-475 of the 1986 IMPORTED CARS & TRUCKS SERVICE & REPAIR manual is incomplete. Use the procedure contained in the 1987 edition of this manual for 1986 vehicles.

Replacement procedure also appears on page 6-475 in the 1986 ENGINE, CLUTCH & DRIVE AXLE SERVICE & REPAIR, IMPORTED CARS & TRUCKS supplement.

10 *1984-1986 TOYOTA 2.0L ENGINE: TIMING BELT INSTALLATION REVISION* – The illustration titled *Installing Engine Timing Belt & Sprockets* under TIMING BELT

Latest Changes & Corrections

FOR 1987 & EARLIER MODELS (Cont.)

installation is incorrect. The "Preset Mark" is actually the TDC mark. The preset mark referred to in text is 90 degrees clockwise from the TDC mark. See following figure for correct illustration.

Installation Engine Timing Belt & Sprockets On 1984-86 2.0L Toyota Engines

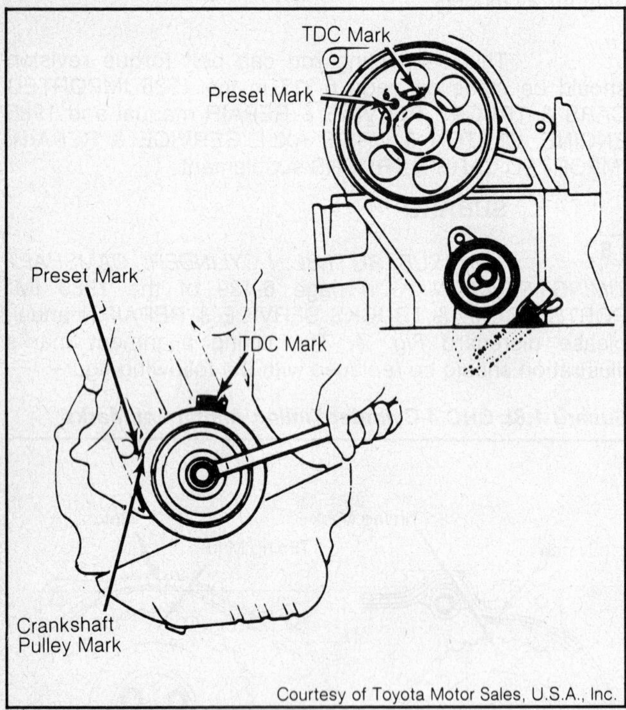

The figure should be corrected in the following publications.

IMPORTED CARS & TRUCKS SERVICE & REPAIR manual and ENGINE, CLUTCH & DRIVE AXLE SERVICE & REPAIR, IMPORTED CARS & TRUCKS supplement.

1984 – page 6-356, Fig. 4.
1985 – page 6-418, Fig. 4.
1986 – page 6-449, Fig. 8.

DRIVE AXLES

CHRYSLER MOTORS & MITSUBISHI

11 *1986 MONTERO, PICKUP AND RAM-50 (4WD): REVISED FRONT DIFFERENTIAL OVERHAUL PROCEDURE* – On page 8-36 of the 1986 IMPORTED CARS & TRUCKS SERVICE & REPAIR manual and the 1986 ENGINE, CLUTCH & DRIVE AXLE supplement, revise the drive pinion depth measurement procedure in the following manner.

Reassembly & Adjustment (Drive Pinion Depth)

1) Press drive pinion front and rear outer bearing races into carrier. Ensure race does not cock and seats in bore of carrier. Install drive pinion bearings on Dummy Pinion (MB990905-2-01) and Pinion Depth Gauge (MB990905-4-01). *See Fig. 3.*

2) Gradually tighten handle on special tool until standard value of drive pinion rotating torque is reached, 3.9-4.3 INCH lbs.(4.5-5.0 N.m) without oil seal. Ensure side bearing seat is clean and gauge firmly contacts seat. Also cut-outs on gauge must be in correct position. Select drive pinion depth adjusting shim that just fit gap between Cylinder Gauge (MB990903-01) and Pinion Gauge (MB990909-4-01).

3) Use the FEWEST number of adjustment shims possible. Install drive pinion adjusting shim(s) between drive pinion and front pinion bearing. Press front pinion bearing onto drive pinion.

12 *1986 MONTERO, PICKUP AND RAM-50 (4WD): REVISED REAR DIFFERENTIAL OVERHAUL PROCEDURE* – On page 8-42 of the 1986 IMPORTED CARS & TRUCKS SERVICE & REPAIR manual, revise the differential reassembly procedures with the following text.

Drive Pinion Depth

2) Install drive pinion bearings with Dummy Pinion Shaft (MB990905-2-01) and Pinion Gauge (MB990905-4-01) into gear carrier. *See Fig. 8.* Gradually increase preload of drive pinion bearings by tightening pinion gauge to 3-5-4.3 INCH lbs. (.40-.49 N.m).

Steps **1)**, **3)** and **4)** are unchanged.

Drive Pinion Preload

2) Preload of front and rear drive pinion bearing (without oil seal) is 3.5-4.3 INCH lbs. (.40-.49 N.m). If measurement is not within standard value, adjust bearing preload by changing pinion spacer shim and/or pinion spacer.

Steps **1)**, **3)** and **4)** are unchanged.

This revision should also be made on page 8-42 in the 1986 ENGINE, CLUTCH & DRIVE AXLE SERVICE & REPAIR, IMPORTED CARS & TRUCKS supplement.

13 *1986 CONQUEST AND STARION: REVISED REAR DIFFERENTIAL OVERHAUL PROCEDURE* – On page 8-49 of the 1986 IMPORTED CARS & TRUCKS SERVICE & REPAIR manual and 1986 ENGINE, CLUTCH & DRIVE AXLE supplement, replace the differential reassembly procedures with the following text.

Drive Pinion Depth

2) Install drive pinion bearings with Dummy Pinion Shaft (MB990905-2-01) and Pinion Height Gauge (MB990905-4-01) into gear carrier. *See Fig. 10.* Gradually increase preload of drive pinion bearings by tightening height gauge to 1.3-2.2 INCH lbs. (.15-2.9 N.m).

Steps **1)**, **3)** and **4)** are unchanged.

Drive Pinion Preload

2) Preload of front and rear drive pinion bearings (without oil seal) is 1.3-2.2 INCH lbs. If measurement is not within standard value, adjust bearing preload by changing pinion front spacer shim and/or pinion spacer.

4) Apply thin coat of multipurpose grease to spline coupling washer. Align mating marks and install spline coupling, washer and nut. Tigthen nut to specification. Measure preload of front and rear drive pinion bearings (with oil seal). Preload should be 3.5-4.3 INCH lbs. (.40-.49 N.m).

Steps **1)** and **3)** are unchanged.

14 *1983-86 ISUZU INTEGRAL HOUSING DRIVE AXLE: PINION DEPTH ADJUSTMENT REVISION* – The PINION DEPTH ADJUSTMENT procedure for Impulse and RWD I-Mark vehicles with this differential has been

FOR 1987 & EARLIER MODELS (Cont.)

revised. The correct procedure appears in the 1987 IMPORTED CARS & TRUCKS SERVICE & REPAIR manual.

This revision to the pinion depth adjustment should also be made in the following manuals.

IMPORTED CARS & TRUCKS SERVICE & REPAIR manual and ENGINE, CLUTCH & DRIVE AXLE SERVICE & REPAIR, IMPORTED CARS & TRUCKS supplement.
1983 - page 8-44.
1984 - page 8-43.
1985 - page 8-57.
1986 - page 8-70.

15 *1986 ISUZU P'UP AND TROOPER II: REAR AXLE BEARING LOCK NUT* - On page 8-63 of the 1986 IMPORTED CARS & TRUCKS SERVICE & REPAIR manual, please replace step **5)** of BEARING REPLACEMENT - EXCEPT IMPULSE with the following text.

5) Place lock nut between vise jaws. Tighten lock nut to 188-195 ft. lbs. (255-264 N.m). Bend over portion of lock washer opposite to locating tab to prevent lock nut from turning.

This bearing replacement revision should also be made on page 8-63 in the 1986 ENGINE, CLUTCH & DRIVE AXLE SERVICE & REPAIR, IMPORTED CARS & TRUCKS supplement.

16 *1986 ISUZU IMPULSE TURBO, P'UP AND TROOPER II: DIFFERENTIAL OVERHAUL REVISION* - On page 8-65 of the 1986 IMPORTED CARS & TRUCKS SERVICE & REPAIR manual, change the drive pinion depth reassembly and adjustment to read as follows.

Reassembly & Adjustments

2) Rotate bearing to ensure proper seating. Tigthten pinion lock nut to 8-10 INCH lbs. (.9-1.1 N.m) for used bearings and 20 INCH lbs. (2.3 N.m) for new bearings. Clean differential case bearing bores.

3) Place Mounting Discs (J-23597-8) on Arbor (J-23597-1). Place assembly in position in side bearing bores. Install bearing caps. Tighten cap nuts to 69-76 ft. lbs. (94-103 N.m). Mount dial indicator on arbor post and preload dial indicator 1/2 turn. Tigthen indicator in this position.

Steps **1)** and **4)** through **8)** are unchanged.

The drive pinion depth revision should also be made on page 8-65 in the 1986 ENGINE, CLUTCH & DRIVE AXLE SERVICE & REPAIR, IMPORTED CARS & TRUCKS supplement.

WHEEL ALIGNMENT

MERCEDES-BENZ

17 *1980-84 MERCEDES-BENZ 380SL: REVISED WHEEL ALIGNMENT SPECIFICATIONS* - The wheel alignment specifications for this model should be changed as follows:

CASTER - 3 1/4° ± 1/3°.
CAMBER - 0° ± 1/6°.
TOE-IN - 1/4° ± 1/6°.
TOE-OUT ON TURNS - Inner 20° and Outer 19.5°.

These wheel alignment specifications should be changed in the following publications.

IMPORTED CARS & TRUCKS SERVICE & REPAIR manual and the CHASSIS SERVICE & REPAIR, IMPORTED CARS & TRUCKS supplement.
1980 - page 8-4.
1981 - page 9-4.
1982 - page 10-4.
1983 - page 10-4.
1984 - page 10-4.

TOYOTA TOE-IN SPECIFICATIONS

Application	Toe-In In.
Camry	
Front	5/64 ± 1/32
Rear	5/32 ± 5/64
Celica	
Front	
Manual Steering	5/32 ± 1/32
Power Steering	13/64 ± 1/32
Rear	0 ± 5/64
Corolla	
FWD	
Front	0 ± 1/32
Rear	5/32 ± 5/64
RWD	
Front	1/32 ± 1/32
Rear	Nonadjustable
Cressida	
Front	5/64 ± 1/32
Rear (Sedan Only)	1/8 ± 5/64
Land Cruiser	
Front	
Bias Tire	5/32 ± 1/32
Radial Tire	
10R-15 & 7.50-16	-1/32 ± 1/32
All Others	1/32 ± 1/32
MR2	
Front	1/32 ± 1/32
Rear	13/64 ± 1/32
Pickup	
1/2 Ton (Short Bed)	
Front	
Bias Tire	5/32 ± 1/32
Radial Tire	1/32 ± 1/32
1/2 Ton (Long Bed)	
Front	
Bias Tire	15/64 ± 1/32
Radial Tire	1/8 ± 1/32
1/2 Ton (All 4WD)	
Front	
Bias Tire	5/32 ± 1/32
Radial Tire	1/32 ± 1/32
All Other Pickups	
Front	
Radial Tire	5/32 ± 1/32
Supra	
Front	-1/32 ± 1/32
Rear	0 ± 1/32
Van	0 ± 1/32
4Runner	1/8 ± 1/32

Latest Changes & Corrections

FOR 1987 & EARLIER MODELS (Cont.)

TOYOTA

18

1984-85 TOYOTA: REVISED WHEEL ALIGNMENT SPECIFICATIONS – The toe-in specifications for all 1984 and 1985 Toyota models should be modified as follows.

These wheel alignment specifications should be changed in the following publications.

IMPORTED CARS & TRUCKS SERVICE & REPAIR manual and CHASSIS SERVICE & REPAIR, IMPORTED CARS & TRUCKS supplement.
1984 – page 10-5.
1985 – page 10-5.

SUSPENSION

CHRYSLER MOTORS

19

1986 COLT VISTA (4WD): REAR WHEEL BEARING REPLACEMENT – On page 11-123 of the 1986 IMPORTED CARS & TRUCKS SERVICE & REPAIR manual, the wheel bearing removal and installation does not apply to Colt Vista 4WD models. Use procedure in the 1987 edition of the manual for 2WD and 4WD wheel bearing replacement.

This revision should also be made on page 11-123 in the 1986 CHASSIS SERVICE & REPAIR IMPORTED CARS & TRUCKS supplement.

20

1986 COLT VISTA (4WD): REAR AXLE SHAFT NUT TIGHTENING SPECIFICATIONS – On page 11-126 of the 1986 IMPORTED CARS & TRUCKS SERVICE & REPAIR manual, add Colt Vista (4WD) rear axle shaft nut to the tightening specification table. The correct torque is 116-159 ft. lbs. (160-220 N.m).

The tightening specification should also be changed on page 11-126 in the 1986 CHASSIS SERVICE & REPAIR IMPORTED CARS & TRUCKS supplement.

21

1984-86 CONQUEST: REAR AXLE SHAFT NUT TIGHTENING SPECIFICATIONS – In the 1984-86 IMPORTED CARS & TRUCKS SERVICE & REPAIR manuals, please revise step **4)** of rear wheel bearing installation for Conquest models.

4) Attach axle flange. Mount axle housing in vise and tighten companion flange mount nut to 188-217 ft. lbs. (260-300 N.m). Measure axle shaft starting torque. Starting torque should be 4 INCH lbs. (.5 N.m). If starting torque exceeds specification, replace spacer.

This wheel bearing installation text should be changed in the following publications.

IMPORTED CARS & TRUCKS SERVICE & REPAIR manual and CHASSIS SERVICE & REPAIR, IMPORTED CARS & TRUCKS supplement.

- 1984 – page 11-85.
- 1985 – page 11-99.
- 1986 – page 11-127.

HONDA

22

1986 HONDA FRONT SUSPENSION: FRONT BALL JOINT REPLACEMENT – On page 11-33 of the 1986 IMPORTED CARS & TRUCKS SERVICE & REPAIR manual, the ball joint removal and installation applies to both Accord and Prelude models.

This revision should also be noted on page 11-33 in the 1986 CHASSIS SERVICE & REPAIR IMPORTED CARS & TRUCKS supplement.

23

1986 HONDA FRONT SUSPENSION: STEERING KNUCKLE REPLACEMENT – On page 11-34 of the 1986 IMPORTED CARS & TRUCKS SERVICE & REPAIR manual, please replace paragraphs **4)** and **5)** under STEERING KNUCKLE, REMOVAL with the following text.

4) Break loose lower control (radius) arm ball joint, and pull down until ball joint is clear of knuckle. on Civic models, remove strut assmbly locking bolt. Tap knuckle down until it is comes off strut.

5) On Accord and Prelude models, remove upper ball joint sield. Remove cotter pin from upper ball joint and remove castle nut. Break loose upper ball joint.

This steering knuckle revision should also be made on page 11-34 in the 1986 CHASSIS SERVICE & REPAIR IMPORTED CARS & TRUCKS supplement.

MAZDA

24

1986 MAZDA RX7 AND 626 FRONT AND REAR SUSPENSIONS: REVISED TIGHTENING SPECIFICATIONS – The tightening specifications for suspension components have been revised as follows.

TIGHTENING SPECIFICATIONS

Application	Ft. Lbs. (N.m)
Front Shock (RX7 & 626)	
Mount Block-to-Suspension Tower Nuts	
RX7	22-27 (29-36)
626	34-46 (46-63)
Piston Rod-to-Mount Nut	47-59 (64-80)
Rear Shock (RX7 & 626)	
Mount Block-to-Suspension Tower Nuts	
RX7	17-22 (23-29)
626	34-46 (46-63)
Piston Rod-to-Mount Nut	
RX7	41-59 (55-80)
626	42-59 (64-80)

Please revise the tightening specification tables on the follow pages of the 1986 IMPORTED CARS & TRUCKS SERVICE & REPAIR manual and the 1986 CHASSIS SERVICE & REPAIR IMPORTED CARS & TRUCKS supplement.

- RX7 & 626 Front Suspension – page 11-52.
- RX7 Rear Suspension – page 11-148.
- 626 Rear Suspension – page 11-150.

25

1986 MAZDA RX7 REAR SUSPENSION: SERVICE MANUAL CORRECTION – On page 11-148 of the 1986 IMPORTED CARS & TRUCKS SERVICE & REPAIR manual, please note that *Fig. 4.* is an illustration of a front suspension.

The figure revision should also be noted on page 11-148 in the 1986 CHASSIS SERVICE & REPAIR IMPORTED CARS & TRUCKS supplement.

MITSUBISHI

26

1983-86 MITSUBISHI: REAR AXLE SHAFT NUT TIGHTENING SPECIFICATIONS – In the 1983-86 IMPORTED CARS & TRUCKS SERVICE & REPAIR manuals, please revise step **4)** of rear wheel bearing installation for Conquest models.

4) Attach axle flange. Mount axle housing in vise and tighten companion flange mount nut to 188-217 ft. lbs. (260-300 N.m). Measure axle shaft starting torque. Starting torque should be 4 INCH lbs. (.5 N.m). If starting torque exceeds specification, replace spacer.

Revise the wheel beariing installation text in the following publications.

IMPORTED CARS & TRUCKS SERVICE & REPAIR manual and CHASSIS SERVICE & REPAIR, IMPORTED CARS & TRUCKS supplement.

- 1983 – page 11-97.
- 1984 – page 11-85.
- 1985 – page 11-99.
- 1986 – page 11-127.

English-Metric Conversion Chart

CONVERSION FACTORS

Unit	To Unit	Multiply By
LENGTH		
Millimeters	Inches	.03937
Inches	Millimeters	25.4
Meters	Feet	3.28084
Feet	Meters	.3048
Kilometers	Miles	.62137
Miles	Kilometers	1.60935
AREA		
Square Centimeters	Square Inches	.155
Square Inches	Square Centimeters	6.45159
VOLUME		
Cubic Centimeters	Cubic Inches	.06103
Cubic Inches	Cubic Centimeters	16.38703
Liters	Cubic Inches	61.025
Cubic Inches	Liters	.01639
Liters	Quarts	1.05672
Quarts	Liters	.94633
Liters	Pints	2.11344
Pints	Liters	.47317
Liters	Ounces	33.81497
Ounces	Liters	.02957

Unit	To Unit	Multiply By
WEIGHT		
Grams	Ounces	.03527
Ounces	Grams	28.34953
Kilograms	Pounds	2.20462
Pounds	Kilograms	.45359
WORK		
Centimeter Kilograms	Inch Pounds	.8676
Inch Pounds	Centimeter Kilograms	1.15262
Meter Kilograms	Foot Pounds	7.23301
Foot Pounds	Newton Meters	1.3558
PRESSURE		
Kilograms/ Sq. Centimeter	Pounds/Sq. Inch	14.22334
Pounds/Sq. Inch	Kilograms/Sq. Centimeter	.07031
Bar	Pounds/Sq. Inch	14.504
Pounds/Sq. Inch	Bar	.06895
Atmosphere	Pounds/Sq. Inch	14.696
Pounds/Sq. Inch	Atmosphere	.06805
TEMPERATURE		
Centigrade Degrees	Fahrenheit Degrees	$(C° \times 9/5)+32$
Fahrenheit Degrees	Centigrade Degrees	$(F° - 32) \times 5/9$

Inches	Decimals	MM
1/64	.016	.397
1/32	.031	.794
3/64	.047	1.191
1/16	.063	1.588
5/64	.078	1.984
3/32	.094	2.381
7/64	.109	2.778
1/8	.125	3.175
9/64	.141	3.572
5/32	.156	3.969
11/64	.172	4.366
3/16	.188	4.763
13/64	.203	5.159
7/32	.219	5.556
15/64	.234	5.953
1/4	.250	6.350
17/64	.266	6.747
9/32	.281	7.144
19/64	.297	7.541
5/16	3.13	7.938
21/64	.328	8.334
11/32	.344	8.731
23/64	.359	9.128
3/8	.375	9.525
25/64	.391	9.922
13/32	.406	10.319
27/64	.422	10.716
7/16	.438	11.113
29/64	.453	11.509
15/32	.469	11.906
31/64	.484	12.303
1/2	.500	12.700

Inches	Decimals	MM
33/64	.516	13.097
17/32	.531	13.494
35/64	.547	13.891
9/16	.563	14.288
37/64	.578	14.684
19/32	.594	15.081
39/64	.609	15.478
5/8	.625	15.875
41/64	.641	16.272
21/32	.656	16.669
43/64	.672	17.066
11/16	.687	17.463
45/64	.703	17.859
23/32	.719	18.256
47/64	.734	18.653
3/4	.750	19.050
49/64	.766	19.447
25/32	.781	19.844
51/64	.797	20.241
13/16	.813	20.638
53/64	.828	21.034
27/32	.844	21.431
55/64	.859	21.828
7/8	.875	22.225
57/64	.891	22.622
29/32	.906	23.019
59/64	.922	23.416
15/16	.938	23.813
61/64	.953	24.209
31/32	.969	24.606
63/64	.984	25.003

METRIC CONVERSIONS

Metric conversions are making life more difficult for the mechanic. In addition to doubling the number of tools required, metric-dimensioned nuts and bolts are used alongside English components in many new vehicles. The mechanic has to decide which tool to use, slowing down the job. The tool problem can be solved by trial and error, but some metric conversions aren't so simple.

Converting temperature, lengths or volumes requires a calculator and conversion charts, or else a very nimble mind. Conversion charts are only part of the answer though, becuase they don't help you "think" metric, or "vizualize" what you are converting. The following examples are intended to help you "see" metric sizes:

LENGTH

Meters are the standard unit of length in the metric system.The smaller units are 10ths (decimeter), 100ths (centimeter), and 1000ths (millimeter) of a meter. These common examples might help you to visualize the metric units:

* A meter is slightly longer than a yard (about 40 inches).
* An aspirin tablet is about one centimeter across (.4 inches).
* A millimeter is about the thickness of a dime.

VOLUME

Cubic meters and centimeters are used to measure volume, just as we normally think of cubic feet and inches. Liquid volume measurements include the liter and milliliter, like the English quarts or ounces.

* One teaspoon is about 5 cubic centimeters.
* A liter is about one quart.
* A liter is about 61 cubic inches.

WEIGHT

The metric weight system is based on the gram, with the most common unit being the kilogram (1000 grams). Our comparable units are ounces and pounds:

* A kilogram is about 2.2 pounds.
* An ounce is about 28 grams.

TORQUE

Torque is somewhat complicated. The term describes the amount of effort exerted to turn something. A chosen unit of weight or force is applied to a lever of standard length. The resulting leverage is called torque. In our standard system, we use the weight of one pound applied to a lever a foot long—resulting in the unit called a foot-pound. A smaller unit is the inch-pound (the lever is one inch long). Metric units include the meter kilogram (lever one meter long with a kilogram of weight applied) and the Newton-meter(lever one meter long with force of one Newton applied). Some conversions are:

* A meter kilogram is about 7.2 foot pounds.
* A Newton-meter is about 1.4 foot pounds.
* A centimeter kilogram (cmkg) is equal to .9 inch pounds.

PRESSURE

Pressure is another complicated measurement. Pressure is described as a force or weight applied to a given area. Our common unit is pounds per square inch. Metric units can be expressed in several ways. One is the kilogram per square centimeter (kg/cm^2). Another unit of pressure is the Pascal (force of one Newton on an area of one square meter), which equals about 4 ounces on a square yard. Since this is a very small amount of pressure, we usually see the kiloPascal, or kPa (1000 Pascals). Another common automotive term for pressure is the bar (used by German manufacturers), which equals 10 Pascals. Thoroughly confused? Try the examples below:

* Atmospheric pressure at sea level is about 14.7 psi.
* Atmospheric pressure at sea level is about 1 bar.
* Atmospheric pressure at sea level is about 1 kg/cm^2.
* One pound per square inch is about 7 kPa.

WE ENCOURAGE PROFESSIONALISM

THROUGH TECHNICIAN CERTIFICATION

SECTION I

GENERAL INDEX

CONTENTS

VEHICLE COMPONENTS — **Page**

Air Bag I-2
Alignment I-2
Alternator I-2
Ammeter I-2
Automatic Choke I-2
Automatic Level I-2
Automatic Transmission I-2
Battery I-2
Belts I-2
Brakes I-3
Camshaft I-4
Capacities I-4
Carburetors I-5
Clutches I-5
Compression Pressure I-5
Computerized Engine Controls I-5
Connecting Rods I-6
Cooling I-6
Cruise Controls I-6
Defoggers I-6
Distributors I-6
Drive Axles I-6
Emission Reset Lights I-8
Engines I-8
Engine Identification I-12
Filter Replacement Interval I-12

VEHICLE COMPONENTS (Cont.) — **Page**

Firing Order I-13
Front Wheel Drive Axles I-13
Fuel Injection - Diesel I-13
Fuel Injection - Gas I-13
Fuel Pump I-13
Fuel Pump Specifications I-13
Fuel Tank Capacities I-14
Fuses I-15
Gauges I-15
Glow Plugs I-15
Horn Button/Pad I-15
Identification I-15
Ignition I-15
Ignition Switch I-16
Ignition Timing I-16
Injection Pump Timing I-16
Jacking & Hoisting I-16
Locking Hubs I-16
Manifolds I-16
Manual Steering I-16
Manual Transmission I-17
Master Cylinder I-17
Oil Capacities I-17
Oil Pressure Gauge I-17
Oil Pump I-17
Piston I-17
Piston Rings I-17
Power Steering I-17
Rear Suspension I-17
Rear Window Defogger I-17
Regulator I-17
Riding Height I-17
Spark Plugs I-17
Starter I-17
Steering I-18
Supplemental Restraint System I-19
Suspension I-19
Switches I-22
Thermostat I-22
Transmission Servicing I-22
Transmission Removal I-22
Trouble Shooting I-22
Tune-Up I-22
Turbocharger I-23
Turn Signal I-23
Valve Clearance I-23
Water Pump I-23
Wheel Alignment I-24
Wheel Bearings I-24
Wheels I-24
Wiper/Washer System I-25
Wire Resistance I-26
Wiring Diagrams I-26

1987 General Index

A

AIR BAG
Mercedes-Benz SRS 5-79
ALIGNMENT – *See Wheel Alignment*

ALTERNATOR
All Models
Applications 3-54
General Servicing 3-58
Bosch
Alfa Romeo
Description 3-59
Overhaul 3-61
Testing 3-59
Audi
Description 3-59
Overhaul 3-61
Testing 3-59
BMW
Description 3-59
Overhaul 3-61
Testing 3-59
Ford Motor Co.
Description 3-59
Overhaul 3-61
Testing 3-59
Mercedes-Benz
Description 3-59
Overhaul 3-61
Testing 3-59
Saab
Description 3-59
Overhaul 3-61
Testing 3-59
Volkswagen
Description 3-59
Overhaul 3-61
Testing 3-59
Volvo
Description 3-59
Overhaul 3-61
Testing 3-59
Yugo
Description 3-59
Overhaul 3-61
Testing 3-59
Ducellier & Paris-Rhone
Peugeot
Description 3-62
Overhaul 3-62
Testing 3-62
Hitachi
Isuzu
Description 3-63
Overhaul 3-66
Testing 3-63
Nissan
Description 3-63
Overhaul 3-66
Testing 3-63
Subaru
Description 3-63
Overhaul 3-66
Testing 3-63
Lucas
Jaguar
Description 3-67
Overhaul 3-87
Testing 3-69
Mitsubishi
Chrysler Motors
Description 3-70
Overhaul 3-72
Testing 3-70
Hyundai
Description 3-70
Overhaul 3-72
Testing 3-70
Mazda
Description 3-70
Overhaul 3-72
Testing 3-70
Mitsubishi
Description 3-70
Overhaul 3-72
Testing 3-70
Nissan (300ZX)
Description 3-70
Overhaul 3-72
Testing 3-70
Motorola
Jaguar
Description 3-73
Overhaul 3-76
Testing 3-73
Nippondenso
Acura
Description 3-77
Overhaul 3-82
Testing 3-78
General Motors
Description 3-77
Overhaul 3-82
Testing 3-78
Honda
Description 3-77
Overhaul 3-82
Testing 3-78
Isuzu
Description 3-77
Overhaul 3-82
Testing 3-78
Sterling
Description 3-77
Overhaul 3-82
Testing 3-78
Toyota
Description 3-77
Overhaul 3-82
Testing 3-78
SEV Motorola
Peugeot, Volkswagen
Description 3-84
Overhaul 3-85
Testing 3-84

AMMETER – *See Gauge*

AUTOMATIC CHOKE – *See Carburetor*

AUTOMATIC LEVEL CONTROL – *See Suspension*

AUTOMATIC TRANSMISSION – *See Transmission*

AXLE SHAFT – *See Drive Axle*

B

BATTERY
Acura
4-Cylinder 1-8
V6 1-13
Alfa Romeo
V6 1-17
Audi
4-Cylinder 1-20
5-Cylinder 1-25
BMW
6-Cylinder 1-27
Chrysler Motors 1-33
Ford Motor Co. 1-37
General Motors 1-42
Honda 1-50
Hyundai 1-54
Isuzu
4-Cylinder Gas 1-60
4-Cylinder Diesel 1-62
Jaguar
6-Cylinder 1-65
V12 1-67
Mazda
4-Cylinder Gas 1-74
Rotary Engine 1-79
Mercedes-Benz
4-Cylinder Gas 1-81
6-Cylinder Gas 1-83
5 & 6-Cylinder Diesel 1-85
V8 1-88
Mitsubishi 1-33
Nissan
4-Cylinder 1-94
V6 1-99
Peugeot
4-Cylinder 1-104
Porsche
4-Cylinder 1-109
6-Cylinder 1-112
Saab 1-116
Subaru 1-122
Sterling 1-13
Suzuki 1-126
Toyota
4-Cylinder 1-135
6-Cylinder 1-141
Volkswagen
4-Cylinder 1-148
5-Cylinder Gas 1-25
Volvo
4-Cylinder 1-151
V6 Gas 1-154
Yugo 1-156

BELTS
Acura
4-Cylinder Gas 1-8
V6 1-13
Alfa Romeo
V6 1-17
Audi
4-Cylinder Gas 1-20
5-Cylinder Gas 1-25
BMW
6-Cylinder 1-27
Chrysler Motors 1-33

1987 General Index

BELTS (Cont.)
Ford Motor Co. 1-37
General Motors 1-42
Honda 1-51
Hyundai 1-55
Isuzu
4-Cylinder Gas 1-60
4-Cylinder Diesel 1-62
Jaguar
6-Cylinder 1-65
V12 1-68
Mazda
4-Cylinder Gas 1-75
Rotary Engine 1-79
Mercedes-Benz
4-Cylinder Gas 1-81
6-Cylinder Gas 1-83
5 & 6-Cylinder Diesel 1-86
V8 1-88
Mitsubishi 1-33
Nissan
4-Cylinder 1-95
V6 1-99
Peugeot
4-Cylinder 1-104
V6 1-106
Porsche
4-Cylinder 1-109
6-Cylinder 1-113
Saab 1-117
Subaru 1-123
Sterling 1-14
Suzuki 1-127
Toyota
4-Cylinder 1-136
6-Cylinder 1-142
Volkswagen
4-Cylinder 1-148
5-Cylinder Gas 1-25
Volvo
4-Cylinder 1-151
V6 1-154

BRAKES
All Models
Trouble Shooting 9-2
Hydraulic Brake Bleeding 9-3
Anti-Locking Brake Systems
Acura 9-157
Audi 9-163
BMW 9-176
Chrysler Motors 9-185
Jaguar 9-189
Mazda 9-192
Mercedes-Benz 9-194
Mitsubishi 9-185
Peugeot 9-203
Porsche 9-209
Saab 9-222
Sterling 9-225
Toyota 9-230
Volvo 9-242
Brake Systems
Acura
Adjustments 9-4
Description 9-4
Overhaul 9-7
Removal & Installation 9-5
Testing 9-4

Audi
Adjustments 9-14
Description 9-14
Overhaul 9-19
Removal & Installation 9-16
Testing 9-15
BMW
Adjustments 9-22
Description 9-22
Overhaul 9-25
Removal & Installation 9-23
Testing 9-22
Chrysler Motors
Adjustments 9-27
Description 9-27
Overhaul 9-33
Removal & Installation 9-28
Ford Motor Co. - Festiva & Merkur XR4Ti
Adjustments 9-37
Description 9-37
Overhaul 9-41
Removal & Installation 9-38
Ford Motor Co. - Tracer
Adjustments 9-44
Description 9-44
Overhaul 9-48
Removal & Installation 9-45
Testing 9-45
General Motors - Chevrolet
Adjustments 9-53
Description 9-53
Overhaul 9-55
Removal & Installation 9-53
Hyundai Excel
Adjustments 9-58
Description 9-58
Overhaul 9-60
Removal & Installation 9-58
Testing 9-58
Honda
Adjustments 9-4
Description 9-4
Overhaul 9-7
Removal & Installation 9-5
Testing 9-4
Isuzu - I-Mark
Adjustments 9-53
Description 9-53
Overhaul 9-55
Removal & Installation 9-53
Isuzu - Impulse
Adjustments 9-63
Description 9-63
Overhaul 9-65
Removal & Installation 9-63
Isuzu - P'UP & Trooper II
Adjustments 9-68
Description 9-68
Overhaul 9-73
Removal & Installation 9-70
Testing 9-68
Jaguar
Adjustments 9-76
Description 9-76
Overhaul 9-79
Removal & Installation 9-76
Testing 9-76

Mazda
Adjustments 9-44
Description 9-44
Overhaul 9-48
Removal & Installation 9-45
Testing 9-45
Mercedes-Benz
Adjustments 9-82
Description 9-82
Overhaul 9-84
Removal & Installation 9-82
Testing 9-82
Mitsubishi - Except Precis
Adjustments 9-27
Description 9-27
Overhaul 9-33
Removal & Installation 9-28
Mitsubishi - Precis
Adjustments 9-58
Description 9-58
Overhaul 9-60
Removal & Installation 9-58
Testing 9-58
Nissan
Adjustments 9-86
Description 9-86
Overhaul 9-91
Removal & Installation 9-87
Peugeot
Adjustments 9-97
Description 9-97
Removal & Installation 9-97
Porsche
Adjustments 9-101
Description 9-101
Overhaul 9-103
Removal & Installation 9-101
Saab
900, 900S & 900 Turbo
Adjustments 9-106
Description 9-106
Overhaul 9-108
Removal & Installation 9-106
9000
Adjustments 9-110
Description 9-110
Overhaul 9-111
Removal & Installation 9-110
Subaru
Adjustments 9-115
Description 9-115
Overhaul 9-118
Removal & Installation 9-115
Sterling
Adjustments 9-113
Description 9-113
Overhaul 9-114
Removal & Installation 9-113
Suzuki
Adjustments 9-121
Description 9-121
Overhaul 9-122
Removal & Installation 9-121
Toyota
Adjustments 9-126
Description 9-126
Overhaul 9-138
Removal & Installation 9-129

1987 General Index

BRAKES (Cont.)
Volkswagen
Adjustments 9-142
Description 9-142
Overhaul 9-146
Removal & Installation 9-143
Volvo
Adjustments 9-149
Description 9-149
Overhaul 9-151
Removal & Installation 9-149
Yugo
Adjustments 9-154
Description 9-154
Overhaul 9-155
Removal & Installation 9-155

C

CAMSHAFT – *See Engine*

CAPACITIES – *See Fuel Tank, Oil or Cooling*

CARBURETORS
Trouble Shooting
All Models 2-2
Chrysler Motors, All Models
Mikuni (Solex) 2-Bbl.
Adjustments 2-47
Description 2-47
Identification 2-47
Overhaul 2-48
Ford Motor Co., Festiva
Asian 2 Bbl.
Adjustments 2-6
Description 2-6
Overhaul 2-7
Specifications 2-9
General Motors, Spectrum
Nippon (Stromberg) 2-Bbl.
Adjustments 2-55
Description 2-55
Overhaul 2-58
Specifications 2-58
General Motors, Sprint
Hitachi DFB 306 2-Bbl.
Adjustments 2-28
Description 2-28
Identification 2-28
Overhaul 2-30
Specifications 2-32
Honda, Accord, Civic, CRX
Keihin 2-Bbl.
Adjustments 2-39
Description 2-39
Identification 2-39
Testing 2-42
Honda, Prelude
Keihin 1-Bbl.
Adjustments 2-33
Description 2-33
Overhaul 2-37
Testing 2-34
Hyundai, Excel
Mikuni (Solex) 2-Bbl.
Adjustments 2-47
Description 2-47
Identification 2-47
Overhaul 2-48
Isuzu, I-Mark
Nippon (Stromberg) 2-Bbl.
Adjustments 2-55
Description 2-55
Overhaul 2-58
Specifications 2-58
Isuzu, PUP, Trooper II
Stromberg 2-Bbl.
Adjustments 2-59
Description 2-59
Identification 2-59
Overhaul 2-60
Specifications 2-60
Mazda, B2600
Mikuni (Solex) 2-Bbl.
Adjustments 2-47
Description 2-47
Identification 2-47
Overhaul 2-48
Mazda, B2200
Nikki 2-Bbl.
Adjustments 2-51
Description 2-51
Overhaul 2-52
Specifications 2-54
Mitsubishi, All Models
Mikuni (Solex) 2-Bbl.
Adjustments 2-47
Description 2-47
Identification 2-47
Overhaul 2-48
Nissan, Pickup
Hitachi 2-Bbl.
Adjustments 2-23
Description & Identification 2-23
Overhaul 2-24
Specifications 2-27
Nissan, Sentra
Hitachi 2-Bbl.
Adjustments 2-21
Description 2-21
Identification 2-21
Overhaul 2-22
Specifications 2-27
Subaru
Hitachi 2-Bbl.
Adjustments 2-21
Description 2-21
Identification 2-21
Overhaul 2-22
Specifications 2-27
Suzuki, Samurai
Hitachi DFB 306 2-Bbl.
Adjustments 2-28
Description 2-28
Identification 2-28
Overhaul 2-30
Specifications 2-32
Toyota
2F – Aisan 2-Bbl.
Adjustments 2-10
Description 2-10
Identification 2-10
Overhaul 2-11
Specifications 2-13
3A-C, 4A-C – Aisan 2-Bbl.
Adjustments 2-17
Description 2-17
Identification 2-17
Overhaul 2-19
Specifications 2-20
22R – Aisan 2-Bbl.
Adjustments 2-14
Description 2-14
Identification 2-14
Overhaul 2-15
Specifications 2-16
Tercel – Toyota .... 1-Bbl.
Adjustments 2-62
Description 2-62
Identification 2-62
Overhaul 2-63

CLUTCHES
All Models
Trouble Shooting 7-2
Acura 7-4
Adjustments 7-6
Description 7-4
Removal & Installation 7-4
Alfa Romeo Milano 7-7
Adjustments 7-7
Description 7-7
Overhaul 7-7
Removal & Installation 7-7
Audi
Coupe GT & 4000S 7-8
Adjustments 7-9
Description 7-8
Removal & Installation 7-8
4000CS Quattro & 5000S 7-10
Adjustments 7-11
Description 7-10
Removal & Installation 7-10
BMW 7-12
Adjustments 7-13
Description 7-12
Overhaul 7-13
Removal & Installation 7-12
Chrysler Motors
FWD Models 7-14
Adjustments 7-15
Description 7-14
Overhaul 7-15
Removal & Installation 7-14
RWD Models 7-16
Adjustments 7-19
Description 7-16
Removal & Installation 7-16
Ford Motor Co.
Festiva & Merkur XR4Ti 7-20
Adjustments 7-22
Description & Operation 7-20
Removal & Installation 7-20
Tracer 7-33
Adjustments 7-35
Description 7-33
Overhaul 7-35
Removal & Installation 7-33
General Motors
Spectrum & Sprint 7-24
Adjustments 7-25
Description 7-24
Removal & Installation 7-24

CLUTCHES (Cont.)
Honda
Accord, Civic & Prelude 7-4
Adjustments 7-6
Description 7-4
Removal & Installation 7-4
Hyundai
Excel 7-26
Adjustments 7-26
Description 7-26
Removal & Installation 7-26
Isuzu
I-Mark 7-27
Adjustments 7-27
Description 7-27
Removal & Installation 7-27
Impulse 7-28
Adjustments 7-29
Description 7-28
Overhaul 7-29
Removal & Installation 7-28
P'UP & Trooper II 7-30
Adjustments 7-32
Description 7-30
Overhaul 7-31
Removal & Installation 7-30
Mazda
FWD 7-33
Adjustments 7-35
Description 7-33
Overhaul 7-35
Removal & Installation 7-33
RWD 7-37
Adjustments 7-38
Description 7-37
Overhaul 7-38
Removal & Installation 7-37
Mercedes-Benz
190 Series 7-39
Adjustments 7-40
Description 7-39
Removal & Installation 7-39
Mitsubishi
FWD Models 7-14
Adjustments 7-15
Description 7-14
Overhaul 7-15
Removal & Installation 7-14
RWD Models 7-16
Adjustments 7-19
Description 7-16
Removal & Installation 7-16
Nissan
All Except Pulsar NX, Sentra & Stanza 7-41
Adjustments 7-43
Description 7-41
Overhaul 7-42
Removal & Installation 7-41
Pulsar NX, Sentra & Stanza 7-44
Adjustments 7-45
Description 7-44
Removal & Installation 7-44
Peugeot 7-46
Description 7-46
Removal & Installation 7-46
Porsche
911 Carrera & Turbo 7-47
Adjustments 7-47
Description 7-47
Removal & Installation 7-47
Saab 900 7-48
Adjustments 7-49
Description 7-48
Overhaul 7-49
Removal & Installation 7-48
Saab 9000 7-50
Adjustments 7-51
Description 7-50
Overhaul 7-51
Removal & Installation 7-50
Sterling 7-52
Adjustments 7-52
Description 7-52
Removal & Installation 7-52
Subaru 7-53
Adjustments 7-54
Description 7-53
Removal & Installation 7-53
Suzuki
Samurai 7-55
Adjustments 7-55
Description 7-55
Removal & Installation 7-55
Toyota
Except Tercel 7-56
Adjustments 7-57
Description 7-56
Overhaul 7-57
Removal & Installation 7-56
Tercel 7-58
Adjustments 7-58
Description 7-58
Removal & Installation 7-58
Volkswagen
Cabriolet, Golf, GTI, Jetta & Scirocco 7-60
Adjustments 7-60
Description 7-60
Removal & Installation 7-60
Quantum 7-62
Adjustments 7-62
Description 7-62
Removal & Installation 7-62
Vanagon 7-63
Description 7-63
Removal & Installation 7-63
Volvo
DL, GL, Turbo, 760 GLE 7-64
Adjustments 7-65
Description 7-64
Overhaul 7-65
Removal & Installation 7-64
Yugo 7-66
Adjustments 7-66
Description 7-66
Removal & Installation 7-66

COMPRESSION PRESSURE
Acura
4-Cylinder 1-6
V6 1-10
Alfa Romeo
V6 1-15
Audi
4-Cylinder 1-18
5-Cylinder 1-21
BMW
6-Cylinder 1-26
Chrysler Motors 1-29
Ford Motor Co. 1-34
General Motors 1-38
Honda 1-44
Hyundai 1-52
Isuzu
4-Cylinder 1-56
4-Cylinder Diesel 1-61
Jaguar
6-Cylinder 1-63
V12 1-66
Mazda
4-Cylinder 1-69
Rotary Engine 1-76
Mercedes-Benz
4-Cylinder 1-80
6-Cylinder 1-82
5 & 6-Cylinder Diesel 1-84
V8 1-87
Mitsubishi 1-29
Nissan
4-Cylinder 1-89
V6 Gas 1-96
Peugeot
4-Cylinder 1-101
V6 1-105
Porsche
4-Cylinder 1-107
6-Cylinder 1-110
V8 1-115
Saab 1-114
Sterling 1-10
Subaru 1-118
Suzuki 1-124
Toyota
4-Cylinder 1-128
6-Cylinder 1-137
Volkswagen
4-Cylinder 1-143
5-Cylinder 1-21
Volvo
4-Cylinder 1-149
V6 1-152
Yugo 1-155

COMPUTERIZED ENGINE CONTROLS
Acura
Description & Operation 1a-2
Testing 1a-4
Trouble Shooting 1a-3
Alfa-Romeo
Description 1a-36
Testing 1a-36
Audi
Except Coupe GT (2.3L) & 5000S (2.3L)
Description & Operation 1a-39
Testing 1a-41
Removal & Installation 1a-52
Coupe GT (2.3L) & 5000S (2.3L)
Description & Operation 1a-63
Testing 1a-66
Removal & Installation 1a-71
BMW Motronic
Description & Operation 1a-72
Motronic Testing 1a-73

1987 General Index

COMPUTERIZED ENGINE CONTROLS (Cont.)

General Motors
Chevrolet Spectrum
Description & Operation 1a-79
Diagnosis & Testing 1a-79
Chevrolet Sprint
Description & Operation 1a-91
Testing 1a-91
Chrysler Motors
Electronically Controlled Injection
Adjustments 1a-125
Description & Operation 1a-120
Testing & Diagnosis 1a-121
Feedback Carburetor
Description & Operation 1a-98
Testing & Diagnosis 1a-98
Multi-point Fuel Injection (MPFI)
Adjustments 1a-149
Description & Operation 1a-141
Testing & Diagnosis 1a-143
Ford Motor Co.
Festiva
Description & Operation 1a-157
Testing 1a-158
Merkur
Circuit Tests 1a-169
Description & Operation 1a-164
Diagnosis & Testing 1a-164
Diagnosis By Symptom Test 1a-169
Quick Test 1a-166
Tracer
Description & Operation 1a-186
Diagnosis 1a-187
Testing 1a-191
Honda
Electronic Control
Description & Operation 1a-201
ECM System Trouble Shooting 1a-205
Testing 1a-202
Feedback Carburetor
Description & Operation 1a-213
Testing 1a-213
Trouble Shooting 1a-218
Hyundai
Description & Operation 1a-226
Testing 1a-227
Isuzu
Closed Loop Emission
Description & Operation 1a-231
Diagnosis & Testing 1a-232
Removal & Installation 1a-240
I-TEC Control
Description & Operation 1a-246
Diagnosis & Testing 1a-246
Test Charts 1a-248
I-Mark Feedback Control
Description & Operation 1a-79
Diagnosis & Testing 1a-79
Mazda
323, 626 & 626 Turbo
Description & Operation 1a-186
Diagnosis 1a-187
Testing 1a-191
Test Charts 1a-195
RX& & RX7 Turbo
Description & Operation 1a-254
Testing 1a-254
Test Charts 1a-255

Mercedes-Benz CIS-E System
Component Testing
190E, 260E & 300E Series 1a-275
420 & 560 Series 1a-273
Description 1a-266
Diagnostic Testing
420 & 560 Series 1a-271
Operation 1a-267
Trouble Shooting
420 & 560 Series 1a-270
Mitsubishi
Feedback Carburetor
Description & Operation 1a-226
Testing 1a-227
Test Charts 1a-228
Electronic Control Injection (ECI)
Adjustments 1a-125
Description & Operation 1a-120
Testing & Diagnosis 1a-121
Test Charts 1a-132
Multi-Point Injection System
Adjustments 1a-149
Description & Operation 1a-141
Testing & Diagnosis 1a-143
Nissan
Electronically Controlled Carburetor
Description & Operation 1a-288
Testing 1a-289
Electronic Concentrated Engine Control
Description & Operation 1a-295
Testing & Diagnosis 1a-304
Test Charts 1a-306
Porsche (DME) Digital Engine Control
Adjustments 1a-475
Description & Operation 1a-472
Diagnosis & Testing 1a-475
Removal & Installation 1a-478
Sterling
Description & Operation 1a-2
Testing 1a-4
Trouble Shooting 1a-3
Subaru
Electronic Carburetor
Description & Operation 1a-482
Diagnosis & Testing 1a-484
Emission Controls 1a-482
Test Charts 1a-485
Multi-Point Fuel Injection (MPFI)
Description & Operation 1a-502
Inspection & Adjustment 1a-503
Trouble Shooting 1a-505
Test Charts 1a-507
Single-Point Fuel Injection SPFI
Description & Operation 1a-528
Inspection & Adjustments 1a-528
Trouble Shooting 1a-530
Trouble Shooting Charts 1a-532
Suzuki
Component Diagnosis & Testing 1a-555
Description 1a-551
Electronic Control Module 1a-554
Operation 1a-552
Diagnosis & Testing
Components 1a-555
Electronic Control Module Circuits 1a-554
Feedback Carburetor 1a-552

Toyota
Computer Controlled Emission System
Description & Operation 1a-558
Diagnosis & Testing 1a-558
Computer Control System
Description & Operation 1a-563
Diagnosis & Testing 1a-573
TCCS Voltage/Resistance Charts 1a-580
Volvo
Computerized Engine Control
Description & Operation 1a-634
Diagnosis & Testing 1a-636
Trouble Shooting 1a-635
Volkswagen Bosch CIS-E
Quantum, Quantum Syncro & Scirocco
Description & Operation 1a-39
Testing 1a-41
Removal & Installation 1a-52
Digifant - Vanagon & Vanagon Syncro
Description & Operation 1a-630
Testing 1a-630
Adjustments 1a-632

CONNECTING ROD – *See Engine*

COOLING
Capacities 6-544
Electric Cooling Fans 6-543
Servicing 6-542
Trouble Shooting 6-541

CRUISE CONTROL SYSTEMS
Acura 5-2
Audi 5-12
BMW 5-23
Chrysler Motors Imports
Conquest 5-25
Honda 5-2
Jaguar 5-34
Mazda 5-36
Mercedes-Benz 5-38
Mitsubishi
Cordia & Tredia 5-41
Starion 5-15
Nissan 5-44
Porsche 5-49
Saab 5-51
Subaru 5-53
Toyota
Diagnostic 5-57
Non-Diagnostic 5-72

D

DEFOGGERS
All Models 5-78

DISTRIBUTOR
All Models
Application Tables 3-3
Bosch Electronic Ignition
Yugo
Adjustments 3-6
Description & Operation 3-6
Testing 3-6
Bosch EZK Electronic Ignition
Peugeot, Volvo
Description & Operation 3-8
Testing 3-8

1987 General Index

DISTRIBUTOR (Cont.)
Bosch Hall Effect Electronic Ignition
Audi, Saab, Volkswagen
Adjustments ... 3-17
Description & Operation ... 3-17
Specifications ... 3-18
Pre-Test Procedures ... 3-17
Testing
Audi 5000CS Quattro & 5000CS Turbo ... 3-22
Audi 5000S & Coupe GT (2.3L) ... 3-24
All Others ... 3-18
Computer Controlled Distributors
BMW ... 1a-72
Chrysler Motors
Electronic Controlled Injection ... 1a-120
Feedback Carburetor ... 1a-79
Honda ... 1a-74
Isuzu
Closed Loop Emission ... 1a-91
I-TEC Control ... 1a-107
Mazda ... 1a-115
Mitsubishi
Feedback Carburetor ... 1a-14
Electronically Controlled Injection ... 1a-31
Nissan
Electronically Controlled Carburetor ... 1a-123
Porsche ... 1a-154
Subaru ... 1a-162
Toyota
Computer Control System ... 1a-175
EFI Electronic Control System ... 1a-219
Volvo ... 1a-241
Ducellier Electronic Ignition
Peugeot
Adjustments ... 3-26
Description & Operation ... 3-26
Testing ... 3-27
Hitachi Computerized Ignition
Nissan, Subaru (Fuel Injected Models)
Description & Operation ... 3-28
Testing ... 3-29
Hitachi Electronic Ignition
Honda
Adjustments ... 3-32
Description & Operation ... 3-31
Overhaul ... 3-33
Testing ... 3-32
Lucas Constant Energy Ignition
Jaguar
Adjustments ... 3-34
Description & Operation ... 3-34
Overhaul ... 3-36
Testing ... 3-35
Mitsubishi Electronic Ignition
Chrysler Motors, Ford Motor Co. (Exc. Merkur), Hyundai, Isuzu (P'UP & Trooper II), Mazda (Exc. RX7), Mitsubishi, Subaru Justy
Adjustments ... 3-37
Description & Operation ... 3-37
Overhaul ... 3-39
Testing ... 3-37
Mitsubishi Electronic Ignition
Mazda RX7
Inspection & Adjustments ... 3-40
Description & Operation ... 3-40
Overhaul ... 3-41
Testing ... 3-40
Motorcraft TFI-IV Ignition
Ford Motor Co. Merkur
Adjustments ... 3-42
Description & Operation ... 3-42
Overhaul ... 3-43
Testing ... 3-43
Trouble Shooting ... 3-42
Nippondenso Electronic Ignition
General Motors, Isuzu (Exc. P'UP & Trooper II), Subaru (Exc. Justy), Suzuki, Toyota
Adjustments ... 3-44
Description & Operation ... 3-44
Overhaul ... 3-50
Testing ... 3-45
Trouble Shooting ... 3-45
Nissan Direct Ignition
Pulsar NX SE
Description & Operation ... 3-16
Testing ... 3-16
Toyo Denso Electronic Ignition
Acura, Honda
Adjustments ... 3-52
Description & Operation ... 3-51
Overhaul ... 3-53
Testing ... 3-52

DRIVE AXLES
Trouble Shooting
All Models ... 8-2
Gear Tooth Patterns
All Models ... 8-4
FWD Axle Shafts
All Models ... 8-5
Audi 4000CS Quattro & 5000CS Quattro
Adjustments ... 8-29
Axle Ratio & Identification ... 8-29
Description & Operation ... 8-29
Removal & Installation ... 8-30
BMW Integral Carrier
Axle Ratio & Identification ... 8-33
Description ... 8-33
Overhaul ... 8-34
Removal & Installation ... 8-33
Chrysler Motors & Mitsubishi
Front Axles (4WD)
Axle Ratio & Identification ... 8-46
Description ... 8-46
Overhaul ... 8-47
Removal & Installation ... 8-46
Integral Axles
Axle Ratio & Identification ... 8-37
Description ... 8-37
Overhaul ... 8-38
Removal & Installation ... 8-37
Rear Axles
Axle Ratio & Identification ... 8-51
Description ... 8-51
Overhaul ... 8-52
Removal & Installation ... 8-51
Integral Housing
Axle Ratio & Identification ... 8-44
Description ... 8-44
Overhaul ... 8-44
Removal & Installation ... 8-44
Ford Motor Co.
Axle Ratio & Identification ... 8-57
Description ... 8-57
Overhaul ... 8-59
Removal & Installation ... 8-57
Honda Rear Axle (Civic Wagon 4WD)
Axle Ratio & Identification ... 8-62
Description ... 8-62
Overhaul ... 8-63
Removal & Installation ... 8-62
Isuzu Front
(P'UP & Trooper II)
Axle Ratio & Identification ... 8-66
Description ... 8-66
Overhaul ... 8-67
Removal & Installation ... 8-66
Isuzu Integral Housing
Axle Ratio & Identification ... 8-71
Description ... 8-71
Overhaul ... 8-71
Removal & Installation ... 8-71
Isuzu Rear
Impulse Turbo, P'UP & Trooper II
Axle Ratio & Identification ... 8-76
Description ... 8-76
Overhaul ... 8-76
Removal & Installation ... 8-76
Jaguar
Axle Ratio & Identification ... 8-82
Description ... 8-82
Overhaul ... 8-85
Removal & Installation ... 8-82
Mazda
Axle Ratio Identification ... 8-88
Description ... 8-88
Overhaul ... 8-89
Removal & Installation ... 8-88
Mercedes-Benz Integral Carrier
Axle Ratio & Identification ... 8-94
Description ... 8-94
Overhaul ... 8-97
Removal & Installation ... 8-94
Mitsubishi – See Chrysler Motors
Nissan
Front Axle
Axle Ratio & Identification ... 8-102
Description ... 8-102
Overhaul ... 8-103
Removal & Installation ... 8-103
Integral Housing
Axle Ratio & Identification ... 8-109
Description ... 8-109
Overhaul ... 8-110
Removal & Installation ... 8-109
Model C200 Rear Axle
Axle Ratio & Identification ... 8-119
Description ... 8-119
Overhaul ... 8-121
Removal & Installation ... 8-119
Separate Carrier
Axle Ratio & Identification ... 8-115
Description ... 8-115
Overhaul ... 8-115
Removal & Installation ... 8-115
Peugeot Split Housing – IRS
Axle Ratio & Identification ... 8-124
Description ... 8-124
Overhaul ... 8-124
Removal & Installation ... 8-124
Porsche
Description ... 8-132
Removal & Installation ... 8-132

1987 General Index

DRIVE AXLES (Cont.)

Subaru 4WD Rear Axle
Axle Ratio & Identification 8-135
Description 8-135
Overhaul 8-136
Removal & Installation 8-135
Suzuki Samurai
Axle Ratio 8-139
Description 8-139
Overhaul 8-139
Removal & Installation 8-139
Toyota Integral Housing - Except Van
Axle Ratio & Identification 8-143
Description 8-143
Overhaul 8-145
Removal & Installation 8-143
Toyota Integral Housing - Van (4WD Front)
Axle Ratio & Identification 8-152
Description 8-152
Overhaul 8-152
Removal & Installation 8-152
Toyota Separate Carrier
Axle Ratio & Identification 8-154
Description 8-154
Overhaul 8-157
Removal & Installation 8-154
Volvo
Axle Ratio & Identification 8-164
Description 8-164
Overhaul 8-165
Removal & Installation 8-164
Volkswagen Quantum Syncro
Adjustments 8-29
Axle Ratio & Identification 8-29
Description & Operation 8-29
Removal & Installation 8-30
Locking Hubs
Description 8-169
Identification 8-169
Overhaul 8-170
Removal & Installation 8-169

E

EMISSIONS

Maintenance Reminder Lights
All Models - *See Front of Manual*

ENGINES

Engine Identification
All Models 6-3
Trouble Shooting
Gasoline Engine 6-9
Diesel Engine 6-12
Engine Overhaul Procedures
All Engines 6-14
Acura Integra 1.6L 4-Cylinder
Camshaft 6-31
Crankshaft & Rod Bearings 6-35
Engine Coding 6-29
Engine, Manifolds & Cylinder Heads 6-29
Engine Cooling 6-37
Engine Oiling 6-36
Engine Removal 6-29
Pistons, Pins & Rings 6-34
Specifications 6-37
Thermostat 6-544
Tightening Specifications 6-37
Valves 6-33
Acura Integra 2.5L & 2.7L V6
Camshafts 6-43
Crankshaft & Rod Bearings 6-49
Engine Coding 6-39
Engine, Manifolds & Cylinder Heads 6-39
Engine Cooling 6-50
Engine Oiling 6-48
Engine Removal 6-39
Pistons, Pins & Rings 6-46
Specifications 6-51
Thermostat 6-544
Tightening Specifications 6-50
Valves 6-45
Alfa Romeo Milano 2.5L V6
Camshaft 6-55
Crankshaft & Rod Bearings 6-59
Engine Coding 6-53
Engine Cooling 6-61
Engine & Cylinder Head 6-53
Engine Oiling 6-61
Engine Removal 6-53
Pistons, Pins & Rings 6-58
Specifications 6-61
Thermostat 6-544
Tightening Specifications 6-61
Valves 6-57
Audi 1.8L & 1.8L 16-Valve 4-Cylinder
Camshaft 6-64
Crankshaft & Rod Bearings 6-69
Engine Coding 6-63
Engine, Manifolds & Cylinder Head 6-63
Engine Cooling 6-71
Engine Oiling 6-70
Engine Removal 6-63
Intermediate Shaft 6-70
Pistons, Pins & Rings 6-69
Specifications 6-72
Thermostat 6-544
Tightening Specifications 6-72
Valves 6-67
Audi 2.22L & 2.3L 5-Cylinder
Camshaft 6-76
Crankshaft & Rod Bearings 6-77
Engine Coding 6-74
Engine Cooling 6-80
Engine, Manifolds & Cylinder Head 6-74
Engine Oiling 6-78
Engine Removal 6-74
Pistons, Pins & Rings 6-77
Specifications 6-80
Thermostat 6-544
Tightening Specifications 6-80
Valves 6-79
BMW 2.5L & 2.7L 6-Cylinder
Camshaft 6-83
Crankshaft & Rod Bearings 6-86
Engine Coding 6-82
Engine Cooling 6-87
Engine, Manifolds & Cylinder Heads 6-82
Engine Oiling 6-87
Engine Removal 6-82
Pistons, Pins & Rings 6-86
Specifications 6-88
Thermostat 6-544
Tightening Specifications 6-87
Valves 6-85
BMW 3.5L 6-Cylinder
Camshaft 6-93
Crankshaft & Rod Bearings 6-95
Engine Coding 6-90
Engine Cooling 6-96
Engine, Manifolds & Cylinder Heads 6-90
Engine Oiling 6-95
Engine Removal 6-90
Pistons, Pins & Rings 6-94
Specifications 6-96
Thermostat 6-544
Tightening Specifications 6-96
Valves 6-93
Chrysler Motors - See Mitsubishi
Ford Motor Co.
1.3L 4-Cylinder (Festiva)
Camshaft 6-99
Crankshaft & Rod Bearings 6-102
Engine Coding 6-98
Engine Cooling 6-104
Engines, Cylinder Head & Manifolds 6-98
Engine Oiling 6-103
Engine Removal 6-98
Pistons, Pins & Rings 6-101
Specifications 6-105
Thermostat 6-544
Tightening Specifications 6-104
Valves 6-101
1.6L 4-Cylinder (Tracer)
Camshaft 6-203
Crankshaft & Rod Bearings 6-206
Cylinder Block 6-205
Engine Coding 6-202
Engine Cooling 6-207
Engine, Manifolds & Cylinder Heads 6-202
Engine Oiling 6-208
Engine Removal 6-202
Pistons, Pins & Rings 6-205
Specifications 6-207
Thermostat 6-544
Tightening Specifications 6-207
Valves 6-204
2.3L 4-Cylinder
Camshaft 6-108
Crankshaft & Rod Bearings 6-111
Cylinder Block Assembly 6-110
Engine Coding 6-106
Engine Cooling 6-113
Engines, Cylinder Head & Manifolds 6-106
Engine Oiling 6-112
Engine Removal 6-106
Pistons, Pins & Rings 6-110
Specifications 6-113
Thermostat 6-544
Tightening Specifications 6-114
Valves 6-109
General Motors - Sprint
1.0L 3-Cylinder
Camshaft 6-116
Crankshaft & Rod Bearings 6-120

1987 General Index

ENGINES (Cont.)
Engine Cooling ... 6-122
Engine Oiling ... 6-122
Engine, Manifolds & Cylinder Heads ... 6-115
Engine Removal ... 6-115
Pistons, Pins & Rings ... 6-119
Specifications ... 6-123
Thermostat ... 6-544
Tightening Specifications ... 6-124
Valves ... 6-118
General Motors – Spectrum 1.5L 4-Cylinder
Camshaft ... 6-126
Crankshaft & Rod Bearings ... 6-129
Engine Coding ... 6-125
Engine Cooling ... 6-130
Engine, Manifolds & Cylinder Heads ... 6-125
Engine Oiling ... 6-130
Engine Removal ... 6-125
Pistons, Pins & Rings ... 6-128
Specifications ... 6-131
Thermostat ... 6-544
Tightening Specifications ... 6-132
Valves ... 6-127
Honda Accord, Civic & Prelude 4-Cylinder
Camshaft ... 6-139
Crankshaft & Rod Bearings ... 6-146
Cylinder Block ... 6-143
Engine Coding ... 6-133
Engine Cooling ... 6-149
Engine, Manifolds & Cylinder Heads ... 6-133
Engine Oiling ... 6-148
Engine Removal ... 6-133
Pistons, Pins & Rings ... 6-143
Specifications ... 6-149
Thermostat ... 6-544
Tightening Specifications ... 6-153
Valves ... 6-140
Hyundai Excel 1.5L 4-Cylinder
Camshaft ... 6-252
Crankshaft & Rod Bearings ... 6-257
Engine Cooling ... 6-258
Engine, Manifolds & Cylinder Head ... 6-251
Engine Coding ... 6-251
Engine Oiling ... 6-257
Engine Removal ... 6-251
Pistons, Pins & Rings ... 6-257
Specifications ... 6-259
Thermostat ... 6-544
Tightening Specifications ... 6-259
Valves ... 6-255
Isuzu I-Mark 1.5L 4-Cylinder
Camshaft ... 6-126
Crankshaft & Rod Bearings ... 6-129
Engine Coding ... 6-125
Engine Cooling ... 6-130
Engine, Manifolds & Cylinder Heads ... 6-125
Engine Oiling ... 6-130
Engine Removal ... 6-125
Pistons, Pins & Rings ... 6-128
Specifications ... 6-131
Thermostat ... 6-544
Tightening Specifications ... 6-132
Valves ... 6-127
Isuzu 1.9L, 2.0L Turbo & 2.3L 4-Cylinder (Gasoline)
Camshaft ... 6-155
Crankshaft & Rod Bearings ... 6-160
Engine Coding ... 6-154
Engine Cooling ... 6-161
Engine, Manifolds & Cylinder Heads ... 6-154
Engine Oiling ... 6-160
Engine Removal ... 6-154
Pistons, Pins & Rings ... 6-159
Specifications ... 6-162
Thermostat ... 6-544
Tightening Specifications ... 6-162
Valves ... 6-158
Isuzu 2.2L 4-Cylinder Diesel
Camshaft ... 6-165
Crankshaft & Rod Bearings ... 6-168
Engine Coding ... 6-164
Engine Cooling ... 6-170
Engine, Manifolds & Cylinder Heads ... 6-164
Engine Oiling ... 6-169
Engine Removal ... 6-164
Pistons, Pins & Rings ... 6-167
Specifications ... 6-170
Thermostat ... 6-544
Tightening Specifications ... 6-170
Valves ... 6-167
Jaguar XJ6 4.2L 6-Cylinder
Camshaft ... 6-174
Crankshaft & Rod Bearings ... 6-176
Engine Coding ... 6-179
Engine Cooling ... 6-172
Engine, Manifolds & Cylinder Heads ... 6-172
Engine Oiling ... 6-178
Engine Removal ... 6-172
Front Crankshaft Oil Seal & Front Cover ... 6-176
Pistons, Pins & Rings ... 6-174
Specifications ... 6-179
Thermostat ... 6-544
Timing Chains ... 6-176
Tightening Specifications ... 6-179
Valves ... 6-174
Jaguar XJS 5.3L V12
Camshaft ... 6-183
Crankshaft & Rod Bearing ... 6-185
Engine Coding ... 6-181
Engine Cooling ... 6-187
Engine Front Cover, Oil Seal & Timing Chain ... 6-183
Engine, Manifolds & Cylinder Heads ... 6-181
Engine Oiling ... 6-186
Engine Removal ... 6-181
Pistons, Pins & Rings ... 6-185
Specifications ... 6-187
Thermostat ... 6-544
Tightening Specifications ... 6-187
Valves ... 6-184
Mazda 1.6L 323 4-Cylinder
Camshaft ... 6-203
Crankshaft & Rod Bearings ... 6-206
Cylinder Block ... 6-205
Engine Coding ... 6-202
Engine Cooling ... 6-207
Engine, Manifolds & Cylinder Heads ... 6-202
Engine Oiling ... 6-208
Engine Removal ... 6-202
Pistons, Pins & Rings ... 6-205
Specifications ... 6-207
Thermostat ... 6-544
Tightening Specifications ... 6-207
Valves ... 6-204
Mazda 2.0L & 2.2L 4-Cylinder
Camshaft ... 6-211
Crankshaft & Rod Bearings ... 6-214
Cylinder Block Assembly ... 6-213
Engine Coding ... 6-210
Engine Cooling ... 6-215
Engine, Manifolds & Cylinder Heads ... 6-210
Engine Oiling ... 6-214
Engine Removal ... 6-210
Pistons, Pins & Rings ... 6-213
Specifications ... 6-216
Thermostat ... 6-544
Tightening Specifications ... 6-216
Valves ... 6-212
Mazda B2600 2.6L 4-Cylinder
Camshaft ... 6-272
Crankshaft & Rod Bearings ... 6-275
Engine Coding ... 6-271
Engine Cooling ... 6-276
Engine, Cylinder Head & Manifolds ... 6-271
Engine Oiling ... 6-276
Engine Removal ... 6-271
Pistons, Pins & Rings ... 6-275
Specifications ... 6-277
Thermostat ... 6-544
Tightening Specifications ... 6-276
Valves ... 6-273
Mazda RX7 1.3L Rotary
Engine Coding ... 6-189
Engine Cooling ... 6-199
Engine Oiling ... 6-197
Engine Removal ... 6-189
Specifications ... 6-200
Thermostat ... 6-544
Tightening Specifications ... 6-199
Mercedes-Benz 190E 2.3L 4-Cylinder
Camshaft ... 6-218
Crankshaft & Rod Bearings ... 6-223
Engine Coding ... 6-218
Engine Cooling ... 6-224
Engine, Manifolds & Cylinder Heads ... 6-218
Engine Oiling ... 6-224
Engine Removal ... 6-218
Pistons, Pins & Rings ... 6-222
Specifications ... 6-224
Thermostat ... 6-544
Tightening Specifications ... 6-226
Valves ... 6-221
Mercedes-Benz 190E, 260E & 300E 2.6L & 3.0L 6-Cylinder
Camshaft ... 6-236
Crankshaft & Rod Bearings ... 6-239
Engine Coding ... 6-235
Engine Cooling ... 6-240

1987 General Index

ENGINES (Cont.)
Engine, Manifolds & Cylinder Heads ... 6-235
Engine Oiling ... 6-240
Engine Removal ... 6-235
Pistons, Pins & Rings ... 6-239
Specifications ... 6-241
Thermostat ... 6-544
Tightening Specifications ... 6-242
Valves ... 6-237

Mercedes-Benz 420 & 560 Series 4.2L & 5.6L V-8
Camshaft ... 6-244
Connecting Rod ... 6-246
Crankshaft & Rod Bearings ... 6-247
Cylinder Block Assembly ... 6-246
Engine Cooling ... 6-248
Engine, Manifolds & Cylinder Heads ... 6-243
Engine Identification ... 6-243
Engine Oiling ... 6-248
Engine Removal ... 6-243
Pistons & Pins & Rings ... 6-246
Specifications ... 6-249
Thermostat ... 6-544
Tightening Specifications ... 6-248
Timing Chain ... 6-245
Valves ... 6-245
Water Pump ... 6-248

Mercedes-Benz 190D 2.5L 5-Cylinder & 300D, 300TD & SDL 3.0L 6-Cylinder
Camshaft ... 6-228
Connecting Rod ... 6-231
Crankshaft & Rod Bearing ... 6-231
Cylinder Block Assembly ... 6-231
Engine Coding ... 6-227
Engine Cooling ... 6-233
Engine, Manifolds & Cylinder Heads ... 6-227
Engine Oiling ... 6-232
Engine Removal ... 6-227
Pistons, Pins & Rings ... 6-231
Specifications ... 6-234
Thermostat ... 6-544
Tightening Specifications ... 6-233
Timing Chain ... 6-
Valves ... 6-229
Water Pump ... 6-232

Mitsubishi 1.5L & 1.6L Turbo 4-Cylinder
Camshaft ... 6-252
Crankshaft & Rod Bearings ... 6-257
Engine Cooling ... 6-258
Engine, Manifolds & Cylinder Head ... 6-251
Engine Coding ... 6-251
Engine Oiling ... 6-257
Engine Removal ... 6-251
Pistons, Pins & Rings ... 6-257
Specifications ... 6-259
Thermostat ... 6-544
Tightening Specifications ... 6-259
Valves ... 6-255

Mitsubishi 1.8L Turbo, 2.0L & 2.4L 4-Cy
Camshaft ... 6-263
Crankshaft & Rod Bearings ... 6-268
Engine Coding ... 6-261
Engine Cooling ... 6-269
Engine, Manifolds & Cylinder Heads ... 6-261
Engine Oiling ... 6-268
Engine Removal ... 6-261
Pistons, Pins & Rings ... 6-267
Specifications ... 6-270
Thermostat ... 6-544
Tightening Specifications ... 6-269
Valves ... 6-266

Mitsubishi 2.6L & 2.6L Turbo 4-Cylinder
Camshaft ... 6-272
Crankshaft & Rod Bearings ... 6-275
Engine Coding ... 6-271
Engine Cooling ... 6-276
Engine, Cylinder Head & Manifolds ... 6-271
Engine Oiling ... 6-276
Engine Removal ... 6-271
Pistons, Pins & Rings ... 6-275
Specifications ... 6-277
Thermostat ... 6-544
Tightening Specifications ... 6-276
Valves ... 6-273

Nissan Pathfinder & Pickup 2.4L 4-Cylinder
Camshaft ... 6-309
Crankshaft & Rod Bearings ... 6-313
Engine Coding ... 6-306
Engine Cooling ... 6-315
Engine, Manifolds & Cylinder Head ... 6-306
Engine Oiling ... 6-314
Engine Removal ... 6-306
Pistons, Pins & Rings ... 6-312
Specifications ... 6-316
Thermostat ... 6-544
Tightening Specifications ... 6-317
Valves ... 6-310

Nissan Pulsar NX & Sentra 1.6L 4-Cylinder
Camshaft ... 6-281
Crankshaft & Rod Bearings ... 6-286
Engine Coding ... 6-279
Engine Cooling ... 6-288
Engine, Manifolds & Cylinder Head ... 6-279
Engine Oiling ... 6-287
Engine Removal ... 6-279
Pistons, Pins & Rings ... 6-285
Specifications ... 6-288
Thermostat ... 6-544
Tightening Specifications ... 6-288
Valves ... 6-284

Nissan Pulsar NX 1.6L 16-Valve 4-Cylinder
Camshaft ... 6-291
Crankshaft & Rod Bearings ... 6-294
Engine Coding ... 6-290
Engine Cooling ... 6-296
Engine, Manifolds & Cylinder Head ... 6-290
Engine Oiling ... 6-295
Engine Removal ... 6-290
Pistons, Pins & Rings ... 6-293
Specifications ... 6-297
Thermostat ... 6-544
Tightening Specifications ... 6-296
Valves ... 6-292

Nissan Stanza & 200SX 2.0L Turbo
Camshaft ... 6-299
Crankshaft & Rod Bearings ... 6-302
Engine Coding ... 6-298
Engine Cooling ... 6-304
Engine, Manifolds & Cylinder Head ... 6-298
Engine Oiling ... 6-303
Engine Removal ... 6-298
Pistons, Pins & Rings ... 6-301
Specifications ... 6-304
Thermostat ... 6-544
Tightening Specifications ... 6-304
Valves ... 6-300

Nissan Maxima, Pickup, 200SX & 300SX 3.0L Turbo V6
Camshaft ... 6-320
Crankshaft & Rod Bearings ... 6-321
Engine Coding ... 6-318
Engine Cooling ... 6-323
Engine, Manifolds & Cylinder Head ... 6-318
Engine Oiling ... 6-323
Engine Removal ... 6-318
Pistons, Pins & Rings ... 6-321
Specifications ... 6-324
Thermostat ... 6-544
Tightening Specifications ... 6-323
Valves ... 6-320

Peugeot 505 2.0L 4-Cylinder
Camshaft ... 6-328
Crankshaft & Rod Bearings ... 6-330
Engine Coding ... 6-326
Engine Cooling ... 6-331
Engine, Manifolds & Cylinder Head ... 6-326
Engine Oiling ... 6-330
Engine Removal ... 6-326
Pistons, Pins & Rings ... 6-329
Specifications ... 6-331
Thermostat ... 6-544
Tightening Specifications ... 6-331
Valves ... 6-328

Peugeot 505 2.2L 4-Cylinder Turbo
Camshaft ... 6-335
Crankshaft & Rod Bearings ... 6-336
Engine Coding ... 6-333
Engine Cooling ... 6-337
Engine, Manifolds & Cylinder Head ... 6-333
Engine Oiling ... 6-337
Engine Removal ... 6-333
Pistons, Pins & Rings ... 6-336
Specifications ... 6-337
Thermostat ... 6-544
Tightening Specifications ... 6-337
Valves ... 6-335

Peugeot 2.8L V6
505 STI & 505 STX
Camshaft ... 6-342
Crankshaft & Rod Bearings ... 6-346
Engine Coding ... 6-339
Engine Cooling ... 6-348
Engine, Manifolds & Cylinder Head ... 6-339
Engine Oiling ... 6-347
Engine Removal ... 6-339
Pistons, Pins & Rings ... 6-345

1987 General Index

ENGINES (Cont.)
- Specifications 6-348
- Thermostat 6-544
- Tightening Specifications 6-348
- Valves 6-345

Porsche 2.5L 4-Cylinder
924-S, 944, 944-S & 944 Turbo
- Camshaft 6-352
- Crankshaft & Rod Bearings 6-359
- Engine Coding 6-350
- Engine Cooling 6-541
- Engine, Manifolds & Cylinder Head 6-350
- Engine Oiling 6-361
- Engine Removal 6-350
- Pistons, Pins & Rings 6-357
- Specifications 6-363
- Thermostat 6-544
- Tightening Specifications 6-364
- Valves 6-356

Porsche 3.2L & 3.3L 6-Cylinder
911 Carrera & 911 Turbo
- Camshaft 6-368
- Crankshaft & Rod Bearings 6-378
- Engine Coding 6-365
- Engine Cooling 6-381
- Engine, Manifolds & Cylinder Head 6-365
- Engine Oiling 6-381
- Engine Removal 6-365
- Pistons, Pins & Rings 6-374
- Specifications 6-382
- Thermostat 6-544
- Tightening Specifications 6-382
- Valves 6-370

Saab 2.0L 4-Cylinder
900, 900S, 900S Turbo, 9000S & 9000 Turbo
- Camshaft 6-385
- Crankshaft & Rod Bearings 6-388
- Engine Coding 6-384
- Engine Cooling 6-388
- Engine, Manifolds & Cylinder Head 6-384
- Engine Oiling 6-388
- Engine Removal 6-384
- Pistons, Pins & Rings 6-387
- Specifications 6-389
- Thermostat 6-544
- Tightening Specifications 6-390
- Valves 6-387

Subaru 1.2L 4-Cylinder
Justy
- Camshaft 6-392
- Crankshaft & Rod Bearings 6-396
- Engine Coding 6-391
- Engine Cooling 6-398
- Engine, Manifolds & Cylinder Head 6-391
- Engine Oiling 6-398
- Engine Removal 6-391
- Pistons, Pins & Rings 6-395
- Specifications 6-399
- Thermostat 6-544
- Tightening Specifications 6-399
- Valves 6-393

Subaru 1.6L & 1.8L 4-Cylinder
Brat & Hatchback
- Camshaft 6-403
- Crankshaft & Rod Bearings 6-405
- Engine Coding 6-401
- Engine Cooling 6-406
- Engine, Manifolds & Cylinder Head 6-401
- Engine Oiling 6-406
- Engine Removal 6-401
- Pistons, Pins & Rings 6-404
- Specifications 6-407
- Thermostat 6-544
- Tightening Specifications 6-408
- Valves 6-404

Subaru 1.8L OHC 4-Cylinder
Coupe, Sedan, Station Wagon & XT Coupe
- Camshaft 6-411
- Crankshaft & Rod Bearings 6-414
- Engine Coding 6-409
- Engine Cooling 6-415
- Engine, Manifolds & Cylinder Head 6-409
- Engine Oiling 6-415
- Engine Removal 6-409
- Pistons, Pins & Rings 6-413
- Specifications 6-416
- Thermostat 6-544
- Tightening Specifications 6-417
- Valves 6-413

Suzuki 1.3L 4-Cylinder
Samurai
- Camshaft 6-418
- Crankshaft & Rod Bearings 6-422
- Engine Coding 6-418
- Engine Cooling 6-426
- Engine, Manifolds & Cylinder Head 6-418
- Engine Oiling 6-425
- Engine Removal 6-418
- Pistons, Pins & Rings 6-421
- Specifications 6-426
- Thermostat 6-544
- Tightening Specifications 6-427
- Valves 6-420

Toyota 1.5L & 1.6L 8-Valve 4-Cylinder
Corolla & Tercel Wagon
- Camshaft 6-431
- Crankshaft & Rod Bearings 6-435
- Engine Coding 6-428
- Engine Cooling 6-436
- Engine, Manifolds & Cylinder Head 6-428
- Engine Oiling 6-435
- Engine Removal 6-428
- Pistons, Pins & Rings 6-434
- Specifications 6-437
- Thermostat 6-544
- Tightening Specifications 6-437
- Valves 6-432

Toyota 1.5L 12-Valve 4-Cylinder
Tercel (Except Wagon)
- Camshaft 6-440
- Crankshaft & Rod Bearings 6-445
- Engine Coding 6-439
- Engine Cooling 6-447
- Engine, Manifolds & Cylinder Head 6-439
- Engine Oiling 6-446
- Engine Removal 6-439
- Pistons, Pins & Rings 6-444
- Specifications 6-448
- Thermostat 6-544
- Tightening Specifications 6-449
- Valves 6-442

Toyota 1.6L 16-Valve 4-Cylinder
Corolla & MR2
- Camshaft 6-453
- Crankshaft & Rod Bearings 6-456
- Engine Coding 6-450
- Engine Cooling 6-458
- Engine, Manifolds & Cylinder Head 6-450
- Engine Oiling 6-457
- Engine Removal 6-450
- Pistons, Pins & Rings 6-455
- Specifications 6-458
- Thermostat 6-544
- Tightening Specifications 6-460
- Valves 6-454

Toyota 2.0L 3S-FE & 3S-GE 4-Cylinder
Camry & Celica
- Camshaft 6-463
- Crankshaft & Rod Bearings 6-469
- Engine Coding 6-461
- Engine Cooling 6-471
- Engine, Manifolds & Cylinder Head 6-461
- Engine Oiling 6-470
- Engine Removal 6-461
- Pistons, Pins & Rings 6-468
- Specifications 6-472
- Thermostat 6-544
- Tightening Specifications 6-472
- Valves 6-468

Toyota 2.0L 3S-FE & 3S-GE 4-Cylinder
Van
- Camshaft 6-475
- Crankshaft & Rod Bearings 6-479
- Engine Coding 6-474
- Engine Cooling 6-480
- Engine, Manifolds & Cylinder Head 6-474
- Engine Oiling 6-479
- Engine Removal 6-474
- Pistons, Pins & Rings 6-478
- Specifications 6-480
- Thermostat 6-544
- Tightening Specifications 6-480
- Valves 6-477

Toyota 2.4L 4-Cylinder
Pickup & 4Runner
- Camshaft 6-482
- Crankshaft & Rod Bearings 6-486
- Engine Coding 6-482
- Engine Cooling 6-487
- Engine, Manifolds & Cylinder Head 6-482
- Engine Oiling 6-487
- Engine Removal 6-482
- Pistons, Pins & Rings 6-485
- Specifications 6-488
- Thermostat 6-544
- Tightening Specifications 6-489
- Valves 6-485

Toyota 2.8L 6-Cylinder
Cressida
- Camshaft 6-491

1987 General Index

ENGINES (Cont.)
Crankshaft & Rod Bearings 6-495
Engine Coding 6-490
Engine Cooling 6-496
Engine, Manifolds & Cylinder Head 6-490
Engine Oiling 6-495
Engine Removal 6-490
Pistons, Pins & Rings 6-494
Specifications 6-497
Thermostat 6-544
Tightening Specifications 6-496
Valves 6-493
Toyota 3.0L Twin Camshaft 6-Cylinder
Supra
Camshaft 6-501
Crankshaft & Rod Bearings 6-505
Engine Coding 6-499
Engine Cooling 6-508
Engine, Manifolds & Cylinder Head 6-499
Engine Oiling 6-506
Engine Removal 6-499
Pistons, Pins & Rings 6-504
Specifications 6-508
Thermostat 6-544
Tightening Specifications 6-508
Valves 6-503
Toyota 4.2L 6-Cylinder
Land Cruiser
Camshaft 6-510
Crankshaft & Rod Bearings 6-513
Engine Coding 6-510
Engine Cooling 6-515
Engine, Manifolds & Cylinder Head 6-510
Engine Oiling 6-514
Engine Removal 6-510
Pistons, Pins & Rings 6-512
Specifications 6-515
Thermostat 6-544
Tightening Specifications 6-515
Valves 6-511
Volkswagen Except 2.1L Opposed 4-Cylinder – See Audi Engines
Volkswagen 2.1L Opposed 4-Cylinder
Vanagon & Vanagon Syncro
Camshaft 6-520
Crankshaft & Rod Bearings 6-520
Engine Coding 6-517
Engine Cooling 6-524
Engine, Manifolds & Cylinder Head 6-517
Engine Oiling 6-523
Engine Removal 6-517
Pistons, Pins & Rings 6-519
Specifications 6-524
Thermostat 6-544
Tightening Specifications 6-524
Valves 6-518
Volvo 2.3L. 4-Cylinder
240 Series, 740 Series & 760 GLE Turbo
Camshaft 6-527
Crankshaft & Rod Bearings 6-529
Engine Coding 6-526
Engine Cooling 6-530
Engine, Manifolds & Cylinder Head 6-526
Engine Oiling 6-529
Engine Removal 6-526
Pistons, Pins & Rings 6-512
Specifications 6-531
Thermostat 6-544
Tightening Specifications 6-530
Valves 6-527
Volvo 2.8L V6
760 GLE & 780 GLE
Camshaft 6-342
Crankshaft & Rod Bearings 6-346
Engine Coding 6-339
Engine Cooling 6-348
Engine, Manifolds & Cylinder Head 6-339
Engine Oiling 6-347
Engine Removal 6-339
Pistons, Pins & Rings 6-345
Specifications 6-348
Thermostat 6-544
Tightening Specifications 6-348
Valves 6-345
Yugo 1.1L 4-Cylinder
GV
Camshaft 6-533
Crankshaft & Rod Bearings 6-537
Engine Coding 6-533
Engine Cooling 6-539
Engine, Manifolds & Cylinder Head 6-533
Engine Oiling 6-538
Engine Removal 6-533
Pistons, Pins & Rings 6-535
Specifications 6-539
Thermostat 6-544
Tightening Specifications 6-539
Valves 6-534

ENGINE COOLING
Cooling System Service 6-542
Engine Coolant Specifications 6-544
Electric Cooling Fans 6-543
Trouble Shooting 6-541

ENGINE IDENTIFICATION NUMBER
Acura
4-Cylinder 1-6, 6-3
V6 .... 1-10, 6-3
Alfa Romeo
V6 .... 1-15, 6-3
Audi
4-Cylinder 1-18, 6-3
5-Cylinder 1-21, 6-3
BMW
6-Cylinder 1-26, 6-3
Chrysler Motors
4-Cylinder 1-29, 6-3
Ford Motor Co.
4-Cylinder 1-34, 6-4
General Motors
Sprint
3-Cylinder 1-38, 6-4
Spectrum
4-Cylinder 1-38, 6-4
Honda 1-44, 6-4
Hyundai 1-52, 6-4
Isuzu
4-Cylinder 1-56, 6-4
4-Cylinder Diesel 1-61, 6-5
Jaguar
6-Cylinder 1-63, 6-5
V12 .... 1-66, 6-5
Mazda
4-Cylinder 1-69, 6-5
Rotary Engine 1-76, 6-5
Mercedes-Benz
4-Cylinder 1-80, 6-5
6-Cylinder 1-82, 6-5
V8 .... 1-87, 6-5
5 & 6-Cylinder Diesel 1-84, 6-5
Mitsubishi
4-Cylinder 1-29, 6-3
Nissan
4-Cylinder 1-89, 6-6
V6 .... 1-96, 6-6
Peugeot
4-Cylinder 1-100, 6-6
V6 .... 1-105, 6-6
Porsche
4-Cylinder 1-107, 6-6
6-Cylinder 1-110, 6-6
Saab 1-114, 6-7
Sterling 1-10, 6-7
Subaru 1-118, 6-7
Suzuki 1-124, 6-7
Toyota
4-Cylinder 1-128, 6-7
6-Cylinder 1-137, 6-7
Volkswagen
4-Cylinder 1-143, 6-8
5-Cylinder 1-21, 6-8
Volvo
4-Cylinder 1-149, 6-8
V6 .... 1-152, 6-8
Yugo 1-155, 6-8

F

FILTER REPLACEMENT INTERVAL
Acura
4-Cylinder Gas 1-8
V6 1-13
Alfa Romeo
V6 1-17
Audi
4-Cylinder 1-20
5-Cylinder 1-25
BMW
6-Cylinder 1-27
Chrysler Motors 1-33
Ford Motor Co. 1-37
General Motors 1-42
Honda 1-51
Hyundai 1-55
Isuzu
4-Cylinder Gas 1-60
4-Cylinder Diesel 1-62
Jaguar
6-Cylinder 1-65
V12 1-68
Mazda
4-Cylinder 1-75
Rotary Engine 1-79

1987 General Index

FILTER REPLACEMENT INTERVAL (Cont.)

Mercedes-Benz
4-Cylinder Gas 1-81
6-Cylinder Gas 1-83
5 & 6-Cylinder Diesel 1-86
V8 1-88
Mitsubishi 1-33
Nissan
4-Cylinder 1-95
V6 1-99
Peugeot
4-Cylinder 1-104
V6 1-106
Porsche
4-Cylinder 1-109
6-Cylinder 1-113
Saab 1-117
Subaru 1-123
Sterling 1-14
Suzuki 1-127
Toyota
4-Cylinder 1-136
6-Cylinder 1-142
Volkswagen
4-Cylinder 1-148
5-Cylinder 1-25
Volvo
4-Cylinder 1-151
V6 1-154
Yugo 1-156

FIRING ORDER

Acura
4-Cylinder 1-6
V6 1-10
Alfa Romeo
V6 1-15
Audi
4-Cylinder 1-18
5-Cylinder 1-21
BMW
6-Cylinder 1-26
Chrysler Motors 1-29
Ford Motor Co. 1-34
General Motors 1-38
Honda 1-44
Hyundai 1-52
Isuzu
4-Cylinder Gas 1-56
4-Cylinder Diesel 1-61
Jaguar
6-Cylinder 1-63
V12 1-66
Mazda
4-Cylinder 1-71
Mercedes-Benz
4-Cylinder Gas 1-80
6-Cylinder Gas 1-82
5 & 6-Cylinder Diesel 1-84
V8 1-87
Mitsubishi 1-29
Nissan
4-Cylinder 1-89
V6 1-100
Peugeot
4-Cylinder 1-100
V6 1-105
Porsche
4-Cylinder 1-107
6-Cylinder 1-110
Saab 1-121
Sterling 1-10
Subaru 1-118
Suzuki 1-124
Toyota
4-Cylinder 1-128
6-Cylinder 1-137
Volkswagen
4-Cylinder 1-143
5-Cylinder 1-21
Volvo
4-Cylinder 1-149
V6 1-152
Yugo 1-155

FRONT WHEEL DRIVE AXLE SHAFTS

All Models 8-5

FUEL INJECTION

All Models
Trouble Shooting 2-4
Acura
Integra, Legend
PGM-FI System
Adjustments 2-151
Description & Operation 2-146
Removal & Installation 2-152
Testing 2-148
Alfa Romeo
Bosh AFC
Adjustments 2-76
Description & Operation 2-66
Removal & Installation 2-74
Special Features 2-68
Testing 2-69
Audi
CIS-E (Electronic Control)
All Information – *See Article in Computerized Engine Control Section*
Chrysler Motors
Colt, Conquest
ECI System
Adjustments 2-118
Description & Operation 2-112
Overhaul 2-117
Removal & Installation 2-116
Testing 2-115
Colt Vista
MPI System
Description 2-119
Testing 2-121
Ford Motor Co.
Merkur XR4Ti, Tracer
Bosh AFC
Adjustments 2-76
Description & Operation 2-66
Removal & Installation 2-74
Special Features 2-68
Testing 2-69
Honda
Accord, Civic, Prelude
PGM-FI System
Adjustments 2-151
Description & Operation 2-146
Removal & Installation 2-152
Testing 2-148
Isuzu Impulse – I-Tec
Adjustments 2-126
Description & Operation 2-123
Diagnosis & Testing 2-123
Removal & Installation 2-126
Jaguar
XJ6 III
Lucas-Bosch AFC
Adjustments 2-131
Description & Operation 2-127
Removal & Installation 2-130
Testing 2-129
XJS
Lucas-Bosch "P" Type
Adjustments 2-138
Description 2-132
Operation 2-133
Removal & Installation 2-136
Testing 2-134
Mazda
323 & 626
Bosh AFC
Adjustments 2-76
Description & Operation 2-66
Removal & Installation 2-74
Special Features 2-68
Testing 2-69
RX7, RX7 Turbo
Adjustments 2-175
Description & Operation 2-140
Removal & Installation 2-145
Testing 2-140
Mitsubishi
Cordia, Mirage, Syarion, Tredia
Adjustments 2-118
Description & Operation 2-112
Overhaul 2-117
Removal & Installation 2-116
Testing 2-115
Galant, Van/Wagon
MPI System
Description 2-119
Testing 2-121
Nissan
Maxima, Stanza, 200SX, 300ZX
Bosh AFC
Adjustments 2-76
Description & Operation 2-66
Removal & Installation 2-74
Special Features 2-68
Testing 2-69
Peugeot 505
Bosh AFC
Adjustments 2-76
Description & Operation 2-66
Removal & Installation 2-74
Special Features 2-68
Testing 2-69
Bosh CIS (Lambda) System
Description & Operation 2-79
Lambda Control System Checks 2-85
Removal & Installation 2-86
Special Features 2-81
Testing 2-81
Porsche
911 Turbo
Bosh CIS (Lambda) System
Description & Operation 2-79
Lambda Control System Checks 2-85
Removal & Installation 2-86

1987 General Index

FUEL INJECTION (Cont.)
Special Features 2-81
Testing 2-81
928S
Bosch LH Jetronic System
Adjustments 2-103
Description 2-92
Removal & Installation 2-125
Trouble Shooting 2-94
Testing 2-96
Saab 900
Bosh CIS (Lambda) System
Description & Operation 2-79
Lambda Control System Checks 2-85
Removal & Installation 2-86
Special Features 2-81
Testing 2-81
Saab 900S, 900 Turbo, 9000 Turbo
Bosch LH Jetronic System
Adjustments 2-103
Description 2-92
Removal & Installation 2-125
Trouble Shooting 2-94
Testing 2-96
Sterling
825
PGM-FI System
Adjustments 2-151
Description & Operation 2-146
Removal & Installation 2-152
Testing 2-148
Subaru
GL Turbo, XT Coupe
Bosh AFC
Adjustments 2-76
Description & Operation 2-66
Removal & Installation 2-74
Special Features 2-68
Testing 2-69
Single Point Fuel Injection
Description & Operation 2-153
Inspection & Adjustments 2-154
Overhaul 2-193
Removal & Installation 2-155
Trouble Shooting 2-156
Toyota
Bosh AFC
Adjustments 2-76
Description & Operation 2-66
Removal & Installation 2-74
Special Features 2-68
Testing 2-69
Volkswagen
Bosh CIS (Lambda) System
Description & Operation 2-79
Lambda Control System Checks 2-85
Removal & Installation 2-86
Special Features 2-81
Testing 2-81
CIS-E (Electronic Control)
All Information – *See Article in Computerized Engine Control Section*
Volvo
Bosch LH Jetronic System
Adjustments 2-103
Description 2-92
Removal & Installation 2-125
Trouble Shooting 2-94
Testing 2-100

Diesel Fuel Injection
All Models
Trouble Shooting 2-4
Isuzu
P'UP, Trooper II
Adjustments 2-161
Description & Operation 2-158
Component Disassembly & Reassembly 2-161
Removal & Installation 2-159
Testing 2-158
Trouble Shooting 2-158
Mercedes-Benz
190D
Adjustments 2-168
Description & Operation 2-163
Removal & Installation 2-167
Testing 2-165
Trouble Shooting 2-164
300D, 300TD, 300 SDL
Adjustments 2-175
Description & Operation 2-169
Removal & Installation 2-174
Testing 2-171

FUEL PUMP
Electric Fuel Pumps
Acura
Integra, Legend
Description & Operation 2-199
Removal & Installation 2-199
Testing 2-199
Alfa Romeo
Description & Operation 2-200
Removal & Installation 2-200
Testing 2-200
Audi
Description & Operation 2-200
Removal & Installation 2-200
Testing 2-200
BMW
Description & Operation 2-200
Removal & Installation 2-200
Testing 2-200
Chrysler Motors
Colt Turbo, Conquest
Description 2-200
Operation 2-201
Removal & Installation 2-201
Testing 2-201
Ford Motor Co.
Merkur XR4Ti
Description & Operation 2-201
Removal & Installation 2-203
Testing 2-202
Honda
Accord, Civic, Prelude
Description & Operation 2-199
Removal & Installation 2-199
Testing 2-199
Isuzu
Impulse
Description 2-203
Removal & Installation 2-203
Jaguar
Description & Operation 2-200
Removal & Installation 2-200
Testing 2-200
Mazda
Description & Operation 2-204
Removal & Installation 2-204
Testing 2-204
Mercedes-Benz
All Information – *See CIS-E article in Computerized Engine Control Section*
Mitsubishi
Cordia, Galant, Mirage Turbo, Starion, Tredia Turbo
Description 2-200
Operation 2-201
Removal & Installation 2-201
Testing 2-201
Nissan
Pathfinder, Pickup, Maxima, Stanza, 200SX, 300ZX
Description 2-200
Operation 2-201
Removal & Installation 2-201
Testing 2-201
Peugeot
Description & Operation 2-200
Removal & Installation 2-200
Testing 2-200
Porsche
Description & Operation 2-200
Removal & Installation 2-200
Testing 2-200
Renault
Description & Operation 2-200
Removal & Installation 2-200
Testing 2-200
Saab
Description & Operation 2-200
Removal & Installation 2-200
Testing 2-200
Subaru
Description & Operation 2-205
Removal & Installation 2-205
Testing 2-205
Sterling
825
Description & Operation 2-199
Removal & Installation 2-199
Testing 2-199
Toyota
Description & Operation 2-205
Removal & Installation 2-206
Testing 2-205
Volkswagen
Description & Operation 2-200
Removal & Installation 2-200
Testing 2-200
Volvo
Description & Operation 2-200
Removal & Installation 2-200
Testing 2-200

FUEL PUMP SPECIFICATIONS
Acura
4-Cylinder 1-8
V6 1-13
Alfa Romeo
V6 1-17

FUEL PUMP SPECIFICATIONS (Cont.)
Audi
4-Cylinder ... 1-19
5-Cylinder ... 1-24
BMW
6-Cylinder ... 1-27
Chrysler Motors ... 1-32
Ford Motor Co. ... 1-36
General Motors ... 1-42
Honda ... 1-50
Isuzu
4-Cylinder Gas ... 1-59
4-Cylinder Diesel ... 1-62
Jaguar
6-Cylinder ... 1-64
V12 ... 1-67
Mazda
4-Cylinder Gas ... 1-74
Rotary Engine ... 1-79
Mercedes-Benz
4-Cylinder Gas ... 1-81
6-Cylinder Gas ... 1-83
V8 ... 1-88
Mitsubishi ... 1-32
Nissan
4-Cylinder ... 1-94
V6 ... 1-99
Peugeot
4-Cylinder ... 1-103
V6 ... 1-106
Porsche
4-Cylinder ... 1-108
6-Cylinder ... 1-112
Saab ... 1-116
Sterling ... 1-13
Subaru ... 1-122
Toyota
4-Cylinder ... 1-135
6-Cylinder ... 1-141
Volkswagen
4-Cylinder ... 1-147
5-Cylinder ... 1-24
Volvo
4-Cylinder ... 1-150
V6 ... 1-153

FUEL TANK CAPACITIES
Acura
4-Cylinder Gas ... 1-8
V6 ... 1-13
Alfa Romeo
V6 ... 1-17
Audi
4-Cylinder ... 1-20
5-Cylinder ... 1-25
BMW
6-Cylinder ... 1-27
Chrysler Motors ... 1-33
Ford Motor Co. ... 1-37
General Motors ... 1-42
Honda ... 1-51
Hyundai ... 1-55
Isuzu
4-Cylinder Gas ... 1-60
4-Cylinder Diesel ... 1-62
Jaguar
6-Cylinder ... 1-65
V12 ... 1-68
Mazda
4-Cylinder Gas ... 1-75
Rotary Engine ... 1-79
Mercedes-Benz
4-Cylinder Gas ... 1-81
6-Cylinder Gas ... 1-83
5 & 6-Cylinder Diesel ... 1-86
V8 ... 1-88
Mitsubishi ... 1-33
Nissan
4-Cylinder ... 1-95
V6 ... 1-99
Peugeot
4-Cylinder ... 1-104
V6 ... 1-106
Porsche
4-Cylinder ... 1-109
6-Cylinder ... 1-113
Saab ... 1-117
Subaru ... 1-123
Sterling ... 1-14
Suzuki ... 1-127
Toyota
4-Cylinder ... 1-136
6-Cylinder ... 1-142
Volkswagen
4-Cylinder ... 1-148
5-Cylinder Gas ... 1-25
Volvo
4-Cylinder ... 1-151
V6 ... 1-154
Yugo ... 1-156

FUSES – See appropriate Wiring Diagram

G

GAUGES
Acura ... 5-84
Audi ... 5-86
BMW ... 5-92
Chevrolet
Spectrum ... 5-95
Sprint ... 5-97
Chrysler Motors
Electronic ... 5-105
Standard ... 5-99
Ford Motors Co. ... 5-108
Honda ... 5-115
Hyundai ... 5-123
Isuzu
I-Mark ... 5-95
All Others ... 5-126
Mazda
Electronic ... 5-134
Standard ... 5-130
Mercedes-Benz ... 5-136
Mitsubishi
Electronic ... 5-105
Standard ... 5-99
Precis ... 5-123
Nissan
Electronic
Maxima ... 5-145
300ZX ... 5-152
Standard ... 5-138
Peugeot ... 5-158
Porsche ... 5-159
Saab ... 5-161
Subaru
Electronic ... 5-177
Standard ... 5-162
Suzuki ... 5-195
Toyota
Electronic ... 5-200
Standard ... 5-197
Volkswagen ... 5-203
Volvo ... 5-205
Yugo ... 5-207

GLOW PLUGS
Isuzu
P'UP, Trooper II
Adjustments ... 2-161
Description & Operation ... 2-158
Component Disassembly & Reassembly . 2-161
Removal & Installation ... 2-159
Testing ... 2-158
Trouble Shooting ... 2-158
Mercedes-Benz
190D
Adjustments ... 2-168
Description & Operation ... 2-163
Removal & Installation ... 2-167
Testing ... 2-165
Trouble Shooting ... 2-164
300D, 300TD, 300 SDL
Adjustments ... 2-175
Description & Operation ... 2-169
Removal & Installation ... 2-174
Testing ... 2-171

H

HEATER CORE REPLACEMENT
Removal & Installation
All Models ... 6-548

HORN BUTTON/PAD
Removal & Installation
All Models ... 12-6

I

IDENTIFICATION – *See Engine or Vehicle Identification Number*

IGNITION
All Models
Application Tables ... 3-3
Bosch Electronic Ignition
Yugo
Adjustments ... 3-6
Description & Operation ... 3-6
Testing ... 3-6
Bosch EZK Electronic Ignition
Peugeot, Volvo
Description & Operation ... 3-8
Testing ... 3-8
Bosch Hall Effect Electronic Ignition
Audi, Saab, Volkswagen
Adjustments ... 3-17
Description & Operation ... 3-17
Specifications ... 3-18
Pre-Test Procedures ... 3-17

1987 General Index

IGNITION (Cont.)
Testing
Audi 5000CS Quattro & 5000CS Turbo 3-22
Audi 5000S & Coupe GT (2.3L) 3-24
All Others 3-18
Computer Controlled Distributors
BMW 1a-72
Chrysler Motors
Electronic Controlled Injection 1a-120
Feedback Carburetor 1a-79
Honda 1a-74
Isuzu
Closed Loop Emission 1a-91
I-TEC Control 1a-107
Mazda 1a-115
Mitsubishi
Feedback Carburetor 1a-14
Electronically Controlled Injection 1a-31
Nissan
Electronically Controlled Carburetor 1a-123
Porsche 1a-154
Subaru 1a-162
Toyota
Computer Control System 1a-175
EFI Electronic Control System 1a-219
Volvo 1a-241
Ducellier Electronic Ignition
Peugeot
Adjustments 3-26
Description & Operation 3-26
Testing 3-27
Hitachi Computerized Ignition
Nissan, Subaru (Fuel Injected Models)
Description & Operation 3-28
Testing 3-29
Hitachi Electronic Ignition
Honda
Adjustments 3-32
Description & Operation 3-31
Overhaul 3-33
Testing 3-32
Lucas Constant Energy Ignition
Jaguar
Adjustments 3-34
Description & Operation 3-34
Overhaul 3-36
Testing 3-35
Mitsubishi Electronic Ignition
Chrysler Motors, Ford Motor Co. (Exc. Merkur), Hyundai, Isuzu (P'UP & Trooper II), Mazda (Exc. RX7), Mitsubishi, Subaru (Justy)
Adjustments 3-37
Description & Operation 3-37
Overhaul 3-39
Testing 3-37
Mitsubishi Electronic Ignition
Mazda RX7
Inspection & Adjustments 3-40
Description & Operation 3-40
Overhaul 3-41
Testing 3-40
Motorcraft TFI-IV Ignition
Ford Motor Co. Merkur
Adjustments 3-42
Description & Operation 3-42
Overhaul 3-43
Testing 3-43
Trouble Shooting 3-42
Nippondenso Electronic Ignition
General Motors, Isuzu (Exc. P'UP & Trooper II), Subaru (Exc. Justy), Suzuki, Toyota
Adjustments 3-44
Description & Operation 3-44
Overhaul 3-50
Testing 3-45
Trouble Shooting 3-45
Nissan Direct Ignition
Pulsar NX SE
Description & Operation 3-16
Testing 3-16
Toyo Denso Electronic Ignition
Acura, Honda
Adjustments 3-52
Description & Operation 3-51
Overhaul 3-53
Testing 3-52

IGNITION SWITCH
Removal & Installation
All Models 12-6

IGNITION TIMING
Acura
4-Cylinder 1-6
V6 1-11
Alfa Romeo
V6 1-15
Audi
4-Cylinder 1-18
5-Cylinder 1-22
BMW
6-Cylinder 1-27
Chrysler Motors 1-30
Ford Motor Co. 1-35
General Motors 1-39
Honda 1-45
Hyundai 1-53
Isuzu 1-57
Jaguar
6-Cylinder 1-64
V12 1-66
Mazda
4-Cylinder 1-70
Rotary Engine 1-76
Mercedes-Benz
4-Cylinder 1-80
6-Cylinder 1-82
V8 1-87
Mitsubishi 1-30
Nissan
4-Cylinder 1-90
V6 1-96
Peugeot
4-Cylinder 1-101
V6 1-105
Porsche
4-Cylinder 1-107
6-Cylinder 1-111
Saab 1-115
Sterling 1-11
Subaru 1-119
Suzuki 1-124
Toyota
4-Cylinder 1-132
6-Cylinder 1-139
Volkswagen
4-Cylinder 1-144
5-Cylinder 1-22
Volvo
4-Cylinder 1-149
V6 1-152
Yugo 1-156

INDICATOR LIGHTS
Audi 5-86
BMW 5-92
Chevrolet
Spectrum 5-96
Sprint 5-97
Ford Motor Co. 5-113
Honda 5-115
Hyundai 5-124
Isuzu
I-Mark 5-96
Mercedes-Benz 5-136
Porsche 5-159
Subaru
Electronic 5-177
Standard 5-162
Suzuki 5-195
Toyota
Electronic 5-200
Standard 5-197

INJECTION PUMP TIMING – *See Tune-Up*

J

JACKING & HOISTING
Acura 10-20
Alfa Romeo 10-20
Audi 10-20
BMW 10-20
Chrysler Motors 10-21
Ford Motor Co. 10-21
General Motors 10-20
Honda 10-22
Hyundai 10-22
Isuzu 10-22
Jaguar 10-22
Mazda 10-22
Mercedes-Benz 10-22
Mitsubishi 10-21, 10-22
Nissan 10-22, 10-23
Peugeot 10-23
Porsche 10-23
Saab 10-23
Subaru 10-24
Suzuki 10-24
Toyota 10-24
Volkswagen 10-24, 10-25
Volvo 10-24

L

LOCKING HUBS
All Manufacturers 8-169

M

MANIFOLD – *See Engine*

MANUAL STEERING – *See Steering*

MANUAL TRANSMISSION – *See Transmission*
MASTER CYLINDER – *See Brakes*
MAINTENANCE REMINDER LIGHTS
All Models – *See Front of Manual*

O

OIL CAPACITIES
Acura
4-Cylinder Gas 1-8
V6 1-13
Alfa Romeo
V6 1-17
Audi
4-Cylinder 1-20
5-Cylinder 1-25
BMW
6-Cylinder 1-27
Chrysler Motors 1-33
Ford Motor Co. 1-37
General Motors 1-42
Honda 1-51
Hyundai 1-55
Isuzu
4-Cylinder Gas 1-60
4-Cylinder Diesel 1-62
Jaguar
6-Cylinder 1-65
V12 1-68
Mazda
4-Cylinder Gas 1-75
Rotary Engine 1-79
Mercedes-Benz
4-Cylinder Gas 1-81
6-Cylinder Gas 1-83
5 & 6-Cylinder Diesel 1-86
V8 1-88
Mitsubishi 1-33
Nissan
4-Cylinder 1-95
V6 1-99
Peugeot
4-Cylinder Gas 1-104
V6 1-106
Porsche
4-Cylinder 1-109
6-Cylinder 1-113
Saab 1-117
Subaru 1-123
Sterling 1-14
Suzuki 1-127
Toyota
4-Cylinder 1-136
6-Cylinder 1-142
Volkswagen
4-Cylinder 1-148
5-Cylinder Gas 1-25
Volvo
4-Cylinder 1-151
V6 1-154
Yugo 1-156
OIL PRESSURE GAUGE – *See Gauge*
OIL PUMP – *See Engine*

P

PARKING BRAKE – *See Brakes*
PISTON – *See Engine*
PISTON RINGS – *See Engine*
POWER BRAKE UNIT – *See Brakes*
POWER STEERING – *See Steering*

R

REAR SUSPENSION – *See Suspension*
REAR WINDOW DEFOGGER
All Models 5-78
REGULATOR
All Models
General Servicing 3-58
Bosch
Alfa Romeo, Audi, BMW, Ford Motor Co., Mercedes-Benz, Saab, Volkswagen, Volvo & Yugo 3-59
Ducellier & Paris Rhone
Peugeot 505 3-62
Hitachi
Isuzu, Nissan & Subaru 3-63
Lucas (Integral)
Jaguar XJ6 III & XJS 3-67
Mitsubishi
Chrysler Motors, Hyundai Mazda, Mitsubishi & Nissan 300ZX Turbo 3-70
Motorola (Integral)
Jaguar XJ6 III 3-73
Nippondenso (Internal)
Acura, General Motors, Honda Accord, Civic, Prelude, Isuzu Impulse, I-Mark, Sterling & Toyota 3-77
Nippondenso (External)
Honda Prelude & Toyota Tercel 3-81
SEV Motorola 3-84
RIDING HEIGHT SPECIFICATIONS – *See Wheel Alignment*

SPARK PLUGS
Acura
4-Cylinder 1-6
V6 1-10
Alfa Romeo
V6 1-15
Audi
4-Cylinder 1-18
5-Cylinder 1-21
BMW
6-Cylinder 1-26
Chrysler Motors 1-29
Ford Motor Co. 1-34
General Motors 1-38
Honda 1-44
Hyundai 1-52
Isuzu
4-Cylinder Gas 1-56
4-Cylinder Diesel 1-61
Jaguar
6-Cylinder 1-63
V12 1-66
Mazda
4-Cylinder 1-69
Rotary Engine 1-76
Mercedes-Benz
4-Cylinder Gas 1-80
6-Cylinder 1-82
5 & 6-Cylinder Diesel 1-84
V8 1-87
Mitsubishi 1-29
Nissan
4-Cylinder Gas 1-89
V6 1-96
Peugeot
4-Cylinder 1-100
V6 1-105
Porsche
4-Cylinder 1-107
6-Cylinder 1-110
Saab 1-114
Subaru 1-125
Sterling 1-10
Suzuki 1-124
Toyota
4-Cylinder 1-128
6-Cylinder 1-137
Volkswagen
4-Cylinder 1-143
5-Cylinder 1-21
Volvo
4-Cylinder 1-149
V6 1-152
Yugo 1-155
STARTER
All Models
Applications 3-86
Trouble Shooting 3-89
Bosch
Alfa Romeo, Audi, BMW, Mercedes-Benz, Peugeot, Porsche, Saab, Volkswagen, Volvo & Yugo
Description 3-91
Overhaul 3-92
Removal & Installation 3-91
Specifications 3-91
Testing 3-91
Trouble Shooting 3-91
Ducellier & Paris-Rhone
Peugeot
Description 3-93
Overhaul 3-93
Testing 3-93
Hitachi & Mitsubishi
Chrysler Motors, General Motors Spectrum, Honda Civic, Hyundai, Isuzu, Mazda, Mitsubishi & Nissan
Description 3-94
Overhaul 3-97
Removal & Installation 3-95
Specifications 3-94
Testing 3-94
Lucas
Jaguar XJ6 III & XJS
Description 3-99
Overhaul 3-100
Testing 3-99

1987 General Index

STARTER (Cont.)
Mitsuba & Nippondenso Reduction Gear
Acura, General Motors Sprint
Honda, Sterling,
Subaru 1.8L & Toyota
Description 3-101
Overhaul 3-102
Testing 3-101
Motorcraft
Ford Motor Co.
Merkur XR4Ti
Bench Testing 3-103
Description 3-103
Operation 3-103
Overhaul 3-105
On Vehicle Testing 3-103
Nippondenso Direct Drive
Honda Civic (Calif.), Subaru 1.6L
& Toyota Tercel
Description 3-106
Overhaul 3-108
Testing 3-106

STEERING
Columns
Acura 12-8
Audi 4000 Series 12-10
Audi 5000 Series 12-11
BMW 12-13
Chevrolet 12-14
Chrysler Motors
FWD Models 12-15
RWD Models 12-17
Ford Motor Co. 12-19
Honda 12-8
Hyundai 12-15
Isuzu
I-Mark & Impulse 12-21
P'UP & Trooper II 12-22
Jaguar 12-23
Mazda 12-24
Mercedes Benz 12-26
Mitsubishi
FWD Models 12-15
RWD Models 12-17
Nissan 12-27
Peugeot 12-30
Porsche 12-30
Saab 12-31
Sterling 12-8
Subaru 12-32
Suzuki 12-35
Toyota
Non-Tilt Wheel 12-41
Tilt-Wheel 12-36
Volkswagen
All Except Quantum & Vanagon 12-43
Quantum 12-44
Vanagon 12-45
Volvo 12-46
Yugo 12-47
Electronic Power Steering
Mazda RX7 & 626
Description 12-176
Diagnosis 12-176
Testing 12-177
Mitsubishi Galant
Description 12-178
Testing & Trouble Shooting 12-178
Overhaul 12-180
Toyota Cressida
Description 12-181
Testing & Trouble Shooting 12-181
Manual Gears & Linkage
Chevrolet Spectrum & Sprint
Adjustments & Description 12-49
Overhaul 12-49
Removal & Installation 12-49
Chrysler Motors
Rack & Pinion
Adjustments & Description 12-50
Overhaul 12-50
Removal & Installation 12-50
Recirculating Ball
Adjustments & Description 12-53
Overhaul 12-53
Removal & Installation 12-53
Ford Motor Co.
Rack & Pinion
Adjustments & Description 12-55
Overhaul 12-55
Removal & Installation 12-55
Honda
Adjustments & Description 12-58
Overhaul 12-58
Removal & Installation 12-58
Hyundai
Adjustments & Description 12-50
Overhaul 12-50
Removal & Installation 12-50
Isuzu
Rack & Pinion
Adjustments & Description 12-49
Overhaul 12-49
Removal & Installation 12-49
Recirculating Ball
Adjustments & Description 12-61
Overhaul 12-61
Removal & Installation 12-61
Mazda
Rack & Pinion
Adjustments & Description 12-55
Overhaul 12-55
Removal & Installation 12-55
Mazda
Recirculating Ball
Adjustmentss & Description 12-63
Overhaul 12-63
Removal & Installation 12-63
Mitsubishi
Rack & Pinion
Adjustments & Description 12-50
Overhaul 12-50
Removal & Installation 12-50
Nissan
Rack & Pinion
Adjustments & Description 12-65
Overhaul 12-65
Removal & Installation 12-65
Recirculating Ball
Adjustments & Description 12-67
Overhaul 12-67
Removal & Installation 12-67
Porsche Rack & Pinion
Adjustments & Description 12-68
Overhaul 12-68
Removal & Installation 12-68
Subaru Rack & Pinion
Adjustments & Description 12-69
Overhaul 12-69
Removal & Installation 12-69
Suzuki Recirculating Ball
Adjustments & Description 12-71
Overhaul 12-71
Removal & Installation 12-71
Toyota
Rack & Pinion
Adjustments & Description 12-72
Overhaul 12-72
Removal & Installation 12-72
Recirculating Ball
Adjustmentss & Description 12-74
Overhaul 12-74
Removal & Installation 12-74
Volkswagen
Rack & Pinion
All Except Vanagon
Adjustmentss & Description 12-76
Removal & Installation 12-77
Vanagon
Adjustmentss & Description 12-77
Overhaul 12-77
Removal & Installation 12-77
Yugo Rack & Pinion
Adjustments & Description 12-78
Overhaul 12-78
Removal & Installation 12-78
Power Gears & Linkage
Acura Rack & Pinion
Adjustments & Description 12-80
Lubrication 12-80
Overhaul 12-83
Removal & Installation 12-82
Audi Rack & Pinion
Adjustments 12-88
Lubrication & Description 12-87
Testing 12-88
Overhaul 12-89
Removal & Installation 12-89
BMW
Rack & Pinion
Description 12-91
Lubrication & Testing 12-91
Overhaul 12-91
Removal & Installation 12-91
Recirculating Ball
Adjustments 12-92
Description & Lubrication 12-91
Overhaul 12-93
Removal & Installation 12-93
Testing 12-93
Chevrolet Spectrum Rack & Pinion
Description 12-94
Adjustmentss & Lubrication 12-94
Overhaul 12-96
Testing 12-94
Removal & Installation 12-96
Chrysler Motors
Rack & Pinion
Description & Lubrication 12-98
Overhaul 12-100
Removal & Installation 12-99
Testing 12-99
Recirculating Ball
Adjustments & Testing 12-103

1987 General Index

STEERING (Cont.)
Description & Lubrication 12-102
Overhaul 12-103
Removal & Installation 12-103
Ford Motor Co. Festiva
Description & Lubrication 12-116
Overhaul 12-118
Removal & Installation 12-118
Testing 12-117
Ford Motor Co. Merkur XR4Ti
Adjustments & Lubrication 12-107
Description 12-106
Lubrication 12-107
Overhaul 12-108
Removal & Installation 12-107
Honda Rack & Pinion
Adjustments & Description 12-80
Lubrication 12-80
Overhaul 12-83
Removal & Installation 12-82
Isuzu
Rack & Pinion
Description 12-94
Adjustmentss & Lubrication 12-94
Overhaul 12-96
Testing 12-94
Removal & Installation 12-96
Recirculating Ball
Adjustments & Testing 12-110
Description & Lubrication 12-110
Overhaul 12-111
Removal & Installation 12-110
Jaguar Rack & Pinion
Adjustments & Description 12-113
Lubrication 12-113
Overhaul 12-115
Removal & Installation 12-113
Testing 12-113
Mazda Rack & Pinion
Description & Lubrication 12-116
Overhaul 12-118
Removal & Installation 12-118
Testing 12-117
Mazda Recirculating Ball
Adjustments 12-119
Description & Lubrication 12-119
Overhaul 12-120
Removal & Installation 12-120
Testing 12-120
Mercedes Benz Recirculating Ball
Description & Lubrication 12-122
Overhaul 12-122
Removal & Installation 12-122
Mitsubishi – See Chrysler Motors
Nissan
Rack & Pinion
Adjustments 12-125
Description & Lubrication 12-124
Overhaul 12-126
Removal & Installation 12-126
Testing 12-125
Recirculating Ball
Adjustments & Lubrication 12-135
Description 12-135
Overhaul 12-136
Removal & Installation 12-135
Testing 12-135
Peugeot Rack & Pinion
Adjustments & Description 12-138
Lubrication 12-138
Overhaul 12-140
Removal & Installation 12-140
Testing 12-139
Porsche Rack & Pinion
Adjustments 12-142
Description & Lubrication 12-141
Overhaul 12-143
Removal & Installation 12-142
Saab Rack & Pinion
Description 12-143
Lubrication & Overhaul 12-143
Removal & Installation 12-143
Sterling
Adjustments & Description 12-80
Lubrication 12-80
Overhaul 12-83
Removal & Installation 12-82
Subaru Rack & Pinion
Adjustments & Description 12-146
Lubrication 12-146
Removal & Installation 12-146
Overhaul 12-148
Toyota
Rack & Pinion
Adjustments & Description 12-150
Lubrication 12-150
Overhaul 12-152
Removal & Installation 12-151
Testing 12-152
Recirculating Ball
Adjustments 12-160
Description & Lubrication 12-159
Overhaul 12-161
Removal & Installation 12-161
Testing 12-160
Volkswagen Rack & Pinion
Adjustments & Description 12-164
Lubrication & Testing 12-164
Overhaul 12-165
Removal & Installation 12-165
Volvo Rack & Pinion
Adjustments & Description 12-166
Lubrication 12-166
Overhaul 12-167
Removal & Installation 12-167

Steering Wheel Removal
All Models 12-6

SUPPLEMENTAL RESTRAINT SYSTEM
Mercedes-Benz 5-79

SUSPENSION
Automatic Level Control
Mercedes-Benz
Description & Operation 11-255
Removal & Installation 11-256
Testing 11-255
Electronic Suspension
Mazda RX7 & 626
Description & Operation 11-258
Testing & Diagnosis 11-259
Mazda 323
Description & Operation 11-264
Removal & Installation 11-266
Testing & Diagnosis 11-265
Mitsubishi Galant
Description & Operation 11-267
ESC Self-Diagnosis 11-269
Removal & Installation 11-271
Nissan Maxima & 300ZX
Description & Operation 11-278
Removal & Installation 11-280
Testing & Diagnosis 11-278
Subaru Sedan, Wagon, 3-Door & XT
Description & Operation 11-283
Removal & Installation 11-288
Trouble Shooting 11-283
Toyota Cressida & Supra
Description & Operation 11-293
Removal & Installation 11-296
Testing & Diagnosis 11-293
Front
Trouble Shooting 11-2
Acura
Adjustments & Inspection 11-3
Description 11-3
Removal & Installation 11-3
Tightening Specifications 11-7
Audi
Adjustments & Inspection 11-8
Description 11-8
Removal & Installation 11-8
Tightening Specifications 11-10
BMW
Adjustments & Inspection 11-11
Description 11-11
Removal & Installation 11-11
Tightening Specifications 11-13
Chrysler Motors
Colt, Colt Vista
Adjustments & Inspection 11-24
Description 11-24
Removal & Installation 11-25
Tightening Specifications 11-29
Conquest
Adjustments & Inspection 11-14
Description 11-14
Removal & Installation 11-14
Tightening Specifications 11-16
Ram-50 2WD Pickup
Adjustments & Inspection 11-17
Description 11-17
Removal & Installation 11-17
Tightening Specifications 11-17
Ram-50 4WD Pickup & Raider
Adjustments & Inspection 11-18
Description 11-18
Removal & Installation 11-18
Tightening Specifications 11-23
Ford Motor Co.
Festiva
Adjustments & Inspection 11-30
Description 11-30
Removal & Installation 11-30
Tightening Specifications 11-34

1987 General Index

SUSPENSION (Cont.)
Merkur XR4Ti
Adjustments & Inspection 11-35
Description 11-35
Removal & Installation 11-35
Tightening Specifications 11-38
Tracer
Adjustments & Inspection 11-39
Description 11-39
Removal & Installation 11-40
Tightening Specifications 11-42
General Motors Imports
Spectrum
Adjustments & Inspection 11-43
Description 11-43
Removal & Installation 11-43
Tightening Specifications 11-44
Sprint
Adjustments & Inspection 11-45
Description 11-45
Removal & Installation 11-45
Tightening Specifications 11-46
Honda
Adjustments & Inspection 11-47
Description 11-47
Removal & Installation 11-47
Tightening Specifications 11-53
Hyundai
Adjustments & Inspection 11-24
Description 11-24
Removal & Installation 11-25
Tightening Specifications 11-29
Isuzu
I-Mark
Adjustments & Inspection 11-43
Description 11-43
Removal & Installation 11-43
Tightening Specifications 11-44
Impulse
Adjustments & Inspection 11-54
Description 11-54
Removal & Installation 11-54
Tightening Specifications 11-55
P'UP & Trooper II
Adjustments & Inspection 11-56
Description 11-56
Removal & Installation 11-56
Tightening Specifications 11-61
Jaguar
Adjustments & Inspection 11-62
Description 11-62
Removal & Installation 11-62
Tightening Specifications 11-64
Mazda RX7, 323 & 626
Adjustments & Inspection 11-39
Description 11-39
Removal & Installation 11-40
Tightening Specifications 11-42
Mazda B2200 & B2600
Adjustments & Inspection 11-65
Description 11-65
Removal & Installation 11-65
Tightening Specifications 11-67
Mercedes-Benz
190 Series, 260E & 300 Series
Adjustments & Inspection 11-68
Description 11-68
Removal & Installation 11-68
Tightening Specifications 11-70
300SDL, 420SEL & 560 Series
Adjustments & Inspection 11-71
Description 11-71
Removal & Installation 11-71
Tightening Specifications 11-73
Mitsubishi
Cordia, Mirage, Precis & Tredia
Adjustments & Inspection 11-24
Description 11-24
Removal & Installation 11-25
Tightening Specifications 11-29
Galant
Adjustments & Inspection 11-74
Description 11-74
Removal & Installation 11-74
Tightening Specifications 11-76
Starion
Adjustments & Inspection 11-14
Description 11-14
Removal & Installation 11-14
Tightening Specifications 11-16
Van/Wagon
Adjustments & Inspection 11-77
Description 11-77
Removal & Installation 11-77
Tightening Specifications 11-78
2WD Pickup
Adjustments & Inspection 11-17
Description 11-17
Removal & Installation 11-17
Tightening Specifications 11-17
4WD Pickup & Montero
Adjustments & Inspection 11-18
Description 11-18
Removal & Installation 11-18
Tightening Specifications 11-23
Nissan
Maxima
Adjustments & Inspection 11-79
Description 11-79
Removal & Installation 11-79
Tightening Specifications 11-80
Pathfinder & Pickup
Adjustments & Inspection 11-81
Description 11-81
Removal & Installation 11-83
Testing 11-83
Tightening Specifications 11-86
Pulsar, Sentra, Stanza, Stanza Wagon
Adjustments & Inspection 11-87
Description 11-87
Removal & Installation 11-89
Tightening Specifications 11-91
Van
Adjustments & Inspection 11-93
Description 11-93
Removal & Installation 11-94
Tightening Specifications 11-96
200SX & 300ZX
Adjustments & Inspection 11-97
Description 11-97
Removal & Installation 11-98
Tightening Specifications 11-98
Peugeot
Adjustments & Inspection 11-99
Description 11-99
Removal & Installation 11-99
Tightening Specifications 11-100
Porsche
911 Carrera & 911 Turbo
Adjustments & Inspection 11-103
Description 11-103
Removal & Installation 11-103
Tightening Specifications 11-104
924-S & 944 Series
Adjustments & Inspection 11-101
Description 11-101
Removal & Installation 11-101
Tightening Specifications 11-102
Saab 900 Series & 9000 Series
Adjustments & Inspection 11-105
Description 11-105
Removal & Installation 11-105
Tightening Specifications 11-107
Sterling
Adjustments & Inspection 11-108
Description 11-108
Removal & Installation 11-108
Tightening Specifications 11-111
Subaru
Adjustments & Inspection 11-113
Description 11-112
Removal & Installation 11-113
Tightening Specifications 11-114
Suzuki
Adjustments & Inspection 11-115
Description 11-115
Removal & Installation 11-116
Tightening Specifications 11-118
Toyota
Camry, Celica, Corolla FWD & Tercel
Adjustments & Inspection 11-119
Description 11-119
Removal & Installation 11-119
Tightening Specifications 11-123
Corolla RWD, Cressida & Supra
Adjustments & Inspection 11-124
Description 11-124
Removal & Installation 11-124
Tightening Specifications 11-127
MR2
Adjustments & Inspection 11-128
Description 11-128
Removal & Installation 11-128
Tightening Specifications 11-129
2WD Pickup & Van
Adjustments & Inspection 11-130
Description 11-130
Removal & Installation 11-130
Tightening Specifications 11-133
4WD Pickup & 4Runner
Adjustments & Inspection 11-134
Description 11-134
Removal & Installation 11-134
Tightening Specifications 11-138
Volkswagen Cabriolet, Golf, GTI & Jetta
Adjustments & Inspection 11-139
Description 11-139

1987 General Index

SUSPENSION (Cont.)

Removal & Installation 11-139
Tightening Specifications 11-140
Volkswagen Fox, Quantum & Scirocco
Adjustments & Inspection 11-141
Description 11-141
Removal & Installation 11-141
Tightening Specifications 11-142
Volkswagen 2WD Vanagon
Adjustments & Inspection 11-143
Description 11-143
Removal & Installation 11-143
Tightening Specifications 11-144
Volkswagen 4WD Vanagon
Adjustments & Inspection 11-145
Description 11-145
Removal & Installation 11-145
Tightening Specifications 11-147
Volvo
Adjustments & Inspection 11-148
Description 11-148
Removal & Installation 11-148
Tightening Specifications 11-149
Yugo
Adjustments & Inspection 11-150
Description 11-150
Removal & Installation 11-150
Tightening Specifications 11-151

Rear

Acura
Adjustments & Inspection 11-152
Description 11-152
Removal & Installation 11-152
Tightening Specifications 11-156
Audi
Adjustments & Inspection 11-157
Description 11-157
Removal & Installation 11-157
Tightening Specifications 11-159
BMW
Adjustments & Inspection 11-160
Description 11-160
Removal & Installation 11-160
Tightening Specifications 11-161
Chrysler Motors
Colt & Colt Vista
Adjustments & Inspection 11-165
Description 11-165
Removal & Installation 11-165
Tightening Specifications 11-169
Conquest
Adjustments & Inspection 11-162
Description 11-162
Removal & Installation 11-162
Tightening Specifications 11-162
Ford Motor Co.
Festiva
Adjustments & Inspection 11-170
Description 11-170
Removal & Installation 11-171
Tightening Specifications 11-173
Merkur XR4Ti
Adjustments & Inspection 11-174
Description 11-174
Removal & Installation 11-174
Tightening Specifications 11-177
Tracer
Adjustments & Inspection 11-178
Description 11-178
Removal & Installation 11-178
Tightening Specifications 11-179
General Motors
Spectrum
Adjustments & Inspection 11-180
Description 11-180
Removal & Installation 11-180
Tightening Specifications 11-181
Sprint
Adjustments & Inspection 11-182
Description 11-182
Removal & Installation 11-182
Tightening Specifications 11-182
Honda
Accord, Civic & Prelude
Adjustments & Inspection 11-184
Description 11-183
Removal & Installation 11-184
Tightening Specifications 11-186
4WD Civic Wagon
Adjustments & Inspection 11-188
Description 11-188
Removal & Installation 11-188
Tightening Specifications 11-188
Hyundai
Adjustments & Inspection 11-165
Description 11-165
Removal & Installation 11-165
Tightening Specifications 11-169
Isuzu
I-Mark
Adjustments & Inspection 11-180
Description 11-180
Removal & Installation 11-180
Tightening Specifications 11-181
Impulse
Adjustments & Inspection 11-189
Description 11-189
Removal & Installation 11-189
Tightening Specifications 11-190
Jaguar
Adjustments & Inspection 11-191
Description 11-191
Removal & Installation 11-191
Tightening Specifications 11-192
Mazda
RX7
Adjustments & Inspection 11-193
Description 11-193
Removal & Installation 11-193
Tightening Specifications 11-195
323 & 626
Adjustments & Inspection 11-174
Description 11-174
Removal & Installation 11-174
Tightening Specifications 11-175
Mercedes-Benz
190 Series, 260E & 300 Series
Adjustments & Inspection 11-198
Description 11-198
Removal & Installation 11-198
Tightening Specifications 11-200
300SDL, 420SEL & 560 Series
Adjustments & Inspection 11-196
Description 11-196
Removal & Installation 11-196
Tightening Specifications 11-197
Mitsubishi
Cordia, Mirage, Precis & Tredia
Adjustments & Inspection 11-165
Description 11-165
Removal & Installation 11-165
Tightening Specifications 11-169
Galant
Adjustments & Inspection 11-201
Description 11-201
Removal & Installation 11-201
Tightening Specifications 11-202
Starion
Adjustments & Inspection 11-162
Description 11-162
Removal & Installation 11-162
Tightening Specifications 11-162
Nissan
Maxima
Adjustments & Inspection 11-203
Description 11-203
Removal & Installation 11-203
Tightening Specifications 11-204
Pulsar NX & Sentra
Adjustments & Inspection 11-205
Description 11-205
Removal & Installation 11-205
Tightening Specifications 11-206
Stanza
Adjustments & Inspection 11-207
Description 11-207
Removal & Installation 11-207
Tightening Specifications 11-209
Stanza Wagon
Adjustments & Inspection 11-210
Description 11-210
Removal & Installation 11-211
Tightening Specifications 11-214
Van
Adjustments & Inspection 11-215
Description 11-215
Removal & Installation 11-215
Tightening Specifications 11-215
200SX & 300ZX
Adjustments & Inspection 11-216
Description 11-216
Removal & Installation 11-217
Tightening Specifications 11-217
Peugeot
Adjustments & Inspection 11-218
Description 11-218
Removal & Installation 11-218
Tightening Specifications 11-220
Porsche
911 Carrera & 911 Turbo
Description 11-223
Removal & Installation 11-223
Tightening Specifications 11-224
924-S & 944 Series
Adjustments & Inspection 11-221
Description 11-221

1987 General Index

SUSPENSION (Cont.)

Removal & Installation 11-221
Tightening Specifications 11-222
Saab 900 Series & 9000 Series
Adjustments & Inspection 11-225
Description 11-225
Removal & Installation 11-225
Tightening Specifications 11-226
Sterling
Adjustments & Inspection 11-227
Description 11-227
Removal & Installation 11-227
Tightening Specifications 11-228
Subaru
Justy
Adjustments & Inspection 11-231
Description 11-231
Removal & Installation 11-231
Tightening Specifications 11-232
All Other Models
Adjustments & Inspection 11-229
Description 11-229
Removal & Installation 11-229
Tightening Specifications 11-230
Toyota
Camry, Celica, Corolla FWD & Tercel Wagon
Adjustments & Inspection 11-238
Description 11-238
Removal & Installation 11-238
Tightening Specifications 11-240
Corolla RWD, Cressida Wagon, 4WD Tercel Wagon & Van
Adjustments & Inspection 11-233
Description 11-233
Removal & Installation 11-233
Tightening Specifications 11-234
Cressida Sedan
Adjustments & Inspection 11-235
Description 11-235
Removal & Installation 11-235
Tightening Specifications 11-237
MR2
Adjustments & Inspection 11-241
Description 11-241
Removal & Installation 11-241
Tightening Specifications 11-242
Supra
Adjustments & Inspection 11-243
Description 11-243
Removal & Installation 11-244
Tightening Specifications 11-244
Volkswagen
Fox, Golf, GTI, Jetta & Scirocco
Adjustments & Inspection 11-245
Description 11-245
Removal & Installation 11-245
Tightening Specifications 11-246
Quantum Syncro
Adjustments & Inspection 11-247
Description 11-247
Removal & Installation 11-247
Vanagon
Adjustments & Inspection 11-248
Description 11-248
Removal & Installation 11-248
Tightening Specifications 11-249
Volvo
Adjustments & Inspection 11-250
Description 11-250
Removal & Installation 11-250
Tightening Specifications 11-252
Yugo
Adjustments & Inspection 11-253
Description 11-253
Removal & Installation 11-253
Tightening Specifications 11-254

SWITCHES
Headlight Dimmer, Turn Signal & Wipers
All Models 12-6

T

THERMOSTAT – *See Engine*

TRANSMISSION SERVICING
Automatic Transmission Application
All Models 13-2
Automatic Transmission Servicing
Acura 13-8
Audi 13-10
BMW 13-13
Chrysler Motors 13-15
Ford Motor Co. 13-19
General Motors 13-21
Honda 13-24
Hyundai 13-26
Isuzu 13-28
Jaguar 13-30
Mazda 13-32
Mercedes-Benz 13-36
Mitsubishi 13-39
Nissan 13-44
Peugeot 13-47
Porsche 13-48
Saab 13-50
Sterling 13-52
Subaru 13-53
Toyota 13-55
Volkswagen 13-57
Volvo 13-60
Manual Transmission Application
All Models 13-5
Manual Transmission Servicing
Acura 13-62
Audi 13-62
BMW 13-64
Chrysler Motors 13-64
Ford Motor Co. 13-65
General Motors 13-66
Honda 13-67
Hyundai 13-68
Isuzu 13-68
Mazda 13-69
Mercedes-Benz 13-70
Mitsubishi 13-70
Nissan 13-71
Peugeot 13-72
Porsche 13-72
Saab 13-73
Sterling 13-74
Subaru 13-74
Suzuki 13-74
Toyota 13-75
Volkswagen 13-76
Volvo 13-79
Yugo 13-80

TRANSMISSION REMOVAL
Automatic
Acura 13-81
Audi 13-81
BMW 13-82
Chrysler Motors 13-83
Ford Motor Co. 13-84
General Motors 13-83
Honda 13-85
Hyundai 13-85
Isuzu 13-85
Jaguar 13-86
Mazda 13-87
Mercedes-Benz 13-88
Mitsubishi 13-89
Nissan 13-90
Peugeot 13-91
Porsche 13-91
Saab 13-91
Sterling 13-92
Subaru 13-92
Toyota 13-93
Volkswagen 13-97
Volvo 13-98
Manual – *See Clutches*

TROUBLE SHOOTING
All Models
Brakes 9-2
Carburetor 2-2
Charging System 3-57
Clutch 7-2
Diesel Fuel Injection 2-4
Drive Axles 8-2
Engine
Diesel 6-12
Gasoline 6-9
Gasoline Fuel Injection 2-3
Ignition Systems 3-2
Manual Steering Gear 12-3
Power Steering Gear 12-4
Starting System 3-89
Suspension 11-2
Tune-Up 1-2
Turbocharger 2-5
Wheel Alignment 10-2

TUNE-UP
Acura
4-Cylinder 1-6
V6 1-10
Alfa Romeo
V6 1-15
Audi
4-Cylinder 1-18
5-Cylinder 1-21
BMW
6-Cylinder 1-26
Chrysler Motors 1-29
Ford Motor Co. 1-34

TUNE-UP (Cont.)

General Motors 1-38
Honda 1-44
Hyundai 1-52
Isuzu
 4-Cylinder Gas 1-56
 4-Cylinder Diesel 1-61
Jaguar
 6-Cylinder 1-63
 V12 1-66
Mazda
 4-Cylinder 1-69
 Rotary Engine 1-76
Mercedes-Benz
 4-Cylinder Gas 1-80
 6-Cylinder 1-82
 5 & 6-Cylinder Diesel 1-84
 V8 1-87
Mitsubishi 1-29
Nissan
 4-Cylinder Gas 1-89
 V6 1-96
Peugeot
 4-Cylinder 1-100
 V6 1-105
Porsche
 4-Cylinder 1-107
 6-Cylinder 1-110
Saab 1-114
Subaru 1-125
Sterling 1-10
Suzuki 1-124
Toyota
 4-Cylinder 1-128
 6-Cylinder 1-137
Volkswagen
 4-Cylinder 1-143
 5-Cylinder 1-21
Volvo
 4-Cylinder 1-149
 V6 1-152
Yugo 1-155

TURBOCHARGER
Trouble Shooting
 All Models 2-5
Audi, 5000CS
 Description & Operation 2-177
 Removal & Installation 2-178
 Testing 2-177
Chrysler Motors
 Description & Operation 2-178
 Disassembly & Reassembly 2-179
 Trouble Shooting 2-179
 Removal & Installation 2-179
Ford Motor Co.
 Description & Operation 2-180
 Removal & Installation 2-182
 Testing 2-180
General Motors 2-180
Isuzu
 Description & Operation 2-182
 Inspection 2-183
 Trouble Shooting 2-182
 Removal & Installation 2-183
Mazda
 Description 2-183
 Inspection 2-184
 Operation 2-184
 Removal & Installation 2-184
 Trouble Shooting 2-184
Mercedes-Benz
 Description & Operation 2-185
 Lubrication 2-186
 Removal & Installation 2-186
 Testing 2-186
Mitsubishi
 Description & Operation 2-178
 Disassembly & Reassembly 2-179
 Trouble Shooting 2-179
 Removal & Installation 2-179
Nissan
 Description & Operation 2-187
 Inspection 2-187
 Removal & Installation 2-187
 Trouble Shooting 2-187
Peugeot
 Description & Operation 2-188
 Testing 2-189
 Trouble Shooting 2-189
Porsche
 Description & Operation 2-189
 Removal & Installation 2-190
Saab
 Adjustments 2-192
 Description & Operation 2-190
 Removal & Installation 2-193
Subaru
 Description & Operation 2-193
 Removal & Installation 2-194
 Testing 2-194
 Trouble Shooting 2-194
Toyota
 Description 2-194
 Removal & Installation 2-196
 Testing 2-195
 Trouble Shooting 2-195
Volvo
 Description & Operation 2-196
 Overhaul 2-198
 Removal & Installation 2-197
 Testing 2-197
 Trouble Shooting 2-197

TURN SIGNAL – *See Switches*

V

VALVE CLEARANCE
Acura
 4-Cylinder 1-6
 V6 1-10
Alfa Romeo
 V6 1-15
Audi
 4-Cylinder 1-18
 5-Cylinder 1-21
BMW
 6-Cylinder 1-26
Chrysler Motors 1-29
Ford Motor Co. 1-34
General Motors 1-38
Honda 1-44
Hyundai 1-52
Isuzu
 4-Cylinder Gas 1-56
 4-Cylinder Diesel 1-61
Jaguar
 6-Cylinder 1-63
 V12 1-66
Mazda
 4-Cylinder 1-69
 Rotary Engine 1-76
Mercedes-Benz
 4-Cylinder Gas 1-80
 6-Cylinder 1-82
 5 & 6-Cylinder Diesel 1-84
 V8 1-87
Mitsubishi 1-29
Nissan
 4-Cylinder Gas 1-89
 V6 1-96
Peugeot
 4-Cylinder 1-100
 V6 1-105
Porsche
 4-Cylinder 1-107
 6-Cylinder 1-110
Saab 1-114
Subaru 1-125
Sterling 1-10
Suzuki 1-124
Toyota
 4-Cylinder 1-128
 6-Cylinder 1-137
Volkswagen
 4-Cylinder 1-143
 5-Cylinder 1-21
Volvo
 4-Cylinder 1-149
 V6 1-152
Yugo 1-155

W

WATER PUMP
Acura
 1.6 4-Cylinder 6-37
 2.5L V6 6-50
Alfa Romeo
 V6 6-61
Audi
 1.8L & 1.8L 16-Valve
  4-Cylinder 6-71
 2.22L & 2.3L 5-Cylinder 6-80
BMW
 2.5L & 2.7L 6-Cylinder 6-87
 3.5L 6-Cylinder 6-96
Ford Motor Co.
 1.3L 4-Cylinder 6-104
 1.6L 4-Cylinder 6-207
 2.3L 4-Cylinder 6-113
Chrysler Motors – See Mitsubishi

1987 General Index

WATER PUMP (Cont.)
General Motors
Chevrolet
1.0L 3-Cylinder 6-122
1.5L 4-Cylinder 6-135
Honda Accord, Civic
& Prelude 4-Cylinder 6-149
Hyundai 1.5L 4-Cylinder 6-258
Isuzu
Impulse, P'UP & Trooper II
4-Cylinder (Gasoline) 6-161
I-Mark 4-Cylinder (Gasoline) 6-130
P'UP 4-Cylinder & Trooper II
4-Cylinder (Diesel) 6-170
Jaguar
4.2L 6-Cylinder 6-179
5.3L V12 6-187
Mazda
B2200 & 626 2.0L/2.2L 4-Cyl. 6-215
B2600 2.6L 4-Cyl. 6-276
323 1.6L 4-Cylinder 6-207
RX7 1.3L Rotary 6-199
Mercedez-Benz
2.3L 4-Cylinder (Gas) 6-224
2.5L & 3.0L 5/6-Cyl. (Diesel) 6-233
2.6L & 3.0 6-Cylinder 6-240
4.2L & 5.6L V8 6-248
Mitsubishi
1.5L & 1.6L Turbo 4-Cylinder 6-258
1.8L Turbo, 2.0L & 2.4L 4-Cylinder 6-269
2.6L & 2.6L Turbo 4-Cylinder 6-276
Nissan
1.6L 4-Cylinder 6-288
1.6L 16-Valve 4-Cylinder 6-296
2.0L 4-Cylinder 6-304
2.4L 4-Cylinder 6-315
3.0L & 3.0L Turbo V6 6-323
Peugeot
2.0L 4-Cylinder 6-331
2.2L 4-Cylinder 6-337
2.8L V6 6-348
Porsche
2.5L 4-Cylinder 6-362
3.2L & 3.3L Turbo 6-Cylinder 6-381
Saab
2.0L 4-Cylinder 6-388
Sterling
2.5L V6 6-50
Subaru
1.2L 6-398
1.6L & 1.8L 4-Cylinder 6-406
1.8L OHC 4-Cylinder 6-415
Suzuki
1.3L 4-Cylinder 6-426
Toyota
1.5L & 1.6L 8-Valve 4-Cylinder 6-436
1.5L 12-Valve 4-Cylinder 6-447
1.6L 16-Valve 4-Cylinder 6-458
2.0L 3S FE & 3S-GE 6-471
2.2L 4-Cylinder 6-480
2.4L 4-Cylinder 6-487
2.8L 6-Cylinder 6-496
3.0L DOHC 6-Cylinder 6-508
4.2L 6-Cylinder 6-515
Volkswagen
1.8L 4-Cylinder (In-Line) 6-71
2.1L Opposed 4-Cylinder 6-524
2.2L 5-Cylinder 6-80
Volvo
2.3L 4-Cylinder 6-530
2.8L V6 6-348
Yugo
1.1L 4-Cylinder 6-539

WIRE RESISTANCE – *See Spark Plugs*

WHEEL ALIGNMENT
Trouble Shooting
All Models 10-2
Riding Height Specifications
Acura to Toyota (Celica) 10-3
Toyota (Celica to Van) 10-4
Wheel Alignment Specifications
Acura 10-6
Alfa Romeo 10-6
Audi 10-6
BMW 10-6
Chevrolet 10-6
Chrysler Motors 10-6
Ford Motor Co. 10-6
Honda 10-6
Hyundai 10-8
Isuzu 10-8
Jaguar 10-8
Mazda 10-8
Mercedes-Benz 10-8
Mitsubishi 10-10
Nissan 10-10
Peugeot 10-10
Porsche 10-12
Saab 10-12
Subaru 10-12
Suzuki 10-12
Toyota 10-12, 10-14
Volkswagen 10-14
Volvo 10-14
Yugo 10-14
Wheel Alignment Procedures
All Models 10-16

WHEELS
Wheel Lug Nut Torques
All Models 10-19

WHEEL BEARINGS
Front
Acura
Adjustments & Inspection 11-3
Removal & Installation 11-3
Audi
Adjustments & Inspection 11-8
Removal & Installation 11-9
BMW
Adjustments & Inspection 11-11
Removal & Installation 11-11
Chrysler Motors
Colt & Colt Vista
Adjustments & Inspection 11-124
Removal & Installation 11-125
Conquest
Adjustments & Inspection 11-14
Removal & Installation 11-14
Chrysler Motors Ram-50 Pickup
2WD
Adjustments & Inspection 11-17
Removal & Installation 11-17
Raider & 4WD
Adjustments & Inspection 11-18
Removal & Installation 11-18
Ford Motor Co.
Festiva
Adjustments & Inspection 11-30
Removal & Installation 11-31
Merkur XR4Ti
Adjustments & Inspection 11-35
Removal & Installation 11-35
Tracer
Adjustments & Inspection 11-39
Removal & Installation 11-40
General Motors
Spectrum
Adjustments & Inspection 11-43
Removal & Installation 11-44
Sprint
Adjustments & Inspection 11-45
Removal & Installation 11-45
Honda
Adjustments & Inspection 11-47
Removal & Installation 11-47
Hyundai
Adjustments & Inspection 11-124
Removal & Installation 11-125
Isuzu
I-Mark
Adjustments & Inspection 11-43
Removal & Installation 11-44
Impulse
Adjustments & Inspection 11-54
Removal & Installation 11-54
Isuzu P'UP & Trooper II
Adjustments & Inspection 11-56
Removal & Installation 11-56
Jaguar
Adjustments & Description 11-62
Removal & Installation 11-62
Mazda RX7, 323 & 626
Adjustments & Inspection 11-39
Removal & Installation 11-40
Mazda B2200 & B2600
Adjustments & Inspection 11-65
Removal & Installation 11-65
Mercedes-Benz
190 Series, 260E & 300 Series
Adjustments & Inspection 11-68
Removal & Installation 11-68
300 SDL, 420SEL & 560 Series
Adjustments & Inspection 11-71
Removal & Installation 11-71
Mitsubishi
Cordia, Mirage, Precis & Tredia
Adjustments & Inspection 11-124
Removal & Installation 11-125

1987 General Index

WHEEL BEARINGS (Cont.)

Galant
- Adjustments & Inspection 11-74
- Removal & Installation 11-74

Montero & 4WD Pickup
- Adjustments & Inspection 11-18
- Removal & Installation 11-18

Starion
- Adjustments & Inspection 11-14
- Removal & Installation 11-14

2WD Pickup
- Adjustments & Inspection 11-17
- Removal & Installation 11-17

Van/Wagon
- Adjustments & Inspection 11-77
- Removal & Installation 11-77

Nissan

Maxima
- Adjustments & Description 11-79
- Removal & Installation 11-79

Pathfinder & Pickup
- Adjustments & Inspection 11-81

Pulsar NX, Sentra, Stanza & Stanza Wagon
- Adjustments & Description 11-87
- Removal & Installatiion 11-89

Van
- Adjustments & Inspection 11-93
- Removal & Installation 11-94

200SX & 300ZX
- Adjustments & Inspection 11-97
- Removal & Installation 11-98

Peugeot
- Adjustments & Inspection 11-99
- Removal & Installation 11-99

Porsche

911 Carrera & 911 Turbo
- Adjustments & Inspection 11-103
- Removal & Installation 11-103

924-S & 944 Series
- Adjustments & Inspection 11-101
- Removal & Installation 11-101

Saab

900 Series & 9000 Series
- Adjustments & Inspection 11-105
- Removal & Installation 11-105

Sterling
- Adjustments & Inspection 11-108
- Removal & Installation 11-108

Subaru
- Adjustments & Inspection 11-113
- Removal & Installation 11-113

Suzuki
- Adjustments & Inspection 11-115
- Removal & Installation 11-116

Toyota

Camry, Celica, Corolla FWD & Tercel
- Adjustments & Inspection 11-119
- Removal & Installation 11-119

Corolla RWD, Cressida & Supra
- Adjustments & Inspection 11-124
- Removal & Installation 11-124

MR2
- Adjustments & Inspection 11-128
- Removal & Installation 11-128

2WD Pickup & Van
- Adjustments & Description 11-130
- Removal & Installation 11-130

4WD Pickup & 4Runner
- Adjustments & Inspection 11-134
- Removal & Installation 11-134

Volkswagen Cabriolet, Golt, GTI & Jetta
- Adjustments & Inspection 11-139
- Removal & Installation 11-139

Volkswagen Fox, Quantum & Scirocco
- Adjustments & Inspection 11-141
- Removal & Installation 11-141

Volkswagen 2WD Vanagon
- Adjustments & Inspection 11-143
- Removal & Installation 11-143

Volkswagen 4WD Vanagon
- Adjustments & Inspection 11-145
- Removal & Installation 11-145

Volvo
- Adjustments & Inspection 11-148
- Removal & Installation 11-148

Yugo
- Adjustments & Inspection 11-150
- Removal & Installation 11-150

Rear

Acura
- Adjustments & Inspection 11-152
- Removal & Installation 11-153

Audi
- Adjustments & Inspection 11-157
- Removal & Installation 11-157

BMW
- Adjustments & Inspection 11-160
- Removal & Installation 11-160

Chrysler Motors

Colt, Colt Vista (2WD & 4WD)
- Adjustments & Inspection 11-165
- Removal & Installation 11-165

Conquest
- Adjustments & Inspection 11-162
- Removal & Installation 11-162

Ford Motor Co.

Festiva
- Adjustments & Inspection 11-170
- Removal & Installation 11-171

Merkur XR4Ti
- Adjustments & Inspection 11-174
- Removal & Installation 11-174

Tracer
- Adjustments & Inspection 11-178
- Removal & Installation 11-178

General Motors

Spectrum
- Adjustments & Inspection 11-180
- Removal & Installation 11-180

Sprint
- Adjustments & Inspection 11-182
- Removal & Installation 11-182

Honda

Accord, Civic & Prelude
- Adjustments & Inspection 11-184
- Removal & Installation 11-184

4WD Civic Wagon
- Adjustments & Inspection 11-188

Hyundai
- Adjustments & Inspection 11-165
- Removal & Installation 11-165

Isuzu

I-Mark
- Adjustments & Inspection 11-180
- Removal & Installation 11-180

Impulse
- Adjustments & Inspection 11-181

Jaguar
- Adjustments & Inspection 11-191
- Removal & Installation 11-191

Mazda RX7
- Adjustments & Inspection 11-193
- Removal & Installation 11-193

323 & 626
- Adjustments & Inspection 11-174
- Removal & Installation 11-174

Mercedes-Benz

190 Series, 260E & 300 Series
- Removal & Installation 11-198

300 SDL, 420SEL & 560 Series
- Removal & Installation 11-196

Mitsubishi Cordia, Mirage, Precis & Tredia
- Adjustments & Inspection 11-165
- Removal & Installation 11-165

Mitsubishi Galant
- Adjustments & Inspection 11-201
- Removal & Installation 11-201

Mitsubishi Starion
- Adjustments & Inspection 11-162
- Removal & Installation 11-162

Nissan

Maxima
- Adjustments & Inspection 11-203
- Removal & Installation 11-203

Pulsar NX & Sentra
- Adjustments & Inspection 11-205
- Removal & Installation 11-205

Stanza
- Adjustments & Inspection 11-207
- Removal & Installation 11-207

Stanza Wagon
- Adjustments & Inspection 11-210
- Removal & Installation 11-210

200SX & 300ZX
- Adjustments & Inspection 11-216
- Removal & Installation 11-217

Peugeot
- Adjustments & Inspection 11-218
- Removal & Installation 11-218

Porsche

911 Carrera & 911 Turbo
- Removal & Installation 11-223

924-S & 944 Series
- Adjustments & Inspection 11-221

Saab

900 Series & 9000 Series
- Adjustments & Inspection 11-225
- Removal & Installation 11-225

Sterling
- Adjustments & Inspection 11-227
- Removal & Installation 11-227

1987 General Index

WHEEL BEARINGS (Cont.)

Subaru
Justy
Adjustments & Inspection 11-231
Removal & Installation 11-231
All Other Models
Adjustments & Inspection 11-229
Removal & Installation 11-229
Toyota
Camry, Celica, Corolla FWD & Tercel
Adjustments & Inspection 11-238
Removal & Installation 11-239
Cressida Sedan
Adjustments & Inspection 11-235
Removal & Installation 11-236
MR2
Adjustments & Inspection 11-241
Removal & Installation 11-241
Supra
Adjustments & Inspection 11-243
Removal & Installation 11-244
Volkswagen Fox, Golf, GTI, Jetta & Scirocco
Description & Adjustments 11-245
Volkswagen Quantum Syncro
Adjustments & Inspection 11-247
Removal & Installation 11-247
Volkswagen Vanagon
Removal & Installation 11-248
Yugo
Description 11-253
Removal & Installation 11-253

WIPER/WASHER SYSTEM

Acura 5-208
Audi 5-210
BMW 5-211
Chevrolet 5-212
Chrysler Motors 5-213
Ford Motor Co. Imports 5-215
Honda 5-208
Hyundai 5-216
Isuzu 5-217
Jaguar 5-218
Mazda 5-220
Mercedes-Benz 5-222
Mitsubishi 5-213
Nissan 5-224
Porsche 5-227
Saab 5-228
Subaru 5-229
Suzuki 5-230
Toyota 5-231
Volkswagen 5-233
Volvo 5-235
Yugo 5-236

WIRING DIAGRAMS

Acura
Integra 4-4
Legend Coupe 4-12
Legend Sedan 4-26
Alfa Romeo
Graduate, Quadrifoglio & Spider Veloce 4-36
Milano 4-41
Audi
Coupe GT, 4000S & 4000CS Quattro 4-49
5000S 4-58
5000CS Turbo & Quattro 4-69
BMW
325, 325e, 325es, 325i,
325is & 325i Convertible 4-80
528e 4-92
535i 535is & M5 4-101
635CSi, L6 & M6 4-113
735i & L7 4-127
Chrysler Motors
Colt 4-138
Colt Vista 4-144
Conquest 4-150
Raider 4-160
Ram-50 4-164
Ford Motor Co.
Festiva 4-168
Merkur XR4Ti 4-172
Tracer 4-178
General Motors
Chevrolet Spectrum 4-184
Chevrolet Sprint 4-188
Honda
Accord 4-193
Civic Hatchback, Wagon, Sedan
& 4WD Wagon 4-203
Civic CRX & CRX Si 4-209
Prelude 4-218
Hyundai
Excel 4-227
Isuzu
I-Mark 4-184
Impulse 4-231
P'UP 4-239
Trooper II 4-244
Jaguar
XJ6 III 4-248
XJS 4-254
Mazda
B2000 & B2600 4-261
RX7 4-266
323 4-274
626 & 626 Turbo 4-281
Mercedes-Benz
190 Series 4-290
260E, 300D, 300E & 300TD 4-304
300SDL 4-315
420SEL, 560SEC & 560SEL 4-326
560SL 4-336
Mitsubishi
Cordia & Tredia 4-345
Galant 4-352
Mirage 4-138
Montero 4-160
Pickup 4-164
Precis 4-227
Starion 4-150
Van/Wagon 4-362
Nissan
Maxima 4-368
Pathfinder & Pickup 4-380
Pulsar NX 4-387
Sentra 4-394
Stanza 4-402
Stanza Wagon 4-409
Van 4-415
200SX 4-423
300ZX & 300ZX Turbo 4-432
Peugeot
505 Series & 505 Turbo 4-445
Porsche
911 Carrera & 911 Turbo 4-456
924S 4-465
928-S4 4-471
944 944S & 944 Turbo 4-483
Saab
900 Series 4-493
9000S & 9000 Turbo 4-504
Sterling
825 & 825SL 4-515
Subaru
Brat, Coupe & Hatchback,
Sedan & Wagon 4-525
Justy 4-536
XT Coupe 4-541
Suzuki
Samurai 4-550
Toyota
Camry 4-553
Celica 4-564
FWD Corolla & FX-16 4-576
RWD Corolla 4-584
Cressida 4-591
Land Cruiser 4-602
MR2 4-605
Pickup & 4Runner 4-612
Supra 4-620
Tercel 4-632
1987½ Tercel 4-637
Van 4-643
Volkswagen
Cabriolet & Scirocco 4-649
Fox 4-656
Golf & GTI 4-660
Jetta & Jetta GLI 4-667
Quantum & Quantum Syncro 4-675
Vanagon 4-681
Volvo
240 DL & 240 GL 4-687
740 Series & 760 Series 4-693
Yugo
GV & GVX 4-703

Notes

Notes

Notes

Notes

Notes

Notes

Notes

Notes

Notes

Notes

Notes

Notes

Please be sure to fill out this form completely.

"WE LISTEN"

Do you have any comments or recommended changes to this book?
We will appreciate receiving them so that we may continue to publish the world's best Service & Repair manuals. **Mail this card today. We'd like to hear from you!**

☐ Domestic Cars ☐ Imported Cars & Trucks ☐ Domestic Light Trucks ☐ Medium & Heavy Duty Trucks
☐ Tune-Up ☐ Electrical ☐ Engine ☐ Chassis ☐ Transmission
☐ Emission ☐ Air Conditioning ☐ Electrical Component Locators ☐ Other ______

Section No. ______ Page No. ______ Vehicle Model & Year ______

Comments: ______

Name ______ Company ______

Address ______ City ______ State ______ Zip ______

Phone (   ) ______ Date ______ THANK YOU

ADIC87

Please be sure to fill out this form completely.

"WE LISTEN"

Do you have any comments or recommended changes to this book?
We will appreciate receiving them so that we may continue to publish the world's best Service & Repair manuals. **Mail this card today. We'd like to hear from you!**

☐ Domestic Cars ☐ Imported Cars & Trucks ☐ Domestic Light Trucks ☐ Medium & Heavy Duty Trucks
☐ Tune-Up ☐ Electrical ☐ Engine ☐ Chassis ☐ Transmission
☐ Emission ☐ Air Conditioning ☐ Electrical Component Locators ☐ Other ______

Section No. ______ Page No. ______ Vehicle Model & Year ______

Comments: ______

Name ______ Company ______

Address ______ City ______ State ______ Zip ______

Phone (   ) ______ Date ______ THANK YOU

ADIC87

Please be sure to fill out this form completely.

"WE LISTEN"

Do you have any comments or recommended changes to this book?
We will appreciate receiving them so that we may continue to publish the world's best Service & Repair manuals. **Mail this card today. We'd like to hear from you!**

☐ Domestic Cars ☐ Imported Cars & Trucks ☐ Domestic Light Trucks ☐ Medium & Heavy Duty Trucks
☐ Tune-Up ☐ Electrical ☐ Engine ☐ Chassis ☐ Transmission
☐ Emission ☐ Air Conditioning ☐ Electrical Component Locators ☐ Other ______

Section No. ______ Page No. ______ Vehicle Model & Year ______

Comments: ______

Name ______ Company ______

Address ______ City ______ State ______ Zip ______

Phone (   ) ______ Date ______ THANK YOU

ADIC87

Name ______________________

Address ______________________

City ____________ State ______ Zip ________

NO POSTAGE
NECESSARY
IF MAILED
IN THE
UNITED STATES

BUSINESS REPLY MAIL

FIRST CLASS PERMIT NO. 3701 SAN DIEGO, CA

POSTAGE WILL BE PAID BY ADDRESSEE

MITCHELL INTERNATIONAL, INC.
P.O. BOX 26260
San Diego, California 92126-9984

Name ______________________

Address ______________________

City ____________ State ______ Zip ________

NO POSTAGE
NECESSARY
IF MAILED
IN THE
UNITED STATES

BUSINESS REPLY MAIL

FIRST CLASS PERMIT NO. 3701 SAN DIEGO, CA

POSTAGE WILL BE PAID BY ADDRESSEE

MITCHELL INTERNATIONAL, INC.
P.O. BOX 26260
San Diego, California 92126-9984

Name ______________________

Address ______________________

City ____________ State ______ Zip ________

NO POSTAGE
NECESSARY
IF MAILED
IN THE
UNITED STATES

BUSINESS REPLY MAIL

FIRST CLASS PERMIT NO. 3701 SAN DIEGO, CA

POSTAGE WILL BE PAID BY ADDRESSEE

MITCHELL INTERNATIONAL, INC.
P.O. BOX 26260
San Diego, California 92126-9984

GOSHEN PUBLIC LIBRARY
3 9531 00033 8797